Stanley Gibbons
SIMPLIFIED
CATALOGUE

Stamps of the World 1994

An illustrated and priced three-volume guide to the postage stamps of the whole world, excluding changes of paper, perforation, shade and watermark

VOLUME 2

FOREIGN COUNTRIES K—Z

STANLEY GIBBONS LTD
London and Ringwood

By Appointment to
Her Majesty the Queen
Stanley Gibbons Limited
London
Philatelists

60th Edition

Published in Great Britain by
Stanley Gibbons Ltd
Publications Editorial, Sales Offices and Distribution Centre
5, Parkside, Christchurch Road,
Ringwood, Hampshire BH24 3SH
Telephone 0425 472363

ISBN: 085259-379-1

Published as Stanley Gibbons Simplified Stamp Catalogue from 1934 to 1970, renamed Stamps of the World in 1971, and produced in two (1982–88) or three (from 1989) volumes as Stanley Gibbons Simplified Catalogue of Stamps of the World.
This volume published October 1994

S.G. Item No. 2882 (94)

Origination by BPC Whitefriars Ltd, Tunbridge Wells, Kent
Printed in Great Britain by Bemrose Security Printing, London & Derby

Stanley Gibbons
SIMPLIFIED CATALOGUE
Stamps of the World

This popular catalogue is a straightforward three-volume listing of the stamps that have been issued everywhere in the world since the very first–Great Britain's famous Penny Black in 1840.

This edition continues the three-volume format. Volume 1 (Foreign countries A–J) appears in September, Volume 2 (Foreign countries K–Z) in October, and Volume 3 covering Commonwealth countries in November.

Readers are reminded that the Catalogue Supplements, published in each issue of **Gibbons Stamp Monthly,** can be used to update the listings in **Stamps of the World** as well as our twenty-two part standard catalogue. To make the supplement even more useful the Type numbers given to the illustrations are now the same in the Stamps of the World as in the standard catalogues. The first Catalogue Supplement to this Volume appeared in the September 1994 issue of **Gibbons Stamp Monthly**.

Gibbons Stamp Monthly can be obtained through newsagents or on postal subscription from Stanley Gibbons Publications, 5, Parkside, Christchurch Road, Ringwood, Hants BH24 3SH.

The catalogue has many important features:

- As an indication of current values virtually every stamp is priced. Thousands of alterations have been made since the last edition.
- By being set out on a simplified basis that excludes changes of paper, perforation, shade, watermark, gum or printer's and date imprints it is particularly easy to use. (For its exact scope see "Information for users" pages following.)
- The thousands of illustrations and helpful descriptions of stamp designs make it of maximum appeal to collectors with thematic interests.
- Its catalogue numbers are the world-recognised Stanley Gibbons numbers throughout.
- Helpful introductory notes for the collector are included, backed by much historical, geographical and currency information.
- A very detailed index gives instant location of countries in this volume, and a cross-reference to those included in the other volumes.

Over 2,610 stamps and 879 new illustrations have been added to the listings in this volume. The last year's three-volume edition contained over 304,000 stamps and 72,500 illustrations.

The listings in this volume are based on the standard catalogues: Part 1 (British Commonwealth) (1994 edition), Part 2 (Austria & Hungary) (4th edition), Part 3 (Balkans) (3rd edition), Part 4 (Benelux) (4th edition), Part 5 (Czechoslovakia & Poland) (4th edition), Part 6 (France) (4th edition), Part 7 (Germany) (4th edition), Part 8 (Italy & Switzerland) (4th edition), Part 9 (Portugal & Spain) (3rd edition), Part 10 (Russia) (4th edition), Part 11 (Scandinavia) (3rd edition), Part 12 (Africa since Independence A-E) (2nd edition), Part 13 (Africa since Independence F-M) (1st edition), Part 14 (Africa since Independence N-Z) (1st edition), Part 15 (Central America) (2nd edition), Part 16 (Central Asia) (3rd edition), Part 17 (China) (4th edition), Part 18 (Japan & Korea) (3rd edition), Part 19 (Middle East) (4th edition), Part 20 (South America) (3rd edition), Part 21 (South-East Asia) (2nd edition) and Part 22 (United States) (4th edition).

Important price revisions made specially for this edition include Latvia, Lithuania, Paraguay, Poland, Rumania (from 1945), Rwanda, Slovakia, Sudan, Uruguay, Zaire and, since independence, St. Thomas and Prince Is, Somalia, Togo, Tunisia and Upper Volta.

Stanley Gibbons Stamp Catalogue
Complete List of Parts

1 British Commonwealth
(Annual in two volumes)

Foreign Countries

2 Austria & Hungary (5th edition, 1994)
Austria · Bosnia & Herzegovina · U.N. (Vienna) · Hungary

3 Balkans (3rd edition, 1987)
Albania · Bulgaria · Greece & Islands · Rumania · Yugoslavia

4 Benelux (4th edition, 1993)
Belgium & Colonies · Netherlands & Colonies · Luxembourg

5 Czechoslovakia & Poland (4th edition, 1991)
Czechoslovakia · Bohemia & Moravia · Slovakia · Poland

6 France (4th edition, 1993)
France · Colonies · Andorra · Monaco

7 Germany (4th edition, 1992)
Germany · States · Colonies · Post Offices

8 Italy & Switzerland (4th edition, 1993)
Italy & Colonies · Fiume · San Marino · Vatican City · Trieste · Liechtenstein · Switzerland · U.N. (Geneva)

9 Portugal & Spain (3rd edition, 1991)
Andorra · Portugal & Colonies · Spain & Colonies

10 Russia (4th edition, 1991)
Russia · Baltic States · Mongolia · Tuva

11 Scandinavia (4th edition, 1994)
Aland Islands · Denmark · Faroe Islands · Finland · Greenland · Iceland · Norway · Sweden

12 Africa since Independence A-E (2nd edition, 1983)
Algeria · Angola · Benin · Bophuthatswana · Burundi · Cameroun · Cape Verde · Central African Republic · Chad · Comoro Islands · Congo · Djibouti · Equatorial Guinea · Ethiopia

13 Africa since Independence F-M (1st edition, 1981)
Gabon · Guinea · Guinea-Bissau · Ivory Coast · Liberia · Libya · Malagasy Republic · Mali · Mauritania · Morocco · Mozambique

14 Africa since Independence N-Z (1st edition, 1981)
Niger Republic · Rwanda · St. Thomas & Prince · Senegal · Somalia · Sudan · Togo · Transkei · Tunisia · Upper Volta · Venda · Zaire

15 Central America (2nd edition, 1984)
Costa Rica · Cuba · Dominican Republic · El Salvador · Guatemala · Haiti · Honduras · Mexico · Nicaragua · Panama

16 Central Asia (3rd edition, 1992)
Afghanistan · Iran · Turkey

17 China (4th edition, 1989)
China · Taiwan · Tibet · Foreign P.O.s

18 Japan & Korea (3rd edition, 1992)
Japan · Ryukyus · Korean Empire · South Korea · North Korea

19 Middle East (4th edition, 1990)
Bahrain · Egypt · Iraq · Israel · Jordan · Kuwait · Lebanon · Oman · Qatar · Saudi Arabia · Syria · U.A.E. · Yemen A.R. · Yemen P.D.R.

20 South America (3rd edition, 1989)
Argentina · Bolivia · Brazil · Chile · Colombia · Ecuador · Paraguay · Peru · Surinam · Uruguay · Venezuela

21 South-East Asia (2nd edition, 1985)
Bhutan · Burma · Indonesia · Kampuchea · Laos · Nepal · Philippines · Thailand · Vietnam

22 United States (4th edition, 1994)
U.S. & Possessions · Canal Zone · Marshall Islands · Micronesia · Palau · U.N. (New York, Geneva, Vienna)

Thematic Catalogues

Stanley Gibbons Catalogues for use with **Stamps of the World.**
Collect Aircraft on Stamps (forthcoming)
Collect Birds on Stamps (3rd edition, 1992)
Collect Butterflies and Other Insects on Stamps (1st edition, 1991)
Collect Chess on Stamps (1st edition, 1992)
Collect Fungi on Stamps (1st edition, 1991)
Collect Mammals on Stamps (1st edition, 1986)
Collect Railways on Stamps (2nd edition, 1990)
Collect Ships on Stamps (2nd edition, 1993)

Information for users

Aim

The aim of this catalogue is to provide a straightforward illustrated and priced guide to the postage stamps of the whole world to help you to enjoy the greatest hobby of the present day.

Arrangement

The catalogue lists countries in alphabetical order and there is a complete index at the end of each volume. For ease of reference country names are also printed at the head of each page.

Within each country, postage stamps are listed first. They are followed by separate sections for such other categories as postage due stamps, parcel post stamps, express stamps, official stamps, etc.

All catalogue lists are set out according to dates of issue of the stamps, starting from the earliest and working through to the most recent. New issues received too late for inclusion in the main lists will be found as "Addenda" at the end of each volume.

Scope of the Catalogue

The *Simplified Catalogue of Stamps of the World* contains listings of postage stamps only. Apart from the ordinary definitive, commemorative and air-mail stamps of each country – which appear first in each list – there are sections for the following where appropriate:

- postage due stamps
- parcel post stamps
- official stamps
- express and special delivery stamps
- charity and compulsory tax stamps
- newspaper and journal stamps
- printed matter stamps
- registration stamps
- acknowledgement of receipt stamps
- late fee and too late stamps
- military post stamps
- recorded message stamps
- personal delivery stamps

We receive numerous enquiries from collectors about other items which do not fall within the categories set out above and which consequently do not appear in the catalogue lists. It may be helpful, therefore, to summarise the other kinds of stamp that exist but which we deliberately exclude from this postage stamp catalogue.

We do *not* list the following:

Fiscal or revenue stamps: stamps used solely in collecting taxes or fees for non-postal purposes. Examples would be stamps which pay a tax on a receipt, represent the stamp duty on a contract or frank a customs document. Common inscriptions found include: Documentary, Proprietary, Inter. Revenue, Contract Note.

Local stamps: postage stamps whose validity and use are limited in area, say to a single town or city, though in some cases they provided, with official sanction, services in parts of countries not covered by the respective government.

Local carriage labels and Private local issues: many labels exist ostensibly to cover the cost of ferrying mail from one of Great Britain's offshore islands to the nearest mainland post office. They are not recognised as valid for national or international mail. Examples: Calf of Man, Davaar, Herm, Lundy, Pabay, Stroma. Items from some other places have only the status of tourist souvenir labels.

Telegraph stamps: stamps intended solely for the prepayment of telegraphic communication.

Bogus or "phantom" stamps: labels from mythical places or non-existent administrations. Examples in the classical period were Sedang, Counani, Clipperton Island and in modern times Thomond and Monte Bello Islands. Numerous labels have also appeared since the War from dissident groups as propaganda for their claims and without authority from the home governments. Common examples are labels for "Free Albania", "Free Rumania" and "Free Croatia" and numerous issues for Nagaland, Indonesia and the South Moluccas ("Republik Maluku Selatan").

Railway letter fee stamps: special stamps issued by railway companies for the conveyance of letters by rail. Example: Talyllyn Railway. Similar services are now offered by some bus companies and the labels they issue likewise do not qualify for inclusion in the catalogue.

Perfins ("perforated initials"): numerous postage stamps may be found with initial letters or designs punctured through them by tiny holes. These are applied by private and public concerns as a precaution against theft and do not qualify for separate mention.

Information for users

Labels: innumerable items exist resembling stamps but – as they do not prepay postage – they are classified as labels. The commonest categories are:

— propaganda and publicity labels: designed to further a cause or campaign;

— exhibition labels: particularly souvenirs from philatelic events;

— testing labels: stamp-size labels used in testing stamp-vending machines;

— Post Office training school stamps: British stamps overprinted with two thick vertical bars or SCHOOL SPECIMEN are produced by the Post Office for training purposes;

— seals and stickers: numerous charities produce stamp-like labels, particularly at Christmas and Easter, as a means of raising funds and these have no postal validity.

Cut-outs: items of postal stationery, such as envelopes, cards and wrappers, often have stamps impressed or imprinted on them. They may usually be cut out and affixed to envelopes, etc., for postal use if desired, but such items are not listed in this catalogue.

Collectors wanting further information about exact definitions are referred to *Philatelic Terms Illustrated,* published by Stanley Gibbons and containing many illustrations in colour (third edition price £7.50 plus £3 postage and packing).

There is also a priced listing of the postal fiscals of Great Britain in our Part 1 *(British Commonwealth)* Catalogue and in Volume 1 of the *Great Britain Specialised* Catalogue (5th and later editions).

Although, as stated, none of the above qualify for inclusion in this postage stamp catalogue, this does not imply that they are of no interest to certain collectors. Indeed, in the 1950s, a group was formed in Great Britain called the "Cinderella Stamp Club", whose object is the study of all those stamps which Stanley Gibbons do *not* list in their catalogues.

Catalogue Numbers

Stanley Gibbons catalogue numbers are recognised universally and any individual stamp can be identified by quoting the catalogue number (the one at the left of the column) prefixed by the name of the country and the letters "S.G.". Do not confuse the catalogue number with the type numbers which refer to illustrations.

Prices

Prices in the left-hand column are for unused stamps and those in the right-hand column for used. Prices are given in pence and pounds:

100 pence (p) = 1 pound (£1).

Prices are shown as follows:

10 means 10p (10 pence);
1.75 means £1.75 (1 pound and 75 pence);
For £100 and above, prices are in whole pounds.

Our prices are for stamps in fine average condition, and in issues where condition varies we may ask more for the superb and less for the sub-standard.

The minimum price quoted is 5p which represents a handling charge rather than a basis for valuing common stamps.

The prices quoted are generally for the cheapest variety of stamps but it is worth noting that differences of watermark, perforation, or other details, outside the scope of this catalogue, may often increase the value of the stamp.

Where prices are not given in either column it is either because the stamps are not known to exist in that particular condition, or, more usually, because there is no reliable information as to value.

All prices are subject to change without prior notice and we give no guarantee to supply all stamps priced. Prices quoted for albums, publications, etc. advertised in this catalogue are also subject to change without prior notice.

Unused Stamps

In the case of stamps from *Great Britain* and the *Commonwealth,* prices for unused stamps of Queen Victoria to King George V are for lightly hinged examples; unused prices of King Edward VIII to Queen Elizabeth II issues are for unmounted mint. The prices of unused *Foreign* stamps are for lightly hinged examples for those issued before 1946, thereafter for examples unmounted mint.

Used Stamps

Prices for used stamps generally refer to postally used examples, though for certain issues it is for cancelled-to-order.

Information for users

Guarantee

All stamps supplied by us are guaranteed originals in the following terms:

If not as described, and returned by the purchaser, we undertake to refund the price paid to us in the original transaction. If any stamp is certified as genuine by the Expert Committee of the Royal Philatelic Society, London, or by B.P.A. Expertising Ltd., the purchaser shall not be entitled to make any claim against us for any error, omission or mistake in such certificate.

Consumers' statutory rights are not affected by the above guarantee.

Currency

At the beginning of each country brief details give the currencies in which the values of the stamps are expressed. The dates, where given, are those of the earliest stamp issues in the particular currency. Where the currency is obvious, e.g. where the colony has the same currency as the mother country, no details are given.

Illustrations

Illustrations of stamps of Commonwealth countries (in Volume 3) and of any surcharges and overprints which are shown and not described are actual size; stamps of all foreign countries are reduced to $\frac{3}{4}$ linear, unless otherwise stated.

"Key-Types"

A number of standard designs occur so frequently in the stamps of the French, German, Portuguese and Spanish colonies that it would be a waste of space to repeat them. Instead these are all illustrated on page xii together with the descriptive names and letters by which they are referred to in the lists.

Type Numbers

These are the bold figures found below each illustration. References to "Type **6**", for example, in the lists of a country should therefore be understood to refer to the illustration below which the number **"6"** appears. These type numbers are also given in the second column of figures alongside each list of stamps, thus indicating clearly the design of each stamp. In the case of Key-Types – see above – letters take the place of the type numbers.

Where an issue comprises stamps of similar design, represented in this catalogue by one illustration, the corresponding type numbers should be taken as indicating this general design.

Where there are blanks in the type number column it means that the type of the corresponding stamps is that shown by the last number above in the type column of the same issue.

A dash (–) in the type column means that no illustration of the stamp is shown.

Where type numbers refer to stamps of another country, e.g. where stamps of one country are overprinted for use in another, this is always made clear in the text.

Stamp Designs

Brief descriptions of the subjects of the stamp designs are given either below or beside the illustrations, at the foot of the list of the issue concerned, or in the actual lists. Where a particular subject, e.g. the portrait of a well-known monarch, recurs frequently the description is not repeated, nor are obvious designs described.

Generally, the unillustrated designs are in the same shape and size as the one illustrated, except where otherwise indicated.

Surcharges and Overprints

Surcharges and overprints are usually described in the headings to the issues concerned. Where the actual wording of a surcharge or overprint is given it is shown in bold type.

Some stamps are described as being "Surcharged in words", e.g. **TWO CENTS,** and others "Surcharged in figures and words", e.g. **20 CENTS,** although of course many surcharges are in foreign languages and combinations of words and figures are numerous. There are often bars, etc., obliterating old values or inscriptions but in general these are only mentioned where it is necessary to avoid confusion.

No attention is paid in this catalogue to colours of overprints and surcharges so that stamps with the same overprints in different colours are not listed separately.

Numbers in brackets after the descriptions of overprinted or surcharged stamps are the catalogue numbers of the unoverprinted stamps.

Note – the words "inscribed" or "inscription" always refer to wording incorporated in the design of a stamp and not surcharges or overprints.

Coloured Papers

Where stamps are printed on coloured paper the description is given as e.g. "4 c. black on blue" – a stamp printed in black on blue paper. No attention is paid in this catalogue to differences in the texture of paper, e.g. laid, wove.

Information for users

Watermarks

Stamps having different watermarks, but otherwise the same, are not listed separately. No reference is therefore made to watermarks in this volume.

Stamp Colours

Colour names are only required for the identification of stamps, therefore they have been made as simple as possible. Thus "scarlet", "vermilion", "carmine" are all usually called red. Qualifying colour names have been introduced only where necessary for the sake of clearness.

Where stamps are printed in two or more colours the central portion of the design is in the first colour given, unless otherwise stated.

Perforations

All stamps are perforated unless otherwise stated. No distinction is made between the various gauges of perforation but early stamp issues which exist both imperforate and perforated are usually listed separately.

Where a heading states "Imperf. or perf." or "Perf. or rouletted" this does not necessarily mean that all values of the issue are found in both conditions.

Dates of Issue

The date given at the head of each issue is that of the appearance of the earliest stamp in the series. As stamps of the same design or issue are usually grouped together a list of King George VI stamps, for example, headed "1938" may include stamps issued from 1938 to the end of the reign.

Miniature Sheets

These are outside the scope of this catalogue but are listed in all other Stanley Gibbons catalogues.

"Appendix" Countries

We regret that, since 1968, it has been necessary to establish an Appendix (at the end of each country as appropriate) to which numerous stamps have had to be consigned. Several countries imagine that by issuing huge quantities of unnecessary stamps they will have a ready source of income from stamp collectors – and particularly from the less-experienced ones. Stanley Gibbons refuse to encourage this exploitation of the hobby and we do not stock the stamps concerned.

Two kinds of stamp are therefore given the briefest of mentions in the Appendix, purely for the sake of record. Administrations issuing stamps greatly in excess of true postal needs have the offending issues placed there. Likewise it contains stamps which have not fulfilled all the normal conditions for full catalogue listing.

These conditions are that the stamps must be issued by a legitimate postal authority, recognised by the government concerned, and are adhesives, valid for proper postal use in the class of service for which they are inscribed. Stamps, with the exception of such categories as postage dues and officials, must be available to the general public at face value with no artificial restrictions being imposed on their distribution.

The publishers of this catalogue have observed, with concern, the proliferation of 'artificial' stamp-issuing territories. On several occasions this has resulted in separately inscribed issues for various component parts of otherwise united states or territories.

Stanley Gibbons Publications have decided that where such circumstances occur, they will not, in the future, list these items in the SG catalogue without first satisfying themselves that the stamps represent a genuine political, historical or postal division within the country concerned. Any such issues which do not fulfil this stipulation will be recorded in the Catalogue Appendix only.

Stamps in the Appendix are kept under review in the light of any newly acquired information about them. If we are satisfied that a stamp qualifies for proper listing in the body of the catalogue it is moved there.

"Undesirable Issues"

The rules governing many competitive exhibitions – including the Melville Competition – are set by the Fédération Internationale de Philatelie and stipulate a downgrading of marks for stamps classed as "undesirable issues".

This catalogue can be taken as a guide to status. All stamps in the main listings and Addenda are acceptable. Stamps in the Appendix should not be entered for competition as these are the "undesirable issues".

Particular care is advised with Aden Protectorate States, Ajman, Bhutan, Chad, Fujeira, Khor Fakkan, Manama, Ras al Khaima, Sharjah, Umm al Qiwain and Yemen. Totally bogus stamps exist (as explained in Appendix notes) and these are to be avoided also for competition. As distinct from "undesirable stamps" certain categories are not covered in this catalogue purely by reason of its scope (see page v). Consult the particular competition rules to see if such are admissible even though not listed by us.

Information for users

Where to Look for More Detailed Listings

The present work deliberately omits details of paper, perforation, shade and watermark. But as you become more absorbed in stamp collecting and wish to get greater enjoyment from the hobby you may well want to study these matters.

All the information you require about any particular postage stamp will be found in the main Stanley Gibbons Catalogues.

Commonwealth countries in Volume 3 are covered by the Part 1 (British Commonwealth) Catalogue published annually in two volumes.

For foreign countries you can easily find which catalogue to consult by looking at the country headings in the present book.

To the right of each country name are code letters specifying which volume of our main catalogues contains that country's listing.

The code letters are as follows:

Pt. 2 Part 2
Pt. 3 Part 3 etc.

(See page iv for complete list of Parts.)

So, for example, if you want to know more about Chinese stamps than is contained in the *Simplified Catalogue of Stamps of the World* the reference to

CHINA Pt. 17

guides you to the Gibbons Part 17 *(China)* Catalogue listing for the details you require.

New editions of Parts 2 to 22 appear at irregular intervals.

Correspondence

Whilst we welcome information and suggestions we must ask correspondents to include the cost of postage for the return of any stamps submitted plus registration where appropriate. Letters should be addressed to The Catalogue Editor at Ringwood.

Where information is solicited purely for the benefit of the enquirer we regret we cannot undertake to reply unless stamps or reply coupons are sent to cover the postage.

Identification of Stamps

We regret we do not give opinions as to the genuineness of stamps, nor do we identify stamps or number them by our Catalogue.

Users of this catalogue are referred to our companion booklet entitled *Stamp Collecting — How to Identify Stamps.* It explains how to look up stamps in this catalogue, contains a full checklist of stamp inscriptions and gives help in dealing with unfamiliar scripts. It is available from Stanley Gibbons at £2.95, postage extra.

Stanley Gibbons would like to complement your collection

At Stanley Gibbons we offer a range of services which are designed to complement your collection.

Our modern stamp shop, the largest in Europe, together with our rare stamp department has one of the most comprehensive stocks of Great Britain in the world, so whether you are a beginner or an experienced philatelist you are certain to find something to suit your special requirements.

Alternatively through our Mail Order services you can control the growth of your collection from the comfort of your own home. Our Postal Sales Department regularly sends out mailings of Special Offers. We can also help with your wants list—so why not ask us for those elusive items?

And don't forget Stanley Gibbons Auctions which holds, on average, 8–10 sales each year. Come along in person or send in a written bid for the items you require. For details of current subscription rates for Auction catalogues write to Stanley Gibbons Auctions, 399 Strand, London WC2R 0LX.

Why not take advantage of the many services we have to offer? Visit our premises in the Strand or, for more information, write to the appropriate address on page x.

Stanley Gibbons Holdings Plc Addresses

Stanley Gibbons Limited,
Stanley Gibbons Auctions
399 Strand, London WC2R 0LX
Telephone 071 836 8444 Fax 071 836 7342 for all departments.

Auction Room and Specialist Stamp Departments. Open Monday–Friday 9.30 a.m. to 5 p.m.

Shop. Open Monday–Friday 8.30 a.m. to 6 p.m. and Saturday 10 a.m. to 4.00 p.m.

Stanley Gibbons Publications
5 Parkside, Christchurch Road, Ringwood, Hants BH24 3SH.
Telephone 0425 472363 (24 hour answerphone service) Fax 0425 470247.

Publication Showroom (at above address). Open Monday–Friday 8.30 a.m. to 5 p.m.

Publications Mail Order. FREEPHONE 0800 611622. Monday–Friday 8.30 a.m. to 5 p.m.

Urch Harris & Co.
(a division of Stanley Gibbons Ltd),
1 Osprey Court, Hawkfield Way, Bristol BS14 0BE.
Telephone 0272 465656 Fax 0272 465225.

Monday–Friday 8.30 a.m. to 5 p.m.

U.H. New Issue Service, Osprey (Postal) Auctions, U.H. Digest.

Stanley Gibbons Publications Overseas Representation

Stanley Gibbons Publications are represented overseas by the following sole distributors (*), main distributors (**) or licensees (***).

Australia*
Lighthouse Philatelic (Aust.) Pty. Ltd., P.O. Box 763, Strawberry Hills, New South Wales, 2012 Australia.

Stanley Gibbons (Australia) Pty. Ltd.*** P.O. Box 863J, Melbourne 3001, Australia.

Belgium and Luxembourg**
Davo c/o Philac, Rue du Midi 48, Bruxelles, 1000 Belgium.

Canada*
Lighthouse Publications (Canada) Ltd., 255 Duke Street, Montreal, Quebec, Canada H3C 2M2

Denmark**
Davo c/o Lindner Falzlos, Gl Randers vej 28, 8450 Hammel, Denmark.

Finland**
Davo c/o Suomen Postimerkkeily Ludvingkatu 5 SF-00130 Helsinki, Finland.

France*
Davo France (Casteilla), 10, Rue Leon Foucault, 78184 St. Quentin Yvelines Cesex, France.

Germany and Austria*
Leuchtturm Albenverlag, Paul Koch KG Am Spakenberg 45, Postfach 1340, D-2054 Geesthacht, Germany.

Hong Kong**
Po-on Stamp Service, G.P.O. Box 2498, Hong Kong.

Israel**
Capital Stamps, P.O. Box 3769, Jerusalem 91036, Israel.

Italy*
Secrian Srl, Via Pantelleria 2, I-20156, Milan, Italy.

Japan**
Japan Philatelic Co. Ltd., P.O. Box 2, Suginami-Minami, Tokyo, Japan.

Netherlands*
Davo Publications, P.O. Box 411, 7400 AK Deventer, Netherlands.

New Zealand***
Stanley Gibbons (New Zealand) Ltd., P.O. Box 80, Wellington, New Zealand.

Norway**
Davo Norge A/S, P.O. Box 738 Sentrum, N-0105, Oslo, Norway.

Singapore***
Stanley Gibbons (Singapore) Pte Ltd., Raffles City P.O. Box 1689, Singapore 9117.

South Africa***
Philatelic Holdings (Pty) Ltd., P.O. Box 930, Parklands, RSA 2121.

Republic Coin and Stamp Accessories (Pty) Ltd.,** P.O. Box 11199, Johannesburg, RSA 2000.

Sweden*
Chr Winther Soerensen AB, Box 43, S-310 Knaered, Sweden.

Switzerland**
Phila Service, Burgstrasse 160, CH 4125, Riehen, Switzerland.

USA*
Lighthouse Publications Inc., P.O. Box 750, 274 Washington Avenue, Hackensack, New Jersey 07602–0705, U.S.A.

West Indies/Caribbean**
Hugh Dunphy, P.O. Box 413, Kingston 10, Jamaica, West Indies.

Abbreviations

Anniv.	denotes	Anniversary
Assn.	,,	Association
Bis.	,,	Bistre
Bl.	,,	Blue
Bldg.	,,	Building
Blk.	,,	Black
Br.	,,	British *or* Bridge
Brn.	,,	Brown
B.W.I.	,,	British West Indies
C.A.R.I.F.T.A.	,,	Caribbean Free Trade Area
Cent.	,,	Centenary
Chest.	,,	Chestnut
Choc.	,,	Chocolate
Clar.	,,	Claret
Coll.	,,	College
Commem.	,,	Commemoration
Conf.	,,	Conference
Diag.	,,	Diagonally
E.C.A.F.E.	,,	Economic Commission for Asia and Far East
Emer.	,,	Emerald
E.P.T. Conference	,,	European Postal and Telecommunications Conference
Exn.	,,	Exhibition
F.A.O.	,,	Food and Agriculture Organization
Fig.	,,	Figure
G.A.T.T.	,,	General Agreement on Tariffs and Trade
G.B.	,,	Great Britain
Gen.	,,	General
Govt.	,,	Government
Grn.	,,	Green
Horiz.	,,	Horizontal
H.Q.	,,	Headquarters
Imperf.	,,	Imperforate
Inaug.	,,	Inauguration
Ind.	,,	Indigo
Inscr.	,,	Inscribed or inscription
Int.	,,	International
I.A.T.A.	,,	International Air Transport Association
I.C.A.O.	,,	International Civil Aviation Organization
I.C.Y.	,,	International Co-operation Year
I.G.Y.	,,	International Geophysical Year
I.L.O.	,,	International Labour Office (or later, Organization)
I.M.C.O.	,,	Inter-Governmental Maritime Consultative Organization
I.T.U.	,,	International Telecommunication Union
Is.	,,	Islands
Lav.	,,	Lavender
Mar.	,,	Maroon
mm.	,,	Millimetres
Mult.	,,	Multicoloured

Mve.	denotes	Mauve
Nat.	,,	National
N.A.T.O.	,,	North Atlantic Treaty Organization
O.D.E.C.A.	,,	Organization of Central American States
Ol.	,,	Olive
Optd.	,,	Overprinted
Orge. *or* oran.	,,	Orange
P.A.T.A.	,,	Pacific Area Travel Association
Perf.	,,	Perforated
Post.	,,	Postage
Pres.	,,	President
P.U.	,,	Postal Union
Pur.	,,	Purple
R.	,,	River
R.S.A.	,,	Republic of South Africa
Roul.	,,	Rouletted
Sep.	,,	Sepia
S.E.A.T.O.	,,	South East Asia Treaty Organization
Surch.	,,	Surcharged
T.	,,	Type
T.U.C.	,,	Trades Union Congress
Turq.	,,	Turquoise
Ultram.	,,	Ultramarine
U.N.E.S.C.O.	,,	United Nations Educational, Scientific & Cultural Organization
U.N.I.C.E.F.	,,	United Nations Children's Fund
U.N.O.	,,	United Nations Organization
U.N.R.W.A.	,,	United Nations Relief and Works Agency for Palestine Refugees in the Near East
U.N.T.E.A.	,,	United Nations Temporary Executive Authority
U.N.R.R.A.	,,	United Nations Relief and Rehabilitation Administration
U.P.U.	,,	Universal Postal Union
Verm.	,,	Vermilion
Vert.	,,	Vertical
Vio.	,,	Violet
W.F.T.U.	,,	World Federation of Trade Unions
W.H.O.	,,	World Health Organization
Yell.	,,	Yellow

Arabic Numerals

As in the case of European figures, the details of the Arabic numerals vary in different stamp designs, but they should be readily recognised with the aid of this illustration:

٠	١	٢	٣	٤
0	1	2	3	4
٥	٦	٧	٨	٩
5	6	7	8	9

Key-Types

(see note on page vii)

French Group

A. "Blanc."

B. "Mouchon."

C. "Merson."

D. "Tablet."

E.

F.

G.

H.

"International Colonial Exhibition."

I. "Faidherbe."

J. "Palms."

K. "Balay."

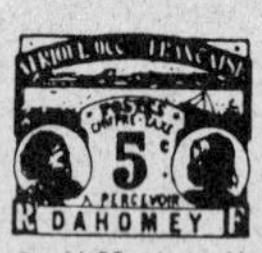
L. "Natives."

M. "Figure."

German Group

N. "Yacht."

O. "Yacht."

Spanish Group

X. "Alfonso XII."

Y. "Baby."

Z. "Curly Head"

Portuguese Group

P. "Crown."

Q. "Embossed."

R. "Figures."

S. "Carlos."

T. "Manoel."

U. "Ceres."

V. "Newspaper."

W. "Due."

STANLEY GIBBONS SIMPLIFIED CATALOGUE OF STAMPS OF THE WORLD—VOLUME 2 COUNTRIES K-Z

KAMPUCHEA Pt. 21

Following the fall of the Khmer Rouge government, which had terminated the Khmer Republic, the People's Republic of Kampuchea was proclaimed on 10 January 1979.

100 cents = 1 riel.

105. Soldiers with Flag and Independence Monument, Phnom Penh.

106. Moscow Kremlin and Globe.

1980. Multicoloured.
402. 0.1 r. Type **105** 60 60
403. 0.2 r. Khmer people and flag .. .. 1·25 1·25
404. 0.5 r. Fisherman pulling in nets .. .. 2·50 2·50
405. 1 r. Armed forces and Kampuchean flag .. 5·50 5·50

1982. 60th Anniv. of U.S.S.R. Mult.
406. 50 c. Type **106** 15 5
407. 1 r. Industrial complex and map of U.S.S.R. .. 45 20

107. Arms of Kampuchea.

1983. 4th Anniv. of People's Republic of Kampuchea. Multicoloured.
408. 50 c. Type **107** 15 5
409. 1 r. Open book illustrating national flag and arms (horiz.) 40 20
410. 3 r. Stylized figures and map .. .. .. 1·40 45

108. Runner with Olympic Torch.

109. "Salatura genutia".

1983. Olympic Games, Los Angeles (1984) (1st issue). Multicoloured.
412. 20 c. Type **108** 8 5
413. 50 c. Javelin throwing .. 15 5
414. 80 c. Pole vaulting .. 25 10
415. 1 r. Discus throwing .. 40 15
416. 1 r. 50 Relay (horiz.) .. 70 20
417. 2 r. Swimming (horiz.) .. 1·10 35
418. 3 r. Basketball .. .. 1·75 45
See also Nos. 526/32.

1983. Butterflies. Multicoloured.
420. 20 c. Type **109** 10 10
421. 50 c. "Euploea althaea juvia" 25 10
422. 80 c. "Byasa polyeuctes termessus" (horiz.) .. 40 15
423. 1 r. "Stichophthalma howqua" (horiz.) .. 60 25
424. 1 r. 50 "Kallima inachus formosana" .. .. 1·10 35
425. 2 r. "Precis orithya orithya" 2·00 65
426. 3 r. "Catopsilia pomona pomona" .. .. 2·75 85

110. Srah Srang.

1983. Khmer Culture. Multicoloured.
427. 20 c. Type **110** 8 5
428. 50 c. Bakong 20 8
429. 80 c. Ta Som (vert.) .. 25 12
430. 1 r. North gate, Angkor Thom (vert.) 45 20
431. 1 r. 50 Kennora (winged figures) (vert.) 80 25
432. 2 r. Apsara (carved figures), Angkor (vert.) 95 35
433. 3 r. Banteai Srei (goddess), Tevoda (vert.) .. 1·50 45

111. Dancers with Castanets.

112. Detail of Fresco.

1983. Folklore. Multicoloured.
434. 50 c. Type **111** 25 8
435. 1 r. Dancers with grass headdresses 60 25
436. 3 r. Dancers with scarves 1·25 45

1983. 500th Birth Anniv. of Raphael.
438. **112.** 20 c. multicoloured .. 8 5
439. – 50 c. multicoloured .. 20 8
440. – 80 c. multicoloured .. 25 12
441. – 1 r. multicoloured .. 45 20
442. – 1 r. 50 multicoloured .. 80 25
443. – 2 r. multicoloured .. 95 35
444. – 3 r. multicoloured .. 1·50 45
DESIGNS: Nos. 439/44, different details of frescoes by Raphael.

113. Montgolfier Balloon.

114. Cobra.

1983. Bicentenary of Manned Flight. Mult.
446. 20 c. Type **113** 10 10
447. 30 c. "La Ville d'Orleans", 1870 .. .. .. 20 10
448. 50 c. Charles' hydrogen balloon 25 15
449. 1 r. Blanchard and Jeffries crossing the Channel, 1785 45 25
450. 1 r. 50 Balloon descent in Arctic 85 30
451. 2 r. Stratosphere balloon .. 1·00 40
452. 3 r. Hot-air balloon race .. 1·60 50

1983. Reptiles. Multicoloured.
454. 20 c. Crested lizard (horiz.) 8 5
455. 30 c. Type **114** 20 8
456. 80 c. Trionyx turtle (horiz.) 25 12
457. 1 r. Chameleon 45 20
458. 1 r. 50 Boa constrictor .. 80 25
459. 2 r. Crocodile (horiz.) .. 95 35
460. 3 r. Turtle (horiz.) .. 1·50 45

115. Rainbow Lory.

116. Sunflower.

1983. Birds Multicoloured.
461. 20 c. Type **115** 15 10
462. 50 c. Barn swallow .. 35 20
463. 80 c. Golden eagle (horiz.) 45 30
464. 1 r. Griffon vulture (horiz.) 80 45
465. 1 r. 50 Javanese collared dove (horiz.) .. .. 1·40 55
466. 2 r. Magpie .. .. .. 1·60 85
467. 3 r. Great Indian hornbill 2·50 1·00

1983. Flowers. Multicoloured.
468. 20 c. Type **116** 8 5
469. 50 c. Caprifoliaceae .. 20 8
470. 80 c. Bougainvillea .. 25 12
471. 1 r. Ranunculaceae .. 45 20
472. 1 r. 50 Nyctagynaeceae .. 80 25
473. 2 r. Cockscomb 95 35
474. 3 r. Roses .. .. .. 1·50 45

117. Luge.

1983. Winter Olympic Games, Sarajevo (1984) (1st issue). Multicoloured.
475. 1 r. Type **117** 45 20
476. 2 r. Biathlon 95 30
477. 4 r. Ski-jumping .. .. 2·00 70
478. 5 r. Two-man bobsleigh .. 2·25 85
479. 7 r. Ice hockey .. .. 3·50 1·25
See also Nos. 496/502.

118. Cyprinidae.

1983. Fishes. Multicoloured.
481. 20 c. Type **118** 8 5
482. 50 c. Trout 20 8
483. 80 c. Catfish 25 12
484. 1 r. Moray eel 45 20
485. 1 r. 50 Cyprinidae (different) 80 25
486. 2 r. Cyprinidae (different) 95 35
487. 3 r. Cyprinidae (different) 1·50 45

119. Factory and Gearwheel.

1983. Festival of Rebirth. Multicoloured.
488 50 c. Type **119** 25 10
489 1 r. Tractor and cow (horiz) 45 20
490 3 r. Bulk carrier, train, car and bridge .. .. 2·50 60

120. Red Cross and Sailing Ship

1984. 5th Anniv. of National Liberation Multicoloured.
492. 50 c. Type **120** 25 8
493. 1 r. Three soldiers, flags and temple 45 20
494. 3 r. Crowd surrounding temple .. .. .. 1·40 50

121. Speed Skating.

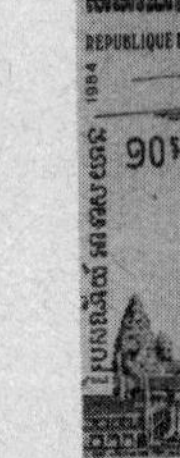

122. Jet over Angkor Vat.

1984. Winter Olympic Games, Sarajevo (2nd issue). Multicoloured.
496. 20 c. Type **121** 8 5
497. 50 c. Ice hockey 20 8
498. 80 c. Skiing 25 12
499. 1 r. Ski jumping 45 20
500. 1 r. 50 Skiing (different) .. 80 25
501. 2 r. Cross-country skiing .. 95 35
502. 3 r. Ice skating (pairs) .. 1·50 45

1984. Air.
504. **122.** 5 r. multicoloured .. 2·25 85
505. 10 r. multicoloured .. 4·50 1·40
506. 15 r. multicoloured .. 7·00 2·25
507. 25 r. multicoloured .. 13·00 4·00

123. Cattle Egret.

124. Doves and Globe.

1984. Birds. Multicoloured.
508. 10 c. Type **123** 10 10
509. 40 c. Black-headed shrike 35 20
510. 80 c. Slaty-headed parakeet 60 30
511. 1 r. Golden-fronted leafbird 1·00 45
512. 1 r. 20 Red-winged crested cuckoo .. .. 1·60 55
513. 2 r. Grey wagtail .. 1·75 75
514. 2 r. 50 Forest wagtail .. 3·00 1·00

1984. International Peace in South-East Asia Forum, Phnom Penh. Multicoloured, background colour given.
515. **124.** 50 c. green 25 8
516. 1 r. blue 45 20
517. 3 r. violet .. .. 1·40 50

125. "Luna 2".

1984. Space Research. Multicoloured.

518. 10 c. "Luna 1" 5 5
519. 40 c. Type **125** 15 8
520. 80 c. "Luna 3" 25 12
521. 1 r. "Soyuz 6" and cosmonauts (vert.) 45 20
522. 1 r. 20 "Soyuz 7" and cosmonautes (vert.) .. 75 25
523. 2 r. "Soyuz 8" and cosmonauts (vert.) 90 35
524. 2 r. 50 Book, rocket and S. P. Korolev (Russian spaceship designer) (vert.) 1·40 45

126. Throwing the Discus.

1984. Olympic Games, Los Angeles (2nd issue). Multicoloured.

526. 20 c. Type **126** 8 5
527. 50 c. Long jumping .. 20 8
528. 80 c. Hurdling 25 12
529. 1 r. Relay 45 20
530. 1 r. 50 Pole vaulting .. 80 25
531. 2 r. Throwing the javelin 95 35
532. 3 r. High jumping .. .. 1·50 45

128. Coyote.

1984. Dog Family. Multicoloured.

535. 10 c. Type **128** 8 5
536. 40 c. Dingo 20 12
537. 80 c. Hunting dog 35 20
538. 1 r. Golden jackal 65 30
539. 1 r. 20 Red fox .. .. 1·00 35
540. 2 r. Maned wolf (vert.) .. 1·25 55
541. 2 r. 50 Wolf .. .. 1·75 70

129. "BB-1002" Type Diesel Locomotive (1966).

1984. Locomotives. Multicoloured.

542 10 c. Type **129** 5 5
543 40 c. "BB-1052" type diesel locomotive (1966) .. 15 8
544 80 c. Franco-Belgian steam locomotive (1945) .. 25 12
545 1 r. "231-505" type steam locomotive (1929) .. 50 20
546 1 r. 20 "803" type railcar (1968) 80 25
547 2 r. "BDE-405" type diesel locomotive (1957) .. 1·10 35
548 2 r. 50 "DS-01" type diesel railcar (1929) .. .. 1·60 50

130. Magnolia.

1984. Flowers. Multicoloured.

549. 10 c. Type **130** 5 5
550. 40 c. "Plumeria" sp. .. 15 8
551. 80 c. "Himenoballis" sp. .. 25 12
552. 1 r. "Peltophorum roxburghii" 45 20
553. 1 r. 20 "Couroupita guianensis" 70 25
554. 2 r. "Lagerstroemia" sp. .. 95 35
555. 2 r. 50 "Thevetia perubiana" 1·40 45

131. Mercedes Benz.

1984. Cars. Multicoloured.

556. 20 c. Type **131** 8 5
557. 50 c. Bugatti 20 8
558. 80 c. Alfa Romeo 25 12
559. 1 r. Franklin 45 20
560. 1 r. 50 Hispano-Suiza .. 80 25
561. 2 r. Rolls Royce 95 35
562. 3 r. Tatra .. .. .. 1·50 45

132. Sra Lai (Rattle).

133. Gazelle.

1984. Musical Instruments. Multicoloured.

564. 10 c. Type **132** 5 5
565. 40 c. Skor drum (horiz.) .. 15 8
566. 80 c. Skor drums (different) 25 12
567. 1 r. Thro khmer (stringed instrument) (horiz.) .. 45 20
568. 1 r. 20 Raneat ek (xylophone) (horiz.) .. 70 25
569. 2 r. Raneat kong (bells) (horiz.) 95 35
570. 2 r. 50 Thro khe (stringed instrument) (horiz.) .. 1·40 45

1984. Mammals. Multicoloured.

571. 10 c. Type **133** 5 5
572. 40 c. Roe deer 15 8
573. 80 c. Hare (horiz.) 25 12
574. 1 r. Red deer 45 20
575. 1 r. 20 Indian elephant .. 70 25
576. 2 r. Genet (horiz.) 90 35
577. 2 r. 50 Kouprey (horiz.) .. 1·40 45

134. "Madonna and Child".

136. Footballers.

135. Bullock Cart.

1984. 450th Death Anniv. of Correggio (artist). Multicoloured.

578. 20 c. Type **134** 8 5
579. 50 c. Detail showing man striking monk 20 8
580. 80 c. "Madonna and Child" (different) 25 12
581. 1 r. "Madonna and Child" (different) 45 20
582. 1 r. 50 "Mystical Marriage of St. Catherine" .. 80 25
583. 2 r. "Pieta" 95 35
584. 3 r. Detail showing man descending ladder .. 1·50 45

1985. 6th Anniv. of People's Republic National Festival. Multicoloured.

586. 50 c. Type **135** 20 5
587. 1 r. Horse-drawn passenger cart 45 20
588. 3 r. Elephants .. .. 1·50 45

1985. World Cup Football Championship, Mexico. Designs showing footballers.

590. **136.** 20 c. multicoloured .. 8 5
591. – 50 c. multicoloured .. 20 8
592. – 80 c. multicoloured .. 25 12
593. – 1 r. multicoloured .. 45 20
594. – 1 r. 50 multicoloured 80 25
595. – 2 r. multicoloured .. 95 35
596. – 3 r. multicoloured .. 1·50 45

137. Eska-Mofa Motor Cycle, 1939

1985. Centenary of Motor Cycle. Mult.

598. 20 c. Type **137** 8 5
599. 50 c. Wanderer, 1939 .. 20 8
600. 80 c. Premier, 1929 .. 25 12
601. 1 r. Ardie, 1939 .. .. 45 20
602. 1 r. 50 Jawa, 1932 .. .. 80 25
603. 2 r. Simson, 1983 .. .. 95 35
604. 3 r. "CZ 125, 1984 .. .. 1·50 45

138. "Gymnopilus spectabilis".

1985. Fungi. Multicoloured.

606 20 c. Type **138** 8 5
607 50 c. "Coprinus micaceus" 20 8
608 80 c. "Amanita panther-ina" 25 12
609 1 r. "Hebeloma crustuliniforme" 45 20
610 1 r. 50 "Amanita muscaria" 80 25
611 2 r. "Coprinus comatus" .. 90 35
612 3 r. "Amanita caesarea" .. 1·50 45

139. "Sputnik 1".

1985. Space Exploration. Multicoloured.

613. 20 c. Type **139** 8 5
614. 50 c. Rocket on transporter and Yuri Gagarin (first man in space) 20 8
615. 80 c. "Vostok 6" and Valentina Tereshkova (first woman in space) .. 25 12
616. 1 r. Space walker 45 20
617. 1 r. 50 "Salyut"–"Soyuz" link 80 25
618. 2 r. "Lunokhod 1" (lunar vehicle) 95 35
619. 3 r. "Venera" (Venus probe) .. .. .. 1·50 45

140. Absara Group.

1985. Traditional Dances. Multicoloured.

621. 50 c. Type **140** 20 8
622. 1 r. Tepmonorom dance .. 45 20
623. 3 r. Absara solo dancer (vert.) .. .. .. 1·50 45

141. Tortoiseshell Cat.

142. "Black Dragon" Lily.

1985. Domestic Cats. Multicoloured.

624. 20 c. Type **141** 8 5
625. 50 c. Tortoiseshell (different) 20 8
626. 80 c. Tabby 25 12
627. 1 r. Long-haired Siamese .. 45 20
628. 1 t. 50 Sealpoint Siamese .. 80 25
629. 2 r. Grey cat 95 35
630. 3 r. Black cat .. .. 1·50 45

1985. Flowers. Multicoloured.

631. 20 c. Type **142** 8 5
632. 50 c. "Iris delavayi" .. 20 8
633. 80 c. "Crocus aureus" .. 25 12
634. 1 r. "Cyclamen persicum" 45 20
635. 1 r. 50 "Primula malacoides" 80 25
636. 2 r. "Viola tricolor Ullswater"" 95 35
637. 3 r. "Crocus purpureus grandiflorus" .. .. 1·50 45

143. "Per Italiani" (Antoine Watteau).

144. Lenin and Arms.

1987. International Music Year. Mult.

638. 20 c. Type **143** 5 8
639. 50 c. "St. Cecilia" (Carlos Saraceni) 20 8
640. 80 c. "Still Life with Violin" (Jean Baptiste Oudry) (horiz.) 25 12
641. 1 r. "Three Musicians" (Fernand Leger) .. 45 20
642. 1 r. 50 Orchestra 80 25
643. 2 r. "St. Cecilia" (Bartholomeo Schedoni) 90 35
644. 3 r. "Harlequin with Violin" (Christian Caillard) .. .. .. 1·50 45

1985. 115th Birth Anniv. of Lenin. Mult.

646. 1 r. Type **144** 45 20
647. 3 r. Lenin on balcony and map .. .. .. 1·50 45

145. Saffron-cowled Blackbird.

1985. "Argentina '85" International Stamp Exhibition, Buenos Aires. Birds. Mult.

648. 20 c. Type **145** 15 10
649. 50 c. Saffron finch (vert.) .. 35 15
650. 80 c. Blue and yellow tanager (vert.) 45 20
651. 1 r. Scarlet-headed blackbird 85 30
652. 1 r. 50 Amazon kingfisher (vert.) .. .. .. 1·40 40
653. 2 r. Toco toucan (vert.) .. 1·60 55
654. 3 r. Rufous-bellied thrush 2·75 70

146. River Launch, 1942.

1985. Water Craft. Multicoloured.

655.	10 c. Type **146**	15	10
656.	40 c. River launch, Cambodia, 1948	35	15
657.	80 c. Tug, Japan, 1913	50	25
658.	1 r. Dredger, Holland	75	35
659.	1 r. 20 Tug, U.S.A.	90	35
660.	2 r. River freighter	1·50	50
661.	2 r. 50 River tanker, Panama	1·90	50

147. "The Flood" (Michelangelo).

148. Son Ngoc Minh.

1985. "Italia '85" International Stamp Exhibition, Rome. Paintings. Multicoloured.

662.	20 r. Type **147**	8	5
663.	50 r. "The Virgin of St. Marguerite" (Mazzola)	20	8
664.	80 r. "The Martyrdom of St. Peter" (Zampieri Domenichino)	25	12
665.	1 r. "Allegory of Spring" (detail) (Sandro Botticelli)	45	20
666.	1 r. 50 "The Sacrifice of Abraham" (Caliari)	80	25
667.	2 r. "The Meeting of Joachim and Anne" (Giotto)	95	35
668.	3 r. "Bacchus" (Michel Angelo Carravaggio)	1·50	45

1985. Festival of Rebirth.

670.	**148.** 50 c. multicoloured	25	10
671.	1 r. multicoloured	50	20
672.	3 r. multicoloured	1·50	50

149. Five-banded Barb.

1985. Fishes. Multicoloured.

673.	20 c. Type **149**	5	5
674.	50 c. "Ophiocephalus micropeltes"	15	5
675.	80 c. Goldfish	25	5
676.	1 r. "Trichogaster leeri"	50	5
677.	1 r. 50 "Puntius hexazona"	70	20
678.	2 r. "Betta splendens"	90	30
679.	3 r. "Datnioides microlepis"	1·25	40

150. Footballers.

152. Jet over Angkor Vat.

151. Cob.

1986. World Cup Football Championship, Mexico. Various footballing scenes.

680.	20 c. multicoloured	5	5
681.	50 c. multicoloured	15	5
682.	80 c. multicoloured	25	10
683.	1 r. multicoloured	45	15
684.	1 r. 50 multicoloured	65	20
685.	2 r. multicoloured	80	30
686.	3 r. multicoloured	1·25	40

1986. Horses. Multicoloured.

688	20 c. Type **151**	5	5
689	50 c. Arab	15	5
690	80 c. Australian pony	25	10
691	1 r. Appaloosa	45	15
692	1 r. 50 Quarter horse	65	20
693	2 r. Vladimir heavy draught horse	65	30
694	3 r. Andalusian	1·25	40

1986. Air.

695.	**152.** 5 r. multicoloured	2·25	75
696.	10 r. multicoloured	4·50	1·25
697.	15 r. multicoloured	6·50	2·00
698.	25 r. multicoloured	12·00	3·50

153. Edaphosaurus.

1986. Prehistoric Animals. Multicoloured.

699	20 c. Type **153**	5	5
700	50 c. Sauroctonus	15	5
701	80 c. Mastodonsaurus	25	10
702	1 r. Rhamphorhynchus (vert)	45	15
703	1 r. 50 Brachiosaurus brancai (vert)	65	20
704	2 r. Tarbosaurus bataar (vert)	80	30
705	3 r. Indricotherium (vert)	1·25	40

154. "Luna 3".

1986. 25th Anniv. of First Man in Space. Multicoloured.

706.	10 c. Type **154**	5	5
707.	40 c. "Vostok"	15	5
708.	80 c. "Vostok" with rocket	25	10
709.	1 r. Cosmonaut Leonov on space walk	45	15
710.	1 r. 20 "Salyut" and "Soyuz" preparing to dock	55	20
711.	2 r. Soviet space station	80	30
712.	2 r. 50 Cosmonaut Leonov and spacecraft	1·00	40

155. Baksei Chmkrong Temple, 920.

1986. Khmer Culture. Multicoloured.

713.	20 c. Type **155**	5	5
714.	50 c. Buddha's head	15	5
715.	80 c. Prea Vihear monastery, Dangrek	25	10
716.	1 r. Fan with design of man and woman	45	15
717.	1 r. 50 Fan with design of men fighting	65	20
718.	2 r. Fan with design of dancer	80	30
719.	3 r. Fan with design of dragon-drawn chariot	1·25	40

156. Tricar, 1885.

1986. Centenary (1985) of Motor Car. Mercedes Benz Models. Multicoloured.

720.	20 c. Type **156**	5	5
721.	50 c. Limousine, 1935	15	5
722.	80 c. Open tourer, 1907	25	10
723.	1 r. Light touring car, 1920	45	15
724.	1 r. 50 Cabriolet, 1932	65	20
725.	2 r. "SKK" tourer, 1938	80	30
726.	3 r. "190", 1985	1·25	40

157. "Danaus genutia".

159. Solar System, Copernicus, Galileo and Tycho Brahe (astronomers).

158. English Kogge of Richard II's Reign.

1986. Butterflies. Multicoloured.

727.	20 c. Type **157**	10	10
728.	50 c. "Graphium amtiphates"	25	10
729.	80 c. "Papilio demoleus"	45	20
730.	1 r. "Danaus sita"	80	30
731.	1 r. 50 "Idea blanchardi"	1·10	45
732.	2 r. "Papilio polytes"	1·50	65
733.	3 r. "Dabasa payeni"	2·40	95

1986. Medieval Ships.

734.	20 c. Type **158**	10	10
735.	50 c. Kogge	20	10
736.	80 c. Knarr	35	10
737.	1 r. Galley	60	15
738.	1 r. 50 Norman ship	90	25
739.	2 r. Mediterranean usciere	1·10	35
740.	3 r. French kogge	1·75	45

1986. Appearance of Halley's Comet. Mult.

741.	10 c. Type **159**	5	5
742.	20 c. "Nativity" (Giotto) and comet from Bayeux Tapestry	5	5
743.	50 c. Comet, 1910, and Mt. Palomar observatory, U.S.A.	15	5
744.	80 c. Edmond Halley and "Planet A" space probe	25	10
745.	1 r. 20 Diagram of comet's trajectory and "Giotto" space probe	55	20
746.	1 r. 50 "Vega" space probe and camera	65	20
747.	2 r. Thermal pictures of comet	80	30

160. Ruy Lopez Segura.

1986. "Stockholmia 86" International Stamp Exhibition. Chess. Multicoloured.

749	20 c. Type **160**	5	5
750	50 c. Francois-Andre Philidor	15	5
751	80 c. Karl Anderssen and Houses of Parliament, London	25	10
752	1 r. Wilhelm Steinitz and Charles Bridge, Prague	45	15
753	1 r. 50 Emanuel Lasker and medieval knight	65	20
754	2 r. Jose Capablanca and Morro Castle, Cuba	80	30
755	3 r. Aleksandr Alekhine	1·25	40

161. "Parodia maassii".

162. Bananas.

1986. Cacti. Multicoloured.

757.	20 c. Type **161**	5	5
758.	50 c. "Rebutia marsoneri"	15	5
759.	80 c. "Melocactus evae"	25	10
760.	1 r. "Gymnocalycium valnicekianum"	45	15
761.	1 r. 50 "Discocactus silichromus"	70	20
762.	2 r. "Neochilenia simulans"	90	30
763.	3 r. "Weingartia chiquichuquensis"	1·25	40

1986. Fruit. Multicoloured.

764.	10 c. Type **162**	5	5
765.	40 c. Papaya	15	5
766.	80 c. Mangoes	25	10
767.	1 r. Breadfruit	45	15
768.	1 r. 20 Lychees	55	20
769.	2 r. Pineapple	90	30
770.	2 r. 50 Grapefruit (horiz.)	1·10	45

163. "Concorde".

1986. Aircraft. Multicoloured.

771.	20 c. Type **163**	10	10
772.	50 c. "DC-10"	20	10
773.	80 c. Boeing "747"	35	10
774.	1 r. Ilyushin "IL-62"	60	15
775.	1 r. 50 Ilyushin "IL-86"	95	25
776.	2 r. "AN-124"	1·25	35
777.	3 r. "A-300" airbus	1·60	45

164. Elephant and Silver Containers on Tray.

1986. Festival of Rebirth. Silverware. Mult.

778.	50 c. Type **164**	25	10
779.	1 r. Tureen	50	20
780.	3 r. Dish on stand	1·50	50

165. Kouprey.

1986. Endangered Animals. Cattle. Mult.

781.	20 c. Type **165**	5	5
782.	20 c. Gaur	5	5
783.	80 c. Bateng cow and calf	25	10
784.	1 r. 50 Asiatic water buffalo	70	20

166. Tou Samuth (revolutionary).

1987. National Festival. 8th Anniv. of People's Republic.
785. **166.** 50 c. multicoloured .. 5 5
786. 1 r. multicoloured .. 12 5
787. 3 r. multicoloured .. 35 10

167. Biathlon.

1987. Winter Olympic Games, Calgary (1988) (1st issue). Multicoloured.
788. 20 c. Type **167** 5 5
789. 50 c. Figure skating .. 5 5
790. 80 c. Speed skating .. 8 5
791. 1 r. Ice hockey 12 5
792. 1 r. 50 Two-man luge .. 15 5
793. 2 r. Two-man bobsleigh .. 25 10
794. 3 r. Cross-country skiing .. 35 10
See also Nos. 864/70.

168. Weightlifting.

1987. Olympic Games, Seoul (1988) (1st issue). Multicoloured.
796. 20 c. Type **168** 5 5
797. 50 c. Archery (horiz.) .. 5 5
798. 80 c. Fencing (horiz.) .. 8 5
799. 1 r. Gymnastics 12 5
800. 1 r. 50 Discus throwing (horiz.) 15 5
801. 2 r. Javelin throwing .. 25 10
802. 3 r. Hurdling 35 10
See also Nos. 875/81.

169. Papillon.

1987. Dogs. Multicoloured.
804. 20 c. Type **169** 5 5
805. 50 c. Greyhound 5 5
806. 80 c. Great dane 8 5
807. 1 r. Doberman 12 5
808. 1 r. 50 Samoyed 15 5
809. 2 r. Borzoi 25 10
810. 3 r. Rough collie 35 10

170. "Sputnik 1".

171. Flask.

1987. Space Exploration. Multicoloured.
811. 20 c. Type **170** 5 5
812. 50 c. "Soyuz 10" 5 5
813. 80 c. "Proton" 8 5
814. 1 r. "Vostok 1" 12 5
815. 1 r. 50 "Salyut" 15 5
816. 2 r. "Kosmos" 25 10
817. 3 r. "Luna 2" 35 10

1987. Metalwork. Multicoloured.
819. 50 c. Type **171** 5 5
820. 1 r. Repousse box 12 5
821. 1 r. 50 Teapot and cups on tray 15 5
822. 3 r. Ornamental sword .. 35 10

172. Carmine Bee Eater.

1987. "Capex '87" International Stamp Exhibition, Toronto. Birds. Multicoloured.
823 20 c. Type **172** 15 10
824 50 c. Hoopoe (vert) .. 15 10
825 80 c. South African crowned crane (vert) .. 20 10
826 1 r. Barn owl (vert) .. 30 10
827 1 r. 50 Grey-headed kingfisher (vert) 40 15
828 2 r. Red-whiskered bulbul 65 20
829 3 r. Purple heron (vert) .. 90 25

173. Horatio F. Phillips's Machine, 1893.

1987. Experimental Aircraft Designs. Mult.
831. 20 c. Type **173** 10 10
832. 50 c. John Stringfellow, 1848 .. .. .. 10 10
833. 80 c. Thoms Moy, 1875 .. 15 10
834. 1 r. Leonardo da Vinci, 1490 .. .. .. 20 10
835. 1 r. 50 Sir George Cayley, 1840 .. .. .. 25 10
836. 2 r. Sir Hiram Maxim, 1894 40 15
837. 3 r. William Samuel Henson, 1842 .. .. 55 15

174. Giant Tortoise.

1987. Reptiles. Multicoloured.
839. 20 c. Type **174** 5 5
840. 50 c. "Uromastix acanthinuros" 5 5
841. 80 c. "Cyclura macleayi" 8 5
842. 1 r. "Phrynosoma coronatum" 12 5
843. 1 r. 50 "Sauromalus obesus" 15 5
844. 2 r. "Ophisaurus apodus" 25 10
845. 3 r. "Thamnophis sirtalis tetrataenia" 35 10

175. "KA-15".

1987. "Hafnia 87" International Stamp Exhibition, Copenhagen. Helicopters. Mult.
846. 20 c. Type **175** 10 10
847. 50 c. "KA-18" 10 10
848. 80 c. "Lynx" ("WG-13") .. 15 10
849. 1 r. "Gazelle" 20 10
850. 1 r. 50 "Puma" 25 10
851. 2 r. Boeing "CH-47" "Chinook" 40 15
852. 3 r. Boeing "UTTAS" .. 55 15

176. Magirus-Deutz No. 21.

1987. Fire Engines. Multicoloured.
854. 20 c. Type **176** 5 5
855. 50 c. "SIL-131" rescue vehicle 5 5
856. 80 c. "Cas-25" fire pump .. 8 5
857. 1 r. Sirmac Saab "424" .. 12 5
858. 1 r. 50 Rosenbaum-Falcon 15 5
859. 2 r. Tatra "815-PRZ" .. 25 10
860. 3 r. Chubbfire "C-44-20" .. 35 10

177. Earth Station Dish Aerial.

178. Speed Skating.

1987. Telecommunications. Multicoloured.
861. 50 c. Type **177** 5 5
862. 1 r. Technological building with radio microwave aerial 12 5
863. 3 r. Intersputnik programme earth station (horiz.) 35 10

1988. Winter Olympic Games, Calgary (2nd issue). Multicoloured.
864. 20 c. Type **178** 5 5
865. 50 c. Ice hockey 5 5
866. 80 c. Slalom 8 5
867. 1 r. Ski jumping 12 5
868. 1 r. 50 Biathlon 15 5
869. 2 r. Ice dancing 25 10
870. 3 r. Cross-country skiing .. 35 10

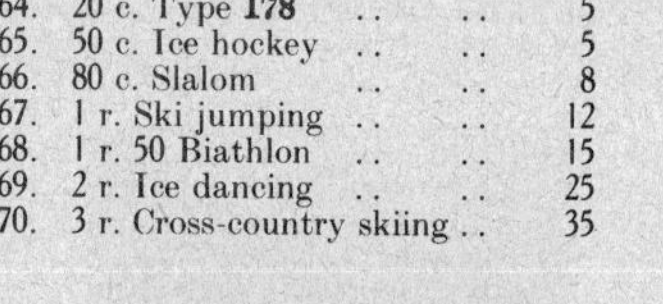

179. Irrigation Canal Bed.

1988. Irrigation Projects. Multicoloured.
872. 50 c. Type **179** 5 5
873. 1 r. Dam construction .. 12 5
874. 3 r. Dam and bridge .. 35 10

180. Beam Exercise.

1988. Olympic Games, Seoul (2nd issue). Women's Gymnastics. Multicoloured.
875. 20 c. Type **180** 5 5
876. 50 c. Bar exercise (horiz.) 5 5
877. 80 c. Ribbon exercise .. 8 5
878. 1 r. Hoop exercise 12 5
879. 1 r. 50 Baton exercise .. 15 5
880. 2 r. Ball exercise (horiz.) .. 25 10
881. 3 r. Floor exercise (horiz.) 35 10

181. White Long-haired Cat.

1988. "Juvalux 88" 9th Youth Philately Exhibition, Luxembourg. Cats. Multicoloured.
883. 20 c. Type **181** 5 5
884. 50 c. Abyssinian (vert.) .. 5 5
885. 80 c. Ginger and white long-haired cat (vert.) .. 8 5
886. 1 r. Tortoiseshell queen and kitten 12 5
887. 1 r. 50 Brown cat (vert.) .. 15 5
888. 2 r. Black long-haired cat (vert.) 25 10
889. 3 r. Grey cat (vert.) .. 35 10

182. "Emerald Seas" (liner).

1988. "Essen 88" International Stamp Fair. Ships. Multicoloured.
891 20 c. Type **182** 10 10
892 50 c. Car ferry 10 10
893 80 c. Freighter 10 10
894 1 r. "Kosmonavt Yury Gagarin" (research ship) 20 10
895 1 r. 50 Tanker 25 10
896 2 r. Hydrofoil 40 10
897 3 r. Hovercraft 55 10

183. Satellite.

185. "Helicostyla florida".

184. "Xiphophorus helleri".

1988. Space Exploration. Designs showing different satellites.
899. **183.** 20 c. multicoloured .. 5 5
900. – 50 c. multicoloured .. 5 5
901. – 80 c. multicoloured .. 8 5
902. – 1 r. mult. (horiz.) .. 12 5
903. – 1 r. 50 mult. (horiz) .. 15 5
904. – 2 r. mult. (horiz.) .. 25 10
905. – 3 r. mult. (horiz.) .. 35 10

1988. "Finlandia 88" International Stamp Exhibition, Helsinki. Tropical Fish. Mult.
907. 20 c. Type **184** 5 5
908. 50 c. "Hemigrammus ocellifer ocellifer" .. 5 5
909. 80 c. "Macropodus opercularis" 8 5
910. 1 r. "Carassius auratus auratus" 12 5
911. 1 r. 50 "Hyphessobrycon ineai" 15 5
912. 2 r. "Corynopoma riisei" .. 25 10
913. 3 r. "Mollienisia latipinna" 35 10

1988. Sea Shells. Multicoloured.
915. 20 c. Type **185** 5 5
916. 50 c. "Helicostyla marinduquensis" .. 5 5
917. 80 c. "Helicostyla fulgens" 8 5
918. 1 r. "Helicostyla woodiana" 12 5
919. 1 r. 50 "Chloraea sirena" .. 15 5
920. 2 r. "Helicostyla mirabilis" 25 10
921. 3 r. "Helicostyla limansauensis" 35 10

186 "Coccinella septempunctata"

1988. Insects. Multicoloured.
922 20 c. Type **186** 30 30
923 50 c. "Zonabride geminata" 35 30
924 80 c. "Carabus auronitens" 60 30
925 1 r. "Apis mellifera" .. 85 30
926 1 r. 50 "Mantis sp." .. 1·00 30
927 2 r. "Aeshna sp." .. 1·60 50
928 3 r. "Malachius aeneus" .. 2·40 50

187 "Cattleya aclandiae"

1988. Orchids. Multicoloured.

929	20 c. Type **187**	5	5
930	50 c. "Odontoglossum" "Royal Sovereign" ..	5	5
931	80 c. "Cattleya labiata" ..	8	5
932	1 r. "Ophrys apifera" ..	12	5
933	1 r. 50 "Laelia anceps" ..	15	5
934	2 r. "Laelia pumila" ..	25	10
935	3 r. "Stanhopea tigrina" (horiz)	35	10

188 Egyptian Banded Cobra

189 Walking Dance

1988. Reptiles. Multicoloured.

936	20 c. Type **188**	5	5
937	50 c. Common iguana ..	5	5
938	80 c. Long-nosed vine snake (horiz)	8	5
939	1 r. Common box turtle (horiz)	12	5
940	1 r. 50 Iguana (horiz) ..	15	5
941	2 r. Viper (horiz)	25	10
942	3 r. Common cobra ..	35	10

1988. Festival of Rebirth. Khmer Culture. Multicoloured.

943	50 c. Type **189**	5	5
944	1 r. Peacock dance ..	12	5
945	3 r. Kantere dance ..	35	10

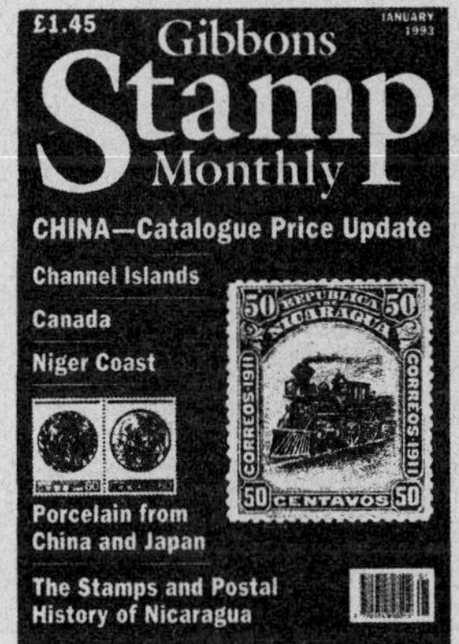

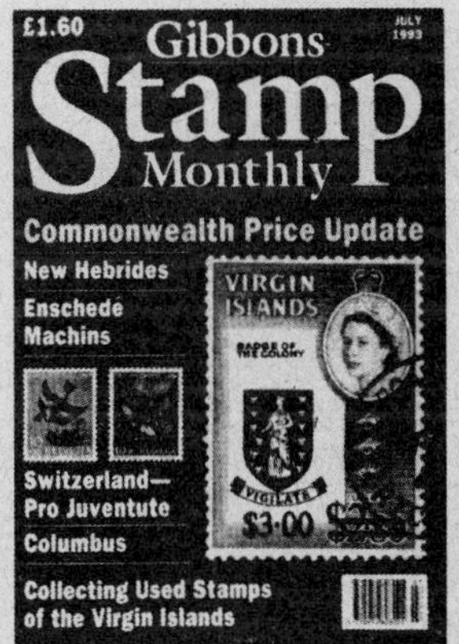

KATANGA Pt. 14

The following stamps were issued by Mr. Tshombe's Government for independent Katanga. In 1963 Katanga was reunited with the Central Government of Congo.

1960. Various stamps of Belgian Congo optd. **KATANGA** and bar or surch. also.

(a) Masks issue of 1948.

1. 1 f. 50 on 1 f. 25 mauve & blue 50 20
2. 3 f. 50 on 2 f. 50 green & brn. 50 25
3. 20 f. purple and red .. .. 1·75 90
4. 50 f. black and brown .. 4·00 3·25
5. 100 f. black and red .. .. 30·00 22·00

(b) Flowers issue of 1952. Flowers in natural colours; colours given are of backgrounds and inscriptions.

6. 10 c. yellow and purple .. 8 8
7. 15 c. green and red .. 8 8
8. 20 c. grey and green .. 12 12
9. 25 c. orange and green .. 15 15
10. 40 c. salmon and green .. 12 12
11. 50 c. turquoise and red .. 20 20
12. 60 c. purple and green .. 15 15
13. 75 c. grey and lake 20 20
14. 1 f. lemon and red 25 25
15. 2 f. buff and olive 30 30
16. 3 f. pink and green 40 35
17. 4 f. lavender and sepia .. 60 50
18. 5 f. green and purple .. 60 50
19. 6 f. 50 lilac and red .. 60 45
20. 7 f. brown and green .. 80 70
21. 8 f. yellow and green .. 80 70
22. 10 f. olive and purple .. 11·50 9·00

(c) Wild animals issue of 1959.

23. 10 c. brown, sepia and blue 12 10
24. 20 c. blue and red 12 10
25. 40 c. brown and blue .. 15 10
26. 50 c. multicoloured .. 15 10
27. 1 f. black, green and brown 5·25 3·25
28. 1 f. 50 black and yellow .. 8·75 6·00
29. 2 f. black, brown and red .. 40 10
30. 3 f. black, purple and slate 3·25 2·50
31. 5 f. brown, green and sepia 60 25
32. 6 f. 50 brown, yellow & blue 75 25
33. 8 f. bistre, violet and brown 1·10 35
34. 10 f. multicoloured .. 1·60 50

(d) Madonna.

35. **102.** 50 c. brn., ochre & chest. 15 15
36. 1 f. brown, violet & blue 15 15
37. 2 f. brown, blue and slate 20 20

(e) African Technical Co-operation Commission. Inscr. in French or Flemish.

38. **103.** 3 f. salmon and slate .. 7·00 7·00
39. 3 f. 50 on 3 f. sal. & slate 2·10 2·10

1960. Independence. Independence issue of Congo optd. **11 JUILLET DE L'ETAT DU KATANGA.**

40. **106.** 20 c. bistre 5 5
41. 50 c. red 5 5
42. 1 f. green 8 8
43. 1 f. 50 brown 8 8
44. 2 f. mauve 10 10
45. 3 f. 50 violet 12 10
46. 5 f. blue 12 10
47. 6 f. 50 black 15 10
48. 10 f. orange 25 20
49. 20 f. blue 45 30

5. 6. Pres. Tshombe.

1961. Katanga Art.

50. **5.** 10 c. green 5 5
51. 20 c. violet 5 5
52. 50 c. blue 5 5
53. 1 f. 50 green 5 5
54. 2 f. brown 5 5
55. – 3 f. 50 blue 5 5
56. – 5 f. turquoise 8 5
57. – 6 f. brown 10 5
58. – 6 f. 50 blue 10 8
59. – 8 f. purple 12 8
60. – 10 f. brown 15 10
61. – 20 f. myrtle 25 20
62. – 50 f. brown 50 40
63. – 100 f. turquoise 85 70

DESIGNS: 3 f. 50 to 8 f. "Preparing food". 10 f. to 100 f. "Family circle".

1961. 1st Anniv. of Independence. Portrait in brown.

64. **6.** 6 f. 50+5 f. red, green & gold .. .. .. 1·25 1·00
65. 8 f.+5 f. red, green and gold .. .. .. 1·25 1·00
66. 10 f.+5 f. red, green and gold .. .. .. 1·25 1·00

7. "Tree".

8. Early Aircraft, Train and Safari.

1961. Katanga International Fair. Vert. symbolic designs as T 7.

67. **7.** 50 c. red, green and black 10 10
68. – 1 f. black and blue .. 10 10
69. – 2 f. 50 black and yellow .. 12 12
70. **7.** 3 f. red, brown and black 15 15
71. – 5 f. black and violet .. 25 25
72. – 6 f. 50 black and orange .. 30 30

1961. Air.

73. **8.** 3 f. 50 multicoloured .. 3·00 3·00
74. – 6 f. 50 multicoloured .. 1·10 1·10
75. **8.** 8 f. multicoloured .. 3·25 3·00
76. – 10 f. multicoloured .. 2·10 1·10

DESIGNS: 6 f. 50, 10 f. Tail of aeroplane.

9. Gendarme in armoured Vehicle.

1962. Katanga Gendarmerie.

77. **9.** 6 f. multicoloured .. 2·25 2·25
78. 8 f. multicoloured .. 35 35
79. 10 f. multicoloured .. 45 45

POSTAGE DUE STAMPS

1960. Postage Due stamps of Belgian Congo handstamped **KATANGA.**

(a) On Nos. D 270/4.

D 50. **D 86.** 10 c. olive 80 80
D 51. 20 c. blue 80 80
D 52. 50 c. green .. .. 1·00 1·00
D 53. 1 f. brown .. ..
D 54. 2 f. orange .. ..

(b) On Nos. D 330/6.

D 55. **D 99.** 10 c. brown .. 3·25 3·25
D 56. 20 c. purple .. 3·25 3·25
D 57. 50 c. green .. .. 3·25 3·25
D 58. 1 f. blue .. .. 1·00 1·00
D 59. 2 f. red .. .. 2·00 2·00
D 60. 4 f. violet .. .. 2·75 2·75
D 61. 6 f. blue .. .. 3·25 3·25

KHMER REPUBLIC Pt. 21

Cambodia was renamed Khmer Republic on 9th October 1970.

100 cents = 1 riel.

78. "Attack".

1971. Defence of Khmer Territory.

285. **78.** 1 r. multicoloured .. 5 5
286. 3 r. multicoloured .. 10 8
287. 10 r. multicoloured .. 40 20

79. "World Races" and U.N. Emblem.

1971. Racial Equality Year.

288. **79.** 3 r. multicoloured .. 10 8
289. 7 r. multicoloured .. 30 15
290. 8 r. multicoloured .. 40 25

80. General Post Office, Phnom Penh.

1971.

291. **80.** 3 r. multicoloured .. 15 15
292. 9 r. multicoloured .. 35 20
293. 10 r. multicoloured .. 40 30

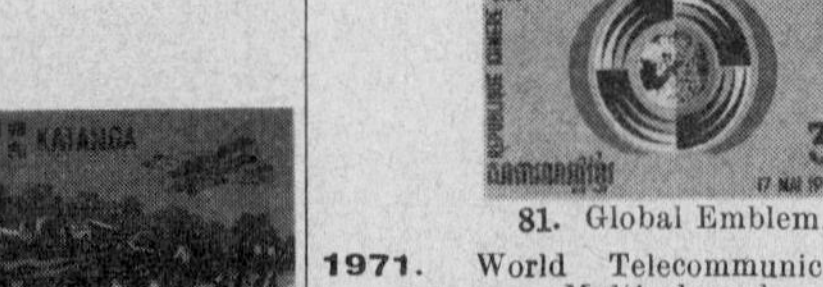
81. Global Emblem.

1971. World Telecommunications Day. Multicoloured.

294. 3 r. Type **81** 10 5
295. 4 r. Type **81** 20 8
296. 7 r. I.T.U. emblem .. 25 15
297. 8 r. I.T.U. emblem .. 35 15

82. "Erythrina indica".

1971. Wild Flowers. Multicoloured.

298. 2 r. Type **82** 15 15
299. 3 r. "Bauhinia variegata" 20 20
300. 6 r. "Butea frondosa" .. 40 20
301. 10 r. "Lagerstroemia floribunda" (vert.) .. 55 45

83. Arms of the Republic. 84. Monument and Flag.

1971. 1st Anniv of Republic.

302 **83** 3 r. bistre and green .. 15 5
303 **84** 3 r. multicoloured .. 10 5
304 4 r. multicoloured .. 15 8
305 **83** 8 r. bistre and orange .. 20 10
306 10 r. bistre and brown 40 15
307 **84** 10 r. multicoloured .. 40 20

85. U.N.I.C.E.F. Emblem. 86. Book Year Emblem.

1971. 25th Anniv. of U.N.I.C.E.F.

309. **85.** 3 r. purple 15 10
310. 5 r. blue 20 15
311. 9 r. red and violet .. 45 30

1972. Int. Book Year.

312. **86.** 3 r. grn., pur. & blue .. 15 8
313. 8 r. blue, grn. & purple 25 15
314. 9 r. bistre, blue & green 40 20

87. Lion of St. Mark's.

1972. U.N.E.S.C.O. "Save Venice" Campaign.

316. **87.** 3 r. brn., buff & pur. .. 15 10
317. – 5 r. brn., buff & grn. .. 30 15
318. – 10 r. brn., bl. & grn. .. 50 20

DESIGNS—HORIZ. 5 r. St. Mark's Basilica. VERT. 10 r. Bridge of Sighs.

88. U.N. Emblem. 89. Dancing Apsaras (relief), Angkor.

1972. 25th Anniv. of Economic Commission for Asia and the Far East (C.E.A.E.O.).

320. **88.** 3 r. red 15 5
321. 6 r. blue 20 10
322. 9 r. red 40 20

1972.

324. **89.** 1 r. brown 8 5
325. 3 r. violet 8 5
326. 7 r. red 20 15
327. 8 r. brown 30 15
328. 9 r. green 35 20
329. 10 r. blue 50 20
330. 12 r. purple 65 25
331. 14 r. blue 80 40

INDEX

Countries can be quickly located by referring to the index at the end of this volume.

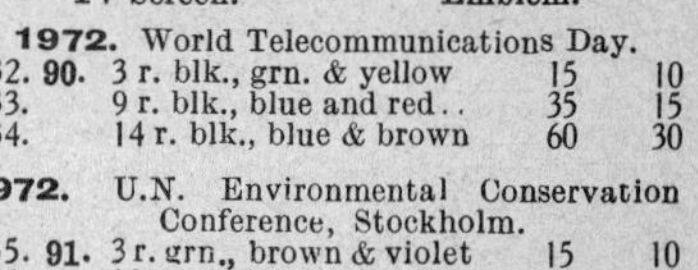
90. "UIT" on TV Screen. 91. Conference Emblem.

1972. World Telecommunications Day.

332. **90.** 3 r. blk., grn. & yellow 15 10
333. 9 r. blk., blue and red .. 35 15
334. 14 r. blk., blue & brown 60 30

1972. U.N. Environmental Conservation Conference, Stockholm.

335. **91.** 3 r. grn., brown & violet 15 10
336. 12 r. violet and green .. 40 20
337. 15 r. green and violet .. 55 35

92. Javan Rhinoceros. 94. Hoisting Flag.

1972. Wild Animals.

339. **92.** 3 r. blk., red and violet 25 10
340. – 4 r. violet, brn. & purple 35 10
341. – 6 r. brn., green & blue .. 60 20
342. – 7 r. brn., green & bistre 60 20
343. – 8 r. blk., green and blue 85 20
344. – 10 r. black, blue & green 1·25 30

DESIGNS: 4 r. Mainland serow. 6 r Thamin. 7 r. Banteng. 8 r. Water buffalo. 10 r. Gaur.

1972. Olympic Games, Munich. Nos. 164 of Cambodia and 302, 306 and 336/7 of Khmer Republic optd **XXe JEUX OLYMPIQUES MUNICH 1972**, Olympic rings and emblem.

345 **83** 3 r. brown and green .. 25 20
346 10 r. bistre and brown 60 50
347 – 12 r. green and brown .. 1·50 50
348 **91** 12 r. violet and green .. 65 50
349 15 r. green and violet .. 65 50

1972. 2nd Anniv. of Republic.

350. **94.** 3 r. multicoloured .. 10 8
351. 5 r. multicoloured .. 15 10
352. 9 r. multicoloured .. 35 20

1972. Red Cross Aid for War Victims. No. 164 of Cambodia and 302, 306 and 336/7 of Khmer Republic surch **SECOURS AUX VICTIMES DE GUERRE**, red cross and value.

353 **83** 3 r.+2 r. brown & green 20 20
354 10 r.+6 r. bistre & brn 45 45
355 – 12 r.+7 r. green & brn 1·75 55
356 **91** 12 r.+7 r. violet & green 55 55
357 15 r.+8 r. green & violet 1·00 1·00

96. Garuda. 97. Crest and Temple.

1973. Air.

358. **96.** 3 r. red 15 15
359. 30 r. blue .. .. 1·25 70
360. 50 r. lilac .. .. 2·40 1·40
361. 100 r. green .. .. 4·00 2·25

1973. New Constitution.

362. **97.** 3 r. multicoloured .. 10 10
363. 12 r. multicoloured .. 15 15
364. 14 r. multicoloured .. 30 20

98. Apsara.

99. Interpol Emblem.

1973. Angkor Sculptures.

366. **98.** 3 r. black 10 8
367. – 8 r. blue 15 8
368. – 10 r. brown 30 15

DESIGNS: 8 r. Devata (12th century). 10 r. Devata (10th century).

1973. 50th Anniv. of International Criminal Police Organization (Interpol).

370.	**99.**	3 r. green and turquoise	10	10
371.		7 r. green and brown ..	15	15
372.		10 r. green and brown ..	30	15

100. Marshal Lon Nol.

1973. Honouring Marshal Lon Nol, 1st President of Republic.

374.	**100.**	3 r. blk., brn. & grn. ..	10	8
375.		8 r. brn., blk. and green	15	10
376.		14 r. brown and black ..	20	15

102. Copernicus and Space Rocket.

1974. 500th Birth Anniv. of Nicolas Copernicus (astronomer). Multicoloured.

382.	1 r. Type **102** (postage) ..	5	5
383.	5 r. Copernicus and "Mariner II"	5	5
384.	10 r. Copernicus and "Apollo"	10	5
385.	25 r. Copernicus and "Telstar"	25	12
386.	50 r. Copernicus and space-walker	45	25
387.	100 r. Copernicus and spaceship landing on Moon	1·00	50
388.	150 r. Copernicus, and Moon-landing craft leaving "Apollo" ..	1·40	70
389.	200 r. Copernicus and "Skylab III' (air) ..	1·75	90
390.	250 r. Copernicus and "Concorde"	3·25	1·40

1974. 4th Anniv. of Republic. Various stamps optd. **4E ANNIVERSAIRE DE LA REPUBLIQUE.**

391.	**78.**	10 r. multicoloured ..	50	35
392.	**77.**	50 r. on 3 r. multicoloured	1·40	1·10
393.	**94.**	100 r. on 5 r. multi-colured	3·00	2·25

No. 392 is additionally optd. **REPUBLIQUE KHMERE** in French and Cambodian.

104. Xylophone.

1975. Unissued stamps of Cambodia showing musical instruments, surch **"REPUBLIQUE KHMERE"** in French and Cambodian and new value. Multicoloured.

394.	5 r. on 8 r. Type **104** ..	
395.	20 r. on 1 r. So (two string violin)	
396.	160 r. on 7 r. Khoung vong (bronze gongs)	
397.	180 r. on 14 r. Two drums	
398.	235 r. on 12 r. Barrel-shaped drum	
399.	500 r. on 9 r. Xylophone (different)	
400.	1000 r. on 10 r. Boat-shaped xylophone ..	
401.	2000 r. on 3 r. Twenty-stringed guitar on legs .. Set of 8	£150

POSTAGE DUE STAMPS

D 101. Frieze, Angkor Vat.

1974.

D 378.	**D101.**	2 r. brown	10	10
D 379.		6 r. green	20	20
D 380.		8 r. mauve	20	20
D 381.		10 r. blue	30	30

APPENDIX

The following stamps have either been issued in excess of postal needs or have not been available to the public in reasonable quantities at face value. Such stamps may later be given full listing if there is evidence of regular postal use.

1972.

Moon Landing of "Apollo 16". Embossed on gold foil. Air 900 r. × 2.

Visit of Pres. Nixon to China. Embossed on gold foil. Air 900 r. × 2.

Olympic Games, Munich. Embossed on gold foil. Air 900 r. × 2.

1973.

Gold Medal Winners, Munich Olympics. Embossed on gold foil. Air 900 r. × 2.

World Cup Football Championships, West Germany (1974). Embossed on gold foil. Air 900 r. × 4.

1974.

Pres. Kennedy and "Apollo 11". Embossed on gold foil. Air 1100 r. × 2.

500th Birth Anniv. of Nicolas Copernicus (astronomer). Embossed on gold foil. Air 1200 r.

Centenary of U.P.U. (1st issue). Postage 10, 60 r.; Air 700 r., 1200 r. Embossed on gold foil.

1975.

Olympic Games, Montreal (1976). Postage 5, 10, 15, 25 r.; Air 50, 100, 150, 200, 250 r., 1200 r. embossed on gold foil.

World Cup Football Championships, West Germany (1974). Postage 1, 5, 10, 25 r.; Air 50, 100, 150, 200, 250 r., 1200 r. embossed on gold foil.

Centenary of U.P.U. (2nd issue). Postage 15, 20, 70, 160, 180, 235 r.; Air 500, 1000, 2000 r., 2000 r. embossed on gold foil.

KHOR FAKKAN

From 1965 various issues were produced for this dependency, some being overprinted on, or in the same designs as, issues for Sharjah.

APPENDIX

The following stamps have either been issued in excess of postal needs or have not been available to the public in reasonable quantities at face value. Such stamps may later be given full listing if there is evidence of regular postal use.

1965.

Views. Nos. 75/80 of Sharjah optd. Air 10, 20, 30, 40, 75, 100 n.p.

Boy and Girl Scouts. Nos. 74 and 89 of Sharjah optd. 2, 2 r.

Birds. Nos. 101/6 of Sharjah optd. Air 30, 40, 75, 150 n.p., 2, 3 r.

Olympic Games, Tokyo 1964. Nos. 95/7 of Sharjah optd. 40, 50 n.p. 2 r.

New York World's Fair. Nos. 81/3 of Sharjah optd. Air 20, 40 n.p. 1 r.

Pres. Kennedy Commem. Nos. 98/100 of Sharjah optd. Air 40, 60, 100 n.p.

Centenary of I.T.U. Postage 1, 2, 3, 4, 5, 50 n.p., 1 r., 120 n.p.

Pan-Arab Games, Cairo. 50 p. × 5.

1966.

International Co-operation Year. 50 n.p. × 8.

Churchill Commemoration. 2, 3, 4, 5 r.

Roses. 20, 35, 60, 80 n.p. 1 r., 125 n.p.

Fish. 1, 2, 3, 4, 5, 15, 20, 30, 40, 50, 75 n.p., 1, 2, 3, 4, 5, 10 r.

Int. Stamp Exhibition, Washington D.C. (SIPEX). 80, 120 n.p., 2 r.

New Currency Surcharges in Rials and Piastres.

(a) 1965 I.T.U. Cent., issue. 10 p. on 50 n.p., 16 p. on 120 n.p., 1 r. on 1 r.

(b) Churchill issue. 1 r. on 2 r., 2 r. on 3 r., 3 r. on 4 r., 4 r. on 5 r.

(c) Roses issue. 1 p. on 20 n.p., 2 p. on 35 n.p., 4 p. on 60 n.p., 6 p. on 80 n.p., 10 p. on 125 n.p., 12 p. on 1 r.

New Currency Surcharges in Dirhams and Riyals.

(a) 1965 Pan-Arab Games issue. 20 d. on 50 p. × 5.

(b) Fish issue. 1 d. on 1 n.p., 2 d. on 2 n.p., 3 d. on 3 n.p., 4 d. on 4 n.p., 5 d. on 5 n.p., 15 d. on 15 n.p., 20 d. on 20 n.p., 30 d. on 30 n.p., 40 d. on 40 n.p., 50 d. on 50 n.p., 75 d. on 75 n.p., 1 r. on 1 r., 2 r. on 2 r., 3 r. on 3 r., 4 r. on 4 r., 5 r. on 5 r., 10 r. on 10 r.

3rd Death Anniv. of Pres. J. Kennedy. Optd. on 1966 Int. Stamp Exhibition issue. 80 d. on 80 n.p., 120 d. on 120 n.p., 2 r. on 2 r.

World Football Cup Championship, England. ½ r. × 7.

1967.

4th Death Anniv. of Pres. J. Kennedy. Optd. on 1966 Int. Stamp Exhibition issue. 80 d. on 80 n.p., 120 d. on 120 n.p., 2 r. on 2 r.

1968.

Famous Paintings. Optd. on Sharjah. Postage **1, 2, 3, 4, 5, 30, 40, 60, 75 d.; Air 1, 2, 3, 4, 5 r.**

Winter Olympic Games, Grenoble. Optd. on Sharjah. Postage 1, 2, 3, 4, 5 d.: Air 1, 2, 3 r.

Previous Olympic Games. Optd. on Sharjah. Air 25, 50, 75 d., 1 r. 50, 3, 4 r.

Olympic Games, Mexico. Optd. on Sharjah. 10, 20, 30 d., 2, 2 r. 40, 5 r.

1969.

12th World Jamboree. Optd. on 1968 issue of Sharjah. Postage 1, 2, 3, 4, 5, 10 d.; Air 30, 50, 60 d., 1 r. 50.

Martyrs of Liberty. Optd. on 1968 issue of Sharjah. Air 35 d. × 4, 60 d. × 4, 1 r. × 4.

Sportsmen and women. Optd. on 1968 issue of Sharjah. Postage 20, 30, 40, 60 d., 1 r. 50, 2 r. 50; Air 35, 50 d., 1, 2, 3 r. 25, 4, 4 r.

A number of issues on gold or silver foil also exist, but it is understood that these were mainly for presentation purposes, although valid for postage.

In common with the other states of the United Arab Emirates the Khor Fakkan stamp contract was terminated on 1 August 1972, and any further new issues released after that date were unauthorised.

KIAUTSCHOU (KIAOCHOW) Pt. 7

A port in Shantung, China, leased by Germany from China in 1898. It was occupied by Japan in 1914, but reverted to China in 1922.

1900. 100 pfennige = 1 mark.
1905. 100 cents = 1 dollar (Chinese).

1900. No. 9 of German P.O.s in China surch **5 Pfg.**

3.	**9.**	5 pf. on 10 pf. red ..	42·00	48·00

1901. " Yacht " key-types inscr. " KIAUTSCHOU ".

11.	N.	3 pf. brown	1·25	1·25
12.		5 pf. green	1·40	50
13.		10 pf. red	2·50	1·00
14.		20 pf. blue	5·50	5·50
15.		25 pf. black & red on yell.	13·00	18·00
16.		30 pf. blk. & orge. on buff	13·00	14·00
17.		40 pf. black and red ..	14·00	18·00
18.		50 pf. blk. & pur. on buff	14·00	18·00
19.		80 pf. blk. & red on rose	25·00	42·00
20.	O.	1 m. red	48·00	75·00
21.		2 m. blue	60·00	£160
22.		3 m. black	£225	£450
23.		5 m. red and black ..	£450	£800

1905. ''Yacht'' key-types inscr. ''KIAUTSCHOU''.

34.	N.	1 c. brown	75	1·00
35.		2 c. green	75	1·00
36.		4 c. red	85	75
37.		10 c. blue	1·00	1·10
38.		20 c. black and red ..	1·50	18·00
39.		40 c. black and red on rose	2·25	55·00
40.	O.	½ dol. red	5·00	55·00
41.		1 dol. blue	5·50	60·00
42.		1½ dol. black	6·50	£150
43.		2½ dol. red and black ..	32·00	£450

KIONGA Pt. 9

Part of German E. Africa, occupied by the Portuguese during the 1914/18 war, and now incorporated in Mozambique.

1916. '' King Carlos'' key-type of Lourenco Marques optd. **REPUBLICA** and surch. **KIONGA** and new value.

1.	S.	½ c. on 100 r. blue on blue	3·50	3·25
2.		1 c. on 100 r. blue on blue	3·50	3·25
3.		2½ c. on 100 r. blue on blue	3·50	3·25
4.		5 c. on 100 r. blue on blue	3·50	3·25

KOREA Pt. 18

A peninsula to the S. of Manchuria in E. Asia. Formerly an empire under Chinese suzerainty, it was annexed by Japan in 1910 and used Japanese stamps. After the defeat of Japan in 1945, Russian and United States Military administrations were set up in Korea to the north and south of the 38th Parallel respectively; in 1948 South Korea and North Korea became independent republics.

1884. 100 mon = 1 tempo.
1895. 5 poon = cheun.
1900. 10 re (or rin) = 1 cheun. 100 cheun = 1 weun.

EMPIRE OF KOREA

1. 3. Korean flag. (4.)

1884.

1.	**1.**	5 m. red	32·00	£1600
2.		10 m. blue	7·50	£1500

1895.

7.	**3.**	5 p. green	10·00	9·00
8.		10 p. blue	16·00	7·00
9.		25 p. lake	10·00	12·00
10a.		50 p. violet	10·00	6·50

1897. Optd. with T **4.**

12.	**3.**	5 p. green	12·00	10·00
13.		10 p. blue	20·00	18·00
14.		25 p. lake	24·00	22·00
16.		50 p. violet	30·00	20·00

1899. Surch in Korean characters.

17	3	1 (p.) on 5 p. green (No. 7)	£800	£450
20		1 (p.) on 5 p. grn (No. 12)	£250	£200
18		1 (p.) on 25 p. red (No. 9)	£110	75·00
21		1 (p.) on 25 p. red (No. 14)	50·00	32·00

6. 7. 8.
National Emblems.

1900. T **6, 7** (2 ch.), **8** (2 ch.) and similar designs.

22a	2 r. grey	75	1·50
23	1 ch. green	5·50	4·00
24	2 ch. blue (T **7**)	35·00	38·00
25	2 ch. blue (T 8)	8·00	7·00
26	3 ch. orange	7·50	7·50
27	4 ch. red	10·00	9·00
28	5 ch. pink	10·00	10·00
29	6 ch. blue	12·00	11·00
30	10 ch. purple	18·00	16·00
31a	15 ch. purple	30·00	25·00
32	20 ch. red	50·00	38·00
33	50 ch. green and pink ..	£180	£120
34	1 wn. multicoloured ..	£225	£180
35	2 wn. green and purple ..	£325	£225

9. Imperial Crown. **17.** Falcon, Sceptre and Orb.

1902. 40th Anniv of Emperor's Accession as King.

36	**9**	3 ch. orange	32·00	25·00

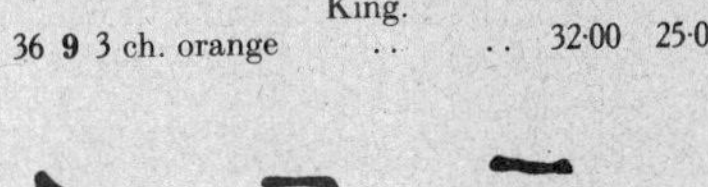

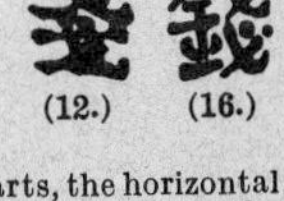
(10.) (11.) (12.) (16.)

Types **10** to **12** are in two parts, the horizontal strokes (one, two or three) representing the value figures and the bottom part being the character for "cheun".

Some variation can be found in these wood-block overprints.

1902.

(a) Surch as Types **10** to **12**.

37	**3**	1 ch. on 25 p. red (No. 9)	8·50	6·50
38		1 ch. on 25 p. red (No. 14)	45·00	45·00
39		2 ch. on 25 p. red (No. 9)	8·50	7·00
40		1 ch. on 25 p. red (No. 14)	42·00	40·00
42		2 ch. on 50 p. vio (No. 10a)	—	£350
43		3 ch. on 25 p. red (No. 9)	42·00	90·00
44		3 ch. on 25 p. red (No. 14)		
46		3 ch. on 50 p. vio (No. 10a)	8·00	10·00
47		3 ch. on 50 p. vio (No. 16)	12·00	12·00

(b) Surch. as T **16** (Japanese "sen" character) and strokes.

49	**3.**	3 ch. on 50 p. violet ..	£650	£500

1903.

50.	**17.**	2 r. grey	50	75
51.		1 ch. purple	4·50	4·50
52.		2 ch. green	4·50	4·50
53.		3 ch. orange	5·50	5·50
54.		4 ch. red	6·50	6·00
55.		5 ch. brown	9·00	8·00
56.		6 ch. lilac	9·00	8·50
57.		10 ch. blue	12·00	10·00
58.		15 ch. red on yellow ..	22·00	22·00
59.		20 ch. purple on yellow	30·00	32·00
60.		50 ch. red on green ..	90·00	95·00
61.		1 wn. lilac on lilac ..	£150	£160
62.		2 wn. purple on orange	£250	£250

SOUTH KOREA

1946. 100 cheun = 1 weun.
1953. 100 weun = 1 hwan.
1962. 100 chon = 1 won.

A. UNITED STATES MILITARY GOVERNMENT

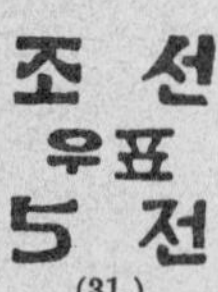

(31.)

33. National Emblem.

1946. Stamps of Japan surch as T **31**.

69	5 ch. on 5 s. purple (No. 396)	6·00	6·50
70	5 ch. on 14 s. red and brown (No. 324)	1·50	1·75
71	10 ch. on 40 s. pur (No. 406)	1·50	1·50
72	20 ch. on 6 s. blue (No. 397)	1·50	1·25
73	30 ch. on 27 s. red (No. 404)	1·50	1·25
74	5 wn. on 17 s. vio (No. 402)	6·50	5·00

1946. Liberation from Japanese Rule.

No.	Type	Description		
75.	–	3 ch. yellow	55	65
76.	–	5 ch. green	55	55
77.	–	10 ch. red	55	45
78.	–	20 ch. blue	55	45
79.	**33.**	50 ch. purple	1·00	80
80.		1 wn. brown	1·00	70

DESIGN: 3 ch. to 20 ch. Family and flag.

34. Dove of Peace and Map of Korea.

1946. 1st Anniv. of Liberation.

No.	Type	Description		
81.	**34.**	50 ch. violet	4·50	2·50

35. U.S. and Korean Flags.

36. Kyongju Observatory.

39. Golden Crown of Silla.

40. Admiral Li Sun Sin.

1946. Resumption of Postal Service between Korea and U.S.A.

No.	Type	Description		
82.	**35.**	10 wn. red	4·50	3·50

1946.

No.	Type	Description		
83.	**36.**	50 ch. blue	60	40
84.	–	1 wn. brown	1·25	55
85.	–	2 wn. blue	1·50	40
86.	**39.**	5 wn. mauve	12·00	4·50
87.	**40.**	10 wn. green	12·00	4·00

DESIGNS—As Type **36**: 1 wn. Hibiscus. 2 wn. Map of Korea.

41. Korean Alphabet.

42. Li Jun, patriot.

44. 16th-century "Turtle" Ship. **45.** Letters Surrounding Globe.

1946. 500th Anniv. of Creation of Korean Alphabet.

No.	Type	Description		
88.	**41.**	50 ch. blue	3·50	1·75

1947.

No.	Type	Description		
89.	**42.**	5 w. green	7·50	2·50
90.	–	10 w. blue	7·50	2·50
91.	–	20 w. red	2·00	50
92.	**44.**	50 w. brown	30·00	8·50

DESIGNS: 10 w. Admiral Li Sun Sin. 20 w. Independence Arch, Seoul.

1947. Resumption of Int. Postal Service.

No.	Type	Description		
93.	**45.**	10 w. blue	10·00	4·25

46. Aeroplane and Globe.

1947. Air. Inauguration of Air Mail Service.

No.	Type	Description		
94.	**46.**	50 w. red	4·75	2·00
126.		150 w. blue	75	70
127.		150 w. green	6·75	

47. Hand and Ballot Slip.

48. Casting Votes.

1948. South Korea Election.

No.	Type	Description		
95.	**47.**	2 w. orange	9·00	6·00
96.		5 w. mauve	9·00	5·00
97.		10 w. violet	18·00	7·00
98.	**48.**	20 w. red	24·00	15·00
99.		50 w. blue	28·00	15·00

49. Korean Flag and Laurel Wreath.

1948. Olympic Games.

No.	Type	Description		
100.	**49.**	5 w. green	50·00	25·00
101.	–	10 w. violet	22·00	10·00

DESIGN—VERT. 10 w. Runner with torch.

50. Capitol and Ears of Rice.

51. Korean Family.

1948. Meeting of First National Assembly.

No.	Type	Description		
102.	**50.**	4 w. brown	14·00	5·50

1948. Promulgation of Constitution.

No.	Type	Description		
103.	**51.**	4 w. green	38·00	14·00
104.	–	10 w. brown	32·00	8·00

DESIGN—HORIZ. 10 w. Flag of Korea.

52. Dr. Syngman Rhee (First President).

53. Hibiscus.

1948. Election of First President.

No.	Type	Description		
105.	**52.**	5 w. blue	50·00	20·00

B. REPUBLIC OF KOREA

1948. Proclamation of Republic.

No.	Type	Description		
106.	–	4 w. blue	25·00	15·00
107.	**53.**	5 w. mauve	25·00	12·00

DESIGN: 4 w. Dove and olive branch.

54. Li Jun.

55. Kyongju Observatory.

1948.

No.	Type	Description		
108.	**54.**	4 w. red	25	15
109.	**55.**	14 w. blue	25	15

56. Doves and U.N. Emblem.

57. Citizen and Date.

1949. Arrival of U.N. Commission.

No.	Type	Description		
110.	**56.**	10 w. blue	28·00	12·00

1949. National Census.

No.	Type	Description		
111.	**57.**	15 w. violet	30·00	12·00

58. Children and Plant.

1949. 20th Anniv. of Children's Day.

No.	Type	Description		
112.	**58.**	15 w. violet	13·00	5·50

59. Hibiscus.

60. Map of Korea and Magpies.

61. Dove and Globe.

62. Admiral Li Sun Sin.

1949.

No.	Type	Description		
113.	–	1 w. red	3·00	1·50
114.	–	2 w. grey	1·50	60
115.	–	5 w. green	6·50	2·25
116.	–	10 w. green	2·00	50
117.	**59.**	15 w. red	45	20
118.	–	20 w. brown	45	20
119.	–	30 w. green	50	20
120.	–	50 w. blue	45	20
121.	**60.**	65 w. blue	1·50	50
122.	–	100 w. olive	50	20
123.	**61.**	200 w. green	60	35
124.	–	400 w. brown	60	40
125.	**62**	500 w. blue	60	45

DESIGNS—VERT. As Type **59**: 1 w. Postman. 2 w. Worker and factory. 5 w. Harvesting rice. 10 w. Manchurian Cranes. 20 w. Diamond Mountains. 30 w. Ginseng plant. 50 w. South Gate, Seoul. 100 w. Tabo Pogoda, Kyongju. HORIZ. As Type **61**: 400 w. Diamond Mountains.

63. Symbol and Phoenix.

64. Steam Train.

1949. 1st Anniv. of Independence.

No.	Type	Description		
128.	**63.**	15 w. blue	18·00	6·00

1949. 50th Anniv. of Korean Railways.

No.	Type	Description		
129.	**64.**	15 w. blue	40·00	22·00

65. Korean Flag.

66. Post-horse Warrant.

1949. 75th Anniv. of U.P.U.

No.	Type	Description		
130.	**65.**	15 w. multicoloured	8·00	8·00

1950. 50th Anniv. of Membership of U.P.U.

No.	Type	Description		
131.	**66.**	15 w. green	15·00	6·00
132.		65 w. brown	10·00	3·50

67. Aeroplane and Globe. **68.** Demonstrators. **69.** Capitol, Seoul.

1950. Air. Opening of Internal Air Mail Service.

No.	Type	Description		
133.	**67.**	60 w. blue	10·00	3·25

1950. 31st Anniv. of Abortive Proclamation of Independence.

No.	Type	Description		
134.	**68.**	15 w. olive	14·00	6·00
135.		65 w. violet	6·00	2·50

1950. 2nd South Korean Election.

No.	Type	Description		
136.	**69.**	30 w. multicoloured	8·00	2·50

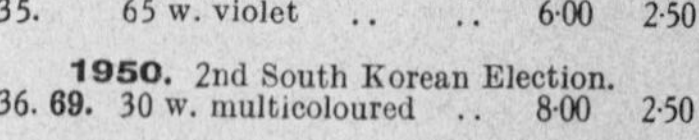

70. Dr. Syngman Rhee.

71. Flag and Mountains.

1950. Unification of Korea.

No.	Type	Description		
137.	**70.**	100 w. blue	2·50	1·00
138.	**71.**	100 w. green	3·50	1·00
139.	–	200 w. green	2·00	75

DESIGN—HORIZ. 200 w. Map of Korea and flags of U.N. and Korea (35 × 24 mm.).

73. Manchurian Crane. **76.** Post-horse Warrant. **77.** Fairy (8th Cent. painting).

1951. Perf. or roul.

No.	Type	Description		
140	**73**	5 w. brown	2·25	50
181	–	20 w. violet	70	30
187	–	50 w. green	2·00	30
183	**76**	100 w. blue	1·00	25
193	**77**	1,000 w. green	2·00	40

DESIGNS—HORIZ. 20 w. Astrological Tiger (ancient painting). 50 w. Dove and Korean flag.

1951. Surch with new value.

No.	Type	Description		
145	**54**	100 w. on 4 w. red	2·00	75
146	**59**	200 w. on 15 w. red	4·50	2·00
147	**54**	300 w. on 4 w. red	1·50	1·00
156	–	300 w. on 10 w. (116)	6·00	20
149	**55**	300 w. on 14 w. blue	2·25	75
150	**59**	300 w. on 15 w. red	1·75	75
151	–	300 w. on 20 w. (118)	2·50	85
152	–	300 w. on 30 w. (119)	2·00	75
153	–	300 w. on 50 w. (120)	2·00	80
154	**60**	300 w. on 65 w. blue	4·50	1·10
155	–	300 w. on 100 w. (122)	2·25	75

80. Statue of Liberty and Flags.

1951. Participation in Korean War. Flags in national colours. A. As Type **80** in green. B. As Type **80** but showing U.N. Emblem and doves in blue.

No.	Description	A	B
158.	500 w. Australia	6·00	6·00
159.	500 w. Belgium	6·00	6·00
160.	500 w. Britain	6·00	6·00
161.	500 w. Canada	6·00	6·00
162.	500 w. Colombia	6·00	6·00
163.	500 w. Denmark	12·00	15·00
164.	500 w. Ethiopia	6·00	6·00
165.	500 w. France	6·00	6·00
166.	500 w. Greece	6·00	6·00
167.	500 w. India	10·00	10·00
168.	500 w. Italy (with crown)	15·00	15·00
169.	500 w. Italy (without crown)	7·00	7·00
170.	500 w. Luxembourg	10·00	10·00
171.	500 w. Netherlands	6·00	6·00
172.	500 w. New Zealand	6·00	6·00
173.	500 w. Norway	10·00	10·00
174.	500 w. Philippines	6·00	6·00

175.		500 w. Sweden	6·00	6·00
176.		500 w. Thailand	6·00	6·00
177.		500 w. Turkey	6·00	6·00
178.		500 w. Union of S. Africa	6·00	6·00
179.		500 w. U.S.A.	5·00	5·00

The prices are the same for unused or used.

1951. Air. No. 126 surch **500 WON.**

180	46	500 w. on 150 w. blue ..	1·00	50

82. Buddha of Sokkuram.

83. Pulguksa Temple, Kyongju.

84. Monument to King Muryol, Kyongju.

85. Shrine of Admiral Li Sun Sin, Tongyong.

1952. Inscr "KOREA".

184	82	200 w. red	1·00	25
185	83	300 w. green	70	25
191	84	500 w. red	2·00	40
192		500 w. blue	7·50	5·00
194	85	2,000 w. blue	1·50	40

86. President Syngman Rhee.

1952. President's Election to 2nd Term of Office.

195.	86.	1,000 w. green	1·00	60

87. Airplane over Freighter.

1952. Air.

196.	87.	1,200 w. brown	1·10	40
197.		1,800 w. blue	1·10	40
198.		4,200 w. violet	1·10	30

For stamps in new currency, see Nos. 210/12.

88. Tree-planting.

89. Monument to King Muryol, Kyongju.

91. Pagoda Park, Seoul.

92. Sika Deer. **93.** Sika Deer.

1953. New currency. With character "hwan" after figure of value.

244	88	1 h. blue	25	10
200	84	2 h. blue	50	10
201		5 h. green	60	10
203	88	10 h. green	80	10
204	–	10 h. brown	2·50	10
205	85	20 h. brown	3·00	10
206	91	30 h. blue	1·00	10
242	92	100 h. brown	7·50	30
243	91	200 h. violet	3·50	25
208	93	500 h. orange	25·00	1·40
209		1000 h. brown	55·00	2·10

DESIGN: No. 204, "Metopta rectifasciata" (moth) and Korean flag.

For designs without character after figure of value, see Nos. 273 etc.

1953. Air. New Currency.

210.	87.	12 h. blue	1·25	40
211.		18 h. violet	1·25	40
212.		42 h. green	2·00	40

94. Field Hospital.

DESIGN — VERT. No. 214, Nurses supporting wounded soldier.

1953. Red Cross Fund. Crosses in red.

213.	94.	10 h. + 5 h. green ..	5·00	1·50
214.	–	10 h. + 5 h. blue ..	5·00	1·50

95. Y.M.C.A. Badge and Map.

96. Aeroplane over East Gate, Seoul.

1953. 50th Anniv of Korean Y.M.C.A.

215	95	10 h. red and black ..	1·40	55

1954. Air.

216.	96.	25 h. brown	1·60	30
217.		35 h. bright purple ..	2·25	30
218.		38 h. green	2·25	30
219.		58 h. blue	2·75	30
296.		70 h. turquoise	4·25	40
220.		71 h. deep blue ..	3·25	30
297.		110 h. brown	4·00	40
298.		205 h. mauve	4·00	40

98. Tokto Island.

99. Erosion Control.

1954.

221.	–	2 h. purple	90	15
222.	–	5 h. blue	60	15
223.	98.	10 h. green	1·00	15

DESIGN: 2 h., 5 h. Rocks off Tokto Is.

1954. 4th World Forestry Congress, Dehru Dun.

224.	99.	10 h. green	50	15
225.		19 h. green	60	15

100. Presidents Syngman Rhee and Eisenhower.

101. "Rebirth of Industry."

1954. Korea–United States Mutual Defence Treaty.

226.	100.	10 h. blue	1·25	35
227.		19 h. brown	1·00	35
228.		71 h. green	1·50	70

1955. Reconstruction.

229	101	10 h. brown	2·25	15
230		15 h. violet	2·25	15
231		20 h. blue	2·25	15
232		50 h. mauve	2·25	25
269		50 h. red	4·50	15

102. Rotary Emblem.

103. Pres. Syngman Rhee.

1955. 50th Anniv. of Rotary International.

236	102.	20 h. violet	1·40	85
237.		25 h. green	1·10	45
238.		71 h. purple	1·10	50

1955. 80th Birthday of President.

239.	103.	20 h. blue	2·50	70

104. Independence Arch, Seoul.

1955. 10th Anniv. of Liberation.

240.	104.	40 h. green	1·25	55
241.		100 h. brown	1·50	85

105. Hibiscus.

106. King Sejong.

107. Kyongju Observatory.

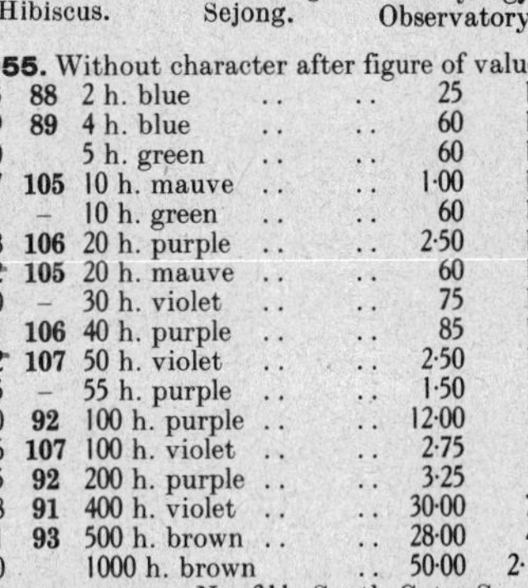

1955. Without character after figure of value.

273	88	2 h. blue	25	10
309	89	4 h. blue	60	10
310		5 h. green	60	10
247	105	10 h. mauve	1·00	10
311	–	10 h. green	60	10
248	106	20 h. purple	2·50	10
312	105	20 h. mauve	60	10
280	–	30 h. violet	75	15
281	106	40 h. purple	85	15
282	107	50 h. violet	2·50	15
315	–	55 h. purple	1·50	10
250	92	100 h. purple	12·00	10
316	107	100 h. violet	2·75	10
285	92	200 h. purple	3·25	15
318	91	400 h. violet	30·00	70
251	93	500 h. brown	28·00	40
320		1000 h. brown	50·00	2·10

DESIGNS—HORIZ. No. 311, South Gate, Seoul. 280, Tiger. VERT. No. 315, Haegumgang.

108. Runners and Torch.

109. U.N. Emblem.

1955. 36th National Athletic Meeting.

252.	108.	20 h. purple	1·25	55
253.		55 h. green	2·00	70

1955. 10th Anniv. of U.N.

254.	109.	20 h. green	1·25	35
255.		55 h. blue	1·25	35

110. Admiral Li Sun Sin and 16th-century "Turtle" Ship.

1955. 10th Anniv. of Korean Navy.

256.	110.	20 h. blue	3·00	1·50

111. Admiration Pagoda.

112. Pres. Syngman Rhee.

1956. 81st Birthday of President.

257.	111.	20 h. green	1·50	70

1956. President's Election to Third Term of Office.

261.	112.	20 h. brown	10·00	3·00
262.		55 h. blue	6·50	1·50

113. Torch and Olympic Rings.

114. Central P.O., Seoul.

1956. Olympic Games.

263.	113.	20 h. brown	2·25	70
264.		55 h. green	2·25	70

1956. Stamp Day. Inscr. "4289.12.4".

265.	114.	20 h. turquoise	2·75	55
266.	–	50 h. red	3·75	1·00
267.	–	55 h. green	1·50	55

DESIGNS—VERT. 50 h. Stamp of 1884. HORIZ. 55 h. Man leading post-pony.

119. I.T.U. Emblem and Radio Mast.

120. Korean Scout and Badge.

1957. 5th Anniv. of Korea's Admission to Int. Telecommunications Union.

290.	119.	40 h. blue	1·00	40
291.		55 h. green	1·00	40

1957. 50th Anniv. of Boy Scout Movement.

293.	120.	40 h. purple	1·00	40
294.		55 h. purple	1·00	40

1957. Flood Relief Fund. As No. 281 but Korean inscr. and premium added and colour changed.

299.		40 h. + 10 h. green ..	2·00	40

123. Mercury, Flags and Freighters.

124. Star of Bethlehem and Pine Cone.

1957. Korean–American Friendship Treaty.

301.	123.	40 h. orange	1·10	40
302.		205 h. green	1·40	40

1957. Christmas and New Year Issue.

304.	124.	15 h. brown, grn. & orge.	2·25	30
305.	–	25 h. green, red & yellow	2·00	20
306.	–	30 h. blue, green & yell.	4·00	1·10

DESIGNS: 25 h. Christmas tree and tassels. 30 h. Christmas tree and dog by window.

125. Winged Letter.

126. Korean Children regarding future.

1958. Postal Week.

321.	125.	40 h. blue and red ..	70	25

1958. 10th Anniv. of Republic of Korea.

323.	126.	20 h. grey	55	25
324.	–	40 h. red	70	25

DESIGN—HORIZ. 40 h. Hibiscus flowers forming figure "10".

127. U.N.E.S.C.O. Headquarters, Paris.

128. Children flying Kites.

1958. Inaug. of U.N.E.S.C.O. Building, Paris.

326.	127.	40 h. orange and green	50	25

1958. Christmas and New Year.

330.	128.	15 h. green	75	15
331.	–	25 h. red, yellow & blue	75	15
332.	–	30 h. red, blue & yellow	1·50	25

DESIGNS—VERT. 25 h. Christmas tree, tassels and wicker basket (cooking sieve). 30 h. Children in traditional festive costume.

129. Rejoicing Crowds in Pagoda Park, Flag and Torch.

1959. 40th Anniv. of Abortive Proclamation of Independence.

334.	129.	40 h. purple and brown	50	25

130. Marines going Ashore from Landing-craft.

1959. 10th Anniv. of Korean Marine Corps.

336.	130.	40 h. green	70	25

131.

1959. 10th Anniv. of Korea's Admission to W.H.O.

339. **131.** 40 h. purple and pink 50 25

132. Diesel Train.

1959. 60th Anniv. of Korean Railways.

341. **132.** 40 h. sepia and brown .. 1·40 75

133. Runners in Relay Race.

1959. 40th Korean National Games.

343. **133.** 40 h. brown and blue .. 50 25

134. Red Cross and Korea.

1959. Red Cross. Inscr. "1959 4292".

345. **134.** 40 h. red and green .. 50 25
346. – 55 h. red and mauve .. 50 25
DESIGN: 55 h. Red Cross on Globe.

135. Korean Postal Flags Old and New.

136. Mice in Korean Costume and New Year Emblem.

1959. 75th Anniv. of Korean Postal Service.

348. **135.** 40 h. red and blue .. 50 25

1959. Christmas and New Year.

350. **136.** 15 h. pink, blue and grey 1·00 15
351. – 25 h. red, green and blue 80 15
352. – 30 h. red, black & mauve 1·25 15
DESIGNS: 25 h. Carol singers. 30 h. Crane.

137. U.P.U. Monument.

138. Honey Bee and Clover.

1960. 60th Anniv. of Admission of Korea to U.P.U.

354. **137.** 40 h. brown & turquoise 1·00 50

1960. Children's Savings Campaign.

356. **138.** 10 h. yell., sepia & green 50 10
357. – 20 h. brn., blue & pink 50 10
DESIGN: 20 h. Snail and Korean money-bag.
For these stamps in new currency, see Nos. 452 etc.

139. "Uprooted Tree".

140. Pres. Eisenhower.

1960. World Refugee Year.

358. **139.** 40 h. red, blue & green 20 10

1960. Visit of President Eisenhower of United States.

360 **140** 40 h. blue, red & green 2·10 70

141. Schoolchildren.

1960. 75th Anniv. of Educational System.

362. **141.** 40 h. pur., brn. & olive 50 25

142. Assembly.

143. "Liberation".

1960. Inauguration of House of Councillors.

364. **142.** 40 h. blue 50 25

1960. 15th Anniv. of Liberation.

366. **143.** 40 h. lake, blue & ochre 50 25

144. Weightlifting.

145. Barn Swallow and Insulators.

1960. Olympic Games.

368. **144.** 20 h. brn., flesh & turq. 50 25
369. – 40 h. brn., blue & turq. 50 25
DESIGN: 40 h. South Gate, Seoul.

1960. 75th Anniv. of Korean Telegraph Service.

371. **145.** 40 h. vio., grey & blue 50 30

146. "Rebirth of Republic".

147. "Torch of Culture".

1960. Establishment of New Government.

373 **146** 40 h. green, blue & orge 50 25

1960. Cultural Month.

376. **147.** 40 h. yellow, pale blue and blue 50 25

148. U.N. Flag.

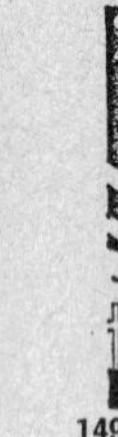

149. U.N. Emblem and Gravestones.

1960. 15th Anniv of U.N.

378 **148** 40 h. blue, green & mve 50 25

1960. Establishment of U.N. Memorial Cemetery.

380. **149.** 40 h. brown & orange 50 25

150. "National Stocktaking".

151. Festival Stocking.

1960. Census of Population and Resources.

382. **150.** 40 h. red, drab & blue 50 25

1960. Christmas and New Year Issue.

384. – 15 h. brn., yell. & grey 40 15
385. **151.** 25 h. red, grn. & blue 30 10
386. – 30 h. red, yell & blue 55 15
DESIGNS: 15 h. Ox's head. 30 h. Girl bowing in New Year's greeting.

152. Wind-sock and Ancient Rain-gauge.

1961. World Meteorological Day.

388. **152.** 40 h. ultram. and blue 70 25

153. Family, Sun and Globe.

1961. World Health Day.

390. **153.** 40 h. brown & salmon 50 25

154. Students' Demonstration.

155. Workers and Conference Emblem.

1961. 1st Anniv. of April Revolution (Overthrow of Pres. Syngman Rhee).

392. **154.** 40 h. green, red & blue 75 30

1961. Int. Community Development Conf., Seoul.

394. **155.** 40 h. turquoise .. 50 25

156. Girl Guide, Camp and Badge.

157. Soldier's Grave.

1961. 15th Anniv. of Korean Girl Guide Movement.

396. **156.** 40 h. turquoise .. 60 25

1961. Memorial Day.

398. **157.** 40 h. black and drab .. 70 30

158. Soldier with Torch.

159. "Three Liberations".

1961. Revolution of 16 May (Seizure of Power by Gen. Pak Chung Hi).

400. **158.** 40 h. brown and yellow 70 30

1961. Liberation Day.

402. **159.** 40 h. multicoloured .. 70 30

160. Korean Forces, Flag and Destroyer.

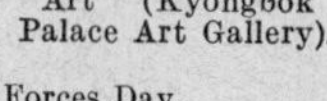

161. "Korean Art" (Kyongbok Palace Art Gallery).

1961. Armed Forces Day.

404. **160.** 40 h. multicoloured .. 1·25 30

1961. 10th Korean Art Exhibition.

406. **161.** 40 h. chocolate & brown 50 25

162. Birthday Candle.

1961. 15th Anniv. of U.N.E.S.C.O.

408. **162.** 40 h. blue and green 50 25

163. Mobile X-Ray Unit.

1961. T.B. Vaccination Week.

410 **163** 40 h. brn, blk & lt brn 50 25

164. Ginseng.

165. King Sejong.

166. White-bellied Black Woodpecker.

167. Rice Harvester.

168. Korean Drum.

169. Plane over Pagoda.

1961.

412. **164.** 20 h. red 80 10
413. **165.** 30 h. lilac 80 10
414. **166.** 40 h. blue and red .. 3·25 20
415. **167.** 40 h. green .. .. 1·10 10
416. **168.** 100 h. brown .. 1·75 10
See also Nos. 467, etc., and for stamps inscribed "REPUBLIC OF KOREA", see Nos. 641, etc. and 785/95.

1961. Air.

417. **169.** 50 h. violet and blue .. 4·50 70
418. – 100 h. brown & blue .. 4·50 35
419. – 200 h. brown & blue .. 9·00 55
420. – 400 h. green & blue .. 6·50 35
DESIGNS—Plane over: 100 h. West Gate, Suwon. 200 h. Gateway and wall of Toksu Palace, Seoul. 400 h. Pavilion, Kyongbok Palace, Seoul.
See also Nos. 454 etc.

170. I.T.U. Emblem as Satellite.

1962. 10th Anniv. of Admission into I.T.U.

421. **170.** 40 h. red and blue .. 1·00 25

171. Triga Mark II Reactor.

1962. 1st Korean Atomic Reactor.

423. **171.** 40 h. green, drab & blue 70 25

172. Mosquito and Emblem.

1962. Malaria Eradication.

424. **172.** 40 h. red and green .. 25 25

173. Girl and Y.W.C.A. Emblem.

1962. 40th Anniv. of Korean Y.W.C.A.
426. **173.** 40 h. blue and orange .. 60 25

174. Emblem of Asian Film Producers' Federation.

175. Soldiers crossing Han River Bridge.

1962. 9th Asian Film Festival, Seoul.
427. **174.** 40 h. violet, red & turq. 1·25 25

1962. 1st Anniv of 16th May Revolution.
428 – 30 h. green and brown 1·10 40
429 **175** 40 h. brn, grn & turq 1·10 40
430 – 200 h. yellow, red & bl 7·50 1·50
DESIGNS—HORIZ. 30 h. "Industrial Progress" (men moving cogwheel up slope). 200 h. "Egg" containing Korean badge and industrial skyline.

176. 20-oared "Turtle" Ship.

1962. 370th Anniv of Hansan Naval Victory over Japanese.
433 **176** 2 w. blue and light blue 1·25 70
434 – 4 w. black, vio & turq 1·60 80
DESIGN: 4 w. 16-oared "turtle" ship.

177. Chindo Dog.

178. "Hanabusaya asiatica".

179. Statue of Goddess Mikuk Besal.

213. Longhorn Beetle.

180. Farmers' Dance.

181. 12th-century Wine-jug.

214. Factory, Fishes and Corn.

182. Mison.

183. 13th-century Printing-block and Impression used for "Tripitaka Koreana".

191. Sika Deer.

192. Bell of King Kyongbok.

215. Boddhisatva Sokkuram Shrine.

216. Tile, Silla Dynasty.

217. "Azure Dragon", Koguryo period.

1962. New Currency.
537 177 20 ch. brown 25 10
468 **178** 40 ch. blue .. 25 10
469 **179** 50 ch. brown 25 10
540 **213** 60 ch. brown 40 10
541 **180** 1 w. blue 85 10
542 **179** 1 w. 50 grey 30 10
543 **164** 2 w. red .. .. 1·25 10
472 **165** 3 w. purple .. .. 2·25 10
545 **167** 4 w. green 30 10
422 **181** 5 w. blue .. .. 3·50 10
547 **214** 7 w. mauve .. .. 1·10 10
548 **168** 10 w. brown .. .. 2·00 10
549 **182** 20 w. mauve .. .. 3·00 10
550 **183** 40 w. purple .. .. 4·50 10
551 **191** 50 w. brown .. .. 6·00 10
552 **192** 100 w. green .. .. 12·00 10
553 **215** 200 w. dp green & grn 5·00 10
554 **216** 300 w. green and ochre 10·00 10
555 **217** 500 w. blue & lt blue .. 6·00 10
See also Nos. 641/9 and 785/95.

184. Scout Badge and Korean Flag.

185. Mackerel, Trawler and Nets.

1962. 40th Anniv. of Korean Scout Movement.
446. **184.** 4 w. brn., red and blue 60 25
447. 4 w. green, red & blue 65 25

1962. 10th Indo-Pacific Fishery Council Meeting, Seoul.
449. **185.** 4 w. blue & turquoise 1·00 25

186. I.C.A.O. Emblem.

1962. 10th Anniv. of Korea's Entry into International Civil Aviation Organization.
450. **186.** 4 w. blue and brown.. 1·00 25

1962. Children's Savings Campaign. As Nos. 356/7 but new currency.
452 1 w. yellow, brn & grn .. 3·25 10
570 2 w. brown, blue and pink 3·25 10

1962. Air. New Currency.
454 **169** 5 w. blue and violet .. 12·50 2·50
512 – 10 w. brown and turquoise (As No. 418) .. .. 3·25 30
513 – 20 w. brown and green (As No. 419) .. 4·00 40
563 **169** 39 w. drab and blue .. 2·50 20
514 – 40 w. green and blue (As No. 420) .. 4·50 50
564 – 64 w. green and blue (As No. 418) .. 2·50 20
565 – 78 w. blue and green (As No. 419) .. 3·25 30
566 – 112 w. green and blue (As No. 420) .. 3·25 30

DESIGN: No. 459, Irrigation Dam.

187. Electric Power Plant.

1962. Inauguration of 1st Korean Economic Five Year Plan.
458 **187** 4 w. violet and orange 1·00 25
459 – 4 w. ultram. and blue 1·00 25
See also Nos. 482/3, 528/9, 593/4 and 634/5.

188. Campaign Emblem.

1963. Freedom from Hunger.
460. **188.** 4 w. green, buff & blue 35 25

189. Globe and Letters.

1963. 1st Anniv. of Asian-Oceanic Postal Union.
462. **189.** 4 w. mve., olive & blue 50 25

190. Centenary Emblem and Map.

1963. Centenary of Red Cross.
464. **190.** 4 w. red, grey and blue 70 25
465. 4 w. red, grey & salmon 70 25

1963. Flood Relief. As No. 545, but new colour and inscr with premium.
479 4 w. + 1 w. blue .. .. 1·10 45

193. "15" and Hibiscus.

1963. 15th Anniv. of Republic.
480. **193.** 4 w. red, violet & blue 1·00 30

194. Nurse and Emblem.

1963. 15th Anniv. of Korean Army Nursing Corps.
481. **194.** 4 w. blk., turq. & grn. 75 25

1963. Five Year Plan. Dated "1963". As T **187.**
482. 4 w. violet and blue .. 90 25
483. 4 w. chocolate and brown 1·10 50
DESIGNS: No. 482, Cement Factory, Mun'gy-ong, and bag of cement. No. 483, Miner and coal train, Samch'ok region.

195. Rock Temples of Abu Simbel **196.**

1963. Nubian Monuments Preservation.
484 **195** 3 w. green and drab .. 2·25 40
485 **196** 4 w. green and drab .. 2·25 40
Nos. 484/5 were issued together, se-tenant, forming a composite design.

197. Rugby Football and Athlete.

198. Nurse and Motor Clinic.

1963. 44th National Games.
487. **197.** 4 w. green, brown & blue 80 25

1963. 10th Anniv. of Korean T.B. Prevention Society.
488. **198.** 4 w blue and red .. 65 25

199. Eleanor Roosevelt.

200. U.N. Headquarters.

1963. 15th Anniv. of Declaration of Human Rights.
489. **199.** 3 w. brown and blue.. 40 25
490. – 4 w. blue, olive & buff 40 25
DESIGN: 4 w. Freedom torch and globe.

1963. 15th Anniv. of U.N. Recognition of Korea.
492. **200.** 4 w. olive, blue & black 60 25

201. Pres. Pak Chong Hi and Capitol.

202. "Tai-Keum" (Bamboo Flute).

1963. Inaug. of President Pak Chong Hi.
494. **201.** 4 w. blue, turq. & blk. 9·50 2·00

1963. Musical Instruments and Players. As T **202.**
495. 4 w. olive, brown and drab 1·75 45
496. 4 w. blk., blue & light blue 1·75 45
497. 4 w. olive, mauve & pink 1·75 45
498. 4 w. sepia, violet & grey.. 1·75 45
499. 4 w. blue, brown and pink 1·75 45
500. 4 w. turq., black and blue 1·75 45
501. 4 w. violet, bistre & yellow 1·75 45
502. 4 w. blue, brown & mauve 1·75 45
503. 4 w. black, blue and purple 1·75 45
504. 4 w. black, brown and pink 1·75 45
MUSICAL INSTRUMENTS (and players): VERT. No. 495, Type **202**. No. 496 "Wul-keum" (banjo). No. 497, "Tang-piri" (flageolet). No. 498, "Na-bal" (trumpet). No. 499, "Hyang-pipa" (lute). No. 500, "Pyenkyeng" (jade chimes). No. 501, "Taipyeng-so" (clarinet). No. 502, "Chang-ko" (double-ended drum). HORIZ. No. 503, "Wa-kong-hu" (harp). No. 504, "Kaya-ko" (zither).

203. Symbols of Metric System.

204. "U.N.E.S.C.O.".

1964. Introduction of Metric System in Korea.
505. **203.** 4 w. multicoloured .. 50 25

1964. 10th Anniversary of Korean U.N.E.S.C.O. Committee.
506. **204.** 4 w. ultram., red & blue 65 25

205. Symbols of Industry and Census.

1964. National Industrial Census (1963).
507. **205.** 4 w. brown, black & grey 90 50

206. Y.M.C.A. Emblem and Profile of Young Man.

1964. 50th Anniv. of Korean Y.M.C.A.
508. **206.** 4 w. red, blue & green 50 25

207. Fair Emblem, Ginseng Root and Freighter.

1964. New York World's Fair.
509. **207.** 40 w. brn., grn. & buff 1·75 35
510. – 100 w. blue, brown and pale blue .. .. 6·50 70
DESIGN: 100 w. Korean pavilion at Fair.

208. Secret Garden.

1964. Background in pale blue.
517. **208.** 1 w. green 50 20
518. – 2 w. olive 65 25
519. – 3 w. turquoise .. 70 25
520. – 4 w. green .. .. 1·10 30
521. – 5 w. violet .. .. 1·25 30
522. – 6 w. blue .. .. 1·40 40
523. – 7 w. brown .. .. 2·00 40
524. – 8 w. brown .. .. 1·75 40
525. – 9 w. violet .. .. 1·75 40
526. – 10 w. green .. .. 2·25 45
DESIGNS: 2 w. Whahong Gate. 3 w. Uisang Pavilion. 4 w. Mt. Songni. 5 w. Paekma River. 6 w. Anab Pond. 7 w. Choksok Pavilion. 8 w. Kwanghan Pavilion. 9 w. Whaom Temple. 10 w. Chonjeyon Falls.

1964. Five Year Plan. Dated "1964". As T 187.
528. 4 w. black and turquoise .. 1·25 25
529. 4 w. blue and yellow .. 90 25
DESIGNS: No. 528, Trawlers and fish. No. 529, Oil refinery and barrels.

209. Wheel and Globe.

1964. Colombo Plan Day.
530 **209** 4 w. lt brn, brn & grn 50 25

210. "Helping Hand".

1964. 15th Anniv. of Korea's Admission to W.H.O.
532. **210.** 4 w. blk., olive & green 50 25

211. Running.
218. Federation Emblem.

219. Olympic "V" Emblem.
212. U.P.U. Monument, Berne, and Ribbons.

1964. 45th National Games, Inchon.
534. **211.** 4 w. pink, green & pur. 1·00 25

1964. 90th Anniv. of U.P.U.
535. **212.** 4 w. brown, blue & pink 50 25

1964. 5th Meeting of Int. Federation of Asian and Western Pacific Contractors' Assns.
556. **218.** 4 w. green, light green and brown 50 25

1964. Olympic Games, Tokyo.
557. **219.** 4 w. blue, turq. & brn. 80 30
558. – 4 w. mve., blue & grn. 80 30
559. – 4 w. brn., ultram. & bl. 80 30
560. – 4 w. mve., brn. & blue 80 30
561. – 4 w. brn., pur. and blue 80 30
DESIGNS—HORIZ. No. 558, Running. No. 559, Rowing. No. 560, Horse-jumping. No. 561, Gymnastics.

220. Unissued 1884 100 m. Stamp.
221. Pine Cone.

1964. 80th Anniv. of Korean Postal Services.
567. **220.** 3 w. blue, vio. & mauve 85 25
568. – 4 w. blk., violet & olive 1·40 1·40
DESIGNS: 4 w. Hong Yong Sik, 1st Korean Postmaster-general.

1965. Korean Plants. Plants multicoloured background colours given.
571. **221.** 4 w. turquoise .. 70 25
572. – 4 w. grey (Plum blossom) 70 25
573. – 4 w. blue (Forsythia) .. 70 25
574. – 4 w. green (Azalea) .. 70 25
575. – 4 w. pink (Lilac) .. 70 25
576. – 4 w. grey (Wild rose) .. 70 25
577. – 4 w. green (Balsam) .. 70 25
578. – 4 w. grey (Hibiscus) .. 70 25
579. – 4 w. flesh (Crepe myrtle) 70 25
580. – 4 w. turquoise-blue (Ullung chrysanthemum) 70 25
581. – 4 w. buff (Paulownia, tree) 70 25
582. – 4 w. blue (Bamboo) .. 70 25

222. Folk Dancing.

1965. Pacific Area Travel Assn. Conf., Seoul.
584. **222.** 4 w. violet, brn. & turq. 40 25

223. Flag and Doves.

1965. Military Aid for Vietnam.
586 **223** 4 w. brown, blue & yell 50 20

224. "Food Production". **225.** "Family Scales".

1965. Agricultural Seven Year Plan.
588 **224** 4 w. brown, grn & blk 40 25

1965. Family-Planning Month.
589 **225** 4 w. grn, drab & lt grn 50 25

226. I.T.U. Emblem and Symbols.

1965. Centenary of I.T.U.
591. **226.** 4 w. black, red & blue 65 20

1965. Five-Year Plan. Dated "1965". As T 187.
593. 4 w. blue and pink .. 1·00 25
594. 4 w. sepia and brown .. 50 25
DESIGNS: No. 593, "Korea" (freighter) at quayside and crates. No. 594, Fertiliser plant and wheat.

227. Flags of Australia, Belgium, Great Britain, Canada and Colombia.

1965. 15th Anniv. of Outbreak of Korean War.
595. **227.** 4 w. multicoloured .. 80 25
596. – 4 w. multicoloured .. 80 25
597. – 4 w. multicoloured .. 80 25
598. – 4 w. multicoloured .. 80 25
599. – 10 w. multicoloured .. 2·00 40
DESIGNS (U.N. Emblem and flags of): No. 596, Denmark, Ethiopia, France, Greece and India. No. 597, Italy, Luxemburg, Netherlands, New Zealand and Norway. No. 598, Philippines, Sweden, Thailand, Turkey and South Africa. No. 599, General MacArthur and flags of Korea, U.N. and U.S.A.

228. Flag and Sky-writing ("20"). **229.** Ants and Leaf.

1965. 20th Anniv. of Liberation.
601. **228.** 4 w. red, violet & blue 55 25
602. – 10 w. red, blue & violet 85 30
DESIGN: 10 w. South Gate and fireworks.

1965. Savings Campaign.
603. **229.** 4 w. sepia, ochre & grn. 35 25

230. Hoisting Flag. **231.** Radio Aerial.

1965. 15th Anniv. of Recapture of Seoul.
604. **230.** 3 w. olive, bl. & salmon 1·10 35

1985. 80th Anniv. of Korean Telecommunications.
605. **231.** 3 w. green, black & blue 50 25
606. – 10 w. blk., blue & yell. 75 30
DESIGN: 10 w. Telegraphist of 1885.

1965. Flood Relief. As No. 545, but colour changed and inscr. with premium.
607. 4 w. + 2 w. blue 75 20

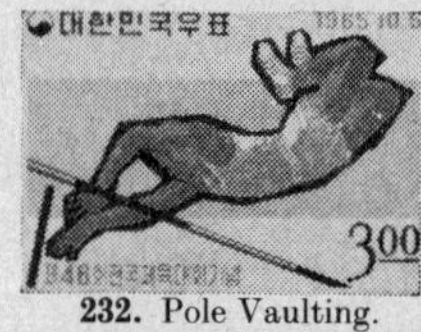

232. Pole Vaulting.

1965. National Athletic Meeting, Kwangju.
608. **232.** 3 w. multicoloured .. 85 25

1965. Aid for Children. As No. 545, but colour changed and inscr with premium.
609 4 w. + 2 w. purple .. 85 20

233. I.C.Y. Emblem.

1965. International Co-operation Year and 20th Anniv of United Nations.
610 **233** 3 w. red, grn & dp grn 45 25
611 – 10 w. ultram, grn & bl 90 25
DESIGN—VERT. 10 w. U.N. flag and headquarters, New York.

234. Child posting Letter. **235.** Children with Toboggan.

1965. 10th Communications Day.
613. **234.** 3 w. multicoloured .. 1·00 25
614. – 10 w. red, blue & green 1·50 30
DESIGN: 10 w. Airmail envelope and telephone receiver.

1965. Christmas and New Year.
615. **235.** 3 w. blue, red & green 55 25
616. – 4 w. blue, red & turq. 55 25
DESIGN: 4 w. Boy and girl in traditional costume.

236. Freedom House. **237.** Mandarin.

1966. Opening of Freedom House, Panmunjom.
618. **236.** 7 w. black, emer. & grn. 75 25
619. 39 w. black, lilac & grn. 4·00 40

1966. Korean Birds. Multicoloured.
621. 3 w. Type **237** .. .. 1·50 25
622. 5 w. Manchurian Crane .. 1·50 25
623. 7 w. Ring-necked Pheasant 2·00 25

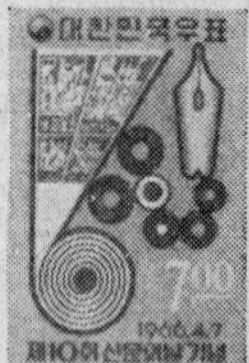

238. Pine Forest. **239.** Printing Press and Pen.

1966. Reafforestation Campaign.
625. **238.** 7 w. brown and green 55 15

1966. 10th Newspaper Day.
626. **239.** 7 w. pur., yell. & turq. 55 15

240. Curfew Bell and Young Koreans. **241.** W.H.O. Building.

1966. Youth Guidance Month.
627. **240.** 7 w. orge., grn. & blue 45 15

1966. Inauguration of W.H.O. Headquarters, Geneva.
628 **241** 7 w. black, blue & yell 60 15
629 39 w. red, grey & yell 3·25 40

242. Pres. Pak, Handclasp and Flags.

1966. Pres. Pak Chung-Hi's State Tour of South-East Asia.
631. **242.** 7 w. multicoloured .. 2·75 70

243. Girl Scout and Flag.

1966. 20th Anniv. of Korean Girl Scouts.
632. **243.** 7 w. blk., grn. & yellow 1·00 15

244. Student and Ewha Women's University.

246. Alaska Pollack.

1966. 80th Anniv. of Korean Women's Education.
633. **244.** 7 w. multicoloured .. 1·00 15

1966. 5-Year Plan. Dated " 1966 ". As T **187.**
634. 7 w. ultramarine and blue 1·10 50
635. 7 w. black and yellow .. 90 25
DESIGNS: No. 634, Map and transport. No. 635, Radar aerials and telephone.

1966. Korean Fishes. Multicoloured.
637. 3 w. Type **246** 90 25
638. 5 w. Manchurian trout .. 90 25
639. 7 w. Yellow corvina .. 1·00 25

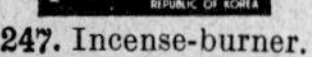
247. Incense-burner.

249. Buddha, Kwanchok Temple.

1966. Inscr. " REPUBLIC OF KOREA ".
641. **213.** 60 ch. green 20 10
642. **180.** 1 w. green .. .. 1·10 10
643. **164.** 2 w. green 15 10
644. **165.** 3 w. brown 15 10
645. **181.** 5 w. blue .. .. 2·00 10
646. **214.** 7 w. blue .. .. 1·75 10
647. **247.** 13 w. blue .. .. 1·90 10
709. **182.** 20 w. grn. & light grn. 4·25 10
710. **183.** 40 w. green & olive .. 4·00 10
711. **191.** 50 w. brown & bistre 3·25 10
648. – 60 w. green .. .. 2·25 10
649. **249.** 80 w. green .. .. 2·25 10
DESIGN—As Type **247.** 60 w. 12th-century Porcelain vessel.

250. Children and Hemispheres.

1966. 15th Assembly of World Conf. of Teaching Profession (WCOTP), Seoul.
650. **250.** 7 w. violet, brn. & blue 45 15

251. Factory within Pouch.

1966. Savings Campaign.
652. **251.** 7 w. multicoloured .. 45 15

252. People on Map of Korea.

1966. National Census.
653. **252.** 7 w. multicoloured .. 45 15

253. "Lucida lateralis".

1966. Insects. Multicoloured.
654 3 w. Type **253** 90 50
655 5 w. "Hexacentrus japonicus" (grasshopper) 90 50
656 7 w. "Sericinus montela" (butterfly) .. .. 1·00 50

254. C.I.S.M. Emblem and " Round Table " Meeting.

255. Soldiers and Flags.

1966. 21st General Assembly of International Military Sports Council (C.I.S.M.), Seoul.
658 **254** 7 w. multicoloured .. 50 15

1966. 1st Anniv. of Korean Troops in Vietnam.
660. **255.** 7 w. multicoloured .. 2·25 70

256. Wrestling.

257. Lions Emblem and Map.

1966. 47th Athletic Meeting, Seoul.
661. **256.** 7 w. multicoloured .. 1·50 35

1966. 5th Orient and South-East Asian Lions Convention, Seoul.
662. **257.** 7 w. multicoloured .. 40 15

258. University Emblem " 20 " and Shields.

1966. 20th Anniv. of Seoul University.
664. **258.** 7 w. multicoloured .. 40 15

259. A.P.A.C.L. Emblem.

1966. 12th Conference of Asian People's Anti-Communist League (A.P.A.C.L.), Seoul.
665 **259** 7 w. multicoloured .. 40 25

260. Presidents Pak and Johnson.

261. U.N.E.S.C.O. Symbols and Emblem.

1966. President Johnson's Visit to Korea.
667. **260.** 7 w. multicoloured .. 1·00 25
668. 83 w. multicoloured .. 5·00 70

1966. 20th Anniv. of U.N.E.S.C.O.
670. **261.** 7 w. multicoloured .. 55 20

1966. Hurricane Relief. As No. 646 but colour changed and premium added.
672. 7 w.+2 w. red 80 15

262. "Lucky Bag".

263. Eurasian Badger.

1966. Christmas and New Year. Multicoloured.
673. 5 w. Type **262** 45 15
674. 7 w. Sheep (vert.) 45 15

1966. Korean Fauna. Multicoloured.
676. 3 w. Type **263** 85 25
677. 5 w. Asiatic black bear .. 85 25
678. 7 w. Tiger .. .. .. 1·10 25

264. " Syncom " Satellite.

265. Presidents Pak and Lubke.

1967. 15th Anniv. of Korea's Admission to I.T.U.
680. **264.** 7 w. multicoloured .. 55 25

1967. Visit of Pres. Lubke of West Germany to Korea.
682. **265.** 7 w. multicoloured .. 1·40 70

266. Coin, Factories and Houses.

267. Okwangdae Mask.

1967. 1st Anniv. of Korean Revenue Office.
684. **266.** 7 w. sepia and green .. 45 25

1967. Folklore. Multicoloured.
685. 4 w. Type **267** 70 25
686. 5 w. Sandi mask 70 25
687. 7 w. Mafoe mask 80 25
The 5 w. is horiz.

268. J.C.I. Emblem and Pavilion.

269. Map Emblem.

1967. International Junior Chamber of Commerce Conference, Seoul.
689 **268** 7 w. multicoloured .. 50 25

1967. 5th Asian Pacific Dental Congress, Seoul.
691. **269.** 7 w. multicoloured .. 55 25

270. Korean Pavilion. 271. Worker and Soldier.

1967. World Fair, Montreal.
693. **270.** 7 w. black, red & yellow 1·00 35
694. 83 w. black, red & blue 4·75 70

1967. Veterans' Day.
696. **271.** 7 w. multicoloured .. 45 25

272. Railway Wheel and Rail.

273. Sword Dance.

1967. 2nd Five Year Plan.
697. **272.** 7 w. blk., yell. and brn. 90 45
698. – 7 w. orge., brn. and blk. 70 30
DESIGN: No. 698, Nut and bolt.
See also 773/4, 833/4, 895/6 and 981/2.

1967. Folklore. Multicoloured.
699. 4 w. Type **273** 85 25
700. 5 w. Peace dance (vert.) .. 85 25
701. 7 w. Buddhist dance (vert.) 1·10 50

274. Soldier and Family.

275. President Pak and Phoenix.

1967. Fund for Korean Troops Serving in Vietnam.
703 **274** 7 w.+3 w. black & pur 80 15

1967. Inaug. of President Pak for 2nd Term.
704. **275.** 7 w. multicoloured .. 3·50 70

276. Scout, Badge and Camp.

1967. 3rd Korean Scout Jamboree. Mult.
706. 7 w. Type **276** .. .. 2·75 20
707. 20 w. Scout badge, bridge and tent .. .. 2·25 40

280. Girls on Swing.

1967. Folklore. Multicoloured.
712. 4 w. Type **280** 75 25
713. 5 w. Girls on seesaw (vert.) 85 25
714. 7 w. Girls dancing (vert.) .. 1·25 25

281. Freedom Centre.

282. Boxing.

1967. 1st World Anti-Communist League Conf., Taipei. Multicoloured.
716. 5 w. Type **281** 45 25
717. 7 w. Hand grasping chain (vert.) 45 25

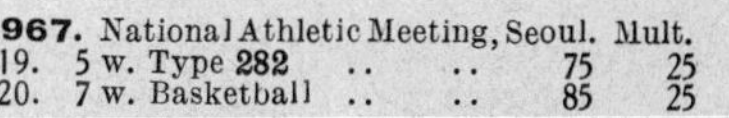

1967. National Athletic Meeting, Seoul. Mult.
719. 5 w. Type **282** 75 25
720. 7 w. Basketball 85 25

283. Student's Memorial, Kwangjoo.

284. Decade Emblem.

1967. Student's Day.
721. **283.** 7 w. multicoloured .. 40 25

1967. Int. Hydrological Decade.
722. **284.** 7 w. multicoloured .. 50 25

285. Children spinning Top.

286. Playing Shuttlecock.

1967. Christmas and New Year.
723. **285.** 5 w. blue, red and pink 50 15
724. – 7 w. brn., blue & bistre 50 15
DESIGN: 7 w. Monkey and Signs of the Zodiac.

1967. Folklore. Multicoloured.
726. 4 w. Type **286** 75 25
727. 5 w. "Dalmaji" (horiz.) .. 75 25
728. 7 w. Archery .. .. 1·00 25

287. Microwave Transmitter.

1967. Inauguration of Microwave Telecommunications Service.
730 **287** 7 w. black, green & blue 40 25

288. Carving, King Songdok's Bell.

289. 5th-6th century Earrings.

290. Korean Flag.

1968.
732. **288.** 1 w. brown & yellow 15 10
733. **289.** 5 w. yellow & green .. 1·25 10
734. **290.** 7 w. red and blue .. 65 10
For designs similar to Type **290** see Nos. 771, 780, 787/8, 790 and 827.

291. W.H.O. Emblem

292. E.A.T.A. Emblem and Korean Motif.

1968. 20th Anniv. of W.H.O.
735. **291.** 7 w. multicoloured .. 55 25

1968. 2nd East Asia Travel Association Conference, Seoul.
737. **292.** 7 w. multicoloured .. 40 25

293. C.A.C.C.I. Emblem, Korean Door-knocker and factories.

294. Pres. Pak and Emperor Haile Selassie.

1968. 2nd Conference of Confederation of Asian Chambers of Commerce and Industry (C.A.C.C.I.), Seoul.
739. **293.** 7 w. multicoloured .. 40 25

1968. Visit of Emperor of Ethiopia.
741. **294.** 7 w. multicoloured .. 1·75 55

295. Post-bag.

296. Atomic and Development Symbols.

1968. Postman's Day. Multicoloured.
743. 5 w. Type **295** 90 45
744. 7 w. Postman 40 25

1968. Promotion of Science and Technology.
745. **296.** 7 w. bl., green & red 40 25

297. Kyung Hi University and Conference Emblem.

298. "Liberation".

1968. 2nd Conf. of Int. Assn. of University Presidents.
746. **297.** 7 w. multicoloured .. 40 25

1968. Liberation of Suppressed People's Campaign.
748. **298.** 7 w. multicoloured .. 40 25

299. Reservist.

300. Stylised Peacock.

1968. Army Reservists' Fund.
749. **299.** 7 w.+3 w. black & grn. 1·00 25

1968. 20th Anniv. of Republic.
750. **300.** 7 w. multicoloured .. 60 25

301. Fair Entrance.

302. Assembly Emblem.

1968. 1st Korean Trade Fair, Seoul.
751. **301.** 7 w. multicoloured .. 40 25

1968. 3rd General Assembly of Asian Pharmaceutical Assn. Federation.
752. **302.** 7 w. multicoloured .. 35 25

303. Scout Badge.

304. Soldier and Battle Scene.

1968. 6th Far East Scout Conf., Seoul.
753. **303.** 7 w. multicoloured .. 1·10 25

1968. 20th Anniv of Korean Armed Forces.
754 **304** 7 w. orange and green 1·50 40
755 – 7 w. blue and light blue 1·50 40
756 – 7 w. blue and orange 1·50 40
757 – 7 w. light blue and blue 1·50 40
758 – 7 w. green and orange 1·50 40

DESIGNS: No. 755, Sailor and naval guns. 756, Servicemen and flags. 757, Airman and fighter planes. 758, Marine and landings.

305. Colombo Plan Emblem and Globe.

1968. 19th Meeting of Colombo Plan Consultative Committee, Seoul.
759. **305.** 7 w. multicoloured .. 40 15

306. (I). Olympic Emblems. **307.** (II).

1968. Olympic Games, Mexico. Multicoloured.
760. 7 w. Type **306** .. .. 1·00 25
761. 7 w. Type **307** .. .. 1·00 25
762. 7 w. Cycling (I) .. .. 1·00 25
763. 7 w. Cycling (II) .. .. 1·00 25
764. 7 w. Boxing (I) .. .. 1·00 25
765. 7 w. Boxing (II) .. .. 1·00 25
766. 7 w. Wrestling (I) .. 1·00 25
767. 7 w. Wrestling (II) .. 1·00 25

The two types of each design may be identified by the position of the country name at the foot of the design—ranged right in types I, and left in types II. On three of the designs (excluding "Cycling") the figures of value are on left and right respectively. Types I and II of each design were issued together horizontally se-tenant within the sheets of 50 stamps.

308. Statue of Woman.

309. Coin and Symbols.

1968. 60th Anniv. of Women's Secondary Education.
769. **308.** 7 w. multicoloured .. 40 20

1968. National Wealth Survey.
770. **309.** 7 w. multicoloured .. 40 20

1968. Disaster Relief Fund. As No. 734, but with additional inscr and premium added.
771 **290** 7 w.+3 w. red and blue 2·00 15

310. Shin Eui Ju Memorial.

311. Demonstrators.

1968. Anniv. of Student Uprising, Shin Eui Ju (1945).
772. **310.** 7 w. multicoloured .. 40 20

1968. 2nd Five Year Plan. As T **272.** Dated "1968". Multicoloured.
773. 7 w. Express motorway .. 55 25
774. 7 w. "Clover-leaf" road junction 55 25

1968. Human Rights Year.
775. **311.** 7 w. multicoloured .. 40 20

312. Christmas Lanterns.

314. Korean House and UN Emblems.

1968. Christmas and New Year. Mult.
776. 5 w. Type **312** 55 10
777. 7 w. Cockerel 55 10

1968. 20th Anniv. of South Korea's Admission to U.N.
779. **314.** 7 w. multicoloured .. 40 20

1969. Military Helicopter Fund. As No. 734 but colours changed and inscr. with premium added.
780. **290.** 7 w.+3 w. red, bl. & grn. 1·10 40

315. Torch and Monument, Pagoda Park, Seoul.

316. Hyun Choong Sa and "Turtle" Ships.

1969. 50th Anniv. of Samil (Independence) Movement.
781. **315.** 7 w. multicoloured .. 55 25

1969. Dedication of Rebuilt Hyun Choong Sa (Shrine of Admiral Li Sun Sin).
782. **316.** 7 w. multicoloured .. 75 25

317. President Pak and Yang di-Pertuan Agong.

318. Stone Temple Lamp.

1969. Visit of Yang di-Pertuan Agong (Malaysian Head-of-State).
783. **317.** 7 w. multicoloured .. 1·40 60

1969.
785. **178.** 40 ch. green (18 × 22 mm.) 25 10
786. **318.** 5 w. purple 45 10
787. **290.** 7 w. blue 45 10
788. 7 w. blue* 30 10
789. **168.** 10 w. blue (22 × 18 mm.) 3·50 10
790. **290.** 10 w. blue 60 10
791. – 20 w. green .. .. 1·50 10
792. – 30 w. green .. .. 2·25 10
793. **183.** 40 w. blue and pink (18 × 22 mm.) .. 6·50 10
794. – 40 w. mauve and blue 1·75 10
795. – 100 w. brn. & purple 28·00 10

DESIGNS—As Type **318.** VERT. 20 w. Wine jug. 40 w. (No. 794), Porcelain Jar, Yi Dynasty. 100 w. Seated Buddha (bronze). HORIZ. 30 w. "Duck" Vase.

*No. 788 has the face value shown as "7" only, omitting the noughts shown on No. 787.

323. "Red Cross" between Faces.

324. "Building the Nation's Economy".

1969. 50th Anniv. of League of Red Cross Societies.
796. **323.** 7 w. multicoloured .. 85 20

1969. "Second Economy Drive".
798. **324.** 7 w. multicoloured .. 40 15

325. Presidents Pak and Nguyen van Thieu.

1969. Visit of President Nguyen van Thieu of South Vietnam.
799. **325.** 7 w. multicoloured .. 1·50 55

326. Reafforestation and Flooded Fields.

327. Ignition of Second-stage Rocket.

1969. Flood and Drought Damage Prevention Campaign. Multicoloured.
801. 7 w. Type **326** 40 25
802. 7 w. Withered and flourishing plants 40 25

1969. First Man on the Moon.
803 **327** 10 w. blue, black & red 1·10 25
804 – 10 w. blue, black & red 1·10 25
805 – 20 w. multicoloured .. 1·10 25
806 – 20 w. multicoloured .. 1·10 25
807 – 40 w. blue, red & black 1·10 25

DESIGNS: No. 804, Separation of modules from rocket. No. 805, Diagram of lunar orbit. No. 806, Astronauts on Moon. No. 807, Splash-down of "Apollo 11".

328. Stepmother admonishing Kongji.

332. Steam Locomotive of 1899.

1969. Korean Fairy Tales (1st series). "Kongji and Patji". Multicoloured.
809. 5 w. Type **328** 55 25
810. 7 w. Kongji and Sparrows 55 25
811. 10 w. Kongji and Ox .. 75 25
812. 20 w. Kongji in Sedan-chair 95 25

See also Nos. 828/31, 839/42, 844/7 and 853/6.

1969. 70th Anniv. of Korean Railways. Multicoloured.
814. 7 w. Type **332** .. .. 1·00 40
815. 7 w. Early steam and modern diesel locomotives .. 1·25 40

333. "F-5A" Fighters. **334.** Game of Cha-jun.

1969. 20th Anniv. of Korean Air Force. Multicoloured.
816. 10 w. Type **333** 90 25
817. 10 w. "F-4D Phantom" fighter .. .. .. 1·10 25

1969. 10th Korean Traditional Arts Contest, Taegu.
818. **334.** 7 w. multicoloured .. 40 15

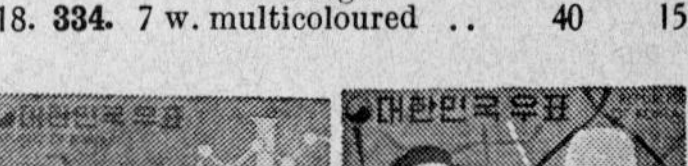

335. Molecule and Institute Building.

336. Presidents Pak and Hamani.

1969. Completion of Korean Institute of Science and Technology.
819. **335.** 7 w. multicoloured .. 45 15

1969. Visit of President Hamani of Niger Republic.
820. **336.** 7 w. multicoloured .. 75 15

337. Football.

342. Students ringing "Education".

1969. 50th Anniv. of National Athletic Meeting. Multicoloured.
822. 10 w. Type **337** 85 25
823. 10 w. Volleyball 85 25
824. 10 w. Korean wrestling .. 85 25
825. 10 w. Fencing 85 25
826. 10 w. Korean karate .. 85 25

Nos. 824/6 are horiz.

1969. Searchlight Fund. As T **290,** but inscr. "7+3" only.
827. 7 w.+3 w. blue and red.. 75 25

1969. Korean Fairy Tales. (2nd series). "The Hare's Liver". As T **328.** Mult.
828. 5 w. Princess and Doctors 55 25
829. 7 w. Hare arriving at Palace 55 25
830. 10 w. Preparing to remove the Hare's liver.. 75 25
831. 20 w. Escape of the Hare 95 25

1969. Second Five-year Plan. As T **272.** Dated "1969". Multicoloured.
833. 7 w. "Agriculture and Fisheries" 60 15
834. 7 w. Emblems of Industry 50 15

1969. 1st Anniv. of National Education Charter.
835. **342.** 7 w. multicoloured .. 40 15

343. Toy Dogs. **344.** Woman with Letter and U.P.U. Monument, Berne.

1969. Lunar New Year ("Year of the Dog"). Multicoloured.
836. 5 w. Type **343** 55 25
837. 7 w. Candle and lattice doorway 55 25

1970. 70th Anniv. of Korea's Admission to U.P.U.
838. **344.** 10 w. multicoloured .. 2·50 55

1970. Korean Fairy Tales (3rd series). "The Sun and the Moon". As T **328.** Mult.
839. 5 w. Mother meets the tiger 55 25
840. 7 w. Tiger in disguise .. 55 25
841. 10 w. Children chased up a tree 75 25
842. 20 w. Children escape to Heaven 95 25

1970. Korean Fairy Tales (4th series). "The Woodcutter and the Fairy". As T **328.** Mult.
844. 10 w. Woodcutter hiding Fairy's dress 75 25
845. 10 w. Fairy as Woodcutter's Wife 75 25
846. 10 w. Fairy and children fly to Heaven 75 25
847. 10 w. Happy reunion .. 75 25

353. I.E.Y. Emblem and Open Book. **354.** Seated Buddha and Korean Pavilion.

1970. Int. Education Year.
849. **353.** 10 w. multicoloured .. 2·75 55

1970. "EXPO 70" World Fair, Osaka, Japan.
850. **354.** 10 w. multicoloured .. 2·00 40

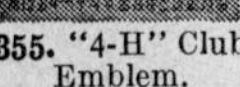

355. "4-H" Club Emblem. **356.** Bank Emblem and Cash.

1970. 15th "4-H" Club (young farmers' organization) Central Contest, Suwon.
851. **355.** 10 w. multicoloured .. 75 30

1970. 3rd General Meeting of Asian Development Bank, Seoul.
852. **356.** 10 w. multicoloured .. 60 30

1970. Korean Fairy Tales (5th series). "Heungbu and Nolbu". As T **328.** Mult.
853. 10 w. Heungbu tending swallow 85 25
854. 10 w. Heungbu finds treasure in pumpkin 85 25
855. 10 w. Nolbu with pumpkin 85 25
856. 10 w. Nolbu chased by devil 85 25

361. Royal Palanquin (Yi dynasty). **362.** New Headquarters Building.

1970. Early Korean Transport.
858 **361** 10 w. multicoloured .. 75 25
859 – 10 w. multicoloured .. 85 25
860 – 10 w. multicoloured .. 75 25
861 – 10 w. black, ochre & bl 1·25 25
DESIGN—HORIZ. No. 859, Tramcar, 1899. 860, Emperor Sunjong's cadillac, 1903. 861, An Chang Nam's Nieuport biplane, 1922.

1970. Opening of New U.P.U. Headquarters Building, Berne.
862. **362.** 10 w. multicoloured .. 60 30

363. Dish Aerial and Hemispheres.

1970. Inauguration of Satellite Communications Station, Kum San.
863. **363.** 10 w. multicoloured .. 1·10 30

364. "PEN" and Quill Pen. **366.** Postal Code Symbol.

365. Section of Motorway.

1970. 37th Int. P.E.N. (literary organization) Congress, Seoul.
864. **364.** 10 w. multicoloured .. 60 25

1970. Opening of Seoul-Pusan Motorway.
865. **365.** 10 w. multicoloured .. 1·00 30

1970. Introduction of Postal Codes.
866. **366.** 10 w. multicoloured .. 60 25

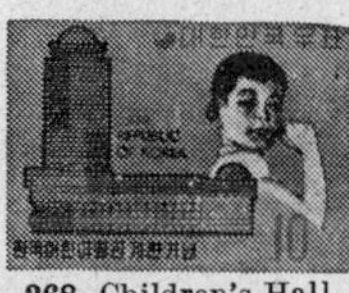

367. Parcel Sorting Area. **368.** Children's Hall and Boy.

1970. Inauguration of Postal Mechanization.
867 **367** 10 w. multicoloured .. 60 25

1970. Opening of Children's Hall, Seoul.
869. **368.** 10 w. multicoloured .. 60 30

369. "Mountain and River" (Yi In Moon).

1970. Korean Paintings of Yi Dynasty (1st series). Multicoloured.
870. 10 w. Type **369** .. .. 1·25 30
871. 10 w. "Jongyangsa Temple" (Chong Son) .. 1·25 30
872. 10 w. "Mountain and River by Moonlight" (Kim Doo Ryang) (vert.) .. 1·25 30
See also Nos. 887/89, 897/899, 947/52, 956/8 and 961/5.

370. P.T.T.I. Emblem. **371.** WAC and Corps Badge.

1970. Councillors' Meeting, Asian Chapter of Postal, Telegraph and Telephone International (Post Office Trade Union Federation).
874. **370.** 10 w. multicoloured .. 55 25

1970. 20th Anniv. of Korean Women's Army Corps.
875. **371.** 10 w. multicoloured .. 55 25

372. Pres. Pak and Flag.

1970.
876. **372.** 10 w. multicoloured 3·00 55
877. – 10 w. blk., grn. & blue 3·00 55
DESIGN—VERT. No. 877, Pres. Pak and industrial complex.

373. Presidents Pak and Sanchez Hernandez.

1970. Visit of Pres. Hernandez of El Salvador.
878. **373.** 10 w. multicoloured .. 1·50 45

374. "People and Houses".

1970. National Census.
880. **374.** 10 w. multicoloured .. 85 25

375. Diving.

1970. 51st National Athletic Games, Seoul. Multicoloured.
881. 10 w. Type **375** .. .. 1·25 35
882. 10 w. Hockey .. .. 1·25 35
883. 10 w. Baseball .. .. 1·25 35

376. Police Badge and Activities. **377.** Bell and Globe.

1970. National Police Day.
885. **376.** 10 w. multicoloured 1·00 30

1970. 25th Anniv. of United Nations.
886. **377.** 10 w. multicoloured .. 65 30

1970. Korean Paintings of the Yi Dynasty (2nd series). Vert. designs as T **369**, showing animals. Multicoloured.
887 30 w. "Fierce Tiger" (Shim Sa Yung) .. .. 1·50 30
888 30 w. "Cats and Sparrows" (Pyun Sang Byuk) .. 1·50 30
889 30 w. "Dog with Puppies" (Yi Am) .. .. 1·50 30

378. Kite and Reel. **380.** Fields ("Food Production").

379. Quotation and Emblems on Globe.

1970. Lunar New Year ("Year of the Pig"). Multicoloured.
891. 10 w. Type **378** 65 20
892. 10 w. Toy pig 65 20

1970. 15th Communications Day.
894. **379.** 10 w. multicoloured .. 65 30

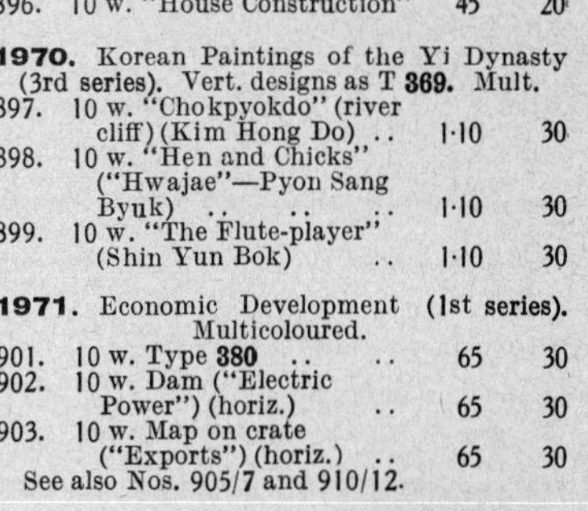

1970. 2nd Five Year Plan. As T **272.** Dated "1970". Multicoloured.
895. 10 w. "Port Development" 45 20
896. 10 w. "House Construction" 45 20

1970. Korean Paintings of the Yi Dynasty (3rd series). Vert. designs as T **369.** Mult.
897. 10 w. "Chokpyokdo" (river cliff) (Kim Hong Do) .. 1·10 30
898. 10 w. "Hen and Chicks" ("Hwajae"—Pyon Sang Byuk) .. .. .. 1·10 30
899. 10 w. "The Flute-player" (Shin Yun Bok) .. 1·10 30

1971. Economic Development (1st series). Multicoloured.
901. 10 w. Type **380** 65 30
902. 10 w. Dam ("Electric Power") (horiz.) .. 65 30
903. 10 w. Map on crate ("Exports") (horiz.) .. 65 30
See also Nos. 905/7 and 910/12.

381. Coal-mining. **382.** Globe, Torch and Spider.

1971. Economic Development (2nd series). Multicoloured.
905. 10 w. Type **381** 45 20
906. 10 w. Cement works (vert.) 45 20
907. 10 w. Fertilizer plant .. 45 20

1971. Anti-Espionage Month.
909. **382.** 10 w. multicoloured .. 60 20

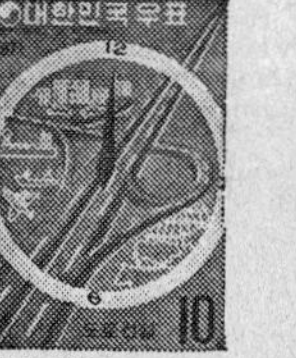

383. Motorway Junction. **384.** Reservist and Badge.

1971. Economic Development (3rd series). Multicoloured.
910. 10 w. Type **383** 45 20
911. 10 w. Scales ("Gross National Income") (horiz.) 45 20
912. 10 w. Bee and coins ("Increased Savings") (horiz.) 45 20

1971. Home Reserve Forces Day.
914. **384.** 10 w. multicoloured .. 80 30

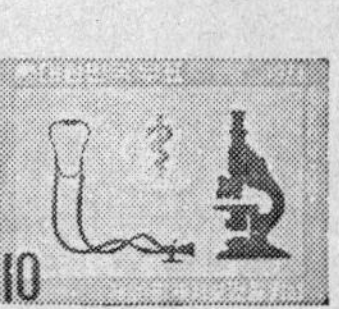
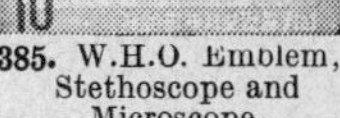

385. W.H.O. Emblem, Stethoscope and Microscope. **386.** Underground Train.

1971. 20th World Health Day.
915. **385.** 10 w. multicoloured .. 45 30

1971. Construction of Seoul Underground Railway System.
916. **386.** 10 w. multicoloured .. 1·00 20

387. Footballer. **388.** Veteran and Association Flag.

1971. First Asian Soccer Games, Seoul.
917. **387.** 10 w. multicoloured .. 1·25 30

1971. 20th Korean Veterans' Day.
918. **388.** 10 w. multicoloured .. 45 20

389. Girl Scouts. **390.** Torch and Economic Symbols.

1971. 25th Anniv. of Korean Girl Scouts Federation.
919. **389.** 10 w. multicoloured .. 55 20

1971. 10th Anniv. of May 16th Revolution.
920. **390.** 10 w. multicoloured .. 45 20

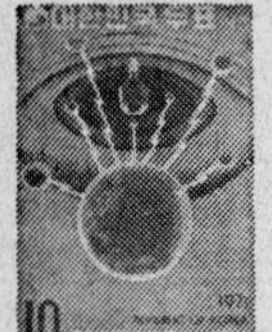

391. "Telecommunications". **392.** I.L.O. Emblem.

1971. 3rd World Telecommunications Day.
921. **391.** 10 w. multicoloured .. 45 20

1971. "The Work of the United Nations Organization".
922. **392.** 10 w. mauve, blk. & grn 1·00 30
923. – 10 w. bl., blk. & mauve 1·00 30
924. – 10 w. multicoloured .. 1·00 30
925. – 10 w. bl., blk. & mauve 1·00 30
926. – 10 w. mauve, blk. & grn 1·00 30
927. – 10 w. bl., blk. & mauve 1·00 30
928. – 10 w. mauve, blk. & bl. 1·00 30
929. – 10 w. blk., grn. & mauv 1·00 30
930. – 10 w. mauve, blk. & bl. 1·00 30
931. – 10 w. bl., blk. & mauve 1·00 30
932. – 10 w. mauve, blk. & bl. 1·00 30
933. – 10 w. blk., mauve & grn 1·00 30
934. – 10 w. mauve, bl. & blk. 1·00 30
935. – 10 w. blk., mauve & grn 1·00 30
936. – 10 w. mauve, blk. & blu 1·00 30
937. – 10 w. bl., blk. & mauve 1·00 30
938. – 10 w. mauve, blk. & blu 1·00 30
939. – 10 w. blk. mauve & grn. 1·00 30
940. – 10 w. mauve, blk. & blu 1·00 30
941. – 10 w. blue, blk. & mauv 1·00 30
942. – 10 w. mauve, blk. & grr 1·00 30
943. – 10 w. blk., blue & mauv 1·00 30
944. – 10 w. multicoloured .. 1·00 30
945. – 10 w. blk., blue & mauv 1·00 30
946. – 10 w. blk., mauve & grr 1·00 30

EMBLEMS: No. 923, Food and Agriculture Organization. No. 924, General Assembly and New York Headquarters. No. 925, U.N.E.S.C.O. No. 926, W.H.O. No. 927, World Bank. No. 928, International Development Association. No. 929, Security Council. No. 930, International Finance Corporation. No. 931, International Monetary Fund. No. 932, International Civil Aviation Organization. No. 933, Economic and Social Council. No. 934, South Korean Flag. No. 935, Trusteeship Council. No. 936, U.P.U. No. 937, I.T.U. No. 938, World Meteorological Organization. No. 939, Int. Court of Justice. No. 940, I.M.C.O. No. 941, U.N.I.C.E.F. No. 942, International Atomic Energy Agency. No. 943, United Nations Industrial Development Organization. No. 944, United Nations Commission for the Unification and Rehabilitation of Korea. No. 945, United Nations Development Programme. No. 946, United Nations Conference on Trade and Development.

393. "Boating" (Shin Yun Bok).

1971. Korean Paintings of the Yi Dynasty (4th series). Multicoloured.
947. 10 w. Type **393** .. .. 2·00 45
948. 10 w. "Greeting Travellers" 2·00 45
949. 10 w. "Tea Ceremony" .. 2·00 45
950. 10 w. "Lady and Servants on Country Road" .. 2·00 45
951. 10 w. "Couple Walking" .. 2·00 45
952. 10 w. "Fairy and Boy beneath Pine Tree" (Li Chae Kwan) (vert.) .. 2·00 45

Nos. 947/51 show "Folk Customs" paintings by Shin Yun Bok.

394. Pres. Pak, Emblem and Motorway. **395.** Camp Fire and Badge.

1971. Re-election of Pres. Pak for 3rd Term.
954. **394.** 10 w. multicoloured .. 1·75 80

1971. Korean Paintings of the Yi Dynasty (5th series). As T **393.** Multicoloured.
956. 10 w. "Chasing the Cat" (Kim Deuk Shin) .. 1·50 30
957. 10 w. "Valley Family" (Li Chae Kwan) (vert.) .. 1·50 30
958. 10 w. "Man Reading" (Li Chae Kwan) (vert.) .. 1·50 30

1971. 13th World Scout Jamboree, Asagiri, Japan.
960. **395.** 10 w. multicoloured .. 55 20

1971. Korean Paintings of the Yi Dynasty (6th series). As T **393.** Multicoloured.
961. 10 w. "Classroom" .. 1·75 45
962. 10 w. "Wrestling Match" 1·75 45
963. 10 w. "Dancer with Musicians" 1·75 45
964. 10 w. "Weavers" .. 1·75 45
965. 10 w. "Drawing Water at the Well" .. .. 1·75 45

Nos. 961/5 depict genre paintings by Kim Hong Do.

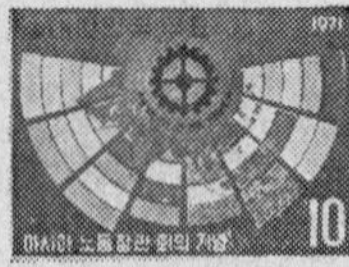

396. Cogwheel and Asian Map.

1971. 3rd Asian Labour Minister's Conference, Seoul.
967. **396.** 10 w. multicoloured .. 45 20

397. Judo.

1971. 52nd National Athletic Meeting, Seoul. Multicoloured.
969 10 w. Type **397** 75 30
970 10 w. Archery 75 30

398. Korean symbol on Palette.

1971. 20th National Fine Art Exhib.
972. **398.** 10 w. multicoloured .. 45 20

399. Doctor and Globe. **400.** Emblems and "Vocational Skills".

1971. 7th Congress of Medical Associations from Asia and Oceania.
973. **399.** 10 w. multicoloured .. 55 20

1971. 2nd National Vocational Skill Contest for High School Students.
974. **400.** 10 w. multicoloured .. 45 20

401. Callipers and "K" Emblem.

1971. 10th Anniv. of Industrial Standardisation.
976. **401.** 10 w. multicoloured .. 45 20

402. Fairy Tale Rats. **403.** Emblem and Hangul Alphabet.

1971. Lunar New Year ("Year of the Rat"). Multicoloured.
977. 10 w. Type **402** 60 20
978. 10 w. Flying Crane .. 65 20

1971. 50th Anniv. of Hangul Hakhoe (Korean Language Research Society).
980. **403.** 10 w. multicoloured .. 45 20

1971. 2nd Five-Year Plan. As T **272.** Dated "1971". Multicoloured.
981. 10 w. Atomic power plant 60 20
982. 10 w. Hydro-electric power project 65 20

404. Korean Red Cross Building on Map. **405.** Globe and Open Book.

1971. South-North Korean Red Cross Conference, Panmunjom.
983. **404.** 10 w. multicoloured .. 80 30

1971. Int. Book Year.
985. **405.** 10 w. multicoloured .. 55 20

406. "Intelsat 4" and Korean Earth Station. **407.** Speed-skating.

1971. 20th Anniv. of Korea's Membership of I.T.U.
987. **406.** 10 w. multicoloured .. 45 20

1972. Winter Olympic Games, Sapporo, Japan. Multicoloured.
988. 10 w. Type **407** .. 75 30
989. 10 w. Figure-skating .. 75 30

408. Forestry Map. **410.** E.C.A.F.E. Emblem and Industrial Symbols.

409. Scarab Beetles and Emblem.

1972. "Trees for Unity" Campaign.
991. **408.** 10 w. multicoloured .. 45 20

1972. 20th Anniv. of Korean Junior Chamber of Commerce.
992. **409.** 10 w. multicoloured .. 60 20

1972. 25th Anniv. of U.N. Economic Commission for Asia and the Far East.
993. **410.** 10 w. multicoloured .. 45 20

411. Flags of Member Countries. **412.** Reserve Forces' Flag.

1972. 10th Anniv. of Asian and Oceanic Postal Union.
994. **411.** 10 w. multicoloured .. 45 20

1972. Home Reserve Forces Day.
995. **412.** 10 w. multicoloured .. 80 30

413. Emblem and "Terias harina". **414.** Rural Activities.

1972. 50th Anniv. of Korean Young Women's Christian Association.
996. **413.** 10 w. multicoloured .. 1·00 30

1972. "New Community" (rural development) Movement.
997. **414.** 10 w. multicoloured .. 45 20

415. "Anti-Espionage" and Korean Flag. **416.** Children with Balloons.

1972. Anti-Espionage Month.
998. **415.** 10 w. multicoloured .. 45 20

1972. 50th Children's Day.
999. **416.** 10 w. multicoloured .. 45 20

417. Leaf Ornament from Gold Crown. **419.** Kalkot, Koje Island, Hanryo Straits Park.

418. Lake Paengnokdam, Mt. Halla Park.

1972. Treasures from King Munyong's Tomb. Multicoloured.
1000. 10 w. Type **417** 60 20
1001. 10 w. Gold earrings (horiz.) 65 20

1972. National Parks (1st series).
1002. **418.** 10 w. multicoloured 50 20
1003. **419.** 10 w. multicoloured 50 20
See also Nos. 1018/19 and 1026/7.

420. Marguerite and Conference Emblem. **421.** Gwanghwa Gate and National Flags.

1972. U.N. Environmental Conservation Conference, Stockholm.
1004. **420.** 10 w. multicoloured 45 20

1972. 7th Asian and Pacific Council (ASPAC) Ministerial Meeting, Seoul.
1006. **421.** 10 w. multicoloured 60 25

422. Pasture ("Development of Rural Economy"). **423.** "Love Pin".

1972. 3rd Five-Year Plan. Dated "1972". Multicoloured.
1007. 10 w. Type **422** 60 25
1008. 10 w. Foundry ladle ("Heavy Industries") 60 25
1009. 10 w. Crate and Globe ("Increased Exports") 60 25

1972. Disaster Relief Fund.
1010 **423** 10 w.+5 w. red & blue 45 20

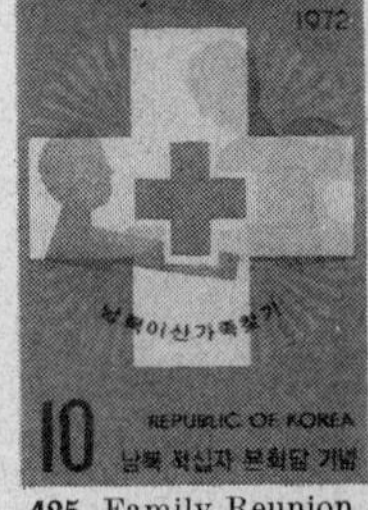

424. Judo. **425.** Family Reunion through Red Cross.

1972. Olympic Games, Munich. Multicoloured.
1011. 20 w. Type **424** 45 20
1012. 20 w. Weightlifting .. 45 20
1013. 20 w. Wrestling 45 20
1014. 20 w. Boxing 45 20

1972. 1st Plenary Meeting of South-North Korean Red Cross Conference, Pyongyang.
1016. **425.** 10 w. multicoloured 80 30

426. Bulkuk Temple, Kyongju Park. **428.** Conference Emblem within "5".

427. Statue and Bopju Temple, Mt. Sokri Park.

1972. National Park (2nd series).
1018. **426.** 10 w. multicoloured 55 20
1019. **427.** 10 w. multicoloured 55 20

1972. 5th Asian Judicial Conf., Seoul.
1020. **428.** 10 w. multicoloured 45 20

429. Lions Badge between Korean Emblems.

1972. 11th Orient and South-East Asian Lions Convention, Seoul.
1021. **429.** 10 w. multicoloured 50 20

430. Scout taking Oath. **431.** Dolls and Ox's Head.

1972. 50th Anniv. of Korean Boy Scouts Movement.
1022. **430.** 10 w. multicoloured 85 25

1972. Lunar New Year ("Year of the Ox"). Multicoloured.
1023. 10 w. Type **431** 60 20
1024. 10 w. Revellers in balloon 60 20

432. Temple, Mt. Naejang Park. **433.** Madeungryong Pass, Mt. Sorak Park.

1972. National Parks. (3rd series).
1026. **432.** 10 w. multicoloured 55 20
1027. **433.** 10 w. multicoloured 55 20

434. President Pak, Flag and "Development".

1972. Re-election of President Pak.
1028. **434.** 10 w. multicoloured 1·50 65

435. National Central Museum, Kyongbok Palace. **437.** Korean Family.

436. Temple, Mt. Sorak.

1973. Korean Tourist Attractions (1st series).
1030. **435.** 10 w. multicoloured 40 15
1031. **436.** 10 w. multicoloured 40 15
See also Nos. 1042/3, 1048/9, 1057/8 and 1075/6.

1973. Korean Unification Campaign.
1032. **437.** 10 w. multicoloured 40 15

438. "V" Sign and and Flags. **439.** Construction Workers and Cogwheel.

1973. Return of Korean Forces from South Vietnam.
1033. **438.** 10 w. multicoloured 45 20

1973. 10th Workers' Day.
1034. **439.** 10 w. multicoloured 40 15

440. W.M.O. Emblem and Satellite. **442.** Wonsam costume (woman's ceremonial).

1973. Centenary of World Meteorological Organization.
1035. **440.** 10 w. multicoloured .. 40 15

1973. Korean Court Costumes of the Yi Dynasty (1st series). Multicoloured. Background colours given.
1037. – 10 w. orange 80 25
1038. **442.** 10 w. orange 80 25
DESIGN: No. 1037, Kujangbok (king's ceremonial costume).
See also Nos. 1045/6, 1053/4, 1060/1 and 1078/9.

443. Nurse with Lamp. **444.** Reservists and Flag.

1973. 50th Anniv. of Korean Nurses' Association.
1040. **443.** 10 w. multicoloured 55 15

1973. Home Reserve Forces Day.
1041. **444.** 10 w. multicoloured .. 75 25

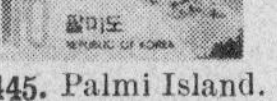

445. Palmi Island. **446.** Sain-am Rock, Mt. Dokjol.

1973. Korean Tourist Attractions (2nd series).
1042. **445.** 10 w. multicoloured 40 15
1043. **446.** 10 w. multicoloured 40 15

447. Table Tennis Player.

1973. Victory of South Korean Women's Team in World Table Tennis Championships, Sarajevo.
1044 **447** 10 w. multicoloured .. 1·00 30

1973. Korean Court Costumes of the Yi Dynasty (2nd series). As T **442**. Multicoloured. Background colours given.
1045. 10 w. purple 75 15
1046. 10 w. green 75 15
DESIGNS: No. 1045, Konryongpo (king's costume). No. 1046, Jokui (queen's ceremonial costume).

450. Admiral Li Sun Sin's Shrine, Asan. **451.** Limestone Cavern, Kusan-ni.

1973. Korean Tourist Attractions (3rd series).
1048. **450.** 10 w. multicoloured 40 10
1049. **451.** 10 w. multicoloured 40 10

452. Children's Choir.

1973. 20th Anniv. of World Vision Int.
1050. **452.** 10 w. multicoloured 45 20

453. Love Pin and "Disasters".

1973. Disaster Relief Fund.
1051. **453.** 10 w.+5 w. mult. .. 20 15

454. Steel Converter. **457.** Table Tennis Bat and Ball.

1973. Inauguration of Pohang Steel Works.
1052. **454.** 10 w. multicoloured 50 15

1973. Korean Court Costumes of the Yi Dynasty. (3rd series). As T **442**. Multicoloured. Background colours given.
1053. 10 w. blue 75 15
1054. 10 w. pink 75 15
DESIGNS: No. 1053, Kangsapo (crown prince's) costume. No. 1054, Tangui (princess's) costume.

1973. Table Tennis Gymnasium Construction Fund.
1056 457 10w.+5 w. mve & grn 45 20

458. Namhae Suspension Bridge. **459.** Hongdo Island.

1973. Korean Tourist Attractions (4th series).
1057. **458.** 10 w. multicoloured 40 10
1058. **459.** 10 w. multicoloured 40 10

460. Interpol and Korean Police Emblems.

1973. 50th Anniv. of International Criminal Police Organization (Interpol).
1059. **460.** 10 w. multicoloured 65 10

1973. Korean Court Costumes of the Yi Dynasty (4th series). As Type **442**. Multicoloured. Background colours given.
1060. 10 w. yellow 75 10
1061. 10 w. blue 75 10
DESIGNS: No. 1060, Kumkwanchobok (court official's) costume. No. 1061, Hwalot (queen's wedding) costume.

465. Manchurian Cranes. **466.** Sommal Lily. **467.** Motorway and Farm.

1973.

1063.	–	1 w. brown	15	10
1063a.	–	3 w. black and blue	25	10
1064.	–	5 w. brown	10	10
1064a.	–	6 w. turquoise & grn.	20	10
1065.	**465.**	10 w. ultramarine & bl.	40	10
1066.	**466.**	10 w. red, blk & grn.	25	10
1067.	**467.**	10 w. green and red	25	10
1068.	–	30 w. brown & yellow	35	10
1068a.	–	50 w. green & brown	30	10
1068b.	–	60 w. brown & yellow	35	10
1068c.	–	80 w. black & brown	45	10
1069.	–	100 w. yell. & brn. ..	5·50	15
1069a.	–	100 w. red	55	10
1069b.	–	200 w. brn. & pink ..	1·10	10
1069c.	–	300 w. red & lilac ..	1·75	10
1069d.	–	500 w. multicoloured	5·50	10
1069e.	–	500 w. purple & brn.	3·00	10
1069f.	–	1,000 w. green ..	4·25	30

DESIGNS—VERT. 1 w. Mask of old man. 5 w. Siberian chipmunk. 6 w. Lily. 30 w. Honey Bee. 50 w. Pot with Lid. 60 w. Jar. 100 w. (No. 1069) Gold Crown, Silla dynasty. 100 w. (No. 1069a) Admiral Yi Soon Shin. 300 w. Pobjusa Temple. 500 w. (No. 1069d) Gold Crown. 500 w. (No. 1069e) Carved dragon (tile Baekje Dynasty). LARGER (24×33 mm.) 100 w. Flying deities (relief from bronze bell, Sangwe on Temple). HORIZ. 3 w. Magpie. 80 w. Ceramic horseman. 200 w. Muryangsujeon Hall, Busok Temple.

For designs similar to Type **465** but with frame, see Type **703**.

470. Tennis.

1973. 54th National Athletic Meeting, Pusan. Multicoloured.
1070. 10 w. Type **470** 40 10
1071. 10 w. Hurdling 40 10

471. Children with Stamp Albums.

1973. Philatelic Week.
1072. **471.** 10 w. multicoloured 35 10

472. Soyang River Dam.

1973. Inauguration of Soyang River Dam.
1074 **472** 10 w. multicoloured .. 30 10

473. Mt. Mai, Chinan. **474.** Tangerine Grove, Cheju Island.

1973. Korean Tourist Attractions (5th Series).
1075. **473.** 10 w. multicoloured 40 10
1076. **474.** 10 w. multicoloured 40 10

475. Match, Cigarette and Flames.

478. Tiger and Candles.

1973. 10th Fire Prevention Day.
1077. **475.** 10 w. multicoloured 25 10

1973. Korean Court Costumes of the Yi Dynasty (5th series). As T **442.** Multicoloured. Background colours given.
1078. 10 w. orange 75 10
1079. 10 w. pink 75 10
DESIGNS: No. 1078, Pyongsangbok (official's wife) costume. No. 1079, Kokunbok (military officer's) costume.

1973. Lunar New Year ("Year of the Tiger"). Multicoloured.
1081. 10 w. Type **478** 40 10
1082. 10 w. Decorated top .. 45 10

479. Korean Girl and Flame Emblem.

1973. 25th Anniv. of Declaration of Human Rights.
1084. **479.** 10 w. multicoloured 25 10

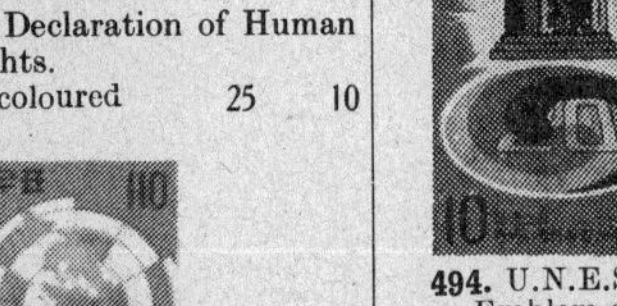

480. Jetliner and Polar Zone.

1973. Air.
1085. **480.** 110 w. blue and pink 2·75 20
1086. - 135 w. red and green 2·75 20
1087. - 145 w. red and blue 2·75 25
1088. - 180 w. yellow and lilac 2·75 25
DESIGNS—Jetliner and Postal Zones on Map. 135 w. South-east Asia. 145 w. India, Australasia and North America. 180 w. Europe, Africa and South America.

481. "Komunko" (zither).

1974. Traditional Musical Instruments (1st series). Mult. Background colours given.
1089. **481.** 10 w. blue 75 10
1090. – 30 w. orange.. .. 85 15
DESIGN: 30 w. "Nagak" (conch trumpet).
See also Nos. 1098/9, 1108/9, 1117/18 and 1132/3.

483. Apricots.

485. Reservist and Factory.

1974. Fruits (1st series). Multicoloured.
1092. 10 w. Type **483** 25 10
1093. 30 w. Strawberries .. 45 15
See also Nos. 1104/5, 1111/2, 1120/1 and 1143/4.

1974. Home Reserve Forces Day.
1095. **485.** 10 w. multicoloured 30 10

486. W.P.Y. Emblem.

489. Mail Train and Communications Emblem.

1974. World Population Year.
1096. **486.** 10 w. multicoloured 25 10

1974. Traditional Musical Instruments (2nd series). As T **481.** Multicoloured. Background colours given.
1098. 10 w. blue 60 10
1099. 30 w. green .. .. 1·25 15
CEREMONIAL INSTRUMENTS: 10 w. "Tchouk". 30 w. "Eu".

1974. Communications Day.
1101. **489.** 10 w. multicoloured 60 15

490. C.A.F.E.A.-I.C.C. Emblem on Globe.

491. Port Installations.

1974. 22nd Session of Int., Chamber of Commerce's Commission on Asian and Far Eastern Affairs, Seoul.
1102. **490.** 10 w. multicoloured 25 10

1974. Inaug. of New Port Facilities, Inchon.
1103. **491.** 10 w. multicoloured 40 10

1974. Fruits (2nd series). As T **483.** Mult.
1104. 10 w. Peaches 40 10
1105. 30 w. Grapes 60 15

494. U.N.E.S.C.O. Emblem and Extended Fan.

499. Cross and Emblems.

1974. 20th Anniv. of South Korean U.N.E.S.C.O. Commission.
1107. **494.** 10 w. multicoloured 25 10

1974. Traditional Musical Instruments (3rd series). As T **481.** Multicoloured. Background colours given.
1108. 10 w. orange 65 10
1109. 30 w. pink .. .. 1·25 15
DESIGNS: 10 w. "A-chaing" (stringed instrument). 30 w. "Kyobang-ko" (drum).

1974. Fruits (3rd series). As T **483.** Mult.
1111. 10 w. Pears 40 10
1112. 30 w. Apples 60 15

1974. "Explo 74"—2nd International Training Congress on Evangelism. Mult.
1114. 10 w. Type **499** 20 10
1115. 10 w. Emblem and Korean map on Globe 20 10

501. Underground Train.

1974. Opening of Seoul Underground Railway.
1116. **501.** 10 w. multicoloured 85 10

1974. Traditional Musical Instruments (4th series). As T **481.** Multicoloured. Background colours given.
1117. 10 w. blue 65 10
1118. 30 w. pink .. .. 1·10 15
DESIGNS: No. 1117, So ("Pan pipes"). No. 1118, Haikem (Two-stringed fiddle).

1974. Fruits (4th series). As T **483.** Mult.
1120. 10 w. Cherries 40 10
1121. 30 w. Persimmons 60 10

506. Rifle Shooting.

1974. 55th National Athletic Meeting, Seoul. Multicoloured.
1123. 10 w. Type **506** 25 10
1124. 30 w. Rowing 65 10

508. U.P.U. Emblem.

509. Symbols of Member Countries.

1974. Cent. of U.P.U.
1125. **508.** 10 w. mult. (postage) 20 10
1126. 110 w. mult. (air) .. 95 45

1974. First World Conference of People-to-People International.
1128. **509.** 10 w. multicoloured 20 10

510. Korean Stamps of 1884.

1974. Philatelic Week and 90th Anniv. of First Korean Stamps.
1129. **510.** 10 w. multicoloured 30 10

511. Taekwondo Contestants.

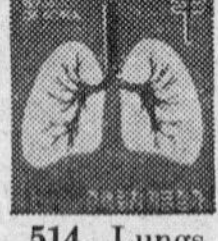

514. Lungs.

1974. First Asian Taekwondo Championships, Seoul.
1131 **511** 10 w. multicoloured .. 30 10

1974. Traditional Musical Instruments (5th series). As T **481.** Multicoloured. Background colours given.
1132. 10 w. pink 40 10
1133. 30 w. ochre 60 15
DESIGNS: 10 w. Pak (clappers). 30 w. Pyenchong (chimes).

1974. Tuberculosis Control Fund.
1135. **514.** 10 w.+5 w. red & grn. 25 10

515. Presidents Pak and Ford.

516. Yook Young Soo (wife of Pres. Pak).

1974. State Visit of President Ford of United States.
1136 **515** 10 w. multicoloured .. 40 20

1974. Yook Young Soo Memorial Issue.
1138. **516.** 10 w. green 40 15
1139. 10 w. orange.. .. 40 15
1140. 10 w. violet 40 15
1141. 10 w. blue 40 15

1974. Fruits (5th series). As T **483.** Mult.
1143. 10 w. Tangerines .. 40 10
1144. 30 w. Chestnuts.. .. 50 15

519. "Good Luck" Purse.

521. U.P.U. Emblem and "75".

1974. Lunar New Year ("Year of the Rabbit"). Multicoloured.
1146. 10 w. Type **519** 35 10
1147. 10 w. Toy rabbits .. 35 10

1975. 75th Anniv of Korea's Membership of U.P.U. Multicoloured.
1149 10 w. Type **521** 25 10
1150 10 w. U.P.U. emblem and paper dart 25 10

523. Dove with "Good Luck" Card.

1975. Inauguration of National Welfare Insurance System.
1151 **523** 10 w. multicoloured .. 20 10

524. Dr. Schweitzer, Map and Syringe.

525. Salpuli Dancer.

1975. Birth Cent. of Dr. Albert Schweitzer.
1152. **524.** 10 w. bistre 40 15
1153. 10 w. mauve.. .. 40 15
1154. 10 w. orange.. .. 40 15
1155. 10 w green 40 15

1975. Korean Folk Dances (1st series). Multicoloured, background colour given.
1156 **525** 10 w. green 40 10
1157 – 10 w. blue 40 10
DESIGN: No. 1157, Exorcism in dance.
See also Nos. 1168/9, 1175/6, 1193/4 and 1208/9.

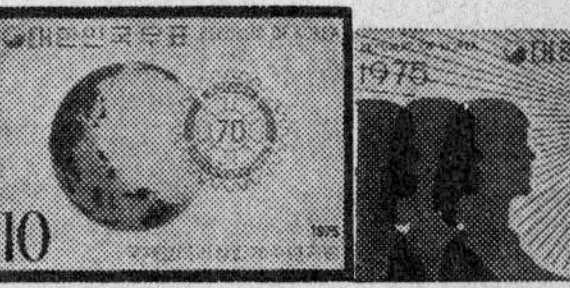

527. Globe and Rotary Emblem.

528. Women and I.W.Y. Emblem.

1975. 70th Anniv. of Rotary International.
1159. **527.** 10 w. multicoloured 25 10

1975. International Women's Year.
1160. **528.** 10 w. multicoloured 20 10

529. Violets.

531. Saemaeul Township.

1975. Flowers (1st series). Mult.
1161. 10 w. Type **529** 35 10
1162. 10 w. Anemones 35 10
See also Nos. 1171/2, 1184/5, 1199/200 and 1213/4.

1975. National Afforestation Campaign. Multicoloured.
1163. 10 w. Type **531** 50 10
1164. 10 w. Lake and trees .. 50 10
1165. 10 w. "Green" forest .. 50 10
1166. 10 w. Felling timber .. 50 10
Nos. 1163/6 were issued together se-tenant in horizontal strips of four within the sheet, forming a composite design.

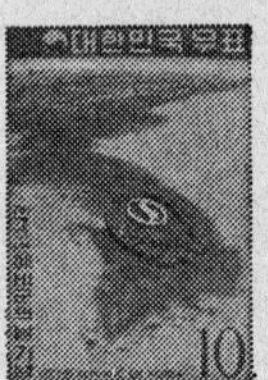

535. H.R.F. Emblem on Map of Korea.

536. Butterfly Dance.

1975. Homeland Reserve Forces Day.
1167. **535.** 10 w. multicoloured 30 10

1975. Folk Dances (2nd series). Multicoloured, background colour given.
1168 **536** 10 w. green 45 10
1169 – 10 w. yellow 45 10
DESIGN: No. 1169, Victory dance.

538. Rhododendron.

540. Metric Symbols.

1975. Flowers (2nd series). Multicoloured.
1171. 10 w. Type **538** 40 10
1172. 10 w. Clematis 40 10

1975. Cent. of Metric Convention.
1173. **540.** 10 w. multicoloured 25 10

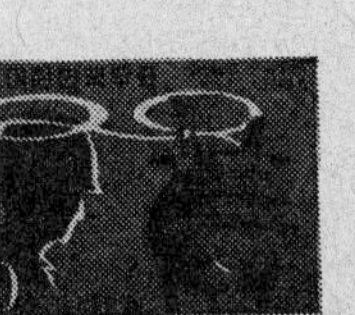

541. Soldier and Incense Pot.

542. Mokjoong Dance.

1975. 20th Memorial Day.
1174. 541. 10 w. multicoloured . . 20 10

1975. Folk Dances (3rd series). Multicoloured, background colour given.
1175 542 10 w. blue 45 10
1176 – 10 w. pink 45 10
DESIGN: No. 1176, Malttungi dancer.

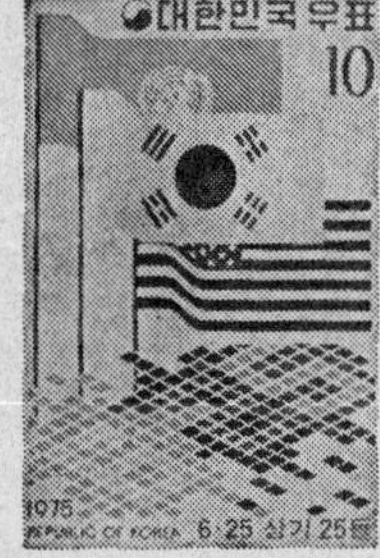
544. Flags of South Korea, U.N. and U.S.

1975. 25th Anniv. of Korean War. Mult.
1178. 10 w. Type 544 . . . . 35 10
1179. 10 w. Flags of Ethiopia, France, Greece, Canada and South Africa . . 35 10
1180. 10 w. Flags of Luxembourg, Australia, U.K., Colombia and Turkey 35 10
1181. 10 w. Flags of Netherlands, Belgium, Philippines, New Zealand and Thailand 35 10

548. Presidents Pak and Bongo.

549. Iris.

1975. State Visit of President Bongo of Gabon.
1182. 548. 10 w. multicoloured 30 10

1975. Flowers (3rd series). Mult.
1184. 10 w. Type 549 . . . . 40 10
1185. 10 w. Thistle 40 10

551. Scout Scarf.

552. Freedom Flame.

1975. "Nordjamb 75" World Scout Jamboree, Norway. Multicoloured.
1186. 10 w. Type 551 . . . . 30 10
1187. 10 w. Scout oath . . 30 10
1188. 10 w. Scout camp . . 30 10
1189. 10 w. Axe and rope . . 30 10
1190. 10 w. Camp fire 30 10

1975. 30th Anniv. of Liberation. Mult.
1191. 20 w. Type 552 . . . . 35 10
1192. 20 w. Balloon emblems . . 35 10

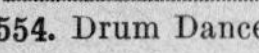
554. Drum Dance.

556. Taekwondo Contestant.

1975. Folk Dances (4th series). Multicoloured, background colour given.
1193 554 20 w. yellow 45 10
1194 – 20 w. orange 45 10
DESIGN: No. 1194, Bara dance.

1975 Second World Taekwondo Championships, Seoul.
1196 556 20 w. multicoloured . . 25 10

557. Assembly Hall.

1975. Completion of National Assembly Hall.
1197. 557. 20 w. multicoloured . . 25 10

558. Dumper Truck and Emblem.

559. Broad-bell Flower.

1975. Contractors' Association Convention, Seoul.
1198. 558. 20 w. multicoloured 20 10

1975. Flowers (4th series). Mult.
1199. 20 w. Type 559 . . . . 40 10
1200. 20 w. Bush clover . . 40 10

561. Morse Key and Dish Aerial.

1975. 90th Anniv. of Korean Telecommunications.
1201. 561. 20 w. blk., orge. & pur. 35 10

562. Yeongweol Caves.

564. Flag and Missiles.

1975. International Tourism Day. Mult.
1202. 20 w. Type 562 . . . . 25 10
1203. 20 w. Mount Sorak . . 25 10

1975. Korean Armed Forces Day.
1204. 564. 20 w. multicoloured 25 10

565. "Gymnastics".

567. "Kangaroo" Collector.

1975. 56th National Athletic Meeting. Mult.
1205. 20 w. Type 565 . . . . 20 10
1206. 20 w. "Handball" . . 20 10

1975. Philatelic Week.
1207. 567. 20 w. multicoloured 25 10

568. Sogo Dance.

570. U.N. Emblem and Handclasps.

1975. Folk Dances (5th series). Multicoloured, background colour given.
1208 568 20 w. blue 45 10
1209 – 20 w. yellow 55 10
DESIGNS: No. 1209, Bupo Nori dance.

1975. 30th Anniv. of United Nations.
1211. 570. 20 w. multicoloured 20 10

571. Red Cross and Emblems.

572. Camellia.

1975. 70th Anniv. of Korean Red Cross.
1212. 571. 20 w. multicoloured 35 10

1975. Flowers (5th series). Multicoloured.
1213. 20 w. Type 572 . . . . 40 10
1214. 20 w. Gentian 40 10

574. Union Emblem.

575. Children Playing.

1975. 10th Anniv. of Asian Parliamentary Union.
1215. 574. 20 w. multicoloured 20 10

1975. Lunar New Year. Multicoloured.
1216. 20 w. Type 575 . . . . 30 10
1217. 20 w. Dragon ("Year of the Dragon") 30 10

577. Electric Train.

1975. Opening of Cross-country Electric Railway.
1219. 577. 20 w. multicoloured 30 10

578. "Dilipa fenestra".

1976. Butterflies (1st series). Multicoloured, background colour given.
1220 578 20 w. red 65 10
1221 – 20 w. blue 65 10
DESIGN: No. 1221, "Luehdorfia puziloi".
See also Nos. 1226/7, 1246/7, 1254/5 and 1264/5.

580. Institute Emblem and Science Emblems.

581. Japanese White-necked Crane.

1976. 10th Anniv. of Korean Institute of Science and Technology.
1222. 580. 20 w. multicoloured 25 10

1976. Birds (1st series). Multicoloured.
1223. 20 w. Type 581 . . . . 55 15
1224. 20 w. Great Bustard . . 55 15
See also Nos. 1243/4, 1251/2, 1257/8 and 1266/7.

583. Globe and Telephones.

1976. Telephone Centenary.
1225. 583. 20 w. multicoloured . . 20 10

584. "Papilio xuthus".

1976. Butterflies (2nd series). Multicoloured, background colour given.
1226 584 20 w. yellow 65 10
1227 – 20 w. green 65 10
DESIGN: No. 1227, "Parnassius bremeri".

586. "National Development".

587. Eye and People.

1976. Homeland Reserve Forces Day.
1228. 586. 20 w. multicoloured 30 10

1976. World Health Day. Prevention of Blindness.
1229 587 20 w. multicoloured . . 30 10

588. Pres. Pak and Flag.

589. Ruins of Moenjodaro.

1976. 6th Anniv of Saemaul Movement (community self-help programme). Mult.
1230 20 w. Type 588 . . . . 45 15
1231 20 w. People ("Intellectual edification") . . 45 15
1232 20 w. Village ("Welfare") 45 15
1233 20 w. Produce and fields ("Production") . . 45 15
1234 20 w. Produce and factory ("Increase of Income") 45 15

1976. Moenjodaro (Pakistan) Preservation Campaign.
1235. 589. 20 w. multicoloured 40 10

590. U.S. Flags of 1776 and 1976.

591. Camp Scene on Emblem.

1976. Bicent. of American Revolution.
1236. 590. 100 w. red, blue & blk. 1·40 30
1237. – 100 w. red, blue & blk. 1·40 30
1238. – 100 w. red, blue & blk. 1·40 30
1239. – 100 w. red, blue & blk. 1·40 30
1240. – 100 w. red, blue & blk. 1·40 30
DESIGNS: No. 1237, Statue of Liberty. No. 1238, Map of United States. No. 1239, Liberty Bell. No. 1240, American astronaut.

1976. 30th Anniv. of Korean Girl Scouts Federation.
1242. 591. 20 w. multicoloured . . 40 10

592. Blue-winged Pitta.

594. Buddha and Temple.

1976. Birds (2nd series). Mult.
1243. 20 w. Type 592 . . . . 55 10
1244. 20 w. White-bellied Black Woodpecker . . 55 10

1976. U.N.E.S.C.O. Campaign for Preservation of Borobudur Temple (in Indonesia).
1245. 594. 20 w. multicoloured 25 10

595. Eastern Pale Clouded Yellow

1976. Butterflies (3rd series). Multicoloured, background colour given.
1246 595 20 w. olive 55 10
1247 – 20 w. violet 55 10
DESIGN: No. 1247, Chinese windmill.

597. Protected Family. **598.** Volleyball.

1976. National Life Insurance.
1248. **597.** 20 w. multicoloured . . 30 10

1976. Olympic Games, Montreal. Mult.
1249. 20 w. Type **598** 35 10
1250. 20 w. Boxing 35 10

600. Black Wood Pigeon. **602.** Children and Books.

1976. Birds (3rd series). Mult.
1251. 20 w. Type **600** 55 10
1252. 20 w. Oystercatcher . . 55 10

1976. Books for Children.
1253. **602.** 20 w. multicoloured . . 25 10

603. " Hestina assimilis ".

1976. Butterflies (4th series). Multicoloured, background colour given.
1254 **603** 20 w. brown 55 10
1255 – 20 w. drab 55 10
Design: No. 1255, Blue triangle.

604a. Corps Members and Flag. **605.** Black-faced Spoonbill.

1976. 1st Anniv. of Korean Civil Defence Corps.
1256. **604a.** 20 w. multicoloured . . 30 10

1976. Birds (4th series). Mult.
1257. 20 w. Type **605** . . 55 10
1258. 20 w. Black Stork . . 55 10

607. Chamsungdan, Mani Mountain.

1976. International Tourism Day. Mult.
1259. 20 w. Type **607** 25 10
1260. 20 w. Ilchumun Gate, Tongdosa 25 10

609. Cadet and Parade. **610.** "Musa basjoo" (flower arrangement, Cheong Jo the Great).

1976. 30th Anniv. of Korean Military Academy.
1261. **609.** 20 w. multicoloured . . 25 10

1976. Philatelic Week.
1262. **610.** 20 w. blk., red & drab 25 10

611. Yellow-legged Tortoiseshell. **613.** European Black Vulture.

1976. Butterflies (5th series). Multicoloured, background colour given.
1264 **611** 20 w. light green . . 55 10
1265 – 20 w. purple . . 55 10
Design: No. 1265, "Fabriciana nerippe".

1976. Birds (5th series). Mult.
1266. 20 w. Type **613** 65 15
1267. 20 w. Whistling Swan . . 65 15

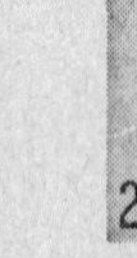

615. Snake (bas-relief, Kim Yu Shin's tomb). **619.** Dish Aerial.

617. " Training Technicians ".

1976. Lunar New Year (Year of the Snake). Multicoloured.
1268 20 w. Type **615** 30 10
1269 20 w. Door knocker with Manchurian cranes . . 30 10

1977. 4th Five Year Economic Development Plan. Multicoloured.
1271 20 w. Type **617** 40 10
1272 20 w. Tanker ("Heavy Industries") 40 10

1977. 25th Anniv. of Korea's I.T.U. Membership.
1273. **619.** 20 w. multicoloured . . 30 10

620. Korean Broadcasting Centre. **621.** Jar with Grape Design.

1977. 50th Anniv. of Broadcasting in Korea.
1274. **620.** 20 w. multicoloured . . 35 10

1977. Korean Ceramics (1st series). Multicoloured, background colours given.
1275. 20 w. Type **621** (brn.) . . 75 10
1276. 20 w. Celadon vase (grey) 75 10
See also 1285/6, 1287/8, 1290/1 and 1300/1.

623. " Two-children " Family. **624.** Reserve Soldier.

1977. Family Planning.
1277 **623** 20 w. grn, turq & orge 20 10

1977. Ninth Homeland Reserve Forces Day.
1278. **624.** 20 w. multicoloured 30 10

625. Diagram of Brain. **626.** Medical Book and Equipment.

1977. 10th Anniv. of Science Day.
1279. **625.** 20 w. multicoloured 20 10

1977. 35th International Military Medicine Meeting.
1280. **626.** 20 w. multicoloured 45 10

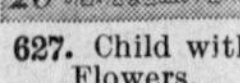

627. Child with Flowers. **628.** Veterans' Flag and Emblem.

1977. 20th Anniv. of Children's Charter.
1281. **627.** 20 w. multicoloured 20 10

1977. 25th Anniv. of Korean Veteran's Day.
1282. **628.** 20 w. multicoloured 40 10

629. Statue of Buddha, Sokkulam Grotto. **630.** Celadon Jar.

1977. 2600th Birth Anniv. of Buddha.
1283. **629.** 20 w. olive 30 10

1977. Korean Ceramics (2nd series). Multicoloured, background colours given.
1285. 20 w. Type **630** (pink) . . 45 10
1286. 20 w. Porcelain vase (blue) (vert.) 45 10

632. "Buddha" Celadon Wine Jar.

1977. Korean Ceramics (3rd series). Multicoloured, background colours given.
1287. 20 w Type **632** (mauve) 45 10
1288. 20 w. Celadon vase (pale blue) 45 10

수해구제
+10
(**634.**)

635. Celadon Vase, Black Koryo Ware.

1977. Flood Relief. No. 791 Surch. with T **634**.
1289. 20 w. + 10 w. green . . 1·00 20

1977. Korean Ceramics (4th series). Multicoloured, background colours given.
1290. 20 w. Type **635** (stone) . . 45 10
1291. 20 w. White porcelain bowl (green) (horiz.) . . 45 10

637. Ulleung-do Island. **639.** Servicemen.

1977. World Tourism Day. Multicoloured.
1292. 20 w. Type **637** 30 10
1293. 20 w. Haeundae Beach . . 30 10

1977. Armed Forces Day.
1294. **639.** 20 w. multicoloured 20 10

640. "Mount Inwang-Clearing-up after **641.** the Rain" (detail from drawing by Chung Seon).

1977. Philatelic Week.
1295. **640.** 20 w. multicoloured 40 10
1296. **641.** 20 w. multicoloured 40 10
Nos. 1294/5 were issued in se-tenant pairs throughout the sheet, forming a composite design.

642. Rotary Emblem and Koryo Dynasty Bronze Bell. **643.** South Korean Flag over Everest.

1977. 50th Anniv. of Korean Rotary Club.
1298. **642.** 20 w. multicoloured 50 10

1977. South Korean Conquest of Mount Everest.
1299. **643.** 20 w. multicoloured 50 10

644. Punch'ong Bottle. **646.** Hands preserving Nature.

1977. Korean Ceramics (5th series). Multicoloured, background colours given.
1300. 20 w. Type **644** (brown) 50 10
1301. 20 w. Celadon cylindrical bottle (pale brown) . . 50 10

1977. Nature Conservation.
1302. **646.** 20 w. bl., grn. & brn. 15 10

647. Children with Kites. **649.** Clay Pigeon Shooting.

1977. Lunar New Year ("Year of the Horse"). Multicoloured.
1303 20 w. Type **647** 25 10
1304 20 w. Horse (bas-relief, Kim Yu Shin's tomb) 25 10

1977. 42nd World Shooting Championships, Seoul. Multicoloured.
1306 20 w. Type **649** 20 10
1307 20 w. Air pistol shooting 20 10
1308 20 w. Air rifle shooting . . 20 10

652. Korean Airlines Boeing "747".

1977. 25th Anniv. of Korean Membership of I.C.A.O.
1310. **652.** 20 w. multicoloured 45 10

653. "Exports".

1977. Korean Exports.
1311. **653.** 20 w. multicoloured 35 10

654. Ships and World Map

1978. National Maritime Day.
1312. **654.** 20 w. multicoloured .. 30 10

655. Three-storey Pagoda, Hwaom Temple.

656. Seven-storey Pagoda, T'app'yong-ri.

1978. Stone Pagodas (1st series).
1313. **655.** 20 w multicoloured 35 10
1314. **656.** 20 w multicoloured 35 10
See also Nos. 1319/20, 1322/5 and 1340/1.

657. Ants with coins.

658. Seoul Sejong Cultural Centre, Hahoe Mask and Violin.

1978. Savings Encouragement.
1315. **657.** 20 w. multicoloured 30 10

1978. Opening of Seoul Sejong Cultural Centre.
1316 **658** 20 w. multicoloured .. 60 10

659. Standard Bearer.

660. Pigeon and Young.

1978. Tenth Homeland Reserve Forces Day.
1317. **659.** 20 w. multicoloured .. 25 10

1978. Family Planning.
1318. **660.** 20 w. black and green 20 10

661. Pagoda, Punhwang Temple.

662. Pagoda, Miruk Temple.

1978. Stone Pagodas (2nd series).
1319. **661.** 20 w. multicoloured .. 35 10
1320. **662.** 20 w. multicoloured .. 35 10

663. National Assembly.

1978. 30th Anniv. of National Assembly.
1321. **663.** 20 w. multicoloured .. 20 10

664. Tabo Pagoda, Pulguk Temple.

665. Three-storey Pagoda, Pulguk Temple.

1978. Stone Pagodas (3rd series).
1322. **664.** 20 w. multicoloured .. 35 10
1323. **665.** 20 w. multicoloured .. 35 10

666. Ten-storey Pagoda, Kyongch'on Temple.

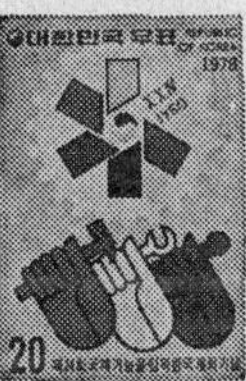
667. Nine-storey Octagonal Pagoda, Wolchong Temple.

1978. Stone Pagodas (4th series).
1324. **666.** 20 w. multicoloured .. 45 10
1325. **667.** 20 w. multicoloured .. 45 10

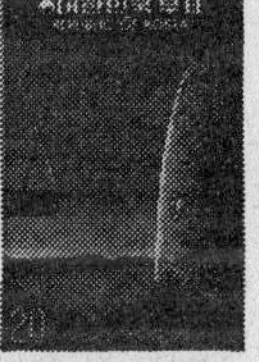
668. Emblem and Hands with Tools.

669. Crater Lake, Mt. Baeguda and Bell of Joy.

1978. 24th International Youth Skill Olympics, Pusan.
1326 **668** 20 w. multicoloured .. 20 10

1978. 30th Anniv. of Republic of Korea.
1328. **669.** 20 w. multicoloured .. 20 10

670. Army Nursing Officer.

671. Sobaeksan Observatory and Telescope.

1978. 30th Anniv. of Army Nursing Corps.
1329. **670.** 20 w. multicoloured .. 20 10

1978. Opening of Sobaeksan Observatory.
1330. **671.** 20 w. multicoloured .. 40 10

672. Kyonghoeru Pavilion, Kyonbok Palace.

673. Baeg-do Island.

1978. World Tourism Day.
1331. **672.** 20 w. multicoloured .. 20 10
1332. **673.** 20 w. multicoloured .. 20 10

674. Customs Officers and Flag.

1978. Cent. of Custom House.
1333. **674.** 20 w. multicoloured .. 25 10

675. Armed Forces.

676. Earthenware Figures, Silla Dynasty.

1978. 30th Anniv. of Korean Armed Forces.
1334. **675.** 20 w. multicoloured .. 30 10

1978. Culture Month.
1335. **676.** 20 w. black and green 20 10

677. Painting of a Lady. (Shin Yoo n-bok).

678. Young Men and Y.M.C.A. Emblem.

1978. Philatelic Week.
1336. **677.** 20 w. multicoloured .. 30 10

1978. 75th Anniv. of Korean Y.M.C.A.
1338. **678.** 20 w. multicoloured .. 20 10

679. Hand smothering Fire.

1978. Fire Prevention Campaign.
1339 **679** 20 w. multicoloured .. 20 10

680. Thirteen-storey Pagoda, Jeonghye Temple.

681. Three-storey Pagoda, Jinjeon Temple.

1978. Stone Pagodas (5th series).
1340. **680.** 20 w. multicoloured .. 30 10
1341. **681.** 20 w. multicoloured .. 30 10

682. Snow Scene.

684. People within Hibiscus.

1978. Lunar New Year ("Year of the Sheep"). Multicoloured.
1342 20 w. Type **682** 25 10
1343 20 w. Sheep (bas-relief, Kim Yu Shin's tomb) 25 10

1978. 10th Anniv. of National Education Charter.
1345. **684.** 20 w. multicoloured .. 20 10

685. President Pak.

1978. Re-election of Pres. Pak.
1346. **685.** 20 w. multicoloured .. 30 10

686. Golden Mandarinfish.

687. Lace Bark Pine.

1979. Nature Conservation.
1348 **686** 20 w. multicoloured .. 25 10
1349 **687** 20 w. multicoloured .. 25 10

688. Samil Monument.

689. Worker and Bulldozer.

1979. 60th Anniv. of Samil Independence Movement.
1350. **688.** 20 w. multicoloured .. 20 10

1979. Labour Day.
1351. **689.** 20 w. multicoloured .. 20 10

690. Tabo Pagoda, Pulgak Temple.

695. Hand Holding Symbols of Security.

1979. Korean Art. Multicoloured.
1352 20 w. Type **690** 25 10
1353 20 w. Gilt-bronze Maitreya 25 10
1354 20 w. Gold crown of Silla 25 10
1355 20 w. Celadon vase .. 25 10
1356 60 w. "Tano Day Activities" (silk screen) (50×33 mm) 45 10

1979. Strengthening National Security.
1358. **695.** 20 w. multicoloured .. 20 10

696. Pulguk Temple and P.A.T.A. Emblem.

1979. 28th Pacific Area Travel Association Conference, Seoul.
1359. **696.** 20 w. multicoloured .. 25 10

697. Presidents Pak and Senghor.

1979. Visit of President Senghor of Senegal.
1360. **697.** 20 w. multicoloured .. 20 10

698. Basketball.

699. Children playing.

1979. 8th World Women's Basketball Championships, Seoul.
1362. **698.** 20 w. multicoloured . . 40 10

1979. International Year of the Child.
1363. **699.** 20 w. multicoloured . . 25 10

700. Children on Swing.

1979. Family Planning.
1364. **700.** 20 w. multicoloured . . 20 10

701. Mandarins. **702.** "Neofinettia falcata" (orchid).

1979. Nature Conservation.
1365 **701** 20 w. multicoloured . . 40 10
1366 **702** 20 w. multicoloured . . 40 10

703 Manchurian Cranes

1979.

No.	Type	Description	Unused	Used
1367	**703**	10 w. black & green	30	10
1368	–	15 w. dp green & grn	15	10
1369	–	20 w. bistre, blk & bl	10	10
1370	–	30 w. multicoloured	20	10
1371	–	40 w. multicoloured	20	10
1372	–	50 w. brn, red & orge	15	10
1373	–	60 w. grey, purple and mauve . .	25	10
1374	–	70 w. multicoloured . .	35	10
1375	–	80 w. yell, blk & red	25	10
1376	–	90 w. buff, green and orange	50	10
1377	–	100 w. purple & mve	40	10
1377a	–	100 w. black . .	45	10
1378	–	150 w. black, bistre and blue	45	10
1379	–	200 w. brown & grn	80	10
1380	–	300 w. blue . .	1·00	10
1381	–	400 w. green, brown and deep green	2·25	10
1381a	–	400 w. blue, ochre, brown and grey . .	1·25	10
1382	–	450 w. brown	1·60	10
1383	–	500 w. dp grn & grn	1·75	15
1383a	–	550 w. black . .	1·75	20
1384	–	600 w. multicoloured	1·25	20
1385	–	700 w. multicoloured	2·10	20
1386	–	800 w. multicoloured	1·60	20
1387	–	1000 w. lt brn & brn	3·00	30
1388	–	1000 w. lt brn & brn	3·00	30
1389	–	5000 w. mult . .	14·00	1·50

DESIGNS—As T **703**. HORIZ. 15 w. Mt. Sorak. 50 w. Earthenware model of wagon. 90 w. Paikryung Island. 1000 w. Duck earthenware vessels (1387 facing right; 1388 facing left). VERT. 20 w. Tolharubang (stone grandfather). 30 w. National flag. 40 w. "Hibiscus syriacus". 60 w. Porcelain jar, Yi Dynasty. 70 w. Kyongju Observatory. 80 w. Mounted warrior (pottery vessel). 100 w. (1377) Ryu Kwan Soon. 100 w. (1377a) Chung Yak Yong (writer). 150 w. Porcelain jar, Chosun Dynasty. 200 w. Ahn Joong Geun. 300 w. Ahn Chang Ho. 400 w. Koryo celadon incense burner. 450, 550 w. Kim Ku (organizer of Korean Independence Party). 500 w. Brick with mountain landscape. 600 w. Hong Yung Sik (postal reformer). 700 w. Duck (lid of incense burner). 29×41 mm. 800 w. Dragon's head flagpole finial. 5000 w. Tiger.
See also No. 1065.

725. People suffering from Traffic Pollution.

1979. Environmental Protection.
1390. **725.** 20 w. brown & grn. 20 10

726. Common Goral. **727.** "Convallaria leiskei" Miquel.

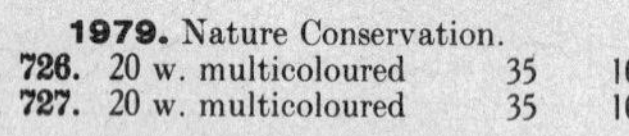

1979. Nature Conservation.
1391. **726.** 20 w. multicoloured 35 10
1392. **727.** 20 w. multicoloured 35 10

728. Presidents Pak and Carter.

1979. Visit of President Carter of United States.
1393. **728.** 20 w. multicoloured 20 10

729. Exhibition Building and Emblem.

1979. Opening of Korea Exhibition Centre.
1395. **729.** 20 w. multicoloured 20 10

730. Airplane and Globe.

1979. 10th Anniv. of Korean Air Lines.
1396. **730.** 20 w. multicoloured 30 10

731. "The Courtesans' Sword Dance" (Shin Yun-bok).

1979. United States "5000 Years of Korean Art" Exhibition (1st issue).
1397. **731.** 60 w. multicoloured 40 10
See also Nos. 1402/3, 1406/7, 1420/1, 1426/7, 1433/4, 1441/2 and 1457/8.

732. Mount Mai, North Cholla Province. **733.** Dragon's Head Rock, Cheju Island.

1979. World Tourism Day.
1399. **732.** 20 w. multicoloured 20 10
1400. **733.** 20 w. multicoloured 20 10

734. Heart, Donors and Blood Drop.

1979. Blood Donors.
1401. **734.** 20 w. red & grn. . . 30 10

735. White Porcelain Jar with Grape Design. **736** Mounted Warrior (pottery vessel).

1979. "5000 Years of Korean Art" Exhibition (2nd issue).
1402. **735.** 20 w. multicoloured 40 10
1403. **736.** 20 w. multicoloured 40 10

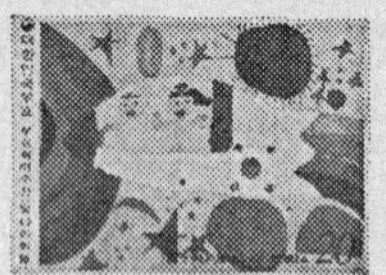

737. "Moon Travel" (Park Chung Jae).

1979. Philatelic Week.
1404. **737.** 20 w. multicoloured 20 10

738. Hahoe Mask. **739.** Golden Amitabha with Halo.

1979. "5000 Years of Korean Art" Exhibition (3rd issue).
1406. **738.** 20 w. multicoloured 40 10
1407. **739.** 20 w. multicoloured 40 10

740. Rain Frog. **741.** Asian Polypody.

1979. Nature Conservation.
1408. **740.** 20 w. multicoloured 45 10
1409. **741.** 20 w. multicoloured 45 10

742. Monkey (bas-relief, Kim Yun Shin's tomb). **743.** Children playing Yut.

1979. Lunar New Year ("Year of the Monkey").
1410. **742.** 20 w. multicoloured 15 10
1411. **743.** 20 w. multicoloured 15 10

744. President Choi Kyu Hah.

1979. Presidential Inauguration.
1413. **744.** 20 w. multicoloured 20 10

MORE DETAILED LISTS
are given in the Stanley Gibbons Catalogues referred to in the country headings.
For lists of current volumes see Introduction.

745. Firefly. **746.** Meesun Tree.

1980. Nature Conservation (5th series).
1415. **745.** 30 w. multicoloured 45 10
1416. **746.** 30 w. multicoloured 45 10

747. President Pak. **748.** Earthenware Kettle.

749. "Landscape" (Kim Hong Do).

1980. President Pak Commemoration.
1417 **747** 30 w. red 20 10
1418 30 w. purple 20 10

1980. Exhibition "5000 Years of Korean Art" (4th issue).
1420. **748.** 30 w. multicoloured 40 10
1421. **749.** 60 w. multicoloured 50 10

750. "Lotus". **751.** "Magpie and Tiger".

1980. Folk Paintings (1st series).
1423. **750.** 30 w. multicoloured 30 15
1424. **751.** 60 w. multicoloured 50 25
See also Nos. 1429/31, 1437/40 and 1453/6.

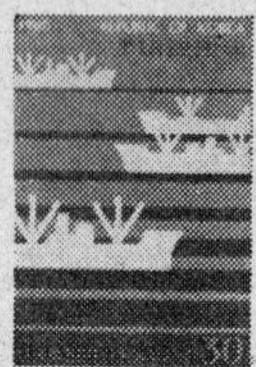

752. Merchant Ships.

1980. Korean Merchant Navy.
1425. **752.** 30 w. multicoloured 30 10

753. "Heavenly Horse" (tomb painting). **754.** Banner Staff with Dragon-head Finial.

1980. Exhibition "5000 Years of Korean Art" (5th series).
1426. **753.** 30 w. multicoloured 40 10
1427. **754.** 30 w. multicoloured 40 10

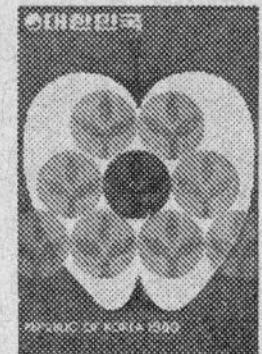

755. "Fruition".

1980. 10th Anniv of Saemaul Movement (community self-help programme).

1428 **755** 30 w. multicoloured . . 20 10

756. "Red Phoenix".

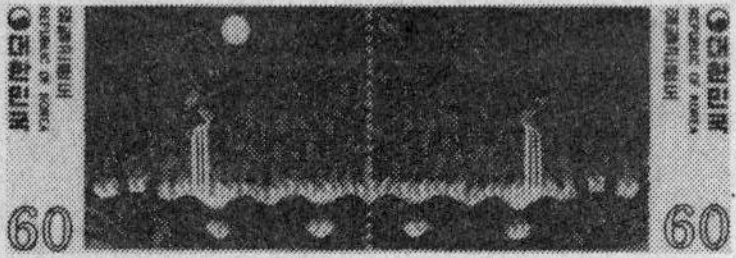

757/8. "Sun and Moon over Mt. Konryun". (½-size illustration).

1980. Folk Paintings (2nd series).

1429. **756.** 30 w. multicoloured 20 10
1430. **757.** 60 w. multicoloured 30 10
1431. **758.** 60 w. multicoloured 30 10

Nos. 1430/1 were issued together in se-tenant pairs within the sheet, forming a composite design.

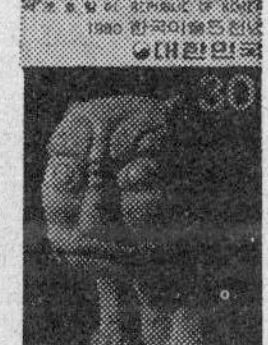

759. "Man on a Horse" (mural, Koguryo period).

760. "Tiger" (granite sculpture).

1980. Exhibition "5000 Years of Korean Art" (6th issue).

1433. **759.** 30 w. multicoloured 40 10
1434. **760.** 30 w. multicoloured 40 10

761. U.N. Flag and Rifle.

762. "Venus de Milo" and Contestants.

1980. 30th Anniv. of Intervention of U.N. Forces in Korean War.

1435. **761.** 30 w. multicoloured 30 10

1980. "Miss Universe" Beauty Contest, Seoul.

1436. **762.** 30 w. multicoloured 30 10

763. "Rabbits pounding Grain in a Mortar".

764. "Dragon in Cloud".

1980. Folk Paintings (3rd series).

1437. **763.** 30 w. multicoloured 40 10
1438. **764.** 30 w. multicoloured 40 10

765. "Pine Tree".

766. "Flowers and Manchurian Cranes" (detail, folding screen).

1980. Folk Paintings (4th series).

1439. **765.** 30 w. multicoloured 40 10
1440. **766.** 30 w. multicoloured 50 15

767. Human faced Roof Tile.

768. "White Tiger" (mural).

1980. Exhibition "5000 Years of Korean Art" (7th issue).

1441. **767.** 30 w. multicoloured 30 10
1442. **768.** 30 w. multicoloured 30 10

769. Football.

770. President Chun Doo Hwan.

1980. 10th President's Cup Football Tournament.

1443. **769.** 30 w. multicoloured 25 10

1980. Presidental Inauguration.

1444. **770.** 30 w. multicoloured 25 10

771. Woman Soldier and Emblem.

1980. 30th Anniv. of Women's Army Corps.

1446. **771.** 30 w. multicoloured 20 10

772. River Baegma.

773. Three Peaks of Dodam.

1980. World Tourism Day.

1447. **772.** 30 w. pink & purple 25 10
1448. **773.** 30 w. yellow, green and blue 25 10

774. Corn-cob and Micrometer.

775. Tree.

1980. Population and Housing Census.

1449. **774.** 30 w. multicoloured 25 10

1980. 75th Anniv. of Korean Red Cross.

1450. **775.** 30 w. multicoloured 35 10

776. "Angels Delivering Mail" (Kim Ki Chul).

1980. Philatelic Week.

1451. **776.** 30 w. multicoloured 25 10

777. "Ten Long-life Symbols".

781. Deva King (sculpture).

1980. Folk Paintings (5th series). Mult.

1453. 30 w. Type **777** 30 10
1454. 30 w. "Herb of eternal youth" and deer . . 30 10
1455. 30 w. Pine and deer eating herb 30 10
1456. 30 w. Pine, water and rock 30 10

Nos. 1453/6 were issued together in horiz setenant strips of four within the sheet, each strip forming a composite design.

1980. Exhibition "5000 Years of Korean Art" (8th series).

1457. **781.** 30 w. black 40 10
1458. 30 w. red 40 10

782. Cable Ship and Cross-section of Cable.

1980. Inauguration of Korea-Japan Submarine Cable.

1459. **782.** 30 w. multicoloured 30 10

783. Cock (bas-relief Kim Yu Shin's tomb).

784. Cranes.

1980. Lunar New Year ("Year of the Cock").

1460. **783.** 30 w. multicoloured 30 10
1461. **784.** 30 w. multicoloured 30 10

785. President Chun Doo Hwan and Factory within "Hibiscus syriacus".

1981. Presidential Inauguration.

1463. **785.** 30 w. multicoloured 20 10

786. "Korea Sun" (tanker).

787. "Asia Yukho" (freighter).

1981. Ships (1st series).

1465. **786.** 30 w. multicoloured 50 15
1466 **787.** 90 w. multicoloured 75 15

See also Nos. 1470/1, 1482/5 and 1501/2.

788. National Assembly Building.

1981. Inaugural Session of 11th National Assembly.

1467 **788** 30 w. brown and gold 20 10

789. Symbols of Disability and I.Y.D.P. Emblem.

790. Disabled Person in Wheelchair at Foot of Steps.

1981. International Year of Disabled Persons.

1468. **789.** 30 w. multicoloured 20 10
1469. **790.** 90 w. multicoloured 45 15

791. "Saturn" (bulk-carrier).

792. "Hanjin Seoul" (container ship).

1981. Ships (2nd series).

1470. **791.** 30 w. deep purple, purple and blue . . 45 15
1471. **792.** 90 w. grey, blue & red 80 15

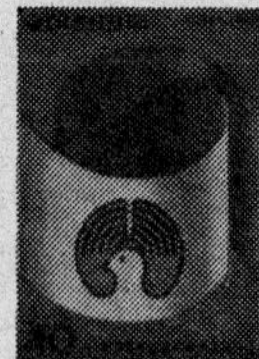

793. Council Emblem on Ribbon.

1981. Advisory Council on Peaceful Unification Policy.
1472. **793.** 40 w. multicoloured 20 10

794. "Clean Rivers and Air". **795.** Birds visiting Breeding Grounds.

1981. World Environment Day.
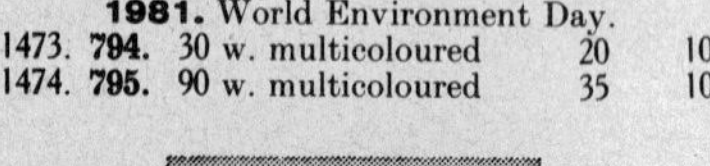
1473. **794.** 30 w. multicoloured 20 10
1474. **795.** 90 w. multicoloured 35 10

796. Presidents Chun and Suharto of Indonesia.

1981. Presidential Visit to A.S.E.A.N. Countries. Multicoloured.
1475. 40 w. Type **796** 20 10
1476. 40 w. Pres. Chun and Sultan of Malaysia .. 20 10
1477. 40 w. Handshake and flags of South Korea and Singapore .. 20 10
1478. 40 w. Pres. Chun and King of Thailand .. 20 10
1479. 40 w. Presidents Chun and Marcos of Philippines 20 10
1480. 40 w. Pres. Chun and flags of Korea, Singapore, Thailand, Indonesia, Malaysia and Philippines (39 × 43 mm.) 20 10

802. "Chung Ryong No. 3" (tug).

803. "Soo Gong No. 71" (trawler).

1981. Ships (3rd series).
1482 **802** 40 w. multicoloured .. 55 15
1483 **803** 100 w. multicoloured 85 15

804. "Aldebaran" (log carrier).

805. "Hyundai No. 1" (car carrier).

1981. Ships (4th series).
1484. **804.** 40 w. multicoloured 55 15
1485. **805.** 100 w. multicoloured 85 15

806. Korean with Flag and Dates on Graph. **812.** W.H.O. Emblem and Citizens.

807. Glider.

1981. 36th Anniv. of Liberation.
1486. **806.** 40 w. multicoloured 25 20

1981. Third Model Aeronautic Competition. Multicoloured.
1487. 10 w. Type **807** 35 15
1488. 20 w. Rubber-powered plane 35 15
1489. 40 w. Line-controlled plane 35 15
1490. 50 w. Radio-controlled plane 35 15
1491. 80 w. Radio-controlled helicopter 35 15

1981. 32nd Session of W.H.O. Regional Committee for the Western Pacific, Seoul.
1492 **812** 40 w. multicoloured .. 20 10

813. Seoul Communications Tower. **814.** Ulreung Island.

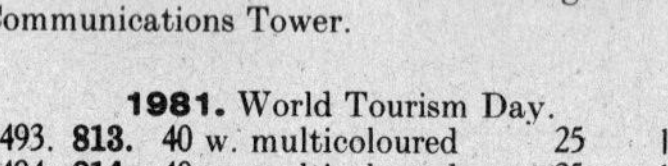

1981. World Tourism Day.
1493. **813.** 40 w. multicoloured 25 10
1494. **814.** 40 w. multicoloured 25 10

815. Cycling.

816. Swimming.

1981. 62nd National Sports Meeting, Seoul.
1495. **815.** 40 w. multicoloured 30 10
1496. **816.** 40 w. multicoloured 30 10

817. Presidents Chun and Carazo Odio. **818.** Hand holding Plate with F.A.O. Emblem.

1981. Visit of President Carazo Odio of Costa Rica.
1497. **817.** 40 w. multicoloured 20 10

1981. World Food Day.
1498. **818.** 40 w. multicoloured 25 10

819. Airplane and Clouds. **820.** South Gate of Seoul and Olympic Rings.

1981. National Aviation Day.
1499. **819.** 40 w. orange, brown and silver 40 10

1981. Choice of Seoul as 1988 Olympic Host City.
1500. **820.** 40 w. multicoloured 30 10

821. "Stolt Hawk" (chemical carrier).

822. Passenger Ferry.

1981. Ships (5th series).
1501. **821.** 40 w. black 55 15
1502. **822.** 100 w. blue 85 15

823. "Hang gliding" (Kim Kyung Jun).

1981. Philatelic Week.
1503. **823.** 40 w. multicoloured 25 10

824. Camellia and Dog. **825.** Children flying kite.

1981. Lunar New Year ("Year of the Dog").
1505. **824.** 40 w. multicoloured 25 10
1506. **825.** 40 w. multicoloured 25 10

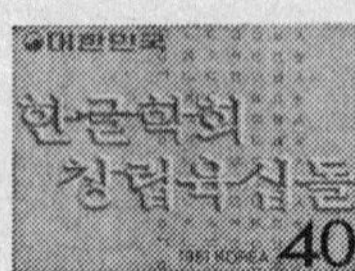

826. "Hangul Hakhoe".

1981. 60th Anniv. of Hangul Hakhoe (Korean Language Society).
1508. **826.** 40 w. multicoloured 30 10

827. Telephone and Dish Aerial. **828.** Scout Emblem and Logs forming "75".

1982. Inauguration of Korea Telecommunication Authority.
1509. **827.** 60 w. multicoloured 35 10

1982. 75th Anniv. of Boy Scout Movement.
1510. **828.** 60 w. multicoloured 50 10

829. Young Woman. **830.** Dividers and World Map.

1982. 60th Anniv. of Korean Young Women's Christian Association.
1511. **829.** 60 w. multicoloured 25 10

1982. Cent. of International Polar Year.
1512. **830.** 60 w. multicoloured 50 10

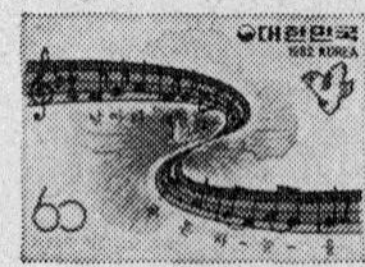

831. Music and "Hibiscus syriacus".

1982. Children's Day.
1513. **831.** 60 w. multicoloured 35 10

832. President Chun and Samuel Doe.

1982. Visit of Samuel Doe (Liberian Head of State).
1514. **832.** 60 w. multicoloured 20 10

833. Centenary Emblem.

1982. Centenary of Korea-United States Friendship Treaty.
1516 **833** 60 w. multicoloured .. 20 10
1517 – 60 w. multicoloured .. 20 10
DESIGN: No. 1517, Statue of Liberty and Seoul South Gate.

835. Presidents Chun and Mobutu.

1982. Visit of President Mobutu of Zaire.
1519. **835.** 60 w. multicoloured 20 10

836. "Territorial Expansion by Kwanggaeto the Great" (Lee Chong Sang).

837. "General Euljimunduck's Great Victory at Salsoo" (Park Kak Soon).

1982. Documentary Paintings (1st series).
1521. **836.** 60 w. multicoloured 30 10
1522. **837.** 60 w. multicoloured 30 10
See also Nos. 1523/4, 1537/8 and 1548/9.

838. "Shilla's Repulse of Invading Tang Army" (Oh Seung Woo).

839. "General Kang Kam Chan's Great Victory at Kyiju" (Lee Yong Hwan).

1982. Documentary Paintings (2nd series).
1523. **838.** 60 w. multicoloured 30 10
1524. **839.** 60 w. multicoloured 30 10

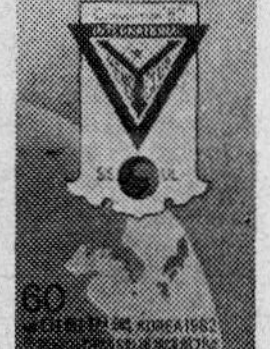
840. Convention Emblem and Globe.

841. Presidents Chun and Moi of Kenya.

1982. 55th International Y's Men's Club Convention, Seoul.
1525. **840.** 60 w. multicoloured 20 10

1982. Presidential Visits to Africa and Canada. Multicoloured.
1526 60 w. Type **841** 25 10
1527 60 w. Presidents Chun and Shagari of Nigeria .. 25 10
1528 60 w. Presidents Chun and Bongo of Gabon .. 25 10
1529 60 w. Presidents Chun and Diouf of Senegal .. 25 10
1530 60 w. Flags of South Korea and Canada .. 25 10

846. National Flag.

1982. Centenary of National Flag.
1532. **846.** 60 w. multicoloured 30 10

847. Emblem and Player.

1982. Second Seoul Table Tennis Championships.
1534. **847.** 60 w. multicoloured 40 10

848. Baseball Player.

1982. 27th World Baseball Championship Series, Seoul.
1535. **848.** 60 w. brown 25 10

849. Exhibition Centre.

1982. Seoul International Trade Fair.
1536. **849.** 60 w. multicoloured 20 10

850. "Admiral Yi Sun Sin's Great Victory at Hansan" (Kim Hyung Ku).

851. "General Kim Chwa Jin's Chungsanri Battle" (Sohn Soo Kwang).

1982. Documentary Paintings (3rd series).
1537. **850.** 60 w. multicoloured 50 10
1538. **851.** 60 w. multicoloured 25 10

852. "Miners reading Consolatory Letters" (Um Soon Keun).

1982. Philatelic Week.
1539. **852.** 60 w. multicoloured 20 10

853. Presidents Chung and Suharto.

1982. Visit of President Suharto of Indonesia.
1541. **853.** 60 w. multicoloured 20 10

854. J.C.I. Emblem over World Map.

855. "Intelsat 5" and "4-A" orbiting globe.

1982. 37th Junior Chamber International World Congress, Seoul.
1543. **854.** 60 w. multicoloured 20 10

1982. Second U.N. Conference on the Exploration and Peaceful Uses of Outer Space, Vienna.
1544. **855.** 60 w. multicoloured 30 10

856. Pig (bas-relief, Kim Yu Shin's tomb).

1982. Lunar New Year ("Year of the Pig").
1545. 60 w. Type **856** 30 10
1546. 60 w. Magpies & Korean moneybag 30 10

858. "General Kwon Yul's Great Victory at Haengju" (Oh Seung Woo).

859. "Kim Chong Suh's Exploitation of Yukin" (Kim Tae).

1982. Documentary Paintings (4th series).
1548. **858.** 60 w. multicoloured 35 10
1549. **859.** 60 w. multicoloured 35 10

860. Flags of South Korea and Turkey.

861. Hand writing Letter.

1982. Visit of President Evran of Turkey.
1550. **860.** 60 w. multicoloured 25 10

1982. Letter Writing Campaign.
1552. **861.** 60 w. multicoloured 20 10

862. Emblem, Airliner, Container Ship and Cranes.

863. Hyundai "Pony 2".

1983. International Customs Day.
1553. **862.** 60 w. multicoloured 50 15

1983. Korean-made Vehicles (1st series). Multicoloured.
1554. 60 w. Type **863** 45 10
1555. 60 w. Keohwa Jeep .. 45 10
See also Nos. 1558/9, 1564/5, 1572/3 and 1576/7.

865. President Chun and Sultan of Malaysia.

1983. Visit of Sultan of Malaysia.
1556 **865** 60 w. multicoloured .. 20 10

866. Daewoo "Maepsy". **867.** Kia "Bongo" Minibus.

1983. Korean-made Vehicles (2nd series).
1558. **866.** 60 w. multicoloured 45 10
1559. **867.** 60 w. multicoloured 45 10

INDEX
Countries can be quickly located by referring to the index at the end of this volume.

868. Former General Bureau of Postal Administration.

869. Central Post Office, Seoul.

1983. "Philakorea 84" International Stamp Exhibition, Seoul. Centenary of Korean Postal Service (1st series).
1560. **868.** 60 w. multicoloured 25 10
1561. **869.** 60 w. multicoloured 25 10
See also Nos. 1566/7, 1574/5 and 1603/6.

870. Old Village Schoolroom.

1983. Teachers' Day.
1562. **870.** 60 w. multicoloured 20 10

871. Asia Motor Co. Bus. **872.** Kia "Super Titan" Truck.

1983. Korean-made Vehicles (3rd series).
1564. **871.** 60 w. multicoloured 45 10
1565. **872.** 60 w. multicoloured 45 10

873. Early Postman.

1983. "Philakorea 84" International Stamp Exhibition, Seoul. Centenary of Korean Postal Service (2nd series).
1566. **873.** 70 w. multicoloured 30 10
1567. – 70 w. multicoloured 30 10
DESIGN: No. 1567, Modern postman on motorcycle..

875. "Communications in Outer Space" (Chun Ja Eun).

1983. World Communications Year.
1568. **875.** 70 w. multicoloured 20 10

876. Whooper Swans at Sunrise.

877. Emblems of Science and Engineering.

1983. Inaug. of Communications Insurance.
1570. **876.** 70 w. multicoloured 45 10

1983. Korean Symposium on Science and Technology, Seoul.
1571. **877.** 70 w. multicoloured 20 10

878. Daewoo Dump Truck.
879. Hyundai Cargo Lorry.

1983. Korean-made Vehicles (4th series).
1572. **878.** 70 w. multicoloured 45 10
1573. **879.** 70 w. multicoloured 45 10

880. Mail carried by Horse.

1983. "Philakorea 84" International Stamp Exhibition, Seoul. Centenary of Korean Postal Service (3rd series). Multicoloured.
1574 70 w. Type **880** 30 10
1575 70 w. Mail truck and aircraft 30 10

882. Dong-A Concrete Mixer Truck.
883. Dong-A Tanker.

1983. Korean-made Vehicles (5th series).
1576. **882.** 70 w. multicoloured 45 10
1577. **883.** 70 w. multicoloured 45 10

884. President Chun and King Hussein.
885. Woman with Fan.

1983. Visit of King Hussein of Jordan.
1578. **884.** 70 w. multicoloured 20 10

1983. 53rd American Society of Travel Agents World Congress, Seoul.
1580. **885.** 70 w. multicoloured 25 10

886. I.P.U. Emblem and Flags.

1983. 70th Inter-Parliamentary Union Conference, Seoul.
1581. **886.** 70 w. multicoloured 30 10

887. Gymnastics.

888. Football.

1983. 64th National Sports Meeting, Inchon.
1583. **887.** 70 w. multicoloured 25 10
1584. **888.** 70 w. multicoloured 25 10

889. Presidents Chun and U San Yu of Burma.

894. Rain Drops containing Symbols of Industry, Light and Food.

1983. Presidential Visits. Multicoloured.
1585. 70 w. Type **889** 50 50
1586. 70 w. Presidents Chun and Giani Zail Singh of India 50 50
1587. 70 w. Presidents Chun and Jayewardene of Sri Lanka 50 50
1588. 70 w. Flags of South Korea and Australia .. 50 50
1589. 70 w. Flags of South Korea and New Zealand 50 50

1983. Development of Water Resources and 10th Anniv of Soyang-gang Dam.
1591 **894** 70 w. multicoloured .. 25 10

895. Centenary Dates.
896. Tree with Lungs and Cross of Lorraine.

1983. Centenary of 1st Korean Newspaper "Hansong Sunbo".
1592 **895** 70 w. multicoloured .. 25 10

1983. 30th Anniv. of Korean National Tuberculosis Association.
1593. **896.** 70 w. multicoloured 25 10

897. Presidents Chun and Reagan.

898. Child collecting Stamps.

1983. Visit of President Reagan of United States of America.
1594. **897.** 70 w. multicoloured 25 10

1983. Philatelic Week.
1596. **898.** 70 w. multicoloured 20 5

899. Rat (bas-relief, Kim Yu Shin's tomb).

1983. Lunar New Year ("Year of the Rat"). Multicoloured.
1598. 70 w. Type **899** 30 10
1599. 70 w. Manchurian cranes and pine 30 10

901. Bicentenary Emblem.

902. 5 m. and 10 m. Stamps, 1884.

1984. Bicent. of Catholic Church in Korea.
1601. **901.** 70 w. red, violet & silver 25 10

1984. "Philakorea 84" International Stamp Exhibition, Seoul. Centenary of Korean Postal Service (4th series). Multicoloured.
1603. 70 w. Type **902** 25 10
1604. 70 w. 5000 w. stamp, 1983 25 10

904. Old Postal Emblem and Post Box.

1984. "Philakorea 84" International Stamp Exhibition, Seoul. Centenary of Korean Postal Service (5th series). Multicoloured.
1605. 70 w. Type **904** 30 10
1606. 70 w. Modern postal emblem and post box 30 10

906. President Chun and Sultan.

1984. Visit of Sultan of Brunei.
1607. **906.** 70 w. multicoloured 25 10

907. President Chun and Sheikh Khalifa.

1984. Visit of Sheikh Khalifa of Qatar.
1609. **907.** 70 w. multicoloured 25 10

908. Child posting Letter.

1984. Centenary of Korean Postal Administration. Multicoloured.
1611. 70 w. Type **908** 25 10
1612. 70 w. Postman in city .. 25 10

910. Pope John Paul II.

911. Cogwheel, Worker's Tools and Flowers.

1984. Visit of Pope John Paul II.
1614. **910.** 70 w. black 35 10
1615. 70 w. multicoloured 35 10

1984. Labour Festival.
1617. **911.** 70 w. multicoloured 20 10

912. Globe, Airliner, Container Ship and Emblem.

913. Map and Flag. of S. Korea and Sri Lanka.

1984. 63rd/64th Sessions of Customs Co-operation Council, Seoul.
1618. **912.** 70 w. multicoloured 65 15

1984. Visit of President Jayewardene of Sri Lanka.
1619. **913.** 70 w. multicoloured 30 10

914. Symbols and Punctuation Marks.

915. Expressway.

1984. 14th Asian Advertising Congress, Seoul.
1621. **914.** 70 w. multicoloured 25 10

1984. Opening of 88 Olympic Expressway.
1622. **915.** 70 w. multicoloured 30 10

916. Laurel, "Victory" and Olympic Rings.
917. A.B.U. Emblem and Microphone.

1984. 90th Anniv. of International Olympic Committee.
1623. **916.** 70 w. multicoloured 30 10

1984. 20th Anniv. of Asia-Pacific Broadcasting Union.
1624. **917.** 70 w. multicoloured 25 10

918. Flags of S. Korea and Senegal.

1984. Visit of President Abdou Diouf of Senegal.
1625. **918.** 70 w. multicoloured 20 10

919. Archery.

921. Crucifixion.

1984. Olympic Games, Los Angeles. Multicoloured.

1627. 70 w. Type **919** 40 10
1628. 440 w. Fencing .. .. 1·60 35

1984. Cent. of Korean Protestant Church. Multicoloured.

1629 70 w. Type **921** 20 10
1630 70 w. Cross, vine and dove 20 10

923. Man carrying Silk-covered Lantern.

1984. Folk Customs (1st series). "Wedding" (Kim Kyo Man). Multicoloured.

1632 70 w. Type **923** 20 10
1633 70 w. Bridegroom on horse 20 10
1634 70 w. Man playing clarinet 20 10
1635 70 w. Bride in sedan chair (51 × 35 mm) 20 10

See also Nos. 1657/8, 1683/4, 1734/8, 1808/11, 1840/3, 1858/61 and 1915/18.

927. Pres. Chun and Mt. Fuji.

1984. Pres. Chun's Visit to Japan.

1637. **927.** 70 w. multicoloured 35 10

928. Flags of S. Korea and Gambia.

1984. Visit of President Sir Dawada Kairaba Jawara of Gambia.

1639 **928** 70 w. multicoloured .. 30 10

929. Symbols of International Trade.

930. Namsan Tower and National Flags.

1984. "Sitra '84" International Trade Fair, Seoul.

1641. **929.** 70 w. multicoloured 30 10

1984. Visit of President El Hadj Omar Bongo of Gabon.

1642 **930** 70 w. multicoloured .. 30 10

931. Badminton.

932 Magnifying Glass and Exhibition Emblem

1984. 65th National Sports Meeting, Taegu. Multicoloured.

1644. 70 w. Type **931** 30 10
1645. 70 w. Wrestling 30 10

1984. "Philakorea 1984" International Stamp Exhibition, Seoul. Multicoloured.

1646 70 w. Type **932** 30 10
1647 70 w. South Gate, Seoul, and stamps (horiz) .. 30 10

934 Presidents Chun and Gayoom

1984. Visit of President Maumoon Abdul Gayoom of the Maldives.

1650 **934** 70 w. multicoloured .. 30 10

935 "100" and Industrial Symbols

1984. Centenary of Korea Chamber of Commerce and Industry.

1652 **935** 70 w. multicoloured .. 30 10

936 Children playing Jaegi-chagi

937 Ox (bas-relief, Kim Yu Shin's tomb)

1984. Lunar New Year. ("Year of the Ox").

1653 **936** 70 w. multicoloured .. 30 10
1654 **937** 70 w. multicoloured .. 30 10

938 I.Y.Y. Emblem

1985. International Youth Year.

1656 **938** 70 w. multicoloured .. 15 5

939 Pounding Rice for New Year Rice Cake

940 Welcoming Year's First Full Moon

1985. Folk Customs (2nd series).

1657 **939** 70 w. multicoloured 30 10
1658 **940** 70 w. multicoloured 30 10

941 Seoul Olympic Emblem

1985. Olympic Games, Seoul (1988) (1st issue). Multicoloured.

1659 70 w. + 30 w. Type **941** .. 40 20
1660 70 w. + 30 w. Hodori (mascot) 40 20

See also Nos. 1673/4, 1687/8, 1694/5, 1703/10, 1747/50, 1752/5, 1784/7, 1814/17, 1826/7, 1835/6 and 1844/7.

943 "Still Life with Doll" (Lee Chong Woo)

944 "Rocky Mountain in Early Spring Morning" (Ahn Jung Shik)

1985. Modern Art (1st series).

1662 **943** 70 w. multicoloured 30 10
1663 **944** 70 w. multicoloured 30 10

See also Nos. 1680/1, 1757/60, 1791/4 and 1875/8.

945 Flags, Statue of Liberty and President Chun

946 Flags, Seoul South Gate and National Flower

1985. Presidential Visit to United States.

1664 **945** 70 w. multicoloured .. 30 10

1985. Visit of President Mohammad Zia-ul-Haq of Pakistan.

1666 **946** 70 w. multicoloured .. 30 10

947 Underwood Hall

1985. Centenary of Yonsei University.

1668 **947** 70 w. black, buff & grn 30 10

948 Flags and Map

1985. Visit of President Luis Alberto Monge of Costa Rica.

1669 **948** 70 w. multicoloured .. 30 10

949 Silver Carp

950 Sailfish

1985. Fishes (1st series).

1671 **949** 70 w. multicoloured 40 10
1672 **950** 70 w. multicoloured 40 10

See also Nos. 1730/3, 1797/1800, 1881/4, 1903/6 and 1951/4.

951 Rowing

952 National Flags

1985. Olympic Games, Seoul (1988) (2nd issue). Multicoloured.

1673 70 w. + 30 w. Type **951** .. 40 20
1674 70 w. + 30 w. Hurdling .. 40 20

1985. Visit of President Hussain Muhammad Ershad of Bangladesh.

1676 **952** 70 w. multicoloured .. 35 10

953 National Flags

1985. Visit of President Joao Bernardo Vieira of Guinea-Bissau.

1678 **953** 70 w. multicoloured .. 30 10

954 "Spring Day on the Farm" (Huh Paik Ryun)

955 "The Exorcist" (Kim Chung Hyun)

1985. Modern Art (2nd issue).

1680 **954** 70 w. multicoloured 35 10
1681 **955** 70 w. multicoloured 35 10

956 Heavenly Lake, Paekdu and National Flower

1985. 40th Anniv of Liberation.

1682 **956** 70 w. multicoloured .. 35 10

957 Wrestling

958 Janggi

1985. Folk Customs (3rd series).
1683 **957** 70 w. multicoloured 35 10
1684 **958** 70 w. multicoloured 35 10

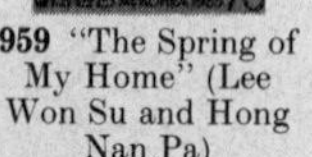
959 "The Spring of My Home" (Lee Won Su and Hong Nan Pa)

960 "A Leaf Boat" (Park Hong Keun and Yun Yong Ha)

1985. Korean Music (1st series).
1685 **959** 70 w. multicoloured 10 5
1686 **960** 70 w. multicoloured 10 5
See also Nos. 1728/9, 1776/7, 1854/5, 1862/3, 1893/4, 1935/6, 1996/7 and 2064/5.

1985. Olympic Games, Seoul (1988) (3rd issue). As T **951**. Multicoloured.
1687 70 w.+30 w. Basketball 40 20
1688 70 w.+30 w. Boxing .. 40 10

961 Satellite, "100" and Dish Aerial

962 Meetings Emblem

1985. Centenary of First Korean Telegraph Service.
1690 **961** 70 w. multicoloured .. 35 10

1985. World Bank and International Monetary Fund Meetings, Seoul.
1691 **962** 70 w. multicoloured .. 35 10

963 U.N. Emblem and Doves

964 Red Cross and Hands (detail, "Creation of Adam", Michelangelo)

1985. 40th Anniv of U.N.O.
1692 **963** 70 w. multicoloured .. 35 10

1985. 80th Anniv of Korea Red Cross.
1693 **964** 70 w. black, red & blue 45 10

1985. Olympic Games, Seoul (1988) (4th issue). As T **951**. Multicoloured.
1694 70 w.+30 w. Cycling .. 40 20
1695 70 w.+30 w. Canoeing .. 40 20

965 Cancelled Stamp on Envelope

966 Tiger (bas-relief, Kim Yu Shin's tomb)

1985. Philatelic Week.
1697 **965** 70 w. multicoloured .. 35 10

1985. Lunar New Year ("Year of the Tiger").
1698 **966** 70 w. multicoloured .. 35 10

967 Mount Fuji and KAL Aircraft

1985. 20th Anniv of Korea–Japan Treaty on Basic Relations.
1699 **967** 70 w. mult (postage) 60 10
1700 370 w. mult (air) 1·40 25

968 Doves and Globe

970 Pres. Chun, Big Ben and Korean and British Flags

1986. International Peace Year.
1701 **968** 70 w. multicoloured .. 35 10
1702 400 w. multicoloured 1·40 25

1986. Olympic Games, Seoul (188) (5th series). As T **951**. Multicoloured.
1703 70 w.+30 w. Show jumping (postage) 40 20
1704 70 w.+30 w. Fencing .. 40 20
1705 70 w.+30 w. Football .. 40 20
1706 70 w.+30 w. Gymnastics 40 20
1707 370 w.+100 w. As No. 1703 (air) .. .. 1·60 70
1708 400 w.+100 w. As No. 1704 .. .. .. 1·75 70
1709 440 w.+100 w. As No. 1705 .. .. .. 1·90 70
1710 470 w.+100 w. As No. 1706 .. .. .. 2·00 70

1986. Presidential Visit to Europe. Mult.
1711 70 w. Type **970** 40 10
1712 70 w. Pres. Chun, Eiffel Tower and Korean and French flags 40 10
1713 70 w. Pres. Chun, Belgian Parliament and Korean and Belgian flags .. 40 10
1714 70 w. Pres. Chun, Cologne Cathedral and Korean and West German flags 40 10

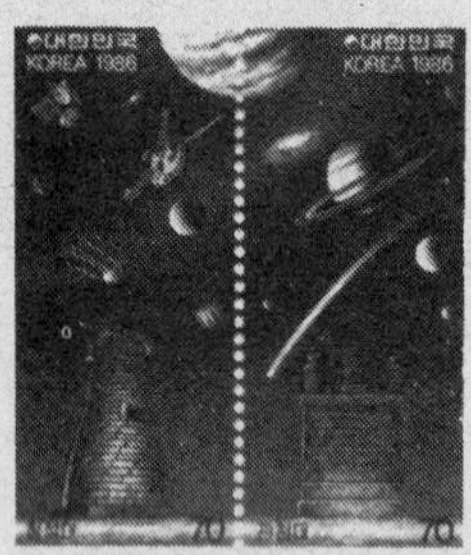
974 Kyongju Observatory

975 Kwanchon Observatory

1986. Science (1st series). Appearance of Halley's Comet.
1716 **974** 70 w. multicoloured .. 30 10
1717 **975** 70 w. multicoloured .. 30 10
See also Nos. 1781/2, 1833/4, 1864/5 and 1898/9.

976 General Assembly Emblem

977 Swallowtail and Flowers

1986. 5th Association of National Olympic Committees General Assembly, Seoul.
1718 **976** 70 w. multicoloured .. 40 10

1986. "Ameripex '86" International Stamp Exhibition, Chicago. Multicoloured.
1719 70 w. Type **977** .. .. 1·75 50
1720 370 w. "Papilio bianor" .. 1·75 50
1721 400 w. Swallowtails .. 1·75 60
1722 440 w. Swallowtail and frog .. .. .. 1·75 60
1723 450 w. Swallowtail .. 1·75 60
1724 470 w. "Papilio bianor" .. 1·75 60
Nos. 1719/24 were printed together, se-tenant, forming a composite design.

983 Male and Female Symbols in Balance

1986. Cent of Korean Women's Education.
1725 **983** 70 w. multicoloured .. 35 10

984 National Flags

1986. Visit of President Andre Kolingba of Central African Republic.
1726 **984** 70 w. multicoloured .. 35 10

985 "Half Moon" (Yun Keuk Young)

986 "Let's Go and Pick the Moon" (Yun Seok Juna and Park Tae Hyun)

1986. Korean Music (2nd series).
1728 **985** 70 w. multicoloured .. 35 10
1729 **986** 70 w. multicoloured .. 35 10

987 Eoreumchi

988 Sweetfish

989 Sardine

990 Hammerhead Sharks

1986. Fishes (2nd series).
1730 **987** 70 w. multicoloured .. 45 10
1731 **988** 70 w. multicoloured .. 45 10
1732 **989** 70 w. multicoloured .. 45 10
1733 **990** 70 w. multicoloured .. 45 10

991 Flag Carrier and Gong Player

996 Child

1986. Folk Customs (4th series). Farm Music. Multicoloured.
1734 70 w. Type **991** 30 10
1735 70 w. Drummer and piper 30 10
1736 70 w. Drummer and gong player 30 10
1737 70 w. Men with ribbons .. 30 10
1738 70 w. Man and woman with child 30 10
Nos. 1734/8 were printed together, se-tenant, forming a composite design.

1986. Family Planning.
1739 **996** 80 w. multicoloured .. 40 10

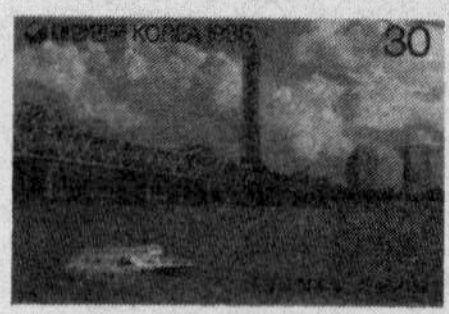
997 Bridge and "63" Building

1986. Completion of Han River Development. Multicoloured.
1740 30 w. Type **997** 40 10
1741 60 w. Buildings and excursion boat .. 40 10
1742 80 w. Rowing boat and Seoul Tower 40 10
Nos. 1740/2 were printed together, se-tenant, forming a composite design.

1000 Emblem

1004 Boy Fishing for Stamp

1002 "5", Delegates and Juan Antonio Samaranch (President of Int. Olympic Committee)

1986. 10th Asian Games, Seoul. Multicoloured.
1743 80 w. Type **1000** .. 40 10
1744 80 w. Firework display .. 40 10

1986. 5th Anniv of Choice of Seoul as 1988 Olympic Games Host City.
1746 **1002** 80 w. multicoloured 45 10

1986. Olympic Games, Seoul (1988) (6th issue). As T **951**. Multicoloured.
1747 80 w.+50 w. Weightlifting (postage) .. .. 1·25 60
1748 80 w.+50 w. Handball .. 1·25 60
1749 370 w.+100 w. As No. 1747 (air) .. .. 1·75 75
1750 400 w.+100 w. As No. 1748 .. .. .. 1·90 75

1986. Olympic Games, Seoul (1988) (7th issue). As T **951**. Multicoloured.
1752 80 w.+50 w. Judo (postage) .. .. 1·10 60
1753 80 w.+50 w. Hockey .. 1·10 60
1754 440 w.+100 w. As No. 1752 (air) .. .. 1·75 70
1755 470 w.+100 w. As No. 1753 .. .. .. 1·90 70

1986. Philatelic Week.
1756 **1004** 80 w. multicoloured 40 10

MINIMUM PRICE

The minimum price quoted is 5p which represents a handling charge rather than a basis for valuing common stamps. For further notes about prices see introductory pages.

1005 "Chunhyang-do" (Kim Un Ho)

1006 "Flowers" (Lee Sang Bum)

1007 "Portrait of a Friend" (Ku Bon Wung)

1008 "Woman in a Ski Suit" (Son Ung Seng)

1986. Modern Art (3rd series).

1757 **1005** 80 w. multicoloured 35 10
1758 **1006** 80 w. multicoloured 35 10
1759 **1007** 80 w. multicoloured 35 10
1760 **1008** 80 w. multicoloured 35 10

1009 Rabbit

1010 Eastern Broad-billed Roller

1986. Lunar New Year ("Year of the Rabbit").

1761 **1009** 80 w. multicoloured 35 10

1986. Birds. Multicoloured.

1762 80 w. Type **1010** .. 50 10
1763 80 w. Japanese waxwing 50 10
1764 80 w. Black-naped oriole 50 10
1765 80 w. Black-capped kingfisher 50 10
1766 80 w. Hoopoe 50 10

1011 Siberian Tiger

1012 Bleeding Heart

1987. Endangered Animals. Multicoloured.

1767 80 w. Type **1011** .. 40 10
1768 80 w. Leopard cat .. 40 10
1769 80 w. Red fox 40 10
1770 80 w. Wild boar 40 10

1987. Flowers. Multicoloured.

1771 550 w. Type **1012** .. 1·25 25
1772 550 w. Diamond bluebell 1·25 25
1773 550 w. "Erythronium japonicum" .. .. 1·25 25
1774 550 w. Pinks .. 1·25 25
1775 550 w. "Chrysanthemum zawadskii" .. .. 1·25 25

1013 "Barley field" (Park Wha Mok and Yun Yong Ha)

1014 "Magnolia" (Cho Young Shik and Kim Dong Jin)

1987. Korean Music (3rd series).

1776 **1013** 80 w. multicoloured 40 10
1777 **1014** 80 w. multicoloured 40 10

1015 National Flags and Korean National Flower

1987. Visit of President Ahmed Abdallah Abderemane of Comoros.

1778 **1015** 80 w. multicoloured 30 10

1016 "100", Light Bulb and Hyang Woen Jeong

1987. Centenary of Electric Light in Korea.

1780 **1016** 80 w. multicoloured 35 10

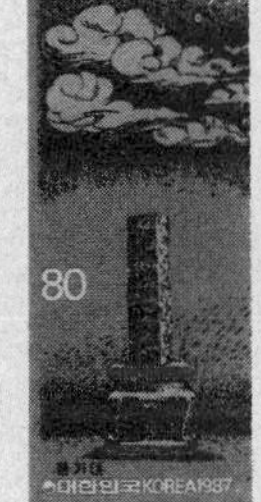

1017 Punggi Wind Observatory

1019 Globes, Crane and Ship

1987. Science (2nd series).

1781 **1017** 80 w. dp brn & brn 40 10
1782 – 80 w. brn & dp brn 40 10

DESIGN: Rain gauge.

1987. 15th International Association of Ports and Harbours General Session, Seoul.

1783 **1019** 80 w. multicoloured 40 10

1987. Olympic Games, Seoul (1988) (8th issue). As T **951**. Multicoloured.

1784 80 w. + 50 w. Wrestling .. 80 25
1785 80 w. + 50 w. Tennis .. 80 25
1786 80 w. + 50 w. Diving .. 80 25
1787 80 w. + 50 w. Show jumping 80 25

1020 Flags and Doves

1987. Visit of President U San Yu of Burma.

1789 **1020** 80 w. multicoloured 40 10

1021 "Valley of Peach Blossoms" (Pyen Kwan Sik)

1022 "Rural Landscape" (Lee Yong Wu)

1023 "Man" (Lee Ma Dong)

1024 "Woman with Water Jar on Head", (sculpture Yun Hyo Chung)

1987. Modern Art (4th series).

1791 **1021** 80 w. multicoloured 35 10
1792 **1022** 80 w. multicoloured 35 10
1793 **1023** 80 w. multicoloured 35 10
1794 **1024** 80 w. multicoloured 35 10

1025 Map and Digital Key Pad

1987. Completion of Automatic Telephone Network (1795) and Communications for Information Year (1796).

1795 80 w. Type **1025** .. 35 10
1796 80 w. Emblem 35 10

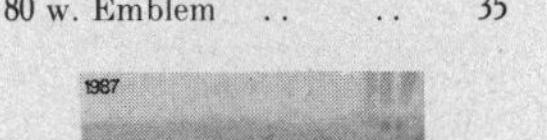

1027 Pilchards

1028 Eel

1029 Barbel

1030 Ray

1987. Fishes (3rd series).

1797 **1027** 80 w. multicoloured 40 10
1798 **1028** 80 w. multicoloured 40 10
1799 **1029** 80 w. multicoloured 40 10
1800 **1030** 80 w. multicoloured 40 10

1031 Statue of Indomitable Koreans (detail) and Flags

1033 Map and Pen within Profile

1987. Opening of Independence Hall. Mult.

1801 80 w. Type **1031** .. 35 10
1802 80 w. Monument of the Nation and aerial view of Hall 35 10

1987. 16th Pacific Science Congress, Seoul.

1804 **1033** 80 w. multicoloured 35 10

1034 Flags and Seoul South Gate

1987. Visit of President Virgilio Barco of Colombia.

1806 **1034** 80 w. multicoloured 40 10

1035/1038 Festivities (½-size illustration)

1987. Folk Customs (5th series). Harvest Moon Day.

1808 **1035** 80 w. multicoloured 35 10
1809 **1036** 80 w. multicoloured 35 10
1810 **1037** 80 w. multicoloured 35 10
1811 **1038** 80 w. multicoloured 35 10

Nos. 1808/11 were issued together, se-tenant, forming a composite design.

1039 Telephone Dials forming Number

1040 Service Flags and Servicemen

1987. Installation of over 10,000,000 Telephone Lines.

1812 **1039** 80 w. multicoloured 40 10

1987. Armed Forces Day.

1813 **1040** 80 w. multicoloured 40 10

1987. Olympic Games, Seoul (1988) (9th issue). As T **951**. Multicoloured.

1814 80 w. + 50 w. Table tennis 65 20
1815 80 w. + 50 w. Shooting .. 65 20
1816 80 w. + 50 w. Archery .. 65 20
1817 80 w. + 50 w. Volleyball .. 65 20

1041 Stamps around Child playing Trumpet

1042 Korean Scientist and Map

1987. Philatelic Week.
1819 **1041** 80 w. multicoloured 35 10

1987. 1st Anniv of South Korea's Signing of Antarctic Treaty.
1820 **1042** 80 w. multicoloured 35 10

1043 Dragon

1044 Scattered Sections of Apple

1987. Lunar New Year ("Year of the Dragon").
1821 **1043** 80 w. multicoloured 35 10

1988. Compulsory Pension Programme.
1822 **1044** 80 w. multicoloured 30 10

1045 Base and Gentoo Penguins

1046 Flag, Olympic Stadium and President Roh Tae Woo

1988. Completion of Antarctic Base.
1823 **1045** 80 w. multicoloured 30 10

1988. Presidential Inauguration.
1824 **1046** 80 w. multicoloured 30 10

1047 Yachting

1049 Crane

1988. Olympic Games, Seoul (10th issue). Multicoloured.
1826 80 w.+20 w. Type **1047** .. 35 20
1827 80 w.+20 w. Taekwondo 35 20

1988. Japanese White-necked Crane. Mult.
1829 80 w. Type **1049** .. 30 10
1830 80 w. Crane taking off .. 30 10
1831 80 w. Crane with wings spread 30 10
1832 80 w. Two cranes in flight 30 10

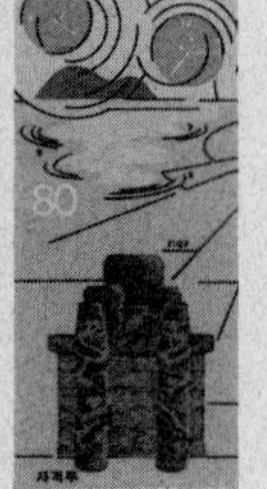

1053 Water Clock

1055 Torch Carrier

1988. Science (3rd series). Multicoloured.
1833 80 w. Type **1053** .. 30 10
1834 80 w. Sundial 30 10
Nos. 1833/4 were issued together, se-tenant, forming a composite design.

1988. Olympic Games, Seoul (11th issue). Multicoloured.
1835 80 w.+20 w. Type **1055** .. 35 20
1836 80 w.+20 w. Stadium .. 35 20

1057 Globe and Red Cross as Candle

1058 Computer Terminal

1988. 125th Anniv of International Red Cross.
1838 **1057** 80 w. multicoloured 30 10

1988. 1st Anniv of National Use of Telepress.
1839 **1058** 80 w. multicoloured 30 10

1059 Woman sitting by Pool and Woman on Swing

1063 Olympic Flag and Pierre de Coubertin (founder of modern Games)

1988. Folk Customs (6th series). Tano Day. Multicoloured.
1840 80 w. Type **1059** .. 30 10
1841 80 w. Women dressing their hair 30 10
1842 80 w. Woman on swing and boy smelling flowers 30 10
1843 80 w. Boys wrestling .. 30 10
Nos. 1840/3 were issued together, se-tenant, forming a composite design.

1988. Olympic Games, Seoul (12th issue). Multicoloured.
1844 80 w. Type **1063** .. 30 10
1845 80 w. Olympic monument 30 10
1846 80 w. View of Seoul (vert) 30 10
1847 80 w. Women in Korean costume (vert) .. 30 10

1067 Stamps forming Torch Flame

1068 Pouring Molten Metal from Crucible

1988. "Olymphilex '88" Olympic Stamps Exhibition, Seoul.
1849 **1067** 80 w. multicoloured 30 10

1988. 22nd International Iron and Steel Institute Conference, Seoul.
1851 **1068** 80 w. multicoloured 30 10

1069 Gomdoori (mascot)

1988. Paralympic Games, Seoul.
1852 80 w. Type **1069** .. 30 10
1853 80 w. Archery 30 10

1071 "Homesick" (Lee Eun Sang and Kim Dong Jin)

1072 "The Pioneer" (Yoon Hae Young and Cho Doo Nam)

1988. Korean Music (4th series).
1854 **1071** 80 w. multicoloured 30 10
1855 **1072** 80 w. multicoloured 30 10

1073 Girls on See-saw

1074 Dancers

1988. Lunar New Year ("New Year of the Snake").
1856 **1073** 80 w. multicoloured 30 10

1989. Folk Customs (7th series). Mask Dance. Multicoloured.
1858 80 w. Type **1074** .. 25 10
1859 80 w. Dancer with fans .. 25 10
1860 80 w. Dancer holding branch 25 10
1861 80 w. Dancer with "Lion" 25 10
Nos. 1858/61 were issued together, se-tenant, forming a composite design.

1079 "Arirang"

1080 "Doraji-taryong"

1989. Korean Music (5th series).
1862 **1079** 80 w. multicoloured 25 10
1863 **1080** 80 w. multicoloured 25 10

1081 Wooden Type Printing

1082 Metal Type Printing

1989. Science (4th series).
1864 **1081** 80 w. brown, bistre and stone .. 25 10
1865 **1082** 80 w. brown, bistre and stone .. 25 10
Nos. 1864/5 were issued together, se-tenant, forming a composite design.

1083 Teeth, Globe, Pencil and Book

1084 Hand with Stick in Heart

1989. 14th Asian–Pacific Dental Congress.
1866 **1083** 80 w. multicoloured 25 10

1989. Respect for the Elderly.
1867 **1084** 80 w. multicoloured 25 10

1085 Emblem

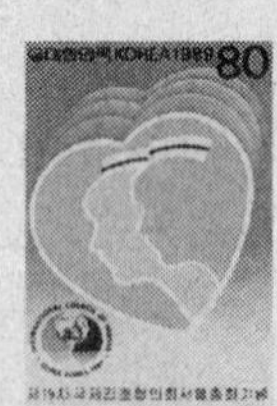

1086 Profiles within Heart

1989. Rotary Int. Convention, Seoul.
1868 **1085** 80 w. multicoloured 25 10

1989. 19th International Council of Nurses Congress, Seoul.
1869 **1086** 80 w. multicoloured 25 10

1087 "Communication"

1088 "Longevity"

1989. Nat. Information Technology Month.
1870 **1087** 80 w. multicoloured 25 10

1989. World Enviroment Day.
1871 **1088** 80 w. multicoloured 25 10

1089 Satellite, Globe and Dish Aerial

1090 "Liberty guiding the People" (detail, Eugene Delacroix)

1989. 10th Anniv of Asia-Pacific Telecommunity.
1872 **1089** 80 w. multicoloured 25 10

1989. Bicentenary of French Revolution.
1873 **1090** 80 w. multicoloured 25 10

1091 Apple and Flask

1989. 5th Asian and Oceanic Biochemists Federation Congress, Seoul.
1874 **1091** 80 w. multicoloured 25 10

1092 "White Ox" (Lee Joong Sub)

1093 "Street Stall" (Park Lae Hyun)

1094 "Little Girl" (Lee Bong Sang)

1095 "Autumn Scene" (Oh Ji Ho)

1989. Modern Art (5th series).
1875 **1092** 80 w. multicoloured 25 10
1876 **1093** 80 w. multicoloured 25 10
1877 **1094** 80 w. multicoloured 25 10
1878 **1095** 80 w. multicoloured 25 10

1096 Hunting Scene

1097 Goddess of Law and Ancient Law Code

1989. Seoul Olympics Commemorative Festival and World Sports Festival for Ethnic Koreans.
1879 1096 80 w. multicoloured 25 10

1989. 1st Anniv of Constitutional Court.
1880 1097 80 w. multicoloured 25 10

1098 Japanese Parrot Fish

1099 Spined Loach

1100 Torrent Catfish

1101 Pinecone Fish

1989. Fishes (4th series).
1881 1098 80 w. multicoloured 25 10
1882 1099 80 w. multicoloured 25 10
1883 1100 80 w. multicoloured 25 10
1884 1101 80 w. multicoloured 25 10

1102 Emblem

1989. 44th International Eucharistic Congress, Seoul.
1885 1102 80 w. multicoloured 25 10

1103 Control Tower and Airplane

1989. 29th International Civil Aiports Association World Congress, Seoul.
1886 1103 80 w. multicoloured 35 10

1104 Scissors cutting burning Banner

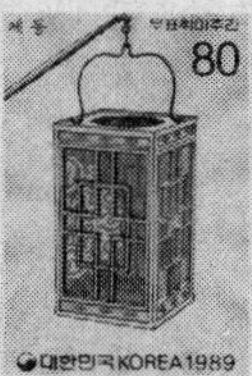
1105 Lantern

1989. Fire Precautions Month.
1887 1104 80 w. multicoloured 25 10

1989. Philatelic Week.
1888 1105 80 w. multicoloured 25 10

1106 Cranes

1107 New Year Custom

1989. Lunar New Year ("Year of the Horse").
1890 1106 80 w. multicoloured 25 10
1891 1107 80 w. multicoloured 25 10

1108 "Pakyon Fall"

1109 "Chonan Samgori"

1990. Koream Music (6th series).
1893 1108 80 w. multicoloured 25 10
1894 1109 80 w. multicoloured 25 10

1110 Clouds, Umbrella and Satellite

1111 Child with Rose

1990. World Meteorological Day.
1895 1110 80 w. multicoloured 25 10

1990. 40th Anniv of U.N.I.C.E.F. Work in Korea.
1896 1111 80 w. multicoloured 25 10

1112 Cable, Fish and Route Map

1990. Completion of Cheju Island–Kohung Optical Submarine Cable.
1897 1112 80 w. multicoloured 25 10

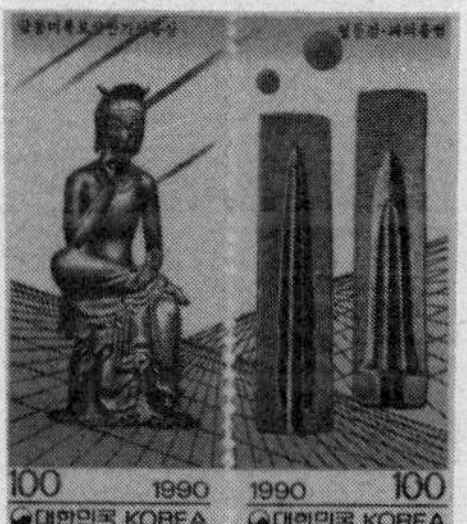
1113 Gilt-bronze Maitreya
1114 Spear and Dagger Moulds

1990. Science (5th series). Metallurgy.
1898 1113 100 w. multicoloured 25 10
1899 1114 100 w. multicoloured 25 10

1115 Housing and "20"

1990. 20th Anniv of Saemaul Movement (community self-help programme).
1900 1115 100 w. multicoloured 25 10

1116 Youths

1117 Butterfly Net catching Pollution

1990. Youth Month.
1901 1116 100 w. multicoloured 25 10

1990. World Envirnmental Day.
1902 1117 100 w. multicoloured 25 10

1118 Belted Beard Grunt

1119 Puffer

1120 Salmon Trout

1121 Butterling

1990. Fishes (5th series).
1903 1118 100 w. multicoloured 25 10
1904 1119 100 w. multicoloured 25 10
1905 1120 100 w. multicoloured 25 10
1906 1121 100 w. multicoloured 25 10

1122 Automatic Sorting Machines

1123 Bandaged Teddy Bear in Hospital Bed

1990. Opening of Seoul Mail Centre.
1907 1122 100 w. multicoloured 25 10

1990. Road Safety Campaign.
1909 1123 100 w. multicoloured 25 10

1124 Campfire

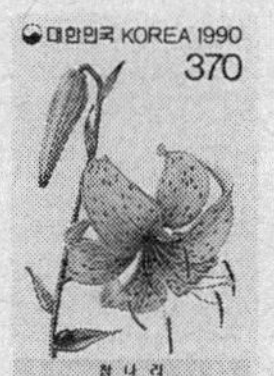
1125 Lily

1990. 8th Korean Boy Scouts Jamboree, Kosong.
1910 1124 100 w. multicoloured 25 10

1990. Wild Flowers (1st series). Multicoloured.
1911 370 w. Type 1125 .. 75 30
1912 400 w. Asters 80 30
1913 440 w. Pheasant's eye .. 85 30
1914 470 w. Scabious .. 90 30
See also Nos. 1956/9 and 1992/5.

1129 Washing Wool
1133 Church

1990. Folk Customs (8th series). Hand Weaving.
1915 1129 100 w. red, yell & blk 25 10
1916 – 100 w. multicoloured 25 10
1917 – 100 w. multicoloured 25 10
1918 – 100 w. multicoloured 25 10
DESIGNS: No. 1916, Spinning; 1917, Dyeing spun yarn; 1918, Weaving.

1990. Centenary of Anglican Church in Korea.
1919 1133 100 w. multicoloured 25 10

1134 Top of Tower

1135 Peas in Pod

1990. 10th Anniv of Seoul Communications Tower.
1920 1134 100 w. black, bl & red 25 10

1990. Census.
1921 1135 100 w. multicoloured 25 10

1136 "40" and U.N. Emblem

1137 Inlaid Case with Mirror

1990. 40th Anniv of U.N. Development Programme.
1922 1136 100 w. multicoloured 25 10

1990. Philatelic Week.
1923 1137 100 w. multicoloured 25 10

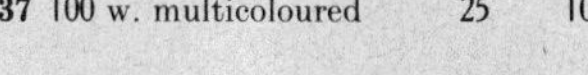

1138 Children feeding Ram

1140 Mascot

1990. Lunar New Year ("Year of the Sheep"). Multicoloured.
1925 100 w. Type 1138 .. 25 10
1926 100 w. Crane flying above mountains 25 10

1990. "Expo '93" World's Fair, Taejon (1st issue). Multicoloured.
1928 100 w. Type 1140 .. 25 10
1929 440 w. Yin and Yang (exhibition emblem) .. 90 30
See also Nos. 1932/3, 2000/1 and 2058/61.

1142 Books and Emblem

1143 Earth

1991. 30th Anniv of Saemaul Minlibrary.
1931 1142 100 w. multicoloured 25 10

1991. "Expo '93" World's Fair, Taejon (2nd issue). Multicoloured.
1932 100 w. Type 1143 .. 25 10
1933 100 w. Expo Tower .. 25 10

1145 "In a Flower Garden" (Uh Hyo Sun and Kwon Kil Sang)

1146 "Way to the Orchard" (Park Hwa Mok and Kim Kong Sun)

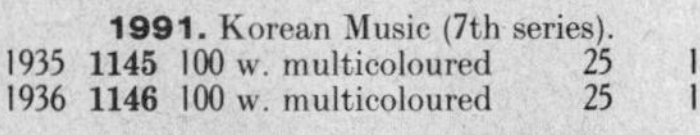
1991. Korean Music (7th series).

1935 **1145** 100 w. multicoloured 25 10
1936 **1146** 100 w. multicoloured 25 10

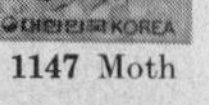
1147 Moth

1148 Beetle

1149 Butterfly

1150 Beetle

1151 Cicada

1152 Water beetle

1153 Hornet

1154 Ladybirds

1155 Dragonfly

1156 Grasshopper

1991. Insects.

1937 **1147** 100 w. multicoloured 25 10
1938 **1148** 100 w. multicoloured 25 10
1939 **1149** 100 w. multicoloured 25 10
1940 **1150** 100 w. multicoloured 25 10
1941 **1151** 100 w. multicoloured 25 10
1942 **1152** 100 w. multicoloured 25 10
1943 **1153** 100 w. multicoloured 25 10
1944 **1154** 100 w. multicoloured 25 10
1945 **1155** 100 w. multicoloured 25 10
1946 **1156** 100 w. multicoloured 25 10

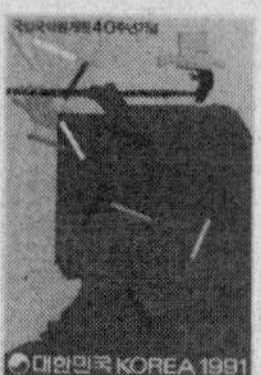
1157 Flautist and Centre

1158 Flag and Provisional Government Building

1991. 40th Anniv of Korean Traditional Performing Arts Centre.

1947 **1157** 100 w. multicoloured 25 10

1991. 72nd Anniv of Establishment of Korean Provisional Government in Shanghai.

1948 **1158** 100 w. multicoloured 25 10

1159 Urban Landscape and Emblem

1991. Employment for Disabled People.

1949 **1159** 100 w. multicoloured 25 10

1160 Bouquet

1991. Teachers' Day.

1950 **1160** 100 w. multicoloured 25 10

1161 "Microphysogobio longidorsalis"

1162 "Gnathopogon majimae"

1163 "Therapon oxyrhynchus"

1164 "Psettina ijimae"

1991. Fishes (6th series).

1951 **1161** 100 w. multicoloured 25 10
1952 **1162** 100 w. multicoloured 25 10
1953 **1163** 100 w. multicoloured 25 10
1954 **1164** 100 w. multicoloured 25 10

1165 Animals waiting to Board Bus

1166 "Aerides japonicum"

1991. "Waiting One's Turn" Campaign.

1955 **1165** 100 w. multicoloured 25 10

1991. Wild Flowers (2nd series). Mult.

1956 100 w. Type **1166** .. 25 10
1957 100 w. "Heloniopsis orientalis" 25 10
1958 370 w. "Aquilegia buergeriana" 75 30
1959 440 w. "Gentiana zollingeri" 90 30

1167 Scout with Semaphore Flags

1168 "Y.M.C.A."

1991. 17th World Scout Jamboree.

1960 **1167** 100 w. multicoloured 25 10

1991. Young Men's Christian Association World Assembly, Seoul.

1962 **1168** 100 w. multicoloured 25 10

1169 Rusted Train and Family Members Reunited

1170 Globe, Rainbow, Dove and U. N. Emblem

1991. "North–South Reunification".

1963 **1169** 100 w. multicoloured 25 10

1991. Admission of South Korea to United Nations Organization.

1964 **1170** 100 w. multicoloured 25 10

1171 Unra

1172 Jing

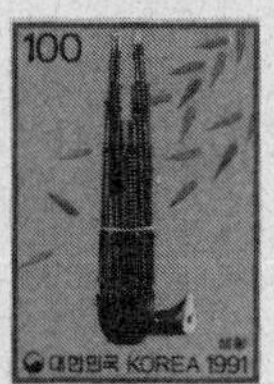
1173 Galgo

1174 Saeng-hwang

1991. Traditional Musical Instruments (1st series).

1965 **1171** 100 w. multicoloured 25 10
1966 **1172** 100 w. multicoloured 25 10
1967 **1173** 100 w. multicoloured 25 10
1968 **1174** 100 w. multicoloured 25 10
See also Nos. 1981/4.

1175 Film and Theatrical Masks

1176 Globe and Satellite

1991. Culture Month.

1969 **1175** 100 w. multicoloured 25 10

1991. "Telecom 91" International Telecommunications Exhibition, Geneva.

1970 **1176** 100 w. multicoloured 25 10

1177 Hexagonals

1178 Bamboo

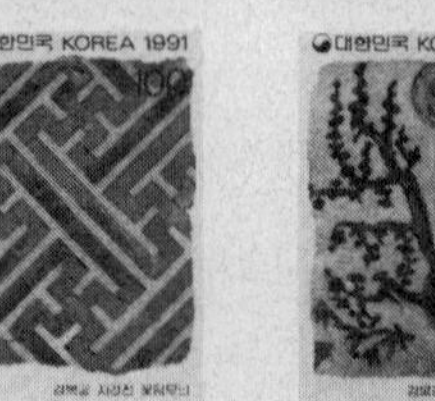
1179 Geometric

1180 Tree

1991. Korean Beauty (1st series). Kottams (patterns on walls).

1971 **1177** 100 w. multicoloured 25 10
1972 **1178** 100 w. multicoloured 25 10
1973 **1179** 100 w. multicoloured 25 10
1974 **1180** 100 w. multicoloured 25 10
See also Nos. 2006/9.

1181 Light Bulb turning off Switch

1182 Stamps

1991. Energy Saving Campaign.

1975 **1181** 100 w. multicoloured 25 10

1991. Philatelic Week.

1976 **1182** 100 w. multicoloured 25 10

1183 Landscape

1991. Lunar New Year ("Year of the Monkey"). Multicoloured.

1978 100 w. Type **1183** .. 25 10
1979 100 w. Flying kites .. 25 10

1185 Yonggo

1186 Chwago

1187 Kkwaenggwari

1188 T'ukchong

1992. Traditional Musical Instruments (2nd series).

1981 **1185** 100 w. multicoloured 25 10
1982 **1186** 100 w. multicoloured 25 10
1983 **1187** 100 w. multicoloured 25 10
1984 **1188** 100 w. multicoloured 25 10

1189 White Hibiscus

1191 Satellite

1992. "Hibiscus syriacus" (national flower). Multicoloured.

1985 100 w. Type **1189** .. 15 10
1986 100 w. Pink hibiscus .. 15 10

1992. Science Day.

1987 **1191** 100 w. multicoloured 15 10

1192 Pong-Gil Yoon

1193 Children and Heart

1992. 60th Death Anniv of Pong-Gil Yoon (Independence fighter).

1988 **1192** 100 w. multicoloured 15 10

1992. Child Protection.

1989 **1193** 100 w. multicoloured 15 10

1194 Warship attacking Settlement

1195 Farmer

1992. 400th Anniv of Start of Im-Jin War.
1990 **1194** 100 w. multicoloured 15 10

1992. 60th International Fertilizer Industry Association Conference, Seoul.
1991 **1195** 100 w. multicoloured 15 10

1992. Wild Flowers (3rd series). As T **1166**. Multicoloured.
1992 100 w. "Lychnis wilfordii" 15 10
1993 100 w. "Lycoris radiata" 15 10
1994 370 w. "Commelina communis" 60 20
1995 440 w. "Calanthe striata" 70 20

1196 "Longing for Mt. Keumkang" (Han Sang Ok and Choi Young Shurp)

1197 "The Swing" (Kim Mal Bong and Geum Su Hyeon)

1992. Korean Music (8th series).
1996 **1196** 100 w. multicoloured 15 10
1997 **1197** 100 w. multicoloured 15 10

1198 Gymnastics

1199 Stylized View of Exhibition

1992. Olympic Games, Barcelona. Mult.
1998 100 w. Type **1198** .. 15 10
1999 100 w. Pole vaulting .. 15 10

1992. "Expo '93" World's Fair, Taejon (3rd issue). Multicoloured.
2000 100 w. Type **1199** .. 15 10
2001 100 w. "Expo 93" .. 15 10

1201 Korea Exhibition Centre and South Gate, Seoul

1992. 21st Universal Postal Union Congress, Seoul. Multicoloured.
2003 100 w. Type **1201** .. 15 10
2004 100 w. Tolharubang (stone grandfather), Cheju .. 15 10

1203 Woven Pattern

1204 Fruit and Flower Decorations

1205 Carved Decorations

1206 Coral, Butterfly and Pine Resin Decorations

1992. Korean Beauty (2nd series). Maedeups (tassels).
2006 **1203** 100 w. multicoloured 15 10
2007 **1204** 100 w. multicoloured 15 10
2008 **1205** 100 w. multicoloured 15 10
2009 **1206** 100 w. multicoloured 15 10

1207 Pong Chang Yi

1208 Hwang Young Jo (Barcelona, 1992)

1992. 60th Death Anniv of Pong Chang Yi (independence fighter).
2010 **1207** 100 w. brown & orge 15 10

1992. Korean Winners of Olympic Marathon. Multicoloured.
2011 100 w. Type **1208** .. 15 10
2012 100 w. Shon Kee Chung (Berlin, 1936) 15 10

1209 Sails on Map of Americas

1210 Heads and Speech Balloon

1992. 500th Anniv of Discovery of America by Columbus.
2014 **1209** 100 w. multicoloured 15 10

1992. Campaign for Purification of Language.
2015 **1210** 100 w. multicoloured 15 10

1211 Flowers and Stamps

1212 Cockerels in Snow-covered Yard

1992. Philatelic Week.
2016 **1211** 100 w. multicoloured 15 10

1992. Lunar New Year ("Year of the Cock"). Multicoloured.
2018 100 w. Type **1212** .. 15 10
2019 100 w. Flying kites .. 15 10

1214 Emblem, Globe and Woman holding Bowl

1992. International Nutrition Conference, Rome.
2021 **1214** 100 w. multicoloured 15 10

1215 View of Centre and Logo

1993. Inauguration of Seoul Arts Centre's Opera House.
2022 **1215** 110 w. multicoloured 20 10

1216 Pres. Kim Young Sam, Flag and Mt. Paektu Lake

1217 National Flag

1993. Inauguration of 14th President.
2023 **1216** 110 w. multicoloured 20 10

1993. Multicoloured.
2025 10 w. Type **1217** .. 10 10
2026 20 w. White stork 10 10
2027 30 w. Magnolia (horiz) .. 10 10
2028 40 w. Korean white pine 10 10
2034 110 w. "Hibiscus syriacus" 20 10
2035 160 w. Pine tree (horiz) .. 25 10
2038 370 w. Drum dance (horiz) 60 20
2040 440 w. Hahoi mask and Ssirum wrestlers (horiz) 75 25
2044 710 w. King Sejong .. 1·25 40
2046 900 w. Statuette of Buddha .. .. 1·50 50

1243 Student and Computer

1244 Emblem and Map

1993. Korean Student Inventions Exhibition.
2051 **1243** 110 w. mauve & silver 20 10

1993. International Human Rights Conf, Vienna, Austria.
2052 **1244** 110 w. multicoloured 20 10

1245 Hand scooping Globe from Water

1246 Matsu-take Mushroom ("Tricholoma matsutake")

1993. "Water is Life".
2053 **1245** 110 w. multicoloured 20 10

1993. Fungi. Multicoloured.
2054 110 w. Type **1246** .. 20 10
2055 110 w. "Ganoderma lucidum" 20 10
2056 110 w. "Lentinula edodes" 20 10
2057 110 w. Oyster fungus ("Pleurotus ostreatus") 20 10

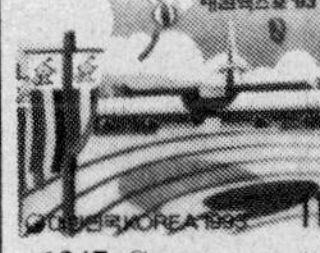
1247 Government Pavilion

1248 International Pavilion and Mascot

1249 Recycling Art Pavilion

1250 Telecom Pavilion

1993. "Expo '93" World's Fair, Taejon (4th issue).
2058 **1247** 110 w. multicoloured 20 10
2059 **1248** 110 w. multicoloured 20 10
2060 **1249** 110 w. multicoloured 20 10
2061 **1250** 110 w. multicoloured 20 10

1251 Emblems

1993. 19th Congress of International Society of Orthopaedic and Trauma Surgery.
2063 **1251** 110 w. multicoloured 20 10

1252 "O Dol Ddo Gi" (Cheju Island folk song)

1253 "Ong He Ya" (barley threshing song)

1993. Korean Music (9th series).
2064 **1252** 110 w. multicoloured 20 10
2065 **1253** 110 w. multicoloured 20 10

1254 Janggu Drum Dance

1255 Emblem

1993. "Visit Korea" Year (1994).
2066 **1254** 110 w. multicoloured 20 10
2067 **1255** 110 w. multicoloured 20 10

C. NORTH KOREAN OCCUPATION.

(1. "Democratic People's Republic of Korea".)

1950. Nos. 116 and 118/9, optd. with Type **1**.
1. 10 w. green .. .. .. 30·00
2. 20 w. brown .. .. .. 8·50
3. 30 w. green .. .. .. 9·50

NORTH KOREA

100 cheun = 1 won

GUM. All stamps of North Korea up to No. N1506 are without gum, except where otherwise stated.

A. RUSSIAN OCCUPATION

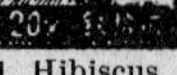

1. Hibiscus.

2. Diamond Mountains.

1946. Perf., roul. or imp.

N1 **1** 20 ch. red .. .. 45·00 32·00
N2 **2** 50 ch. green .. .. 15·00 15·00
N4b 50 ch. red .. .. 8·50 8·50
N5b 50 ch. violet .. .. 10·00 12·00

4. Gen. Kim Il Sung and Flag.

5. Peasants.

1946. 1st Anniv of Liberation from Japan.

N6 **4** 50 ch. brown £150 £110

1947. Perf., roul or imp..

N 7. **5.** 1 wn. green .. .. 5·00 4·00
N 8. 1 wn. violet .. .. 15·00 10·00
N 9. 1 wn. blue on buff .. 5·50 4·50
N 10. 1 wn. blue .. .. 3·25 2·50

6.

7.

8.

1948. 2nd Anniv. of Labour Law.

N 11. **6.** 50 ch. blue £225 £180

1948. 3rd Anniv. of Liberation from Japan.

N 12. **7.** 50 ch. red .. .. — £175

1948. Promulgation of Constitution.

N 13. **8.** 50 ch. blue and red .. £160 40·00

B. KOREAN PEOPLE'S DEMOCRATIC REPUBLIC

9. North Korean Flag.

10.

1948. Establishment of People's Republic. Roul.

N 16. **9.** 25 ch. violet .. .. 3·50 3·50
N 17. 50 ch. blue .. .. 6·00 6·00

1949. Roul or perf.

N18 **10** 6 wn. red and blue .. 2·00 2·00

11. Kim Il Sung University, Pyongyang.

12. North Korean Flags.

11a. Kim Il Sung University, Pyongyang.

1949. Roul.

N 19. **11.** 1 wn. violet .. .. 45·00 20·00
N 20. **11a.** 1 wn. blue .. .. 45·00 20·00

1949. 4th Anniv. of Liberation from Japan. Roul or perf.

N 22. **12.** 1 wn. red, grn. & blue 35·00 14·00

13. Order of the National Flag.

14. Liberation Monument, Pyongyang.

15. Soldier and Flags.

16. Peasant and Worker.

17. Tractor.

18. Capitol, Seoul.

1950. Perf., roul. or imp. Various sizes.

N 24. **13.** 1 wn. green (A) .. 2·00 1·00
N 25. 1 wn. orange (A) .. — 25·00
N 26. 1 wn. orange (B) .. 12·00 12·00
N 27. 1 wn. green (C) .. 1·75 1·25
N 28. 1 wn. olive (D) .. 5·50 4·50

SIZES: (A) 23½ × 37½ mm. (B) 20 × 32½ mm. (C) 22 × 35½ mm. (D) 22½ × 36½ mm.

1950. 5th Anniv. of Liberation from Japan. Roul., perf. or imperf. Various sizes.

N29 **14** 1 wn. red, ind. & blue 90 90
N30 1 wn. orange .. .. 6·00 5·00
N31 **15** 2 wn. blk., bl. & red.. 90 90
N32 **16** 6 wn. green (A) .. 1·25 1·25
N36 6 wn. red (B) .. .. 12·50 11·00
N33 **17** 10 wn. brown (C) .. 2·00 2·00
N37 10 wn. brown (D) .. 18·00 13·50

SIZES: (A) 20 × 30 mm. (B) 22 × 33 mm. (C) 20 × 28 mm. (D) 22 × 30 mm.

1950. Capture of Seoul by North Korean Forces. Roul.

N 38. **18.** 1 wn. red, bl. & green 35·00 32·00

19.

20. Kim Gi Ok and Aeroplane.

1951. Order of Admiral Li Sun Sin. Imperf or perf.

N39 **19** 6 wn. orange .. .. 6·50 5·00

1951. Air Force Hero Kim Gi Ok. Imperf.

N 40. **20.** 1 wn. blue .. .. 5·00 2·00

21. Russian and North Korean Flags. 22. Kim Ki U (hero).

23. N. Korean and Chinese Soldiers.

1951. 6th Anniv. of Liberation from Japan. Roul. or perf.

N 41. **21.** 1 wn. blue .. .. 3·50 2·50
N 42. 1 wn. red .. .. 3·50 2·50
N 43. **22.** 1 wn. blue .. .. 3·50 2·50
N 44. 1 wn. red .. .. 3·75 2·50
N 45. **23.** 2 wn. blue .. .. 6·50 5·00
N 46. 2 wn. red .. .. 8·50 7·50

All values exist on buff and on white paper.

24. Order of Soldier's Honour.

25. 26. Woman Partisan, Li Su Dok.

1951. Imperf. or perf.

N 47. **24.** 40 wn. red .. .. 7·50 4·50

1951. Co-operation of Chinese People's Volunteers. Imperf. or perf.

N 49. **25.** 10 wn. blue .. .. 5·00 3·25

1952. Partisan Heroes. Imperf. or perf.

N 50. **26.** 70 wn. brown.. .. 3·00 1·00

27. 28. Gen. P'eng Teh-huai. 29. Munition Worker.

1952. Peace Propaganda. Imperf. or perf.

N 51. **27.** 20 wn. bl., grn. & red 4·00 2·00

1952. Honouring Commander of Chinese People's Volunteers. Imperf.

N 52. **28.** 10 wn. purple.. .. 6·00 3·00

1952. Labour Day. Imperf. or perf.

N 53. **29.** 10 wn. red .. .. 13·00 13·00

30.

31.

32.

1952. 6th Anniv of Labour Law. Imperf or perf.

N54a **30** 10 wn. blue .. .. 7·00 7·00

1952. Anti-U.S. Imperialism Day. Imperf or perf.

N55 **31** 10 wn. red .. .. 13·00 13·00

1952. North Korean and Chinese Friendship. Imperf or perf.

N56b **32** 20 wn. deep blue .. 9·00 9·00

33.

34.

1952. 7th Anniv. of Liberation from Japan. Imperf. or perf.

N 57. **33.** 10 wn. red .. .. 10·00 10·00
N 58. **34.** 10 wn. red .. .. 12·00 12·00

35. 36. 37.

1952. Int. Youth Day. With gum. Imperf. or perf.

N 59. **35.** 10 wn. green .. .. 6·00 6·00

1953. 5th Anniv. of People's Army. Imperf. or perf.

N 60. **36.** 10 wn. red .. .. 12·50 12·50
N 61. **37.** 40 wn. purple.. .. 12·50 12·50

38.

39.

1953. Int. Women's Day. With gum. Imperf. or perf.

N 62. **38.** 10 wn. red .. .. 8·00 8·00
N 63. **39.** 40 wn. green .. .. 8·00 8·00

40.

41.

1953. Labour Day. Imperf. or perf.

N 64. **40.** 10 wn. green .. .. 7·50 7·50
N 65. **41.** 40 wn. orange .. 7·50 7·50

42.

43.

1953. Anti-U.S. Imperialism Day. With gum. Imperf. or perf.

N 66. **42.** 10 wn. turquoise .. 13·00 13·00
N 67. **43.** 40 wn. red .. .. 13·00 13·00

44.

45.

1953. 4th World Youth Festival, Bucharest. With gum. Imperf. or perf.

N 68. **44.** 10 wn. blue and green 3·25 2·75
N 69. **45.** 20 wn. green and pink 3·25 2·75

46.

47.

1953. Armistice and Victory Issue. With gum. Imperf. or perf.

N 70a. **46.** 10 wn. brn. & yellow 38·00 32·00

1953. 8th Anniv. of Liberation from Japan. Imperf.

N 71. **47.** 10 wn. red .. .. £120 90·00

48.

49. Liberation Monument, Pyongyang.

1953. 5th Anniv. of People's Republic. Imperf. or perf.

N 72. **48.** 10 wn. blue and red .. 11·00 11·00

1953. With gum. Imperf. or perf.

N 73. **49.** 10 wn. slate .. .. 3·75 3·50

(50.)

(51.)

1954. No. N18 optd "Fee Collected" in Korean characters, T **50**.

N74 **10** 6 wn. red and blue .. £120 £120

1954. Nos. N18 and N39 surch with T **51**.

N75 **10** 5 wn. on 6 wn. red & bl 8·00 8·00
N76 **19** 5 wn. on 6 wn. orange 45·00 40·00

52.

53.

1954. Post-war Economic Reconstruction. With gum. Imperf of perf.

N77 **52** 10 wn. blue .. .. 6·00 6·00

1954. 6th Anniv. of People's Army. With gum. Imperf. or perf.

N 78. **53.** 10 wn. red .. .. 10·00 10·00

54.

55.

1954. Int. Women's Day. With gum. Imperf. or perf.
N 79. **54.** 10 wn. red .. .. 5·50 5·50

1954. Labour Day. With gum. Imperf. or perf.
N 80. **55.** 10 wn. red .. .. 6·00 6·00

56.

57. Taedong Gate, Pyongyang.

1954. Anti-U.S. Imperialism Day. With gum. Imperf or perf.
N81 **56** 10 wn. red .. .. 15·00 15·00

1954. Imperf. or perf.
N 82. **57.** 5 wn. lake .. .. 2·00 75
N 83. 5 wn. brown .. .. 2·00 75

58.

59. Soldier.

1954. National Young Activists' Conf. With gum. Imperf. or perf.
N 84. **58.** 10 wn. red, bl. & slate 3·00 3·00

1954. 9th Anniv of Liberation from Japan. With gum. Imperf or perf.
N85 **59** 10 wn. red .. .. 6·00 6·00

60. North Korean Flag.

61. Hwanghae Iron Works.

62. Hwanghae Iron Works and Workers.

1954. 6th Anniv. of People's Republic. With gum. Imperf. or perf.
N 86. **60.** 10 wn. bl. & red .. 5·00 5·00

1954. Economic Reconstruction. Imperf. or perf.
N 87. **61.** 10 wn. blue .. .. 2·00 50
N 88. **62.** 10 wn. brown .. .. 2·00 50

63.

64.

1955. 7th Anniv. of People's Army. With gum. Imperf. or perf.
N 89. **63.** 10 wn. red .. .. 3·50 3·50

1955. Int. Women's Day. With gum. Imperf. or perf.
N 90. **64.** 10 wn. deep blue .. 3·50 3·50

HAVE YOU READ THE NOTES AT THE BEGINNING OF THIS CATALOGUE?
These often provide answers to the enquiries we receive.

65.

66.

1955. Labour Day. With gum. Imperf. or perf.
N 91. **65.** 10 wn. green .. .. 3·25 3·25
N 92. **66.** 10 wn. red .. .. 3·25 3·25

67. Admiral Li Sun Sin.

68.

1955. Imperf. or perf.
N 93. **67.** 1 wn. blue on green .. 1·25 20
N 94. 2 wn. red on buff .. 1·75 25
N 95. 2 wn. red .. 3·00 50

1955. 9th Anniv. of Labour Law. With gum. Imperf. or perf.
N 96. **68.** 10 wn. red .. .. 3·50 2·50

69. Liberation Monument and Flags.

1955. 10th Anniv of Liberation from Japan. Imperf or perf.
N 97. **69.** 10 wn. green .. 2·00 1·50
N 98. 10 wn. red, blue and brown ($29\frac{1}{2} \times 42\frac{1}{2}$ mm.) .. 1·25 1·00

70.

71.

1955. Soviet Union Friendship Month. Imperf. or perf.
N 99. **70.** 10 wn. red .. .. 1·50 1·00
N 100. 10 wn. red & blue .. 2·25 1·50
N 101. **71.** 20 wn. red & slate .. 3·25 2·50
N 102. 20 wn. red & blue .. 1·50 1·25
SIZES: No. N 99, $22 \times 32\frac{1}{2}$ mm. No. N 100, $29\frac{1}{2} \times 43$ mm. No. N 101, $18\frac{3}{4} \times 32$ mm. No. N 102, 25×43 mm.

72. Son Rock.

73.

74.

1956. Haegumgang Maritime Park. Imperf. or perf.
N 103. **72.** 10 wn. blue on blue 3·00 1·75

1956. 8th Anniv. of People's Army. Imperf. or perf.
N 104. **73.** 10 wn. red on green .. 5·50 5·50

1956. Labour Day. Imperf. or perf.
N 105. **74.** 10 wn. blue .. .. 3·50 2·75

75. Machinist.

76. Taedong Gate, Pyongyang.

77. Woman Harvester.

78. Moranbong Theatre, Pyongyang.

1956. Imperf. or perf.
N 106. **75.** 1 wn. brown 90 60
N 107. **76.** 2 wn. blue 90 60
N 108. **77.** 10 wn. red 90 60
N 109. **78.** 40 wn. green .. .. 5·00 3·50

79. Miner.

80. Boy Bugler and Girl Drummer.

1956. 10th Anniv. of Labour Law. Imperf. or perf.
N 110. **79.** 10 wn. brown .. 1·75 1·00

1956. 10th Anniv. of Children's Union. Imperf. or perf.
N 111. **80.** 10 wn. brown .. 4·00 2·75

81. Workers.

82. Industrial Plant.

1956. 10th Anniv. of Sex Equality Law. Imperf. or perf.
N 112. **81.** 10 wn. brown .. 2·00 1·40

1956. 10th Anniv. of Nationalization of Industry. Imperf. or perf.
N 113. **82.** 10 wn. brown .. 27·00 11·50

83. Liberation Tower.

84. Kim Il Sung University.

1956. 11th Anniv. of Liberation from Japan. Imperf. or perf.
N 114. **83.** 10 wn. red .. .. 1·50 80

1956. 10th Anniv. of Kim Il Sung University. Imperf. or perf.
N 115. **84.** 10 wn. brown .. 2·50 1·75

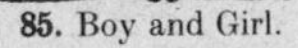
85. Boy and Girl.

86. Pak Ji Won.

1956. 4th Democratic Youth League Congress. Imperf. or perf.
N 116. **85.** 10 wn. brown .. 2·50 1·50

1957. 220th Birth Anniv. of Pak Ji Won ("Yonam"), statesman. Imperf. or perf.
N 117. **86.** 10 wn. blue .. .. 1·50 90

87. Tabo Pagoda, Pulguksa.

88. Ulmil Pavilion, Pyongyang.

89. Furnaceman.

1957. Imperf., perf. or roul.
N 118. **87.** 5 wn. blue .. .. 1·00 75
N 119. **88.** 40 wn. green .. .. 2·00 1·25

1957. Production and Economy Campaign. With or without gum. Imperf. or perf.
N 121. **89.** 10 wn. blue .. .. 2·50 1·25

90. Furnaceman.

91. Voters and Polling Booth.

1957. 2nd General Election. Imperf. or perf.
N 122. **90.** 1 wn. orange .. 45 30
N 123. 2 wn. brown .. 45 30
N 124. **91.** 10 wn. red .. .. 2·50 1·25

92. Ryongwangjong, Pyongyang.

93. Lenin and Flags.

94. Kim Il Sung at Pochonbo.

95. Lenin.

96. Pouring Steel.

1957. 1530th Anniv. of Pyongyang. Imperf. or perf.
N 125. **92.** 10 wn. green 60 25

1957. 40th Anniv. of Russian Revolution. Imperf. or perf.
N 126. **93.** 10 wn. green 75 40
N 127. **94.** 10 wn. red 75 40
N 128. **95.** 10 wn. blue 75 40
N 129. **96.** 10 wn. orange .. 1·25 40
No. N 126 exists with gum.

97. Congress Emblem.

98. Liberation Monument, Spassky Tower and Flags.

1957. 4th World Trade Unions Federation Congress, Leipzig. Imperf (with or without gum) or perf.
N130 **97** 10 wn. blue and green 80 50

1957. Russian Friendship Month. Imperf. or perf.
N 131. **98.** 10 wn. green .. .. 1·75 50

99. Weighing a Baby.

100. Bandaging a Hand.

1957. Red Cross. Imperf., perf. or roul.
N132 **99** 1 wn. red .. .. 3·50 2·00
N133 2 wn. red .. .. 3·50 2·00
N134 **100** 10 wn. red .. .. 10·00 4·50
No. N 133 exists with or without gum.

101. Koryo Celadon Jug (12th century). **102.** Koryo Incense-burner (12th cent.).

1958. Korean Antiquities. Imperf. (with or without gum) or perf.
N 135. **101.** 10 wn. blue.. .. 3·00 50
N 136. **102.** 10 wn. green .. 3·00 50

103. Woljong Temple Pagoda. **104.** Soldier.

1958. With gum (5 wn.), without gum (10 wn.). Imperf. or perf.
N 137. **103.** 5 wn. green.. .. 1·00 50
N 138. 10 wn blue.. .. 1·50 75

1958. 10th Anniv. of People's Army. No gum (No. N 139) with or without gum (No. N 140). Imperf. or perf.
N 139. **104.** 10 wn. blue.. .. 1·25 50
N 140. – 10 wn. red .. .. 1·75 65
Design—horiz. ($37\frac{1}{2} \times 26$ mm.): No. N 140, Soldier, flag and Hwanghae Iron Works.

106. Airliner over Pyongyang.

1958. Air. Imperf. or perf.
N 141. **106.** 20 wn. blue.. .. 4·25 1·00

107. Sputniks. **108.** Sputnik encircling Globe.

1958. I.G.Y. Inscr. "1957–1958". Imperf. or perf.
N 142. **107.** 10 wn. slate .. 45 10
N 143. **108.** 20 wn. slate .. 45 10
N 144. – 40 wn. slate .. 3·00 30
N 145. **107.** 70 wn. slate .. 50 20
Design—horiz. 40 wn. Sputnik over Pyongyang Observatory.
Nos. N 142/4 exist with or without gum.

109. Furnaceman. **110.** Hwanghae Iron Works.

1958. Young Socialist Constructors' Congress, Pyongyang. Imperf. or perf.
N 146. **109.** 10 wn. blue .. 1·75 50

1958. Opening of Hwanghae Iron Works. Imperf. or perf.
N 147. **110.** 10 wn. blue .. 2·50 65

111. Commemorative Badge. **112.** Federation Emblem.

1958. Farewell to Chinese People's Volunteers (1st issue). Imperf. or perf.
N148 **111** 10 wn. purple & blue 1·00 40
See also Nos. N158.

1958. 4th Int. Women's Federation Democratic Congress. Imperf. or perf.
N 149. **112.** 10 wn. blue .. 80 35

113. Conference Emblem.

1958. 1st World Young Worker's Trade Union Federation Conference, Prague. Imperf. of perf.
N 150. **113.** 10 wn. brn. & grn. 1·25 35

114. Flats, East Ward, Pyongyang. **115.** Workers' Flats, Pyongyang.

1958. Rehousing Progress. Imperf. or perf.
N151 **114** 10 wn. blue .. .. 2·00 50
N152 **115** 10 wn. green .. 2·00 50

117. Pyongyang Railway Station. **119.** Textile Worker.

1958. 10th Anniv of Korean People's Republic. Imperf or perf.
N153 – 10 wn. green .. 3·00 50
N154 **117** 10 wn. green .. 7·50 1·50
N155 – 10 wn. brown & buff 1·50 50
N156 **119** 10 wn. brown .. 5·25 1·75
N157 – 10 wn. brown .. 4·00 1·00
Designs—horiz. No. N 153, Hungnam Fertiliser Plant. No. N 157, Yongp'ung Dam, Pyongyang. vert. No. N 155, Arms of People's Republic.

121. Volunteer and Troop Train. **122.** Transplanting Rice.

1958. Farewell to Chinese People's Volunteers (2nd issue). Imperf. or perf.
N 158. **121.** 10 wn. sepia .. 20·00 6·50

1958. Imperf. or perf.
N 159. **122.** 10 wn. sepia .. 40 15

123. Winged Horse of Chollima. **124.** N. Korean and Chinese Flags.

1958. National Production Executives' Meeting, Pyongyang. With or without gum. Imperf. or perf.
N 160. **123.** 10 wn. red .. 1·60 30

1958. N. Korean-Chinese Friendship Month. With or without gum. Imperf. or perf.
N161 **124** 10 wn. red, blue & grn 75 30

125. Farm Workers. **126.** Gen. Ulji Mun Dok.

1959. National Co-operative Farming Congress, Pyongyang. With or without gum. Imperf. or perf.
N 162. **125.** 10 wn. blue.. .. 65 25

1959. With gum. Imperf. or perf.
N163 **126** 10 wn. red and yellow 1·50 50
See also Nos. N165/7 and N216/19.

127. Women with Banner. **128.** Rocket and Moon.

1959. National Conference of Women Socialist Constructors, Pyongyang. With or without gum.
N164 **127** 10 ch. brown and red 75 30

1959. Revalued currency. Portraits as T **126**. Imperf (with or without gum) or perf (with gum).
N165 – 2 ch. blue on green .. 60 10
N166 – 5 ch. purple on buff 70 10
N167 **126** 10 ch. red on cream 85 10
Portraits: 2 ch. General Kang Gam Chan. 5 ch. General Chon Bong Jun.

1959. Launch of Soviet Moon Rocket. With or without gum. Imperf. or perf.
N 168. **128.** 2 ch. purple on buff 1·50 40
N 169. 10 ch. bl. on grn.. . 2·75 50

129. "Irrigation". **130.** Inscribed Tree at Partisan H.Q. Chongbong.

131. Kim Il Sung Statue. **132.** Mt. Paekdu.

1959. Land Irrigation Project. Imperf. or perf.
N 170. **129.** 10 ch. multicoloured 2·00 45

1959. Partisan Successes against Japanese 1937-39. With gum (No. N 172) or no gum (others). Perf. (N 172) or imperf. or perf. (others).
N 171. **130.** 5 ch. multicoloured 1·50 35
N 172. **131.** 10 ch. blue and turq. 1·00 10
N 173. **132.** 10 ch. violet .. 1·75 40

133. "Flying Horse" Tractor.

1959. "Great Perspectives" (1st issue): Development of Industrial Mechanisation). With or without gum. Perf, roul or imperf.
N174 1 ch. red, olive and green 45 10
N175 2 ch. multicoloured .. 2·50 40
N176 2 ch. red, pink and violet 60 10
N177 5 ch. orange, brn & ochre 60 15
N178 10 ch. blue, green & brn 70 15
N179 10 ch. grn, lt grn & brn 1·00 20
Designs: No. N175, Electric shunting locomotive. N176, "Red Star 58" bulldozer. N 177, "Flying Horse" excavator. N178, "SU-50" universal lathe. N179, "Victory 58" lorry.
See also Nos. N189a/200 and N275/79.

134. Armistice Building, Panmunjom. **135.** Protest Meeting.

136. "Hoisting link between N. and S. Korea". **137.** Emigration "Pickets".

1959. Campaign for Withdrawal of U.S. Forces from S. Korea. With gum. Perf. (20 ch.) or imperf. or perf. (others).
N180 **134** 10 ch. blue & ultram 55 20
N181 **135** 20 ch. deep blue & bl 75 30
N182 **136** 70 ch. brown, cream and purple .. 4·00 1·60

1959. Campaign Against Emigration of South Koreans. With gum.
N 183. **137.** 20 ch. brn. & sepia 90 30

138. Korean Type of "1234". **139.** Books breaking Chains.

141. Korean Alphabet of 1443. **140.** Emblems of Peace, Labour and Letters.

1959. Int. Book Exn., Leipzig. With gum (No. N 184, N 186) or no gum (others).
N 184. **138.** 5 ch. sepia .. 4·00 40
N 185. **139.** 5 ch. red & grn. .. 1·50 30
N 186. **140.** 10 ch. blue .. 2·50 75
N 187. **141.** 10 ch. violet & blue 2·50 50

142. Pig Farm. **143.** Rotary Cement Kiln.

1959. Animal Husbandry. With gum (5 ch.) or no gum (2ch.).
N188 – 2 ch. brn, grn & buff 40 15
N189 **142** 5 ch. cream, bl & brn 60 20
Design—horiz. 2 ch. Cow-girl with Cattle.

1959. "Great Perspectives" (2nd issue: Production Targets). With gum (Nos. N190 and N192) or no gum (others). Perf (N197/8 and N200), perf or imperf (others).
N189a **143** 1 ch. bn, choc & bl 25 10
N190 – 2 ch. multicoloured 50 10
N191 – 5 ch. multicoloured 90 25
N192 – 10 ch. multicoloured 1·10 35
N193 – 10 ch. pur, yell & bl 50 10
N194 – 10 ch. yellow, green and red 75 10
N195 – 10 ch. multicoloured 50 10
N196 – 10 ch. blue, light blue and green .. 60 10
N197 – 10 ch. multicoloured 50 10
N198 – 10 ch. green, buff and brown .. 75 10
N199 – 10 ch. brown & orge 50 10
N200 – 10 ch. multicoloured 95 15
Designs—vert. No. N 190, Electric power lines and dam. No. N 191, Loading fertilizers into truck. horiz. No. N 192, Factory, electric power lines and dam. No. N 193, Harvesting. No. N 194, Sugar-beet, factory and pieces of sugar. No. N 195, Steel furnace. No. N 196, Trawlers. No. N 197, Pig-iron workers. No. N 198, Coal miners. No. N 199, Girl picking apples. No. N 200, Textile worker.

144. Sika Deer. **145.** Congress Emblem.

1959. Game Preservation. No gum (5 ch.), with gum (10 ch.).
N201 – 5 ch. multicoloured 90 20
N202 – 5 ch. yellow, brn & bl 90 10
N203 – 5 ch. sepia, grn & brn 90 10
N204 – 5 ch. brown, blk & bl 90 35
N205 **144** 10 ch. multicoloured 1·50 25
N206 – 10 ch. red, brown and green on cream .. 2·75 50
Designs—horiz. No. N 201, Chinese water deer. No. N 202, Siberian weasel. No. N 203, Steppe polecat. No. N 204, European otter. No. N 206, Ring-necked Pheasant.

1960. 3rd Korean Trade Unions Federation Congress. With gum.
N 207. **145.** 5 ch. multicoloured 35 10

146. "Chungnyon-ho" (freighter).

147. Soldier, Tractor and Plough.

148. Knife Dance.

1959. Transport. With gum.
N 208. – 5 ch. purple .. 7·50 1·00
N 209. **146.** 10 ch. green .. 2·25 60
DESIGN: 5 ch. Electric train.

1960. 12th Anniv. of Korean People's Army. With gum.
N 210. **147.** 5 ch. vio. & blue .. 32·00 28·00

1960. Korean National Dances. Mult.
N 211. 5 ch. Type **148** .. .. 1·60 10
N 212. 5 ch. Drum dance .. 1·60 10
N 213. 10 ch. Farmers' dance .. 1·60 20

149. Women of Three Races.

150. Kim Jong Ho (geographer).

1960. 50th Anniv. of Int. Women's Day. With gum.
N 214. **149.** 5 ch. mauve and blue 40 15
N 215. — 10 ch. grn. & orange 50 25
DESIGN—VERT. 10 ch. Woman operating lathe.

1960. Korean Celebrities. With gum.
N216 **150** 1 ch. grey and green 50 10
N217 – 2 ch. blue and yellow 70 10
N218 – 5 ch. blue and yellow 2·75 20
N219 – 10 ch. brown & ochre 70 10
PORTRAITS: 2 ch. Kim Hong Do (painter). 5 ch. Pak Yon (musician). 10 ch. Chong Da San (scholar).

151. Grapes.

152. Lenin.

1960. Wild Fruits. Fruits in natural colours. With or without gum (N221/2), with gum (others).
N 220. 5 ch. olive & turquoise .. 55 15
N 221. 5 ch. drab and blue .. 55 15
N 222. 5 ch. olive and blue .. 55 15
N 223. 10 ch. olive & orange .. 70 20
N 224. 10 ch. green & pink .. 70 20
FRUITS: No. N 220, T **151**. No. N 221, Fruit of "Actinidia arguta planch". No. N 222, Pine-cone. No. N 223, Hawthorn berries. No. N 224, Horse-chestnut.

1960. 90th Birth Anniv. of Lenin. With gum.
N 225. **152.** 10 ch. purple .. 40 15

153. Koreans and American Soldier (caricature).

154. Arch of Triumph Square, Pyongyang.

1960. Campaign Day for Withdrawal of U.S. Forces from South Korea. With gum.
N 226. **153.** 10 ch. blue 90 20

1960. Views of Pyongyang.
N 227. **154.** 10 ch. green .. 60 10
N 228. – 20 ch. slate 90 20
N 229. – 40 ch. green .. 2·00 35
N 230. – 70 ch. green .. 2·75 45
N 231. – 1 wn. blue .. .. 4·00 70
VIEWS OF PYONGYANG: 20 ch. River Taedong promenade. 40 ch. Youth Street. 70 ch. People's Army Street. 1 wn. Sungri Street.

155. Russian Flag on Moon (14.9.59).

156. "Mirror Rock".

1960. Russian Cosmic Rocket Flights. With gum (5 ch.) or no gum (10 ch.).
N 232. – 5 ch. turquoise .. 2·25 1·60
N 233. **155.** 10 ch. mult. .. 2·50 75
DESIGN: 5 ch. "Lunik 3" approaching Moon (4.10.59).

1960. Diamond Mountains Scenery (1st issue). Multicoloured.
N 234. 5 ch. Type **156** 60 10
N 235. 5 ch. Devil-faced Rock 60 10
N 236. 10 ch. Dancing Dragon Bridge (horiz.) .. 2·50 2·00
N 237. 10 ch. Nine Dragon Falls 2·75 1·50
N 238. 10 ch. Mt. Diamond on the Sea (horiz.) .. 90 10
See also Nos. N 569/72, N 599/601 and N 1180/4.

157. Lily.

158. Guerrillas in the Snow.

1960. Flowers. Multicoloured. With gum (N242), with or without gum (others).
N 239. 5 ch. Type **157** 15 25
N 240. 5 ch. Rhododendron .. 75 15
N 241. 10 ch. Hibiscus .. .. 1·25 20
N 242. 10 ch. Blue campanula 1·25 20
N 243. 10 ch. Mauve campanula 1·25 20

1960. Revolutionary Leadership of Kim Il Sung.
N 244. **158.** 5 ch. red 20 10
N 245. – 10 ch. blue 45 10
N 246. – 10 ch. red 45 10
N 247. – 10 ch. blue 45 10
N 248. – 10 ch. red 45 10
DESIGNS: No. N 245, Kim Il Sung talks to guerrillas. No. N 246, Kim Sung at Pochonbo. No. 247, Kim Il Sung on bank of Amnok River. No. N 248, Kim Il Sung returns to Pyongyang.

159. Korean and Soviet Flags.

160. "North Korean-Soviet Friendship".

1960. 15th Anniv. of Liberation from Japan.
N 249. **159.** 10 ch. red, bl. & brn. 60 15

1960. North Korean-Soviet Friendship Month.
N 250. **160.** 10 ch. lake on cream 35 15

161. Okryu Bridge, Pyongyang.

1960. Pyongyang Buildings.
N 251. **161.** 10 ch. blue .. .. 1·50 20
N 252. – 10 ch. violet .. 1·10 15
N 253. – 10 ch. green .. 50 10
DESIGNS: No. N 252, Grand Theatre, Pyongyang. No. N 253, Okryu Restaurant.

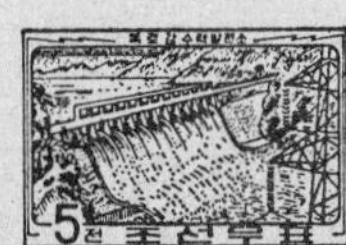
162. Tokro River Dam.

1960. Inaug. of Tokro River Hydro-electric Power Station. With gum.
N 254. **162.** 5 ch. blue 70 10

163.

164. Quayside welcome.

1960. 15th Anniv of World Federation of Trade Unions.
N255 **163** 10 ch. light blue, ultramarine & blue 25 10

1960. Repatriation of Korean Nationals from Japan.
N 256. **164.** 10 ch. purple .. 2·50 20

165. Lenin and Workers.

166. Football.

1960. Korea–Soviet Friendship. With gum.
N257 **165** 10 ch. brown and flesh 25 10

1960. Liberation Day Sports Meeting, Pyongyang. Multicoloured.
N 258. 5 ch. Running (vert.) .. 60 10
N 259. 5 ch. Weightlifting (vert.) 60 10
N 260. 5 ch. Cycling (vert.) .. 2·25 15
N 261. 5 ch. Gymnastics (vert.) 60 10
N 262. 5 ch. Type **166** .. .. 1·10 15
N 263. 10 ch. Swimming .. 60 10
N 264. 10 ch. Moranbong Stadium, Pyongyang 60 10

167. Friendship Monument, Pyongyang.

168. Federation Emblem.

1960. 10th Anniv. of Entry of Chinese Volunteers into Korean War. With gum.
N 265. – 5 ch. mauve .. 20 10
N 266. **167.** 10 ch. blue 20 10
DESIGN—HORIZ. 5 ch. Chinese and Korean soldiers celebrating.

1960. 15th Anniv. of World Democratic Youth Federation.
N267 **168** 10 ch. multicoloured 30 10

169. White-backed Woodpecker.

170. Korean Wrestling.

1960. Birds.
N 268. **169.** 2 ch. multicoloured 2·25 15
N 268a. – 5 ch. multicoloured 2·50 15
N 269. – 5 ch. brn., yell & bl. 3·75 35
N 270. – 10 ch. yell., brn. & grn. 2·75 20
DESIGNS—HORIZ. 5 ch. (N268a), Mandarin ducks. 10 ch. Black-naped oriole. VERT. 5 ch. (N269), Scops owl.

1960. Sports and Games. Multicoloured.
N 271. 5 ch. Type **170** 45 10
N 272. 5 ch. Riding on swing (vert.) 45 10
N 273. 5 ch. Archery .. .. 1·40 20
N 274. 10 ch. Jumping on see-saw (vert.) 45 10

171. Cogwheel and Corn. ("Mechanization of Rural Economy").

172. Cultivated Ginseng.

1961. "Great Perspectives" (3rd issue: Targets of Seven-Year Plan, 1961-67. Inscr. "1961"). Multicoloured.
N 275. 5 ch. Type **171** 60 10
N 276. 5 ch. Cogwheel and textiles 1·10 10
N 277. 10 ch. Hammer, sickle and torch on flag (vert.) .. 30 10
N 278. 10 ch. Cogwheels around power station .. 60 10
N 279. 10 ch. Cogwheel and molten steel 45 10

1961. Multicoloured.
N 280. 5 ch. Type **172** .. .. 1·50 10
N 281. 10 ch. Wild ginseng (perennial herb) .. 1·50 10

173. Aldehyde Shop.

1961. Construction of Vinalon Factory. With gum.
N282 **173** 5 ch. red and yellow 60 10
N283 – 10 ch. green & yellow 1·10 10
N284 – 10 ch. blue & yellow 1·10 10
N285 – 20 ch. purple & yell 1·25 15
DESIGNS: No. N 283, Glacial acetic acid shop. No. N 284, Polymerization and saponification shop. No. N 285, Spinning shop.
See also Nos. N 338/41.

174. Construction Work.

175. Museum Building.

1961. Construction of Children's Palace, Pyongyang. With gum.
N 286. **174.** 2 ch. red on yellow 35 12

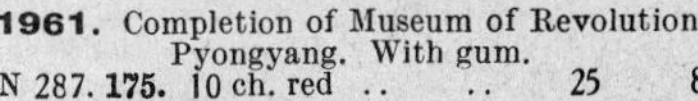
1961. Completion of Museum of Revolution, Pyongyang. With gum.
N 287. **175.** 10 ch. red 25 8

176. Cosmic Rocket.

177. Wheat Harvester.

1961. Launching of Soviet Venus Rocket.
N288 **176** 10 ch. red, yellow & bl 60 15

1961. Agricultural Mechanisation. With gum.
N 289. – 5 ch. violet 50 10
N 290. – 5 ch. green 50 10
N 291. **177.** 5 ch. green 50 10
N 292. – 10 ch. blue 60 10
N 293. – 10 ch. purple .. 60 10
DESIGNS: No. N 289, Tractor-plough. No. N 290, Disc-harrow. No. N 292, Maize-harvester. No. N 293, Tractors.

178.

179. Agriculture.

1961. Opening of Training Institute.
N 294. **178.** 10 ch. brn. on buff 25 10

1961. 15th Anniv. of Land Reform Law. With gum.
N 295. **179.** 10 ch. grn. on yell. 45 15

180.

181. Mackerel.

1961. 15th Anniv. of National Programme. With gum.
N 296. **180.** 10 ch. pur. & yell.. 20 10

1961. Marine Life.
N 297. **181.** 5 ch. multicoloured 90 10
N 298. – 5 ch. blk. & blue .. 2·00 25
N 299. – 10 ch. bl., blk. & lt. bl. 2·50 25
N 300. – 10 ch. multicoloured 90 10
N 301. – 10 ch. brn., yell. & grn. 90 10
DESIGNS: No. N 298, Common dolphin. No. N 299, Whale sp. No. N 300, Tunny, No. N 301, Pollack.

182. Tractor-crane. **183.** Tree-planting.

1961. With gum.
N302 182 1 ch. brown .. 40 10
N303 – 2 ch. brown .. 45 10
N304 – 5 ch. green 60 10
N305 – 10 ch. violet .. 75 20
DESIGNS—HORIZ. 2 ch. Heavy-duty lorry. 5 ch. Eight-metres turning lathe. VERT. 10 ch. 3000-ton press.
See also Nos. N378/9c.

1961. Re-afforestation Campaign. With gum.
N 306. **183.** 10 ch. green .. 75 15

184. "Peaceful Unification" Banner. **185.** Pioneers visiting Battlefield.

1961. Propaganda for Peaceful Reunification of Korea.
N 307. **184.** 10 ch. multicoloured 5·50 1·50

1961. 15th Anniv. of Children's Union. Mult.
N 308. 5 ch. Pioneers bathing .. 40 10
N 309. 10 ch. Pioneer bugler .. 1·25 20
N 310. 10 ch. Type **185** 40 10

186. "Labour Law". **187.** Apples.

1961. 15th Anniv. of Labour Law. With gum.
N 311. **186.** 10 ch. blue on yellow 20 10

1961. Fruit. Multicoloured.
N312 5 ch. Peaches .. 60 10
N313 5 ch. Plums .. 60 10
N314 5 ch. Type **187** 60 10
N315 10 ch. Persimmons .. 60 10
N316 10 ch. Pears 60 10

188. Yuri Gagarin and "Vostok-I".

1961. World's First Manned Space Flight.
N 317. **188.** 10 ch. ultram. & blue 35 10
N 318. 10 ch. violet & blue 35 10

189. Power Station.

1961. 15th Anniv. of Nationalization of Industries Law. With gum.
N 319. **189.** 10 ch. brown .. 2·75 60

190. Women at Work. **191.** Children planting Tree.

1961. 15th Anniv. of Sex Equality Law. With gum.
N 320. **190.** 10 ch. red 35 10

1961. Children. Multicoloured.
N 321. 5 ch. Type **191** 60 10
N 322. 5 ch. Reading book .. 30 10
N 323. 10 ch. Playing with ball 30 10
N 324. 10 ch. Building a house 30 10
N 325. 10 ch. Waving flag .. 30 10

192. Poultry and Stock-breeding. **193.** Soldiers on March (statue).

1961. Improvement in Living Standards. Mult.
N 326. 5 ch. Type **192** 60 10
N 327. 10 ch. Fabrics and textile factory .. .. 1·10 10
N 328. 10 ch. Trawler and fish (horiz.) .. .. 1·00 20
N 329. 10 ch. Grain-harvesting (horiz.) 50 10

1961. 25th Anniv. of Fatherland Restoration Association. With gum.
N 330. – 10 ch. violet .. 40 10
N 331. – 10 ch. violet .. 25 10
N 332. **193.** 10 ch. blue & buff 25 10
DESIGNS—Marshal Kim Il Sung. No. N 330, Seated under tree. No. N 331, Working at desk.

194. Party Emblem and Members. **195.** Miner.

1961. Fourth Korean Workers' Party Congress. Pyongyang. With gum.
N 333. **194.** 10 ch. green .. 20 10
N 334. – 10 ch. purple .. 20 10
N 335. – 10 ch. red 20 10
DESIGNS—VERT. No. N334, "Chollima" statue, Pyongyang. HORIZ. No. N335, Marshal Kim Il Sung.

1961. Miners' Day. With gum.
N 336. **195.** 10 ch. brown .. 1·75 60

196. Pak in Ro. **197.** Aldehyde Shop.

1961. 400th Birth Anniv. of Pak in Ro (poet).
N 337. **196.** 10 ch. indigo on blue 45 15

1961. Completion of Vinalon Factory. With gum.
N338 **197** 5 ch. red and yellow 60 10
N339 – 10 ch. brown & yell 90 10
N340 – 10 ch. blue & yellow 90 10
N341 – 20 ch. purple & yell 1·40 20
DESIGNS: No. N 339, Glacial-acetic shop. No. N 340, Polymerization and saponification shop. No. N 341, Spinning shop.

198. Korean and Chinese Flags. **199.** Basketball.

1961. North Korean Friendship Treaties with China and the U.S.S.R.
N 342. – 10 ch. multicoloured 40 10
N 343. **198.** 10 ch. red, bl. & yell. 40 10
DESIGN: No. N 342, Korean and Soviet flags.

1961. Physical Culture Day. With gum.
N 344. – 2 ch. grey 50 10
N 345. – 5 ch. blue 75 10
N 346. **199.** 10 ch. blue 75 10
N 347. – 10 ch. blue 75 10
N 348. – 10 ch. purple .. 75 10
N 349. – 20 ch. red 50 10
DESIGNS: 2 ch. Table tennis. 5 ch. Flying model aircraft. 10 ch. (No. N347) Rowing. 10 ch. (No. N348) High jumping. 20 ch. Sports emblem.

(200.)

201. General Rock.

1961. Centenary of Publication of Map "Taidong Yu Jido" by Kim Jung Ho. No. N 216 surch. with T **200.**
N350 150 5 ch. on 1 ch. grey and green .. 35·00 24·00

1961. Mt. Chilbo Scenery. With gum.
N 351. **201.** 5 ch. blue 45 10
N 352. – 5 ch. brown .. 45 10
N 353. – 10 ch. violet .. 90 20
N 354. – 10 ch. blue .. 90 20
N 355. – 10 ch. blue 90 20
DESIGNS—HORIZ. No. N 352, Chonbul Peak. No. N 354, Tiled House Rock. No. N 355, Rainbow Rock. VERT. No. N 353, Mansa Peak.

202. "Agriculture and Industry". **203.** Winged Horse and Congress Emblem.

1961. With gum.
N 356. **202.** 10 ch. green .. 35 10

1961. Fifth World Federation of Trade Unions Congress, Moscow. With gum.
N 357 **203.** 10 ch. bl., pur. & vio. 25 10

204. "Red Banner" Class Electric Locomotive. **205.** Ice Hockey.

1961. Railway Electrification. With gum.
N 358. **204.** 10 ch. vio. & yellow 4·00 1·60

1961. Winter Sports. With gum.
N359 – 10 ch. brown & grey 45 10
N360 – 10 ch. brown & green 45 10
N361 **205** 10 ch. brown and blue 45 10
N362 – 10 ch. brown and blue 45 10
DESIGNS: No. N359, Figure skating. No. N360, Speed skating. No. N 362, Skiing.

206. Grain Harvest. **207.** Tiger.

1962. "Six Heights" of Production Targets (1st series.) Inscr. "1962". With gum.
N 363. – 5 ch. red, vio. & grey 30 10
N 364. – 5 ch. brown & grey 1·75 30
N 365. **206.** 10 ch. yell., blk. & bl. 30 10
N 366. – 10 ch. red, yell. & bl. 90 10
N 367. – 10 ch. black & blue 75 15
N 368. – 10 ch. yell., brn. & bl. 30 10
DESIGNS: No. N363, Ladle and molten steel. No. N364, Coal trucks. No. N366, Fabrics and mill. No. N367, Trawler and catch. No. N368, Construction of flats.
See also Nos. N440/5.

1962. Animals.
N369 **207** 2 ch. multicoloured 1·75 15
N370 – 2 ch. brown & green 1·25 10
N371 – 5 ch. yellow & green 1·25 10
N372 – 10 ch. brown & green 1·50 15
ANIMALS—HORIZ. 2 ch. (No. N 370), Racoon-dog. 5 ch. Chinese ferret-badger. 10 ch. Asiatic black bear.

208. Kayagum Player. **209.** "Leuhdorfia puziloi".

1962. Musical Instruments and Players (1st series). Multicoloured.
N373 10 ch. Type **208** .. 1·75 20
N374 10 ch. Man playing haegum (two-stringed bowed instrument) .. 1·75 20
N375 10 ch. Woman playing wolgum (banjo) .. 1·75 20
N376 10 ch. Man playing chotdae (flute) .. 1·75 20
N377 10 ch. Woman playing wagonghu (harp) .. 1·75 20
See also Nos. N473/7.

1962. As T **182**. Inscr. "1962". With gum (Nos. N 379 and 379b), no gum (others).
N 378. 5 ch. green 50 10
N 379. 10 ch. blue 75 15
N 379a. 10 ch. brown .. .. — 3·75
N 379b. 5 wn. brown .. .. 9·50 3·00
N 379c. 10 wn. purple .. .. 11·50 6·00
DESIGNS—VERT. 5 ch. Hydraulic press. 10 ch. (2), Three-ton hammer. 10 wn. Tunnel drill. HORIZ. 5 wn. Hobbing machine.
See also Nos. N 415/22, N 513/15 and 573.

1962. Butterflies. Multicoloured.
N380 5 ch. Type **209** .. 2·25 15
N381 10 ch. "Sericinus telamon" (purple background) .. 2·25 15
N382 10 ch. Keeled apollo (lilac background) .. 2·25 15
N383 10 ch. Peacock (green background) .. 2·25 15

210. G. S. Titov and "Vostok-2".

1962. Second Soviet Manned Space Flight.
N 384. **210.** 10 ch. multicoloured 45 15

211. Marshal Kim Il Sung and (inset) addressing Workers. **212.** Kim Chaek.

1962. Marshal Kim Il Sung's 50th Birthday. With gum.
N 385. **211.** 10 ch. red 45 15
N 386. 10 ch. green .. 45 15
N 387. – 10 ch. blue 45 10
DESIGN: No. 387, Kim Il Sung in fur hat and (inset) inspecting battle-front.

1962. Korean Revolutionaries (1st series). With gum.
N 388. **212.** 10 ch. sepia 35 10
N 389. – 10 ch. blue 35 10
N 390. – 10 ch. red 35 10
N 391. – 10 ch. purple .. 35 10
N 392. – 10 ch. green .. 35 10
N 393. – 10 ch. blue 35 10
N 394. – 10 ch. brown .. 35 10
PORTRAITS: No. N 389, Kang Gon. N 390, An Gil. N 391, Ryu Gyong Su. N 392/3, Kim Jong Suk. N 394, Choe Chun Guk.
See also Nos. N 478/82 and N 733/5.

213. Mother with Children. **214.** Black-faced Spoonbill.

1962. National Mothers' Meeting, Pyongyang.
N 395. **213.** 10 ch. multicoloured 30 10

1962. Birds. Inscr. "1962". Multicoloured.
N 396. 5 ch. Type **214** .. .. 1·00 15
N 397. 5 ch. Brown Hawk Owl 3·50 20
N 398. 10 ch. Eastern Broad-billed Roller .. .. 2·00 20
N 399. 10 ch. Black Paradise Flycatcher .. .. 2·00 20
N 400. 20 ch. Whistling Swan .. 2·50 20

215. Victory Flame. 216. Gilthead.

1962. 25th Anniv. of Battle of Pochonbo.
N 401. 215. 10 ch. multicoloured 55 10

1962. Fish. Inscr. "1962". Multicoloured.
N 402. 5 ch. Type 216 .. .. 90 10
N 403. 5 ch. Hairtail 90 10
N 404. 10 ch. Shad .. .. 1·25 15
N 405. 10 ch. Sea bass .. .. 1·25 15
N 406. 10 ch. Stonehead .. 1·25 15

217. 218. 219.
Waterdropper. Radial Drill. Chong Da San.

1962. Antiques. With gum.
N 407. – 4 ch. black & blue .. 60 10
N 408. 217. 5 ch. black & ochre 60 10
N 409. A. 10 ch. black & green 75 10
N 410. B. 10 ch. black & orange 75 10
N 411. C. 10 ch. black & purple 75 10
N 412. D. 10 ch. black & brown 75 10
N 413. E. 10 ch. black & yellow 75 10
N 414. – 40 ch. black & grey 2·50 35
DESIGNS—VERT. 4 ch. Brush pot. 40 ch. Porcelain decanter. HORIZ. A, Inkstand. B, Brushstand. C, Turtle paperweight. D, Inkstone. E, Document case.

1962. Double frame-line. With gum.
N415 – 2 ch. green .. 25 10
N415a – 2 ch. brown .. — 3·75
N416 – 4 ch. blue 75 10
N417 218 5 ch. blue 35 10
N418 – 5 ch. purple .. 35 10
N419 – 10 ch. purple .. 40 10
N420 – 40 ch. blue .. 2·75 20
N421 – 90 ch. blue .. 1·40 30
N422 – 1 wn. brown .. 4·50 50
DESIGNS—VERT. 2 ch. Vertical milling machine. 5 ch. (No. N418), Hydraulic hammer. 1 wn. Spindle drill. HORIZ. 4 ch. "Victory April 15" motor-car. 10 ch. All-purpose excavator. 40 ch. Trolley-bus. 90 ch. Planing machine.
See also Nos. No. N513/15 and N573.

1962. Birth Bicentenary of Chong Da San (philosopher).
N423 219 10 ch. purple .. 35 10

220. Voter. 222. Globe and "Vostok 3" and "4".

221. Pyongyang.

1962. Election of Deputies to National Assembly. Multicoloured.
N 424. 10 ch. Type 220 .. 60 10
N 425. 10 ch. Family going to poll. 60 10

1962. 1535th Anniv. of Pyongyang. With gum.
N 426. 221. 10 ch. black and blue 65 10

1962. 1st "Team" Manned Space Flight.
N 427. 222. 10 ch. ind., bl. & red 75 30

223. Spiraea. 224. "Uibang Ryuchui".

1962. Korean Plants. Plants in natural colours; frame and inscr colours given.
N428 223 5 ch. lt green & green 70 10
N429 – 10 ch. green and red 70 10
N430 – 10 ch. blue & purple 70 10
N431 – 10 ch. green and olive 70 10
PLANTS: No. N429, Ginseng. No. N430, Campanula. No. N431, "Rheumcoreanum makai (Polyonaceae)".

1962. 485th Anniv. of Publication of "Uibang Ryuchui" (medical encyclopaedia).
N 432. 224. 10 ch. multicoloured 1·75 30

225. Science Academy. 226. Fisherwomen.

1962. 10th Anniv. of Korean Science Academy.
N 433. 225. 10 ch. bl. & turq. .. 1·00 10

1962.
N 434. 226. 10 ch. blue 70 10

227. European Mink.

1962. Animals.
N 435. 227. 4 ch. brn. & grn. .. 45 10
N 436. – 5 ch. bl., drab & grn. 45 10
N 437. – 10 ch. bl. & yell. .. 60 10
N 438. – 10 ch. sepia & turq. 60 10
N 439. – 20 ch. brn. & blue 1·25 15
ANIMALS—HORIZ. No. N 436, Chinese hare. VERT. No N 437, Eurasian red squirrel. No. N 438, Common goral. No. N 439, Siberian Chipmunk.

228. Harvesting.

1963. "Six Heights" of Production Targets (2nd issue). Inscr "1963". Multicoloured.
N440 5 ch. Miner 70 20
N441 10 ch. Type 228 .. 40 10
N442 10 ch. Furnaceman .. 30 10
N443 10 ch. Construction worker 30 10
N444 10 ch. Textiles loom operator 65 10
N445 40 ch. Fisherman and trawler .. .. 1·75 40

229. Soldier. 230. Peony.

1963. 15th Anniv. of Korean People's Army. With gum.
N 446. – 5 ch. brown .. 50 10
N 447. 229. 10 ch. red .. 60 10
N 448. – 10 ch. blue .. 85 10
DESIGNS: 5 ch. Airman. 10 ch. blue, Sailor.

1963. Korean Flowers. Multicoloured.
N 449. 5 ch. Type 230 .. .. 45 10
N 450. 10 ch. Rugosa rose .. 75 10
N 451. 10 ch. Azalea 75 10
N 452. 10 ch. Campion 75 10
N 453. 40 ch. Orchid .. .. 2·25 35

231. "Sadangch'um" (Korean folk dance). 232. Revolutionaries.

1963. Int. Music and Dancing Contest, Pyongyang. Multicoloured.
N 454. 10 ch. Type 231 .. .. 1·25 15
N 455. 10 ch. Dancer with fan .. 1·25 15

1963. 3rd Anniv. of South Korean Rising of April, 1960.
N 456. 232. 10 ch. mult. .. 25 10

233. Karl Marx. 234. Children in Chemistry Class.

1963. 145th Birth Anniv. of Karl Marx. With gum.
N 457. 233. 10 ch. blue 30 10

1963. Child Care and Amenities. Mult.
N 458. 2 ch. Type 234 .. .. 65 10
N 459. 5 ch. Children running 50 10
N 460. 10 ch. Boy conducting choir .. .. .. 1·50 10
N 461. 10 ch. Girl chasing butterfly .. .. 2·75 20

235. Armed Koreans and American Soldier (caricature).

1963. Campaign Month for Withdrawal of U.S. Forces from South Korea.
N 462. 235. 10 ch. multicoloured 45 10

236. "Cyrtoclytus capra".

1963. Korean Beetles. Multicoloured designs. Colours of beetles given.
N 463. 5 ch. Type 236 .. .. 65 10
N 464. 10 ch. multicoloured .. 95 10
N 465. 10 ch. red and blue .. 95 10
N 466. 10 ch. ind., blue & purple 95 10
BEETLES: No. N 464, "Cicindela chinenis". No. N 465, "Purpuricenus lituratus". No. N 466, "Agapanthia pilicornis".

237. Soldier with Flag. 238. North Korean Flag.

1963. 10th Anniv. of Victory in Korean War.
N 467. 237. 10 ch. mult. .. 30 10

1963. 15th Anniv. of People's Republic. Mult.
N 468. 10 ch. Type 238 .. 30 10
N 469. 10 ch. N. Korean Badge 30 10

239. Namdae Gate, Kaesong. 240. Ajaeng (bowed zither).

1963. Ancient Korean Buildings (1st series). With gum.
N 470. 239. 5 ch. black 20 10
N 471. – 10 ch. blue 40 10
N 472. – 10 ch. brown .. 40 10
BUILDINGS: No. N471, Taedong Gate, Pyongyang. No. N472, Potong Gate, Pyongyang.
See also Nos. N537/8.

1963. Musical Instruments and Players (2nd series). Multicoloured. Nos. N 473 and 476 with gum.
N473 3 ch. Type 240 .. .. 75 10
N474 5 ch. Pyongyon (jade chimes) 75 10
N475 10 ch. Saenap (brass bowl) .. .. .. 1·40 10
N476 10 ch. Rogo (drums in frame) .. .. 1·40 10
N477 10 ch. Piri ("wooden pipe") .. .. 1·40 10

1963. Korean Revolutionaries (2nd issue). As T 212. With gum.
N 478. 5 ch. brown 25 10
N 479. 5 ch. purple 25 10
N 480. 10 ch. rose 30 10
N 481. 10 ch. slate 30 10
N 482. 10 ch. dull purple .. 30 10
PORTRAITS: No. N 478, Kwon Yong Byok. No. N 479, Ma Dong Hui. No. N 480, Li Je Sun. No. N 481, Pak Dal. No. N 482, Kim Yong Bom.

241. Nurse with Children. 242. Hwajang Hall.

1963. Child Welfare. Multicoloured.
N 483. 10 ch. Type 241 .. 30 10
N 484. 10 ch. Children in play ground 30 10

1963. Mount Myohyang Resort. Mult.
N 485. 5 ch. Type 242 .. .. 35 10
N 486. 10 c. Mountain stream and chalet 75 10
N 487. 10 ch. Kwanum Pavilion and stone pagoda .. 65 10
N 488. 10 ch. Rope bridge across river .. .. 1·75 15
Nos. N 487/8 are horiz.

243. Furnaceman. 244. Children hoeing.

1963. Seven Year Plan. With gum.
N489 243 5 ch. red 20 10
N490 – 10 ch. grey .. .. 1·50 20
N491 – 10 ch. red .. .. 1·50 10
N492 – 10 ch. lilac 85 10
DESIGNS—VERT. No. N 490, Construction workers. HORIZ. No. N 491, Power technicians. No. N 492, Miners.

1963. "Hung Bo" (fairytale). Multicoloured.
N 493. 5 ch. Type 244 .. .. 30 10
N 494. 10 ch. Tying up broken leg of swallow .. 90 10
N 495. 10 ch. Barn swallow dropping gourd seed .. 90 10
N 496. 10 ch. Sawing through giant gourd .. 50 10
N 497. 10 ch. Treasure inside gourd 50 10

245. Marksman.

1963 Marksmanship. Multicoloured.
N 498. 5 ch. Type 245 .. .. 30 10
N 499. 10 ch. Marksman with small-bore rifle .. 55 10
N 500. 10 ch. Marksman with standard rifle .. 55 10

246. Sinuiju Chemical Fibre Factory. 248. Korean Alphabet.

247. Strikers. 249. Lenin.

1964. Chemical Fibres Factories. With gum.
N 501. **246.** 10 ch. slate 75 10
N 502. – 10 ch. purple .. 75 10
DESIGN: No. N 502, Chongjin Chemical Fibre Factory.

1964. 35th Anniv. of Wonsan General Strike. With gum.
N 503. **247.** 10 ch. brown .. 60 10

1964. 520th Anniv. of Korean Alphabet.
N 504. **248.** 10 ch. grn., buff & brn. 20 10

1964. 40th Death Anniv. of Lenin. With gum.
N 505. **249.** 10 ch. red 30 10

250. Whale-catcher.

1964. Fishing Industry. Multicoloured.
N506 5 ch. Type **250** .. 40 10
N507 5 ch. Trawler No. 051 .. 40 10
N508 10 ch. Trawler No. 397 .. 85 20
N509 10 ch. Trawler No. 738 .. 85 20

251. Insurgents. **252.** Warring Peasants.

1964. 45th Anniv. of Rising of 1st March. With gum.
N 510. **251.** 10 ch. purple .. 30 10

1964. 70th Anniv. of Kabo Peasant's War. With gum.
N 511. **252.** 10 ch. purple .. 30 10

253. Students' Palace, Pyongyang. **254.** "Changbaek" Excavator.

1964. With gum.
N 512. **253.** 10 ch. green .. 30 10

1964. Single frame-line. Dated "1964" or "1965" (No. N 573). With gum.
N 513. – 5 ch. violet 25 10
N 514. **254.** 10 ch. green .. 50 10
N 515. – 10 ch. blue 50 10
N 573. – 10 ch. violet .. 45 10
DESIGNS—VERT. 5 ch. 200 Metre drill. 10 ch. (N 573) "Horning 500" machine. HORIZ. 10 ch. (N 515) 400 h.p. Diesel engine.

255. "On the March".

1964. 5th Korean Democratic Youth League Congress, Pyongyang.
N 516. **255.** 10 ch. multicoloured 30 10

256. Electric Train.

1964. Inauguration of Pyongyang-Sinuiju Electric Railway.
N 517. **256.** 10 ch. multicoloured 2·50 20

257. Rejoicing in Chongsan-ri Village.

1964. Popular movement at Chongsan-ri. With gum.
N 517a. **257.** 5 ch. brown ..

258. Drum Dance. **259.** Li Su Bok in Battle.

1964. Korean Dances.
N 518. **258.** 2 ch. mve., buff & blk. 1·50 15
N 519. – 5 ch. red, blk. & yell. 1·75 15
N 520. – 10 ch. multicoloured 2·00 15
DANCES: 5 ch. "Ecstasy" (solo). 10 ch. Tabor.

1964. Li Su Bok Commem. With gum.
N 521. **259.** 5 ch. red 20 10

260. Nampo Smelting Works.

1964. With gum.
N 522. **260.** 5 ch. green 85 10
N 523. – 10 ch. slate .. .. 1·40 20
DESIGNS: 10 ch. Hwanghae iron works.

261. Torch, Chollima statue and Cogwheel.

1964. Asian Economic Seminar, Pyongyang. Multicoloured.
N 524. 5 ch. Type **261** 15 10
N 525. 10 ch. Flags, statue and cogwheel 30 10

262. Korean People and Statue of Kang Ho Yong (war hero).

1964. Struggle for Reunification of Korea.
N 526. **262.** 10 ch. multicoloured 45 10

263. Hawk Fowl.

1964. Domestic Poultry. Multicoloured.
N 527. 2 ch. Type **263** 35 10
N 528. 4 ch. White fowl .. 35 10
N 529. 5 ch Ryongyon fowl .. 55 10
N 530. 5 ch. Black fowl 55 10
N 531. 40 ch. Helmet guineafowl 1·75 60

264. Skiing.

1964. Winter Olympic Games, Innsbruck.
N 532. **264.** 5 ch. red, bl. & buff 50 10
N 533. – 10 ch. bl., grn. & buff 75 10
N 534. – 10 ch. bl., red & buff 75 10
DESIGNS: No. N533, Ice skating. N534, Skiing (slalom).

INDEX

Countries can be quickly located by referring to the index at the end of this volume.

265. "Tobolsk" (passenger ship) and Flags. **266.** Tonggun Pavilion Uiju.

1964. 5th Anniv. of Agreement for Repatriation of Koreans in Japan.
N 535. **265.** 10 ch. red, bl. & lt. bl. 1·00 20
N 536. – 30 ch. multicoloured 80 15
DESIGN: 30 ch. Return of repatriates.

1964. Ancient Korean Buildings (2nd series). With gum.
N 537. **266.** 5 ch. purple .. 10 10
N 538. – 10 ch. green .. 30 10
DESIGN: 10 ch. Inpang Pavilion, Kanggye City.

267. Cycling. **268.** Burning of the "General Sherman".

1964. Olympic Games, Tokyo.
N 539. – 2 ch. brown and slate 25 10
N 540. **267.** 5 ch. brown & green 75 10
N 541. – 10 ch. orange & blue 35 10
N 542. – 10 ch. orge. & green 35 10
N 543. – 40 ch. brown & blue 60 35
DESIGNS—HORIZ. 2 ch. Rifle-shooting. 10 ch. blue, Running. VERT. 10 ch. green, Wrestling. 40 ch. Volleyball.

1964. The "General Sherman" Incident, 1866. With gum.
N 544. **268.** 30 ch. brown .. 2·00 30

269. Organizing Guerrillas.

DESIGNS: 5 ch. Kim Il Sung addressing guerrillas. 10 ch. Battle scene at Xiaowangqing.

1964. Guerrilla Operations in the 1930's against the Japanese. With gum.
N 545. **269.** 2 ch. violet 15 10
N 546. – 5 ch. blue 20 10
N 547. – 10 ch. black .. 30 10

270. Students attacking. **271.** Weightlifting.

1964. Kwangju Students Rising, 1929. With gum.
N 548. **270.** 10 ch. violet .. 1·60 15

1964. "GANEFO" Athletic Games, Djakarta, Indonesia (1963). Multicoloured.
N 549. 2 ch. Type **271** 25 10
N 550. 5 ch. Athlete breasting tape 30 10
N 551. 5 ch. Boxing 30 10
N 552. 10 ch. Football 75 15
N 553. 10 ch. Globe emblem .. 30 15
Nos. N551/3 are horiz.

272. Lynx. **273.** Vietnamese Attack.

1964. Animals. With gum.
N 554. 2 ch. sepia (Type **272**) .. 60 10
N 555. 5 ch. sepia (Leopard cat) 1·50 10
N 556. 10 ch. brown (Leopard) 2·00 10
N 557. 10 ch. sepia (Yellow-throated marten) .. 2·00 10

1964. Support for People of Vietnam.
N 558. **273.** 10 ch. multicoloured 30 10

274. Prof. Kim Bong Han and Emblems.

1964. Kyongrak Biological Systems.
N 559. **274.** 2 ch. purple & olive 50 10
N 560. – 5 ch. grn., orge. & bl. 75 10
N 561. – 10 ch. red, yell. & bl. 1·10 10
DESIGNS ($33 \times 23\frac{1}{2}$ mm.): 5 ch. "Bonghan" duct. 10 ch. "Bonghan" corpuscle. Each include emblems as in Type **274**.

275. Farmers, Tractor and Lorry.

1964. Agrarian Programme. Multicoloured.
N 562. 5 ch. Type **275** 10 10
N 563. 10 ch. Peasants with scroll and book .. 30 10
N 564. 10 ch. Peasants—one writing in book .. 30 10

276. Chung Jin gets a Pistol. **277.** Girl with Korean Products.

1964. The Struggle to capture Japanese Arms. With gum.
N 565. **276.** 4 ch. brown .. 25 10

1964. Economic 7 Year Plan. Multicoloured. With gum (5 ch.) or no gum (others).
N 566. 5 ch. Type **277** 20 10
N 567. 10 ch. Farm girl .. 30 10
N 568. 10 ch. Couple on winged horse ($23\frac{1}{2} \times 23\frac{1}{2}$ mm.) 30 10

278. Three Fairies Rock. **280.** Soldiers Advancing, Fusong.

1964. Diamond Mountains Scenery (2nd issue). Inscr. "1964". Multicoloured. Without gum (2,4 ch.) or with gum (others).
N 569. 2 ch. Type **278** 60 10
N 570. 4 ch. Ryonju Falls .. 2·00 10
N 571. 10 ch. The Ten Thousand Rocks, Manmulsang .. 70 10
N 572. 10 ch. Chinju Falls .. 2·00 10

1965. Guerrilla Operations against the Japanese, 1934–40. With gum.
N 574. **280.** 10 ch. violet .. 30 10
N 575. – 10 ch. violet .. 30 10
N 576. – 10 ch. green .. 30 10
DESIGNS: No. N 575, Soldiers descending hill, Hongqihe. No. N 576, Soldiers attacking hill post, Luozigou.

281. Tuman River. **282.** Union Badge.

1965. Korean Rivers. Multicoloured.
N 577 2 ch. Type **281** .. 35 5
N 578 5 ch. Taedong (vert) .. 1·25 15
N 579 10 ch. Amnok .. 50 10

1965. First Congress of Landworkers' Union, Pyongyang. With gum.
N 580. **282** 10 ch. multicoloured 30 10

283. Furnacemen and Workers.

1965. 10 Major Tasks of 7 Year Plan. With gum.

N 581. **283.** 10 ch. multicoloured 30 10

284. Miners' Strike, Sinhung Colliery.

1965. 35th Anniv. of Strikes and Peasants' Revolt. With gum.

N 582. **284.** 10 ch. olive .. 1·00 10
N 583. – 10 ch. brown .. 1·00 10
N 584. – 40 ch. purple .. 1·00 20

DESIGNS: 10 ch. Strikers at Pyongyang Rubber Factory. 40 ch. Revolt of Tanchon peasants.

285. Embankment Construction. **286.** Hand holding Torch.

1965. Sunhwa River Works. With gum.

N 585. **285.** 10 ch. multicoloured 30 10

1965. 5th Anniv. of South Korean Rising of April 19th. Mult. With gum.

N 586. 10 ch. Type **286** .. 20 10
N 587. 40 ch. Student-hero, Kim Chio 45 20

287. Power Station under Construction.

1965. Construction of Thermal Power Station. Pyongyang. With gum.

N588 **287** 5 ch. brown and blue 25 10

288. African and Asian.

1965. 10th Anniv. of 1st Afro-Asian Conf. Bandung. With gum.

N 589. **288.** 10 ch. multicoloured 30 10

289. Rejoicing Koreans.

1965. 10th Anniv. of General Assn. of Koreans in Japan. With gum.

N 590. **289.** 10 ch. bl. & red .. 25 10
N 591. – 40 ch. ind., blue & red 45 15

DESIGN: 40 ch. Patriot and flag.

290. Workers in Battle. **291.** "Victory 64" 10-ton Lorry.

1965. 2nd Afro-Asian Conf., Algiers. With gum.

N 592. **290.** 10 ch. black, yell. & red 55 10
N 593. – 40 ch. black, yell. & red 1·10 25

DESIGN: 40 ch. Korean and African soldiers. The Algiers Conf. did not take place.

1965. With gum.

N 594. **291.** 10 ch. green .. 75 10

292. Kim Chang Gol.

1965. War Heroes (1st series). With gum.

N 595. **292.** 10 ch. green .. 30 10
N 596. – 10 ch. brown .. 30 10
N 597. – 40 ch. purple .. 75 20

PORTRAITS: No. N 596, Cho Gun Sil and machine-gun. No. N 597, An Hak Ryong and machine-gun.
See also Nos. N 781/3 and N 850/1.

293. Marx and Lenin.

1965. Postal Ministers' Congress, Peking. With gum.

N 598. **293.** 10 ch. blk., yell & red 1·50 15

294. Lake Samil.

1965. Diamond Mountains Scenery (3rd issue). Multicoloured. With gum.

N 599. 2 ch. Type **294** 60 10
N 600. 5 ch. Chipson Peak .. 1·00 10
N 601. 10 ch. Kwanum Falls .. 2·75 25

295. Amnok River, Kusimuldong. **296.** Footballer and Games' Emblem.

1965. Scenes of Japanese War. With gum.

N 602. **295.** 5 ch. green & blue.. 35 10
N 603. – 10 ch. turq. & blue.. 60 10

DESIGN: 10 ch. Lake Samji.

1965. "GANEFO" Football Games, Pyongyang. Multicoloured. With gum.

N 604. 10 ch. Type **296** .. 90 10
N 605. 10 ch. Games emblem and Moranbong Stadium 90 10

297. Workers and Map. **298.** Engels.

1965. 20th Anniv. of Liberation from Japan. With gum.

N 606. **297.** 10 ch. multicoloured 30 10

1965. 145th Birth Anniv. of Engels. With gum.

N 607. **298.** 10 ch. brown .. 30 10

299. Pole Vaulting. **302.** Kim Chaek Iron Works.

301. Korean Fighters.

1965. Sports. Multicoloured. With gum.

N608 2 ch. Type **299** 25 10
N609 4 ch. Throwing the javelin .. .. 1·50 20
N610 10 ch. Throwing the discus 35 10
N611 10 ch. High jumping (horiz) 35 10
N612 10 ch. Putting the shot (horiz) 35 10

1965. 20th Anniv. of Korean Workers' Party. Each black, yellow and red. With gum.

N 613. 10 ch. Type **301** .. 45 10
N 614. 10 ch. Party emblem .. 45 10
N 615. 10 ch. Lenin and Marx 45 10
N 616. 10 ch. Workers marching 45 10
N 617. 10 ch. Fighters 45 10
N 618. 40 ch. Workers 45 10

Nos. N 613/8 each have a red banner in the background and were issued together in blocks of 6 (3×2), forming a composite design, within the sheet.

1965. With gum.

N 620. **302.** 10 ch. purple .. 95 10
N 621. – 10 ch. brown .. 95 10

DESIGN: 10 ch. Chongjin Steel Works.

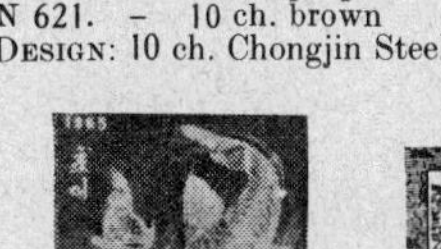

303. Grass carp. **304.** Building House.

1965. Freshwater Fish. Multicoloured. With gum.

N 622. 2 ch. Rainbow trout .. 50 10
N 623. 4 ch. Dolly Varden trout 65 10
N 624. 10 ch. Brown trout (surfacing water) .. 1·40 15
N 625. 10 ch. Carp diving (date at left) .. .. .. 1·40 15
N 626. 10 ch. Type **303** .. 1·40 15
N 627. 40 ch. Crucian carp .. 2·25 30

1965. Kim Hong Do's Drawings. With gum.

N 628. 2 ch. green (Type **304**) .. 20 10
N 629. 4 ch. purple (Weaving) .. 55 10
N 630. 10 ch. brown (Wrestling) 35 10
N 631. 10 ch. blue (School class) 35 10
N 632. 10 ch. red (Dancing) .. 85 10
N 633. 10 ch. violet (Blacksmiths) 75 10

305. Children in Workshop. **306.** Whale-catcher.

1965. Life at Pyongyang Children's and Students' Palace. Multicoloured. With gum.

N634 2 ch. Type **305** 20 10
N635 4 ch. Boxing 20 10
N636 10 ch. Chemistry .. 75 10
N637 10 ch. Playing violin and accordion 75 10

1965. Korean Fishing Boats. With gum.

N 638. **306.** 10 ch. blue .. .. 1·10 15
N 639. – 10 ch. green .. 1·10 15

DESIGN: 10 ch. Fishing Fleet Service Vessel.

307. Great Tit. **308.** Silkworm Moth ("Bombyx mori") and Cocoon.

1965. Korean Birds. Inscr. "1965". Multicoloured. With gum.

N 640. 4 ch. Black-capped Kingfisher (vert.) .. 1·25 10
N 641. 10 ch. Type **307** .. 1·75 15
N 642. 10 ch. Pied Wagtail (facing left) .. .. 1·75 15
N 643. 10 ch. Azure-winged Magpie (facing right) 1·75 15
N 644. 40 ch. Black-tailed Hawfinch .. .. 4·00 45

1965. Korean Sericulture. With gum.

N 645. **308.** 2 ch. green .. .. 3·75 20
N 646. – 10 ch. brown .. 3·75 30
N 647. – 10 ch. purple .. 3·75 30

MOTHS AND COCOONS: No. N646, Ailathus silk moth ("Samia cynthia"). No. N647, Chinese oak silk moth ("Antheraea pernyi").

309. Hooded Crane. **310.** Squid.

1965. Wading Birds. With gum.

N648 **309** 2 ch. brown .. 2·25 10
N649 – 10 ch. blue .. .. 2·25 20
N650 – 10 ch. purple .. 2·25 20
N651 – 40 ch. green .. 4·75 45

BIRDS: No. N 649, Japanese White-necked Crane. No. N 650, Manchurian Crane. No. N 651, Grey Heron.

1965. Korean Molluscs. Mult. With gum.

N 652. 5 ch. Type **310** .. .. 1·25 10
N 653. 10 ch. Octopus .. .. 1·25 10

311. Spotbill Duck. **312.** Circus Theatre, Pyongyang.

1965. Korean Ducks. Mult. With gum.

N 654. 2 ch. Type **311** .. .. 1·75 10
N 655. 4 ch. Ruddy Shelduck .. 1·75 15
N 656. 10 ch. Mallard .. .. 2·50 20
N 657. 40 ch. Baikal Teal .. 3·75 60

1965. Korean Circus. With gum except No. N 661.

N 658. **312.** 2 ch. blue, blk. & brn. 50 10
N 659. – 10 ch. blue, red & blk. 1·25 10
N 660. – 10 ch. red., blk. & grn. 1·25 10
N 661. – 10 ch. orge., sepia & grn. 1·25 10
N 662. – 10 ch. red, yell. & turq. 1·25 10

DESIGNS—VERT. No. N 659, Trapeze artistes. No. N 660, Performer with hoops on seesaw. No. N 661, Tightrope dancers. No. N 662, Performer with revolving cap on stick.

313. "Marvel of Peru" ("Mirabilis jalapa"). **314.** "Finn" Class Yacht.

1965. Korean Flowers. Multicoloured. With gum except No. N663.

N663 4 ch. Type **313** 70 10
N664 10 ch. Peony .. .. 1·10 10
N665 10 ch. Moss rose .. 1·10 10
N666 10 ch. Magnolia .. 1·10 10

1965. Yachts. Multicoloured. With gum.

N 667. 2 ch. Type **314** 50 15
N 668. 10 ch. "5.5" 85 30
N 669. 10 ch. "Dragon" .. 85 30
N 670. 40 ch. "Star" .. .. 1·60 60

315. Cuban, Korean and African.

316. Hosta.

1966. African-Asian and Latin American Friendship Conf., Havana. With gum.
N 671. **315.** 10 ch. multicoloured 30 10

1966. Wild Flowers. Mult. With gum.
(a) 1st series.
N 672. 2 ch. Type **316** 40 10
N 673. 4 ch. Dandelion .. 40 10
N 674. 10 ch. Pink convolvulus 60 10
N 675. 10 ch. Lily-of-the-Valley 60 10
N 676. 40 ch. Catalpa blossom 1·75 20
(b) 2nd series.
N 677. 2 ch. Polyanthus .. 40 10
N 678. 4 ch. Lychnis 40 10
N 679. 10 ch. Adonis 60 10
N 680. 10 ch. Orange Lily .. 60 10
N 681. 90 ch. Rhododendron .. 2·75 30

317. Farmer and Wife.

1966. 20th Anniv. of Land Reform Law. With gum.
N 682. **317.** 10 ch. multicoloured 20 10

318. Troops advancing, Dashahe.

319. Silla Bowl.

1966. Paintings of Guerrilla Battles, 1937–39. With gum, except No. N684.
N 683. **318.** 10 ch. red 30 10
N 684. – 10 ch. turquoise .. 30 10
N 685. – 10 ch. purple .. 30 10
Designs and battles: No. N 684, Troops firing from trees, Taehongdan. No. N 685, Troops on hillside, Jiansanfeng.

1966. Art Treasures of Silla Dynasty. With gum.
N 686. **319.** 2 ch. ochre 65 10
N 687. – 5 ch. black 65 10
N 688. – 10 ch. violet .. 90 10
Designs: 5 ch. Earthenware jar. 10 ch. Censer.

320. Hands holding Torch, Rifle and Hammer.

321. Torch and Patriots.

1966. 80th Anniv. of Labour Day. With gum.
N 689. **320.** 10 ch. multicoloured 30 10

1966. 30th Anniv of Association for Restoration of Fatherland.
N 690. **321.** 10 ch. red & yellow 30 10

322. Harvester.

1966. Aid for Agriculture. Multicoloured.
N 691. 5 ch. Type **322** 25 10
N 692. 10 ch. Labourer .. 35 10

323. Young Pioneers.

1966. 20th Anniv. of Korean Children's Union. Without gum.
N 693. **323.** 10 ch. multicoloured 30 10

324. Kangson Steel Works.

1966. Korean Industries. With gum.
N 694. **324.** 10 ch. grey .. 1·10 15
N 695. – 10 ch. red (Pongung Chemical Works) 1·10 15

325. Saury.

1966. Korean Fishes. With gum except Nos. 699/700.
N 696. **325.** 2 ch. blue, grn. & pur. 50 10
N 697. – 5 ch. pur., grn. & brn. 65 10
N 698. – 10 ch. bl., buff & grn. 1·00 20
N 699. – 10 ch. purple & green 1·00 20
N 700. – 40 ch. grn., buff & blue 2·50 35
Fishes: 5 ch. Cod. 10 ch. (No. N 698), Salmon, (No. N 699), "Pleurogrammus azonus". 40 ch. "Pink" salmon.

326. Professor Kim Bong Han.

1966. Kyungrak Biological System. With gum.

1966. Kyungrak Biological System. With gum.
N701 **326** 2 ch. blue, grn & yell 45 10
N702 – 4 ch. multicoloured 45 10
N703 – 5 ch. multicoloured 45 10
N704 – 10 ch. multicoloured 45 10
N705 – 10 ch. multicoloured 45 10
N706 – 10 ch. multicoloured 45 10
N707 – 15 ch. multicoloured 45 10
N708 – 40 ch. multicoloured 45 10
Designs: No. N704, Kyongrak Institute. N708, Figure of Man. N702/3, 705/7 Diagram of system.
Nos. N701/8 were issued together, se-tenant, forming a composite design.

327. Leonov in Space ("Voskhod 2").

1966. Cosmonauts Day. Multicoloured.
N 710 5 ch. Type **327** .. 20 10
N 711 10 ch. "Luna 9" .. 55 10
N 712 40 ch. "Luna 10" .. 1·10 20

328. Footballers.

1966. World Cup Football Championship. Multicoloured.
N 713. 10 ch. Type **328.** .. 1·25 25
N 714. 10 ch. Jules Rimet Cup, football and boots .. 1·25 25
N 715. 10 ch. Goalkeeper saving goal (vert.) .. .. 1·25 25

329. Defence of Seoul.

1966. Korean War of 1950–53. With gum.
N 716. **329.** 10 ch. green .. 35 10
N 717. – 10 ch. purple .. 35 10
N 718. – 10 ch. purple .. 35 10
Designs: No. N 717, Battle on Mt. Napal. No. N 718, Battle for Height 1211.

330. Women in Industry.

1966. 20th Anniv. of Sex Equality Law.
N 719. **330.** 10 ch. multicoloured 30 10

331. Industrial Workers.

332. Water-jar Dance.

1966. 20th Anniv. of Industrial Nationalization.
N 720. **331.** 10 ch. multicoloured 60 10

1966. Korean Dances. Multicoloured. 5 ch., 40 ch. with or without gum; others without.
N 721. 5 ch. Type **332** 60 10
N 722. 10 ch. Bell dance .. 1·25 15
N 723. 10 ch. "Dancer in a Mural Painting" .. .. 1·25 15
N 724. 15 ch. Sword dance .. 1·50 20
N 725. 40 ch. Gold Cymbal dance 2·40 30

333. Korean attacking U.S. Soldier.

334. Crop-spraying.

1966. Korean Reunification Campaign. With gum.
N 726. **333.** 10 ch. green .. 40 10
N 727. – 10 ch. purple .. 40 10
N 728. – 10 ch. lilac .. .. 2·25 45
Designs: No. N727, Korean with young child. No. N728, Korean with shovel, industrial scene and electric train.

1966. Industrial Uses of Aircraft. With gum except 2 ch. and 5 ch.
N 729. **334.** 2 ch. green & purple 40 10
N 730. – 5 ch. brn. & green .. 3·25 15
N 731. – 10 ch. sepia and blue 1·25 10
N 732. – 40 ch. brn. & blue .. 1·25 10
Designs (each with aircraft): 5 ch. Forest-fire observation. 10 ch. Geological survey. 40 ch. Detection of fish shoals.

1966. Korean Revolutionaries (3rd issue). As T **212.** With gum.
N 733. 10 ch. violet (O Jung Hub) .. .. ..
N 734. 10 ch. green (Kim Gyong Sok) .. .. ..
N 735. 10 ch. blue (Li Dong Gol)

335. Kim Il Sung University.

1966. 20th Anniv. of Kim Il Sung University. With gum.
N 736. **335.** 10 ch. violet .. 50 10

336. Judo.

337. Hoopoe.

1966. Ganefo Games, Phnom-Penh.
N 737. **336.** 5 ch. blk., grn. & bl. 45 10
N 738. – 10 ch. black, myrtle and green .. 45 10
N 739. – 10 ch. black and red 45 10
Designs: No. N738, Basketball. No. N739, Table tennis.

1966. Korean Birds. Mult. Inscr. "1966".
N 740. 2 ch. Common Rosefinch 70 10
N 741. 5 ch. Type **337** .. 90 10
N 742. 10 ch. Black-breasted Thrush (blue background) .. 1·10 15
N 743. 10 ch. Crested Lark (green background) .. 1·10 15
N 744. 40 ch. White-bellied Black Woodpecker .. .. 2·50 40
The 2 ch. and 10 ch. (both) are horiz.

338. Building Construction.

1966. "Increased Production with Economy". Multicoloured. Without gum (40 ch.) or with gum (others).
N 745. 5 ch. Type **338** 25 10
N 746. 10 ch. Furnaceman and graph 45 10
N 747. 10 ch. Machine-tool production 45 10
N 748. 40 ch. Miners and pithead 1·40 15

339. Parachuting.

1966. National Defence Sports. With gum.
N749 **339** 2 ch. brown .. 65 10
N750 – 5 ch. red .. 55 10
N751 – 10 ch. blue .. 2·00 10
N752 – 40 ch. green .. 1·60 20
Designs: 5 ch. Show jumping. 10 ch. Motor cycle racing. 40 ch. Radio receiving and transmitting competition.

340. "Samil Wolgan" (Association Magazine).

341. Red Deer.

1966. 30th Anniv of "Samil Wolgan" Magazine.
N 753. **340.** 10 ch. multicoloured 50 10

1966. Korean Deer. Multicoloured.
N 754. 2 ch. Type **341** 20 5
N 755. 5 ch. Sika deer 35 10
N 756. 10 ch. Indian muntjac (erect) 70 10
N 757. 10 ch. Reindeer (grazing) 70 10
N 758. 70 ch. Fallow deer .. 2·50 25

342. Blueberries.

343. Onpo Rest Home.

1966. Wild Fruit. Multicoloured.
N 759. 2 ch. Type **342** 25 10
N 760. 5 ch. Wild pears .. 35 10
N 761. 10 ch. Wild raspberries .. 50 10
N 762. 10 ch. Schizandra .. 50 10
N 763. 10 ch. Wild plums .. 50 10
N 764. 40 ch. Jujube .. .. 1·40 15

1966. Korean Rest Homes. With gum.
N 765. **343.** 2 ch. violet .. 25 10
N 766. – 5 ch. turquoise .. 35 10
N 767. – 10 ch. green .. 50 10
N 768. – 40 ch. black .. 80 20
Rest homes: 5 ch. Mt. Myohyang. 10 ch. Songdowon. 40 ch. Hongwon.

344. Soldier.

1967. 19th Anniv. of Army Day. Without gum.
N 769. **344.** 10 ch. grn., yell. & red 25 10

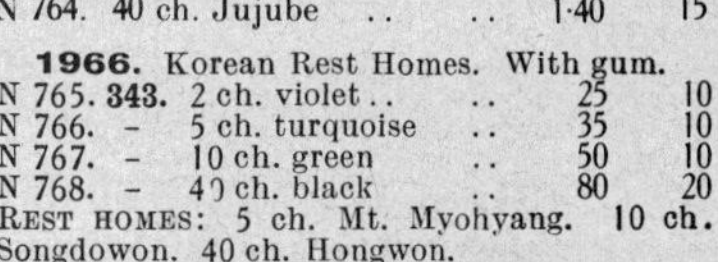
MORE DETAILED LISTS
are given in the Stanley Gibbons Catalogues referred to in the country headings.
For lists of current volumes see Introduction.

345. Sow.

1967. Domestic Animals. Multicoloured. Without gum. 40 ch. also with gum.
N 770. 5 ch. Type **345** 25 10
N 771. 10 ch. Goat 35 10
N 772. 40 ch. Ox 85 25

346. Battle Scene.

1967. 30th Anniv of Battle of Pochonbo. With gum.
N773 **346** 10 ch. orge, red & grn 50 10

347. Students.

1967. Compulsory Technical Education for Nine Years.
N 774. **347.** 10 ch. multicoloured 25 10

348. Table Tennis Player.

1967. 29th International Table Tennis Championships, Pyongyang. Designs showing players in action. 5 ch. with or without gum.
N 775. **348.** 5 ch. multicoloured 25 5
N 776. – 10 ch. multicoloured 50 10
N 777. – 40 ch. multicoloured 95 15

349. Anti-aircraft Defences.

1967. Paintings of Guerrilla War against the Japanese. With gum.
N 778. **349.** 10 ch. blue 35 10
N 779. – 10 ch. purple .. 1·40 25
N 780. – 10 ch. violet .. 35 10
PAINTINGS: No. N 779, Blowing-up railway bridge. No. N 780, People helping guerrillas in Wangyugou.

1967. War Heroes (2nd series). As T **292.** Designs showing portraits and combat scenes. With gum.
N 781. 10 ch. slate 40 10
N 782. 10 ch. violet 40 10
N 783. 10 ch. blue 75 10
PORTRAITS: No. N 781, Li Dae Hun and grenade-throwing. No. N 782, Choe Jong Un and soldiers charging. No. N 783, Kim Hwa Ryong and air dog-fight.

350. Workers.

1967. Labour Day.
N 784. **350.** 10 ch. multicoloured 25 10

351. Card Game.

1967. Korean Children. Multicoloured.
N 785. 5 ch. Type **351** 55 10
N 786. 10 ch. Children modelling tractor 45 10
N 787. 40 ch. Children playing with ball 90 20

352. Victory Monument.

1967. Unveiling of Battle of Ponchonbo Monument.
N 788. **352.** 10 ch. multicoloured 30 10

353. Attacking Tank.

354. "Polygonatum japonicum".

1967. Monuments to War of 1950–53. 2 ch. with or without gum.
N 789. **353.** 2 ch. green & turquoise 20 10
N 790. – 5 ch. sepia and green 85 10
N 791. – 10 ch. brown and buff 30 10
N 792. – 40 ch. brown and blue 60 15
MONUMENTS: 5 ch. Soldier-musicians. 10 ch. Soldier. 40 ch. Soldier with children.

1967. Medicinal Plants. Multicoloured; background colour of 10 ch. values given to aid identification. Nos. 793/5 797 with or without gum.
N 793. 2 ch. Type **354** 35 10
N 794. 5 ch. "Hibiscus manihot" 40 10
N 795. 10 ch. "Scutellaria baicalensis" (turq.) 55 10
N 796. 10 ch. "Pulsatilla koreana" (blue) .. 55 10
N 797. 10 ch. "Rehmannian glutinosa" (yellow) .. 55 10
N 798. 40 ch. "Tanacetum boreale" .. .. 1·75 35

355. Servicemen.

1967. People's Army. Multicoloured. 5 ch. with or without gum.
N 799. 5 ch. Type **355** 20 10
N 800. 10 ch. Soldier & Farmer 25 10
N 801. 10 ch. Officer decorating soldier 25 10

356. Freighter "Chollima".

1967. With gum.
N 802. **356.** 10 ch. green .. 60 10

357. "Reclamation of Tideland".

1967. "Heroic Struggle of the Chollima Riders". Paintings. Without gum (5 ch.) or with gum (others).
N 803. – 5 ch. agate 40 10
N 804. **357.** 10 ch. slate 55 10
N 805. – 10 ch. green .. 55 10
DESIGNS—VERT. 5 ch. "Drilling Rock Precipice". 10 ch. (N 805), "Felling Trees".

358. "Erimaculus isenbeckii".

1967. Crabs. Multicoloured.
N 806. 2 ch. Type **358** 75 15
N 807. 5 ch. "Neptunus trituberculatus" 95 15
N 808. 10 ch. "Paralithodes camtschatica" .. 1·40 15
N 809. 40 ch. "Chionoecetes opilio" .. .. .. 2·25 40

359. Electric Train and Hand switching points.

1967. Propaganda for Reunification of Korea.
N 810. **359.** 10 ch. multicoloured 2·25 40

360. Tongrim Waterfall.

361. Chollima Flying Horse and Banners.

1967. Korean Waterfalls. 2 ch. with or without gum. Multicoloured.
N 811. 2 ch. Type **360** .. .. 1·75 15
N 812. 10 ch. Sanju waterfall, Mt. Myohyang .. 2·50 20
N 813. 40 ch. Sambang waterfall, Mt. Chonak .. 4·50 45

1967. "The Revolutionary Surge Upwards". Various designs incorporating the Chollima Flying Horse.
N 814. – 5 ch. blue 75 20
N 815. – 10 ch. red 25 10
N 816. – 10 ch. green .. 25 10
N 817. – 10 ch. lilac 25 10
N 818. **361.** 10 ch. red 20 10
DESIGNS—HORIZ. 5 ch. Ship, train and lorry (Transport). No. N 815, Bulldozers (Building construction). No. N 816, Tractors (Rural development). No. N 817, Heavy presses (Machine-building industry).

362. Lenin.

1967. 50th Anniv. of Russian October Revolution.
N 819. **362.** 10 ch. brn., yell. & red 25 10

363. Voters and Banner.

1967. Korean Elections. Multicoloured.
N 820. 10 ch. Type **363** .. 35 10
N 821. 10 ch. Woman casting vote (vert.) 35 10

364. European Black Vulture.

1967. Birds of Prey. Multicoloured. With gum.
N 822. 2 ch. Type **364** .. 1·50 25
N 823. 10 ch. Booted Eagle (horiz.) 2·75 35
N 824. 40 ch. White-bellied Sea Eagle .. 3·50 55

365. Chongjin.

1967. North Korean Cities. With gum.
N 825. **365.** 5 ch. green 45 10
N 826. – 10 ch. lilac 45 10
N 827. – 10 ch. violet .. 45 10
DESIGNS: No. N 826, Humhung. No. N 827, Sinuiju.

366. Kim Il Sung at Head of Columns.

1967. Battle of Pochonbo Monument. Detail of Monument. Multicoloured.
N 828. 10 ch. Type **366** .. 25 10
N 829. 10 ch. Head of right-hand column 25 10
N 830. 10 ch. Tail of right-hand column 25 10
N 831. 10 ch. Head of left-hand column 25 10
N 832. 10 ch. Tail of left-hand column 25 10
N 833. 10 ch. Centre of right-hand column 25 10
N 834. 10 ch. Centre of left-hand column 25 10
SIZES—HORIZ. Nos. N 829/32, 43×28 mm. Nos. 833/34, 56×28 mm.
The centrepiece of the Monument is flanked by two columns of soldiers, headed by Kim Il Sung.

367. Soldier brandishing Red Book.

1967. "Let us carry out the Decisions of the Workers' Party Conference!". Mult.
N 835. 10 ch. Type **367** .. 25 10
N 836. 10 ch. Militiaman holding bayonet 25 10
N 837. 10 ch. Foundryman and bayonet 25 10

368. Whaler firing Harpoon.

1967. With gum.
N 838. **368.** 10 ch. blue .. .. 1·25 25

369. Airman, Soldier and Sailor.

1968. 20th Anniv. of People's Army. Mult. With gum.
N 839. 10 ch. Type **369** .. 30 10
N 840. 10 ch. Soldier below attack in snow .. 30 10
N 841. 10 ch. Soldier below massed ranks .. 30 10
N 842. 10 ch. Soldier holding flag 30 10
N 843. 10 ch. Soldier holding book 30 10
N 844. 10 ch. Soldiers and armed workers with flag .. 30 10
N 845. 10 ch. Furnaceman and soldier 30 10
N 846. 10 ch. Soldier saluting 30 10
N 847. 10 ch. Charging soldiers
N 848. 10 ch. Soldier, sailor and airman below flag .. 30 10
30 10

1968. War Heroes (3rd series). As T **292**. With gum.

N 850. 10 ch. violet 25 10
N 851. 10 ch. purple 25 10

PORTRAITS: No. N 850, Han Gye Ryol firing Bren gun. No. N 851, Li Su Bok charging up hill.

370. Dredger "September 2".

371. Ten-storey Flats, East Pyongyang.

372. Palace of Students and Children, Kaesong.

1968. With gum.

N 852. **370.** 5 ch. green 30 10
N 853. **371.** 10 ch. blue 30 10
N 854. **372.** 10 ch. blue 30 10

373. Marshal Kim Il Sung.

1968. Marshal Kim Il Sung's 56th Birthday. With gum.

N 855. **373.** 40 ch. multicoloured 65 40

374. Kim Il Sung with Mother.

1968. Childhood of Kim Il Sung. Mult.

N856 10 ch. Type **374** .. 35 10
N857 10 ch. Kim Il Sung with his father 35 10
N858 10 ch. Setting out from home, aged 13 .. 35 10
N859 10 ch. Birthplace at Mangyongdae .. 35 10
N860 10 ch. Mangyong Hill .. 35 10

375. Matsu-take Mushroom

1968. Mushrooms. With gum.

N 861 **375** 5 ch. brown & green 2·00 25
N 862 – 10 ch. ochre, brown and green .. 3·25 35
N 863 – 10 ch. brown & grn 3·25 35

DESIGNS: No. N862, Black mushroom. No. N863, Cultivated mushroom.

376. Leaping Horseman.

1968. 20th Anniv. of Korean People's Democratic Republic. Mult. With gum.

N 864. 10 ch. Type **376** .. 70 10
N 865. 10 ch. Four servicemen 70 10
N 866. 10 ch. Soldier with bayonet 70 10
N 867. 10 ch. Advancing with banners 70 10
N 868. 10 ch. Statue 70 10
N 869. 10 ch. Korean flag .. 70 10
N 870. 10 ch. Soldier and peasant with flag 70 10
N 871. 10 ch. Machine-gunner with flag 70 10

377. Domestic Products.

378. Proclaiming the Ten Points.

1968. Development of Light Industries. Multicoloured. With gum.

N 872. 2 ch. Type **377** 25 10
N 873. 5 ch. Textiles .. .. 1·00 10
N 874. 10 ch. Tinned produce .. 40 40

1968. Kim Il Sung's Ten Point Political Programme. Multicoloured.

N 875. 2 ch. Type **378** 15 10
N 876. 5 ch. Soldier and artisan (horiz.) 20 10

379. Livestock.

1968. Development of Agriculture. Mult. With gum.

N 877. 5 ch. Type **379** 25 10
N 878. 10 ch. Fruit-growing .. 25 10
N 879. 10 ch. Wheat-harvesting 25 10

380. Scallop.

1968. Shellfish. Multicoloured. With gum.

N 880. 5 ch. Type **380** 75 10
N 881. 5 ch. Venus clam .. 75 10
N 882. 10 ch. Mussel .. .. 1·25 10

381. Museum of the Revolution, Pochonbo.

382. Grand Theatre, Pyongyang.

1968.

N 883. **381.** 2 ch. green 20 10
N 884. **382.** 10 ch. brown .. 65 10

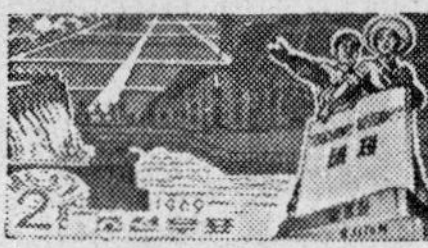

383. Irrigation.

1969. Rural Development. Multicoloured.

N 885. 3 ch. Type **383** 20 10
N 886. 5 ch. Agricultural mechanisation 20 10
N 887. 10 ch. Electrification .. 40 10
N 888. 40 ch. Applying fertilisers and spraying trees 60 10

384. Grey rabbits.

1969. Rabbits. Mult. With or without gum.

N 889. 2 ch. Type **384** 35 10
N 890. 10 ch. Black rabbits .. 35 10
N 891. 10 ch. Brown rabbits .. 35 10
N 892. 10 ch. White rabbits .. 35 10
N 893. 40 ch. Doe and young .. 1·10 15

385. "Age and Youth".

1969. Public Health Service.

N 894. **385.** 2 ch. brn. & bl. .. 35 10
N 895. – 10 ch. blue and red 65 10
N 896. – 40 ch. grn. & yell. 1·40 20

DESIGNS: 10 ch. Nurse with syringe. 40 ch. Auscultation by woman doctor.

386. Sowing Rice Seed.

1969. Agricultural Mechanisation.

N 897. **388.** 10 ch. green .. 45 10
N 898. – 10 ch. pink .. 45 10
N 899. – 10 ch. black .. 45 10
N 900. – 10 ch. brown .. 45 10

DESIGNS: No. N 898, Rice harvester. No. N 899, Weed-spraying machine. No. N 900, Threshing machine.

387. Ponghwa.

1969. Revolutionary Historical Sites. Multicoloured.

N 901. 10 c. Type **387** 25 10
N 902. 10 ch. Mangyongdae birthplace of Kim Il Sung 25 10

388. Kim crosses into Manchuria, 1926, aged 13.

1969. Kim Il Sung in Manchuria. Multicoloured. No. N907 with gum.

N 903. 10 ch. Type **388** 40 10
N 904. 10 ch. Leading strike of Yuwen Middle School boys, 1927 .. .. 40 10
N 905. 10 ch. Leading anti-Japanese demonstration in Kirin, 1928 .. 40 10
N 906. 10 ch. Presiding at meeting of Young Communist League, 1930 .. .. .. 40 10
N 907. 10 ch. Meeting of young revolutionaries .. 40 10

389. Birthplace at Chilgol.

1969. Commemoration of Mrs. Kang Ban Sok, mother of Kim Il Sung. Multicoloured.

N 908. 10 ch. Type **389** 30 10
N 909. 10 ch. With members of Women's Association 30 10
N 910. 10 ch. Resisting Japanese police .. .. .. 2·50 40

390. Pegaebong Bivouac.

1969. Bivouac Sites in the Guerrilla War against the Japanese. Multicoloured.

N 911. 5 ch. Type **390** 20 10
N 912. 10 ch. Mupo site (horiz.) 30 10
N 913. 10 ch. Chongbong site .. 30 10
N 914. 40 ch. Konchang site (horiz.) .. .. 1·00 20

391. Chollima Statue.

392. Museum of the Revolution, Pyongyang.

1969.

N 915. **391.** 10 ch. blue .. 25 10
N 916. **392.** 10 ch. green .. 25 10

393. Mangyong Chickens.

395. Statute of Marshal Kim Il Sung.

394. Marshal Kim Il Sung and Children.

1969. Korean Poultry.

N 917. **393.** 10 ch. blue .. 45 10
N 918. – 10 ch. violet .. 1·25 15

DESIGN: No. N 918, Kwangpo ducks.

1969. Kim Il Sung's Educational System. Multicoloured.

N 919. 2 ch. Type **394** 25 10
N 920. 10 ch Worker with books 25 10
N 921. 40 ch. Students with books 50 20

1969. Memorials on Pochonbo Battlefield. Inscr. "1937.6.4". Multicoloured.

N 922. 5 ch. Machine-gun post 25 10
N 923. 10 ch. Type **395** 25 10
N 924. 10 ch. "Aspen-tree" monument 25 10
N 925. 10 ch. Glade Konjang Hill 25 10

396. Teaching at Myongsin School.

1969. Commemoration of Kim Hyong Jik, father of Kim Il Sung. Multicoloured.

N 926. 10 ch. Type **396** 30 10
N 927. 10 ch. Secret meeting with Korean National Association members 30 10

397. Relay Runner.

1969. 20th Anniv. of Sports Day.

N 928. **397.** 10 ch. multicoloured 35 10

398. President Nixon attacked by Pens.

1969. Anti-U.S. Imperialism Journalists' Conference, Pyongyang.

N 929. **398.** 10 ch. multicoloured 35 10

399. Fighters and Battle.

1969. Implementation of Ten-point Programme of Kim Il Sung. Multicoloured.

N 930. 5 ch. Type **399** (Reunification of Korea) .. 20 10
N 931. 10 ch. Workers upholding slogan (vert.) .. 20 10

400. Bayonet Attack over U.S. Flag.

1969. Anti-American Campaign.

N 932. **400.** 10 ch. multicoloured 35 10

401. Armed Workers.

1969. Struggle for the Reunification of Korea. Multicoloured.

N 933. 10 ch. Workers stabbing U.S. soldier 20 10
N 934. 10 ch. Kim Il Sung and crowd with flags .. 20 10
N 935. 50 ch. Type **401** 50 20
Nos. N933/5 are vert.

402. Yellowtail.

1969. Korean Fishes. Multicoloured.

N936 5 ch. Type **402** 60 10
N937 10 ch. Dace 90 10
N938 40 ch. Mullet .. .. 1·75 25

403. Freighter "Taesungsan".

1969.

N 939. **403.** 10 ch. purple .. 60 10

405. Dahwangwai (1935).

1970. Guerrilla Conference Places.

N 940. **405.** 2 ch. blue & green 25 10
N 941. – 5 ch. brn. & grn... 25 10
N 942. – 10 ch. light green and green .. 25 10
DESIGNS: 5 ch. Yaoyinggou (barn) (1935). 10 ch. Xiaohaerbaling (tent) (1940).

406. Lake Chon. **407.** Vietnamese Soldier and Furnaceman.

1970. Mt. Paekdu, Home of Revolution (1st issue). Inscr. "1970".

N 943. **406.** 10 ch. black, brown and green .. 40 10
N 944. 10 ch. black, green and yellow .. 40 10
N 945. – 10 ch. purple, blue and yellow .. 40 10
N 946. – 10 ch. black, blue and pink .. 40 10
DESIGNS: No. N 944, Piryu Peak. No. N 945, Pyongsa (Soldier) Peak. No. N 946, Changgun (General) Peak.
See also Nos. 979/81.

1970. Help for the Vietnamese People.

N 947. **407.** 10 ch. green, brown and red 20 10

408. Receiving his Father's Revolvers from his Mother.

1970. Revolutionary Career of Kim Il Sung. Multicoloured.

N 948. 10 ch. Type **408** 65 20
N 949. 10 ch. Receiving smuggled weapons from his mother 65 20
N 950. 10 ch. Talking to farm workers 65 20
N 951. 10 ch. At Kalun meeting, 1930 .. .. .. 65 20

409. Lenin. **410.** March of Koreans.

1970. Birth Centenary of Lenin.

N 952. **409.** 10 ch. brn. & cinn... 30 10
N 953. – 10 ch. brown & green 30 10
DESIGN: No. N 953, Lenin making a speech.

1970. 15th Anniv. of Association of Koreans in Japan.

N 954. **410.** 10 ch. red 20 10
N 955. 10 ch. purple .. 20 10

411. Uniformed Factory Worker. **412.** Students and Newspapers.

1970. Workers' Militia.

N 956. **411.** 10 ch. grn., brn. & mve. 20 10
N 957. – 10 ch. grn., brn. & bl. 20 10
DESIGN—HORIZ. No. N 957, Militiaman saluting.

1970. Peasant Education. Multicoloured.

N 958. 2 ch. Type **412** .. 35 10
N 959. 5 ch. Peasant with book 20 10
N 960. 10 ch. Students in class 20 10

413. "Electricity Flows".

1970. Commemoration of Army Electrical Engineers.

N 961. **413.** 10 ch. brown .. 40 10

414. Soldier with Rifle.

1970. Campaign Month for Withdrawal of U.S. Troops from South Korea.

N 962. **414.** 5 ch. violet 15 10
N 963. – 10 ch. purple .. 30 10
DESIGN: 10 ch. Soldier and partisan.

415. Rebel wielding Weapons.

1970. Struggle in South Korea against U.S. Imperialism.

N 964. **415.** 10 ch. violet .. 20 10

416. Labourer ("Fertilisers"). **417.** Railway Guard.

1970. Encouragement of Increased Productivity.

N 965. **416.** 10 ch. grn., pink & brn. 30 10
N 966. – 10 ch. grn., red & brn. 50 10
N 967. – 10 ch. bl., grn. & brn. 30 10
N 968. – 10 ch. bistre, brn. & grn. 30 10
N 969. – 10 ch. vio., grn. & brn. 30 10
DESIGNS: No. N 966, Furnaceman ("Steel"). No. N 967, Operative ("Machines"). No. 968, Labourer ("Building Construction"). No. N 969, Miner ("Mining").

1970. "Speed the Transport System".

N 970. **417.** 10 ch. bl., orge. & grn. 65 15

418. Agriculture.

1970. Executive Decisions of the Workers' Party Congress. Designs embodying book.

N 971. **418.** 5 ch. red 20 10
N 972. 10 ch. green .. 70 15
N 973. – 40 ch. green .. 70 15
DESIGNS: 10 ch. Industry. 40 ch. The Armed Forces.

419. Chollima Statue and Workers' Party Banner. **421.** Emblem of League.

1970. 25th Anniv. of Korean Workers' Party.

N 974. **419.** 10 ch. red, brn. & buff 20 10

1971. 25th Anniv. of League of Socialist Working Youth.

N 976. **421.** 10 ch. red, brn. & bl. 15 10

422. Log Cabin, Nanhutou.

1971. 35th Anniv. of Nanhutou Guerrilla Conference.

N 977. **422.** 10 ch. multicoloured 20 10

423. Tractor Driver.

1971. 25th Anniv. of Land Reform Law.

N 978. **423.** 2 ch. red, grn. & blk. 20 10

1971. Mt. Paekdu, Home of Revolution (2nd issue). As T **406** but inscr "1971".

N 979. 2 ch. blk., olive & grn... 35 10
N 980. 5 ch. pink, blk. & slate.. 1·50 15
N 981. 10 ch. blk., red & grey .. 60 10
DESIGNS—HORIZ. 2 ch. General view. 10 ch. Western peak. VERT. 5 ch. Waterfall.

424. Popyong Museum.

1971. Museums of the Revolution.

N 982. **424.** 10 ch. brn. & yell. 20 10
N 983. – 10 ch. bl. & orge... 20 10
N 984. – 10 ch. grn. & orge. 20 10
DESIGNS: No. N 983, Mangyongdae Museum. No. N 984, Chunggang Museum.

425. Miner.

1971. Six Year Plan for Coal Industry.

N 985. **425.** 10 ch. multicoloured 40 10

426. Kim Il Sung.

1971. Founding of Anti-Japanese Guerrilla Army. Multicoloured.

N 986. 10 ch. Type **426** 35 10
N 987. 10 ch. Kim Il Sung founding Anti-Japanese Guerrilla Army 35 10
N 988. 10 ch. Kim Il Sung addressing the people 35 10
N 989. 10 ch. Kim Il Sung and members of Children's Corps 35 10

Nos. N 987/9 are horiz.

428. Hands holding Hammer and Rifle.

1971. 85th Anniv. of Labour Day.

N 990. **428.** 1 w. red, brown & buff .. .. 1·75 40

429. Soldiers and Map.

430. Monument.

1971. 35th Anniv. of Association for Restoration of Fatherland.

N 991. **429.** 10 ch. red, buff & black 35 10

1971. Battlefields in Musan Area, May 1939. Multicoloured.

N 992. 5 ch. Type **430** 15 10
N 993. 10 ch. Machine guns in perspex cases (horiz.) 20 10
N 994. 40 ch. Huts among birch trees (horiz.) 55 15

431. Koreans Marching.

432. Flame Emblem.

1971. Solidarity of Koreans in Japan.

N 995. **431.** 10 ch. brown .. 20 10

1971. 25th Anniv. of Korean Childrens' Union.

N 996. **432.** 10 ch. red, yellow and blue .. 20 10

433. Marchers and Banners.

434. Foundryman.

1971. 6th Congress of League of Socialist Working Youth.

N 997. **433.** 5 ch. red, buff & black 10 10
N 998. – 10 ch. red, green & black. 20 10

DESIGN: 10 c. Marchers and banner under globe.

1971. 25th Anniv. of Labour Law.

N 999. **434.** 5 ch. black, purple & buff 20 10

435. Young Women.

1971. 25th Anniv. of Sex Equality Law.

N 1000. **435.** 5 ch. multicoloured 20 10

436. Schoolchildren.

1971. 15th Anniv. of Compulsory Primary Education.

N 1001. **436.** 10 ch. multicoloured 35 10

437. Choe Yong Do and Combat Scene.

1971. Heroes of the Revolutionary Struggle in South Korea.

N 1002. **437.** 5 ch. black & grn. 25 10
N 1003. – 10 ch. red & brn. 25 10
N 1004. – 10 ch. black & red 25 10

DESIGNS: No. N 1003, Revolutionary with book. No. N 1004, Kim Jong Tae and scene of triumph.

438. Two Foundrymen.

1971. 25th Anniv. of Nationalization of Industry Law.

N 1005. **438.** 5 ch. black, green and brown .. 65 10

439. Struggle in Korea.

1971. The Anti-Imperialist and Anti-U.S. Imperialist Struggles.

N 1006. **439.** 10 ch. red, black and brown .. 15 10
N 1007. – 10 ch. brown, black and blue .. 25 10
N 1008. – 10 ch. red, black and pink .. 35 10
N 1009. – 10 ch. black, olive and green .. 15 10
N 1010. – 10 ch. orange, black and red .. 15 10
N 1011. – 40 ch. green, black and pink .. 35 15

DESIGNS: No. N 1007, Struggle in Vietnam. No. N 1008, Soldier with rifle and 'plane marked "EC". No. N 1009, Struggle in Africa. No. N 1010, Cuban soldier and Central America. No. N 1011, Bayonetting U.S. soldier.

440. Kim Il Sung University.

1971. 25th Anniv. of Kim Il Sung University.

N 1012. **440.** 10 ch. grey, red & yellow 20 10

441. Iron-ore Ladle (Mining).

1971. Tasks of Six Year Plan. Multicoloured.

N 1013. 10 ch. Type **441** .. 1·00 15
N 1014. 10 ch. Workers and text 20 10
N 1015. 10 ch. Railway track (Transport) .. 1·00 15
N 1016. 10 ch. Hand and wrench (Industry) .. 25 10
N 1017. 10 ch. Mechanical scoop (Construction) .. 1·00 15
N 1018. 10 ch. Manufactured goods (Trade) 25 10
N 1019. 10 ch. Crate on hoists (Exports) .. 20 10
N 1020. 10 ch. Lathe (Heavy Industries) .. .. 1·00 15
N 1021. 10 ch. Freighter (Shipping) 55 10
N 1022. 10 ch. Household equipment (Light Industries) .. 20 10
N 1023. 10 ch. Corncob and wheat (Agriculture) .. 30 10

442. Technicians.

1971. Cultural Revolution. Multicoloured.

N 1024. 2 ch. Type **442** .. 20 10
N 1025. 5 ch. Mechanic .. 25 10
N 1026. 10 ch. Schoolchildren 30 10
N 1027. 10 ch. Chemist .. 50 10
N 1028. 10 ch. Composer at piano 85 15

443. Workers with Red Books.

1971. Ideological Revolution. Mult.

N 1029. 10 ch. Type **443** .. 20 10
N 1030. 10 ch. Workers reading book 20 10
N 1031. 10 ch. Workers' lecture 20 10
N 1032. 10 ch. Worker and pneumatic drill .. 20 10

444. Korean Family.

1971. Improvement in Living Standards.

N 1033. **444.** 10 ch. multicoloured 15 10

445. Furnaceman.

1971. Implementation of Decisions of Fifth Workers' Party Conference.

N1034 **445** 10 ch. multicoloured 60 10

INDEX

Countries can be quickly located by referring to the index at the end of this volume.

446.

447. 6000-ton Press.

1971. Solidarity with South Korean Revolutionaries.

N1036 **446** 10 ch. brown, blue and black .. 30 10
N1037 – 10 ch. brown, flesh and red 30 10
N1038 – 10 ch. multicoloured 30 10
N1039 – 10 ch. multicoloured 30 10

DESIGNS—VERT. No. N 1037, U.S. soldier attacked by poster boards. No. N 1038, Hands holding rifles aloft. HORIZ. No. N 1039, Men advancing with rifles.

1971.

N 1040. 447. 2 ch. brown .. 50 10
N 1041. – 5 ch. blue 90 15
N 1042. – 10 ch. green .. 90 10
N 1043. – 10 ch. green .. 90 10

DESIGNS: No. N1041, Refrigerated freighter "Ponghwasan". No. N1042, 300 h.p. bulldozer. No. N1043, "Sungrisan" lorry.

448. Title-page and Militants.

1971. 35th Anniv. of "Samil Wolgan" Magazine.

N 1044. **448.** 10 ch. red, grn. & blk. 45 10

452. Poultry Chicks.

1972. Poultry Breeding.

N 1051. **452.** 5 ch. yellow, black & brown .. 25 10
N 1052. – 10 ch. orange, bistre and brown 35 10
N 1053. – 40 ch. blue, orange and deep blue .. 55 15

DESIGNS: 10 ch. Chickens and battery egg house. 40 ch. Eggs and fowls suspended from hooks.

453. Scene from "Village Shrine".

1972. Films of Guerrilla War.

N1054 **453** 10 ch. grey & green 60 10
N1055 – 10 ch. bl, pur & orge 60 10
N1056 – 10 ch. pur, bl & yell 60 10

DESIGNS: No. N1055, Patriot with pistol ("A Sea of Blood"). No. N1056, Guerrilla using bayonet ("The Lot of a Self-defence Corps Member").

454. Kim Il Sung acknowledging Greetings.

1972. Kim Il Sung's 60th Birthday. Scenes in the life of Kim Il Sung, dated "1912-1972". Multicoloured.

N1057 5 ch. Type **454** .. 20 10
N1058 5 ch. In campaign H.Q. 20 10
N1059 5 ch. Military conference (horiz) 20 10
N1060 10 ch. In wheatfield (horiz) 30 10
N1061 10 ch. Directing construction (horiz) 1·50 40
N1062 10 ch. Talking to foundry workers (horiz) 20 10
N1063 10 ch. Aboard whaler (horiz) 45 10
N1064 10 ch. Visiting a hospital (horiz) 40 10
N1065 10 ch. Viewing orchard (horiz) 20 10
N1066 10 ch. With survey party on Haeju-Hasong railway line (horiz) .. .. 1·50 40
N1067 10 ch. Meeting female workers at silk factory (horiz) .. 50 15
N1068 10 ch. Village conference (horiz) 20 10
N1069 10 ch. Touring chicken factory (horiz) .. 20 10
N1070 40 ch. Relaxing with children 45 20
N1071 1 wn. Giant portrait and marchers 70 40

455. Bugler sounding "Charge".

1972. 40th Anniv. of Guerrilla Army.

N 1073. **455.** 10 ch. multicoloured 45 10

456. Pavilion of Ryongpo.

1972. Historic Sites of the 1950-53 War. Multicoloured.

N 1074. 2 ch. Type **456** .. 15 10
N 1075. 5 ch. Houses at Onjong 15 10
N 1076. 10 ch. Headquarters, Kosanjin 15 10
N 1077. 40 ch. Victory Museum, Chonsung-dong .. . 30 10

457. Volleyball.

1972. Olympic Games, Munich. Multicoloured.

N 1078. 2 ch. Type **457** .. 25 10
N 1079. 5 ch. Boxing (horiz.) .. 35 10
N 1080. 10 ch. Judo 40 10
N 1081. 10 ch. Wrestling (horiz.) 40 10
N 1082. 40 ch. Rifle-shooting .. 95 10

458. Chollima Street, Pyongyang.

1971. Chollima Street, Pyongyang. Mult.

N 1083. 5 ch. Bridge and sky-scraper blocks .. 1·60 35
N 1084. 10 ch. Type **458** .. 60 15
N 1085. 10 ch. Another view of street 60 15

459. Dredger.

1972. Development of Natural Resources. Multicoloured.

N 1086. 5 ch. Type **459** .. 35 10
N 1087. 10 ch. Forestry .. 50 10
N 1088. 40 ch. Reclaiming land from the sea .. 60 15

460. Ferrous Industry.

1972. Tasks of the Six-Year Plan. The Metallurgical Industry. Inscr. "1971-1976". Multicoloured.

N 1089. 10 ch. Type **460** .. 80 10
N 1090. 10 ch. Non-ferrous Industry 40 10

461. Iron Ore Industry.

1972. Tasks of the Six-year Plan. The Mining Industry. Inscr. "1971-1976". Multicoloured.

N 1091. 10 ch. Type **461** .. 40 10
N 1092. 10 ch. Coal mining industry .. .. 1·10 15

462. Electronic and Automation Industry.

1972. Tasks of the Six-Year Plan. The Engineering Industry. Inscr. "1971-1976". Multicoloured.

N 1093. 10 ch. Type **462** .. 40 10
N 1094. 10 ch. Single-purpose machines 40 10
N 1095. 10 ch. Machine tools .. 40 10

463. Clearing Virgin Soil.

1972. Tasks of the Six-Year Plan. Rural Economy. Multicoloured.

N 1096. 10 ch. Type **463** .. 45 10
N 1097. 10 ch. Irrigation .. 45 10
N 1098. 10 ch. Harvesting .. 45 10

464. Automation.

1972. Tasks of the Six-Year Plan. Inscr. "1971-1976". Multicoloured.

N 1099. 10 ch. Type **464** .. 60 10
N 1100. 10 ch. Agricultural mechanisation .. 45 10
N 1101. 10 ch. Lightening of house-hold chores .. 45 10

465. Chemical Fibres and Materials.

1972. Tasks of the Six-Year Plan. The Chemical Industry. Inscr. "1971-1976". Multicoloured.

N 1102. 10 ch. Type **465** .. 45 10
N 1103. 10 ch. Fertilisers, insecticides and weed killers 45 10

466. Textiles.

1972. Tasks of the Six-Year Plan. Consumer Goods Inscr. "1971-1976". Multicoloured.

N 1104. 10 ch. Type **466** .. 45 10
N 1105. 10 ch. Kitchen ware and overalls .. 45 10
N 1106. 10 ch. Household goods 45 10

467. Fish, Fruit and Vegetables.

1972. Tasks of the Six-Year Plan. The Food Industry. Multicoloured.

N 1107. 10 ch. Type **467** .. 45 10
N 1108. 10 ch. Tinned foods .. 45 10
N 1109. 10 ch. Food packaging 45 10

468. Electrifying Railway Lines.

1972. Tasks of the Six-Year Plan. Transport. Inscr. "1971–1976". Multicoloured.

N 1110. 10 ch. Type **468** .. 35 10
N 1111. 10 ch. Laying new railway track 35 10
N 1112. 10 ch. Freighters .. 40 10

469. Soldier with Shell.

1972. North Korean Armed Forces. Multicoloured.

N 1113. 10 ch. Type **469** .. 35 10
N 1114. 10 ch. Marine 35 10
N 1115. 10 ch. Air Force pilot 35 10

470. "Revolution of 19 April 1960".

1972. The Struggle for Reunification of Korea. Multicoloured.

N1116 10 ch. Type **470** .. 15 10
N1117 10 ch. Marchers with banners 15 10
N1118 10 ch. Insurgents with red banner 15 10
N1119 10 ch. Attacking U.S. and South Korean soldiers 15 10
N1120 10 ch. Workers with posters 15 10
N1121 10 ch. Workers acclaiming revolution .. 1·75 45
N1122 10 ch. Workers and manifesto 15 10

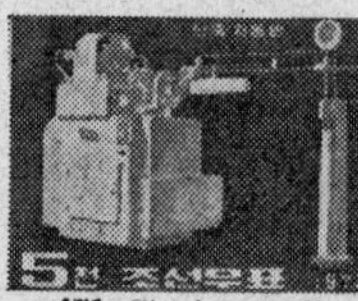

471. Single-spindle Automatic Lathe.

1972. Machine Tools.

N 1123. **471.** 5 ch. green & pur. 25 10
N 1124. – 10 ch. blue & grn. 35 10
N 1125. – 40 ch. grn. & brn. 80 15

DESIGNS—HORIZ. 10 ch. "Kusong-3" lathe. VERT. 40 ch. 2,000 ton crank press.

472. Casting Vote.

1972. National Elections. Multicoloured.

N 1126. 10 ch. Type **472** .. 25 10
N 1127. 10 ch. Election campaigner 25 10

475. Soldier.

1973. 25th Anniv. of Founding of Korean People's Army. Multicoloured.

N 1130. 5 ch. Type **475** .. 20 10
N 1131. 10 ch. Sailor 30 10
N 1132. 40 ch. Airman 70 25

476. Wrestling Site.

1973. Scenes of Kim Il Sung's Childhood, Mangyongdae. Multicoloured.

N 1133. 2 ch. Type **476** .. 15 10
N 1134. 5 ch. Warship rock .. 15 10
N 1135. 10 ch. Swinging site (vert.) 20 10
N 1136. 10 ch. Sliding rock .. 20 10
N 1137. 40 ch. Fishing site .. 60 15

477. Monument to Socialist Revolution and Construction, Mansu Hill.

1973. Museum of the Korean Revolution.

N1138 **477** 10 ch. multicoloured 25 10
N1139 – 10 ch. multicoloured 25 10
N1140 – 40 ch. multicoloured 50 15
N1141 – 3 wn. green & yell 2·50 60

DESIGNS—As Type **477**: 10 ch. (No. 1139) Similar monument but men in military clothes. 40 ch. Statue of Kim Il Sung. HORIZ. (60 × 29 mm): 3 wn. Museum building.

478. Karajibong Camp.

1973. Secret Camps by Tuman-Gang in Guerrilla War, 1932. Multicoloured.

N 1142. 10 ch. Type **478** .. 15 10
N 1143. 10 ch. Soksaegol Camp 15 10

479.

1973. Menace of Japanese Influence in South Korea.

N 1144. **479.** 10 ch. multicoloured 20 10

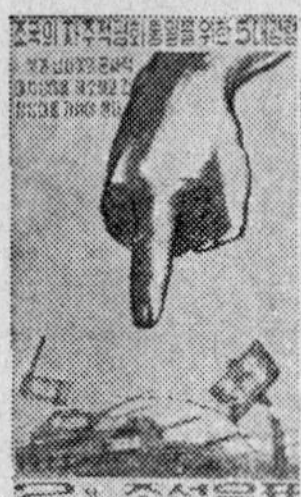
480. Wrecked U.S. Tanks.

1973. Five-point Programme for Reunification of Korea. Multicoloured.

N 1145	2 ch. Type **480** ..	25	10
N 1146	5 ch. Train and crane lifting tractor ..	1·40	15
N 1147	10 ch. Leaflets falling on crowd	15	10
N 1148	10 ch. Hand holding leaflet and map of Korea	25	10
N 1149	40 ch. Banner and globe	40	20

481. Lorries.

482. Volleyball.

1973. Lorries and Tractors. Multicoloured.

N1150	10 ch. Type **481** ..	35	10
N1151	10 ch. Tractors and earth-moving machine	35	10

1973. Socialist Countries' Junior Women's Volleyball Games, Pyongyang.

N 1152. **482.** 10 ch. multicoloured 30 10

483. Battlefield.

1973. 20th Anniv. of Victory in Korean War.

N 1153.	**483.**	10 ch. green, red and black ..	20	10
N 1154.	–	10 ch. brown, blue and black ..	20	10

Design: 10 ch. Urban fighting.

484. "The Snow Falls".

1973. Mansudae Art Troupe. Dances. Multicoloured.

N 1155.	10 ch. Type **481** ..	50	10
N 1156.	25 ch. "A Bumper Harvest of Apples"	1·10	25
N 1157.	40 ch. "Azalea of the Fatherland" ..	1·40	30

485. Schoolchildren.

1973. Ten Years Compulsory Secondary Education.

N 1158. **485.** 10 ch. multicoloured 25 10

486. "Fervour in the Revolution".

1973. The Works of Kim Il Sung. (1st series).

N 1159.	**486.**	10 ch. brown, red and yellow. ..	15	10
N 1160.	–	10 ch. brown, green and yellow ..	15	10
N 1161.	–	10 c. lake, brown and yellow ..	15	10

Designs: No. N 1160, Selected works. No. N 1161, "Strengthen the Socialist System".

See also Nos. N 1217/8.

487. Celebrating Republic.

1973. 25th Anniv. of People's Republic. Multicoloured.

N 1162.	5 ch. Type **487** ..	10	10
N 1163.	10 ch. Fighting in Korean War	10	10
N 1164.	40 ch. Peace and reconstruction	1·60	40

488. Pobwang Peak.

1973. Mt. Myohyang. Multicoloured.

N 1165.	2 ch. Type **488** ..	25	10
N 1166.	5 ch. Inhodae Pavilion	35	10
N 1167.	10 ch. Taeha Falls (vert.)	1·25	30
N 1168.	40 ch. Rongyon Falls (vert.)	1·75	30

489. Party Memorial Building.

1973. Party Memorial Building.

N 1169. **489.** 1 wn. brown, grey and buff 95 30

490. Football and Handball.

1973. National People's Sports Meeting. Mult.

N 1170.	2 ch. Type **490** ..	50	10
N 1171.	5 ch. High jumper and woman sprinter ..	25	10
N 1172.	10 ch. Skaters and skiers	40	10
N 1173.	10 ch. Wrestling and swinging	30	10
N 1174.	40 ch. Parachutist and motor cyclists ..	1·60	25

491. Weightlifting.

492. Chongryu Cliff.

1973. Junior Weightlifting Championships of Socialist Countries.

N 1175. **491.** 10 ch. blue, brown and green .. 25 10

1973. Scenery of Moran Hill, Pyongyang. Multicoloured.

N 1176.	2 ch. Type **492** ..	40	15
N 1177.	5 ch. Moran Waterfall	1·75	40
N 1178.	10 ch. Pubyok Pavilion	50	10
N 1179.	40 ch. Ulmil Pavilion	65	15

493. Rainbow Bridge.

494. Magnolia Flower.

1973. Diamond Mountains Scenery (4th issue). Multicoloured.

N 1180.	2 ch. Type **493** ..	85	15
N 1181.	5 ch. Suspension foot-bridge, Okryudong (horiz.)	85	15
N 1182.	10 ch. Chonnyo Peak ..	50	10
N 1183.	10 ch. Chilchung Rock and Sonji peak (horiz.)	50	10
N 1184.	40 ch. Sujong and Pari Peaks (horiz.) ..	60	15

1973.

N 1185. **494.** 10 ch. multicoloured 40 10

495. S. Korean Revolutionaries.

1973. South Korean Revolution. Mult.

N 1186.	10 ch. Type **495** ..	15	10
N 1187.	10 ch. Marching revolutionaries	15	10

496. Cock sees Butterflies.

1973. Scenes from "Cock Chasing Butterflies". Fairy Tale. Multicoloured.

N 1188.	2 ch. Type **496** ..	75	10
N 1189.	5 ch. Butterflies discuss how to repel cock ..	90	10
N 1190.	10 ch. Cock chasing butterflies with basket	1·40	15
N 1191.	10 ch. Cock chasing butterfly up cliff ..	1·60	20
N 1192.	40 ch. Cock chasing butterflies over cliff	1·90	25
N 1193.	90 ch. Cock falls into sea and butterflies escape	2·40	30

497. Yonpung.

1973. Historical Sites of War and Revolution (40 ch.). Multicoloured.

N 1196.	2 ch. Type **497** ..	10	10
N 1197.	5 ch. Hyangha ..	10	10
N 1198.	10 ch. Changgol ..	15	10
N 1199.	40 ch. Paeksong ..	55	10

498. Science Library, Kim Il Sung University.

1973. New Buildings in Pyongyang.

N 1200.	**498.**	2 ch. violet ..	50	10
N 1201.	–	5 ch. green ..	15	10
N 1202.	–	10 ch. brown ..	25	10
N 1203.	–	40 ch. brown & buff	55	10
N 1204.	–	90 ch. buff ..	95	15

Designs—horiz. 10 ch. Victory Museum. 40 ch. People's Palace of Culture. 90 ch. Indoor stadium. vert. 5 ch. Building No. 2, Kim Il Sung University.

499. Red Book.

1973. Socialist Constitution of North Korea. Multicoloured.

N 1205.	10 ch. Type **499** ..	15	10
N 1206.	10 ch. Marchers with red book & banners	15	10
N 1207.	10 ch. Marchers with red book & emblem	15	10

500. Oriental Great Reed Warbler.

1973. Korean Songbirds. Multicoloured.

N1208	5 ch. Type **500** ..	1·25	15
N1209	10 ch. Grey starling (facing right) ..	1·75	20
N1210	10 ch. Daurian starling (facing left)	1·75	20

503. Chollima Statue.

1974. The works of Kim Il Sung (2nd series). Multicoloured.

N 1217.	10 ch. Type **503** ..	65	10
N 1218.	10 ch. Bayonets threatening U.S. soldier ..	15	10

504. Train in Station.

1974. Opening of Pyongyang Metro. **Mult.**

N 1219. 10 ch. Type **504** .. 45 10
N 1220. 10 ch. Escalators .. 45 10
N 1221. 10 ch. Station Hall .. 45 10

505. Capital Construction Front.

1974. Five Fronts of Socialist Construction. Multicoloured.

N 1222. 10 ch. Type **505** .. 15 10
N 1223. 10 ch. Agricultural front 25 10
N 1224. 10 ch. Transport front 75 15
N 1225. 10 ch. Fisheries front .. 50 10
N 1226. 10 ch. Industrial front (vert.) 25 10

506. Marchers with Banners.

1974. 10th Anniv. of Publication of "Theses on the Socialist Rural Question in Our Country". Multicoloured.

N 1227. 10 ch. Type **506** .. 15 10
N 1228. 10 ch. Book and rejoicing crowd 15 10
N 1229. 10 ch. Tractor & banners 15 10

Nos. 1227/9 were issued together se-tenant forming a composite design.

507. Manure Spreader.

1974. Farm Machinery.

N 1230. **507.** 2 ch. grn., blk. & red 40 10
N 1231. – 5 ch. red, blk. & bl. 40 10
N 1232. – 10 ch. red, blk. & grn. 40 10

DESIGNS: 5 ch. "Progress" tractor. 10 ch. "Mount Taedoksan" tractor.

508. Archery (Grenoble).

1974. North Korean Victories at International Sports Meetings. Multicoloured.

N1233 2 ch. Type **508** .. 65 15
N1234 5 ch. Gymnastics (Varna) 15 10
N1235 10 ch. Boxing (Bucharest) 25 10
N1236 20 ch. Volleyball (Pyongyang) .. 15 10
N1237 30 ch. Rifle shooting (Sofia) 45 10
N1238 40 ch. Judo (Tbilisi) .. 65 15
N1239 60 ch. Model aircraft flying (Vienna) (horiz) 95 20
N1240 1 wn. 50 Table tennis (Peking) (horiz) .. 1·75 30

INDEX

Countries can be quickly located by referring to the index at the end of this volume.

509. Book and rejoicing Crowd.

1974. First Country with No Taxes.

N 1241. **509.** 10 ch. multicoloured 20 10

510. Drawing up Programme in Woods.

1974. Kim Il Sung during the Anti-Japanese Struggle. Multicoloured.

N 1242. 10 ch. Type **510** .. 25 10
N 1243. 10 ch. Giving directions to Pak Dal 25 10
N 1244. 10 ch. Presiding over Nanhutou Conference 25 10
N 1245. 10 ch. Supervising creation of strongpoint 25 10

511. Sun Hui loses her Sight.

1974. Scences from "The Flower Girl" (revolutionary opera). Multicoloured.

N 1246. 2 ch. Type **511** .. 40 10
N 1247. 5 ch. Death of Ggot Bun's mother 40 10
N 1248. 10 ch. Ggot Bun throws boiling water at landlord 75 10
N 1249. 40 ch. Ggot Bun joins revolutionaries .. 1·25 15

512. Leopard Cat.

1974. 15th Anniv. of Pyongyang Zoo. Multicoloured.

N 1251. 2 ch. Type **512** .. 50 10
N 1252. 5 ch. Lynx 50 10
N 1253. 10 ch. Red fox .. 50 10
N 1254. 10 ch. Wild boar .. 50 10
N 1255. 20 ch. Dhole 50 15
N 1256. 40 ch. Brown bear .. 60 25
N 1257. 60 ch. Leopard .. 1·00 25
N 1258. 70 ch. Tiger .. .. 1·40 30
N 1259. 90 ch. Lion .. .. 1·75 35

513. "Rosa acucularis lindly".

1974. Roses. Multicoloured.

N1261 2 ch. Type **513** .. 40 10
N1262 5 ch. Yellow sweet briar 45 10
N1263 10 ch. Pink aromatic rose 55 10
N1264 10 ch. Aronia sweet briar (yellow centres) 55 10
N1265 40 ch. Multi-petal sweet briar .. .. 1·40 10

515. Weigela.

1974. Flowering Plants of Mt. Paekdu. Mult.

N 1267. 2 ch. Type **515** .. 30 10
N 1268. 5 ch. Amaryllis .. 30 10
N 1269. 10 ch. Red lily .. 30 10
N 1270. 20 ch. Orange lily .. 40 10
N 1271. 40 ch. Azalea 65 10
N 1272. 60 ch. Yellow lily .. 1·10 10

516. Postwoman and Construction Site.

1974. Cent of U.P.U. and Admission of North Korea to Union. Multicoloured.

N 1273. 10 ch. Type **516** .. 1·25 15
N 1274. 25 ch. Chollima monument.. .. .. 10 10
N 1275. 40 ch. Globe and airliners 90 15

517. "Rana nigromaculata".

1974. Frogs and Toad. Multicoloured.

N 1276. 2 ch. Type **517** .. 50 10
N 1277. 5 ch. "Bombina orientalis" 60 10
N 1278. 10 ch. "Rana catesbiana" 75 15
N 1279. 40 ch. "Bufo bufo" .. 1·60 25

518. "Women of Namgang Village".

1974. Korean Paintings. Multicoloured.

N1281 2 ch. Type **518** .. 50 10
N1282 5 ch. "An Old Man on the Rakdong River" (60 × 49 mm) .. 60 10
N1283 10 ch. "Morning in the Nae-kumgang" (bridge) 75 10
N1284 20 ch. "Mt. Kumgang" (60 × 49 mm) .. 1·00 15

519. "Elektron 1" and "Elektron 2", 1964.

1974. Cosmonauts Day. Multicoloured.

N 1286. 10 ch. Type **519** .. 15 10
N 1287. 20 ch. "Proton 1", 1965 25 10
N 1288. 30 ch. "Venera 3", 1966 40 10
N 1289. 40 ch. "Venera 5" and "Venera 6", 1969 .. 50 10

521.

1974. Civil Aviation.

N 1292. **521.** 2 ch. mult. .. 30 10
N 1293. – 5 ch. mult. .. 30 10
N 1294. – 10 ch. mult. .. 40 10
N 1295. – 40 ch. mult. .. 75 25
N 1296. – 60 ch. mult. .. 1·25 50

DESIGNS: 5 ch. to 60 ch. Various aircraft.

522. "Rhododendron redowskianum".

1974. Plants of Mt. Paekdu. Multicoloured.

N1298 2 ch. Type **522** .. 35 10
N1299 5 ch. "Dryas octopetala" 35 10
N1300 10 ch. "Potentilla fruticosa" 40 10
N1301 20 ch. "Papaver somniferum" 50 10
N1302 40 ch. "Phyllodoce caerulea 70 20
N1303 60 ch. "Oxytropis anertii" .. .. 1·25 40

523. "Sobaek River in the Morning".

1974. Modern Korean Paintings. (1st series). Multicoloured.

N 1304. 10 ch. Type **523** .. 60 10
N 1305. 20 ch. "Combatants of Mt. Laohei" (60 × 40 mm.) .. 65 10
N 1306. 30 ch. "Spring in the Fields" 75 15
N 1307. 40 ch "Tideland Night" 2·50 20
N 1308. 60 ch. "Daughter" (60 × 54 mm.) .. 90 40

See also Nos. N 1361/5, N 1386/96 and N 1485/9.

525. Log cabin, Unha Village.

1974. Historic Sites of the Revolution.

N 1310. – 5 ch. mult. .. 10 10
N 1311. **525.** 10 ch. mult. .. 10 10

DESIGN: 5 ch. Munmyong.

526. Sesame.

1974. Oil-producing Plants. Multicoloured.

N 1312. 2 ch. Type **526** .. 40 10
N 1313. 5 ch. "Perilla frutescens" 45 10
N 1314. 10 ch. Sunflower .. 50 10
N 1315. 40 ch. Castor bean .. 85 40

527. Kim Il Sung as Guerrilla Leader.

1974. Kim Il Sung. Multicoloured.

N 1316.	10 ch. Type **527** ..	20	10
N 1317.	10 ch. Commander of the People's Army (52 × 35 mm.)	20	10
N 1318.	10 ch. "The commander is also a son of the people" (52 × 35 mm.)	20	10
N 1319.	10 ch. Negotiating with the Chinese anti-Japanese unit (52 × 35 mm.)	20	10

528.

1974. Grand Monument on Mansu Hill. Mult.

N 1320.	10 ch. Type **528** ..	15	10
N 1321.	10 ch. As T **528** but men in civilian clothes	15	10
N 1322.	10 ch. As T **528** but men facing left ..	15	10
N 1323.	10 ch. As No. N 1322 but men in civilian clothes	15	10

529. Factory Ship "Chilbosan".

1974. Deep-sea Fishing. Multicoloured.

N1324	2 ch. Type **529** ..	70	25
N1325	5 ch. Trawler support ship "Paekdusan" ..	70	25
N1326	10 ch. Freighter "Moranbong" ..	70	25
N1327	20 ch. Whale-catcher ..	70	25
N1328	30 ch. Trawler ..	70	25
N1329	40 ch. Stern trawler ..	70	25

539. Kim Il Sung crosses River Agrok.

1975. 50th Anniv. of Kim Il Sung's crossing of River Agrok.

N 1349.	**539.**	10 ch. mult. ..	25	10

540. Pak Yong Sun " World Table Tennis Queen ".

1975. Pak Yong Sun, Winner of 33rd World Table Tennis Championships, Calcutta.

N 1350.	**540.**	10 ch. multicoloured	50	10

541. Common Zebra.

1975. Pyongyang Zoo. Multicoloured.

N 1352.	10 ch. Type **541** ..	30	10
N 1353.	10 ch. African buffalo	30	10
N 1354.	20 ch. Giant panda (horiz.)	80	10
N 1355.	25 ch. Bactrian camel	70	15
N 1356.	30 ch. Indian elephant	1·25	20

542. " Blue Dragon ".

1975. 7th-century Mural Paintings from Koguryo Tombs, Kangso.

N 1357.	10 ch. Type **542**	65	10
N 1358.	15 ch. " White Tiger "	85	10
N 1359.	25 ch. " Red Phoenix " (vert.)	1·00	10
N 1360.	40 ch. " Snake-turtle "	1·40	25

543. " Spring in the Guerrilla Base " (1968).

1975. Modern Korean Paintings (2nd series). Anti-Japanese struggle. Multicoloured.

N1361	10 ch. Type **543** ..	35	10
N1362	10 ch. "Revolutionary Army landing at Unggi" (1969) ..	35	10
N1363	15 ch. "Sewing Team Members" (1961) ..	55	10
N1364	20 ch. "Girl Watering Horse" (1969) ..	1·00	15
N1365	30 ch. "Kim Jong Suk giving Guidance to Children's Corps" (1970)	80	20

544. Cosmonaut.

1975. Cosmonaut's Day. Multicoloured.

N1366	10 ch. Type **544** ..	15	10
N1367	30 ch. "Lunokhod" moon vehicle (horiz)	40	10
N1368	40 ch. "Soyuz" spacecraft and "Salyut" space laboratory (horiz)	55	15

546. The Beacon lit at Pochonbo, 1937.

1975. Kim Il Sung during the Guerrilla War against the Japanese. Multicoloured.

N 1370.	10 ch. Type **546** ..	25	10
N 1371.	10 ch. "A Bowl of Parched-rice Powder", 1938 ..	25	10
N 1372.	10 ch. Guiding the Nanpaizi meeting, November, 1938 ..	25	10
N 1373.	10 ch. Welcoming helpers	25	10
N 1374.	10 ch. Lecturing the guerrillas	25	10
N 1375.	15 ch. Advancing into the homeland, May 1939	35	10
N 1376.	25 ch. By Lake Samji, May 1939	45	10
N 1377.	30 ch. At Sinsadong, May 1939	55	10
N 1378.	40 ch. Xiaohaerbaling meeting, 1940 ..	65	15

547. Vase of Flowers and Kim Il Sung's Birthplace.

1975. Kim Il Sung's 63rd Birthday. Mult.

N1379	10 ch. Type **547** ..	10	10
N1379a	40 ch. Kim Il Sung's birthplace, Mangyongdae	35	10

548. South Korean Insurgent.

1975. 15th Anniv. of April 19th Rising.

N 1380.	**548.**	10 ch. multicoloured	15	10

549. "Kingfisher at a Lotus Pond".

1975. Paintings of Li Dynasty. Mult.

N 1381.	5 ch. Type **549** ..	1·10	10
N 1382.	10 ch. "Crabs" ..	75	10
N 1383.	15 ch. "Rose of Sharon"	1·10	15
N 1384.	25 ch. "Lotus and Water Cock ..	1·50	30
N 1385.	30 ch. "Tree Peony and Red Junglefowl" ..	2·25	30

1975. Modern Korean Paintings (3rd series). Fatherland Liberation War. Dated designs at T **543**. Multicoloured.

N 1386.	5 ch. "On the Advance Southward" (1966) (vert.)	20	10
N 1387.	10 ch. "The Assigned Post" (girl sentry) (1968) (vert) ..	25	10
N 1388.	15 ch. "The Herosim of Li Su Bok" (1965) ..	30	10
N 1389.	25 ch. "Retaliation" (woman machine-gunner) (1970) ..	50	20
N 1390.	30 ch. "The awaited Troops" (1970) ..	60	20

1975. Modern Korean Paintings 4th series). Socialist Construction. Dated designs as T **543**. Multicoloured.

N 1391.	10 ch. "Pine Tree' (1966) (vert.) ..	45	10
N 1392.	10 ch. "The Blue Signal Lamp" (1960) (vert.)	1·40	10
N 1393.	15 ch. "A Night of Snowfall" (1963) ..	50	10
N 1394.	20 ch. "Smelters" (1968)	60	15
N 1395.	25 ch. "Tideland Reclamation" (1961) ..	60	15
N 1396.	30 ch. "Mount Paekdusan" (1966)	60	20

550. Flag and Building. **552.** " Feet first " entry (man).

1975. 20th Anniv. of "Chongryon" Assn. of Koreans in Japan.

N1397	**550**	10 ch. multicoloured	15	10
N1398		3 wn. multicoloured	2·50	55

1975. Diving. Multicoloured.

N 1400.	10 ch. Type **552** ..	15	10
N 1401.	25 ch. Piked somersault (man)	40	10
N 1402.	40 ch. " Head first " entry (woman) ..	85	15

553.

1975. Campaign against U.S. Imperialism.

N 1403.	**553.**	10 ch. multicoloured	15	10

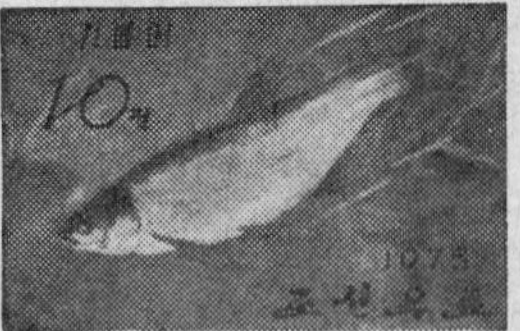

554. Memorial Fish.

1975. Fresh-water Fish. Multicoloured.

N 1404.	10 ch. Type **554** ..	40	10
N 1405.	10 ch. Whitefish (fish swimming to right)	40	10
N 1406.	15 ch. "Opsanichthys bidens"	60	10
N 1407.	25 ch. Naere	1·00	15
N 1408.	30 ch. Catfish (fish swimming to right)	1·25	20
N 1409.	30 ch. Snakehead (fish swimming to left) ..	1·25	20

MINIMUM PRICE

The minimum price quoted is 5p which represents a handling charge rather than a basis for valuing common stamps. For further notes about prices see introductory pages.

555.

1975. 10th Socialist Countries' Football Tournament, Pyongyang.

N 1410. 555. 5 ch. multicoloured 25 10
N 1411. – 10 ch. multicoloured 25 10
N 1412. – 15 ch. multicoloured 30 10
N 1413. – 20 ch. multicoloured 40 15
N 1414. – 50 ch. multicoloured 75 35

DESIGNS: 10 ch. to 50 ch. Various footballers.

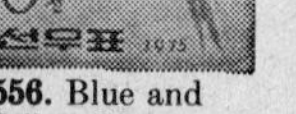

556. Blue and Yellow Macaw.

557. Flats.

1975. Birds. Multicoloured.

N 1416. 10 ch. Type **556** .. 90 10
N 1417. 15 ch. Sulphur-crested cockatoo .. .. 1·10 10
N 1418. 20 ch. Blyth's parakeet .. .. .. 1·40 20
N 1419. 25 ch. Rainbow lory .. 1·60 30
N 1420. 30 ch. Budgerigar .. 1·90 30

1975. New Buildings in Pyongyang. Mult.

N 1421. 90 ch. Saesallim (formerly Sangwon) St. .. 1·50 40
N 1422. 1 wn. Type **557** .. 1·75 45
N 1423. 2 wn. Potonggang Hotel 2·75 60

558. White Peach Blossom.

559. Sejongbong.

1975. Blossoms of Flowering Trees. Mult.

N 1424. 10 ch. Type **558** .. 30 10
N 1425. 15 ch. Red peach blossom 30 10
N 1426. 20 ch. Red plum blossom 45 15
N 1427. 25 ch. Apricot blossom 60 15
N 1428. 30 ch. Cherry blossom 85 20

1975. Landscapes in the Diamond Mountains. Multicoloured.

N 1429. 5 ch. Type **559** .. 40 10
N 1430. 10 ch. Chonsondae .. 65 10
N 1431. 15 ch. Pisamun .. 85 10
N 1432. 25 ch. Manmulsang .. 1·10 20
N 1433. 30 ch. Chaehabong .. 1·25 20

560. Azalea.

1975. Flowers of the Azalea Family. Mult.

N 1434. 5 ch. Type **560** .. 35 10
N 1435. 10 ch. White Azalea .. 35 10
N 1436. 15 ch. Wild Rhododendron 50 10
N 1437. 20 ch. White Rhododendron 50 15
N 1438. 25 ch. Rhododendron 65 15
N 1439. 30 ch. Yellow Rhododendron 90 20

561. Gliders.

1975. Training for National Defence. Mult.

N 1440. 5 ch. Type **561** .. 30 10
N 1441. 5 ch. Radio-controlled model aircraft .. 30 10
N 1442. 10 ch. "Free fall parachutist" (vert.) .. 45 10
N 1443. 10 ch. Parachutist landing on target (vert.) 45 10
N 1444. 20 ch. Parachutist with bouquet of flowers (vert.) 55 15

562. Wild Apple.

1975. Fruit Tree Blossom. Multicoloured.

N1446 10 ch. Type **562** .. 30 10
N1447 15 ch. Wild pear .. 30 10
N1448 20 ch. Hawthorn .. 40 15
N1449 25 ch. Chinese quince .. 55 15
N1450 30 ch. Flowering quince 65 60

563. Torch of Juche.

1975. 30th Anniv. of Korean Workers' Party. Multicoloured.

N 1451. 2 ch. "Victory" and American graves .. 10 10
N 1452. 2 ch. Sunrise over Mt. Paekdu-san.. .. 10 10
N 1453. 5 ch. Type **563** .. 10 10
N 1454. 5 ch. Chollima Statue and sunset over Pyongyang 10 10
N 1455. 10 ch. Korean with Red Book 10 10
N 1456. 10 ch. Chollima Statue 10 10
N 1457. 25 ch. Crowds and burning building .. 35 10
N 1458. 70 ch. Flowers and map of Korea 95 15

564. Welcoming Crowd.

1975. 30th Anniv. of Kim Il Sung's Return to Pyongyang.

N 1460. **564.** 20 ch. multicoloured 25 15

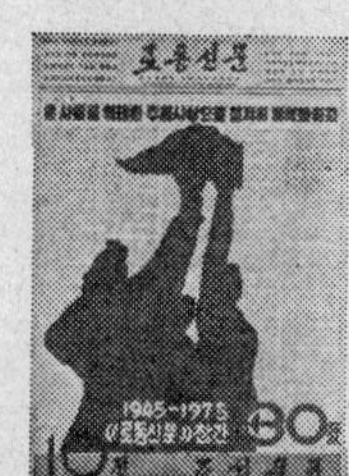

565. Workers holding "Juche" Torch.

1975. 30th Anniv. of "Rodong Simmun" (Journal of the Central Committee of the Worker's Party.)

N 1461. **565.** 10 ch. multicoloured 50 10

566. Hyonmu Gate.

1975. Ancient Wall-Gates of Pyongyang. Multicoloured.

N 1463 10 ch. Type **566** .. 10 10
N 1464 10 ch. Taedong Gate .. 10 10
N 1465 15 ch. Potong Gate .. 20 10
N 1466 20 ch. Chongum Gate 35 15
N 1467 30 ch. Chilsong Gate (vert.) 45 25

567.

1975. Views of Mt. Chilbo.

N 1468. **567.** 10 ch. mult. .. 40 10
N 1469. – 10 ch mult. .. 40 10
N 1470. – 15 ch. mult. .. 65 10
N 1471. – 20 ch. mult. .. 75 15
N 1472. – 30 ch. mult. .. 85 20

DESIGNS: Nos. N 1468/72, Various views.

568. Right-hand Section of Monument.

1975. Historic Site of Revolution in Wangjaesan. Multicoloured.

N 1473. 10 ch. Type **568** .. 10 10
N 1474. 15 ch. Left-hand section of monument .. 20 10
N 1475. 25 h. Centre section of monument .. 30 15
N 1476. 30 ch. Centre section, close-up 40 20

No. N 1475 is 38 × 60 mm. and No. N 1476, 60 × 38 mm.

569. Marchers with Flags.

1976. 30th Anniv. of Korean League of Socialist Working Youth. Multicoloured.

N 1477. 2 ch. Flags and Emblem 15 10
N 1478. 70 ch. Type **569** .. 90 40

570. Geese.

1976. Ducks and Geese. Multicoloured.

N 1479. 10 ch. Type **570** .. 40 10
N 1480. 20 ch. "Perennial" duck 90 10
N 1481. 40 ch. Kwangpo duck 1·60 20

571. "Oath".

1976. Korean Peoples Army (sculptural works). Multicoloured.

N 1482. 5 ch. Type **571** .. 10 10
N 1483. 10 ch. "Union of Officers with Men" (horiz.) 15 10
N 1484. 10 ch. "This Flag to the Height" .. 15 10

572. "Rural Road at Evening".

1976. Modern Korean Paintings (5th series). Social Welfare. Multicoloured.

N 1485. 10 ch. Type **572** .. 35 10
N 1486. 15 ch. "Passing on Technique" (1970) 45 10
N 1487. 25 ch. "Mother (and Child)' (1965) .. 55 15
N 1488. 30 ch. "Medical Examination at School" (1970) (horiz.) .. 75 15
N 1489. 40 ch. "Lady Doctor of Village" (1970) (horiz.) 90 20

573. Worker holding Text of Law.

1976. 30th Anniv. of Agrarian Reform Law.

N 1490. **573.** 10 ch. multicoloured 20 10

574. Telephones and Satellite.

1976. Centenary of First Telephone Call. Multicoloured. With or without gum.

N 1491. 2 ch. Type **574** .. 40 10
N 1492. 5 ch. Satellite and antenna 40 10
N 1493. 10 ch. Satellite and telecommunications systems 40 10
N 1494. 15 ch. Telephone and linesman .. .. 1·10 10
N 1495. 25 ch. Satellite and map of receiving stations .. .. 1·50 15
N 1496. 40 ch. Satellite and cable-laying barge .. 1·75 20

575. Cosmos.

1976. Flowers. Multicoloured.

N 1498. 5 ch. Type **575** .. 25 10
N 1499. 10 ch. Dahlia 25 10
N 1500. 20 ch. Zinnia 45 15
N 1501. 40 ch. China aster .. 70 25

576. Fruit and Products.

1976. Pukchong Meeting of Korean Workers' Party Presidium. Multicoloured.

N 1502. 5 ch. Type **576** .. 45 10
N 1503. 10 ch. Fruit and orchard scene 45 10

577. "Pulgunji" Type Electric Locomotive.

1976. Railway Locomotives. Multicoloured.

N1504 5 ch. Type **577** .. 25 10
N1505 10 ch. "Chaju" type underground train .. 55 10
N1506 15 ch. "Saebyol" type diesel lcomotive .. 70 15

GUM. All the following stamps were issued with gum, except were otherwise stated.

578. Satellite.

1976. Space Flight. With or without gum.

N 1507. **578.** 2 ch. multicoloured 15 10
N 1508. – 5 ch. multicoloured 15 10
N 1509. – 10 ch. multicoloured 20 10
N 1510. – 15 ch. multicoloured 30 10
N 1511. – 25 ch. multicoloured 45 15
N 1512. – 40 ch. multicoloured 70 20

DESIGNS: 5 ch. to 40 ch. Various satellites and space craft.

579. Kim Il Sung beside Car.

1976. Kim Il Sung's 64th Birthday.

N1514 **579** 10 ch. multicoloured 40 10

580. Bat and Ribbon.

1976. 3rd Asian Table Tennis Championships. Multicoloured. Without gum.

N 1516. 5 ch. Type **580** .. 25 10
N 1517. 10 ch. Three women players with flowers 25 10
N 1518. 20 ch. Player defending 45 10
N 1519. 25 ch. Player making attacking shot .. 75 15

581. Kim Il Sung announcing Establishment of Association.

1976. 40th Anniv of Association for the Restoration of the Fatherland. Without gum.

N1521 **581** 10 ch. multicoloured 10 10

582. Golden Pheasant.

1976. Pheasants. Multicoloured. With or without gum.

N 1522. 2 ch. Type **582** .. 60 10
N 1523. 5 ch. Lady Amherst's pheasant 60 15
N 1524. 10 ch. Silver pheasant 70 20
N 1525. 15 ch. Reeve's pheasant 80 20
N 1526. 25 ch. Temminck's tragopan .. .. 1·00 25
N 1527. 40 ch. Ringed-necked pheasant (albino) .. 1·25 35

583. Monument and Map of River.

585. Bronze Medal (Hockey, Pakistan).

584. Running.

1976. Potong River Monument. Without gum.

N1529 **583** 10 ch. brown & green 20 10

1976. Olympic Games, Montreal. Mult.

N 1530. 2 ch. Type **584** .. 20 10
N 1531. 5 ch. Diving 20 10
N 1532. 10 ch. Judo 20 10
N 1533. 15 ch. Gymnastics .. 30 10
N 1534. 25 ch. Gymnastics .. 80 15
N 1535. 40 ch. Fencing .. 1·25 20

1976. Olympic Medal Winners (1st issue). Multicoloured.

N 1537. 2 ch. Type **585** .. 25 10
N 1538. 5 ch. Bronze medal (shooting, Rudolf Dollinger) 25 10
N 1539. 10 ch. Silver medal (boxing, Li Byong Uk) 25 15
N 1540. 15 ch. Silver medal (cycling, Daniel Morelon) .. .. 1·50 15
N 1541. 25 ch. Gold medal (marathon, Waldemar Cierpinski) 90 20
N 1542. 40 ch. Gold medal (boxing, Ku Yong Jo) .. .. .. 1·40 25

INDEX

Countries can be quickly located by referring to the index at the end of this volume.

586. Boxing (Ku Yong Jo).

1976. Olympic Medal Winners (2nd issue). Multicoloured.

N1544 2 ch. Type **586** .. 25 10
N1545 5 ch. Gymnastics (Nadia Comaneci) 25 10
N1546 10 ch. Pole vaulting (Tadeusz Slusarki) .. 25 10
N1547 15 ch. Hurdling (Guy Drut) 30 10
N1548 20 ch. Cycling (Bernt Johansson) .. .. 2·50 15
N1549 40 ch. Football (East Germany) .. .. 1·50 20

587. U.P.U. Headquarters, Berne.

1976. International Festivities. Mult.

N 1551. 2 ch. Type **587** .. 40 10
N 1552. 5 ch. Footballers (World Cup) .. 40 10
N 1553. 10 ch. Olympic Stadium 40 10
N 1554. 15 ch. Olympic Village 40 10
N 1555. 25 ch. Junk and satellite 70 20
N 1556. 40 ch. Satellites .. 75 20

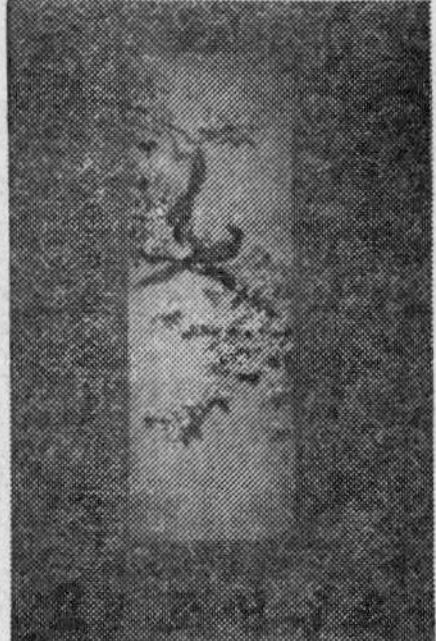

588. Azure-winged Magpies.

1976. Embroidery. Multicoloured. With or without gum.

N 1558. 2 ch. Type **588** .. 1·25 15
N 1559. 5 ch. White magpie .. 90 15
N 1560. 10 ch. Roe deer .. 30 10
N 1561. 15 ch. Black-naped oriole and magnolias 1·40 15
N 1562. 25 ch. Fairy with flute (horiz.) 70 15
N 1563. 40 ch. Tiger .. .. 1·60 40

589. Roman "5" and Flame.

1976. 5th Non-aligned States' Summit Conference, Colombo. Without gum.

N1565 **589** 10 ch. multicoloured 10 10

590. Trophy and Certificate.

1976. World Model Plane Championships (1975). Multicoloured. Without gum.

N 1566. 5 ch. Type **590** .. 20 10
N 1567. 10 ch. Trophy and medals 30 10
N 1568. 20 ch. Model plane and emblem 45 10
N 1569. 40 ch. Model glider and medals 75 15

591. "Pulgungi" Type Diesel Shunting Locomotive.

1976. Locomotives. Multicoloured.

N1570 2 ch. Type **591** .. 40 10
N1571 5 ch. "Saebyol" type diesel locomotive .. 55 10
N1572 10 ch. "Saebyol" type diesel shunting locomotive 65 10
N1573 15 ch. Electric locomotive 75 10
N1574 25 ch. "Kumsung" type diesel locomotive .. 95 15
N1575 40 ch. "Pulgungi" type electric locomotive 1·10 20

592. House of Culture.

1976. House of Culture. Without gum.

N1577 **592** 10 ch. brown & black 15 10

593. Kim Il Sung visiting Tosongrang.

1976. Revolutionary Activities of Kim Il Sung. Multicoloured.

N 1578. 2 ch. Type **593** .. 20 10
N 1579. 5 ch. Kim Il Sung vists peasants 20 10
N 1580. 10 ch. Kim Il Sung on hilltop 25 10
N 1581. 15 ch. Kim Il Sung giving house to farmhand 30 10
N 1582. 25 ch. Kim Il Sung near front line .. 70 10
N 1583. 40 ch. Kim Il Sung walking in rain .. 70 15

594. Kim Il Sung with Union Members.

1976. 50th Anniv of Down-with-Imperialism Union. Without gum.

N 1585. **594.** 20 ch. multicoloured 35 15

604. Searchlights and Kim Il Sung's Birthplace.

605. Spring Costume.

1977. New Year. Without gum.
N1589 **604** 10 ch. multicoloured .. 10 10

1977. National Costumes of Li Dynasty. Mult.
N 1590. 10 ch. Type **605** (postage) 45 10
N 1591. 15 ch. Summer costume 60 10
N 1592. 20 ch. Autumn costume 70 15
N 1593. 40 ch. Winter costume (air.) .. .. .. 1·10 20

606. Two Deva Kings (Koguryo Dynasty).

1977. Korean Cultural Relics. Multicoloured.
N 1594 2 ch. Type **606** (post) 25 10
N 1595 5 ch. Gold-copper decoration, Koguryo Dynasty 25 10
N 1596 10 ch. Copper Buddha, Koryo Dynasty .. 35 10
N 1597 15 ch. Gold-copper Buddha, Paekje Dynasty 45 10
N 1598 25 ch. Gold crown, Koguryo Dynasty .. 55 15
N 1599 40 ch. Gold-copper sun decoration, Koguryo Dynasty (horiz) .. 70 20
N 1600 50 ch. Gold crown, Silla Dynasty (air) .. 90 35

607. Worker with Five-Point Programme.

1977. Five-point Programme for Remaking Nature. Without gum.
N1601 **607** 10 ch. multicoloured 20 10

608. Pine Branch and Map of Korea.

1977. 60th Anniv of Korean National Association. Without gum.
N1602 **608** 10 ch. multicoloured 35 10

609. Championship Emblem and Trophy.

1977. 34th World Table Tennis Championships. Multicoloured. Without gum.
N 1603. 10 ch. Type **609** (postage) 20 10
N 1604. 15 ch. Pak Yong Sun .. 30 10
N 1605. 20 ch. Pak Yong Sun with trophy .. 50 15
N 1606. 40 ch. Pak Yong Ok and Yang Ying (air) 95 20

610. Kim Il Sung founds Guerrilla Army at Mingyuegou.

1977. Kim Il Sung's 65th Birthday. Mult.
N 1607. 2 ch. Type **610** .. 10 10
N 1608. 5 ch. In command of army 10 10
N 1609. 10 ch. Visiting steel workers in Kangson 25 10
N 1610. 15 ch. Before battle .. 20 10
N 1611. 25 ch. In schoolroom .. 25 10
N 1612. 40 ch. Viewing bumper harvest 35 10

611. " Chollima 72 " Trolleybus.

1977. Trolleybuses. Without gum.
N1614 **611** 5 ch. bl, lilac & blk 75 10
N1615 – 10 ch. red, grn & blk 75 10
DESIGN: 10 ch. "Chollima 74" trolleybus.

612. Red Flag and Hand holding Rifle.

1977. 45th Anniv of Korean People's Revolutionary Army. Without gum.
N1616 **612** 40 ch. red, yell & blk 50 20

613. Proclamation and Watchtower.

1977. 40th Anniv of Pochonbo Battle. Without gum.
N1617 **613** 10 ch. multicoloured 10 10

614. Koryo White Ware Teapot.

1977. Korean Porcelain. Multicoloured.
N 1618. 10 ch. Type **614** (postage) 30 10
N 1619. 15 ch. White vase, Li Dynasty 40 10
N 1620. 20 ch. Celadon vase, Koryo Dynasty .. 65 10
N 1621. 40 ch. Celadon vase with lotus decoration, Koryo Dynasty (air) .. .. 1·10 15

615. Postal Transport.

1977. Postal Services. Multicoloured. Without gum.
N 1623. 2 ch. Type **615** .. 60 15
N 1624. 10 ch. Postwoman delivering letter .. 25 10
N 1625. 30 ch. Postal helicopter 90 30
N 1626. 40 ch. Airliner and world map 90 30

616. " Rapala arata ".

1977. Butterflies and Dragonflies. Mult.
N1627 2 ch. Type **616** (postage) 35 10
N1628 5 ch. "Colias aurora" .. 55 10
N1629 10 ch. Poplar admiral .. 75 10
N1630 15 ch. "Anax parthenope" .. .. 1·00 10
N1631 25 ch. "Sympetrum pedemontanum elatum" .. .. 1·25 10
N1632 50 ch. "Papilio maackii" (air) .. .. .. 1·50 20

617. Grey Cat.

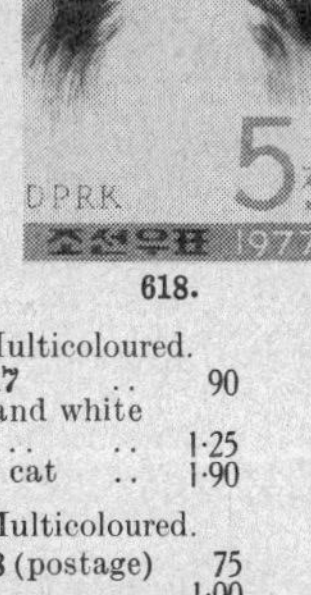

618.

1977. Cats. Multicoloured.
N 1634. 2 ch. Type **617** .. 90 10
N 1635. 10 ch. Black and white cat .. .. 1·25 15
N 1636. 25 ch. Ginger cat .. 1·90 20

1977. Dogs. Multicoloured.
N 1638. 5 ch. Type **618** (postage) 75 10
N 1639. 15 ch. Chow .. .. 1·00 10
N 1640. 50 ch. Pungsang dog (air) 1·60 15

619. Kim Il Sung and Pres. Tito.

1977. Visit of President Tito.
N 1642. **619.** 10 ch. multicoloured 10 10
N 1643. 15 ch. multicoloured 15 10
N 1644. 20 ch. multicoloured 25 10
N 1645. 40 ch. multicoloured 35 10

620. Girl and Symbols of Education.

1977. 5th Anniv of 11-year Compulsory Education. Without gum.
N1646 **620** 10 ch. multicoloured 10 10

621. " Mactra sulcataria ".

622. Students and " Theses ".

1977. Shellfish and Fish. Multicoloured.
N 1647. 2 ch. Type **621** (postage) 30 10
N 1648. 5 ch. " Natica fortunei " 45 15
N 1649. 10 ch. " Arca inflata" 65 15
N 1650. 25 ch. " Rapana thomasiana " 90 20
N 1651. 50 ch. " Sphoeroides porphyreus " (air) .. 1·45 25

1977. Kim Il Sung's "Theses on Socialist Education". Multicoloured. Without gum.
N 1653. 10 ch. Type **622** .. 10 10
N 1654. 20 ch. Students, crowd and text 15 10

623. " Juche " Torch.

624. Jubilant Crowd.

1977. Seminar on the Juche Idea. Multicoloured. Without gum.
N 1655. 2 ch. Type **623** .. 10 10
N 1656. 5 ch. Crowd and red book 10 10
N 1657. 10 ch. Chollima Statue and flags 10 10
N 1658. 15 ch. Handclasp and red flag on world map 10 10
N 1659. 25 ch. Map of Korea and anti-U.S. slogans 15 10
N 1660. 40 ch. Crowd and Mt. Paekdu-san 20 10

1977. Election of Deputies to Supreme People's Assembly. Without gum.
N1662 **624** 10 ch. multicoloured 10 10

625. Footballers.

1977. World Cup Football Championship, Argentina. Without gum.
N 1663. **625.** 10 ch. multicoloured 50 15
N 1664. 15 ch. multicoloured 90 20
N 1665. – 40 ch. multicoloured 1·60 25
DESIGNS: 15, 40 ch. Different football scenes.

626. Kim Il Sung with Rejoicing Crowds.

1977. Re-election of Kim Il Sung. Without gum.
N1667 **626** 10 ch. multicoloured 10 10

627. Chollima Statue and Symbols of Communication.

1977. 20th Anniv of Socialist Countries' Communication Organization. Without gum.
N1668 **627** 10 ch. multicoloured 20 10

HAVE YOU READ THE NOTES AT THE BEGINNING OF THIS CATALOGUE?
These often provide answers to the enquiries we receive.

638. Chollima Statue and City Skyline.

1978. New Year. Without gum.

N1687 **638** 10 ch. multicoloured .. 10 10

639. Skater in 19th-century Costume.

640. Post-rider and "Horse-ticket".

1978. Winter Olympic Games, Sapporo and Innsbruck. Multicoloured.

N 1688. 2 ch. Type **639** (postage) 40 10
N 1699. 5 ch. Skier 40 10
N 1690. 10 ch. Woman skater 40 10
N 1691. 15 ch. Hunter on skis 50 10
N 1692. 20 ch. Woman (in 19th-century costume) on skis 50 10
N 1693. 25 ch. Viking with long-bow .. .. 1·25 15
N 1694. 40 ch. Skier (air) .. 1·40 15

1978. Postal Progress. Multicoloured.

N 1696. 2 ch. Type **640** (postage) 25 10
N 1697. 5 ch. Postman on motorcycle .. 1·50 10
N 1698. 10 ch. Electric train and postvan .. .. 1·50 15
N 1699. 15 ch. Mail steamer and helicopter .. 65 15
N 1700. 25 ch. Aeroplane and satellite 75 15
N 1701. 40 ch. Dove and U.P.U. Headquarters (air) 50 15

641. "Self-portrait". **643.** Show Jumping.

642. "Chungsong" Tractor.

1978. 400th Birth Anniv of Rubens.

N 1703. **641.** 2 ch. multicoloured 25 10
N 1704. 5 ch. multicoloured 25 10
N 1705. 40 ch. multicoloured 1·50 20

1978. Farm Machines. Without gum.

N 1707. **642.** 10 ch. red and black 35 10
N 1708. – 10 ch. brn. & blk. .. 35 10

DESIGN: No. N 1708, Sprayer.

1978. Olympic Games, Moscow (1980). Equestrian Events. Multicoloured.

N1709 2 ch. Type **643** .. 25 10
N1710 5 ch. Jumping bar .. 35 10
N1711 10 ch. Cross-country .. 45 10
N1712 15 ch. Dressage .. 50 10
N1713 25 ch. Water splash .. 75 15
N1714 40 ch. Dressage (different) .. .. 1·25 15

644. Soldier.

1978. Korean People's Army Day. Multicoloured. Without gum.

N 1716. 5 ch. Type **644** .. 10 10
N 1717. 10 ch. Servicemen saluting 10 10

645. "Mangyongbong" (Freighter).

1978. Korean Ships. Multicoloured.

N1718 2 ch. Type **645** (postage) 1·75 45
N1719 5 ch. "Hyoksin" (freighter) 35 15
N1720 10 ch. "Chongchon-gang" (gas carrier) .. 35 15
N1721 30 ch. "Sonbong" (tanker) 60 20
N1722 50 ch. "Taedonggang" (freighter) (air) .. 1·10 40

646. Uruguayan Footballer.

1978. World Cup Football Championship Winners. Multicoloured.

N 1724. 5 ch. Type **646** (postage) 40 10
N 1725. 10 ch. Italian player .. 40 10
N 1726. 15 ch. West German player 40 10
N 1727. 25 ch. Brazilian player 40 10
N 1728. 40 ch. English player .. 75 10
N 1729. 50 ch. Hands holding World Cup (vert.) (air) 65 35

647. Footballers (1930 Winners, Uruguay).

1978. History of World Cup Football Championship. Multicoloured.

N 1731. 20 ch. Type **647** (postage) 75 15
N 1732. 20 ch. Italy, 1934 .. 75 15
N 1733. 20 ch. France, 1938 .. 75 15
N 1734. 20 ch. Brazil, 1950 .. 75 15
N 1735. 20 ch. Switzerland, 1954 75 15
N 1736. 20 ch. Sweden, 1958 .. 75 15
N 1737. 20 ch. Chile, 1962 .. 75 15
N 1738. 20 ch. England, 1966 .. 75 15
N 1739. 20 ch. Mexico, 1970 .. 75 15
N 1740. 20 ch. West Germany, 1974 .. .. 75 15
N 1741. 20 ch. Argentina, 1978 75 15
N 1742. 50 ch. Footballers and emblem (air) .. 75 15

648. "Sea of Blood" (opera).

1978. Art from the Period of Anti-Japanese Struggle. Multicoloured.

N1744 10 ch. Type **648** .. 25 10
N1745 15 ch. Floral kerchief embroidered with map of Korea .. 35 10
N1746 20 ch. "Tansimjul" (maypole dance) .. 50 15

649. Red Flag and "7", Electricity and Coal.

1978. Second 7 Year Plan. Multicoloured. Without gum.

N 1748. 5 ch. Type **649** 25 10
N 1749. 10 ch. Steel and non-ferrous metal .. 30 10
N 1750. 15 ch. Engineering and chemical fertilizer .. 35 10
N 1751. 30 ch. Cement and fishing 55 10
N 1752. 50 ch. Grain and tideland reclimation 75 10

650. Gymnastics (Alfred Flatow).

1978. Olympic Games History and Medal-winners. Multicoloured.

N 1753. 20 ch. Type **650** .. 60 15
N 1754. 20 ch. Runners (Michel Theato) 60 15
N 1755. 20 ch. Runners (Wyndham Halswelle) .. 60 15
N 1756. 20 ch. Rowing (William Kinnear) 60 15
N 1757. 20 ch. Fencing (Paul Anspach) .. .. 1·25 25
N 1758. 20 ch. Runners (Ugo Frigerio) 60 15
N 1759. 20 ch. Runners (Ahmed El Quafi) 60 15
N 1760. 20 ch. Cycling (Robert Charpentier) .. 1·50 35
N 1761. 20 ch. Gymnastics (Josep Stalder) 60 15
N 1762. 20 ch. Boxing (Lazio Papp) 85 20
N 1763. 20 ch. Runners (Ronald Delany) 60 15
N 1764. 20 ch. High jump (Jolanda Balas) .. 60 15
N 1765. 20 ch. High jump (Valery Brumel) .. 60 15
N 1766. 20 ch. Gymnastics (Vera Caslavska) 60 15
N 1767. 20 ch. Rifle shooting (Li Ho Jun) .. 60 15

651. Swissair Douglas "DC-8".

1978. Aeroplanes. Multicoloured.

N 1769. 2 ch. Type **651** .. 40 10
N 1770. 10 ch. Czechoslovakian "DK" jet .. 50 10
N 1771. 15 ch. Italia Douglas "DC-8" 65 10
N 1772. 20 ch. Aeroflot airliner 75 10
N 1773. 25 ch. Korean airliner 75 10
N 1774. 30 ch. Korean airliner 75 10
N 1775. 40 ch. Air France "Concorde" .. 1·75 40

652. White-bellied Black Woodpecker and Map. **653.** Demonstrators and Korean Map.

1978. White-bellied Black Woodpecker Preservation. Multicoloured.

N 1777. 5 ch. Type **652** .. 55 15
N 1778. 10 ch. Woodpecker and eggs 65 20
N 1779. 15 ch. Woodpecker feeding young 85 25
N 1780. 25 ch. Woodpecker feeding young (different) 1·00 35
N 1781. 50 ch. Adult woodpecker on tree trunk .. 1·60 40

1978. 30th Anniv of Democratic People's Republic of Korea. Multicoloured. Without gum.

N 1783. 10 ch. Type **653** 10 10
N 1784. 10 ch. Flag and soldiers 10 10
N 1785. 10 ch. Flag and "Juche" 10 10
N 1786. 10 ch. Red Flag 10 10
N 1787. 10 ch. Chollima Statue and city skyline .. 10 10
N 1788. 10 ch. "Juche" torch and men of three races 10 10

654. Cat and Pup. **668.** Red Flag and Pine Branch.

655. Footballers.

1978. Animal Paintings by Li Am. Mult.

N 1789. 10 ch. Type **654** .. 1·75 30
N 1790. 15 ch. Cat up a Tree .. 1·75 30
N 1791. 40 ch. Wild Geese .. 1·75 30

1978. Argentina's Victory in World Cup Football Championship. Without gum.

N 1792. **655.** 10 ch. mult. .. 65 10
N 1793. – 15 ch. mult. .. 75 15
N 1794. – 25 ch. mult. .. 90 20

DESIGNS: 15, 25 ch. Different football scenes.

1979. New Year. Without gum.

N1812 **668** 10 ch. multicoloured 15 10

669. Kim Il Sung with Children's Corps Members, Maanshan.

1979. International Year of the Child (1st issue). Multicoloured.

(a) Paintings of Kim Il Sung and children.

N 1813. 5 ch. Type **669** 15 10
N 1814. 10 ch. Kim Il Sung and Children's Corps members in classroom.. .. .. 25 10
N 1815. 15 ch. New Year gathering .. 30 10

N 1816. 20 ch. Kim Il Sung and children in snow .. 45 10
N 1817. 30 ch. Kim Il Sung examines children's schoolbooks (vert.) 50 10

(b) Designs showing children.
N 1818. 10 ch. Tug-of-war .. 15 10
N 1819. 15 ch. Dance "Growing up Fast" 40 15
N 1820. 20 ch. Children of many races and globe 40 10
N 1821. 25 ch. Children singing 65 15
N 1822. 30 ch. Children in toy spaceships 40 10
See also Nos. N 1907/17.

670. Rose.

1979. Roses. Multicoloured.
N1824 1 wn. Red rose ..
N1825 3 wn. White rose ..
N1826 5 wn. Type **670** ..
N1827 10 wn. Deep pink rose
See also Nos. N1837/42.

671. Warriors on Horseback.
672. Red Guard and Industrial Skyline.

1979. "The Story of Two Generals". Multicoloured. Without gum.
N1828 5 ch. Type **671** .. 20 10
N1829 10 ch. Farm labourer blowing feather .. 30 10
N1830 10 ch. Generals fighting on foot 30 10
N1831 10 ch. Generals on horseback .. 30 10

1979. 20th Anniv of Worker-Peasant Red Guards. Without gum.
N1832 **672** 10 ch. multicoloured 15 10

673. Airship "Fleurus".

1979. Airships. Multicoloured. Without gum.
N1833 10 ch. Type **673** .. 75 15
N1834 20 ch. N 1 "Norge" .. 75 15

674. Crowd of Demonstrators.

1979. 60th Anniv of 1st March Popular Uprising. Without gum.
N1836 **674** 10 ch. blue and red 15 10

1979. Roses. As Nos. N1824/7. Multicoloured.
N1837 5 ch. Type **670** (postage) 25 10
N1838 10 ch. As No. N1827 .. 30 10
N1839 15 ch. As No. N1824 .. 35 10
N1840 20 ch. Yellow rose .. 45 10
N1841 30 ch. As No. 1825 .. 60 10
N1842 50 ch. Deep pink rose (different) (air) .. 80 15

675. Table Tennis Trophy.
676. Marchers with Red Flag.

1979. 35th World Table Tennis Championship, Pyongyang. Multicoloured. With or without gum.
N 1843. 5 ch. Type **675** .. 15 10
N 1844. 10 ch. Women's doubles 15 10
N 1845. 15 ch. Women's singles 25 10
N 1846. 20 ch. Men's doubles .. 40 10
N 1847. 30 ch. Men's singles .. 60 10

1979. Socialist Construction under Banner of Juche Idea. Multicoloured. Without gum.
N1849 5 ch. Type **676** .. 10 10
N1850 10 ch. Map of Korea .. 10 10
N1851 10 ch. Juche torch .. 10 10

677. Badge.
678. Emblem, Satellite orbiting Globe and Aerials.

1979. Order of Honour of the Three Revolutions. Without gum.
N1852 **677** 10 ch. blue .. 10 10

1979. World Telecommunications Day. Without gum.
N1853 **678** 10 ch. multicoloured 25 10

679. Advancing Soldiers and Monument.

1979. 40th Anniv of Battle in Musan Area. Without gum.
N1854 **679** 10 ch. mauve, light blue and blue .. 20 10

680. Exhibition Entrance.

1979. International Friendship Exhibition. Without gum.
N1855 **680** 10 ch. multicoloured 10 10

681. "Peonies".

1979. 450th Death Anniv of Albrecht Durer (artist). Multicoloured.
N1856 15 ch. Type **681** .. 45 20
N1857 20 ch. "Columbines" .. 90 20
N1858 25 ch. "A Great Tuft of Grass" 90 20
N1859 30 ch. "Wing of a Bird" 1·25 40

682. Fencing.

1979. Olympic Games, Moscow (2nd issue). Multicoloured. With gum (10, 40 ch. only).
N 1861. 5 ch. Type **682** .. 30 10
N 1862. 10 ch. Gymnastics .. 45 10
N 1863. 20 ch. Yachting .. 60 15
N 1864. 30 ch. Athletics .. 75 15
N 1865. 40 ch. Weightlifting .. 85 15

683. Hunting.

1979. Horse-riding (people of Koguryo Dynasty). Multicoloured.
N 1867. 5 ch. Type **683** .. 15 10
N 1868. 10 ch. Archery contest 40 10
N 1869. 15 ch. Man beating drum on horseback 40 10
N 1870. 20 ch. Man blowing horn 60 10
N 1871. 30 ch. Man and horse, armoured with chain-mail 45 10
N 1872. 50 ch. Hawking (air) .. 2·00 15

684. Judo.
685. Warrior's Costume.

1979. Olympic Games, Moscow (3rd issue). Multicoloured. With gum (5, 15, 20, 30 ch. only).
N 1873. 5 ch. Type **684** .. 30 10
N 1874. 10 ch. Volleyball .. 30 10
N 1875. 15 ch. Cycling .. .. 1·25 25
N 1876. 20 ch. Basketball .. 50 15
N 1877. 25 ch. Canoeing .. 50 15
N 1878. 30 ch. Boxing 75 25
N 1879. 40 ch. Shooting .. 70 20

1979. Warrior Costumes of Li Dynasty.
N 1881. **685.** 5 ch. mult. .. 20 10
N 1882. – 10 ch. mult. .. 20 10
N 1883. – 15 ch. mult. .. 30 10
N 1884. – 20 ch. mult. .. 45 10
N 1885. – 30 ch. mult. .. 60 10
N 1886. – 50 ch. mult. (air) 90 15
Designs: 10 ch. to 50 ch. Different costumes.

686. Wrestling.
687. Monument.

1979. Olympic Games, Moscow (4th issue). Multicoloured.
N 1887. 10 ch. Type **686** .. 25 10
N 1888. 15 ch. Handball .. 30 10
N 1889. 20 ch. Archery .. 90 25
N 1890. 25 ch. Hockey .. .. 2·00 45
N 1891. 30 ch. Rowing .. .. 1·00 15
N 1892. 40 ch. Football .. 1·50 25

1979. Chongbong Monument. Without gum.
N1894 **687** 10 ch. multicoloured 20 10

688. Bottle-feeding Fawn.

1979. Sika Deer. Multicoloured.
N 1895. 5 ch. Type **688** (post.) 25 10
N 1896. 10 ch. Doe and fawn .. 25 10
N 1897. 15 ch. Stag drinking from stream .. 25 15
N 1898. 20 ch. Stag 35 15
N 1899. 30 ch. Stag and doe .. 50 25
N 1900. 50 ch. Antlers and deer (air) 85 35

689. Moscovy Ducks.

1979. Central Zoo, Pyongyang. Multicoloured.
N1901 5 ch. Type **689** (postage) 40 10
N1902 10 ch. Ostrich 40 10
N1903 15 ch. Common turkey 40 10
N1904 20 ch. Dalmatian pelican 65 15
N1905 30 ch. Vulturine guinea-fowl 80 15
N1906 50 ch. Mandarin ducks (air) .. .. .. 1·25 35

690. Girl with Model Viking Ship.

1979. International Year of the Child. (2nd issue). Multicoloured.
N 1907. 20 ch. Type **690** .. 1·00 20
N 1908. 20 ch. Boys with model train .. .. .. 2·50 85
N 1909. 20 ch. Boy with model biplane .. .. 1·25 20
N 1910. 20 ch. Boy with model spaceman 80 20
N 1911. 30 ch. Boy with model speedboat .. .. 1·50 30
N 1912. 30 ch. Boy sitting astride toy train .. 2·50 85
N 1913. 30 ch. Boy and model airplane .. .. 1·60 30
N 1914. 30 ch. Boy and flying spaceman .. .. 1·00 30

691. Footballers.

1979. International Year of the Child (3rd issue). Multicoloured.
N 1916. 20 ch. Type **691** .. 1·00 20
N 1917. 30 ch. Footballers (different) .. .. 1·50 30

MINIMUM PRICE

The minimum price quoted is 5p which represents a handling charge rather than a basis for valuing common stamps. For further notes about prices see introductory pages.

692. "Inimicus japonicus".

1979. Marine Life. Multicoloured.

N 1919.	20 ch. Type **699** ..	75	10
N 1920.	30 ch. "Sebastes schlegeli" (fish) ..	1·00	20
N 1921.	50 ch. Northern sealion	1·60	30

693. Cross-country Skiing (Sergei Saveliev).

1979. Winter Olympic Games, Lake Placid. Multicoloured.

N1922	10 ch. Figure skating (Irina Rodnina and Aleksandr Zaitsev) (horiz)	50	15
N1923	20 ch. Ice hockey (Russian team) (horiz)	75	20
N1924	30 ch. Ladies 5 km relay (horiz)	1·25	25
N1925	40 ch. Type **693** ..	1·50	30
N1926	50 ch. Ladies' speed skating (Tatiana Averina)	1·90	35

694. Bee collecting Nectar.

1979. Bees. Multicoloured.

N 1928.	20 ch. Type **694** ..	90	10
N 1929.	30 ch. Bee and flowers	1·10	15
N 1930.	50 ch. Bee hovering over flower	1·25	25

695. Kim Jong Suk's Birthplace, Heoryong.

1979. Historic Revolutionary Sites.

N 1931.	**695.**	10 ch. mult. ..	15	10
N 1932.	–	10 ch. brown, blue and black ..	15	10

DESIGN: No. N1932, Sinpa Revolutionary Museum.

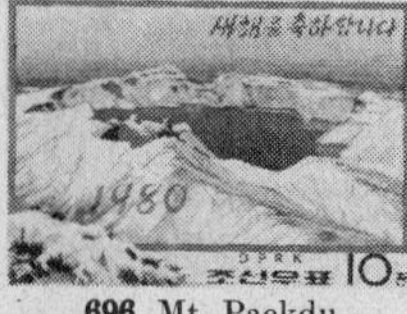
696. Mt. Paekdu.

1980. New Year.

N 1933.	**696.**	10 ch. mult. ..	55	10

697. Student and Books.

1980. Studying.

N 1934.	**697.**	10 ch. multicoloured	25	10

698. Conveyor Belt.

1980. Unryul Mine Conveyor Belt.

N1935	**698**	10 ch. multicoloured	55	10

699. Children of Three Races.

1980. International Day of the Child. Multicoloured.

N1936	10 ch. Type **699** ..	30	10
N1937	10 ch. Girl dancing to accordion	50	10
N1938	10 ch. Children in fair-ground aeroplane ..	40	10
N1939	10 ch. Children as astronauts	30	10
N1940	10 ch. Children on tricycles	1·00	30
N1941	10 ch. Children with toy train	1·40	45
N1942	10 ch. "His loving care for the children, future of the father-land" (59½ × 38 mm)	30	10

700. Monument.

1980. Chongsan-ri Historic Site. Mult.

N 1944.	5 ch. Type **700** ..	10	10
N 1945.	10 ch. Meeting place of the General Membership	15	10

701. Monument.

1980. Monument marking Kim Jong Suk's Return.

N 1946.	**701.**	10 ch. multicoloured	15	10

702. Vasco Nunez de Balboa.

1980. Conquerors of the Earth. Mult.

N 1947.	10 ch. Type **702** ..	50	10
N 1948.	20 ch. Francisco de Orellana	75	20
N 1949.	30 ch. Haroun Tazieff	1·00	35
N 1950.	40 ch. Edmund Hillary and Sherpa Tenzing	1·50	45

703. Museum.

1980. Ryongpo Revolutionary Museum.

N1952	**703**	10 ch. blue and black	20	10

704. Rowland Hill and Stamps.

1980. Death Centenary (1979) of Sir Rowland Hill. Multicoloured.

N 1953.	30 ch. Type **704** ..	3·25	75
N 1954.	50 ch. Rowland Hill and stamps (different)	3·25	75

705. North Korean Red Cross Flag.

1980. World Red Cross Day. Multicoloured.

N 1955.	10 ch. Type **705** ..	70	20
N 1956.	10 ch. Henri Dunant (founder)	70	20
N 1957.	10 ch. Nurse and child	70	20
N 1958.	10 ch. Red Cross aeroplane and ship ..	1·00	25
N 1959.	10 ch. Red Cross hellcopter	1·00	25
N 1960.	10 ch. Children playing at nurses	70	20
N 1961.	10 ch. Red Cross Map over Korea and forms of transport ..	2·50	60

706. Fernando Magellan.

1980. Conquerors of the Sea. Multicoloured.

N1963	10 ch. Type **706** ..	1·50	25
N1964	20 ch. Fridtjof Nansen	1·50	25
N1965	30 ch. Auguste and Jacques Piccard ..	2·00	25
N1966	40 ch. Jacques-Yves Cousteau	2·25	55

707. Korean Stamps and Penny Black.

1980. "London 1980" International Stamp Exhibition. Multicoloured.

N 1968.	10 ch. Type **707** (postage)	1·50	40
N 1969.	20 ch. Korean cover and British Guiana 1 c. black and red ..	1·50	30
N 1970.	30 ch. Early Korean stamp and modern cover	1·25	25
N 1971.	50 ch. Korean stamps	2·00	35
N 1972.	40 ch. Korean stamp and miniature sheet (air)	1·50	35

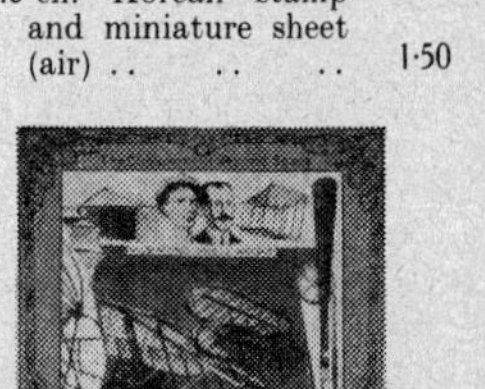
708. Wright Brothers.

1980. Conquerors of Sky and Space. Multicoloured.

N 1974.	10 ch. Type **708** ..	60	15
N 1975.	20 ch. Louis Bleriot ..	90	25
N 1976.	30 ch. Anthony Fokker	1·25	40
N 1977.	40 ch. Secondo Campini and Frank Whittle	1·75	45

709. Space Station on Planet.

710. Flag and Banners.

1980. Conquerors of the Universe. Multicoloured.

N 1979.	10 ch. Orbiting space station	30	10
N 1980.	20 ch. Type **709** ..	40	20
N 1981.	30 ch. Prehistoric animals and space ships	1·00	35
N 1982.	40 ch. Prehistoric animals and birds and spaceship ..	1·40	45

1980. 25th Anniv of General Association of Korean Residents in Japan (Chongryon).

N1984	**710**	10 ch. multicoloured	20	10

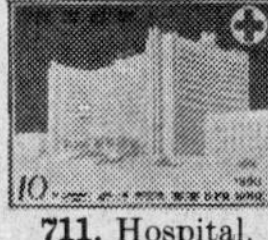
711. Hospital.

1980. Pyongyang Maternity Hospital.

N 1985.	**711.**	10 ch. blue, purple and black ..	45	15

712. Health Centre.

1980. Changgangwon Health Centre, Pyongyang.

N 1986.	**712.**	2 ch. black & blue	15	10

713. Hand holding Rifle.

714. Workers' Hostel, Samjiyon.

1980. 50th Anniv. of Revolutionary Army.

N 1987.	**713.**	10 ch. mult. ..	25	10

1980.

N1988	**714**	10 ch. brn, bl & blk	30	10
N1989	–	10 ch. black & green	50	20

N1990 – 10 ch. black and red 50 20
N1991 – 10 ch. black & yell 50 20
N1992 – 10 ch. multicoloured 30 10
N1993 – 10 ch. multicoloured 30 10
N1994 – 10 ch. multicoloured 1·00 35
N1995 – 10 ch. green & black 75 25
N1996 – 10 ch. grey, bl & blk 3·50 60
N1997 – 10 ch. multicoloured 3·50 60

DESIGNS: No. N1989, "Taedonggang" rice transplanter. N1990, "Chongsan-ri" rice harvester. N1991, Maize harvester. N1992, Revolutionary building, Songmun-ri. N1993, Revolutionary building, Samhwa. N1994, Sundial of 1438. N1995, 16th-century "turtle" ship. N1996, Pungsan dog. N1997, Japanese quail.

715. Party Emblem.

1980. Sixth Korean Workers' Party Congress. Multicoloured.
N 1998. 10 ch. Type **715** .. 15 10
N 1999. 10 ch. Students and Laurel leaf on globe 15 10
N 2000. 10 ch. Group with accordion 45 15
N 2001. 10 ch. Group with banner, microscope, book and trophy .. 25 10
N 2002. 10 ch. Worker with book and flag .. 75 25
N 2003. 10 ch. Worker with spanner and flag .. 75 25
N 2004. 10 ch. Marchers with torch and flags .. 15 10
N 2005. 10 ch. Emblem, marchers and map 20 10

716. Dribbling Ball.

1980. World Cup Football Championship, 1978–1982. Multicoloured.
N 2007. 20 ch. Type **716** .. 3·00 90
N 2008. 30 ch. Tackle .. .. 4·50 1·10

717. Irina Rodnina and Aleksandr Zaitsev.

1980. Winter Olympic Gold Medal Winners.
N 2010. **717.** 20 ch. mult. .. 5·50 1·75

718. "Soldier with Horse".

719. Kepler, Astrolabe and Satellites.

1980. 450th Death Anniv. (1978) of Albrecht Durer (artist).
N 2012. **718.** 20 ch. mult. .. 5·00 1·50

1980. 350th Death Anniv. of Johannes Kepler (astronomer).
N 2014. **719.** 20 ch. mult. .. 3·00 1·25

720. German 1 m. and Russian 30 k. "Zeppelin" Stamps.

1980. Third International Stamp Fair, Essen. Multicoloured.
N 2016. 10 ch. Type **720** .. 90 25
N 2017. 20 ch. As 10 ch. but 2 m. and 35 k. stamps .. .. 1·90 45
N 2018. 30 ch. As 10 ch. but 4 m. and 1 r. stamps 2·50 65

721. Shooting (Aleksandr Melentev).

1980. Olympic Medal Winners. Multicoloured.
N2020 10 ch. Type **721** .. 50 15
N2021 20 ch. Cycling (Robert Dill-Bundi) .. .. 2·75 75
N2022 25 ch. Gymnastics (Stoyan Deltchev) 1·00 25
N2023 30 ch. Wrestling (Chang Se Hong and Li Ho Pyong) .. .. 1·00 25
N2024 35 ch. Weightlifting (Ho Bong Chol) .. .. 1·00 25
N2025 40 ch. Running (Marita Koch) .. .. 1·50 30
N2026 50 ch. Modern Pentathlon (Anatoli Starostin) .. .. 1·60 35

722. Tito.

723. Convair "CV 340".

1980. President Tito of Yugoslavia Commemoration.
N 2028. **722.** 20 ch. mult. .. 30 10

1980. 25th Anniv. of First Post-War Flight of Lufthansa.
N 2029. **723.** 20 ch. mult. .. 4·00 1·75

724. "The Rocket".

1980. 150th Anniv. of Liverpool–Manchester Railway.
N 2031. **724.** 20 ch. mult. .. 5·00 1·75

725. Steam and Electric Locomotives.

1980. Cent. of First Electric Train.
N 2033. **725.** 20 ch. mult. .. 5·00 1·75

726. Hammarskjold.

727. Fischer and Spassky.

1980. 75th Birth Anniv. of Dag Hammarskjold (Former Secretary General of United Nations).
N 2035. **726.** 20 ch. mult. .. 2·50 1·25

1980. World Chess Championship, Merano.
N2037 **727** 20 ch. multicoloured 5·50 1·75

728. Stolz.

729. Chollima Statue.

1980. Birth Cent. of Robert Stolz (composer).
N 2039. **728.** 20 ch. mult. .. 3·75 1·50

1981. New Year. Without gum.
N2043 **729** 10 ch. multicoloured 1·50 40

730. Russian Fairy Tale.

1981. International Year of the Child (1979) (4th issue). Fairy Tales. Multicoloured.
N 2042. 10 ch. Type **730** .. 1·50 40
N 2043. 10 ch. Icelandic tale .. 1·50 40
N 2044. 10 ch. Swedish tale .. 1·50 40
N 2045. 10 ch. Irish tale .. 1·50 40
N 2046. 10 ch. Italian tale .. 1·50 40
N 2047. 10 ch. Japanese tale .. 1·50 40
N 2048. 10 ch. German tale .. 1·50 40

731. Changgwang Street.

1981. Changgwang Street, Pyongyang.
N 2050. **731.** 10 ch mult. .. 35 10

732. Footballers.

1981. World Cup Football Championship, Spain (1982) (1st issue). Multicoloured.
N 2051. 10 ch. Type **732** .. 2·75 65
N 2052. 20 ch. Hitting ball past defender .. .. 2·75 65
N 2053. 30 ch. Disputing possession of ball .. 2·75 65

See also Nos. N 2055/9 and N 2201/6.

733. Map, Emblem and World Cup.

1981. World Cup Football Championship, Spain (1982) (2nd issue). Multicoloured.
N 2055. 10 ch. Type **733** .. 1·75 45
N 2056. 15 ch. Footballers .. 1·75 45
N 2057. 20 ch. Heading ball .. 1·75 45
N 2058. 25 ch. Footballers (different) .. .. 1·75 45
N 2059. 30 ch. Footballers (different) .. .. 1·75 45

734. Workers with Book and Marchers with Banner.

1981. Implementation of Decision of the 6th Koreans' Party Congress. Multicoloured.
N 2061. 2 ch. Type **734** .. 10 10
N 2062. 10 ch. Worker with book 10 10
N 2063. 10 ch. Workers and industrial plant .. 25 10
N 2064. 10 ch. Electricity and coal (horiz.) 70 25
N 2065. 10 ch. Steel and non-ferrous metals (horiz. 25 10
N 2067. 10 ch. Cement and fertilizers (horiz.) .. 25 10
N 2067. 30 ch. Fishing and fabrics (horiz.) 25 10
N 2068. 40 ch. Grain and harbour (horiz.) .. 25 10
N 2069. 70 ch. Clasped hands .. 20 10
N 2070. 1 w. Hand holding torch 30 15

735. Footballers.

1981. Gold Cup Football Championship, Uruguay.
N 2071. **735.** 20 ch. mult. .. 3·00 1·00

736. Dornier "Do X" Flying Boat.

1981. "Naposta '81" International Stamp Exhibition, Stuttgart. Multicoloured.
N 2073. 10 ch. Type **736** .. 2·50 50
N 2074. 20 ch. Zepplin "LZ 120" "Bodensee" .. 2·50 50
N 2075. 30 ch. "Gotz von Berlichingen" .. 1·25 40

737. Telecommunications Equipment.

1981. World Telecommunication Day.
N 2077. **737.** 10 ch. mult. .. 1·75 20

738. "Iris pseudacorus".

1981. Flowers. Multicoloured.
N 2078. 10 ch. Type **738** .. 75 15
N 2079. 20 ch. "Iris pallasii" .. 1·00 20
N 2080. 30 ch. "Gladiolus gandavensis" .. 1·40 30

739. Austrian "WIPA 1981" and Rudolf Kirchschlager Stamps.

1981. "WIPA 1981" International Stamp Exhibition, Vienna. Multicoloured.
N 2081. 20 ch. Type **739** .. 1·90 60
N 2082. 30 ch. Austrian Maria Theresa and Franz Joseph stamps .. 2·50 80

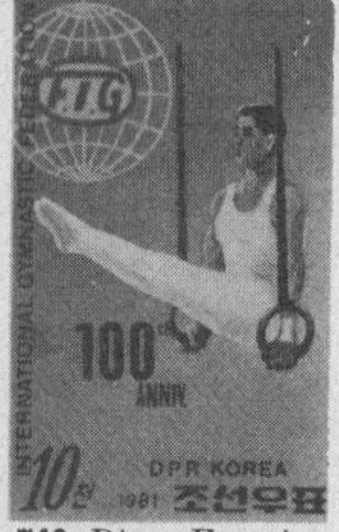

740. Rings Exercise.

1981. Centenary of International Gymnastic Federation. Multicoloured.
N 2084. 10 ch Type **740** .. 55 20
N 2085. 15 ch. Horse exercise .. 75 25
N 2086. 20 ch. Backwards somersault .. .. 1·10 35
N 2087. 25 ch. Floor exercise .. 1·25 40
N 2088. 30 ch. Exercise with hoop .. .. .. 1·40 45

741. Armed Workers.

1981. 50th Anniv of Mingyuehgou Meeting.
N2090 741 10 ch. multicoloured 20 10

742. Farm Building, Sukchon.

1981. 20th Anniv. of Agricultural Guidance System and Taean Work System.
N 2091. **742.** 10 ch. green, black and gold .. 20 10
N 2092. – 10 ch. blue, black and gold .. 20 10
DESIGN: No. N 2092, Taean Revolutionary Museum.

743. Woman and Banner.

1981. 55th Anniv. of Formation of Women's Anti-Japanese Association.
N 2093. **743** 5 wn. mult. .. 2·75 1·10

743a. Scene from Opera.

1981. 10th Anniv. of "Sea of Blood" (opera).
N 2094. **743a.** 10 wn. mult. ..

744. Joan of Arc.

1981. 550th Death Anniv. of Joan of Arc. Multicoloured.
N 2095. 10 ch. Type **744** .. 2·50 60
N 2096. 10 ch. Archangel Michael .. .. 2·75 75
N 2097. 70 ch. Joan of Arc in armour .. .. 2·75 75

745. Torch, Mountains and Flag.

1981. 55th Anniv. of Down with Imperialism Union.
N 2099. **745.** 1 wn. 50 mult. .. 40 20

746. "Young Girl by the Window".

1981. 375th Birth Anniv. of Rembrandt (artist). Multicoloured.
N 2100. 10 ch. Type **746** .. 55 25
N 2101. 20 ch. "Rembrandt's Mother" .. .. 1·25 45
N 2102. 30 ch. "Saskia van Uylenburgh" .. 1·75 70
N 2103. 40 ch. "Pallas Athene" 2·25 90

747. Emblem and Banners over Pyongyang.

1981. Symposium of Non-Aligned Countries on Food Self-Sufficiency, Pyongyang. Mult.
N 2105. 10 ch. Type **747.** .. 20 10
N 2106. 50 ch. Harvesting .. 50 10
N 2107. 90 ch. Factories, tractors and marchers with banner .. 70 15

748. St. Paul's Cathedral.

1981. Wedding of Prince of Wales (1st issue). Multicoloured.
N 2108. 10 ch. Type **748** .. 2·00 45
N 2109. 20 ch. Great Britain Prince of Wales Investiture Stamp .. 2·00 45
N 2110. 30 ch. Lady Diana Spencer .. .. 2·00 45
N 2111. 40 ch. Prince Charles in military uniform .. 2·00 45
See also Nos. N 2120/3.

749. "Four Philosophers" (detail).

1981. Paintings by Rubens. Multicoloured.
N 2113. 10 ch. Type **749** .. 55 25
N 2114. 15 ch. "Portrait of Helena Fourment" 85 35
N 2115. 20 ch. "Portrait of Isabella Brandt" .. 1·25 45
N 2116. 25 ch. "Education of Maria de Medici" .. 1·50 60
N 2117. 30 ch. "Helena Fourment and her Child" 1·75 70
N 2118. 40 ch. "Helena Fourment in her Wedding Dress" .. .. 2·25 90

750. Royal Couple.

1981. Wedding of Prince of Wales (2nd issue). Multicoloured.
N 2120. 10 ch. Type **750** .. 3·00 90
N 2121. 20 ch. Couple on balcony after wedding 3·00 90
N 2122. 30 ch. Couple outside St. Paul's Cathedral 3·00 90
N 2123. 70 ch. Full-length wedding portrait of couple .. .. 3·00 90

751. Rowland Hill and Stamps.

1981. "Philatokyo '81" International Stamp Exhibition. Multicoloured.
N 2125. 10 ch. Korean 2 ch. Seminar on Juche Idea stamp (41 × 29 mm.) 75 20
N 2126. 10 ch. Korean 10 and 70 ch. stamps (41 × 29 mm.) .. .. 2·00 75
N 2127. 10 ch. Type **751** .. 2·00 75
N 2128. 20 ch. Korean Fairy Tales stamps .. 1·75 40
N 2129. 30 ch. Japanese stamps 3·00 90

752. League Members and Flag.

1981. Seventh League of Socialist Working Youth Congress, Pyongyang.
N 2131. **752.** 10 ch. mult. .. 20 10
N 2132. 80 ch. mult. .. 60 10

753. Government Palace, Sofia, Bulgarian Arms and Khan Asparuch.

1981. 1300th Anniv. of Bulgarian State.
N 2133. **753.** 10 ch. mult. .. 15 10

754. Dimitrov.

1981. Birth Centenary of Georgi Dimitrov (Bulgarian statesman).
N 2134. **754.** 10 ch. mult. .. 15 10

755. Emblem, Lufthansa "B 747", City Hall and Mercedes "500".

1981. "Philatelia '81" International Stamp Fair, Frankfurt-am-Main.
N 2135. **755.** 20 ch. mult. .. 2·25 35

756. "Concorde" and Zeppelin.

1981. "Philexfrance 82" International Stamp Exhibition, Paris. Multicoloured.

(a) As T **756**.

N 2136. 10 ch. Type **756** .. 2·75 40
N 2137. 20 ch. "Concorde" Breguet "Provence", and Breguet's and Santos-Dumont's aircraft .. .. 3·25 75
N 2138. 30 ch. "Mona Lisa" and stamps .. .. 1·75 30

(b) Size 32 × 53 mm.

N 2140. 10 ch. Hotel des Invalides, Paris .. 1·50 45
N 2141. 20 ch. President Mitterand of France 1·50 45
N 2142. 30 ch. International Friendship Exhibition building 1·50 45
N 2143. 70 ch. Kim Il Sung .. 1·50 45

757. Rising Sun.

758. Emblem and Flags.

1982. New Year.

N 2144. **757.** 10 ch. mult. .. 30 10

1982. "Prospering Korea". Multicoloured.

N2145 2 ch. Type **758** .. 15 10
N2146 10 ch. Industry .. 25 10
N2147 10 ch. Agriculture .. 25 10
N2148 10 ch. Mining 45 10
N2149 10 ch. Arts 25 10
N2150 10 ch. Al Islet lighthouse, Uam-ri .. 75 15
N2151 40 ch. Buildings .. 50 15

759. "The Hair-do".

1982. Birth Centenary of Pablo Picasso (artist). Multicoloured.

N 2152. 10 ch. Type **759** .. 75 20
N 2153. 10 ch. "Paulo on a donkey" .. .. 1·75 35
N 2154. 20 ch. "Woman Leaning on Arm" .. 90 25
N 2155. 20 ch. "Harlequin" .. 1·75 35
N 2156. 25 ch. "Child with Pigeon" .. .. 1·90 50
N 2157. 25 ch. "Reading a Letter" .. .. 1·75 35
N 2158. 35 ch. "Portrait of Gertrude Stein" .. 1·50 30
N 2159. 35 ch. "Harlequin" (different) .. .. 1·75 35
N 2160. 80 ch. "Minotaur" .. 1·75 35
N 2161. 90 ch. "Mother with Child" .. .. 1·75 35

760. Fireworks over Pyongyang.

1982. Kim Il Sung's 70th Birthday. Mult.

N2163 10 ch. Kim Il Sung's birthplace, Mangyongdae .. 20 10
N2164 10 ch. Type **760** .. 20 10
N2165 10 ch. "The Day will dawn on down-trodden Korea" .. 20 10
N2166 10 ch. Signalling start of Pochonbo Battle .. 20 10
N2167 10 ch. Kim Il Sung starting Potong River project 20 10
N2168 10 ch. Embracing bereaved children .. 20 10
N2169 10 ch. Kim Il Sung as Supreme Commander 20 10
N2170 10 ch. "On the Road of Advance" 20 10
N2171 10 ch. Kim Il Sung kindling flame of Chollima Movement, Kansong Steel Plant 75 25
N2172 10 ch. Kim Il Sung talking to peasants .. 20 10
N2173 10 ch. Kim Il Sung fixing site of reservoir 30 10
N2174 20 ch. Kim Il Sung visiting Komdok Valley 75 25
N2175 20 ch. Kim Il Sung visiting Red Flag Company 20 10
N2176 20 ch. Kim Il Sung teaching Juche farming methods .. 20 10
N2177 20 ch. Kim Il Sung visiting iron works .. 35 10
N2178 20 ch. Kim Il Sung talking with smelters 35 10
N2179 20 ch. Kim Il Sung at chemical plant .. 45 10
N2180 20 ch. Kim Il Sung with fishermen 40 10

Nos. N2165/80 are horiz designs.

761. Soldier saluting.

1982. 50th Anniv. of People's Army.

N 2182. **761.** 10 ch. mult. .. 25 10

762. "The Bagpiper" (Durer).

763. Surveyors.

1982. Fourth Essen International Stamp Fair.

N 2183. **762.** 30 ch. mult. .. 3·75 40

1982. Implementation of Four Nature-remaking Tasks.

N 2184. **763.** 10 ch. mult. .. 25 10

764. Princess as Baby.

765. Tower of the Juche Idea Pyongyang.

1982. 21st Birthday of Princess of Wales.

N 2185. **764.** 10 ch. mult. .. 60 20
N 2186. – 20 ch. mult. .. 1·25 35
N 2187. – 30 ch. mult. .. 1·50 45
N 2188. – 50 ch. mult. .. 2·00 60
N 2189. – 60 ch. mult. .. 2·00 60
N 2190. – 70 ch. mult. .. 2·00 60
N 2191. – 80 ch. mult. .. 2·00 60

DESIGNS: 20 to 80 ch. Princess at various ages.

1982.

2193. **765.** 2 wn. mult. .. 1·25 30
2194. – 3 wn. orge. & blk. 1·75 40

DESIGN: (26 × 38 mm.) 3 wn. Arch of Triumph.

766. Tiger.

1982. Tigers.

N 2195. **766.** 20 ch. mult. .. 1·25 35
N 2196. – 30 ch. mult. .. 1·90 35
N 2197. – 30 ch. mult. (horiz.) 2·75 45
N 2198. – 40 ch. mult. (horiz.) 2·75 45
N 2199. – 80 ch. mult. (horiz.) 2·75 45

DESIGNS: 30 to 80 ch. Tigers.

767. Group 1 Countries.

1982. World Cup Football Championship, Spain (3rd issue). Multicoloured.

N 2201. 10 ch. Type **767** .. 60 20
N 2202. 20 ch. Group 2 countries .. .. 1·25 25
N 2203. 30 ch. Group 3 countries .. .. 1·75 30
N 2204. 40 ch. Group 4 countries .. .. 2·10 40
N 2205. 50 ch. Group 5 countries .. .. 2·50 50
N 2206. 60 ch. Group 6 countries .. .. 3·00 50

768. Rocket Launch.

769. Charlotte von Stein.

1982. The Universe. Multicoloured.

N 2208. 10 ch. Type **768** .. 1·50 60
N 2209. 20 ch. Spaceship over globe .. .. 1·50 60
N 2210. 80 ch. Spaceship between globe and moon .. .. 1·50 60

1982. 150th Death Anniv. of Johann von Goethe (writer). Multicoloured.

N 2212. 10 ch. Type **769** .. 50 25
N 2213. 10 ch. Goethe's mother 1·50 45
N 2214. 20 ch. Goethe's sister .. 75 30
N 2215. 20 ch. Angelika Kauffmann .. .. 1·50 45
N 2216. 25 ch. Charlotte Buff .. 90 35
N 2217. 25 ch. Anna Amalia .. 1·50 45
N 2218. 35 ch. Lili Schonemann 1·25 40
N 2219. 35 ch. Charlotte von Lengefeld .. 1·50 45
N 2220. 80 ch. Goethe .. .. 1·60 45

770. Player holding aloft World Cup.

1982. World Cup Football Championship Results. Multicoloured.

N 2222. 20 ch. Type **770** .. 1·25 30
N 2223. 30 ch. Group of players with World Cup .. 1·75 50
N 2224. 30 ch. Type **770** .. 2·50 65
N 2225. 40 ch. As No. N 2203 .. 2·50 65
N 2226. 80 ch. King Juan Carlos of Spain and two players with World Cup .. .. 2·50 65

771. Princess and Prince William of Wales.

1982. 1st Wedding Anniv. of Prince and Princess of Wales.

N 2228. **771.** 30 ch. mult. .. 4·50 1·75

772. Royal Couple with Prince William.

1982. Birth of Prince William of Wales. Multicoloured.

N 2230. 10 ch. Couple with Prince William (different) .. .. 1·50 50
N 2231. 10 ch. Princess of Wales holding bouquet .. 3·00 1·50
N 2232. 20 ch. Couple with Prince William (different) .. .. 1·75 60
N 2233. 20 ch. Prince Charles carrying baby, and Princess of Wales .. 3·00 1·50
N 2234. 30 ch. Type **772** .. 2·00 75
N 2235. 30 ch. Prince Charles carrying baby, and Princess of Wales (different) .. .. 3·00 1·50
N 2236. 40 ch. Princess with baby .. .. .. 2·75 90
N 2237. 40 ch. Prince and Princess of Wales (horiz.) .. .. 4·75 1·90
N 2238. 50 ch. Princess with baby (different) .. 3·50 1·00
N 2239. 50 ch. Prince and Princess of Wales in evening dress (horiz.) 4·75 1·90
N 2240. 80 ch. Couple with Prince William (different) .. .. 3·00 1·50
N 2241. 80 ch. Prince Charles holding baby, and Princess of Wales (horiz.) .. .. 4·75 1·90

773. Baldwin's Airship, 1908.

1982. Bicentenary of Manned Flight (1st issue). Multicoloured.

N 2243. 10 ch. Type **773** .. 1·25 40
N 2244. 10 ch. Pauley and Durs Egg's airship, 1818 .. 2·50 60
N 2245. 20 ch. Tissandier brothers' airship, 1883 .. .. 1·50 50
N 2246. 20 ch. Guyot's balloon, 1784 .. .. .. 2·50 60
N 2247. 30 ch. Parseval "PL VII", 1912 .. .. 2·00 60
N 2248. 30 ch. George Cayley's airship, 1837 .. 2·50 60
N 2249. 40 ch. Count Lennox's "Eagle", 1834 .. 2·25 60
N 2250. 40 ch. Camille Vert's "Poisson Volant", 1859 .. .. .. 2·50 60
N 2251. 80 ch. Dupuy de Lome's airship, 1872 2·50 60

774. "Utopic Post Balloon" (Balthasar Antoine Dunker).

1982. Bicentenary of Manned Flight (2nd issue). Multicoloured.

N 2253. 10 ch. Type **774** .. 1·50 40
N 2254. 10 ch. Balloon at Versailles, 1783 .. 3·00 60
N 2255. 20 ch. ". . . and they fly into heaven and have no wings . . ." 2·00 50
N 2256. 20 ch. Montgolfier Brothers' balloon, 1783 .. .. .. 3·00 60
N 2257. 30 ch. Pierre Testu-Brissy's test flight, 1798 .. .. .. 2·50 60
N 2258. 30 ch. Balloon landing at Nesle .. .. 3·00 60
N 2259. 40 ch. Test flight of Zenith, 1875 .. 3·00 60
N 2260. 40 ch. Blanchard's flight over English Channel .. .. 3·00 60
N 2261. 80 ch. Gas balloon at World Fair, 1878 .. 3·00 60

775. Turtle with Scroll.

1982. Tale of the Hare. Multicoloured.

N 2263. 10 ch. Type **775** .. 90 15
N 2264. 20 ch. Hare riding on turtle .. .. 1·25 20
N 2265. 30 ch. Hare and turtle before Dragon King 1·50 30
N 2266. 40 ch. Hare back on land .. .. .. 2·00 40

776. Flag, Red Book and City.
777. Tower of Juche Idea.

1982. 10th Anniv. of Socialist Constitution.

N 2267. **776.** 10 ch. mult. .. 25 10

1983. New Year.

N 2268. **777.** 10 ch. mult. .. 15 10

778. Children reading "Saenal".

1983. 55th Anniv. of "Saenal" Newspaper.

N 2269. **778.** 10 ch. mult. .. 50 10

779. "Man in Oriental Costume".

1983. Paintings by Rembrandt. Mult.

N 2270. 10 ch. Type **779** .. 75 30
N 2271. 10 ch. "Child with dead Peacocks" (detail) .. 2·50 60
N 2272. 20 ch. "The Noble Slav" .. .. 1·50 40
N 2273. 20 ch. "Old Man in Fur Hat" .. .. 2·50 60
N 2274. 30 ch. "Dr. Tulp's Anatomy Lesson" (detail) .. .. 2·75 75
N 2275. 30 ch. "Portrait of a fashionable Couple" 2·50 60
N 2276. 40 ch. "Two Scholars disputing" .. .. 2·00 50
N 2277. 40 ch. "Woman with Child" .. .. 2·50 60
N 2278. 80 ch. "Woman holding an Ostrich Feather Fan" .. .. 2·50 60

780. Airship over Cologne.

1983. "Luposta" International Air Mail Exhibition, Cologne. Multicoloured.

N 2280. 30 ch. Type **780** .. 3·00 90
N 2281. 40 ch. Airship over Cologne (different) .. 3·00 90

781. Banner and Monument.

1983. 50th Anniv. of Wangjaesan Meeting.

N 2283. **781.** 10 ch. mult. .. 20 10

782. Karl Marx.

1983. Death Centenary of Karl Marx.

N 2284. **782.** 10 ch. mult. .. 50 25

783. Scholar, Marchers and Map of Journey.

1983. 60th Anniv. of Thousand-ri Journey for Learning.

N 2285. **783.** 10 ch. mult. .. 50 10

784. "Madonna of the Goldfinch".

1983. 500th Birth Anniv. of Raphael. Multicoloured.

N 2286. 10 ch. Type **784** .. 1·50 40
N 2287. 20 ch. "The School of Athens" (detail) .. 2·25 60
N 2288. 30 ch. "Madonna of the Grand Duke" .. 2·50 55
n 2289. 50 ch. "Madonna of the Chair" .. .. 2·75 55
N 2290. 50 ch. "Madonna of the Lamb" .. .. 2·25 60
N 2291. 80 ch. "The Beautiful Gardener" .. .. 2·25 60

785. Department Store No. 1.

1983. Pyongyang Buildings. Multicoloured.

N 2293. 2 ch. Chongryu Restaurant 20 10
N 2294. 10 ch. Part of Munsu Street 30 10
N 2295. 10 ch. Ice Rink .. 40 10
N 2296. 40 ch. Type **785** .. 60 15
N 2297. 70 ch. Grand People's Study House .. 75 25

786. Emblem and Crowd.

1983. 5th Anniv. of International Institute of Juche Idea.

N 2298. **786.** 10 ch. mult. .. 15 10

787. Judo.

1983. Olympic Games, Los Angeles (1st issue). Multicoloured.

N 2299. 20 ch. Type **787** .. 1·00 50
N 2300. 20 ch. Wrestling .. 1·90 50
N 2301. 30 ch. Judo (different) (value in gold) .. 1·00 50
N 2302. 30 ch. Judo (different) (value in black) .. 1·90 50
N 2303. 40 ch. Boxing .. .. 1·00 50
N 2304. 40 ch. Li Ho Jun (1972 shooting gold medal- 1·90 50
list) .. .. .. 1·00 50
N 2305. 50 ch. Weightlifting ..
N 2306. 50 ch. Wrestling (different) .. .. 1·90 50
N 2307. 80 ch. Boxing (different) 1·90 50

See also Nos. N 2359/64.

788. Satellite, Masts and Dish Aerial.

1983. World Communications Year (1st issue).

N 2309. **788.** 10 ch. mult. .. 1·50 20

See also Nos. N 2349/53.

789. Emblem, Giant Panda and Stamp.

1983. "Tembal 83" International Thematic Stamp Exhibition, Basel. Multicoloured.

N 2310. 20 ch. Type **789** .. 1·75 35
N 2311. 30 ch. Emblem, flag and Basel Town Post stamp .. .. 1·90 35

790. "Colourful Cow" (kogge), 1402.

1983. Old Ships. Multicoloured.

N2312 20 ch. Type **790** .. 1·10 45
N2313 20 ch. "Turtle" ship, 1592 .. .. 2·40 75
N2314 35 ch. "Great Harry" (warship), 1555 .. 1·50 55
N2315 35 ch. Admiral Li Sun Sin and "turtle" ship 2·40 75
N2316 50 ch. "Eagle of Lubeck" (galleon), 1567 .. .. 2·10 70
N2317 50 ch. "Merkur" (full-rigged sailing ship), 1847 .. .. 2·40 75
N2318 80 ch. "Herzogin Elisabeth" (cadet ship) .. .. 2·40 75

791. "Locomotion", 1825.

1983. Railway Locomotives. Multicoloured.

N 2320 20 ch. Type **791** .. 1·25 60
N 2321 20 ch. "Drache", 1848 3·50 1·00
N 2322 35 ch. "Der Adler", 1835 .. .. 1·75 80
N 2323 35 ch. Korean steam locomotive, 1853 .. 3·50 1·00
N 2324 50 ch. "Austria", 1837 2·75 80
N 2325 50 ch. Bristol and Exeter Railway steam locomotive, 1853 .. .. 3·50 1·00
N 2326 80 ch. Caledonian Railway locomotive, 1859 3·50 1·00

792. Map, Hand and Weapons.

1983. 10th Anniv. of Publication of Five-point Policy for Korea's Reunification.
N 2328. **792.** 10 ch. mult. .. 25 10

793. Emblem, Tower of Juche Idea and Fireworks.

1983. World Conference on Journalists against Imperialism and for Friendship and Peace, Pyongyang. Multicoloured.
N 2329. 10 ch. Type **793** .. 30 10
N 2330. 40 ch. Emblem and rainbow and clasped hands 50 15
N 2331. 70 ch. Emblem, map and hand with raised forefinger 75 20

794. Worker and Banners.

1983. "Let's Create the Speed of the 80s".
N2332 **794** 10 ch multicoloured 25 10

795. Soldier and Rejoicing Crowd.

1983. 30th Anniv. of Victory in Liberation War.
N 2333. **795.** 10 ch. mult. .. 25 10

796. "Gorch Foch" (cadet barque) and Korean 1978 2 ch. Stamp.

1983. "Bangkok 1983" International Stamp Exhibition.
N2334 **796** 40 ch. multicoloured 3·00 1·25

797. Skiing.

1983. Winter Olympic Games, Sarajevo (1984). Multicoloured.
N2336 10 ch. Type **797** .. 75 35
N2337 20 ch. Figure skating (vert) .. .. 2·50 60
N2338 30 ch. Skating (pair) .. 2·00 90
N2339 50 ch. Ski jumping .. 2·00 90
N2340 50 ch. Ice hockey (vert) 2·50 60
N2341 80 ch. Speed skating (vert) .. .. 2·50 60

798. Workers and Soldier with Books.

1983. 35th Anniv. of Korean People's Democratic Republic.
N 2343. **798.** 10 ch. mult. .. 35 10

799. Archery.

800. Girls holding Hands.

1983. Folk Games. Multicoloured.
N 2344. 10 ch. Type **799** .. 1·75 40
N 2345. 10 ch. Flying kites .. 90 20
N 2346. 40 ch. See-sawing .. 75 20
N 2347. 40 ch. Swinging .. 90 20

1983. Korean-Chinese Friendship.
N 2348. **800.** 10 ch. mult. .. 15 10

801. Envelopes and Forms of Transport.

802. Portrait.

1983. World Communications Year (2nd issue). Multicoloured.
N 2349. 30 ch. Mail van, motor-cyclist and hand holding magazines .. 3·75 1·10
N 2350. 30 ch. Satellite, globe and dish aerial .. 1·75 70
N 2351. 40 ch. Type **801** .. 3·75 1·10
N 2352. 40 ch. Television camera-man .. .. .. 1·75 70
N 2353. 80 ch. Telephone and aerial .. .. 1·75 70

1983. Paintings by Rubens. Multicoloured.
N2355 40 ch. Type **802** .. 2·00 90
N2356 40 ch. Portrait (different) (horiz) .. 2·50 1·00
N2357 80 ch. "The Sentencing of Midas" (horiz) .. 2·50 1·00

803. Sprinting.

1983. Olympic Games, Los Angeles (2nd issue). Multicoloured.
N 2359. 10 ch. Type **803** .. 75 20
N 2360. 20 ch. Show jumping .. 1·75 45
N 2361. 30 ch. Cycling .. 3·00 55
N 2362. 50 ch. Handball .. 2·00 60
N 2363. 50 ch. Fencing .. 1·75 45
N 2364. 80 ch. Gymnastics .. 1·75 45

804. "St. Catherine".

805. Kimilsungflower.

804a. Cat.

1983. 450th Death Anniv of Antonio Correggio (artist) (1984). Multicoloured.
N2366 20 ch. Type **804** .. 1·75 60
N2367 20 ch. "Morning" (detail) .. .. 2·50 75
N2368 35 ch. "Madonna" .. 1·75 60
N2369 35 ch. "Morning" (different) .. .. 2·50 75
N2370 50 ch. "Madonna with St. John" .. .. 1·75 60
N2371 50 ch. "St. Catherine" (different) .. .. 2·50 75
N2372 80 ch. "Madonna and Child" .. .. 2·50 75

1983. Cats. Multicoloured, frame colour given.
N2373a **804a** 10 ch. green .. 50 10
N2373b – 10 ch. gold .. 50 10
N2373c – 10 ch. blue .. 50 10
N2373d – 10 ch. red .. 50 10
N2373e – 10 ch. silver .. 50 10
DESIGNS: Different cat's heads.

1984. New Year.
N 2374. **805.** 10 ch. mult. .. 65 10

806. Worker and Workers' Party Flag.

1984. "Under the Leadership of the Workers' Party". Multicoloured.
N 2375. 10 ch. Type **806** .. 25 10
N 2376. 10 ch. Ore-dressing plant No. 3, Komdok General Mining Enterprise, and Party Flag 40 10

807. Farm Worker, Rice and Maize.

1984. 20th Anniv. of Publication of "Theses of the Socialist Rural Question in Our Country".
N 2377. **807.** 10 ch. mult. .. 25 10

808. Changdok School, Chilgol.

1984. Kim Il Sung's 72nd Birthday.
N 2378. **808.** 5 ch. green, black and blue .. 25 10
N 2379. – 10 ch. mult. .. 25 10
DESIGN: 10 ch. Birthplace, Mangyongdae, and rejoicing crowd.

INDEX

Countries can be quickly located by referring to the index at the end of this volume.

809. "Spanish Riding School" (Julius von Blaas).

1984. "Espana 84" International Stamp Exhibition, Madrid. Multicoloured.
N 2380. 10 ch. Type **809** .. 1·75 50
N 2381. 20 ch. "Ferdinand of Austria" (Rubens) .. 1·75 50

810. "La Donna Velata".

812. Construction Site.

811. Map and Second Stage Pumping Station.

1984. 500th Birth Anniv. (1983) of Raphael (artist). Multicoloured.
N 2383. 10 ch. "Portrait of Agnolo Doni" .. 1·50 50
N 2384. 20 ch. Type **810** .. 1·50 50
N 2385. 30 ch. "Portrait of Jeanne d'Aragon" .. 1·50 50

1984. 25th Anniv. of Kiyang Irrigation System.
N 2387. **811.** 10 ch. multicoloured 50 10

1984. Construction on Five District Fronts.
N2388 **812** 10 ch. red, blk & yell 50 10

813. Bobsleighing (East Germany).

1984. Winter Olympic Games Medal Winners. Multicoloured.
N2389 10 ch. Ski jumping (Matti Nykaenen) .. 1·75 50
N2390 20 ch. Speed skating (Karin Enke) .. 1·50 40
N2391 20 ch. Slalom (Max Julen) .. .. 1·75 50
N2392 30 ch. Type **813** .. 1·50 40
N2393 30 ch. Downhill skiing (Maria Walliser) .. 1·75 50
N2394 40 ch. Cross-country skiing (Thomas Wassberg) .. .. 2·75 60
N2395 80 ch. Cross-country skiing (Marja-Liisa Hamalainen) .. 2·75 60

814. Type "E" Goods Locomotive.

1984. Essen International Stamp Fair. Mult.
N2397 20 ch. Type "202" express locomotive .. 3·25 65
N2398 30 ch. Type **814** .. 3·25 65

815. "Mlle. Fiocre in the Ballet 'La Source'".

1984. 150th Birth Anniv of Edgar Degas (artist). Multicoloured.

N2400 10 ch. Type **815** .. 1·50 25
N2401 20 ch. "The Dance Foyer at the Rue le Peletier Opera" .. 2·50 25
N2402 30 ch. "Race Meeting" 3·75 40

816. Map of Pyongnam Irrigation System and Reservoir.

1984. Irrigation Experts Meeting, Pyongyang.
N2404 **816** 2 ch. multicoloured 40 10

817. Korean Stamp and Building.

818. Crowd and Banners.

1984. U.P.U. Congress Stamp Exn, Hamburg.
N2405 **817** 20 ch. multicoloured 3·00 40

1984. Proposal for Tripartite Talks.
N2407 **818** 10 ch. multicoloured 40 10

819. Nobel experimenting.

1984. 150th Birth Anniv (1983) of Alfred Bernhard Nobel (inventor). Multicoloured.

N2408 20 ch. Type **819** .. 3·00 45
N2409 30 ch. Portrait of Nobel 3·00 45

820. Drinks, Tinned Food, Clothes and Flats.

1984. Improvements of Living Standards.
N2411 **820** 10 ch. multicoloured 40 10

821. Sunhwa School, Mangyongdae.

1984. School of Kim Hyong Jik (Kim Il Sung's Father).
N2412 **821** 10 ch. multicoloured 40 10

822. Armed Crowd with Banners.

1984. 65th Anniv. of Kuandian Conference.
N 2413. **822.** 10 ch. multicoloured 40 10

823. "Thunia bracteata".

1984. Flowers. Multicoloured.

N 2414. 10 ch. "Cattleya loddigesii" 60 10
N 2415. 20 ch. Type **823** .. 90 25
N 2416. 30 ch. "Phalaenopsis amabilis" .. .. 1·25 40

824. Swordfish and Trawler.

1984. Fishing Industry. Multicoloured.

N2418 5 ch. Type **824** .. 50 15
N2419 10 ch. Marlin and trawler 70 25
N2420 40 ch. "Histiophorus orientalis" and game fishing launch .. 2·25 95

825. Revolutionary Museum, Chilgol.

1984.
N 2421. **825.** 10 ch. multicoloured 40 10

826. Kim Hyok, Cha Gwang Su and Youth.

828. Clock Face.

827. Inauguration of a French Railway Line, 1860.

1984. "Let's All become the Kim Hyoks and Cha Gwang Sus of the '80s".
N2422 **826** 10 ch. multicoloured 40 10

1984. Centenary (1983) of "Orient Express". Multicoloured.

N 2423. 10 ch. Type **827** .. 90 25
N 2424. 20 ch. Opening of a British railway line, 1821 .. .. .. 2·00 55
N 2425. 30 ch. Inauguration of Paris-Rouen line, 1843 .. .. .. 2·75 85

1984. Centenary of Greenwich Meridian.
N 2427. **828.** 10 ch. multicoloured 2·50 1·00

829. Grand Theatre, Hamhung.

830. Turning on Machinery.

1984.
N 2429. **829.** 10 ch. blue .. 40 10

1984. Automation of Industry.
N 2430. **830.** 40 ch. multicoloured 60 30

831 "Dragon Angler"

1984. Paintings. Multicoloured.

N2431 10 ch. Type **831** .. 60 10
N2432 20 ch. "Ox Driver" (Kim Du Ryang) (47 × 35 mm) .. 90 25
N2433 30 ch. "Bamboo" (Kim Jin U) (47 × 35 mm) 1·25 40

832 Tsiolkovsky

1984. K. E. Tsiolkovsky (space scientist). Multicoloured.

N2435 20 ch. Type **832** .. 90 25
N2436 30 ch. "Sputnik" orbiting Earth .. 1·25 40

833 "Pongdaesan"

1984. Container Ships. Multicoloured.

N2438 10 ch. Type **833** .. 80 15
N2439 20 ch. "Ryongnamsan" 1·10 35
N2440 30 ch. "Rungrado" .. 1·60 50

834 Caracal

1984. Animals. Multicoloured.

N2442 10 ch. Spotted hyenas 60 10
N2443 20 ch. Type **834** .. 90 25
N2444 30 ch. Black-backed jackals .. .. 1·25 40
N2445 40 ch. Foxes .. .. 1·60 60

835 Marie Curie

836 Chestnut-eared Aracari

1984. 50th Anniv of Marie Curie (physicist).
N2447 **835** 10 ch. multicoloured 60 10

1984. Birds. Multicoloured.

N2449 10 ch. Hoopoe 70 10
N2450 20 ch. South African crowned cranes .. 1·10 25
N2451 30 ch. Saddle-bill stork 1·50 40
N2452 40 ch. Type **836** .. 1·90 60

837 Cosmonaut

1984. Space Exploration. Multicoloured.

N2454 10 ch. Type **837** .. 60 10
N2455 20 ch. Cosmonaut on space-walk 90 25
N2456 30 ch. Cosmonaut (different) .. .. 1·25 40

838 "Arktika"

1984. Russian Ice-breakers. Multicoloured.

N2458 20 ch. Type **838** .. 1·25 35
N2459 30 ch. "Ermak" .. 1·75 50

839 Mendeleev

1984. 150th Birth Anniv of Dmitri Mendeleev (chemist).
N2461 **839** 10 ch. multicoloured 60 10

840 Kim Il Sung in U.S.S.R.

1984. Kim Il Sung's Visits to Eastern Europe. Multicoloured.

N2463 10 ch. Type **840** .. 60 10
N2464 10 ch. In Poland .. 60 10
N2465 10 ch. In German Democratic Republic 60 10
N2466 10 ch. In Czechoslovakia 60 10
N2467 10 ch. In Hungary .. 60 10
N2468 10 ch. in Bulgaria .. 60 10
N2469 10 ch. In Rumania .. 60 10

841 Freesia

1985. New Year.
N2471 **841** 10 ch. multicoloured 40 10

842 Journey Route, Steam Locomotive and Memorials

1985. 60th Anniv of 1000 ri Journey by Kim Il Sung. Multicoloured.
N2472 5 ch. Type **842** .. 40 10
N2473 10 ch. Boy trumpeter and schoolchildren following route .. 40 10
Nos. N2472/3 were issued together, se-tenant, forming a composite design.

843 Cugnot's Steam Car, 1769 — **844** Camp, Mt. Paekdu

1985. History the of Motor Car (1st series). Multicoloured.
N2474 10 ch. Type **843** .. 60 10
N2475 15 ch. Goldsworthy Gurney steam omnibus, 1825 .. 75 15
N2476 20 ch. Gottlieb Daimler diesel car, 1885 .. 90 25
N2477 25 ch. Benz three-wheeled diesel car, 1886 .. .. .. 1·10 35
N2478 30 ch. Peugeot diesel car, 1891 .. .. 1·25 40
See also Nos. N2562/6.

1985. Korean Revolution Headquarters.
N2480 **844** 10 ch. multicoloured 40 20

845 Taechodo Lighthouse — **846** Hedgehog challenges Tiger

1985. Lighthouses. Multicoloured.
N2481 10 ch. Type **845** .. 75 10
N2482 20 ch. Sodo .. .. 1·10 30
N2483 30 ch. Pido .. .. 1·60 45
N2484 40 ch. Suundo .. .. 2·00 70

1985. "The Hedgehog defeats the Tiger" (fable). Multicoloured.
N2485 10 ch. Type **846** .. 60 10
N2486 20 ch. Tiger goes to stamp on rolled-up hedgehog 90 25
N2487 30 ch. Hedgehog clings to tiger's nose .. 1·25 40
N2488 35 ch. Tiger flees .. 1·40 50
N2489 40 ch. Tiger crawls before hedgehog .. 1·60 60

MORE DETAILED LISTS

are given in the Stanley Gibbons Catalogues referred to in the country headings.
For lists of current volumes see Introduction.

847 "Pleurotus cornucopiae" — **848** West Germany v. Hungary, 1954

1985. Fungi. Multicoloured.
N2490 10 ch. Type **847** .. 60 10
N2491 20 ch. Oyster fungus .. 90 25
N2492 30 ch. "Catathelasma ventricosum" .. 1·25 40

1985. World Cup Football Championship Finals.
N2493 **848** 10 ch. black, buff and brown .. 60 10
N2494 – 10 ch. multicoloured 60 10
N2495 – 20 ch. black, buff and brown .. 90 25
N2496 – 20 ch. multicoloured 90 25
N2497 – 30 ch. black, buff and brown .. 1·25 40
N2498 – 30 ch. multicoloured 1·25 40
N2499 – 40 ch. black, buff and brown .. 1·60 60
N2500 – 40 ch. multicoloured 1·60 60
DESIGNS—VERT. N2496, West Germany v. Netherlands, 1974; N2499, England v. West Germany, 1966. HORIZ. N2494, Brazil v. Italy, 1970; N2495, Brazil v. Sweden, 1958; N2497, Brazil v. Czechoslovakia, 1962; N2498, Argentina v. Netherlands, 1968; N2500, Italy v. West Germany, 1982.

849 Date and Kim Il Sung's Birthplace — **850** Horn Player

1985. 73rd Birthday of Kim Il Sung.
N2502 **849** 10 ch. multicoloured 40 10

1985. 4th-century Musical Instruments. Mult.
N2503 10 ch. Type **850** .. 60 10
N2504 20 ch. So (pipes) player 90 25

851 Chongryon Hall, Tokyo — **852** Common Marmoset

1985. 30th Anniv of Chongryon (General Association of Korean Residents in Japan).
N2505 **851** 10 ch. brown .. 40 10

1985. Mammals. Multicoloured.
N2506 5 ch. Type **852** .. 45 10
N2507 10 ch. Ring-tailed lemur 45 10

854 Buenos Aires and Argentina 1982 Stamp — **855** Dancer and Gymnast

1985. "Argentina '85" International Stamp Exhibition, Buenos Aires. Multicoloured.
N2509 10 ch. Type **854** .. 60 10
N2510 20 ch. Iguacu Falls and Argentina 1984 and North Korea 1978 stamps (horiz) 90 25

1985. 12th World Youth and Students' Festival, Moscow. Multicoloured.
N2512 10 ch. Type **855** .. 60 10
N2513 20 ch. Spassky Tower, Moscow, and Festival emblem 90 25
N2514 40 ch. Youths of different races .. 1·60 60

856 Peace Pavilion, Youth Park — **857** Liberation Celebrations

1985. Pyongyang Buildings.
N2515 **856** 2 ch. black & green 20 10
N2516 – 40 ch. brn & lt brn 45 20
DESIGN: 40 ch. Multi-storey flats, Chollima Street.

1985. 40th Anniv of Liberation.
N2517 – 5 ch. red, black & bl 20 10
N2518 – 10 ch. multicoloured 40 10
N2519 – 10 ch. brown, black and green .. 40 10
N2520 – 10 ch. multicoloured 40 10
N2521 **857** 10 ch. yellow, black and red 40 10
N2522 – 10 ch. red, orange and black .. 40 10
N2523 – 40 ch. multicoloured 60 20
DESIGNS—HORIZ. No. N2517, Soldiers with rifles and flag; N2518, Crowd with banners and Flame of Juche; N2519, Korean and Soviet soldiers raising arms; N2520, Japanese soldiers laying down weapons; N2523, Students bearing banners. VERT. N2522, Liberation Tower, Moran Hill, Pyongyang.

858 Halley and Comet

1985. Appearance of Halley's Comet. Mult.
N2525 10 ch. Type **858** .. 60 10
N2526 20 ch. Diagram of comet's flight and space probe 90 25

859 "Camellia japonica" — **861** Party Founding Museum

860 "Hunting"

1985. Flowers. Multicoloured.
N2528 10 ch. "Hippeastrum hybridum" .. 60 10
N2529 20 ch. Type **859** .. 90 25
N2530 30 ch. "Cyclamen persicum" .. .. 1·25 40

1985. Koguryo Culture.
N2531 10 ch. "Hero" (vert) .. 60 10
N2532 15 ch. "Heroine" (vert) 75 15
N2533 20 ch. "Flying Fairy" 90 25
N2534 25 ch. Type **860** .. 1·10 35

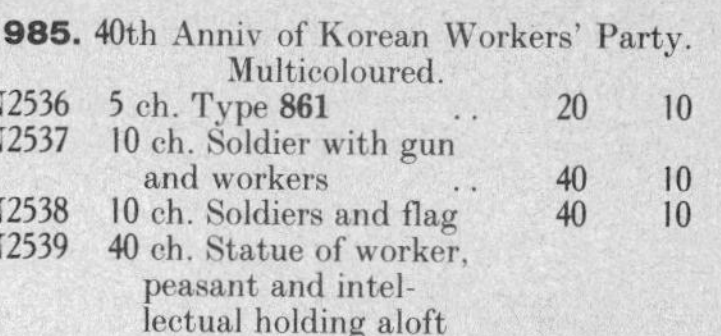

1985. 40th Anniv of Korean Workers' Party. Multicoloured.
N2536 5 ch. Type **861** .. 20 10
N2537 10 ch. Soldier with gun and workers .. 40 10
N2538 10 ch. Soldiers and flag 40 10
N2539 40 ch. Statue of worker, peasant and intellectual holding aloft party emblem .. 60 20

862 Arch of Triumph, Pyongyang — **863** Colosseum, Rome, and N. Korea 1975 10 ch. Stamp

1985. 40th Anniv of Kim Il Sung's Return.
N2541 **862** 10 ch. brown & green 40 10

1985. "Italia '85" International Stamp Exhibition, Rome. Multicolourd.
N2542 10 ch. Type **863** .. 60 10
N2543 20 ch. "The Holy Family" (Raphael) (vert) 90 25
N2544 30 ch. Head of "David" (statue, Michelangelo) (vert) .. .. 1·25 40

864 Mercedes Benz Type "300"

1985. South-West German Stamp Fair, Sindelfingen. Multicoloured.
N2546 10 ch. Type **864** .. 60 10
N2547 15 ch. Mercedes Benz Type "770" .. 75 15
N2548 20 ch. Mercedes Benz "W 150" 90 25
N2549 30 ch. Mercedes Type "600" .. .. 1·25 40

865 Tackle

1985. World Cup Football Championship, Mexico (1st issue). Multicoloured.
N2551 20 ch. Type **865** .. 90 25
N2552 30 ch. Three players .. 1·25 40
See also Nos. N2558/9 and N2577/82.

866 Dancers

1985. International Youth Year. Mult.
N2554 10 ch. Type **866** .. 60 10
N2555 20 ch. Sports activities 90 25
N2556 30 ch. Technology .. 1·25 40

867 Players

1985. World Cup Football Championship, Mexico (2nd issue). Multicoloured.
N2558 20 ch. Type **867** .. 90 25
N2559 30 ch. Goalkeeper and players .. .. 1·25 40

868 Juche Torch

869 Amedee Bollee and Limousine, 1901

1986. New Year.
N2561 **868** 10 ch. multicoloured 40 10

1986. History of the Motor Car (2nd series). Multicoloured.
N2562 10 ch. Type **869** .. 60 10
N2563 20 ch. Stewart Rolls, Henry Royce and "Silver Ghost", 1906 90 25
N2564 25 ch. Giovanni Agnelli and Fiat car, 1912 .. 1·10 35
N2565 30 ch. Ettore Bugatti and "Royal" coupe, 1928 .. .. .. 1·25 40
N2566 40 ch. Louis Renault and fiacre, 1906 .. 1·60 60

870 Gary Kasparov

872 Tongdu Rock, Songgan

871 Cemetery Gate

1986. World Chess Championship, Moscow.
N2568 **870** 20 ch. multicoloured 90 25

1986. Revolutionary Martyrs' Cemetery, Pyongyang. Multicoloured.
N2570 5 ch. Type **871** .. 20 10
N2571 10 ch. Bronze sculpture (detail) 40 10

1986. 37th Anniv of Pres. Kim Il Sung's Visit to Songgan Revolutionary Site.
N2572 **872** 10 ch. multicoloured 40 10

873 Buddhist Scriptures Museum

1986. Mt. Myohyang Buildings.
N2573 **873** 10 ch. brown & grn 40 10
N2574 – 20 ch. violet and red 50 10
DESIGN: 20 ch. Taeung Hall.

874 "Amphiprion frenatus"

1986. Fishes. Multicoloured.
N2575 10 ch. Pennant coralfish 60 10
N2576 20 ch. Type **874** .. 90 25

875 Footballers and Flags of Italy, Bulgaria and Argentina

1986. World Cup Football Championship, Mexico (3rd issue). Designs showing footballers and flags of participating countries. Multicoloured.
N2577 10 ch. Type **875** .. 60 10
N2578 20 ch. Mexico, Belgium, Paraguay and Iraq .. 90 25
N2579 25 ch. France, Canada, U.S.S.R. and Hungary .. .. 1·10 35
N2580 30 ch. Brazil, Spain, Algeria and Northern Ireland .. .. 1·25 40
N2581 35 ch. West Germany, Uruguay, Scotland and Denmark .. 1·40 50
N2582 40 ch. Poland, Portugal, Morocco and England 1·60 60

876 Singer, Pianist and Emblem

1986. 4th Spring Friendship Art Festival, Pyongyang.
N2584 **876** 1 wn. multicoloured 1·25 55

877 Daimler "Motorwagen", 1886

878 Mangyong Hill

1986. 60th Anniv of Mercedes-Benz (car manufacturers). Multicoloured.
N2585 10 ch. Type **877** .. 60 10
N2586 10 ch. Benz "velo", 1894 60 10
N2587 20 ch. Mercedes car, 1901 90 25
N2588 20 ch. Benz limousine, 1909 .. .. 90 25
N2589 30 ch. Mercedes "tourenwagen", 1914 1·25 40
N2590 30 ch. Mercedes-Benz "170" 6-cylinder, 1931 1·25 40
N2591 40 ch. Mercedes-Benz "380", 1933 .. 1·60 60
N2592 40 ch. Mercedes-Benz "540 K", 1936 .. 1·60 60

1986. 74th Birthday of Kim Il Sung.
N2594 **878** 10 ch. multicoloured 30 10

879 Crowd

1986. 50th Anniv of Association for the Restoration of the Fatherland.
N2595 **879** 10 ch. multicoloured 30 10

880 Dove carrying Letter

881 "Mona Lisa" (Leonardo da Vinci)

1986. International Peace Year. Mult.
N2596 10 ch. Type **880** .. 60 10
N2597 20 ch. U.N. Headquarters, New York 90 25
N2598 30 ch. Dove, globe and broken missiles .. 1·25 40

1986.
N2600 **881** 20 ch. multicoloured 90 25

882 Pink Iris

883 Kim Un Suk

1986. Irises. Multicoloured.
N2601 20 ch. Type **882** .. 90 25
N2602 30 ch. Violet iris .. 1·25 40

1986. Tennis Players. Multicoloured.
N2604 10 ch. Type **883** (postage) 60 10
N2605 20 ch. Ivan Lendl .. 90 25
N2606 30 ch. Steffi Graf .. 1·25 40
N2607 50 ch. Boris Becker (air) 1·75 75

884 Sulphur-crested Cockatoo

1986. "Stampex '86" Stamp Exhibition, Adelaide, Australia.
N2608 **884** 10 ch. multicoloured 60 10

885 First Issue of "L'Unita"

886 "Express II" (icebreaker) and Sweden 1872 20 ore Stamp

1986. National "L'Unita" (Italian Communist Party newspaper) Festival, Milan. Mult.
N2610 10 ch. Type **885** .. 60 10
N2611 20 ch. Milan Cathedral 90 25
N2612 30 ch. "Pieta" (Michelangelo) (vert) 1·25 40

1986. "Stockholmia 86" International Stamp Exhibition, Stockholm.
N2614 **886** 10 ch. multicoloured 90 20

887 Reprint of First Stamp

1986. 40th Anniv of First North Korean Stamps (1st issue). Multicoloured.
N2616 10 ch. Type **887** (postage) 60 10
N2617 15 ch. Imperforate reprint of first stamp 75 15
N2618 50 ch. 1946 50 ch. violet stamp (air) .. .. 1·75 75
See also Nos. N2619/21.

888 Postal Emblems and 1962 and 1985 Stamps

1986. 40th Anniv of First North Korean Stamps (2nd issue). Multicoloured.
N2619 10 ch. Type **888** (postage) 60 10
N2620 15 ch. General Post Office and 1976 and 1978 stamps 75 15
N2621 50 ch. Kim Il Sung, first stamp and reprint (vert) (air) .. .. 1·75 75

1986. World Cup Football Championship Results. Nos. N2577/82 optd **1st: ARG 2nd: FRG 3rd: FRA 4th: BEL**.
N2622 10 ch. multicoloured .. 60 10
N2623 20 ch. multicoloured .. 90 25
N2624 25 ch. multicoloured .. 1·10 35
N2625 30 ch. multicoloured .. 1·25 40
N2626 35 ch. multicoloured .. 1·40 50
N2627 40 ch. multicoloured .. 1·60 60

890 Flag and Man with raised Fist

892 Schoolchildren

891 Gift Animals House

1986. 60th Anniv of Down-with-Imperialism Union.
N2629 **890** 10 ch. multicoloured 30 10

1986. 1st Anniv of Gift Animals House, Central Zoo, Pyongyang.
N2630 **891** 2 wn. multicoloured 3·00 1·10

1986. 40th Anniv of U.N.E.S.C.O. Mult.
N2631 10 ch. Type **892** .. 60 10
N2632 50 ch. Anniversary emblem, Grand People's Study House and telecommunications (horiz) .. 1·75 75

893 Communications Satellite

1986. 15th Anniv of Intersputnik.
N2633 **893** 5 wn. multicoloured 7·00 3·00

894 Oil tanker leaving Lock

1986. West Sea Barrage.
N2634 **894** 10 ch. multicoloured 30 10
N2635 – 40 ch. green, black and gold .. 90 20
N2636 – 1 wn. 20 mult .. 2·25 60
DESIGNS: 20 ch. Aerial view of dam; 1 wn. 20, Aerial view of lock.

895 Common Morel

896 Machu Picchu, Peru, and N. Korea Taedong Gate Stamp

1986. Minerals and Fungi. Multicoloured.

N2637 10 ch. Lengenbachite (postage) 60 10
N2638 10 ch. Common funnel cap 60 10
N2639 15 ch. Rhodochrosite .. 75 15
N2640 15 ch. Type **895** .. 75 15
N2641 50 ch. Annabergite (air) 1·75 75
N2642 50 ch. Blue russula .. 1·75 75

1986. North Korean Three-dimensional Photographs and stamps exhibition, Lima, Peru.

N2643 **896** 10 ch. multicoloured 60 10

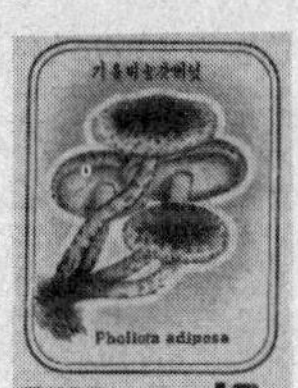

897 Pine Tree

898 "Pholiota adiposa"

1987. New Year. Multicoloured.

N2645 10 ch. Type **897** .. 30 10
N2646 40 ch. Hare 75 25

1987. Fungi. Multicoloured.

N2647 10 ch. Type **898** .. 40 10
N2648 20 ch. Chanterelle .. 70 20
N2649 30 ch. "Boletus impolitus" .. .. 1·00 30

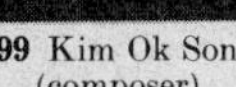

899 Kim Ok Song (composer)

901 East Pyongyang Grand Theatre

1987. Musicians' Death Anniversaries. Mult.

N2651 10 ch. Maurice Ravel (composer, 50th anniv) 40 10
N2652 10 ch. Type **899** (22nd anniv) 40 10
N2653 20 ch. Giovanni Lully (composer, 300th anniv) 70 20
N2654 30 ch. Franz Liszt (composer, centenary (1986)) .. .. 1·00 30
N2655 40 ch. Violins (250th anniv of Antonio Stradivari (violin maker)) .. .. 1·25 40
N2656 40 ch. Christoph Gluck (composer, bicent) .. 1·25 40

1987 Buildings.

N2658 **901** 5 ch. green .. 15 10
N2659 – 10 ch. brown .. 25 10
N2660 – 3 wn. blue .. .. 4·00 1·25

DESIGNS—VERT. 10 ch. Pyongyang Koryo Hotel. HORIZ. 3 wn. Rungnado Stadium.

INDEX

Countries can be quickly located by referring to the index at the end of this volume.

902 "Gorch Foch" (German cadet barque)

1987. Sailing Ships. Multicoloured.

N2661 20 ch. Type **902** (postage) 70 20
N2662 30 ch. "Tovarishch" (Russian cadet barque) (vert) .. 1·00 30
N2663 50 ch. "Belle Poule" (cadet schooner) (vert) (air) .. .. 1·50 45
N2664 50 ch. "Sagres II" (Portuguese cadet barque) (vert) .. 1·50 45
N2665 1 wn. Koryo period merchantman 3·00 95
N2666 1 wn. "Dar Mlodziezy" (Polish cadet full-rigged ship) (vert) .. 3·00 95

903 Road Signs

1987. Road Safety.

N2667 **903** 10 ch. blue, red and black (postage) .. 40 10
N2668 – 10 ch. red and black 40 10
N2669 – 20 ch. bl, red & blk 70 20
N2670 – 50 ch. red and black (air) .. .. 1·50 50

DESIGNS: Nos. N2668/70, Different road signs.

904 Fire Engine

1987. Fire Engines.

N2671 **904** 10 ch. multicoloured (postage) .. 40 10
N2672 – 20 ch. multicoloured 70 20
N2673 – 30 ch. multicoloured 1·00 30
N2674 – 50 ch. mult (air) .. 1·50 50

DESIGNS: N2672/4, Different machines.

905 "Apatura ilia" and Spiraea

1987. Butterflies and Flowers. Multicoloured.

N2675 10 ch. Type **905** .. 40 10
N2676 10 ch. "Ypthima argus" and fuchsia 40 10
N2677 20 ch. "Neptis philyra" and aquilegia .. 70 20
N2678 20 ch. "Papilio protenor" and chrysanthemum .. 70 20
N2679 40 ch. "Parantica sita" and celosia .. .. 1·25 40
N2680 40 ch. "Vanessa indica" and hibiscus .. 1·25 40

906 Association Monument, Pyongyang

907 Doves, Emblem and Tree

1987. 70th Anniv of Korean National Association (independence movement).

N2681 **906** 10 ch. red, sil & blk 25 10

1987. 5th Spring Friendship Art Festival, Pyongyang.

N2682 **907** 10 ch. multicoloured 25 10

908 Mangyong Hill

909 Bay

1987. 75th Birthday of Kim Il Sung. Mult.

N2683 10 ch. Type **908** .. 25 10
N2684 10 ch. Kim Il Sung's birthplace, Mangyongdae (horiz) 25 10
N2685 10 ch. "A Bumper Crop of Pumpkins" (62 × 41 mm) 25 10
N2686 10 ch. "Profound Affection for the Working Class" .. 25 10

1987. Horses. Multicoloured.

N2687 10 ch. Type **909** .. 40 10
N2688 10 ch. Bay (different) .. 40 10
N2689 40 ch. Grey rearing .. 1·25 40
N2690 40 ch. Grey on beach .. 1·25 40

910 "Sputnik 1" (first artificial satellite)

1987. Transport. Multicoloured.

N2691 10 ch. Type **910** (30th anniv of flight) .. 40 10
N2692 10 ch. Electric train "Juche" (horiz) .. 40 10
N2693 10 ch. Electric locomotive "Mangyongdae" (horiz) .. 40 10
N2694 20 ch. Laika (30th anniv of first animal in space) 70 20
N2695 20 ch. Tupolev "Tu-144" supersonic airplane (horiz) 70 20
N2696 20 ch. "Concorde" (11th anniv of first commercial flight) (horiz) 70 20
N2697 30 ch. Count Ferdinand von Zeppelin (70th death anniv) and "LZ4" airship (horiz) 1·00 30
N2698 80 ch. Zeppelin and diagrams and drawings of airships (horiz) 3·00 1·00

911 Musk Ox

1987. "Capex '87" International Stamp Exhibition, Toronto. Multicoloured.

N2699 10 ch. Type **911** .. 40 10
N2700 40 ch. Jacques Cartier, his ship "Grande Hermine" and ice-breaker (horiz) .. 1·25 40
N2701 60 ch. Ice hockey (Winter Olympics, Calgary, 1988) (horiz) 1·75 60

912 Trapeze Artistes

1987. International Circus Festival, Monaco. Multicoloured.

N2702 10 ch. Type **912** .. 40 10
N2703 10 ch. "Brave Sailors" (North Korean acrobatic act) (vert) 40 10
N2704 20 ch. Clown and elephant (vert) .. 70 20
N2705 20 ch. North Korean artiste receiving "Golden Clown" award 70 20
N2706 40 ch. Performing horses and cat act .. .. 1·25 40
N2707 50 ch. Prince Rainier and his children applauding .. .. 1·50 50

913 Attack on Watch Tower

1987. 50th Anniv of Battle of Pochonbo.

N2708 **913** 10 ch. brown, black and ochre .. 25 10

914 Sports

1987. Angol Sports Village.

N2709 **914** 5 ch. brown & gold 15 10
N2710 – 10 ch. blue and gold 25 10
N2711 – 40 ch. brown & gold 75 25
N2712 – 70 ch. blue and gold 1·25 40
N2713 – 1 wn. red and gold 1·90 60
N2714 – 1 wn. 20 violet 2·25 70

DESIGNS: Exteriors of—10 ch. Indoor swimming pool; 40 ch. Weightlifting gymnasium; 70 ch. Table tennis gymnasium; 1 wn. Football stadium; 1 wn. 20, Handball gymnasium.

915 Mandarins

1987. Mandarins. Multicoloured.

N2715 20 ch. Type **915** .. 70 15
N2716 20 ch. Mandarins on shore 70 15
N2717 20 ch. Mandarins on branch 70 15
N2718 40 ch. Mandarins in water .. .. 1·25 40

916 Exhibition Site and 1987 3 wn. Stamp

1987. "Olymphilex '87" Olympic Stamps Exhibition, Rome.

N2719 **916** 10 ch. multicoloured 40 10

917 Underground Station and Guard

1987. Railway Uniforms. Multicoloured.
N2721 10 ch. Type **917** .. 25 10
N2722 10 ch. Underground train and station supervisor 25 10
N2723 20 ch. Guard and train 40 10
N2724 30 ch. Guard and train 55 20
N2725 40 ch. "Orient Express" guard 75 25
N2726 40 ch. German ticket controller and steam train 75 25

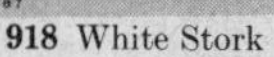
918 White Stork

920 Victory Column

919 Ice Skating

1987. "Hafnia 87" International Stamp Exhibition, Copenhagen. Multicoloured.
N2727 40 ch. Type **918** .. 1·00 30
N2728 60 ch. "Danmark" (cadet ship) and "Little Mermaid", Copenhagen .. 1·25 40

1987. Winter Olympic Games, Calgary (1988). Multicoloured.
N2729 40 ch. Type **919** .. 1·00 30
N2730 40 ch. Ski jumping .. 1·00 30
N2731 40 ch. Skiing (value on left) (horiz) .. .. 1·00 30
N2732 40 ch. Skiing (value on right) (horiz) .. 1·00 30

1987. 750th Anniv of Berlin and "Philatelia '87" International Stamp Exhibition, Cologne. Multicoloured.
N2734 10 ch. Type **920** .. 40 10
N2735 20 ch. Reichstag (horiz) 70 20
N2736 30 ch. Pfaueninsel Castle 1·00 30
N2737 40 ch. Charlottenburg Castle (horiz) .. 1·25 40

921 Garros and Airplane

1987. Birth Centenary of Roland Garros (aviator) and Tennis as an Olympic Sport. Multicoloured.
N2739 20 ch. Type **921** .. 70 20
N2740 20 ch. Ivan Lendl (tennis player) .. 70 20
N2741 40 ch. Steffi Graf (tennis player) .. .. 1·25 40

923 Pyongyang Buildings

1988. New Year. Multicoloured.
N2744 10 ch. Type **923** .. 20 10
N2745 40 ch. Dragon 75 25

924 Banner and Newspaper

925 Birthplace, Mt. Paekdu

1988. 60th Anniv of "Saenal" Newspaper.
N2746 **924** 10 ch. multicoloured 20 10

1988. Kim Jong Il's Birthday.
N2747 **925** 10 ch. multicoloured 20 10

926 Henry Dunant (founder)

1988. 125th Anniv of International Red Cross. Multicoloured.
N2749 10 ch. Type **926** .. 20 10
N2750 20 ch. North Korean Red Cross emblem and map 40 15
N2751 20 ch. International Committee headquarters, Geneva .. 40 15
N2752 40 ch. Pyongyang Maternity Hospital, doctor and baby .. 75 25

927 "Santa Maria"

1988. 500th Anniv (1992) of Discovery of America by Christopher Columbus. Mult.
N2754 10 ch. Type **927** .. 25 15
N2755 20 ch. "Pinta" .. 55 20
N2756 30 ch. "Nina" 75 25
Nos. N2754/6 were issued together, se-tenant, forming a composite design of Columbus's ships leaving Palos.

928 Hot-air Balloons

929 Dancers

1988. "Juvalux '88" International Youth Stamp Exhibition, Luxembourg. Mult.
N2758 40 ch. Type **928** .. 75 25
N2759 60 ch. Early railway locomotive and railway map of Luxembourg, 1900 .. 1·10 35

1988. 6th Spring Friendship Art Festival, Pyongyang. Multicoloured.
N2760 10 ch. Singer (poster) .. 20 10
N2761 1 wn. 20 Type **929** .. 2·25 75

930 Inaugural Congress Emblem

931 Birthplace, Mangyongdae

1988. 10th Anniv of International Institute of the Juche Idea.
N2762 **930** 10 ch. multicoloured 20 10

1988. 76th Birthday of Kim Il Sung.
N2763 **931** 10 ch. multicoloured 20 10

932 "Urho" (ice-breaker)

1988. "Finlandia 88" International Stamp Exhibition, Helsinki. Multicoloured.
N2765 40 ch. Type **932** .. 1·00 25
N2766 60 ch. Matti Nykaenen (Olympic Games ski-jumping medallist) 1·10 35

933 Postcard for 1934 Championship

934 Emblem

1988. World Cup Football Championship, Italy (1st issue). Multicoloured.
N2767 10 ch. Football match 20 10
N2768 20 ch. Type **933** .. 40 15
N2769 30 ch. Player tackling (horiz) 55 20
See also Nos. N2924/7.

1988. 13th World Youth and Students' Festival, Pyongyang (1st issue). Mult.
N2771 5 ch. Type **934** .. 10 10
N2772 10 ch. Dancer .. 20 10
N2773 10 ch. Gymnast and gymnasium, Angol Sports Village .. 20 10
N2774 10 ch. Map of Korea, globe and doves .. 20 10
N2775 10 ch. Finger pointing at shattered nuclear rockets 20 10
N2776 1 wn. 20 Three differently coloured hands and dove .. 2·25 75
See also Nos. N2860/3 and N2879/80.

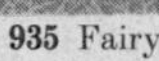
935 Fairy

936 Mallards

1988. "Eight Fairies of Mt. Kumgang" (tale). Multicoloured.
N2777 10 ch. Type **935** .. 20 10
N2778 15 ch. Fairy at pool and fairies on rainbow .. 30 10
N2779 20 ch. Fairy and woodman husband .. 40 15
N2780 25 ch. Couple with baby 50 15
N2781 30 ch. Couple with son and daughter .. 55 20
N2782 35 ch. Family on rainbow 65 20

1988. "Praga '88" International Stamp Exhibition, Prague. Multicoloured.
N2783 20 ch. Type **936** .. 40 15
N2784 40 ch. Vladimir Remek (Czechoslovak cosmonaut) 75 25

937 Red Crossbill

1988. Birds. Multicoloured.
N2785 10 ch. Type **937** .. 30 15
N2786 15 ch. Stonechat .. 60 15
N2787 20 ch. European nut-hatch 75 25
N2788 25 ch. Great spotted woodpecker 95 25
N2789 30 ch. Common king-fisher .. .. 1·10 30
N2790 35 ch. Bohemian wax-wing .. .. 1·25 30

938 Fair Emblem

1988. 40th Int. Stamp Fair, Riccione.
N2791 **938** 20 ch. multicoloured. 40 15

939 Emu

1988. Bicent of Australian Settlement. Mult.
N2793 10 ch. Type **939** .. 45 20
N2794 15 ch. Satin bowerbirds 65 20
N2795 25 ch. Laughing kookaburra (vert) .. .. 1·10 30

940 Floating Crane "5-28"

1988. Ships. Multicoloured.
N2797 10 ch. Type **940** .. 25 10
N2798 20 ch. Freighter "Hwanggumsan" .. 50 20
N2799 30 ch. Freighter "Changjasan Chongnyon-ho" .. 70 25
N2800 40 ch. Liner "Samjiyon" 1·00 30

941 Hansa

1988. 150th Birth Anniv of Count Ferdinand von Zeppelin (airship pioneer). Mult.

N2801 10 ch. Type **941** .. 20 10
N2802 20 ch. "Schwaben" .. 40 15
N2803 30 ch. "Viktoria Luise" 55 20
N2804 40 ch. "LZ 3" .. 75 25

942 Kim Il Sung and Jambyn Batmunkh

944 Tower of Juche Idea

943 Hero and Labour Hero of the D.P.R.K. Medals

1988. Kim Il Sung's Visit to Mongolia.

N2806 **942** 10 ch. multicoloured 20 10

1988. National Heroes Congress.

N2807 **943** 10 ch. multicoloured 20 10

1988. 40th Anniv of Democratic Republic. Multicoloured.

N2808 5 ch. Type **944** .. 10 10
N2809 10 ch. Smelter and industrial buildings 20 10
N2810 10 ch. Soldier and Mt. Paekdu 20 10
N2811 10 ch. Map of Korea and globe 20 10
N2812 10 ch. Hand holding banner, globe and doves 20 10

945 "Sunflowers" (Vincent van Gogh)

946 Emblem

1988. "Filacept 88" Stamp Exhibition, The Hague. Multicoloured.

N2814 40 ch. Type **945** .. 75 25
N2815 60 ch. "The Chess Game" (Lucas van Leyden) (horiz) .. 1·10 35

1988. 16th Session of Socialist Countries' Post and Telecommunications Conference, Pyongyang.

N2816 **946** 10 ch. multicoloured 20 10

947 Chaju "82" 10-ton Truck

948 "Owl"

1988. Tipper Trucks. Multicoloured.

N2817 20 ch. Type **947** .. 40 15
N2818 40 ch. Kumsusan-ho 40-ton truck 75 25

1988. Paintings by O Un Byol. Multicoloured.

N2819 10 ch. Type **948** .. 20 10
N2820 15 ch. "Dawn" (cockerel) 30 10
N2821 20 ch. "Beautiful Rose received by Kim Il Sung" 40 15
N2822 25 ch. "Sun and Bamboo" 50 15
N2823 30 ch. "Autumn" (fruit tree) 55 20

949 "Chunggi" Type Steam Locomotive No. 35

1988. Railway Locomotives. Multicoloured.

N2824 10 ch. Type **949** .. 20 10
N2825 20 ch. "Chunggi" type steam locomotive No. 22 .. .. 40 15
N2826 30 ch. "Chongiha" type electric locomotive No. 3 .. .. 55 20
N2827 40 ch. "Chunggi" type steam locomotive No. 307 .. .. 75 25

950 Pirmen Zurbriggen (downhill skiing)

1988. Winter Olympic Games, Calgary, Medal Winners. Multicoloured.

N2828 10 ch. Type **950** .. 20 10
N2829 20 ch. Yvonne van Gennip (speed skating) 40 15
N2830 30 ch. Marjo Matikainen (cross-country skiing) 55 20
N2831 40 ch. U.S.S.R. (ice hockey) (horiz) .. 75 25

951 Yuri Gagarin

1988. 1st Man and Woman in Space. Mult.

N2833 20 ch. Type **951** .. 40 15
N2834 40 ch. Valentina Tereshkova 75 25

952 Nehru

953 Chollima Statue

1988. Birth Centenary of Jawaharlal Nehru (Indian statesman) and "India 89" International Stamp Exhibition, New Delhi.

N2835 **952** 20 ch. purple, black and gold .. 40 15

1989. New Year. Multicoloured.

N2837 10 ch. Type **953** .. 20 10
N2838 20 ch. "The Dragon Angler" (17th-century painting) 40 15
N2839 40 ch. "Tortoise and Serpent" (Kangso tomb painting) (horiz) 75 25

954 Archery

1989. National Defence Training. Mult.

N2840 10 ch. Type **954** .. 20 10
N2841 15 ch. Rifle shooting .. 30 10
N2842 20 ch. Pistol shooting .. 40 15
N2843 25 ch. Parachuting .. 50 15
N2844 30 ch. Launching model glider 55 20

955 Dobermann Pinscher

957 Agriculture

1989. Animals presented to Kim Il Sung. Multicoloured.

N2845 10 ch. Type **955** .. 20 10
N2846 20 ch. Labrador .. 40 15
N2847 25 ch. German shepherd 50 15
N2848 30 ch. Rough collies (horiz) 55 20
N2849 35 ch. Serval (horiz) .. 65 20

1989. 25th Anniv of Publication of "Theses on the Socialist Rural Question in our Country" by Kim Il Sung.

N2852 **957** 10 ch. multicoloured 20 10

958 The Gypsy and Grapes

959 Korean Girl

MINIMUM PRICE

The minimum price quoted is 5p which represents a handling charge rather than a basis for valuing common stamps. For further notes about prices see introductory pages.

1989. Fungi and Fruits. Multicoloured.

N2853 10 ch. Type **958** .. 20 10
N2854 20 ch. Caesar's mushroom and magnolia vine 40 15
N2855 25 ch. "Lactarius hygrophoides" and "Eleagnus crispa" .. 50 15
N2856 30 ch. "Agaricus placomyces" and Chinese gooseberries 55 20
N2857 35 ch. Horse mushroom and "Lycium chinense" 65 20
N2858 40 ch. Elegant boletus and "Juglans cordiformis" .. 75 25

1989. 13th World Youth and Students' Festival, Pyongyang (2nd issue). Mult.

N2860 10 ch. Type **959** .. 20 10
N2861 20 ch. Children of different races .. 40 15
N2862 30 ch. Fairy and rainbow 55 20
N2863 40 ch. Young peoples and Tower of Juche Idea 75 25

960 "Parnassius eversmanni"

1989. Insects. Multicoloured.

N2864 10 ch. Type **960** .. 20 10
N2865 15 ch. "Colias heos" .. 30 10
N2866 20 ch. "Dilipa fenestra" 40 15
N2867 25 ch. "Buthus martensis" 50 15
N2868 30 ch. "Trichogramma ostriniae" 55 20
N2869 40 ch. "Damaster constricticollis" .. 75 25

961 Dancers (poster)

962 Birthplace, Mangyongdae

1989. Spring Friendship Art Festival, Pyongyang.

N2871 **961** 10 ch. multicoloured 20 10

1989. 77th Birthday of Kim Il Sung.

N2872 **962** 10 ch. multicoloured 20 10

963 Battle Plan and Monument to the Victory

1989. 50th Anniv of Battle of the Musan Area.

N2873 **963** 10 ch. bl, flesh & red 20 10

964 Modern Dance

1989. Chamo System of Dance Notation. Multicoloured.

N2874 10 ch. Type **964** .. 20 10
N2875 20 ch. Ballet 40 15
N2876 25 ch. Modern dance (different) 50 15
N2877 30 ch. Traditional dance 55 20

965 Hands supporting Torch

966 Victorious Badger

1989. 13th World Youth and Students' Festival, Pyongyang (3rd issue).

N2879 **965** 5 ch. blue 10 10

N2880 – 10 ch. brown .. 20 10

DESIGN: 10 ch. Youth making speech.

1989. "Badger measures the Height" (cartoon film). Multicoloured.

N2881 10 ch. Cat, bear and badger race to flag pole 20 10

N2882 40 ch. Cat and bear climb pole while badger measures shadow 75 25

N2883 50 ch. Type **966** .. 95 30

967 Kyongju Observatory and Star Chart

969 Pele (footballer) and 1978 25 ch. Stamp

1989. Astronomy.

N2884 **967** 20 ch. multicoloured 40 15

1989. "Brasiliana 89" International Stamp Exhibition, Rio de Janeiro.

N2887 **969** 40 ch. multicoloured 75 25

970 Nurse and Ambulance

1989. Emergency Services. Multicoloured.

N2888 10 ch. Type **970** .. 20 10

N2889 20 ch. Surgeon and ambulance 40 15

N2890 30 ch. Fireman and fire engine 55 20

N2891 40 ch. Fireman and engine (different) .. 75 25

971 Kaffir Lily

972 Air Mail Letter and Postal Transport

1989. Plants presented to Kim Il Sung. Mult.

N2892 10 ch. Type **971** .. 20 10

N2893 15 ch. Tulips .. 30 10

N2894 20 ch. Flamingo lily .. 40 15

N2895 25 ch. "Rhododendron obtusum" .. 50 15

N2896 30 ch. Daffodils .. 55 20

1989. 150th Anniv of the Penny Black and "Stamp World London 90" International Stamp Exhibition (1st issue). Multicoloured.

N2898 5 ch. Type **972** .. 10 10

N2899 10 ch. Post box and letters 20 10

N2900 20 ch. Stamps, tweezers and magnifying glass 40 15

N2901 30 ch. First North Korean stamps .. 55 20

N2902 40 ch. Universal Postal Union emblem and headquarters, Berne 75 25

N2903 50 ch. Sir Rowland Hill and Penny Black .. 95 30

See also No. N2956.

973 "Bistorta incana"

1989. Alpine Flowers. Multicoloured.

N2904 10 ch. "Iris setosa" .. 20 10

N2905 15 ch. "Aquilegia japonica" 30 10

N2906 20 ch. Type **973** .. 40 15

N2907 25 ch. "Rodiola elongata" 50 15

N2908 30 ch. "Sanguisorba sitchensis" 55 20

974 Tree, Mt. Paekdu

975 Skipping

1989. Slogan-bearing Trees (1st series). Mult.

N2910 10 ch. Type **974** .. 20 10

N2911 3 wn. Tree, Oun-dong, Pyongyang .. .. 5·50 1·75

N2912 5 wn. Tree, Mt. Kanbaek .. .. 9·50 3·25

See also No. N2931.

1989. Children's Games. Multicoloured.

N2913 10 ch. Type **975** .. 20 10

N2914 20 ch. Windmill .. 40 15

N2915 30 ch. Kite .. 55 20

N2916 40 ch. Whip and top .. 75 25

977 Diesel Train and Sinpa Youth Station

1989. Railway Locomotives. Multicoloured.

N2918 10 ch. Type **977** .. 20 10

N2919 20 ch. "Pulgungi" type electric locomotive .. 40 15

N2920 25 ch. Diesel locomotive 50 15

N2921 30 ch. Diesel locomotive (different) .. 55 20

N2922 40 ch. Steam locomotive 75 25

N2923 50 ch. Steam locomotive (different) 95 30

978 Players and Map of Italy

1989. World Cup Football Championship, Italy (2nd issue). Multicoloured.

N2924 10 ch. Type **978** .. 20 10

N2925 20 ch. Free kick .. 40 15

N2926 30 ch. Goal mouth scrimmage .. 55 20

N2927 40 ch. Goalkeeper diving for ball 75 25

979 Magellan (navigator)

1989. "Descobrex '89" International Stamp Exhibition, Portugal.

N2928 **979** 30 ch. multicoloured 75 20

980 Mangyong Hill and Pine Branches

981 Ryukwoli

1990. New Year. Multicoloured.

N2929 10 ch. Type **980** .. 20 10

N2930 20 ch. Koguryo mounted archers .. 40 15

1990. Slogan-bearing trees (2nd series). As T **974**. Multicoloured.

N2931 5 ch. Tree, Mt. Paekdu 10 10

1990. Dogs. Multicoloured.

N2932 20 ch. Type **981** .. 40 15

N2933 30 ch. Palryuki .. 55 20

N2934 40 ch. Komdungi .. 75 25

N2935 50 ch. Oulruki 95 30

982 Birthplace, Mt. Paekdu

983 Stone Instruments and Primitive Man

1990. Birthday of Kim Jong Il.

N2936 **982** 10 ch. brown .. 20 10

1990. Evolution of Man. Multicoloured.

N2937 10 ch. Type **983** .. 20 10

N2938 40 ch. Palaeolithic and Neolithic man .. 75 25

984 Rungna Bridge, Pyongyang

1990. Bridges. Multicoloured.

N2939 10 ch. Type **984** .. 20 10

N2940 20 ch. Potong bridge, Pyongyang .. 40 15

N2941 30 ch. Sinuiji–Ryucho Island Bridge .. 55 20

N2942 40 ch. Chungsongui Bridge, Pyongyang .. 75 25

985 Infantryman

987 Dancers (poster)

986 "Atergatis subdentatus"

1990. Warriors' Costumes. Multicoloured.

N2943 20 ch. Type **985** .. 40 15

N2944 30 ch. Archer 55 20

N2945 50 ch. Military commander in armour 95 30

N2946 70 ch. Oficer's costume, 10th–14th centuries) 1·25 40

Nos. N2943/5 depict costumes from the 3rd century B.C. to the 7th century A.D.

1990. Crabs. Multicoloured.

N2947 20 ch. Type **986** .. 40 15

N2948 30 ch. "Platylambrus validus" 55 20

N2949 50 ch. "Uca arcuata" .. 95 30

1990. Spring Friendship Art Festival, Pyongyang.

N2950 **987** 10 ch. multicoloured 20 10

988 Monument at Road Folk, Mangyongdae

989 "Gymnocalycium sp."

1990. 78th Birthday of Kim Il Sung.

N2951 **988** 10 ch. green and gold 20 10

1990. Cacti. Multicoloured.

N2953 10 ch. Type **989** .. 20 10

N2954 30 ch. "Pyllocactus hybridus" 55 20

N2955 50 ch. "Epiphyllum truncatum" .. 95 30

990 Exhibition Emblem

991 Congo Peafowl

1990. "Stamp World London 90" International Stamp Exhibition (2nd issue).

N2956 **990** 20 ch. red and black 40 15

1990. Peafowl. Multicoloured.

N2958 10 ch. Type **991** .. 30 10

N2959 20 ch. Common peafowl 70 20

992 Dolphin and Submarine

1990. Bio-engineering. Multicoloured.

N2961 10 ch. Type **992** .. 20 10

N2962 20 ch. Bat and dish aerial 40 15

N2963 30 ch. Eagle and aircraft 70 20

N2964 40 ch. Octopus and rockets 75 25

993 "Self-portrait" (Rembrandt)

994 K. H. Rummenigge (footballer)

1990. "Belgica 90" International Stamp Exhibition, Brussels. Multicoloured.

N2965 10 ch. Type **993** .. 20 10
N2966 20 ch. "Self-portrait" (Raphael) 40 15
N2967 30 ch. "Self-portrait" (Rubens) 55 20

1990. "Dusseldorf '90" International Youth Stamp Exhibition. Multicoloured.

N2968 20 ch. Steffi Graf (tennis player) 40 15
N2969 30 ch. Exhibition emblem 55 20
N2970 70 ch. Type **994** .. 1·25 40

995 Workers' Stadium, Peking, and Games Mascot

1990. 11th Asian Games, Peking (Nos. N2971/2) and 3rd Asian Winter Games, Samjiyon (N2973). Multicoloured.

N2971 10 ch. Type **995** .. 20 10
N2972 30 ch. Chollima Statue and sportsmen .. 55 20
N2973 40 ch. Sportsmen and Games emblem .. 75 25

996 Ball

1990. West Germany, Winners of World Cup Football Championship. Multicoloured.

N2974 15 ch. Emblem of F.I.F.A. (International Federation of Football Associations) 30 10
N2975 20 ch. Jules Rimet .. 40 15
N2976 25 ch. Type **996** .. 50 15
N2977 30 ch. Olympic Stadium, Rome (venue of final) 55 20
N2978 35 ch. Goalkeeper .. 65 20
N2979 40 ch. Emblem of West German Football Association .. 75 25

997 Kakapo and Map of New Zealand

1990. "New Zealand 1990" International Stamp Exhibition, Auckland.

N2981 **997** 30 ch. multicoloured 70 20

999 Head of Procession

1990. Koguryo Wedding Procession. Mult.

N2983 10 ch. Type **999** .. 20 10
N2984 30 ch. Bridegroom .. 55 20
N2985 50 ch. Bride in carriage 95 30
N2986 1 wn. Drummer on horse .. .. 1·90 65

Nos. N2983/6 were issued together, se-tenant, forming a composite design.

1000 Marchers descending Mt. Paekdu

1990. Rally for Peace and Reunification of Korea.

N2987 **1000** 10 ch. multicoloured 20 10

1001 Praying Mantis

1990. Insects. Multicoloured.

N2989 20 ch. Type **1001** .. 40 15
N2990 30 ch. Ladybird .. 55 20
N2991 40 ch. "Pheropsophus jessoensis" 75 25
N2992 70 ch. "Phyllium siccifolium" .. .. 1·25 40

1002 Footballers

1990. North–South Reunification Football Match, Pyongyang. Multicoloured.

N2993 10 ch. Type **1002** .. 20 10
N2994 20 ch. Footballers (different) 40 15

1003 Concert Emblem

1004 Ox

1990. National Reunification Concert.

N2996 **1003** 10 ch. multicoloured 20 10

1990. Farm Animals.

N2997 **1004** 10 ch. brown & grn 20 10
N2998 – 20 ch. lilac & yell 40 15
N2999 – 30 ch. grey and red 55 20
N3000 – 40 ch. green & yell 75 25
N3001 – 50 ch. brown & bl 95 30

DESIGNS: 20 ch. Pig; 30 ch. Goat; 40 ch. Sheep; 50 ch. Horse.

1005 Chinese and North Korean Soldiers

1006 Anniversary Emblem

1990. 40th Anniv of Participation of Chinese Volunteers in Korean War. Multicoloured.

N3002 10 ch. Type **1005** .. 20 10
N3003 20 ch. Populace welcoming volunteers (horiz) 40 15
N3004 30 ch. Rejoicing soldiers and battle scene (horiz) 55 20
N3005 40 ch. Post-war reconstruction (horiz) 75 25

1990. 40th Anniv of United Nations Development Programme.

N3007 **1006** 1 wn. blue, silver and black .. 1·90 65

1007 Sturgeon

1008 Sheep

1990. Fishes.

N3008 **1007** 10 ch. brown & grn 20 10
N3009 – 20 ch. green & blue 40 15
N3010 – 30 ch. blue & pur 55 20
N3011 – 40 ch. brown & bl 75 25
N3012 – 50 ch. violet & grn 95 30

DESIGNS: 20 ch. Sea bream; 30 ch. Flying fish; 40 ch. Fat greenling; 50 ch. Ray.

1990. New Year.

N3013 **1008** 40 ch. multicoloured 75 25

1009 Moorhen

1010 Giant Panda

1990. Birds.

N3014 **1009** 10 ch. bl, grn & blk 25 10
N3015 – 20 ch. brown, bistre and black .. 50 15
N3016 – 30 ch. green, grey and black .. 65 20
N3017 – 40 ch. brown, orange and black 90 30
N3018 – 50 ch. ochre, brown and black .. 1·10 35

DESIGNS: 20 ch. Jay; 30 ch. Three-toed woodpecker; 40 ch. Whimbrel; 50 ch. Water rail.

1991. "Phila Nippon '91" International Stamp Exhibition, Tokyo. Multicoloured.

N3019 10 ch. Type **1010** .. 20 10
N3020 20 ch. Two giant pandas feeding 40 15
N3021 30 ch. Giant panda clambering onto branch 55 20
N3022 40 ch. Giant panda on rock 75 25
N3023 50 ch. Two giant pandas 95 30
N3024 60 ch. Giant panda in tree fork .. .. 1·10 35

1011 Changsan

1991. Revolutionary Sites.

N3026 5 ch. Type **1011** .. 10 10
N3027 10 ch. Oun 20 10

1012 Black-faced Spoonbills

1014 Hedgehog Fungus

1013 "Clossiana angarensis"

1991. Endangered Birds. Multicoloured.

N3028 10 ch. Type **1012** .. 20 10
N3029 20 ch. Grey herons .. 35 10
N3030 30 ch. Great egrets .. 50 15
N3031 40 ch. Manchurian cranes 75 20
N3032 50 ch. Japanese white-necked cranes .. 90 25
N3033 70 ch. White storks .. 1·10 30

1991. Alpine Butterflies. Multicoloured.

N3034 10 ch. Type **1013** .. 10 10
N3035 20 ch. "Erebia embla" 25 10
M3036 30 ch. Camberwell beauty 35 10
N3037 40 ch. Comma 50 15
N3038 50 ch. Eastern pale clouded yellow .. 60 20
N3039 60 ch. "Thecla betulae" 70 25

1991. Fungi. Multicoloured.

N3040 10 ch. Type **1014** .. 10 10
N3041 20 ch. "Phylloporus rhodoxanthus" .. 25 10
N3042 30 ch. "Calvatia craniiformis" .. 35 10
N3043 40 ch. Cauliflower clavaria 50 15
N3044 50 ch. "Russula integra" 60 20

1015 Kumchon

1991. Revolutionary Sites. Multicoloured.

N3045 10 ch. Type **1015** .. 10 10
N3046 40 ch. Samdung .. 50 15

1016 Dr. Kye Ung Sang (researcher)

1017 Emblem and Venue

1991. Silkworm Research. Multicoloured.

N3047 10 ch. Type **1016** .. 10 10
N3048 20 ch. Chinese oak silk moth 25 10
N3049 30 ch. "Attacus ricini" 35 10
N3050 40 ch. "Antheraea yamamai" 50 15
N3051 50 ch. Silkworm moth 60 20
N3052 60 ch. "Aetias artemis" 70 25

1991. 9th Spring Friendship Art Festival, Pyongyang.

N3053 **1017** 10 ch. multicoloured 10 10

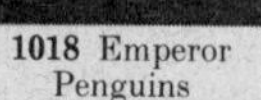
1018 Emperor Penguins

1020 Map and Kim Jong Ho

1019 People's Palace of Culture (venue)

1991. Antarctic Exploration. Multicoloured.

N3054	10 ch. Type **1018** ..	10	10
N3055	20 ch. Research station	25	10
N3056	30 ch. Elephant seals ..	35	10
N3057	40 ch. Research ship ..	75	25
N3058	50 ch. Southern black-backed gulls ..	60	20

1991. 85th Interparliamentary Union Conference, Pyongyang.

N3060	**1019** 10 ch. deep green, green and silver	10	10
N3061	– 1 wn. 50 mult ..	1·75	60

DESIGN: 1 wn. 50, Conference emblem and azalea.

1991. 130th Anniv of Publication of Kim Jong Ho's Map of Korea.

N3062	**1020** 90 ch. black, stone and silver ..	1·10	35

1021 Cynognathus

1991. Dinosaurs. Multicoloured.

N3063	10 ch. Type **1021** ..	10	10
N3064	20 ch. Brontosaurus ..	25	10
N3065	30 ch. Stegosaurus and allosaurus	35	10
N3066	40 ch. Pterosauria ..	50	15
N3067	50 ch. Ichthyosaurus ..	60	20

1022 Sprinting

1991. Olympic Games, Barcelona (1992). Mult.

N3068	10 ch. Type **1022** ..	10	10
N3069	10 ch. Hurdling ..	10	10
N3070	20 ch. Long jumping ..	25	10
N3071	20 ch. Throwing the discus	25	10
N3072	30 ch. Putting the shot	35	10
N3073	30 ch. Pole vaulting ..	35	10
N3074	40 ch. High jumping ..	50	15
N3075	40 ch. Throwing the javelin	50	15

1023 Cats and Birds

1991. Cats. Multicoloured.

N3077	10 ch. Type **1023** ..	10	10
N3078	20 ch. Cat and rat ..	15	10
N3079	30 ch. Cat and butterfly	20	10
N3080	40 ch. Cats with ball ..	25	10
N3081	50 ch. Cat and frog ..	30	10

1025 Wild Horse

1991. Horses. Multicoloured.

N3083	10 ch. Type **1025** ..	10	10
N3084	20 ch. Hybrid of wild ass and wild horse ..	15	10
N3085	30 ch. Przewalski's horse	20	10
N3086	40 ch. Wild ass ..	25	10
N3087	50 ch. Wild horse (different) ..	30	10

1026 Pennant Coralfish

1991. Fishes. Multicoloured.

N3088	10 ch. Type **1026** ..	10	10
N3089	20 ch. Big-spotted triggerfish ..	15	10
N3090	30 ch. Anemonefish ..	20	10
N3091	40 ch. Blue surgeon fish	25	10
N3092	50 ch. Angelfish ..	30	10

1027 Rhododendrons

1991. Flowers. Multicoloured.

N3094	10 ch. Begonia ..	10	10
N3095	20 ch. Gerbera ..	15	10
N3096	30 ch. Type **1027** ..	20	10
N3097	40 ch. Phalaenopsis ..	25	10
N3098	50 ch. "Impatiens sultanii"	30	10
N3099	60 ch. Streptocarpus ..	35	10

Nos. N3097/9 commemorate "CANADA '92" International Youth Stamp Exhibition, Montreal.

1028 Panmunjom

1029 Magnolia

1991.

N3100	**1028** 10 ch. multicoloured	10	10

1991. National Flower.

N3101	**1029** 10 ch. multicoloured	10	10

1030 Players

1991. Women's World Football Championship, China. Multicoloured.

N3102	10 ch. Type **1030** ..	10	10
N3103	20 ch. Dribbling the ball	15	10
N3104	30 ch. Heading the ball	20	10
N3105	40 ch. Overhead kick ..	25	10
N3106	50 ch. Tackling ..	30	10
N3107	60 ch. Goalkeeper ..	35	10

1031 Squirrel Monkeys

1992. Monkeys. Multicoloured.

N3108	10 ch. Type **1031** ..	10	10
N3109	20 ch. Pygmy marmosets	15	10
N3110	30 ch. Red-handed tamarins ..	20	10

1032 Eagle Owl

1992. Birds of Prey. Multicoloured.

N3112	10 ch. Type **1032** ..	10	10
N3113	20 ch. Common buzzard	15	10
N3114	30 ch. African fish eagle	20	10
N3115	40 ch. Steller's sea eagle	25	10
N3116	50 ch. Golden eagle ..	30	10

1033 Birthplace, Mt. Paekdu

1992. Birthday of Kim Jong Il. Mt. Paekdu. Multicoloured.

N3118	10 ch. Type **1033** ..	10	10
N3119	20 ch. Mountain summit	15	10
N3120	30 ch. Mountain lake ..	20	10
N3121	40 ch. Mountain lake (different)	25	10

1034 Service Bus

1992. Transport.

N3123	**1034** 10 ch. mult ..	10	10
N3124	– 20 ch. mult ..	15	10
N3125	– 30 ch. mult ..	20	10
N3126	– 40 ch. mult ..	25	10
N3127	– 50 ch. mult ..	30	10
N3128	– 60 ch. mult ..	35	10

DESIGNS: 20 ch. to 60 ch. Different buses and trams.

1035 Dancers and Emblem

1992. Spring Friendship Art Festival, Pyongyang.

N3129	**1035** 10 ch. multicoloured	10	10

1036 Birthplace, Mangyongdae

1992. 80th Birthday of Kim Il Sung. Revolutionary Sites. Multicoloured.

N3130	10 ch. Type **1036** (post)	10	10
N3131	10 ch. Party emblem and monument ..	10	10
N3132	10 ch. Map and house on stilts	10	10
N3133	10 ch. Statue of soldier and house	10	10
N3134	40 ch. Cogwheels and building	25	10
N3135	40 ch. Chollima Statue and building ..	25	10
N3136	1 wn. 20 Monument and West Sea Barrage (air)	70	25

1038 Soldiers on Parade

1992. 60th Anniv of People's Army. Mult.

N3139	10 ch. Type **1038** ..	10	10
N3140	10 ch. Couple greeting soldier	10	10
N3141	10 ch. Army, air force and navy personnel	10	10

1039 Hurdling

1992. Olympic Games, Barcelona. Mult.

N3142	10 ch. Type **1039** ..	10	10
N3143	20 ch. High jumping ..	15	10
N3144	30 ch. Putting the shot	20	10
N3145	40 ch. Sprinting ..	25	10
N3146	50 ch. Long jumping ..	30	10
N3147	60 ch. Throwing the javelin	35	10

1040 Planting Crops

1992. Evolution of Man. Designs showing life in the New Stone Age (10, 20 ch.) and The Bronze Age (others). Multicoloured.

N3149	10 ch. Type **1040** (post)	10	10
N3150	20 ch. Family around cooking pot ..	15	10
N3151	30 ch. Ploughing fields	20	10
N3152	40 ch. Performing domestic chores ..	25	10
N3153	50 ch. Building a dolmen (air) ..	30	10

1041 White-bellied Black Woodpecker

1042 Map and Hands holding Text

1992. Birds. Multicoloured.

N3154	10 ch. Type **1041** ..	10	10
N3155	20 ch. Ring-necked pheasant	15	10
N3156	30 ch. White stork ..	20	10
N3157	40 ch. Blue-winged pitta	25	10
N3158	50 ch. Pallas's sand-grouse	30	10
N3159	60 ch. Black grouse ..	35	10

1992. 20th Anniv of Publication of North–South Korea Joint Agreement.

N3161 **1042**	1 wn. 50 mult ..	90	30

1043 "Bougainvillea spectabilis"

1044 Venus, Earth, Mars and Satellite

1992. Flowers. Multicoloured.

N3163	10 ch. Type **1043** ..	10	10
N3164	20 ch. "Ixora chinensis"	15	10
N3165	30 ch. "Dendrobium taysuwie"	20	10
N3166	40 ch. "Columnea gloriosa"	25	10
N3167	50 ch. Crinum	30	10
N3168	60 ch. "Ranunculus asiaticus"	35	10

1992. The Solar System. Multicoloured.

N3169	50 ch. Type **1044** ..	30	10
N3170	50 ch. Jupiter	30	10
N3171	50 ch. Saturn	30	10
N3172	50 ch. Uranus	30	10
N3173	50 ch. Neptune and Pluto	30	10

Nos. N3169/73 were issued together, se-tenant, forming a composite design.

1045 Yacht

1046 Moreno Mannini (defender)

1992. "Riccione '92" Stamp Fair. Mult.

N3175	10 ch. Type **1045** ..	10	10
N3176	20 ch. Sailboard ..	15	10
N3177	30 ch. Sailing dinghy ..	20	10
N3178	40 ch. Sailing dinghy (different)	25	10
N3179	50 ch. Yacht (different)	30	10
N3180	60 ch. Emblem ..	35	10

1992. Sampdoria, Italian Football Champion, 1991. Multicoloured.

N3181	20 ch. Type **1046** ..	15	10
N3182	30 ch. Gianluca Vialli (forward)	20	10
N3183	40 ch. Pietro Vierchowod (defender) ..	25	10
N3184	50 ch. Fausto Pari (defender)	30	10
N3185	60 ch. Roberto Mancini (forward)	35	10
N3186	1 wn. Paolo Mantovani (club president) ..	60	20

1047 Black-belts warming up

1992. 8th World Taekwondo Championship, Pyongyang. Multicoloured.

N3188	10 ch. Type **1047** ..	10	10
N3189	30 ch. "Roundhouse" kick	20	10
N3190	50 ch. High kick ..	30	10
N3191	70 ch. Flying kick ..	40	15
N3192	90 ch. Black-belt breaking tiles with fist	55	20

1048 Common Toad ("Bufo bufo")

1992. Frogs and Toads. Multicoloured.

N3194	40 ch. Type **1048** (post)	25	10
N3195	40 ch. Moor frog ("Rana arvalis")	25	10
N3196	40 ch. "Rana chosenica"	25	10
N3197	70 ch. Common pond frog ("Rana nigromaculata")	40	15
N3198	70 ch. Japanese tree toad ("Hyla japonica")	40	15
N3199	70 ch. "Rana coreana" (air)	40	15

1049 "Rhododendron mucronulatum"

1992. World Environment Day. Mult.

N3200	10 ch. Type **1049** (post)	10	10
N3201	30 ch. Barn swallow ..	20	10
N3202	40 ch. "Stewartia koreana" (flower) ..	25	10
N3203	50 ch. "Dictyoptera aurora" (insect) ..	30	10
N3204	70 ch. "Metasequoia glyptostroboides" (tree)	40	15
N3205	90 ch. Chinese salamander	55	20
N3206	1 wn. 20 "Ginkgo biloba" (plant) (air)	70	25
N3207	1 wn. 40 Spotted sculpin	80	25

1050 Fin Whale ("Balaenoptera physalis")

1992. Whales and Dolphins. Multicoloured.

N3208	50 ch. Type **1050** (post)	30	10
N3209	50 ch. Common dolphin ("Delphinus delphis")	30	10
N3210	50 ch. Killer whale ("Orcinus orca") ..	30	10
N3211	50 ch. Hump-backed whale ("Megaptera nodosa")	30	10
N3212	50 ch. Bottle-nosed whale ("Berardius bairdii")	30	10
N3213	50 ch. Sperm whale ("Physeter catadon") (air)	30	10

1051 Mother and Chicks

1992. New Year. Roosters in various costumes. Multicoloured.

N3214	10 ch. Type **1051** ..	10	10
N3215	20 ch. Lady	15	10
N3216	30 ch. Warrior ..	20	10
N3217	40 ch. Courtier ..	25	10
N3218	50 ch. Queen	30	10
N3219	60 ch. King	35	10

1052 Choe Chol Su (boxing)

1992. Gold Medal Winners at Barcelona Olympics. Multicoloured.

N3221	10 ch. Type **1052** ..	10	10
N3222	20 ch. Pae Kil Su (gymnastics) ..	15	10
N3223	30 ch. Flags of Spain and North Korea, flame, gold medal and archer	20	10
N3224	40 ch. Church of the Holy Family (Barcelona) and games mascot and emblem	25	10
N3225	50 ch. Ri Hak Son (freestyle wrestling)	30	10
N3226	60 ch. Kim Il (freestyle wrestling)	35	10

1053 Golden Mushroom

1055 League Members and Flag

1054 "Keumkangsania asiatica"

1993. Fungi. Multicoloured.

N3227	10 ch. Type **1053** ..	10	10
N3228	20 ch. Shaggy caps ..	15	10
N3229	30 ch. "Ganoderma lucidum"	20	10
N3230	40 ch. Brown mushroom	25	10
N3231	50 ch. "Volvaria bombycina" ..	30	10
N3232	60 ch. "Sarcodon aspratus"	35	10

1993. Plants. Multicoloured.

N3234	10 ch. Type **1054** ..	10	10
N3235	20 ch. "Echinosophora koreensis"	15	10
N3236	30 ch. "Abies koreana"	20	10
N3237	40 ch. "Benzoin angustifolium" ..	25	10
N3238	50 ch. "Abeliophyllum distichum"	30	10
N3239	60 ch. "Abelia mosanensis" ..	35	10

1993 8th League of Socialist Working Youth Congress. Multicoloured.

N3241	10 ch. Type **1055** ..	10	10
N3242	40 ch. Flame, League emblem and text ..	25	10

1056 Phophyong Revolutionary Site Tower and March Corps Emblem

1057 Tower of Juche Idea and Grand Monument, Mt. Wangjae

1993. 70th Anniv of Thousand-ri Journey for Learning.

N3243 **1056**	10 ch. multicoloured	10	10

1993. 60th Anniv of Wangjaesan Meeting.

N3244 **1057**	5 ch. multicoloured	10	10

1058 "Kimjongil" (begonia)

1059 Pilot Fish

1993. 51st Birthday of Kim Jong Il.

N3245 **1058**	10 ch. multicoloured	10	10

1993. Fishes. Multicoloured.

N3247	10 ch. Type **1059** ..	10	10
N3248	20 ch. Japanese stingray	15	10
N3249	30 ch. Moonfish ..	20	10
N3250	40 ch. Coelacanth ..	25	10
N3251	50 ch. Grouper ..	30	10

1060/64 "Spring on the Hill" (½-size illustration)

1993. 18th-century Korean Painting.

N3253 **1060**	40 ch. mult ..	25	10
N3254 **1061**	40 ch. mult ..	25	10
N3255 **1062**	40 ch. mult ..	25	10
N3256 **1063**	40 ch. mult ..	25	10
N3257 **1064**	40 ch. mult ..	25	10

Nos. N3253/7 were issued together, se-tenant, forming the composite design illustrated.

1065 Violinist, Dancers and Emblem

1993. Spring Friendship Art Festival, Pyongyang.

N3258 **1065**	10 ch. multicoloured	10	10

1066 Books

1993. 80th Birthday of Kim Il Sung and Publication of his "Reminiscences with the Century".

N3259 **1066**	10 ch. multicoloured	10	10

1067 Kwangbok Street

1993. Pyongyang. Multicoloured.

N3261	10 ch. Type **1067** ..	10	10
N3262	20 ch. Chollima Street	15	10
N3263	30 ch. Munsu Street ..	20	10
N3264	40 ch. Moranbong Street	25	10
N3265	50 ch. Thongil Street ..	30	10

1068 "Trichogramma dendrolimi" (fly)

1069 Ri In Mo

1993. Insects. Multicoloured.

N3267 10 ch. Type **1068** .. 10 10
N3268 20 ch. "Brachymeria obscurata" (fly) .. 15 10
N3269 30 ch. "Metrioptera brachyptera" (cricket) 20 10
N3270 50 ch. European field cricket 30 10
N3271 70 ch. "Geocoris pallidipennis" (beetle) 45 15
N3272 90 ch. "Cyphonony x dorsalis" (wasp) fighting spider .. 55 20

1993. Return from Imprisonment of Ri In Mo (war correspondent).

N3273 **1069** 10 ch. multicoloured 10 10

1070 Footballers

1071 Grey-headed Green Woodpecker

1993. World Cup Football Championship, U.S.A.

N3275 **1070** 10 ch. mult .. 10 10
N3276 – 20 ch. mult .. 15 10
N3277 – 30 ch. mult .. 20 10
N3278 – 50 ch. mult .. 30 10
N3279 – 70 ch. mult .. 45 15
N3280 – 90 ch. mult .. 55 20

DESIGNS: 20 ch. to 90 ch. Various footballing scenes.

1993. Birds. Multicoloured.

N3281 10 ch. Type **1071** .. 10 10
N3282 20 ch. King bird of paradise 15 10
N3283 30 ch. Lesser bird of paradise 20 10
N3284 40 ch. "Steganura paradisea" 25 10
N3285 50 ch. Magnificent bird of paradise 30 10
N3286 60 ch. Greater bird of paradise 40 15

Nos. N3283/4 also commemorate "Indopex'93" International Stamp Exhibition, Surabaya.

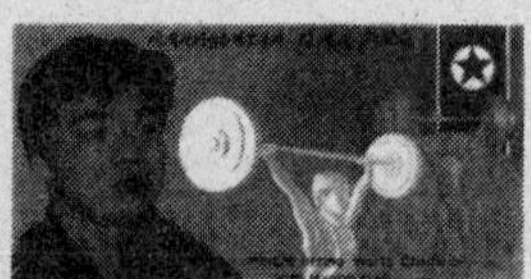

1072 Kim Myong Nam (weightlifting, 1990)

1993 World Champions. Multicoloured.

N3293 10 ch. Type **1072** .. 10 10
N3294 20 ch. Kim Kwang Suk (gymnastics, 1991) .. 15 10
N3295 30 ch. Pak Yong Sun (table tennis, 1975, 1977) 20 10
N3296 50 ch. Kim Yong Ok (radio direction-finding, 1990) .. 30 10
N3297 70 ch. Han Yun Ok (taekwondo, 1987, 1988, 1990) 45 15
N3298 90 ch. Kim Yong Sik (free-style wrestling, 1986, 1989) 55 20

1073 Cabbage and Chilli Peppers

1074 State Arms

1993. Fruits and Vegetables. Multicoloured.

N3299 10 ch. Type **1073** .. 10 10
N3300 20 ch. Squirrels and horse chestnuts .. 15 10
N3301 30 ch. Grapes and peach 20 10
N3302 40 ch. Birds and persimmon 25 10
N3303 50 ch. Tomatoes, aubergine and cherries 30 10
N3304 60 ch. Radish, onion and garlic 40 15

1993.

N3305 **1074** 10 ch. orange .. 10 10

1075 Soldiers and Civilians

1993. 40th Anniv of Victory in Liberation War. Multicoloured.

N3306 10 ch. Type **1075** .. 10 10
N3307 10 ch. Officer and soldier 10 10
N3308 10 ch. Guided missiles on low-loaders on parade 10 10
N3309 10 ch. Anti-aircraft missiles on lorries on parade 10 10
N3310 10 ch. Self-propelled missile launchers (tracked vehicles) on parade 10 10
N3311 10 ch. Machine gun placement (30 × 48 mm) 10 10
N3312 10 ch. Soldier with flag (30 × 48 mm) .. 10 10
N3313 10 ch. Soldier and flags (30 × 48 mm) .. 10 10
N3314 10 ch. Kim Il Sung at strategic policy meeting 10 10
N3315 10 ch. Kim Il Sung directing battle for Height 1211 .. .. 10 10
N3316 10 ch. Kim Il Sung at munitions factory .. 10 10
N3317 10 ch. Kim Il Sung with tank commanders .. 10 10
N3318 10 ch. Kim Il Sung with triumphant soldiers 10 10
N3319 20 ch. Kim Il Sung with artillery unit .. 15 10
N3320 20 ch. Kim Il Sung encouraging machine gun crew 15 10
N3321 20 ch. Kim Il Sung studying map of Second Front .. 15 10
N3322 20 ch. Kim Il Sung with airmen 15 10
N3323 20 ch. Musicians ("Alive is art of Korea") .. 15 10

1076 Choe Yong Do

1077 "Robinia sp."

1993. National Reunification Prize Winners. Multicoloured.

N3325 10 ch. Type **1076** .. 10 10
N3326 20 ch. Kim Ku .. 15 10
N3327 30 ch. Hong Myong Hui 20 10
N3328 40 ch. Ryo Un Hyong 25 10
N3329 50 ch. Kim Jong Thae 30 10
N3330 60 ch. Kim Chaek .. 40 15

1993. "Taipei '93" International Stamp Exhibition, Taipeh. Multicoloured.

N3331 20 ch. Type **1077** .. 15 10
N3332 30 ch. Hippeastrum .. 20 10

1078 Newton

1993. 350th Birth Anniv (1992) of Sir Isaac Newton (mathematician and scientist). Multicoloured.

N3334 10 ch. Type **1078** .. 10 10
N3335 20 ch. Apple tree and formula of law of gravitation 15 10
N3336 30 ch. Satellite, reflecting telescope, dish aerial, globe and rocket 20 10
N3337 50 ch. Formula of binomial theorem .. 30 10
N3338 70 ch. Newton's works and statue 45 15

APPENDIX

The following stamps have either been issued in excess of postal needs or have not been available to the public in reasonable quantities at face value. Such stamps may later be given full listing if there is evidence of regular postal use.

1976.

Olympic Games, Montreal. Three-dimensional stamps showing Olympic events. 5, 10, 15, 20, 25, 40 ch.

1977.

Olympic Games, Montreal. Three-dimensional stamps showing medals. 5, 10, 15, 20, 25, 40 ch. Olympic Games, Montreal. 1976 Olympic Games issue optd. with winners' names. 5, 10, 15, 20, 25, 40 ch.

1979.

XIII Winter Olympic Games, 1980. Nos. N 1688/94 optd. 2, 5, 10, 15, 20, 25, 40 ch.

1981.

Nobel Prizes for Medicine. Nos. N 1955/61 optd. 7 × 10 ch.

World Cup Football Championship, Spain (1982). Nos. N 1731/41 optd. 12 × 20 ch.

World Cup Football Championship, Spain (1982). Three-dimensional stamps. Air 20, 30 ch.

1982.

21st Birthday of Princess of Wales. Nos. N 2108/11 and N 2120/3 optd. 10, 20, 30, 40 ch. 10, 20, 30, 70 ch.

Birth of Prince William of Wales. Nos. N 2185/91 optd. 10, 20, 30, 50, 60, 70, 80 ch.

Birth of Prince William of Wales. Three-dimensional stamps. 3 × 30 ch.

1983.

XXIII Olympic Games, Los Angeles, 1984. Nos. N2084/8 optd 10, 15, 20, 25, 30 ch.

1984.

European Royal History. 81x10 ch.

KOUANG TCHEOU (KWANGCHOW) Pt. 17

An area and port of S. China, leased by France from China in April 1898. It was returned to China in February 1943.

1906. 100 centimes = 1 franc.
1919. 100 cents = 1 piastre.

Unless otherwise stated the following are optd. or surch. on stamps of Indo-China.

1906. Surch. **Kouang Tcheou-Wan** and value in Chinese.

1. **8.** 1 c. olive .. .. .. 1·50 1·50
2. 2 c. red on yellow .. 1·50 1·40
3. 4 c. purple on grey .. 2·00 1·90
4. 5 c. green .. .. .. 2·00 2·00
5. 10 c. red .. .. .. 2·00 2·00
6. 15 c. brown on blue .. 5·00 4·75
7. 20 c. red on green .. 2·00 2·00
8. 25 c. blue .. .. .. 2·00 2·00
9. 30 c. brown on cream .. 2·50 2·50
10. 35 c. black on yellow .. 3·50 3·25
11. 40 c. black on grey .. 2·50 2·50
12. 50 c. brown on cream .. 10·00 10·00
13. D. 75 c. brown on orange .. 15·00 15·00
14. **8.** 1 f. green .. .. .. 18·00 18·00
15. 2 f. brown on yellow .. 18·00 18·00
16. D. 5 f. mauve on lilac .. £120 £120
17. **8.** 10 f. red on green .. £150 £150

1908. Native types surch **KOUANG-TCHEOU** and value in Chinese.

18 **10** 1 c. black and brown .. 40 45
19 2 c. black and brown .. 40 50
20 4 c. black and blue .. 45 50
21 5 c. black and green .. 45 45
22 10 c. black and red .. 45 45
23 15 c. black and violet .. 1·10 1·10
24 **11** 20 c. black and violet .. 2·00 2·00
25 25 c. black and blue .. 2·50 2·50
26 30 c. black and brown .. 4·25 4·50
27 35 c. black and green .. 5·75 6·00
28 40 c. black and brown .. 6·00 6·00
29 50 c. black and red .. 6·50 6·50
30 **12** 75 c. black and orange .. 6·50 6·50
31 – 1 f. black and red .. 7·50 7·50
32 – 2 f. black and green .. 20·00 20·00
33 – 5 f. black and blue .. 40·00 40·00
34 – 10 f. black and violet .. 60·00 60·00

1919. Nos. 18/34 surch in figures and words.

35 **10** 2/5 on 1 c. black & brown 40 45
36 4/5 c. on 2 c. black & brn 35 45
37 1 3/5 c. on 4 c. black & bl 50 55
38 2 c. on 5 c. black & green 55 55
39 4 c. on 10 c. black & red 1·40 85
40 6 c. on 15 c. black & vio 55 45
41 **11** 8 c. on 20 c. black & vio 2·00 1·90
42 10 c. on 25 c. black & bl 5·50 5·00
43 12 c. on 30 c. black & brn 1·10 85
44 14 c. on 35 c. black & grn 1·25 1·10
45 16 c. on 40 c. black & brn 90 70
46 20 c. on 50 c. black & red 90 65
47 **12** 30 c. on 75 c. blk & orge 3·50 3·50
48 – 40 c. on 1 f. black and red 4·25 4·25
49 – 80 c. on 2 f. black & green 5·00 4·25
50 – 2 p. on 5 f. black & blue 95·00 90·00
51 – 4 p. on 10 f. black & vio 12·00 11·50

1923. Native types optd **KOUANG-TCHEOU** only. (Value in cents and piastres).

52 **10** 1/10 c. red and grey .. 15 30
53 1/5 c. black and blue .. 15 30
54 2/5 c. black and brown .. 20 30
55 4/5 c. black and red .. 25 35
56 1 c. black and brown .. 35 35
57 2 c. black and green .. 55 55
58 3 c. black and violet .. 55 55
59 4 c. black and orange .. 55 55
60 5 c. black and red .. 55 55
61 **11** 6 c. black and red .. 70 55
62 7 c. black and green .. 55 70
63 8 c. black on lilac .. 90 55
64 9 c. black & yell on grn 90 85
65 10 c. black and blue .. 85 85
66 11 c. black and violet .. 85 85
67 12 c. black and brown .. 85 85
68 15 c. black and orange .. 1·40 1·40
69 20 c. black & blue on buff 90 85
70 40 c. black and red .. 1·75 1·75
71 1 p. black & green on grn 4·75 4·75
72 2 p. black & pur on pink 7·50 7·75

1927. Pictorial types optd. **KOUANG-TCHEOU.**

73. **22.** 1/10 c. olive 15 30
74. 1/5 c. yellow 20 30
75. 2/5 c. blue 25 35
76. 4/5 c. brown 30 35
77. 1 c. orange 40 45
78. 2 c. green 55 55
79. 3 c. blue 55 55
80. 4 c. mauve 55 55
81. 5 c. violet 55 55
82. **23.** 6 c. red 50 55
83. 7 c. brown 50 55
84. 8 c. olive 55 55
85. 9 c. purple 65 65
86. 10 c. blue 65 65
87. 11 c. orange 65 70
88. 12 c. green 65 65
89. **24.** 15 c. brown and red .. 1·10 1·10
90. 20 c. grey and violet .. 1·40 1·40
91. – 25 c. mauve and brown .. 1·40 1·40
92. – 30 c. olive and blue .. 95 95
93. – 40 c. blue and red .. 90 85
94. – 50 c. grey and green .. 1·00 1·00
95. – 1 p. blk., yellow & blue .. 2·50 2·50
96. – 2 p. blue, orange & red .. 2·75 2·75

1937. 1931 issue optd. **KOUANG-TCHEOU.**

98. **33.** 1/10 c. blue 15 30
99. 1/5 c. lake 20 30
100. 2/5 c. red 15 30
101. 1/2 c. brown 15 25
102. 4/5 c. violet 30 30
103. 1 c. brown 20 30
104. 2 c. green 20 30
126. – 3 c. brown 30 30
105. – 3 c. green 50 45
106. – 4 c. blue 55 55
127. – 4 c. green 30 30
128. – 4 c. yellow .. .. 1·00 1·00
107. – 5 c. purple 55 55
129. – 5 c. green 35 35
108. – 6 c. red 35 45
130. – 7 c. black 35 45
131. – 8 c. lake 35 45
132. – 9 c. black on yellow .. 40 45
109. – 10 c. blue 65 65
133. – 10 c. blue on pink .. 50 55
110. – 15 c. blue 40 45
134. – 18 c. blue 20 30
111. – 20 c. red 40 45
112. – 21 c. green 40 45
135. – 22 c. green 35 35
113. – 25 c. purple .. .. 1·60 1·60
136. – 25 c. blue 45 45
114. – 30 c. brown 35 45
115. **36.** 50 c. brown 55 60
116. 60 c. purple 60 60
137. 70 c. blue 45 45
117. 1 p. green 85 90
118. 2 p. red .. .. .. 1·00 1·00

1939. New York World's Fair. As T **28** of Mauritania.

119. 13 c. red 50 55
120. 23 c. deep blue & blue 50 55

1939. 150th Anniv. of French Revolution. As T **29** of Mauritania.

121. 6 c.+2 c. green .. 3·75 3·75
122. 7 c.+3 c. brown .. 3·75 3·75
123. 9 c.+4 c. orange .. 3·75 3·75
124. 13 c.+10 c. red .. 3·75 3·75
125. 23 c.+20 c. blue .. 3·75 3·75

KUWAIT Pt. 19

An independent Arab Shaikhdom on the N.W. coast of the Persian Gulf with Indian and later British postal administration. On 1st February, 1959, the Kuwait Government assumed responsibility for running its own postal service. In special treaty relations with Great Britain until 19 June 1961 when Kuwait became completely independent.

For stamps issued by Indian and British postal administrations, see Vol. 3.

1958. 100 naye paise = 1 rupee.
1961. 1,000 fils = 1 dinar.

20. Shaikh Abdullah.

21. Dhow.

1958.

131. **20.** 5 n.p. green 15 10
132. 10 n.p. red 20 10
133. 15 n.p. brown 20 10
134. 20 n.p. violet 20 10
135. 25 n.p. salmon 35 10
136. 40 n.p. purple 75 20
137. **21.** 40 n.p. blue 45 10
138. – 50 n.p. red 40 10
139. – 75 n.p. green 45 15
140. – 1 r. purple 50 10
141. – 2 r. blue and brown .. 2·50 25
142. – 5 r. turquoise .. .. 4·00 1·50
143. – 10 r. lilac .. .. 13·00 3·75

DESIGNS—HORIZ. As Type **21**: 50 n.p. Oil pipelines. 75 n.p. Power Station. (36×20 mm.). 1 r. Oil rig. 2 r. Single-masted dhow. 5 r. Kuwait Mosque. 10 r. Main Square, Kuwait Town.

22. Shaikh Abdullah and Flag.

1960. 10th Anniv. of Shaikh's Accession.

144. **22.** 40 n.p. red and olive .. 25 10
145. 60 n.p. red and blue .. 35 15

1961. As 1958 issue but currency changed and new designs.

146 **20** 1 f. green 15 10
147 2 f. red 15 10
148 4 f. brown 15 10
149 5 f. violet 15 10
150 8 f. red 20 10
151 15 f. purple 25 10
152 – 20 f. green (as 5 r.) .. 50 10
153 – 25 f. blue 90 10
154 – 30 f. blue & brn (as 2 r.) 1·25 10
155 – 35 f. black & red .. 75 40
156 **21** 40 f. blue (32×22 mm) 1·25 15
157 – 45 f. brown 50 10
158 – 75 f. brn & grn (as 2 r.) 2·50 60
159 – 90 f. brown & blue .. 1·75 35
160 – 100 f. red .. .. 3·25 10
161 **21** 250 f. grn (32×22 mm) 7·00 1·50
162 – 1 d. orange .. .. 10·00 1·50
163 – 3 d. red (as 5 r.) .. 25·00 18·00

NEW DESIGNS (37×20 mm). 25 f., 100 f. Vickers "Viscount" airliner over South Pier, Mina al Ahmadi. 35 f., 90 f. Shuwaikh Secondary School. 45 f., 1 d. Wara Hill.

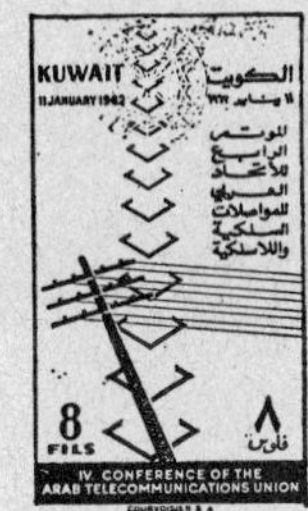

23. Telegraph Pole.

1962. 4th Arab Telecommunications Union Conference.

164. **23.** 8 f. blue and black .. 15 10
165. 20 f. red and black .. 30 20

1962. Arab League Week. As T **76** of Libya.

166. 20 f. purple 10 10
167. 45 f. brown 30 20

25. Mubarakiya School, Shaikh Abdullah and Shaikh Mubarak.

1962. Golden Jubilee of Mubarakiya School.

168. **25.** 8 f. multicoloured .. 15 10
169. 20 f. multicoloured .. 40 15

26. National Flag and Crest.

1962. National Day.

170. **26.** 8 f. multicoloured .. 10 10
171. 20 f. multicoloured .. 35 20
172. 45 f. multicoloured .. 80 30
173. 90 f. multicoloured .. 1·25 1·00

1962. Malaria Eradication. As T **26a** of Yemen.

174. 4 f. green and turquoise 10 10
175. 25 f. grey and green .. 30 25

28. "Industry and Progress".

1962. Bicent. of Sabah Dynasty.

176. **28.** 8 f. multicoloured .. 10 10
177. 20 f. multicoloured .. 25 15
178. 45 f. multicoloured .. 55 15
179. 75 f. multicoloured .. 95 50

29. Mother and Child.

31. "Education from Oil".

30. Campaign Emblem, Palm and Domestic Animals.

1963. Mothers' Day. Centres black and green; value black; country name red.

180. **29.** 8 f. yellow 10 10
181. 20 f. blue 20 15
182. 45 f. olive 45 25
183. 75 f. grey 70 40

1963. Freedom from Hunger. Design in brown and green. Background colours given.

184. **30.** 4 f. blue 10 10
185. 8 f. yellow 25 15
186. 20 f. lilac 50 25
187. 45 f. pink .. .. 1·25 90

1963. Education Day.

188. **31.** 4 f. brown, blue & yellow 10 10
189. 20 f. green, blue & yellow 30 10
190. 45 f. purple, blue & yell. 60 25

32. Shaikh Abdullah and Flags.

1963. 2nd Anniv. of National Day. Flags in green, black and red; values in black.

191. **32.** 4 f. blue 40 30
192. 5 f. ochre 60 55
193. 20 f. violet .. .. 3·00 2·25
194. 50 f. olive .. .. 6·00 3·75

33. Human Lungs, and Emblems of W.H.O. and Kuwait.

1963. W.H.O. "Tuberculosis Control" Campaign. Emblem yellow: Arms black, green and red.

195. **33.** 2 f. black and ochre .. 10 10
196. 4 f. black and green .. 10 10
197. 8 f. black and blue .. 20 10
198. 20 f. black and lake .. 80 35

34. Municipal Hall and Scroll.

1963. New Constitution. Centres dull purple; Amir red.

199. **34.** 4 f. red 10 20
200. 8 f. green 15 25
201. 20 f. purple 25 30
202. 45 f. brown 45 35
203. 75 f. violet 65 65
204. 90 f. blue .. .. .. 1·40 2·00

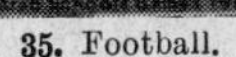

35. Football. **36.** Scales of Justice and Globe.

1963. Arab Schools Games. Multicoloured.

205. 1 f. Type **35** 10 10
206. 4 f. Basketball 10 10
207. 5 f. Swimming 10 10
208. 8 f. Running 15 10
209. 15 f. Throwing the javelin 30 15
210. 20 f. Pole-vaulting .. 40 20
211. 35 f. Gymnastics 90 35
212. 45 f. Gymnastics .. .. 1·25 75

Nos. 207, 209/11 are horiz.

1963. 15th Anniv. of Declaration of Human Rights.

213. **36.** 8 f. black, turq. & violet 10 10
214. 20 f. black, yellow & grey 40 20
215. 25 f. black, buff & blue 60 30

37. Shaikh Abdullah.

38. Rameses II in War Chariot.

1964. Multicoloured.

216. **37.** 1 f. 10 10
217. 2 f. 10 10
218. 4 f. 15 10
219. 5 f. 15 10
220. 8 f. 25 10
221. 10 f. 25 10
222. 15 f. 35 10
223. 20 f. 35 10
224. 25 f. 40 10
225. 30 f. 55 10
226. 40 f. 75 10
227. 45 f. 90 10
228. 50 f. 95 10
229. 70 f. .. .. .. 1·00 20
230. 75 f. .. .. .. 1·50 30
231. 90 f. .. .. .. 1·50 30
232. 100 f. .. .. .. 1·75 20
233. – 250 f. .. .. .. 5·50 50
234. – 1 d. .. .. .. 15·00 2·50

Nos. 233/4 are larger (25×30 mm.).

1964. Nubian Monuments Preservation.

235. **38.** 8 f. purple, blue & buff 15 10
236. 20 f. vio., blue & lt. blue 35 15
237. 30 f. violet, blue & turq. 45 25

39. Mother and Child.

1964. Mother's Day.

238. **39.** 8 f. blue, green and grey 10 10
239. 20 f. blue, green and red 25 10
240. 30 f. blue, green & bistre 35 20
241. 45 f. blue, green & blue 50 20

40. Nurse giving B.C.G. Vaccine to Patient, and Bones of Chest.

41. Dhow and Microscope.

1964. World Health Day.

242. **40.** 8 f. green and brown .. 35 10
243. 20 f. red and green .. 90 20

1964. Education Day.

244 **41.** 8 f. multicoloured .. 15 10
245. 15 f. multicoloured .. 30 10
246. 20 f. multicoloured .. 35 15
247. 30 f. multicoloured .. 60 25

42. Dhow and Doves.

1964. 3rd Anniv. of National Day. Badge in blue, brown, black, red and green.

248. **42.** 8 f. black and bistre .. 15 10
249. 20 f. black and green .. 25 10
250. 30 f. black and grey .. 40 15
251. 45 f. black and blue .. 55 25

43. A.P.U. Emblem. **44.** "Comet" and "Dakota" Airliners.

1964. 10th Anniv. of Arab Postal Union's Permanent Office, Cairo.

252. **43.** 8 f. brown and blue .. 35 10
253. 20 f. blue and yellow .. 50 10
254. 45 f. brown and olive .. 90 35

1964. Air. 10th Anniv. of Kuwait Airways. Sky in blue; aircraft blue, red and black.

255. **44.** 20 f. black and bistre .. 45 15
256. 25 f. black and brown .. 55 15
257. 30 f. black and olive .. 65 20
258. 45 f. black and brown .. 85 35

45. Conference Emblem. 46. Dhow, Doves and Oil-drilling Rig.

1965. 1st Arab Journalists' Conf., Kuwait.
259. 45. 8 f. multicoloured .. 15 10
260. 20 f. multicoloured .. 35 15

1965. 4th Anniv. of National Day.
261. 46. 10 f. multicoloured .. 15 10
262. 15 f. multicoloured .. 30 15
263. 20 f. multicoloured .. 45 20

47. I.C.Y. Emblem. 48. Mother and Children.

1965. Int. Co-operation Year.
264. 47. 8 f. black and red .. 30 10
265. 20 f. black and blue .. 75 30
266. 30 f. black and green .. 1·10 50
The stamps are inscribed "CO-OPERATIVE".

1965. Mothers' Day.
267. 48. 8 f. multicoloured .. 20 10
268. 15 f. multicoloured .. 30 20
269. 20 f. multicoloured .. 50 25

49. Weather Kite.

1965. World Meteorological Day.
270. 49. 4 f. blue and yellow .. 30 10
271. 5 f. blue and orange .. 30 10
272. 20 f. blue and green .. 1·40 50

50. Census Graph.

1965. Population Census.
273. 50. 8 f. black, brown & turq. 20 10
274. 20 f. black, pink & green 60 20
275. 50 f. black, green & red 1·40 60

1965. Deir Yassin Massacre. As T **52a** of Yemen.
276. 4 f. red and blue 25 10
277. 45 f. red and green .. 1·75 60

51. Atomic Symbol and Tower of Shuwaikh Secondary School.

1965. Education Day.
278. 51. 4 f. multicoloured .. 15 10
279. 20 f. multicoloured .. 40 15
280. 45 f. multicoloured .. 75 35

52. I.T.U. Emblem and Symbols. 53. Saker Falcon.

1965. I.T.U. Cent.
281. 52. 8 f. red and blue .. 30 10
282. 20 f. red and green .. 75 20
283. 45 f. blue and red .. 1·75 55

1965. Reconstitution of Burnt Algiers Library. As T **53a** of Yemen.
284. 8 f. green, red and black.. 30 10
285. 15 f. red, green and black.. 80 15

1965. Centre in sepia.
286. 53. 8 f. purple 75 10
287. 15 f. olive .. .. 1·10 10
288. 20 f. blue .. .. 1·25 10
289. 25 f. red .. .. 1·25 15
290. 30 f. green .. .. 1·75 20
291. 45 f. blue .. .. 2·75 30
292. 50 f. purple .. .. 3·25 40
293. 90 f. red .. .. 5·00 1·25

54. Open Book. 55. Shaikh Sabah.

1966. Education Day.
294. 54. 8 f. multicoloured .. 20 10
295. 20 f. multicoloured .. 45 10
296. 30 f. multicoloured .. 70 25

1966.
297. 55. 4 f. multicoloured .. 15 10
298. 5 f. multicoloured .. 15 10
299. 20 f. multicoloured .. 40 10
300. 30 f. multicoloured .. 55 10
301. 40 f. multicoloured .. 70 15
302. 45 f. multicoloured .. 75 20
303. 70 f. multicoloured .. 1·75 50
304. 90 f. multicoloured .. 2·00 75

56. Fishes and Ears of Wheat.

1966. Freedom from Hunger.
305. 56. 20 f. multicoloured .. 1·50 25
306. 45 f. multicoloured .. 2·00 55

57. Eagle and Scales of Justice.

1966. 5th Anniv. of National Day.
307. 57. 20 f. multicoloured .. 85 20
308. 25 f. multicoloured .. 95 25
309. 45 f. multicoloured .. 1·75 65

58. Cogwheel and Map of Arab States. 59. Mother and Children.

1966. Arab Countries Industrial Development Conf. Kuwait.
310. 58. 20 f. grn. black & blue 60 10
311. 50f. grn., black & brown 1·00 35

1966. Mothers' Day.
312. 59. 20 f. multicoloured .. 30 12
313. 40 f. multicoloured .. 70 35

60. Red Crescent Emblem of Medicine. 61. "Man and his Cities".

1966. 5th Arab Medical Conf., Kuwait.
314. 60. 15 f. red and blue .. 35 10
315. 30 f. red, blue and pink 75 20

1966. World Health Day.
316. 61. 8 f. multicoloured .. 25 10
317. 10 f. multicoloured .. 35 10

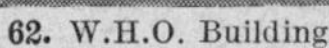
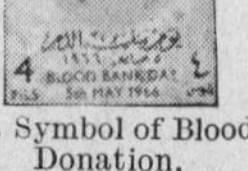

62. W.H.O. Building. 63. Symbol of Blood Donation.

1966. Inaug. of W.H.O. Headquarters, Geneva.
318. 62. 5 f. green, blue and red 45 10
319. 10 f. green, blue & turq. 80 10

1966. Traffic Day. As T **66** of Yemen.
320. 10 f. red, emerald & green 50 10
321. 20 f. emerald, red & green 75 20

1966. Blood Bank Day.
322. 63. 4 f. multicoloured .. 40 10
323. 8 f. multicoloured .. 85 25

64. Shaikh Ahmad and "British Fusilier" (tanker).

1966. 20th Anniv. of 1st Crude Oil Shipment.
324. 64. 20 f. multicoloured .. 60 20
325. 45 f. multicoloured .. 1·40 60

65. Ministry Building.

1966. Inauguration of Ministry of Guidance and Information. Building.
326. 65. 4 f. red and brown .. 15 10
327. 5 f. brown and green .. 15 10
328. 8 f. green and violet .. 20 10
329. 20 f. orange and blue.. 60 15

66. Dhow, Lobster, Fish and Crab. 67. U.N. Flag.

1966. F.A.O. Near East Countries Fisheries Conf., Kuwait.
330. 66. 4 f. multicoloured .. 35 20
331. 20 f. multicoloured .. 1·40 55

1966. U.N. Day.
332. 67. 20 f. multicoloured .. 75 20
333. 45 f multicoloured .. 1·50 65

68. U.N.E.S.C.O. Emblem. 69. Ruler and University Shield.

1966. 20th Anniv. of U.N.E.S.C.O.
334. 68. 20 f. multicoloured .. 75 20
335. 45 f. multicoloured .. 1·50 65

1966. Opening of Kuwait University.
336. 69. 8 f. multicoloured .. 25 10
337. 10 f. multicoloured .. 25 10
338. 20 f. multicoloured .. 75 20
339. 45 f. multicoloured .. 1·50 70

70. Ruler and Heir-Apparent.

1966. Appointment of Heir-Apparent.
340. 70. 8 f. multicoloured .. 25 10
341. 20 f. multicoloured .. 60 15
342. 45 f. multicoloured .. 1·25 55

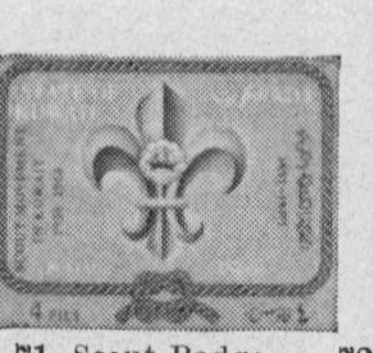

71. Scout Badge. 72. Symbol of Learning.

1966. 30th Anniv. of Kuwait Scouts.
343. 71. 4 f. brown and green .. 75 15
344. 20 f. green and brown.. 2·50 70

1967. Education Day.
345. 72. 10 f. multicoloured .. 25 10
346. 45 f. multicoloured .. 70 25

73. Fertiliser Plant.

1967. Inaug. of Chemical Fertiliser Plant.
347. 73. 8 f. purple, green & blue 40 10
348. 20 f. blue, green & buff 1·00 20

74. Ruler, Dove and Olive-Branch.

1967. 6th Anniv. of National Day.
349. 74. 8 f. multicoloured .. 25 10
350. 20 f. multicoloured .. 65 20

75. Map and Municipality Building. 76. Arab Family.

1967. 1st Arab Cities Organization Conf., Kuwait.
351. 75. 20 f. multicoloured .. 1·00 25
352. 30 f. multicoloured .. 1·50 1·75

1967. Family's Day.
353. 76. 20 f. multicoloured .. 1·00 25
354. 45 f. multicoloured .. 1·50 60

77. Arab League Emblem. 78. Sabah Hospital.

1967. Arab Cause Week.
355. 77. 8 f. blue and grey .. 15 10
356. 10 f. green and yellow 15 10

1967. World Health Day.
357. 78. 8 f. multicoloured .. 45 10
358. 20 f. multicoloured .. 1·40 15

79. Nubian Statues.

1967. Arab Week for Nubian Monuments Preservation.
359. 79. 15 f. green, brown & yell. 60 15
360. 20 f. green, purple & blue 90 25

80. Traffic Policeman.

81. I.T.Y. Emblem. 82. "Reaching for Knowledge".

1967. Traffic Day.
361. **80.** 8 f. multicoloured .. 75 15
362. 20 f. multicoloured .. 1·75 45

1967. Int. Tourist Year.
363. **81.** 20 f. black, blue & turq. 55 15
364. 45 f. black, blue & mve. 1·25 50

1967. "Eliminate Illiteracy" Campaign.
365. **82.** 8 f. multicoloured .. 75 10
366. 20 f. multicoloured .. 1·50 40

83. Map of Palestine. **84.** Factory and Cogwheels.

1967. U.N. Day.
367. **83.** 20 f. red and blue .. 60 15
368. 45 f. red and orange .. 1·40 75

1967. 3rd Arab Labour Ministers' Conf.
369. **84.** 20 f. yellow and red .. 60 15
370. 45 f. yellow and slate .. 1·40 70

85. Open Book and Kuwaiti Flag. **86.** Oil Rig and Map.

1968. Education Day.
371. **85.** 20 f. multicoloured .. 45 10
372. 45 f. multicoloured .. 1·25 55

1968. 30th Anniv. of Oil Discovery in Greater Burgan Field.
373. **86.** 10 f. multicoloured .. 65 15
374. 20 f. multicoloured .. 1·25 55

87. Ruler and Sun Rays. **88.** Book, Eagle and Sun.

1968. 7th Anniv. of National Day.
375. **87.** 8 f. multicoloured .. 20 10
376. 10 f. multicoloured .. 20 10
377. 15 f. multicoloured .. 30 10
378. 20 f. multicoloured .. 45 15

1968. Teachers' Day.
379. **88.** 8 f. multicoloured .. 25 10
380. 20 f. multicoloured .. 55 15
381. 45 f. multicoloured .. 1·25 55

89. Family Picnicking.

1968. Family Day.
382. **89.** 8 f. multicoloured .. 20 10
383. 10 f. multicoloured .. 20 10
384. 15 f. multicoloured .. 30 10
385. 20 f. multicoloured .. 45 20

90. Ruler, W.H.O. and State Emblems.

1968. World Health Day and 20th Anniv. of W.H.O.
386. **90.** 20 f. multicoloured .. 60 20
387. 45 f. multicoloured .. 1·40 60

INDEX

Countries can be quickly located by referring to the index at the end of this volume.

91. Dagger on Deir Yassin, and Scroll.

1968. 20th Anniv. of Deir Yassin Massacre.
388. **91.** 20 f. red and blue .. 80 25
389. 45 f. red and violet .. 2·75 70

92. Pedestrians on Road Crossing.

1968. Traffic Day.
390. **92.** 10 f. multicoloured .. 75 20
391. 15 f. multicoloured .. 1·25 25
392. 20 f. multicoloured .. 1·75 50

93. Torch and Map. **94.** Palestine Refugees.

1968. Palestine Day.
393. **93.** 10 f. multicoloured .. 80 25
394. 20 f. multicoloured .. 1·40 30
395. 45 f. multicoloured .. 2·75 1·00

1968. Human Rights Year.
396. **94.** 20 f. multicoloured .. 25 15
397. 30 f. multicoloured .. 35 25
398. 45 f. multicoloured .. 65 30
399. 90 f. multicoloured .. 1·25 1·00

95. National Museum. **96.** Man reading Book.

1968.
400. **95.** 1 f. green and sepia .. 10 10
401. 2 f. green and plum .. 10 10
402. 5 f. red and black .. 15 10
403. 8 f. green and brown .. 20 10
404. 10 f. purple and blue .. 20 10
405. 20 f. blue and brown .. 40 10
406. 25 f. orange and blue .. 50 10
407. 30 f. green and blue .. 65 20
408. 45 f. slate and purple .. 95 20
409. 50 f. red and green .. 1·40 40

1968. Int. Literacy Day.
410. **96.** 15 f. multicoloured .. 25 10
411. 20 f. multicoloured .. 60 15

97. Refugee Children and U.N. Headquarters.

1968. United Nations Day.
412. **97.** 20 f. multicoloured .. 25 10
413. 30 f. multicoloured .. 40 20
414. 45 f. multicoloured .. 60 25

98. Chamber of Commerce Building.

1968. Inauguration of Kuwait Chamber of Commerce and Industry Building.
415. **98.** 10 f. purple and orange 25 10
416. 15 f. blue and mauve .. 25 10
417. 20 f. green and brown .. 35 15

99. Conference Emblem.

1968. 14th Arab Chambers of Commerce, Industry and Agriculture Conference.
418. **99.** 10 f. multicoloured .. 25 10
419. 15 f. multicoloured .. 30 10
420. 20 f. multicoloured .. 40 20
421. 30 f. multicoloured .. 60 35

100. Refinery Plant. **101.** Holy Koran, Scales and People.

1968. Inaug. of Shuaiba Refinery.
422. **100.** 10 f. multicoloured .. 30 15
423. 20 f. multicoloured .. 55 15
424. 30 f. multicoloured .. 80 35
425. 45 f. multicoloured .. 1·40 60

1968. 1,400th Anniv. of the Holy Koran.
426. **101.** 8 f. multicoloured .. 30 10
427. 20 f. multicoloured .. 75 15
428. 30 f. multicoloured .. 1·10 40
429. 45 f. multicoloured .. 1·40 60

102. Boeing "707" Airliner.

1969. Inaug. of Boeing "707" Aircraft by Kuwait Airways.
430. **102.** 10 f. multicoloured .. 40 15
431. 20 f. multicoloured .. 80 25
432. 25 f. multicoloured .. 1·00 45
433. 45 f. multicoloured .. 2·00 80

103. Globe and Symbols of Engineering and Science.

1969. Education Day.
434. **103.** 15 f. multicoloured .. 30 15
435. 20 f. multicoloured .. 50 25

104. Hilton Hotel. **105.** Family and Teachers' Society Emblem.

1969. Inaug. of Kuwait Hilton Hotel.
436. **104.** 10 f. multicoloured .. 25 15
437. 20 f. multicoloured .. 50 15

1969. Education Week.
438. **105.** 10 f. multicoloured .. 25 15
439. 20 f. multicoloured .. 50 15

106. Flags and Laurel. **107.** Emblem, Teacher and Class.

1969. 8th Anniv. of National Day.
440. **106.** 15 f. multicoloured .. 25 15
441. 20 f. multicoloured .. 30 15
442. 30 f. multicoloured .. 50 30

1969. Teachers' Day.
443. **107.** 10 f. multicoloured .. 20 15
444. 20 f. multicoloured .. 40 15

108. Kuwaiti Family.

1969. Family Day.
445. **108.** 10 f. multicoloured .. 25 15
446. 20 f. multicoloured .. 45 15

109. Ibn Sina, Nurse with Patient and W.H.O. Emblem. **110.** Motor-cycle Police.

1969. World Health Day.
447. **109.** 15 f. multicoloured .. 50 15
448. 20 f. multicoloured .. 60 15

1969. Traffic Day.
449. **110.** 10 f. multicoloured .. 1·00 20
450. 20 f. multicoloured .. 2·00 30

111. I.L.O. Emblem.

1969. 50th Anniv. of I.L.O.
451. **111.** 10 f. gold, black and red 20 10
452. 20 f. gold, black & green 35 15

112. Tanker "Al Sabahiah".

1969. 4th Anniv. of Kuwait Shipping Company.
453. **112.** 20 f. multicoloured .. 90 30
454. 45 f. multicoloured .. 1·90 95

113. Woman writing Letter. **114.** Amir Shaikh Sabah.

1969. Int. Literacy Day.
455. **113.** 10 f. multicoloured .. 20 10
456. 20 f. multicoloured .. 40 20

1969. Portraits multicoloured; background colours given.
457. **114.** 8 f. blue 25 10
458. 10 f. red 25 10
459. 15 f. grey 35 10
460. 20 f. yellow 40 10
461. 25 f. lilac 50 10
462. 30 f. orange 70 10
463. 45 f. drab 95 10
464. 50 f. green .. .. 1·25 10
465. 70 f. blue .. .. 1·50 25
466. 75 f. blue .. .. 1·75 30
467. 90 f. brown .. .. 2·25 35
468. 250 f. purple .. .. 7·00 60
469. 500 f. green .. .. 11·00 1·75
470. 1 d. purple .. .. 18·00 2·50

115. "Appeal to World Conscience". 116. Earth Station.

1969. United Nations Day.

471. 115.	10 f. blue, black & green	25	15
472.	20 f. blue, black & ochre	50	15
473.	45 f. blue, black & red	1·00	45

1969. Inauguration of Kuwait Satellite Communications Station. Multicoloured.

474.	20 Type 116	90	20
475.	45 f. Dish aerial on Globe (vert.)	1·90	70

117. Refugee Family. 118. Globe, Symbols and I.E.Y. Emblem.

1969. Palestinian Refugee Week.

476. 117.	20 f. multicoloured ..	1·25	25
477.	45 f. multicoloured ..	2·75	75

1970. Int. Education Year.

478. 118.	20 f. multicoloured ..	40	20
479.	45 f. multicoloured ..	1·00	60

119. Shoue.

1970. Kuwait Sailing Dhows. Multicoloured.

480	8 f. Type 119	40	10
481	10 f. Sambuk	40	10
482	15 f. Baggala	60	20
483	20 f. Battela	75	15
484	25 f. Bum	90	35
485	45 f. Baggala	1·75	40
486	50 f. Dhow-building ..	2·00	60

120. Kuwaiti Flag.

1970. 9th Anniv. of National Day.

487. 120.	15 f. multicoloured ..	40	15
488.	20 f. multicoloured ..	50	15

121. Young Commando and Dome of the Rock, Jerusalem.

1970. Support for Palestine Commandos. Multicoloured.

489.	10 f. Type 121	60	20
490.	20 f. Commando in battle-dress	1·25	20
491.	45 f. Woman commando ..	2·75	90

122. Parents with "Children".

1970. Family Day.

492. 122.	20 f. multicoloured ..	30	15
493.	30 f. multicoloured ..	50	25

123. Arab League Flag, Emblem and Map.

1970. 25th Anniv. of Arab League.

494. 123.	20 f. ochre, green & blue	25	10
495.	45 f. violet, green & pink	50	20

124. Census Emblem and Graph.

1970. Population Census.

496. 124.	15 f. multicoloured ..	25	10
497.	20 f. multicoloured ..	35	15
498.	30 f. multicoloured ..	60	30

125. Cancer the Crab in "Pincers". 126. Traffic Lights and Road Signs.

1970. World Health Day.

499. 125.	20 f. multicoloured ..	35	10
500.	30 f. multicoloured ..	55	25

1970. Traffic Day.

501. 126.	20 f. multicoloured ..	1·25	25
502.	30 f. multicoloured ..	1·75	60

127. Red Crescent.

1970. Int. Red Cross and Crescent Day.

503. 127.	10 f. multicoloured ..	40	15
504.	15 f. multicoloured ..	60	15
505.	30 f. multicoloured ..	1·50	55

128. New Headquarters Building.

1970. Opening of New U.P.U. Headquarters Building, Berne.

506. 128.	20 f. multicoloured ..	50	10
507.	30 f. multicoloured ..	75	40

129. Amir Shaikh Sabah. 130. U.N. Symbols.

1970.

508. 129.	20 f. multicoloured ..	50	20
509.	45 f. multicoloured ..	1·50	65

1970. 25th Anniv. of United Nations.

511 130	20 f. multicoloured ..	30	15
512	45 f. multicoloured ..	60	25

131. "Medora" (tanker) at Sea Island Jetty.

1970. Oil Shipment Facilities, Kuwait.

513. 131.	20 f. multicoloured ..	1·00	25
514.	45 f. multicoloured ..	2·00	70

132. Kuwaiti and U.N. Emblems and Hand writing.

1970. International Literacy Day.

515. 132.	10 f. multicoloured ..	60	20
516.	15 f. multicoloured ..	80	20

133. Guards and Badge.

1970. First Graduation of National Guards.

517. 133.	10 f. multicoloured ..	50	20
518.	20 f. multicoloured ..	1·00	20

134. Symbols and Flag. 136. Map of Palestine on Globe.

135. Dr. C. Best, Sir F. Banting (discoverers of insulin) and syringe.

1971. 10th Anniv. of National Day.

519. 134.	20 f. multicoloured ..	65	15
520.	30 f. multicoloured ..	90	30

1971. World Health Day, and 50th Anniv of Discovery of Insulin.

521 135	20 f. multicoloured ..	75	15
522	45 f. multicoloured ..	1·75	45

1971. Palestine Week.

523. 136.	20 f. multicoloured ..	1·00	20
524.	45 f. multicoloured ..	2·25	55

137. I.T.U. Emblem. 138. "Three Races".

1971. World Telecommunications Day.

525. 137.	20 f. blk., brn. & silver	1·00	20
526.	45 f. blk., brn. & gold ..	2·25	55

1971. Racial Equality Year.

527. 138.	15 f. multicoloured ..	30	10
528.	30 f. multicoloured ..	60	35

139. A.P.U. Emblem.

1971. 25th Anniv. of Founding of Arab Postal Union at Sofar Conference.

529. 139.	20 f. multicoloured ..	50	15
530.	45 f. multicoloured ..	1·25	40

140. Book, Pupils, Globes and Pen.

1971. Int. Literacy Day.

531. 140.	25 f. multicoloured ..	55	15
532.	60 f. multicoloured ..	1·40	70

141. Footballers.

1971. Regional Sports Tournament, Kuwait. Multicoloured.

533	20 f. Type 141	60	15
534	30 f. Footballer blocking attack	1·25	45

142. Emblems of U.N.I.C.E.F. and Kuwait.

1971. 25th Anniv. of U.N.I.C.E.F.

535. 142.	25 f. multicoloured ..	50	20
536.	60 f. multicoloured ..	1·10	75

143. Book Year Emblem.

1972. Int. Book Year.

537. 143.	20 f. black and brown	50	10
538.	45 f. black and green ..	1·10	55

144. Crest and Laurel.

1972. 11th Anniv. of National Day.

539. 144.	20 f. multicoloured ..	60	10
540.	45 f. multicoloured ..	1·50	55

145. Telecommunications Centre.

1972. Inauguration of Telecommunications Centre, Kuwait.

541. 145.	20 f. multicoloured ..	1·25	20
542.	45 f. multicoloured ..	2·75	80

146. Human Heart. 147. Nurse and Child.

1972. World Health Day and World Heart Month.
543. **146.** 20 f. multicoloured .. 1·25 20
544. 45 f. multicoloured .. 2·75 80

1972. Int. Red Cross and Crescent Day.
545. **147.** 8 f. multicoloured .. 50 10
546. 40 f. multicoloured .. 2·50 70

148. Football.

1972. Olympic Games, Munich. Mult.
547. 2 f. Type **148** 10 10
548. 4 f. Running 10 10
549. 5 f. Swimming 15 10
550. 8 f. Gymnastics 25 10
551. 10 f. Throwing the discus 30 10
552. 15 f. Show jumping .. 40 10
553. 20 f. Basketball 45 15
554. 25 f. Volleyball 50 40

149. Produce and Fishing Boat. **151.** Ancient Capitals.

150. Bank Emblem.

1972. 11th F.A.O. Near East, Regional Conf., Kuwait.
555. **149.** 5 f. multicoloured .. 30 10
556. 10 f. multicoloured .. 55 10
557. 20 f. multicoloured .. 1·10 30

1972. 20th Anniv. of National Bank of Kuwait.
558. **150.** 10 f. multicoloured .. 25 10
559. 35 f. multicoloured .. 1·00 50

1972. Archaeological Excavations on Failaka Island. Multicoloured.
560. 2 f. Type **151** 10 15
561. 5 f. View of excavations .. 25 10
562. 10 f. " Leaf " capital .. 40 10
563. 15 f. Excavated building .. 60 20

152. Floral Emblem. **153.** Interpol Emblem.

1973. 12th Anniv. of National Day.
564. **152.** 10 f. multicoloured .. 25 10
565. 20 f. multicoloured .. 55 15
566. 30 f. multicoloured .. 90 40

1973. 50th Anniv. of Int. Criminal Police Organization ((Interpol).
567. **153.** 10 f. multicoloured .. 50 15
568. 15 f. multicoloured .. 90 25
569. 20 f. multicoloured .. 1·40 60

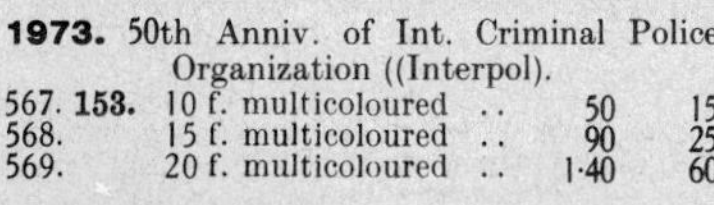

154. C.I.S.M. Emblem and Flags. **155.** Airways Building.

1973. 25th Anniv. of Int. Military Sports Council (C.I.S.M.)
570. **154.** 30 f. multicoloured .. 75 30
571. 40 f. multicoloured .. 85 40

1973. Opening of Kuwait Airways H.Q. Building.
572. **155.** 10 f. multicoloured .. 30 10
573. 15 f. multicoloured .. 50 20
574. 20 f. multicoloured .. 60 25

156. Weather Map of Middle East.

1973. Centenary of World Meteorological Organization.
575. **156.** 5 f. multicoloured .. 30 20
576. 10 f. multicoloured .. 50 20
577. 15 f. multicoloured .. 80 45

157. Shaikhs Ahmed and Sabah.

1973. 50th Anniv. of 1st Kuwait Stamp Issue (overprints on India of 1923).
578. **157.** 10 f. multicoloured .. 40 10
579. 20 f. multicoloured .. 75 15
580. 70 f. multicoloured .. 2·50 1·25

158. Mourning Dove.

1973. Birds and Hunting Equipment. Multicoloured.
581. 5 f. Type **158** 40 15
582. 5 f. Hoopoe 40 15
583. 5 f. Rock dove 40 15
584. 5 f. Stone-curlew 40 15
585. 8 f. Great grey shrike .. 40 15
586. 8 f. Red-backed shrike .. 40 15
587. 8 f. Black-headed shrike .. 40 15
588. 8 f. Golden oriole 40 15
589. 10 f. Willow warbler .. 40 15
590. 10 f. Great reed warbler .. 40 15
591. 10 f. Blackcap 40 15
592. 10 f. Barn swallow .. 40 15
593. 15 f. Rock thrush 65 15
594. 15 f. Redstart 65 15
595. 15 f. Common wheatear .. 65 15
596. 15 f. Bluethroat 65 15
597. 20 f. Houbara bustard .. 85 20
598. 20 f. Pin-tailed sandgrouse 85 20
599. 20 f. Giant wood rail .. 85 20
600. 20 f. Spotted crake .. 85 20
601. 25 f. American kestrel .. 1·00 30
602. 25 f. Great black-backed gull .. .. .. 1·00 30
603. 25 f. Purple heron .. .. 1·00 30
604. 25 f. Wryneck .. .. 1·00 30
605. 30 f. European bee eater .. 1·40 40
606. 30 f. Saker falcon .. .. 1·40 40
607. 30 f. Grey wagtail .. .. 1·40 40
608. 30 f. Pied wagtail .. .. 1·40 40
609. 45 f. Bird snares .. .. 1·75 75
610. 45 f. Driving great grey shrike into net .. .. 1·75 75
611. 45 f. Stalking rock dove with hand net .. .. 1·75 75
612. 45 f. Great grey shrike and disguised lure .. .. 1·75 75
Nos. 602/12 are size 38 × 38 mm.

159. Flame Emblem. **160.** Congress Emblem.

1973. 25th Anniv. of Declaration of Human Rights.
613. **159.** 10 f. multicoloured .. 30 10
614. 40 f. multicoloured .. 1·00 30
615. 75 f. multicoloured .. 1·75 90

1974. 4th Congress of Arab Veterinary Union, Kuwait.
616. **160.** 30 f. multicoloured .. 55 25
617. 40 f. multicoloured .. 70 60

161. Flag and Wheat Ear Symbol. **163.** Tournament Emblem.

162. A.M.U. Emblem.

1974. 13th Anniv. of National Day.
618. **161.** 20 f. multicoloured .. 30 10
619. 30 f. multicoloured .. 50 25
620. 70 f. multicoloured .. 1·25 1·00

1974. 12th Conference of Arab Medical Union and 1st Conference of Kuwait Medical Society.
621. **162.** 30 f. multicoloured .. 1·25 30
622. 40 f. multicoloured .. 1·75 70

1974. 3rd Arabian Gulf Trophy Football Tournament, Kuwait.
623. **163.** 25 f. multicoloured .. 70 15
624. 45 f. multicoloured .. 1·50 80

164. Institute Buildings.

1974. Inauguration of Kuwait Institute for Scientific Research.
625. **164.** 15 f. multicoloured .. 70 25
626. 20 f. multicoloured .. 1·10 30

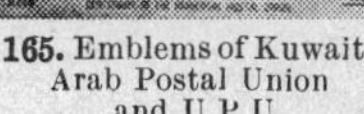

165. Emblems of Kuwait, Arab Postal Union and U.P.U. **167.** Council Emblem and Flags of Member States.

166. Symbolic Telephone Dial.

1974. Cent. of U.P.U.
627. **165.** 20 f. multicoloured .. 20 15
628. 30 f. multicoloured .. 25 30
629. 60 f. multicoloured .. 45 50

1974. World Telecommunications Day.
630 **166.** 10 f. multicoloured .. 40 15
631. 30 f. multicoloured .. 80 30
632. 40 f. multicoloured .. 1·00 40

1974. 17th Anniv. of Signing Arab Economic Unity Agreement.
633. **167.** 20 f. grn., blk. and red 45 10
634. 30 f. red, blk. & green 80 30

168. 'Population Growth".

1974. World Population Year.
635. **168.** 30 f. multicoloured .. 75 20
636. 70 f. multicoloured .. 1·75 90

169. Fund Building.

1974. Kuwait Fund for Arab Economic Development.
637. **169.** 10 f. multicoloured .. 30 15
638. 20 f. multicoloured .. 70 50

170. Shuaiba Emblem.

1974. 10th Anniv. of Shuaiba Industrial Area.
639. **170.** 10 f. multicoloured .. 30 10
640. 20 f. multicoloured .. 70 15
641. 30 f. multicoloured .. 1·10 60

171. Arms of Kuwait and " 14 ".

1975. 14th Anniv. of National Day.
642. **171.** 20 f. multicoloured .. 40 10
643. 70 f. multicoloured .. 1·25 80
644. 75 f. multicoloured .. 1·50 95

172. Census Symbols.

1975. Population Census.
645. **172.** 8 f. multicoloured .. 15 10
646. 20 f. multicoloured .. 35 10
647. 30 f. multicoloured .. 55 25
648. 70 f. multicoloured .. 1·60 75
649. 100 f. multicoloured .. 2·00 90

173. I.W.Y. and Kuwait Women's Union Emblems.

1975. International Women's Year.
650. **173.** 15 f. multicoloured .. 50 15
651. 20 f. multicoloured .. 50 15
652. 30 f. multicoloured .. 80 45

174. Classroom within Open Book.

1975. International Literacy Day.
653. **174.** 20 f. multicoloured .. 50 15
654. 30 f. multicoloured .. 75 40

175. I.S.O. Emblem. **176.** U.N. Flag, Rifle and Olive-branch.

1975. World Standards Day.
655. **175.** 10 f. multicoloured .. 25 15
656. 20 f. multicoloured .. 55 15

1975. 30th Anniv. of U.N.O.
657. **176.** 20 f. multicoloured .. 35 10
658. 45 f. multicoloured .. 75 45

177. Shaikh Sabah.

1975.
659. **177.** 8 f. multicoloured .. 35 10
660. 20 f. multicoloured .. 70 10
661. 30 f. multicoloured .. 1·00 10
662. 50 f. multicoloured .. 1·50 10
663. 90 f. multicoloured .. 3·50 40
664. 100 f. multicoloured .. 4·00 40

178. Kuwait " Skyline ".

1976. 15th Anniv. of National Day.
665. **178.** 10 f. multicoloured .. 30 15
666. 20 f. multicoloured .. 60 15

178a. Emblem, Microscope and Operation.
179. Early and Modern Telephones.

1976. 2nd Annual Conference of Kuwait Medical Association.
667. **178a.** 5 f. multicoloured .. 30 15
668. 10 f. multicoloured .. 60 15
669. 30 f. multicoloured .. 1·75 55

1976. Telephone Centenary.
670. **179.** 5 f. black and orange .. 20 15
671. 15 f. black and blue .. 55 15

180. Eye.

1976. World Health Day.
672. **180.** 10 f. multicoloured .. 40 15
673. 20 f. multicoloured .. 75 15
674. 30 f. multicoloured .. 1·25 55

181. Red Crescent Emblem.

1976. 10th Anniv. of Kuwait Red Crescent Society.
675. **181.** 20 f. multicoloured .. 40 15
676. 30 f. multicoloured .. 70 30
677. 45 f. multicoloured .. 1·25 55
678. 75 f. multicoloured .. 2·00 1·40

182. Suburb of Manama.
183. Basketball.

1976. U.N. Human Settlements Conference.
679. **182.** 10 f. multicoloured .. 30 15
680. 20 f. multicoloured .. 60 15

1976. Olympic Games, Montreal. Mult.
681. 4 f. Type **183** 10 10
682. 8 f. Running 15 10
683. 10 f. Judo 15 10
684. 15 f. Handball 20 10
685. 20 f. Figure-skating .. 25 10
686. 30 f. Volleyball 40 25
687. 45 f. Football 55 35
688. 70 f. Swimming 75 85

184. Ethnic Heads and Map of Sri Lanka.
185. Torch, U.N.E.S.C.O. Emblem and Kuwaiti Arms.

1976. Non-Aligned Countries' Congress, Colombo.
689. **184.** 20 f. multicoloured .. 30 10
690. 30 f. multicoloured .. 55 15
691. 45 f. multicoloured .. 75 45

1976. 30th Anniv. of U.N.E.S.C.O.
692 **185.** 20 f. multicoloured .. 40 10
693. 45 f. multicoloured .. 1·00 40

186. Pot-throwing.
187. Diseased Knee.

1977. Popular Games. Multicoloured.
694. 5 f. Type **186** 15 10
695. 5 f. Kite-flying 15 10
696. 5 f. Balancing sticks .. 15 10
697. 5 f. Spinning tops 15 10
698. 10 f. Blind-man's-buff (horiz.) 15 10
699. 10 f. Rowing (horiz.) .. 15 10
700. 10 f. Rolling hoops (horiz.) 15 10
701. 10 f. Rope game (horiz.) .. 15 10
702. 15 f. Skipping 20 10
703. 15 f. Marbles 20 10
704. 15 f. Carting 20 10
705. 15 f. Teetotum (tops) .. 20 10
706. 20 f. Halma (horiz.) .. 30 15
707. 20 f. Model boating (horiz.) 30 15
708. 20 f. Pot and candle (horiz.) 30 15
709. 20 f. Hide-and-seek (horiz.) 30 15
710. 30 f. Knuckle bones .. 30 15
711. 30 f. Hiding the stone .. 30 15
712. 30 f. Hopscotch 30 15
713. 30 f. Catch-as-catch-can .. 30 15
714. 40 f. Bowls (horiz.) .. 60 30
715. 40 f. Hockey (horiz.) .. 60 30
716. 40 f. Guessing game (horiz.) 60 30
717. 40 f. Jacks (horiz.) .. 60 30
718. 60 f. Hiding the cake (horiz.) 70 45
719. 60 f. Chess (horiz.) .. 70 45
720. 60 f. Story-telling (horiz.) 70 45
721. 60 f. Treasure hunt (horiz.) 70 45
722. 70 f. Hobby horses (horiz.) 85 60
723. 70 f. Hide-and-seek (horiz.) 85 60
724. 70 f. Catch shadow (horiz.) 85 60
725. 70 f. Throwing game (horiz.) 85 60

1977. World Rheumatism Year.
726. **187.** 20 f. multicoloured .. 40 15
727. 30 f. multicoloured .. 60 15
728. 45 f. multicoloured .. 90 35
729. 75 f. multicoloured .. 1·25 1·00

188. Shaikh Sabah.
189. Kuwait Tower.

1977. 16th National Day.
730. **188.** 10 f. multicoloured .. 15 10
731. 15 f. multicoloured .. 20 10
732. 30 f. multicoloured .. 45 15
733. 80 f. multicoloured .. 1·00 70

1977. Inauguration of Kuwait Tower.
734. **189.** 30 f. multicoloured .. 75 15
735. 80 f. multicoloured .. 2·25 70

MINIMUM PRICE

The minimum price quoted is 5p which represents a handling charge rather than a basis for valuing common stamps. For further notes about prices see introductory pages.

190. A.P.U. Emblem and Flags.
191. Printed Circuit.

1977. 25th Anniv. of Arab Postal Union.
736. **190.** 5 f. multicoloured .. 10 10
737. 15 f. multicoloured .. 20 10
738. 30 f. multicoloured .. 50 15
739. 80 f. multicoloured .. 1·40 80

1977. World Telecommunications Day.
740. **191.** 30 f. orange and brown 65 15
741. 80 f. orange and green 1·50 95

192. Shaikh Sabah.
193. Championship Emblem.

1977.
742. **192.** 15 f. brn., blk. and blue 40 10
743. 25 f. brn., blk. and yell. 70 10
744. 30 f. brn.. blk. and red 90 10
745. 80 f. brn., blk. and vio. 2·00 15
746. 100 f. brn., blk. & orge. 2·75 20
747. 150 f. brn., blk. & blue 4·50 45
748. 200 f. brn., blk. & olive 5·50 70

1977. 4th Asian Youth Basketball Championships.
749. **193.** 30 f. multicoloured .. 50 15
750. 80 f. multicoloured .. 1·25 70

194. " Popular Dancing " (O. Al-Nakeeb).

1977. Children's Paintings. Multicoloured.
751. 15 f. Type **194** 25 10
752. 15 f. " Al Deirah " (A. M. al-Onizi) 25 10
753. 30 f. " Fishing " (M. al-Jasem) 55 20
754. 30 f. " Dug al-Harees " (B. al-Sa'adooni) (vert.) .. 55 20
755. 80 f. " Fraisa Dancing " (M. al-Mojaibel) (vert.) .. 1·40 75
756. 80 f. " Kuwaiti Girl " (K. Ghazi) (vert.) .. 1·40 75

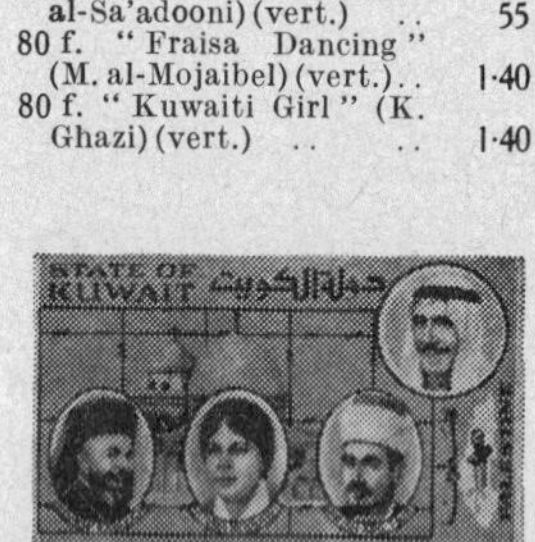

195. Dome of the Rock and Palestinian Freedom Fighters.

1978. Palestinian Freedom Fighters.
757. **195.** 30 f. multicoloured .. 90 25
758. 80 f. multicoloured .. 2·25 1·25

196. Dentist treating Patient.

1978. 10th Arab Dental Union Congress.
759. **196.** 30 f. multicoloured .. 70 15
760. 80 f. multicoloured .. 1·60 85

197. Carrying Water from Dhows.

1978. Water Resources. Multicoloured.
761. 5 f. Type **197** 15 10
762. 5 f. Camel 10 10
763. 5 f. Water carrier 10 10
764. 5 f. Pushing water in cart 15 10
765. 10 f. Irrigation with donkey 10 10
766. 10 f. Water troughs .. 10 10
767. 10 f. Water pool 10 10
768. 10 f. Watering crops .. 10 10
769. 15 f. Bedouin watering sheep 10 10
770. 15 f. Women at pool .. 10 10
771. 15 f. Animals drinking .. 10 10
772. 15 f. Camp site 10 10
773. 20 f. Oasis 15 10
774. 20 f. Washing and drinking at home 15 10
775. 20 f. Water urn 15 10
776. 20 f. Piped water 15 10
777. 25 f. Desalination plant .. 20 15
778. 25 f. Water tanker .. 20 15
779. 25 f. Filling water tankers 20 15
780. 25 f. Modern water tanks .. 20 15
781. 30 f. Catching water during storm (vert.) 25 15
782. 30 f. Water tank (vert.) .. 25 15
783. 30 f. " Umbrella " catching water (vert.) .. 25 15
784. 30 f. Two water tanks (vert.) 25 15
785. 80 f. Carrying water on donkey (vert.) 85 50
786. 80 f. Woman carrying water can (vert.) 85 50
787. 80 f. Woman with water-skins (vert.) 85 50
788. 80 f. Tanker delivering water (vert.) 85 50
789. 100 f. Piping water into tank (vert.) .. .. 1·00 70
790. 100 f. Water cistern (vert.) 1·00 70
791. 100 f. Filling cistern (vert.) 1·00 70
792. 100 f. Drawing water from well (vert.) .. .. 1·00 70

198. Symbols of Development.

1978. 17th National Day.
793. **198.** 30 f. multicoloured .. 35 10
794. 80 f. multicoloured .. 90 50

199. Face infected with Smallpox.

1978. Global Eradication of Smallpox.
795. **199.** 30 f. multicoloured .. 45 10
796. 80 f. multicoloured .. 1·10 60

200. Microwave Antenna.
201. Shaikh Jabir.

1978. 10th World Telecommunications Day.
797. **200.** 30 f. multicoloured .. 35 10
798. 80 f. multicoloured .. 1·10 60

1978. Portrait in brown; background colour given.
799. **201.** 15 f. green 35 10
800. 30 f. orange 70 10
801. 80 f. purple .. .. 1·50 15
802. 100 f. green .. .. 1·75 15
803. 130 f. brown .. .. 2·75 45
804. 180 f. violet .. .. 4·00 55
805. 1 d. red .. .. 11·00 75
806. 4 d. blue .. .. 40·00 4·75
Nos. 805/6 are larger, 24 × 29 mm.

202. Mount Arafat, Pilgrims and Kaaba.

1978. Pilgrimage to Mecca.
807. **202.** 30 f. multicoloured .. 50 15
808. 80 f. multicoloured .. 1·25 70

203. U.N. and Anti-Apartheid Emblems.

1978. International Anti-Apartheid Year.

809.	203.	30 f. multicoloured ..	40	15
810.		80 f. multicoloured ..	95	55
811.		180 f. multicoloured ..	1·75	1·25

204. Refugees.

1978. 30th Anniv. of Declaration of Human Rights.

812.	204.	30 f. multicoloured ..	40	15
813.		80 f. multicoloured ..	80	50
814.		100 f. multicoloured ..	1·40	1·25

205. Information Centre.

1978. Kuwait Information Centre.

815.	205.	5 f. multicoloured ..	10	10
816.		15 f. multicoloured ..	20	10
817.		30 f. multicoloured ..	50	20
818.		80 f. multicoloured ..	1·10	65

206. Kindergarten. 207. Kuwaiti Flag and Doves.

1979. International Year of the Child.

819.	206.	30 f. multicoloured ..	40	15
820.		80 f. multicoloured ..	1·00	75

1979. 18th National Day.

821.	207.	30 f. multicoloured ..	30	10
822.		80 f. multicoloured ..	70	55

208. Crops and Greenhouse.

1979. 4th Arab Agriculture Ministers Congress.

823.	208.	30 f. multicoloured ..	35	15
824.		80 f. multicoloured ..	90	70

209. World Map, Koran and symbols of Arab Achievements. 210. Children flying Kites.

1979. The Arabs.

825.	209.	30 f. multicoloured ..	35	15
826.		80 f. multicoloured ..	90	70

1979. Children's Paintings. Multicoloured.

827.		30 f. Type 210	35	15
828.		30 f. Girl and doves ..	35	15
829.		30 f. Crowd and balloons ..	35	15
830.		80 f. Boys smiling (horiz.)	95	70
831.		80 f. Children in landscape (horiz.)	95	70
832.		80 f. Tug-of-war (horiz.) ..	95	70

211. Wave Pattern and Television Screen. 212. International Military Sports Council Emblem.

1979. World Telecommunications Day.

833.	211.	30 f. multicoloured ..	35	15
834.		80 f. multicoloured ..	90	65

1979. 29th International Military Football Championship.

835.	212.	30 f. multicoloured ..	35	15
836.		80 f. multicoloured ..	90	65

213. Child and Industrial Landscape.

1979. World Environment Day.

837.	213.	30 f. multicoloured ..	45	15
838.		80 f. multicoloured ..	1·40	75

214. Children supporting Globe. 215. Children with Television.

1979. 50th Anniv. of International Bureau of Education.

839.	214.	30 f. multicoloured ..	35	15
840.		80 f. multicoloured ..	90	60
841.		130 f. multicoloured ..	1·40	90

1979. 25th Anniv. of Kuwaiti Kindergartens. Children's Drawings. Multicoloured.

842.		30 f. Type 215	40	15
843.		80 f. Children with flags ..	1·00	65

216. The Kaaba, Mecca. 217. Figure, with Dove and Torch, clothed in Palestinian Flag.

1979. Pilgrimage to Mecca.

844.	216.	30 f. multicoloured ..	50	15
845.		80 f. multicoloured ..	1·25	65

1979. International Day of Solidarity with Palestinians.

846.	217.	30 f. multicoloured ..	1·50	20
847.		80 f. multicoloured ..	2·50	1·25

218. Boeing "747" and Douglas "DC 3".

1979. 25th Anniv. of Kuwait Airways.

848.	218.	30 f. multicoloured ..	50	15
849.		80 f. multicoloured ..	1·40	90

219. Oyster Shell with Pearl bearing Map of Kuwait.

1980. 19th National Day.

850.	219.	30 f. multicoloured ..	35	15
851.		80 f. multicoloured ..	90	60

220. Graph with Human Figures.

1980. Population Census.

852.	220.	30 f. blk., silver & blue	40	15
853.		80 f. blk., gold & orge.	1·00	60

221. Campaign Emblem. 222. Municipality Building.

1980. World Health Day. Anti-Smoking Campaign.

854.	221.	30 f. multicoloured ..	65	15
855.		80 f. multicoloured ..	1·60	80

1980. 50th Anniv. of Kuwait Municipality.

856.	222.	15 f. multicoloured ..	25	10
857.		30 f. multicoloured ..	45	20
858.		80 f. multicoloured ..	1·10	80

223. "The Future".

1980. Children's Imagination of Future Kuwait. Multicoloured.

859.		30 f. Type 223	50	15
860.		80 f. Motorways	1·40	75

224. Hand blotting out Factory.

1980. World Environment Day.

861.	224.	30 f. multicoloured ..	55	20
862.		80 f. multicoloured ..	1·50	80

225. Volleyball. 226. O.P.E.C. Emblem and Globe.

1980. Olympic Games, Moscow. Mult.

863.		15 f. Type 225	20	15
864.		15 f. Tennis	20	15
865.		30 f. Swimming	30	20
866.		30 f. Weightlifting ..	30	20
867.		30 f. Basketball	30	20
868.		30 f. Judo	30	20
869.		80 f. Gymnastics	75	50
870.		80 f. Badminton	75	50
871.		80 f. Fencing	75	50
872.		80 f. Football	75	50

1980. 20th Anniv. of Organization of Petroleum Exporting Countries.

873.	226.	30 f. multicoloured ..	60	15
874.		80 f. multicoloured ..	1·40	80

227. Mosque and Kaaba, Mecca.

1980. 1400th Anniv. of Hegira.

875.	227.	15 f. multicoloured ..	25	10
876.		30 f. multicoloured ..	50	20
877.		80 f. multicoloured ..	1·25	80

228. Dome of the Rock. 229. Ibn Sina (Avicenna).

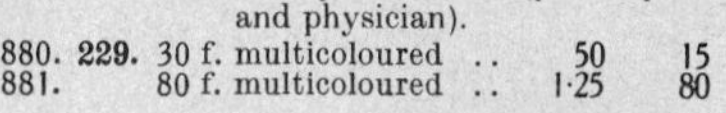

1980. International Day of Solidarity with Palestinian People.

878.	228.	30 f. multicoloured ..	1·25	25
879.		80 f. multicoloured ..	2·75	1·50

1980. Birth Millenary of Ibn Sina (philosopher and physician).

880.	229.	30 f. multicoloured ..	50	15
881.		80 f. multicoloured ..	1·25	80

230. Islamic Symbols. 231. Person in Wheelchair playing Snooker.

1981. First Islamic Medicine Conference, Kuwait.

882.	230.	30 f. multicoloured ..	65	15
883.		80 f. multicoloured ..	1·60	90

1981. International Year of Disabled People. Multicoloured.

884.		30 f. Type 231	65	15
885.		80 f. Girl in wheelchair ..	1·60	90

232. Symbols of Development and Progress.

1981. 20th National Day.

886.	232.	30 f. multicoloured ..	70	15
887.		80 f. multicoloured ..	1·60	90

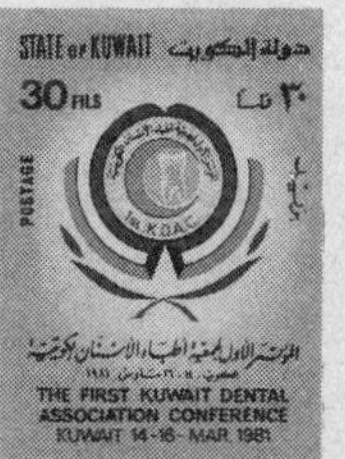

233. Emblem of Kuwait Dental Association. 234. "Lamp".

1981. First Kuwait Dental Association Conference.

888.	233.	30 f. multicoloured ..	1·00	20
889.		80 f. multicoloured ..	2·50	1·25

1981. World Red Cross and Red Crescent Day.

890.	234.	30 f. multicoloured ..	90	20
891.		80 f. multicoloured ..	2·25	1·25

235. Emblems of I.T.U. and W.H.O. and Ribbons forming Caduceus. 236. Tanker polluting Sea and Car polluting Atmosphere.

1981. World Telecommunications Day.

892.	235.	30 f. multicoloured ..	90	20
893.		70 f. multicoloured ..	2·00	1·25

1981. World Environment Day.

894.	236.	30 f. multicoloured ..	85	30
895.		80 f. multicoloured ..	2·10	1·25

237. Sief Palace.

1981.

896.	237.	5 f. multicoloured ..	10	10
897.		10 f. multicoloured ..	10	10
898.		15 f. multicoloured ..	10	10
899.		25 f. multicoloured ..	15	10
900.		30 f. multicoloured ..	15	10
901.		40 f. multicoloured ..	20	10
902.		60 f. multicoloured ..	30	10
903.		80 f. multicoloured ..	40	10
904.		100 f. multicoloured ..	50	10
905.		115 f. multicoloured ..	55	15
906.		130 f. multicoloured ..	60	10
907.		150 f. multicoloured ..	70	15
908.		180 f. multicoloured ..	85	20
909.		250 f. multicoloured ..	1·10	25
910.		500 f. multicoloured ..	2·50	35
911.		1 d. multicoloured ..	4·75	55
912.		2 d. multicoloured ..	9·50	1·50
913.		3 d. multicoloured ..	14·00	3·00
914.		4 d. multicoloured ..	19·00	8·00

Nos. 911/14 are larger, 33 × 28 mm. and have a different border.

238. Pilgrims.

1981. Pilgrimage to Mecca.

915.	238.	30 f. multicoloured ..	1·00	20
916.		80 f. multicoloured ..	2·50	90

239. Palm Trees, Sheep, Camel, Goat and F.A.O. Emblem.

1981. World Food Day.

917.	239.	30 f. multicoloured ..	90	20
918.		80 f. multicoloured ..	2·25	90

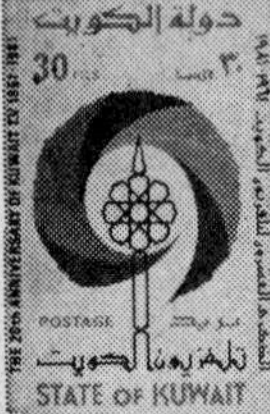

240. Television Emblem.

241. Blood Circulation Diagram.

1981. 20th Anniv. of Kuwait Television.

919.	240.	30 f. multicoloured ..	80	20
920.		80 f. multicoloured ..	1·75	80

1982. First International Symposium on Pharmacology of Human Blood Vessels.

921.	241.	30 f. multicoloured ..	1·00	25
922.		80 f. multicoloured ..	2·50	1·00

242. Symbols of Development, Progress and Peace.

1982. 21st National Day.

923.	242.	30 f. multicoloured ..	45	20
924.		80 f. multicoloured ..	1·10	80

243. Emblem of Kuwait Boy Scouts Association on Globe.

1982. 75th Anniv. of Boy Scout Movement.

925.	243.	30 f. multicoloured ..	70	20
926.		80 f. multicoloured ..	1·60	90

244. Emblem of Arab Pharmacists Union.

1982. Arab Pharmacists Day.

927.	244.	30 f. multicoloured ..	1·00	25
928.		80 f. multicoloured ..	2·50	1·00

245. Red Crescent, Arab and W.H.O. Emblem.

246. A.P.U. Emblem.

1982. World Health Day.

929.	245.	30 f. multicoloured ..	75	25
930.		80 f. multicoloured ..	2·00	1·00

1982. 30th Anniv. of Arab Postal Union.

931.	246.	30 f. black, pink and green	1·00	25
932.		80 f. black, green and pink	2·50	1·00

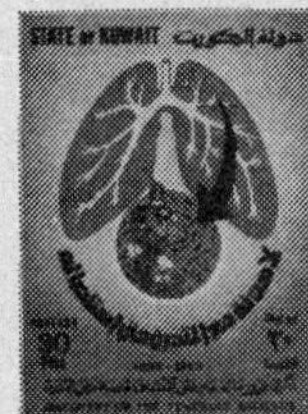

247. Lungs and Microscope.

249. Museum Exhibits.

248. Crest and Emblems of Kuwait Football Association and Olympic Committee.

1982. Centenary of Discovery of Tubercle Bacillus.

933.	247.	30 f. multicoloured ..	1·25	25
934.		80 f. multicoloured ..	2·75	1·25

1982. World Cup Football Championship, Spain.

935.	248.	30 f. multicoloured ..	75	25
936.		80 f. multicoloured ..	2·00	1·00

1982. 10th Anniv. of Science and Natural History Museum.

937.	249.	30 f. multicoloured ..	1·00	30
938.		80 f. multicoloured ..	2·50	1·40

250. Container Ship.

1982. 6th Anniv. of United Arab Shipping Company. Multicoloured.

939.	30 f. Type **250**	65	30
940.	80 f. Freighter	1·90	95

251. Palm Trees.

1982. Arab Palm Tree Day.

941.	251.	30 f. multicoloured ..	40	25
942.		80 f. multicoloured ..	1·00	85

252. Pilgrims.

1982. Pilgrimage to Mecca.

943.	252.	15 f. multicoloured ..	35	10
944.		30 f. multicoloured ..	75	25
945.		80 f. multicoloured ..	1·75	90

253. Desert Flower.

1983. Desert Plants. Multicoloured; background colours given.

946.	10 f. green (vert.)	10	10
947.	10 f. violet	10	10
948.	10 f. pink	10	10
949.	10 f. red	10	10
950.	10 f. brown	10	10
951.	10 f. green	10	10
952.	10 f. orange	10	10
953.	10 f. red	10	10
954.	10 f. brown	10	10
955.	10 f. blue	10	10
956.	15 f. green	15	15
957.	15 f. purple	15	15
958.	15 f. blue	15	15
959.	15 f. blue	15	15
960.	15 f. green	15	15
961.	15 f. red	15	15
962.	15 f. brown	15	15
963.	15 f. blue	15	15
964.	15 f. mauve	15	15
965.	15 f. red	15	15
966.	30 f. brown	30	30
967.	30 f. red	30	30
968.	30 f. blue	30	30
969.	30 f. green	30	30
970.	30 f. red	30	30
971.	30 f. blue	30	30
972.	30 f. green	30	30
973.	30 f. mauve	30	30
974.	30 f. brown	30	30
975.	30 f. yellow	30	30
976.	40 f. red (horiz.)	40	30
977.	40 f. green	40	30
978.	40 f. violet	40	30
979.	40 f. blue	40	30
980.	40 f. violet	40	30
981.	40 f. green	40	30
982.	40 f. mauve	40	30
983.	40 f. brown	40	30
984.	40 f. blue	40	30
985.	40 f. green	40	30
986.	80 f. violet	80	60
987.	80 f. green	80	60
988.	80 f. yellow	80	60
989.	80 f. brown	80	60
990.	80 f. blue	80	60
991.	80 f. yellow	80	60
992.	80 f. green	80	60
993.	80 f. violet	80	60
994.	80 f. brown	80	60
995.	80 f. yellow	80	60

DESIGNS: Various plants.

254. Peace Dove on Map of Kuwait.

1983. 22nd National Day.

996.	254.	30 f. multicoloured ..	60	20
997.		80 f. multicoloured ..	1·40	85

255. I.M.O. Emblem.

1983. 25th Anniv. of International Maritime Organization.

998.	255.	30 f. multicoloured ..	60	20
999.		80 f. multicoloured ..	1·40	85

256. Virus and Map of Africa.

1983. Third International Conference on Impact of Viral Diseases on Development of Middle East and African Countries.

1000.	256.	15 f. multicoloured ..	30	15
1001.		30 f. multicoloured ..	60	25
1002.		80 f. multicoloured ..	1·50	90

257. Stylized Figures exercising.

1983. World Health Day.

1003.	257.	15 f. multicoloured ..	35	15
1004.		30 f. multicoloured ..	70	25
1005.		80 f. multicoloured ..	1·60	95

258. U.P.U., W.C.Y. and I.T.U. Emblems.

1983. World Communications Year.

1006.	258.	15 f. multicoloured ..	35	15
1007.		30 f. multicoloured ..	70	25
1008.		80 f. multicoloured ..	1·60	95

259. Map of Kuwait and Dhow.

1983. World Environment Day.

1009.	259.	15 f. multicoloured ..	45	15
1010.		30 f. multicoloured ..	90	25
1011.		80 f. multicoloured ..	2·00	95

260. Walls of Jerusalem.

1983. World Heritage Convention.

1012.	260.	15 f. multicoloured ..	40	15
1013.		30 f. multicoloured ..	80	25
1014.		80 f. multicoloured ..	1·75	90

261. Pilgrims in Mozdalipha.

1983. Pilgrimage to Mecca.

1015.	261.	15 f. multicoloured ..	40	15
1016.		30 f. multicoloured ..	80	25
1017.		80 f. multicoloured ..	1·75	90

262. Arab within Dove.

1983. International Day of Solidarity with Palestinian People.

1018. **262.** 15 f. multicoloured . . 45 15
1019. 30 f. multicoloured . . 90 25
1020. 80 f. multicoloured . . 2·00 90

263. Kuwait Medical Association and Congress Emblems.

1984. 21st Pan-Arab Medical Congress.

1021. **263.** 15 f. multicoloured . . 40 15
1022. 30 f. multicoloured . . 80 25
1023. 80 f. multicoloured . . 1·75 90

264. State Arms within Key.

1984. Inauguration of New Health Establishments.

1024. **264.** 15 f. multicoloured . . 40 15
1025. 30 f. multicoloured . . 80 25
1026. 80 f. multicoloured . . 1·75 90

265. Dove and Globe **266.** Symbols of Medicine within Head.

1984. 23rd National Day.

1027. **265.** 15 f. multicoloured . . 40 15
1028. 30 f. multicoloured . . 80 25
1029. 80 f. multicoloured . . 1·75 90

1984. Second International Medical Science Conference.

1030. **266.** 15 f. multicoloured . . 40 15
1031. 30 f. multicoloured . . 80 25
1032. 80 f. multicoloured . . 1·75 90

267. Douglas "Dakota".

1984. 30th Anniv. of Kuwait Airways Corporation.

1033. **267.** 30 f. light blue, blue and yellow . . 75 20
1034. 80 f. light blue, blue and mauve . . 2·00 90

268. Magazine Covers. **269.** Family and Emblems.

1984. 25th Anniv. of "Al-Arabi" Magazine.

1035. **268.** 15 f. multicoloured . . 25 15
1036. 30 f. multicoloured . . 60 25
1037. 80 f. multicoloured . . 1·50 90

1984. World Health Day.

1038 **269.** 15 f. multicoloured . . 40 15
1039 30 f. multicoloured . . 80 25
1040 80 f. multicoloured . . 1·75 90

270. Sudanese Orphan and Village.

1984. Hanan Kuwaiti Village, Sudan.

1041. **270.** 15 f. multicoloured . . 35 15
1042. 30 f. multicoloured . . 70 25
1043. 80 f. multicoloured . . 1·50 90

271. I.C.A.O., Kuwait Airport and Kuwait Airways Emblems.

1984. 40th Anniv. of I.C.A.O.

1044. **271.** 15 f. multicoloured . . 40 15
1045. 30 f. multicoloured . . 80 25
1046. 80 f. multicoloured . . 1·75 90

272. Map of Arab Countries and Youths.

1984. Arab Youth Day.

1047. **272.** 30 f. multicoloured . . 80 25
1048. 80 f. multicoloured . . 1·60 90

273. Swimming.

1984. Olympic Games, Los Angeles. Multicoloured

1049. 30 f. Type **273** 40 40
1050. 30 f. Hurdling 40 40
1051. 80 f. Judo 40 40
1052. 80 f. Equestrian 40 40

274. Anniversary Emblem, Camera, Glider, Al-Aujairy Observatory and Wind Tower.

1984. 10th Anniv. of Science Club.

1053. **274.** 15 f. multicoloured . . 50 15
1054. 30 f. multicoloured . . 95 25
1055. 80 f. multicoloured . . 1·90 90

275. Stoning the Devil.

1984. Pilgrimage to Mecca.

1056. **275.** 30 f. multicoloured . . 80 25
1057. 80 f. multicoloured . . 1·75 90

276. Anniversary Emblem.

1984. 20th Anniv. of International Telecommunications Satellite Consortium (Intelsat).

1058. **276.** 30 f. multicoloured . . 80 25
1059. 80 f. multicoloured . . 1·75 90

277. Council Emblem. **278.** Hands breaking Star.

1984. 5th Supreme Council Session of Gulf Co-operation Council.

1060. **277.** 30 f. multicoloured . . 70 25
1061. 80 f. multicoloured . . 1·40 85

1984. International Day of Solidarity with Palestinian People.

1062. **278.** 30 f. multicoloured . . 80 25
1063. 80 f. multicoloured . . 1·75 90

279. Company Emblem as Satellite. **280.** I.Y.Y. Emblem.

1984. 50th Anniv. of Kuwait Oil Company.

1064. **279.** 30 f. multicoloured . . 80 25
1065. 80 f. multicoloured . . 1·75 90

1985. International Youth Year.

1066. **280.** 30 f. multicoloured . . 40 20
1067. 80 f. multicoloured . . 1·00 60

281. "24", Hand holding Flame and Dove. **282.** Programme Emblem.

1985. 24th National Day.

1068. **281.** 30 f. multicoloured . . 70 25
1069. 80 f. multicoloured . . 1·60 80

1985. International Programme for Communications Development.

1070. **282.** 30 f. multicoloured . . 80 25
1071. 80 f. multicoloured . . 1·75 90

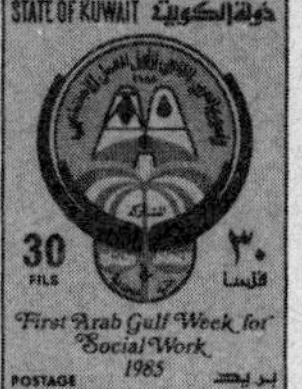

283. Emblem. **284.** Molar.

1985. First Arab Gulf Social Work Week.

1072. **283.** 30 f. multicoloured . . 80 25
1073. 80 f. multicoloured . . 1·75 90

1985. Third Kuwait Dental Association Conference.

1074. **284.** 30 f. multicoloured . . 1·00 25
1075. 80 f. multicoloured . . 2·25 1·00

285. Emblem. **286.** Globe and Figures.

1985. Population Census.

1076. **285.** 30 f. multicoloured . . 80 25
1077. 80 f. multicoloured . . 1·75 90

1985. World Health Day.

1078. **286.** 30 f. multicoloured . . 90 25
1079. 80 f. multicoloured . . 2·00 95

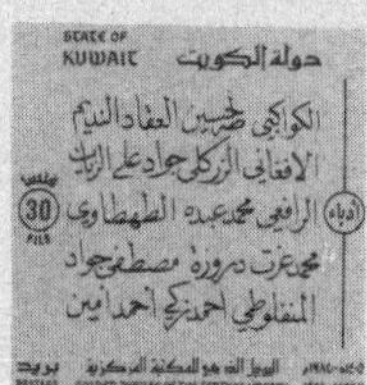

287. Arabic Script.

No. 1080.

No. 1081.

No. 1082.

No. 1083.

No. 1084.

No. 1085.

No. 1086.

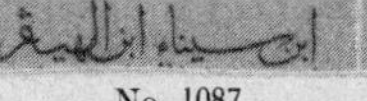
No. 1087.

1985. 50th Anniv. of Central Library. Square designs showing titles of books and names of authors in Arabic script (first line of text illustrated above).

1080. 30 f. gold 65 55
1081. 30 f. gold 65 55
1082. 30 f. gold 65 55
1083. 30 f. gold 65 55
1084. 80 f. black and gold . . 1·50 1·25
1085. 80 f. black and gold . . 1·50 1·25
1086. 80 f. black and gold . . 1·50 1·25
1087. 80 f. black and gold . . 1·50 1·25

288. Seascape.

1985. World Environment Day.
1088. **288.** 30 f. multicoloured .. 1·40 30
1089. 80 f. multicoloured .. 3·00 1·10

289. Anniversary Emblem.

1985. 25th Anniv. of Organization of Petroleum Exporting Countries.
1090. **289.** 30 f. deep blue, blue and mauve .. 1·00 25
1091. 80 f. deep blue, blue and brown .. 2·25 1·25

290. Emblem and Heads.

1985. Introduction of Civilian Identity Cards.
1092. **290.** 30 f. multicoloured .. 80 20
1093. 80 f. multicoloured .. 1·75 1·00

291. Flag on Globe within Symbolic Design.

1985. International Day of Solidarity with Palestinian People.
1094. **291.** 15 f. multicoloured .. 65 20
1095. 30 f. multicoloured .. 1·25 40
1096. 80 f. multicoloured .. 2·75 1·25

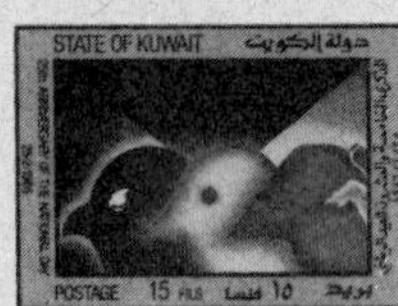

292. Birds.

1986. 25th National Day.
1097. **292.** 15 f. multicoloured .. 50 20
1098. 30 f. multicoloured .. 1·00 40
1099. 80 f. multicoloured .. 2·50 1·40

293. Emblem. **294.** W.H.O. Emblem as Flower.

1986. 20th Anniv. of Kuwait Red Crescent.
1100. **293.** 20 f. multicoloured .. 70 20
1101. 25 f. multicoloured .. 80 30
1102. 70 f. multicoloured .. 2·25 1·25

1986. World Health Day.
1103. **294.** 20 f. multicoloured .. 70 20
1104. 25 f. multicoloured .. 80 30
1105. 70 f. multicoloured .. 2·25 1·25

295. I.P.Y. Emblem.

1986. International Peace Year.
1106 **295** 20 f. green, blue & blk 65 20
1107 25 f. blue, yell & blk 75 30
1108 70 f. blue, mve & blk 2·00 1·25

296. "Al Mirqab" (container ship).

1986. 10th Anniv of United Arab Shipping Company. Multicoloured.
1109 20 f. Type **296** .. .. 1·00 20
1110 70 f. "Al Mubarakiah" (container ship) .. 2·75 1·50

297. Bank Emblem on Map.

1986. 25th Anniv. of Gulf Bank.
1111. **297.** 20 f. multicoloured .. 65 20
1112. 25 f. multicoloured .. 75 30
1113. 70 f. multicoloured .. 2·00 1·40

298. Zig-zags and Diamonds.

1986. Sadu Art. Multicoloured.
1114 20 f. Type **298** 60 20
1115 70 f. Triangles and symbols .. .. 1·75 90
1116 200 f. Stripes and triangles 4·50 2·50

299. Dove on Manacled Hand pointing to Map.

1986. International Day of Solidarity with Palestinian People.
1117. **299.** 20 f. multicoloured .. 90 20
1118. 25 f. multicoloured .. 1·25 40
1119. 70 f. multicoloured .. 2·75 1·50

300. Conference Emblem.

1987. 5th Islamic Summit Conference.
1120. **300.** 25 f. multicoloured .. 60 20
1121. 50 f. multicoloured .. 1·25 40
1122. 150 f. multicoloured 2·75 1·50

301. Map in National Colours and Symbols of Development.

1987. 26th National Day.
1123. **301.** 50 f. multicoloured .. 80 25
1124. 150 f. multicoloured 2·00 1·25

302. Health Science Centre.

1987. 3rd Kuwait International Medical Sciences Conference: Infectious Diseases in Developing Countries.
1125. **302.** 25 f. multicoloured .. 40 20
1126. 150 f. multicoloured 2·00 1·25

303. Campaign Emblem.

1987. World Health Day. Child Immunization Campaign.
1127. **303.** 25 f. multicoloured .. 40 20
1128. 50 f. multicoloured .. 80 30
1129. 150 f. multicoloured 2·00 1·40

304. Jerusalem.

1987. "Jerusalem is an Arab City".
1130. **304.** 25 f. multicoloured .. 30 15
1131. 50 f. multicoloured .. 60 30
1132. 150 f. multicoloured 1·75 1·00

305. Pilgrims in Miqat Wadi Mihrim.

1987. Pilgrimage to Mecca.
1133. **305.** 25 f. multicoloured .. 25 15
1134. 50 f. multicoloured .. 50 25
1135. 150 f. multicoloured 1·40 75

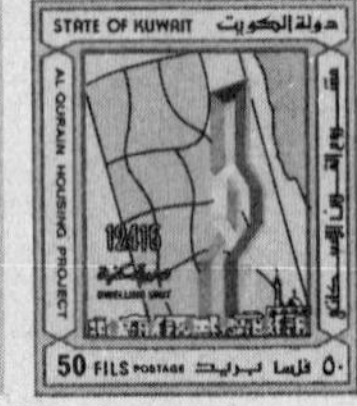

306. Emblem. **308.** Project Monument and Site Plan.

307. Buoy and Container Ship.

1987. Arab Telecommunications Day.
1136. **306.** 25 f. multicoloured .. 25 15
1137. 50 f. multicoloured .. 50 20
1138. 150 f. multicoloured 1·40 75

1987. World Maritime Day.
1139. **307.** 25 f. multicoloured .. 30 20
1140. 50 f. multicoloured .. 65 30
1141. 150 f. multicoloured 1·75 90

1987. Al-Qurain Housing Project.
1142. **308.** 25 f. multicoloured .. 25 15
1143. 50 f. multicoloured .. 50 20
1144. 150 f. multicoloured 1·40 75

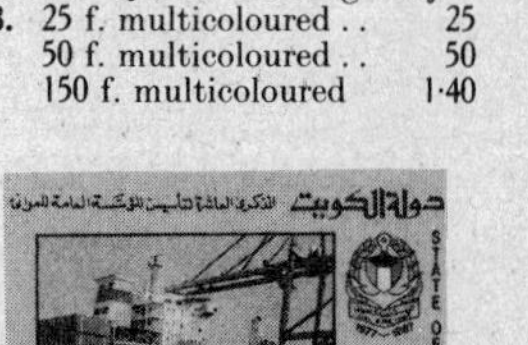

309. Unloading Container Ship.

1987. 10th Anniv. of Ports Public Authority.
1145. **309.** 25 f. multicoloured .. 20 10
1146. 50 f. multicoloured .. 40 20
1147. 150 f. multicoloured 1·10 60

310. Symbolic Design. **311.** Emblem.

1987. International Day of Solidarity with Palestinian People.
1148. **310.** 25 f. multicoloured .. 20 10
1149. 50 f. multicoloured .. 40 20
1150. 150 f. multicoloured 1·10 60

1988. 25th Anniv. of Women's Cultural and Social Society.
1151. **311.** 25 f. multicoloured .. 20 10
1152. 50 f. multicoloured .. 40 20
1153. 150 f. multicoloured 1·10 60

312. Emblem. **313.** Hands holding W.H.O. Emblem.

1988. 27th National Day.
1154. **312.** 25 f. multicoloured .. 20 10
1155. 50 f. multicoloured .. 40 20
1156. 150 f. multicoloured 1·10 60

1988. World Health Day. 40th Anniv. of W.H.O.
1157. **313.** 25 f. multicoloured .. 15 10
1158. 50 f. multicoloured .. 35 20
1159. 150 f. multicoloured 1·00 50

314. Regional Marine Protection Organization Emblem. **315.** Society Emblem.

1988. 10th Anniv. of Kuwait Regional Convention for Protection of Marine Environment.
1160. **314.** 35 f. deep blue, blue and brown .. 25 15
1161. 50 f. deep blue, blue and green 35 20
1162. 150 f. deep blue, blue and lilac .. .. 1·00 50

1988. 25th Anniv. of Kuwait Teachers' Society.
1163. **315.** 25 f. multicoloured .. 15 10
1164. 50 f. multicoloured .. 35 20
1165. 150 f. multicoloured 1·00 50

316. Pilgrims at al-Sail al-Kabir Miqat.

1988. Pilgrimage to Mecca.
1166. **316.** 25 f. multicoloured .. 15 10
1167. 50 f. multicoloured .. 35 20
1168. 150 f. multicoloured 1·00 50

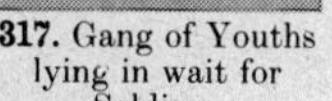

317. Gang of Youths lying in wait for Soldiers.

318. Ring of Dwellings around Key.

1988. Palestinian "Intifida" Movement.
1169. **317.** 50 f. multicoloured .. 35 20
1170. 150 f. multicoloured 1·00 50

1988. Arab Housing Day.
1171. **318.** 50 f. multicoloured .. 35 20
1172. 100 f. multicoloured 70 35
1173. 150 f. multicoloured 1·00 50

319. Map of Palestine highlighted on Globe.

320. Volunteers embracing Globe.

1988. International Day of Solidarity with Palestinian People.
1174. **319.** 50 f. multicoloured .. 35 20
1175. 100 f. multicoloured 70 35
1176. 150 f. multicoloured 1·00 50

1988. International Volunteer Day.
1177. **320.** 50 f. multicoloured .. 35 20
1178. 100 f. multicoloured 70 35
1179. 150 f. multicoloured 1·00 50

321 Conference, Kuwait Society of Engineers and Arab Engineers Union Emblems

1989. 18th Arab Engineering Conference.
1180 **321** 50 f. multicoloured .. 35 20
1181 100 f. multicoloured 70 35
1182 150 f. multicoloured 1·00 50

322 Flags as Figures supporting Map

323 Conference Emblem

1989. 28th National Day.
1183 **322** 50 f. multicoloured .. 35 20
1184 100 f. multicoloured 70 35
1185 150 f. multicoloured 1·00 50

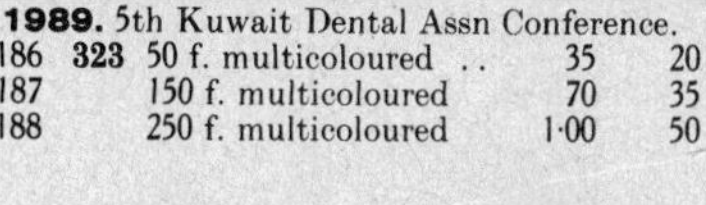

1989. 5th Kuwait Dental Assn Conference.
1186 **323** 50 f. multicoloured .. 35 20
1187 150 f. multicoloured 70 35
1188 250 f. multicoloured 1·00 50

324 Emblems

325 Anniversary Emblem

1989. World Health Day.
1189 **324** 50 f. multicoloured .. 35 20
1190 150 f. multicoloured 70 35
1191 250 f. multicoloured 1·00 50

1989. 10th Anniv of Arab Board for Medical Specializations.
1192 **325** 50 f. multicoloured .. 35 20
1193 150 f. multicoloured 70 35
1194 250 f. multicoloured 1·00 50

326 Torch, Pen and Flag

1989. 25th Anniv of Kuwait Journalists' Association.
1195 **326** 50 f. multicoloured .. 35 20
1196 200 f. multicoloured 85 45
1197 250 f. multicoloured 1·00 50

327 Attan'eem Migat, Mecca

1989. Pilgrimage to Mecca.
1198 **327** 50 f. multicoloured .. 30 15
1199 150 f. multicoloured 60 30
1200 200 f. multicoloured 85 45

328 Al-Qurain Housing Project

329 Tree

1989. Arab Housing Day.
1201 **328** 25 f. multicoloured .. 10 10
1202 50 f. multicoloured 30 15
1203 150 f. multicoloured 60 30

1989. Greenery Week.
1204 **329** 25 f. multicoloured .. 10 10
1205 50 f. multicoloured 25 15
1206 150 f. multicoloured 60 30

330 Dhow

331 Emblem and Map

1989. Coil stamps.
1207 **330** 50 f. gold and green 45 20
1208 100 f. gold and blue 80 25
1209 200 f. gold and red .. 1·50 55

1989. 5tn Anniv of Gulf Investment Corporation.
1210 **331** 25 f. multicoloured .. 10 10
1211 50 f. multicoloured .. 25 15
1212 150 f. multicoloured 60 30

332 Emblem

333 Zakat House

1989. 1st Anniv of "Declaration of Palestine State".
1213 **332** 50 f. multicoloured .. 25 10
1214 150 f. multicoloured 60 30
1215 200 f. multicoloured 85 45

1989. Orphanage Sponsorship Project.
1216 **333** 25 f. multicoloured .. 10 10
1217 50 f. multicoloured .. 25 10
1218 150 f. multicoloured 60 30

334 Shaikh Sabah al-Salem as-Sabah (former Chief) and Officers

335 Globe and Dove

1989. 50th Anniv (1988) of Kuwait Police.
1219 **334** 25 f. multicoloured .. 10 10
1220 50 f. multicoloured 20 10
1221 150 f. multicoloured .. 60 30

1990. 29th National Day.
1222 **335** 25 f. multicoloured .. 10 10
1223 50 f. multicoloured .. 20 10
1224 150 f. multicoloured .. 60 30

336 Earth, Clouds and Weather Balloon

1990. World Meteorological Day.
1225 **336** 50 f. multicoloured .. 20 10
1226 100 f. multicoloured .. 40 20
1227 150 f. multicoloured .. 60 30

337 Map bordered by National Flag

338 Lanner Falcon

1990. World Health Day.
1228 **337** 50 f. multicoloured .. 20 10
1229 100 f. multicoloured .. 40 20
1230 150 f. multicoloured .. 60 30

1990.
1231 **338** 50 f. gold and blue .. 25 15
1232 100 f. gold and red .. 45 25
1233 150 f. gold and green 70 35

339 Soldiers carrying Kuwait Flag

340 Dove and Map

1991. Liberation (1st issue).
1234 **339** 25 f. multicoloured .. 10 10
1235 50 f. multicoloured .. 20 10
1236 150 f. multicoloured .. 60 30
See also Nos. 1243/84.

1991. Peace.
1237 **340** 50 f. multicoloured .. 20 10
1238 100 f. multicoloured .. 40 20
1239 150 f. multicoloured .. 60 30

341 Flag, Map, and Globe

342 Sweden

1991. Reconstruction.
1240 **341** 50 f. multicoloured .. 20 10
1241 150 f. multicoloured .. 60 30
1242 200 f. multicoloured .. 80 40

1991. Liberation (2nd issue). Each showing a dove coloured with the flag of one of the assisting nations. Multicoloured.
1243 50 f. Type **342** 20 10
1244 50 f. Soviet Union .. 20 10
1245 50 f. United States of America 20 10
1246 50 f. Kuwait 20 10
1247 50 f. Saudi Arabia .. 20 10
1248 50 f. United Nations .. 20 10
1249 50 f. Singapore 20 10
1250 50 f. France 20 10
1251 50 f. Italy 20 10
1252 50 f. Egypt 20 10
1253 50 f. Morocco 20 10
1254 50 f. United Kingdom .. 20 10
1255 50 f. Philippines 20 10
1256 50 f. United Arab Emirates 20 10
1257 50 f. Syria 20 10
1258 50 f. Poland 20 10
1259 50 f. Australia 20 10
1260 50 f. Japan 20 10
1261 50 f. Hungary 20 10
1262 50 f. Netherlands .. 20 10
1263 50 f. Denmark 20 10
1264 50 f. New Zealand .. 20 10
1265 50 f. Czechoslovakia .. 20 10
1266 50 f. Bahrain 20 10
1267 50 f. Honduras 20 10
1268 50 f. Turkey 20 10
1269 50 f. Greece 20 10
1270 50 f. Oman 20 10
1271 50 f. Qatar 20 10
1272 50 f. Belgium 20 10
1273 50 f. Sierra Leone .. 20 10
1274 50 f. Argentina 20 10
1275 50 f. Norway 20 10
1276 50 f. Canada 20 10
1277 50 f. Germany 20 10
1278 50 f. South Korea .. 20 10
1279 50 f. Bangladesh .. 20 10
1280 50 f. Bulgaria 20 10
1281 50 f. Senegal 20 10
1282 50 f. Spain 20 10
1283 50 f. Niger 20 10
1284 50 f. Pakistan 20 10

343 "Human Terror"

1991. 1st Anniv of Iraqi Invasion. Mult.
1286 50 f. Type **343** 20 10
1287 100 f. "Invasion of Kuwait" 40 20
1288 150 f. "Environmental Terrorism" (horiz) .. 60 30

POSTAGE DUE STAMPS

D **34.**

D **51.**

1963.

No.	Type	Description		
D 199.	D 34.	1 f. brown and black	10	20
D 200.		2 f. violet and black	15	25
D 201.		5 f. blue and black	25	20
D 202.		8 f. green and black	45	35
D 203.		10 f. yellow and black	65	65
D 204.		25 f. red and black	1·40	2·00

The above stamps were not sold to the public unused until 1st July, 1964.

1965.

No.	Type	Description		
D 276.	D 51.	4 f. red and yellow . .	15	30
D 277.		15 f. red and blue . .	45	50
D 278.		40 f. blue and green	95	1·25
D 279.		50 f. green & mauve	1·25	1·50
D 280.		100 f. blue & yellow	2·25	3·00

KYRGYZSTAN Pt. 10

Formerly Kirghizia, a constituent republic of the Soviet Union, Kyrgyzstan became independent in 1991. Its capital Frunze reverted to its previous name of Bishkek.

100 kopeks = 1 rouble

1 Sary-Chelek Nature Reserve

2 Eagle

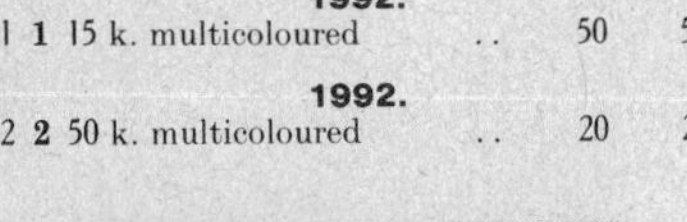

1992.

1	1	15 k. multicoloured . .	50	50

1992.

2	2	50 k. multicoloured . .	20	20

3 "Cattle at Issyk-kule" (G. A. Aitiev)

1992.

3	3	1 r. multicoloured . .	50	50

4 Carpet and Samovar

1992.

4	4	1 r. 50 multicoloured . .	70	70

LA AGUERA Pt. 9

An administrative district of Spanish Sahara whose stamps it later used.

1920. Rio de Oro stamps optd. LA AGUERA.

No.	Type	Description		
1.	15.	1 c. green	1·40	1·40
2.		2 c. brown	1·40	1·40
3.		5 c. green	1·40	1·40
4.		10 c. red	1·40	1·40
5.		15 c. yellow	1·40	1·40
6.		20 c. violet	1·40	1·40
7.		25 c. blue	1·40	1·40
8.		30 c. brown	1·40	1·40
9.		40 c. pink	1·40	1·40
10.		50 c. blue	3·75	3·50
11.		1 p. red	8·50	6·50
12.		4 p. purple	25·00	22·00
13.		10 p. orange	45·00	45·00

2.

1923.

No.	Type	Description		
14	2	1 c. blue	70	70
15		2 c. green	70	70
16		5 c. green	70	70
17		10 c. red	70	70
18		15 c. brown	70	70
19		20 c. yellow	70	70
20		25 c. blue	70	70
21		30 c. brown	70	70
22		40 c. red	85	85
23		50 c. purple	3·00	2·75
24		1 p. mauve	7·50	5·75
25		4 p. violet	17·00	16·00
26		10 p. orange	20·00	19·00

LAOS Pt. 21

Laos (previously part of Fr. Indo-China) became independent in 1951.

1951. 100 cents = 1 piastre.
1955. 100 cents = 1 kip.

1. River Mekong. 2. King Sisavang Vong.

1951.

No.	Type	Description		
1.	1.	10 c. green and turquoise	10	10
2.		20 c. red and claret . .	10	10
3.		30 c. blue and indigo . .	65	55
4.	–	50 c. brown . .	20	15
5.	–	60 c. orange and red . .	20	20
6.	–	70 c. turquoise and blue . .	20	20
7.	–	1 p. violet and purple . .	20	20
8.	2.	1 p. 50 purple and brown	55	45
9.	–	2 p. green and grey . .	9·00	2·25
10.	–	3 p. red and claret . .	55	50
11.	–	5 p. blue and indigo . .	80	55
12.	–	10 p. purple and brown . .	1·75	90

DESIGNS—HORIZ. As Type **1**: 50 c. to 70 c. Luang Prabang. 1 p. and 2 p. to 10 p. Vientiane.

3. Laotian Woman.

4. Laotian Woman Weaving.

1952.

No.	Type	Description		
13.	3.	30 c. violet and blue (post.)	20	15
14.		80 c. turquoise and green	20	20
15.		1 p. 10 red	50	20
16.		1 p. 90 blue and dk. blue	80	55
17.		3 p. sepia and purple . .	80	55
18.	–	3 p. 30 purple & violet (air)	55	35
19.	4.	10 p. green and blue . .	1·25	80
20.		20 p. red	1·90	1·40
21.		30 p. purple and sepia . .	3·00	2·50

DESIGN—As Type **4**: 3 p. 30, Vat Pra Keo shrine.

5. King Sisavang Vong and U.P.U. Monument.

1952. 1st Anniv. of Admission to U.P.U.

No.	Type	Description		
22.	5.	80 c. vio., bl. & ind. (post.)	45	45
23.		1 p. brown, red and lake . .	45	45
24.		1 p. 20 blue and violet . .	45	45
25.		1 p. 50 brn., emer. & grn.	45	45
26.		1 p. 90 turquoise and sepia	70	70
27.		25 p. indigo and blue (air)	3·00	3·00
28.		50 p. sepia, purple & brn.	3·50	3·50

6. Girl carrying her Brother. 7. Native Musicians.

1953. Red Cross Fund. Cross in red.

No.	Type	Description		
29.	6.	1 p. 50+1 p. brn. & blue . .	1·60	1·60
30.		3 p.+1 p. 50 red & green . .	1·60	1·60
31.		3 p. 90+2 p. 50 brn. & sep.	1·60	1·60

1953.

No.	Type	Description		
32.	7.	4 p. 50 turquoise and blue	55	40
33.		6 p. brown and slate . .	55	50

8. Buddha.

1953. Air. Statues of Buddha.

No.	Type	Description		
34.	–	4 p. green	65	45
35.	–	6 p. 50 green	90	65
36.	–	9 p. green	1·25	1·00
37.	8.	11 p. 50 orge., brn. & red	1·60	1·40
38.	–	40 p. purple	3·25	1·60
39.	–	100 p. bistre	9·00	6·00

Nos. 34 and 37 are horiz. and the rest vert.

9. Vientiane.

1954. Jubilee of King Sisavang Vong.

No.	Type	Description		
40.	9.	2 p. violet and blue (post.)	35·00	19·00
41.		3 p. red and brown . .	35·00	25·00
42.		50 p. turq. and blue (air)	£110	£110

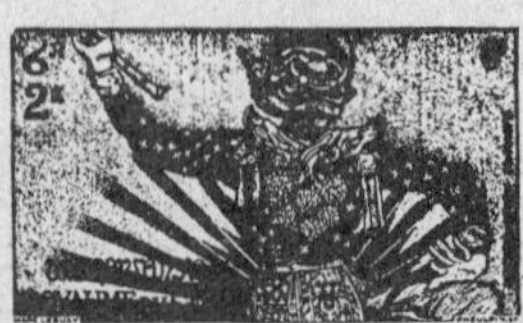

10. Ravana.

1955. Air. "Ramayana" (dramatic poem).

No.	Type	Description		
43.	10.	2 k. blue and green . .	65	55
44.	–	4 k. red and brown . .	80	65
45.	–	5 k. olive, brown and red	1·40	1·00
46.	–	10 k. black, orge. & brn.	2·75	1·60
47.	–	20 k. olive, grn. & violet	3·25	2·25
48.	–	30 k. black, brown & blue	4·50	3·25

DESIGNS—HORIZ. 4 k. Hanuman, the white monkey. 5 k. Ninh Laphath, the black monkey. VERT. 10 k. Sita and Rama. 20 k. Luci and Ravana's friend. 30 k. Rama.

11. Buddha and Worshippers.

1956. 2500th Anniv. of Buddhist Era.

No.	Type	Description		
49.	11.	2 k. brown (postage) . .	2·25	1·60
50.		3 k. black	2·25	1·60
51.		5 k. sepia	2·25	1·90
52.		20 k. red (air)	22·00	17·00
53.		30 k. olive and green . .	22·00	17·00

Nos. 49/53 were wrongly inscribed as commemorating the birth centenary of Buddha.

12. U.N. Emblem. 13.

1956. 1st Anniv. of Admission to U.N.

No.	Type	Description		
54.	12.	1 k. black (postage) . .	45	45
55.		2 k. blue	55	50
56.		4 k. red	80	70
57.		6 k. violet	1·00	85
58.	13.	15 k. blue (air)	4·50	4·50
59.		30 k. lake	6·50	6·50

14. Flute-player.

1957. Native Musical Instruments.

No.	Type	Description		
60.	14.	2 k. multicoloured (post.)	1·10	80
61.	–	4 k. multicoloured . .	1·10	80
62.	–	8 k. blue, brown & orge.	1·60	95
63.	–	12 k. ol., vio. & red (air)	1·50	1·50
64.	–	14 k. brown, blue and red	1·90	1·90
65.	–	20 k. turquoise, green and violet	2·25	2·25

DESIGNS: Natives playing instruments—VERT. 4 k. Pipes. 14 k. Violin. 20 k. Drum. HORIZ. 8 k. Xylophone. 12 k. Bells.

DESIGNS—VERT. 5 k. Drying rice. 16 k. Winnowing rice. HORIZ. 26 k. Polishing rice.

15. Harvesting Rice.

1957. Rice Cultivation.

No.	Type	Description		
66.	15.	3 k. multicoloured . .	55	40
67.	–	5 k. brown, red and green	55	50
68.	–	16 k. violet, olive and blue	1·40	80
69.	–	26 k. choc., brn. & green	1·60	1·40

16. "The Offertory". 18. Mother and Child.

17. Carrier Elephants.

1957. Air. Buddhism Commem.

No.	Type	Description		
70.	16.	10 k. blue, brown & violet	50	50
71.	–	15 k. brn., yell. & choc.	70	70
72.	–	18 k. bistre and green . .	1·00	1·00
73.	–	24 k. lake, black & yellow	1·90	1·90

DESIGNS—HORIZ. 15 k. "Meditation" (children on river craft). 24 k. (48×36½ mm.) "The Great Renunciation" (natives with horse). VERT. 18 k. "Serenity" (head of Buddhist).

1958. Laotian Elephants. Multicoloured.
74. 10 c. Type **17** 35 20
75. 20 c. Elephant's head with head-dress 35 20
76. 30 c. Elephant with howdah (vert.) 35 20
77. 2 k. Elephant hauling log.. 45 35
78. 5 k. Elephant walking with calf (vert.) .. .. 1·40 80
79. 10 k. Caparisoned elephant (vert.) .. .. .. 1·40 1·00
80. 13 k. Elephant bearing throne (vert.) .. .. .. 2·50 1·60

1958. Air. 3rd Anniv. of Laotian Red Cross. Cross in red.
81. **18.** 8 k. black and violet .. 85 85
82. 12 k. olive and brown .. 85 85
83. 15 k. turq. and green .. 1·10 1·10
84. 20 k. violet and bistre .. 1·10 1·10

19.

1958. Inaug. of U.N.E.S.C.O. Headquarters Building, Paris.
85. **19.** 50 c. multicoloured .. 25 20
86. – 60 c. multicoloured .. 25 20
87. – 70 c. multicoloured .. 25 20
88. – 1 k. multicoloured .. 35 20
DESIGNS—VERT. 60 c. Woman, children and part of exterior of U.N.E.S.C.O. building. 70 c. Woman and children hailing U.N.E.S.C.O. building superimposed on globe. HORIZ. 1 k. General view of U.N.E.S.C.O. building and Eiffel Tower.

20. King Sisavang Vong.

1959.
89. **20.** 4 k. lake 35 35
90. 6 k. 50 brown 35 35
91. 9 k. mauve 35 35
92. 13 k. green 45 45

21. Stage Performance. **22.** Portal of Vat Phou Temple, Pakse.

1959. Education and Fine Arts.
93. **21.** 1 k. multicoloured .. 15 15
94. – 2 k. lake, violet and black 20 15
95. – 3 k. black, green & purple 30 20
96. – 5 k. green, yellow & violet 45 35
DESIGNS—VERT. 2 k. Student and " Lamp of Learning ". 5 k. Stage performers and Buddhist temple. HORIZ. 3 k. Teacher and children with " Key to Education ".

1959. Laotian Monuments. Multicoloured.
97. 50 c. Type **22** 15 15
98. 1 k. 50 That Ing Hang, Savannakhet 20 20
99. 2 k. 50 Vat Phou Temple, Pakse 30 30
100. 7 k. That Luang, Vientiane 50 40
101. 11 k. As 7 k., different view 65 55
102. 12 k. 50 Phou-si Temple, Luang Prabang.. .. 85 65
The 1 k. 50, 2 k. 50 and 11 k. are horiz. and the rest vert.

1960. World Refugee Year. Nos. 89 and 79 surch. **ANNEE MONDIALE DU REFUGIE 1959-1960** and premium.
103. 4 k.+1 k. lake .. 1·90 1·90
104. 10 k.+1 k. multicoloured 3·00 3·00

24. Plain of Jars, Xieng Khouang. **25.** Funeral Urn.

1960. Air. Tourist Propaganda. Multicoloured.
105. 9 k. 50 Type **24** 50 50
106. 12 k. Papheng Falls, Champassak 70 70
107. 15 k. Pair of bullocks with cart .. .. .. 1·00 1·00
108. 19 k. Buddhist monk and village .. .. .. 1·10 1·10
The 12 k. and 15 k. are horiz. and the rest vert.

1961. Funeral of King Sisavang Vong.
109. **25.** 4 k. bistre, black and red 85 85
110. – 6 k. 50 brown and black 85 85
111. – 9 k. brown and black .. 85 85
112. – 25 k. black .. .. 2·25 2·25
DESIGNS: 6 k. 50, Urn under canopy. 9 k. Catafalque on dragon carriage. 25 k. King Sisavang Vong.

26. Temples and Statues (" Pou Gneu Nha Gneu "). **27.** King Savang Vatthana.

1962. Air. Festival of Makha Bousa.
113. **26.** 11 k. green, red & yellow 70 70
114. – 14 k. blue and orange .. 70 70
115. – 20 k. multicoloured .. 1·10 1·10
116. – 25 k. multicoloured .. 1·40 1·40
DESIGNS: 14 k. Bird (" Garuda "). 20 k. Flying deities (" Hanuman "). LARGER (36×48 mm.): 25 k. Warriors (" Nang Teng One ").

1962.
117. **27.** 1 k. purple, red and blue 10 10
118. 2 k. purple, red & mauve 20 15
119. 5 k. purple, red & turq. 30 20
120. 10 k. pur., red & bistre 50 30

28. Laotian Boy. **29.** Royal Courier.

1962. Malaria Eradication.
121. **28.** 4 k. olive, black & green 20 10
122. – 9 k. brown, blk. & turq. 35 30
123. – 10 k. red, yellow & olive 50 35
DESIGNS: 9 k. Laotian girl. 10 k. Campaign emblem.

1962. Philatelic Exn., Vientiane and Stamp Day. Multicoloured.
124. 50 c. Modern mail transport (horiz.) 60 80
125. 70 c. Dancer and globe (horiz.) 40 40
126. 1 k. Royal courier on elephant 60 60
127. 1 k. 50 Type **29** 55 55

30. Fisherman.

1963. Freedom from Hunger. Multicoloured.
128. 1 k. Type **30** 20 15
129. 4 k. Threshing rice (vert.) 25 20
130. 5 k. Planting rice and oxen in paddy field 30 30
131. 9 k. Harvesting rice (vert.) 50 40

31. Queen of Laos. **32.** Laotian supporting U.N. Emblem.

1963. Red Cross Centenary.
132. **31.** 4 k. multicoloured .. 40 40
133. 6 k. multicoloured .. 45 45
134. 10 k. multicoloured .. 65 65

1963. Declaration of Human Rights. 15th Anniv. Imperf. or perf.
135. **32.** 4 k. purple, blue and red 85 65

33. Temple, Map and Rameses II.

1964. Nubian Monuments Preservation.
136. **33.** 4 k. multicoloured .. 30 30
137. 6 k. multicoloured .. 40 40
138. 10 k. multicoloured .. 45 45

34. Offertory Vase and Horn.

1964. "Constitutional Monarchy". Mult.
139. 10 k. Type **34** 20 15
140. 15 k. Seated Buddha of Vat Pra Keo 30 20
141. 20 k. Laotians walking across map 35 30
142. 40 k. Royal Palace, Luang Prabang 70 55

35. Phra Vet and wife. **36.** Meo Warrior.

1964. Folklore. Phra Vet Legend. Mult.
143. 10 k. Type **35** 35 35
144. 32 k. "Benediction" .. 45 45
145. 45 k. Phame and wife .. 65 65
146. 55 k. Arrest of Phame .. 80 80

1964. "People of Laos".
147. – 25 k. black, brown and green (post.).. .. 45 45
148. **36.** 5 k. multicoloured (air) 20 15
149. – 10 k. flesh, slate & purple 30 15
150. – 50 k. brn., drab & lilac 1·00 80
DESIGNS: 10 k. Kha hunter. 25 k. Girls of three races. 50 k. Thai woman.

37. " Cethoeia biblis ".

1965. Laotian Butterflies.
151. **37.** 10 k. multicoloured (postage) 70 35
152. – 25 k. violet, black & yell. 1·25 55
153. – 40 k. yell., brn. and grn. 2·25 1·00
154. – 20 k. brown & ochre (air) 80 55
BUTTERFLIES—As Type **37**: 25 k. " Precis cebrene ". HORIZ. (48×27 mm.): 20 k. " Attacus atlas ". 40 k. " Dysphania militaris ".

38. Wattay Airport (" French Aid ").

1965. Foreign Aid.
155. **38.** 25 k. mve., brn. & turq. 30 20
156. – 45 k. brown and green.. 40 35
157. – 55 k. brown and blue .. 55 45
158. – 75 k. multicoloured .. 70 60
DESIGNS—VERT. 45 k. Mother bathing child (water resources: " Japanese Aid "). 75 k. School and plants (education and cultivation: " American Aid "). HORIZ. 55 k. Studio of radio station (" British Aid ").

39. Hophabang.

1965.
159. **39.** 10 k. multicoloured .. 20 15

40. Teleprinter operator, Globe and Map.

1965. I.T.U. Cent.
160. **40.** 5 k. brn., violet and pur. 25 15
161. – 30 k. brn., blue and grn. 40 35
162. – 50 k. multicoloured .. 70 45
DESIGNS: 30 k. Globe, map, telephonist and radio operator. 50 k. Globe, radio receiver and mast.

1965. Surch.
163. **20.** 1 k. on 4 k. lake .. 20 15
164. 5 k. on 6 k. 50 brown.. 25 20

42. Mother and Baby. **43.** Leopard Cat.

1965. 6th Anniv. of U.N. "Protection of Mother and Child".
165. **42.** 35 k. blue and red .. 60 45

1965. Air. Laotian Fauna.
166. **43.** 25 k. yell., brn. & grn. 40 30
167. – 55 k. brown, sepia & blue 55 45
168. – 75 k. brown and green.. 70 60
169. – 100 k. brown, blk. & yell. 1·10 85
170. – 200 k. black and red .. 2·75 2·25
DESIGNS: 55 k. Phayre's flying squirrel. 75 k. Javan mongoose. 100 k. Chinese porcupine. 200 k. Binturong.

44. U.N. Emblem on Map. **45.** Bulls in Combat.

1965. 20th Anniv. of U.N.
171. **44.** 5 k. blue, drab & green 20 20
172. 25 k. blue, drab & purple 30 25
173. 40 k. blue, drab & blue 50 50

1965. Laotian Folklore. Multicoloured.
174. 10 k. Type **45** 25 20
175. 20 k. Tikhy (form of hockey) 30 20
176. 25 k. Pirogue race .. 45 30
177. 50 k. Rocket festival .. 55 40

46. Slaty-headed Parakeet.

1966. Laotian Birds.
178. **46.** 5 k. green, brown & red 80 40
179. – 15 k. brown, black & turq. 90 50
180. – 20 k. sepia, ochre & blue 1·10 70
181. – 45 k. blue, sepia & violet 2·50 1·75
BIRDS: 15 k. White-crested Laughing Thrush. 20 k. Osprey. 45 k. Indian Roller.

47. W.H.O. Building.

1966. Inaug. of W.H.O. Headquarters, Geneva.

182. **47.** 10 k. blue and turquoise .. 20 20
183. 25 k. green and red .. 30 25
184. 50 k. black and blue .. 50 45

48. Ordination of Priests.

1966. Laotian Folklore. Multicoloured.

186. 10 k. Type **48** 30 20
187. 25 k. Sand-hills ceremony 35 30
188. 30 k. " Wax pagoda " procession (vert.) 50 35
189. 40 k. " Sou-Khouan " ceremony (vert.) 55 40

49. U.N.E.S.C.O. Emblem.

1966. 20th Anniv. of U.N.E.S.C.O.

190. **49.** 20 k. orange and black 20 15
191. 30 k. blue and black .. 30 25
192. 40 k. green and black .. 35 30
193. 60 k. red and black .. 50 45

50. Letter, Carrier Pigeon and Emblem.

1966. Int. Correspondence Week.

195. **50.** 5 k. blue, brown and red 20 15
196. 20 k. purple, black & grn. 30 20
197. 40 k. brown, red & blue 40 35
198. 45 k. black, green & pur. 50 40

51. Flooded Village.

52. Carving, Siprapouthbat Pagoda.

1967. Mekong Delta Flood Relief. Mult.

200. 20 k. + 5 k. Type **51** .. 45 45
201. 40 k. + 10 k. Flooded market-place 65 65
202. 60 k. + 15 k. Flooded airport 1·10 1·10

1967. Buddhist Art.

204. **52.** 5 k. green and brown .. 15 15
205. – 20 k. blue and sepia .. 30 20
206. – 50 k. purple and sepia .. 65 40
207. – 70 k. drab and purple .. 85 55

Designs (carvings in temple pagodas, Luang Prabang): 30 k. Visoun. 50 k. Xiengthong. 70 k. Visoun (different).

53. General Post Office.

1967. Opening of New G.P.O. Building, Vientiane.

208. **53.** 25 k. brn., grn. and pur. 25 25
209. 50 k. blue, grn. and slate 40 35
210. 70 k. red, grn. and brn. 65 55

54. " Ophicephalus micropeltes ".

55. " Cassia fistula ".

1967. Fishes.

211. **54.** 20 k. black, bistre & blue 40 25
212. – 35 k. slate, bistre & turq. 45 35
213. – 45 k. sepia, ochre & grn. 65 45
214. – 60 k. black, bistre & grn. 1·00 55

Designs: 35 k. " Pangasianodon gigas ". 45 k. " Mastocembelus armatus ". 60 k. " Notopterus ".

1967. Flowers. Multicoloured.

215. 30 k. Type **55** 30 35
216. 55 k. "Curcuma singularia" 50 45
217. 75 k. "Poinciana regia" .. 70 60
218. 80 k. "Plumeria acutifolia" 80 65

56. Harvesting.

1967. 10th Anniv. of Laotian Red Cross.

219. **56.** 20 k. + 5 k. multicoloured 30 30
220. 50 k. + 10 k. mult. .. 55 55
221. 60 k. + 15 k. mult. .. 75 75

57. Banded Krait.

1967. Reptiles. Multicoloured.

223. 5 k. Type **57** 20 15
224. 40 k. Marsh crocodile .. 45 40
225. 100 k. Pit viper .. .. 1·90 1·10
226. 200 k. Water monitor (lizard) .. .. .. 3·25 2·25

58. Human Rights Emblem.

1968. Human Rights Year. Emblem in red and green.

227. **58.** 20 k. green 20 20
228. 30 k. brown 30 25
229. 50 k. blue 60 45

59. Military Parade.

60. W.H.O. Emblem.

1968. Army Day. Multicoloured.

231. 15 k. Type **59** (postage) .. 20 15
232. 20 k. Soldiers and tank in battle 30 20
233. 60 k. Soldiers and Laotian flag 50 40
234. 200 k. Parade of colours before National Assembly building (air) .. .. 1·10 65
235. 300 k. As 200 k. .. .. 1·60 1·00

1968. 20th Anniv. of W.H.O.

237. **60.** 15 k. brown, red & pur. 25 20
238. 30 k. brown, green & bl. 30 20
239. 70 k. brown, pur. & red 45 30
240. 110 k. brown and purple 65 50
241. 250 k. brown, blue & grn. 1·60 1·25

MINIMUM PRICE

The minimum price quoted is 5p which represents a handling charge rather than a basis for valuing common stamps. For further notes about prices see introductory pages.

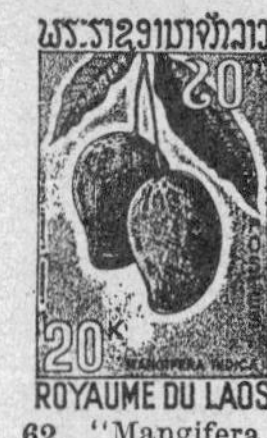

61. " Chrysochroa mnizechi ".

62. " Mangifera indica ".

1968. Insects.

243. **61.** 30 k. blue, yellow and green (postage) .. 45 25
244. – 50 k. blk., orge. and pur. 55 30
245. – 90 k. blue, orge. & ochre 1·00 55
246. – 120 k. blk. & orge. (air) 95 55
247. – 160 k. multicoloured .. 1·40 75

Insects—vert. 50 k. " Aristobia approximator ". 90 k. " Eutaenia corbetti ". horiz. 120 k. " Dorysthenes walkeri ". 160 k. " Megaloxantha bicolor ".

1968. Laotian Fruits.

248. **62.** 20 k. green, blue & blk. 15 15
249. – 50 k. green, red & blue 40 30
250. – 180 k. grn., brn. & orge. 1·10 80
251. – 250 k. grn., brn. & yell. 1·90 1·25

Designs—vert. 50 k. " Tamarindus indica ". horiz. 180 k. " Artocarpus intregrifolia ". 250 k. " Citrullus vulgaris ".

63. Hurdling.

1968. Olympic Games, Mexico.

252. **63.** 15 k. grn., blue and brn. 20 15
253. – 80 k. brn., turq. & blue 40 35
254. – 100 k. blue, brn. & grn. 45 35
255. – 110 k. brn., red and blue 50 40

Designs: 80 k. Tennis. 100 k. Football. 110 k. High-jumping.

64. Oriental Door, Wat Ongtu (detail).

1969. Wat Ongtu Temple.

256. **64.** 150 k. gold, blk. & red 1·25 90
257. – 200 k. gold, black & red 1·90 1·40

Design: 200 k. Central door, Wat Ongtu.

65. " Pharak praying to the Gods ".

1969. Laotian "Ballet Royal". Designs showing dance characters. Multicoloured.

258. 10 k. Type **65** (postage) .. 30 15
259. 15 k. "Soukhib ordered to attack" 45 25
260. 20 k. "Thotsakan reviewing troops" 55 35
261. 30 k. "Nang Sida awaiting punishment" 70 45
262. 40 k. "Pharam inspecting his troops" 90 50
263. 60 k. "Hanuman about to rescue Nang Sida" .. 1·60 80
264. 110 k. "Soudagnou battling with Thotsakan" (air) .. 2·25 1·60
265. 300 k. "Pharam dancing with Thotsakan" .. 4·50 3·00

66. Handicrafts Workshop, Vientiane.

1969. 10th Anniv. of I.L.O.

267. **66.** 30 k. violet & red (post.) 30 30
268. 60 k. purple and green 55 50
269. – 300 k. black & brown (air) 2·75 1·90

Design: 300 k. Elephants moving logs.

67. Chinese Pangolin.

1969. "Wild Animals" (1st series). Mult.

270. 15 k. Type **67** (postage) .. 20 15
271. 30 k. Type **67** 50 35
272. 70 k. Sun bear (air) .. 70 50
273. 120 k. Common gibbon (vert.) .. .. .. 1·40 70
274. 150 k. Tiger .. .. 1·75 95

See also Nos. 300/3 and 331/5.

68. Royal Mausoleum, Luang Prabang.

1969. 10th Death Anniv. of King Sisavang Vong.

275. **68.** 50 k. ochre, blue & grn. 40 35
276. – 70 k. ochre and lake .. 45 35

Design: 70 k. King Sisavang Vong (medallion).

69. "Lao Woman being Groomed" (Leguay).

1969. Air. Paintings by Marc Leguay (1st series). Multicoloured.

277. 10 k. Type **69** .. .. 1·10 65
278. 150 k. "Village Market" (horiz.) .. .. 1·40 1·00

See also Nos. 285, 307/9 and 357/61.

70. Carved Capital, Wat Xiengthong.

1970. Laotian Pagodas. Multicoloured.

279. 70 k. Type (**70** postage) .. 50 40
280. 100 k. Library, Wat Sisaket (air) 60 35
281. 120 k. Wat Xiengthong (horiz.) 95 65

71. "Noon" Drum.

1970. Laotian Drums.
282. 71. 30 k. mult. (post.) .. 45 40
283. – 55 k. black, grn. & brn. 55 45
284. – 125 k. brown, yellow and flesh (air) 90 60
DESIGNS—HORIZ. 55 k. Bronze drum. VERT. 125 k. Wooden drum.

1970. Air. Paintings by Marc Leguay (2nd series). As T **69**. Multicoloured.
285. 150 k. "Banks of the Mekong" .. .. 1·25 90

72. Franklin D. Roosevelt.

1970. Air. 25th Death Anniv. of Franklin D. Roosevelt (American statesman).
286. 72. 120 k. slate and green 95 55

73. "Lenin explaining Electrification Plan" (L. Shmatko).

1970. Birth Cent. of Lenin.
287. 73. 30 k. multicoloured .. 25 20
288. 70 k. multicoloured .. 40 35

1970. "Support for War Victims". Nos. 258/65 ("Ballet Royal") surch. **Soutien aux Victimes de la Guerre** and value.
289. 10 k. + 5 k. mult. (post.) 35 35
290. 15 k. + 5 k. multicoloured 35 35
291. 20 k. + 5 k. multicoloured 35 35
292. 30 k. + 5 k. multicoloured 35 35
293. 40 k. + 5 k. multicoloured 65 65
294. 60 k. + 5 k. multicoloured 80 80
295. 110 k. + 5 k. mult. (air) .. 1·40 1·40
296. 300 k. + 5 k. multicoloured 2·50 2·50

75. Weaving Silk.

1970. "EXPO 70" World Fair, Osaka, Japan Laotian Silk Industry.
297. 75. 30 k. bl., brn. & red (post.) 35 30
298. – 70 k. multicoloured .. 65 55
299. – 125 k. mult. (air) .. 95 65
DESIGNS: 70 k. Silk-spinning. 125 k. Winding skeins.

76. Wild Boar.

77. Buddha, U.N. Emblem and New York H.Q.

1970. Wild Animals (2nd series).
300. 76. 20 k. brn. & grn. (postage 35 25
301. – 60 k. brn. and olive .. 65 40
302. – 210 k. black, red and yellow (air) .. .. 1·75 1·10
303. – 500 k. green, brn. & orge. 4·00 2·25
ANIMALS: 210 k. Leopard. 500 k. Gaur.

1970. 25th Anniv. of U.N.O. Mult.
304. 30 k. Type **77** (postage) .. 30 25
305. 70 k. Type **77** 55 40
306. 125 k. Nang Thorani ("Goddess of the Earth") and New York H.Q. (air) .. .. 1·10 80

1970. Air. Paintings by Marc Leguay (3rd series). As T **69**. Multicoloured.
307. 100 k. "Village Track" .. 65 45
308. 120 k. "Paddy-field in Rainy Season" (horiz.) .. 1·00 60
309. 150 k. "Village Elder" .. 1·10 70

78. "Nakhanet".

1971. Laotian Mythology (1st series). Frescoes from Triumphal Arch, Vientiane. Mult.
310. 78. 70 k. orge., brn. & red (postage) 45 35
311. – 85 k. green, yell. & blue 55 45
312. – 125 k. mult. (air) .. 1·10 65
DESIGNS—DIAMOND. 85 k. "Rahu". HORIZ. 49×36 mm. 125 k. "Underwater duel between Nang Matsa and Hanuman".
See also Nos. 352/4 and 385/7.

79. Silversmiths.

1971. Laotian Traditional Crafts. Mult.
313. 30 k. Type **79** 20 20
314. 50 k. Potters 35 20
315. 70 k. Pirogue-builder (horiz. 49×36 mm.) .. 45 30

80. Laotian and African Children.

1971. Racial Equality Year.
316. 80. 30 k. blue, red and green 20 15
317. – 60 k. vio., red & yellow 40 30
DESIGN: 60 k. Laotian dancers and musicians.

81. Buddhist Monk at That Luang.

1971. 50th Anniv. of Vientiane Rotary Club.
318. 81. 30 k. violet, brn. & blue 30 20
319. – 70 k. grey, red & blue .. 45 35
DESIGN—VERT. 70 k. Laotian girl on "Dragon" staircase.

82. "Dendrobium agregatum".

83. Dancers from France and Laos.

1971. Laotian Orchids. Multicoloured.
320. 30 k. Type **82** (postage) .. 35 20
321. 40 k. "Rynchostylis giganterum" 40 30
322. 50 k. "Ascocentrum miniatur" (horiz.) 45 35
323. 60 k. "Paphiopedilum exul" 45 40
324. 70 k. "Trichoglottis fasciata" (horiz.) 55 45
325. 80 k. Cattleya (horiz.) .. 65 45
326. 125 k. Brasilian cattleya (horiz.) (air) .. .. 1·25 70
327. 150 k. "Vanda teres" (horiz.) 1·40 1·00
Nos. 321, 323 and 325 are smaller 22×36 or, 36×22 mm. Nos. 326/7 are larger, 48×27 mm. The orchid on No. 320 is depicted in its normal (inverted) position.

1971. Air. "Twin Cities" of St. Astier (France) and Keng-Kog (Laos).
328. 83. 30 k. lake and brown .. 20 15
329. 70 k. purple and plum .. 30 20
330. 100 k. green & deep green 50 35

1971. Wild Animals (3rd series). As T **76** but with square format (36×36 mm.)
331. 25 k. blk., vio. & blue (post.) 35 25
332. 40 k. blk., green & olive .. 45 35
333. 50 k. orange and green .. 70 45
334. 85 k. brn., green & emerald 1·10 80
335. 300 k. brn. and green (air) 2·75 1·90
DESIGNS: 25 k., 40 k. Common palm civet. 50 k. Lesser Malay chevrotain. 85 k. Sambar. 300 k. Javan rhinoceros.

85. Laotian Woman (design from 1952 issue).

1971. 20th Anniv. of Laotian Stamps.
336. 85. 30 k. chocolate, brown & violet (postage) .. 30 20
337. 40 k. multicoloured .. 35 25
338. – 50 k. blk., flesh and blue 50 35
339. – 125 k. vio., brn. & grn. (air) 1·10 80
DESIGNS—VERT. (36×48 mm.). 40 k. Violinist As No. 64). 50 k. Rama (As No. 48). 125 k. The Offertory" (As Type **16**).

86. "Sunset on the Mekong" (Prisayane).

1971. Air. Paintings by Chamnane Prisayane. Multicoloured.
341. 125 k. Type **86** 85 65
342. 150 k. "Quiet Morning at Ban Tane Pieo" .. 1·10 80

87. Children reading Book

1972. Int. Book Year.
343. 87. 30 k. green (postage) .. 20 15
344. – 70 k. brown 40 30
345. – 125 k. violet (air) .. 85 55
DESIGNS: 70 k. Laotian illustrating manuscript. (48×27 mm.) 125 k. Father showing manuscripts to children.

88. Nam Ngum Dam and Obelisk.

1972. 25th Anniv. of E.C.A.F.E. (Economic Commission for Asia and the Far East). Multicoloured.
346. 40 k. Type **88** (postage) .. 20 20
347. 80 k. Type **88** 45 30
348. 145 k. Lake and Spill-way, Nam Ngum Dam (air) .. 90 55

HAVE YOU READ THE NOTES
AT THE BEGINNING OF
THIS CATALOGUE?
These often provide answers to the
enquiries we receive.

89. "The Water-carrier".

1972. 25th Anniv. of U.N.I.C.E.F. Drawings by Lao Schoolchildren. Multicoloured.
349. 50 k. Type **89** 40 25
350. 80 k. "Teaching Bamboo-weaving" 45 40
351. 120 k. "Riding a Water-buffalo" 85 55

90. "Nakharath".

1972. Laotian Mythology (2nd series).
352. 90. 100 k. green 55 40
353. – 120 k. lilac 80 45
354. – 150 k. brown 90 55
DESIGNS: 120 k. "Nang Kinnali". 150 k. "Norasing".

91. Festival Offerings.

1972. Air. That Luang Religious Festival.
355. 91. 110 k. brown 50 35
356. – 125 k. purple 70 50
DESIGN: 125 k. Festival procession.

1972. Air. Paintings by Marc Leguay (4th series). As T **69**. Multicoloured.
357. 50 k. "In the Paddy Field" (detail) 35 35
358. 50 k. "In the Paddy Field" (different detail) .. 35 35
359. 70 k. "Village in the Rainy Season" (detail) .. 45 30
360. 70 k. "Village in the Rainy Season" (different detail) 45 30
361. 120 k. "Laotian Mother" .. 95 55
Nos. 357/8 and 359/60 when placed together form the complete painting in each case.

92. Attopeu Religious Costume.

93. "Lion" Guardian, That Luang.

1973. Regional Costumes.
362. 92. 40 k. yell., mve. & brn. (postage) 35 20
363. – 90 k. blk., lake & brn. .. 65 45
364. – 120 k. brn., sepia & mve. (air) 65 45
365. – 150 k. ochre, lake & brn. 85 55
DESIGNS: 90 k. Phongsaly festival costume. 120 k. Luang Prabang wedding costume. 150 k. Vientiane evening dress.

1973. 55th Anniv. of Lions International.
366. 93. 40 k. red, purple & blue 35 25
367. 80 k. red, yellow & blue 55 40
368. – 150 k. mult. (air) .. 95 80
DESIGN: 150 k. Lions emblems and statue of King Saysetthathirath, Vientiane.

94. Satellite passing Rahu.

1973. Space in Retrospect. Multicoloured.
369. 80 k. Type **94** 40 20
370. 150 k. Landing module and Laotian festival rocket .. 70 45

95. Dr. Gerhard Hansen and Map of Laos.

1973. Centenary of Identification of Leprosy Bacillus by Hansen.
371. **95.** 40 k. pur., dull pur. & orge. 45 35
372. 80 k. red, brn. & yellow 65 45

96. "Benediction". **97.** "Nang Mekhala". (Goddess of the Sea).

1973. 25th Anniv. of Laotian Boy Scouts Association.
373. **96.** 70 k. yell. & brn. (post.) 45 35
374. – 110 k. vio. & orge. (air) 45 20
375. – 150 k. bl., drab & brn... 65 35
DESIGNS—HORIZ. 110 k. Camp-fire entertainment. 150 k. Scouts helping flood victims, Vientiane, 1966.

1973. Air. I.M.O. Cent.
376. **97.** 90 k. brn., red & mauve 45 35
377. – 150 k. brn., red & light-brn. 80 50
DESIGN: 150 k. "Chariot of the Sun".

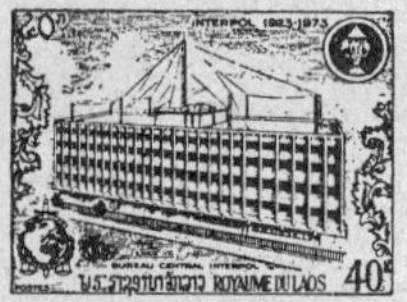

99. Interpol H.Q., Paris.

1973. 50th Anniv. of Int. Criminal Police Organization (Interpol).
382. **99.** 40 k. blue (postage) .. 30 20
383. 80 k. brown and bistre 35 20
384. – 150 k. violet, red and green (air) .. 70 40
DESIGN: (48×27 mm.). 150 k. Woman in opium-poppy field.

100. "Phra Sratsvady".

1974. Air. Laotian Mythology (3rd series).
385. **100.** 100 k. red, brn. & lilac .. 55 35
386. – 110 k. brn., lilac & red .. 65 45
387. – 150 k. vio., brn. & orge. 1·00 70
DESIGNS: 110 k. "Phra Indra". 150 k. "Phra Phrom".

101. Boy and Postbox. **102.** "Eranthemum nervosum".

1974. Cent. of U.P.U.
388. **101.** 70 k. brn., grn. & bl. (post.) 40 30
389. 80 k. brn., bl. & grn. .. 45 35
390. – 200 k. brn. & red (air) .. 1·40 95
DESIGN—HORIZ. (48×36 mm.). 200 k. Laotian girls with letters, and U.P.U. Monument, Berne (Type **105**).

1974. Laotian Flora.
391. **102.** 30 k. vio. & grn. (post.) 35 30
392. – 50 k. multicoloured .. 45 35
393. – 80 k. red, grn. & brn. 70 50
394. – 500 k. grn. & brn. (air) 3·00 2·25
DESIGNS—HORIZ. (36×26 mm.). 50 k. "Nenuphar nymphea lotus". 80 k. "Kapokier des falaises Schefflera". SQUARE. (36×36 mm.) 500 k. "Nepenthes phillamphora".

103. Mekong Ferry carrying Bus.

1974. Laotian Transport.
395. **103.** 25 k. brn. & orge. (post.) 45 20
396. – 90 k. brn. and bistre .. 70 55
397. – 250 k. brn. & grn. (air) 2·00 1·25
DESIGNS—VERT. 90 k. Bicycle rickshaw. HORIZ. 250 k. Mekong house boat.

104. Marconi, and Laotians with Transistor Radio.

1974. Birth Centenary of Guglielmo Marconi (radio pioneer).
398. **104.** 60 k. grey, grn. & brn. (postage) 30 20
399. 90 k. gry, brn. & grn. 40 35
400. – 200 k. bl. & brn. (air) .. 1·75 85
DESIGN: 200 k. Communications methods.

105. U.P.U. Monument and Laotian Girls.

1974. Air. Cent. of U.P.U.
401. **105.** 500 k. lilac and red .. 2·75 1·90

106. "Diastocera wallichi".

1974. Insects. Beetles.
403. **106.** 50 k. brn., blk. & grn. (postage) .. 50 45
404. – 90 k. blk., turq. & grn. 80 55
405. – 100 k. blk., orge. & brn. 1·40 75
406. – 110 k. vio., brn. & grn. (air) .. .. .. 1·40 70
DESIGNS: 90 k. "Macrochenus isabellunis". 100 k. "Purpuricenus malaccensis". 110 k. "Sternocera multipunctata".

107. Pagoda and Sapphire.

1974. "Mineral Riches".
407. **107.** 100 k. brn., green & blue 50 35
408. – 110 k. brn., blue & yell. 60 35
DESIGN: 110 k. Gold-panning and necklace.

108. King Savang Vatthana, Prince Souvanna Phouma, and Prince Souvanouvong.

1975. 1st Anniv. (1974) of Laotian Peace Treaty.
409. **108.** 80 k. brn., ochre & grn. 40 30
410. 300 k. brn., ochre & pur. 85 70
411. 420 k. brn., ochre & turq. 1·00 85

109. Fortune-teller's Chart.

1975. Chinese New Year "Year of the Rabbit". Multicoloured.
413. 40 k. Type **109** 30 20
414. 200 k. Fortune-teller .. 85 55
415. 350 k. Lao woman riding rabbit (vert.) .. .. 1·90 1·10

110. U.N. Emblem and Frieze. **112.**

1975. International Women's Year.
416. **110.** 100 k. blue and green .. 40 30
417. – 200 k. orange and blue 55 40
DESIGN: 200 k. I.W.Y. emblem.

1975. "Pravet Sandone" Religious Festival. Laotian Legends.
420. **112.** 80 k. multicoloured .. 35 25
421. – 110 k. multicoloured .. 45 30
422. – 120 k. multicoloured .. 45 35
423. – 130 k. multicoloured .. 70 55
DESIGNS: 110 k. to 130 k. various legends.

113. Buddha and Stupas.

1975. U.N.E.S.C.O. Campaign to Save the Temple of Borobudur.
424. **113.** 100 k. grn., blue & brn. 45 35
425. – 200 k. brn., grn. & bist. 90 60
DESIGN: 200 k. Temple sculptures.

114. Laotian Arms. **115.** Thatiang, Vien-Tran.

1976.
427. **114.** 1 k. multicoloured .. 5 5
428. 2 k. multicoloured .. 5 5
429. 5 k. multicoloured .. 10 8
430. 10 k. multicoloured .. 15 15
431. 200 k. multicoloured .. 1·90 1·40

1976. Pagodas. Multicoloured.
433. 1 k. Type **115** 5 5
434. 2 k. Phonsi, Luang Prabang 12 12
435. 30 k. Type **115** 45 35
436. 80 k. As 2 k. 90 60
437. 100 k. As 2 k. .. .. 1·10 85
438. 300 k. Type **115** .. 2·75 1·90

116. Silversmith.

1977. Laotian Crafts. Multicoloured.
440. 1 k. Type **116** 5 5
441. 2 k. Weaver 10 8
442. 20 k. Potter 40 20
443. 50 k. Basket-weaver .. 65 35

117. Gubarev, Grechko and "Salyut" Space Station.

1977. 60th Anniv. of Russian Revolution. Multicoloured.
445. 5 k. Type **117** 5 5
446. 20 k. Lenin 15 10
447. 50 k. As 20 k. 40 20
448. 60 k. Type **117** 45 35
449. 100 k. Kremlin and Government Palace, Vientiane 80 55
450. 250 k. As 100 k. .. .. 1·75 1·50

118. Laotian Arms. **119.** Soldiers with Flag.

1978.
452. **118.** 5 k. yellow and black 8 8
453. 10 k. sepia and black 8 8
454. 50 k. purple and black 15 10
455. 100 k. green and black 40 20
456. 250 k. violet and blk. 1·00 60

1978. Army Day. Multicoloured.
457. 20 k. Type **119** 10 10
458. 40 k. Soldiers attacking village (horiz.) 15 10
459. 300 k. Anti-aircraft guns 1·60 75

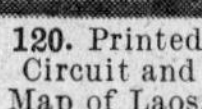

120. Printed Circuit and Map of Laos. **121.** Marchers with Banner.

1978. World Telecommunications Day.
460. **120.** 30 k. orge, brn. & silver 10 8
461. – 250 k. multicoloured .. 1·00 55
DESIGN: 250 k. Printed circuit, map and transmitter tower.

1979. National Day. Multicoloured.
462. 20 k. Type **121** 8 8
463. 50 k. Women with flag .. 15 12
464. 400 k. Dancer .. .. 1·40 85

122. Woman posting Letter.

1978. 15th Anniv. of Asian-Oceanic Postal Union. Multicoloured.
466. 5 k. Type **122** 8 8
467. 10 k. Post Office counter .. 8 8
468. 80 k. As 10 k. 35 30
469. 100 k. Type **122** 45 35

123. Children playing Ball.

1979. International Year of the Child (1st series). Multicoloured. Without gum.

No.	Description	Unused	Used
470.	20 k. Type **123**	10	10
471.	50 k. Children at school (horiz.)	20	15
472.	200 k. Mother feeding child	90	55
473.	500 k. Nurse inoculating child	2·75	1·40

124. Elephant, Buffalo and Pirogues.

1979. Transport. Multicoloured.

No.	Description	Unused	Used
475.	5 k. Type **124**	15	10
476.	10 k. Buffalo carts	10	10
477.	70 k. As No. 476	45	15
478.	500 k. Type **124**	2·25	1·25

125. Dancing Child.

1979. International Year of the Child (2nd series). Multicoloured. Without gum.

No.	Description	Unused	Used
479.	100 k. Children playing musical instruments (horiz.)	45	30
480.	200 k. Child releasing dove	80	50
481.	600 k. Type **125**	2·75	1·40

126. Forest and Paddy Field.

1980. 5th Anniv. of Republic (1st issue) and 25th Anniv. of People's Front. Multicoloured. Without gum.

No.	Description	Unused	Used
483.	30 c. Type **126**	15	10
484.	50 c. Classroom and doctor examining baby (horiz.)	20	10
485.	1 k. Three women	40	20
486.	2 k. Dam and electricity pylons (horiz.)	95	65

127. Lenin Reading.

1980. 110th Birth Anniv. of Lenin. Mult.

No.	Description	Unused	Used
488.	1 k. Type **127**	15	5
489.	2 k. Lenin writing	30	15
490.	3 k. Lenin and red flag (vert.)	45	20
491.	4 k. Lenin making speech (vert.)	60	30

128. Workers in Field.

1980. 5th Anniv. of Republic (2nd issue). Multicoloured. Without gum.

No.	Description	Unused	Used
493.	50 c. Type **128**	10	5
494.	1 k. 60 Loading logs on lorry and elephant hauling logs	25	15
495.	4 k. 60 Veterinary workers tending animals	65	35
496.	5 k. 40 Workers in paddy field	90	45

129. Emblems of Industry, Technology, Transport, Sport and Art.

1981. 26th P.C.U.S. (Communist Party) Congress. Multicoloured.

No.	Description	Unused	Used
498.	60 c. Type **129**	8	5
499.	4 k. 60 Communist star breaking manacles and globe	70	35
500.	5 k. Laurel branch and broken bomb	90	40

131. Player heading Ball.  **132.** Disabled person on Telephone.

1981. World Cup Football Championship, Spain (1982) (1st issue). Multicoloured.

No.	Description	Unused	Used
503.	1 k. Type **131**	15	5
504.	2 k. Receiving ball	30	10
505.	3 k. Passing ball	45	15
506.	4 k. Goalkeeper diving for ball (horiz.)	60	20
507.	5 k. Dribbling	85	35
508.	6 k. Kicking ball	95	45

See also Nos. 545/50.

1981. International Year of Disabled Persons. Multicoloured.

No.	Description	Unused	Used
509.	3 k. Type **132**	45	45
510.	5 k. Disabled teacher	80	80
511.	12 k. Person in wheelchair mending net	1·90	1·90

133. Wild Cat.

1981. Wild Cats. Multicoloured.

No.	Description	Unused	Used
512.	10 c. Type **133**	20	20
513.	20 c. Fishing cat	20	20
514.	30 c. Caracal	20	20
515.	40 c. Clouded Leopard	25	25
516.	50 c. Flat-headed cat	25	25
517.	9 k. Jungle cat	4·00	4·00

134. Dish Aerial and Flag.

1981. Sixth National Day Festival. Mult.

No.	Description	Unused	Used
518.	3 k. Type **134**	50	35
519.	4 k. Soldier and flag	60	45
520.	5 k. Girls presenting flowers to soldier, flag and map of Laos	85	55

135. Indian Elephant.

1982. Indian Elephant. Multicoloured.

No.	Description	Unused	Used
521.	1 k. Type **135**	25	10
522.	2 k. Elephant carrying log	45	10
523.	3 k. Elephant with passengers	75	20
524.	4 k. Elephant in trap	90	45
525.	5 k. Elephant and young	1·25	45
526.	5 k. Herd of elephants	1·40	60

136. Laotian Wrestling.

1982. Laotian Wrestling.

No.	Type	Description	Unused	Used
527.	**136.**	50 c. multicoloured	8	5
528.	–	1 k. 20 multicoloured	15	8
529.	–	2 k. multicoloured	30	15
530.	–	2 k. 50 multicoloured	45	25
531.	–	4 k. multicoloured	60	30
532.	–	5 k. multicoloured	90	40

DESIGNS: 1 k. 20 to 5 k. Various wrestling scenes.

137. "Nymphaea zanzibariensis".

1982. Water Lillies. Multicoloured.

No.	Description	Unused	Used
533.	30 c. Type **137**	5	5
534.	40 c. "Nelumbo nucifera" "Great Rose"	5	5
535.	60 c. "Nymphaea rosea"	8	5
536.	3 k. "Nymphaea nouchali"	45	30
537.	4 k. "Nymphaea White"	65	35
538.	7 k. "Nelumbo nucifera" "Gaertn White"	1·25	45

138. Barn Swallow.

1982. Birds. Multicoloured.

No.	Description	Unused	Used
539.	50 c. Type **138**	25	15
540.	1 k. Hoopoe	55	30
541.	2 k. Common Kingfisher	95	50
542.	3 k. Black-naped Blue Monarch	1·25	70
543.	4 k. Grey Wagtail (horiz.)	1·60	1·00
544.	10 k. Long-tailed Tailor Bird (horiz.)	4·50	2·40

139. Football.

1982. World Cup Football Championship, Spain (2nd issue).

No.	Type	Description	Unused	Used
545.	**139.**	1 k. multicoloured	15	5
546.	–	2 k. multicoloured	30	10
547.	–	3 k. multicoloured	45	20
548.	–	4 k. multicoloured	60	20
549.	**139.**	5 k. multicoloured	85	35
550.	–	6 k. multicoloured	1·00	40

DESIGNS: 2 k. to 6 k. Various designs showing football scenes.

140. "Herona marathus".

1982. Butterflies. Multicoloured.

No.	Description	Unused	Used
552.	1 k. Type **140**	25	10
553.	2 k. "Neptis paraka"	60	20
554.	3 k. "Euripus halitherses"	85	30
555.	4 k. "Lebadea martha"	1·10	40
556.	5 k. "Iton semamora" (42 × 26 mm.)	1·50	75
557.	6 k. "Elymnias hypermnestra" (59 × 41 mm.)	1·75	1·00

142. Raft.

1982. River Craft. Multicoloured.

No.	Description	Unused	Used
559	50 c. Type **142**	10	10
560	60 c. Sampan	10	10
561	1 k. House boat	30	10
562	2 k. Passenger steamer	45	25
563	3 k. Ferry	60	35
564	8 k. Self-propelled barge	1·75	70

143. Vat Chanh.

1982. Pagodas. Multicoloured.

No.	Description	Unused	Used
565.	50 c. Type **143**	8	5
566.	60 c. Vat Inpeng	8	5
567.	1 k. Vat Dong Mieng	15	5
568.	2 k. Ho Tay	35	15
569.	3 k. Vat Ho Pha Keo	45	20
570.	8 k. Vat Sisaket	1·40	55

145. Poodle

1982. Dogs. Multicoloured.

No.	Description	Unused	Used
591.	50 c. Type **145**	8	5
592.	60 c. Samoyed	8	5
593.	1 k. Boston terrier	15	5
594.	2 k. Chairn terrier	40	15
595.	3 k. Chihuahua	50	20
596.	8 k. Bulldog	1·25	55

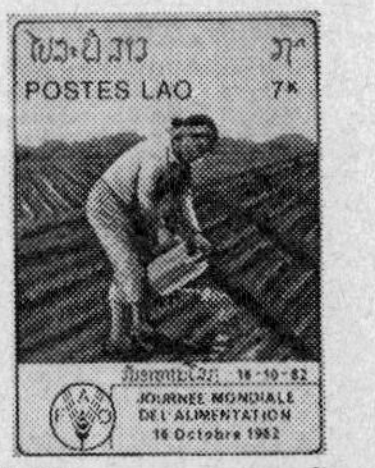

146. Woman watering Crops.

1982. World Food Day. Multicoloured.

No.	Description	Unused	Used
597.	7 k. Type **146**	1·10	45
598.	8 k. Woman transplanting rice	1·40	55

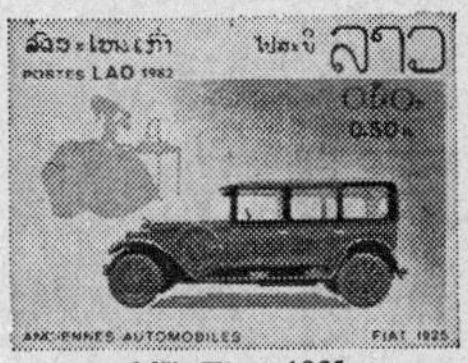

147. Fiat, 1925.

1982. Cars. Multicoloured.

No.	Description	Unused	Used
599.	50 c. Type **147**	8	5
600.	60 c. Peugeot, 1925	8	5
601.	1 k. Berliet, 1925	15	5
602.	2 k. Ballot, 1925	40	15
603.	3 k. Renault, 1926	50	20
604.	8 k. Ford, 1925	1·25	55

148. President Souphanouvong.

1982. 7th Anniv. of Republic. Mult.

605. 50 c. Type **148** 8 5
606. 1 k. Tractors (horiz.) .. 15 5
607. 2 k. Cow (horiz.) 30 15
608. 3 k. Lorry passing dish aerial (horiz.) 45 30
609. 4 k. Nurse examining child 60 30
610. 5 k. Classroom (horiz.) .. 80 40
611. 6 k. Dancer 95 45

149. Dimitrov, Flag and Arms of Bulgaria.

1982. Birth Centenary of Georgi Dimitrov (Bulgarian statesman).

612. **149.** 10 k. multicoloured .. 1·60 90

150. Kremlin and Arms of U.S.S.R. **151.** Hurdling.

1982. 60th Anniv. of U.S.S.R. Mult.

613. 3 k. Type 150 .. .. 50 35
614. 4 k. Doves and maps of U.S.S.R. and Laos .. 70 55

1983. Olympic Games, Los Angeles. Mult.

616. 50 c. Type **151** 8 5
617. 1 k. Javelin 15 5
618. 2 k. Basketball 30 10
619. 3 k. Diving.. .. .. 45 20
620. 4 k. Gymnastics 60 35
621. 10 k. Weightlifting .. 1·75 55

152. Bucking Horse.

1983. Horses. Multicoloured.

623. 50 c. Type **152** 8 5
624. 1 k. Rearing black horse .. 15 5
625. 2 k. Trotting brown horse 30 10
626. 3 k. Dappled horse .. 45 20
627. 4 k. Wild horse crossing snow .. .. .. 1·00 60
628. 10 k. Horse in paddock .. 1·75 55

153. "St. Catherine of Alexandria". **154.** Soviet and Czech Cosmonauts.

1983. 500th Birth Anniv. of Raphael (artist). Multicoloured.

629. 50 c. Type **153** 8 5
630. 1 k. "Adoration of the Kings" 15 5
631. 2 k. "Madonna of the Grand Duke" 30 10
632. 3 k. "St. George and the Dragon" 55 20
633. 4 k. "The Vision of Ezekiel" 70 30
634. 10 k. "Adoration of the Kings" (different) .. 1·75 55

1983. Cosmonauts. Multicoloured.

636. 50 c. Type **154** 8 5
637. 50 c. Soviet cosmonaut and Miroslaw Hermaszewski (Polish) 8 5
638. 1 k. Soviet cosmonaut and Sigmund Jahn (East German) 15 5
639. 1 k. Nikolai Rukavishnikov (Soviet) and Georgi Ivanov (Bulgarian) 15 5
640. 2 k. V. Kubasov (Soviet) and Bertalan Farkas (Hungarian) 30 10
641. 3 k. V. Dzhanibekov (Soviet) and Gurragchaa (Mongolian) 55 20
642. 4 k. Soviet and Rumanian cosmonauts 65 25
643. 6 k. Soviet cosmonaut and Arnaldo Tamayo (Cuban) 95 35
644. 10 k. Soviet and French cosmonauts .. .. 1·75 55

155. Early Balloon Flight.

1983. Bicent. of Manned Flight. Mult.

646. 50 c. Type **154** 10 10
647. 1 k. Balloon with winged gondola 15 10
648. 2 k. Balloon, Tower of London and map .. 30 10
649. 3 k. Modern hot-air balloon over city.. .. 60 20
650. 4 k. Massed balloon ascent 65 30
651. 10 k. Stratosphere balloon 1·75 65

157. "Dendrobium sp."

1983. Flowers. Multicoloured.

654. 1 k. Type **157** 15 5
655. 2 k. "Aerides odoratum" .. 30 10
656. 3 k. "Dendrobium aggregatum" 60 20
657. 4 k. "Dendrobium" .. 65 25
658. 5 k. "Moschatum" .. 80 35
659. 6 k. "Dendrobium sp." (different) .. .. 1·10 40

158. Downhill Skiing.

1983. Winter Olympic Games, Sarajevo (1984) (1st issue). Multicoloured.

660. 50 c. Type **158** 8 5
661. 1 k. Slalom.. .. .. 15 5
662. 2 k. Ice hockey 30 10
663. 3 k. Speed skating .. 60 20
664. 4 k. Ski-jumping 65 25
665. 10 k. Luge .. .. .. 1·75 60

See also Nos 696/702.

160. "Notopterus chitala".

1983. Fishes of Mekong River. Multicoloured.

668. 1 k. Type **160** 15 5
669. 2 k. "Cyprinus carpio" .. 30 10
670. 3 k. "Pangasius sp." .. 60 20
671. 4 k. "Catlocarpio siamensis" 65 25
672. 5 k. "Morulius sp." .. 80 35
673. 6 k. "Tilapia nilotica" .. 1·10 40

161. Magellan and "Vitoria".

1983. Explorers and their Ships. Mult.

674 1 k. Type **161** 30 15
675 2 k. Jacques Cartier and "Grande Hermine" .. 65 20
676 3 k. Columbus and "Santa Maria" .. .. .. 1·40 55
677 4 k. Pedro Alvares Cabral and "El Ray" .. .. 1·40 60
678 5 k. Cook and H.M.S. "Resolution" .. .. 1·75 85
679 6 k. Charcot and "Pourquoi-pas?" .. 2·25 1·00

No. 679 is inscribed "Cabot".

162. Tabby Cat.

1983. Domestic Cats. Multicoloured.

680. 1 k. Type **168** 15 5
681. 2 k. Long-haired Persian .. 30 10
682. 3 k. Siamese 60 20
683. 4 k. Burmese 65 25
684. 5 k. Persian 80 35
685. 6 k. Tortoiseshell .. .. 1·10 40

163. Marx, Book, Sun and Signature.

1983. Death Cent. of Karl Marx. Mult.

686. 1 k. Marx, dove, globe and flags 15 5
687. 4 k. Type **163** 75 25
688. 6 k. Marx and flags .. 1·40 60

164. Elephant dragging Log.

1983. 8th Anniv. of Republic. Mult.

689. 1 k. Type **164** 15 5
690. 4 k. Cattle and pig (horiz.) 75 25
691. 6 k. Crops .. .. .. 1·40 60

165. Carrier Pigeon and Telex Machine.

1983. World Communications Year. Mult.

692. 50 c. Type **165** 8 5
693. 1 k. Early telephone, handset and receiver.. .. 15 5
694. 4 k. Television tube and aerial 70 25
695. 6 k. Satellite and dish aerial .. .. .. 1·40 60

166. Ice Skating. **167.** Tiger.

1984. Winter Olympic Games, Sarajevo (2nd issue). Multicoloured.

696. 50 c. Type **166** 8 5
697. 1 k. Speed skating .. 20 8
698. 2 k. Biathlon 35 12
699. 4 k. Luge (horiz.) 70 25
700. 5 k. Downhill skiing (horiz.) 80 30
701. 6 k. Ski-jumping .. .. 1·10 40
702. 7 k. Slalom.. .. .. 1·40 45

1984. Endangered Animals. The Tiger. Multicoloured.

704. 25 c. Type **167** 8 8
705. 25 c. Tigers (horiz.) .. 8 8
706. 3 k. Tiger and cubs (horiz.) 1·10 85
707. 4 k. Tiger cubs .. .. 1·60 1·25

168. Diving.

1984. Olympic Games, Los Angeles (2nd issue). Multicoloured.

708. 50 c. Type **168** 8 5
709. 1 k. Volleyball 20 8
710. 2 k. Running 35 12
711. 4 k. Basketball 70 25
712. 5 k. Judo 90 35
713. 6 k. Football .. .. 1·00 40
714. 7 k. Gymnastics .. .. 1·40 50

169. Tuned Drums.

1984. Musical Instruments. Multicoloured.

716. 1 k. Type **169** 20 8
717. 2 k. Xylophone 35 12
718. 3 k. Pair of drums .. 50 20
719. 4 k. Hand drum 70 25
720. 5 k. Barrel drum 85 30
721. 6 k. Pipes and string instrument .. .. 1·10 50

170. National Flag. 171. "Great Chess".

1984. National Day. Multicoloured.
722. 60 c. Type **170** 12 5
723. 1 k. National arms 25 10
724. 2 k. As No. 723 .. .. 40 20

1984. 60th Anniv of International Chess Federation. Multicoloured.
725 50 c. Type **171** 8 5
726 1 k. Renaissance game ("The Three Ages of Man" (15th-century miniature attr. to Estienne Porchier)) .. 20 8
727 2 k. Teaching chess .. 35 12
728 2 k. Margrave Otto IV of Brandenburg playing chess with his wife (German early 14th-century drawing) .. 35 12
729 3 k. Four men at chess-board 65 25
730 4 k. Two women playing 75 30
731 8 k. Two men playing .. 1·40 50
Nos. 725, 727 and 729/31 show illustrations from King Alfonso X's "Book of Chess, Dice and Tablings".

172. "Cardinal Nino de Guevara" (El Greco). 173. "Adonis aestivalis".

1984. "Espana 84" International Stamp Exhibition, Madrid. Multicoloured.
733. 50 c. Type **172** 8 5
734. 1 k. "Gaspar de Guzman, Duke of Olivares, on Horseback" (Velazquez) 20 8
735. 2 k. "The Annunciation" (Murillo) 35 12
736. 2 k. "Portrait of a Lady" (Zurbaran) 35 12
737. 3 k. "The Family of Charles IV" (Goya) .. 65 25
738. 4 k. "Two Harlequins" (Picasso) 75 30
739. 8 k. "Abstract" (Miro) .. 1·40 50

1984. Woodland Flowers. Multicoloured.
741. 50 c. Type **173** 8 5
742. 1 k. "Alpinia speciosa" .. 20 8
743. 2 k. "Cassia lechenaultiana" 35 12
744. 2 k. "Aeschynanthus speciosus" 35 12
745. 3 k. "Datura meteloides" 65 25
746. 4 k. "Quamoclit pennata" 75 30
747. 8 k. "Commelina benghalensis" .. .. .. 1·40 50

174. Nazzaro.

1984. 19th Universal Postal Union Congress Philatelic Salon, Hamburg. Cars. Mult.
748. 50 c. Type **174** 8 5
749. 1 k. Daimler 20 8
750. 2 k. Delage 35 12
751. 2 k. Fiat "S 57/14B" .. 35 12
752. 3 k. Bugatti 65 25
753. 4 k. Itala 75 30
754. 8 k. Blitzen Benz .. .. 1·40 50

175. "Madonna and Child".

1984. 450th Death Anniv. of Correggio (artist). Multicoloured.
756. 50 c. Type **175** 8 5
757. 1 k. Detail showing horsemen resting 20 8
758. 2 k. "Madonna and Child" (different) 35 12
759. 2 k. "Mystical Marriage of St. Catherine" 35 12
760. 3 k. "Four Saints" .. 65 25
761. 4 k. "Noli me Tangere" .. 75 30
762. 8 k. "Christ bids Farewell to the Virgin May" .. 1·40 50

176. "Luna 1".

1984. Space Exploration. Multicoloured.
764. 50 c. Type **176** 8 5
765. 1 k. "Luna 2" 20 8
766. 2 k. "Luna 3" 35 12
767. 2 k. Kepler & "Sputnik 2" 35 12
768. 3 k. Newton & Lunokhod 2 65 25
769. 4 k. Jules Verne and "Luna 13" 75 30
770. 8 k. Copernicus and space station .. .. .. 1·40 50

177. Malaclemys Terrapin.

1984. Reptiles. Multicoloured.
771. 50 c. Type **177** 8 5
772. 1 k. Banded krait 20 8
773. 2 k. Indian python (vert.) 35 12
774. 2 k. Reticulated python .. 35 12
775. 3 k. Tokay gecko 65 25
776. 4 k. "Natrix subminiata" 75 30
777. 8 k. Dappled ground gecko 1·40 50

178. Greater Glider.

1984. "Ausipex 84" International Stamp Exhibition, Melbourne. Marsupials. Mult.
778. 50 c. Type **178** 8 5
779. 1 k. Platypus 20 8
780. 2 k. Southern hairy-nosed wombat 35 12
781. 2 k. Tasmanian devil .. 35 12
782. 3 k. Thylacine 65 25
783. 4 k. Tiger cat 75 30
784. 8 k. Wallaby .. .. 1·40 50

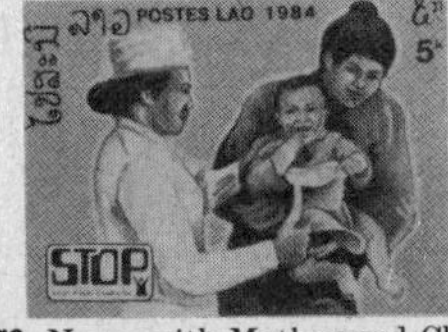

179. Nurse with Mother and Child.

1984. Anti-poliomyelitis Campaign. Mult.
786. 5 k. Type **179** 90 35
787. 6 k. Doctor inoculating child .. .. .. 1·00 40

180. Dragon Stair-rail.

1984. Laotian Art. Multicoloured.
788. 50 c. Type **180** 8 5
789. 1 k. Capital of column .. 20 8
790. 2 k. Decorative panel depicting god 35 12
791. 2 k. Decorative panel depicting leaves .. 35 12
792. 3 k. Stylized leaves (horiz.) 65 25
793. 4 k. Triangular flower decoration (horiz.) .. 75 30
794. 8 k. Circular lotus flower decoration .. .. 1·40 50

181. River House Boat.

1984. 9th Anniv of Republic. Multicoloured.
795 1 k. Type **181** 45 10
796 2 k. Passengers boarding Fokker Friendship airplane 45 15
797 4 k. Building a bridge .. 75 30
798 10 k. Building a road .. 1·50 55

182. Players with Ball.

1985. World Cup, Mexico (1986) (1st issue). Multicoloured.
799. 50 c. Type **183** 8 5
800. 1 k. Heading the ball .. 20 8
801. 2 k. Defending the ball .. 35 12
802. 3 k. Running with ball .. 65 25
803. 4 k. Taking possession of ball 75 30
804. 5 k. Heading the ball (different) 85 35
805. 6 k. Saving a goal .. .. 1·00 40
See also Nos. 868/74.

183. Motor Cycle.

1985. Centenary of Motor Cycle. Mult.
807. 50 c. Type **183** 5 5
808. 1 k. Gnome Rhone, 1920 .. 5 5
809. 2 k. F.N. "M67C", 1928 .. 8 5
810. 3 k. Indian "Chief", 1930 .. 12 5
811. 4 k. Rudge Multi, 1914 .. 15 5
812. 5 k. Honda "Benly J", 1953 .. .. .. 20 8
813. 6 k. CZ, 1938 .. .. 25 8

184. "Amanita muscaria".

1985. Fungi. Multicoloured.
814 50 c. Type **184** 5 5
815 1 k. "Boletus edulis" .. 5 5
816 2 k. "Coprinus comatus" 8 5
817 2 k. "Amanita rubescens" 8 5
818 3 k. "Xerocomus subtomentosus" .. 12 5
819 4 k. "Lepiota procera" .. 15 5
820 8 k. "Paxillus involutus" 30 10

184a Battle Plan and Scene

1985. 40th Anniv of End of World War II. Multicoloured.
820a 1 k. Type **184a** .. 5 5
820b 2 k. Monument and military parade, Red Square, Moscow .. 8 5
820c 4 k. Street battle and battle plan, Stalingrad 15 5
820d 5 k. Battle plan and Reichstag, Berlin .. 20 10
820e 6 k. Soviet Memorial, Berlin-Treptow, and military parade at Brandenburg Gate .. 25 10

185. Lenin reading "Pravda".

1985. 115th Birth Anniv. of Lenin. Multicoloured.
821. 1 k. Type **185** 5 5
822. 2 k. Lenin 8 5
823. 10 k. Lenin addressing meeting 40 15

186. "Cattleya percivaliana".

1985. "Argentina '85" International Stamp Exhibition, Buenos Aires. Orchids. Multicoloured.
824. 50 c. Type **186** 5 5
825. 1 k. "Odontoglossum luteo-purpureum" .. 5 5
826. 2 k. "Cattleya lueddemanniana" 8 5
827. 2 k. "Maxillaria sanderiana" 8 5
828. 3 k. "Miltonia vexillaria" 12 5
829. 4 k. "Oncidium varicosum" 15 5
830. 8 k. "Cattleya dowiana" .. 30 10

187. Rhesus Macaque. 188. "Apollo" Rocket on Launch Pad.

1985. Mammals. Multicoloured.
832. 2 k. Type **187** 8 5
833. 3 k. Kouprey 12 5
834. 4 k. Porcupine (horiz.) .. 15 5
835. 5 k. Asiatic black bear (horiz.) 20 8
836. 10 k. Chinese pangolin .. 40 15

1985. 10th Anniv. of "Soyuz"—"Apollo" Flight. Multicoloured.

No.	Description	Unused	Used
837.	50 c. Type **188**	5	5
838.	1 k. "Soyuz" rocket on launch pad	5	5
839.	2 k. "Apollo" approaching "Soyuz" (horiz.)	8	5
840.	2 k. "Soyuz" approaching "Apollo" (horiz.)	8	5
841.	3 k. "Apollo" and crew (horiz.)	12	5
842.	4 k. "Soyuz" and crew (horiz.)	15	5
843.	8 k. "Apollo" and Soyuz docked (horiz.)	30	10

189. Fiat.

1985. "Italia '85" International Stamp Exhibition, Rome. Multicoloured.

(a) Aircraft.

No.	Description	Unused	Used
844.	50 c. Type **189**	10	10
845.	1 k. Cant "z.501"	10	10
846.	2 k. Flying boat "MF-5"	10	10
847.	3 k. Macchi "Castoldi"	20	10
848.	4 k. Anzani	25	10
849.	5 k. Ambrosini	30	10
850.	6 k. Piaggio	40	15

(b) Columbus and his ships.

No.	Description	Unused	Used
852.	1 k. "Pinta"	30	15
853.	2 k. "Nina"	35	15
854.	3 k. "Santa Maria"	45	15
855.	4 k. Christopher Columbus	15	10
856.	5 k. Map of Columbus's first voyage	20	10

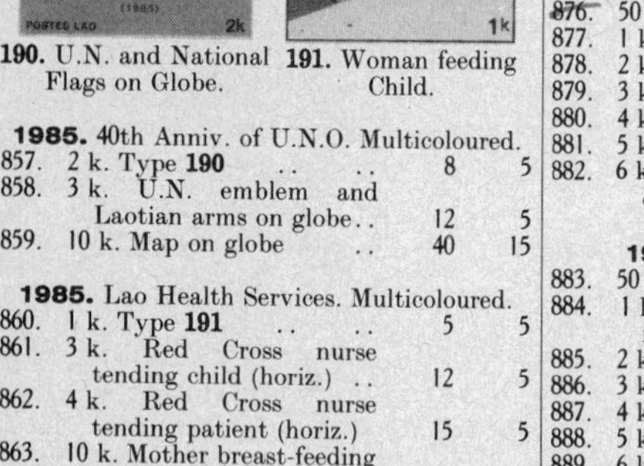

190. U.N. and National Flags on Globe. **191.** Woman feeding Child.

1985. 40th Anniv. of U.N.O. Multicoloured.

No.	Description	Unused	Used
857.	2 k. Type **190**	8	5
858.	3 k. U.N. emblem and Laotian arms on globe	12	5
859.	10 k. Map on globe	40	15

1985. Lao Health Services. Multicoloured.

No.	Description	Unused	Used
860.	1 k. Type **191**	5	5
861.	3 k. Red Cross nurse tending child (horiz.)	12	5
862.	4 k. Red Cross nurse tending patient (horiz.)	15	5
863.	10 k. Mother breast-feeding baby	40	15

192. Soldier, Workers and Symbols of Industry and Agriculture.

1985. 10th Anniv. of Republic. Mult.

No.	Description	Unused	Used
864.	3 k. Type **192**	12	5
865.	10 k. Soldier, workers and symbols of transport and communications	40	15

193. Soldier with Flag and Workers.

1985. 30th Anniv. of People's Revolutionary Party. Multicoloured.

No.	Description	Unused	Used
866.	2 k. Type **193**	8	5
867.	8 k. Soldier with flag and workers (different)	30	10

194. Footballers. **194a** Cosmonaut, "Mir" Space Complex and Earth

1986. World Cup Football Championship, Mexico (2nd issue).

No.	Type	Description	Unused	Used
868.	**194.**	50 c. multicoloured	5	5
869.	–	1 k. multicoloured	5	5
870.	–	2 k. multicoloured	8	5
871.	–	3 k. multicoloured	12	5
872.	–	4 k. multicoloured	15	5
873.	–	5 k. multicoloured	20	8
874.	–	6 k. multicoloured	25	10

DESIGNS: 1 k. to 6 k. Various football scenes.

1986. 17th Soviet Communist Party Congress. Multicoloured.

No.	Description	Unused	Used
875a	4 k. Type **194a**	15	5
875b	20 k. Lenin and Red flag	80	25

195. "Pelargonium grandiflorum". **196.** "Aporia hippia".

1986. Flowers. Multicoloured.

No.	Description	Unused	Used
876.	50 c. Type **195**	5	5
877.	1 k. "Aquilegia vulgaris"	5	5
878.	2 k. "Fuchsia globosa"	8	5
879.	3 k. "Crocus aureus"	12	5
880.	4 k. "Althaea rosea"	15	5
881.	5 k. "Gladiolus purpureo"	20	8
882.	6 k. "Hyacinthus orientalis"	25	10

1986. Butterflies. Multicoloured.

No.	Description	Unused	Used
883.	50 c. Type **196**	10	10
884.	1 k. "Euthalia irrubescens"	15	10
885.	2 k. "Japonica lutea"	20	10
886.	3 k. "Pratapa ctesia"	30	10
887.	4 k. "Kallina inachus"	35	10
888.	5 k. "Ixias pyrene"	50	20
889.	6 k. "Parantica sita"	60	25

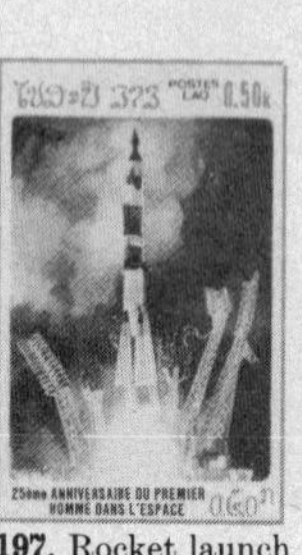

197. Rocket launch at Baikanur Space Centre.

198. Giraffe.

1986. 25th Anniv. of First Man in Space. Multicoloured.

No.	Description	Unused	Used
890.	50 k. Type **197**	5	5
891.	1 k. "Molniya" communications satellite	5	5
892.	2 k. "Salyut" space station (horiz.)	8	5
893.	3 k. Yuri Gargarin, "Sputnik 1" and rocket debris (horiz.)	12	5
894.	4 k. "Luna 3" and moon	15	5
895.	5 k. Komarov on first space walk	20	8
896.	6 k. "Luna 16" lifting off from moon	25	10

1986. Animals. Multicoloured.

No.	Description	Unused	Used
898.	50 c. Type **198**	5	5
899.	1 k. Lion	5	5
900.	2 k. African elephant	8	5
901.	3 k. Red kangaroo	12	5
902.	4 k. Koala	15	5
903.	5 k. Greater flamingo	1·00	30
904.	6 k. Giant panda	25	10

199. Boeing "747".

1986. Air. Airplanes. Multicoloured.

No.	Description	Unused	Used
906.	20 k. Type **199**	1·00	40
907.	50 k. Ilyushin "Il 86"	2·50	85

200. Great Argus Pheasant. (half-size illustration)

1986. Pheasants. Multicoloured.

No.	Description	Unused	Used
908.	50 c. Type **200**	15	10
909.	1 k. Silver pheasant	15	10
910.	2 k. Ring-necked pheasant	30	10
911.	3 k. Lady Amherst's pheasant	45	10
912.	4 k. Reeves's pheasant	60	10
913.	5 k. Golden pheasant	75	20
914.	6 k. Copper pheasant	90	30

201. "Elaphe guttata".

1986. Snakes. Multicoloured.

No.	Description	Unused	Used
915.	50 c. Type **201**	5	5
916.	1 k. "Lampropeltis doliata annulata" (horiz.)	5	5
917.	1 k. "Thalerophis richardi"	5	5
918.	2 k. "Diadophis amabilis" (horiz.)	8	5
919.	4 k. "Boiga dendrophila" (horiz.)	15	5
920.	5 k. Python (horiz.)	20	8
921.	8 k. Cobra	25	10

202. Bayeux Tapestry (detail) and Comet Head.

1986. Appearance of Halley's Comet. Mult.

No.	Description	Unused	Used
922.	50 c. Comet over Athens (65 × 21 mm.)	5	5
923.	1 k. Type **202** (44 × 21 mm.)	5	5
924.	2 k. Edmond Halley and comet tail (20 × 21 mm.)	8	5
925.	3 k. "Vega" space probe and comet head (44 × 21 mm.)	12	5
926.	4 k. Galileo and comet tail (20 × 21 mm.)	15	5
927.	5 k. Comet head (20 × 21 mm.)	20	8
928.	6 k. "Giotto" space probe and comet tail (44 × 21 mm.)	25	10

Nos. 923/4 were printed together, se-tenant, forming a composite design. Nos. 925/6 and 927/8 were similarly arranged.

HAVE YOU READ THE NOTES AT THE BEGINNING OF THIS CATALOGUE?
These often provide answers to the enquiries we receive.

203. Keeshond.

204. "Mammillaria matudae".

1986. "Stockholmia 86" International Stamp Exhibition. Dogs. Multicoloured.

No.	Description	Unused	Used
930.	50 c. Type **203**	5	5
931.	1 k. Elkhound	5	5
932.	2 k. Bernese	8	5
933.	3 k. Pointing griffon	12	5
934.	4 k. Sheepdog	15	5
935.	5 k. Irish terrier	20	8
936.	6 k. Briard	25	10

1986. Cacti. Multicoloured.

No.	Description	Unused	Used
938.	50 c. Type **204**	5	5
939.	1 k. "Mammillaria theresae"	5	5
940.	2 k. "Ariocarpus trigonus"	8	5
941.	3 k. "Notocactus crassigibbus"	12	5
942.	4 k. "Astrophytum asterias hybridum"	15	5
943.	5 k. "Melocactus manzanus"	20	8
944.	6 k. "Astrophytum ornatum hybridum"	25	10

205. Arms and Dove on Globe. **206.** Vat Phu Champasak.

1986. International Peace Year. Mult.

No.	Description	Unused	Used
945.	3 k. Type **205**	12	5
946.	5 k. Dove on smashed bomb	20	8
947.	10 k. People supporting emblem	40	15

1986. 40th Anniv. of U.N.E.S.C.O. Mult.

No.	Description	Unused	Used
948.	3 k. Type **206**	12	5
949.	4 k. Dish aerial and map on globe	15	5
950.	9 k. People reading books (horiz.)	35	10

207. Speed Skating.

1987. Winter Olympic Games, Calgary (1988). Multicoloured.

No.	Description	Unused	Used
951.	50 c. Type **207**	5	5
952.	1 k. Biathlon	5	5
953.	2 k. Figure skating (pairs)	10	5
954.	3 k. Luge (horiz.)	10	5
955.	4 k. Four-man bobsleigh (horiz.)	15	5
956.	5 k. Ice hockey (horiz.)	20	8
957.	6 k. Ski-jumping (horiz.)	20	8

208. Gymnast and Urn.

1987. Olympic Games, Seoul (1988) (1st issue). Sports and Greek Pottery. Multicoloured.
959. 50 c. Type **208** 5 5
960. 1 k. Discus-thrower and vase (horiz.) 5 5
961. 2 k. Runner and urn .. 10 5
962. 3 k. Show-jumper and bowl (horiz.) 10 5
963. 4 k. Javelin-thrower and plate 15 5
964. 5 k. High-jumper and bowl with handles (horiz.) .. 20 8
965. 6 k. Wrestlers and urn .. 20 8
See also Nos. 1053/9.

209. Great Dane.

1987. Dogs. Multicoloured.
967. 50 c. Type **209** 5 5
968. 1 k. Black labrador .. 5 5
969. 2 k. St. Bernard 10 5
970. 3 k. Black German shepherd 10 5
971. 4 k. German shepherd .. 15 5
972. 5 k. Beagle 20 8
973. 6 k. Golden retriever .. 20 8

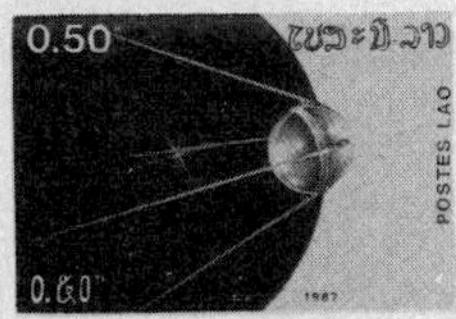

210. "Sputnik 1".

1987. 30th Anniv. of Launch of First Artificial Satellite. Multicoloured.
974. 50 c. Type **210** 5 5
975. 1 k. "Sputnik 2" 5 5
976. 2 k. "Cosmos 97" 10 5
977. 3 k. "Cosmos" 10 5
978. 4 k. "Mars" 15 5
979. 5 k. "Luna 1" 20 8
980. 9 k. "Luna 3" (vert.) .. 30 10

211. "MONTREAL" Handstamp on Letter to Quebec and Schooner.

1987. "Capex 87" International Stamp Exhibition, Toronto. Ships and Covers. Multicoloured.
981. 50 c. Type **211** 10 10
982. 1 k. "PAID MONTREAL" on letter and schooner .. 10 10
983. 2 k. Letter from Montreal to London and full-rigged ship 15 10
984. 3 k. 1840 letter to Williamsburgh and early screw-steamer .. 15 10
985. 4 k. 1844 letter to London and early screw-steamer 25 10
986. 5 k. 1848 letter and early paddle-steamer 35 10
987. 6 k. 1861 letter and river paddle-steamer 35 10

212 Horse

1987. Horses. Multicoloured.
989 50 c. Type **212** 5 5
990 1 k. Chestnut horse .. 5 5
991 2 k. Black horse with sheepskin noseband .. 10 5
992 3 k. Dark chestnut horse 10 5
993 4 k. Black horse 15 5
994 5 k. Chestnut horse with plaited mane 20 8
995 6 k. White horse 20 8

213 Volvo "480"

1987. Motor Cars. Multicoloured.
996 50 c. Type **213** 5 5
997 1 k. Alfa Romeo "33" .. 5 5
998 2 k. Ford "Fiesta" .. 10 5
999 3 k. Ford "Fiesta" (different) 10 5
1000 4 k. Ford "Granada" .. 15 5
1001 5 k. Citroen "AX" .. 20 8
1002 6 k. Renault "21" .. 20 8

214 "Vanda teres"

1987. Orchids. Multicoloured.
1004 3 k. Type **214** 5 5
1005 7 k. "Laeliocattleya" sp. 5 5
1006 10 k. "Paphiopedilum" hybrid 5 5
1007 39 k. "Sobralia" sp. .. 12 5
1008 44 k. "Paphiopedilum" hybrid (different) .. 15 5
1009 47 k. "Paphiopedilum" hybrid (different) .. 20 8
1010 50 k. "Cattleya trianaei" 20 8

215 Elephants

1987. "Hafnia 87" International Stamp Exhibition, Copenhagen. Elephants. Mult.
1012 50 c. Type **215** 5 5
1013 1 k. Three elephants .. 5 5
1014 2 k. Elephant feeding .. 10 5
1015 3 k. Elephant grazing on grass 10 5
1016 4 k. Baby elephant with adult elephant feeding from tree 15 5
1017 5 k. Elephant walking .. 20 8
1018 6 k. Elephant (vert) .. 20 8

216 Building Bamboo House

1987. International Year of Shelter for the Homeless. Multicoloured.
1020 1 k. Type **216** 5 5
1021 27 k. Building wooden house 12 5
1022 46 k. House on stilts .. 20 8
1023 70 k. Street of houses on stilts 25 10

217 "Botia macracantha"

1987. Fishes. Multicoloured.
1024 3 k. Type **217** 5 5
1025 7 k. "Oxymocanthus longirostris" 5 5
1026 10 k. "Adioryx caudimaculatus" 5 5
1027 39 k. "Synchiropus splendidus" 12 5
1028 44 k. "Cephalopolis miniatus" 15 5
1029 47 k. "Dendrochirus zebra" 20 8
1030 50 k. "Pomacantus semicirculatus" .. 20 8

218 Watering Seedlings

1987. World Food Day. Multicoloured.
1031 1 k. Type **218** 5 5
1032 3 k. Harvesting maize (vert) 5 5
1033 5 k. Harvesting rice .. 5 5
1034 63 k. Children with fish (vert) 25 10
1035 142 k. Tending pigs and poultry 50 20

219 Wounded Soldiers on Battlefield

1987. 70th Anniv of Russian Revolution. Multicoloured.
1036 1 k. Type **219** 5 5
1037 2 k. Mother and baby .. 5 5
1038 4 k. Storming the Winter Palace 5 5
1039 8 k. Lenin amongst soldiers and sailors .. 5 5
1040 10 k. Lenin labouring in Red Square 5 5

220 Hoeing

1987. Rice Culture in Mountain Regions. Multicoloured.
1041 64 k. Type **220** 20 8
1042 100 k. Working in paddy fields 35 15

221 Laotheung Costume

1987. Ethnic Costumes. Multicoloured.
1043 7 k. Type **221** 5 5
1044 38 k. Laoloum costume .. 12 5
1045 144 k. Laosoun costume 50 20

222 Two-man Bobsleigh

1988. Winter Olympic Games, Calgary (2nd issue). Multicoloured.
1046 1 k. Type **222** 5 5
1047 4 k. Biathlon (shooting) 5 5
1048 20 k. Cross-country skiing 8 5
1049 42 k. Ice hockey .. 15 5
1050 63 k. Speed skating .. 20 8
1051 70 k. Slalom 25 8

223 Throwing the Javelin

1988. Olympic Games, Seoul (2nd issue). Mult.
1053 2 k. Type **223** 5 5
1054 5 k. Triple-jumping .. 5 5
1055 10 k. Men's gymnastics 5 5
1056 12 k. Pirogue racing .. 5 5
1057 38 k. Women's gymnastics 5 5
1058 46 k. Fencing 5 5
1059 100 k. Wrestling .. 15 5

224 Trachodon

1988. "Juvalux 88" Youth Philately Exn., Luxembourg. Prehistoric Animals. Mult.
1061 3 k. Type **224** 5 5
1062 7 k. Tyrannosaurus (vert) 5 5
1063 39 k. "Iguanodon bernissartensis" (vert) 5 5
1064 44 k. Scolosaurus (vert) .. 5 5
1065 47 k. Phororhacus (vert) 20 10
1066 50 k. "Ceratosaurus nasicornis" 10 10
The inscriptions on the 7 and 50 k. values have been transposed.

225 Adults in Hygiene Class

1988. 40th Anniv of W.H.O. Multicoloured.
1068 5 k. Type **225** 5 5
1069 27 k. Fumigating houses 5 5
1070 164 k. Woman pumping fresh water (vert) .. 25 8

226 "Sans Pareil"

227 "Plumieria rubra"

1988. "Essen 88" International Stamp Fair. Early Steam Locomotives. Multicoloured.
1071 6 k. Type **226** 5 5
1072 15 k. "Rocket" 5 5
1073 20 k. "Royal George" (horiz) 5 5
1074 25 k. "Trevithick" (horiz) 5 5
1075 30 k. "Novelty" (horiz) 5 5
1076 100 k. "Tom Thumb" (horiz) 15 5

1988. "Finlandia 88" International Stamp Exhibition, Helsinki. Flowers. Multicoloured.
1078 8 k. Type **227** 5 5
1079 9 k. "Althaea rosea" 5 5
1080 15 k. "Ixora coccinea" 5 5
1081 33 k. "Cassia fistula" 5 5
1082 64 k. "Dahlia coccinea" (red) 10 5
1083 69 k. "Dahlia coccinea" (yellow) 10 5

228 Sash Pattern

1988. Decorative Stencil Patterns.
1085 **228** 1 k. multicoloured 5 5
1086 – 2 k. yellow, red & blk 5 5
1087 – 3 k. multicoloured 5 5
1088 – 25 k. multicoloured 5 5
1089 – 163 k. multicoloured 25 8
DESIGNS (stencils for): VERT. 2 k. Pagoda doors; 3 k. Pagoda walls. HORIZ. 25 k. Pagoda pillars; 163 k. Skirts.

229 Dove and Figures
230 Stork-billed Kingfisher

1988. 125th Anniv of Red Cross Movement. Multicoloured.
1090 4 k. Type **229** 5 5
1091 52 k. Red Cross workers with handicapped people 8 5
1092 144 k. Red Cross worker vaccinating baby (horiz) 20 8

1988. Birds. Multicoloured.
1093 6 k. Type **230** 10 10
1094 10 k. Japanese quail 10 10
1095 13 k. Blossom-headed parakeet 10 10
1096 44 k. Orange-breasted green pigeon 70 20
1097 63 k. Black-crested bulbul 1·50 30
1098 64 k. Mountain imperial pigeon 1·50 30

231 Red Cross Workers loading Supplies into Pirogue

1988. Completion of First Five-Year Plan. Multicoloured.
1099 20 k. Type **231** 10 10
1100 40 k. Library 10 10
1101 50 k. Irrigating fields 10 10
1102 100 k. Improvement in communications 20 10

232 Ruy Lopez Segura

1988. Chess Players. Multicoloured.
1103 1 k. Type **232** 5 5
1104 2 k. A. Anderssen 5 5
1105 3 k. P. Murphy 5 5
1106 6 k. Wilhelm Steinitz 5 5
1107 7 k. Emanuel Lasker 5 5
1108 12 k. Jose Raul Capablanca 5 5
1109 172 k. Aleksandr Alekhine 25 8

233 Tortoiseshell Cat

1989. "India 89" International Stamp Exhibition, New Dehli. Cats. Multicoloured.
1110 5 k. Type **233** 5 5
1111 6 k. Brown cat 5 5
1112 10 k. Black and white cat 5 5
1113 20 k. Ginger cat 5 5
1114 50 k. Black cat 8 5
1115 172 k. Grey and white cat 25 8

234 Gunboat, Tank, Soldiers and Flags

1989. 40th Anniv of People's Army. Mult.
1117 1 k. Type **234** 10 10
1118 2 k. Soldier teaching mathematics (vert) 10 10
1119 3 k. Army medics vaccinating civilians 10 10
1120 250 k. Peasant, revolutionary, worker and soldiers 40 15

235 Footballers

1989. World Cup Football Championship, Italy (1990) (1st issue). Multicoloured.
1121 10 k. Type **235** 5 5
1122 15 k. Footballer looking to pass ball 5 5
1123 20 k. Ball hitting player on chest 5 5
1124 25 k. Tackle 5 5
1125 45 k. Dribbling ball 5 5
1126 105 k. Kicking ball 15 5
See also Nos. 1168/73.

236 Couple planting Sapling

1989. Preserve Forests Campaign. Mult.
1128 4 k. Type **236** 5 5
1129 10 k. Burning and fallen trees 5 5
1130 12 k. Man felling tree (vert) 5 5
1131 200 k. Trees on map (vert) 30 10

INDEX
Countries can be quickly located by referring to the index at the end of this volume.

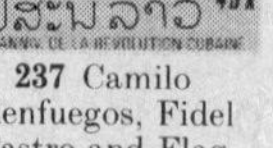
237 Camilo Cienfuegos, Fidel Castro and Flag

238 Skaters

1989. 30th Anniv of Cuban Revolution. Mult.
1132 45 k. Type **237** 5 5
1133 50 k. Cuban and Laotian flags 8 5

1989. Winter Olympic Games, Albertville (1992) (1st issue). Ice Skating. Multicoloured.
1134 9 k. Type **238** 5 5
1135 10 k. Pair figure skating (horiz) 5 5
1136 15 k. Ice dancing 5 5
1137 24 k. Female skater 5 5
1138 29 k. Pair 5 5
1139 114 k. Male skater 15 5
See also Nos. 1196/1201, 1237/41 and 1276/80.

239 High jumping

241 Sapodillas

240 "Poor on Seashore"

1989. Olympic Games, Barcelona (1992) (1st issue). Multicoloured.
1141 5 k. Type **239** 5 5
1142 15 k. Gymnastics 5 5
1143 20 k. Cycling (horiz) 5 5
1144 25 k. Boxing (horiz) 5 5
1145 70 k. Archery 10 5
1146 120 k. Swimming 20 8
See also Nos. 1179/84, 1231/5 and 1282/6.

1989. "Philexfrance '89" International Stamp Exn., Paris. Paintings by Picasso. Mult.
1148 5 k. Type **240** 5 5
1149 7 k. "Motherhood" 5 5
1150 8 k. "Portrait of Jaime S. le Bock" 5 5
1151 9 k. "Harlequins" 5 5
1152 105 k. "Boy with Dog" 15 5
1153 114 k. "Girl on Ball" 15 5

1989. Fruits. Multicoloured.
1155 5 k. Type **241** 5 5
1156 20 k. Sugar-apples 5 5
1157 20 k. Guavas 5 5
1158 30 k. Durians 5 5
1159 50 k. Pomegranates 8 5
1160 172 k. "Moridica charautia" 25 8

242 Sikhotabong Temple, Khammouane

243 Nehru and Woman

1989. Temples. Multicoloured.
1161 5 k. Type **242** 5 5
1162 15 k. Dam Temple, Vientiane 5 5
1163 61 k. Ing Hang Temple, Savannakhet 10 5
1164 161 k. Ho Vay Phra Luang Temple, Vientiane 25 8

1989. Birth Centenary of Jawaharlal Nehru (Indian statesman). Multicoloured.
1165 1 k. Type **243** 5 5
1166 60 k. Nehru and group of children (horiz) 8 5
1167 200 k. Boy garlanding Nehru 30 10

244 Footballer

1990. World Cup Football Championship, Italy (2nd issue).
1168 **244** 10 k. multicoloured 5 5
1169 – 15 k. multicoloured 5 5
1170 – 20 k. multicoloured 5 5
1171 – 25 k. multicoloured 5 5
1172 – 45 k. multicoloured 10 5
1173 – 105 k. multicoloured 20 10
DESIGNS: 15 to 105 k. Different footballing scenes.

245 Teacher and Adult Class

1990. International Literacy Year. Mult.
1175 10 k. Type **245** 5 5
1176 50 k. Woman teaching child (vert) 10 5
1177 60 k. Monk teaching adults 10 5
1178 150 k. Group reading and writing under tree 25 10

246 Basketball

1990. Olympic Games, Barcelona (1992) (2nd issue). Multicoloured.
1179 10 k. Type **246** 5 5
1180 30 k. Hurdling 5 5
1181 45 k. High jumping 10 5
1182 50 k. Cycling 10 5
1183 60 k. Throwing the javelin 10 5
1184 90 k. Tennis 15 5

247 Great Britain 1840 Penny Black and Mail Coach

1990. "Stamp World London 90" International Stamp Exhibition. Multicoloured.
1186 15 k. Type **247** 10 10
1187 20 k. U. S. 1847 5 c. stamp and early steam locomotive 10 10
1188 40 k. France 1849 20 c. stamp and hot-air balloons 10 10
1189 50 k. Sardinia 1851 5 c. stamp and post rider .. 10 10
1190 60 k. Indo-China 1892 1 c. stamp and elephant .. 10 10
1191 100 k. Spain 1850 6 c. stamp and galleon .. 30 10

248 Ho Chi Minh addressing Crowd

1990. Birth Centenary of Ho Chi Minh. Mult.
1193 40 k. Type **248** 5 5
1194 60 k. Ho Chi Minh and Laotian President .. 10 5
1195 160 k. Ho Chi Minh and Vietnamese flag (vert) 30 10

249 Speed Skating

1990. Winter Olympic Games, Albertville (1992) (2nd issue). Multicoloured.
1196 10 k. Type **249** 5 5
1197 25 k. Cross-country skiing (vert) 5 5
1198 30 k. Downhill skiing .. 5 5
1199 35 k. Tobogganing .. 5 5
1200 80 k. Figure skating (pairs) (vert) 15 5
1201 90 k. Biathlon 15 5

250 That Luang, 1867

1990. 430th Anniv of That Luang. Mult.
1203 60 k. Type **250** 10 5
1204 70 k. That Luang, 1930 .. 15 5
1205 130 k. That Luang, 1990 (vert) 25 10

251 Tui

1990. "New Zealand '90" International Stamp Exhibition, Auckland. Multicoloured.
1206 10 k. Type **251** 5 5
1207 15 k. Sky lark 5 5
1208 20 k. New Zealand sooty oystercatcher 5 5
1209 50 k. Common cormorant 10 5
1210 60 k. "Demigretta sacra" 10 5
1211 100 k. Brown kiwi .. 20 5

252 Brown-antlered Deer

1990. Mammals. Multicoloured.
1213 10 k. Type **252** 5 5
1214 20 k. Gaur 5 5
1215 40 k. Wild water buffalo 5 5
1216 45 k. Kouprey 10 5
1217 120 k. Javan rhinoceros .. 20 5

253 Surgeons Operating

1990. 40th Anniv of U.N. Development Programme. Multicoloured.
1218 30 k. Type **253** 10 10
1219 45 k. Fishermen inspecting catch .. 10 10
1220 80 k. Air-traffic controller (vert) 15 10
1221 90 k. Electricity plant workers .. 15 10

254 Rice Ceremony

1990. New Year. Multicoloured.
1222 5 k. Type **254** 5 5
1223 10 k. Elephant in carnival parade 5 5
1224 50 k. Making offerings at temple 10 5
1225 150 k. Family ceremony 25 10

255 Memorial, Wreath and Eternal Flame

1990. 15th National Day Festival. Mult.
1226 15 k. Type **255** 5 5
1227 20 k. Celebration parade 5 5
1228 80 k. Hospital visit .. 15 5
1229 120 k. Girls parading with banner 20 5

257 Two-man Kayak

1991. Olympic Games, Barcelona (1992) (3rd issue). Multicoloured.
1231 22 k. Type **257** 5 5
1232 32 k. Canoeing 5 5
1233 285 k. Diving (vert) .. 50 20
1234 330 k. Yachting (vert) .. 60 20
1235 1000 k. Swimming .. 1·75 60

258 Bobsleighing

1991. Winter Olympic Games, Albertville (1992) (3rd issue). Multicoloured.
1237 32 k. Type **258** 5 5
1238 135 k. Cross-country skiing (horiz) 25 10
1239 250 k. Ski jumping (horiz) 45 15
1240 275 k. Biathlon (horiz) .. 50 20
1241 900 k. Speed skating (horiz) .. .. 1·60 55

259 Pha Pheng Falls, Champassak

1991. Tourism. Multicoloured.
1243 155 k. Type **259** 30 10
1244 220 k. Pha Tang mountains, Vanvieng .. 40 15
1245 235 k. Tat Set waterfall, Saravane (vert) .. 40 15
1246 1000 k. Plain of Jars, Xieng Khouang (vert) 1·75 60

260 Match Scene

1991. World Cup Football Championship, U.S.A. (1994) (1st issue). Multicoloured.
1247 32 k. Type **260** 5 5
1248 330 k. Goalkeeper catching ball 60 20
1249 340 k. Player controlling ball (vert) 60 20
1250 400 k. Player dribbling ball 70 25
1251 500 k. Tackle 90 30
See also Nos. 1292/6.

261 Planting Saplings

1991. National Tree Planting Day. Mult.
1253 250 k. Type **261** 45 15
1254 700 k. Planting saplings (different) .. .. 1·25 45
1255 800 k. Removing saplings from store .. .. 1·40 50

262 "Mallard"

1991. "Espamer '91" Spain–Latin American Stamp Exhibition, Buenos Aires. Railway Locomotives. Multicoloured.
1256 25 k. Type **262** 5 5
1257 32 k. Pacific "231" steam locomotive 5 5
1258 285 k. American locomotive 50 20
1259 650 k. "Canadian Pacific" steam locomotive .. 1·10 40
1260 750 k. "Beyer-Garratt" (wrongly inscr "Garrant") locomotive 1·40 50

263 Spindle Festival

1991. Traditional Music. Multicoloured.
1262 20 k. Type **263** 5 5
1263 220 k. Mong player (vert) 40 15
1264 275 k. Siphandone singer (vert) 50 20
1265 545 k. Khap ngum singer 1·00 35
1266 690 k. Phouthaydam dance .. .. .. 1·25 45

264 Great Purple

1991. "Phila Nippon '91" Int Stamp Exhibition, Tokyo. Butterflies. Mult.
1267 55 k. Type **264** 10 5
1268 90 k. "Luehdorfia puziloi" (wrongly inscr "Luendorfia") .. 15 5
1269 255 k. "Papilio bianor" .. 45 15
1270 285 k. Swallowtail .. 50 20
1271 900 k. Mikado swallowtail 1·60 55

265 Emblem and Pattern

266 Bobsleigh

1991. International Decade for Cultural Development (1988–97). Multicoloured.
1273 285 k. Type **265** 55 20
1274 330 k. Emblem and drum 60 20
1275 1000 k. Emblem and pipes 1·90 65

1992. Winter Olympic Games, Albertville (4th issue). Multicoloured.
1276 200 k. Type **266** 35 10
1277 220 k. Slalom skiing .. 40 15
1278 250 k. Downhill skiing (horiz) 45 15
1279 500 k. One-man luge .. 95 35
1280 600 k. Figure skating .. 1·10 40

267 Running

269 Argentinian and Italian Players and Flags

268 Pest Control

1992. Olympic Games, Barcelona (4th issue). Multicoloured.
1282 32 k. Type **267** 5 5
1283 245 k. Baseball 45 15
1284 275 k. Tennis 50 20
1285 285 k. Basketball .. 55 20
1286 900 k. Boxing (horiz) .. 1·75 60

1992. World Health Day. Multicoloured.
1288 200 k. Type **268** 35 10
1289 255 k. Anti-smoking campaign 50 20
1290 330 k. Donating blood .. 60 20
1291 1000 k. Vaccinating child (vert) .. .. 1·90 65

1992. World Cup Football Championship, U.S.A. (1994) (2nd issue). Multicoloured.

1292 260 k. Type **269** 50 20
1293 305 k. German and English players and flags 55 20
1294 310 k. American flag, ball and trophy 60 20
1295 350 k. Italian and English players and flags .. 65 25
1296 800 k. German and Argentinian players and flags .. .. .. 1·50 55

270 Boy Drumming

272 Doorway and Ruins

271 Common Cobra

1992. International Children's Day. Children at Play. Multicoloured.

1298 220 k. Type **270** 40 15
1299 285 k. Girls skipping (horiz) 55 20
1300 330 k. Boys racing on stilts 60 20
1301 400 k. Girls playing "escape" game (horiz) 75 25

1992. Snakes. Multicoloured.

1302 280 k. Type **271** 50 20
1303 295 k. Common cobra .. 55 20
1304 420 k. "Trimeresurus wagleri" 80 30
1305 700 k. King cobra (vert) 1·25 45

1992. Restoration of Wat Phou. Mult.

1306 185 k. Type **272** 35 10
1307 220 k. Doorway (different) 40 15
1308 1200 k. Doorway with collapsed porch (horiz) 2·25 80

273 "Pinta" and Juan Martinez's Map

1992. "Genova '92" International Thematic Stamp Exhibition. Multicoloured.

1309 100 k. Type **273** 20 5
1310 300 k. Piri Reis's letter and caravelle (vert) .. 55 20
1311 350 k. Magellan's ship and Paolo del Pozo Toscanelli's world map 65 25
1312 400 k. Gabriel de Vallseca's map and Vasco da Gama's ship 75 25
1313 455 k. Juan Martinez's map and Portuguese four-masted caravel .. 85 30

274 Woman in Traditional Costume

1992. Traditional Costumes of Laotian Mountain Villages.

1315 **274** 25 k. multicoloured .. 5 5
1316 – 55 k. multicoloured .. 10 5
1317 – 400 k. multicoloured 75 25
1318 – 1200 k. multicoloured 2·25 80

DESIGNS: 55 to 1200 k. Different costumes.

275 Crested Gibbon

1992. Climbing Mammals. Multicoloured.

1319 10 k. Type **275** 5 5
1320 100 k. Variegated langur 20 5
1321 250 k. Pileated gibbon .. 45 15
1322 430 k. Francois's monkey 80 30
1323 800 k. Lesser slow loris .. 1·50 55

POSTAGE DUE STAMPS

D 5. Vat Sisaket Shrine.

D 6. Sampans

D 98. Serpent.

1952.

D 22. **D 5.** 10 c. brown 10 10
D 23. 20 c. violet 10 10
D 24. 50 c. red 8 8
D 25. 1 p. green 15 15
D 26. 2 p. blue 15 15
D 27. 5 p. purple 55 55
D 28. **D 6.** 10 p. blue 80 80

1973.

D 378. **D 98.** 10 k. blk., brn. & yell. 5 5
D 379. 15 k. blk., yell. & grn. 8 8
D 380. 20 k. blk., grn. & bl. 15 15
D 381. 50 k. blk., bl. & red 30 30

APPENDIX

The following stamps have either been issued in excess of postal needs or have not been available to the public in reasonable quantities at face value. Such stamps may later be given full listing if there is evidence of regular postal use.

1975

Centenary of U.P.U. Postage 10, 15, 30, 40 k; Air 1000, 1500 k. On gold foil 2500, 3000 k.
"Apollo-Soyuz" Space Link. Postage 125, 150, 200, 300 k.; Air 450, 700 k.

Bicentenary of American Revolution. Postage 10, 15, 40, 50, 100, 125, 150, 200 k.: Air 1000, 1500 k.

LATAKIA Pt. 19

The former state of the Alaouites which changed its name to Latakia in 1930.

Latakia was merged with Syria in 1936.

100 centiemes = 1 piastre.

1931. As 1930 stamps of Syria (T **26/7**) optd. **LATTAQUIE** and in Arabic.

64 0 p. 10 purple 20 15
66 0 p. 20 blue 20 20
67 0 p. 20 red 30 30
68 0 p. 25 green 30 30
69 0 p. 25 violet 50 50
70 0 p. 50 violet 50 50
71 0 p. 75 red 50 50
72 1 p. green 50 50
73 1 p. 50 brown 80 80
74 1 p. 50 green 90 90
75 2 p. violet 90 90
76 3 p. green .. .. 1·60 1·60
77 4 p. orange .. .. 1·50 1·50
78 4 p. 50 red .. .. 1·50 1·50
79 6 p. green .. .. 1·60 1·60
80 7 p. 50 blue .. .. 1·60 1·60
81 10 p. brown .. .. 2·25 2·25
82 15 p. green .. .. 3·00 3·00
83 25 p. purple .. .. 7·00 7·00
84 50 p. brown .. .. 6·00 6·00
85 100 p. red .. .. 16·00 16·00

1931. Air. As 1931 air stamps of Syria optd. **LATTAQUIE** and in Arabic.

86 0 p. 50 yellow 25 25
87 0 p. 50 brown 40 40
88 1 p. brown 70 70
89 2 p. blue 90 90
90 3 p. green .. .. 1·10 1·10
91 5 p. purple .. .. 2·50 2·50
92 10 p. blue .. .. 3·50 3·50
93 15 p. red .. .. 4·50 4·50
94 25 p. orange .. .. 8·00 8·00
95 50 p. black .. .. 12·00 12·00
96 100 p. mauve .. .. 12·00 12·00

POSTAGE DUE STAMPS

1931. Nos. D 197/8 of Syria optd. **LATTAQUIE** and in Arabic.

D 86. 8 p. black on blue .. 8·50 8·50
D 87. 15 p. black on red .. 6·50 6·50

LATVIA Pt. 10

A country on the Baltic Sea. Previously part of the Russian Empire, Latvia was independent from 1918 to 1940 when it became part of the U.S.S.R.

Following the dissolution of the U.S.S.R. in 1991, Latvia once again became an independent republic.

1918. 100 kapeikas = 1 rublis.
1923. 100 santimu = 1 lats.
1991. 100 kopeks = 1 (Russian) rouble.
July 1992. 100 kopeks = 1 Latvian rouble.
1993. 100 santimu = 1 lats.

1.

4.

5. Rising Sun.

1918. Printed on back of German war maps. Imperf or perf.

1 **1** 5 k. red 35 50

1919. On plain or ruled paper. Imperf. or perf.

15 **1** 3 k. lilac 10 10
16 5 k. red 10 10
17 10 k. blue 10 10
18 15 k. green 10 10
41 20 k. orange 10 10
20 25 k. grey 50 35
21 35 k. brown 20 20
42 40 k. purple 30 10
22 50 k. violet 20 20
44 75 k. green 25 15
29 3 r. red and blue .. .. 1·25 75
30 5 r. red and brown .. 1·00 85

1919. Liberation of Riga. Imperf.

24. **4.** 5 k. red 20 15
25. 15 k. green 20 15
26. 35 k. brown 35 10

For stamps of Type **1** and **4** optd. with a cross, with or without Russian letters "Z A", see under North-West Russia Nos. 21/42.

1919. Imperf. or perf.

27. **5.** 10 k. blue 45 35

6.

7.

1919. 1st Anniversary of Independence.

(a) Size 33×45 mm.

32 **6** 10 k. red and brown .. 35 35

(b) Size 28×38 mm.

33 **6** 10 k. red and brown .. 20 20
34 35 k. green and blue .. 20 20
35 1 r. red and green .. 50 50

1919. Liberation of Courland.

36. **7.** 10 k. red and brown .. 10 10
37. 25 k. green and blue .. 20 20
38. 35 k. blue and black .. 30 30
39. 1 r. brown and green .. 85 85

8.

1920. Red Cross stamps.

A. On backs of blue Bolshevist notes. Perf.

46 **8** 20–30 k. red and brown .. 1·00 1·40
47 40–55 k. red and blue .. 1·00 1·40
48 50–70 k. red and green .. 85 2·00
49 1 r.–1 r. 30 red and grey .. 1·10 2·00

B. On backs of green Western Army notes. Perf.

50 **8** 20–30 k. red and brown .. 1·00 1·25
51 40–55 k. red and blue .. 1·00 1·25
52 50–70 k. red and green .. 85 1·60
53 1 r.–1 r. 30 red and grey .. 1·50 3·25

C. On backs of red, green and brown Bolshevist notes. Imperf.

54 **8** 20–30 k. red and brown .. 1·50 3·00
55 40–55 k. red and blue .. 1·50 3·00
56 50–70 k. red and green .. 1·50 3·00
57 1 r.–1 r. 30 red and grey .. 3·75 4·75

CHARITY PREMIUMS. In the above and later issues where two values are expressed, the lower value represents the franking value and the higher the price charged, the difference being the charity premium.

9.

10.

1920. Liberation of Latgale.

58. **9.** 50 k. pink and green .. 65 20
59. 1 r. brown and green .. 65 30

1920. 1st Constituent Assembly.

60. **10.** 50 k. red 50 20
61. 1 r. blue 50 15
62. 3 r. green and brown .. 65 70
63. 5 r. purple and grey .. 1·60 80

1920. Surch. in white figures on black oval.

64. **6.** 10 r. on 1 r. red and green 2·00 1·60
65. 20 r. on 1 r. red and green 4·00 2·75
66. 30 r. on 1 r. red and green 5·00 5·00

1920. Surch. **2 DIWI RUBLI.** Perf.

67. **1.** 2 r. on 10 k. blue .. 2·75 75
68. **4.** 2 r. on 35 k. brown .. 50 30

1920. (a) Surch **WEENS** or **DIVI**, value and **RUBLI**.

69 **7** 1 (WEENS) r. on 35 k. blue and black .. 30 30
70 2 (DIVI) r. on 10 k. red and brown 85 85
71 2 (DIVI) r. on 25 k. green and blue 70 30

(b) Surch **DIWI RUBLI 2**.

72 **6** 2 r. on 35 k. green & blue 50 40

(c) Surch **DIVI 2 RUB. 2**.

73 **10** 2 r. on 50 k. red 25 25

(d) Surch **Desmit rubli**

74 **6** 10 r. on 10 r. on 1 r. red and green (No. 64) .. 2·00 65

1921. Red Cross. Nos. 51/3 surch **RUB 2 RUB**.

75 **8** 2 r. on 20–30 k. red & brn 2·75 5·00
76 2 r. on 40–55 k. red & blue 2·75 5·00
77 2 r. on 50–70 k. red & grn 2·75 5·00
78 2 r. on 1 r.–1 r. 30 k. red and grey .. .. 2·75 5·00

1921. Surch. in figures and words over thick bar of crossed lines.

79. **9.** 10 r. on 50 k. pink & green 1·60 70
80. 20 r. on 50 k. pink & green 5·00 4·00
81. 30 r. on 50 k. pink & green 4·00 3·75
82. 50 r. on 50 k. pink & green 10·00 6·75
83. 100 r. on 50 k. pink & grn. 20·00 17·00

19.

1921. Air. Value in "RUBLU". Imperf or perf.

84 **19** 10 r. green .. .. 5·00 1·50
85 20 r. blue .. .. 5·00 1·60

See also Nos. 155/7.

21. Latvian Coat of Arms. **22.** Great Seal of Latvia.

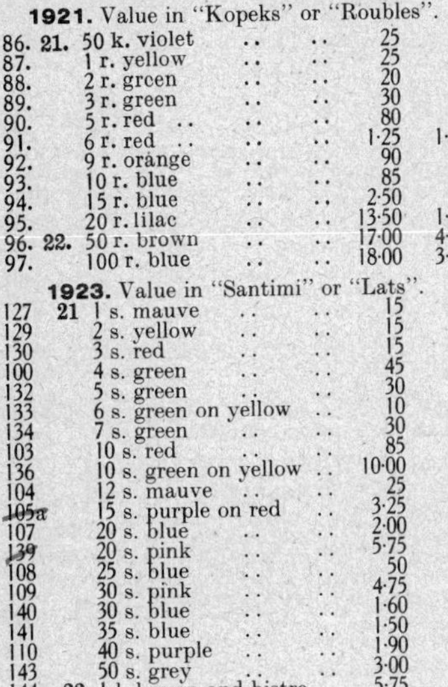

1921. Value in "Kopeks" or "Roubles".
86. **21.** 50 k. violet 25 10
87. 1 r. yellow 25 25
88. 2 r. green 20 10
89. 3 r. green 30 25
90. 5 r. red 80 10
91. 6 r. red .. .. 1·25 1·00
92. 9 r. orange 90 50
93. 10 r. blue 85 10
94. 15 r. blue .. .. 2·50 60
95. 20 r. lilac .. .. 13·50 1·40
96. **22.** 50 r. brown .. .. 17·00 4·25
97. 100 r. blue .. .. 18·00 3·75

1923. Value in "Santimi" or "Lats".
127 **21** 1 s. mauve 15 10
129 2 s. yellow 15 10
130 3 s. red 15 10
100 4 s. green 45 10
132 5 s. green 30 10
133 6 s. green on yellow .. 10 10
134 7 s. green 30 15
103 10 s. red 85 10
136 10 s. green on yellow .. 10·00 10
104 12 s. mauve 25 20
105a 15 s. purple on red .. 3·25 10
107 20 s. blue .. .. 2·00 10
139 20 s. pink .. .. 5·75 10
108 25 s. blue 50 10
109 30 s. pink .. .. 4·75 15
140 30 s. blue .. .. 1·60 10
141 35 s. blue .. .. 1·50 10
110 40 s. purple .. .. 1·90 15
143 50 s. grey .. .. 3·00 15
144 **22** 1 l. brown and bistre .. 5·75 15
116 2 l. blue and light blue 18·00 1·60
117 5 l. green & light green 55·00 4·75
118 10 l. red and light red 5·00 6·00

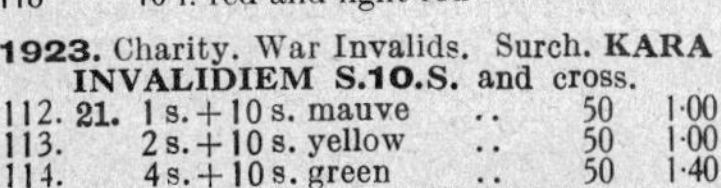

1923. Charity. War Invalids. Surch. **KARA INVALIDIEM S.10.S.** and cross.
112. **21.** 1 s.+10 s. mauve .. 50 1·00
113. – 2 s.+10 s. yellow .. 50 1·00
114. – 4 s.+10 s. green .. 50 1·40

24. Town Hall. **28.** Pres. J. Cakste.

1925. 300th Anniv. of City of Libau.
119. – 6–12 s. blue and red .. 1·75 4·00
120. **24.** 15–25 s. brown and blue 1·00 2·75
121. – 25–35 s. green and violet 3·25 2·75
122. – 30–40 s. lake and blue .. 5·75 11·50
123. – 50–60 s. violet and green 7·75 15·00
DESIGNS—HORIZ. 6–12 s. Harbour and lighthouse. 25–35 s. Spa health pavlion. VERT. 30–40 s. St. Anna's Church. 50–60 s. Arms of Libau.

1927. Surch.
124. **1.** 15 s. on 40 k. purple .. 50 40
125. 15 s. on 50 k. violet .. 1·50 1·60
126. **10.** 1 l. on 3 r. green & brown 6·75 13·50

1928. Death of President Cakste and Memorial Fund.
150. **28.** 2–12 s. orange .. .. 4·00 3·25
151. 6–16 s. green .. .. 4·00 3·25
152. 15–25 s. lake .. .. 4·00 3·25
153. 25–35 s. blue .. .. 4·00 3·25
154. 30–40 s. red .. .. 4·00 3·25

1928. Air. Value in "SANTIMU" or "SANTIMI".
155 **19** 10 s. green .. .. 1·60 1·00
156 15 s. red .. .. 2·40 80
157 25 s. blue .. .. 3·25 90

29. Ruins at Rezekne. **30.** Venta.

1928. 10th Anniv of Independence. Views.
158 **29** 6 s. purple and green .. 1·00 15
159 – 15 s. green and brown .. 1·00 15
160 – 20 s. green and red .. 1·40 50
161 – 30 s. brown and blue .. 1·60 20
162 – 50 s. pink and grey .. 2·00 2·00
163 – 1 l. sepia and brown .. 4·00 1·75
DESIGNS: 15 s. Jelgava (Mitau). 20 s. Cesis (Wenden). 30 s. Liepaja (Libau). 50 s. Riga. 1 l. National Theatre, Riga.

1928. Liberty Memorial Fund. Imperf. or perf.
164. **30.** 6–16 s. green .. .. 3·25 3·25
165. – 10–20 s. red .. .. 3·25 3·25
166. – 15–25 s. brown .. .. 3·25 3·25
167. – 30–40 s. blue .. .. 3·25 3·25
168. – 50–60 s. black .. .. 3·25 3·25
169. – 1 l.–1 l. 10 s. purple .. 3·25 3·25
DESIGNS: 10–20 s. "Latvia" (Woman). 15–25 s. Mitau. 30–40 s. National Theatre, Riga. 50–60 s. Wenden. 1 l.–1 l. 10 s. Trenches, Riga Bridge.

32. Z. A. Meierovics. **33.** J. Rainis.

1929. 3rd Death Anniv. of Meierovics (Foreign Minister). Imperf. or perf.
170 **32** 2–4 s. yellow .. .. 4·00 4·00
171 6–12 s. green .. .. 4·00 4·00
172 15–25 s. purple .. .. 4·00 4·00
173 25–35 s. blue .. .. 4·00 4·00
174 30–40 s. blue .. .. 4·00 4·00

1930. Memorial Fund for J. Rainis (writer and politician). Imperf or perf.
175 **33** 1–2 s. purple .. .. 1·00 1·50
176 2–4 s. orange .. .. 1·00 1·50
177 4–8 s. green .. .. 1·00 1·50
178 6–12 s. brown and green 1·00 1·50
179 10–20 s. red .. .. 17·00 30·00
180 15–30 s. green & brown 17·00 30·00

34. Durbe Castle.

1930. Air. J. Rainis Memorial Fund. Imperf or perf.
181 **34** 10–20 s. green and red .. 10·00 11·50
182 15–30 s. red and green .. 10·00 11·50

35. **36.**

1930. Anti-T.B. Fund.
183 – 1–2 s. red and purple .. 50 50
184 – 2–4 s. red and orange .. 50 50
185 **35** 4–8 s. red and green .. 1·00 80
186 – 5–10 s. brown and green 1·40 1·10
187 – 6–12 s. yellow & green .. 1·40 1·10
188 – 10–20 s. black and red .. 2·00 1·60
189 – 15–30 s. green & brown 1·50 1·50
190 – 20–40 s. blue and red .. 2·00 2·00
191 – 25–50 s. lilac, blue & red 3·00 2·50
192 **36** 30–60 s. lilac, green & bl 3·25 4·25
DESIGNS—VERT. As Type **35**: 1–2 s., 2–4 s. The Crusaders' Cross. 5–10 s. G. Zemgalis. 6–12 s. Tower. 10–20 s. J. Cakste. 15–30 s. Floral design. 20–40 s. A. Kviesis. HORIZ. As Type **36**: 25–50 s. Sanatorium.

1931. Nos. 183/92 surch.
196 9 on 6–12 s. yellow & grn 65 1·60
197 16 on 1–2 s. red and purple 13·50 20·00
198 17 s. 2–4 s. red and orange 1·25 1·60
199 19 on 4–8 s. red and green 4·75 7·50
200 20 on 5–10 s. brown & grn 2·50 7·50
201 23 on 15–30 s. green & brn 1·00 1·00
202 25 on 10–20 s. black & red 2·75 4·25
203 35 on 20–40 s. blue and red 4·00 6·00
204 45 on 25–50 s. lilac, blue and red .. .. 11·50 18·00
205 55 on 30–60 s. lilac, green and blue .. .. 13·50 28·00

1931. Air. Charity. Nos. 155/7 surch **LATVIJAS AIZSARGI** and value. Imperf or perf.
206 **19.** 50 on 10 s. green .. 13·50 18·00
207. 1 l. on 15 s. red .. 13·50 18·00
208. 1 l. 50 on 25 s. blue .. 13·50 18·00

38. Foreign Invasion.

1932. Militia Maintenance Fund. Imperf. or perf.
209. – 1–11 s. blue and purple 3·25 3·75
210. **38.** 2–17 s. orange and olive 3·25 3·75
211. – 3–23 s. red and brown 3·25 3·75
212. – 4–34 s. green .. .. 3·25 3·75
213. – 5–45 s. green .. .. 3·25 3·75
DESIGNS: 1–11 s. The Holy Oak and Kriva telling stories. 3–23 s. Lacplesis, the deliverer. 4–34 s. The Black Knight (enemy) slaughtered. 5–45 s. Laimdota, the spirit of Latvia, freed.

39. Infantry Manoeuvres.

1932. Militia Maintenance Fund. Imperf. or perf.
214. – 6–25 s. purple & brown 5·75 6·75
215. **39.** 7–35 s. blue and green .. 5·75 6·75
216. – 10–45 s. sepia and green 5·75 6·75
217. – 12–55 s. green & red .. 5·75 6·75
218. – 15–75 s. violet and red 5·75 6·75
DESIGNS—HORIZ. 6–25 s. Troops on march. VERT. 10–45 s. First aid to soldier. 12–55 s. Army kitchen. 15–75 s. Gen. J. Balodis.

41.

1932. Air. Charity. Imperf. or perf.
219. **41.** 10–20 s. black and green 13·50 18·00
220. 15–30 s. red and grey .. 13·50 18·00
221. 25–50 s. blue and grey .. 13·50 18·00

1932. Riga Exn. of Lettish Products. Optd. **Latvijas razojumu izstade Riga. 1932.g.10.-18.IX.**
222. **21.** 3 s. red 50 40
223. 10 s. green on yellow .. 1·50 80
224. 20 s. pink .. .. 2·00 70
225. 35 s. blue .. .. 3·25 85

43. Leonardo da Vinci. **44.** "Mourning Mother" Memorial, Riga.

1932. Air. Charity. Pioneers of Aviation. Imperf or perf.
226 – 5–25 s. green and brown 13·50 17·00
227 **43** 10–50 s. green and brown 13·50 17·00
228 – 15–75 s. green and red .. 13·50 17·00
229 – 20–100 s. mauve & green 13·50 17·00
230 – 25–125 s. blue and brown 13·50 17·00
DESIGNS—VERT. 5–25 s. Icarus. 15–75 s. Charliere's balloon. HORIZ. 20–100 s. Wright's biplane. 25–125 s. Bleriot's monoplane.

1933. Air. Wounded Latvian Airmen Fund. Imperf. or perf.
231. – 2-52 s. brown and black 9·25 12·50
232. **44.** 3-53 s. red and black .. 9·25 12·50
233. – 10-60 s. green and black 9·25 12·50
234. – 20-70 s. red and black .. 9·25 12·50
DESIGNS: 2 s. Fall of Icarus. 10 s., 20 s. Proposed tombs for airmen.

1933. Air. Charity. Riga–Bathurst Flight. Nos. 155/7 ptd **LATVIJA-AFRIKA 1933** or surch also.
235. 10 s. green .. .. 20·00 27·00
236. 15 s. red .. .. 20·00 27·00
237. 25 s. blue .. .. 20·00 32·00
238. 50 s. on 15 s. red .. £110 £325
239. 100 s. on 25 s. blue .. £110 £325
In the event the aircraft crashed at Neustettin, Germany, and the mail was forwarded by ordinary post.

46. Biplane under Fire at Riga.

1933. Air Charity. Wounded Latvian Airmen Fund. Imperf. or perf.
240. – 3-53 s. blue and orange 20·00 23·00
241. **46.** 7-57 s. brown and blue 20·00 23·00
242. – 35-135 s. black and blue 20·00 23·00
DESIGNS: 3 s. Monoplane taking off. 35 s. Map and planes.

47. American "Gee-Bee" Plane.

1933. Air. Charity. Wounded Latvian Airmen Fund. Imperf. or perf.
243. **47.** 8-68 s. grey and brown 27·00 50·00
244. – 12-112 s. green & pur... 27·00 50·00
245. – 30-130 s. grey and blue 38·00 50·00
246. – 40-190 s. blue & purple 27·00 50·00
DESIGNS: 12 s. British "S6S" plane. 30 s. "Graf Zeppelin" airship over Riga. 40 s. Dornier "Do X".

48. President's Palace. **50.** A. Kronvalds. **51.**

1934. 15th Anniv. of New Constitution.
247. **48.** 3 s. red 10 15
248. – 5 s. green 15 10
249. – 10 s. green .. .. 2·00 10
250. – 20 s. red .. .. 2·00 10
251. – 35 s. blue 10 15
252. **48.** 40 s. brown 10 15
DESIGNS: 5, 10 s. Arms and shield. 20 s. Allegory of Latvia. 35 s. Government Building.

1936. Lettish Intellectuals.
253. **50.** 3 s. red .. .. .. 1·60 4·25
254. – 10 s. green .. .. 1·60 4·25
255. – 20 s. mauve .. .. 1·60 5·00
256. – 35 s. blue .. .. 1·60 5·00
PORTRAITS: 10 s. A. Pumpurs. 20 s. J. Maters. 35 s. Auseklis.

1936. White Cross Fund. Designs incorporating Cross and Stars device as in T **51.**
257 **51** 3 s. red .. .. 1·50 3·25
258 – 10 s. green .. .. 1·50 3·25
259 – 20 s. mauve .. .. 1·50 4·00
260 – 35 s. blue .. .. 1·50 4·00
DESIGNS: 10 s. Oak leaves. 20 s. Doctors and patient. 35 s. Woman holding shield.

53. Independence Monument, Rauna (Ronneburg). **54.** President Ulmanis.

1937. Monuments.
261. **53.** 3 s. red .. .. .. 35 1·40
262. – 5 s. green 35 60
263. – 10 s. green 35 35
264. – 20 s. red .. .. 85 1·00
265. – 30 s. blue .. .. 1·40 1·25
266. – 35 s. blue .. .. 1·40 1·50
267. – 40 s. brown .. .. 2·25 2·50
DESIGNS—VERT. 10 s. Independence Monument, Jelgava (Mitau). 20 s. War Memorial, Valka (Walk). 30 s. Independence Monument, Iecava (Eckau). 35 s. Independence Monument, Riga. 40 s. Col. Kalpak's Grave, Visagalas Cemetery. HORIZ. 5 s. Cemetery Gate, Riga.

1937 President Ulmanis's 60th Birthday.
268 **54** 3 s. red and orange .. 15 10
269 5 s. light green & green 15 15
270 10 s. deep green & green 25 35
271 20 s. purple and red .. 55 35
272 25 s. grey and blue .. 1·10 65
273 30 s. deep blue and blue 1·10 60
274 35 s. indigo and blue .. 1·00 50
275 40 s. lt brown & brown 85 75
276 50 s. green and black .. 90 80

56. Gaizinkalns, Livonia. **57.** General J. Balodis.

1938. 20th Anniv. of Independence.
278. **56.** 3 s. red 10 10
279. – 5 s. green 10 10
280. **57.** 10 s. green 20 10
281. – 20 s. mauve 20 10
282. – 30 s. blue 60 20
283. – 35 s. slate 65 10
284. – 40 s. mauve 80 15
DESIGNS—As Type **56**: 5 s. Latgale landscape. 30 s. City of Riga. 35 s. Rumba waterfall, Courland. 40 s. Zemgale landscape. As Type **57**: 20 s. President Ulmanis.

INDEX

Countries can be quickly located by referring to the index at the end of this volume.

58. Elementary School, Riga.

DESIGNS: 5 s. Jelgava Castle. 10 s. Riga Castle. 2 s. Independence Memorial. 30 s. Eagle and National Flag. 35 s. Town Hall, Daugavpils. 40 s. War Museum and Powder-magazine, Riga 50 s. Pres. Ulmanis.

1939. 5th Anniv of Authoritarian Government.

285. 58. 3 s. brown 50 85
286. – 5 s. green 50 85
287. – 10 s. green .. .. 1·40 1·00
288. – 20 s. red .. .. 1·60 1·40
289. – 30 s. blue .. .. 1·25 1·00
290. – 35 s. blue .. .. 1·60 1·50
291. – 40 s. purple .. .. 2·75 1·00
292. – 50 s. black .. .. 3·25 1·00

59. Reaping.

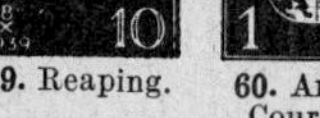

60. Arms of Courland, Livonia and Latgale.

61. Arms of Latvian Soviet Socialist Republic.

1939. Harvest Festival. Dated "8 X 1939".

294. 59. 10 s. green 65 20
295. – 20 s. red (Apples) .. 1·00 15

1940.

296. 60. 1 s. violet 15 20
297. 2 s. yellow 15 20
298. 3 s. red 10 15
299. 5 s. brown 10 10
300. 7 s. green 10 40
301. 10 s. green 60 10
302. 20 s. red 60 10
303. 30 s. brown 75 25
304. 35 s. blue 10 70
305. 50 s. green 85 30
306. 1 l. olive .. .. 1·60 35

1940. Incorporation of Latvia in U.S.S.R.

307. 61. 1 s. violet 15 20
308. 2 s. yellow 15 15
309. 3 s. red 10 10
310. 5 s. olive 10 10
311. 7 s. green 10 45
312. 10 s. green 30 10
313. 20 s. red 65 10
314. 30 s. blue .. .. 1·40 30
315. 35 s. blue 10 55
316. 40 s. brown 60 65
317. 50 s. grey .. .. 1·40 65
318. 1 l. brown .. .. 1·60 1·10
319. 5 l. green .. .. 11·50 7·50

63 Latvian Arms 64

1991.

320 63 5 k. silver, brn & lt brn 10 10
321 10 k. silver, brn & drab 10 10
322 15 k. silver, sepia & brn 10 10
323 20 k. silver, blue & lt bl 35 35
324 40 k. silver, green and light green 65 65
325 50 k. silver, brown & lil 85 85
326 64 100 k. multicoloured .. 1·60 1·60
327 200 k. multicoloured .. 3·25 3·25

1991. Nos. 4672, 6073 and 6077 of Russia surch **LATVIJA** and new value.

328 100 k. on 7 k. blue .. 20 20
329 300 k. on 2 k. brown .. 65 65
330 500 k. on 2 k. brown .. 1·10 1·10
331 1000 k. on 2 k. brown .. 2·25 2·25
358 25 r. on 4 k. red .. .. 2·40 2·40

67 Main Statue, Liberty Monument, Riga

68 Olympic Committee Symbol

1991.

336 67 10 k. multicoloured .. 10 10
337 15 k. multicoloured .. 10 10
338 20 k. multicoloured .. 10 10
339 30 k. multicoloured .. 10 10
340 50 k. multicoloured .. 55 55
341 100 k. multicoloured .. 1·10 1·10

1992. Recognition of Latvian Olympic Committee.

342 68 50 k. + 25 k. red, silver and drab 65 65
343 – 50 k. + 25 k. red, silver and grey 65 65
344 68 100 k. + 50 k. red, gold and bistre .. .. 1·40 1·40

DESIGN: No. 343, As T 68 but symbols smaller and inscribed "BERLIN 18.09.91." at left.

69 Vaidelotis

72 Children in Fancy Dress around Christmas Tree

1992. Statues from the base of the Liberty Monument, Riga.

345 – 10 k. black and brown 10 10
346 69 20 k. brown and grey .. 10 10
347 – 30 k. deep lilac and lilac 10 10
348 69 30 k. dp brown & brown 10 10
349 – 40 k. blue and grey .. 35 35
350 69 50 k. green and grey .. 40 40
351 – 50 k. brown and grey .. 40 40
352 – 100 k. purple and mauve 85 85
353 – 200 k. deep blue & blue 1·60 1·60

DESIGNS: Nos. 345, 347 and 353, Kurzeme (warrior with shield); Nos. 349 and 351/2, Lachplesis (two figures).

1992. Birds of the Baltic. As Nos. 506/9 of Lithuania.

359 5 r. black and red .. 15 15
360 5 r. brown, black and red 15 15
361 5 r. sepia, brown and red 15 15
362 5 r. brown, black and red 15 15

DESIGNS: No. 359, Osprey ("Pandion haliaetus"); 360, Black-tailed godwit ("Limosa limosa"); 361, Goosander ("Mergus merganser"); 362, Common shelducks ("Tadorna tadorna").

1992. Christmas. Multicoloured.

363 2 r. Type 72 .. .. 20 20
364 3 r. Angel choir 50 50
365 10 r. Type 72 .. .. 1·75 1·75
366 15 r. Adoration of the Kings .. .. .. 2·50 2·50

1993. Nos. 4855, 5296 and 5295 of Russia surch **LATVIJA** and new value.

367 50 r. on 6 k. multicoloured 25 25
368 100 r. on 6 k. multicoloured 50 50
369 300 r. on 6 k. multicoloured 1·75 1·75

74 Kuldiga Couple

75 Emblem

1993. Costumes. Multicoloured.

370 5 s. Type 74 .. .. 10 10
371 10 s. Alsunga 25 25
372 20 s. Lielvarde 45 45
373 50 s. Rucava .. .. 1·25 1·25
374 100 s. Zemgale .. .. 2·40 2·40
375 500 s. Ziemellatgale .. 12·00 12·00

1993. National Song Festival.

377 75 3 s. black, gold & brown 10 10
378 5 s. black, gold and lilac 10 10
379 – 15 s. multicoloured .. 35 35

DESIGN: 15 s. Abstract.

76 Pope John Paul II

77 Flags

1993. Papal Visit.

380 76 15 s. multicoloured .. 35 35

1993. 75th Anniv of First Republic.

381 77 5 s. multicoloured .. 10 10
382 15 s. multicoloured .. 35 35

LEBANON Pt. 19

A territory N. of the Holy Land, formerly part of the Turkish Empire. Greater Lebanon was given a separate status under French Mandate in 1920. Until September, 1923, the French occupation stamps of Syria were used and these were followed by the joint issue of 1923, Nos. 97 etc., of Syria. Independence was proclaimed in 1941, but the country was not evacuated by French troops until 1946.

100 centiemes = 1 piastre.
100 piastres = 1 Lebanese pound.

1924. Stamps of France surch. **GRAND LIBAN** and value.

1. 11. 10 c. on 2 c. red .. 40 40
2. 18. 25 c. on 5 c. orange .. 40 30
3. 50 c. on 10 c. green .. 35 30
4. 15. 75 c. on 15 c. green .. 1·10 85
5. 18. 1 p. on 20 c. brown .. 40 30
6. 1 p. 25 on 25 c. blue .. 2·40 1·10
7. 1 p. 50 on 30 c. orange .. 1·00 45
8. 1 p. 50 on 30 c. red .. 85 45
9. 15. 2 p. 50 on 50 c. blue .. 85 45
10. 13. 2 p. on 40 c. red & blue .. 2·50 1·90
11. 3 p. on 60 c. vio. & blue .. 4·50 3·25
12. 5 p. on 1 f. red & green .. 4·50 4·25
13. 10 p. on 2 f. orge. & grn. 6·75 4·75
14. 25 p. on 5 f. blue & yell. 12·00 10·00

1924. Air. Nos. 10/13 optd. **Poste par Avion.**

22. 13. 2 p. on 40 c. red & blue .. 5·50 5·50
23. 3 p. on 60 c. vio. & bl. .. 5·50 5·50
24. 5 p. on 1 f. red & green .. 5·50 5·50
25. 10 p. on 2 f. orge. & grn. 5·50 5·50

1924. "Pasteur" issue of France surch. **GRAND LIBAN** and value.

15. 30. 50 c. on 10 c. green .. 40 30
16. 1 p. 50 on 30 c. red .. 1·00 90
17. 2 p. 50 on 50 c. blue .. 90 35

1924. "Olympic Games" issue of France surch. **GRAND LIBAN** and value.

18. 31. 50 c. on 10 c. green .. 25·00 25·00
19. – 1 p. 25 on 25 c. red .. 25·00 25·00
20. – 1 p. 50 on 30 c. red & blk. 25·00 25·00
21. – 2 p. 50 on 50 c. blue .. 25·00 25·00

1924. Stamps of France surch. **Gd Liban** and value in English and Arabic.

26. 11. 10 c. on 2 c. red .. 15 20
27. 18. 25 c. on 5 c. orange .. 30 30
28. 50 c. on 10 c. green .. 40 40
29. 15. 75 c. on 15 c. green .. 55 55
30. 18. 1 p. on 20 c. brown .. 30 30
31. 1 p. 25 on 25 c. blue .. 85 85
32. 1 p. 50 on 30 c. red .. 40 40
33. 1 p. 50 on 30 c. orange 32·00 32·00
34. 2 p. on 35 c. violet .. 85 85
35. 13. 2 p. on 40 c. red & blue 30 30
36. 2 p. on 45 c. grn. & bl. 9·50 9·50
37. 3 p. on 60 c. violet & bl. 85 85
38. 15. 3 p. on 60 c. violet .. 1·10 1·10
39. 4 p. on 85 c. red .. 1·10 1·10
40. 13. 5 p. on 1 f. red & green 1·60 1·60
41. 10 p. on 2 f. orge. & turq. 4·25 4·25
42. 25 p. on 5 f. blue & yell. 6·00 6·00

1924. "Pasteur" issue of France surch. **Gd Liban** and value in English and Arabic.

43. 30. 50 c. on 10 c. green .. 30 20
44. 75 c. on 15 c. green .. 40 60
45. 1 p. 50 on 30 c. red .. 75 60
46. 2 p. on 45 c. red .. 1·40 1·10
47. 2 p. 50 on 50 c. blue 60 20
48. 4 p. on 75 c. blue .. 1·40 1·10

1924. Nos. 401/4 (Olympic Games) and Ronsard stamps of France surch. **Gd Liban** and value in English and Arabic.

49. 31. 50 c. on 10 c. green .. 28·00 28·00
50. – 1 p. 25 on 25 c. red .. 28·00 28·00
51. – 1 p. 50 on 30 c. red & blk. .. .. .. 28·00 28·00
52. – 2 p. 50 on 50 c. blue .. 28·00 28·00
53. 35. 4 p. on 75 c. blue .. 1·25 1·25

1924. Air. Stamps of France surch. **Gd Liban Avion** and value in English and Arabic.

54. 13. 2 p. on 40 c. red & blue .. 5·50 5·50
55. 3 p. on 60 c. vio. & bl. .. 5·50 5·50
56. 5 p. on 1 f. red & green .. 5·50 5·50
57. 10 p. on 2 f. red & grn. .. 5·50 5·50

5. Cedar of Lebanon.

7. Tripoli.

6. Beirut.

1925. Views.

58. 5. 10 c. violet 20 10
59. 6. 25 c. black 30 20
60. – 50 c. green (Tripoli) .. 20 10
61. – 75 c. red (Beit ed-Din) .. 35 20
62. – 1 p. red (Baalbek) .. 80 40
63. – 1 p. 25 c. grn. (Mouktara) 75 85
64. – 1 p. 50 c. red (Tyre) .. 35 15
65. – 2 p. sepia (Zahle).. .. 55 20
66. – 2 p. 50 c. blue (Baalbek).. 85 65
67. – 3 p. brn. (Deir el-Kamar) 90 75
68. – 5 p. violet (Sidon) .. 1·25 1·10
69. 7. 10 p. plum .. .. 2·25 1·60
70. – 25 p. blue (Beirut) .. 6·75 6·25

1925. Air. Stamps as last optd. **AVION** in English and Arabic.

71. – 2 p. sepia .. .. .. 2·25 2·25
72. – 3 p. brown .. .. 2·25 2·25
73. – 5 p. violet.. .. .. 2·25 2·25
74. 7. 10 p. plum .. .. 2·25 2·25

1926. Air. Same stamps but optd. with aeroplane instead.

75. – 2 p. sepia .. .. .. 2·25 2·25
76. – 3 p. brown .. .. 2·25 2·25
77. – 5 p. violet.. .. .. 2·25 2·25
78. 7. 10 p. plum .. .. 2·25 2·25

1926. War Refugee Charity. As 1925 but surch. **Secours aux Refugies Afft.** and premium in English and Arabic.

79. 6. 25 c.+25 c. black .. 2·25 2·25
80. – 50 c.+25 c. green .. 2·25 2·25
81 – 75 c.+25 c. red .. 2·25 2·25
82. – 1 p.+50 c. red .. 2·25 2·25
83. – 1 p. 25+50 c. green .. 3·00 3·00
84. – 1 p. 50+50 c. red .. 3·00 3·00
85. – 2 p.+75 c. sepia .. .. 2·50 2·50
86. – 2 p. 50+75 c. blue .. 3·00 3·00
87. – 3 p.+1 p. brown .. .. 3·00 3·00
88. – 5 p.+1 p. violet .. .. 3·00 3·00
89. 7. 10 p.+2 p. plum .. .. 3·25 3·25
90. – 25 p.+5 p. blue .. .. 3·25 3·25

1926. Air. Nos. 75/78 surch. **Secours aux Refugies Afft.** and premium in English and Arabic.

91. – 2 p.+1 p. sepia .. .. 5·50 5·50
92. – 3 p.+2 p. brown .. .. 5·50 5·50
93. – 5 p.+3 p. violet .. .. 5·50 5·50
94. 7. 10 p.+5 p. plum .. .. 5·50 5·50

1926. As 1925 surch. in English and Arabic figures and bars.

95. – 3 p. 50 c. on 75 c. red .. 40 40
96b. 6. 4 p. on 25 c. black .. 85 85
98. – 4 p. 50 on 75 c. red .. 1·10 1·10
99. – 6 p. on 2 p. 50 blue .. 75 75
100. – 7 p. 50 on 2 p. 50 blue.. 1·10 1·10
101. – 12 p. on 1 p. 25 green .. 80 80
102. – 15 p. on 25 p. blue .. 1·10 1·10
103. – 20 p. on 1 p. 25 green .. 3·00 3·00

1927. Pictorial and provisional stamps of Lebanon optd. **Republique Libanaise.**

104. 5. 10 c. violet 10 10
105. – 50 c. green 10 10
106. – 1 p. red 10 10
107. – 1 p. 50 red 20 20
108. – 2 p. sepia 40 30
109. – 3 p. brown 30 15
110. 6. 4 p. on 25 c. blk. (No. 96) 20 10
111. – 4 p. 50 on 75 c. red .. 20 15
112. – 5 p. violet .. .. 1·10 35
113. – 7 p. 50 on 2 p. 50 blue (No. 100) 30 15
114. 7. 10 p. plum .. .. 1·25 60
115. – 15 p. on 25 p. blue (No. 102) .. .. 3·50 2·50
117. – 25 p. blue .. .. 5·25 4·25

1927. Air. Nos. 75/78 optd. **Republique Libanaise** in one or two lines and bar.

118. – 2 p. sepia .. .. 2·25 2·25
119. – 3 p. brown .. .. 2·25 2·25
120. – 5 p. violet .. .. 2·25 2·25
121. 7. 10 p. plum .. .. 2·25 2·25

الجمهورية اللبنانية

(10.)

1928. Nos. 104/117 optd. with T **10** and in some cases surch. also.

145. 5. 5 c. on 10 c. violet .. 10 10
124. 10 c. violet 15 15
125. – 50 c. green .. .. 1·00 1·00
146. – 50 c. on 75 c. red .. 30 30
126. – 1 p. red 30 30
127. – 1 p. 50 red .. .. 1·00 1·00
128. – 2 p. sepia 60 60
147 – 2 p. on 1 p. 25 green .. 30 30
129. – 3 p. brown 80 80
148. 6. 4 p. on 25 c. black .. 30 30
131. – 4 p. 50 on 75 c. red .. 1·00 1·00
132. – 5 p. violet .. .. 1·90 1·90
149. – 7 p. 50 on 2 p. 50 blue 90 90
134. 7. 10 p. plum .. .. 2·75 2·75
135. – 15 p. on 25 p. blue .. 4·75 4·75
136. – 25 p. blue .. .. 5·50 5·50

1928. Air. Optd. **Republique Libanaise** in English and Arabic (latter as T 10) and aeroplane.

151. – 50 c. green 25 25
152 – 50 c. on 75 c. (No. 146) 25 25
153. – 1 p. red 30 30
141. – 2 p. sepia .. .. 1·60 1·60
154. – 2 p. on 1 p. 25 (No. 147) 70 70
142. – 3 p. brown .. .. 1·10 1·10
143. – 5 p. violet .. .. 1·60 1·60
144. 7. 10 p. plum .. .. 1·60 1·60
155. – 15 p. on 25 p. (No. 135) £170 £170
156. – 25 p. blue £110 £110

14. "Bombyx mori" Larva, Cocoon and Moth.

1930. Silk Congress.

157. 14. 4 pi. sepia .. .. 8·75 8·75
158. 4½ pi. red .. .. 8·75 8·75
159. 7½ pi. blue .. .. 8·75 8·75
160. 10 pi. violet .. .. 8·75 8·75
161. 15 pi. green .. .. 8·75 8·75
162. 25 pi. red .. .. 8·75 8·75

15. Cedars of Lebanon. 16a. Baalbek.

1930. Views.

163. – 10 c. orange (Beirut) .. 10 10
164. 15. 20 c. brown 10 10
165. – 25 c. blue (Baalbek) .. 15 15
166. – 50 c. brown (Bickfaya) .. 70 35
166b. – 75 c. brown (Baalbek).. 35 25
167. – 1 p. green (Saida) .. 50 25
167a. – 1 p. plum (Saida) .. 50 25
168. – 1 p. 50 plum (Beit ed-Din) 80 80
168a. – 1 p. 50 green (Beit ed-Din) 50 25
169. – 2 p. blue (Tripoli) .. 1·00 40
170. – 3 p. sepia (Baalbek) .. 1·00 40
171. – 4 p. brown (Nahr-el-Kelb) 1·25 15
172. – 4 p. 50 red (Beaufort).. 1·25 50
173. – 5 p. black (Beit ed-Din) 65 25
251. – 5 p. blue (Nahr el-Kalb) 80 15
174. – 6 p. purple (Tyre) .. 1·10 95
175. 16a. 7 p. 50 blue .. .. 1·25 30
176. 10 p. green (Hasbaya).. 2·50 30
177. – 15 p. purple (Afka Falls) 3·75 90
178. – 25 p. green (Beirut) .. 4·75 1·10
179. – 50 p. grn. (Deir el-Kamar) 18·00 5·00
180. – 100 p. black (Baalbek) 18·00 7·25

17. Jebeil (Byblos).

1930. Air. Aeroplane and views as T **17.**

181. 50 c. purple (Rachaya) .. 25 20
182. 1 p. green (Broumana) .. 25 20
183. 2 p. orange (Baalbek) .. 55 60
184. 3 p. red (Hasroun) .. 55 40
185. 5 p. green (Byblos) .. 55 40
186. 10 p. red (Kadisha) .. 1·10 1·10
187. 15 p. brown (Beirut) .. 80 95
188. 25 p. violet (Tripoli) .. 1·50 1·40
189. 50 p. lake (Kabelais) .. 4·75 4·50
190. 100 p. brown (Zahle) .. 6·50 6·00

18. Skiing.

1936. Air. Tourist Propaganda.

191. 18. 50 c. green .. .. 1·25 1·50
192. – 1 p. orange .. .. 1·90 1·75
193. 18. 2 p. violet .. .. 1·90 1·75
194. – 3 p. green .. .. 1·90 1·75
195. 18. 5 p. red .. .. 1·90 1·75
196. – 10 p. brown .. .. 1·50 1·75
197. – 15 p. red .. .. 27·00 27·00
198. 18. 25 p. green .. .. 75·00 75·00

Design: 1, 3, 10, 15 p. Jounieh Bay.

20. Cedar of Lebanon.

22. Lebanese Landscape. 21. President Edde.

1937.

199. 20. 10 c. red 15 10
200. 20 c. blue 15 10
201. 25 c. lilac 20 10
202. 50 c. red 20 10
203. 75 c. brown 25 15
207. 21. 3 p. violet 80 40
208. 4 p. brown 40 10
209. 4 p. 50 red 50 20
211. 22. 10 p. red 90 30
212. 12½ p. blue 45 15
213. 15 p. green 75 35
214. 20 p. brown 60 15
215. 25 p. red 65 20
216. 50 p. violet .. .. 1·50 45
217. 100 p. sepia .. .. 2·25 1·00

23. Exhibition Pavilion, Paris.

1937. Air. Paris Int. Exn.

218. 23. 50 c. black 85 85
219. 1 p. green 85 85
220. 2 p. brown 85 85
221. 3 p. green 85 85
222. 5 p. green .. .. 1·10 1·10
223. 10 p. red .. .. 5·00 5·00
224. 15 p. red .. .. 5·00 5·00
225. 25 p. brown .. .. 10·00 10·00

25. Ruins of Baalbek.

1937. Air.

226. – 50 c. blue 10 10
227. – 1 p. brown 15 10
228. – 2 p. sepia 25 15
229. – 3 p. red 60 50
230. – 5 p. green 30 40
231. 25. 10 p. violet 30 20
232. 15 p. blue 90 95
233. 25 p. violet .. .. 2·75 2·75
234. 50 p. green .. .. 5·50 4·25
235. 100 p. brown .. .. 2·75 2·25

Design: 50 c. to 5 p. Beit ed-Din.

1938. Surch. in English and Arabic figures.

236. 21. 2 p. on 3 p. violet .. 40 35
237. 2½ p. on 4 p. brown .. 40 35

27. Medical College, Beirut.

1938. Air. Medical Congress.

238. 27. 2 p. green .. .. 1·60 1·60
239. 3 p. orange .. .. 1·60 1·60
240. 5 p. violet .. .. 3·00 3·00
241. 10 p. red .. .. 7·25 7·25

28. M. Nogues and Aeroplane over Beirut. 32. Emir Bechir Chehab.

1938. Air. 10th Anniv. of 1st France-Lebanese Air Service.

242. 28. 10 p. purple .. .. 2·40 2·40

1938. Surch.

243. – 6 p. on 7 p. 50 (No. 175) 90 90
244. – 7 p. 50 on 50 p. (No. 179) 90 90
245. – 7 p. 50 on 100 p. (180) 90 90
246. 22. 12 p. 50 on 7 p. 50 blue 2·10 2·10
247. 12½ on 7 p. 50 blue .. 25 25

1939. As T **16a.** but with differing figures and Arabic inscriptions in side panels, and imprint at foot "IMP. CATHOLIQUE-BEYROUTH-LIBAN" instead of "HELIO VAUGIRARD".

248. 1 p. green 75 10
249. 1 p. 50 purple 85 40
250. 7 p. 50 red .. .. 1·10 50

Design: Beit ed-Din.

1942. 1st Anniv. of Proclamation of Independence.

252. 32. 50 c. green (postage) .. 1·75 1·75
253. 1 p. 50 purple .. .. 1·75 1·75
254. 6 p. red .. .. 1·75 1·75
255. 15 p. blue .. .. 1·75 1·75

256. – 10 p. purple (air) .. 3·00 3·00
257. – 50 p. green .. .. 3·00 3·00

Design: 10 p., 50 p. (air), Aeroplane over mountains.

1943. Surch. in English and Arabic and with old values cancelled with ornaments.

258. 2 p. on 4 p. brown (208) .. 3·50 3·00
259. 6 p. on 7 p. 50 red (250) .. 65 35
260. 10 p. on 12½ p. blue (212).. 65 40

37. Parliament House.

38. Behamoun.

1944. 2nd Anniv. of Proclamation of Independence.

265. 37. 25 p. red (postage) .. 6·75 6·75
266. – 50 p. blue .. .. 6·75 6·75
267. 37. 150 p. blue .. .. 6·75 6·75
268. – 200 p. purple .. .. 6·75 6·75

Design: 50 p. 200 p. Government House.

269. 38. 25 p. green (air) .. 2·00 1·90
270. 50 p. orange .. .. 3·00 2·25
271. – 100 p. brown .. .. 3·00 1·75
272. – 200 p. violet .. .. 4·25 3·25
273. – 300 p. green .. .. 13·50 10·50
274. – 500 p. brown .. .. 30·00 22·00

Designs: 100 p., 200 p. Rachaya Citadel. 300 p., 500 p. Beirut.

38a. Beirut Isolation Hospital.

المؤتمر الطبي العربي السادس

١٩٤٤

(39.)

1944. 10th Medical Congress. Horiz designs optd with T **39.**

275 38a 10 p. red (postage) .. 4·25 4·25
276 20 p. blue .. .. 4·25 4·25

277 – 20 p. orange (air) .. 1·90 1·90
278 – 50 p. blue .. .. 1·90 1·90
279 – 100 p. purple .. .. 3·00 3·00

Design: Nos. 277/9, Bhannes Sanatorium.

(40. Trans " Nov. 23, 1943 ").

1944. President's Return to Office. 1st Anniv. Nos. 265/74 optd. with T **40.**

280. 37. 25 p. red (postage) .. 9·00 9·00
281. – 50 p. blue .. .. 9·00 9·00
282. 37. 150 p. blue .. .. 9·00 9·00
283. – 200 p. purple .. .. 9·00 9·00

284. 38. 25 p. green (air) .. 3·25 3·25
285. 50 p. orange .. .. 5·50 5·50
286. – 100 p. brown .. .. 7·25 7·25
287. – 200 p. violet .. .. 14·00 14·00
288. – 300 p. green .. .. 18·00 18·00
289. – 500 p. brown .. .. 32·00 32·00

1945. Surch. in English and Arabic figures and ornaments.

261. – 2 p. on 5 p. blue (251) 40 20
262. – 3 p. on 5 p. blue (251) 40 20
263. 22. 6 p. on 12½ pi. blue .. 55 35
264. 7½ pi. on 12½ pi. blue .. 75 95

41. Crusader Castle, Byblos. 42. Falls of R. Litani.

1945.

397. 41. 7 p. 50 red (postage) .. 2·50 10
398. 10 p. purple .. .. 4·50 10
399. 12 p. 50 blue .. .. 11·00 30
290. 15 p. brown .. .. 2·00 1·75
291. 20 p. green .. .. 2·00 1·75
292. – 25 p. blue .. .. 2·00 1·75
400. 41. 25 p. violet .. .. 17·00 45
293. – 50 p. red .. .. 4·00 2·25
401. 41. 50 p. green .. .. 35·00 2·75

294. 42. 25 p. brown (air) .. 1·25 1·00
295. 50 p. purple .. .. 1·75 1·40
296. – 200 p. violet .. .. 7·25 2·50
297. – 300 p. black .. .. 15·00 5·25

Designs—Horiz. Nos. 292, 293, Crusader Castle, Tripoli. Nos. 296/7, Cedar of Lebanon and skier.

HAVE YOU READ THE NOTES AT THE BEGINNING OF THIS CATALOGUE?
These often provide answers to the enquiries we receive.

43. V(ictory) and National Flag.

44. V(ictory) and Lebanese Soldiers at Bir-Hakeim.

1946. Victory. " V " in design. (a) Postage.
298. **43.** 7 p. 50 brn., red & pink 80 10
299. 10 p. mauve, pink & red 1·00 10
300. 12 p. 50 lake, red & mve. 1·00 15
301. 15 p. green, emer. & red 1·90 15
302. 20 p. myrtle, grn. & red 1·60 10
303. 25 p. dp. blue, lt. blue and red .. .. 2·75 45
304. 50 p. blue, pink & red .. 5·00 1·25
305. 100 p. black, grey & red 8·25 3·00

(b) Air.
306. **44.** 15 p. green, yell. & red 45 15
307. 20 p. red and blue .. 45 30
308. 25 p. blue, yell. & red .. 50 30
309. 50 p. grey, vio. & red .. 85 30
310. 100 p. violet and red .. 2·75 95
311. 150 p. brown and red .. 3·25 1·50

1946. As T **43** but without " V " sign.
312. 7 p. 50 lake, red & mauve 60 10
313. 10 p. dp. blue, pale mve. and red 90 10
314. 12 p. 50 brn., grn. and red 1·00 10
315. 15 p. brown, pink and red 1·90 20
316. 20 p. blue, orange and red 1·60 20
317. 25 p. myrtle, green and red 2·75 30
318. 50 p. dp. blue, lt. blue and red .. .. .. 5·00 1·25
319. 100 p. dp. grey, lt. grey & red .. .. .. 8·25 3·00

45. Grey Herons.

1946.
320. **45.** 12 p. 50 c. red (postage) 11·00 25
321. 10 p. orange (air) .. 4·25 65
322. 25 p. blue .. .. 5·25 35
323. 50 p. green .. .. 10·50 1·00
324. 100 p. purple .. .. 18·00 4·50

46 Cedar of Lebanon. **47.**

1946.
325. **46.** 50 c. brown 10 10
326. 1 p. purple 10 10
327. 2 p. 50 violet 20 10
328. 5 p red 45 10
329. 6 p. grey 50 10

1946. Air. Arab Postal Congress.
330. **47.** 25 p. blue 70 35
331. 50 p. green 85 55
332. 75 p. red .. .. 1·40 95
333. 150 p. violet .. .. 2·75 2·00

48. Cedar of Lebanon.

49. President, Bridge and Tablet.

1947.
333a. **48.** 50 c. brown 45 10
333b. 2p. 50 green 95 10
333c. 5 p. red .. .. 1·40 10

1947. Air. Evacuation of Foreign Troops from Lebanon.
334. **49.** 25 p. blue 80 50
335. 50 p. red 90 90
336. 75 p. black .. .. 1·50 1·25
337. 150 p. green .. .. 3·00 2·25

50. Crusader Castle, Tripoli.

51. Jounieh Bay.

DESIGN: 150 p. to 300 p. Grand Serail Palace.

1947.
338. **50.** 12 p. 50 red (postage) 4·25 20
339. 25 p. blue .. .. 5·25 25
340. 50 p. green .. .. 16·00 45
341. 100 p. violet .. .. 22·00 4·00

342. **51.** 5 p. green (air) 25 10
343. 10 p. mauve 20 10
344. 15 p. red 40 10
344a. 15 p. green .. .. 5·00 80
345. 20 p. orange 60 10
345a. 20 p. red 60 10
346. 25 p. blue 90 10
347. 50 p. red .. .. 1·90 20
348. 100 p. purple .. .. 4·25 35
349. – 150 p. purple .. .. 9·00 70
350. – 200 p. slate .. .. 14·00 3·50
351. – 300 p. black .. .. 19·00 8·25

54. Phoenician Galley.

DESIGN—VERT. 10 p. to 25 p. Posthorn.

1947. Air. 12th Congress of U.P.U., Paris.
352. – 10 p. blue 60 25
353. – 15 p. red 75 35
354. – 25 p. blue .. .. 1·00 60
355. **54.** 50 p. green .. .. 2·75 75
356. 75 p. violet .. .. 3·50 1·25
357. 100 p. brown .. .. 5·00 2·50

55. Faraya Bridge and Statue.

DESIGN: 50 p. to 100 p. Djounie Bay and statue.

1947. Air. Red Cross Fund. Cross in red.
358. **55.** 12 p. 50+25 p. green .. 5·50 4·50
359. 25 p.+50 p. blue .. 6·00 5·00
360. – 50 p.+100 p. brown .. 8·25 6·00
361. – 75 p.+150 p. violet .. 17·00 12·00
362. – 100 p.+200 p. grey .. 27·00 17·00

56. Cedar of Lebanon.

58. Lebanese Landscape.

1948.
363. **56.** 50 c. blue (postage) .. 15 10
407. 50 c. red 10 10
364. 1 p. brown 35 10
408. 1 p. orange 30 10
365. 2 p. 50 mauve 65 10
409. 2 p. 50 violet .. .. 1·25 10
366. 3 p. green 90 10
367. 5 p. red .. .. 1·00 10
410. 5 p. purple .. .. 1·00 10
368. – 7 p. 50 red .. .. 2·00 10
369. – 10 p. purple .. .. 2·75 10
370. – 12 p. 50 blue .. .. 6·75 20
371. – 25 p. blue .. .. 8·25 70
372. – 50 p. green .. .. 17·00 4·75
DESIGN—HORIZ. 7 p. 50 to 50 p. Zebaide Aqueduct.

373. **58.** 5 p. red (air) 30 10
374. 10 p. mauve 65 10
375. 15 p. brown .. .. 1·60 10
376. 20 p. slate .. .. 2·75 15
377. 25 p. blue .. .. 6·75 65
378. 50 p. black .. .. 11·00 1·25

59. Europa on Bull.

61. Apollo on Sun Chariot.

1948. 3rd Meeting of U.N.E.S.C.O., Beirut.
379. **59.** 10 p. red (postage) .. 1·60 1·00
380. 12 p. 50 violet .. 2·25 1·50
381. 25 c. olive .. .. 2·75 1·50
382. – 30 p. brown .. .. 2·75 1·60
383. – 40 p. green .. .. 4·50 1·75
DESIGN—VERT. 30 p. 40 p. Avicenna (philosopher and scientist).

384. **61.** 7 p. 50 blue (air) .. 1·10 85
385. 15 p. black .. .. 1·40 85
386. 20 p. brown .. .. 2·50 1·75
387. – 35 p. red .. .. 4·00 2·25
388. – 75 p. green .. .. 7·75 4·50
DESIGN—HORIZ. 35 p. 75 p. Symbolical figure.

64. Helicopter.

63. Camel.

66. Nahr el-Kalb Bridge.

1949. 75th Anniv. of U.P.U.
389. **63.** 5 p. violet (postage) .. 75 50
390. 7 p. 50, red .. .. 1·40 80
391. 12 p. 50 blue .. .. 1·60 1·10
392. **64.** 25 p. blue (air) .. .. 4·25 1·75
393. 50 p. green .. .. 7·50 2·50

1950.
411. **66.** 7 p. 50 red .. .. 1·90 15
412. 10 p. lilac .. .. 2·75 10
413. 12 p. 50 pale blue .. 5·50 20
414. 25 p. deep blue .. 8·25 65
415. 50 p. green .. .. 17·00 4·75
See also Nos. 433/7.

67. Congressional Flags.

DESIGNS—HORIZ. 5 p., 15 p. House Martins. 25 p., 35 p. Pres. Bishara al-Khoury and bldg.

1950. Lebanese Emigrants' Congress. Inscr. " MOIS DES EMIGRES—ETE 1950 ".
416. **67.** 7 p. 50 green (postage) .. 40 10
417. 12 p. mauve 40 10
418. – 5 p. blue (air) .. .. 1·40 25
419. – 15 p. violet .. .. 2·25 45
420. – 25 p. brown 80 35
421. – 35 p. green .. .. 1·50 75

70. Crusader Castle, Sidon.

1950. Air.
422. **70.** 10 p. brown 60 10
423. 15 p. green 80 10
424. 20 p. red .. .. 1·60 30
425. 25 p. blue .. .. 3·50 1·00
426. 50 p. grey .. .. 5·00 2·00

1950. Surch. with figures and bars.
427. **56.** 1 p. on 3 p. green .. 45 10
428. **46.** 2 p. 50 on 6 p. grey .. 55 10

73. Cedar of Lebanon.

74. Nahr el-Kalb Bridge.

75. Crusader Castle, Sidon.

Type **74** is similar to Type **66** but left value tablets differ.

1951.
429. **73.** 50 c. red (postage) .. 35 10
430. 1 p. brown 35 10
431. 2 p. 50 grey .. .. 1·60 10
432. 5 p. red .. .. 1·50 10
433. **74.** 7 p. 50 red .. .. 1·90 20
434. 10 p. purple .. .. 2·75 10
435. 12 p. 50 turquoise .. 5·50 30
436. 25 p. blue .. .. 8·25 60
437. 50 p. green .. .. 17·00 4·75
438. **75.** 10 p. turquoise (air) .. 80 10
439. 15 p. brown .. .. 1·75 10
440. 20 p. red .. .. 1·75 10
441. 25 p. blue .. .. 2·00 15
442. 35 p. mauve .. .. 5·00 1·60
443. 50 p. violet .. .. 9·00 1·10
For other values as Type **74** see Nos. 561/3.

76. Cedar.

77. Baalbek.

1952.
444. **76.** 50 c. green (postage) .. 40 10
445. 1 p. brown 45 10
446. 2 p. 50 blue 65 10
447. 5 p. red .. .. 1·00 15
448. **77.** 7 p. 50 red .. .. 1·40 30
449. 10 p. violet .. .. 3·00 40
450. 12 p. 50 blue .. .. 3·00 40
451. 25 p. blue .. .. 4·00 1·00
452. – 50 p. green .. .. 12·00 1·75
453. – 100 p. brown .. .. 22·00 4·75
454. – 5 p. red (air) 30 10
455. – 10 p. grey 45 10
456. – 15 p. mauve 80 10
457. – 20 p. orange .. .. 1·25 25
458. – 25 p. blue .. .. 1·25 25
459. – 35 p. blue .. .. 2·00 25
460. – 50 p. green .. .. 7·00 35
461. – 100 p. blue .. .. 48·00 1·50
462. – 200 p. green .. .. 28·00 2·75
463. – 300 p. sepia .. .. 38·00 6·50
DESIGNS—HORIZ. As Type **77**. Postage: 50 p., 100 p. Beaufort Castle. Air: 5 p. to 35 p. Beirut Airport. 50 p. to 300 p. Amphitheatre, Byblos.

78. Cedar of Lebanon.

79. General Post Office.

80. Mail-plane.

1953.
464. **78.** 50 c. blue (postage) .. 40 10
465. 1 p. red 40 10
466. 2 p. 50 lilac 50 10
560. 2 p. 50 red 35 10
467. 5 p. green .. .. 1·00 12
468. **79.** 7 p. 50 red .. .. 1·75 25
469. 10 p. green .. .. 2·10 40
470. 12 p. 50 turquoise .. 3·00 50
471. 25 p. blue .. .. 4·75 65
472. 50 p. brown .. .. 8·25 1·75
473. **80.** 5 p. green (air) 30 10
474. 10 p. red 55 10
475. 15 p. red 80 10
476. 20 p. turquoise .. .. 1·25 10
477. 25 p. blue .. .. 3·25 10
478. 35 p. brown .. .. 4·50 15
479. 50 p. blue .. .. 6·50 30
480. 100 p. sepia .. .. 12·00 2·75
For 20 p. green as Type **79** see No. 636.

81. Cedar of Lebanon.

82. Beit ed-Din Palace.

83. Baalbek.

DESIGN — HORIZ. 50 p. to 300 p. Litani Irrigation Canal.

1954.
481. **81.** 50 c. blue (postage) .. 15 10
482. 1 p. orange 15 10
483. 2½ p. violet 55 10
484. 5 p. green 60 10
485. **82.** 7 p. 50 red .. .. 1·40 30
486. 10 p. green .. .. 2·00 30
487. 12 p. 50 blue .. .. 3·00 40
488. 25 p. deep blue .. 4·50 1·25
489. 50 p. turquoise .. 7·75 2·75
490. 100 p. sepia .. .. 16·00 5·00
491. **83.** 5 p. green (air) 40 10
492. 10 p. violet 70 10
493. 15 p. red 80 10
494. 20 p. brown .. .. 1·10 10
495. 25 p. blue .. .. 1·25 10
496. 35 p. sepia .. .. 1·75 20
497. – 50 p. green .. .. 5·50 25
498. – 100 p. red .. .. 9·00 35
499. – 200 p. sepia .. .. 20·00 1·10
500. – 300 p. blue .. .. 32·00 2·25
For other values in this design see Nos. 564/7.

84. Khalde Airport, Beirut.

1954. Air. Opening of Beirut Int. Airport.

501. 84. 10 p. red and pink .. 60 25
502. 25 p. blue and ultram... 1·50 40
503. 35 p. brown and sepia.. 1·60 55
504. 65 p. green and grey .. 4·25 1·90

1955. Arab Postal Union. As T 96a of Syria but smaller, 27×37 mm. Inscr. "LIBAN" at top.

505. 12 p. 50 green (postage) .. 25 15
506. 25 p. violet 35 15
507. 2 p. 50 brown (air) .. 20 15

85. Rotary Emblem. 86. Cedar of Lebanon.

87. Jeita Grotto. 88. Skiers.

1955. Air. 50th Anniv. of Rotary Int.

508. 85. 35 p. green 70 50
509. 65 p. blue .. .. 1·25 75

1955.

510. 86. 50 c. blue (postage) .. 15 10
511. 1 p. red 15 10
512. 2 p. 50 violet .. 25 10
552. 2 p. 50 blue .. 2·25 10
513. 5 p. green .. 45 10
514. 87. 7 p. 50 red .. 55 10
515. 10 p. green .. 95 10
516. 12 p. 50 blue .. 1·10 10
517. 25 p. blue .. 2·75 10
518. 50 p. green .. 3·50 30
519. 88. 5 p. turquoise (air) .. 40 20
520. 15 p. red .. 55 15
521. 20 p. violet .. 1·00 15
522. 25 p. blue .. 1·90 20
523. 35 p. brown .. 3·00 35
524. 50 p. brown .. 6·75 60
525. 65 p. blue .. 9·50 1·40

For other colours and new values as Type 88 see Nos. 568/70 and for redrawn Type 86 see Nos. 582/5, 686 and 695/7.

89. Visitor from Abroad. 90. Cedar of Lebanon. 91. Globe and Columns.

92. Oranges.

1955. Air. Tourist Propaganda.

526. 89. 2 p. 50 slate and purple 10 10
527. 12 p. 50 blue & ultram. 30 15
528. 25 p. blue and indigo.. 75 20
529. 35 p. blue and green .. 1·00 30

1955.

530. 90. 50 c. blue (postage) .. 15 10
531. 1 p. orange .. 30 10
532. 2 p. 50 violet .. 15 10
533. 5 p. green .. 20 10
534. 91. 7 p. 50 red and yellow.. 35 10
535. 10 p. green and brown.. 40 10
536. 12 p. 50 blue and green 60 10
537. 25 p. blue and mauve.. 1·40 15
538. 50 p. myrtle and blue.. 1·60 15
539. 100 p. sepia and pink .. 2·75 60
540. 92. 5 p. yellow & green (air) 15 10
541. 10 p. orange and green 35 10
542. 15 p. red and green .. 40 10
543. 20 p. orange and brown 60 10
544. – 25 p. violet and blue .. 85 10
545. – 35 p. lake and green .. 1·40 15
546. – 50 p. yellow and black.. 1·40 15
547. – 65 p. yellow and green.. 3·00 20
548. – 100 p. orange and green 4·75 60
549. – 200 p. red and green .. 6·75 3·00

DESIGNS—VERT. 25 p. to 50 p. Grapes. HORIZ. 4 p. to 200 p. Quinces.

93. U.N. Emblem. 94. Masks, Columns and Gargoyle.

1956. Air. 10th Anniv. of U.N.

550. 93. 35 p. blue .. .. 3·00 2·25
551. 65 p. green .. .. 3·50 2·75

1956. Air. Baalbek Int. Drama Festival. Inscr. "FESTIVAL INTERNATIONAL DE BAALBECK".

553. 94. 2 p. 50 sepia 40 15
554. 10 p. green 55 25
555. – 12 p. 50 blue 55 30
556. – 25 p. violet 80 40
557. – 35 p. purple .. .. 1·60 50
558. – 65 p. slate .. .. 1·90 1·25

DESIGNS—HORIZ. 12 p. 50, 25 p. Temple ruins at Baalbek. VERT. 35 p., 65 p. Double bass, masks and columns.

1957. As T 74 but inscr. " LIBAN ".

561. 7 p. 50 red 70 10
562. 10 p. brown .. .. 1·10 10
563. 12 p. 50 blue .. .. 1·25 10

1957. Air. Arabic inscription changed. New values and colours.

564. – 10 p. violet 20 10
565. – 15 p. orange 35 10
566. – 20 p. green 40 10
567. – 25 p. blue 50 10
568. 88. 35 p. green .. .. 1·25 20
569. 65 p. purple .. .. 2·75 50
570. 100 p. brown .. .. 4·50 90

DESIGN: 10 p. to 25 p. As Nos. 497/500.

95. Pres. Chamoun and King Faisal II of Iraq. 97. Runners.

1957. Air. Arab Leaders' Conf., Beirut.

571. 95. 15 p. orange 50 25
572. – 15 p. blue 50 25
573. – 15 p. purple 50 25
574. – 15 p. mauve 50 25
575. – 15 p. green 50 25
576. – 25 p. turquoise.. .. 50 25
577. – 100 p. brown .. .. 3·25 1·60

DESIGNS—HORIZ. 15 p. values as Type 95 show Pres. Chamoun and King Hussein of Jordan (No. 572), Abdallah Khalil of Sudan (No. 573), Pres. Shukri Bey al-Quwatli of Syria (No. 574) and King Saud of Saudi Arabia (No. 575). 25 p. Map and Pres. Chamoun. 100 p. (44×44 mm. Diamond shape), The six Arab Leaders.

1957. 2nd Pan-Arabian Games, Beirut.

578. 97. 2 p. 50 c. sepia (post.).. 40 15
579. – 12½ p. blue 60 20
580. – 35 p. purple (air) .. 1·50 60
581. – 50 p. green .. .. 2·00 95

DESIGNS—VERT. 12½ p. Footballers. HORIZ. 35 p. Fencers. 50 p. Stadium.

98. Miners.

DESIGNS—POSTAGE—As Type 86: 50 c., 2 p. 50 c. Figures in uniform size. 1 p., 5 p. Short dash under "P". As Type 98—VERT. 25 p. to 100 p. Potter. AIR—As Type 98—HORIZ. 5 p. to 25 p. Cedar of Lebanon with signs of the Zodiac, bird and ship. 35 p. to 100 p. Chamoun Electric Power Station.

1957.

582 86 50 c. blue (16½ × 20½ mm) (postage) .. 15 10
582a 50 c. violet (17 × 21½ mm) .. 25 10
583 1 p. brown (16½ × 20½ mm) .. 20 10
583a 1 p. red (17 × 21½ mm) 25 10
584 2 p. 50 violet (16½ × 20½ mm) .. 25 10
584a 2 p. 50 blue (17 × 21½ mm) .. 45 10
584b 2 p. 50 green (17 × 21½ mm) .. 30 10
585 5 p. green (16½ × 20½ mm) .. 45 10
586 98 7½ p. pink .. 70 10
587 10 p. brown .. 65 10
588 12½ p. blue .. 85 10
589 – 25 p. blue .. 1·00 10
590 – 50 p. green .. 1·50 15
591 – 100 p. brown .. 3·25 45
592 – 5 p. green (air) .. 25 10
593 – 10 p. orange 15 10
594 – 15 p. brown 20 10
595 – 20 p. red 35 10
596 – 25 p. blue 60 10
597 – 35 p. purple 85 15
598 – 50 p. green .. .. 1·25 20
599 – 65 p. brown .. .. 1·75 25
600 – 100 p. grey .. .. 2·25 75

99. Cedar of Lebanon. 100. Soldier and Flag.

101. Airliner at Khalde Airport.

1959.

601. 99. 50 c. blue (postage) .. 15 10
602. 1 p. orange 35 10
603. 2 p. 50 c. violet .. 35 10
604. 5 p. green 30 10
605. 100. 12 p. 50 c. blue .. 55 10
606. 25 p. blue 60 10
607. 50 p. brown .. .. 1·10 15
608. 100 p. sepia .. .. 2·25 30
609. 101. 5 p. green (air).. .. 55 10
610. 10 p. purple 55 10
611. 15 p. violet 80 10
612. 20 p. red .. .. 1·10 10
613. 25 p. violet .. .. 1·50 20
614. – 35 p. myrtle 80 20
615. – 50 p. turquoise.. .. 1·00 20
616. – 65 p. sepia .. .. 1·60 30
617. – 100 p. blue .. .. 2·25 45

DESIGN—HORIZ. Nos. 614/7, Factory cogwheel and telegraph pylons.

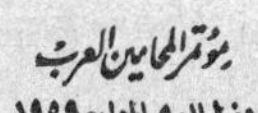

30P ٣٠ق

(102.)

1959. Lawyers' Conf. Nos. 538 and 546 (air) surch. as T 102.

618. 30 p. on 50 p. myrtle and blue (postage) .. 60 45
619. 40 p. on 50 p. yellow and black (air) .. 55 40

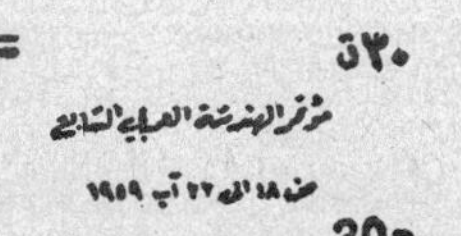

30P

(103.)

1959. Air. Engineers' Conf. Nos. 614 and 616 surch. as T 103.

620. 30 p. on 35 p. myrtle .. 50 30
621. 40 p. on 65 p. sepia .. 75 40

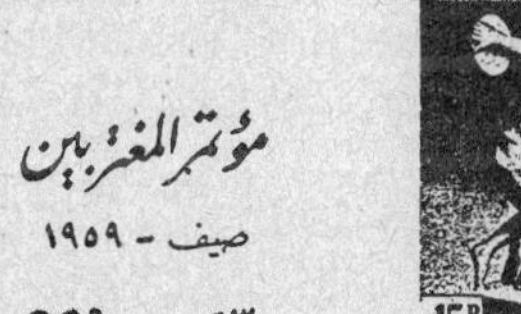

30P ٣٠ق (104.) 105. Discus Thrower.

1959. Emigrants' Conf. No. 590 surch. as T 104.

622. 30 p. on 50 p. green .. 50 15
623. 40 p. on 50 p. green .. 75 35

1959. Air. 3rd Mediterranean Games, Beirut.

624. 105. 15 p. green 40 15
625. – 30 p. brown 60 25
626. – 40 p. blue .. .. 1·25 35

DESIGNS—VERT. 30 p. Weightlifting. HORIZ. 40 p. Games emblem.

INDEX
Countries can be quickly located by referring to the index at the end of this volume.

106. Soldiers with Standard. 108. Planting Tree.

1959. Air. 16th Anniv. of Independence.

627. 106. 40 p. red and black .. 65 35
628. 60 p. red and green .. 95 55

1959. Surch.

629. 100. 7 p. 50 on 12 p. 50 blue 15 10
630. 10 p. on 12 p. 50 blue.. 20 10
631. 15 p. on 25 p. blue .. 30 10
632. – 40 p. on 50 p .green (No. 590) 65 30
633. 88. 40 p. on 65 p. pur. (air) 1·40 45

1960. Air. 25th Anniv. of Friends of the Tree Society.

634. 108. 20 p. purple and green 45 20
635. 40 p. sepia and green .. 65 40

1960. Air. As T 79 but colours of name and value tablets reversed.

636. 50. 20 p. green 40 20

109. Pres. Chehab.

1960. Air.

637. 109. 5 p. green 10 10
638. 10 p. blue 15 10
639. 15 p. brown 15 10
640. 20 p. sepia 20 10
641. 30 p. olive 35 10
642. 40 p. red 35 10
643. 50 p. blue 60 15
644. 70 p. purple 65 25
645. 100 p. green .. .. 1·40 60

110. Arab League Centre. 111. " Uprooted Tree ".

1960. Inaug. of Arab League Centre, Cairo.

646. 110. 15 p. turquoise.. .. 25 20

1960. Air. World Refugee Year.

(a) Size 20½ × 36½ mm.

647. 111. 25 p. brown 30 35
648. 40 p. green 50 45

(b) Size 19½ × 35½ mm.

648b. 111. 25 p. brown 50 50
648c. 40 p. green .. .. 90 1·10

112. Martyrs' Monument.

1960. Air. Martyrs' Commem.

649. 112. 20 p. purple and green 45 15
650. 40 p. blue and green .. 40 20
651. – 70 p. olive and black .. 1·00 55

DESIGN—VERT. 70 p. Detail of statues on monument.

113. Pres. Chehab and King Mohammed V. 114. Pres. Chehab.

1960. Air. Visit of King Mohammed V of Morocco.

652. 113. 30 p. brn. & dp. brn... 50 20
653. 70 p. brn. & blk. .. 1·00 55

1960.

654. 114. 50 c. green 10 10
655. 2 p. 50 olive 10 10
656. 5 p. green 15 10
657. 7 p. 50 brown 30 10
658. 15 p. blue 45 10
659. 50 p. purple 90 15
660. 100 p. brown .. .. 1·40 35

115. Child. 116. Dove, Map and Flags.

1960. Air. Mother and Child Days.

661. 115. 20 p. red and yellow .. 45 10
662. 20 p. + 10 p. red & yell. 55 30
663. – 60 p. blue & pale blue 1·00 40
664. – 60 p. + 15 p. blue and pale blue .. .. 1·25 65

DESIGN: Nos. 663/4, Mother and child.

1960. Air. World Lebanese Union Meeting. Beirut. Multicoloured.

665. 20 p. Type 116 .. .. 20 10
666. 40 p. Cedar of Lebanon and homing pigeons .. 40 15
667. 70 p. Globes and Cedar of Lebanon (horiz.) .. 65 30

(117.) 119. Boxing.

1960. Arabian Oil Congress, Beirut. Optd. with T 117.

668. 86. 5 p. green (No. 585) .. 10 10
669. 110. 15 p. turquoise .. 35 15

1960. Air. World Refugee Year. Nos. 647/8 surch. in English and Arabic.

669a. 111. 20 p. + 10 p. on 40 p. grn. 5·00 5·00
669b. 30 p. + 15 p. on 25 p. brn. 7·75 7·75

1961. Olympic Games.

670. 119. 2 p. 50 + 2 p. 50 brn. and blue (postage) .. 10 10
671. – 5 p. + 5 p. brown and orge. 15 15
672. – 7 p. 50 + 7 p. 50 brn. & vio. 25 20
673. – 15 p. + 15 p. brn. & red (air) 1·75 1·50
674. – 25 p. + 25 p. brn. & grn. 1·75 1·50
675. – 35 p. + 35 p. brn. & blue 1·75 1·50

DESIGNS: 5 p. Wrestling. 7 p. 50, Putting the shot. 15 p. Fencing. 25 p. Cycling. 35 p. Swimming.

120. Pres. Chehab. 121. Pres. Chehab and Map of Lebanon. 122. U.N. Emblem and Map.

1961.

676. 120. 2 p. 50 ultram. & blue (postage) .. 15 10
677. 7 p. 50 purple and blue 25 10
678. 10 p. brown and yellow 35 10
679. 121. 5 p. grn. & lt. grn. (air) 15 10
680. 10 p. brown and ochre .. 35 10
681. 70 p. violet and mauve 1·10 45
682. – 200 p. blue and bistre .. 2·50 1·50

DESIGN—HORIZ. 200 p. Casino, Maameltein.

1961. Air. 15th Anniv. of U.N.O.

683. 122. 20 p. purple and blue .. 30 10
684. – 30 p. green and brown .. 45 15
685. – 50 p. light blue & ultram. 75 35

DESIGNS—VERT. 40 p. U.N. emblem and Baalbek ruins. HORIZ. 50 p. View of U.N. Headquarters and Manhattan.

123. Cedar.

124. Bay of Maameltein.

1961. Redrawn version of T 86 (different arrangement at foot).

(a) Shaded background

686. 123. 2 p. 50 myrtle 45 10

(b) As T 123 but plain background.

695. 2 p. 50 yellow .. 15 10
696. 5 p. lake 25 10
697. 10 p. black 35 10

1961. Air.

687. 124. 15 p. lake 20 10
688. 30 p. blue 35 15
689. 40 p. sepia 45 20

125. Weaving.

DESIGN: 30 p. Pottery.

1961. Air. Labour Day.

690. – 30 p. red 85 25
691. 125. 70 p. blue .. .. 1·25 70

126. Water-skiers.

DESIGNS — VERT. 15 p. Firework display. HORIZ. 70 p. Tourists in punt.

1961. Air. Tourist Month.

692. – 15 p. violet and blue .. 45 15
693. 126. 40 p. blue and flesh .. 65 45
694. – 70 p. olive & flesh .. 1·00 70

127. G.P.O., Beirut.

1961.

698. 127. 2 p. 50 mauve (postage) 35 10
699. 5 p. green 50 10
700. 15 p. blue 45 10
701. – 35 p. green (air) .. 35 20
702. – 50 p. brown 55 30
703. – 100 p. black 80 60

DESIGN: 35 p. to 100 p. Motor highway, Dora.

128. Cedars of Lebanon.

129. Tyre Waterfront.

1961.

704. 128. 50 c. green 10 10
705. 1 p. brown 15 10
706. 2 p. 50 blue 20 10
707. 5 p. red 25 10
708. 7 p. 50 violet 40 10
709. – 10 p. purple 55 10
710. – 15 p. blue 65 10
711. – 50 p. green .. .. 8·50 45
712. – 100 p. black .. .. 1·90 70
713. 129. 5 p. red (air) .. 20 10
714. 10 p. violet 20 10
715. 15 p. blue 30 10
716. 20 p. orange 30 10
717. 30 p. green 40 10
718. – 40 p. purple 50 20
719. – 50 p. blue 60 20
720. – 70 p. green 85 45
721. – 100 p. sepia .. .. 1·50 60

DESIGNS—HORIZ. Nos. 709/12, Zahle. VERT. Nos. 718/21, Afka Falls.

See also Nos. 729/34.

130. U.N.E.S.C.O. Building, Beirut.

1961. Air. 15th Anniv. of U.N.E.S.C.O. Mult.

722. 20 p. Type 130 .. .. 35 10
723. 30 p. U.N.E.S.C.O. emblem and cedar (vert.) .. 45 20
724. 50 p. U.N.E.S.C.O. Building, Paris 85 40

131. Tomb of Unknown Soldier.

132. Scout Bugler.

1961. Independence and Evacuation of Foreign Troops Commem. Multicoloured.

725. 10 p. Type 131 (postage) 25 10
726. 15 p. Soldier and flag .. 35 10
727. 25 p. Cedar emblem (air) 30 20
728. 50 p. Emirs Bashir and Fakhreddine 55 45

The 25 p. and 50 p. are horiz.

1962. As Nos. 704/21 but with larger figures of value.

729. 128. 50 c. green (postage) .. 15 10
730. 1 p. brown 15 10
731. 2 p. 50 blue 20 10
732. – 15 p. blue .. .. 1·90 15
733. 129. 5 p. red (air) 35 10
734. – 40 p. purple .. .. 4·00 50

1962. Lebanese Scout Movement Commem.

735. ½ p. blk., yell. & grn. (post.) 10 10
736. 1 p. multicoloured .. 10 10
737. 2½ p. green, black and red 10 10
738. 6 p. multicoloured .. 20 10
739. 10 p. yellow, black & blue 35 10
740. 15 p. multicoloured (air) .. 35 20
741. 20 p. yell., blk. and violet 50 30
742. 25 p. multicoloured .. 85 40

DESIGNS—VERT. ½ p. Type 132. 6 p. Lord Baden-Powell. 20 p. Saluting hand. HORIZ. 1 p. Scout with flag, cedar and badge. 2½ p. Stretcher party, badge and laurel. 10 p. Scouts and camp fire. 15 p. Cedar and Guide badge. 25 p. Cedar and Scout badge.

133. Arab League Centre, Cairo, and Emblem.

134. Blacksmith.

1962. Air. Arab League Week.

743. 133. 20 p. blue & turquoise 40 20
744. 30 p. lake and pink .. 45 30
745. 50 p. green & turquoise 75 45

See also Nos. 792/5.

1962. Air. Labour Day.

746. 134. 5 p. green and blue .. 25 10
747. 10 p. blue and pink .. 30 10
748. – 25 p. violet and pink .. 35 15
749. – 35 p. mauve and blue 45 25

DESIGN—HORIZ. 25 p., 35 p. Tractor.

1962. European Shooting Championships Nos. 670/5 otpd. CHAMPIONNAT D'EUROPE DE TIR/2 JUIN 1962 in English and Arabic.

750. 119. 2 p. 50 + 2 p. 50 (post.) 30 30
751. – 5 p. + 5 p. 55 40
752. – 7 p. 50 + 7 p. 50 .. 70 40
753. – 15 p. + 15 p. (air) .. 65 65
754. – 25 p. + 25 p. .. .. 1·40 1·40
755. – 35 p. + 35 p. .. .. 1·90 1·90

136. Hand grasping Emblem. 137. Rock Temples of Abu Simbel.

1962. Air. Malaria Eradication.

756. 136. 30 p. brown & lt. brown 40 30
757. – 70 p. violet and lilac .. 60 55

DESIGN: 70 p. Campaign emblem.

1962. Nubian Monuments.

758. 137. 5 p. bl. & ultram. (post.) 30 10
759. 15 p. lake and brown .. 40 15
760. – 30 p. yell. and grn. (air) 85 45
761. – 50 p. olive and grey .. 1·40 90

DESIGNS: 30 p., 50 p. Bas-relief.

138. Playing-card Symbols.

139. Schoolboy.

1962. Air. European Bridge Championships.

762. 138. 25 p. multicoloured .. 1·60 1·10
763. 40 p. multicoloured .. 1·90 1·10

1962. Schoolchildren's Day.

764. 139. 30 p. mult. (postage) .. 35 15
765. – 45 p. mult. (air) .. 55 25

DESIGN: 45 p. Teacher.

140.

141. Cherries.

1962. Air. 19th Anniv. of Independence.

766. 140. 25 p. grn., red & turq. 55 35
767. 25 p. vio., red & turq. 55 35
768. 25 p. blue, red & turq. 55 35

1962. Fruits. Multicoloured.

769. 50 c. Type 141 (postage) .. 15 10
770. 1 p. Figs. 15 10
771. 2 p. 50 Type 141 .. .. 20 10
772. 5 p. Figs. 30 10
773. 7 p. 50 Type 141 .. .. 30 10
774. 10 p. Grapes 40 10
775. 17 p. 50 Grapes 50 10
776. 30 p. Grapes 80 15
777. 50 p. Oranges .. .. 1·25 40
778. 100 p. Pomegranates .. 3·00 90
779. 5 p. Apricots (air) .. 30 10
780. 10 p. Plums 40 10
781. 20 p. Apples 50 10
782. 30 p. Plums 65 20
783. 40 p. Apples 80 20
784. 50 p. Pears .. .. 1·00 25
785. 70 p. Medlars .. .. 1·40 40
786. 100 p. Lemons .. .. 1·90 70

142. Reaping.

143. Nurse tending Baby.

1963. Air. Freedom from Hunger.

787. 142. 2 p. 50 yellow and blue 15 10
788. 5 p. yellow and green .. 15 10
789. 7 p. 50 yellow & purple 30 10
790. – 15 p. green and red .. 30 15
791. – 20 p. green and red .. 40 20

DESIGN—HORIZ. 15 p., 20 p. Three ears of wheat within hand.

1963. Air. Arab League Week. As T 133 but inscr. "1963".

792. 5 p. violet and blue .. 15 10
793. 10 p. green and blue .. 30 15
794. 15 p. brown and blue .. 20 25
795. 20 p. grey and blue .. 40 40

1963. Air. Red Cross Cent.

796. – 5 p. green and red .. 15 10
797. – 20 p. blue and red .. 40 10
798. 143. 35 p. red and black .. 45 25
799. 40 p. violet and red .. 55 35

DESIGN—HORIZ. 5 p., 20 p. Blood transfusion.

144. Allegory of Music.

145. Flag and rising Sun.

1963. Air. Baalbek Festival.

800. 144. 35 p. orange and blue 55 35

1963. Air. 20th Anniv. of Independence. Flag and Sun in red and yellow.

801. **145.** 5 p. turquoise 20 10
802. 10 p. green 30 15
803. 25 p. blue 35 40
804. 40 p. drab 55 65

146. Cycling. **147.** Hyacinth.

1964. 4th Mediterranean Games, Naples (1963).

805. **146.** 2 p. 50 brown & purple (postage) 10 10
806. – 5 p. orange and blue .. 25 10
807. – 10 p. brown and violet 35 10
808. – 15 p. orge. & grn. (air) 35 10
809. – 17 p. 50 brown & blue 55 15
810. – 30 p. brown & turq... 55 30

DESIGNS—VERT. 5 p. Basketball. 10 p. Running. 15 p. Tennis. HORIZ. 17 p. 50, Swimming. 30 p. Skiing.

1964. Flowers. Multicoloured.

811. 50 c. Type **147** (postage) .. 20 10
812. 1 p. Type **147** 20 10
813. 2 p. 50 Type **147** 20 10
814. 5 p. Cyclamen 20 10
815. 7 p. 50 Cyclamen 20 10
816. 10 p. Poinsettia 30 10
817. 17 p. 50 Anemone .. 55 10
818. 30 p. Iris .. .. .. 1·00 20
819. 50 p. Poppy .. .. 1·60 45
820. 5 p. Lily (air) 20 10
821. 10 p. Ranunculus .. 50 10
822. 20 p. Anemone 40 10
823. 40 p. Tuberose 70 25
824. 45 p. Rhododendron .. 1·00 25
825. 50 p. Jasmine 95 25
826. 70 p. Yellow broom .. 1·40 55

Nos. 816/26 are vert., size 26½ × 37 mm.

148. Cedar of Lebanon. **149.**

1964.

827. **148.** 50 c. green 20 10
828. **149.** 50 c. green 15 10
829. 2 p. 50 blue 20 10
830. 5 p. mauve 30 10
831. 7 p. 50 orange .. 30 10
832. 17 p. purple 50 10

150. Child on Rocking-horse. **152.** " Flame of Freedom ".

151. League Session.

1964. Air. Children's Day.

833. – 5 p. multicoloured .. 20 10
834. – 10 p. multicoloured .. 25 10
835. **150.** 20 p. multicoloured .. 40 20
836. 40 p. multicoloured .. 45 55

DESIGN—HORIZ. 5 p., 10 p. Girls skipping.

1964. Air. Arab League Meeting.

837. **151.** 5 p. buff, brn. and blk. 35 15
838. 10 p. black 20 20
839. 15 p. turquoise .. 45 30
840. 20 p. mauve, brown and sepia 95 40

1964. Air. 15th Anniv. of Declaration of Human Rights.

841. **152.** 20 p. red, salmon & brn. 25 10
842. – 40 p. orge., grey & blue 45 25

DESIGN: 40 p. Flame on pedestal bearing U.N. emblem.

153. Sick Child. **154.** Clasped Wrists.

1964. Air. "Bal des Petits Lits Blancs" (Ball for children's charity).

843. **153.** 2 p. 50 multicoloured 15 10
844. 5 p. multicoloured .. 15 10
845. 15 p. multicoloured .. 20 10
846. – 17 p. 50 multicoloured 30 15
847. – 20 p. multicoloured .. 35 15
848. – 40 p. multicoloured .. 40 25

DESIGN—HORIZ. (55 × 25½ mm.): 17 p. 50, to 40 p. Children in front of palace (venue of ball).

1964. Air. World Lebanese Union Congress, Beirut.

849. **154.** 20 p. blk., yell. & grn. 35 20
850. 40 p. blk., yell. & pur. 55 40

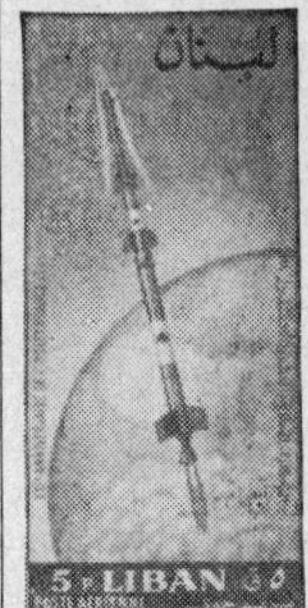

156. Temple Columns.

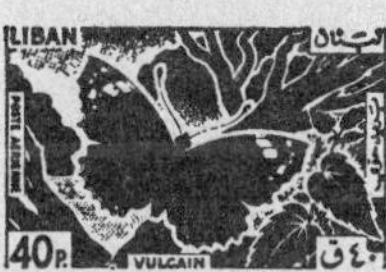

155. Rocket in Flight. **157.** Swimming.

1964. Air. 21st Anniv. of Independence.

851. **155.** 5 p. multicoloured .. 20 15
852. 10 p. multicoloured .. 20 15
853. – 40 p. blue and black .. 55 40
854. – 70 p. purple and black 1·00 75

DESIGNS—HORIZ. 40 p., 70 p. " Struggle for Independence " (battle scene).

1965. Baalbek Festival.

855. **156.** 2 p. 50 blk. & orge. (post.) 15 10
856. – 7 p. 50 black & blue .. 50 20
857. – 10 p. mult. (air) .. 15 10
858. – 15 p. multicoloured .. 30 10
859. – 25 p. multicoloured .. 30 25
860. – 40 p. multicoloured .. 55 35

DESIGNS—VERT. (28 × 55 mm.): 10 p., 15 p. Man in costume. 25 p., 40 p. Woman in costume.

1965. Olympic Games, Tokyo.

861 **157** 2 p. 50 black, blue and mauve (postage) .. 10 10
862 – 7 p. 50 pur, grn & brn 40 25
863 – 10 p. grey, brn & grn 50 35
864 – 15 p. black & grn (air) 20 10
865 – 25 p. green and purple 35 15
866 – 40 p. brown and blue 50 25

DESIGNS—HORIZ. 7 p. 50 Fencing. 15 p. Horse-jumping. 40 p. Gymnastics. VERT. 10 p. Basket-ball. 25 p. Rifle-shooting.

159. Pope Paul and Pres. Helou.

1965. Air. Pope Paul's Visit to Lebanon.

883. **159.** 45 p. violet and gold .. 1·90 1·10

160. Sheep.

1965.

884. – 50 c. multicoloured .. 15 10
885. – 1 p. grey, black & mve. 50 10
886. **160.** 2 p. 50 yell., sep. & grn. 35 10

DESIGNS: 50 c. Cow and calf. 1 p. Rabbit.

161. " Cedars of Friendship ". **162.** " Silk Manufacture ".

1965. Air.

887. **161.** 40 p. multicoloured .. 45 15

1965. Air. World Silk Congress. Beirut. Multicoloured.

888. 2 p. 50 Type **162** 10 10
889. 5 p. Type **162** 10 10
890. 7 p. 50 Type **162** 15 10
891. 15 p. Weaver and loom .. 20 10
892. 30 p. As 15 p. 35 15
893. 40 p. As 15 p. 50 20
894. 50 p. As 15 p. 65 35

163. Parliament Building.

1965. Air. Cent. of Lebanese Parliament.

895. **163.** 35 p. brn., ochre & red 50 15
896. 40 p. brn., ochre & grn. 60 20

164. U.N. Emblem and Headquarters. **165.** Playing-card " King ".

1965. Air. 20th Anniv. of U.N.

897. **164.** 2 p. 50 blue 10 10
898. 10 p. red 15 10
899. 17 p. 50 violet .. 20 10
900. 30 p. green 35 15
901. 40 p. brown 50 30

1965. Air. World Bridge Championships, Beirut.

902. **165.** 2 p. 50 multicoloured 20 10
903. 15 p. multicoloured .. 30 10
904. 17 p. 50 multicoloured 35 20
905. 40 p. multicoloured .. 65 30

166. Dagger on Deir Yassin, Palestine. **167.** I.T.U. Emblem and Symbols.

1965. Air. Deir Yassin Massacre.

906. **166.** 50 p. multicoloured .. 45 35

1966. Air. Centenary (1965) of I.T.U.

907. **167.** 2 p. 50 multicoloured 15 10
908. 15 p. multicoloured .. 35 10
909. 17 p. 50 multicoloured 50 15
910. 25 p. multicoloured .. 50 25
911. 40 p. multicoloured .. 60 45

168. Stage Performance.

1966. Air. Baalbek Festival. Multicoloured.

912. 2 p. 50 Type **168** 15 10
913. 5 p. Type **168** 15 10
914. 7 p. 50 Ballet performance 15 10
915. 15 p. Ballet performance .. 35 10
916. 30 p. Concert 20 20
917. 40 p. Concert 40 30

The 7 p. 50 and 15 p. are vert.

169. Tabarja. **170.** W.H.O. Building.

1966. Tourism. Multicoloured.

918 50 c. Hippodrome, Beirut (postage) 10 10
919 1 p. Pigeon Grotto, Beirut 10 10
920 2 p. 50 Type **169** 10 10
921 5 p. Ruins, Beit-Mery .. 15 10
922 7 p. 50 Ruins, Anfar .. 15 10
923 10 p. Djezzine Falls (air) .. 20 10
924 15 p. Sidon Castle .. 25 10
925 20 p. Amphitheatre, Byblos 30 10
926 30 p. Sun Temple, Baalbek 45 10
927 50 p. Palace, Beit ed-Din 50 10
928 60 p. Nahr-el-Kalb .. 65 30
929 75 p. Tripoli 90 45

1966. Air. Inauguration of W.H.O. Headquarters, Geneva.

930. **170.** 7 p. 50 green 25 10
931. 17 p. 50 red 15 10
932. 25 p. blue 20 20

171. Skiing. **173.** Child in Bath.

172. Inscribed Sarcophagus.

1966. Air. Int. Cedars Festival.

933. **171.** 2 p. 50 brn., red & grn. 25 10
934. – 5 p. multicoloured .. 25 10
935. – 17 p. 50 multicoloured 40 15
936. – 25 p. red, brn. & grn. 45 30

DESIGNS: 5 p. Toboganning. 17 p. 50, Cedar in snow. 25 p. Ski-lift.

1966. Air. Phoenician Invention of the Alphabet.

937. **172.** 10 p. brn., blk. & grn. 15 10
938. – 15 p. brn., ochre & mve. 25 10
939. – 20 p. sep., bl. & grn. 35 20
940. – 30 p. brn., orge. & yell. 40 30

DESIGNS: 15 p. Phoenician sailing ship. 20 p. Mediterranean route map showing spread of Phoenician alphabet. 30 p. Kadmus with alphabet tablet.

1966. Air. Int. Children's Day. Multicoloured.

941 2 p. Type **173** 10 10
942 5 p. Boy and doll in rowing boat 15 10
943 7 p. 50 Girl skiing .. 30 10
944 15 p. Girl giving food to bird 20 15
945 20 p. Boy doing homework 30 25

174. Decade Emblem. **175.** Rev. Daniel Bliss (founder).

158. "Vanessa atalanta".

1965. (a) Postage. Birds.

867. – 5 p. multicoloured .. 30 10
868. – 10 p. multicoloured .. 45 10
869. – 15 p. choc., orge. & brn. 85 10
870. – 17 p. 50 pur., red & bl. 1·25 10
871. – 20 p. blk., yell. & grn. 1·40 15
872. – 32 p. 50 yell., brn. & grn. 2·50 40

(b) Air. Butterflies.

873. – 30 p. yell., brn. & red 15 10
874. – 35 p. bl., red & bistre 30 15
875. **158.** 40 p. brn., red & grn. 35 15
876. – 45 p. brn., yell. & bl. 45 20
877. – 70 p. multicoloured .. 50 35
878. – 85 p. blk., orge. & grn. 80 35
879. – 100 p. blue & plum .. 1·10 35
880. – 200 p. brn., bl. & pur. 2·50 55
881. – 300 p. sepia, yellow & green .. .. 3·25 1·10
882. – 500 p. brown & blue .. 7·25 2·75

DESIGNS—BIRDS: 5 p. Bullfinch. 10 p. Goldfinch. 15 p. Hoopoe. 17 p. 50, Red-legged partridge. 20 p. Golden oriole. 32 p. 50, European bee eater. BUTTERFLIES: 30 p. "Pericallia matronula". 35 p. "Heliconius cyrbia". 45 p. "Satyrus semele". 70 p. "Papilio machaon". 85 p. "Anthocharis cardamines". 100 p. "Morpho cypris". 200 p. "Erasmia sanguiflua". 300 p. Papilio crassus". LARGER (35½ × 25 mm): 500 p. "Charaxes ameliae".

1966. Air. International Hydrological Decade.
947. 174. 5 p. ultram., bl. & orge. 15 10
948. 10 p. red, bl. & orge.. 15 10
949. – 15 p. sep., grn. & orge. 25 15
950. – 20 p. bl., grn & orge. 20 20
DESIGN: 15 p., 20 p. Similar "wave" pattern.

1966. Air. Centenary of American University, Beirut.
951. 175. 20 p. brn., yell. & grn. 35 10
952. – 30 p. grn., brn. & blue 40 15
DESIGN: 30 p. University Chapel.

176. I.T.Y. Emblem.

177. Beit ed-Din Palace.

1967. Int. Tourist Year (1st issue).
(a) Postage.
954. 176. 50 c. multicoloured .. 10 10
955. 1 p. multicoloured .. 10 10
956. 2 p. 50 multicoloured 10 10
957. 5 p. multicoloured .. 15 10
958. 7 p. 50 multicoloured 25 10

(b) Air. Multicoloured.
959. 10 p. Tabarja 25 10
960. 15 p. Pigeon Rock, Beirut 30 10
961. 17 p. 50 Type 177 .. 30 10
962. 20 p. Sidon 30 10
963. 25 p. Tripoli 35 10
964. 30 p. Byblos 20 10
965. 35 p. Ruins, Tyre .. 30 10
966. 40 p. Temple, Baalbek .. 45 10
See also Nos. 977/80.

178. Signing Pact, and Flags.

1967. Air. 22nd Anniv. of Arab League Pact.
967. 178. 5 p. multicoloured .. 10 10
968. 10 p. multicoloured .. 15 10
969. 15 p. multicoloured .. 30 15
970. 20 p. multicoloured .. 20 30

179. Veterans War Memorial Building, San Francisco.

1967. Air. San Francisco Pact of 1945. Mult.
971. 2 p. 50 Type 179 .. 15 20
972. 5 p. Type 179 .. 15 20
973. 7 p. 50 Type 179 .. 15 20
974. 10 p. Scroll and flags of U.N. and Lebanon .. 15 10
975. 20 p. As 10 p. .. 20 10
976. 30 p. As 10 p. .. 30 20

180. Temple Ruins, Baalbek.

1967. Air. Int. Tourist Year (2nd issue). Multicoloured.
977. 5 p. Type 180 .. 15 10
978. 10 p. Ruins, Anjar .. 20 10
979. 15 p. Ancient bridge, Nahr-Ibrahim .. 30 10
980. 20 p. Grotto, Jeita .. 35 15

181.

1967. Air. India Day.
981. 181. 2 p. 50 red 10 10
982. 5 p. red 15 10
983. 7 p. 50 brown 15 10
984. 10 p. blue 15 10
985. 15 p. green 40 15

182.

1967. Air. 22nd Anniv. of Lebanon's Admission to U.N.
986. 182. 2 p. 50 red 10 10
987. 5 p. blue 10 10
988. 7 p. 50 green 10 10
989. – 10 p. red 10 10
990. – 20 p. blue 25 10
991. – 30 p. green 45 15
DESIGN: 10, 20, 30 p. U. N. Emblem.

183. Goat and Kid.

1967. Animals and Fishes. Multicoloured.
992. 50 c. Type 183 (postage) 10 10
993. 1 p. Cattle 10 10
994. 2 p. 50 Sheep 10 10
995. 5 p. Dromedaries .. 15 10
996. 10 p. Donkey 20 10
997. 15 p. Horses 40 10
998. 20 p. Shark (air) .. 40 10
999. 30 p. Needle-fish .. 40 10
1000. 40 p. Pollack 60 10
1001. 50 p. Wrasse 70 15
1002. 70 p. Red mullet .. 90 25
1003. 100 p. Salmon .. .. 1·10 35

184. Ski Jumping.

1968. Air. Int. Ski Congress. Beirut.
1004. 184. 2 p. 50 multicoloured 15 10
1005. – 5 p. multicoloured .. 25 10
1006. – 7 p. 50 multicoloured 25 10
1007. – 10 p. multicoloured .. 35 15
1008. – 25 p. multicoloured .. 25 25
DESIGNS: 5 p. to 10 p. Skiing (all different). 25 p. Congress emblem of Cedar and skis.

185. Princess Khaskiah.

1968. Air. Emir Fakhreddine II Commem. Multicoloured.
1009. 2 p. 50 Type 185 .. 15 10
1010. 5 p. Emir Fakhreddine II 15 10
1011. 10 p. Sidon Citadel .. 20 5
1012. 15 p. Chekif Citadel .. 30 10
1013. 17 p. 50 Beirut Citadel .. 15 15
The 10 p., 15 p. and 17 p. 50, are horiz. designs.

186. Colonnade.

1968. Air. Tyre Antiquities.
1014. – 2 p. 50 brown, cream and pink 15 10
1015. 186. 5 p. brn., bl. & yell. 25 10
1016. – 7 p. 50 brn., buff & grn. 30 10
1017. – 10 p. brn., bl. & orge. 15 15
DESIGNS—VERT. 2 p. 50, Roman Bust. 10 p. Bas-relief. HORIZ. 7 p. 50, Arch.

187. Justinian and Mediterranean Map.

1968. Air. 1st Anniv. of Faculty of Law, Beirut.
1019. 5 p. Justinian (vert.) .. 10 10
1020. 10 p. Justinian (vert.) .. 15 10
1021. 15 p. Type 187 .. .. 20 10
1022. 20 p. Type 187 .. .. 30 15

188. Arab League Emblem.
190. Jupiter's Temple Ruins, Baalbek.

189. Cedar on Globe.

1968. Air. Arab Appeal Week.
1023. 188. 5 p. multicoloured .. 10 10
1024. 10 p. multicoloured.. 15 10
1025. 15 p. multicoloured.. 25 10
1026. 20 p. multicoloured.. 30 15

1968. Air. 3rd World Lebanese Union Congress, Beirut.
1027. 189. 2 p. 50 multicoloured 10 10
1028. 5 p. multicoloured .. 15 10
1029. 7 p. 50 multicoloured 20 10
1030. 10 p. multicoloured.. 30 15

1968. Air. Baalbek Festival. Multicoloured.
1031. 5 p. Type 190 .. .. 10 10
1032. 10 p. Bacchus's Temple.. 10 10
1033. 15 p. Corniche, Jupiter's Temple 25 15
1034. 20 p. Portal, Bacchus's Temple 35 20
1035. 25 p. Columns, Bacchus's Temple 55 25

191. Long Jumping and Atlantes.

1968. Air. Olympic Games, Mexico.
1036. 191. 5 p. blk., yell. & blue 15 10
1037. – 10 p. blk., blue & pur. 20 10
1038. – 15 p. multicoloured.. 20 10
1039. – 20 p. multicoloured.. 25 15
1040. – 25 p. brown .. 45 25
DESIGNS (each incorporating Aztec relic): 10 p. High-jumping. 15 p. Fencing. 20 p. Weightlifting. 25 p. " Sailing boat " with oars.

192. Lebanese driving Tractor ("Work protection").
193. Minshiya Stairs.

1968. Air. Human Rights Year. Mult.
1041. 10 p. Type 192 .. .. 15 10
1042. 15 p. Citizens ("Social Security") 20 10
1043. 25 p. Young men of three races ("Unity") .. 25 15

1968. Air. Centenary of 1st Municipal Council (Deir el-Kamar). Multicoloured.
1044. 10 p. Type 193 .. .. 15 10
1045. 15 p. Serai kiosk.. .. 20 10
1046. 25 p. Ancient highway .. 25 15

194. Nurse and Child.

1969. Air. U.N.I.C.E.F. Commem. Mult.
1047. 194. 5 p. blk., brn. & blue 10 10
1048. – 10 p. blk., grn. & yell. 15 10
1049. – 15 p. blk., red & pur. 25 10
1050. – 20 p. blk., blue & yell. 30 10
1051. – 25 p. blk., ochre & mve. 35 15
DESIGNS: 10 p. Produce. 15 p. Mother and child. 20 p. Child with book. 25 p. Children with flowers.

195. Ancient Coin.

1969. Air. 20th Anniv. of Int. Museums Council (I.C.O.M.) Exhibits in National Museum Beirut. Multicoloured.
1052. 2 p. 50 Type 195 .. 15 10
1053. 5 p. Gold dagger, Byblos 20 10
1054. 7 p. 50 Detail of Ahiram's Sarcophagus 20 10
1055. 30 p. Jewelled pectoral .. 15 30
1056. 40 p. Khalde "bird" vase 30 45

196. Water-skiing.

1969. Air. Water-Sports. Multicoloured.
1057. 2 p. 50 Type 196 .. 15 10
1058. 5 p. Water-skiing (group) 20 10
1059. 7 p. 50 Water-skiing with parachute 35 10
1060. 30 p. Sailing 30 30
1061. 40 p. Yacht-racing .. 50 50
The 7 p. 50 and 30 p. are vert.

197. Frontier Guard.

1969. Air. 25th Anniv. of Independence. The Lebanese Army.
1062. 2 p. Type 197 .. .. 15 10
1063. 5 p. Unknown Soldier's Tomb 25 10
1064. 7 p. 50 Army Foresters .. 30 10
1065. 15 p. Road-making .. 10 15
1066. 30 p. Military Ambulance and Helicopter .. 20 25
1067. 40 p. Skiing Patrol .. 25 45

198. Concentric Red Crosses.

1971. Air. 25th Anniv. of Lebanese Red Cross.
1068. 198. 15 p. red and black.. 15 10
1069. – 85 p. red and black.. 80 80
DESIGN: 85 p. Red Cross in shape of cedar of Lebanon.

199. Foil and Flags of Arab States.

1971. Air. 10th Int. Fencing Championships. Multicoloured.

1070. 10 p. Type **199** 20 10
1071. 15 p. Foil and flags of foreign nations .. 25 10
1072. 35 p. Contest with foils .. 30 35
1073. 40 p. Epee contest .. 40 35
1074. 50 p. Contest with sabres 50 40

200. " Farmers at Work " (12th-Century Arab Painting).

1971. Air. 50th Anniv. (1969) of I.L.O.

1075. **200.** 10 p. multicoloured .. 15 10
1076. 40 p. multicoloured .. 55 30

201. U.P.U. Monument and New H.Q. Building, Berne.

1971. Air. New U.P.U. Headquarters Building, Berne.

1077. **201.** 15 p. red, blk. & yell. 15 10
1078. 35 p. yell., blk. & pink 30 25

202. "Ravens setting fire to Owls" (14th-century painting).

1971. Air. Children's Day. Multicoloured.

1079. 15 p. Type **202** 30 10
1080. 85 p. "The Lion and the Jackal" (13th-century painting (horiz. 39 × 29 mm.) 90 45

203. Arab League Flag and Map.

1971. Air. 25th Anniv. of Arab League.

1081. **203.** 30 p. multicoloured .. 40 15
1082. 70 p. multicoloured .. 55 45

204. Jamhour Electricity Sub-station.

1971. Air. Multicoloured.

1083. 5 p. Type **204** 15 10
1084. 10 p. Maameltein Bridge 20 10
1085. 15 p. Hoteliers' School .. 20 10
1086. 20 p. Litani Dam .. 40 10
1087. 25 p. Interior of T.V. set 15 10
1088. 35 p. Bziza Temple .. 30 10
1089. 40 p. Jounieh Harbour .. 30 15
1090. 45 p. Radar scanner, Beirut Airport 35 15
1091. 50 p. Hibiscus 50 20
1092. 70 p. School of Sciences Building 65 20
1093. 85 p. Oranges 95 35
1094. 100 p. Satellite Communications Station, Arbanieh 1·10 60

205. Insignia of Imam al Ouzai (theologian).

1971. Air. Lebanese Celebrities.

1095. **205.** 25 p. brn. gold & grn. 15 15
1096. – 25 p. brn., gold & yell. 15 15
1097. – 25 p. brn., gold & yell. 15 15
1098. – 25 p. brn., gold & grn. 15 15

PORTRAITS: No. 1096, Bechara el Khoury (poet and writer). No. 1097, Hassan Kamel el Sabbah (scientist). No. 1098, Gibran Khalil Gibran (writer).

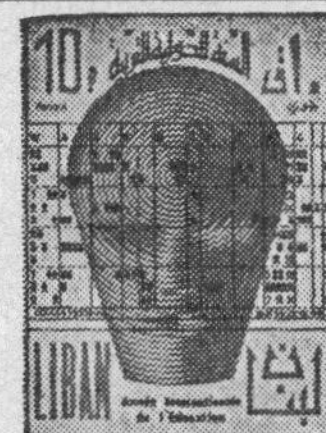

206. I.E.Y. Emblem and Computer Card.

1971. Air. Int. Education Year.

1099. **206.** 10 p. multicoloured .. 15 10
1100. 40 p. multicoloured .. 25 25

207. Dahr-el-Basheq Sanatorium. **208.** " Solar Wheel " Emblem.

1971. Air. Tuberculosis Relief Campaign.

1101. **207.** 50 p. multicoloured .. 45 30
1102. – 100 p. multicoloured 65 45

DESIGN: 100 p. Different view of Sanatorium.

1971. Air. 16th Baalbek Festival.

1103. **208.** 15 p. orge. & blue .. 25 10
1104. – 85 p. blk., bl. & orge. 65 55

DESIGN: 85 p. Corinthian capital.

209. Field-gun.

1971. Air. Army Day. Multicoloured.

1105. 15 p. Type **209** 15 10
1106. 25 p. "Mirage" jet fighters 80 20
1107. 40 p. Army Command H.Q. 35 25
1108. 70 p. "Tarablous" naval patrol-boat .. .. 1·25 45

210. Interior Decoration. **212.** U.N. Emblem.

211. Lenin.

1971. Air. 2nd Anniv. of Burning of Al-Aqsa Mosque, Jerusalem.

1109. **210.** 15 p. bistre and brown 20 10
1110. 35 p. bistre and brown 45 20

1971. Air. Birth Cent. of Lenin. Mult.

1111. 30 p. Type **211** 30 20
1112. 70 p. Lenin in profile .. 55 60

1971. Air. 25th Anniv. of United Nations.

1113. **212.** 15 p. multicoloured .. 20 10
1114. 85 p. multicoloured .. 65 35

213. "Europa" Mosaic, Byblos.

1971. Air. World Lebanese Union.

1115. **213.** 10 p. multicoloured .. 25 10
1116. 40 p. multicoloured .. 65 20

1972. Various stamps surch.

1117. 5 p. on 7 p. 50 (No. 922) (postage) 15 10
1118. 5 p. on 7 p. 50 (No. 958) .. 15 10
1119. 25 p. on 32 p. 50 (No. 872) 65 10
1120. 5 p. on 7 p. 50 (No. 1016) (air) 15 10
1121. 100 p. on 300 p. (No. 881) 1·00 55
1122. 100 p. on 500 p. (No. 882) 1·00 55
1123. 200 p. on 300 p. (No. 881) 2·10 1·10

217. Morning Glory. **218.** Ornate Arches.

1973. Air. Multicoloured.

1124. 2 p. 50 Type **217** .. 15 10
1125. 5 p. Roses 30 10
1126. 15 p. Tulips 20 10
1127. 25 p. Lilies 35 10
1128. 40 p. Carnations 45 15
1129. 50 p. Iris 65 10
1130. 70 p. Apples .. .. 1·00 15
1131. 75 p. Grapes .. .. 1·10 25
1132. 100 p. Peaches .. .. 1·40 35
1133. 200 p. Pears .. .. 2·75 35
1134. 300 p. Cherries .. .. 4·00 70
1135. 500 p. Oranges .. .. 5·50 1·25

1973. Air. Lebanese Domestic Architecture.

1136 – 35 p. multicoloured .. 35 25
1137 **218** 50 p. multicoloured .. 45 40
1138 – 85 p. multicoloured .. 80 50
1139 – 100 p. multicoloured 95 70

DESIGNS: Nos. 1136 and 1138/39, Various Lebanese dwellings.

219. Girl with Lute.

1973. Air. Ancient Costumes. Multicoloured.

1140. 5 p. Woman with rose .. 25 10
1141. 10 p. Shepherd 30 10
1142. 20 p. Horseman 15 15
1143. 25 p. Type **219** 20 20

220. Swimming.

1973. Air 5th Pan-Arab Schools' Games, Beirut. Multicoloured.

1144. 5 p. Type **220** 20 10
1145. 10 p. Running 20 10
1146. 15 p. Gymnastics 30 10
1147. 20 p. Volleyball 40 10
1148. 25 p. Basketball 30 15
1149. 50 p. Table-tennis .. 80 30
1150. 75 p. Handball 65 50
1151. 100 p. Football .. .. 1·25 75

221. Brasilia.

1973. Air. 150th Anniv. of Brazil's Independence. Multicoloured.

1153. 5 p. Type **221** 15 10
1154. 20 p. Salvador (Bahia) in 1823 .. .. .. 15 20
1155. 25 p. Map and Phoenician galley .. 15 20
1156. 50 p. Emperor Pedro I & Emir Fakhreddine II 40 20

222. Marquetry. **223.** Cedar of Lebanon.

1973. Air. Lebanese Handicrafts. Mult.

1157. 10 p. Type **222** 15 10
1158. 20 p. Weaving 25 10
1159. 35 p. Glass-blowing .. 45 10
1160. 40 p. Pottery 60 15
1161. 50 p. Metal-working .. 70 15
1162. 70 p. Cutlery-making .. 70 30
1163. 85 p. Lace-making .. 1·00 40
1164. 100 p. Handicrafts Museum 1·60 45

1974.

1165. **223.** 50 c. grn., brn. & orge. 15 10

224. Camp Site and Emblems.

1974. Air. 11th Arab Scout Jamboree, Smar-Jubeil, Lebanon. Multicoloured.

1166. 2 p. 50 Type **224** .. 20 10
1167. 5 p. Scout badge and map 20 10
1168. 7 p. 50 Map of Arab countries 20 10
1169. 10 p. Lord Baden-Powell and Baalbek 25 10
1170. 15 p. Guide and camp .. 35 10
1171. 20 p. Lebanese Guide and Scout badge 20 15
1172. 25 p. Scouts around campfire 30 15
1173. 30 p. Globe and Scout badge 35 20
1174. 35 p. Flags of participating countries 45 30
1175. 50 p. Scout chopping wood for old man 50 20

225. Mail Train.

1974. Cent. of U.P.U. Mult.

1176. 5 p. 50 Type **225** .. 10 10
1177. 20 p. Container ship .. 40 10
1178. 25 p. Congress building, Lausanne, and U.P.U. H.Q., Berne 40 10
1179. 50 p. Mail-plane 50 45

226. Congress Building, Sofar. **227.** " Mountain Road " (O. Onsi).

1974. Air. 25th Anniv. of Arab Postal Union. Multicoloured.

1180. 5 p. Type **226** 10 10
1181. 20 p. View of Sofar . 30 10
1182. 25 p. A.P.U. H.Q., Cairo 40 15
1183. 50 p. Ministry of Posts, Beirut 80 45

1974. Air. Lebanese Paintings. Mult.

1184. 50 p. Type **227** 75 35
1185. 50 p. " Clouds " (M. Farroukh) .. 75 35
1186. 50 p. " Woman " (G. K. Gebran) .. 75 35
1187. 50 p. " Embrace " (C. Gemayel) 75 35
1188. 50 p. " Self-portrait " (H. Serour) 75 35
1189. 50 p. " Portrait " (D. Corm) 75 35

228. Hunter killing Lion.

1974. Air. Hermel Excavations. Mult.

1190. 5 p. Type **228** 15 10
1191. 10 p. Astarte 20 10
1192. 25 p. Dogs hunting boar .. 60 25
1193. 35 p. Greco-Roman tomb 95 55

229. Book Year Emblem.

1974. Air. International Book Year (1972).

1194. **229.** 5 p. multicoloured .. 10 10
1195. 10 p. multicoloured .. 15 10
1196. 25 p. multicoloured .. 50 25
1197. 35 p. multicoloured .. 75 50

230. Magnifying Glass.

231. Georgina Rizk in Lebanese Costume.

1974. Air. Stamp Day. Multicoloured.

1198. 5 p. Type **230** 10 10
1199. 10 p. Linked posthorns .. 10 10
1200. 15 p. Stamp-printing .. 25 10
1201. 20 p. "Stamp" in mount 35 15

1974. Air. Miss Universe 1971 (Georgina Rizk). Multicoloured.

1202. 5 p. Type **231** 10 10
1203. 20 p. Head-and-shoulders portrait 30 10
1204. 25 p. Type **231** 35 15
1205. 50 p. As 20 p. 40 45

232. Winds.

234. Discus-throwing.

233. U.N.I.C.E.F. Emblem and Helicopter.

1974. Air. U.N. Conference on Human Environment, Stockholm, 1972. Mult.

1207. 5 p. Type **232** 10 10
1208. 25 p. Mountains and plain 20 15
1209. 30 p. Trees and flowers .. 20 15
1210. 10 p. Sea 35 40

1974. Air. 25th Anniv. of U.N.I.C.E.F. Mult.

1212. 20 p. Type **233** 45 10
1213. 25 p. Emblem and child welfare clinic 35 15
1214. 35 p. Emblem and kindergarten class 50 20
1215. 70 p. Emblem and schoolgirls in laboratory .. 55 35

1974. Air. Olympic Games, Munich, 1972. Multicoloured.

1217. 5 p. Type **234** 15 10
1218. 10 p. Putting the shot .. 20 10
1219. 15 p. Weight-lifting .. 25 10
1220. 35 p. Running 45 20
1221. 50 p. Wrestling 45 25
1222. 85 p. Javelin-throwing .. 90 35

235. Symbols of Archaeology.

1975. Air. "Beirut—University City". Multicoloured.

1224 20 p. Type **235** 25 30
1225 25 p. Science and medicine 30 25
1226 35 p. Justice and commerce 45 35
1227 70 p. Industry and commerce 75 35

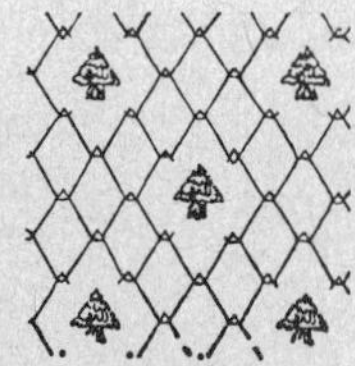
(**236.**)

1978. Air. Various stamps optd. with different patterns as T **236**.

(a) Tourist Views. Nos. 1090, 1092/3.

1228. 45 p. Radar scanner, Beirut Airport .. 40 10
1229. 70 p. School of Sciences Building 80 20
1230. 85 p. Oranges 80 25

(b) Flowers and Fruits. Nos. 1124/35.

1231. 2 p. 50 Morning glory .. 10 10
1232. 5 p. Type **217** 10 10
1233. 15 p. Tulips 20 10
1234. 25 p. Lilies 45 10
1235. 40 p. Carnations .. 40 15
1236. 50 p. Iris 55 15
1237. 70 p. Apples .. .. 1·00 20
1238. 75 p. Grapes .. .. 1·25 20
1239. 100 p. Peaches .. .. 1·10 30
1240. 200 p. Pears .. .. 2·25 1·25
1241. 300 p. Cherries .. .. 3·25 2·25
1242. 500 p. Oranges .. .. 6·75 3·25

(c) Lebanese Domestic Architecture. Nos. 1136/9.

1243. – 35 p. multicoloured .. 55 10
1244. **218.** 50 p. multicoloured .. 75 15
1245. – 85 p. multicoloured .. 90 25
1246. – 100 p. multicoloured 1·10 30

(d) Ancient Costumes. Nos. 1140/3.

1247. 5 p. Woman with rose .. 10 10
1248. 10 p. Shepherd 15 10
1249. 20 p. Horseman 35 10
1250. 25 p. Type **219** 20 10

(e) Lebanese Handicrafts. Nos. 1157/8, 1160/4.

1251. 10 p. Type **222** 15 10
1252. 20 p. Weaving 30 10
1253. 40 p. Pottery 40 15
1254. 50 p. Metal-working .. 55 15
1255. 70 p. Cutlery-making .. 90 20
1256. 85 p. Lace-making .. 1·10 25
1257. 100 p. Handicraft Museum 1·10 30

237. Mikhail Naimy (poet) and View of al-Chakroub Baskinta.

1978. Air. Mikhail Naimy Festival Week. Multicoloured.

1258. 25 p. Mikhail Naimy and Sannine mountains .. 40 15
1259. 50 p. Type **237** 60 30
1260. 75 p. Mikhail Naimy (vert.) 70 45

238. Heart and Arrow.

239. Army Badge.

1978. Air. World Health Day.

1261 **238** 50 p. blue, red & black 45 35

1980. Army Day. Multicoloured.

1262 25 p. Type **239** (postage) 40 15
1263 50 p. Statue of Emir Fakhr el Dine on horseback (air) 55 35
1264 75 p. Soldiers with flag (horiz) 85 40

240. 13th-century European King.

1980. Air. 50th Anniv (1974) of International Chess Federation. Multicoloured.

1265 50 p. Rook, knight and anniv emblem (horiz) 1·50 50
1266 75 p. Type **240** .. .. 2·00 90
1267 100 p. Rook and Lebanese Chess Federation emblem .. .. 2·00 1·00
1268 150 p. 18th-century French rook, king and knight .. .. 2·75 1·50
1269 200 p. Painted faience rook, queen and bishop 3·50 2·00

241. Congress, U.P.U. and Lebanon Postal Emblems.

1981. Air. 18th U.P.U. Congress, Rio de Janeiro (1979).

1270. **241.** 25 p. bl., gold and blk. 20 20
1271. 50 p. pink, gold & blk. 45 35
1272. 75 p. grn., gold & blk. 70 30

242. Children on Raft.

243. President Sarkis.

1981. Air. International Year of the Child (1979).

1273 **242** 100 p. multicoloured .. 85 45

1981. 5th Anniv. of Election of President Sarkis.

1274. **243.** 125 p. multicoloured 1·00 40
1275. 300 p. multicoloured 2·50 95
1276. 500 p. multicoloured 4·00 1·25

244. Society Emblem and Children.

1981. Air. Cent. (1978) of Al-Makassed Islamic Welfare Society. Multicoloured.

1277. 50 p. Type **244** 50 25
1278. 75 p. Institute building .. 75 35
1279. 100 p. Al-Makassed (founder) 90 30

245. Stork carrying Food.

1982. World Food Day (1981). Multicoloured.

1280. 50 p. Type **245** 50 25
1281. 75 p. Ear of wheat and globe 50 35
1282. 100 p. Fruit, fish & grain 65 60

246. W.C.Y. Emblem.

247. Phoenician Galley flying Scout Flag.

1983. World Communications Year.

1283. **246.** 300 p. multicoloured 1·60 95

1983. 75th Anniv. of Boy Scout Movement. Multicoloured.

1284. 200 p. Type **247** .. .. 1·40 65
1285. 300 p. Scouts lowering flag and signalling by semaphore .. .. 1·90 95
1286. 500 p. Camp .. .. 3·25 1·40

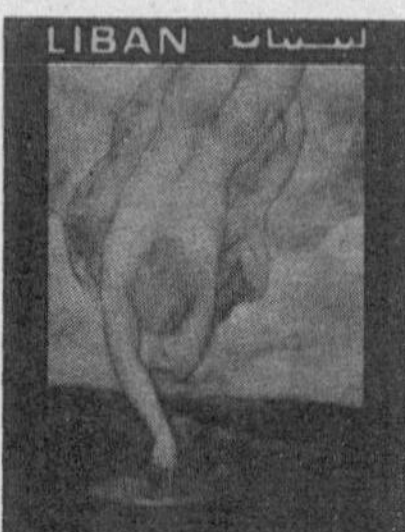

248. "The Soul is Back".

1983. Birth Cent. of Gibran (poet and painter). Multicoloured.

1287. 200 p. Type **248** .. .. 1·50 65
1288. 300 p. "The Family" .. 2·00 95
1289. 500 p. "Gibran" .. .. 3·25 1·40
1290. 1000 p. "The Prophet" .. 6·75 3·25

249. Cedar of Lebanon.

250. Iris.

1984.

1292. **249.** 5 p. multicoloured .. 10 10

1984. Flowers. Multicoloured.

1293. 10 p. Type **250** 15 10
1294. 25 p. Periwinkle 30 15
1295. 50 p. Barberry 40 30

251. Dove with Laurel over Buildings.

1984. Lebanese Army. Multicoloured.

1296. 75 p. Type **251** 50 40
1297. 150 p. Cedar and soldier holding rifle .. .. 1·00 75
1298. 300 p. Broken chain, hand holding laurel wreath and cedar .. 2·10 1·10

252. Temple Ruins, Fakra.

1984. Multicoloured.

1299. 100 p. Type **252** 85 45
1300. 200 p. Temple ruins, Bziza .. .. .. 1·40 55
1301. 500 p. Roman arches and relief, Tyre .. .. 3·25 1·40

253. President taking Oath.

1988. Installation of President Amin Gemayel.

1302. **253.** L£25 multicoloured 50 40

254. Map of South America and Cedar of Lebanon.

1988. 1st World Festival of Lebanese Youth in Uruguay.

1303. **254.** L£5 multicoloured .. 20 10

255. Satellite, Flags and Earth.

256. Children.

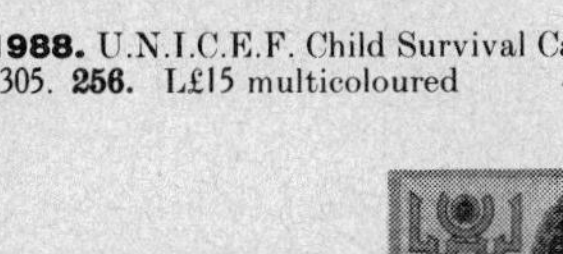

1988. "Arabsat" Telecommunications Satellite.

1304.	**255.**	L£10 multicoloured	25	15

1988. U.N.I.C.E.F. Child Survival Campaign.

1305.	**256.**	L£15 multicoloured	40	30

257. Arabic "75" and Scout Emblems.

258. President, Map and Dove.

1988. 75th Anniv (1987) of Arab Scouts Movement.

1306	**257**	L£20 multicoloured ..	60	15

1988. International Peace Year (1986).

1307.	**258.**	L£50 multicoloured	1·00	40

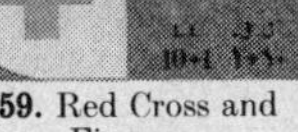

259. Red Cross and Figures.

260 Cedar of Lebanon

1988. Red Cross.

1308.	**259.**	L£10+L£1 red, silver and black	25	25
1309.	–	L£20+L£2 multicoloured ..	50	20
1310.	–	L£30+L£3 silver, green and red ..	75	35

Designs: L£20, Helmeted heads. L£30, Globe, flame, and dove holding map of Lebanon.

1989.

1314	**260**	L£50 green and mauve	10	10
1315		L£70 green and brown	35	10
1316		L£100 green & yellow	55	10
1317		L£200 green and blue	1·10	55
1318		L£500 dp green & grn	2·75	1·40

POSTAGE DUE STAMPS

1924. Postage Due stamps of France surch. **GRAND LIBAN** and value in "CENTIEMES" or "PIASTRES".

D 26.	**D 11.**	50 c. on 10 c. brown	2·50	2·50
D 27.		1 p. on 20 c. olive ..	2·50	2·50
D 28.		2 p. on 30 c. red	2·50	2·50
D 29.		3 p. on 50 c. purple ..	2·50	2·50
D 30.		5 p. on 1 f. red on yell.	2·50	2·50

1924. Postage Due stamps of France surch. **GdLiban** and value in English and Arabic.

D 58.	**D 11.**	50 c. on 10 c. brown ..	2·75	2·50
D 59.		1 p. on 20 c. olive ..	2·75	2·50
D 60.		2 p. on 30 c. red	2·75	2·50
D 61.		3 p. on 50 c. purple ..	2·75	2·50
D 62.		5 p. on 1 f. red on yell.	2·75	2·50

D 7. Nahr el-Kelb.

Designs—horiz. 1 p. Pine Forest, Beirut. 2 p. Pigeon Grotto, Beirut. 3 p. Beaufort Castle. 5 p. Baalbek.

1925.

D 75.	**D 7.**	50 c. brown on yellow	30	30
D 76.	–	1 p. black on red ..	45	45
D 77.	–	2 p. black on blue ..	70	70
D 78.	–	3 p. brown on orange	1·50	1·50
D 79.	–	5 p. black on green ..	2·00	2·00

1927. Optd. **Republique Libanaise** and bars.

D 122.	**D 7.**	50 c. brown on yellow	30	30
D 123.	–	1 p. black on red ..	50	50
D 124.	–	2 p. black on blue ..	75	75
D 125.	–	5 p. brown on orange	2·00	2·00
D 126.	–	5 p. black on green	2·75	2·75

1928. Nos. D 16/20 optd. with T **10.**

D 145.	**D 7.**	50. c brown on yellow	70	70
D 146.	–	1 p. black on red ..	70	70
D 147.	–	2 p. black on blue ..	1·40	1·40
D 148.	–	3 p. brown on orange	3·00	2·75
D 149.	–	5 p. black on green	3·25	3·00

D 18.

D 19. Bas-relief from Sarcophagus of King Ahiram at Byblos.

D 32.

Designs: 1 p. Bas-relief of Phoenician galley. 2 p. Arabesque. 3 p. Garland. 15 p. Statuettes.

1931.

D 191.	**D 18.**	50 c. black on red ..	25	25
D 192.	–	1 p. black on blue ..	50	50
D 193.	–	2 p. black on yellow	60	60
D 194.	–	3 p. black on green ..	60	60
D 195.	**D 32.**	5 p. black on orange	3·75	3·75
D 196.	**D 19.**	8 p. black on red ..	2·25	2·25
D 252.	**D 32.**	10 p. green	3·50	3·50
D 197.	–	15 p. black	2·00	2·00

D 43. National Museum.

1945.

D 298.	**D 43.**	2 p. black on lemon	2·50	2·40
D 299.		5 p. blue on red ..	3·00	3·00
D 300.		25 p. blue on green	4·00	4·00
D 301.		50 p. purple on blue	4·50	4·50

D 53.

1947.

D 352.	**D 53.**	5 p. black on green	2·75	70
D 353.		25 p. black on yellow	24·00	1·60
D 354.		50 p. black on blue	14·50	3·25

D 59. Monument at Hermel.

1948.

D 379.	**D 59.**	2 p. black on yellow	1·60	45
D 380.		3 p. black on red ..	4·00	1·50
D 381.		10 p. black on blue	10·00	3·00

D 67.

1950.

D 416.	**D 67.**	1 p. red	70	10
D 417.		5 p. blue	1·60	50
D 418.		10 p. green	3·50	90

D 78.

1952.

D 464.	**D 78.**	1 p. mauve	20	10
D 465.		2 p. violet	15	10
D 466.		3 p. green	50	20
D 467.		5 p. blue	40	20
D 468.		10 p. brown ..	90	40
D 469.		25 p. black	6·50	85

D 81. **D 93.**

1953.

D 481.	**D 81.**	1 p. red	15	10
D 482.		2 p. green	15	10
D 483.		3 p. orange ..	20	10
D 484.		5 p. purple ..	30	15
D 485.		10 p. brown ..	40	20
D 486.		15 p. blue	1·00	50

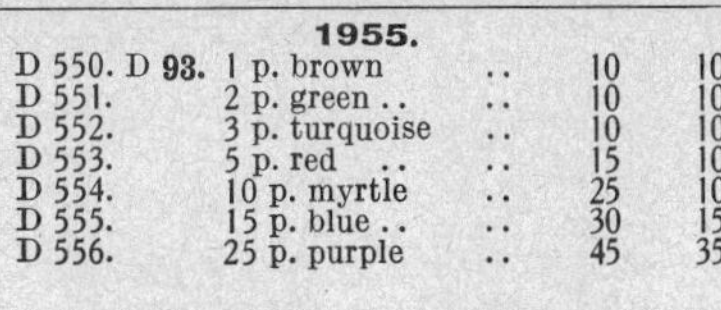

1955.

D 550.	**D 93.**	1 p. brown ..	10	10
D 551.		2 p. green	10	10
D 552.		3 p. turquoise ..	10	10
D 553.		5 p. red	15	10
D 554.		10 p. myrtle ..	25	10
D 555.		15 p. blue	30	15
D 556.		25 p. purple ..	45	35

D 178. **D 184.** Emir Fakhreddine II

1967.

D 967.	**D 178.**	1 p. green	10	20
D 968.		5 p. mauve ..	15	20
D 969.		15 p. blue	15	15

1968.

D 1004.	**D 184.**	1 p. slate and grey	10	20
D 1005.		2 p. turq. & green	10	20
D 1006.		3 p. orge. & yell.	10	20
D 1007		5 p. purple & red	15	15
D 1008.		10 p. olive & yell.	25	25
D 1009.		15 p. blue and pale violet	15	15
D 1010		25 p. bl. & pale blue	40	40

POSTAL TAX STAMPS

These were issued between 1946 and 1962 for compulsory use on inland mail (and sometimes on mail to Arab countries) to provide funds for various purposes.

(T 41.)

(T 42.)

1946. Lebanese Army. Fiscal stamp as Type T **41** surch. with Type T **42.**

T 289.	**T 41.**	5 p. on 30 c. brown	17·00	1·25

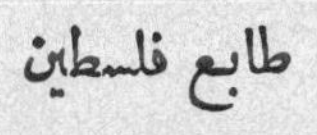

(T 50.) (T 56.)

1947. Aid to War in Palestine. Surch. as Type T **42** but with top lines as Type T **50.**

T 338.	**T 41.**	5 p. on 25 c. green	12·00	1·50
T 339.		5 p. on 30 c. brown	17·00	1·50
T 340.		5 p. on 60 c. blue ..	25·00	1·50
T 341.		5 p. on 3 p. pink ..	12·00	1·50
T 343.		5 p. on 10 p. red ..	55·00	2·75
T 342.		5 p. on 15 p. blue	12·00	1·50

The top line of the overprint on No. T 343 differs from Type T **50**, and No. T 341 comes either as Type T **50** or with a similar inscription.

1947. Aid to War in Palestine. As No. T 341 but with figure "5" at left instead of "0" and without inscr. between figures.

T 345.	**T 41.**	5 p. on 3 p. pink ..	£225	16·00

1948. Lebanese Army. No. T289 optd with T **56.**

T 363.	**T 41.**	5 p. on 30 c. brown	17·00	1·75

T 95. Family and Ruined House.

1956. Earthquake Victims.

T 559.	**T 95.**	2 p. 50 brown ..	2·25	10

T 99. Rebuilding.

T 100. Rebuilding.

1957. Earthquake Victims.

T 601.	**T 99.**	2 p. 50 brown ..	2·50	15
T 602.		2 p. 50 green ..	1·00	15
T 603.	**T 100.**	2 p. 50 brown ..	2·00	10

T 132. Rebuilding. **T 133.** Rebuilding.

1961. Earthquake Victims.

T 729.	**T 132.**	2 p. 50 brown ..	1·25	10
T 730.	**T 133.**	2 p. 50 blue ..	1·00	10

LIBERIA Pt. 13

A republic on the W. coast of Africa, founded as a home for freed slaves.

100 cents = 1 dollar.

1.

2.

1860.

7 1. 6 c. red .. .. .. 20·00 35·00
8. 12 c. blue .. .. .. 18·00 30·00
9. 24 c. green .. .. .. 20·00 35·00

1880.

13. 1. 1 c. blue .. .. .. 2·25 3·50
14. 2 c. red .. .. .. 2·25 3·50
15. 6 c. mauve .. .. .. 1·75 3·50
16. 12 c. yellow .. .. .. 2·50 4·50
17. 24 c. red .. .. .. 3·00 5·00

1881.

18. 2. 3 c. black .. .. .. 2·50 4·50

3.

4.

5. "Alligator" (first settlers' ship).

1882.

19. 3. 8 c. blue .. .. .. 15·00 5·50
20. 16 c. red .. .. .. 3·50 3·00

1886.

49. 3. 1 c. red .. .. .. 60 1·00
50. 2 c. green 60 75
23. 3 c. mauve .. .. .. 70 1·50
52. 4 c. brown .. .. .. 80 1·25
27. 6 c. grey .. .. .. 1·00 1·50
54. 4. 8 c. grey .. .. .. 2·50 3·00
55. 16 c. yellow .. .. .. 3·00 3·50
29. 5. 32 c. blue .. .. .. 12·00 12·00

7. Liberian Star.

8. African Elephant.

9. Oil Palm.

10. Pres. H. R. W. Johnson.

11. Vai Woman.

12. Seal.

13. Star.

15. Hippopotamus.

17. President Johnson.

1892.

75. 7. 1 c. red 30 30
76. 2 c. blue 30 30
77. 8. 4 c. black and green .. 2·50 2·25
78. 9. 6 c. green 45 45
79. 10. 8 c. black and brown .. 60 1·00
80. 11. 12 c. red .. .. .. 60 1·25
81. 12. 16 c. lilac .. .. .. 2·50 3·50
82. 13. 24 c. green on yellow .. 1·50 1·75
83. 12. 32 c. blue .. .. .. 3·50 5·00
84. 15. $1 black and blue .. 6·00 8·00
85. 13. $2 brown on buff .. 3·25 3·75
86. 17. $5 black and red .. 5·00 8·00

1893. Surch. **5 5 Five Cents.**

103. 9. 5 c. on 6 c. green .. 1·50 2·00

24.

1894. Imperf. or roul.

117. 24. 5 c. black and red .. 3·00 3·00

35.

36.

1897.

144. 9. 1 c. purple 45 35
145. 1 c. green 55 50
146. 15. 2 c. black and bistre .. 2·50 1·75
147. 2 c. black and red .. 2·50 2·00
148. 8. 5 c. black and lake .. 3·50 3·00
149. 5 c. black and blue .. 2·00 1·75
150. 10. 10 c. blue and yellow .. 1·00 1·50
151. 11. 15 c. black .. .. 1·50 2·00
152. 12. 20 c. red .. .. 2·50 3·00
153. 13. 25 c. green .. .. 1·75 2·50
154. 12. 30 c. blue .. .. 3·50 5·00
155. 35. 50 c. black and brown 1·40 3·50

The prices in the "used" column of sets marked with a dagger (†) against the date of issue are for stamps "cancelled to order" from remainder stocks. Postally used specimens are worth appreciably more.

†1897.

156. 36. 3 c. red and green .. 25 8

1901. Official stamps of 1892–98 optd. **ORDINARY**

175. 9. 1 c. purple (No. O 157) 50·00 35·00
176. 1 c. green (O 158) .. 18·00 18·00
177. 7. 2 c. blue (O 120) .. 50·00 50·00
178. 15. 2 c. blk. and brn. (O 159) £100 45·00
179. 2 c. blk. and red (O 160) 25·00 30·00
180. 24. 5 c. grn. and lilac (O 130) £130 £130
181. 8. 5 c. blk. and red (O 161) £100 £100
182. 5 c. black and bl. (O 162) 20·00 25·00
183. 10. 8 c. blk. and brn. (O 122) 75·00
184. 10 c. bl. and yell. (O 163) 25·00 30·00
169. 11. 12 c. red (O 92) .. £100 £100
185. 15 c. black (O 164) .. 18·00 25·00
170. 12. 16 c. lilac (O 93) .. ..
186. 16 c. lilac (O 124) .. £140 £140
187. 20 c. red (O 165) .. 22·00 28·00
171. 13. 24 c. grn. and yell. (O 94) £200 £250
188. 24 c. grn. on yell. (O 125) 25·00 30·00
189. 25 c. green (O 166) .. 28·00 35·00
190. 12. 30 c. blue (O 167) .. 20·00 26·00
191. 13. 32 c. blue (O 126) .. £150
192. 35. 50 c. blk. & brn. (O 168) 25·00 30·00
172. 15. $1 blk. and bl. (O 96) £900
193. $1 blk. and bl. (O 127) £150 £250
194. 13. $2 brn. on buff (O 128) £1300
174. 17. $5 blk. and red (O 98) .. £2500
196. $5 blk. and red (O 129) £1400

1902. Surch. **75 c.** and bar.

206. 15. 75 c. on $1 blk. & blue 7·50 10·00

40. Liberty.

1903.

209. 40. 3 c. black 25 15

1903. Surch. in words.

216. 12. 10 c. on 16 c. lilac .. 2·50 4·50
217. 13. 15 c. on 24 c. grn. on yell. 2·50 5·00
218. 12. 20 c. on 32 c. blue .. 3·50 4·50

1904. Surch.

219. 9. 1 c. on 5 c. on 6 c. green (No. 103) 60 80
220. 8. 2 c. on 4 c. black and green (No. O 89) .. 3·50 4·50
221. 12. 2 c. on 30 c. blue (No. 154) 5·00 7·50

50. African Elephant.

51. Head of Mercury.

52. Mandingo Tribesman.

53. Pres. Barclay and Executive Mansion.

†1906.

224. 50. 1 c. black and green .. 1·00 50
225. 51. 2 c. black and red .. 15 12
226. – 5 c. black and blue .. 2·75 50
227. – 10 c. black and red .. 6·50 90
228. – 15 c. green and violet .. 5·50 2·00
229. – 20 c. black & orange .. 7·00 1·60
230. – 25 c. grey and blue .. 75 20
231. – 30 c. violet 70 15
232. – 50 c. black and green .. 1·25 20
233. – 75 c. black & brown .. 6·00 1·60
234. – $1 black and pink .. 1·50 25
235. 52. $2 black and green .. 2·50 35
236. 53. $5 grey and red .. 5·00 50

DESIGNS—As TYPE **50**: 5 c. Chimpanzee. 15 c. Agama lizard. 75 c. Pygmy hippopotamus. As Type **51**: 10 c. Great Blue Turaco. 20 c. Great Egret. 25 c. Head of Liberty on coin. 30 c. Figures "30". 50 c. Liberian flag. As Type **53**: $1, Head of Liberty.

55. Coffee Plantation.

56. Gunboat "Lark".

57. Commerce.

†1909. The 10 c. is perf. or roul.

250. 55. 1 c. black and green .. 25 15
251. – 2 c. black and red .. 25 15
252. 56. 5 c. black and blue .. 1·75 35
254. 57. 10 c. black and purple 25 20
255. – 15 c. black and blue .. 1·25 35
256. – 20 c. green and red .. 2·50 50
257. – 25 c. black and brown 1·75 35
258. – 30 c. brown .. .. 1·75 35
259. – 50 c. black and green .. 2·75 60
260. – 75 c. black and brown .. 2·25 45

DESIGNS—As Type **55**: 2 c. Pres. Barclay. 15 c. Vai woman spinning cotton. 20 c. Pepper plant. 25 c. Village hut. 30 c. Pres. Barclay (in picture frame). As Type **56**: 50 c. Canoeing. 75 c. Village (design shaped like a book).

1909. No. 227 surch. **Inland 3 Cents.**

261. – 3 c. on 10 c. blk. and red 3·50 5·00

†1910. Surcharged **3 CENTS INLAND POSTAGE.** Perf. or rouletted.

274. 57. 3 c. on 10 c. blk. & pur. 35 25

1913. Various types surch. with new value and bars or ornaments.

322. – 1 c. on 2 c. blk. & red (No. 251) .. .. 2·25 3·00
290. 57. +2 c. on 3 c. on 10 c. blk. and purple .. 60 1·25
323. 56. 2 c. on 5 c. blk. & blue 2·25 3·50
292. – 2 c. on 15 c. black and blue (No. 255) .. 2·00 2·50
279. – 2 c. on 25 c. grey & blue (A) (No. 230) .. 7·50 5·00
281. – 2 c. on 25 c. black and brown (A) (No. 257) 7·50 5·00
295. – 2 c. on 25 c. black and brown (B) (No. 257) 4·50 4·50
296. – 5 c. on 20 c. grn. & red (No. 256) .. .. 1·50 2·00
280. – 5 c. on 30 c. violet (C) (No. 231) .. 7·50 5·00
282. – 5 c. on 30 c. brown (C) (No. 258) .. 7·50 10·00
297. – 5 c. on 30 c. brown (D) (No. 258) .. 3·50 3·50
278. 36. 8 c. on 3 c. red & green 60 30
283. – 10 c. on 50 c. black and green (E) (No. 259) .. 9·00 9·00
301. – 10 c. on 50 c. black and green (F) (No. 259) .. 6·50 6·00
303. – 20 c. on 75 c. black and brown (No. 260) .. 6·00 6·50
304. 53. 25 c. on $1 blk. & pink 18·00 22·00
305. – 50 c. on $2 black and green (No. 235) .. 12·50 15·00
308. – $1 on $5 grey and red (No. 236) .. 22·00 25·00

Descriptions of surcharges. (A) **1914 2 CENTS.** (B) **2** over ornaments. (C) **1914 5 CENTS.** (D) **5** over ornaments. (E) **1914 10 CENTS.** (F) **10** and ornaments.

64. House on Providence Is.

65. Monrovia Harbour, Providence Is.

†1915.

288. 64. 2 c. red 20 8
289. 65. 3 c. violet 20 8

1916. Liberian Frontier Force. Surch. **LFF 1 C.**

332. 9. 1 c. on 1 c. green .. 45·00 45·00
333. 50. 1 c. on 1 c. blk. and grn. £250 £250
334. 55. 1 c. on 1 c. blk. and grn. 1·75 3·50
335. – 1 c. on 2 c. black and red (No. 251) .. 1·75 4·00

1916. Surch. **1916** over new value.

339. 1. 3 c. on 6 c. mauve .. 22·00 22·00
340. 5 c. on 12 c. yellow .. 4·00 5·00
341. 10 c. on 24 c. red .. 4·00 4·50

1917. Surch. **1917** and value in words.

342. 13. 4 c. on 25 c. green .. 6·00 7·50
343. 52. 5 c. on 30 c. violet (No. 231) .. .. 30·00 35·00

1918. Surch. **3 CENTS.**

345. 57. 3 c. on 10 c. black & pur. 2·00 5·00

91. Bongo.

93.

92. African Palm Civet.

94. Traveller's Tree.

†1918.

349. 91. 1 c. black and green .. 1·00 25
350. 92. 2 c. black and red .. 1·00 25
351. – 5 c. black and blue .. 45 10
352. 93. 10 c. green 20 10
353. – 15 c. green and black .. 1·75 20
354. – 20 c. black and red .. 50 15
355. 94. 25 c. green .. .. 2·40 25
356. – 30 c. black and mauve .. 11·00 70
357. – 50 c. black and blue .. 6·00 70
358. – 75 c. black and olive .. 1·00 25
359. – $1 blue and brown .. 3·50 25
360. – $2 black and violet .. 4·50 30
361. – $5 brown .. .. 5·00 40

DESIGNS—As Type **91**: 5 c. Coat of Arms. 15 c. Oil palm. 20 c. Statue of Mercury. 75 c. Heads of Mandingos. $5, "Liberia" seated. As Type **92**: 50 c. Lungfish (or Mudskipper). $1, Coast view. $2, Liberia College. As Type **93**: 30 c. Palm-nut Vulture.

1918. Geneva Red Cross Fund. Surch. **TWO CENTS** and red cross.

375. 91. 1 c.+2 c. black & green 75 75
376. 92. 2 c.+2 c. black & red .. 75 75
377. – 5 c.+2 c. black & blue .. 25 1·00
378. 93. 10 c.+2 c. green .. 50 1·00
379. – 15 c.+2 c. green & blk. 2·00 1·50
380. – 20 c.+2 c. black & red 1·25 2·50
381. 94. 25 c.+2 c. green .. 3·00 3·00
382. – 30 c.+2 c. blk. & mve. 8·50 5·00
383. – 50 c.+2 c. blk. & blue .. 6·00 5·00
384. – 75 c.+2 c. blk. & olive 1·75 4·50
385. – $1+2 c. blue & brown 3·75 6·00
386. – $2+2 c. black & violet 5·00 10·00
387. – $5+2 c. brown .. 12·00 20·00

1920. Surch. **1920** and value and two bars.

393. 91. 3 c. on 1 c. blk. & grn. 1·50 2·25
394. 92. 4 c. on 2 c. blk. & red 1·50 2·50
395. R 42. 5 c. on 10 c. blk. & bl. 3·50 4·00
396. 5 c. on 10 c. blk. & red 3·50 4·00
397. 5 c. on 10 c. blk. & grn. 3·00 3·50
398. 5 c. on 10 c. blk. & vio. 3·00 3·50
399. 5 c. on 10 c. blk. & red 3·50 4·00

100. Cape Mesurado.

101. Pres. D. E. Howard.

†1921.

402. 100. 1 c. green 20 10
403. 101. 5 c. black and blue .. 25 10
404. – 10 c. blue and red .. 80 10
405. – 15 c. green and purple .. 2·75 50
406. – 20 c. green and red .. 1·50 25
407. – 25 c. black and yellow .. 2·75 50
408. – 30 c. purple and green .. 1·00 15
409. – 50 c. blue and yellow .. 1·00 25
410. – 75 c. sepia and red .. 1·00 40
411. – $1 black and red .. 18·00 1·00
412. – $2 violet and yellow .. 25·00 1·75
413. – $5 red and purple .. 23·00 1·50

DESIGNS—VERT. 10 c. Arms. HORIZ. 15 c. Crocodile. 20 c. Pepper plant. 25 c. Leopard. 30 c. Village. 50 c. Kru boatman. 75 c. St. Paul's R. $1, Bongo (antelope). $2, Great Indian Hornbill. $5, African elephant.

†1921. Optd. **1921.**

414. 100. 1 c. green .. .. 3·00 50
415. 64. 2 c. red .. .. 3·00 50
416. 65. 3 c. violet .. .. 3·50 50
417. 101. 5 c. black and blue .. 2·25 50
418. – 10 c. blue and red .. 5·50 50
419. – 15 c. green and purple .. 7·50 1·00
420. – 20 c. green and red .. 3·50 60
421. – 25 c. black and yellow .. 7·50 1·00
422. – 30 c. purple and green .. 3·50 50
423. – 50 c. blue and yellow .. 3·00 70
424. – 75 c. sepia and red .. 3·00 50
425. – $1 black and red .. 20·00 1·50
426. – $2 violet and yellow .. 28·00 2·50
427. – $5 red and purple .. 23·00 3·50

107. Arrival of First Settlers in "Alligator".

†1923. Centennial issue.

466. 107. 1 c. black and blue .. 16·00 70
467. 2 c. brown and red .. 16·00 70
468. 5 c. blue and olive .. 8·50 70
469. 10 c. mauve and green .. 4·75 70
470. $1 brown and red .. 7·00 70

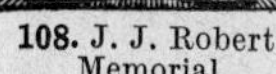

108. J. J. Roberts Memorial. **109.** House of Representatives, Monrovia.

110. Rubber Plantation.

†1923.

471. **108.** 1 c. green .. .. 1·50 8
472. **109.** 2 c. brown and red .. 1·50 8
473. – 3 c. black and lilac .. 50 10
474. – 5 c. black and blue .. 5·00 15
475. – 10 c. brown and grey .. 1·00 10
476. – 15 c. blue and bistre .. 13·00 50
477. – 20 c. mauve and green 10·00 50
478. – 25 c. brown and red .. 30·00 50
479. – 30 c. mauve and brown 1·50 20
480. – 50 c. orange and purple 3·50 40
481. – 75 c. blue and grey .. 2·00 40
482. **110.** $1 violet and red .. 3·00 70
483. – $2 blue and orange .. 4·50 65
484. – $5 brown and green .. 7·50 65

DESIGNS—As Type **108:** 3 c. Star. 5 c., 10 c. Pres. King. 50 c. Pineapple. As Type **109:** 15 c. Hippopotamus. 20 c. Kob (antelope). 25 c. African buffalo. 30 c. Natives making palm oil. 75 c. Carrying elephant tusk. As Type **110:** $2, Stockton lagoon. $5, Styles of huts.

1926. Surch. **Two Cents** and thick bar or wavy lines or ornamental scroll.

504. **91.** 2 c. on 1 c. black & green 2·50 4·00

116. Palm Trees.

117. Map of Africa. **118.** President King.

1928.

511. **116.** 1 c. green 15 12
512. 2 c. violet 20 20
513. 3 c. brown 35 20
514. **117.** 5 c. blue 55 35
515. **118.** 10 c. grey 70 35
516. **117.** 15 c. purple .. .. 3·00 1·40
517. $1 brown .. .. 27·00 13·00

1936. Nos. O 518 and 512/13 surch. **AIR MAIL SIX CENTS.**

525. **116.** 6 c. on 1 c. green .. £110 65·00
526. 6 c. on 2 c. violet .. £110 65·00
527. 6 c. on 3 c. brown .. £110 65·00

122. Fokker "F18".

1936. Air. First Air Mail Service of 28th February.

530. **122.** 1 c. black and green .. 25 10
531. 2 c. black and red .. 25 10
532. 3 c. black and violet .. 40 10
533. 4 c. black and orange 40 15
534. 5 c. black and blue .. 45 15
535. 6 c. black and green .. 45 20

1936. Nos. 350/61 surch. **1936** and new values in figures.

536. 1 c. on 2 c. black and red 30 50
537. 3 c. on 5 c. black and blue 30 45
538. 4 c. on 10 c. green 25 40
539. 6 c. on 15 c. green and black 30 55
540. 8 c. on 20 c. black & red .. 20 60
541. 12 c. on 30 c. black & mauve 2·75 2·25
542. 14 c. on 50 c. black & blue 1·50 1·75
543. 16 c. on 75 c. black & olive 50 1·00
544. 18 c. on $1 blue and brown 60 25
545. 22 c. on $2 black & violet 60 1·50
546. 24 c. on $5 brown .. .. 75 2·00

1936. Nos. O 363/74 optd. with Star and **1936** or surch. also in figures and words.

547. 1 c. on 2 c. black and red .. 30 50
548. 3 c. on 5 c. black and blue 25 50
549. 4 c. on 10 c. green 20 45
550. 6 c. on 15 c. green & brown 25 60
551. 8 c. on 20 c. black and lilac 30 60
552. 12 c. on 30 c. black & violet 2·50 2·00
553. 14 c. on 50 c. black & brown 1·00 1·50
554. 16 c. on 75 c. black & brown 45 90
555. 18 c. on $1 blue and olive .. 50 1·00
556. 22 c. on $2 black and olive 60 1·25
557. 24 c. on $5 green .. .. 75 1·50
558. 25 c. green and brown .. 1·00 2·00

126. Hippopotamus.

1937.

559. – 1 c. black and green .. 1·00 35
560. – 2 c. black and red .. 1·00 30
561. – 3 c. black and purple .. 1·00 35
562. **126.** 4 c. black and orange .. 1·50 60
563. – 5 c. black and blue .. 2·25 50
564. – 6 c. black and green .. 45 20

DESIGNS: 1 c. Black and white casqued hornbill. 2 c. Bushbuck. 3 c. African buffalo. 5 c. Western reef heron. 6 c. Pres. Barclay.

127. Tawny Eagle in Flight. **128.** Sikorsky Flying-boat.

129. Little Egrets.

1938. Air.

565. **127.** 1 c. green 40 10
566. **128.** 2 c. red 15 10
567. – 3 c. olive 30 10
568. **129.** 4 c. orange 35 10
569. – 5 c. green 50 10
570. **128.** 10 c. violet 25 10
571. – 20 c. mauve 30 15
572. – 30 c. grey .. .. 1·10 15
573. **127.** 50 c. brown .. .. 2·25 25
574. – $1 blue .. .. 1·40 25

DESIGNS—VERT. 20 c., $1, Bimotor flying-boat. HORIZ. 3 c., 30 c. Lesser Black-backed Gull in flight.

130. Immigrant Ships nearing Liberian Coast.

1940. Centenary of Founding of Liberian Commonwealth.

575. **130.** 3 c. blue 50 15
576. – 5 c. brown 20 10
577. – 10 c. green 25 15

DESIGNS: 5 c. Seal of Liberia and Flags of original Settlements. 10 c. Thos. Buchanan's house and portrait.

1941. Cent. of First Postage Stamps. Nos. 575/7 optd. **POSTAGE STAMP CENTENNIAL 1840-1940** and portrait of Rowland Hill.

578. **130.** 3 c. blue (postage) .. 1·75 1·75
579. – 5 c. brown .. .. 1·75 1·75
580. – 10 c. green .. .. 1·75 1·75
581. **130.** 3 c. blue (air) .. .. 1·40 1·40
582. – 5 c. brown .. .. 1·40 1·40
583. – 10 c. green .. .. 1·40 1·40

Nos. 581/3 are additionally optd. **AIR MAIL** and aeroplane.

1941. Red Cross Fund. Nos. 575/7 surch. **RED CROSS** plus Red Cross and **TWO CENTS.**

584. **130.** +2 c. on 3 c. blue (post.) 1·40 1·40
585. – +2 c. on 5 c. brown .. 1·40 1·40
586. – +2 c. on 10 c. green .. 1·40 1·40
587. **130.** +2 c. on 3 c. blue (air) 1·40 1·40
588. – +2 c. on 5 c. brown .. 1·40 1·40
589. – +2 c. on 10 c. green .. 1·40 1·40

Nos. 587/9 are additionally optd. **AIR MAIL** and aeroplane.

1941. Air. 1st Flight to U.S.A. Nos. 565/74 surch. **First Flight LIBERIA-U.S. 1941, 50 c.** and bar.

594. **127.** 50 c. on 1 c. £2000 £250
595. **128.** 50 c. on 2 c. .. .. £150 75·00
596. – 50 c. on 3 c. .. .. £225 75·00
597. **129.** 50 c. on 4 c. .. .. 70·00 35·00
598. 50 c. on 5 c. .. .. 70·00 35·00
599. **128.** 50 c. on 10 c. .. .. 45·00 35·00
600. – 50 c. on 20 c. £1500 £150
601. – 50 c. on 30 c. .. .. 80·00 30·00
602. **127.** 50 c. brown .. .. 80·00 35·00
603. – $1 blue .. .. 45·00 30·00

The first flight was cancelled and covers were sent by ordinary mail. The flight took place in 1942 and the stamps were reissued but with the date obliterated.

1942. As Nos. 594/601 but with date "1941" obliterated by two bars.

604. **127.** 50 c. on 1 c. green .. 8·50 8·50
605. **128.** 50 c. on 2 c. red .. 6·00 6·50
606. – 50 c. on 3 c. green .. 7·50 7·50
607. **129.** 50 c. on 4 c. orange .. 7·00 7·00
608. 50 c. on 5 c. green .. 7·00 7·00
609. **128.** 50 c. on 10 c. violet .. 5·00 6·00
610. – 50 c. on 20 c. mauve .. 5·00 6·00
611. – 50 c. on 30 c. grey .. 7·50 7·50
612. **127.** 50 c. brown .. .. 7·50 7·50
613. – $1 blue .. .. .. 6·00 7·00

138. Miami-Monrovia Air Route. **139.** Bushbuck.

1942. Air.

614. **138.** 10 c. red 20 10
615. – 12 c. blue 30 10
616. – 24 c. green 35 10
617. **138.** 30 c. green 35 10
618. 35 c. lilac 40 15
619. 50 c. purple 50 15
620. 70 c. olive 55 30
621. $1·40 red .. .. 1·00 50

DESIGN: 12 c., 24 c. Aeroplane over Liberian Agricultural and Industrial Fair.

1942.

622. – 1 c. brown and violet .. 80 20
623. – 2 c. brown and blue .. 80 20
624. – 3 c. brown and green .. 1·25 45
625. **139.** 4 c. red and black .. 2·00 70
626. – 5 c. brown and olive .. 1·75 70
627. – 10 c. black and red .. 3·50 1·10

DESIGNS—HORIZ. 1 c. Royal antelope. 2 c. Water chevrotain. 3 c. Jentink's duiker. 5 c. Banded duiker. VERT. 10 c. Diana monkey.

1944. Stamps of 1928 and 1937 surch.

628. **116.** 1 c. on 2 c. violet .. 7·50 7·50
634. **126.** 1 c. on 4 c. blk. & orge. .. .. 45·00 38·00
629. **118.** 1 c. on 10 c. grey .. 9·00 5·50
635. – 2 c. on 3 c. black and purple (No. 561) .. 45·00 38·00
630. **117.** 2 c. on 5 c. blue .. 3·00 3·00
632. **116.** 3 c. on 2 c. violet .. 25·00 30·00
636. – 4 c. on 5 c. black and blue (No. 563) 28·00 28·00
633. **118.** 4 c. on 10 c. grey .. 3·00 3·00
637. – 5 c. on 1 c. black and green (No. 559) .. 85·00 55·00
638. – 6 c. on 2 c. black and red (No. 560) 12·00 15·00
639. – 10 c. on 6 c. black and green (No. 564) .. 13·50 15·00

1944. Air stamps of 1936 and 1938 surch.

643. **128.** 10 c. on 2 c. red .. 25·00 28·00
644. **129.** 10 c. on 5 c. green .. 12·50 17·00
640. **122.** 30 c. on 1 c. blk. and grn. 60·00 45·00
645. 30 c. on 3 c. olive (No. 567) .. £160 £125
646. **129.** 30 c. on 4 c. orange .. 14·00 14·00
641. **122.** 50 c. on 3 c. blk. and vio. 20·00 22·00
642. 70 c. on 2 c. black & red 40·00 45·00
647. – $1 on 3 c. olive (No. 567) 65·00 65·00
648. **127.** $1 on 50 c. brown .. 40·00 32·00

150. Pres. Roosevelt reviewing Troops.

1945. Pres. Roosevelt Memorial.

650. **150.** 3 c. black & pur. (post.) 15 15
651. 5 c. black and blue .. 30 25
652. 70 c. black & brown (air) 1·50 2·00

151. Opening Monrovia Harbour Project.

1946. Opening of Monrovia Harbour Project by Pres. Tubman.

653. **151.** 5 c. blue (postage) .. 25 15
654. 24 c. green (air) .. 2·00 2·50

1947. As T **151**, but without inscr. at top.

655. 5 c. violet (postage) .. 15 12
656. 25 c. red (air) .. .. 1·00 1·50

152. 1st Postage Stamps of United States and Liberia.

1947. U.S. Postage Stamps Cent. and 87th Anniv. of Liberian Postal Issues.

657. **152.** 5 c. red (postage) .. 20 12
658. 12 c. green (air) .. 30 15
659. 25 c. violet 40 20
660. 50 c. blue 50 25

153. Matilda Newport Firing Cannon. **154.** Liberty.

1947. 125th Anniv. of Defence of Monrovia.

662. **153.** 1 c. black & grn. (post.) 15 8
663. 3 c. black and violet .. 20 10
664. 5 c. black and blue .. 20 15
665. 10 c. black and yellow 95 45
666. 25 c. black and red (air) 95 35

1947. Cent. of National Independence.

667. – 1 c. green (postage) .. 20 10
668. **154.** 2 c. purple 20 10
669. – 3 c. purple 30 12
670. – 5 c. blue 40 15
671. – 12 c. orange (air) .. 60 20
672. – 25 c. red 75 35
673. – 50 c. brown 90 70

DESIGNS—VERT. 1 c. Liberian star. 3 c. Arms of Liberia. 4 c. Map of Liberia. 12 c. J. J. Roberts Monument. 25 c. Liberian Flag 50 c. ($26\frac{1}{2} \times 33$ mm.) Centenary Monument.

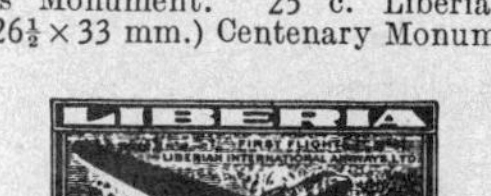

156.

1948. Air. First Liberian Int. Airways Flight (Monrovia-Dakar).

674. **156.** 25 c. red .. .. 1·50 1·00
675. 50 c. blue .. .. 2·00 1·50

157. Joseph J. Roberts.

158. Colonists and Map. **158.** Hand Holding Book.

1949. Liberian Presidents. Portrait and name in black. (a) Postage.

676. – 1 c. green (Roberts) .. 3·00 3·50
677. **157.** 1 c. green 12 10
678. – 1 c. pink (Roberts) .. 25 12
679. – 2 c. pink (Benson) .. 35 35
680. – 2 c. yellow (Benson) 35 15
681. – 3 c. mauve (Warner) 35 35
682. – 4 c. olive (Payne) .. 35 55
683. – 5 c. blue (Mansion) .. 45 55
684. – 6 c. orange (Roye) .. 55 95
685. – 7 c. green (Gardner and Russell) .. 70 1·25
686. – 8 c. red (Johnson) .. 70 1·40
687. – 9 c. pur. (Cheeseman) 1·10 1·40
688. – 10 c. yell. (Coleman) 1·00 35
689. – 10 c. grey (Coleman) .. 40 20
690. – 15 c. orange (Gibson) .. 85 40
691. – 15 c. blue (Gibson) .. 25 15
692. – 20 c. grey (A. Barclay) 1·25 70
693. – 20 c. red (A. Barclay) 50 45
694. – 25 c. red (Howard) .. 1·60 1·10
695. – 25 c. blue (Howard) .. 50 45
696. – 50 c. turquoise (King) 3·25 95
697. – 50 c. purple (King) .. 70 60
698. – $1 mve. (E. Barclay) 5·50 70
699. – $1 brown (E. Barclay) 3·50 55

(b) Air.

700. – 25 c. blue (Tubman) .. 1·00 55
701. – 25 c. green (Tubman) 75 35

Nos. 676 and 678 have a different portrait of Roberts wearing a moustache.

1949. Multicoloured.

702. 1 c. Settlers approaching village (postage) .. 50 75
703. 2 c. Rubber tapping and planting 50 75
704. 3 c. Landing of first colonists in 1822 .. .. 1·00 1·50
705. 5 c. Jehudi Ashmun and Matilda Newport defending stockade 50 75
706. 25 c. Type 158 (air) .. 1·25 1·50
707. 50 c. Africans and coat of arms .. .. 3·25 3·25

1950. National Literacy Campaign.

708. 159. 5 c. blue (postage) .. 20 12
709. – 25 c. red (air) .. 70 70

DESIGN—VERT. 25 c. Open book and rising sun.

160. U.P.U. Monument, Berne. 161. Carey, Ashmun and Careysburg.

1950. 75th Anniv. of U.P.U.

711. 160. 5 c. blk. and grn. (post.) 20 15
712. – 10 c. black and mauve 30 30
713. – 25 c. pur. & orge. (air) 2·75 2·75

DESIGNS—HORIZ. 10 c. Standehaus, Berne. VERT. 25 c. U.P.U. Monument, Berne.

1952. Designs all show portrait of Ashmun.

715. – 1 c. green (postage) .. 8 8
716. 161. 2 c. blue and red .. 10 8
717. – 3 c. green and purple .. 10 8
718. – 4 c. green and brown 12 10
719. – 5 c. red and blue .. 20 15
720. – 10 c. blue and red .. 25 20
721. – 25 c. black & pur. (air) 35 35
722. – 50 c. red and blue .. 70 45

DESIGNS—VERT. 1 c. Seal of Liberia. 3 c. Harper and Harper City. 5 c. Buchanan and Upper Buchanan. HORIZ. 4 c. Marshall and Marshall City. 10 c. Roberts and Robertsport. 25 c. Monroe and Monrovia. 50 c. Tubman and map.

162. U.N. Headquarters. 163. Flags and U.N. Emblem.

1952. U.N. Commem.

724. 162. 1 c. blue (postage) .. 10 8
725. – 4 c. blue and pink .. 15 10
726. – 10 c. brown and yellow 25 20
727. 163. 25 c. red and blue (air) 55 45

DESIGNS—HORIZ. 4 c. Liberian and U.N. flags and scroll. 10 c. Liberian and U.N. emblems.

164. Modern Road-building.

1953. Air. Transport.

729. 164. 12 c. brown 15 15
730. – 25 c. purple 75 30
731. – 35 c. violet .. .. 1·00 35
732. – 50 c. orange 65 25
733. – 70 c. green .. .. 1·00 40
734. – $1 blue .. .. 1·40 55

DESIGNS: 25 c. "African Glen" (freighter) in Monrovia Harbour. 35 c. Diesel locomotive. 50 c. Free Port of Monrovia. 70 c. Roberts Field Airport. $1, Tubman Bridge.

165. Common Bulbul.

166. Blue-throated Roller.

1953. Imperf. or perf.

735. 165. 1 c. red and blue .. 60 15
736. 166. 3 c. blue and salmon .. 60 15
737. – 4 c. brown and yellow 85 20
738. – 5 c. turquoise & mauve 1·00 20
739. – 10 c. mauve and green 1·00 20
740. – 12 c. orange and brown 1·60 30

BIRDS—As Type 165: 4 c. Yellow-casqued Hornbill. 5 c. Giant Kingfisher. As Type 166: 10 c. African Jacana. 12 c. Broad-tailed Paradise Whydah.

167. Hospital.

DESIGNS—As Type 167: 5 c. Medical research workers. 10 c. Nurses. Larger (46 × 35 mm.): 25 c. Doctor examining patient.

1954. Liberian Govt. Hospital Fund.

741. – 5 c. + 5 c. black and purple (postage) .. 20 15
742. – 10 c.+5 c. black and red (air) 15 20
743. 167. 20 c.+5 c. black & grn. 25 25
744. – 25 c.+5 c. black, red and blue 30 20

168. Children of the World.

1954. Air. U.N.I.C.E.F.

745. 168. $5 ultram., red & blue 25·00 20·00

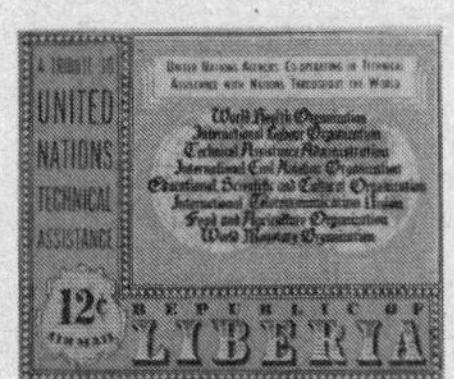

169. U.N. Organizations.

1954. Air. U.N. Technical Assistance.

746. 169. 12 c. black and blue .. 25 15
747. – 15 c. brown and yellow 25 15
748. – 20 c. black and green .. 30 20
749. – 25 c. blue and red .. 35 25

DESIGNS: 15 c. Printers. 20 c. Mechanic. 25 c. Teacher and students.

1954. Air. Visit of Pres. Tubman to U.S.A. As Nos. 729/34 but colours changed and inscr. "COMMEMORATING PRESIDENTIAL VISIT U.S.A.".

750. 12 c. orange 20 20
751. 25 c. blue 80 25
752. 35 c. red .. .. 3·25 1·40
753. 50 c. mauve 80 30
754. 70 c. brown .. .. 1·10 50
755. $1 green .. .. 1·60 65

170. Football. 171. "Callichilia Stenosepala".

1955. Sports.

756. – 3 c. red & grn. (post) 15 10
757. 170. 5 c. black and orange 15 10
758. – 25 c. violet and yellow 25 20
759. – 10 c. bl. & mve. (air) 20 12
760. – 12 c. brown and blue 12 12
761. – 25 c. red and green .. 20 20

DESIGNS—VERT. 3 c. Tennis. 25 c. Boxing (No. 758). HORIZ. 10 c. Baseball. 12 c. Swimming. 25 c. Running (No. 761).

1955. Flowers.

763. 171. 6 c. yellow, salmon & green (postage) .. 15 10
764. – 7 c. red, yell. & green 15 10
765. – 8 c. buff, blue & green 20 10
766. – 9 c. green and orange 25 15
767. – 20 c. yellow, green and violet (air) .. 12 12
768. – 25 c. yell., green & red 20 20

FLOWERS—VERT. 7 c. "Gomphia subcordata". 8 c. "Listrostachys chudata". 9 c. "Mussaenda isertiana". HORIZ. 20 s. "Costus". 25 c. "Barteria nigritiana".

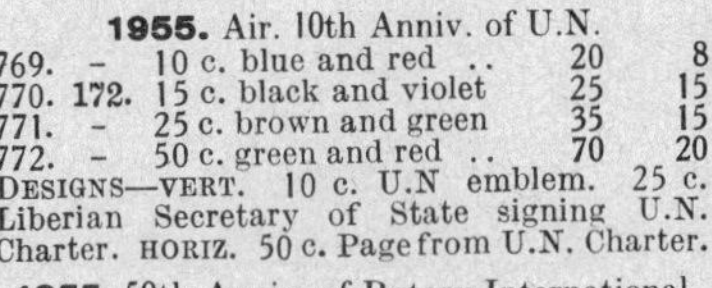

172. U.N. General Assembly. 173. Tapping Rubber and Rotary Emblem.

1955. Air. 10th Anniv. of U.N.

769. – 10 c. blue and red .. 20 8
770. 172. 15 c. black and violet 25 15
771. – 25 c. brown and green 35 15
772. – 50 c. green and red .. 70 20

DESIGNS—VERT. 10 c. U.N emblem. 25 c. Liberian Secretary of State signing U.N. Charter. HORIZ. 50 c. Page from U.N. Charter.

1955. 50th Anniv. of Rotary International.

773. 173. 5 c. grn. & yell. (post.) 25 15
774. – 10 c. blue and red (air) 12 25
775. – 15 c. brown, yell. & red 20 35

DESIGNS: 10 c. Rotary Int. H.Q., Evanston. 15 c. View of Monrovia.

174. Coliseum, New York.

DESIGNS—VERT. 3 c., 15 c. Statue of Liberty. HORIZ. 6 c., 12 c. The Globe.

1956. 5th Int. Philatelic Exn., New York.

777. – 3 c. brown and green (postage) 15 10
778. 174. 4 c. brown and green .. 8 25
779. – 6 c. purple and black .. 20 10
780. 174. 10 c. blue and red (air) 25 12
781. – 12 c. violet and orange 20 15
782. – 15 c. purple & turquoise 25 20

175. Chariot Race.

DESIGNS—HORIZ. 4 c. Olympic rings, eastern grey kangaroo and emu. 8 c. Goddess of Victory. 12 c., 20 c. Olympic torch superimposed on map of Australia. VERT. 6 c. Discus thrower.

1956. Olympic Games.

784. – 4 c. brn. & olive (post.) 15 15
785. – 6 c. black and green .. 15 10
786. – 8 c. brown and blue .. 20 10
787. 175. 10 c. black and red .. 25 10
788. – 12 c. pur. and grn. (air) 20 15
789. – 20 c. multicoloured .. 30 20

176. Pan-American Clipper "John Alden" at Idlewild Airport.

DESIGN: 5 c., 15 c., 50 c. President Tubman and clipper "John Alden" at Roberts Field, Liberia.

1957. 1st Anniv. of Inauguration of Liberia U.S. Direct Air Service.

791. 176. 3 c. blue & orge. (post.) 15 15
792. – 5 c. black and mauve .. 20 20
793. 176. 12 c. blue & green (air) 30 25
794. – 15 c. black and brown 30 25
795. 176. 25 c. blue and red .. 45 25
796. – 50 c black and blue .. 85 30

177. Children's Playground.

DESIGNS: 5 c. Teacher with pupil. 6 c. National anthem with Choristers. 10 c. Children viewing welfare home. 15 c. Nurse inoculating youth. 35 c. Kamara triplets.

1957. Inaug. of Antoinette Tubman Child Welfare Foundation. Inscr. as in T 177.

797. 177. 4 c. green & red (post.) 10 8
798. – 5 c. brown & turquoise 15 10
799. – 6 c. violet and bistre .. 15 10
800. – 10 c. blue and red .. 20 12
801. – 15 c. brn. & blue (air) 20 15
802. – 35 c. purple and grey 35 25

178. German Flag and Brandenburg Gate.

1958. Pres. Tubman's European Tour. Flags in national colours.

804. 178. 5 c. blue (postage) .. 15 10
805. – 5 c. brown 15 10
806. – 5 c. red 15 10
807. – 10 c. black (air) .. 25 15
808. – 15 c. green 25 20
809. – 15 c. blue 25 20
810. – 15 c. violet 25 20

DESIGNS: Flags of: Netherlands and windmill (No. 805); Sweden and Royal Palace, Stockholm (No. 806); Italy and Colosseum (No. 807); France and Arc de Triomphe (No. 808); Switzerland and Alpine chalet (No. 809); Vatican City and St. Peter's Basilica (No. 810).

179. Map of the World. 180. Africans and Map.

1958. 10th Anniv. of Declaration of Human Rights.

811. 179. 3 c. blue and black .. 25 15
812. – 5 c. brown and blue .. 20 20
813. – 10 c. orange and black 30 75
814. – 12 c. black and red .. 40 35

DESIGNS: 5 c. U.N. Emblem and H.Q. building. 10 c. U.N. Emblem. 12 c. U.N. Emblem and initials of U.N. Agencies.

1959. Africa Freedom Day.

816. 180. 20 c. orge. & brn. (post.) 30 30
817. – 25 c. brn. & blue (air) 35 20

DESIGN: 25 c. Two Africans looking at Pres. Tubman's declaration of Africa Freedom Day.

181. 182. Abraham Lincoln.

1959. Inaug. of U.N.E.S.C.O. Building, Paris.

818. 181. 25 c. pur. & grn. (post.) 35 40
819. – 25 c. red & blue (air) .. 35 30

DESIGN—HORIZ. No. 819 U.N.E.S.C.O. Headquarters, Paris.

1959. 150th Birth Anniv. of Abraham Lincoln.

821. 182. 10 c. blk. & blue (post.) 25 30
822. 15 c. black and orange 30 30
823. 25 c. black & grn. (air) 55 50

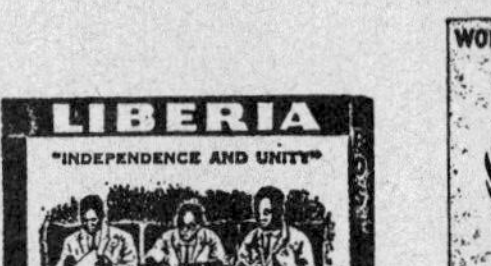

183. Presidents Toure, Tubman and Nkrumah at Conference Table. 184. "Care of Refugees".

1960. "Big Three" Conf., Saniquellie, Liberia.

825. 183. 25 c. black & red (post.) 35 25
826. – 25 c. blk., bl. & buff (air) 35 25

DESIGN: No. 826, Medallion portraits of Presidents Toure (Guinea), Tubman (Liberia) and Nkrumah (Ghana).

1960. World Refugee Year.

827. 184. 25 c. grn. & blk. (post.) 35 30
828. 25 c. blue & black (air) 55 40

185. 186. Weightlifting.

1960. 10th Anniv. of African Technical Co-operation (C.C.T.A.).

830. 185. 25 c. grn. & blk. (post.) 35 25
831. – 25 c. brn. and blue (air) 45 35

DESIGN: No. 831, Map of Africa with symbols showing fields of assistance.

1960. Olympic Games, Rome.

832. 186. 5 c. brn. and grn. (post.) 20 15
833. – 10 c. brown and purple 40 75
834. – 15 c. brown and orange 35 30
835. – 25 c. brown & blue (air) 70 45

DESIGNS—HORIZ. 10 c. Rowing. 25 c. Javelin-throwing. VERT. 15 c. Walking.

187. Stamps of 1860 and Map.

188. " Guardians of Peace".

1960. Liberian Stamp Cent. Stamps, etc., in green, red and blue. Colours of map and inscriptions given.
837. **187.** 5 c. black (postage) .. 25 15
838. 20 c. brown 40 40
839. 25 c. blue (air) .. 50 40

1961. Membership of U.N. Security Council.
841. **188.** 25 c. blue & red (post.) 45 35
842. – 25 c. blue and red (air) 45 25
DESIGN—HORIZ. No. 842, Dove of Peace, Globe and U.N. Emblem.

189. Anatomy Class, University of Liberia.

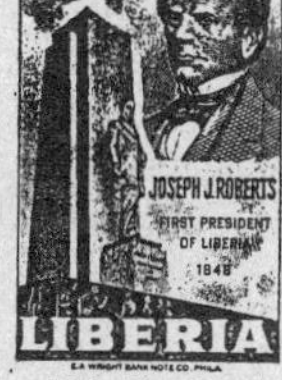

190. President Roberts.

1961. 15th Anniv. of U.N.E.S.C.O.
845. **189.** 25 c. brn. & grn. (post.) 35 35
846. – 25 c. brn. & violet (air) 35 25
DESIGN: No. 846, Science class, University of Liberia.

1961. 150th Birth Anniv. of Joseph J. Roberts (first President of Liberia).
848. **190.** 5 c. sepia & orge. (post.) 20 15
849. – 10 c. sepia and blue .. 35 15
850. – 25 c. sepia & green (air) 45 35
DESIGNS—HORIZ. 10 c. Pres. Roberts and old and new presidential mansions. 25 c. Pres. Roberts and Providence Is.

DESIGNS—HORIZ. 10 c. Scout badge and scouts in camp. VERT. 25 c. Scout and badge.

191. Scout and Sports.

1961. Liberian Boy Scout Movement.
852. **191.** 5 c. sepia & vio. (post.) 25 20
853. – 10 c. ochre and blue .. 30 20
854. – 25 c. sepia & green (air) 40 30

192. Hammarskjold and U.N. Emblem.

193. Campaign Emblem.

1962. Dag Hammarskjold Commem.
856. **192.** 20 c. blk. & blue (post.) 30 20
857. 25 c. black & pur. (air) 35 25

1962. Malaria Eradication.
859. **193.** 25 c. grn. & red (post.) 35 25
860. – 25 c. orge. & violet (air) 35 25
DESIGN—HORIZ. No. 860, Campaign emblem and slogan.

194. Pres. Tubman and New York Skyline. **195.** U.N. Emblem.

1962. Air. President's Visit to U.S.A.
862. **194.** 12 c. multicoloured .. 25 15
863. 25 c. multicoloured .. 35 30
864. 50 c. multicoloured .. 70 55

1962. U.N. Day.
865. **195.** 20 c. bistre & grn. (post.) 35 30
866. – 25 c. blue & dp. blue (air) 45 30
DESIGN: 25 c. U.N. emblem and flags.

196. Treasury Building.

197. F.A.O. Emblem, Bowl and Spoon.

1962. Liberian Government Buildings.
868. – 1 c. orge. & blue (post.) 5 15
869. **196.** 5 c. violet and blue .. 15 10
870. – 10 c. brown and buff .. 20 12
871. – 15 c. blue and salmon 25 20
872. – 80 c. yellow and brown 1·25 70
873. – 12 c. lake & green (air) 25 50
874. – 50 c. blue and orange .. 70 65
875. – 70 c. blue and mauve .. 1·00 70
876. **196.** $1 black and orange .. 1·40 30
BUILDINGS: 1 c., 80 c. Executive. 10 c., 50 c. Information. 12 c., 15 c., 70 c. Capitol.

1963. Freedom from Hunger.
877. **197.** 5 c. pur. & turq. (post.) 15 10
878. – 25 c. yellow & green (air) 35 20
DESIGN: 25 c. F.A.O. emblem and Globe.

DESIGNS — HORIZ. 15 c. Space capsule. VERT. 25 c. " Telstar ". TV satellite.

198. Rocket.

1963. Space Exploration.
880. **198.** 10 c. yell. & blue (post.) 20 15
881. – 15 c. brown and blue .. 35 70
882. – 25 c. grn. & orge. (air) 45 30

199. Red Cross.

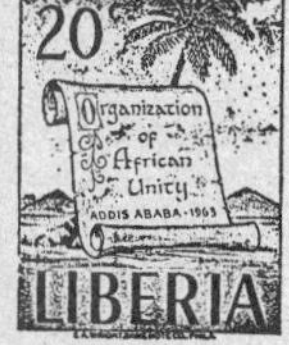

200. " Unity " Scroll.

1963. Red Cross Centenary.
884. **199.** 5 c. green & red (post.) 15 15
885. – 10 c. grey and red .. 20 20
886. – 25 c. violet & red (air) 35 30
887. – 50 c. blue and red .. 70 50
DESIGNS—VERT. 10 c. Emblem and torch. HORIZ. 25 c. Red Cross and Globe. 50 c. Emblem and Globe.

1963. Conference of African Heads of State, Addis Ababa.
888. **200.** 20 c. brn. & grn. (post. 40 35
889. – 25 c. red and green (air) 45 30
DESIGN : 25 c. Map of Africa (insc. "AFRICAN SUMMIT CONFERENCE").

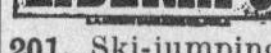

201. Ski-jumping.

202. President Kennedy.

1963. Winter Olympic Games, Innsbruck. (1964).
890. **201.** 5 c. blue and red (post.) 20 20
891. – 10 c. red and blue (air) 25 25
892. – 25 c. orange and green 35 35
DESIGNS—VERT. 10 c. Olympic flame. HORIZ. 25 c. Olympic rings. All have mountain scenery as backgrounds.

1964. President Kennedy Memorial Issue.
894. **202.** 20 c. blk. & blue (post.) 35 20
895. – 25 c. black & pur. (air) 45 30
DESIGN—VERT. 25 c. Pres. Kennedy, full face portrait.

203. "Relay I" Satellite.

204. Mt. Fuji.

1964. Space Communications.
897. – 10 c. orange and green 20 15
898. **203.** 15 c. blue and mauve .. 25 20
899. – 25 c. yell., blk. and blue 45 25
SATELLITES—HORIZ. 10 c. " Syncom ". 25 c " Mariner II ".

1964. Olympic Games, Tokyo.
901. **204.** 10 c. green and yellow 15 10
902. – 15 c. purple and red .. 20 15
903. – 25 c. red and buff .. 45 20
DESIGNS: 15 c. Japanese arch and Olympic Flame. 25 c. Cherry blossom and stadium.

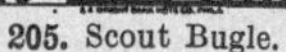

205. Scout Bugle.

5¢ LINCOLN CENTENNIAL MEMORIAL 1965 LIBERIA
206. " The Great Emancipator " (statue).

1965. Liberian Boy Scouts.
905. – 5 c. brown and blue (postage) 25 15
906. **205.** 10 c. ochre and green .. 40 25
907. – 25 c. blue & red (air) .. 50 35
DESIGNS—VERT. 5 c. Scout badge and saluting hand. 25 c. Liberian flag within scout badge.

1965. Death Cent. of Abraham Lincion.
909. **206.** 5 c. brown and sepia .. 20 70
910. – 20 c. green & pale brown 35 30
911. – 25 c. blue and purple .. 40 40
DESIGNS—HORIZ. 20 c. Bust of Lincoln, and Pres. Kennedy. VERT. 25 c. Lincoln statue Chicago (after St. Gaudens).

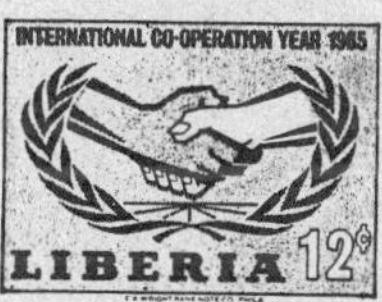

207. I.C.Y. Emblem.

1965. Int. Co-operation Year.
913. **207.** 12 c. brown and orange 70 25
914. 25 c. brown and blue .. 40 25
915. 50 c. brown and green 80 70

208. I.T.U. Emblem and Symbols.

1965. Cent. of I.T.U.
917. **208.** 25 c. brn. & grn. (post.) 40 25
918. 35 c. mauve and black 60 50
919. 50 c. blue and red (air) 80 45

209. Pres. Tubman and Flag.

210. Sir Winston Churchill.

1965. Pres. Tubman's 70th Birthday. Mult
921. 25 c. Type **209** (postage) .. 35 30
922. 25 c. President and Liberian arms (air) 35 25

1966. Churchill Commem.
924. **210.** 15 c. black & orge. (post.) 30 30
925. – 20 c. black and green .. 35 25
926. – 25 c. black and blue (air) 40 30
DESIGNS—HORIZ. 20 c. Churchill in uniform of Trinity House Elder Brother. 25 c. Churchill and Houses of Parliament.

211. Pres. Roberts.

212. Footballers and Hemispheres.

1966. Liberian Presidents.
928. **211.** 1 c. black and pink .. 5 5
929. – 2 c. black and yellow .. 5 5
930. – 3 c. black and violet .. 8 8
931. – 4 c. black and yellow .. 75 50
932. – 5 c. black and orange .. 10 8
933. – 10 c. black and green .. 15 10
934. – 25 c. black and blue .. 35 20
935. – 50 c. black and mauve 70 65
936. – 80 c. black and red .. 1·25 95
937. – $1 black and brown .. 1·40 15
938. – $2 black and purple .. 3·00 2·50
939. – 25 c. black & green (air) 35 25
PRESIDENTS: 2 c. Benson. 3 c. Warner. 4 c. Payne. 5 c. Roye. 10 c. Coleman. 25 c. (postage), Howard. 25 c. (air), Tubman. 50 c. King. 80 c. Johnson. $1, Barclay. $2, Cheesman.

1966. World Cup Football Championships.
940. **212.** 10 c. brown & turquoise 15 15
941. – 25 c. brown and mauve 35 30
942. – 35 c. brown and orange 50 45
DESIGNS—VERT. 25 c. Presentation cup football and boots. 35 c. Footballer.

213. Pres. Kennedy Taking Oath.

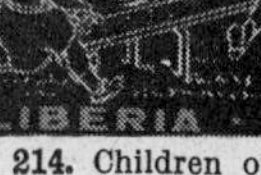

214. Children on See-saw.

1966. 3rd Death Anniv. (Nov. 22nd) of Pres. Kennedy.
944. **213.** 15 c. black & red (post.) 25 15
945. – 20 c. purple and blue .. 35 20
946. – 25 c. blue, black and ochre (air) 45 30
947. – 35 c. blue and pink .. 60 45
DESIGNS: 20 c. Kennedy stamps of 1964. 25 c. U.N. General Assembly and Pres. Kennedy. 35 c. Pres. Kennedy and rocket on launching pad.

1966. 20th Anniv. of U.N.I.C.E.F.
949. **214.** 5 c. blue and red .. 20 20
950. – 80 c. brown and green 1·25 1·25
DESIGN: 80 c. Child playing " Doctors".

215. Giraffe.

216. Scout Emblem and Various Sports.

1966. Wild Animals. Multicoloured.
951. 2 c. Type **215** 10 5
952. 3 c. Lion 20 15
953. 5 c. Crocodile (horiz.) .. 15 10
954. 10 c. Chimpanzees 40 20
955. 15 c. Leopard (horiz.) .. 50 25
956. 20 c. Black rhinoceros (horiz.) 60 40
957. 25 c. African elephant .. 70 50

1967. World Scout Jamboree, Idaho.
958. – 10 c. purple and green 20 15
959. **216.** 25 c. red and blue .. 35 20
960. – 40 c. brown and green 60 60
DESIGNS—VERT. 10 c. Jamboree emblem. HORIZ. 40 c. Scout by campfire, and Moon landing.

217. Pre-Hispanic Sculpture.

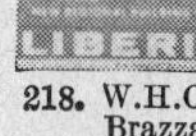

218. W.H.O. Building, Brazzaville.

1967. Publicity for Olympic Games, Mexico (1968).
962. **217.** 10 c. violet & orange 75 50
963. – 25 c. orge., blk & bl. 35 40
964. – 40 c. red and green .. 60 90
DESIGNS—VERT. 25 c. Aztec calendar. HORIZ. 40 c. Mexican sombrero, guitar and ceramics.

1967. Inauguration of W.H.O.'s Regional Office, Brazzaville.
966. **218.** 5 c. yellow and blue .. 20 20
967. – 80 c. green and yellow 1·25 1·25
DESIGN—VERT. 80 c. As Type **218** but in vertical format.

219. Boy with Rattle.

220. Ice-hockey.

1967. Musicians and Instruments. Mult.
968. 2 c. Type **219** 15 15
969. 3 c. Tomtom and soko violin 20 20
970. 5 c Mang harp 25 25
971. 10 c. Alimilim 30 30
972. 15 c. Xylophone drums .. 35 35
973. 25 c. Tomtoms 50 40
974. 35 c. Oral harp 75 60
The 3 c. and 5 c. are horiz. designs.

1967. Publicity for Winter Olympic Games, Grenoble (1968).
975. **220.** 10 c. blue and green .. 15 20
976. – 25 c. violet and blue .. 35 30
977. – 40 c. brown and orange 60 50
DESIGNS: 25 c Ski-jumping. 40 c. Tobogganing.

221. Pres. Tubman.

222. Human Rights Emblem.

1967. Re-election of Pres. Tubman for 6th Term.
979. **221.** 25 c. brown and blue 35 25

1968. Human Rights Year.
981. **222.** 3 c. blue and red .. 10 40
982. 80 c. green and brown 1·25 1·25

223. Dr. King and Hearse.

224. Throwing the Javelin and Statue of Diana.

1968. Martin Luther King Commem.
984. **223.** 15 c. brown and blue 25 20
985. – 25 c. brown and blue 40 30
986. – 35 c. black and olive 60 40
DESIGNS—VERT. 25 c. Dr. Martin Luther King. HORIZ. 35 c. Dr. King and Lincoln Monument.

1968. Olympic Games, Mexico.
988. **224.** 15 c. violet and brown 25 12
989. – 25 c. blue and red .. 35 15
990. – 35 c. brown and green 50 30
DESIGNS: 25 c. Throwing the discus and Quetzalcoatl sculpture. 35 c. High-diving and Xochilcalco bas-relief.

225. President Tubman.

226. I.L.O. Symbol.

1968. 25th Anniv. of Pres. Tubman's Administration.
992. **225.** 25 c. blk., brn. & silver 45 50

1969. 50th Anniv. of I.L.O.
994. **226.** 25 c. blue & gold (post.) 35 35
995. – 80 c. green & gold (air) 1·50 1·00
DESIGN: 80 c. As Type **226**. but vertical.

227. "Prince Balthasar Carlos" (Velasquez).

228. Bank Emblem on "Tree".

1969. Paintings (1st series). Multicoloured.
996. 3 c. Type **227** 10 10
997. 5 c. "Red Roofs" (Pissarro) 20 10
998. 10 c. "David and Goliath" (Caravaggio) 30 12
999. 12 c. "Still Life" (Chardin) 30 12
1000. 15 c. "The Last Supper" (Leonardo da Vinci) .. 35 15
1001. 20 c. "Regatta at Argenteuil" (Monet) 50 20
1002. 25 c. "Judgement of Solomon" (Giorgione) 45 25
1003. 35 c. "The Sistine Madonna" (Raphael) 60 30
Nos. 997/1001 are horiz.
See also Nos. 1010/1017.

1969. 5th Anniv. of African Development Bank.
1004. **228.** 25 c. brown and blue 45 40
1005. 80 c. red and green .. 1·50 1·50

229. Memorial Plaque. **230.** Peace Dove and Emblems.

1969. 1st Man on the Moon.
1006. **229.** 15 c. blue and ochre 25 15
1007. – 25 c. blue and orange 35 20
1008. – 35 c. red and slate .. 50 25
DESIGNS—VERT. 25 c. Moon landing and Liberian 35 c. "Kennedy" stamp of 1966. 35 c. Module lifting off from Moon.

1969. Paintings (2nd series). As T **227**. Multicoloured.
1010. 3 c. "The Gleaners" (Millet) 15 10
1011. 5 c. "View of Toledo" (El Greco) 20 12
1012. 10 c. "Heads of Negroes" (Rubens) 30 15
1013. 12 c. "The Last Supper" (El Greco) 30 20
1014. 15 c. "Peasants Dancing" (Brueghel) 35 20
1015. 20 c. "Hunters in the Snow" (Brueghel) .. 40 25
1016. 25 c. "Descent from the Cross" (detail, Weyden) 45 30
1017. 35 c. "The Conception" (Murillo) 60 40
Nos. 1010, 1012/15 are horiz.

1970. 25th Anniv. of United Nations.
1018. **230.** 5 c. grn. & silver (post.) 15 25
1019. – $1 blue & silver (air) 1·25 1·50
DESIGN: $1, U.N. emblem and olive branch.

231. World Cup "Football" Emblem.

1970. World Cup Football Championships, Mexico.
1020. **231.** 5 c. brown and blue .. 20 15
1021. – 10 c. brown and green 25 20
1022. – 25 c. gold and purple 45 30
1023. – 35 c. red and blue .. 60 45
DESIGNS—VERT. 10 c. Tlaloc, Mexican Rain God. 25 c. Jules Rimet Cup. HORIZ. 35 c. Football in sombrero.

232. Japanese Singer and Festival Plaza.

1970. Expo 70. Multicoloured.
1025. 2 c. Type **232** 10 5
1026. 3 c. Japanese singer and Expo hall 15 8
1027. 5 c. Aerial view of "EXPO 70" 15 10
1028. 7 c. "Tanabata" Festival 30 10
1029. 8 c. "Awa" Dance Festival 30 12
1030. 25 c. "Sado-Okesa" Dance Festival .. 45 25

233. New H.Q. Building.

1970. Inauguration of New U.P.U. Headquarters Building, Berne.
1032. **233.** 25 c. brown and blue 35 35
1033. – 80 c. brn. & chestnut 1·25 1·50
DESIGN—VERT. 80 c. Similar to Type **233** but with larger U.P.U. monument.

234. "The First Consul" (Vien).

1970. Birth Bicent. of Napoleon Bonaparte. Multicoloured.
1034. 3 c. Type **234** 20 10
1035. 5 c. "Napoleon visiting school" (unknown artist) 30 12
1036. 10 c. "Napoleon Bonaparte" (detail, Gerard) 35 15
1037. 12 c. "The French Campaign" (Meissonier) .. 40 20
1038. 20 c. "The Abdication" (Bouchot) 50 30
1039. 25 c. "Meeting of Napoleon and Pope Pius VII" (Demarne) 60 35
Design of 10 c. is incorrectly attributed to Gerard on the stamp.

235. Pres. Tubman.

1970. Pres. Tubman's 75th Birthday.
1041. **235.** 25 c. multicoloured .. 35 25

236. "Adoration of the Magi" (Van der Weyden).

1970. Christmas. "The Adoration of the Magi" by artists as below. Multicoloured.
1043. 3 c. Type **236** 10 8
1044. 5 c. H. Memling 15 10
1045. 10 c. S. Lochner 25 12
1046. 12 c. A. Altdorfer (vert.) 30 15
1047. 20 c. H. van der Goes .. 35 18
1048. 25 c. H. Bosch (vert.) .. 40 30

237. Bapende Mask.

238. Astronauts on Moon.

239. Pres. Tubman and Women at Ballot Box.

1971. African Ceremonial Masks. Mask from different tribes. Multicoloured.
1050. 2 c. Type **237** 10 8
1051. 3 c. Dogon 12 10
1052. 5 c. Baoule 15 12
1053. 6 c. Dedougou 20 12
1054. 9 c. Dan 25 15
1055. 15 c. Bamileke 30 20
1056. 20 c. Bapende (different) 40 30
1057. 25 c. Bamileke costume .. 60 30

1971. "Apollo 14". Moon Mission. Mult.
1058. 3 c. Type **238** 15 10
1059. 5 c. Astronaut and Moon vehicle 15 10
1060. 10 c. Erecting U.S. flag on Moon 20 10
1061. 12 c. Splashdown .. 40 15
1062. 20 c. Astronauts leaving capsule 45 15
1063. 25 c. "Apollo 14" crew 60 20

1971. 25th Anniv. of Liberian Women's Suffrage.
1065. **239.** 3 c. blue and brown .. 15 30
1066. – 80 c. brown and green 1·25 1·50
DESIGN—HORIZ. 80 c. Pres. Tubman, women and map.

240. Hall of Honour, Munich.

1971. Olympic Games, Munich (1972) (1st issue). Views of Munich. Multicoloured.
1067. 3 c. Type **240** 15 8
1068. 5 c. View of central Munich 15 8
1069. 10 c. National Museum .. 20 10
1070. 12 c. Max Joseph's Square 25 10
1071. 20 c. Propylaen, King's Square 40 15
1072. 25 c. Liesel-Karlstadt Fountain 60 20

241. American Scout.

242. Pres. William Tubman.

1971. World Scout Jamboree, Asagiri, Japan. Scouts in national uniforms. Multicoloured.
1074. 3 c. Type **241** 15 5
1075. 5 c. West Germany .. 15 10
1076. 10 c. Australia 20 12
1077. 12 c. Great Britain .. 25 15
1078. 20 c. Japan 40 20
1079. 25 c. Liberia 60 30

1971. Pres. Tubman Memorial Issue.
1081. **242.** 3 c. brn., blue & blk. 8 8
1082. 25 c. brn., pur. & blk. 35 35

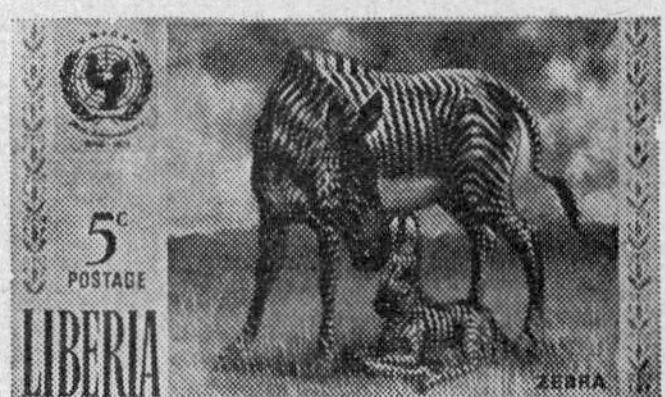

243. Common Zebra and Foal.

1971. 25th Anniv. of U.N.I.C.E.F. Animals with young. Multicoloured.
1083. 5 c. type **243** 20 10
1084. 7 c. Koalas 30 12
1085. 8 c. Guanaco 35 15
1086. 10 c. Red fox and cubs .. 45 15
1087. 20 c. Savanna monkeys 65 25
1088. 25 c. Brown bears .. 90 35

244. Cross-country Skiing and Sika Deer.

1971. Winter Olympic Games, Sapporo, Japan. Sports and Hokkaido Animals. Multicoloured.
1090. 2 c. Type **244** 10 10
1091. 3 c. Tobogganing and black woodpecker .. 40 15
1092. 5 c. Ski-jumping and Brown bear 15 10
1093. 10 c. Bob-sleighing and common guillemots .. 75 15
1094. 15 c. Figure-skating and Northern pika .. 30 20
1095. 25 c. Slalom-skiing and Manchurian cranes .. 1·50 45

245. A.P.U. Emblem, Dove and Letter.

246. "Elizabeth" (emigrant ship) at Providence Island.

1971. 10th Anniv. of African Postal Union.

1097.	**245.**	25 c. orange and blue	35	25
1098.		80 c. brown and grey	1·25	1·50

1972. 150th Anniv. of Liberia.

1099.	**246.**	3 c. green and blue ..	50	50
1100.	–	20 c. blue and orange	35	20
1101.	**246.**	25 c. purple & orange	1·50	55
1102.	–	35 c. purple and green	60	40

DESIGNS—VERT. 20 c., 35 c. Arms and Founding Fathers Monument, Monrovia.

247. Pres. Tolbert and Map.

1972. Inaug. of Pres. Wm. R. Tolbert Jnr.

1104.	**247.**	25 c. brown and green	35	25
1105.	–	80 c. brown and blue	1·25	80

DESIGN—VERT. 80 c. Pres. Tolbert standing by desk.

248. Football.

1972. Olympic Games, Munich (2nd issue). Multicoloured.

1106.	3 c. Type **248**	10	5
1107.	5 c. Swimming	15	8
1108.	10 c. Show-jumping ..	25	10
1109.	12 c. Cycling	30	15
1110.	20 c. Long-jumping ..	45	20
1111.	25 c. Running	60	25

249. Globe and Emblem.

251. Emperor Haile Selassie.

250. Astronaut and Moon Rover.

1972. 50th Anniv. of Int. Y's Men's Clubs.

1113.	**249.**	15 c. violet and gold	40	15
1114.	–	90 c. green and blue	1·50	2·00

DESIGN: 90 c. Club emblem on World Map.

1972. Moon Mission of "Apollo 16". Mult.

1115.	3 c. Type **250**	8	5
1116.	5 c. Reflection on visor ..	10	8
1117.	10 c. Astronauts with cameras ..	15	10
1118.	12 c. Setting up equipment	20	15
1119.	20 c. "Apollo 16" emblem	40	20
1120.	25 c. Astronauts in Moon Rover	50	25

1972. Emperor Haile Selassie of Ethiopia's 80th Birthday.

1122.	**251.**	20 c. green and yellow	40	30
1123.		25 c. purple & yellow	45	40
1124.		35 c. brown & yellow	60	60

252. H.M.S. "Ajax" (ship of the line), 1809.

1972. Famous Ships of the British Royal Navy. Multicoloured.

1125	3 c. Type **252**	35	25
1126	5 c. H.M.S. "Hogue" (screw ship of the line), 1848	65	25
1127	7 c. H.M.S. "Ariadne" (frigate), 1816	85	30
1128	15 c. H.M.S. "Royal Adelaide" (ship of the line), 1828	1·00	55
1129	20 c. H.M.S. "Rinaldo" (screw sloop), 1860 ..	1·40	70
1130	25 c. H.M.S. "Nymphe" (screw sloop), 1888 ..	1·90	1·00

253. Pres. Tolbert taking Oath.

1972. First Year President Tolbert Presidency.

1132.	**253.**	15 c. multicoloured ..	35	15
1133.		25 c. multicoloured ..	70	70

254. Klaus Dibiasi and Italian Flag.

1973. Olympic Games, Munich. Gold-medal Winners. Multicoloured.

1135.	5 c. Type **254**	10	8
1136.	8 c. Borzov and Soviet flag	12	8
1137.	10 c. Yanagida and Japanese flag	15	10
1138.	12 c. Spitz and U.S. flag	20	12
1139.	15 c. Keino and Kenyan flag	25	15
1140.	25 c. Meade and Union Jack	35	25

255. Astronaut on Moon.

1973. Moon Flight of "Apollo 17". Mult.

1142.	2 c. Type **255**	5	5
1143.	3 c. Testing lunar rover at Cape Kennedy ..	10	5
1144.	10 c. Collecting Moon rocks	12	10
1145.	15 c. Lunar rover on Moon	20	15
1146.	20 c. "Apollo 17" crew at Cape Kennedy ..	30	20
1147.	25 c. Astronauts on Moon	35	25

256. British G.W.R. Locomotive.

1973. Historical Railways. Steam locomotives of 1895–1905. Multicoloured.

1149.	2 c. Type **256**	20	5
1150.	3 c. Holland	30	5
1151.	10 c. France	55	15
1152.	15 c. U.S.A.	75	20
1153.	20 c. Japan	1·60	25
1154.	25 c. Germany	2·25	30

257. O.A.U. Emblem.

1973. 10th Anniv. of Organization of African Unity.

1156.	**257.**	3 c. multicoloured ..	10	8
1157.		5 c. multicoloured ..	10	8
1158.		10 c. multicoloured ..	12	10
1159.		15 c. multicoloured ..	20	15
1160.		25 c. multicoloured ..	35	25
1161.		50 c. multicoloured ..	70	70

258. Edward Jenner and Roses.

1973. 25th Anniv. of W.H.O. Mult.

1162.	1 c. Type **258**	15	5
1163.	4 c. Sigmund Freud and violets	15	8
1164.	10 c. Jonas Salk and chrysanthemums	25	10
1165.	15 c. Louis Pasteur and scabious	40	15
1166.	20 c. Emil von Behring and mallow	45	20
1167.	25 c. Sir Alexander Fleming and rhododendrons	75	25

259. Stanley Steamer, 1910.

1973. Vintage Cars. Multicoloured.

1169.	2 c. Type **259**	5	5
1170.	3 c. Cadillac Model A, 1903	10	8
1171.	10 c. Clement-Baynard, 1904	15	10
1172.	15 c. Rolls-Royce Silver Ghost tourer, 1907 ..	25	15
1173.	20 c. Maxwell gentleman's speedster, 1905 ..	35	20
1174.	25 c. Chadwick, 1907 ..	50	25

260. Copernicus, Armillary Sphere and Satellite Communications System.

1973. 500th Birth Anniv. of Copernicus. Mult.

1176.	1 c. Type **260**	5	5
1177.	4 c. Eudoxus solar system	8	5
1178.	10 c. Aristotle, Ptolemy and Copernicus ..	15	8
1179.	15 c. "Saturn" and "Apollo" spacecraft	25	15
1180.	20 c. Astronomical observatory satellite ..	35	20
1181.	25 c. Satellite tracking-station	50	25

261. Radio Mast and Map of Africa.

1974. 20th Anniv. of "Eternal Love Winning Africa". Radio Station. Multicoloured.

1183.	13 c. Type **261**	25	25
1184.	15 c. Radio Mast and map of Liberia	35	25
1185.	17 c. Type **261**	35	50
1186.	25 c. As 15 c.	50	40

262. "Thomas Coutts" (full-rigged sailing ship) and "Aureol" (liner).

1974. Cent of U.P.U. Multicoloured.

1187.	2 c. Type **262**	20	10
1188.	3 c. Mail-plane and liner, satellite and Monrovia Post Office	30	10
1189.	10 c. U.S. and Soviet Telecommunications satellites	15	10
1190.	15 c. Postal runner and aircraft	25	20
1191.	20 c. British Rail High-speed Train and Liberian mail-van ..	55	25
1192.	25 c. American Pony Express rider	50	35

263. Fox Terrier.

1974. Dogs. Multicoloured.

1194.	5 c. Type **263**	15	8
1195.	10 c. Boxer	20	10
1196.	16 c. Chihuahua	30	15
1197.	19 c. Beagle	35	20
1198.	25 c. Golden retriever ..	40	25
1199.	50 c. Collie	75	50

264. West Germany v. Chile Match.

1974. World Cup Football Championships, West Germany. Scenes from semi-final matches. Multicoloured.

1201.	1 c. Type **264**	5	5
1202.	2 c. Australia v. East Germany	10	5
1203.	5 c. Brazil v. Yugoslavia	15	8
1204.	10 c. Zaire v. Scotland ..	20	10
1205.	12 c. Netherlands v. Uruguay	25	12
1206.	15 c. Sweden v. Bulgaria	30	15
1207.	20 c. Italy v. Haiti ..	40	20
1208.	25 c. Poland v. Argentina	60	25

265. "Chrysiridia Madagascariensis".

1974. Tropical Butterflies. Multicoloured.

1210.	1 c. Type **265**	10	10
1211.	2 c. "Catagramma sorana"	10	10
1212.	5 c. "Erasmia pulchella"	20	10
1213.	17 c. "Morpho cypris"	50	25
1214.	25 c. "Agrias amydon"	70	35
1215.	40 c. "Vanessa cardui"	1·40	45

266. Pres. Tolbert and Gold Medallion.

1974. "Family of Man" Award to President Tolbert. Multicoloured.

1217.	3 c. Type **266**	5	25
1218.	$1 Pres. Tolbert, medallion and flag	1·40	1·40

267. Churchill with Troops.

1974. Birth Centenary of Sir Winston Churchill. Multicoloured.

1219	3 c. Type **267**	10	5
1220	10 c. Churchill and aerial combat	30	10
1221	15 c. Churchill aboard "Liberty" ship in Channel	55	15
1222	17 c. Churchill reviewing troops in desert ..	30	15
1223	20 c. Churchill crossing Rhine	40	20
1224	25 c. Churchill with Roosevelt	50	25

268. Marie Curie.

1975. International Women's Year. Mult.

1226.	2 c. Type **268**	10	5
1227.	3 c. Mahalia Jackson .. .	5	5
1228.	5 c. Joan of Arc.. ..	8	5
1229.	10 c. Eleanor Roosevelt	15	8
1230.	25 c. Matilda Newport..	50	25
1231.	50 c. Valentina Tereshkova	70	55

269. Old State House, Boston, and U.S. 2 c. "Liberty Bell" Stamp of 1926.

1975. Bicent. of American Independence.

1233.	5 c. Type **269**	15	8
1234.	10 c. George Washington and 1928 "Valley Forge" stamp ..	30	10
1235.	15 c. Philadelphia & 1937 "Constitution" stamp	45	12
1236.	20 c. Benjamin Franklin & 1938 "Ratification" stamp	50	15
1237.	25 c. Paul Revere's Ride & 1925 "Lexington-Concord" stamp ..	70	20
1238.	50 c. "Santa Maria" and 1893 "Columbus' Landing" stamp ..	2·00	55

270. Dr. Schweitzer, Yellow Baboon and Lambarene Hospital.

1975. Birth Cent. of Dr Albert Schweitzer. Multicoloured.

1240.	1 c. Type **270**	10	10
1241.	3 c. Schweitzer, African elephant and canoe ..	15	10
1242.	5 c. Schweitzer, African buffalo and canoe ..	75	20
1243.	6 c. Schweitzer, kob and dancer	30	10
1244.	25 c. Schweitzer, lioness and village woman ..	75	25
1245.	50 c. Schweitzer, Common zebras and clinic scene	1·40	65

271. "Apollo" Spacecraft.

1975. "Apollo-Soyuz" Space Link. Mult.

1247.	5 c. Type **271**	8	5
1248.	10 c. "Soyuz" spacecraft	12	8
1249.	15 c. American-Russian hand-clasp	20	12
1250.	20 c. Flags and maps of America and Russia ..	25	15
1251.	25 c. Leonov and Kubasov	35	20
1252.	50 c. Slayton, Brand and Stafford	70	50

272. Presidents Tolbert and Stevens, and Signing Ceremony.

1975. Liberia-Sierra Leone Mano River Union Agreement.

1254. **272.**	2 c. multicoloured ..	5	5
1255.	3 c. multicoloured ..	5	5
1256.	5 c. multicoloured ..	10	8
1257.	10 c. multicoloured ..	15	10
1258.	25 c. multicoloured ..	35	25
1259.	50 c. multicoloured ..	70	70

273. Figure-skating.

1976. Winter Olympic Games, Innsbruck. Multicoloured.

1260.	1 c. Type **273**	10	10
1261.	4 c. Ski-jumping ..	20	20
1262.	10 c. Skiing (slalom) ..	30	20
1263.	25 c. Ice-hockey	60	30
1264.	35 c. Speed-skating ..	90	40
1265.	50 c. Two-man bobsledding	1·25	1·60

274. Pres. Tolbert taking Oath.

1976. Inauguration of President William R. Tolbert, Jr. Multicoloured.

1267.	3 c. Type **274**	5	5
1268.	25 c. Pres. Tolbert in Presidential Chair (vert.)..	35	25
1269.	$1 Liberian crest, flat and commemorative gold coin	1·40	1·40

275. Weightlifting.

1976. Olympic Games, Montreal. Mult.

1270.	2 c. Type **275**	10	10
1271.	3 c. Pole-vaulting ..	10	10
1272.	10 c. Hammer and shot-put	30	15
1273.	25 c. Sailing	65	35
1274.	35 c. Gymnastics ..	90	60
1275.	50 c. Hurdling	1·25	65

276. Bell's Telephone and Receiver.

1976. Telephone Centenary. Multicoloured.

1277.	1 c. Type **276**	10	10
1278.	4 c. Mail-coach	10	10
1279.	5 c. "Intelsat 4" satellite	15	10
1280.	25 c. Cable-ship "Dominia", 1926 ..	1·00	30
1281.	40 c. Futuristic train ..	1·00	50
1282.	50 c. Wright brothers plane, "Graf Zeppelin" and "Concorde" ..	1·75	60

277. Gold Nugget Pendant.

1976. Liberian Products (1st series). Mult.

1284.	1 c. Mano River Bridge..	10	10
1285.	3 c. Type **277**	10	10
1286.	5 c. "V" ring	10	10
1286a.	7 c. As No. 1286.. ..	15	25
1287.	10 c. Rubber tree and tyre	15	10
1287a.	15 c. Combine harvester	20	10
1287b.	17 c. As No. 1289 ..	35	10
1287c.	20 c. Hydro-electric plant	30	15
1288.	25 c. Mesurado shrimp..	35	25
1288a.	27 c. Dress and woman tie-dying cloth ..	40	25
1289.	55 c. Barracuda.. ..	1·40	35
1289a.	$1 Train carrying iron ore	1·60	25

For designs as Type **277** but in a smaller size, see Nos. 1505/8.

278. Black Rhinoceros.

1976. Animals. Multicoloured.

1290.	2 c. Type **278**	10	10
1291.	3 c. Bongo	10	10
1292.	5 c. Chimpanzee (vert.)	15	10
1293.	15 c. Pygmy hippopotamus	40	15
1294.	25 c. Leopard	80	40
1295.	$1 Gorilla	2·75	90

279. Statue of Liberty and Unification Monument on Maps of U.S.A. and Liberia.

1976. Bicentenary of American Revolution. Multicoloured.

1297.	25 c. Type **279**	35	25
1298.	$1 Presidents Washington & Ford (U.S.A.), Roberts and Tolbert (Liberia)	1·40	1·25

280. Baluba Masks.

1977. Second World Black and African Festival of Arts and Culture, Lagos (Nigeria). Tribal Masks. Multicoloured.

1300.	5 c. Type **280**	8	5
1301.	10 c. Bateke	15	10
1302.	15 c. Basshilele	20	12
1303.	20 c. Igungun	30	15
1304.	25 c. Maisi	35	20
1305.	50 c. Kifwebe	70	45

281. Latham's Francolin.

1977. Liberian Wild Birds. Multicoloured.

1307.	5 c. Type **281**	40	10
1308.	10 c. Narina trogon ..	60	15
1309.	15 c. Rufous-crowned roller	60	20
1310.	20 c. Brown-cheeked hornbill	65	25
1311.	25 c. Common bulbul ..	75	30
1312.	50 c. African fish eagle ..	1·50	80

282. Alwin Schockemohle (individual jumping).

1977. Olympic Games, Montreal. Equestrian Gold-medal Winners. Multicoloured.

1314.	5 c. Edmund Coffin (military dressage) (postage)	15	10
1315.	15 c. Type **282**	40	20
1316.	20 c. Christine Stuckelberger (dressage) ..	50	30
1317.	25 c. "Nations Prize" (French team).. ..	70	35
1318.	55 c. Military dressage (U.S.A. team) (air) ..	1·25	70

283. Queen Elizabeth II.

1977. Silver Jubilee of Queen Elizabeth II. Multicoloured.

1320.	15 c. Type **283**	35	15
1321.	25 c. Queen Elizabeth and Prince Philip with President and Mrs. Tubman of Liberia	55	25
1322.	80 c. Queen Elizabeth, Prince Philip and Royal Arms	1·75	70

284. "Blessing the Children".

1977. Christmas. Multicoloured.

1324.	20 c. Type **284**	50	25
1325.	25 c. "The Good Shepherd"	70	35
1326.	$1 "Jesus and the Woman of Samaria at the Well"	2·00	1·00

285. Dornier "Do-X" Flying-boat.

1978. "Progress in Aviation". Multicoloured.

1327.	2 c. Type **285**	10	10
1328.	3 c. Space shuttle on carrier plane	10	10
1329.	5 c. Edward Rickenbacker and Douglas "DC-3"	10	10
1330.	25 c. Lindbergh and "Spirit of St. Louis"	45	20
1331.	35 c. Bleriot and "XI" monoplane	65	35
1332.	50 c. Wright Brothers and "Flying Machine" ..	90	55

286. Santos-Dumont's Airship.

1978. 75th Anniv. of First Zeppelin Flight. Multicoloured.

1334.	2 c. Type **286**	10	10
1335.	3 c. Baldwin's airship, 1908	10	10
1336.	5 c. Tissandier brothers' dirigible, 1883 ..	10	10
1337.	25 c. Parseval "PL VII", 1912	40	20
1338.	40 c. "Nulli Secundus II", 1908	75	35
1339.	50 c. "R 34" rigid airship, 1919	85	55

287. Tackling. **288.** Coronation Chair.

1978. World Cup Football Championship, Argentina.

1341. **287.**	2 c. multicoloured ..	5	5
1342. –	3 c. mult. (horiz.) ..	5	5
1343. –	10 c. mult. (horiz.) ..	15	8
1344. –	25 c. mult. (horiz.) ..	35	20
1345. –	35 c. multicoloured ..	50	25
1346. –	50 c. mult. (horiz.) ..	70	50

DESIGNS: Nos. 1342/6 Different match scenes.

1978. 25th Anniv. of Coronation. Mult.

1348.	5 c. Type **288**	8	25
1349.	25 c. Imperial State Crown	35	25
1350.	$1 Buckingham Palace (horiz.)..	1·40	1·00

289. Mohammed Ali Jinnah and Flags.

1978. Birth Centenary of Mohammed Ali Jinnah (first Governor-General of Pakistan).
1352. **289.** 30 c. multicoloured .. 1·10 1·10

290. Carter and Tolbert Families.

1978. Visit of President Carter of U.S.A. Multicoloured.
1353. 5 c. Type **290** 8 8
1354. 25 c. Presidents Carter and Tolbert with Mrs. Carter at microphones 25 20
1355. $1 Presidents Carter and Tolbert in open car .. 1·40 1·40

291. Italy v. France. **292.** Timber Truck.

1978. Argentina's Victory in World Cup Football Championship. Multicoloured.
1356. 1 c. Brazil v. Spain (horiz.) 5 5
1357. 2 c. Type **291** 5 5
1358. 10 c. Poland v. West Germany (horiz.) 15 10
1359. 27 c. Peru v. Scotland .. 40 25
1360. 35 c. Austria v. West Germany 50 25
1361. 50 c. Argentinian players with Cup 70 50

1978. 8th World Forestry Congress, Djakarta. Multicoloured.
1363. 5 c. Chopping up log (horiz.) 8 8
1364. 10 c. Type **292** 15 8
1365. 25 c. Felling trees (horiz.) 25 20
1366. 50 c. Loggers (horiz.) .. 70 70

293. Presidents Gardner and Tolbert with Monrovia Post Office.

1979. Centenary of U.P.U. Membership. Multicoloured.
1367. 5 c. Type **293** 8 8
1368. 35 c. Presidents Gardner and Tolbert with U.P.U. emblem 50 25

294. "25" and Radio Waves.

1979. 25th Anniv. of Radio ELWA. Mult.
1369. 35 c. Type **294** 50 25
1370. $1 Radio tower .. .. 1·40 1·40

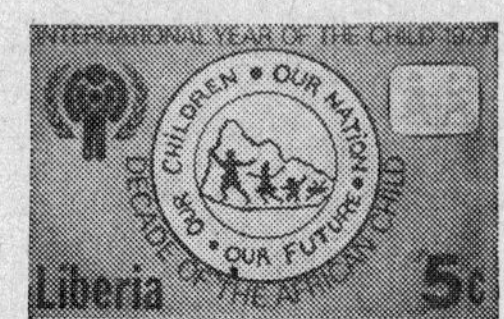

295. I.Y.C., Decade of the African Child. and S.O.S. Villages Emblems.

1979. International Year of the Child. Multicoloured.
1371. 5 c. Type **295** 8 8
1372. 25 c. As Type **295** but with UNICEF instead of S.O.S. Villages emblem 25 20
1373. 35 c. Type **295** 50 25
1374. $1 As No. 1372 .. .. 1·40 1·40

296. Clasped Arms and Torches.

1979. Organization for African Unity Summit Conference, Monrovia. Multicoloured.
1375. 5 c. Type **296** 8 8
1376. 27 c. Masks 40 25
1377. 35 c. African animals .. 50 50
1378. 50 c. Thatched huts and Common Bulbuls .. 1·25 70

297. Sir Rowland Hill and Liberian 15 c. Stamp, 1974.

1979. Death Centenary of Sir Rowland Hill. Multicoloured.
1379 3 c. Type **297** 10 10
1380 10 c. Pony Express rider 15 10
1381 15 c. British mail coach .. 20 10
1382 25 c. "John Penn" (paddle-steamer) .. 75 25
1383 27 c. Stanier Pacific locomotive 75 25
1384 50 c. Concorde .. .. 1·50 90

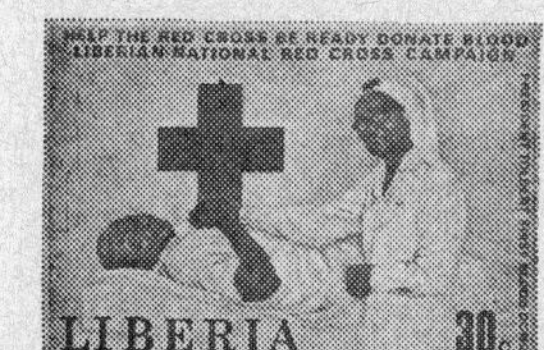

298. President Tolbert giving Blood.

1979. National Red Cross Blood Donation Campaign. Multicoloured.
1386. 30 c. Type **298** 45 25
1387. 50 c. President Tolbert and Red Cross .. 70 70

299. "World Peace" (tanker).

1979. 2nd World Maritime Day and 30th Anniv of Liberia Maritime Programme. Multicoloured.
1388 5 c. Type **299** 30 15
1389 $1 "World Peace" (different) .. .. 2·25 1·60

300. "A Good Turn".

1979. Scout Paintings by Norman Rockwell Multicoloured.
1390. 5 c. Scout giving first aid to pup ("A Good Scout") 20 15
1391. 5 c. Type **300** 20 15
1392. 5 c. "Good Friends" .. 20 15
1393. 5 c. "Spirit of America" 20 15
1394. 5 c. "Scout Memories" 20 15
1395. 5 c. "The Adventure Trail" 20 15
1396. 5 c. "On My Honour" 20 15
1397. 5 c. "A Scout is Reverent" 20 15
1398. 5 c. "The Right Way" 20 15
1399. 5 c. "The Scoutmaster" 20 15
1400. 10 c. "A Scout is Loyal" 35 20
1401. 10 c. "An Army of Friendship" 35 20
1402. 10 c. "Carry on" 35 20
1403. 10 c. "A Good Scout" .. 35 20
1404. 10 c. "The Campfire Story" 35 20
1405. 10 c. "High Adventure" 35 20
1406. 10 c. "Mighty Proud" 35 20
1407. 10 c. "Tomorrow's Leader" 35 20
1408. 10 c. "Ever Onward" .. 35 20
1409. 10 c. "Homecoming" .. 35 20
1410. 15 c. "Scouts of Many Trails" 40 25
1411. 15 c. "America builds for Tomorrow" 40 25
1412. 15 c. "The Scouting Trail" 40 25
1413. 15 c. "A Scout is Reverent" 40 25
1414. 15 c. "A Scout is Helpful" 40 25
1415. 15 c. "Pointing the Way" 40 25
1416. 15 c. "A Good Sign All Over the World" .. 40 25
1417. 15 c. "To Keep Myself Physically Strong" .. 40 25
1418. 15 c. "A Great Moment" 40 25
1419. 15 c. "Growth of a Leader" 40 25
1420. 25 c. "A Scout is Loyal" 60 35
1421. 25 c. "A Scout is Friendly" 60 35
1422. 25 c. "We Too, Have a Job to Do" 60 35
1423. 25 c. "I Will do my Best" 60 35
1424. 25 c. "A Guiding Hand" 60 35
1425. 25 c. "Breakthrough for Freedom" 60 35
1426. 25 c. "Scouting is Outing" 60 35
1427. 25 c. "Beyond the Easel" 60 35
1428. 25 c. "Come and Get It" 60 35
1429. 25 c. "America's Manpower begins with Boypower" 60 35
1430. 35 c. "All Together" .. 80 45
1431. 35 c. "Men of Tomorrow" 80 45
1432. 35 c. "Friend in Need" 80 45
1433. 35 c. "Our Heritage" .. 80 45
1434. 35 c. "Forward America" 80 45
1435. 35 c. "Can't Wait" .. 80 45
1436. 35 c. "From Concord to Tranquillity" 80 45
1437. 35 c. "We Thank Thee" 80 45
1438. 35 c. "So Much Concern" 80 45
1439. 35 c. "Spirit of '76" .. 80 45

301. Mrs. Tolbert and Children.

1979. S.O.S. Children's Village, Monrovia. Multicoloured.
1440. 25 c. Mrs. Tolbert and children (different) (horiz.) 35 25
1441. 40 c. Type **301** 60 60

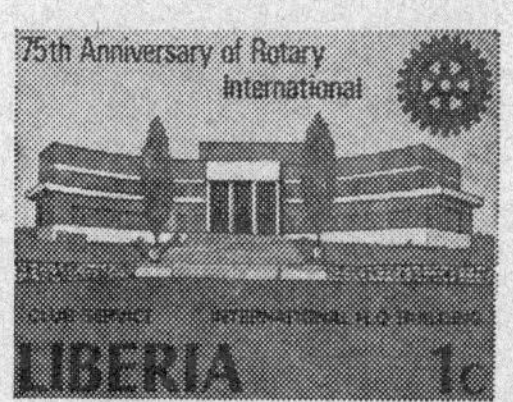

302. International Headquarters, Evanston, Illinois.

1979. 75th Anniv. of Rotary International. Multicoloured.
1442. 1 c. Type **302** 5 5
1443. 5 c. Vocational services .. 8 8
1444. 17 c. Wheelchair patient and nurse (community service) (vert.) .. 20 10
1445. 27 c. Flags (international service) 40 25
1446. 35 c. Different races holding hands around globe (health, hunger and humanity) 50 50
1447. 50 c. President Tolbert and map of Africa (Monrovia Rotary Club. 17th anniv.) (vert.) .. 70 70

303. Ski-jumping.

1980. Winter Olympic Games, Lake Placid. Multicoloured.
1449. 1 c. Type **303** 5 5
1450. 5 c. Pairs figure skating .. 8 8
1451. 17 c. Bobsleigh 20 10
1452. 27 c. Cross-country skiing 50 25
1453. 35 c. Speed skating .. 50 50
1454. 50 c. Ice hockey 70 70

304. Presidents Tolbert of Liberia and Stevens of Sierra Leone and View of Mano River.

1980. 5th Anniv. of Mano River Union and 1st Anniv. (1979) of Postal Union.
1456. **304.** 8 c. multicoloured .. 10 8
1457. 27 c. multicoloured .. 40 25
1458. 35 c. multicoloured .. 50 50
1459. 80 c. multicoloured .. 1·25 1·25

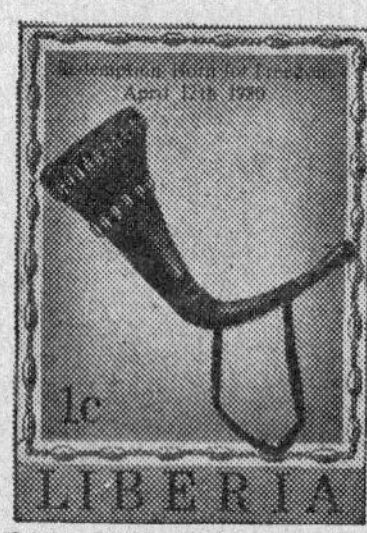

305. Redemption Horn.

1981. People's Redemption Council (1st series). Multicoloured.
1460. 1 c. Type **305** 5 5
1461. 10 c. M/Sgt. Doe and allegory of redemption (horiz.) 10 10
1462. 14 c. Map, soldier and citizens (horiz.) .. 12 12
1463. $2 M/Sgt. Samuel Doe (chairman of Council) 3·00 3·00

See also Nos. 1475/8.

306. Players and Flags of Argentine, Uruguay, Italy and Czechoslovakia.

1981. World Cup Football Championships, Spain (1982). Multicoloured.
1464. 3 c. Type **306** 5 5
1465. 5 c. Players and flags of Hungary, Italy, Germany, Brazil and Sweden 5 5
1466. 20 c. Players and flags of Italy, Germany, Brazil and Sweden 20 20
1467. 27 c. Players and flags of Czechoslovakia, Brazil, Great Britain and Germany 25 25
1468. 40 c. Players and flags of Italy, Brazil, Germany and Netherlands .. 60 60
1469. 55 c. Players and flags of Netherlands and Uruguay 80 80

307. M/Sgt. Doe and Crowd.

1981. 1st Anniv. of People's Redemption Council. Multicoloured.
1471. 22 c. Type **307** 20 20
1472. 27 c. M/Sgt. Doe and national flag 25 25
1473. 30 c. Hands clasping arms, sunrise and map .. 45 45
1474. $1 M/Sgt. Doe, "Justice" and soldiers .. 1·40 1·40

1981. People's Redemption Council (2nd series).
1475. 6 c. Type **305** 5 5
1476. 23 c. As No. 1461 .. 20 20
1477. 31 c. As No. 1462 .. 45 45
1478. 41 c. As No. 1463 .. 60 60

INDEX

Countries can be quickly located by referring to the index at the end of this volume.

329. Queen Mother in Garter Robes.
330. Alamo, San Antonio, Texas.

1985. 85th Birthday of Queen Elizabeth the Queen Mother. Multicoloured

1621.	31 c. Type **329**	35	30
1622.	41 c. At the races	55	50
1623.	62 c. Waving to the crowds	80	70

1986. "Ameripex '86" International Stamp Exhibition, Chicago. Multicoloured.

1625.	25 c. Type **330**	30	20
1626.	31 c. Liberty Bell, Philadelphia	40	30
1627.	80 c. Magnifying glass, emblem and Liberian stamps	1·00	80

331. Unveiling Ceremony, 1886 (after E. Moran).
333. Royal Theatre. Gendarmenmarkt.

332. Max Julen. (Men's Giant Slalom).

1986. Centenary of Statue of Liberty. Multicoloured.

1628.	20 c. Type **331**	30	20
1629.	31 c. Frederic-Auguste Bartholdi (sculptor) and statue	40	30
1630.	$1 Head of statue	1·40	1·25

1987. Winter Olympic Games, Calgary (1988). 1984 Games Gold Medallists. Multicoloured.

1631.	3 c. Type **332**	5	5
1632.	6 c. Debbi Armstrong (women's giant slalom)	8	5
1633.	31 c. Peter Angerer (biathlon)	35	25
1634.	60 c. Bill Johnson (men's downhill)	70	60
1635.	80 c. East German team (four-man bobsleigh)	90	80

1987. Liberian–German Friendship. 750th Anniv. of Berlin. Multicoloured.

1637.	6 c. Type **333**	8	5
1638.	31 c. Kaiser Friedrich Museum, River Spree	35	25
1639.	60 c. Charlottenburg Palace	70	60
1640.	80 c. Kaiser Wilhelm Memorial Church	90	80

334. Othello and Desdemona ("Othello").

1987. William Shakespeare. Multicoloured.

1642.	3 c. Type **334**	5	5
1643.	6 c. Romeo and Juliet ("Romeo and Juliet")	8	5
1644.	10 c. Falstaff ("The Merry Wives of Windsor")	15	10
1645.	15 c. Falstaff, Doll Tearsheet and Prince Hal ("Henry IV", Part 2)	20	15
1646.	31 c. Hamlet holding Yorick's skull ("Hamlet")	35	25
1647.	60 c. Macbeth and the three witches ("Macbeth")	70	60
1648.	80 c. Lear and companions in the storm ("King Lear")	90	80
1649.	$2 William Shakespeare and Globe Theatre, Southwark	2·40	2·10

335. Emblem.

1987. Amateur Radio Week. 25th Anniv. of Liberia Radio Amateur Association. Mult.

1650.	10 c. Type **335**	15	10
1651.	10 c. Amateur radio enthusiasts	15	10
1652.	35 c. Certificate awarded to participants in anniversary "On the Air" activity	40	30
1653.	35 c. Globe, flags and banner	40	30

336. Illuminated Torch Flame.

1987. Centenary of Statue of Liberty. Mult.

1654	6 c. Type **336**	10	10
1655	6 c. Scaffolding around statue's head	10	10
1656	6 c. Men working on head	10	10
1657	6 c. Men working on crown	10	10
1658	6 c. Statue's toes	10	10
1659	15 c. Statue behind "Sir Winston Churchill" (cadet schooner)	35	20
1660	15 c. "Bay Queen" (harbour ferry)	35	20
1661	15 c. Posters on buildings and crowd	20	15
1662	15 c. Tug and schooner in bay	35	20
1663	15 c. Decorated statues around building	20	15
1664	31 c. Fireworks display around statue	35	25
1665	31 c. Statue floodlit	35	25
1666	31 c. Statue's head	35	25
1667	31 c. Fireworks display around statue (different)	35	25
1668	31 c. Statue (half-length)	35	25
1669	60 c. Wall poster on building (vert)	70	60
1670	60 c. Yachts and cabin cruisers on river (vert)	1·25	75
1671	60 c. Measuring statue's nose (vert)	70	60
1672	60 c. Plastering nose (vert)	70	60
1673	60 c. Finishing off repaired nose (vert)	70	60

337. Dr. Doe (President), Dr. Moniba (Vice-President), Flags and Hands.

1988. 2nd Anniv. of Second Republic.

1674.	**337.**	10 c. multicoloured	15	10
1675.		35 c. multicoloured	40	30

338. Breast-feeding.

1988. U.N.I.C.E.F. Child Survival and Development Campaign. Multicoloured.

1676.	3 c. Type **338**	5	5
1677.	6 c. Oral rehydration therapy (vert.)	8	5
1678.	31 c. Immunization	35	25
1679.	$1 Growth monitoring (vert.)	1·25	1·00

339. Chief Justice Emmanuel N. Gbalazeh swearing-in Dr. Samuel Kanyon Doe.

1988. Inauguration of Second Republic.

1680.	**339.**	6 c. multicoloured	8	5

340. Footballer and Stadium.

1988. 2nd Anniv. of Opening of Samuel Kanyon Doe Sports Complex.

1681.	**340.**	31 c. multicoloured	35	25

341. Child and Volunteer reading.

1988. 25th Anniv. of U.S. Peace Corps in Liberia.

1682.	**341.**	10 c. multicoloured	10	5
1683.		35 c. multicoloured	40	30

342. Pres. Doe, Farm Workers and Produce.

1988. Green Revolution.

1684.	**342.**	10 c. multicoloured	10	5
1685.		35 c. multicoloured	40	30

344. Emblem.
345. "GP 10" Locomotive, Nimba.

1988. 25th Anniv. of Organization of African Unity.

1687.	**344.**	10 c. multicoloured	10	5
1688.		35 c. multicoloured	40	30
1689.		$1 multicoloured	1·25	1·00

1988. Locomotives. Multicoloured.

1690.	10 c. Type **345**	10	5
1691.	35 c. Triple engined iron ore train	40	30

346. Helping Boy to Walk.
347. Baseball.

1988. 25th Anniv of St. Joseph's Catholic Hospital. Multicoloured.

1693.	10 c. Type **346**	10	5
1694.	10 c. Medical staff and hospital	10	5
1695.	35 c. Monk, child, candle and hospital	40	30
1696.	$1 Map behind doctor with nurse holding baby	1·25	1·00

1988. Olympic Games, Seoul. Multicoloured.

1697.	10 c. Type **347**	10	10
1698.	35 c. Hurdling	40	30
1699.	45 c. Fencing	50	40
1700.	80 c. Synchronised swimming	90	70
1701.	$1 Yachting	1·50	1·00

348. Monkey Bridge.
349. Tending Crops.

1988.

1703	10 c. Type **348**	10	5
1704	35 c. Sasa players (horiz)	40	30
1705	45 c. Snake dancers	50	40

1988. 10th Anniv. of International Fund for Agricultural Development. Multicoloured.

1706.	10 c. Type **349**	10	5
1707.	35 c. Farmers tending livestock and spraying crops	40	30

350. Destruction of Royal Exchange, 1838.

1988. 300th Anniv. of Lloyd's of London. Multicoloured.

1708.	10 c. Type **350**	10	10
1709.	35 c. Air Liberia "BN2A" aircraft (horiz.)	60	30
1710.	45 c. "Chevron Antwerp" (tanker) (horiz.)	70	40
1711.	$1 "Lakonia" (liner) ablaze, 1963	1·50	1·00

351 Honouring Head of Operational Smile Team

1989. 3rd Anniv of Second Republic.

1712	**351**	10 c. black and blue	10	5
1713		35 c. black and red	40	30
1714	–	50 c. black & mve	55	45

DESIGN: 50 c. Pres. Samuel Doe at John F. Kennedy Memorial Hospital.

1989. Presidents of United States (5th series). As T **308**. Multicoloured.

1715	$1 George Bush	1·25	1·00

352 "Harmony"

353 Union Glass Factory, Gardersville, Monrovia

1989. Liberia–Japan Friendship. 50th Anniv of Rissho Kosei-Kai (lay Buddhist association). Multicoloured.

1716	10 c. Type **352**	10	5
1717	10 c. Nikkyo Niwano (founder and president of association) ..	10	5
1718	10 c. Rissho Kosei-Kai headquarters, Tokyo ..	10	5
1719	50 c. Eternal Buddha, Great Sacred Hall ..	55	45

1989. 15th Anniv of Mano River Union. Multicoloured.

1721	10 c. Type **353**	12	5
1722	35 c. Presidents of Guinea, Sierra Leone and Liberia	40	30
1723	45 c. Monrovia–Freetown highway	55	45
1724	50 c. Flags, map and mail van	60	50
1725	$1 Presidents at 1988 Summit	1·25	1·00

354 Symbols of International Co-operation

357 Recovery Ship U.S.S. "Okinawa"

1989. World Telecommunication Day.

1726	**354** 50 c. multicoloured ..	60	50

1989. 20th Anniv of First Manned Landing on Moon. Multicoloured.

1728	10 c. Type **357**	30	10
1729	35 c. Edwin Aldrin, Neil Armstrong and Michael Collins (crew) (28 × 28 mm)	40	30
1730	45 c. "Apollo 11" flight emblem (28 × 28 mm) ..	55	45
1731	$1 Aldrin descending to Moon's surface ..	1·25	1·00

358 Renovation of Statue of Liberty

360 Nehru and Flag

1989. "Philexfrance '89" International Stamp Exhibition, Paris, and "World Stamp Expo '89" International Stamp Exhibition, Washington D.C. Multicoloured.

1733	25 c. Type **358**	30	20
1734	25 c. French contingent at statue centenary celebrations	30	20
1735	25 c. Statue, officials and commemorative plaque	30	20

1989. Birth Centenary of Jawaharlal Nehru (Indian statesman). Multicoloured.

1737	45 c. Type **360**	55	45
1738	50 c. Nehru	60	50

361 Close View of Station

1990. New Standard A Earth Satellite Station. Multicoloured.

1739	10 c. Type **361**	12	5
1740	35 c. Distant view of station	40	30

362 Emblem

1990. 25th Anniv of United States Educational and Cultural Foundation in Liberia. Multicoloured.

1741	10 c. Type **362**	12	5
1742	45 c. Similar to Type **362** but differently arranged	55	45

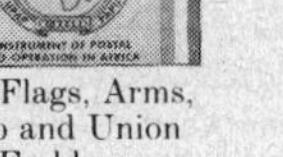

363 Flags, Arms, Map and Union Emblem

364 Bomi County

1990. 10th Anniv of Pan-African Postal Union.

1743	**363** 35 c. multicoloured ..	40	30

1990. County Flags. Multicoloured.

1744	10 c. Type **364**	10	5
1745	10 c. Bong	10	5
1746	10 c. Grand Bassa	10	5
1747	10 c. Grand Cape Mount ..	10	5
1748	10 c. Grand Gedeh	10	5
1749	10 c. Grand Kru	10	5
1750	10 c. Lofa	10	5
1751	10 c. Margibi	10	5
1752	10 c. Maryland	10	5
1753	10 c. Montserrado	10	5
1754	10 c. Nimba	10	5
1755	10 c. Rivercess	10	5
1756	10 c. Sinoe	10	5
1757	35 c. Type **364**	40	30
1758	35 c. Bong	40	30
1759	35 c. Grand Bassa	40	30
1760	35 c. Grand Cape Mount ..	40	30
1761	35 c. Grand Gedeh	40	30
1762	35 c. Grand Kru	40	30
1763	35 c. Lofa	40	30
1764	35 c. Margibi	40	30
1765	35 c. Maryland	40	30
1766	35 c. Montserrado	40	30
1767	35 c. Nimba	40	30
1768	35 c. Rivercess	40	30
1769	35 c. Sinoe	40	30
1770	45 c. Type **364**	50	40
1771	45 c. Bong	50	40
1772	45 c. Grand Bassa	50	40
1773	45 c. Grand Cape Mount ..	50	40
1774	45 c. Grand Gedeh	50	40
1775	45 c. Grand Kru	50	40
1776	45 c. Lofa	50	40
1777	45 c. Margibi	50	40
1778	45 c. Maryland	50	40
1779	45 c. Montserrado	50	40
1780	45 c. Nimba	50	40
1781	45 c. Rivercess	50	40
1782	45 c. Sinoe	50	40
1783	50 c. Type **364**	55	45
1784	50 c. Bong	55	45
1785	50 c. Grand Bassa	55	45
1786	50 c. Grand Cape Mount ..	55	45
1787	50 c. Grand Gedeh	55	45
1788	50 c. Grand Kru	55	45
1789	50 c. Lofa	55	45
1790	50 c. Margibi	55	45
1791	50 c. Maryland	55	45
1792	50 c. Montserrado	55	45
1793	50 c. Nimba	55	45
1794	50 c. Rivercess	55	45
1795	50 c. Sinoe	55	45
1796	$1 Type **364**	1·10	95
1797	$1 Bong	1·10	95
1798	$1 Grand Bassa	1·10	95
1799	$1 Grand Cape Mount ..	1·10	95
1800	$1 Grand Gedeh	1·10	95
1801	$1 Grand Kru	1·10	95
1802	$1 Lofa	1·10	95
1803	$1 Margibi	1·10	95
1804	$1 Maryland	1·10	95
1805	$1 Montserrado	1·10	95
1806	$1 Nimba	1·10	95
1807	$1 Rivercess	1·10	95
1808	$1 Sinoe	1·10	95

365 Lady Elizabeth Bowes-Lyon as Girl

368 Boxing

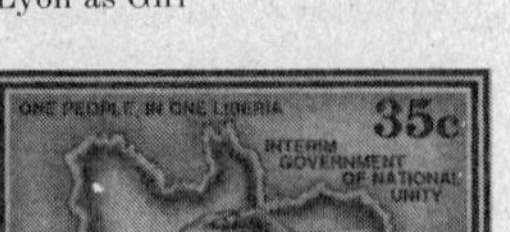

367 Clasped Hands and Map

1991. 90th Birthday (1990) of Queen Elizabeth the Queen Mother. Multicoloured.

1809	10 c. Type **365**	12	8
1810	$2 As Duchess of York (29 × 36½ mm)	2·25	1·40

1991. National Unity. Multicoloured.

1812	35 c. Type **367**	40	25
1813	45 c. National flag and map of Africa (ECOMOG (West African States Economic Community peace-keeping forces))	50	30
1814	50 c. Brewer, Konneh and Michael Francis (co-chairmen) and national flag (All-Liberia Conference) ..	60	40

1992. Olympic Games, Barcelona. Mult.

1815	45 c. Type **368**	60	40
1816	50 c. Football	70	45
1817	$1 Weightlifting ..	1·40	85
1818	$2 Water polo	2·75	1·75

369 "Disarm Today"

1993. Peace and Redevelopment. Mult.

1820	50 c. Type **369**	70	45
1821	$1 "Join your Parents and build Liberia" ..	1·40	85
1822	$2 "Peace must prevail in Liberia"	2·75	1·75

OFFICIAL STAMPS

1892. 1892 stamps optd. **OFFICIAL.**

O 87.	**7.**	1 c. red	30	40
O 88.		2 c. blue	30	50
O 89.	**8.**	4 c. black and green ..	2·50	4·00
O 104.	**9.**	5 c. on 6 c. grn. (No. 89)	1·00	1·75
O 90.		6 c. green	60	90
O 91.	**10.**	8 c. black and brown	1·00	1·25
O 92.	**11.**	12 c. red	1·50	1·75
O 93.	**12.**	16 c. lilac	2·00	2·50
O 94.	**13.**	24 c. green on yellow	1·40	1·75
O 95.	**12.**	32 c. blue	3·00	4·50
O 96.	**15.**	$1 black and blue ..	15·00	18·00
O 97.	**13.**	$2 brown on buff ..	10·00	12·00
O 98.	**17.**	$5 black and red ..	12·00	15·00

1894. 1892 stamps optd. **O S.**

O 119.	**7.**	1 c. red	30	60
O 120.		2 c. blue	35	70
O 121.	**8.**	4 c. black and green ..	2·75	3·00
O 122.	**10.**	8 c. black and brown	1·50	2·00
O 123.	**11.**	12 c. red	1·75	2·50
O 124.	**12.**	16 c. lilac	2·50	3·00
O 125.	**13.**	24 c. green on yellow	2·00	2·50
O 126.	**12.**	32 c. blue	3·50	4·00
O 127.	**15.**	$1 black and blue ..	20·00	22·00
O 128.	**13.**	$2 brown on buff ..	12·50	16·00
O 129.	**17.**	$5 black and red ..	30·00	35·00

1894. 1894 stamp in different colours optd. **O S** Imperf. or roul.

O 130.	**24.**	5 c. green and lilac ..	1·75	2·00

1898. 1897 stamps optd. **O S.**

O 157.	**9.**	1 c. purple	35	35
O 158.		1 c. green	35	35
O 159.	**15.**	2 c. black and bistre	1·50	2·00
O 160.		2 c. black and red ..	2·00	2·50
O 161.	**8.**	5 c. black and lake ..	2·25	1·75
O 162.		5 c. black and blue ..	2·50	2·50
O 163.	**10.**	10 c. blue and yellow	1·00	1·25
O 164.	**11.**	15 c. black	1·00	1·50
O 165.	**12.**	20 c. red	1·25	2·00
O 166.	**13.**	25 c. green	1·50	2·00
O 167.	**12.**	30 c. blue	2·00	2·75
O 168.	**35.**	50 c. black and brown	1·75	2·50

†1903. Stamp of 1903, but different colour, optd. **O S.**

O 210.	**40.**	3 c. green	20	15

1904. Nos. O 104 and 167 surch. **ONE O S.** and bars or **O S 2** and bars.

O 222.	**9.**	1 c. on 5 c. on 6 c. green	1·10	1·50
O 223.	**12.**	2 c. on 30 c. blue ..	5·50	6·50

†1906. Stamps of 1906, but different colours, optd. **O S.**

O 237.	**50.**	1 c. black and green ..	50	50
O 238.	**51.**	2 c. black and red ..	15	8
O 239.	–	5 c. black and blue ..	2·00	35
O 240.	–	10 c. black and violet	5·00	60
O 241.	–	15 c. black and brown	4·00	75
O 242.	–	20 c. black and green	5·00	75
O 243.	–	25 c. grey and purple	60	15
O 244.	–	30 c. brown	50	15
O 245.	–	50 c. green and brown	90	20
O 246.	–	75 c. black and blue ..	3·00	75
O 247.	–	$1 black and green ..	1·00	25
O 248.	**52.**	$2 black and purple ..	1·50	25
O 249.	**53.**	$5 black and orange	3·50	30

†1909. Stamps of 1909, but different colours, optd **OS.** 10 c. perf or roul.

O 262.	**55.**	1 c. black and green ..	15	10
O 263.	–	2 c. brown and red ..	15	10
O 264.	**56.**	5 c. black and blue ..	1·00	15
O 266.	**57.**	10 c. blue and black ..	50	25
O 267.	–	15 c. black and purple	50	25
O 268.	–	20 c. green and bistre	1·25	45
O 269.	–	25 c. green and blue ..	70	50
O 270.	–	30 c. blue	1·00	40
O 271.	–	50 c. green and brown	2·25	40
O 272.	–	75 c. black and violet	1·50	40

1910. No. O266 surch **3 CENTS INLAND POSTAGE**. Perf or roul.

O276	**57**	3 c. on 10 c. blue & blk	90	45

1914. Official stamps surch.: (A) **1914 2 CENTS.** (B) **+2 c.** (C) **5.** (D) **CENTS 20 OFFICIAL.**

O 291.	**57.**	+2 c. on 3 c. on 10 c. blue and black (B) (No. O 275) ..	60	1·25
O 284.	–	2 c. on 25 c. grey and pur. (A) (No. O 243)	15·00	7·50
O 285.	–	5 c. on 30 c. blue (C) (No. O 270) ..	11·00	4·50
O 286.	–	20 c. on 75 c. black and violet (D) (No. O272)	11·00	4·50

1914. No. 233 surch. **CENTS 20 OFFICIAL.**

O 287.		20 c. on 75 c. black and brown	11·00	4·50

1915. Official stamps of 1906 and 1909 surch. in different ways.

O 325.	–	1 c. on 2 c. brown and red (No. O 263) ..	2·25	2·50
O 326.	**56.**	2 c. on 5 c. black and blue (No. O 264) ..	2·50	3·00
O 310.	–	2 c. on 15 c. black and purple (No. O 267)	95	1·25
O 311.	–	2 c. on 25 c. green and blue (No. O 269) ..	5·50	5·50
O 312.	–	5 c. on 20 c. green and bistre (No. O 268)	1·25	1·50
O 313.	–	5 c. on 30 c. blue (No. O 270) ..	5·50	5·50
O 314.	–	10 c. on 50 c. green and brown (No. O 271)	6·50	7·50
O 316.	–	20 c. on 75 c. black and violet (No. O 272)	2·75	3·50
O 317.	–	25 c. on $1 black and green (No. O 247) ..	11·00	12·00
O 318.	**52.**	50 c. on $2 black and purple (No. O 248)	13·00	15·00
O 320.	**53.**	$1 on $5 black and orange (No. O 249)	15·00	18·00

1915. No. O 168 surch. **10 10** and ornaments and bars.
O 321. **35.** 10 c. on 50 c. blk. & brn. 9·00 9·00

1915. Military Field Post. Official stamps surch. **L E F 1c.**
O 336. **50.** 1 c. on 1 c. black and green (No. O 237) £325 £325
O 337. **55.** 1 c. on 1 c. black and green (No. O 262) 2·00 3·00
O 338. – 1 c. on 2 c. brown and red (No. O 263) .. 2·00 3·00

1917. No. O 244 surch. **FIVE CENTS 1917** and bars.
O 344. – 5 c. on 30 c. brown .. 13·00 15·00

1918. No. O 266 surch. **3 CENTS.**
O 348. **57.** 3 c. on 10 c. blue & blk. 1·40 2·00

†1918. Stamps of 1918, but in different colours, optd. **O S.**
O 362. **91.** 1 c. brown and green 50 15
O 363. **92.** 2 c. black and red .. 50 15
O 364. – 5 c. black and blue .. 45 10
O 365. **93.** 10 c. blue 35 8
O 366. – 15 c. green and brown 1·75 40
O 367. – 20 c. black and lilac .. 55 10
O 368. **94.** 25 c. green and brown 3·25 45
O 369. – 30 c. black and violet 6·00 50
O 370. – 50 c. black and brown 4·75 50
O 371. – 75 c. black and brown 2·00 15
O 372. – $1 blue and olive .. 3·50 30
O 373. – $2 black and olive .. 6·00 50
O 374. – $5 green .. .. 8·50 60

1920. Nos. O 362/3 surch. **1920** and value and two bars.
O 400. **91.** 3 c. on 1 c. brn. & grn. 1·50 2·00
O 401. **92.** 4 c. on 2 c. blk. & red 2·00 2·50

†1921. Stamps of 1915 and 1921, in different colours, optd. **O S** or **OFFICIAL.**
O 428. **100.** 1 c. green 70 8
O 429. **64.** 2 c. red 70 10
O 430. **65.** 3 c. brown 70 10
O 431. **101.** 5c. brown and blue .. 70 10
O 432. – 10 c. black and purple 1·25 15
O 433. – 15 c. green and black 3·50 50
O 434. – 20 c. blue and brown 1·50 25
O 435. – 25 c. green and orange 3·50 50
O 436. – 30 c. red and brown .. 1·40 15
O 437. – 50 c. green and black 1·50 25
O 438. – 75 c. purple and blue 1·50 25
O 439. – $1 black and blue .. 12·00 1·50
O 440. – $2 green and orange 16·00 1·50
O 441. – $5 blue and green .. 17·00 1·75

†1921. Nos. O 400/41 optd. **1921.**
O 442. **100.** 1 c. green .. .. 1·40 20
O 443. **64.** 2 c. red .. .. 1·40 20
O 444. **65.** 3 c. brown .. .. 1·50 25
O 445. **101.** 5 c. brown and blue .. 70 25
O 446. – 10 c. black and purple 1·75 25
O 447. – 15 c. green and black 2·50 60
O 448. – 20 c. blue and brown 2·25 35
O 449. – 25 c. green and orange 3·50 70
O 450. – 30 c. red and brown .. 1·75 30
O 451. – 50 c. green and black 3·50 40
O 452. – 75 c. purple and blue 2·00 40
O 453. – $1 black and blue .. 10·00 1·50
O 454. – $2 green and orange .. 15·00 2·50
O 455. – $5 blue and green .. 16·00 3·00

†1923. Stamps of 1923, but different colours, optd. **O S.**
O 485. **108.** 1 c. black and green .. 50 8
O 486. **109.** 2 c. brown and red .. 50 8
O 487. – 3 c. black and blue .. 50 10
O 488. – 5 c. green and orange 1·25 10
O 489. – 10 c. purple and olive 80 10
O 490. – 15 c. blue and green .. 4·50 40
O 491. – 20 c. blue and lilac .. 4·50 40
O 492. – 25 c. brown .. .. 8·00 40
O 493. – 30 c. brown and blue 1·25 20
O 494. – 50 c. brown and bistre 2·50 30
O 495. – 75 c. green and grey .. 1·50 25
O 496. **110.** $1 green and red .. 2·50 40
O 497. – $2 red and purple .. 3·50 50
O 498. – $5 brown and blue .. 5·00 1·00

1926. No. O 362 surch. **Two Cents** and thick bar of wavy lines or ornamental scroll or two bars.
O 506. **91.** 2 c. on 1 c. brn. & grn. 3·00 3·50

1928. Stamps of 1928 optd. **OFFICIAL SERVICE.**
O 518. **116.** 1 c. green 20 10
O 519. 2 c. violet 25 12
O 520. 3 c. brown 50 12
O 521. **117.** 5 c. blue 80 15
O 522. **118.** 10 c. grey .. .. 1·25 45
O 523. **117.** 15 c. lilac .. .. 2·40 60
O 524. $1 brown .. .. 24·00 12·00

1944. No. O 484 surch.
O 649. 4 c. on 10 c. grey .. 8·00 8·00

POSTAGE DUE STAMPS

1892. Stamps of 1886 surch **POSTAGE DUE** and value in frame.
D 99. **4.** 3 c. on 3 c. mauve .. 2·00 3·00
D 100. 6 c. on 6 c. grey .. 3·50 4·50

D 23.

1894.
D 110. **D 23.** 2 c. black and orange on yellow .. 70 1·00
D 111. 4 c. blk. & red on rose 70 1·00
D 112. 6 c. blk. & brn. on buff 70 1·00
D 113. 8 c. blk. & bl. on bl. 1·00 1·50
D 114. 10 c. black and green on mauve .. 1·00 2·00
D 115. 20 c. black and violet on grey .. .. 1·25 2·00
D 116. 40 c. black and brown on green .. .. 1·75 2·50

REGISTRATION STAMPS

R 22.

1893.
R 105. **R 22.** (10 c.) black (Buchanan) .. £275 £350
R 106. (10 c.) black ("Grenville") .. £1000 £1250
R 107. (10 c.) blk. (Harper) £1000 £1250
R 108. (10 c.) black (Monrovia) .. 40·00 £175
R 109. (10 c.) blk. (Robertsport) £500 £575

1894. Surch **10 CENTS 10** twice.
R140 **R 22** 10 c. blue on pink (Buchanan) .. 3·00 3·50
R141 10 c. green on buff (Harper) .. 3·00 3·50
R142 10 c. red on yellow (Monrovia) .. 3·00 3·50
R143 10 c. red on blue (Robertsport) .. 3·00 3·50

R 42. Pres. Gibson.

R 96. Patrol Boat "Quail".

†1903.
R211 **R 42** 10 c. black and blue (Buchanan) .. 1·50 25
R212 10 c. black and red ("Grenville") .. 1·50 25
R213 10 c. black & green (Harper) .. 1·50 25
R214 10 c. black & violet (Monrovia) .. 1·50 25
R215 10 c. black & purple (Robertsport) .. 1·50 25

1919. Roul or perf.
R388 **R 96** 10 c. blue and black (Buchanan) .. 90 5·00
R389 10 c. black & brown ("Grenville") .. 90 6·50
R390 10 c. black & green (Harper) .. 90 4·50
R391 10 c. blue and violet (Monrovia) .. 90 5·00
R392 10 c. black and red (Robertsport) .. 90 6·50

R 106. Gabon Viper.

†1921.
R456 **R 106** 10 c. black and red (Buchanan) .. 25·00 2·50
R457 10 c. black and red (Greenville) .. 15·00 2·50
R458 10 c. black & blue (Harper) .. 20·00 2·50
R459 10 c. black & orge (Monrovia) .. 15·00 2·50
R460 10 c. black & green (Robertsport) .. 15·00 2·50

†1921. Optd. **1921.**
R 461. **R 106.** 10 c. blk. & lake .. 17·00 4·50
R 462. 10 c. blk. & red .. 18·00 4·50
R 463. 10 c. blk. & blue .. 17·00 4·50
R 464. 10 c. blk. & orge. 18·00 4·50
R 465. 10 c. blk. & grn... 17·00 4·50

R 111. Sailing Skiff (Buchanan).

†1923. Various sea views.
R 499. **R 111.** 10 c. red & black 8·50 55
R 500. – 10 c. green & black 8·50 55
R 501. – 10 c. orge. & black 8·50 55
R 502. – 10 c. blue & black 8·50 55
R 503. – 10 c. vio. & black 8·50 55

DESIGNS: No. R500, Lighter (Greenville). R501, Full-rigged sailing ship (Harper). R502, "George Washington" (liner) (Monrovia). R503, Canoe (Robertsport).

1941. No. 576 surch. **REGISTERED** and **10 CENTS 10.**
R 592. 10 c. on 5 c. brn. (post.) 1·40 1·40
R 593. 10 c. on 5 c. brown (air) 1·40 1·40
No. R 593 additionally optd. **AIR MAIL** and aeroplane.

SPECIAL DELIVERY STAMPS

1941. No. 576 surch. **SPECIAL DELIVERY** and **10 CENTS 10.**
S 590. 10 c. on 5 c. brn (post.) 1·40 1·40
S 591. 10 c. on 5 c. brown (air) 1·40 1·40
No. S 591 additionally optd. **AIR MAIL,** aeroplane and postman.

LIBYA Pt. 8; Pt. 13

A former Italian colony in N. Africa, comprising the governorates of Cyrenaica and Tripolitania. From the end of 1951 an independent kingdom including the Fezzan also. Following a revolution in 1969 the country became the Libyan Arab Republic.

1912. 100 centesimi = 1 lira.
1952. 1000 milliemes = 1 Libyan pound.
1972. 1000 dirhams = 1 dinar.

A. ITALIAN COLONY.

1912. Stamps of Italy optd **LIBIA** (No. 5) or **Libia** (others).
1. **30.** 1 c. brown 10 55
2. **31.** 2 c. brown 10 25
3. **37.** 5 c. green 10 10
4. 10 c. red 10 10
5. **41.** 15 c. black .. .. 18·00 1·10
6. **37.** 15 c. grey .. .. 1·90 3·25
7. **33.** 20 c. orange 25 25
8. **41.** 20 c. orange .. .. 1·10 2·75
9. **39.** 25 c. blue 45 35
10. 40 c. brown .. .. 70 1·00
11. **33.** 45 c. olive .. .. 7·50 9·50
12. **39.** 50 c. mauve .. .. 2·25 85
13. 60 c. red .. .. 4·25 9·50
14. **34.** 1 l. brown and green .. 24·00 1·90
15. 5 l. blue and red .. £120 £150
16. 10 l. olive and red .. 9·50 35·00

1915. Red Cross stamps of Italy optd. **LIBIA.**
17 **53.** 10 c.+5 c. red .. .. 80 3·50
18. **54.** 15 c.+5 c. grey .. 3·75 8·00
19. 20 c. on 15 c.+5 c. grey 3·75 8·00
20. 20 c.+5 c. orange .. 1·25 4·75

1916. No. 100 of Italy optd. **LIBIA.**
21. **41.** 20 c. on 15 c. grey .. 16·00 4·50

4. Roman Legionary.

5. Goddess of Plenty.

9. "Libyan Sibyl" by Michelangelo.

6. Roman Galley leaving Tripoli.

7. Victory.

10. Bedouin Woman.

1921.
22 **4** 1 c. brown and black .. 20 90
23 2 c. brown and black .. 20 90
24 5 c. green and black .. 40 55
50 7½ c. brown and black .. 30 1·25
51 **5** 10 c. pink and black .. 30 10
52 15 c. orange and brown 1·90 60
41 **9** 20 c. green 30 10
27 **5** 25 c. blue and deep blue 30 15
54 **6** 30 c. brown and black .. 10 35
42 **9** 40 c. brown .. .. 1·10 40
55 **6** 50 c. green and black .. 10 10
30 55 c. violet and black .. 1·90 5·00
43 **9** 60 c. blue 30 10
57 **7** 75 c. red and purple .. 10 10
58a 1 l. brown .. .. 1·25 10
59 **6** 1 l. 25 blue and indigo .. 10 10
44 **9** 1 l. 75 orange 10 10
45 2 l. red .. .. 1·60 80
46 2 l. 55 violet .. .. 1·60 2·75
32 **7** 5 l. blue and black .. 9·00 7·00
33 10 l. green and blue .. 40·00 55·00

1922. Victory stamps of Italy optd. **LIBIA.**
34. **62.** 5 c. green .. .. 30 1·75
35. 10 c. red .. .. 30 1·75
36. 15 c. grey .. .. 35 3·00
37. 25 c. blue .. .. 35 3·00

1922. Nos. 9 and 12 of Libya surch.
38. **39.** 40 c. on 50 c. mauve .. 1·10 1·40
39. 80 c. on 25 c. blue .. 1·60 5·00

1928. Air. Air stamps of Italy optd. **Libia.**
63. **88.** 50 c. red .. .. 2·75 4·50
64. 80 c. brown and purple 5·00 19·00

1928. Types of Italy optd **LIBIA** (No. 67) or **Libia** (others).
65. **92.** 7½ c. brown .. .. 5·00 15·00
66. **34.** 1 l. 25 blue .. .. 23·00 11·00
67. **91.** 1 l. 75 brown .. .. 28·00 1·25

1936. 10th Tripoli Trade Fair.

68. 10. 50 c. violet .. .. 70 1·40
69. 1 l. 25 blue .. .. 90 4·25

1936. Air. Nos. 96 and 99 of Cyrenaica optd. LIBIA.

70. – 50 c. violet 80 10
71. 17. 1 l. black .. .. 2·75 19·00

1937. Air. Stamps of Tripolitania optd. LIBIA.

72. 18. 50 c. red 20 10
73. 60 c. orange 35
74. 75 c. blue .. .. 35 12·00
75. 80 c. purple .. .. 35 12·00
76. 19. 1 l. blue 90 60
77. 1 l. 20 brown .. .. 35 15·00
78. 1 l. 50 orange 35
79. 5 l. green 35

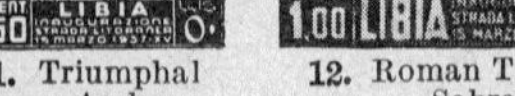

11. Triumphal Arch. **12.** Roman Theatre, Sabrata.

1937. Inaug. of Coastal Highway.

80. 11. 50 c. red (postage) .. 1·10 2·75
81. 1 l. 25 blue .. .. 1·10 6·50
82. 12. 50 c. purple (air) .. 1·10 3·75
83. 1 l. black .. .. 1·10 6·00

1937. 11th Tripoli Trade Fair. Optd XI FIERA DI TRIPOLI.

84. 11. 50 c. red (postage) .. 4·00 12·00
85. 1 l. 25 blue .. .. 4·00 12·00
86. 12. 50 c. purple (air) .. 4·00 12·00
87. 1 l. black .. .. 4·00 12·00

14. Benghazi Waterfront.

1938. 12th Tripoli Trade Fair.

88. 14. 5 c. brown (postage) .. 15 35
89. – 10 c. sepia 15 35
90. 14. 25 c. green 35 35
91. – 50 c. violet 35 20
92. 14. 75 c. red .. .. 40 1·60
93. – 1 l. 25 blue .. .. 50 1·75

DESIGN: 10 c., 50 c., 1 l. 25 Fair Buildings.

94. 50 c. olive (air) 70 75
95. 1 l. blue .. .. 70 2·75

DESIGN—VERT. View of Tripoli.

16. Statue of Augustus. **17.** Eagle and Serpent.

1938. Birth Bimillenary of Augustus.

96. 16. 5 c. olive 15 85
97. – 10 c. red 15 85
98. 16. 25 c. green 40 65
99. – 50 c. mauve 40 35
100. 16. 75 c. red .. .. 60 1·40
101. – 1 l. 25 blue .. .. 60 1·40
102. 17. 50 c. olive (air) .. .. 35 1·10
103. 1 l. mauve .. .. 50 2·50

DESIGN: 10, 50 c., 1 l. 25, Statue of Goddess of Plenty.

18. Agricultural Landscape.

1939. 13th Tripoli Trade Fair. Inscr. "XIII FIERA CAMPIONARIA DI TRIPOLI" etc.

104. 18. 5 c. olive (postage) .. 10 55
105. – 20 c. brown 30 55
106. 18. 50 c. mauve 35 30
107. – 75 c. red 40 90
108. 18. 1 l. 25 blue 40 90
109. – 25 c. green (air) .. 25 1·10
110. – 50 c. green 30 90
111. – 1 l. mauve .. .. 35 1·10

DESIGNS: 20, 75 c. Ghadames. 25 c., 1 l. Arab, camel and airliner over desert. 50 c. Airliner over Fair entrance.

19. Buildings.

1940. Naples Exhibition.

112 19 5 c. brown (postage) .. 10 35
113 – 10 c. orange 10 35
114 – 25 c. green 50 85
115 19 50 c. violet 50 85
116 – 75 c. red .. .. 50 1·25
117 – 1 l. 25 blue .. .. 50 1·40
118 – 2 l. + 75 c. red .. .. 50 2·00

DESIGNS—HORIZ. 10, 75 c., 2 l. Oxen and plough. VERT. 25 c., 1 l. 25, Mosque.

119 – 50 c. black (air) .. 30 1·40
120 – 1 l. brown .. .. 30 1·40
121 – 2 l. + 75 c. blue .. 55 2·25
122 – 5 l. + 2 l. 50 brown .. 55 2·25

DESIGNS—HORIZ. 50 c., 2 l. Airplane over city. 1, 5 l. Airplane over oasis.

20. Hitler and Mussolini.

1941. Rome-Berlin Axis Commemoration.

123. 20. 5 c. orange (postage) .. 10 3·00
124. 10 c. brown .. .. 10 3·00
125. 20 c. purple .. .. 40 3·00
126. 25 c. green .. .. 40 3·00
127. 50 c. violet .. .. 40 3·00
128. 75 c. red .. .. 40 5·00
129. 1 l. 25 blue .. .. 40 5·00
130. 50 c. green (air) .. 45 10·00

B. INDEPENDENT.

ليبيا (20.) LIBYA — ٤ ليرة ع. -- ليبيا -- (21.) 4 MAL. LIBYA — ٨ فرنك -- ليبيا -- (22.) 8 FRANCS LIBYA

1951. Stamps of Cyrenaica optd.

(a) For use in Cyrenaica. Optd. as T 20.

131. 24. 1 m. brown 15 15
132. 2 m. red 20 20
133. 3 m. yellow 25 25
134. 4 m. green .. .. 30·00 18·00
135. 5 m. brown 35 35
136. 8 m. orange 40 40
137. 10 m. violet 60 60
138. 12 m. red 85 85
139. 20 m. blue .. .. 1·25 1·25
140. 25. 50 m. blue and brown 11·00 11·00
141. 100 m. red and black .. 25·00 22·00
142. 200 m. violet and blue 42·00 38·00
143. 500 m. yellow & green £120 £110

(b) For use in Tripolitania. Surch. as T 21 in Military Authority lire.

151. 24. 1 mal. on 2 m. red .. 25 25
152. 2 mal. on 4 m. green .. 25 25
153. 4 mal. on 8 m. orange 25 25
154. 5 mal. on 10 m. violet 35 35
155. 6 mal. on 12 m. red .. 35 35
156. 10 mal. on 20 m. blue .. 65 65
157. 25. 24 mal. on 50 m. blue and brown .. 2·50 2·50
158. 48 mal. on 100 m. red 7·00 7·00
159. 96 mal. on 200 m. violet and blue .. 22·00 22·00
160. 240 mal. on 500 m. yellow and green .. 60·00 60·00

(c) For use in the Fezzan. Surch. as T 22.

166. 24. 2 f. on 2 m. red .. 20 20
167. 4 f. on 4 m. green .. 30 30
168. 8 f. on 8 m. orange .. 35 40
169. 10 f. on 10 m. violet .. 50 50
170. 12 f. on 12 m. red .. 75 75
171. 20 f. on 20 m. blue .. 1·40 1·40
172. 25. 48 f. on 50 m. bl. & brn. 40·00 40·00
173. 96 f. on 100 m. red and black .. 40·00 40·00
174. 192 f. on 200 m. violet and blue .. 90·00 80·00
175. 480 f. on 500 m. yellow and green .. £150 £140

23. King Idris. (28.) **30.**

1952.

176. 23. 2 m. brown 8 8
177. 4 m. grey 8 8
178. 5 m. green .. .. 9·00 35
179. 8 m. red 40 25
180. 10 m. violet .. .. 9·00 15
181. 12 m. red 75 15
182. 20 m. blue .. .. 9·50 45
183. 25 m. brown .. .. 9·50 45
184. – 50 m. blue and brown .. 1·25 65
185. – 100 m. red and black .. 2·50 1·40
186. – 200 m. violet and blue .. 4·50 2·50
187. – 500 m. orange & green .. 14·00 9·00

Nos. 184/7 are larger.

1955. Arab Postal Union. As T 96a of Syria but inscr. "LIBYE" at top.

200. 5 m. brown 90 60
201. 10 m. green .. .. 1·25 90
202. 30 m. violet .. .. 1·90 1·40

1955. 2nd Arab Postal Congress, Cairo. Nos. 200/2 optd. with T 28.

203. 5 m. brown 40 30
204. 10 m. green 70 50
205. 30 m. violet .. .. 1·40 85

1955. No. 177 surch.

206. 23. 5 m. on 4 m. grey .. 65 45

1955.

207. 30. 1 m. black on yellow .. 5 5
208. 2 m. bistre .. .. 1·00 50
209. 2 m. brown 8 5
210. 3 m. blue 8 5
211. 4 m. black .. .. 1·25 50
212. 4 m. lake 20 15
213. 5 m. green 40 20
214. 10 m. lilac 65 25
215. 18 m. red 15 8
216. 20 m. orange 25 15
217. 30 m. blue 50 20
218. 35 m. brown 65 25
219. 40 m. lake 75 40
220. 50 m. olive 85 25
221. – 100 m. purple and slate 1·25 50
222. – 200 m. lake and blue .. 5·00 95
223. – 500 m. orange & green 9·00 5·00
224. – £L1 grn. & brn. on yell. 12·00 7·50

Nos. 221/4 are larger (27 × 32 mm.).
See also Nos. 242/57.

33. Imam's Tomb at Djaghboub. **34.** Map of Libya.

35. **36.**

1956. Death Centenary of Imam Essayed Mohamed Aly el Senussi.

225. 33. 5 m. green 20 20
226. 10 m. lilac 35 20
227. 15 m. red 40 40
228. 30 m. blue 80 60

1956. 1st Anniv. of Admission to U.N.

229. 34. 15 m. buff and blue .. 30 15
230. 35 m. buff, purple & blue 65 30

1957. Arab Postal Congress, Tripoli.

231. 35. 15 m. blue 25 65
232. 500 m. brown .. .. 8·50 4·50

1958. 10th Anniv. of Declaration of Human Rights.

233. 36. 10 m. violet 20 12
234. 15 m. green 25 20
235. 30 m. blue 65 50

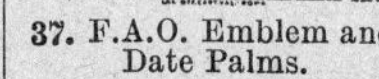

37. F.A.O. Emblem and Date Palms. **39.**

1959. 1st Int. Dates Conf., Tripoli.

236. 37. 10 m. black and violet 20 15
237. 15 m. black and green 25 20
238. 45 m. black and blue .. 60 50

1960. Inauguration of Arab League Centre, Cairo. As T 154a of Syria. but with Arms of Libya and inscr. "LIBYA".

239. 10 m. black and green .. 25 20

1960. World Refugee Year.

240. 39. 10 m. black and violet 25 15
241. 45 m. black and blue .. 65 50

1960. As Nos. 207 etc. On coloured paper.

242. 30. 1 m. black on grey .. 5 5
243. 2 m. brown on buff .. 5 5
244. 3 m. indigo on blue .. 5 5
245. 4 m. lake on red .. 5 5
246. 5 m. green on green .. 8 5
247. 10 m. lilac on violet .. 10 5
248. 15 m. sepia on buff .. 10 5
249. 20 m. orange on orange 20 10
250. 30 m. red on pink .. 20 15
251. 40 m. lake on red .. 30 20
252. 45 m. blue on blue .. 35 20
253. 50 m. olive on bistre .. 35 20
254. – 100 m. purple & slate on blue 60 35
255. – 200 m. lake & blue on blue .. .. 1·60 90
256. – 500 m. orange & green on green .. .. 14·00 3·50
257. – £L1 grn. & brn. on brn. 14·00 8·50

40. Palm Tree and Radio Mast. **41.** Military Watch-tower (medallion).

1960. 3rd Arab Telecommunications Conf. Tripoli.

258. 40. 10 m. violet 15 8
259. 15 m. turquoise .. 20 10
260. 45 m. lake 70 35

1961. Army Day.

261. 41. 5 m. brown and green .. 20 8
262. 15 m. brown and blue .. 30 15

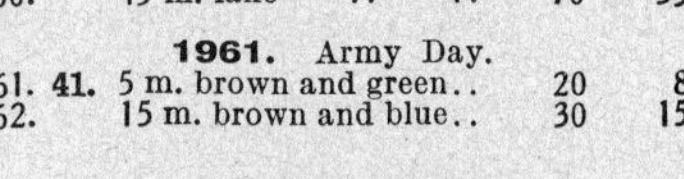

42. Zelten Field and Marsa Brega Port.

1961. Inaug. of First Libyan Petrol Pipeline.

263. 42. 15 m. green and buff .. 25 10
264. 50 m. brown & lavender 75 40
265. 100 m. blue & pale blue 1·75 50

43. Broken Chain and Agricultural Scenes.

1961. 10th Anniv. of Independence.

266. 43. 15 m. sepia, turquoise and green 15 10
267. – 50 m sep., brn. & buff 45 25
268. – 100 m. sep., bl. & salmon 1·10 45

DESIGNS (embodying broken chain): 50 m. Modern highway and buildings. 100 m. Industrial machinery.

44. Tuareg Camel Riders.

1962. Int. Fair, Tripoli.

269. 44. 10 m. chestnut & brown 25 10
270. – 15 m. green and purple 40 25
271. – 50 m. blue and green .. 1·00 80

DESIGNS: 15 m. Well. 50 m. Oil derrick.

45. Campaign Emblem. **46.** Ahmed Rafik.

1962. Malaria Eradication.
273. 45. 15 m. multicoloured .. 25 20
274. 50 m. multicoloured .. 60 45

1962. 1st Death Anniv. of Ahmed Rafik el Mehdawi (poet).
276. 46. 15 m. green 15 10
277. 20 m. brown 25 20

47. Scout Badge and Handclasp. 48. City within Oildrop.

1962. 3rd Boy Scouts' Meeting, Tripoli.
278. 47. 5 m. sepia, red & yellow 10 8
279. – 10 m. sepia, yell. & blue 20 10
280. – 15 m. sep., yell. & grey 25 20
DESIGNS: 10 m. Scouts and badge. 15 m. Badge and camp.

1962. Inauguration of Essider Terminal, Sidrah Oil Pipeline.
282. 48. 15 m. purple and green 20 15
283. 50 m. olive and brown.. 60 45

49. Red Crescent encircling Globe.

1963. Int. Red Cross Cent.
284. 49. 10 m. multicoloured .. 20 15
285. 15 m. multicoloured .. 25 20
286. 20 m. multicoloured .. 40 30

50. Rainbow over Map of Tripoli.

1963. International Trade Fair, Tripoli.
287. 50. 15 m. multicoloured .. 25 20
288. 30 m. multicoloured .. 35 20
289. 50 m. multicoloured .. 70 35

51. Palm and Well. 52. "Emancipation".

1963. Freedom from Hunger.
290. 51. 10 m. green, brown & bl. 20 10
291. – 15 m. ochre, pur. & grn. 25 20
292. – 45 m. sep., bl. & salmon 50 35
DESIGNS: 15 m. Camel and sheep. 45 m. Farmer sowing and tractor.

1963. 15th Anniv. of Declaration of Human Rights.
293. 52. 5 m. brown and blue .. 10 5
294. 15 m. purple and blue.. 20 10
295. 50 m. green and blue .. 45 30

55. Child playing in Sun.

54. Map and Fair Entrance. 56. Lungs and Stethoscope.

1964. International Fair, Tripoli.
300. 54. 10 m. green, brown and red 35 15
301. 15 m. grn., brn. & purple 45 20
302. 30 m. green, brown & bl. 65 45

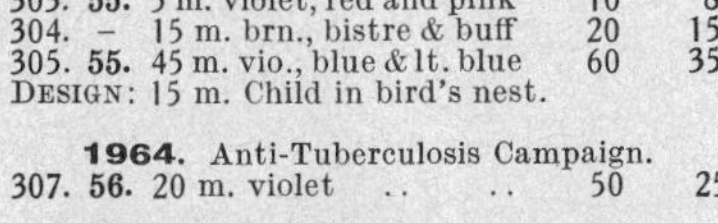

1964. Children's Day. Sun gold.
303. 55. 5 m. violet, red and pink 10 8
304. – 15 m. brn., bistre & buff 20 15
305. 55. 45 m. vio., blue & lt. blue 60 35
DESIGN: 15 m. Child in bird's nest.

1964. Anti-Tuberculosis Campaign.
307. 56. 20 m. violet 50 25

57. Crown and Map. 58. Libyan Woman, Silk Moth and Cocoon.

1964. 1st Anniv. of Libyan Union.
308. 57. 5 m. orange and green.. 12 8
309. 50 m. yellow and blue.. 60 25

1964. Emancipation of Libyan Women.
310. 58. 10 m. blue and green .. 15 10
311. 20 m. blue and yellow.. 25 35
312. 35 m. blue and pink .. 40 45

59. Flags and Scout Salute. 60. Bayonet.

1964. Libyan Scouts. Multicoloured.
314. 10 m. Type 59 .. .. 35 20
315. 20 m. Scout badge and saluting hands 60 35

1964. Foundation of the Senussi Arby.
317. 60. 10 m. brown and green 15 8
318. 20 m. black and orange 25 15

61. Ahmed Bahloul (poet). 62. Football.

1964. Ahmed Bahloul El-Sharef Commem.
319 61. 15 m. purple 20 8
320. 20 m. blue 35 20

1964. Olympic Games, Tokyo. Rings in Gold.
321. 5 m. black & blue (Type 62) 25 20
322. 10 m. blk. & pur. (Cycling) 25 20
323. 20 m. blk. & red (Boxing) 25 20
324. 30 m. blk. & buff (Runner) 35 25
325. 35 m. blk. & olive (High-diving) 35 25
326. 50 m. blk. & grn. (Hurdling) 35 25
Nos. 321/6 were arranged together se-tenant in the sheets, each block of six being superimposed with the Olympic "rings" symbol.

63. A.P.U. Emblem. 64. I.C.Y. Emblem.

1964. 10th Anniv. of Arab Postal Union.
328. 63. 10 m. blue and yellow.. 10 8
329. 15 m. brown and lilac.. 20 10
330. 30 m. brown and green 65 35

1965. Int. Co-operation Year.
331. 64. 5 m. gold & blue (post.) 25 8
332. 15 m. gold and red .. 65 25
333. 50 m. gold & violet (air) 75 35

65. European Bee Eater.

1965. Birds. Multicoloured.
335. 5 m. Long-legged Buzzard 65 15
336. 10 m. Type 65 .. .. 85 15
337. 15 m. Black-bellied Sandgrouse .. .. .. 1·25 15
338. 20 m. Houbara Bustard.. 1·50 25
339. 30 m. Spotted Sandgrouse 1·90 45
340. 40 m. Barbary Partridge.. 2·25 65
The 5 m. and 40 m. are vert.

66. Fair Emblem.

1965. Int. Trade Fair, Tripoli.
341. 66. 50 m. multicoloured .. 35 20

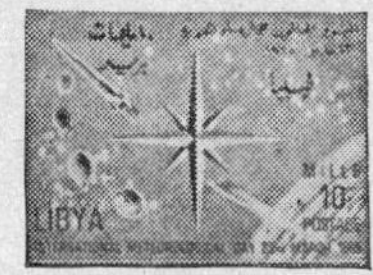
67. Compass, Rocket and Balloons.

1965. World Meteorological Day.
342. 67. 10 m. multicoloured .. 10 8
343. 15 m. multicoloured .. 20 15
344. 50 m. multicoloured .. 60 45

68. I.T.U. Emblem and Symbols.

1965. Cent. of I.T.U.
345. 68. 10 m. brown 8 8
346. 20 m. purple 15 10
347. 50 m. mauve 40 25

69. Lamp and Burning Library. 70. Rose.

1965. Reconstitution of Burnt Algiers Library.
348. 69. 15 m. multicoloured .. 20 8
349. 50 m. multicoloured .. 45 25

1965. Flowers. Multicoloured.
351. 1 m. Type 70 .. .. 8 5
352. 2 m. Iris 8 5
353. 3 m. Cactus flower .. 10 5
354. 4 m. Sunflower 20 10

71. Airliner over Globe. 72. Forum, Cyrene.

1965. Inaug. of Kingdom of Libya Airlines.
355. 71. 5 m. multicoloured .. 10 10
356. 10 m. multicoloured .. 20 10
357. 15 m. multicoloured .. 40 10

1965.
358. 72. 50 m. olive and blue .. 35 25
359. – 100 m. brown and blue 65 45
360. – 200 m. blue and purple 1·60 65
361. – 500 m. green and red .. 3·25 1·60
362. – £L1 brown and green.. 6·50 3·50
DESIGNS—VERT. 100 m. Trajan's Arch, Leptis Magna. 200 m. Apollo's Temple, Cyrene. HORIZ. 500 m. Antonine Temple, Sabratha. £L1, Theatre, Sabratha.

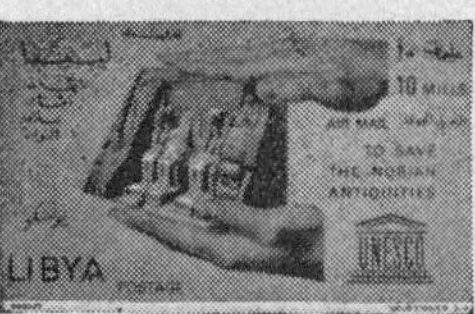
73. "Helping Hands".

1966. Air. Nubian Monuments Preservation.
363. 73. 10 m. brown and bistre 20 8
364. 15 m. brown and green 25 10
365. 40 m. brown & chestnut 50 25

74. Germa Mausoleum.

Nos. 367 and E 368 have the Libyan crest printed in green on the back.

1966.
367. 74. 70 m. violet & brown .. 60 35
See also No. E 368.

75. Globe and Satellites.

1966. Int. Trade Fair, Tripoli.
369. 75. 15 m. blk., gold & grn. 20 8
370. 45 m. black, gold & blue 40 20
371. 55 m. black, gold & pur. 55 30

76. League Centre, Cairo, and Emblem. 77. W.H.O. Building.

1966. Arab League Week.
372. 76. 20 m. red, green & blk. 10 10
373. 55 m. blue, red & blk. 35 25

1966. Air. Inauguration of W.H.O. Headquarters, Geneva.
374. 77. 20 m. blk., yellow & blue 20 8
375. 50 m. black, green & red 40 25
376. 65 m. blk., salmon & lake 50 40

78. Tuareg with Camel. 80. Leaping Deer.

1966. Tuaregs.
378. 78. 10 m. red 20 20
379. – 20 m. blue 35 30
380. – 50 m. multicoloured .. 90 50
DESIGNS—VERT. 20 m. As Type 78 but positions of Tuareg and camel reversed. HORIZ. (62×39 mm.). 50 m. Tuareg with camel (different).

1966. 1st Arab Girl Scouts Camp (5 m.) and 7th Arab Boy Scouts Camp (25 and 65 m.). Multicoloured.
382. 5 m. Type 80 .. .. 8 5
383. 25 m. } Boy Scouts 20 10
384. 65 m. } Camp Emblem (vert.) 45 25

81. Airline Emblem. 82. U.N.E.S.C.O. Emblem.

1966. Air. 1st Anniv. of Kingdom of Libya Airlines.
385. 81. 25 m. multicoloured .. 20 15
386. 60 m. multicoloured .. 45 35
387. 85 m. multicoloured .. 65 50

1967. 20th Anniv. of U.N.E.S.C.O.
388. 82. 15 m. multicoloured .. 20 8
389. 25 m. multicoloured .. 40 20

83. Castle of Columns, Tolemaide. **85.** Fair Emblem.

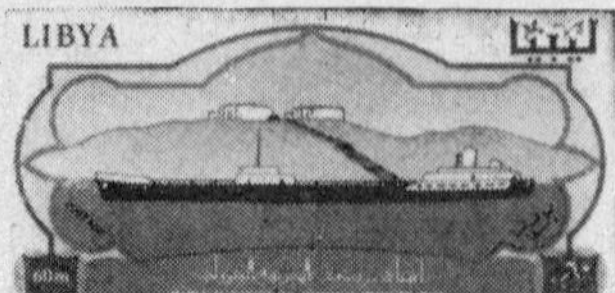

84. "British Confidence" (tanker) at Oil Terminal.

1967. Tourism.
390. **83.** 25 m. blk., brn. & violet 20 10
391. – 55 m. brn., violet & blk. 40 25
DESIGN—HORIZ. 55 m. Sebha Fort.

1967. Inaug. of Marsa al Hariga Oil Terminal.
392. **84.** 60 m. multicoloured .. 85 30

1967. Int. Fair, Tripoli.
393. **85.** 15 m. multicoloured .. 25 5
394. 55 m. multicoloured .. 40 25

86. I.T.Y. Emblem. **87.** Running.

1967. Int. Tourist Year.
395. **86.** 5 m. black and blue .. 5 5
396. 10 m. blue and black .. 8 5
397. 45 m. black, blue & pink 30 15

1967. Mediterranean Games, Tunisia. Designs showing action "close-ups".
398. **87.** 5 m. blk., orge. and blue 5 5
399. – 10 m. blk., brn. & blue 5 5
400. – 15 m. blk., violet & blue 10 8
401. – 45 m. blk., red & blue .. 30 25
402. – 75 m. blk., grn. and blue 45 30
DESIGNS: 10 m. Throwing the javelin. 15 m. Cycling. 45 m. Football. 75 m. Boxing.

88. Open Book and Arab League Emblem. **89.** Human Rights Emblem.

1967. Literacy Campaign.
403. **88.** 5 m. orange and violet .. 5 5
404. 10 m. green and violet 10 5
405. 15 m. purple and violet 12 8
406. 25 m. blue and violet .. 20 12

1968. Human Rights Year.
407. **89.** 15 m. red and green .. 15 5
408. 60 m. blue and orange .. 35 25

90. Cameleers, Aircraft, Oil Rig and Map.

1968. Int. Fair, Tripoli.
409. **90.** 55 m. multicoloured .. 60 30

91. Arab League Emblem.

1968. Arab League Week.
410 **91** 10 m. red and blue .. 10 8
411 45 m. green and orange 35 25

92. Children "Wrestling" (statue). **93.** W.H.O. Emblem and Reaching Hands.

1968. Children's Day. Multicoloured.
412. 25 m. Type **92** 20 12
413. 55 m. Libyan mother and children 40 25

1968. 20th Anniv. of W.H.O.
414. **93.** 25 m. blue and purple .. 25 12
415. 55 m. brown and blue .. 40 25

94. Oil Pipeline Map.

1968. Inaug. of Zueitina Oil Terminal.
416. **94.** 10 m. multicoloured .. 20 10
417. 60 m. multicoloured .. 55 25

95. "Teaching the People".

1968. "Eliminate Illiteracy".
418. **95.** 5 m. mauve 8 5
419. 10 m. orange 10 8
420. 15 m. blue 10 8
421. 20 m. green 20 20

96. Conference Emblem.

1968. 4th Session of Arab Labour Ministries Conf., Tripoli.
422. **96.** 10 m. multicoloured 8 8
423. 15 m. multicoloured .. 20 10

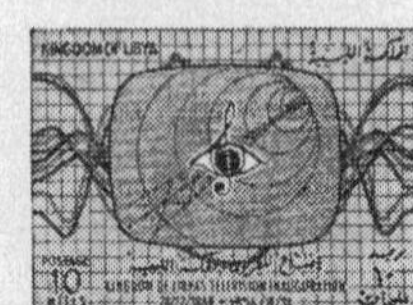

97. Treble Clef, Eye and T.V. Screen.

1968. Inaug. of Libyan Television Service.
424. **97.** 10 m. multicoloured 10 5
425. 30 m. multicoloured .. 35 20

98. Bridge, Callipers and Road Sign.

1968. Opening of Wadi El Kuf Bridge.
426. **98.** 25 m. multicoloured .. 15 12
427. 60 m. multicoloured .. 35 25

99. Melons. **100.** Fair Emblem.

1969. Fruits. Multicoloured.
428. 5 m. Type **99** 5 5
429. 10 m. Dates 8 5
430. 15 m. Lemons 10 5
431. 20 m. Oranges 15 8
432. 25 m. Peaches 20 15
433. 35 m. Pears 40 25

1969. 8th Int. Trade Fair, Tripoli.
434. **100.** 25 m. multicoloured .. 15 10
435. 35 m. multicoloured .. 25 15
436. 40 m. multicoloured .. 30 20

101. Hoisting Weather Balloon.

1969. World Meteorological Day.
437. **101.** 60 m. multicoloured 45 30

102. Family on Staircase within Cogwheel. **103.** I.L.O. Emblem.

1969. 10th Anniv. of Libyan Social Insurance.
438. **102.** 15 m. multicoloured .. 15 8
439. 55 m. multicoloured .. 30 25

1969. 50th Anniv. of I.L.O.
440. **103.** 10 m. grn., blk. & turq. 8 8
441. 60 m. green, black & red 35 25

104. Emblem and Desert Scene.

1969. African Tourist Year.
442. **104.** 15 m. multicoloured .. 15 10
443. 30 m. multicoloured .. 30 25

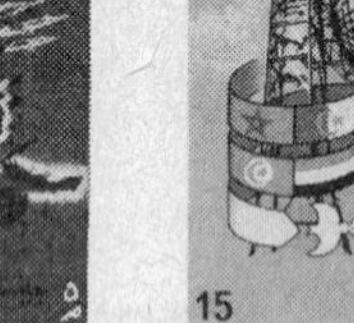

105. Members of the Armed Forces and Olive Branch. **106.** Dish Aerial and Flags.

1969. Revolution of 1st September.
444. **105.** 5 m. multicoloured .. 25 10
445. 10 m. multicoloured .. 35 20
446. 15 m. multicoloured .. 55 25
447. 25 m. multicoloured .. 85 40
448. 45 m. multicoloured .. 1·00 60
449. 60 m. multicoloured .. 1·75 70
On Nos. 444/9 the value is in white and the designers name appears at the foot of design.

1970. 5th Anniv. of Arab Satellite Communications Co-operation Agreement.
450. **106.** 15 m. multicoloured .. 25 15
451. 20 m. multicoloured .. 40 20
452. 25 m. multicoloured .. 50 25
453. 40 m. multicoloured .. 65 40

107. Arab League Flag, Arms and Map.

1970. Silver Jubilee of Arab League.
454. **107.** 10 m. sepia, grn. & blue 10 10
455. 15 m. brn., grn., orge. 15 12
456. 20 m. pur., grn. & olive 25 25

1970. Revolution of 1st September. Designs as T **105**, but without imprint "M. A. Siala" at foot, and figures of value differently inscr.
457. **87.** 5 m. multicoloured .. 25 10
458. 10 m. multicoloured .. 35 20
459. 15 m. multicoloured .. 55 25
460. 25 m. multicoloured .. 85 40
461. 45 m. multicoloured .. 1·00 60
462. 60 m. multicoloured .. 1·75 70

108. New Headquarters Building. **109.** Arms and Soldiers.

1970. New U.P.U. Headquarters Building, Berne.
463. **108.** 10 m. multicoloured .. 12 10
464. 25 m. multicoloured .. 20 20
465. 60 m. multicoloured .. 40 30

1970. Nos. 358 and 360/2 with "KINGDOM OF LIBYA" inscriptions obliterated.
465a. **72.** 50 m. olive and blue ..
466. – 200 m. blue and purple
467. – 500 m. green and pink
468. – £L1 brown and green ..
These stamps were sold only for use on parcel post items. Other values may exist so overprinted, but were unauthorised.
See also Nos. 518/23.

1970. Evacuation of Foreign Military Bases in Libya.
469. **109.** 15 m. black and red .. 15 15
470. 25 m. yell., bl. & red .. 20 20
471. 45 m. yell., red & grn. .. 50 30

110. Soldiers and Libyan Flag. **111.** U.N. Emblem, Dove and Scales.

1970. 1st Anniv. of Libyan Arab Republic.
472. **110.** 20 m. multicoloured .. 25 15
473. 25 m. multicoloured .. 40 15
474. 30 m. multicoloured .. 65 35

1970. 25th Anniv. of United Nations.
475. **111.** 5 m. brn., red & grn. .. 25 8
476. 10 m. grn., red & emerald 40 15
477. 60 m. grn., red & blue 95 40

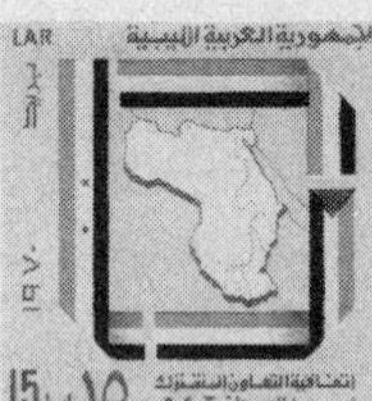

112. Map and Flags. **113.** Dove, U.N. Emblem and Globe.

1970. Signing of Tripoli Charter of Co-operation.
478. **112.** 15 m. grn., blk. & red .. 75 40

1971. 10th Anniv. of U.N. De-colonisation Declaration.
479. **113.** 15 m. multicoloured .. 25 15
480. 20 m. multicoloured .. 40 20
481. 60 m. multicoloured .. 95 40

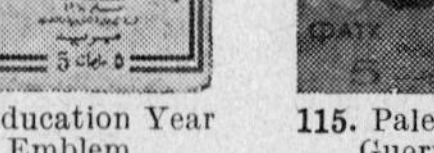

114. Education Year Emblem. **115.** Palestinian Guerrilla.

1971. Int. Education Year.
482. **114.** 5 m. brn., red & blk. .. 15 5
483. 10 m. grn., red & blk. .. 25 8
484. 20 m. bl., red & blk. .. 50 15

1971. "Al-Fatah" Movement for the Liberation of Palestine.
485. **115.** 5 m. multicoloured .. 15 8
486. 10 m. multicoloured .. 25 15
487. 100 m. multicoloured .. 90 55

116. Fair Emblem. **117.** O.P.E.C. Emblem.

1971. 9th Int. Trade Fair, Tripoli.
488. **116.** 15 m. multicoloured .. 15 10
489. 30 m. multicoloured .. 35 20

1971. Organization of Petroleum Exporting Countries (O.P.E.C.).
490. **117.** 10 m. brown and yellow 15 8
491. 70 m. violet and pink .. 60 40

118. Global Symbol. **119.** Soldier, Torch and Flag.

1971. World Telecommunications Day (Nos. 494/5) and Pan-African Telecommunications Network.
492. – 5 m. multicoloured .. 8 5
493. – 15 m. multicoloured .. 10 8
494. **118.** 25 m. multicoloured .. 20 12
495. 35 m. multicoloured .. 50 25
DESIGN: 5 m., 15 m. Telecommunications map of Africa.

1971. 1st Anniv. of Evacuation of Foreign Troops.
496. **119.** 5 m. multicoloured .. 8 5
497. 10 m. multicoloured .. 15 10
498. 15 m. multicoloured .. 20 15

120. Ramadan Suehli. **121.** Palm and Dates.

1971. Ramadan Suehli (patriot). Commem.
499. **120.** 15 m. multicoloured .. 12 10
500. 55 m. multicoloured .. 40 35
For similar portraits see Nos. 503/4, 507/8, 526/7 and 553/4.

1971. 2nd Anniv. of 1st September Revolution.
501. **121.** 5 m. multicoloured .. 20 8
502. 15 m. multicoloured .. 45 15

1971. 40th Death Anniv. of Omar el Mukhtar (patriot). As T **120**.
503. 5 m. multicoloured .. 8 8
504. 100 m. multicoloured .. 95 60

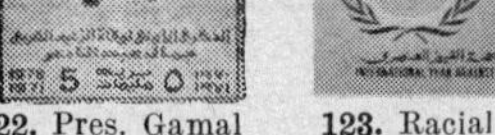

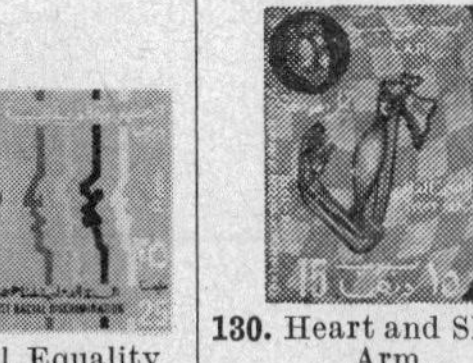

122. Pres. Gamal Nasser. **123.** Racial Equality Year Emblem.

1971. 1st Death Anniv. of Pres. Nasser of Egypt.
505. **122.** 5 m. blk., grn. and pur. 10 8
506. 15 m. blk., pur. and grn. 15 10

1971. 21st Death Anniv. of Ibrahim Usta Omar (poet). As T **120**.
507. 25 m. multicoloured .. 25 15
508. 30 m. multicoloured .. 45 20

1971. Racial Equality Year.
509. **123.** 25 m. multicoloured .. 25 12
510. 35 m. multicoloured .. 35 15

124. A.P.U. Emblem. **125.** Arab Postal Union. Emblem and Envelope.

1971. 25th Anniv. of Founding of Arab Postal Union at Sofar Conf.
511. **124.** 5 m. multicoloured .. 5 5
512. 10 m. multicoloured .. 20 8
513. 15 m. multicoloured .. 15 10

1971. 10th Anniv. of African Postal Union. Multicoloured.
514. 10 m. Type **125** 10 5
515. 15 m. Type **125** 15 10
516. 25 m. A.P.U. Emblem and dove with letter .. 25 15
517. 55 m. As 25 m. 50 35

1971. Nos. 428/33 with "KINGDOM OF LIBYA" inscriptions obliterated.
518. 5 m. Type **99** .. ..
519. 10 m. Dates .. ..
520. 15 m. Lemons .. ..
521. 20 m. Oranges .. ..
522. 25 m. Peaches .. ..
523. 35 m. Pears .. ..

126. Book Year Emblem. **127.** Libyan Arms.

1972. Int. Book Year.
524. **126.** 15 m. multicoloured .. 15 10
525. 20 m. multicoloured .. 25 20

1972. Ahmed Gnaba (poet). Commem. As T **120**.
526. 20 m. multicoloured .. 25 10
527. 35 m. multicoloured .. 35 20

1972. Values in Milliemes.
528. **127.** 5 m. multicoloured .. 5 5
529. 10 m. multicoloured .. 10 5
530. 25 m. multicoloured .. 15 5
531. 30 m. multicoloured .. 20 8
532. 35 m. multicoloured .. 25 10
533. 40 m. multicoloured .. 25 12
534. 45 m. multicoloured .. 35 15
535. 55 m. multicoloured .. 45 20
536. 60 m. multicoloured .. 75 35
537. 90 m. multicoloured .. 75 40

128. Tombs, Ghirza. **129.** Fair Emblem.

1972. Libyan Antiquities. Multicoloured.
538. 5 m. Type **128** 8 5
539. 10 m. Cufic inscription, Ajdabiya 10 5
540. 15 m. Marcus Aurelius' Arch, Tripoli (horiz.) .. 15 10
541. 25 m. Exchanging Weapons (cave painting, Wadi Zigza) 20 15
542. 55 m. Garamantian chariot (wall drawing, Wadi Zigza) 50 25
543. 70 m. "Libya crowning Cyrene" (Roman relief, Cyrene) 75 45

1972. 10th Int. Trade Fair, Tripoli.
544. **129.** 25 m. multicoloured .. 20 15
545. 35 m. multicoloured .. 25 20
546. 50 m. multicoloured .. 50 25
547. 70 m. multicoloured .. 65 35

130. Heart and Skeletal Arm. **131.** "Unity" Symbol on Map.

1972. World Health Day.
548. **130.** 15 m. multicoloured .. 65 25
549. 25 m. multicoloured .. 95 40

1972. 1st Anniv. of Libyan–Egyptian Federation Agreement.
550. **131.** 15 m. yell., blue & blk. 10 8
551. 20 m. yell., grn. & emer. 20 10
552. 25 m. yell., red & black 35 20

1972. Birth Centenary (1970) of Suleiman el Baruni (writer). As T. **120**.
553. 10 m. multicoloured .. 25 15
554. 70 m. multicoloured .. 65 50

1972. New Currency (Dirhams and Dinars). As Type **127**.
(a) Size 19 × 24 mm.
555. **127.** 15 dh. multicoloured .. 10 5
556. 65 dh. multicoloured .. 35 25
557. 70 dh. multicoloured .. 45 30
558. 80 dh. multicoloured .. 65 35
(b) Size 27 × 32 mm.
559. **127.** 100 dh. multicoloured 90 50
560. 200 dh. multicoloured 1·50 1·00
561. 500 dh. multicoloured 3·75 3·00
562. 1 D. multicoloured .. 7·00 5·00

132.

1972.
563. **132.** 5 m. multicoloured .. 95 15
564. 20 m. multicoloured .. 3·50 40
565. 50 m. multicoloured .. 8·50 1·40
Nos. 563/5 were also issued with the Arabic face values expressed in the new currency. See also Nos. 657/9.

133. Environmental Emblem. **134.** Olympic Emblems.

1972. U.N. Environmental Conservation Conf., Stockholm.
566. **133.** 15 dh. multicoloured .. 20 10
567. 55 dh. multicoloured .. 45 35

1972. Olympic Games, Munich.
568. **134.** 25 dh. multicoloured .. 65 35
569. 35 dh. multicoloured .. 90 65

135. Symbolic Tree and "Fruit". **136.** Dome of the Rock.

1972. 3rd Anniv. of 1st September Revolution.
570. **135.** 15 dh. multicoloured .. 15 8
571. 25 dh. multicoloured .. 35 15

1973. Dome of the Rock, Jerusalem.
572. **136.** 10 dh. multicoloured .. 10 5
573. 25 dh. multicoloured .. 20 15

137. Nicolas Copernicus. **138.** Libyan Eagle and Fair.

1973. 500th Birth Anniv. of Copernicus. Multicoloured.
574. 15 dh. Type **137** 15 8
575. 25 dh. "Copernicus in his Observatory" (horiz.) .. 25 15

1973. 11th Int. Trade Fair, Tripoli.
576. **138.** 5 dh. multicoloured .. 15 5
577. 10 dh. multicoloured .. 20 10
578. 15 dh. multicoloured .. 25 15

139. Blind Persons and Occupations. **140.** Map and Laurel.

1973. Role of the Blind in Society.
579. **139.** 20 dh. multicoloured .. 1·25 40
580. 25 dh. multicoloured .. 3·25 1·25

1973. 10th Anniv. of Organization of African Unity.
584. **140.** 15 dh. multicoloured .. 20 10
585. 25 dh. multicoloured .. 40 20

141. Interpol H.Q., Paris.

1973. 50th Anniv. of Int. Criminal Police Organization (Interpol).
586. **141.** 10 dh. multicoloured .. 10 8
587. 15 dh. multicoloured .. 15 10
588. 25 dh. multicoloured .. 20 20

142. Map and Emblems. **143.** W.M.O. Emblem.

1973. Census.
589. **142.** 10 dh. bl., blk. & red 95 20
590. 25 dh. grn., blk. & bl. 1·25 45
591. 35 dh. orge., blk. & grn. 2·25 65

1973. W.M.O. Centenary.
592. **143.** 5 dh. blue, black & red 8 5
593. 10 dh. blue, blk. & grn. 15 10

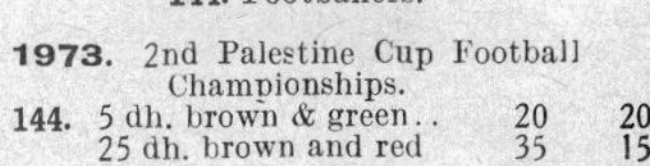

144. Footballers.

1973. 2nd Palestine Cup Football Championships.
594. **144.** 5 dh. brown & green .. 20 20
595. 25 dh. brown and red 35 15

145. Revolutionary Torch. **146.** "Writing Ability".

1973. 4th Anniv. of September 1st Revolution.
596. **145.** 15 dh. multicoloured .. 20 8
597. 25 dh. multicoloured .. 35 10

1973. Literacy Campaign.
598. **146.** 25 dh. multicoloured .. 25 12

147. Doorway of Old City Hall. **148.** Militiamen and Flag.

1973. Cent. of Tripoli Municipality. Mult.
599. 10 dh. Type **147** 20 5
600. 25 dh. Khondok fountain 25 10
601. 35 dh. Clock tower .. 35 15

1973. Libyan Militia.
602. **148.** 15 dh. multicoloured .. 15 8
603. 25 dh. multicoloured .. 25 10

149. Arabic Quotation from Speech of 15 April 1973.

1973. Declaration of Cultural Revolution by Col. Gaddafi. Multicoloured.
604. 25 dh. Type **149** 20 8
605. 70 dh. As Type **149** but text in English 60 30

150. Ploughing with Camel. **151.** Human Rights Emblem.

1973. 10th Anniv. of World Food Programme.
606. **150.** 10 dh. multicoloured . . 10 5
607. 25 dh. multicoloured . . 20 10
608. 35 dh. multicoloured . . 30 15

1973. 25th Anniv. of Declaration of Human Rights.
609. **151.** 25 dh. red, pur. & bl. . . 20 10
610. 70 dh. red, grn. & bl. . . 50 30

152. Mullet. **154.** Emblem formed with National Flags.

153. Lookout Post and Scout Salute.

1973. Fishes. Multicoloured.
611. 5 dh. Type **152** 8 5
612. 10 dh. Sea-bream 15 8
613. 15 dh. Perch 20 10
614. 20 dh. Sea-perch 30 15
615. 25 dh. Tunny 45 20

1974. 20th Anniv. of Scouting in Libya.
616. **153.** 5 dh. multicoloured . . 25 10
617. 20 dh. multicoloured . . 75 20
618. 25 dh. multicoloured . . 1·50 45

1974. 12th Int. Trade Fair, Tripoli.
619. **154.** 10 dh. multicoloured . . 20 5
620. 25 dh. multicoloured . . 25 15
621. 35 dh. multicoloured . . 40 35

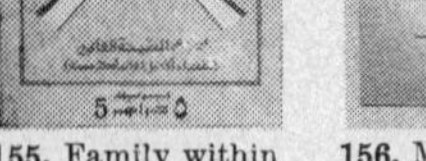

155. Family within Protective Hands. **156.** Minaret within Star.

1974. World Health Day.
622. **155.** 5 dh. multicoloured . . 15 8
623. 25 dh. multicoloured . . 25 20

1974. Inauguration of Benghazi University.
624. **156.** 10 dh. multicoloured . . 20 8
625. 25 dh. multicoloured . . 35 15
626. 35 dh. multicoloured . . 50 25

157. U.P.U. Emblem within Star. **158.** Traffic Lights and Signs.

1974. Cent. of U.P.U.
627. **157.** 25 dh. multicoloured . . 1·60 40
628. 70 dh. multicoloured . . 3·50 90

1974. Motoring and Touring Club of Libya.
629. **158.** 5 dh. multicoloured . . 8 5
630. 10 dh. multicoloured . . 15 8
631. 25 dh. multicoloured . . 15 10

159. Tank, Refinery and Pipeline. **160.** W.P.Y. Emblem and People.

1974. 5th Anniv. of 1st September Revolution.
632. **159.** 5 dh. multicoloured . . 5 5
633. 20 dh. multicoloured . . 15 8
634. 25 dh. multicoloured . . 15 10
635. 35 dh. multicoloured . . 20 12

1974. World Population Year.
637. **160.** 25 dh. multicoloured . . 20 10
638. 35 dh. multicoloured . . 25 20

161. **162.** Congress Emblem.

1975. 13th International Trade Fair, Tripoli. Libyan Costumes.
639. **161.** 5 dh. multicoloured . . 5 5
640. – 10 dh. multicoloured . . 8 5
641. – 15 dh. multicoloured . . 10 5
642. – 20 dh. multicoloured . . 20 8
643. – 25 dh. multicoloured . . 20 10
644. – 50 dh. multicoloured . . 45 20

DESIGNS: 10 dh. to 50 dh. Various costumes.

1975. Arab Workers' Congress.
645. **162.** 10 dh. multicoloured . . 8 5
646. 25 dh. multicoloured . . 15 12
647. 35 dh. multicoloured . . 25 12

163. Teacher at Blackboard. **164.** Human Figures, Text and Globe.

1975. Teachers' Day.
648. **163.** 10 dh. multicoloured . . 10 5
649. 25 dh. multicoloured . . 20 10

1975. World Health Day.
650. **164.** 20 dh. multicoloured . . 15 8
651. 25 dh. multicoloured . . 20 10

165. Readers and Bookshelves. **166.** Festival Emblem.

1975. Arab Book Exhibition.
652. **165.** 10 dh. multicoloured . . 10 5
653. 20 dh. multicoloured . . 20 10
654. 25 dh. multicoloured . . 25 12

1975. 2nd Arab Youth Festival.
655. **166.** 20 dh. multicoloured . . 15 10
656. 25 dh. multicoloured . . 20 12

1975. As Nos. 563/5 but without "L.A.R.".
657. **132.** 5 dh. blk., orge. & blue 10 5
658. 20 dh. blk., yell. & blue 20 5
659. 50 dh. blk., grn. & blue 35 12

167. Games Emblem. **168.** Dove of Peace.

1975. 7th Mediterranean Games, Algiers.
660. **167.** 10 dh. multicoloured . . 10 5
661. 25 dh. multicoloured . . 20 8
662. 50 dh. multicoloured . . 35 20

1975. 6th Anniv. of September 1st Revolution. Multicoloured.
663. 25 dh. Type **168** 20 10
664. 70 dh. Peace dove with different background . . 50 25

169. Khalil Basha Mosque. **170.** Arms and Crowds.

1975. Mohamed's 1405th Birthday. Mosques. Multicoloured.
666. 5 dh. Type **169** 5 5
667. 10 dh. Sidi Abdulla El Shaab 8 5
668. 15 dh. Sidi Ali El Fergani 10 8
669. 20 dh. Al Kharruba (vert.) 15 8
670. 25 dh. Katiktha (vert.) . . 20 8
671. 30 dh. Murad Agha (vert.) 20 12
672. 35 dh. Maulai Mohamed (vert.) 25 15

1976. National People's Congress.
673. **170.** 35 dh. multicoloured 20 10
674. 40 dh. multicoloured 25 10

171. Dialogue Emblem. **172.** Woman blowing Bugle.

1976. Islamic-Christian Dialogue Seminar.
675. **171.** 40 dh. multicoloured . . 25 12
676. 115 dh. multicoloured 75 30

1976. Int. Trade Fair, Tripoli. Multicoloured.
677. 10 dh. Type **171** 8 5
678. 20 dh. Lancer 15 8
679. 30 dh. Drummer 20 10
680. 40 dh. Bagpiper 25 20
681. 100 dh. Woman with jug on head 70 35

173. Early and Modern Telephones.

1976. Telephone Centenary. Multicoloured.
682. 40 dh. Type **173** 25 12
683. 70 dh. Alexander Graham Bell 75 25

174. Mother and Child. **175.** Hands supporting Eye.

1976. International Children's Day.
685. **174.** 85 dh. multicoloured . . 45 30
686. 110 dh. multicoloured 65 40

1976. World Health Day.
687. **175.** 30 dh. multicoloured . . 20 10
688. 35 dh. multicoloured . . 20 10
689. 40 dh. multicoloured . . 25 15

176. Little Bittern.

1976. Libyan Birds. Multicoloured.
690. 5 dh. Type **176** 45 20
691. 10 dh. Great Grey Shrike 85 30
692. 15 dh. Fulvous Babbler . . 1·25 40
693. 20 dh. European Bee Eater (vert.) . . . . . . 1·60 55
694. 25 dh. Hoopoe . . . . 1·90 75

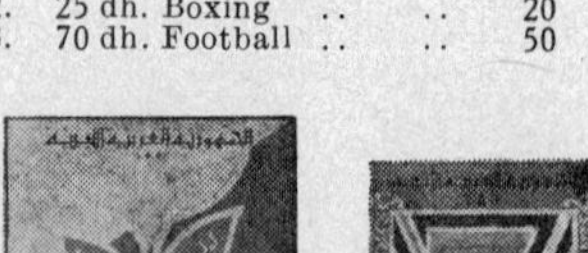

177. Barabekh Plant. **178.** Cycling.

1976. Natural History Museum. Mult.
695. 10 dh. Type **177** 8 5
696. 15 dh. Fin whale (horiz.) . . 15 10
697. 30 dh. Lizard (horiz.) . . 20 10
698. 40 dh. Elephant's skull (horiz.) 25 15
699. 70 dh. Bonnelli's Eagle . . 1·50 40
700. 115 dh. Barbary sheep . . 75 40

1976. Olympic Games, Montreal. Mult.
701. 15 dh. Type **178** 10 5
702. 25 dh. Boxing 20 10
703. 70 dh. Football 50 20

179. Global "Tree". **180.** Agricultural and Industrial Symbols.

1976. Non-Aligned Countries' Colombo Conference.
705. **179.** 115 dh. multicoloured 50 35

1976. 7th Anniv. of Revolution.
706. **180.** 30 dh. multicoloured . . 15 10
707. 40 dh. multicoloured . . 20 12
708. 100 dh. multicoloured 40 30

181. Various Sports. **182.** Chessboard and Pieces.

1976. 5th Arab Games, Damascus.
710. **181.** 15 dh. multicoloured . . 10 5
711. 30 dh. multicoloured . . 15 10
712. 100 dh. multicoloured 50 30

1976. Arab Chess Olympiad, Tripoli.
714. **182.** 15 dh multicoloured . . 30 15
715. 30 dh. multicoloured . . 60 30
716. 100 dh. multicoloured 1·25 50

183. Ratima. **186.** Kaaba, Mecca.

184. Emblem and Text.

1976. Libyan Flora. Multicoloured.
717. 15 dh. Type **183** 12 5
718. 20 dh. "Sword of Crow" 15 8
719. 35 dh. Lasef 20 10
720. 40 dh. Yadid 30 15
721. 70 dh. Esparto grass . . 60 25

1976. International Archives Council.
722. **184.** 15 dh. multicoloured . . 5 5
723. 35 dh. multicoloured . . 15 10
724. 70 dh. multicoloured . . 30 20

1976. Pilgrimage to Mecca.
729. 186. 15 dh. multicoloured .. 5 5
730. 30 dh. multicoloured .. 12 8
731. 70 dh. multicoloured .. 30 20
732. 100 dh. multicoloured 45 30

187. 188. Basket.

1977. Coil Stamps.
733. 187. 5 dh. multicoloured .. 5 5
734. 20 dh. multicoloured .. 10 5
735. 50 dh. multicoloured .. 25 15

1977. 15th International Trade Fair, Tripoli. Multicoloured.
736. 10 dh. Type 188 .. .. 5 5
737. 20 dh. Leather bag .. 8 5
738. 30 dh. Vase 15 8
739. 40 dh. Slippers 20 15
740. 50 dh. Saddle 25 15

189. Girl with Flowers.

1977. Children's Day. Multicoloured.
742. 10 dh. Type 189 .. .. 5 5
743. 30 dh. Clothes shop .. 15 8
744. 40 dh. Orchard 20 15

190. Fighters and Machine-gun. 191. Protected Child.

1977. 9th Anniv. of Battle of Al-Karamah.
745. 190. 15 dh. multicoloured .. 10 5
746. 25 dh. multicoloured .. 12 8
747. 70 dh. multicoloured .. 35 25

1977. World Health Day.
748. 191. 15 dh. multicoloured .. 10 5
749. 30 dh. multicoloured .. 15 8

192. A.P.U. Emblem.

1977. 25th Anniv. of Arab Postal Union.
750. 192. 15 dh. multicoloured .. 10 5
751. 20 dh. multicoloured .. 15 8
752. 40 dh. multicoloured .. 20 15

193. Maps of Libya and Africa. 194. Heart on Map of Libya.

1977. Organization of African Unity Conference, Tripoli.
753. 193. 40 dh. multicoloured .. 45 20
754. 70 dh. multicoloured .. 55 30

1977. Red Crescent Commemoration.
755. 194. 5 dh. multicoloured .. 10 5
756. 10 dh. multicoloured .. 15 8
757. 30 dh. multicoloured .. 30 12

HAVE YOU READ THE NOTES AT THE BEGINNING OF THIS CATALOGUE?
These often provide answers to the enquiries we receive.

195. Messenger and Jet Aircraft.

1977. Communications Progress. Mult.
758. 20 dh. Type 195 .. .. 15 10
759. 25 dh. Arab rider and "Concorde" 30 15
760. 60 dh. Satellite and aerial 30 20
761. 115 dh. Television relay via satellite 65 35
762. 150 dh. Camel rider and aircraft loading .. 1·25 60
763. 200 dh. "Apollo-Soyuz" link .. .. .. 1·25 65

196. Mosque. 197. Archbishop Capucci.

1977. Libyan Mosques.
765. 196. 40 dh. multicoloured .. 20 12
766. – 50 dh. multicoloured .. 25 15
767. – 70 dh. multicoloured .. 30 20
768. – 90 dh. multicoloured .. 40 30
769. – 100 dh. multicoloured 45 35
770. – 115 dh. multicoloured 55 40
DESIGNS: 50 dh. to 115 dh. Various mosques. The 50 dh. and 100 dh. are vertical.

1977. 3rd Anniv. of Archbishop Capucci's Imprisonment.
771. 197. 30 dh. multicoloured .. 15 10
772. 40 dh. multicoloured .. 20 12
773. 115 dh. multicoloured 55 35

198. Clasped Hands and Emblems.

1977. 8th Anniv. of Revolution.
774. 198. 15 dh. multicoloured .. 10 5
775. 30 dh. multicoloured .. 15 10
776. 85 dh. multicoloured .. 45 25

199. Swimming.

1977. Arab School Sports. Multicoloured.
778. 5 dh. Type 199 .. .. 5 5
779. 10 dh. Handball (horiz.) .. 8 5
780. 15 dh. Football 12 10
781. 25 dh. Table tennis (horiz.) 25 20
782. 40 dh. Basketball 35 25

200. Championship Emblem.

1977. 1st International Turf Championships, Tripoli. Multicoloured.
783. 5 dh. Horse jumping (facing left) 5 5
784. 10 dh. Arab horseman .. 5 5
785. 15 dh. Type 200 .. .. 12 5
786. 45 dh. Horse jumping fence (facing right) 30 15
787. 115 dh. Arab horseman racing 60 40

201. Dome of the Rock. 202. Fort, and Hands writing Arabic Script in Book.

1977. Palestine Welfare.
789. 201. 5 dh. multicoloured .. 5 5
790. 10 dh. multicoloured .. 10 5

1977. "The Green Book". Multicoloured.
791. 35 dh. Type 202 .. .. 15 10
792. 40 dh. Type 202 (text in English) 20 12
793. 115 dh. Dove with "Green Book" and map .. 55 40

203. Emblem.

1977. World Standards Day.
794. 203. 5 dh. multicoloured .. 5 5
795. 15 dh. multicoloured .. 8 5
796. 30 dh. multicoloured .. 15 10

204. Giraffe.

1978. Rock Drawings from Wadi Mathendous. Multicoloured.
797. 10 dh. Crocodiles (horiz.) .. 5 5
798. 15 dh. Elephant hunt (horiz.) 10 5
799. 20 dh. Type 204 .. .. 15 10
800. 30 dh. Antelope (horiz.) .. 20 12
801. 40 dh. Elephant (horiz.) .. 25 20

205. Silver Pendant. 206. Compass and Lightning Flash.

1978. 16th Tripoli International Fair.
802. 205. 5 dh. silver, blk. & red 5 5
803. – 10 dh. silver, blk. & vio. 5 5
804. – 20 dh. silver, blk. & grn. 10 5
805. – 25 dh. silver, blk. & blue 12 8
806. – 115 dh. silver, blk. & blue 60 35
DESIGNS: 10 dh. Silver ornamental plate. 20 dh. Necklace with three pendants. 25 dh. Crescent-shaped silver brooch. 115 dh. Silver armband.

1978. Arab Cultural Education Organisation.
807. 206. 30 dh. multicoloured .. 20 12
808. 115 dh. multicoloured 75 35

207. Dancing a Round.

1978. Children's Day. Children's Paintings. Multicoloured.
809. 40 dh. Type 207 .. .. 20 12
810. 40 dh. Children with Placards 20 12
811. 40 dh. Shopping Street .. 20 12
812. 40 dh. Playground .. 20 12
813. 40 dh. Wedding Ceremony 20 12

208. Brickwork Clenched Fist.

1978. The Arabs.
814. 208. 30 dh. multicoloured .. 20 12
815. 115 dh. multicoloured 60 35

209. Blood Pressure Meter. 211. Games Emblem.

210. Microwave Antenna.

1978. World Hypertension Month.
816. 209. 30 dh. multicoloured .. 15 12
817. 115 dh. multicoloured 55 35

1978. World Telecommunications Day.
818. 210. 30 dh. multicoloured .. 15 12
819. 115 dh. multicoloured 60 35

1978. Third African Games, Algiers.
820. 211. 15 dh. copper, vio. & blk. 5 5
821. 30 dh. silver, lilac & blk. 12 10
822. 115 dh. gold, pur. & blk. 60 35

212. Aerial View of Airport. 213. Ankara.

1978. Inauguration of Tripoli International Airport. Multicoloured.
823. 40 dh. Type 212 .. .. 30 10
824. 115 dh. Terminal building 95 40

1978. Turkish-Libyan Friendship.
825. 213. 30 dh. multicoloured .. 12 5
826. 35 dh. multicoloured .. 15 10
827. 115 dh. multicoloured 60 35

214. "Armed Forces". 215. Crater.

1978. 9th Anniv. of 1st September Revolution. Multicoloured.
828. 30 dh. Type 214 .. .. 40 15
829. 35 dh. Tower, Green Book and symbols of progress 15 10
830. 115 dh. "Industry" .. 50 35

1978. Second Symposium on Geology of Libya. Multicoloured.
832. 30 dh. Type 215 .. .. 12 5
833. 40 dh. Oasis 20 12
834. 115 dh. Crater (different) .. 50 35

216. "Green Book" and different Races.

1978. International Anti-Apartheid Year.
835. **216.** 30 dh. multicoloured .. 12 5
836. 40 dh. multicoloured .. 20 12
837. 115 dh. multicoloured 50 35

217. Pilgrims, Minarets and Kaaba.

218. Clasped Hands and Globe.

1978. Pilgrimage to Mecca.
838. **217.** 5 dh. multicoloured .. 5 5
839. 10 dh. multicoloured .. 5 5
840. 15 dh. multicoloured .. 10 5
841. 20 dh. multicoloured .. 12 10

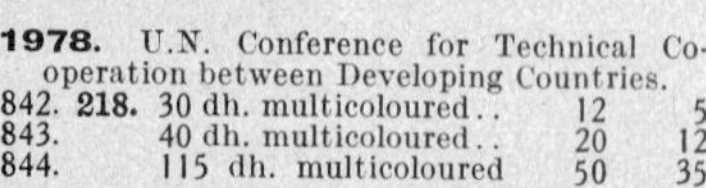
1978. U.N. Conference for Technical Co-operation between Developing Countries.
842. **218.** 30 dh. multicoloured .. 12 5
843. 40 dh. multicoloured .. 20 12
844. 115 dh. multicoloured 50 35

219. Workers, Rifles, Torch and Flag.

220. Human Figure and Scales.

1978. Arab Countries Summit Conference. Multicoloured.
845. 30 dh. Type **219** 12 5
846. 40 dh. Map of Middle East, eagle and crowd (horiz.) 20 12
847. 115 dh. As 40 dh... .. 50 35
848. 145 dh. Type **219** 60 45

1978. 30th Anniv. of Declaration of Human Rights.
849. **220.** 15 dh. multicoloured .. 10 5
850. 30 dh. multicoloured 20 12
851. 115 dh. multicoloured 50 35

221. Horse Racing and Fort.

222. Lilienthal's Glider.

1978. Libyan Study Centre.
852. **221.** 20 dh. multicoloured .. 12 5
853. 40 dh. multicoloured .. 20 12
854. 115 dh. multicoloured 50 35

1978. 75th Anniv. of First Powered Flight. Multicoloured.
855. 20 dh. Type **222** 10 10
856. 25 dh. Lindbergh's "Spirit of St. Louis" 10 10
857. 30 dh. Admiral Byrd's Polar flight 90 25
858. 50 dh. Flying boat and Zeppelin .. .. 1·25 35
859. 115 dh. Wright brothers and "Flyer" 50 40

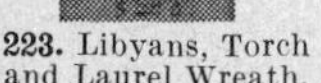
223. Libyans, Torch and Laurel Wreath.

224. Mounted Dorcas gazelle head.

1979.
861. **223.** 5 dh. multicoloured .. 5 5
862. 10 dh. multicoloured .. 5 5
863. 15 dh. multicoloured .. 10 5
864. 30 dh. multicoloured .. 20 10
865. 50 dh. multicoloured .. 20 10
866. 60 dh. multicoloured .. 25 12
867. 70 dh. multicoloured .. 30 15
868. 100 dh. multicoloured 45 25
869. 115 dh. multicoloured 50 30
870. 200 dh. multicoloured 75 45
870a. 250 dh. multicoloured 1·25 1·10
871. 500 dh. multicoloured 1·90 95
872. 1000 dh. multicoloured 4·00 2·50
872a. 1500 dh. multicoloured 7·00 6·25
872b. 2500 dh. multicoloured 11·00 10·00
Nos. 861/9 measure 18×23 mm. and Nos. 870/2b 26×32 mm.

1979. Coil Stamps.
873. **224.** 5 dh. multicoloured .. 12 10
874. 20 dh. multicoloured .. 25 10
875. 50 dh. multicoloured .. 45 25

225. Tortoise.

1979. Libyan Animals. Multicoloured.
876. 5 dh. Type **225** 5 5
877. 10 dh. Addax (vert.) .. 8 5
878. 15 dh. Algerian hedgehog 20 10
879. 20 dh. North African crested porcupine 20 10
880. 30 dh. Dromedaries .. 30 12
881. 35 dh. Wild Cat (vert.) .. 40 15
882. 45 dh. Dorcas gazelle (vert.) 50 25
883. 115 dh. Cheetah .. .. 1·10 40

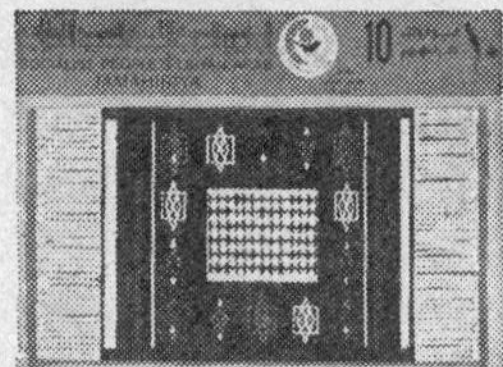
226. Carpet.

1979. 17th Tripoli International Trade Fair.
884. **226.** 10 dh. multicoloured .. 5 5
885. – 15 dh. multicoloured .. 10 5
886. – 30 dh. multicoloured .. 12 8
887. – 45 dh. multicoloured .. 15 10
888. – 115 dh. multicoloured 50 35
DESIGNS: 15 dh. to 115 dh. Different carpets.

227. Aircraft and People.

1979. International Year of the Child. Children's Paintings (1st series). Mult.
889. 20 dh. Type **227** 10 5
890. 20 dh. Shepherd with Flock 10 5
891. 20 dh. Open Air Cafe 10 5
892. 20 dh. Boat in Storm .. 10 5
893. 20 dh. Policeman on Traffic Duty 10 5
See also Nos. 975/9.

228. World Map, Koran and Symbols of Arab Achievements.

229. Radar Tower and Map.

1979. The Arabs.
894. **228.** 45 dh. multicoloured .. 20 12
895. 70 dh. multicoloured .. 30 20

1979. World Meteorological Day.
896. **229.** 15 dh. multicoloured .. 5 5
897. 30 dh. multicoloured .. 12 10
898. 50 dh. multicoloured .. 20 12

230. Medical Care.

1979. World Health Day.
899. **230.** 40 dh. multicoloured .. 20 12

231. "Carpobrotus acinaciformis".
232. Farmer and Sheep.

1979. Libyan Flowers. Multicoloured.
900. 10 d. Type **231** 5 5
901. 15 d. "Caralluma europaea" 10 5
902. 20 d. "Arum cirenaicum" 10 5
903. 35 d. "Lavatera arborea" 20 12
904. 40 d. "Capparis spinosa" 20 12
905. 50 d. "Ranunculus asiaticus" 25 15

1979. 10th Anniv. of Revolution. Mult.
906. 15 dh. Type **232** 10 5
907. 15 dh. Crowd with Green Book 10 5
908. 15 dh. Oil field 10 5
909. 15 dh. Refinery 10 5
910. 30 dh. Dish aerial 15 10
911. 30 dh. Hospital 15 10
912. 30 dh. Doctor examining patient 15 10
913. 30 dh. Surgeon 15 10
914. 40 dh. Street, Tripoli .. 20 12
915. 40 dh. Steel mill 20 12
916. 40 dh. Tanks 20 12
917. 40 dh. Tuareg horsemen .. 20 12
918. 70 dh. Revolutionaries and Green Book 35 20
919. 70 dh. Crowd within map of Libya 35 20
920. 70 dh. Mullah 35 20
921. 70 dh. Student 35 20

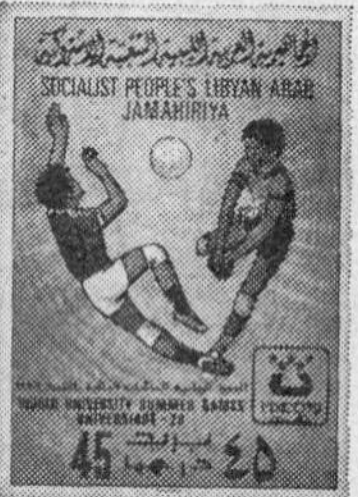
233. Volleyball.

234. Emblem.

1979. "Universiada '79" World University Games, Mexico City. Multicoloured.
923. 45 dh. Type **233** 20 12
924. 115 dh. Football 60 30

1979. Third World Telecommunications Exhibition, Geneva.
925. **234.** 45 dh. multicoloured .. 20 12
926. 115 dh. multicoloured 60 30

235. Seminar Emblem and Crowd.

1979. International Seminar on the "Green Book". Multicoloured.
927. 10 dh. Type **235** 5 5
928. 35 dh. Seminar in progress 20 12
929. 100 dh. Colonel Gaddafi with "Green Book" .. 50 30
No. 928 is horizontal, 70×43 mm.

236. Horsemen in Town.

1979. Evacuation of Foreign Forces. Mult.
931. 30 dh. Type **236** 15 10
932. 40 dh. Tuareg horsemen .. 20 15

237. Football Match.

1979. Mediterranean Games, Split.
934. **237.** 15 dh. multicoloured .. 10 5
935. 30 dh. multicoloured .. 15 10
936. 70 dh. multicoloured .. 35 20

238. Cyclist and Emblem.

1979. Junior Cycling Championships, Tripoli. Multicoloured.
937. 15 dh. Type **238** 10 5
938. 30 dh. Cyclists and emblem 15 10

239. Horse-jumping.

1979. Pre-Olympics. Multicoloured.
939. 45 dh. Type **239** 20 15
940. 60 dh. Javelin 30 15
941. 115 dh. Hurdles 60 30
942. 160 dh. Football 70 40
Nos. 939/42 exist from sheets on which an overall Moscow Olympics emblem in silver was superimposed on the stamps.

240. Figure clothed in Palestinian Flag.

241. Ploughing.

1979. Solidarity with Palestinian People.
944. **240.** 30 dh. multicoloured .. 15 10
945. 115 dh. multicoloured 60 30

1980. World Olive Oil Year.
946. **241.** 15 dh. multicoloured .. 10 5
947. 30 dh. multicoloured .. 15 10
948. 45 dh. multicoloured .. 20 12

242. Hockey (left).

243. Pipes.

1980. National Sports. Multicoloured.
949. 10 dh. Type **242** 5 5
950. 10 dh. Hockey (right) .. 5 5
951. 10 dh. Leap-frog (left) .. 5 5
952. 10 dh. Leap-frog (right) .. 5 5
953. 15 dh. Long jump (left) .. 10 5
954. 15 dh. Long jump (right) .. 10 5
955. 15 dh. Ball catching (left) 10 5
956. 15 dh. Ball catching (right) 10 5
957. 20 dh. Wrestling (left) .. 10 5
958. 20 dh. Wrestling (right) .. 10 5
959. 20 dh. Stone throwing (left) 10 5
960. 20 dh. Stone throwing (right) 10 5
961. 30 dh. Tug-of-war (left) .. 15 10
962. 30 dh. Tug-of-war (right) .. 15 10
963. 30 dh. Jumping (left) .. 15 10
964. 30 dh. Jumping (right) .. 15 10
965. 45 dh. Horsemen (left) .. 20 12
966. 45 dh. Horsemen (right) .. 20 12
967. 45 dh. Horsemen with whips (left) 20 12
968. 45 dh. Horsemen with whips (right) 20 12
Nos. 949/68 were issued together, divided into se-tenant blocks of four within the sheet, each horizontal pair forming a composite design.

1980. 18th Tripoli International Fair. Mult.
969. 5 dh. Drum (horiz.) .. 5 5
970. 10 dh. Drum (different) (horiz.) 5 5
971. 15 dh. Type **243** 10 5
972. 20 dh. Bagpipes (horiz.) .. 10 5
973. 25 dh. Stringed instrument and bow (horiz.) .. 15 8

1980. International Year of the Child (1979) (2nd issue). As T **227**. Multicoloured.
975. 20 dh. " Horse Riding " .. 10 5
976. 20 dh. " Beach scene " .. 10 5
977. 20 dh. " Fish " 10 5
978. 20 dh. " Birthday party " 10 5
979. 20 dh. " Sheep Festival " 10 5

244. Mosque and Kaaba.

1980. 400th Anniv. of Hejira.
980. **244.** 50 dh. multicoloured .. 25 15
981. 115 dh. multicoloured 60 30

245. Surgical Operation and Hospital.

1980. World Health Day.
982. **245.** 20 dh. multicoloured .. 10 5
983. 50 dh. multicoloured .. 25 15

246. Battle of Shoghab " Shahat ", 1913.

1980. Battles (1st series). Multicoloured.
984. 20 dh. Gardabia, 1915 .. 20 15
986. 20 dh. Type **246** 10 10
988. 20 dh. Fundugh al-Shibani " Garian " 10 10
990. 20 dh. Yefren 10 10
992. 20 dh. Ghira " Brak " .. 20 15
994. 20 dh. El Hani (Shiat) .. 35 15
996. 20 dh. Sebah 20 15
998. 20 dh. Sirt 10 10
985. 35 dh. Gardabia 10 10
987. 35 dh. Shoghab " Shahat " 20 15
989. 35 dh. Fundagh al-Shibani " Garian " 20 15
991. 35 dh. Yefren 20 15
993. 35 dh. Ghira " Brak " .. 20 15
995. 35 dh. El Hani (Shiat) .. 60 25
997. 35 dh. Sebah 20 15
999. 35 dh. Sirt 10 10

The two values commemorating each battle were issued in se-tenant pairs, each pair forming a composite design.

See also Nos. 1027/50, 1132/51 and 1232/39.

247. Flame.

248. Ghadames.

1980. Sheikh Zarruq Festival.
1000. **247.** 40 dh. multicoloured 20 12
1001. 115 dh. multicoloured 60 30

1980. Arabian Towns Organization. Mult.
1003. 15 dh. Type **248** 10 5
1004. 30 dh. Derna 15 10
1005. 50 dh. Ahmad Pasha Mosque, Tripoli .. 25 15

249. Guides on Hike.

1980. 14th Pan-Arab Scout Jamboree. Multicoloured.
1006. 15 dh. Type **249** 10 5
1007. 30 dh. Guides cooking .. 15 10
1008. 50 dh. Cub Scouts cooking 25 15
1009. 115 dh. Scouts map-reading 60 30

250. Oil Refinery.

1980. 11th Anniv. Revolution. Mult.
1011. 5 dh. Type **250** 10 10
1012. 10 dh. Recreation and youth 10 10
1013. 15 dh. Agriculture .. 10 10
1014. 25 dh. Aeroplane and liner 50 15
1015. 40 dh. Education .. 20 15
1016. 115 dh. Housing 60 30

251. Camels, Map of Libya and Conference Emblem.

1980. World Tourism Conference, Manila. Multicoloured.
1018. 45 dh. Type **251** .. 20 12
1019. 115 dh. Emblem, map and camel riders 60 30

252. Figures supporting O.P.E.C. Emblem.

254. Map of Libya and Science Symbols.

253. Death of Omar el Mukhtar.

1980. 20th Anniv. of Organization of Petroleum Exporting Countries. Mult.
1020. 45 dh. O.P.E.C. emblem and globe 20 12
1021. 115 dh. Type **252** 60 30

1980. 49th Death Anniv. of Omar el Mukhtar (patriot).
1022. **253.** 20 dh. multicoloured 10 5
1023. 35 dh. multicoloured 20 12

1980. Birth Millenary of Avicenna (philosopher) and School Scientific Exhibition. Multicoloured.
1025. 45 dh. Type **254** 20 12
1026. 115 d. Avicenna and Exhibition Emblem .. 60 30

1981. Battles (2nd series). As T **246**. Mult.
1027. 20 dh. Zuara 8 8
1029. 20 dh. Tawargha .. 8 8
1031. 20 dh. Dernah 8 8
1033. 20 dh. Bir Tagreft .. 8 8
1035. 20 dh. Funduk El Jamel " Misurata " 8 8
1037. 20 dh. Sidi El Khemri " Gusbat " 8 8
1039. 20 dh. El Khoms .. 8 8
1041. 20 dh. Roghdalin " Menshia " 8 8
1043. 20 dh. Ain Zara " Tripoli " 8 8
1045. 20 dh. Rughbat el Naga " Benina " 8 8
1047. 20 dh. Tobruk 8 8
1049. 20 dh. Ikshadia " Werfella " 8 8
1028. 35 dh. Zuara 12 12
1030. 35 dh. Tawargha .. 12 12
1032. 35 dh. Dernah 12 12
1034. 35 dh. Bir Tagreft .. 12 12
1036. 35 dh. Funduk El Jamel " Misurata " 12 12
1038. 35 dh. Sidi El Khemri " Gusbat " 12 12
1040. 35 dh. El khoms .. 12 12
1042. 35 dh. Roghdalin " Menshia " 12 12
1044. 35 dh. Ain Zara " Tripoli " 12 12
1046. 35 dh. Rughbat el Naga " Benina " 12 12
1048. 35 dh. Tobruk 12 12
1050. 35 dh. Ikshadia " Werfella " 12 12

The two values commemorating each battle were issued in se-tenant pairs, each pair forming a composite design.

254. Tent, Trees and Sun.

1981. Children's Day. Children's Paintings. Multicoloured.
1051. 20 dh. Type **254** 8 8
1052. 20 dh. Women 8 8
1053. 20 dh. Picnic 8 8
1054. 20 dh. Aeroplane and playing children .. 8 8
1055. 20 dh. Mosque and man with camel 8 8

255. Central Bank.

257. Crowd and " Green Book " Stamp of 1977.

256. Pots.

1981. 25th Anniv. of Central Bank of Libya.
1056. **255.** 45 dh. multicoloured 15 15
1057. 115 dh. multicoloured 35 35

1981. Tripoli International Fair. Multicoloured.
1059. 5 dh. Type **256** 5 5
1060. 10 dh. Silver coffee pot (vert.) 5 5
1061. 15 dh. Long-necked vase (vert.) 5 5
1062. 45 dh. Round-bellied vase 15 15
1063. 115 dh. Jug 35 35

1981. People's Authority Declaration.
1064. **257.** 50 dh. multicoloured 15 15
1065. 115 dh. multicoloured 35 35

258. Tajoura Hospital, Medical Complex, Patients, receiving Treatment and W.H.O. Emblem.

1981. World Health Day.
1066. **258.** 45 dh. multicoloured 15 15
1067. 115 dh. multicoloured 35 35

259. Eye and Man on Crutches.

1981. International Year of Disabled People.
1068. **259.** 20 dh. grn., blue & blk. 8 8
1069. – 45 dh. grn., blk. & blue 15 15
1070. – 115 dh. blue and green 35 35

DESIGNS: 45 dh. Globe and I.Y.D.P. emblem. 115 dh. Hands holding shield with I.Y.D.P. emblem, eye and man on crutch.

260. Horse.

1981. Libyan Mosaics. Multicoloured.
1071. 10 dh. Type **260** 5 5
1072. 20 dh. Ship 8 8
1073. 30 dh. Birds, fish and flowers 10 10
1074. 40 dh. Leopard 12 12
1075. 50 dh. Man playing musical instrument 15 15
1076. 115 dh. Fishes 35 35

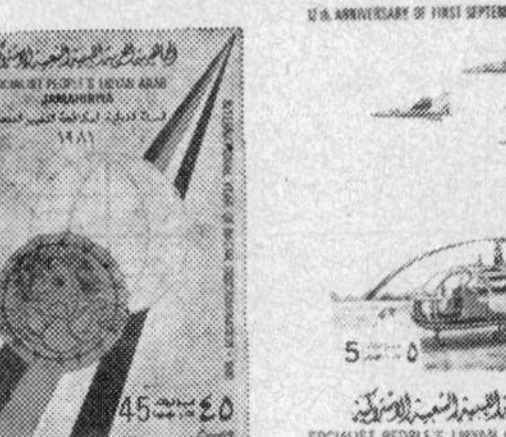
261. Racial Discrimination Emblem.

262. Jet Fighters and Helicopter (Left-hand stamp).

1981. International Year Against Racial Discrimination.
1077. **261.** 45 dh. multicoloured 25 25
1078. 50 dh. multicoloured 30 30

1981. 12th Anniv. of Revolution.
1079. **262.** 5 dh. blue & light blue 15 10
1080. – 5 dh. blue & light blue 15 10
1081. – 5 dh. blue & light blue 10 10
1082. – 5 dh. blue & light blue 10 10
1083. – 10 dh. black and blue 10 10
1084. – 10 dh. black and blue 10 10
1085. – 10 dh. black and blue 10 10
1086. – 10 dh. black and blue 10 10
1087. – 15 dh. brn. & light brn. 15 10
1088. – 15 dh. brn. & light brn. 10 10
1089. – 15 dh. brn. & light brn. 10 10
1090. – 15 dh. brn. & light brn. 10 10
1091. – 20 dh. blue and green 15 15
1092. – 20 dh. blue and green 15 15
1093. – 20 dh. blue and green 15 15
1094. – 20 dh. blue and green 15 15
1095. – 25 dh. brn. and yell. 15 15
1096. – 25 dh. brn. and yell. 15 15
1097. – 25 dh. brn. and yell. 15 15
1098. – 25 dh. brn. and yell. 15 15

DESIGNS—VERT. No. 1080, Jet fighter (right-hand stamp). Nos. 1081/2, Parachutists. Nos. 1083/4, Tank parade. Nos. 1085/6, Marching frogmen. Nos. 1087/8, Anti-aircraft rocket trucks. Nos. 1089/90, Missile trucks. HORIZ. Nos. 1091/2, Marching sailors. Nos. 1093/4, Jeeps and anti-aircraft rocket trucks. Nos. 1095/6, Armoured vehicles and land-rovers. Nos. 1097/8, Tank parade.

Each pair forms a horizontal composite design, the first number being the left-hand stamp in each instance.

263. Wheat and Plough.

1981. World Food Day.
1100. **263.** 45 dh. multicoloured 25 25
1101. 200 dh. multicoloured 95 95

264. "Pseudotergumia fidia".

1981. Butterflies. Multicoloured.
1102 5 dh. Type **264** 15 10
1103 5 dh. "Chazara prieuri" (sun in background) .. 15 10
1104 5 dh. "Polygonia c-album" (trees in background) 15 10

1105 5 dh. "Colias crocea" (mosque in background) 15 10
1106 10 dh. "Anthocharis bellia" (face value bottom right) 15 10
1107 10 dh. "Pandoriana pandora" (face value bottom left) 15 10
1108 10 dh. "Melanargia ines" (face value top right) .. 15 10
1109 10 dh. "Charaxes jasius" (face value top left) .. 15 10
1110 15 dh. "Nymphales antiopa" (face value bottom right) 30 30
1111 15 dh. "Eurodryas desfontainii" (face value bottom left) .. 30 30
1112 15 dh. "Iphiclides podalirius" (face value top right) 30 30
1113 15 dh. "Glaucopsyche melanops" (face value top left) 30 30
1114 25 dh. "Spialia sertorius" (face value bottom right) 50 45
1115 25 dh. "Pieris brassicae" (face value bottom left) 50 45
1116 25 dh. "Lysandra albicans" (face value top right) 50 45
1117 25 dh. "Celastrina argiolus" (face value top left) 50 45

The four designs of each value were issued together in small sheets of four, showing composite background designs.

265. Grapes.

266. I.Y.D.P. Emblem and Globe.

1981. Fruit. Multicoloured.
1119. 5 dh. Type **265** 5 5
1120. 10 dh. Dates 5 5
1121. 15 dh. Lemons 10 10
1122. 20 dh. Oranges 12 12
1123. 35 dh. Barbary figs .. 20 20
1124. 55 dh. Pomegranate .. 30 30

1981. International Year of Disabled Persons.
1125. **266.** 45 dh. multicoloured 25 25
1126. 115 dh. multicoloured 55 55

267. Animals (looking right).

1982. Libyan Mosaics. Multicoloured.
1127. 45 dh. Type **267** 25 25
1128. 45 dh. Orpheus 25 25
1129. 45 dh. Animals (looking left) 25 25
1130. 45 dh. Fishes 25 25
1131. 45 dh. Fishermen .. 25 25
1132. 45 dh. Fishes and ducks 25 25
1133. 45 dh. Farm 25 25
1134. 45 dh. Birds and fruit .. 25 25
1135. 45 dh. Milking 25 25

268. Koran Texts leading to Ka'aba.

269. Grinding Flour.

1982. Third Koran Reading Contest. Multicoloured.
1136. 10 dh. Type **249** 5 5
1137. 35 dh. Koran and formation of the World .. 20 20
1138. 115 dh. Reading the Koran 55 55

1982. Battles (3rd series). As T **246.** Multicoloured.
1140. 20 dh. Hun "Gioffra" .. 12 12
1142. 20 dh. Gedabia 12 12
1144. 20 dh. El Asaba "Gianduba" 12 12
1146. 20 dh. El Habela .. 12 12
1148. 20 dh. Suk El Ahad "Tarhuna" 12 12
1150. 20 dh. El Tangi 12 12
1152. 20 dh. Sokna 12 12
1154. 20 dh. Wadi Smalus "Jabel El Akdar" .. 12 12
1156. 20 dh. Sidi Abuagela "Agelat" 12 12
1158. 20 dh. Sidi Surur "Zeliten" 12 12
1160. 20 dh. Kuefia 12 12
1162. 20 dh. Abunjeim 12 12
1141. 35 dh. Hun "Gioffra" .. 20 20
1143. 35 dh. Gedabia 20 20
1145. 35 dh. El Asaba "Gianduba" 20 20
1147. 35 dh. El Habela .. 20 20
1149. 35 dh. Suk El Ahad "Tarhuna" 20 20
1151. 35 dh. El Tangi 20 20
1153. 35 dh. Sokna 20 20
1155. 35 dh. Wadi Smalus "Jabel El Akdar" .. 20 20
1157. 35 dh. Sidi Abuagela "Agelat" 20 20
1159. 35 dh. Sidi Surur "Zeliten" 20 20
1161. 35 dh. Kuefia 20 20
1163. 35 dh. Abunjeim .. 20 20

The two values commemorating each battle were issued in se-tenant pairs, each pair forming a composite design.

1982. Tripoli International Fair. Mult.
1164. 5 dh. Type **269** 5 5
1165. 10 dh. Ploughing .. 5 5
1166. 25 dh. Stacking Hay .. 15 15
1167. 35 dh. Weaving 20 20
1168. 45 dh. Cooking 25 25
1169. 100 dh. Harvesting .. 50 50

270. "ALFATAH" forming Farm Vehicle.

1982. People's Authority Declaration. Multicoloured.
1170. 100 dh. Type **270** .. 50 50
1171. 200 dh. Colonel Gaddafi, old man, "Green Book" and guns 95 95
1172. 300 dh. Rejoicing crowd 1·40 1·40

271. Scout flying Balloon.

272. Map of Africa and A.F.C. Emblem.

1982. 75th Anniv. of Boy Scout Movement. Multicoloured.
1173. 100 dh. Type **271** .. 50 50
1174. 200 dh. Scouts helping injured dog 95 95
1175. 300 dh. Scout reading to old man .. .. 1·40 1·40
1176. 400 dh. Scout with model rocket .. .. .. 1·90 1·90

1982. African Football Cup Competition.
1178. **272.** 100 dh. multicoloured 50 50
1179. 200 dh. multicoloured 95 95

273. Footballer.

1982. World Cup Football Championship, Spain. Multicoloured.
1180. 45 dh. Type **273** 25 25
1181. 100 dh. Footballer (different) 50 50
1182. 200 dh. As No. 1173 95 95
1183. 300 dh. Footballer and goalkeeper .. .. 1·40 1·40

274. Palestinian Children. 275. Lanner Falcon.

1982. Palestinian Children's Day. Mult.
1185. 20 dh. Type **274** .. 12 12
1186. 20 dh. Girl with dish .. 12 12
1187. 20 dh. Child with turban 12 12
1188. 20 dh. Young child .. 12 12
1189. 20 dh. Young boy .. 12 12

1982. Birds. Multicoloured.
1190. **275.** 15 dh. Lanner falcon 35 30
1191. – 15 dh. Common swift 35 30
1192. – 15 dh. Peregrine falcon 35 30
1193. – 15 dh. Greater flamingo 35 30
1194. – 25 dh. Whitethroat 60 40
1195. – 25 dh. Turtle dove .. 60 40
1196. – 25 dh. Black-bellied sandgrouse .. 60 40
1197. – 25 dh. Egyptian vulture 60 40
1198. – 45 dh. Golden oriole 1·00 70
1199. – 45 dh. European bee eater .. .. 1·00 70
1200. – 45 dh. Common kingfisher .. .. 1·00 70
1201. – 45 dh. Common roller 1·00 70
1202. – 95 dh. Barbary partridge .. .. 1·90 1·40
1203. – 95 dh. Barn owl .. 1·90 1·40
1204. – 95 dh. Cream-coloured courser .. 1·90 1·40
1205. – 95 dh. Hoopoe .. 1·90 1·40

The four designs of each value were printed together in se-tenant blocks of four, forming a composite design.

276. Nurses' Class, Operating Theatre and Doctor examining Child. 277. Map of Libya and A.P.U. Emblem.

1982. Teaching Hospitals.
1207. **276.** 95 dh. multicoloured 50 50
1208. 100 dh. multicoloured 50 50
1209. 205 dh. multicoloured 1·10 1·10

1982. 30th Anniv. of Arab Postal Union.
1210. **277.** 100 dh. multicoloured 50 50
1211. 200 dh. multicoloured 95 95

278. 19th-century Chinese King and diagram of Fischer v Spassky, 1972.

1982. World Chess Championship, Moscow. Multicoloured.
1212 100 dh. Type **278** .. 50 50
1213 100 dh. African king and diagram of Karpov v Korchnoi, 1978 .. 50 50
1214 100 dh. Modern bishop and diagram of Smyslov v Karpov, 1971 50 50
1215 100 dh. 19th-century European rook and diagram of Tal v Vadasz, 1977 .. 50 50

Nos. 1212/15 were printed together, se-tenant, forming a composite design.

279. Hexagonal Pattern.

1982. World Telecommunications Day.
1217. **279.** 100 dh. multicoloured 50 50
1218. 200 dh. multicoloured 95 95

280. Map of Libya and "Green Book".

1982. 51st Anniv. of International Philatelic Federation (F.I.P.).
1219. **280.** 200 dh. multicoloured 95 95

281. Family & Flag. 283. Palm Tree and Red Crescent.

282. Pres. Gaddafi and Aircraft.

1982. Organization of African Unity Summit. Multicoloured.
1221. 50 dh. Type **281** 30 30
1222. 100 dh. Map, dove and symbols of industry and agriculture 50 50
1223. 200 dh. Pres. Gaddafi and crowd with "Green Book" (65 x 36 mm.) .. 95 95

1982. 13th Anniv. of Revolution. Mult.
1225. 15 dh. Type **282** 15 10
1226. 20 dh. Gaddafi, soldiers and rockets 15 10
1227. 30 dh. Gaddafi, sailors and naval vessels .. 50 25
1228. 45 dh. Gaddafi, soldiers and tanks .. 25 25
1229. 70 dh. Gaddafi, and armed forces 35 35
1230. 100 dh. Gaddafi and women soldiers .. 50 50

1982. 25th Anniv. of Libyan Red Crescent. Multicoloured.
1232. 100 dh. Type **283** .. 50 50
1233. 200 dh. "25" within crescents 95 95

284. Globe, Dove and Rifle. 286. Philadelphus.

285. Gaddafi, Crowd, "Green Book" and Emblems.

1982. Solidarity with Palestinian People.
1234. **284.** 100 dh. black, mauve and green .. 45 40
1235. 200 dh. black, blue and green .. 90 80

1982. Al Fateh University Symposium on the "Green Book". Multicoloured.

1236. 100 dh. Type **285** .. 50 45
1237. 200 dh. Gaddafi, "Green Book", map and emblems .. .. .. 1·00 95

1983. Flowers. Multicoloured.

1238. 25 dh. Type **286** 12 10
1239. 25 dh. Hypericum .. 12 10
1240. 25 dh. Antirrhinum .. 12 10
1241. 25 dh. Lily 12 10
1242. 25 dh. Capparis 12 10
1243. 25 dh. Tropaeolum .. 12 10
1244. 25 dh. Roses 12 10
1245. 25 dh. Chrysanthemum 12 10
1246. 25 dh. "Nigella damascena" 12 10
1247. 25 dh. "Guilladia lanceolata" 12 10
1248. 25 dh. Dahlia 12 10
1249. 25 dh. "Dianthus caryophyllus" 12 10
1250. 25 dh. "Notobasis syriaca" 12 10
1251. 25 dh. "Nerium oleander" 12 10
1252. 25 dh. "Iris histroides" 12 10
1253. 25 dh. "Scolymus hispanicus" 12 10

287. Customs Council Building, Brussels, and Warrior on Horseback.

288. Camel.

1983. 30th Anniv. of Customs Co-operation Council. Multicoloured.

1254. 25 dh. Type **287** 12 10
1255. 50 dh. Customs building and warrior on camel .. 25 20
1256. 100 dh. Customs building and warrior with sword 50 45

1983. Battles (4th series). As T **246**.

(a) Battle of Ghaser Ahmed.

1257. 50 dh. multicoloured .. 25 20
1258. 50 dh. multicoloured .. 25 20

(b) Battle of Sidi Abuarghub.

1259. 50 dh. multicoloured .. 25 20
1260. 50 dh. multicoloured .. 25 20

(c) Battle of Ghar Yunes.

1261. 50 dh. multicoloured .. 25 20
1262. 50 dh. multicoloured .. 25 20

(d) Battle of Bir Otman.

1263. 50 dh. multicoloured .. 25 20
1264. 50 dh. multicoloured .. 25 20

(e) Battle of Sidi Sajeh.

1265. 50 dh. multicoloured .. 25 20
1266. 50 dh. multicoloured .. 25 20

(f) Battle of Ras el-Hamam.

1267. 50 dh. multicoloured .. 25 20
1268. 50 dh. multicoloured .. 25 20

(g) Battle of Zawiet Ishghefa.

1269. 50 dh. multicoloured .. 25 20
1270. 50 dh. multicoloured .. 25 20

(h) Battle of Wadi Essania.

1271. 50 dh. multicoloured .. 25 20
1272. 50 dh. multicoloured .. 25 20

(i) Battle of El-Meshiashta.

1273. 50 dh. multicoloured .. 25 20
1274. 50 dh. multicoloured .. 25 20

(j) Battle of Gharara.

1275. 50 dh. multicoloured .. 25 20
1276. 50 dh. multicoloured .. 25 20

(k) Battle of Abughelan

1277. 50 dh. multicoloured .. 20 20
1278. 50 dh. multicoloured .. 20 20

(l) Battle of Mahruka

1279. 50 dh. multicoloured .. 20 20
1280. 50 dh. multicoloured .. 20 20

The two values for each battle were printed together in se-tenant pairs, forming composite designs.

1983. Farm Animals. Multicoloured.

1281. 25 dh. Type **288** 12 10
1282. 25 dh. Cow 12 10
1283. 25 dh. Horse 12 10
1284. 25 dh. Bull 12 10
1285. 25 dh. Goat 12 10
1286. 25 dh. Sheep dog .. 12 10
1287. 25 dh. Ewe 12 10
1288. 25 dh. Ram 12 10
1289. 25 dh. Duck 12 10
1290. 25 dh. Guinea fowl .. 12 10
1291. 25 dh. Rabbit 12 10
1292. 25 dh. Pigeon 12 10
1293. 25 dh. Turkey 12 10
1294. 25 dh. Cockerel 12 10
1295. 25 dh. Hen 12 10
1296. 25 dh. Goose 12 10

289. Musician with Twin-horned Pipe.

1983. Tripoli International Fair. Mult.

1297. 40 dh. Type **289** 20 15
1298. 45 dh. Bagpipes (horiz.) .. 25 20
1299. 50 dh. Horn 25 20
1300. 55 dh. Flute (horiz.) .. 30 25
1301. 75 dh. Pipe 40 35
1302. 100 dh. Man and woman at well 50 45

290. Phoenician Galley.

1983. 25th Anniv of International Maritime Organization. Multicoloured.

1303 100 dh. Type **290** .. 80 55
1304 100 dh. Ancient Greek galley 80 55
1305 100 dh. Ancient Egyptian ship 80 55
1306 100 dh. Roman sailing ship 80 55
1307 100 dh. Viking longship .. 80 55
1308 100 dh. Libyan xebec .. 80 55

291. Motorist.

1983. Children's Day. Multicoloured.

1309. 20 dh. Type **291** 10 8
1310 20 dh. Tractor and trailer 10 8
1311. 20 dh. Child with dove and globe 10 8
1312. 20 dh. Scout camp .. 10 8
1313. 20 dh. Dinosaur 10 8

292. Pres. Gaddafi with Children.

1983. World Health Day. Multicoloured.

1314. 25 dh. Type **292** 12 10
1315. 50 dh. Gaddafi and old man in wheelchair .. 25 20
1316. 100 dh. Gaddafi visiting sick girl (horiz.) .. 50 45

293. Gaddafi, Map and "Green Book".

294. Economic Emblems on Map of Africa.

1983. First World "Green Book" Symposium. Multicoloured.

1317. 50 dh. Type **293** 25 20
1318. 70 dh. Symposium in session and emblem (56 × 37 mm.) 35 30
1319. 80 dh. Gaddafi, "Green Book", emblem and "Jamahiriya" .. 40 35

1983. 25th Anniv. of African Economic Committee.

1321. **294.** 50 dh. multicoloured 25 20
1322. 100 dh. multicoloured 50 45
1323. 250 dh. multicoloured 1·25 1·10

296. "Labrus bimaculatus".

1983. Fishes. Multicoloured.

1325. 25 dh. Type **296** 12 10
1326. 25 dh. "Trigoporus lastoviza" 12 10
1327. 25 dh. "Thalassoma pavo" 12 10
1328. 25 dh. "Apogon imberbis" 12 10
1329. 25 dh. "Scomber scombrus" 12 10
1330. 25 dh. "Spondyliosoma cantharus" 12 10
1331. 25 dh. "Trachinus draco" 12 10
1332. 25 dh. "Blennius pavo" 12 10
1333. 25 dh. "Scorpaena notata" 12 10
1334. 25 dh. "Serranus scriba" 12 10
1335. 25 dh. "Lophius piscatorius" 12 10
1336. 25 dh. "Uranoscopus scaber" 12 10
1337. 25 dh. "Auxis thazard" .12 10
1338. 25 dh. "Zeus faber" .. 12 10
1339. 25 dh. "Dactylopterus volitans" 12 10
1340. 25 dh. "Umbrina cirrosa" 12 10

297. "Still-life" (Gauguin).

1983. Paintings. Multicoloured.

1341. 50 dh. Type **297** 25 20
1342. 50 dh. Abstract 25 20
1343. 50 dh. "The Conquest of Tunis by Charles V" (Rubens) 25 20
1344 50 dh. "Arab Band in Horse-drawn Carriage" 25 20
1345. 50 dh. "Apotheosis of Gaddafi" (vert.) .. 25 20
1346. 50 dh. Horses (detail of Raphael's "The Triumph of David over the Assyrians") (vert.) .. 25 20
1347. 50 dh. "Workers" (vert.) 25 20
1348. 50 dh. "Sunflowers" (Van Gogh) (vert.) 25 20

298. Basketball.

1983. Olympic Games, Los Angeles. Mult.

1349. 10 dh. Type **298** 5 5
1350. 15 dh. High jumping .. 8 5
1351. 25 dh. Running 12 10
1352. 50 dh. Gymnastics .. 25 20
1353. 100 dh. Windsurfing .. 65 45
1354. 200 dh. Shot-putting .. 1·00 95

299. I.T.U. Building, Antenna and W.C.Y. Emblem.

1983. World Communications Year.

1356. **299.** 10 dh. multicoloured 5 5
1357. 50 dh. multicoloured 25 20
1358. 100 dh. multicoloured 50 45

300. "The House is to be served by its Residents".

1983. Extracts from the Green Book. Mult.

1359. 10 dh. Type **300** 5 5
1360. 15 dh. "Power, wealth and arms are in the hands of the people" 8 5
1361. 20 dh. "Masters in their own castles" (vert.) .. 10 8
1362. 35 dh. "No democracy without popular congresses" 20 15
1363. 100 dh. "The authority of the people" (vert.) 50 45
1364. 140 dh. "The Green Book is the guide of humanity for final release" 75 70

301. Handball.

1983. 2nd African Youth Festival. Mult.

1366 100 dh. Type **301** .. 50 45
1367 100 dh. Basketball .. 50 45
1368 100 dh. High jumping .. 50 45
1369 100 dh. Running .. 50 45
1370 100 dh. Football .. 50 45

302. Marching Soldiers.

1983. 14th Anniv. of September Revolution. Multicoloured.

1371. 65 dh. Type **302** 35 30
1372. 75 dh. Weapons and communications training .. 40 35
1373. 90 dh. Women with machine-guns and bazookas .. 45 40
1374. 100 dh. Machine-gun training 50 45
1375. 150 dh. Bazooka training 75 70
1376. 250 dh. Rifle training .. 1·25 1·10

303. Saluting Scouts.

1983. Scout Jamborees. Multicoloured.

1378. 50 dh. Type **303** 25 20
1379. 100 dh. Scouts around camp fire 50 45

Events. 50 dh. Second Islamic Scout Jamboree. 100 dh. 15th Pan Arab Scout Jamboree.

304. Traffic Cadets.

305. Saadun.

1983. Traffic Day. Multicoloured.

1381. 30 dh. Type **304** 15 12
1382. 70 dh. Traffic policeman 35 30
1383. 200 dh. Police motorcyclists .. .. .. 1·00 95

1983. 90th Birth Anniv. of Saadun (patriot soldier).

1384. **305.** 100 dh. multicoloured 50 45

306. "Americana", 1910.

1983. Bicent. of Manned Flight. Mult.

No.	Description	Unused	Used
1385.	100 dh. Type **306**	1·00	55
1386.	100 dh. " Nulli Secundus ", 1907	1·00	55
1387.	100 dh. J. B. Meusnier balloon, 1785	1·00	55
1388.	100 dh. Blanchard and Jeffries' Channel crossing, 1785 (vert.) ..	1·00	55
1389.	100 dh. Pilatre de Rozier's balloon flight, 1784 (vert.)	1·00	55
1390.	100 dh. First Montgolfier balloon, 1783 (vert.) ..	1·00	55

307. Globe and Dove.

1983. Solidarity with Palestinian People.

No.	Description	Unused	Used
1393 **307**	200 dh. green, bl & blk	1·00	95

308. Gladiators fighting.

1983. Mosaics. Multicoloured.

No.	Description	Unused	Used
1394.	50 dh. Type **308**	25	20
1395.	50 dh. Gladiators fighting (different)	25	20
1396.	50 dh. Gladiators and slave	25	20
1397.	50 dh. Two musicians ..	25	20
1398.	50 dh. Three musicians ..	25	20
1399.	50 dh. Two gladiators ..	25	20
1400.	50 dh. Two Romans and bound victim	25	20
1401.	50 dh. Leopard and man hunting deer	25	20
1402.	50 dh. Deer and man with boar	25	20

309. Traditional Architecture.

1983. Achievements of the Revolution. Multicoloured.

No.	Description	Unused	Used
1403	10 dh. Type **309**	10	10
1404	15 dh. Camels drinking and mechanization of farming	10	10
1405	20 dh. Computer operator and industrial scene ..	10	10
1406	35 dh. Modern architecture	15	10
1407	100 dh. Surgeons and nurses treating patients and hospital	45	40
1408	140 dh. Airport and airplane	1·25	75

310. Flooding a River Bed.

311. Mahmud Burkis.

1983. Colonel Gaddafi-River Builder. Multicoloured.

No.	Description	Unused	Used
1410.	50 dh. Type **310**	20	15
1411.	50 dh. Irrigation pipe and agricultural produce ..	20	15
1412.	100 dh. Colonel Gaddafi, irrigation pipe and farmland (62 × 44 mm.)	45	40
1413.	100 dh. Colonel Gaddafi and map (68 × 32 mm.)	45	40
1414.	150 dh. Colonel Gaddafi explaining irrigation project (35 × 32 mm.) ..	70	65

Nos 1410/12 were printed together in se-tenant strips of three forming a composite design.

1984. Personalities. Multicoloured.

No.	Description	Unused	Used
1416.	100 dh. Type **311** ..	45	40
1417.	100 dh. Ahmed el-Bakbak	45	40
1418.	100 dh. Mohamed el-Misurati	45	40
1419.	100 dh. Mahmud Ben Musa	45	40
1420.	100 dh. Abdulhamid el-Sherif	45	40
1421.	100 dh. Mehdi el-Sherif ..	45	40
1422.	100 dh. Mahmud Mustafa Dreza	45	40
1423.	100 dh. Hosni Fauzi el-Amir	45	40
1424.	100 dh. Ali Haidar el-Saati	45	40
1425.	200 dh. Ahmed el-Feghi Hasan	90	80
1426.	200 dh. Bashir el-Jawab	90	80
1427.	200 dh. Ali el-Gariani ..	90	80
1428.	200 dh. Muktar Shakshuki	90	80
1429.	200 dh. Abdurrahman el-Busayri	90	80
1430.	200 dh. Ibbrahim Bakir	90	80
1431.	200 dh. Mahmud el-Janzuri	90	80

312. Windsurfing.

313. Col. Gaddafi with Schoolchildren.

1984. Water Sports. Multicoloured.

No.	Description	Unused	Used
1432.	25 dh. Type **312**	20	10
1433.	25 dh. Dinghy sailing (orange and red sails)	20	10
1434.	25 dh. Dinghy sailing (mauve sails)	20	10
1435.	25 dh. Hang-gliding on water skis	20	10
1436.	25 dh. Water-skiing ..	20	10
1437.	25 dh. Angling from boat	20	10
1438.	25 dh. Men in speed boat	20	10
1439.	25 dh. Water-skiing (different)	20	10
1440.	25 dh. Fishing	20	10
1441.	25 dh. Canoeing	20	10
1442.	25 dh. Surfing	20	10
1443.	25 dh. Water-skiing (different)	20	10
1444.	25 dh. Scuba diving ..	20	10
1445.	25 dh. Diving	20	10
1446.	25 dh. Swimming in snorkel and flippers ..	20	10
1447.	25 dh. Scuba diving for fish	20	10

1984. African Children's Day. Multicoloured.

No.	Description	Unused	Used
1448.	50 dh. Type **313**	20	15
1449.	50 dh. Colonel Gaddafi and children in national dress	20	15
1450.	100 dh. Colonel Gaddafi on map and children at various activities (62 × 43 mm.)	70	40

314. Women in National, Casual and Military Dress.

1984. Libyan Women's Emancipation. Multicoloured.

No.	Description	Unused	Used
1451.	55 dh. Type **314**	25	20
1452.	70 dh. Women in traditional, casual and military dress (vert.)	30	25
1453.	100 dh. Colonel Gaddafi and women in military dress	45	40

315 Theatre, Sabratha.

1984. Roman Ruins of Cyrenaica. Mult.

No.	Description	Unused	Used
1454.	50 dh. Type **315**	20	15
1455.	60 dh. Temple, Cyrene ..	25	20
1456.	70 dh. Monument, Sabratha (vert.)	30	25
1457.	100 dh. Amphitheatre, Leptis Magna	45	40
1458.	150 dh. Temple, Cyrene (different)	70	65
1459.	200 dh. Basilica, Leptis Magna	90	80

316. Silver Dirham, 115 h.

318. Muktar Shiaker Murabet.

317. Men at Tea Ceremony.

1984. Arabic Islamic Coins (1st series).

No.	Description	Unused	Used
1460. **316.**	200 dh. silver, yellow and black	90	85
1461. –	200 dh. silver, mauve and black	90	85
1462. –	200 dh. silver, green and black	90	85
1463. –	200 dh. silver, orange and black	90	85
1464. –	200 dh. silver, blue and black	90	85

Designs: No. 1461, Silver dirham, 93 h. 1462, Silver dirham, 121 h. 1463, Silver dirham, 49 h. 1464, Silver dirham, 135 h.

See also Nos. 1643/5.

1984. International Trade Fair, Tripoli. Mult.

No.	Description	Unused	Used
1465.	25 dh. Type **317**	12	10
1466.	35 dh. Woman making tea	15	12
1467.	45 dh. Men taking tea ..	20	15
1468.	55 dh. Family taking tea	25	20
1469.	75 dh. Veiled women pouring tea	35	30
1470.	100 dh. Robed men taking tea	45	40

1984. Musicians. Multicoloured.

No.	Description	Unused	Used
1471.	100 dh. Type **318** ..	45	40
1472.	100 dh. El-Aref el-Jamal	45	40
1473.	100 dh. Ali Shiaalia ..	45	40
1474.	100 dh. Bashir Fehmi ..	45	40

319. Playing among Trees.

1984. Children's Day. Designs showing children's paintings. Multicoloured.

No.	Description	Unused	Used
1475.	20 dh. Type **319** ..	10	8
1476.	20 dh. A rainy day ..	10	8
1477.	20 dh. Weapons of war ..	10	8
1478.	20 dh. Playing on the swing	10	8
1479.	20 dh. Playing in the park	10	8

320. Crest and "39".

1984. 39th Anniv. of Arab League.

No.	Description	Unused	Used
1480. **320.**	30 dh. multicoloured	15	12
1481.	40 dh. multicoloured	20	15
1482.	50 dh. multicoloured	25	20

321. Red Four-seater Car.

1984. Motor Cars and Locomotives. Mult.

No.	Description	Unused	Used
1483.	100 dh. Type **321** ..	45	40
1484.	100 dh. Red three-seater car	45	40
1485.	100 dh. Yellow two-seater car with three lamps	45	40
1486.	100 dh. Covered red four-seater car	45	40
1487.	100 dh. Yellow two-seater car with two lamps	45	40
1488.	100 dh. Cream car with spare wheel at side ..	45	40
1489.	100 dh. Green car with spare wheel at side ..	45	40
1490.	100 dh. Cream four-seater car with spare wheel at back	45	40
1491.	100 dh. Locomotive pulling wagon and coach	70	35
1492.	100 dh. Purple and blue locomotive	70	35
1493.	100 dh. Cream locomotive	70	35
1494.	100 dh. Lavender and brown locomotive ..	70	35
1495.	100 dh. Lavender and black locomotive with red wheels	70	35
1496.	100 dh. Cream and red locomotive	70	35
1497.	100 dh. Purple and black locomotive with red wheels	70	35
1498.	100 dh. Green and orange locomotive	70	35

322. Stylised People and Campaign Emblem.

1984. World Health Day. Anti-Polio Campaign. Multicoloured.

No.	Description	Unused	Used
1499.	20 dh. Type **322**	10	8
1500.	30 dh. Stylised people and 1981 20 dh. stamp	15	12
1501.	40 dh. Stylised people and Arabic emblem ..	20	15

323. Man making Slippers.

1984. Handicrafts. Multicoloured.

1502. 150 dh. Type **323** .. 70 65
1503. 150 dh. Man making decorative harness .. 70 65
1504. 150 dh. Women forming cotton into skeins .. 70 65
1505. 150 dh. Woman spinning by hand 70 65
1506. 150 dh. Man weaving .. 70 65
1507. 150 dh. Women weaving 70 65

324. Telephones, Dial and Mail.

1984. Postal and Telecommunications Union Congress. Multicoloured.

1508. 50 dh. Type **324** 25 20
1509. 50 dh. Woman working at computer console, dial and man working on computer 25 20
1510. 100 dh. Satellite, map, laurel branches and telephone handset .. 45 40

325. Armed Soldiers and Civilians.

326. Children behind Barbed Wire.

1984. Abrogation of 17th May Treaty. Multicoloured.

1511. 50 dh. Type **325** 25 20
1512. 50 dh. Map, dove and burning banner (30 × 40 mm.) 25 20
1513. 50 dh. Soldiers shaking hands and crowd with banners (30 × 40 mm.) 25 20
1514. 100 dh. Hands tearing treaty, Gaddafi and crowd (62 × 40 mm.) .. 45 40
1515. 100 dh. Gaddafi addressing crowd 45 40

Nos. 1512/14 were printed together in se-tenant strips of three, forming a composite design.

1984. Child Victims of Invasion Day. Multicoloured.

1516. 70 dh. Torn flags on barbed wire 30 25
1517. 100 dh. Type **326** .. 45 40

327. "The Party System Aborts Democracy".

328. Man in Brown Robes.

1984. Quotations from "The Green Book". Multicoloured.

1518. 100 dh. Type **327** .. 45 40
1519. 100 dh. Colonel Gaddafi 45 40
1520. 100 dh. "Partners not wage-workers" .. 45 40
1521. 100 dh. "No representation in lieu of the people. Representation is falsification" .. 45 40
1522. 100 dh. The Green Book 45 40
1523. 100 dh. "Committees everywhere" 45 40
1524. 100 dh. "Forming parties splits societies" .. 45 40
1525. 100 dh. Skyscraper and earthmover 45 40
1526. 100 dh. "No democracy without popular congresses" 45 40

1984. Costumes. Multicoloured.

1527. 100 dh. Type **328** .. 45 40
1528. 100 dh. Woman in green dress and red shawl .. 45 40
1529. 100 dh. Man in ornate costume and turban .. 45 40
1530. 100 dh. Man in short trousers and plain shirt 45 40
1531. 100 dh. Woman in shift and trousers with white shawl 45 40
1532. 100 dh. Man in long white robe and red shawl 45 40

329. Footballer tackling.

1984. World Cup Football Championship. Multicoloured.

1533. 70 dh. Type **329** 30 25
1534. 70 dh. Footballers in magenta and green shirts 30 25
1535. 70 dh. Footballers in orange and lemon shirts 30 25
1536. 70 dh. Goalkeeper failing to save ball 30 25
1537. 70 dh. Footballers in yellow and brown shirts 30 25
1538. 70 dh. Top of Trophy and footballer in green striped shirt 30 25
1539. 70 dh. Top of Trophy and footballers in blue and pink shirts .. 30 25
1540. 70 dh. Footballers in black and white striped and green and red striped shirts .. 30 25
1541. 70 dh. Footballers in green and red striped shirts 30 25
1542. 70 dh. Foot of trophy and footballers in orange striped and blue shirts 30 25
1543. 70 dh. Foot of trophy and goalkeeper .. 30 25
1544. 70 dh. Goalkeeper saving headed ball 30 25
1545. 70 dh. Referee and footballers 30 25
1546. 70 dh. Footballers in white with red striped sleeves and orange shirts 30 25
1547. 70 dh. Footballers in white and green striped and orange shirts 30 25
1548. 70 dh. Footballer in pink shirt 30 25

Nos. 1533/48 were printed in sheetlets of 16 stamps, the backgrounds to the stamps forming an overall design of a stadium.

330. Football.

331. Palm Trees.

1984. Olympic Games, Los Angeles. Mult.

1549 100 dh. Type **330** .. 45 40
1550 100 dh. Swimming .. 45 40
1551 100 dh. Throwing the discus 45 40
1552 100 dh. Windsurfing .. 70 40
1553 100 dh. Basketball .. 45 40
1554 100 dh. Running .. 45 40

1984. 9th World Forestry Congress. Mult.

1556. 100 dh. Four types of forest 45 40
1557. 200 dh. Type **331** .. 90 85

332. Modern Building.

1984. 15th Anniv. of Revolution. Mult.

1558. 25 dh. Type **332** 12 10
1559. 25 dh. Front of building 12 10
1560. 25 dh. Building by pool 12 10
1561. 25 dh. Col. Gaddafi (three-quarter portrait) 12 10
1562. 25 dh. High-rise block .. 12 10
1563. 25 dh. Crane and mosque 12 10
1564. 25 dh. Motorway interchange 12 10
1565. 25 dh. House and garden 12 10
1566. 25 dh. Shepherd and flock 12 10
1567. 25 dh. Combine harvester 12 10
1568. 25 dh. Tractors 12 10
1569. 25 dh. Scientific equipment 12 10
1570. 25 dh. Col. Gaddafi (full face) 12 10
1571. 25 dh. Water pipeline .. 12 10
1572. 25 dh. Lighthouse .. 12 10
1573. 25 dh. Liner at quay .. 30 10

333. Armed Man.

334. Soldier flogging Civilian.

1984. Evacuation of Foreign Forces. Mult.

(a) As T **333**.

1574. 50 dh. Type **333** 25 20
1575. 50 dh. Armed man (different) 25 20
1576. 100 dh. Men on horseback charging (62 × 40 mm.) 45 40

(b) As T **334**.

1577. 100 dh. Type **334** .. 45 40
1578. 100 dh. Girl on horse charging soldiers .. 45 40
1579. 100 dh. Mounted soldiers and wounded being tended by women .. 45 40

335. Woman riding Skewbald Showjumper.

1984. Equestrian Events. Multicoloured.

1580. 25 dh. Type **335** 12 10
1581. 25 dh. Man riding black showjumper (stands in background) 12 10
1582. 25 dh. Jockey riding chestnut horse (stands in background) .. 12 10
1583. 25 dh. Man on chestnut horse jumping in cross-country event .. 12 10
1584. 25 dh. Man riding bay horse in showjumping competition 12 10
1585. 25 dh. Woman on black horse in dressage competition 12 10
1586. 25 dh. Man on black horse in dressage competition 12 10
1587. 25 dh. Woman riding chestnut horse in cross-country event .. 12 10
1588. 25 dh. Jockey riding bay horse 12 10
1589. 25 dh. Woman on bay horse in dressage competition 12 10
1590. 25 dh. Man on grey horse in dressage competition 12 10
1591. 25 dh. Jockey riding grey steeplechaser 12 10
1592. 25 dh. Woman riding grey showjumper .. 12 10
1593. 25 dh. Woman riding through water in cross-country competition .. 12 10
1594. 25 dh. Woman on chestnut horse in cross-country competition .. 12 10
1595. 25 dh. Man riding dun showjumper 12 10

Nos. 1580/95 were printed together in sheetlets of 16 stamps, the backgrounds of the stamps forming an overall design of an equestrian ring.

336. Man cleaning Corn.

337. Map and Pharmaceutical Equipment.

1984. Traditional Agriculture. Multicoloured.

1596. 100 dh. Type **336** .. 45 40
1597. 100 dh. Man using oxen to draw water from well 45 40
1598. 100 dh. Man making straw goods 45 40
1599. 100 dh. Shepherd with sheep 45 40
1600. 100 dh. Man treating animal skin 45 40
1601. 100 dh. Man climbing coconut tree 45 40

1984. Arab Pharmacists Union. 9th Conference.

1602. **337.** 100 dh. multicoloured 45 40
1603. 200 dh. multicoloured 90 80

338. Crowd with Banner showing Map of North Africa.

1984. Arab-African unity. Multicoloured.

1604. 100 dh. Type **338** .. 45 40
1605. 100 dh. Crowd and men holding flags 45 40

339. 1982 and 1983 Solidarity Stamps and Map of Palestine.

1984. Solidarity with Palestinian People.

1606. **339.** 100 dh. multicoloured 45 40
1607. 150 dh. multicoloured 70 65

340. Boeing "747 SP", 1975.

1984. 40th Anniv. of International Civil Aviation Organization. Multicoloured.

1608. 70 dh. Type **340** 50 30
1609. 70 dh. "Concorde", 1969 50 30
1610. 70 dh. Lockheed "L 1011-500 Tristar" 1978 50 30
1611. 70 dh. "Airbus A310", 1982 .. .. .. 50 30
1612. 70 dh. Tupolev "TU 134A", 1962 .. .. 50 30
1613. 70 dh. Short "360", 1981 50 30
1614. 70 dh. Boeing "727", 1963 50 30
1615. 70 dh. "Caravelle 10", 1965 .. .. .. 50 30
1616. 70 dh. Fokker "F27", 1955 .. .. .. 50 30
1617. 70 dh. Lockheed "749 A Constellation", 1946 .. 50 30
1618. 70 dh. Martin "130", 1955 50 30
1619. 70 dh. Douglas "DC-3", 1936 .. .. .. 50 50
1620. 70 dh. Junkers "JU-52", 1932 .. .. .. 50 30
1621. 70 dh. Spirit of St. Louis (Lindbergh's airplane), 1927 .. .. .. 50 30
1622. 70 dh. De Havilland "Moth", 1925 .. .. 50 30
1623. 70 dh. Wright Brothers' Flyer I, 1903 .. .. 50 30

Nos. 1608/23 were printed together in sheetlets of 16 stamps, the backgrounds of the stamps forming an overall design of a runway.

341. Coin. **342.** Mother and Son.

1984. 20th Anniv. of African Development Bank. Multicoloured.

1624. 50 dh. Type **341** 25 20
1625. 70 dh. Map of Africa and "20" 30 25
1626. 100 dh. "20" and symbols of industry and agriculture 45 40

1985. U.N.I.C.E.F. Child Survival Campaign. Multicoloured.

1627 70 dh. Type **342** 30 20
1628 70 dh. Couple and children 30 20
1629 70 dh. Col. Gaddafi and children 30 20
1630 70 dh. Boys in uniform .. 30 20

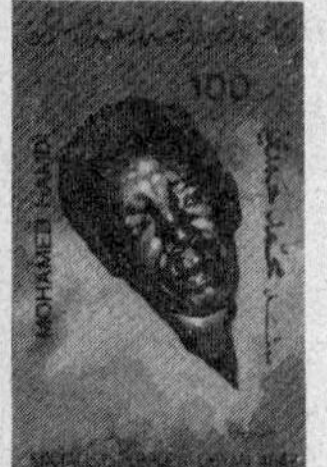

343. Mohamed Hamdi. **344.** Pipeline, River, Plants and Map.

1985. Musicians and Instruments. Mult.

1631. 100 dh. Kamel el-Ghadi 45 35
1632. 100 dh. Fiddle rebab .. 45 35
1633. 100 dh. Ahmed el-Khogia 45 35
1634. 100 dh. Violin 45 35
1635. 100 dh. Mustafa el-Fallah 45 35
1636. 100 dh. Zither 45 35
1637. 100 dh. Type **343** .. 45 35
1638. 100 dh. Mask 45 35

1985. Col. Gaddafi—River Builder. Mult.

1639. 100 dh. Type **344**. .. 45 35
1640. 100 dh. Water droplet, river and flowers .. 45 35
1641. 100 dh. Dead tree with branch thriving in water droplet 45 35

345. Gold Dinar, 105 h.

1985. Arabic Islamic Coins (2nd series). Multicoloured.

1643. 200 dh. Type **345** .. 90 80
1644. 200 dh. Gold dinar, 91 h 90 80
1645. 200 dh. Gold dinar, 77 h. 90 80

346. Fish. **347.** Gaddafi in Robes and Hat.

1985. Fossils. Multicoloured.

1647. 150 dh. Type **346** .. 65 55
1648. 150 dh. Frog 65 55
1649. 150 dh. Mammal .. 65 55

1985. People's Authority Declaration. Mult.

1650. 100 dh. Type **347** .. 45 35
1651. 100 dh. Gaddafi in black robe holding book .. 45 35
1652. 100 dh. Gaddafi in dress uniform without cap .. 45 35
1653. 100 dh. Gaddafi in black dress uniform with cap 45 35
1654. 100 dh. Gaddafi in white dress uniform 45 35

348. Cymbal Player.

1985. International Trade Fair, Tripoli. Multicoloured.

1655. 100 dh. Type **348** .. 45 35
1656. 100 dh. Piper and drummer 45 35
1657. 100 dh. Drummer and bagpipes player .. 45 35
1658. 100 dh. Drummer .. 45 35
1659. 100 dh. Tambour player 45 35

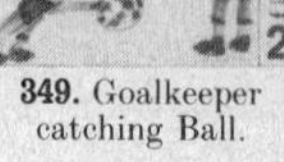

349. Goalkeeper catching Ball. **350.** Emblem, Radio Transmitter and Satellite.

1985. Children's Day. Multicoloured.

1660. 20 dh. Type **349** 10 5
1661. 20 dh. Child on touchline with ball 10 5
1662. 20 dh. Letters of alphabet as players 10 5
1663. 20 dh. Goalkeeper saving ball 10 5
1664. 20 dh. Player heading ball 10 5

1985. International Communications Development Programme.

1665. **350.** 30 dh. multicoloured 15 8
1666. 70 dh. multicoloured 35 25
1667. 100 dh. multicoloured 45 35

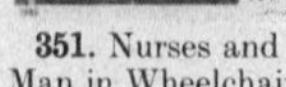

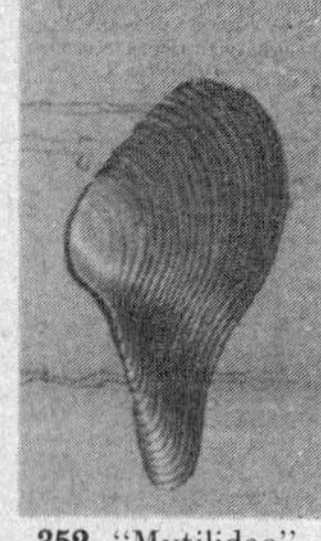

351. Nurses and Man in Wheelchair. **352.** "Mytilidae".

1985. World Health Day. Multicoloured.

1668. 40 dh. Type **351** 15 8
1669. 60 dh. Nurse and doctors 25 15
1670. 100 dh. Nurse and child 45 35

1986. Sea Shells. Multicoloured.

1671. 25 dh. Type **352** 12 5
1672. 25 dh. "Muricidae" .. 12 5
1673. 25 dh. "Cardiidae" .. 12 5
1674. 25 dh. "Corallophilidae" 12 5
1675. 25 dh. "Muricidae" (different) 12 5
1676. 25 dh. "Muricacea" .. 12 5
1677. 25 dh. "Turridae" .. 12 5
1678. 25 dh. "Argonautidae" .. 12 5
1679. 25 dh. "Tonnidae" .. 12 5
1680. 25 dh. "Aporrhaidae" .. 12 5
1681. 25 dh. "Trochidae" .. 12 5
1682. 25 dh. "Cancellariidae" 12 5
1683. 25 dh. "Epitoniidae" .. 12 5
1684. 25 dh. "Turbnidae" .. 12 5
1685. 25 dh. "Mitridae" .. 12 5
1686. 25 dh. "Pectinidae" .. 12 5

Nos. 1671/86 were printed se-tenant, the backgrounds forming an overall design of the sea bed.

353. Books and Emblem. **354.** Girls Skipping.

1985. International Book Fair, Tripoli.

1687. **353.** 100 dh. multicoloured 45 35
1688. 200 dh. multicoloured 90 80

1985. International Youth Year. Mult.

1689. 20 dh. Type **354** 10 5
1690. 20 dh. Boys playing with stones 10 5
1691. 20 dh. Girls playing hopscotch 10 5
1692. 20 dh. Boys playing with sticks 10 5
1693. 20 dh. Boys playing with spinning top 10 5

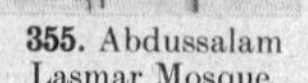

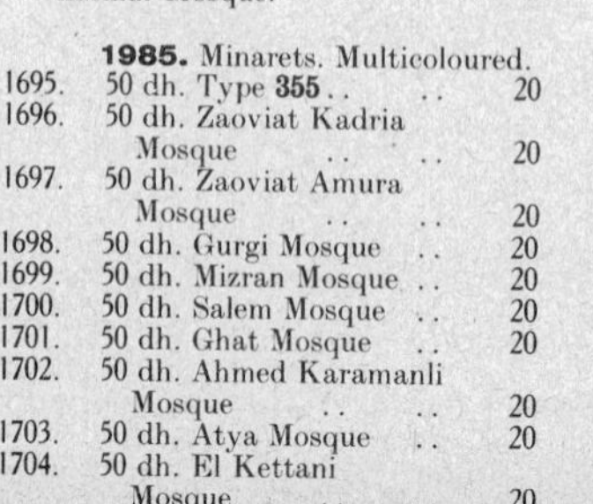

355. Abdussalam Lasmar Mosque. **356.** Jamila Zemerli.

1985. Minarets. Multicoloured.

1695. 50 dh. Type **355** 20 12
1696. 50 dh. Zaoviat Kadria Mosque 20 12
1697. 50 dh. Zaoviat Amura Mosque 20 12
1698. 50 dh. Gurgi Mosque .. 20 12
1699. 50 dh. Mizran Mosque .. 20 12
1700. 50 dh. Salem Mosque .. 20 12
1701. 50 dh. Ghat Mosque .. 20 12
1702. 50 dh. Ahmed Karamanli Mosque 20 12
1703. 50 dh. Atya Mosque .. 20 12
1704. 50 dh. El Kettani Mosque 20 12
1705. 50 dh. Benghazi Mosque 20 12
1706. 50 dh. Derna Mosque .. 20 12
1707. 50 dh. El Derug Mosque 20 12
1708. 50 dh. Ben Moussa Mosque 20 12
1709. 50 dh. Ghadames Mosque 20 12
1710. 50 dh. Abdulwahab Mosque 20 12

1985. Teachers' Day. Multicoloured.

1711. 100 dh. Type **356** .. 45 35
1712. 100 dh. Hamida El-Anezi 45 35

357. "Philadelphia" exploding. **358.** Gaddafi and Followers.

1985. Battle of the "Philadelphia". Mult.

1713. 50 dh. Type **357** 60 20
1714. 50 dh. Men with swords 60 20
1715. 100 dh. Men fighting and ship's rigging (59 × 45 mm.) .. .. 1·25 45

Nos 1713/15 were printed together, se-tenant, forming a composite design.

1986. Colonel Gaddafi's Islamic Pilgrimage. Multicoloured.

1716. 200 dh. Gaddafi writing 90 80
1717. 200 dh. Gaddafi praying 90 80
1718. 200 dh. Gaddafi, crowds and Kaaba 90 80
1719. 200 dh. Gaddafi and mirror 90 80
1720. 200 dh. Type **358** .. 90 80

359. "Leucopaxillus lepistoides".

1985. Mushrooms. Multicoloured.

1722 50 dh. Type **359** 30 15
1723 50 dh. "Amanita caesarea" 30 15
1724 50 dh. "Coriolus hirsutus" 30 15
1725 50 dh. "Cortinarius subfulgens" 30 15
1726 50 dh. "Dermocybe pratensis" 30 15
1727 50 dh. "Macrolepiota excoriata" 30 15
1728 50 dh. "Amanita curtipes" 30 15
1729 50 dh. "Trametes ljubarskyi" 30 15
1730 50 dh. "Pholiota aurivella" 30 15
1731 50 dh. "Boletus edulis" .. 30 15
1732 50 dh. "Geastrum sessile" 30 15
1733 50 dh. "Russula sanguinea" 30 15
1734 50 dh. "Cortinarius herculeus" 30 15
1735 50 dh. "Pholiota lenta" .. 30 15
1736 50 dh. "Amanita rubescens" 30 15
1737 50 dh. "Seleroderma polyrhizum" 30 15

Nos. 1722/37 were printed together, se-tenant, the backgrounds of the stamps forming an overall design of map of Mediterranean.

360. Woman in Purple Striped Dress. **361.** "In Need Freedom is Latent".

1985. Traditional Women's Costumes. Multicoloured.
1738. 100 dh. Type **360** .. 45 35
1739. 100 dh. Woman in robes covering her face .. 45 35
1740. 100 dh. Woman in colourful robes with heavy jewellery .. 45 35
1741. 100 dh. Woman in long blue striped dress .. 45 35
1742. 100 dh. Woman in red dress and trousers .. 45 35

1985. Quotations from "The Green Book".
1743. **361.** 100 dh light green, green and black .. 45 35
1744. – 100 dh. multicoloured 45 35
1745. – 100 dh. light green, green and black .. 45 35
1746. – 100 dh. light green, green and black .. 45 35
1747. – 100 dh. multicoloured 45 35
1748. – 100 dh. light green, green and black .. 45 35
1749. – 100 dh. light green, green and black .. 45 35
1750. – 100 dh. multicoloured 45 35
1751. – 100 dh. light green, green and black .. 45 35

DESIGNS: No. 1744, Gaddafi in uniform reading. 1745, "To make a party you split society". 1746, "Public sport is for all the masses". 1747, "Green Books" and doves. 1748, "Wage-workers are a type of slave, however improved their wages may be". 1749, "People are only harmonious with their own arts and heritages". 1750, Gaddafi addressing crowd. 1751, "Democracy means popular rule not popular expression".

362. Tree and Citrus Fruits.

1985. 16th Anniv. of Revolution. Mult.
1752. 100 dh. Type **362** .. 45 35
1753. 100 dh. Oil pipeline and tanks .. 45 35
1754. 100 dh. Capital and olive branch .. 45 35
1755. 100 dh. Mosque and modern buildings .. 45 35
1756. 100 dh. Flag and mountains .. 45 35
1757. 100 dh. Telecommunications .. 45 35

363. Zauiet Amoura, Janzour.

364. Players in Red No. 5 and Green Shirts.

1985. Mosque Gateways. Multicoloured.
1759. 100 dh. Type **363** .. 45 35
1760. 100 dh. Shiaieb El-Ain, Tripoli .. 45 35
1761. 100 dh. Zauiet Abdussalam El-Asmar, Zliten .. 45 35
1762. 100 dh. Karamanli, Tripoli .. 45 35
1763. 100 dh. Gurgi. Tripoli .. 45 35

1985. Basketball. Multicoloured.
1764. 25 dh. Type **364** .. 12 5
1765. 25 dh. Players in green number 7 and red shirts .. 12 5
1766. 25 dh. Players in green number 8 and red shirts .. 12 5
1767. 25 dh. Players in red number 6 and green shirts .. 12 5
1768. 25 dh. Players in red number 4 and green number 7 shirts .. 12 5
1769. 25 dh. Players in green numbers 6 and 5 and red number 9 shirts .. 12 5
1770. 25 dh. Basket and one player in red and two in green shirts .. 12 5
1771. 25 dh. Players in red number 8 and green number 7 shirts .. 12 5
1772. 25 dh. Two players in green shirts and two in red shirts, one number 4 .. 12 5
1773. 25 dh. Players in red numbers 4 and 7 and green shirts .. 12 5
1774. 25 dh. Players in red numbers 4 and 9 and green numbers 7 and 4 shirts .. 12 5
1775. 25 dh. Players in red number 6 and green shirts .. 12 5
1776. 25 dh. Players in red number 9 and green number 8 shirts .. 12 5
1777. 25 dh. Players in red number 8 and green number 5 shirts .. 12 5
1778. 25 dh. Players in red number 4 and green shirts .. 12 5
1779. 25 dh. Players in red number 5 and green number 10 shirts .. 12 5

Nos. 1764/79 were printed together se-tenant, the backgrounds of the stamps forming an overall design of baseball court and basket.

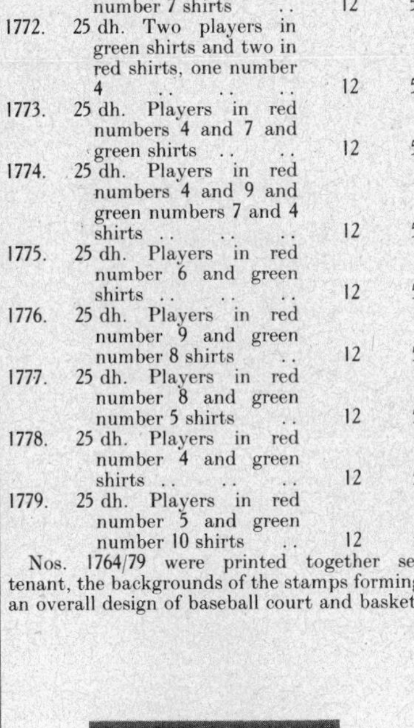

365. People in Light Ray.

1985. Evacuation of Foreign Forces. Multicoloured.
1780. 100 dh. Man on crutches in web and light shining on tree .. 45 35
1781. 100 dh. Hands pulling web away from man .. 45 35
1782. 100 dh. Type **365** .. 45 35

366. Stockbook, Magnifying Glass and Stamps.

367. Players.

1985. Stamp Day. "Italia '85" International Stamp Exhibition, Rome. Multicoloured.
1783. 50 dh. Man and desk on flying stamp above globe .. 20 12
1784. 50 dh. Type **366** .. 20 12
1785. 50 dh. Stamps escaping from wallet .. 20 12

1986. World Cup Football Championship, Mexico (1st issue). Multicoloured.
1786. 100 dh. Type **367** .. 45 35
1787. 100 dh. Players in red and white number 10 and yellow shirts .. 45 35
1788. 100 dh. Goalkeeper and player defending goal against attack .. 45 35
1789. 100 dh. Goalkeeper diving to make save .. 45 35
1790. 100 dh. Goalkeeper jumping to make save 45 35
1791. 100 dh. Player in red and white shirt tackling player in lime shirt .. 45 35

See also Nos. 1824/9.

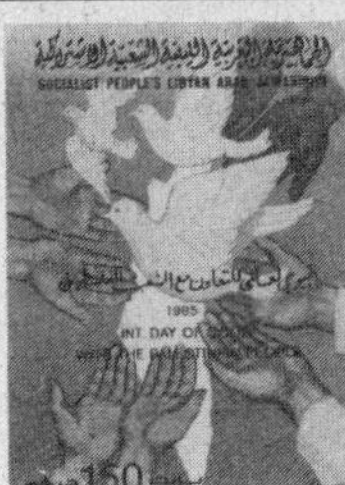

368. Hands releasing Doves.

1985. Solidarity with Palestinian People.
1793. **368.** 100 dh. multicoloured 45 35
1794. 150 dh. multicoloured 45 35

370. Headquarters and Dish Aerial.

371. Paper and Quill in Hand.

1986. 1st Anniv. of General Posts and Telecommunications Corporation.
1807. **370.** 100 dh. multicoloured 40 30
1808. 150 dh. multicoloured 60 50

1986. Peoples' Authority Declaration. Mult.
1809. 50 dh. Type **371** .. 20 12
1810. 50 dh. Paper and globe in hand .. 20 12
1811. 100 dh. "Green Books" and dove (53 × 37 mm.) 40 30

372. Flute.

1986. International Trade Fair, Tripoli. Multicoloured.
1812. 100 dh. Type **372** .. 40 30
1813. 100 dh. Drums .. 40 30
1814. 100 dh. Double pipes .. 40 30
1815. 100 dh. Tambourines .. 40 30
1816. 100 dh. Drum hung from shoulder .. 40 30

373. Boy Scout with Fish on Hook.

1986. Children's Day. Multicoloured.
1817. 50 dh. Type **373** .. 20 12
1818. 50 dh. Boy on camel .. 20 12
1819. 50 dh. Boy catching butterflies .. 20 12
1820. 50 dh. Boy playing drum 20 12
1821. 50 dh. Boy and giant goalkeeper on football pitch .. 20 12

374. Emblem, Man and Skull in Blood Droplet.

1986. World Health Day. Multicoloured, background colours given.
1822. **374.** 250 dh. silver .. 1·00 80
1823. 250 dh. gold .. 1·00 80

375. Footballers.

1986. World Cup Football Championship, Mexico (2nd issue). Multicoloured.
1824. 50 dh. Type **375** .. 20 12
1825. 50 dh. Player jumping over player on ground 20 12
1826. 50 dh. Referee and players .. 20 12
1827. 50 dh. Goalkeeper trying to save ball .. 20 12
1828. 50 dh. Player about to tackle .. 20 12
1829. 50 dh. Player jumping over ball .. 20 12

376. Peas.

377. Health Programmes.

1986. Vegetables. Multicoloured
1831. 50 dh. Type **376** .. 20 12
1832. 50 dh. Marrow .. 20 12
1833. 50 dh. Beans .. 20 12
1834. 50 dh. Aubergine .. 20 12
1835. 50 dh. Corn on the cob .. 20 12
1836. 50 dh. Tomato .. 20 12
1837. 50 dh. Red pepper .. 20 12
1838. 50 dh. Zucchini .. 20 12
1839. 50 dh. Garlic .. 20 12
1840. 50 dh. Cabbage .. 20 12
1841. 50 dh. Cauliflower .. 20 12
1842. 50 dh. Celery .. 20 12
1843. 50 dh. Onions .. 20 12
1844. 50 dh. Carrots .. 20 12
1845. 50 dh. Potato .. 20 12
1846. 50 dh. Radishes .. 20 12

Nos. 1831/46 were printed together in sheetlets of 16 stamps, the backgrounds of the stamps forming an overall design of a garden.

1986. Jamahiriya Thought. Multicoloured.
1847. 50 dh. Type **377** .. 20 12
1848. 50 dh. Education programmes .. 20 12
1849. 100 dh. "Green Book", agricultural scenes and produce (agriculture programmes) (62 × 41 mm.) .. 40 30

378. Gaddafi studying Plans.

1986. Colonel Gaddafi, "Great Man-made River Builder". Multicoloured.
1850. 100 dh. Type **378** .. 40 30
1851. 100 dh. Gaddafi showing planned route on map 40 30
1852. 100 dh. Gaddafi and old well .. 40 30
1853. 100 dh. Gaddafi in desert 40 30
1854. 100 dh. Gaddafi and pipe 40 30
1855. 100 dh. Gaddafi at pumping station .. 40 30
1856. 100 dh. Gaddafi and storage tank .. 40 30
1857. 100 dh. Workers' hut .. 40 30
1858. 100 dh. Water in cupped hands and irrigation equipment .. 40 30
1859. 100 dh. Gaddafi turning wheel at opening ceremony .. 40 30
1860. 100 dh. Laying pipes .. 40 30
1861. 100 dh. Pipe sections on lorries .. 40 30
1862. 100 dh. Gaddafi in robes holding "Green Book" 40 30
1863. 100 dh. Boy giving Gaddafi bowl of fruit 40 30
1864. 100 dh. Boy drinking from tap .. 40 30
1865. 100 dh. Gaddafi praying 40 30

379. Gaddafi with Children.

1986. Colonel Gaddafi, "Man of Peace". Multicoloured.

1866.	100 dh. Type **379**	40	30
1867.	100 dh. Reading book in tent	40	30
1868.	100 dh. With his mother	40	30
1869.	100 dh. Praying in tent with his sons	40	30
1870.	100 dh. Talking to hospital patient	40	30
1871.	100 dh. Driving tractor	40	30

380. "F 111" Exploding above Man with injured Child.

381. Gaddafi, Ruined buildings and Stretcher-bearers.

1986. Battle of the U.S.S. "Philadelphia" and American Attack on Libya. Mult.

(a) As T **380**.

1872	50 dh. Type **380**	40	25
1873	50 dh. American aircraft carrier and escaping family	40	25
1874	100 dh. "Philadelphia" exploding (59 × 38 mm)	1·00	50

(b) As T **381**.

1875.	70 dh. Type **381**	30	20
1876.	70 dh. Burning wreckage of car and man and boy in rubble	30	20
1877.	70 dh. Woman and child by burning ruin	30	20
1878.	70 dh. Men running from bomb strike	30	20
1879.	70 dh. Covered body and rescue workers searching ruins	30	20
1880.	70 dh. Libyans and airplane tail and wing	50	25
1881.	70 dh. Libyans waving fists	30	20
1882.	70 dh. Rescue workers lifting child from rubble	30	20
1883.	70 dh. Weeping women and soldier carrying baby	30	20
1884.	70 dh. Libyans and glare of explosion	30	20
1885.	70 dh. Libyans and airplane wing and nose	50	25
1886.	70 dh. Man carrying girl	30	20
1887.	70 dh. Coffins held aloft by crowd	30	20
1888.	70 dh. Crowd carrying pictures of Gaddafi	30	20
1889.	70 dh. Wounded being tended	30	20
1890.	70 dh. Hands tending wounded baby	30	20

(c) Size 89 × 32 mm.

1891.	100 dh. Bomber aircraft, Gaddafi and anti-aircraft rockets	80	35

Nos 1872/4 were printed together in se-tenant strips of three within the sheet, each strip forming a composite design.

INDEX
Countries can be quickly located by referring to the index at the end of this volume.

382. "The House must be served by its own Tenant".

1986. Quotations from the "Green Book".

1892.	**382.**	100 dh. light green, green and black	40	30
1893.	–	100 dh. multicoloured	40	30
1894.	–	100 dh. light green, green and black	40	30
1895.	–	100 dh. light green, green and black	40	30
1896.	–	100 dh. multicoloured	40	30
1897.	–	100 dh. light green, green and black	40	30
1898.	–	100 dh. light green, green and black	40	30
1899.	–	100 dh. multicoloured	40	30
1900.	–	100 dh. light green, green and black	40	30

DESIGNS: No. 1893, Gaddafi. 1894, "The Child is raised by his Mother". 1895, "Democracy is the Supervision of the People by the People". 1896, "Green Books". 1897, "Representation is a Falsification of Democracy. 1898, "The Recognition of Profit is an Acknowledgement of Exploitation". 1899, Vase of roses, iris, lilies and jasmine. 1900, "Knowledge is a Natural Right of every Human Being which Nobody has the Right to deprive him of under any Pretext".

383. Map, Chrysanthemum and Health Services.

1986. 17th Anniv. of Revolution, Mult.

1901.	200 dh. Type **383**	80	70
1902.	200 dh. Map, sunflower and agriculture programme	80	70
1903.	200 dh. "Sunflowers" (Van Gogh)	80	70
1904.	200 dh. Map, rose and defence programme	80	70
1905.	200 dh. Map, campanula and oil exploration programme	80	70

384. Moroccan and Libyan Women.

1986. Arab–African Union. Multicoloured.

1906.	250 dh. Type **384**	1·00	80
1907.	250 dh. Libyan and Moroccan horsemen	1·00	80

385. Libyan Horseman.

1986. Evacuation of Foreign Forces. Mult.

1908.	50 dh. Type **385**	20	12
1909.	100 dh. Libyan horsemen trampling Italian soldiers	40	30
1910.	150 dh. Italian soldiers charging	60	50

386. Globe and Rose.

1986. International Peace Year Multicoloured, background colours given.

1911.	**386.**	200 dh. green	80	70
1912.		200 dh. blue	80	70

387. Brick "Fists" and Maps within Laurel Wreath.

1986. Solidarity with Palestinian People. Multicoloured, background colours given.

1913.	**387.**	250 dh. blue	1·00	80
1914.		250 dh. red	1·00	80

388. Drummer.

1986. Folk Music. Multicoloured.

1915.	70 dh. Type **388**	30	20
1916.	70 dh. Masked stick dancer	30	20
1917.	70 dh. Woman dancer with pot headdress	30	20
1918.	70 dh. Bagpipe player	30	20
1919.	70 dh. Tambour player	30	20

389. Gazelles.

1987. Endangered Animals. Sand Gazelle. Multicoloured.

1920.	100 dh. Type **389**	40	30
1921.	100 dh. Mother and calf	40	30
1922.	100 dh. Gazelle drinking	40	30
1923.	100 dh. Gazelle lying down	40	30

390. Oil Derricks and Crowd.

391. Sheep and Shepherd.

1987. People's Authority Declaration. Mult.

1924.	500 dh. Type **390**	2·00	1·75
1925.	500 dh. Buildings and crowd	2·00	1·75
1926.	1000 dh. Gaddafi addressing crowd and globe (40 × 38 mm.)	3·75	3·25

1987. 18th Anniv. of Revolution. Mult.

1927.	150 dh. Type **391**	60	50
1928.	150 dh. Col. Gaddafi in robes	60	50
1929.	150 dh. Mosque	60	50
1930.	150 dh. Water flowing from irrigation pipe	60	50
1931.	150 dh. Combine harvester	60	50
1932.	150 dh. Col. Gaddafi in army uniform with microphone	60	50
1933.	150 dh. Harvesting crop	60	50
1934.	150 dh. Irrigation	60	50
1935.	150 dh. Soldier with rifle	60	50
1936.	150 dh. Buildings behind Libyan with rifle	60	50
1937.	150 dh. Fountain	60	50
1938.	150 dh. Buildings and beach	60	50
1939.	150 dh. Fort and girls	60	50
1940.	150 dh. Children and hand on rifle butt	60	50
1941.	150 dh. Theatre	60	50
1942.	150 dh. Couple	60	50

392. Omar Abed Anabi al Mansusri.

1988. Personalities. Multicoloured.

1943.	100 dh. Type **392**	40	30
1944.	200 dh. Ahmed Ali al Emrayd	80	70
1945.	300 dh. Khalifa Said Ben Asker	1·25	1·00
1946.	400 dh. Mohamed Ben Farhat Azawi	1·60	1·40
1947.	500 dh. Mohamed Souf al Lafi al Marmori	2·00	1·75

393. Gaddafi and Crowd with Raised Fists around Earthmover Bucket.

1988. Freedom Festival Day.

1948.	**393.**	100 dh. multicoloured	40	30
1949.		150 dh. multicoloured	60	50
1950.		250 dh. multicoloured	1·00	85

394 Woman and Children running

1988. 2nd Anniv of American Attack on Libya. Multicoloured.

1951	150 dh. Type **394**	60	50
1952	150 dh. Gaddafi playing chess with boy	60	50
1953	150 dh. Gaddafi and children	60	50
1954	150 dh. Gaddafi in robes	60	50
1955	150 dh. Gaddafi and boys praying	60	50
1956	150 dh. Gaddafi and injured girl	60	50
1957	150 dh. Gaddafi in robes with children (horiz)	60	50
1958	150 dh. Gaddafi making speech (horiz)	60	50
1959	150 dh. Gaddafi and family (horiz)	60	50

395 Roses

1988. 19th Anniv of Revolution.

1961	**395**	100 dh. multicoloured	40	30
1962		250 dh. multicoloured	1·00	80
1963		300 dh. multicoloured	1·25	1·00
1964		500 dh. multicoloured	2·10	1·75

396 Relay **397** Dates

1988. Olympic Games, Seoul. Multicoloured.

1965 150 dh. Type **396** .. 60 50
1966 150 dh. Cycling 60 50
1967 150 dh. Football .. 60 50
1968 150 dh. Tennis 60 50
1969 150 dh. Running .. 60 50
1970 150 dh. Showjumping .. 60 50

1988. The Palm Tree. Multicoloured.

1972 500 dh. Type **397** .. 2·10 1·75
1973 1000 dh. Tree .. .. 4·00 3·50

398 Petrol Bomb, Sling and Map **399** Globe, Declaration and Dove

1988. Palesintian "Intifada" Movement. Multicoloured.

1974 100 dh. Type **398** .. 40 30
1975 200 dh. Boy holding stones (45 × 38 mm) .. 80 70
1976 300 dh. Map and flag .. 1·25 1·00

1989. People's Authority Declaration.

1977 **399** 260 dh. multicoloured 1·10 65
1978 500 dh. multicoloured 2·00 1·25

400 Crowd and Green Books (½ size Illustration)

1989. 20th Anniv of Revolution. Mult.

1979 150 dh. Type **400** .. 60 40
1980 150 dh. Soldiers, Colonel Gaddafi and water pipeline 60 40
1981 150 dh. Military hardware, Gaddafi in uniform, education, communications and medicine .. 60 40
1982 150 dh. Armed horsemen 60 40
1983 150 dh. U.S.S. "Philadelphia" exploding .. 1·00 55

401 Execution Victims, Soldiers and Colonel Gaddafi

1989. 78th Anniv of Deportation of Libyans to Italy. Multicoloured.

1985 100 dh. Type **401** .. 40 25
1986 100 dh. Colonel Gaddafi and Libyans 40 25
1987 100 dh. Soldiers, deportees and Gaddafi 40 25
1988 100 dh. Deportees on jetty and in boats 55 25
1989 100 dh. Gaddafi and corpses 40 25

402 Demolition of Wall **403** Emblem of Committee for supporting "Intifida"

1989. "Demolition of Borders".

1991 **402** 150 dh. multicoloured 60 40
1992 200 dh. multicoloured 80 55

1989. Palestinian "Intifida" Movement. Mult.

1993 100 dh. Type **403** .. 40 25
1994 300 dh. Crowd of youths 1·25 85
1995 500 dh. Emblem (first anniv of declaration of State of Palestine) .. 2·00 1·25

404 Circulation Diagram and Annafis

1989. Ibn Annafis (physician) Commem.

1996 **404** 100 dh. multicoloured 40 25
1997 150 dh. multicoloured 60 40

405 Green Books and Fort **406** Libyan People and Soldier

1990. People's Authority Declaration.

1998 **405** 300 dh. multicoloured 1·25 85
1999 500 dh. multicoloured 2·00 1·25

1990. 20th Anniv of American Forces Evacuation.

2000 **406** 100 dh. multicoloured 40 25
2001 400 dh. multicoloured 1·60 1·00

407 Eagle **408** Anniversary Emblem

1990. 21st Anniv of Revolution.

2002 **407** 100 dh. multicoloured 40 25
2003 400 dh. multicoloured 1·60 1·00
2004 1000 dh. multicoloured 4·00 2·75

1990. 30th Anniv of Organization of Petroleum Exporting Countries.

2006 **408** 100 dh. multicoloured 40 25
2007 400 dh. multicoloured 1·60 1·00

409 I.L.Y. Emblem and Figures **410** Player, Globe and Ball

1990. International Literacy Year.

2008 **409** 100 dh. multicoloured 40 25
2009 300 dh. multicoloured 1·25 85

1990. World Cup Football Championship, Italy.

2010 **410** 100 dh. multicoloured 40 25
2011 400 dh. multicoloured 1·60 1·00
2012 500 dh. multicoloured 2·00 1·25

411 Hand holding Ears of Wheat **412** Members' Flags

1990. World Food Day. Multicoloured.

2014 500 dh. Type **411** .. 2·00 1·25
2015 2000 dh. Ploughing .. 8·25 5·25

1991. 2nd Anniv of Union of Arab Maghreb.

2016 **412** 100 dh. multicoloured 40 25
2017 300 dh. multicoloured 1·25 85

413 Flame, Scroll and Koran

1991. People's Authority Declaration.

2018 **413** 300 dh. multicoloured 1·25 85
2019 400 dh. multicoloured 1·60 1·00

414 Girl and International Year of the Child Emblem **415** World Health Organization Emblem

1991. Children's Day. Multicoloured.

2020 100 dh. Type **414** .. 40 25
2021 400 dh. Boy and Day of the African Child emblem .. .. 1·60 1·00

1991. World Health Day. Multicoloured.

2022 100 dh. Type **415** .. 40 25
2023 200 dh. As Type **415** but with emblem additionally inscr "W.H.O. O.M.S." 80 55

416 Wadi el Hayat **417** Digging Riverbed and laying Pipes

1991. Scenes from Libya. Multicoloured.

2024 100 dh. Type **416** .. 50 25
2025 250 dh. Mourzuk (horiz) 1·25 65
2026 500 dh. Ghadames (horiz) 2·40 1·25

1991. Great Man-made River. Multicoloured.

2027 50 dh. Type **417** 25 15
2028 50 dh. Col. Gaddafi, agricultural projects and livestock (59 × 37 mm) 25 15
2029 50 dh. Produce 25 15

Nos. 2027/9 were printed together, se-tenant, forming a composite design.

418 "22", Roses and Broken Chain

1991. 22nd Anniv of Revolution. Mult.

2030 300 dh. Type **418** .. 1·40 70
2031 400 dh. "22" within wheat/cogwheel wreath and broken chain .. 1·90 95

419 Emblem and Globe

1991. "Telecom 91" International Telecommunications Exhibition, Geneva. Mult.

2033 100 dh. Type **419** .. 50 25
2034 500 dh. Buildings and dish aerial (horiz) .. .. 2·40 1·25

420 Monument and Soldier

1991. 80th Anniv of Deportation of Libyans to Italy. Multicoloured.

2035 100 dh. Type **420** .. 50 25
2036 400 dh. Naval transport, Libyans and soldiers .. 2·50 95

421 Map **424** State Arms

423 Gaddafi and Camels

1991. Arab Unity.

2038 **421** 50 dh. multicoloured 20 10
2039 100 dh. multicoloured 40 20

1992. "Gaddafi, Man of Peace 1992". Multicoloured, colour of frame given.

2056 **423** 100 dh. green .. 40 20
2057 100 dh. grey 40 20
2058 100 dh. red 40 20
2059 100 dh. ochre 40 20

1992.

2061 **424** 100 dh. grn, brn & yell 40 20
2062 150 dh. green, brown and grey 60 30
2063 200 dh. grn, brn & bl 85 45
2064 250 dh. green, brown and orange .. 1·10 55
2065 300 dh. grn, brn & vio 1·25 65
2066 400 dh. green, brown and mauve .. 1·75 90
2067 450 dh. emerald, brown and green .. 1·90 95

425 1991 100 dh. Stamp, Tweezers, Magnifying Glass and Stamps

1992. 3rd Anniv of Union of Arab Maghreb.

2068	**425**	75 dh. multicoloured	30	15
2069		80 dh. multicoloured	35	20

426 Horse-drawn Carriage

1992. International Trade Fair, Tripoli. Multicoloured.

2070	50 dh. Type **426**	20	10
2071	100 dh. Horse-drawn cart	40	20

427 Emblem

429 Fish with Spines

428 Emblem and Camel Rider

1992. People's Authority Declaration.

2072	**427**	100 dh. multicoloured	40	20
2073		150 dh. multicoloured	60	30

1992. African Tourism Year.

2074	**428**	50 dh. multicoloured	20	10
2075		100 dh. multicoloured	40	20

1992. Fishes. Multicoloured.

2076	100 dh. Type **429**	40	20
2077	100 dh. Pike	40	20
2078	100 dh. Fish with seven spines on back ..	40	20
2079	100 dh. Light brown fish with continuous dorsal fin	40	20
2080	100 dh. Fish with four spines on back ..	40	20
2081	100 dh. Red fish with whiskers	40	20

430 Horsewoman with Rifle

431 Long Jumping

1992. Horse Riders. Multicoloured.

2082	100 dh. Type **430** ..	40	20
2083	100 dh. Man on rearing white horse	40	20
2084	100 dh. Man on brown horse with ornate bridle	40	20
2085	100 dh. Roman soldier on brown horse ..	40	20
2086	100 dh. Man in blue coat on brown horse ..	40	20
2087	100 dh. Arab on white horse	40	20

1992. Olympic Games, Barcelona. Mult.

2089	50 dh. Type **431**	20	10
2090	50 dh. Throwing the discus	20	10
2091	50 dh. Tennis	20	10

432 Palm Trees

1992. Achievements of the Revolution. Mult.

2093	100 dh. Type **432** ..	40	20
2094	150 dh. Ingots and foundry	60	30
2095	250 dh. Container ship ..	1·10	55
2096	300 dh. Airplane ..	1·25	65
2097	400 dh. Assembly hall ..	1·75	90
2098	500 dh. Water pipes and Gaddafi	2·10	1·10

433 Gaddafi

434 Laurel Wreath, Torch and "23"

1992. Multicoloured, background colours given.

2099	**433**	500 dh. green ..	2·10	1·10
2100		1000 dh. pink ..	4·25	2·25
2101		2000 dh. blue ..	8·25	4·25
2102		5000 dh. violet ..	21·00	10·50
2103		6000 dh. orange ..	25·00	12·50

1992. 23rd Anniv of Revolution. Mult.

2104	50 dh. Type **434**	20	10
2105	100 dh. Laurel wreath, flag, sun and "23" ..	40	20

435 Antelope drinking

436 Horse and Broken Chain

1992. Oases. Multicoloured.

2107	100 dh. Type **435** ..	40	20
2108	200 dh. Sun setting behind camel train (vert) ..	85	45
2109	300 dh. Camel rider ..	1·25	65

1992. Evacuation of Foreign Forces. Mult.

2110	75 dh. Type **436**	30	15
2111	80 dh. Flag and broken chain	35	20

437 Monument and Dates

1992. 81st Anniv of Deportation of Libyans to Italy.

2112	**437**	100 dh. multicoloured	40	20
2113		250 dh. multicoloured	1·10	55

438 Dome of the Rock and Palestinian

1992. Palestinian "Intifida" Movement. Multicoloured.

2114	100 dh. Type **438** ..	40	20
2115	300 dh. Map, Dome of the Rock, flag and fist (vert)	1·25	65

439 Red and White Striped Costume

1992. Women's Costumes. Multicoloured.

2116	50 dh. Type **439**	20	10
2117	50 dh. Large red hat with silver decorations, white tunic and red wrap ..	20	10
2118	50 dh. Brown and orange striped costume with small gold necklace and horseshoe brooch ..	20	10
2119	50 dh. Purple and white costume	20	10
2120	50 dh. Orange striped costume	20	10

CONCESSIONAL LETTER POST

1929. No. CL227 of Italy optd **LIBIA**.

CL68	CL **93**	10 c. blue	11·00	12·00

1941. No. CL267 of Italy optd **LIBIA**.

CL123	CL **109**	10 c. brown ..	3·50	4·25

EXPRESS LETTER STAMPS

A. ITALIAN ISSUES.

1915. Express Letter stamps of Italy optd **Libia**.

E17	E **35**	25 c. red	7·00	7·00
E18	E **41**	30 c. blue and red ..	4·50	14·00

1921. As Type **E 17** of Somalia, but inscr "LIBIA".

E34	30 c. red and blue ..	1·10	2·75
E35	50 c. brown and red ..	1·60	4·25
E42	60 c. brown and red ..	2·50	7·00
E43	2 l. red and blue ..	5·00	15·00

Nos. E34 and E43 are inscr "EXPRES".

1922. Nos. E17/18 surch.

E40	E **35**	60 c. on 25 c. red ..	3·75	7·00
E41	E **41**	1 l. 60 on 30 c. blue and red	5·00	17·00

1926. Nos. E42/3 surch.

E62	70 c. on 60 c. brown & red	3·25	7·00
E64	1 l. 25 on 60 c. brown & red	2·75	1·00
E63	2 l. 50 on 2 l. red and blue	3·75	14·00

B. INDEPENDENT ISSUE.

1966. Design similar to T **74** inscr. "EXPRES".

E 368.	90 m. red and green ..	85	65

DESIGN—HORIZ. 90 m. Saracen Castle, Zuela.

OFFICIAL STAMPS

1952. Optd. **Official** in English and Arabic.

O 192.	**23.**	2 m. brown	40	35
O 193.		4 m. grey	65	50
O 194.		5 m. green	3·25	2·50
O 195.		8 m. red	2·25	75
O 196.		10 m. violet	3·00	2·25
O 197.		12 m. red	4·25	4·50
O 198.		20 m. blue	7·00	4·50
O 199.		25 m. brown	9·00	5·00

PARCEL POST STAMPS

Unused prices are for complete stamps.

1915. Parcel Post stamps of Italy optd **LIBIA** on each half of the stamp.

P 17.	P **53.**	5 c. brown	60	20
P 18.		10 c. blue	60	20
P 19.		20 c. black	80	20
P 20.		25 c. red	85	20
P 21.		50 c. orange	1·60	20
P 22.		1 l. violet	1·40	20
P 23.		2 l. green	1·90	20
P 24.		3 l. yellow	2·25	20
P 25.		4 l. grey	2·25	20
P 26.		10 l. purple	30·00	6·00
P 27.		12 l. brown	55·00	6·00
P 28.		15 l. olive	55·00	8·00
P 29.		20 l. purple	55·00	9·50

1927. Parcel Post stamps of Italy optd. **LIBIA** on each half of the stamp.

P 62.	P **92.**	5 c. brown	£8000	
P 63.		10 c. blue	1·40	30
P 64.		25 c. red	1·40	30
P 65.		30 c. blue	20	30
P 66.		50 c. orange	55·00	7·00
P 67.		60 c. red	20	30
P 68.		1 l. violet	19·00	3·00
P 69.		2 l. green	24·00	3·00
P 70.		3 l. yellow	70	30
P 71.		4 l. grey	70	30
P 72.		10 l. mauve	£160	11·00
P 73.		20 l. purple	£160	11·00

POSTAGE DUE STAMPS

A. ITALIAN ISSUES.

1915. Postage Due stamps of Italy optd **Libia**.

D 17.	D **12.**	5 c. purple & orange	40	1·90
D 18.		10 c. pur. & orge. ..	60	1·90
D 19.		20 c. pur. & orge. ..	1·10	3·25
D 20.		30 c. pur. & orge. ..	1·40	3·25
D 21.		40 c. pur. & orge. ..	1·90	3·25
D 22.		50 c. pur. & orge. ..	1·25	3·25
D 23.		60 c. pur. & orge. ..	2·25	4·75
D 24.		60 c. brn. & orge. ..	38·00	70·00
D 25.		1 l. pur. & blue ..	1·25	75
D 26.		2 l. pur. & blue ..	19·00	32·00
D 27.		5 l. pur. & blue ..	24·00	45·00

1934. Postage Due stamps of Italy optd **LIBIA**.

D 68.	D **141.**	5 c. brown ..	15	70
D 69.		10 c. blue	15	70
D 70.		20 c. red	80	55
D 71.		25 c. green ..	80	55
D 72.		30 c. orange ..	80	1·10
D 73.		40 c. brown ..	80	1·75
D 74.		50 c. violet ..	1·10	20
D 75.		60 c. blue	1·60	2·75
D 76.	D **142.**	1 l. orange ..	1·40	20
D 77.		2 l. green	24·00	4·50
D 78.		5 l. violet	48·00	15·00
D 79.		10 l. blue	7·00	15·00
D 80.		20 l. red	7·00	17·00

B. INDEPENDENT ISSUES

1951. Postage Due stamps of Cyrenaica optd.

(a) For use in Cyrenaica. Optd. as T **20**.

D 144.	D **26.**	2 m. brown ..	4·00	5·00
D 145.		4 m. green ..	4·00	5·00
D 146.		8 m. red	6·00	7·00
D 147.		10 m. orange ..	7·50	10·00
D 148.		20 m. yellow ..	12·00	14·00
D 149.		40 m. blue ..	25·00	22·00
D 150.		100 m. black ..	35·00	28·00

(b) For use in Tripolitania. Surch. as T **21**.

D 161.	D **26.**	1 mal. on 2 m. brn.	3·75	3·25
D 162.		2 mal. on 4 m. grn.	6·00	6·00
D 163.		4 mal. on 8 m. red	9·50	9·50
D 164.		10 mal. on 20 m. yellow	19·00	19·00
D 165.		20 mal. on 40 m. blue	32·00	35·00

D 25.

D 53. Government Building, Tripoli.

1952.

D 188.	D **25.**	2 m. brown ..	40	25
D 189.		5 m. green ..	65	50
D 190.		10 m. red	90	65
D 191.		50 m. blue ..	2·50	1·50

1964.

D 296.	D **53.**	2 m. brown ..	10	8
D 297.		6 m. green ..	20	10
D 298.		10 m. red	20	15
D 299.		50 m. blue ..	40	30

D 185. Men in Boat.

1976. Ancient Mosaics. Multicoloured.

D 725.	5 dh. Type D **185** ..	5	5
D 726.	10 dh. Head of Medusa	5	5
D 727.	20 dh. Peacock	10	8
D 728.	50 dh. Fish	25	12

LIECHTENSTEIN Pt. 8

A small independent principality lying between Austria and Switzerland.

1912. 100 heller = 1 krone.
1921. 100 rappen = 1 franc. (Swiss).

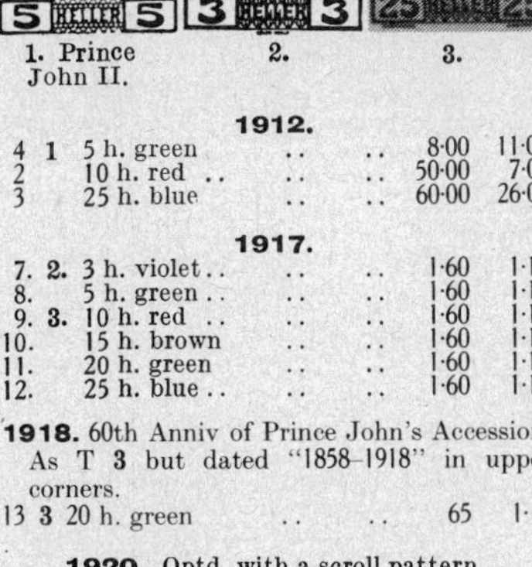

1. Prince John II. 2. 3.

1912.

1	1	5 h. green	8·00	11·00
2		10 h. red	50·00	7·00
3		25 h. blue	60·00	26·00

1917.

7.	2.	3 h. violet	1·60	1·10
8.		5 h. green	1·60	1·10
9.	3.	10 h. red	1·60	1·10
10.		15 h. brown	1·60	1·10
11.		20 h. green	1·60	1·10
12.		25 h. blue	1·60	1·10

1918. 60th Anniv of Prince John's Accession. As T 3 but dated "1858–1918" in upper corners.

13	3	20 h. green	65	1·10

1920. Optd. with a scroll pattern.

14.	2.	5 h. green	2·00	5·50
15.	3.	10 h. red	2·00	5·50
16.		25 h. blue	2·00	5·50

1920. Surch.

17	2	40 h. on 3 h. violet	2·00	5·50
18	3	1 k. on 15 h. brown	2·00	5·50
19		2½ k. on 20 h. green	2·00	5·50

7. 8. Castle of Vaduz.

1920. Imperf.

20.	7.	5 h. bistre	15	3·50
21.		10 h. orange	15	3·50
22.		15 h. blue	15	3·50
23.		20 h. brown	15	3·50
24.		25 h. green	15	3·50
25.		30 h. grey	15	3·50
26.		40 h. red	15	3·50
27.	8.	1 k. blue	15	3·50

9. Prince John I. 10. Arms.

1920. Perf.

28.	7.	5 h. bistre	15	40
29.		10 h. orange	15	40
30.		15 h. blue	15	40
31.		20 h. brown	15	40
32.	–	25 h. olive	15	40
33.	7.	30 h. grey	15	40
34.	–	40 h. red	15	40
35.	–	50 h. green	15	40
36.	–	60 h. brown	15	40
37.	–	80 h. red	15	40
38.	8.	1 k. lilac	15	40
39.	–	2 k. blue	25	70
40.	9.	5 k. grey	50	1·25
41.	–	7½ k. slate	65	1·50
42.	10.	10 k. yellow	75	2·00

DESIGNS—VERT. As Type 8. 25 h. St. Mamertus Chapel. 40 h. Gutenberg Castle. 50 h. Courtyard, Vaduz Castle. 60 h. Red House, Vaduz. 80 h. Church Tower, Schaan. 2 k. Bendern. As Type 9: 7½ k. Prince John II.

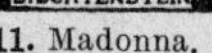

11. Madonna. 15. St. Mamertus Chapel.

14. Arms. 16. Vaduz.

1920. Prince John's 80th Birthday. Imperf. or perf.

43.	11.	50 h. olive	30	1·10
44.		80 h. red	30	1·10
45.		2 k. blue	30	1·10

1921. Surch. **2 Rp.** and bars.

47.	7.	2 r. on 10 h. orge. (No. 21)	35	16·00

1921.

47a.	14.	2 r. yellow	55	8·00
48.		2½ r. brown	55	8·00
49.		3 r. orange	55	8·00
50.		5 r. olive	7·50	1·25
51.		7½ r. blue	3·75	25·00
65.		10 r. green	20·00	1·10
53.		13 r. brown	7·50	60·00
54.		15 r. violet	14·00	12·00
55.	15.	20 r. black and violet	55·00	1·00
56.	–	25 r. black and red	2·00	1·75
57.	–	30 r. black and green	60·00	8·00
66.	–	30 r. black and blue	15·00	1·10
58.	–	35 r. black and brown	3·25	8·50
59.	–	40 r. black and blue	5·00	2·75
60.	–	50 r. black and olive	7·00	2·75
61.	–	80 r. black and grey	20·00	55·00
62.	16.	1 f. black and lake	40·00	30·00

DESIGNS—As Type 15: 25 r. Vaduz Castle. 30 r. Bendern. 35 r. Prince John II. 40 r. Church Tower at Schaan. 50 r. Gutenberg Castle. 80 r. Red House, Vaduz.

1924. Surch.

63.	14.	5 on 7½ r. blue	1·00	2·00
64.		10 on 13 r. brown	60	1·25

19. Vine-dresser. 21. Government Bldg. and Church, Vaduz.

1924.

67	19	2½ r. mauve and green	1·25	4·75
68		5 r. blue and brown	2·25	70
69		7½ r. brown and green	1·40	4·75
70	–	10 r. green	9·00	55
71	19	15 r. green and purple	6·50	25·00
72	–	20 r. red	32·00	70
73	21	1½ f. blue	75·00	75·00

DESIGN—As Type 19: 10, 20 r. Castle of Vaduz.

22. Prince John II. 23.

1925. Charity. 85th Birthday of Prince.

74.	22.	10+5 r. green	35·00	13·00
75.		20+5 r. red	18·00	13·00
76.		30+5 r. blue	5·50	4·25

1927. Charity. 87th Birthday of Prince. Arms multicoloured.

77	23	10+5 r. green	6·50	17·00
78		20+5 r. lake	6·50	17·00
79		30+5 r. blue	6·50	14·00

DESIGNS — HORIZ. 5 r. Railway bridge. 10 r. Ruggell. 30 r. Salvage work by Swiss soldiers.

24. Salvage work by Austrian soldiers.

1928. Flood Relief.

80.	–	5 r.+5 r. brn. & red	18·00	17·00
81.	–	10 r.+10 r. brn. & grn.	17·00	21·00
82.	24.	20 r.+10 r. brn. & red	17·00	21·00
83.	–	30 r.+10 r. brn. & blue	17·00	21·00

DESIGN — VERT. 10 r. to 60 r. Prince John II.

26. Prince John II, 1858–1928.

1928. 70th Anniv. of Accession of John II.

84.	–	10 r. olive and brown	1·75	3·25
85.	–	20 r. olive and red	3·00	5·50
86.	–	30 r. olive and blue	17·00	14·00
87.	–	60 r. olive and mauve	45·00	80·00
88.	26.	1 f. 20 r. blue	40·00	80·00
89.		1 f. 50 r. sepia	70·00	£160
90.		2 f. lake	70·00	£160
91.		5 f. green	70·00	£170

28. Prince Francis I. 31. Girl Vintager.

32. Prince Francis I and Princess Elsa. 34. Monoplane over Vaduz Castle and Rhine Valley.

1929. Accession of Prince Francis I.

92.	–	10 r. green	60	2·50
93.	28.	20 r. red	75	3·50
94.	–	30 r. blue	1·75	15·00
95.	–	70 r. brown	16·00	85·00

PORTRAITS: 10 r. Prince Francis I when a boy. 30 r. Princess Elsa. 70 r. Prince Francis I and Princess Elsa.

1930.

96	31	3 r. red	55	85
97	–	5 r. green	1·25	80
98	–	10 r. lilac	1·40	50
99	–	20 r. red	22·00	60
100	–	25 r. green	5·00	30·00
101	–	30 r. blue	4·00	75
102	–	35 r. green	6·00	14·00
103	–	40 r. brown	6·50	3·00
104	–	50 r. black	70·00	13·00
105	–	60 r. green	55·00	16·00
106	–	90 r. purple	60·00	80·00
107	–	1 f. 20 brown	80·00	£140
108	–	1 f. 50 blue	35·00	40·00
109	32	2 f. brown and green	45·00	80·00

DESIGNS—VERT. 5 r. Mt. Three Sisters—Edelweiss. 10 r. Alpine cattle—Alpine roses. 20 r. Courtyard of Vaduz Castle. 25 r. Mt. Naafkopf. 30 r. Valley of Samina. 35 r. Rofenberg Chapel. 40 r. St. Mamertus' Chapel. 50 r. Kurhaus at Malbun. 60 r. Gutenberg Castle. 90 r. Schellenberg Monastery. 1 f. 20 r. Vaduz Castle. 1 f. 50 r. Pfaelzer Club Hut.

1930. Air.

110.	–	15 r. sepia	5·00	8·00
111.	–	20 r. green	12·00	13·00
112.	–	25 r. brown	6·00	22·00
113.	–	35 r. blue	12·00	22·00
114.	34.	45 r. green	25·00	55·00
115.		1 f. red	38·00	35·00

DESIGNS—VERT. 15 r., 20 r. Biplane over mountains. HORIZ. 25 r., 35 r. Biplane over Vaduz Castle.

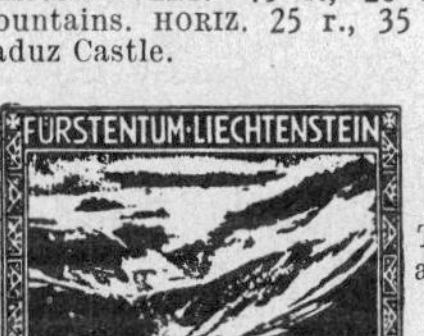

The 2 f. shows a different view.

35. Zeppelin over Alps.

1931. Air.

116.	35.	1 f. green	38·00	80·00
117.	–	2 f. blue	80·00	£225

37. Princess Elsa. 38. Mt. Naafkopf. 39. Prince Francis I.

1932. Youth Charities.

118.	–	10 r.+5 r. green	16·00	25·00
119.	37.	20 r.+5 r. red	16·00	25·00
120.	–	30 r.+10 r. blue	16·00	32·00

DESIGNS—VERT. (Smaller: 22 × 29 mm.) 10 r. Arms of Liechtenstein. (As Type 37). 30 r. Prince Francis.

1933.

121.	38.	25 r. orange	£190	50·00
122.	–	90 r. green	7·50	65·00
123.	–	1 f. 20 brown	80·00	£200

DESIGNS: 90 r. Gutenberg Castle. 1 f. 20, Vaduz Castle.

1933. Prince Francis's 80th Birthday.

124	39	10 r. violet	18·00	30·00
125		20 r. red	18·00	30·00
126		30 r. blue	18·00	30·00

40. 41. "Three Sisters"

42. Vaduz Castle. 44. Prince Francis I.

45. Arms of Liechtenstein. 46. Golden Eagle.

1933.

127.	40.	3 r. red	15	45
128.	41.	5 r. green	2·25	50
129.	–	10 r. violet	50	40
130.	–	15 r. red	20	85
131.	–	20 r. red	50	45
132.	–	25 r. brown	18·00	42·00
133.	–	30 r. blue	3·25	90
134.	–	35 r. green	70	5·50
135.	–	40 r. brown	90	3·50
136.	42.	50 r. brown	18·00	13·00
137.	–	60 r. red	1·25	4·75
138.	–	90 r. green	5·50	16·00
139.	–	1 f. 20 blue	1·75	16·00
140.	–	1 f. 50 lake	2·00	21·00
141.	–	2 f. brown	55·00	£150
142.	44.	3 f. blue	75·00	£150
143.	45.	5 f. purple	£350	£850

DESIGNS—VERT. As Type 41: 10 r. Schaan Church. 15 r. Bendern am Rhein. 20 r. Town Hall, Vaduz. 25 r. Saminatal. As Type 44: 2 f. Princess Elsa. HORIZ. As Type 42: 30 r. Saminatal. 35 r. Schellenberg ruins. 40 r. Government Building, Vaduz. 60 r. Vaduz Castle. 90 r. Gutenberg Castle. 1 f. 20, Pfalzer Hut, Bettlerjoch. 1 f. 50, Valuna.

See also Nos. 174, 225/6 and 258.

1934. Air.

145.	46.	10 r. violet	8·00	20·00
146.	–	15 r. orange	18·00	30·00
147.	–	20 r. red	18·00	30·00
148.	–	30 r. blue	18·00	30·00
149.	–	50 r. green	14·00	25·00

DESIGNS: 10 r. to 20 r. Golden Eagles in flight. 30 r. Osprey in nest. 50 r. Golden Eagle on rock.

1935. Air. No. 115 surch **60 Rp.**

150	34	60 r. on 1 f. red	24·00	40·00

DESIGN: 2 f. "Graf Zeppelin" over Schaan Airport.

49. "Hindenburg" and Schaan Church.

1936. Air.

151.	49.	1 f. red	26·00	65·00
152.	–	2 f. violet	22·00	65·00

51. Masescha am Triesenberg. 52. Schellenberg Castle.

1937.

154	–	3 r. brown	15	50
155	51	5 r. green and buff	15	20
156	–	10 r. violet and buff	15	15
157	–	15 r. black and buff	20	60
158	–	20 r. red and buff	20	30
159	–	25 r. brown and buff	55	2·00
160	–	30 r. blue and buff	3·00	60
161	52	40 r. green and buff	2·25	1·50
162	–	50 c. brown and buff	85	2·00
163	–	60 r. purple and buff	2·25	2·00
164	–	90 r. violet and buff	9·00	13·00
165	–	1 f. purple and buff	2·00	10·00
166	–	1 f. 20 brown and buff	8·00	20·00
167	–	1 f. 50 r. grey and buff	2·50	20·00

DESIGNS—VERT. As Type 51: 3 r. Schalun ruins. 10 r. Knight and Vaduz Castle. 15 r. Upper Saminatal. 20 r. Church and Bridge at Bendern. 25 r. Steg Chapel and girl. HORIZ. As Type 52: 30 r. Farmer and orchard, Triesenberg. 50 r. Knight and Gutenberg Castle. 60 r. Baron von Brandis and Vaduz Castle. 90 r. "Three Sisters" mountain. 1 fr. Boundary-stone on Luziensteig. 1 f. 20 r. Minstrel and Gutenberg Castle. 1 f. 50 r. Lawena (Schwarzhorn).

53. Roadmakers at Triesenberg.

1937. Workers' Issue.

No.	Type	Description	Unused	Used
168	–	10 r. mauve	80	70
169	53	20 r. red	1·10	1·25
170	–	30 r. blue	1·50	1·50
171	–	50 r. brown	1·00	2·50

DESIGNS: 10 r. Bridge at Malbun. 30 r. Binnen Canal Junction. 50 r. Francis Bridge, near Planken.

1938. Death of Prince Francis I.

No.	Type	Description	Unused	Used
174.	44.	3 f. black on yellow	8·50	65·00

54. Josef Rheinberger. 55. Black-headed Gulls.

1939. Birth Cent. of Rheinberger (composer).

No.	Type	Description	Unused	Used
175.	54.	50 r. green	75	3·25

1939. Air.

No.	Type	Description	Unused	Used
176.	–	10 r. violet (Barn swallows)	40	45
177.	55.	15 r. orange	65	1·50
178.	–	20 r. red (Herring gull)	1·75	45
179.	–	30 r. blue (Common buzzard)	1·60	1·25
180.	–	50 r. green (Northern goshawk)	5·00	2·00
181.	–	1 f. red (Lammergeier)	4·25	13·00
182.	–	2 f. violet Lammergeier	4·00	13·00

56. Offering Homage to First Prince.

1939. Homage to Francis Joseph II.

No.	Type	Description	Unused	Used
183.	56.	20 r. red	60	1·40
184.		30 r. blue	60	1·40
185.		50 r. green	60	1·40

57. Francis Joseph II.

DESIGNS: 2 f. Cantonal Arms. 3 f. Arms of Principality.

1939.

No.	Type	Description	Unused	Used
186	–	2 f. green on cream	6·00	32·00
187	–	3 f. violet on cream	4·50	32·00
188	57	5 f. brown on cream	11·00	20·00

58. Prince John when a child.

1940. Birth Cent of Prince John II.

No.	Type	Description	Unused	Used
189.	58.	20 r. red	40	1·50
190.	–	30 r. blue	55	2·50
191.	–	50 r. green	1·00	8·00
192.	–	1 f. violet	6·00	55·00
193.	–	1 f. 50 black	4·50	45·00
194.	–	3 f. brown	3·50	20·00

DESIGNS: HORIZ.—As Type **58**: Portraits of Prince John in early manhood (30 r.), in middle age (50 r.) and in later life (1 f.), and Memorial tablet (1 f. 50). VERT.—As Type **44**: 3 f. Framed portrait of Prince John II.

60. Wine Press.

1941. Agricultural Propaganda.

No.	Type	Description	Unused	Used
195.	–	10 r. brown	35	80
196.	60.	20 r. red	60	1·25
197.	–	30 r. blue	60	2·00
198.	–	50 r. green	1·60	13·00
199.	–	90 r. violet	1·60	15·00

DESIGNS: 10 r. Harvesting maize. 30 r. Sharpening scythe. 50 r. Milkmaid and cow. 90 r. Girl wearing traditional headdress.

61. Madonna and Child. 62. Prince Hans Adam.

1941.

No.	Type	Description	Unused	Used
200.	61.	10 f. red on buff	45·00	95·00

1941. Princes (1st issue).

No.	Type	Description	Unused	Used
201	62	20 r. red	30	1·25
202	–	30 r. blue (Wenzel)	35	2·00
203	–	1 f. grey (Anton Florian)	1·40	14·00
204	–	1 f. 50 green (Joseph)	1·50	14·00

See also Nos. 210/13 and 217/20.

63. St. Lucius preaching.

1942. 600th Anniv of Separation from Estate of Montfort.

No.	Type	Description	Unused	Used
205	63	20 r. red on pink	90	80
206	–	30 r. blue on pink	90	2·00
207	–	50 r. green on pink	1·75	6·00
208	–	1 f. brown on pink	2·25	12·00
209	–	2 f. blue on pink	2·25	12·00

DESIGNS: 30 r. Count of Montfort replanning Vaduz. 50 r. Counts of Montfort-Werdenberg and Sargans signing treaty. 1 f. Battle of Gutenberg. 2 f. Homage to Prince of Liechtenstein.

64. Prince John Charles. 65. Princess Georgina.

1942. Princes (2nd issue).

No.	Type	Description	Unused	Used
210.	64.	20 r. red	30	80
211.	–	30 r. blue (Francis Joseph I)	45	1·50
212.	–	1 f. purple (Alois I)	1·40	13·00
213.	–	1 f. 50 r. brn. (John I)	1·40	13·00

1943. Marriage of Prince Francis Joseph II and Countess Georgina von Wildczek.

No.	Type	Description	Unused	Used
214.	–	10 r. purple	45	80
215.	65.	20 r. red	45	80
216.	–	30 r. blue	45	80

PORTRAITS—VERT: 10 r. Prince Francis Joseph II. Horiz (44×25 mm). 30 r. Prince and Princess.

66. Alois II. 67. Marsh Land.

1943. Various Princes (3rd issue).

No.	Type	Description	Unused	Used
217.	66.	20 r. brown	30	65
218.	–	30 r. blue	60	1·25
219.	–	1 f. brown	90	6·50
220.	–	1 f. 50 green	90	6·50

PORTRAITS—HORIZ. 30 r. John II. 1 f. Francis I. 1 f. 50, Francis Joseph II.

1943. Completion of Irrigation Canal.

No.	Type	Description	Unused	Used
221.	67.	10 r. violet	20	40
222.	–	30 r. blue	40	1·90
223.	–	50 r. green	75	7·00
224.	–	2 f. brown	2·00	11·00

DESIGNS: 30 r. Draining the canal. 50 r. Ploughing reclaimed land. 2 f. Harvesting.

1943. Castles. As T 41.

No.	Type	Description	Unused	Used
225.		10 r. grey (Vaduz)	40	35
226.		20 r. brown (Gutenberg)	55	80

69. Planken. 70. Prince Francis Joseph II.

1944. Various designs. Buff backgrounds.

No.	Type	Description	Unused	Used
227.	69.	3 r. brown	15	20
228.	–	5 r. green (Bendern)	15	10
228a.	–	5 r. brown (Bendern)	28·00	60
229.	–	10 r. violet (Triesen)	20	10
230.	–	15 r. blue (Ruggell)	30	85
231.	–	20 r. red (Vaduz)	30	20
232.	–	25 r. pur. (Triesenberg)	30	1·00
233.	–	30 r. blue (Schaan)	30	25
234.	–	40 r. brown (Balzers)	60	1·10
235.	–	50 r. grey (Mauren)	70	1·50
236.	–	60 r. green (Schellenberg)	3·75	4·25
237.	–	90 r. olive (Eschen)	3·75	4·50
238.	–	1 f. red (Vaduz Castle)	2·25	3·75
239.	–	1 f. 20 brown (Valunatal)	2·50	5·00
240.	–	1 f. 50 r. blue (Lawena)	2·50	5·00

1944.

No.	Type	Description	Unused	Used
241	70	2 f. brown	4·75	14·00
242	–	3 f. green	3·00	11·00

DESIGN: 3 f. Princess Georgina.
See also Nos. 302/3.

72. 73.

1945. Birth of Crown Prince Johann Adam Pius (known as Prince Hans Adam).

No.	Type	Description	Unused	Used
243.	72.	20 r. brn., yellow & gold	1·00	40
244.		30 r. blue, yellow & gold	1·00	1·40
245.		100 r. grey, yell. & gold	2·25	5·00

1945.

No.	Type	Description	Unused	Used
246.	73.	5 f. blue on buff	19·00	28·00
247		5 f. brown on buff	24·00	38·00

74. First Aid. 75. St. Lucius.

1945. Red Cross. Cross in red.

No.	Type	Description	Unused	Used
248.	–	10 r.+10 r. vio. on buff	1·25	1·50
249.	74.	20 r.+20 r. red on buff	1·25	2·25
250.	–	1 f.+1 f. 40 r. grey on buff	8·00	22·00

DESIGNS: 10 r. Mother and children. 1 f. Nurse and invalid.

1946.

No.	Type	Description	Unused	Used
251.	75.	10 f. grey on buff	35·00	28·00

76. Red Deer. 79. Wilbur Wright.

1946. Wild Life.

No.	Type	Description	Unused	Used
252.	76.	20 r. red	2·25	2·25
255.	–	20 r. red (Chamois)	4·00	4·00
283.	–	20 r. red (Roebuck)	8·50	3·75
253.	–	30 r. blue (Arctic hare)	3·00	3·00
256.	–	30 r. blue (Alpine marmot)	5·50	4·25
284.	–	30 r. grn. (Black grouse)	22·00	6·00
285.	–	80 r. brown (Eurasian badger)	35·00	38·00
254.	–	1 f. 50 r. olive (Capercaillie)	9·50	11·00
257.	–	1 f. 50 r. brown (Golden eagle)	9·50	14·00

1947. Death of Princess Elsa. As No. 141.

No.	Type	Description	Unused	Used
258.	–	2 f. black on yellow	3·50	12·00

1948. Air. Pioneers of Flight.

No.	Type	Description	Unused	Used
259	–	10 r. green	65	20
260	–	15 r. violet	65	1·10
261	–	20 r. brown	80	20
262	–	25 r. red	1·25	1·90
263	–	40 r. blue	1·75	1·00
264	–	50 r. blue	1·75	1·75
265	–	1 f. purple	2·50	3·00
266	–	2 f. purple	4·50	4·75
267	79	5 f. green	5·50	6·50
268	–	10 f. black	32·00	16·00

PORTRAITS: 10 r. Leonardo da Vinci. 15 r. Joseph Montgolfier. 20 r. Jakob Degen. 25 r. Wilhelm Kress. 40 r. E. G. R. Robertson. 50 r. William Henson. 1 f. Otto Lilienthal. 2 f. Salomon Andree. 10 f. Icarus.

80. "Ginevra de Benci" (Da Vinci). 82. Posthorn and Map of World.

1949. Paintings. Size 27×31 mm.

No.	Type	Description	Unused	Used
269	80	10 r. green	45	30
270	–	20 r. red	1·25	60
271	–	30 r. brown	3·00	1·25
272	–	40 r. blue	6·00	65
273	–	50 r. violet	5·00	6·50
274	–	60 r. grey	11·00	5·50
275	–	80 r. brown	2·50	4·00
276	–	90 r. green	11·00	5·00
277	–	120 r. mauve	2·50	4·75

DESIGNS: 20 r. "Portrait of a Young Girl" (Rubens). 30 r. Self-portrait of Rembrandt in plumed hat. 40 r. "Stephan Gardiner, Bishop of Winchester" (Quentin Massys). 50 r. "Madonna and Child" (Hans Memling). 60 r. "Franz Meister in 1456" (Jehan Fouquet). 80 r. "Lute Player" (Orazio Gentileschi). 90 r. "Portrait of a Man" (Bernhardin Strigel). 120 r. "Portrait of a Man (Duke of Urbino)" (Raphael).

1949. No. 227 surch **5 Rp.** and bars.

No.	Type	Description	Unused	Used
278	69	5 r. on 3 r. brown & buff	60	40

1949. 75th Anniv of U.P.U.

No.	Type	Description	Unused	Used
279	82	40 r. blue	3·00	3·75

83. Rossauer Castle. 86. Boy cutting Loaf.

1949. 250th Anniv of Acquisition of Domain of Schellenberg.

No.	Type	Description	Unused	Used
280	83	20 r. purple	2·00	2·00
281	–	40 r. blue	7·00	6·50
282	–	1 f. 50 red	9·50	8·50

DESIGN—HORIZ. 40 r. Bendern Church. VERT. 1 f. 50, Prince Johann Adam I.

1950. Surch **100 100**.

No.	Type	Description	Unused	Used
286	82	100 r. on 40 r. blue	23·00	42·00

1951. Agricultural scenes.

No.	Type	Description	Unused	Used
287.	86.	5 r. red	20	10
288.	–	10 r. green	45	10
289.	–	15 r. brown	4·50	5·00
290.	–	20 r. sepia	1·00	20
291.	–	25 r. red	4·50	4·50
292.	–	30 r. green	3·25	55
293.	–	40 r. blue	8·50	7·00
294.	–	50 r. brown	7·50	3·00
295.	–	60 r. brown	7·00	3·00
296.	–	80 r. brown	9·00	8·00
297.	–	90 r. olive	18·00	4·75
298.	–	1 f. violet	55·00	6·00

DESIGNS: 10 r. Man whetting scythe. 15 r. Mowing. 20 r. Girl and sweet corn. 25 r. Haywain. 30 r. Gathering grapes. 40 r. Man with scythe. 50 r. Herdsman with cows. 60 r. Ploughing. 80 r. Girl carrying basket of fruit. 90 r. Woman gleaning. 1 f. Tractor hauling corn.

87. "Lock on the Canal" (Aelbert Cuyp). 88. "Willem von Heythuysen, Burgomaster of Haarlem" (Frans Hals).

1951. Charity. Paintings.

No.	Type	Description	Unused	Used
299.	87.	10 r.+10 r. olive	8·00	6·00
300.	88.	20 r.+10 r. sepia	8·00	12·00
301.	–	40 r.+10 r. blue	8·00	8·00

DESIGN—As Type **87**: 40 r. "Landscape" (Jacob van Ruysdael).

90. Vaduz Castle. 96. Lord Baden-Powell.

1951.

No.	Type	Description	Unused	Used
302	70	2 f. blue	13·00	30·00
303	–	3 f. brown	£150	90·00
304	90	5 f. green	£170	£150

DESIGN: 3 f. Princess Georgina.

1952. No. 281 surch **1.20.**

No.	Type	Description	Unused	Used
308		1 f. 20 on 40 r. blue	23·00	45·00

1952. Paintings from Prince's Collection. (a) As T **80** but size 25×30 mm.

No.	Type	Description	Unused	Used
309.		10 r. green	80	70
305.		20 r. plum	32·00	3·00
307.		40 r. deep blue	12·00	5·00
312.		40 r. blue	27·00	38·00

PAINTINGS: No. 309, "Portrait of a Young Man" (A.G.). 305, "Portrait" (Giovanni Salvoldo). 307, "St. John" (Andrea Del Sarto). 312, "Leonhard, Count of Hag" (Hans von Kulmbach).

(b) As T **88** (22½×24 mm.)

No.	Type	Description	Unused	Used
310.		20 r. bistre	12·00	2·00
306.		30 r. olive	22·00	6·00
311.		30 r. brown	25·00	6·50

PAINTINGS: No. 310, "St. Nicholas" (Bartholomaus Zeitblom). 306, "Madonna and Child" (Giovanni Botticelli). 311, "St. Christopher" (Lucas Cranach the elder).

1953. 14th Int. Scout Conf.

No.	Type	Description	Unused	Used
313.	96.	10 r. green	1·60	1·40
314.		20 r. brown	13·00	2·00
315.		25 r. red	11·00	15·00
316.		40 r. blue	9·00	5·00

97. Alemannic Ornamental Disc, (c. A.D. 600).

98. Prehistoric Walled Settlement, Borscht.

1953. Opening of National Museum, Vaduz.

No.	Type	Description	Unused	Used
317.	97.	10 r. brown	8·00	12·00
318.	98.	20 r. green	8·00	10·00
319.	–	1 f. 20, blue	42·00	26·00

DESIGN—VERT. 1 f. 20, Rossen jug (3000 B.C.).

99. Footballers.

100. Madonna and Child.

1954. Football.

No.	Type	Description	Unused	Used
320	99	10 r. brown and red	1·90	80
321	–	20 r. deep green & green	6·50	1·25
322	–	25 r. dp brown & brown	16·00	28·00
323	–	40 r. violet and grey	14·00	8·00

DESIGNS—HORIZ. 20 r. Footballer kicking ball. 25 r. Goal-keeper. 40 r. Two footballers.

For stamps in similar designs see Nos. 332/5, 340/3, 351/4 and 363/6.

1954. Nos 299/301 surch. in figures.

No.	Type	Description	Unused	Used
324.	87.	35 r. on 10 r.+10 r. olive	3·00	2·00
325.	88.	60 r. on 20 r.+10 r. sepia	15·00	9·00
326.	–	65 r. on 40 r.+10 r. bl.	5·00	7·00

1954. Termination of Marian Year.

No.	Type	Description	Unused	Used
327.	100.	20 r. brown	2·00	2·00
328.		40 r. green	15·00	17·00
329.		1 f. sepia	16·00	16·00

101. Princess Georgina.

102. Crown Prince John Adam Pius.

1955.

No.	Type	Description	Unused	Used
330.	–	2 f. brown	65·00	35·00
331.	73.	3 f. green	65·00	35·00

PORTRAIT: 2 f. Prince Francis Joseph II.

1955. Mountain Sports designs as T **99.**

No.	Type	Description	Unused	Used
332.		10 r. plum and turquoise	90	70
333.		20 r. myrtle and bistre	5·00	70
334.		25 r. sepia and blue	15·00	14·00
335.		40 r. olive and red	15·00	6·00

DESIGNS: 10 r. Slalom racer. 20 r. Mountaineer hammering in piton. 25 r. Skier. 40 r. Mountaineer resting on summit.

1955. 10th Anniv. of Liechtenstein Red Cross. Cross in red.

No.	Type	Description	Unused	Used
336.	102.	10 r. blue	1·25	60
337.	–	20 r. green	4·50	1·75
338.	–	40 r. bistre	6·50	7·00
339.	–	60 r. lake	6·50	3·50

PORTRAITS—VERT. 20 r. Prince Philip. 40 r. Prince Nicholas. 60 r. Princess Nora.

1956. Athletic designs as T **99.**

No.	Type	Description	Unused	Used
340.		10 r. green and brown	80	60
341.		20 r. purple and green	3·00	70
342.		40 r. brown and blue	4·50	4·50
343.		1 f. brown and red	10·00	12·00

DESIGNS: 10 r. Throwing the javelin. 20 r. Hurdling. 40 r. Pole vaulting. 1 f. Running.

103.

104. Prince Francis Joseph II.

1956. 150th Anniv. of Sovereignty of Liechtenstein.

No.	Type	Description	Unused	Used
344.	103.	10 r. purple and gold	2·00	75
345.		1 f. 20 blue and gold	9·00	3·50

1956. 50th Birthday of Prince Francis Joseph II.

No.	Type	Description	Unused	Used
346.	104.	10 r. green	1·40	40
347.		15 r. blue	3·00	2·50
348.		25 r. purple	3·25	2·50
349.		60 r. brown	7·00	2·50

1956. 6th Philatelic Exn., Vaduz. As T **102** but inscr. "6 BRIEFMARKEN-AUSSTELLUNG".

No.	Type	Description	Unused	Used
350.		20 r. olive	2·25	40

1957. Gymnastic designs as T **99.**

No.	Type	Description	Unused	Used
351.		10 r. olive and pink	1·25	75
352.		15 r. purple and green	4·50	6·00
353.		25 r. green and drab	6·00	7·00
354.		1 f. 50, sepia and yellow	16·00	14·00

DESIGNS: 10 r. Somersaulting. 15 r. Vaulting. 25 r. Exercising with rings. 1 f. 50, Somersaulting on parallel bars.

105. Norway Spruce.

106. Lord Baden-Powell.

1957. Liechtenstein Trees and Bushes.

No.	Type	Description	Unused	Used
355.	105.	10 r. purple	3·50	1·75
356.	–	20 r. lake	3·50	70
357.	–	1 f. green	5·50	5·50

DESIGNS: 20 r. Wild rose bush. 1 f. Silver birch.

See also Nos. 369/71, 375/7 and 401/3.

1957. 50th Anniv of Boy Scout Movement and Birth Centenary of Lord Baden-Powell (founder).

No.	Type	Description	Unused	Used
358.	–	10 r. blue	1·00	1·25
359.	106.	20 r. brown	1·00	1·25

DESIGN: 10 r. Torchlight procession.

107. St. Mamertus Chapel.

108. Relief Map of Liechtenstein.

1957. Christmas.

No.	Type	Description	Unused	Used
360	107	10 r. sepia	70	20
361	–	40 r. blue	2·75	6·00
362	–	1 f. 50 brown	8·00	9·50

DESIGNS: (from St. Mamertus Chapel). 40 r. Altar shrine. 1 f. 50, "Pieta" (sculpture).

See also Nos. 372/4 and 392/4.

1958. Sports designs as T **99.**

No.	Type	Description	Unused	Used
363.		15 r. purple and blue	1·00	1·25
364.		30 r. olive and purple	4·75	6·00
365.		40 r. slate and salmon	7·50	7·50
366.		90 r. sepia and apple	2·50	3·50

DESIGNS: 15 r. Swimmer. 30 r. Fencers. 40 r. Tennis player. 90 r. Racing cyclists.

1958. Brussels Int. Exn.

No.	Type	Description	Unused	Used
367.	108.	25 r. vio., ochre & red	35	55
368.		40 r. violet, blue and red	45	55

1958. Liechtenstein Trees and Bushes. As T **105.**

No.	Type	Description	Unused	Used
369		20 r. brown (Sycamore)	3·00	60
370		50 r. green (Holly)	12·00	3·50
371		90 r. violet (Yew)	3·00	2·75

1958. Christmas. As T **107.**

No.	Type	Description	Unused	Used
372.		20 r. myrtle	2·50	2·25
373.		35 r. violet	2·50	2·25
374.		80 r. sepia	2·75	2·25

DESIGNS: 20 r. "St. Maurice and St. Agatha". 35 r. "St. Peter". 80 r. St. Peter's Chapel, Mals-Balzers.

1959. Liechtenstein Tress and Bushes. As T **105.**

No.	Type	Description	Unused	Used
375		20 r. lilac (Larch)	4·50	2·25
376		50 r. red (Red-berried elder)	4·00	2·25
377		90 r. green (Linden)	3·50	3·00

109.

111. Harvester.

110. Flags of Vaduz Castle and Rhine Valley.

1959. Pope Pius XII Mourning.

No.	Type	Description	Unused	Used
378.	109.	30 r. purple and gold	65	75

1959. Views.

No.	Type	Description	Unused	Used
379	–	5 r. brown	10	10
380	110	10 r. purple	10	10
381	–	20 r. mauve	25	10
382	–	30 r. red	30	15
383	–	40 r. green	75	35
384	–	50 r. blue	45	30
385	–	60 r. blue	65	40
386	111	75 r. brown	1·00	1·25
387	–	80 r. green	75	55
388	–	90 r. purple	90	65
389	–	1 f. brown	90	50
390	–	1 f. 20 red	1·25	1·00
390a	–	1 f. 30 green	1·00	90
391	–	1 f. 50 blue	1·50	1·00

DESIGNS—HORIZ: 5 r. Bendern Church. 20 r. Rhine Dam. 30 r. Gutenberg Castle. 40 r. View from Schellenberg. 50 r. Vaduz Castle. 60 r. Naafkopf-Falknis Mountains (view from the Bettlerjoch). 1 f. 20, Harvesting apples. 1 f. 30, Farmer and wife. 1 f. 50, Saying grace at table. VERT. 80 r. Alpine haymaker. 90 r. Girl in vineyard. 1 f. Mother in kitchen.

1959. Christmas. As T **107.**

No.	Type	Description	Unused	Used
392.		5 r. myrtle	50	15
393.		60 r. olive	5·00	4·50
394.		1 f. purple	4·50	2·50

DESIGNS: 5 r. Bendern Church belfry. 60 r. Relief on bell of St. Theodul's Church. 1 f. Sculpture on tower of St. Lucius's Church.

112. Bell "47-J" Helicopter.

1960. Air. 30th Anniv. of 1st Liechtenstein Air Stamps.

No.	Type	Description	Unused	Used
395.	112.	30 r. orange	2·00	2·25
396.	–	40 r. blue	3·50	2·25
397.	–	50 r. purple	8·50	4·00
398.	–	75 r. green	1·50	2·50

DESIGNS (Airliners in flight): 40 r. Boeing "707". 50 r. Convair "600". 75 r. Douglas "DC-8".

1960. World Refugee Year. Surch **WELTFLUCHTLINGS JAHR 1960,** uprooted tree and new value.

No.	Type	Description	Unused	Used
399.	108.	30+10 r. on 40 r. violet, blue and red	60	85
400.		50+10 r. on 25 r. violet, ochre and red	80	1·40

1960. Liechtenstein Trees and Bushes. As T **105.**

No.	Type	Description	Unused	Used
401.		20 r. brown (Beech)	6·00	3·50
402.		30 r. purple (Juniper)	6·00	7·00
403.		50 r. turquoise (Pines)	19·00	9·00

114. Europa "Honeycomb".

1960. United Europe.

No.	Type	Description	Unused	Used
404.	114.	50 r. multicoloured	85·00	45·00

115. Princess Gina.

116. Heinrich von Frauenberg.

1960.

No.	Type	Description	Unused	Used
404a.	–	1 f. 70 violet	80	85
405.	115.	2 f. blue	1·40	1·40
406.	–	3 f. brown	1·40	1·50

PORTRAITS: 1 f. 70, Crown Prince Hans Adam. 3 f. Prince Francis Joseph II.

1961. Minnesingers (1st issue). Multicoloured. Reproductions from the Manessian Manuscript of Songs.

No.	Type	Description	Unused	Used
407.		15 r. Type **116**	30	35
408.		25 r. Ulrich von Liechtenstein	50	50
409.		35 r. Ulrich von Gutenberg	60	70
410.		1 f. Konrad von Altstatten	1·40	1·50
411.		1 f. 50 Walther von der Vogelweide	7·25	12·00

See also Nos. 415/8 and 428/31.

117. "Power Transmission".

118. Clasped Hands.

1961. Europa.

No.	Type	Description	Unused	Used
412.	117.	50 r. multicoloured	20	25

1962. Europa.

No.	Type	Description	Unused	Used
413.	118.	50 r. red and blue	40	40

119. Campaign Emblem.

120. Pieta.

1962. Malaria Eradication.

No.	Type	Description	Unused	Used
414.	119.	50 r. turquoise	35	35

1962. Minnesingers (2nd issue). As T **116.** Multicoloured.

No.	Type	Description	Unused	Used
415.		20 r. King Konradin	20	20
416.		30 r. Kraft von Toggenburg	60	60
417.		40 r. Heinrich von Veldig..	60	60
418.		2 f. Tannhauser	1·50	1·50

1962. Christmas.

No.	Type	Description	Unused	Used
419.	120.	30 r. mauve	40	40
420.	–	50 r. orange	55	55
421.	–	1 f. 20 blue	95	95

DESIGNS: 50 r. Fresco with Angel. 1 f. 20, View of Mauren.

See also Nos. 438/40.

121. Prince Francis Joseph II.

122. Milk and Bread.

1963. 25th Anniv. of Reign of Prince Francis Joseph II.

No.	Type	Description	Unused	Used
422.	121.	5 f. green	3·50	2·75

1963. Freedom from Hunger.

No.	Type	Description	Unused	Used
423.	122.	50 r. brown, pur. & red	35	35

HAVE YOU READ THE NOTES AT THE BEGINNING OF THIS CATALOGUE?
These often provide answers to the enquiries we receive.

123. "Angel of Annunciation". **124.** "Europa".

1963. Red Cross Cent. Cross in red; background grey.
424. **123.** 20 r. olive and green .. 25 25
425. – 80 r. violet and mauve .. 60 60
426. – 1 f. grey and blue .. 80 80
DESIGNS: 80 r. "The Epiphany". 1 f. "Family".

1963. Europa.
427. **124.** 50 r. multicoloured .. 75 65

1963. Minnesingers (3rd issue). As T **116.** Multicoloured.
428. 25 r. Heinrich von Sax .. 25 25
429. 30 r. Kristan von Hamle .. 40 40
430. 75 r. Werner von Teufen .. 75 75
431. 1 f. 70 Hartmann von Aue 1·50 1·50

125. Olympic Rings and Flags. **126.** Arms of Counts of Werdenberg, Vaduz.

1964. Olympic Games, Tokyo.
432. **125.** 50 r. red, black & blue .. 30 30

1964. Arms (1st issue). Multicoloured.
433 20 f. Type **126** 15 15
434 30 f. Barons of Brandis .. 20 20
435 80 r. Counts of Sulz .. 65 65
436 1 f. 50 Counts of Hohenems 90 90
See also Nos. 443/6.

127. Roman Castle, Schaan. **128.** P. Kaiser

1964. Europa.
437. **127.** 50 f. multicoloured .. 1·10 70

1964. Christmas. As T **120.**
438. 10 r. purple 10 10
439. 40 r. blue 25 25
440. 1 f. 30 purple 80 80
DESIGNS: 10 f. Masescha Chapel. 40 r. "Mary Magdalene" (altar paintings). 1 f. 30, "St. Sebastian, Madonna and Child, and St. Roche" (altar painting).

1964. Death Cent. of Peter Kaiser (historian).
441. **128.** 1 f. green on cream .. 30 45

129. "Madonna" (wood sculpture, c. 1700). **130.** Europa "Links" (ancient belt-buckle).

1965.
442. **129.** 10 f. red .. .. 5·50 3·50

1965. Arms (2nd issue). As T **126.** Multicoloured.
443. 20 r. Von Schellenberg .. 15 15
444. 30 r. Von Gutenberg .. 20 20
445. 80 r. Von Frauenberg .. 70 70
446. 1 f. Von Ramschwag .. 70 70

1965. Europa.
447. **130.** 50 r. brown, grey & blue 30 40

131. "Jesus in the Temple". **132.** Princess Gina and Prince Franz (after painting by Pedro Leitao).

1965. Birth Centenary of Ferdinand Nigg (painter).
448 – 10 r. dp green & green 10 10
449 – 30 f. brown & orange 15 15
450 **131** 1 f. 20 green and blue 40 40
DESIGNS—VERT. 10 r. "The Annunciation". 30 r. "The Magi".

1965. Special Issue.
451. **132.** 75 r. multicoloured .. 30 40
See also No. 457.

133. Telecommunication Symbols. **134.** Tree ("Wholesome Earth").

1965. Cent. of I.T.U.
452. **133.** 25 r. multicoloured .. 20 20

1966. Nature Protection.
453. **134.** 10 r. green and yellow 10 10
454. – 20 r. indigo and blue .. 15 15
455. – 30 r. blue and green .. 15 15
456. – 1 f. 50 red and yellow 45 45
DESIGNS: 20 r. Bird ("Pure Air"). 30 r. Fish ("Clean Water"). 1 f. 50, Sun ("Protection of Nature").

1966. Prince Franz Joseph II's 60th Birthday. As T **132**, but with portrait of Prince Franz and inscr. "1906–1966".
457. – 1 f. multicoloured .. 30 45

135. Arms of Herren von Richenstein. **136.** Europa "Ship".

1966. Arms of Triesen Families. Mult.
458. 20 r. Type **135** 15 15
459. 30 r. Junker Vaistli .. 20 20
460. 60 r. Edle von Trisun .. 25 25
461. 1 f. 20 Die von Schiel .. 50 50

1966. Europa.
462. **136.** 50 r. multicoloured .. 30 30

137. Vaduz Parish Church. **138.** Cogwheels.

1966. Restoration of Vaduz Parish Church.
463 **137** 5 r. green and red .. 10 10
464 – 20 r. purple and bistre 15 10
465 – 30 r. blue and red .. 20 20
466 – 1 f. 70 brown and green 60 90
DESIGNS: 20 f. St. Florin. 30 f. Madonna. 1 f. 70, God the Father.

1967. Europa.
467. **138.** 50 r. multicoloured .. 30 30

139. "The Manfrom Malanser". **141.** "Alpha and Omega".

1967. Liechtenstein Sagas. (1st series). Multicoloured.
468. 20 r. Type **139** 10 10
469. 30 r. "The Treasure of Gutenberg" 15 15
470. 1 f. 20 "The Giant of Guflina" 40 40
See also Nos. 492/4 and 516/18.

1967. Christian Symbols. Multicoloured.
472. 20 r. Type **141** 10 10
473. 30 r. "Tropaion" (Cross as victory symbol) .. 10 10
474. 70 r. Christ's monogram .. 30 30

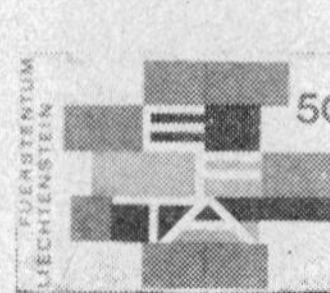

142. Father J. B. Buchel (educator, historian and poet). **143.** "E.F.T.A.".

1967. Buchel Commem.
475. **142.** 1 f. lake and green .. 35 35

1967. European Free Trade Assn.
476. **143.** 50 r. multicoloured .. 30 25

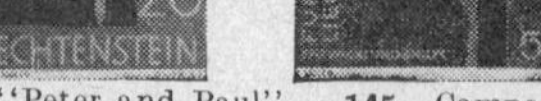

144. "Peter and Paul", Mauren. **145.** Campaign Emblem.

1967. "Patrons of the Church". Mult.
477. 5 r. "St. Joseph", Planken 10 10
478. 10 r. "St. Lawrence", Schaan 10 10
479. 20 r. Type **144** 15 10
480. 30 r. "St. Nicholas", Balzers 20 10
480a. 40 r. "St. Sebastian", Nendeln 45 25
481. 50 r. "St. George", Schellenberg 35 20
482. 60 r. "St. Martin", Eschen 50 30
483. 70 r. "St. Fridolin", Ruggell 55 40
484. 80 r. "St. Gallus", Triesen 65 45
485. 1 f. "St. Theodolus", Triesenberg .. 70 40
486. 1 f. 20 "St. Anna", Vaduz Castle 85 70
487. 1 f. 50 "St. Marie", Bendern-Camprin .. .. 1·10 80
488. 2 f. "St. Lucius", (patron saint of Liechtenstein) .. 1·50 1·10

1967. "Technical Assistance".
489. **145.** 50 r. + 20 r. mult. .. 30 30

146. Europa "Key".

1968. Europa.
490. **146.** 50 r. multicoloured .. 30 25

147. Arms of Liechtenstein and Wilczek. **148.** Sir Rowland Hill.

1968. Silver Wedding Anniv. of Prince Francis Joseph II and Princess Gina.
491. **147.** 75 r. multicoloured .. 45 40

1968. Liechtenstein Sagas (2nd series). As T **139.** Multicoloured.
492. 30 r. "The Treasure of St. Mamerten" 20 15
493. 50 r. "The Hobgoblin in the Bergerwald" .. 25 25
494. 80 r. "The Three Sisters" 40 40

1968. "Pioneers of Philately". (1st series).
495. **148.** 20 r. green 15 10
496. – 30 r. brown 20 15
497. – 1 f. black 50 40
PORTRAITS: 30 r. Philippe de Ferrari. 1 f. Maurice Burrus.
See also Nos. 504/5 and 554/6.

150. Arms of Liechtenstein. **151.** Colonnade.

1969.
498 **150** 3 f. 50 brown .. .. 1·50 1·25

1969. Europa.
499. **151.** 50 r. multicoloured .. 30 30

152. "Biology".

1969. 250th Anniv. of Liechtenstein. Mult.
500. 10 r. Type **152** 10 10
501. 30 r. "Physics" 20 15
502. 50 r. "Astronomy" .. 40 30
503. 80 r. "Art" 60 60

1969. "Pioneers of Philately" (2nd series). As T **148.**
504. 80 r. brown 40 40
505. 1 f. 20 blue 60 60
PORTRAITS: 80 r. Carl Lindenberg 1 f. 20, Theodore Champion.

153. Arms of St. Luzi Monastery. **154.** Symbolic "T".

1969. Arms of Church Patrons. Multicoloured.
506. 20 r. St. Johann's Abbey .. 20 10
507. 30 r. Type **153** 25 20
508. 30 r. Ladies' Priory, Schanis 25 20
509. 30 r. Knights Hospitallers, Feldkirch 25 20
510. 50 r. Pfafers Abbey .. 35 30
511. 50 r. Weingarten Abbey .. 35 30
512. 75 r. St. Gallen Abbey .. 70 50
513. 1 f. 20 Ottobeuren Abbey 1·10 80
514. 1 f. 50 Chur Episcopate .. 1·40 90

1969. Cent. of Liechtenstein Telegraph System.
515. **154.** 30 r. multicoloured .. 15 15

1969. Liechtenstein Sagas (3rd series). As T **139.** Multicoloured.
516. 20 r. "The Cheated Devil" 15 15
517. 50 r. "The Fiery Red Goat" 40 25
518. 60 r. "The Grafenberg Treasure" 50 35

155. Orange Lily. **156.** "Flaming Sun".

1970. Nature Conservation Year. Mult.
519. 20 r. Type **155** 20 15
520. 30 r. Wild orchid 40 20
521. 50 r. Ranunculus 55 40
522. 1 f. 20 Bog bean .. .. 1·10 1·00
See also Nos. 532/5 and 548/51.

1970. Europa.
523. **156.** 50 r. yellow, blue & grn. 30 30

MINIMUM PRICE

The minimum price quoted is 5p which represents a handling charge rather than a basis for valuing common stamps. For further notes about prices see introductory pages.

157. Prince Wenzel. 158. Prince Francis Joseph II.

1970. 25th Anniv. of Liechtenstein Red Cross.
524. 157. 1 f. multicoloured .. 45 45

1970.
526. – 1 f. 70 green 80 80
526a. – 2 f. 50 blue .. .. 1·25 1·25
527. 158. 3 f. black .. .. 1·40 1·40
DESIGNS: 1 f. 70, Prince Hans Adam. 2 f. 50, Princess Gina.

159. "Mother and Child" (R. Schadler). 160. Bronze Boar (La Tene period).

1970. Christmas.
528. 159. 30 r. multicoloured .. 20 15

1971. Nat. Museum Inaug.
529. 160. 25 r. blk., blue & ultram. 15 15
530. – 30 r. brown and green 20 15
531. – 75 r. multicoloured .. 60 40
DESIGNS: 30 r. Ornamental peacock (Roman, 2nd-century). 75 r. Engraved bowl (13th-century).

161. Europa Chain.

1971. Liechtenstein Flowers (2nd series). As T 155. Multicoloured.
532. 10 r. Cyclamen 10 10
533. 20 r. Moonwort 15 15
534. 50 r. Superb pink 40 35
535. 1 f. 50 Alpine columbine .. 1·25 1·00

1971. Europa.
536. 161. 50 r. yellow, bl. & black 30 30

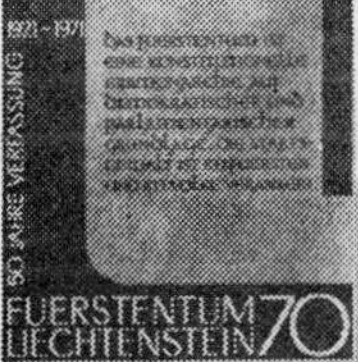

162. Part of Text. 163. Cross-country Skiing.

1971. 50th Anniv. of 1921 Constitution. Mult.
537. 70 r. Type 162 .. .. 60 50
538. 80 r. Princely crown .. 65 55

1971. Winter Olympic Games, Sapporo, Japan (1972). Multicoloured.
539. 15 r. Type 163 .. .. 15 10
540. 40 r. Ice hockey 30 25
541. 65 r. Downhill skiing .. 45 40
542. 1 f. 50 Figure skating .. 95 95

164. "Madonna and Child" (sculpture, Andrea della Robbia). 165. Gymnastics.

1971. Christmas.
543. 164. 30 r. multicoloured .. 20 15

1972. Olympic Games, Munich. Mult.
544 10 r. Type 165 .. .. 10 10
545 20 r. High jumping .. 15 15
546 40 r. Running 30 25
547 60 r. Throwing the discus 40 35

1972. Liechtenstein Flowers (3rd series). As T 155. Multicoloured.
548. 20 r. Sulphur anemone .. 15 15
549. 30 r. Turk's-cap lily .. 25 20
550. 60 r. Alpine centaury .. 55 40
551. 1 f. 20 Reed-mace .. 85 75

166. "Communications". 168. "Faun".

1972. Europa.
552. 136. 40 r. multicoloured .. 30 25

1972. "Pioneers of Philately" (3rd series). As T 148.
554. 30 r. green 25 25
555. 40 r. purple 30 30
556. 1 f. 30 blue .. .. .. 1·10 85
PORTRAITS: 30 r. Emilio Diena. 40 r. Andre de Cock. 1 f. 30, Theodore E. Steinway.

1972. "Natural Art". Motifs fashioned from roots and branches. Multicoloured.
557. 20 r. Type 168 .. .. 15 15
558. 30 r. "Dancer" 20 20
559. 1 f. 10 "Owl" 65 65

169. "Madonna with Angels" (F. Nigg). 170. Lawena Springs.

1972. Christmas.
560. 169. 30 r. multicoloured .. 25 20

1972. Landscapes.
561 – 5 r. purple and yellow 10 10
562 170 10 r. green & lt green 10 10
563 – 15 r. brown and green 10 10
564 – 25 r. purple and blue 25 20
565 – 30 r. lilac and brown .. 30 10
566 – 40 r. mauve and brown 40 20
567 – 50 r. blue and lilac .. 30 20
568 – 60 r. green and yellow 30 30
569 – 70 r. blue & light blue 35 35
570 – 80 r. green & lt green 40 40
571 – 1 f. brown and green .. 60 45
572 – 1 f. 30 blue and green 75 75
573 – 1 f. 50 brown and blue 75 75
574 – 1 f. 80 brown & lt brn 1·25 1·10
575 – 2 f. brown and blue .. 1·60 1·00
DESIGNS: 5 r. Silum. 15 r. Ruggeller Reed. 25 r. Steg Kirchlispitz. 30 r. Feld Schellenberg. 40 r. Rennhof Mauren. 50 r. Tidrufe. 60 r. Eschner Riet. 70 r. Mittagspitz. 80 r. Schaan Forest. 1 f. St. Peter's Chapel, Mals. 1 f. 30, Frommenhaus. 1 f. 50, Ochsenkopf. 1 f. 80, Hehlawangspitz. 2 f. Saminaschlucht.

171. Europa "Posthorn".

1973. Europa.
576. 171. 30 r. multicoloured .. 25 20
577. 40 r. multicoloured .. 35 30

172. Nautilus Goblet. 173. Arms of Liechtenstein.

1973. Treasures from Prince's Collection (1st issue). Drinking Vessels. Mult.
578. 30 r. Type 172 .. .. 25 20
579. 70 r. Ivory tankard .. 60 45
580. 1 f 10 Silver cup 80 70
See also Nos. 589/92.

1973.
581. 173. 5 f. multicoloured .. 3·00 2·40

174. False Ringlet. 175. "Madonna" (Bartolomeo di Tommaso da Foligno).

1973. "Small Fauna of Liechtenstein". (1st series). Multicoloured.
582. 30 r. Type 174 .. .. 35 20
583. 40 r. Curlew .. .. 1·25 30
584. 60 r. Edible frog 55 40
585. 80 r. Grass snake 70 55
See also Nos. 596/9.

1973. Christmas.
586. 175. 30 r. multicoloured .. 25 20

176. "Shouting Horseman" (sculpture, Andrea Riccio). 177. Footballers.

1974. Europa. Multicoloured.
587 30 r. Type 176 .. .. 25 20
588 40 r. "Squatting Aphrodite" (sculpture, Antonio Susini) 35 30

1974. Treasures from Prince's Collection (2nd issue). Porcelain. As T 172. Multicoloured.
589 30 r. Vase, 19th century .. 25 20
590 50 r. Vase, 1740 .. .. 40 30
591 60 r. Vase, 1830 .. .. 50 40
592 1 f. Vase, c. 1700 .. .. 80 75

1974. World Cup Football Championship, West Germany.
593 177 80 f. multicoloured .. 70 55

178. Posthorn and U.P.U. Emblem. 179. Bishop Marxer.

1974. Cent. of Universal Postal Union.
594. 178. 40 r. blk., grn. & gold .. 30 25
595. 60 r. blk, red & gold .. 40 40

1974. Small Fauna of Liechtenstein (2nd series). As T 174. Multicoloured.
596 15 r. Mountain newt .. 15 10
597 25 r. Adder 20 15
598 70 r. Cynthia's fritillary (butterfly) .. .. 1·75 60
599 1 f. 10 Three-toed woodpecker .. .. .. 2·25 85

1974. Death Cent. of Bishop Franz Marxer.
600. 179. 1 f. multicoloured .. 40 50

180. Prince Francis Joseph II and Princess Gina.

1974.
601. 180. 10 f. brown and gold .. 4·50 4·50

181. "St. Florian". 182. Prince Constantin.

1974. Christmas. Local Art. Glass Paintings. Multicoloured.
602. 30 r. Type 181 .. .. 20 15
603. 50 r. "St. Wendelin" .. 35 30
604. 60 r. "St. Mary, Anna and Joachim" 45 40
605. 70 r. "Jesus in Manger" .. 55 50

1975. Royal Princes.
606. 182. 70 r. green and gold .. 55 50
607. – 80 r. purple and gold .. 70 60
608. – 1 f. 20 blue and gold .. 95 85
PORTRAITS—80 r. Prince Maximilian. 1 f. 20, Prince Alois.

183. "Cold Sun" (M. Frommelt). 184. Imperial Cross.

1975. Europa. Multicoloured.
609. 30 r. Type 183 .. .. 25 20
610. 60 r. "Village" (L. Jager) .. 55 45

1975. Imperial Insignia. (1st series). Multicoloured.
611. 30 r. Type 184 .. .. 25 20
612. 60 r. Imperial sword .. 40 35
613. 1 f. Imperial orb 80 70
614. 1 f. 30 Coronation robe (50 × 32 mm.) .. .. 10·00 8·50
615. 2 f. Imperial crown .. 2·00 1·75
See also Nos. 670/3.

185. "Red Cross Activities". 186. St. Mamerten, Triesen.

1975. 30th Anniv. of Liechtenstein Red Cross.
616. 185. 60 r. multicoloured .. 45 35

1975. European Architectural Heritage Year. Multicoloured.
617. 40 r. Type 186 .. .. 25 25
618. 50 r. Red House, Vaduz .. 30 30
619. 70 r. Prebendary buildings, Eschen 50 60
620. 1 f. Gutenberg Castle, Balzers 75 85

187. Speed Skating. 188. "Daniel in the Lions' Den".

1975. Winter Olympic Games, Innsbruck (1976). Multicoloured.
621. 20 r. Type 187 .. .. 15 10
622. 25 r. Ice hockey 20 15
623. 70 r. Downhill skiing .. 60 50
624. 1 f. 20 Slalom 90 85

1975. Christmas and Holy Year. Capitals in Chur Cathedral.
625 188 30 r. violet and gold .. 25 20
626 – 60 r. green and gold .. 50 40
627 – 90 r. red and gold .. 95 65
DESIGNS: 60 r. "Madonna". 90 r. "St. Peter".

189. Mouflon. 190. Crayfish.

1976. Europa. Ceramics by Prince Hans von Liechtenstein. Multicoloured.
628. 40 r. Type 189 .. .. 50 25
629. 80 r. "Pheasant and Brood" 75 60

1976. World Wildlife Fund. Multicoloured.
630. 25 r. Type 190 .. .. 20 20
631. 40 r. Turtle 30 30
632. 70 r. European otter .. 60 65
633. 80 r. Lapwing .. .. 2·00 90

191. Roman Fibula. 193. Judo.

1976. 75th Anniv. of Liechtenstein Historical Society.

634. 191. 90 r. multicoloured .. 60 60

1970. Olympic Games, Montreal. Mult.

636 35 r. Type **193** 25 20
637 50 r. Volleyball 35 35
638 80 r. Relay 50 50
639 1 f. 10 Long jumping .. 70 75

194. "Singing Angels" 195. "Pisces".

1976. 400th Birth Anniv (1977) of Peter Paul Rubens (painter). Multicoloured.

640. 50 r. Type **194** 50 50
641. 70 r. "Sons of Rubens" .. 75 85
642. 1 f. "Daughters of Cecrops" (49 × 39 mm.) .. 3·50 4·25

1976. Signs of the Zodiac (1st series). Mult.

643. 20 r. Type **195** 15 15
644. 40 r. "Aries" 30 25
645. 80 r. "Taurus" 50 55
646. 90 r. "Gemini" 70 75

See also Nos. 666/9 and 710/13.

196. "Child Jesus of Prague". 197. Sarcophagus Statue, Chur Cathedral.

1976. Christmas. Monastic Works in Wax. Multicoloured.

647 20 r. Type **196** 15 10
648 50 r. "The Flight into Egypt" (vert) 40 35
649 80 r. "Holy Trinity" (vert) 60 55
650 1 f. 50 "Holy Family" .. 1·10 1·00

1976. Bishop Ortlieb von Brandis of Chur Commemoration.

651 **197** 1 f. 10 brown and gold 70 65

199. Map of Liechtenstein, 1721 (J. Heber). 200. Coin of Emperor Constantine II.

1977. Europa. Multicoloured.

664 40 r. Type **199** 20 20
665 80 r. "View of Vaduz, 1815" (F. Bachmann) .. 45 45

1977. Signs of the Zodiac (2nd series). As T **195**. Multicoloured.

666. 40 r. "Cancer" 25 20
667. 70 r. "Leo" 45 45
668. 80 r. "Virgo" 55 55
669. 1 f. 10 "Libra" 65 70

1977. Imperial Insignia (2nd series). As T **184**. Multicoloured.

670 40 r. Holy Lance and Reliquary with Particle of the Cross 30 25
671 50 r. "St. Matthew" (Imperial Book of Gospels) 35 30
672 80 r. St. Stephen's Purse .. 55 55
673 90 r. Tabard of Imperial Herald 75 75

1977. Coins (1st series). Multicoloured.

674 35 r. Type **200** 30 25
675 70 r. Lindau Brakteat .. 50 50
676 80 r. Coin of Ortlieb von Brandis 60 60

See also Nos. 707/9.

201. Frauenthal Castle, Styria. 202. Children in Costume.

1977. Castles.

677 **201.** 20 r. green and gold .. 15 15
678. – 50 r. red and gold .. 30 30
679. – 80 r. lilac and gold .. 45 50
680. – 90 r. blue and gold .. 50 60

DESIGNS: 50 r. Gross-Ullersdorf, Moravia. 80 r. Liechtenstein Castle, near Modling, Austria. 90 r. Palais Liechtenstein, Alserbachstrasse, Vienna.

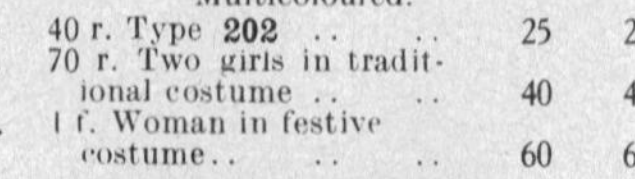

1977. Liechtenstein National Costumes. Multicoloured.

681. 40 r. Type **202** 25 25
682. 70 r. Two girls in traditional costume 40 45
683. 1 f. Woman in festive costume 60 65

203. Princess Tatjana.

1977. Princess Tatjana.

684. **203.** 1 f. 10, light brown, brown and gold .. 1·00 80

204. "Angel". 205. Palais Liechtenstein, Bankgasse, Vienna.

1977. Christmas. Sculptures by Erasmus Kern. Multicoloured.

685 20 r. Type **204** 15 15
686 50 r. "St. Rochus" .. 30 30
687 80 r. "Madonna" 45 55
688 1 f. 50 "God the Father" 85 1·00

1978. Europa.

689 **205** 40 r. blue and gold .. 30 25
690 – 80 r. red and gold .. 70 55

DESIGN: 80 r. Feldsberg Castle.

206. Farmhouse, Triesen. 207. Vaduz Castle.

1978. Buildings. Multicoloured.

691 10 r. Type **206** 10 10
692 20 r. Upper village of Triesen 15 10
693 35 r. Barns at Balzers .. 30 20
694 40 r. Monastery building, Bendern 30 10
695 50 r. Rectory tower, Balzers-Mals 40 25
696 70 r. Rectory, Mauren .. 50 30
697 80 r. Farmhouse, Schellenberg 70 45
698 90 r. Rectory, Balzers .. 75 70
699 1 f. Rheinberger House, Vaduz 80 55
700 1 f. 10 Vaduz Mitteldorf .. 90 70
701 1 f. 50 Town Hall, Triesenberg .. .. .. 1·25 95
702 2 f. National Museum and Administrator's residence, Vaduz .. .. 1·50 1·10

1978. 40th Anniv of Prince Francis Joseph II's Accession. Royal Residence. Multicoloured.

703. 40 r. Type **207** 40 40
704. 50 r. Courtyard 40 40
705. 70 r. Hall 65 65
706. 80 r. High Altar, Castle Chapel 75 75

208. Coin of Prince Charles. 209. "Portrait of a Piebald" (J. von Hamilton and A. Faistenberger).

1978. Coins (2nd series). Multicoloured.

707 40 r. Type **208** 30 30
708 50 r. Coin of Prince John Adam 40 40
709 80 r. Coin of Prince Joseph Wenzel 65 65

1978. Signs of the Zodiac (3rd series). As T **195**. Multicoloured.

710. 40 r. "Scorpio" 30 25
711. 50 r. "Sagittarius" .. 40 35
712. 80 r. "Capricorn" .. 65 60
713. 1 f. 50 "Aquarius" .. 1·25 1·10

1978. Paintings. Multicoloured.

714 70 r. Type **209** 50 50
715 80 r. "Portrait of a Blackish Brown Stallion" (J. von Hamilton) 65 65
716 1 f. 10 "Golden Carriage of Prince Joseph Wenzel" (Martin von Meytens) ($48\frac{1}{2} \times 38$ mm) 85 85

210. "Adoration of the Shepherds". 211. Mailplane over Schaan.

1978. Christmas. Church Windows, Triesenberg. Multicoloured.

717. 20 r. Type **210** 15 15
718. 50 r. "Enthroned Madonna with St. Joseph" .. 40 30
719. 80 r. "Adoration of the Magi" 70 65

1979. Europa. Multicoloured.

720. 40 r. Type **211** 45 45
721. 80 r. Zeppelin over Vaduz Castle 70 70

212. Child Drinking. 213. Ordered Wave-field.

1979. International Year of the Child. Multicoloured.

722. 80 r. Type **212** 40 50
723. 90 r. Child eating 50 60
724. 1 f. 10 Child reading .. 55 70

1979. 50th Anniv. of International Radio Consultative Committee (CCIR).

725. **213.** 50 r. blue and black .. 40 30

214. Abstract Composition. 215. Sun rising over Continents.

1979. Liechtenstein's Entry into Council of Europe.

726. **214.** 80 r. multicoloured .. 70 55

1979. Development Aid.

727. **215.** 1 f. multicoloured .. 80 70

216. Arms of Carl Ludwig von Sulz. 217. Sts. Lucius and Florian (fresco, Waltensberg-Vuorz Church).

1979. Heraldic Windows in the Liechtenstein National Museum. Multicoloured.

728 40 r. Type **216** 30 25
729 70 r. Arms of Barbara von Sulz 65 55
730 1 f. 10 Arms of Ulrich von Ramschwag and Barbara von Hallwil .. 90 80

1979. Patron Saints.

731 **217** 20 f. multicoloured .. 8·00 8·50

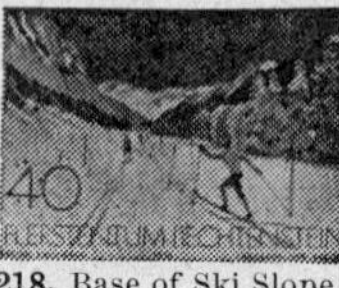

218. Base of Ski Slope, Valuna.

1979. Winter Olympic Games, Lake Placid (1980). Multicoloured.

732. 40 r. Type **218** 35 25
733. 70 r. Malbun and Ochsenkopf 65 55
734. 1 f. 50 Ski-lift, Sareis .. 1·25 1·00

219. "The Annunciation".

1979. Christmas. Embroideries by Ferdinand Nigg. Multicoloured.

735. 20 r. Type **219** 15 10
736. 50 r. "Christmas" .. 40 30
737. 80 r. "Blessed are the Peacemakers" 60 50

220. Maria Leopoldine von Esterhazy (bust by Canova). 221. Arms of Andreas Buchel, 1690.

1980. Europa.

738 **220** 40 r. green, turq & gold 35 35
739 – 80 r. brown, red & gold 50 50

DESIGN: 80 r. Maria Theresia von Liechtenstein (after Martin von Meytens).

1980. Arms of Bailiffs (1st series). Mult.

740. 40 r. Type **221** 30 25
741. 70 r. Georg Marxer, 1745 .. 60 55
742. 80 r. Luzius Frick, 1503 .. 70 60
743. 1 f. 10 Adam Oehri, 1634 .. 85 80

See also Nos. 763/6, and 788/91.

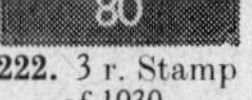

222. 3 r. Stamp of 1930. 223. Milking Pail.

1980. 50th Anniv. of Postal Museum.

744. **222.** 80 r. lake, turq. & grey 65 60

1980. Alpine Dairy Farming Implements. Multicoloured.

745. 20 r. Type **223** 15 15
746. 50 r. Wooden heart dairy herd descent marker .. 40 30
747. 80 r. Butter churn .. 65 55

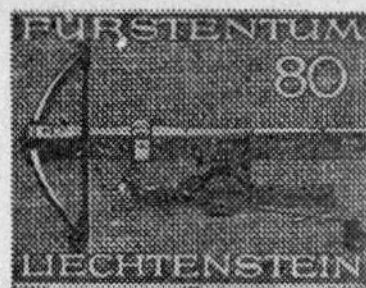

224. Crossbow.

1980. Hunting Weapons.

748 **224** 80 r. brown and lilac .. 70 60
749 – 90 r. black and green 80 70
750 – 1 f. 10 black and brown 90 80

DESIGNS: 90 r. Spear and knife. 1 f. 10, Rifle and powder-horn.

225. Triesenberg Costumes.

1980. Costumes. Multicoloured.

751. 40 r. Type **225** 30 25
752. 70 r. Dancers, Schellenberg 65 55
753. 80 r. Brass band, Mauren 70 65

226. Beech Trees, Matrula (spring).

227. Angel bringing Shepherds Good Tidings.

1980. The Forest in the Four Seasons. Multicoloured.

754. 40 r. Type **226** 30 30
755. 50 r. Firs in the Valorsch (summer) 45 40
756. 80 r. Beech tree, Schaan (autumn) 70 60
757. 1 f. 50 Edge of forest at Oberplanken (winter) .. 1·25 1·25

1980. Christmas. Multicoloured.

758. 20 r. Type **227** 15 15
759. 50 r. Crib 40 30
760. 80 r. Epiphany 65 60

228. National Day Procession.

230. Scout Emblems.

1981. Europa. Multicoloured.

761. 40 r. Fireworks at Vaduz Castle 35 25
762. 80 r. Type **228** 75 65

1981. Arms of Bailiffs (2nd series). As T **221.** Multicoloured.

763. 40 r. Anton Meier, 1748 .. 30 25
764. 70 r. Kaspar Kindle, 1534 60 50
765. 80 r. Hans Adam Negele, 1600 .. .. .. 70 60
766. 1 f. 10 Peter Matt, 1693 .. 90 80

1981. 50th Anniv. of Boy Scout and Girl Guide Movements.

768. **230.** 20 r. multicoloured .. 30 15

231. Symbols of Disability.

232. St. Theodul (sculpture).

1981. International Year of Disabled People.

769. **231.** 40 r. multicoloured .. 30 25

1981. 1600th Birth Anniv. of St. Theodul.

770. **232.** 80 r. multicoloured .. 65 55

233. " Xanthoria parietina ". **234.** Gutenberg Castle.

1981. Mosses and Lichens. Multicoloured.

771. 40 r. Type **233** 30 25
772. 50 r. " Parmelia physodes " 50 40
773. 70 r. " Sphagnum palustre " 65 55
774. 80 r. " Amblystegium serpens " 80 65

1981. Gutenberg Castle. Multicoloured.

775. 20 r. Type **234** 20 15
776. 40 r. Courtyard 30 25
777. 50 r. Parlour 40 35
778. 1 f. 10 Great Hall .. 95 85

235. Cardinal Karl Borromaus von Mailand.

236. St. Nicholas blessing Children.

1981. Famous Vistors to Liechtenstein (1st series). Multicoloured.

779. 40 r. Type **235** 30 30
780. 70 r. Johann Wolfgang von Goethe (writer) .. 65 60
781. 80 r. Alexander Dumas the younger (writer) .. 75 65
782. 1 f. Hermann Hesse (writer) 85 80

See also Nos. 804/7 and 832/5.

1981. Christmas. Multicoloured.

783. 20 r. Type **236** 15 15
784. 50 r. Adoration of the Kings 40 30
785. 80 r. Holy Family 70 55

237. Peasant Revolt, 1525.

1982. Europa. Multicoloured.

786. 40 r. Type **237** 40 30
787. 80 r. King Wenceslaus with Counts (Imperial direct rule, 1396) .. 85 65

1982. Arms of Baliffs (3rd series). As T **221.** Multicoloured.

788. 40 r. Johann Kaiser, 1664 40 30
789. 70 r. Joseph Anton Kaufmann, 1748 .. .. .. 70 60
790. 80 r. Christoph Walser, 1690 80 75
791. 1 f. 10 Stephan Banzer, 1658 .. .. .. 1·10 1·00

238. Triesenberg Sports Ground. **239.** Crown Prince Hans Adam.

1982. World Cup Football Championship, Spain. Multicoloured.

792 15 r. Type **238** 20 15
793 25 r. Eschen/Mauren playing fields 25 25
794 1 f. 80 Rheinau playing fields, Balzers .. .. 1·75 1·60

1982. " Liba 82 " Stamp Exhibition. Multicoloured.

795. 1 f. Type **239** 90 85
796. 1 f. Princess Marie Aglae .. 90 85

240. Tractor (agriculture).

1982. Rural Industries. Multicoloured.

797. 30 r. Type **240** 30 25
798. 50 r. Cutting flowers (horticulture) 50 40
799. 70 r. Worker with logs (forestry) 70 65
800. 150 r. Worker and milk (dairy farming) .. 1·50 1·40

241. "Neu-Schellenberg".

243. Angel playing Lute.

1982. 150th Birth Anniv. of Mortiz Menzinger (artist). Multicoloured.

801. 40 r. Type **241** 30 25
802. 50 r. " Vaduz " 55 40
803. 100 r. " Bendern " .. 90 80

1982. Famous Visitors to Liechtenstein (2nd series). As T **235.** Multicoloured.

804 40 r. Emperor Maximilian I (after Benhard Strigel) 30 25
805 70 f. Georg Jenatsch (liberator of Grisons) .. 65 50
806 80 r. Angelika Kaufmann (artist, self-portrait) .. 75 60
807 1 f. St. Fidelis of Sigmaringen .. .. 1·00 90

1982. Christmas. Details from High Altar by Jakob Russ, Chur Cathedral. Mult.

808. 20 r. Type **243** 15 15
809. 50 r. Madonna and child .. 45 35
810. 80 r. Angel playing organ 70 60

244. Notker Balbulus of St. Gall.

245. Shrove Thursday.

1983. Europa. Multicoloured.

811. 40 r. Type **244** 30 25
812. 80 r. Hildegard of Bingen 70 55

1983. Shrovetide and Lent Customs. Mult.

813 40 r. Type **245** 30 25
814 70 r. Shrovetide carnival .. 55 50
815 1 f. 80 Lent Sunday bonfire 1·40 1·40

246. River Bank.

247. "Schaan".

1983. Anniversaries and Events. Mult.

816. 20 r. Type **246** 30 20
817. 40 r. Montgolfier Brothers' balloon 35 30
818. 50 r. Airmail envelope .. 50 35
819. 80 r. Plant and hands holding spade 70 65

EVENTS: 20 r. Council of Europe river and coasts protection campaign. 40 r. Bicentenary of manned flight. 50 r. World Communications Year. 80 r. Overseas aid.

1983. Landscape Paintings by Anton Ender. Multicoloured.

820. 40 r. Type **247** 35 25
821. 50 r. "Gutenberg Castle" .. 55 45
822. 200 r. "Steg Reservoir" .. 2·00 2·00

248. Princess Gina.

249. Pope John Paul II.

1983. Multicoloured.

823. 2 f. 50 Type **248** .. .. 2·25 1·75
824. 3 f. Prince Francis Joseph II .. .. 2·75 2·00

1983. Holy Year.

825. **249.** 80 r. multicoloured .. 75 60

250. Snowflakes and Stripes.

251. Seeking Shelter.

1983. Winter Olympic Games, Sarajevo. Multicoloured.

826. 40 r. Type **250** 35 25
827. 80 r. Snowflake 75 65
828. 1 f. 80 Snowflake and rays 1·75 1·75

1983. Christmas. Multicoloured.

829. 20 r. Type **251** 15 15
830. 50 r. Infant Jesus 50 35
831. 80 r. Three Kings 75 65

1984. Famous Visitors to Liechtenstein (3rd series). As T **235.** Multicoloured.

832 40 r. Aleksandr Vassilievich Suvorov (Russian General) 40 30
833 70 r. Karl Rudolf von Buol-Schauenstein, Bishop of Chur .. 65 60
834 80 r. Carl Zuckmayer (dramatist) 75 65
835 1 f. Curt Goetz (actor) .. 95 90

253. Bridge.

1984. Europa. 25th Anniv of C.E.P.T.

836 **253** 50 r. light blue & blue 50 40
837 80 r. red and brown .. 75 70

254. The Warning Messenger.

255. Pole Vaulting.

1984. Liechtenstein Legends. The Destruction of Trisona. Each brown, grey and blue.

838. 35 r. Type **254** 30 25
839. 50 r. The buried town .. 55 40
840. 80 r. The spared family .. 80 70

1984. Olympic Games, Los Angeles. Mult.

841 70 r. Type **255** 60 55
842 80 r. Throwing the discus 70 65
843 1 f. Putting the shot .. 85 80

256. Currency (trade and banking).

1984. Occupations. Multicoloured.

844 5 r. Type **256** 10 10
845 10 r. Plumber adjusting pipe (building trade) .. 15 10
846 20 r. Operating machinery (industry—production) 20 15
847 35 r. Draughtswoman (building trade—planning) 35 20
848 45 r. Office worker and world map (industry—sales) 50 35
849 50 r. Cook (tourism) .. 55 30
850 60 r. Carpenter (building trade—interior decoration) 70 45
851 70 r. Doctor injecting patient (medical services) 75 60
852 80 r. Scientist (industrial research) 80 55
853 100 r. Bricklayer (building trade) 90 65
854 120 r. Flow chart (industry—administration) .. 1·25 1·10
855 150 r. Handstamping covers (post and communications) .. 1·60 1·00

257. Princess Marie. **258.** Annuniciation.

1984. Multicoloured.
856. 1 f. 70 Type **227** .. .. 1·50 1·25
857. 2 f. Prince Hans Adam .. 2·00 1·50

1984. Christmas. Multicoloured.
858. 35 r. Type **258** 30 25
859. 50 r. Holy Family 50 40
860. 80 r. The three kings .. 80 70

259. Apollo and the Muses playing Music (detail from 18th-century harpsichord lid).

1985. Europa. Music Year. Multicoloured.
861. 50 r. Type **259** 60 50
862. 80 r. Apollo and the Muses playing music (different) 80 75

260. St. Elisabeth Convent, Schaan.

1985. Monasteries. Multicoloured.
863. 50 r. Type **260** 50 40
864. 1 f. Schellenberg Convent 1·00 1·00
865. 1 f. 70 Gutenberg Mission, Balzers .. .. .. 1·75 1·75

261. Princess Gina and handing out of Rations. **262.** Justice.

1985. 40th Anniversary of Liechtenstein Red Cross. Multicoloured.
866. 20 r. Type **261** 30 30
867. 50 r. Princess Gina and Red Cross ambulance .. 75 75
868. 120 r. Princess Gina with refugee children .. 1·50 1·50

1985. Cardinal Virtues. Multicoloured.
869. 35 r. Type **262** 30 30
870. 50 r. Temperance 50 50
871. 70 r. Prudence 70 70
872. 1 f. Fortitude .. .. 1·10 1·10

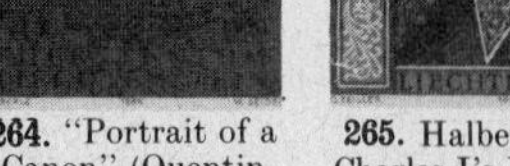

264. "Portrait of a Canon" (Quentin Massys). **265.** Halberd used by Charles I's Bodyguard.

1985. Paintings from Metropolitan Museum, New York. Multicoloured.
874. 50 r. Type **264** 60 60
875. 1 f. "Clara Serena Rubens" (Rubens) .. .. 1·50 1·50
876. 1 f. 20 "Duke of Urbino" (Raphael) .. .. 1·25 1·25

1985. Guards' Weapons and Armour. Mult.
877 35 r. Type **265** 35 30
878 50 r. Morion used by Charles I's bodyguard .. 70 70
879 80 r. Halberd used by Carl Eusebius's bodyguard .. 90 90

266. Frankincense. **267.** Puppets performing Tragedy.

1985. Christmas. Multicoloured.
880. 35 r. Type **266** 35 25
881. 50 r. Gold 60 50
882. 80 r. Myrrh 90 90

1985. Theatre. Multicoloured.
883. 50 r. Type **267** 70 70
884. 80 r. Puppets performing comedy 90 90
885. 1 f. 50 Opera .. .. 1·75 1·75

268. Courtyard. **269.** Barn Swallows.

1986. Vaduz Castle. Multicoloured.
886 20 r. Type **268** 20 15
887 25 r. Keep 40 30
888 50 r. Castle 60 45
889 90 r. Inner gate 75 60
890 1 f. 10 Castle from gardens 1·40 1·25
891 1 f. 40 Courtyard (different) .. .. 1·75 1·40

1986. Europa. Birds. Multicoloured.
892 50 r. Type **269** .. .. 1·00 75
893 90 r. European robin .. 1·50 1·75

270. "Offerings". **271.** Palm Sunday.

1986. Lenten Fast.
894 **270** 1 f. 40 multicoloured .. 1·50 1·50

1986. Religious Festivals. Multicoloured.
895 35 r. Type **271** 40 30
896 50 r. Wedding 70 60
897 70 r. Rogation Day procession 90 80

272. Karl Freiherr Haus von Hausen. **273.** Francis Joseph II.

1986. 125th Anniv. of Liechtenstein Land Bank.
898 **272** 50 r. brown, ochre & buff 55 55

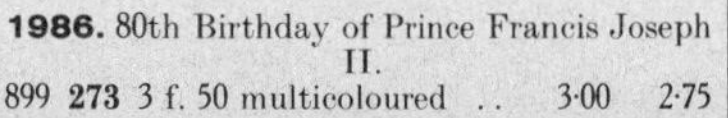

1986. 80th Birthday of Prince Francis Joseph II.
899 **273** 3 f. 50 multicoloured .. 3·00 2·75

274. Roebuck in Ruggeller Riet. **275.** Cabbage and Beetroot.

1986. Hunting. Multicoloured.
900 35 r. Type **274** 45 45
901 50 r. Chamois at Rappenstein 80 80
902 1 f. 70 Stag in Lawena .. 2·25 2·25

1986. Field Crops. Multicoloured.
903 50 r. Type **275** 70 70
904 80 r. Red cabbages .. 1·00 1·00
905 90 r. Potatoes, onions and garlic .. .. .. 1·25 1·25

276. Archangel Michael. **277.** Silver Fir.

1986. Christmas. Multicoloured.
906 35 r. Type **276** 35 30
907 50 r. Archangel Gabriel .. 70 70
908 90 r. Archangel Raphael .. 1·40 1·40

1986. Tree Bark. Multicoloured.
909 25 r. Type **277** 30 30
910 90 r. Norway spruce .. 1·40 1·40
911 1 f. 40 Pedunculate oak .. 1·90 1·90

278. Gamprin Primary School. **280.** Niklaus von Flue.

1987. Europa. Multicoloured.
912 50 c. Type **278** 60 60
913 90 c. Schellenberg parish church .. .. .. 1·40 1·40

1986. 500th Death Anniv. of Niklaus von Flue (martyr).
914 **280** 1 f. 10 multicoloured .. 1·25 1·25

281. Miller's Thumb. **282.** Princes Alois (frame as in first stamps).

1987. Fishes (1st series). Multicoloured.
915 50 r. Type **281** 70 70
916 90 r. Brook trout .. .. 1·25 1·25
917 1 f. 10 European grayling 1·75 1·75
See also Nos. 959/61.

1987. 75th Anniv. of First Liechtenstein Stamps.
918 **282** 2 f. multicoloured .. 2·40 2·40

283. Staircase. **284.** Arms.

1987. Liechtenstein City Palace, Vienna. Multicoloured.
919 35 r. Type **283** 35 30
920 50 r. Minoritenplatz doorway 70 70
921 90 r. Staircase (different) 1·25 1·25

1987. 275th Anniv. of Transfer of County of Vaduz to House of Liechtenstein.
922 **284** 1 f. 40 multicoloured .. 1·50 1·50

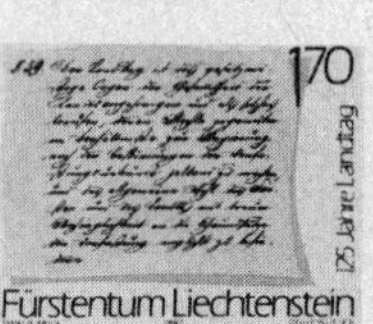

285. Constitution Charter, 1862. **286.** St. Matthew.

1987. 125th Anniv. of Liechtenstein Parliament.
923 **285** 1 f. 70 multicoloured .. 1·75 1·75

1987. Christmas. Illuminations from "Golden Book" of Pfafers Abbey. Multicoloured.
924 35 r. Type **286** 35 30
925 50 r. St. Mark 75 75
926 60 r. St. Luke 85 85
927 90 r. St. John .. .. 1·40 1·40

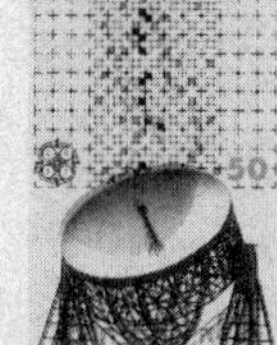

287. "The Toil of the Cross-Country Skier". **288.** Dish Aerial.

1987. Winter Olympic Games, Calgary (1988). Multicoloured.
928 25 r. Type **287** 30 30
929 90 r. "The Courageous Pioneers of Skiing" .. 1·40 1·40
930 1 f. 10 "As our Grandfathers used to ride on a Bobsled" .. .. 1·60 1·60

1988. Europa, Transport and Communications. Multicoloured.
931 50 r. Type **288** 50 50
932 90 r. Maglev monorail .. 1·25 1·25

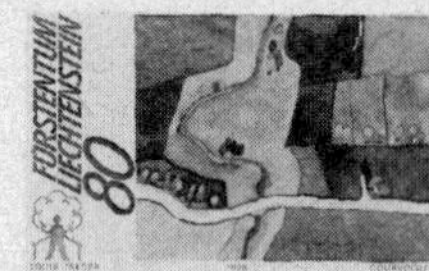

289. Agriculture.

1988. European Campaign for Rural Areas. Multicoloured.
933 80 r. Type **289** .. .. 1·00 1·00
934 90 r. Village centre .. 1·40 1·40
935 1 f. 70 Road .. .. 1·75 1·75

290. Headphones on Books (Radio Broadcasts). **292.** St. Barbara's Shrine, Balzers.

1988. Costa Rica–Liechtenstein Cultural Co-operation.
936 **290.** 50 r. multicoloured .. 65 65
937 – 1 f. 40 red, brown and green .. .. 2·00 2·00
Design: 1 f. 40 Man with pen and radio (Adult education).

1988. Wayside Shrines. Multicoloured.
939 25 r. Type **292** 40 40
940 35 r. Shrine containing statues of Christ, St. Peter and St. Paul at Oberdorf, Vaduz .. 50 50
941 50 r. St. Anthony of Egypt's shrine, Fallagass, Ruggel 85 85

293. Cycling.

294. Joseph and Mary.

1988. Olympic Games, Seoul. Multicoloured.
942 50 r. Type **293** 70 70
943 80 r. Gymnastics .. .. 1·25 1·25
944 90 r. Running .. .. 1·50 1·50
945 1 f. 40 Equestrian event .. 2·10 2·10

1988. Christmas. Multicoloured.
946 35 r. Type **294** 35 30
947 50 r. Baby Jesus 70 70
948 90 r. Wise Men presenting gifts to Jesus .. .. 1·40 1·40

295. Letter beside Footstool (detail).

296 "Cat and Mouse"

1988. "The Letter" (portrait of Marie-Theresa, Princesse de Lamballe by Anton Hickel). Multicoloured.
949 50 r. Type **295** 65 65
950 90 r. Desk and writing materials (detail) .. 1·10 1·10
951 2 f. "The Letter" (complete painting) .. 2·00 2·00

1989. Europa. Children's Games. Mult.
952 50 r. Type **296** 90 90
953 90 r. "Hide and Seek" .. 1·50 1·50

298 Rheinberger and Score

299 Little Ringed Plover

1989. 150th Birth Anniv of Josef Gabriel Rheinberger (composer).
954 **298** 2 f. 90 black, blue & pur 3·00 3·00

1989. Endangered Animals. Multicoloured.
955 25 r. Type **299** 40 40
956 35 r. Green tree frog .. 50 50
957 50 r. "Libelloides coccajus" (owl-fly) 75 75
958 90 r. Polecat .. .. 1·50 1·50

1989. Fishes (2nd series). As T **281**. Mult.
959 50 r. Pike 60 60
960 1 f. 10 Lake trout .. 1·40 1·40
961 1 f. 40 Stone loach .. 1·90 1·90

301 Return of Cattle from Alpine Pastures

302 Falknis

1989. Autumn Customs. Multicoloured.
962 35 r. Type **301** 40 40
963 50 r. Peeling corn cobs .. 65 65
964 80 r. Cattle market .. 1·10 1·10

1989. Mountains. Watercolours by Josef Schadler.
965 – 5 r. multicoloured .. 10 10
966 – 10 r. multicoloured .. 10 10
967 – 35 r. multicoloured .. 30 25
968 – 40 r. multicoloured .. 35 25
969 – 45 r. multicoloured .. 40 30
970 **302** 50 r. multicoloured .. 45 35
971 – 60 r. multicoloured .. 55 40
972 – 70 r. multicoloured .. 65 50
973 – 75 r. multicoloured .. 70 55
974 – 80 r. violet, brn & blk 75 60
975 – 1 f. multicoloured .. 90 70
976 – 1 f. 20 multicoloured .. 1·10 85
977 – 1 f. 50 multicoloured .. 1·40 1·00
978 – 1 f. 60 multicoloured .. 1·50 1·10
979 – 2 f. multicoloured .. 1·90 1·90
DESIGNS: 5 r. Augstenberg; 10 r. Hahenespiel; 35 r. Nospitz; 40 r. Ochsenkopf; 45 r. Three Sisters; 60 r. Kuhgrat; 70 r. Galinakopf; 75 r. Plassteikopf; 80 pf. Naafkopf; 1 f. Schonberg; 1 f. 20, Bleikaturm; 1 f. 50, Garselliturm; 1 f. 60, Schwarzhorn; 2 f. Scheienkopf.

303 "Melchior and Balthasar"

304 Mace Quartz

1989. Christmas. Details of triptych by Hugo van der Goes. Multicoloured.
981 35 r. Type **303** 50 50
982 50 r. "Kaspar and Holy Family" (27 × 34 mm) .. 75 70
983 90 r. "St. Stephen" .. 1·25 1·25

1989. Minerals. Multicoloured.
984 50 r. Type **304** 80 80
985 1 f. 10 Globe pyrite .. 1·50 1·50
986 1 f. 50 Calcite .. .. 2·10 2·10

305 Nendeln Forwarding Agency, 1864

306 Penny Black

1990. Europa. Post Office Buildings. Mult.
987 50 r. Type **305** 70 70
988 90 r. Vaduz post office, 1976 .. .. 1·10 1·10

1990. 150th Anniv of the Penny Black.
989 **306** 1 f. 50 multicoloured .. 1·90 1·90

307 Footballers

308 Tureen, Oranges and Grapes

1990. World Cup Football Championship, Italy.
990 **307** 2 f. multicoloured .. 2·40 2·40

1990. 9th Death Anniv of Benjamin Steck (painter). Multicoloured.
991 50 r. Type **308** 70 70
992 80 r. Apples and pewter bowl .. .. 1·00 1·00
993 1 f. 50 Basket, apples, cherries and pewter jug 1·90 1·90

309 Princess Gina

310 Ring-necked Pheasant

1990. Prince Francis Joseph II and Princess Gina Commemoration. Multicoloured.
994 2 f. Type **309** .. .. 2·40 2·40
995 3 f. Prince Francis Joseph II .. .. 3·50 3·50

1990. Game Birds. Multicoloured.
996 25 r. Type **310** 30 30
997 50 r. Black grouse .. 60 60
998 2 f. Mallard .. .. 2·40 2·40

311 Annunciation

312 St. Nicholas

1990. Christmas. Paintings. Multicoloured.
999 35 r. Type **311** 45 45
1000 50 r. Nativity 60 60
1001 90 r. Adoration of the Magi 1·00 1·00

1990. Winter Customs. Multicoloured.
1002 35 r. Type **312** 45 45
1003 50 r. Awakening on New Year's Eve 60 60
1004 1 f. 50 Giving New Year greetings .. .. 1·60 1·60

313 Mounted Courier

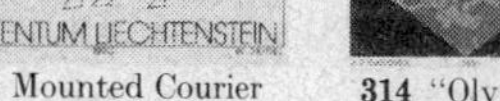
314 "Olympus 1" Satellite

1990. 500th Anniv of Regular European Postal Services.
1005 **313** 90 r. multicoloured .. 1·00 1·00

1991. Europa. Europe in Space. Mult.
1006 50 r. Type **314** 55 55
1007 90 r. "Meteosat" satellite 95 95

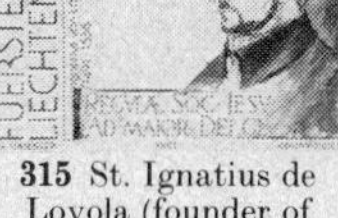

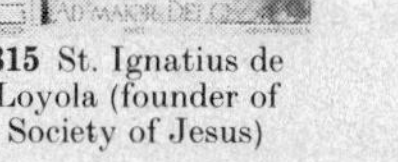

315 St. Ignatius de Loyola (founder of Society of Jesus)

316 U.N. Emblem and Dove

1991. Anniversaries. Multicoloured.
1008 80 r. Type **315** (500th birth anniv) 85 85
1009 90 r. Wolfgang Amadeus Mozart (composer, death bicentenary) .. 95 95

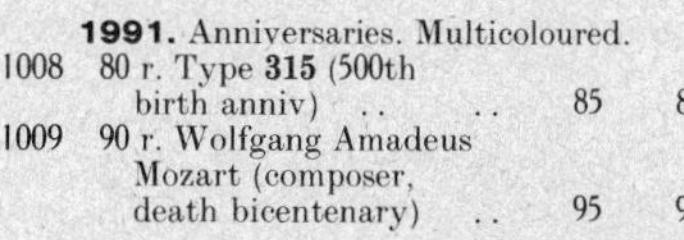

1991. Admission to U. N. Membership (1990).
1010 **316** 2 f. 50 multicoloured 2·75 2·75

317 Non-Commissioned Officer and Private

318 "Near Maloja" (Giovanni Giacometti)

1991. 125th Anniv of Last Mobilization of Liechtenstein's Military Contingent (to the Tyrol). Multicoloured.
1011 50 r. Type **317** 55 55
1012 70 r. Tunic, chest and portrait 75 55
1013 1 f. Officer and private .. 1·10 1·10

1991. 700th Anniv of Swiss Confederation. Paintings by Swiss artists. Multicoloured.
1014 50 r. Type **318** 55 55
1015 80 r. "Rhine Valley" (Ferdinand Gehr) .. 85 85
1016 90 r. "Bergell" (Augusto Giacometti) 95 95
1017 1 f. 10 "Hoher Kasten" (Hedwig Scherrer) .. 1·25 1·25

319 Stampless and Modern Covers

320 Princess Marie

1991. "Liba 92" National Stamp Exhibition, Vaduz.
1018 **319** 90 r. multicoloured .. 90 90

1991. Multicoloured.
1019 3 f. Type **320** .. .. 3·00 3·00
1020 3 f. 40 Prince Hans Adam II .. .. .. 3·50 3·50

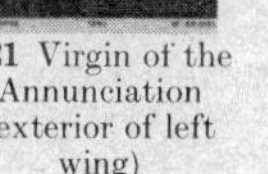
321 Virgin of the Annunciation (exterior of left wing)

322 Cross-country Skiers and Testing for Drug Abuse

1991. Christmas. Details of the altar from St. Mamertus Chapel, Triesen. Mult.
1021 50 r. Type **321** 50 50
1022 80 r. Madonna and Child (wood-carving attr. Jorg Syrlin, inner shrine) 80 80
1023 90 r. Angel Gabriel (exterior of right wing) 90 90

1991. Winter Olympic Games, Albertville. Multicoloured.
1024 70 r. Type **322** 70 70
1025 80 r. Ice hockey player tackling opponent and helping him after fall .. 80 80
1026 1 f. 60 Downhill skier and fallen skier caught in safety net .. .. 1·60 1·60

323 Relay Race, Drugs and Shattered Medal

324 Aztecs

1992. Olympic Games, Barcelona. Mult.
1027 50 r. Type **323** 45 45
1028 70 r. Cycling road race .. 65 65
1029 2 f. 50 Judo .. .. 2·25 2·25

1992. Europa. 500th Anniv of Discovery of America by Columbus. Multicoloured.
1030 80 r. Type **324** 75 75
1031 90 r. Statue of Liberty and New York skyline 85 85

325 Clown in Envelope ("Good Luck")

327 "Blechnum spicant"

1992. Greetings Stamps. Multicoloured.
1032 50 r. Type **325** 45 45
1033 50 r. Wedding rings in envelope and harlequin violinist 45 45
1034 50 r. Postman blowing horn (31 × 21 mm) .. 45 45
1035 50 r. Flying postman carrying letter sealed with heart (31 × 21 mm) 45 45

1992. Ferns. Multicoloured.
1037 40 r. Type **327** 35 35
1038 50 r. Maidenhair spleenwort 45 45
1039 70 r. Hart's-tounge .. 65 65
1040 2 f. 50 "Asplenium ruta-muraria" .. .. 2·25 2·25

328 Reading Edict

329 Chapel of St. Mamertus, Triesen

1992. 650th Anniv of County of Vaduz.
1041 **328** 1 f. 60 multicoloured 1·50 1·50

1992. Christmas. Multicoloured.
1042 50 r. Type **329** 45 45
1043 90 r. Crib, St. Gallus's Church, Triesen .. 85 85
1044 1 f. 60 St. Mary's Chapel, Triesen .. .. 1·50 1·50

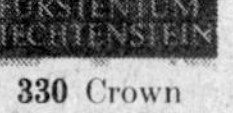
330 Crown Prince Alois

331 "Nafkopf and Huts, Steg"

1992.
1045 **330** 2 f. 50 multicoloured 2·25 2·25

1993. Paintings by Hans Gantner. Mult.
1046 50 r. Type **331** 45 45
1047 60 r. "Hunting Lodge, Sass" 55 55
1048 1 f. 80 "Red House, Vaduz" .. .. 1·60 1·60

332 "910805" (Bruno Kaufmann)

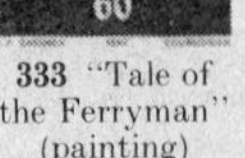
333 "Tale of the Ferryman" (painting)

1993. Europa. Contemporary Art. Mult.
1049 80 r. Type **332** 70 70
1050 1 f. "The little Blue" (Evi Kliemand) 90 90

1993. Tibetan Collection in the National Museum. Multicoloured.
1051 60 r. Type **333** 55 55
1052 80 r. Religious dance mask 75 75
1053 1 f. "Tale of the Fish" (painting) 95 95

334 "Tree of Life"

335 "The Black Hatter"

1993. Missionary Work.
1054 **334** 1 f. 80 multicoloured 1·75 1·75

1993. Homage to Liechtenstein.
1055 **335** 2 f. 80 multicoloured 2·75 2·75

337 Origanum

338 Eurasian Badger

1993. Flowers. Illustrations from "Hortus Botanicus Liechtensteinensis". Mult.
1057 50 r. Type **337** 50 50
1058 60 r. Meadow sage .. 55 55
1059 1 f. Seseli annuum .. 95 95
1060 2 f. 50 Large self-heal .. 2·40 2·40

1993. Animals. Multicoloured.
1061 60 r. Type **338** 55 55
1062 80 r. Beech marten .. 75 75
1063 1 f. Red fox 95 95

339 "Now that the Quiet Days are Coming..." (Rainer Maria Rilke)

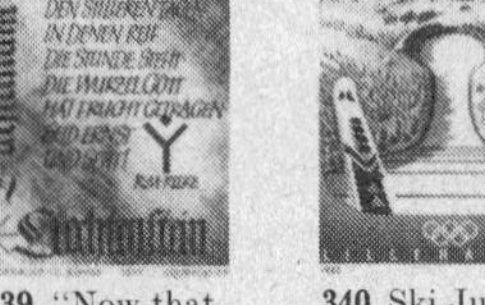
340 Ski Jumping

1993. Christmas. Multicoloured.
1064 60 r. Type **339** 55 55
1065 80 r. "Can You See the Light..." (Th. Friedrich) 75 75
1066 1 f. "Christmas, Christmas..." (R. A. Schroder) 95 95

1993. Winter Olympic Games, Lillehammer, Norway (1994). Multicoloured.
1067 60 r. Type **340** 55 55
1068 80 r. Slalom 75 75
1069 2 f. 40 Bobsleighing .. 2·25 2·25

OFFICIAL STAMPS

1932. Stamps of 1930 optd. **REGIERUNGS DIENSTSACHE** under crown.
O 118. 5 r. green (No. 97) .. 8·00 8·00
O 119. 10 r. purple .. .. 50·00 8·00
O 120. 20 r. red .. .. .. 55·00 8·00
O 121. 30 r. blue .. .. 12·00 8·00
O 122. 35 r. green .. .. 7·00 18·00
O 123. 50 r. sepia .. .. 45·00 13·00
O 124. 60 r. olive .. .. 9·50 28·00
O 125. 1 f. 20 brown £100 £250

1933. Nos. 121 and 123 optd **REGIERUNGS DIENSTSACHE** in circle round crown.
O126 **38** 25 r. orange .. .. 35·00 32·00
O127 – 1 f. 20 brown .. .. 60·00 £225

1934. Nos. 128 etc. optd **REGIERUNGS DIENSTSACHE** in circle round crown.
O 150. **41.** 5 r. green .. .. 70 1·50
O 151. – 10 r. violet .. .. 60 1·25
O 152. – 15 r. red .. .. 35 1·40
O 153. – 20 r. red .. .. 40 1·40
O 155. – 25 r. brown .. .. 1·50 11·00
O 156. – 30 r. blue .. .. 3·00 4·50
O 157. **42.** 50 r. brown .. .. 1·00 2·00
O 158. – 90 r. green .. .. 5·50 30·00
O 159. – 1 f. 50 lake .. .. 26·00 £130

1937. Stamps of 1937 optd **REGIERUNGS DIENSTSACHE** in circle round crown.
O174 **51** 5 r. green and buff .. 20 50
O175 – 10 r. violet and buff .. 40 90
O176 – 20 r. red and buff .. 75 1·25
O177 – 25 r. brown and buff 30 1·25
O178 – 30 r. blue and buff .. 1·00 70
O179 – 50 r. brown and buff 75 90
O180 – 1 f. purple and buff .. 75 5·50
O181 – 1 f. 50 grey and buff .. 2·10 9·00

1947. Stamps of 1944 optd. **DIENSTMARKE** and crown.
O 255. 5 r. green .. .. 1·25 60
O 256. 10 r. violet .. .. 1·25 85
O 257. 20 r. red .. .. .. 1·50 85
O 258. 30 r. blue .. .. 2·00 1·40
O 259. 50 r. grey .. .. 2·00 3·00
O 260. 1 f. red .. .. .. 9·00 10·00
O 261. 1 f. 50 blue .. .. 9·00 10·00

O 86.

O 198. Government Building, Vaduz.

1950. Buff paper.
O 287. O **86**. 5 r. purple and grey .. 10 10
O 288. 10 r. olive and red .. 10 10
O 289. 20 r. brown and blue 15 15
O 290. 30 r. lake and red .. 30 25
O 291. 40 r. blue and brown 30 30
O 292. 55 r. green and red .. 1·00 1·00
O 293. 60 r. grey and red .. 1·00 1·00
O 294. 80 r. orange and grey 75 75
O 295. 90 r. speia and blue .. 80 1·00
O 296. 1 f. 20 green & orange 1·50 1·50

1968. White paper.
O 495. O **86**. 5 r. brown and orange 10 10
O 496. 10 r. violet and red .. 10 10
O 497. 20 r. red and green .. 15 15
O 498. 30 r. green and red .. 25 25
O 499. 50 r. blue and red .. 40 40
O 500. 60 r. orange and blue 50 50
O 501. 70 r. red and green .. 60 60
O 502. 80 r. green and red .. 70 70
O 503. 95 r. green and red .. 1·00 1·00
O 504. 1 f. purple & turquoise 90 90
O 505. 1 f. 20 brown & turq. 1·40 1·40
O 506. 2 f. brown and orange 1·60 1·60

1976.
O 652 O **198** 10 r. brown & vio 10 10
O 653 20 r. red and blue 15 15
O 654 35 r. blue and red 20 20
O 655 40 r. violet & grn 25 25
O 656 50 r. green & mve 30 30
O 657 70 r. purple & grn 40 40
O 658 80 r. green & pur 50 50
O 659 90 r. violet & blue 60 60
O 660 1 f. grey & purple 65 65
O 661 1 f. 10 brown & bl 70 70
O 662 1 f. 50 green & red 90 90
O 663 2 f. orange & blue 1·40 1·40
O 664 5 f. purple & orge 3·75 3·50

POSTAGE DUE STAMPS

D 11.

D 25.

D 58.

1920.
D 43. D **11.** 5 h. red 10 25
D 44. 10 h. red 10 25
D 45. 15 h. red 10 25
D 46. 20 h. red 10 25
D 47. 25 h. red 15 30
D 48. 30 h. red 15 30
D 49. 40 h. red 15 30
D 50. 50 h. red 15 30
D 51. 80 h. red 15 30
D 52. 1 k. blue 20 50
D 53. 2 k. blue 20 50
D 54. 5 k. blue 20 50

1928.
D 84. D **25.** 5 r. orange & violet .. 1·00 2·50
D 85. 10 r. orange & violet 1·25 2·50
D 86. 15 r. orange & violet 2·50 10·00
D 87. 20 r. orange & violet 2·50 2·50
D 88. 25 r. orange & violet 2·50 7·50
D 89. 30 r. orange & violet 7·00 11·00
D 90. 40 r. orange & violet 8·00 12·00
D 91. 50 r. orange & violet 8·50 15·00

1940.
D 189. D **58.** 5 r. red and blue .. 1·25 4·25
D 190. 10 r. red and blue .. 50 75
D 191. 15 r. red and blue .. 75 4·50
D 192. 20 r. red and blue .. 80 1·25
D 193. 25 r. red and blue .. 1·40 3·25
D 194. 30 r. red and blue .. 3·00 5·00
D 195. 40 r. red and blue .. 3·00 4·50
D 196. 50 r. red and blue .. 3·00 5·50

LITHUANIA Pt. 10

A country on the Baltic Sea, under Russian rule until occupied by the Germans in the first World War (see German Eastern Command). It was an independent republic from 1918 to 1940, when it was incorporated into the U.S.S.R.

Lithuania declared its independence in 1990, and the U.S.S.R. formally recognised the republic in 1991.

1918. 100 skatiku = 1 auksinas.
1922. 100 centu = 1 litas.
1990. 100 kopeks = 1 rouble.
1992. Talons.

1.

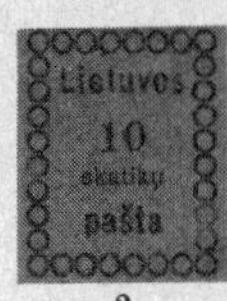

2.

1918.
3 **1** 10 s. black on buff .. 50·00 20·00
4 15 s. black on buff .. 50·00 20·00
5 20 s. black on buff .. 3·25 2·40
6 30 s. black on buff .. 3·25 2·40
7 40 s. black on buff .. 3·25 2·40
8 50 s. black on buff .. 3·25 2·40

1919.
9 **2** 10 s. black on buff .. 5·00 1·90
10 15 s. black on buff .. 5·00 1·90
11 20 s. black on buff .. 5·00 1·90
12 30 s. black on buff .. 5·00 1·90

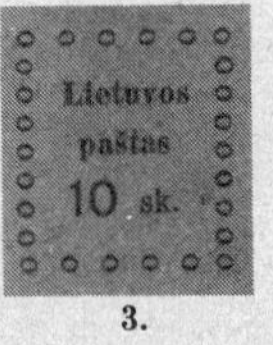

3.

Lietuvos paštas sk. 10 sk.
(4.)

1919.
13 **3** 10 s. black on buff .. 1·40 1·00
14 15 s. black on buff .. 1·40 1·00
15 20 s. black on buff .. 1·40 1·00
16 30 s. black on buff .. 1·40 1·00
17 40 s. black on buff .. 1·40 1·40
18 50 s. black on buff .. 1·40 1·40
19 60 s. black on buff .. 1·40 1·40

1919.
20 **4** 10 s. black on buff .. 1·60 80
21 15 s. black on buff .. 1·60 80
22 20 s. black on buff .. 1·60 80
23 30 s. black on buff .. 1·60 80
24 40 s. black on buff .. 1·60 1·10
25 50 s. black on buff .. 1·60 1·10
26 60 s. black on buff .. 1·60 1·40

5. Arms.

6.

7.

1919. "auksinas" in lower case letters on 1 to 5 a.
40 **5** 10 s. pink 15 15
50 10 s. orange 15 10
51 15 s. violet 15 10
52 20 s. blue 15 10
43 30 s. orange 15 15
53 30 s. bistre 15 10
54 40 s. brown 15 10
55 **6** 50 s. green 15 10
56 60 s. red and violet .. 15 10
57 75 s. red and yellow .. 15 10
37 **7** 1 a. red and grey 35 20
38 3 a. red and brown .. 35 20
39 5 a. red and green .. 40 30

1921. As T **4**, but "AUKSINAS" or "AUKSINAI" in capital letters.
58. **7.** 1 a. red and grey .. 15 10
59. 3 a. red and brown .. 25 15
60. 5 a. red and green .. 40 25

MINIMUM PRICE

The minimum price quoted is 5p which represents a handling charge rather than a basis for valuing common stamps. For further notes about prices see introductory pages.

11. Lithuania receiving Independence.

12. Lithuania arises.

1920. 2nd Anniv of Independence.

No.	Type	Description	Unused	Used
65.	11.	10 s. lake	2·00	2·00
66.		15 s. lilac	2·00	2·00
67.		20 s. blue	2·00	2·00
68.	12.	30 s. brown	2·00	2·00
69.	–	40 s. green and brown	2·00	2·00
70.	12.	50 s. red	2·00	2·00
71.		60 s. lilac	2·00	2·00
72.	–	80 s. red and violet	2·00	2·00
73.	–	1 a. red and green	2·00	2·00
74.	–	3 a. red and brown	2·00	2·00
75.	–	5 a. red and green	2·00	2·00

DESIGNS—VERT. 40 s., 80 s., 1 a. Lithuania with chains broken. 3 a., 5 a. (25×25 mm.) Arms.

16. Arms.

17. Vytautas.

1920. National Assembly.

No.	Type	Description	Unused	Used
76.	16.	10 s. red	30	25
77.		15 s. violet	45	35
78.	17.	20 s. green	45	35
79.	16.	30 s. brown	45	45
80.	–	40 s. violet and green	45	45
81.	17.	50 s. brown and orange	45	45
82.		60 s. red and orange	55	45
83.	–	80 s. red, grey and black	55	55
84.	–	1 a. yellow and black	55	55
85.	–	3 a. green and black	65	65
86.	–	5 a. violet and black	1·60	1·60

DESIGNS—As Type **17**: 40 s., 80 s. Gediminas. As Type **16**: 1 a. to 5 a. Sacred Oak and Altar.

20. Sower.

21. Kestutis.

22. Reaper.

23.

28. Allegory of Flight.

24. Flying Posthorn.

25. Junkers "F-13" over R. Niemen.

1921.

No.	Type	Description	Unused	Used
87.	20.	10 s. red	15	1·40
88.		15 s. mauve	15	1·60
89.		20 s. blue	10	10
90.	22.	30 s. brown	40	4·00
91.	21.	40 s. red	15	10
92.	22.	50 s. olive	10	10
93.		60 s. mauve and green	30	5·00
94.	21.	80 s. red and orange	20	15
95.		1 a. green and brown	15	10
96.		2 a. red and blue	15	10
97.	23.	3 a. blue and brown	40	85
124.	20.	4 a. blue and yellow	30	20
98.	23.	5 a. red and grey	50	2·00
125.	20.	8 a. black and green	65	20
99.	23.	10 a. mauve and red	1·00	35
100.		25 a. green and brown	1·10	65
101.		100 a. grey and red	4·00	10·00

1921. Air. Inauguration of Kaunas-Konigsberg Air Service.

No.	Type	Description	Unused	Used
102.	24.	20 s. blue	1·00	85
103.		40 s. orange	1·00	85
104.		60 s. green	1·00	65
105.		80 s. red	1·10	1·00
106.	25.	1 a. green and red	2·00	1·25
107.	–	2 a. brown and blue	2·00	1·50
108.	–	5 a. grey and yellow	2·75	2·75

DESIGNS—As Type **25**: 2 a. Three planes in flight. 5 a. Plane over Gediminas Castle.

1921. Air. Inauguration of Air Mail Service.

No.	Type	Description	Unused	Used
109.	28.	20 s. lilac and orange	1·10	1·50
110.		40 s. red and blue	1·10	1·50
111.		60 s. olive and blue	1·10	1·60
112.		80 s. green and yellow	1·10	1·60
113.		1 a. blue and green	1·10	1·60
114.		2 a. red and grey	1·10	1·50
115.		5 a. green and purple	1·10	1·50

1922. Surch. **4 AUKSINAI** with or without frame.

No.	Type	Description	Unused	Used
116.	6.	4 a. on 75 s. red & yellow	40	40

30.

1922. Air.

No.	Type	Description	Unused	Used
118.	30.	1 a. red and brown	1·60	2·25
119.		3 a. green and violet	1·60	1·40
120.		5 a. yellow and blue	1·60	2·50

31. Gediminas Castle.

33. Pte. Luksis.

1922. Air.

No.	Type	Description	Unused	Used
121.	31.	2 a. red and blue	1·00	90
122.		4 a. red and brown	1·00	90
123.		10 a. blue and black	2·40	1·90

1922. "De jure" Recognition of Lithuania by League of Nations. Inscr. "LIETUVA DE JURE".

No.	Type	Description	Unused	Used
126.	33.	20 s. red and black	35	35
127.	–	40 s. violet and green	25	15
128.	–	50 s. blue and purple	25	15
129.	–	60 s. orange and violet	25	15
130.	–	1 a. blue and red	25	20
131.	–	2 a. brown and blue	35	35
132.	–	3 a. blue and brown	35	35
133.	–	4 a. purple and green	35	35
134.	–	5 a. red and brown	35	35
135.	–	6 a. blue	45	35
136.	–	8 a. yellow and blue	65	35
137.	–	10 a. green and violet	1·00	1·00

DESIGNS—VERT. 40 s. Lt. Juozapavicius. 50 s. Dr. Basanavicius. 60 s. Mrs. Petkevicaite. 1 a. Prof. Voldemaras. 2 a. Dovidaitis. 3 a. Dr. Slezevicius. 4 a. Dr. Galvanauskas. 5 a. Dr. Grinius. 6 a. Dr. Stulginskis. 8 a. Pres. Smetona. HORIZ. (39 × 27 mm.): 10 a. Stauguitis, Pres. Smetona and Silingas.

1922. Surch.

No.	Type	Description	Unused	Used
138	5	1 c. on 10 s. orange (postage)	25	5·00
139		1 c. on 15 s. violet	25	5·00
143		1 c. on 20 s. blue	25	5·00
144		1 c. on 30 s. orange	35·00	60·00
145		1 c. on 30 s. bistre	15	40
146		1 c. on 40 s. brown	50	4·00
148	22	1 c. on 50 s. olive	10	10
149	6	2 c. on 50 s. green	65	4·00
150		2 c. on 60 s. red & violet	10	10
151		2 c. on 75 s. red & yellow	75	5·00
152	20	3 c. on 10 s. red	1·50	6·00
153		3 c. on 15 s. mauve	15	15
154		3 c. on 20 s. blue	20	3·25
155	22	3 c. on 30 s. brown	1·60	8·25
156	21	3 c. on 40 s. red	15	60
157	7	3 c. on 1 a. (No. 37)	85·00	£130
158		3 c. on 1 a. (No. 58)	15	1·25
159		3 c. on 3 a. (No. 38)	70·00	£120
160		3 c. on 3 a. (No. 59)	10	65
161		3 c. on 5 a. (No. 39)	40·00	50·00
162		3 c. on 5 a. (No. 60)	10	80
163	22	5 c. on 50 s. olive	10	10
164		5 c. on 60 s. mve & grn	85	15·00
165	21	5 c. on 80 s. red & orge	10	40
166	6	5 c. on 4 a. on 75 s. red and yellow	30	12·50
168	21	10 c. on 1 a. grn & brn	25	10
169		10 c. on 2 a. red & blue	10	10
170	20	15 c. on 4 a. blue & yell	10	10
171	23	25 c. on 3 a. blue & grn	5·00	25·00
172		25 c. on 5 a. red & grey	1·60	6·75
173		25 c. on 10 a. mve & red	1·00	1·60
174	20	30 c. on 8 a. black & grn	65	35
175	23	50 c. on 25 a green & brn	1·50	3·00
176		1 l. on 100 a. grey & red	2·75	3·25
177	24	10 c. on 20 s. blue (air)	1·40	3·75
178		10 c. on 40 s. orange	1·40	5·75
179		10 c. on 60 s. green	1·10	5·75
180		10 c. on 80 s. red	1·40	5·75
181	25	20 c. on 1 a. green & red	4·75	12·50
182	–	20 c. on 2 a. (No. 107)	8·00	18·00
183	31	25 c. on 2 a. red & blue	1·00	85
184		30 c. on 4 a. red & brn	1·00	80
185	–	50 c. on 5 a. (No. 108)	1·40	1·25
186	31	50 c. on 10 a. blue & blk	65	1·25
187	30	1 l. on 5 a. yellow & blue	12·50	27·00

38. Wayside Cross.

39. Ruins of Kaunas Castle.

40. Seminary Church.

1923.

No.	Type	Description	Unused	Used
201	38	2 c. brown	60	30
202		3 c. green	85	25
203		5 c. green	85	10
204		10 c. violet	2·00	10
189		15 c. red	1·40	10
190		20 c. green	1·40	15
191		25 c. blue	1·40	10
206		36 c. brown	7·50	65
192	39	50 c. green	1·40	15
193		60 c. red	1·40	10
194	40	1 l. orange and green	6·75	10
195		3 l. red and grey	5·25	55
196		5 l. brown and blue	10·00	90

43. Arms of Memel.

44. Ruins of Trakai.

1923. Union of Memel with Lithuania.

No.	Type	Description	Unused	Used
210.	43.	1 c. red and green	1·10	1·25
211.	–	2 c. mauve	1·10	1·25
212.	–	3 c. yellow	1·25	1·25
213.	43.	5 c. buff and blue	1·40	1·25
214.	–	10 c. red	1·50	1·50
215.	–	15 c. green	1·50	1·50
216.	44.	25 c. violet	2·40	2·40
217.	–	30 c. red	2·75	3·25
218.	–	60 c. green	2·75	3·25
219.	–	1 l. green	3·00	3·00
220.	–	2 l. red	6·75	10·00
221.	44.	3 l. blue	7·50	10·00
222.	–	5 l. blue	10·00	11·50

DESIGNS—As Type **43**: 3 c., 2 l. Chapel of Biruta. 10 c., 15 c. War Memorial, Kaunas. As Type **44**: 2 c., 30 c. Arms of Lithuania. 60 c., 5 l. Memel Lighthouse. 1 l. Memel Harbour.

45.

46.

1924. Air.

No.	Type	Description	Unused	Used
223.	45.	20 c. yellow	1·40	85
224.		40 c. green	1·40	85
225.		60 c. red	1·60	65
226.	46.	1 l. brown	3·25	55

1924. Charity. War Orphans Fund. Surch **KARO NASLAICIAMS** and premium.

No.	Type	Description	Unused	Used
227.	38.	2 c.+2 c. brn. (postage)	1·00	90
228.		3 c.+3 c. olive	1·00	90
229.		5 c.+5 c. green	1·00	90
231.		10 c.+10 c. violet	1·40	1·50
232.		15 c.+15 c. red	1·50	1·50
233.		20 c.+20 c. olive	2·00	2·00
235.		25 c.+25 c. blue	4·75	4·75
236.		36 c.+34 c. brown	5·00	5·00
237.	39.	50 c.+50 c. green	5·00	5·00
238.		60 c.+60 c. red	6·75	6·75
239.	40.	1 l.+1 l. orange & green	6·75	6·75
240.		3 l.+2 l. red and grey	11·50	11·50
241.		5 l.+3 l. brown and blue	17·00	17·00
242.	45.	20 c.+20 c. yellow (air)	6·75	6·75
243.		40 c.+40 c. green	6·75	6·75
244.		60 c.+60 c. red	6·75	6·75
245.	46.	1 l.+1 l. brown	8·50	9·00

49. Swallow carrying Letter.

56.

57.

1926. Air.

No.	Type	Description	Unused	Used
246.	49.	20 c. red	70	30
247.		40 c. orange and mauve	70	30
248.		60 c. black and blue	2·10	40

1926. Charity. War Invalids. Nos. 227/39 surch. with new values and small ornaments.

No.	Type	Description	Unused	Used
249.	38.	1 c.+1 c. on 2 c.+2 c.	55	65
250.		2 c.+2 c. on 3 c.+3 c.	55	65
251.		2 c.+2 c. on 5 c.+5 c.	55	65
253.		5 c.+5 c. on 10 c.+10 c.	1·40	1·40
254.		5 c.+5 c. on 15 c.+15 c.	1·40	1·40
255.		10 c.+10 c. on 20 c.+20 c.	1·40	1·40
257.		10 c.+10 c. on 25 c.+25 c.	3·25	3·25
258.		14 c.+14 c. on 36 c.+34 c.	4·00	4·00
259.	39.	20 c.+20 c. on 50 c.+50 c.	3·25	3·25
260.		25 c.+25 c. on 60 c.+60 c.	5·00	5·00
261.	40.	30 c.+30 c. on 1 l.+1 l.	8·25	8·25

1926. Charity. War Orphans. Nos. 227/39 surch. **V.P.** and new values in circular ornament.

No.	Type	Description	Unused	Used
262.	38.	1 c.+1 c. on 2 c.+2 c.	55	65
263.		2 c.+2 c. on 3 c.+3 c.	55	65
264.		2 c.+2 c. on 5 c.+5 c.	55	65
266.		5 c.+5 c. on 10 c.+10 c.	1·40	1·40
267.		10 c.+10 c. on 15 c.+15 c.	1·40	1·25
268.		15 c.+15 c. on 20 c.+20 c.	1·60	1·40
270.		15 c.+15 c. on 25 c.+25 c.	3·25	3·25
271.		19 c.+19 c. on 36 c.+34 c.	3·25	3·25
272.	39.	25 c.+25 c. on 50 c.+50 c.	4·00	4·00
273.		30 c.+30 c. on 60 c.+60 c.	6·75	6·75
274.	40.	50 c.+50 c. on 1 l.+1 l.	10·00	10·00

1927.

No.	Type	Description	Unused	Used
275	56	2 c. orange	55	10
276		3 c. brown	55	10
277		5 c. green	1·10	10
278		10 c. violet	2·00	10
279		15 c. red	1·60	10
280		25 c. blue	1·60	10
283		30 c. blue	5·25	10

1927. Dr. Basanavicius Mourning issue.

No.	Type	Description	Unused	Used
285.	57.	15 c. red	1·40	40
286.		25 c. blue	1·40	40
287.		50 c. green	1·40	50
288.		60 c. violet	2·75	1·40

58. "Vytis" of the Lithuanian Arms.

1927.

No.	Type	Description	Unused	Used
289.	58.	1 l. green and grey	1·25	65
290.		3 l. violet and green	3·25	50
291.		5 l. brown and grey	6·25	1·25

59. President Antanas Smetona.

60. Lithuania liberated.

1928. 10th Anniv. of Independence.

No.	Type	Description	Unused	Used
292.	59.	5 c. green and brown	15	10
293.		10 c. black and violet	15	10
294.		15 c. brown and orange	15	10
295.		25 c. slate and blue	50	10
296.	60.	50 c. purple and blue	90	20
297.		60 c. black and red	1·10	35
298.	–	1 l. brown	1·40	1·00

DESIGN—HORIZ. 1 l. Lithuania's resurrection (angel and soldiers). Dated 1918-1928.

62.

63.

64. J. Tubelis.

66. Railway Station, Kaunas.

1930. 500th Death Anniv. of Grand Duke Vytautas.

(a) Postage.

No.	Type	Description	Unused	Used
299.	62.	2 c. brown	25	10
300.		3 c. violet and brown	25	10
301.		5 c. red and green	25	10
302.		10 c. green and violet	25	10
303.		15 c. violet and red	25	10
304.		30 c. purple and blue	50	10
305.		36 c. olive and purple	35	15
306.		50 c. blue and green	35	20
307.		60 c. red and blue	60	35
308.	63.	1 l. purple, grey & grn.	2·00	65
309.		3 l. violet, pink & mauve	2·75	1·25
310.		5 l. red, grey and brown	5·00	1·40
311.		10 l. black and blue	15·00	10·00
312.		25 l. green and brown	32·00	48·00

(b) Air.

No.	Type	Description	Unused	Used
313	64	5 c. brown, yellow & blk	35	35
314		10 c. black, drab & blue	40	40
315		15 c. blue, grey & purple	40	40
316	–	20 c. red, orange & brn	1·00	55
317	–	40 c. violet, lt blue & bl	1·40	80
318	–	60 c. black, lilac & green	1·60	1·40
319	–	1 l. black, lilac and red	3·00	1·50

DESIGNS—HORIZ. 20 c., 40 c. Vytautas and Kaunas. 60 c., 1 l. Vytautas and Smetona.

1932. Orphans' Fund. Imperf. or perf.

No.	Type	Description	Unused	Used
320.	66.	5 c. blue and brown	30	30
321.		10 c. purple and brown	30	30
322.	–	15 c. brown and green	30	30
323.	–	25 c. blue and green	45	50
324.	–	50 c. grey and olive	1·00	1·60
325.	–	60 c. grey and mauve	1·40	5·00
326.	–	1 l. blue and grey	2·00	2·75
327.	–	3 l. purple and green	3·00	5·00

DESIGNS—As Type **66**: 15, 25 c. "The Two Pines" (painting). 50 c. G.P.O. VERT. 60 c., 1, 3 l. Vilnius Cathedral.

68. Map of Lithuania, Memel and Vilna.

1932. Air. Orphans' Fund. Imperf. or perf.

No.	Type	Description	Unused	Used
328.	68.	5 c. red and green	25	25
329.		10 c. purple and brown	25	25
330.	–	15 c. blue and buff	40	40
331.	–	20 c. black and brown	2·40	2·00
332.	–	40 c. purple and yellow	3·25	3·25
333.	–	60 c. blue and buff	4·00	6·00
334.	–	1 l. purple and green	5·00	6·00
335.	–	2 l. blue and green	5·00	6·75

DESIGNS: 15 c., 20 c. Aeroplane over R. Niemen. 40 c., 60 c. Town Hall, Kaunas. 1 l., 2 l. Vytautas Church, Kaunas.

69. Vytautas escapes from Prison.

71. Coronation of Mindaugas.

1932. 15th Anniv. of Independence. Imperf. or perf.

No.	Type	Description	Unused	Used
336.	69.	5 c. purple & red (post.)	50	50
337.		10 c. brown and grey	50	50
338.	–	15 c. green and red	50	50
339.	–	25 c. brown and purple	1·00	1·60
340.	–	50 c. brown and green	1·40	2·40
341.	–	60 c. red and green	1·60	5·00
342.	–	1 l. black and blue	2·00	3·25
343.	–	3 l. green and purple	2·75	6·75
344.	–	5 c. lilac and green (air)	15	20
345.	–	10 c. red and green	15	25
346.	71.	15 c. brown and violet	20	30
347.		20 c. black and red	45	45
348.	–	40 c. black and purple	1·00	2·00
349.	–	60 c. black and orange	1·40	6·00
350.	–	1 l. green and violet	2·10	3·25
351.	–	2 l. brown and blue	3·00	6·00

DESIGNS—POSTAGE. As Type **69**: 15, 25 c. Vytautas and Jagello preaching the gospel. 50, 60 c. Battle of Grunewald. 1, 3 l. Proclamation of Independence. AIR. As Type **71**: 5, 10 c. Battle of Saules. 40 c. Gediminas in Council. 60 c. Founding of Vilnius. 1 l. Russians surrendering to Gediminas. 2 l. Algirdas before Moscow.

72. A. Visteliauskas.

PORTRAITS: 15 c., 25 c. P. Vileisis. 50 c., 60 c. J. Sliupas. 1 l., 3 l. J. Basanavicius.

1933. 50th Anniv. of Publication of "Ausra".

No.	Type	Description	Unused	Used
352.	72.	5 c. red and green	20	25
353.		10 c. red and blue	20	25
354.	–	15 c. red and orange	20	25
355.	–	25 c. brown and blue	85	1·00
356.	–	50 c. blue and green	1·25	1·60
357.	–	60 c. dp. brn. & lt. brn.	3·00	5·00
358.	–	1 l. purple and red	3·25	4·25
359.	–	3 l. purple and blue	5·75	6·75

73. Trakai Castle.

1933. Air. 550th Death Anniv. of Grand Duke Kestutis.

No.	Type	Description	Unused	Used
360.	73.	5 c. blue and green	20	35
361.		10 c. brown and violet	20	35
362.	–	15 c. violet and blue	20	35
363.	–	20 c. purple and brown	55	80
364.	–	40 c. purple and blue	1·40	1·90
365.	–	60 c. blue and red	2·25	7·75
366.	–	1 l. blue and green	2·75	6·75
367.	–	2 l. green and violet	4·00	10·00

DESIGNS: 15. 20 c. Kestutis encounters Birute. 40, 60 c. Birute. 1, 2 l. Kestutis and Algirdas.

74. Mother and Child.

75. J. Tumas Vaizgantas.

1933. Child Welfare. (a) Postage.

No.	Type	Description	Unused	Used
373.	74.	5 c. brown and green	15	20
374.		10 c. blue and red	15	20
375.	–	15 c. purple and green	20	25
376.	–	25 c. black and orange	65	1·00
377.	–	50 c. red and green	1·00	1·60
378.	–	60 c. orange and black	2·40	5·00
379.	–	1 l. blue and brown	2·75	5·00
380.	–	3 l. green and purple	4·75	8·25

DESIGNS—VERT. 15, 25 c. Boy reading a book. 50, 60 c. Boy with building bricks. 1, 3 l. Mother and child weaving.

(b) Air. Various medallion portraits in triangular frames.

No.	Type	Description	Unused	Used
381.	–	5 c. blue and red	15	15
382.	–	10 c. green and violet	15	15
383.	75.	15 c. brown and green	15	15
384.		20 c. blue and red	25	35
385.	–	40 c. green and lake	1·40	1·60
386.	–	60 c. brown and blue	1·75	3·75
387.	–	1 l. blue and yellow	2·40	3·75
388.	–	2 l. lake and green	3·75	6·00

DESIGNS: 5, 10 c. Maironis. 40, 60 c. Vincas Kudirka. 1, 2 l. Zemaite.

76. Captains S. Darius and S. Girenas.

78. "Flight" mourning over Wreckage.

81. President A. Smetona.

1934. Air. Death of Darius and Girenas (trans-Atlantic airmen).

No.	Type	Description	Unused	Used
389.	76.	20 c. red and black	10	10
390.	–	40 c. blue and red	10	10
391.	76.	60 c. violet and black	10	10
392.	78.	1 l. black and red	35	15
393.	–	3 l. orange and green	1·00	2·00
394.	–	5 l. blue and brown	4·00	4·25

DESIGNS—HORIZ. 40 c. Airplane "Lituanica" over Atlantic. VERT. 3 l. "Lituanica" and globe. 5 l. "Lituanica" and Vytis.

1934. President's 60th Birthday.

No.	Type	Description	Unused	Used
395.	81.	15 c. red	3·25	10
396.		30 c. green	6·75	15
397.		60 c. blue	13·50	70

82.

83.

84. Gleaner.

85.

1934.

No.	Type	Description	Unused	Used
398.	82.	2 c. red and orange	25	10
399.		5 c. green	30	10
400.	83.	10 c. brown	1·00	10
401.	84.	25 c. brown and green	2·40	10
402.	83.	35 c. red	2·40	10
403.	84.	50 c. blue	4·00	10
404.	85.	1 l. purple and red	17·00	10
405.		3 l. green	20	10
406.	–	5 l. purple and blue	20	20
407.	–	10 l. brown and yellow	1·60	1·25

DESIGN—HORIZ. as Type **85**: 5 l., 10 l. Knight.

For design as Type **82** but smaller, see Nos. 411/12.

1935. Air. Honouring Atlantic Flyer Vaitkus. No. 390 optd **F. VAITKUS nugalejo Atlanta 21-22-IX-1935**.

No.	Type	Description	Unused	Used
407a	–	40 c. blue and red	£300	£325

87. Vaitkus and Air Route.

88. President Smetona.

1936. Air. Vaitkus' New York–Ireland Flight.

No.	Type	Description	Unused	Used
408.	87.	15 c. purple	1·25	45
409.		30 c. green	1·60	1·10
410.		60 c. blue	2·75	1·10

1936. As T **82** but smaller (18 × 23 mm.).

No.	Type	Description	Unused	Used
411.	82.	2 c. orange	10	10
412.		5 c. green	10	10

1936.

No.	Type	Description	Unused	Used
413.	88.	15 c. red	4·00	10
414.		30 c. green	11·50	10
415.		60 c. blue	6·75	10

89.

90. Archer.

1937.

No.	Type	Description	Unused	Used
416.	89.	10 c. green	1·10	10
417.		25 c. mauve	10	10
418.		35 c. red	60	10
419.		50 c. brown	30	10
419a.		1 l. blue	15	30

1938. 1st National Olympiad Fund.

No.	Type	Description	Unused	Used
420.	90.	5 c. + 5 c. green	8·25	10·00
421.	–	15 c. + 5 c. red	9·25	10·00
422.	–	30 c. + 10 c. blue	13·50	13·50
423.	–	60 c. + 15 c. brown	20·00	20·00

DESIGNS: 15 c. Throwing the javelin. 30 c. Diving. 60 c. Relay runner breasting tape.

1938. Scouts' and Guides' National Camp Fund. Nos. 420/3 optd. **TAUTINE SKAUCIU** (or **SKAUTU**) **STOVYKLA** and badge.

No.	Type	Description	Unused	Used
424.	90.	5 c. + 5 c. green	10·00	10·00
425.	–	15 c. + 5 c. red	10·00	10·00
426.	–	30 c. + 10 c. blue	10·00	13·50
427.	–	60 c. + 15 c. brown	20·00	22·00

92. President Smetona.

93. Scoring a Goal.

1939. 20th Anniv. of Independence.

No.	Type	Description	Unused	Used
428.	–	15 c. red	30	10
429.	92.	30 c. green	85	45
430.	–	35 c. mauve	1·00	55
431.	92.	60 c. blue	1·40	85

DESIGN: 15, 35 c. Dr. Basanavicius proclaiming Lithuanian independence.

1939. 3rd. European Basketball Championship and Physical Culture Fund.

No.	Type	Description	Unused	Used
432.	–	15 c. + 10 c. brown	6·75	6·75
433.	93.	30 c. + 15 c. green	6·75	6·75
434.	–	60 c. + 40 c. violet	17·00	20·00

DESIGNS—VERT. 15 c. Scoring a goal. HORIZ. ($40\frac{1}{2} \times 36$ mm). 60 c. International flags and ball.

1939. Recovery of Vilnius. Nos. 428/31 optd **VILNIUS 1939-X-10** and trident.

No.	Type	Description	Unused	Used
435.	–	15 c. red	55	30
436.	92.	30 c. green	1·00	40
437.	–	35 c. mauve	1·10	55
438.	92.	60 c. blue	1·50	85

95. Vytis.

96. Vilnius.

1940. "Liberty" Issue.

No.	Type	Description	Unused	Used
439.	95.	5 c. brown	10•	10
440.	–	10 c. green	65•	30
441.	–	15 c. orange	10	10
442.	–	25 c. brown	10	30
443.	–	30 c. green	10	10
444.	–	35 c. orange	10	45

DESIGNS: 10 c. Angel. 15 c. Woman releasing a dove. 25 c. Mother and children. 30 c. "Liberty Bell". 35 c. Mythical animal.

1940. Recovery of Vilnius.

No.	Type	Description	Unused	Used
445.	96.	15 c. brown	30	15
446.	–	30 c. green	85	25
447.	–	60 c. blue	1·60	90

DESIGNS—VERT. 30 c. Portrait of Gediminas. HORIZ. 60 c. Ruins of Trakai Castle.

1940. Incorporation of Lithuania in U.S.S.R. Optd. **LTSR 1940 VII 21.**

No.	Type	Description	Unused	Used
448.	82.	2 c. red and orange	15	40
449.	95.	5 c. brown	15	40
450.	–	10 c. green (No. 440)	4·00	5·00
451.	–	15 c. orange (No. 441)	15	50
452.	–	25 c. brown (No. 442)	20	75
453.	–	30 c. green (No. 443)	25	80
454.	–	35 c. orange (No. 444)	60	1·50
455.	89.	50 c. brown	50	1·40

From 1940 to 1990 Lithuania used stamps of Russia.

99 Angel and Map

1990. No gum. Imperf.

No.	Type	Description	Unused	Used
456	99	5 k. green	10	10
457		10 k. lilac	20	20
458		20 k. blue	40	40
459		50 k. red	1·50	1·50

1990. No gum. Imperf (simulated perfs).

No.	Type	Description	Unused	Used
460	99	5 k. green and brown	10	10
461		10 k. purple and brown	20	20
462		20 k. blue and brown	40	40
463		50 k. red and brown	1·00	1·00

100 Vytis

101 Hill of Crosses, Siauliai

1991.

No.	Type	Description	Unused	Used
464	100	10 k. black, gold & brn	20	20
465		15 k. black, gold & grn	30	30
466		20 k. black, gold & blue	40	40
467		30 k. black, gold & red	60	60
468		40 k. black and gold	20	20
469		50 k. black, gold & vio	25	25
470	101	50 k. brown, chestnut and black	1·00	1·00
471	100	100 k. blk, gold & grn	50	50
472	–	200 k. brown, chestnut and black	3·25	3·25
473	100	500 k. black, gold & bl	2·40	2·40

DESIGN: As T **101**—200 k. Lithuanian Liberty Bell.

See also No. 482 and 488/9.

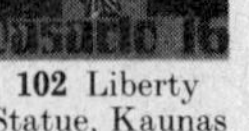

102 Liberty Statue, Kaunas

103 Angel with Trumpet

1991. National Day.

No.	Type	Description	Unused	Used
480	102	20 k. mauve, sil & blk	40	40

1991. 1st Anniv of Declaration of Independence from U.S.S.R.

No.	Type	Description	Unused	Used
481	103	20 k. dp green & green	40	40

1991. No gum. Imperf (simulated perfs).

No.	Type	Description	Unused	Used
482	100	15 k. green	30	30

104 Wayside Crosses

1991.

No.	Type	Description	Unused	Used
483	104	40 k. green and silver	55	55
484	–	70 k. brn, buff & gold	95	95
485	–	100 k. brown, yellow and silver	1·40	1·40

DESIGNS: 70 k. "Madonna" (icon from Pointed Gate Chapel, Vilnius; 100 k. Towers of St. Anne's Church, Vilnius.

105 Candle

1991. 50th Anniv of Resistance to Soviet and German Occupations.

No.	Type	Description	Unused	Used
486	105	20 k. yellow, blk & bis	40	40
487	–	50 k. rose, black & red	1·00	1·00
488	–	70 k. multicoloured ..	1·10	1·10

DESIGNS: 50 k. Shield pierced by swords; 70 k. Sword and wreath

1991. No gum. Imperf.

No.	Type	Description	Unused	Used
489	100	25 k. black and brown	50	50
490		30 k. black and purple	60	60

106 World Map and Games Emblem

107 Lithuanian Flag on Ice-axe and Mt. Everest

1991. 4th International Lithuanians' Games.

No.	Type	Description	Unused	Used
491	106	20 k. green, blk & yell	40	40
492	–	50 k. green, blk & yell	1·40	1·40

DESIGN: 50 k. Symbolic female athlete.

1991. Lithuanian Expedition to Mt. Everest.

No.	Type	Description	Unused	Used
493	107	20 k. multicoloured ..	40	40
494		70 k. multicoloured ..	1·75	1·75

108 Trakai Castle

109 Black Storks

1991. 650th Death Anniv of Grand Duke Gediminas. Each brown, ochre and green.

No.	Type	Description	Unused	Used
495		30 k. Type 108	60	60
496		50 k. Gediminas	75	75
497		70 k. Vilnius in 14th century	1·10	1·10

1991. Birds in the Red Book. Multicoloured.

No.	Type	Description	Unused	Used
498		30 k.+15 k. Type 109 ..	90	90
499		50 k. Common cranes ..	1·00	1·00

110 U.N. and National Emblems and National Flag

111 National Team Emblem and Colours

1992. Admission to U.N.O.

No.	Type	Description	Unused	Used
500	110	100 k. multicoloured ..	50	50

1992. Winter Olympic Games, Albertville, and Summer Games, Barcelona. Multicoloured.

No.	Type	Description	Unused	Used
501		50 k.+25 k. Type 111 ..	35	35
502		130 k. Winter Games emblem	60	60
503		280 k. Summer Games emblem	1·10	1·10

112 Slipper Orchid

113 Goosander ("Mergus merganser")

1992. Plants in the Red Book. Multicoloured.

No.	Type	Description	Unused	Used
504		200 k. Type 112	65	65
505		300 k. Sea holly	1·00	1·00

1992. Birds of the Baltic. No value expressed.

No.	Type	Description	Unused	Used
506	113	B (15 t.) black & green	20	20
507	–	B (15 t.) brn, blk & grn	20	20
508	–	B (15 t.) sepia, brown and green	20	20
509	–	B (15 t.) brn, blk & grn	20	20

DESIGNS: No. 506, Osprey ("Pandion haliaetus"); 507, Black-tailed godwit ("Limosa limosa"); 509, Common shelduck ("Tadorna tadorna").

114 Kedainiai

115 Couple

1992. Arms. Multicoloured.

No.	Type	Description	Unused	Used
510		2 t. Type 114	15	15
511		3 t. Vilnius	20	20
512		10 t. State arms	65	65

See also Nos. 531/3.

1992. Costumes of Suvalkija.

No.	Type	Description	Unused	Used
513	115	2 t. multicoloured ..	15	15
514	–	5 t. multicoloured ..	30	30
515	–	7 t. multicoloured ..	45	45

DESIGNS: 5, 7 t. Different costumes.

116 Zapyskis Church

1993. Churches.

No.	Type	Description	Unused	Used
516	116	3 t. black and stone ..	15	15
517	–	10 t. black and blue	55	55
518	–	15 t. black and grey ..	85	85

DESIGNS: 10 t. Church of St. Peter and St. Paul, Vilnius; 15 t. Church of the Resurrection, Kaunas.

1993. Nos. 467, 490 and 468 surch.

No.	Type	Description	Unused	Used
519	100	1 t. on 30 k. black, gold and red	10	10
520		1 t. on 30 k. blk & pur	10	10
521		3 t. on 40 k. blk & gold	35	35

118 Jonas Basanavicius (statesman)

1993. National Day. No value expressed.

No.	Type	Description	Unused	Used
522	118	A (3 t.) red, cinnamon and brown	15	15
523	–	B (15 t.) green, stone and brown	85	85

DESIGN: No. 523, Jonas Vileisis (politician).

119 Vytautas

120 Simonas Daukantas (historian)

1993. 600th Anniv (1987) of Accession of Grand Duke Vytautas.

No.	Type	Description	Unused	Used
524	–	5 t. gold, red and black	25	25
525	119	10 t. green, black & red	55	55
526	–	15 t. black, yell & red	80	80

DESIGNS: 5 t. Seal; 15 t. "Battle of Grunwald" (Jan Matejka).

1993. Birth Anniversaries. Each brown and yellow.

No.	Type	Description	Unused	Used
528		1000 t. Type 120 (bicent)	50	50
529		2000 t. Vydunas (125th anniv)	1·25	1·25
530		4500 t. Vincas Mykolaitis-Putinas (philosopher, centenary)	2·75	2·75

1993. Town Arms. As T 114. Multicoloured.

No.	Type	Description	Unused	Used
531		5 c. Skuodas	10	10
532		30 c. Telsiai	10	10
533		50 c. Klaipeda	20	20

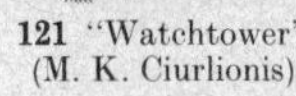

121 "Watchtower" (M. K. Ciurlionis)

122 State Arms

1993. World Unity Day (5 t.) and Trans-atlantic Flight (80 t.). Multicoloured.

No.	Type	Description	Unused	Used
534		5 c. Type 121	10	10
535		80 c. S. Dariaus and S. Gireno	30	30

1993. No value expressed.

No.	Type	Description	Unused	Used
536	122	A, green, brown & red	10	10
537		B, red, green & bistre	30	30

123 Pope John Paul II and View of Siluva

124 Couple

1993. Papal Visit. Multicoloured.

No.	Type	Description	Unused	Used
538		60 c. Type 123	20	20
539		60 c. Pope and Hill of Crosses	20	20
540		80 c. Pope and Kaunas ..	30	30
541		80 c. Pope and Ausra Gates, Vilnius	30	30

1993. Costumes of Dzukai.

No.	Type	Description	Unused	Used
542	124	60 c. multicoloured ..	20	20
543	–	80 c. multicoloured ..	30	30
544	–	1 t. multicoloured ..	35	35

DESIGNS: 80 c. to 1 t. Different costumes.

LOMBARDY AND VENETIA Pt. 2

Formerly known as Austrian Italy. Although these Provinces used a different currency the following issues were valid throughout Austria. Lombardy was annexed by Sardinia in 1859 and Venetia by Italy in 1866.

1850. 100 centesimi = 1 lira.
1858. 100 soldi = 1 florin.
100 kreuzer = 1 gulden.

1. Arms of Austria.

1850. Imperf.

No.	Type	Description	Unused	Used
1c.	1.	5 c. orange	£600	45·00
2c.		10 c. black	£700	38·00
7.		15 c. red	£180	60
8.		30 c. brown	£850	1·40
9.		45 c. blue	£2250	6·50

1859. As T 4 and 5 of Austria (Emperor Francis Joseph I) but value in soldi. Perf.

No.	Type	Description	Unused	Used
16.	5.	2 s. yellow	£200	35·00
17.	4.	3 s. black	£450	£100
18.		3 s. green	£160	30·00
19.	5.	5 s. red	90·00	2·00
20.		10 s. brown	£120	18·00
21.		15 s. blue	£425	8·00

3. Emperor Francis Joseph I.

4. Arms of Austria.

1861.

No.	Type	Description	Unused	Used
25.	3.	5 s. red	£475	1·25
26.		10 s. brown	£425	10·00

1863.

No.	Type	Description	Unused	Used
27.	4.	2 s. yellow	42·00	70·00
33.		3 s. green	8·50	6·50
34.		5 s. red	1·50	80
35.		10 s. blue	8·00	2·75
36.		15 s. brown	13·00	16·00

JOURNAL STAMPS

J 5.

1858. Imperf.

No.	Type	Description	Unused	Used
J 22.	J5.	1 k. black	£600	£2000
J 23.		2 k. red	£120	35·00
J 24.		4 k. red	£12000	£2250

LOURENCO MARQUES Pt. 9

A Portuguese colony in E. Africa, now part of Mozambique, whose stamps it uses.

1895. 1000 reis = 1 milreis.
1913. 100 centavos = 1 escudo.

1895. "Figures" key-type inscr. "LOURENCO MARQUES"

No.	Type	Description	Unused	Used
1	R	5 r. yellow	20	15
2		10 r. mauve	25	15
3		15 r. brown	40	35
4		20 r. lilac	40	35
10		25 r. green	30	15
12		50 r. blue	35	15
18		75 r. red	80	40
14		80 r. green	1·25	90
7		100 r. brown on yellow	85	50
16		150 r. red on rose ..	90	75
8		200 r. blue on blue ..	1·50	1·00
9		300 r. blue on brown ..	1·50	1·00

1895. 700th Death Anniv of St. Anthony. Optd **L. MARQUES CENTENARIO DE S. ANTONIO MDCCCXCV** on (a) "Embossed" key-type inscr "PROVINCIA DE MOCAMBIQUE".

No.	Type	Description	Unused	Used
19.	Q.	5 r. black	5·00	4·50
20.		10 r. green	7·50	5·00
21.		20 r. red	9·00	6·00
22.		25 r. purple	11·00	8·00
23.		40 r. brown	9·00	7·50
27a.		50 r. blue	6·00	5·00
25.		100 r. brown	17·00	12·00
26.		200 r. violet	13·00	12·00
27.		300 r. orange	20·00	17·00

(b) "Figures" key-type inscr. "MOCAMBIQUE"

No.	Type	Description	Unused	Used
28.	R.	5 r. orange	5·00	4·00
29.		10 r. mauve	9·00	7·50
30.		50 r. blue	14·00	8·00
35.		75 r. red	15·00	10·00
32.		80 r. green	25·00	18·00
33.		100 r. brown on yellow ..	27·00	25·00
35a.		150 r. red on rose ..	17·00	14·00

1897. No. 9 surch **50 reis.**
36 R 50 r. on 300 r. blue on brn .. 50·00 42·00

1898. "King Carlos" key-type inscr. "LOURENCO MARQUES".
37. S. 2½ r. grey .. 15 15
38. 5 r. orange .. 15 15
39. 10 r. green .. 15 15
40. 15 r. brown .. 15 15
83. 15 r. green .. 25 20
41. 20 r. lilac .. 30 15
42. 25 r. green .. 35 15
84. 25 r. red .. 20 15
43. 50 r. blue .. 50 15
85. 50 r. brown .. 45 30
86. 65 r. blue .. 2·00 1·75
44. 75 r. red .. 80 65
87. 75 r. purple .. 60 50
45. 80 r. mauve .. 70 55
46. 100 r. blue on blue .. 50 25
88. 115 r. brown on pink .. 2·10 2·00
89. 130 r. brown on yellow .. 2·25 2·00
47. 150 r. brown on yellow .. 90 80
48. 200 r. purple on pink .. 1·60 70
49. 300 r. blue on pink .. 1·00 75
90. 400 r. blue on yellow .. 2·25 2·00
50. 500 r. black on blue .. 1·25 1·25
51. 700 r. mauve on yellow .. 3·50 2·50

1899. Green and brown fiscal stamps of Mozambique, as T 9 of Macao, bisected and each half surch. **Correio de Lourenco Marques** and value. Imperf.
55. – 5 r. on half of 10 r. .. 60 30
56. – 25 r. on half of 10 r. .. 60 30
57. – 50 r. on half of 30 r. .. 60 30
58. – 50 r. on half of 800 r. .. 90 50

1899. Nos. 44 and 86 surch **50 Reis.**
91. S. 50 r. on 65 r. blue .. 1·00 1·00
59. 50 r. on 75 r. red .. 1·25 1·00

1902. "Figures" and "Newspaper" key-types surch.
60. V. 65 r. on 2½ r. brown .. 1·10 1·00
62. R. 65 r. on 5 r. yellow .. 1·10 1·00
63. 65 r. on 15 r. brown .. 1·10 1·00
64. 65 r. on 20 r. lilac .. 1·10 1·00
66. 115 r. on 10 r. mauve .. 1·10 1·00
67. 115 r. on 200 r. bl. on bl. .. 1·10 1·00
68. 115 r. on 300 r. bl. on brn. .. 1·10 1·00
70. 130 r. on 25 r. green .. 1·10 1·00
72. 130 r. on 80 r. green .. 85 75
73. 130 r. on 150 r. red on rose .. 85 75
74. 400 r. on 50 r. blue .. 3·00 1·75
76. 400 r. on 75 r. red .. 2·50 2·00
78. 400 r. on 100 r. brown on yellow .. 1·75 1·25

1902. "King Carlos" key-type inscr. "LOURENCO MARQUES" optd. **PROVISORIO**
79. S. 15 r. brown .. 70 50
80. 25 r. green .. 60 35
81. 50 r. blue .. 80 55
82. 75 r. red .. 1·25 70

1911. "King Carlos" key-type inscr. "LOURENCO MARQUES" optd. **REPUBLICA.**
92. S. 2½ r. grey .. 10 10
93. 5 r. orange .. 10 10
94. 10 r. green .. 20 15
95. 15 r. green .. 20 15
96. 20 r. lilac .. 35 20
97. 25 r. red .. 20 15
98. 50 r. brown .. 35 25
99. 75 r. purple .. 35 25
100. 100 r. blue on blue .. 35 25
178. 115 r. brown on pink .. 35 35
102. 130 r. brown on yellow .. 30 30
103. 200 r. purple on pink .. 30 30
104. 400 r. blue on yellow .. 60 35
105. 500 r. black on blue .. 70 60
106. 700 r. mauve on yellow .. 75 60

1913. Surch. **REPUBLICA LOURENCO MARQUES** and value on "Vasco da Gama" issues of

(a) **Portuguese Colonies.**
107. ¼ c. on 2½ r. green .. 50 45
108. ½ c. on 5 r. red .. 50 45
109. 1 c. on 10 r. purple .. 35 35
110. 2½ c. on 25 r. green .. 35 35
111. 5 c. on 50 r. blue .. 50 45
112. 7½ c. on 75 r. brown .. 85 75
113. 10 c. on 100 r. brown .. 65 45
114. 15 c. on 150 r. bistre .. 40 40

(b) **Macao.**
115. ¼ c. on ½ a. green .. 60 45
116. ½ c. on 1 a. red .. 60 45
117. 1 c. on 2 a. purple .. 40 45
118. 2½ c. on 4 a. green .. 40 45
119. 5 c. on 8 a. blue .. 60 45
120. 7½ c. on 12 a. brown .. 1·00 85
121. 10 c. on 16 a. brown .. 75 45
122. 15 c. on 24 a. bistre .. 75 45

(c) **Timor.**
123. ¼ c. on ½ a. green .. 60 45
124. ½ c. on 1 a. red .. 60 45
125. 1 c. on 2 a. purple .. 40 45
126. 2½ c. on 4 a. green .. 40 45
127. 5 c. on 8 a. blue .. 60 45
128. 7½ c. on 12 a. brown .. 1·00 85
129. 10 c. on 16 a. brown .. 75 45
130. 15 c. on 24 a. bistre .. 75 45

1914. "Ceres" key-type inscr. "LOURENCO MARQUES".
147. U. ¼ c. olive .. 10 10
148. ½ c. black .. 10 10
149. 1 c. green .. 10 10
150. 1½ c. brown .. 15 15
151. 2 c. red .. 15 15
152. 2½ c. violet .. 15 15
153. 5 c. blue .. 20 20
154. 7½ c. brown .. 20 20
155. 8 c. grey .. 20 20
140. 10 c. brown .. 70 30
157. 15 c. red .. 40 40
142. 20 c. green .. 50 40
143. 30 c. brown on green .. 50 40
144. 40 c. brown on red .. 2·75 1·75
145. 50 c. orange on pink .. 90 80
146. 1 e. green on blue .. 1·00 80

1914. Provisionals of 1902 overprinted **REPUBLICA.**
166 R 115 r. on 10 r. mauve .. 30 30
167 115 r. on 200 r. bl. on bl. 35 30
168 115 r. on 300 r. blue on brown .. 30 30
161 130 r. on 25 r. green .. 50 40
164 130 r. on 80 r. green .. 35 30
169 130 r. on 150 r. red on rose .. 30 30
184 400 r. on 50 r. blue .. 60 45
185 400 r. on 75 r. red .. 75 20

1915. Nos. 93 and 148 perf. diagonally and each half surch. ½.
170. S. ½ on half of 5 r. orange .. 1·00 90
171. U. ½ on half of ½ c. black .. 1·00 90
Prices of Nos. 170/1 are for whole stamps.

1915. Surch **Dois centavos.**
172 S 2 c. on 15 r. (No. 83) .. 40 35
173 2 c. on 15 c. (No. 95) .. 40 35

1918. Red Cross Fund. "Ceres" key-type inscr. "LOURENCO MARQUES", optd. **9-3-18** and Red Cross or surch. with value in figures and bars also.
188. U ¼ c. olive .. 50 50
189. ½ c. black .. 50 50
190. 1 c. green .. 50 50
191. 2½ c. violet .. 50 50
192. 5 c. blue .. 50 50
193. 10 c. red .. 1·00 90
194. 20 c. on 1½ c. brown .. 1·00 90
195. 30 c. brown on green .. 1·00 90
196. 40 c. on 2 c. red .. 1·00 90
197. 50 c. on 7½ c. brown .. 1·00 90
198. 70 c. on 8 c. grey .. 1·00 90
199. 1 e. on 15 c. red .. 1·00 90

1920. No. 166 surch. **Um quarto de centavo.**
200. R. ¼ c. on 115 r. on 10 r. mauve .. 25 20

1920. No. 152 surch. in figures or words.
201. U. 1 c. on 2½ c. violet .. 20 15
202. 1½ c. on 2½ c. violet .. 20 15
203. 4 c. on 2½ c. violet .. 20 15
For other surcharges on "Ceres" key-type of Lourenzo Marques, see Mozambique Nos. 309/10 and Nos. D 44 and 46.

NEWSPAPER STAMPS

1893. "Newspaper" key-type inscr. "LOURENCO MARQUES".
N 1. V. 2½ r. brown .. 15 15

1895. 700th Death Anniv of St. Anthony. "Newspaper" key-type inscr "MOCAMBIQUE" optd **L. MARQUES CENTENARIO DE S. ANTONIO MDCCCXCV.**
N36 V 2½ r. brown .. 2·50 2·00

LUBECK Pt. 7

Formerly one of the free cities of the Hanseatic League. In 1868 joined the North German Confederation.

16 schillinge = 1 mark.

1. 3.

1859. Imperf.
9. 1. ½ s. lilac .. 14·50 £1300
10. 1 s. orange .. 26·00 £1300
3. 2 s. brown .. 16·00 £200
4. 2½ s. red .. 40·00 £600
6. 4 s. green .. 16·00 £325

1863. Rouletted.
11. 3. ½ s. green .. 38·00 65·00
13. 1 s. orange .. £110 £120
14. 2 s. red .. 20·00 50·00
16. 2½ s. blue .. 45·00 £325
17. 4 s. bistre .. 35·00 95·00

4. 5.

1864. Imperf.
19. 4. 1¼ s. brown .. 21·00 48·00

1865. Roul.
21. 5. 1½ s. mauve .. 20·00 75·00

LUXEMBOURG Pt. 4

An independent Grand Duchy lying between Belgium and the Saar District. Under German Occupation from 1940 to 1944.

1852. 12½ centimes = 1 silver groschen. 100 centimes = 1 franc.
1940. 100 pfennig = 1 reichsmark.
1944. 100 centimes = 1 franc (Belgian).

1. Grand Duke William III. 3. 4.

1852. Imperf.
2. 1. 10 c. black .. £2000 35·00
3a. 1 s. red .. £1300 60·00

1859. Imperf or roul.
23 3 1 c. brown .. 32·00 3·50
21 1 c. orange .. 30·00 5·50
17 2 c. black .. 12·00 9·00
8 4 c. yellow .. £180 £160
20 4 c. green .. 32·00 19·00
10 4 10 c. blue .. £190 11·00
24 10 c. purple .. £100 1·40
25 10 c. lilac .. £110 1·40
28 12½ c. red .. £170 4·50
30 20 c. brown .. £110 6·00
12 25 c. brown .. £375 £250
32 25 c. blue .. £850 8·50
13 30 c. purple .. £300 £180
14 37½ c. green .. £300 £170
35 37½ c. bistre .. £300 £275
39 40 c. orange .. 32·00 80·00

1872. Surch. **UN FRANC.** Roul.
37. 4. 1 f. on 37½ c. bistre .. £1000 70·00

1874. Perf.
64 3 1 c. brown .. 7·00 5·50
65 2 c. black .. 6·00 1·00
42 4 c. green .. 1·00 8·00
43 5 c. yellow .. £170 15·00
67 4 10 c. lilac .. £160 70
61 12½ c. red .. £180 £160
69 20 c. brown .. 40·00 13·00
70 25 c. blue .. £250 2·75
71 30 c. red .. 2·50 19·00
55 40 c. orange .. 75 8·00

1879. Surch. **Un Franc.** Perf.
56. 4. 1 f. on 37½ c. bistre .. 6·00 20·00

7. Agriculture and Trade. 8. Grand Duke Adolf. 9.

1882.
116 7 1 c. grey .. 15 25
117 2 c. brown .. 10 20
118 4 c. bistre .. 35 1·00
119 5 c. green .. 50 20
120 10 c. red .. 6·00 20
98 12½ c. blue .. 1·00 18·00
122 20 c. orange .. 3·00 1·50
123 25 c. blue .. £150 1·00
101 30 c. green .. 17·00 12·00
124 50 c. brown .. 65 6·00
103 1 f. lilac .. 70 20·00
104 5 f. orange .. 27·00 £120

1891.
127 8 10 c. red .. 15 25
145 12½ c. green .. 50 50
146 20 c. orange .. 8·00 50
147 25 c. blue .. 40 30
148 30 c. green .. 1·00 1·00
149 37½ c. green .. 2·00 3·00
150 50 c. brown .. 6·00 3·50
151 1 f. purple .. 18·00 5·00
135 2½ f. black .. 1·00 15·00
136 5 f. lake .. 30·00 45·00

1895.
152. 9. 1 c. grey .. 1·00 30
153. 2 c. brown .. 10 20
154. 4 c. bistre .. 15 70
155. 5 c. green .. 1·25 20
156. 10 c. red .. 5·00 20

10. 11. Grand Duke William IV. 13. Grand Duchess Adelaide.

1906.
157. 10. 1 c. grey .. 10 20
158. 2 c. brown .. 10 20
159. 4 c. bistre .. 15 25
160. 5 c. green .. 25 20
231. 5 c. mauve .. 15 20
161. 6 c. lilac .. 10 30
161a. 7½ c. orange .. 10 2·50
162. 11. 10 c. red .. 80 20
163. 12½ slate .. 1·00 40
164. 15 c. brown .. 1·00 60
165. 20 c. orange .. 1·50 50
166. 25 c. blue .. 38·00 30
166a. 30 c. olive .. 55 50
167. 37½ c. green .. 55 50
168. 50 c. brown .. 1·75 60
169. 87½ c. blue .. 1·25 8·00
170. 1 f. purple .. 3·00 1·00
171. 2½ f. red .. 40·00 80·00
172. 5 f. purple .. 7·00 40·00

1912. Surch. **62½ cts.**
173. 11. 62½ c. on 87½ c. blue .. 1·00 2·00
173a. 62½ c. on 2½ f. red .. 1·00 3·50
173b. 62½ c. on 5 f. purple .. 40 1·50

1914.
174 13 10 c. purple .. 10 20
175 12½ c. green .. 10 20
176 15 c. brown .. 10 20
176a 17½ c. brown .. 10 40
177 25 c. blue .. 10 20
178 30 c. brown .. 10 40
179 35 c. blue .. 10 40
180 37½ c. brown .. 10 40
181 40 c. red .. 20 40
182 50 c. grey .. 20 40
183 62½ c. green .. 30 2·25
183a 87½ c. orange .. 30 2·25
184 1 f. brown .. 80 25
185 2½ f. red .. 40 2·50
186 5 f. violet .. 7·00 35·00

1916. Surch. in figures and bars.
187. 10. 2½ on 5 c. green .. 10 20
188. 3 on 2 c. brown .. 10 20
212. 5 on 1 c. grey .. 10 20
213. 5 on 4 c. bistre .. 10 40
214. 5 on 7½ c. orange .. 10 20
215. 6 on 2 c. brown .. 20 25
189. 13. 7½ on 10 c. red .. 10 20
190. 17½ on 30 c. brown .. 10 40
191. 20 on 17½ c. brown .. 10 20
216. 25 on 37½ c. sepia .. 10 20
217. 75 on 62½ c. green .. 10 20
218. 80 on 87½ c. orange .. 10 20
192. 87½ on 1 f. brown .. 50 5·50

17. Grand Duchess Charlotte. 18. Vianden Castle.

1921. Perf.
194 17 2 c. brown .. 10 20
195 3 c. green .. 10 20
196 6 c. purple .. 10 20
197 10 c. green .. 10 20
193a 15 c. red* .. 10 20
198 15 c. green .. 10 20
234 15 c. orange .. 10 20
199 20 c. orange .. 10 30
235 20 c. green .. 10 20
200 25 c. green .. 10 20
201 30 c. red .. 10 20
202 40 c. orange .. 10 20
203 50 c. blue .. 10 40
236 50 c. red .. 10 20
204 75 c. red .. 10 1·10
237 75 c. blue .. 10 20
205 80 c. black .. 10 85
206a 18 1 f. red .. 10 30
238 1 f. blue .. 10 50
207 – 2 f. blue .. 50 50
239 – 2 f. brown .. 1·10 1·50
208 – 5 f. violet .. 15·00 6·00

DESIGNS—As Type **18**: 2 f. Factories at Esch. 5 f. Bridge over Alzette.

*No. 193a was originally issued on the occasion of the birth of Crown Prince Jean.

See also Nos. 219/20.

21. Monastery at Clervaux.

DESIGNS—HORIZ. 15 c. Pfaffenthal. 25 c. as Type **26**.

1921. War Monument Fund.
209. 21. 10 c.+5 c. green .. 15 3·00
210. – 15 c.+10 c. orange .. 15 5·00
211. – 25 c.+10 c. green .. 15 3·00

1922. Philatelic Exn. Imperf.
219. 17. 25 c. green .. 1·40 5·00
220. 30 c. red .. 1·40 5·00

26. Luxembourg. 28. Echternach.

1923.
222a 26 10 f. black .. .. 2·75 8·00

1923. Unveiling of War Memorial by Prince Leopold of Belgium. Nos. 209/11 surch. **27 mai 1923** and additional values.
223. 21. 10+5+25 c. green .. 1·00 13·00
224. – 15+10+25 c. orange .. 1·00 20·00
225. – 25+10+25 c. green .. 1·00 13·00

1923.
226a. 28. 3 f. blue 60 50

1924. Charity. Death of Grand Duchess Marie Adelaide. Surch. **CARITAS** and new value.
227. 13. 12½ c.+7½ c. green .. 10 1·50
228. 35 c.+10 c. blue.. .. 10 1·50
229. 2½ f.+1 f. red .. .. 35 20·00
230. 5 f.+2 f. violet .. .. 35 15·00

1925. Surch **5.**
240 17 5 on 10 c. green .. 10 20

31. 32. Grand Duchess Charlotte.

1925. Anti-T.B. Fund.
241. 31. 5 c.+5 c. violet .. 10 60
242. 30 c.+5 c. orange .. 10 2·00
243. 50 c.+5 c. brown .. 10 4·00
244. 1 f.+10 c. blue .. 25 12·00

1926.
245. 32. 5 c. mauve 10 20
246. 10 c. olive 10 10
246a. 15 c. black 10 20
247. 20 c. orange 10 30
248. 25 c. green 10 30
248a. 25 c. brown 10 30
248b. 30 c. green 10 30
248c. 30 c. violet 30 20
248d. 35 c. violet 70 30
248e. 35 c. green 10 20
249. 40 c. brown 10 20
250. 50 c. brown 10 20
250a. 60 c. green 65 20
251. 65 c. brown .. .. 15 1·40
251a 70 c. violet 10 10
252. 75 c. red 10 50
252a. 75 c. brown 10 20
253. 80 c. brown .. .. 15 1·10
253a. 90 c. red .. .. 20 1·40
254. 1 f. black 40 30
254a. 1 f. red 40 25
255. 1¼ f. blue 10 50
255a. 1¼ f. yellow .. .. 5·50 1·50
255b. 1½ f. green 30 20
255c. 1½ f. red .. .. 12·00 1·50
255d. 1½ f. blue .. .. 50 1·00
255e. 1¾ f. blue 70 25

33. Prince Jean. 34. Grand Duchess and Prince Felix.

1926. Child Welfare.
256. 33. 5 c.+5 c. blk. and mauve 10 50
257. 40 c.+10 c. black & grn. 10 1·00
258. 50 c.+15 c. black & yell. 10 1·00
259. 75 c.+20 c. black & red 20 10·00
260. 1 f. 50 c.+30 c. black and blue .. .. 20 10·00

1927. Int. Philatelic Exn.
261. 34. 25 c. purple .. .. 1·00 10·00
262. 50 c. green .. .. 1·50 12·00
263. 75 c. red .. .. 1·00 10·00
264. 1 f. black .. .. 1·00 10·00
265. 1½ f. blue .. .. 1·00 10·00

35. Princess Elisabeth. 37. Clervaux.

1927. Child Welfare.
266. 35. 10 c.+5 c. blk. & blue 10 50
267. 50 c.+10 blk. & brn. 10 1·00
268. 75 c.+20 c. blk. & orge. 10 1·25
269. 1 f.+30 c. blk. & red 20 10·00
270. 1½ f.+50 c. blk. & bl. 20 10·00

1927. Stamps of 1921 and 1926 surch.
270a 32 10 on 30 c. green .. 30 40
271 17 15 on 20 c. green .. 10 20
272 32 15 on 25 c. green .. 20 60
273 17 35 on 40 c. orange .. 10 20
274 32 60 on 65 c. brown .. 10 40
275 17 60 on 75 c. blue .. 10 20
276 32 60 on 75 c. red .. 10 40
277 17 60 on 80 c. black .. 20 40
278 32 60 on 80 c. brown .. 15 50
278a 70 on 75 c. brown .. 3·50 30
278b 75 on 90 c. red .. 1·00 40
278c 1¾ on 1½ f. blue .. 2·25 1·50

1928. Perf.
279a 37 2 f. black 75 60
See also No. 339.

38. Princess Marie Adelaide. 39. Princess Marie Gabrielle.

1928. Child Welfare.
280. 38. 10 c.+5 c. pur. & green 20 1·00
281. 60 c.+10 c. olive & brn. 30 3·50
282. 75 c.+15 c. grn. & red 50 5·00
283. 1 f.+25 c. brn. & grn. 1·00 16·00
284. 1½ f.+50 c. blue & yell. 1·00 16·00

1928. Child Welfare.
285. 39. 10 c.+10 c. grn. & brn. 20 50
286. 35 c.+15 c. brn. & grn. 70 5·00
287. 75 c.+30 c. blk. & red 70 7·00
288. 1¼ f.+50 c. grn. & red 2·00 20·00
289. 1¾ f.+75 c. blk. & blue 2·00 25·00

40. Prince Charles. 41. Arms of Luxembourg.

1930. Child Welfare.
290. 40. 10 c.+5 c. brn. & grn. 20 70
291. 75 c.+10 c. grn. & brn. 1·25 4·00
292. 1 f.+25 c. violet & red 2·50 12·00
293. 1¼ f.+75 c. blk. & yell. 4·00 20·00
294. 1¾ f.+1 f. 50 brn. & bl. 4·50 20·00

1930.
295. 41. 5 c. red 50 30
296. 10 c. green 60 20

42. Aeroplane over the Alzette. 43. Luxembourg, Lower Town.

1931. Air.
296a. 42. 50 c. green .. .. 55 1·00
297. 75 c. brown .. .. 50 1·00
298. 1 f. red .. .. 50 1·25
299. 1¼ f. purple .. .. 50 1·50
300. 1¾ f. blue .. .. 50 1·50
300a. 3 f. black .. .. 1·00 4·50

1931.
301. 43. 20 f. green .. .. 2·75 15·00

44. Princess Alix. 45. Countess Ermesinde. 46. Emperor Henry VII.

1931. Child Welfare.
302. 44. 10 c.+5 c. grey & brn. 20 1·00
303. 75 c.+10 c. grn. & red 3·00 12·00
304. 1 f.+25 c. grey & grn. 5·00 25·00
305. 1¼ f.+75 c. grn. & vio. 5·00 25·00
306. 1¾ f.+1 f. 50 grey & bl. 10·00 50·00

1932. Child Welfare.
307. 45. 10 c.+5 c. brown .. 30 80
308. 75 c.+10 c. violet .. 2·00 12·00
309. 1 f.+25 c. red .. .. 8·00 35·00
310. 1¼ f.+75 c. lake .. 8·00 35·00
311. 1¾ f.+1 f. 50 blue .. 8·00 35·00

1933. Child Welfare.
312. 46. 10 c.+5 c. brown .. 30 80
313. 75 c.+10 c. purple .. 3·00 15·00
314. 1 f.+25 c. red .. .. 10·00 35·00
315. 1¼ f.+75 c. brown .. 12·00 45·00
316. 1¾ f.+1 f. 50 blue .. 12·00 55·00

47. Gateway of the Three Towers. 48. Arms of John the Blind.

1934.
317 47 5 f. green .. .. 1·00 6·00

1934. Child Welfare.
318. 48. 10 c.+5 c. violet .. 10 70
319. 35 c.+10 c. green .. 2·50 10·00
320. 75 c.+15 c. red .. .. 2·50 10·00
321. 1 f.+25 c. red .. .. 13·00 50·00
322. 1¼ f.+75 c. orange .. 15·00 55·00
323. 1¾ f+1½ f. blue .. .. 14·00 55·00

50. Surgeon.

1935. Int. Relief Fund for Intellectuals.
324. – 5 c. violet .. .. 15 1·40
325. – 10 c. red .. .. 30 1·40
326. – 15 c. olive .. .. 30 2·00
327. – 20 c. orange .. .. 45 2·50
328. – 35 c. green .. .. 80 3·50
329. – 50 c. black .. .. 90 5·00
330. – 70 c. green .. .. 2·50 6·00
331. 50. 1 f. red .. .. 2·00 7·00
332. – 1 f. 25 turquoise .. 8·00 55·00
333. – 1 f. 75 blue .. .. 10·00 55·00
334. – 2 f. brown .. .. 32·00 £120
335. – 3 f. brown .. .. 45·00 £160
336. – 5 f. blue .. .. 70·00 £300
337. – 10 f. purple £180 £500
338. 50. 20 f. green £200 £600

DESIGNS—HORIZ. 5 c., 10 f. Schoolteacher. 15 c., 3 f. Journalist. 20 c. 1 f. 75, Engineer. 35 c., 1 f. 25, Chemist. VERT. 10 c., 2 f. "The Arts". 50 c., 5 f. Barrister. 70 c. University.

This set was sold at the P.O. at double face value.

1935. Esch Philatelic Exn. Imperf.
339. 37. 2 f. (+50 c.) black .. 4·25 13·00

52. Vianden. 53. Charles I.

1935.
340 52 10 f. green .. .. 1·40 10·00

1935. Child Welfare.
341. 53. 10 c.+5 c. violet .. 10 40
342. 35 c.+10 c. green .. 30 60
343. 70 c.+20 c. brown .. 70 1·50
344. 1 f.+25 c. red .. .. 12·00 40·00
345. 1 f. 25+75 c. brown .. 12·00 40·00
346. 1 f. 75+1 f. 50 blue .. 12·00 50·00

54. Town Hall. 55. Wenceslas I. 56. Wenceslas II.

1936. 11th Int. Philatelic Federation Congress.
347. 54. 10 c. brown 20 50
348. 35 c. green .. .. 30 1·00
349. 70 c. orange .. .. 35 1·50
350. 1 f. red .. .. 1·00 9·00
351. 1 f. 25 violet .. .. 1·60 12·00
352. 1 f. 75 blue .. .. 1·00 10·00

1936. Child Welfare.
353. 55. 10 c.+5 c. brown .. 10 30
354. 35 c.+10 c. green .. 20 60
355. 70 c.+20 c. slate .. 40 80
356. 1 f.+25 c. red .. .. 2·00 12·00
357. 1 f. 25+75 c. violet .. 4·00 30·00
358. 1 f. 75+1 f. 50 blue .. 4·00 18·00

1937. Child Welfare.
360. 56. 10 c.+5 c. blk. & red.. 10 40
361. 35 c.+10 c. grn. & pur. 20 50
362. 70 c.+20 c. red & bl. .. 20 50
363. 1 f.+25 c. red & green.. 1·00 12·00
364. 1 f. 25+75 c. purple and brown .. 1·25 15·00
365. 1 f. 75+1 f. 50 blue and black .. 1·25 16·00

57. St. Willibrord. 61. Sigismond of Luxembourg.

1938. Echternach Abbey Restoration Fund (1st issue). 1200th Death Anniv of St. Willibrord.
366. 57. 35 c.+10 c. green .. 25 50
367. – 70 c.+10 c. black .. 70 60
368. – 1 f. 25+25 c. red .. 90 2·00
369. – 1 f. 75+50 c. blue .. 1·50 2·00
370. – 3 f.+2 f. red .. .. 5·00 8·00
371. – 5 f.+5 f. violet .. 5·00 8·00

DESIGNS—As Type **57**: 70 c. Town Hall, Echternach. 1 f. 25, Pavilion, Echternach Municipal Park. 31×51 mm: 1 f 75, St. Willibrord (from miniature). 42×38 mm: 3 f. Echternach Basilica. 5 f. Whitsuntide dancing procession.

See also Nos. 492/7 and 569/70.

1938. Child Welfare.
372. 61. 10 c.+5 c. blk. & mve. 10 40
373. 35 c.+10 c. blk. & grn. 20 50
374. 70 c.+20 c. blk. & brn. 30 50
375. 1 f.+25 c. blk. & red 1·60 14·00
376. 1 f. 25+75 c. blk. & grey 1·60 14·00
377. 1 f. 75+1 f. 50 black and blue .. .. 1·90 20·00

62. Arms of Luxembourg. 63. William I.

1939. Centenary of Independence.
378. 62. 35 c. green 15 20
379. 63. 50 c. orange 25 20
380. – 70 c. green 10 20
381. – 75 c. olive .. .. 50 1·00
382. – 1 f. red .. .. 1·25 2·00
383. – 1 f. 25 violet 15 20
384. – 1 f. 75 blue 15 20
385. – 3 f. brown 30 50
386. – 5 f. black .. .. 30 6·50
387. – 10 f. red .. .. 1·00 8·00

PORTRAITS—As Type **63**: 70 c. William II. 75 c. William III. 1 f. Prince Henry. 1 f. 25, Grand Duke Adolphe. 1 f. 75, William IV. 3 f. Marie-Anne, wife of William IV. 5 f. Grand Duchess Marie Adelaide. 10 f. Grand Duchess Charlotte.

1939. Surch. in figures.
388. 32. 30 c. on 60 c. green .. 10 1·25

65. Allegory of Medicinal Spring. 66. Prince Jean.

1939. Mondorf-les-Bains Propaganda.
389 65 2 f. red .. .. .. 30 2·50

1939. 20th Anniv of Reign and of Royal Wedding.
390 66 10 c.+5 c. brn on cream 10 30
391 – 35 c.+10 c. grn on cream 20 1·00
392 – 70 c.+20 c. black on cream .. .. 55 1·50
393 66 1 f.+25 c. red on cream 2·50 30·00
394 – 1 f. 25+75 c. violet on cream .. 3·25 40·00
395 – 1 f. 75+1 f. 50 blue on cream 4·00 60·00

PORTRAITS: 35 c., 1 f. 25, Prince Felix. 70 c., 1 f. 75, Grand Duchess Charlotte.

1940. Anti-T.B. Fund. Surch with Cross of Lorraine and premium.

396 65 2 f.+50 c. grey . . . . 1·00 12·00

1940-44. GERMAN OCCUPATION.

1940. T 94 of Germany optd. **Luxemburg.**

397. 94. 3 pf. brown 10 35
398. 4 pf. slate 10 50
399. 5 pf. green 10 50
400. 6 pf. green 10 35
401. 8 pf. orange 10 35
402. 10 pf. brown 10 50
403. 12 pf. red 10 35
404. 15 pf. red 20 65
405. 20 pf. blue . . . . 20 1·10
406. 25 pf. blue . . . . 40 1·25
407. 30 pf. olive 20 65
408. 40 pf. mauve . . . . 40 1·25
409. 50 pf. black and green . . 40 1·75
410. 60 pf. black and red . . 60 5·00
411. 80 pf. black and blue . . 3·00 16·00
412. 100 pf. black and yellow 60 4·50

1940. Types of Luxembourg surch.

413 32 3 Rpf. on 15 c. black . . 10 50
414 4 Rpf. on 20 c. orange 10 50
415 5 Rpf. on 35 c. green . . 10 50
416 6 Rpf. on 10 c. green . . 10 50
417 8 Rpf. on 25 c. brown . . 10 50
418 10 Rpf. on 40 c. brown 10 50
419 12 Rpf. on 60 c. green . . 10 50
420 15 Rpf. on 1 f. red . . 15 3·25
421 20 Rpf. on 50 c. brown 10 1·00
422 25 Rpf. on 5 c. mauve 35 3·25
423 30 Rpf. on 70 c. violet 15 1·00
424 40 Rpf. on 75 c. brown 15 1·00
425 50 Rpf. on 1½ f. green . . 15 1·00
426 65 60 Rpf. on 2 f. red . . 65 16·00
427 47 80 Rpf. on 5 f. green . . 20 3·25
428 52 100 Rpf. on 10 f. green 20 3·25

1941. Nos. 739/47 of Germany optd. **Luxemburg.**

429. 3 pf.+2 pf. brown . . 20 55
430. 4 pf.+3 pf. grey 20 55
431. 5 pf.+3 pf. green . . 20 55
432. 6 pf.+4 pf. green . . 20 55
433. 8 pf.+4 pf. orange . . 20 55
434. 12 pf.+6 pf. red 20 55
435. 15 pf.+10 pf. purple . . 1·25 7·50
436. 25 pf.+15 pf. blue . . 1·00 7·50
437. 40 pf.+35 pf. red . . 1·00 7·50

1944. INDEPENDENCE REGAINED

70. Grand Duchess Charlotte.

71. "Britannia".

1944.

438. 70. 5 c. brown 10 10
439. 10 c. slate 10 10
440. 20 c. orange 20 10
441. 25 c. brown 10 10
442. 30 c. red 30 30
443. 35 c. green 15 30
444. 40 c. blue 30 30
445. 50 c. violet 10 10
445a. 60 c. orange . . . . 1·50 15
446. 70 c. red 15 20
447. 70 c. green 50 70
448. 75 c. brown 30 20
449. 1 f. olive 10 10
450. 1¼ f. orange 20 20
451. 1½ f. orange 30 15
452. 1¾ f. blue 30 30
453. 2 f. red . . . . 3·50 15
454. 2½ f. mauve . . . . 6·50 5·50
455. 3 f. green 50 50
456. 3½ f. blue 60 85
457. 5 f. green 20 20
458. 10 f. red . . . . 30 1·40
459. 20 f. blue . . . . 50 16·00

1945. Liberation.

460. – 60 c.+1 f. 40 green . . 10 20
461. – 1 f. 20+1 f. 80 red . . 10 20
462. 71. 2 f. 50+3 f. 50 blue . . 10 20
463. – 4 f. 20+4 f. 80 violet . . 10 20

DESIGNS. 60 c. Ship symbol of Paris between Cross of Lorraine and Arms of Luxembourg. 1 f. 20, Man killing snake between Arms of Russia and Luxembourg. 4 f. 20, Eagle between Arms of U.S.A. and Luxembourg.

72. Statue of the Madonna in Procession.

DESIGNS — VERT. As Type **72**: 1 f. 20, The Madonna. 2 f. 50, The Madonna and Luxembourg. 5 f. 50, Portal of Notre Dame Cathedral.

73. Altar and Shrine of the Madonna.

1945. Our Lady of Luxembourg.

464. 72. 60 c.+40 c. green . . 20 80
465. – 1 f. 20+80 c. red . . 20 80
466. – 2 f. 50+2 f. 50 blue . . 30 4·00
467. – 5 f. 50+6 f. 50 violet . . 95 50·00
468. 73. 20 f.+20 f. brown . . 95 50·00

74. Lion of Luxembourg.

75. Members of the Maquis.

1945.

469. 74. 20 c. black 20 20
470. 30 c. green 20 20
470a. 60 c. violet 30 20
471. 75 c. brown 30 20
472. 1 f. 20 red 20 20
473. 1 f. 50 violet 20 20
474. 2 f. 50 blue 30 30

1945. National War Victims Fund.

475 75 20 c.+30 c. green & buff 20 1·00
476 – 1 f. 50+1 f. red and buff 20 1·00
477 – 3 f. 50+3 f. 50 bl & buff 40 10·00
478 – 5 f.+10 f. brown & buff 30 10·00

DESIGNS: 1 f. 50, Mother and children. 3 f. 50, Political prisoner. 5 f. Executed civilian.

76.

77. John the Blind, King of Bohemia.

1946. Air.

479 – 1 f. green and blue . . 20 20
480 76 2 f. brown and yellow . . 20 20
481 – 3 f. brown and yellow . . 20 20
482 – 4 f. violet and grey . . 30 30
483 76 5 f. purple and yellow 25 25
484 – 6 f. purple and blue . . 30 30
485 – 10 f. brown and yellow 1·00 30
486 76 20 f. blue and grey . . 1·25 1·00
487 – 50 f. green & light green 2·00 1·00

DESIGNS: 1, 4, 10 f. Airplane wheel. 3, 6, 50 f. Airplane engine and castle.

1946. 600th Death Anniv of John the Blind.

488 77 60 c. +40 c. grn & grey 15 1·50
489 1 f. 50+50 c. red & buff 25 2·00
490 3 f. 50+3 f. 50 bl & grey 95 22·00
491 5 f.+10 f. brown & grey 50 18·00

78. Exterior Ruins of St. Willibrord Basilica.

79. St. Willibrord.

1947. Echternach Abbey Restoration (2nd issue). Inscr. "ECHTERNACH"

492. 78. 20 c.+10 c. black . . 30 30
493. – 60 c.+10 c. green . . 60 50
494. – 75 c.+25 c. red . . 1·00 80
495. – 1 f. 50 c.+50 c. brown 1·25 80
496. – 3 f. 50 c.+2 f. 50 blue 4·00 3·75
497. 79. 25 f.+25 f. purple . . 25·00 25·00

DESIGNS—As Type **78**: 60 c. Statue of Abbot Bertels. 75 c. Echternach Abbey emblem. 1 f. 50, Ruined interior of Basilica. 3 f. 50, St. Irmine and Pepin II carrying model of Abbey.

80. U.S. Military Cemetery, Hamm.

82. Michel Lentz (national poet).

1947. Honouring Gen. George S. Patton.

498 80 1 f. 50 red and buff . . 20 20
499 – 3 f. 50 blue and buff . . 1·25 2·00
500 80 5 f. green and grey . . 1·25 1·40
501 – 10 f. purple and grey . . 5·00 32·00

PORTRAIT: 3 f. 50, 10 f. Gen. G. S. Patton.

1947. National Welfare Fund.

502 82 60 c.+40 c. brn & buff 55 60
503 1 f. 50+50 c. pur & buff 55 60
504 3 f. 50+3 f. 50 bl & grey 5·50 18·00
505 10 f.+5 f. green & grey 5·50 19·00

83. L'Oesling.

85. "Dicks" (Edmund de la Fontaine).

86. Grand Duchess Charlotte.

1948. Tourist Propaganda.

505a – 2 f. 50 brown & choc 1·50 40
505b – 3 f. violet . . . . 6·00 1·25
505c – 4 f. blue . . . . 4·00 1·25
506 83 7 f. brown . . . . 22·00 80
507 – 10 f. green . . . . 1·75 20
508 – 15 f. red . . . . 2·00 40
509 – 20 f. blue . . . . 2·00 40

DESIGNS—HORIZ. 2 f. 50, Television transmitter, Dudelange. 3 f. Radio Luxembourg. 4 f. Victor Hugo's house, Vianden. 10 f. River Moselle. 15 f. Mining district. VERT. 20 f. Luxembourg.

1948. National Welfare Fund.

510 85 60 c.+40 c. brown & bis 45 50
511 1 f. 50+50 c. red & pink 60 70
512 3 f. 50+3 f. 50 bl & grey 9·50 15·00
513 10 f.+5 f. green & grey 8·50 15·00

1948.

513a. 86. 5 c. orange 10 10
513b. 10 c. blue 10 10
514. 15 c. olive 15 10
514a. 20 c. purple 20 10
515. 25 c. grey 20 10
515a. 30 c. olive 20 10
515b. 40 c. red 30 30
515c. 50 c. orange 40 15
516. 60 c. bistre 30 20
517. 80 c. green 30 20
518. 1 f. red . . . . 1·00 10
518a. 1 f. 20 black . . . . 1·00 30
518b. 1 f. 25 brown . . . . 1·00 40
519. 1 f. 50 turquoise . . 1·00 10
520. 1 f. 60 grey . . . . 1·00 1·00
521. 2 f. purple . . . . 1·00 10
521a. 2 f. 50 red . . . . 1·75 10
521b. 3 f. blue . . . . 13·00 40
521c. 3 f. 50 red . . . . 4·00 40
522. 4 f. blue . . . . 4·00 40
522a. 5 f. violet . . . . 11·00 40
523. 6 f. purple . . . . 6·50 40
524. 8 f. green . . . . 5·50 80

87. Date-stamp and Map.

1949. 75th Anniv of U.P.U.

525 87 80 c. green, lt grn & blk 50 60
526 2 f. 50 red, pink & black 2·25 1·50
527 4 f. ultram, blue & black 3·75 5·50
528 8 f. brown, buff & black 12·00 25·00

88. Michel Rodange.

89. Young Girl.

1949. National Welfare Fund.

529 88 60 c.+40 c. green & grey 50 50
530 2 f.+1 f. purple & claret 5·00 6·00
531 4 f.+2 f. blue and grey 8·00 12·00
532 10 f.+5 f. brown & buff 8·00 14·00

1950. War Orphans Relief Fund.

533. – 60 c.+15 c. turquoise . . 1·50 50
534. 89. 1 f.+20 c. red . . . . 4·00 1·25
535. – 2 f.+30 c. brown . . 2·00 1·25
536. 89. 4 f.+75 c. blue . . 12·00 15·00
537. – 8 f.+3 f. black . . 32·00 42·00
538. 89. 10 f.+5 f. purple . . 32·00 42·00

DESIGN: 60 c., 2 f., 8 f. Mother and boy.

90. J. A. Zinnen. (composer).

91. Ploughman and Factories.

1950. National Welfare Fund.

539. 90. 60 c.+10 c. vio. & grey 55 30
540. 2 f.+15 c. red & buff 1·00 40
541. 4 f.+15 c. blue & grey 5·00 7·00
542. 8 f.+5 f. brown & buff 22·00 25·00

1951. To Promote United Europe.

543 91 80 c. green & light green 10·00 10·00
544 – 1 f. violet & light violet 5·50 50
545 – 2 f. brown and grey . . 25·00 50
546 91 2 f. 50 red and orange . . 26·00 21·00
547 – 3 f. brown and yellow . . 45·00 32·00
548 – 4 f. blue and light blue 60·00 40·00

DESIGNS: 1, 3 f. Map, people and "Rights of Man" Charter. 2, 4 f. Scales balancing "United Europe" and "Peace".

92. L. Menager (composer).

1951. National Welfare Fund.

549 92 60 c.+10 c. black & grey 40 40
550 2 f.+15 c. green & grey 40 40
551 4 f.+15 c. blue and grey 4·00 3·00
552 8 f.+5 f. purple & grey 25·00 30·00

92a. T 1 and 86.

92b. T 1.

1952. National Philatelic Exhibition ("CENTILUX") and Stamp Centenary.

552a 92a 80 c. black, purple and green (air) . . 50 50
552b 2 f. 50 blk, pur & red 1·50 1·50
552c 4 f. black, pur & bl 3·00 3·00
552d 8 f. black, pur & red 50·00 55·00
552e 10 f. blk, pur & brn 40·00 45·00

552f 92b 2 f. black and green (postage) . . . . 35·00 50·00
552g 4 f. red and green . . 35·00 50·00

93. Hurdling.

1952. 15th Olympic Games, Helsinki.
553. 93. 1 f. black & green .. 60 30
554. – 2 f. black and lt. brown (Football) .. .. 2·00 30
555. – 2 f. 50 black and pink (Boxing) .. .. 4·00 90
556. – 3 f. blk. & drab (Water polo) .. .. .. 5·00 90
557. – 4 f. blk. & bl. (Cycling) 25·00 6·50
558. – 8 f. blk. & lilac (Fencing) 16·00 3·75

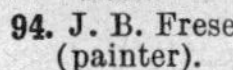

94. J. B. Fresez (painter). **95.** Prince Jean and Princess Josephine Charlotte.

1952. National Welfare Fund.
559 94 60 c.+15 c. green & blue 40 40
560 2 f.+25 c. brown & orge 40 40
561 4 f.+25 c. violet & grey 3·00 4·00
562 8 f.+4 f. 75 pur & lt pur 26·00 32·00

1953. Royal Wedding.
563 95 80 c. violet & dp mauve 45 35
564 1 f. 20 dp brown & brn 45 35
565 2 f. deep green & green 1·25 35
566 3 f. deep purple & purple 1·25 50
567 4 f. deep blue and blue 5·50 1·00
568 9 f. brown and red .. 5·50 1·00

96. Echternach Basilica. **97.** Pierre D'Aspelt.

1953. Echternach Abbey Restoration (3rd issue).
569. 96. 2 f. red .. .. .. 3·50 35
570. – 2 f. 50 olive .. .. .. 5·00 5·50
DESIGN: 2 f. 50 Interior of Basilica.

1953. 7th Birth Cent. of Pierre D'Aspelt.
571. 97. 4 f. black .. .. 7·00 4·25

98. "Candlemas Singing". **99.** Foils, Mask and Gauntlet.

1953. National Welfare Fund.
572 98 25 c.+15 c. carmine and red 30 40
573 – 80 c.+20 c. blue & brn 30 40
574 – 1 f. 20+30 c. grn & turq 70 80
575 98 2 f.+25 c. brown & red 30 40
576 – 4 f.+50 c. blue & turq 4·75 7·00
577 – 7 f.+3 f. 35 lilac & violet 13·00 18·00
DESIGNS: 80 c., 4 f. "The Rattles". 1 f. 20, 7 f. "The Easter-eggs".

1954. World Fencing Championships.
578 99 2 f. deep brown and brown on cream .. 4·00 50

100. Fair Emblem. **101.** Earthenware Whistle.

1954. Luxembourg International Fair.
579. 100. 4 f. multicoloured .. 9·50 2·75

1954. National Welfare Fund.
580 101 25 c.+5 c. red & orge 40 50
581 – 80 c.+20 c. grey & blk 40 50
582 – 1 f. 20+30 c. green and cream .. .. 1·50 1·50
583 101 2 f.+25 c. brn & buff 60 60
584 – 4 f.+50 c. dp blue & bl 5·00 7·00
585 – 7 f.+3 f. 45 vio & mve 24·00 25·00
DESIGNS: 80 c., 4 f. Sheep and drum. 1 f. 20, 7 f. Merry-go-round horses.

102. Tulips. **103.**

1955. Mondorf-les-Bains Flower Show.
586. 102. 80 c. red, green & brown 30 30
587. – 2 f. yellow, green & red 40 30
588. – 3 f. pur., green & emer. 3·50 3·50
589. – 4 f. orange, green & blue 5·50 5·50
FLOWERS: 2 f. Daffodils. 3 f. Hyacinths. 4 f. Parrot tulips.

1955. 1st National Crafts Exhibition.
590 103 2 f. black and grey .. 1·00 25

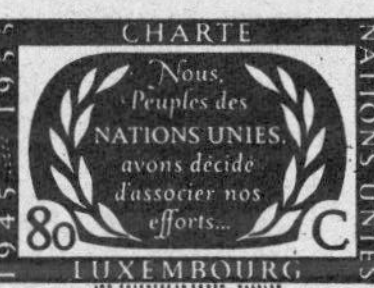

104. "Charter". **105.** "Christmas Day".

1955. 10th Anniv. of U.N.
591. 104. 80 c. blue and black .. 45 50
592. – 2 f. brown and red .. 3·25 15
593. – 4 f. red and blue .. 2·25 3·00
594. – 9 f. green and brown 75 75
SYMBOLIC DESIGNS: 2 f. "Security". 4 f. "Justice". 9 f. "Assistance".

1955. National Welfare Fund.
595 – 25 c.+5 c. red and pink 30 30
596 105 80 c.+20 c. blk & grey 30 30
597 – 1 f. 20+30 c. deep green and green .. 60 80
598 – 2 f.+25 c. deep brown and brown 60 30
599 105 4 f.+50 c. blue & lt bl 6·00 10·00
600 – 7 f.+3 f. 45 pur & mve 12·00 14·00
ALLEGORICAL DESIGNS: 25 c., 2 f. "St. Nicholas's Day". 1 f. 20, 7 f. "Twelfth Night".

1956. Mondorf-les-Bains Flower Show. As T 102 but inscription at top in one line. Multicoloured.
601 2 f. Anemones 65 30
602 3 f. Crocuses .. .. 2·50 2·25

1956. Roses. As T 102 but inscr at top "LUXEMBOURG—VILLE DES ROSES". Multicoloured.
603 2 f. 50 Yellow roses .. 6·00 4·50
604 4 f. Red roses .. .. 3·00 2·25

108. Steel Plant and Girder. **109.** Blast Furnaces and Map.

1956. 50th Anniv. of Esch-sur-Alzette.
605. 108. 2 f. red, black and turq. 1·75 40

1956. European Coal and Steel Community. Inscr. as in T 109.
606. 109. 2 f. red .. .. 30·00 1·00
607. – 3 f. blue .. .. 30·00 22·00
608. – 4 f. green .. .. 6·00 4·25
DESIGNS—VERT. 3 f. Girder supporting City of Luxemburg. HORIZ. 4 f. Chain and miner's lamp.

MORE DETAILED LISTS are given in the Stanley Gibbons Catalogues referred to in the country headings. For lists of current volumes see Introduction.

110. **111.** Luxembourg Central Station.

1956. Europa.
609. 110. 2 f. black and brown £200 25
610. 3 f. red and orange .. 40·00 40·00
611. 4 f. deep blue and blue 2·25 3·00

1956. Electrification of Luxembourg Railways.
612. 111. 2 f. sepia and black .. 3·00 50

112. I. de la Fontaine. **113.** Arms of Echternach.

1956. Council of State Cent. Inscr. as in T 112.
613. 112. 2 f. sepia .. .. 1·00 30
614. – 7 f. purple .. .. 2·00 80
DESIGN: 7 f. Grand Duchess Charlotte.

1956. National Welfare Fund. Inscr. "CARITAS 1956". Arms. Multicoloured.
615. 25 c.+5 c. Type 113 .. 25 30
616. 80 c.+20 c. Esch-sur-Alzette 25 30
617. 1 f. 20+30 c. Grevenmacher 30 45
618. 2 f.+25 c. Type 113 .. 25 30
619. 4 f.+50 c. Esch-sur-Alzette .. .. 2·25 3·50
620. 7 f.+3 f. 45 Grevenmacher 6·00 11·00

114. Lord Baden-Powell and Scout Emblems. **115.** Prince Henri.

1957. Birth Cent. of Lord Baden-Powell, and 50th Anniv. of Scouting Movement.
621. 114. 2 f. brown and green .. 1·00 30
622. – 2 f. 50 red and violet .. 2·25 3·75
DESIGN: 2 f. 50, as Type 114 but showing Girl Guide emblems.

1957. "Prince Jean and Princess Josephine-Charlotte Foundation" Child Welfare Clinic.
623 115 2 f. dp brown & brown 1·00 20
624 – 3 f. dp green and green 2·50 2·75
625 – 4 f. deep blue and blue 2·00 2·75
DESIGNS—HORIZ. 3 f. Children's Clinic Project. VERT. 4 f. Princess Marie-Astrid.

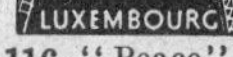

116. "Peace". **117.** Fair Entrance and Flags.

1957. Europa.
626. 116. 2 f. brown .. .. 2·00 15
627. 3 f. red .. .. 35·00 15·00
628. 4 f. purple .. .. 30·00 15·00

1957. National Welfare Fund. Arms as T 113 inscr. "CARITAS 1957". Multicoloured.
629. 25 c.+5 c. Luxembourg .. 30 40
630. 80 c.+20 c. Mersch .. 30 40
631. 1 f. 20+30 c. Vianden .. 40 50
632. 2 f.+25 c. Luxembourg .. 30 30
633. 4 f.+50 c. Mersch .. 2·00 4·25
634. 7 f.+3 f. 45 Vianden .. 4·75 7·50

1958. 10th Anniv of Luxembourg Int Fair.
635 117 2 f. multicoloured .. 15 15

118. Luxembourg Pavilion. **119.** St. Willibrord holding Child (after Puseel).

1958. Brussels Exhibition.
636 118 2 f. 50 blue and red .. 15 15

1958. 1300th Birth Anniv. of St. Willibrord.
637. – 1 f. red 20 30
638. 119. 2 f. 50 sepia 25 15
639. – 5 f. blue 60 90
DESIGNS: 1 f. St. Willibrord and St. Irmina holding inscribed plaque. 5 f. St. Willibrord and Suppliant. (Miracle of the wine-cask).

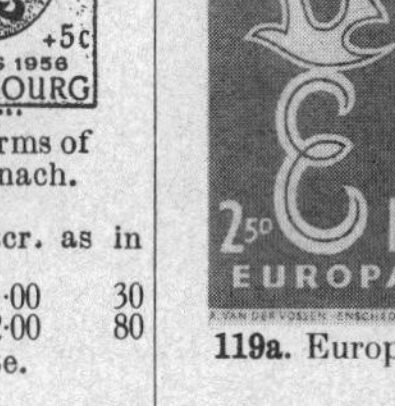

119a. Europa. **120.** Open-air Theatre at Wiltz.

1958. Europa.
640. 119a. 2 f. 50 blue and red .. 15 15
641. 3 f. 50 brown & grn. 20 25
642. 5 f. red and blue .. 50 75

1958. Wiltz Open-air Theatre Commem.
643. 120. 2 f. 50 sepia and grey 30 15

121. Vineyard. **122.** Grand Duchess Charlotte.

1958. Bimillenary of Moselle Wine Industry.
644. 121. 2 f. 50 brown and green 30 15

1958. National Welfare Fund. Arms as T 113 inscr. "CARITAS 1958". Multicoloured.
645. 30 c.+10 c. Capellen .. 30 30
646. 1 f.+25 c. Diekirch .. 30 30
647. 1 f. 50+25 c. Redange .. 50 50
648. 2 f. 50+50 c. Capellen .. 30 30
649. 5 f.+50 c. Diekirch .. 1·50 4·00
650. 8 f. 50+4 f. 60 Redange 4·25 7·50

1959. 40th Anniv of Accession of Grand Duchess Charlotte.
651 122 1 f. 50 dp green & green 35 25
652 2 f. 50 brown & lt brn 35 20
653 5 f. lt blue & ultram .. 75 90

123. N.A.T.O. Emblem. **123a.** Europa.

1959. 10th Anniv. of N.A.T.O.
654. 123. 2 f. 50 blue and olive .. 15 10
655. 8 f. 50 blue and brown .. 40 40

1959. Mondorf-les-Bains Flower Show. As T 102 but inscr. "1959".
656. 1 f. violet, yellow and turq. 25 30
657. 2 f. 50 red, green and blue 30 20
658. 3 f. blue, green and purple 50 70
FLOWERS: 1 f. Iris. 2 f. 50, Peony. 3 f. Hortensia.

1959. Europa.
659. 123a. 2 f. 50 green 40 15
660. 5 f. blue 55 75

124. Early Locomotive and First Bars of Hymn "De Feierwon".

1959. Railways Centenary.

661. 124. 2 f. 50 blue and red .. 1·25 40

1959. National Welfare Fund. Arms as T 113 inscr. "CARITAS 1959". Multicoloured.

662. 30 c.+10 c. Clervaux .. 30 30
663. 1 f.+25 c. Remich .. 30 30
664. 1 f. 50+25 c. Wiltz .. 50 50
665. 2 f. 50+50 c. Clervaux .. 30 30
666. 5 f.+50 c. Remich .. 1·00 2·00
667. 8 f. 50+4 f. 60 Wiltz .. 4·25 11·00

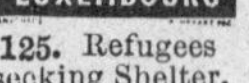

125. Refugees seeking Shelter. 126. Steel Worker.

1960. World Refugee Year.

668. 125. 2 f. 50 blue & salmon .. 15 15
669. – 5 f. blue and violet .. 20 35

DESIGN—HORIZ. 5 f. "The Flight into Egypt" (Biblical scene).

1960. 10th Anniv. of Schuman Plan.

670. 126. 2 f. 50 lake 20 15

127. European School, Luxembourg. 128. Grand Duchess Charlotte.

1960. European School Commem.

671. 127. 5 f. black and blue .. 1·25 1·00

1960.

672. 128. 10 c. red 10 20
673. 20 c. red 10 20
673a. 25 c. orange 20 20
674. 30 c. drab 10* 20
675. 50 c. green 50 20
676. 1 f. violet 50* 10
677. 1 f. 50 mauve 50 15
678. 2 f. turquoise 60 10
679. 2 f. 50 purple .. .. 1·50 15
680. 3 f. dull purple .. .. 2·75 10
680a. 3 f. 50 turquoise .. 3·00 2·00
681. 5 f. brown .. .. 1·75 20
681a. 6 f. turquoise .. .. 2·75 20

129. Heraldic Lion, and Tools.

1960. 2nd National Crafts Exn.

682. 129. 2 f. 50 multicoloured .. 90 20

129a. Conference Emblem. 130. Princess Marie-Astrid.

1960. Europa.

683. 129a. 2 f. 50 green and black 20 15
684. 5 f. black and red .. 30 25

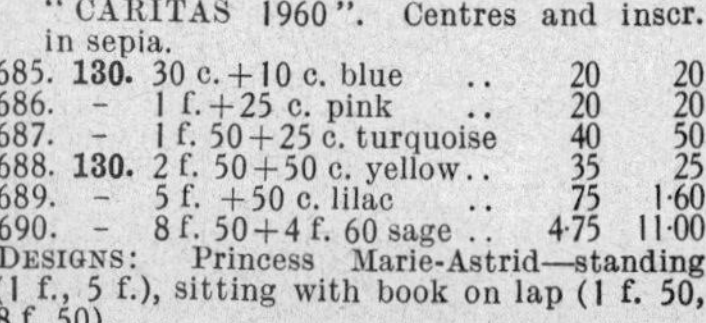

1960. National Welfare Fund. Inscr. "CARITAS 1960". Centres and inscr. in sepia.

685. 130. 30 c.+10 c. blue .. 20 20
686. – 1 f.+25 c. pink .. 20 20
687. – 1 f. 50+25 c. turquoise 40 50
688. 130. 2 f. 50+50 c. yellow .. 35 25
689. – 5 f. +50 c. lilac .. 75 1·60
690. – 8 f. 50+4 f. 60 sage .. 4·75 11·00

DESIGNS: Princess Marie-Astrid—standing (1 f., 5 f.), sitting with book on lap (1 f. 50, 8 f. 50).

131. Great Spotted Woodpecker. 132. Patton Monument, Ettelbruck.

1961. Animal Protection Campaign. Inscr. "PROTECTION DES ANIMAUX".

691. 131. 1 f. multicoloured .. 40 15
692. – 1 f. 50 buff, blue and black 25 25
693. – 3 f. brown, buff and violet 40 40
694. – 8 f. 50 multicoloured .. 70 50

DESIGNS—VERT. 8 f. 50, Dachshund. HORIZ. 1 f. 50, Cat. 3 f. Horse.

1961. Tourist Publicity.

695. 132. 2 f. 50 blue and black .. 20 20
696. – 2 f. 50 green 20 20

DESIGN—VERT. No. 696, Clervaux.

133. Doves. 134. Prince Henri.

1961. Europa.

697. 133. 2 f. 50 red 10 10
698. 5 f. blue 20 20

1961. National Welfare Fund. Inscr. "CARITAS 1961". Centres and inscr. in sepia.

699. 134. 30 c.+10 c. mauve .. 20 20
700. – 1 f.+25 c. lavender .. 20 20
701. – 1 f. 50+25 c. salmon .. 35 45
702. 134. 2 f. 50+50 c. green .. 35 30
703. – 5 f.+50 c. yellow .. 70 1·60
704. – 8 f. 50+4 f. 60 grey .. 2·00 5·50

DESIGNS: Prince Henri when—young boy (1 f., 5 f.); youth in formal dress (1 f. 50, 8 f. 50).

135. Cyclist Carrying Cycle. 136. Europa "Tree".

1962. World Cross-country Cycling Championships, Esch-sur-Alzette.

705. 135. 2 f. 50 multicoloured .. 30 15
706. – 5 f. mult. (Emblem) .. 30 40

1962. Europa.

707. 136. 2 f. 50 multicoloured .. 15 10
708. 5 f. brn., grn. & purple 15 20

137. St. Laurent's Church, Diekirch. 138. Prince Jean and Princess Margaretha as Babies.

1962.

709. 137. 2 f. 50 black and brown 30 15

1962. National Welfare Fund. Inscr. "CARITAS 1962". Centres and inscr. in sepia.

710. 138. 30 c.+10 c. buff .. 20 20
711. – 1 f.+25 c. blue .. 20 20
712. – 1 f. 50+25 c. olive .. 30 40
713. – 2 f. 50+50 c. pink .. 30 25
714. – 5 f.+50 c. green .. 65 1·50
715. – 8 f. 50+4 f. 60 violet .. 1·60 4·50

PORTRAITS—VERT. 1 f., 2 f. 50, Prince Jean and: 2 f. 50, 5 f., Princess Margaretha, at various stages of childhood. HORIZ. 8 f. 50, The Royal Children.

HAVE YOU READ THE NOTES AT THE BEGINNING OF THIS CATALOGUE?
These often provide answers to the enquiries we receive.

139. Blackboard. 140. Benedictine Abbey, Munster.

1963. 10th Anniv. of European Schools.

716. 139. 2 f. 50 green, red & grey 10 10

1963. Millenary of City of Luxembourg and International Philatelic Exhibition.

(a) Horiz views.

717 – 1 f. blue 15 30
718 140 1 f. 50 red 15 30
719 – 2 f. 50 green 15 30
720 – 3 f. brown 15 30
721 – 5 f. violet 15 30
722 – 11 f. blue .. .. 1·10 1·75

VIEWS: 1 f. Bock Rock. 2 f. 50, Rham Towers. 3 f. Grand Ducal Palace. 5 f. Castle Bridge. 11 f. Millenary Buildings.

(b) Vert multicoloured designs.

723 1 f. "Three Towers" Gate 10 10
724 1 f. 50 Great Seal 15 15
725 2 f. 50 "The Black Virgin" (statue), St. John's Church 15 15
726 3 f. Citadel 15 15
727 5 f. Town Hall 35 70

141. Colpach Castle. 142. "Human Rights".

1963. Red Cross Cent.

728. 141. 2 f. 50 red & slate .. 15 10

1963. 10th Anniv. of European "Human Rights" Convention.

729. 142. 2 f. 50 blue on gold .. 20 10

143. "Co-operation". 144. Trout snapping Bait.

1963. Europa.

730. 143. 3 f. grn., orge. & turq. 20 10
731. 6 f. orge., red & brn. .. 20 25

1963. World Fishing Championships, Wormeldange.

732. 144. 3 f. slate 15 15

145. Telephone Dial. 146. St. Roch (patron saint of bakers).

1963. Inaug. of Automatic Telephone System.

733. 145. 3 f. green, blk. & blue 15 15

1963. National Welfare Fund. Patron Saints of Crafts and Guilds. Inscr. "CARITAS 1963". Multicoloured.

734. 50 c.+10 c. Type 146 .. 15 15
735. 1 f.+25 c. St. Anne (tailors) .. 15 15
736. 2 f.+25 c. St. Eloi (smiths) 15 15
737. 3 f.+50 c. St. Michel (haberdashers) .. 15 15
738. 6 f.+50 c. St. Barthelemy (butchers) .. 1·25 2·00
739. 10 f.+5 f. 90 St. Thibaut (seven crafts) .. .. 2·00 3·00

147. Power House. 148. Barge entering Canal.

1964. Inaug. of Vianden Reservoir.

740. 147. 2 f. blue, brown & red 20 15
741. – 3 f. lt. bl., turq. & red 20 15
742. – 6 f. brn., blue & green 30 15

DESIGNS—HORIZ. 3 f. Upper reservoir. VERT. 6 f. Lohmuhle Dam.

1964. Inauguration of Moselle Canal.

743 148 3 f. indigo and blue .. 30 15

149. Europa "Flower". 150. Students thronging "New Athenaeum".

1964. Europa.

744. 149. 3 f. blue, brn. & cream 15 10
745. 6 f. sepia, green & yell. 15 20

1964. Opening of "New Athenaeum" (education centre).

746. 150. 3 f. black and green .. 10 10

150a. King Baudouin, Queen Juliana and Grand Duchess Charlotte.

1964. 20th Anniv. of "BENELUX".

747. 150a. 3 f. brn., yell. & blue 10 10

151. Grand Duke Jean and Princess Josephine-Charlotte. 152. Three Towers.

1964. Accession of Grand Duke Jean.

748. 151. 3 f. dp. blue & pale bl. 30 10
749. 6 f. sepia & pale brown 30 20

1964. National Welfare Fund. Inscr. "CARITAS 1964". Multicoloured.

750. 50 c.+10 c. Type 152 .. 15 15
751. 1 f.+25 c. Grand Duke Adolphe Bridge .. 15 15
752. 2 f.+25 c. Lower Town .. 15 15
753. 3 f.+50 c. Type 152 .. 15 15
754. 6 f.+50 c. Grand Duke Adolphe Bridge .. 1·00 1·50
755. 10 f.+5 f. 90 Lower Town 1·00 2·00

153. Rotary Emblem and Cogwheels. 154. Grand Duke Jean.

1965. 60th Anniv. of Rotary Int.

756. 153. 3 f. multicoloured .. 15 10

1965.

757	154	25 c. brown	10	10
758		50 c. red	10	10
759		1 f. blue	10	10
760		1 f. 50 purple ..	10	10
761a		2 f. red	10	10
762		2 f. 50 orange ..	10	10
763a		3 f. green	20	10
763b		3 f. 50 brown ..	20	20
764a		4 f. purple	20	10
764ba		5 f. green	20	10
765a		6 f. lilac	30	10
765b		7 f. orange	30	10
765c		8 f. blue	50	10
766		9 f. green	40	20
766a		10 f. black	60	10
767		12 f. red	50	10
767a		14 f. blue	50	40
767b		16 f. green	70	25
767c		18 f. green	80	30
767d		20 f. blue	80	20
767e		22 f. brown ..	80	60

155. I.T.U. Emblem and Symbols.

1965. Cent. of I.T.U.
768. **155.** 3 f. blue, lake & violet 10 10

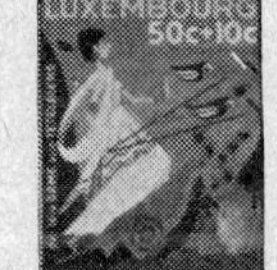

156. Europa "Sprig". 157. "The Roman Lady of the Titelberg".

1965. Europa.
769. **156.** 3 f. turq., red and black 15 10
770. 6 f. brown, blue & green 15 20

1965. National Welfare Fund. Fairy Tales. Inscr. "CARITAS 1965". Multicoloured.
771. 50 c.+10 c. Type **157** .. 15 20
772. 1 f.+25 c. "Schappchen, the Huntsman" .. 15 20
773. 2 f.+25 c. "The Witch of Koerich" 15 20
774. 3 f.+50 c. "The Goblins of Schoendels" .. 15 20
775. 6 f.+50 c. "Tollchen, Watchman of Hesperange" 30 1·00
776. 10 f.+5 f. 90 "The Old Spinster of Heispelt" 75 2·75

158. "Flag" and Torch. 159. W.H.O. Building.

1966. 50th Anniv. of Luxembourg Workers' Union.
777. **158.** 3 f. red and grey .. 10 10

1966. Inaug. of W.H.O. Headquarters, Geneva.
778. **158.** 3 f. green 10 10

160. Golden Key. 161. Europa "Ship".

1966. Tercentenary of Solemn Promise to Our Lady of Luxembourg.
779. **160.** 1 f. 50 green 10 20
780. – 2 f. red 10 20
781. – 3 f. blue 10 20
782. – 6 f. brown 20 30
DESIGNS: 2 f. Interior of Luxembourg Cathedral (after painting by J. Martin). 3 f. Our Lady of Luxembourg (after engraving by R. Collin). 6 f. Gallery pillar, Luxembourg Cathedral (after sculpture by D. Muller).

1966. Europa.
783. **161.** 3 f. blue and grey .. 10 10
784. 6 f. green and brown .. 20 20

162. Diesel Locomotive.

1966. Luxembourg Railwaymen's Philatelic Exn. Multicoloured.
785. 1 f. 50 Type **162** 30 25
786. 3 f. Electric locomotive .. 30 20

163. Grand Duchess Charlotte Bridge. 164. Kirchberg Building and Grand Duke Adolphe Railway Bridge.

1966. Tourism.
787. **163.** 3 f. lake 10 10
See also Nos. 807/8, 828 and 844/5.

1966. "Luxembourg-European Centre".
788. **164.** 1 f. 50 green 20 20
789. – 13 f. blue (Robert Schuman monument) 30 15

165. "Mary, Veiled Matron of Wormeldange". 166. City of Luxembourg, 1850 (after engraving by N. Liez).

1966. National Welfare Fund. Luxembourg Fairy Tales. Multicoloured.
790 50 c.+10 c. Type **165** .. 10 20
791 1 f. 50+25 c. "Jekel Warden of the Wark" .. 10 20
792 2 f.+25 c. "The Black Gentleman of Vianden" 10 20
793 3 f.+50 c. "The Gracious Fairy of Rosport" .. 15 20
794 6 f.+1 f. "The Friendly Shepherd of Donkolz" .. 35 1·00
795 13 f.+6 f. 90 "The Little Sisters of Trois-Vierges" 45 2·25

1967. Cent. of Treaty of London.
796. **166.** 3 f. brn., blue & green 25 10
797. – 6 f. red, brown & blue 20 30
DESIGN—VERT. 6 f. Plan of Luxembourg fortress c. 1850 (after T. de Cederstolpe).

167. Cogwheels. 168. Lion on Globe.

1967. Europa.
798. **167.** 3 f. purple, grey & buff 15 10
799. 6 f. sepia, purple & blue 15 20

1967. 50th Anniv. of Lions Int.
800. **168.** 3 f. yellow, pur. & black 10 10

169. European Institutions Building, Luxembourg. 170. Hikers and Hostel.

1967. N.A.T.O. Council Meeting, Luxembourg.
801. **169.** 3 f. turquoise and green 10 10
802. 6 f. red and pink .. 25 35

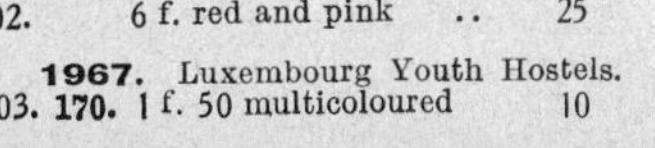

1967. Luxembourg Youth Hostels.
803. **170.** 1 f. 50 multicoloured 10 15

171. Shaving-dish (after Degrotte). 172. "Gardener".

1967. "200 Years of Luxembourg Pottery".
804. **171.** 1 f. 50 multicoloured 10 15
805. – 3 f. multicoloured .. 20 15
DESIGN—VERT. 3 f. Vase, circa 1820.

1967. "Family Gardens" Congress, Luxembourg.
806. **172.** 1 f. 50 orange and green 10 15

1967. Tourism. As T **163**.
807 3 f. indigo and blue .. 20 15
808 3 f. purple, green and blue 20 15
DESIGNS—HORIZ. No. 807, Moselle River and quayside, Mertert. VERT. No. 808, Moselle, Church and vines, Wormeldange.

173. Prince Guillaume. 174. Football.

1967. National Welfare Fund. Royal Children and Residence.
809 173 50 c.+10 c. brn & buff 15 20
810 – 1 f. 50+25 c. brn & bl 15 20
811 – 2 f.+25 c. brown & red 15 20
812 – 3 f.+50 c. brown & yell 40 20
813 – 6 f.+1 f. brown and lavender .. .. 40 1·00
814 – 13 f.+6 f. 90 brown, green and blue .. 45 2·75
DESIGNS: 1 f. 50, Princess Margaretha. 2 f. Prince Jean. 3 f. Prince Henri. 6 f. Princess Marie-Astrid. 13 f. Berg Castle.

1968. Olympic Games, Mexico.
815 – 50 c. light blue & blue 10 15
816 174 1 f. 50 green & emerald 10 15
817 – 2 f. yellow and green 10 15
818 – 3 f. lt orange & orange 10 10
819 – 6 f. green and blue .. 15 20
820 – 13 f. red and crimson 30 30
DESIGNS: 50 c. Diving. 2 f. Cycling. 3 f. Running. 6 f. Walking. 13 f. Fencing.

175. Europa "Key". 176. Thermal Bath Pavilion, Mondorf-les-Bains.

1968. Europa.
821. **175.** 3 f. brown, black & grn. 10 10
822. 6 f. green, black & orge. 20 30

1968. Mondorf-les-Bains Thermal Baths.
823. **176.** 3 f. multicoloured .. 15 10

177. Fair Emblem.

1968. 20th Anniv. of Luxembourg Int. Fair.
824. **177.** 3 f. multicoloured .. 15 10

178. Village Project. 179. "Blood Transfusion".

1968. Luxembourg SOS Children's Village.
825. **178.** 3 f. purple and green .. 10 10
826. – 6 f. black, blue & pur. 20 30
DESIGN—VERT. 6 f. Orphan with foster-mother.

1968. Blood Donors of Luxembourg Red Cross.
827. **179.** 3 f. red and blue .. 20 10

180. "Luxair" Airliner over Luxembourg. 181. Cap Institute.

1968. Tourism.
828 180 50 f. dp blue, brn & bl 1·75 40

1968. National Welfare Fund. Luxembourg Handicapped Children.
829. **181.** 50 c.+10 c. brown and blue .. 15 20
830. – 1 f. 50+25 c. brown and green .. 15 20
831. – 2 f.+25 c. brn. & yell. 20 30
832. – 3 f.+50 c. brn. & bl. 25 20
833. – 6 f.+1 f. brn. & buff 40 1·00
834. – 13 f.+6 f. 90 brown and pink .. 85 3·00
DESIGNS: 1 f. 50, Deaf and dumb child. 2 f. Blind child. 3 f. Nurse supporting handicapped child. 6 f. and 13f. Mentally handicapped children (different).

183. Colonnade.

1969. Europa.
836. **183.** 3 f. multicoloured .. 15 10
837. 6 f. multicoloured .. 30 30

184. "The Wooden Horse" (Kutter).

1969. 75th Birth Anniv. of Joseph Kutter (painter). Multicoloured.
838. 3 f. Type **184**. 50 15
839. 6 f. "Luxembourg" (Kutter) 50 30

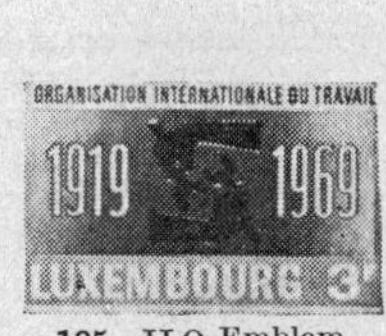

185. ILO Emblem. 186. National Colours.

1969. 50th Anniv. of Int. Labour Organization.
840. **185.** 3 f. gold, violet & green 10 10

1969. 25th Anniv. of "BENELUX" Customs Union.
841. **186.** 3 f. multicoloured .. 20 10

187. N.A.T.O. Emblem. **188.** Ear of Wheat and Agrocentre, Mersch.

1969. 20th Anniv of N.A.T.O.
842 **187** 3 f. orange and brown 20 10

1969. "Modern Agriculture".
843. **188.** 3 f. grey and green .. 10 10

189. Echternach. **190.** Vianden Castle.

1969. Tourism.
844 **189** 3 f. indigo and blue .. 20 10
845 – 3 f. blue and green .. 20 10
DESIGN: No. 845, Wiltz.

1969. National Welfare Fund. Castles (1st series). Multicoloured.
846. 50 c.+10 c. Type **190** .. 15 20
847. 1 f. 50+25 c. Lucilinburhuc 15 20
848. 2 f.+25 c. Bourglinster .. 15 20
849. 3 f.+50 c. Hollenfels .. 15 20
850. 6 f.+1 f. Ansembourg .. 45 1·50
851. 13 f.+6 f. 90 Beaufort .. 65 3·00
See also Nos. 862/7.

191. Pasque Flower. **192.** Firecrest.

1970. Nature Conservation Year. Mult.
852. 3 f. Type **191** 20 10
853. 6 f. West European hedgehogs 60 40

1970. 50 Years of Bird Protection.
854. **192.** 1 f. 50 grn., blk. & orge. 50 15

193. "Flaming Sun".

1970. Europa.
855. **193.** 3 f. multicoloured .. 10 10
856. 6 f. multicoloured .. 20 30

194. Road Safety Assoc. Emblem and Traffic.

1970. Road Safety.
857. **194.** 3 f. black, red and lake 30 15

195. "Empress Kunegonde and Emperor Henry II" (stained-glass windows, Luxembourg Cathedral).

1970. Cent. of Luxembourg Diocese.
858. **195.** 3 f. multicoloured .. 15 20

196. Population Pictograph. **197.** Facade of Town Hall, Luxembourg.

1970. Population Census.
859. **196.** 3 f. red, blue & green 15 10

1970. 50th Anniv. of Union of Four Suburbs with Luxembourg City.
860. **197.** 3 f. brown, ochre & blue 15 10

198. U.N. Emblem. **199.** Monks in the Scriptorium.

1970. 25th Anniv. of United Nations.
861. **198.** 1 f. 50 violet and blue 10 10

1970. National Welfare Fund. Castles (2nd series). Designs as T **190.**
862. 50 c.+10 c. Clervaux .. 15 20
863. 1 f. 50+25 c. Septfontaines 15 20
864. 2 f.+25 c. Bourschied .. 15 20
865. 3 f.+50 c. Esch-sur-Sure 15 20
866. 6 f.+1 f. Larochette .. 60 1·50
867. 13 f.+6 f. 90 Brandenbourg 1·10 3·25

1971. Medieval Miniatures produced at Echternach. Multicoloured.
868. 1 f. 50 Type **199** 10 15
869. 3 f. Vine-growers going to work 15 10
870. 6 f. Vine-growers at work and returning home .. 25 20
871. 13 f. Workers with spades and hoe 45 55

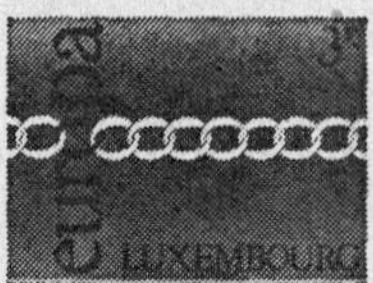

200. Europa Chain.

1971.
872. **200.** 3 f. blk., brn. & red .. 20 15
873. 6 f. black, brn. & green 35 50

201. Olympic Rings and Arms of Luxembourg. **202.** "50" and Emblem.

1971. Int. Olympic Committee Meeting, Luxembourg.
874. **201.** 3 f. red, gold and blue 10 10

1971. 50th Anniv. of Luxembourg's Christian Workers' Union (L.C.G.B.).
875. **202.** 3 f. purple, orge. & yell. 10 10

203. Artificial Lake, Upper Sure Valley. **204.** Child with Coin.

1971. Man-made Landscapes.
876. **203.** 3 f. blue, grey & brn... 40 20
877. – 3 f. brn., green & blue 40 25
878. – 15 f. blk., blue & brn. 60 20
DESIGNS: No. 877, Water-processing plant, Esch-sur-Sure. No. 878, ARBED (United Steelworks) Headquarters Building, Luxembourg.

1971. Schoolchildren's Saving Campaign.
879. **204.** 3 f. multicoloured .. 30 10

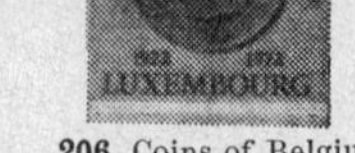

205. "Bethlehem Children". **206.** Coins of Belgium and Luxembourg.

1971. National Welfare Fund. "The Nativity" — wood-carvings in Beaufort Church. Multicoloured.
880. 1 f.+25 c. Type **205** .. 30 20
881. 1 f. 50+25 c. "Shepherds" 30 20
882. 3 f.+50 c. "Virgin, Child Jesus and St. Joseph" 30 20
883. 8 f.+1 f. "Herdsmen" .. 1·25 2·00
884. 18 f.+6 f. 50 "One of the Magi" .. .. .. 2·00 5·00

1972. 50th Anniv. of Belgium-Luxembourg Economic Union.
885. **206.** 1 f. 50 silver, blk. & grn. 15 15

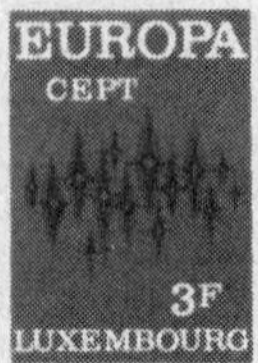

207. Bronze Mask (1st cent.). **208.** "Communications".

1972. Gallo-Roman Exhibits from Luxembourg State Museum. Multicoloured.
886. 1 f. Samian bowl (2nd cent.) (horiz.) 15 15
887. 3 f. Type **207** 30 15
888. 8 f. Limestone head (2nd/3rd cent.) 60 80
889. 15 f. Glass "head" flagon (4th cent.) 50 60

1972. Europa.
890. **208.** 3 f. multicoloured .. 40 10
891. 8 f. multicoloured .. 85 85

209. Archer. **210.** R. Schuman (after bronze by R. Zilli.)

1972. 3rd European Archery Championships, Luxembourg.
892. **209.** 3 f. multicoloured .. 30 10

1972. 20th Anniv. of Establishment of European Coal and Steel Community in Luxembourg.
893 **210** 3 f. green and grey .. 40 15

211. National Monument. **212.** "Renert".

1972. Monuments and Buildings.
894. **211.** 3 f. brn., grn. & violet 50 15
895. – 3 f. brn., green & blue 50 15
DESIGN: No. 895, European Communities' Court of Justice.

1972. Cent. of Publication of Michel Rodange's "Renert" (satirical poem).
896. **212.** 3 f. multicoloured .. 30 10

213. "Angel". **214.** "Epona on Horseback".

1972. National Welfare Fund. Stained Glass Windows in Luxembourg Cathedral. Mult.
897. 1 f.+25 c. Type **213** .. 15 20
898. 1 f. 50+25 c. "St. Joseph" 15 20
899. 3 f.+50 c. "Holy Virgin with Child Jesus" .. 15 20
900. 8 f.+1 f. "People of Bethlehem" .. .. 1·00 2·00
901. 18 f.+6 f. 50 "Angel" (facing left) .. .. 3·00 7·00

1973. Archaeological Relics. Multicoloured.
902. 1 f. Type **214** 15 20
903. 4 f. "Panther attacking swan" (horiz.) 30 10
904. 8 f. Celtic gold coin .. 1·10 1·10
905. 15 f. Bronze boar (horiz.) .. 90 65

215. Europa "Posthorn". **216.** Bee on Honeycomb.

1973. Europa.
906 **215** 4 f. orange, blue & vio 35 10
907 8 f. green, yellow & pur 90 1·00

1973. Bee-keeping.
908. **216.** 4 f. multicoloured .. 30 10

217. Nurse and Child. **218.** Capital, Vianden Castle.

1973. Day Nurseries in Luxembourg.
909 **217** 4 f. multicoloured .. 30 10

1973. Romanesque Architecture in Luxembourg.
910. **218.** 4 f. purple and green .. 20 10
911. – 8 f. blue and brown .. 45 75
DESIGN: 8 f. Detail of altar, St. Irmina's Chapel, Rosport.

219. Labour Emblem. **220.** J. de Busleyden.

1973. 50th Anniv. of Luxembourg Board of Labour.
912. **219.** 3 f. multicoloured .. 20 10

1973. 500th Anniv of Great Council of Malines.
913 **220** 4 f. purple and brown 20 10

221. Monument, Wiltz. **222.** Joachim and St. Anne.

1973. National Strike Monument.
914 **221** 4 f. green, brown & grey 20 10

1973. National Welfare Fund. "The Nativity". Details from 16th-century reredos, Hachiville Hermitage. Mult.
915. 1 f.+25 c. Type **222** .. 15 20
916. 3 f.+25 c. "Mary meets Elizabeth" 15 20
917. 4 f.+50 c. "Magus presenting gift" 20 20
918. 8 f.+1 f. "Shepherds at the manger" .. .. 75 2·00
919. 15 f.+7 f. "St. Joseph with Candle" .. .. .. 2·25 6·00

223. Princess Marie-Astrid, Association President.
224. Flame Emblem.

1974. Luxembourg Red Cross Youth Association.
920. **223.** 4 f. multicoloured .. 60 15

1974. 50th Anniv. of Luxembourg Mutual Insurance Federation.
921. **224.** 4 f. multicoloured .. 20 10

225. Seal of Henry VII, King of the Romans.
226. "Hind" (A. Tremont).

1974. Seals in Luxembourg State Archives.
922. **225.** 1 f. brn., yell. & purple 10 10
923. – 3 f. brn., yell. & green 20 25
924. – 4 f. dark brn., yell. & brn. 30 10
925. – 19 f. brn., yell. & blue 75 90
DESIGNS: 3 f. Equestrian seal of John the Blind, King of Bohemia. 4 f. Municipal seal of Diekirch. 19 f. Seal of Marienthal Convent.

1974. Europa. Sculptures. Multicoloured.
926. 4 f. Type **226** 40 10
927. 8 f. "Abstract" (L. Wercollier) .. .. .. 1·00 1·25

227. Churchill Memorial, Luxembourg.
228. Diagram of Fair.

1974. Birth Cent. of Sir Winston Churchill.
928. **227.** 4 f. multicoloured .. 30 10

1974. New Int. Fair, Luxembourg-Kirchberg.
929. **228.** 4 f. multicoloured .. 20 10

229. "Theis the Blind" (artist unknown).
230. "Crowning of St. Cecily and St. Valerien" (Hollenfels Church).

1974. 150th Death Anniv of "Theis the Blind" (Mathias Schou, folk singer).
930 **229** 3 f. multicoloured .. 20 30

1974. Gothic Architecture.
931. **230.** 4 f. brn., grn. & violet 30 30
932. – 4 f. blk., brn. & blue.. 30 20
DESIGN: No. 932, Interior of Septfontaines Church.

231. U.P.U. Emblem on "100".

1974. Cent. of Universal Postal Union.
933. **231.** 4 f. multicoloured .. 20 10
934. 8 f. multicoloured .. 50 70

232. "Benelux".

1974. 30th Anniv of Benelux (Customs Union).
935 **232** 4 f. turquoise, grn & bl 60 15

233. Differdange.

1974. Tourism.
936 **233** 4 f. purple 45 15

234. "Annunciation".
236. The Fish Market, Luxembourg.

1974. National Welfare Fund. Illustrations from "Codex Aureus Epternacensis". Mult.
937. 1 f.+25 c. Type **234** .. 15 20
938. 3 f.+25 c. "Visitation".. 15 20
939. 4 f.+50 c. "Nativity" .. 20 20
940. 8 f.+1 f. "Adoration of the Magi" .. .. .. 90 2·00
941. 15 f.+7 f. "Presentation at the Temple" .. .. 1·75 5·00

1975. European Architectural Heritage Year.
943 **236** 1 f. green 70 20
944 – 3 f. brown .. .. 1·25 30
945 – 4 f. lilac .. .. 1·40 15
946 – 19 f. red .. .. 1·50 1·00
DESIGNS—HORIZ. 3 f. Bourglinster Castle. 4 f. Market Square, Echternach. VERT. 19 f. St. Michael's Square, Mersch.

237. "Joseph Kutter" (self-portrait).
238. Dr. Albert Schweitzer.

1975. Luxembourg Culture, and Europa. Paintings. Multicoloured.
947. 1 f. Type **237** 15 15
948. 4 f. "Remich Bridge" (N. Klopp) (horiz.) .. .. 1·00 20
949. 8 f. "Still Life" (J. Kutter) (horiz.) .. .. 2·00 1·90
950. 20 f. "The Dam" (D. Lang) 1·25 45

1975. Birth Centenary of Dr Albert Schweitzer (medical missionary).
951 **238** 4 f. blue .. .. 1·00 15

239. Robert Schuman, G. Martino and P.-H Spaak.
240. Civil Defence Emblem.

1975. 25th Anniv of Robert Schuman Declaration for European Unity.
952 **239** 4 f. black, gold & green 1·00 15

1975. 15th Anniv. of Civil Defence Reorganization.
953. **240.** 4 f. multicoloured .. 60 10

241. Ice Skating.
242. Fly Orchid.

1975. Sports. Multicoloured.
954 **241** 3 f. purple, blue & grn 45 25
955 – 4 f. brn, grn & dp brn 65 15
956 – 15 f. blue, brown & grn 1·40 65
DESIGNS—HORIZ. 4 f. Water-skiing. VERT. 15 f. Rock-climbing.

1975. National Welfare Fund. Protected Plants. (1st series). Multicoloured.
957. 1 f.+25 c. Type **242** 20 20
958. 3 f.+25 c. Pyramid orchid 40 35
959. 4 f.+50 c. Marsh helleborine 50 15
960. 8 f.+1 f. Pasque flower .. 1·50 2·00
961. 15 f.+7 f. Bee orchid 3·50 6·00
See also Nos. 976/80 and 997/1001.

243. Grand Duchess Charlotte (80th).
244. 7th-century Disc-shaped Brooch.

1976. Royal Birthdays. Multicoloured.
962. 6 f. Type **243** .. .. 1·00 20
963. 6 f. Prince Henri (21st) .. 1·00 20

1976. Luxembourg Culture. Ancient Treasures from Merovingian Tombs. Mult.
964. 2 f. Type **244** 15 20
965. 5 f. 5th–6th cent. glass beaker (horiz.) 30 30
966. 6 f. Ancient pot (horiz.) .. 30 15
967. 12 f. 7th cent. gold coin .. 1·00 1·00

245. Soup Tureen.

1976. Europa. 19th century Pottery. Mult.
968. 6 f. Type **245** 50 15
969. 12 f. Bowl .. .. .. 1·25 1·25

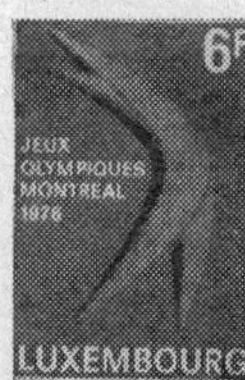

246. Independence Hall, Philadelphia.
247. Symbol representing "Strength and Impetus".

1976. Bicent. of American Revolution.
970. **246.** 6 f. multicoloured .. 30 10

1976. Olympic Games, Montreal.
971 **247** 6 f. gold, magenta and mauve 20 10

248. Association Emblem and "Sound Vibrations".
249. "Virgin and Child".

1976. 30th Anniv of "Jeunesses Musicales" (Youth Music Association).
972 **248** 6 f. multicoloured .. 30 10

1976. Renaissance Art. Multicoloured.
973. 6 f. Type **249** 30 10
974. 12 f. Bernard de Velbruck, Lord of Beaufort (funeral monument) 50 80

250. Alexander Graham Bell.

1976. Telephone Centenary.
975. **250.** 6 f. green 30 10

1976. National Welfare Fund. Protected Plants (2nd series). As T **242**. Multicoloured.
976. 2 f.+25 c. Gentian .. 20 20
977. 5 f.+25 c. Wild daffodil .. 20 20
978. 6 f.+50 c. Red helleborine (orchid) 40 25
979. 12 f.+1 f. Late spider orchid 1·25 1·50
980. 20 f.+8 f. Twin leaved squill 3·25 5·00

251. Johann von Goethe (poet).
252. Fish Market, Luxembourg.

1977. Luxembourg Culture. Famous Visitors to Luxembourg.
981 **251** 2 f. purple 15 10
982 – 5 f. violet 25 20
983 – 6 f. black 60 15
984 – 12 f. violet .. .. 1·25 75
DESIGNS: 5 f. Joseph Mallard William Turner (painter). 6 f. Victor Hugo (writer). 12 f. Franz Liszt (musician).

1977. Europa. Multicoloured.
985 6 f. Type **252** 35 10
986 12 f. Grand Duke Adolphe railway bridge and European Investment Bank 90 1·00

253. Esch-sur-Sure.
254. Marguerite de Busbach (founder).

1977. Tourism.
987. **253.** 5 f. blue 50 20
988. – 6 f. brown 40 10
DESIGNS: 6 f. Ehnen.

1977. Anniversaries. Multicoloured.
989 6 f. Type **254** 40 15
990 6 f. Louis Braille (after Filippi) 40 15
ANNIVERSARIES: No. 989, 350th anniv of foundation of Notre Dame Congregation. No. 990, 125th death anniv.

256. St. Gregory the Great.
257. Head of Medusa.

1977. Baroque Art. Sculpture from Feulen Parish Church pulpit attributed to J.-G. Scholtus.
992 **256** 6 f. purple 40 15
993 – 12 f. grey 80 80
DESIGN: 12 f. St Augustine.

1977. Roman Mosaic at Diekirch.
994. **257.** 6 f. multicoloured .. 60 20

258. Scene from "Orpheus and Eurydice" (Gluck).

1977. 25th Wiltz International Festival.
995. 258. 6 f. multicoloured .. 60 15

259. Map of E.E.C. and "Europa" (R. Zilli).

1977. 20th Anniv. of Rome Treaties.
996. 259. 6 f. multicoloured .. 40 15

1977. National Welfare Fund. Protected Plants (3rd series). As T 242. Multicoloured.
997. 2 f.+25 c. Lily of the Valley 15 15
998. 5 f.+25 c. Columbine .. 30 25
999. 6 f.+50 c. Mezereon .. 50 25
1000. 12 f.+1 f. Early Spider Orchid .. .. .. 1·75 1·50
1001. 20 f.+8 f. Spotted Orchid 3·00 5·00

262. Charles IV. 263. Head of Our Lady of Luxembourg.

1978. Europa.
1004. 262. 6 f. lilac 40 10
1005. – 12 f. red .. .. 1·25 1·00
DESIGN: 12 f. Pierre d'Aspelt (funeral monument, Mainz Cathedral).

1978. Anniversaries. Multicoloured.
1006. 6 f. Type 263 (300th anniv. of election as patron saint) 40 15
1007. 6 f. Trumpeters (135th anniv. of Grand Ducal Military Band) .. 65 15

264. Emile Mayrisch (after T. van Rysselberghe). 265. Child with Ear of Millet.

1978. 50th Death Anniv. of Emile Mayrisch (iron and steel magnate).
1008. 264. 6 f. multicoloured .. 55 15

1978. "Solidarity 1978". Multicoloured.
1009. 2 f. Type 265 (Terre des Hommes) 10 20
1010. 5 f. Flower and lungs (70th anniv. of Luxembourg Anti-Tuberculosis League) 30 20
1011. 6 f. Open cell (Amnesty International and 30th anniv. of Declaration of Human Rights) .. 35 15

266. Perfect Ashlar. 267. "St. Matthew".

1978. 175th Anniv. of Luxembourg Grand Lodge.
1012. 266. 6 f. blue 60 15

1979. National Welfare Fund. Glass Paintings (1st series). Multicoloured.
1013. 2 f.+25 c. Type 267 .. 15 20
1014. 5 f.+25 c. "St. Mark" .. 30 30
1015. 6 f.+50 c. "Nativity" .. 40 30
1016. 12 f.+1 f. "St. Luke" .. 1·25 1·00
1017. 20 f.+8 f. "St. John" .. 2·00 4·50
See also Nos. 1035/9 and 1055/8.

268. Denarius of Gaius Julius Caesar. 269. Mondorf-les-Bains.

1979. Luxembourg Culture. Roman Coins in the State Museum. Multicoloured.
1018 5 f. Type 268 .. .. 30 15
1019 6 f. Sestertius of Faustina I 50 15
1020 9 f. Follis of Helena .. 80 50
1021 26 f. Solidus of Valens .. 1·75 1·40
See also Nos. 1040/3 and 1060/3.

1979. Tourism.
1022 269 5 f. green, brown & bl 25 20
1023 – 6 f. red 75 10
DESIGN: 6 f. Luxembourg Central Station.

270. Stage Coach. 271. Antoine Meyer (poet).

1979. Europa. Multicoloured.
1024. 6 f. Type 270 .. .. 1·75 15
1025. 12 f. Old wall telephone (vert.) .. .. .. 1·75 1·50

1979. Anniversaries.
1026. – 2 f. purple 35 20
1027. 271. 5 f. red 35 20
1028. – 6 f. turquoise .. 35 20
1029. – 9 f. grey-black .. 40 25
DESIGNS—36×36 mm: 2 f. Michel Pintz on trial (after L. Piedboeuf) and monument to rebels (180th anniv of peasant uprising against French). 22×36 mm: 5 f. Type 271 (150th anniv of first publication in Luxembourg dialect. 6 f. S. G. Thomas (centenary of purchase of Thomas patent for steel production). 9 f. "Abundance crowing Work and Saving" (ceiling painting by August Vinet) (50th anniv of Stock Exchange).

272. "European Assembly". 273. Blindfolded Cherub with Chalice.

1979. First Direct Elections to European Assembly.
1030 272 6 f. multicoloured .. 2·25 60

1979. Rococo Art. Details from altar of St. Michael's Church by Barthelemy Namur. Multicoloured.
1031 6 f. Type 273 .. .. 40 15
1032 12 f. Cherub with anchor 70 70

274. Child with Traffic Symbol Balloons jumping over Traffic.

1979. International Year of the Child.
1033. 274. 2 f. bl., brn. & red .. 15 15

275. Radio Waves, "RTL" and Dates.

1979. 50th Anniv. of Broadcasting in Luxembourg.
1034. 275. 6 f. blue and red .. 50 15

1979. National Welfare Fund. Glass Paintings (2nd series). As T 267. Multicoloured.
1035. 2 f.+25 c. "Spring" .. 15 15
1036. 5 f.+25 c. "Summer" .. 30 30
1037. 6 f.+50 c. "Charity" .. 40 30
1038. 12 f.+1 f. "Autumn" .. 80 1·50
1039. 20 f.+8 f. "Winter" .. 1·50 4·50

1980. Luxembourg Culture. Medieval Coins in the State Museum. As T 268. Multicoloured.
1040 2 f. Grosso of Emperor Henry VII 20 20
1041 5 f. Grosso of John the Blind of Bohemia .. 20 20
1042 6 f. "Mouton d'or" of Wenceslas I and Jeanne, Duke and Duchess of Brabant .. 80 15
1043 20 f. Grosso of Wenceslas II, Duke of Luxembourg .. .. .. 1·60 80

276. State Archives Building. 277. Jean Monnet (statesman).

1980. Tourism.
1044. 276. 6 f. purple, ultramarine and blue .. 50 15
1045. – 6 f. red and brown .. 60 15
DESIGN—VERT. No. 1045, Ettelbruck Town Hall.

1980. Europa.
1046. 277. 6 f. black 50 15
1047. – 12 f. olive .. .. 1·00 85
DESIGNS: 12 f. St. Benedict of Nursia (founder of Benedictine Order) (statue in Echternach Abbey).

278 Sports Equipment. 279. Gloved Hand protecting Worker from Machinery.

1980. "Sports for All".
1048. 278. 6 f. blk., orge. & grn. 1·40 30

1980. 9th World Congress on the Prevention of Accidents at Work and Occupational Diseases, Amsterdam.
1049. – 2 f. multicoloured .. 20 15
1050. 279. 6 f. brn., grey & red .. 40 15
DESIGN:—VERT. 2 f. Worker pouring molten iron.

280. "Mercury" (Jean Mich). 281. Postcoded Letter.

1980. Art Nouveau Sculpture. Statues beside entrance to Sate Savings Bank.
1051 280 8 f. lilac 45 15
1052 – 12 f. blue 55 60
DESIGN: 12 f. "Ceres" (Jean Mich).

1980. Postcode Publicity.
1053. 281. 4 f. brn., ochre & red 35 15

282. Policemen and Patrol Car.

1980. 50th Anniv. of National Police Force.
1054. 282. 8 f. multicoloured .. 80 20

1980. National Welfare Fund. Glass Paintings (3rd series). As T 267. Multicoloured.
1055. 4 f.+50 c. "St. Martin" 30 20
1056. 6 f.+50 c. "St. Nicholas" 30 25
1057. 8 f.+1 f. "Virgin and child" .. .. .. 40 1·00
1058. 30 f.+10 f. "St. George" 2·25 4·50

1981. Luxembourg Culture. Coins in the State Museum. As T 268.
1060 4 f. Patagon of Philip IV of Spain, 1635 .. .. 25 20
1061 6 f. 12 sols coin of Maria Theresa, 1775 .. .. 30 20
1062 8 f. 12 sols coin of Emperor Joseph II, 1789 .. .. .. 30 15
1063 30 f. Siege crown of Emperor Francis II, 1795 .. .. .. 1·40 80

284. European Parliament Building, Luxembourg. 285. Cock-shaped Whistle sold at Easter Monday Market.

1981. Tourism.
1064. 284. 8 f. brown and blue .. 30 15
1065. – 8 f. red and blue .. 30 15
DESIGN: No. 1065, National Library.

1981. Europa. Multicoloured.
1066. 8 f. Procession of beribboned sheep and town band to local fair .. 40 15
1067. 12 f. Type 285 .. .. 60 50

286. Staunton Knight on Chessboard. 287. Prince Henri and Princess Maria Teresa.

1981. Anniversaries.
1068. 286. 4 f. multicoloured .. 40 15
1069. – 8 f. ochre, brn. & silver 40 15
1070. – 8 f. multicoloured .. 40 15
DESIGNS—VERT. 4 f. Type 286 (50th anniv of Luxembourg Chess Federation). 8 f. (1070), Passbook and State Savings Bank (125th anniv of State Savings Bank). HORIZ. 8 f. (1069), First Luxembourg banknote (125th anniv of International Bank of Luxembourg's issuing rights).

1981. Royal Wedding.
1071. 287. 8 f. multicoloured .. 50 40

288. Gliders over Useldange. 289. Flame.

1981. Aviation. Multicoloured.
1072. 8 f. Type 288 .. .. 30 15
1073. 16 f. Sports planes .. 55 60
1074. 35 f. Boeing over Luxembourg-Findel airport terminal .. .. 1·25 85

1981. Energy Conservation.
1075. 289. 8 f. multicoloured .. 30 15

290. Arms of Petange. 291. "Apple Trees in Blossom" (Frantz Seimetz).

1981. National Welfare Fund. Arms of Local Authorities (1st series). Multicoloured.
1076. 4 f.+50 c. Type 290 .. 15 15
1077. 6 f.+50 c. Larochette .. 25 25
1078. 8 f.×1 f. "Adoration of the Magi" (School of Rubens) 40 30
1079. 16 f.+2 f. Stadtbredimus 80 1·50
1080. 35 f.+12 f. Weiswampach 2·50 5·00
See also Nos. 1097/1101 and 1119/23.

1982. Luxembourg Culture. Landscapes through the Four Seasons. Multicoloured.
1081 4 f. Type **291** 20 15
1082 6 f. "Landscape" (Pierre Blanc) 30 30
1083 8 f. "The Larger Hallerbach" (Guido Oppenheim) 45 15
1084 16 f. "Winter Evening" (Eugene Mousset) .. 70 70

292. Cross of Hinzert and Statue "Political Prisoner" (Lucien Wercollier).
293. Treaty of London, 1867, and Luxembourg Fortress.

1982. National Monument of the Resistance and Deportation, Notre-Dame Cemetery.
1085. **292.** 8 f. multicoloured .. 40 15

1982. Europa. Multicoloured.
1086. 8 f. Type **293** 50 15
1087. 16 f. Treaty of Paris, 1951, and European Coal and Steel Community Building, Luxembourg 90 75

294. St. Theresa of Avila (wood statue, Carmel Monastery.)
295. State Museum.

1982. Anniversaries. Multicoloured.
1088 4 f. Type **294** (400th death anniv) 30 15
1089 8 f. Raoul Follereau (social worker for lepers, 5th death anniv) 50 15

1982. Tourism.
1090 **295** 8 f. brown, blue & blk 50 15
1091 – 8 f. buff, black & blue 75 15
DESIGN: No. 1091, Luxembourg Synagogue.

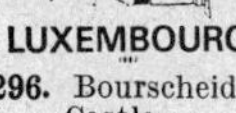

296. Bourscheid Castle.
297. Key in Lock.

1982. Classified Monuments (1st series).
1092. **296.** 6 f. blue 30 15
1093. – 8 f. red 50 15
DESIGN—HORIZ. 8 f. Vianden Castle.
See also Nos. 1142/3, and 1165/6.

1982. Anniversaries. Multicoloured.
1094 4 f. Type **297** (50th anniv of International Youth Hostel Federation) .. 50 15
1095 8 f. Scouts holding hands around globe (75th anniv of Scouting Movement) (vert) .. 60 15

298. Monument to Civilian and Military Deportation.

1982. Civilian and Military Deportation Monument, Hollerich Station.
1096. **298.** 8 f. multicoloured .. 40 15

1982. National Welfare Fund. Arms of Local Authorities (2nd series) and Stained Glass Window (8 f.). As T **290**. Multicoloured.
1097 4 f. + 50 c. Bettembourg 25 20
1098 6 f. + 50 c. Frisange .. 30 25
1099 8 + 1 f. "Adoration of the Shepherds" (Gustav Zanter, Hoscheid parish church) 45 30
1100 16 f. + 2 f. Mamer .. 90 1·30
1101 35 f. + 12 f. Heinerscheid 2·25 5·00

299. Modern Fire Engine.
300. "Mercury" (Auguste Tremont).

1983. Centenary of National Federation of Fire Brigades. Multicoloured.
1102. 8 f. Type **299** 65 15
1103. 16 f. Hand fire-pump (18th century) .. .. 1·25 65

1983. Anniversaries and Events.
1104. **300.** 4 f. multicoloured .. 20 20
1105. – 6 f. multicoloured .. 50 30
1106. – 8 f. brown, black and blue 50 15
1107. – 8 f. deep blue and blue 50 15
DESIGNS: No. 1104, Type **300** (25th Congress of International Association of Foreign Exchange Dealers). 1105, N.A.T.O. emblem surrounded by flags of member countries (25th anniv. of N.A.T.O.). 1106, Echternach Cross of Justice (30th Congress of International Union of Barristers). 1107, Globe and customs emblem (30th anniv. of Customs Co-operation Council).

301. Robbers attacking Traveller.

1983. Europa. Miniatures from "Codex Aureus Escorialensis", illustrating Parable of the Good Samaritan. Multicoloured.
1108. 8 f. Type **301** 75 20
1109. 16 f. Good Samaritan helping traveller .. 1·25 80

302. Initial "H" from "Book of Baruch".
303. Despatch Rider and Postcode.

1983. Luxembourg Culture. Echternach Abbey Giant Bible. Multicoloured
1110. 8 f. Type **302** 45 20
1111. 35 f. Initial "B" from letter of St. Jerome to Pope Damasius I .. 1·50 1·25

1983. World Communications Year. Mult.
1112. 8 f. Type **303** 80 20
1113. 8 f. European Communications Satellite (horiz.) 1·25 30

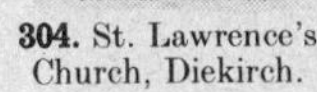

304. St. Lawrence's Church, Diekirch.
305. Basketball.

1983. Tourism.
1114. **304.** 7 f. orange, brown and blue 30 15
1115. – 10 f. orange, brown and blue 40 20
DESIGN—HORIZ. 10 f. Dudelange Town Hall.

1983. Anniversaries and Events. Mult.
1116. 7 f. Type **305** (50th anniv. of Luxembourg basketball Federation) .. 55 20
1117. 10 f. Sheepdog (European Working Dog Championships) 80 20
1118. 10 f. City of Luxembourg ("The Green Heart of Europe") 80 20

1983. National Welfare Fund. Arms of Local Authorities (3rd series) and Painting. As T **290**. Multicoloured.
1119. 4 f. + 1 f. Winseler .. 30 20
1120. 7 f. + 1 f. Beckerich .. 40 30
1121. 10 f. + 1 f. "Adoration of the Shepherds" (Lucas Bosch) 50 35
1122. 16 f. + 2 f. Feulen .. 1·10 1·50
1123. 40 f. + 13 f. Mertert .. 2·75 5·00

306. Lion and First Luxembourg Stamp.
307. Pedestrian Precinct.

1984. Anniversaries. Each black, red and blue.
1124. 10 f. Type **306** 70 30
1125. 10 f. Lion and ministry buildings 70 30
1126. 10 f. Lion and postman's bag 70 30
1127. 10 f. Lion and locomotive 70 30
ANNIVERSARIES. No. 1124, 50th anniv. of Federation of Luxembourg Philatelic Societies. No. 1125, 75th anniv. of Civil Service Trade Union Movement. No. 1126, 75th anniv. of Luxembourg Postmen's Trade Union. No. 1127, 125th anniv. of Luxembourg Railways.

1984. Environmental Protection. Mult.
1128. 7 f. Type **307** 30 30
1129. 10 f. City of Luxembourg sewage treatment plant 40 20

308. Hands supporting European Parliament Emblem.
309. Bridge.

1984. 2nd Direct Elections to European Parliament.
1130. **308.** 10 f. multicoloured .. 60 20

1984. Europa. 25th Anniv. of European Post and Telecommunications Conference.
1131. **309.** 10 f. green, dp. green and black .. .. 1·00 20
1132. 16 f. orge., brn. & blk. 2·00 75

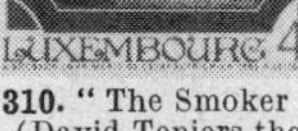

310. "The Smoker" (David Teniers the Younger).
311. "The Race" (Jean Jacoby).

1984. Paintings. Multicoloured.
1133. 4 f. Type **310** 50 30
1134. 7 f. "Young Turk caressing his Horse" (Eugene Delacroix) (horiz.) 70 30
1135. 10 f. "Epiphany" (Jan Steen) (horiz.) .. 1·00 20
1136. 50 f. "The Lacemaker" (Pieter van Slingelandt) .. .. 3·50 1·50

1984. Olympic Games, Los Angeles.
1137. **311.** 10 f. orge. blk. & blue 65 20

312. "Pecten sp."
313. "American Soldier" (statue by Michel Heitz at Clervaux)

1984. Luxembourg Culture. Fossils in the Natural History Museum. Mult.
1138. 4 f. Type **312** 35 20
1139. 7 f. "Gryphaea arcuata" 65 30
1140. 10 f. "Coeloceras raquinianum" (ammonite) .. .. 1·25 15
1141. 16 f. "Dapedius sp." (fish) .. .. .. 1·50 95

1984. Classified Monuments (2nd series). As T **296**.
1142. 7 f. turquoise 35 30
1143. 10 f. brown 45 15
DESIGNS: 7 f. Hollenfels Castle. 10 f. Larochette Castle.

1984. 40th Anniv. of Liberation.
1144. **313.** 10 f. blk., red & blue 1·25 20

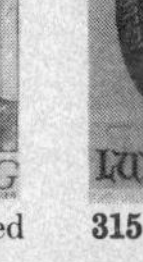

314. Infant astounded by Surroundings.
315. Jean Bertels (abbot of Echternach Abbey).

1984. National Welfare Fund. The Child. Multicoloured.
1145. 4 f. + 1 f. Type **314** .. 40 40
1146. 7 f. + 1 f. Child dreaming 60 60
1147. 10 f. + 1 f. "Nativity" (crib, Steinsel church) 1·00 50
1148. 16 f. + 2 f. Child sulking 2·50 2·50
1149. 40 f. + 13 f. Girl admiring flower .. .. .. 7·00 8·00

1985. Luxembourg Culture. Portrait Medals in State Museum (1st series). Multicoloured.
1150. 4 f. Type **315** (steatite medal, 1595) 20 20
1151. 7 f. Emperor Charles V (bronze medal, 1537) .. 30 30
1152. 10 f. King Philip II of Spain (silver medal, 1555) 40 20
1153. 30 f. Maurice of Orange-Nassau (silver medal, 1615) .. .. .. 1·25 90
See also Nos. 1173/6.

316. Fencing.
317. Papal Arms.

1985. Anniversaries. Multicoloured.
1154. 10 f. Type **316** (50th anniv. of Luxembourg Fencing Federation) .. 60 20
1155. 10 f. Benz "Velo" (centenary of automobile) .. 60 20
1156. 10 f. Telephone within concentric circles (centenary of Luxembourg telephone service) .. 60 20

1985. Visit of Pope John Paul II.
1157. **317.** 10 f. multicoloured .. 60 20

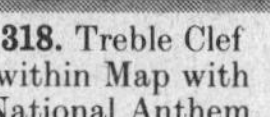

318. Treble Clef within Map with National Anthem. **320.** Little Owl.

1985. Europa. Music Year. Multicoloured.

1158. 10 f. Type **318** (Grand Duke Adolphe Union of choral, instrumental and folklore societies) 1·25 30
1159. 16 f. Neck of violin, music school and score of Beethoven's Violin Concerto opus 61 .. 2·25 95

1985. Endangered Animals. Multicoloured.

1161. 4 f. Type **320** .. .. 1·00 30
1162. 7 f. European wildcat (horiz.) .. .. 1·50 30
1163. 10 f. Red admiral (horiz.) 2·00 30
1164. 50 f. European tree frog 5·00 1·25

1985. Classified Monuments (3rd series). As T **296.**

1165. 7 f. red 50 20
1166. 10 f. green 50 15

Designs—horiz. 7 f. Echternach orangery. vert. 10 f. Mohr de Waldt house.

321. Mansfeld Arms (book binding). **322.** Application.

1985. Luxembourg Culture.

1167. **321.** 10 f. multicoloured .. 50 30

1985. National Welfare Fund. Multicoloured.

1168. 4 f.+1 f. Type **322** .. 40 30
1169. 7 f.+1 f. Friendship .. 60 50
1170. 10 f.+1 f. "Adoration of the Magi" (16th century alabaster sculpture) .. .. 1·00 50
1171. 16 f.+2 f. Child identifying with his favourite characters .. 2·50 2·50
1172. 40 f.+13 f. Shame .. 7·50 9·00

1986. Luxembourg Culture. Portrait Medals in State Museum (2nd series). As T **315.**

1173. 10 f. multicoloured .. 50 30
1174. 12 f. multicoloured .. 60 20
1175. 18 f. black, grey and blue 80 50
1176. 20 f. multicoloured .. 1·25 50

Designs: 10 f. Count of Monterey (silver medal, 1675). 12 f. Louis XIV of France (silver medal, 1684). 18 f. Pierre de Weyms (president of Provincial Council) (pewter medal, 1700). 20 f. Duke of Marlborough (silver medal, 1706).

323. Bee on Flower. **324.** Forest and City.

1986. Anniversaries. Multicoloured.

1177. 12 f. Type **323** (Centenary of Federation of Luxembourg Beekeeper's Associations) 80 20
1178. 12 f. Table tennis player (50th anniv. of Luxembourg Table Tennis Federation) 80 20
1179. 11 f. Mosaic of woman with water jar (centenary of Mondorf State Spa) 80 20

1986. Europa. Multicoloured.

1180. 12 f. Type **324** 75 15
1181. 20 f. Mankind, industry and countryside .. 1·50 75

325. Fort Thungen. **326.** Schuman.

1986. Luxembourg Town Fortifications. Mult.

1182 15 f. Type **325** 60 50
1183 18 f. Invalids' Gate (vert) 80 50
1184 50 f. Malakoff Tower (vert) .. .. .. 2·00 1·50

1986. Birth Centenary of Robert Schuman (politician).

1185. **326.** 2 f. black and red .. 10 10
1186. 10 f. black and blue 40 30

327. Road through Red Triangle on Map. **328.** Ascent to Chapel of the Cross, Grevenmacher.

1986. European Road Safety Year.

1187. **327.** 10 f. multicoloured .. 75 20

1986. Tourism.

1188. **328.** 12 f. multicoloured .. 70 30
1189. – 12 f. brn, stone & red 70 30

Design: No. 1189, Relief from Town Hall facade, Esch-sur-Alzette.

329. Presentation of Letter of Freedom to Echternach (after P. H. Witkamp). **330.** Annunciation.

1986. 800th Birth Anniv. of Countess Ermesinde of Luxembourg.

1190. **329.** 12 f. brown and stone 60 30
1191. – 30 f. buff, black and grey .. .. 1·50 80

Design: 30 f. Seal, 1238.

1986. National Welfare Fund. Illustrations from 15th-century "Book of Hours". Multicoloured.

1192. 6 f.+1 f. Type **330** .. 1·00 30
1193. 10 f.+1 f. Angel appearing to shepherds .. 50 40
1194. 12 f.+2 f. Nativity .. 1·00 50
1195. 18 f.+2 f. Adoration of the Magi .. .. 2·50 2·50
1196. 20 f.+8 f. Flight into Egypt .. .. .. 5·00 5·00

331. Garden Dormouse. **332.** Network Emblem.

1987. Endangered Animals. Multicoloured.

1197 6 f. Type **331** 50 30
1198 10 f. Banded agrion (vert) 65 55
1199 12 f. Dipper (vert) .. 1·25 55
1200 25 f. Salamander .. 2·00 80

1987. 50th Anniversaries. Multicoloured.

1201. 12 f. Type **232** (Amateur Short Wave Network) 55 30
1202. 12 f. Anniversary emblem (International Fair) 55 30

333. "St. Bernard of Siena and St. John the Baptist". **334.** National Swimming Centre (Roger Taillibert).

1987. Paintings by Giovanni Ambrogio Bevilacqua in State Museum. Multicoloured.

1203 10 f. Type **333** 50 40
1204 18 f. "St. Jerome and St. Francis of Assisi" .. 90 60

1987. Europa. Architecture. Multicoloured.

1205. 12 f. Type **334** .. .. 1·00 30
1206. 20 f. European Communities' Court of Justice .. .. .. 2·00 80

335. "Consecration" (stained glass window by Gustav Zanter). **336.** Charles Metz (first President) (after Jean-Baptiste Fresez).

1987. Millenary of St. Michael's Church. Multicoloured.

1207. 12 f. Type **335** 50 30
1208. 20 f. Baroque organ-chest .. .. .. 1·10 70

1987. Chamber of Deputies.

1209. **336.** 6 f. brown 30 20
1210. – 12 f. blue 50 40

Design: 12 f. Chamber of Deputies building.

337. Hennesbau, Niederfeulen. **338.** Annunciation.

1987. Rural Architecture. Each ochre, brown and blue.

1211. 10 f. Type **337** .. 60 30
1212. 12 f. 18th-century dwelling house converted to health centre, Mersch 60 30
1213. 100 f. 18th-century house converted to Post Office, Bertrange .. 4·00 1·75

1987. National Welfare Fund. Illustrations from 15th-century Paris "Book of Hours". Multicoloured.

1214. 6 f.+1 f. Type **338** .. 70 50
1215. 10 f.+1 f. Visitation .. 1·25 1·00
1216. 12 f.+2 f. Adoration of the Magi .. .. 1·50 1·00
1217. 18 f.+2 f. Presentation in the Temple .. 2·00 2·00
1218. 20 f.+8 f. Flight into Egypt .. .. .. 4·00 5·00

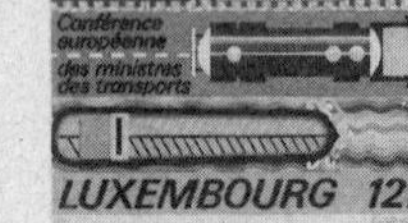

339. Lilies and Water-lily. **340.** Rail, Road and Water Transport.

1988. Luxembourg Culture. Flower Illustrations by Pierre-Joseph Redoute. Mult.

1219 6 f. Type **339** 75 30
1220 10 f. Primulas and double narcissus 75 40
1221 12 f. Tulips and chrysanthemums .. 1·50 20
1222 50 f. Irises and gorterias 2·50 1·25

1988. European Conference of Ministers of Transport, Luxembourg (1223) and 25th Anniv of Eurocontrol (air safety organization) (1224). Multicoloured.

1223 12 f. Type **340** 60 35
1224 20 f. Boeing 747 airplane 1·25 80

342. Wiltz Town Hall and Cross of Justice.

1988. Tourism. Multicoloured.

1226 10 f. Type **342** 70 30
1227 12 f. Differdange Castle (vert) 70 30

See also Nos. 1254/5 and 1275/6.

343. Athletes.

1988. 50th Anniv. of League of Luxembourg Student Sports Associations.

1228. **343.** 12 f. multicoloured .. 60 15

344. Automated Mail Sorting.

1988. Europa. Transport and Communications. Multicoloured.

1229 12 f. Type **344** .. .. 1·50 20
1230 20 f. Electronic communications .. .. 2·00 90

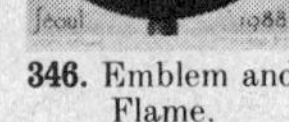

345. Jean Monnet (statesman, birth centenary). **346.** Emblem and Flame.

1988. European Anniversaries.

1231. **345.** 12 f. pink, brown and light brown .. 75 20
1232. – 12 f. brown and green 1·25 20

Design: No. 1232, European Investment Bank headquarters, Kirchberg (30th anniv).

1988. Olympic Games, Seoul.

1233. **346.** 12 f. multicoloured .. 60 15

347. Septfontaines Castle. **348.** Annunciation to Shepherds.

1988. Doorways.

1234. **347.** 12 f. black and brown 45 15
1235. – 25 f. black and green 90 80
1236. – 50 f. black and brown 1·75 1·25

Designs: 25 f. National Library. 50 f. Holy Trinity Church.

1988. National Welfare Fund. Illustrations from 16th-century Book of Hours. Mult.
1237 9 f.+1 f. Type **348** .. 60 40
1238 12 f.+2 f. Adoration of the Magi 70 40
1239 18 f.+2 f. Madonna and Child .. .. .. 2·25 2·25
1240 20 f.+8 f. Pentecost .. 2·75 2·75

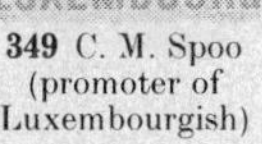

349 C. M. Spoo (promoter of Luxembourgish)

350 Grand Ducal Family Vault Bronze (Auguste Tremont)

1989. Anniversaries.
1241 **349** 12 f. black, red & brn 60 25
1242 – 18 f. multicoloured .. 90 50
1243 – 20 f. red, black & grey 1·25 75
DESIGNS: 12 f. Type **349** (75th death anniv); 18 f. Stylized inking pad (125th anniv of Book Workers' Federation); 20 f. Henri Dunant (founder of International Red Cross) (75th anniv of Luxembourg Red Cross).

1989. 150th Anniv of Independence.
1244 **350** 12 f. multicoloured .. 60 30

351 "Astra" Satellite and Map on T.V. Screens

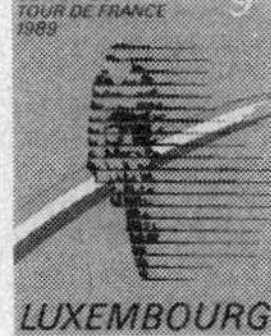

352 Cyclist

1989. Launch of 16-channel T.V. Satellite.
1245 **351** 12 f. multicoloured .. 60 30

1989. Start in Luxembourg of Tour de France Cycling Race.
1246 **352** 9 f. multicoloured .. 70 30

353 Assembly and Flag

354 Emblem

1989. 40th Anniv of Council of Europe.
1247 **353** 12 f. multicoloured .. 70 30

1989. Cent of Interparliamentary Union.
1248 **354** 12 f. yellow, bl & ind 70 30

355 Hands

356 "Three Children in a Park" (anon)

1989. 3rd Direct Elections to European Parliament.
1249 **355** 12 f. multicoloured .. 70 30

1989. Europa. Children's Games and Toys. Multicoloured.
1250 12 f. Type **356** 75 30
1251 20 f. "Child with Drum" (anon) .. .. 1·75 95

357 Grand Duke Jean

358 Charles IV

1989. 25th Anniv of Accession of Grand Duke Jean.
1252 **357** 3 f. black and orange 10 10
1253 9 f. black and green 50 30

1989. Tourism. As T **342**. Multicoloured.
1254 12 f. Clervaux Castle .. 50 30
1255 18 f. 1st-century bronze wild boar, Titelberg .. 90 65

1989. Luxembourg History. Stained Glass Windows by Joseph Oberberger, Luxembourg Cathedral. Multicoloured.
1256 12 f. Type **358** 75 30
1257 20 f. John the Blind .. 1·25 85
1258 25 f. Wenceslas II .. 1·25 85

359 St. Lambert and St. Blase, Fennange

360 Funfair (650th anniv of Schueberfouer)

1989. National Welfare Fund. Restored Chapels (1st series). Multicoloured.
1259 9 f.+1 f. Type **359** .. 50 30
1260 12 f.+2 f. St. Quirinus, Luxembourg (horiz) .. 60 50
1261 18 f.+3 f. St. Anthony the Hermit, Reisdorf (horiz) 1·50 1·50
1262 25 f.+8 f. The Hermitage, Hachiville .. .. 2·00 2·00
See also Nos. 1280/3 and 1304/7.

1990. Anniversaries.
1263 **360** 9 f. multicoloured .. 45 30
1264 – 12 f. brn, pink & blk 55 30
1265 – 18 f. multicoloured .. 90 50
DESIGNS: 12 f. Batty Weber (writer, 50th death anniv); 18 f. Dish aerial (125th anniv of International Telecommunications Union).

361 Troops at Fortress

1990. Luxembourg Culture. Etchings of the Fortress by Christoph Wilhelm Selig. Mult.
1266 9 f. Type **361** 60 30
1267 12 f. Soldiers by weir .. 70 40
1268 20 f. Distant view of fortress .. .. 1·25 60
1269 25 f. Walls .. .. 1·75 90

362 Paul Eyschen (75th anniv)

363 "Psallus pseudoplatani" (male and female) on Maple

1990. Statesmen's Death Anniversaries.
1270 **362** 9 f. brown and blue .. 50 30
1271 – 12 f. blue and brown 60 40
DESIGN: 12 f. Emmanuel Servais (centenary).

1990. Centenary of Luxembourg Naturalists' Society.
1272 **363** 12 f. multicoloured .. 70 40

364 General Post Office, Luxembourg City

365 Hammelsmarsch Fountain (Will Lofy)

1990. Europa. Post Office Buildings.
1273 **364** 12 f. black and brown 75 30
1274 – 20 f. black and blue .. 1·50 70
DESIGN—VERT. 20 f. Esch-sur-Alzette Post Office.

1990. Tourism. As T **342**. Multicoloured.
1275 12 f. Mondercange administrative offices 65 30
1276 12 f. Schifflange town hall and church 65 30

1990. Fountains. Multicoloured.
1277 12 f. Type **365** 60 30
1278 25 f. Doves Fountain .. 1·25 80
1279 50 f. Maus Ketty Fountain, Mondorf-les-Bains (Will Lofy) .. 2·25 1·50

366 Congregation of the Blessed Virgin Mary, Vianden

368 "Geastrum varians"

1990. National Welfare Fund. Restored Chapels (2nd series). Multicoloured.
1280 9 f.+1 f. Type **366** .. 60 40
1281 12 f.+2 f. Notre Dame, Echternach (horiz) .. 70 50
1282 18 f.+3 f. Consoler of the Afflicted, Grentzingen (horiz) .. 1·25 1·25
1283 25 f.+8 f. St. Pirmin, Kaundorf .. .. 1·75 1·75

1991. Fungi. Illustrations by Pierre-Joseph Redoute. Multicoloured.
1285 14 f. Type **368** .. .. 1·00 40
1286 14 f. "Agaricus (Gymnopus) thiebautii" 1·00 40
1287 18 f. "Agaricus (Lepiota) lepidocephalus" .. 1·50 75
1288 25 f. "Morchella favosa" 2·00 1·25

369 "View from the Trier Road"

370 Dicks (after Jean Goedert)

1991. Luxembourg Culture. 50th Death Anniv of Sosthene Weis (painter). Multicoloured.
1289 14 f. Type **369** 80 40
1290 18 f. "Vauban Street and the Viaduct" .. .. 1·00 60
1291 25 f. "St. Ulric Street" (vert) .. .. .. 1·50 75

1991. Death Centenary of Edmond de la Fontaine (pen-name Dicks) (poet).
1292 **370** 14 f. multicoloured .. 70 40

MINIMUM PRICE

The minimum price quoted is 5p which represents a handling charge rather than a basis for valuing common stamps. For further notes about prices see introductory pages.

371 Claw grasping Piece of Metal (after Emile Kirscht)

372 National Miners' Monument, Kayl

1991. 75th Anniv of Trade Union Movement in Luxembourg.
1293 **371** 14 f. multicoloured .. 70 40

1991. Tourism. Multicoloured.
1294 14 f. Type **372** 75 40
1295 14 f. Magistrates' Court, Redange-sur-Attert (horiz) 75 40

373 Earth and Orbit of "Astra 1A" and "1B" Satellites

374 Telephone

1991. Europa. Europe in Space. Mult.
1296 14 f. Type **373** 90 40
1297 18 f. Betzdorf Earth Station .. .. 1·50 85

1991. Posts and Telecommunications.
1298 **374** 4 f. brown 50 20
1299 – 14 f. blue 60 20
DESIGN: 14 f. Postbox.

375 1936 International Philatelic Federation Congress Stamp

376 Girl's Head

1991. 50th Stamp Day.
1300 **375** 14 f. multicoloured .. 60 40
The stamp illustrated on No. 1300 incorrectly shows a face value of 10 f.

1991. Mascarons (stone faces on buildings) (1st series).
1301 **376** 14 f. black, buff & brn 60 40
1302 – 25 f. blk, buff & pink 1·25 80
1303 – 50 f. black, buff & bl 2·25 1·60
DESIGNS: 25 f. Woman's head; 50 f. Man's head.
See also Nos. 1320/22.

377 Chapel of St. Donatus, Arsdorf

378 Jean-Pierre Pescatore Foundation

1991. National Welfare Fund. Restored Chapels (3rd series). Multicoloured.
1304 14 f.+2 f. Type **377** .. 80 60
1305 14 f.+2 f. Chapel of Our Lady of Sorrows, Brandenbourg (horiz) 80 60
1306 18 f.+3 f. Chapel of Our Lady, Luxembourg (horiz) .. .. 1·25 1·25
1307 22 f.+7 f. Chapel of the Hermitage, Wolwelange 1·75 1·75

1992. Buildings. Multicoloured.

No.	Type	Description	Mint	Used
1308		14 f. Type **378**	55	35
1309		14 f. Higher Technology Institute, Kirchberg	55	35
1310		14 f. New Fairs and Congress Centre, Kirchberg	55	35

379 Inner Courtyard, Bettembourg Castle

1992. Tourism. Multicoloured.

No.	Type	Description	Mint	Used
1311		18 f. Type **379**	75	45
1312		25 f. Walferdange Railway Station	1·00	60

380 Athlete (detail of mural, Armand Strainchamps)

1992. Olympic Games, Barcelona.

No.	Type	Description	Mint	Used
1313	**380**	14 f. multicoloured	55	35

381 Luxembourg Pavilion

382 Lions Emblem

1992. "Expo '92" World's Fair, Seville.

No.	Type	Description	Mint	Used
1314	**381**	14 f. multicoloured	55	35

1992. 75th Anniv of Lions International.

No.	Type	Description	Mint	Used
1315	**382**	14 f. multicoloured	55	35

383 Memorial Tablet (Lucien Wercollier)

384 Nicholas Gonner (editor)

1992. 50th Anniv of General Strike.

No.	Type	Description	Mint	Used
1316	**383**	18 f. brown, grey & red	75	45

1992. Europa. 500th Anniv of Discovery of America by Columbus. Luxembourg Emigrants to America.

No.	Type	Description	Mint	Used
1317	**384**	14 f. brown, blk & grn	55	35
1318	–	22 f. blue, blk & orge	90	55

DESIGN: 22 f. Nicolas Becker (writer).

385 Star and European Community Emblem

386 Posthorn and Letters

1992. Single European Market.

No.	Type	Description	Mint	Used
1319	**385**	14 f. multicoloured	55	35

1992. Mascarons (2nd series). As T **376**.

No.	Type	Description	Mint	Used
1320		14 f. black, buff and green	55	35
1321		22 f. black, buff and blue	90	55
1322		50 f. black, buff & purple	2·00	1·25

DESIGNS: 14 f. Ram's head; 22 f. Lion's head; 50 f. Goat's head.

1992. 150th Anniv of Post and Telecommunications Office. Designs showing stained glass windows by Auguste Tremont. Mult.

No.	Type	Description	Mint	Used
1323		14 f. Type **386**	55	35
1324		22 f. Post rider	90	55
1325		50 f. Telecommunications	2·00	1·25

387 Hazel Grouse

388 Grand Duke Jean

1992. National Welfare Fund. Birds. Mult.

No.	Type	Description	Mint	Used
1326		14 f.+2 f. Type **387**	65	50
1327		14 f.+2 f. Golden oriole (vert)	65	50
1328		18 f.+3 f. Black stork	85	85
1329		22 f.+7 f. Red kite (vert)	1·10	1·10

1993.

No.	Type	Description	Mint	Used
1332	**388**	5 f. black and yellow	20	10
1334		7 f. black and brown	30	20
1337		14 f. black and purple	55	35
1340		18 f. black and yellow	75	45
1343		22 f. black and green	90	55
1345		25 f. black and blue	1·00	60

389 Old Ironworks Cultural Centre, Steinfort

1993. Tourism. Multicoloured.

No.	Type	Description	Mint	Used
1350		14 f. Type **389**	55	35
1351		14 f. "Children with Grapes" Fountain, Schwebsingen	55	35

390 Collage by Maurice Esteve

1993. New Surgical Techniques.

No.	Type	Description	Mint	Used
1352	**390**	14 f. multicoloured	55	35

391 Hotel de Bourgogne (Prime Minister's offices)

1993. Historic Houses. Multicoloured.

No.	Type	Description	Mint	Used
1353		14 f. Type **391**	55	35
1354		20 f. Simons House (now Ministry of Agriculture)	85	50
1355		50 f. Cassal House	2·00	1·25

392 "Rezlop" (Fernand Roda)

1993. Europa. Contemporary Art. Mult.

No.	Type	Description	Mint	Used
1356		14 f. Type **392**	55	35
1357		22 f. "So Close" (Sonja Roef)	90	55

393 Monument (detail, D. Donzelli), Tetange Cemetery

394 Emblem

1993. 75th Death Anniv of Jean Schortgen (first worker elected to parliament).

No.	Type	Description	Mint	Used
1358	**393**	14 f. multicoloured	55	35

1993. Centenary of Artistic Circle of Luxemburg.

No.	Type	Description	Mint	Used
1359	**394**	14 f. mauve and violet	55	35

395 European Community Ecological Label

396 Tram Motor Unit No. 1 (Transport Museum, Luxembourg)

1993. Protection of Environment.

No.	Type	Description	Mint	Used
1360	**395**	14 f. blue, grn & emer	55	35

1993. Museum Exhibits. Multicoloured.

No.	Type	Description	Mint	Used
1361		14 f. Type **396**	55	35
1362		22 f. Iron ore tipper wagon (National Mining Museum, Rumelange)	85	55
1363		60 f. Horse-drawn carriage (Arts and Ancient Crafts Museum, Wiltz)	2·25	1·40

OFFICIAL STAMPS

1875. Stamps of 1859–72 optd **OFFICIEL**. Roul.

No.	Type	Description	Mint	Used
O79	**3**	1 c. brown	22·00	40·00
O80		2 c. black	22·00	40·00
O81	**4**	10 c. lilac	£2250	£2500
O82		12½ c. red	£450	£550
O83		20 c. brown	40·00	60·00
O84		25 c. blue	£250	£150
O85		30 c. purple	28·00	70·00
O88		40 c. orange	£170	£250
O87		1 f. on 37½ c. bistre (No. 37)	£140	18·00

1875. Stamps of 1874–79 optd **OFFICIEL**. Perf.

No.	Type	Description	Mint	Used
O 89	**3**	1 c. brown	7·00	30·00
O 90		2 c. black	8·00	30·00
O 91		4 c. green	£100	£140
O 92		5 c. yellow	50·00	70·00
O 93a	**4**	10 c. lilac	80·00	£100
O111		12½ c. red	55·00	80·00
O 98		20 c. brown		
O 99a		25 c. blue	2·00	2·50
O 96		1 f. on 37½ c. bistre (No. 56)	30·00	50·00

1881. Stamp of 1859 optd **S. P.** Roul.

No.	Type	Description	Mint	Used
O116	**3**	40 c. orange	30·00	70·00

1881. Stamps of 1874–79 optd **S. P.** Perf.

No.	Type	Description	Mint	Used
O128	**3**	1 c. brown	7·00	8·00
O129		2 c. black	8·00	10·00
O118		4 c. green	£180	£200
O123		5 c. yellow	70·00	90·00
O124	**4**	10 c. lilac	£100	£130
O131		12½ c. red	£120	£160
O132		20 c. brown	65·00	80·00
O133		25 c. blue	65·00	80·00
O134		30 c. red	65·00	80·00
O120		1 f. on 37½ c. bistre (No. 56)	26·00	50·00

1882. Stamps of 1882 optd **S. P.**

No.	Type	Description	Mint	Used
O 141.	**7.**	1 c. grey	25	40
O 142.		2 c. brown	25	40
O 143.		4 c. olive	25	50
O 144.		5 c. green	30	60
O 181.		10 c. red	11·00	15·00
O 158.		12½ c. blue	2·00	5·00
O 159.		20 c. orange	2·00	4·00
O 183.		25 c. blue	16·00	22·00
O 149.		30 c. olive	4·00	9·00
O 150.		50 c. brown	1·00	3·00
O 151.		1 f. lilac	1·00	4·00
O 152.		5 f. orange	12·00	24·00

1891. Stamps of 1891 optd **S. P.**

No.	Type	Description	Mint	Used
O188	**8**	10 c. red	25	50
O191		12½ c. green	7·00	7·00
O192		20 c. orange	10·00	9·00
O193		25 c. blue	30	55
O194		30 c. green	8·50	9·00
O195		37½ c. green	9·00	9·00
O196		50 c. brown	8·00	10·00
O197		1 f. purple	8·00	12·00
O198		2½ f. black	38·00	75·00
O199		5 f. lake	27·00	55·00

1898. Stamps of 1895 optd **S. P.**

No.	Type	Description	Mint	Used
O 213.	**9.**	1 c. grey	2·00	2·00
O 214.		2 c. brown	1·25	1·50
O 215.		4 c. bistre	1·25	1·50
O 216.		5 c. green	4·00	5·00
O 217.		10 c. red	20·00	38·00

1908. Stamps of 1906 optd **Officiel**.

No.	Type	Description	Mint	Used
O218	**10**	1 c. grey	10	30
O219		2 c. brown	10	30
O220		4 c. bistre	10	30
O221		5 c. green	10	30
O271		5 c. mauve	10	30
O222		6 c. lilac	10	30
O223		7½ c. yellow	10	30
O224	**11**	10 c. red	20	40
O225		12½ c. slate	20	50
O226		15 c. brown	30	50
O227		20 c. orange	30	60
O228		25 c. blue	30	60
O229		30 c. olive	3·00	6·00
O230		37½ c. green	50	60
O231		50 c. brown	80	1·25
O232		87½ c. blue	2·00	3·50
O233		1 f. purple	3·00	4·00
O234		2½ f. red	60·00	60·00
O235		5 f. purple	50·00	50·00

1915. Stamps of 1914 optd **Officiel**.

No.	Type	Description	Mint	Used
O236	**13**	10 c. purple	20	70
O237		12½ c. green	20	70
O238		15 c. brown	20	70
O239		17½ c. brown	20	70
O240		25 c. blue	20	70
O241		30 c. brown	1·50	4·50
O242		35 c. blue	20	1·25
O243		37½ c. brown	20	1·50
O244		40 c. red	30	1·25
O245		50 c. grey	30	1·00
O246		62½ c. green	30	1·50
O247		87½ c. orange	30	1·75
O248		1 f. brown	30	1·50
O249		2½ f. red	30	2·50
O250		5 f. violet	30	3·00

1922. Stamps of 1921 optd **Officiel**.

No.	Type	Description	Mint	Used
O251	**17**	2 c. brown	10	20
O252		3 c. green	10	20
O253		6 c. purple	10	40
O272		10 c. green	10	30
O273		15 c. green	10	30
O274		15 c. orange	10	30
O256		20 c. orange	10	40
O275		20 c. green	10	30
O257		25 c. green	10	40
O258		30 c. red	10	40
O259		40 c. orange	10	40
O260		50 c. blue	20	60
O276		50 c. red	20	50
O261		75 c. red	20	60
O277		75 c. blue	20	50
O266		80 c. black	20	50
O263	**18**	1 f. red	30	2·00
O278		1 f. blue	30	1·00
O267	–	2 f. blue	1·00	2·00
O279	–	2 f. brown	1·50	4·00
O269	–	5 f. violet	5·00	10·00

1922. Stamps of 1923 optd **Officiel**.

No.	Type	Description	Mint	Used
O268b	**28**	3 f. blue	40	1·75
O270	**26**	10 f. black	8·00	25·00

1926. Stamps of 1926 optd **Officiel**.

No.	Type	Description	Mint	Used
O280	**32**	5 c. mauve	10	20
O281		10 c. green	10	20
O298		15 c. black	30	80
O282		20 c. orange	10	20
O283		25 c. green	10	20
O300		25 c. brown	20	60
O301		30 c. green	30	1·40
O302		30 c. violet	30	80
O303		35 c. violet	30	80
O304		35 c. green	30	80
O286		40 c. brown	10	20
O287		50 c. brown	10	20
O307		60 c. green	30	60
O288		65 c. brown	10	40
O308		70 c. violet	3·00	6·00
O289		75 c. red	10	40
O309		75 c. brown	30	60
O291		80 c. brown	10	40
O292		90 c. red	20	60
O293		1 f. black	20	50
O312		1 f. red	40	1·60
O294		1¼ f. blue	10	50
O313		1¼ f. yellow	2·00	6·00
O314		1¼ f. green	1·90	4·00
O315		1½ f. blue	30	1·40
O316		1¾ f. blue	40	1·50

1928. Stamp of 1928 optd **Officiel**.

No.	Type	Description	Mint	Used
O317	**37**	2 f. black	40	1·50

1931. Stamp of 1931 optd **Officiel**.

No.	Type	Description	Mint	Used
O318	**43**	20 f. green	2·00	7·00

1934. Stamp of 1934 optd **Officiel**.

No.	Type	Description	Mint	Used
O319	**47**	5 f. green	1·40	5·00

1935. No. 340 optd **Officiel**.

No.	Type	Description	Mint	Used
O341	**52**	10 f. green	1·25	6·00

POSTAGE DUE STAMPS

D 12. Arms of Luxembourg.

D 77.

1907.

D 173. D 12.	5 c. black and green	10	20
D 174.	10 c. black and green	1·10	20
D 175.	12½ c. black & green	30	80
D 176.	20 c. black and green	60	80
D 177.	25 c. black and green	10·00	1·25
D 178.	50 c. black and green	50	3·00
D 179.	1 f. black and green	30	3·00

1920. Surch.

D 193. D 12.	15 on 12½ c. blk. & grn.	1·00	6·00
D 194.	30 on 25 c. blk. & grn.	1·25	7·00

1922.

D 221. D 12.	5 c. red and green ..	20	40
D 222.	10 c. red and green ..	20	30
D 223.	20 c. red and green ..	20	30
D 224.	25 c. red and green ..	20	30
D 225.	30 c. red and green ..	40	30
D 226.	35 c. red and green ..	40	20
D 227.	50 c. red and green ..	40	30
D 228.	60 c. red and green ..	30	30
D 229.	70 c. red and green ..	40	30
D 230.	75 c. red and green ..	40	20
D 231.	1 f. red and green ..	20	50
D 232.	2 f. red and green ..	40	6·50
D 233.	3 f. red and green ..	1·25	13·00

1946.

D 488. D 77.	5 c. green	30	30
D 489.	10 c. green	30	30
D 490.	20 c. green	30	30
D 491.	30 c. green	30	30
D 492.	50 c. green	30	30
D 493.	70 c. green	40	55
D 494.	75 c. green	1·25	30
D 495.	1 f. red	30	30
D 496.	1 f. 50 red	30	30
D 497.	2 f. red	30	30
D 498.	3 f. red	40	30
D 499.	5 f. red	60	30
D 500.	10 f. red	1·00	1·50
D 501.	20 f. red	3·00	16·00

MACAO Pt. 9

A Portuguese territory in China at the mouth of the Canton River.

1884. 1,000 reis = 1 milreis.
1894. 78 avos = 1 rupee.
1913. 100 avos = 1 pataca.

1884. "Crown" key-type insc. "MACAU".

1 P	5 r. black	2·25	1·75
2	10 r. orange	3·50	3·00
21	10 r. green	3·25	3·00
3	20 r. olive	6·00	6·00
27	20 r. red	6·50	4·75
13	25 r. red	2·00	1·25
22	25 r. lilac	1·90	1·60
14	40 r. blue	7·00	5·50
23	40 r. yellow	4·75	3·50
15	50 r. green	9·50	6·50
24	50 r. blue	1·90	1·25
31	80 r. grey	9·00	7·00
7	100 r. lilac	3·00	2·25
17	200 r. orange	4·50	3·25
9	300 r. brown	4·00	3·25

1885. "Crown" key type of Macao surch in Reis diagonally and with bar.

19. P.	80 r. on 100 r. lilac ..	6·00	5·00

1885. "Crown" key type of Macao surch. thus **5 Reis** diagonally and with bar.

32 P	5 r. on 25 r. red	2·25	2·00
33	10 r. on 25 r. red	3·75	3·00
38	10 r. on 50 r. green ..	17·00	15·00
35	20 r. on 50 r. green ..	3·25	2·50
40	40 r. on 50 r. green ..	13·00	11·00

1885. "Crown" key-type of Macao surch. with figure of value only and bar.

41. P.	5 on 25 r. red	2·50	2·25
42a.	10 on 50 r. green ..	2·75	2·25

1887. "Crown" key-type of Macao surch. horizontally with new value and bar.

43. P.	5 r. on 80 r. grey	2·25	2·00
46.	5 r. on 100 r. lilac ..	7·00	6·00
44.	10 r. on 80 r. grey ..	3·75	3·50
47.	10 r. on 200 r. orange ..	12·00	10·00
45.	20 r. on 80 r. grey ..	4·25	3·50

9.

1887. Fiscal stamps as T 9 surch. **CORREIO** and new value.

50.	5 r. on 10 r. green & brn.	16·00	14·00
51.	5 r. on 20 r. green & brn.	16·00	14·00
52.	5 r. on 60 r. green & brn.	16·00	14·00
53.	10 r. on 10 r. green & brn.	20·00	15·00
54.	10 r. on 60 r. green & brn.	22·00	17·00
55.	40 r. on 20 r. green & brn.	20·00	16·00

1888. "Embossed" key-type inscr. "PROVINCIA DE MACAU"

56 Q	5 r. black	2·00	1·75
57	10 r. green	2·00	1·75
58	20 r. red	2·50	1·75
59	25 r. mauve	3·50	2·25
67	40 r. brown	3·25	2·25
68	50 r. blue	2·25	1·75
69	80 r. grey	2·50	2·00
70	100 r. brown	2·50	2·00
71	200 r. lilac	5·50	3·50
72	300 r. orange	6·50	3·75

1892. No. 71 surch **30 30**.

73 Q	30 on 200 r. lilac	5·00	4·50

1894. "Embossed" key-type of Macao surch **PROVISORIO**, value and Chinese characters.

75b Q	1 a. on 5 r. black ..	70	50
76	3 a. on 20 r. red	2·25	1·75
77	4 a. on 25 r. mauve ..	2·25	1·40
89	5 a. on 30 on 200 r. lilac (No. 73)	4·00	3·75
78	6 a. on 40 r. brown ..	2·75	1·40
79	8 a. on 50 r. blue ..	4·50	2·25
80	13 a. on 80 r. grey ..	3·25	2·75
81	16 a. on 100 r. brown ..	3·25	2·75
88	31 a. on 200 r. lilac ..	8·00	6·00
83	47 a. on 300 r. orange ..	8·00	6·00

1894. "Figures" key-type inscr. "MACAU".

91. R.	5 r. yellow	1·25	90
92.	10 r. mauve	1·25	90
93.	15 r. brown	1·50	1·25
94.	20 r. lilac	1·50	1·25
95.	25 r. green	4·00	3·00
96.	50 r. blue	5·00	4·50
97.	75 r. red	4·50	4·00
98.	80 r. green	4·25	3·50
99.	100 r. brown on buff ..	3·25	3·25
100.	150 r. red on rose ..	4·00	3·25
101.	200 r. blue on blue ..	4·50	4·00
102.	300 r. blue on brown ..	5·50	5·00

1898. As Vasco da Gama types of Portugal but inscr. "MACAU".

104.	½ a. green	1·00	70
105.	1 a. red	1·00	70
106.	2 a. purple	1·10	70
107.	4 a. green	1·10	70
108.	8 a. blue	1·40	1·00
109.	12 a. brown	2·25	1·60
110.	16 a. brown	2·25	1·50
111.	24 a. bistre	2·25	2·00

1898. "King Carlos" key-type inscr "MACAU". Name and value in black.

112. S.	½ a. grey	30	20
113.	1 a. yellow	40	20
114.	2 a. green	45	25
115.	2½ a. brown	70	55
116.	3 a. lilac	70	55
174.	3 a. grey	80	75
117.	4 a. green	1·00	80
175.	4 a. red	80	75
176.	5 a. brown	90	80
177.	6 a. brown	95	80
119.	8 a. blue	1·10	80
178.	8 a. brown	1·75	1·40
120.	10 a. blue	1·10	80
121.	12 a. red	1·75	1·25
179.	12 a. purple	5·50	4·25
122.	13 a. mauve	1·75	1·25
123.	15 a. green	4·50	3·50
124.	16 a. blue on blue ..	2·00	1·75
181.	18 a. brown on pink ..	4·50	3·25
125.	20 a. brown on yellow ..	2·00	1·75
126.	24 a. brown on yellow ..	2·00	1·75
127.	31 a. purple on pink ..	2·25	1·90
128.	47 a. blue on pink ..	3·50	2·75
183.	47 a. blue on yellow ..	6·00	4·25
129.	78 a. black on blue ..	4·50	4·00

1900. "King Carlos" key-type of Macao surch. **PROVISORIO** and new value.

132. S.	5 on 13 a. mauve ..	90	70
133.	10 on 16 a. blue on blue ..	1·00	80
134.	15 on 24 a. brown on yell.	1·25	1·00
135.	20 on 31 a. purple on pink	1·25	1·00

1902. Various types of Macao surch.

138 Q	6 a. on 5 r. black ..	90	70
142 R	6 a. on 5 r. yellow ..	80	60
136 P	6 a. on 10 r. orange ..	2·00	1·75
137	6 a. on 10 r. green ..	1·25	1·10
139 Q	6 a. on 10 r. green ..	90	70
143 R	6 a. on 10 r. mauve ..	1·00	70
144	6 a. on 15 r. brown ..	1·00	70
145	6 a. on 25 r. green ..	85	60
140 Q	6 a. on 40 r. brown ..	90	70
146 R	6 a. on 80 r. green ..	85	65
148	6 a. on 100 r. brn on buff	85	60
149	6 a. on 200 r. blue on bl	90	60
151 V	18 a. on 2½ r. brown ..	1·25	1·10
153 Q	18 a. on 20 r. red ..	1·75	1·25
162 R	18 a. on 20 r. lilac ..	2·10	1·50
154 Q	18 a. on 25 r. mauve ..	12·00	9·50
163 R	18 a. on 50 r. blue ..	2·10	1·75
165	18 a. on 75 r. red ..	2·25	1·75
155 Q	18 a. on 80 r. grey ..	15·00	15·00
156	18 a. on 100 r. brown ..	2·50	2·25
166 R	18 a. on 150 r. red on rose	2·25	1·75
158 Q	18 a. on 200 r. lilac ..	15·00	14·00
160	18 a. on 300 r. orange ..	2·50	2·00
167 R	18 a. on 300 r. bl on brn	2·25	1·75

1902. "King Carlos" type of Macao optd. **PROVISORIO.**

168. S.	2 a. green	2·25	1·60
169.	4 a. green	2·00	1·50
170.	8 a. blue	2·00	1·50
171.	10 a. blue	2·00	1·50
172.	12 a. red	3·75	2·75

1905. No. 179 surch. **10 AVOS** and bar.

184. S.	10 a. on 12 a. purple ..	2·25	2·00

1910. "Due" key-type of Macao, but with words "PORTEADO" and "RECEBER" cancelled.

185. W.	½ a. green	1·00	80
186.	1 a. green	1·00	80
187.	2 a. grey	1·10	1·00

1911. "King Carlos" key-type of Macao optd **REPUBLICA**.

188 S	½ a. grey	25	20
189	1 a. orange	25	20
190	2 a. green	25	20
191	3 a. grey	25	20
192	4 a. red	70	65
193	5 a. brown	70	65
194	6 a. brown	70	65
195	8 a. brown	70	65
196	10 a. blue	70	65
197	13 a. lilac	90	70
198	16 a. blue on blue ..	90	70
199	18 a. brown on pink ..	1·75	1·60
200	20 a. brown on cream ..	1·75	1·60
201	31 a. purple on pink ..	1·75	1·60
202	47 a. blue and yellow ..	3·00	3·25
203	78 a. black and blue ..	3·75	3·25

30. 32.

1911. Fiscal stamp surch **POSTAL 1 AVO** and bar.

204 30	1 a. on 5 r. brown, yellow and black ..	85	70

1911. Stamps bisected and surch.

205 S	2 a. on half of 4 a. red (No. 175)	1·00	1·00
206	5 a. on half of 10 a. blue (No. 120)	2·00	2·00
207	5 a. on half of 10 a. blue (No. 171)	1·75	1·75

1911.

208 32	1 a. black	80·00	80·00
209	2 a. black	85·00	85·00

1913. Provisionals of 1902 surch. in addition with new value and bars over old value and optd. **REPUBLICA.**

212. R.	2 a. on 18 a. on 20 r. lilac (No. 162)	90	80
213.	2 a. on 18 a. on 50 r. blue (No. 163)	90	80
215.	2 a. on 18 a. on 75 r. red (No. 165)	90	80
216.	2 a. on 18 a. on 150 r. red on rose (No. 166) ..	90	80

1913. Provisionals of 1902 optd **REPUBLICA**.

218 Q	6 a. on 5 r. (No. 138) ..	1·25	1·10
284 R	6 a. on 5 r. (No. 142) ..	75	65
217 P	6 a. on 10 r. (No. 137) ..	3·00	2·50
285 Q	6 a. on 10 r. (No. 139) ..	55	40
286 R	6 a. on 10 r. (No. 143) ..	55	40
287	6 a. on 15 r. (No. 144) ..	45	40
288	6 a. on 25 r. (No. 145) ..	45	40
220 Q	6 a. on 40 r. (No. 140) ..	1·40	1·10
289 R	6 a. on 80 r. (No. 146) ..	45	40
291	6 a. on 100 r. (No. 148) ..	95	70
292	6 a. on 200 r. (No. 149) ..	45	40
283 S	10 a. on 12 a. (No. 184)	40	35
293 V	18 a. on 2½. r. (No. 151)	70	45
229 Q	18 a. on 20 r. (No. 153)	1·75	1·60
295 R	18 a. on 20 r. (No. 162) ..	95	85
296	18 a. on 50 r. (No. 163)	1·10	95
298	18 a. on 75 r. (No. 165) ..	1·10	1·00
230 Q	18 a. on 100 r. (No. 156)	7·50	7·00
299 R	18 a. on 150 r. (No. 166)	1·10	1·00
233 Q	18 a. on 300 r. (No. 160)	3·00	3·00
300 R	18 a. on 300 r. (No. 167)	1·10	1·00

1913. Stamps of 1911 issue surch.

252. S.	½ a. on 5 a. brown ..	80	70
255.	1 a. on 13 a. lilac ..	80	70
253.	4 a. on 8 a. brown ..	1·25	95

1913. Vasco da Gama stamps of Macao optd. **REPUBLICA**, and the 12 a. surch. **10 A.**

256.	½ a. green	60	45
257.	1 a. red	60	45
258.	2 a. purple	60	45
259.	4 a. green	60	45
260.	8 a. blue	95	70
261.	10 a. on 12 a. brown ..	1·75	1·00
262.	16 a. brown	1·10	80
263.	24 a. bistre	1·60	1·10

1913. "Ceres" key-type inscr. "MACAU".

264 U	½ a. olive	35	25
265	1 a. black	35	25
311	1½ a. green	25	20
208	2 a. green	35	25
313	3 a. orange	1·00	1·00
267	4 a. red	90	35
315	4 a. yellow	1·00	1·00
268	5 a. brown	1·00	75
269	6 a. violet	1·00	70
270	8 a. brown	1·00	70
271	10 a. blue	1·00	70
272	12 a. brown	1·00	70
320	14 a. mauve	2·50	2·00
273	16 a. grey	2·00	1·40
274	20 a. brown	2·25	1·75
322	24 a. green	2·50	2·00
323	32 a. brown	2·25	2·00
275	40 a. purple	2·25	1·75
324	56 a. red	3·75	2·75
276	58 a. brown on green ..	3·50	2·50
325	72 a. brown	6·50	4·00
277	76 a. brown on red ..	4·25	3·75
278	1 p. orange on pink ..	4·50	4·00
326	1 p. orange	10·00	8·00
279	3 p. green on blue ..	16·00	12·00
327	3 p. blue	23·00	22·00
328	5 p. red	32·00	38·00

1915. Nos. 170/1 optd. **REPUBLICA.**

281. S.	8 a. blue	40	35
282.	10 a. blue	40	35

1919. Surch.

301. U.	½ a. on 5 a. brn. (No. 268)	5·50	4·50
330.	1 a. on 24 a. grn. (No. 322)	70	65
302. R.	2 a. on 6 a. on 25 r. green (No. 288)	9·00	9·00
303.	2 a. on 6 a. on 80 r. green (No. 289)	5·00	4·50
304. S.	"2 avos" on 6 a. (No. 202)	7·50	6·00
331. U.	2 a. on 32 a. (No. 323) ..	70	65
332.	4 a. on 12 a. (No. 272) ..	70	65
333.	5 a. on 6 a. vio. (No. 269)	2·00	1·75
334.	7 a. on 8 a. brn. (No. 270)	1·10	1·00
335.	12 a. on 14 a. (No. 320)	1·10	1·00
336.	15 a. on 16 a. (No. 273)	1·10	1·00
337.	20 a. on 56 a. red (No. 324)	1·60	1·40

1934. As T **40** of Portuguese India ("Portugal" and Galeasse).
338. **40.** ½ a. sepia 25 25
339. 1 a. sepia 25 25
340. 2 a. green 25 25
341. 3 a. mauve 25 25
342. 4 a. black 35 25
343. 5 a. grey 35 25
344. 6 a. brown 35 25
345. 7 a. red 35 30
346. 8 a. blue 35 30
347. 10 a. red 55 50
348. 12 a. blue 55 50
349. 14 a. olive 55 50
350. 15 a. red 55 50
351. 20 a. orange 55 50
352. 30 a. green .. .. 1·50 1·00
353. 40 a. violet .. .. 1·50 1·00
354. 50 a. brown .. .. 2·75 1·50
355. 1 p. blue .. .. 8·00 2·40
356. 2 p. brown .. .. 11·00 4·25
357. 3 p. green .. .. 14·25 7·25
358. 5 p. mauve .. .. 27·00 11·00

1936. Air. Stamps of 1934 optd. **Aviao** and with Greek characters or surch. also.
359. **40.** 2 a. green 90 80
360. 3 a. mauve 90 80
361. 5 a. on 6 a. brown 90 80
362. 7 a. red 90 80
363. 8 a. blue .. .. 1·60 1·40
364. 15 a. red .. .. 5·50 2·75

54. Vasco da Gama. **56.** Aircraft over Globe.

1938. Name and value in black.
365. **54.** 1 a. olive (postage) .. 20 20
366. 2 a. brown 20 20
367. 3 a. violet 20 20
368. 4 a. green 20 20
369. – 5 a. red 20 20
370. – 6 a. slate 20 20
371. – 8 a. purple 20 20
372. – 10 a. mauve 40 40
373. – 12 a. red 40 40
374. – 15 a. orange 40 40
375. – 20 a. blue 50 45
376. – 40 a. black .. .. 1·10 70
377. – 50 a. brown .. .. 1·10 70
378. – 1 p. red .. .. 3·50 1·50
379. – 2 p. olive .. .. 7·50 3·25
380. – 3 p. blue .. .. 12·00 4·50
381. – 5 p. brown .. .. 20·00 70·00
382. **56.** 1 a. red (air) 15 15
383. 2 a. violet 15 15
384. 3 a. orange 25 25
385. 5 a. blue 35 30
386. 10 a. red 65 35
387. 20 a. green 95 75
388. 50 a. brown .. .. 1·40 95
389. 70 a. red .. .. 2·75 1·40
390. 1 p. mauve .. .. 6·00 2·40
DESIGNS: Nos 369/71, Mousinho de Albuquerque. Nos. 372/4, Henry the Navigator. Nos. 375/7, Dam. Nos 378/81, Afonso de Albuquerque.

1940. Surch.
391. **40.** 1 a. on 6 a. brn. (No. 344) 1·50 1·00
394. 2 a. on 6 a. brn. (No. 344) 90 80
395. 3 a. on 6 a. brn. (No. 344) 90 80
401. – 3 a. on 6 a. slate (No. 370) 10·00 9·00
396. **40.** 5 a. on 7 a. red (No. 345) 90 80
397. 5 a. on 8 a. blue (No. 346) 90 80
398. 8 a. on 30 a. (No. 352) .. 1·90 1·75
399. 8 a. on 40 a. (No. 353) .. 1·90 1·75
400. 8 a. on 50 a. (No. 354) .. 1·90 1·75

61. Mountain Fort. **62.** Our Lady of Fatima.

1948.
410 – 1 a. brown and orange 30 25
427 – 1 a. violet and pink .. 45 35
411 **61** 2 a. purple 30 20
428 2 a. brown and yellow 45 35
412 – 3 a. purple 35 30
429 – 3 a. orange 80 35
413 – 8 a. red 35 20
430 – 8 a. grey 80 35
414 – 10 a. purple 75 30
431 – 10 a. brown and orange 90 45
415 – 20 a. blue 75 30
416 – 30 a. grey .. .. 1·10 40
432 – 30 a. blue .. .. 1·75 85
417 – 50 a. brown and buff .. 1·50 55
433 – 50 a. olive and green .. 3·00 95
418 – 1 p. green .. .. 11·00 2·75
419 – 1 p. blue .. .. 8·50
434 – 1 p. brown .. .. 4·25 1·60
420 – 2 p. red .. .. 10·00 2·25
421 – 3 p. green .. .. 12·00 3·00
422 – 5 p. violet .. .. 18·00 4·00

DESIGNS—HORIZ. 1 a. Macao house. 3 a. Macao. 8 a. Pria, Grande Bay. 10 a. Leal Senado Sq. 20 a. St. Jerome Hill. 30 a. Street scene. 50 a. Goddess Ma. 5 p. Forest road. VERT. 1 p. Cerco Gateway. 2 p. Barra Pagoda. 3 p. Post Office.

1948. Honouring the Statue of Our Lady of Fatima.
423. **62.** 8 a. red .. .. 2·00 1·40

64. Globe and Letter. **65.** Bells and Dove.

1949. 75th Anniv. of U.P.U.
424. **64.** 32 a. purple .. .. 30·00 8·00

1950. Holy Year.
425. 32 a. black .. .. 1·75 1·25
426. 50 a. red .. .. 1·75 1·25
DESIGN: 50 a. Angel holding candelabra.

66. Arms and Dragon.

1950.
435 **66** 1 a. yellow on cream .. 30 35
436 2 a. green on green .. 30 35
437 10 a. purple on green .. 30 35
438 10 a. mauve on green .. 30 35

67. F. Mendes Pinto. **68.** Junk.

1951.
439 **67** 1 a. indigo and blue .. 15 10
440 – 2 a. brown and green .. 15 10
441 – 3 a. green & light green 20 10
442 – 6 a. violet and blue .. 30 15
443 – 10 a. brown and orange 90 30
444 **67** 20 a. purple & lt purple 2·75 80
445 – 30 a. brown and green 2·75 80
446 – 50 a. red and orange .. 6·50 2·25
447 – 1 p. ultramarine & blue 4·50 1·25
448 – 3 p. black and blue .. 16·00 3·00
449 **68** 5 p. brown and orange 32·00 11·00
DESIGNS—As Type **67**: 2, 10 a. St. Francis Xavier. 3, 50 a. J. Alvares. 6, 30 a. L. de Camoens. As Type **68**—HORIZ. 1 p. Sampan. VERT. 3 p. Junk.

69. Our Lady of Fatima. **71.** St. Raphael Hospital.

1951. Termination of Holy Year.
450 **69** 60 a. mauve and pink .. 1·50 1·25

1952. 1st Tropical Medicine Congress, Lisbon.
451. **71.** 6 a. mauve and black .. 80 60

72. St. Francis Xavier Statue. **73.** The Virgin.

1952. 400th Death Anniv. of St. Francis Xavier.
452. **72.** 3 a. black on cream .. 20 20
453. – 16 a. brown on buff .. 80 40
454. – 40 a. black on blue .. 1·60 80
DESIGNS: 16 a. Miraculous Arm of St. Francis. 40 a. Tomb of St. Francis.

1953. Missionary Art Exn.
455. **73.** 8 a. brown and drab .. 25 25
456. 10 a. blue and brown .. 95 30
457. 50 a. green and drab .. 2·25 1·25

74. Honeysuckle. **75.** Portuguese Stamp of 1853 and Arms of Portuguese Overseas Provinces.

1953. Flowers.
458 **74** 1 a. yellow, green & red 10 10
459 – 3 a. purple, green & yell 10 10
460 – 5 a. red, green & brown 15 15
461 – 10 a. multicoloured .. 15 15
462 – 16 a. yellow, green & brn 15 15
463 – 30 a. pink, brown & grn 20 15
464 – 39 a. multicoloured .. 30 25
465 – 1 p. yellow, green & pur 1·40 65
466 – 3 p. red, brown and grey 2·75 1·10
467 – 5 p. yellow, green & red 5·00 1·50
FLOWERS: 3 a. Myosotis. 5 a. Dragon claw. 10 a. Nunflower. 16 a. Narcissus. 30 a. Peach blossom. 39 a. Lotus blossom. 1 p. Chrysanthemum. 3 p. Plum blossom. 5 p. Tangerine blossom.

1954. Portuguese Postage Stamp Cent.
468 **75** 10 a. multicoloured .. 50 50

76. Father M. de Nobrega and Sao Paulo. **77.** Map of Macao.

1954. 4th Centenary of Sao Paulo.
469 **76** 39 a. multicoloured .. 1·00 85

1956. Map multicoloured. Values in red, inscr. in brown. Colours given are of the backgrounds.
470. **77.** 1 a. drab 10 10
471. 3 a. slate 10 10
472. 5 a. brown 10 10
473. 10 a. buff 10 10
474. 30 a. blue 30 15
475. 40 a. green 45 25
476. 90 a. grey .. .. 1·50 55
477. 1 p. 50 pink .. .. 2·00 1·40

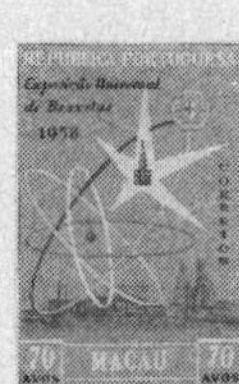

78. Exhibition Emblem and Atomic Emblems. **79.** "Cinnamomum camphora".

1958. Brussels Int. Exn.
478. **78.** 70 a. multicoloured .. 55 55

1958. 6th Int. Congress of Tropical Medicine.
479. **79.** 20 a. multicoloured .. 2·00 1·60

80. Globe girdled by Signs of the Zodiac. **81.** Airliner over Ermida da Penha.

1960. 500th Death Anniv. of Prince Henry the Navigator.
480. **80.** 2 p. multicoloured .. 70 60

1960. Air. Multicoloured.
481 50 a. Praia Grande Bay .. 60 30
482 76 a. Type **81** 80 45
483 3 p. Macao .. .. 1·60 60
484 5 p. Mong Ha .. .. 2·75 1·00
485 10 p. Shore of Praia Grande Bay .. .. 5·50 1·00

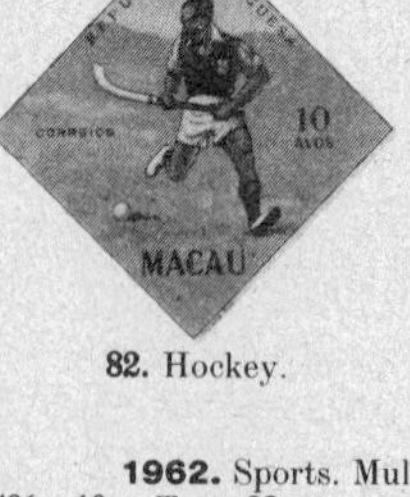
82. Hockey. **83.** "Anopheles hycranus".

1962. Sports. Multicoloured.
486 10 a. Type **82** 35 30
487 16 a. Wrestling 95 60
488 20 a. Table tennis .. 80 45
489 50 a. Motor cycling .. 80 45
490 1 p. 20 Relay racing .. 1·40 1·25
491 2 p. 50 Badminton .. 2·40 2·40

1962. Malaria Eradication.
492. **83.** 40 a. multicoloured .. 55 55

84. Bank Building. **85.** I.T.U. Emblem and St. Gabriel.

1964. Cent. of National Overseas Bank.
493. **84.** 20 a. multicoloured .. 1·10 1·00

1965. Centenary of I.T.U.
494. **85.** 10 a. multicoloured .. 70 60

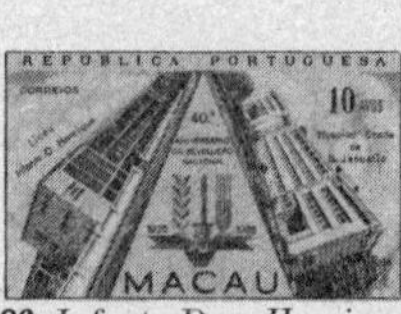

86. Infante Dom Henrique Academy and Visconde de Sao Januario Hospital. **87.** Drummer, 1548.

1966. 40th Anniv. of National Revolution.
495. **86.** 10 a. multicoloured .. 70 60

1966. Portuguese Military Uniforms. Mult.
496. 10 a. Type **87** 20 15
497. 15 a. Soldier, 1548 .. 30 20
498. 20 a. Arquebusier, 1649 .. 30 20
499. 40 a. Infantry officer, 1783 50 15
500. 50 a. Infantryman, 1783 .. 60 40
501. 60 a. Infantryman, 1902 .. 75 50
502. 1 p. Infantryman, 1903 .. 1·50 90
503. 3 p. Infantryman, 1904 .. 2·50 1·50

88. O. E. Carmo and Patrol Boat "Vega". **89.** Arms of Pope Paul VI, and "Golden Rose".

1967. Cent of Military Naval Assn. Mult.
504 10 a. Type **88** 60 35
505 20 a. Silva Junior and sail frigate "Don Fernando" 1·90 1·10

1967. 50th Anniv. of Fatima Apparitions.
506. **89.** 50 a. multicoloured .. 80 75

90. Cabral Monument, Lisbon. **91.** Adm. Gago Coutinho with Sextant.

1968. 500th Birth Anniv. of Pedro Cabral (explorer). Multicoloured.
507. 20 a. Type **90** 50 40
508. 70 a. Cabral's statue, Belmonte .. .. .. 1·00 80

1969. Birth Cent. of Admiral Gago Coutinho.
509. **91.** 20 a. multicoloured .. 30 30

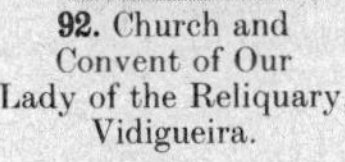

92. Church and Convent of Our Lady of the Reliquary, Vidigueira.

93. L. A. Rebello da Silva.

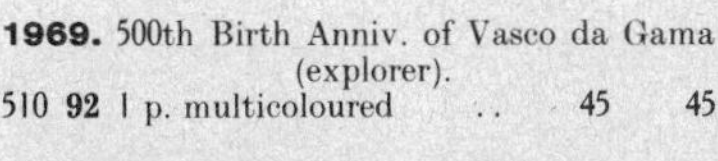

1969. 500th Birth Anniv. of Vasco da Gama (explorer).
510 **92** 1 p. multicoloured .. 45 45

1969. Centenary of Overseas Administrative Reforms.
511. **93.** 90 a. multicoloured .. 45 45

94. Bishop D. Belchoir Carneiro.

95. Facade of Mother Church, Golega.

1969. 400th Anniv. of Misericordia Monastery, Macao.
512. **94.** 50 a. multicoloured .. 45 30

1969. 500th Birth Anniv of King Manoel I.
513 **95** 30 a. multicoloured .. 45 35

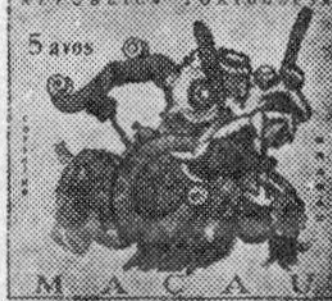

96. Marshal Carmona.

97. Dragon Mask.

1970. Birth Cent. of Marshal Carmona.
514. **96.** 5 a. multicoloured .. 40 30

1971. Chinese Carnival Masks. Multicoloured.
515. 5 a. Type **97** 20 20
516. 10 a. Lion mask 35 35

98. Portugese Traders at the Chinese Imperial Court.

100. Seaplane " Santa Cruz" arriving at Rio de Janeiro.

99. Hockey.

101. Lyre Emblem and Theatre Facade

1972. 400th Anniv of Camoens' "The Lusiads" (epic poem).
517 **98** 20 a. multicoloured .. 1·50 1·10

1972. Olympic Games, Munich.
518 **99.** 50 a. multicoloured .. 40 30

1972. 50th Anniv of First Flight from Lisbon to Rio de Janeiro.
519 **100.** 5 p. multicoloured .. 3·75 2·75

1972. Cent. of Dom Pedro V Theatre, Macao.
520. **101.** 2 p. multicoloured .. 1·25 1·10

102. W.M.O. Emblem

103. Visconde de Sao Januario.

1973. Centenary of W.M.O.
521. **102.** 20 a. multicoloured .. 70 60

1974. Cent. of Visconde de Sao Januario Hospital. Multicoloured.
522. 15 a. Type **103** 25 15
523. 60 a. Hospital buildings of 1874 and 1974 .. .. 65 35

104. Chinnery (self-portrait).

105. Macao-Taipa Bridge.

1974. Birth Bicent. of George Chinnery (painter).
524. **104.** 30 a. multicoloured .. 80 60

1975. Inauguration of Macao-Taipa Bridge. Multicoloured.
525. 20 a. Type **105** 50 35
526. 2 p. 20 View of Bridge from below .. .. .. 1·75 1·00

106. Man waving Banner.

1975. 1st. Anniv of Portuguese Revolution.
527 **106** 10 a. multicoloured .. 1·00 1·00
528 1 p. multicoloured .. 2·25 2·00

107. Pou Chai Pagoda.

1976. Pagodas. Multicoloured.
529. 10 p. Type **107** .. .. 3·50 1·25
530. 20 p. Tin Hau Pagoda .. 6·00 2·25

108. Symbolic Figure.

1977. Legislative Assembly.
531. **108.** 5 a. blue, dp. blue & blk. 1·50 80
532. 2 p. brown and black .. 4·00 1·75
533. 5 p. yellow, grn. & blk. 5·00 3·75

1979. Nos. 462, 464, 469, 482, 523 and 526 surch.
536 – 10 a. on 16 a. yellow, green and brown .. 1·75 1·25
537 – 30 a. on 39 a. mult .. 1·75 1·25
538 **76** 30 a. on 39 a. mult .. 8·00 5·50
539 – 30 a. on 60 a. mult .. 2·75 2·00
540 **81** 70 a. on 76 a. mult .. 9·00 1·00
541 – 2 p. on 2 p. 20 mult .. 2·40 1·75

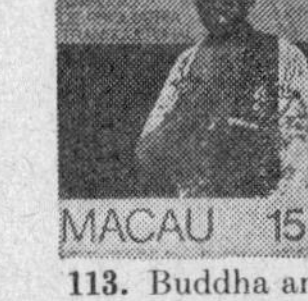

111. Camoes and Macao Harbour.

113. Buddha and Macao Cathedral.

1981. 400th Death Anniv. (1980) of Camoes (Portuguese poet).
542. **111.** 10 a. multicoloured 20 20
543. 30 a. multicoloured 20 20
544. 1 p. multicoloured 50 35
545. 3 p. multicoloured 1·60 95

1981. Transcultural Psychiatry Symposium.
547. **113.** 15 a. multicoloured 15 15
548. 40 a. multicoloured 15 15
549. 50 a. multicoloured 20 15
550. 60 a. multicoloured 25 20
551. 1 p. multicoloured 35 25
552. 2 p. 20 multicoloured 80 45

115. Health Services Buildings.

1982. Buildings.
554 – 10 a. grey, blue & yell 10 10
555 – 20 a. blk, grn & lt grn 10 10
556 **115** 30 a. grn, grey & stone 10 10
557 – 40 a. yell, lt grn & grn 10 10
558 – 60 a. orange, chocolate and brown 15 10
559 – 80 a. pink, green & brn 15 10
560 – 90 a. purple, blue & red 20 10
561 – 1 p. multicoloured .. 20 10
562 – 1 p. 50 yell, brn & grey 30 15
563 – 2 p. purple, ultramarine and blue .. 35 20
564 – 2 p. 50 ultramarine, red and blue 50 30
565 – 3 p. yell, dp grn & grn 65 40
566 – 7 p. 50 lilac, blue & red 1·40 85
567 – 10 p. grey, lilac & mve 1·90 1·10
568 – 15 p. yellow, brn & red 2·75 1·50

DESIGNS: 10 a. Social Welfare Institute. 20 a. Holy House of Mercy. 40 a. Guia lighthouse. 60 a. St. Lawrence's Church. 80 a. St. Joseph's Seminary. 90 a. Pedro V Theatre. 1 p. Cerco city gate. 1 p. 50 St. Domenico's Church. 2 p. Luis de Camoes Museum. 2 p. 50, Ruins of St. Paul's Church. 3 p. Palace of St. Sancha (Governor's residence). 7 p. 50, Senate House. 10 p. Schools Welfare Service building. 15 p. Barracks of the Moors (headquarters of Port Captaincy and Maritime Police).

116. Heng Ho (Moon goddess).

117. Aerial View of Macao, Taipa and Coloane Islands.

1982. Autumn Festival. Multicoloured
569. 40 a. Type **116** 15 15
570. 1 p. Decorated gourds .. 30 15
571 2 p. Paper lantern .. 60 40
572. 5 p. Warrior on lion .. 1·40 1·00

1982. Macao's Geographical Situation. Multicoloured.
573. 50 a. Type **117** 20 15
574. 3 p. Map of South China .. 90 70

118. "Switchboard Operators" (Lou Sok Man).

1983. World Communications Year. Children's Drawings. Multicoloured.
575. 60 a. Type **118** 20 15
576. 3 p. Postman and pillar box (Lai Sok Pek) .. 90 70
577. 6 p. Globe with methods of communication (Loi Chak Keong) .. .. 2·00 1·10

INDEX
Countries can be quickly located by referring to the index at the end of this volume.

119. " Asclepias curassavica ".

120. Galleon and Map of Macao (left).

1983. Medicinal Plants. Multicoloured.
578. 20 a. Type **119** 25 25
579. 40 a. "Acanthus ilicifolius" 30 30
580 60 a. "Melastoma sanguineum" 55 35
581. 70 a. Indian lotus ("Nelumbo nucifera") .. 75 40
582. 1 p. 50 " Bombax malabaricum" .. .. 1·40 90
583. 2 p. 50 "Hibiscus mutabilis" .. .. .. 2·25 1·40

1983. 16th Century Portuguese Discoveries. Multicoloured.
585 4 p. Type **120** .. .. 1·60 1·25
586 4 p. Galleon, astrolabe and map of Macao (right) .. 1·60 1·25

Nos. 585/6 were printed together, se-tenant, forming a composite design.

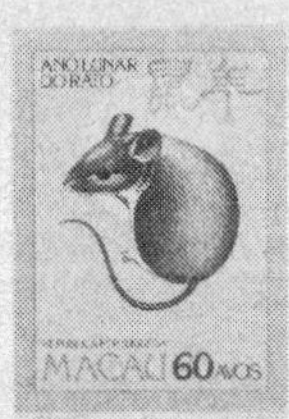

121. Rat.

122. Detail of first Macao Stamp, 1884.

1984 New Year. "Year of the Rat".
587a **121** 60 a. multicoloured .. 1·75 1·60

1984. Centenary of Macao Postage Stamps.
588 **122** 40 a. black and red .. 20 15
589 3 p. black and red .. 80 55
590 5 p. black and brown 1·25 90

123. Jay.

1984. "Ausipex 84" International Stamp Exhibition, Melbourne. Birds. Mult.
592 30 a. White-breasted kingfisher and common kingfisher 25 15
593 40 a. Type **123** 25 15
594 50 a. Japanese white eye .. 40 20
595 70 a. Hoopoe 55 30
596 2 p. 50 Peking robin .. 1·25 75
597 6 p. Mallard .. .. 2·75 1·90

124. Hok Lou T'eng.

1984. "Philakorea 84" International Stamp Exhibition, Seoul. Fishing Boats. Mult.
598 20 a. Type **124** 20 15
599 60 a. Tai Tong 40 25
600 2 p. Tai Mei Chai .. 1·00 60
601 5 p. Ch'at Pong T'o .. 2·00 1·50

125. Ox and Moon.

126. Open Hand with Stylized Doves.

1985. New Year. Year of the Ox.

602a 125 1 p. multicoloured .. 1·10 1·10

1985. International Youth Year. Mult.

603. 2 p. 50 Type **126** 65 35
604. 3 p. Open hands and plants 75 40

127. President Ramalho Eanes.

1985. Visit of President Eanes of Portugal.

605. **127.** 1 p. 50 multicoloured 70 30

128. Riverside Scene. **129.** "Euploea midamus".

1985. 25th Anniv. of Luis de Camoes Museum. Paintings by Cheng Chi Yun. Multicoloured.

606. 2 p. 50 Type **128** 60 40
607. 2 p. 50 Man on seat and boy filling jar from river 60 40
608. 2 p. 50 Playing harp in summerhouse 60 40
609. 2 p. 50 Three men by river 60 40

1985. World Tourism Day. Butterflies. Mult.

610 30 a. Type **129** 15 10
611 50 a. "Hebomoia glaucippe" 25 15
612 70 a. "Lethe confusa" .. 35 20
613 2 p. "Heliophorus epicles" 80 45
614 4 p. "Euthalia phemius seitzi" .. .. 1·25 70
615 7 p. 50 "Troides helena" .. 2·25 90

130. Tou (sailing barge). **131.** Tiger and Moon.

1985. "Italia '85" International Stamp Exhibition, Rome. Cargo Boats. Multicoloured.

617. 50 a. Type **130** 30 25
618. 70 a. "Veng Seng Lei" (motor junk) 40 25
619. 1 p. "Tong Heng Long No. 2" (motor junk) .. 60 25
620. 6 p. "Fong Vong San" (container ship) .. .. 3·00 1·75

1986. New Year. Year of the Tiger.

621. **131.** 1 p. 50 multicoloured 90 40

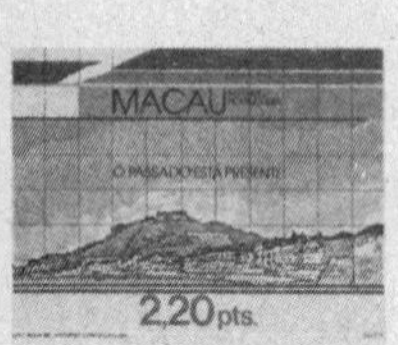

132. View of Macao. **133.** Suo-na.

1986. Macao, "the Past is still Present".

622 **132** 2 p. 20 multicoloured .. 75 45

1986. "Ameripex '86" International Stamp Exhibition, Chicago. Musical Instruments. Multicoloured.

623. 20 a. Type **133** 10 10
624. 50 a. Sheng (pipes) .. 15 15
625. 60 a. Er-hu (bowed instrument) 20 15
626. 70 a. Ruan (string instrument) 25 20
627. 5 p. Cheng (harp) .. .. 1·50 80
628. 8 p. Pi-pa (lute) .. .. 2·00 95

134. Hydrofoil.

1986. "Stockholmia 86" International Stamp Exhibition. Passenger Ferries. Mult.

630 10 a. Type **134** 20 20
631 40 a. "Tejo" (hovercraft) 25 20
632 3 p. "Tercera" (jetfoil) .. 1·40 80
633 7 p. 50 High speed ferry .. 3·75 3·00

135. Taipa Fortress. **136.** Sun Yat-sen.

1986. 10th Anniv. of Security Forces. Fortresses. Multicoloured.

634. 2 p. Type **135** 90 90
635. 2 p. St. Paul on the Mount 90 90
636. 2 p. St. Francis 90 90
637. 2 p. Guia 90 90

Nos. 634/7 were printed together, se-tenant, forming a composite design.

1986. 120th Birth Anniv. of Dr. Sun Yat-sen.

638. **136.** 70 a. multicoloured .. 1·75 1·25

137. Hare and Moon. **138.** Wa To (physician).

1987. New Year. Year of the Hare.

640. **137.** 1 p. 50 multicoloured 55 20

1987. Shek Wan Ceramics. Multicoloured.

641. 2 p. 20 Type **138** 45 35
642. 2 p. 20 Choi San, God of Fortune 45 35
643. 2 p. 20 Yi, Sun God .. 45 35
644. 2 p. 20 Cung Kuei, Keeper of Demons 45 35

139. Dragon Boats.

1987. Dragon Boat Festival. Multicoloured.

645 50 a. Type **139** 20 15
646 5 p. Dragon boat figure-head .. .. .. 1·40 75

140. Circular Fan. **141.** Fantan.

1987. Fans. Multicoloured.

647 30 a. Type **140** 10 10
648 70 a. Folding fan with tree design 15 10
649 1 p. Square-shaped fan with peacock design .. 45 15
650 6 p. Heart-shaped fan with painting of woman and tree .. .. .. 1·25 1·00

1987. Casino Games. Multicoloured.

652. 20 a. Type **141** 10 10
653. 40 a. Cussec 15 10
654. 4 p. Baccarat 85 65
655. 7 p. Roulette .. .. 1·40 90

142. Goods Hand-cart. **143.** Dragon and Moon.

1987. Traditional Vehicles. Multicoloured.

656 10 a. Type **142** 10 10
657 70 a. Open sedan chair .. 20 10
658 90 a. Rickshaw 20 20
659 10 p. Cycle rickshaw .. 2·00 1·25

1988. New Year. Year of the Dragon.

661. **143.** 2 p. 50 multicoloured 40 30

144. West European Hedgehog.

1988. Protected Mammals. Multicoloured.

662. 3 p. Type **144** 60 50
663. 3 p. Eurasian badger .. 60 50
664. 3 p. European otter .. 60 50
665. 3 p. Chinese pangolin .. 60 50

145. Breastfeeding.

1988. 40th Anniv. of W.H.O. Multicoloured.

666 60 a. Type **145** 15 10
667 80 a. Vaccinating child .. 20 10
668 2 p. 40 Donating blood .. 35 25

146. Bicycles.

1988. Transport. Multicoloured.

669 20 a. Type **146** 10 10
670 50 a. Lambretta and Vespa 10 10
671 3 p. 30 Open-sided motor car 55 45
672 5 p. Renault delivery truck, 1912 .. .. 80 70

147. Hurdling. **148.** Intelpost (electronic mail).

1988. Olympic Games, Seoul. Multicoloured.

674. 40 a. Type **147** 10 10
675. 60 a. Basketball 15 10
676. 1 p. Football 20 10
677. 8 p. Table tennis .. .. 1·25 90

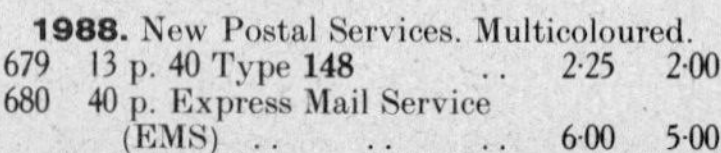

1988. New Postal Services. Multicoloured.

679 13 p. 40 Type **148** .. 2·25 2·00
680 40 p. Express Mail Service (EMS) .. .. .. 6·00 5·00

149. B.M.W. Saloon Car. **150.** Snake and Moon.

1988. 35th Macao Grand Prix. Multicoloured.

681. 80 a. Type **149** 20 10
682. 2 p. 80, Motor cycle .. 40 30
683. 7 p. Formula 3 car .. 1·25 90

1989. New Year. Year of the Snake.

685. **150.** 3 p. multicoloured .. 50 40

151 Water Carrier **152** White Building

1989. Traditional Occupations (1st series). Multicoloured.

686 50 a. Type **151** 10 10
687 1 p. Tan-kya (boat) woman 20 10
688 4 p. Tin-tin man (pedlar) 60 50
689 5 p. Tao-fu-fa (soya bean cheese) vendor 80 70

See also Nos. 714/17 and 743/6.

1989. Paintings by George Vitalievich Smirnoff in Luis Camoes Museum Mult.

690 2 p. Type **152** 30 20
691 2 p. Building with railings 30 20
692 2 p. Street scene 30 20
693 2 p. White, thatched cottage 30 20

153 Common Cobra **154** Talu

1989. "Philexfrance 89" International Stamp Exhibition, Paris. Snakes of Macao. Mult.

694 2 p. 50 Type **153** 40 30
695 2 p. 50 Banded krait ("Bungarus fasciatus") 40 30
696 2 p. 50 Bamboo pit viper ("Trimeresurus albolabris") 40 30
697 2 p. 50 Rat snake ("Elaphe radiata") 40 30

1989. Traditional Games. Multicoloured.

698 10 a. Type **154** 10 10
699 60 a. Triol (marbles) .. 10 10
700 3 p. 30 Chiquia (shuttle-cock) 50 40
701 5 p. Chinese chequers .. 50 40

155 Flying Boat **156** Malacca

1989. Aircraft. Multicoloured.

702 50 a. Type **155** 10 10
703 70 a. Pan Am "Clipper" (flying boat) 15 10
704 2 p. 80 Fairey seaplane .. 65 55
705 4 p. Hawker "Osprey" (seaplane) .. .. 1·00 65

1989. "World Stamp Expo '89" International Stamp Exhibition, Washington D.C. Portuguese Presence in Far East. Mult.

707 40 a. Type **156** 10 10
708 70 a. Thailand 10 10
709 90 a. India 15 10
710 2 p. 50 Japan 40 30
711 7 p. 50 China .. .. 1·10 85

157 Horse and Moon

159 Long-finned Grouper ("Epinephelus megachir")

1990. New Year. Year of the Horse.
713 157 4 p. multicoloured . . 60 50

1990. Traditional Occupations (2nd series). As T **151**. Multicoloured.
714 30 a. Long-chau singer . . 10 10
715 70 a. Cobbler 10 10
716 1 p. 50 Travelling penman 20 10
717 7 p. 50 Fisherman with wide nets . . . . 1·25 1·00

1990. Fishes. Multicoloured.
719 2 p. 40 Type **159** 30 20
720 2 p. 40 Malabar snapper ("Lutianus malabaricus") 30 20
721 2 p. 40 Snakehead ("Ophiocepalus maculatus") 30 20
722 2 p. 40 Common paradise fish ("Macropodus opercularis") 30 20

160 Porcelain

1990. "New Zealand 1990" International Stamp Exhibition, Auckland. Industrial Diversification. Multicoloured.
723 3 p. Type **160** 40 30
724 3 p. Furniture 40 30
725 3 p. Toys 40 30
726 3 p. Artificial flowers . . 40 30

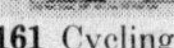

161 Cycling

162 Rose by Lazaro Luis

1990. 11th Asian Games, Peking. Mult.
728 80 a. Type **161** 10 10
729 1 p. Swimming 15 10
730 3 p. Judo 40 30
731 4 p. 20 Shooting 55 40

1990. Compass Roses. Designs showing roses from ancient charts by cartographer named. Multicoloured.
733 50 a. Type **162** 15 15
734 1 p. Diogo Homem 15 25
735 3 p. 50 Diogo Homem (different) 75 55
736 6 p. 50 Fernao Vaz Dourado . . . . 1·40 60

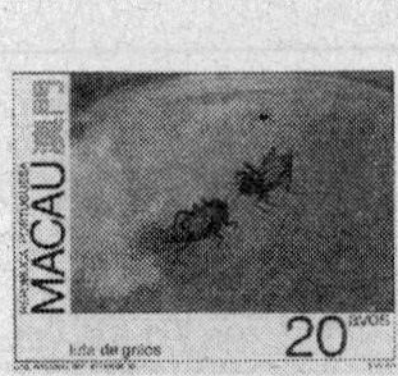

163 Cricket Fight

164 Goat and Moon

1990. Betting on Animals. Multicoloured.
738 20 a. Type **163** 10 10
739 80 a. Hwamei fight 25 15
740 1 p. Greyhound racing . . 15 10
741 10 p. Horse racing . . 1·40 1·00

1991. New Year. Year of the Goat.
742 164 4 p. 50 multicoloured . . 60 35

1991. Traditional Occupations (3rd series). As T **151**. Multicoloured.
743 80 a. Knife-grinder . . 10 10
744 1 p. 70 Flour-puppets vendor 20 10
745 3 p. 50 Street barber . . 45 25
746 4 p. 20 Fortune-teller . . 55 35

165 Swollen Harp ("Harpa harpa")

1991. Sea Shells. Multicoloured.
747 3 p. Type **165** 45 30
748 3 p. Oil lamp cone ("Tonna zonata") 45 30
749 3 p. Skeleton shell ("Murex pecten") 45 30
750 3 p. Rosary shell ("Chicoreus rosarius") 45 30

166 Character and Backcloth

167 "Delonix regia" and Lou Lim Ioc Garden

1991. Chinese Opera. Multicoloured.
751 166 60 a. multicoloured . . 10 10
752 – 80 a. multicoloured . . 10 10
753 – 1 p. multicoloured . . 15 10
754 – 10 p. multicoloured . . 1·40 1·00
DESIGNS: Nos. 752/4 Different backcloths and costumes.

1991. Flowers and Gardens (1st series). Mult.
755 1 p. 70 Type **167** 25 15
756 3 p. "Ipomoea cairica" and Sao Francisco Garden . . 45 30
757 3 p. 50 "Jasminum mesyi" and Sun Yat Sen Park 50 35
758 4 p. 20 "Bauhinia variegata" and Seac Pai Van Park 60 45
See also Nos. 815/18.

168 Portuguese Traders unloading Boats

169 Firework Display

1991. Cultural Exchange. Nambam Paintings attr. Kano Domi. Multicoloured.
760 4 p. 20 Type **168** 85 55
761 4 p. 20 Portuguese traders displaying goods to buyers 60 45

1991. Christmas. Multicoloured.
763 1 p. 70 Type **169** 15 15
764 3 p. Father Christmas . . 45 30
765 3 p. 50 Man dancing . . 50 35
766 4 p. 20 January 1st celebrations 60 45

170 Concertina Door

1992. Doors and Windows. Multicoloured.
767 1 p. 70 Type **170** 30 20
768 3 p. Window with four shutters 50 35
769 3 p. 50 Window with two shutters 60 45
770 4 p. 20 Louvred door . . 70 50

171 Monkey and Moon

172 T'it Kuai Lei

1992. New Year. Year of the Monkey.
771 171 4 p. 50 multicoloured . . 75 55

1992. Gods of Chinese Mythology (1st series). Multicoloured.
772 3 p. 50 (1) Type **172** . . 60 45
773 3 p. 50 (2) Chong Lei Kun 60 45
774 3 p. 50 (3) Cheong Kuo Lou on donkey 60 45
775 3 p. 50 (4) Loi Tong Pan . . 60 45
See also Nos. 796/9.

173 Lion Dance

174 High Jumping

1992. "World Columbian Stamp Expo '92", Chicago. Chinese Dances. Multicoloured.
776 1 p. Type **173** 15 10
777 2 p. 70 Lion dance (different) 45 30
778 6 p. Dragon dance . . 1·00 75

1992. Olympic Games, Barcelona. Mult.
779 80 a. Type **174** 15 10
780 4 p. 20 Badminton . . 70 50
781 4 p. 70 Roller hockey . . 80 60
782 5 p. Yachting 85 60

175 Na Cha Temple

1992. Temples (1st series). Multicoloured.
784 1 p. Type **175** 15 10
785 1 p. 50 Kun Iam 25 15
786 1 p. 70 Hong Kon 30 20
787 6 p. 50 A Ma . . . . 1·10 80
See also Nos. 792/5.

176 Tung Sin Tong Services

177 Rooster and Dragon

1992. Centenary of Tung Sin Tong (medical and educational charity).
788 176 1 p. multicoloured . . 15 10

1992. Portuguese–Chinese Friendship.
789 177 10 p. multicoloured . . 1·75 1·75

178 Cock

179 Children carrying Banners

1992. New Year. Year of the Cock.
791 178 5 p. multicoloured . . 85 60

1993. Temples (2nd series). As T **175**. Mult.
792 50 a. T'am Kong 10 10
793 2 p. T'in Hau 35 25
794 3 p. 50 Lin Fong 60 45
795 8 p. Pau Kong . . . . 1·40 1·00

1993. Gods of Chinese Mythology (2nd series). As T **172**. Multicoloured.
796 3 p. 50 (1) Lam Ch'oi Wo flying on crane . . 60 45
797 3 p. 50 (2) Ho Sin Ku (goddess) on peach blossom 60 45
798 3 p. 50 (3) Hon Seong Chi crossing sea on basket of flowers 60 45
799 3 p. 50 (4) Ch'ou Kuok K'ao crossing river on plank 60 45

1993. Chinese Wedding. Multicoloured.
800 3 p. Type **179** 50 35
801 3 p. Bride 50 35
802 3 p. Bridegroom 50 35
803 3 p. Wedding guests . . 50 35
Nos. 800/3 were issued together, se-tenant, forming a composite design.

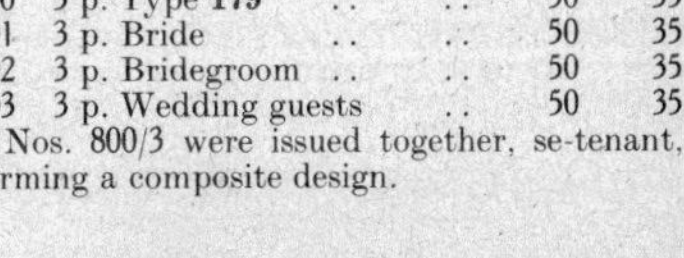

180 Bird perched on Hand

181 Long-eared Owl

1993. Environmental Protection.
805 180 1 p. multicoloured . . 15 10

1993. Birds of Prey. Multicoloured.
806 3 p. Type **181** 50 35
807 3 p. Barn owl ("Tyto alba") 50 35
808 3 p. Peregrine falcon ("Falco peregrinus") . . 50 35
809 3 p. Golden eagle ("Aquila obrysaetos") 50 35

182 Town Hall

1993. Union of Portuguese-speaking Capital Cities.
811 182 1 p. 50 green, blue & red 25 15

183 Portuguese Missionaries

1993. 450th Anniv of First Portuguese Visit to Japan. Multicoloured.
812 50 a. Japanese man with musket 10 10
813 3 p. Type **183** 50 35
814 3 p. 50 Traders carrying goods 60 45

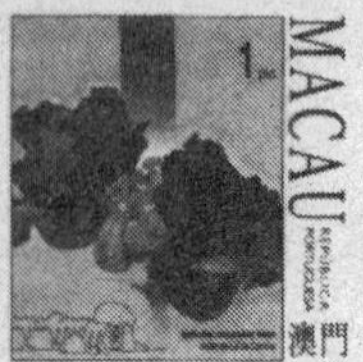

184 "Spathodea campanulata" and Luis de Camoes Garden

1993. Flowers and Gardens (2nd series). Multicoloured.
815 1 p. Type **184** 15 10
816 2 p. "Tithonia diversifolia" and Montanha Russa Garden 35 25
817 3 p. "Rhodomyrtus tomentosa" and Cais Garden 50 35
818 8 p. "Passiflora foetida" and Flora Garden .. 1·40 1·00

185 Caravel

1993. Sailing Ships. Multicoloured.
820 1 p. Type **185** 15 10
821 2 p. Caravel (different) .. 35 25
822 3 p. 50 Nau 60 45
823 4 p. 50 Galleon 75 55

186 Saloon Car

1993. 40th Anniv of Macao Grand Prix. Multicoloured.
825 1 p. 50 Type **186** 25 15
826 2 p. Motor cycle 35 25
827 4 p. 50 Racing car .. 75 55

CHARITY TAX STAMPS

The notes under this heading in Portugal also apply here.

1919. Fiscal stamp optd. **TAXA DE GUERRA.**
C 305. 2 a. green .. .. 1·75 1·25
C 306. 11 a. green .. .. 2·25 2·00
The above was for use in Timor as well as Macao.

1925. Marquis de Pombal issue of Portugal but inscr. " MACAU ".
C 329. C **73.** 2 a. red 60 60
C 330. - 2 a. red 60 60
C 331. C **75.** 2 a. red 60 60

C **48.** Our Lady of Charity (altarpiece, Macao Cathedral).

1930.
C 332. C **48.** 5 a. brown & buff .. 5·50 4·50

1945. As Type C **48** but values in Arabic and Chinese numerals left and right, at bottom of design.
C486 1 a. olive and green .. 20 20
C487 2 a. purple and grey .. 20 20
C415 5 a. brown and yellow .. 4·00 3·75
C416 5 a. blue and pale blue .. 3·50 3·00
C417 10 a. green and pale green 3·00 2·50
C470 10 a. blue and green .. 25 20
C418 15 a. orange & pale orge 2·50 2·00
C419 20 a. red and orange .. 4·50 4·00
C489 20 a. brown and yellow .. 30 20
C414 50 a. lilac and buff .. 4·00 3·75
C472 50 a. red and pink .. 3·00 2·00

1981. No. C487 and similar higher (fiscal) values surch **20 avos** and Chinese characters.
C546 20 a. on 2 a. pur on grey 35 35
C534 20 a. on 1 p. grn & lt grn 80 50
C535 20 a. on 3 p. black & pink 45 25
C536 20 a. on 5 p. brown & yell

1981. No. C418 surch. **10 avos** and Chinese characters.
C 553. 10 a. on 15 a. orange and pale orange 25 25

NEWSPAPER STAMPS

1892. " Embossed " key-type of Macao surch. **JORNAES** and value in figures.
N 73. Q. 2½ r. on 10 r. green .. 65 50
N 74. 2½ r. on 40 r. brown .. 65 50
N 75. 2½ r. on 80 r. grey .. 65 50

1893. "Newspaper" key-type inscr. "Macau".
N 79. V. 2½ r. brown 45 40

1894. "Newspaper" key-type of Macao surch. ½ **avo PROVISORIO** and Chinese characters.
N 82. V. ½ a. on 2½ r. brown .. 70 60

POSTAGE DUE STAMPS

1904. " Due " key-type inscr. " MACAU."
D 184. W. ½ a. green 35 35
D 185. 1 a. green 40 40
D 186. 2 a. grey 40 40
D 187. 4 a. brown 40 40
D 188. 5 a. orange 85 60
D 189. 8 a. brown 85 60
D 190. 12 a. brown .. .. 1·25 60
D 191. 20 a. blue .. .. 2·25 2·00
D 192. 40 a. red .. .. 2·50 2·25
D 193. 50 a. orange .. .. 6·00 6·00
D 194. 1 p. lilac .. .. 12·00 9·00

1911. "Due" key-types of Macao optd **REPUBLICA.**
D204 W ½ a. green 30 30
D205 1 a. green 30 30
D206 2 a. grey 30 30
D207 4 a. brown 30 30
D208 5 a. orange 30 30
D209 8 a. brown 30 30
D287 12 a. brown 65 40
D211 20 a. blue .. .. 1·00 80
D212 40 a. red .. .. 1·75 1·40
D290 50 a. orange .. .. 2·50 2·25
D214 1 p. lilac .. .. 4·50 3·75

1925. Marquis de Pombal issue, as Nos. C 329/31 optd. **MULTA.**
D 329. C **73.** 4 a. red 45 45
D 330. - 4 a. red 45 45
D 331. C **75.** 4 a. red 45 45

1947. As Type D **1** of Portuguese Colonies, but inscr "MACAU".
D410 D **1** 1 a. black and purple 70 70
D411 2 a. black and violet 70 70
D412 4 a. black & blue .. 70 70
D413 5 a. black and brown 70 70
D414 8 a. black and purple 70 70
D415 12 a. black & brown 70 70
D416 20 a. black and green 1·25 1·25
D417 40 a. black and red 2·10 2·10
D418 50 a. black & yellow 3·75 3·75
D419 1 p. black and blue 3·75 3·75

1949. Postage stamps of 1934 surch. **PORTEADO** and new value.
D 424. **40.** 1 a. on 4 a. black .. 60 60
D 425. 2 a. on 6 a. brown .. 60 60
D 426. 4 a. on 8 a. blue .. 60 60
D 427. 5 a. on 10 a. red .. 70 60
D 428. 8 a. on 12 a. blue .. 70 70
D 429. 12 a. on 30 a. green .. 1·25 1·10
D 430. 20 a. on 40 a. violet .. 1·25 1·10

1951. Optd **PORTEADO** or surch also.
D439 **66** 1 a. yellow on cream .. 25 25
D440 2 a. green on green .. 25 25
D441 7 a. on 10 a. mauve on green 25 25

D **70.**

1952. Numerals in red. Name in black.
D 451. D **70.** 1 a. blue and green 10 10
D 452. 3 a. brown & salmon 10 10
D 453. 5 a. slate and blue .. 10 10
D 454. 10 a. red and blue .. 20 20
D 455. 30 a. blue and brown 25 25
D 456. 1 p. brown & grey .. 1·10 1·10

MACEDONIA Pt. 3

GERMAN OCCUPATION.

100 stotinki = 1 lev.

Македония
8. IX. 1944
1 лв.
(**1.**)

1944. Stamps of Bulgaria, 1940-44.
(a) Surch as T **1.**
1. 1 l. on 10 st. orange .. .. 3·75 9·25
2. 3 l. on 15 st. blue .. .. 3·75 9·25
(b) Surch similar to T **1** but larger.
3. 6 l. on 10 st. blue .. .. 6·25 14·00
4. 9 l. on 15 st. green .. .. 6·25 14·00
5. 9 l. on 15 st. green .. .. 7·75 19·00
6. 15 l. on 4 l. black .. .. 15·00 40·00
7. 20 l. on 7 l. blue .. .. 15·00 40·00
8. 30 l. on 14 l. brown .. .. 30·00 75·00

MADAGASCAR AND DEPENDENCIES Pt. 6

A large island in the Indian Ocean off the east coast of South Africa. French Post Offices operated there from 1885.

In 1896 the island was declared a French colony, absorbing Diego-Suarez and Ste. Marie de Madagascar in 1898 and Nossi-Be in 1901.

Madagascar became autonomous as the Malagasy Republic in 1958.

100 centimes = 1 franc.

A. FRENCH POST OFFICES

1889. Stamps of French Colonies " Commerce " type surch. with value in figures.
1. **J.** 05 on 10 c. black on lilac .. £475 £150
2. 05 on 25 c. black on red .. £475 £140
4. 05 on 40 c. red on yellow .. £110 70·00
5. 5 on 10 c. black on lilac .. £160 90·00
6. 5 on 25 c. black on red .. £160 95·00
7. 15 on 25 c. black on red .. £110 70·00
3. 25 on 40 c. red on yellow .. £425 £120

5.

1891. No gum. Imperf.
9 **5** 5 c. black on green .. £100 17·00
10 10 c. black on blue .. 70·00 22·00
11 15 c. blue on blue .. 75·00 24·00
12 25 c. brown on buff .. 14·00 8·50
13 1 f. black on yellow .. £800 £200
14 5 f. black and lilac on lilac £1500 £900

1895. Stamps of France optd. **POSTE FRANCAISE Madagascar.**
15. **10.** 5 c. green .. .. .. 4·75 3·75
16. 10 c. black on lilac .. 30·00 19·00
17. 15 c. blue .. .. .. 40·00 7·00
18. 25 c. black on red .. 55·00 6·00
19. 40 c. red on yellow .. 45·00 12·00
20. 50 c. red .. .. .. 65·00 12·00
21. 75 c. brown on orange .. 60·00 27·00
22. 1 f. olive .. .. .. 85·00 18·00
23. 5 f. mauve on lilac .. £110 50·00

1896. Stamps of France surch with value in figures in oval.
29. **10.** 5 c. on 1 c. black on blue £4000 £1500
30. 15 c. on 2 c. brn. on yell. £1500 £750
31. 25 c. on 3 c. grey £1700 £750
32. 25 c. on 4 c. red on grey £4250 £1400
33. 25 c. on 40 c. red on yell. £900 £550

B. FRENCH COLONY

1896. "Tablet" key-type inscr "MADAGASCAR ET DEPENDANCES".
1 D 1 c. black & red on blue 50 50
2 2 c. brown & bl on buff 60 60
2a 2 c. brn & blk on buff 2·75 2·75
3 4 c. brn & bl on grey 85 40
17 5 c. green and red .. 75 30
6 10 c. blk & bl on lilac 4·75 60
18 10 c. red and blue .. 1·00 25
7 15 c. blue and red .. 6·00 55
19 15 c. grey and red .. 1·10 30
8 20 c. red & blue on grn 3·50 85
9 25 c. blk & red on pink 4·75 40
20 25 c. blue and red .. 12·50 14·00
10 30 c. brn & bl on drab 4·75 1·50
21 35 c. blk & red on yell 28·00 3·50
11 40 c. red & blue on yell 5·25 1·00
12 50 c. red & bl on pink 6·75 85
22 50 c. brown & red on bl 20·00 16·00
13 75 c. vio & red on orge 2·25 1·50
14 1 f. green and red .. 7·00 1·90
15 1 f. green and blue .. 12·50 8·00
16 5 f. mauve & bl on lilac 25·00 16·00

1902. "Tablet" key-type stamps as above surch.
27 D 0,01 on 2 c. brown and blue on buff .. .. 4·50 3·00
27a 0,01 on 2 c. brown and black on buff .. 2·50 4·00
29 0,05 on 30 c. brown and blue on drab .. 3·50 3·50
23 05 on 50 c. red and blue on pink .. .. 2·00 1·50
31 0,10 on 50 c. red and blue on pink .. 3·00 3·50
24 10 on 5 f. mauve and blue on lilac .. 14·00 12·00
32 0,15 on 75 c. violet and red on orange .. 1·75 1·75
33 0,15 on 1 f. green & red 1·75 2·50
25 15 on 1 f. green and red 3·50 1·75

1902. Nos. 59 and 61 of Diego-Suarez surch.
35 D 0,05 on 30 c. brown and blue on drab .. 85·00 £100
36 0,10 on 50 c. red and blue on pink £3250 £3000

4. Zebu and Lemur.

5. Transport in Madagascar.

1903.
38 **4** 1 c. purple 55 30
39 2 c. brown 50 50
40 4 c. brown 55 55
41 5 c. green .. .. 4·75 55
42 10 c. red .. .. 5·00 50
43 15 c. red .. .. 5·00 65
44 20 c. orange .. .. 3·00 1·25
45 25 c. blue .. .. 20·00 1·50
46 30 c. red .. .. 22·00 8·00
47 40 c. lilac .. .. 20·00 3·25
48 50 c. brown .. .. 35·00 13·50
49 75 c. yellow .. .. 38·00 14·50
50 1 f. green .. .. 38·00 23·00
51 2 f. blue .. .. 50·00 24·00
52 5 f. black .. .. 50·00 55·00

1908.
53a **5** 1 c. green and violet .. 10 20
54 2 c. green and red .. 10 20
55 4 c. brown and green .. 10 25
56 5 c. olive and green .. 40 15
90 5 c. red and black .. 20 10
57 10 c. brown and pink .. 25 15
91 10 c. olive and green .. 20 20
92 10 c. purple and brown 30 20
58 15 c. red and lilac .. 30 20
93 15 c. green and olive .. 25 40
94 15 c. red and blue .. 90 1·00
59 20 c. brown and orange 25 30
60 25 c. black and blue .. 1·25 25
95 25 c. black and violet .. 40 15
61 30 c. black and brown 1·25 1·40
96 30 c. brown and red .. 45 40
97 30 c. purple and green 50 30
98 30 c. light green & green 80 80
62 35 c. black and red .. 95 60
63 40 c. black and brown 65 60
64 45 c. black and green .. 50 50
99 45 c. red and scarlet .. 50 75
100 45 c. purple and lilac .. 85 90
65 50 c. black and violet .. 50 45
101 50 c. black and blue .. 45 20
102 50 c. yellow and black 60 25
103 60 c. violet on pink .. 50 65
104 65 c. blue and black .. 70 75
66 75 c. black and red .. 45 35
105 85 c. red and green .. 85 1·25
67 1 f. green and brown .. 45 30
106 1 f. blue 65 70
107 1 f. green and mauve .. 3·50 3·75
108 1 f. 10 green and brown 85 1·00
68 2 f. green and blue .. 2·25 95
69 5 f. brown and violet .. 7·50 3·75

1912. "Tablet" key-type surch.
70 D 05 on 15 c. grey and red 35 30
71 05 on 20 c. red and blue on green 40 65
72 05 on 30 c. brown and blue on drab .. 40 65
73 10 on 75 c. violet and red on orange .. .. 3·00 6·00
81 0,60 on 75 c. violet and red on orange .. 4·50 4·50
82 1 f. on 5 f. mauve and blue on lilac 45 85

1912. Surch.
74 **4** 05 on 2 c. brown 25 45
75 05 on 20 c. orange .. 35 50
76 05 on 30 c. red 35 80
77 10 on 40 c. lilac 50 95
78 10 on 50 c. brown .. 85 2·00
79 10 on 75 c. brown .. 2·50 4·50
83 1 f. on 5 f. black .. .. 20·00 20·00

1915. Surch **5c** and red cross.
80 5 10 c.+5 c. brown and pink 50 90

1921. Surch **1 cent.**
84 5 1 c. on 15 c. red and lilac 40 70

1921. Type **5** (some colours changed) surch.
109 5 25 c. on 15 c. red and lilac 40 45
85 0,25 on 35 c. black & red 3·00 3·00
86 0,25 on 40 c. black & brn 2·50 2·75
87 0,25 on 45 c. black & grn 2·00 2·25
110 25 c. on 2 f. green & blue 30 40
112 25 c. on 5 f. brown & vio 50 60
88 0,30 on 40 c. black & brn 1·10 1·10
113 50 c. on 1 f. green & brn 80 20
89 0,60 on 75 c. black & red 1·90 2·00
114 60 on 75 c. violet on pink 40 40
115 65 c. on 75 c. black & red 90 1·50
116 85 c. on 45 c. black & grn 90 1·50
117 90 c. on 75 c. pink & red 45 55
118 1 f. 25 on 1 f. blue .. 30 40
119 1 f. 50 on 1 f. lt blue & bl 50 20
120 3 f. on 5 f. violet & grn 1·50 1·00
121 10 f. on 5 f. mauve & red 4·50 3·25
122 20 f. on 5 f. blue & mauve 6·25 5·50

14. Sakalava Chief.

15. Zebus.

17. Betsileo Woman.

18. General Gallieni.

1930.
123 18 1 c. blue 20 40
124 15 1 c. green and blue .. 20 25
125 14 2 c. brown and red .. 10 10
177 18 3 c. blue 15 25
126 14 4 c. mauve and brown 15 35
127 15 5 c. red and green .. 15 15
128 – 10 c. green and red .. 10 10
129 17 15 c. red 10 10
130 15 20 c. blue and brown .. 20 20
131 – 25 c. brown and lilac .. 20 10
132 17 30 c. green 40 30
133 14 40 c. red and green .. 30 35
134 17 45 c. lilac 55 50
178 18 45 c. green 35 40
179 50 c. brown 20 10
180 60 c. mauve 15 30
136 15 65 c. mauve and brown 55 25
181 18 70 c. red 35 35
137 17 75 c. brown 50 25
138 15 90 c. red 85 80
182 18 90 c. brown 30 15
139 – 1 f. blue and brown .. 1·00 90
140 – 1 f. red and scarlet .. 45 45
140a – 1 f. 25 brown and blue 95 75
183 18 1 f. 40 orange 50 35
141 14 1 f. 50 ultramarine & bl 4·50 1·25
142 1 f. 50 red and brown 50 55
278 1 f. 50 brown and red 20 50
184 18 1 f. 60 violet 50 40
143 14 1 f. 75 red and brown 2·50 1·00
185 18 2 f. red 35 20
186a 3 f. green 55 60
146 14 5 f. brown and mauve 70 40
147 18 10 f. orange .. .. 2·75 1·90
148 14 20 f. blue and brown .. 1·40 1·40
DESIGN—VERT. 10 c., 25 c., 1 f., 1 f. 25, Hova girl.

1931. "Colonial Exhibition" key-types inscr "MADAGASCAR".
149 E 40 c. black and green .. 55 55
150 F 50 c. black and mauve .. 1·25 70
151 G 90 c. black and red .. 85 90
152 H 1 f. 50 black and blue .. 1·40 1·00

19. Aeroplane over Madagascar.

20. J. Laborde and Tananarivo Palace.

1935. Air.
153 19 50 c. red and green .. 50 55
154 90 c. red and green .. 35 40
155 1 f. 25 red and lake .. 35 40
156 1 f. 50 red and blue .. 40 45
157 1 f. 60 red and blue .. 20 25
158 1 f. 75 red and orange .. 5·25 3·25
159 2 f. red and blue .. 50 30
160 3 f. red and orange .. 35 30
161 3 f. 65 red and black .. 35 40
162 3 f. 90 red and green .. 30 30
163 4 f. red and carmine .. 35·00 1·90
164 4 f. 50 red and black .. 18·00 80
165 5 f. 50 red and green .. 45 40
166 6 f. red and mauve .. 40 40
167 6 f. 90 red and purple .. 40 40
168 8 f. red and mauve .. 70 90
169 8 f. 50 red and green .. 80 95
170 9 f. red and green .. 45 50
171 12 f. red and brown .. 55 65
172 12 f. 50 red and violet .. 1·25 95
173 15 f. red and orange .. 60 60
174 16 f. red and green .. 1·25 1·25
175 20 f. red and brown .. 1·90 1·40
176 50 f. red and blue .. 3·25 3·00

1937. International Exhibition, Paris. As Nos. 211/16 of New Caledonia.
187 20 c. violet 60 75
188 30 c. green 75 85
189 40 c. red 50 50
190 50 c. brown and agate .. 45 60
191 90 c. red 45 60
192 1 f. 50 blue 45 90

1938. 60th Death Anniv. of Jean Laborde (explorer).
193. 20. 35 c. green 35 45
194. 55 c. violet 40 45
195. 65 c. red 35 50
196. 80 c. purple 45 40
197. 1 f. red 35 30
198. 1 f. 25 red 45 40
199. 1 f. 75 blue 90 35
200. 2 f. 15 brown .. .. 1·75 1·25
201. 2 f. 25 blue 75 75
202. 2 f. 50 brown 40 45
203. 10 f. green 60 60

1938. Int. Anti-Cancer Fund. As T **22** of Mauritania.
204. 1 f. 75+50 c. blue .. .. 3·75 6·00

1939. New York World's Fair. As T **28** of Mauritania.
205. 1 f. 25 red 75 80
206. 2 f. 25 blue 80 85

1939. 150th Anniv of French Revolution. As T **29** of Mauritania.
207 45 c.+25 c. green and black (postage) .. 4·75 5·75
208 70 c.+30 c. brown & black 5·25 5·75
209 90 c.+35 c. orange & black 4·75 5·75
210 1 f. 25+1 f. red and black 4·75 5·75
211 2 f. 25+2 f. blue and black 5·00 5·75
212 4 f. 50+4 f. black and orange (air) .. 9·00 10·00

1942. Surch **50** and bars.
213 15 50 on 65 c. mauve & brn 95 35

1942. Free French Administration. Optd **FRANCE LIBRE** or surch also.
214 14 2 c. brown and red (postage) 65 65
215 18 3 c. blue .. .. 85·00 90·00
216 15 0,05 on 1 c. green & blue 50 60
217 20 0,10 on 55 c. violet 75 90
218 17 15 c. red .. .. 6·25 6·25
219 20 0,30 on 65 c. red 50 60
220 15 0 f. 50 on 0,05 on 1 c. green and blue 50 65
221 50 on 65 c. mauve & brn 55 25
222 18 50 on 90 c. brown .. 40 20
223 15 65 c. mauve and brown 65 65
224 18 70 c. red 55 60
225 20 80 c. purple .. .. 1·40 1·40
226 – 1,00 on 1 f. 25 brown and blue (No. 140a) .. 1·40 1·40
227 20 1,00 on 1 f. 25 red 5·00 5·00
228 18 1 f. 40 orange .. 60 60
229 5 1 f. 50 on 1 f. blue 90 85
230 14 1 f. 50 ultramarine & bl 90 90
231 1 f. 50 red and brown 90 90
232 18 1,50 on 1 f. 60 violet 55 55
233 14 1,50 on 1 f. 75 red & brn 55 50
234 20 1,50 on 1 f. 75 blue .. 55 55
235 18 1 f. 60 violet .. 50 60
236 20 2,00 on 2 f. 15 brown 50 50
237 2 f. 25 blue .. 55 55
238 – 2 f. 25 blue (No. 206) .. 55 55
239 20 2 f. 50 brown .. 2·00 2·25
240 5 10 f. on 5 f. mauve & red 5·50 5·25
241 20 10 f. green .. 2·75 3·00
242 5 20 f. on 5 f. blue & mve 7·75 8·00
243 14 20 f. blue and brown .. £550 £650
244 19 1,00 on 1 f. 25 red and lake (air) .. .. 3·00 3·25
245 1 f. 50 red and blue .. 3·75 3·75
246 1 f. 75 red and orange .. 55·00 60·00
247 3,00 on 3 f. 65 red & blk 65 25
248 8 f. red and purple .. 80 75
249 8,00 on 8 f. 50 red & grn 60 30
250 12 f. red and brown .. 1·75 1·60
251 12 f. 50 red and violet .. 90 85
252 16 f. red and green .. 3·25 3·25
253 50 f. red and blue .. 2·75 2·75

24. Traveller's Tree.

29. Gen. Gallieni.

36. Gen. Gallieni and View.

1943. Free French Issue.
254. 24. 5 c. brown 10 25
255. 10 c. mauve 10 10
256. 25 c. green 10 20
257. 30 c. orange 10 10
258. 40 c. blue 20 20
259. 80 c. purple 10 10
260. 1 f. blue 15 15
261 1 f. 50 c. red 20 15
262. 2 f. yellow 15 10
263. 2 f. 50 c. blue 20 25
264. 4 f. blue and red .. 20 10
265. 5 f. green and black .. 45 15
266. 10 f. red and blue .. 60 20
267. 20 f. violet and brown 40 40

1943. Free French Administration. Air. As T **30** of New Caledonia, but inscr. "MADAGASCAR".
268. 32. 1 f. orange 40 40
269. 1 f. 50 c. red 40 40
270. 5 f. purple 40 40
271. 10 f. black 40 40
272. 25 f. blue 85 45
273. 50 f. green .. .. 1·40 70
274. 100 f. red 50 80

1944. Mutual Aid and Red Cross Funds. As T **31** of New Caledonia.
275. 5 f.+20 f. green .. 50 80

1944. Surch **1 f. 50**.
276 24 1 f. 50 on 5 c. brown .. 35 55
277 1 f. 50 on 10 c. mauve .. 50 80

1945. Eboue. As T **32** of New Caledonia.
279. 2 f. black 20 35
280. 25 f. green 50 85

1946. Air. Victory. As T **34** of New Caledonia.
281. 8 f. red 40 40

1945. Surch with new value.
282 24 50 c. on 5 c. brown .. 35 35
283 60 c. on 5 c. brown .. 40 45
284 70 c. on 5 c. brown .. 35 40
285 1 f. 20 on 5 c. brown .. 35 35
286 2 f. 40 on 25 c. green .. 35 45
287 3 f. on 25 c. green .. 30 30
288 4 f. 50 on 25 c. green .. 45 50
289 15 f. on 2 f. 50 blue .. 35 45

1946. Air. From Chad to the Rhine. As Nos. 300/305 of New Caledonia.
290. 5 f. blue 75 85
291. 10 f. red 80 90
292. 15 f. green 80 90
293. 20 f. brown .. .. 1·00 1·10
294. 25 f. violet .. .. 1·25 1·40
295. 50 f. red .. .. 1·10 1·40

1946.
296. – 10 c. green (postage) .. 10 25
297. – 30 c. orange 10 15
298. – 40 c. olive 10 25
299. – 50 c. purple 10 10
300. – 60 c. blue 10 25
301. – 80 c. green 10 25
302. – 1 f. sepia 10 10
303. – 1 f. 20 green 20 20
304. 29. 1 f. 50 red 10 10
305. 2 f. black 10 10
306. 3 f. purple 10 10
307. – 3 f. 60 red 60 60
308. – 4 f. blue 25 20
309. – 5 f. orange 35 15
310. – 6 f. blue 20 10
311. – 10 f. lake 25 25
312. – 15 f. brown 35 20
313. – 20 f. blue 45 35
314. – 25 f. brown 80 45
315. – 50 f. blue and red (air) .. 90 45
316. – 100 f. brown and red .. 1·75 85
317. – 200 f. brown and green 3·50 2·00
DESIGNS—VERT. 10 c. to 50 c. Native with spear. 6 f., 10 f. Gen. Duchesne. 15 f., 20 f., 25 f. Lt.-Col. Joffre. 100 f. (28×51 mm.) Allegory of flight. HORIZ. 60 c., 80 c. Zebus. 1 f., 1 f. 20 Sakalava man and woman. 3 f. 60, 4 f., 5 f. Betsimisaraka mother and child. 50 f. (49×28 mm.) Aerial view of Port of Tamatave. 200 f. (51×28 mm.) Aeroplane and map.

1946. 50th Anniv. of French Protectorate.
318. 36. 10 f.+5 f. purple .. 35 45

1948. Air. Discovery of Adelie Land, Antarctic. No. 316 optd. **TERRE ADELIE DUMONT D'URVILLE 1840.**
319. – 100 f. brown and red .. 35·00 50·00

1949. Air. 75th Anniv of U.P.U. As T **38** of New Caledonia.
320 25 f. multicoloured .. 2·75 1·90

1950. Colonial Welfare Fund. As T **39** of New Caledonia.
321. 10 f.+2 f. purple & green 3·50 4·00

38. Cacti and Succulents.

39. Long-tailed Ground Roller.

40. Woman and Forest Road.

1952.
322. 38. 7 f. 50 grn. & blue (post.) 70 35
323. 39. 8 f. lake .. .. 1·25 35
324. 15 f. blue and green .. 2·75 30
325. – 50 f. green and blue (air) 2·25 40
326. – 100 f. black, brn. & blue 8·50 1·50
327. – 200 f. brown and green 12·50 4·50
328. 40. 500 f. brn., sepia & green 21·00 5·00
DESIGNS: As Type **40**: 50 f. Palm trees. 100 f. Antsirabe Viaduct. 200 f. Ring-tailed lemurs.

1952. Military Medal Cent. As T **40** of New Caledonia.
329. 15 f. turquoise, yell. & grn. 1·50 1·90

1954. Air. 10th Anniv. of Liberation. As T **42** of New Caledonia.
330. 15 f. purple and violet .. 2·00 1·50

41. Marshal Lyautey.

1954. Birth Cent. of Marshal Lyautey.
331. 41. 10 f. indigo, bl. & ultram. 65 10
332. 40 f. lake, grey & black 1·00 10

42. Gallieni School.

43. Cassava.

1956. Economic and Social Development Fund.
333. – 3 f. brown and grey .. 20 10
334. 42. 5 f. brown & chestnut .. 15 10
335. – 10 f. blue and grey .. 30 15
336. – 15 f. green & turquoise 40 15
DESIGNS: 3 f. Tamatave and tractor. 10 f. Dredging canal. 15 f. Irrigation.

1956. Coffee. As T **44** of New Caledonia.
337. 20 f. sepia and brown .. 40 15

1957. Plants.
338 43 2 f. green, brown & blue 25 10
339 – 4 f. red, brown & green 25 15
340 – 12 f. green, brown & vio 45 15
DESIGNS: 4 f. Cloves. 12 f. Vanilla.

PARCEL POST STAMPS

1919. Receipt stamp of France surch **MADAGASCAR ET DEPENDANCES 0fr.10 COLIS POSTAUX.**
P81 0 f. 10 on 10 c. grey .. 2·75 2·75

1919. Fiscal stamp of Madagascar surch **COLIS POSTAUX 0f.10.**
P82 0 f. 10 on 1 f. pink .. 70·00 42·00

1919. Fiscal stamps surch **Madagascar et Dependances** (in capitals on No. P83) **COLIS POSTAUX 0f.10.**
P83 0 f. 10 pink .. .. 6·25 4·75
P84 0 f. 10 red and green .. 1·50 1·25
P85 0 f. 10 black and green .. 1·75 1·25

POSTAGE DUE STAMPS

1896. Postage Due stamps of Fr. Colonies optd. **Madagascar et DEPENDANCES.**
D 17. U 5 c. blue .. .. 5·00 4·75
D 18. 10 c. brown .. .. 5·00 4·25
D 19. 20 c. yellow .. .. 4·50 5·00
D 20. 30 c. red .. .. 5·50 5·00
D 21. 40 c. mauve .. .. 50·00 30·00
D 22. 50 c. violet .. .. 6·00 5·00
D 23. 1 f. green .. .. 55·00 35·00

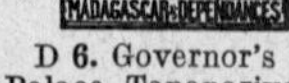

D 6. Governor's Palace, Tananarive. D 37.

1908.

D 70. D 6. 2 c. red 10 10
D 71. 4 c. violet 10 15
D 72. 5 c. green 10 20
D 73. 10 c. red 10 20
D 74. 20 c. olive 10 30
D 75. 40 c. brown on cream 15 30
D 76. 50 c. brown on blue 15 25
D 77. 60 c. red 20 45
D 78. 1 f. blue 25 55

1924. Surch. in figures.

D 123. D 6. 60 c. on 1 f. red .. 1·00 1·40
D 124. 2 f. on 1 f. purple .. 45 60
D 125. 3 f. on 1 f. blue .. 45 60

1942. Free French Administration. Optd **FRANCE LIBRE** or surch also.

D254 D 6 10 c. red 55 65
D255 20 c. green 55 65
D256 0,30 on 5 c. green .. 55 65
D257 40 c. brown on cream 55 65
D258 50 c. brown and blue 55 65
D259 60 c. red 55 65
D260 1 f. blue 55 65
D261 1 f. on 2 c. purple .. 3·00 3·50
D262 2 f. on 4 c. violet .. 1·25 1·50
D263 2 f. on 1 f. mauve .. 55 65
D264 3 f. on 1 f. blue .. 55 65

1947.

D 319. D 37. 10 c. mauve .. 10 25
D 320. 30 c. brown .. 10 25
D 321. 50 c. green 10 25
D 322. 1 f. brown 10 25
D 323. 2 f. red 20 30
D 324. 3 f. brown 15 30
D 325. 4 f. blue 15 40
D 326. 5 f. red 25 45
D 327. 10 f. green 35 55
D 328. 20 f. blue .. .. 40 1·00

For later issues see **MALAGASY REPUBLIC.**

MADEIRA Pt. 9

A Portuguese island in the Atlantic Ocean off the N.W. coast of Africa. Regarded as part of Portugal for administrative purposes, it now uses Portuguese stamps. Some separate issues for Madeira were introduced from 1980 onwards.

1868. 1000 reis = 1 milreis
1912. 100 centavos = 1 escudo.

Nos. 1/77 are stamps of Portugal optd. **MADEIRA.**

1868. With curved value label. Imperf.

1. 14. 20 r. olive .. .. 90·00 70·00
2. 50 r. green .. .. 90·00 70·00
3. 80 r. orange .. .. £100 75·00
4. 100 r. lilac .. .. £100 75·00

1868. With curved value label. Perf.

10. 14. 5 r. black .. .. .. 20·00 18·00
13. 10 r. yellow .. .. 42·00 38·00
14. 20 r. olive .. .. 65·00 55·00
15b. 25 r. red .. .. .. 25·00 4·00
16. 50 r. green .. .. 85·00 70·00
17. 80 r. orange .. .. 90·00 70·00
19. 100 r. mauve .. .. 85·00 70·00
20. 120 r. blue .. .. 55·00 35·00
21. 240 r. mauve £200 £190

1871. With straight value label.

57 15 5 r. black .. .. 3·50 2·25
31 10 r. yellow .. .. 12·00 9·00
72a 10 r. green .. .. 26·00 20·00
32 15 r. brown .. .. 6·50 4·50
49 20 r. olive .. .. 13·00 10·00
50 25 r. red .. .. .. 5·00 1·60
51 50 r. green .. .. 27·00 11·00
71 50 r. blue.. .. .. 55·00 28·00
27 80 r. orange .. .. 40·00 32·00
53 100 r. mauve .. .. 35·00 24·00
38 120 r. blue .. .. 55·00 38·00
55 150 r. blue .. .. 85·00 75·00
74 150 r. yellow £130 £110
39 240 r. mauve £275 £225
67 300 r. lilac .. .. 35·00 30·00

1880. Stamps of 1880.

75 16 5 r. black .. .. 12·00 11·00
78 25 r. grey .. .. 12·00 5·00
78b 25 r. brown .. .. 12·00 5·00
77 17 25 r. grey .. .. 12·00 11·00

1898. Vasco da Gama. As Nos. 378/85 of Portugal.

134. 2½ r. green .. .. 1·25 75
135. 5 r. red .. .. 1·25 75
136. 10 r. purple .. .. 2·00 90
137. 25 r. green .. .. 1·25 75
138. 50 r. blue .. .. 3·00 1·75
139. 75 r. brown .... 4·00 3·25
140. 100 r. brown .. .. 3·50 2·75
141. 150 r. brown .. .. 6·00 5·00

For Nos. 134/41 with **REPUBLICA** opt., see Nos. 455/62 of Portugal.

6. Cercs. 7. 20 r. Stamp, 1868.

1929. Funchal Museum Fund.

148. 6. 3 c. violet 20 20
149. 4 c. yellow 20 20
150. 5 c. blue 20 20
151. 6 c. brown 25 25
152. 10 c. red 25 25
153. 15 c. green 25 25
154. 16 c. brown 25 25
155. 25 c. red 30 30
156. 32 c. green 30 30
157. 40 c. brown 30 30
158. 50 c. black 30 30
159. 64 c. turquoise 35 35
160. 80 c. brown 35 35
161. 96 c. red 40 40
162. 1 e. black 40 40
163. 1 e. 20 red 35 35
164. 1 e. 60 blue 35 35
165. 2 e. 40 yellow 75 75
166. 3 e. 36 olive 80 80
167. 4 e. 50 red 80 80
168. 7 e. blue .. .. .. 1·50 1·50

1980. 112th Anniv of First Overprinted Madeira Stamps.

169. 7. 6 e. 50 blk., bistre & grn. 15 10
170. – 19 e. 50 blk., pur. and red 40 25

DESIGN: 19 e. 50, 100 r. stamp, 1868.

8. Ox Sledge.

1980. World Tourism Conference, Manila, Philippines. Multicoloured.

172 50 c Type 8 .. .. 10 10
173. 1 e. Wine and grapes .. 10 10
174. 5 e. Map of Madeira 15 10
175. 6 e. 50 Basketwork .. 20 10
176. 8 e. Orchid 35 20
177. 30 e. Fishing boat 80 35

9. O Bailinho (folk dance).

1981. Europa.

178. 9. 22 e. multicoloured .. 50 30

10. Portuguese Caravel approaching Madeira. 11. " Dactylorhiza foliosa ".

1981. 560th Anniv (1980) of Dicovery of Madeira. Multicoloured.

180 8 e. 50 Type 10 .. .. 25 10
181 33 e. 50 Prince Henry the Navigator and map of Atlantic Ocean .. 85 40

1981. Regional Flowers. Multicoloured.

182. 7 e. Type 11 .. .. 10 10
183. 8 e. 50 "Geranium maderense" 15 10
184. 9 e. "Goodyera macrophylla" 15 10
185. 10 e. "Armeria maderensis" 15 10
186. 12 e. 50 "Matthiola maderensis" 20 10
187. 20 e. "Isoplexis sceptrum" 35 20
188. 27 e. "Viola paradoxa" .. 40 20
189. 30 e. "Erica maderensis" .. 40 25
190. 33 e. 50 "Scilla maderensis" 50 30
191. 37 e. 50 "Cirsium latifolium" 55 30
192. 50 e. "Echium candicans" 85 55
193. 100 e. "Clethra arborea" .. 1·40 65

12. First Sugar Mill. 13. Dancer holding Dolls on Staff.

1982. Europa.

199. 12. 33 e. 50 multicoloured 1·00 40

1982. O Brinco Dancing Dolls. Mult.

201. 27 e. Type 13 .. .. 60 40
202. 33 e. 50 Dancers 80 50

14. Los Levadas Irrigation Channels.

1983. Europa.

203. 14. 37 e. 50 multicoloured 90 30

15. Flag of Madeira. 16. Rally Car.

1983. Flag.

205. 15. 12 e. 50 multicoloured 30 10

1984. Europa. As T 398 of Portugal but additionally inscr "MADEIRA".

206 51 e. multicoloured .. 95 50

1984. 25th Anniv. of Madeira Rally. Multicoloured.

208. 16 e. Type 16 .. .. 30 15
209. 51 e. Rally car (different) 1·00 40

17. Basket Sledge. 18. Braguinha Player.

1984. Transport (1st series). Multicoloured.

210 16 e. Type 17 .. .. 20 10
211 35 e. Hammock 40 30
212 40 e. Borracheiros (wine carriers) 50 30
213 51 e. Local sailing boat .. 70 35

See also Nos. 218/21.

1985. Europa.

214 18 60 e. multicoloured .. 1·40 55

19. Black Scabbard Fish.

1985. Fishes (1st series). Multicoloured.

216 40 e. Type 19 .. .. 70 30
217 60 e. Moon fish .. .. 1·10 45

See also Nos. 222/3 and 250/3.

1985. Transport (2nd series). As T 17. Mult.

218 20 e. Ox sledge 20 10
219 40 e. Mountain railway .. 50 35
220 46 e. Fishing boat and basket used by pesquitos (itinerant fish sellers) .. 65 35
221 60 e. Coastal ferry .. 75 40

1986. Fishes (2nd series). As T 19. Mult.

222. 20 e. Big eye tuna 40 10
223. 75 e. Red bream .. .. 1·40 55

20 Cory's Shearwater and Tanker

1986. Europa.

224 20 68 e. 50 multicoloured .. 1·25 60

21 Sao Lourenco Fort, Funchal

1986. Fortresses. Multicoloured.

226 22 e. 50 Type 21 .. .. 20 10
227 52 e. 50 Sao Joao do Pico Fort, Funchal 45 30
228 68 e. 50 Sao Tiago Fort, Funchal 60 35
229 100 e. Nossa Senhora do Amparo Fort, Machico 90 80

22 Firecrest 24 Funchal Cathedral

23 Social Services Centre, Funchal (Raul Chorao Ramalho)

1987. Birds (1st series). Multicoloured.

230 25 e. Type 22 .. .. 35 15
231 57 e. Trocaz pigeon .. 65 35
232 74 e. 50 Barn owl 85 45
233 125 e. Soft-plumaged petrel 1·25 80

See also Nos. 240/3.

1987. Europa. Architecture.

234 23 74 e. 50 multicoloured .. 90 45

1987. Historic Buildings. Multicoloured.

236 51 e. Type 24 .. .. 45 20
237 74 e. 50 Old Town Hall, Santa Cruz 65 30

25 "Maria Cristina" (mail boat).

1988. Europa. Transport and Communications.

238 25 80 e. multicoloured .. 75 40

1988. Birds (2nd series). As T 22. Mult.

240. 27 e. European robin .. 30 15
241. 60 e. Rock sparrow .. 50 25
242. 80 e. Chaffinch 80 45
243. 100 e. European sparrow hawk 90 55

26 Columbus and Funchal House

27 Child flying Kite

1988. Christopher Columbus's Houses in Madeira. Multicoloured.

244	55 e. Type **26**	40	20
245	80 e. Columbus and Porto Santo house (horiz) ..	70	35

1989. Europa. Children's Games and Toys.

246 **27**	80 e. multicoloured ..	65	30

28 Church of St. John the Evangelist

29 Silver Hatchetfish

1989. "Brasiliana 89" Stamp Exhibition, Rio de Janeiro. Madeiran Churches. Multicoloured.

248	29 e. Type **28**	20	10
249	87 e. St. Clara's Church and Convent	65	35

1989. Fishes (3rd series). Multicoloured.

250	29 e. Type **29**	25	10
251	60 e. "Pseudolepidaplois scrofa"	45	20
252	87 e. Rainbow wrasse ..	70	35
253	100 e. Scorpion fish ..	80	40

30 Zarco Post Office

31 Bananas

1990. Europa. Post Office Buildings.

254 **30**	80 e. multicoloured ..	60	30

1990. Sub-tropical Fruits. Multicoloured.

256	5 e. Type **31**	10	10
256b	10 e. Thorn apple ..	10	10
257	32 e. Avocado	25	10
257b	35 e. Mangoes	30	15
257c	38 e. Tomatoes	35	15
258	60 e. Sugar apple ..	45	20
258b	65 e. Surinam cherries ..	50	25
258c	70 e. Brazilian guavas ..	55	25
258d	85 e. Delicious fruits ..	80	35
259	100 e. Passion fruit ..	80	35
260	110 e. Papayas	90	40
261	125 e. Guava	1·10	50

32 Tunny Boat

1990. Boats. Multicoloured.

270	32 e. Type **32**	25	10
271	50 e. Desert Islands boat	50	20
272	70 e. Maneiro type of fishing boat	60	35
275	95 e. Chavelha type of fishing boat	85	40

33 Trocaz Pigeon

1991. The Trocaz Pigeon. Multicoloured.

274	35 e. Type **33**	35	15
275	35 e. Two pigeons ..	35	15
276	35 e. Pigeon on nest ..	35	15
277	35 e. Pigeon alighting on twig	35	15

Nos. 264/7 were issued together, se-tenant, forming a composite design.

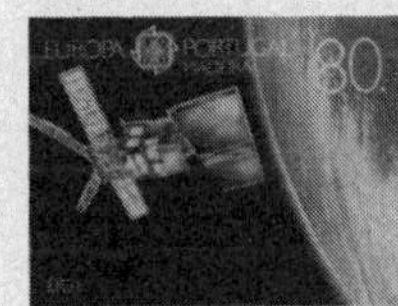

34 European Remote Sensing ("ERS1") Satellite

1991. Europa. Europe in Space.

278 **34**	80 e. multicoloured ..	65	30

35 Columbus and Funchal House

1992. Europa. 500th Anniv of Discovery of America by Columbus.

280 **35**	85 e. multicoloured ..	80	35

36 "Gaviao" (ferry)

1992. Island Boats. Multicoloured.

281	38 e. Type **36**	35	15
282	65 e. "Independencia" (catamaran ferry) ..	65	25
283	85 e. "Madeirense" (car ferry)	85	40
284	120 e. "Funchalense (freighter)	1·10	55

37 "Shadow thrown by Christa Maar" (Lourdes Castro)

39 Window of St. Francis's Convent, Funchal

38 Seals Swimming

1993. Europa. Contemporary Art.

285 **37**	90 e. multicoloured ..	70	30

1993. Mediterranean Monk Seal. Mult.

287	42 e. Type **38**	30	15
288	42 e. Seal basking ..	30	15
289	42 e. Two seals on rocks ..	30	15
290	42 e. Mother suckling young	30	15

Nos. 287/90 were issued together, se-tenant, forming a composite design.

1993. Regional Architecture. Multicoloured.

291	42 e. Type **39**	30	15
292	130 e. Window of Mercy, old hospital	1·00	45

CHARITY TAX STAMPS

The note under this heading in Portugal also applies here.

1925. Marquis de Pombal stamps of Portugal inscr. "MADEIRA".

C 142. C **73.**	15 c. grey	70	70
C 143. –	15 c. grey	70	70
C 144. C **75.**	15 c. grey	70	70

NEWSPAPER STAMP

1876. Newspaper stamp of Portugal optd. **MADEIRA.**

N69 N 17	2½ r. green	3·25	1·40

POSTAGE DUE STAMPS

1925. Marquis de Pombal stamps as Nos. C 1/3 optd. **MULTA.**

D 145. C **73.**	30 c. grey	70	70
D 146. –	30 c. grey	70	70
D 147. C **75.**	30 c. grey	70	70

Sep '94

Oct '94

Nov '94

MALAGASY REPUBLIC Pt. 6; Pt. 13

The former areas covered by Madagascar and Dependencies were renamed the Malagasy Republic within the French Community on 14 Oct., 1958.

1958. 100 centimes = 1 franc.
1976. 5 francs = 1 ariary.

1958. 10 Anniv. of Declaration of Human Rights. As T **48** of New Caledonia.

1.	10 f. brown and blue ..	65	45

1959. Tropical Flora. As T **47** of New Caledonia.

2.	6 f. green, brown and yellow	15	10
3.	25 f. multicoloured	40	15

DESIGNS—HORIZ. 6 f. "Datura". 25 f. Poinsettia.

1. Malagasy Flag and Assembly Hall.

DESIGNS — VERT. 25 f. Malagasy flag on map of Madagascar. 60 f. Natives holding French and Malagasy flags.

1959. Proclamation of Malagasy Republic and "French Community" Commem (60 f.).

4 1	20 f. red, green and purple	30	20
5 –	25 f. red, green and grey ..	40	25
6 –	60 f. multicoloured ..	75	45

2. "Chionaema pauliani" (butterfly).

3. Reafforestation.

1960.

7 –	30 c. multicoloured (post.)	15	10
8 –	40 c. brown, choc. & green	15	10
9 –	50 c. turquoise and purple	15	10
10 **2**	1 f. red, purple and black	20	15
11 –	3 f. black, red and olive ..	35	20
12 –	5 f. green, brown and red	10	10
13 –	6 f. yellow and green ..	10	10
14 –	8 f. black, green and red ..	15	10
15 –	10 f. grn., brn. & turquoise	20	10
16 –	15 f. green and brown ..	25	15
17 –	30 f. multicoloured (air) ..	75	25
18 –	40 f. brown & turquoise ..	85	30
19 –	50 f. multicoloured ..	2·50	50
20 –	100 f. multicoloured ..	4·00	85
21 –	200 f. yellow and violet ..	7·50	1·50
22 –	500 f. brown, blue & green	7·50	2·00

BUTTERFLIES—As Type **2**: 30 c. Purple-tip. 40 c. "Acraea hova". 50 c. Clouded mother-of-pearl. 3 f. "Hypolimnas dexithea". 48 × 27 mm: 50 f. "Charaxes antamboulou". 100 f. Sunset moth. 27 × 48 mm: 200 f. Tailed comet moth.

OTHER DESIGNS—As Type **2**: HORIZ. 5 f. Sisal. 8 f. Pepper. 15 f. Cotton. VERT. 6 f. Ylang ylang (vegetable). 10 f. Rice. 48½ × 27 mm: 30 f. Sugar-cane trucks. 40 f. Tobacco plantation. 500 f. Mandrare Bridge.

1960. Trees Festival.

23 **3**	20 f. brown, green & ochre	35	25

4.

5. Pres. Philibert Tsiranana.

1960. 10th Anniv. of African Technical Co-operation Commission.

24. **4.**	25 f. lake and green ..	45	35

1960.

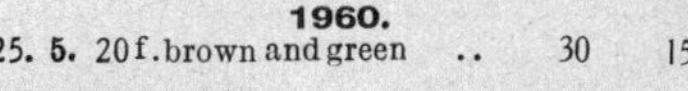

25. **5.**	20 f. brown and green ..	30	15

6. Young Athletes.

7. Pres. Tsiranana.

1960. 1st Youth Games, Tananarive.

26. **6.**	25 f. brown, chest. & blue	50	30

1960.

27. **7.**	20 f. black, red and green	25	10

1960. Independence. Surch. **+10 F FETES DE L'INDEPENDANCE.**

28. **7.**	20 f. + 10 f. blk., red & grn.	55	35

9. Ruffed Lemur.

LEMURS:—POSTAGE—Vert. as Type **9**: 2 f. Grey gentle lemur. 12 f. Mongoose-lemur. AIR (48 × 27 mm.): 65 f. Diadem sifaka. 85 f. Indris. 250 f. Verreaux's sifaka.

1961. Lemurs.

29.	–	2 f. purple & tur. (post.)	15	15
30.	9.	4 f. black, brown & myrtle	20	15
31.	–	12 f. brown and green	50	30
32.		65 f. brown, sepia and myrtle (air)	1·75	65
33.	–	85 f. black, sepia and green	2·25	1·00
34.	–	250 f. pur., blk. & turq.	6·50	2·75

10. Diesel Train.

12. Ranomafana.

11. U.N. and Malagasy Flags, and Govt. Building, Tananarive.

1962.

35.	10.	20 f. myrtle	90	20
36.	–	25 f. blue	35	15

DESIGN: 25 f. President Tsirianana Bridge.

1962. Admission into U.N.O.

37.	11.	25 f. multicoloured	35	20
38.		85 f. multicoloured	95	55

1962. Malaria Eradication. As T **43** of Mauritania.

39.	25 f. + 5 f. green	50	50

1962. Tourist Publicity.

40.	12.	10 f. purple, myrtle and blue (postage)	20	15
41.	–	30 f. pur., blue & myrtle	40	15
42.	–	50 f. blue, myrtle & pur.	60	25
43.	–	60 f. myrtle, pur. & blue	80	35
44.	–	100 f. brown, myrtle and blue (air)	1·75	95

DESIGNS—As Type **12**: 30 f. Tritriva Lake. 50 f. Foulpointe. 60 f. Fort Dauphin. VERT. (27 × 47½ mm.): 100 f. Boeing airliner over Nossi-Be.

13. G.P.O., Tamatave.

1962. Stamp Day.

45.	13.	25 f. + 5 f. brown, myrtle and blue	35	40

14. Malagasy and U.N.E.S.C.O. Emblems.

15. Hydro-electric Station.

1962. U.N.E.S.C.O. Conf. on Higher Education in Africa, Tananarive.

46.	14.	20 f. black, green and red	35	25

1962. 1st Anniv. of Union of African and Malagassy States. As T **45** of Mauritania.

47.	30 f. green	45	35

1962. Malagasy Industrialisation.

48.	15.	5 f. multicoloured	10	10
49.	–	8 f. multicoloured	15	10
50.	–	10 f. multicoloured	20	10
51.	–	15 f. brown, black & blue	35	15
52.	–	20 f. multicoloured	35	20

DESIGNS—HORIZ. 8 f. Atomic plant. 15 f. "Esso Gasikara" (tanker). 20 f. Hertzian aerials at Tananarive-Fianarantsoa. VERT. 10 f. Oilwell.

16. Globe and Factory.

1963. Int. Fair, Tamatave.

53.	16.	25 f. orange and black	30	20

1963. Freedom from Hunger. As T **51** of Mauritania.

54.	25 f. + 5 f. lake, brown & red	60	60

17. Douglas "DC-8" Airliner.

1963. Air. Malagasy Commercial Aviation.

55.	17.	500 f. blue, red and green	8·50	3·25

18. Central Post Office, Tananarive.

19. Madagascar Blue Pigeon.

1963. Stamp Day.

56.	18.	20 f. + 5 f. brn. & turq.	30	35

1963. Malagasy Birds and Orchids (8 f. to 12 f.). Multicoloured. (a) Postage as T **19**.

57.	1 f. Type **19**	60	30
58.	2 f. Blue Madagascar Coucal	60	30
59.	3 f. Madagascar Red Fody	60	30
60.	6 f. Madagascar Pygmy Kingfisher	70	30
61.	8 f. "Gastrorchis humblotii"	20	15
62.	10 f. "Eulophiella roempleriana"	30	25
63.	12 f. "Angraceum sesquipedale"	30	25

(b) Air. Horiz. (49½ × 28 mm.).

64.	40 f. Helmet Bird	2·50	45
65.	100 f. Pitta-like Ground Roller	5·50	1·00
66.	200 f. Crested Wood Ibis	12·00	3·00

20. Centenary Emblem and Map.

21. U.P.U. Monument, Berne, and Map of Malagasy.

1963. Red Cross Cent.

67.	20.	30 f. multicoloured	80	60

1963. Air. African and Malagasy Posts and Telecommunications Union. As T **56** of Mauritania.

68.	85 f. multicoloured	1·00	90

1963. Air. 2nd Anniv. of Malagasy's admission to U.P.U.

69.	21.	45 f. blue, red & turquoise	50	25
70.		85 f. blue, red and violet	90	50

22. Arms of Fianarantsoa.

23. Flame, Globe and Hands.

1963. Town Arms (1st series). Multicoloured.

71.	1 f. 50 Antsirabe	10	10
72.	5 f. Antalaha	15	10
73.	10 f. Tulear	20	10
74.	15 f. Majunga	30	15
75.	20 f. Type **22**	40	15
75a.	20 f. Manajary	25	10
76.	25 f. Tananarive	45	15
76a.	30 f. Nossi Be	35	15
77.	50 f. Diego-Suarez	85	50
77a.	90 f. Antsohihy	1·40	55

See also Nos. 174/7 and 208/9.

1963. 15th Anniv. of Declaration of Human Rights.

78.	23.	60 f. ochre, bronze & mauve	55	45

24. Met. Station, Tananarive.

1964. Air. World Meteorological Day.

79.	24.	90 f. brown, blue & grey	1·50	1·25

25. Postal Cheques and Savings Bank Building, Tananarive.

26. Scouts beside Camp-fire.

1964. Stamp Day.

80.	25.	25 f. + 5 f. brn., bl. & grn.	50	60

1964. 40th Anniv. of Malagasy Scout Movement.

81.	26.	20 f. multicoloured	55	25

27. Symbolic Bird and Globe within "Egg".

28. Statuette of Woman.

1964. "Europafrique".

82.	27.	45 f. brown and green	45	35

1964. Malagasy Art.

83.	28.	6 f. brown, blue & indigo (postage)	25	15
84.	–	30 f. brown, bistre & grn.	45	20
85.	–	100 f. brn., red & vio. (air)	1·50	95

DESIGNS: 30 f. Statuette of squatting vendor. (27 × 48½): 100 f. Statuary of peasant family, ox and calf.

1964. French, African and Malagasy Co-operation. As T **68** of Mauritania.

86.	25 f. brn., chestnut & black	40	25

29. Tree on Globe.

30. Cithern.

1964. University of Malagasy Republic.

87.	29.	65 f. black, red & green	50	25

1965. Malagasy Musical Instruments.

88.	–	3 f. brown, blue and mauve (postage)	20	10
89.	30.	6 f. sepia, purple & green	25	10
90.	–	8 f. brown, black & green	35	10
91.	–	25 f. multicoloured	90	50
92.	–	200 f. brown, orange and green (air)	4·00	2·25

DESIGNS—As Type **30**: 3 f. Kabosa (lute). 8 f. Hazolahy (sacred drum). LARGER—VERT. (35½ × 48 mm.): 25 f. "Valiha Player" (after E. Ralambo). (27 × 48 mm.): 200 f. Bara violin.

31. Foulpointe Post Office.

1965. Stamp Day.

93.	31.	20 f. brn., green & orge.	20	15

32. I.T.U. Emblem.

33. J.-J. Rabearivelo (poet).

1965. I.T.U. Cent.

94.	32.	50 f. green, blue and red	1·00	45

1965. Rabearivelo Commem.

95.	33.	40 f. brown and orange	40	25

34. Nurse weighing Baby.

1965. Air. Int. Co-operation Year.

96.	34.	50 f. black, bistre & blue	60	35
97.	–	100 f. purple, brn. & blue	1·25	60

DESIGN: 100 f. Boy and girl.

35. Pres. Tsiranana.

36. Bearer.

1965. Pres. Tsiranana's 55th Birthday.

98.	35.	20 f. multicoloured	25	15
99.		25 f. multicoloured	30	20

1965. Postal Transport.

102.	–	3 f. violet, blue & brown	30	15
103.	–	4 f. blue, brown & green	25	15
104.	36.	10 f. multicoloured	25	15
105.	–	12 f. multicoloured	30	20
106.	–	20 f. multicoloured	50	20
107.	–	25 f. multicoloured	50	20
108.	–	30 f. red, brown & blue	1·25	60
109.	–	65 f. brn., blue & violet	1·50	50

DESIGNS—HORIZ. 3 f. Early car. 4 f. Filanzane (litter). 12 f. Pirogue. 20 f. Horse-drawn mail-cart. 25 f. Bullock cart. 30 f. Early railway postal carriage. 65 f. Hydrofoil, "Porthos", Betsiboka.

37. Diseased Hands.

1966. World Leprosy Day.

110.	37.	20 f. purple, red & grn.	35	20

38. Planting Trees.

1966. Reafforestation Campaign.

111.	38.	20 f. violet, brn. & turq.	35	20

39. "Cicindelidae chaetodera andriana."

1966. Malagasy Insects. Multicoloured.

112.	1 f. Type **39**	10	10
113.	6 f. "Mantodea tisma freiji"	20	10
114.	12 f. "Cerambycini mastododera nodicollis"	45	20
115.	45 f. "Trachelophoru giraffa"	85	30

40. Madagascar 1 c. Stamp of 1903.

41. Betsileo Dance.

1966. Stamp Day.

116.	40.	25 f. bistre and red	35	25

1966. Folk Dances. Multicoloured.

117.	2 f. Bilo Sakalava dance (vert.) (postage)	15	10
118.	5 f. Type **41**	25	15
119.	30 f. Antandroy dance (vert.)	55	20
120.	200 f. Southern Malagasy dancer (air)	3·50	1·50
121.	250 f. Sakalava Net Dance	4·00	2·25

Nos. 120/1 are size 27 × 48 mm.

43. "Tree" of Emblems.

1966. O.C.A.M. Conf., Tananarive.
122. **43.** 25 f. multicoloured .. 30 15
The above was issued with "Janvier 1966" obliterated by bars, and optd. **"JUIN 1966"**.

45. U.N.E.S.C.O. Emblem.

44. Singing Anthem.

47. Harvesting Rice. **46.** Lions Emblem.

1966. National Anthem.
123. **44.** 20 f. brn., mauve & grn. 25 10

1966. 20th Anniv. of U.N.E.S.C.O.
124. **45.** 30 f. blue, bistre & red.. 35 20

1967. 50th Anniv. of Lions Int.
125. **46.** 30 f. multicoloured .. 40 20

1967. Int. Rice Year.
126. **47.** 20 f. multicoloured .. 30 15

48. Adventist Temple, Tanambao-Tamatave.

1967. Religious Buildings (1st series).
127. **48.** 3 f. ochre, blue and green 10 10
128. – 5 f. lilac, purple & green 10 10
129. – 10 f. purple, blue & grn. 25 10
BUILDINGS.—VERT. 5 f. Catholic Cathedral, Tananarive. HORIZ. 10 f. Mosque, Tamatave.
See also Nos. 148/50.

49. Raharisoa at Piano.

1967. 4th Death Anniv. of Norbert Raharisoa (composer).
130. **49.** 40 f. multicoloured .. 55 20

50. Jean Raoult's Flight of 1911.

1967. "History of Malagasy Aviation".
131. **50.** 5 f. brown, blue and green (postage) .. 35 15
132. – 45 f. black, blue & brn. 90 35
133. – 500 f. black, blue and ochre (air) .. .. 8·75 3·75
DESIGNS: 45 f. Bernard Bougault and flying-boat, 1926. (48×27 mm.): 500 f. Dagnaux-Dufert and biplane, 1927.

51. Ministry of Communications, Tananarive. **52.** Church, Torch and Map.

1967. Stamp Day.
134. **51.** 20 f. green, blue & orge. 25 15

1967. Air. 5th Anniv. of U.A.M.P.T. As T **101** of Mauritania.
135. 100 f. mauve, bistre & red 1·25 60

1967. Cent. of Malagasy Lutheran Church.
136. **52.** 20 f. multicoloured .. 30 15

53. Map and Decade Emblem. **54.** Woman's Face and Scales of Justice.

1967. Int. Hydrological Decade.
137. **53.** 90 f. brown, red & blue 85 45

1967. Women's Rights Commission.
138. **54.** 50 f. blue, ochre & green 50 25

55. Human Rights Emblem. **56.** Congress and W.H.O. Emblems.

1968. Human Rights Year.
139. **55.** 50 f. red, green and blk. 40 25

1968. Air. 20th Anniv. of W.H.O. and Int. Medical Sciences Congress, Tananarive.
140. **56.** 200 f. red, blue & ochre 2·00 1·25

57. International Airport, Tananarive-Ivato.

1968. Air. Stamp Day.
141. **57.** 500 f. blue, green & brn. 4·25 3·00

1968. Nos. 33 and 38 surch.
142. **11.** 20 f. on 85 f. (postage) 40 30
143. – 20 f. on 85 f. (No. 33)(air) 50 30

59. "Industry and Construction". **61.** Isotry Protestant Church, Fitiavana, Tananarive.

60. Church and Open Bible.

1968. Five-Year Plan. (1st issue).
144. **59.** 10 f. plum, red & green 15 10
145. – 20 f. black, red & green 20 15
146. – 40 f. bl., brn. & ultram. 85 35
DESIGNS—VERT. 20 f. "Agriculture". HORIZ. 40 f. "Transport".
See also Nos. 156/7.

1968. 150th Anniv. of Christianity in Madagascar.
147. **60.** 20 f. multicoloured .. 25 10

1968. Religious Buildings (2nd series).
148. **61.** 4 f. brown, green & red 10 10
149. – 12 f. brown, blue & violet 20 10
150. – 50 f. indigo, blue & grn. 45 25
DESIGNS: 12 f. Catholic Cathedral, Fianarantsoa. 50 f. Aga Khan Mosque, Tananarive.

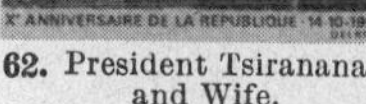

62. President Tsiranana and Wife. **63.** Cornucopia, Coins and Map.

1968. 10th Anniv. of Republic.
151. **62.** 20 f. brown, red & yell. 20 10
152. 30 f. brown, red and blue 25 15

1968. 50th Anniv. of Malagasy Savings Bank.
154. **63.** 20 f. multicoloured .. 25 10

64. "Dance of the Whirlwind".

1968. Air.
155. **64.** 100 f. multicoloured .. 1·10 65

65. Malagasy Family.

1968. Five Year Plan (2nd issue).
156. **65.** 15 f. red, yellow & blue 15 10
157. – 45 f. multicoloured .. 40 25
DESIGN—VERT. 45 f. Allegory of "Achievement".

1968. Air. "Philexafrique" Stamp Exn., Abidjan (1969) (1st issue). As T **113a** of Mauritania.
158. 100 f. multicoloured .. 1·75 80
DESIGN: 100 f. "Young Woman sealing a Letter". (J. B. Santerre.)

1969. Air. "Philexafrique" Stamp Exn., Abidjan, Ivory Coast (2nd issue). As T **114a** of Mauritania.
159. 50 f. red, green and drab 1·00 90
DESIGN: 50 f. Malagasy Arms, map and Madagascar stamp of 1946.

68. "Queen Adelaide receiving Malagasy Mission, London" (1836–37).

1969.
160. **68.** 250 f. multicoloured .. 3·00 2·50

69. Hand with Spanner, Cogwheels and I.L.O. Emblem.

1969. 50th Anniv. of I.L.O.
161. **69.** 20 f. multicoloured .. 25 15

70. Post and Telecommunications Building, Tananarive.

1969. Stamp Day.
162. **70.** 30 f. multicoloured .. 35 20

71. Map, Steering Wheel and Vehicles. **72.** President Tsiranana making Speech.

1969. 20th Anniv. of Malagasy Motor Club.
163. **71.** 65 f. multicoloured .. 60 35

1969. 10th Anniv. of President Tsiranana's Assumption of Office.
164. **72.** 20 f. multicoloured .. 20 10

73. Bananas. **74.** Start of Race and Olympic Flame.

1969. Fruits.
165. **73.** 5 f. green, brown & blue 15 10
166. – 15 f. red, myrtle & green 30 10
DESIGN: 15 f. Lychees.

1969. Olympic Games, Mexico (1968).
167. **74.** 15 f. brown, red & green 25 20

75. "Malagasy Seashore, East Coast" (A. Razafinjohany).

1969. Air. Paintings by Malagasy Artists. Multicoloured.
168. 100 f. Type **75** .. .. 1·25 80
169. 150 f. "Sunset on the High Plateaux (H. Ratovo).. 2·50 1·40

76. Imerino House, High Plateaux. **77.** Ambalavao Arms.

1969. Malagasy Traditional Dwellings (1st series).
170. – 20 f. red, blue and grn. 20 10
171. – 20 f. brn., red and blue 20 10
172. **76.** 40 f. red, blue & indigo 40 20
173. – 60 f. purple, grn. & blue 60 25
HOUSES—HORIZ. 20 f. (No. 170), Tsimihety hut, East Coast. 60 f. Betsimisaraka dwellings, East Coast. VERT. 20 f. (No. 171), Betsileo house, High Plateaux.
See also Nos. 205/6.

1970. Town Arms (2nd series). Multicoloured.
174. 10 f. Type **77** 20 10
175. 25 f. Morondava 35 15
176. 25 f. Ambatondrazaka .. 35 15
177. 80 f. Tamatave 90 35
See also Nos. 208/9.

78. Agate. **80.** U.N. Emblem and Symbols.

1970. Semi-precious Stones. Multicoloured.
178. 5 f. Type **78** 55 20
179. 20 f. Ammonite .. .. 1·75 45

1970. New U.P.U. Headquarters Building, Berne. As T **81** of New Caledonia.
180. 20 f. blue, brn. & mauve.. 30 20

1970. 25th Anniv. of United Nations.
181. **80.** 50 f. black, blue & orge 40 25

81. Astronaut and Module on Moon.

1970. Air. 1st Anniv. of "Apollo 11" Moon-landing.
182. **81.** 75 f. green, slate and blue. 85 40

82. Malagasy Fruits.

1970.
183. **82.** 20 f. multicoloured .. 30 15

83. "Volute delessertiana".

1970. Sea-shells (1st series). Multicoloured.
184. 5 f. Type **83** 25 15
185. 10 f. "Murex tribulus" .. 35 15
186. 20 f. "Spondylus" .. 70 20

84. Aye-aye.

1970. Int. Nature Conservation Conference, Tananarive.
187. **84.** 20 f. multicoloured .. 40 30

85. Boeing "737" in Flight.

1970. Air.
188. **85.** 200 f. red, green & blue 2·40 1·25

86. Pres. Tsiranana. 87. Calcite.

1970. Pres. Tsiranana's 60th Birthday.
189. **86.** 30 f. brown and green.. 30 15

1971. Minerals. Multicoloured.
190. 12 f. Type **87** 75 20
191. 15 f. Quartz .. .. 1·10 35

88. Soap Works, Tananarive.

1971. Malagasy Industries.
192. **88.** 5 f. multicoloured .. 15 10
193. – 15 f. black, brown & blue 25 10
194. – 50 f. multicoloured .. 55 15
DESIGNS: 15 f. Chrome works, Comina-Andriamena. 50 f. Textile complex, Sotema-Majunga.

89. Globe and Emblems.

1971. Council Meeting of Common Market Countries with African and Malagasy Associated States, Tananarive.
195. **89.** 5 f. multicoloured .. 15 15

90. Rural Mobile Post Office. **91.** Gen. De Gaulle.

1971. Stamp Day.
196. **90.** 25 f. multicoloured .. 35 15

1971. Death (1970) of Gen. Charles de Gaulle.
197 **91** 30 f. black, red and blue 70 35

92. Palm Beach Hotel, Nossi-Be. **93.** Forestry Emblem.

1971. Malagasy Hotels.
198. **92.** 25 f. multicoloured .. 30 20
199. – 65 f. brn., blue & green 60 30
DESIGN: 65 f. Hilton Hotel, Tananarive.

1971. Forest Preservation Campaign.
200. **93.** 3 f. multicoloured .. 15 10

94. Jean Ralaimongo. **96.** Vezo Dwellings, South-east Coast.

1971. Air. Malagasy Celebrities.
201. **94.** 25 f. brn., red & orange 30 15
202. – 65 f. brn., myrtle & grn. 40 25
203. – 100 f. brown, ultram. and blue 90 40
CELEBRITIES: 65 f. Albert Sylla. 100 f. Joseph Ravoahangy Andrianavalona.

1971. Air. 10th Anniv. of African and Malagasy Posts and Telecommunications Union. As T **139a** of Mauritania.
204. 100 f. U.A.M.P.T. H.Q. Brazzaville, and painting "Mpisikidy" (G. Rakotovao) .. .. 1·00 60

1971. Malagasy Traditional Dwellings (2nd series). Multicoloured.
205. 5 f. Type **96** 15 10
206. 10 f. Antandroy hut, South coast 20 10

97. "Children and Cattle in Meadow" (G. Rasoaharijaona).

1971. 25th Anniv. of U.N.I.C.E.F.
207. **97.** 50 f. multicoloured .. 65 30

1972. Town Arms (3rd series). As T **77.** Multicoloured.
208. 1 f. Maintirano Arms .. 10 10
209. 25 f. Fenerive-Est.. .. 35 20

99. Cable-laying train.

1972. Co-axial Cable Link, Tananarive-Tamatave.
210. **99.** 45 f. brn., grn. and red 1·40 80

100. Telecommunications Station.

1972. Inauguration of Philibert Tsiranana Satellite Communications Station.
211. **100.** 85. f. multicoloured .. 75 45

101. Pres. Tsiranana and Voters. **102.** "Moped" Postman.

1972. Presidential Elections
212. **101.** 25 f. multicoloured .. 40 35

1972. Stamp Day.
213. **102.** 10 f. multicoloured .. 40 20

1972. De Gaulle Memorial. No. 197 surch. **MEMORIAL + 20F.**
214. **91.** 30 f. + 20 f. blk., red & bl. 60 60

104. Exhibition. Emblem and Stamps. **105.** Road and Monument.

1972. 2nd Nat. Stamp Exn., Antanarive.
215. **104.** 25 f. multicoloured .. 25 20
216. 40 f. multicoloured .. 40 25
217. 100 f. multicoloured .. 90 55

1972. Opening of Andapa-Sambava Highway.
219. **105.** 50 f. multicoloured .. 35 25

106. Petroleum Refinery, Tamatave. **107.** R. Rakotobe.

1972. Malagasy Economic Development.
220. **106.** 2 f. blue, grn. & yell... 20 10
221. – 100 f. multicoloured .. 2·40 40
DESIGN: 100 f. "3600 CV" railway locomotive.

1972. Air. 1st Death Anniv. of Rene Rakotobe (poet).
222. **107.** 40 f. brn., purple & orge. 40 20

108. College Buildings.

1972. 150th Anniv. of Razafindrahety College, Tananarive.
223. **108.** 10 f. purple, brn. & blue 15 10

109. Volleyball.

1972. African Volleyball Championships.
224. **109.** 12 f. blk., orge. & brn. 40 15

110. Runners breasting Tape.

1972. Air. Olympic Games, Munich. Mult.
225. 100 f. Type **110** .. .. 1·00 60
226. 200 f. Judo .. .. 1·75 90

111. Hospital Complex.

1972. Inauguration of Ravoahangy Andrianavalona Hospital.
227. **111.** 6 f. multicoloured .. 20 15

112. Mohair Goat.

1972. Air. Malagasy Wool Production.
228. **112.** 250 f. multicoloured .. 3·50 2·25

113. Ploughing with Oxen.

1972. Agricultural Expansion.
229. **113.** 25 f. multicoloured .. 25 15

114. "Virgin and Child" (15th-cent. Florentine School).

1972. Air. Christmas. Religious Paintings. Multicoloured.
230. 85 f. Type **114** 85 55
231. 150 f. "Adoration of the Magi" (A. Mantegna) (horiz.) .. .. .. 2·00 85

115. Betsimisarka Women.

1972. Traditional Costumes. Multicoloured.
232. 10 f. Type **115** 20 10
233. 15 f. Merina mother and child 30 20

116. Astronauts on Moon. 117. "Natural Produce".

1973. Air. Moon Flight of "Apollo 17".
234. **116.** 300 f. pur., brn. & grey 3·00 1·75

1973. 10th Anniv. of Malagasy Freedom from Hunger Campaign Committee.
235. **117.** 25 f. multicoloured .. 30 15

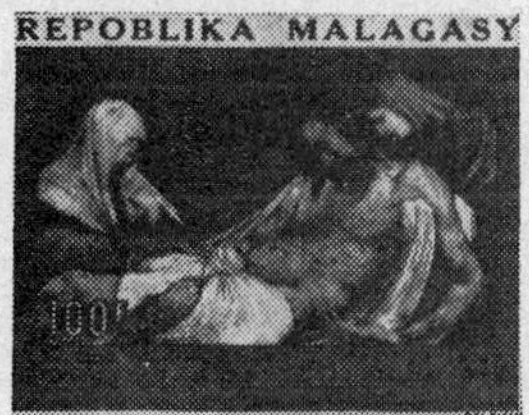

118. "The Entombment" (Grunewald).

1973. Air. Easter. Multicoloured.
236. 100 f. Type **118** .. .. 1·00 55
237. 200 f. "The Resurrection" (Grunewald) (vert.) .. 2·00 1·10

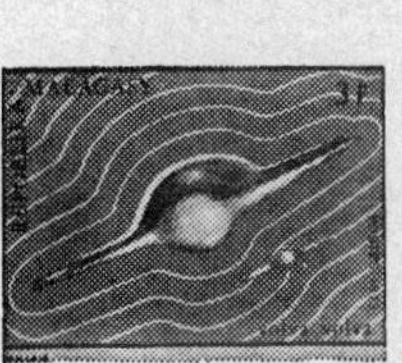

119. "Volva volva" Shell. 120. Postal Courier, Tsimandoa.

1973. Sea-shells (2nd series). Multicoloured.
238. 3 f. Type **119** 10 10
239. 10 f. "Lambis chiragra" .. 15 15
240. 15 f. "Harpa major" .. 30 20
241. 25 f. Type **119** 40 30
242. 40 f. As 15 f. 65 35
243. 50 f. As 10 f. .. .. 1·25 40

1973. Stamp Day.
244. **120.** 50 f. blue, grn. & brn. 45 20

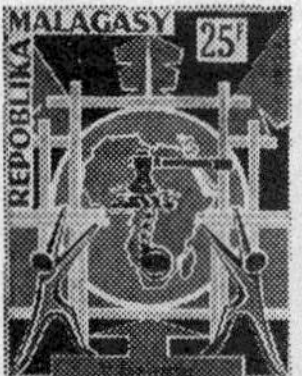

121. "Africa" within Scaffolding. 122. "Cameleon campani".

1973. 10th Anniv. of Organization of African Unity.
245. **121.** 25 f. multicoloured .. 30 15

1973. Malagasy Chameleons. Multicoloured.
246. 1 f. Type **122** 10 10
247. 5 f. "Cameleon nasutus" (male) 10 10
248. 10 f. "Cameleon nasutus" (female) 15 10
249. 40 f. As 5 f. 55 25
250. 60 f. Type **122** 85 35
251. 85 f. As 10 f. .. .. 1·25 65

123. Excursion Carriage.

1973. Air. Early Malagasy Railways. Mult.
252. 100 f. Type **123** .. .. 1·75 80
253. 150 f. Steam locomotive .. 2·50 1·25

124. "Cypripedium".

1973. Orchids. Multicoloured.
254. 10 f. Type **124** 30 15
255. 25 f. "Nepenthes pervillei" 50 20
256. 40 f. As 25 f. .. .. 1·00 35
257. 100 f. Type **124** .. .. 2·25 85

1973. Pan African Drought Relief. No. 235 surch. **SECHERESSE SOLIDARITE AFRICAINE** and value.
258. **117.** 100 f. on 25 f. mult. .. 1·10 60

126. Dish Aerial and Met. Station. 128. Greater Dwarf Lemur.

1973. Air. W.M.O. Cent.
259. **126.** 100 f. orge., bl. & blk. 1·25 65

1973. 12th Anniv. of African and Malagasy Posts and Telecommunications. As T **155a** of Mauritania.
260. 100 f. red, violet and green 90 45

1973. Malagasy Lemurs.
261. **128.** 5 f. brn., grn. & purple (postage) 30 15
262. – 25f. brn., sepia & grn. 80 35
263. – 150 f. brn., grn. & sepia (air) .. .. 2·25 1·25
264. **128.** 200 f. brn., tur. & blue 3·25 1·75
DESIGN—VERT. 25 f., 150 f. Weasel-lemur.

129. Pres. Kennedy.

1973. Air. 10th Death Anniv. of Pres. John Kennedy.
265. **129.** 300 f. multicoloured .. 2·25 1·75

130. Footballers.

1973. Air. World Cup Football Championships. West Germany.
266. **130.** 500 f. mauve, brown and light brown .. 5·50 2·50

CURRENCY. Issues from No. 267 to No. 389 have face values shown as "Fmg". This abbreviation denotes the Malagasy Franc which was introduced in 1966.

131. Copernicus, Satellite and Diagram.

1974. Air. 500th Birth Anniv. of Copernicus.
267. **131.** 250 f. bl., brn. & green 2·75 1·50

1974. No. 76a surch.
268. 25 f. on 30 f. multicoloured 25 15

133. Agricultural Training. 135. Family and House.

134. Male Player, and Hummingbird on Hibiscus.

1974. 25th World Scouting Conference, Nairobi, Kenya.
269. **133.** 4 f. grey, blue & green (postage) 10 10
270. – 15 f. pur., grn. & blue 20 15
271. – 100 f. ochre, red & blue (air) 80 45
272. – 300 f. brn., bl. & blk... 2·75 1·50
DESIGNS—VERT. 15 f. Building construction. HORIZ. 100 f. First Aid training. 300 f. Fishing.

1974. Air. Asia, Africa and Latin America Table-Tennis Championships, Peking.
273. **134.** 50 f. red, blue & brown 80 30
274. – 100 f. red, blue & vio. 1·60 70
DESIGN: 100 f. Female player, and stylised bird.

1974. World Population Year.
275. **135.** 25 f. red, orange & blue 25 10

136. Micheline Rail Car.

1974. Air. Malagasy Railway Locomotives.
276. **136.** 50 f. grn., red & brn... 65 40
277. – 85 f. red, blue & green 1·10 50
278. – 200 f. bl., light bl. & brown .. .. 2·75 1·25
DESIGNS: 85 f. Track-inspection trolley. 200 f. Garratt steam locomotive.

137. U.P.U. Emblem and Letters.

1974. Air. Centenary of U.P.U.
279. **137.** 250 f. red, bl. & violet 1·75 1·40

138. Rainibetsimisaraka.

1974. Rainibetsimisaraka Commemoration.
280. **138.** 25 f. multicoloured .. 35 20

1974. Air. West Germany's Victory in World Cup Football Championships. No. 266 optd. **R.F.A. 2 HOLLANDE 1.**
281. **130.** 500 f. mauve, brown & light brown .. .. 4·75 2·50

140. "Apollo" and "Soyuz" spacecraft.

1974. Air. Soviet-U.S. Space Co-operation.
282. **140.** 150 f. orge., grn. & blue 1·10 60
283. – 250 f. grn., bl. & brown 2·00 1·00
DESIGN: No. 283, As Type **140** but different view.

141. Marble Slabs. 143. Faces and Maps.

1974. Marble Industry. Multicoloured.
284. 4 f. Type **141** 25 15
285. 25 f. Quarrying 75 25

1974. Air. Universal Postal Union. Cent. (2nd issue). No. 279 optd. **100 ANS COLLABORATION INTERNATIONALE.**
286. **137.** 250 f. red, blue & violet 1·40 1·00

1974. Europafrique.
287. **143.** 150 f. brn., red & orge. 1·40 70

144. "Food in Hand".

1974. "Freedom from Hunger".
288. **144.** 80 f. bl., brn. & grey .. 65 35

145. "Coton". 146. Malagasy People.

1974. Malagasy Dogs. Multicoloured.
289. 50 f. Type **145** .. .. 1·40 45
290. 100 f. Hunting Dog .. 2·00 1·10

1974. Founding of "Fokonolona" Commune.
291. **146.** 5 f. multicoloured .. 15 10
292. 10 f. multicoloured .. 15 10
293. 20 f. multicoloured .. 20 10
294. 60 f. multicoloured .. 60 30

147. "Discovering Talent".

1974. National Development Council.
295. **147.** 25 f. multicoloured .. 20 10
296. 35 f. multicoloured .. 30 15

148. "Adoration of the Magi" (David). 149. Malagasy Girl and Rose.

1974. Air. Christmas. Multicoloured.
297. 200 f. Type **148** .. .. 1·75 95
298. 300 f. "Virgin of the Cherries and Child" (Metzys).. .. .. 3·00 1·25

1975. International Women's Year.
299. **149.** 100 f. brn., orge. & grn. 85 40

150. Colonel Richard Ratsimandrava (Head of Government).

1975.

300. **150.** 15 f. brn., blk. & yell. 15 10
301. 25 f. brn., blk. & blue 20 15
302. 100 f. brn., blk. & grn. 80 35

151. Sofia Bridge.

1975.

303. **151.** 45 f. multicoloured .. 50 20

152. U.N. Emblem and Part of Globe.

1975. Air. 30th Anniv. of U.N. Charter.

304. **152.** 300 f. multicoloured .. 2·25 1·25

153. De Grasse (after Mauzaisse) and " Randolph ".

1975. Bicentenary of American Revolution. (1st issue). Multicoloured.

305. 40 f. Type **153** (postage) 55 25
306. 50 f. Lafayette, " Lexington " and H.M.S. " Edward " .. 65 30
307. 100 f. D'Estaing and " Languedoc " (air). .. 1·25 50
308. 200 f. Paul Jones, " Bonhomme Richard " and H.M.S. " Serapis " 2·25 1·10
309. 300 f. Benjamin Franklin, " Millern " and " Montgomery " .. .. 3·25 1·60

154. " Euphorbia viguieri ".

1975. Malagasy Flora. Multicoloured.

311. 15 f. Type **154** (postage) .. 25 15
312. 25 f. " Hibiscus rosesinensis " 40 20
313. 30 f. " Plumeria rubra acutitolia " 55 20
314. 40 f. " Pachypodium rosulatum " .. .. 1·00 30
315. 85 f. " Turraea sericea " (air) .. .. .. 1·75 1·00

1975. Air. "Apollo – Soyuz" Space Link Nos. 282/3 optd **JONCTION 17 JUILLET 1975.**

316. **140.** 150 f. orge., grn. & blue 1·00 60
317. – 250f. grn., blue & brn. 2·00 1·00

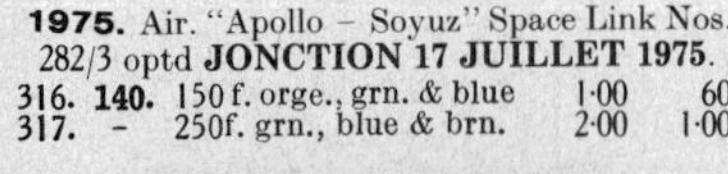

156. Temple Frieze.

1975. Air. " Save Borobudur Temple " (in Indonesia) Campaign.

318. **156.** 50 f. red, orange & blue 1·00 50

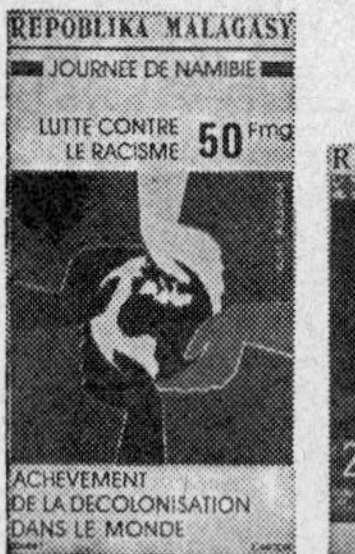

157. " Racial Unity ". **159.** Lily Waterfall.

158. Pryer's Woodpecker.

1975. Namibia Day.

319. **157.** 50 f. multicoloured .. 45 20

1975. International Exposition, Okinawa. Fauna. Multicoloured.

320. 25 f. Type **158** (postage) .. 2·00 35
321. 40 f. Ryukyu rabbit .. 50 20
322. 50 f. Toad 70 30
323. 75 f. Tortoise .. .. 1·10 40
324. 125 f. Sika deer (air) .. 1·50 55

1975. Lily Waterfall. Multicoloured.

326. 25 f. Type **159** 40 15
327. 40 f. Lily Waterfall (distant view) 60 15

160. Hurdling.

1975. Air. " Pre-Olympic Year ". Olympic Games, Montreal (1976). Multicoloured.

328. 75 f. Type **160** 60 35
329 200 f. Weightlifting (vert.) 1·50 75

161. Bobsleigh " Fours ".

1975. Winter Olympic Games, Innsbruck. Multicoloured.

330. 75 f. Type **161** (postage) .. 50 25
331. 100 f. Ski-jumping .. 80 35
332. 140 f. Speed-skating .. 1·25 50
333. 200 f. Cross-country skiing (air) .. .. .. 1·75 75
334. 245 f. Downhill skiing .. 2·00 90

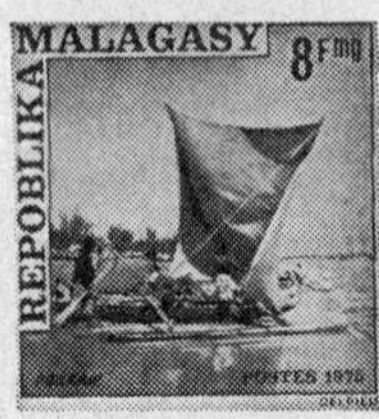

162. Pirogue.

1975. Malagasy Sailing-vessels. Mult.

336. 8 f. Type **162** 15 15
337. 45 f. Malagasy schooner .. 60 25

163. Canoeing.

1976. Olympic Games, Montreal. Mult.

338. 40 f. Type **163** (postage) .. 25 15
339. 50 f. Sprinting and hurdling 35 20
340. 100 f. Putting the shot, and long-jumping (air) .. 65 35
341. 200 f. Gymnastics-horse and parallel bars .. .. 1·40 75
342. 300 f. Trampoline-jumping and high-diving .. .. 2·00 1·00

164. " Apollo 14 " Lunar Module and Flight Badge.

1976. Air. 5th Anniv. of "Apollo 14" Mission.

344. **164.** 150 f. blue, red & grn. 1·25 65

1976. Air. 5th Anniv. of "Apollo 14" Mission. No. 344 optd. **5e Anniversaire de la mission APOLLO XIV.**

345. **164.** 150 f. blue, red & grn. 1·25 75

166. " Graf Zeppelin " over Fujiyama.

1976. 75th Anniv. of Zeppelin. Mult.

346. 40 f. Type **166** (postage) .. 35 15
347. 50 f. Zeppelin over Rio de Janeiro 40 15
348. 75 f. Zeppelin over New York 80 25
349. 100 f. Zeppelin over Sphinx and Pyramids 95 35
350. 200 f. Zeppelin over Berlin (air) .. .. .. 2·00 75
351. 300 f. Zeppelin over London 3·00 1·00

167. " Prevention of Blindness ".

1976. World Health Day.

353. **167.** 100 f. multicoloured .. 1·25 55

168. Aragonite.

1976. Minerals and Fossils. Multicoloured.

354. 25 f. Type **168** 50 15
355. 50 f. Fossilised wood .. 85 30
356. 150 f. Celestyte .. .. 2·75 1·10

169. Alexander Graham Bell and Early Telephone.

1976. Telephone Centenary. Multicoloured.

357. 25 f. Type **169** 15 10
358. 50 f. Cable maintenance, 1911 .. .. .. 30 15
359. 100 f. Telephone operator and switchboard, 1895 .. 60 25
360. 200 f. "Emile Baudot" cable ship .. .. 1·75 70
361. 300 f. Man with radio-telephone .. .. .. 2·00 80

170. Children reading Book.

1976. Children's Books Promotion. Multicoloured.

363. 10 f. Type **170** 15 10
364. 25 f. Children reading book (vert.) 35 15

1976. Medal winners, Winter Olympic Games, Innsbruck. Nos. 330/4 optd. **VAINQUEUR** and medal winner.

365. 75 f. Type **161** (postage) .. 50 25
366. 100 f. Ski-jumping .. 80 40
367. 140 f. Skating .. .. 1·25 50
368. 200 f. Cross-country skiing (air) .. .. .. 1·40 75
369. 245 f. Downhill skiing .. 1·90 1·00

OPTS: 75 f. **ALLEMAGNE FEDERALE.** 100 f. **KARL SCHNABL, AUTRICHE.** 140 f. **SHEILA YOUNG, ETATS-UNIS.** 200 f. **IVAR FORMO, NORVEGE.** 245 f. **ROSI MITTERMAIER, ALLEMAGNE DE L'OUEST.**

The subject depicted on No. 367 is speed-skating, an event in which the gold medal was won by J. E. Storholt, Norway.

1976. Bicent of American Revolution. (2nd issue). Nos. 305/9 optd. **"4 JUILLET 1776-1976".**

371. **153.** 40 f. multicoloured (postage) 35 25
372. – 50 f. multicoloured .. 40 30
373. – 100 f. multicoloured (air) 75 50
374. – 200 f. multicoloured .. 1·50 85
375. – 300 f. multicoloured .. 2·25 1·25

173. Descent Trajectory.

1976. " Viking " Landing on Mars. Mult.

377. 75 f. Type **173** 40 20
378. 100 f. " Viking " landing module separation .. 60 25
379. 200 f. " Viking " on Martian surface .. .. .. 1·25 55
380. 300 f. " Viking " orbiting Mars .. .. .. 2·00 80

174. Rainandriampandry. **175.** Doves over Globe.

1976. 30th Anniv. of Treaties signed by Rainandriamampandry (Foreign Minister).

382. **174.** 25 f. multicoloured .. 30 20

1976. Indian Ocean – " Zone of Peace ". Multicoloured.

383. 60 f. Type **175** 35 20
384. 160 f. Doves flying across Indian Ocean (horiz.) .. 1·10 55

1976. Olympic Games Medal – winners. Nos. 338/342 optd. with names of two winners on each stamp.

385. **163.** 40 f. multicoloured (postage) 25 15
386. – 50 f. multicoloured .. 35 25
387. – 100 f. multicoloured (air) 70 40
388. – 200 f. multicoloured .. 1·40 65
389. – 300 f. multicoloured .. 2·00 1·00

OVERPRINTS: 40 f. **V. DIBA, A. ROGOV.** 50 f. **H. CRAWFORD, J. SCHALLER.** 100 f. **U. BEYER, A. ROBINSON.** 200 f. **N. COMANECI, N. ANDRIANOV,** 300 f. **K. DIBIASI, E. VAYTSEKHOVSKAIA.**

177. Malagasy Arms.

1976. 1st Anniv. of Malagasy Democratic Republic.
391. **177.** 25 f. multicoloured .. 20 10

178. Rabezavana (Independence Movement leader).

1977. National Heroes. Multicoloured.
392. 25 f. Type **178** 20 10
393. 25 f. Lt. Albert Randriamaromanana .. 20 10
394. 25 f. Ny Avana Ramanantoanina (politician) .. 20 10
395. 100 f. Fasam-Pirenena National Mausoleum, Tananarive (horiz.) .. 75 40

179. Family.

1977. World Health Day.
396. **179.** 5 f. multicoloured .. 15 10

180. Medical School, Antananarivo.

1977. 80th Anniv. of Medical School Antananarivo.
397. **180.** 250 f. multicoloured .. 1·75 95

181. Rural Post Van.

1977. Rural Mail.
398. **181.** 35 f. multicoloured .. 30 15

182. Morse Key and Man with Headphones.

1977. 90th Anniv. of Antananarivo–Tamatave Telegraph.
399. **182.** 15 f. multicoloured .. 15 10

183. Academy Emblem.

1977. 75th Anniv. of Malagasy Academy.
400. **183.** 10 f. multicoloured .. 15 10

184. Lenin and Russian Flag.

1977. 60th Anniv. of Russian Revolution.
401. **184.** 25 f. multicoloured .. 15 10

185. Raoul Follereau.

1978. 25th Anniv. of World Leprosy Day.
402. **185.** 5 f. multicoloured .. 20 10

186. Microwave Antenna.

187. " Co-operation ".

1978. World Telecommunications Day.
403. **186.** 20 f. multicoloured .. 15 10

1978. Anti-Apartheid Year.
404. **187.** 60 f. red, blk. & yell... 40 25

188. Children with Instruments of Revolution.

189. Tractor, Factory and Labourers.

1978. " Youth—Pillar of the Revolution ".
405. **188.** 25 f. multicoloured .. 75 45

1978. Socialist Co-operatives.
406. **189.** 25 f. multicoloured .. 15 10

190. Women at Work.

191. Children with Books, Instruments and Fruit.

1979. " Women, Pillar of the Revolution ".
407. **190.** 40 f. multicoloured .. 25 15

1979. International Year of the Child.
408. **191.** 10 f. multicoloured .. 20 10

192. Ring-tailed Lemur.

193. J. V. S. Razakandraina.

1979. Animals. Multicoloured.
409. 25 f. Type **192** (postage) .. 25 15
410. 125 f. Black lemur .. 1·10 30
411. 1000 f. Malagasy civet .. 8·00 2·25
412. 20 f. Tortoise (air).. .. 20 20
413. 95 f. Black lemur (different) .. .. .. 1·00 40

1979. J. V. S. Razakandraina (poet) Commem.
414. **193.** 25 f. multicoloured .. 15 10

194. " Centella asiatica ".

1979. Medicinal Plant.
415. **194.** 25 f. multicoloured .. 15 10

195. Map of Malagasy and Ste. Marie Telecommunications Station.

1979. Telecommunications.
416. **195.** 25 f. multicoloured .. 20 10

196. Post Office, Antsirabe.

1979. Stamp Day.
417. **196.** 500 f. multicoloured .. 2·75 1·10

197. Palestinians with Flag.

1979. Air. Palestinian Solidarity.
418. **197.** 60 f. multicoloured .. 50 20

198. "Concorde" and Map of Africa.

1979. 20th Anniv. of ASECNA (African Air Safety Organization).
419. **198.** 50 f. multicoloured .. 60 20

199. Lenin addressing Meeting.

1980. 110th Birth Anniv. of Lenin.
420. **199.** 25 f. multicoloured .. 20 10

200. Taxi-Bus.

201. Map illuminated by Sun.

1980. 5th Anniv. of Socialist Revolution.
421. **200.** 30 f. multicoloured .. 20 10

1980. 20th Anniv. of Independence.
422. **201.** 75 f. multicoloured .. 50 30

202. Military Parade.

1980. 20th Anniv. of Army.
423. **202.** 50 f. multicoloured .. 35 15

203. Joseph Raseta.

1980. Dr. Joseph Raseta Commemoration.
424. **203.** 30 f. multicoloured .. 20 10

204. Anatirova Temple.

1980. Anatirova Temple Centenary.
425. **204.** 30 f. multicoloured .. 20 10

205. Boxing.

1980. Olympic Games, Moscow. Multicoloured.
426. 30 f. Hurdling 20 10
427. 75 f. Type **205** 45 25
428. 250 f. Judo .. .. 1·50 75
429. 500 f. Swimming .. .. 2·75 1·50

206. Emblem, Map and Sun.

1980. 5th Anniv. of Malagasy Democratic Republic.
430. **206.** 30 f. multicoloured .. 20 10

207. Skier.

1981. Winter Olympic Games, Lake Placid (1980).

431. 207. 175 f. multicoloured .. 1·10 55

208. " Angraecum leonis ".

209. Handicapped Student.

1981. Flowers. Multicoloured.

432. 5 f. Type 208 .. .. 10 10
433. 80 f. " Angraecum ramosum " 60 25
434. 170 f. " Angraecum sesquipedale " .. .. 1·25 55

1981. International Year of Disabled People. Multicoloured.

435. 25 f. Type 209 .. .. 20 10
436. 80 f. Disabled carpenter .. 55 25

210. Ribbons forming Caduceus, I.T.U. and W.H.O. Emblems.

1981. World Telecommunications Day.

437. 210. 15 f. blue, blk. and yell. 15 10
438. 45 f. multicoloured .. 35 15

211. Valentina Tereshkova (first woman in space).

1981. Space Achievements. Multicoloured.

439. 30 f. Type 211 .. .. 15 10
440. 80 f. Astronaut on Moon .. 55 25
441. 90 f. Yuri Gagarin (first man in space) 65 30

212. Raphael-Louis Rafiringa.

1981. Raphael-Louis Rafiringa Commemoration.

442. 212. 30 f. multicoloured .. 20 10

213. Child writing Alphabet.

1981. World Literary Day.

443. 213. 30 f. multicoloured .. 20 10

214. Ploughing and Sowing.

1981. World Food Day.

444. 214. 200 f. multicoloured .. 1·25 60

215. Magistrates' Oath.

1981. Renewal of Magistrates' Oath.

445. 215. 30 f. mauve and black 20 10

216. " Dove ".

1981. Birth Centenary of Pablo Picasso.

446. 216. 80 f. multicoloured .. 60 25

217. U.P.U. Emblem and Malagasy Stamps.

1981. 20th Anniv. of Admission to U.P.U.

447. 217. 5 f. multicoloured .. 10 10
448. 30 f. multicoloured .. 20 10

218. Stamps forming Map of Malagasy.

1981. Stamp Day.

449. 218. 90 f. multicoloured .. 65 30

219. Hook-billed Vanga.

1982. Birds. Multicoloured.

450. 25 f. Type 219 .. .. 75 30
451. 30 f. Courol 75 30
452. 200 f. Madagascar Fish Eagle (vert.) .. .. 4·50 1·90

220. Vaccination.

221. Jeannettee Mpihira.

1982. Centenary of Discovery of Tubercule Bacillus.

453. 220. 30 f. multicoloured .. 30 15

1982. Jeannette Mpihira Commemoration.

454. 221. 30 f. multicoloured .. 20 10

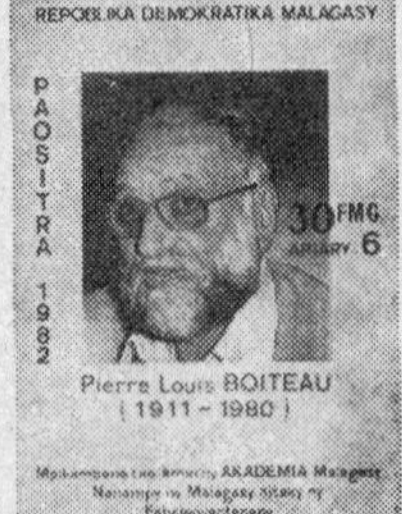

222. Womans' Head formed from Map of Africa.

223. Pierre Louis Boiteau.

1982. Air. 20th Anniv. of Panafrican Women's Organization.

455. 222. 80 f. multicoloured .. 60 30

1982. Pierre Louis Boiteau Commemoration.

456. 223. 30 f. multicoloured .. 20 15

224. Andekaleka Dam.

1982. Air. Andekaleka Hydro-electric Complex.

457. 224. 80 f. multicoloured .. 60 30

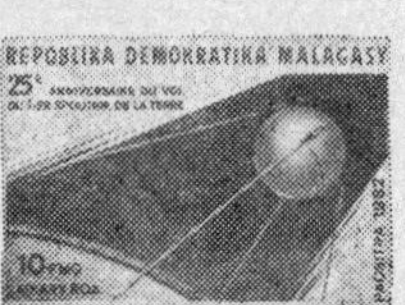

225. "Sputnik I".

1982. 25th Anniv. of First Artificial Satellite. Multicoloured.

458. 10 f. Type 225 .. .. 10 10
459. 80 f. Yuri Gagarin .. 60 30
460. 100 f. "Soyuz-Salyut" space station 75 35

226. Heading Ball.

1982. World Cup Football Championship, Spain. Multicoloured.

461. 30 f. Type 226 .. .. 20 10
462. 40 f. Running with ball .. 30 15
463. 80 f. Tackle 60 30

227. Ploughing, Sowing and F.A.O. Emblem.

1982. World Food Day.

465. 227. 80 f. multicoloured .. 50 30

228. Bar Scene.

1982. 150th Anniv. of Edouard Manet (artist). Multicoloured.

466. 5 f. Type 228 .. .. 15 15
467. 30 f. Woman in white .. 25 10
468. 170 f. Man with pipe .. 1·40 65

229. " Lutianus sebae ".

1982. Fishes. Multicoloured.

470. 5 f. Type 229 .. .. 15 15
471. 20 f. " Istiophorus platypterus " 20 15
472. 30 f. " Pterois volitans " .. 25 15
473. 50 f. " Thunnus albacares " 40 15
474. 200 f. " Epinephelus fasciatus " .. .. .. 1·75 65

230. Fort Mahavelona.

1982. Landscapes. Multicoloured.

476. 10 f. Type 230 (postage) .. 10 10
477. 30 f. Ramena coast .. 20 10
478. 400 f. Jacarandas in flower (air) .. .. .. 2·75 1·50

231. Flags of Russia and Malagasy, Clasped Hands and Tractors.

1982. 60th Anniv. of U.S.S.R. Mult.

479. 10 f. Type 231 .. .. 10 10
480. 15 f. Flags, clasped hands and radio antenna .. 10 10
481. 30 f. Map of Russia, Kremlin and Lenin 15 10
482. 150 f. Flags, clasped hands, statue and arms of Malagasy .. .. 1·00 45

232. Television, Drums, Envelope and Telephone.

1983. World Communications Year. Mult.

483. 30 f. Type 232 .. .. 15 10
484. 80 f. Stylized figures holding cogwheel 55 25

MINIMUM PRICE

The minimum price quoted is 5p which represents a handling charge rather than a basis for valuing common stamps. For further notes about prices see introductory pages.

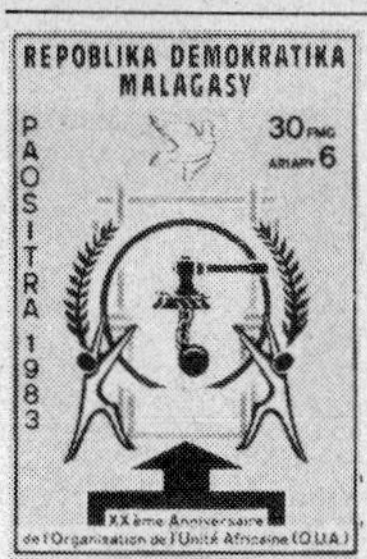

233. Axe breaking Chain on Map of Africa.

234. Henri Douzon.

1983. 20th Anniv. of Organization of African Unity.

485. **233.** 30 f. multicoloured .. 20 10

1983. Henri Douzon (lawyer) Commem.

486. **234.** 30 f. multicoloured .. 20 10

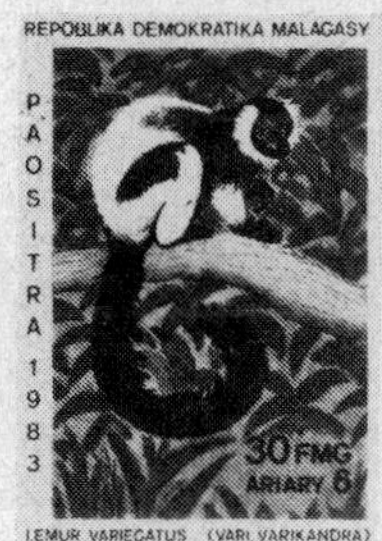

237. Ruffed Lemur.

1984. Lemurs. Multicoloured.

489. 30 f. Type **237** 35 20
490. 30 f. Verreaux's sifaka .. 35 20
491. 30 f. Lesser mouse-lemur (horiz.) 35 20
492. 30 f. Aye-aye (horiz.) .. 35 20
493. 200 f. Indri (horiz.) .. 2·00 1·10

238. Ski-jumping.

1984. Winter Olympic Games, Sarajevo. Multicoloured.

495. 20 f. Type **238** 15 10
496. 30 f. Ice-hockey 20 10
497. 30 f. Downhill skiing .. 20 10
498. 30 f. Speed skating .. 20 10
499. 200 f. Ice-dancing.. .. 1·40 70

239. Renault, 1907.

1984. Early Motor Cars. Multicoloured.

501. 15 f. Type **239** 20 10
502. 30 f. Benz, 1896 .. .. 30 15
503. 30 f. Baker, 1901 .. .. 30 15
504. 30 f. Blake, 1901 .. .. 30 15
505. 200 f. F.I.A.L., 1908 .. 2·00 75

240. Pastor Ravelojaona.

241. "Noli me Tangere".

1984. Pastor Ravelojaona (encyclopedist) Commemoration.

507. **240.** 30 f. multicoloured .. 20 15

1984. 450th Death Anniv. of Correggio. Paintings by Artist.

508. **241.** 5 f. multicoloured .. 10 10
509. 20 f. multicoloured .. 15 10
510. 30 f. multicoloured .. 25 15
511. 80 f. multicoloured .. 45 25
512. 200 f. multicoloured .. 1·40 65

242. Paris Landmarks and Emblem.

243. Football.

1984. 60th Anniv of International Chess Federation. Multicoloured.

514 5 f. Type **242** 15 15
515 20 f. Wilhelm Steinitz and stylized king 20 15
516 30 f. Vera Menchik and stylized queen 35 15
517 30 f. Anatoly Karpov and trophy 35 15
518 215 f. Nona Gaprindashvili and trophy .. .. 2·75 90

1984. Olympic Games, Los Angeles.

520. **243.** 100 f. multicoloured .. 45 30

244. "Eudaphaenura splendens".

245. Ralaimongo.

1984. Butterflies. Multicoloured.

521. 15 f. Type **244** 20 15
522. 50 f. "Acraea hova" .. 60 20
523. 50 f. "Othreis boesae" .. 60 20
524. 50 f. "Pharmocophagus antenor" 60 20
525. 200 f. "Epicausis smithii" 2·25 1·00

1984. Birth Centenary of Jean Ralaimongo (politician).

527. **245.** 50 f. multicoloured .. 30 15

246. Children in Brief-case.

247. "Disa incarnata".

1984. 25th Anniv. of Children's Rights Legislation.

528. **246.** 50 f. multicoloured .. 40 15

1984. Orchids. Multicoloured.

529. 20 f. Type **247** (postage) .. 20 10
530. 235 f. "Eulophiella roempleriana" .. .. 2·25 85
531. 50 f. "Eulophiella roempleriana" (horiz.) (air) .. 60 25
532. 50 f. "Grammangis ellisii" (horiz.) 60 25
533. 50 f. "Grammangis spectabilis" 60 25

248. U.N. Emblem and Cotton Plant.

249. "Sun Princess" (Sadio Diouf).

1984. 20th Anniv. of United Nations Conference on Commerce and Development.

535. **248.** 100 f. multicoloured .. 60 30

1984. 40th Anniv. of International Civil Aviation Organization.

536. **249.** 100 f. multicoloured .. 65 30

250. Bible, Map and Gothic Letters.

1985. 150th Anniv. of First Bible in Malagasy Language.

537. **250.** 50 f. brown, pink and black 30 15

251. Farming Scenes, Census-taker and Farmer.

252. Lap-dog.

1985. Agricultural Census.

538. **251.** 50 f. grey, black and mauve 30 15

1985. Cats and Dogs. Multicoloured.

539. 20 f. Type **252** 20 15
540. 20 f. Siamese cat 20 15
541. 50 f. Abyssinian cat (vert.) 60 20
542. 100 f. Cocker spaniel (vert.) 1·25 35
543. 235 f. Poodle .. .. 2·50 90

253. Russian Soldiers in Berlin.

1985. 40th Anniv. of Victory in Second World War.

545. 20 f. Type **253** 15 10
546. 50 f. Arms of French squadron and fighter planes 40 15
547. 100 f. Victory parade, Red Square, Moscow .. 75 30
548. 100 f. French troops entering Paris (vert.) .. 75 30

254. Parade in Stadium.

1985. 10th Anniv. of Malagasy Democratic Republic.

549. **254.** 50 f. multicoloured .. 40 15

255. Medal and Independence Obelisk.

256. Peace Dove and Stylised People.

1985. 25th Anniv. of Independence.

550. **255.** 50 f. multicoloured .. 40 15

1985. 12th World Youth and Students' Festival, Moscow.

551. **256.** 50 f. multicoloured .. 40 15

257. I.Y.Y. Emblem and Map of Madagascar.

258. Red Cross Centres and First Aid Post.

1985. International Youth Year.

552. **257.** 100 f. multicoloured .. 60 25

1985. 70th Anniv. of Malagasy Red Cross.

553. **258.** 50 f. multicoloured .. 60 25

259. "View of Sea at Saintes-Maries" (Vincent van Gogh).

260. Indira Gandhi.

1985. Impressionist Paintings. Multicoloured.

554. 20 f. Type **259**. 20 10
555. 20 f. "Rouen Cathedral in the Evening" (Claude Monet) (vert.) 15 10
556. 45 f. "Young Girls in Black" (Pierre-Auguste Renoir) (vert.) 30 20
557. 50 f. "Red Vineyard at Arles" (van Gogh) .. 30 20
558. 100 f. "Boulevard des Capucines, Paris" (Monet) 85 40

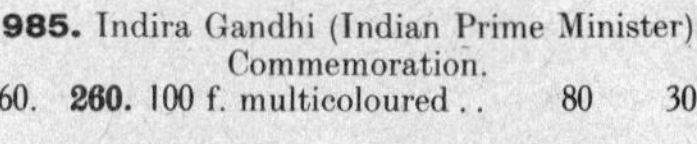

1985. Indira Gandhi (Indian Prime Minister) Commemoration.

560. **260.** 100 f. multicoloured .. 80 30

261. Figures and Dove on Globe and Flag.

262. "Aeranthes grandiflora".

1985. 40th Anniv. of U.N.O.

561. **261.** 100 f. multicoloured .. 65 25

1985. Orchids. Multicoloured.

562. 20 f. Type **262** 20 10
563. 45 f. "Angraecum magdalenae" and "Nephele oenopion" (insect) (horiz.) 35 15
564. 50 f. "Aerangis stylosa" .. 35 15
565. 100 f. "Angraecum eburneum longicalcar" and "Hippotion batschi" (insect) 80 35
566. 100 f. "Angraecum sesquipedale" and "Xanthopan morganipredicta" (insect) .. 80 35

263. Russian and Czechoslovakian Cosmonauts.

1985. Russian "Interkosmos" Space Programme. Multicoloured.

568. 20 f. Type **263** 15 10
569. 20 f. Russian and American flags and "Apollo"–"Soyuz" link 15 10
570. 50 f. Russian and Indian cosmonauts 30 15
571. 100 f. Russian and Cuban cosmonauts 50 25
572. 200 f. Russian and French cosmonauts .. .. 1·25 60

264. Emblem in "10".

265. Headquarters.

1985. 10th Anniv. of Malagasy Democratic Republic.
574. **264.** 50 f. multicoloured .. 30 15

1986. 10th Anniv. of ARO (State insurance system).
575. **265.** 50 f. yellow and brown 30 15

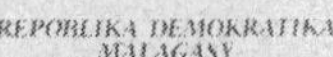

266. "David and Uriah" (Rembrandt).

268. Sombrero, Football and Player.

267. Comet.

1986. Foreign Paintings in Hermitage Museum, Leningrad. Multicoloured.
576. 20 f. Type **266** 20 10
577. 50 f. "Portrait of Old Man in Red" (Rembrandt) .. 35 20
578. 50 f. "Danae" (Rembrandt) (horiz.) .. 35 20
579. 50 f. "Marriage of Earth and Water" (Rubens) .. 35 20
580. 50 f. "Portrait of Infanta Isabella's Maid" (Rubens) 35 20

1986. Air. Appearance of Halley's Comet.
582. **267.** 150 f. multicoloured .. 1·00 50

1986. Russian Paintings in the Tretyakov Gallery, Moscow. As T **266**. Multicoloured.
583. 20 f. "Fruit and Flowers" (I. Khroutsky) (horiz.) .. 15 10
584. 50 f. "The Rooks have Returned" (A. Savrasov) 30 20
585. 50 f. "Unknown Woman (I. Kramskoi) (horiz.) .. 30 20
586. 50 f. "Aleksandr Pushkin" (O. Kiprenski) 30 20
587. 100 f. "March, 1895" (I. Levitan) (horiz.) .. 60 40

1986. World Cup Football Championship, Mexico.
589. **268.** 150 f. multicoloured .. 1·10 30

269. Child Care.

270. Jungle Cat.

1986. U.N.I.C.E.F. Child Survival Campaign.
590. **269.** 60 f. multicoloured .. 40 15

1986. Wild Cats. Multicoloured.
591. 10 f. Type **270** 20 10
592. 10 f. Wild cat 20 10
593. 60 f. Caracal 45 20
594. 60 f. Leopard cat 45 20
595. 60 f. Serval 45 20

271. Dove above Hands holding Globe.

1986. International Peace Year. Mult.
597. 60 f. Type **271** 40 15
598. 150 f. Doves above emblem and map .. .. .. 1·00 45

272. U.P.U. Emblem on Dove.

273. U.P.U. Emblem on Globe.

1986. World Post Day.
599. **272.** 60 f. multicoloured (postage) 40 15
600. 150 f. blue, black and red (air) .. .. 1·10 50

1986. Air. 25th Anniv. of Admission to U.P.U.
601. **273.** 150 f. multicoloured .. 1·10 50

274. Giant Madagascar Coucal.

1986. Birds. Multicoloured.
602. 60 f. Type **274** .. .. 1·10 40
603. 60 f. Crested Madagascar coucal .. .. .. 1·10 40
604. 60 f. Rufous vangas (vert.) 1·10 40
605. 60 f. Red-tailed vangas (vert.) .. .. 1·10 40
606. 60 f. Sicklebill .. .. 1·10 40

275. Tortoise.

1987. Endangered Animals. Multicoloured.
608 60 f. Type **275** 50 20
609 60 f. Crocodile 50 20
610 60 f. Crested wood ibis (vert) 50 20
611 60 f. Black coucal .. 50 20

276. Crowd in "40".

1987. 40th Anniv. of Anti-Colonial Uprising.
613. **276.** 60 f. brn., red & yell. 35 15
614. – 60 f. multicoloured .. 35 15
DESIGN: No. 614, Hands in broken manacles, map, rifleman and spearman.

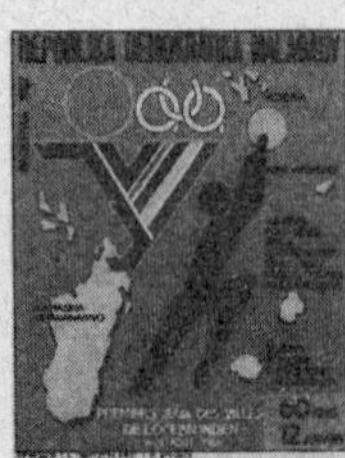
277. Emblems, Map and Pictogram.

1987. 1st Indian Ocean Towns Games.
615. **277.** 60 f. multicoloured .. 35 15
616. 150 f. multicoloured .. 1·10 35

278. "Sarimanok".

1987. The "Sarimanok" (replica of early dhow). Multicoloured.
617. 60 f. Type **278** 40 15
618. 150 f. "Sarimanok" (diff.) 1·10 35

279. Coffee Plant.

280. Rifle Shooting and Satellite.

1987. 25th Anniv. of African and Malagasy Coffee Producers Organization. Mult.
619. 60 f. Type **279** 35 15
620. 150 f. Map showing member countries .. 1·10 35

1987. Winter Olympic Games, Calgary (1988). Multicoloured.
621. 60 f. Type **280** 25 10
622. 150 f. Slalom 60 20
623. 250 f. Luge .. .. .. 1·25 40
624. 350 f. Speed skating .. 1·40 50
625. 400 f. Ice hockey .. .. 1·60 60
626. 450 f. Ice skating (pairs) .. 2·00 70

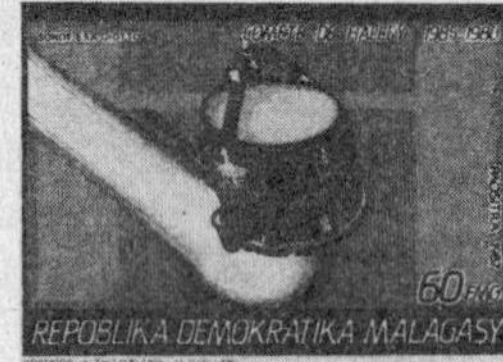
281. "Giotto" Space Probe.

1987. Appearance of Halley's Comet (1986). Space Probes. Multicoloured.
628. 60 f. Type **281** 25 10
629. 150 f. "Vega 1" 60 20
630. 250 f. "Vega 2" .. .. 1·25 40
631. 350 f. "Planet A 1" .. 1·40 50
632. 400 f. "Planet A 2" .. 1·60 60
633. 450 f. "I.C.E." .. .. 2·00 70

282. Piper "Aztec".

283. Rabearivelo.

1987. Air. 25th Anniv. of Air Madagascar. Multicoloured.
635. 60 f. Type **282** 40 20
636. 60 f. "Twin otter" .. 40 20
637. 150 f. Boeing "747" .. 1·00 40

1987. 50th Death Anniv. of Jean-Joseph Rabearivelo (poet).
638. **283.** 60 f. multicoloured .. 30 15

284. Communications Equipment Robot and Print-out Paper.

285. Emblem.

1987. National Telecommunications Research Laboratory.
639. **284.** 60 f. grn., blk. & red 30 15

1987. 150th Anniv. of Execution of Rafaravavy Rasalama (Christian martyr).
640. **285.** 60 f. black, deep blue and blue 30 15

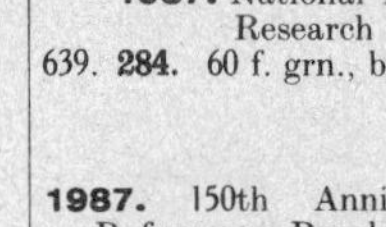

286. Hand using Key and Telegraphist.

1987. Centenary of Antananarivo–Tamatave Telegraph.
641. **286.** 60 f. multicoloured .. 30 15

287. Bartholomeu Dias and Departure from Palos, 1492.

1987. 500th Anniv. (1992) of Discovery of America by Columbus. Multicoloured.
642. 60 f. Type **287** 20 10
643. 150 f. Route around Samana Cay and Henry the Navigator 45 20
644. 250 f. Columbus and crew disembarking, 1492, and A. de Marchena 75 30
645. 350 f. Building Fort Navidad and Paolo del Pozzo Toscanelli .. 1·10 40
646. 400 f. Columbus in Barcelona, 1493, and Queen Isabella of Spain 1·25 50
647. 450 f. Columbus and "Nina" .. .. .. 1·50 50

288. Showjumping and "Harlequin" (Picasso).

1987. Olympic Games, Barcelona (1992). Multicoloured.
649. 60 f. Type **288** (postage) .. 15 10
650. 150 f. Weightlifting and Barcelona Cathedral .. 40 20
651. 250 f. Hurdling and Canaletas Fountain .. 70 30
652. 350 f. High jumping and Parc d'Attractions .. 1·00 40
653. 400 f. Gymnast on bar and church (air) .. .. 1·40 50
654. 450 f. Gymnast with ribbon and Triumphal Arch .. 1·50 50

289. Anniversary Emblem, T.V. Tower and Interhotel "Berlin".

290. Musician and Dancers.

1987. 750th Anniv. of Berlin.
656. **289.** 150 f. multicoloured .. 25 15

1987. Schools Festival.
657. **290.** 60 f. multicoloured .. 15 10

291. Madagascar Pasteur Institute and Pasteur.

1987. Centenary of Pasteur Institute, Paris.
658. **291.** 250 f. multicoloured .. 60 25

292. "After the Shipwreck" (Eugene Delacroix).

1987. Paintings in Pushkin Museum of Fine Arts, Moscow. Multicoloured.
659. 10 f. Type **292** 15 10
660. 60 f. "Jupiter and Callisto" (François Boucher) (vert.) 15 10
661. 60 f. "Still Life with Swan" (Frans Snyders) 15 10
662. 60 f. "Chalet in the Mountains" (Gustave Courbet) 15 10
663. 150 f. "At the Market" (Joachim Bueckelaer) .. 40 15

293. Emblem. **294.** Family and House on Globe.

1987. 10th Anniv. of Pan-African Telecommunications Union.
665. **293.** 250 f. multicoloured .. 40 20

1988. International Year of Shelter for the Homeless (1987). Multicoloured.
666. 80 f. Type **294** 15 10
667. 250 f. Hands forming house protecting family from rain 35 20

295. Lenin addressing Crowd.

1988. 70th Anniv. of Russian Revolution. Multicoloured.
668. 60 f. Type **295** 15 10
669. 60 f. Revolutionaries .. 15 10
670. 150 f. Lenin in crowd .. 25 15

296. Broad-nosed Gentle Lemur.

1988. Endangered Species. Multicoloured.
671. 60 f. Type **296** 15 10
672. 150 f. Diadem sifaka .. 20 15
673. 250 f. Indri 35 15
674. 350 f. Ruffed lemur .. 60 25
675. 550 f. Purple herons (horiz.) 90 70
676. 1500 f. Nossi-be chameleon (horiz.) .. .. .. 2·40 1·25

297. Ice Skating.

1988. Winter Olympic Games, Calgary. Mult.
678. 20 f. Type **297** 10 10
679. 60 f. Speed-skating .. 10 10
680. 60 f. Slalom 10 10
681. 100 f. Cross-country skiing 20 10
682. 250 f. Ice hockey 45 20

298. Dove, Axe breaking Chain and Map.

1988. 25th Anniv. of Organization of African Unity.
684. **298.** 80 f. multicoloured .. 15 10

299. Institute Building.

1988. 20th Anniv. of National Posts and Telecommunications Institute.
685. **299.** 80 f. multicoloured .. 15 10

300. College.

1988. Centenary of St. Michael's College.
686. **300.** 250 f. multicoloured .. 30 20

301. Pierre and Marie Curie in Laboratory. **302.** Emblem.

1988. 90th Anniv. of Discovery of Radium.
687. **301.** 150 f. brown & mve. 40 15

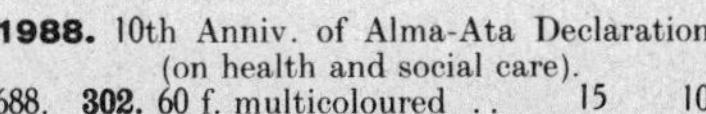
1988. 10th Anniv. of Alma-Ata Declaration (on health and social care).
688. **302.** 60 f. multicoloured .. 15 10

303. Emblem. **304.** Ring-tailed Lemurs on Island.

1988. 40th Anniv. of W.H.O.
689. **303.** 150 f. brown, blue and black 20 15

1988. 50th Anniv. of Tsimbazaza Botanical and Zoological Park. Multicoloured.
690. 20 f. Type **304** 15 10
691. 80 f. Ring-tailed lemur with young (25 × 37 mm.) 20 10
692. 250 f. Palm tree and ring-tailed lemur within "Zoo" (47 × 32 mm.) .. 40 20

305. Hoopoe and Blue Madagascar Coucal. **306** Cattle grazing

1988. Scouts, Birds and Butterflies. Mult.
694. 80 f. Type **305** 30 20
695. 250 f. "Chrysiridia croesus" (butterfly) 40 20
696. 270 f. Weaver and red forest fody 70 35
697. 350 f. "Papilio dardanus" (butterflies) 60 40
698. 550 f. Crested Madagascar coucal .. .. 1·25 75
699. 1500 f. "Argema mittrei" (butterfly) .. .. 2·50 2·00

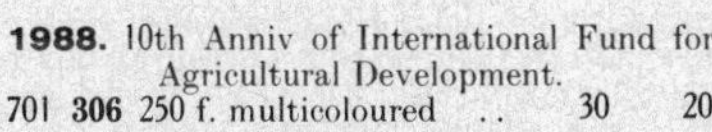
1988. 10th Anniv of International Fund for Agricultural Development.
701 **306** 250 f. multicoloured .. 30 20

307 Karl Bach and Clavier **308** Books

1988. Musicians' Anniversaries. Mult.
702 80 f. Type **307** (death bicentenary) 15 10
703 250 f. Franz Schubert and piano (160th death) .. 40 15
704 270 f. Georges Bizet and scene from "Carmen" (150th birth) 40 20
705 350 f. Claude Debussy and scene from "Pelleas et Melisande" (70th death) 50 25
706 550 f. George Gershwin at piano writing score of "Rhapsody in Blue" (90th birth) 75 45
707 1500 f. Elvis Presley (10th death (1987)) .. .. 2·50 1·25

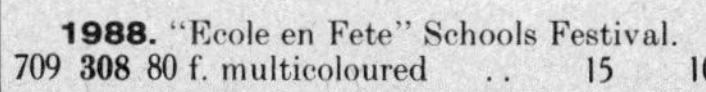
1988. "Ecole en Fete" Schools Festival.
709 **308** 80 f. multicoloured .. 15 10

309 "Black Sea Fleet at Feodosiya" (Ivan Aivazovski) **310** "Tragocephala crassicornis"

1988. Paintings of Sailing Ships. Mult.
710 20 f. Type **309** 25 15
711 80 f. "Lesnoie" (N. Semenov) 25 15
712 80 f. "Seascape with Sailing Ships" (Simon de Vlieger) 25 15
713 100 f. "Orel" (N. Golitsine) (horiz) 30 15
714 250 f. "Naval Battle Exercises" (Adam Silo) 75 25

1988. Endangered Beetles. Multicoloured.
716 20 f. Type **310** 15 10
717 80 f. "Polybothris symptuosa-gema" .. 15 10
718 250 f. "Euchroea auripigmenta" 50 25
719 350 f. "Stellognata maculata" 70 35

311 Stretcher Bearers and Anniversary Emblem **312** Symbols of Human Rights

1988. 125th Anniv of International Red Cross. Multicoloured.
720 80 f. Type **311** 15 10
721 250 f. Red Cross services, emblem and Henri Dunant (founder) .. 35 20

1988. 40th Anniv of Declaration of Human Rights. Multicoloured.
722 80 f. Type **312** 15 10
723 250 f. Hands with broken manacles holding "40" 35 15

313 Mercedes-Benz "Blitzen-Benz", 1909

1989. Cars and Trains. Multicoloured.
724 80 f. Type **313** 15 10
725 250 f. Micheline "ZM 517 Tsikirity" Antananarivo–Moramanga line 35 15
726 270 f. Bugatti coupe binder, "41" 40 20
727 350 f. German class "1020" electric locomotive .. 60 25
728 1500 f. Souleze "710" diesel train, Malagasy .. 2·25 1·25
729 2500 f. Opel racing car, 1913 3·50 2·00

314 Tyrannosaurus

1989. Prehistoric Animals. Multicoloured.
731 20 f. Type **314** 15 10
732 80 f. Stegosaurus 20 10
733 250 f. Arsinoitherium .. 40 15
734 450 f. Triceratops .. 80 30

315 "Tahitian Girls"

1989. Woman in Art. Multicoloured.

736 20 f. Type **315** 10 10
737 80 f. "Portrait of a Girl" (Jean-Baptiste Greuze) 15 10
738 80 f. "Portrait of a Young Woman" (Titian) .. 15 10
739 100 f. "Woman in Black" (Auguste Renoir) .. 20 10
740 250 f. "The Lace-maker" (Vasily Tropinine) .. 35 15

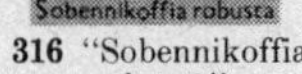

316 "Sobennikoffia robusta" **317** Nehru

1989. Orchids. Multicoloured.

742 5 f. Type **316** 15 10
743 10 f. "Grammangis fallax" (horiz) 15 10
744 80 f. "Angraecum sororium" 20 10
745 80 f. "Cymbidiella humblotii" 20 10
746 250 f. "Oenia oncidiiflora" 60 20

1989. Birth Centenary of Jawaharlal Nehru (Indian statesman).

748 **317** 250 f. multicoloured .. 45 15

318 Mahamasina Sports Complex, Lake Anosy and Ampefiloha Quarter

1989. Antananarivo. Multicoloured.

749 5 f. Type **318** 10 10
750 20 f. Andravoahangy and Anjanahary Quarters .. 10 10
751 80 f. Zoma market and Faravohitra Quarter .. 15 10
752 80 f. Andohan'Analekely Quarter and 29 March Column 15 10
753 250 f. Avenue de l'Independance and Jean Ralaimongo Column .. 35 15
754 550 f. Lake Anosy, Queen's Palace and Andohalo School 70 35

319 Rose Quartz

1989. Ornamental Minerals. Multicoloured.

755 80 f. Type **319** 20 10
756 250 f. Fossilized wood .. 60 20

MINIMUM PRICE

The minimum price quoted is 5p which represents a handling charge rather than a basis for valuing common stamps. For further notes about prices see introductory pages.

320 Pope and Rasoamanarivo **321** Map and Runner with Torch

1989. Visit of Pope John Paul II and Beatification of Victoire Rasoamanarivo. Mult.

757 80 f. Type **320** 20 10
758 250 f. Map and Pope .. 55 20

1989. Town Games.

759 **321** 80 f. + 20 f. mult .. 15 15

322 "Storming the Bastille"

1989. Bicent of French Revolution (1st issue).

760 **322** 250 f. multicoloured .. 35 15

See also Nos. 773/5.

323 Mirabeau and Gabriel Riqueti at Meeting of States General

1989. "Philexfrance 89" International Stamp Exhibition, Paris. Multicoloured.

761 250 f. Type **323** 30 15
762 350 f. Camille Desmoulins' call to arms 45 20
763 1000 f. Lafayette and crowd demanding bread 1·25 60
764 1500 f. Trial of King Louis XVI .. .. .. 2·00 80
765 2500 f. Assassination of Marat .. .. .. 3·25 1·25

324 "Mars 1"

1989. Space Probes. Multicoloured.

767 20 f. Type **324** 10 10
768 80 f. "Mars 3" 15 10
769 80 f. "Zond 2" 15 10
770 250 f. "Mariner 9" .. 35 15
771 270 f. "Viking 2" 40 20

325 "Liberty guiding the People" (Eugene de la Croix)

1989. Bicentenary of French Revolution (2nd issue). Multicoloured.

773 5 f. Type **325** (postage) .. 10 10
774 80 f. "La Marseillaise" (Francois Rude) .. 15 10
775 250 f. "Oath of the Tennis Court" (Jacques Louis David) (air) 35 15

326 Rene Cassin (founder) **327** Mother and Young on Bamboo

1989. 25th Anniv of Int. Human Rights Institute for French Speaking Countries.

776 **326** 250 f. multicoloured .. 30 15

1989. Golden Gentle Lemur.

777 **327** 250 f. multicoloured .. 40 20

328 Footballer and Cavour Monument, Turin

1989. World Cup Football Championship, Italy. Multicoloured.

778 350 f. Type **328** 50 20
779 1000 f. Footballer and Christopher Columbus monument, Genoa .. 1·40 50
780 1500 f. Florentine footballer, 1530, and "David" (sculpture, Michelangelo) .. .. 2·00 75
781 2500 f. Footballer and "Rape of Proserpina" (sculpture, Bernini), Rome .. .. .. 3·25 1·40

329 Pennant Coralfish

1990. Fishes. Multicoloured.

783 5 f. Type **329** 10 10
784 20 f. Snub-nosed parasitic eel (vert) 10 10
785 80 f. Southern guitar-fish (vert) 15 10
786 250 f. Red-banded grouper 40 15
787 320 f. Common hammerhead shark 55 20

330 Long Jumping **331** "Queen of the Isalo" (rock)

1990. Olympic Games, Barcelona (1992). Mult.

789 80 f. Type **330** 10 10
790 250 f. Pole vaulting .. 35 15
791 550 f. Hurdling 65 25
792 1500 f. Cycling .. .. 2·00 60
793 2000 f. Baseball .. .. 2·50 80
794 2500 f. Tennis .. .. 3·25 1·25

1990. Natural Features. Multicoloured.

796 70 f. Type **331** 15 10
797 150 f. Lonjy Island (as T **332**) 25 15

332 Pipe

1990. Sakalava Craft. Multicoloured.

798 70 f. Type **332** 15 10
799 150 f. Combs (as T **331**) 25 15

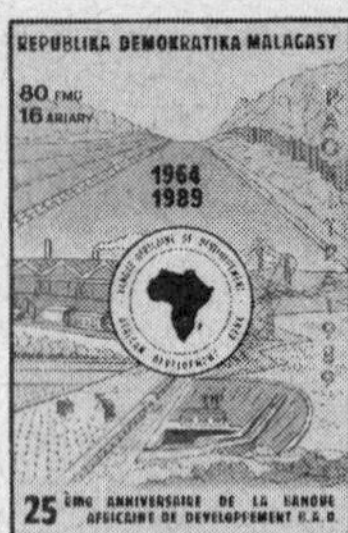

333 Emblem and Projects

1990. 25th Anniv of African Development Bank.

800 **333** 80 f. multicoloured .. 15 10

334 "Voyager II" and Neptune

1990. 20th Anniv of First Manned Landing on Moon. Multicoloured.

801 80 f. Type **334** 15 10
802 250 f. Flying boats .. 40 15
803 550 f. "Noah" satellite tracking elephants .. 70 25
804 1500 f. Venus and "Magellan" space probe 1·25 55
805 2000 f. Halley's Comet and "Concorde" .. .. 2·25 90
806 2500 f. "Apollo 11" landing capsule and crew .. 3·00 1·00

335 Liner on Globe **336** Maps showing Development between 1975 and 1990

1990. 30th Anniv of International Maritime Organization.

808 **335** 250 f. ultra, bl & blk .. 45 15

1990. Air. 15th Anniv of Malagasy Socialist Revolution.

809 **336** 100 f. multicoloured .. 15 10
810 – 350 f. black and grey 45 25

DESIGN: 350 f. Presidential Palaces, 1975 and 1990.

337 Oral Vaccination **338** Four-man Bobsleigh

1990. Anti-Polio Campaign.
811 **337** 150 f. multicoloured .. 30 15

1990. Winter Olympic Games, Albertville (1992). Multicoloured.
812 350 f. Type **338** 40 20
813 1000 f. Speed skating .. 1·25 40
814 1500 f. Cross-country skiing 2·00 65
815 2500 f. Downhill skiing .. 3·00 1·10

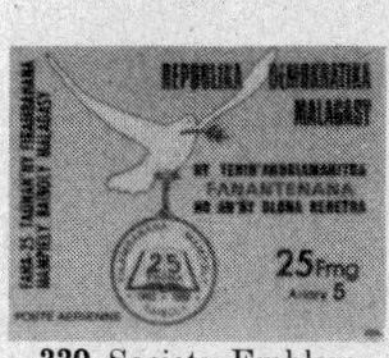

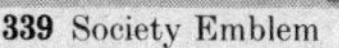
339 Society Emblem **340** Mascot

1990. Air. 25th Anniv of Malagasy Bible Society.
817 **339** 25 f. multicoloured .. 10 10
818 – 100 f. blue, black & grn 15 10
DESIGN—VERT. 100 f. Society emblem.

1990. 3rd Indian Ocean Island Games, Malagasy (1st issue).
819 **340** 100 f.+20 f. on 80 f. +20 f. multicoloured 15 15
820 350 f.+20 f. on 250 f. +20 f. multicoloured 45 40

The games were originally to be held in 1989 and the stamps were printed for release then. The issued stamps are handstamped with the correct date and new value.

See also Nos. 822/3.

341 Symbols of Agriculture and Industry **342** Torch

1990. 30th Anniv of Independence.
821 **341** 100 f. multicoloured .. 15 10

1990. 3rd Indian Ocean Island Games, Malagasy (2nd issue).
822 **342** 100 f. multicoloured .. 15 10
823 350 f. multicoloured .. 45 20

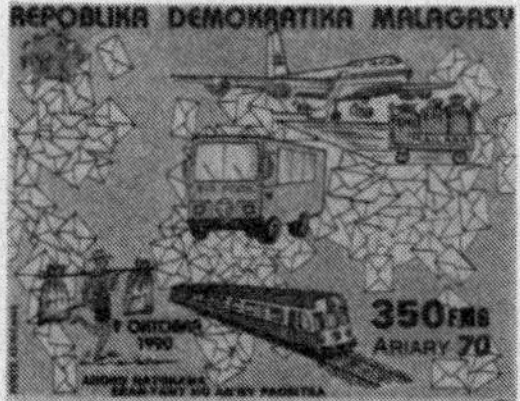

343 Envelopes forming Map and Mail Transportation

1990. Air. World Post Day.
824 **343** 350 f. multicoloured .. 75 30

344 Ho Chi Minh **345** "Avahi laniger"

1990. Birth Centenary of Ho Chi Minh (President of North Vietnam, 1945–69).
825 **344** 350 f. multicoloured .. 40 20

1990. Lemurs. Multicoloured.
826 10 f. Type **345** 10 10
827 20 f. "Lemur fulvus albifrons" 10 10
828 20 f. "Lemur fulvus sanfordi" 10 10
829 100 f. "Lemur fulvus collaris" 25 15
830 100 f. "Lepulemur ruficaudatus" .. 25 15

346 "Tridacna squamosa" **347** Letters in Book

1990. Shells. Multicoloured.
832 40 f. Type **346** 15 10
833 50 f. "Terebra dimidiata" and "Terebra subulata" 15 10

1990. International Literacy Year. Mult.
834 20 f. Type **347** 10 10
835 100 f. Open book and hand holding pen (horiz) .. 20 15

348 Cep **349** De Gaulle, Leclerc and Parod under Arc de Triomphe, 1944

1991. Fungi. Multicoloured.
836 25 f. Type **348** 10 10
837 100 f. Butter mushroom .. 10 10
838 350 f. Fly agaric 25 10
839 450 f. Scarlet-stemmed boletus 35 15
840 680 f. Flaky-stemmed witches' mushroom .. 50 25
841 800 f. Brown birch bolete 55 25
842 900 f. Orange birch bolete 65 30

1991. Multicoloured.
844 100 f. Type **349** 10 10
845 350 f. "Galileo" space probe near Jupiter .. 25 10
846 800 f. Crew of "Apollo 11" on moon 55 25
847 900 f. De Gaulle and Free France emblem, 1942 .. 65 30
848 1250 f. "Concorde" aircraft and German "ICE" high speed train .. .. 1·40 55
849 2500 f. Gen. Charles de Gaulle (French statesman) .. .. 1·90 95

350 Industrial and Agricultural Symbols and Arms **351** Baobab Tree

1991. 15th Anniv (1990) of Republic.
851 **350** 100 f. multicoloured .. 10 10

1991. Trees. Multicoloured.
852 140 f. Type **351** 10 10
853 500 f. "Dideria madagascariensis" 35 15

352 Whippet

1991. Dogs. Multicoloured.
854 30 f. Type **352** 10 10
855 50 f. Japanese spaniel .. 10 10
856 140 f. Toy terrier 10 10
857 350 f. Chow-chow .. 25 10
858 500 f. Chihuahua 35 15
859 800 f. Afghan hound .. 55 25
860 1140 f. Papillon 85 40

POSTAGE DUE STAMPS

D 13. Independence Obelisk.

1962.
D 45. D **13.** 1 f. green 10 10
D 46. 2 f. brown 10 10
D 47. 3 f. violet 10 10
D 48. 4 f. slate 10 10
D 49. 5 f. red 10 10
D 50. 10 f. green 15 15
D 51. 20 f. purple 20 20
D 52. 40 f. blue 50 45
D 53. 50 f. red 75 70
D 54. 100 f. black .. .. 1·40 1·25

APPENDIX

The following stamps have either been issued in excess of postal needs or have not been available to the public in reasonable quantities at face value.

1987

Winter Olympic Games, Calgary (1988). 1500 f. (on gold foil).

1989

Scout and Butterfly. 5000 f. (on gold foil).

"Philexfrance 89" Int. Stamp Exhibition, Paris. 5000 f. (on gold foil).

World Cup Football Championship, Italy. 5000 f. (on gold foil).

1990

Winter Olympic Games, Albertville (1992). 5000 f. (on gold foil).

1991

Birth Cent of De Gaulle. 5000 f. (on gold foil).

MALI Pt. 6; Pt. 13

Federation of French Sudan and Senegal, formed in 1959 as an autonomous republic within the French Community. In August 1960 the Federation was split up and the French Sudan part became the independent Mali Republic.

100 centimes = 1 franc.

A. FEDERATION.

1. Map, Flag, Mali and Torch.

1959. Establishment of Mali Federation.
1. **1.** 25 f. multicoloured .. 50 50

2.

1959. Air. 300th Anniv of St. Louis, Senegal.
2 **2** 85 f. multicoloured .. 1·50 1·25

3. Parrot Fish.  **4.** Violet Starling

1960. (a) Postage. Fish as T **3**.
3. **3.** 5 f. orange, blue & bronze 30 15
4. – 10 f. black, brown & turq. 30 25
5. – 15 f. brown, slate and blue 40 25
6. – 20 f. black, bistre & grn. .. 50 35
7. – 25 f. yellow, sepia & green 60 40
8. – 30 f. red, purple and blue .. 80 50
9. – 85 f. red, blue and green .. 1·75 1·50

(b) Air. Birds as T **4**.
10. **4.** 100 f. multicoloured .. 5·50 1·60
11. – 200 f. multicoloured .. 12·00 5·00
12. – 500 f. multicoloured .. 32·00 13·50

DESIGNS—HORIZ. 10 f. Trigger fish. 15 f. Batfish. 20 f. Threadfish. 25 f. Butterfly fish. 30 f. Surgeon. 85 f. Sea bream. 200 f. Bateleur. VERT. 500 f. Common gonolek.

1960. 10th Anniv of African Technical Cooperation Commission. As T 4 of Malagasy Republic.
13 25 f. purple and violet .. 1·00 75

B. REPUBLIC.

1960. Nos. 6, 7, 9 and 10/12 optd. **REPUBLIQUE DU MALI** and bar or bars or surch. also.
14. 20 f. black, bistre and green postage) .. 1·25 60
15. 25 f. red, purple and blue .. 1·75 60
16. 85 f. red, blue and green .. 3·00 1·50
17. 100 f. multicoloured (air) .. 4·50 1·50
18. 200 f. multicoloured .. 7·00 3·25
19. 300 f. on 500 f. multicoloured 12·00 5·50
20. 500 f. multicoloured .. 25·00 14·00

7. Pres. Mamadou Konatc.

DESIGN: 25 f., 300 f. President Keita. Nos. 23/4 are larger (27×38 mm.).

1961.
21. **7.** 20 f. sepia & green (post.) 25 15
22. – 25 f. black and purple .. 35 15
23. **7.** 200 f. sepia & red (air) .. 3·00 1·00
24. – 300 f. black and green .. 4·25 1·25

8. U.N. Emblem, Flag and Map.

1961. Air. Proclamation of Independence and Admission into U.N.
25. 8. 100 f. multicoloured .. 1·25 90

9. Sankore Mosque, Timbuktu.

1961. Air.
26. 9. 100 f. brown, blue & sepia 1·75 55
27. – 200 f. brown, red & green 4·00 1·50
28. – 500 f. green, brown & blue 11·00 3·25
DESIGN: 200 f. View of Timbuktu. 500 f. Arms and view of Bamako.

10. Africans learning Vowels.

1961. 1st Anniv. of Independence.
29. 10. 25 f. multicoloured .. 45 30

11. Sheep at Pool. 12. African Map and King Mohammed V of Morocco.

1961.
30. 11. 50 c. sepia, myrtle & red 15 15
31. A. 1 f. bistre, green and blue 15 15
32. B. 2 f. red, green and blue.. 15 15
33. C. 3 f. brown, green and blue 15 15
34. D. 4 f. blue, green and bistre 15 15
35. 11. 5 f. purple, green and blue 20 15
36. A. 10 f. brown, myrtle & blue 20 15
37. B. 15 f. brown, green & blue 20 15
38. C 20 f. red, green and blue 30 25
39. D. 25 f. brown and blue .. 40 20
40. 11. 30 f. brown, green & violet 55 30
41. A. 40 f. brown, green & blue 1·25 30
42. B. 50 f. lake, green and blue 50 30
43. C. 60 f. brown, green and blue 1·40 30
44. D. 85 f. brown, bistre & blue 1·75 35
DESIGNS: A, Oxen at pool. B, House of Arts, Mali. C, Land tillage. D, Combine-harvester in rice field.

1962. 1st Anniv. of African Conf. Casablanca.
45. 12. 25 f. multicoloured .. 25 15
46. 50 f. multicoloured .. 50 20

13. Patrice Lumumba.

1962. 1st Death Anniv. of Patrice Lumumba (Congo leader).
47. 13. 25 f. brown & bistre .. 20 20
48. 100 f. brown and green.. 75 50

1962. Malaria Eradication. As T 43 of Mauritania.
49. 25 f.+5 f. blue 50 60

14. Pegasus and U.P.U. Emblem.

1962. 1st Anniv. of Admission into U.P.U.
50 14. 85 f. multicoloured .. 1·00 65

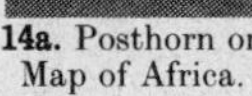

14a. Posthorn on Map of Africa. 15. Sansanding Dam.

1962. African Postal Union Commem.
51. 14a. 25 f. green and brown 25 20
52. 85 f. orange and green 75 50

1962.
53. 15. 25 f. black, green & blue 30 20
54. – 45 f. multicoloured .. 1·10 50
DESIGN—HORIZ. 45 f. Cotton plant.

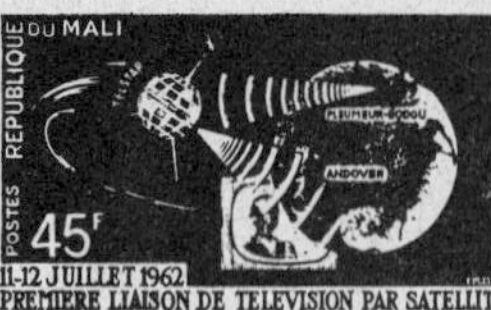

16. "Telstar" Satellite, Globe and Television Receiver.

1962. 1st Trans-Atlantic Telecommunications Satellite Link.
55. 16. 45 f. brn., violet & lake.. 70 40
56. 55 f. violet, olive & green 80 60

17. Soldier and Family. 18. Bull's Head, Laboratory Equipment and Chicks.

1962. Mali-Algerian Solidarity.
57. 17. 25 f.+5 f. multicoloured 30 30

1963. Zoological Research Centre, Sotuba.
58. 18. 25 f. turq. & brn. (post.) 35 25
59. – 200 f. turquoise, purple and bistre (air) .. 3·00 1·25
DESIGN: 200 f. As Type 18 but horiz. (48 × 27 mm.).

19. Tractor and Campaign Emblem.

1963. Freedom from Hunger.
60. 19. 25 f. pur., black and blue 35 20
61. 45 f. brn., green & turq. 65 35

20. Balloon and W.M.O. Emblem.

1963. Atmospheric Research.
62. 20. 25 f. multicoloured .. 30 20
63. 45 f. multicoloured .. 60 35
64. 60 f. multicoloured .. 80 50

21. Race Winners. 22. Centenary Emblem and Globe.

1963. Youth Week. Multicoloured.
65. 5 f. Type 21 .. .. 15 10
66. 10 f. Type 21 .. .. 20 15
67. 20 f. Acrobatic dance .. 35 20
68. 85 f. Football .. .. 1·40 55
Nos. 67/8 are horiz.

1963. Red Cross Cent. Inscr. in black.
69. 22. 5 f. multicoloured .. 20 15
70. 10 f. red, yellow and grey 30 20
71. 85 f. red, yellow and grey 1·10 60

23. Stretcher case entering Ambulance 'Plane "Aero 145".

1963. Air.
72. 23. 25 f. brown, blue & green 35 20
73. – 55 f. blue, ochre & brown 1·00 40
74. – 100 f. blue, brown & green 1·60 75
DESIGNS: 55 f. Airliner on tarmac. 100 f. Airliner taking off.

24. South African Crowned Crane standing on Giant Tortoise. 26. "Kaempferia aethiopica".

25. U.N. Emblem, Doves and Banner.

1963. Air. Fauna Protection.
75. 24. 25 f. brn., red & orange.. 1·75 50
76. 200 f. multicoloured .. 5·50 2·10

1963. Air. 15th Anniv. of Declaration of Human Rights.
77. 25. 50 f. yellow, red & green 75 40

1963. Tropical Flora. Multicoloured.
78. 30 f. Type 26 .. .. 45 25
79. 70 f. "Bombax costatum" 1·40 50
80. 100 f. "Adenium honghel" 2·75 65

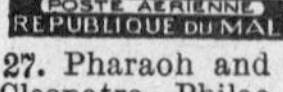

27. Pharaoh and Cleopatra, Philae. 28. Locust on Map of Africa.

1964. Air. Nubian Monuments Preservation.
81. 27. 25 f. brown and purple.. 60 25
82. 55 f. olive and purple .. 1·40 50

1964. Anti-Locust Campaign.
83. 28. 5 f. brown, green & purple 20 15
84. – 10 f. brown, green & olive 30 20
85. – 20 f. brown, green & bistre 50 25
DESIGNS—VERT. 10 f. Locust and map. HORIZ. 20 f. Air-spraying, locust and village.

29. Football.

1964. Olympic Games, Tokyo.
86. 29. 5 f. purple, green & red.. 15 10
87. – 10 f. brown, blue & sepia 20 20
88. – 15 f. red and violet .. 25 20
89. – 85 f. green, brn. & violet 1·00 70
DESIGNS—VERT. 10 f. Boxing. 15 f. Running and Olympic Flame. HORIZ. 85 f. Hurdling. Each design has a stadium in the background.

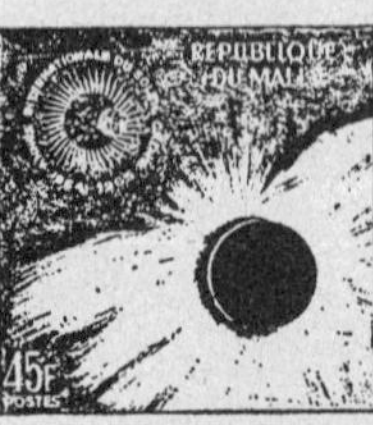

30. Solar Flares. 32. Map of Vietnam.

31. President Kennedy.

1964. Int. Quiet Sun Years.
90. 30. 45 f. olive, red and blue.. 60 35

1964. Air. 1st Death Anniv. of Pres. Kennedy.
91. 31. 100 f. multicoloured .. 1·40 1·25

1964. Mali—South Vietnam Workers' Solidarity Campaign.
92. 32. 30 f. multicoloured .. 30 20

33. Knysna Turacos.

1965. Air. Birds.
93. 33. 100 f. green, blue and red 4·75 1·60
94. – 200 f. black, red and blue 11·00 3·25
95. – 300 f. black, ochre & grn. 16·00 4·50
96. – 500 f. red, brn. & green 24·00 8·25
BIRDS—VERT. 200 f. Abyssinian Ground Hornbills. 300 f. Egyptian Vultures. HORIZ. 500 f. Goliath Herons.

34. I.C.Y. Emblem and U.N. Headquarters. 36. Abraham Lincoln.

35. African Buffalo.

1965. Air. Int. Co-operation Year.
97. 34. 55 f. ochre, purple & blue 75 40

1965. Animals.
98. – 1 f. brn., blue & green.. 10 10
99. 35. 5 f. brn., orge. & green 15 10
100. – 10 f. brn., mauve & grn. 40 25
101. – 30 f. brn., green & red.. 75 30
102. – 90 f. brown, grey & grn. 2·25 95
ANIMALS—VERT. 1 f. Waterbuck. 10 f. Scimitar oryx. 90 f. Giraffe. HORIZ. 30 f. Leopard.

1965. Death Cent. of Abraham Lincoln.
103. 36. 45 f. multicoloured .. 60 40
104. 55 f. multicoloured .. 65 50

37. Hughes' Telegraph. 38. "Lungs" and Mobile X-Ray Unit (Anti-T.B.).

1965. Cent. of I.T.U.
105. – 20 f. black, blue & orge. 30 25
106. 37. 30 f. green, brn. & orge. 45 25
107. – 50 f. grn., brn. & orge. 75 45
DESIGNS—VERT. 20 f. Denis's Pneumatic tube. 50 f. Lescurre's heliograph.

1965. Mali Health Service.
108. 38. 5 f. violet, red & crimson 15 15
109. – 10 f. green, bistre & red 25 15
110. – 25 f. green and brown.. 40 20
111. – 45 f. green and brown.. 75 40
DESIGNS: 10 f. Mother and children (Maternal and Child Care). 25 f. Examining patient (Marchoux Institute). 45 f. Nurse (Biological Laboratory).

39. Diving.

1965. 1st African Games, Brazzaville, Congo.
112. 39. 5 f. red, brown and blue 15 10
113. – 15 f. turquoise, brown and red (Judo) .. 60 30

40. Pope John XXIII. 41. Sir Winston Churchill.

1965. Air. Pope John Commem.
114. **40.** 100 f. multicoloured .. 1·90 75

1965. Air. Churchill Commem.
115. **41.** 100 f. blue and brown 1·75 75

42. Dr. Schweitzer and Young African.

1965. Air. Dr. Albert Schweitzer Commem.
116. **42.** 100 f. multicoloured .. 2·00 75

43. Leonov.

1966. Int. Astronautic Conf., Athens (1965). Multicoloured.
117. 100 f. Type **43** .. .. 1·60 60
118. 100 f. White .. .. 1·60 60
119. 300 f. Cooper, Conrad, Leonov and Beliaiev (vert.) .. 4·25 2·00

44. Vase, Quill and Cornet.

1966. World Festival of Negro Arts, Dakar, Cameroun.
120. **44.** 30 f. black, red & ochre 30 20
121. – 55 f. red, black and green 60 35
122. – 90 f. brn., orge. & blue 1·10 60
DESIGNS: 55 f. Mask, brushes and palette, microphones. 90 f. Dancers, Mask, patterned cloth.

45. W.H.O. Building.

1966. Inaug. of W.H.O. Headquarters, Geneva.
123. **45.** 30 f. grn., blue & yellow 40 20
124. 45 f. red, blue & yellow 60 35

46. Fisherman with Net.

1966. River Fishing.
125. **46.** 3 f. brown and blue .. 15 15
126. – 4 f. purple, blue & brown 20 15
127. – 20 f. purple, grn. & blue 35 15
128. **46.** 25 f. purple, blue & grn. 50 20
129. – 60 f. purple, lake & grn. 85 35
130. – 85 f. plum, grn. & blue 1·25 50
DESIGNS: 4 f., 60 f. Collective shore fishing. 20 f., 85 f. Fishing pirogue.

HAVE YOU READ THE NOTES AT THE BEGINNING OF THIS CATALOGUE?
These often provide answers to the enquiries we receive.

47. Papal Arms, U.N. and Peace Emblems.

1966. Air. Pope Paul's Visit to U.N.
131. **47.** 200 f. blue, green & turq. 2·50 1·10

48. Initiation Ceremony. 49. People and U.N.E.S.C.O. Emblem.

1966. Mali Pioneers. Multicoloured.
132. 5 f. Type **48** 15 15
133. 25 f. Pioneers dancing .. 50 20

1966. Air. 20th Anniv. of U.N.E.S.C.O.
134. **49.** 100 f. red, green & blue 1·75 70

50. Footballers, Globe, Cup and Football.

1966. Air. World Cup Football Championships, England.
135. **50.** 100 f. multicoloured .. 1·75 70

51. Cancer ("The Crab"). 52. U.N.I.C.E.F. Emblem and Children.

1966. Air. 9th Int. Cancer Congress, Tokyo.
136. **51.** 100 f. multicoloured .. 1·60 55

1966. 20th Anniv. of U.N.I.C.E.F.
137. **52.** 45 f. blue, purple & brn. 60 25

53. Inoculating Cattle.

1967. Campaign for Preventing Cattle Plague.
138. **53.** 10 f. multicoloured .. 25 10
139. 30 f. multicoloured .. 50 20

54. Desert Vehicles in Pass.

1967. Air. Crossing of the Hoggar (1924).
140. **54.** 200 f. green, brn. & vio. 4·50 2·25

55. "Diamant" Rocket and Lana's "Aerial Ship". 56. Ancient City.

1967. Air. French Space Rockets and Satellites.
141. **55.** 50 f. blue, turq. & pur. 70 30
142. – 100 f. lake, pur. & turq. 1·40 50
143. – 200 f. pur., olive & blue 2·40 1·00
DESIGNS: 100 f. Satellite "A 1" and Jules Verne's "rocket". 200 f. Satellite "D 1" and Da Vinci's "bird-powered" flying machine.

1967. Int. Tourist Year.
144. **56.** 25 f. orge., blue & violet 30 20

57. Amelia Earhart and Mail Route-map.

1967. Air. 30th Anniv. of Amelia Earhart's Flight, via Gao.
145. **57.** 500 f. multicoloured .. 7·00 3·25

58. "The Bird Cage". 59. Scout Emblems and Rope Knots.

1967. Air. Picasso Commem. Designs showing paintings. Multicoloured.
146. 50 f. Type **58** .. .. 1·00 30
147. 100 f. "Paul as Harlequin" 1·75 70
148. 250 f. "The Pipes of Pan" 3·50 1·50
See also Nos. 158/9 and 164/7.

1967. Air. World Scout Jamboree, Idaho.
149. **59.** 70 f. red and green .. 1·00 30
150. – 100 f. black, lake & grn. 1·25 45
DESIGN: 100 f. Scout with "walkie-talkie" radio.

60. "Chelorrhina polyphemus". 61. School Class.

62. "Europafrique". 63. Lions Emblem and Crocodile.

1967. Insects.
151. **60.** 5 f. green, brown & blue 30 20
152. – 15 f. purple, brn. & grn. 50 25
153. – 50 f. red, brn. & green .. 1·10 55
INSECTS—HORIZ. 15 f. "Ugada grandicollis". 50 f. "Phymateus cinctus".

1967. Int. Literary Day.
154. **61.** 50 f. black, red & green 60 20

1967. Europafrique.
155. **62.** 45 f. multicoloured .. 70 25

1967. 50th Anniv. of Lions Int.
156. **63.** 90 f. multicoloured .. 95 55

64. "Water Resources". 65. Block of Flats, Grenoble.

1967. Int. Hydrological Decade.
157. **64.** 25 f. black, blue & bistre 30 20

1967. Air. Toulouse-Lautrec Commem. Paintings as T **58**. Multicoloured.
158. 100 f. "Gazelle" (horse's head (horiz.) .. .. 2·00 1·10
159. 300 f. "Gig drawn by Cob" (vert.) .. .. 4·75 2·25

1968. Air. Winter Olympic Games, Grenoble.
160. **65.** 50 f. brown, green & blue 70 35
161. – 150 f. brown, blue and ultramarine .. 1·60 65
DESIGN: 150 f. Bob-sleigh course, Huez mountain.

66. W.H.O. Emblem.

1968. 20th Anniv. of W.H.O.
162. **66.** 90 f. blue, lake & green 70 30

67. Human Figures and Entwined Hearts.

1968. World "Twin Towns" Day.
163. **67.** 50 f. red, violet & green 40 15

1968. Air. Flower Paintings. As T **58**. Mult.
164. 50 f. "Roses and Anemones" (Van Gogh) 50 25
165. 150 f. "Vase of Flowers" (Manet) .. .. 1·50 55
166. 300 f. "Bouquet of Flowers" (Delacroix) .. .. 3·00 1·10
167. 500 f. "Marguerites" (Millet) .. .. 4·50 2·00
SIZES: 50 f., 300 f. 40 × 41½ mm. 150 f. 36 × 47½ mm. 500 f. 50 × 36 mm.

68. Dr. Martin Luther King. 69. "Draisienne" Bicycle, 1809.

1968. Air. Martin Luther King Commem.
168. **68.** 100 f. black, pink & pur. 85 35

1968. Veteran Bicycles and Motor Cars.
169. **69.** 2 f. brown, mauve and green (post.) .. 20 15
170. – 5 f. red, blue and bistre 30 20
171. – 10 f. blue, brown & grn. 50 25
172. – 45 f. black, grn. & brn. 80 40
173. – 50 f. red, grn. & brn. (air) 1·00 25
174. – 100 f. blue, mve. & bistre 2·00 60
DESIGNS—HORIZ. 5 f. De Dion-Bouton, 1894. 45 f. Panhard-Levassor, 1914. 100 f. Mercedes-Benz, 1927. VERT. 10 f. Michaux Bicycle, 1861. 50 f. "Bicyclette, 1918"

70. Books, Graph and A.D.B.A. Emblem.

1968. 10th Anniv. of Int. African Libraries and Archives Development Assn.
175. **70.** 100 f. red, black & brn... 65 30

71. Football.

1968. Air. Olympic Games, Mexico. Mult.
176. 100 f. Type **71** 75 40
177. 150 f. Long-jumping (vert.) 1·25 60

1968. Air. "Philexafrique" Stamp Exn., Abidjan, Ivory Coast, 1969 (1st issue). As T **113a** of Mauritania. Multicoloured.
178. 200 f. "The Editors" (F. M. Granet) .. .. 2·00 1·50

1969. Air. "Philexafrique" Stamp Exn. Abidjan, Ivory Coast (2nd issue). As T **114a** of Mauritania.
179. 100 f. purple, red & violet 1·25 1·25
DESIGN: 100 f. Carved animal and French Sudan stamp of 1931.

1969. Air. Birth Bicent. of Napoleon Bonaparte. Multicoloured. As T **114b** of Mauritania.
180. 150 f. "Napoleon Bonaparte, First Consul" (Gros) .. 2·25 1·25
181. 200 f. "The Bivouac—Battle of Austerlitz" (Lejeune) (horiz.) .. 4·00 1·75

73. Montgolfier's Balloon.

1969. Air. Aviation History. Multicoloured.
182. 50 f. Type **73** 50 20
183. 150 f. Ferber's "No. 5" Biplane .. .. 1·50 40
184. 300 f. "Concorde" .. 3·00 1·40
See also Nos. 202/4

74. African Tourist Emblem.

1969. African Tourist Year.
185. **74.** 50 f. red, green & blue .. 25 20

75. "O.I.T." and I.L.O. Emblem.

1969. 50th Anniv. of I.L.O.
186. **75.** 50 f. violet, blue & green 30 20
187. 60 f. slate, red & brown 35 20

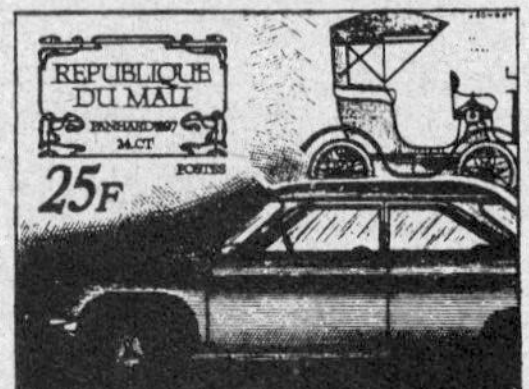

76. Panhard of 1897 and Model "24-CT".

1969. French Motor Industry.
188. **76.** 25 f. lake, black and bistre (postage) 50 20
189. – 30 f. green and black .. 60 20
190. – 55 f. red, black and purple (air) .. 1·00 35
191. – 90 f. blue, blk. & red .. 1·40 45
DESIGNS: 30 f. Citroen of 1923 and Model "DS-21". 55 f. Renault of 1898 and Model "16". 90 f. Peugeot of 1893 and Model "404".

77. Clarke (Australia), 10,000 metres (1965).

1969. Air. World Athletics Records.
192. **77.** 60 f. brown and blue .. 30 25
193. – 90 f. brown and red .. 45 25
194. – 120 f. brown and green 55 35
195. – 140 f. brown and slate .. 70 35
196. – 150 f. black and red .. 85 50
DESIGNS: 90 f. Lusis (Russia), Javelin (1968). 120 f. Miyake (Japan), Weightlifting (1967). 140 f. Matson (U.S.A.), Shot-putting (1968). 150 f. Keino (Kenya), 3,000 metres (1965).

78. Hollow Blocks.

1969. Int. Toy Fair, Nuremberg.
197. **78.** 5 f. red, yellow and grey 15 10
198. – 10 f. multicoloured .. 15 10
199. – 15 f. green, red and pink 20 10
200. – 20 f. orge., blue and red 25 15
DESIGNS: 10 f. Toy donkey on wheels. 15 f. "Ducks". 20 f. Model car and race-track.

79. "Apollo 8". Earth and Moon.

1969. Air. Moon Flight of "Apollo 8".
201. **79.** 2,000 f. gold .. .. 14·00 14·00
This stamp is embossed on gold foil.

1969. Air. 1st Man on the Moon. Nos. 182/4 optd. **L'HOMME SUR LA LUNE JUILLET 1969** and **Apollo 11.**
202. 50 f. multicoloured .. 95 65
203. 150 f. multicoloured .. 2·00 1·25
204. 300 f. multicoloured .. 3·25 2·50

81. Sheep.

1969. Domestic Animals
205. **81.** 1 f. olive, brown & green 10 10
206. – 2 f. brown, grey and red 10 10
207. – 10 f. olive, brown & blue 20 10
208. – 35 f. slate and red .. 60 30
209. – 90 f. brown and blue .. 1·25 55
ANIMALS: 2 f. Goat. 10 f. Donkey. 35 f. Horse. 90 f. Dromedary.

1969. 5th Anniv. of African Development Bank. As T **122a** of Mauritania.
210. 50 f. brown, green & purple 25 20
211. 90 f. orange, green & brown 45 20

83. "Mona Lisa" (Leonardo da Vinci).

1969. Air. 450th Death Anniv of Leonardo da Vinci.
212 **83** 500 f. multicoloured .. 4·00 3·25

84. Vaccination. **85.** Mahatma Gandhi.

1969. Campaign against Smallpox and Measles.
213. **84.** 50 f. slate, brn. & green 40 15

1969. Air. Birth Cent. Mahatma Gandhi.
214. **85.** 150 f. brown and green 1·60 55

1969. 10th Anniv. of Aerial Navigation Security Agency for Africa and Madagascar (A.S.E.C.N.A.). As T **94a** of Niger.
215 100 f. green 60 25

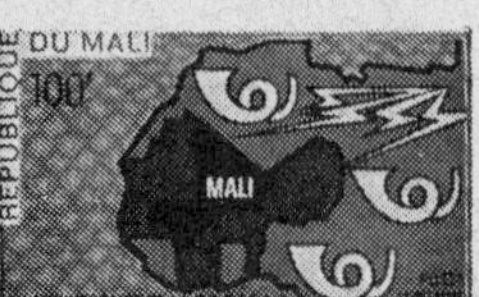

87. West African Map and Posthorns.

1970. Air. 11th Anniv. of West African Postal Union (C.A.P.T.E.A.O.).
216. **87.** 100 f. multicoloured .. 60 35

1970. Air. Religious Paintings. As T **83.** Multicoloured.
217. 100 f. "Virgin and Child" (Van der Weydan School) 70 40
218. 150 f. "The Nativity" (The Master of Flamalle) .. 1·10 65
219. 250 f. "Virgin, Child and St. John the Baptist" (Low Countries School) 2·40 1·40

89. Franklin D. Roosevelt. **91.** Lenin.

90. Women of Mali and Japan.

1970. Air. 25th Death Anniv. of Franklin D. Roosevelt.
220. **89.** 500 f. black, red and blue 3·50 2·00

1970. "EXPO 70" World Fair, Osaka, Japan.
221. **90.** 100 f. orge, brn. & blue 60 20
222. – 150 f. red, grn. & yell... 80 30
DESIGN: 150 f. Flags and maps of Mali and Japan.

1970. Air. Birth Centenary of Lenin.
223 **91** 300 f. black, grn & flesh 2·25 1·00

92. Verne and Moon Rockets.

1970. Air. Jules Verne, "Prophet of Space Travel". Multicoloured.
224. 50 f. Type **92** 60 25
225. 150 f. Moon orbit .. .. 1·50 50
226. 300 f. Splashdown .. .. 2·25 1·10

93. I.T.U. Emblem and Map.

1970. World Telecommunications Day.
227. **93.** 90 f. red, brown & sepia 60 25

1970. New U.P.U. Headquarters Building, Berne. As Type **81** of New Caledonia.
228. 50 f. brown, green & red .. 30 20
229. 60 f. brown, blue & mauve 40 20

1970. Air. Space Flight of "Apollo 13". Nos. 224/6 optd. **APOLLO XIII EPOPEE SPATIALE 11-17 AVRIL 1970** in three lines.
230. 50 f. multicoloured .. 40 25
231. 150 f. multicoloured .. 1·10 45
232. 300 f. multicoloured .. 2·00 1·25

96. "Intelstat 3" Satellite.

1970. Air. Space Telecommunications.
233. **96.** 100 f. indigo, blue & orge. 60 35
234. – 200 f. purple, grey & blue 1·25 50
235. – 300 f. brn., orge & slate 2·25 1·10
236. – 500 f. brn., blue & indigo 3·50 1·60
DESIGNS: 200 f. "Molnya I" satellite. 300 f. Dish aerial, Type PB 2. 500 f. "Symphony Project" satellite.

97. Auguste and Louis Lumiere, Jean Harlow and Marilyn Monroe.

1970. Air. Lumiere Brothers (inventors of the cine camera). Commem.
237. **97.** 250 f. multicoloured .. 2·50 1·25

98. Footballers.

1970. Air. World Cup Football Championships, Mexico.
238. **98.** 80 f. grn., brn. and red 50 25
239. 200 f. red, brown and blue 1·25 55

99. Rotary Emblem, Map and Antelope. **100.** "Supporting United Nations".

1970. Air. Rotary International.
240. **99.** 200 f. multicoloured .. 1·75 60

1970. Air. 25th Anniv. of U.N.O.
241. **100.** 100 f. blue, brn. & violet 70 35

101. Page from 11th century Baghdad Koran.

1970. Air. Ancient Muslim Art. Mult.
242. 50 f. Type **101** 50 25
243. 200 f. "Tree and wild Animals" (Jordanian mosaic, c.730) .. .. 1·25 55
244. 250 f. "The Scribe" (Baghdad miniature, 1287) .. .. .. 2·00 90

1970. Air. Moon Landing of "Luna 16". Nos. 234/5 surch. **LUNA 16 PREMIERS PRELEVEMENTS AUTOMATIQUES SUR LA LUNE SEPTEMBRE 1970** and new values.
245. 150 f. on 200 f. purple, grey and blue .. .. 1·00 40
246. 250 f. on 300 f. brown, orange and grey .. 1·50 60

103. G.P.O., Bamako.

1970. Public Buildings.
247. **103.** 30 f. olive, grn. & brn. 20 20
248. – 40 f. purple, brn. & grn. 30 20
249. – 60 f. grey, green and red 40 20
250. – 80 f. brn., green and grey 50 25
BUILDINGS: 40 f. Chamber of Commerce, Bamako. 60 f. Ministry of Public Works, Bamako. 80 f. Town Hall, Segou.

104. Pres. Nasser.

106. Gallet "0-30-T" Locomotive.

105. " The Nativity " (Antwerp School 1530).

1970. Air. Pres. Gamal Nasser of Egypt. Commemoration.

251. **104.** 1000 f. gold .. .. 7·50 7·50

1970. Air. Christmas. Paintings. Mult.

252. 100 f. Type **105** 70 40
253. 250 f. " Adoration of the Shepherds " (Memling) 1·60 95
254. 300 f. " Adoration of the Magi " (17th century Flemish school) .. .. 2·25 1·25

1970. Mali Railway Locomotives from the Steam Era (1st series).

255. **106.** 20 f. black, red and green 1·40 1·25
256. – 40 f. black, green & brn. 1·75 1·60
257. – 50 f. black, green & brn. 2·10 1·90
258. – 80 f. black, red & green 3·00 2·75
259. – 100 f. black, grn. & brn. 3·50 3·25

LOCOMOTIVES: 40 f. Felou "0-3-0T". 50 f. Bechevel "2-3-0T". 80 f. "231". 100 f. Type "141".

See also No. 367/70.

107. Scouts crossing Log-bridge.

1970. Scouting in Mali. Multicoloured.

260. 5 f. Type **107** 20 15
261. 30 f. Bugler and scout camp (vert.) 35 15
262. 100 f. Scouts canoeing .. 90 35

108. Bambara de San Mask. 109. General De Gaulle.

1971. Mali Masks and Ideograms. Mult.

263. 29 f. Type **108** 15 10
264. 25 f. Dogon de Bandiagara mask 20 10
265. 59 f. Kanaga ideogram .. 45 15
266. 89 f. Bambara ideogram .. 60 25

1971. Air. Charles De Gaulle Commem. Die-stamped on gold foil.

267. **109.** 2000 f. gold, red & blue 30·00 30·00

110. Alfred Nobel.

111. Tennis Player (Davis Cup).

1971. Air. 75th Death Anniv. of Alfred Nobel (philanthropoist).

268. **110.** 300 f. lake, brn & grn. 2·25 1·25

1971. Air. World Sporting Events.

269. **111.** 100 f. slate, pur. & blue 75 25
270. – 150 f. olive, brn. & grn. 1·40 40
271. – 200 f. brn., olive & blue 2·00 60

DESIGNS—HORIZ. 150 f. Steeplechase (inscr. " Derby at Epsom " but probably represents the Grand National). VERT. 200 f. Yacht (America Cup).

112. Youth, Sun and Microscope.

1971. 50th Anniv. of 1st B.C.G. Vaccine Inoculation.

272. **112.** 100 f. brn., grn. & red 85 40

113. "The Thousand and One Nights".

1971. Air. " Tales of the Arabian Nights ". Multicoloured.

273. 120 f. Type **113** 70 30
274. 180 f. "Ali Baba and the Forty Thieves" 1·00 40
275. 200 f. "Aladdin's Lamp" .. 1·40 50

114. Scouts, Japanese Horseman and Mt. Fuji.

1971. 13th World Scout Jamboree, Asagiri, Japan.

276. **114.** 80 f. plum, grn. & blue 60 20

115. Rose between Hands.

116. Rural Costume.

1971. 25th Anniv. of U.N.I.C.E.F.

277. **115.** 50 f. brn., red & orge. 30 20
278. – 60 f. blue, green & brn. 40 20

DESIGN—VERT. 60 f. Nurses and children.

1971. National Costumes. Multicoloured.

279. 5 f. Type **116** 15 10
280. 10 f. Rural costume (female) 20 15
281. 15 f. Tuareg 20 15
282. 60 f. Embroidered " boubou 45 20
283. 80 f. Women's ceremonial costume 60 25

117. Olympic Rings and Events.

1971. Air. Olympic Games Publicity.

284. **117.** 80 f. blue, pur. & grn. 40 20

118. Telecommunications Map.

1971. Pan-African Telecommunications Network Year.

285. **118.** 50 f. multicoloured .. 25 20

119. " Mariner 4 " and Mars.

1971. Air. Exploration of Outer Space.

286. **119.** 200 f. green, bl. & brn. 1·25 50
287. – 300 f. blue, plum & pur. 1·75 60

DESIGN: 300 f. " Venera 5 " and Venus.

120. " Santa Maria " (1492).

1971. Air. Famous Ships.

288. **120.** 100 f. brn., violet & blue 70 35
289. – 150 f. vio., brn. & grn. 1·25 45
290. – 200 f. grn., blue & red 1·60 75
291. – 250 f. red, blue & blk. 2·25 90

DESIGNS: 150 f. " Mayflower " (1620). 200 f. Battleship " Potemkin " (1905). 250 f. Liner " Normandie " (1935).

121. " Hibiscus rose-sinensis ".

1971. Flowers. Multicoloured.

292. 20 f. Type **121** 20 10
293. 50 f. " Euphorbia pulcherrima " 45 15
294. 60 f. " Adenium obesum " 70 20
295. 80 f. "Allamanda cathartica" 1·00 25
296. 100 f. " Satanocrater berhautii " .. .. 1·25 35

122. Allegory of Justice.

1971. 25th Anniv. of Int. Court of Justice, The Hague.

297. **122.** 160 f. choc., red & brn. 80 35

123. Nat King Cole. 124. Statue of Olympic Zeus (by Phidias).

1971. Air. Famous Negro Musicians. Mult.

298. 130 f. Type **123** .. 1·25 25
299. 150 f. Erroll Garner .. 1·25 30
300. 270 f. Louis Armstrong .. 1·75 45

1971. Air. " The Seven Wonders of the Ancient World ".

301. **124.** 70 f. blue, brn. & pur. 35 20
302. – 80 f. blk., brn. & blue 40 20
303. – 100 f. blue, red & violet 50 25
304. – 130 f. blk., pur. & blue 75 30
305. – 150 f. brn., grn. & blue 1·10 35
306. – 270 f. blue, brn. & pur. 1·60 75
307. – 280 f. blue, pur. & brn. 2·00 85

DESIGNS—VERT. 80 f. Pyramid of Cheops, Egypt. 130 f. Pharos of Alexandria. 270 f. Mausoleum of Halicarnassos. 280 f. Colossus of Rhodes. HORIZ. 100 f. Temple of Artemis, Ephesus. 150 f. Hanging Gardens of Babylon.

125. " Family Life " (carving).

1971. 15th Anniv. of Social Security Service.

308. **125.** 70 f. brn., green & red 40 20

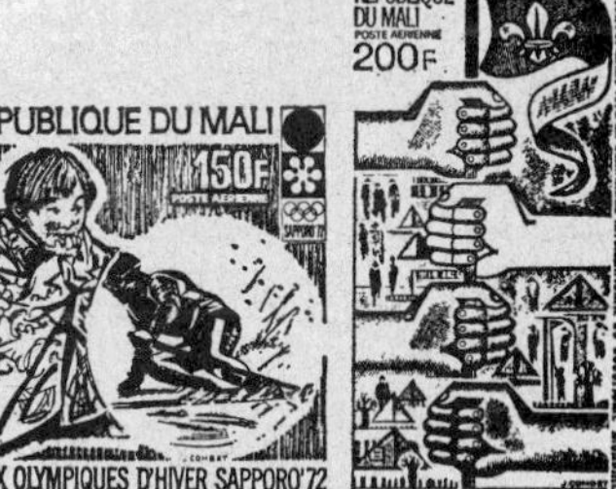

126. Slalom-skiing and Japanese Girl. 128. Hands clasping Flagpole.

127. " Santa Maria della Salute " (Caffi).

1972. Air. Winter Olympic Games, Sapporo, Japan.

309. **126.** 150 f. brn., grn. & orge. 1·00 35
310. – 200 f. grn., brn. & red 1·50 55

DESIGN: 200 f. Ice-hockey and Japanese actor.

1972. Air. U.N.E.S.C.O. " Save Venice " Campaign. Multicoloured.

312. 130 f. Type **127** 70 35
313. 270 f. " Rialto Bridge " 1·40 60
314. 280 f. " St. Mark's Square " (vert.) .. .. .. 1·60 70

1972. Air. Int. Scout Seminar, Cotonou, Dahomey.

315. **128.** 200 f. grn., orge. & brn. 1·40 55

129. Heart and Red Cross Emblems.

1972. Air. World Heart Month.

316. **129.** 150 f. red and blue .. 1·00 40

130. Football.

1972. Air. Olympic Games, Munich (1st issue). Sports and Munich Buildings.

317. **130.** 50 f. blue, brn. & grn. 25 20
318. – 150 f. blue, brn. & grn. 70 30
319. – 200 f. blue, brn. & grn. 80 50
320. – 300 f. blue, brn. & grn. 1·25 70

DESIGNS—VERT. 150 f. Judo. 200 f. Hurdling. HORIZ. 300 f. Running.

See also Nos. 357/62.

131. " Apollo 15 " and Lunar Rover.

1972. Air. History of Transport Development.

322. **131.** 150 f. red, grn. & lake 80 40
323. – 250 f. red, blue & grn. 2·00 1·00

DESIGN: 250 f. Montgolfier's balloon and Cugnot's steam car.

132. " UIT " on T.V. Screen.

1972. World Telecommunications Day.
324. **132.** 70 f. black, blue & red 40 20

133. Clay Funerary Statue. **134.** Samuel Morse, and Early Telegraph.

1972. Mali Archaeology. Multicoloured.
325. 30 f. Type **133** 20 15
326. 40 f. Female Figure (wood-carving) 30 20
327. 50 f. " Warrior " (stone-painting) 40 20
328. 100 f. Wrought-iron ritual figures .. .. .. 1·00 35

1972. Death Centenary of Samuel Morse (inventor of telegraph).
329. **134.** 80 f. purple, grn. & red 45 20

135. " Cinderella ". **136.** Weather Balloon.

1972. Air. Charles Perrault's Fairy Tales.
330. **125.** 70 f. grn., red and brown 45 20
331. – 80 f. brn., red & green 50 25
332. – 150 f. violet, pur. & blue 1·10 35
DESIGNS: 80 f. " Puss in Boots ". 150 f. " The Sleeping Beauty ".

1972. World Meteorological Day.
333. **136.** 130 f. multicoloured .. 60 30

137. Astronauts and Lunar Rover.

1972. Air. Moon Flight of " Apollo 16 ".
334. **137.** 500 f. brn., violet & grn. 3·00 1·25

138. Book Year Emblem.

1972. Air. Int. Book Year.
335. **138.** 80 f. gold, green & blue 40 25

139. Sarakole Dance, Kayes. **140.** Learning the Alphabet.

1972. Traditional Dances. Multicoloured.
336. 10 f. Type **139** 25 15
337. 20 f. Malinke dance, Bamako 30 15
338. 50 f. Hunter's dance, Bougouni 45 20
339. 70 f. Bambara dance, Segou 60 20
340. 80 f. Dogon dance, Sanga .. 70 30
341. 120 f. Targuie dance, Timbuktu 1·25 45

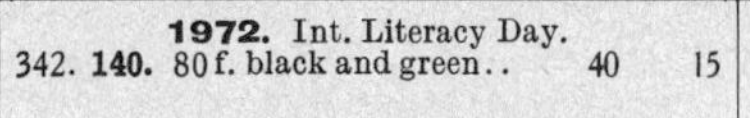
1972. Int. Literacy Day.
342. **140.** 80 f. black and green .. 40 15

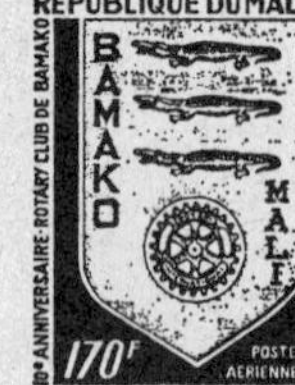

141. Statue and Musical Instruments. **142.** Club Banner.

1972. First Anthology of Malinenne Music.
343. **141.** 100 f. multicoloured .. 70 30

1972. Air. 10th Anniv. of Bamako Rotary Club.
344. **142.** 170 f. purple, blue & red 1·00 40

143. Aries the Ram.

1972. Signs of the Zodiac.
345. **143.** 15 f. brown & purple 25 20
346. – 15 f. black and brown 25 20
347. – 35 f. blue and red .. 40 25
348. – 35 f. red and green .. 40 25
349. – 40 f. brown and blue 50 30
350. – 40 f. brown and purple 50 30
351. – 45 f. red and blue .. 60 35
352. – 45 f. green and red .. 60 35
353. – 65 f. blue and violet 90 35
354. – 65 f. brown and violet 90 35
355. – 90 f. blue and mauve 1·40 65
356. – 90 f. green and mauve 1·40 65
DESIGNS: No. 346, Taurus the Bull. No. 347, Gemini the Twins. No. 348, Cancer the Crab. No. 349, Leo the Lion. No. 350, Virgo the Virgin. No. 351, Libra the Scales. No. 352, Scorpio the Scorpion. No. 353, Sagittarius the Archer. No. 354, Capricornus the Goat. No. 355, Aquarius the Water-carrier. No. 356, Pisces the Fish.

1972. Air. Olympic Games, Munich (2nd issue). Sports and Locations of Games since 1952. As Type **130.**
357. 70 f. blue, brown and red .. 25 15
358. 90 f. green, red and blue .. 35 20
359. 140 f. olive, green and brown 60 20
360. 150 f. brn., green and red 65 25
361. 170 f. blue, brn. and purple 75 30
362. 210 f. blue, red and green .. 90 40
DESIGNS—VERT. 70 f. Boxing, Helsinki Games (1952). 150 f. Weightlifting, Tokyo Games (1964). HORIZ. 90 f. Hurdling, Melbourne Games (1956). 140 f. 200 metres, Rome Games (1960). 170 f. Swimming, Mexico Games (1968). 210 f. Throwing the javelin, Munich Games (1972).

1972. Medal Winners, Munich Olympic Games. Nos. 318/20 and 362 optd. with events and names, etc.
363. 150 f. blue, brown & green 70 30
364. 200 f. blue, brown & green 90 40
365. 210 f. blue, red and green .. 90 40
366. 300 f. blue, brown & green 1·25 70
OVERPRINTS: 150 f. **JUDO RUSKA 2 MEDAILLES D'OR.** 200 f. **STEEPLE KEINO MEDAILLE D'OR.** 210 f. **MEDAILLE D'OR 90 m. 48** 300 f. **100 m.-200m BORZOV 2 MEDAILLES D'OR.**

1972. Mali Locomotives (2nd series). As T **106.**
367. 10 f. blue, green & red .. 1·25 1·00
368. 30 f. blue, green & brn. .. 2·50 2·25
369. 60 f. blue, brn. & grn. .. 3·00 2·75
370. 120 f. purple, grn. & blk. .. 5·00 4·50
LOCOMOTIVES: 10 f. First Locomotive to arrive at Bamako, 1906. 30 f. Locomotive from the Thies-Bamako line, 1920. 60 f. Type " 141 " locomotive, Thies-Bamako line, 1927. 120 f. Alsthom " BB " coupled diesels, Dakar-Bamako line, 1947.

146. Emperor Haile Selassie.

1972. Air. 80th Birth Anniv. of Emperor Haile Selassie.
371. **146.** 70 f. multicoloured .. 30 20

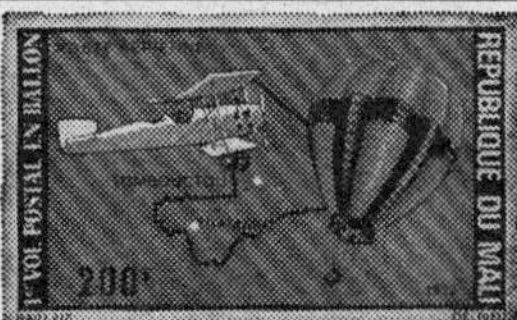

147. Balloon, Aircraft and Map.

1972. Air. First Mali Airmail Flight by Balloon. Bamako to Timbukto. Mult.
372. 200 f. Type **147** .. .. 1·00 45
373. 300 f. Balloon, " Concorde " and map .. 1·40 60

148. High-Jumping.

1973. 2nd African Games, Lagos, Nigeria. Multicoloured.
374. 70 f. Type **148** 30 20
375. 270 f. Throwing the discus 1·25 60
376. 280 f. Football .. .. 1·40 65

149. 14th-century German Bishop. **150.** Interpol Headquarters, Paris.

1973. Air. World Chess Championship, Reykjavik, Iceland.
377 **149** 100 f. lt blue, bl & brn 1·25 35
378 – 200 f. red, lt red & blk 2·50 75
DESIGN: 200 f. 18th-century Indian knight (elephant).

1973. 50th Anniv. of Int. Criminal Police Organization (Interpol).
379. **150.** 80 f. multicoloured .. 65 20

151. Emblem and Dove with letter. **152.** " Fauna Protection " Stamp of 1963.

1973. 10th Anniv. (1971) of African Postal Union.
380. **151.** 70 f. multicoloured .. 35 20

1973. Air. Stamp Day.
381. **152.** 70 f. orge., red & brn. 1·25 30

153. Astronauts on Moon. **155.** Handicapped Africans.

154. Copernicus.

1973. Moon Mission of " Apollo " 17.
382. **153.** 250 f. brown and blue 1·60 65

1973. 500th Birth Anniv. of Copernicus.
384. **154.** 300 f. purple and blue 2·00 1·10

1973. " Help the Handicapped ".
385. **155.** 70 f. orge., black & red 35 20

156. Dr. G. A. Hansen.

1973. Centenary of Hansen's Identification of the Leprosy Bacillus.
386. **156.** 200 f. grn., blk. & red 1·60 60

157. Bentley and Alfa Romeo, 1930.

1973. 50th Anniv. of Le Mans 24 hour Endurance Race.
387. **157.** 50 f. grn., orge. & blue 35 15
388. – 100 f. green, blue & red 75 25
389. – 200 f. blue, green & red 1·75 50
DESIGNS: 100 f. Jaguar and Talbot, 1953. 200 f. Matra and Porsche, 1952.

158. Scouts around Camp-fire.

1973. Int. Scouting Congress, Addis Ababa and Nairobi.
390. **158.** 50 f. brown, red & blue 30 15
391. – 70 f. brown, red & blue 40 20
392. – 80 f. red, brn. & green 50 20
393. – 130 f. grn., blue & brn. 70 30
394. – 270 f. red, violet & grey 1·40 60
DESIGNS—VERT. 70 f. Scouts Saluting flag. 130 f. Lord Baden-Powell. HORIZ. 80 f. Standard-bearers. 270 f. Map of Africa and Scouts and Guides in ring.

159. Swimming and National Flags.

1973. First Afro-American Sports Meeting, Bamako.
395. **159.** 70 f. green, red & blue 30 20
396. – 80 f. green, red and blue 35 25
397. – 330 f. blue and red .. 1·50 70
DESIGNS—VERT. 80 f. Throwing the discus and javelin. HORIZ. 330 f. Running.

1973. Pan-African Drought Relief. No. 296 surch. **SECHERESSE SOLIDARITE AFRICAINE** and value.
398. 200 f. on 100 f. multicoloured 1·10 65

1973. Air. African Fortnight, Brussels. As T **168a** of Niger.
399. 70 f. violet, blue and brn. 30 20

162. " Perseus " (Cellini). **164.** " Apollo 11 " First Landing.

163. Stephenson's " Rocket " and French " Buddicom " Locomotive.

1973. Air. Famous Sculptures.
400. **162.** 100 f. green and red .. 55 25
401. – 150 f. purple and red .. 85 35
402. – 250 f. green and red .. 1·50 65
DESIGNS: 150 f. "Pieta" (Michelangelo). 250 f. "Victory of Samothrace".

1973. Air. Famous Locomotives.
403. **163.** 100 f. blk., blue & brn. 1·25 60
404. – 150 f. multicoloured .. 1·60 65
405. – 200 f. blue, slate and brown .. .. 2·50 1·00
DESIGNS: 150 f. Union Pacific and Santa Fe Railroad locomotives. 200 "Mistral" and "Tokaido" trains.

1973. Conquest of the Moon.
406. **164.** 50 f. purple, red & brn. 25 20
407. – 75 f. grey, blue and red 30 20
408. – 100 f. slate, brown and blue 55 30
409. – 280 f. blue, green & red 1·25 65
410. – 300 f. blue, red & green 1·50 80
DESIGNS: 75 f. "Apollo 13" Recovery capsule. 100 f. "Apollo 14" Lunar trolley. 280 f. "Apollo 15" Lunar rover. 300 f. "Apollo 17" lift off from Moon.

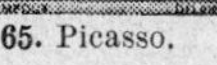
165. Picasso.

166. Pres. John Kennedy.

1973. Air. Pablo Picasso (artist). Commem.
411. **165.** 500 f. multicoloured .. 2·75 1·25

1973. Air. 10th Death Anniv. of Pres. Kennedy.
412. **166.** 500 f. black, pur. & gold 2·50 1·25

1973. Air. Christmas. As T **105** but dated "1973". Multicoloured.
413. 100 f. "The Annunciation" (V. Carpaccio) (horiz.) .. 50 25
414. 200 f. "Virgin of St. Simon" (F. Baroccio) .. .. 1·25 50
415. 250 f. "Flight into Egypt" (A. Solario) .. .. 1·60 70

167. Player and Football.

168. Cora.

1973. Air. World Football Cup Championships, West Germany.
416. **167.** 150 f. red, brn. & grn. 75 35
417. – 250 f. grn., brn. & violet 1·50 60
DESIGN: 250 f. Goalkeeper and ball.

1973. Musical Instruments.
419. **168.** 5 f. brn., red & green .. 20 10
420. – 10 f. brown and blue .. 20 10
421. – 15 f. brown, red & yell. 25 15
422. – 20 f. brown and red .. 30 15
423. – 25 f. brn., red & yell. .. 35 15
424. – 30 f. black and blue .. 50 20
425. – 35 f. sepia, brn. & red 60 20
426. – 40 f. brown and red .. 65 30
DESIGNS—HORIZ. 10 f. Balafon. VERT. 15 f. Djembe. 20 f. Guitar. 25 d. N'Djarka. 30 f. M'Bolon. 35 f. Dozo N'Goni. 40 f. N'Tamani.

169. "Musicians" (mosaic).

INDEX

Countries can be quickly located by referring to the index at the end of this volume.

1974. Air. Roman Frescoes and Mosaics from Pompeii.
427. **169.** 150 f. red, brn. & grey 75 35
428. – 250 f. brn., red & orge. 1·25 60
429. – 350 f. brown, orange and olive .. .. 1·75 75
DESIGNS—VERT. 250 f. "Alexander the Great" (mosaic). 350 f. "Bacchante" (fresco).

170. Corncob, Worker and "Kibaru" Newspaper.
171. Sir Winston Churchill.

1974. 2nd Anniv. of Rural Press.
430. **170.** 70 f. brown and green 35 20

1974. Air. Birth Cent. of Sir Winston Churchill.
431. **171.** 500 f. black .. .. 2·50 1·50

172. Chess-pieces on Board.

1974. Air. 21st Chess Olympiad, Nice.
432 **172** 250 f. indigo, red & blue 2·50 75

173. "The Crucifixion" (Alsace School c. 1380).

1974. Air. Easter. Multicoloured.
433. 400 f. Type **173** .. .. 1·60 1·00
434. 500 f. "The Entombment" (Titian) (horiz.) .. .. 2·25 1·25

174. Lenin.

1974. Air. 50th Death Anniv. of Lenin.
435. **174.** 150 f. purple and violet 70 30

175. Goalkeeper and Globe.

177. Full-rigged Sailing Ship and Modern Liner.

176. Horse-jumping Scenes.

1974. World Cup Football Championships, West Germany.
436. **175.** 270 f. red, grn. & lilac 1·25 80
437. – 280 f. blue, brn. & red 1·60 80
DESIGN: 280 f. World Cup emblem on football.

1974. Air. World Equestrian Championships, La Baule.
438. **176.** 130 f. brn., lilac & blue 1·50 60

1974. Cent. of Universal Postal Union.
439. **177.** 80 f. pur., lilac & brn. 55 25
440. – 90 f. orge., grey & blue 40 30
441. – 270 f. pur., olive & grn. 2·00 90
DESIGNS: 90 f. Bi-plane and jet airliner. 270 f. Early steam and modern electric trains.
See also Nos. 463/4.

178. "Skylab" over Africa.

1974. Air. Survey of Africa by "Skylab" Space Station.
442. **178.** 200 f. indigo, bl. & orge. 1·00 40
443. – 250 f. blue, pur. & orge. 1·25 60
DESIGN: 250 f. Astronaut servicing cameras.

1974. Air. 11th Arab Scout Jamboree, Lebanon. Nos. 391/2 surch. **130 f. 11e JAMBOREE ARABE AOUT 1974 LIBAN** or **170 f. CONGRES PAN-ARABE LIBAN AOUT 1974.**
444. 130 f. on 70 f. brn., red & bl. 70 40
445. 170 f. on 80 f. bl., grn. & red 75 50

1974. Air. 5th Anniv. of First landing on Moon. Nos. 408/9 surch. **130 f. 1er DEBARQUEMENT SUR LA LUNE 20-VII-69** or **300 f. 1er PAS SUR LA LUNE 21-VII-69.**
446. 130 f. on 100 f. slate, brown and blue 70 45
447. 300 f. on 280 f. bl., grn. & red 1·40 70

1974. West Germany's Victory in World Cup Football Championships. Nos. 436/7 surch. **R.F.A. 2 HOLLANDE 1** and value.
448. **175.** 300 f. on 270 f. red, green and lilac .. 1·40 80
449. – 330 f. on 280 f. blue, brown and red .. 1·60 80

182. Weaver.

183. River Niger near Gao.

1974. Crafts and Craftsmen. Mult.
450. 50 f. Type **182** 25 15
451. 60 f. Potter 30 15
452. 70 f. Smith 40 20
453. 80 f. Wood-carver 55 20

1974. Mali Views. Multicoloured.
454. 10 f. Type **183** 15 10
455. 20 f. "The Hand of Fatma" (rock formation, Hombori) (vert.) 15 10
456. 40 f. Waterfall, Gouina .. 35 15
457. 70 f. Hill-dwellings, Dogon (vert.) 60 20

184. "C3-PLM" (1906) and "150-P" (1939) Locomotives.

1974. Air. Steam Locomotives.
458. **184.** 90 f. indigo, red & blue 75 40
459. – 120 f. brn., orge. & blue 85 50
460. – 210 f. brn., orge. & blue 1·60 70
461. – 330 f. blk., grn. & blue 2·40 1·40
DESIGNS: 120 f. Baldwin "2-2-0" (1870) and Pacific (1920) locomotives. 210 f. "241-A1" (1925) and Buddicom (1847) locomotives. 330 f. Hudson (1938) and "La Gironde" (1839) locomotives.

185. Skiing.

1974. Air. 50th Anniv. of Winter Olympics.
462. **185.** 300 f. red, blue & grn. 1·40 80

1974. Berne Postal Convention. Cent. Nos. 439 and 441 surch. **9 OCTOBRE 1974** and value.
463. **177.** 250 f. on 80 f. purple, lilac and brown .. 1·40 80
464. – 300 f. on 270 f. purple olive and green .. 1·90 80

187. Mao Tse-tung and Great Wall of China.

188. "The Nativity" (Memling).

1974. 25th Anniv. of Chinese People's Republic.
465. **187.** 100 f. blue, red & green 50 30

1974. Air. Christmas. Multicoloured.
466. 290 f. Type **188** .. .. 1·25 70
467. 310 f. "Virgin and Child" (Bourgogne School) .. 1·50 75
468. 400 f. "Adoration of the Magi" (Schongauer) .. 1·90 1·10

189. Raoul Follereau (missionary).

191. Dr. Schweitzer.

190. Electric Train and Airliner.

1974. Air. Raoul Follereau, "Apostle of the Lepers".
469. **189.** 200 f. blue .. .. 1·25 55
469a. 200 f. brown .. .. 1·75 1·10

1974. Air. Europafrique.
470. **190.** 100 f. grn., brn. & blue 1·75 65
471. 110 f. bl., vio. & brn. .. 1·75 65

1975. Birth Cent. of Dr Albert Schweitzer.
472. **191.** 150 f. turq., grn. & blue 90 40

192. Patients making Handicrafts, and Lions International Emblem.

1975. 5th Anniv. of Samanko (Leprosy rehabilitation village). Multicoloured.
473. 90 f. Type **192** 50 20
474. 100 f. View of Samanko .. 60 25

193. "The Pilgrims at Emmaus" (Champaigne).

1975. Air. Easter. Multicoloured.
475. 200 f. Type **193** 90 45
476. 300 f. "The Pilgrims at Emmaus" (Veronese) .. 1·25 60
477. 500 f. "Christ in Majesty" (Limoges enamel) (vert.) .. .. .. 2·25 1·25

194. "Journey to the Centre of the Earth".

1975. Air. 70th Death Anniv. of Jules Verne.
478. **194.** 100 f. grn., bl. and brn. 45 25
479. – 170 f. brn., blue and light brown 75 35
480. – 190 f. blue, turq. & brn. 85 40
481. – 220 f. brn., pur. & blue 1·25 50
DESIGNS: 170 f. Jules Verne and "From the Earth to the Moon" 90 f. Giant octopus—"Twenty Thousand Leagues Under the Sea". 220 f. "A Floating City".

195. Head of "Dawn" (Tomb of the Medici). **197.** Astronaut.

196. "Tetrodon fahaka".

1975. Air. 500th Birth Anniv of Michelangelo (artist). Multicoloured.
482. 400 f. Type **195** .. .. 1·75 1·10
483. 500 f. "Moses" (marble statue, Rome) .. 2·25 1·25

1975. Fishes (1st series).
484. **196.** 60 f. brn., yell. and grn. 50 20
485. – 70 f. blk., brn. and grey 55 25
486. – 80 f. multicoloured .. 70 25
487. – 90 f. blue, grey & grn. 1·00 35
488. – 110 f. black and blue .. 1·25 45
FISHES: 70 f. "Malopterurus electricus". 80 f. "Citharinus latus". 90 f. "Hydrocyon forskali". 110 f. "Lates niloticus".
See also Nos. 544/8.

1975. Air. Soviet–U.S. Space Co-operation.
489. **197.** 290 f. red, blue and blk. 1·10 50
490. – 300 f. red, blue and blk. 1·10 60
491. – 370 f. grn., pur. and blk. 1·40 80
DESIGNS: 300 f. "America and Russia". 370 f. New York and Moscow landmarks.

198. Einstein and Equation. **199.** Woman with Bouquet.

1975. Air. 20th Death Anniv. of Albert Einstein.
492. **198.** 90 f. blue, pur. & brn. 55 30
See also Nos. 504, 507 and 519.

1975. International Women's Year.
493. **199.** 150 f. red and green .. 70 35

200. Morris "Oxford", 1913.

1975. Early Motor-cars.
494. **200.** 90 f. violet, brn. & blue 50 20
495. – 130 f. red, grey & blue 80 25
496. – 190 f. deep blue, green and blue .. .. 1·25 40
497. – 230 f. brn., blue & red 1·50 45
MOTOR-CARS: 130 f. Franklin "E", 1907. 190 f. Daimler, 1900. 230 f. Panhard & Levassor, 1895.

201.

1975. Air. "Nordjamb 75" World Scout Jamboree, Norway.
498. **201.** 100 f. blue, brn. & lake 55 25
499. – 150 f. grn., brn. & blue 75 30
500. – 290 f. lake, brn. & blue 1·40 75
DESIGNS: 150 f., 290 f. Scouts and emblem (different).

202. Lafayette and Battle Scene.

1975. Air. Bicentenary of American Revolution. Multicoloured.
501 290 f. Type **202** .. .. 1·50 65
502 300 f. Washington and battle scene .. .. 1·50 65
503 370 f. De Grasse and Battle of the Chesapeake, 1781 1·90 95

1975. 20th Death Anniv of Sir Alexander Fleming (scientist). As T **198**.
504 150 f. brown, purple & blue 80 35

204. Olympic Rings.

1975. Air. "Pre-Olympic Year".
505. **204.** 350 f. violet and blue 1·00 65
506. – 400 f. blue .. 1·10 80
DESIGNS: 400 f. Emblem of Montreal Olympics (1976).

1975. Birth Bicentenary of Andre-Marie Ampere. As T **198**.
507. 90 f. brown, red & violet 45 20

205. Tristater of Carthage.

1975. Ancient Coins.
508. **205.** 130 f. blk., blue & pur. 50 25
509. – 170 f. blk., grn. & brn. 70 35
510. – 190 f. blk., grn. & red 1·00 65
511. – 260 f. blk., blue & orge. 1·40 1·00
COINS: 170 f. Decadrachm of Syracuse. 190 f. Tetradrachm of Acanthe. 260 f. Didrachm of Eretrie.

1975. Air. "Apollo-Soyuz" Space Link. Nos. 489/91 optd. **ARRIMAGE 17 Juil. 1975.**
512. **197.** 290 f. red, blue & blk. 1·25 65
513. – 300 f. red, blue & blk. 1·25 65
514. – 370 f. grn., pur. & blk. 1·50 95

207. U.N. Emblem and Names of Agencies forming "ONU".

1975. 30th Anniv. of United Nations Charter.
515. **207.** 200 f. blue and green 70 45

208. "The Visitation" (Ghirlandaio).

1975. Air. Christmas. Religious Paintings. Multicoloured.
516. 290 f. Type **208** .. .. 1·40 55
517. 300 f. "Nativity" (Fra Filippo Lippi School) 1·40 65
518. 370 f. "Adoration of the Magi" (Velasquez) .. 1·60 1·10

1975. Air. 500th Death Anniv. of Clement Ader (aviation pioneer). As T **198**.
519. 100 f. pur., red & blue .. 55 20

209. "Concorde" in Flight.

1976. Air. "Concorde's" First Commercial Flight.
520. **209.** 500 f. multicoloured .. 3·50 1·50

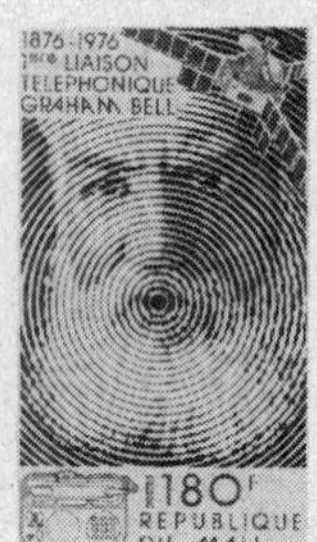

210. Figure-Skating. **211.** Alexander Graham Bell.

1976. Air. Winter Olympic Games, Innsbruck. Multicoloured.
521. 120 f. Type **210** 50 25
522. 420 f. Ski-jumping .. 1·50 65
523. 430 f. Skiing (slalom) .. 1·50 75

1976. Telephone Centenary.
524. **211.** 180 f. blue, brown and light brown .. 65 35

212. Chameleon.

1976. Reptiles. Multicoloured.
525. 20 f. Type **212** 20 15
526. 30 f. Lizard 25 15
527. 40 f. Tortoise 30 20
528. 90 f. Python 65 25
529. 120 f. Crocodile .. .. 1·10 50

213. Nurse and Patient. **215.** Constructing Orbital Space Station.

214. Dr. Adenauer and Cologne Cathedral.

1976. Air. World Health Day.
530. **213.** 130 f. multicoloured .. 55 25

1976. Birth Centenary Dr. Konrad Adenauer.
531. **214.** 180 f. purple & brown 90 40

1976. Air. "The Future in Space".
532. **215.** 300 f. deep blue, blue and orange .. .. 1·25 60
533. – 400 f. blue, red & pur. 1·90 90
DESIGN: 400 f. Sun and space-ship with solar batteries.

216. American Bald Eagle and Liberty Bell.

1976. Air. American Revolution. Bicent. and "Interphil '76" Int. Stamp Exn., Philadelphia.
534. **216.** 100 f. blue, pur. & blk. 1·00 20
535. – 400 f. brn., blue & blk. 3·50 85
536. – 440 f. violet, grn. & blk. 2·75 85
DESIGNS—HORIZ. 400 f. Warships and American bald eagle. VERT. 440 f. Red Indians and American bald eagle.

217. Running. **218.** Scouts marching.

1976. Air. Olympic Games, Montreal.
537. **217.** 200 f. blk., brn. & red 70 40
538. – 250 f. brn., grn. & blue 80 50
539. – 300 f. blk., blue & grn. 1·25 60
540. – 440 f. blk., blue & grn. 1·60 90
DESIGNS: 250 f. Swimming. 300 f. Handball. 440 f. Football.

1976. Air. 1st All-African Scout Jamboree, Nigeria.
541. **218.** 140 f. brn., blue & grn. 70 35
542. – 180 f. brn., grn. & grey 1·00 40
543. – 200 f. violet & brown .. 1·10 50
DESIGNS—HORIZ. 180 f. Scouts tending calf. VERT. 200 f. Scout surveying camp at dusk.

1976. Fishes (2nd series). As T **196**.
544. 100 f. black and blue .. 50 20
545. 120 f. yell., brn. and grn... 55 25
546. 130 f. turq., brn. and blk. 65 25
547. 150 f. yellow, drab & green 75 30
548. 220 f. black, green & brown 1·25 50
DESIGNS: 100 f. "Heterotis niloticus". 120 f. "Synodontis budgetti", 130 f. "Heterobranchus bidorsalis". 150 f. "Tilapia mondodi" 220 f. "Alestes malerolepidotus".

220. Scenes from Children's Book. **221.** "Roi de L'Air".

1976. Literature for Children.
549. **220.** 130 f. grey, grn. & red 45 25

1976. "L'Essor" Newspaper. First Issue.
550. **221.** 120 f. multicoloured .. 1·00 30

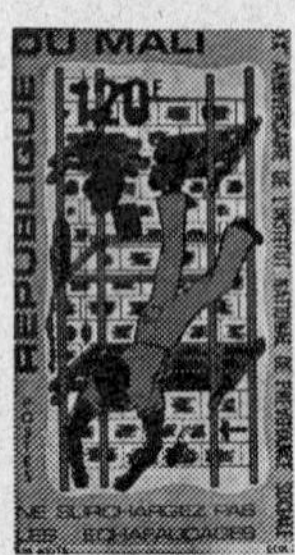

222. Fall from Scaffolding.

1976. 20th Anniv. of National Social Insurance.
551. **222.** 120 f. multicoloured .. 35 25

223. Moenjodaro.

1976. Air. U.N.E.S.C.O. " Save Moenjodaro " (Pakistan) Campaign.
552. **223.** 400 f. pur., blue & blk. 1·75 80
553. – 500 f. red, yell. & blue 2·00 1·25
DESIGN: 500 f. Effigy, animals and remains.

224. Freighter, Aircraft and Map.

1976. Air. Europafrique.
554. **224.** 200 f. purple and blue 1·10 45

225. Cascade of Letters.

1976. 25th Anniv. of U.N. Postal Administration.
555. **225.** 120 f. orge., grn. & lilac 45 25

226. Moto Guzzi " 254 " (Italy).

1976. Motorcycling.
556. **266.** 90 f. red, grey & brown 45 20
557. – 120 f. vio., blue & blk. 55 25
558. – 130 f. red, grey & grn. 70 25
559. – 140 f. blue, grn. & grey 90 30
DESIGNS: 120 f. B.M.W. " 900 " (Germany). 130 f. Honda " Egli " (Japan). 140 f. Motobecane " LT3 " (France).

227. " The Nativity " (Taddeo Gaddi).

1976. Air. Christmas. Religious Paintings. Multicoloured.
560. 280 f. Type **227**. . . . . 1·25 50
561. 300 f. " Adoration of the Magi " (Hans Memling) 1·40 60
562. 320 f. " The Nativity " (Carlo Crivelli) . . . . 1·50 75

228. Muscat Fishing Boat.

1976. Ships.
563. **228.** 160 f. pur., grn. & blue 65 30
564. – 180 f. grn., red & blue 65 35
565. – 190 f. pur., blue & grn. 70 40
566. – 200 f. grn., red & blue 75 40
DESIGNS: 180 f. Cochin Chinese junk. 190 f. Dunkirk lightship. "Ruytingen". 200 f. Nile felucca.

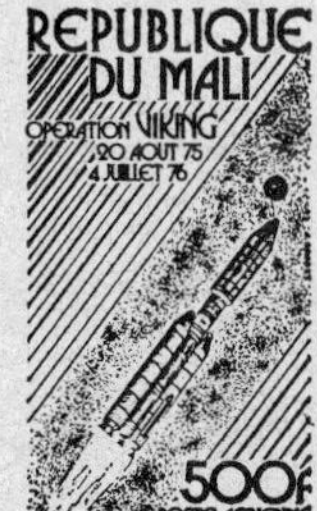

229. Rocket in Flight.

1976. Air. Operation " Viking ".
567. **229.** 500 f. blue, red & lake 1·75 1·25
568. – 1000 f. lake, blue and deep blue . . . . 3·00 1·90
DESIGN: 1000 f. Spacecraft on Mars.

230. Pres. Giscard d'Estaing and Sankore Mosque, Timbuktu.

1977. Air. Visit of Pres. Giscard d'Estaing of France.
570. **230.** 430 f. multicoloured . . 2·00 80

231. Rocket on Launch-pad, Newton and Apple.

1977. Air. 250th Death Anniv. of Isaac Newton.
571. **231.** 400 f. pur., red & grn. 2·00 75

232. Prince Philip and Queen Elizabeth II.

1977. Air. "Personalities of Decolonisation". Multicoloured.
572. 180 f. Type **232** 65 35
573. 200 f. General De Gaulle (vert.) . . . . . . 1·10 50
574. 250 f. Queen Wilhelmina of the Netherlands (vert.) 75 55
575. 300 f. King Baudouin and Queen Fabiola of Belgium 1·10 70
576. 480 f. Crowning of Queen Elizabeth II (vert.) . . 2·00 1·25

233. Lindbergh and " Spirit of St. Louis ".

1977. Air. 50th Anniv. of Lindbergh's Transatlantic Flight.
577. **233.** 420 f. orange and violet 1·90 85
578. – 430 f. blue, orge. & grn. 1·90 85
DESIGN: 430 f. " Spirit of St. Louis " crossing the Atlantic.

234. Village Indigobird. **236.** Printed Circuit.

235. Louis Braille and Hands reading Book.

1977. Mali Birds. Multicoloured.
579. 15 f. Type **234** 45 15
580. 25 f. Yellow-breasted Barbet 75 15
581. 30 f. Vitelline Masked Weaver 75 55
582. 40 f. Carmine Bee Eater . . 90 60
583. 50 f. Senegal Parrot . . 90 60

1977. 125th Death Anniv. of Louis Braille (inventor of "Braille" system of reading and writing for the blind).
584. **235.** 200 f. blue, red & green 1·10 45

1977. World Telecommunications Day.
585. **236.** 120 f. red and brown . . 35 20

236a. Chateau Sassenage, Grenoble.

1977. Air. 10th Anniv. of International French Language Council.
586. **236a.** 300 f. multicoloured 1·00 50

237. Zeppelin LZ–1 over Lake Constance.

1977. Air. History of the Zeppelin.
587. **237.** 120 f. grn., brn. & blue 55 25
588. – 130 f. deep blue, brown and blue 55 25
589. – 350 f. red, blue and deep blue . . . . 1·60 75
590. – 500 f. deep blue, green and blue . . . . 2·25 95
DESIGNS: 130 f. " Graf Zeppelin " over Atlantic. 350 f. Burning of " Hindenburg " at Lakehurst. 500 f. Ferdinand von Zeppelin and " Graf Zeppelin " at mooring mast.

238. "Anax imperator".

1977. Insects. Multicoloured.
591 5 f. Type **238** 20 15
592 10 f. "Sphadromantis viridis" 25 15
593 20 f. "Vespa tropica" . . 25 15
594 35 f. "Melolontha melolantha" 30 15
595 60 f. Stag beetle 55 20

239. Knight and Rook. **240.** Henri Dunant.

1977. Chess Pieces.
596. **239.** 120 f. blk., grn. & brn. 1·00 30
597. – 130 f. grn., red & blk. 1·10 30
598. – 300 f. grn., red & blue 2·50 75
DESIGNS—VERT. 130 f. Pawn and Bishop. HORIZ. 300 f. King and Queen.

1977. Air. Nobel Peace Prize Winners. Multicoloured.
599. 600 f. Type **240** (founder of Red Cross) . . . . 2·00 1·00
600. 700 f. Martin Luther King 2·25 1·10

241. Ship. **242.** " Head of Horse ".

1977. Europafrique.
601. **241.** 400 f. multicoloured . . 1·25 75

1977. 525th Birth Anniv. of Leonardo da Vinci.
602. **242.** 200 f. brown and black 75 50
603. – 300 f. brown . . . . 1·10 60
604. – 500 f. red . . . . 2·00 85
DESIGNS: 300 f. " Head of Young Girl ". 500 f. Self-portrait.

243. Footballers. **245.** Dome of the Rock.

244. Friendship Hotel.

1977. Air. Football Cup Elimination Rounds.
605. – 180 f. brn., grn. & orge. 50 30
606. **243.** 200 f. brn., grn. & orge. 60 35
607. – 420 f. grey, grn. & lilac 1·25 70
DESIGNS—HORIZ. 180 f. Two footballers. 420 f. Tackling.

1977. Friendship Hotel, Bamako. Inauguration.
608. **244.** 120 f. multicoloured . . 35 25

1977. Palestinian Welfare.
609. **245.** 120 f. multicoloured . . 55 20
610. 180 f. multicoloured . . 70 30

246. Mao Tse-tung and " Comatex " Hall, Bamako.

1977. Air. Mao Tse-tung Memorial.
611. **246.** 300 f. red . . . . 1·25 50

1977. Air. First Commercial Paris-New York Flight by " Concorde ". Optd. **PARIS-NEW YORK. 22.11.77.**
612. **209.** 500 f. multicoloured . . 7·00 4·50

248. " Adoration of the Magi " (Rubens).

1977. Air. Christmas. Details from " Adoration of the Magi " by Rubens.
613. **248.** 400 f. multicoloured . . 1·25 75
614. – 500 f. multicoloured . . 1·60 95
615. – 600 f. multicoloured . . 2·00 1·10
The 600 f. is a horizontal design.

249. " Hercules and the Nemean Lion ".

1978. 400th Birth Anniv. of Peter Paul Rubens. Multicoloured.
616. 200 f. " Battle of the Amazons " (horiz.) . . 70 35
617. 300 f. " Return from Labour in the Fields " (horiz.) . . 1·00 55
618. 500 f. Type **249** . . . . 1·75 95

250. Schubert and Mute Swans.

1978. Air. 150th Death Anniv. of Franz Schubert (composer). Multicoloured.

619. 300 f. Schubert and bars of music (vert.) .. .. 1·50 60
620. 420 f. Type **250** .. .. 4·00 70

251. Cook and Shipboard Scene.

1978. Air. 250th Birth Anniv. of Captain James Cook.

621. **251.** 200 f. bl., red & violet 1·25 40
622. – 300 f. brn., blue & grn. 1·75 70
DESIGN: 300 f. Capt. Cook meeting natives.

252. African and Chained Building.

1978. World Anti-Apartheid Year.

623. **252.** 120 f. vio., brn. & blue 40 20
624. – 130 f. vio., blue & orge. 40 20
625. – 180 f. brn., pur. & orge. 60 30
DESIGNS: 130 f. Statue of Liberty and Africans walking to open door. 180 f. African children and mule in fenced enclosure.

253. Players and Ball. 254. "Head of Christ"

1978. Air. World Cup Football Championship, Argentina.

626. **253.** 150 f. red, grn. & brn. 60 30
627. – 250 f. red, brn. & grn. 1·25 45
628. – 300 f. red, brn. & blue 1·50 50
DESIGNS—VERT. 250 f. HORIZ. 300 f. Different football scenes.

1978. Air. Easter. Works by Durer.

630. **254.** 420 f. green & brown 1·60 75
631. – 430 f. blue and brown 1·60 75
DESIGN: 430 f. "The Resurrection".

255. Red-cheeked Cordon-bleu.

1978. Birds. Multicoloured.

632. 20 f. Type **255** 20 15
633. 30 f. Black-faced Fire Finch 45 20
634. 50 f. Red-billed Fire Finch 55 40
635. 70 f. African Collared Dove 95 40
636. 80 f. White-billed Buffalo Weaver .. .. 1·40 50

256. C-3 "Trefle".

1978. Air. Birth Centenary of Andre Citroen (automobile pioneer).

637. **256.** 120 f. brn., lake & grn. 60 20
638. – 130 f. grey, orge. & blue 70 25
639. – 180 f. blue, grn. & red 1·10 30
640. – 200 f. black, red & lake 1·25 40
DESIGNS: 130 f. B-2 "Croisiere Noir" track-laying vehicle, 1924. 180 f. B-14 G Saloon, 1927. 200 f. Model-11 front-wheel drive car, 1934.

1978. 20th Anniv. of Bamako Lions Club. Nos. 473/4 surch. **XXe ANNIVERSAIRE DU LIONS CLUB DE BAMAKO 1958–1978** and value.

641. 120 f. on 90 f. Type **192** .. 45 20
642. 130 f. on 100 f. View of Samanko 55 30

258. Names of 1978 U.P.U. members forming Map of the World.

1978. Centenary of U.P.U. Foundation Congress, Paris.

643. **258.** 120 f. grn., orge. & mve. 45 20
644. – 130 f. yell., red and grn. 45 20
DESIGN: 130 f. Names of 1878 member states across globe.

259. Desert Scene.

1978. Campaign against Desertification.

645. **259.** 200 f. multicoloured .. 70 35

260. Mahatma Gandhi. **262.** Dominoes.

261. "Dermestes bromius".

1978. 30th Anniv. of Gandhi's Assassination.

646. **260.** 140 f. brn., red & black 85 30

1978. Insects. Multicoloured.

647 15 f. Type **261** 20 15
648 25 f. "Calosoma sp." .. 25 15
649 90 f. "Lopocerus variegatus" 45 20
650 120 f. "Coccinella septempunctata" .. 55 25
651 140 f. "Goliathus giganteus" 70 30

1978. Social Games.

652. **262.** 100 f. black, grn. & red 40 20
653. – 130 f. red, blk. & blue 85 25
DESIGN: 130 f. Bridge hand.

263. Ostrich on Nest (Syrian Manuscript).

1978. Air. Europafrique. Multicoloured.

654. 100 f. Type **263** .. .. 1·25 20
655. 110 f. Common zebra (Mansur miniature) .. 50 30

1978. Air. World Cup Football Championship Finalists. Nos. 626/8 optd. with results.

656. **253.** 150 f. red, grn. & brn. 60 25
657. – 250 f. red, brn. & grn. 1·00 45
658. – 300 f. red, brn. & blue 1·25 60
OPTS: 150 f. **CHAMPION 1978 ARGENTINE.** 250 f. **2e HOLLANDE:** 300 f. **3e BRESIL 4e ITALIE.**

265. Coronation Coach.

1978. Air. 25th Anniv. of Coronation of Queen Elizabeth II. Multicoloured.

660. 500 f. Type **265** .. .. 1·50 70
661. 1000 f. Queen Elizabeth II 2·75 1·40

266. Aristotle and African Animals. 267. Douglas "DC 3" and U.S.A. 1918 24c. stamp.

1978. 2300th Death Anniv. of Aristotle (Greek philosopher).

662. **266.** 200 f. brn., red and grn. 90 35

1978. Air. History of Aviation.

663. **267.** 80 f. dp. blue, red & blue 35 15
664. – 100 f. multicoloured .. 40 20
665. – 120 f. blk., blue & red 50 25
666. – 130 f. grn., red & blk. 55 30
667. – 320 f. violet, blue & red 1·25 65
DESIGNS: 100 f. Stampe "SV-4" and Belgium Balloon stamp of 1932. 120 f. Ader's "Avion No. 3" and France "Concorde" stamp of 1976. 130 f. Junker "JU-52" and Germany Biplane stamp of 1919. 320 f. Mitsubishi "A-6M Zero" and Japan Pagoda stamp of 1951.

268. "The Annunciation".

1978. Air. Christmas. Works by Durer.

668 **268** 420 f. brown and black 1·25 60
669 – 430 f. brown & green .. 1·25 60
670 – 500 f. black & brown .. 1·60 75
DESIGNS: 430 f. "Virgin and Child". 500 f. "Adoration of the Magi".

269. Launch of "Apollo 8" and Moon.

1978. Air. 10th Anniv. of First Manned Flight around the Moon.

671. **269.** 200 f. red, grn. & violet 60 30
672. – 300 f. violet, grn. & red 1·10 50
DESIGN: 300 f. "Apollo 8" in orbit around the Moon.

270. U.N. and Human Rights Emblems.

1978. 30th Anniv. of Declaration of Human Rights.

673. **270.** 180 f. red, blue and brown 60 35

271. "Concorde" and Ader's Aircraft.

1979. Air 3rd Anniv of First Commerical "Concorde" Flight. Multicoloured.

674. 120 f. Type **271** 60 25
675. 130 f. "Concorde" and "Flyer" 70 30
676. 200 f. "Concorde" and "Spirit of St. Louis" .. 1·25 45

1979. Air. "Philexafrique" Stamp Exhibition, Libreville, Gabon (1st issue) and Int. Stamp Fair, Essen, West Germany. As T **262** of Niger. Multicoloured.

677. 200 f. Ruff (bird) and Lubeck 1859 ½ s. stamp 1·00 70
678. 200 f. Dromedary and Mali 1965 200 f. stamp .. 1·75 1·25
See also Nos. 704/5.

1979. Air. Birth Centenary of Albert Einstein (physicist). No. 492 surch. **"1879–1979" 130F.**

679. **198.** 130 f. on 90 f. blue, pur. and brown 55 30

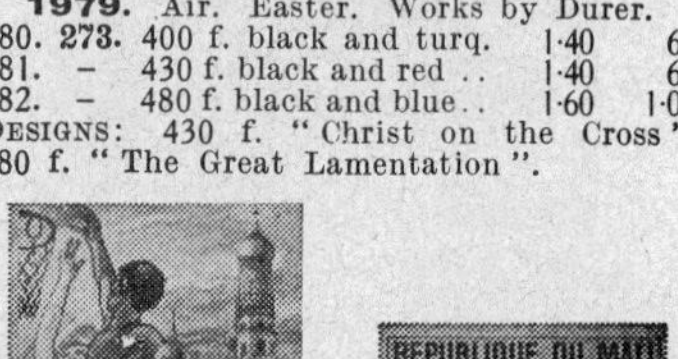
273. "Christ carrying the Cross".

1979. Air. Easter. Works by Durer.

680. **273.** 400 f. black and turq. 1·40 60
681. – 430 f. black and red .. 1·40 60
682. – 480 f. black and blue .. 1·60 1·00
DESIGNS: 430 f. "Christ on the Cross". 480 f. "The Great Lamentation".

274. Basketball and St. Basil's Cathedral, Moscow. 275. African Manatee.

1979. Air. Pre-Olympic Year. Multicoloured.

683. 420 f. Type **274** .. .. 1·50 75
684. 430 f. Footballer and Kremlin .. .. 1·50 75

1979. Endangered Animals. Multicoloured.

685. 100 f. Type **275** 45 20
686. 120 f. Chimpanzee 55 30
687. 130 f. Topi 65 35
688. 180 f. Gemsbok 80 40
689. 200 f. Giant eland 90 55

276. Child and I.Y.C. Emblem.

1979. International Year of the Child.

690. **276.** 120 f. grn., red & brn. 40 20
691. – 200 f. purple and green 70 35
692. – 300 f. brown, mauve and deep brown .. 1·00 50
DESIGNS: 200 f. Girl and scout with birds. 300 f. Children with calf.

277. Judo.

1979. World Judo Championships, Paris.

693. **277.** 200 f. sepia, red & ochre 80 40

278. Wave Pattern and Human Figures. **279.** Goat's Head and Lizard Fetishes.

1979. World Telecommunications Day.
694. 278. 120 f. multicoloured .. 35 20

1979. World Museums Day. Multicoloured.
695. 90 f. Type **279** 30 15
696. 120 f. Seated figures (wood carving).. .. .. 40 20
697. 130 f. Two animal heads and figurine (wood carving).. .. .. 50 25

280. Rowland Hill and Mali 1961 25 f. stamp.

281. Cora Players.

1979. Death Centenary of Sir Rowland Hill.
698. 280. 120 f. multicoloured .. 40 20
699. – 130 f. red, blue & grn. 40 20
700. – 180 f. blk., grn. & blue 60 30
701. – 200 f. blk., red & pur. 70 35
702. – 300 f. blue, deep blue and red .. .. 1·25 50
DESIGNS: 130 f. Zeppelin and Saxony stamp of 1850; 180 f. " Concorde " and France stamp of 1849; 200 f. Stage coach and U.S.A. stamp of 1849; 300 f. U.P.U. emblem and Penny Black.

1979.
703. 281. 200 f. multicoloured .. 1·00 40

282. Sankore Mosque and " Adenium obesum ".

1979. " Philexafrique " Exhibition, Libreville, Gabon (2nd issue).
704. 282. 120 f. multicoloured .. 90 55
705. – 300 f. red, blue & orge. 1·90 1·25
DESIGN: 300 f. Horseman and satellite.

283. Map of Mali showing Conquest of Desert.

1979. Operation " Sahel Vert ". Multicoloured.
706. 200 f. Type **283** 70 30
707. 300 f. Planting a tree .. 1·10 50

284. Lemons.

285. Sigmund Freud.

1979. Fruit (1st series). Multicoloured.
708. 10 f. Type **284** 15 10
709. 60 f. Pineapple 30 15
710. 100 f. Papaw 50 15
711. 120 f. Sweet-sops 55 20
712. 130 f. Mangoes 65 25
See also Nos. 777/81.

1979. 40th Death Anniv. of Sigmund Freud (psychologist).
713. 285. 300 f. sepia and violet 1·25 60

286. Caillie and Camel approaching Fort.

1979. 180th Birth Anniv. of Rene Caillie (explorer).
714. 286. 120 f. sepia, brn. & blue 50 20
715. – 130 f. blue, grn. & brn. 60 25
DESIGN: 130 f. Rene Caillie and map of route across Sahara.

287. " Eurema brigitta ".

1979. Butterflies and Moths (1st series). Mult.
716. 100 f. Type **287** 60 20
717. 120 f. " Papilio pylades " 65 20
718. 130 f. " Melanitis leda satyridae " 80 40
719. 180 f. " Gonimbrasis belina occidentalis " .. .. 1·25 45
720. 200 f. " Bunaea alcinoe " 1·50 50
See also Nos. 800/4.

288. Mali 1970 300 f. Stamp and Modules orbiting Moon.

1979. Air. 10th Anniv of First Moon Landing.
721. 430 f. Type **288** .. .. 1·40 60
722. 500 f. 1973 250 f. stamp and rocket launch .. .. 1·60 95

289. Capt. Cook and H.M.S. "Resolution" off Kerguelen Islands.

1979. Air. Death Bicent. of Captain James Cook.
723 300 f. Type **289** .. .. 1·50 80
724 480 f. Capt Cook and H.M.S. "Resolution" off Hawaii .. .. .. 2·25 1·10

290. Menaka Greyhound. **291.** David Janowski.

1979. Dogs. Multicoloured.
725. 20 f. Type **290** 20 15
726. 50 f. Water spaniel .. 35 15
727. 70 f. Beagle 45 15
728. 80 f. Newfoundland .. 55 20
729. 90 f. Sheepdog 70 20

1979. Air. Chess Grand-masters.
730. 291. 100 f. red and brown .. 70 30
731. – 140 f. red, brn. & blue 1·00 30
732. – 200 f. blue, vio. & grn. 1·60 50
733. – 300 f. brn., ochre & red 2·00 70
DESIGNS: 140 f. Alexander Alekhine. 200 f. Willi Schlage. 300 f. Efim Bogoljubow.

292. " The Adoration of the Magi " 1511 (detail, Durer).

1979. Air. Christmas. Works by Durer.
734. 292. 300 f. brown & orange 1·00 50
735. – 400 f. brown and blue 1·25 75
736. – 500 f. brown and green 1·60 95
DESIGNS: 400 f. "Adoration of the Magi" (1503). 500 f. "Adoration of the Magi" (1511, different).

1979. Air. 20th Anniv. of ASECNA (African Air Safety Organization). As T **198** of Malagasy but 36 × 27 mm.
737. 120 f. multicoloured .. 40 20

293. Globe, Rotary Emblem and Diesel Train. **294.** African Ass.

1980. Air. 75th Anniv. of Rotary International. Multicoloured.
738. 220 f. Type **293** .. .. 1·25 50
739. 250 f. Globe, Rotary emblem and aeroplane 1·00 45
740. 430 f. Bamako Rotary Club and emblem .. .. 1·40 75

1980. Protected Animals. Multicoloured.
741. 90 f. Type **294** 50 20
742. 120 f. Addax 60 20
743. 130 f. Cheetahs 65 35
744. 140 f. Barbary sheep .. 70 45
745. 180 f. African buffalo .. 90 50

295. Speed Skating.

1980. Air. Winter Olympics Game, Lake Placid. Multicoloured.
746. 200 f. Type **295** 70 30
747. 300 f. Ski jump .. .. 1·10 60

296. Stephenson's " Rocket " and Mali 30 f. Stamp, 1972.

1980. Air. 150th Anniv. of Liverpool and Manchester Railway.
749. 296. 200 f. blue, brn., & grn. 90 45
750. – 300 f. blk., brn. & turq. 1·60 80
DESIGN: 300 f. " Rocket " and Mali 50 f. railway stamp, 1970.

297. Horse Jumping.

1980. Air. Olympic Games, Moscow.
751. 297. 200 f. grn., brn., & blue 70 30
752. – 300 f. blue, brn. & grn. 1·00 50
753. – 400 f. red, grn. & lt. grn. 1·50 75
DESIGN: 300 f. Sailing. 400 f. Football.

298. Solar Pumping Station, Koni.

1980. Solar Energy. Multicoloured.
755. 90 f. Type **298** 30 15
756. 100 f. Solar capture tables, Dire 35 15
757. 120 f. Solar energy cooker 50 20
758. 130 f. Solar generating station, Dire 55 25

299. Nioro Horse.

1980. Horses. Multicoloured.
759. 100 f. Mopti 50 15
760. 120 f. Type **299** 55 15
761. 130 f. Koro 65 20
762. 180 f. Lake zone horse .. 80 35
763. 200 f. Banamba 95 40

300. " Head of Christ " (Maurice Denis).

1980. Air. Easter.
764. 300. 480 f. red and brown .. 1·60 95
765. – 500 f. brown and red .. 1·60 95
DESIGN: 500 f. " Christ before Pilate " (Durer).

301. Kepler and Diagram of Earth's Orbit.

1980. Air. 350th Death Anniv. of J. Kepler (astronomer).
766. 301. 200 f. brt. bl., bl. & red 80 35
767. – 300 f. mve., vio. & grn. 1·25 55
DESIGN: 300 f. Kepler, Copernicus and diagram of solar system.

302. Pluto and Diagram of Orbit.

1980. Air. 50th Anniv. of Discovery of Planet Pluto.
768. 302. 420 f. blue, grey & mve. 1·90 85

303. " Lunokhod 1 " (10th Anniv.).

1980. Air. Space Events.
769. 303. 480 f. blk., red and blue 1·50 85
770. – 500 f. grey, blue & red 1·50 85
DESIGN: 500 f. " Apollo " – " Soyuz " link-up.

304. Fleming and Laboratory.

1980. Sir Alexander Fleming (discoverer of penicillin). Commemoration.
771. 304. 200 f. grn., sepia & brn. 80 35

305. Avicenna, Medical Instruments and Herbs.

306. Pilgrim at Mecca.

1980. Birth Millenary of Avicenna (Arab physician and philosopher).
772. 305. 120 f. blue, red & brown 40 20
773. – 180 f. deep brn., turq. and brown 60 25
DESIGN: 180 f. Avicenna as teacher.

1980. 1400th Anniv. of Hegira. Mult.
774. 120 f. Type 306 .. .. 40 15
775. 130 f. Praying hands .. 40 20
776. 180 f. Pilgrims (horiz.) .. 60 30

1980. Fruit (2nd series). As T 284. Mult.
777. 90 f. Guavas 45 20
778. 120 f. Cashews 50 20
779. 130 f. Oranges 65 25
780. 140 f. Bananas 75 25
781. 180 f. Grapefruit 90 35

307. Rochambeau and French Fleet at Rhode Island, 1780.

1980. Air. French Support for American Independence.
782. 307. 420 f. brn., turq. & red 1·50 75
783. – 430 f. blk., blue & red 1·50 80
DESIGN: 430 f. Rochambeau, Washington and Eagle.

308. Dove and U.N. Emblem.

1980. 60th Anniv of League of Nations.
784 308 200 f. blue, red & violet 60 35

309. Scene from "Around the World in 80 Days".

1980. Air. 75th Death Anniv. of Jules Verne (writer).
785. 309. 100 f. red, grn. & brn. 1·50 75
786. – 100 f. brn., chestnut & turquoise .. .. 1·50 30
787. – 150 f. grn., brn. & dark brown .. .. 1·00 40
788. – 150 f. blue, violet and deep blue .. .. 1·00 40
DESIGNS: No. 786, "Concorde". No. 787, "From the Earth to the Moon". No. 788, Astronaut on Moon.

310. Xylophone, Mask and Emblem.

1980. Sixth Arts and Cultural Festival, Bamako.
789. 310. 120 f. multicoloured .. 40 20

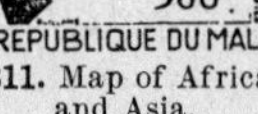

311. Map of Africa and Asia.

313. Conference Emblem.

1980. 25th Anniv. of Afro-Asian Bandung Conference.
790. 311. 300 f. green, red & blue 90 55

1980. Air. Olympic Medal Winners. Nos. 751/3 optd.
791. 200 f. green, brown & blue 70 35
792. 300 f. blue, brown & green 1·00 55
793. 400 f. red, green & lt. green 1·40 75
OVERPRINTS: 200 f. CONCOURS COMPLET INDIVIDUEL ROMAN (It.) BLINOV (Urss) SALNIKOV (Urss). 300 f. FINN RECHARDT (Fin. MAYRHOFER (Autr.) BALACHOV (Urss). 400 f. TCHECO-SLOVAQUIE ALLEMAGNE DE L'EST URSS.

1980. World Tourism Conference, Manila. Multicoloured.
795. 120 f. Type 313 .. .. 35 15
796. 180 f. Encampment outside fort and Conference emblem 50 30

314. Dam and Rural Scene.

1980. 20th Anniv. of Independence. Mult.
797. 100 f. Type 314 .. .. 40 15
798. 120 f. National Assembly Building 40 20
799. 130 f. Independence Monument (vert.) 45 25

1980. Butterflies. (2nd series). As T 287 but dated "1980". Multicoloured.
800. 50 f. "Uterheisa pulchella" (post.) 30 20
801. 60 f. "Mylothis chloris pieridae" 40 20
802. 70 f. "Hypolimnas misippus" 50 20
803. 80 f. "Papilio demodocus" 65 20
804. 420 f. "Denaus chrysippus" (48 × 36 mm.) (air) .. 2·25 1·25

315. Pistol firing Cigarette and Target over Lungs.

1980. Anti-Smoking Campaign.
805. 315. 200 f. multicoloured .. 75 35

316. Train, Aircraft and Globe.

1980. Europafrique.
806. 316. 300 f. multicoloured .. 1·25 60

317. Map of West Africa and Agricultural Symbols.

318. Gen. de Gaulle and Map of France.

1980. 5th Anniv. of West African Economic Council. Multicoloured.
807. 100 f. Type 317 .. .. 35 15
808. 120 f. "Transport" .. 1·40 45
809. 130 f. "Industry" .. 45 25
810. 140 f. "Energy" 50 25

1980. Air. 10th Death Anniv. of Gen. Charles de Gaulle. Multicoloured.
811. 420 f. Type 318 .. .. 1·75 75
812. 430 f. De Gaulle and Cross of Lorraine .. .. 1·75 75

319. "Tokaido" (Japan) and Mali 1972 10 f. Stamp.

1980. Air. Locomotives.
813. 319. 120 f. blue, grn. & red 65 20
814. – 130 f. green, blue & red 75 25
815. – 200 f. orge., blk., & grn. 1·00 40
816. – 480 f. blk., red & green 2·50 95
DESIGNS—HORIZ. 130 f. "RTG" train of Amtrack, U.S.A. and 20 f. locomotive stamp of 1970. 200 f. "Rembrandt" train, Germany and 100 f. locomotive stamp of 1970. VERT. 480 f. "TGV 001" express train, France and 80 f. locomotive stamp of 1970.

320. "Flight into Egypt" (Rembrandt).

321. Nomo Dogon.

1980. Air. Christmas. Multicoloured.
817. 300 f. "St. Joseph showing the infant Jesus to St. Catherine" (Lorenzo Lotto) (horiz.) .. .. 1·00 55
818. 400 f. Type 320 .. .. 1·40 80
819. 500 f. "Christmas Night" (Gauguin) (horiz.) .. 1·60 90

1980. 5th Anniv. of African Posts and Telecommunications Union. As T 292 of Niger.
820. 130 f. multicoloured .. 40 20

1981. Statuettes. Multicoloured.
821. 60 f. Type 321 .. .. 20 15
822. 70 f. Senoufo fertility symbol 25 15
823. 90 f. Bamanan fertility statuette 35 15
824. 100 f. Senoufo captives snuff-box 40 15
825. 120 f. Dogon fertility statuette 50 20

322. "Self-portrait" (Blue period).

323. Mambie Sidibe.

1981. Birth Bicent. of Pablo Picasso (artist).
826. 322. 1000 f. multicoloured 3·25 1·75

1981. Mali Thinkers and Savants.
827. 323. 120 f. brown, buff & red 40 20
828. – 130 f. brn., buff & blk. 40 25
DESIGN: 130 f. Amadou Hampate Ba.

324. Mosque and Ka'aba.

325. Tackle.

1981. 1400th Anniv. of Hejira.
829. 324. 120 f. multicoloured .. 40 20
830. 180 f. multicoloured .. 60 30

1981. Air. World Cup Football Championship Eliminators. Multicoloured.
831. 100 f. Type 325 .. .. 40 20
832. 200 f. Heading the ball .. 85 35
833. 300 f. Running for ball .. 1·40 50

326. Kaarta Zeba.

327. Crinum de Moore "Crinum moorei".

1981. Cattle. Multicoloured.
835. 20 f. Type 326 .. .. 15 15
836. 30 f. Peul du Macina sebu 15 15
837. 40 f. Maure zebu 25 15
838. 80 f. Touareg zebu .. 50 15
839. 100 f. N'Dama cow .. 60 20

1981. Flowers. Multicoloured.
840. 50 f. Type 327 .. .. 30 15
841. 100 f. Double rose hibiscus "Hibiscus rosa-sinensis" 70 15
842. 120 f. Pervenche "Catharanthus roseus" .. 80 20
843. 130 f. Frangipani "Plumeria rubra" 80 25
844. 180 f. Orgueil de Chine "Caesalpinia pulcherrima" .. .. .. 1·25 40

328. Mozart and Musical Instruments.

1981. Air. 225th Birth Anniv. of Mozart. Multicoloured.
845. 420 f. Type 328 .. .. 1·75 85
846. 430 f. Mozart and musical instruments (different) 1·75 85

329. "The Fall on the Way to Calvary" (Raphael).

330. Yuri Gagarin.

1981. Air. Easter.
847. 500 f. Type 329 .. .. 1·50 85
848. 600 f. "Ecce Homo" (Rembrandt) .. .. 2·00 1·25

1981. Air. Space Anniversaries and Events.
849. 330. 200 f. blue, blk. and red 75 30
850. – 200 f. blue, black and light blue 75 30
851. – 380 f. multicoloured .. 1·25 55
852. – 430 f. violet, blk. & blue 1·50 70
DESIGNS—VERT. No. 849, Type 330 first man in space (20th anniv.). No. 850, Alan Shepard first American in space (20th anniv). No. 851, Saturn and moons (exploration of Saturn.) HORIZ. No. 852, Sir William Herschel. and diagram of Uranus, (Discovery. Bicent.)

331. Blind and Sighted Faces.

332. Caduceus (Telecommunications and Health).

1981. International Year of Disabled People.
853. 331. 100 f. light brown, brown and green 35 15
854. – 120 f. violet, blue and purple 45 20
DESIGN: 120 f. Mechanical hand and human hand with spanner.

1981. World Telecommunications Day.
855. 332. 130 f. multicoloured .. 40 25

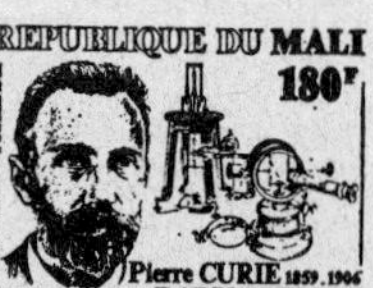

333. Pierre Curie and Instruments.

1981. 75th Death Anniv. of Pierre Curie (discoverer of radioactivity).
856. 333. 180 f. blue, blk. & orge. 90 30

334. Scouts at Well and Dorcas Gazelle.

1981. 4th African Scouting Conference, Abidjan. Multicoloured.

857.	110 f. Type **334**	55	30
858.	160 f. Scouts signalling and patas monkey	1·00	60
859.	300 f. Scouts saluting and cheetah (vert.)	1·50	85

1981. Air. World Railway Speed Record. No. 816 optd. **26 fevrier 1981/Record du monde de vitesse—380 km/h.**

861.	480 f. black, red and blue	2·25	90

336. Columbus, Fleet and U.S. Columbus Stamp of 1892.

1981. Air. 475th Death Anniv. of Christopher Columbus.

862.	**336.**	180 f. brn., blk. & blue	80	40
863.	–	200 f. grn., blue & brn.	1·00	40
864.	–	260 f. blk., violet & red	1·50	60
865.	–	300 f. lilac, red & green	1·60	70

DESIGNS—VERT. 200 f. "Nina" and 1 c. Columbus stamp of Spain. 260 f. "Pinta" and 5 c. Columbus stamp of Spain. HORIZ. 300 f. "Santa Maria" and U.S. 3 c. Columbus stamp.

1981. 23rd World Scouting Conference, Dakar. Nos. 857/9 optd. **"DAKAR 8 AOUT 1981/28e CONFERENCE MOUNDIALE DU SCOUTISME".**

866.	**334.**	110 f. multicoloured ..	40	20
867.	–	160 f. multicoloured ..	50	30
868.	–	300 f. multicoloured ..	1·25	55

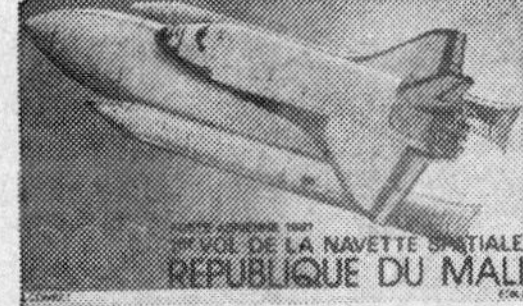

338. Space Shuttle after Launching.

1981. Air. Space Shuttle. Multicoloured.

870.	200 f. Type **338**	75	30
871.	500 f. Space Shuttle in Orbit	2·00	75
872.	600 f. Space Shuttle landing	2·25	1·25

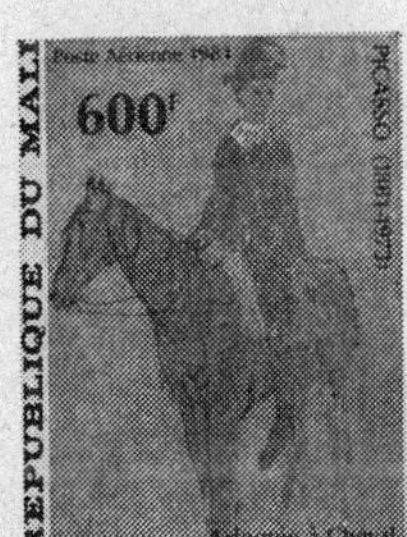

339. "Harlequin on a Horse".

1981. Air. Birth Centenary of Pablo Picasso. Multicoloured.

874.	600 f. Type **339**	2·50	1·25
875.	750 f. "Child with Pigeon"	3·00	1·40

340. Prince Charles, Lady Diana Spencer and St. Paul's Cathedral.

1981. Air. British Royal Wedding. Mult.

876.	500 f. Type **340**	1·25	75
877.	700 f. Prince Charles, Lady Diana Spencer and coach	1·75	1·10

342. Maure Sheep.

343. Heinrich von Stephan (founder of U.P.U.), Early Aeroplane and "Concorde".

1981. Sheep. Multicoloured.

886.	10 f. Type **342**	15	10
887.	25 f. Peul sheep	20	10
888.	140 f. Sahael sheep ..	50	25
889	180 f. Touareg sheep ..	75	35
890.	200 f. Djallonke ram ..	85	35

1981. Universal Postal Union Day.

891.	**343.**	400 f. red and green ..	1·60	70

344. Woman drinking from Bowl.

1981. World Food Day.

892.	**344.**	200 f. brn., orge. & mve.	65	30

345. "The Incarnation of the Son of God" (detail Grunewald).

1981. Air. Christmas. Multicoloured.

893.	500 f. Type **345**	1·75	75
894.	700 f. "The Campori Madonna" (Correggio)	2·25	1·25

347. Transport and Hands holding Map of Europe and Africa.

1981. Europafrique.

896.	**347.**	700 f. blue, brown and orange	3·00	1·60

348. Guerin, Calmette, Syringe and Bacillus.

1981. 60th Anniv. of First B.C.G. Inoculation.

897.	**348.**	200 f. brown, violet and black	85	40

1981. Air. World Chess Championship, Merano. Nos. 731 and 733 optd.

898	140 f. red, brown and blue	1·10	50
899	300 f. brown, ochre and red	2·00	75

OPTS: 140 f. **ANATOLI KARPOV VICTOR KORTCHNOI MERANO (ITALIE) (Octobre–Novembre 1981.** 300 f. **Octobre–Novembre 1981 ANATOLI KARPOV Champion du Monde 1981.**

350. "Nymphaea lotus".

1982. Flowers. Multicoloured.

900.	170 f. Type **350**	75	35
901.	180 f. "Bombax costatum"	80	35
902.	200 f. "Parkia biglobosa"	85	40
903.	220 f. "Gloriosa simplex"	1·10	45
904.	270 f. "Satanocrater berhautii"	1·25	50

351. Lewis Carroll and Characters from "Alice" Books.

1982. Air. 150th Birth Anniv. of Lewis Carroll. (Revd. Charles Dodgson).

905.	110 f. Type **351**	55	25
906.	130 f. Characters from "Alice" books ..	60	30
907.	140 f. Characters from "Alice" books (different)	75	30

352. "George Washington" (Gilbert Stuart).

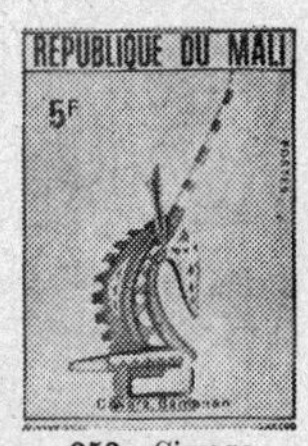

353. Ciwara Bamanan.

1982. Air. 250th Birth Anniv. of George Washington.

908.	**352.**	700 f. multicoloured ..	2·00	1·25

1982. Masks. Multicoloured.

909.	5 f. Type **353**	10	10
910.	35 f. Kanga Dogon ..	15	10
911.	180 f. N Domo Bamanan	75	30
912.	200 f. Cimier (Sogoninkum Bamanan	85	40
913.	250 f. Kpelie Senoufo ..	1·10	45

354. Football.

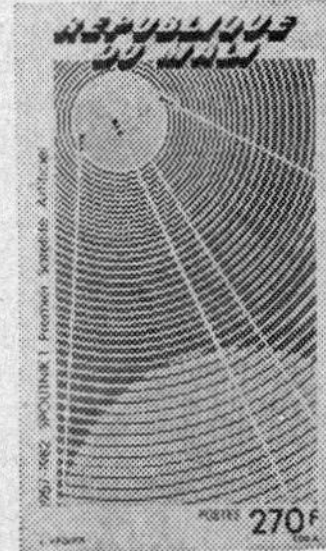

355. "Sputnik 1".

1982. Air. World Cup Football Championship, Spain.

914.	**354.**	220 f. multicoloured ..	80	45
915.	–	420 f. multicoloured ..	1·50	90
916.	–	500 f. multicoloured ..	1·75	90

DESIGNS: 420 f., 500 f. Football scenes.

1982. 25th Anniv. of First Artificial Satellite.

918.	**355.**	270 f. violet, blue and red	1·25	50

356. Lord Baden-Powell, Tent and Scout Badge.

1982. Air. 125th Birth Anniv. of Lord Baden-Powell.

919.	300 f. Type **356**	1·50	50
920.	500 f. Saluting scout ..	2·25	90

357. "The Transfiguration" (Fra Angelico).

1982. Air. Easter. Multicoloured.

921.	680 f. Type **357**	2·00	1·25
922.	1000 f. "Pieta" (Giovanni Bellini")	3·00	1·90

358. Doctor giving Child Oral Vaccine.

360. "En Bon Ami" (N'Teri).

359. Lions Emblem and Blind Person.

1982. Anti-Polio Campaign.

923.	**358.**	180 f. multicoloured ..	80	35

1982. Lions Club Blind Day.

924.	**359.**	260 f. orange, blue and red	1·25	50

1982. Hairstyles. Multicoloured.

925.	140 f. Type **360**	35	30
926.	150 f. Tucked-in pony tail	40	30
927.	160 f. "Pour l'Art" ..	50	35
928.	180 f. "Bozo Kun" ..	75	35
929.	270 f. "Fulaw Kun" ..	1·25	60

361. Arms Stamp of Mali and France.

1982. Air. "Philexfrance 82" International Stamp Exhibition, Paris. Multicoloured.

930.	180 f. Type **361**	60	35
931.	200 f. Dromedary caravan and 1979 "Philexfrique II" stamp	1·00	70

362. Fire-engine, 1850.

1982. Fire-engines, Multicoloured.

932.	180 f. Type **362**	85	35
933.	200 f. Fire-engine, 1921 ..	1·25	40
934.	270 f. Fire-engine, 1982 ..	1·50	50

363. Gobra.

1982. Zebu. Cattle. Multicoloured.

935. 10 f. Type **363** 10 10
936. 60 f. Azaouak 25 15
937. 110 f. Maure 35 25
938. 180 f. Toronke 65 35
939. 200 f. Peul Sambourou .. 75 40

1982. Air. World Cup Football Championship Winners. Nos. 914/16 optd.

940. **354.** 220 f. multicoloured .. 75 45
941. – 420 f. multicoloured .. 1·50 90
942. – 500 f. multicoloured .. 1·75 90

OPTS: 220 f. **1 ITALIE 2 RFA 3 POLOGNE** 420 f. **POLOGNE FRANCE 3-2.** 500 f. **ITALIE RFA 3-1.**

365. " Urchin with Cherries ".

1982. Air. 150th Birth Anniv. of Edouard Manet (painter).

944. **365.** 680 f. multicoloured .. 2·50 1·25

366. " Virgin and Child ". (detail) (Titian). **367.** Wind-surfing.

1982. Air. Christmas. Multicoloured.

945. 500 f. Type **366** .. .. 1·50 90
946. 1000 f. " Virgin and Child " (Giovanni Bellini) .. 2·75 1·90

1982. Introduction of Wind-surfing as Olympic Event. Multicoloured.

947. 200 f. Type **367** 80 45
948. 270 f. Wind-surfer .. 1·25 55
949. 300 f. Wind-surfer (different) 1·40 55

368. Goethe.

1982. Air. 150th Death Anniv. of Goethe (poet).

950. **368.** 500 f. brown, light brown and black 1·75 90

369. Valentina Tereshkova. **370.** Transatlantic Balloon "Double Eagle II".

1983. Air. 20th Anniv. of Launching of Vostok VI.

951. **369.** 400 f. multicoloured 1·25 75

1983. Air. Bicent. of Manned Flight. Mult.

952. 500 f. Type **370** .. .. 2·00 90
953. 700 f. Montgolfier balloon 2·50 1·25

371. Football.

1983. Air. Olympic Games, Los Angeles. Multicoloured.

954. 180 f. Type **371** 50 30
955. 270 f. Hurdles 75 40
956. 300 f. Windsurfing .. 1·10 55

372. " The Transfiguration " (detail). **373.** Martin Luther King.

1983. Air. Easter. Multicoloured.

957. 400 f. Type **372** .. .. 1·25 75
958. 600 f. " The Entombment " (detail from Baglioni Retable) .. .. 2·00 1·10

1983. Celebrities.

959. **373.** 800 f. brn., blue & pur. 2·50 1·40
960. – 800 f. brn., red & dp. red 2·50 1·40

DESIGN: No. 960, President Kennedy.

374. Oua Hairstyle. **375.** " Family of Acrobats with Monkey ".

1983. Hairstyles. Multicoloured.

961. 180 f. Type **374** 60 30
962. 200 f. Nation (Diamani) .. 70 30
963. 270 f. Rond Point .. 90 40
964. 300 f. Naamu-Naamu .. 1·00 45
965. 500 f. Bamba-Bamba .. 2·00 80

1983. Air. 10th Death Anniv. of Picasso.

966. **375.** 680 f. multicoloured .. 2·00 1·25

376. Lions Club Emblem and Lions.

1983. Air. Lions and Rotary Clubs. Mult.

967. 700 f. Type **376** .. .. 2·25 2·00
968. 700 f. Rotary Club emblem, container ship, diesel railcar and aeroplane .. 4·50 2·50

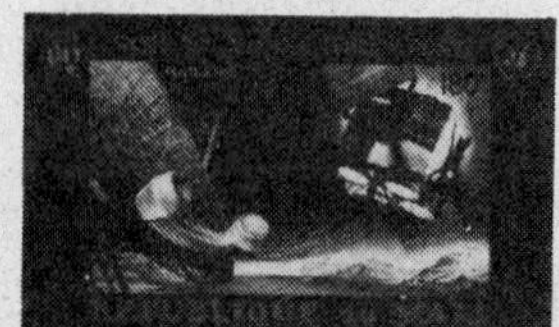

377. Satellite, Antenna and Telephone.

1983. World Communications Year.

969. **377.** 180 f. multicoloured .. 55 30

378. Lavoisier and Apparatus. **379.** Banzoumana Sissoko.

1983. Bicent. of Lavoisier's Analysis of Water.

970. **378.** 300 f. grn., brn. & blue 1·10 50

1983. Mali Musicians. Multicoloured.

971. 200 f. Type **379** 75 30
972. 300 f. Batourou Sekou Kouyate .. .. .. 1·25 45

380. Nicephore Niepce and Camera. **381.** Space Shuttle " Challenger ".

1983. 150th Death Anniv. of Nicephore Niepce (pioneer of photography).

973. **380.** 400 f. blue, grn. & deep green .. .. 1·40 65

1983. Air. Space Shuttle.

974. **381.** 1000 f. multicoloured 3·00 1·75

382. Young People and Map of Africa.

1983. Second Panafrican Youth Festival. Multicoloured.

975. 240 f. Type **382** 75 40
976. 270 f. Hands reaching for map of Africa 75 40

383. Mercedes, 1914.

1983. Air. Paris–Dakar Rally. Multicoloured.

977. 240 f. Type **383** .. .. 1·25 40
978. 270 f. Mercedes SSK, 1929 1·25 50
979. 500 f. Mercedes W 196, 1954 2·25 80

384 Liner and U.P.U. Emblem. **385.** Pawn and Bishop.

1983. U.P.U. Day.

981. **384.** 240 f. red, blk. & blue 1·25 50

1983. Air. Chess Pieces.

982. **385.** 300 f. grey, vio. & grn. 1·60 60
983. – 420 f. grn., pink & grey 2·00 85
984. – 500 f. blue, dp. blue & green .. .. .. 2·75 1·00

DESIGNS: 420 f. Rook and knight. 500 f. King and queen.

386. " Canigiani Madonna ".

1983. Air. Christmas. 500th Birth Anniv. of Raphael. Multicoloured.

986. 700 f. Type **386** .. .. 2·00 1·00
987. 800 f. " Madonna of the Lamb " .. .. .. 2·25 1·25

387. Sahara Goat.

1984. Goats. Multicoloured.

988. 20 f. Type **387** 15 10
989. 30 f. Billy goat 20 10
990. 50 f. Billy goat (different) 25 15
991. 240 f. Kaarta goat .. 1·00 40
992. 350 f. Southern goat .. 1·40 75

388. " Leopold Zborowski " (Modigliani). **389.** Henri Dunant (founder of Red Cross).

1984. Air. Birth Cent. of Modigliani (painter).

993. **388.** 700 f. multicoloured .. 2·50 1·25

1984. Air. Celebrities.

994. **389.** 400 f. dp. bl., red & bl. 1·50 65
995. – 540 f. dp. bl., red & bl. 1·60 85

DESIGN: 540 f. Abraham Lincoln.

390. Sidney Bechet.

1984. Air. Jazz Musicians. Multicoloured.

996. 470 f. Type **390** .. .. 2·25 75
997. 500 f. Duke Ellington .. 2·25 80

391. Micro-light Aircraft.

1984. Air. Micro-light Aircraft. Mult.

998. 270 f. Type **391** .. .. 1·00 40
999. 350 f. " Gemini " micro-light .. .. .. 1·25 55

392. Weightlifting.

1984. Air. Olympic Games, Los Angeles. Multicoloured.

1000 265 f. Type **392** 75 40
1001 440 f. Show jumping .. 90 70
1002 500 f. Hurdles .. .. 1·10 80

393. " Crucifixion " (Rubens).

1984. Air. Easter.

1004. **393.** 940 f. brn. & dp. brn. 3·00 1·50

1005. – 970 f. brown & red .. 3·00 1·50

DESIGN—HORIZ. 970 f. " The Resurrection " (Mantegna).

1984. Currency revaluation. Various stamps surch.

(i) U.P.U. Day (No. 981)

1006. **384.** 120 f. on 240 f. red, black and blue (postage) .. .. 1·10 50

(ii) Goats (Nos. 988/92)

1007. **387.** 10 f. on 20 f. mult. .. 10 10

1008. – 15 f. on 30 f. mult. .. 15 10

1009. – 25 f. on 50 f. mult. .. 20 15

1010. – 125 f. on 240 f. mult. 95 40

1011. – 175 f. on 350 f. mult. 1·75 65

(iii) Paris–Dakar Rally (No. 977)

1012. **383.** 120 f. on 240 f. mult. (air) .. .. 1·10 40

395. Mercedes "Simplex".

1984. Air. 150th Birth Anniv. of Gottlieb Daimler (motor car designer).

1035. **395.** 350 f. olive, blue and mauve .. .. 2·25 1·10

1036. – 470 f. green, violet and plum .. .. 3·00 1·50

1037. – 485 f. blue, violet and plum .. .. 3·25 1·75

DESIGNS: 470 f. Mercedes-Benz Type "370 S". 485 f. Mercedes-Benz "500 S EC".

396. Farm Workers

1984. Progress in Countryside and Protected Essences. Multicoloured.

1038. 5 f. Type **396** 10 10

1039. 90 f. Carpentry 60 30

1040. 100 f. Tapestry making 70 35

1041. 135 f. Metal work .. 80 40

1042. 515 f. "Borassus flabelifer" .. .. 3·25 1·90

1043. 1225 f. "Vitelaria paradoxa" .. .. .. 7·50 3·75

397. Emblem and Child.

1984. United Nations Children's Fund.

1044. **397.** 120 f. red, brown and green 80 40

1045. – 135 f. red, blue and brown 90 50

DESIGN: 135 f. Emblem and two children.

398. U.P.U. Emblem, Anchor and Hamburg.

1984. Universal Postal Union Congress, Hamburg.

1046. **398.** 135 f. mauve, green and blue 80 40

1984. Air. Olympic Winners, Los Angeles. No. 1000/1002 optd.

1047 135 f. on 265 f. Optd **HALTERES 56 KGS / 1. WU (CHINE). 2. LAI (CHINE). 3. KOTAKA (JAPON)** 80 40

1048 220 f. on 440 f. Optd **DRESSAGE / PAR EQUIPES / 1. RFA 2. SUISSE / 3. SUEDE** 1·10 75

1049 250 f. on 500 f. Optd **ATHLETISME 3000 METRES STEEPLE / 1. KORIR (KENYA). / 2. MAHMOUD (FRANCE). / 3. DIEMER (E-U).** .. 1·40 1·00

400. Emblem.

1984. 10th Anniv. of Economic Community of West Africa.

1051. **400.** 350 f. multicoloured 1·75 1·10

401. Dimetrodon.

1984. Prehistoric Animals. Multicoloured.

1052. 10 f. Type **401** 15 15

1053. 25 f. Iguanodon (vert.) .. 25 15

1054. 30 f. Archaeopteryx (vert.) 45 30

1055. 120 f. Type **401** .. .. 1·50 45

1056. 175 f. As No. 1053 .. 1·75 70

1057. 350 f. As No. 1054 .. 3·50 2·50

1058. 470 f. Triceratops .. 5·00 2·50

402. "Virgin and Child between St. Joseph and St. Jerome". (detail, Lorenzo Lotto)

1984. Air. Christmas.

1059. **402.** 500 f. multicoloured 3·00 1·60

1984. Drought Aid. No. 758 surch.

1060. **403.** 470 f. on 130 f. mult. 2·75 1·75

404. Horse Galloping. 405. "Clitocybe nebularis".

1985. Horses. Multicoloured.

1061. 90 f. Type **404** 70 35

1062. 135 f. Beledougou horse 1·25 40

1063. 190 f. Nara horse .. 1·50 70

1064. 530 f. Trait horse .. 4·50 2·00

1985. Fungi. Multicoloured.

1065 120 f. Type **405** .. .. 1·50 55

1066 200 f. "Lepiota cortinarius" .. .. .. 2·00 85

1067 485 f. "Agaricus semotus" 5·00 2·00

1068 525 f. "Lepiota procera" 5·25 2·25

406. Emile Marchoux and Marchoux Institute.

1985. Health. Multicoloured.

1069. 120 f. Type **406** (World Lepers' Day and 40th anniv of Marchoux Institute) (postage) .. 80 30

1070. 135 f. Lions' emblem and Samanto Village (15th anniv.) 85 35

1071. 470 f. Laboratory technicians and polio victim (anti-polio campaign) (air) .. .. 3·50 1·50

407. Profiles and Emblem.

1985. 15th Anniv. of Technical and Cultural Co-operation Agency.

1072. **407.** 540 f. grn. & brown 3·50 1·90

408. Common Kingfisher.

1985. Air. Birth Bicentenary of John J. Audubon (ornithologist). Multicoloured.

1073. 180 f. Type **408** .. .. 1·40 75

1074. 300 f. Great bustard (vert.) 2·25 1·25

1075. 470 f. Ostrich (vert.) .. 3·50 2·00

1076. 540 f. Ruppell's griffon .. 3·75 2·50

409. National Pioneers Movement Emblem.

1985. International Youth Year. Mult.

1077. 120 f. Type **409** 80 40

1078. 190 f. Boy leading oxen 1·40 70

1079. 500 f. Sports motifs and I.Y.Y. emblem .. 3·50 1·75

410. Airplanes and Agency Emblem.

1985. Air. 25th Anniv. of Aerial Navigation Security Agency for Africa and Madagascar (ASECNA).

1080. **410.** 700 f. multicoloured 4·50 2·50

411. Lion, and Scouts collecting Wood.

1985. Air. "Philexafrique" Stamp Exhibition, Lome. Multicoloured.

1081. 200 f. Type **411** .. .. 1·50 1·25

1082. 200 f. Satellite, dish aerial and globe .. 1·50 1·25

412. U.P.U. Emblem, Computer and Reservoir (Development).

1985. "Philexafrique" Stamp Exhibition, Lome, Togo (2nd issue). Multicoloured.

1083. 250 f. Type **412** .. .. 1·75 1·25

1084. 250 f. Satellite, girls writing and children learning from television (Youth) .. .. 1·75 1·25

413. Grey Cat.

1986. Cats. Multicoloured.

1085. 150 f. Type **413** .. .. 1·50 60

1086. 200 f. White cat .. .. 2·25 80

1087. 300 f. Tabby cat .. 2·50 1·10

414. Hands releasing Doves and Globe.

1986. Anti-apartheid Campaign. Mult.

1088. 100 f. Type **414** 65 40

1089. 120 f. People breaking chain around world .. 85 50

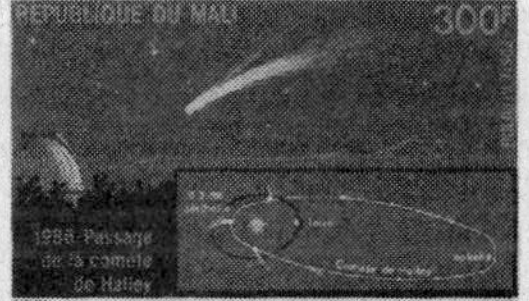

415. Comet and Diagram of Orbit.

1986. Air. Appearance of Halley's Comet.

1090. **415.** 300 f. multicoloured 2·25 1·25

416. Internal Combustion Engine.

1986. Air. Centenaries of First Motor Car with Internal Combustion Engine and Statue of Liberty. Multicoloured.

1091. 400 f. Type **416** .. .. 3·00 1·50

1092. 600 f. Head of statue, and French and American flags .. 4·00 2·25

417. Robeson.

1986. Air. 10th Death Anniv. of Paul Robeson (singer).

1093. **417.** 500 f. multicoloured 4·00 2·00

418. Women tending Crop.

1986. World Communications Day.

1094. **418.** 200 f. multicoloured 1·50 80

419. Players.

1986. World Cup Football Championship, Mexico. Multicoloured.

1095. 160 f. Type **419** .. .. 1·40 65
1096. 225 f. Player capturing ball .. .. .. 1·90 90

420. Watt.

1986. 250th Birth Anniv. of James Watt (inventor).

1098. **420.** 110 f. multicoloured 85 45

421. Eberth and Microscope.

422. Chess Pieces on Board.

1986. Air. 60th Death Anniv. of Karl Eberth (discoverer of typhoid bacillus).

1099. **421.** 550 f. multicoloured 4·00 1·90

1986. Air. World Chess Championship, London and Leningrad. Multicoloured.

1100 400 f. Type **422** .. .. 3·50 1·75
1101 500 f. Knight and board 4·50 2·25

1986. World Cup Winners. Nos. 1095/6 optd. **ARGENTINE 3 R.F.A. 2.**

1102. 160 f. multicoloured .. 1·25 85
1103. 225 f. multicoloured .. 1·60 1·00

424. Head.

1986. Endangered Animals. Giant Eland. Multicoloured.

1105. 5 f. Type **424** 10 10
1106. 20 f. Standing by dead tree 25 10
1107. 25 f. Stepping over fallen branch 25 10
1108. 200 f. Mother and calf .. 1·90 95

425. Mermoz and Airplane "Southern Cross".

1986. Air. 50th Anniv. of Disappearance of Jean Mermoz (aviator). Multicoloured.

1109. 150 f. Type **425** .. .. 1·25 60
1110. 600 f. Cams "53" and Oiseau "Tango" .. 4·25 2·25
1111. 625 f. Map and seaplane "Le Comte de la Vaulx" .. .. 4·50 2·50

1986. 10th Anniv. of "Concorde's" First Commercial Flight. Nos. 674/6 surch. **1986—10e Anniversaire du 1er Vol Commercial Supersonique.**

1112. 175 f. on 120 f. Type **271** 1·40 80
1113. 225 f. on 130 f. "Concorde" and Wright Brothers' "Flyer" .. .. 1·75 1·00
1114. 300 f. on 200 f. "Concorde" and Lindbergh's "Spirit of St. Louis" .. .. 2·75 1·50

427. Hansen and Follereau.

1987. Air. 75th Death Anniv. of Gerhard Hansen (discoverer of bacillus) and 10th Death Anniv. of Raoul Follereau (leprosy pioneer).

1115. **427.** 500 f. multicoloured 3·50 1·90

428. Model "A", 1903.

1987. 40th Death Anniv. of Henry Ford (motor car manufacturer). Multicoloured.

1116. 150 f. Type **428** .. .. 1·25 55
1117. 200 f. Model "T", 1923 .. 1·75 75
1118. 225 f. "Thunderbird", 1968 .. .. .. 1·75 95
1119. 300 f. "Continental", 1963 2·00 1·25

429. Konrad Adenauer.

431. Scenes from "The Jazz Singer".

430. Runners and Buddha's Head.

1987. Air. 20th Death Anniv. of Konrad Adenauer (German statesman).

1120. **429.** 625 f. stone, brown and red .. .. 4·00 2·25

1987. Air. Olympic Games, Seoul (1988). (1st issue).

1121. **430.** 400 f. black & brown 2·00 1·40
1122. – 500 f. deep green, green and red .. 2·75 1·75

DESIGN: 500 f. Footballers.

See also Nos. 1133/4.

1987. Air. 60th Anniv. of First Talking Picture.

1123. **431.** 550 f. red, brown and deep brown .. 4·00 2·25

432. "Apis florea".

1987. Bees. Multicoloured.

1124 100 f. Type **432** 80 50
1125 150 f. "Apis dorsata" .. 1·40 70
1126 175 f. "Apis adonsonii" .. 1·60 80
1127 200 f. "Apis mellifera" .. 1·75 1·00

433. Map, Dove and Luthuli.

1987. Air. 20th Death Anniv. of Albert John Luthuli (Nobel Peace Prize winner).

1128. **433.** 400 f. mauve, blue and brown .. 2·50 1·50

434. Profiles and Lions Emblem.

1987. Air. Lions International and Rotary International. Multicoloured.

1129. 500 f. Type **434** .. .. 3·00 1·75
1130. 500 f. Clasped hands and Rotary emblem .. 3·00 1·75

435. Anniversary Emblem and Symbols of Activities.

1988. 30th Anniv. of Lions International in Mali.

1131. **435.** 200 f. multicoloured 1·25 75

436. Emblem and Doctor examining Boy.

1988. 40th Anniv. of W.H.O.

1132. **436.** 150 f. multicoloured 1·10 60

437. Coubertin and Ancient and Modern Athletes.

1988. Air. Olympic Games, Seoul (2nd issue). 125th Birth Anniv. of Pierre de Coubertin (founder of modern games). Multicoloured.

1133. 240 f. Type **437** .. .. 1·10 90
1134. 400 f. Stadium, Olympic rings and sports pictograms .. .. .. 1·90 1·40

438. "Harlequin".

1988. Air. 15th Death Anniv. of Pablo Picasso (painter).

1135. **438.** 600 f. multicoloured 4·00 2·25

439. "Concorde" and Globe.

1988. Air. 15th Anniv. of First North Atlantic Crossing by "Concorde".

1136. **439.** 500 f. multicoloured 3·75 2·00

440. Pres. Kennedy. **442.** Map.

1988. 25th Death Anniv. of John Fitzgerald Kennedy (American President).

1137. **440.** 640 f. multicoloured 4·00 2·40

1988. Mali Mission Hospital, Mopti. No. 1132 surch. **MISSION MALI HOPITAL de MOPTI 300F** and **MEDECINS DU MONDE** emblem.

1138. **436.** 300 f. on 150 f. mult. 2·40 1·75

1988. 25th Anniv. of Organization of African Unity.

1139. **442.** 400 f. multicoloured 2·50 1·25

443 Map, Leaf and Stove

1989. Air. "Improved Stoves: For a Green Mali". Multicoloured.

1140 5 f. Type **443** 10 10
1141 10 f. Tree and stove .. 10 10
1142 25 f. Type **443** 15 10
1143 100 f. As No. 1141 .. 60 35

444 Astronauts on Moon

1989. Air. 20th Anniv of First Manned Moon Landing.

1144 **444** 300 f. blue, pur & grn 2·00 1·25
1145 – 500 f. purple, bl & brn 3·25 1·75

DESIGN: 500 f. Astronauts on moon (diff).

445 Emblem and Crossed Syringes

1989. Vaccination Programme. Multicoloured.
1146 20 f. Type **445** 15 10
1147 30 f. Doctor vaccinating woman 20 10
1148 50 f. Emblem and syringes 40 15
1149 175 f. Doctor vaccinating child .. .. .. 1·40 65

446 Emblem

1989. 25th Anniv of International Law Institute of French-speaking Countries.
1150 **446** 150 f. multicoloured 1·10 55
1151 200 f. multicoloured 1·40 70

447 Crowd

448 U.P.U. Emblem and Hands holding Envelopes

1989. Air. Bicentenary of French Revolution and "Philexfrance 89" International Stamp Exhibition, Paris.
1152 **447** 400 f. red, blue & pur 2·50 1·25
1153 – 600 f. vio, pur & mve 3·50 2·00
DESIGN: 600 f. Marianne and Storming of Bastille.

1989. World Post Day.
1154 **448** 625 f. multicoloured .. 3·50 2·25

449 Pope and Cathedral

1990. Visit of Pope John Paul II.
1155 **449** 200 f. multicoloured .. 1·60 80

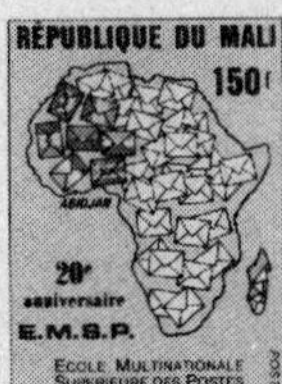

450 Envelopes on Map

1990. 20th Anniv of Multinational Postal Training School, Abidjan.
1156 **450** 150 f. multicoloured .. 1·25 55

451 Footballers

1990. Air. World Cup Football Championship, Italy. Multicoloured.
1157 200 f. Type **451** .. .. 1·50 75
1158 225 f. Footballers (different) .. .. 1·75 85

1990. World Cup Result. Nos. 1157/8 optd. Multicoloured.
1160 200 f. **ITALIE : 2 / ANGLETERE: 1** .. 1·50 85
1161 225 f. **R.F.A. : 1 / ARGENTINE : 0** .. 1·75 85

453 Pres. Moussa Traore and Bamako Bridge

1990. 30th Anniv of Independence.
1163 **453** 400 f. multicoloured .. 2·50 1·50

454 Man writing and Adults learning to Read

455 Woman carrying Water and Cattle at Well

1990. International Literacy Year.
1164 **454** 150 f. multicoloured .. 1·25 55
1165 200 f. multicoloured .. 1·50 75

1991. Lions Club (1166) and Rotary International (1167) Projects. Multicoloured.
1166 200 f. Type **455** (6th anniv of wells project) .. 1·40 75
1167 200 f. Bamako branch emblem and hand (30th anniv of anti-polo campaign .. .. 1·40 75

456 Sonrai Dance, Takamba

457 Bank Emblem and Map of France

1991. Dances. Multicoloured.
1168 50 f. Type **456** 30 15
1169 100 f. Malinke dance, Mandiani 60 30
1170 150 f. Bamanan dance, Kono 90 50
1171 200 f. Dogon dance, Songho .. .. 1·10 75

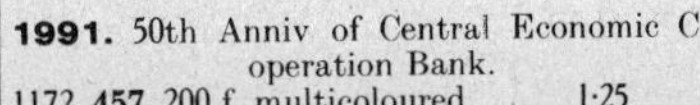
1991. 50th Anniv of Central Economic Co-operation Bank.
1172 **457** 200 f. multicoloured .. 1·25 75

458 Women with Torch and Banner

1992. National Women's Movement for the Safeguarding of Peace and National Unity.
1173 **458** 150 f. multicoloured .. 75 40

1992. Various stamps surch.
1174 – 25 f. on 470 f. mult (No. 1058) (postage) 15 10
1175 **420** 30 f. on 110 f. mult .. 15 10
1176 – 50 f. on 300 f. mult (No. 1087) 25 15
1177 – 50 f. on 1225 f. mult (No. 1043) 25 15
1178 – 150 f. on 135 f. mult (No. 1070) 75 40
1179 – 150 f. on 190 f. mult (No. 1063) 75 40
1180 – 150 f. on 190 f. mult (No. 1078) 75 40
1181 **400** 150 f. on 350 f. mult .. 75 40
1182 – 150 f. on 485 f. mult (No. 1067) 75 40
1183 – 150 f. on 525 f. mult (No. 1068) 75 40
1184 – 150 f. on 530 f. mult (No. 1064) 75 40
1185 **440** 200 f. on 640 f. mult .. 1·00 50
1186 – 240 f. on 350 f. mult (No. 1057) .. .. 1·25 65
1187 **448** 240 f. on 625 f. mult .. 1·25 65
1188 **410** 20 f. on 700 f. mult (air) 10 10
1189 **415** 20 f. on 300 f. mult .. 10 10
1190 – 25 f. on 470 f. mult (No. 1071) 15 10
1191 **408** 30 f. on 180 f. mult .. 15 10
1192 – 30 f. on 500 f. purple, blue and brown (No. 1145) 15 10
1193 – 100 f. on 540 f. mult (No. 1076) 50 25
1194 **438** 100 f. on 600 f. mult .. 50 25
1195 **444** 150 f. on 300 f. blue, purple and green .. 75 40
1196 **447** 150 f. on 400 f. red, blue and purple .. 75 40
1197 – 200 f. on 300 f. mult (No. 1074) .. .. 1·00 50
1198 – 240 f. on 600 f. violet, purple and mauve (No. 1153) .. .. 1·25 65

1992.
(a) Postage. No. 1095 surch **150 f "Euro 92"**.
1199 **419** 150 f. on 160 f. mult .. 75 40
(b) Air. No. 1134 surch **150F "Barcelone 92"**
1200 150 f. on 400 f. mult .. 75 40

OFFICIAL STAMPS

O 9. Dogon Mask.

O 30. Mali Flag and Emblems.

1961.
O 26. **O 9.** 1 f. violet 10 10
O 27. 2 f. red 10 10
O 28. 3 f. slate 10 10
O 29. 5 f. turquoise .. 15 15
O 30. 10 f. brown 20 15
O 31. 25 f. blue 35 15
O 32. 30 f. red 40 20
O 33. 50 f. myrtle 70 25
O 34. 85 f. purple .. .. 1·10 65
O 35. 100 f. green .. .. 1·40 65
O 36. 200 f. purple .. 2·75 1·40

1964. Centre and flag multicoloured; frame colour given.
O 90. **O 30.** 1 f. green 10 10
O 91. 2 f. lavender 10 10
O 92. 3 f. slate 10 10
O 93. 5 f. purple 10 10
O 94. 10 f. blue 15 10
O 95. 25 f. ochre 20 15
O 96. 30 f. green 25 15
O 97. 50 f. orange 35 15
O 98. 85 f. brown 50 20
O 99. 100 f. red 65 30
O 100. 200 f. blue .. .. 1·50 60

O 341. Arms of Gao.

1981. Town Arms. Multicoloured.
O 878. 5 f. Type O **341** .. 10 10
O 879. 15 f. Tombouctou .. 10 10
O 880. 50 f. Mopti 20 10
O 881. 180 f. Segou 60 30
O 882. 200 f. Sikasso 80 30
O 883. 680 f. Koulikoro .. 2·50 95
O 884. 700 f. Kayes .. .. 2·75 1·25
O 885. 1000 f. Bamako .. 4·00 1·50

1984. Nos. O 878/85 surch.
O 1013. 15 f. on 5 f. Type O **341** 15 10
O 1014. 50 f. on 15 f. Tombouctou 30 15
O 1015. 120 f. on 50 f. Mopti .. 70 25
O 1016. 295 f. on 180 f. Segou .. 2·00 90
O 1017. 470 f. on 200 f. Sikasso 3·00 1·50
O 1018. 515 f. on 680 f. Koulikoro .. .. 3·50 1·90
O 1019. 845 f. on 700 f. Kayes 6·00 2·50
O 1020. 1225 f. on 1000 f. Bamako .. .. 7·50 3·75

POSTAGE DUE STAMPS

D 9. Bambara Mask.

1961.
D 26. **D 9.** 1 f. black 10 10
D 27. 2 f. blue 10 10
D 28. 5 f. mauve 20 10
D 29. 10 f. orange 25 15
D 30. 20 f. turquoise .. 50 25
D 31. 25 f. purple 65 30

D 28. "Polyptychus roseus".

1964. Butterflies and Moths. Multicoloured.
D83 1 f. Type D **28** 10 10
D84 1 f. "Deilephila nerii" .. 10 10
D85 2 f. "Bunaea alcinoe" .. 15 15
D86 2 f. "Gynanisa maja" .. 15 15
D87 3 f. "Teracolus eris" .. 35 30
D88 3 f. "Colotis antevippe" .. 35 30
D89 5 f. "Manatha microcera" 35 30
D90 5 f. "Charaxes epijasius" 35 30
D91 10 f. "Hypokopelates otraeda" 45 35
D92 10 f. "Lipaphnaeus leonina" 45 35
D93 20 f. "Lobobunaea christyi" 75 70
D94 20 f. "Gonimbrasia hecate" 75 70
D95 25 f. "Hypolimnas misippus" .. .. 1·10 90
D96 25 f. "Castopsilia florella" 1·10 90

1984. Nos. D 83/96 surch.
D 1021. 5 f. on 1 f. Type D **28** 10 10
D 1022. 5 f. on 1 f. "Deilephila nerii" 10 10
D 1023. 10 f. on 2 f. "Bunaea alcinoe" 10 10
D 1024. 10 f. on 2 f. "Gynanisa maja" 10 10
D 1025. 15 f. on 3 f. "Teracolus eris" 15 10
D 1026. 15 f. on 3 f. "Colotis antevippe" 15 10
D 1027. 25 f. on 5 f. "Manatha microcera" 15 15
D 1028. 25 f. on 5 f. "Charaxes epijasius" 15 15
D 1029. 50 f. on 10 f. "Hypokopelates otraeda" .. 30 30
D 1030. 50 f. on 10 f. "Lipaphnaeus leonina" .. 30 30
D 1031. 100 f. on 20 f. "Lobobunaea christyi" .. 60 60
D 1032. 100 f. on 20 f. "Gonimbrasia hecate" .. 60 60
D 1033. 125 f. on 25 f. "Hypolimnas misippus" .. 75 75
D 1034. 125 f. on 25 f. "Catopsilia florella" .. 75 75

MANAMA Pt. 19

A dependency of Ajman.

100 dirhams = 1 riyal.

1966. Nos. 10, 12, 14 and 18 of Ajman surch. **Manama** in English and Arabic and new value.

1.	40 d. on 40 n.p. multicoloured	40	25
2.	70 d. on 70 n.p. multicoloured	40	25
3.	1 r. 50 on 1 r. 50 mult.	1·25	75
4.	10 r. on 10 r. multicoloured	6·00	6·00

1967. Nos. 140/8 of Ajman optd. **MANAMA** in English and Arabic. (a) Postage.

5.	15 d. blue and brown	10	10
6.	30 d. brown and black	15	10
7.	50 d. black and brown	35	20
8.	70 d. violet and black	60	30
	(b) Air.		
9.	1 r. green and brown	60	40
10.	2 r. mauve and black	1·40	90
11.	3 r. black and brown	2·00	1·75
12.	5 r. brown and black	3·50	3·50
13.	10 r. blue and brown	6·50	6·50

APPENDIX

The following stamps have either been issued in excess of postal needs or have not been available to the public in a reasonable quantities at face value. Such stamps may later be given full listing if there is evidence of regular postal use.

1966.

New Currency Surcharges. Stamps of Ajman surch. **Manama** in English and Arabic and new value.

(a) Nos. 19/20 and 22/4 (Kennedy). 10 d. on 10 n.p., 15 d. on 15 n.p., 1 r. on 1 r., 2 r. on 2 r., 3 r. on 3 r.

(b) Nos. 27, 30 and 35/6 (Olympics). 5 d. on 5 n.p., 25 d. on 25 n.p., 3 r. on 3 r., 5 r. on 5 r.

(c) Nos. 70/2 and 75 (Churchill). 50 d. on 50 n.p., 75 d. on 75 n.p., 1 r. on 1 r., 5 r. on 5 r.

(d) Nos. 85/8 (Space). Air 50 d. on 50 n.p., 1 r. on 1 r., 3 r. on 3 r., 5 r. on 5 r.

1967.

World Scout Jamboree, Idaho. Postage 30, 70 d., 1 r.; Air 2, 3, 4 r.

Olympic Games, Mexico (1968). Postage 35, 65, 75 d., 1 r.; Air 1 r. 25, 2, 3, 4 r.

Winter Olympic Games, Grenoble (1968) Postage 5, 35, 60, 75 d.; Air 1, 1 r. 25, 2, 3 r.

Paintings by Renoir and Terbrugghen. Air 35, 65 d., 1, 2 r. × 3.

1968.

Paintings by Velazquez. Air 1 r. × 2, 2 r. × 2.

Costumes. Air 30 d. × 2, 70 d. × 2, 1 r. × 2, 2 r. × 2.

Olympic Games, Mexico. Postage 1 r. × 4; Air 2 × 4. r.

Satellites and Spacecraft. Air 30 d. × 2, 70 d. × 2, 1 r. × 2, 2 r. × 2, 3 r. × 2.

Human Rights Year. Kennedy Brothers and Martin Luther King. Air 1 r. × 3, 2r. × 3.

Sports Champions, Famous Footballers. Postage 15, 20, 50, 75 d., 1 r.; Air 10 r.

Heroes of Humanity. Circular designs on gold or silver foil. 60 d. × 12.

Olympic Games, Mexico. Circular designs on gold or silver foil. Air 3 r. × 8.

Mothers' Day. Paintings. Postage 1 r × 6.

Kennedy Brothers Commem. Postage 2 r.; Air 5 r.

Cats. (1st series). Postage 1, 2, 3 d.; Air 2, 3 r.

5th Death Anniv. of Pres. Kennedy. Air 10 r.

Space Exploration. Postage 5, 10, 15, 20, 25 d.; Air 15 r.

Olympic Games, Mexico. Gold Medals. Postage 2 r. × 4; Air 5 r. × 4.

Christmas. Air 5 r.

1969.

Sports Champions. Cyclists. Postage 1, 2, 5, 10, 15, 20 d.; Air 12 r.

Sports Champions. German Footballers. Postage 5, 10, 15, 20, 25 d.; Air 10 r.

Sports Champions. Motor-racing Drivers. Postage 1, 5, 10, 15, 25 d.; Air 10 r.

Motor-racing Cars. Postage 1, 5, 10, 15, 25 d.; Air 10 r.

Sports Champions. Boxers. Postage 5, 10, 15, 20 d.; Air 10 r.

Sports Champions. Baseball Players. Postage 1, 2, 5, 10, 15 d.; Air 10 r.

Birds. Air 1 r. × 11.

Roses. 1 r. × 6.

Animals. Air 1 r. × 6.

Paintings by Italian Artists. 5, 10, 15, 20 d., 10 r.

Great Composers. Air 5, 10, 25 d., 10 r.

Paintings by French Artists. 1 r. × 4.

Nude Paintings. Air 2 r. × 4.

Kennedy Brothers. Air 2, 3, 10 r.

Olympic Games, Mexico. Gold Medal Winners. Postage 1, 2 d., 10 r.; Air 10 d., 5, 10 r.

Paintings of the Madonna. Postage 10 d.; Air 10 r.

Space Flight of "Apollo 9". Optd. on 1968 Exploration issue. Air 15 r.

Space Flight of "Apollo 10". Optd. on 1968 Space Exploration issue. Air 15 r.

1st Death Anniv. of Gagarin. Optd. on 1968 Space Exploration issue. 5 d.

2nd Death Anniv. of Edward White (astronaut). Optd. on 1968 Space Exploration issue. 10 d.

1st Death Anniv. of Robert Kennedy. Optd. on 1969 Kennedy Brothers issue. Air 2 r.

Olympic Games, Munich (1972). Optd. on 1969 Mexico Gold Medal Winners issue. Air 10 d., 5, 10 r.

Moon Mission of "Apollo 11". Air 1, 2, 3 r.

Christmas. Paintings by Brueghel. Postage 1, 2, 4, 5, 10 d.; Air 6 r.

1970.

"Soyuz" and "Apollo" Space Programmes. Postage 1, 2, 4, 5, 10 d.; Air 3, 5 r.

Kennedy and Eisenhower Commem. Embossed on gold foil. Air 20 r.

Lord Baden-Powell Commem. Embossed on gold foil. Air 20 r.

World Cup Football Championships, Mexico. Postage, 20, 40, 60, 80 d., 1 r; Air 3 r.

Brazil's Victory in World Cup Football Championships. Optd. on 1970 World Cup issue. Postage 20, 40, 60, 80 d., 1 r; Air 3 r.

Paintings by Michelangelo. Postage 1, 2, 4, 5, 10 d.; Air 6 r.

World Fair "Expo 70", Osaka, Japan. Air 25, 50, 75 d., 1, 2, 3, 12 r.

Paintings by Renoir. Postage 1, 2, 5, 6, 10 d.; Air 5, 12 r.

Olympic Games, Rome, Tokyo, Mexico and Munich. Postage 15, 30, 50, 70 d.; Air 2, 5 r.

Winter Olympic Games, Sapporo (1972) (1st issue). Postage 2, 3, 4, 10 d.; Air 2, 5 r.

Christmas. Flower Paintings by Brueghel. Postage 5, 20, 25, 30, 50 d.; Air 60 d., 1, 2 r.

1971.

Winter Olympic Games, Sapporo (2nd issue). Postage 1, 2, 3, 4, 5, 6, 8, 10, 12, 15, 20, 25, 30, 35, 40, 50 d.; Air 75 d, 1, 2, 2 r.50.

Roses. Postage 5, 20, 25, 30, 50 d.; Air 60 d., 1, 2 r.

Birds. Postage 5, 20, 25, 30, 50 d.; Air 60 d. 1, 2 r.

Paintings by Modigliani. Air 25, 50, 60, 75 d., 1 r. 50, 3 r.

Paintings by Rubens. Postage 1, 2, 3, 4, 5, 10 d.; Air 2, 3 r.

"Philatokyo '71" Stamp Exhibition, Paintings by Hokusai and Hiroshige. Postage 10, 15, 20, 25, 50, 75 d.; Air 1, 2 r.

25th Anniv. of United Nations. Optd on 1970 Christmas issue. Postage 5, 20, 25, 30, 50 d.; Air 60 d., 1, 2 r.

British Military Uniforms. Postage 5, 20, 25, 30, 50 d.; Air 60 d., 1, 2 r.

Space Flight of "Apollo 14". Postage 15, 25, 50, 60, 70 d.; Air 5 r.

Space Flight of "Apollo 15". Postage 25, 40, 50, 60 d.; Air 1, 6 r.

13th World Scout Jamboree, Asagiri, Japan. (1st issue). Postage 1, 2, 3, 5, 7, 10, 12, 15, 20, 25, 30, 35, 40, 50, 65. 80 d.; Air 1, 1 r. 25, 1 r. 50, 2 r.

World Wild Life Conservation. Postage 1, 2, 3, 5, 7, 10, 12, 15, 20, 25, 30, 35, 40, 50, 65, 80 d.; Air 1 r. 1 r.25, 1 r.50, 2 r.

13th World Scout Jamboree, Asagiri, Japan. (2nd issue). Stamps Postage 10, 15, 20, 25, 50, 75 d.; Air 1, 2 r.

Winter Olympic Games, Sapporo (3rd issue). Postage 1, 2, 3, 4, 5, 10 d.; Air 2, 3 r.

Cats (2nd series). Postage 15, 25, 40, 60 d.; Air 3, 10 r.

Lions International Clubs. Optd. on 1971 Uniforms issue. Postage 5, 20, 25, 30, 50 d.; Air 60 d., 1, 2 r.

Paintings of Ships. Postage 15, 20, 25, 30, 50 d.; Air 60 d. 1, 2 r.

Great Olympic Champions. Postage 25, 50, 75 d. 1 r.; Air 5 r.

Prehistoric Animals. Postage 15, 20, 25, 30, 50, 60 d.; Air 1, 2 r.

Footballers. Postage 5, 10, 15, 20, 40 d.; Air 5 r.

Royal Visit of Queen Elizabeth II to Japan. Postage 10, 20, 30, 40, 50 d.; Air 2, 3 r.

Fairy Tales. Stories by Hans Andersen. Postage 1, 2, 4, 5, 10 d.; Air 3 r.

World Fair, Philadelphia (1976). American Paintings. Postage 20, 25, 50, 60, 75 d.; Air 3 r.

Fairy Tales. Well-known stories. Postage 1, 2, 4, 5, 10 d.; Air 3 r.

Space Flight of "Apollo 16". Postage 20, 30, 40, 50, 60 d.; Air 3, 4 r.

Tropical Fishes. Postage 1, 2, 3, 4, 5, 10 d.; Air 2, 3 r.

European Tour of Emperor Hirohito of Japan. Postage 1, 2, 4, 5, 10 d.; Air 6 r.

Meeting of Pres. Nixon and Emperor Hirohito of Japan in Alaska. Optd. on 1971 Emperor's Tour issue. Air 6 r.

2500th Anniv. of Persian Empire. Postage 10, 20, 30, 40, 50 d.; Air 3 r.

Space Flight of "Apollo 15" and Future Developments in Space. Postage 10, 15, 20, 25, 50 d.; Air 1, 2 r.

1972.

150th Death Anniv. (1971) of Napoleon. Postage 10, 20, 30, 40 d.; Air 1, 2, 3, 4 r.

1st Death Anniv. of Gen. de Gaulle. Postage 10, 20, 30, 40 d.; Air 1, 2, 3, 4 r.

Paintings from the "Alte Pinakothek", Munich. Postage 5, 10, 15, 20, 25 d.; Air 5 r.

"Tour de France" Cycle Race. Postage 5, 10 15, 20, 25, 30, 35, 40, 45, 50, 55, 60 d.; Air 65, 70, 75, 80, 85, 90, 95 d., 1 r.

Cats and Dogs. Postage 10, 20, 30, 40, 50 d.; Air 1 r.

25th Anniv. of U.N.I.C.E.F. Optd. on 1971 World Scout Jamboree, Asagiri (2nd issue). Postage 10, 15, 20, 25, 50, 75 d.; Air 1, 2 r.

Past and Present Motorcars. Postage 10, 20, 30, 40, 50 d.; Air 1 r.

Military Uniforms. 1 r. × 11.

The United Arab Emirates Ministry of Communications took over the Manama postal service on 1 August 1972. Further stamps inscribed "Manama" issued after that date were released without authority and had no validity.

MANCHUKUO Pt. 17

Issues for the Japanese puppet Government set up in 1932 under President (later Emperor) Pu Yi.

100 fen = 1 yuan

1. White Pagoda, Liaoyang.

2. Pu Yi, later Emperor Kang-teh.

1932.

(a) With five characters in top panel as T **1** and **2**.

1.	**1.**	½ f. brown	35	25
2.		1 f. lake	35	10
25.		1½ f. mauve	60	75
26.		2 f. slate	1·00	25
27.		3 f. brown	2·00	10
6.		4 f. olive	20	10
7.		5 f. green	30	15
8.		6 f. red	1·50	40
9.		7 f. grey	50	20
10.		8 f. yellow	7·50	5·00
11.		10 f. orange	1·25	15
12.	**2.**	13 f. brown	2·00	2·00
13.		15 f. red	10·00	60
14.		16 f. blue	7·00	2·00
15.		20 f. brown	2·00	40
16.		30 f. orange	2·00	60
17.		50 f. green	3·00	70
31.		1 y. violet	10·00	3·00
		(b) With six characters in top panel.		
40.	**1.**	½ f. sepia	15	10
41.		1 f. lake	15	10
42.		1½ f. mauve	30	40
43.		3 f. brown	30	10
44.		5 f. blue	6·00	60
45.		5 f. slate	1·00	40
46.		6 f. red	75	15
47.		7 f. grey	75	40
48.		9 f. orange	75	20
55.		10 f. blue	3·00	10
56.	**2.**	13 f. brown	2·00	2·50
49.		15 f. red	1·00	25
50.		18 f. green	10·00	3·00
51.		20 f. sepia	1·50	20
52.		30 f. brown	2·00	25
53.		50 f. olive	2·50	30
54.		1 y. violet	4·50	2·40

3. Map and Flags.

6. Emperor's Palace.

1933. 1st Anniv. of Republic.

19.	**3.**	1 f. orange	50	40
20.	–	2 f. green	5·50	6·00
21.	**3.**	4 f. red	50	35
22.	–	10 f. blue	7·50	7·50

DESIGN: 2, 10 f. Council Hall, Hsinking.

1934. Enthronement of Emperor.

32.	**6.**	1½ f. brown	60	40
33.	–	3 f. red	40	20
34.	**6.**	6 f. green	2·75	2·75
35.	–	10 f. blue	4·25	3·00

DESIGN: 3 f., 10 f. Phoenixes.

1934. Stamps of 1932 surch. with four Japanese characters.

36.	**1.**	1 f. on 4 f. olive (No. 6)	1·50	1·00
38.		3 f. on 4 f. olive (No. 6)	2·00	1·50
39.	**2.**	3 f. on 16 f. blue (No. 14)	4·00	4·00

In No. 38 the left hand upper character of the surcharge consists of three horizontal lines.

12. Orchid Crest of Manchukuo.

13. Changpai Mountain and Sacred Lake.

1935. China Mail.

64.	**12.**	2 f. green	30	15
65.		2½ f. violet	20	15
58.	**13.**	4 f. green	50	25
67.		5 f. black	15	10
68.	**12.**	8 f. yellow	1·00	30
63.	**13.**	12 f. brown	3·00	1·75
70.		13 f. brown	15	15

15. Mt. Fuji.

16. Phœnixes.

1935. Visit of Emperor Kang-teh to Japan.

71.	**15.**	1½ f. green	40	40
72.	**16.**	3 f. orange	30	15
73.	**15.**	6 f. red	1·90	1·75
74.	**16.**	10 f. blue	2·00	2·00

17. Symbolic of Accord.

19. State Council Building, Hsinking.

20. Chengte Palace, Jehol.

1936. Japan-Manchukuo Postal Agreement.

75.	**17.**	1½ f. sepia	80	80
76.	–	3 f. mauve	50	10
77.	**17.**	6 f. red	3·75	3·00
78.	–	10 f. blue	3·00	2·00

DESIGN—HORIZ. 3 f., 10 f. Department of Communications.

1936.

79	**19**	½ f. brown	15	15
80		1 f. red	20	10
81		1½ f. violet	1·25	1·25
82	A	2 f. green	10	10
83	**19**	3 f. brown	15	15
84	B	4 f. green	10	10
149	**19**	5 f. grey	10	50
86	A	6 f. red	25	10
87	B	7 f. black	30	10
88		9 f. red	35	20
89	**20**	10 f. blue	35	10
90	B	12 f. orange	15	10
91		13 f. brown	7·00	10·00
92		15 f. red	60	30
93	C	18 f. green	4·50	4·50
94		19 f. green	2·50	1·00
152	A	20 f. brown	25	1·00
153	**20**	30 f. brown	25	1·00
97	D	38 f. blue	7·00	7·00
98		39 f. blue	30	90
99	A	50 f. green	1·00	30
154	**20**	1 y. violet	25	2·00

DESIGNS: A, Carting soya-beans. B, Peiling Mausoleum. C, Aeroplane and grazing sheep (domestic and China air mail). D, Aeroplane over R. Sungari bridge (air mail to Japan).

21. Sun rising over Fields.

22. Shadowgraph of old and new Hsinking

1937. 5th Anniv. of Founding of State.

101.	**21.**	1½ f. red	2·50	3·00
102.	**22.**	3 f. green	75	75

1937. China Mail. Surch in Chinese characters.

108.	**12.**	2½ f. on 2 f. green	1·00	1·00
110.	**13.**	5 f. on 4 f. green	1·25	1·25
111.		13 f. on 12 f. brown	3·25	3·25

27. Pouter Pigeon and Hsinking.

DESIGN: 4 f., 20 f. Flag over Imperial Palace.

1937. Completion of Five Year Reconstruction Plan for Hsinking.

No.	Type	Description	Unused	Used
112.	27.	2 f. mauve	75	75
113.	–	4 f. red	60	10
114.	27.	10 f. green	2·75	1·50
115.	–	20 f. blue	2·75	3·00

29. Manchukuo. **30.** Japanese Residents Assn. Building.

1937. Japan's Relinquishment of Extra-territorial Rights.

No.	Type	Description	Unused	Used
116.	29.	2 f. red	35	15
117.	30.	4 f. green	1·00	25
118.		8 f. orange	1·50	1·10
119.	–	10 f. blue	1·10	30
120.	–	12 f. violet	1·75	1·75
121.	–	20 f. lake	2·00	1·50

DESIGNS—As Type **20**—HORIZ. 10 f., 20 f. Dept. of Communications Bldg. VERT. 12 f. Ministry of Justice.

32. "Twofold Happiness". **33.** Red Cross on Map and Globe.

1937. New Year's Greetings.

No.	Type	Description	Unused	Used
122.	32.	2 f. red and blue	1·25	30

1938. Inaug. of Manchukuo Red Cross Society.

No.	Type	Description	Unused	Used
123.	33.	2 f. red	75	75
124.		4 f. green	75	75

34. Map of Railway Lines. **35.** "Asia" Express.

1939. Completion of 10,000 Kilometres of Manchurian Railways.

No.	Type	Description	Unused	Used
125	34	2f. blue and orange	1·00	1·00
126	35	4 f. deep blue and blue	1·00	1·00

36. Manchurian Cranes over Shipmast. **37.** Census Official and Manchukuo. **38.** Census Slogans in Chinese, and Mongolian.

1940. 2nd Visit of Emperor to Japan.

No.	Type	Description	Unused	Used
127.	36.	2 f. mauve	1·10	2·10
128.		4 f. green	1·25	1·90

1940. National Census.

No.	Type	Description	Unused	Used
129.	37.	2 f. brown and yellow	45	45
130.	38.	4 f. black and green	45	45

39. Message of Congratulation. **40.** Dragon Dance.

1940. 2600th Anniv. of Founding of Japanese Empire.

No.	Type	Description	Unused	Used
131.	39.	2 f. red	10	40
132.	40.	4 f. blue	10	50

紀念新嘉坡
復歸我東亞
年九德康

41. Recruit. (42.)

1941. Enactment of Conscription Law.

No.	Type	Description	Unused	Used
133.	41.	2 f. red	30	60
134.		4 f. blue	45	70

1942. Fall of Singapore. Stamps of 1936 optd. with T **42**.

No.	Type	Description	Unused	Used
135.	A.	2 f. green	50	75
136.	B.	4 f. olive	60	80

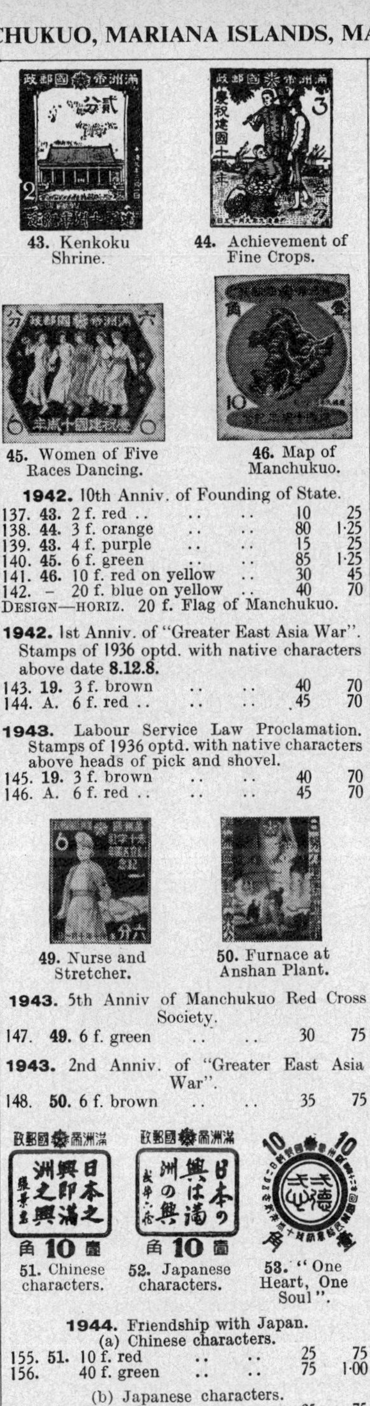

43. Kenkoku Shrine. **44.** Achievement of Fine Crops.

45. Women of Five Races Dancing. **46.** Map of Manchukuo.

1942. 10th Anniv. of Founding of State.

No.	Type	Description	Unused	Used
137.	43.	2 f. red	10	25
138.	44.	3 f. orange	80	1·25
139.	43.	4 f. purple	15	25
140.	45.	6 f. green	85	1·25
141.	46.	10 f. red on yellow	30	45
142.	–	20 f. blue on yellow	40	70

DESIGN—HORIZ. 20 f. Flag of Manchukuo.

1942. 1st Anniv. of "Greater East Asia War". Stamps of 1936 optd. with native characters above date **8.12.8.**

No.	Type	Description	Unused	Used
143.	19.	3 f. brown	40	70
144.	A.	6 f. red	.45	70

1943. Labour Service Law Proclamation. Stamps of 1936 optd. with native characters above heads of pick and shovel.

No.	Type	Description	Unused	Used
145.	19.	3 f. brown	40	70
146.	A.	6 f. red	45	70

49. Nurse and Stretcher. **50.** Furnace at Anshan Plant.

1943. 5th Anniv of Manchukuo Red Cross Society.

No.	Type	Description	Unused	Used
147.	49.	6 f. green	30	75

1943. 2nd Anniv. of "Greater East Asia War".

No.	Type	Description	Unused	Used
148.	50.	6 f. brown	35	75

51. Chinese characters. **52.** Japanese characters. **53.** "One Heart, One Soul".

1944. Friendship with Japan.
(a) Chinese characters.

No.	Type	Description	Unused	Used
155.	51.	10 f. red	25	75
156.		40 f. green	75	1·00

(b) Japanese characters.

No.	Type	Description	Unused	Used
157.	52.	10 f. red	25	75
158.		40 f. green	75	1·00

1945. 10th Anniv. of Emperor's Edict.

No.	Type	Description	Unused	Used
159.	53.	10 f. red	85	2·00

MARIANA ISLANDS Pt. 7

A group of Spanish Islands in the Pacific Ocean of which Guam was ceded to the U.S.A. and the others to Germany. The latter are now under U.S. Trusteeship.

100 pfennig = 1 mark.

1899. German stamps optd. **Marianen.**

No.	Type	Description	Unused	Used
7.	8.	3 pf. brown	12·00	32·00
8.		5 pf. green	14·00	32·00
9.	9.	10 pf. red	18·00	38·00
10.		20 pf. blue	22·00	£110
11.		25 pf. orange	60·00	£160
12.		50 pf. brown	60·00	£190

1901. "Yacht" key-type inscr. "MARIANEN".

No.	Type	Description	Unused	Used
13.	N.	3 pf. brown	70	90
14.		5 pf. green	70	90
15.		10 pf. red	70	2·75
16.		20 pf. blue	1·00	6·00
17.		25 pf. blk. & red on yellow	1·25	13·00
18.		30 pf. blk. & orge. on buff	1·25	13·00
19.		40 pf. black and red	1·25	13·00
20.		50 pf. blk. & pur. on buff	1·40	15·00
21.		80 pf. blk. & red on rose	2·00	24·00
22.	O.	1 m. red	2·25	65·00
23.		2 m. blue	4·00	80·00
24.		3 m. black	6·00	£120
25.		5 m. red and black	£130	£500

MARIENWERDER Pt. 7

A district of E. Prussia where a plebiscite was held in 1920. As a result the district remained part of Germany. After the War of 1939-45 it was returned to Poland and reverted to its original name of Kwidzyn.

100 pfennig = 1 mark.

1.

1920.

No.	Type	Description	Unused	Used
1.	1.	5 pf. green	25	25
2.		10 pf. red	20	15
3.		15 pf. grey	30	35
4.		20 pf. brown	15	15
5.		25 pf. blue	40	45
6.		30 pf. orange	85	65
7.		40 pf. brown	40	45
8.		50 pf. violet	40	40
9.		60 pf. brown	2·75	2·50
10.		75 pf. brown	65	75
11.		1 m. brown and green	60	55
12.		2 m. purple	4·50	2·40
13.		3 m. red	4·00	3·25
14.		5 m. blue and red	24·00	17·00

1920. Stamps of Germany inscr "DEUTSCHES REICH" (a) optd **Commission Interalliee Marienwerder**.

No.	Type	Description	Unused	Used
15	10	5 pf. green	10·00	20·00
16		20 f. blue	3·00	10·00
17		50 pf. blk & pur on buff	£300	£600
18		75 pf. black and green	2·00	5·00
19		80 pf. black & red on rose	60·00	£110
25	12	1 m. red	2·25	4·50
26		1 m. 25 green	2·50	5·00
27		1 m. 50 brown	3·25	7·00
28	13	2 m. 50 purple	2·25	4·50

(b) optd **Commission interalliee Marienwerder** and surch also.

No.	Type	Description	Unused	Used
21	24	1 m. on 2 pf. grey	20·00	35·00
22		2 m. on 2½ pf. grey	7·00	12·00
23	10	3 m. on 3 pf. brown	7·50	14·00
24	24	5 m. on 7½ pf. orange	8·50	14·00

1920. As T **1**, with inscription at top changed to "PLEBISCITE".

No.	Type	Description	Unused	Used
29.		5 pf. green	2·25	2·00
30.		10 pf. red	2·25	2·00
31.		15 pf. grey	8·50	10·00
32.		20 pf. brown	1·25	1·50
33.		25 pf. blue	11·00	11·00
34.		30 pf. orange	1·00	80
35.		40 pf. brown	70	50
36.		50 pf. violet	1·40	1·00
37.		60 pf. brown	4·00	3·75
38.		75 pf. brown	5·00	5·00
39.		1 m. brown and green	75	60
40.		2 m. purple	90	85
41.		3 m. red	1·40	1·10
42.		5 m. blue and red	2·00	1·25

MARSHALL ISLANDS Pt. 7; Pt. 22

A group of islands in the Pacific Ocean, a German protectorate from 1885. From 1920 to 1947 it was a Japanese mandated territory and from 1947 part of the United States Trust Territory of the Pacific Islands, using United States stamps. In 1984 it assumed control of its postal services.

A. GERMAN PROTECTORATE

100 pfennig = 1 mark.

1897. Stamps of Germany optd.
(a) Optd **Marschall-Iseln**

No.	Type	Description	Unused	Used
G 1	8	3 pf. brown	£120	£450
G 2		5 pf. green	£100	£400
G 3	9	10 pf. red	30·00	£110
G 4		20 pf. blue	30·00	£110

(b) Optd **Marshall-Inseln**

No.	Type	Description	Unused	Used
G 5	8	3 pf. brown	3·00	5·00
G 6		5 pf. green	7·50	5·50
G 7	9	10 pf. red	10·00	14·00
G 8		20 pf. blue	13·00	23·00
G 9		25 pf. orange	17·00	40·00
G10		50 pf. brown	27·00	48·00

1901. "Yacht" key types inscr. "MARSHALL INSELN".

No.	Type	Description	Unused	Used
G 11.	N.	3 pf. brown	60	1·00
G 12.		5 pf. green	60	1·10
G 13.		10 pf. red	60	4·00
G 14.		20 pf. blue	75	9·00
G 15.		25 pf. blk. & red on yell.	80	15·00
G 16.		30 pf. blk. & orge. on buff	80	15·00
G 17.		40 pf. black and red	80	15·00
G 18.		50 pf. blk. & pur. on buff	1·10	20·00
G 19.		80 pf. blk. & red on rose	2·00	32·00
G 20.	O.	1 m. red	3·00	60·00
G 21.		2 m. blue	4·25	£110
G 22.		3 m. black	6·00	£180
G 23.		5 m. red and black	£110	£450

B. REPUBLIC

100 cents = 1 dollar.

1. Canoe.

1984. Inauguration of Postal Independence. Multicoloured.

No.	Description	Unused	Used
1.	20 c. Type **1**	55	30
2.	20 c. Fishes and net	55	30
3.	20 c. Navigational stick-chart	55	30
4.	20 c. Islet with coconut palms	55	30

2. Mili Atoll. **3.** German Marshall Islands 1900 3 pf. Optd. Stamp.

1984. Maps. Multicoloured.

No.	Description	Unused	Used
5	1 c. Type **2**	10	10
6	3 c. Likiep Atoll	10	10
7	5 c. Ebon Atoll	15	10
8	10 c. Jaluit Atoll	15	10
9	13 c. Ailinginae Atoll	25	15
10	14 c. Wotho Atoll	25	15
11	20 c. Kwajalein and Ebeye Atolls	40	20
12	22 c. Enewetak Atoll	40	20
13	28 c. Ailinglaplap Atoll	65	35
14	30 c. Majuro Atoll	65	25
15	33 c. Namu Atoll	70	40
16	37 c. Rongelap Atoll	75	45
16a	39 c. Taka and Utirik Atolls	75	45
16b	44 c. Ujelang Atoll	85	50
16c	50 c. Aur and Maloelap Atolls	1·00	65
17	$1 Arno Atoll	2·25	75
18	$2 Wotje and Erikub Atolls	4·00	2·50
19	$5 Bikini Atoll	10·00	8·00
20	$10 Marshallese stick chart (31 × 31 mm)	16·00	13·00

1984. 19th Universal Postal Union Congress Philatelic Salon, Hamburg.

No.	Type	Description	Unused	Used
21.	3.	40 c. brn., blk. & yell.	75	50
22.	–	40 c. brn., blk. & yell.	75	50
23.	–	40 c bl., blk. & yell.	75	50
24.	–	40 c. multicoloured	75	50

DESIGNS: No. 22, German Marshall Islands 1901 3 pf. "Yacht" stamp. 23, German Marshall Islands 1897 20 pf. stamp. 24, German Marshall Islands 1901 5 m. "Yacht" stamp.

4. Common Dolphin.

1984. "Ausipex 84" International Stamp Exhibition, Melbourne. Dolphins. Mult.

No.	Description	Unused	Used
25	20 c. Type **4**	55	35
26	20 c. Risso's dolphin	55	35
27	20 c. Spotter dolphins	55	35
28	20 c. Bottle-nosed dolphin	55	35

5. Star over Bethlehem and Text. **6.** Traditional Chief and German and Marshallese Flags.

1984. Christmas Multicoloured.

29.	20 c. Type **5**	50	30
30.	20 c. Desert landscape	50	30
31.	20 c. Two kings on camels	50	30
32.	20 c. Third king on camel	50	30

1984. 5th Anniv. of Constitution. Mult.

33	20 c. Type **6**	45	30
34	20 c. Pres. Amata Kabua and American and Marshallese flags	45	30
35	20 c. Admiral Chester W. Nimitz and Japanese and Marshallese flags	45	30
36	20 c. Trygve H. Lie (first Secretary-General of United Nations) and U.N. and Marshallese flags	45	30

7. Leach's Storm Petrel.

1985. Birth Bicentenary of John J. Audubon (ornithologist). Multicoloured.

37.	22 c. Type **7** (inscr. "Fork-tailed Petrel") (postage)	65	30
38.	22 c. Pectoral sandpiper	65	30
39.	44 c. Brown booby (inscr "Booby Gannet") (air)	1·25	80
40.	44 c. Whimbrel (inscr. "Great Esquimaux Curlew")	1·25	80

8. Black-spotted Triton.

1985. Sea Shells (1st series). Multicoloured.

41.	22 c. Type **8**	60	35
42.	22 c. Monodon murex	60	35
43.	22 c. Diana conch	60	35
44.	22 c. Great green turban	60	35
45.	22 c. Rose-branch murex	60	35

See also Nos. 85/9, 131/5 and 220/4.

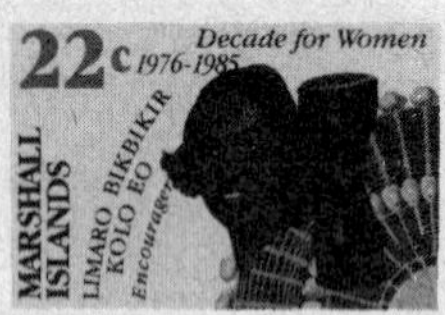

9. Woman as Encourager and Drum.

1985. International Decade for Women. Multicoloured.

46	22 c. Type **9**	50	30
47	22 c. Woman as Peacemaker and palm branches	50	30
48	22 c. Woman as Nurturer and pounding stone	50	30
49	22 c. Woman as Benefactress and lesser frigate bird	50	30

Nos. 46/9 were printed together in se-tenant blocks of four within the sheet, each block forming a composite design.

10. White-barred Surgeon Fish.

1985. Lagoon Fishes. Multicoloured.

50.	22 c. Type **10**	60	40
51.	22 c. White-blotched squirrel fish	60	40
52.	22 c. White-spotted boxfish	60	40
53.	22 c. Saddleback butterfly fish	60	40

11. Basketball.

1985. International Youth Year. Mult.

54.	22 c. Type **11**	45	30
55.	22 c. Elderly woman recording for oral history project	45	30
56.	22 c. Islander explaining navigational stick charts	45	30
57.	22 c. Dancers at inter-atoll music and dance competition	45	30

12. American Board of Commissions for Foreign Missions Stock Certificate.

1985. Christmas. "Morning Star I" (first Christian missionary ship to visit Marshall Islands). Multicoloured.

58	14 c. Type **12**	30	15
59	22 c. Launching of "Morning Star I", 1856	45	30
60	33 c. Departure from Honolulu, 1857	70	50
61	44 c. Entering Ebon Lagoon, 1857	80	60

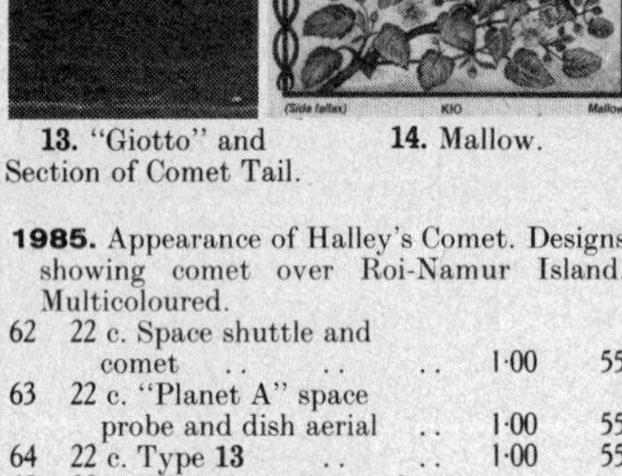

13. "Giotto" and Section of Comet Tail. **14.** Mallow.

1985. Appearance of Halley's Comet. Designs showing comet over Roi-Namur Island. Multicoloured.

62	22 c. Space shuttle and comet	1·00	55
63	22 c. "Planet A" space probe and dish aerial	1·00	55
64	22 c. Type **13**	1·00	55
65	22 c. "Vega" satellite and buildings on island	1·00	55
66	22 c. Sir Edmund Halley, satellite communications ship and airplane	1·00	55

Nos. 62/6 were printed together, se-tenant, forming a composite design.

1985. Medicinal Plants. Multicoloured.

67.	22 c. Type **14**	50	35
68.	22 c. Half-flower	50	35
69.	22 c. "Guettarda speciosa"	50	35
70.	22 c. Love-vine	50	35

15. Triton's Trumpet.

1986. World Wildlife Fund. Marine Life. Multicoloured.

71.	14 c. Type **15**	45	30
72.	14 c. Giant clam	45	30
73.	14 c. Small giant clam	45	30
74.	14 c. Coconut crab	45	30

16. Consolidated "PBY-15A Catalina" Amphibian.

1986. Air. "Ameripex 86" International Stamp Exhibition, Chicago. Mail Planes. Mult.

75.	44 c. Type **16**	85	65
76.	44 c. Grumman "SA-16 Albatross"	85	65
77.	44 c. McDonnell Douglas "DC-6B Super Cloudmaster"	85	65
78.	44 c. Boeing "727-100"	85	65

17. Islanders in Outrigger Canoe.

1986. 40th Anniv. of Operation Crossroads (atomic bomb tests on Bikini Atoll). Multicoloured.

80	22 c. Type **17**	55	35
81	22 c. Advance landing of amphibious DUKW from U.S.S. "Sumner"	55	35
82	22 c. Loading "LST 1108" (tank landing ship) for islanders' departure	55	35
83	22 c. Man planting coconuts as part of reclamation programme	55	35

1986. Sea Shells (2nd series). As T **8**. Mult.

85.	22 c. Rose murex	50	35
86.	22 c. Orange spider conch	50	35
87.	22 c. Red-mouth frog shell	50	35
88.	22 c. Laciniate conch	50	35
89.	22 c. Giant frog shell	50	35

18. Blue Marlin.

1986. Game Fishes. Multicoloured.

90.	22 c. Type **18**	50	40
91.	22 c. Wahoo	50	40
92.	22 c. Dolphin fish	50	40
93.	22 c. Yellowfin tuna	50	40

19. Flowers (top left).

1986. International Peace Year. Mult.

94	22 c. Type **19** (Christmas) (postage)	50	35
95	22 c. Flowers (top right)	50	35
96	22 c. Flowers (bottom left)	50	35
97	22 c. Flowers (bottom right)	50	35
98	44 c. Head of Statue crowned with flowers (24 × 39 mm) (cent of Statue of Liberty) (air)	1·00	70

Nos. 94/7 were issued together, se-tenant, in blocks of four within the sheet, each block forming a composite design of mixed flower arrangement.

20. Girl Scout giving Plant to Patient.

1986. Air. 20th Anniv. of Marshall Island Girl Scouts and 75th Anniv. (1987) of United States Girl Scout Movement. Multicoloured.

99.	44 c. Type **20**	90	70
100.	44 c. Giving salute	90	70
101.	44 c. Girl scouts holding hands in circle	90	70
102.	44 c. Weaving pandana and palm branch mats	90	70

21. Wedge-tailed Shearwater.

1987. Air. Sea Birds. Multicoloured.

103	44 c. Type **21**	90	70
104	44 c. Red-footed booby	90	70
105	44 c. Red-tailed tropic bird	90	70
106	44 c. Lesser frigate bird	90	70

22. "James T. Arnold", 1854.

1987. Whaling Ships. Multicoloured.

107.	22 c. Type **22**	60	45
108.	22 c. "General Scott", 1859	60	45
109.	22 c. "Charles W. Morgan", 1865	60	45
110.	22 c. "Lucretia", 1884	60	45

23. "Spirit of St. Louis" and Congressional Medal of Honour, 1927.

1987. Aviators. Multicoloured.

111	33 c. Type **23**	70	45
112	33 c. Charles Lindbergh and "Corsair", Marshall Islands, 1944	70	45
113	39 c. William Bridgeman and bomber, Kwajalein, 1944	80	60
114	39 c. Bridgeman and Douglas "Skyrocket", 1951	80	60
115	44 c. John Glenn and fighters, Marshall Islands, 1944	1·00	75
116	44 c. Glenn and "Friendship 7" space capsule	1·00	75

24. "Electra" taking off from Lae, New Guinea.

1987. Air. "Capex '87" International Stamp Exhibition, Toronto. 50th Anniv. of Amelia Earhart's Round the World Flight Attempt. Multicoloured.

117	44 c. Type **24**	90	65
118	44 c. U.S. Coastguard cutter "Itasca" waiting off Howland Island for "Electra"	90	65
119	44 c. Islanders and crashed "Electra" on Mili Atoll	90	65
120	44 c. Japanese patrol boat "Koshu" recovering "Electra"	90	65

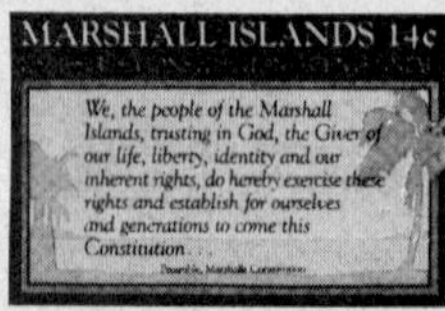

25. "We, the people of the Marshall Islands . . .".

1987. Bicentenary of United States of America Constitution. Multicoloured.

122	14 c. Type **25**	30	25
123	14 c. Marshall Is. and U.S.A. emblems	30	25
124	14 c. "We the people of the United States. . ."	30	25
125	22 c. "All we have and are today as a people. . ."	45	25
126	22 c. Marshall Is. and U.S.A. flags	45	25

127	22 c. ". . . to establish Justice,. . ."	45	25
128	44 c. "With this Constitution. . ."	85	75
129	44 c. Marshall Is. stick chart and U.S. Liberty Bell	85	75
130	44 c. ". . . to promote the general Welfare. . ."	85	75

The three designs of each value were printed together, se-tenant, the left hand stamp of each strip bearing quotations from the preamble to the Marshall Islands Constitution and the right hand stamp, quotations from the United States Constitution preamble.

1987. Sea Shells (3rd series). As T 8. Mult.

131.	22 c. Magnificent cone	55	35
132.	22 c. Partridge tun	55	35
133.	22 c. Scorpion spider conch	55	35
134.	22 c. Hairy triton	55	35
135.	22 c. Chiragra spider conch	55	35

26. Planting Coconut.

1987. Copra Industry. Multicoloured.

136.	44 c. Type **26**	80	65
137.	44 c. Making copra	80	65
138.	44 c. Bottling extracted coconut oil	80	65

27. "We have seen his star in the east, . . .".

1987. Christmas. Multicoloured.

139	14 c. Type **27**	30	25
140	22 c. "Glory to God in the highest;. . ."	40	30
141	33 c. "Sing unto the Lord a new song. . ."	60	40
142	44 c. "Praise him in the cymbals and dances;. . ."	80	65

28. Eastern Reef Heron.

1988. Shore and Water Birds. Multicoloured.

143.	44 c. Type **28**	75	50
144.	44 c. Bar-tailed godwit	75	50
145.	44 c. Blue-faced booby	75	50
146.	44 c. Common shoveler	75	50

29. Damselfish. **30.** Javelin Thrower.

1988. Fishes. Multicoloured.

147	1 c. Type **29**	10	10
148	3 c. Blackface butterfly fish	10	10
149	14 c. Hawkfish	20	10
150	15 c. Balloonfish	20	10
151	17 c. Trunk fish	25	15
152	22 c. Lyretail wrasse	30	20
153	25 c. Parrotfish	30	20
154	33 c. White-spotted boxfish	40	25
155	36 c. Spotted boxfish	45	30
156	39 c. Surgeonfish	50	40
157	44 c. Long-snouted butterfly fish	55	45
158	45 c. Trumpetfish	55	45
159	56 c. Sharp-nosed puffer	70	50
160	$1 Seahorse	1·25	70
161	$2 Ghost pipefish	2·50	1·50
162	$5 Big-spotted triggerfish	6·00	4·50
163	$10 Blue jacks (50 × 28 mm)	12·00	9·00

1988. Olympic Games, Seoul. Multicoloured.

166.	15 c. Type **30**	25	15
167.	15 c. Drawing javelin back and star	25	15
168.	15 c. Javelin drawn back fully (value at left)	25	15
169.	15 c. Commencing throw (value at right)	25	15
170.	15 c. Releasing javelin	25	15
171.	25 c. Runner and star (left half)	35	25
172.	25 c. Runner and star (right half)	35	25
173.	25 c. Runner (value at left)	35	25
174.	25 c. Runner (value at right)	35	25
175.	25 c. Finish of race	35	25

Nos. 166/70 were printed together, se-tenant, forming a composite design of a javelin throw with background of the Marshallese flag. Nos. 171/5 were similarly arranged forming a composite design of a runner and flag.

31. "Casco" sailing through Golden Gate of San Francisco.

1988. Centenary of Robert Louis Stevenson's Pacific Voyages. Multicoloured.

176	25 c. Type **31**	50	35
177	25 c. "Casco" at the Needles of Ua-Pu, Marquesas	50	35
178	25 c. "Equator" leaving Honolulu	50	35
179	25 c. Chieftain's canoe, Majuro Lagoon	50	35
180	25 c. Bronze medallion depicting Stevenson by Augustus St. Gaudens, 1887	50	35
181	25 c. "Janet Nicoll" (inter-island steamer), Majuro Lagoon	50	35
182	25 c. Stevenson's visit to maniap of King Tembinoka of Gilbert Islands	50	35
183	25 c. Stevenson in Samoan Canoe, Apia Harbour	50	35
184	25 c. Stevenson on horse Jack at Valima (Samoan home)	50	35

32. Spanish Ragged Cross Ensign (1516–1785) and Magellan's Ship "Vitoria".

1988. Exploration Ships and Flags. Mult.

185	25 c. Type **32**	50	35
186	25 c. British red ensign (1707–1800), "Charlotte" and "Scarborough"	50	35
187	25 c. American flag and ensign (1837–45), U.S.S. "Flying Fish" and U.S.S. "Peacock"	50	35
188	25 c. German flag and ensign (1867–1919) and "Planet"	50	35

33. Father Christmas in Sleigh. **34.** Nuclear Test on Bikini Atoll.

1988. Christmas. Multicoloured.

189.	25 c. Type **33**	35	25
190.	25 c. Reindeer over island with palm huts and trees	35	25
191.	25 c. Reindeer over island with palm trees	35	25
192.	25 c. Reindeer and flying fish	35	25
193.	25 c. Reindeer over island with outrigger canoe	35	25

1988. 25th Anniv. of Assassination of John F. Kennedy (American President). Mult.

194.	25 c. Type **34**	40	25
195.	25 c. Kennedy signing Test Ban Treaty	40	25
196.	25 c. Kennedy	40	25
197.	25 c. Kennedy using hot-line between Washington and Moscow	40	25
198.	25 c. Peace Corps volunteers	40	25

35 "SV-5D PRIME" Vehicle Launch from Vandenberg Air Force Base

1988. Kwajalein Space Shuttle Tracking Station. Multicoloured.

199	25 c. Type **35** (postage)	45	30
200	25 c. Re-entry of "SV-5D"	45	30
201	25 c. Recovery of "SV-5D" off Kwajalein	45	30
202	25 c. Space shuttle "Discovery" over Kwajalein	45	30
203	45 c. Shuttle and astronaut over Rongelap (air)	75	55

Nos. 199/202 were printed together, se-tenant, forming a composite design.

36 1918 Typhoon Monument, Majuro

1989. Links with Japan. Multicoloured.

204	45 c. Type **36**	80	55
205	45 c. Japanese seaplane base and railway, Djarrej Islet, 1940s	80	55
206	45 c. Japanese fishing boats	80	55
207	45 c. Japanese skin-divers	80	55

37 "Island Woman"

1989. Links with Alaska. Oil Paintings by Claire Fejes. Multicoloured.

208	45 c. Type **37**	75	55
209	45 c. "Kotzebue, Alaska"	75	55
210	45 c. "Marshallese Madonna"	75	55

38 Dornier "Do 228"

1989. Air. Airplanes. Multicoloured.

212	12 c. Type **38**	30	20
214	36 c. Boeing "737"	55	40
215	39 c. H.S. "748"	65	45
216	45 c. Boeing "727"	75	55

1989. Sea Shells (4th series). As T 8. Mult.

220	25 c. Pontifical mitre	50	30
221	25 c. Tapestry turban	50	30
222	25 c. Flame mouthed helmet	50	30
223	25 c. Prickly Pacific drupe	50	30
224	25 c. Blood mouthed conch	50	30

40 Wandering Tattler

1989. Birds. Multicoloured.

226	45 c. Type **40**	85	60
227	45 c. Turnstone	85	60
228	45 c. Pacific golden plover	85	60
229	45 c. Sanderling	85	60

41 "Bussard" (German cruiser) and 1897 Ship's Post Cancellation

1989. "Philexfrance 89" International Stamp Exhibition, Paris. Marshall Islands Postal History. Multicoloured.

230	25 c. Type **41**	80	50
231	25 c. First Day Cover bearing first Marshall Islands stamps and U.S. 10 c. stamp	80	50
232	25 c. Consolidated Catalina flying boats, floating Fleet Post Office ("L.S.T. 119"), Majuro, and 1944 U.S. Navy cancellation	80	50
233	25 c. Nakajima A6M2 seaplane, mailboat off Mili Island and Japanese cancellation	80	50
234	25 c. Majuro Post Office	80	50
235	25 c. Consolidated Catalina amphibian, outrigger canoe and 1951 U.S. civilian mail cancellation	80	50
236	45 c. "Morning Star V" (missionary ship) and 1905 Jaluit cancellation	85	55
237	45 c. 1906 registered cover with Jaluit cancellation	85	55
238	45 c. "Prinz Eitel Freiderich" (auxiliary cruiser) and 1914 German ship's post cancellation	85	55
239	45 c. "Scharnhorst" (cruiser) leading German Asiatic Squadron and 1914 ship's post cancellation	85	55

Nos. 230/5 were printed together, se-tenant, Nos. 231 and 234 forming a composite design to commemorate the 5th anniversary of Marshall Islands Independent Postal Service.

Since August 1989 a considerable number of stamps have appeared, issued on behalf of the Republic of the Marshall Islands. It has only been possible to confirm postal use of the following definitive issues.

44 White-capped Noddy

1990. Birds. Multicoloured.

249	1 c. Type **44**	10	10
250	5 c. Red-tailed tropic bird	10	10
251	9 c. Whimbrel	10	10
252	10 c. Sanderling	15	15
253	12 c. Black-naped tern	15	15
254	15 c. Wandering tattler	20	20
255	20 c. Bristle-thighed curlew	25	25
256	22 c. Greater scaup	30	30
257	23 c. Common (inscr "Northern") shoveler	30	30
258	25 c. Common (inscr "Brown") noddy	35	35
259	27 c. Sooty tern	35	35
260	28 c. Sharp-tailed sandpiper	35	35
261	29 c. Wedge-tailed shearwater	40	40
262	30 c. American (inscr "Pacific") golden plover	40	40
263	35 c. Brown booby	45	45
264	36 c. Red-footed booby	50	50

265 40 c. White tern 55 55
266 45 c. Common teal .. 60 60
267 50 c. Great frigate bird .. 65 65
268 52 c. Crested tern (inscr "Great Crested Tern") 70 70
269 65 c. Lesser sand plover .. 85 85
270 75 c. Little tern .. .. 1·00 1·00
271 $1 Eastern (inscr "Pacific") reef heron .. 1·40 1·40
272 $2 Masked booby .. 2·50 2·50

45 "Britannia"

1993. Ships. Multicoloured.
(a) Size 35 × 21mm.
278 15 c. Type **45** 20 20
279 19 c. "Micro Palm" (inter-island ship) 25 35
281 23 c. H.M.S. "Cornwallis" (sail frigate) 30 30
282 24 c. U.S.S. "Dolphin" (schooner) 30 30
285 29 c. "Morning Star I" (missionary brigantine) 40 40
291 50 c. U.S.S. "Lexington" (aircraft carrier) .. 65 65
292 52 c. H.M.S. "Serpent" (brig) 70 70
294 75 c. "Scarborough" (British transport) .. 1·00 1·00
(b) Size 46 × 27 mm.
295 $1 Enewetak outrigger canoe .. .. 1·40 1·40
296 $2 Jaluit outrigger canoe 2·50 2·50

MARTINIQUE Pt. 6

An island in the West Indies, now an overseas department using the stamps of France.

100 centimes = 1 franc.

1886. Stamp of French Colonies, "Commerce" type. (a) Surch **MARTINIQUE** and new value.
3 J 01 on 20 c. red on green .. 8·75 9·00
1 5 on 20 c. red on green .. 30·00 26·00
4 05 on 20 c. red on green .. 7·00 4·50
2 5 c. on 20 c. red on green .. £10000 £10000
6 015 on 20 c. red on green .. 35·00 35·00
5 15 on 20 c. red on green .. £130 £110
(b) Surch **MQE 15 c.**
7 J 15 c. on 20 c. red on green 60·00 55·00

1888. Stamps of French Colonies, "Commerce" type, surch **MARTINIQUE** and value, thus **01 c.**
9 J 01 c. on 2 c. brn on buff 1·50 1·25
10 01 c. on 4 c. brn on grey 7·00 1·75
11 05 c. on 4 c. brn on grey £800 £675
12 05 c. on 10 c. black & lilac 60·00 30·00
13 05 c. on 20 c. red on green 12·50 9·25
14 05 c. on 30 c. brn on drab 16·00 14·50
15a 05 c. on 35 c. blk on yell 10·00 7·75
16 05 c. on 40 c. red on yell 32·00 25·00
17 15 c. on 4 c. brn on grey £7000 £6000
18 15 c. on 20 c. red on green 70·00 50·00
19 15 c. on 25 c. blk on pink 9·25 8·00
20 15 c. on 75 c. red on pink £110 90·00

1891. Postage Due stamps of French Colonies surch. **TIMBRE - POSTE MARTINIQUE** and value in figures.
21. U. 05 c. on 5 c. black .. 7·75 7·00
25. 05 c. on 10 c. black .. 4·25 5·00
22. 05 c. on 15 c. black .. 5·50 4·00
23. 15 c. on 20 c. black .. 8·00 5·50
24. 15 c. on 30 c. black .. 8·00 6·50

1891. Stamp of French Colonies, "Commerce" type, surch **TIMBRE-POSTE 01c. MARTINIQUE.**
28 J 01 c. on 2 c. brown on buff 5·00 5·00

1892. Stamp of French Colonies, "Commerce" type, surch **1892 MARTINIQUE** and new value.
29 J 05 c. on 25 c. blk on pink 38·00 32·00
31 15 c. on 25 c. blk on pink 15·00 15·00

1892. "Tablet" key-type inscr "MARTINIQUE", in red (1, 5, 15, 25, 75 c., 1 f.) or blue (others).
33 D 1 c. black on blue .. 80 80
34 2 c. brown on buff .. 90 85
35 4 c. brown on grey .. 90 85
36 5 c. green on green .. 1·25 45
37 10 c. black on lilac .. 5·50 70
47 10 c. red .. .. 1·75 50
38 15 c. blue .. .. 21·00 3·50
48 15 c. grey .. .. 6·25 70
39 20 c. red on green .. 10·00 4·00
40 25 c. black on pink .. 11·50 1·00
49 25 c. blue .. .. 8·50 7·50
41 30 c. brown on drab .. 21·00 7·75
50 35 c. black on yellow .. 9·50 4·75
42 40 c. red on yellow .. 21·00 7·50
43 50 c. red on pink .. 20·00 9·75
51 50 c. brown on blue .. 21·00 15·00
44 75 c. brown on orange .. 20·00 10·00
45 1 f. green .. .. 16·00 8·25
52 2 f. violet on pink .. 65·00 50·00
53 5 f. mauve on lilac .. 75·00 60·00

1903. Postage Due stamp of French Colonies surch **TIMBRE POSTE 5 F. MARTINIQUE COLIS POSTAUX.**
53a U 5 f. on 60 c. brn on buff £400 £425
Despite the surcharge No. 53a was for use on letters as well as parcels.

1904. Surch **10 c.**
54 D 10 c. on 30 c. brn on drab 4·75 4·75
55 10 c. on 5 f. mve on lilac 6·25 6·25

1904. Surch **1904 0f10.**
56 D 0 f. 10 on 30 c. brown on drab .. .. .. 10·50 10·50
57 0 f. 10 on 40 c. red on yell 10·50 10·50
58 0 f. 10 on 50 c. red on pink .. .. .. 10·50 10·50
59 0 f. 10 on 75 c. brown on orange .. .. 9·75 9·75
60 0 f. 10 on 1 f. green .. 10·50 10·50
61 0 f. 10 on 5 f. mve on lilac £140 £140

13. Martinique Woman.

15. Woman and Sugar Cane.

14. Fort-de-France.

1908.
62 **13** 1 c. chocolate and brown 15 20
63 2 c. brown and green .. 15 25
64 4 c. brown and purple .. 15 25
65 5 c. brown and green .. 25 15
87 5 c. brown and orange 15 15
66 10 c. brown and red .. 45 25
88 10 c. olive and green .. 20 30
89 10 c. red and purple .. 20 25
67 15 c. red and purple .. 15 30
90 15 c. olive and green .. 20 30
91 15 c. red and blue .. 50 70
68 20 c. brown and lilac .. 50 55
69 **14** 25 c. brown and blue .. 75 20
92 25 c. brown and orange 25 15
93 30 c. brown and red .. 35 35
94 30 c. red and carmine .. 20 35
95 30 c. brown & lt brown 20 25
96 30 c. green and blue .. 70 75
71 35 c. brown and lilac .. 30 45
72 40 c. brown and green .. 30 40
73 45 c. chocolate & brown 35 45
74 50 c. brown and red .. 75 45
97 50 c. brown and blue .. 70 75
98 50 c. green and red .. 30 20
99 60 c. pink and blue .. 20 30
100 65 c. brown and violet 90 95
75 75 c. brown and black .. 70 60
101 75 c. blue and deep blue 20 30
102 75 c. blue and brown .. 1·40 1·50
103 90 c. carmine and red .. 3·25 3·25
76 **15** 1 f. brown and red .. 40 40
104 1 f. blue 30 40
105 1 f. green and red .. 95 1·25
106 1 f. 10 brown and violet 2·00 2·00
107 1 f. 50 light blue & blue 3·50 3·50
77 2 f. brown and grey .. 1·90 1·00
108 3 f. mauve on pink .. 5·25 5·25
78 5 f. brown and red .. 6·25 6·00

1912. Stamps of 1892 surch.
79 05 on 15 c. grey 50 45
80 05 on 25 c. black on pink .. 75 85
81 10 on 40 c. red on yellow .. 90 1·00
82 10 on 5 f. mauve on lilac .. 1·25 1·40

1915. Surch **5c** and red cross.
83 **13** 10 c. + 5 c. brown and red 1·00 1·00

1920. Surch in figures.
115 **13** 0,01 on 2 c. brown & grn 1·10 1·40
109 0,01 on 15 c. red & pur 25 35
110 0,02 on 15 c. red & pur 15 35
84 05 on 1 c. choc & brn 1·00 1·00
111 0,05 on 15 c. red & pur 25 35
116 0,05 on 20 c. brn & lilac 1·25 1·40
85 10 on 2 c. brown & green 85 90
117 **14** 0,15 on 30 c. brn & red 6·50 7·00
86 **13** 25 on 15 c. red & purple 65 70
121 25 c. on 15 c. red & pur 25 35
119 **14** 0,25 on 50 c. brn & red £170 £170
120 0,25 on 50 c. brown & bl 2·75 3·00
122 **15** 25 c. on 2 f. brn & grey 20 35
123 25 c. on 5 f. brown & red 95 60
112 **14** 60 on 75 c. pink and blue 20 35
113 65 on 45 c. brn & lt brn 60 70
114 85 on 75 c. brown & blk 65 80
124 90 c. on 75 c. carmine and red .. .. 1·90 2·00
125 **15** 1 f. 25 on 1 f. blue .. 20 30
126 1 f. 50 on 1 f. ultramarine and blue .. 70 80
127 3 f. on 5 f. green and red 1·25 1·40
128 10 f. on 5 f. red & green 6·00 6·25
129 20 f. on 5 f. violet & brn 9·25 9·00

1931. "Colonial Exhibition" key-types inscr "MARTINIQUE".
130 E 40 c. black and green .. 2·25 2·25
131 F 50 c. black and mauve .. 2·00 2·00
132 G 90 c. black and red .. 2·25 2·25
133 H 1 f. 50 black and blue .. 2·25 2·25

26. Basse Pointe Village.

27. Government House, Fort-de-France.

28. Martinique Women.

1933.
134 **26** 1 c. red on pink .. 15 25
135 **27** 2 c. blue 15 30
136 3 c. purple 20 30
137 **26** 4 c. green 15 30
138 **27** 5 c. purple 15 25
139 **26** 10 c. black on pink .. 15 25
140 **27** 15 c. black on red .. 15 25
141 **28** 20 c. brown 15 25
142 **26** 25 c. purple 20 35
143 **27** 30 c. green 25 25
144 30 c. blue 25 30
145 **28** 35 c. green 25 35
146 40 c. brown 25 35
147 **27** 45 c. brown .. .. 1·00 1·10
148 45 c. green 30 45
149 50 c. red 20 15
150 **26** 55 c. red 45 55
151 60 c. blue 25 35
152 **28** 65 c. red on blue .. 35 30
153 70 c. purple 35 30
154 **26** 75 c. brown 50 50
155 **27** 80 c. violet 35 35
156 **26** 90 c. red .. .. 1·10 95
157 90 c. purple 35 40
158 **27** 1 f. black on green .. 1·10 30
159 1 f. red 40 40
160 **28** 1 f. 25 violet 45 45
161 1 f. 25 red 45 40
162 **28** 1 f. 40 blue 40 40
163 **27** 1 f. 50 blue 35 35
164 1 f. 60 brown 45 45
165 **28** 1 f. 75 green .. .. 5·50 2·50
166 1 f. 75 blue 40 35
167 **26** 2 f. blue on green .. 40 30
168 **28** 2 f. 25 blue 50 45
169 **26** 2 f. 50 purple 55 60
170 **28** 3 f. purple 25 25
171 5 f. red on pink .. 70 40
172 **26** 10 f. blue on blue .. 45 30
173 **27** 20 f. red on yellow .. 85 65

30. Belain d'Esnambuc, 1635.

31. Schœlcher and Abolition of Slavery, 1848.

1935. West Indies Tercentenary.
174. **30.** 40 c. brown .. .. 1·10 1·00
175. 50 c. red .. .. 1·10 1·00
176. 1 f. 50 blue .. .. 8·00 8·00
177. **31.** 1 f. 75 red .. .. 7·25 7·50
178. 5 f. brown .. .. 7·25 7·50
179. 10 f. green .. .. 5·25 5·50

1937. International Exhibition, Paris. As Nos. 211/16 of New Caledonia.
180 20 c. violet 85 95
181 30 c. green 85 95
182 40 c. red 85 95
183 50 c. brown and agate .. 80 1·10
184 90 c. red .. .. 90 1·10
185 1 f. 50 blue .. .. 1·00 1·10

1938. Int. Anti-Cancer Fund. As T **22** of Mauritania.
186. 1 f. 75 + 50 c. blue .. 6·50 6·50

1939. New York World's Fair. As T **28** of Mauritania.
187. 1 f. 25 red 70 70
188. 2 f. 25 blue 70 70

1939. 150th Anniv of French Revolution. As T **29** of Mauritania.
189 45 c. + 25 c. green & black 4·50 4·50
190 70 c. + 30 c. brown & black 4·50 4·50
191 90 c. + 35 c. orange & black 4·50 4·50
192 1 f. 25 + 1 f. red and black 4·50 4·50
193 2 f. 25 + 2 f. blue and black 4·50 4·50

1944. Mutual Aid and Red Cross Funds. As T **31** of New Caledonia.
194. 5 f. + 20 f. violet 65 80

1945. Eboue. As T **32** of New Caledonia.
195. 2 f. black 20 35
196. 25 f. green 55 65

1945. Surch.
197. **27.** 1 f. on 2 c. blue .. 40 40
198. **26.** 2 f. on 4 c. olive .. 40 40
199. **27.** 3 f. on 2 c. blue .. 40 40
200. **28.** 5 f. on 65 c. red on blue .. 60 60
201. 10 f. (DIX f.) on 65 c. red on blue 60 60
202. **27.** 20 f. (VINGT f.) on 3 c. purple 75 75

33. Victor Schœlcher.

1945.
203 33 10 c. blue and violet .. 15 30
204 30 c. brown and red .. 20 30
205 40 c. blue and light blue 25 35
206 50 c. red and purple .. 30 30
207 60 c. orange and yellow 30 40
208 70 c. purple and brown 30 40
209 80 c. green & light green 30 40
210 1 f. blue and light blue 30 40
211 1 f. 20 violet and purple 30 40
212 1 f. 50 red and orange .. 30 40
213 2 f. black and grey .. 30 40
214 2 f. 40 red and pink .. 75 90
215 3 f. pink and light pink 30 20
216 4 f. ultramarine and blue 35 25
217 4 f. 50 turquoise & green 50 35
218 5 f. light brown & brown 40 50
219 10 f. purple and mauve 50 30
220 15 f. red and pink .. 60 45
221 20 f. olive and green .. 80 75

1945. Air. As T 30 of New Caledonia.
222. 50 f. green 50 35
223. 100 f. red 55 45

1946. Air. Victory. As T 34 of New Caledonia.
224. 8 f. blue 50 75

1946. Air. From Chad to the Rhine. As Nos. 300/305 of New Caledonia.
225. 5 f. orange 40 50
226. 10 f. green 40 50
227. 15 f. red 50 60
228. 20 f. brown 50 60
229. 25 f. blue 60 70
230. 50 f. grey 80 90

34. Martinique Woman.

39. Mountains and Palms.

35. Local Fishing Boats and Rocks.

40. West Indians and Flying Boat.

1947.
231. 34. 10 c. lake (postage) .. 20 30
232. 30 c. blue 15 25
233. 50 c. brown 15 30
234. 35. 60 c. green 25 35
235. 1 f. lake 25 35
236. 1 f. 50 violet 25 35
237. – 2 f. green 60 45
238. – 2 f. 50 brown 60 50
239. – 3 f. blue 45 45
240. – 4 f. brown 45 45
241. – 5 f. green 40 45
242. – 6 f. mauve 45 45
243. – 10 f. blue 75 65
244. – 15 f. lake 90 85
245. – 20 f. brown .. .. 1·25 1·00
246. 39. 25 f. violet .. .. 1·40 1·25
247. 40 f. green .. .. 1·50 1·40
248. 40. 50 f. purple (air) .. 2·50 2·00
249. – 100 f. green .. .. 3·75 2·50
250. – 200 f. violet .. .. 38·00 15·00

DESIGNS—HORIZ. As Type **35**: 2 f. to 3 f. Gathering sugar cane. 4 f. to 6 f. Mount Pele. 10 f. to 20 f. Fruit products. As Type **40**—VERT. 100 f. Aeroplane over landscape. HORIZ. 200 f. Wandering Albatross in flight.

POSTAGE DUE STAMPS

1927. Postage Due stamps of France optd. **MARTINIQUE.**
D 130. D 11. 5 c. blue 50 85
D 131. 10 c. brown .. 80 1·00
D 132. 20 c. olive .. .. 90 1·00
D 133. 25 c. red .. .. 1·25 1·50
D 134. 30 c. red .. .. 1·60 1·75
D 135. 45 c. green .. 1·75 1·75
D 136. 50 c. purple .. 3·50 3·75
D 137. 60 c. green .. 4·25 4·25
D 138. 1 f. red on yellow .. 5·25 5·25
D 139. 2 f. mauve .. 7·25 7·25
D 140. 3 f. red .. .. 8·25 8·25

D 29. Fruit.

D 43. Map of Martinique.

1933.
D174 D 29 5 c. blue on green .. 15 40
D175 10 c. brown .. 20 40
D176 20 c. blue 60 65
D177 25 c. red on pink .. 60 65
D178 30 c. purple .. 40 45
D179 45 c. red on yellow 30 35
D180 50 c. brown .. 45 75
D181 60 c. green .. 45 75
D182 1 f. black on red .. 65 90
D183 2 f. purple 55 75
D184 3 f. blue on blue .. 70 85

1947.
D 251. D 43. 10 c. blue 15 20
D 252. 30 c. green .. 15 30
D 253. 50 c. blue 15 30
D 254. 1 f. orange .. 20 35
D 255. 2 f. purple 45 60
D 256. 3 f. purple 45 60
D 257. 4 f. brown 55 70
D 258. 5 f. red 60 70
D 259. 10 f. black .. 90 1·25
D 260. 20 f. green .. 90 1·25

MAURITANIA Pt. 6; Pt. 13

A French colony extending inland to the Sahara, incorporated in French West Africa from 1945 to 1959. In 1960 Mauritania became an independent Islamic republic.

1906. 100 centimes = 1 franc.
1973. 100 cents = 1 ouguiya (um).

1906. "Faidherbe", "Palms" and "Balay" key-types inscr "MAURITANIE" in blue (10, 40 c., 5 f.) or red (others).
1 I 1 c. grey 25 25
2 2 c. brown 50 40
3 4 c. brown on blue .. 75 50
4 5 c. green 45 50
5 10 c. pink .. .. 4·50 3·00
6 J 20 c. black on blue .. 11·00 8·50
7 25 c. blue .. .. 4·50 3·25
8 30 c. brown on pink .. 70·00 40·00
9 35 c. black on yellow .. 4·25 3·00
10 40 c. red on blue .. 4·50 3·50
11 45 c. brown on green .. 4·25 3·50
12 50 c. violet .. .. 4·50 3·50
13 75 c. green on orange .. 4·00 3·50
14 K 1 f. black on blue .. 9·50 8·00
15 2 f. blue on pink .. 35·00 30·00
16 5 f. red on yellow .. £100 85·00

6. Merchants crossing Desert.

1913.
18 6 1 c. brown and lilac .. 10 20
19 2 c. blue and black .. 10 20
20 4 c. black and violet .. 15 25
21 5 c. green and light green 25 40
37 5 c. red and purple .. 10 25
22 10 c. orange and pink .. 55 75
38 10 c. green and light green 10 25
39 10 c. pink on blue .. 15 30
23 15 c. black and brown .. 30 40
24 20 c. orange and brown .. 20 45
25 25 c. ultramarine and blue 80 85
40 25 c. red and green .. 40 65
26 30 c. pink and green .. 50 80
41 30 c. orange and red .. 50 70
42 30 c. yellow and black .. 15 35
43 30 c. light green and green 70 95
27 35 c. violet and brown .. 25 45
44 35 c. light green and green 25 50
28 40 c. green and brown .. 70 1·10
29 45 c. brown and orange .. 35 55
30 50 c. pink and lilac .. 35 50
45 50 c. ultramarine and blue 40 50
46 50 c. blue and green .. 40 60
47 60 c. violet on pink .. 15 35
48 65 c. blue and brown .. 50 70
31 75 c. brown and blue .. 50 70
49 85 c. brown and green .. 40 60
50 90 c. pink and red .. 85 90
32 1 f. black and red .. 40 65
51 1 f. 10 red and mauve .. 6·50 6·75
52 1 f. 25 brown and blue .. 1·10 1·25
53 1 f. 50 blue and light blue 70 75
54 1 f. 75 red and green .. 70 75
55 1 f. 75 ultramarine & blue 75 70
33 2 f. violet and orange .. 1·00 1·40
56 3 f. mauve on pink .. 1·00 1·40
34 5 f. blue and violet .. 1·40 1·50

1915. Surch **5c** and red cross.
35 6 10 c.+5 c. orange & pink 40 70
36 15 c.+5 c. black & brown 40 75

1922. Surch in figures and bars (some colours changed).
60 6 25 c. on 2 f. violet & orge 60 60
57 60 on 75 c. violet on pink 50 70
58 65 on 15 c. black & brown 1·00 1·40
59 85 on 75 c. brown and blue 75 1·10
61 90 c. on 75 c. pink and red 1·40 1·40
62 1 f. 25 on 1 f. ultram & bl 55 75
63 1 f. 50 on 1 f. blue & lt bl 65 80
64 3 f. on 5 f. mauve & brown 5·00 5·00
65 10 f. on 5 f. green & mauve 4·25 4·50
66 20 f. on 5 f. orange & blue 4·25 4·50

1931. "Colonial Exhibition" key-types inscr "MAURITANIE".
67 E 40 c. green and black .. 5·00 5·25
68 F 50 c. purple and black .. 2·50 2·50
69 G 90 c. red and black .. 2·50 2·50
70 H 1 f. 50 blue and black .. 2·50 2·50

1937. Int. Exn., Paris. As Nos. 211/16 of New Caledonia.
71. 20 c. violet 60 75
72. 30 c. green 60 80
73. 40 c. red 50 75
74. 50 c. brown 50 70
75. 90 c. red 50 80
76. 1 f. 50 blue 55 80

22. Pierre and Marie Curie.

1938. Int. Anti-Cancer Fund.
76b. 22. 1 f. 75+50 c. blue .. 3·50 5·00

23. Man on Camel.

24. Warriors.

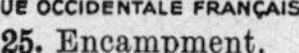

25. Encampment.

26. Mauritanians.

1938.
77. 23. 2 c. purple 15 30
78. 3 c. blue 10 30
79. 4 c. lilac 10 30
80. 5 c. red 10 30
81. 10 c. red 20 35
82. 15 c. violet 15 30
83. 24. 20 c. red 10 30
84. 25 c. blue 30 55
85. 30 c. purple 20 30
86. 35 c. green 35 55
87. 40 c. red 35 50
88. 45 c. green 35 45
89. 50 c. violet 35 55
90. 25. 55 c. lilac 55 70
91. 60 c. violet 40 50
92. 65 c. green 40 55
93. 70 c. red 50 60
94. 80 c. blue .. .. 95 1·00
95. 90 c. lilac 40 55
96. 1 f. red .. .. .. 90 1·10
97. 1 f. green 25 45
98. 1 f. 25 red 50 90
99. 1 f. 40 blue 50 65
100. 1 f. 50 violet 45 70
101. 1 f. 60 brown .. .. 90 1·00
102. 26. 1 f. 75 blue 75 70
103. 2 f. lilac 60 75
104. 2 f. 25 blue 45 65
105. 2 f. 50 brown 65 80
106. 3 f. green 50 70
107. 5 f. red 60 90
108. 10 f. purple .. .. 90 1·40
109. 20 f. red .. .. .. 95 1·40

27. Rene Caillie (explorer).

1939. Caillie.
110. 27. 90 c. orange 50 80
111. 2 f. violet 50 80
112. 2 f. 25 blue 50 80

28.

1939. New York World's Fair.
113. 28. 1 f. 25 red 45 65
114. 2 f. 25 blue 45 65

29. Storming the Bastille.

1939. 150th Anniv of French Revolution.
115 29 45 c.+25 c. green & blk 4·75 5·00
116 70 c.+30 c. brown & blk 4·75 5·00
117 90 c.+35 c. orange & blk 4·75 5·00
118 1 f. 25+1 f. red & black 4·75 5·00
119 2 f. 25+2 f. blue & black 4·75 5·00

30. Aeroplane over Jungle.

1940. Air.
120. 30. 1 f. 90 blue 45 60
121. 2 f. 90 red 45 60
122. 4 f. 50 green 45 60
123. 4 f. 90 olive 60 75
124. 6 f. 90 orange 65 85

1941. National Defence Fund. Surch. **SECOURS NATIONAL** and value.
124a. +1 f. on 50 c. (No. 89) .. 2·00 2·00
124b. +2 f. on 80 c. (No. 94) .. 4·00 4·00
124c. +2 f. on 1 f. 50 (No. 100) 4·00 4·00
124d. +3 f. on 2 f. (No. 103) .. 4·00 4·00

31a. Ox Caravan.

1942. Marshal Petain issue.
124e 31a 1 f. green .. .. 20 1·25
124f 2 f. 50 blue .. .. 15 1·25

1942. Air. Colonial Child Welfare Fund. As Nos. 98g/i of Niger.
124g 1 f. 50+3 f. 50 green .. 15
124h 2 f.+6 f. brown 15
124i 3 f.+9 f. red 15

1942. Air. Imperial Fortnight. As No. 98j of Niger.
124j 1 f. 20+1 f. 80 blue & red 15

32. Airliner over Camel Caravan.

1942. Air. T 32 inscr "MAURITANIE" at foot.
124k 32 50 f. orange and yellow 75 1·10

1944. Surch.
125 25 3 f. 50 on 65 c. green .. 25 20
126 4 f. on 65 c. green .. 30 35
127 5 f. on 65 c. green .. 40 60
128 10 f. on 65 c. green .. 40 50
129 27 15 f. on 90 c. orange .. 65 70

ISLAMIC REPUBLIC.

35. Flag of Republic.

37. Well.

38. Slender-billed Gull.

1960. Inaug. of Islamic Republic.
130. **35.** 25 f. bistre, green and brown on rose .. 40 35

1960. 10th Anniv. of African Technical Co-operation Commission. As T 4 of Malagasy Republic.
131. 25 f. blue and turquoise .. 40 35

1960.

No.	Type	Description	Unused	Used
132.	**37.**	50 c. purple & brn. (post.)	10	10
133.	–	1 f. bistre, brown & green	10	10
134.	–	2 f. brown, green & blue	15	10
135.	–	3 f. red, sepia & turquoise	20	20
136.	–	4 f. buff and green ..	20	20
137.	–	5 f. choc., brown and red	15	10
138.	–	10 f. blue, black & brown	20	15
139.	–	15 f. multicoloured ..	40	15
140.	–	20 f. brown and green ..	30	15
141.	–	25 f. blue and green ..	50	15
142.	–	30 f. blue, violet & bistre	50	15
143.	–	50 f. brown and green ..	80	40
144.	–	60 f. purple, red & green	1·25	40
145.	–	85 f. brown, sepia & blue	3·50	1·50
146.	–	100 f. brown, chocolate and blue (air).. ..	6·00	2·75
147.	–	200 f. myrtle, brn. & sepia	14·00	5·75
148.	**38.**	500 f. sepia, blue & brn.	30·00	11·50

DESIGNS—VERT. (As Type **37**) 2 f. Harvesting dates. 5 f. Harvesting millet. 25 f., 30 f. Seated dance. 50 f. "Telmidi" (symbolic figure). 60 f. Metalsmith. 85 f. Scimitar oryx. 100 f. Greater flamingo. 200 f. African spoonbill. HORIZ. 3 f. Barbary sheep. 4 f. Fennec foxes. 10 f. Cordwainer. 15 f. Fishing-boat. 20 f. Nomad school.

39. Flag and Map.

43. Campaign Emblem.

42. European, African and Airlines.

1960. Proclamation of Independence.
149. **39.** 25 f. grn., brn. and chest. 50 50

1962. Air. "Air Afrique" Airline.
150. **42.** 100 f. green, brown & bistre .. .. 1·75 1·10

1962. Malaria Eradication.
151. **43.** 25 f. + 5 f. olive .. 50 50

44. U.N. Headquarters and View of Nouakchott.

1962. Admission to U.N.O.

No.	Type	Description	Unused	Used
152.	**44.**	15 f. brn., black & blue	20	20
153.		25 f. brown, myrtle & bl.	35	35
154.		85 f. brown, purple & bl.	1·00	1·00

45. Union Flag.

1962. 1st Anniv. of Union of African and Malagasy States.
155. **45.** 30 f. blue 45 45

46. Eagle and Crescent over Nouakchott.

1962. 8th Endemic Diseases Eradication Conf., Nouakchott.
156. **46.** 30 f. green, brown & blue 45 35

47. Diesel Mineral Train.

1962.
157. **47.** 50 f. multicoloured .. 2·25 85

1962. Air. 1st Anniv. of Admission to U.N.O. As T **44** but views from different angles and inscr. "1 er ANNIVERSAIRE 27 OCTOBRE 1962".
158. 100 f. blue, brown & turq. 1·10 90

49. Map and Agriculture.

1962. 2nd Anniv. of Independence.
159. **49.** 30 f. green and purple.. 45 30

50. Congress Representatives.

1962. 1st Anniv. of Unity Congress.
160. **50.** 25 f. brn., myrtle & blue 45 40

51. Globe and Emblem.

1962. Freedom from Hunger.
161. **51.** 25 f. + 5 f. blue, brn. & purple 55 55

52. Douglas DC-3 Airliner over Nouakchott Airport.

1963. Air. Creation of National Airline.
162. **52.** 500 f. myrtle, brn. & bl. 12·00 4·50

53. Open-cast Mining, Zouerate.

1963. Air. Mining Development. Mult.
163. 100 f. Type **53** .. .. 2·50 60
164. 200 f. Port-Etienne .. 4·50 1·75

54. Striped Hyena.

ANIMALS—HORIZ. 1 f. Spotted hyena. 2 f. Guinea baboons. 10 f. Leopard. 15 f. Bongos 20 f. Aardvark. 30 f. North African crested porcupine. 60 f. Chameleon. VERT. 1 f. 50 Cheetah. 5 f. Dromedaries. 25 f. Patas monkeys. 50 f. Dorcas gazelle.

1963. Animals.

No.	Type	Description	Unused	Used
165.	**54.**	50 c. blk., brn. & myrtle	10	10
166.	–	1 f. black, blue and buff	10	10
167.	–	1 f. 50 brn., olive & pur.	20	15
168.	–	2 f. purple, green & red	15	15
169.	–	5 f. bistre, blue & ochre	25	20
170.	–	10 f. black and ochre ..	40	20
171.	–	15 f. purple and blue..	40	20
172.	–	20 f. bistre, pur. & blue	50	20
173.	–	25 f. ochre, brn. & turq.	70	25
174.	–	30 f. bistre, brown & blue	1·25	30
175.	–	50 f. bistre, brn. & grn.	1·75	60
176.	–	60 f. bistre, brn. & turq.	2·25	90

56. "Posts and Telecommunications.

1963. Air. African and Malagasy Posts and Telecommunications Union.
177. **56.** 85 f. multicoloured .. 1·00 65

57. " Telstar " Satellite.

DESIGNS: 100 f. " Syncom" satellite. 150 f. " Relay " satellite.

1963. Air. Space Telecommunications.

No.	Type	Description	Unused	Used
178.	**57.**	50 f. brn., pur. and grn.	65	45
179.	–	100 f. blue, brown & red	1·25	80
180.	–	150 f. turquoise & brown	2·25	1·50

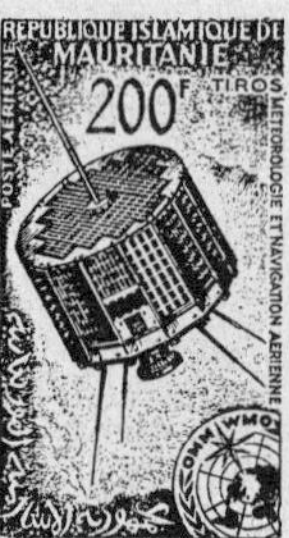

58. " Tiros " Satellite.

60. U.N. Emblem, Sun and Birds.

59. Airline Emblem.

1963. Air. World Meteorological Day.
181. **58.** 200 f. brn., blue & grn. 3·50 1·75

1963. Air. 1st Anniv. of "Air Afrique" and "DC–8" Service Inaug.
182. **59.** 25 f. multicoloured .. 50 25

1963. Air. 15th Anniv. of Declaration of Human Rights.
183. **60.** 100 f. blue, violet & pur. 1·25 85

61. Cogwheels and Wheat.

62. Lichtenstein's Sandgrouse.

1964. Air. European-African Economic Convention.
184. **61.** 50 f. multicoloured .. 1·10 70

1964. Air. Birds.

No.	Type	Description	Unused	Used
185.	**62.**	100 f. ochre, brn. & grn.	7·50	1·60
186.	–	200 f. blk., brn. & blue	12·00	3·75
187.	–	500 f. slate, red & green	26·00	10·00

DESIGNS: 200 f. Reed Cormorant. 500 f. Dark Chanting Goshawk.

63. Temple, Philae.

1964. Air. Nubian Monuments Preservation.

No.	Type	Description	Unused	Used
188.	**63.**	10 f. brown, black & blue	45	30
189.		25 f. slate, brown & blue	70	60
190.		60 f. choc., brown & blue	1·50	1·10

64. W.M.O. Emblem. Sun and Lightning.

65. Radar Antennae and Sun Emblem.

1964. World Meteorological Day.
191. **64.** 85 f. blue, orge. & brn. 1·25 80

1964. Int. Quiet Sun Years.
192. **65.** 25 f. red, green and blue 35 25

66. Bowl depicting Horse-racing.

1964. Air. Olympic Games, Tokyo.

No.	Type	Description	Unused	Used
193.	**66.**	15 f. brown and bistre..	30	25
194.	–	50 f. brown and blue ..	60	50
195.	–	85 f. brown and red ..	1·10	1·00
196.	–	100 f. brown and green	1·50	1·25

DESIGNS—VERT. 50 f. Running (vase). 85 f. Wrestling (vase). HORIZ. 100 f. Chariot-racing (bowl).

67. Grey Mullet.

68. "Co-operation".

1964. Marine Fauna.

No.	Type	Description	Unused	Used
197.	**67.**	1 f. green, blue & brown	15	15
198.	–	5 f. purple, grn. & brown	20	15
199.	–	10 f. green, ochre & blue	35	20
200.	–	60 f. slate, green & brn.	2·00	85

DESIGNS—VERT. 5 f. Lobster (" Panulirus mauritanicus "). 10 f. Lobster (" Panulirus regius "). HORIZ. 60 f. Meagre.

1964. French, African and Malagasy Co-operation.
201. **68.** 25 f. brown, green & mauve 40 30

69. Pres. Kennedy. **70.** "Nymphaea lotus".

1964. Air. 1st Death Anniv. of Pres. Kennedy.
202. **69.** 100 f. multicoloured .. 1·40 1·00

1965. Mauritanian Flowers.
203. **70.** 5 f. green, red and blue 15 15
204. – 10 f. grn., ochre & pur. 25 15
205. – 20 f. brown, red & sepia 45 20
206. – 45 f. turq., purple & grn. 1·10 60
FLOWERS—VERT. 10 f. "Acacia gommier". 45 f. "Caralluma retrospiciens". HORIZ. 20 f. "Adenium obesum".

71. "Hardine" **72.** Abraham Lincoln.

1965. Musical Instruments and Musicians.
207. **71.** 2 f. brown, bistre & blue 15 15
208. – 8 f. brown, bistre & red 30 15
209. – 25 f. brown, black & grn. 60 20
210. – 40 f. black, blue & violet 80 35
DESIGNS: 8 f. "Tobol" (drums). 25 f. "Tidinit" ("Violins"). 40 f. Native band.

1965. Death Cent. of Abraham Lincoln.
211. **72.** 50 f. multicoloured .. 70 35

73. Early Telegraph and Relay Satellite.

1965. Air. Cent. of I.T.U.
212. **73.** 250 f. grn., mve. & blue 4·25 3·25

74. Palms in the Adrar.

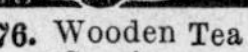

76. Wooden Tea Service. **75.** "Attack on Cancer" (the Crab).

1965. "Tourism and Archaeology" (1st series).
213. **74.** 1 f. green, brown & blue 10 10
214. – 4 f. brown, red & blue .. 15 10
215. – 15 f. multicoloured .. 30 20
216. – 60 f. sepia, brn. & green 90 45
DESIGNS—VERT. 4 f. Chinguetti Mosque. HORIZ. 15 f. Clay-pits. 60 f. Carved doorway, Qualata.
See also Nos. 255/8.

1965. Air. Campaign Against Cancer.
217 **75** 100 f. red, blue and ochre 1·50 60

1965. Native Handicrafts.
218. **76.** 3 f. brn., ochre and slate 15 15
219. – 7 f. purple, orge. & blue 20 20
220. – 25 f. brn., black & red .. 35 20
221. – 50 f. red, green & orge. 75 35
DESIGNS—VERT. 7 f. Snuff-box and pipe. 25 f. Damasquine dagger. HORIZ. 50 f. Mederdra chest.

77. Nouakchott Wharf. **78.** Sir Winston Churchill.

1965. Mauritanian Development.
222. – 5 f. green and brown .. 90 60
223. **77.** 10 f. red, turq. and blue 15 10
224. – 30 f. red, brown & purple 1·75 60
225. – 85 f. violet, lake and blue 1·25 55
DESIGNS—VERT. 5 f., 30 f. Choum Tunnel. HORIZ. 85 f. Nouakchott Hospital.

1965. Air. Churchill Commem.
226. **78.** 200 f. multicoloured .. 2·50 1·25

DESIGNS—HORIZ. 60 f. Satellite "A 1" and Globe. 90 f. Rocket "Scout" and satellite "FR 1".

79. Rocket "Diamant".

1966. Air. French Satellites.
227. **79.** 30 f. green, red and blue 50 25
228. – 60 f. purple, blue & turq. 1·00 45
229. – 90 f. lake, violet & blue 1·50 75

80. Dr. Schweitzer and Hospital Scene.

1966. Air. Schweitzer Commem.
230. **80.** 50 f. multicoloured .. 1·10 50

81. Stafford, Schirra and "Gemini 6".

1966. Air. Space Flights. Multicoloured.
231. 50 f. Type **81** 60 25
232. 100 f. Borman, Lovell and "Gemini 7" .. .. 1·25 60
233. 200 f. Beliaiev, Leonov and "Voskhod 2" .. .. 2·50 1·25

82. African Woman and Carved Head.

1966. World Festival of Negro Arts, Dakar.
234. **82.** 10 f. blk., brn. and grn. 20 10
235. – 30 f. purple, black & blue 35 20
236. – 60 f. purple, red & orge. 75 45
DESIGNS: 30 f. Dancers and hands playing cornet. 60 f. Cine-camera and village huts.

83. "Dove" over Map of Africa. **84.** Satellite "D 1".

1966. Air. Organization of African Unity. (O.A.U.).
237. **83.** 100 f. multicoloured .. 1·00 50

1966. Air. Launching of Satellite "D 1".
238. **84.** 100 f. plum, brn. & blue 1·10 75

85. Breguet "14".

1966. Air. Early Aircraft.
239. **85.** 50 f. indigo, blue & bistre 80 25
240. – 100 f. grn., pur. and blue 1·75 50
241. – 150 f. turq., brn. & blue 2·50 75
242. – 200 f. indigo, blue & pur. 3·50 1·25
AIRCRAFT: 100 f. Farman "Goliath". 150 f. Couzinet "Arc-en-Ciel". 200 f. Latecoere "28".

86. "Acacia ehrenbergiana".

1966. Mauritanian Flowers. Multicoloured.
243. 10 f. Type **86** 25 15
244. 15 f. "Schouwia purpurea" 35 15
245. 20 f. "Ipomaea asarifolia" 45 20
246. 25 f. "Grewia bicolor" .. 55 25
247. 30 f. "Pancratium trianthum" 90 25
248. 60 f. "Blepharis linariifolia" 1·40 55

87. Aircraft and "Air Afrique" Emblem.

1966. Air. "DC–8" Air Services Inaug.
249. **87.** 30 f. grey, blk. and red 40 15

88. "Raft of the Medusa" (after Gericault).

1966. Air. 150th Anniv. of Shipwreck of the "Medusa".
250. **88.** 500 f. multicoloured .. 9·00 6·50

89. "Myrina silenus". **90.** "Hunting" (petroglyph from Tenses, Adrar).

1966. Butterflies. Multicoloured.
251 5 f. Type **89** 30 20
252 30 f. "Colotis danae" .. 1·00 40
253 45 f. "Hypolimnas misippus" .. .. 1·75 60
254 60 f. "Danaus chrysippus" 2·50 85

1966. Tourism and Archaeology (2nd series).
255. **90.** 2 f. chestnut and brown 15 15
256. – 3 f. brown and blue .. 20 20
257. – 30 f. green and red .. 55 25
258. – 50 f. brn., grn. and pur. 1·25 80
DESIGNS: 3 f. "Fighting" (petroglyph from Tenses, Adrar). 30 f. Copper jug (from Le Mreyer, Adrar). 50 f. Camel and caravan.

91. Cogwheels and Ears of Wheat.

1966. Air. Europafrique.
259. **91.** 50 f. multicoloured .. 70 40

92. U.N.E.S.C.O. Emblem.

1966. 20th Anniv. of U.N.E.S.C.O.
260. **92.** 30 f. multicoloured .. 45 20

93. Olympic Village, Grenoble.

1967. Publicity for Olympic Games (1968).
261. – 20 f. brn., blue and grn. 30 20
262. **93.** 30 f. brown, green & blue 40 30
263. – 40 f. brn., pur. and blue 60 40
264. – 100 f. brn., grn. and blk. 1·10 70
DESIGNS—VERT. 20 f. Old and new buildings, Mexico City. 40 f. Ice rink, Grenoble and Olympic torch. HORIZ. 100 f. Olympic stadium, Mexico City.

94. South African Crowned Crane. **95.** Globe, Rockets and Eye.

1967. Air. Birds. Multicoloured.
265. 100 f. Type **94** .. .. 3·75 1·50
266. 200 f. Great Egret .. 7·50 2·10
267. 500 f. Ostrich .. .. 16·00 6·75

1967. Air. World Fair, Montreal.
268. **95.** 250 f. brn., blue & black 2·25 1·25

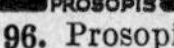

96. Prosopis. **97.** Jamboree Emblem and Scout Kit.

1967. Trees.
269. **96.** 10 f. grn., blue & brown 20 10
270. – 15 f. green, blue & pur. 25 15
271. – 20 f. green, pur. & blue 30 15
272. – 25 f. brown and green .. 40 20
273. – 30 f. brown, green & red 55 25
TREES: 15 f. Jujube. 20 f. Date palm. 25 f. Peltophorum. 30 f. Baobab.

1967. World Scout Jamboree, Idaho.
274. **97.** 60 f. blue, green & brown 70 35
275. – 90 f. blue, green and red 1·10 50
DESIGN—HORIZ. 90 f. Jamboree emblem and scouts.

98. Weaving.

100. Cattle. **99.** Atomic Symbol.

1967. Advancement of Mauritanian Women.
276. **98.** 5 f. red, black and violet 15 10
277. – 10 f. black, violet & grn. 20 10
278. – 20 f. black, purple & blue 35 15
279. – 30 f. blue, black & brown 45 25
280. – 50 f. black, violet & ind. 70 30
DESIGNS—VERT. 10 f. Needlework. 30 f. Laundering. HORIZ. 20 f. Nursing. 50 f. Sewing (with machines).

1967. Air. Int. Atomic Energy Agency.
281. **99.** 200 f. blue, green & red 2·25 1·10

1967. Campaign for Prevention of Cattle Plague.
282. **100.** 30 f. red, blue and green 35 25

101. Map of Africa, Letters and Pylons.

1967. Air. 5th Anniv. of U.A.M.P.T.
283. **101.** 100 f. green, brown and purple .. .. 1·00 60

102. "Francois of Rimini" (Ingres). **103.** Currency Tokens.

1967. Air. Death Cent. of Jean Ingres (painter). Multicoloured.
284 90 f. Type **102** .. .. 1·10 60
285 200 f. "Ingres in his Studio" (Alaux) .. 2·10 1·25
See also Nos. 306/8.

1967. 5th Anniv. of West African Monetary Union.
286. **103.** 30 f. grey and orange 35 15

104. "Hyphaene thebaica". **105.** Human Rights Emblem.

1967. Mauritanian Fruits.
287. **104.** 1 f. brown, grn. & purple 15 10
288. – 2 f. yellow, green & brn. 15 10
289. – 3 f. olive, green & violet 15 10
290. – 4 f. red, green & brown 15 10
291. – 5 f. orange, brown & grn. 20 10
FRUITS—HORIZ. 2 f. "**Balanites aegyptiaca**". 4 f. "**Ziziphus lotus**". VERT. 3 f. "**Adansonia digitata**". 5 f. "**Phoenix dactylifera**".

1968. Human Rights Year.
292. **105.** 30 f. yellow, grn. & black 30 20
293. 50 f. yellow, brn. & black 55 35

106. Chancellor Adenauer. **108.** Mosque, Nouakchott.

107. Skiing.

1968. Air. Adenauer Commem.
294. **106.** 100 f. sepia, brn. & blue 1·25 60

1968. Air. Olympic Games, Grenoble and Mexico.
296. **107.** 20 f. purple, indigo & bl. 30 10
297. – 30 f. brown, green & plum 35 15
298. – 50 f. green, blue & ochre 55 25
299. – 100 f. green, red & brn. 1·00 50
DESIGNS—VERT. 30 f. Horse-vaulting. 50 f. Ski-jumping. HORIZ. 100 f. Hurdling.

1968. Tourism. Multicoloured.
300. 30 f. Type **108** 25 20
301. 45 f. Amogjar Pass .. 35 20
302. 90 f. Cavaliers' Tower, Boutilimit 65 35

109. Man and W.H.O. Emblem.

1968. Air. 20th Anniv. of W.H.O.
303. **109.** 150 f. blue, purple & brn. 1·50 75

110. U.N.E.S.C.O. Emblem and "Movement of Water".

1968. Int. Hydrological Decade.
304. **110.** 90 f. green and lake .. 70 40

111. U.P.U. Building, Berne.

1968. Admission of Mauritania to U.P.U.
305. **111.** 30 f. brown and red .. 35 20

1968. Air. Paintings by Ingres. As T **102**. Multicoloured.
306. 100 f. "Man's Torso" .. 1·10 65
307. 150 f. "The Iliad" .. 1·75 95
308. 250 f. "The Odyssey" .. 2·75 1·60

112. Land-yachts crossing Desert. **113.** Dr. Martin Luther King.

1968. Land-yacht Racing.
309. **112.** 30 f. blue, yell. & orge. 45 25
310. – 40 f. pur., blue & orge. 55 30
311. – 60 f. grn., yell. & orge. 85 50
DESIGNS—HORIZ. 40 f. Racing on shore. VERT. 60 f. Crew making repairs.

1968. Air. "Apostles of Peace".
312. **113.** 50 f. brown, blue & olive 1·00 40
313. – 50 f. brown and blue .. 60 25
DESIGN: No. 313, Mahatma Gandhi.

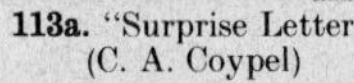

113a. "Surprise Letter" (C. A. Coypel) **114.** Donkey and Foal.

1968. Air. "Philexafrique" Stamp Exn. Abidjan, Ivory Coast, (1969) (1st issue).
315. **113a.** 100 f. multicoloured 1·75 1·75

1968. Domestic Animals. Multicoloured.
316. 5 f. Type **114** 15 10
317. 10 f. Ewe and lamb .. 20 15
318. 15 f. Dromedary and calf 25 15
319. 30 f. Mare and foal .. 45 25
320. 50 f. Cow and calf 70 35
321. 90 f. Goat and kid .. 1·40 50

114a. Forest Scene and Stamp of 1938.

1969. Air. "Philexafrique" Stamp Exn., Abidjan, Ivory Coast (2nd issue).
322. **114a** 50 f. purple, green & brown .. .. 1·10 1·10

114b. "Napoleon at Council of Five Hundred (Bouchot). **115.** Map and I.L.O. Emblem.

1969. Air. Birth Bicentenary of Napoleon Bonaparte. Multicoloured.
323. 50 f. Type **114b** .. .. 1·50 90
324. 90 f. "Napoleon's Installation by the Council of State" (Conder) .. .. 2·00 1·25
325. 250 f. "The Farewell of Fontainebleau" (Vernet) 5·00 3·25

1969. 50th Anniv. of I.L.O.
326. **115.** 50 f. multicoloured .. 50 25

116. Monitor Lizard. **117.** Date Palm, "Parlatoria blanchardi" and "Pharoscymus anchorage".

1969. Reptiles. Multicoloured.
327. 5 f. Type **116** 25 20
328. 10 f. Horned viper 45 30
329. 30 f. Black-collared cobra 1·10 35
330. 60 f. Rock python .. .. 1·75 1·10
331. 85 f. Nile crocodile .. 2·75 1·40

1969. Date-palms. Protection Campaign.
332 **117** 30 f. blue, red and green 30 15

118. Camel and Emblem.

1969. Air. African Tourist Year.
333. **118.** 50 f. purple, blue & orge. 70 35

119. Dancers and Baalbek Columns.

1969. Air. Baalbek Festival, Lebanon.
334. **119.** 100 f. brn., red & bl. 1·25 55

120. "Apollo 8" and Moon.

1969. Air. Moon Flight of "Apollo 8". Embossed on gold foil.
335. **120.** 1,000 f. gold .. .. 14·00 14·00

121. Wolde (marathon). **122a.** Bank Emblem.

122. London-Istanbul Route-Map.

1969. Air. Gold Medal Winners, Mexico Olympic Games.
336. **121.** 30 f. red, brown & blue 25 15
337. – 70 f. red, brown & green 50 30
338. – 150 f. green, bistre & red 1·25 70
DESIGNS: 70 f. Beamon (athletics). 150 f. Vera Caslavska (gymnastics).

1969. Air. London–Sydney Motor Rally.
339. **122.** 10 f. brn., blue & purple 15 10
340. – 20 f. brn., blue & purple 30 15
341. – 50 f. brn., blue & purple 60 25
342. – 70 f. brn., blue & purple 85 30
Route—Maps: 20 f. Ankara-Teheran. 50 f. Kandahar-Bombay. 70 f. Perth-Sydney.

1969. 5th Anniv. of African Development Bank. Multicoloured.
344. **122a.** 30 f. brn., grn. & bl. 30 15

123. Pendant. **124.** Sea-water Desalination Plant, Nouakchott.

1969. Native Handicrafts.
345. **123.** 10 f. brown and purple 20 15
346. – 20 f. red, black and blue 40 20
DESIGN—HORIZ. 20 f. Rahla headdress.

1969. Economic Development.
347. **124.** 10 f. blue, purple and red 20 15
348. – 15 f. black, lake and blue 25 15
349. – 30 f. black, purple & blue 30 20
DESIGNS: 15 f. Fishing quay, Nouadhibou. 30 f. Meat-processing plant, Kaedi.

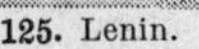

125. Lenin. **126.** "Sternocera interrupta".

1970. Birth Cent. of Lenin.
350. **125.** 30 f. black, red and blue 30 20

1970. Insects.
351. **126.** 5 f. black, buff & brown 25 15
352. – 10 f. brown, yellow & lake 35 15
353. – 20 f. olive, purple & brn. 50 25
354. – 30 f. violet, grn. & brn. 80 45
355. – 40 f. brown, blue & lake 1·50 70
INSECTS: 10 f. "**Anoplocnemis curvipes**". 20 f. "**Julodis aequinoctialis**". 30 f. "**Thermophilum sexmaculatum marginatum**". 40 f. "**Plocaederus denticornis**".

127. Footballers and Hemispheres. **128.** Japanese Musician, Emblem and Map on Palette.

1970. World Cup Football Championships, Mexico.
356. **127.** 25 f. multicoloured .. 30 20
357. – 30 f. multicoloured .. 35 20
358. – 70 f. multicoloured .. 70 30
359. – 150 f. multicoloured .. 1·60 75
DESIGNS: 30 f., 70 f., 150 f. As Type **127**, but with different players.

1970. New U.P.U. Headquarters Building. As T **81** of New Caledonia.
360. 30 f. red, brown and green 35 20

1970. Air. "EXPO 70" World Fair, Osaka, Japan. Multicoloured.
361. 50 f. Type **128** 50 20
362. 75 f. Japanese fan 75 35
363. 150 f. Stylised bird, map and boat .. .. .. 1·40 80

129. U.N. Emblem and Examples of Progress.

1970. Air. 25th Anniv. of U.N.O.
364. **129.** 100 f. grn., brn. & blue 1·00 60

130. Vladimir Komarov. **131.** Descent of "Apollo 13".

1970. Air. "Lost Heroes of Space" (1st series).
365. **130.** 150 f. brn., orge. & slate 1·50 70
366. – 150 f. brn., blue and slate 1·50 70
367. – 150 f. brn., orge. & slate 1·50 70
HEROES: No. 366, Elliott See. 367, Yuri Gagarin. See also Nos. 376/8.

1970. Air. Space Flight of "Apollo 13".
369. **131.** 500 f. red, blue and gold 5·00 5·00

132. Woman in Traditional Costume. **133.** Arms and State House.

1970. Traditional Costumes. As T **132**.
370. **132.** 10 f. orange and brown 20 15
371. – 30 f. blue, red and brown 40 20
372. – 40 f. brn., purple & red 50 30
373. – 50 f. blue and brown .. 70 35
374. – 70 f. brown, choc. & blue 90 45

1970. Air. 10th Anniv. of Independence.
375. **133.** 100 f. multicoloured .. 1·00 45

1970. Air. "Lost Heroes of Space" (2nd series). As T **130**.
376. 150 f. brown, blue & turq. 1·50 70
377. 150 f. brown, blue & turq. 1·50 70
378. 150 f. brown, blue & orange 1·50 70
HEROES: No. 376, Roger Chaffee. No. 377, Virgil Grissom. No. 378, Edward White.

134. Greek Wrestling.

1971. Air. "Pre-Olympics Year".
380. **134.** 100 f. brn., pur. & blue 1·10 75

135. People of Different Races.

1971. Racial Equality Year.
381. **135.** 30 f. plum, blue & brn. 30 15
382. – 40 f. black, red & blue .. 35 20
DESIGN:—VERT. 40 f. European and African hands.

136. Pres. Nasser.

1971. Air. Pres. Gamal Nasser of Egypt Commemoration.
383. **136.** 100 f. multicoloured .. 85 40

137. Gen. De Gaulle in Uniform. **138.** Scout Badge, Scout and Map.

1971. De Gaulle Commem. Multicoloured.
384. 40 f. Type **137** .. .. 1·25 60
385. 100 f. De Gaulle as President of France .. .. 2·75 1·40

1971. Air. 13th World Scout Jamboree, Asagiri, Japan.
387. **138.** 35 f. multicoloured .. 40 20
388. 40 f. multicoloured .. 50 20
389. 100 f. multicoloured .. 1·25 45

139. Diesel Locomotive.

1971. Miferma Iron-ore Mines. Multicoloured.
390. 35 f. Iron ore train .. 1·10 60
391. 100 f. Type **139** .. .. 2·40 1·40
Nos. 390/1 form a composite design.

139a. Headquarters, Brazzaville, and Ardin musicians.

1971. Air. 10th Anniv. of African and Malagasy Posts and Telecommunications Union.
392. **139a.** 100 f. multicoloured 1·10 60

140. A.P.U. Emblem and Airmail Envelope.

1971. Air. 10th Anniv. of African Postal Union.
393. **140.** 35 f. multicoloured .. 40 25

141. U.N.I.C.E.F. Emblem and Child.

1971. 25th Anniv. of U.N.I.C.E.F.
394. **141.** 35 f. blk., brn. & blue .. 35 20

142. "Moslem King" (c. 1218).

1972. Air. Moslem Miniatures. Mult.
395. 35 f. Type **142** 45 20
396. 40 f. "Enthroned Prince" (Egypt, c. 1334) .. 60 25
397. 100 f. "Pilgrims' Caravan" (Maquamat, Baghdad 1237) .. .. 1·50 70

1972. Air. U.N.E.S.C.O. "Save Venice" Campaign. As T **127** of Mali. Multicoloured.
398. 45 f. "Quay and Ducal Palace" (Carlevaris) (vert.) 60 25
399. 100 f. "Grand Canal" (Canaletto) .. .. 1·40 60
400. 250 f. "Grand Canal" (Canaletto) .. .. 3·00 1·50

143. Hurdling.

1972. Air. Olympic Games, Munich.
401. **143.** 75 f. pur., orge. & grn. 55 30
402. 100 f. pur., blue & brn. 75 40
403. 200 f. pur., lake & grn. 1·60 70

144. Nurse tending Baby. **145.** Samuel Morse and Morse Key.

1972. Mauritanian Red Crescent Fund.
405. **144.** 35 f. + 5 f. multicoloured 60 60

1972. World Telecommunications Day. Multicoloured.
406. 35 f. Type **145** 35 20
407. 40 f. "Relay" satellite and hemispheres 45 20
408. 75 f. Alexander Graham Bell and early telephone 70 35

146. Spirifer Shell.

1972. Fossil Shells. Multicoloured.
409. 25 f. Type **146** .. .. 1·00 35
410. 75 f. Trilobite .. .. 2·75 1·10

147. "Luna 16" and Moon probe. **151.** Mediterranean Monk Seal with Young.

149. Africans and 500 f. Coin.

1972. Air. Russian Exploration of the Moon.
411. **147.** 75 f. brn., blue & green 60 30
412. – 100 f. brn., grey & violet 90 50
DESIGN—HORIZ. 100 f. "Lunokhod 1".

1972. Air. Gold Medal-Winners, Munich. Nos. 401/3 optd. as listed below.
413. **143.** 75 f. pur., orge. & grn. 60 30
414. 100 f. pur., blue & brn. 80 50
415. 200 f. pur., lake & grn. 1·60 1·00
OVERPRINTS: 75 f. **110m. HAIES MILBURN MEDAILLE D'OR.** 100 f. **400m. HAIES AKII-BUA MEDAILLE D'OR.** 200 f. **3,000m. STEEPLE KEINO MEDAILLE D'OR.**

1972. 10th Anniv. of West African Monetary Union.
416. **149.** 35 f. grey, brn. & grn. 30 20

1973. Air. Moon Flight of "Apollo 17". No. 267 surch. **Apollo XVII Decembre 1972** and value.
417. 250 f. on 500 f. multicoloured 4·00 2·00

1973. Seals. Multicoloured.
418. 40 f. Type **151** (postage) .. 1·25 50
419. 135 f. Head of Mediterranean monk seal (air) .. 3·75 2·00

152. "Lion and Crocodile" (Delacroix).

1973. Air. Paintings by Delacroix. Mult.
420. 100 f. Type **152** .. .. 1·50 75
421. 250 f. "Lion attacking Forest Hog" .. .. 3·25 2·00

153. "Horns of Plenty".

1973. 10th Anniv. of World Food Programme.
422. **153.** 35 f. multicoloured .. 30 20

154. U.P.U. Monument, Berne, and Globe.

1973. World U.P.U. Day.
423. **154.** 100 f. bl., orge. & grn. 1·00 65

155. Nomad Encampment and Eclipse.

1973. Total Eclipse of the Sun.
424. **155.** 35 f. purple and green 35 20
425. – 40 f. purple, red & blue 45 20
426. – 140 f. purple and red 1·60 75
DESIGNS—VERT. 40 f. Rocket and "Concorde". HORIZ. 140 f. Observation team.

1973. "Drought Relief". African Solidarity. No. 320 optd. **SECHERESSE SOLIDARITE AFRICAINE** and value.
428. 20 u. on 50 f. multicoloured 65 45

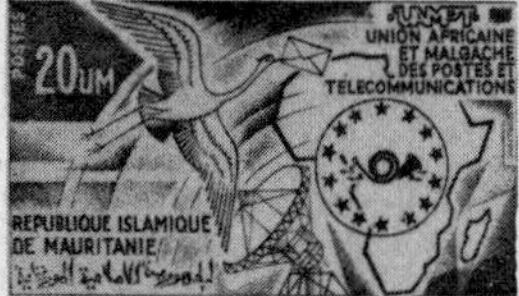

155a. Crane with Letter and Union Emblem.

1973. 12th Anniv. of African and Malagasy Posts and Telecommunications Union.
429. **155a.** 20 u. brown, light brown & orange 70 45

157. Detective making Arrest and Fingerprint.

1973. 50th Anniv. of International Criminal Police Organization (Interpol).
430. **157.** 15 u vio., red & brn... 1·10 45

1974. Various stamps surch. with values in new currency.

(a) Postage.
(i) Nos. 345/6.
431. **123.** 27 u. on 10 f. brn. & pur. 1·50 70
432. – 28 u. on 20 f. red, black and blue 1·75 90
(ii) Nos. 351/5.
433. **126.** 5 u. on 5 f. black, buff and brown 70 50
434. – 7 u. on 10 f. brown, yellow and lake 60 30
435. – 8 u. on 20 f. olive, pur. and brown 70 35
436. – 10 u. on 30 f. violet, purple and brown 1·00 45
437. – 20 u. on 4 f. brown, blue and lake 2·00 1·10
(iii) Nos. 409/10.
438. **146.** 5 u. on 25 f. mult. 60 40
439. – 15 u. on 75 f. mult. 1·75 1·00
(iv) No. 418.
440. **151.** 8 u. on 40 f. mult. 90 45

(b) Air.
(i) Nos. 395/7.
441. **142.** 7 u. on 35 f. mult. 40 20
442. – 8 u. on 40 f. mult. 40 20
443. – 20 u. on 100 f. mult. 1·50 70
(ii) No. 419.
444. – 27 u. on 135 f. mult. 2·25 85
(iii) Nos. 420/1.
445. **152.** 20 u. on 100 f. mult. 1·60 70
446. – 50 u. on 250 f. mult. 3·75 2·00
(iv) Nos. 424/6.
447. **155.** 7 u. on 35 f. purple and green 45 20
448. – 8 u. on 40 f. purple, red and blue 45 20
449. – 28 u. on 140 f. purple and red 1·90 70

159. Footballers.

161. Sir Winston Churchill.

160. Jules Verne and Scenes from Books.

1974. Air. World Cup Football Championships. West Germany.
450. **159.** 7 u. multicoloured 40 20
451. 8 u. multicoloured 40 20
452. 20 u. multicoloured 1·10 50

1974. Air. Jules Verne, "Prophet of Space Travel", and "Skylab" Flights Commem.
454. **160.** 70 u. silver 4·50 4·50
455. – 70 u. silver 4·50 4·50
456. **160.** 250 u. gold 12·00 12·00
457. – 250 u. gold 12·00 12·00
DESIGNS: Nos. 455, 457, "Skylab" in Space.

1974. Air. Birth Cent. of Sir Winston Churchill.
458. **161.** 40 u. red and purple 1·75 95

162. U.P.U. Monument and Globes.

1974. Cent. of U.P.U.
459. **162.** 30 u. red, green and deep green 1·25 75
460. 50 u. red, light blue and blue 2·00 1·25

163. 5 Ouguiya Coin and Banknote.

1974. 1st Anniv. of Introduction of Ouguiya Currency.
461. **163.** 7 u. blk., grn. & blue 35 20
462. – 8 u. blk., mauve & grn. 40 20
463. – 20 u. blk., blue & red 1·00 50
DESIGNS: 8 u. 10 ouguiya coin and banknote. 20 u. 20 ouguiya coin and banknote.

164. Lenin.

166. Two Hunters.

1974. Air. 50th Death Anniv. of Lenin.
464. **164.** 40 u. green and red 2·00 95

1974. Treaty of Berne Centenary. Nos. 459/60 optd. **9 OCTOBRE 100 ANS D'UNION POSTALE INTERNATIONALE.**
465. **162.** 30 u. red, green and deep green 1·60 80
466. 50 u. red, light blue and blue 2·00 1·25

1975. Nos. 287/91 surch. in new currency.
467. – 1 u. on 5 f. orge., brn. and green 10 10
468. – 2 u. on 4 f. red, grn. and brown 15 15
469. – 3 u. on 2 f. yell., green and brown 20 15
470. **104.** 10 u. on 1 f. brn., grn. and purple 60 20
471. – 12 u. on 3 f. olive, grn. and violet 75 30

1975. Rock-carvings, Zemmour.
472. **166.** 4 u. red and brown 40 15
473. – 5 u. purple 45 25
474. – 10 u. blue and light blue 80 35
DESIGNS—VERT: 5 u. Ostrich. HORIZ: 10 u. Elephant.

167. Mauritanian Women.

1975. Air. International Women's Year.
475. **167.** 12 u. pur., brn. & blue 50 25
476. – 40 u. pur., brn. & blue 1·75 85
DESIGN: 40 u. Head of Mauritanian woman.

MINIMUM PRICE

The minimum price quoted is 5p which represents a handling charge rather than a basis for valuing common stamps. For further notes about prices see introductory pages.

168. Combined European and African Heads.

169. Dr. Schweitzer.

1975. Europafrique.
477. **168.** 40 u. brn., red & bistre 1·60 95

1975. Birth Cent. of Dr. Albert Schweitzer.
478. **169.** 60 u. olive, brn. & grn. 2·50 1·50

1975. Pan-African Drought Relief. Nos. 301/2, surch. **SECHERESSE SOLIDARITE AFRICAINE** and value.
479. 15 u. on 45 f. multicoloured 1·00 50
480. 25 u. on 90 f. multicoloured 1·40 75

171. Akjoujt Plant and Man with Camel.

172. Fair Emblem.

1975. Mining Industry.
481. **171.** 10 u. brn., blue & orge. 1·00 30
482. – 12 u. blue, red & brn. 1·25 40
DESIGN: 12 u. Mining operations.

1975. Nouakchott National Fair.
483. **172.** 10 u. multicoloured 40 25

173. Throwing the Javelin.

1975. Air. "Pre-Olympic Year". Olympic Games, Montreal (1976).
484. **173.** 50 u. red, grn. & brn. 1·60 1·40
485. – 52 u. blue, brn. & red 1·75 1·40
DESIGN: 52 u. Running.

174. Commemorative Medal.

1975. 15th Anniv. of Independence. Multicoloured.
486. 10 u. Type **174** 50 30
487. 12 u. Map of Mauritania 60 35

175. "Soyuz" Cosmonauts Leonov and Kubasov.

1975. "Apollo-Soyuz" Space Link. Mult.
488. 8 u. Type **175** (postage) 45 20
489. 10 u. "Soyuz" on launch-pad 55 25
490. 20 u. "Apollo" on launch-pad (air) 70 45
491. 50 u. Cosmonauts meeting astronauts 2·00 1·00
492. 60 u. Parachute splashdown 2·25 1·25

176. Foot-soldier of Lauzun's Legion.

1976. Bicentenary of American Independence. Multicoloured.
494. 8 u. Type **176** (postage) 60 20
495. 10 u. "Green Mountain" infantryman 70 20
496. 20 u. Lauzun Hussar's officer (air) 90 40
497. 50 u. Artillery officer of 3rd Continental Regiment 2·40 1·00
498. 60 u. Grenadier of Gatinais' Regiment 3·00 1·25

1976. 10th Anniv. of Arab Labour Charter. No. 408 surch. **10e ANNIVERSAIRE DE LA CHARTE ARABE DU TRAVAIL** in French and Arabic.
500. 12 u. on 75 f. blue, black and green 55 30

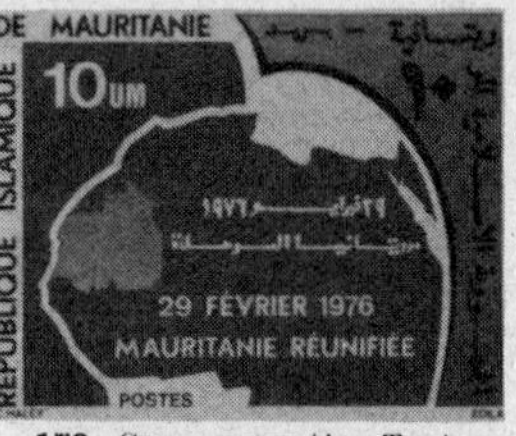

178. Commemorative Text on Map.

1976. Reunification of Mauritania.
501. **178.** 10 u. green, lilac and deep green 45 30

181. Running.

1976. Air. Olympic Games, Montreal.
514. **181.** 10 u. brown, green and violet 40 25
515. – 12 u. brown, green and violet 50 35
516. – 52 u. brown, green and violet 1·75 1·25
DESIGNS: 12 u. Vaulting (gymnastics). 52 u. Fencing.

182. "LZ 4" at Friedrichshafen.

1976. 75th Anniv. of Zeppelin Airship. Mult.
517. 5 u. Type **182** (postage) 25 15
518. 10 u. "LZ 10" over German Landscape 40 20
519. 12 u. "LZ 13" over Heligoland 50 25
520. 20 u. "LZ 120" and Doctor H. Durr 2·25 75
521. 50 u. "LZ 127" over Capitol, Washington (air) 2·25 90
522. 60 u. "LZ 130" crossing Swiss Alps 3·00 1·25

183. Temple and Bas-relief.

1976. U.N.E.S.C.O. "Save Moenjodaro" (Pakistan) Campaign.

524. **183.** 15 u. multicoloured .. 80 40

184. Sacred Ibis and Yellow-billed Stork.

185. Alexander Graham Bell, Early Telephone and Satellite.

1976. Air. Mauritanian Birds. Mult.

525. 50 u. Type **184** .. .. 4·25 1·75

526. 100 u. Marabou storks (horiz.) .. .. .. 7·50 3·75

527. 200 u. Long-crested and Martial eagles .. .. 15·00 6·50

1976. Telephone Cent.

528. **185.** 10 u. blue, lake and red 50 25

186. Mohammed Ali Jinnah.

1976. Birth Centenary of Mohammed Ali Jinnah (first Governor-General of Pakistan).

529. **186.** 10 u. multicoloured .. 35 20

187. Capsule Assembly.

1977. "Viking" Space Mission. Mult.

530. 10 u. Mission Control (horiz.) 50 15

531. 12 u. Type **187** 55 20

532. 20 u. "Viking" in flight (horiz.) (air) .. 80 25

533. 50 u. "Viking" over Mars (horiz.) .. .. .. 2·00 60

534. 60 u. Parachute descent .. 2·25 65

188. Bush Hare.

1977. Mauritanian Animals. Multicoloured.

536. 5 u. Type **188** 30 15

537. 10 u. Golden jackals .. 55 30

538. 12 u. Warthogs 75 40

539. 14 u. Lion and lioness .. 85 50

540. 15 u. African elephants .. 1·75 80

189. Frederic and Irene Joliot-Curie (Chemistry, 1935).

1977. Nobel Prize-winners. Multicoloured.

541. 12 u. Type **189** (postage) 75 15

542. 15 u. Emil von Behring and nurse inoculating patient (1901) 75 20

543. 14 u. George Bernard Shaw and scene from "Androcles and the Lion" (1925) (air) 75 30

544. 55 u. Thomas Mann and scene from "Joseph and his Brethren" (1929) .. 1·90 60

545. 60 u. International Red Cross and scene on Western Front (Peace Prize) (1917) 2·25 70

190. A.P.U. Emblem.

1977. 25th Anniv. of Arab Postal Union.

547. **190.** 12 u. multicoloured .. 45 30

191. Oil Lamp.

192. Skeleton of Hand.

1977. Pottery from Tegdaoust.

548. **191.** 1 u. olive, brn. and blue 10 10

549. – 2 u. mauve, brn. & blue 15 10

550. – 5 u. orge., brn. & blue 25 10

551. – 12 u. brn., grn. and red 55 20

DESIGNS: 2 u. Four-handled tureen. 5 u. Large jar. 12 u. Narrow-necked jug.

1977. World Rheumatism Year.

552. **192.** 40 u. orge., brn. & grn. 2·00 1·25

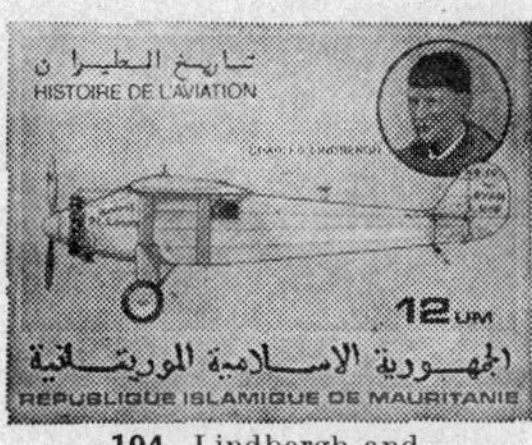

193. Holy Kaaba, Mecca.

1977. Air. Pilgrimage to Mecca.

553. **193.** 12 u. multicoloured .. 60 40

194. Lindbergh and "Spirit of St. Louis".

1977. History of Aviation. Multicoloured.

554. 12 u. Type **194** 50 15

555. 14 u. Clement Ader and "Aeolus" 60 25

556. 15 u. Louis Bleriot and aircraft 70 25

557. 55 u. Italo Balbo and flying-boat .. .. 2·25 70

558. 60 u. "Concorde" .. 2·50 85

195. Dome of the Rock.

197. "Helene Fourment and Her Children" (Rubens).

196. Two Players.

1977. Palestinian Welfare.

560. **195.** 12 u. multicoloured .. 70 30

561. 14 u. multicoloured .. 80 35

1977. World Cup Football Championships—Elimination Rounds. Multicoloured.

562. 12 u. Type **196** (postage) .. 40 15

563. 14 u. Sir Alf Ramsey and Wembley Stadium .. 50 20

564. 15 u. A "throw-in" .. 60 20

565. 50 u. Football and emblems (air) .. .. .. 2·00 60

566. 60 u. Eusebio Ferreira .. 2·40 1·00

1977. 400th Birth Anniv. of Rubens. Paintings. Multicoloured.

568. 12 u. Type **197** 50 15

569. 14 u. "The Marquis of Spinola" 60 20

570. 67 u. "The Four Philosophers" .. .. 2·25 75

571. 69 u. "Steen Castle and Park" (horiz.) .. 2·50 85

198. Addra Gazelles.

1978. Endangered Animals. Multicoloured.

573. 5 u. Scimitar oryx (horiz.) 35 15

574. 12 u. Type **198** 65 25

575. 14 u. African manatee (horiz.) 80 35

576. 55 u. Barbary sheep .. 3·00 1·00

577. 60 u. African elephant (horiz.) .. .. 3·25 1·25

578. 100 u. Ostrich .. .. 4·50 1·75

199. Clasped Hands and President Giscard d'Estaing of France.

1978. Air. Franco-African Co-operation. Embossed on foil.

579. **199.** 250 u. silver .. 7·00 7·00

580. 500 u. gold .. .. 14·00 14·00

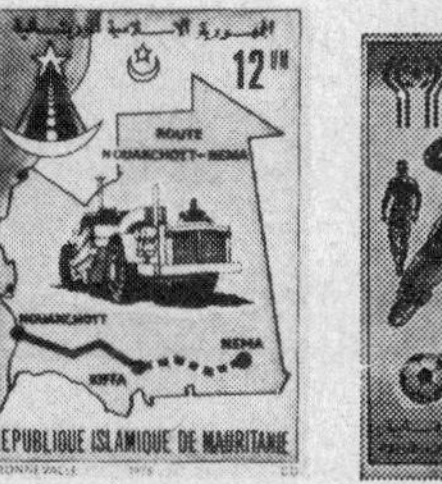

199a. Earth-mover and Route Map.

200. Footballers.

1978. Nouakchott-Nema Highway. Mult.

580a. 12 um. Type **199a** .. 2·00 1·50

580b. 14 um. Bulldozer and route map .. .. .. 2·25 1·75

1978. World Cup Football Championship, Argentina. Multicoloured.

581. 12 u. Type **200** 40 20

582. 14 u. World Cup 50 25

583. 20 u. F.I.F.A. flag and football 85 35

201. Raoul Follereau and St. George fighting Dragon.

1978. 25th Anniv. of Raoul Follereau Foundation.

585 **201** 12 u. brown and green 70 40

202. Emblem and People holding Hands.

203. Charles de Gaulle.

1978. International Anti-Apartheid Year.

586. – 25 u. brn., blue and red 90 60

587. **202.** 30 u. brn., blue & grn. 1·10 70

DESIGN—HORIZ. 25 m. Emblem and people behind fence.

1978. Personalities. Multicoloured.

588. 12 u. Type **203** 90 30

589. 14 u. King Baudouin of Belgium 90 30

590. 55 u. Queen Elizabeth II (25th anniv. of Coronation) .. .. .. 2·00 90

1978. Air. "Philexafrique" Stamp Exhibition, Libreville (Gabon) (1st issue), and 2nd Int. Stamp Fair, Essen (West Germany). As T **262** of Niger. Multicoloured.

591 20 u. Water rail and Hamburg 1859 ½ s. stamp .. .. .. 1·00 65

592 20 u. Spotted hyena and Mauritania 1967 100 f. South African crowned crane stamp .. .. 1·00 65

See also Nos. 619/20.

1978. Argentina's Victory in World Cup Football Championship. Nos. 562/6 optd **ARGENTINE—PAYS BAS 3-1** in English and Arabic.

593 **196** 12 u. mult (postage) .. 50 25

594 – 14 u. multicoloured .. 55 30

595 – 15 u. multicoloured .. 65 30

596 – 50 u. mult (air) .. 1·75 1·10

597 – 60 u. multicoloured .. 2·25 1·40

205. View of Nouakchott.

1978. 20th Anniv. of Nouakchott.

599. **205.** 12 um. multicoloured 45 30

206. Human Rights Emblem.

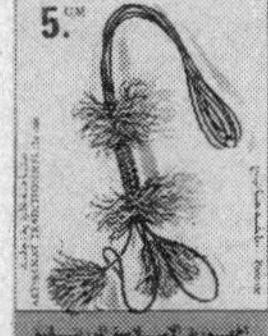

208. Key Chain.

207. Ader's Flying Machine and Wright Brothers' "Flyer".

1978. 30th Anniv. of Declaration of Human Rights.

600. **206.** 55 um. red and blue .. 1·60 1·25

1979. Air. 75th Anniv. of First Powered Flight.

601. **207.** 15 um. grey, red and blue 75 35

602. – 40 um. violet, blue and brown .. .. 1·75 1·10

DESIGN: 40 um. "Concorde" and Wright "Flyer".

1979. Handicrafts. Multicoloured.

603. 5 um. Type **208** 25 15

604. 7 um. Tooth-brush case .. 30 20

605. 10 um. Knife sheath .. 45 25

209. " Market Peasant and Wife ". **210.** Seated Buddha, Temple of Borobudur.

1979. 450th Birth Anniv. of Albrecht Durer (artist).

606. **209.** 12 u. black and red .. 50 25
607. – 14 u. black and red .. 60 25
608. – 55 u. black and red .. 1·60 75
609. – 60 u. black and red .. 1·90 1·00

DESIGNS: 14 u. " Young Peasant and his Wife ". 55 u. " Mercenary with Banner ". 60 u. " St. George and the Dragon ".

1979. U.N.E.S.C.O. Campaign for Preservation of Historic Monuments. Mult.

611. 12 u. Type **210** 50 30
612. 14 u. Carthaginian warrior and hunting dog .. 60 30
613. 55 u. Erechtheum Caryatid, Acropolis .. .. 1·75 1·25

211. Rowland Hill and Paddle-steamer "Sirius".

1979. Death Centenary of Sir Rowland Hill. Multicoloured.

614 12 u. Type **211** 50 25
615 14 u. Hill and "Great Republic" (paddle-steamer) 65 25
616 55 u. Hill and "Mauretania I" (liner) .. .. 2·00 60
617 60 u. Hill and "Stirling Castle" (liner) .. .. 2·50 85

212. Satellite over Earth.

1979. " Philexafrique " Exhibition, Libreville (2nd issue).

619. – 12 u. multicoloured .. 60 50
620. **212.** 30 u. red, blue and lilac 1·40 1·25

DESIGN—HORIZ. 12 u. Embossed leather cushion cover.

213. Mother and Children. **215.** Sprinter on Starting-blocks.

1979. International Year of the Child. Multicoloured.

621. 12 u. Type **213** 45 25
622. 14 u. Mother with sleeping baby 55 35
623. 40 u. Children playing with ball .. .. .. 1·50 90

1979. 10th Anniv. of "Apollo II" Moon Landing. Nos. 530/4 optd. **ALUNISSAGE APOLLO XI JUILLET 1969**, with Lunar module, or surch. also.

624. 10 u. Mission Control (horiz.) 40 25
625. 12 u. Type **187** 45 30
626. 14 u. on 20 u. " Viking " in flight (horiz.) (air) .. 60 25
627. 50 u. " Viking " over Mars (horiz.) .. .. 1·60 1·00
628. 60 u. Parachute descent .. 1·90 1·10

1979. Pre-Olympic Year. Multicoloured.

630. 12 u. Type **215** 35 15
631. 14 u. Female runner .. 40 15
632. 55 u. Male runner leaving start .. .. .. 1·50 60
633. 60 u. Hurdling .. .. 1·60 60

215a. " Scomberesox saurus ".

1979. Fishes. Multicoloured.

634a 1 u. Type **215a** 10 10
634b 2 u. Swordfish 10 10
634c 3 u. "Trigla lucerna" .. 15 15

216. Ice Hockey.

1979. Winter Olympic Games, Lake Placid (1980). Ice Hockey. Multicoloured.

635. 10 u. Type **216** 40 20
636. 12 u. Saving a goal .. 45 25
637. 14 u. Goalkeeper and player 55 25
638. 55 u. Two players .. .. 2·00 60
639. 60 u. Goalkeeper .. .. 2·25 65
640. 100 u. Tackle .. .. 3·50 1·25

217. Woman pouring out Tea.

1980. Taking Tea.

641. **217.** 1 u. multicoloured .. 10 10
642. 5 u. multicoloured .. 20 10
643. 12 u. multicoloured .. 45 20

218. Koran, World Map and Symbols of Arab Achievements.

1980. The Arabs.

644. **218.** 12 u. multicoloured .. 40 25
645. 15 u. multicoloured .. 50 30

1980. Winter Olympics Medal Winners. Nos. 635/40 optd.

646. 10 u. **Medaille de bronze SUEDE** 35 20
647. 12 u. **MEDAILLE DE BRONZE SUEDE** .. 40 20
648. 14 u. **Medaille d'argent U.R.S.S.** 45 25
649. 55 u. **MEDAILLE D'ARGENT U.R.S.S.** .. 1·50 80
650. 60 u. **MEDAILLE D'OR ETATS-UNIS** .. 1·75 90
651. 100 u. **Medaille d'or ETATS-UNIS** .. 3·00 1·50

220. Holy Kaaba, Mecca. **221.** Mother and Child.

1980. Pilgrimage to Mecca. Multicoloured.

652. 10 u. Type **220** 40 20
653. 50 u. Pilgrims outside Mosque .. .. .. 1·60 1·10

1980. World Red Cross Societies Day.

654. **221.** 20 u. multicoloured .. 70 40

222. Crowd greeting Armed Forces.

1980. Armed Forces Festival.

655. **222.** 12 u. multicoloured .. 35 20
656. 14 u. multicoloured .. 40 25

223. Horse jumping Bar. **224.** Trees on Map of Mauritania.

1980. Olympic Games, Moscow. Mult.

657. 10 u. Type **223** 30 20
658. 20 u. Water polo 55 30
659. 50 u. Horse jumping brick wall (horiz.) .. .. 1·40 55
660. 70 u. Horse jumping stone wall .. .. 1·90 75

1980. Tree Day.

662. **224.** 12 u. multicoloured .. 35 20

225. " Rembrandt's Mother ".

1980. Paintings by Rembrandt. Mult.

663. 10 u. " Self-portrait " .. 30 20
664. 20 u. Type **225** 55 30
665. 50 u. " Portrait of a Man in Oriental Costume " .. 1·40 55
666. 70 u. " Titus Lisant " .. 1·90 75

226. Footballers.

1980. Air. World Cup Football Championship, Spain (1982). Multicoloured.

668. 10 u. Type **226** 30 20
669. 12 u. Goalkeeper and players 35 20
670. 14 u. Goalkeeper catching ball 40 25
671. 20 u. Fighting for possession 55 30
672. 67 u. Tackle .. .. 1·90 75

1980. Olympic Medal Winners. Nos. 657/60 optd.

674. 10 u. **VAINQUEUR KOWALCZYK (POL)** .. 30 20
675. 20 u. **VAINQUEUR THEURER (AUTR)** .. 55 30
676. 50 u. **VAINQUEUR URSS** 1·40 55
677. 70 u. **VAINQUEUR ROMAN (IT)** .. .. 1·90 75

228. Giovi " Mastodont ".

1980. Locomotives. Multicoloured.

679 10 u. Type **228** 40 15
680 12 u. SNIM-SEM diesel ore train 45 15
681 14 u. Steam locomotive of Chicago, Milwaukee and St. Paul Railway .. 55 20
682 20 u. Bury steam locomotive 1837 .. .. 75 25
683 67 u. Steam locomotive of French Reseau du Nord line .. .. 2·50 55
684 100 u. Steam locomotive of Berlin–Potsdam line .. 3·75 95

229. Palm Tree, Crescent and Star, Maize and Map.

1980. 20th Anniv. of Independence.

685. **229.** 12 u. multicoloured .. 40 20
686. 15 u. multicoloured .. 50 30

230. El Haram Mosque.

1981. 15th Century of Hegira. Multicoloured.

687. 2 um. Type **230** 10 10
688. 12 um. Medine Mosque .. 40 20
689. 14 um. Chinguetti Mosque 50 30

231. Space Shuttle in Orbit.

1981. Air. Space Shuttle. Multicoloured.

690. 12 um. Type **231** 40 20
691. 20 um. Shuttle and space station 70 30
692. 50 um. Shuttle performing experiment .. .. 1·60 75
693. 70 um. Shuttle landing .. 2·25 1·00

232. " The Harlequin ".

1981. Air. Birth Centenary of Pablo Picasso. Multicoloured.

695. 12 um. Type **232** 50 20
696. 20 um. " Vase of Flowers " 75 30
697. 50 um. " Three Women at a Fountain " (horiz.) .. 1·40 75
698. 70 um. " Dinard Landscape " (horiz.) .. .. 2·25 1·00
699. 100 um. " Le Dejeuner sur l'Herbe " (horiz.) .. 3·00 1·50

233. I.Y.D.P. Emblem.

1981. International Year of Disabled People.

700. **233.** 12 um. vio., gold & blue 45 30

234. Open Landau.

1981. British Royal Wedding. Multicoloured.

701. 14 um. Type **234** 40 20
702. 18 um. Light carriage .. 45 20
703. 77 um. Closed coupe .. 1·40 1·10

235. George Washington.

1981. Bicentenary of Battles of Yorktown and Chesapeake Bay. Multicoloured.

705. 14 um. Type **235** 45 25
706. 18 um. Admiral de Grasse 55 25
707. 63 um. Surrender of Cornwallis at Yorktown (horiz.) 1·75 95
708. 81 um. Battle of Chesapeake Bay (horiz.) .. .. 2·25 1·50

236. Columbus and " Pinta ".

1981. 450th Death Anniv. of Christopher Columbus. Multicoloured.

709. 19 um. Type **236** .. .. 1·00 40
710. 55 um. Columbus and " Santa Maria " .. 2·75 1·10

237. Wheat and F.A.O. Emblem.

238. Kemal Ataturk.

1981. World Food Day.

711. **237.** 19 um. multicoloured 60 40

1981. Birth Centenary of Kemal Ataturk (Turkish statesman).

712. **238.** 63 um. multicoloured 2·00 1·25

239. Eastern White Pelicans.

1981. Birds of the Arguin. Multicoloured.

713. 2 um. Type **239** 30 15
714. 18 um. Greater Flamingoes 1·25 70

240. Hand holding Torn Flag.

1981. Battle of Karameh Commemoration.

715. **240.** 14 um. multicoloured 45 30

241. " Dermochelys coiacer ".

1981. Turtles. Multicoloured.

716. 1 um. Type **241** 20 15
717. 3 um. " Chelonia mydas " 30 15
718. 4 um. " Eretmochelys imbricata " 35 15

242. Sea Scouts.

1982. 75th Anniv. of Boy Scout Movement. Multicoloured.

719. 14 um. Type **242** 55 25
720 19 um. Scouts boarding rowing boat 90 35
721. 22 um. Scouts in rowing boat .. .. .. 1·00 40
722. 92 um. Scouts in yacht .. 3·00 1·25

243. Deusenberg, 1921.

1982. 75th Anniv. of French Grand Prix Motor Race. Multicoloured.

724. 7 um. Type **243** 40 20
725. 12 um. Alfa Romeo, 1932 50 20
726. 14 um. Juan Fangio .. 60 35
727. 18 um. Renault, 1979 .. 75 40
728. 19 um. Niki Lauda .. 75 45

244. A.P.U. Emblem.

245. Hexagonal Pattern.

1982. 30th Anniv. of Arab Postal Union.

730. **244.** 14 um. orange & brown 45 30

1982. World Telecommunications Day.

731. **245.** 21 um. multicoloured 65 45

246. Environmental Emblem on Map.

1982. 10th Anniv. of U.N. Environmental Programme.

732. **246.** 14 um. blue & light blue 45 30

247. Princess of Wales.

1982. 21st Birthday of Princess of Wales. Multicoloured.

733. 21 um. Type **247** 75 35
734. 77 um. Princess of Wales (different) .. .. 2·40 1·10

248. Straw Hut.

1982. Traditional Houses. Multicoloured.

736. 14 um. Type **248** 45 30
737. 18 um. Thatched hut .. 55 45
738. 19 um. Tent 60 45

1982. Birth of Prince William of Wales. Nos. 701/3 surch. **NAISSANCE ROYALE 1982.**

739. 14 um. Type **234** .. 45 35
740. 18 um. Light Carriage .. 55 40
741 77 um. Closed coupe .. 2·40 1·25

1982. Air. World Cup Football Championship Results Nos 668/72 optd. **ITALIE 3 ALLEMAGNE (R.F.A.) 1.**

743. 10 um. Type **226** .. 40 25
744. 12 um. Goalkeeper punching ball 40 30
745. 14 um. Goalkeeper catching ball 45 30
746. 20 um. Three players .. 70 40
747. 67 um. Tackle .. .. 2·25 1·40

251. Cattle at Collinaire Dam, Hodh El Gharbi.

1982. Agricultural Development.

749. 14 um. Type **251** .. .. 1·25 1·10
750. 18 um. Irrigation canal, Gorgol .. .. .. 1·75 1·25

252. Desert Rose.

1982. Desert Rose.

751. **252.** 21 um. multicoloured 1·50 1·00

253. Montgolfier Balloon, 1783.

1983. Bicent. of Manned Flight. Mult.

752. 14 um. Type **253** 65 20
753. 18 um. First hydrogen balloon ascent, 1783 (horiz.) 65 30
754. 19 um. Zeppelin 65 30
755. 55 um. Nieuport biplane (horiz.) .. .. .. 1·75 70
756. 63 um. " Concorde " (horiz.) 3·00 1·00
757. 77 um. " Apollo 11 " on Moon .. .. .. 2·50 1·00

254. Ouadane.

1983. Protection of Ancient Sites. Mult.

758. 14 um. Type **254** 40 25
759. 18 um. Chinguetti .. 50 30
760. 24 um. Oualata 70 45
761. 30 um. Tichitt .. .. 1·00 55

255. Manuscript.

256. I.M.O. Emblem.

1983. Ancient Manuscripts. Multicoloured.

762. 2 um. Type **255** 10 10
763. 5 um. Decorated manuscript 15 15
764. 7 um. Shield-shaped patterned manuscript .. 25 20

1983. 25th Anniv. of I.M.O.

765. **256.** 18 um. multicoloured 50 30

257. W.C.Y. Emblem.

1983. World Communications Year.

766. **257.** 14 um. multicoloured 55 30

258. Customs Emblems.

1983. 30th Anniv. of Customs Co-operation Council.

767. **258.** 14 um. multicoloured 45 30

259. Pilatre de Rozier and Montgolfier Balloon.

260. Grinding Stone.

1983. Bicent. of Manned Flight. Mult.

768. 10 um. Type **259** (postage) 40 20
769. 14 um. John Wise and balloon " Atlantic " .. 50 30
770. 25 um. Charles Renard and dirigible " La France " (horiz.) 85 35
771. 100 um. Henri Julliot and " Patrie " (air) (horiz.) .. 3·75 1·25

1983. Prehistoric Grindstones. Multicoloured.

773. 10 um. Type **260** 50 30
774. 14 um. Pestle and mortar 75 40
775. 18 um. Grinding dish .. 1·00 60

261. Basketball.

1983. Pre-Olympic Year. Multicoloured.

776. 1 um. Type **261** (postage) 10 10
777. 20 um. Wrestling 60 25
778. 50 um. Show-jumping .. 1·50 80
779. 77 um. Running (air) .. 2·25 1·25

262. Lord Baden-Powell (founder of Scout Movement).

1984. Celebrities. Multicoloured.

781. 5 um. Type **262** (postage) 15 10
782. 14 um. Goethe (poet) .. 45 20
783. 25 um. Rubens and detail of painting " The Virgin and Child " 75 45
784. 100 um. P. Harris (founder of Rotary International) (air) .. .. .. 3·00 1·40

263. Tunny.

1984. Fishing Resources. Multicoloured.
786. 1 um. Type **263** 10 10
787. 2 um. Mackerel 10 10
788. 5 um. Hake 25 15
789. 14 um. Chinchard 70 45
790. 18 um. Building a fishing boat 85 55

264. Durer and "Madonna and Child".

1984. Multicoloured.
791. 10 um. Type **254** (postage) 35 20
792. 12 um. "Apollo 11" and astronaut (15th anniv of first manned Moon landing) 40 25
793. 50 um. Chess pieces and globe .. .. .. 2·00 80
794. 77 um. Prince and Princess of Wales (air) .. .. 2·25 1·40

265. Start of Race.

1984. Olympic Games, Los Angeles. Multicoloured.
796. 14 um. Type **265** 40 25
797. 18 um. Throwing the discus (vert.) 55 25
798. 19 um. Hurdling (vert.) .. 55 25
799. 44 um. Trowing the javelin (vert.) .. .. .. 1·25 65
800. 77 um. High jumping .. 2·00 1·25

266. Feeding Dehydrated Child from Glass.

267. Aerial View of Complex.

1984. Infant Survival Campaign. Mult.
802. 1 um. Type **266** 10 10
803. 4 um. Breast-feeding baby 15 10
804. 10 um. Vaccinating baby 30 20
805. 14 um. Weighing baby .. 45 30

1984. Nouakchott Olympic Complex.
806. **267.** 14 um. multicoloured 50 40

268. Tents and Mosque Courtyard.

1984. Pilgrimage to Mecca. Multicoloured.
807. 14 um. Type **268** 50 30
808. 18 um. Tents and court-yard (different) 75 40

269. Emblem.

1984. 10th Anniv. of West African Economic Community.
809. **269.** 14 um. multicoloured 45 30

270. S. van den Berg (windsurfing).

1984. Air. Olympic Games Yachting Gold Medallists. Multicoloured.
810. 14 um. Type **270** 55 25
811. 18 um. R. Coutts ("Finn" class) 75 25
812. 19 um. Spain ("470" class) 1·00 25
813. 44 um. U.S.A. ("Soling" class) .. .. .. 1·90 60

1984. Drought Relief. No. 537 surch. **Aide au Sahel 84.**
815. 18 um. on 10 um. mult. .. 70 50

272. Profiles and Emblem.

1985. 15th Anniv. of Technical and Cultural Co-operation Agency.
816. **272.** 18 um. blue, deep blue and red 60 45

273. Animal Drinking in Water Droplet and Skeletons.

274. Replanting Trees.

1985. Campaign against Drought. Mult.
817. 14 um. Type **273** .. .. 1·10 50
818. 18 um. Lush trees by river in water droplet and dead trees .. .. 1·10 50

1985. Anti-desertification Campaign. Mult.
819. 10 um. Type **274** 35 25
820. 14 um. Animals fleeing from forest fire 55 30
821. 18 um. Planting grass to hold sand dunes .. 65 50

275. Emblem.

1985. 30th Anniv. (1984) of Arab League.
822. **275.** 14 um. green & black 45 30

276. Map, I.Y.Y. Emblem and Youths.

1985. Air. "Philexafrique" Stamp Exhibition, Lome. Multicoloured.
823. 40 um. Type **276** (International Youth Year) .. 1·50 1·25
824. 40 um. Nouadhibou oil refinery .. .. .. 1·50 1·25

277. Bonaparte's Gulls.

1985. Air. Birth Bicentenary of John J. Audubon (ornithologist). Multicoloured.
825. 14 um. Western tanager and scarlet tanager .. 80 35
826. 18 um. Type **277** .. .. 1·00 40
827. 19 um. Blue jays .. .. 1·10 60
828. 44 um. Black skimmer .. 3·25 2·00

278. "Der Adler", 1835

1985. Anniversaries. Multicoloured.
830. 12 um. Type **278** (German railways. 150th anniv.) 60 25
831. 18 um. Class 10 locomotive, 1956 (German railways. 150th anniv.) 90 25
832. 44 um. Johann Sebastian Bach (composer, 300th birth anniv. European Music Year) .. .. 1·60 70
833. 77 um. Georg Frederick Handel (composer, 300th birth anniv. European Music Year) .. .. 2·75 1·25
834. 90 um. Statue of Liberty (centenary) (vert.) .. 2·75 1·40

279. Globe and Emblem.

1985. World Food Day.
836. **279.** 18 um. multicoloured 55 35

280. Tending Sheep and reading Book.

1985. Air. "Philexafrique" Stamp Exhibition, Lome, Togo (2nd issue). Mult.
837. 50 um. Type **280** .. .. 2·00 1·50
838. 50 um. Dock, iron ore mine and train .. .. 2·00 1·50

281. Map showing Industries.

1985. 25th Anniv. of Independence.
839. **281.** 18 um. multicoloured 60 40

282. Development.

1986. International Youth Year. Mult.
840. 18 um. Type **282** 60 30
841. 22 um. Re-afforestation (voluntary work) .. 70 40
842. 25 um. Hands reaching from globe to dove (peace) (vert.) 75 50

283. Seaplane and Map.

1986. Air. 55th Anniv. (1985) of First Commercial South Atlantic Flight. Multicoloured.
843. 18 um. Type **283** 60 35
844. 50 um. Airplanes crossing between maps of Africa and South America .. 1·75 1·25

284. Toujounine Earth Receiving Station.

1986.
845. **284.** 25 um. multicoloured 90 50

285. Heads of Mother and Pup.

1986. World Wildlife Fund. Mediterranean Monk Seal. Multicoloured.
846. 2 um. Type **285** 20 15
847. 5 um. Mother and pup on land 25 15
848. 10 um. Mother and pup swimming 40 15
849. 18 um. Seal family .. 80 25

286. Player and 1970 25 f. Stamp.

1986. Air. World Cup Football Championship, Mexico. Multicoloured.
851. 8 um. Type **286** 25 10
852. 18 um. Player and 1970 30 f. stamp 60 20
853. 22 um. Player and 1970 70 f. stamp 70 30
854. 25 um. Player and 1970 150 f. stamp 85 35
855. 40 um. Player and World Cup trophy on "stamp" 1·25 60

287. Weaving.

1986.
857. **287.** 18 um. multicoloured 60 35

288. Emblem, Airplanes and Map.

1986. Air. 25th Anniv. of Air Afrique.
858. **288.** 26 um. multicoloured 1·00 40

289. Indian, "Santa Maria" and Route Map.

1987. 500th Anniv. (1992) of Discovery of America by Christopher Columbus. Mult.
859. 2 um. Type **289** (postage) 10 10
860. 22 um. Indian, "Nina" and map 65 30
861. 35 um. Indian, "Pinta" and map .. .. .. 1·10 50
862. 150 um. Indian, map and Christopher Columbus (air) .. .. .. 4·50 1·60

290. J. H. Dort, Comet Picture and Space Probe "Giotto".

1986. Appearance of Halley's Comet. Multicoloured.
864. 5 um. Type **290** (postage) 15 10
865. 18 um. William Huggins (astronomer) and "Ariane" space rocket .. 60 20
866. 26 um. E. J. Opik and space probes "Giotto" and "Vega" 80 30
867. 80 um. F. L. Whipple and "Planet A" space probe (air) .. .. .. 2·75 1·25

291. Astronauts.

1986. "Challenger" Astronauts Commemoration. Multicoloured.
869. 7 um. Type **291** (postage) 20 10
870. 22 um. Judith Resnik and astronaut 60 30
871. 32 um. Ellison Onizuka and Ronald McNair .. 1·00 45
872. 43 um. Christa Corrigan McAuliffe (air) .. .. 1·50 60

292. Sea Bream.

1986. Fishes and Birds. Multicoloured.
874. 4 um. Type **292** 20 15
875. 22 um. White spoonbills .. 1·50 70
876. 32 um. Bridled terns .. 1·75 90
877. 98 um. Sea trout .. .. 3·25 2·25
See also Nos. 896/900.

293. Arrow through Victim. 294. Fisherman.

1986. 4th Anniv. of Massacre of Palestinian Refugees in Sabra and Shatila Camps, Lebanon.
878. **293.** 22 um. blk., gold & red 80 40

1986. World Food Day.
879. **294.** 22 um. multicoloured 80 40

295. Dome of the Rock.

1987. "Arab Jerusalem".
880. **295.** 22 um. multicoloured 80 40

296. Boxing.

1987. Air. Olympic Games, Seoul (1988) (1st issue). Multicoloured.
881. 30 um. Type **296** 80 40
882. 40 um. Judo .. .. 1·00 55
883. 50 um. Fencing .. .. 1·25 70
884. 75 um. Wrestling .. .. 2·00 1·10
See also Nos. 902/5.

297. Cordoue Mosque.

1987. 1200th Anniv. of Cordoue Mosque.
886. **297.** 30 um. multicoloured 1·00 50

298. Women's Slalom.

1987. Air. Winter Olympic Games, Calgary (1988). Multicoloured.
887. 30 um. Type **298** .. .. 1·10 40
888. 40 um. Men's speed skating 1·40 55
889. 50 um. Ice hockey .. 1·60 75
890. 75 um. Women's downhill skiing .. .. .. 2·50 1·10

299. Adults at Desks.

1987. Literacy Campaign. Multicoloured.
892. 18 um. Type **299** 60 40
893. 20 um. Adults and children reading 80 50

300. People queueing for Treatment.

1987. World Health Day.
894. **300.** 18 um. multicoloured 70 40

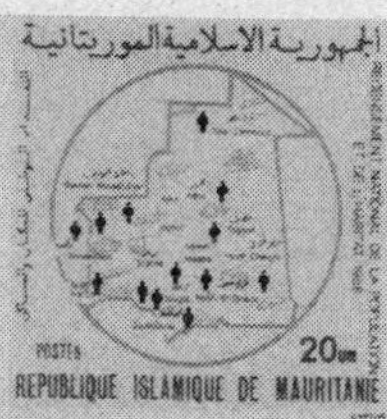
301. Map within Circle.

1988. National Population and Housing Census.
895. **301.** 20 um. multicoloured 60 35

1988. Fishes and Birds. Horiz designs as T **292**. Multicoloured.
896. 1 um. White wrasse .. 10 10
897. 7 um. Trigger fish 30 15
898. 15 um. Striped bonitos .. 50 30
899. 18 um. Cormorants .. 70 40
900. 80 um. Royal terns .. 3·00 2·00

302. People with Candles. 303. Hammer Throwing.

1988. 40th Anniv. of W.H.O.
901. **302.** 30 um. multicoloured 1·00 40

1988. Air. Olympic Games, Seoul (2nd issue). Multicoloured.
902. 20 um. Type **303** 50 25
903. 24 um. Discus 60 30
904. 30 um. Putting the shot .. 80 40
905. 150 um. Javelin throwing 4·00 2·10

1988. Winter Olympic Games Gold Medal Winners. Nos. 887/90 optd.
907 30 um. Optd **Medaille d'or/Vreni Schneider (Suisse)** .. .. 1·00 50
908 40 um. Optd **Medaille d'or/1500 m./Andre Hoffman (R.D.A.)** .. 1·10 75
909 50 um. Optd **Medaille d'or/U.R.S.S.** .. 1·50 1·00
910 75 um. Optd **Medaille d'or/Marina Kiehl (R.F.A.)** .. .. 2·25 1·50

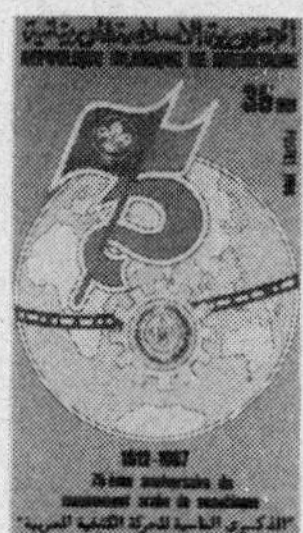
305. Flags and Globe.

1988. 75th Anniv. of Arab Scout Movement.
912. **305.** 35 um. multicoloured 1·25 55

306 Men at Ballot Box

1988. 1st Municipal Elections. Multicoloured.
913 20 um. Type **306** 60 30
914 24 um. Woman at ballot box 80 40

307 Emblem 308 Ploughing with Oxen

1988. 25th Anniv of Organization of African Unity.
915 **307** 40 um. multicoloured .. 1·25 60

1988. 10th Anniv of International Agricultural Development Fund.
916 **308** 35 um. multicoloured .. 1·10 70

309 Port Activities

1989. 1st Anniv of Nouakchott Free Port.
917 **309** 24 um. multicoloured .. 1·25 65

310 "Heliothis armigera" 311. "Nomadacris septemfasciata".

1989. Plant Pests. Multicoloured.
918 2 um. Type **310** 15 15
919 6 um. "Aphis gossypii" .. 20 15
920 10 um. "Agrotis ypsilon" 35 15
921 20 um. "Chilo sp." 75 30
922 24 um. "Plitella xylostella" 85 40
923 30 um. "Henosepilachna elaterii" .. .. 1·25 55
924 42 um. "Trichoplusia ni" 1·50 70

1989. Locusts. Multicoloured.
925 5 um. Type **311** .. 15 10
926 20 um. Locusts mating .. 60 30
927 24 um. Locusts emerging from chrysallis .. 70 40
928 40 um. Locusts flying 1·25 75
929 88 um. Locust (different) 3·00 1·25

312 Men of Different Races embracing 313 Footballers

1989. "Philexfrance '89" Int Stamp Exn., Paris, and Bicent of French Revolution.
930 **312** 35 um. multicoloured .. 1·10 60

1989. World Cup Football Championship, Italy (1990) (1st issue).
913 **313** 20 um. multicoloured .. 70 40
See also Nos. 937/41.

314 Attan'eem Migat, Mecca

1989. Pilgrimage to Mecca.

932	314	20 um. multicoloured ..	75	30

315 Emblem 317 Youths

316 Carpet

1989. 25th Anniv of African Development Bank.

933	315	37 um. black & mauve	1·00	50

1989.

934	316	50 um. multicoloured ..	1·50	80

1989. 2nd Anniv of Palestinian "Intifida" Movement.

935	317	35 um. multicoloured ..	1·25	50

318 Member Countries' Leaders (½ size Illustration)

1990. 1st Anniv of Arab Maghreb Union.

936	318	50 um. multicoloured ..	1·50	70

319 Players 320 Envelopes on Map

1990. Air. World Cup Football Championship, Italy (2nd issue).

937	319	50 um. multicoloured	1·50	50
938	–	60 um. multicoloured	1·90	60
939	–	70 um. multicoloured	2·00	75
940	–	90 um. multicoloured	2·75	75
941	–	150 um. multicoloured	4·50	1·25

DESIGNS: 60 to 150 um. Show footballers.

1990. 20th Anniv of Multinational Postal Training School, Abidjan.

942	320	50 um. multicoloured ..	1·10	50

321 Books and Desk

1990. International Literacy Year.

943	321	60 um. multicoloured ..	1·75	1·00

322 Maps and Earth-moving Vehicles

1990. Mineral Resources.

944	322	60 um. multicoloured ..	2·25	1·25

323 Dressage 324 Emblem

1990. Olympic Games, Barcelona (1992). Mult.

945		5 um. Type **323** (postage)	20	15
946		50 um. Archery	1·40	40
947		60 um. Throwing the hammer	1·50	50
948		75 um. Football	2·00	50
949		90 um. Basketball ..	2·75	65
950		220 um. Table tennis (air)	6·00	1·40

1990. 2nd Anniv of Declaration of State of Palestine.

952	234	85 um. multicoloured ..	1·75	1·10

325 Camp

1990. Integration of Repatriates from Senegal. Multicoloured.

953		50 um. Type **325**	90	60
954		75 um. Women's sewing group	1·25	1·00
955		85 um. Water collection ..	1·40	1·00

326 Map, Dove and Mandela

1990. Release from South African Prison of Nelson Mandela.

956	326	85 um. multicoloured ..	1·60	1·10

327 Downhill skiing

1990. Winter Olympic Games, Albertville (1992). Multicoloured.

957		60 um. Type **327** (postage)	1·00	60
958		75 um. Cross-country skiing	1·50	75
959		90 um. Ice hockey ..	1·75	95
960		220 um. Figure skating (pairs) (air)	3·75	2·25

328 Blue Leg

1991. Scouts, Fungi and Butterflies. Mult.

962		5 um. Type **328** (postage)	15	10
963		50 um. "Agaricus bitorquis edulis"	1·40	60
964		60 um. "Bunea alcinoe" (butterfly)	2·00	75
965		90 um. "Salamis cytora" (butterfly)	2·50	1·10
966		220 um. "Bronze boletus"	4·50	2·25
967		75 um. "Cyrestis camillus" (butterfly) (air) ..	2·00	85

329 Dish Aerials and Transmitting Tower

330 Woman carrying Bucket of Water

1991. 30th Anniv of Independence. Mult.

968		50 um. Type **329** ..	1·00	65
969		60 um. Container ship in dock	2·00	85
970		100 um. Workers in field ..	1·75	1·00

1991. World Meteorological Day.

972	330	100 um. multicoloured	1·75	1·10

331 Health Centre

1991. 20th Anniv of Medecins sans Frontieres (international medical relief organization).

973	331	60 um. multicoloured ..	70	45

332 Cats

1991. Domestic Animals. Multicoloured.

974		50 um. Type **332**	55	35
975		60 um. Basenji dog ..	70	45

333 Globe and Stylized Figures

1991. World Population Day.

976	333	90 um. multicoloured ..	1·00	60

334 Blind Woman with Sight restored

1991. Anti-blindness Campaign.

977	334	50 um. multicoloured ..	55	35

335 Nouakchott Electricity Station

1991. 2nd Anniv of Nouakchott Electricity Station.

978	335	50 um. multicoloured ..	55	35

OFFICIAL STAMPS

O **41.** Cross of Trarza. O **179.**

1961.

O 150.	O **41.**	1 f. purple and blue	10	10
O 151.		3 f. myrtle and red ..	10	10
O 152.		5 f. brown & green ..	10	10
O 153.		10 f. blue and turq.	20	10
O 154.		15 f. orange and blue	30	15
O 155.		20 f. green & myrtle	35	20
O 156.		25 f. red and orange	40	30
O 157.		30 f. green & purple	45	30
O 158.		50 f. sepia and red ..	1·00	45
O 159.		100 f. blue & orange	1·60	75
O 160.		200 f. red and green	3·00	1·60

1976.

O 502.	O **179.**	1 u. multicoloured ..	10	10
O 503.		2 u. multicoloured ..	15	10
O 504.		5 u. multicoloured ..	20	15
O 505.		10 u. multicoloured	40	20
O 506.		12 u. multicoloured	55	30
O 507.		40 u. multicoloured	1·75	1·00
O 508.		50 u. multicoloured	2·25	1·25

POSTAGE DUE STAMPS

1906. Stamps of 1906 optd **T** in a triangle.

D18	I	5 c. green and red ..	–	27·00
D19		10 c. pink and blue	–	27·00
D20	J	20 c. black & red on blue	–	40·00
D21		25 c. blue and red ..	–	40·00
D22		30 c. brn & red on pink	–	£110
D23		50 c. violet and red ..	–	£110
D24	K	1 f. black & red on blue	–	£160

1906. "Natives" key-type inscr "MAURITANIE" in blue (10, 30 c.) or red (others).

D25	L	5 c. green	1·25	1·25
D26		10 c. purple	1·75	1·75
D27		15 c. blue on blue ..	4·00	3·25
D28		20 c. black on yellow ..	6·00	6·00
D29		30 c. red on cream ..	6·00	6·75
D30		50 c. violet	9·25	9·25
D31		60 c. black on buff ..	6·50	6·75
D32		1 f. black on pink ..	11·50	9·25

1914. "Figure" key-type inscr. "MAURITANIE".

D 35.	M.	5 c. green	10	25
D 36.		10 c. red	15	25
D 37.		15 c. grey	15	30
D 38.		20 brown	15	30
D 39.		30 c. blue	25	40
D 40.		50 c. black	50	95
D 41.		60 c. orange	40	50
D 42.		1 f. violet	60	80

1927. Surch. in figures.

D 67.	M.	2 F. on 1 f. purple ..	1·25	1·75
D 68.		3 F. on 1 f. brown ..	1·25	2·00

D **40.** Qualata Motif. D **55.** Ruppell's Griffon.

1961.

D 150.	D **40.**	1 f. yellow and purple	10	10
D 151.		2 f. grey and red ..	10	10
D 152.		5 f. pink and red ..	20	15
D 153.		10 f. green & myrtle	25	15
D 154.		15 f. brown and drab	30	15
D 155.		20 f. blue and red ..	35	20
D 156.		25 f. red and green ..	55	35

1963. Birds. Multicoloured.

D 177.	50 c. Type D **55**	45	20
D 178.	50 c. Common crane ..	45	20
D 179.	1 f. Eastern white pelican	55	25
D 180.	1 f. Garganey	55	25
D 181.	2 f. Golden oriole ..	65	25
D 182.	2 f. Variable sunbird ..	65	25
D 183.	5 f. Great snipe	75	55
D 184.	5 f. Common shoveler ..	75	55
D 185.	10 f. Vulturine guinea-fowl	1·40	1·00
D 186.	10 f. Black stork ..	1·40	1·00
D 187.	15 f. Grey heron.. ..	1·60	1·40
D 188.	15 f. White stork ..	1·60	1·40
D 189.	20 f. Paradise whydah ..	1·90	1·60
D 190.	20 f. Red-legged partridge	1·90	1·60
D 191.	25 f. Little stint.. ..	2·25	2·00
D 192.	25 f. Arabian bustard ..	2·25	2·00

D **180.**

1976.

D 509.	D **180.**	1 u. multicoloured	10	10
D 510.		3 u. multicoloured	15	15
D 511.		10 u. multicoloured	35	35
D 512.		12 u. multicoloured	40	40
D 513.		20 u. multicoloured	70	70

APPENDIX

The following stamps have either been issued in excess of postal needs or have not been available to the public in a reasonable quantities at face value. Such stamps may later be given full listing if there is evidence of regular postal use.

1962.

World Refugee Year (1960). Optd. on 1960–61 Definitive issue, 30, 50, 60 f.

Olympic Games in Rome (1960) and Tokyo (1964). Surch. on 1960–61 Definitive issue 75 f. on 15 f., 75 f. on 20 f.

European Coal and Steel Community and Exploration of Iron-ore in Mauritania. Optd. on 1960–61 Definitive issue. Air 500 f.

Malaria Eradication. Optd. on 1960–61 Definitive issue. Air. 100, 200 f.

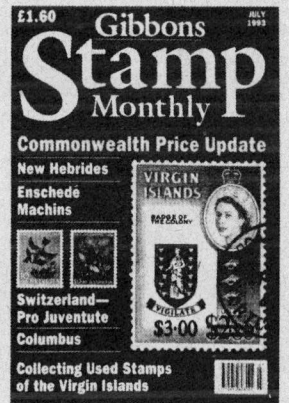

MAYOTTE Pt. 6

One of the Comoro Is. adjacent to Madagascar.

100 centimes = 1 franc.

1892. "Tablet" key-type inscr "MAYOTTE".

1	D	1 c. black and red on blue	40	40
2		2 c. brown & blue on buff	50	50
3		4 c. brown & blue on grey	70	60
4		5 c. green & red on green	1·50	1·00
5		10 c. black & blue on lilac	2·00	2·00
15		10 c. red and blue ..	26·00	20·00
6		15 c. blue and red ..	6·00	4·00
16		15 c. grey and red ..	60·00	45·00
7		20 c. red & blue on green	5·25	4·50
8		25 c. black & red on pink	3·75	2·50
17		25 c. blue and red ..	4·00	3·50
9		30 c. brown & bl on drab	8·25	5·75
18		35 c. black & red on yell	2·50	2·50
10		40 c. red & blue on yellow	6·75	5·75
19		45 c. black on green	7·50	6·00
11		50 c. red and blue on pink	12·50	8·00
20		50 c. brown & red on blue	6·25	8·25
12		75 c. brown & red on orge	14·00	9·00
13		1 f. green and red ..	10·50	8·00
14		5 f. mauve & blue on lilac	70·00	60·00

1912. Surch in figures.

21	D	05 on 20 c. brown and blue on buff	90	90
22		05 on 4 c. brown and blue on grey	35	30
23		05 on 15 c. blue and red	50	50
24		05 on 20 c. red and blue on green	50	60
25		05 on 25 c. black and red on pink	50	60
26		05 on 30 c. brown and blue on drab	60	65
27		10 on 40 c. red and blue on yellow	50	70
28		10 on 45 c. black and red on green	55	55
29		10 on 50 c. red and blue on pink	1·50	1·75
30		10 on 75 c. brown and red on orange	85	1·00
31		10 on 1 f. green and red	1·00	1·10

MECKLENBURG-SCHWERIN Pt. 7

In northern Germany. Formerly a Grand Duchy, Mecklenburg-Schwerin joined the North German Confederation in 1868.

48 schilling = 1 thaler.

1. 2.

1856. Imperf.

1a	1	¼ s. red	9·50	8·00
1		⁴⁄₄ s. red	£130	£110
3	2	3 s. yellow	75·00	42·00
4		5 s. blue	£200	£250

See note below No. 7.

1864. Roul.

5a	1	¼ s. red	£120	£140
6a		¼ s. red	6·00	6·00
5		⁴⁄₄ s. red	£2250	£1800
6		⁴⁄₄ s. red	48·00	48·00
11	2	2 s. purple	£200	£225
9		3 s. yellow	£150	95·00
7		5 s. bistre	£130	£225

Nos. 1, 1a, 5, 5a have a dotted background, Nos. 6 and 6a a plain background. Prices for Nos. 1a, 5a and 6a are for quarter stamps; prices for Nos. 1, 5 and 6 are for the complete stamp (four quarters) as illustrated in Type 1.

MECKLENBURG-STRELITZ Pt. 7

In northern Germany. Formerly a Grand Duchy, Mecklenburg-Strelitz joined the North German Confederation in 1868.

30 silbergroschen = 1 thaler.

1 2

1864. Roul. Various frames.

2	1	¼ sgr. orange	£150	£2250
3		⅓ sgr. green	50·00	£1200
6		1 sch. mauve	£275	£3500
7	2	1 sgr. red.. ..	£130	£190
9		2 sgr. blue	28·00	£750
11		3 sgr. bistre	28·00	£1200

MEMEL Pt. 7

A seaport and district on the Baltic Sea, formerly part of Germany. Under Allied control after the 1914–18 war, it was captured and absorbed by Lithuania in 1923 and returned to Germany in 1939. From 1945 the area has been part of Lithuania.

1920. 100 pfennig = 1 mark.
16.4.23. 100 centu = 1 litas.

1920. Stamps of France surch **MEMEL** and **pfennig** or **mark** with figure of value.

1.	18.	5 pf. on 5 c. green ..	10	20
2.		10 pf. on 10 c. red ..	10	20
3.		20 pf. on 25 c. blue ..	10	20
4.		30 pf. on 30 c. orange ..	10	20
5.		40 pf. on 20 c. brown ..	10	20
6.		50 pf. on 35 c. violet ..	10	35
7.	13.	60 pf. on 40 c. red & blue	20	55
8.		80 pf. on 45 c. grn. & blue	15	35
9.		1 m. on 50 c. brown & lav.	10	20
10.		1 m. 25 on 60 c. vio. & blue	70	1·75
11.		2 m. on 1 f. red and yellow	15	25
12.		3 m. on 2 f. orge. & grn.	9·00	22·00
13.		3 m. on 5 f. blue & yellow	9·50	22·00
14.		4 m. on 2 f. orge. & green	15	35
15.		10 m. on 5 f. blue & yellow	1·50	4·00
16.		20 m. on 5 f. blue & yell.	30·00	55·00

1920. Stamps of Germany inscr. "DEUTSCHES REICH" optd. **Memel-gebiet** or **Memelgebiet.**

17.	10.	5 pf. green	20	35
18.		10 pf. red	2·00	6·50
19.		10 pf. orange	15	35
20.	24.	15 pf. purple	2·25	6·00
21.	10.	20 pf. blue	15	15
22.		30 pf. blk. & orge. on buff	1·25	2·00
23.		30 pf. blue	15	35
24.		40 pf. black and red ..	10	15
25.		50 pf. blk. & pur. on buff	10	15
26.		60 pf. olive	45	2·00
27.		75 pf. black and green ..	2·00	5·00
28.		80 pf. blue	90	2·75
29.		1 m. red	20	45
30.		1 m. 25 green	11·00	26·00
31.		1 m. 50 brown	3·50	7·00
32.	13.	2 m. blue	1·50	3·25
33.		2 m. 50 red	9·50	22·00

The following are all surch. on stamps of France.

1921. Stamps of 1920 further surch in large figures.

34	18	15 on 10 pf. on 10 c. red	15	35
35		15 on 20 pf. on 25 c. blue	20	55
36		15 on 50 pf. on 35 c. violet	15	45
37	13	60 on 40 pf. on 20 c. brn	15	15
38		75 on 60 pf. on 40 c. red and blue	40	1·00
39		1,25 on 1 m. on 50 c. brown and lavender ..	15	40
40		5,00 on 2 m. on 1 f. red and yellow	45	1·25

1921. Surch **MEMEL** and **Pfennig** or **Mark** with figure of value.

54	18	5 pf. on 5 c. orange ..	10	20
55		10 pf. on 10 c. red ..	40	1·10
56		10 pf. on 10 c. green ..	10	20
57		15 pf. on 10 c. green ..	10	30
58		20 pf. on 20 c. brown ..	2·75	8·50
59		20 pf. on 25 c. blue ..	2·75	8·50
60		25 pf. on 5 c. orange ..	10	15
61		30 pf. on 30 c. red ..	40	1·75
86		35 pf. on 35 c. violet ..	10	20
64	13	40 pf. on 40 c. red & blue	10	15
62	15	50 pf. on 50 c. blue ..	10	15
41	13	60 pf. on 40 c. red & blue	2·25	6·50
87	15	75 pf. on 15 c. green ..	10	15
63	18	75 pf. on 35 c. violet ..	10	15
65	13	80 pf. on 45 c. grn & bl	10	15
88	18	1 m. on 25 c. blue ..	10	15
66	13	1 m. on 40 c. red & blue	10	15
89	18	1¼ m. on 30 c. red ..	10	20
67	13	1 m. 25 on 60 c. vio & bl	10	20
68		1 m. 50 on 45 c. grn & bl	10	25
90		2 m. on 45 c. green & bl	10	20
69		2 m. on 1 f. red & green	10	20
91		2¼ m. on 40 c. red & blue	10	20
92		2¼ m. on 60 c. vio & bl	20	25
113	18	3 m. on 5 c. orange ..	10	1·10
70	13	3 m. on 60 m. vio & bl	45	85
93		4 m. om 45 c. green & bl	10	15
71		5 m. on 1 f. red & green	15	45
114	15	6 m. on 15 c. green ..	15	80
94	13	6 m. on 60 c. violet & bl	10	15
72		6 m. on 2 f. orge & grn	15	45
115	18	8 m. on 30 c. red ..	35	2·25
95	13	9 m. on 1 f. red & green	15	30
73		9 m. on 5 f. blue & buff	20	60
116		10 m. on 45 c. green & bl	35	1·00
43		10 m. on 5 f. blue & buff	55	1·40
96		12 m. on 40 c. red & blue	15	30
117		20 m. on 40 c. red & blue	35	1·60
44		20 m. on 45 c. green & bl	2·75	10·00
97		20 m. on 2 f. orge & grn	15	40
118		30 m. on 60 c. violet & bl	35	1·50
98		30 m. on 5 f. blue & buff	2·25	6·50
119		40 m. on 1 f. red & green	35	1·75
99		50 m. on 2 f. orge & grn	7·00	18·00
120		80 m. on 2 f. orge & grn	35	1·75
121		100 m. on 5 f. bl & buff	45	3·00

1921. Air. Optd **FLUGPOST** in double-lined letters.

47	13	60 pf. on 40 c. red and blue (No. 7)	22·00	60·00
48		60 pf. on 40 c. red and blue (No. 41)	2·00	6·50
49		80 pf. on 45 c. green & bl	2·00	6·00
50		1 m. on 50 c. brown & lav	1·40	4·50
51		2 m. on 1 f. red & yellow	2·00	4·50
52		3 m. on 60 c. violet and blue (No. 42)	2·00	6·50
53		4 m. on 2 f. orange & grn	2·25	10·00

1922. Air. Optd **Flugpost** in script letters.

74	13	40 pf. on 40 c. red and blue (No. 64)	25	1·00
75		80 pf. on 45 c. green and blue (No. 65)	25	1·00
76		1 m. on 40 c. red and blue (No. 66)	25	1·00
77		1 m. 25 on 60 c. violet and blue (No. 67) ..	40	1·75
78		1 m. 50 on 45 c. green and blue (No. 68)	40	1·75
79		2 m. on 1 f. red and green (No. 69)	40	1·75
80		3 m. on 60 c. violet and blue (No. 70)	40	1·75
81		3 m. on 60 c. violet and blue (No. 70)	90·00	£550
82		4 m. on 2 f. orange and green (No. 14) ..	40	1·75
83		5 m. on 1 f. red and green (No. 71)	45	2·00
84		6 m. on 2 f. orange and green (No. 72) ..	45	2·00
85		9 m. on 5 f. blue and buff (No. 73)	55	2·00

1922. air. Surch as in 1921 and optd **FLUGPOST** in ordinary capitals.

100.	13.	40 pf. on 40 c. red & bl.	80	6·00
101.		1 m. on 40 c. red & blue	80	6·00
102.		1 m. 25 on 60 c. violet and blue	80	6·00
103.		1 m. 50 on 45 c. green and blue	80	6·00
104.		2 m. on 1 f. brn. & yellow	80	6·00
105.		3 m. on 60 c. violet & bl.	80	6·00
106.		4 m. on 2 f. orge. & grn.	80	6·00
107.		5 m. on 1 f. brn. & yell.	80	6·00
108.		6 m. on 2 f. orge. & grn.	80	6·00
109.		9 m. on 5 f. blue & brn.	80	6·00

1922. Surch as in 1921 but with additional surch **Mark** obliterating **Pfennig**.

110.	18.	10 m. on 10 pf. on 10 c. green (No. 56) ..	50	2·50
111.		20 m. on 20 pf. on 20 c. brown (No. 58) ..	40	85
112.	15.	50 m. on 50 pf. on 50 c. blue (No. 62) ..	1·25	5·50

1923. Nos. 64 and 67 with additional surch.

122.	13.	(40) Mark on 40 pf. on 40 c. red and blue ..	40	1·25
123.		"80" on 1 m. 25 on 60 c. violet and blue..	40	1·75

1923. Nos. 90 and 88 surch. with large figures.

124.	13.	10 on 2 m. on 45 c. green and blue	85	2·50
125.	18.	25 on 1 m. on 25 c. blue	85	2·50

LITHUANIAN OCCUPATION

The port and district of Memel was captured by Lithuanian forces in 1923 and incorporated in Lithuania.

1. 5.

1923. Surch. **KLAIPEDA (MEMEL)** and value over curved line and **MARKIU.**

1.	1.	10 m. on 5 c. blue ..	35	75
2.		25 m. on 5 c. blue ..	35	75
3.		50 m. on 25 c. red ..	35	75
4.		100 m. on 25 c. red ..	50	1·40
5.		400 m. on 1 l. brown ..	1·25	2·50

1923. Surch. **Klaipeda (Memel)** and value over two straight lines and **Markiu.**

6.	1.	10 m. on 5 c. blue ..	65	1·75
7.		25 m. on 5 c. blue ..	65	1·75
8.		50 m. on 25 c. red ..	65	1·75
9.		100 m. on 25 c. red ..	65	1·75
10.		400 m. on 1 l. brown ..	70	2·25
11.		500 m. on 1 l. brown ..	70	2·25

1923. Surch. **KLAIPEDA (Memel)** and value over four stars and **MARKIU.**

12.	1.	10 m. on 5 c. blue ..	55	1·75
13.		20 m. on 5 c. blue ..	55	1·75
14.		25 m. on 24 c. red ..	55	1·75
15.		50 m. on 25 c. red ..	65	2·25
16.		100 m. on 1 l. brown ..	80	2·75
17.		200 m. on 1 l. brown ..	80	2·75

1923.

18.	5.	10 m. brown	20	45
19.		20 m. yellow	20	45
20.		25 m. orange	20	45
21.		40 m. violet	20	45
22.		50 m. green	75	85
23.		100 m. red	40	40
24.		300 m. olive	2·50	45·00
25.		400 m. brown	45	65
26.		500 m. purple	2·50	45·00
27.		1,000 m. blue	65	80

7. Memel Port. 8. Memel Arms. 9. Memel Lighthouse.

1923. Uniting of Memel with Lithuania and amalgamation of Memel Harbours.

28.	7.	40 m. olive	2·50	10·00
29.		50 m. brown	2·50	10·00
30.		80 m. green	2·50	10·00
31.		100 m. red	2·50	10·00
32.	8.	200 m. blue	2·50	10·00
33.		300 m. brown	2·50	10·00
34.		400 m. purple	2·50	10·00
35.		500 m. orange	2·50	10·00
36.		600 m. olive	2·50	10·00
37.	9.	800 m. blue	2·50	10·00
38.		1000 m. purple	2·50	10·00
39.		2000 m. red	2·50	10·00
40.		3000 m. green	2·50	10·00

1923. No. 123 of Memel surch. **Klaipeda,** value and large **M** between bars, sideways.

41.		100 on 80 on 1 m. 25 on 60 c.	3·25	8·50
42.		400 m. on 80 on 1 m. 25 on 60 c.	3·25	8·50
43.		500 m. on 80 on 1 m. 25 on 60 c.	3·25	8·50

1923. Surch (thin or thick figures) in **CENT.** or **LITAS** and bars.

60	5	2 c. on 10 m. brown ..	1·25	5·50
44		2 c. on 20 m. yellow ..	2·25	3·25
45		2 c. on 50 m. green ..	2·25	3·25
63		3 c. on 10 m. brown ..	2·00	5·50
46		3 c. on 40 m. violet ..	2·50	3·50
47		3 c. on 300 m. olive ..	2·50	3·50
48		5 c. on 100 m. red ..	2·50	3·50
49		5 c. on 300 m. olive ..	3·00	4·25
50		10 c. on 400 m. brown ..	5·00	7·00
67		15 c. on 25 m. orange ..	70·00	£350
51		30 c. on 500 m. purple ..	3·00	3·50
68		50 c. on 1000 m. blue ..	1·50	4·75
69		1 l. on 1000 m. blue ..	3·25	9·00

1923. Surch in **CENTU** and bars.

53.	5.	2 c. on 300 m. olive ..	3·75	6·25
54.		3 c. on 300 m. olive ..	3·75	6·25
55.		10 c. on 25 m. orange ..	3·75	6·25
56.		15 c. on 25 m. orange ..	3·75	6·25
57.		20 c. on 500 m. purple ..	3·75	7·75
58.		30 c. on 500 m. purple ..	3·75	6·25
59.		50 c. on 500 m. purple ..	10·00	17·00

1923. Surch in **CENT.** or **LITAS**.

70.	7.	15 c. on 40 m. olive ..	3·25	12·00
71.		30 c. on 50 m. brown ..	2·50	6·50
72.		30 c. on 80 m. green ..	3·25	10·00
73.		30 c. on 100 m. red ..	2·50	6·50
74.	8.	50 c. on 200 m. blue ..	3·25	10·00
75.		50 c. on 300 m. brown ..	2·50	6·50
76.		50 c. on 400 m. purple ..	3·25	11·00
77.		50 c. on 500 m. orange ..	2·50	6·50
78.		1 l. on 600 m. olive ..	3·25	11·00
79.	9.	1 l. on 800 m. blue ..	3·25	11·00
80.		1 l. on 1000 m. purple ..	3·25	11·00
81.		1 l. on 2000 m. red ..	3·25	11·00
82.		1 l. on 3000 m. green ..	3·25	11·00

1923. Surch. in large figures and **Centu** and bars reading upwards.

83.	1.	10 c. on 25 m. on 5 c. blue (No. 2)	17·00	40·00
84.		15 c. on 100 m. on 25 c. red (No. 4)	20·00	£110
85.		30 c. on 400 m. on 1 l. brown (No. 5) ..	4·00	16·00
86.		60 c. on 50 m. on 25 c. red (No. 8)	20·00	£130

1923. Surch. in large figures and **CENT.** and bars.

87.	7.	15 c. on 50 m. brown ..	£225	£450
88.		25 c. on 100 m. red ..	£110	£225
89.	8.	30 c. on 300 m. brown ..	£180	£1000
90.		60 c. on 500 m. orange ..	£110	£900

1923. Surch in **Centu** or **Centai** (25 c.) between bars.

91.	5.	15 c. on 10 m. brown ..	5·00	20·00
92.		15 c. on 20 m. yellow ..	2·25	10·00
93.		15 c. on 25 m. orange ..	2·75	12·00
94.		15 c. on 40 m. violet ..	2·25	10·00
95.		15 c. on 50 m. green ..	1·50	8·00
96.		15 c. on 100 m. red ..	1·50	8·00
97.		15 c. on 400 m. brown..	1·25	6·00
98.		15 c. on 1000 m. blue ..	45·00	£250
99.		25 c. on 10 m. brown ..	3·25	16·00
100.		25 c. on 20 m. yellow ..	2·25	9·50
101.		25 c. on 25 m. orange ..	2·75	12·00
102.		25 c. on 40 m. violet ..	2·25	10·00
103.		25 c. on 50 m. green ..	1·40	7·50
104.		25 c. on 100 m. red ..	1·40	7·50
105.		25 c. on 400 m. brown..	1·25	6·00
106.		25 c. on 1000 m. blue ..	50·00	£275
107.		30 c. on 10 m. brown ..	4·50	19·00
108.		30 c. on 20 m. yellow ..	2·50	10·00
109.		30 c. on 25 m. orange ..	3·25	12·00
110.		30 c. on 40 m. violet ..	2·50	10·00
111.		30 c. on 50 m. green ..	1·40	6·50
112.		30 c. on 100 m. red ..	1·40	7·00
113.		30 c. on 400 m. brown..	1·25	6·00
114.		30 c. on 1000 m. blue ..	45·00	£250

INDEX

Countries can be quickly located by referring to the index at the end of this volume.

MEXICO Pt. 15

A republic of Central America. From 1864-67 an Empire under Maximilian of Austria.

8 reales = 100 centavos = 1 peso.

1. Miguel Hidalgo y Costilla. 2.

1856. With or without optd district name. Imperf.

1c 1 ½ r. blue .. .. 12·50 14·00
8c ½ r. black on buff .. 12·50 17·00
6 1 r. orange .. .. 11·00 1·60
9b 1 r. black on green .. 2·50 2·75
7b 2 r. green .. .. 10·50 1·60
10c 2 r. black on red .. 1·40 3·25
4b 4 r. red .. .. 55·00 75·00
11b 4 r. black on yellow .. 22·00 35·00
12a 4 r. red on yellow .. 50·00 60·00
5c 8 r. lilac .. .. 75·00 95·00
13a 8 r. black on brown .. 48·00 95·00
14a 8 r. green on brown .. 60·00 80·00

1864. Perf.

15a. 2. 1 r. red 10
16a. 2 r. blue 15
17a. 4 r. brown 25
18a. 1 p. black 95

3. Arms of Mexico. 4. Emperor Maximilian.

1864. Imperf.

30 3 3 c. brown £600 £1200
19a ½ r. brown .. .. 85·00 £225
31 ½ r. purple .. .. 35·00 28·00
31c ½ r. grey .. .. 40·00 40·00
32b 1 r. blue .. .. 8·25 5·00
33 2 r. orange .. .. 2·50 1·60
34 4 r. green .. .. 55·00 32·00
35b 8 r. red .. .. 80·00 48·00

1864. Imperf.

40. 4. 7 c. purple £225 £2500
36c. 7 c. grey .. .. 32·00 60·00
41. 13 c. blue .. .. 3·75 5·50
42. 25 c. orange .. .. 3·25 5·00
39c. 50 c. green .. .. 11·50 11·50

7. Hidalgo. 8. Hidalgo. 9. Hidalgo.

10. Hidalgo. 15. Benito Juarez. 16.

1868. Imperf. or perf.

67. 7. 6 c. black on brown .. 4·50 2·50
68. 12 c. black on green .. 1·90 60
69. 25 c. blue on pink .. 3·50 45
70b. 50 c. black on yellow .. 60·00 7·50
71. 100 c. black on brown .. 60·00 22·00
76. 100 c. brown on brown .. 95·00 28·00

1872. Imperf. or perf.

87. 8. 6 c. green .. .. 6·25 6·25
88. 12 c. blue 80 65
94. 25 c. red .. .. 3·50 75
90. 50 c. yellow .. .. 70·00 16·00
91. 100 c. lilac .. .. 48·00 25·00

1874. Various frames. Perf.

102a. 9. 4 c. orange .. .. 3·50 6·25
97. 10. 5 c. brown .. .. 2·10 1·40
98. 9. 10 c. black 85 50
105. 10 c. orange 85 50
99. 10. 25 c. blue 35 30
107. 9. 50 c. green .. .. 7·00 6·25
108. 100 c. red .. .. 9·50 8·25

1879.

115 15 1 c. brown .. .. 1·90 1·75
116 2 c. violet .. .. 1·75 1·50
117 5 c. orange .. .. 1·25 60
118 10 c. blue .. .. 1·60 1·25
127a 10 c. brown .. .. 1·25
128 12 c. brown .. .. 3·25 3·25
129 18 c. brown .. .. 3·75 3·25
130 24 c. mauve .. .. 3·75 3·25
119 25 c. red .. .. 4·00 4·75
132 25 c. brown .. .. 2·10
120 50 c. green .. .. 6·25 6·00
134 50 c. yellow .. .. 35·00 38·00
121 85 c. violet .. .. 11·00 9·50
122 100 c. black .. .. 12·50 11·00
137 100 c. orange .. .. 40·00 48·00

1882.

138. 16. 2 c. green .. .. 3·25 2·50
139. 3 c. red .. .. 3·25 2·50
140. 6 c. blue .. .. 2·50 1·90

17. Hidalgo. 18.

1884.

141. 17. 1 c. green .. .. 1·25 15
142. 2 c. green .. .. 1·90 25
157. 2 c. red .. .. 6·25 1·40
143. 3 c. green .. .. 3·75 80
158. 3 c. brown .. .. 8·75 2·50
144. 4 c. green .. .. 5·00 80
159. 4 c. red .. .. 12·50 7·50
145. 5 c. green .. .. 5·00 60
160. 5 c. blue .. .. 8·75 1·60
146. 6 c. green .. .. 4·50 45
161. 6 c. brown .. .. 10·00 2·50
147. 10 c. green .. .. 4·75 15
162. 10 c. orange .. .. 7·50 45
148. 12 c. green .. .. 8·75 1·25
163. 12 c. brown .. .. 16·00 3·75
149. 20 c. green .. .. 25·00 95
150. 25 c. green .. .. 45·00 1·90
164. 25 c. blue .. .. 55·00 8·75
151. 50 c. green .. .. 40 1·25
152. 1 p. blue .. .. 40 4·75
153. 2 p. blue .. .. 40 8·75
154. 5 p. blue .. .. £120 80·00
155. 10 p. blue .. .. £170 95·00

1886.

196. 18. 1 c. green 30 10
209. 2 c. red 35 10
167. 3 c. lilac .. .. 2·50 1·25
189. 3 c. red 30 10
198. 3 c. orange 95 35
168. 4 c. lilac .. .. 4·50 95
211. 4 c. red 75 50
199. 4 c. orange .. .. 1·10 50
191. 5 c. blue 20 10
170. 6 c. lilac .. .. 5·00 60
213. 6 c. red 95 60
200. 6 c. orange .. .. 1·40 35
171. 10 c. lilac .. .. 5·00 15
193. 10 c. red 10 10
185a. 10 c. brown .. .. 8·75 1·90
201. 10 c. orange .. .. 7·50 35
172. 12 c. lilac .. .. 5·00 3·25
215. 12 c. red .. .. 3·25 3·75
173. 20 c. lilac .. .. 40·00 22·00
194. 20 c. red 50 20
202. 20 c. orange .. .. 12·50 1·60
174. 25 c. lilac .. .. 16·00 3·75
217. 25 c. red 95 25
203. 25 c. orange .. .. 4·00 1·10
206. 5 p. red £350 £225
207. 10 p. red £550 £350

19. Foot Postman. 20. Mounted Postman and Pack Mules. 21. Statue of Cuauhtemoc.

22. Mailcoach. 23. Steam Train.

1895.

253. 19. 1 c. green 20 10
219. 2 c. red 30 10
220. 3 c. brown 30 10
221. 20. 4 c. orange .. .. 1·50 25
257. 21. 5 c. blue 35 10
223. 22. 10 c. purple 50 10
224. 20. 12 c. olive .. .. 8·25 3·75
225. 22. 15 c. blue .. .. 4·00 80
226. 20 c. red .. .. 4·00 40
227. 50 c. mauve .. .. 12·00 4·75
228. 23. 1 p. brown .. .. 23·00 11·50
229. 5 p. red .. .. 80·00 48·00
230. 10 p. blue .. .. £130 85·00

27. 28. Juanacatlan Falls.

29. Popocatepetl. 30. Cathedral, Mexico.

1899. Various frames for T 27.

266. 27. 1 c. green 80 10
276. 1 c. purple 60 10
267. 2 c. red .. .. 2·40 10
277. 2 c. green 80 10
268. 3 c. brown .. .. 1·60 10
278. 4 c. red .. .. 2·50 20
269. 5 c. blue .. .. 2·50 10
279. 5 c. orange 45 10
270. 10 c. brown and purple 3·25 15
280. 10 c. orange and blue .. 2·50 10
271. 15 c. purple & lavender 4·25 10
272. 20 c. blue and red .. 4·75 15
273a. 28. 50 c. black and purple 19·00 1·25
281. 50 c. black and red .. 40·00 3·50
274. 29. 1 p. black and blue .. 42·00 1·90
275. 30. 5 p. black and red .. £130 6·25

32. Josefa Ortiz. 40. Hidalgo at Dolores.

1910. Cent. of First Independence Movement.

282. 32. 1 c. purple 10 10
283. – 2 c. green 10 10
284. – 3 c. brown 25 10
285. – 4 c. red .. .. 1·25 20
286. – 5 c. orange 10 10
287. – 10 c. orange and blue .. 80 10
288. – 15 c. lake and slate .. 4·50 20
289. – 20 c. blue and lake .. 2·50 10
290. 40. 50 c. black and brown .. 6·25 95
291. – 1 p. black and blue .. 7·50 1·10
292. – 5 p. black and red .. 28·00 2·75

DESIGNS—As Type **32**: 2 c. L. Vicario. 3 c. L. Rayon. 4 c. J. Aldama. 5 c. M. Hidalgo. 10 c. I. Allende. 15 c. E. Gonzalez. 20 c. M. Abasolo. As Type **40**: 1 p. Mass on Mt. of Crosses. 5 p. Capture of Granaditas.

REVOLUTIONARY PROVISIONALS

For full list of the provisional issues made during the Civil War from 1913 onwards, see the Stanley Gibbons Part 15 (Central America) Catalogue.

CONSTITUTIONALIST GENERAL ISSUES

CT 1.

1914. "Transitorio".

CT 1. CT 1. 1 c. blue 20 15
CT 2. 2 c. green 30 15
CT 3. 4 c. blue .. .. 7·00 1·60
CT 4. 5 c. green .. .. 7·00 1·90
CT 9. 5 c. green 10 10
CT 5. 10 c. red 15 15
CT 6. 20 c. brown 25 25
CT 7. 50 c. red .. .. 1·60 2·10
CT 8. 1 p. violet .. .. 8·75 10·00

The words of value on No. CT4, are 2 × 14mm. and on No. CT 9 are 2½ × 16mm.

1914. Victory of Torreon. Nos. CT 1/7 optd. **Victoria de TORREON ABRIL 2 - 1914.**

CT 10. CT 1. 1 c. blue .. .. 95·00 80·00
CT 11. 2 c. green .. .. £110 95·00
CT 12. 4 c. blue £130 £160
CT 13. 5 c. green .. .. 11·50 12·50
CT 14. 10 c. red .. .. 60·00 60·00
CT 15. 20 c. brown £1100 £1100
CT 16. 50 c. red £1200 £1200

(CT 3.) CT 4.

1914. Handstamped with Type CT 3.

(a) Nos. D 282/6.

CT 17. D 1. 1 c. blue .. .. 8·75 10·00
CT 18. 2 c. blue .. .. 8·75 10·00
CT 19. 4 c. blue .. .. 8·75 10·00
CT 20. 5 c. blue .. .. 8·75 10·00
CT 21. 10 c. blue .. .. 8·75 10·00

(b) Nos. 282/92.

CT 22. 32. 1 c. purple 35 30
CT 23. – 2 c. green 95 80
CT 24. – 3 c. brown 95 80
CT 25. – 4 c. red .. .. 1·60 1·25
CT 26. – 5 c. orange 20 10
CT 27. – 10 c. orge. and blue .. 1·90 1·25
CT 28. – 15 c. lake and slate .. 3·25 1·90
CT 29. – 20 c. blue and lake .. 6·25 3·75
CT 30. 40. 50 c. black & brown .. 7·50 5·00
CT 31. – 1 p. black and blue .. 16·00 6·25
CT 32. – 5 p. black and red .. £100 95·00

1914.

CT 33. CT 4. 1 c. pink .. .. 80 12·50
CT 34. 2 c. green .. .. 80 11·50
CT 35. 3 c. orange .. .. 80 12·50
CT 36. 5 c. red .. .. 60 5·00
CT 37. 10 c. green .. .. 60 22·00
CT 38. 25 c. blue .. .. 10·00

CT 5.

1914. "Denver" issue.

CT 39. CT 5. 1 c. blue 15 20
CT 40. 2 c. green 15 15
CT 41. 3 c. orange 25 15
CT 42. 5 c. red 25 15
CT 43. 10 c. red 35 40
CT 44. 15 c. mauve .. .. 60 1·10
CT 45. 50 c. yellow .. .. 1·25 1·60
CT 46. 1 p. violet .. .. 5·25 7·50

1914. Optd. **GOBIERNO CONSTITUCIONALISTA.**

(a) Nos. 279 and 271/2.

CT 50. – 5 c. orange .. .. 48·00 35·00
CT 51. – 15 c. pur. and lavender 95·00 95·00
CT 52. – 20 c. blue and red .. £300 £250

(b) Nos. D 282/6.

CT 53. D 32. 1 c. blue .. .. 1·10 1·10
CT 54. 2 c. blue .. .. 1·25 1·25
CT 55. 4 c. blue .. .. 9·50 9·50
CT 56. 5 c. blue .. .. 9·50 9·50
CT 57. 10 c. blue .. .. 1·60 1·60

(c) Nos. 282/92.

CT 58. 32. 1 c. purple 10 10
CT 59. – 2 c. green 10 10
CT 60. – 3 c. brown 20 20
CT 61. – 4 c. red 25 25
CT 62. – 5 c. orange 10 10
CT 63. – 10 c. orange & blue .. 10 10
CT 64. – 15 c. lake and slate .. 35 30
CT 65. – 20 c. blue and lake .. 35 35
CT 66. 40. 50 c. black and brown 1·10 75
CT 67. – 1 p. black and blue .. 4·75 3·25
CT 68. – 5 p. black and red .. 25·00 19·00

CONVENTIONIST ISSUES

(CV 1.) Villa-Zapata Monogram.

1914. Optd. with Type CV 1.

(a) Nos. 266/75.

CV 1. 27. 1 c. green .. .. 60·00
CV 2. 2 c. red .. .. 60·00
CV 3. 3 c. brown .. .. 32·00
CV 4. 5 c. blue .. .. 60·00
CV 5. 10 c. brown & pur. .. 60·00
CV 6. 15 c. pur. & lavender 60·00
CV 7. 20 c. blue and red .. 60·00
CV 8. 28. 50 c. black and red .. £160
CV 9. 29. 1 p. black and blue .. £160
CV 10. 30. 5 p. black and red .. £300

(b) Nos. 276/80.

CV 11. 27. 1 c. purple .. .. 60·00
CV 12. 2 c. green .. .. 60·00
CV 13. 4 c. red .. .. 60·00
CV 14. 5 c. orange .. .. 7·75
CV 15. 10 c. orange & blue .. 48·00

(c) Nos. D 282/6.

CV 16. D 32. 1 c. blue .. .. 6·00 6·25
CV 17. 2 c. blue .. .. 6·00 6·25
CV 18. 4 c. blue .. .. 6·00 6·25
CV 19. 5 c. blue .. .. 6·00 6·25
CV 20. 10 c. blue .. .. 60·00 6·25

(d) Nos. 282/92.

CV 21. 32. 1 c. purple 40 40
CV 22. – 2 c. green 45 20
CV 23. – 3 c. brown 30 30
CV 24. – 4 c. red .. .. 1·25 1·25
CV 25. – 5 c. orange 10 10
CV 26. – 10 c. orange and blue 95 95
CV 27. – 15 c. lake and slate .. 95 95
CV 28. – 20 c. blue and lake .. 95 95
CV 29. 40. 50 c. black & brown .. 6·25 6·25
CV 30. – 1 p. black and blue .. 9·50 9·50
CV 31. – 5 p. black and red .. 95·00 95·00

CONSTITUTIONALIST PROVISIONAL ISSUES

(CT 10.) (CT 11.) Carranza Monogram.

1914. Nos. 282/92 handstamped with Type CT 10.

CT 69. 32. 1 c. purple .. .. 6·00 5·50
CT 70. – 2 c. green .. .. 6·00 5·50
CT 71. – 3 c. brown .. .. 6·00 5·50
CT 72. – 4 c. red .. .. 7·50 7·00
CT 73. – 5 c. orange 90 90
CT 74. – 10 c. orange and blue 7·00 6·25
CT 75. – 15 c. lake and slate .. 7·00 6·25
CT 76. – 20 c. blue and lake .. 8·75 5·75
CT 77. 40. 50 c. black and brown 19·00 19·00
CT 78. – 1 p. black and blue .. 28·00
CT 79. – 5 p. black & red .. £100

1915. Optd. with Type CT **11.**

(a) No. 271.

CT 80. – 15 c. pur. & lavender 50·00 50·00

(b) No. 279.

CT 81. – 5 c. orange .. .. 12·50 12·50

(c) Nos. D 282/6.

CT 82. D **32.** 1 c. blue .. .. 7·00
CT 83. 2 c. blue .. .. 7·00
CT 84. 4 c. blue .. .. 7·00
CT 85. 5 c. blue .. .. 7·00
CT 86. 10 c. blue .. .. 7·00

(d) Nos. 282/92.

CT 87. **32.** 1 c. purple 35 35
CT 88. – 2 c. green 35 30
CT 89. – 3 c. brown 35 35
CT 90. – 4 c. red .. .. 1·25 1·25
CT 91. – 5 c. orange 10 10
CT 92. – 10 c. orange and blue 75 75
CT 93. – 15 c. lake and slate.. 75 75
CT 94. – 20 c. blue and lake .. 75 75
CT 95. **40.** 50 c. black and brown 6·25 6·25
CT 96. – 1 p. black and blue.. 9·50 9·50
CT 97. – 5 p. black and red .. 95·00 95·00

GENERAL ISSUES

43. Coat of Arms. **44.** Statue of Cuauhtemoc. **45.** Ignacio Zaragoza.

1915. Portraits as T **45.** Roul. or perf.

293. **43.** 1 c. violet 10 10
294. **44.** 2 c. green 20 15
304. **45.** 3 c. brown 20 15
305. 4 c. red (Morelos) .. 20 20
306. 5 c. orange (Madero) .. 25 15
308. 10 c. blue (Juarez) .. 15 10

46. Map of Mexico. **47.** Lighthouse, Veracruz.

48. Post Office, Mexico City.

1915.

299. **46.** 40 c. grey 30 30
433. 40 c. mauve .. .. 1·25 25
300. **47.** 1 p. grey and brown .. 35 60
411. 1 p. grey and blue .. 22·00 60
301. **48.** 5 p. blue and lake .. 5·00 5·50
412. 5 p. grey and green .. 50 60

(**49.**) **50.** V. Carranza.

1916. Silver Currency. Optd. with T **49.**

(a) No. 271.

309. – 15 c. pur. & lavender .. £250 £250

(b) No. 279.

309a. – 5 c. orange .. .. 55·00 55·00

(c) Nos. 282/92.

310. **32.** 1 c. purple .. .. 2·10 3·25
311. – 2 c. green 25 15
312. – 3 c. brown 25 15
313. – 4 c. red.. .. .. 3·75 5·00
314. – 5 c. orange 10 10
315. – 10 c. orange and blue.. 60 95
316. – 15 c. lake and slate .. 1·10 1·90
317. – 20 c. blue and lake .. 1·10 1·90
318. **40.** 50 c. black and brown.. 5·25 3·25
319. – 1 p. black and blue .. 9·50 4·00
320. – 5 p. black and red .. 95·00 80·00

(d) Nos. CT 1/3 and CT 5/8.

320b. CT **1.** 1 c. blue .. .. 15·00
320c. 2 c. green .. .. 7·50
320d. 4 c. blue £160
320e. 10 c. red .. .. 1·40
320f. 20 c. brown.. .. 1·90
320g. 50 c. red .. .. 9·50
320h. 1 p. violet .. .. 15·00

(e) Nos. CT 39/46.

321. CT **5.** 1 c. blue .. .. 2·40 12·00
322. 2 c. green .. .. 2·40 7·00
323. 3 c. orange .. .. 45 7·00
324. 5 c. red .. .. 45 7·00
325. 10 c. red .. .. 45 3·25
326. 15 c. mauve .. .. 45 7·00
327. 50 c. yellow .. .. 70 8·00
328. 1 p. violet .. .. 6·00 15·00

(f) Nos. CT 58/68.

329. **32.** 1 c. purple .. .. 1·60 2·50
330. – 2 c. green 35 30
331. – 3 c. brown 30 30
332. – 4 c. red.. .. .. 30 30
333. – 5 c. orange 50 15
334. – 10 c. orange and blue .. 35 30
335. – 15 c. lake and slate .. 40 40
336. – 20 c. blue and lake .. 40 40
337. **40.** 50 c. black and brown.. 4·75 3·75
338. – 1 p. black and blue .. 10·00 10·00
339. – 5 p. black and red .. 95·00 85·00

(g) Nos. CV 22/9.

340. **32.** 1 c. purple .. .. 7·00 9·50
341. – 2 c. green 75 45
342. – 3 c. brown .. .. 2·00 2·75
343. – 4 c. red.. .. .. 8·25 9·50
344. – 5 c. orange .. .. 2·75 3·75
345. – 10 c. orange and blue .. 7·50 8·75
346. – 15 c. lake and slate .. 7·50 8·75
347. 20 c. blue and lake .. 7·50 8·75

(h) Nos. CT 87/97.

348. **32.** 1 c. purple .. .. 1·60 2·10
349. – 2 c. green 30 30
350. – 3 c. brown 25 20
351. – 4 c. red.. .. .. 3·25 3·75
352. – 5 c. orange 40 10
353. – 10 c. orange and blue .. 75 1·25
354. – 15 c. lake and slate .. 60 30
355. – 20 c. blue and red .. 60 55
356. **40.** 50 c. black and brown.. 4·75 5·50
357. – 1 p. black and blue .. 7·00 7·50

1916. Carranza's Triumphal Entry into Mexico City.

358. **50.** 10 c. brown .. .. 7·50 8·25
359. 10 c. blue 60 30

(**51.**)

1916. Optd. with T **51.**

(a) Nos. D 282/6.

360. D **32.** 5 c. on 1 c. blue .. 1·60 1·60
361. 10 c. on 2 c. blue .. 1·60 1·60
362. 20 c. on 4 c. blue .. 1·60 1·60
363. 25 c. on 5 c. blue .. 1·60 1·60
364. 60 c. on 10 c. blue .. 75 75
365. 1 p. on 1 c. blue .. 75 75
366. 1 p. on 2 c. blue .. 75 75
367. 1 p. on 4 c. blue .. 40 40
368. 1 p. on 5 c. blue .. 1·60 1·60
369. 1 p. on 10 c. blue .. 1·60 1·60

(b) Nos. 282, 286 and 283

370. **32.** 5 c. on 1 c. purple .. 10 10
371. 10 c. on 1 c. purple .. 10 10
372. – 20 c. on 5 c. orange .. 10 10
373. – 25 c. on 5 c. orange .. 15 15
374. – 60 c. on 2 c. green .. 10·50 12·50

(c) Nos. CT 39/40.

375. CT **5.** 60 c. on 1 c. blue .. 1·90 3·75
376. 60 c. on 2 c. green .. 1·90 3·75

(d) Nos. CT 58, CT 62 and CT 59.

377. **32.** 5 c. on 1 c. purple .. 10 10
378. – 10 c. on 1 c. purple .. 60 60
379. – 25 c. on 5 c. purple .. 15 15
380. – 60 c. on 2 c. green .. £130 £170

(e) No. CV **25.**

381. – 25 c. on 5 c. orange .. 15 10

(f) Nos. CT 87, CT 91 and CT 88.

382. **32.** 5 c. on 1 c. purple .. 9·50 12·50
383. – 10 c. on 1 c. purple .. 3·25 4·75
385. – 25 c. on 5 c. orange .. 50 95
386. – 60 c. on 2 c. green .. £140

1916. Nos. D 282/6 surch. **GPM** and value.

387. D **32.** $2·50 on 1 c. blue .. 60 60
388. $2·50 on 2 c. blue .. 6·25 6·25
389. $2·50 on 4 c. blue .. 6·25 6·25
390. $2·50 on 5 c. blue .. 6·25 6·25
391. $2·50 on 10 c. blue .. 6·25 6·25

52a. Arms. **53.** Zaragoza.

1916.

392. **52a.** 1 c. purple 15 15

1917. Portraits. Roul. or perf.

393. **53.** 1 c. violet 25 10
393a. 1 c. grey 70 20
394. – 2 c. green (Vazquez) .. 35 8
395. – 3 c. brown (Suarez) .. 35 8
396. – 4 c. red (Carranza) .. 60 20
397. – 5 c. blue (Herrera) .. 85 10
398. – 10 c. blue (Madero) .. 1·40 8
399. – 20 c. lake (Dominguez) 14·00 35
400. – 30 c. purple (Serdan).. 38·00 60
401. – 30 c. black (Serdan) .. 45·00 60

1919. Red Cross Fund. Surch. with cross and premium.

413. 5 c.+3 c. blue (No. 397).. 9·00 9·50
414. 10 c.+5 c. blue (No. 398) 11·00 9·50

56. Meeting of Iturbide and Guerrero.

1921. Cent. of Declaration of Independence.

415. **56.** 10 c. brown and blue .. 9·50 1·90
416. – 10 p. black and brown .. 9·50 22·00

DESIGN: 10 p. Entry into Mexico City.

58. Golden Eagle.

1922. Air.

454. **58.** 25 c. sepia and lake .. 70 20
455. 25 c. sepia and green .. 75 25
456. 50 c. red and blue .. 1·00 35

59. Morelos Monument. **60.** Fountain and Aqueduct.

61. Pyramid of the Sun, Teotihuacan. **62.** Castle of Chapultepec.

63. Columbus Monument. **74.** Benito Juarez.

64. Juarez Colonnade. **65.** Monument to Dona Josefa Ortiz de Dominguez.

66. Cuauhtemoc Monument. **68.** Ministry of Communications.

69. National Theatre and Palace of Fine Arts.

1923. Roul. or perf.

436 **59** 1 c. brown 25 10
437 **60** 2 c. red.. .. .. 15 10
438 **61** 3 c. brown 10 8
429 **62** 4 c. green 60 10
440 **63** 4 c. green 15 10
~~441~~ 5 c. orange 10 10
453 **74** 8 c. orange 15 10
423 **64** 10 c. brown .. .. 4·75 10
~~442~~ **66** 10 c. lake 15 10
443 **65** 20 c. blue 35 10
426 **66** 30 c. green .. .. 35·00 2·50
432 **64** 30 c. green 45 10
434 **68** 50 c. brown 30 10
435 **69** 1 p. blue and lake .. 50 25

70. **72.** Sr. Francisco Garcia y Santos.

73. Post Office, Mexico City.

DESIGN—VERT. as Type **70:** 4 c., 10 c. Map of North and South America.

1926. 2nd Pan-American Postal Congress. Inscr. as in T **70/3.**

445. **70.** 2 c. red .. .. .. 1·25 35
446. – 4 c. green .. .. 1·25 40
447. **70.** 5 c. orange .. .. 1·25 25
448. – 10 c. red .. .. 1·90 25
449. **72.** 20 c. blue .. .. 1·90 50
450. 30 c. green .. .. 3·25 1·90
451. 40 c. mauve .. .. 6·25 1·60
452. **73.** 1 p. blue and brown .. 12·50 3·75

1929. Child Welfare. Optd. **Protection a la Infancia.**

457. **59.** 1 c. brown 25 12

77. **79.** Capt. Emilio Carranza.

1929. Obligatory Tax. Child Welfare.

459. **77.** 1 c. violet 10 8
461. 2 c. green 20 8
462. 5 c. brown 15 8

1929. Air. 1st Death Anniv. of Carranza (airman).

463. **79.** 5 c. sepia and green .. 55 30
464. 10 c. red and sepia .. 65 35
465. 15 c. green and violet.. 1·90 60
466. 20 c. black and sepia .. 60 35
467. 50 c. black and red .. 3·75 1·25
468. 1 p. sepia and black .. 7·75 1·75

80.

1929. Air. (a) Perf.

469. **80.** 10 c. violet 15 10
470. 15 c. red 65 10
471. 20 c. sepia .. .. 17·00 60
472. 30 c. black 10 10
473. 35 c. blue 15 10
473b. 50 c. lake 60 30
474. 1 p. blue and black .. 60 30
475. 5 p. blue and red .. 2·50 2·10
476. 10 p. sepia and violet .. 3·75 4·50

(b) Rouletted.

476a. **80.** 5 c. blue 10 10
477. 10 c. violet 10 10
478. 15 c. red 15 10
479. 20 c. sepia 75 10
480. 25 c. purple 45 40
481. 50 c. lake 45 35

81. **87.**

1929. Air. Aviation Week.

482. **81.** 20 c. violet 60 50
483. 40 c. green .. .. 55·00 48·00

1930. 2nd Pan-American Postal Congress issue optd. **HABILITADO 1930.**

484. **70.** 2 c. red .. .. 2·10 1·40
485. – 4 c. green .. .. 2·10 1·25
486. **70.** 5 c. orange .. .. 2·10 1·10
487. – 10 c. red .. .. 3·75 1·25
488. **72.** 20 c. blue .. .. 5·00 1·90
489. 30 c. green .. .. 4·50 2·10
490. 40 c. mauve .. .. 6·25 4·50
491. **73.** 1 p. blue and brown .. 5·50 3·75

1930. Air. National Tourist congress. Optd. **Primer Congreso Nacional de Turismo. Mexico. Abril 20-27 de 1930.**
492. **80.** 10 c. violet (No. 477) .. 1·25 60

1930. Obligatory Tax. Child Welfare. Surch. **HABILITADO $0.01.**
494. **77.** 1 c. on 2 c. green .. 30 15
495. 1 c. on 5 c. brown .. 60 15

1930. Air. Optd. **HABILITADO 1930.**
496. **79.** 5 c. sepia and green .. 3·50 2·75
497. 15 c. green and violet .. 5·50 4·75

1930. Air. Optd. **HABILITADO Aereo 1930-1931.**
498. **79.** 5 c. sepia and green .. 3·75 4·00
499. 10 c. red and sepia .. 2·10 2·50
500. 15 c. green and violet .. 4·00 4·50
501. 20 c. black and sepia .. 4·50 3·50
502. 50 c. black and red .. 8·75 6·25
503. 1 p. sepia and black .. 2·50 1·75

1931. Obligatory Tax. Child Welfare. No. CT 58 optd. **PRO INFANCIA.**
504. **32.** 1 c. purple 20 12

1931. Fourth Cent. of Puebla.
505. **87.** 10 c. brown and blue .. 1·60 25

88. **92.** Fray Bartolome de las Casas.

1931. Air. Aeronautic Exn.
506. **88.** 25 c. lake .. .. 2·00 1·60

1931. Nos. 446/52 optd. **HABILITADO 1931.**
508. – 4 c. green .. .. 35·00
509. **70.** 5 c. orange .. .. 6·25
510. – 10 c. red .. .. 6·25
511. **72.** 20 c. blue .. .. 6·25
512. 30 c. green .. .. 11·00
513. 40 c. mauve .. .. 16·00
514. **73.** 1 p. blue & brown .. 14·00

1931. Air. Surch. **HABILITADO Quince centavos.** Perf. or rouletted.
516. **80.** 15 c. on 20 c. sepia .. 20 10

1932. Air. Surch. in words and figures. Perf. or roul.
517. **88.** 20 c. on 25 c. lake .. 30 15
521. **80.** 30 c. on 20 c. sepia .. 15 10
519. **58.** 40 c. on 25 c. sep. & lake 90 65
520. 40 c. on 25 c. sep. & grn. 25·00 25·00
522. **80.** 80 c. on 25 c. (No. 480) 90 60

1932. Air. 4th Death Anniv of Emilio Carranza. Optd **HABILITADO AEREO–1932.**
523. **79.** 5 c. sepia and green .. 3·75 3·25
524. 10 c. red and sepia .. 3·25 1·90
525. 15 c. green and violet .. 3·75 2·50
526 20 c. black and sepia .. 3·25 1·75
527. 50 c. black and red .. 22·00 22·00

1933. Roul.
528. **92.** 15 c. blue 15 5

93. Mexican Geographical and Statistical Society's Arms.

94. National Theatre and Palace of Fine Arts.

1933. 21st Int. Statistical Congress and Cent. of Mexican Geographical and Statistical Society.
529. **93.** 2 c. green (postage) .. 75 20
530. 5 c. brown .. .. 1·10 25
531. 10 c. blue 35 10
532. 1 p. violet .. .. 32·00 38·00
533. **94.** 20 c. violet & red (air) .. 2·10 85
534. 30 c. violet and brown .. 4·25 3·75
535. 1 p. violet and green .. 42·00 45·00

95. Mother and Child.

98. Nevada de Toluca.

1934. National University. Inscr. "PRO-UNIVERSIDAD".
543. **95.** 1 c. orange (postage) .. 10 10
544. – 5 c. green .. .. 1·00 15
545. – 10 c. lake .. .. 1·25 30
546. – 20 c. blue .. .. 5·00 3·25
547. – 30 c. black .. .. 8·75 7·50
548. – 40 c. brown .. .. 15·00 10·00
549. – 50 c. blue .. .. 28·00 32·00
550. – 1 p black and red .. 32·00 30·00
551. – 5 p. brown and black .. £120 £160
552. – 10 p. violet and brown £500 £650
DESIGNS: 5 c. Archer. 10 c. Festive headdress. 20 c. Woman decorating pot. 30 c. Indian and Inca Lily. 40 c. Potter. 50 c. Sculptor. 1 p. Gold craftsman. 5 p. Girl offering fruit. 10 p. Youth burning incense.

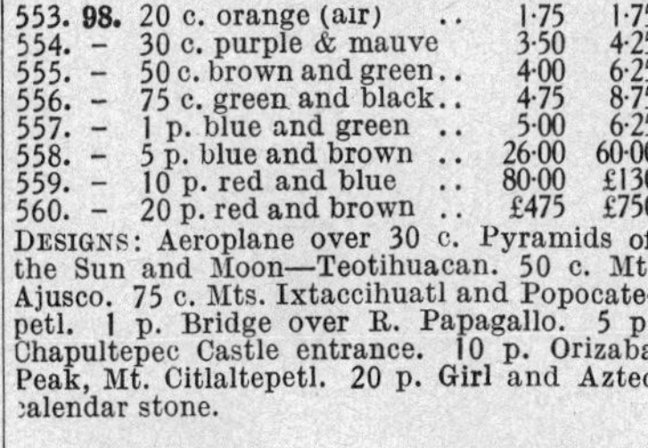

553. **98.** 20 c. orange (air) .. 1·75 1·75
554. – 30 c. purple & mauve 3·50 4·25
555. – 50 c. brown and green .. 4·00 6·25
556. – 75 c. green and black .. 4·75 8·75
557. – 1 p. blue and green .. 5·00 6·25
558. – 5 p. blue and brown .. 26·00 60·00
559. – 10 p. red and blue .. 80·00 £130
560. – 20 p. red and brown .. £475 £750
DESIGNS: Aeroplane over 30 c. Pyramids of the Sun and Moon—Teotihuacan. 50 c. Mt. Ajusco. 75 c. Mts. Ixtaccihuatl and Popocatepetl. 1 p. Bridge over R. Papagallo. 5 p. Chapultepec Castle entrance. 10 p. Orizaba Peak, Mt. Citlaltepetl. 20 p. Girl and Aztec calendar stone.

101. Zapoteca Indian Woman.

110. Coat of Arms.

1934. Pres. Cardenas' Assumption of Office. Designs as Type **101** and **110.** Imprint "OFICINA IMPRESORA DE HACIENDA-MEXICO" at foot of stamp. (a) Postage.
561. – 1 c. orange 30 8
562. **101.** 2 c. green 30 8
563. – 4 c. red 45 15
564. – 5 c. brown 30 8
565. – 10 c. blue 40 8
565a. – 10 c. violet 80 8
566. – 15 c. blue .. .. 2·50 15
567. – 20 c. green .. .. 1·25 10
567a. – 20 c. blue 85 8
568. – 30 c. red 35 8
653. – 30 c. blue 40 8
569. – 40 c. brown 40 8
570. – 50 c. black 45 8
571. **110.** 1 p. red and brown .. 1·60 8
572. – 5 p. violet and orange .. 4·75 55
DESIGNS: 1 c. Yalalteca Indian. 4 c. Revolution Monument. 5 c. Los Remedios Tower. 10 c. Cross of Palenque. 15 c. Independence Monument, Mexico City. 20 c. Independence Monument, Puebla. 30 c. "Heroic Children" Monument, Mexico City. 40 c. Sacrificial Stone. 50 c. Ruins of Mitla, Oaxaca. 5 p. Mexican "Charro" (Horseman).

112. Mictlantecuhtli.

120. "Peasant admiration".

(b) Air.
573. **112.** 5 c. black 20 10
574. – 10 c. brown 45 10
575. – 15 c. green 90 10
576. – 20 c. red .. .. 1·90 10
577. – 30 c. olive 35 10
577a. – 40 c. blue 60 10
578. – 50 c. green .. .. 1·60 10
579. – 1 p. red and green .. 2·50 10
580. **120.** 5 p. black and red .. 4·50 25
DESIGNS—HORIZ. 10 c. Temple at Quetzalcoatl. 15 c. Aeroplane over Citlaltepetl. 20 c. Popocatepetl. 30 c. Pegasus. 50 c. Uruapan Pottery. 1 p. "Warrior Eagle". VERT. 40 c. Aztec Idol.

121. Tractor.

122. Arms of Chiapas.

1935. Industrial Census.
581. **121.** 10 c. violet .. .. 2·50 25

1935. Air. Amelia Earhart Flight to Mexico. No. 576 optd. **AMELIA EARHART VUELO DE BUENA VOLUNTAD MEXICO 1935.**
581a. 20 c. red £1900 £2500

1935. Annexation of Chiapas Centenary.
582. **122.** 10 c. blue 35 15

123. E. Zapata.

124. Francisco Madero.

1935. 25th Anniv. of Revolutionary Plans of Ayala and San Luis Potosi.
583. **123.** 10 c. violet (postage) .. 35 10
584. **124.** 20 c. red (air) 20 10

129. Nuevo Laredo Road.

131. Rio Corona Bridge.

1936. Opening of Nuevo Laredo Highway (Mexico City-U.S.A.).
591. – 5 c. red & green (post) .. 15 10
592. – 10 c. grey 25 10
593. **129.** 20 c. green and brown .. 75 50
DESIGNS—As Type **129:** 5 c. Symbolical Map of Mexico-U.S.A. road. 10 c. Matalote Bridge.
594. – 10 c. blue (air) 30 10
595. **131.** 20 c. orange and violet 30 10
596. – 40 c. green and blue .. 40 30
DESIGNS—As Type **131:** 10 c. Tasquillo Bridge over Rio Tula. 40 c. Guayalejo Bridge.

1936. 1st Congress of Industrial Medicine and Hygeine. Optd. **PRIMER CONGRESO NAL. DE HIGIENE V MED. DEL TRABAJO.**
597. – 10 c. violet (No. 565a.) 30 20

1937. As Nos. 561/4, 565a and 576, but smaller. Imprint at foot changed to "TALLERES DE IMP.(RESION) DE EST.(AMPILLAS) Y VALORES-MEXICO".
708. 1 c. orange (postage) 25 8
709. 2 c. green 25 8
600. 4 c. red 40 8
601. 5 c. brown 35 8
602. 10 c. violet 25 8
603. 20 c. red (air) 80 8

134. Blacksmith.

DESIGNS—VERT. 10 c. Peasant revolutionary. 20 c. Preaching revolt. HORIZ. 20 c. Horseman. 40 c. Aeroplane. 1 p. Mounted horseman.

1938. Carranza's "Plan of Guadelupe". 25th Anniv. Inscr. "CONMEMORATIVO PLAN DE GUADALUPE", etc.
604. **134.** 5 c. brown & blk. (post.) 30 10
605. – 10 c. brown 10 10
606. – 20 c. orange and brown 3·25 50
607. – 20 c. blue and red (air) .. 20 10
608. – 40 c. red and blue .. 45 15
609. – 1 p. blue and yellow .. 3·00 1·40

140. Arch of the Revolution.

141. Cathedral and Constitution Square.

1938. 16th Int. Town Planning and Housing Congress, Mexico City. Inscr. as in T **140/1.**
610. **140.** 5 c. brown (postage) .. 80 30
611. 5 c. olive .. .. 1·60 1·40
612. – 10 c. orange .. .. 8·75 7·00
613. – 10 c. brown 30 10
614. – 20 c. black .. .. 2·10 2·50
615. – 20 c. lake .. .. 11·50 9·50
DESIGNS—As Type **140.** 10 c. National Theatre. 20 c. Independence Column.
616. **141.** 20 c. red (air) 15 10
617. 20 c. violet .. .. 8·75 6·25
619. – 40 c. green .. .. 4·50 3·25
620. – 1 p. slate .. .. 4·50 3·25
621. – 1 p. light blue .. .. 4·50 3·25
DESIGNS—As Type **141:** 40 c. Chichen Itza Ruins (Yucatan). 1 p. Acapulco Beach.

142. Mosquito and Malaria Victim.

1939. Obligatory Tax. Anti-Malaria Campaign.
622. **142.** 1 c. blue 95 10

MINIMUM PRICE

The minimum price quoted is 5p which represents a handling charge rather than a basis for valuing common stamps. For further notes about prices see introductory pages.

143. Statue of an Indian.

144. Statue of Woman Pioneer and Child.

1939. Tulsa Philatelic Convention, Oklahoma.
623. **143.** 10 c. red (postage) .. 20 10
624. **144.** 20 c. brown (air) .. 50 20
625. 40 c. green .. .. 1·25 60
626. 1 p. violet 80 45

145. Mexican Pavilion, World's Fair.

146. Morelos Statue on Mexican Pavilion.

1939. Air. F. Sarabia non-stop Flight to New York. Optd. **SARABIA Vuela MEXICO-NUEVA YORK.**
626a. **146.** 20 c. blue and red .. £160 £300

1939. New York World's Fair.
627. **145.** 10 c. grn. & blue (post.) 30 10
628. **146.** 20 c. green (air) .. 60 25
629. 40 c. purple .. .. 1·60 60
630. 1 p. brown and red .. 1·00 50

147. J. de Zumarraga.

152. "Building".

154. "Transport".

1939. 400th Anniv. of Printing in Mexico.
631. **147.** 2 c. black (postage) .. 35 10
632. – 5 c. green 35 10
633. – 10 c. red 10 10
634. – 20 c. blue (air) .. 10 10
635. – 40 c. green 30 10
636. – 1 p. red and brown .. 55 35
DESIGNS: 5 c. First printing works in Mexico. 10 c. Antonio D. Mendoza. 20 c. Book frontispiece. 40 c. Title page of first law book printed in America. 1 p. Oldest Mexican Colophon.

1939. National Census. Inscr. "CENSOS 1939 1940".
637. **152.** 2 c. red (postage) .. 60 10
638. – 5 c. green 10 10
639. – 10 c. brown 10 10
640. **154.** 20 c. blue (air) .. 70 25
641. – 40 c. orange 35 10
642. – 1 p. violet and blue .. 1·75 35
DESIGNS—As Type **152:** 5 c. "Agriculture". 10 c. "Commerce". As Type **154:** 40 c. "Industry". 1 p. "Seven Censuses".

155. "Penny Black".

156. Roadside Monument.

1940. Cent. of First Adhesive Postage Stamps.

643. 155. 5 c. yell. & black (post.) .. 45 25
644. 10 c. purple 10 10
645. 20 c. red and blue .. 15 10
646. 1 p. red and grey .. 4·50 2·50
647. 5 p. blue and black .. 23·00 19·00

648. 5 c. green & black (air) 45 30
649. 10 c. blue and brown .. 35 10
650. 20 c. violet and red .. 25 10
651. 1 p. brown and red .. 2·10 3·25
652. 5 p. brown and green .. 25·00 35·00

1940. Opening of Highway from Mexico City to Guadalajara.

654. 156. 6 c. green 35 10

159. Original College at Patzcuaro.

1940. 4th Cent. of National College of St. Nicholas de Hidalgo.

655. – 2 c. violet (postage) .. 65 25
656. – 5 c. red 40 10
657. – 10 c. olive 40 10

658. 159. 20 c. green (air) .. 20 10
659. – 40 c. orange 25 10
660. – 1 p. violet, brn. & orge. 60 45

DESIGNS—VERT. 2 c. V. de Quiroga. 5 c. M. Ocampo. 10 c. St. Nicholas College Arms. 40 c. Former College at Morelia. HORIZ. 1 p. Present College at Morelia.

163. Pirate Galleon.

1940. 400th Anniv. of Campeche. Inscr. as in T 163.

661. – 10 c. red & brown (post.) 1·90 60

662. 163. 20 c. brown & red (air) 70 35
663. – 40 c. green and black .. 75 25
664. – 1 p. black and blue .. 3·25 1·90

DESIGNS: 10 c. Campeche City Arms. 40 c. St. Miguel Castel. 1 p. Temple of San Francisco.

165. Helmsman. 166. Miguel Hidalgo y Costilla.

1940. Inauguration of Pres. Camacho.

665. 165. 2 c. orge. & black (post.) 1·00 30
666. 5 c. blue and brown .. 3·75 2·10
667. 10 c. olive and brown .. 1·40 40

668. 20 c. grey & orge. (air) .. 1·25 60
669. 40 c. brown and green .. 1·25 95
670. 1 p. purple and red .. 2·10 1·25

1940. Compulsory Tax. Dolores Hidalgo Memorial Fund.

671. 166. 1 c. red 30 8

168. Javelin throwing. 169. Dark Nebula in Orion.

1941. National Athletic Meeting.

675. 168. 10 c. green .. .. 2·10 25

1942. Inauguration of Astro-physical Observatory at Tonanzintla, Puebla.

676. 169. 2 c. blue & vio. (post.) 80 50
677. – 5 c. blue .. .. 5·50 1·25
678. – 10 c. blue and orange 5·50 25

679. – 20 c. blue & grn. (air) 7·75 1·90
680. – 40 c. blue and red .. 7·00 2·50
681. – 1 p. black and orange 7·00 2·75

DESIGNS: 5 c. Solar Eclipse. 10 c. Spiral Galaxy of the "Hunting Dog". 20 c. Extra-Galactic Nebula in Virgo. 40 c. Ring Nebula in Lyra. 1 p. Russell Diagram.

171. Ruins of Chichen-Itza. 172. Merida Nunnery.

1942. 400th Anniv. of Merida. Inscr. as in T 171/2.

682. 171. 2 c. brown (postage) .. 70 30
683. – 5 c. red .. .. 1·40 30
684. – 10 c. violet 80 10

685. 172. 20 c. blue (air) .. 95 25
686. – 40 c. green .. .. 1·40 1·25
687. – 1 p. red .. .. 1·60 1·25

DESIGNS—VERT. 5 c. Mayan sculpture. 10 c. Arms of Merida. 40 c. Montejo University Gateway. HORIZ. 1 p. Campanile of Merida Cathedral.

173. "Mother Earth". 175. Hidalgo Monument.

1942. 2nd Inter-American Agricultural Conf.

688. 173. 2 c. brown (postage) .. 40 20
689. – 5 c. blue .. .. 1·90 55
690. – 10 c. orange 60 25

691. – 20 c. green (air) .. 1·25 25
692. – 40 c. brown 75 25
693. – 1 p. violet .. .. 1·60 1·25

DESIGNS: 5 c. Sowing wheat. 10 c. Western Hemisphere carrying torch. 20 c. Corn. 40 c. Coffee. 1 p. Bananas.

1942. 400th Anniv. of Guadalajara.

694. 175. 2 c. brn. & blue (post.) 15 15
695. – 5 c. red and black .. 60 25
696. – 10 c. blue and red .. 60 20

697. – 20 c. black & grn. (air) 80 35
698. – 40 c. green and olive .. 1·10 50
699. – 1 p. violet and brown 80 60

DESIGNS—VERT. 5 c. Government Palace. 10 c. Guadalajara. HORIZ. 20 c. St. Paul's Church, Zapopan. 40 c. Sanctuary of Our Lady of Guadalupe. 1 p. Arms of Guadalajara.

186. Saltillo Athenaeum, Coahuila.

1942. 75th Anniv. of Saltillo Athenaeum.

700. 186. 10 c. black 90 20

189. Birthplace of Allende.

1943. 400th Anniv. of San Miguel de Allende.

701. – 2 c. blue (postage) .. 50 15
702. – 5 c. brown 55 15
703. – 10 c. black .. 2·10 50

704. – 20 c. green (air) .. 60 30
705. 189. 40 c. purple 45 30
706. – 1 p. red .. .. 1·75 1·60

DESIGNS—VERT. 2 c. Cupola de las Monjas. 5 c. Gothic Church. 10 c. Gen. de Allende. HORIZ. 20 c. San Miguel de Allende. 1 p. Church seen through cloisters.

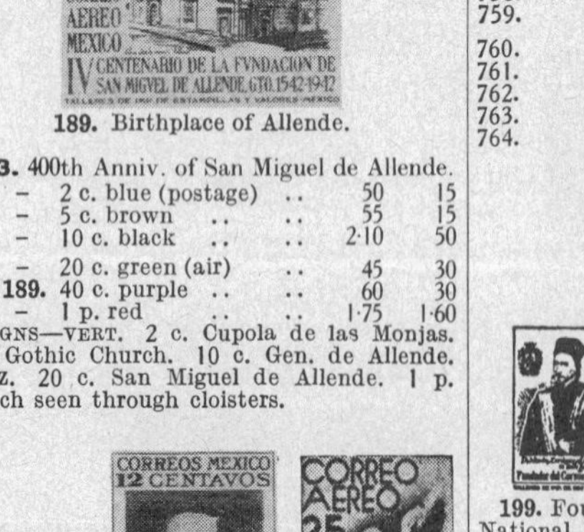

190. "Liberty". 192. Dr. de Castorena. 194. "Flight".

1944.

707. 190. 12 c. brown 20 8

1944. 3rd National Book Fair.

732. 192. 12 c. brown (postage) 40 10
733. – 25 c. green (air) .. 45 10

DESIGN: 25 c. Microphone, book and camera.

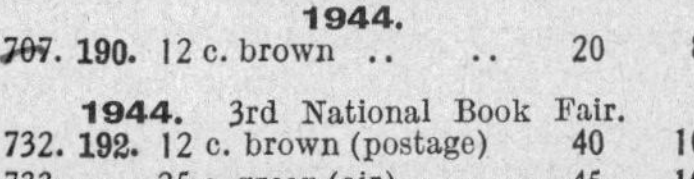

1944. Air.

734. 194. 25 c. brown 30 8

195. Hands clasping Globe.

1945. Inter-American Conf.

735. 195. 12 c. red (postage) .. 25 10
736. 1 p. green 45 10
737. 5 p. brown .. .. 3·50 2·75
738. 10 p. black .. .. 6·25 5·00

739. 25 c. orange (air) .. 10 10
740. 1 p. green 15 10
741. 5 p. blue .. .. 1·25 1·10
742. 10 p. red .. .. 3·50 2·75
743. 20 p. blue .. .. 7·25 7·00

196. La Paz Theatre, San Luis Potosi.

1945. Reconstruction of La Paz Theatre, San Luis Potosi.

744. 196. 12 c. pur. & blk. (post.) 20 10
745. 1 p. blue and black .. 30 10
746. 5 p. red and black .. 3·50 3·25
747. 10 p. green and black 7·75 7·50

748. 30 c. green (air) .. 10 10
749. 1 p. purple and green 15 10
750. 5 p. black and green 1·40 1·25
751. 10 p. blue and green .. 2·75 2·10
752. 20 p. green and black .. 6·00 5·25

197. Fountain of Diana the Huntress. 198. Removing Bandage.

1945.

753. 197. 3 c. violet 40 8

1945. Literacy Campaign.

754. 198. 2 c. blue (postage) .. 15 10
755. 6 c. orange 20 10
756. 12 c. blue 20 10
757. 1 p. olive 25 10
758. 5 p. red and black .. 2·10 1·90
759. 10 p. green and blue 12·50 12·50

760. 30 c. green (air) .. 10 10
761. 1 p. red 15 10
762. 5 p. blue .. .. 1·60 1·40
763. 10 p. red .. .. 2·75 2·75
764. 20 p. brown and green 13·00 12·50

199. Founder of National Post Office. 200. O.N.U., Olive Branch and Globe.

201. O.N.U. and Flags of United Nations.

1946. Foundation of Posts in Mexico in 1580.

765. 199. 8 c. black 60 5

1946. United Nations.

766. 200. 2 c. olive (postage) .. 15 10
767. 6 c. brown 15 10
768. 12 c. blue 10 10
769. 1 p. green 30 10
770. 5 p. red .. .. 3·25 3·25
771. 10 p. blue .. .. 14·00 12·50

772. 201. 30 c. brown (air) .. 10 10
773. 1 p. grey 10 10
774. 5 p. green and brown .. 70 50
775. 10 p. brown and sepia 2·75 2·00
776. 20 p. red and slate .. 6·00 4·75

202. Zacatecas City Arms. 205. Don Genaro Codina and Zacatecas.

1946. 400th Anniv. of Zacatecas.

777. 202. 2 c. brown (postage) .. 25 10
778. 12 c. blue 12 10
779 – 1 p. mauve 30 10
780. – 5 p. red .. .. 3·50 1·90
781. – 10 p. black and blue .. 19·00 6·25

DESIGNS: 1 p. Statur of Gen. Ortega. 5 p. R. L. Velarde (poet). 10 p. F. G. Salinas.

782. – 30 c. grey (air) .. 10 10
783. 205. 1 p. green and brown .. 15 10
784. – 5 p. green and red .. 1·60 1·60
785. – 10 p. brown and green 5·50 2·75

PORTRAITS: 30 c. Fr. Margil de Jesus. 5 p. Gen. Enrique Estrada. 10 p. D. Fernando Villalpando.

207. Learning Vowels. 208. Postman.

1946. Education Plan.

786. 207. 1 c. sepia 20 8

1947.

787. 208. 15 c. blue 15 8

209. Roosevelt and First Mexican Stamp. 210. 10 c. U.S.A. 1847 and Mexican Eagle.

1947. U.S.A. Postage Stamp Cent.

788. 209. 10 c. brown (postage) 80 60
789. – 15 c. green 10 10

790. – 25 c. blue (air) .. 35 20
791. 210. 30 c. black 25 10
792. – 1 p. blue and red .. 50 15

DESIGNS: 15 c. as Type 209, but vert. 25 c., 1 p. as Type 210 but horiz.

213. Justo Sierra.

214. Ministry of Communications.

DESIGN—HORIZ. 10p. E. Carranza.

212. Douglas DC4.

1947.

795. 213. 10 p. green and brown (postage) .. .. 55·00 9·50
796. 214. 20 p. mauve & green .. 80 1·25

793. – 10 p. red & brn. (air) .. 75 80
794. 212. 20 p. red and blue .. 1·50 1·25

215. Manuel Rincon. **217.** Vicente Suarez.

1947. Battle Centenaries. Portraits of "Child Heroes" etc., inscr. "1er CENTENARIO CHAPULTEPEC ("CHURUBUSCO" or "MOLINO DEL REY") 1847 1947".

797. – 2 c. black (postage) .. 30 8
798. – 5 c. red 15 8
799. – 10 c. brown 15 8
800. – 15 c. green 15 8
801. **215.** 30 c. olive 20 8
802. – 1 p. blue 30 15
803. – 5 p. red and blue .. 1·25 1·25

DESIGNS—VERT. 2 c. Francisco Marquez. 5 c. Fernando Montes de Oca. 10 c. Juan Escutin. 15 c. Agustin Melgar. 1 p. Lucas Balderas. 5 p. Flag of San Blas Battalion.

804. **217.** 25 c. violet (air) .. 15 8
805. – 30 c. blue 15 8
806. – 50 c. green 25 8
807. – 1 p. violet 30 8
808. – 5 p. brown and blue .. 80 80

DESIGNS—HORIZ. 30 c. Juan de la Barrera. 50 c. Military Academy. 1 p. Pedro Maria Anaya. 5 p. Antonio de Leon.

218. Puebla Cathedral. **221.** Dance of the Half Moons, Puebla.

1950. (a) Postage. As T **218.**

835. – 3 c. blue 15 8
874. – 5 c. brown 25 8
875. – 10 c. green .. .. 1·50 8
876. – 15 c. green 20 8
877e. **218.** 20 c. blue 30 5
840. – 30 c. red 25 8
879. – 30 c. brown 35 8
880b. – 40 c. orange 95 5
1346b. – 50 c. blue 10 5
1327b. – 80 c. green 35 5
843. – 1 p. brown .. .. 2·75 8
1346f. – 1 p. green 10 5
1011ab. – 1 p. grey 30 5
1327d. – 3 p. red 55 5
1012a. – 5 p. blue and green .. 1·10 60
1013ab. – 10 p. black and blue .. 2·50 1·25
846. – 20 p. violet and green 6·25 6·25
1014a. – 20 p. violet and black 5·00 2·50
1327e. – 50 p. orange and green 6·25 4·75

DESIGNS: 3 c, 3p. La Purisima Church, Monterrey. 5 c. Modern building, Mexico City. 10 c. Convent of the Nativity, Tepoztlan. 15 c, 50 p. Benito Juarez. 30 c., 80 c. Indian dancer, Michoacan. 40 c. Sculpture, Tabasco. 50 c. Carved head, Veracruz. 1 p. Actopan Convent and carved head. 5 p. Galleon, Campeche. 10 p. Francisco Madero. 20 p. Modern building, Mexico City.

(b) Air. As T **221.**

897 – 5 c. blue 15 10
898 – 10 c. brown 85 15
899a – 20 c. red 35 10
850 – 25 c. brown 60 10
851 – 30 c. olive 15 10
852 – 35 c. violet .. .. 1·25 10
1327f – 40 c. blue 10 10
904c – 50 c. green 35 10
1056 – 80 c. red 60 70
906a. **221.** 1 p. grey 45 10
1327h – 1 p. 60 red 60 10
1327i – 1 p. 90 red 35 5
907a – 2 p. brown .. .. 6·25 25
908 – 2 p. 25 purple .. 60 45
1327j – 4 p. 30 blue 45 5
1017a – 5 p. orange and brown 2·75 35
1327k – 5 p. 20 lilac 70 25
1327l – 5 p. 60 green .. 1·40 30
895 – 10 p. blue and black .. 3·00 60
1019a – 20 p. blue and red .. 4·50 4·75

DESIGNS: 5 c. 1 p. 90. Bay of Acapulco. 10 c. 4 p. 30. Dance of the Plumes, Oaxaca. 20 c. Mayan frescoes, Chiapas. 25 c. 2 p. 25, 5 p. 60. Masks, Michoacan. 30 c. Cuauhtemoc. 35 c. 2 p., 5 p. 20., Taxco, Guerrero. 40 c. Sculpture, San Louis Potosi. 50 c. 1 p. 60., Ancient carvings, Chiapas. 80 c. University City, Mexico City. 5 p. Architecture, Queretaro. 10 p. Hidalgo. 20 p. National Music Conservatoire, Mexico City.

222. Arterial Road. **224.** Train and Map.

1950. Opening of Mexican Section of Pan-American Highway. Inscr. "CARRETERA INTERNACIONAL 1950".

860. – 15 c. violet (postage) 30 10
861. **222.** 20 c. blue 20 10
862. – 25 c. pink (air) .. 1·60 20
863. – 35 c. green 10 10

DESIGNS—HORIZ. 15 c. Bridge. 25 c. Pres. M. Aleman, bridge and map. 35 c. B. Juarez and map.

1950. Inaug. of Mexico–Yucatan Rly.

864. – 15 c. purple (postage) 80 10
865. **224.** 20 c. red 25 10
866. – 25 c. green (air) .. 25 10
867. – 35 c. blue 40 30

DESIGNS—VERT. 15 c. Rail-laying. HORIZ. 25 c. Diesel trains. 35 c. M. Aleman and suspension bridge.

227. Hands and Globe.

DESIGNS — HORIZ. 25 c. Aztec runner. VERT. 50 c. Letters "U.P.U.".

1950. 75th Anniv. of U.P.U.

868. – 50 c. violet (postage) 25 10
869. – 25 c. red (air) .. 35 10
870. **227.** 80 c. blue 30 20

228. Miguel Hidalgo. **229.**

1953. Birth Bicent. of Hidalgo.

871. **228.** 20 c. sepia & blue (post.) 1·10 10
872. – 25 c. lake and blue (air) 35 10
873. **229.** 35 c. green 35 10

DESIGN—As Type **229**: 25 c. Full face portrait.

231. Aztec Athlete. **232.** View and Mayan Bas-relief.

1954. 7th Central American and Caribbean Games.

918. **231.** 20 c. blue & pink (post.) 55 10
919. **232.** 25 c. brown and green (air) 35 15
920. – 35 c. turq. and purple 30 10

DESIGN: 35 c. Stadium.

233. **234.**

1954. Mexican National Anthem Cent.

921. **233.** 5 c. lilac & blue (post.) 45 12
922. 20 c. brown & purple 55 10
923. 1 p. green and red .. 30 20
924. **234.** 25 c. blue & lake (air) 45 15
925. 35 c. purple and blue 20 10
926. 80 c. green and blue 25 15

235. Torchbearer and Stadium. **236.** Aztec God and Map.

1955. 2nd Pan-American Games, Mexico City. Inscr. "II JUEGOS DEPORTIVOS PANAMERICANOS".

927. **235.** 20 c. grn. & brn. (post) 40 10
928. **236.** 25 c. blue & brown (air) 30 10
929. – 35 c. brown and red .. 30 10

DESIGN—As Type **236**: 35 c. Stadium and map.

237. Olin Design.

238. Feathered Serpent and Mask.

1956. Mexican Stamp Centenary.

930. **237.** 5 c. grn. & brn. (post.) 30 10
931. – 10 c. blue and grey .. 30 10
932. – 30 c. purple and red .. 20 10
933. – 50 c. brown and blue .. 25 10
934. – 1 p. black and green .. 35 10
935. – 5 p. sepia and bistre .. 1·25 1·40

DESIGNS—As Type **237**: 10 c. Tohtli bird. 30 c. Zochitl flower. 50 c. Centli corn. 1 p. Mazatl deer. 5 p. Teheutli man's head.

937. **238.** 5 c. black (air) .. 15 10
938. – 10 c. blue 15 10
939. – 50 c. purple 10 10
940. – 1 p. violet 15 10
941. – 1 p. 20 mauve .. 15 10
942. – 5 p. turquoise 50 50

DESIGNS—As Type **238**: 10 c. Bell tower, coach and Viceroy Enriquez de Almanza. 50 c. Morelos and cannon. 1 p. Mother, child and mounted horseman. 1 p. 20, Sombrero and spurs. 5 p. Emblems of food and education and pointing hand.

239. Stamp of 1856.

1956. Centenary Int. Philatelic Exn., Mexico City.

944. **239.** 30 c. blue and brown .. 45 15

240. F. Zarco. **241.** V. Gomez Farias and M. Ocampo.

1956. Inscr. "CONSTITUYENTE(S) DE 1857".

945 – 25 c. brown (postage) 35 10
946 – 45 c. blue 15 10
947 – 60 c. purple 15 10
1346d **240.** 70 c. blue 20 10
1327c – 2 p. 30 blue 55 5
949 **241.** 15 c. blue (air) .. 20 10
1327g – 60 c. green 15 15
950 – 1 p. 20 violet & green 35 15
951 **241.** 2 p. 75 purple .. 50 30

PORTRAITS—As T **240** (postage): 25, 45 c., 2 p. 30, G. Prieto. 60 c. P. Arriagan. As T **241** (air): 60 c., 1 p. 20, L. Guzman and I. Ramirez.

242. Paricutin Volcano.

1956. Air. 20th Int. Geological Congress.

952. **242.** 50 c. violet 30 8

243. Map of Central America and the Caribbean

1956. Air. 4th Inter-American Congress of Caribbean Tourism.

953. **243.** 25 c. blue and grey .. 20 8

244. Assembly of 1857. **245.** Mexican Eagle and Scales.

1957. Cent. of 1857 Constitution.

958. – 30 c. gold & lake (post.) 35 8
959. **244.** 1 p. green and sepia .. 25 10
960. **245.** 50 c. brn. & green (air) 20 8
961. – 1 p. lilac and blue .. 30 15

DESIGNS—VERT. 30 c. Emblem of Constitution. HORIZ. 1 p. (Air), "Mexico" drafting the Constitution.

246. Globe, Weights and Dials.

1957. Air. Centenary of Adoption of Metric System in Mexico.

962. **246.** 50 c. black and silver .. 30 8

247. Train Disaster. **248.** Oil Derrick.

1957. Air. 50th Anniv. of Heroic Death of J. Garcia (engine driver) at Nacozari.

963. **247.** 50 c. purple and red .. 20 25

1958. 20th Anniv. of Nationalization of Oil Industry.

964. **248.** 30 c. blk. & blue (post.) 25 10
965. – 5 p. red and blue .. 2·50 2·50
966. – 50 c. grn. & black (air) 10 10
967. – 1 p. black and red .. 20 10

DESIGNS—HORIZ. 50 c. Oil storage tank and "AL SERVICIO DE LA PATRIA" ("At the service of the Fatherland"). 1 p. Oil refinery at night. VERT. 5 p. Map of Mexico and silhouette of oil refinery.

249. Angel, Independence Monument, Mexico City. **250.** U.N.E.S.C.O. Headquarters, Paris.

1958. Air. 10th Anniv. of Declaration of Human Rights.

968. **249.** 50 c. blue 20 8

1959. Inaug. of U.N.E.S.C.O. Headquarters Building, Paris.

969. **250.** 30 c. black and purple 30 8

251. U.N. Headquarters, New York. **252.** President Carranza.

1959. U.N. Economic and Social Council Meeting, Mexico City.

970. **251.** 30 c. blue and yellow .. 30 8

1960. "President Carranza Year" (1959) and his Birth Centenary.

971. **252.** 30 c. pur. & grn. (post.) 20 8
972. – 50 c. viol. & salmon (air) 20 8

DESIGN—HORIZ. 50 c. Inscription "Plan de Guadalupe Constitucion de 1917" and portrait as Type **252**.

253. Alexander von Humboldt (statue). **254.** Alberto Braniff's Aeroplane of 1910, and Britannia Airliner.

1960. Death Centenary of Alexander von Humboldt (naturalist).

973. **253.** 40 c. green and brown 20 8

1960. Air. 50th Anniv. of Mexican Aviation.
974. **254.** 50 c. brown and violet 40 10
975. 1 p. brown and green .. 40 15

255. Francisco I. Madero. **257.** Dolores Bell. **259.** Children at Desk, University and School Buildings.

1960. Visit to Mexico of Members of Elmhurst Philatelic Society (American Society of Mexican Specialists). Inscr. "HOMENAJE AL COLECCIONISTA".
976. **255.** 10 p. sepia, green and purple (postage) .. 22·00 26·00
977. – 20 p. sepia, green and purple (air) .. .. 26·00 50·00
Design—As No. 1019a. 20 p. National Music Conservatoire inscr. "MEX. D.F.".

1960. 150th Anniv. of Independence.
978. **257.** 30 c. red & grn. (post.) 60 10
979. – 1 p. sepia and green .. 25 10
980. – 5 p. blue and purple .. 3·25 3·25
981. – 50 c. red & grn. (air) .. 15 10
982. – 1 p. 20 sepia and blue 20 10
983. – 5 p. sepia and green .. 2·75 1·10
Designs—vert. No. 979, Independence Column. No. 980, Hidalgo, Dolores Bell and Mexican Eagle. horiz. No. 981, Mexican Flag. No. 982, Eagle breaking chain and bell tolling. No. 983, Dolores Church.

1960. 50th Anniv. of Mexican Revolution.
984. – 10 c. multicoloured (postage) 30 10
985. – 15 c. brown and green 1·75 10
986. – 20 c. blue and brown .. 50 10
987. – 30 c. violet and sepia .. 20 10
988. **259.** 1 p. slate and purple .. 25 10
989. – 5 p. grey and purple .. 2·10 2·10
990. – 50 c. blk. & blue (air) 20 10
991. – 1 p. green and red .. 20 10
992. – 1 p. 20 sepia and green 20 10
993. – 5 p. lt. bl., bl. & mauve 1·25 45
Designs: No. 984, Pastoral scene (35½×45½ mm.). As Type **259**—vert. No. 985, Worker and hospital buildings. No. 986, Peasant, soldier and marine. No. 987, Power lines and pylons. No. 989, Coins, banknotes and bank entrance. horiz. No. 990, Douglas DC-8 airliner. No. 991, Riggers on oil derrick. No. 992, Main highway and map. No. 993, Barrage.

261. Count S. de Revillagigedo. **262.** Railway Tunnel. **263.** Mosquito Globe and Instruments.

1960. Air. National Census.
994. **261.** 60 c. black and lake .. 35 8

1961. Opening of Chihuahua State Railway.
995. **262.** 40 c. blk. & grn. (post.) 25 25
996. – 60 c. blue & black (air) 20 30
997. – 70 c. black and blue .. 20 10
Designs—horiz. 60 c. Railway track and outline map of Mexico. 70 c. Railway viaduct.

1962. Malaria Eradication.
998. **263.** 40 c. brown and blue .. 25 8

264. Pres. Goulart of Brazil. **265.** Soldier and Memorial Stone.

1962. Visit of President of Brazil.
999. **264.** 40 c. bistre 65 10

1962. Cent. of Battle of Puebla.
1000. **265.** 40 c. sepia and green (postage) 25 8
1001. – 1 p. olive & green (air) 35 10
Design—horiz. 1 p. Statue of Gen. Zaragoza.

266. Draughtsman and Surveyor. **267.** Plumb-line.

1962. 25th Anniv. of National Polytechnic Institute.
1002. **266.** 40 c. turquoise & blue (postage) 65 10
1003. – 1 p. olive and blue (air) 35 10
Design—horiz. 1 p. Scientist and laboratory assistant.

1962. Mental Health.
1004. **267.** 20 c. blue and black 90 15

268. Pres. J. F. Kennedy. **269.** Tower and Cogwheels.

1962. Air. Visit of U.S. President.
1005. **268.** 80 c. blue and red .. 75 15

1962. "Century 21" Exn. ("World's Fair"), Seattle.
1006. **269.** 40 c. black and green 35 8

270. Globe and O.E.A. Emblem. **271.** Pres. Alessandri of Chile. **272.** Balloon over Mexico City.

1962. Inter-American Economic and Social Council.
1007. **270.** 40 c. sepia & grey (post.) 25 8
1008. – 1 p. 20 sepia & vio. (air) 35 15
Design—horiz. 1 p. 20, Globe, Scroll and O.E.A. emblem.

1962. Visit of President of Chile.
1009. **271.** 20 c. brown 45 10

1962. Air. 1st Mexican Balloon Flight Cent.
1010. **272.** 80 c. black and blue 90 25

273. "ALALC" Emblem. **274.** Pres. Betancourt of Venezuela.

1963. Air. 2nd "ALALC" Session.
1023. **273.** 80 c. purple & orange 65 20

1963. Visit of President of Venezuela.
1024. **274.** 20 c. blue 35 10

275. Petroleum Refinery. **276.** Congress Emblem.

1963. Air. 25th Anniv. of Nationalization of Mexican Petroleum Industry.
1025. **275.** 80 c. slate and orange 35 10

1963. 19th Int. Chamber of Commerce Congress, Mexico City.
1026. **276.** 40 c. brown and black (postage) 45 10
1027. – 80 c. black & blue (air) 55 20
Design—horiz. 80 c. World map and "C.I.C." emblem.

277. Campaign Emblem. **278.** Arms and Mountain. **279.** B. Dominguez.

1963. Freedom from Hunger.
1028. **277.** 40 c. red and blue .. 45 12

1963. 4th Centenary of Durango.
1029. **278.** 20 c. brown and blue 45 12

1963. Birth Centenary of B. Dominguez (revolutionary).
1030. **279.** 20 c. olive and green 45 12

280. Exhibition Stamp of 1956. **281.** Pres. Tito.

1963. 77th American Philatelic Society Convention, Mexico City.
1031. **280.** 1 p. brn. & bl. (post.) 60 45
1032. – 5 p. red (air) .. .. 1·40 75
Design—horiz. 5 p. EXMEX "stamp" and "postmark".

1963. Air. Visit of President of Yugoslavia.
1033 **281** 2 p. green and violet 1·10 30

283. Part of U.I.A. Building. **284.** Red Cross on Tree. **285.** Pres. Estenssoro.

1963. Air. Int. Architects' Day.
1034. **283.** 80 c. grey and blue .. 45 15

1963. Red Cross Centenary.
1035. **284.** 20 c. red & grn. (post.) 30 12
1036. – 80 c. red & green (air) 70 25
Design—horiz. 80 c. Red Cross on dove.

1963. Visit of President of Bolivia.
1037. **285.** 40 c. purple & brown 45 12

286. Jose Morelos. **287.** Don Quixote as skeleton.

289. Diesel Train. **288.** University Arms.

1963. 150th Anniv. of First Anahuac Congress.
1038. **286.** 40 c. bronze & green 40 12

1963. Air. 50th Death Anniv. of Jose Posada (satirical artist).
1039. **287.** 1 p. 20 black .. 75 20

1963. 90th Anniv. of Sinaloa University.
1040. **288.** 40 c. bistre and green 45 12

1963. 11th Pan-American Railways Congress, Mexico City.
1041. **289.** 20 c. brn. & blk. (post.) 55 30
1042. – 1 p. 20 blue and violet (air) 50 20
Design: 1 p. 20, Steam and diesel locomotives and horse-drawn tramcar.

290. "F.S.T.S.E." Emblem. **291.** Mrs. Roosevelt, Flame and U.N. Emblem.

1964. 25th Anniv. of Workers' Statute.
1075. **290.** 20 c. sepia and orange 30 8

1964. Air. 15th Anniv. of Declaration of Human Rights.
1076. **291.** 80 c. blue and orange 50 10

292. Pres. De Gaulle.

1964. Air. Visit of President of France.
1077. **292.** 2 p. blue and brown .. 1·25 35

293. Pres. Kennedy and Pres. A. Lopez Mateos.

1964. Air. Ratification of Chamizal Treaty (1963).
1078. **293.** 80 c. black and blue .. 55 15

294. Queen Juliana and Arms. **295.** Academy Emblem.

1964. Air. Visit of Queen Juliana of the Netherlands.
1079. **294.** 20 c. bistre and blue 70 15

1964. Cent. of National Academy of Medicine.
1080. **295.** 20 c. gold and black .. 30 8

296. Lieut. Jose Azueto and Cadet Virgilio Uribe.

1964. Air. 50th Anniv. of Heroic Defence of Veracruz.
1081. **296.** 40 c. green and brown 30 10

297. Arms and World Map.

1964. Air. Int. Bar Assn. Conf., Mexico City.
1082. **297.** 40 c. blue and brown 45 10

298. Colonel G. Mendez. **299.** Dr. Jose Rizal. **300.** Zacatecas.

1964. Cent. of Battle of the Jahuactal Tabasco.
1083. **298.** 40 c. olive and brown 35 10

1964. 400 Years of Mexican–Philippine Friendship. Inscr. "1564 AMISTAD MEXICANO-FILIPINA 1964".
1084. **299.** 20 c. blue & grn. (post.) 35 10
1085. – 40 c. blue and violet .. 40 10
1086. – 80 c. blue & lt. bl. (air) 1·40 25
1087. – 2 p. 75 black & yellow 1·75 70
Designs—As Type **299**—vert. 40 c. Legaspi. horiz. 80 c. Galleon. larger (44×36 mm.): 2 p. 75, Ancient map of Pacific Ocean.

1964. 50th Anniv. of Conquest of Zacatecas.
1088. **300.** 40 c. green and red .. 40 10

301. Morelos Theatre, Aguascalientes. **302.** Andres Manuel del Rio.

1965. 50th Anniv. of Aguascalientes Convention.
1089. **301.** 20 c. purple and grey 30 8

1965. Andres M. del Rio Commem.
1090. **302.** 30 c. black 35 8

303. Netzahualcoyotl Dam. **304.** J. Morelos (statue).

1965. Air. Inaug. of Netzahualcoyotl Dam.
1091. **303.** 80 c. slate and purple 30 10

1965. 150th Anniv. (1964) of First Constitution.
1092. **304.** 40 c. brown and green 40 10

305. Microwave Tower. **306.** Fir Trees.

1965. Air. Centenary of I.T.U.
1093. **305.** 80 c. blue and indigo 40 20
1094. – 1 p. 20 green and black 45 20
DESIGN: 1 p. 20, Radio-electric station.

1965. Forest Conservation.
1095. **306.** 20 c. green and blue.. 30 8
The inscription "¡CUIDALOS!" means "CARE FOR THEM!".

307. I.C.Y. Emblem.

1965. Int. Co-operation Year.
1096. **307.** 40 c. brown and green 25 8

308. Camp Fire and Tent.

1965. Air. World Scout Conf., Mexico City.
1097. **308.** 80 c. ultramarine & blue 40 20

309. King Baudouin and Queen Fabiola.

1965. Air. Visit of Belgian King and Queen.
1098. **309.** 2 p. blue and green .. 75 20

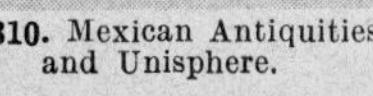

310. Mexican Antiquities and Unisphere. **311.** Dante (after R. Sanzio).

1965. Air. New York World's Fair.
1099. **310.** 80 c. green and yellow 30 15

1965. Air. Dante's 700th Birth Anniv.
1100. **311.** 2 p. red .. .. 1·00 55

312. Sling-thrower. **313.** Jose M. Morelos y Pavon (leader of independence movement).

1965. Olympic Games (1968) Propaganda (1st series). Museum pieces.
1101. **312.** 20 c. blue & olive (post.) 45 10
1102. – 40 c. sepia and red .. 15 10
1103. – 80 c. slate & red (air) 35 10
1104. – 1 p. 20 indigo & blue 45 15
1105. – 2 p. brown & blue .. 35 10
DESIGNS—As Type **312**—VERT. 40 c. Batsman. HORIZ. 2 p. Ball game. HORIZ. (36×20 mm.): 80 c. Fieldsman. 1 p. 20, Scoreboard.

1965. 150th Anniv. of Morelos's Execution.
1108. **313.** 20 c. black and blue.. 30 10

314. Agricultural Produce. **315.** Ruben Dario.

1966. Cent. of Agrarian Reform Law.
1109. **314.** 20 c. red 30 8
1110. – 40 c. black 40 10
DESIGN: 40 c. Emilio Zapata, pioneer of agrarian reform.

1966. Air. 50th Death Anniv. of Ruben Dario (Nicaraguan poet).
1111. **315.** 1 p. 20 sepia .. 55 20

316. Father Andres de Urdaneta and Compass Rose. **317.** Flag and Postal Emblem.

1966. Air. 400th Anniv. of Father Andres de Urdaneta's Return from the Philippines.
1112. **316.** 2 p. 75 black .. 85 45

1966. 9th Postal Union of Americas and Spain Congress (U.P.A.E.), Mexico City.
1113. **317.** 40 c. blk. & grn. (post.) 35 8
1114. – 80 c. blk. & mve. (air) 30 12
1115. – 1 p. 20 black and blue 35 15
DESIGNS—VERT. 80 c. Flag and posthorn. HORIZ. 1 p. 20, U.P.A.E. emblem and flag.

318. Friar B. de Las Casas. **319.** E.S.I.M.E. Emblem and Diagram

1966. 400th Death Anniv. of Friar Bartolome de Las Casas ("Apostle of the Indies").
1116. **318.** 20 c. black on buff .. 35 8

1966. 50th Anniv. of Higher School of Mechanical and Electrical Engineering.
1117. **319.** 20 c. green and grey.. 30 8

320. U Thant and U.N. Emblem.

321. "1966 Friendship Year".

322. F.A.O. Emblem. **323.** Running and Jumping.

1966. Air. U.N. Secretary-General U Thant's Visit to Mexico.
1118. **320.** 80 c. black and blue.. 30 15

1966. Air. "Year of Friendship" with Central American States.
1119. **321.** 80 c. green and red .. 25 10

1966. Int. Rice Year.
1120. **322.** 40 c. green 30 8

1966. Olympic Games (1968) Propaganda (2nd series).
1121. **323.** 20 c. blk. & blue (post.) 55 10
1122. – 40 c. black and lake.. 25 8
1124. – 80 c. blk. & brn. (air) 35 10
1125. – 2 p. 25 black & green 55 25
1126. – 2 p. 75 black & violet 60 35
DESIGNS: 40 c. Wrestling. LARGER (57×20 mm.): 80 c. Obstacle race. 2 p. 25, American football. 2 p. 75, Lighting Olympic flame.

324. U.N.E.S.C.O. Emblem.

1966. Air. 20th Anniv. of U.N.E.S.C.O.
1128. **324.** 80 c. multicoloured .. 30 10

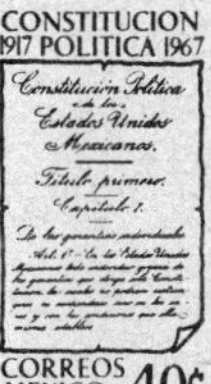

325. Constitution of 1917. **326.** Earth and Satellite. **327.** Oil Refinery.

1967. 50th Anniv. of Mexican Constitution.
1129. **325.** 40 c. black (postage) 45 10
1130. – 80 c. brn. & ochre (air) 35 10
DESIGN: 80 c. President V. Carranza.

1967. Air. World Meteorological Day.
1131. **326.** 80 c. blue and black.. 30 20

1967. 7th World Petroleum Congress, Mexico City.
1132. **327.** 40 c. black and blue 30 8

328. Nayarit Indian. **329.** Degollado Theatre.

1967. 50th Anniv. of Nayarit State.
1133. **328.** 20 c. black and green 30 8

1967. Cent. of Degollado Theatre, Guadalajara.
1134. **329.** 40 c. brown and mauve 10 10

330. Mexican Eagle and Crown. **331.** School Emblem.

1967. Cent. of Triumph over the Empire.
1135. **330.** 20 c. black and ochre 30 10

1967. Air. 50th Anniv. of Military Medical School.
1136. **331.** 80 c. green and yellow 35 15

332. Capt. H. Ruiz Gavino. **333.** Marco Polo.

1967. Air. 50th Anniv. of 1st Mexican Airmail Flight. Pachuca-Mexico City.
1137. **332.** 80 c. brown and black 30 10
1138. – 2 p. brown and black 70 20
DESIGN—HORIZ. 2 p. Biplane.

1967. Air. Int. Tourist Year.
1139. **333.** 80 c. red and black.. 20 10

334. Canoeing. **335.** A. del Valle-Arizpe (writer).

337. P. Moreno. **336.** Hertz and Clark Maxwell.

1967. Olympic Games (1968) Propaganda (3rd series).
1140. **334.** 20 c. blk. & blue (post.) 20 10
1141. – 40 c. black and red.. 15 10
1142. – 50 c. black and green 15 10
1143. – 80 c. black and violet 25 10
1144. – 2 p. black and orange 40 15
1146. – 80 c. black & mve. (air) 15 10
1147. – 1 p. 20 black & green 15 10
1148. – 2 p. black and lemon 60 20
1149. – 5 p. black and yellow 1·00 35
DESIGNS: 40 c. Basketball. 50 c. Hockey. 80 c. (No. 1143), Cycling. 80 c. (No. 1146), Diving. 1 p. 20, Running. 2 p. (No. 1144), Fencing. 2 p. (No. 1148), Weightlifting. 5 p. Football.

1967. Cent. of Fuente Athenaeum, Saltillo.
1151. **335.** 20 c. slate and brown 30 10

1967. Air. Int. Telecommunications Plan Conf. Mexico City.
1152. **336.** 80 c. green and black 30 10

1967. 150th Death Anniv. of Pedro Moreno (revolutionary).
1153. **337.** 40 c. black and blue.. 30 12

338. Gabino Berreda (founder of Preparatory School). **339.** Exhibition Emblem.

1968. Centenary of Nat. Preparatory and Engineering Schools.
1154. **338.** 40 c. red and blue .. 35 10
1155. – 40 c. blue and black.. 35 10
DESIGN: No. 1155, Staircase, Palace of Mining.

1968. Air. "Efimex '68" Int. Stamp Exn., Mexico City.
1156. **339.** 80 c. green and black 25 30
1157. 2 p. red and black .. 25 30
The emblem reproduces the "Hidalgo" Official stamp design of 1884

1968. Olympic Games (1968) Propaganda (4th series). Designs as T **334**. but inscr. "1968".
1158. 20 c. black & olive (post.) 25 10
1159. 40 c. black and purple .. 25 10
1160. 50 c. black and green .. 25 10
1161. 80 c. black and mauve 25 10
1162. 1 p. black and brown .. 1·50 25
1163. 2 p. black and grey .. 1·75 95
1165. 80 c. black and blue (air) 30 10
1166. 1 p. black and turquoise 35 15
1167. 2 p. black and yellow .. 35 20
1168. 5 p. black and brown .. 80 70
DESIGNS: 20 c. Wrestling. 40 c. Various sports. 50 c. Water-polo. 80 c. (No. 1161) Gymnastics. 80 c. (No. 1165) Yachting. 1 p. (No. 1162) Boxing. 1 p. (No. 1166) Rowing. 2 p. (No. 1163) Pistol-shooting. 2 p. (No. 1167) Volley-ball. 5 p. Horse-racing.

340. Dr. Martin Luther King.

1968. Air. Martin Luther King Commem.
1170. **340.** 80 c. black and grey 35 12

341. Olympic Flame. **342.** Emblems of Games.

1968. Olympic Games, Mexico.
(i) Inaug. Issue.
1171. **341.** 10 p. multicoloured .. 2·00 1·25

(ii) Games Issue. Multicoloured designs as T **341.** (20, 40, 50 c. post. and 80 c., 1 p., 2 p. air) or as T **342** (others).
1172. 20 c. Dove of Peace on map (post.) 25 8
1173. 40 c. Stadium 30 10
1174. 50 c. Telecommunications Tower, Mexico City .. 30 10
1175. 2 p. Palace of Sport, Mexico City 55 25
1176. 5 p. Cultural symbols of Games .. .. 1·50 80
1178. 80 c. Dove and Olympic rings (air) .. 15 10
1179. 1 p. "The Discus-thrower" 15 10
1180. 2 p. Olympic medals .. 45 25
1181. 5 p. Type **342** .. 1·75 85
1182. 10 p. Line-pattern based on "Mexico 68" & rings 1·50 95

343. Arms of Vera Cruz. **344.** "Father Palou" (M. Guerrero).

1969. 450th Anniv. of Vera Cruz.
1185. **343.** 40 c. multicoloured .. 30 8

1969. Air. 220th Anniv. of Arrival in Mexico of Father Serra (coloniser of California).
1186. **344.** 80 c. multicoloured 35 10

It was intended to depict Father Serra in this design, but the wrong detail of the painting by Guerrero, which showed both priests, was used.

345. Football and Spectators.

1969. Air. World Cup Football Championship (1st issue). Multicoloured.
1187. 80 c. Type **345** 25 10
1188. 2 p. Foot kicking ball .. 35 10
See also Nos. 1209/10.

346. Underground Train.

1969. Inauguration of Mexico City Underground Railway System.
1189. **346.** 40 c. multicoloured .. 20 10

347. Mahatma Gandhi.

348. Footprint on Moon.

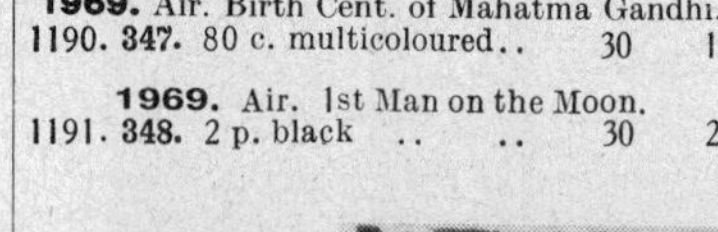

1969. Air. Birth Cent. of Mahatma Gandhi.
1190. **347.** 80 c. multicoloured .. 30 10

1969. Air. 1st Man on the Moon.
1191. **348.** 2 p. black 30 25

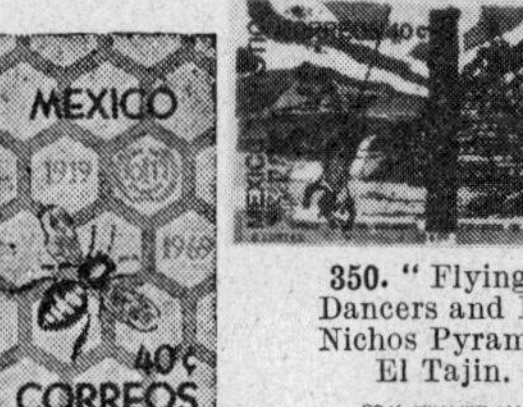

349. Bee and Honeycomb.

350. "Flying" Dancers and Los Nichos Pyramid, El Tajin.

351. Red Crosses and Sun. **352.** "General Allende" (D. Rivera).

1969. 50th Anniv. of I.L.O.
1192. **349.** 40 c. brn., blue & yell. 20 8

1969. Tourism (1st series). Multicoloured.
1193. 40 c. Type **350** 25 10
1193a. 40 c. Puerto Vallarta, Jalisco (vert.) 25 10
1194. 80 c. Acapulco (air) .. 60 15
1195. 80 c. Pyramid, Teotihuacan 60 15
1196. 80 c. "El Caracol" (Maya ruin), Yucatan .. 60 15
See also Nos. 1200/2 and 1274/7.

1969. Air. 50th Anniv. of League of Red Cross Societies.
1197. **351.** 80 c. multicoloured .. 30 10

1969. Birth Bicent. of General Ignacio Allende ("Father of Mexican Independence").
1198. **352.** 40 c. multicoloured .. 20 8

353. Dish Aerial. **354.** Question Marks.

1969. Air. Inauguration of Satellite Communications Station, Tulancingo.
1199. **353.** 80 c. multicoloured .. 35 10

1969. Tourism (2nd series). As T **350** but dated "1970". Multicoloured.
1200. 40 c. Puebla Cathedral .. 40 10
1201. 40 c. Anthropological Museum, Mexico City 40 10
1202. 40 c. Belaunzaran street, Guanajuato 40 10

1970. 9th National and 5th Agricultural Census. Multicoloured.
1204. 20 c. Type **354** 30 8
1205. 40 c. Horse's head and agricultural symbols .. 25 8

355. Diagram of Human Eye.

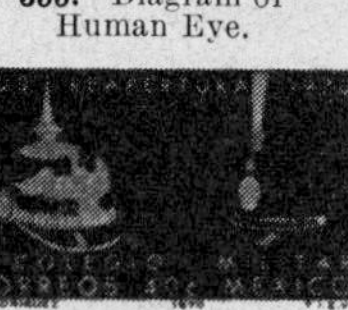

356. Cadet Ceremonial Helmet and Kepi. **357.** Jose Pino Suarez.

1970. 21st Int. Ophthalmological Congress, Mexico City.
1206. **355.** 40 c. multicoloured .. 25 8

1970. 50th Anniv. of Military College Reorganization.
1207. **356.** 40 c. multicoloured .. 20 8

1970. Birth Centenary (1969) of Jose Maria Pino Suarez (statesman).
1208. **357.** 40 c. multicoloured .. 20 8

358. Football and Masks. **360.** Composition by Beethoven.

1970. Air. World Cup Football Championship (2nd issue). Multicoloured.
1209. 80 c. Type **358** 30 15
1210. 2 p. Football and Mexican idols 25 25

1970. Air. Birth Bicent. of Beethoven.
1212. **360.** 2 p. multicoloured .. 50 25

361 Arms of Celaya. **362.** "General Assembly".

1970. 400th Anniv. of Celaya.
1213. **361.** 40 c. multicoloured .. 20 8

1970. Air. 25th Anniv. of U.N.O.
1214. **362.** 80 c. multicoloured .. 30 10

363. "Eclipse de Sol". **364.** "Galileo" (Susterman).

1970. Total Eclipse of the Sun (7.3.70).
1215. **363.** 40 c. black 20 8

1971. Air. Conquest of Space. Early Astronomers. Multicoloured.
1216. 2 p. Type **364** 25 10
1217. 2 p. "Kepler" (unknown artist) 25 10
1218. 2 p. "Sir Isaac Newton" (Kneller) 25 10

365. "Sister Juana" (M. Cabrera).

1971. Air. Mexican Arts and Sciences (1st series). Paintings. Multicoloured.
1219. 80 c. Type **365** 40 15
1220. 80 c. "El Paricutin" (volcano) (G. Murillo) .. 40 15
1221. 80 c. "Men of Flames" (J. C. Orozco) 40 15
1222. 80 c. "Self-portrait" (J. M. Velasco) .. 40 15
1223. 80 c. "Mayan Warriors" ("Dresden Codex") .. 40 15

See also Nos. 1243/7, 1284/8, 1323/7, 1351/5, 1390/4, 1417/21, 1523/7, 1540/4, 1650/4, 1688/92, 1834 and 1845.

366. Stamps from Venezuela, Mexico and Colombia.

1971. Air. "Philately for Peace". Latin-American Stamp Exhibitions 1968-70.
1224. **366.** 80 c. multicoloured .. 35 15

367. Lottery Balls.

1971. Bicent. of National Lottery.
1225. **367.** 40 c. black and green 25 8

368. "Francisco Clavijero" (P. Carlin).

1971. Air. Return of the Remains of Francisco Javier Clavijero (historian) to Mexico (1970).
1226. **368.** 2 p. brown and green 50 25

369. Vasco de Quiroga and "Utopia" (O'Gorman). **370.** "Amado Nervo" (artist unkown).

1971. 500th Birth Anniv. of Vasco de Quiroga, Archbishop of Michoacan.
1227. **369.** 40 c. multicoloured .. 20 8

1971. Birth Cent. of Amado Nervo (writer).
1228. **370.** 80 c. multicoloured .. 20 8

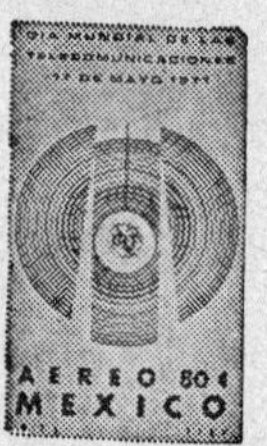

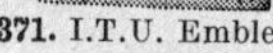

371. I.T.U. Emblem. **372.** Mariano Matamoros" (D. Rivera).

1971. Air. World Telecommunications Day.
1229. **371.** 80 c. multicoloured .. 25 10

1971. Air. Birth Bicentenary of Mariano Matamoros (patriot).
1230. **372.** 2 p. multicoloured .. 45 25

373. "General Guerrero". (O'Gorman). **374.** Loudspeaker and Sound Waves.

1971. Air. 150th Anniv. of Independence from Spain.
1231. **373.** 2 p. multicoloured .. 45 25

1971. 50th Anniv. of Radio Broadcasting in Mexico.
1232. **374.** 40 c. blk., blue & grn. 25 8

375. Pres. Cardenas and Banners. **376.** Stamps of Venezuela, Mexico, Colombia and Peru.

1971. 1st Death Anniv. of General Lazaro Cardenas.
1233. **375.** 40 c. black and lilac .. 25 8

1971. Air. "EXFILIMA 71" Stamp Exhib. Lima, Peru.
1234. **376.** 80 c. multicoloured .. 45 15

377. Abstract of Circles. **378.** Piano Keyboard.

1971. Air. 25th Anniv. of U.N.E.S.C.O.
1235. **377.** 80 c. multicoloured .. 30 15

1971. 1st Death Anniv. of Agustin Lara (composer).
1236. **378.** 40 c. blk., blue & yell. 30 8

379. "Mental Patients". **380.** City Arms of Monterrey.

1971. Air. 5th World Psychiatric Congress, Mexico City.
1237. **379.** 2 p. multicoloured .. 25 20

1971. 375th Anniv. of Monterrey.
1238. **380.** 40 c. multicoloured .. 5 5

381. Durer's Bookplate.

1971. Air. 500th Anniv. of Albrecht Durer (artist).
1239. **381.** 2 p. black and brown 40 25

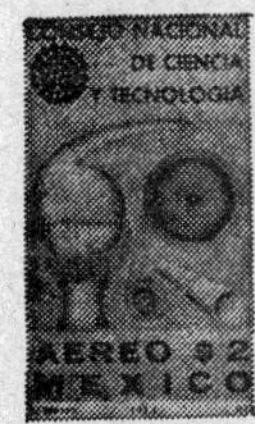

382. Scientific Symbols. **383.** Emblem of Mexican Cardiological Institute.

1972. Air. 1st Anniv. of National Council of Science and Technology.
1240. **382.** 2 p. multicoloured .. 20 5

1972. World Health Month. Multicoloured.
1241. 40 c. Type **383** (postage) 8 5
1242. 80 c. Heart specialists (air) 8 5

1972. Air. Mexican Arts and Sciences (2nd series). Portraits. As T **365**.
1243. 80 c. brown and black .. 75 15
1244. 80 c. green and black .. 75 15
1245. 80 c. brown and black .. 75 15
1246. 80 c. blue and black .. 75 15
1247. 80 c. red and black .. 75 15
PORTRAITS: No. 1243, King Netzahualcoyotl of Texcoco (patron of the arts). No. 1244, J. R. de Alarcon (lawyer). No. 1245, J. J. Fernandez de Lizardi (writer). No. 1246, E. G. Martinez (poet). No. 1247, R. L. Velardc (author).

384. Rotary Emblems. **385.** Indian Laurel and Fruit.

1972. Air. 50th Anniv. of Rotary Movement in Mexico.
1248. **384.** 80 c. multicoloured .. 8 5

1972. Centenary of Chilpancingo as Capital of Guerrero State.
1249. **385.** 40 c. blk., gold & grn. 8 5

386. Track of Car Tyre.

1972. Air. 74th Assembly of Int. Tourist Alliance, Mexico City.
1250. **386.** 80 c. black and grey .. 10 5

387. First issue of "Gaceta De Mexico". **388.** Emblem of Lions Organization.

1972. 250th Anniv. of Publication of "Gaceta De Mexico". (1st newspaper to be published in Latin America).
1251. **387.** 40 c. multicoloured .. 8 5

1972. Lions' Clubs Convention, Mexico City.
1252. **388.** 40 c. multicoloured .. 8 5

389. "Zaragoza" (cadet sail corvette). **390.** "Margarita Maza de Juarez" (artist unknown).

1972. 75th Anniv. of Naval Academy, Veracruz.
1253. **389.** 40 c. multicoloured .. 30 10

1972. Death Cent. of Pres. Benito Juarez.
1254. **390.** 20 c. mult. (postage) 35 8
1255. – 40 c. multicoloured .. 35 8
1256. – 80 c. blk. & blue (air) 10 5
1257. – 1 p. 20 multicoloured 12 5
1258. – 2 p. multicoloured .. 20 5
DESIGNS: 40 c. "Benito Juarez" (D. Rivera). 80 c. Page of Civil Register with Juarez signature. 1 p. 20 "Benito Juarez" (P. Clave). 2 p. "Benito Juarez" (J. C. Orozco).

391. "Emperor Justinian I" (mosaic). **392.** Atomic Emblem.

1972. 50th Anniv. of Mexican Bar Association.
1259. **391.** 40 c. multicoloured .. 55 8

1972. Air. 16th General Conference of Int. Atomic Energy Organization, Mexico City.
1260 **392.** 2p. blk., blue and grey 15 5

393. Caravel on "Stamp". **394.** "Sobre las Olas" (sheet-music cover by O'Brandstetter).

1972. Stamp Day of the Americas.
1261. **393.** 80 c. violet and brown 12 5

1972. Air. 28th Int. Author's and Composers' Society Congress. Mexico City.
1262. **394.** 80 c. brown 12 5

395. "Mother and Child". (G. Galvin).

1972. Air. 25th Anniv. of U.N.I.C.E.F.
1263. **395.** 80 c. multicoloured .. 50 10

396. "Father Pedro de Gante" (Rodriguez y Arangorti). **397.** Olympic Emblems.

1972. Air. 400th Death Anniv. of Father Pedro de Gante (founder of first school in Mexico).
1264. **396.** 2 p. multicoloured .. 25 5

1972. Olympic Games, Munich.
1265. **397.** 40 c. multicoloured (postage) 8 5
1266. – 80 c. multicoloured (air) 12 5
1267. – 2 p. blk., grn. & blue 25 5
DESIGNS—HORIZ. 80 c. "Football". VERT. 2 p. Similar to Type **397**.

398. Books on Shelves. **400.** "Footprints on the Americas".

399. Fish ("Pure Water").

1972. Int. Book Year.
1268. **398.** 40 c. multicoloured .. 8 5

1972. Anti-Pollution Campaign.
1269. **399.** 40 c. blk. & blue (post.) 8 5
1270. – 80 c. blk. & blue (air) 12 5
DESIGN—VERT. 80 c. Pigeon on cornice ("Pure Air").

1972. Air. Tourist Year of the Americas.
1271. **400.** 80 c. multicoloured 12 5

401. Stamps of Mexico, Colombia, Venezuela, Peru and Brazil.

1973. Air. "EXFILBRA 72" Stamp Exhibition, Rio de Janeiro, Brazil.
1272. **401.** 80 c. multicoloured .. 12 5

402. "Metlac Viaduct" (J. M.Velasco).

1973. Cent. of Mexican Railways.
1273. **402.** 40 c. multicoloured 90 10

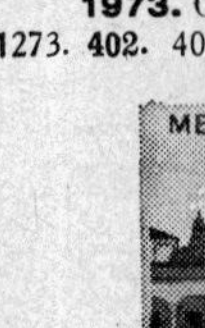

403. Ocotlan Abbey.

1973. Tourism (3rd series). Multicoloured.
1274. 40 c. Type **403** (postage) .. 20 8
1275. 40 c. Indian hunting dance, Sonora (vert.) .. 20 8
1276. 80 c. Girl in local costume (vert.) (air) 35 15
1277. 80 c. Sport fishing, Lower California 35 10

404. "God of the Winds".

1973. Air. Centenary of W.M.O.
1278. **404.** 80 c. blk., blue & mauve 35 10

405. Copernicus. **406.** Cadet.

1973. Air. 500th Birth Anniv. of Copernicus (astronomer).
1279. **405.** 80 c. green 12 5

1973. 150th Anniv. of Military College.
1280. **406.** 40 c. multicoloured .. 8 8

407. "Francisco Madero" (D. Rivera). **408.** Antonio Narro (founder).

1973. Birth Centenary of Pres. Francisco Madero.
1281. **407.** 40 c. multicoloured .. 8 5

1973. 50th Anniv. of "Antonio Narro" Agricultural School, Saltillo.
1282. **408.** 40 c. grey 8 5

409. San Martin Statue. **410.** Caryon Molecules.

1973. Air. Argentina's Gift of San Martin Statue to Mexico City.
1283. **409.** 80 c. multicoloured .. 12 5

1973. Air. "Mexican Arts and Sciences". (3rd series). Astronomers. As T **365** but dated "1973". Multicoloured.
1284. 80 c. green and red .. 10 10
1285. 80 c. multicoloured .. 10 10
1286. 80 c. multicoloured .. 10 10
1287. 80 c. multicoloured .. 10 10
1288. 80 c. multicoloured .. 10 10
DESIGNS: No. 1284, Aztec "Sun" stone. No. 1285, Carlos de Siguenza y Gongora. No. 1286, Francisco Diaz Covarrubias. No. 1287, Joaquin Gallo. No. 1288, Luis Enrique Erro.

1973. 25th Anniv. of Chemical Engineering School.
1289. **410.** 40 c. blk., yell. & red 8 5

411. Fist with Pointing Finger. 412. "EXMEX 73" Emblem.

1974. Promotion of Exports.
1294. **411.** 40 c. black and green 8 5

1974. "EXMEX 73" National Stamp Exhibition, Cuernavaca.
1295. **412.** 40 c. black (postage) 8 5
1296. – 80 c. mult. (air) .. 12 8
DESIGN: 80 c. Cortes' Palace, Cuernavaca.

413. Manuel Ponce.

1974. 25th Death Anniv. (1973) of Manuel M. Ponce (composer).
1297. **413.** 40 c. multicoloured.. 8 5

414. Gold Brooch, Mochica Culture.

1974. Air. Exhibition of Peruvian Gold Treasures, Mexico City.
1298. **414.** 80 c. multicoloured.. 15 10

415. C.E.P.A.L. Emblem and Flags. 416. Baggage.

1974. Air. 25th Anniv. of U.N. Economic Commission for Latin America (C.E.P.A.L.).
1299. **415.** 80 c. multicoloured .. 12 5

1974. Air. 16th Confederation of Latin American Tourist Organizations (C.O.T.A.L.) Convention, Acapulco.
1300. **416.** 80 c. multicoloured.. 12 5

417. Silver Statuette. 419. "Dancing Dogs" (Indian statuette).

418. "The Enamelled Saucepan" (Picasso).

1974. 1st International Silver Fair, Mexico City.
1301. **417.** 40 c. multicoloured.. 8 5

1974. Air. 1st Death Anniv. of Pablo Picasso (artist).
1302. **418.** 80 c. multicoloured.. 12 5

1974. 6th Season of Dog Shows.
1303. **419.** 40 c. multicoloured.. 8 5

420. Mariano Azuela.

1974. Birth Cent. (1973) of Mariano Azuela (writer).
1304. **420.** 40 c. multicoloured.. 8 5

421. Tepotzotlan Viaduct.

1974. National Engineers' Day.
1305. **421.** 40 c. black and blue.. 55 12

422. R. Robles (surgeon).

1974. 25th Anniv. of W.H.O.
1306. **422.** 40 c. brown and green 8 5

423. U.P.U. Emblem.

1974. "Exfilmex 74" Inter-American Stamp Exhibition, Mexico City.
1307. **423.** 40 c. black and green on yell (postage) .. 8 5
1308. 80 c. black and brown on yellow (air) .. 12 5

424. Demosthenes. 426. Map and Indian Head.

425. Early Biplane.

1974. 2nd Spanish-American Reading and Writing Studies Congress, Mexico City.
1309. **424.** 20 c. green and brown 35 8

1974. Air. 50th Anniv. of "Mexicana" (Mexican Airlines). Multicoloured.
1310. 80 c. Type **425** 15 10
1311. 2 p. Jetliner 40 10

1974. Union with Chiapas. 150th Anniv.
1312. **426.** 20 c. green and brown 5 5

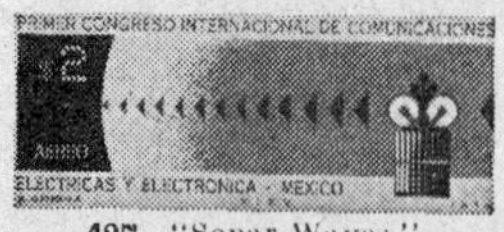

427. "Sonar Waves".

1974. Air. 1st International Electrical and Electronic Communications Congress, Mexico City.
1313. **427.** 2 p. multicoloured .. 15 5

428. S. Lerdo de Tejada. 429. Manuscript of Constitution.

1974. Cent. of Restoration of Senate.
1314. **428.** 40 c. black and blue.. 8 5

1974. 150th Anniv. of Federal Republic.
1315. **429.** 40 c. black and green 8 5

430. Ball in Play.

1974. Air. 8th World Volleyball Championships, Mexico City.
1316. **430.** 2 p. blk., brn. & orge. 15 5

432. F. C. Puerto. 433. Mask, bat and Catcher's glove.

1974. Air. Birth Centenary of Felipe Carrillo Puerto (politician and journalist).
1318. **432.** 80 c. brown & green 8 5

1974. Air. 50th Anniv. of Mexican Baseball League.
1319. **433.** 80 c. brown and green 8 5

434. U.P.U. Monument.

1974. Cent. of U.P.U.
1320. **434.** 40 c. brown & blue (post.) 10 5
1321. – 80 c. multicoloured (air) 8 5
1322. – 2 p. brown & green.. 20 5
DESIGNS: 80 c. Man's face as letter-box, Colonial period. 2p. Heinrich von Stephan, founder of U.P.U.

1974. Air. Mexican Arts and Sciences (4th series). Music and Musicinas. As T **365** but dated "1974". Multicoloured.
1323. 80 c. "Musicians"-Mayan painting, Bonampak .. 12 5
1324. 80 c. First Mexican-printed score, 1556 .. .. 12 5
1325. 80 c. Angela Peralta (soprano and composer) 12 5
1326. 80 c. "Miguel Lerdo de Tejada" (composer) (F. S. Rayon) .. 12 5
1327. 80 c. "Silvestre Revueltas" (composer) (bronze by Carlos Bracho) .. 12 5

435. I.W.Y. Emblem. 436. Economic Charter.

1975. Air. International Women's Year.
1328. **435.** 1 p. 60 black and red 15 5

1975. Air. U.N. Declaration of Nations' Economic Rights and Duties.
1329. **436.** 1 p. 60 multicoloured 15 5

437. Jose Maria Mora. 439. Dr. M. Jimenez.

438. Balsa raft "Acali".

1975. 150th Anniv. of Federal Republic.
1330. **437.** 20 c. multicoloured .. 5 5

1975. Air. Trans-Atlantic Voyage of "Acali". Canary Islands to Yucatan (1973).
1331. **438.** 80 c. multicoloured .. 30 10

1975. Air. Fifth World Gastroenterological Congress.
1332. **439.** 2 p. multicoloured .. 15 5

440. Aztec Merchants with Goods ("Codex Florentino").

1975. Centenary (1974) of Mexican Chamber of Commerce.
1333. **440.** 80 c. multicoloured.. 8 5

441. Miguel de Cervantes Saavedra (Spanish author). 442. 4-reales Coin of 1675.

1975. Air. Third International Cervantes Festival, Guanajuato.
1334. **441.** 1 p. 60 red and black 15 5

1975. Air. International Numismatics Convention "Mexico 74".
1335. **442.** 1 p. 60 bronze and blue 15 5

443. Salvador Novo.

1975. Air. 1st Death Anniv. of Salvador Novo (poet and writer).

1336. **443.** 1 p. 60 multicoloured 15 5

444. " Self-portrait " (Siqueiros).

1975. Air. 1st Death Anniv. of David Alfaro Siqueiros (painter).

1337. **444.** 1 p. 60 multicoloured 15 5

445. General Juan Aldama (detail from mural by Diego Rivera).

1975. Birth Bicentenary (1974) of General Aldama.

1338. **445.** 80 c. multicoloured .. 8 5

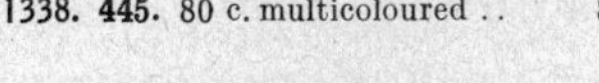

446. U.N. and I.W.Y. Emblems.

1975. Air. International Women's Year and World Conference.

1339. **446.** 1 p. 60 blue and pink 12 5

447. Eagle and Snake (" Codex Duran ").

1975. 650th Anniv. of Tenochtitlan (now Mexico City). Multicoloured.

1340. 80 c. Type **447** (postage) 8 5

1341. 1 p. 60 Arms of Mexico City (air) 15 5

448. Domingo F. Sarmiento (educator and statesman).

449. Teacher's Monument, Mexico City.

1975. Air. 1st Int. Congress of " Third World " Educators, Acapulco.

1342. **448.** 1 p. 60 grn. & brown 15 5

1975. Air. Mexican-Lebanese Friendship.

1343. **449.** 4 p. 30 green & brown 25 5

450. Games' Emblem.

1975. Air. 7th Pan-American Games, Mexico City.

1344. **450.** 1 p. 60 multicoloured 15 5

451. Julian Carrillo (composer.)

452. Academy Emblem.

1975. Birth Centenary of J. Carrillo.

1345. **451.** 80 c. brown and grn. 5 5

1975. Cent. of Mexican Languages Academy.

1346. **452.** 80 c. yellow and brn. 5 5

453. University Building.

1975. 50th Anniv. of Guadalajara University.

1347. **453.** 80 c. blk., brn. & pink 8 5

454. Dr. Atl.

455. Road Builders.

1975. Air. Atl (Gerardo Murillo-painter and writer). Birth Centenary.

1348. **454.** 4 p. 30 multicoloured 25 10

1975. " 50 Years of Road Construction " and 15th World Road Congress, Mexico City.

1349. **455.** 80 c. blk. & grn. (post.) 8 5

1350. – 1 p. 60 blk. & blue (air) 12 5

DESIGN: 1 p. 60 Congress emblem.

1975. Air. Mexican Arts and Sciences (5th series). As T **365**, but dated " 1975 ". Multicoloured.

1351. 1 p. 60 Title page, F. Hernandez' " History of New Spain " .. 12 5

1352. 1 p. 60 A. L. Herrera (naturalist) .. 12 5

1353. 1 p. 60 Page from " Badiano Codex " (Aztec herbal) 12 5

1354. 1 p. 60 A. Rosenblueth Stearns (neurophysiologist) .. 12 5

1355. 1 p. 60 A. A. Duges (botanist and zoologist) .. 12 5

456. Car Engine Parts.

457. Aguascalientes Cathedral.

1975. Mexican Exports. Multicoloured.

No.	Type	Description	Unused	Used
1356	–	5 c. blue (postage)	35	5
1471	–	20 c. black ..	35	5
1356b	–	40 c. brown ..	30	5
1356c	**456**	50 c. blue ..	35	5
1472		50 c. black ..	5	5
1473	–	80 c. red	5	5
1474	–	1 p. violet & yellow	8	5
1358a	–	1 p. black & orge	5	5
1475	–	2 p. blue & turq ..	45	5
1476	–	3 p. brown ..	25	5
1359b	–	4 p. red and brown	25	8
1359e	–	5 p. brown ..	8	5
1359ed	–	6 p. red	8	5
1359ee	–	6 p. grey ..	8	5
1359f	–	7 p. blue ..	8	5
1359g	–	8 p. brown ..	8	5
1359h	–	9 p. blue	8	5
1479	–	10 p. lt green & grn	95	45
1360ac	–	10 p. red	5	5
1360ad	–	15 p. orange & brn	15	8
1360b	–	20 p. black ..	15	10
1360bc	–	20 p. black & red	5	5
1360be	–	25 p. brown ..	25	10
1360bh	–	35 p. yellow & mve	25	10
1360bk	–	40 p. yellow & brn	25	10
1360bl	–	40 p. gold & green	25	10
1360bm	–	40 p. black ..	10	10
1360c	–	50 p. multicoloured	1·25	35
1360d	–	50 p. yellow & blue	35	20
1360da	–	50 p. red & green	35	20
1360db	–	60 p. brown ..	30	15
1360dc	–	70 p. brown ..	35	20
1360de	–	80 p. gold & mauve	20	50
1360df	–	80 p. blue ..	80	50
1360dg	–	90 p. blue & green	85	55
1360e	–	100 p. red, green and grey ..	70	35
1360ea	–	100 p. brown ..	5	5
1360f	–	200 p. yellow, green and grey ..	1·90	30
1360fb	–	200 p. yellow & grn	8	5
1360g	–	300 p. blue, red and grey	60	60
1360gb	–	300 p. blue and red	15	8
1360h	–	400 p. bistre, brown and grey ..	95	35
1360hb	–	450 p. brown & mve	20	8
1360i	–	500 p. green, orange and grey ..	1·90	30
1360ib	–	500 p. grey & blue	20	8
1360j	–	600 p. mult ..	30	5
1360k	–	700 p. black, red and green ..	35	5
1360kb	–	750 p. black, red anf green ..	30	10
1360l	–	800 p. brn & dp brn	40	5
1360m	**456**	900 p. black ..	50	8
1360n	–	950 p. blue ..	40	20
1481a	–	1000 p. black, red and grey ..	50	20
1360pa	–	1000 p. red & black	40	8
1360q	–	1100 p. grey ..	60	30
1360r	–	1300 p. red, green and grey ..	60	30
1360rb	–	1300 p. red & green	50	25
1360rg	–	1400 p. black ..	50	20
1360s	–	1500 p. brown ..	55	45
1360t	–	1600 p. orange ..	65	30
1360u	–	1700 p. green and deep green ..	70	30
1360w	–	1900 p. blue & grn	1·25	50
1481b	–	2000 p. blk & grey	1·25	50
1360xa	–	2000 p. black ..	80	55
1360y	–	2100 p. black, orange and grey	80	55
1360ya	–	2100 p. black & red	80	55
1360yb	–	2200 p. red ..	90	60
1360z	–	2500 p. blue & grey	95	65
1360za	–	2500 p. blue ..	95	65
1360zc	–	2800 p. black ..	1·10	75
1481c	–	3000 p. green, grey and orange ..	1·75	75
1360zf	**456**	3600 p. blk & grey	1·50	1·00
1360zg	–	3900 p. grey & blue	1·60	1·10
1481d	–	4000 p. yellow, grey and red ..	2·40	1·25
1360zj	–	4800 p. red, green and grey ..	1·90	1·25
1481e	–	5000 p. grey, green and orange ..	3·00	1·50
1360zn	–	6000 p. green, yellow and grey	2·40	1·60
1360zq	–	7200 p. mult ..	3·00	2·00
1361	–	30 c. bronze (air)	30	5
1482	–	50 c. green & brn	5	5
1361a	–	80 c. blue ..	10	5
1483	–	1 p. 60 blk & orge	5	5
1484	–	1 p. 90 red & green	15	8
1361d	–	2 p. gold and blue	25	8
1485	–	2 p. 50 red & green	5	5
1361e	–	4 p. yellow & brn	25	8
1361f	–	4 p. 30 mve & grn	10	20
1361g	–	5 p. blue & yellow	95	20
1361h	–	5 p. 20 black & red	25	25
1361i	–	5 p. 60 green & yell	10	30
1488	–	10 p. green and light green ..	55	40
1361j	–	20 p. black, red and green	2·75	85
1361k	–	50 p. multicoloured	1·60	95

DESIGNS—POSTAGE. 5 c., 6, 1600 p. Steel tubes. 20 c., 40 (1360bm), 1400, 2800 p. Laboratory flasks. 40 c., 100 p. (1360ea) Cup of coffee. 80 c., 10 p. (1360ac), 2200 p. Steer marked with beef cuts. 1, 3000 p. Electric cable. 2, 90, 1900 p. Sea shell. 3, 60 p. Men's shoes. 4 p. Ceramic tiles. 5, 1100 p. Chemical formulae. 7, 8, 9, 80 (1360df), 2500 p. Textiles. 10 (1479), 1700 p. Tequila. 15 p. Honeycomb. 20 p. (1360b), 2000 p. Wrought iron. 20 (1360bc), 2100 p. Bicycles. 25, 70, 1500 p. Hammered copper vase. 35, 40 (1360bk/bl), 50 (1360d), 80 p. (1360de) Books. 50 p. (1360c), 600 p. Jewellery. 50 p. (1360da), 4800 p. Tomato. 100 p. (1360e), 1300 p. Strawberries. 200, 6000 p. Citrus fruit. 300 p. Motor vehicles. 400, 450 p. Printed circuit. 500 p. (1360i), 5000 p. Cotton boll. 500 p. (1360ib), 3900 p. Valves (petroleum) industry. 700, 750, 7200 p. Film. 800 p. Construction materials. 1000 p. Farm machinery. 4000 p. Bee and honeycomb. AIR. 30 c. Hammered copper vase. 50 c. Electronic components. 80 c. Textiles. 1 p. 60, Bicycles. 1 p. 90, Valves (petroleum) industry. 2 p. Books. 2 p. 50, Tomato. 4p. Bee and honeycombe. 4 p. 30, Strawberry. 5 p. Motor vehicles. 5 p. 20, Farm machinery. 5 p. 60, Cotton boll. 10 p. Citrus fruit. 20 p. Film. 50 p. Cotton.

1975. 400th Anniv of Aguascalientes.

1362 **457** 50 c. black and green 35 5

458. J. T. Bodet.

460. " Death of Cuautemoc " (Chavez Morado).

459. " Fresco " (J. C. Orozco).

1975. 1st Death Anniv. of Jaime T. Bodet (author and late Director-General of U.N.E.S.C.O.).

1363. **458.** 80 c. brown and blue 8 5

1975. 150th Anniv. of Mexican Supreme Court of Justice.

1364. **459.** 80 c. multicoloured .. 8 5

1975. 450th Death Anniv. of Emperor Cuautemoc.

1365. **460.** 80 c. multicoloured .. 8 5

461. Allegory of Irrigation.

1976. 50th Anniv. of Nat. Irrigation Commission.

1366. **461.** 80 c. dark blue & blue 8 5

462. City Gateway.

1976. 400th Anniv. of Leon de los Aldamas, Guanajuato.

1367. **462.** 80 c. yellow & purple 8 5

463. Early Telephone.

464. Gold Coin.

1976. Air. Telephone Centenary.

1368. **463.** 1 p. 60 black and grey 10 5

1976. Air. 4th Int. Numismatics Convention.

1369. **464.** 1 p. 60 gold, brn. & blk. 10 5

465. Tlaloc (Aztec god of rain) and Calles Dam.

1976. Air. 12th Int. Great Dams Congress.

1370. **465.** 1 p. 60 purple & green 20 10

466. Perforation Gauge.

1976. Air. " Interphil '76 " Int. Stamp Exn., Philadelphia.

1371. **466.** 1 p. 60 blk., red & blue 20 10

467. Rainbow over Industrial Skyline.

470. Liberty Bell.

1976. Air. U.N. Conf. on Human Settlements.
1372. **467.** 1 p. 60 multicoloured 20 10

1976. Air. Bicentenary of American War of Independence.
1378. **470.** 1 p. 60 blue & mauve 20 10

471. Forest Fire.

1976. Fire Prevention Campaign
1379 **471.** 80 c. multicoloured .. 8 5

472. Peace Texts. **473.** Children on TV Screen.

1976. Air. 30th International Asian and North American Science and Humanities Congress, Mexico City.
1380. **472.** 1 p. 60 multicoloured 15 10

1976. Air. 1st Latin-American Forum on Children's Television.
1381. **473.** 1 p. 60 multicoloured 20 10

474. Scout's Hat. **475.** Exhibition Emblem.

1976. 50th Anniv. of Mexican Boy Scout Movement.
1382. **474.** 80 c. olive and brown 8 5

1976. "Mexico Today and Tomorrow" Exhibition.
1383. **475.** 80 c. blk., red & turq. 8 5

476. New Buildings. **477.** Dr. R. Vertiz.

1976. Inaug. of New Military College Buildings.
1384. **476.** 50 c. brown and ochre 8 5

1976. Centenary of Ophthalmological Hospital of Our Lady of the Light.
1385 **477** 80 c. brown and black 8 5

478. Guadalupe Basilica.

1976. Inaug. of Guadalupe Basilica.
1386. **478.** 50 c. bistre and black 8 5

479. "40" and Emblem.

1976. 40th Anniv. of National Polytechnic Institute.
1387. **479.** 80 c. blk., red and grn. 8 5

480. Blast Furnace.

1976. Inauguration of Lazaro Cardenas Steel Mill, Las Truchas.
1388. **480.** 50 c. multicoloured .. 5 5

481. Natural Elements.

1976. Air. World Urbanisation Day.
1389. **481.** 1 p. 60 multicoloured 10 5

1976. Air. Mexican Arts and Sciences (6th series). As T **365** but dated "1976". Multicoloured.
1390. 1 p. 60 black and red .. 10 5
1391. 1 p. 60 multicoloured .. 10 5
1392. 1 p. 60 black and yellow 10 5
1393. 1 p. 60 multicoloured .. 10 5
1394. 1 p. 60 brown and black 10 5
DESIGNS: No. 1390, "The Signal" (Angela Gurria). No. 1391, "The God of Today" (L. Ortiz Monasterio). No. 1392, "The God Coatlicue" (traditional Mexican sculpture). No. 1393, "Tlahuicole" (Manuel Vilar). No. 1394, "The Horseman" (Manuel Tolsa).

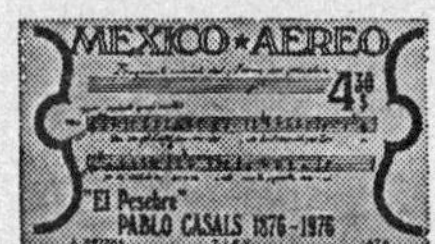

482. Score of "El Pesebre".

1977. Air. Birth Cent. of Pablo Casals (cellist).
1395. **482.** 4 p. 30 blue and brown 12 5

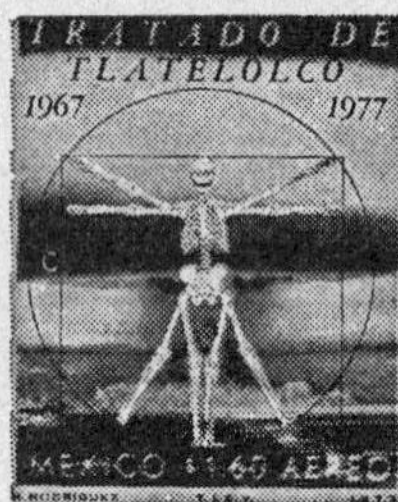

483. "Man's Destruction".

1977. Air. 10th Anniv. of Treaty of Tlatelolco.
1396. **483.** 1 p. 60 multicoloured 8 5

484. Saltillo Cathedral. **485.** Light Switch, Pylon and Engineers.

1977. 400th Anniv. of Founding of Saltillo.
1397. **484.** 80 c. brown & yellow 5 5

1977. 40 years of Development in Mexico. Federal Electricity Commission.
1398. **485.** 80 c. multicoloured .. 5 5

486. Footballers.

1977. Air. 50th Anniv. of Mexican Football Federation.
1399. **486.** 1 p. 60 multicoloured 8 5
1400. – 4 p. 30 yell., blue & blk. 15 5
DESIGN: 4 p. 30 Football emblem.

487. Hands and Scales.

1977. Air. 50th Anniv. of Federal Council of Reconciliation and Arbitration.
1401. **487.** 1 p. 60 orge., brn. & blk. 8 5

488. Flags of Spain and Mexico. **489.** Tlaloc (weather god).

1977. Resumption of Diplomatic Relations with Spain.
1402. **488.** 50 c. multicoloured (postage) 5 5
1403. 80 c. multicoloured .. 5 5
1404. – 1 p. 60 blk. & grey (air) 5 5
1405. – 1 p. 90 red, green and pale green 8 5
1406. – 4 p. 30 grey, brn. & grn. 12 5
DESIGNS: 1 p. 60, Arms of Mexico and Spain. 1 p. 90, Maps of Mexico and Spain. 4 p. 30, President Jose Lopez Portillo and King Juan Carlos.

1977. Air. Centenary of Central Meteorological Observatory.
1407. **489.** 1 p. 60 multicoloured 8 5

490. Ludwig van Beethoven. **491.** A. Serdan.

1977. Air. 150th Death Anniv. of Beethoven.
1408. **490.** 1 p. 60 grn. & brown 8 5
1409. 4 p. 30 red and blue .. 12 5

1977. Birth Centenary of Aquiles Serdan (revolutionary martyr).
1410. **491.** 80 c. blk., turq. & grn. 5 5

492. Mexico City-Guernavaca Highway.

1977. Air. 25th Anniv. of First National Highway.
1411. **492.** 1 p. 60 multicoloured 8 5

493. Poinsettia. **494.** Arms of Campeche.

1977. Christmas.
1412. **493.** 50 c. multicoloured .. 5 5

1977. Air. Bicent. of Naming of Campeche.
1413. **494.** 1 p. 60 multicoloured 8 5

495. Tractor and Dam.

1977. Air. U.N. Desertification Conference, Mexico City.
1414. **495.** 1 p. 60 multicoloured 8 5

496. Congress Emblem.

1977. Air. 20th World Education, Hygiene and Recreation Congress.
1415. **496.** 1 p. 60 multicoloured 8 5

497. Freighter "Rio Yaqui". **498.** Mayan Dancer.

1977. Air. 60th Anniv. of National Merchant Marine.
1416. **497.** 1 p. 60 multicoloured 40 10

1977. Air. Mexican Arts and Sciences (7th series). Pre-colonial statuettes.
1417. **498.** 1 p. 60 red, blk. & pink 8 5
1418. – 1 p. 60 blue, black and pale blue .. 8 5
1419. – 1 p. 60 grey, black and yellow 8 5
1420. – 1 p. 60 green, black and turquoise .. 8 5
1421. – 1 p. 60 red, black and grey 8 5
DESIGNS: No. 1418, Aztec god of dance. No. 1419, Snake dance. No. 1420, Dancer, Monte Alban. No. 1421, Dancer, Totonaca.

499. Hospital Scene.

1978. Air. 35th Anniv. of Mexican Social Insurance Institute. Multicoloured.
1422. 1 p. 60 Type **499** 8 5
1423. 4 p. 30 Workers drawing benefits 15 5

500. Moorish Fountain.

1978. Air. 450th Anniv. of Chiapa de Corzo, Chiapas.
1424. **500.** 1 p. 60 multicoloured 8 5

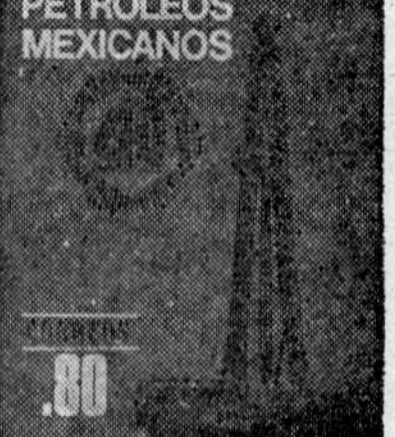

501. Telephones. 1878 and 1978. **502.** Oilwell.

1978. Cent. of Mexican Telephone.
1425. **501.** 80 c. red and salmon 5 5

1978. 40th Anniv. of Nationalization of Oil Resources.
1426. **502.** 80 c. red and salmon (postage) 10 10
1427. – 1 p. 60 blue & red (air) 10 10
1428. – 4 p. 30 black, light blue and blue .. 35 10
DESIGNS: 1 p. 60, General I. Cardenas (President, 1938). 4 p. 30, Oil rig, Gulf of Mexico.

503. Arms of San Cristobal las Casas.

1978. Air. 450th Anniv. of San Cristobal de las Casas, Chiapas.
1429. **503.** 1 p. 60 purple, pink and black 5 5

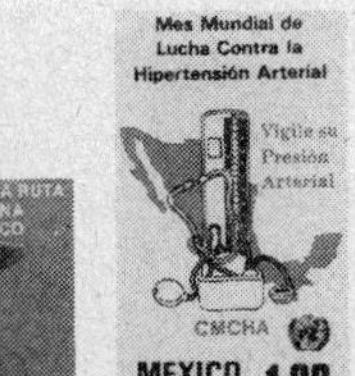

504. 1928 Mail Plane. **506.** Blood Pressure Gauge and Map of Mexico.

505. Globe and Cogwheel.

1978. Air. 50th Anniv. of First Mexican Airmail Route.
1430. **504.** 1 p. 60 multicoloured 20 10
1431. 4 p. 30 multicoloured 30 10

1978. Air. World Conference on Technical Co-operation between Underdeveloped Countries. Multicoloured.
1432. 1 p. 60 Type **505** .. 8 5
1433. 4 p. 30 Globe and cog-wheel joined by flags .. 12 5

1978. Air. World Hypertension Month and World Health Day.
1434. **506.** 1 p. 60 blue and red .. 8 5
1435. – 4 p. 30 salmon & blue 12 5
Design: 4 p. 30, Hand with stethoscope.

507. Kicking Ball. **508.** Francisco (Pancho) Villa.

1978. Air. World Cup Football Championship, Argentina.
1436. **507.** 1 p. 60 blue, pale orange and orange 8 5
1437. – 1 p. 90 blue, brown and orange .. 10 5
1438. – 4 p. 30 blue, green and orange .. 12 5
Designs: 1 p. 90, Saving a goal. 4 p. 30, Footballer.

1978. Air. Birth Centenary of Francisco Villa (revolutionary leader).
1439. **508.** 1 p. 60 multicoloured 8 5

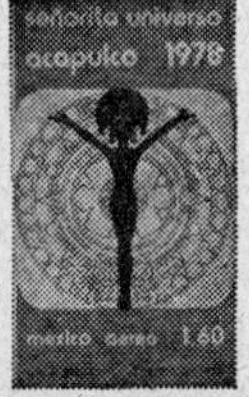

509. Emilio Carranza Stamp of 1929. **510.** Woman and Calendar Stone.

1978. Air. 50th Anniv. of Mexico–Washington Flight by Emilio Carranza.
1440. **509.** 1 p. 60 red and brown 8 5

1978. Air. Miss Universe Contest, Acapulco.
1441. **510.** 1 p. 60 blk., brn. & red 8 5
1442. 1 p. 90 blk., brn. & grn. 10 5
1443. 4 p. 30 blk., brn. & red 15 8

511. Alvaro Obregon (J. Romero).

1978. Air. 50th Death Anniv. of Alvaro Obregon (statesman).
1444. **511.** 1 p. 60 multicoloured 8 5

512. Institute Emblem.

1978. 50th Anniv. of Pan-American Institute for Geography and History.
1445. **512.** 80 c. blue and black (postage) 5 5
1446. – 1 p. 60 grn. & blk. (air) 8 5
1447. – 4 p. 30 brown & black 12 5
Designs: 1 p. 60, 4 p. 30, Designs as Type **512**, showing emblem.

513. Sun rising over Ciudad Obregon. **514.** Mayan Statue, Rook and Pawn.

1978. Air. 50th Anniv. of Ciudad Obregon.
1448. **513.** 1 p. 60 multicoloured 8 5

1978. Air. World Youth Team Chess Championship, Mexico City.
1449. **514.** 1 p. 60 multicoloured 8 5
1450. 4 p. 30 multicoloured 20 5

515. Aristotle. **516.** Mule Deer.

1978. Air. 2300th Death Anniv. of Aristotle.
1451. **515.** 1 p. 60 grey, blue and yellow 8 5
1452. – 4 p. 30 grey, red and yellow 20 5
Design: 4 p. 30, Statue of Aristotle.

1978. Air. World Youth Team Chess Championship, Mexico City.
1453. 1 p. 60 Type **516** .. 20 10
1454. 1 p. 60 Ocelot 20 10
See also Nos. 1548/9, 1591/2, 1638/9 and 1683/4.

517. Man's Head and Dove. **518.** " Dahlia coccinea ". (" Dalia " on stamp).

1978. Air. International Anti-Apartheid Year.
1455. **517.** 1 p. 60 grey, red and black 8 5
1456. – 4 p. 30 grey, lilac and black 12 5
Design: 4 p. 30, Woman's head and dove.

1978. Mexican Flowers (1st series). Mult.
1457. 50 c. Type **518** 5 5
1458. 80 c. " Plumeria rubra " 5 5
See also Nos. 1550/1, 1593/4, 1645/6, 1681/2, 1791/2 and 1913/14.

519. Emblem. **520.** Dr. Rafael Lucio.

1978. Air. 12th World Architects' Congress.
1459. **519.** 1 p. 60 red black and orange 8 5

1978. Air. 11th International Leprosy Congress.
1460. **520.** 1 p. 60 green 8 5

521. Franz Schubert and " Death and the Maiden ". **522.** Decorations and Candles.

1978. Air. 150th Death Anniv. of Franz Schubert (composer).
1461. **521.** 4 p. 30 brown, black and green 12 5

1978. Christmas. Multicoloured.
1462. 50 c. Type **522** (postage) 8 5
1463. 1 p. 60 Children and decoration (air) .. 8 5

523. Antonio Vivaldi. **524.** Wright " Flyer ".

1978. Air. 300th Birth Anniv. of Antonio Vivaldi (composer).
1464. **523.** 4 p. 30 red, stone and brown 12 5

1978. Air. 75th Anniv. of First Powered Flight.
1465. **524.** 1 p. 60 orange, yellow and mauve .. 15 10
1466. – 4 p. 30 yell., red & flesh 30 10
Design: 4 p. 30, Side view of Wright "Flyer".

525. Albert Einstein and Equation.

1979. Air. Birth Centenary of Albert Einstein (physicist).
1467. **525.** 1 p. 60 multicoloured 8 5

526. Arms of Hermosillo. **527.** Sir Rowland Hill.

1979. Cent. of Hermosillo, Sonora.
1468. **526.** 80 c. multicoloured .. 5 5

1979. Air. Death Centenary of Sir Rowland Hill.
1469. **527.** 1 p. 60 multicoloured 8 5

528. " Children " (Adriana Blas Casas).

1979. Air. International Year of the Child.
1470. **528.** 1 p. 60 multicoloured 8 5

529. Registered Letter from Mexico to Rome, 1880.

1979. Air. " Mepsipex 79 ", Third International Exhibition of Elmhurst Philatelic Society, Mexico City.
1499. **529.** 1 p. 60 multicoloured 8 5

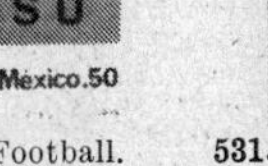

530. Football. **531.** Josefa Ortiz de Dominguez.

1979. " Universiada 79 ", 10th World University Games, Mexico City (1st issue).
1500. **530.** 50 c. grey, black and blue (postage) .. 5 5
1501. – 80 c. multicoloured .. 5 5
1502. – 1 p. multicoloured .. 5 5
1504. – 1 p. 60 multicoloured (air) 8 5
1505. – 4 p. 30 multicoloured 15 10
Designs—Vert. 80 c. Aztec ball player. 1 p. Wall painting of athletes. 1 p. 60, Games emblem. 4 p. 30, Flame and doves.
See also Nos. 1514/19.

1979. 150th Death Anniv. of Josefa Ortiz de Dominguez (Mayor of Queretaro).
1507. **531.** 80 c. pink, black and bright pink .. 5 5

532. " Allegory of National Culture " (Alfaro Siqueiros).

1979. 50th Anniv. of National University's Autonomy. Multicoloured.
1508. 80 c. Type **532** (postage) 5 5
1509. 3 p. " The Conquest of Energy " (Chavez Morado) 20 10
1510. 1 p. 60 " The Return of Quetzalcoatl " (Chavez Morado) (air) .. 8 5
1511. 4 p. 30 " Students reaching for Culture " (Alfaro Siqueiros) .. 15 10

533. Messenger and U.P.U. Emblem. **534.** Emiliano Zapata (after Diego Rivera).

1979. Air. Centenary of Mexico's Admission to U.P.U.
1512. **533.** 1 p. 60 yellow, black and brown .. 8 5

1979. Birth Centenary of Emiliano Zapata (revolutionary).
1513. **534.** 80 c. multicoloured .. 5 5

535. Football. 536. Tepoztlan, Morelos.

1979. "Universiada '79", 10th World University Games, Mexico City (2nd issue). Multicoloured.

1514. 50 c. Type **535** (postage) 5 5
1515. 80 c. Volleyball 5 5
1516. 1 p. Basketball 8 5
1518. 1 p. 60 Tennis (air) .. 8 5
1519. 5 p. 50 Swimming .. 30 20

1979. Tourism (1st series). Multicoloured.

1526. 80 c. Type **536** (postage) 5 5
1527. 80 c. Mexacaltitan, Nayarit 5 5
1528. 1 p. 60 Agua Azul waterfall, Chipas (air) .. 8 5
1529. 1 p. 60 King Coliman statue, Colima 8 5

See also Nos. 1631/4 and 1675/8.

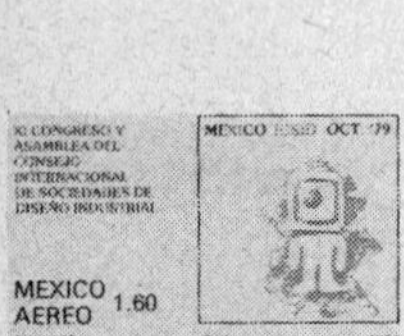

537. Congress Emblem. 538. Edison Lamp.

1979. Air. 11th Congress and Assembly of International Industrial Design Council.

1530. **537.** 1 p. 60 black, mauve and turquoise .. 10 5

1979. Air. Cent. of Electric Light.

1531. **538.** 1 p. 60 multicoloured 10 5

539. Martin de Olivares (postmaster). 540. Assembly Emblem.

1979. 400th Anniv. of Royal Proclamation of Mail Services in the New World. Mult.

1532. 80 c. Type **539** (postage) .. 5 5
1533. 1 p. 60 Martin Enriquez de Almanza (viceroy of New Spain) (air) .. 10 5
1534. 5 p. 50 King Philip II of Spain 35 20

1979. Air. Eighth General Assembly of Latin American Universities Union.

1536. **540.** 1 p. 60 multicoloured 10 5

541. Shepherd. 542. Moon Symbol from Mexican Codex.

1979. Christmas. Multicoloured.

1537. 50 c. Type **541** (postage) 5 5
1538. 1 p. 60 Girl and Christmas tree (air) .. 10 5

1979. Air. 10th Anniv. of First Man on Moon.

1539. **542.** 2 p. 50 multicoloured 15 10

543. Church, Yanhuitlan.

1980. Air. Mexican Arts and Sciences (8th series). Multicoloured.

1540. 1 p. 60 Type **543** 10 5
1541. 1 p. 60 Monastery, Yuriria 10 5
1542. 1 p. 60 Church, Tlayacapan 10 5
1543. 1 p. 60 Church, Actopan .. 10 5
1544. 1 p. 60 Church, Acolman 10 5

544. Steps and Snake's Head.

1980. National Pre-Hispanic Monuments (1st series). Multicoloured.

1545. 80 c. Type **544** (postage) 5 5
1546. 1 p. 60 Doble Tlaloc (rain god (air) 10 5
1547. 5 p. 50 Coyolzauhqui (moon goddess) 35 20

See also Nos. 1565/7 and 1605/7.

1980. Mexican Fauna (2nd series). As Type **516**. Multicoloured.

1548. 80 c. Common Turkey (postage) 35 10
1549. 1 p. 60 Greater Flamingo (air) 80 25

1980. Mexican Flowers (2nd series). As T **518**. Multicoloured.

1550. 80 c. "Tajetes erecta" (postage) 15 5
1551. 1 p. 60 "Vanilla planifolia" (air) 25 5

545. Jules Verne.

1980. Air. 75th Death Anniv. of Jules Verne (author).

1552. **545.** 5 p. 50 brn. & blk. .. 35 20

546. Skeleton smoking Cigar (after Guadalupe Posada). 547. China Poblana, Puebla.

1980. Air. World Health Day. Anti-Smoking Campaign.

1553. **546.** 1 p. 60 pur., bl. & red 10 5

1980. National Costumes (1st series). Mult.

1554. 50 c. Type **547** 5 5
1555. 80 c. Jarocha, Veracruz (postage) 5 5
1556. 1 p. 60 Chiapaneca, Chiapas (air) 10 5

See also Nos. 1588/90.

548. Family. 549. Cuauhtemoc (last Aztec Emperor).

1980. 10th Population and Housing Census.

1557. **548.** 3 p. blk. & silver .. 20 10

1980. Pre-Hispanic Personages (1st series). Multicoloured.

1558. 80 c. Type **549** 5 5
1559. 1 p. 60 Nezahualcoyotl (governor of Tetzcoco) 10 5
1560. 5 p. 50 Eight Deer Tiger's Claw (11th Mixtec king) 35 20

Also see Nos. 1642/4 and 1846/8.

550. Xipe (Aztec god of medicine). 551. Bronze Medal.

1980. 22nd World Biennial Congress of International College of Surgeons, Mexico City.

1561. **550.** 1 p. 60 multicoloured 10 5

1980. Olympic Games, Moscow.

1562. **551.** 1 p. 60 bronze, blk., & turquoise 10 5
1563. – 3 p. silver, blk., & bl. 20 10
1564. – 5 p. 50 gold, blk. & red 35 20

DESIGNS: 3 p. Silver medal. 5 p. 50, Gold medal.

1980. National Pre-Hispanic Monuments (2nd series). As T **554**. Multicoloured.

1565. 80 c. Sacred glass .. 5 5
1566. 1 p. 60 Stone snail .. 10 5
1567. 5 p. 50 Chac Mool (god) .. 35 20

552. Sacromonte Sanctuary, Amecameca.

1980. Colonial Architecture (1st series).

1568. **552.** 2 p. 50 grey and black 20 8
1569. – 2 p. 50 grey and black 20 8
1570. – 3 p. grey and black .. 25 10
1571. – 3 p. grey and black .. 25 10

DESIGNS—HORIZ. No. 1552, St. Catherine's Convent, Patzcuaro. No. 1554, Hermitage, Cuernavaca. VERT. No. 1553, Basilica, Culiapan.

See also Nos. 1617/20, 1660/3, 1695/8 and 1784/7.

553. Quetzalcoatl (god). 554. Arms of Sinaloa.

1980. World Tourism Conference, Manila, Philippines.

1572. **553.** 2 p. 50 multicoloured 12 8

1980. 150th Anniv. of Sinaloa State.

1573. **554.** 1 p. 60 multicoloured 10 5

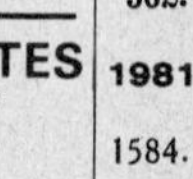

555. Straw Angel. 556. Congress Emblem.

1980. Christmas. Multicoloured.

1574. 50 c. Type **555** 5 5
1575. 1 p. 60 Poinsettia in a jug 10 5

1980. 4th International Civil Justice Congress.

1576. **556.** 1 p. 60 multicoloured 10 5

557. Glass Demijohn and Animals. 558. "Simon Bolivar" (after Paulin Guerin).

1980. Mexican Crafts (1st series). Mult.

1577. 50 c. Type **557** 5 5
1578. 1 p. Poncho 8 8
1579. 3 p. Wooden mask .. 20 12

Add also Nos. 1624/6.

1980. 150th Death Anniv. of Simon Bolivar.

1580. **558.** 4 p. multicoloured .. 30 20

559. Vicente Guerrero. 560. Valentin Gomez Farias.

1981. 150th Death Anniv. of Vicente Guerrero (liberator).

1581. **559.** 80 c. multicoloured 5 5

1981. Birth Bicent. of Valentin Gomez Farias.

1582. **560.** 80 c. black and green 5 5

561. Table Tennis Balls in Flight.

1981. First Latin-American Table Tennis Cup.

1583. **561.** 4 p. multicoloured .. 30 20

562. Jesus Gonzalez Ortega. 563. Gabino Barreda.

1981. Death Centenary of Jesus Gonzalez Ortega.

1584. **562.** 80 c. light brn. & brn. 5 5

1981. Death Centenary of Gabino Barreda (politician).

1585. **563.** 80 c. pink, blk., & grn. 5 5

564. Benito Juarez. **565.** Foundation Monument.

1981. 175th Birth Anniv. of Benito Juarez (patriot).
1586. **564.** 1 p. 60 grn., brn. and light brown .. 12 8

1981. 450th Anniv. of Puebla City.
1587. **565.** 80 c. multicoloured 5 5

1981. National Costumes (2nd series). Vert. Designs as T **547.** Multicoloured.
1588. 50 c. Purepecha, Michoacan 5 5
1589. 80 c. Charra, Jalisco .. 5 5
1590. 1 p. 60 Mestiza, Yucatan 12 8

1981. Mexican Fauna (3rd series). Vert. designs as T **516.** Multicoloured.
1591. 80 c. Northern Mockingbird 45 15
1592. 1 p. 60 Mountain Trogon 85 40

1981. Mexican Flowers (3rd series). Vert. designs as T **518.** Multicoloured.
1593. 80 c. Avocado 5 5
1594. 1 p. 60 Cacao 12 8

566. " Martyrs of Cananea " (David A. Siqueiros).

1981. 75th Anniv. of Martyrs of Cananea.
1595. **566.** 1 p. 60 multicoloured 12 8

567. Toy Drummer with One Arm. **568.** Arms of Queretaro.

1981. International Year of Disabled People.
1596. **567.** 4 p. multicoloured .. 30 20

1981. 450th Anniv. of Queretaro City.
1597. **568.** 80 c. multicoloured 5 5

569. Mexican Stamp of 1856 and Postal Service Emblem.

1981. 125th Anniv. of First Mexican Stamp.
1598. **569.** 4 p. multicoloured .. 30 20

570. Sir Alexander Fleming. **572.** St. Francisco Xavier Claver.

571. Union Congress Building and Emblem.

1981. Birth Centenary of Sir Alexander Fleming (discoverer of penicillin).
1599. **570.** 5 p. blue and orange 35 10

1981. Opening of New Union Congress Building.
1600. **571.** 1 p. 60 green and red 10 8

1981. 250th Birth Anniv. of St. Francis Xavier Claver.
1601. **572.** 80 c. multicoloured .. 5 5

573. " Desislava " (detail of Bulgarian Fresco).

1981. 1300th Anniv. of Bulgarian State. Multicoloured.
1602. 1 p. 60 Type **573** .. 10 8
1603. 4 p. Horse-headed cup from Thrace 25 20
1604. 7 p. Madara Horseman (relief) 40 30

1981. Pre-Hispanic Monuments. As Type **544.** Multicoloured.
1605. 80 c. Seated God 5 5
1606. 1 p. 60 Alabaster deer's head 12 8
1607. 4 p. Jade Fish 30 20

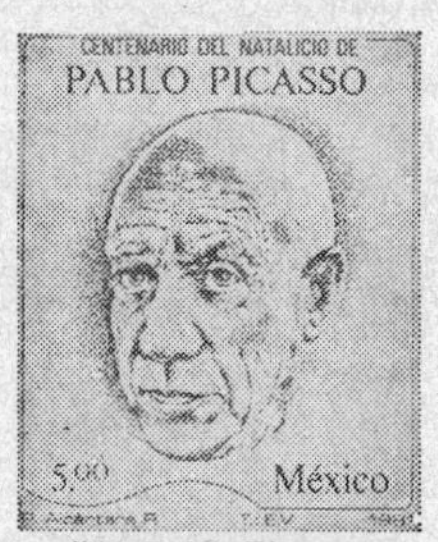

574. Pablo Picasso.

1981. Birth Cent. of Pablo Picasso (artist).
1608. **574.** 5 p. deep grn. & grn. 35 20

575. Shepherd. **576.** Wheatsheaf.

1981. Christmas. Multicoloured.
1609. 50 c. Type **575** 5 5
1610. 1 p. 60 Praying girl .. 12 8

1981. World Food Day.
1611. **576.** 4 p. multicoloured .. 25 15

577. Thomas Edison, Lightbulb and Gramophone.

1981. 50th Death Anniv. of Thomas Edison (inventor).
1612. **577.** 4 p. stone, brn. & grn. 25 15

578. Co-operation Emblem and Wheat.

1981. International Meeting on Co-operation and Development, Cancun.
1613. **578.** 4 p. blue, grey & black 25 20

579. Globe and Diesel Locomotive.

1981. 15th Pan-American Railway Congress.
1614. **579.** 1 p. 60 multicoloured 35 10

580. Film Frame.

1981. 50th Anniv. of Mexican Sound Movies.
1615. **580.** 4 p. grey, blk. & grn. 25 20

581. Postcode and Bird (delivering Letter).

1981. Inauguration of Postcodes.
1616. **581.** 80 c. multicoloured .. 5 5

1981. Colonial Architecture (2nd series). As T **522.** Multicoloured.
1617. 4 p. Mascarones House .. 25 15
1618. 4 p. La Merced Convent .. 25 15
1619. 5 p. Chapel of the Third Order, Texcoco .. 30 20
1620. 5 p. Father Tembleque Aqueduct, Otumba .. 30 20

582. " Martyrs of Rio Blanco " (Orozco).

1982. 75th Anniv. of Martyrs of Rio Blanco.
1621. **582.** 80 c. multicoloured .. 5 5

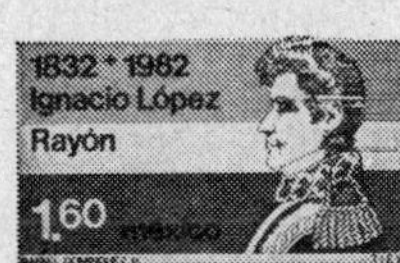

583. Ignacio Lopez Rayon.

1982. 150th Death Anniv. of Ignacio Lopez Rayon.
1622. **583.** 1 p. 60 grn., red & blk. 10 5

MINIMUM PRICE

The minimum price quoted is 5p which represents a handling charge rather than a basis for valuing common stamps. For further notes about prices see introductory pages.

584. Postal Headquarters.

1982. 75th Anniv. of Postal Headquarters.
1623. **584.** 4 p. pink and green .. 25 20

1982. Mexican Crafts (2nd series). As T **557.** Multicoloured.
1624. 50 c. " God's Eye " (Huichol art) 5 5
1625. 1 p. Ceramic snail .. 8 5
1626. 3 p. Tiger mask 20 12

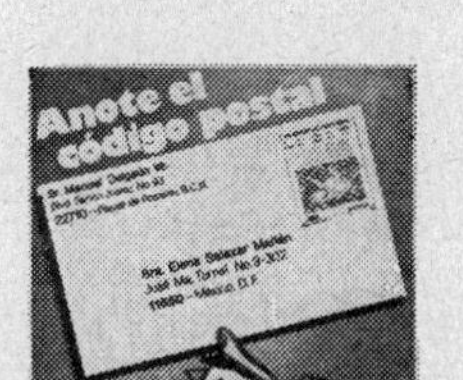

585. Postcoded Letter and Bird.

1982. Postcode Publicity.
1627. **585.** 80 c. multicoloured .. 5 5

586. Dr. Robert Koch and Cross of Lorraine.

1982. Cent. of Discovery of Tubercle Bacillus.
1628. **586.** 4 p. multicoloured .. 15 10

587. Military Academy. **588.** Arms of Oaxaca.

1982. 50th Anniv. of Military Academy.
1629. **587.** 80 c. yell., blk. & gold 5 5

1982. 450th Anniv. of Oaxaca City.
1630. **588.** 1 p. 60 multicoloured 8 5

1982. Tourism (2nd series). As T **563.** Multicoloured.
1631. 80 c. Basaseachic Falls, Chihuahua 5 5
1632. 80 c. Natural rock formation, Pueblo Nuevo, Durango 5 5
1633. 1 p. 60 Mayan City of Edzna, Campeche .. 8 5
1634. 1 p. 60 La Venta (Olmeca sculpture), Tabasco .. 8 5

589. Footballers.

1982. World Cup Football Championship, Spain. Multicoloured.
1635. 1 p. 60 Type **589** .. 5 5
1636. 4 p. Dribbling 15 10
1637. 7 p. Tackling 25 15

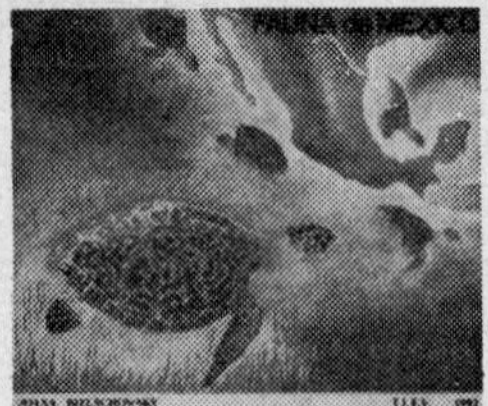

590. Hawksbill Turtles.

1982. Mexican Fauna. Multicoloured.

1638. 1 p. 60 Type **590** .. 8 5
1639. 4 p. Grey Whales .. 15 30

591. Vicente Guerrero.

1982. Birth Bicentenary of Vicente Guerrero (independence fighter).

1640. **591.** 80 c. multicoloured .. 5 5

592. Symbols of Peace and Communication.

1982. Second U.N. Conference on the Exploration and Peaceful Uses of Outer Space, Vienna.

1641. **592.** 4 p. multicoloured .. 10 8

1982. Pre-Hispanic Personalities (2nd series). As T **549**. Multicoloured.

1642. 80 c. Tariacuri 5 5
1643. 1 p. 60 Acamapichtli .. 5 5
1644. 4 p. Ten Deer Tiger's breastplate 10 8

593. Pawpaw (" Carica papaya ").

1982. Mexican Flora. Multicoloured.

1645. 80 c. Type **593** 5 5
1646. 1 p. 60 Maize (" Zea mays ") 5 5

594. Astrologer.

1982. Native Mexican Codices. Florentine Codex. Multicoloured.

1647. 80 c. Type **594** 5 5
1648. 1 p. 60 Arriving at School 5 5
1649. 4 p. Musicians 10 8

595. Manuel Gamio (anthropologist).

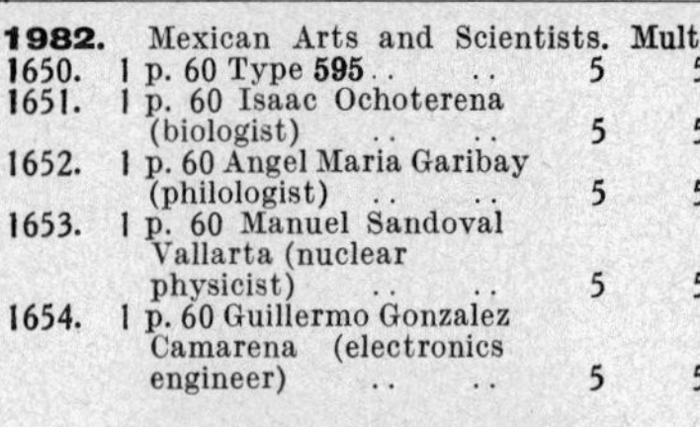

1982. Mexican Arts and Scientists. Mult.

1650. 1 p. 60 Type **595** 5 5
1651. 1 p. 60 Isaac Ochoterena (biologist) 5 5
1652. 1 p. 60 Angel Maria Garibay (philologist) 5 5
1653. 1 p. 60 Manuel Sandoval Vallarta (nuclear physicist) 5 5
1654. 1 p. 60 Guillermo Gonzalez Camarena (electronics engineer) 5 5

596. State Archives Building.

1982. Inaug. of State Archives Building.

1655. **596.** 1 p. 60 blk. and grn. 5 5

597. Dove and Peace Text.

1982. Christmas. Multicoloured.

1656. 50 c. Type **597** 5 5
1657. 1 p. 60 Dove & Peace text (different) 5 5

598. Hands holding Food.

1982. Mexican Food System.

1658. **598.** 1 p. 60 multicoloured 5 5

599. " Revolutionary Mexico " Stamp, 1956.

1982. Inauguration of Revolution Museum, Chihuahua.

1659. **599.** 1 p. 60 grey & green 5 5

1982. Colonial Architecture (3rd series). As T **552**. Multicoloured.

1660. 1 p. 60 College of Sts. Peter and Paul, Mexico City 5 5
1661. 8 p. Convent of Jesus Maria, Mexico City .. 15 10
1662. 10 p. Open Chapel, Tlalmanalco 20 12
1663. 14 p. Convent, Actopan .. 25 20

600. Alfonso Garcia Robles and Laurel.

601. Jose Vasconcelos.

1982. Alfonso Garcia Robles (Nobel Peace Prize Winner) Commemoration.

1664. **600.** 1 p. 60 grey, blk. & gold 5 5
1665. – 14 p. pink, blk. & gold 25 20

DESIGN: 14 p. Robles and medal.

1982. Birth Centenary of Jose Vasconcelos (philosopher).

1666. **601.** 1 p. 60 black & blue 5 5

602. W.C.Y. Emblem and Methods of Communication.

1983. World Communications Year.

1667. **602.** 16 p. multicoloured .. 20 15

603. Sonora State Civil War Stamp, 1913.

1983. " Herflex 83 " Mexican Revolution Stamp Exhibition.

1668. **603.** 6 p. brn., blk. & grn. 8 5

604. "Nauticas Mexico" (container ship), World Map and I.M.O. Emblem.

1983. 25th Anniv. of International Maritime Organization.

1669. **604.** 16 p. multicoloured .. 80 20

605. Doctor treating Patient.

1983. Constitutional Right to Health Protection.

1670. **605.** 6 p. green and red .. 8 5

606. Valentin Gomez Farias (founder) and Arms of Society.

1983. 150th Anniv. of Mexican Geographical and Statistical Society.

1671. **606.** 6 p. multicoloured .. 8 5

607. Football.

1983. Second World Youth Football Championship, Mexico.

1672. **607.** 6 p. black and green 8 5
1673. 13 p. black and red .. 15 10
1674. 14 p. black and blue 20 12

1983. Tourism. As T **536**. Multicoloured.

1675 6 p. Federal Palace, Queretaro 10 10
1676 6 p. Water tank, San Luis Potosi 10 10
1677 13 p. Cable car, Zacatecas 15 10
1678 14 p. Carved head of Kohunlich, Quintana Roo 20 15

608. Bolivar on Horseback.

1983. Birth Bicent. of Simon Bolivar.

1679. **608.** 21 p. multicoloured .. 25 15

609. Angela Peralta. **610.** Agave.

1983. Death Centenary of Angela Peralta (opera singer).

1680. **609.** 9 p. lt. brn. & brn. 10 8

1983. Mexican Flora and Fauna (5th series). Multicoloured.

1681. 9 p. Type **610** 10 8
1682. 9 p. Sapodilla 10 8
1683. 9 p. Swallowtail 30 10
1684. 9 p. Boa constrictor .. 10 8

611. Two Candles.

1983. Christmas. Multicoloured.

1685. 9 p. Type **611** 10 8
1686. 20 p. Three candles .. 25 15

612. S.C.T. Emblem.

1983. Integral Communications and Transport System.

1687. **612.** 13 p. blue and black 15 10

613. Carlos Chavez (musician).

1983. Mexican Arts and Sciences (10th series). Contemporary Artists. Mult.

1688. **613.** 9 p. brown, light brn. and deep brown .. 10 8
1689. – 9 p. brown, light brn. and deep brown .. 10 8
1690. – 9 p. deep brown, light brown and brown .. 10 8
1691. – 9 p. light brown, deep brown and brown .. 10 8
1692. – 9 p. deep brown, stone and brown .. 10 8

DESIGNS: No. 1689, Franciso Goitia (painter). No. 1690, S. Diaz Miron (poet). No. 1691, Carlos Bracho (sculptor). No. 1692, Fanny Anitua (singer).

614. Orozco (self-portrait).

1983. Birth Centenary of Jose Clemente Orozco (artist).

1693. **614.** 9 p. multicoloured .. 10 8

615. Human Rights Emblem.

1983. 35th Anniv. of Human Rights Declaration.

1694. **615.** 20 p. deep blue, yellow and blue 25 15

1983. Colonial Architecture (4th series). As T **552**. Each grey and black.

1695. 9 p. Convent, Malinalco .. 10 8
1696. 20 p. Cathedral, Cuernavaca 25 15
1697. 21 p. Convent, Tepeji del Rio 25 15
1698. 24 p. Convent, Atlatlahucan 30 20

616. Antonio Caso and Books.

1983. Birth Centenary of Antonio Caso (philosopher).

1699. **616.** 9 p. blue, lilac & red 10 8

617. Joaquin Velazquez.

1983. Bicent. of Royal Legislation on Mining.

1700. **617.** 9 p. multicoloured .. 10 8

618. Book and Envelopes.

1984. Centenary of First Postal Laws.

1701. **618.** 12 p. multicoloured .. 12 10

619. Children dancing around Drops of Anti-Polio Serum.

1984. World Anti-polio Campaign.

1702. **619.** 12 p. multicoloured 12 10

620. Muscovy Duck.

1984. Mexican Fauna (6th series). Multicoloured.

1703. 12 p. Type **620** 40 20
1704. 20 p. Red-billed whistling duck .. 65 30

621. Xoloitzcuintle Dog.

1984. World Dog Show.

1705. **621.** 12 p. multicoloured 12 10

622. Bank Headquarters.

1984. Centenary of National Bank.

1706. **622.** 12 p. multicoloured 12 10

623. Hands holding Trees.

624. Throwing the Discus.

1984. Protection of Forest Resources.

1707. **623.** 20 p. multicoloured 20 15

1984. Olympic Games, Los Angeles. Multicoloured.

1708. 14 p. Type **624** 15 12
1709. 20 p. Show jumping .. 20 15
1710. 23 p. Gymnastics (floor exercise) 25 20
1711. 24 p. Diving 25 20
1712. 25 p. Boxing 25 20
1713. 26 p. Fencing 25 20

INDEX

Countries can be quickly located by referring to the index at the end of this volume.

625. Mexican and Russian flags.

1984. 60th Anniv. of Diplomatic Relations with U.S.S.R.

1715. **626.** 23 p. multicoloured 25 20

626. Hand holding U.N. emblem.

1984. International Population Conference.

1716. **623.** 20 p. multicoloured 20 15

627. Gen. Mugica.

1984. Birth Centenary of General Francisco Mugica (politician).

1717. **627.** 14 p. brown & black 15 12

628. Emblem and Dates.

629. Airline Emblem.

1984. 50th Anniv. of Economic Culture Fund.

1718. **628.** 14 p. brown, black and red 15 12

1984. 50th Anniv of Aeromexico (state airline).

1719 – 14 p. multicoloured .. 15 12
1720 **629** 20 p. black and red .. 20 15

DESIGN—36 × 44 mm. 14 p. "Red Cactus" (sculpture, Sebastian).

630. Palace of Fine Arts.

1984. 50th Anniv. of Palace of Fine Arts.

1721. **630.** 14 p. blue, black and brown 15 12

631. Metropolitan Cathedral (detail of facade).

633. Dove and Hand holding Flame.

632. Coatzacoalcos Bridge.

1984. 275th Anniv. of Chihuahua City.

1722. **631.** 14 p. brown & black 15 12

1984. Inaug. of Coatzacoalcos Bridge.

1723. **632.** 14 p. multicoloured 15 12

1984. World Disarmament Week.

1724. **633.** 20 p. multicoloured 20 15

634. Christmas Tree and Toy Train.

1984. Christmas. Multicoloured.

1725. 14 p. Type **634** 45 12
1726. 20 p. Breaking the pinata (balloon filled with gifts) (vert.) 20 15

635. Ignacio Manuel Altamirano.

1984. 150th Birth Anniv. of Ignacio Manuel Altamirano (politician and journalist).

1727. **635.** 14 p. red and black 15 12

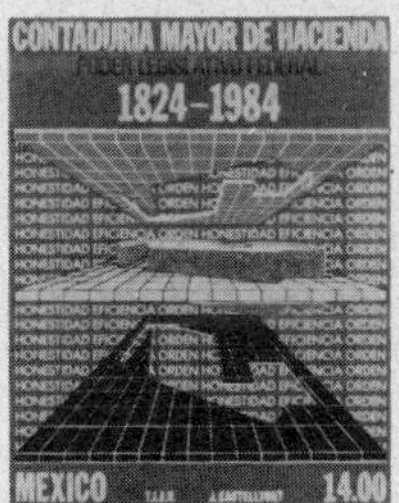

636. Maps, Graph and Text.

1984. 160th Anniv. of State Audit Office.

1728. **636.** 14 p. multicoloured 15 12

637. Half a Football and Mexican Colours.

1984. Mexico, Site of 1986 World Cup Football Championship. Multicoloured.

1729. 20 p. Type **637** 20 15
1730. 24 p. Football and Mexican colours .. 25 20

638. Romulo Gallegos. **639.** State Arms and Open Register.

1984. Birth Cent. of Romulo Gallegos.

1731. **638.** 20 p. black and blue 20 15

1984. 125th Anniv. of Mexican Civil Registration.

1732. **639.** 24 p. blue 25 20

640. Mexican Flag. **641.** Johann Sebastian Bach.

1985. 50th Anniv. of National Flag.

1733. **640.** 22 p. multicoloured 25 20

1985. 300th Birth Anniv. of Johann Sebastian Bach (composer).

1734. **641.** 35 p. red and black 15 30

642. I.Y.Y. Emblem. **643.** Children and Fruit within Book.

1985. International Youth Year.

1735. **642.** 35 p. purple, gold and black 15 30

1985. Child Survival Campaign.

1736. **643.** 36 p. multicoloured 12 10

644. Commemorative Medallion.

1985. 450th Anniv. of State Mint.

1737. **644.** 35 p. gold, mve. & bl. 12 10

645. Victor Hugo, Text and Gateway.

1985. Death Cent. of Victor Hugo (novelist).

1738. **645.** 35 p. grey 12 10

646. Hidalgo 8 r. Stamp, 1856.

1985. "Mexifil 85" Stamp Exhibition.

1739. **646.** 22 p. grey, black and purple 8 5
1740. – 35 p. grey, black and blue 12 10
1741. – 36 p. multicoloured 12 10

DESIGNS: 35 p. Carranza 10 c. stamp, 1916. 36 p. Juarez 50 p. stamp, 1975.

647. Rockets, Satellite, Nurse and Computer Operator.

1985. Launching of First Morelos Satellite. Multicoloured.

1743. 22 p. Type **647** 8 5
1744. 36 p. Camera, dish aerial, satellite and computers 12 10
1745. 90 p. Camera, dish aerial, satellite, television and couple telephoning .. 25 20

Nos. 1743/5 were printed together, se-tenant, forming a composite design.

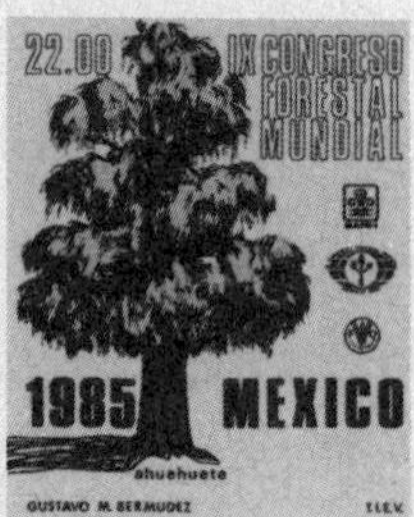

648. Conifer.

1985. Ninth World Forestry Congress, Mexico.

1747. **648.** 22 p. brown, black and green 8 5
1748. – 35 p. brown, black and green 12 10
1749. – 36 p. brown, black and green 12 10

DESIGNS: 35 p. Silk-cotton tree. 36 p. Mahogany tree.

649. Martin Luis Guzman.

1985. Mexican Arts and Sciences (11th series). Contemporary Writers.

1750. **649.** 22 p. grey and blue 8 5
1751. – 22 p. grey and blue 8 5
1752. – 22 p. grey and blue 8 5
1753. – 22 p. grey and blue 8 5
1754. – 22 p. grey and blue 8 5

DESIGNS: No. 1751, Augustin Yanez. 1752, Alfonso Reyes. 1753, Jose Ruben Romero. 1754, Artemio de Valle-Arizpe.

650. Miguel Hidalgo.

1985. 175th Anniv. of Independence Movement. Each green, black and red.

1755. 22 p. Type **650** 5 5
1756. 35 p. Jose Ma. Morelos .. 5 5
1757. 35 p. Ignacio Allende .. 5 5
1758. 36 p. Leona Vigario .. 5 5
1759. 110 p. Vicente Guerrero 20 15

651. San Ildefonso.

1985. 75th Anniv. of National University. Multicoloured.

1761. 26 p. Type **651** 5 5
1762. 26 p. Emblem 5 5
1763. 40 p. Modern building .. 5 5
1764. 45 p. 1910 crest and Justo Sierra (founder) .. 8 5
1765. 90 p. University crest .. 15 10

652. Rural and Industrial Landscapes.

1985. 25th Anniv. of Inter-American Development Bank.

1766. **652.** 26 p. multicoloured 5 5

653. Guns and Doves. **654.** Hands and Dove.

1985. United Nations Disarmament Week.

1767. **653.** 36 p. multicoloured 5 5

1985. 40th Anniv. of U.N.O.

1768. **654.** 26 p. multicoloured 5 5

655. "Girls Skipping" (Mishinoya K. Maki).

1985. Christmas. Children's Paintings. Mult.

1769. 26 p. Disabled and able-bodied children playing (Margarita Salazar) 5 5
1770. 35 p. Type **655** 5 5

656. Soldadera.

1985. 75th Anniv. of 1910 Revolution. Each red, black and green.

1771. 26 p. Type **656** 5 5
1772. 35 p. Pancho Villa .. 5 5
1773. 40 p. Emiliano Zapata .. 5 5
1774. 45 p. Venustiano Carranza 8 5
1775. 110 p. Francisco I. Madero 20 15

657. "Vigilante" (Federico Silva).

1985. Second "Morelos" Telecommunications Satellite Launch.

1777. – 26 p. black and blue 5 5
1778. **657.** 35 p. grey, pink and black 5 5
1779. – 45 p. multicoloured 8 5

DESIGNS—VERT. 26 p. "Cosmonaut" (sculpture by Sebastian). HORIZ. 45 p. "Mexican Astronaut" (painting by Cauduro).

658. "Mexico" holding Book.

1985. 25th Anniv. of Free Textbooks National Commission.

1781. **658.** 26 p. multicoloured 5 5

659. Olympic Stadium, University City.

1985. World Cup Football Championship, Mexico. Each grey and black.

1782. 26 p. Type **659** 5 5
1783. 45 p. Azteca Stadium .. 8 5

1985. Colonial Architecture (5th series). Vert. designs as T **552**. Each brown and black.

1784. 26 p. Vizcayan College, Mexico City 5 5
1785. 35 p. Counts of Heras y Soto Palace, Mexico City 5 5
1786. 40 p. Counts of Calimaya Palace, Mexico City .. 5 5
1787. 45 p. St. Carlos Academy, Mexico City 8 5

661. Luis Enrique Erro Planetarium.

1986. 50th Anniv. of National Polytechnic Institute. Multicoloured.
1788. 40 p. Type **661** 5 5
1789. 65 p. National School of Arts and Crafts .. 10 5
1790. 75 p. Founders, emblem and "50" 10 5

1985. Mexican Flowers (6th series). As T **518**. Multicoloured.
1791. 40 p. Calabash 5 5
1792. 65 p. "Nopalea coccinellifera" (cactus) 10 5

663. Doll.

1986. World Health Day.
1793. **663.** 65 p. multicoloured 10 5

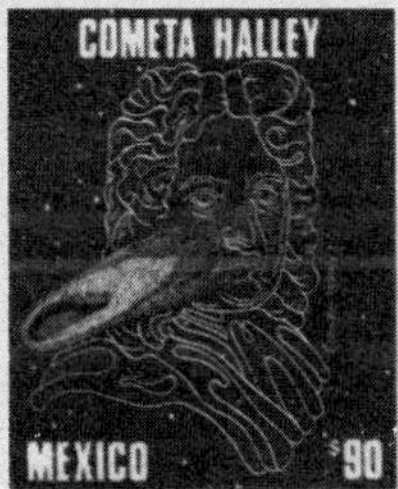

664. Halley and Comet.

1986. Appearance of Halley's Comet.
1794. **664.** 90 p. multicoloured 15 10

665. Emblem.

1986. Centenary of Geological Institute.
1795. **665.** 40 p. multicoloured 5 5

666. "Three Footballers with Berets".

1986. World Cup Football Championship, Mexico (2nd issue). Paintings by Angel Zarraga. Multicoloured.
1796 30 p. Type **666** 5 5
1797. 40 p. "Portrait of Ramon Novaro" 5 5
1798. 65 p. "Sunday" 10 5
1799. 70 p. "Portrait of Ernest Charles Gimpel" .. 10 5
1800. 90 p. "Three Footballers" 15 10

667. Ignacio Allende.

1986. 175th Death Annivs. of Independence Heroes. Multicoloured.
1802. 40 p. Type **667** 5 5
1803. 40 p. Miguel Hidalgo (after J. C. Orozco) .. 5 5
1804. 65 p. Juan Aldama .. 10 5
1805. 75 p. Mariano Jimenez .. 10 5

668. Mexican Arms over "FTF". **669.** Nicolas Bravo.

1986. 50th Anniv. of Fiscal Tribunal.
1806. **668.** 40 p. blk., bl. & grey 5 5

1986. Birth Bicentenary of Nicolas Bravo (independence fighter).
1807. **669.** 40 p. multicoloured 5 5

670. "Zapata Landscape".

1986. Paintings by Diego Rivera. Multicoloured.
1808. 50 p. Type **670** 5 5
1809. 80 p. "Nude with Arum Lilies" 10 5
1810. 110 p. "Vision of a Sunday Afternoon Walk on Central Avenue" (horiz.) .. 20 15

671. Guadalupe Victoria.

1986. Birth Bicentenary of Guadalupe Victoria (first President).
1811. **671.** 50 p. multicoloured 5 5

672. People depositing Produce.

1986. 50th Anniv. of National Depositories.
1812. **672.** 40 p. multicoloured 5 5

673. Pigeon above Hands holding Posthorn. **674.** Emblem.

1986. World Post Day.
1813. **673.** 120 p. multicoloured 20 15

1986. Foundation of National Commission to Mark 500th Anniv. (1992) of Discovery of America.
1814. **674.** 50 p. black and red 8 5

675. Ministry of Mines. **676.** Liszt.

1986. 15th Pan-American Roads Congress.
1815. **675.** 80 p. grey and black 10 5

1986. 175th Birth Anniv. of Franz Liszt (composer).
1816. **676.** 100 p. brown & black 15 10

677. U.N. and "Pax Cultura" Emblems.

1986. International Peace Year.
1817. **677.** 80 p. bl., red & blk. 10 5

678. Jose Maria Pino Suarez (1st Vice-President of Revolutionary Govt.).

1986. Famous Mexicans buried in The Rotunda of Illustrious Men (1st series).
1818. **678.** 50 p. multicoloured 8 5
See also Nos. 1823/4, 1838 and 1899.

679. King. **680.** "Self-portrait".

1986. Christmas. Multicoloured.
1819. 50 p. Type **679** 8 5
1820. 80 p. Angel 10 5

1986. Birth Centenary of Diego Rivera (artist).
1821. **680.** 80 p. multicoloured 10 5

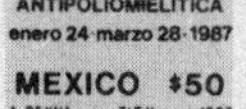

681. Baby receiving Vaccination. **682.** Perez de Leon College.

1987. National Days for Poliomyelitis Vaccination.
1822. **681.** 50 p. multicoloured 5 5

1987. Famous Mexicans buried in The Rotunda of Illustrious Men (2nd series). As T **678**. Multicoloured.
1823. 100 p. Jose Maria Iglesias 5 5
1824. 100 p. Pedro Sainz de Baranda 5 5

1987. Centenary of Higher Education.
1825. **682.** 100 p. multicoloured 5 5

683. Kino and Map.

1987. 300th Anniv. of Father Eusebio Francisco Kino's Mission to Pimeria Alta.
1826. **683.** 100 p. multicoloured 5 5

684. Baby's Head.

1987. Child Immunization Campaign.
1827. **684.** 100 p. dp. bl. & bl 5 5

685. Staircase. **686.** "5th of May. 1862, and the Siege of Puebla" Exhibition Poster, 1887.

1987. 50th Anniv. of Puebla Independent University.
1828. **685.** 200 p. grey, pink and black 10 5

1987. 125th Anniv. of Battle of Puebla.
1829. **686.** 100 p. multicoloured 5 5

687. Stylized City.

1987. "Metropolis 87" World Association of Large Cities Congress.

1830. **687.** 310 p. red, black and green 45 30

688. Lacquerware Tray, Uruapan, Michoacan. **689.** Genaro Estrada (author and pioneer of democracy).

1987. Handicrafts. Multicoloured.

1831. 100 p. Type **688** 5 5

1832. 200 p. Woven blanket, Santa Ana Chiautempan, Tlaxcala 10 5

1833. 230 p. Ceramic jar with lid, Puebla, Puebla .. 15 8

1987. Mexican Arts and Sciences (12th series).

1834. **689.** 100 p. brown, black and pink 5 5

See also Nos. 1845, 1880 and 1904/5.

690. "Native Traders" (mural, P. O'Higgins).

1987. 50th Anniv. of National Foreign Trade Bank.

1835. **690.** 100 p. multicoloured 5 5

691. Diagram of Longitudinal Section through Ship's Hull.

1987. 400th Anniv. of Publication of First Shipbuilding Manual in America, Diego Garcia de Palacio's "Instrucion Nautica".

1836. **691.** 100 p. grn., bl. & brn. 5 5

692. Man carrying Sack of Maize Flour.

1987. 50th Anniv. of National Food Programme.

1837. **692.** 100 p. multicoloured 5 5

1987. Mexicans in Rotunda of Illustrious Men (3rd series). As T **678.** Multicoloured.

1838. 100 p. Leandro Valle .. 5 5

693. "Self-portrait with Skull".

1987. Paintings by Saturnino Herran.

1839 **693** 100 p. brown & black 15 5

1840 – 100 p. multicoloured 15 5

1841 – 400 p. multicoloured 60 50

DESIGNS: No. 1840, "The Offering". 1841, "Creole with Shawl".

694. Flags of Competing Countries.

1987. 10th Pan-American Games, Indianapolis.

1842. **694.** 100 p. multicoloured 5 5

1843. – 200 p. black, red and green 10 5

DESIGN: 200 p. Running.

695. Electricity Pylon.

1987. 50th Anniv. of Federal Electricity Commission.

1844. **695.** 200 p. multicoloured 10 5

1987. Mexican Arts and Sciences (13th series). As T **689.** Multicoloured.

1845. 100 p. J. E. Hernandez y Davalos (author) .. 5 5

1987. Pre-Hispanic Personages (3rd series). As T **549.** Multicoloured.

1846. 100 p. Xolotl (Chichimeca commander) 5 5

1847. 200 p. Nezahualpilli (leader of Tezcoco tribe) 10 5

1848. 400 p. Motecuhzoma Ilhuicamina (leader of Tenochtitlan tribe) .. 45 10

696. Stylized Racing Car.

1987. Mexico Formula One Grand Prix.

1849. **696.** 100 p. multicoloured 5 5

697. Mexican Cultural Centre, Mexico City. **698.** "Santa Maria" and 1922 Mexican Festival Emblem.

1987. Mexican Tourism.

1850. **697.** 100 p. multicoloured 5 5

1987. 500th Anniv of "Meeting of Two Worlds" (discovery of America by Columbus) (1st issue).

1851. **698.** 150 p. multicoloured 30 15

See also Nos. 1902, 1941, 1979, 2038 and 2062/6.

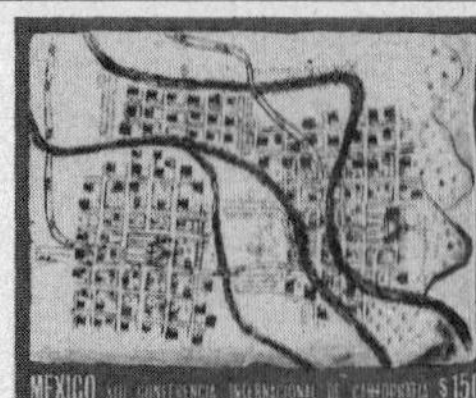

699. 16th-century Spanish Map of Mexico City.

1987. 13th International Cartography Conference.

1852. **699.** 150 p. multicoloured 8 5

1987. Mexican Tourism. As T **697.** Mult.

1853. 150 p. Michoacan .. 15 10

1854. 150 p. Garcia Caves, Nuevo Leon 10 10

1855. 150 p. View of Mazatlan, Sinaloa 10 10

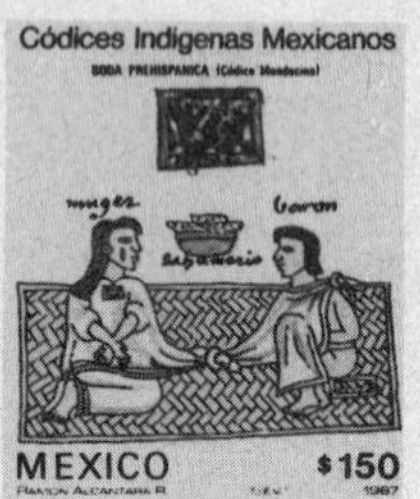

700. Pre-Hispanic Wedding Ceremony.

1987. Native Codices. Mendocino Codex. Multicoloured.

1856. 150 p. Type **700** 8 5

1857. 150 p. Moctezuma's council chamber .. 8 5

1858. 150 p. Foundation of Tenochtitlan 8 5

701. Dove with Olive Twig.

1987. Christmas.

1859. **701.** 150 p. mauve .. 8 5

1860. – 150 p. blue 8 5

DESIGN: No. 1860, As T **701** but dove facing left.

702. "Royal Ordinance for the Carriage of Maritime Mail" Title Page.

1987. World Post Day.

1861. **702.** 150 p. green and grey 8 5

703. Circle of Flags.

1987. 1st Meeting of Eight Latin-American Presidents, Acapulco. Multicoloured.

1863. 250 p. Type **703** 10 5

1864. 500 p. Flags and doves .. 25 10

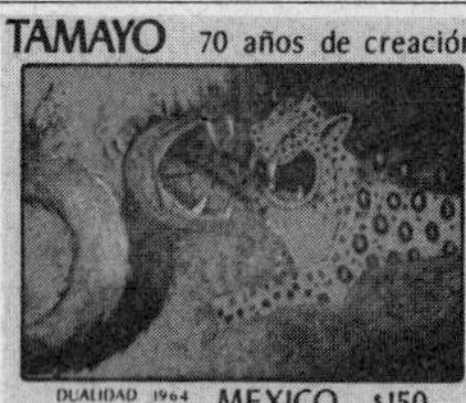

704. "Dualidad 1964".

1987. Rufino Tamayo (painter), "70 Years of Creativity".

1865. **704.** 150 p. multicoloured 8 5

705. Train on Metlac Railway Bridge.

1987. 50th Anniv of Railway Nationalization.

1866 **705** 150 p. multicoloured .. 35 5

706. Stradivarius at Work (detail, 19th-century engraving).

1987. 250th Death Anniv. of Antonio Stradivarius (violin-maker).

1867. **706.** 150 p. light violet and violet .. 8 5

707. Statue of Manuel Crescensio Rejon (promulgator of Yucatan State Constitution).

1988. Constitutional Tribunal, Supreme Court of Justice.

1868. **707.** 300 p. multicoloured 15 8

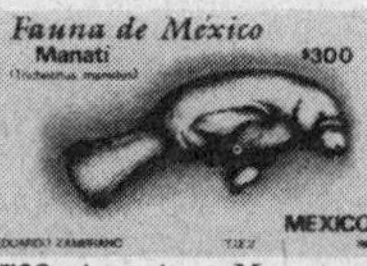

708. American Manatee.

1988. Animals. Multicoloured.

1869. 300 p. Type **708** 15 5

1870. 300 p. Mexican mole salamander 15 5

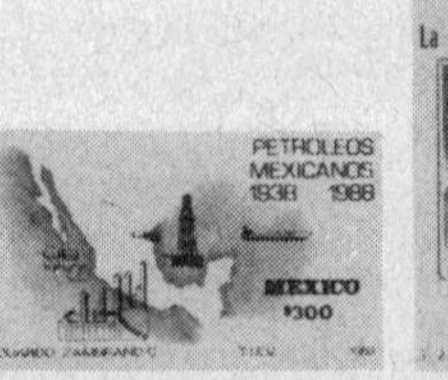

709. Map and Oil Industry Symbols. **710.** "The Vaccination".

1988. 50th Anniv. of Pemex (Nationalized Petroleum Industry).

1871. **709.** 300 p. blue and black 20 10

1872. – 300 p. multicoloured 15 10

1873. – 500 p. multicoloured 25 10

DESIGNS—36×43 mm. No. 1872, PEMEX emblem. 43×36 mm. No. 1873, "50" and oil exploration platform.

1988. World Health Day (1874) and 40th Anniv. of W.H.O. (1875). Paintings by Diego Rivera.
1874. **710.** 300 p. brown & green 15 5
1875. – 300 p. multicoloured 15 5
DESIGN—43 × 36 mm. No. 1875, "The People demand Health".

711. "Death Portrait" (Victor Delfin).

1988. 50th Death Anniv. of Cesar Vallejo (painter and poet). Multicoloured.
1876. 300 p. Type **711** 15 5
1877. 300 p. Portrait by Arnold Belkin and "Hoy me palpo. . ." 15 5
1878. 300 p. Portrait as in T **711** but larger (30 × 35 mm) 15 5
1879. 300 p. Portrait as in No. 1877 but larger (23 × 35 mm.) 15 5

1988. Mexican Arts and Sciences (14th series). As T **689**.
1880. 300 p. brown, black and violet 15 5
DESIGN: 300 p. Carlos Pellicer (poet).

712. Girl and Boy holding Stamp in Tweezers.

1988. "Mepsirrey '88" Stamp Exhibition, Monterrey. Multicoloured.
1881. 300 p. Type **712** 15 5
1882. 300 p. Envelope with "Monterey" handstamp 15 5
1883. 500 p. Exhibition emblem 25 10

713. Hernandos Rodriguez Racing Circuit, Mexico City.

1988. Mexico Formula One Grand Prix.
1884. **713.** 500 p. multicoloured 25 10

714. Lopez Verlarde and Rose.

715. Emblem.

1988. Birth Centenary of Ramon Lopez Velarde (poet). Multicoloured.
1885. 300 p. Type **714** 15 5
1886. 300 p. Abstract 15 5

1988. 50th Anniv. of Military Sports.
1887. **715.** 300 p. multicoloured 15 5

716. Chrysanthemum, Container Ship and Flags.

1988. Centenary of Mexico–Japan Friendship, Trade and Navigation Treaty.
1888. **716.** 500 p. multicoloured 35 10

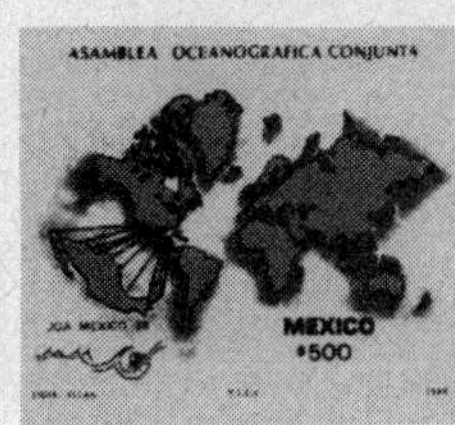

717. Map. **718.** Runners.

1988. Oceanographical Assembly.
1889. **717.** 500 p. multicoloured 25 10

1988. Olympic Games Seoul.
1890. **718.** 500 p. multicoloured 25 10

719. Boxer and Flags.

1988. 25th Anniv. of World Boxing Council.
1892. **719.** 500 p. multicoloured 25 10

720. Hospital and Emblem.

1988. 125th Anniv. of Red Cross.
1893. **720.** 300 p. grey, red and black 15 5

721 Posada

1988. 75th Death Anniv of Jose Guadalupe Posada (painter).
1894 **721** 300 p. black and silver 15 5

722 "Danaus plexippus"

1988. Endangered Insects. The Monarch Butterfly. Multicoloured.
1895 300 p. Type **722** 30 10
1896 300 p. Butterflies on wall 30 10
1897 300 p. Butterflies on leaves 30 10
1898 300 p. Caterpillar, butterfly and chrysalis . . 30 10

1988. Mexicans in Rotunda of Illustrious Persons (4th series). As T **678**. Multicoloured.
1899 300 p. Manuel Sandoval Vallarta 15 5

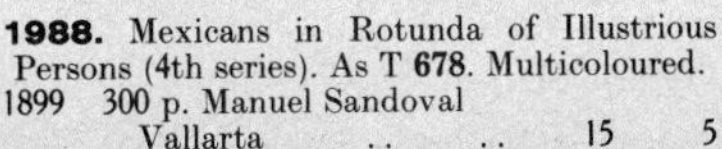

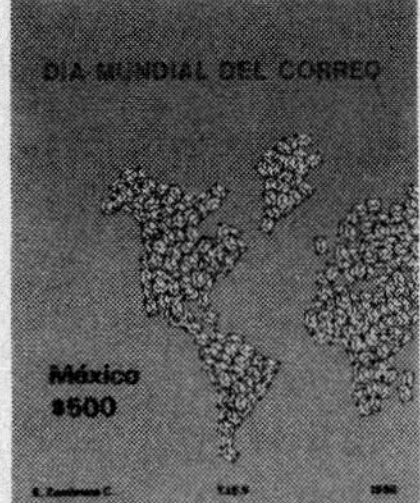

723 Envelopes forming Map

1988. World Post Day.
1900 **723** 500 p. black and blue 20 8

724 Indian and Monk writing

1988 500th Anniv of "Meeting of Two Worlds" (2nd issue). Yanhuitian Codex.
1902 **724** 500 p. multicoloured . . 20 8

725 Man watering Plant

1988. World Food Day. "Rural Youth".
1903 **725** 500 p. multicoloured . . 20 8

1988. Mexican Arts and Sciences (15th series). As T **689**.
1904 300 p. black and grey . . 15 5
1905 300 p. brown, black & yell 15 5
DESIGNS: No. 1904, Alfonso Caso; 1905, Vito Alessio Robles.

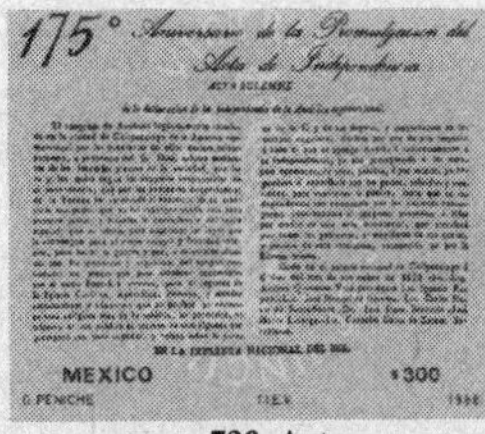

726 Act

1988. 175th Anniv of Promulgation of Act of Independence.
1906 **726** 300 p. flesh and brown 15 5

727 "Self-portrait 1925" 728 Children and Kites

1988. 25th Death Anniv of Antonio Ruiz (painter). Multicoloured.
1907 300 p. Type **727** 15 5
1908 300 p. "La Malinche" . . 15 5
1909 300 p. "March Past" . . 15 5

1988. Christmas. Multicoloured.
1910 300 p. Type **728** 15 5
1911 300 p. Food (horiz) . . 15 5

729 Emblem

1988. 50th Anniv of Municipal Workers Trade Union.
1912 **729** 300 p. black and brown 15 5

1988. Mexican Flowers (7th series). As T **518**. Multicoloured.
1913 300 p. "Mimosa tenuiflora" 15 5
1914 300 p. "Ustilago maydis" 15 5

731 "50" and Emblem

1989. 50th Anniv of State Printing Works.
1915 **731** 450 p. brn, grey & red 20 8

732 Arms and Score of National Anthem

1989. 145th Anniv of Dominican Independence.
1916 **732** 450 p. multicoloured . . 20 8

733 Emblem

1989. Centenary of International Boundary and Water Commission.
1917 **733** 1100 p. multicoloured 50 50

734 Emblem

1989. 10th International Book Fair, Mineria.
1918 **734** 450 p. multicoloured . . 20 8

735 Composer at Work

1989. 25th Anniv of Society of Authors and Composers.
1919 **735** 450 p. multicoloured . . 20 8

736 People

1989. Anti-Aids Campaign.
1920 **736** 450 p. multicoloured .. 20 8

737 Vicario

738 Statue of Reyes

1989. Birth Bicentenary of Leona Vicario (Independence fighter).
1921 **737** 450 p. brown, deep brown and black .. 20 8

1989. Birth Cent of Alfonso Reyes (writer).
1922 **738** 450 p. multicoloured .. 20 8

739 Speeding Cars

1989. Mexico Formula One Grand Prix.
1923 **739** 450 p. multicoloured .. 20 8

740 Sea and Mountains

741 Huehueteotl (god)

1989. 14th Travel Agents' Meeting, Acapulco.
1924 **740** 1100 p. multicoloured 50 50

1989. 14th International Congress on Ageing.
1925 **741** 450 p. pink, black and stone 20 8

742 Revolutionary and Battle Site

1989. 75th Anniv of Battle of Zacatecas.
1926 **742** 450 p. black 20 8

743 Catchers

1989. Baseball Professionals' Hall of Fame. Multicoloured.
1927 550 p. Type **743** 20 8
1928 550 p. Striker 20 8
Nos. 1927/8 were printed together, se-tenant, forming a composite design.

744 Bows and Arrows

1989. World Archery Championships, Switzerland. Multicoloured.
1929 650 p. Type **744** 25 10
1930 650 p. Arrows and target 25 10
Nos. 1929/30 were printed together, se-tenant, forming a composite design.

745 Arms

1989. Centenary of Tijuana.
1931 **745** 1100 p. multicoloured 50 20

746 Storming the Bastille

1989. Bicentenary of French Revolution.
1932 **746** 1300 p. multicoloured 60 50

747 Mina

1989. Birth Bicentenary of Francisco Xavier Mina (independence fighter).
1933 **747** 450 p. multicoloured .. 20 8

748 Cave Paintings

1989. 25th Anniv of National Anthropological Museum, Chapultepec.
1934 **748** 450 p. multicoloured .. 20 8

749 Runners

1989. 7th Mexico City Marathon.
1935 **749** 450 p. multicoloured .. 20 8

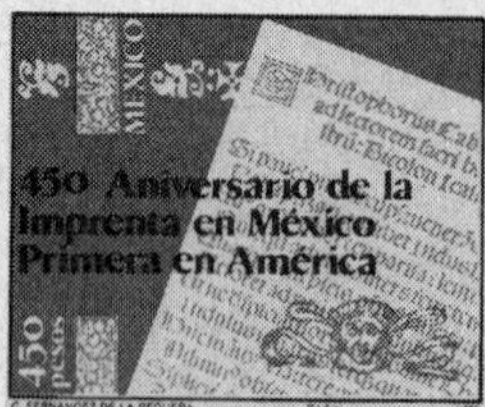

750 Printed Page

1989. 450th Anniv of First American and Mexican Printed Work.
1936 **750** 450 p. multicoloured .. 20 8

751 Posthorn and Cancellations

1989. World Post Day.
1937 **751** 1100 p. multicoloured 50 20

752 "Aguascalientes in History" (Osvaldo Barra)

1989. 75th Anniv of Aguascalientes Revolutionary Convention.
1938 **752** 450 p. multicoloured .. 20 8

753 Patterns

1989. America. Pre-Columbian Culture.
1939 450 p. Type **753** 20 8
1940 450 p. Traditional writing 20 8

754 Old and New World Symbols

755 Cross of Lorraine

1989. 500th Anniv of "Meeting of Two Worlds" (3rd issue).
1941 **754** 1300 p. multicoloured 60 25

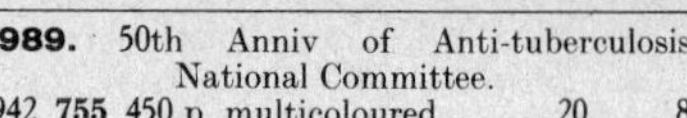
1989. 50th Anniv of Anti-tuberculosis National Committee.
1942 **755** 450 p. multicoloured .. 20 8

756 Mask of God Murcielago

1989.
1943 **756** 450 p. grn, blk & mve 20 8

757 Bank

1989. 125th Anniv of Serfin Commercial Bank.
1944 **757** 450 p. blue, gold & blk 20 8

758 Cortines

759 Man with Sparkler

1989. Birth Centenary of Adolfo Ruiz Cortines (President, 1952–58).
1945 **758** 450 p. multicoloured .. 20 8

1989. Christmas. Multicoloured.
1946 450 p. Type **759** 20 8
1947 450 p. People holding candles (horiz) .. 20 8

760 Emblem

1989. 50th Anniv of National Institute of Anthropology and History.
1948 **760** 450 p. gold, red & blk 20 8

761 Steam Locomotive, Modern Train and Felipe Pescador

1989. 80th Anniv of Nationalization of Railways.
1949 **761** 450 p. multicoloured .. 20 8

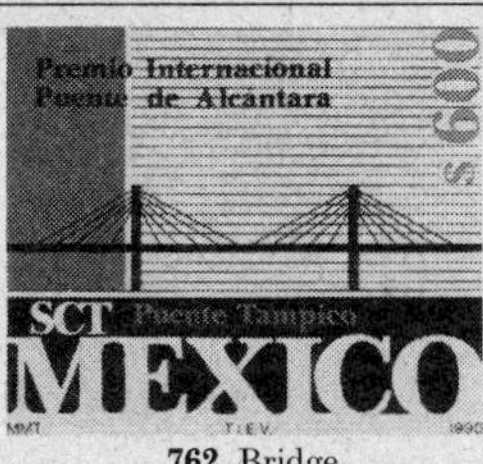

762 Bridge

1990. Opening of Tampico Bridge.
1950 **762** 600 p. blk, gold & red 20 8

763 Smiling Children

1990. Child Vaccination Campaign.
1951 **763** 700 p. multicoloured .. 25 10

764 People in Houses

1990. 11th General Population and Housing Census.
1952 **764** 700 p. grn, yell & lt grn 25 10

765 Stamp under Magnifying Glass

1990. 10th Anniv of Mexican Philatelic Association.
1953 **765** 700 p. multicoloured .. 25 10

766 Archive

1990. Bicentenary of National Archive.
1954 **766** 700 p. blue 25 10

767 Emblem and "90"

1990. 1st International Poster Biennale.
1955 **767** 700 p. multicoloured .. 25 10

MORE DETAILED LISTS

are given in the Stanley Gibbons Catalogues referred to in the country headings.
For lists of current volumes see Introduction.

768 Messenger, 1790

1990. "Stamp World London 90" International Stamp Exhibition.
1956 **768** 700 p. yell, red & blk 25 10

769 Penny Black

1990. 150th Anniv of the Penny Black.
1957 **769** 700 p. blk, red & gold 25 10

770 National Colours and Pope John Paul II

1990. Papal Visit.
1958 **770** 700 p. multicoloured .. 25 10

771 Church 772 Mother and Child

1990. 15th Travel Agents' Congress.
1959 **771** 700 p. multicoloured .. 25 10

1990. Mother and Child Health Campaign.
1960 **772** 700 p. multicoloured .. 25 10

773 Smoke Rings forming Birds 774 Globe as Tree

1990. World Anti-Smoking Day.
1961 **773** 700 p. multicoloured .. 25 10

1990. World Environment Day.
1962 **774** 700 p. multicoloured .. 25 10

775 Racing Car and Chequered Flag

1990. Mexico Formula One Grand Prix.
1963 **775** 700 p. black, red & grn 25 10

776 Aircraft Tailfin

1990. 25th Anniv of Airports and Auxiliary Services.
1964 **776** 700 p. multicoloured .. 25 10

777 Family

1990. United Nations Anti-drugs Decade.
1965 **777** 700 p. multicoloured .. 25 10

778 Tree Trunk

1990. Forest Conservation.
1966 **778** 700 p. multicoloured .. 25 10

779 Emblem

1990. "Solidarity".
1967 **779** 700 p. multicoloured .. 25 10
See also No. 2047.

780 Columns and Native Decoration

1990. World Heritage Site. Oaxaca.
1968 **780** 700 p. multicoloured .. 25 10

781 Elegant Tern

1990. Conservation of Rasa Island, Gulf of California.
1969 **781** 700 p. grey, blk & red 70 20

782 Institute Activities

1990. 25th Anniv of Mexican Petroleum Institute.
1970 **782** 700 p. blue and black 25 10

783 National Colours, City Monuments and Runners

1990. 18th International Mexico City Marathon.
1971 **783** 700 p. black, red & grn 25 10

784 Facade

1990. 50th Anniv of Colima University.
1972 **784** 700 p. multicoloured .. 25 10

785 Abstract

1990. Mexico City Consultative Council.
1973 **785** 700 p. multicoloured .. 25 10

786 Electricity Worker

1990. 30th Anniv of Nationalization of Electricity Industry.
1974 **786** 700 p. multicoloured .. 25 10

787 Violin and Bow

1990. 50th Death Anniv of Silvestre Revueltas (violinist).
1975 **787** 700 p. multicoloured .. 25 10

788 Building

1990. 450th Anniv of Campeche.
1976 **788** 700 p. multicoloured .. 25 15

789 Crossed Rifle and Pen

1990. 80th Anniv of San Luis Plan.
1977 **789** 700 p. multicoloured .. 25 15

1990. 14th World Supreme Councils Conf.
1978 **790** 1500 p. multicoloured 55 35

791 Spanish Tower and Mexican Pyramid

1990. 500th Anniv of "Meeting of Two Worlds" (4th issue).
1979 **791** 700 p. multicoloured .. 25 15

792 Glass of Beer, Ear of Barley and Hop

793 Carving

1990. Centenary of Brewing Industry.
1980 **792** 700 p. multicoloured .. 25 15

1990. Bicentenary of Archaeology in Mexico.
1981 **793** 1500 p. multicoloured 55 35

794 Ball-game Field

795 Globe and Poinsettia

1990. 16th Central American and Caribbean Games. Multicoloured.
1982 750 p. Type **794** 30 20
1983 750 p. Amerindian ball-game player 30 20
1984 750 p. Amerindian ball-game player (different) (horiz) 30 20
1985 750 p. Yutsil and Balam (mascots) (horiz) .. 30 20

1990. Christmas. Multicoloured.
1986 700 p. Type **795** 25 15
1987 700 p. Fireworks and candles 25 15

796 Dog (statuette)

1990. 50th Anniv of Mexican Canine Federation.
1988 **796** 700 p. multicoloured .. 25 15

797 Microscope, Dolphin and Hand holding Map

1991. 50th Anniv of Naval Secretariat.
1989 **797** 1000 p. gold, blk & bl 40 25

798 Means of Transport

1991. Accident Prevention.
1990 **798** 700 p. multicoloured .. 40 15

799 Products in Bags

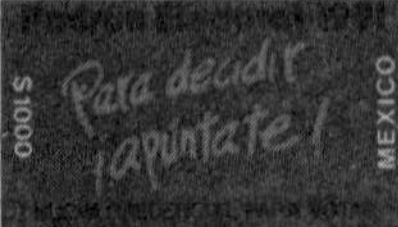
800 "In order to Decide, Register"

1991. 15th Anniv of National Consumer Institute.
1991 **799** 1000 p. multicoloured 40 25

1991. Electoral Register.
1992 **800** 1000 p. orge, grn & blk 40 25

MINIMUM PRICE

The minimum price quoted is 5p which represents a handling charge rather than a basis for valuing common stamps. For further notes about prices see introductory pages.

801 Basketball Player

802 Flowers and Caravel

1991. Olympic Games, Barcelona (1992). (1st issue).
1993 **801** 1000 p. black & yellow 40 25
See also Nos. 2050, 2057 and 2080/9.

1991. America (1990). Natural World. Mult.
1994 700 p. Type **802** 40 15
1995 700 p. Right half of caravel, parrot and flowers 40 15
Nos. 1994/5 were issued together, se-tenant, forming a composite design.

803 Children in Droplet

1991. Children's Month. Vaccination Campaign.
1996 **803** 1000 p. multicoloured 40 25

804 Map

805 Dove and Children

1991. World Post Day (1990).
1997 **804** 1500 p. multicoloured 55 35

1991. Children's Days for Peace and Development.
1998 **805** 1000 p. multicoloured 40 25

806 Dove

807 Mining

1991. Family Health and Unity.
1999 **806** 1000 p. multicoloured 40 25

1991. 500th Anniv of Mining.
2000 **807** 1000 p. multicoloured 40 25

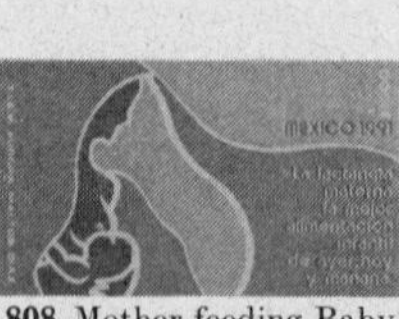
808 Mother feeding Baby

809 Emblem

1991. Breastfeeding Campaign.
2001 **808** 1000 p. buff, bl & brn 40 25

1991. 16th Tourism Fair, Acapulco.
2002 **809** 1000 p. green & dp grn 40 25

810 Rotary Emblem and Independence Monument, Mexico City

811 "Communication"

1991. Rotary International Convention. "Let us Preserve the Planet Earth".
2003 **810** 1000 p. gold and blue 40 25

1991. Centenary of Ministry of Transport and Communications (S.C.T.). Multicoloured.
2004 1000 p. Type **811** .. 40 35
2005 1000 p. Airplane landing 40 25
2006 1000 p. Facsimile machine 40 25
2007 1000 p. Van 40 25
2008 1000 p. Satellites and Earth 40 25
2009 1000 p. Railway freight cars on bridge .. 40 25
2010 1000 p. Telephone users .. 40 25
2011 1000 p. Road bridge over road 40 25
2012 1000 p. Road bridge and cliffs 40 25
2013 1000 p. Stern of container ship and dockyard .. 40 25
2014 1000 p. Television camera and presenter 40 25
2015 1000 p. Front of truck at toll gate 40 25
2016 1000 p. Roadbuilding ("Solidarity") .. 40 25
2017 1500 p. Airplane and control tower 55 35
2018 1500 p. Part of fax machine, transmitters and dish aerials on S.C.T. building .. 55 35
2019 1500 p. Satellite (horiz) .. 55 35
2020 1500 p. Railway locomotives 55 35
2021 1500 p. S.C.T. building .. 55 35
2022 1500 p. Road bridge over ravine 55 35
2023 1500 p. Bow of container ship and dockyard .. 55 35
2024 1500 p. Bus at toll gate .. 55 35
2025 1500 p. Rear of truck and trailer at toll gate .. 55 35
Nos. 2005/25 were issued together, se-tenant, each block containing several composite designs.

812 Jaguar

1991. Lacandona Jungle Conservation.
2026 **812** 1000 p. blk, orge & red 40 25

813 Driver and Car

814 Emblem and Left-hand Sections of Sun and Earth

1991. Mexico Formula 1 Grand Prix.
2027 **813** 1000 p. multicoloured 40 25

1991. Total Eclipse of the Sun. Multicoloured.
2028 1000 p. Type **814** .. 40 25
2029 1000 p. Emblem and right-hand sections of sun and Earth .. 40 25
2030 1500 p. Emblem and centre of sun and Earth showing north and central America .. 55 35
Nos. 2028/30 were issued together, se-tenant, forming a composite design.

815 "Solidarity" (Rufino Tamayo) **816** Bridge

1991. 1st Latin American Presidential Summit, Guadalajara.
2031 **815** 1500 p. blk, orge & yell 55 35

1991. Solidarity between Nuevo Leon and Texas.
2032 **816** 2000 p. multicoloured 1·10 75

817 Runners **819** Emblem

818 Cogwheel

1991. 9th Mexico City Marathon.
2033 **817** 1000 p. multicoloured 40 25

1991. 50th Anniv (1990) of National Chambers of Industry and Commerce.
2034 **818** 1500 p. multicoloured 55 35

1991. 55th Anniv of Federation Fiscal Tribunal.
2035 **819** 1000 p. silver and blue 40 25

820 National Colours forming Emblem

1991. "Solidarity—Let us Unite in order to Progress".
2036 **820** 1000 p. multicoloured 40 25

821 Dove with Letter **822** World Map

1991. World Post Day.
2037 **821** 1000 p. multicoloured 40 25

1991. 500th Anniv of "Meeting of Two Worlds" (5th issue).
2038 **822** 1000 p. multicoloured 40 25

823 Caravel, Sun and Trees

1991. America. Voyages of Discovery. Mult.
2039 1000 p. Type **823** .. 40 25
2040 1000 p. Storm cloud, caravel and broken snake 40 25

824 Flowers and Pots

1991. Christmas. Multicoloured.
2041 1000 p. Type **824** .. 40 25
2042 1000 p. Children with decoration 40 25

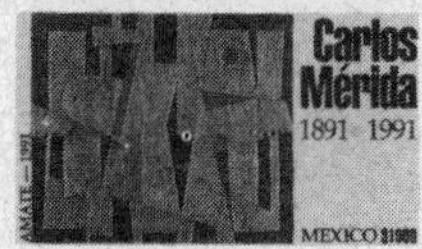

825 Abstract

1991. Carlos Merida (artist) Commemoration.
2043 **825** 1000 p. multicoloured 40 25

826 Score and Portrait

1991. Death Bicentenary of Wolfgang Amadeus Mozart (composer).
2044 **826** 1000 p. multicoloured 40 25

827 Kidney Beans and Maize

1991. Self-sufficiency in Kidney Beans and Maize.
2045 **827** 1000 p. multicoloured 40 25

828 City Plan

1991. 450th Anniv of Morelia.
2046 **828** 1000 p. brown, stone and red 40 25

1991. "Solidarity". As No. 1967 but new value.
2047 **779** 1000 p. multicoloured 40 25

INDEX

Countries can be quickly located by referring to the index at the end of this volume.

829 Merida

1992. 450th Anniv of Merida.
2048 **829** 1300 p. multicoloured 60 40

830 Colonnade

1992. Bicentenary of Engineering Training in Mexico.
2049 **830** 1300 p. blue and red .. 60 40

831 Horse Rider

1992. Olympic Games, Barcelona (2nd issue).
2050 **831** 2000 p. multicoloured 90 60

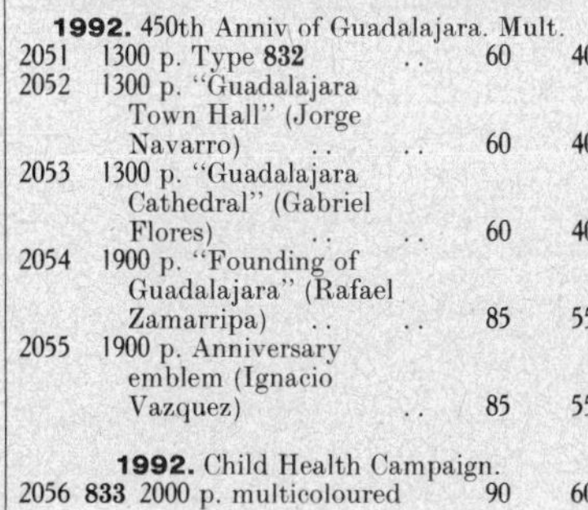

832 City Arms **833** Children and Height Gauge

1992. 450th Anniv of Guadalajara. Mult.
2051 1300 p. Type **832** .. 60 40
2052 1300 p. "Guadalajara Town Hall" (Jorge Navarro) 60 40
2053 1300 p. "Guadalajara Cathedral" (Gabriel Flores) 60 40
2054 1900 p. "Founding of Guadalajara" (Rafael Zamarripa) 85 55
2055 1900 p. Anniversary emblem (Ignacio Vazquez) .. 85 55

1992. Child Health Campaign.
2056 **833** 2000 p. multicoloured 90 60

834 Olympic Torch and Rings

1992. Olympic Games, Barcelona (3rd issue).
2057 **834** 2000 p. multicoloured 90 60

835 Horse and Racing Car

1992. "500th Anniv of the Wheel and the Horse in America". Mexico Formula 1 Grand Prix.
2058 **835** 1300 p. multicoloured 60 40

836 Satellite and Map of Americas **837** Human Figure and Cardiograph

1992. "Americas Telecom '92" Telecommunications Exhibition.
2059 **836** 1300 p. multicoloured 60 40

1992. World Health Day.
2060 **837** 1300 p. black, red & bl 60 40

838 Emblem

1992. 60th Anniv of Military Academy.
2061 **838** 1300 p. red, yell & blk 60 40

839 "Inspiration of Christopher Columbus" (Jose Maria Obregon) **840** Complex

1992. 500th Anniv of "Meeting of Two Worlds" (6th issue). "Granada '92" International Stamp Exhibition.
2062 1300 p. Type **839** .. 60 40
2063 1300 p. "Racial Encounter" (Jorge Gonzalez Camarena) .. 60 40
2064 2000 p. "Origin of the Sky" (Selden Codex) .. 90 60
2065 2000 p. "Quetzalcoatl and Tezcatlipoca" (Borhomico Codex) .. 90 60
2066 2000 p. "From Spaniard and Indian, mestizo" .. 90 60

1992. National Medical Centre.
2068 **840** 1300 p. multicoloured 60 40

841 Children, Dove and Globe **842** New-born Baby

1992. Children's Rights.
2069 **841** 1300 p. multicoloured 60 40

1992. Traditional Childbirth.
2070 **842** 1300 p. multicoloured 60 40

1992. "World Columbian Stamp Expo '92", Chicago. Nos. 2062/6 optd **WORLD COLUMBIAN STAMP EXPO '92 MAY 22-31, 1992 –CHICAGO** and emblem.
2071 1300 p. mult (No. 2062) .. 50 35
2072 1300 p. mult (No. 2063) .. 50 35
2073 2000 p. mult (No. 2064) .. 80 55
2074 2000 p. mult (No. 2065) .. 80 55
2075 2000 p. mult (No. 2066) .. 80 55

845 Arms of Colleges

1992. Bicentenary of Mexico Notary College.
2078 **845** 1300 p. multicoloured 50 35

846 Trees and Cacti

1992. Tree Day.

2079 **846** 1300 p. multicoloured .. 50 35

847 Boxing **848** Athlete

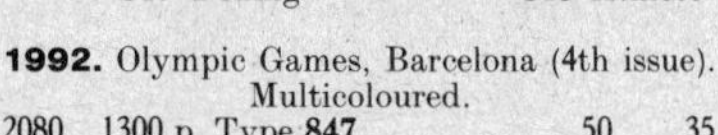

1992. Olympic Games, Barcelona (4th issue). Multicoloured.

2080 1300 p. Type **847** 50 35
2081 1300 p. High jumping 50 35
2082 1300 p. Fencing 50 35
2083 1300 p. Shooting 50 35
2084 1300 p. Gymnastics 50 35
2085 1900 p. Rowing 75 50
2086 1900 p. Running 75 50
2087 1900 p. Football 75 50
2088 1900 p. Swimming 75 50
2089 2000 p. Equestrian 80 55

1992. 10th Mexico City Marathon.

2091 **848** 1300 p. multicoloured .. 50 35

849 Emblem

1992. "Solidarity".

2092 **849** 1300 p. multicoloured .. 50 35

851 Television, Map and Radio

1992. 50th Anniv of National Chamber of Television and Radio Industry.

2094 **851** 1300 p. multicoloured .. 50 35

852 Letter orbiting Globe

1992. World Post Day.

2095 **852** 1300 p. multicoloured .. 50 35

853 Satellite above South and Central America and Flags

1992. American Cadena Communications System.

2096 **853** 2000 p. multicoloured .. 80 55

854 Gold Compass Rose

1992. America. 500th Anniv of Discovery of America by Columbus. Multicoloured.

2097 2000 p. Type **854** 80 55
2098 2000 p. Compass rose (different) and fish .. 80 55

Nos. 2097/8 were issued together, se-tenant, forming a composite design.

855 Scroll

1992. 400th Anniv of San Luis Potosi.

2099 **855** 1300 p. black & mauve .. 50 35

856 Berrendos Deer

1992. Conservation.

2100 **856** 1300 p. multicoloured .. 50 35

857 Schooner, Landing Ship, Emblem and Sailors **858** Christmas Tree, Children and Crib

1992. Navy Day.

2101 **857** 1300 p. multicoloured .. 50 35

1992. Christmas. Children's drawings. Mult.

2102 1300 p. Type **858** 50 35
2103 2000 p. Street celebration (horiz) 80 55

Currency Reform. 1 (new) peso = 1000 (old) pesos.

859 Anniversary Emblem **860** Emblem

1993. 50th Anniv of Mexican Social Security Institute (1st issue).

2104 **859** 1 p. 50 grn, gold & blk .. 60 40

See also No. 2110.

1993. Centenary of Mexican Ophthalmological Society.

2105 **860** 1 p. 30 multicoloured .. 50 35

861 Children **862** Society Arms and Founders

1993. Children's Month.

2106 **861** 1 p. 30 multicoloured .. 50 35

1993. 160th Anniv of Mexican Geographical and Statistical Society.

2107 **862** 1 p. 30 multicoloured .. 50 35

863 1824 Constitution **864** Gomez, Children and Hospital

1993. 150th Death Anniv of Miguel Ramos Arizpe, "Father of Federalism".

2108 **863** 1 p. 30 multicoloured .. 50 35

1993. 50th Anniv of Federico Gomez Children's Hospital.

2109 **864** 1 p. 30 multicoloured .. 50 35

865 Doctor with Child

1993. 50th Anniv of Mexican Social Security Institute (2nd issue). Medical Services.

2110 **865** 1 p. 30 multicoloured .. 50 35

866 Mother feeding Baby

1993. "Health begins at Home".

2111 **866** 1 p. 30 multicoloured .. 50 35

867 Seal and Map

1993. Upper Gulf of California Nature Reserve.

2112 **867** 1 p. 30 multicoloured .. 50 35

868 Cantinflas

1993. Mexican Film Stars. Mario Moreno (Cantinflas).

2113 **868** 1 p. 30 black and blue .. 50 35

869 Campeche

1993. Tourism. Multicoloured.

2114 90 c. Type **869** 35 25
2115 1 p. Guanajuato 40 25
2116 1 p. 30 Colima 50 35
2117 1 p. 90 Michoacan (vert) .. 75 50
2118 2 p. Coahuila 80 55
2119 2 p. 20 Queretaro 90 60
2120 2 p. 50 Sonora .. .. 1·00 65
2121 2 p. 80 Zacatecas (vert) .. 1·10 75
2122 3 p. 70 Sinaloa .. .. 1·50 1·00
2123 4 p. 40 Yucatan .. .. 1·75 1·10
2124 4 p. 80 Chiapas .. .. 1·90 1·25
2125 6 p. Mexico City .. .. 2·40 1·60

870 Dr. Maximiliano Ruiz Castaneda

1993. 50th Anniv of Health Service. Mult.

2126 1 p. 30 Type **870** 50 35
2127 1 p. 30 Dr. Bernardo Sepulveda Gutierrez .. 50 35
2128 1 p. 30 Dr. Ignacio Chavez Sanchez 50 35
2129 1 p. 30 Dr. Mario Salazar Mallen 50 35
2130 1 p. 30 Dr. Gustavo Baz Prada 50 35

871 Brazil 30 r. "Bull's Eye" Stamp **872** Runners

1993. 150th Anniv of First Brazilian Stamps.

2131 **871** 2 p. multicoloured .. 80 55

1993. 11th Mexico City Marathon.

2132 **872** 1 p. 30 multicoloured .. 50 35

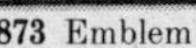

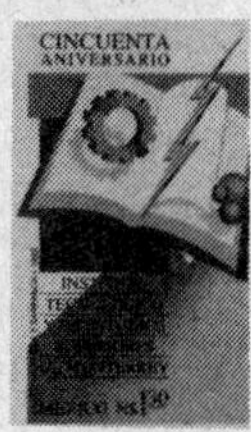

873 Emblem **874** Open Book and Symbols

1993. "Solidarity".

2133 **873** 1 p. 30 multicoloured .. 50 35

1993. 50th Anniv of Monterrey Institute of Technology and Higher Education. Mult.

2134 1 p. 30 Type **874** 50 35
2135 2 p. Buildings and mountains 80 55

Nos. 2134/5 were issued together, se-tenant, forming a composite design.

875 Cogwheels and Emblem **876** Torreon

1993. 75th Anniv of Concamin.

2136 **875** 1 p. 30 multicoloured .. 50 35

1993 Centenary of Torreon.

2137 **876** 1 p. 30 multicoloured .. 50 35

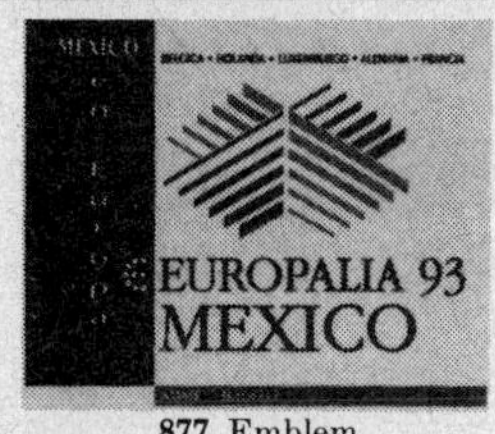

877 Emblem

1993. "Europalia 93 Mexico" Festival.

2138	877	2 p. multicoloured ..	80	55

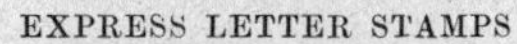

EXPRESS LETTER STAMPS

E 55. Express Service Messenger.

1919.

E 445.	E 55.	20 c. black and red	35	15

E 95.

1934.

E 536.	E 95.	10 c. blue and red ..	15	30

E 121. Indian Archer. E 222.

1934. New President's Assumption of Office. Imprint "OFICINA IMPRESORA DE HACIENDA-MEXICO".

E 581.	E 121.	10 c. violet ..	1·00	20

1938. Imprint "TALLERES DE IMP. DE EST. Y VALORES-MEXICO".

E 610.	E 121.	10 c. violet ..	55	20
E 731.		20 c. orange ..	25	30

1940. Optd. **1940.**

E 665.	E 55.	20 c. black and red	20	15

1950.

E 860.	E 222.	25 c. orange ..	20	10
E 910.	–	60 c. green ..	1·10	35

DESIGN: 60 c. Hands and letter.

E 244.

E 245.

1956.

E 954	E 244	35 c. purple ..	25	10
E1065		50 c. green ..	45	10
E 956	E 245	80 c. red ..	50	80
E1066		1 p. 20 lilac ..	1·50	75
E1346p	E 244	2 p. orange ..	20	15
E1346q	E 245	5 p. blue ..	20	60

E 468. Watch Face.

1979.

E 1373.	E 468.	2 p. black & orge.	5	60

INSURED LETTER STAMPS

IN 125. Safe. IN 222. P.O. Treasury Vault.

1935. Inscr. as in Type IN 1.

IN 583.	–	10 c. red ..	1·10	30
IN 733.	–	50 c. blue ..	75	25
IN 734.	IN 125.	1 p. green ..	75	35

DESIGNS: 10 c. Bundle of insured letters. 50 c. Registered mailbag.

1950.

IN 911.	IN 222.	20 c. blue ..	15	10
IN 912.		40 c. purple ..	15	10
IN 913.		1 p. green	20	10
IN 914.		5 p. green & bl.	65	60
IN 915.		10 p. blue & red	3·00	1·50

IN 469. Padlock.

1976.

IN 1374.	IN 469.	40 c. blk. & turq.	5	5
IN 1522.		1 p. blk. & turq.	5	5
IN 1376.		2 p. blk. & bl.	5	5
IN 1380.		5 p. blk. & turq.	5	5
IN 1524.		10 p. blk. & turq.	10	5
IN 1525.		20 p. blk. & turq.	10	10
IN 1383.		50 p. blk. & turq.	95	95
IN 1384.		100 p. black and turquoise ..	60	60

The 5, 10, 20 p. exist with the padlock either 31 or 32½ mm. high.

OFFICIAL STAMPS

O 18. Hidalgo.

1884. No value shown.

O 156.	O 18.	Red	30	20
O 157.		Brown	15	10
O 158.		Orange	80	15
O 159.		Green	30	15
O 160.		Blue	45	35

1894. Stamps of 1895 handstamped **OFICIAL.**

O 231.	19.	1 c. green	3·75	1·25
O 232.		2 c. red	4·50	1·25
O 233.		3 c. brown	3·75	1·25
O 234.	20.	4 c. orange	5·50	2·50
O 235.	21.	5 c. blue	7·50	2·50
O 236.	22.	10 c. purple	7·00	50
O 237.	20.	12 c. olive	15·00	6·25
O 238.	22.	15 c. blue	8·75	3·75
O 239.		20 c. red	8·75	3·75
O 240.		50 c. mauve	19·00	9·50
O 241.	23.	1 p. brown	48·00	19·00
O 242.		5 p. red	£110	55·00
O 243.		10 p. blue	£190	£100

1899. Stamps of 1899 handstamped **OFICIAL.**

O 276.	27.	1 c. green	9·50	60
O 286.		1 c. purple	8·75	95
O 277.		2 c. red	12·50	95
O 287.		2 c. green	8·75	95
O 278.		3 c. brown	12·50	60
O 288.		4 c. red	16·00	45
O 279.		5 c. blue	12·50	1·10
O 289.		5 c. orange	16·00	3·25
O 280.		10 c. brown & purple	16·00	1·40
O 290.		10 c. orange and blue	19·00	95
O 281.		15 c. purple & lavender	16·00	1·40
O 282.		20 c. blue and red ..	19·00	45
O 283.	28.	50 c. black & purple ..	38·00	6·25
O 291.		50 c. black and red ..	48·00	6·25
O 284.	29.	1 p. black and blue ..	80·00	6·25
O 285.	30.	5 p. black and red ..	50·00	19·00

1911. Independence stamps optd. **OFICIAL.**

O 301.	32.	1 c. purple	1·25	1·25
O 302.	–	2 c. green	75	45
O 303.	–	3 c. brown	1·25	45
O 304.	–	4 c. red	1·90	45
O 305.	–	5 c. orange	3·25	1·75
O 306.	–	10 c. orge. and blue ..	1·90	45
O 307.	–	15 c. lake and slate ..	3·25	2·00
O 308.	–	20 c. blue and lake ..	2·50	45
O 309.	40.	50 c. black & brown ..	8·75	3·75
O 310.	–	1 p. black and blue ..	15·00	6·25
O 311.	–	5 p. black and red ..	55·00	32·00

1915. Stamps of 1915 optd. **OFICIAL.**

O 321.	43.	1 c. violet	30	55
O 322.	44.	2 c. green	30	55
O 323.	45.	3 c. brown	30	55
O 324.		4 c. red	30	55
O 325.		5 c. orange	30	55
O 326.		10 c. blue	30	55

1915. Stamps of 1915 optd. **OFICIAL.**

O 318.	46.	40 c. grey	2·50	3·75
O 455.		40 c. mauve ..	3·75	1·90
O 319.	47.	1 p. grey and brown	3·25	3·75
O 456.		1 p. grey and blue ..	9·50	6·25
O 320.	48.	5 p. blue and lake ..	19·00	16·00
O 457.		5 p. grey and green ..	55·00	95·00

1916. Nos. O301/11 optd with T **49**.

O 358.	32.	1 c. purple	1·90	
O 359.	–	2 c. green	30	
O 360.	–	3 c. brown	35	
O 361.	–	4 c. red	2·00	
O 362.	–	5 c. orange	35	
O 363.	–	10 c. orange and blue	35	
O 364.	–	15 c. lake and slate ..	35	
O 365.	–	20 c. blue and lake ..	40	
O 366.	40.	50 c. black and brown	55·00	
O 367.	–	1 p. black and blue ..	3·25	
O 368.	–	5 p. black and red ..	£1600	

1918. Stamps of 1917 optd. **OFICIAL.**

O 424.	53.	1 c. violet	1·25	60
O 446.		1 c. grey	30	20
O 447.	–	2 c. green	20	20
O 448.	–	3 c. brown	25	20
O 449.	–	4 c. red	3·75	45
O 450.	–	5 c. blue	20	20
O 451.	–	10 c. blue	30	15
O 452.	–	20 c. lake	2·50	2·50
O 454.	–	30 c. black	3·75	1·40

1923. No. 416 optd. **OFICIAL.**

O 485.		10 p. black and brown	60·00	95·00

1923. Stamps of 1923 optd. **OFICIAL.**

O 471.	59.	1 c. brown	20	20
O 473.	60.	2 c. red	25	25
O 475.	61.	3 c. brown	55	40
O 461.	62.	4 c. green	1·90	1·90
O 476.	63.	4 c. green	40	40
O 477.		5 c. orange	70	65
O 489.	74.	8 c. orange	3·75	2·50
O 479.	66.	10 c. lake	55	55
O 480.	65.	20 c. blue	3·25	2·50
O 464.	64.	30 c. green	35	25
O 467.	68.	50 c. brown	55	55
O 469.	69.	1 p. blue and lake ..	4·75	4·75

1929. Air. Optd. **OFICIAL.**

O 501.	80.	5 c. blue (roul.) ..	45	25
O 502.	81.	20 c. violet	55	55
O 492.	58.	25 c. sepia and lake	3·50	2·75
O 490.		25 c. sepia and green	1·75	1·25

1929. Air. As 1926 Postal Congress stamp optd. **HABILITADO Servicio Oficial Aereo.**

O 493.	70.	2 c. black	26·00	26·00
O 494.	–	4 c. black	26·00	26·00
O 495.	70.	5 c. black	26·00	26·00
O 496.	–	10 c. black	26·00	26·00
O 497.	72.	20 c. black	26·00	26·00
O 498.		30 c. black	26·00	26·00
O 499.		40 c. black	26·00	26·00
O 500.	73.	1 p. black	£950	£950

O 85.

1930. Air.

O 503.	O 85.	20 c. grey	2·75	2·75
O 504.		35 c. violet	40	95
O 505.		40 c. blue and brown	50	90
O 506.		70 c. sepia and violet	50	95

1931. Air. Surch **HABILITADO Quince centavos.**

O 515.	O 85.	15 c. on 20 c. grey ..	45	45

1932. Air. Optd. **SERVICIO OFICIAL** in one line. T **62** perf. or roul.

O 532.	80.	10 c. violet	30	30
O 533.		15 c. red	85	85
O 534.		20 c. sepia	85	85
O 531.	58.	50 c. red and blue ..	90	70

1932. Stamps of 1923 optd **SERVICIO OFICIAL** in two lines.

O 535.	59.	1 c. brown	15	15
O 536.	60.	2 c. red	10	10
O 537.	61.	3 c. brown	95	95
O 538.	63.	4 c. green	3·25	2·50
O 539.		5 c. red	3·75	2·50
O 540.	66.	10 c. lake	1·10	75
O 541.	65.	20 c. blue	4·75	3·25
O 544.	64.	30 c. green	2·50	95
O 545.	46.	40 c. mauve	4·75	1·90
O 546.	68.	50 c. brown	80	95
O 547.	69.	1 p. blue and lake ..	95	95

1933. Air. Optd. **SERVICIO OFICIAL** in two lines.

O 553.	58.	50 c. red and blue ..	1·00	70

1933. Air. Optd. **SERVICIO OFICIAL** in two lines.

O 548.	80.	5 c. blue (No. 476a) ..	30	30
O 549.		10 c. violet (No. 477)	30	30
O 550.		20 c. sepia (No. 479) ..	30	60
O 551.		50 c. lake (No. 481) ..	40	95

1934. Optd. **OFICIAL.**

O 565.	92.	15 c. blue	35	35

1938. Nos. 561/71 optd. **OFICIAL.**

O 622.		1 c. orange ..	70	1·25
O 623.		2 c. green	45	45
O 624.		4 c. red	45	45
O 625.		10 c. violet	45	80
O 626.		20 c. blue	55	80
O 627.		30 c. red	70	1·25
O 628.		40 c. brown	70	1·25
O 629.		50 c. black	1·00	1·00
O 630.		1 p. red and brown ..	2·50	3·75

PARCEL POST STAMPS

P 167. Mail Train.

1941.

P 732.	P 167.	10 c. red	1·75	40
P 733.		20 c. violet	2·00	50

P 228. Mail Train.

1951.

P 916. P 228. 10 c. pink .. 1·25 15
P 917. 20 c. violet .. 1·75 25

POSTAGE DUE STAMPS

D 32.

1908.

D 282. D 32. 1 c. blue .. .. 1·00 1·00
D 283. 2 c. blue .. .. 1·00 1·00
D 284. 4 c. blue .. .. 1·00 1·00
D 285. 5 c. blue .. .. 1·00 1·00
D 286. 10 c. blue .. .. 1·00 1·00

MICRONESIA Pt. 22

A group of islands in the Pacific, from 1899 to 1914 part of the German Caroline Islands. Occupied by the Japanese in 1914 the islands were from 1920 a Japanese mandated territory, and from 1947 part of the United States Trust Territory of the Pacific Islands, using United States stamps. Micronesia assumed control of its postal services in 1984.

100 cents = 1 dollar.

1. Yap.

1984. Inauguration of Postal Independence. Maps. Multicoloured.

1. 20 c. Type **1** 60 45
2. 20 c. Truk 60 45
3. 20 c. Pohnpei 60 45
4. 20 c. Kosrae 60 45

2. Fernandez de Quiros.

3. Air Micronesia "727–100".

1984.

5 2 1 c. blue 10 10
6 – 2 c. brown 10 10
7 – 3 c. blue 10 10
8 – 4 c. green 10 10
9 – 5 c. brown and olive .. 10 10
10 – 10 c. purple 15 10
11 – 13 c. blue 20 10
11a – 15 c. red 20 10
12 – 17 c. brown 25 10
13 2 19 c. purple 30 10
14 – 20 c. green 30 10
14a – 22 c. green 30 15
14b – 25 c. orange 30 15
15 – 30 c. red 45 15
15a – 36 c. blue 50 20
16 – 37 c. violet 50 20
16a – 45 c. green 60 30
17 – 50 c. brown and sepia .. 80 35
18 – $1 olive .. .. .. 1·50 85
19 – $2 blue .. .. .. 3·00 1·50
20 – $5 brown .. .. .. 8·00 4·50
20a – $10 blue .. .. .. 15·00 11·00

DESIGNS: 2, 20 c. Louis Duperrey. 3, 30 c. Fyodor Lutke. 4, 37 c. Jules Dumont d'Urville. 5 c. Men's house, Yap. 10, 45 c. Sleeping Lady (mountains), Kosrae. 13, 15 c. Liduduhriap waterfall, Pohnpei. 17, 25 c. Tonachau Peak, Truk. 22, 36 c. "Senyavin" (full-rigged sailing ship). 50 c. Devil mask, Truk. $1 Sokehs Rock, Pohnpei. $2 Outrigger canoes, Kosrae. $5 Stone money, Yap. $10 Official seal.

1984. Air. Multicoloured.

21. 28 c. Type **3** 55 30
22. 35 c. Pan American "SA-16 Albatross" 70 50
23. 40 c. Transocean Airlines "PBY-5A" 90 60

4. Truk Post Office.

1984. "Ausipex 84" International Stamp Exhibition, Melbourne. Multicoloured.

24 20 c. Type **4** (postage) .. 50 20
25 28 c. German Caroline Islands 1919 3 pf. yacht stamp (air) 60 40
26 35 c. German 1900 20 pf. stamp optd for Caroline Islands 70 50
27 40 c. German Caroline Islands 1915 5 m. yacht stamp 80 65

5. Baby in Basket.

1984. Christmas. Multicoloured.

28. 20 c. Type **5** (postage) .. 50 25
29. 28 c. Open book showing Christmas scenes (air) .. 60 40
30. 35 c. Palm tree decorated with lights 70 50
31. 40 c. Women preparing food 80 65

6. U.S.S. "Jamestown" (warship).

1985. Ships.

32. 6. 22 c. blk. & brn. (post.) 65 35
33. – 33 c. black and lilac (air) 85 50
34. – 39 c. black and green .. 1·00 70
35. – 44 c. black and red .. 1·40 85

DESIGNS: 33 c. "L'Astrolabe" (D'Urville's ship); 39 c. "La Coquille" (Duperrey's ship); 44 c. "Shenandoah" (Confederate warship).

7. Lelu Protestant Church, Kosrae.

1985. Christmas.

36 7 22 c. black and orange (postage) 70 30
37 – 33 c. black and violet (air) 95 50
38 – 44 c. black and green .. 1·50 70

DESIGNS: 33 c. Dublon Protestant Church. 44 c. Pohnpei Catholic Church.

8. "Noddy Tern".

1985. Birth Bicentenary of John J. Audubon (ornithologist). Multicoloured.

39 22 c. Type **8** (postage) .. 70 50
40 22 c. "Turnstone" .. 70 50
41 22 c. "Golden Plover" .. 70 50
42 22 c. "Black-bellied Plover" 70 50
43 44 c. "Sooty Tern" (air) .. 1·25 80

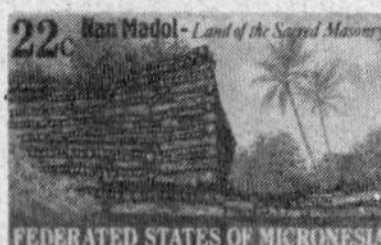

9. Land of Sacred Masonry.

1985. Nan Madol, Pohnpei. Multicoloured.

44. 22 c. Type **9** (postage) .. 45 25
45. 33 c. Nan Tauas inner courtyard (air) 60 45
46. 39 c. Nan Tauas outer wall 75 60
47. 44 c. Nan Tauas burial vault 90 70

10. Doves, "LOVE" and Hands.

12. Bully Hayes.

1986. Anniversaries and Events. Mult.

48 22 c. Type **10** (International Peace Year) 60 35
49 44 c. Halley's comet .. 1·40 80
50 44 c. "Trienza" (cargo liner) arriving at jetty (40th anniv of return of Nauruans from Truk) .. 1·40 80

1986. Nos. 1/4 surch.

51 22 c. on 20 c. Type **1** .. 55 45
52 22 c. on 20 c. Truk .. 55 45
53 22 c. on 20 c. Pohnpei .. 55 45
54 22 c. on 20 c. Kosrae .. 55 45

1986. "Ameripex 86" Int. Stamp Exhibition, Chicago. Bully Hayes (buccaneer). Mult.

55. 22 c. Type **12** (postage) .. 50 30
56. 33 c. Angelo (crew member) forging Hawaii 5 c. blue stamp (air) 65 50
57. 39 c. "Leonora" sinking off Kosrae 75 60
58. 44 c. Hayes escaping capture on Kosrae .. 95 75
59. 75 c. Cover of book "Bully Hayes, Buccaneer" by Louis Becke .. .. 1·50 1·25

13. "Madonna and Child".

1986. Christmas. "Madonna and Child" Paintings.

61. – 5 c. mult. (postage) .. 15 10
62. – 22 c. multicoloured .. 70 30
63. – 33 c. multicoloured (air) 95 65
64. 13. 44 c. multicoloured .. 1·25 1·00

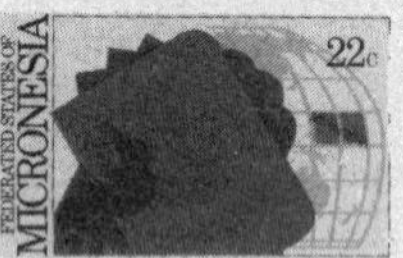

14. Passports on Globe.

1986. 1st Micronesian Passport.

65 14 22 c. blue, black & yellow 60 35

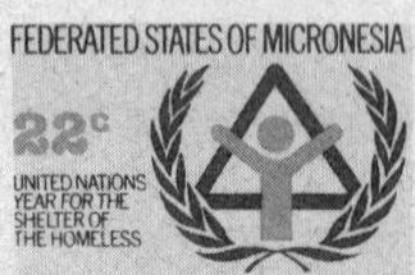

15. Emblem (International Year of Shelter for the Homeless).

1987. Anniversaries and Events.

66. 15. 22 c. blue, red and black (postage) 35 30
67. – 33 c. green, red and black (air) 50 40
68. – 39 c. blue, black and red 60 50
69. – 44 c. blue, red and black 75 60

DESIGNS: 33 c. Dollar sign (bicentenary of dollar currency). 39 c. Space capsule (25th anniv of first American to orbit Earth). 44 c. "200 USA" (bicentenary of US constitution).

16. Archangel Gabriel appearing to Mary.

1987. Christmas. Multicoloured.

71. 22 c. Type **16** (postage) .. 40 30
72. 33 c. Joseph praying and Mary with baby Jesus (air) 60 45
73. 39 c. Shepherds with their sheep 75 60
74. 44 c. Wise men 90 75

17. Spanish Missionary and Flag.

1988. Micronesian History. Multicoloured.

75 22 c. Type **17** (postage) .. 50 35
76 22 c. Natives producing copra and German flag .. 50 35
77 22 c. School pupils and Japanese flag 50 35
78 22 c. General store and U.S. flag 50 35
79 44 c. Traditional boatbuilding and fishing skills (air) 1·00 75
80 44 c. Welcoming tourists from airplane and divers investigating World War II wreckage .. .. 1·00 75

18. Ponape White Eye.

19. Marathon.

1988. Birds. Multicoloured.

81 3 c. Type **18** (postage) .. 10 10
82 14 c. Truk monarch .. 25 10
83 22 c. Ponape starling .. 35 20
84 33 c. Truk white eye (air) .. 55 35
85 44 c. Blue-faced parrot finch 75 60
86 $1 Yap monarch .. .. 1·50 1·25

1988. Olympic Games, Seoul. Multicoloured.

87. 25 c. Type **19** 45 25
88. 25 c. Hurdling 45 25
89. 45 c. Basketball 70 55
90. 45 c. Volleyball 70 55

20. Girls decorating Tree.

1988. Christmas. Multicoloured.

91. 25 c. Type **20** 45 30
92. 25 c. Dove with mistletoe in beak and children holding decorations 45 30
93. 25 c. Boy in native clothing and girl in floral dress sitting at base of tree .. 45 30
94. 25 c. Boy in T-shirt and shorts and girl in native clothing sitting at base of tree 45 30

Nos. 91/4 were printed together in blocks of four, se-tenant, forming a composite design.

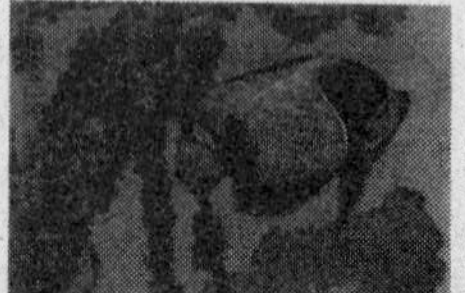
21. Sun and Stars Angelfish.

1988. Truk Lagoon, "Micronesia's Living War Memorial". Multicoloured.

95 25 c. Type **21** 40 30
96 25 c. Jellyfish and shoal of small fishes 40 30
97 25 c. Snorkel divers 40 30
98 25 c. Two goldenjack (black-striped fishes facing left) 40 30
99 25 c. Blacktip reef shark 40 30
100 25 c. Deck railings of wreck and fishes 40 30
101 25 c. Squirrelfish (red fish) 40 30
102 25 c. Batfish and aircraft cockpit 40 30
103 25 c. Three Moorish idols (fishes with long dorsal fins) 40 30
104 25 c. Four barracuda and shoal 40 30
105 25 c. Two spot-banded butterfly fishes (facing alternate directions) 40 30
106 25 c. Three-spot damselfish and aircraft propeller 40 30
107 25 c. Foxface (fish) and shoal 40 30
108 25 c. Lionfish (fish with spines) 40 30
109 25 c. Scuba diver 40 30
110 25 c. Tubular corals 40 30
111 25 c. Ornate butterfly fish and brain coral 40 30
112 25 c. Clown fish, clam and sea plants 40 30

Nos. 95/112 were printed together, se-tenant, in sheetlets of 18 stamps, the backgrounds of the stamps forming an overall design of the remains of a Japanese ship and "Zero" fighter plane on the Lagoon bed colonized by marine life.

22 Flag of Pohnpei

1989. Air. State Flags. Multicoloured.

113 45 c. Type **22** 85 60
114 45 c. Truk 85 60
115 45 c. Kosrae 85 60
116 45 c. Yap 85 60

23 Plumeria and Headdress

1989. Mwarmwarms (floral decorations). Multicoloured.

117 45 c. Type **23** 85 60
118 45 c. Hibiscus and lei 85 60
119 45 c. Jasmine and Yap religious mwarmwarm 85 60
120 45 c. Bougainvillea and Truk dance mwarmwarm 85 60

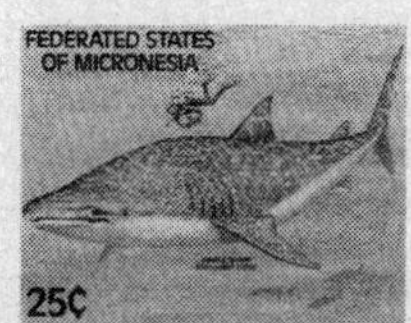

24 White Shark

1989. Sharks. Multicoloured.

121 25 c. Type **24** 65 40
122 25 c. Hammerhead shark 65 40
123 45 c. Tiger shark (vert) 1·10 75
124 45 c. Great white shark (vert) 1·10 75

26 "Explorer 1" Satellite over North America

1989. 20th Anniv of First Manned Landing on the Moon. Multicoloured.

126 25 c. "X-15" rocket plane 40 30
127 25 c. Type **26** 40 30
128 25 c. Ed White on space walk during "Gemini 4" mission 40 30
129 25 c. "Apollo 18" space-craft 40 30
130 25 c. "Gemini 4" space capsule over South America 40 30
131 25 c. Space shuttle "Challenger" 40 30
132 25 c. Italian "San Marco 2" satellite 40 30
133 25 c. Russian "Soyuz 19" spacecraft 40 30
134 25 c. Neil Armstrong descending ladder to Moon's surface during "Apollo 11" mission 40 30
135 $2.40 Lunar module "Eagle" on Moon (34 × 46 mm) 3·50 2·75

Nos 126/34 were printed together in se-tenant sheetlets of nine stamps, the backgrounds of the stamps forming an overall design of Earth as viewed from the Moon.

27 Horse's Hoof

1989. Sea Shells. Multicoloured.

136 1 c. Type **27** 10 10
137 3 c. Rare spotted cowrie 10 10
138 15 c. Commercial trochus 20 10
139 20 c. General cone 25 10
140 25 c. Triton's trumpet 30 20
141 30 c. Laciniated conch 35 25
142 36 c. Red-mouthed olive 45 35
143 45 c. Map cowrie 55 45
144 50 c. Textile cone 60 50
145 $1 Orange spider conch 1·25 1·00
146 $2 Golden cowrie 2·50 2·00
147 $5 Episcopal mitre 6·00 4·50

28 Oranges

1989. "World Stamp Expo '89" International Stamp Exhibition, Washington D.C. "Kosrae—the Garden State". Multicoloured.

155 25 c. Type **28** 45 30
156 25 c. Limes 45 30
157 25 c. Tangerines 45 30
158 25 c. Mangoes 45 30
159 25 c. Coconuts 45 30
160 25 c. Breadfruit 45 30
161 25 c. Sugar cane 45 30
162 25 c. Kosrae house 45 30
163 25 c. Bananas 45 30
164 25 c. Children with fruit and flowers 45 30
165 25 c. Pineapples 45 30
166 25 c. Taro 45 30
167 25 c. Hibiscus 45 30
168 25 c. Ylang ylang 45 30
169 25 c. White ginger 45 30
170 25 c. Plumeria 45 30
171 25 c. Royal poinciana 45 30
172 25 c. Yellow allamanda 45 30

29 Angel over Micronesian Village

1989. Christmas. Multicoloured.

173 25 c. Type **29** 50 25
174 45 c. Truk children dressed as Three Kings 75 60

HAVE YOU READ THE NOTES AT THE BEGINNING OF THIS CATALOGUE?

These often provide answers to the enquiries we receive.

30 Young Kingfisher and Sokehs Rock, Pohnpei

1990. World Wide Fund for Nature. Micronesian Kingfisher and Micronesian Pigeon.

175 10 c. Type **30** 15 10
176 15 c. Adult kingfisher and rain forest, Pohnpei 25 15
177 20 c. Pigeon flying over lake at Sleeping Lady, Kosrae 35 25
178 25 c. Pigeon perched on leaf, Tol Island, Truk 45 35

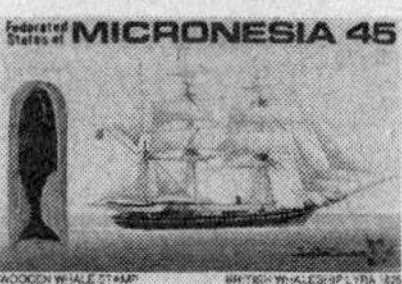

31 Wooden Whale Stamp and "Lyra"

1990. "Stamp World London 90" International Stamp Exhibition. 19th-century British Whaling Ships. Multicoloured.

179 45 c. Type **31** 55 45
180 45 c. Harpoon heads and "Prudent" 55 45
181 45 c. Carved whale bone and "Rhone" 55 45
182 45 c. Carved whale tooth and "Sussex" 55 45

33 Beech Model 18E3 over Kosrae Airport

34 School Building

1990. Air. Airplanes. Multicoloured.

185 22 c. Type **33** 30 15
186 36 c. Boeing 727 landing at Truk 50 30
187 39 c. Britten Norman Islander over Pohnpei 50 30
188 45 c. Beech Queen Air over Yap 60 35

1990. 25th Anniv of Pohnpei Agriculture and Trade School. Multicoloured.

190 25 c. Type **34** 25 15
191 25 c. Fr. Costigan (founder) and students 25 15
192 25 c. Fr. Hugh Costigan 25 15
193 25 c. Ispahu Samuel Hadley (Metelanim chief) and Fr. Costigan 25 15
194 25 c. Statue of Liberty, New York City Police Department badge and Empire State Building 25 15

36 Loading Mail Plane at Pohnpei Airport

1990. Pacific Postal Transport. Mult.

196 25 c. Type **36** 35 20
197 45 c. Launch meeting "Nantaku" (inter-island freighter) in Truk Lagoon to exchange mail, 1940 65 40

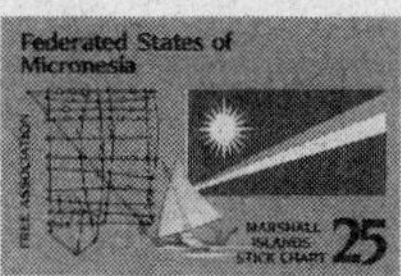

37 Marshallese Stick Chart, Outrigger Canoe and Flag

1990. 4th Anniv of Ratification of Micronesia and Marshall Islands Compacts of Free Association. Multicoloured.

198 25 c. Type **37** 35 20
199 25 c. Frigate bird, U.S.S. "Constitution" (frigate), U.S. flag and bald eagle 35 20
200 25 c. Micronesian outrigger canoe and flag 35 20

38 "Caloptilia sp." and New Moon

1990. Moths. Multicoloured.

201 45 c. Type **38** 60 50
202 45 c. "Anticrates sp." (inscr "Yponomeatidae") and waxing moon 60 50
203 45 c. "Cosmopterigidae" family and full moon 60 50
204 45 c. "Cosmopterigidae" family and waning moon 60 50

39 Cherub above Roof

41 Hawksbill Turtle returning to Sea

1990. Christmas. "Micronesian Holy Night". Multicoloured.

205 25 c. Type **39** 30 20
206 25 c. Two cherubs and Star of Bethlehem 30 20
207 25 c. Cherub blowing horn 30 20
208 25 c. Lambs, goat, pig and chickens 30 20
209 25 c. Native wise men offering gifts to Child 30 20
210 25 c. Children and dog beside lake 30 20
211 25 c. Man blowing conch shell 30 20
212 25 c. Adults and children on path 30 20
213 25 c. Man and children carrying gifts 30 20

Nos. 205/13 were printed together, se-tenant, forming a composite design.

1991 Sea Turtles. Multicoloured.

215 29 c. Type **41** 45 25
216 29 c. Green turtles swimming underwater 45 25
217 50 c. Hawksbill turtle swimming underwater 45 25
218 50 c. Leatherback turtle swimming underwater 45 25

42 Boeing E-3 "Sentry"

1991. Operations Desert Shield and Desert Storm (liberation of Kuwait). Mult.

219 29 c. Type **42** 40 25
220 29 c. Grumman F-14 "Tomcat" 40 25
221 29 c. U.S.S. "Missouri" (battleship) 40 25
222 29 c. Multiple Launch Rocket System 40 25
223 $2.90 Great frigate bird with yellow ribbon and flag of Micronesia (50 × 37 mm) 3·75 2·75

MORE DETAILED LISTS

are given in the Stanley Gibbons Catalogues referred to in the country headings.
For lists of current volumes see Introduction.

43 "Evening Flowers, Toloas, Truk"

1991. "Phila Nippon '91" International Stamp Exhibition, Tokyo. 90th Birth Anniv (1992) of Paul Jacoulet (artist). Micronesian Ukiyo-e Prints by Jacoulet. Multicoloured.

No.	Description	Unused	Used
225	29 c. Type **43**	40	25
226	29 c. "The Chief's Daughter, Mogomog"	40	25
227	29 c. "Yagourouh and Mio, Yap"	40	25
228	50 c. "Yap Beauty and Orchids"	70	45
229	50 c. "The Yellow-Eyed Boys, Ohlol"	70	45
230	50 c. "Violet Flowers, Tomil, Yap"	70	45

44 Sheep and Holy Family

1991. Christmas. Shell Cribs. Multicoloured.

No.	Description	Unused	Used
232	29 c. Type **44**	40	25
233	40 c. Three Kings arriving at Bethlehem	55	35
234	50 c. Sheep around manger	65	45

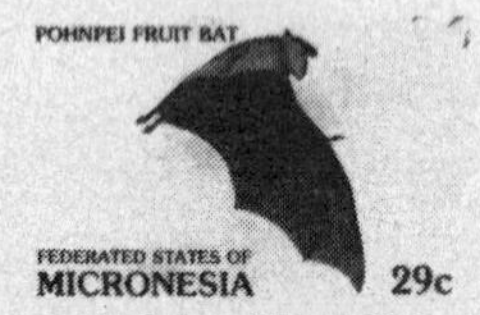

45 Pohnpei Fruit Bat

1991. Pohnpei Rain Forest. Multicoloured.

No.	Description	Unused	Used
235	29 c. Type **45**	40	25
236	29 c. Purple-capped fruit dove	40	25
237	29 c. Micronesian kingfisher	40	25
238	29 c. Birdnest fern	40	25
239	29 c. Island swiftlets	40	25
240	29 c. Pohnpei white-eye ("Long-billed white-eye")	40	25
241	29 c. Brown noddy	40	25
242	29 c. Pohnpei lory	40	25
243	29 c. Pohnpei flycatcher	40	25
244	29 c. Caroline ground dove	40	25
245	29 c. White-tailed tropic bird	40	25
246	29 c. Micronesian honey-eater	40	25
247	29 c. Ixora	40	25
248	29 c. Pohnpei fantail	40	25
249	29 c. Grey white-eye	40	25
250	29 c. Blue-faced parrot finch	40	25
251	29 c. Cicadabird	40	25
252	29 c. Green skink	40	25

Nos. 235/52 were issued together, se-tenant, forming a composite design.

46 Airplane and Outrigger Canoe

47 Volunteers learning Crop Planting

1992. Air. Multicoloured.

No.	Description	Unused	Used
253	40 c. Type **46**	55	35
254	50 c. Airplane and outrigger canoe (different)	65	45

1992. 25th Anniv of Presence of United States Peace Corps in Micronesia. Multicoloured.

No.	Description	Unused	Used
255	29 c. Type **47**	40	25
256	29 c. Education	40	25
257	29 c. Pres. John Kennedy announcing formation of Peace Corps	40	25
258	29 c. Public health nurses	40	25
259	29 c. Recreation	40	25

48 Queen Isabella of Spain

1992. 500th Anniv of Discovery of America by Christopher Columbus. Multicoloured.

No.	Description	Unused	Used
260	29 c. Type **48**	40	25
261	29 c. "Santa Maria"	40	25
262	29 c. Christopher Columbus	40	25

49 Flags

1992. 1st Anniv of U. N. Membership.

No.	Type	Description	Unused	Used
263	**49**	29 c. multicoloured	40	25
264		50 c. multicoloured	65	45

50 Bouquet

1992. Christmas.

No.	Type	Description	Unused	Used
266	**50**	29 c. multicoloured	40	25

MIDDLE CONGO Pt. 6

One of three colonies into which Fr. Congo was divided in 1906. Became part of Fr. Equatorial Africa in 1937. Became part of the Congo Republic within the French Community on 28th November, 1958.

100 centimes = 1 franc.

1. Leopard in Ambush.

2. Bakalois Woman.

3. Coconut Palms, Libreville.

1907.

No.	Type	Description	Unused	Used
1	**1**	1 c. olive and brown	10	10
2		2 c. violet and brown	10	10
3		4 c. blue and brown	10	10
4		5 c. green and blue	10	10
21		5 c. yellow and blue	35	45
5		10 c. red and blue	15	10
22		10 c. green and light green	1·25	1·25
6		15 c. purple and pink	85	55
7		20 c. brown and blue	1·25	1·00
8	**2**	25 c. blue and green	45	35
23		25 c. green and grey	35	45
9		30 c. pink and green	55	45
24		30 c. red	75	75
10		35 c. brown and blue	55	55
11		40 c. green and brown	55	55
12		45 c. violet and orange	2·10	1·90
13		50 c. green and orange	75	70
25		50 c. blue and green	85	85
14		75 c. brown and blue	3·50	2·50
15	**3**	1 f. green and violet	6·00	4·50
16		2 f. violet and green	5·00	3·25
17		5 f. blue and pink	18·00	16·00

1916. Surch **5c** and red cross.

No.	Type	Description	Unused	Used
20	**1**	10 c. + 5 c. red and blue	45	55

1924. Surch **AFRIQUE EQUATORIALE FRANCAISE** and new value.

No.	Type	Description	Unused	Used
26	**3**	25 c. on 2 f. green & violet	35	35
27		25 c. on 5 f. pink and blue	35	35
28		65 on 1 f. brown & orange	45	55
29		85 on 1 f. brown & orange	55	55
30	**2**	90 on 75 c. scarlet and red	65	55
31		1 f. 25 on 1 f. ultram & bl	25	25
32		1 f. 50 on 1 f. bl & ultram	85	65
33		3 f. on 5 f. pink and brown	1·10	85
34		10 f. on 5 f. green and red	5·50	4·00
35		20 f. on 5 f. purple & brn	8·00	5·50

1924. Optd **AFRIQUE EQUATORIALE FRANCAISE.**

No.	Type	Description	Unused	Used
36	**1**	1 c. olive and brown	15	20
37		2 c. violet and brown	20	20
38		4 c. blue and brown	20	20
39		5 c. yellow and blue	20	20
40		10 c. green and light green	20	20
41		10 c. red and grey	20	20
42		15 c. purple and pink	25	25
43		20 c. brown and blue	25	25
44		20 c. green and light green	25	25
45		20 c. brown and mauve	45	25
46	**2**	25 c. green and grey	25	25
47		30 c. red	45	25
48		30 c. grey and mauve	20	10
49		30 c. deep green and green	25	25
50		35 c. brown and blue	25	25
51		40 c. green and brown	40	25
52		45 c. violet and orange	75	45
53		50 c. blue and green	50	25
54		50 c. yellow and black	25	15
55		65 c. brown and blue	1·10	90
56		75 c. brown and blue	35	25
57		90 c. red and pink	2·25	1·60
58	**3**	1 f. green and violet	75	55
59		1 f. 10 mauve and brown	1·75	1·10
60		1 f. 50 ultramarine & blue	3·25	2·40
61		2 f. violet and green	85	65
62		3 f. mauve on pink	3·50	3·00
63		5 f. blue and pink	2·50	1·25

1931. "Colonial Exhibition" key-types inscr "MOYEN CONGO".

No.	Type	Description	Unused	Used
65	E	40 c. green and black	2·00	1·90
66	F	50 c. mauve and black	1·10	1·00
67	G	90 c. red and black	1·40	1·10
68	H	1 f. 50 blue and black	2·00	1·10

15. Mindouli Viaduct.

DESIGN: 40 c. to 1 f. 50, Pasteur Institute, Brazzaville. 1 f. 75 to 20 f. Govt. Building, Brazzaville.

1933.

No.	Type	Description	Unused	Used
69.	**15.**	1 c. brown	10	50
70.		2 c. blue	10	50
71.		4 c. olive	10	50
72.		5 c. red	20	30
73.		10 c. green	40	50
74.		15 c. purple	75	1·25
75.		20 c. red on rose	4·50	3·00
76.		25 c. orange	75	75
77.		30 c. green	1·75	1·25
78.	–	40 c. brown	85	55
79.	–	45 c. black on green	90	65
80.	–	50 c. purple	55	35
81.	–	65 c. red on green	55	45
82.	–	75 c. black on red	5·50	3·50
83.	–	90 c. red	55	55
84.	–	1 f. red	55	45
85.	–	1 f. 25 green	90	60
86.	–	1 f. 50 blue	3·25	1·50
87.	–	1 f. 75 violet	1·00	75
88.	–	2 f. olive	85	65
89.	–	3 f. black on red	1·75	1·60
90.	–	5 f. grey	8·00	6·50
91.	–	10 f. black	35·00	18·00
92.	–	20 f. brown	22·00	14·00

POSTAGE DUE STAMPS

1928. Postage Due type of France optd **MOYEN-CONGO A. E. F.**

No.	Type	Description	Unused	Used
D 64.	D **11.**	5 c. blue	25	25
D 65.		10 c. brown	25	25
D 66.		20 c. olive	55	55
D 67.		25 c. red	55	55
D 68.		30 c. red	55	55
D 69.		45 c. green	55	55
D 70.		50 c. purple	65	75
D 71.		60 c. brown on cream	95	95
D 72.		1 f. red on cream	1·00	1·00
D 73.		2 f. red	1·75	1·90
D 74.		3 f. violet	3·25	3·25

D **13.** Village.

1930.

No.	Type	Description	Unused	Used
D 75.	D **13.**	5 c. olive and blue	35	45
D 76.		10 c. brown and red	55	55
D 77.		20 c. brown and green	1·50	1·50
D 78.		25 c. brown and blue	2·00	2·25
D 79.		30 c. green and brown	3·00	3·25
D 80.		45 c. olive and green	3·00	3·25
D 81.		50 c. brown & mauve	3·00	3·25
D 82.		60 c. black and violet	3·50	3·50
D 83.	–	1 f. black and brown	6·00	6·00
D 84.	–	2 f. brown & mauve	6·50	6·50
D 85.	–	3 f. brown and red	6·50	6·50

DESIGN: 1 to 3 f. "William Guinet" (steamer) on the River Congo.

1. Arms of Este.

1933.

No.	Type	Description	Unused	Used
D 93.	D**17.**	5 c. green	40	45
D 94.		10 c. blue on blue	45	45
D 95.		20 c. red on yellow	55	55
D 96.		25 c. red	55	55
D 97.		30 c. red	65	75
D 98.		45 c. purple	65	75
D 99.		50 c. black	1·25	1·25
D 100.		60 c. black on red	1·75	1·75
D 101.		1 f. red	2·50	2·50
D 102.		2 f. orange	3·75	3·75
D 103.		3 f. blue	6·25	6·25

For later issues see **FRENCH EQUATORIAL AFRICA.**

MODENA Pt. 8

A state in Upper Italy, formerly a duchy and now part of Italy. Used stamps of Sardinia after the cessation of its own issues in 1860. Now uses Italian stamps.

100 centesimi = 1 lira.

5. Cross of Savoy.

1852. Imperf.

No.	Type	Description	Unused	Used
9	**1**	5 c. black on green	10·00	23·00
3		10 c. black on pink	£200	55·00
4		15 c. black on yellow	15·00	13·00
5		25 c. black on buff	18·00	14·00
12		40 c. black on blue	19·00	85·00
13		1 l. black on white	35·00	£1800

1859. Imperf.

No.	Type	Description	Unused	Used
48.	**5.**	5 c. green	£600	£500
50.		15 c. brown	£1000	£2250
51.		15 c. grey	£130	
53.		20 c. black	£900	75·00
54.		20 c. lilac	30·00	£400
56.		40 c. red	80·00	£700
58.		80 c. brown	80·00	£15000

NEWSPAPER STAMPS

1853. As T 1 but in the value tablet inscr "B.G. CEN" and value. Imperf.

N3 1 9 c. black on mauve .. £140 40·00
N4 10 c. black on lilac .. 20·00 £160

N 4.

1859. Imperf.

N 5. N 4. 10 c. black £400 £1800

MOHELI Pt. 6

An island in the Comoro Archipelago, adjacent to Madagascar. A separate French dependency until 1914 when the whole archipelago was placed under Madagascar whose stamps were used until 1950. Now part of the Comoro Islands.

100 centimes = 1 franc.

1906. "Tablet" key-type inscr "MOHELI" in blue (2, 4, 10, 20, 30, 40 c., 5 f.) or red (others).

1 D 1 c. black on blue .. 85 80
2 2 c. brown on buff .. 85 60
3 4 c. brown on grey .. 90 1·10
4 5 c. green .. .. 1·25 1·00
5 10 c. red .. .. 1·60 1·00
6 20 c. red on green .. 6·00 4·00
7 25 c. blue .. .. 6·25 3·00
8 30 c. brown on drab .. 9·50 7·00
9 35 c. black on yellow .. 4·75 2·25
10 40 c. red on yellow .. 7·00 4·25
11 45 c. black on green .. 45·00 30·00
12 50 c. brown on blue .. 13·00 8·00
13 75 c. brown on orange .. 13·00 11·50
14 1 f. green .. .. 8·50 8·25
15 2 f. violet on pink .. 21·00 19·00
16 5 f. mauve on lilac .. 90·00 75·00

1912. Surch in figures.

17 D 05 on 4 c. brown and blue on grey 55 70
18 05 on 20 c. red and blue on green .. .. 90 2·00
19 05 on 30 c. brown and blue on drab .. .. 80 1·00
20 10 on 40 c. red and blue on yellow .. .. 80 1·00
21 10 on 45 c. black and red on green 60 80
22 10 on 50 c. brown and red on blue .. .. 90 1·25

MOLDOVA Pt.10

Formerly Moldavia, a constituent republic of the Soviet Union. Moldova declared its sovereignty within the Union in 1990 and became independent in 1991.

100 kopeks = 1 rouble.

1 Arms

2 Codrii Nature Reserve

1991. 1st Anniv of Declaration of Sovereignty. Multicoloured. Imperf.

1 7 k. Type **1** 10 10
2 13 k. Type 1 .. .. 20 20
3 30 k. Flag (35 × 23 mm) .. 45 45

1992.

4 2 25 k. multicoloured .. 45 45

3 Arms

4 "TU-144" Aircraft

1992.

5 3 35 k. green 10 10
6 50 k. red 20 20
7 65 k. brown 30 30
8 1 r. purple 45 45
9 1 r. 50 blue 75 75

1992. Air.

15 4 1 r. 75 red 30 30
16 2 r. 50 mauve 45 45
17 7 r. 75 violet .. .. 1·50 1·50
18 8 r. 50 green .. .. 1·90 1·90

5 European Bee Eater

6 St. Panteleimon Church

1992. Birds. Multicoloured.

19 50 k. Type **5** 20 20
20 65 k. Golden oriole .. 25 25
21 2 r. 50 Green woodpecker .. 65 65
22 6 r. Common roller .. 1·10 1·10
23 7 r. 50 Hoopoe .. .. 1·25 1·25
24 15 r. European cuckoo .. 2·50 2·50

1992. Centenary (1991) of St. Panteleimon Church, Chisinau.

25 6 1 r. 50 multicoloured .. 35 35

7 Wolf suckling Romulus and Remus

9 High Jumping

1992. Trajan Memorial, Chisinau.

26 7 5 r. multicoloured .. 95 95

1992. Various stamps of Russia surch **MOLDOVA** and value.

27 2 r. 50 on 4 k. red (No. 4672) 25 25
28 6 r. on 3 k. red (No. 4671) 65 65
29 8 r. 50 on 4 k. red (No. 4672) 95 95
30 10 r. on 3 k. turq (No. 5941) 1·25 1·25

1992. Olympic Games, Barcelona. Mult.

31 35 k. Type **9** 10 10
32 65 k. Wrestling 45 45
33 1 r. Archery 65 65
34 2 r. 50 Swimming .. 1·00 1·00
35 10 r. Show jumping .. 1·50 1·50

1992. Moldovan Olympic Games Medal Winners.

37 1 r. Optd **NATALIA VALEEV / bronz** and emblem 50 50
38 2 r. 50 Optd **IURIE BASCATOV / argint** and emblem .. .. 1·40 1·40

12 Moldovan Flag, Statue of Liberty and U.N. Emblem and Building

1992. Admission of Moldova to U.N.O. Mult.

40 1 r. 30 Type **12** 15 15
41 12 r. As Type **12** but with motifs differently arranged .. .. 1·25 1·25

13 Moldovan Flag and Prague Castle

1992. Admission of Moldova to European Security and Co-operation Conf. Mult.

42 2 r. 50 Type **13** 20 20
43 25 r. Helsinki Cathedral and Moldovan flag .. 1·60 1·60

1992. Nos. 4533 and 4670 of Russia surch **MOLDOVA**, new value and bunch of grapes.

44 – 45 k. on 2 k. mauve .. 15 15
45 – 46 k. on 2 k. mauve .. 15 15
46 1753 63 k. on 1 k. green .. 25 25
47 70 k. on 1 k. green .. 15 15
48 4 r. on 1 k. green .. 80 80

15 Carpet and Pottery

16 Galleon

1992. Folk Art.

49 15 7 r. 50 multicoloured .. 2·50 2·50

1992. 500th Anniv of Discovery of America by Columbus. Multicoloured.

50 1 r. Type **16** 15 15
51 6 r. Carrack .. .. 1·10 1·10
52 6 r. Caravel .. .. 1·10 1·10

17 Letter Sorter, Train, State Flag and U.P.U. Emblem

1992. Admission to U.P.U. Multicoloured.

54 5 r. Type **17** 95 95
55 10 r. Airplane, computerized letter sorting equipment, state flag and U.P.U. emblem .. .. .. 1·75 1·75

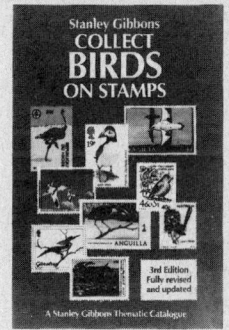

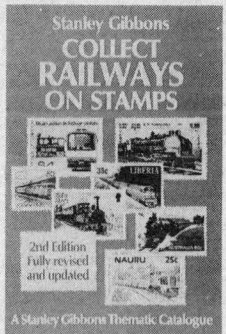

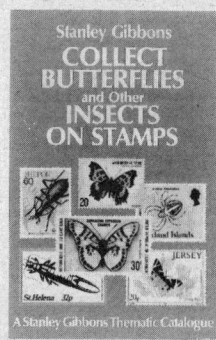

MONACO Pt. 6

A principality on the S. coast of France including the town of Monte Carlo.

100 centimes = 1 French franc.

1. Prince Charles III. 2. Prince Albert. 4. War Widow and Monaco.

1885.

1. 1. 1 c. olive .. .. .. 7·50 8·50
2. 2 c. lilac .. .. .. 20·00 18·00
3. 5 c. blue .. .. .. 35·00 26·00
4. 10 c. brown on yellow .. 40·00 30·00
5. 15 c. red .. .. .. £150 9·00
6. 25 c. green .. .. .. £350 45·00
7. 40 c. blue on red .. .. 32·00 27·00
8. 75 c. black on red .. .. 80·00 50·00
9. 1 f. black on yellow .. £1000 £350
10. 5 f. red on green £2500 £1500

1891.

11 2 1 c. green 40 50
12 2 c. purple 40 50
13 5 c. blue .. .. .. 25·00 2·00
22 5 c. green 45 25
14 10 c. brown on yellow .. 70·00 9·00
23 10 c. red .. .. .. 1·00 30
15 15 c. pink .. .. £100 4·00
24 15 c. brown on yellow .. 1·50 60
25 15 c. green .. .. 1·75 1·75
16 25 c. green .. .. £225 25·00
26 25 c. blue .. .. 4·25 1·50
17 40 c. black on pink .. 2·00 1·25
18 50 c. brown on orange .. 3·50 3·00
19 75 c. brown on buff .. 15·00 8·00
20 1 f. black on yellow .. 12·00 6·00
21 5 f. red on green .. 80·00 40·00
28 5 f. mauve £180 £170
29 5 f. green .. .. 20·00 22·00

1914. Surcharged +5c.

30. 2. 10 c.+5 c. red .. .. 3·75 4·50

1919. War Orphans Fund.

31. 4. 2 c.+3 c. mauve .. .. 10·00 13·00
32. 5 c.+5 c. green .. .. 6·50 9·50
33. 15 c.+10 c. red .. .. 6·50 9·50
34. 25 c.+15 c. blue .. 15·00 24·00
35. 50 c.+50 c. brn. on orge. 70·00 90·00
36. 1 f.+1 f. black on yellow £250 £300
37. 5 f.+5 f. red £850 £950

1920. Princess Charlotte's Marriage. Nos. 33/7 optd **20 mars 1920** or surch also.

38. 4. 2 c.+3 c. on 15 c.+10 c. 28·00 28·00
39. 2 c.+3 c. on 25 c.+15 c. 28·00 28·00
40. 2 c+3 c. on 50 c.+50 c.. 28·00 28·00
41. 5 c.+5 c. on 1 f.+1 f. 28·00 28·00
42. 5 c.+5 c. on 5 f.+5 f. 28·00 28·00
43. 15 c.+10 c. red .. 17·00 20·00
44. 25 c.+15 c. blue .. 7·00 7·00
45. 50 c.+50 c. brn. on orge.. 30·00 35·00
46. 1 f.+1 f. black on yellow 40·00 42·00
47. 5 f.+5 f. red £5000 £5000

1921. Princess Antoinette's Baptism. Optd **28 DECEMBRE 1920** or surch also.

48 2 5 c. green 45 50
49 75 c. brown on buff .. 3·50 5·00
50 2 f. on 5 f. mauve .. 27·00 35·00

1922. Surch.

51. 2. 20 c. on 15 c. green .. 1·00 1·00
52. 25 c. on 10 c. red .. 55 60
53. 50 c. on 1 f. black on yellow 4·25 5·00

8. Prince Albert I. 9. St. Devote Viaduct.

1922.

54. 8. 25 c. brown .. .. 2·25 3·25
55. – 30 c. green .. .. 65 1·10
56. – 30 c. red 40 45
57. 9. 40 c. brown 50 50
58. – 50 c. blue .. .. .. 3·75 4·00
59. – 60 c. grey 20 25
60. – 1 f. black on yellow .. 20 20
61a.– 2 f. red 40 35
62. – 5 f. brown .. .. .. 28·00 32·00
63. – 5 f. green on blue .. 5·00 6·50
64. – 10 f. red .. .. .. 11·00 13·00

DESIGNS—As Type **9**: 30 c., 50 c. Oceanographic Museum. 60 c., 1 f., 2 f. The Rock. 5 f., 10 f. Prince's Palace, Monaco.

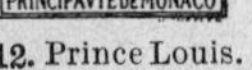

12. Prince Louis. 13. Prince Louis and Palace.

1923.

65. 12. 10 c. green 35 35
66. 15 c. red 50 50
67. 20 c. brown 30 30
68. 25 c. purple 25 30
69. 13. 50 c. blue 25 30

1924. Surch. with new value and bars.

70. 2. 45 c. on 50 c. brn. on orge. 50 50
71. 75 c. on 1 f. black on yell. 30 30
72. 85 c. on 5 f. green 30 30

14. 15. 16.

17. St. Devote Viaduct.

1924.

73 14 1 c. grey 10 10
74 2 c. brown 10 10
75 3 c. mauve .. .. 1·75 45
76 5 c. orange 20 20
77 10 c. blue 10 10
78 15 15 c. green 10 10
79 15 c. violet .. .. 1·50 80
80 20 c. mauve 15 10
81 20 c. pink 20 10
82 25 c. pink 10 10
83 25 c. red on yellow .. 15 15
84 30 c. orange 10 10
85 40 c. brown 10 10
86 40 c. blue on blue .. 15 10
87 45 c. black 70 40
88 16 50 c. green 15 15
89 15 50 c. brown on yellow .. 10 10
90 16 60 c. brown 10 15
91 15 60 c. green on green .. 10 10
92 75 c. green on green .. 20 15
93 75 c. red on yellow .. 15 10
94 75 c. black 40 20
95 80 c. red on yellow .. 25 20
96 90 c. red on yellow .. 75 75
97 17 1 f. black on yellow .. 20 15
98 1 f. 05 mauve 20 35
99 1 f. 10 green .. .. 8·00 3·50
100 15 1 f. 25 blue on blue .. 15 15
101 1 f. 50 blue on blue .. 1·40 90
102 – 2 f. brown and mauve .. 70 60
103 – 3 f. lilac & red on yellow 12·00 6·50
104 – 5 f. red and green .. 5·00 3·75
105 – 10 f. blue and brown .. 12·00 10·00

DESIGN—As Type **17**: 2 f. to 10 f. Monaco.

1926. Surch.

106 15 30 c. on 25 c. pink .. 20 10
107 50 c. on 60 c. grn on grn 70 15
108 17 50 c. on 1 f. 05 mauve .. 40 35
109 50 c. on 1 f. 10 green .. 4·50 2·75
110 15 50 c. on 1 f. 25 blue on bl 35 30
111 1 f. 25 on 1 f. blue on bl 35 20
112 – 1 f. 50 on 2 f. brown and mauve (No. 102) .. 2·50 2·25

20. Princes Charles III, Louis II and Albert I.

1926. Int. Philatelic Exn, Monte Carlo.

113. 20. 50 c. red 65 65
114. 1 f. 50 blue 65 65
115. 3 f. violet 65 65

20a. 21. Palace Entrance.

22. St. Devote's Church. 23. Prince Louis II.

1933.

116. 20a. 1 c. plum 10 10
117. 2 c. green 10 10
118. 3 c. purple 10 10
119. 5 c. red 10 10
120. 10 c. blue 10 10
121. 15 c. violet 75 70
122. 21. 15 c. red 40 10
123. 20 c. brown 40 10
124. A. 25 c. sepia 60 30
125. 22. 30 c. green 70 30
126. 23. 40 c. sepia .. .. 1·10 1·10
127. B. 45 c. brown .. .. 2·25 60
128. 23. 50 c. violet .. .. 1·00 60
129. C. 65 c. green .. .. 2·00 40
130. D. 75 c. blue .. .. 2·40 1·25
131. 23. 90 c. red .. .. 3·25 2·00
132. 22. 1 f. brown .. .. 14·00 5·00
133. D. 1 f. 25 red .. .. 3·00 2·00
134. 23. 1 f. 50 blue .. .. 16·00 6·50
135. A. 1 f. 75 red .. .. 18·00 4·00
136. 1 f. 75 red .. .. 15·00 5·00
137. B. 2 f. blue .. .. 4·25 2·00
138. 21. 3 f. violet .. .. 10·00 3·00
139. A. 3 f. 50 orange .. .. 38·00 22·00
140. 22. 5 f. purple .. .. 14·00 9·00
141. A. 10 f. blue .. .. 85·00 32·00
142. C. 20 f. black .. .. £130 85·00

DESIGNS—As Type **21**—HORIZ. A, The Prince's Residence. B, The Rock of Monaco. C, Palace Gardens. D, Fortifications and Harbour.

For other stamps in Type **20a** see Nos. 249, etc.

1933. Air. Surch. with aeroplane and value.

143. – 1 f. 50 on 5 f. red and green (No. 104) .. 22·00 22·00

28. Palace Gardens.

DESIGNS — HORIZ. 90 c. Exotic gardens. 1 f. 50, The Bay of Monaco. VERT. 2 f., 5 f. Prince Louis II.

1937. Charity.

144. 28. 50 c.+50 c. green .. 1·75 2·25
145. – 90 c.+90 c. red .. 1·75 2·25
146. – 1 f. 50+1 f. 50 blue .. 3·50 4·50
147. – 2 f.+2 f. violet .. 5·50 5·50
148. – 5 f.+5 f. red.. .. 60·00 60·00

1937. Postage Due stamps optd **POSTES** or surch also.

149 D 18 5 on 10 c. violet .. 70 70
150 10 c. violet 70 70
151 15 on 30 c. bistre .. 70 70
152 20 on 30 c. bistre .. 70 70
153 25 on 60 c. red .. 1·25 1·25
154 30 c. bistre .. .. 1·90 1·75
155 40 on 60 c. red .. 2·00 1·60
156 50 on 60 c. red .. 2·00 2·00
157 65 on 1 f. blue .. 1·60 1·60
158 85 on 1 f. blue .. 3·50 3·50
159 1 f. blue .. .. 4·50 4·50
160 2 f. 15 on 2 f. red .. 5·50 5·50
161 2 f. 25 on 2 f. red .. 11·00 11·00
162 2 f. 50 on 2 f. red .. 18·00 18·00

31. Prince Louis II. 33. Monaco Hospital.

1938.

164. 31. 55 c. brown .. .. 1·75 70
165. 65 c. violet .. .. 16·00 7·00
166. 70 c. brown 15 15
167. 90 c. violet 15 15
168. 1 f. red .. .. .. 3·25 2·50
169. 1 f. 25 red 20 15
170. 1 f. 75 blue .. .. 7·00 4·50
171. 2 f. 25 blue 20 15

1938. Anti-Cancer Fund. 40th Anniv. of Discovery of Radium.

172. – 65 c.+25 c. green .. 5·00 5·00
173. 33. 1 f. 75+50 c. blue .. 6·00 6·00

DESIGN—VERT. 65 c. Pierre and Marie Curie.

34. The Cathedral. 38. Monaco Harbour.

1939.

174. 34. 20 c. mauve 15 15
175. – 25 c. brown 30 20
176. – 30 c. green 20 20
177. – 40 c. red 20 20
178. – 45 c. purple 20 20
179. – 50 c. green 25 15
180. – 60 c. red 20 20
181. – 60 c. green 20 20
182. 38. 70 c. lilac 20 20
183. 75 c. green 35 20
184. – 1 f. black 20 20
185. – 1 f. 30 brown 20 20
186. – 2 f. purple 20 20
187. – 2 f. 50 red .. .. 16·00 9·50
188. – 2 f. 50 blue 70 30
189. 38. 3 f. red 40 20
190. 34. 5 f. blue .. .. 1·40 60
191. – 10 f. green 80 65
192. – 20 f. blue .. .. 1·00 65

DESIGNS—VERT. 25 c., 40 c., 2 f. Place St. Nicholas. 30 c., 60 c., 20 f. Palace Gateway. 50 c., 1 f., 1 f. 30, Palace of Monaco. HORIZ. 45c., 2 f. 50, 10 f. Aerial view of Monaco.

See also Nos. 250 etc.

40. Louis II Stadium. 41. Lucien.

1939. Inauguration of Louis II Stadium, Monaco.

198. 40. 10 f. green .. .. 95·00 95·00

1939. National Relief. XVI–XVIII-century portrait designs and view.

199. 41. 5 c.+5 c. black.. .. 1·00 1·00
200. – 10 c.+10 c. purple .. 1·00 1·00
201. – 45 c.+15 c. green .. 3·00 3·00
202. – 70 c.+30 c. mauve .. 4·50 5·00
203. – 90 c.+35 c. violet .. 5·50 6·50
204. – 1 f.+1 f. blue .. .. 15·00 15·00
205. – 2 f.+2 f. red .. .. 16·00 18·00
206. – 2 f. 25+1 f. 25 blue .. 28·00 28·00
207. – 3 f.+3 f. red .. .. 40·00 40·00
208. – 5 f.+5 f. red .. .. 60·00 65·00

DESIGNS—VERT. 10 c. Honore II. 45 c. Louis I. 70 c. Charlotte de Gramont. 90 c. Antoine I. 1 f. Marie de Lorraine. 2 f. Jacques I. 2 f. 25, Louise-Hippolyte. 3 f. Honore III. HORIZ. 5 f. The Rock of Monaco.

1939. 8th Int. University Games. As T **40** but inscr. "VIIIeme JEUX UNIVERSITAIRES INTERNATIONAUX 1939".

209. 40 c. green 75 90
210. 70 c. brown .. .. 85 1·00
211. 90 c. violet .. .. 1·00 1·25
212. 1 f. 25 red .. .. 1·00 1·25
213. 2 f. 25 blue .. .. 2·50 2·50

1940. Red Cross Ambulance Fund. As Nos. 174/92 in new colours surch. with Red Cross and premium.

214. 34. 20 c.+1 f. violet .. 1·25 1·25
215. – 25 c.+1 f. green .. 1·25 2·25
216. – 30 c.+1 f. red .. 1·25 2·25
217. – 40 c.+1 f. blue .. 1·25 2·25
218. – 45 c.+1 f. red .. 1·25 2·25
219. – 50 c.+1 f. brown .. 1·25 2·25
220. – 60 c.+1 f. green .. 1·25 2·25
221. 38. 75 c.+1 f. black .. 1·90 2·25
222. – 1 f.+1 f. red .. .. 1·75 2·40
223. – 2 f.+1 f. slate .. 1·75 2·40
224. – 2 f. 50+1 f. green .. 7·00 6·50
225. 38. 3 f.+1 f. blue .. 9·50 7·75
226. 34. 5 f.+1 f. black .. 9·50 7·75
227. – 10 f.+5 f. blue .. 17·00 17·00
228. – 20 f.+5 f. purple .. 25·00 25·00

44. Prince Louis II.

1941.

229. 44. 40 c. red 20 20
230. 80 c. green 20 20
231. 1 f. violet 10 10
232. 1 f. 20 green 10 10
233. 1 f. 50 red 10 10
234. 1 f. 50 violet 10 10
235. 2 f. green 10 10
236. 2 f. 40 red 10 10
237. 2 f. 50 blue 35 35
238. 4 f. blue 10 10

45. 46.

1941. National Relief Fund.

239. 45. 25 c.+25 c. purple .. 50 1·00
240. 46. 50 c.+25 c. brown .. 50 1·00
241. 75 c.+50 c. purple .. 1·25 1·60
242. 45. 1 f.+1 f. blue .. .. 1·25 1·60
243. 46. 1 f. 50+1 f. 50 red .. 1·40 2·25
244. 45. 2 f.+2 f. green .. 1·40 2·25
245. 46. 2 f. 50+2 f. blue .. 1·60 2·75
246. 45. 3 f.+3 f. brown .. 1·75 2·75
247. 46. 5 f.+5 f. green.. .. 4·50 2·75
248. 45. 10 f.+8 f. sepia .. 10·00 6·00

1941. New values and colours.

249	**20a**	10 c. black	10	10
250	–	30 c. red (as No. 176)..	20	15
251	**20a**	30 c. green	10	10
252		40 c. red	10	10
253		50 c. violet	10	10
362	**34**	50 c. brown	10	10
254	**20a**	60 c. blue	10	10
363	–	60 c. pink (as No. 175)	10	15
255	**20a**	70 c. brown	10	10
256	**34**	80 c. green	10	10
257	–	1 f. brown (as No. 178)	10	10
258	**38**	1 f. 20 blue	15	15
259	–	1 f. 50 blue (as No. 175)	15	15
260	**38**	2 f. blue	10	10
261	–	2 f. grn. (as No. 179)..	10	10
262	–	3 f. black (as No. 175)	10	10
364	–	3 f. purple (as No. 176)	20	20
391	–	3 f. green (as No. 175)	40	20
263	**34**	4 f. mauve	10	20
365	–	4 f. green (as No. 175)	20	20
264	–	4 f. 50 violet (as No. 179)	10	10
265	–	5 f. green (as No. 176)	10	10
392	–	5 f. green (as No. 178)	20	10
393	–	5 f. red (as No. 176)..	35	35
266	–	6 f. violet (as No. 179)	20	30
368	–	8 f. brown (as No. 179)	65	40
267	**34**	10 f. blue	10	10
370	–	10 f. brn. (as No. 179)	1·00	45
394	**38**	10 f. yellow	60	20
268		15 f. red	20	15
269	–	20 f. brn. (as No. 178)	20	15
373	–	20 f. red (as No. 178)..	45	25
270	**38**	25 f. green	90	60
374		25 f. black	17·00	8·50
397	–	25 f. blue (as No. 176)	13·50	8·50
398	–	25 f. red (as No. 179)..	90	55
399	–	30 f. blue (as No. 176)	2·75	2·75
400	–	35 f. blue (as No. 179)	3·00	1·10
401	**34**	40 f. red	2·25	2·00
402		50 f. violet	2·00	65
403	–	65 f. violet (as No. 178)	3·50	3·75
404	**34**	70 f. yellow	3·75	5·00
405	–	75 f. grn. (as No. 175)	8·75	4·50
406	–	85 f. red (as No. 175)	6·00	4·50
407	–	100 f. turquoise (as No. 178)	4·50	4·50

47. Aeroplane over Monaco.

48. Propeller and Palace.

49. Arms, Aeroplane and Globe.

50. Charles II.

1942. Air.

271	**47**	5 f. green	20	20
272		10 f. blue	20	30
273	**48**	15 f. brown	55	35
274	–	20 f. brown	55	45
275	–	50 f. purple	3·00	1·75
276	**49**	100 f. red and purple ..	3·00	1·75

DESIGNS—VERT. 20 f. Pegasus. HORIZ. 50 f. Common gull over Bay of Monaco.

1942. National Relief Fund. Royal Personages.

277.	–	2 c.+3 c. blue	10	10
278.	**50.**	5 c.+5 c. red	10	10
279.	–	10 c.+5 c. black ..	10	10
280.	–	20 c.+10 c. green ..	10	10
281.	–	30 c.+30 c. purple ..	10	10
282.	–	40 c.+40 c. red ..	10	10
283.	–	50 c.+50 c. violet ..	10	10
284.	–	75 c.+75 c. purple ..	10	10
285.	–	1 f.+1 f. green ..	10	10
286.	–	1 f. 50+1 f. red ..	10	10
287.	–	2 f. 50+2 f. 50 violet ..	1·50	2·25
288.	–	3 f.+3 f. blue ..	1·50	2·25
289.	–	5 f.+5 f. sepia ..	2·00	3·50
290.	–	10 f.+5 f. purple ..	2·00	3·50
291.	–	20 f.+5 f. blue ..	2·25	4·00

PORTRAITS: 2 c. Rainier Grimaldi. 10 c. Jeanne Grimaldi. 20 c. Charles Auguste, Goyon de Matignon. 30 c. Jacques I. 40 c. Louise-Hippolyte. 50 c. Charlotte Grimaldi. 75 c. Marie Charles Grimaldi. 1 f. Honore III. 1 f. 50, Honore IV. 2 f. 50, Honore V. 3 f. Florestan I. 5 f. Charles III. 10 f. Albert I. 20 f. Princess Marie-Victoire.

52. Prince Louis II.

1943.

292.	**52.**	50 f. violet	55	55

53. St. Devote.

54. Blessing the Sea.

55. Arrival of St. Devote at Monaco.

1944. Charity. Festival of St. Devote.

293.	**53.**	50 c.+50 c. brown ..	15	15
294.	–	70 c.+80 c. blue ..	15	15
295.	–	80 c.+70 c. green ..	15	15
296.	–	1 f.+1 f. purple ..	15	15
297.	–	1 f. 50+1 f. 50 red ..	15	15
298.	**54.**	2 f.+2 f. purple ..	20	30
299.	–	5 f.+2 f. violet .	35	35
300.	–	10 f.+40 f. blue ..	35	35
301.	**55.**	20 f.+60 f. blue ..	2·75	3·25

DESIGNS—VERT. 70 c., 1 f. Various processional scenes. 1 f. 50 Burning the boat. 10 f. Trial scene. HORIZ. 80 c. Procession. 5 f. St. Devote's Church.

1945. Air. For War Dead and Deported Workers. As Nos. 272/6 (colours changed) surch.

302.	**1 f.+4 f. on 10 f. red ..**	35	35
303.	**1 f.+4 f. on 15 f. brown**	35	35
304.	**1 f.+4 f. on 20 f. brown**	35	35
305.	**1 f.+4 f. on 50 f. blue ..**	35	35
306.	**1 f.+4 f. on 100 f. purple..**	35	35

57. Prince Louis II. **58.**

1946.

361.	**57.**	30 c. black	10	10
389.		50 c. olive	10	10
390.		1 f. violet	10	10
307.		2 f. 50 green	15	10
308.		3 f. mauve	15	10
366.		5 f. brown	20	15
309.		6 f. red	15	10
367.		6 f. purple	1·00	20
310.		10 f. blue	15	10
369.		10 f. orange	10	10
371.		12 f. red	1·60	50
395.		12 f. slate	2·75	2·00
396.		15 f. lake	2·75	2·25
372.		18 f. blue	3·75	2·75
311.	**58.**	50 f. grey	90	1·10
312.		100 f. red	1·25	1·60

59. Child Praying.

60. Nurse and Baby.

1946. Child Welfare Fund.

313.	**59.**	1 f.+3 f. green ..	20	20
314.		2 f.+4 f. red ..	20	20
315.		4 f.+6 f. blue ..	20	20
316.		5 f.+40 f. mauve ..	55	55
317.		10 f.+60 f. red ..	55	55
318.		15 f.+100 f. blue ..	90	90

1946. Anti-tuberculosis Fund.

319.	**60.**	2 f.+8 f. blue ..	35	35

1946. Air. Optd. **POSTE AERIENNE** over aeroplane.

320.	**58.**	50 f. grey	1·75	1·40
321.		100 f. red	2·75	2·00

62. Steamship and Chart.

1946. Stamp Day.

322.	**62.**	3 f.+2 f. blue	20	20

63.

1946. Air.

323	**63**	40 f. red	60	40
324		50 f. brown	70	50
325		100 f. green	1·40	1·00
326		200 f. violet	1·50	1·40
326a		300 f. blue & ultram	28·00	35·00
326b		500 f. green & dp green	22·00	30·00
326c		1000 f. violet & brown	28·00	35·00

64. Pres. Roosevelt and Palace of Monaco.

66. Pres. Roosevelt.

1946. President Roosevelt Commem.

327.	**66.**	10 c. mauve (postage)..	10	10
328.	–	30 c. blue	15	15
329.	**64.**	60 c. green	15	15
330.	–	1 f. sepia	30	30
331.	–	2 f.+3 f. green ..	55	55
332.	–	3 f. violet	1·00	1·00
333.	–	5 f. red (air)	30	30
334.	–	10 f. black	60	40
335.	**66.**	15 f.+10 f. orange ..	75	65

DESIGNS—HORIZ. 30 c., 5 f. Rock of Monaco. 2 f. Viaduct and St. Devote. VERT. 1 f., 3 f., 10 f. Map of Monaco.

67. Prince Louis II.

68. Pres. Roosevelt as a Philatelist.

69. Statue of Liberty and New York Harbour.

70. Prince Charles III.

1947. Participation in the Cent. International Philatelic Exn., New York.

(a) Postage.

336.	**67.**	10 f. blue	2·00	2·00

(b) Air. Dated "1847 1947".

337.	**68.**	50 c. violet	40	35
338.	–	1 f. 50 mauve	30	25
339.	–	3 f. orange	30	20
340.	–	10 f. blue	2·00	2·00
341.	**69.**	15 f. red	3·00	3·00

DESIGNS—HORIZ. As Type **68:** 1 f. 50, G.P.O., New York. 3 f. Oceanographic Museum, Monte Carlo. As Type **69:** 10 f. Bay of Monaco.

1948. Stamp Day.

342.	**70.**	6 f.+4 f. green on blue	20	20

71. Diving.

72. Tennis.

1948. Olympic Games, Wembley. Inscr. "JEUX OLYMPIQUES 1948".

343.	–	50 c. green (postage) ..	15	15
344.	–	1 f. red	15	15
345.	–	2 f. blue	40	40
346.	–	2 f. 50 red	1·00	1·00
347.	**71.**	4 f. slate	1·50	1·50
348.	–	5 f.+5 f. brown (air) ..	4·50	7·25
349.	–	6 f.+9 f. violet ..	6·50	9·50
350.	**72.**	10 f.+15 f. red ..	11·00	16·00
351.	–	15 f.+25 f. blue ..	15·00	25·00

DESIGNS—HORIZ. 50 c. Hurdling. 15 f. Yachting. VERT. 1 f. Running. 2 f. Throwing the discus. 2 f. 50, Basketball. 5 f. Rowing. 6 f. Skiing.

75. The Salmacis Nymph.

77. F. J. Bosio (wrongly inscr. "J. F.").

1948. Death Centenary of Francois Joseph Bosio (sculptor).

352.	**75.**	50 c. green (postage) ..	10	10
353.	–	1 f. red	20	20
354.	–	2 f. blue	30	30
355.	–	2 f. 50 violet	80	80
356.	**77.**	4 f. mauve	1·40	1·40
357.	–	5 f.+5 f. blue (air) ..	3·75	6·50
358.	–	6 f.+9 f. green ..	5·50	8·25
359.	–	10 f.+15 f. red ..	6·00	8·75
360.	–	15 f.+25 f. brown ..	7·75	12·00

DESIGNS—VERT. 1 f., 5 f. Hercules struggling with Achelous. 2 f., 6 f. Aristaeus (Garden God). 15 f. The Salmacis Nymph (36×48 mm.). HORIZ. 2 f. 50, 10 f. Hyacinthus awaiting his turn to throw a quoit.

79. Exotic Gardens.

80. "Princess Alice II".

1949. Birth Cent. of Prince Albert I.

375.	–	2 f. blue (postage) ..	25	20
376.	**79.**	3 f. green	10	10
377.	–	4 f. brown and blue ..	20	20
378.	**80.**	5 f. red	40	40
379.	–	6 f. violet	45	45
380.	–	10 f. sepia	80	65
381.	–	12 f. pink	1·25	85
382.	–	18 f. orange and brown	2·50	2·50
383.	–	20 f. brown (air) ..	30	55
384.	–	25 f. blue	30	55
385.	–	40 f. green	55	80
386.	–	50 f. green, brn. & blk...	65	1·10
387.	–	100 f. red	3·00	4·00
388.	–	200 f. orange	5·50	7·00

DESIGNS—HORIZ. 2 f. Yacht "Hirondelle I" (1870). 4 f. Oceanographic Museum, Monaco. 10 f. "Hirondelle II" (1914). 12 f. Albert harpooning whale. 18 f. Buffalo (Palaeolithic mural). 20 f. Constitution Day, 1911. 25 f. Paris Institute of Palaeontology. 200 f. Coin with effigy of Albert. VERT. 6 f. Statue of Albert at tiller. 40 f. Anthropological Museum. 50 f. Prince Albert I. 100 f. Oceanographic Institute, Paris.

83. Palace of Monaco and Globe.

1949. 75th Anniv. of U.P.U.

410.	**83.**	5 f. green (postage) ..	10	10
411.		10 f. orange	2·75	2·75
412.		15 f. red	20	25
413.		25 f. blue (air)	55	45
414.		40 f. sepia and brown..	45	65
415.		50 f. blue and green ..	55	75
416.		100 f. blue and red ..	1·50	1·60

84. Prince Rainier III and Monaco Palace.

85. Prince Rainier III.

1950. Accession of Prince Rainier III.

417 84 10 c. purple & red (post) 10 10
418 50 c. brown, light brown and orange 10 10
419 1 f. violet 10 10
420 5 f. deep green & green 85 55
421 15 f. carmine and red .. 1·50 1·50
422 25 f. blue, green and ultramarine .. .. 3·50 2·75
423 50 f. brown & black (air) 3·00 2·25
424 100 f. blue, deep brown and brown .. .. 4·50 3·75

1950.

425. 85. 50 c. violet 10 10
426. 1 f. brown 10 10
434. 5 f. green .. .. 6·00 2·25
427. 6 f. green 65 20
428. 8 f. green .. .. 3·50 1·10
429. 8 f. orange 90 35
435. 10 f. orange .. .. 10·00 4·50
430. 12 f. blue .. .. 1·25 25
431. 15 f. red .. .. 2·25 35
432. 15 f. blue .. .. 1·10 20
433. 18 f. red .. .. 3·00 80

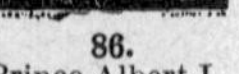

86. Prince Albert I.

87. Edmond and Jules de Goncourt.

1951. Unveiling of Prince Albert Statue.

436. 86. 15 f. blue .. .. 6·00 4·00

1951. 50th Anniv. of Goncourt Academy.

437. 87. 15 f. purple .. .. 3·50 3·50

88. St. Vincent de Paul.

90. St. Peter's Keys and Papal Bull.

89. Judgment of St. Devote.

1951. Holy Year.

438 88 10 c. blue, ultram & red 15 15
439 – 50 c. violet and red .. 15 15
440 89 1 f. green and brown .. 20 20
441 90 2 f. red and purple .. 30 30
442 – 5 f. green 30 30
443 – 12 f. violet 40 40
444 – 15 f. red .. .. 2·75 2·00
445 – 20 f. brown .. .. 4·00 2·50
446 – 25 f. blue .. .. 5·00 2·75
447 – 40 f. violet and mauve 6·50 3·50
448 – 50 f. brown and olive .. 7·75 5·00
449 – 100 f. brown .. .. 25·00 15·00

DESIGNS—TRIANGULAR: 50 c. Pope Pius XII. As Type **90**—HORIZ. 5 f. Mosaic. VERT. 12 f. Prince Rainier III in St. Peter's. 15 f. St. Nicholas of Patara. 20 f. St. Romain. 25 f. St. Charles Borromeo. 40 f. Coliseum. 50 f. Chapel of St. Devote. As Type **89**—VERT. 100 f. Rainier of Westphalia.

INDEX

Countries can be quickly located by referring to the index at the end of this volume.

93. Wireless Mast and Monaco.

94. Seal of Prince Rainier III.

1951. Monte Carlo Radio Station.

450. 93. 1 f. orange, red and blue 55 20
451. 15 f. purple, red & violet 2·75 55
452. 30 f. brown and blue .. 10·00 2·00

1951.

453. 94. 1 f. violet 65 30
454. 5 f. black .. .. 2·50 1·10
455. 5 f. violet .. .. 2·25 65
512. 6 f. red .. .. 2·75 80
513. 8 f. red .. .. 4·50 2·50
514. 8 f. brown .. .. 3·25 1·10
456. 15 f. green .. .. 9·00 5·00
515. 15 f. blue .. .. 11·00 2·50
457. 30 f. blue .. .. 14·00 7·00
516. 30 f. green .. .. 14·00 4·00

95. Gallery of Hercules.

1952. Monaco Postal Museum.

460. 95. 5 f. chestnut and brown 30 30
461. 15 f. violet and purple .. 55 30
462. 30 f. indigo and blue .. 1·00 40

96. Football.

1953. 15th Olympic Games, Helsinki. Inscr. "HELSINKI 1952".

463. – 1 f. mauve & violet (post.) 20 15
464. 96. 2 f. blue and green .. 20 20
465. – 3 f. pale and deep blue .. 25 20
466. – 5 f. green and brown .. 70 30
467. – 8 f. red and lake .. 1·25 80
468. – 15 f. brown, grn. & blue 90 55
469. – 40 f. black (air) .. 9·00 6·50
470. – 50 f. violet .. .. 9·00 6·50
471. – 100 f. green .. .. 14·00 10·00
472. – 200 f. red .. .. 18·00 11·00

DESIGNS: 1 f. Basketball. 3 f. Yachting. 5 f. Cycling. 8 f. Gymnastics. 15 f. Louis II Stadium, Monaco. 40 f. Running. 50 f. Fencing. 10 f. Rifle, target and Arms of Monaco. 200 f. Olympic torch.

97. "Journal Inedit".

1953. Centenary of Publication of Journal by E. and J. de Goncourt.

473. 97. 5 f. green 40 25
474. 15 f. brown .. .. 1·50 50

98. Physalia, Yacht "Princess Alice", Prince Albert, Richet and Portier.

1953. 50th Anniv. of Discovery of Anaphylaxis.

475. 98. 2 f. violet, green & brn. 10 10
476. 5 f. red, lake and green 40 25
477. 15 f. lilac, blue and green 2·25 1·10

99. F. Ozanam.

100. St. Jean-Baptiste de la Salle.

1954. Death Centenary of Ozanam (founder of St. Vincent de Paul Conferences).

478. 99. 1 f. red 10 10
479. – 5 f. blue 25 25
480. 99. 15 f. black .. .. 1·25 55

DESIGN: 5 f. Outline drawing of Sister of Charity.

1954. St. J.-B. de la Salle (educationist).

481. 100. 1 f. red 10 10
482. – 5 f. sepia 25 25
483. 100. 15 f. blue .. .. 1·25 40

DESIGN: 5 f. Outline drawing of De la Salle and two children.

101.

102.

103.

1954. Arms.

484 – 50 c. red, black & mve 10 10
485 – 70 c. red, black & blue 10 10
486 101 80 c. red, black & green 10 10
487 – 1 f. red, black and blue 10 10
488 102 2 f. red, black & orange 10 10
489 – 3 f. red, black & green 10 10
490 103 5 f. multicoloured .. 10 10

DESIGNS—HORIZ. 50 c. as Type **101**. VERT. 70 c., 1, 3 f. as Type **102**.

104. Seal of Prince Rainier III.

1954. Precancelled.

491. 104. 4 f. red 65 20
492. 5 f. blue 20 10
493. 8 f. green 65 30
494. 8 f. purple 55 20
495. 10 f. green 20 10
496. 12 f. violet .. .. 2·75 80
497. 15 f. orange 80 55
498. 20 f. green 80 55
499. 24 f. brown .. .. 5·50 2·75
500. 30 f. blue .. .. 1·10 65
501. 40 f. brown .. .. 3·25 1·00
502. 45 f. red .. .. 2·25 1·00
503. 55 f. blue .. .. 5·50 1·60

See also Nos. 680/3.

105. Lambarene.

106. Dr. Albert Schweitzer.

1955. 80th Birthday of Dr. Schweitzer (humanitarian).

504. 105. 2 f. green, turquoise and blue (postage) .. 10 10
505. 106. 5 f. blue and green .. 65 65
506. – 15 f. pur., blk. and grn. 1·75 1·75
507. – 200 f. slate, green and blue (air) .. .. 28·00 17·00

DESIGNS—As Type **106**: 15 f. Lambarene Hospital. HORIZ. (48 × 27 mm.): 200 f. Schweitzer and jungle scene.

107. Common Cormorants.

1955. Air.

508a. – 100 f. indigo and blue 15·00 12·00
509. – 200 f. black and blue 18·00 9·50
510. – 500 f. grey and green 30·00 16·00
511a. 107. 1,000 f. black, turquoise and green 75·00 45·00

DESIGNS—As Type **107**: 100 f. Roseate tern 200 f. Herring gull. 500 f. Wandering albatrosses.

108 Eight Starting Points.

109. Prince Rainier III.

1955. 25th Monte Carlo Car Rally.

517. 108. 100 f. red and brown .. 60·00 50·00

1955.

518. 109. 6 f. purple and green .. 10 10
519. 8 f. violet and red .. 10 10
520. 12 f. green and red .. 20 10
521. 15 f. blue and purple .. 30 15
522. 18 f. blue and orange .. 60 20
523. 20 f. turquoise 70 30
524. 25 f. black and orange .. 45 20
525. 30 f. sepia and blue .. 11·00 3·75
526. 30 f. violet .. .. 2·00 75
527. 35 f. brown .. .. 3·50 90
528. 50 f. lake and green .. 2·75 90

See also Nos. 627/41.

110. "La Maison a Vapeur".

111. "The 500 Millions of the Begum".

113. U.S.S. "Nautilus".

112. "Round the World in Eighty Days".

1955. 50th Death Anniv. of Jules Verne (author). Designs illustrating his works.

529. – 1 f. blue & brown (post.) 10 10
530. – 2 f. sepia, indigo & blue 10 10
531. 110. 3 f. blue, black & brown 10 10
532. – 5 f. sepia and red .. 10 10
533. 111. 6 f. grey and sepia .. 25 25
534. – 8 f. turquoise and olive 35 35
535. – 10 f. sepia, turq. & indigo 80 80
536. 112. 15 f. red and brown .. 75 55
537. – 25 f. black and green .. 1·75 1·10
538. 113. 30 f. blk., pur. and turq. 4·00 3·25
539. – 200 f. indigo & blue (air) 24·00 22·00

DESIGNS—As Type **111**—VERT. 1 f. "Five Weeks in a Balloon". HORIZ. 5 f. "Michael Strogoff". 8 f. "Le Superbe Orenoque". As Type **110**—HORIZ. 2 f. "A Floating Island". 10 f. "Journey to the Centre of the Earth". 25 f. "20,000 Leagues under the Sea". 200 f. "From Earth to Moon".

DESIGNS — As Type **114**: 10 f. "Madonna" (L. Brea). As Type **113**: 15 f. Bienheureux Rainier.

114. "The Immaculate Virgin" (F. Brea).

1955. Marian Year.
540. **114.** 5 f. grn., grey & brown 20 20
541. – 10 f. green, grey & brown 30 30
542. – 15 f. brown and sepia .. 40 40

115. Rotary Emblem.

1955. 50th Anniv. of Rotary International.
543. **115.** 30 f. blue and yellow .. 70 70

116. George Washington. **118.** President Eisenhower.

117. Abraham Lincoln.

1956. 5th International Stamp Exhibition, New York.
544 **116** 1 f. violet and lilac .. 10 10
545 – 2 f. lilac and purple .. 10 10
546 **117** 3 f. blue and violet .. 10 10
547 **118** 5 f. red 20 20
548 – 15 f. brown & chocolate 45 45
549 – 30 f. black, indigo & bl 2·25 1·75
550 – 40 f. brown .. .. 1·60 1·60
551 – 50 f. red .. .. 2·25 2·25
552 – 100 f. green .. .. 2·75 2·75

DESIGNS—As Type **117**: 2 f. F. D. Roosevelt. As Type **116**—HORIZ. 15 f. Monaco Palace in the 18th century. 30 f. Landing of Columbus. LARGER (48 × 36 mm.): 50 f. Aerial view of Monaco Palace in the 18th century. 100 f. Louisiana landscape in 18th century. As Type **118**: 40 f. Prince Rainier III.

120.

1956. 7th Winter Olympic Games, Cortina d'Ampezzo and 16th Olympic Games, Melbourne.
553. – 15 f. brn., green & pur. 90 55
554. **120.** 30 f. red .. .. 1·50 1·00
DESIGN: 15 f. "Italia" ski-jump.

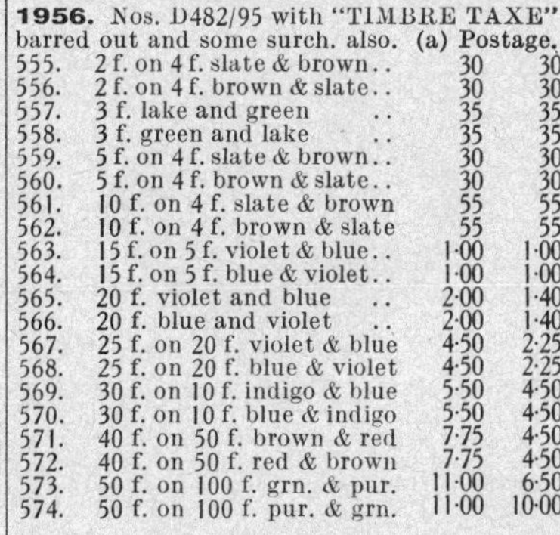

1956. Nos. D482/95 with "TIMBRE TAXE" barred out and some surch. also. (a) Postage.
555. 2 f. on 4 f. slate & brown .. 30 30
556. 2 f. on 4 f. brown & slate .. 30 30
557. 3 f. lake and green .. 35 35
558. 3 f. green and lake .. 35 35
559. 5 f. on 4 f. slate & brown .. 30 30
560. 5 f. on 4 f. brown & slate .. 30 30
561. 10 f. on 4 f. slate & brown 55 55
562. 10 f. on 4 f. brown & slate 55 55
563. 15 f. on 5 f. violet & blue .. 1·00 1·00
564. 15 f. on 5 f. blue & violet .. 1·00 1·00
565. 20 f. violet and blue .. 2·00 1·40
566. 20 f. blue and violet .. 2·00 1·40
567. 25 f. on 20 f. violet & blue 4·50 2·25
568. 25 f. on 20 f. blue & violet 4·50 2·25
569. 30 f. on 10 f. indigo & blue 5·50 4·50
570. 30 f. on 10 f. blue & indigo 5·50 4·50
571. 40 f. on 50 f. brown & red 7·75 4·50
572. 40 f. on 50 f. red & brown 7·75 4·50
573. 50 f. on 100 f. grn. & pur. 11·00 6·50
574. 50 f. on 100 f. pur. & grn. 11·00 10·00

(b) Air. Optd. **POSTE AERIENNE** also.
575. 100 f. on 20 f. violet & blue 8·00 8·00
576. 100 f. on 20 f. blue & violet 8·00 8·00

121. Route Map from Glasgow.

1956. 26th Monte Carlo Car Rally.
577. **121.** 100 f. brown and red .. 17·00 14·00

122. Princess Grace and Prince Rainier III.

1956. Royal Wedding.
578. **122.** 1 f. blk. & grn. (post.) 10 10
579. 2 f. black and red .. 10 10
580. 3 f. black and blue .. 20 15
581. 5 f. black and green .. 55 25
582. 15 f. black and brown 80 40
583. 100 f. brn. & pur. (air) 90 60
584. 200 f. brown & red .. 1·10 65
585. 500 f. brown & grey .. 2·50 2·00

123. Princess Grace. **124.** Princess Grace with Princess Caroline.

1957. Birth of Princess Caroline.
586. **123.** 1 f. grey 10 10
587. 2 f. olive 10 10
588. 3 f. brown 10 10
589. 5 f. red 10 10
590. 15 f. pink 10 10
591. 25 f. blue 50 10
592. 30 f. violet 50 10
593. 50 f. red .. .. 1·00 20
594. 75 f. orange .. .. 1·50 40

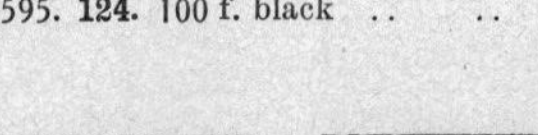

1958. Birth of Prince Albert.
595. **124.** 100 f. black .. .. 4·50 3·50

125. Order of St. Charles. **126.** Route Map from Munich.

1958. Centenary of Creation of National Order of St. Charles.
596. **125.** 100 f. multicoloured .. 1·60 1·40

1958. 27th Monte Carlo Rally.
597. **126.** 100 f. multicoloured .. 5·50 5·00

127. Statue of the Holy Virgin and Popes Pius IX and Pius XII.

1958. Centenary of Apparition of Virgin Mary at Lourdes.
598. **127.** 1 f. grey & brn. (post.) 10 10
599. – 2 f. violet and blue .. 10 10
600. – 3 f. sepia and green .. 10 10
601. – 5 f. blue and sepia .. 10 10
602. – 8 f. multicoloured .. 15 15
603. – 10 f. multicoloured .. 15 10
604. – 12 f. multicoloured .. 20 15
605. – 20 f. myrtle and purple 30 20
606. – 35 f. myrtle, bistre and brown 40 30
607. – 50 f. blue, grn. & lake 65 55
608. – 65 f. turq. and blue .. 90 70
609. – 100 f. grey, myrtle and blue (air) .. .. 1·40 1·10
610. – 200 f. brn. & chestnut 2·00 1·75

DESIGNS—VERT. (26½ × 36 mm.): 2 f. St. Bernadette. 3 f. St. Bernadette at Bartres. 5 f. The Miracle of Bourriette. 20 f. St. Bernadette at prayer. 35 f. St. Bernadette's canonization. (22 × 36 mm.): 8 f. Stained-glass window. As Type **127**: 50 f. St. Bernadette, Pope Pius XI, Mgr. Laurence and Abbe Peyramale. HORIZ. (48 × 36 mm.): 10 f. Lourdes grotto. 12 f. Interior of Lourdes grotto. (36 × 26½ mm.): 65 f. Shrine of St. Bernadette. (48 × 27 mm.): 100 f. Lourdes Basilica. 200 f. Pope Pius X and subterranean interior of Basilica.

128. Princess Grace and Clinic.

1959. Opening of new hospital block in "Princess Grace" Clinic, Monaco.
611. **128.** 100 f. grey, brn. & grn. 1·25 80

129. U.N.E.S.C.O. Headquarters, Paris, and Cultural Emblems.

1959. Inaug. of U.N.E.S.C.O. Headquarters Building.
612. **129.** 25 f. multicoloured .. 15 10
613. – 50 f. turq., blk. & olive 35 30
DESIGN: 50 f. As Type **129** but with heads of children and letters of various alphabets in place of the emblems.

130. Route Map from Athens. **131.** Prince Rainier and Princess Grace.

1959. 28th Monte Carlo Rally.
614. **130.** 100 f. blue, red & grn. on blue .. .. 4·00 3·50

1959. Air.
615. **131.** 300 f. violet .. .. 7·75 3·75
616. 500 f. blue .. .. 13·50 6·00
See also Nos. 642/3.

132. "Princess Caroline" Carnation.

1959. Flowers.
617. **132.** 5 f. mve., grn. and brn. 10 10
618. – 10 f. on 3 f. pink, green and brown 10 10
619. – 15 f. on 1 f. yell. & grn. 15 10
620. – 20 f. purple and green 35 25
621. – 25 f. on 6 f. red, yell. and green 55 30
622. – 35 f. pink and green .. 1·40 80
623. – 50 f. green and sepia .. 2·00 1·10
624. – 85 f. on 65 f. lavender, bronze and green .. 2·00 1·40
625. – 100 f. red and green .. 3·25 2·00

FLOWERS—As Type **132**: 10 f. "Princess Grace" carnation. 100 f. "Grace of Monaco" rose. VERT. (22 × 36 mm.): 15 f. Mimosa. 25 f. Geranium. HORIZ. (36 × 22 mm.): 20 f. Bougainvillaea. 35 f. "Laurier" rose. 50 f. Jasmine. 85 f. Lavender.

(New currency. 100 (old) francs = 1 (new franc.)

133. "Uprooted Tree". **134.** Oceanographic Museum.

1960. World Refugee Year.
626. **133.** 25 c. green, blue & blk. 15 15

1960. Prince Rainier types with values in new currency.
627. **109.** 25 c. blk. & orge. (post.) 10 10
628. 30 c. violet 20 10
629. 40 c. red and brown .. 20 10
630. 45 c. brown and grey .. 30 10
631. 50 c. red and green .. 40 20
632. 50 c. red and brown .. 40 10
633. 60 c. brown and green .. 50 20
634. 60 c. brown and purple 90 30
635. 65 c. blue and brown .. 5·50 1·00
636. 70 c. blue and plum .. 80 10
637. 85 c. green and violet .. 1·00 40
638. 95 c. blue .. .. 1·50 40
639. 1 f. 10 blue and brown 1·50 80
640. 1 f. 30 brown and red .. 2·75 1·10
641. 2 f. 30 purple and orange 1·40 45
642. **131.** 3 f. violet (air) .. .. 35·00 13·00
643. 5 f. blue .. .. 35·00 16·00

1960.
644 – 5 c. green, black & blue 10 10
645 **134** 10 c. brown and blue 15 10
646 – 10 c. blue, violet & grn 10 10
647 – 40 c. pur, grn & dp grn 45 10
648 – 45 c. brown, green & bl 2·00 20
649 – 70 c. brown, red & grn 40 20
650 – 80 c. red, green & blue 90 40
651 – 85 c. black, brn & grey 5·25 1·10
652 – 90 c. red, blue & black 1·00 40
653 – 1 f. multicoloured .. 1·25 25
654 – 1 f. 15 black, red & bl 1·25 65
655 – 1 f. 30 brown, grn & bl 80 35
656 – 1 f. 40 orge, grn & vio 2·00 80

DESIGNS—HORIZ. 5 c. Palace of Monaco. 10 c. (No. 646), Aquatic Stadium. 40 c., 45 c., 80 c., 1 f. 40, Aerial view of Palace. 70 c., 85 c., 90 c., 1 f. 15, 1 f. 30, Court of Honour, Monaco Palace. 1 f. Palace floodlit.

134a. St. Devote.

1960. Air.
668. **134a.** 2 f. violet, blue and green .. .. 1·40 75
669. 3 f. brn., grn. & blue 2·00 1·10
670. 5 f. red .. .. 3·50 90
671. 10 f. brown, grey and green .. .. 5·50 3·25

135. Sea Horse.

136. Route Map from Lisbon.

1960. Marine Life and Plants.
(a) Marine Life.
672. – 1 c. red and turquoise 10 10
673. – 12 c. brown and blue .. 55 10
674. **135.** 15 c. green and red .. 65 10
675. – 20 c. multicoloured .. 60 10
DESIGNS—HORIZ. 1 c. "Macrocheira kampferi" (crab). 20 c. "Pterois volitans". VERT. 12 c. "Fasciolaria trapezium" (shell).

(b) Plants.
676. – 2 c. multicoloured .. 10 10
677. – 15 c. orge., brn. & olive 65 10
678. – 18 c. multicoloured .. 55 10
679. – 20 c. red, olive & brn. 55 10
PLANTS—VERT. 2 c. "Selenicereus sp.". 15 c. "Cereus sp." 18 c. "Aloe ciliaris". 20 c. "Nopalea dejecta".

1960. Prince Rainier Seal type with values in new currency. Precancelled.
680. **104.** 8 c. purple 65 20
681. 20 c. green .. .. 1·00 35
682. 40 c. brown .. .. 1·60 65
683. 55 c. blue .. .. 4·50 1·00

1960. 29th Monte Carlo Rally.
684 **136** 25 c. black, red and blue on blue .. 1·40 1·40

137. Stamps of Monaco 1885, France and Sardinia, 1860.

1960. 75th Anniv. of 1st Stamp.
685. **137.** 25 c. bistre, blue & vio. 70 70

138. Aquarium.

1960. 50th Anniv. of Oceanographic Museum, Monaco.
686. – 5 c. black, blue & purple 20 15
687. **138.** 10 c. grey, brn. and grn. 35 35
688. – 15 c. blk., bistre & blue 20 15
689. – 20 c. blk., blue & mve. 45 20
690. – 25 c. turquoise .. 90 65
691. – 50 c. brown and blue .. 1·75 1·00
DESIGNS—VERT. 5 c. Oceanographic Museum (similar to Type **134**). HORIZ. 15 c. Conference Hall. 20 c. Hauling-in catch. 25 c. Museum, aquarium and under-water research equipment. 50 c. Prince Albert, "Hirondelle I" (schooner) and "Princess Alice" (steam yacht).

139. Horse-jumping.

1960. Olympic Games.
692. **139.** 5 c. brn., red and grn. 10 10
693. – 10 c. brn., blue & grn. 20 20
694. – 15 c. red, brn. & purple 20 20
695. – 20 c. blk., blue & grn. 2·00 2·00
696. – 25 c. pur., turq. & grn. 55 55
697. – 50 c. pur., blue & turq. 90 90
DESIGNS: 10 c. Swimming. 15 c. Long jumping. 20 c. Throwing the javelin. 25 c. Free-skating. 50 c. Skiing.

140. Rally Badge, Old and Modern Cars.

1961. 50th Anniv. of Monte Carlo Rally.
698. **140.** 1 f. vio., red and brn. 1·40 1·00

141. Route Map from Stockholm.

142. Marine-life.

1961. 30th Monte Carlo Rally.
699 **141** 1 f. multicoloured .. 1·10 1·10

1961. World Aquariological Congress. Orange network background.
700. **142.** 25 c. red, sep. & violet 15 15

143. Leper in Town of Middle Ages.

145. Insect within Protective Hand.

144. Semi-submerged Sphinx of Ouadi-es-Saboua.

1961. Sovereign Order of Malta.
701 **143** 25 c. black, red & brn 15 15

1961. U.N.E.S.C.O. Campaign for Preservation of Nubian Monuments.
702. **144.** 50 pur., blue and brn. 65 65

1961. Nature Preservation.
703. **145.** 25 c. mauve & purple 15 15

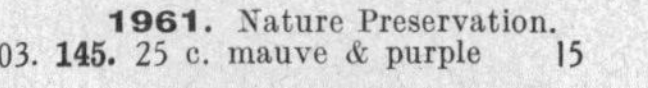

146. Chevrolet, 1912.

1961. Veteran Motor Cars.
704 1 c. brown, green and chest 10 10
705 2 c. blue, purple and red .. 10 10
706 3 c. purple, black & mauve 10 10
707 4 c. blue, brown and violet 10 10
708 5 c. green, red and olive .. 10 10
709 10 c. brown, red and blue 10 10
710 15 c. green and turquoise 15 15
711 20 c. brown, red and violet 20 20
712 25 c. violet, red and brown 35 35
713 30 c. lilac and green .. 60 60
714 45 c. green, purple & brown 1·40 1·10
715 50 c. blue, red and brown 1·40 1·10
716 65 c. brown, red and grey 1·40 1·10
717 1 f. blue, red and violet 2·75 2·75
MOTOR CARS: 1 c. Type **146**: 2 c. Peugeot, 1898. 3 c. Fiat, 1901. 4 c. Mercedes, 1901. 5 c. Rolls Royce, 1903. 10 c. Panhard-Lavassor, 1899. 15 c. Renault, 1898. 20 c. Ford "N", 1906 (wrongly inscr. "FORD-S-1908"). 25 c. Rochet-Schneider, 1894. 30 c. FN-Herstal, 1901. 45 c. De Dion Bouton, 1900. 50 c. Buick, 1910. 65 c. Delahaye, 1901. 1 f. Cadillac, 1906.

147. Racing Car and Race Route.

1962. 20th Monaco Motor Grand Prix.
718. **147.** 1 f. purple .. .. 1·40 1·00

148. Route Map from Oslo.

1962. 31st Monte Carlo Rally.
719. **148.** 1 f. multicoloured .. 1·10 90

149. Louis XII and Lucien Grimaldi.

DESIGNS: 50 c. Parchment bearing declaration of sovereignty. 1 f. Seals of two Sovereigns.

1962. 450th Anniv. of Recognition of Monegasque Sovereignty by Louis XII.
720. **149.** 25 c. black, red & blue 20 20
721. – 50 c. brn., lake & blue 20 20
722. – 1 f. red, green & brown 55 55

150. Mosquito and Swamp.

1962. Malaria Eradication.
723. **150.** 1 f. green and olive .. 50 30

151. Sun, Bouquet and "Hope Chest".

1962. National Multiple Sclerosis Society, New York.
724. **151.** 20 c. multicoloured .. 15 10

152. Harvest Scene.

DESIGN: 2 f. Mercury in flight over Europe.

1962. Europa.
725. **152.** 25 c. brown, green and blue (postage) .. 15 15
726. 50 c. olive & turquoise 25 25
727. 1 f. olive and purple .. 55 55
728. – 2 f. slate, brown and green (air) .. 1·00 90

153. Atomic Symbol and Scientific Centre, Monaco.

1962. Air. Scientific Centre, Monaco.
729. **153.** 10 f. vio., brn. & blue 5·50 5·00

INDEX

Countries can be quickly located by referring to the index at the end of this volume.

154. Yellow Wagtails.

155. Galeazzi's Diving Turret.

1962. Protection of Birds useful to Agriculture.
730. **154.** 5 c. yell., brown & green 10 10
731. – 10 c. red, bistre & pur. 10 10
732. – 15 c. multicoloured .. 15 10
733. – 20 c. sepia, grn. & mve. 15 10
734. – 25 c. multicoloured .. 50 20
735. – 30 c. brn., blue & myrtle 60 40
736. – 45 c. brown and violet 90 50
737. – 50 c. black, olive & turq. 1·40 60
738. – 85 c. multicoloured .. 1·90 1·10
739. – 1 f. sepia, red & green 2·50 1·25
BIRDS: 10 c. European robins. 15 c. Goldfinches. 20 c. Blackcaps. 25 c. Greater spotted woodpeckers. 30 c. Nightingale. 45 c. Barn owls. 50 c. Common starlings. 85 c. Red crossbills. 1 f. White storks.

1962. Underwater Exploration.
740 – 5 c. black, violet & bl 10 10
741 **155** 10 c. blue, violet & brn 10 10
742 – 25 c. bistre, green & bl 10 10
743 – 45 c. black, blue & grn 35 25
744 – 50 c. green, bistre & bl 35 35
745 – 85 c. blue & turquoise 65 60
746 – 1 f. brown, green & bl 90 90
DESIGNS—HORIZ. 5 c. Divers. 25 c. Williamson's photosphere (1914) and bathyscape "Trieste". 45 c. Klingert's diving-suit (1797) and modern diving-suit. 50 c. Diving saucer. 85 c. Fulton's "Nautilus" (1800) and modern submarine. 1 f. Alexander the Great's diving bell and Beebe's bathysphere.

156. Donor's Arm and Globe.

158. Feeding Chicks in Nest.

157. "Ring-a-ring o' Roses".

1962. 3rd Int. Blood Donors' Congress' Monaco.
747. **156.** 1 f. red, sepia & orange 40 40

1963. U.N. Children's Charter.
748. **157.** 5 c. red, blue and ochre 10 10
749. **158.** 10 c. green, sepia & bl. 10 10
750. – 15 c. blue, red & green 10 10
751. – 20 c. multicoloured .. 10 10
752. – 25 c. blue, pur. & brn. 20 20
753. – 50 c. multicoloured .. 30 30
754. – 95 c. multicoloured .. 65 45
755. – 1 f. purple, red & turq. 1·10 90
DESIGNS—As Type **157**: 1 f. Prince Albert and Princess Caroline. Children's paintings as Type **158**—HORIZ. 15 c. Children on scales. 50 c. House and child. VERT. 20 c. Sun's rays and children of three races. 25 c. Mother and child. 95 c. Negress and child.

159. Ship's Figurehead.

160. Racing Cars.

1963. Int. Red Cross Cent.
756. **159.** 50 c. red, brown & turq. 25 25
757. – 1 f. multicoloured .. 55 55
DESIGN—HORIZ. 1 f. Moynier, Dunant and Dufour.

1963. European Motor Grand Prix.
758. **160.** 50 c. multicoloured .. 40 35

161. Emblem and Charter.

1963. Founding of Lions Club of Monaco.
759. **161.** 50 c. blue, bistre & violet 40 40

162. Hotel des Postes and U.P.U. Monument, Berne.

1963. Paris Postal Conference Cent.
760. **162.** 50 c. lake, grn. & yell. 30 30

163. "Telstar" Satellite and Globe.

1963. 1st Link Trans-Atlantic T.V. Satellite.
761. **163.** 50 c. brown, grn. & pur. 40 40

164. Route Map from Warsaw.

1963. 32nd Monte Carlo Rally.
762. **164.** 1 f. multicoloured .. 90 80

165. Feeding Chicks.

1963. Freedom from Hunger.
763. **165.** 1 f. multicoloured .. 50 50

166. Allegory.

1963. 2nd Ecumenical Council, Vatican City.
764. **166.** 1 f. turquoise, green and red 40 40

167. Henry Ford and Ford "A" Car of 1903.

1963. Birth Centenary of Henry Ford (motor pioneer).
765. **167.** 20 c. green and purple 20 20

168. H. Garin (winner of 1903 race) cycling through Village.

DESIGN: 50 c. Cyclist passing Desgrange Monument, Col du Galibier, 1963.

1963. 50th "Tour de France" Cycle Race.
766. **168.** 25 c. grn., brn. & blue 20 20
767. – 50 c. sep., grn. & blue 25 25

169. P. de Coubertin and Discus-thrower.

1963. Birth Centenary of Pierre de Coubertin (reviver of Olympic Games).
768. **169.** 1 f. brown, red & lake 40 40

170. R. Garros and Aircraft.

1963. Air. 50th Anniv. of 1st Aerial Crossing of Mediterranean Sea.
769. **170.** 2 f. sepia and blue .. 1·10 90

171. Route Map from Paris. 173. "Europa".

172. Children with Stamp Album.

1963. 33rd Monte Carlo Rally.
770. **171.** 1 f. red, turq. and blue 70 60

1963. "Scolatex" Int. Stamp Exn., Monaco.
771. **172.** 50 c. blue, violet & red 20 20

1963. Europa.
772. **173.** 25 c. brown, red & green 20 20
773. 50 c. sepia, red & blue 30 30

174. Wembley Stadium.

1963. Cent. of (English) Football Association.
774. **174.** 1 c. violet, green & red 10 10
775. – 2 c. red, black & green 10 10
776. – 3 c. orange, olive & red 10 10
777. – 4 c. multicoloured .. 10 10

Multicoloured horiz. designs depicting

(a) "Football Through the Centuries".
778. 10 c. "Calcio", Florence (16th cent.) 10 10
779. 15 c. "Soule", Brittany (19th cent.) 10 10
780. 20 c. English military college (after Cruickshank, 1827) 10 10
781. 25 c. English game (after Overend, 1890) 10 10

(b) "Modern Football".
782. 30 c. Tackling 20 20
783. 50 c. Saving goal 55 55
784. 95 c. Heading ball .. 80 80
785. 1 f. Corner kick .. .. 1·00 1·00

DESIGNS—As Type **174**: 4 c. Louis II Stadium, Monaco. This stamp is optd. in commemoration of the Association Sportive de Monaco football teams in the French Championships and in the Coupe de France, 1962-63. HORIZ. (36 × 22 mm.): 2 c. Footballer making return kick. 3 c. Goalkeeper saving ball.

Nos. 778/81 and 782/5 were respectively issued together in sheets and arranged in blocks of 4 with a football in the centre of each block.

175. Communications in Ancient Egypt, and Rocket.

1964. "PHILATEC 1964" Int. Stamp Exn., Paris.
786. **175.** 1 f. brown, indigo & bl. 40 40

176. Reproduction of Rally Postcard Design.

1964. 50th Anniv. of 1st Aerial Rally, Monte Carlo.
787. 1 c. olive, blue & grn. (post.) 10 10
788. 2 c. bistre, brown and blue 10 10
789. 3 c. brown, blue & green 10 10
790. 4 c. red, turquoise & blue 10 10
791. 5 c. brown, red and violet 10 10
792. 10 c. violet, brown & blue 10 10
793. 15 c. orange, brown & blue 10 10
794. 20 c. sepia, green and blue 20 10
795. 25 c. brown, blue and red 30 10
796. 30 c. myrtle, purple & blue 40 20
797. 45 c. sepia, turq. & brown 55 35
798. 50 c. ochre, olive & violet 65 45
799. 65 c. red, slate & turquoise 90 55
800. 95 c. turq., red and bistre 1·40 90
801. 1 f. brown, blue & turq. .. 1·50 1·00
802. 5 f. sep., bl. & brn. (air) .. 3·00 3·00

DESIGNS: 1 c. Type **176**. HORIZ. (48 × 27 mm.)—Rally planes: 2 c. Renaux's "Farman". 3 c. Espanet's "Nieuport". 4 c. Moineau's "Breguet". 5 c. Garros' and B. des Moulinais' "Morane-Saulnier". 10 c. Hirth's "Albatros". 15 c. Prevost's "Deperdussin". Famous planes and flights: 20 c. "Vickers-Vimy" (Ross Smith: London-Port Darwin, 1919). 25 c. Douglas,-"Liberty" (U.S. World Flight, 1924). 30 c. Savoia Marchetti "S 16ter" (De Pinedo's World Flight, 1925). 45 c. Fokker "F-7" (First Flight over North Pole, Byrd and Bennett, 1925). 50 c. Ryan– "Spirit of St. Louis" (First solo crossing of N. Atlantic, Lindbergh, 1927). 65 c. "Breguet-19" (Paris—New York, Coste and Bellonte 1930). 95 c. "Late-28" (Dakar—Natal, first S. Atlantic airmail flight, Mermoz, 1930). 1 f. Dornier "DO-X" (Germany—Rio de Janeiro, Christiansen, 1930), 5 f. Convair B-58 "Hustler" (New York—Paris in 3 hours, 19′ 41″ Major Payne, U.S.A.F., 1961).

177. Aquatic Stadium. 178. Europa "Flower".

1964. Precancelled.
803. **177.** 10 c. multicoloured .. 1·50 20
803a. 15 c. multicoloured .. 75 20
804. 25 c. turq., blue & blk. 75 20
805. 50 c. vio., turq. & blk. 1·40 65

The "1962" date has been obliterated with two bars.

See also Nos. 949/51a and 1227/1230.

1964. Europa.
806. **178.** 25 c. red, green & blue 20 20
807. 50 c. brn., bistre & blue 40 40

179. Weightlifting.

1964. Olympic Games, Tokyo and Innsbruck.
808 **179** 1 c. red, brown and blue (postage) .. 10 10
809 – 2 c. red, green & olive 10 10
810 – 3 c. blue, brown & red 10 10
811 – 4 c. green, olive & red 10 10
812 – 5 f. red, brown and blue (air) 2·25 2·25

DESIGNS: 2 c. Judo. 3 c. Pole vaulting. 4 c. Archery. 5 f. Bobsleighing.

180. Pres. Kennedy and Space Capsule.

1964. Pres. Kennedy Commem.
813. **180.** 50 c. indigo and blue .. 40 40

181. Monaco and Television Set.

1964. 5th Int. Television Festival, Monte Carlo.
814. **181.** 50 c. brown, blue & red 30 30

182. F. Mistral and Statue.

1964. 50th Death Anniv. of Frederic Mistral (poet).
815. **182.** 1 f. brown and olive .. 35 35

183. Scales of Justice.

1964. 15th Anniv of Declaration of Human Rights.
816 **183** 1 f. green and brown .. 40 40

184. Route Map from Minsk.

1964. 34th Monte Carlo Rally.
817. **184.** 1 f. brn., turq. & ochre 55 40

185. FIFA Emblem.

1964. 60th Anniv. of Federation Internationale de Football Associations (FIFA).
818. **185.** 1 f. bistre, blue & red 60 60

186. "Syncom 2" and Globe.

1965. Cent. of I.T.U.
819. **186.** 5 c. grn. & ult. (post.) 10 10
820. – 10 c. chest., brn. & blue 10 10
821. – 12 c. pur., red & grey 10 10
822. – 18 c. blue, red & purple 10 10
823. – 25 c. vio., bistre & pur. 10 10
824. – 30 c. bistre, brn. & sepia 20 20
825. – 50 c. blue and green .. 25 25
826. – 60 c. blue and brown .. 25 25
827. – 70 c. sepia, orge. & blue 40 40
828. – 95 c. blk., indigo & blue 65 65
829. – 1 f. brown and blue .. 90 90
830. – 10 f. green, blue and brown (air) .. .. 4·00 4·00

DESIGNS—As Type **186**—HORIZ. 10 c. "Echo 2". 18 c. "Lunik 3". 30 c. A. G. Bell and telephone. 50 c. S. Morse and telegraph. 60 c. E. Belin and "belinograph". VERT. 12 c. "Relay". 10 f. Monte Carlo television transmitter. LARGER ($48\frac{1}{2} \times 27$ mm.): 25 c. "Telstar" and Pleumeur-Bodou Station. 70 c. Roman beacon and Chappe's telegraph. 95 c. Cable-laying ships "Great Eastern" and "Alsace". 1 f. E. Branly, G. Marconi and English Channel.

187. Europa "Sprig".

1965. Europa.

831	187	30 c. brown and green	15	15
832		60 c. violet and red ..	30	30

188. Monaco Palace (18th cent.).

1966. 750th Anniv. of Monaco Palace.

833	188	10 c. violet, grn. & blue	10	10
834	–	12 c. bistre, blue & blk.	10	10
835	–	18 c. grn., blk. & blue	15	15
836	–	30 c. brn., blk. & blue	20	20
837	–	60 c. grn., blue & bistre	30	30
838	–	1 f. 30 brown and green	80	80

DESIGNS (Different views of Palace): 12 c. 17th cent. 18 c. 18th cent. 30 c. 19th cent. 60 c. 19th cent. 1 f. 30, 20th cent.

189. Dante.

1966. 700th Anniv of Dante's Birth.

839	189	30 c. green, deep green and red	20	20
840	–	60 c. blue, turq & grn	40	40
841	–	70 c. black, green & red	55	55
842	–	95 c. blue, violet & pur	80	80
843	–	1 f. turq, blue & dp bl	80	80

DESIGNS (Scenes from Dante's works): 60 c. Dante harassed by the panther (envy). 70 c. Crossing the 5th circle. 95 c. Punishment of the arrogant. 1 f. Invocation of St. Bernard.

190. "The Nativity".

1966. World Assn. of Children's Friends (A.M.A.D.E.).

844	190	30 c. brown	20	20

191. Route Map from London.

1966. 35th Monte Carlo Rally.

845	191	1 f. blue, purple and red	55	55

192. Princess Grace with Children.

1966. Air. Princess Stephanie's 1st Birthday.

846	192	3 f. brown, blue & vio	2·00	1·60

193. Casino in 19th Century.

194. Europa "Ship".

1966. Centenary of Monte Carlo.

847.	–	12 c. black, red & blue (postage) ..	10	10
848.	193.	25 c. multicoloured ..	10	10
849.	–	30 c. multicoloured ..	10	10
850.	–	40 c. multicoloured ..	20	20
851.	–	60 c. multicoloured ..	30	30
852.	–	70 c. blue and lake ..	65	65
853.	–	95 c. black and purple		
854.	–	1 f. 30 purple, brown and chestnut ..	90	90
855.	–	5 f. lake, ochre and blue (air) ..	2·25	2·25

DESIGNS—VERT. 12 c. Prince Charles III. HORIZ. 40 c. Charles III Monument. 95 c. Massenet and Saint-Saens. 1 f. 30, Faure and Ravel. LARGER (48 × 27 mm.): 30 c. F. Blanc, originator of Monte Carlo, and view of 1860. 60 c. Prince Rainier III and projected esplanade. 70 c. Rene Blum and Diaghilev, ballet character from "Petrouchka". (36 × 36 mm.): 5 f. Interior of Opera House, 1879.

1966. Europa.

856.	194.	30 c. orange ..	15	15
857.		60 c. green	25	25

195. Prince Rainier and Princess Grace.

197. "Learning to Write".

196. Prince Albert I and Yachts "Hirondelle I" and "Princess Alice".

1966. Air.

858.	195.	2 f. slate and red ..	90	40
859.		3 f. slate and green ..	2·00	70
860.		5 f. slate and blue ..	2·25	90
860a.		10 f. slate and bistre	4·50	3·00
860b.		20 f. brn. & orange	50·00	30·00

1966. 1st Int. Oceanographic History Congress, Monaco.

861.	196.	1 f. lilac and blue ..	1·40	1·00

1966. 20th Anniv. of U.N.E.S.C.O.

862.	197.	30 c. purple and mauve	10	10
863.		60 c. brown and blue ..	25	25

198. T.V. Screen, Cross and Monaco Harbour.

200. W.H.O. Building.

199. "Precontinent III".

1966. 10th Meeting of Int. Catholic Television Assn. (U.N.D.A.), Monaco.

864.	198.	60 c. red, pur. & crim.	20	15

1966. 1st Anniv of Underwater Research Craft "Precontinent III".

865	199	1 f. yellow, brown & bl	35	30

1966. Inaug. of W.H.O. Headquarters, Geneva.

866.	200.	30 c. brn., grn. & blue	10	10
867.		60 c. brn., red & grn.	20	20

201. Bugatti, 1931

202. Dog (Egyptian bronze).

1967. 25th Motor Grand Prix, Monaco. Multicoloured. (a) Postage.

868.	1 c. Type **201**	10	10
869.	2 c. Alfa-Romeo, 1932 ..	10	10
870.	5 c. Mercedes, 1936 ..	10	10
871.	10 c. Maserati, 1948 ..	10	10
872.	18 c. Ferrari, 1955 ..	10	10
873.	20 c. Alfa-Romeo, 1950 ..	10	10
874.	25 c. Maserati, 1957 ..	15	15
875.	30 c. Cooper-Climax, 1958	15	15
876.	40 c. Lotus-Climax, 1960 ..	20	20
877.	50 c. Lotus-Climax, 1961 ..	40	20
878.	60 c. Cooper-Climax, 1962	65	40
879.	70 c. B.R.M., 1963–6 ..	80	55
880.	1 f. Walter Christie, 1907 ..	1·00	80
881.	2 f. 30 Peugeot, 1910 ..	2·00	1·50

(b) Air. Diamond. 50 × 50 mm.

882.	3 f. black and blue ..	1·50	1·25

DESIGN: Panhard-Phenix, 1895.

1967. Int. Cynological Federation Congress, Monaco.

883.	202.	30 c. black, pur. & grn.	25	25

203. View of Monte Carlo.

1967. International Tourist Year.

884	203	30 c. brown, green & bl	15	10

204. Pieces on Chessboard.

1967. Int. Chess Grand Prix, Monaco.

885.	204.	60 c. blk., plum & bl.	65	50

205. Melvin Jones (founder), Lions Emblem and Monte Carlo.

1967. 50th Anniv. of Lions Int.

886.	205.	60 c. blue, ult. and brn.	30	20

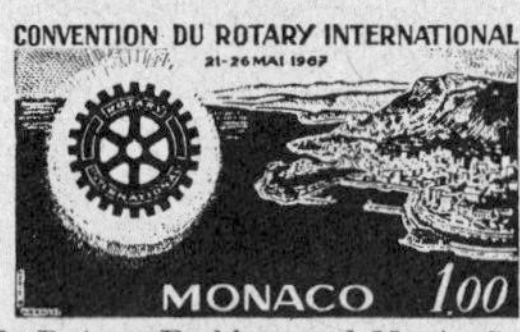

206. Rotary Emblem and Monte Carlo.

1967. Rotary Int. Convention.

887.	206.	1 f. bistre, blue & green	40	30

207. Fair Buildings.

1967. World Fair, Montreal.

888.	207.	1 f. red, slate and blue	30	30

208. Squiggle on Map of Europe.

209. Cogwheels.

1967. European Migration Committee (C.I.M.E.).

889.	208.	1 f. brown, bistre & blue	30	25

1967. Europa.

890.	209.	30 c. violet, pur. & red	20	20
891.		60 c. green, turq. & emer.	30	30

210. Dredger and Coastal Chart.

1967. 9th Int. Hydrographic Congress, Monaco.

892.	210.	1 f. brown, blue & green	35	30

211. Marie Curie and Scientific Equipment.

1967. Birth Cent. of Marie Curie.

893.	211.	1 f. blue, olive & brown	35	30

212. Skiing.

1967. Winter Olympic Games, Grenoble.

894.	212.	2 f. 30 brn., blue & slate	1·00	80

213. "Prince Rainier I" (E. Charpentier).

1967. Paintings. "Princes and Princesses of Monaco". Multicoloured.

895.	1 f. Type **213**	40	40
896.	1 f. "Lucien Grimaldi" (A. di Predis)	40	40

See also Nos. 932/3, 958/9, 1005/6, 1023/4, 1070/1, 1108/9, 1213/14, 1271/2, 1325, 1380/1, 1405/6, 1460/1 and 1531/2.

214. Putting the Shot.

1968. Olympic Games, Mexico.

897	214.	20 c. blue, brown and green (postage) ..	10	10
898.	–	30 c. brn., bl. & plum	10	10
899.	–	60 c. blue, pur. & red	20	20
900.	–	70 c. red, bl. & ochre	25	25
901.	–	1 f. blue, brown and orange ..	50	50
902.	–	2 f. 30 ol., bl. & lake	1·10	1·10
903.	–	3 f. blue, vio. & grn. (air)	1·50	1·25

DESIGNS: 30 c. High-jumping. 60 c. Gymnastics. 70 c. Water-polo. 1 f. Greco-Roman wrestling. 2 f. 30, Gymnastics (different). 3 f. Hockey.

215. "St. Martin".

1968. 20th Anniv. of Monaco Red Cross.
904. **215.** 2 f. 30 blue and brown 90 90

216. "Anemones" (after Raoul Dufy).

217. Insignia of Prince Charles III and Pope Pius IX.

1968. Monte Carlo Floral Exns.
905. **216.** 1 f. multicoloured .. 55 55

1968. Cent. of "Nullius Diocesis" Abbey.
906. **217.** 10 c. brown and red .. 10 10
907. – 20 c. red, green & brn. 10 10
908. – 30 c. brown and blue .. 20 20
909. – 60 c. brown, blue & grn. 25 25
910. – 1 f. indigo, bistre & blue 40 40
DESIGNS—VERT. 20 c. "St. Nicholas" (after Louis Brea). 30 c. "St. Benedict" (after Simone Martini). 60 c. Subiaco Abbey. HORIZ. 1 f. Old St. Nicholas' Church (on site of present cathedral).

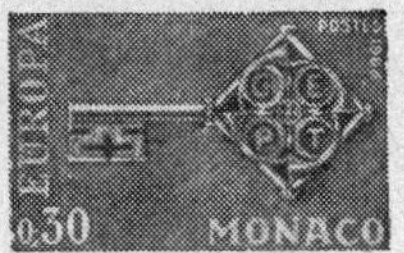

218. Europa "Key".

1968. Europa.
911. **218.** 30 c. red and orange .. 20 20
912. 60 c. blue and red .. 30 30
913. 1 f. brown and green 90 65

219. Type 0-3-0 Steam Locomotive (1868).

1968. Cent. of Nice–Monaco Railway.
914. **219.** 20 c. black, blue & pur. 30 25
915. – 30 c. black, blue & olive 40 35
916. – 60 c. black, blue & ochre 90 40
917. – 70 c. black, vio. & brn. 1·40 75
918. – 1 f. black, blue and red 2·00 1·40
919. – 2 f. 30 blue, blk. & red 2·75 2·40
DESIGNS: 30 c. Type "C-220" steam locomotive (1898). 60 c. Type "230-C" steam locomotive (1910). 70 c. Type "231-F" steam locomotive (1925) 1 f. Type "241-A" steam locomotive (1952). 2 f. 30, Type "BB" electric locomotive (1968).

220. Chateaubriand and Combourg Castle.

1968. Birth Cent. of Chateaubriand (novelist).
920. **220.** 10 c. plum, grn. & myrtle 10 10
921. – 20 c. violet, pur. & blue 10 10
922. – 25 c. brown, vio. & blue 10 10
923. – 30 c. vio., choc. & brn. 15 15
924. – 60 c. brn., grn. & red 25 25
925. – 2 f. 30 brn., mve. & blue 90 90
Scenes from Chateaubriand's novels: 20 c. "Le Genie du Christianisme". 25 c. "Rene". 30 c. "Le Dernier Abencerage". 60 c. "Les Martyrs". 2 f. 30, "Atala".

221. Law Courts, Paris, and statues—"La France et la Fidelite".

1968. Birth Centenary of J. F. Bosio (Monegasque sculptor).
926. **221.** 20 c. brown and purple 10 10
927. – 25 c. brown and red .. 10 10
928. – 30 c. blue and green .. 10 10
929. – 60 c. green and myrtle 25 20
930. – 2 f. 30 black and slate 75 65
DESIGNS—VERT. (26 × 36 mm.): 25 c. "Henry IV as a Child". 30 c. "J. F. Bosio" (lithograph). 60 c. "Louis XIV". HORIZ.—As Type **221**: 2 f. 30, "Napoleon I, Louis XVIII and Charles X".

222. W.H.O. Emblem.

1968. 20th Anniv. of W.H.O.
931. **222.** 60 c. multicoloured .. 25 20

1968. Paintings. "Princes and Princesses of Monaco". As T **213**. Multicoloured.
932. 1 f. "Prince Charles II" (Mimault) 30 30
933. 2 f. 30 "Princess Jeanne Grimaldi (Mimault) .. 70 70

223. The Hungarian March.

1969. Death Centenary of Hector Berlioz (composer).
934 **223** 10 c. brown, violet and green (postage) .. 10 10
935 – 20 c. brown, ol & mve 10 10
936 – 25 c. brown, bl & mve 10 10
937 – 30 c. black, green & bl 10 10
938 – 40 c. red, black & slate 10 10
939 – 50 c. brn, slate & pur 15 15
940 – 70 c. brn, slate & grn 25 20
941 – 1 f. black, mve & brn 35 25
942 – 1 f. 15 black, bl & turq 50 40
943 – 2 f. blk, bl & grn (air) 90 80
DESIGNS—HORIZ. 20 c. Mephistopheles appears to Faust. 25 c. Auerbach's tavern. 30 c. Sylphs' ballet. 40 c. Minuet of the goblins. 50 c. Marguerite's bedroom. 70 c. "Forests and caverns". 1 f. The journey to Hell. 1 f. 15, Heaven. All scenes from Berlioz's "The Damnation of Faust". VERT. 2 f. Bust of Berlioz.

224. "St. Elisabeth of Hungary".

1969. Monaco Red Cross.
944. **224.** 3 f. blue, brown & red 1·40 1·10

225. "Napoleon I" (P. Delaroche).

1969. Birth Bicent. of Napoleon Bonaparte.
945. **225.** 3 f. multicoloured .. 1·10 1·00

226. Colonnade. 227. "Head of Woman" (Da Vinci).

1969. Europa.
946. **226.** 40 c. red and purple .. 30 10
947. 70 c. blue, brown & blk. 80 45
948. 1 f. ochre, brn. & blue 1·00 65

1969. Precancelled. As T **177**. No date.
949 22 c. brown, blue & black 35 10
949a 26 c. violet, blue & black 40 15
949b 30 c. multicoloured .. 65 15
950 35 c. multicoloured .. 45 10
950a 45 c. multicoloured .. 65 10
951 70 c. black and blue .. 65 35
951a 90 c. green, blue & black 1·25 35

1969. 450th Death Anniv. of Leonardo da Vinci.
952. **227.** 30 c. brown 10 10
953. – 40 c. red and brown .. 15 10
954. – 70 c. green 25 20
955. – 80 c. sepia 35 25
956. – 1 f. 15 brown 55 45
957. – 3 f. brown .. .. 1·40 80
DRAWINGS: 40 c. Self-portrait. 70 c. "Head of an Old Man". 80 c. "Head of St. Madeleine". 1 f. 15, "Man's Head". 3 f. "The Condottiere".

1969. Paintings. "Princes and Princesses of Monaco". As T **213**. Multicoloured.
958 1 f. "Prince Honore II" (Champaigne) 35 35
959 3 f. "Princess Louise-Hippolyte" (Champaigne) .. .. 1·00 1·00

228. Marine Fauna, King Alfonso XIII of Spain and Prince Albert I of Monaco.

229. I.L.O. Emblem.

1969. 50th Anniv. of Int. Commission for Scientific Exploration of the Mediterranean, Madrid.
960. **228.** 40 c. blue and black .. 20 20

1969. 50th Anniv. of I.L.O.
961. **229.** 40 c. multicoloured .. 20 20

230. Aerial View of Monaco and T.V. Camera.

1969. 10th Int. Television Festival.
962. **230.** 40 c. purple, lake & blue 15 15

231. J.C.C. Emblem.

1969. 25th Anniv. of Junior Chamber of Commerce.
963. **231.** 40 c. vio., bistre & blue 15 15

232. Alphonse Daudet and Scenes from "Lettres".

1969. Centenary of Daudet's "Lettres de Mon Moulin".
964 **232** 30 c. lake, violet & grn 10 10
965 – 40 c. green, brown & bl 20 20
966 – 70 c. multicoloured .. 30 25
967 – 80 c. violet, brn & grn 30 30
968 – 1 f. 15 brown, orge & bl 50 50
DESIGNS: (Scenes from the book)—40 c. "Installation" (Daudet writing). 70 c. "Mule, Goat and Wolf". 80 c. "Gaucher's Elixir" and "The Three Low Masses". 1 f. 15, Daudet drinking, "The Old Man" and "The Country Sub-Prefect".

233. Conference Building, Albert I and Rainier III.

1970. Interparliamentary Union's Spring Meeting, Monaco.
969. **233.** 40 c. black, red & pur. 15 10

234. Baby Common Seal.

1970. Protection of Baby Seals.
970. **234.** 40 c. drab, blue & purple 40 30

235. Japanese Print.

236. Dobermann.

1970. Expo 70.
971 **235** 20 c. brown, grn & red 10 10
972 – 30 c. brown, buff & grn 25 20
973 – 40 c. bistre and violet 15 15
974 – 70 c. grey and red .. 50 50
975 – 1 f. 15 red, green & pur 55 55
DESIGNS—VERT. 30 c. Manchurian Cranes (birds). 40 c. Shinto temple gateway. HORIZ. 70 c. Cherry blossom. 1 f. 15, Monaco Palace and Osaka Castle.

1970. Int. Dog Show, Monte Carlo.
976. **236.** 40 c. black and brown 65 40

237. Apollo.

1970. 20th Anniv. of World Federation for Protection of Animals.
977. **237.** 30 c. black, red & blue 40 20
978. – 40 c. brown, blue & grn. 40 20
979. – 50 c. brown, ochre & bl. 55 40
980. – 80 c. brown, blue & grn. 80 55
981. – 1 f. brown, bistre & slate 1·50 90
982. – 1 f. 15 brn., green & blue 2·00 1·10
DESIGNS—HORIZ. 40 c. Basque ponies. 50 c. Common seal. VERT. 80 c. Chamois. 1 f. White-tailed sea eagles. 1 f. 15, European otter.

238. "St. Louis" (King of France).

1970. Monaco Red Cross.
983. **238.** 3 f. grn., brn. & slate 1·25 1·10
See also Nos. 1022, 1041, 1114, 1189 and 1270.

239. "Roses and Anemones" (Van Gogh).

1970. Monte Carlo Flower Show.
984. 239. 3 f. multicoloured .. 1·50 1·25
See also Nos. 1042 and 1073.

240. Moon Plaque, Presidents Kennedy and Nixon.

1970. 1st Man on the Moon (1969). Mult.
985. 40 c. Type 240 .. .. 15 10
986. 80 c. Astronauts on Moon 65 40

241. New U.P.U. Building and Monument. 242. "Flaming Sun".

1970. New U.P.U. Headquarters Building.
987. 241. 40 c. brn., black & grn. 15 10

1970. Europa.
988. 242. 40 c. purple 20 10
989. 80 c. green 55 30
990. 1 f. blue 90 55

243. Camargue Horse.

1970. Horses.
991. 243. 10 c. slate, olive & blue (postage) 10 10
992. – 20 c. brn., olive and blue 20 10
993. – 30 c. brn., grn. and blue 20 15
994. – 40 c. grey, brn. & slate 30 20
995. – 50 c. brn., olive & blue 65 35
996. – 70 c. brn., orge. & grn. 1·00 65
997. – 85 c. blue, grn. & olive 1·50 90
998. – 1 f. 15 black, grn & blue 2·00 1·40
999. – 3 f. multicoloured (air) 1·50 1·40
HORSES—HORIZ. 20 c. Anglo-Arab. 30 c. French saddle-horse. 40 c. Lippizaner. 50 c. Trotter. 70 c. English thoroughbred. 85 c. Arab. 1 f. 15, Barbary. DIAMOND (50 × 50 mm.) 3 f. Rock-drawings of horses in Lascaux grotto.

244. Dumas, D'Artagnan and the Three Musketeers.

1970. Birth Centenary of Alexandre Dumas (pere) (author).
1000. 244. 30 c. slate, brn. & blue 10 10

245. H. Rougier and Bleriot Aircraft.

1970. 60th Anniv. of First Mediterranean Flight.
1001. 245. 40 c. brown, blue & slate 20 10

246. De Lamartine and scene from "Meditations Poetiques".

1970. 150th Birth Anniv. of A. de Lamartine (writer).
1002. 246. 80 c. brn., blue & turq. 30 15

247. Beethoven.

1970. Birth Bicent. of Beethoven.
1003. 247. 1 f. 30 brown and red 1·00 65

1970. 50th Death Anniv. of Modigliani. Vert. Painting as T 213. Multicoloured.
1004. 3 f. "Portrait of Dedie" 1·60 1·25

1970. Paintings. "Princes and Princesses of Monaco". As T 213.
1005. 1 f. red and black .. 30 30
1006. 3 f. multicoloured .. 1·00 90
PORTRAITS: 1 f. "Prince Louis I" (F. de Troy). 3 f. "Princess Charlotte de Gramont" (S. Bourdon).

248. Cocker Spaniel. 249. Razorbill.

1971. Int. Dog Show, Monte Carlo.
1007. 248. 50 c. multicoloured .. 1·40 90
See also Nos. 1036, 1082, 1119, 1218 and 1239.

1971. Campaign Against Pollution of the Sea.
1008. 249. 50 c. indigo and blue 65 35

250. Hand holding Emblem.

1971. 7th Int. Blood-Donors Federation Congress.
1009. 250. 80 c. red, violet & grey 35 30

251. Sextant, Scroll and Underwater Scene.

1971. 50th Anniv. of Int. Hydrographic Bureau.
1010. 251. 80 c. brn., grn. & slate 40 30

252. Detail of Michelangelo painting ("The Arts").

1971. 25th Anniv. of U.N.E.S.C.O.
1011. 252. 30 c. brn., blue & vio. 10 10
1012. – 50 c. blue and brown 20 10
1013. – 80 c. brown and green 30 15
1014. – 1 f. 30 green 40 40
DESIGNS—VERT. 50 c. Alchemist and dish aerial ("Sciences"). 1 f. 30, Prince Pierre of Monaco (National U.N.E.S.C.O. Commission). HORIZ. 80 c. Ancient scribe, book and T.V. screen ("Culture").

253. Europa Chain.

1971. Europa.
1015. 253. 50 c. red 30 10
1016. 80 c. blue 65 40
1017. 1 f. 30 green .. 1·40 90

254. Old Bridge, Sospel.

1971. Protection of Historic Monuments.
1018. 254. 50 c. brn., blue & grn. 15 10
1019. – 80 c. brn., grn. & grey 25 15
1020. – 1 f. 30 red, grn. & brn. 55 40
1021. – 3 f. slate, blue & olive 1·10 1·00
DESIGNS—HORIZ. 80 c. Roquebrune Chateau. 1 f. 30, Grimaldi Chateau, Cagnes-sur-Mer. VERT. 3 f. Roman "Trophy of the Alps", La Turbie.

1971. Monaco Red Cross. As T 238.
1022. 3 f. brown, olive & green 1·25 1·10
DESIGN: 3 f. St. Vincent de Paul.

1972. Paintings. "Princes and Princesses of Monaco". As T 213. Multicoloured.
1023. 1 f. "Prince Antoine I" (Rigaud) 40 20
1024. 3 f. "Princess Marie de Lorraine" (18th-cent. French School) .. 1·10 1·00

255. La Fontaine and Animal Fables (350th).

1972. Birth Annivs. (1971).
1025. 255. 50 c. brn., emer. & grn. 30 20
1026. – 1 f. 30 pur., blk. & red 55 40
DESIGNS: 1 f. 30, Baudelaire, nudes and cats (150th).

256. Saint-Saens and scene from Opera, "Samson and Delilah".

1972. 50th Death Anniv. (1971) of Camile Saint-Saens.
1027. 256. 90 c. brown and sepia 40 25

257. Battle Scene.

1972. 400th Anniv. (1971) of Battle of Lepanto.
1028. 257. 1 f. blue, brn. & red .. 60 40

258. "Christ before Pilate" (engraving by Durer).

1972. 500th Birth Anniv. (1971) of Albrecht Durer.
1029. 258. 2 f. black and brown 1·00 80

259. "The Cradle" (B. Morisot).

1972. 25th Anniv. (1971) of U.N.I.C.E.F.
1030. 259. 2 f. multicoloured .. 90 65

260. "Gilles" (Watteau).

1972. 250th Death Anniv. (1971) of Watteau.
1031. 260. 3 f. multicoloured .. 1·40 1·25

261. Santa Claus.

1972. Christmas (1971).
1032. 261. 30 c. red, blue & brn. 10 10
1033. 50 c. red, grn. & orge. 25 10
1034. 90 c. red, blue & brn. 40 20

262. Steam Locomotive and Modern Turbo Express.

1972. 50th Anniv. of Int. Railway Union.
1035. 262. 50 c. pur., lilac & red 50 30

1972. Int. Dog Show, Monte Carlo. As T 248. Inscr. "1972".
1036. 60 c. mult. (Great Dane) 1·40 90

263. "Pollution Kills".

1972. Anti-Pollution Campaign.
1037. 263. 90 c. brn., grn. & blk. 50 30

264. Ski-jumping.

1972. Winter Olympic Games, Sapporo, Japan.
1038. 264. 90 c. blk., red & grn. 40 30

265. "Communications".

266. "SS. Giovanni e Paolo" (detail, Canaletto).

1972. Europa.

1039. **265.** 50 c. blue and orge. .. 80 30
1040. 90 c. blue and grn. .. 1·50 1·00

1972. Monaco Red Cross. As T **238**.

1041 3 f. brown and purple .. 1·25 1·10
DESIGN: 3 f. St. Francis of Assisi.

1972. Monte Carlo Flower Show. As T **239**.

1042. 3 f. multicoloured .. 2·00 1·00
DESIGN: 3 f. "Vase of Flowers" (Cezanne).

1972. U.N.E.S.C.O. "Save Venice" Campaign.

1043. **266.** 30 c. red 25 20
1044. – 60 c. violet 35 20
1045. – 2 f. blue .. .. 1·10 1·00
DESIGNS—27 × 48 mm: 60 c. "S. Pietro di Castello" (F. Guradi). As Type **266**: 2 f. "Piazzetta S. Marco" (B. Bellotto).

267. Dressage.

1972. Olympic Games, Munich. Equestrian Events.

1046. **267.** 60 c. brn., blue & lake 40 40
1047. – 90 c. lake, brn. & blue 90 90
1048. – 1 f. 10 blue, lake & brn. 1·25 1·25
1049. – 1 f. 40 brn., lake & blue 2·25 2·25
DESIGNS: 90 c. Cross country. 1 f. 10, Show jumping (wall). 1 f. 40, Show jumping (parallel bars).

268. Escoffier and Birthplace.

1972. 125th Birth Anniv. of Auguste Escoffier (master chef).

1050. **268.** 45 c. black and brown 25 15

269. Drug Addiction. **270.** Globe, Birds and Animals.

1972. Campaign Against Drugs.

1051. **269.** 50 c. red, brn. & orange 25 20
1052. 90 c. grn., brn. & blue 35 30
See also Nos. 1088/91 and 1280/1.

1972. 17th Int. Congress of Zoology, Monaco.

1053. **270.** 30 c. grn., brn. & red 10 10
1054. – 50 c. brn., purple & red 25 10
1055. **270.** 90 c. blue, brn. & red 35 20
DESIGN—HORIZ. 50 c. Similar to Type **270**.

271. Bouquet. **272.** "The Nativity" and Child's face.

1972. Monte Carlo Flower Show, 1973 (1st issue). Multicoloured.

1056. 30 c. Lilies in vase .. 20 10
1057. 50 c. Type **271** 65 20
1058. 90 c. Flowers in Vase .. 1·00 65
See also Nos. 1073, 1105/7, 1143/4, 1225/6, 1244, 1282/3 and 1316/17.

1972. Christmas.

1059 **272** 30 c. grey, blue & pur 10 10
1060 50 c. red, purple & brn 20 10
1061 90 c. vio, plum & pur 40 20

273. Bleriot and Aircraft.

1972. Birth Annivs.

1062. **273.** 30 c. blue and brown 15 10
1063. – 50 c. blue, turquoise and new blue .. 40 30
1064. – 90 c. brown and buff 55 35
DESIGNS AND ANNIVERSARIES: 30 c. (birth cent.). 50 c. Amundsen and polar scene (birth cent). 90 c. Pasteur and laboratory scene (150th birth anniv.).

274. "Gethsemane".

1972. Protection of Historical Monuments. Frescoes by J. Canavesio. Chapel of Notre-Dame des Fontaines, La Brigue.

1065. **274.** 30 c. red 10 10
1066. – 50 c. grey 20 15
1067. – 90 c. green 40 25
1068. – 1 f. 40 red 55 40
1069. – 2 f. purple .. .. 1·10 65
DESIGNS: 50 c. "Christ Outraged". 90 c. "Ascent to Calvary". 1 f. 40, "The Resurrection". 2 f. "The Crucifixion".

1972. Paintings. "Princes and Princesses of Monaco". As T**213**. Multicoloured.

1070. 1 f. "Prince Jacques I" (N. Largilliere) .. 40 25
1071. 3 f. "Princess Louise-Hippolyte" (J. B. Vanloo) .. .. 1·25 1·00

1973. Monte Carlo Flower Show. (2nd issue). As T **239**.

1073. 3 f. 50 multicoloured .. 3·00 2·25
DESIGN: 3 f. 50, "Bouquet of Flowers".

276. Europa "Posthorn".

1973. Europa.

1074. **276.** 50 c. orange .. 1·10 40
1075. 90 c. green .. .. 2·50 1·60

277. Moliere and Characters from "Le Malade Imaginaire". **278.** Colette, Cat and Books.

1973. 300th Death Anniv. of Moliere.

1076. **277.** 20 c. red, brown & blue 30 20

1973. Birth Anniversaries.

1077 **278** 30 c. black, blue & red 35 20
1078 – 45 c. multicoloured .. 1·40 50
1079 – 50 c. lilac, purple & bl 30 20
1080 – 90 c. multicoloured .. 45 30
DESIGNS AND ANNIVERSARIES—HORIZ. 30 c. (nature writer—birth cent.). 45 c. J. H. Fabre and insects (entomologist—150th birth anniv.). 90 c. Sir George Cayley and early flying machines (aviation pioneer—birth bicent.). VERT. 50 c. Blaise Pascal (philosopher and writer—350th birth anniv.).

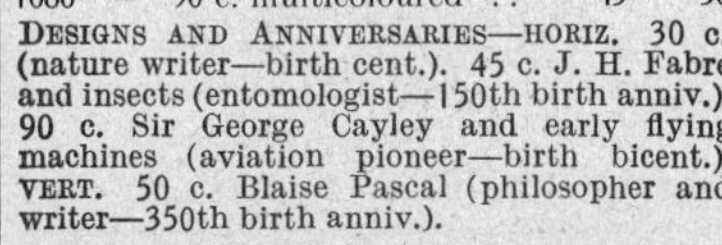

279. E. Ducretet, "Les Invalides" and Eiffel Tower.

1973. 75th Anniv. of Eugene Ducretet's First Hertzian Radio Link.

1081. **279.** 30 c. purple and brown 20 15

1973. Int. Dog Show, Monte Carlo. As T **248**. Inscr. "1973". Multicoloured.

1082. 45 c. Alsatian .. .. 3·75 2·25

280. C. Peguy and Chartres Cathedral.

1973. Birth Bicent. of Charles Peguy (writer).

1083. **280.** 50 c. brn., mauve & grey 30 25

281. Telecommunications Equipment. **282.** Stage Characters.

1973. 5th World Telecommunications Day.

1084. **281.** 60 c. violet, blue & brn. 30 20

1973. 5th World Amateur Theatre Festival.

1085. **282.** 60 c. lilac, blue & red 35 20

283. Ellis and Rugby Tackle.

1973. 150th Anniv of Founding of Rugby Football by William Webb Ellis.

1086 **283** 90 c. red, lake & brown 55 35

284. St. Theresa.

1973. Birth Cent. of St. Theresa of Lisieux.

1087. **284.** 1 f. 40 multicoloured 65 40

285. Drug Addiction.

1973. Campaign Against Drugs.

1088. **285.** 50 c. red, grn. & blue 20 15
1089. – 50 c. multicoloured .. 20 15
1090. **285.** 90 c. violet, grn. & red 40 30
1091. – 90 c. multicoloured .. 60 40
DESIGN: Nos. 1089, 1091, Children, syringes and addicts.

286. "Institution of the Creche" (Giotto).

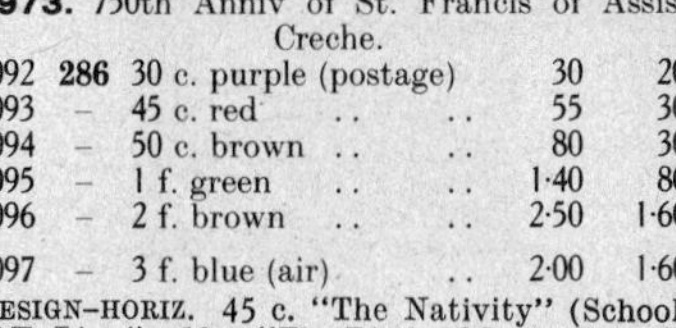

1973. 750th Anniv of St. Francis of Assisi Creche.

1092 **286** 30 c. purple (postage) 30 20
1093 – 45 c. red 55 30
1094 – 50 c. brown 80 30
1095 – 1 f. green .. .. 1·40 80
1096 – 2 f. brown .. .. 2·50 1·60
1097 – 3 f. blue (air) .. 2·00 1·60
DESIGN—HORIZ. 45 c. "The Nativity" (School of F. Lippi). 50 c. "The Birth of Jesus Christ" (Giotto). VERT. 1 f. "The Nativity" (15th century miniature). 2 f. "The Birth of Jesus" (Fra Angelico). 3 f. "The Nativity" (Flemish school).

287. Country Picnic.

1973. 50th Anniv. of National Committee for Monegasque Traditions.

1098. **287.** 10 c. blue, grn. & brn. 10 10
1099. – 20 c. vio., blue & grn. 10 10
1100. – 30 c. sepia, brn. & grn. 15 15
1101. – 45 c. red, violet & pur. 20 20
1102. – 50 c. blk., red & brn. 30 30
1103. – 60 c. red, violet & blue 30 30
1104. – 1 f. violet blue & brown 45 45
DESIGNS—VERT. 20 c. Maypole dance. HORIZ. 30 c. "U Bradi" (local dance). 45 c. St. Jean fire-dance. 50 c. Blessing the Christmas loaf. 60 c. Blessing the sea – Festival of St. Devote. 1 f. Corpus Christi procession.

1973. Monte Carlo Flower Show, 1974. As T **271**. Multicoloured.

1105. 45 c. Roses and Strelitzia 55 25
1106. 60 c. Mimosa and myosotis 90 40
1107. 1 f. "Vase of Flowers" (Odilon Redon) .. 2·00 1·00

1973. Paintings. "Princesses of Monaco". As T **213**. Multicoloured.

1108. 2 f. "Charlotte Grimaldi" (in day dress, P. Gobert) 1·00 90
1109. 2 f. "Charlotte Grimaldi" (in evening dress, P. Gobert) .. .. 1·00 90

289. U.P.U. Emblem and Symbolic Heads. **290.** Farman and Aircraft of 1909 and 1919.

1974. Cent. of Universal Postal Union.

1111. **289.** 50 c. purple & brown 25 10
1112. – 70 c. multicoloured .. 35 20
1113. – 1 f. 10 multicoloured 80 55
DESIGNS: 70 c. Hands holding letters. 1 f. 10, "Countries of the World" (famous buildings).

1974. Monaco Red Cross. As T **238**.

1114. 3 f. blue, green & purple 1·25 1·25
DESIGN: 3 f. St. Bernard of Menthon.

1974. Birth Centenary of Henri Farman (aviation pioneer).

1115. **290.** 30 c. brn., pur. & blue 10 10

291. Marconi, Circuit Plan and Destroyers.

1974. Birth Centenary of Guglielmo Marconi (radio pioneer).

1116. **291.** 40 c. red, dark bl. & bl. 20 10

292. Duchesne and "Penicillium glaucum".

1974. Birth Centenary of Ernest Duchesne (microbiologist).

1117. **292.** 45 c. blk., blue & pur. 25 10

INDEX

Countries can be quickly located by referring to the index at the end of this volume.

293. Forest and Engine.

1974. 60th Death Anniv. of Fernand Forest (motor engineer and inventor).
1118. **293.** 50 c. pur., red & blk. 20 10

1974. International Dog Show, Monte Carlo. As T **248**, inscr. "1974".
1119. 60 c. multicoloured .. 2·40 1·40
DESIGN: 60 c. Schnauzer.

294. Ronsard and Characters from "Sonnet to Helene".

1974. 450th Birth Anniv. of Pierre de Ronsard (poet).
1120. **294.** 70 c. brown and red .. 40 35

295. Sir Winston Churchill (after bust by O. Nemon).

297. "The King of Rome" (Bosio).

296. Interpol Emblem, and Views of Monaco and Vienna.

1974. Birth Cent. of Sir Winston Churchill.
1121. **295.** 1 f. brown and grey .. 50 30

1974. 60th Anniv. of 1st Int. Police Judiciary Congress and 50th Anniv. of Int. Criminal Police Organization (Interpol).
1122. **296.** 2 f. bl., brn. & grn... 1·00 80

1974. Europa. Sculptures by J. F. Bosio.
1123. **297.** 45 c. green & brown .. 1·10 65
1124. – 1 f. 10 bistre & brown 1·75 1·10
DESIGN: 1 f. 10 "Madame Elizabeth".

298. " The Box " (A. Renoir).

1974. " The Impressionists ". Multicoloured.
1126. 1 f. Type **298** .. .. 1·40 65
1127. 1 f. " The Dance Class " (E. Degas) .. 1·40 65
1128. 2 f. " Impression-Sunrise " (C. Monet) (horiz.) .. 2·50 1·10
1129. 2 f. " Entrance to Voisins Village " (C. Pissarro) (horiz.) .. .. 2·50 1·10
1130. 2 f. " The Hanged Man's House " (P. Cezanne) (horiz.) .. .. 2·50 1·10
1131. 2 f. " Floods at Port Marly " (A. Sisley) (horiz.) .. 2·50 1·10

299. Tigers and Trainer.

1974. First International Circus Festival, Monaco.
1132. **299.** 2 c. brown, grn. & bl. 10 10
1133. – 3 c. brown & purple 10 10
1134. – 5 c. blue, brn. & red 10 10
1135. – 45 c. brn., blk. & red 40 20
1136. – 70 c. multicoloured .. 65 30
1137. – 1 f. 10 brn., grn. & red 1·25 65
1138. – 5 f. green, bl. & brn. 4·25 2·75
DESIGNS—VERT. 3 c. Performing horses. 45 c. Equestrian act. 1 f. 10, Acrobats. 5 f. Trapeze act. HORIZ. 5 c. Performing elephants. 70 c. Clowns.

300. Honore II on Medal.

1974. 350th Anniv of Monegasque Numismatic Art.
1139 **300** 60 c. green and red .. 25 35

301. Marine Flora and Fauna.

1974. 24th Congress of the International Commission for the Scientific Exploration of the Mediterranean. Multicoloured.
1140. 45 c. Type **301** 40 20
1141. 70 c. Sea-bed flora and fauna 80 30
1142. 1 f. 10 Sea-bed flora and fauna (different) .. 1·60 55
Nos. 1141/2 are larger, size 52 × 31 mm.

1974. Monte Carlo Flower Show. As T **271**. Multicoloured.
1143. 70 c. Honeysuckle and violets 65 40
1144. 1 f. 10 Iris and chrysanthemums .. .. 1·10 65

302. Prince Rainier III (F. Messina). **303.**

1974.
1145 **302** 60 c. green (postage) 30 15
1146 80 c. red 40 25
1147 80 c. green 40 10
1148 1 f. brown 90 35
1149 1 f. red 50 10
1149a 1 f. green 40 10
1149b 1 f. 10 green .. 40 10
1150 1 f. 20 violet .. 1·75 1·40
1150a 1 f. 20 red 65 10
1150b 1 f. 20 green .. 65 10
1151 1 f. 25 blue 80 55
1151a 1 f. 30 red 65 15
1152 1 f. 40 red 80 10
1152a 1 f. 50 black .. 75 40
1153 1 f. 60 grey 80 20
1153a 1 f. 70 blue 90 40
1153b 1 f. 80 blue .. .. 1·00 50
1154 2 f. mauve .. .. 2·00 75
1154a 2 f. 10 brown .. 1·10 55
1155 2 f. 30 violet .. 1·10 55
1156 2 f. 50 black .. 1·75 90
1157 9 f. violet .. .. 5·00 2·50
1158 **303** 10 f. violet (air) .. 4·00 1·75
1159 15 f. red .. .. 6·50 3·50
1160 20 f. blue .. .. 8·50 4·50

304. Coastline, Monte Carlo. **305.** " Haageocereus chosicensis ".

1974.
1161 **304** 25 c. blue, green & brn 25 10
1162 – 25 c. brown, grn & bl 20 20
1163 – 50 c. brown and blue 35 10
1164 **304** 65 c. blue, brn & grn 30 20
1165 – 70 c. multicoloured .. 30 20
1166 **304** 1 f. 10 brown, grn & bl 90 30
1167 – 1 f. 10 black. brn & bl 55 30
1168 – 1 f. 30 brown, grn & bl 65 30
1169 – 1 f. 40 grn, grey & brn 1·10 40
1170 – 1 f. 50 green, bl & blk 1·00 55
1171 – 1 f. 70 brown, grn & bl 1·60 1·00
1172 – 1 f. 80 brown, grn & bl 1·10 65
1173 – 2 f. 30 brn, grey & bl 1·40 90
1174 – 3 f. brown, grey & grn 3·50 1·50
1175 – 5 f. brown, green, & bl 5·50 2·00
1176 – 6 f 50 brown, bl & grn 3·00 2·00
DESIGNS—VERT. 50 c. Palace clock tower. 70 c. Botanical gardens. 1 f. 40, Monaco Cathedral. 1 f. 40, 1 f. 50, Prince Albert I statue and Museum. 3 f. Fort Antoine. HORIZ. 25 c. (1162), 1 f. 70, "All Saints" Tower. 1 f. 10 (1167), Palais de Justice. 1 f. 80, 5 f. 50, La Condamine. 2 f. 30, North Galleries of Palace. 6 f. 50, Aerial view of hotels and harbour.

1975. Plants. Multicoloured.
1180. 10 c. Type **305** 10 10
1181. 20 c. " Matucana madisoniarum " .. 10 10
1182. 30 c. " Parodia scopaioides " 35 10
1183. 85 c. " Mediolobivia arachnacantha " .. 1·10 40
1184. 1 f. 90 " Matucana yanganucensis " .. 2·25 1·25
1185. 4 f. " Echinocereus marksianus " .. .. 4·50 2·50

306. " Portrait of a Sailor " (P. Florence). **308.** " Prologue ".

307. " St. Bernardin de Sienne ".

1975. Europa.
1186. **306.** 80 c. purple .. .. 1·10 65
1187. – 1 f. 20 blue .. .. 1·60 90
DESIGN: 1 f. 20 " St. Devote " (Ludovic Brea).

1975. Monaco Red Cross.
1189. **307.** 4 f. blue and purple .. 2·25 1·50

1975. Centenary of "Carmen" (opera by Georges Bizet).
1190 **308** 30 c. violet, brn & blk 10 10
1191 – 60 c. grey, green & red 20 10
1192 – 80 c. green, brn & blk 40 25
1193 – 1 f. 40 purple, brown and ochre 80 60
DESIGNS—HORIZ. 60 c. Lilla Pastia's tavern. 80 c. "The Smuggler's Den" 1 f. 40, "Confrontation at Seville".

309. Saint-Simon. **310.** Dr. Albert Schweitzer.

1975. 300th Birth Anniv. of Louis de Saint-Simon (writer).
1194. **309.** 40 c. blue 25 15

1975. Birth Cent. of Dr. Schweitzer (Nobel Peace Prize winner).
1195. **310.** 60 c. red and brown 40 20

311. " Stamp " and Calligraphy.

1975. " Arphila 75 " International Stamp Exhibition, Paris.
1196. **311.** 80 c. brown & orange 50 35

312. Seagull and Sunrise.

1975. International Exposition, Okinawa.
1197 **312** 85 c. blue, grn & orge 55 30

313. Pike smashing Crab.

1975. Anti-Cancer Campaign.
1198. **313.** 1 f. multicoloured .. 65 30

314. Christ with Crown of Thorns.

1975. Holy Year.
1199. **314.** 1 f. 15 black, brown and purple .. 70 40

315. Villa Sauber, Monte Carlo.

1975. European Architectural Heritage Year.
1200. **315.** 1 f. 20 grn., brn. & bl. 90 55

316. Woman's Head and Globe.

1975. International Women's Year.
1201. **316.** 1 f. 20 multicoloured 90 60

317. Rolls-Royce " Silver Ghost " (1907).

1975. Evolution of the Motor Car.
1202 **317** 5 c. blue, green & brn 10 10
1203 – 10 c. indigo and blue 10 10
1204 – 20 c. bl, ultram & blk 20 10
1205 – 30 c. purple & mauve 40 20
1206 – 50 c. blue, pur & mve 80 40
1207 – 60 c. red and green .. 1·10 65
1208 – 80 c. indigo and blue 1·60 90
1209 – 85 c. brn, orge & grn 2·25 1·50
1210 – 1 f. 20 blue, red & grn 2·25 1·60
1211 – 1 f. 40 green and blue 3·50 2·00
1212 – 5 f. 50 blue, emerald and green .. .. 9·00 5·50
MOTOR CARS: 10 c. Hispano-Suiza "H.6B" (1926). 20 c. Isotta Fraschini "8A" (1928). 30 c. Cord "L.29". 50 c. Voisin "V12" (1930). 60 c. Duesenberg "SJ" (1933). 80 c. Bugatti "57 C" (1938). 85 c. Delahaye "135 M" (1940). 1 f. 20, Cisitalia "Pininfarina" (1945). 1 f. 40, Mercedes-Benz "300 SL" (1955). 5 f. 50, Lamborghini "Countach" (1974).

1975. Paintings. "Princes and Princesses of Monaco". As T **213**. Multicoloured.
1213. 2 f. "Prince Honore III" 1·10 65
1214. 4 f. "Princess Catherine de Brignole" .. .. 2·50 1·60

318. Dog behind Bars.

319. Maurice Ravel

1975. 125th Birth Anniv. of Gen. J. P. Delmas de Grammont (author of Animal Protection Code).
1215. **318.** 60 c. black and brown 65 40
1216. – 80 c. black and brown 90 65
1217. – 1 f. 20 green & purple 1·40 70
DESIGNS—VERT. 80 c. Cat chased up tree. HORIZ. 1 f. 20, Horse being ill-treated.

1975. International Dog Show, Monte Carlo. As T **248**. but inscr. "1975". Multicoloured.
1218. 60 c. black and purple .. 2·00 1·10
DESIGN: 60 c. French poodle.

1975. Birth Cent. of Musicians.
1219. **319.** 60 c. brown & purple 55 30
1220. – 1 f. 20 black & purple 1·00 80
DESIGN: 1 f. 20, Johann Strauss (the younger).

320. Circus Clown.

322. Andre Ampere with Electrical Meter.

321. Monaco Florin Coin, 1640.

1975. 2nd International Circus Festival.
1221. **320.** 80 c. multicoloured .. 80 40

1975. Monaco Numismatics.
1222 **321** 60 c. brown and blue 50 30
See also Nos. 1275, 1320 and 1448.

1975. Birth Bicentenary of Andre Ampere (physicist).
1223 **322** 85 c. indigo and blue 60 35

323. "Lamentations for the Dead Christ".

1975. 500th Birth Anniv. of Michelangelo.
1224. **323.** 1 f. 40 olive and black 80 60

1975. Monte Carlo Flower Show (1976). As T **271**. Multicoloured.
1225. 60 c. Bouquet of wild flowers 90 35
1226. 80 c. Ikebana flower arrangement .. .. 1·00 40

1975. Precancelled. Surch.
1227. 42 c. on 26 c. violet, blue and black (No. 949a) 1·40 60
1228. 48 c. on 30 c. red, blue, lilac & blk. (No. 949b) 2·00 80
1229. 70 c. on 45 c. blue, violet, turq. & blk. (No. 950a) 3·50 1·25
1230. 1 f. 35 on 90 c. green, blue and black (951a) .. 4·50 2·00

HAVE YOU READ THE NOTES AT THE BEGINNING OF THIS CATALOGUE?
These often provide answers to the enquiries we receive.

325. Prince Pierre de Monaco.

1976. 25th Anniv of Literary Council of Monaco.
1231 **325** 10 c. black 10 10
1232 – 20 c. blue and red .. 20 10
1233 – 25 c. blue and red .. 20 10
1234 – 30 c. brown 20 15
1235 – 50 c. blue, red & pur 30 20
1236 – 60 c. brn, grn & lt brn 40 25
1237 – 80 c. purple and blue 65 40
1238 – 1 f. 20 vio, bl & mve 1·10 90
COUNCIL MEMBERS—HORIZ. 20 c. A. Maurois and Colette. 25 c. Jean and Jerome Tharaud. 30 c. E. Henriot, M. Pagnol and G. Duhamel. 50 c. Ph. Heriat, J. Supervielle and L. Pierard. 60 c. R. Dorgeles, M. Achard and G. Bauer. 80 c. F. Hellens, A. Billy and Mgr. Grente. 1 f. 20, J. Giono, L. Pasteur Vallery-Radot and M. Garcon.

326. Dachshunds.

1976. Int. Dog Show, Monte Carlo.
1239. **326.** 60 c. multicoloured .. 2·50 1·50

327. Bridge Table and Monte Carlo Coast.

1976. 5th Bridge Olympiad, Monte Carlo.
1240. **327.** 60 c. brn., grn. & red 55 30

328. Alexander Graham Bell and Early Telephone.

1976. Telephone Centenary.
1241. **328.** 80 c. brown, light brown and grey 50 30

329. Federation Emblem on on Globe.

1976. 50th Anniv of International Philatelic Federation.
1242 **329** 1 f. 20 red, blue & grn 80 60

330. U.S.A. 2 c. Stamp, 1926.

1976. Bicent. of American Revolution.
1243. **330.** 1 f. 70 black & purple 1·10 80

331. "The Fritillaries" (Van Gogh).

1976. Monte Carlo Flower Show.
1244. **331.** 3 f. multicoloured .. 4·75 3·00

332. Diving.

333. Decorative Plate.

1976. Olympic Games, Montreal.
1245. **332.** 60 c. brown and blue 25 20
1246. – 80 c. blue, brn. & grn. 40 30
1247. – 85 c. blue, grn. & brn. 50 40
1248. – 1 f. 20 brn., grn. & blue 80 60
1249. – 1 f. 70 brn., blue & grn. 1·00 1·00
DESIGNS—VERT. 80 c. Gymnastics. 85 c. Hammer-throwing. HORIZ. 1 f. 20, Rowing. 1 f. 70, Boxing.

1976. Europa. Monegasque Ceramics. Mult.
1251. 80 c. Type **333** 80 60
1252. 1 f. 20 Grape-harvester (statuette) .. .. 1·10 80

334. Palace Clock Tower.

335. "St. Louise de Marillac" (altar painting).

1976. Precancelled.
1254. **334.** 50 c. red 60 30
1255. 52 c. orange 30 15
1256. 54 c. green 40 20
1257. 60 c. green 60 40
1258. 62 c. mauve 40 20
1259. 68 c. yellow 60 30
1260. 90 c. violet 90 65
1261. 95 c. red 65 35
1262. 1 f. 05 brown .. 60 35
1263. 1 f. 60 blue .. .. 1·50 90
1264. 1 f. 70 turquoise .. 1·50 60
1265. 1 f. 85 brown .. 1·25 80

1976. Monaco Red Cross.
1270. **335.** 4 f. blk., pur. and grn. 2·25 1·40

1976. Paintings. "Princes and Princesses of Monaco". As T **213**.
1271. 2 f. purple .. .. 1·10 80
1272. 4 f. multicoloured .. 2·25 1·40
DESIGNS: 2 f. "Prince Honore IV". 4 f. "Princess Louise d'Aumont-Mazarin".

336. St. Vincent-de-Paul.

337. Marie de Rabutin Chantal.

1976. Centenary of St. Vincent-de-Paul Conference, Monaco.
1273 **336** 60 c. black, brown & bl 30 20

1976. 350th Birth Anniv. of Marquise de Sevigne (writer).
1274. **337.** 80 c. blk., violet & red 40 25

338. Monaco 2 g. "Honore II" Coin, 1640.

1976. Monaco Numismatics.
1275. **338.** 80 c. blue and green 55 30

339. Admiral R. E. Boyd with Fokker Trimotor Aircraft and Roald Amundsen with "Norge" Airship.

1976. 50th Anniv of First Flights over North Pole.
1276 **339** 85 c. black, blue & grn 1·00 65

340. Gulliver and Lilliputians.

341. Girl's Head and Christmas Decorations.

1976. 250th Anniv. of Jonathan Swift's "Gulliver's Travels".
1277. **340.** 1 f. 20 multicoloured 60 45

1976. Christmas.
1278 **341** 60 c. multicoloured .. 40 20
1279 1 f. 20 grn, orge & pur 65 40

342. "Drug" Dagger piercing Man and Woman.

343. Circus Clown.

1976. Campaign against Drug Abuse.
1280 **342** 80 c. bl, orge & bronze 50 30
1281 1 f. 20 lilac, pur & brn 75 40

1976. Monte Carlo Flower Show (1977). As T **271**. Mult.
1282. 80 c. Flower arrangement 80 40
1283. 1 f. Bouquet of flowers .. 1·40 65

1976. 3rd International Circus Festival, Monte Carlo.
1284. **343.** 1 f. multicoloured .. 1·00 55

344. Schooner "Hirondelle".

1977. 75th Anniv of Publication of "Career of a Navigator" by Prince Albert I (1st issue). Illustrations by L. Tinayre.
1285. **344.** 10 c. brn., blue & turq. 10 10
1286. – 20 c. blk., brn. & lake 10 10
1287. – 30 c. grn., blue & orge. 15 15
1288. – 80 c. blk., blue & red 35 25
1289. – 1 f. black and brown 55 30
1290. – 1 f. 25 olive, grn. & vio. 65 40
1291. – 1 f. 40 brn., olive & grn. 1·00 80
1292. – 1 f. 90 blue, pale blue and red .. .. 1·40 1·25
1293. – 2 f. 50 brn., blue and turquoise .. .. 2·25 2·00
DESIGNS—VERT. 20 c. Prince Albert I. 1 f. Helmsman. 1 f. 90, Bringing in the trawl. HORIZ. 30 c. Crew-members. 80 c. "Hirondelle" in a gale. 1 f. 25, Securing the lifeboat. 1 f. 40, Shrimp fishing. 2 f. 50, Capture of a moon-fish.
See also Nos. 1305/13.

345. Pyrenean Sheep and Mountain Dogs.

1977. International Dog Show, Monte Carlo.

1294. **345.** 80 c. multicoloured .. 2·25 1·10

346. " Maternity " (M. Cassatt).

1977. World Association of the " Friends of Children ".

1295. **346.** 80 c. deep brown, brown and black 55 35

347. Archers.

1977. 10th International Archery Championships.

1296. **347.** 1 f. 10 blk., brn. & bl. 60 40

348. Charles Lindbergh and " Spirit of St. Louis ".

1977. 50th Anniv. of Lindbergh's Transatlantic Flight.

1297. **348.** 1 f. 90 light blue, blue and brown .. 1·60 1·00

349. " Harbour, Deauville ".

1977. Birth Cent. of Raoul Dufy (painter).

1298. **349.** 2 f. multicoloured .. 2·25 2·00

350. " Portrait of a Young Girl ".

351. " L'Oreillon " Tower.

1977. 400th Birth Anniv of Peter Paul Rubens (painter).

1299 **350** 80 c. orge, brn & blk 40 30

1300 – 1 f. red 65 35

1301 – 1 f. 40 orange and red 1·40 90

DESIGNS: 1 f. "Duke of Buckingham". 1 f. 40, "Portrait of a Child".

1977. Europa. Monaco Views.

1302. **351.** 1 f. brown and blue.. 90 30

1303. – 1 f. 40 blue, brown and bistre .. .. 1·40 65

DESIGN: 1 f. 40, St. Michael's Church, Menton.

1977. 75th Anniv of Publication of "Career of a Navigator" by Prince Albert I (2nd issue). Illustrations by L. Tinayre. As T **344**.

1305. 10 c. black and blue .. 10 10

1306. 20 c. blue 10 10

1307. 30 c. blue, light blue and green 20 20

1308. 80 c. brn., blk. and grn. 30 30

1309. 1 f. grey and green .. 50 30

1310. 1 f. 25 blk., brn. and lilac 60 40

1311. 1 f. 40 purple, blue & brn. 90 60

1312. 1 f. 90 black, blue and light blue .. .. 1·50 1·25

1313. 3 f. blue, brown & green 2·25 1·60

DESIGNS—HORIZ. 10 c. "Princess Alice" (steam yacht) at Kiel. 20 c. Ship's laboratory. 30 c. "Princess Alice" in ice floes. 1 f. Polar scene. 1 f. 25, Bridge of "Princess Alice" during snowstorm. 1 f. 40, Arctic camp. 1 f. 90, Ship's steam launch in floating ice. 3 f. "Princess Alice" passing iceberg. VERT. 80 c. Crewmen in Arctic dress.

352. Santa Claus and Sledge.

353. Face, Poppy and Syringe.

1977. Christmas.

1314. **352.** 80 c. red, green & blue 35 25

1315. 1 f. 40 multicoloured 65 35

1977. Monte Carlo Flower Show. As T **271**. Multicoloured.

1316. 80 c. Snapdragons and campanula 80 40

1317. 1 f. Ikebana .. .. 1·00 65

1977. Campaign Against Drug Abuse.

1318 **353** 1 f. black, red & violet 55 30

354. Clown and Flags.

1977. 4th International Festival of Circus, Monaco.

1319. **354.** 1 f. multicoloured .. 1·00 55

355. Gold Coin of Honore II.

1977. Monaco Numismatics.

1320. **355.** 80 c. brown and red 50 35

356. Mediterranean divided by Industry.

1977. Protection of the Mediterranean Environment.

1321. **356.** 1 f. blk., grn. & blue 60 35

357. Dr. Guglielminetti and Road Tarrers.

1977. 75th Anniv. of First Experiments at Road Tarring in Monaco.

1322. **357.** 1 f. 10 black, bistre and brown 50 35

358. F.M.L.T. Badge and Monte Carlo.

1977. 50th Anniv. of Monaco Lawn Tennis Federation.

1323. **358.** 1 f. bl., red & brn. .. 60 30

359. Wimbledon and First Championships.

1977. Centenary of Wimbledon Lawn Tennis Championships.

1324. **359.** 1 f. 40 grey, green & brown .. .. 1·00 55

1977. Paintings. " Princes and Princesses of Monaco ". As T **213**. Multicoloured.

1325. 6 f. " Prince Honore V " 3·00 1·60

360. St. Jean Bosco.

1977. Monaco Red Cross. Monegasque Art.

1326. **360.** 4 f. grn., brn. and blue 2·00 1·10

1978. Precancelled. Surch.

1327. **334.** 58 c. on 54 c. green.. 60 30

1328. 73 c. on 68 c. yellow.. 70 40

1329. 1 f. 15 on 1 f. 05 brn. 1·00 65

1330. 2 f. on 1 f. 85 brown.. 1·75 1·10

362. Aerial Shipwreck from " L'Ile Mysterieuse ".

1978. 150th Birth Anniv. of Jules Verne.

1331. **362.** 5 c. brown, red & olive 10 10

1332. – 25 c. turq., blue & red 10 10

1333. – 30 c. blue, brn. & pale blue 15 10

1334. – 80 c. blk., grn. & orge. 35 20

1335. – 1 f. brn., lake & blue 55 30

1336. – 1 f. 40 bistre, brn. and green 80 65

1337. – 1 f. 70 brn., pale blue and blue .. .. 1·10 80

1338. – 5 f. 50 violet and blue 3·00 2·25

DESIGNS: 25 c. The abandoned ship from " L'Ile Mysterieuse ". 30 c. The secret of the island from " L'Ile Mysterieuse ". 80 c. " Robur the Conqueror ". 1 f. " Master Zacharius ". 1 f. 40, " The Castle in the Carpathians ". 1 f. 70, " The Children of Captain Grant ". 5 f. 50, Jules Verne and allegories.

363. Aerial View of Congress Centre.

1978. Inauguration of Monaco Congress Centre.

1339. **363.** 1 f. brn., blue & grn. 40 30

1340. – 1 f. 40 blue, brn. & grn. 65 40

DESIGN: 1 f. 40, View of Congress Centre from sea.

364. Footballers and Globe.

1978. World Cup Football Championship, Argentina.

1341. **364.** 1 f. blue, slate & grn. 65 55

365. Antonio Vivaldi.

366. "Ramoge" (research vessel) and Grimaldi Palace.

1978. 300th Birth Anniv. of Antonio Vivaldi (composer).

1342. **365.** 1 f. brown and red .. 60 40

1978. Environment Protection. " RAMOGE " Agreement.

1343. **366.** 80 c. multicoloured .. 40 25

1344. – 1 f. red, blue & green 65 40

DESIGN—HORIZ. (48 × 27 mm.) 1 f. Map of coastline between St. Raphael and Genes.

367. Monaco Cathedral.

368. Monaco Congress Centre.

1978. Europa. Monaco Views.

1345. **367.** 1 f. green, brn. & blue 80 45

1346. – 1 f. 40 brn., grn. & blue 1·25 65

DESIGN: 1 f. 40, View of Monaco from the east.

1978. Precancelled.

1348. **368.** 61 c. orange 30 10

1349. 64 c. green 30 10

1350. 68 c. blue 30 10

1351. 78 c. purple 40 20

1352. 83 c. violet 40 20

1353. 88 c. orange 40 20

1354. 1 f. 25 brown .. 70 30

1355. 1 f. 30 red .. 65 40

1356. 1 f. 40 green.. .. 65 40

1357. 2 f. 10 blue .. .. 1·50 75

1358. 2 f. 25 orange .. 1·40 80

1359. 2 f. 35 mauve .. 1·10 80

369. " Cinderella ".

1978. 350th Birth Anniv. of Charles Perrault (writer).

1360. **369.** 5 c. red, olive & violet 10 10

1361. – 25 c. blk., brn. & mve. 10 10

1362. – 30 c. grn., lake & brn. 15 10

1363. – 80 c. multicoloured.. 25 20

1364. – 1 f. red, brn. & olive 40 30

1365. – 1 f. 40 mauve, ultram. and blue 75 65

1366. – 1 f. 70 grn., blue & grey 1·00 65

1367. – 1 f. 90 multicoloured 1·25 90

1368. – 2 f. 50 blue, orge. and green .. .. 1·50 1·10

DESIGNS: 25 c. " Puss in Boots ". 30 c. " The Sleeping Beauty ". 80 c. " Donkey's Skin ". 1 f. " Little Red Riding Hood ". 1 f. 40, " Bluebeard ". 1 f. 70, " Tom Thumb ". 1 f. 90, " Riquet with a Tuft ". 2 f. 50, " The Fairies ".

370. " The Sun-flowers " (Van Gogh).

371. Afghan Hound.

1978. Monte Carlo Flower Show (1979) and 125th Birth Anniv. of Vincent Van Gogh. Multicoloured.

1369. 1 f. Type **370.** .. .. 1·40 65
1370. 1 f. 70 " The Iris " (Van Gogh) .. .. .. 2·00 1·10

1978. International Dog Show, Monte Carlo. Multicoloured.

1371. 1 f. Type **371** .. .. 1·50 1·00
1372. 1 f. 20 Borzoi .. .. 2·50 1·40

372. Girl with Letter.

374. Juggling Seals.

373. Catherine and William Booth.

1978. Christmas.

1373. **372.** 1 f. brn., blue & red 55 40

1978. Centenary of Salvation Army.

1374. **373.** 1 f. 70 multicoloured 1·00 70

1978. 5th International Circus Festival, Monaco.

1375. **374.** 80 c. orge., blk. & blue 40 20
1376. – 1 f. multicoloured .. 65 35
1377. – 1 f. 40 brown, mauve and bistre .. .. 1·00 35
1378. – 1 f. 90 blue, lilac and mauve .. .. 1·40 1·10
1379. – 2 f. 40 multicoloured 2·00 1·50

DESIGNS—HORIZ. 1 f. 40, Horseback acrobatics. 1 f. 90, Musical monkeys. 2 f. 40, Trapeze. VERT. 1 f. Lion tamer.

1978. Paintings. " Princes and Princesses of Monaco ". As T **213.** Multicoloured.

1380. 2 f. " Prince Florestan I " (G. Dauphin) .. .. 1·10 90
1381. 4 f. " Princess Caroline Gilbert de la Metz " (Marie Verroust) .. 2·25 1·90

377. " Jongleur de Notre-Dame " (Massenet).

1979. Centenary of "Salle Garnier" (Opera House) (1st issue).

1384. **377.** 1 f. blue, orge. & mve. 40 20
1385. – 1 f. 20 vio., blk. & turq. 65 30
1386. – 1 f. 50 mar., grn. & turq. 80 65
1387. – 1 f. 70 multicoloured 1·10 90
1388. – 2 f. 10 turq. & violet 1·50 1·10
1389. – 3 f. multicoloured .. 2·00 1·40

DESIGNS—HORIZ. 1 f. 20, "Hans the Flute Player" (L. Ganne). 1 f. 50, "Don Quixote"(J. Massenet). 2 f. 10, "The Child and the Sorcerer" (M. Ravel). 3 f. Charles Garnier (architect) and south facade of Opera House. VERT. 1 f. 70, "L'Aiglon"(A. Honegger and J. Ibert).

See also Nos. 1399/1404.

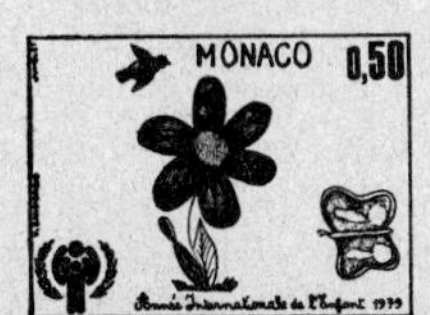

378. Flower, Bird and Butterfly.

1979. International Year of the Child. Children's Paintings.

1390. **378.** 50 c. pink, grn. & blk. 20 15
1391. – 1 f. slate, grn. & orge. 45 25
1392. – 1 f. 20 slate, orge. & mve. 65 30
1393. – 1 f. 50 yell., brn. & blue 90 55
1394. – 1 f. 70 multicoloured 1·10 65

DESIGNS: 1 f. Horse and Child. 1 f. 20, " The Gift of Love ". 1 f. 50, " Peace in the World ". 1 f. 70, " Down with Pollution ".

379. Armed Foot Messenger.

1979. Europa.

1395. **379.** 1 f. 20 brn., grn. & blue 65 30
1396. – 1 f. 50 brn., turq. & blue 80 40
1397. – 1 f. 70 brn., grn. & blue 95 70

DESIGNS: 1 f. 50, 18th cent. felucca. 1 f. 70, Arrival of 1st train at Monaco.

380. " Instrumental Music " (G. Boulanger) (detail of Opera House interior).

1979. Centenary of "Salle Garnier" (Opera House) (2nd issue).

1399. – 1 f. brn., orge. & turq. 55 20
1400. – 1 f. 20 multicoloured 65 40
1401. – 1 f. 50 multicoloured 1·00 65
1402. – 1 f. 70 blue, brn. & red 1·40 1·00
1403. – 2 f. 10 red, violet & blk. 1·60 1·10
1404. **380.** 3 f. green, brown and yellow-green .. 2·10 1·50

DESIGNS: As Type **377.** HORIZ. 1 f. "Les Biches" (F. Poulenc). 1 f. 20, "The Sailors" (G. Auric). 1 f. 70, "Gaiete Parisienne" (J. Offenbach). VERT. 1 f. 50, "La Spectre de la Rose" (C. M. Weber) (after poster by Jean Cocteau). 2 f. 10, "Salome" (R. Strauss).

1979. Paintings. " Princes and Princesses of Monaco". As T **213.** Multicoloured.

1405. 3 f. " Prince Charles III " (B. Biard) .. .. 1·40 1·00
1406. 4 f. " Antoinette de Merode " .. .. 1·75 1·40

381. St. Pierre Claver.

382. " Princess Grace " Orchid.

1979. Monaco Red Cross.

1407. **381.** 5 f. multicoloured .. 2·25 1·75

1979. Monte Carlo Flora 1980.

1408. **382.** 1 f. multicoloured .. 1·40 80

383. "Princess Grace" Rose.

384. Clown balancing on Ball.

1979. Monte Carlo Flower Show.

1409 **383** 1 f. 20 multicoloured 1·60 90

1979. 6th International Circus Festival.

1410. **384.** 1 f. 20 multicoloured 1·00 65

385. Sir Rowland Hill and Penny Black.

386. Albert Einstein.

1979. Death Cent. of Sir Rowland Hill.

1411. **385.** 1 f. 70 brn., blue & blk. 65 45

1979. Birth Centenary of Albert Einstein (physicist).

1412. **386.** 1 f. 70 brn., grey & red 60 50

387. St. Patrick's Cathedral.

388. Nativity Scene.

1979. Centenary of St. Patrick's Cathedral, New York.

1413. **387.** 2 f. 10 blk., blue & brn. 1·00 60

1979. Christmas.

1414. **388.** 1 f. 20 blue, orge. & mve. 40 25

389. Early Racing Cars.

1979. 50th Anniv. of Grand Prix Motor Racing.

1415. **389.** 1 f. multicoloured .. 50 30

390. Arms of Charles V and Monaco.

1979. 450th Anniv. of Visit of Emperor Charles V.

1416. **390.** 1 f. 50 brn., blue & blk. 60 40

391. Setter and Pointer.

1979. International Dog Show, Monte Carlo.

1417. **391.** 1 f. 20 multicoloured 20 10

392. Spring.

1980. Precancels. The Seasons.

1418. **392.** 76 c. brown and green 35 20
1419. 88 c. olive, emer. & grn. 35 20
1420. – 99 c. green and brown 45 30
1421. – 1 f. 14 grn., emer. & brn. 45 30
1422. – 1 f. 60 brown, grey & deep brown .. 90 65
1423. – 1 f. 84 lake, grey & brn. 90 55
1424. – 2 f. 65 brn., lt. bl. & blue 1·40 90
1425. – 3 f. 05, brn., bl. & slate 1·50 1·00

DESIGNS: 99 c., 1 f. 14, Summer. 1 f. 60, 1 f. 84, Autumn. 2 f. 65, 3 f. 05, Winter.

394. Paul P. Harris (founder) and View of Chicago.

1980. 75th Anniv. of Rotary International.

1434. **394.** 1 f. 80 ol., bl. & turquoise 90 65

395. Gymnastics.

1980. Olympic Games, Moscow and Lake Placid.

1435 **395** 1 f. 10 bl, brn & grey 30 20
1436 – 1 f. 30 red, brown & bl 40 30
1437 – 1 f. 60 red, blue & brn 55 40
1438 – 1 f. 80 brn, bis & grn 65 40
1439 – 2 f. 30 grey, vio & mve 1·00 65
1440 – 4 f. green, blue & brn 1·40 1·25

DESIGNS: 1 f. 30, Handball. 1 f. 60, Pistol shooting. 1 f. 80, Volleyball. 2 f. 30, Ice hockey. 4 f. Skiing.

396. Colette (novelist).

397. " La Source ".

1980. Europa. Each black, green and red.

1441 1 f. 30 Type **396** 35 25
1442 1 f. 80 Marcel Pagnol (writer) 45 30

1980. Birth Bicent. of Jean Ingres (artist).

1444. **397.** 4 f. multicoloured .. 4·00 2·25

398. Montaigne.

399. Guillaume Apollinaire (after G. Pieret).

1980. 400th Anniv. of Publication of Montaigne's "Essays".

1445. **398.** 1 f. 30 blk., red & blue 50 25

1980. Birth Centenary of Guillaume Apollinaire (poet).

1446. **399.** 1 f. 10 brown .. 40 30

400. Congress Centre.

1980. Kiwanis International European Convention.

1447. **400.** 1 f. 30 blk., blue & red 50 25

401. Honore II Silver Ecu, 1649.

1980. Numismatics.

1448. **401.** 1 f. 50 black and blue 65 40

402. Lhassa Apso and Shih Tzu.

1980. International Dog Show, Monte Carlo.
1449. **402.** 1 f. 30 multicoloured 2·00 1·25

403. " The Princess and the Pea ".

1980. 175th Birth Anniv. of Hans Christian Andersen.
1450. **403.** 70 c. sepia, red & brn. 25 20
1451. – 1 f. 30 bl., turq. & red 35 25
1452. – 1 f. 50 blk., bl. & turq. 65 55
1453. – 1 f. 60 red, blk. & brn. 80 70
1454. – 1 f. 80 yell., brn. & turq. 1·00 75
1455. – 2 f. 30 brn., pur. & vio. 1·40 90
DESIGNS: 1 f. 30, " The Little Mermaid ". 1 f. 50, " The Chimneysweep and Shepherdess ". 1 f. 60, " The Brave Little Lead Soldier ". 1 f. 80, " The Little Match Girl ". 2 f. 30, " The Nightingale ".

404. " The Road " (M. Vlaminck).

1980. 75th Anniv. of 1905 Autumn Art Exhibition. Multicoloured.
1456. 2 f. Type **404** 1·50 65
1457. 3 f. " Woman at Balustrade " (Van Dongen) 2·50 1·25
1458. 4 f. " The Reader " (Henri Matisse) 3·00 2·00
1459. 5 f. " Three Figures in a Meadow " (A. Derain) 4·25 2·40

1980. Paintings. " Princes and Princesses of Monaco ". As T **213.** Multicoloured.
1460. 4 f. " Prince Albert I " (L. Bonnat) 1·60 1·25
1461. 4 f. " Princess Marie Alice Heine " (L. Maeterlinck) 1·60 1·25

405. " Sunbirds ".

1980. Monaco Red Cross.
1462. **405.** 6 f. red, bistre & brn. 2·75 2·00

406. " MONACO " balanced on Tightrope.

1980. Seventh International Circus Festival, Monaco.
1463. **406.** 1 f. 30 red, turq. & blue 1·00 55

407. Children and Nativity.

1980. Christmas.
1464. **407.** 1 f. 10 blue, carmine and red 35 25
1465. 2 f. 30 violet, orange and pink 85 55

1980. Monte Carlo Flower Show, 1981. As T **383.** Multicoloured.
1466. 1 f. 30 " Princess Stephanie " Rose 80 40
1467. 1 f. 80 Ikebana 1·50 80

408. " Alcyonium ".

409. Fish with Hand for Tail.

1980. Marine Fauna. Multicoloured.
1468. 5 c. " Spirographis spallanzanii " 10 10
1469. 10 c. " Anemonia sulcata " 10 10
1470. 15 c. " Leptopsammia pruvoti " 10 10
1471. 20 c. " Pteroides " 10 10
1472. 30 c. " Paramuricea clavata " (horiz.) 30 10
1473. 40 c. Type **408** 30 10
1474. 50 c. " Corallium rubrum " 40 20
1475. 60 c. " Calliactis parasitica " (horiz.) 50 20
1476. 70 c. " Cerianthus membranaceus " (horiz.) 60 30
1477. 1 f. " Actinia equina " (horiz.) 80 30
1478. 2 f. " Protula " (horiz.) 2·00 50

1981. " Respect the Sea ".
1479. **409.** 1 f. 20 multicoloured 60 40

410. Prince Rainier and Princess Grace.

1981. Royal Silver Wedding.
1480. **410.** 1 f. 20 black and green 1·00 40
1481. – 1 f. 40 black and red 1·10 65
1482. – 1 f. 70 black and green 1·50 80
1483. – 1 f. 80 black and brn. 1·75 1·10
1484. – 2 f. black and blue 2·50 1·50

411. Mozart (after Lorenz Vogel).

412. Palm Cross.

1981. 225th Birth Anniv. of Wolfgang Amadeus Mozart (composer).
1485. **411.** 2 f. brn., dp. brn. & bl. 1·40 60
1486. – 2 f. 50 bl., brn. & dp. brn. 1·50 1·00
1487. – 3 f. 50 dp. brn., bl. & brn. 2·25 1·75
DESIGNS—HORIZ. 2 f. 50, "Mozart at 7 with his Father and Sister" (engraving by Delafoose after drawing by Carmontelle). 3 f. 50, "Mozart directing Requiem two Days before his Death" (painting by Baude).

1981. Europa. Multicoloured.
1488. **412.** 1 f. 40 grn., brn. & red 35 25
1489. – 2 f. multicoloured 60 40
DESIGN. 2 f. Children carrying palm crosses.

413. Paris Football Stadium, Cup and Footballer.

1981. 25th Anniv. of European Football Cup.
1491. **413.** 2 f. black and blue 90 55

414. I.Y.D.P. Emblem and Girl in Wheelchair.

1981. International Year of Disabled Persons.
1492. **414.** 1 f. 40 blue and green 55 40

415. Palace flying Old Flag, National Flag, and Monte Carlo.

1981. Centenary of National Flag.
1493 **415** 2 f. red, blue & brown 85 55

416. Oceanographic Institute, Paris and Oceanographic Museum, Monaco.

1981. 75th Anniv. of Oceanographic Institute.
1494. **416.** 1 f. 20 bl., blk. & brn. 50 40

417. Bureau Building and "Faddey Bellingshausen" (hydrographic research ship).

1981. 50th Anniv. of International Hydrographic Bureau.
1495. **417.** 2 f. 50 sepia, brown & light brown 1·00 80

418. Rough Collies and Shetland Sheepdogs.

1981. International Dog Show, Monte Carlo.
1496. **418.** 1 f. 40 multicoloured 2·00 1·50

419. Rainier III and Prince Albert.

421. Arctic Scene and Map.

1981. (a) 23 × 28 mm.

1497	419	1 f. 40 green (postage)	50	10
1498		1 f. 60 red	60	10
1499		1 f. 60 green	50	10
1500		1 f. 70 green	50	10
1501		1 f. 80 red	60	10
1502		1 f. 80 green	55	10
1503		1 f. 90 green	90	40
1504		2 f. red	75	10
1505		2 f. green	75	10
1506		2 f. 10 red	90	10
1507		2 f. 20 red	60	10
1508		2 f. 30 blue	1·50	80
1509		2 f. 50 brown	1·00	30
1510		2 f. 60 blue	1·60	65
1511		2 f. 80 blue	1·90	75
1512		3 f. blue	2·00	65
1513		3 f. 20 blue	1·60	75
1514		3 f. 40 blue	2·00	90
1515		3 f. 60 blue	1·75	40
1516		4 f. brown	1·60	40
1517		5 f. 50 black	2·50	80
1518		10 f. purple	2·50	1·10
1519		15 f. green	6·00	1·40
1520		20 f. blue	5·50	2·00

(b) 36 × 27 mm.

1521	–	5 f. violet (air)	1·75	60
1522	–	10 f. red	4·00	1·25
1523	–	15 f. green	5·50	1·75
1524	–	20 f. blue	7·00	2·50
1525	–	30 f. brown	6·50	3·50

DESIGN: Nos. 1521/5, Double portrait and monograms.

1981. First International Congress on Discovery and History of Northern Polar Regions, Rome.
1530. **421.** 1 f. 50 multicoloured 1·00 55

1981. Paintings. "Princes and Princesses of Monaco". Vert. designs as T **213.** Mult.
1531. 3 f. "Prince Louis II" (P.-A. de Laszlo) 1·25 90
1532. 5 f. "Princess Charlotte" (P.-A. de Laszlo) 2·00 1·75

422. Hercules fighting the Nemean Lion.

1981. Monaco Red Cross. The Twelve Labours of Hercules (1st series).
1533. **422.** 2 f. 50 + 50 c. green, brown and red 1·00 90
1534. – 3 f. 50 + 50 c. blue, green and red 1·40 1·10
DESIGN: 3 f. 50, Slaying the Hydra of Lerna.
See also Nos. 1584/5, 1631/2, 1699/1700, 1761/2 and 1794/5.

423. Ettore Bugatti (racing car designer) (Cent.).

424. Eglantines and Morning Glory.

1981. Birth Anniversaries.
1535 **423** 1 f. indigo, blue & red 60 30
1536 – 2 f. black, blue & brn 70 55
1537 – 2 f. 50 brown, black and red 1·25 65
1538 – 4 f. multicoloured 2·50 1·75
1539 – 4 f. multicoloured 2·50 1·75
DESIGNS: No. 1536, George Bernard Shaw (dramatist, 125th anniv.). 1537, Fernand Leger (painter, centenary). (LARGER: 37 × 48 mm.). 1538, Pablo Picasso (self-portrait) (centenary). 1539, Rembrandt (self-portrait) (375th anniv.).

1981. Monte Carlo Flower Show (1982). Mult.
1540. 1 f. 40 type **424** 90 40
1541. 2 f. "Ikebana" (painting by Ikenobo) 1·40 80

425. "Catherine Deneuve".

426. Tiger, Clown, Acrobat and Elephants.

1981. 1st International Rose Show, Monte Carlo.
1542. **425.** 1 f. 80 multicoloured 1·40 75

1981. 8th International Circus Festival, Monaco.
1543. **426.** 1 f. 40 violet, mauve & black 1·00 65

427. Praying Children and Nativity.

1981. Christmas.
1544. **427.** 1 f. 20 bl., mve. & brn. 40 25

428. "Lancia-Stratos" Rally Car.

1981. 50th Monte Carlo Rally (1982).
1545. **428.** 1 f. blue, red & turquoise 65 40

430. "Hoya bella".

431. Spring.

1981. Plants in Exotic Garden. Multicoloured.

1547 1 f. 40 Type **430** .. .. 2·00 70
1548 1 f. 60 "Bolivicereus samaipatanus" .. 1·75 70
1549 1 f. 80 "Trichocereus grandiflorus" (horiz) .. 1·75 75
1550 2 f. "Argyroderma roseum" .. .. 1·00 30
1551 2 f. 30 "Euphorbia milii" 1·75 70
1552 2 f. 60 "Echinocereus fitchii" (horiz) .. 1·75 70
1553 2 f. 90 "Rebutia heliosa" (horiz) .. .. 1·90 1·10
1554 4 f. 10 "Echinopsis multiplex cristata" (horiz) .. 2·75 1·60

1982. Precancels. The Seasons of the Peach Tree.

1555. **431.** 97 c. mauve & green 40 25
1556. – 1 f. 25 green, orange and mauve .. 50 30
1557. – 2 f. 03 brown 90 65
1558. – 3 f. 36 brown and blue .. .. 1·25 1·00

DESIGNS: 1 f. 25, Summer. 2 f. 03, Autumn 3 f. 36, Winter.

432. Nutcracker.

433. Capture of Monaco Fortress, 1297.

1982. Birds from Mercantour National Park.

1559. **432.** 60 c. blk., brn. & grn. 50 40
1560. – 70 c. black and mauve 90 50
1561. – 80 c. red, black & orange .. .. 1·00 50
1562. – 90 c. black, red and blue .. .. 1·10 70
1563. – 1 f. 40 brn., blk. & red .. .. 1·75 1·40
1564. – 1 f. 60 brown, black & blue .. .. 2·50 1·50

DESIGNS—VERT. 70 c. Black grouse. 80 c. Rock partridge. 1 f. 60, Golden eagle. HORIZ. 90 c. Wallcreeper. 1 f. 40, Rock ptarmigan.

1982. Europa.

1565. **433.** 1 f. 60 blue, brown and red 50 30
1566. – 2 f. 30 blue, brown and red 75 45

DESIGN: 2 f. 30, Signing the Treaty of Peronne, 1641.

434. Old Quarter.

1982. Fontvieille.

1568. **434.** 1 f. 40 bl., brn. & grn. 50 20
1569. – 1 f. 60 light brown, brown and red .. 65 20
1570. – 2 f. 30 purple .. 1·00 55

DESIGNS: 1 f. 60, Land reclamation. 2 f. 30, Urban development.

435. Stadium.

1982. Fontvieille Sports Stadium (1st series).

1571. **435.** 2 f. 30 green, brown & blue .. .. 1·00 65

See also No. 1616.

436. Arms of Paris.

1982. "Philexfrance" International Stamp Exhibition, Paris.

1572. **436.** 1 f. 40 red, grey and deep red 55 40

437. Old English Sheepdog.

1982. International Dog Show, Monte Carlo. Multicoloured.

1573. 60 c. Type **437** .. .. 1·25 65
1574. 1 f. Briard .. .. 1·75 1·00

438. Monaco Cathedral and Arms.

1982. Creation of Archbishopric of Monaco (1981).

1575. **438.** 1 f. 60 blk., bl. & red 65 40

439. St. Francis of Assisi.

440. Dr. Robert Koch.

1982. 800th Birth Anniv. of St. Francis of Assisi.

1576. **439.** 1 f. 40 grey and light grey 60 30

1982. Cent. of Discovery of Tubercle Bacillus.

1577. **440.** 1 f. 40 purple & lilac 80 40

441. Lord Baden-Powell.

443. St. Hubert (18th-century medallion).

1982. 125th Birth Anniv. of Lord Baden-Powell (founder of Boy Scout Movement).

1578. **441.** 1 f. 60 brn. and black 90 55

1982. 29th Meeting of International Hunting Council, Monte Carlo.

1580 **443** 1 f. 60 multicoloured 65 55

444. Books, Reader and Globe.

1982. International Bibliophile Association General Assembly, Monte Carlo.

1581 **444** 1 f. 60 blue, pur & red 65 40

445. "Casino, 1870".

1982. Monaco in the "Belle Epoque" (1st series). Paintings by Hubert Clerissi. Multicoloured.

1582. 3 f. Type **445** .. .. 1·40 90
1583. 5 f. "Porte d'Honneur, Royal Palace, 1893" .. 2·50 1·40

See also Nos. 1629/30, 1701/2, 1763/4, 1801/2, 1851/2, 1889/90 and 1965/6.

1982. Monaco Red Cross. The Twelve Labours of Hercules (2nd series). As T **422**.

1584. 2 f. 50+50 c. green, red and bright red .. 1·00 1·00
1585. 3 f. 50+50 c. brown, blue and red .. .. 1·40 1·40

DESIGNS: 2 f. 50, Capturing the Erymanthine Boar. 3 f. 50, Shooting the Stymphalian Birds.

446. Nicolo Paganini (violinist and composer, bicent).

447. Vase of Flowers.

1982. Birth Anniversaries.

1586 **446** 1 f. 60 brown & purple 75 55
1587 – 1 f. 80 red, mve & brn 90 55
1588 – 2 f. 60 green and red 1·25 75
1589 – 4 f. multicoloured .. 3·00 1·40
1590 – 4 f. multicoloured .. 3·00 1·40

DESIGNS—VERT. No. 1587, Anna Pavlova (ballerina, centenary). 1588, Igor Stravinsky (composer, centenary). HORIZ. (47 × 36 mm.) 1589, "In a Boat" (Edouard Manet, 150th anniv.). 1590, "The Black Fish" (Georges Braque, centenary).

1982. Monte Carlo Flower Show (1983). Multicoloured.

1591. 1 f. 60 Type **447** .. .. 1·00 40
1592. 2 f. 60 Ikebana arrangement .. .. .. 2·00 65

448. Bowl of Flowers.

449. The Three Kings.

1982.

1593. **448.** 1 f. 60 multicoloured 1·00 40

1982. Christmas.

1594. **449.** 1 f. 60 grn., bl. & orge. 55 30
1595. – 1 f. 80 grn., bl. & orge. 65 30
1596. – 2 f. 60 grn., bl. & orge. 1·00 55

DESIGNS: 1 f. 80, The Holy Family. 2 f. 60, Shepherds and angels.

450. Prince Albert I and Polar Scene.

1982. Cent. of First International Polar Year.

1598. **450.** 1 f. 60 brn., grn. & bl. 1·10 75

451. Viking Longships off Greenland.

1982. Millenary of Discovery of Greenland by Erik the Red.

1599. **451.** 1 f. 60 bl., brn. & blk. 1·40 65

452. Julius Caesar in the Port of Monaco ("Aeneid", Book VI).

1982. 2000th Death Anniv. of Virgil (poet).

1600. **452.** 1 f. 80 deep blue, blue and brown .. 1·10 65

453. Spring.

454. Tourism.

1983. Precancels. The Seasons of the Apple Tree.

1601. **453.** 1 f. 05 purple, green and yellow .. 35 30
1602. – 1 f. 35 lt. grn., dp. grn. and turquoise 40 40
1603. – 2 f. 19 red, brn. & grey 80 55
1604. – 3 f. 63 dp. yellow and brown .. .. 1·50 1·00

DESIGNS: 1 f. 35 Summer. 2 f. 19 Autumn. 3 f. 63 Winter.

1983. 50th Anniv. of Exotic Garden. Mult.

1605. 1 f. 80 Type **454** 75 65
1606. 2 f. Cactus plants (botanical collections) 1·10 75
1607. 2 f. 30 Cactus plants (international flower shows) .. .. .. 1·40 1·10
1608. 2 f. 60 Observatory grotto (horiz.) .. 1·50 90
1609. 3 f. 30 Museum of Prehistoric Anthropology (horiz.) 2·00 1·50

455. Alaskan Malamute.

457. St. Charles Borromee and Church.

1983. International Dog Show. Monte Carlo.

1610. **455.** 1 f. 80 multicoloured 1·75 1·10

1983. Centenary of St. Charles Church, Monte Carlo.

1612. **457.** 2 f. 60 deep blue, blue and green 90 65

458. Montgolfier Balloon, 1783.

459. Franciscan College.

1983. Europa.

1613. **458.** 1 f. 80 blue, brown & grey 55 30
1614. – 2 f. 60 grey, blue & brown 75 40

DESIGN: 2 f. 60, Space shuttle.

1983. Centenary of Franciscan College, Monte Carlo.
1616. **459.** 2 f. grey, brn. & red 65 40

460. Stadium.

1983. Fontvieille Sports Stadium (2nd series).
1617. **460.** 2 f. grn., blue & brn. 65 40

461. Early and Modern Cars.

1983. Cent. of Petrol-driven Motor Car.
1618. **461.** 2 f. 90 blue, brown & green .. .. 1·40 1·10

462. Blue Whale.

1983. International Commission for the Protection of Whales.
1619. **462.** 3 f. 30 blue, light blue and grey .. .. 2·75 1·75

463. Dish Aerial, Pigeon, W.C.Y. Emblem and Satellite.

1983. World Communications Year.
1620. **463.** 4 f. lilac and mauve 1·25 1·00

464. Smoking Moor.

1983. Nineteenth Century Automata from the Galea Collection. Multicoloured.
1621. 50 c. Type **464** 15 10
1622. 60 c. Clown with diabolo 20 10
1623. 70 c. Smoking monkey .. 20 15
1624. 80 c. Peasant with pig .. 30 15
1625. 90 c. Buffalo Bill smoking 40 15
1626. 1 f. Snake charmer .. 40 15
1627. 1 f. 50 Pianist 65 40
1628. 2 f. Young girl powdering herself .. .. .. 1·00 65

1983. Monaco in the "Belle Epoque" (2nd series). As T **445.** Multicoloured.
1629. 3 f. "The Beach, 1902" .. 1·75 1·10
1630. 5 f. "Cafe de Paris, 1905" 2·50 1·75

1983. Monaco Red Cross. The Twelve Labours of Hercules (3rd series). As T **422.**
1631. 2 f. 50+50 c. brn., bl. & red .. .. .. 1·10 1·00
1632. 3 f. 50+50 c. vio., mauve & red .. .. .. 1·40 1·25
DESIGNS: 2 f. 50 Capturing the Hind of Ceryneia. 3 f. 50 Cleaning the Augean stables.

465. Johannes Brahms (composer).

1983. Birth Anniversaries.
1633. **465.** 3 f. deep brown, brown and green .. 1·10 75
1634. – 3 f. black, brown and red .. .. 1·10 75
1635. – 4 f. multicoloured .. 2·50 1·60
1636. – 4 f. multicoloured .. 2·50 1·60
DESIGNS:—HORIZ. No. 1633, T **465** (150th anniv.). 1634, Giacomo Puccini (composer) and scene from "Madame Butterfly" (125th anniv.). VERT. 37 × 48 mm.) 1635, "Portrait of a Young Man" (Raphael (artist), 500th anniv.). 1636, "Cottin Passage" (Utrillo (artist), centenary).

466. Circus Performers.

467. Bouquet.

1983. 9th International Circus Festival, Monaco.
1637. **466.** 2 f. blue, red & green 1·00 65

1983. Monte Carlo Flower Show (1984). Mult.
1638. 1 f. 60 Type **467** 90 35
1639. 2 f. 60 Arrangement of poppies .. .. 1·40 65

468. Provencale Creche.

469. Nobel Literature Prize Medal.

1983. Christmas.
1640. **468.** 2 f. multicoloured .. 1·00 55

1983. 150th Birth Anniv of Alfred Nobel (inventor of dynamite and founder of Nobel Prizes).
1641 **469** 2 f. black, grey and red 75 55

470. O. F. Ozanam (founder) and Paris Headquarters.

471. "Tazerka" (oil rig).

1983. 150th Anniv. of Society of St. Vincent de Paul.
1642. **470.** 1 f. 80 violet and pur. 65 40

1983. Oil Industry.
1643. **471.** 5 f. blue, brn. & turq. 1·75 1·10

474. Skater and Stadium.

1984. Winter Olympic Games, Sarajevo.
1646. **474.** 2 f. blue, green and turquoise 65 55
1647. – 4 f. blue, vio. & pur. 1·40 75
DESIGN: 4 f. Skater and snowflake.

475. Bridge.

476. Balkan Fritillary.

1984. Europa. 25th Anniv. of European Post and Telecommunications Conference.
1648. **475.** 2 f. blue 65 30
1649. 3 f. green .. .. 1·00 75

1984. Butterflies and Moths in Mercantour National Park. Multicoloured.
1651 1 f. 60 Type **476** 75 40
1652 2 f. "Zygaena vesubiana" 1·00 55
1653 2 f. 80 False mnestra ringlet .. .. 1·40 75
1654 3 f. Small apollo (horiz) .. 1·40 75
1655 3 f. 60 Southern swallow-tail (horiz) .. .. 1·75 1·40

477. Auvergne Pointer.

478. Sanctuary and Statue of Virgin.

1984. International Dog Show, Monte Carlo.
1656. **477.** 1 f. 60 multicoloured 1·40 75

1984. Our Lady of Laghet Sanctuary.
1657. **478.** 2 f. blue, brown and green 65 40

479. Stratospheric Balloon.

480. Concert.

1984. Birth Centenary of Auguste Piccard (physicist).
1658. **479.** 2 f. 80 blk., grn. & bl. 90 55
1659. – 4 f. bl., grn. & turq. 1·40 75
DESIGN. 4 f. Bathyscaphe.

1984. 25th Anniv. of Palace Concerts.
1660. **480.** 3 f. 60 blue & dp. blue .. .. 1·40 75

481. Place de la Visitation.

482. Spring.

1984. Bygone Monaco (1st series). Paintings by Hubert Clerissi.
1661. **481.** 5 c. brown 10 15
1662. – 10 c. red 10 10
1663. – 15 c. violet 10 10
1664. – 20 c. blue 10 10
1665. – 30 c. blue 15 10
1666. – 40 c. green 20 10
1667. – 50 c. red 20 10
1668. – 60 c. blue 10 10
1669. – 70 c. orange 60 10
1670. – 80 c. green 20 10
1671. – 90 c. mauve 25 20
1672. – 1 f. blue 30 15
1673. – 2 f. black 60 25
1674. – 3 f. red .. .. 1·00 40
1675. – 4 f. blue .. .. 1·10 80
1676. – 5 f. green .. .. 1·10 65
1677. – 6 f. green .. .. 1·75 75
DESIGNS: 10 c. Town Hall. 15 c. Rue Basse. 20 c. Place Saint-Nicolas. 30 c. Quai du Commerce. 40 c. Rue des Iris. 50 c. Ships in harbour. 60 c. St. Charles's Church. 70 c. Religious procession. 80 c. Olive tree overlooking harbour. 90 c. Quay-side. 1 f. Palace Square. 2 f. Fishing boats in harbour. 3 f. Bandstand. 4 f. Railway station. 5 f. Mail coach. 6 f. Monte Carlo Opera House.
See also Nos. 2015/27.

1984. Precancels. The Seasons of the Quince.
1678. **482.** 1 f. 14 red and green 30 30
1679. – 1 f. 47 dp. grn. & grn. 40 40
1680. – 2 f. 38 olive, turquoise & green 75 55
1681. – 3 f. 95 green .. .. 1·40 1·00
DESIGNS: 1 f. 47, Summer. 2 f. 38, Autumn. 3 f. 95, Winter.

483. Shepherd.

485. Bowl of Mixed Flowers.

484. Gargantua and Cattle.

1984. Christmas. Crib Figures from Provence. Multicoloured.
1682. 70 c. Type **483** 25 15
1683. 1 f. Blind man 35 20
1684. 1 f. 70 Happy man .. 65 35
1685. 2 f. Spinner 75 40
1686. 2 f. Angel playing trumpet 75 40
1687. 2 f. 40 Garlic seller .. 1·00 50
1688. 3 f. Drummer .. .. 1·40 65
1689. 3 f. 70 Knife grinder .. 1·60 90
1690. 4 f. Elderly couple .. 1·75 1·10

1984. 450th Anniv. of First Edition of "Gargantua" by Francois Rabelais.
1691. **484.** 2 f. black, red and brown 65 40
1692. – 2 f. black, red & bl. 65 40
1693. – 4 f. green .. .. 1·40 1·00
DESIGNS:—As T **484.** No. 1692, Panurge's sheep. 36 × 48 mm. 1693, Francois Rabelais.

1984. Monte Carlo Flower Show (1985). Mult.
1694. 2 f. 10 Type **485** .. 1·00 40
1695. 3 f. Ikebana arrangement 1·60 65

486. Television Lights and Emblem.

1984. 25th International Television Festival, Monte Carlo.
1696. **486.** 2 f. 10 blue, grey and mauve 65 40
1697. – 3 f. grey, blue and red .. .. 1·00 65
DESIGN: 3 f. "Golden Nymph" (Grand Prix).

487. Chemical Equipment.

489. "Woman with Chinese Vase"

1984. Pharmaceutical and Cosmetics Industry.
1698. **487.** 2 f. 40 blue, deep blue and green 75 35

1984. Monaco Red Cross. The Twelve Labours of Hercules (4th series). As T **422.**
1699. 3 f. + 50 c. brown, light brown and red .. 1·10 1·00
1700. 4 f. + 50 c. green, brown and red .. .. 1·40 1·25
DESIGNS: 3 f. Killing the Cretan bull. 4 f. Capturing the Mares of Diomedes.

1984. Monaco in the "Belle Epoque" (3rd series). Paintings by Hubert Clerissi. As T **445.** Multicoloured.
1701 4 f. "Grimaldi Street, 1908" (vert) .. .. 1·60 1·25
1702 5 f. "Railway Station, 1910" (vert) .. .. 2·50 1·60

1984. 150th Birth Anniv. of Edgar Degas (artist).
1704. **489.** 6 f. multicoloured .. 2·50 2·00

490. Spring.

1985. Precancels. Seasons of the Cherry.
1705. **490.** 1 f. 22 olive, green and blue 30 30
1706. – 1 f. 57 red, green and yellow 40 40
1707. – 2 f. 55 orange and brown 75 55
1708. – 4 f. 23 purple, green and blue .. .. 1·40 90

DESIGNS: 1 f. 57 Summer. 2 f. 55 Autumn. 4 f. 23 Winter.

491. First Stamp.

1985. Cent. of First Monaco Stamps.
1709. **491.** 1 f. 70 green 65 30
1710. 2 f. 10 red 80 10
1711. 3 f. blue .. .. 1·40 40

493. "Berardia subacaulis".

495. Nadia Boulanger (composer).

1985. Flowers in Mercantour National Park. Multicoloured.
1724. 1 f. 70 Type **493** 65 35
1725. 2 f. 10 "Saxifraga florulenta" (vert.) 75 40
1726. 2 f. 40 "Fritillaria moggridgei" (vert.) .. .. 1·00 65
1727. 3 f. "Sempervivum allionii" (vert.) .. 1·25 90
1728. 3 f. 60 "Silene cordifolia" (vert.) .. .. .. 1·40 1·10
1729. 4 f. "Primula allionii" .. 1·75 1·50

1985. 25th Anniv. of First Musical Composition Competition.
1731. **495.** 1 f. 70 brown .. 55 30
1732. – 2 f. 10 blue 75 40

DESIGN: 2 f. 10, Georges Auric (composer).

496. Stadium and Runners.

1985. Inauguration of Louis II Stadium, Fontvieille, and Athletics and Swimming Championships.
1733. **496.** 1 f. 70 brown, red and violet .. 55 40
1734. – 2 f. 10 blue, brown and green 65 40

DESIGN: 2 f. 10 Stadium and swimmers.

497. Prince Antoine I.

1985. Europa.
1735. **497.** 2 f. 10 blue 65 30
1736. – 3 f. red .. 1·00 50

DESIGN: 3 f. John-Baptiste Lully (composer).

498. Museum, "Hirondelle" (schooner) and "Denise" (midget submarine).

1985. 75th Anniv. of Oceanographic Museum.
1738. **498.** 2 f. 10 black, green and blue 75 40

499. Boxer.

1985. International Dog Show, Monte Carlo.
1739. **499.** 2 f. 10 multicoloured 1·60 90

500. Scientific Motifs.

1985. 25th Anniv. of Scientific Centre.
1740. **500.** 5 f. blue, black and violet .. .. 1·00 55

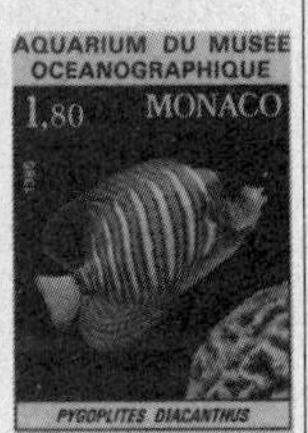

501. Children and Hands holding Seedling and Emblem.

502. Regal Angelfish.

1985. International Youth Year.
1741. **501.** 3 f. brown, green and light brown .. 1·00 55

1985. Fishes in Oceanographic Museum Aquarium (1st series). Multicoloured.
1742 1 f. 80 Type **502** 75 55
1743 1 f. 90 Type **502** .. .. 1·25 55
1744 2 f. 20 Powder blue tang surgeonfish 90 40
1745 3 f. 20 "Chaetodon collare" .. .. 1·40 1·00
1746 3 f. 40 As No. 1745 .. 2·25 1·10
1747 3 f. 90 Spotted triggerfish 2·00 1·40
1748 7 f. Fishes in aquarium (36 × 48 mm) .. .. 3·00 2·00

See also Nos. 1857/62.

504. Rome Buildings and Emblem.

1985. "Italia '85" International Stamp Exhibition, Rome.
1750. **504.** 4 f. black, grn. & red 1·40 90

505. Clown.

506. Decorations.

1985. 11th International Circus Festival, Monaco.
1751. **505.** 1 f. 80 multicoloured 1·00 55

1985. Christmas.
1752. **506.** 2 f. 20 multicoloured 90 40

507. Ship and Marine Life.

508. Arrangement of Roses, Tulips and Jonquil.

1985. Fish Processing Industry.
1753. **507.** 2 f. 20 blue, turquoise and brown .. 65 40

1985. Monte Carlo Flower Show (1986). Mult.
1754. 2 f. 20 Type **508** .. .. 1·00 55
1755. 3 f. 20 Arrangement of chrysanthemums and heather .. .. 1·50 1·00

509. Globe and Satellite.

1985. European Telecommunications Satellite Organization.
1756 **509** 3 f. black, blue & vio 1·10 65

510. Sacha Guitry (actor, centenary).

1985. Birth Anniversaries.
1757. **510.** 3 f. orange & brown 1·00 55
1758. – 4 f. blue, brown and mauve .. .. 1·40 75
1759. – 5 f. turquoise, blue and grey .. .. 1·75 1·10
1760. – 6 f. blue, brown and black .. .. 2·00 1·25

DESIGNS: 4 f. Wilhelm and Jacob Grimm (folklorists, bicentenaries). 5 f. Frederic Chopin and Robert Schumann (composers, 175th annivs). 6 f. Johann Sebastian Bach and Georg Friedrich Handel (composers, 300th annivs).

1985. Monaco Red Cross. The Twelve Labours of Hercules (5th series). As T **422**.
1761. 3 f. + 70 c. green, deep red and red .. .. 1·10 90
1762. 4 f. + 80 c. brn., blue and red .. .. 1·25 1·10

DESIGNS: 3 f. The Cattle of Geryon. 4 f. The Girdle of Hippolyte.

1985. Monaco in the "Belle Epoque" (4th series). As T **445**, showing paintings by Hubert Clerissi. Multicoloured.
1763. 4 f. "Port of Monaco, 1912" .. .. 1·50 1·10
1764. 6 f. "Avenue de la Gare 1920" .. .. .. 2·75 2·00

512. Spring.

1986. Precancels. Seasons of the Hazel Tree.
1766. **512.** 1 f. 28 brown, green and blue 30 30
1767. – 1 f. 65 green, brown and yellow .. 40 40
1768. – 2 f. 67 grey, brown and deep brown .. 75 55
1769. – 4 f. 44 green and brown .. .. 1·40 90

DESIGNS: 1 f. 65, Summer. 2 f. 67, Autumn. 4 f. 44, Winter.

513. Ancient Monaco.

1986. 10th Anniv. of "Annales Monegasques" (historical review).
1770. **513.** 2 f. 20 grey, blue and brown 65 35

514. Scotch Terriers.

1986. International Dog Show, Monte Carlo.
1771. **514.** 1 f. 80 multicoloured 2·25 1·10

515. Mouflon.

516. Research Vessel "Ramoge".

1986. Mammals in Mercantour National Park. Multicoloured.
1772. 2 f. 20 Type **515** 65 30
1773. 2 f. 50 Ibex 75 55
1774. 3 f. 20 Chamois .. .. 1·00 75
1775. 3 f. 90 Alpine marmot (vert.) .. .. 1·40 90
1776. 5 f. Arctic hare (vert.) .. 1·75 1·40
1777. 7 f. 20 Stoat (vert.) .. 2·40 2·00

1986. Europa. Each green, blue and red.
1778. 2 f. 20 Type **516** 80 40
1779. 3 f. 20 Underwater nature reserve, Larvotto beach .. 1·00 65

517. Prince Albert I and National Council Building.

1986. Anniversaries and Events.
1781. **517.** 2 f. 50 brown and green 75 55
1782. – 3 f. 20 brown, red and black .. .. 1·10 90
1783. – 3 f. 90 purple and red 1·50 1·10
1784. – 5 f. green, red and blue .. .. 1·75 1·25

DESIGNS—HORIZ. 2 f. 50, Type **517** (75th anniv. of First Constitution). 3 f. 20, Serge Diaghilev and dancers (creation of new Monte Carlo ballet company). 3 f. 90, Henri Rougier and Turcat-Mery car (75th anniv. of first Monte Carlo Rally). VERT. 5 f. Flags and Statue of Liberty (centenary).

518. Chicago and Flags.

1986. "Ameripex '86" International Stamp Exhibition, Chicago.
1785. **518.** 5 f. blk., red & bl. 1·75 1·00

520. Comet, Telescopes and 1532 Chart by Apian.

1986. Appearance of Halley's Comet.
1787. **520.** 10 f. bl., brn. & grn. 3·00 2·00

521. Monte Carlo. and Congress Centre.

1986. 30th International Insurance Congress.
1788. **521.** 3 f. 20 bl., brn. & grn. 1·00 55

522. Christmas Tree Branch and Holly. **523.** Clown's Face and Elephant on Ball.

1986. Christmas. Multicoloured.
1789. 1 f. 80 Type **522** 65 25
1790. 2 f. 50 Christmas tree branch and poinsettia 90 35

1986. 12th International Circus Festival, Monaco.
1791. **523.** 2 f. 20 multicoloured 1·10 40

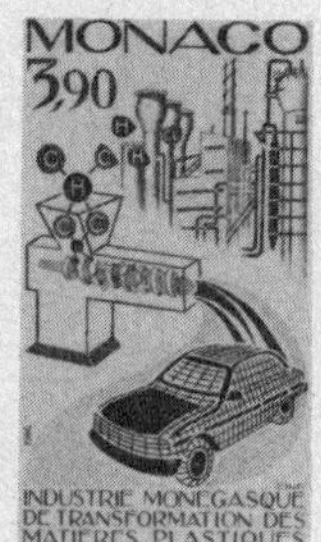

524. Posy of Roses and Acidanthera. **525.** Making Plastic Mouldings for Car Bodies.

1986. Monte Carlo Flower Show (1987). Multicoloured.
1792. 2 f. 20 Type **524** . . . . 1·10 40
1793. 3 f. 90 Lilies and beech in vase . . . . . . 1·75 1·00

1986. Monaco Red Cross. The Twelve Labours of Hercules (6th series). As T **422**.
1794. 3 f + 70 c. grn., yell. & red 1·10 75
1795. 4 f + 80 c. bl., brn. & red 1·25 1·00
DESIGNS: 3 f. The Golden Apples of the Hesperides. 4 f. Capturing Cerberus.

1986. Plastics industry.
1796. **525.** 3 f. 90 turquoise, red and grey . . . . 1·40 55

526. Scenes from "Le Cid" (Pierre Corneille).

1986. Anniversaries.
1797. **526.** 4 f. dp. brn. & brn. 1·40 90
1798. – 5 f. brown and blue 1·75 75
DESIGNS: 4 f. Type **526** (350th anniv. of first performance). 5 f. Franz Liszt (composer) and bible (175th birth anniv.).

527. Horace de Saussure, Mont Blanc and Climbers.

1986. Bicentenary of First Ascent of Mont Blanc by Dr. Paccard and Jacques Balmat.
1799. **527.** 5 f. 80 bl., red & blk. 1·75 1·25

528. "The Olympic Diver" (Emma de Sigaldi).

1986. 25th Anniv of Unveiling of "The Olympic Diver" (statue).
1800 **528** 6 f. multicoloured . . 2·00 1·10

1986. Monaco in the "Belle Epoque" (5th series). Paintings by Hubert Clerissi. As T **445**. Multicoloured.
1801 6 f. "Bandstand and Casino, 1920" (vert) . . 2·25 1·40
1802 7 f. "Avenue du Beau Rivage, 1925" (vert) . . 3·25 2·00

530. Spring.

1987. Precancels. Seasons of the Chestnut.
1804. **530.** 1 f. 31 green, yellow and brown 30 30
1805. – 1 f. 69 green and brown 40 40
1806. – 2 f. 74 brown, yellow and blue 75 65
1807. – 4 f. 56 brown, green and grey . . . . 1·40 1·10
DESIGNS: 1 f. 69, Summer. 2 f. 74, Autumn. 4 f. 56, Winter.

531. Golden Hunter.

1987. Insects in Mercantour National Park. Multicoloured.
1808 1 f. Type **531** 40 20
1809 1 f. 90 Golden wasp (vert) 65 30
1810 2 f. Green tiger beetle . . 65 30
1811 2 f. 20 Brown aeshna (vert) 75 40
1812 3 f. Leaf beetle . . . . 1·10 65
1813 3 f. 40 Grasshopper (vert) 1·40 90

532. St. Devote Church. **533.** Dogs.

1987. Centenary of St. Devote Parish Church.
1814. **532.** 1 f. 90 brown . . 55 25

1987. International Dog Show, Monte Carlo.
1815. **533.** 1 f. 90 grey, black and brown . . 1·00 40
1816. – 2 f. 70 black and green . . . . 1·75 80
DESIGN: 2 f. 70, Poodle.

534. Stamp Album.

1987. Stamp Day.
1817. **534.** 2 f. 20 red, purple and mauve . . 65 20

535. Louis II Stadium, Fontvieille. **536.** Cathedral.

1987. Europa. Each blue, green and red.
1818. 2 f. 20 Type **535** 65 30
1819. 3 f. 40 Crown Prince Albert Olympic swimming pool . . 1·10 55

1987. Centenary of Monaco Diocese.
1821. **536.** 2 f. 50 green 80 30

538. Lawn Tennis.

1987. 2nd European Small States Games, Monaco.
1823. **538.** 3 f. black, red and purple . . . . 1·25 65
1824. – 5 f. blue and black . . 1·75 1·00
DESIGN: 5 f. Sailing dinghies and windsurfer.

539. "Red Curly Tail" (Alexander Calder).

1987. "Monte Carlo Sculpture 1987" Exhibition.
1825. **539.** 3 f. 70 multicoloured 1·25 80

540. Prince Rainier III. **541.** Swallowtail on Stamp.

1987. 50th Anniv. of Monaco Stamp Issuing Office.
1826. **540.** 4 f. blue . . . . 1·40 1·40
1827. – 4 f. red . . . . 1·40 1·40
1828. – 8 f. black . . . . 2·50 2·50
DESIGNS: No. 1827, Prince Louis II. 47 × 37 mm—1829, Villa Miraflores.

1987. International Stamp Exhibition.
1829. **541.** 1 f. 90 deep green and green 55 25
1830. 2 f. 20 purple and red 65 45
1831. 2 f. 50 purple and mauve 90 60
1832. 3 f. 40 deep blue and blue . . . . 1·25 90

542. Festival Poster (J. Ramel). **543.** Christmas Scenes.

1987. 13th International Circus Festival, Monaco (1988).
1833 **542** 2 f. 20 multicoloured 1·10 30

1987. Christmas.
1834. **543.** 2 f. 20 red 60 20

544. Strawberry Plants and Campanulas in Bowl. **545.** Obverse and Reverse of Honore V 5 f. Silver Coin.

1987. Monte Carlo Flower Show (1988). Mult.
1835 2 f. 20 Type **544** 75 25
1836 3 f. 40 Ikebana arrangement of water lilies and dog roses (horiz) . . 1·25 50

1987. 150th Anniv. of Revival of Monaco Coinage.
1837. **545.** 2 f. 50 black and red 75 40

546. Graph, Factory, Electron Microscope and Printed Circuit.

1987. Electro-Mechanical Industry.
1838. **546.** 2 f. 50 blue, green and red 75 40

547. St. Devote.

1987. Monaco Red Cross. St. Devote, Patron Saint of Monaco (1st series). Multicoloured.
1839. 4 f. Type **547** . . . . 1·40 65
1840. 5 f. St. Devote and her nurse . . . . . . 1·75 90
See also Nos. 1898/9, 1956/7, 1980/1, 2062/3 and 2101/2.

548. Oceanographic Museum and I.A.E.A. Headquarters, Vienna.

1987. 25th Anniv. of International Marine Radioactivity Laboratory, Monaco.
1842. **548.** 5 f. black, brown and blue . . . . 1·50 1·00

549. Jouvet.

1987. Birth Centenary of Louis Jouvet (actor).
1843. **549.** 3 f. black . . . . 1·10 65

550. River Crossing.

1987. Bicentenary of First Edition of "Paul and Virginia" by Bernardin de Saint-Pierre.
1844. **550.** 3 f. green, orange and blue 90 65

551. Marc Chagall (painter).

1987. Anniversaries.
1845 551 4 f. black and red .. 1·40 75
1846 – 4 f. purple, red and brown .. .. 1·40 75
1847 – 4 f. red, blue & brown 1·40 65
1848 – 4 f. green, brown and purple .. .. 1·40 65
1849 – 5 f. blue, brown and green .. .. 1·60 90
1850 – 5 f. brown, green and blue .. .. 1·60 90
DESIGNS: No. 1845, Type **551** (birth centenary). 1846, Chapel of Ronchamp and Charles Edouard Jeanneret (Le Corbusier) (architect, birth centenary). 1847, Sir Isaac Newton (mathematician) and diagram (300th anniv. of publication of "Principia Mathematica"). 1848 Key and Samuel Morse (inventor, 150th anniv. of Morse telegraph). 1849, Wolfgang Amadeus Mozart and scene from "Don Juan" (opera, bicentenary of composition). 1850, Hector Berlioz (composer) and scene from "Mass for the Dead" (150th anniv. of composition).

1987. Monaco in the "Belle Epoque" (6th series). As T **445** showing paintings by Hubert Clerissi. Multicoloured.
1851 6 f. "Main Ramp to Palace Square, 1925" (vert) .. .. .. 2·00 1·40
1852 7 f. "Monte Carlo Railway Station, 1925" (vert) .. 3·00 2·00

552. Coat of Arms. 553. Spanish Hogfish.

1987.
1853 552 2 f. multicoloured .. 50 30
1854 2 f. 20 multicoloured 65 30

1988. Fishes in Oceanographic Museum Aquarium (2nd series). Multicoloured.
1857 2 f. Type **553** 75 30
1858 2 f. 20 Longnose butterfly fish ("Chelmon rostratus") 90 30
1859 2 f. 50 Harlequin filefish ("Oxymonacanthus longirostrus") .. 90 55
1860 3 f. Blue trunkfish .. 1·00 40
1861 3 f. 70 Lionfish .. 1·40 65
1862 7 f. Moon wrasse (horiz) 2·00 1·25

554. Spring. 556. Dachshunds.

1988. Precancels. Seasons of the Pear Tree. Multicoloured.
1863 1 f. 36 Type **554** 30 30
1864 1 f. 75 Summer 40 40
1865 2 f. 83 Autumn 75 65
1866 4 f. 72 Winter .. .. 1·40 1·10
See also Nos. 1952/5.

1988. European Dachshunds Show, Monte Carlo.
1868 556 3 f. multicoloured .. 1·40 75

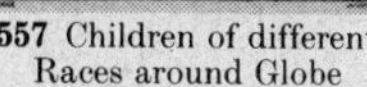

557 Children of different Races around Globe
558 Satellite Camera above Man with World as Brain

1988. 25th Anniv of World Association of Friends of Children.
1869 557 5 f. green, brown & bl 1·60 1·00

1988. Europa. Transport and Communications. Each black, brown and red.
1870 2 f. 20 Type **558** 65 30
1871 3 f. 60 High-speed mail train and aircraft propeller .. .. 1·40 65

559 Coxless Four

1988. Centenary of Monaco Nautical Society (formerly Regatta Society).
1873 559 2 f. blue, green and red 65 30

560 Jean Monnet (statesman)
561 "Leccinum rotundifoliae"

1988. Birth Centenaries.
1874 560 2 f. black, brown & bl 1·75 75
1875 – 2 f. black and blue .. 1·75 75
DESIGN: No. 1875, Maurice Chevalier (entertainer).

1988. Fungi in Mercantour National Park. Multicoloured.
1876 2 f. Type **561** 65 30
1877 2 f. 20 Crimson wax cap 75 30
1878 2 f. 50 "Pholiota flammans" 90 55
1879 2 f. 70 "Lactarius lignyotus" .. .. 1·00 75
1880 3 f. Goaty smell (vert) .. 1·10 75
1881 7 f. "Russula olivacea" (vert) .. .. .. 2·75 1·75

562 Nansen
563 Church and "Miraculous Virgin"

1988. Centenary of First Crossing of Greenland by Fridtjof Nansen (Norwegian explorer).
1882 562 4 f. violet .. .. 1·60 75

1988. Restoration of Sanctuary of Our Lady of Laghet.
1883 563 5 f. multicoloured .. 1·60 1·00

564 Anniversary Emblem

1988. 40th Anniv of W.H.O.
1884 564 6 f. red and blue .. 1·75 1·25

565 Anniversary Emblem

1988. 125th Anniv of Red Cross.
1885 565 6 f. red, grey and black 1·75 1·25

566 Congress Centre

1988. 10th Anniv of Monte Carlo Congress Centre.
1886 566 2 f. green 55 30
1887 – 3 f. red 90 55
DESIGN: 3 f. Auditorium.

1988. Monaco in the "Belle Epoque" (7th series). Paintings by Hubert Clerissi. As T **445**. Multicoloured.
1889 6 f. "Steam packet in Monte Carlo Harbour, 1910" .. .. 2·00 1·40
1890 7 f. "Place de la Gare, 1910" .. .. .. 2·50 1·40

568 Festival Poster (J. Ramel)
569 Star Decoration

1988. 14th International Circus Festival, Monaco (1989).
1891 568 2 f. multicoloured .. 75 20

1988. Christmas.
1892 569 2 f. multicoloured .. 65 25

570 Arrangement of Fuchsias, Irises, Roses and Petunias
571 Models

1988. Monte Carlo Flower Show (1989).
1893 570 3 f. multicoloured .. 1·10 40

1988. Ready-to-Wear Clothing Industry.
1894 571 3 f. green, orge & blk 75 35

572 Lord Byron (bicentenary)
574 "Le Nain and his Brothers" (Antoine Le Nain)

1988. Writers' Birth Anniversaries.
1895 572 3 f. black, brown & bl 90 55
1896 – 3 f. purple and blue .. 90 55
DESIGN: No. 1896, Pierre de Marivaux (300th anniv).

1988. Monaco Red Cross. St. Devote, Patron Saint of Monaco (2nd series). As T **547**. Multicoloured.
1898 4 f. Roman governor Barbarus arriving at Corsica .. .. 1·25 65
1899 5 f. St. Devote at the Roman senator Eutychius's house .. 1·60 1·00

1988. Artists' Birth Anniversaries.
1900 574 5 f. brown olive & red 1·60 90
1901 – 5 f. black, green & bl 1·60 90
DESIGNS: No. 1912, Type **574** (400th anniv); 1913, "The Great Archaeologists" (bronze statue, Giorgio de Chirico) (centenary).

575 Sorcerer

1989. Rock Carvings in Mercantour National Park. Multicoloured.
1902 2 f. Type **575** 55 25
1903 2 f. 20 Oxen in yoke .. 55 25
1904 3 f. Hunting implements 90 40
1905 3 f. 60 Tribal chief .. 1·00 55
1906 4 f. Puppet (vert) .. 1·10 65
1907 5 f. Jesus Christ (vert) .. 1·50 90

576 Rue des Spelugues
577 Prince Rainier

1989. Old Monaco (1 st series). Multicoloured.
1908 2 f. Type **576** 90 40
1909 2 f. 20 Place Saint Nicolas 1·00 45
See also Nos. 1969/70 and 2090/1.

1989.
1910 577 2 f. blue and azure .. 65 10
1911 2 f. 10 blue and azure 55 10
1912 2 f. 20 brown and pink 75 10
1913 2 f. 20 blue and azure 40 10
1914 2 f. 30 brown and pink 55 10
1915 2 f. 40 blue and azure 55 10
1916 2 f. 50 brown and pink 55 10
1918 2 f. 80 brown and pink 60 10
1920 3 f. 20 blue and cobalt 75 30
1922 3 f. 40 blue and cobalt 70 20
1923 3 f. 60 blue and cobalt 1·00 30
1924 3 f. 70 blue and cobalt 80 30
1925 3 f. 80 purple and lilac 90 30
1927 4 f. purple and lilac .. 85 20
1930 5 f. brown and pink .. 1·10 40
1932 10 f. dp green & green 2·00 1·00
1934 15 f. blue and grey 3·25 1·10
1936 20 f. red and pink .. 4·00 1·60
1938 25 f. black and grey .. 5·50 1·60
1940 40 f. brown and pink 8·75 2·75

578 Yorkshire Terrier

1989. International Dog Show, Monte Carlo.
1941 578 2 f. 20 multicoloured 90 55

579 Magician, Dove and Cards

1989. 5th Grand Prix of Magic, Monte Carlo.
1942 579 2 f. 20 black, bl & red 55 30

580 Nuns and Monks around "Our Lady of Misericorde"

1989. 350th Anniv of Archiconfrerie de la Misericorde.
1943 **580** 3 f. brown, black & red 75 40

581 Charlie Chaplin (actor) and Film Scenes

1989. Birth Centenaries.
1944 – 3 f. green, blue & mve 75 55
1945 **581** 4 f. pur, green & red 1·50 90
DESIGN: 3 f. Jean Cocteau (writer and painter), scene from "The Double-headed Eagle" and frescoes in Villefrance-sur-Mer chapel.

583 Boys playing Marbles

586 "Artist's Mother" (Philibert Florence)

1989. Europa. Children's Games. Each mauve, brown and grey.
1947 2 f. 20 Type **583** 65 30
1948 3 f. 60 Girls skipping .. 1·00 55

1989. Precancels. As Nos. 1863/6 but values changed. Multicoloured.
1952 1 f. 39 Type **554** 30 20
1953 1 f. 79 Summer 40 30
1954 2 f. 90 Autumn 75 55
1955 4 f. 84 Winter .. .. 1·40 90

1989. Monaco Red Cross. St. Devote, Patron Saint of Monaco (3rd series). As T **547**. Mult.
1956 4 f. St. Devote beside the dying Eutychius .. 1·25 65
1957 5 f. Barbarus condemns St. Devote to torture for refusing to make a sacrifice to the gods .. 1·50 75

1989. Artists' 150th Birth Anniversaries.
1958 **586** 4 f. brown .. .. 1·25 65
1959 – 6 f. multicoloured .. 1·75 1·10
1960 – 8 f. multicoloured .. 2·25 1·50
DESIGNS—HORIZ. 6 f. "Molesey Regatta" (Alfred Sisley). VERT. 8 f. "Farmyard at Auvers" (Paul Cezanne).

587 Poinsettia, Christmas Roses and Holly

1989. Christmas.
1961 **587** 2 f. multicoloured .. 90 20

588 Map and Emblem

1989. Cent of Interparliamentary Union.
1962 **588** 4 f. black, green & red 1·10 65

590 Monaco Palace, White House, Washington, and Emblem

1989. 20th U.P.U. Congress, Washington D.C.
1964 **590** 6 f. blue, brown & blk 1·60 1·25

1989. Monaco in the "Belle Epoque" (8th series). Paintings by Hubert Clerissi. As T **445**. Multicoloured.
1965 7 f. "Barque in Monte Carlo Harbour, 1915" (vert) .. .. .. 2·00 1·50
1966 8 f. "Gaming Tables, Casino, 1915" (vert) .. 2·25 1·75

591 World Map

592 Clown and Horses

1989. 10th Anniv of Monaco Aide et Presence (welfare organization).
1967 **591** 2 f. 20 brown and red 65 30

1989. 15th International Circus Festival, Monte Carlo.
1968 **592** 2 f. 20 multicoloured 1·00 40

1990. Old Monaco (2nd series). Paintings by Claude Rosticher. As T **576**. Mult.
1969 2 f. 10 La Rampe Major 75 40
1970 2 f. 30 Town Hall Court-yard 90 45

593 Phalaenopsis "Princess Grace"

594 Bearded Collie

1990. International Garden and Greenery Exposition, Osaka, Japan. Multicoloured.
1971 2 f. Type **593** 55 30
1972 3 f. Iris "Grace Patricia" 75 40
1973 3 f. "Paphiopedilum" "Prince Rainier III" .. 75 40
1974 4 f. "Cattleya" "Principessa Grace" .. .. 1·00 55
1975 5 f. Rose "Caroline of Monaco" .. .. 1·25 90

1990. International Dog Show, Monte Carlo.
1976 **594** 2 f. 30 multicoloured 90 40

595 Noghes and Racing Car

1990. Birth Centenary of Antony Noghes (founder of Monaco Grand Prix and Monte Carlo Rally).
1977 **595** 3 f. red, lilac and black 90 40

596 Cyclist and Lancia Rally Car

1990. Centenary of Automobile Club of Monaco (founded as Cycling Racing Club).
1978 **596** 4 f. blue, brown & pur 1·10 55

597 Telephone, Satellite and Dish Aerial

1990. 125th Anniv of I.T.U.
1979 **597** 4 f. lilac, mauve & blue 1·10 65

1990. Monaco Red Cross. St. Devote, Patron Saint of Monaco (4th series). As T **547**. Mult.
1980 4 f. St. Devote being flogged .. .. 1·25 65
1981 5 f. Placing body of St. Devote in fishing boat 1·50 1·75

598 Sir Rowland Hill and Penny Black

1990. 150th Anniv of Penny Black.
1982 **598** 5 f. blue and black .. 1·50 1·00

599 "Post Office, Place de la Mairie"

601 Anatase

1990. Europa. Post Office Buildings. Paintings by Hubert Clerissi. Mult.
1983 2 f. 30 Type **599** 65 30
1984 3 f. 70 "Post Office, Avenue d'Ostende" .. 1·10 60

1990. Minerals in Mercantour National Park. Multicoloured.
1987 2 f. 10 Type **601** 55 25
1988 2 f. 30 Albite 55 25
1989 3 f. 20 Rutile 75 35
1990 3 f. 80 Chlorite .. 1·00 50
1991 4 f. Brookite (vert) .. 1·00 55
1992 6 f. Quartz (vert) .. 1·40 90

602 Powerboat

603 Pierrot writing (mechanical toy)

1990. World Offshore Powerboat Racing Championship.
1993 **602** 2 f. 30 brown, red & bl 1·25 75

1990. Philatelic Round Table.
1994 **603** 3 f. blue 75 35

604 Christian Samuel Hahnemann (founder of homeopathy)

1990. Bicentenaries.
1995 **604** 3 f. purple, grn & blk 75 35
1996 – 5 f. chestnut, brn & bl 1·40 70
DESIGN: 5 f. Jean-Francois Champollion (Egyptologist) and hieroglyphics (birth bicentenary).

605 Monaco Heliport, Fontvieille

606 Petanque Player

1990. 30th International Civil Airports Association Congress, Monte Carlo.
1997 **605** 3 f. black, red & brn 75 35
1998 – 5 f. black, blue & brn 1·40 60
DESIGN: 5 f. Helicopters over Monte Carlo Congress Centre.

1990. 26th World Petanque Championship.
1999 **606** 6 f. blue, brown & orge 1·60 80

607 Spring

608 Miller on Donkey

1990. Precancels. Seasons of the Plum Tree. Multicoloured.
2000 1 f. 46 Type **607** 30 20
2001 1 f. 89 Summer 40 30
2002 3 f. 06 Autumn 65 55
2003 5 f. 10 Winter .. .. 1·10 90

1990. Christmas. Crib figures from Provence. Multicoloured.
2004 2 f. 30 Type **608** 55 20
2005 3 f. 20 Woman carrying faggots 75 30
2006 3 f. 80 Baker .. .. 1·10 55
See also Nos. 2052/4, 2097/9 and 2146/8.

610 Pyotr Ilich Tchaikovsky (composer)

611 Clown playing Concertina

1990. 150th Birth Anniversaries.
2008 **610** 5 f. blue and green .. 1·40 75
2009 – 5 f. bistre and blue .. 1·40 65
2010 – 7 f. multicoloured .. 1·60 1·10
DESIGNS—As T **610**. No. 2009, "Cathedral" (Auguste Rodin, sculptor). 48 × 37 mm. "The Magpie" (Claude Monet, painter).

1991. 16th International Circus Festival, Monte Carlo.
2011 **611** 2 f. 30 multicoloured 55 25
See also No. 2069.

1991. Bygone Monaco (2nd series). Paintings by Hubert Clerissi. As T **481**.
2015 20 c. purple 10 10
2017 40 c. green 10 10
2018 50 c. red 10 10
2019 60 c. blue 15 10
2020 70 c. green 15 10
2021 80 c. blue 20 15
2022 90 c. lilac 30 15
~~2023~~ 1 f. blue 30 15
2024 2 f. red 45 30
2025 3 f. black .. .. 1·10 80
2027 7 f. grey and black .. 1·50 1·10
DESIGNS: 20 c. Rock of Monaco and Fontvieille; 40 c. Place du Casino; 50 c. Place de la Cremailleere and railway station; 60 c. National Council building; 70 c. Palace and Rampe Major; 80 c. Avenue du Beau Rivage; 90 c. Fishing boats, Fontvieille; 1 f. Place d'Armes; 2 f. Marche de la Condamine; 3 f. Yacht; 7 f. Oceanographic Museum.

612 Abdim's Stork

613 Phyto-plankton

1991. International Symposium on Bird Migration. Multicoloured.
2029 2 f. Type **612** 50 35
2030 3 f. Broad-tailed humming birds 85 60
2031 4 f. Garganeys .. .. 1·00 70
2032 5 f. Eastern broad-billed roller .. .. .. 1·40 1·00
2033 6 f. European bee eaters 1·60 1·25

1991. Oceanographic Museum (1st series).
2034 **613** 2 f. 10 multicoloured 55 30
See also Nos. 2095/6.

614 Schnauzer

615 Cyclamen, Lily-of-the-Valley and Pine Twig in Fir-cone

1991. International Dog Show, Monte Carlo.
2035 **614** 2 f. 50 multicoloured 65 40

1991. Monte Carlo Flower Show.
2036 **615** 3 f. multicoloured .. 75 40

616 Corals

617 Control Room, "Eutelsat" Satellite and Globe

1991. "Joys of the Sea" Exhibition. Mult.
2037 2 f. 20 Type **616** 55 40
2038 2 f. 40 Coral necklace .. 55 40

1991. Europa. Europe in Space. Each blue, black and green.
2039 2 f. 30 Type **617** 55 30
2040 3 f. 20 Computer terminal, "Inmarsat" satellite, research ship transmitting signal and man with receiving equipment 90 60

618 Cross-country Skiers and Statue of Skiers by Emma de Sigaldi

1991. 1992 Olympic Games.
(a) Winter Olympics, Albertville
2042 **618** 3 f. green, blue & olive 70 75
2043 – 4 f. green, blue & olive 1·00 1·00

(b) Olympic Games, Barcelona
2044 – 3 f. green, lt br & brn 75 75
2045 – 5 f. black, brn & grn 1·25 1·25
DESIGNS: No. 2043, Right-hand part of statue and cross-country skiers; 2044, Track, relay runners and left part of statue of relay runners by Emma de Sigaldi; 2045, Right part of statue, view of Barcelona and track.

619 Head of "David" (Michelangelo), Computer Image and Artist at Work

620 Prince Pierre, Open Book and Lyre

1991. 25th Int. Contemporary Art Prize.
2046 **619** 4 f. grn, dp grn & lilac 1·00 65

1991. 25th Anniv of Prince Pierre Foundation.
2047 **620** 5 f. black, blue & brn 1·25 90

621 Tortoises

1991. Hermann's Tortoise. Multicoloured.
2048 1 f. 25 Type **621** 25 20
2049 1 f. 25 Head of tortoise .. 25 20
2050 1 f. 25 Tortoise in grass .. 25 20
2051 1 f. 25 Tortoise emerging from among plants .. 25 20

1991. Christmas. As T **608** showing crib figures from Provence. Multicoloured.
2052 2 f. 50 Consul 50 20
2053 3 f. 50 Arlesian woman .. 70 30
2054 4 f. Mayor 90 40

622 Norway Spruce

1991. Conifers in Mercantour National Park. Multicoloured.
2055 2 f. 50 Type **622** 50 20
2056 3 f. 50 Silver fir 70 30
2057 4 f. "Pinus uncinata" .. 90 30
2058 5 f. Scots pine (vert) .. 1·10 55
2059 6 f. Arolla pine .. .. 1·40 75
2060 7 f. European larch (vert) 1·60 90

1991. Monaco Red Cross. St. Devote, Patron Saint of Monaco (5th series). As T **547**. Multicoloured.
2062 4 f. 50 Fishing boat carrying body caught in storm .. .. .. 1·10 90
2063 5 f. 50 Dove guiding boatman to port of Monaco 1·40 1·10

624 "Portrait of Claude Monet"

1991. 150th Birth Anniv of Auguste Renoir (painter).
2064 **624** 5 f. multicoloured .. 1·10 65

625 Prince Honore II of Monaco

1991. 350th Anniv of Treaty of Peronne (giving French recognition of sovereignty of Monaco). Paintings by Philippe de Champaigne. Multicoloured.
2065 6 f. Type **625** .. .. 1·40 75
2066 7 f. King Louis XIII of France .. .. 1·60 90

626 Princess Grace (after R. Samini)

1991. 10th Anniv of Princess Grace Theatre.
2067 **626** 8 f. multicoloured .. 1·60 1·10

1992. 16th International Circus Festival. Monte Carlo. As No. 2011 but value and dates changed.
2069 **611** 2 f. 50 multicoloured 55 30
The 1991 Festival was cancelled.

628 Two-man Bobsleighs

1992. Winter Olympic Games, Albertville (7 f.), and Summer Games, Barcelona (8 f.).
2070 **628** 7 f. blue, turq & blk 1·50 90
2071 – 8 f. purple, blue & grn 1·75 1·00
DESIGN: 8 f. Football.

630 Spring

1992. Precancels. Seasons of the Walnut Tree. Multicoloured.
2073 1 f. 60 Type **630** 35 20
2074 2 f. 08 Summer 50 30
2075 2 f. 98 Autumn 70 40
2076 5 f. 28 Winter .. .. 1·25 75

631 Golden Labrador

1992. International Dog Show, Monte Carlo.
2077 **631** 2 f. 20 multicoloured 50 30

632 Racing along Seafront

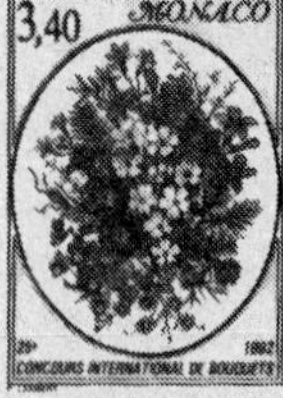

633 Mixed Bouquet

1992. 50th Monaco Grand Prix.
2078 **632** 2 f. 50 black, pur & bl 60 35

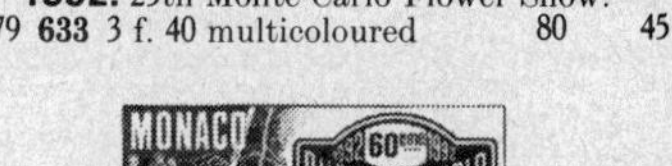

1992. 25th Monte Carlo Flower Show.
2079 **633** 3 f. 40 multicoloured 80 45

634 Ford Sierra Rally Car

1992. 60th Monte Carlo Car Rally.
2080 **634** 4 f. black, green & red 95 55

636 "Pinta" off Palos

1992. Europa. 500th Anniv of Discovery of America by Columbus. Multicoloured.
2082 2 f. 50 Type **636** 60 40
2083 3 f. 40 "Santa Maria" in the Antilles 80 60
2084 4 f. "Nina" off Lisbon .. 95 75

637 Produce

1992. "Ameriflora" Horticultural Show, Columbus, Ohio. Multicoloured.
2086 4 f. Type **637** 95 55
2087 5 f. Vase of mixed flowers 1·10 70

638 Prince Rainier I and Fleet (detail of fresco by E. Charpentier, Spinola Palace, Genoa)

1992. Columbus Exhibition, Genoa (6 f.), and "Expo' 92" World's Fair, Seville (7 f.).
2088 **638** 6 f. brown, red & blue 1·50 1·10
2089 – 7 f. brown, red & blue 1·60 1·10
DESIGN: 7 f. Monaco pavilion.

1992. Old Monaco (3rd series). Paintings by Claude Rosticher. As T **576**. Mult.
2090 2 f. 20 La Porte Neuve (horiz) 50 30
2091 2 f. 50 La Placette Bosio (horiz) 60 35

639 "Christopher Columbus"

1992. "Genova '92" International Thematic Stamp Exhibition. Roses. Multicoloured.
2092 3 f. Type **639** 70 40
2093 4 f. "Prince of Monaco" 95 55

640 Lammergeier

1992.
2094 **640** 2 f. 20 orge, blk & grn 50 30

1992. Oceanographic Museum (2nd series). As T **613**. Multicoloured.
2095 2 f. 20 "Ceratium ranipes" 50 30
2096 2 f. 50 "Ceratium hexacanthum" 60 35

1992. Christmas. As T **608** showing crib figures from Provence. Multicoloured.
2097 2 f. 50 Basket-maker .. 60 35
2098 3 f. 40 Fishwife 80 45
2099 5 f. Rural constable .. 1·10 70

641 "Seabus" (tourist submarine)

1992.
2100 **641** 4 f. blue, red & brown 1·00 80

642 Burning Boat Ceremony, St. Devote's Eve

1992. Monaco Red Cross. St. Devote, Patron Saint of Monaco (6th series).
2101 **642** 6 f. red, blue & brown 1·50 1·10
2102 – 8 f. purple, orge & red 1·90 1·10
DESIGN: 8 f. Procession of reliquary, St. Devote's Day.

643 Athletes, Sorbonne University and Coubertin

1992. Centenary of Pierre de Coubertin's Proposal for Revival of Olympic Games.
2103 **643** 10 f. blue .. .. 2·25 1·40

644 Baux de Provence and St. Catherine's Chapel

1992. Titles of Princes of Monaco. Marquis of Baux de Provence.
2104 **644** 15 f. multicoloured .. 3·50 2·10

646 Clown and Tiger

647 Short-toed Eagles

1993. 17th International Circus Festival, Monte Carlo.
2106 **646** 2 f. 50 multicoloured 60 35

1993. Birds of Prey in Mercantour National Park.
2107 **647** 2 f. chestnut, brown and orange .. 45 30
2108 – 3 f. indigo, orge & bl 70 45
2109 – 4 f. brown, ochre & bl 95 55
2110 – 5 f. brown, chestnut and green .. .. 1·10 70
2111 – 6 f. brown, mve & grn 1·40 85
DESIGNS—HORIZ. 3 f. Peregrine falcon. VERT. 4 f. Eagle owl; 5 f. Honey buzzard; 6 f. Tengmalm's owl.

650 Mixed Bouquet

652 Fire Fighting and Rescue

651 Pennants, Auditorium and Masks

1993. Monte Carlo Flower Show.
2114 **650** 3 f. 40 multicoloured 80 50

1993. 10th International Amateur Theatre Festival.
2115 **651** 4 f. 20 multicoloured 1·00 60

1993. World Civil Protection Day.
2116 **652** 6 f. black, red & green 1·40 85

653 Newfoundland

654 Golfer

1993. International Dog Show, Monte Carlo.
2117 **653** 2 f. 20 multicoloured 50 30

1993. 10th Monte Carlo Open Golf Tournament.
2118 **654** 2 f. 20 multicoloured 50 30

655 Princess Grace

656 Mirror and Candelabra

1993. 10th Death Anniv (1992) of Princess Grace.
2119 **655** 5 f. blue .. .. 1·10 70

1993. 10th Antiques Biennale.
2120 **656** 7 f. multicoloured .. 1·60 1·00

657 "Echinopsis multiplex"

658 Monte Carlo Ballets

1993. Cacti.
2121 **657** 2 f. 50 grn, pur & yell 60 35
2122 – 2 f. 50 green & purple 60 35
2123 – 2 f. 50 grn, pur & yell 60 35
2124 – 2 f. 50 green & yellow 60 35
DESIGNS: No. 2122, "Zygocactus truncatus"; 2123, "Echinocereus procumbens"; 2124, "Euphorbia virosa".
See also Nos. 2154/7.

1993. Europa. Contemporary Art.
2125 **658** 2 f. 50 blk, brn & pink 60 35
2126 – 4 f. 20 grey and brown 1·00 60
DESIGN: 4 f. 20, "Evolution" (sculpture, Emma de Sigaldi).

660 State Arms and Olympic Rings

1993. 110th International Olympic Committee Session, Monaco.
2129 **660** 2 f. 80 red, brown & bl 65 40
2130 – 2 f. 80 blue, lt bl & red 60 40
2131 – 2 f. 80 brn, blue & red 65 40
2132 – 2 f. 80 blue, lt bl & red 65 40
2133 – 2 f. 80 brown, bl & red 65 40
2134 – 2 f. 80 blue, lt bl & red 65 40
2135 – 2 f. 80 brown, bl & red 65 40
2136 – 2 f. 80 blue, lt bl & red 65 40
2137 – 4 f. 50 multicoloured 1·00 60
2138 – 4 f. 50 black, yell & bl 1·00 60
2139 – 4 f. 50 red, yellow & bl 1·00 60
2140 – 4 f. 50 black, yell & bl 1·00 60
2141 – 4 f. 50 red, yellow & bl 1·00 60
2142 – 4 f. 50 black, yell & bl 1·00 60
2143 – 4 f. 50 red, yellow & bl 1·00 60
2144 – 4 f. 50 red, yellow & bl 1·00 60
DESIGNS: Nos. 2129, 2137, Type **660**; 2130, Bobsleighing; 2131, Skiing; 2132, Yachting; 2133, Rowing; 2134, Swimming; 2135, Cycling; 2136, 2144, Commemorative inscription; 2138, Gymnastics (rings exercise); 2139, Judo; 2140, Fencing; 2141, Hurdling; 2142, Archery; 2143, Weightlifting.

661 Examining 1891 1 c. Stamp

1993. Centenary of Monaco Philatelic Union.
2145 **661** 2 f. 40 multicoloured 55 35

1993. Christmas. Crib figures from Provence. As T **608**. Multicoloured.
2146 2 f. 80 Donkey 65 40
2147 3 f. 70 Shepherd holding lamb 85 55
2148 4 f. 40 Ox lying down in barn .. .. .. 1·00 60

662 Grieg, Music and Trolls

1993. 150th Birth Anniv of Edvard Grieg (composer).
2149 **662** 4 f. blue 95 60

663 Abstract Lithograph

664 Monaco Red Cross Emblem

1993. Birth Centenary of Joan Miro (painter and sculptor).
2150 **663** 5 f. multicoloured .. 1·10 70

1993. Monaco Red Cross.
2151 **664** 5 f. red, yellow & blk 1·10 70
2152 – 6 f. red and black .. 1·40 85
DESIGN: 6 f. Crosses inscribed with fundamental principles of the International Red Cross.

665 "St. Joseph the Carpenter"

1993. 400th Birth Anniv of Georges de la Tour (painter).
2153 **665** 6 f. multicoloured .. 1·40 85

1994. Cacti. As Nos. 2121/4 but values changed.
2154 **657** 20 c. green, pur & yell 10 10
2155 – 30 c. green and purple (as No. 2122) .. 10 10
2156 – 40 c. green and yellow (as No. 2124) 10 10
2157 – 4 f. green, purple and yellow (as No. 2123) 95 60

666 Festival Poster

667 Artist/Poet

1994. 18th International Circus Festival, Monte Carlo.
2158 **666** 2 f. 80 multicoloured 65 40

1994. Mechanical Toys.
2159 **667** 2 f. 80 blue 65 40
2160 – 2 f. 80 red 65 40
2161 – 2 f. 80 purple .. 65 40
2162 – 2 f. 80 green 65 40
DESIGNS: No. 2160, Bust of Japanese woman; 2161, Shepherdess with sheep; 2162, Young Parisienne.

POSTAGE DUE STAMPS

D 3.

D 4.

D 18.

1906.
D 29a **D 3** 1 c. green 20 30
D 30 5 c. green 35 45
D 31a 10 c. red 25 30
D 32 10 c. brown .. £350 £110
D 33 15 c. pur on cream 1·40 1·00
D113 20 c. bistre on buff 15 15
D 34 30 c. blue 30 35
D114 40 c. mauve .. 15 15
D 35 50 c. brown on buff 2·75 2·50

D115		50 c. green ..	15	15
D116		60 c. black ..	40	40
D117		60 c. mauve ..	10·00	13·50
D118		1 f. purple on cream	10	10
D119		2 f. red	30	30
D120		3 f. red	30	30
D121		5 f. blue	40	40

1910.

D 36.	D 4.	1 c. olive	20	25
D 37.		10 c. lilac	30	35
D 38.		30 c. bistre	£170	£170

1919. Surch.

D 39.	D 4.	20 c. on 10 c. lilac..	1·75	2·50
D 40.		40 c. on 30 c. bistre	1·75	2·50

1925.

D 106.	D 18.	1 c. olive	15	20
D 107.		10 c. violet ..	15	20
D 108.		30 c. bistre ..	15	30
D 109.		60 c. red	30	30
D 110.		1 f. blue	55·00	48·00
D 111.		2 f. red	90·00	70·00

1925. Surch. **1 franc a percevoir.**

D 112.	D 8.	1 f. on 50 c. brown on buff	65	65

D 64.

D 65.

1946.

D 327.	D 64.	10 c. black ..	10	10
D 328.		30 c. violet ..	10	10
D 329.		50 c. blue	10	10
D 330.		1 f. green	15	15
D 331.		2 f. brown.. ..	15	15
D 332.		3 f. mauve ..	20	20
D 333.		4 f. red	30	35
D 334.	D 65.	5 f. brown.. ..	20	20
D 335.		10 f. blue	30	30
D 336.		20 f. turquoise ..	40	45
D 337.		50 f. red and mauve	32·00	48·00
D 338.		100 f. red and green	5·00	9·00

D 99. Early Steam Locomotive.

1953.

D 478.	–	1 f. red and green ..	10	10
D 479.	–	1 f. green and red ..	10	10
D 480.	–	2 f. turquoise & blue	10	10
D 481.	–	2 f. blue & turquoise	10	10
D 482.	D 99.	3 f. lake and green..	20	20
D 483.	–	3 f. green and lake..	20	20
D 484.	–	4 f. slate and brown	15	15
D 485.	–	4 f. brown and slate	15	15
D 486.	–	5 f. violet and blue..	40	40
D 487.	–	5 f. blue and violet..	40	40
D 488.	–	10 f. indigo and blue	5·50	5·50
D 489.	–	10 f. blue and indigo	5·50	5·50
D 490.	–	20 f. violet and blue	1·75	1·75
D 491.	–	20 f. blue and violet	1·75	1·75
D 492.	–	50 f. brown and red	4·50	4·50
D 493.	–	50 f. red and brown	4·50	4·50
D 494.	–	100 f. green & purple	7·50	7·50
D 495.	–	100 f. purple & green	11·00	11·00

TRIANUGLAR DESIGNS: Nos. D478, Pigeons released from mobile loft. D479, "Sikorsky" helicopter. D480, Brig. D481, "United States" (liner). D483, Streamlined steam locomotive. D484, Old monoplane. D485, "Comet" airliner. D486, Old motor-car. D487, "Sabre" racing-car. D488, Leonardo da Vinci's flying machine. D489, Postal rocket. D490, Balloon. D491, Airship "Graf Zeppelin". D492, Postilion. D493, Motor cycle messenger. D494, Mail coach. D495, Railway mail van.

D 140. 18th-Century Felucca.

1960.

D 698.	D 140.	1 c. brn., grn. & bl.	55	55
D 699.	–	2 c. sep., bl. & grn.	15	15
D 700.	–	5 c. pur., blk. & turq.	15	25
D 701.	–	10 c. blk., grn. & bl.	10	10
D 702.	–	20 c. pur., grn. & bl.	80	80
D 703.	–	30 c. brn., bl. & grn.	90	90
D 704.	–	50 c. bl., brn. & myr.	80	80
D 705.	–	1 f. brn., myr. & bl.	1·60	1·60

DESIGNS: 2 c. Paddle-steamer "La Palmaria". 5 c. Arrival of first railway train at Monaco. 10 c. 15th–16th-century armed messenger. 20 c. 18th-century postman. 30 c. "Charles III" (paddle-steamer). 50 c. 17th-century courier. 1 f. Mail coach (19th-century).

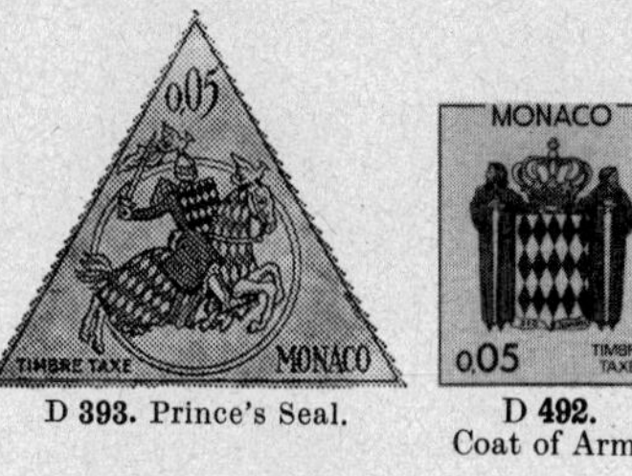

D 393. Prince's Seal.

D 492. Coat of Arms.

1980.

D1426	D 393	5 c. red & brn. ..	10	10
D1427		10 c. orge. & red	10	10
D1428		15 c. vio. & red..	10	10
D1429		20 c. grn. & red..	10	10
D1430		30 c. bl. & red ..	15	15
D1431		40 c. bistre & red	20	20
D1432		50 c. vio. & red..	25	25
D1433		1 f. grey & blue..	40	40
D1434		2 f. brn. & blk...	90	80
D1435		3 f. red & grn. ..	1·40	1·10
D1436		4 f. grn. & red ..	1·75	1·50
D1437		5 f. brn. & mag.	2·25	1·75

1985.

D 1712.	D 492.	5 c. multicoloured	10	10
D 1713.		10 c. multicoloured	10	10
D 1714.		15 c. multicoloured	10	10
D 1715.		20 c. multicoloured	10	10
D 1716.		30 c. multicoloured	10	10
D 1717.		40 c. multicoloured	10	10
D 1718.		50 c. multicoloured	10	10
D 1719.		1 f. multicoloured	30	30
D 1720.		2 f. multicoloured	65	65
D 1721.		3 f. multicoloured	1·00	1·00
D 1722.		4 f. multicoloured	1·40	1·40
D 1723.		5 f. multicoloured	1·50	1·50

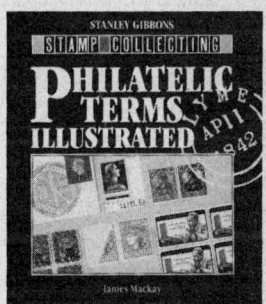

MONGOLIA Pt. 10

A republic in Central Asia between China and Russia, independent since 1921.

1924. 100 cents = 1 dollar (Chinese).
1926. 100 mung = 1 tugrik.

1. Eldev-Otchir Symbol.

2. Soyombo Symbol.

1924. Inscr. in black.
1. 1. 1 c. brown, pink and grey on bistre .. .. 3·25 3·25
2. 2 c. brown, blue and red on brown .. .. 3·25 2·75
3. 5 c. grey, red and yellow .. 20·00 14·00
4. 10 c. blue & brown on blue 7·50 5·50
5. 20 c. grey, blue and white on blue .. .. .. 12·00 8·50
6. 50 c. red & orange on pink 20·00 14·00
7. $1 bistre, red and white on yellow .. .. 32·00 22·00

Stamps vary in size according to the face value.

1926. Fiscal stamps as T 2 optd. **POSTAGE** in frame in English and Mongolian.
8. 2. 1 c. blue .. .. .. 6·50 6·50
9. 2 c. buff .. .. .. 7·50 7·50
10. 5 c. purple .. .. .. 8·50 8·50
11. 10 c. green .. .. .. 10·00 10·00
12. 20 c. brown .. .. .. 13·00 13·00
13. 50 c. brown and yellow .. £120 £120
14. $1 brown and pink .. £325 £375
15. $5 red and olive £350

Stamps vary in size according to the face value.

4. State Emblem: Soyombo Symbol. 5.

1926. New Currency.
16 4 5 m. black and lilac .. 4·00 4·00
17 20 m. black and blue .. 3·50 3·50

1926.
18. 5. 1 m. black and yellow .. 1·00 80
19. 2 m. black and brown .. 1·10 90
20. 5 m. black and lilac (A) .. 2·00 1·40
28. 5 m. black and lilac (B) .. 13·00 8·50
21. 10 m. black and blue .. 1·40 1·10
30. 20 m. black and blue .. 14·00 8·00
22. 25 m. black and green .. 3·00 1·75
23. 40 m. black and yellow .. 4·50 2·00
24. 50 m. black and brown .. 6·00 3·25
25. 1 t. black, green & brown 14·00 6·50
26. 3 t. black, yellow and red 30·00 25·00
27. 5 t. black, red and purple 45·00 40·00

In (A) the Mongolian numerals are in the upper and in (B) in the lower value tablets.

These stamps vary in size according to the face value.

(6).

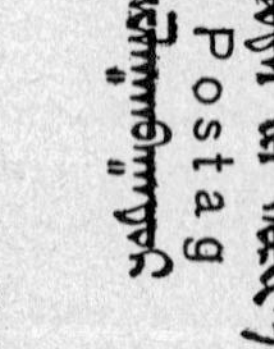

(7).

1930. Surch. as T 6.
32. 5. 10 m. on 1 m. blk. & yell. 20·00 30·00
33. 20 m. on 2 m. black & brn. 30·00 30·00
34. 25 m. on 40 m. blk. & yell. 35·00 35·00

1931. Optd. with T 7.
35. 2. 1 c. blue .. .. .. 17·00 8·00
36. 2 c. buff .. .. .. 12·00 6·00
37. 5 c. purple .. .. .. 18·00 6·00
38. 10 c. green .. .. .. 18·00 6·00
39. 20 c. brown .. .. .. 27·00 8·50
40. 50 c. brown and yellow .. 70·00 70·00
41. $1 brown and pink ..

1931. Surch. **Postage** and value in "Menge".
43. 2. 5 m. on 5 c. purple .. 18·00 6·00
44. 10 m. on 10 c. green .. 30·00 15·00
45. 20 m. on 20 c. brown .. 40·00 20·00

INDEX

Countries can be quickly located by referring to the index at the end of this volume.

9. Govt. Building, Ulan Bator.

11. Sukhe Bator.

12. Lake and Mountain Scenery.

1932.
46. – 1 m. brown .. .. 1·40 1·00
47. – 2 m. red .. .. .. 1·40 1·00
48. – 5 m. blue 35 30
49. 9. 10 m. green 35 30
50. – 15 m. brown 35 30
51. – 20 m. red 35 30
52. – 25 m. violet 45 30
53. 11. 40 m. black 45 40
54. – 50 m. blue 35 30
55. 12. 1 t. green 60 50
56. – 3 t. violet .. .. .. 1·75 1·25
57. – 5 t. brown .. .. .. 10·00 7·50
58. – 10 t. blue .. .. .. 17·00 13·00

DESIGNS—As Type 9: 1 m. Weavers. 5 m. Machinist. As Type 11: 2 m. Telegraphist. 15 m. Revolutionary soldier carrying flag. 20 m. Mongols learning Latin alphabet. 25 m. Soldier. 50 m. Sukhe Bator's monument. As Type 12: 3 t. Sheep-shearing. 5 t. Camel caravan. 10 t. Lassoing wild horses (after painting by Sampilon).

13. Mongol Man.

14. Camel Caravan.

1943. Network background in similar colour to stamps.
59. 13. 5 m. green .. .. .. 3·50 3·50
60. – 10 m. blue .. .. .. 6·00 3·75
61. – 15 m. red .. .. .. 7·00 5·00
62. 14. 20 m. brown .. .. .. 11·00 9·00
63. – 25 m. brown .. .. .. 11·00 11·00
64. – 30 m. red .. .. .. 12·00 12·00
65. – 45 m. purple .. .. .. 17·00 17·00
66. – 60 m. green .. .. .. 28·00 28·00

DESIGNS—VERT. 10 m. Mongol woman. 15 m. Soldier. 30 m. Arms of the Republic. 45 m. Portrait of Sukhe Bator, dated 1894–1923. HORIZ. 25 m. Secondary school. 60 m. Pastoral scene.

15. Marshal Kharloin Choibalsan.

17. Victory Medal.

16. Choibalsan and Sukhe Bator.

1945. 50th Birthday of Choibalsan.
67. 15. 1 t. black .. .. .. 7·50 7·50

1946. 25th Anniv. of Independence. As T 16/17.
68. – 30 m. bistre .. .. .. 4·50 3·50
69. 16. 50 m. purple .. .. .. 5·50 4·00
70. – 60 m. brown .. .. .. 5·50 5·50
71. – 60 m. black .. .. .. 8·00 7·50
72. 17. 80 m. brown .. .. .. 7·50 7·50
73. – 1 t. blue .. .. .. 11·00 12·00
74. – 2 t. brown .. .. .. 14·00 16·00

DESIGNS—VERT. ($21\frac{1}{2}$ × 32 mm): 30 m. Choibalsan, aged four. As Type 17: 60 m. (No. 71), Choibalsan when young man. 1 t. 25th Anniversary Medal. 2 t. Sukhe Bator. HORIZ. As Type 16: 60 m. (No. 70), Choibalsan University.

17a. Flags of Communist Bloc.

1951. Struggle for Peace.
75. 17a. 1 t. multicoloured .. 7·50 7·50

17b. Lenin (after P. Vasilev).

19. Sukhe Bator.

18. State Shop.

1951. Honouring Lenin.
76. 17b. 3 t. multicoloured .. 16·00 16·00

1951. 30th Anniv. of Independence.
77. – 15 m. green on azure .. 3·25 3·25
78. 18. 20 m. orange .. .. 3·25 3·25
79. – 20 m. multicoloured .. 3·75 3·75
80. – 25 m. blue on azure .. 3·75 3·75
81. – 30 m. multicoloured .. 4·25 4·25
82. – 40 m. violet on pink .. 4·50 4·50
83. – 50 m. brown on azure .. 9·00 9·00
84. – 60 m. black on pink .. 8·00 8·00
85. 19. 2 t. brown .. .. 15·00 15·00

DESIGNS—HORIZ. (As Type 18): 15 m. Altai Hotel. 40 m. State Theatre, Ulan Bator. 50 m. Pedagogical Institute. ($55\frac{1}{2}$ × 26 mm.). 25 m. Choibalsan University. VERT. (As Type 19). 20 m. (No. 79), 30 m. Arms and flag. 60 m. Sukhe Bator Monument.

20. School-children.

1952. Culture.
86. – 5 m. brown on pink .. 2·00 1·75
87. 20. 10 m. blue on pink .. 2·50 2·50

DESIGN: 5 m. New houses.

21. Choibalsan in National Costume.

22. Choibalsan and Farm Worker.

1953. 1st Death Anniv. of Marshal Choibalsan. As T 21/22.
88. 21. 15 m. blue .. .. 2·50 2·75
89. 22. 15 m. green .. .. 2·50 2·75
90. 21. 20 m. green .. .. 5·00 6·00
91. 22. 20 m. sepia .. .. 2·50 2·50
92. – 20 m. blue .. .. 2·50 2·50
93. – 30 m. sepia .. .. 3·25 3·25
94. – 50 m. brown .. .. 3·25 3·25
95. – 1 t. red .. .. 4·00 4·00
96. – 1 t. purple .. .. 4·00 4·00
97. – 2 t. red .. .. 4·00 4·00
98. – 3 t. purple .. .. 5·00 5·00
99. – 5 t. red .. .. 19·00 19·00

DESIGNS: As Type 21: 1 t. (96), 2 t. Choibalsan in uniform. (33 × 48 mm): 3, 5 t. Busts of Choibalsan and Sukhe Bator. (33 × 46 mm): 50 m., 1 t. (95), Choibalsan and young pioneer. (48 × 33 mm): 20 m. (92), 30 m. Choibalsan and factory hand.

23. Arms of the Republic.

23a. Lenin.

1954.
100. 23. 10 m. red .. .. 6·50 4·00
101. 20 m. red .. .. 11·00 5·00
102. 30 m. red .. .. 6·00 4·50
103. 40 m. red .. .. 7·00 4·50
104. 60 m. red .. .. 6·50 4·50

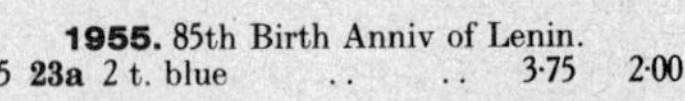

1955. 85th Birth Anniv of Lenin.
105 23a 2 t. blue .. .. 3·75 2·00

23b. Flags of the Communist Bloc.

24. Sukhe Bator and Choibalsan.

1955. Struggle for Peace.
106 23b 60 m. multicoloured .. 1·00 55

1955.
107 24 30 m. green 30 20
108 – 30 m. blue 50 20
109 – 30 m. red 40 40
110 – 40 m. purple .. .. 1·00 40
111 – 50 m. brown .. .. 1·00 45
112 – 1 t. multicoloured .. 2·75 1·25

DESIGNS—HORIZ. 30 m. blue, Lake Khobsogol. 50 m. Choibalsan University. VERT. 30 m. red, Lenin Statue, Ulan Bator. 40 m. Sukhe Bator and dog. 1 t. Arms and flag of the Republic.

24a. Train linking Ulan Bator and Moscow.

25. Arms of the Republic.

1956. Mongol–Soviet Friendship. Mult.
113 1 t. Type 24a .. .. 22·00 10·00
114 2 t. Flags of Mongolia and Russia .. .. .. 3·50 2·00

1956.
115 25 20 m. brown 50 30
116 30 m. brown 65 35
117 40 m. blue 80 45
118 60 m. green .. .. 1·00 65
119 1 t. red .. .. 1·60 80

26. Hunter and Golden Eagle.

27. Arms.

27a. Wrestlers.

1956. 35th Anniv. of Independence.
120. 26. 30 m. brown .. .. 32·00 16·00
121. 27. 30 m. blue .. .. 5·00 4·00
122. 27a. 60 m. green .. .. 15·00 15·00
123. – 60 m. orange .. .. 15·00 15·00

DESIGN—As Type 26: 60 m. (No. 123), Children. Also inscr. "XXXV".

28.

29.

1958. With or without gum.
124. 28. 20 m. red .. .. 1·50 1·00

1958. 13th Mongol People's Revolutionary Party Congress. With or without gum.
125. **29.** 30 m. red and salmon .. 3·00 3·25

1958. As T **27a** but without "xxxv". With or without gum.
126 50 m. brown on pink .. 5·00 3·75

30. Dove and Globe.

1958. 4th Congress of Int. Women's Federation, Vienna. With or without gum.
127. **30.** 60 m. blue .. .. 3·25 2·00

31. Ibex.

32. Yak.

1958. Mongolian Animals. As T **31/2.**
128. – 30 m. pale blue .. 12·00 2·50
129. – 30 m. turquoise .. 12·00 2·50
130. **31.** 30 m. green .. .. 3·00 1·50
131. 30 m. turquoise .. 3·00 1·00
132. **32.** 60 m. bistre .. .. 3·50 2·00
133. 60 m. orange .. .. 3·50 1·25
134. – 1 t. blue .. .. 5·00 2·50
135. – 1 t. light blue .. .. 4·00 1·75
136. – 1 t. red .. .. .. 5·00 3·25
137. – 1 t. red .. .. .. 4·00 2·00
DESIGNS—VERT. 30 m. (Nos. 128/9), Dalmatian pelicans. HORIZ. 1 t. (Nos. 134/5), Yak, facing right. 1 t. (Nos. 136/7), Bactrian camels.

33. Goat.

34. "Tulaga".

1958. Mongolian Animals.
138. **33.** 5 m. sepia and yellow .. 15 10
139. – 10 m. sepia and green.. 20 10
140. – 15 m. sepia and lilac .. 35 10
141. – 20 m. sepia and blue .. 35 10
142. – 25 m. sepia and red .. 40 10
143. – 30 m. purple and mauve 50 10
144. **33.** 40 m. green 50 10
145. – 50 m. brown and salmon 60 20
146. – 60 m. blue 80 20
147. – 1 t. bistre and yellow .. 1·75 50
ANIMALS: 10 m., 30 m. Ram. 15 m., 60 m. Stallion. 20 m., 50 m. Bull. 25 m., 1 t. Bactrian camel.

1959.
148. **34.** 1 t. multicoloured .. 3·25 1·10

35. Taming a Wild Horse.

1959. Mongolian Sports. Centres and inscriptions multicoloured: frame colours given below.
149. **35.** 5 m. yellow and orange 20 10
150. – 10 m purple 20 10
151. – 15 m. yellow and green 20 10
152. – 20 m lake and red .. 25 10
153. – 25 m. blue 40 15
154. – 30 m. yell., grn. & turq. 55 15
155. – 70 m. red and yellow .. 70 30
156. – 80 m. purple .. .. 1·10 60
DESIGNS: 10 m. Wrestlers. 15 m. Introducing young rider. 20 m. Archer. 25 m. Galloping horseman. 30 m. Archery contest. 70 m. Hunting a wild horse. 80 m. Proclaiming a champion.

36. Child Musician.

DESIGNS — VERT. 10 m. Young wrestlers. 20 m. Youth on horse. 25 m. Artists in national costume. HORIZ. 40 m. Festival parade.

1959. Mongolian Youth Festival (1st issue).
157. **36.** 5 m. purple and blue .. 20 10
158. – 10 m. brown and green 25 10
159. – 20 m. green and purple 25 10
160. – 25 m. blue and green .. 50 25
161. – 40 m. violet and myrtle 95 40

38. Kalmuck Script.

37. Festival Badge.

39. Military Monument.

40. Herdswoman and Lamb.

1959. Mongolian Youth Festival (2nd issue).
162. **37.** 30 m. purple and blue.. 30 20

1959. Mongolists' Congress. Designs as T **38** incorporating "MONGOL" in various scripts.
163. – 30 m. multicoloured .. 5·00 5·00
164. – 40 m. red, blue & yellow 5·00 5·00
165. **38.** 50 m. multicoloured .. 7·00 7·00
166. – 60 m. red, blue & yellow 11·00 11·00
167. – 1 t. yellow, turq. & orge. 14·00 14·00
SCRIPTS (29½ × 42½ mm.): 30 m. Stylized Ulghur. 40 m. Soyombo. 60 m. Square (Pagspa). (21½ × 31 mm.): 1 t. Cyrillic.

1959. 20th Anniv of Battle of Khalka River.
168. – 40 m. red, brn. & yellow 55 15
169. **39.** 50 m. multicoloured .. 55 15
DESIGN: 40 m. Mounted horseman with flag (emblem), inscr. "AUGUST 1959 HALHIN GOL".

1959. 2nd Meeting of Rural Economy Co-operatives.
170. **40.** 30 m. green .. .. 3·50 3·50

41. Sable.

1959. Mongolian Fauna.
171. **41.** 5 m. pur., yell. & blue 15 10
172. – 10 m. multicoloured 60 10
173. – 15 m. blk., grn. and red 45 10
174. – 20 m. purple, blue & red 45 15
175. – 30 m. myrtle, pur. & grn. 50 15
176. – 50 m. blk., blue & green 1·10 30
177. – 1 t. black, green and red 1·75 40
ANIMALS—HORIZ. (58 × 21 mm.): 10 m. Ring-necked pheasants. 20 m. European otter. 50 m. Saiga. 1 t. Siberian musk deer. As Type **41**: 15 m. Muskrat. 30 m. Argali.

42. "Lunik 3" in Flight.

44. "Flower" Emblem.

43. Motherhood Badge.

1959. Launching of "Lunik 3" Rocket.
178 **42** 30 m. yellow and violet 65 25
179 – 50 m. red, green & blue 80 35
DESIGN—HORIZ. 50 m. Trajectory of "Lunik 3" around the Moon.

1960. Int. Women's Day.
180. **43.** 40 m. bistre and blue .. 50 15
181. **44.** 50 m. yell., grn. & blue 75 30

45. Lenin.

46. Larkspur.

1960. 90th Birth Anniv. of Lenin.
182. **45.** 40 m. red 60 15
183. 50 m. violet 40 30

1960. Flowers.
184 **46** 5 m. blue, green & bistre 15 10
185 – 10 m. red, green & orge 20 10
186 – 15 m. violet, grn & bis 25 10
187 – 20 m. yellow, green & ol 30 10
188 – 30 m. vio, grn & emerald 35 15
189 – 40 m. orange, grn & vio 65 15
190 – 50 m. violet, green & bl 85 35
191 – 1 t. mauve, grn & lt grn 1·60 80
FLOWERS. 10 m. Tulip. 15 m. Jacob's ladder. 20 m. Asiatic globe flower. 30 m. Clustered bell-flower. 40 m. Grass of Parnassus. 50 m. Meadow cranesbill. 1 t. "Begonia vansiana".

47. Horse-jumping.

1960. Olympic Games. Inscr. "ROMA 1960" or "ROMA MCMLX". Centres in greenish grey.
192. **47.** 5 m. red, black & turq. 10 10
193. – 10 m. violet and yellow 15 10
194. – 15 m. turq., black & red 20 20
195. – 20 m. red and blue .. 20 10
196. – 30 m. ochre, blk. & grn. 35 10
197. – 50 m. blue & turquoise 50 10
198. – 70 m. grn., blk. & violet 60 30
199. – 1 t. mauve and green .. 90 50
DESIGNS—DIAMOND SHAPED: 10 m. Running. 20 m. Wrestling. 50 m. Gymnastics. 1 t. Throwing the discuss. As Type **47**: 15 m. Diving. 30 m. Hurdling. 70 m. High jumping.

48.

1960. Red Cross.
200. **48.** 20 m. red, yellow & blue 70 25

49. Newspapers.

1960. 40th Anniv. of Mongolian Newspaper "Unen" ("Truth").
201. **49.** 20 m. buff, green & red 20 10
202. 30 m. red, yellow & grn. 30 15

50. Hoopoe.

1961. Mongolian Song-birds.
203. – 5 m. mve., blk. and grn. 70 25
204. **50.** 10 m. red, black & green 80 25
205. – 15 m. yell., black & green 90 35
206. – 20 m. grn., blk. & bistre 1·10 35
207. – 50 m. blue, black & red 1·60 35
208. – 70 m. yell., blk. & mve. 1·75 65
209. – 1 t. mauve, orge. & blk. 2·25 90
BIRDS—As Type **50**. 15 m. Golden Oriole. 20 m. Siberian Capercaillie. Inverted triangulars: 5 m. Rose-coloured Starling. 50 m. Eastern broad-billed Roller. 70 m. Tibetan Sandgrouse. 1 t. Mandarin.

51. Foundry Worker.

52. Patrice Lumumba.

1961. 15th Anniv. of World Federation of Trade Unions.
210. **51.** 30 m. red and black .. 30 10
211. – 50 m. red and violet .. 35 20
DESIGN—HORIZ. 50 m. Hemispheres.

1961. Patrice Lumumba (Congolese politician) Commemoration.
212. **52.** 30 m. brown .. .. 1·50 1·00
213. 50 m. purple .. .. 2·00 1·25

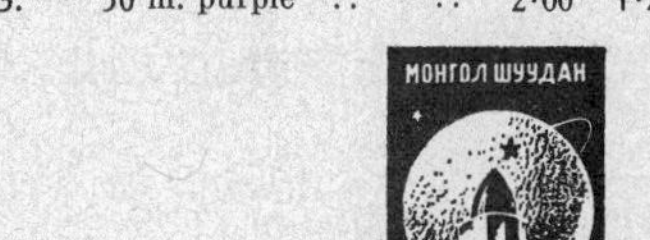

53. Bridge.

54. Gagarin with Capsule.

1961. 40th Anniv. of Independence (1st issue). Mongolian Modernization.
214. **53.** 5 m. green 10 10
215. – 10 m. blue 10 10
216. – 15 m. red 15 10
217. – 20 m. brown 15 10
218. – 30 m. blue 20 15
219. – 50 m. green 30 20
220. – 1 t. violet 50 25
DESIGNS: 10 m. Shoe-maker. 15 m. Store at Ulan Bator. 30 m. Government Building, Ulan Bator. 50 m. Machinist. 1 t. Ancient and modern houses. (59 × 20½ mm.): 20 m. Choibalsan University.

See also Nos. 225/32, 233/41, 242/8 and 249/56.

1961. World's First Manned Space Flight. Multicoloured.
221 20 m. Type **54** 50 15
222 30 m. Gagarin and globe (horiz) 60 30
223 50 m. Gagarin in capsule making parachute descent 90 60
224 1 t. Globe and Gagarin (horiz) .. .. 1·40 90

55. Postman with Reindeer.

1961. 40th Anniv of Independence (2nd issue). Mongolian Postal Service.
225 **55** 5 m. red, brown and blue (postage) .. 15 10
226 – 15 m. violet, brn & bis 30 10
227 – 20 m. blue, black & grn 20 10
228 – 25 m. violet, bis & grn 30 15
229 – 30 m. green, blk & lav 3·50 80
230 – 10 m. orange, black and green (air) .. 35 10
231 – 50 m. black, pink & grn 1·00 25
232 – 1 t. multicoloured .. 1·10 35
DESIGNS—Postman with: 10 m. Horses. 15 m. Camels. 20 m. Yaks. 25 m. Postman on quayside. 30 m. Diesel mail train. 50 m. Mail plane over map. 1 t. Postal emblem.

56. Rams.

1961. 40th Anniv. of Independence (3rd issue). Animal Husbandry.
233. 56. 5 m. black, red and blue 10 10
234. – 10 m. black, green & pur. 15 10
235. – 15 m. black, red & green 20 10
236. – 20 m. sepia, bl. & brn. 25 10
237. – 25 m. black, yell. & grn. 30 15
238. – 30 m. black, red & violet 35 15
239. – 40 m. black, grn. & red 40 15
240. – 50 m. black, brown & bl. 65 25
241. – 1 t. black, violet & olive 90 50
DESIGNS: 10 m. Oxen. 15 m. Camels. 20 m. Pigs and poultry. 25 m. Angora goats. 30 m. Mongolian horses. 40 m. Ewes. 50 m. Cows. 1 t. Combine-harvester.

57. Children Wrestling.

1961. 40th Anniv. of Independence (5th issue). Mongolian Sports.
242. 57. 5 m. multicoloured .. 15 10
243. – 10 m. sepia, red & green 20 10
244. – 15 m. pur., blue & yell. 25 10
245. – 20 m. red, black & green 40 25
246. – 30 m. pur., grn. & lav. 80 30
247. – 50 m. indigo, orge. & bl. 1·00 35
248. – 1 t. purple, blue & grey 1·60 70
DESIGNS: 10 m. Horse-riding. 15 m. Children on camel and pony. 20 m. Falconry. 30 m. Skiing. 50 m. Archery. 1 t. Dancing.

58. Young Mongol.

1961. 40th Anniv. of Independence (6th issue). Mongolian Culture.
249. 58. 5 m. purple and green.. 10 10
250. – 10 m. blue and red .. 10 10
251. – 15 m. brown and blue.. 15 10
252. – 20 m. green and violet.. 25 10
253. – 30 m. red and blue 35 15
254. – 50 m. violet and bistre.. 80 20
255. – 70 m. green and mauve 90 25
256. – 1 t. red and blue .. 1·25 70
DESIGNS—HORIZ. 10 m. Mongol chief. 70 m. Orchestra. 1 t. Gymnast. VERT. 15 m. Sukhe Bator Monument. 20 m. Young singer. 30 m. Young dancer. 50 m. Dombra-player.

59. Mongol Arms.

60. Congress Emblem.

1961. Arms multicoloured; inscr. in blue; background colours given.
257. 59. 5 m. salmon 15 10
258. 10 m. lilac 20 10
259. 15 m. brown 25 10
260. 20 m. turquoise .. 35 10
261. 30 m. ochre 45 15
262. 50 m. mauve 50 20
263. 70 m. olive 60 25
264. 1 t. orange .. .. 1·00 35

1961. 5th World Federation of Trade Unions Congress, Moscow.
265. 60. 30 m. red, yellow & blue 30 15
266. 50 m. red, yellow & sepia 35 20

61. Dove, Map and Globe.

1962. Admission of Mongolia to U.N.O.
267. 61. 10 m. multicoloured 20 10
268. – 30 m. multicoloured .. 30 15
269. – 50 m. multicoloured .. 40 15
270. – 60 m. multicoloured .. 60 25
271. – 70 m. multicoloured .. 70 35
DESIGNS: 30 m. U.N. Emblem and Mongol Arms. 50 m. U.N. and Mongol flags. 60 m. U.N. Headquarters and Mongolian Parliament building. 70 m. U.N. and Mongol flags, and Assembly.

62. Football, Globe and Flags.

1962. World Cup Football Championship, Chile. Multicoloured.
272. 10 m. Type 62 .. .. 10 10
273. 30 m. Footballers, globe and ball 25 10
274. 50 m. Footballers playing in stadium 40 15
275. 60 m. Goalkeeper saving goal 50 25
276. 70 m. Stadium .. .. 1·10 35

63. D. Natsagdorj.

64. Torch and Handclasp.

65. Flags of Mongolia and U.S.S.R.

1962. 3rd Congress of Mongolian Writers.
277. 63. 30 m. brown 20 15
278. 50 m. green 30 15

1962. Afro–Asian People's Solidarity.
279. 64. 20 m. multicoloured .. 15 10
280. 30 m. multicoloured .. 25 20

1962. Mongol–Soviet Friendship.
281. 65. 30 m. multicoloured .. 25 10
282. 50 m. multicoloured .. 35 20

1962. Malaria Eradication. Nos. 184/91 optd. with Campaign emblem and **LUTTE CONTRE LE PALUDISME.**
283. 46. 5 m. 20 20
284. – 10 m. 20 20
285. – 15 m. 20 20
286. – 20 m. 20 20
287. – 30 m. 40 30
288. – 40 m. 40 30
289. – 50 m. 55 50
290. – 1 t .. .. .. 1·10 80

67. Victory Banner.

DESIGNS: 30 m. Engraved lacquer tablets. 50 m. Obelisk. 60 m. Genghis Khan.

1962. 800th Birth Anniv. of Genghis Khan.
291. 67. 20 m. multicoloured .. 5·50 5·50
292. – 30 m. multicoloured .. 5·50 5·50
293. – 50 m. blk., brn. and red 12·00 12·00
294. – 60 m. buff, blue & brn. 12·00 12·00

68. Perch.

1962. Fish. Multicoloured.
295. 5 m. Type 68 .. .. 15 10
296. 10 m. Burbot 15 10
297. 15 m. Arctic Grayling .. 20 10
298. 20 m. Bullhead 30 15
299. 30 m. Pike—perch .. 45 20
300. 50 m. Sturgeon 70 30
301. 70 m. Dace 95 45
302. 1 t. 50 Sculpin .. .. 1·50 70

69. Sukhe Bator.

1963. 70th Birth Anniv. of Sukhe Bator.
303. 69. 30 m. blue 15 10
304. 60 m. lake 30 20

70. Dog "Laika" and "Sputnik 2".

1963. Space Flights. Multicoloured.
305. 5 m. Type 70 .. .. 20 10
306. 15 m. Rocket blasting off.. 35 10
307. 25 m. "Lunik 2" (1959).. 35 15
308. 70 m. Nikolaev and Popovich 65 35
309. 1 t. Rocket "Mars" (1962) 90 55
SIZES—As Type 70: 70 m., 1 t. VERT. (21 × 70 mm.): 15 m., 25 m.

71. Children packing Red Cross Parcels.

1963. Red Cross Cent. Multicoloured.
310. 20 m. Type 71 .. .. 35 10
311. 30 m. Blood transfusion.. 45 15
312. 50 m. Doctor treating child 60 20
313. 60 m. Ambulance at street accident.. .. 75 20
314. 1 t. 30 Centenary emblem 90 40

72. Karl Marx. 73. Woman.

1963. 145th Birth Anniv. of Karl Marx.
315. 72. 30 m. blue 20 10
316. 60 m. lake 25 20

1963. 5th World Congress of Democratic Women, Moscow.
317. 73. 30 m. multicoloured 25 20

74. "Inachis io".

1963. Mongolian Butterflies. Multicoloured.
318. 5 m. Type 74 .. .. 30 10
319. 10 m. "Gonepteryx rhamni L." 35 10
320. 15 m. "Aglais urticae L." 85 15
321. 20 m. "Parnassius apollo L." 55 20
322. 30 m. "Papilio machaon L." 85 25
323. 60 m. "Agrodiaetus damon Schiff" .. 1·25 45
324. 1 t. "Limenitis populi L." 1·75 60

75. Globe and Scales of Justice.

1963. 15th Anniv. of Declaration of Human Rights.
325. 75. 30 m. red, blue & brown 20 15
326. 60 m. black, blue & yell. 30 20

76. "Coprinus comatus".

1964. Mushrooms. Multicoloured.
327. 5 m. Type 76 .. .. 25 10
328. 10 m. "Lactarius torminosus" 35 15
329. 15 m. "Psalliota campestris" 45 15
330. 20 m. "Russula delica".. 50 15
331. 30 m. "Ixocomus granulatus" 75 20
332. 50 m. "Lactarius scobiculatus" .. .. 1·00 45
333. 70 m. "Lactarius deliciosus" .. .. .. 1·40 60
334. 1 t. "Ixocomus variegatus" .. .. .. 1·90 80

77. Lenin when a Young Man.

1964. 60th Anniv. of London Bolshevik (Communist) Party.
335. 77. 30 m. red and brown .. 30 30
336. 50 m. ultramarine & blue 35 30

78. Gymnastics.

1964. Olympic Games, Tokyo. Multicoloured.

337.	5 m. Type **78**	10	10
338.	10 m. Throwing the javelin	10	10
339.	15 m. Wrestling	10	10
340.	20 m. Running	20	10
341.	30 m. Horse-jumping ..	30	15
342.	50 m. High-diving ..	40	20
343.	60 m. Cycling	65	30
344.	1 t. Emblem of Tokyo Games	90	50

79. Congress Emblem.

1964. 4th Mongolian Women's Congress.

345. **79.**	30 m. multicoloured ..	35	20

80. "Lunik 1".

1964. Space research. Multicoloured.

346.	5 m. Type **80**	15	10
347.	10 m. "Vostoks 1 and 2"	15	10
348.	15 m. "Tiros"	20	10
349.	20 m. "Cosmos" ..	20	10
350.	30 m. "Mars Probe" ..	30	10
351.	60 m. "Luna 4" ..	45	15
352.	80 m. "Echo 2" ..	60	25
353.	1 t. Radio Telescope ..	65	45

The 10 m., 80 m. and 1 t. are horiz., the rest are vert.

81. Horseman and Flag.

1964. 40th Anniv. of Mongolian Constitution.

354. **81.**	25 m. multicoloured ..	30	10
355.	50 m. multicoloured ..	35	20

82. Marine Exploration.

1965. Int. Quiet Sun Year. Multicoloured.

356.	5 m. Type **82** (postage) ..	30	10
357.	10 m. Weather balloon ..	15	10
358.	60 m. Northern Lights ..	60	20
359.	80 m. Geomagnetic emblems	70	25
360.	1 t. Globe and I.Q.S.Y. emblem	1·10	50
361.	15 m. Weather satellite (air)	40	10
362.	20 m. Antarctic exploration	3·00	55
363.	30 m. Space exploration ..	55	15

83. Horses Grazing.

1965. Mongolian Horses. Multicoloured.

364.	5 m. Type **83**	30	10
365.	10 m. Hunting with Golden Eagles	80	15
366.	15 m. Breaking-in wild horse	45	15
367.	20 m. Horses racing ..	45	15
368.	30 m. Horses jumping ..	55	15
369.	60 m. Hunting wolves ..	70	25
370.	80 m. Milking a mare ..	85	40
371.	1 t. Mare and colt ..	1·40	60

84. Farm Girl with Lambs.

1965. 40th Anniv. of Mongolian Youth Movement.

372. **84.**	5 m. orge., bistre & grn.	10	10
373. –	10 m. bistre, blue & red	15	10
374. –	20 m. ochre, red & violet	20	15
375. –	30 m. lilac, brown & grn.	45	20
376. –	50 m. orge., buff & blue	75	45

DESIGNS: 10 m. Young drummers. 20 m. Children around campfire. 30 m. Young wrestlers. 50 m. Emblem.

85. Chinese Perch.

1965. Mongolian Fishes. Multicoloured.

377	5 m. Type **85**	20	10
378	10 m. "Brachymistrax lenok"	20	10
379	15 m. Siberian sturgeon ..	25	15
380	20 m. Taimen	35	15
381	30 m. Banded catfish ..	55	20
382	60 m. Amur catfish ..	85	20
383	80 m. Pike	90	40
384	1 t. River perch	1·25	60

86. Marx and Lenin.

87. I.T.U. Emblem and Symbols.

1965. Organization of Socialist Countries' Postal Administrations Conference, Peking.

385 **86**	10 m. black and red ..	25	15

1965. Air. I.T.U. Cent.

386. **87.**	30 m. blue and bistre ..	40	15
387.	50 m. red, bistre & blue	60	20

88. Sable

1966. Mongolian Fur Industry.

388. **88.**	5 m. pur., blk. & yellow	15	10
389. –	10 m. brn., black & grey	15	10
390. –	15 m. brn., black & blue	25	10
391. –	20 m. multicoloured ..	25	10
392. –	30 m. brn., blk. & mve.	35	10
393. –	60 m. brn., blk. and grn.	55	25
394. –	80 m. multicoloured ..	85	40
395. –	1 t. blue, black & olive	1·90	50

DESIGNS (Fur animals)—HORIZ. 10 m. Red fox. 30 m. Pallas's Cat. 60 m. Beech marten. VERT. 15 m. European otter. 20 m. Cheetah. 80 m. Stoat. 1 t. Woman in fur coat.

89. W.H.O. Building.

1966. Inauguration of W.H.O. Headquarters, Geneva.

396 **89**	30 m. blue, gold & green	35	15
397	50 m. blue, gold and red	50	20

90. Footballers.

1966. World Cup Football Championships. Multicoloured.

398.	10 m. Type **90**	15	10
399.	30 m. Footballers (different)	25	10
400.	60 m. Goalkeeper saving goal	40	25
401.	80 m. Footballers (different)	65	30
402.	1 t. World Cup flag ..	1·10	35

92. Sukhe Bator and Parliament Buildings, Ulan Bator.

1966. 15th Mongolian Communist Party Congress.

404. **92.**	30 m. multicoloured ..	15	10

93. Wrestling. **95.** State Emblem.

1966. World Wrestling Championships Toledo (Spain). Similar Wrestling designs.

405. **93.**	10 m. blk., mve. & pur.	10	10
406. –	30 m. blk., mve. & grey	20	15
407. –	60 m. blk., mve. & brn.	30	15
408. –	80 m. blk., mve. & lilac	40	20
409. –	1 t. blk., mve. and turq.	55	20

1966. 45th Anniv. of Independence. Mult.

411.	30 m. Type **95**	75	20
412.	50 m. Sukhe Bator, emblems of agriculture and industry (horiz.) ..	1·75	30

96. "Physochlaena physaloides". **97.** Child with Dove.

1966. Children's Day. Multicoloured.

421.	10 m. Type **97**	20	10
422.	15 m. Children with reindeer	20	10
423.	20 m. Boys wrestling ..	25	10
424.	30 m. Boy riding horse ..	50	15
425.	60 m. Children on camel ..	60	20
426.	80 m. Shepherd boy with sheep	75	25
427.	1 t. Boy archer	1·40	55

The 15 m., 30 m. and 80 m. are horiz.

1966. Flowers. Multicoloured.

413	5 m. Type **97**	20	10
414	10 m. Onion	20	10
415	15 m. Red lily	25	10
416	20 m. "Thermopsis lanceolata"	35	10
417	30 m. "Amygdalus mongolica"	50	20
418	60 m. Bluebeard	60	30
419	80 m. "Piptanthus mongolicus"	75	40
420	1 t. "Iris bungei" ..	95	55

1966. 60th Birth Anniv. of D. Natsagdorj. Nos. 277/8 optd. **1906 1966.**

420a. **63.**	30 m. brown	6·50	6·50
420b.	50 m. green	6·50	6·50

98. "Proton 1".

1966. Space Satellites. Multicoloured.

428.	5 m. "Vostok 2" (vert.) ..	10	10
429.	10 m. Type **98**	10	10
430.	15 m. "Telstar 1" (vert.)	15	10
431.	20 m. "Molniya 1" (vert.)	15	10
432.	30 m. "Syncom 3" (vert.)	20	15
433.	60 m. "Luna 9" (vert.) ..	40	15
434.	80 m. "Luna 12" (vert.)	60	30
435.	1 t. Mars and photographs taken by "Mariner 4"	85	40

99. Tarbosaurus. **100.** Congress Emblem.

1966. Prehistoric Animals. Multicoloured.

436.	5 m. Type **99**	40	10
437.	10 m. Talararus	40	10
438.	15 m. Protoceratops ..	55	15
439.	20 m. Indricotherium ..	55	15
440.	30 m. Saurolophus ..	90	20
441.	60 m. Mastodon	1·40	30
442.	80 m. Mongolotherium ..	1·60	45
443.	1 t. Mammuthus	1·75	70

1967. 9th Int. Students' Union Congress.

444. **100.**	30 m. ultramarine & blue	25	15
445.	50 m. blue and pink ..	35	20

101. Sukhe Bator and Mongolian and Soviet Soldiers. **102.** Vietnamese Mother and Child.

1967. 50th Anniv. of October Revolution.

446. **101.**	40 m. multicoloured ..	35	20
447. –	60 m. multicoloured ..	40	25

DESIGN: 60 m. Lenin, and soldiers with sword.

1967. Help for Vietnam.

448. **102.**	30 m. + 20 m. brown, red and blue ..	30	25
449.	50 m. + 30 m. brown, blue and red	50	40

103. Figure Skating.

1967. Winter Olympic Games, Grenoble. Mult.

450	5 m. Type **103**	10	10
451	10 m. Speed skating ..	10	10
452	15 m. Ice hockey	30	10
453	20 m. Skijumping ..	40	10
454	30 m. Bob sleighing ..	45	20
455	60 m. Figure skating (pairs)	60	30
456	80 m. Downhill skiing ..	80	40

104. Bactrian Camel and Calf.

1968. Young Animals. Multicoloured.
458. 5 m. Type **104** 15 10
459. 10 m. Yak 15 10
460. 15 m. Lamb 20 10
461. 20 m. Foal 30 10
462. 30 m. Calf 30 10
463. 60 m. Bison 40 15
464. 80 m. Roe deer 55 30
465. 1 t. Reindeer 80 40

105. Prickly Rose.

ДЭХБ
20 ЖИЛ
WHO
(106.)

1968. Mongolian Berries.
466. 105. 5 m. ultram. on blue .. 15 10
467. – 10 m. brown on buff .. 15 10
468. – 15 m. emerald on green 20 10
469. – 20 m. red on cream .. 20 10
470. – 30 m. red on pink .. 25 10
471. – 60 m. brown on orange 45 20
472. – 80 m. turquoise on blue 60 25
473. – 1 t. red on cream .. 80 40
DESIGNS: 10 m. Blackcurrant. 15 m. Gooseberry. 20 m. Crabapple. 30 m. Strawberry. 60 m. Redcurrant. 80 m. Cowberry. 1 t. Sea buckthorn.

1968. 20th Anniv. of World Health Organization. Nos. 396/7 optd. with T **106**.
474. 89. 30 m. blue, gold & grn. 2·50 2·50
475. 50 m. blue, gold and red 2·50 2·50

107. Human Rights Emblem.
109. "Portrait of artist Sharab" (A. Sangatzohyo).

108. "Das Kapital".

1968. Human Rights Year.
476. 107. 30 m. green and blue .. 30 10

1968. 150th Birth Anniv. of Karl Marx. Multicoloured.
477. 30 m. Type **108** 20 10
478. 50 m. Karl Marx 35 20

1968. Mongolian Paintings. Multicoloured.
479. 5 m. Type **109** 15 10
480. 10 m. "On Remote Roads" (A. Sangatzohyo) .. 20 10
481. 15 m. "Camel Calf" (B. Avarzad) 25 10
482. 20 m. "The Milk" (B. Avarzad) 30 15
483. 30 m. "The Bowman" (B. Gombosuren) .. 50 30
484. 80 m. "Girl Sitting on a Yak" (A. Sangatzohyo) 70 40
485. 1 t. 40 "Cagan Dara Eke" (Janaivajara) .. .. 1·25 75

110. Volleyball.

1968. Olympic Games, Mexico. Mult.
487. 5 m. Type **110** 10 10
488. 10 m. Wrestling 10 10
489. 15 m. Cycling 15 10
490. 20 m. Throwing the javelin 15 10
491. 30 m. Football 15 15
492. 60 m. Running 35 25
493. 80 m. Gymnastics .. 55 25
494. 1 t. Weightlifting .. 90 40

111. Hammer and Spade.

1968. 7th Anniv of Darkhan Town.
496 111 50 m. orange and blue 20 10

112. Gorky.
113. "Madonna and Child" (Boltraffio).

1968. Birth Cent of Maksim Gorky (writer).
497 112 60 m. ochre and blue .. 20 10

1968. 20th Anniv (1966) of U.N.E.S.C.O. Paintings by European Masters in National Gallery, Budapest. Multicoloured.
498. 5 m. Type **113** 15 10
499. 10 m. "St. Roch healed by an angel" (Moretto of Brescia) 20 10
500. 15 m. "Madonna and Child with St. Anne" (Macchietti) 25 10
501. 20 m. "St. John on Patmos" (Cano) 35 15
502. 30 m. "Young lady with viola da gamba" (Kupetzky) 35 15
503. 80 m. "Study of a head" (Amerling) 60 50
504. 1 t. 40 "The death of Adonis" (Furini) .. 1·25 75

114. Paavo Nurmi (running).

1969. Olympic Games' Gold-medal Winners. Multicoloured.
506. 5 m. Type **114** 10 10
507. 10 m. Jesse Owens (running) 10 10
508. 15 m. F. Blankers-Koen (hurdling) 15 10
509. 20 m. Laszlo Papp (boxing) 15 10
510. 30 m. Wilma Rudolph (running) 25 15
511. 60 m. Boris Sahlin (gymnastics) 35 20
512. 80 m. D. Schollander (swimming) 40 25
513. 1 t. A. Nakayama (ring exercises) 80 45

115. Bayit Costume (woman).

1969. Mongolian Costumes. Multicoloured.
515. 5 m. Type **115** 20 10
516. 10 m. Torgut (man) .. 20 10
517. 15 m. Sakhchin (woman) 25 10
518. 20 m. Khalka (woman) .. 35 10
519. 30 m. Daringanga (woman) 40 15
520. 60 m. Mingat (woman) .. 55 20
521. 80 m. Khalka (man) .. 75 25
522. 1 t. Barga (woman) .. 1·25 40

116. Emblem and Helicopter Rescue.

1969. 30th Anniv. of Mongolian Red Cross.
523. 116. 30 m. red and blue .. 60 20
524. – 50 m. red and violet .. 50 25
DESIGN: 50 m. Shepherd and ambulance.

117. Yellow Lion's-foot.

1969. Landscapes and Flowers. Multicoloured.
525 5 m. Type **117** 15 10
526 10 m. Variegated pink .. 15 10
527 15 m. Superb pink .. 25 10
528 20 m. Meadow cranesbill .. 25 10
529 30 m. Mongolian pink .. 40 15
530 60 m. Asiatic globe flower 50 15
531 80 m. Long-lipped larkspur 70 30
532 1 t. Saxaul 85 40

118. "Bullfight" (O. Tsewegdjaw).

1969. 10th Anniv. of Co-operative Movement. Paintings in National Gallery, Ulan Bator. Multicoloured.
533. 5 m. Type **118** 10 10
534. 10 m. "Colts Fighting" (O. Tsewegdjaw) .. 10 10
535. 15 m. "Horse-herd" (A. Sengetsohyo) .. 20 10
536. 20 m. "Camel Caravan" (D. Damdinsuren) .. 20 10
537. 30 m. "On the Steppe" (N. Tsultem) .. 35 15
538. 60 m. "Milking Mares" (O. Tsewegdjaw) .. 40 15
539. 80 m. "Off to School" (B. Avarzad) 50 30
540. 1 t. "After Work" (G. Odon) 80 40

120. Army Crest.

БНМАУ-ыг
тунхагласны
45
жилийн ой
1969—XI—26
(121.)

1969. 30th Anniv of Battle of Khalka River.
543 120 50 m. multicoloured .. 30 10

1969. 45th Anniv of Mongolian People's Republic. Nos. 411/12 optd with T **121**.
544. 95. 30 m. multicoloured .. 1·50 1·40
545. – 50 m. multicoloured .. 3·00 2·10

122. "Sputnik 3".

1969. Exploration of Space. Multicoloured.
546. 5 m. Type **122** 15 10
547. 10 m. "Vostok 1" 15 10
548. 15 m. "Mercury 7" .. 20 10
549. 20 m. Space-walk from "Voskhod 2" 30 10
550. 30 m. "Apollo 8" in Moon orbit 40 15
551. 60 m. Space-walk from "Soyuz 5" 45 25
552. 80 m. "Apollo 12" and Moon landing 55 30

123. Wolf.

1970. Wild Animals. Multicoloured.
554. 5 m. Type **123** 25 10
555. 10 m. Brown bear 30 10
556. 15 m. Lynx 55 10
557. 20 m. Wild Boar 55 10
558. 30 m. Elk 60 20
559. 60 m. Bobak marmot .. 70 20
560. 80 m. Argali 80 35
561. 1 t. "Hun Hunter and Hound" (tapestry) .. 90 50

124. "Lenin Centenary" (silk panel, Cerenhuu).

1970. Birth Cent. of Lenin. Multicoloured.
562. 20 m. Type **124** 15 10
563. 50 m. "Mongolians meeting Lenin" (Sangatzohyo) (horiz.) 30 15
564. 1 t. "Lenin" (Mazhig) 45 20

125. "Fairy Tale" Pavilion.

1970. "EXPO 70" World Fair, Osaka, Japan.
565. 125. 1 t. 50 multicoloured. 65 55

126. Footballers.

1970. World Cup Football Championships, Mexico.
567. 126. 10 m. multicoloured .. 15 10
568. – 20 m. multicoloured .. 15 10
569. – 30 m. multicoloured .. 20 10
570. – 50 m. multicoloured .. 25 10
571. – 60 m. multicoloured .. 45 15
572. – 1 t. multicoloured .. 55 15
573. – 1 t. 30 multicoloured .. 70 40
DESIGNS: Nos. 568/73, Different football scenes.

127. Common Buzzard.

1970. Birds of Prey. Multicoloured.
575. 10 m. Type **127** 60 10
576. 20 m. Tawny Owls .. 80 10
577. 30 m. Northern Goshawk 95 15
578. 50 m. White-tailed Sea Eagle 1·00 20
579. 60 m. Peregrine Falcon .. 1·50 40
580. 1 t. Common Kestrels .. 1·75 40
581. 1 t. 30 Black Kite .. 2·10 50

128. Soviet Memorial, Treptow, Berlin. **129.** Mongol Archery.

1970. 25th Anniv. of Victory in Second World War.

582. **128.** 60 m. multicoloured .. 35 15

1970. Mongolian Traditional Life. Mult.

583 10 m. Type **129** 30 15
584 20 m. Bogd-gegeen's Palace, Ulan Bator .. 30 15
585 30 m. Mongol horsemen .. 30 20
586 40 m. "The White Goddess-Mother" .. 30 25
587 50 m. Girl in National costume 65 45
588 60 m. "Lion's Head" (statue) 75 45
589 70 m. Dancer's mask .. 85 65
590 80 m. Gateway, Bogd-gegeen's Palace .. 1·00 1·00

131. I.E.Y. and U.N. Emblems with Flag.

1970. Int. Education Year.

592. **131.** 60 m. multicoloured .. 25 15

132. Horseman, "50" and Sunrise.

1970. 50th Anniv. of National Press.

593. **132.** 30 m. multicoloured .. 35 20

133. "Vostok 3" and "4".

1971. Space Research. Multicoloured.

594 10 m. Type **133** 15 10
595 20 m. Space-walk from "Voskhod 2" 15 15
596 30 m. "Gemini 6" and "7" 15 15
597 50 m. Docking of "Soyuz 4" and "5" 25 20
598 60 m. "Soyuz 6", "7" and "8" 35 20
599 80 m. "Apollo 11" and lunar module 50 35
600 1 t. "Apollo 13" damaged 60 30
601 1 t. 30 "Luna 16" .. 75 30

No. 594 is incorrectly inscribed. "12–15 August 1962" refers to flight of "Vostoks 3" and "4".

134. Sukhe Bator addressing Meeting.

1971. 50th Anniv of Revolutionary Party. Multicoloured.

603 30 m. Type **134** 15 10
604 60 m. Horseman with flag 25 10
605 90 m. Sukhe Bator with Lenin 30 15
606 1 t. 20 Mongolians with banner 40 25

136. Tsam Mask.

1971. Mongol Tsam Masks.

608. 10 m. multicoloured .. 15 10
609. 20 m. multicoloured .. 20 10
610. 30 m. multicoloured .. 30 10
611. 50 m. multicoloured .. 30 10
612. 60 m. multicoloured .. 40 20
613. 1 t. multicoloured .. 70 30
614. 1 t. 30 multicoloured .. 90 50

DESIGNS: Nos. 609/14, Different dance masks.

137. Banner and Party Emblems.

1971. 16th Revolutionary Party Congress.

615. **137.** 60 m. multicoloured .. 20 10

138. Steam Locomotive.

1971. "50 Years of Transport Development". Multicoloured.

616. 20 m. Type **138** 60 15
617. 30 m. Diesel locomotive .. 65 15
618. 40 m. Russian "Urals" truck 65 15
619. 50 m. Russian "Moskvich 412" car 75 15
620. 60 m. "PO-2" biplane .. 90 25
621. 80 m. "Antonov AN-24" airliner .. .. .. 1·10 40
622. 1 t. Lake steamer "Sukhe Bator" .. .. .. 2·00 70

139. Soldier. **140.** Emblem and Red Flag.

1971. 50th Anniv. of People's Army and Police. Multicoloured.

623. 60 m. Type **139** 40 10
624. 1 t. 50 Policeman and child 85 20

1971. 50th Anniv of Revolutionary Youth Organization.

625 **140** 60 m. multicoloured .. 30 20

141. Mongolian Flag and Year Emblem.

1971. Racial Equality Year.

626. **141.** 60 m. multicoloured .. 30 15

142. "The Old Man and the Tiger".

1971. Mongolian Folk Tales. Multicoloured.

627 10 m. Type **142** 20 10
628 20 m. "The Boy Giant-killer" 20 10
629 30 m. Cat and mice .. 20 10
630 50 m. Mongolians riding on eagle 25 10
631 60 m. Girl on horseback ("The Wise Bride") .. 40 15
632 80 m. King and courtiers with donkey 55 20
633 1 t. Couple kneeling before empty throne ("Story of the Throne") 80 25
634 1 t. 30 "The Wise Bird" .. 95 40

DESIGNS: Various Mongolian Fairy Tales.

143. Yaks.

1971. Livestock Breeding. Multicoloured.

635. 20 m. Type **143** 20 10
636. 30 m. Bactrian camels .. 20 10
637. 40 m. Sheep 25 10
638. 50 m. Goats 40 10
639. 60 m. Cattle 50 20
640. 80 m. Horses 60 25
641. 1 t. Pony 95 45

144. Cross-country Skiing.

1972. Winter Olympic Games, Sapporo, Japan. Multicoloured.

642 10 m. Type **144** .. 25 10
643 20 m. Bobsleighing .. 30 10
644 30 m. Figure skating .. 30 10
645 50 m. Slalom skiing .. 35 10
646 60 m. Speed skating .. 40 15
647 80 m. Downhill skiing .. 50 20
648 1 t. Ice hockey 70 25
649 1 t. 30 Pairs figure skating 85 40

145. "Horse-breaking" (A. Sengatzohyo).

1972. Paintings by Contemporary Artists from the National Gallery, Ulan Bator. Multicolured.

651 10 m. Type **145** 15 10
652 20 m. "Black Camel" (A. Sengatzohyo) .. 20 10
653 30 m. "Jousting" (A. Sengatzohyo) .. 25 10
654 50 m. "Wrestling Match" (A. Sengatzohyo) .. 30 10
655 60 m. "Waterfall" (A. Sengatzohyo) .. 40 10

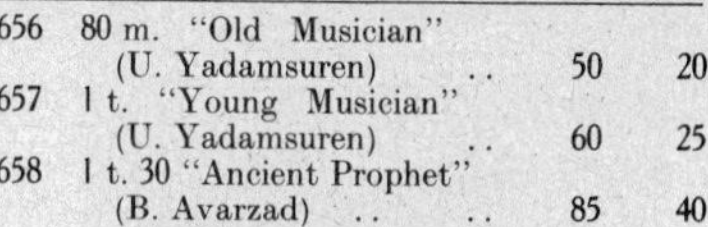
656 80 m. "Old Musician" (U. Yadamsuren) .. 50 20
657 1 t. "Young Musician" (U. Yadamsuren) .. 60 25
658 1 t. 30 "Ancient Prophet" (B. Avarzad) 85 40

147. "Calosoma fischeri".

1972. Insects. Multicoloured.

660. 10 m. Type **147**. 20 10
661. 20 m. "Mylabris mongolica" 25 10
662. 30 m. "Sternoplax zichyi" 30 10
663. 50 m. "Rhaebus komarovi" 40 15
664. 60 m. "Meloe centripubens" 55 15
665. 80 m. "Eodorcadion mongolicum" 75 25
666. 1 t. "Platyope maongolica" 90 30
667. 1 t. 30 "Lixus nigrolineatus" 1·40 50

149. Satellite and Dish Aerial ("Telecommunications").

1972. Air. National Achievements. Mult.

669. 20 m. Type **149** 20 10
670. 30 m. Horse-herd ("Livestock Breeding") 30 10
671. 40 m. Diesel train and air-craft ("Transport") .. 90 15
672. 50 m. Corncob and farm ("Agriculture") 35 15
673. 60 m. Ambulance and hospital ("Public Health") 70 20
674. 80 m. Actors ("Culture") .. 70 25
675. 1 t. Factory ("Industry") 75 40

150. Globe, Flag and Dish Aerial.

1972. Air. World Telecommunications Day.

676. **150.** 60 m. multicoloured .. 40 15

151. Running.

1972. Air. Olympic Games, Munich. Mult.

677 10 m. Type **151** 15 10
678 15 m. Boxing 15 10
679 20 m. Judo 20 10
680 25 m. High jumping .. 20 10
681 30 m. Rifle-shooting .. 30 15
682 60 m. Wrestling 45 20
683 80 m. Weightlifting .. 55 25
684 1 t. Mongolian flag and Olympic emblems .. 80 45

152. E.C.A.F.E. Emblem.

1972. 25th Anniv. of E.C.A.F.E.

686. **152.** 60 m. blue, gold and red 20 10

153. Mongolian Racerunner.

1972. Reptiles. Multicoloured.

687 10 m. Type **153** 20 10
688 15 m. Radde's toad .. 25 10
689 20 m. Halys viper .. 85 10
690 25 m. Toad-headed agama 40 15
691 30 m. Asiatic grass frog .. 55 15
692 60 m. Plate-tailed geckol 70 25
693 80 m. Steppe ribbon snake 85 35
694 1 t. Mongolian agama .. 1·25 55

154. "Technical Knowledge".

1972. 30th Anniv. of Mongolian State University. Multicoloured.

695. 50 m. Type **154** 35 10
696. 60 m. University building 45 15

155. "Madonna and Child with St. John the Baptist and a Holy Woman" (Bellini).

1972. Air. U.N.E.S.C.O. "Save Venice" Campaign. Paintings. Multicoloured.

697 10 m. Type **155** 15 10
698 20 m. "The Transfiguration" (Bellini) (vert) 20 10
699 30 m. "Blessed Virgin with the Child" (Bellini) (vert) 25 10
700 50 m. "Presentation of the Christ in the Temple" (Bellini) 40 15
701 60 m. "St. George" (Bellini) (vert) 50 20
702 80 m. "Departure of Ursula" (detail, Carpaccio) (vert) .. 65 35
703 1 t. "Departure of Ursula" (different detail, Carpaccio) 85 45

156. Manlay-Bator Damdinsuren.

157. Spassky Tower, Moscow Kremlin.

1972. National Heroes. Multicoloured.

705 10 m. Type **156** 15 10
706 20 m. Ard Ayus in chains (horiz) 25 10
707 50 m. Hatan-Bator Magsarzhav 40 15
708 60 m. Has-Bator on the march (horiz) 55 20
709 1 t. Sukhe Bator 85 30

1972. 50th Anniv. of U.S.S.R.

710. **157.** 60 m. multicoloured .. 50 15

158. Snake and "Mars 1".

1972. Air. Animal Signs of the Mongolian Calendar and Progress in Space Exploration. Multicoloured.

711. 60 m. Type **158** 70 25
712. 60 m. Horse and "Apollo 8" (square) 70 25
713. 60 m. Sheep and "Electron 2" (square) 70 25
714. 60 m. Monkey and "Explorer 6" 70 25
715. 60 m. Dragon and "Mariner 2" 70 25
716. 60 m. Pig and "Cosmos 110" (square) 70 25
717. 60 m. Dog and "Ariel 2" (square) 70 25
718. 60 m. Cockerel and "Venus 1" 70 25
719. 60 m. Hare and "Soyuz 5" 70 25
720. 60 m. Tiger and "Gemini 7" (square) 70 25
721. 60 m. Ox and "Venus 4" (square) 70 25
722. 60 m. Rat and "Apollo 15" lunar rover 70 25

The square designs are size 40 × 40 mm.

159. Swimming Gold Medal (Mark Spitz, U.S.A.).

1972. Gold Medal Winners, Munich Olympic Games. Multicoloured.

723 5 m. Type **159** 15 10
724 10 m. High jumping (Ulrike Meyfarth, West Germany) 25 10
725 20 m. Gymnastics (Savao Kato, Japan) 25 10
726 30 m. Show jumping (Andras Balczo, Hungary) 35 10
727 60 m. Running (Lasse Viren, Finland) .. 50 20
728 80 m. Swimming (Shane Gould, Australia) .. 70 25
729 1 t. Putting the shot (Anatoli Bondarchuk, U.S.S.R.) 85 35

160. Monkey on Cycle.

1973. Mongolian Circus (1st series). Mult.

731. 5 m. Type **160** 20 10
732. 10 m. Seal with ball .. 20 10
733. 15 m. Bear on mono-wheel 30 10
734. 20 m. Acrobat on camel .. 30 10
735. 30 m. Acrobat on horse .. 50 10
736. 50 m. Clown playing flute 60 15
737. 60 m. Contortionist .. 70 30
738. 1 t. New circus Hall, Ulan Bator .. .. .. 1·00 45

See also Nos. 824/30.

HAVE YOU READ THE NOTES AT THE BEGINNING OF THIS CATALOGUE?
These often provide answers to the enquiries we receive.

161. Mounted Postman.

162. Sukhe Bator receiving Traditional Gifts.

1973.

739. **161.** 50 m. brown (postage) 60 10
740. – 60 m. green .. .. 1·75 15
741. – 1 t. purple .. .. 1·00 20
742. – 1 t. 50 blue (air) .. 1·75 25

Designs: 60 m. Diesel train. 1 t. Mail truck. 1 t. 50, Airliner.

1973. 80th Birth Anniv of Sukhe Bator. Multicoloured.

743 10 m. Type **162** 15 10
744 20 m. Holding reception .. 25 10
745 50 m. Leading army .. 35 10
746 60 m. Addressing council 45 10
747 1 t. Giving audience (horiz) 65 20

163. W.M.O. Emblem and Meteorological Symbols.

1973. Air. Centenary of World Meteorological Organization.

748 **163** 60 m. multicoloured .. 45 15

164. "Copernicus" (anon.).

167. Marx and Lenin.

Нэгдлийн Холбооны IV Их
Хурал 1973—6—11
(166.)

1973. 500th Birth Anniv. of Nicholas Copernicus (astronomer). Multicoloured.

749. 50 m. Type **164** 40 15
750. 60 m. "Copernicus in his Observatory" (J. Matejko) (55 × 35 mm.) .. 50 15
751. 1 t. "Copernicus" (Jan Matejko).. .. .. 70 30

1973. 4th Agricultural Co-operative Congress, Ulan Bator. No. 538 optd with T **166**.

754 60 m. multicoloured ..

1973. 9th Organization of Socialist States Postal Ministers Congress. Ulan Bator.

755 **167** 60 m. multicoloured .. 30 15

168. Russian Stamp and Emblems.

1973. Air. Council for Mutual Economic Aid Posts and Telecommunications Conference, Ulan Bator. Multicoloured.

756 30 m. Type **168** 30 15
757 30 m. Mongolia 45 20
758 30 m. Bulgaria 45 20
759 30 m. Hungary 45 20
760 30 m. Czechoslovakia .. 45 20
761 30 m. German Democratic Republic 45 20
762 30 m. Cuba 45 20
763 30 m. Rumania 45 20
764 30 m. Poland 70 20

169. Common Shelduck.

1973. Aquatic Birds. Multicoloured.

765 5 m. Type **169** 40 10
766 10 m. Black-throated diver 55 10
767 15 m. Bar-headed geese .. 85 15
768 30 m. Great crested grebe 1·10 20
769 50 m. Mallard .. .. 1·60 40
770 60 m. Mute swan .. .. 1·90 40
771 1 t. Greater scaups .. 2·25 50

170. Siberian Weasel.

1973. Small Fur Animals. Multicoloured.

772 5 m. Type **170** 20 10
773 10 m. Siberian chipmunk 20 10
774 15 m. Siberian flying squirrel 20 10
775 20 m. Eurasian badger .. 25 15
776 30 m. Eurasian red squirrel 35 15
777 60 m. Wolverine 70 30
778 80 m. American mink .. 85 45
779 1 t. Arctic hare .. .. 1·25 60

171. Launching "Soyuz" Spacecraft.

1973. Air. "Apollo" and "Soyuz" Space Programmes. Multicoloured.

780 5 m. Type **171** 15 10
781 10 m. "Apollo 8" .. 15 10
782 15 m. "Soyuz 4" and "5" linked 20 15
783 20 m. "Apollo 11" module on Moon 20 15
784 30 m. "Apollo 14" after splash-down 30 15
785 50 m. Triple flight by "Soyuz 6", "7" and "8" 35 20
786 60 m. "Apollo 16" lunar rover 45 25
787 1 t. "Lunokhod 1" .. 65 30

172. Global Emblem.

1973. 15th Anniv of Review "Problems of Peace and Socialism".

789 **172** 60 m. red, gold and blue 35 15

173. Alpine Aster.

1973. Mongolian Flowers. Multicoloured.

790	5 m. Type 173	15	10
791	10 m. Mongolian catchfly	25	10
792	15 m. "Rosa davurica" ..	30	10
793	20 m. Mongolian dandelion	40	15
794	30 m. "Rhododendron dahuricum"	55	20
795	50 m. "Clematis tangutica"	70	40
796	60 m. Siberian primrose ..	85	55
797	1 t. Pasque flower ..	1·25	65

174. "Limenitis populi".

1974. Butterflies and Moths. Multicoloured.

798.	5 m. Type 174	30	10
799.	10 m. " Arctia hebe " ..	35	10
800.	15 m. " Rhyparia purpurata"	40	10
801.	20 m. " Catocala pacta " ..	55	10
802.	30 m. " Isoceras kaszabi "	70	15
803.	50 m. " Celerio costata " ..	1·00	30
804.	60 m. " Arctia caja " ..	1·10	40
805.	1 t. "Diacrisia sannio" ..	1·50	50

175. "Hebe Namshil" (L. Merdorsh). 176. Comecon Headquarters, Moscow.

1974. Mongolian Opera and Drama. Mult.

806.	15 m. Type 175	25	10
807.	20 m. "Sive Hiagt" (D. Luvsansharav) (horiz.)	25	10
808.	25 m. "Edre" (D. Namdag)	30	10
809.	30 m. "The Three Khans of Sara-gol" (horiz.)	40	15
810.	60 m. " Amarsana " (B. Damdinsuren) ..	65	20
811.	80 m. " Edre " (different scene)	80	25
812.	1 t. " Edre " (different scene)	1·25	55

1974. Air. 25th Anniv. of Communist Council for Mutual Economic Aid ("Comecon").

813.	176. 60 m. multicoloured ..	30	20

177. Government Building and Sukhe Bator Monument, Ulan Bator.

1974. 50th Anniv. of Renaming of Capital as Ulan Bator.

814.	177. 60 m. multicoloured ..	30	20

179. Mounted Courier.

1974. Air. Centenary of U.P.U. Multicoloured.

816	50 m. Type 179	1·50	40
817	50 m. Reindeer mail sledge	1·50	40
818	50 m. Mail coach	1·50	40
819	50 m. Balloon post ..	2·00	40
820	50 m. Lake steamer "Sukhe Bator" and "AN-2" aircraft ..	2·25	40
821	50 m. Mail train and P.O. truck	1·75	40
822	50 m. Rocket in orbit ..	1·50	40

180. Performing Horses.

1974. Mongolian Circus (2nd series). Mult.

824.	10 m. Type 180 (postage)	20	10
825.	20 m. Juggler (vert.) ..	30	10
826.	30 m. Elephant on ball (vert.)	40	15
827.	40 m. Performing yak ..	60	20
828.	60 m. Acrobats (vert.) ..	75	25
829.	80 m. Trick cyclist (vert.)	1·10	45
830.	1 t. Contortionists (vert.) (air)	1·10	45

181. " Training a Young Horse ".

1974. Int. Children's Day. Drawings by Lhamsurem. Multicoloured.

831.	10 m. Type 181	20	10
832.	20 m. " Boy with Calf " ..	30	10
833.	30 m. " Riding untamed Horse "	35	10
834.	40 m. " Boy with Foal " ..	45	20
835.	60 m. " Girl dancing with Doves "	60	20
836.	80 m. " Wrestling " ..	65	30
837.	1 t. " Hobby-horse Dance "	1·10	45

182. Archer on Foot.

1974. "Nadam" Sports Festival. Mult.

838.	10 m. Type 182	20	10
839.	20 m. "Kazlodanie" (Kazakh mounted game)	30	10
840.	30 m. Mounted archer ..	40	10
841.	40 m. Horse-racing ..	50	20
842.	60 m. Bucking horse-riding	60	20
843.	80 m. Capturing wild horse	70	30
844.	1 t. Wrestling	80	45

183. Giant Panda.

1974. Bears. Multicoloured.

845.	10 m. Brown bear	15	10
846.	20 m. Type 183 ..	25	10
847.	30 m. Giant Panda ..	45	15
848.	40 m. Brown bear	45	20
849.	60 m. Sloth bear	70	30
850.	80 m. Asiatic black bear ..	80	50
851.	1 t. Brown bear	1·40	65

184. Red Deer.

1974. Game Reserves. Fauna. Multicoloured.

852.	10 m. Type 184	15	10
853.	20 m. Eurasian beaver ..	30	10
854.	30 m. Leopard	40	15
855.	40 m. Herring gull ..	85	30
856.	60 m. Roe deer	80	30
857.	80 m. Argali	85	35
858.	1 t. Siberian musk deer ..	1·40	65

185. Detail of Buddhist Temple, Palace of Bogdo Gegen.

1974. Mongolian Architecture. Multicoloured.

859.	10 m. Type 185	20	10
860.	15 m. Buddhist temple (now museum)	20	10
861.	30 m. " Charity " Temple, Ulan Bator	40	15
862.	50 m. Yurt (tent)	55	20
863.	80 m. Arbour in court-yard	75	40

186. Spassky Tower, Moscow, and Sukhe Bator Statue, Ulan Bator. 187. Proclamation of the Republic.

1974. Brezhnev's Visit to Mongolia.

864.	186. 60 m. multicoloured ..	30	20

1974. 50th Anniv. of Mongolian People's Republic. Multicoloured.

865.	60 m. Type 187	35	20
866.	60 m. "First Constitution" (embroidery)	35	20
867.	60 m. Mongolian flag ..	35	20

188. Gold Decanter.

1974. Goldsmiths' Treasures of the 19th Century. Multicoloured.

868.	10 m. Type 188	20	10
869.	20 m. Silver jug	30	10
870.	30 m. Night lamp	35	10
871.	40 m. Tea jug	45	20
872.	60 m. Candelabra	55	20
873.	80 m. Teapot	75	30
874.	1 t. Silver bowl on stand ..	1·00	40

189. Lapwing.

1974. Protection of Water and Nature Conservation. Multicoloured.

875	10 m. Type 189 (postage)	50	10
876	20 m. Sturgeon	45	10
877	30 m. Marsh marigolds ..	50	15
878	40 m. Dalmatian pelican ..	90	20
879	60 m. Perch	75	25
880	80 m. Sable	90	40
881	1 t. Hydrologist with jar of water (air)	1·00	40

190. U.S. Mail Coach.

1974. Centenary of U.P.U. Multicoloured.

883	10 m. Type 190	15	10
884	20 m. French postal cart ..	20	10
885	30 m. Changing horses, Russian mail and passenger carriage ..	35	15
886	40 m. Swedish postal coach with caterpillar tracks ..	45	20
887	50 m. First Hungarian mail van	50	25
888	60 m. German Daimler-Benz mail van and trailer	65	40
889	1 t. Mongolian postal courier	95	55

191. Red Flag. 193. Mongolian Woman.

192. "Zygophyllum xanthoxylon" (½-size illustration).

1975. 30th Anniv. of Victory.

891.	191. 60 m. multicoloured ..	35	20

1975. 12th International Botanical Conference. Rare Medicinal Plants. Multicoloured.

892.	10 m. Type 192	25	10
893.	20 m. "Incarvillea potaninii"	35	10
894.	30 m. " Lancea tibetica "	55	15
895.	40 m. " Jurinea mongolica "	55	20
896.	50 m. " Saussurea involucrata "	70	20
897.	60 m. " Allium mongolicum "	80	30
898.	1 t. " Adonis mongolica "	1·40	40

1975. International Women's Year.

899.	193. 60 m. multicoloured ..	45	20

194. " Soyuz " on Launch-pad.

1975. Air. Joint Soviet–American Space Project. Multicoloured.

900	10 m. Type 194	10	10
901	20 m. Launch of "Apollo"	15	10
902	30 m. "Apollo" and "Soyuz" spacecraft ..	30	10
903	40 m. Docking manoeuvre	35	20
904	50 m. Spacecraft docked together	45	20
905	60 m. "Soyuz" in orbit ..	50	30
906	1 t. "Apollo" and "Soyuz" spacecraft and communications satellite ..	80	40

195. Child and Lamb.

1975. International Children's Day. Mult.

908	10 m. Type 195	20	10
909	20 m. Child riding horse ..	40	10
910	30 m. Child with calf ..	40	10
911	40 m. Child and "orphan camel"	40	15
912	50 m. "The Obedient Yak"	50	25
913	60 m. Child riding on swan	60	30
914	1 t. Two children singing	95	45

See also Nos. 979/85.

196. Pioneers tending Tree.

Тээвэр—50
1975—7—15.

(197).

1975. 50th Anniv. of Mongolian Pioneer Organization. Multicoloured.

915. 50 m. Type **196** 30 15
916. 60 m. Children's study circle 50 20
917. 1 t. New emblem of Mongolian pioneers 65 30

1975. 50th Anniv. of Public Transport. Nos. 616/22 optd. with T **197**.

918. **138.** 20 m. multicoloured .. 2·50 2·50
919. – 30 m. multicoloured .. 2·50 2·50
920. – 40 m. multicoloured .. 1·90 1·90
921. – 50 m. multicoloured .. 1·90 1·90
922. – 60 m. multicoloured .. 2·50 2·50
923. – 80 m. multicoloured .. 3·00 3·00
924. – 1 t. multicoloured .. 3·75 3·75

198. Argali.

1975. Air, South Asia Tourist Year.

925 **198** 1 t. 50 multicoloured .. 90 40

199. Golden Eagle attacking Red Fox.

1975. Hunting Scenes. Multicoloured.

926. 10 m. Type **199** 55 10
927. 20 m. Lynx-hunting (vert.) 45 10
928. 30 m. Hunter stalking bobak marmots 50 15
929. 40 m. Hunter riding on reindeer (vert.) 60 20
930. 50 m. Shooting wild boar 60 25
931. 60 m. Wolf in trap (vert.) 75 35
932. 1 t. Hunters with brown bear .. .. .. 1·00 50

200. " Mesocottus haitej ".

1975. Fishes. Multicoloured.

933. 10 m. Type **200** 20 10
934. 20 m. " Pseudaspius leptocephalus " 30 10
935. 30 m. " Oreoleuciscus potanini " 35 15
936. 40 m. " Tinca tinca " .. 45 20
937. 50 m. " Coregonus lavaretus " 65 25
938. 60 m. " Erythroculter mongolicus " 75 30
939. 1 t. " Carassius auratus " 1·25 55

201. " Morin Hur " (musical instrument).

202. Revolutionary with Banner.

1975. Mongolian Handicrafts. Multicoloured.

940 10 m. Type **201** 15 10
941 20 m. Saddle 25 10
942 30 m. Headdress 30 10
943 40 m. Boots 40 15
944 50 m. Cap 50 20
945 60 m. Pipe and tobacco pouch 60 25
946 1 t. Fur hat 90 40

1975. 70th Anniv. of 1905 Russian Revolution.

947. **202.** 60 m. multicoloured .. 35 20

203. " Taming a Wild Horse ".

1975. Mongolian Paintings. Multicoloured.

948 10 m. Type **203** 10 10
949 20 m. "Camel Caravan" (horiz) 25 10
950 30 m. "Man playing Lute" 35 10
951 40 m. "Woman adjusting Headdress" (horiz) .. 40 15
952 50 m. "Woman in ceremonial Costume" .. 40 25
953 60 m. "Woman fetching Water" 50 30
954 1 t. "Woman playing Yaga" (musical instrument) 75 40

204. Ski Jumping.

205. " House of Young Technicians ".

1975. Winter Olympic Games, Innsbruck. Multicoloured.

956 10 m. Type **204** 10 10
957 20 m. Ice hockey 30 10
958 30 m. Slalom skiing .. 35 10
959 40 m. Bobsleighing .. 45 15
960 50 m. Rifle shooting (biathlon) 55 25
961 60 m. Speed skating .. 60 25
962 1 t. Figure skating .. 90 45

1975. Public Buildings.

964. **205.** 50 m. blue 40 10
965. – 60 m. green 50 15
966. – 1 t. brown 70 25

DESIGNS: 60 m. Hotel, Ulan Bator. 1 t. " Museum of the Revolution ".

206. " Molniya " Satellite.

1976. Air. 40th Anniv of Mongolian Meteorological Office.

967 **206** 60 m. blue and yellow 55 20

209. " National Economy " Star.

1976. 17th Mongolian People's Revolutionary Party Congress, Ulan Bator.

970. **209.** 60 m. multicoloured .. 35 20

210. Archery.

1976. Olympic Games, Montreal. Mult.

971 10 m. Type **210** 15 10
972 20 m. Judo 20 10
973 30 m. Boxing 35 10
974 40 m. Gymnastics .. 35 15
975 60 m. Weightlifting .. 45 20
976 80 m. High jumping .. 55 25
977 1 t. Rifle shooting .. 80 35

1976. Int. Children's Day. As T **195**. Mult.

979. 10 m. Gobi Desert landscape 20 10
980. 20 m. Horse-taming .. 30 10
981. 30 m. Horse-riding .. 35 10
982. 40 m. Pioneers' camp .. 45 20
983. 60 m. Young musician .. 60 20
984. 80 m. Children's party .. 80 30
985. 1 t. Mongolian wrestling .. 1·00 45

211. Cavalry Charge.

1976. 55th Anniv of Revolution. Mult.

986 60 m. Type **211** (postage) . 65 20
987 60 m. Man and emblem (vert) 65 20
988 60 m. "Industry and Agriculture" (air) .. 65 20

213. Osprey.

1976. Protected Birds. Multicoloured.

990. 10 m. Type **213** 50 10
991. 20 m. Griffon Vulture .. 65 10
992. 30 m. Lammergeier .. 90 15
993. 40 m. Marsh Harrier .. 1·10 15
994. 60 m. European Black Vulture .. .. 1·40 20
995. 80 m. Golden Eagle .. 1·60 25
996. 1 t. Tawny Eagle .. 1·90 30

214 " Rider on Wild Horse ".

1976. Paintings by O. Tsewegdjaw. Mult.

997 10 m. Type **214** 15 10
998 20 m. "The First Nadam" (game on horse-back) (horiz) 20 10
999 30 m. "Harbour on Khobsogol Lake" (horiz) .. 55 15
1000 40 m. "Awakening the Steppe" (horiz) .. 45 20
1001 80 m. "Wrestling" (horiz) 60 25
1002 1 t. "The Descent" (Yak hauling timber) .. 1·00 50

215. " Industrial Development ".

1976. Mongolian – Soviet Friendship.

1003. **215.** 60 m. multicoloured 90 20

216. John Naber of U.S.A. (Swimming).

217. Tablet on Tortoise.

1976. Olympic Games, Montreal. Gold Medal Winners. Multicoloured.

1004 10 m. Type **216** 10 10
1005 20 m. Nadia Comaneci of Rumania (gymnastics) 15 10
1006 30 m. Kornelia Ender of East Germany (swimming) 30 10
1007 40 m. Mitsuo Tsukahara of Japan (gymnastics) 40 15
1008 60 m. Gregor Braun of West Germany (cycling) 50 25
1009 80 m. Lasse Viren of Finland (running) .. 60 30
1010 1 t. Nikolai Andrianov of U.S.S.R. (gymnastics) 70 35

1976. Archaeology.

1012. **217.** 50 m. brown and blue 40 15
1013. – 60 m. black and green 40 15

DESIGN: 60 m. 6th-century stele.

218. " R – 1 " Biplane.

1976. Mongolian Aircraft. Multicoloured.

1014. 10 m. Type **218** 20 10
1015. 20 m. " R – 5 " biplane .. 30 10
1016. 30 m. " K – 5 " monoplane 40 10
1017. 40 m. " PO – 2 " biplane 45 15
1018. 60 m. " I – 16 " fighter .. 60 20
1019. 80 m. " Yak – 6 " monoplane 75 35
1020. 1 t. Junkers " Ju – 13 " monoplane 95 40

219. Dancers in Folk Costume.

1977. Mongolian Folk Dances. Multicoloured.

1021 10 m. Type **219** 25 10
1022 20 m. Dancing girls in 13th-century costume 35 10
1023 30 m. West Mongolian dance 45 10
1024 40 m. "Ekachi" dance .. 50 15
1025 60 m. "Bielge" ("Trunk") dance 80 20
1026 80 m. "Hodak" dance .. 95 30
1027 1 t. "Dojarka" dance .. 1·10 45

220. Gravitational Effects on " Pioneer ".

1977. 250th Death Anniv. of Sir Isaac Newton (mathematician). Multicoloured.

1028. 60 m. Type **220** (postage) 45 15
1029. 60 m. Apple tree (25×32 mm.) 45 15
1030. 60 m. Planetary motion and sextant 45 15
1031. 60 m. Sir Isaac Newton (25×32 mm.) 45 15
1032. 60 m. Spectrum of light .. 45 15
1033. 60 m. Attraction of Earth 45 15
1034. 60 m. Laws of motion of celestial bodies (25×32 mm.) 45 15
1035. 60 m. Space-walking (air) 45 15
1036. 60 m. " Pioneer 10 " and Jupiter 45 15

221. Natsagdorj, Mongolian Scenes and Extract from poem " Mother ".

1977. Natsagdorj (poet) Commem. Mult.

1037. 60 m. Type **221** 40 25
1038. 60 m. Border stone, landscape and extract from poem " My Homeland " 40 25

222. Horse Race.

1977. Horses. Multicoloured.

1039. 10 m. Type **222** 20 10
1040. 20 m. Girl on white horse 25 10
1041. 30 m. Rangeman on brown horse 30 10
1042. 40 m. Tethered horses .. 40 20
1043. 60 m. White mare with foal 55 20
1044. 80 m. Brown horse with shepherd 70 30
1045. 1 t. White horse 85 45

223. " Mongolemys elegans ".

1977. Prehistoric Animals. Multicoloured.

1046. 10 m. Type **223** 30 10
1047. 20 m. " Embolotherium ergiliense " 45 10
1048. 30 m. " Psittacosaurus mongoliensis " .. 55 15
1049. 40 m. Enthelodon .. 70 20
1050. 60 m. " Spirocerus kiakhtensis " .. .. 1·00 25
1051. 80 m. Hipparion .. 1·40 40
1052. 1 t. " Bos primigenius " 1·60 55

225. Child feeding Lambs.

226. Industrial Plant and Transport.

1977. Children's Day and 1st Balloon Flight in Mongolia. Multicoloured.

1054. 10 m. + 5 m. Type **225** 30 15
1055. 20 m. + 5 m. Boy playing flute and girl dancing 45 15
1056. 30 m. + 5 m. Girl chasing butterflies 55 20
1057. 40 m. + 5 m. Girl with ribbon 60 25
1058. 60 m. + 5 m. Girl with flowers 70 40
1059. 80 m. + 5 m. Girl with bucket 80 50
1060. 1 t. + 5 m. Boy going to school .. .. .. 1·00 60

1977. Erdenet (New Town).

1062. **226.** 60 m. multicoloured 75 20

227. Trade Unions Emblem.

1977. Air. 11th Mongolian Trade Unions Congress.

1063. **227.** 60 m. multicoloured 50 15

228. Mounting Bell-shaped Gear on Rocket. (Illustration reduced. Actual size 66 × 26 mm.)

1977. Air. 11th Anniv of "Intercosmos" Co-operation. Multicoloured.

1064 10 m. Type **228** 10 10
1065 20 m. Launch of "Intercosmos 3" 20 10
1066 30 m. Tracking ship "Kosmonavt Yury Gargarin" 60 15
1067 40 m. Observation of lunar eclipse 50 20
1068 60 m. Earth station's multiple antennae .. 70 25
1069 80 m. Magnetosphere examination, Van Allen Zone 90 35
1070 1 t. Meterological satellites .. .. 1·25 65

229. Fire-fighters' Bucket Chain.

1977. Mongolian Fire-fighting Services. Multicoloured.

1072. 10 m. Type **229** 20 10
1073. 20 m. Horse-drawn hand pump 30 10
1074. 30 m. Horse-drawn steam pump 40 15
1075. 40 m. Fighting forest fire 50 20
1076. 60 m. Mobile foam extinguisher 70 25
1077. 80 m. Modern fire engine 85 30
1078. 1 t. Helicopter spraying fire .. .. .. 1·25 45

230. "Molniya" Satellite and Dish Aerial on TV Screen.

1977. 40th Anniv. of Technical Institute.

1079. **230.** 60 m. bl., blk. & grey 45 20

231. " Aporia crataegi ".

1977. Butterflies and Moths. Multicoloured.

1080. 10 m. Type **231** 20 10
1081. 20 m. " Gastropacha quercifolia " 35 15
1082. 30 m. " Colias chrysoteme " 50 15
1083. 40 m. " Dasychira fascelina " 70 20
1084. 60 m. " Malocosoma neustria " .. .. 1·00 25
1085. 80 m. " Diacrisia sannio " 1·40 35
1086. 1 t. " Heodes virgaureae " 1·60 50

232. Lenin Museum.

233. Cruiser " Aurora " and Soviet Flag.

1977. Inaug. of Lenin Museum, Ulan Bator.

1087 **232** 60 m. multicoloured .. 40 20

1977. 60th Anniv of Russian Revolution. Multicoloured.

1088 50 m. Type **233** 60 15
1089 60 m. Dove and globe (horiz) 50 15
1090 1 t. 50 Freedom banner around the globe (horiz) 75 35

234. Giant Pandas.

1977. Giant Pandas. Multicoloured.

1091. 10 m. Eating bamboo shoot (vert.) 20 10
1092. 20 m. Type **234** 35 10
1093. 30 m. Female and cub in washtub (vert.) .. 45 15
1094. 40 m. Male and cub with bamboo shoot .. 60 20
1095. 60 m. Female and cub (vert.) 80 30
1096. 80 m. Family (horiz.) .. 1·40 50
1097. 1 t. Male on hind legs (vert.) .. .. .. 1·60 65

236. Montgolfier Brothers' Balloon.

1977. Air. Airships and Balloons. Mult.

1099 20 m. Type **236** 25 10
1100 30 m. Zeppelin "LZ-127" over North Pole .. 30 10
1101 40 m. "Osoaviahim" airship over the Arctic .. 40 15
1102 50 m. Soviet airship "North" 55 20
1103 60 m. "Aereon-340" design 65 20
1104 80 m. Nestrenko's planned airship 70 35
1105 1 t. 20 "Flying Crane" .. 1·00 60

237. Ferrari " 312-T2 ".

1978. Racing Cars. Multicoloured.

1107 20 m. Type **237** 25 10
1108 30 m. Ford McLaren "M-23" 30 10
1109 40 m. Soviet experimental car 40 20
1110 50 m. Japanese Mazda .. 50 20
1111 60 m. Porsche "936-Turbo" 60 25
1112 80 m. Model of Soviet car 65 25
1113 1 t. 20 American rocket car "Blue Flame" .. 95 40

238. " Boletus variegatus ". (Illustration reduced. Actual size 75 × 25 mm.)

1978. Mushrooms. Multicoloured.

1114 20 m. Type **238** 35 15
1115 30 m. "Russula cyanoxantha" 50 15
1116 40 m. "Boletus aurantiacus" 60 20
1117 50 m. "Boletus scaber" .. 70 25
1118 60 m. "Russula flava" .. 80 30
1119 80 m. "Lactarius resimus" 1·00 45
1120 1 t. 20 "Flammula spumosa" .. .. 1·40 65

239. A. F. Mozhaiski and Monoplane.

1978. Air. History of Aviation. Multicoloured.

1121. 20 m. Type **239** 20 10
1122. 30 m. Henry Farman and biplane 25 10
1123. 40 m. Geoffrey De Havilland and Hercules " DH-66 " 30 15
1124. 50 m. Charles Lindbergh and " Spirit of St. Louis " 45 20
1125. 60 m. Shagdarsuren, Demberel and aircraft 55 20
1126. 80 m. Chkalov, Baidukov, Beliakov and monoplane 65 35
1127. 1 t. 20 A. N. Tupolev and " TU-154 " 90 55

240. Footballers and View of Rio de Janeiro.

1978. World Cup Football Championship, Argentina. Multicoloured.

1129. 20 m. Type **240** 20 10
1130. 30 m. Footballers and Old Town Tower, Berne .. 25 10
1131. 40 m. Footballers and Stockholm Town Hall 30 15
1132. 50 m. Footballers and University of Chile .. 40 20
1133. 60 m. Footballers, Houses of Parliament and Tower of London 55 25
1134. 80 m. Footballers and Theatre Degolladeo of Guadalajara, Mexico .. 60 25
1135. 1 t. 20 Footballers and Munich Town Hall .. 85 40

241. Mongolian Youth and Girl.

1978. Mongolian Youth Congress, Ulan Bator.

1137. **241.** 60 m. multicoloured 35 15

242. Eurasian Beaver and 1954 Canadian Beaver Stamp.

1978. "CAPEX '78". International Stamp Exhibition, Toronto. Multicoloured.

1138.	20 m. Type **242**	20	10
1139.	30 m. Tibetan sand-grouse and Canada S.G. 620	40	10
1140.	40 m. Black-throated diver and Canada S.G. 495	50	10
1141.	50 m. Argali and Canada S.G. 449	70	35
1142.	60 m. Brown bear and Canada S.G. 447 ..	80	40
1143.	80 m. Elk and Canada S.G. 448	90	45
1144.	1 t. 20 Herring gull and Canada S.G. 474 ..	1·50	25

243. Marx, Engels and Lenin.

1978. 20th Anniv. of Review "Problems of Peace and Socialism".

1146. **243.**	60 m. red, gold & blk.	40	15

244. Map of Cuba, Liner, Aeroplane and Emblem.

1978. Air. 11th World Youth Festival, Havana.

1147. **244.**	1 t. multicoloured ..	90	20

245. "Open-air Repose".

1978. 20th Anniv of Philatelic Co-operation between Mongolia and Hungary. Paintings by P. Angalan. Multicoloured.

1148	1 t. 50 Type **245** ..	90	90
1149	1 t. 50 "Winter Night" ..	90	90
1150	1 t. 50 "Saddling" ..	90	90

247. Butterfly Dog.

1978. Dogs. Multicoloured.

1152	10 m. Type **247**	20	10
1153	20 m. Black Mongolian sheepdog	25	10
1154	30 m. Puli (Hungarian sheepdog)	35	15
1155	40 m. St. Bernard ..	40	20
1156	50 m. German shepherd dog	55	25
1157	60 m. Mongolian watch-dog	65	25
1158	70 m. Semoyedic Spitz ..	75	35
1159	80 m. Laika (space dog)	90	35
1160	1 t. 20 Black and white poodles and cocker spaniel	1·10	55

248. Open Book showing Scenes from Mongolian Literary Works.

1978. 50th Anniv. of Mongolian Writers' Association.

1161. **248.**	60 m. blue and red ..	35	15

249. "Dressed Maja" (Goya – 150th death anniv.).

1978. Painters' Anniversaries. Multicoloured.

1162.	1 t. 50 Type **249**	90	90
1163.	1 t. 50 "Ta Matete" (Gauguin – 75th death anniv.)	90	90
1164.	1 t. 50 "Bridge at Arles" (Van Gogh – 125th birth anniv.)	90	90

250. Young Bactrian Camel.

1978. Bactrian Camels. Multicoloured.

1166.	20 m. Camel with Foal ..	25	15
1167.	30 m. Type **250**	30	15
1168.	40 m. Two camels ..	45	20
1169.	50 m. Woman leading loaded camel	55	25
1170.	60 m. Camel in winter coat	70	30
1171.	80 m. Camel-drawn water waggon	90	45
1172.	1 t. 20 Camel racing ..	1·25	60

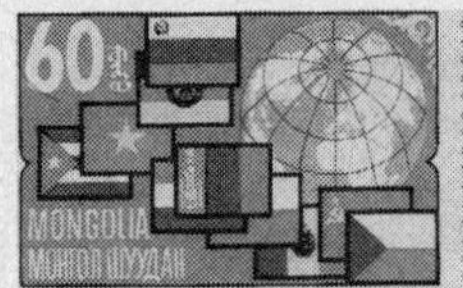

251. Flags of COMECON Countries.

1979. 30th Anniv. of Council of Mutual Economic Assistance.

1173. **251.**	60 m. multicoloured	35	25

252. Children riding Camel.

1979. International Year of the Child. Multicoloured.

1174.	10 m. + 5 m. Type **252** ..	15	15
1175.	30 m. + 5 m. Children feeding chickens ..	25	15
1176.	50 m. + 5 m. Children with deer	35	15
1177.	60 m. + 5 m. Children picking flowers ..	45	20
1178.	70 m. + 5 m. Children watering tree	50	25
1179.	80 m. + 5 m. Young scientists	60	35
1180.	1 t. + 5 m. Making music and dancing	80	50

INDEX

Countries can be quickly located by referring to the index at the end of this volume.

253. Silver Tabby.

1978. Domestic Cats. Multicoloured.

1182.	10 m. Type **253**	20	10
1183.	30 m. White Persian ..	35	15
1184.	50 m. Red Persian ..	55	15
1185.	60 m. Blue-cream Persian	70	20
1186.	70 m. Siamese	80	30
1187.	80 m. Smoke Persian ..	90	35
1188.	1 t. Birman	1·25	50

254. "Potaninia mongolica".

1979. Flowers. Multicoloured.

1189.	10 m. Type **254**	20	10
1190.	30 m. "Sophora alopecuroides"	30	10
1191.	50 m. "Halimodendron halodendron"	35	15
1192.	60 m. "Myosotis asiatica"	50	20
1193.	70 m. "Scabiosa comosa"	50	30
1194.	80 m. "Leucanthemum sibiricum"	60	30
1195.	1 t. "Leontopodium ochroleucum" ..	80	45

255. Finland v. Czechoslovakia.

1979. World Ice Hockey Championships, Moscow. Multicoloured.

1196.	10 m. Type **255**	15	10
1197.	30 m. West Germany v. Sweden	30	10
1198.	50 m. U.S.A. v. Canada ..	50	20
1199.	60 m. Russia v. Sweden ..	60	20
1200.	70 m. Canada v. Russia ..	65	25
1201.	80 m. Swedish goalkeeper	75	25
1202.	1 t. Czechoslovakia v. Russia	1·00	35

256. Lambs (Sanzhid).

1979. Agriculture Paintings. Multicoloured.

1203	10 m. Type **256**	10	10
1204	30 m. "Milking camels" (Budbazar)	20	10
1205	50 m. "Aircraft bringing help" (Radnabazar) .	40	15
1206	60 m. "Herdsmen" (Budbazar)	40	15
1207	70 m. "Milkmaids" (Nanzadsguren) (vert)	50	30
1208	80 m. "Summer Evening" (Sanzhid)	70	40
1209	1 t. "Country Landscape" (Tserendondog) ..	80	50

257. First Mongolian and Bulgarian Stamps.

1979. Death Centenary of Sir Rowland Hill, and "Philaserdica 79" International Stamp Exhibition, Sofia. Each black, grey and brown.

1211	1 t. Type **257**	1·50	1·00
1212	1 t. American mail coach	1·50	1·00
1213	1 t. Travelling post office, London–Birmingham railway	1·50	1·00
1214	1 t. Paddle-steamer "Hindoostan" ..	1·75	1·00

258. Stephenson's "Rocket".

1979. Development of Railways. Mult.

1215	10 m. Type **258**	25	10
1216	20 m. German "Der Adler" locomotive, 1835	30	10
1217	30 m. American locomotive, 1860	40	10
1218	40 m. Mongolian locomotive, 1931	50	15
1219	50 m. Mongolian locomotive, 1936	55	20
1220	60 m. Mongolian locomotive, 1970	65	25
1221	70 m. Japanese high-speed electric train, 1963 ..	80	30
1222	80 m. French "Orleans" aerotrain	90	40
1223	1 t. 20 Russian experimental jet train "Rapidity"	1·00	50

259. Flags of Mongolia and Russia.

262. East German Flag, Berlin Buildings and "Soyuz 31".

260. Pallas's Cat.

1979. 40th Anniv. of Battle of Khalka River.

1224. **259.**	60 m. gold, red and yellow	40	35
1225. –	60 m. red, yell. & blue	40	35

DESIGN: No. 1225, Ribbons, badge and military scene.

1979. Wild Cats. Multicoloured.

1226.	10 m. Type **260**	15	10
1227.	30 m. Lynx	30	15
1228.	50 m. Tiger	55	25
1229.	60 m. Snow leopard ..	65	25
1230.	70 m. Leopard	75	35
1231.	80 m. Cheetah	80	35
1232.	1 t. Lion	1·25	50

1979. 30th Anniv. of German Democratic Republic (East Germany).

1234. **262.**	60 m. multicoloured	60	30

263. Demoiselle Crane.

1979. Air. Protected Birds. Multicoloured.

1235.	10 m. Type **263** ..	35	10
1236.	30 m. Barred Warbler ..	55	10
1237.	50 m. Ruddy Shelduck ..	65	15
1238.	60 m. Azure-winged Magpie	75	15
1239.	70 m. Goldfinch	75	20
1240.	80 m. Great Tit	85	25
1241.	1 t. Golden Oriole ..	1·10	30

264. "Venus 5" and "6".

1979. Air. Space Research. Multicoloured.

1242	10 m. Type **264**	10	10
1243	30 m. "Mariner 5" ..	20	10
1244	50 m. "Mars 3"	35	20
1245	60 m. "Viking 1" and "2"	40	20
1246	70 m. "Luna 1", "2" and "3"	45	25
1247	80 m. "Lunokhod 2" ..	50	25
1248	1 t. "Apollo 15" Moon-rover	65	40

265. Cross-country Skiing.

1980. Winter Olympic Games, Lake Placid. Multicoloured.

1250	20 m. Type **265**	20	10
1251	30 m. Biathlon	25	15
1252	40 m. Ice hockey ..	30	20
1253	50 m. Ski jumping ..	40	25
1254	60 m. Slalom	50	30
1255	80 m. Speed skating ..	60	30
1256	1 t. 20 Four-man bobsleigh	85	45

266. "Andrena scita".

1980. Air. Wasps and Bees. Multicoloured.

1258.	20 m. Type **266**	25	15
1259.	30 m. "Paravespula germanica"	30	20
1260.	40 m. "Perilampus ruficornis"	40	25
1261.	50 m. "Bombus terrestris"	60	30
1262.	60 m. "Apis mellifera"	70	35
1263.	80 m. "Stilbum cyanurum"	80	45
1264.	1 t. 20 "Parnopes grandior"	1·25	60

267. Weightlifting.

1980. Olympic Games, Moscow. Multicoloured.

1266.	20 m. Type **267** ..	15	10
1267.	30 m. Archery	20	15
1268.	40 m. Gymnastics ..	25	15
1269.	50 m. Running	35	20
1270.	60 m. Boxing	40	25
1271.	80 m. Judo	50	25
1272.	1 t. 20 Cycling	75	40

268. "Z-526 AFS" Aeroplane.

1980. Air. World Aerobatic Championship, Oshkosh, Wisconsin. Multicoloured.

1274.	20 m. Type **268**	25	10
1275.	30 m. RS-180 "Sportsman"	30	10
1276.	40 m. Yanki-Anu ..	40	15
1277.	50 m. MJ-2 "Tempete"	55	20
1278.	60 m. "Pits"	65	25
1279.	80 m. "Acrostar" ..	75	35
1280.	1 t. 20 JAK-50	1·00	60

269. Swimming.

1980. Olympic Medal Winners. Multicoloured.

1282.	20 m. Type **269**	15	10
1283.	30 m. Fencing	20	10
1284.	50 m. Judo	30	15
1285.	60 m. Athletics	40	20
1286.	80 m. Boxing	50	25
1287.	1 t. Weightlifting ..	55	30
1288.	1 t. 20 Kayak-canoe ..	75	35

270. Sukhe Bator.

271. Gubarev.

1980. Mongolian Politicians.

1290.	**270.**	60 m. brown	40	20
1291.	–	60 m. blue	40	20
1292.	–	60 m. turquoise ..	40	20
1293.	–	60 m. bronze-green ..	40	20
1294.	–	60 m. deep green ..	40	20
1295.	–	60 m. red	40	20
1296.	–	60 m. brown	40	20

DESIGNS—VERT. No. 1291, Marshal Choibalsan. No. 1292, Yu. Tsedenbal aged 13. No. 1293, Tsedenbal as soldier, 1941. No. 1294, Pres. Tsedenbal in 1979. No. 1295, Tsedenbal with children. HORIZ. No. 1296, Tsedenbal and President Brezhnev of Russia.

1980. "Intercosmos" Space Programme. Multicoloured.

1297.	40 m. Type **271**	30	20
1298.	40 m. Czechoslovak stamp showing Gubarev and Remek	30	20
1299.	40 m. P. Klimuk ..	30	20
1300.	40 m. Polish stamp showing M. Hermaszewski ..	30	20
1301.	40 m. V. Bykovsky ..	30	20
1302.	40 m. East German stamp showing S. Jahn ..	30	20
1303.	40 m. N. Rukavishnikov	30	20
1304.	40 m. Bulgarian stamp showing G. Ivanov ..	30	20
1305.	40 m. V. Kubasov ..	30	20
1306.	40 m. Hungarian stamp showing Kubasov and B. Farkas	30	20

272. Benz, 1885.

1980. Classic Cars. Multicoloured.

1307.	20 m. Type **272**	25	10
1308.	30 m. "President" Czechoslovakia, 1897	30	10
1309.	40 m. Armstrong Siddeley, 1904	35	25
1310.	50 m. Russo-Balt, 1909 ..	45	20
1311.	60 m. Packard, 1909 ..	50	20
1312.	80 m. Lancia, 1911 ..	70	30
1313.	1 t. 60 "Marne" taxi, 1914	1·40	60

MINIMUM PRICE

The minimum price quoted is 5p which represents a handling charge rather than a basis for valuing common stamps. For further notes about prices see introductory pages.

273. Adelie Penguin

276. "The Shepherd speaking the Truth".

1980. Antarctic Exploration. Multicoloured.

1315	20 m. Type **273**	55	15
1316	30 m. Blue whales ..	70	20
1317	40 m. Wandering albatross and Jacques Cousteau's bathysphere	95	30
1318	50 m. Weddell seals and mobile research station	90	30
1319	60 m. Emperor penguins	1·25	35
1320	70 m. Great skuas ..	1·50	40
1321	80 m. Killer whales ..	1·60	55
1322	1 t. 20 Adelie penguins, research station, aircraft and tracked vehicle	2·25	75

1980. Nursery Tales. Multicoloured.

1326.	20 m. Type **276**	25	10
1327.	30 m. Children under umbrella and rainbow ("Above them the Sky is always clear") ..	30	10
1328.	40 m. Children on sledge and skis ("Winter's Joys")	35	15
1329.	50 m. Girl watching boy playing flute ("Little Musicians")	40	15
1330.	60 m. Boys giving girl leaves ("Happy Birthday")	55	20
1331.	80 m. Children with flowers and briefcase ("First Schoolday")	65	30
1332.	1 t. 20 Girls dancing ("May Day")	90	40

277. Soldier.

1981. 60th Anniv. of Mongolian People's Army.

1334.	**277.**	60 m. multicoloured	60	30

278. Economy Emblems within Party Initials.

1981. 60th Anniv. of Mongolian Revolutionary People's Party.

1335.	**278.**	60 m. gold, red & black	45	25

279. Motocross.

1981. Motor Cycle Sports. Multicoloured.

1336	10 m. Type **279**	15	10
1337	20 m. Tour racing ..	25	10
1338	30 m. Ice racing ..	30	15
1339	40 m. Road racing ..	40	20
1340	50 m. Motocross (different)	50	25
1341	60 m. Road racing (different)	55	25
1342	70 m. Speedway ..	60	30
1343	80 m. Sidecar racing ..	70	35
1344	1 t. 20 Road racing (different)	95	45

280. Cosmonauts entering Space Capsule.

1981. Soviet–Mongolian Space Flight. Mult.

1345	20 m. Type **280**	30	10
1346	30 m. Rocket and designer S. P. Korolev	35	10
1347	40 m. "Vostok 1" and Yuri Gagarin	40	15
1348	50 m. "Soyuz"–"Salyut" space station	50	20
1349	60 m. Spectral photography	60	25
1350	80 m. Crystal and space station	70	30
1351	1 t. 20 Space complex, Moscow Kremlin and Sukhe Bator statue, Ulan Bator	90	45

281. Ulan Bator Buildings and 1961 Mongolian Stamp.

1981. Stamp Exhibitions.

1353.	1 t. multicoloured ..	1·75	80
1354.	1 t. multicoloured ..	1·75	80
1355.	1 t. black, blue & magenta	1·75	80
1356.	1 t. multicoloured ..	1·75	80

DESIGNS: No. 1353, Type **281** (Mongolian stamp exhibition). No. 1354, Wurttemberg stamps of 1947 and 1949 and view of Old Stuttgart ("Naposta '81" exhibition). No. 1355, Parliament building and sculpture, Vienna, and Austrian stamp of 1933 ("WIPA 1981" exhibition). No. 1356, Japanese stamp of 1964, cherry blossom and girls in Japanese costume ("Japex '81" exhibition, Tokyo).

282. Star and Industrial and Agricultural Scenes.

1981. 18th Mongolian Revolutionary People's Party Congress.

1357.	**282.**	60 m. multicoloured	45	25

284. Sheep Farming.

1981. "Results of the People's Economy". Multicoloured.

1359.	20 m. Type **284**	30	10
1360.	30 m. Transport	70	15
1361.	40 m. Telecommunications	90	15
1362.	50 m. Public health service	50	20
1363.	60 m. Agriculture ..	60	25
1364.	80 m. Electrical industry	70	30
1365.	1 t. 20 Housing	1·00	45

286. Pharaonic Ship (15th century B.C.).

1981. Sailing Ships. Multicoloured.

1367 10 m. Type **286** 30 10
1368 20 m. Mediterranean sailing ship (9th century) 40 15
1369 40 m. Hanse kogge (12th century) (vert) .. 60 20
1370 50 m. Venetian felucca (13th century) (vert) .. 75 30
1371 60 m. Columbus's "Santa Maria" (vert) 90 35
1372 80 m. Cook's H.M.S. "Endeavour" (vert) .. 1·00 50
1373 1 t. "Poltava" (18th-century Russian ship of the line) (vert) 1·40 60
1374 1 t. 20 American schooner (19th century) (vert) .. 1·60 75

287. Arms of Mongolia and Russia.

1981. Soviet-Mongolian Friendship Pact.

1375. **287.** 60 m. red, bl. and gold 45 25

288. "Hendrickje in Bed".

290. White-tailed Sea Eagle and German 1 m. "Zeppelin" Stamp.

289. Billy Goat (pawn).

1981. 375th Birth Anniv. of Rembrandt (artist). Multicoloured.

1376. 20 m. "Flora" 20 10
1377. 30 m. Type **288** 25 15
1378. 40 m. "Young Woman with Earrings" .. 40 20
1379. 50 m. "Young girl in the Window" .. 45 25
1380. 60 m. "Hendrickje like Flora" 55 30
1381. 80 m. "Saskia with Red Flower" .. 70 35
1382. 1 t. 20 "The Holy Family with Drape" (detail) .. 85 45

1981. Mongolian Chess Pieces. Multicoloured.

1384 20 m. Type **289** 50 15
1385 40 m. Horse-drawn cart (rook) 75 25
1386 50 m. Camel (bishop) .. 90 35
1387 60 m. Horse (knight) .. 1·25 40
1388 80 m. Lion (queen) .. 1·60 60
1389 1 t. 20 Man with dog (king) .. .. .. 2·00 85

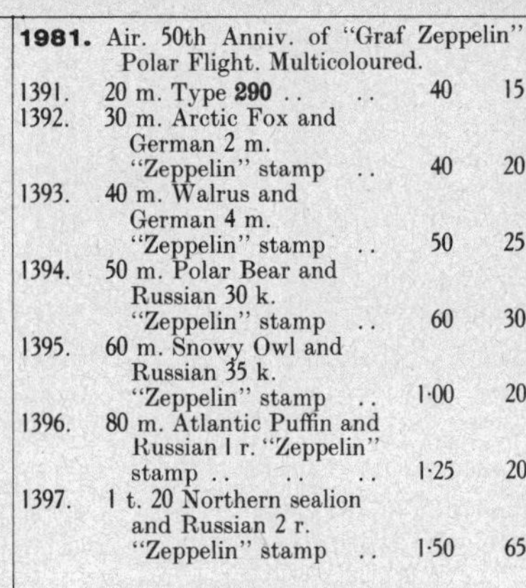

1981. Air. 50th Anniv. of "Graf Zeppelin" Polar Flight. Multicoloured.

1391. 20 m. Type **290** 40 15
1392. 30 m. Arctic Fox and German 2 m. "Zeppelin" stamp .. 40 20
1393. 40 m. Walrus and German 4 m. "Zeppelin" stamp .. 50 25
1394. 50 m. Polar Bear and Russian 30 k. "Zeppelin" stamp .. 60 30
1395. 60 m. Snowy Owl and Russian 35 k. "Zeppelin" stamp .. 1·00 20
1396. 80 m. Atlantic Puffin and Russian 1 r. "Zeppelin" stamp .. .. .. 1·25 20
1397. 1 t. 20 Northern sealion and Russian 2 r. "Zeppelin" stamp .. 1·50 65

291. Circus Camel and Circus Building, Ulan Bator.

1981. Mongolian Sport and Art. Multicoloured.

1399. 10 m. Type **291** 10 10
1400. 20 m. Horsemen and stadium (National holiday calvalcade) 20 15
1401. 40 m. Wrestling and Ulan Bator stadium .. 40 25
1402. 50 m. Archers and stadium 55 30
1403. 60 m. Folk singer-dancer and House of Culture .. 65 35
1404. 80 m. Girl playing jatga (folk instrument) and Ulan Bator Drama Theatre 80 40
1405. 1 t. Ballet dancers and Opera House .. .. 1·25 50
1406. 1 t. 20 Exhibition Hall and statue of man on bucking horse .. .. 1·40 70

292. Mozart and scene from "The Magic Flute".

1981. Composers. Multicoloured.

1407. 20 m. Type **292** 40 15
1408. 30 m. Beethoven and scene from "Fidelio" .. 50 20
1409. 40 m. Bartok and scene from "The Miraculous Mandarin" 60 25
1410. 50 m. Verdi and scene from "Aida" 80 35
1411. 60 m. Tchaikovsky and scene from "The Sleeping Beauty" .. 90 40
1412. 80 m. Dvorak and score of "New World" symphony .. .. 1·25 50
1413. 1 t. 20 Chopin, piano, score and quill pens .. .. 1·60 75

293. "Mongolian Women in Everyday Life" (detail, Davaakhuu).

294. Gorbatko.

1981. International Decade for Women. Multicoloured.

1414. 20 m. Type **293** 25 10
1415. 30 m. "Mongolian Women in Everyday Life" (different detail) .. 35 15
1416. 40 m. "National Day" (detail, Khishigbaiar) .. 40 20
1417. 50 m. "National Day" (detail) (different) .. 50 25
1418. 60 m. "National Day" (detail) (different) .. 60 35
1419. 80 m. "Ribbon Weaver" (Ts. Baidi) 85 40
1420. 1 t. 20 "Expectant Mother" (Senghesokhio) .. 1·25 65

1981. "Intercosmos" Space Programme. Multicoloured.

1422. 50 m. Type **294** 50 30
1423. 50 m. Vietnam stamp showing Gorbatko and Pham Tuan 50 30
1424. 50 m. Romanenko .. 50 30
1425. 50 m. Cuban stamp showing Tamayo 50 30
1426. 50 m. Dzhanibekov .. 50 30
1427. 50 m. Mongolian stamp showing Dzhanibekov and Gurrugchaa .. 50 30
1428. 50 m. Popov 50 30
1429. 50 m. Rumanian stamp showing "Salyut" space station and "Soyuz" space ship 50 30

295. Karl von Drais Bicycle, 1816.

1982. History of the Bicycle. Multicoloured.

1430. 10 m. Type **295** 20 10
1431. 20 m. Macmillan bicycle, 1838 .. .. .. 30 10
1432. 40 m. First American pedal bicycle by Pierre Lallament, 1866 .. 50 20
1433. 50 m. First European pedal bicycle by Ernest Michaux 55 25
1434. 60 m. "Kangaroo" bicycle, 1877 .. .. 60 30
1435. 80 m. Coventry Rotary Tandem, 1870s .. 75 45
1436. 1 t. Chain-driven bicycle, 1878 .. .. .. 95 60
1437. 1 t. 20 Modern bicycle .. 4·50 2·40

296. Footballers (Brazil, 1950).

1982. World Cup Football Championship, Spain. Multicoloured.

1439. 10 m. Type **296** 15 10
1440. 20 m. Switzerland, 1954 25 10
1441. 40 m. Sweden, 1958 .. 40 20
1442. 50 m. Chile, 1962 .. 55 25
1443. 60 m. England, 1966 .. 60 30
1444. 80 m. Mexico, 1970 .. 75 40
1445. 1 t. West Germany, 1974 95 50
1446. 1 t. 20 Argentina, 1978 .. 1·25 55

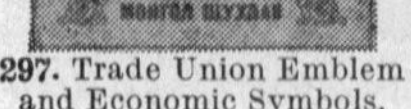

297. Trade Union Emblem and Economic Symbols.

299. Dimitrov.

1982. 12th Mongolian Trade Unions Congress.

1448. **297.** 60 m. multicoloured 50 30

1982. Birth Centenary of Georgi Dimitrov (Bulgarian statesman).

1450 **299** 60 m. blk, grey & gold 55 30

300. Chicks.

1982. Young Animals. Multicoloured.

1451 10 m. Type **300** 20 10
1452 20 m. Colt 30 15
1453 30 m. Lamb 40 20
1454 40 m. Roe deer fawn .. 50 25
1455 50 m. Bactrian camel .. 65 30
1456 60 m. Kid 70 35
1457 70 m. Calf 80 40
1458 1 t. 20 Wild piglet .. 1·10 60

301. Coal-fired Industry.

1982. Coal Mining.

1459. **301.** 60 m. multicoloured .. 70 30

302. Emblem.

304. Revsomol Emblem within "Flower".

303. Siberian Pine.

1982. 18th Revsomol Youth Congress.

1460. **302.** 60 m. multicoloured 55 30

1982. Trees. Multicoloured.

1461 20 m. Type **274** 25 15
1462 30 m. Siberian fir .. 35 20
1463 40 m. Poplar 45 25
1464 50 m. Siberian larch .. 55 30
1465 60 m. Scots pine .. 65 35
1466 80 m. Birch 75 45
1467 1 t. 20 Spruce .. .. 1·10 60

1982. 60th Anniv of Revsomol Youth Organization.

1449 **304** 60 m. multicoloured .. 55 30

305. World Map and Satellite.

1982. Air. I.T.U. Delegates' Conference, Nairobi.

1469. **305.** 60 m. multicoloured 70 30

306. Japanese "Iseki-6500" Tractor.

1982. Tractors. Multicoloured.

1470 10 m. Type **306** 15 10
1471 20 m. West German "Deutz-DX230" .. 25 10
1472 40 m. British "Bonser" .. 40 20
1473 50 m. American "International-884" .. 55 25
1474 60 m. French Renault "TX 145-14" .. 60 30
1475 80 m. Russian "Belarus-611" 75 40
1476 1 t. Russian "K-7100" .. 95 50
1477 1 t. 20 Russian "DT-75" .. 1·10 55

307. Fish and Lake Hevsgel.

1982. Landscapes and Animals. Mult.

1478	20 m. Type **307**	35	15
1479	30 m. Zavkhan Highlands and sheep	40	20
1480	40 m. Lake Hovd and Eurasian beaver ..	50	25
1481	50 m. Lake Uvs and horses	65	30
1482	60 m. Bajankhongor Steppe and goitred gazelle	80	35
1483	80 m. Bajan-Elgii Highlands and rider with golden eagle ..	1·50	35
1484	1 t. 20 Gobi Desert and bactrian camels ..	1·40	65

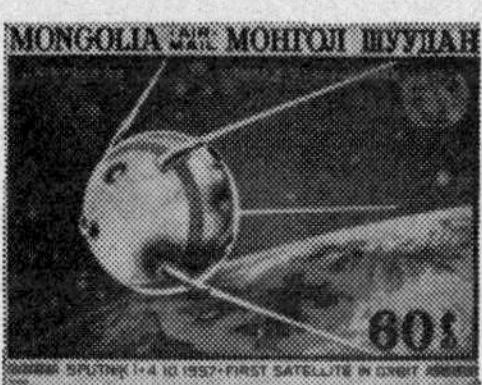

308. " Sputnik 1 ".

1982. Air. Second U.N. Conference on the Exploration and Peaceful Uses of Outer Space. Multicoloured.

1485.	60 m. Type **308**	60	30
1486.	60 m. " Sputnik 2 " and Laika (first dog in space)	60	30
1487.	60 m. " Vostok 1 " and Yuri Gagarin (first man in space)	60	30
1488.	60 m. " Venera 8 " ..	60	30
1489.	60 m. " Vostok 6 " and V. Tereshkova (first woman in space)	60	30
1490.	60 m. Aleksei Leonov and space walker	60	30
1491.	Neil Armstrong and astronaut on Moon's surface	60	30
1492.	60 m. V. Dzhanibekov, Jean-Loup Chretien and " Soyuz T-6 "	60	30

309. Montgolfier Brothers' Balloon, 1783.

1982. Air. Bicent of Manned Flight. Mult.

1494.	20 m Type **309**	30	10
1495.	30 m. Blanchard and Jefferies crossing the Channel, 1785	40	20
1496.	40 m. Green's flight to Germany in " Royal Vauxhall ", 1836 ..	55	25
1497.	50 m. Andree's North Pole flight in " Oernen " 1897	60	30
1498.	60 m. First Gordon Bennett balloon race, Paris, 1906	70	35
1499.	80 m. First stratosphere flight, Switzerland, 1931	90	45
1500.	1 t. 20 " U.S.S.R. VR-62 " flight, 1933	1·25	65

310. Sorcerer tells Mickey Mouse to clean up Quarters.

1983. Drawings from " The Sorcerer's Apprentice " (section of Walt Disney's film " Fantasia "). Multicoloured.

1502.	25 m. Type **310**	20	10
1503.	35 m. Mickey notices Sorcerer has left his cap behind	30	15
1504.	45 m. Mickey puts cap on and commands broom to fetch water	35	20
1505.	55 m. Broom carrying water	40	25
1506.	65 m. Mickey sleeps while broom continues to fetch water, flooding the room	50	30
1507.	75 m. Mickey uses axe on broom to try to stop it	55	35
1508.	85 m. Each splinter becomes a broom which continues to fetch water	65	40
1509.	1 t. 40 Mickey, clinging to Sorcerer's Book of Spells, caught in whirlpool ..	1·00	55
1510.	2 t. Mickey handing cap back to Sorcerer ..	1·40	75

311. Foal with Mother.

1983. " The Foal and the Hare " (folk tale). Multicoloured.

1512.	10 m. Type **311**	10	10
1513.	20 m. Foal wanders off alone	15	10
1514.	30 m. Foal finds sack ..	25	15
1515.	40 m. Foal unties sack ..	30	15
1516.	50 m. Wolf jumps out of sack	40	20
1517.	60 m. Hare appears as wolf is about to eat foal ..	45	25
1518.	70 m. Hare tricks wolf into re-entering sack ..	50	30
1519.	80 m. Hare ties up sack with wolf inside ..	60	35
1520.	1 t. 20 Hare and foal look for foal's mother ..	90	50

312. Antonov " AN24B " Aircraft.

1983. Tourism. Multicoloured.

1524	20 m. Type **312**	35	10
1525	30 m. Skin tent	35	15
1526	40 m. Roe deer	40	20
1527	50 m. Argali	55	25
1528	60 m. Imperial eagle ..	1·25	30
1529	80 m. Khan Museum, Ulan Bator	90	40
1530	1 t. 20 Sukhe Bator statue, Ulan Bator ..	1·00	60

313. Rose.

1983. Flowers. Multicoloured.

1531.	20 m. Type **313**	30	10
1532.	30 m. Dahlia	40	15
1533.	40 m. Marigold	50	20
1534.	50 m. Narcissus	60	25
1535.	60 m. Viola	70	30
1536.	80 m. Tulip	85	40
1537.	1 t. 20 Sunflower ..	1·25	60

MORE DETAILED LISTS
are given in the Stanley Gibbons Catalogues referred to in the country headings. For lists of current volumes see Introduction.

314. Border Guard.

1983. 50th Anniv. of Border Guards.

1538.	**314.** 60 m. multicoloured	1·00	40

316. Karl Marx.

1983. Death Centenary of Karl Marx.

1540.	**316.** 60 m. red, gold & bl.	70	40

317. Agriculture.

1983. 18th Communist Party Congress Five Year Plan. Multicoloured.

1541.	10 m. Type **317**	15	10
1542.	20 m. Power industry ..	25	10
1543.	30 m. Textile industry ..	30	15
1544.	40 m. Science in industry and agriculture ..	45	25
1545.	60 m. Improvement of living standards ..	60	35
1546.	80 m. Communications ..	1·40	50
1547.	1 t. Children (education)	1·00	60

318. Young Inventors.

1983. Children's Year. Multicoloured.

1548.	10 m. Type **318**	15	10
1549.	20 m. In school	25	10
1550.	30 m. Archery	40	15
1551.	40 m. Shepherdess playing flute	50	20
1552.	50 m. Girl with deer ..	65	30
1553.	70 m. Collecting rocks and mushrooms ..	1·00	50
1554.	1 t. 20 Girl playing lute and boy singing ..	1·25	60

319. Skating.

1983. 10th Anniv. of Children's Fund. Multicoloured.

1555.	20 m. Type **319**	15	15
1556.	30 m. Shepherds ..	25	15
1557.	40 m. Tree-planting ..	50	25
1558.	50 m. Playing by the sea	65	35
1559.	60 m. Carrying water ..	80	40
1560.	80 m. Folk dancing ..	1·00	65
1561.	1 t. 20 Ballet	1·75	85

320. Pallas's Pika.

1983. Small Mammals. Multicoloured.

1563.	20 m. Type **320**	35	20
1564.	30 m. Long-eared jerboa	45	25
1565.	40 m. Eurasian red squirrel	55	30
1566.	50 m. Daurian hedghog	65	40
1567.	60 m. Harvest mouse ..	80	45
1568.	80 m. Eurasian water shrew	1·25	70
1569.	1 t. 20 Siberian chipmunk	1·75	95

322. Bobsleighing.

1984. Winter Olympic Games, Sarajevo. Mult.

1571	20 m. Type **322**	30	15
1572	30 m. Cross-country skiing	40	20
1573	40 m. Ice hockey ..	55	30
1574	50 m. Speed skating ..	65	35
1575	60 m. Ski jumping ..	75	40
1576	80 m. Ice dancing ..	1·25	70
1577	1 t. 20 Biathlon (horiz) ..	1·60	90

323. Mail Van.

1984. World Communications Year. Multicoloured.

1579.	10 m. Type **323**	15	10
1580.	20 m. Earth receiving station	30	20
1581.	40 m. Airplane	75	30
1582.	50 m. Central Post Office, Ulan Bator	70	35
1583.	1 t. Transmitter	1·10	70
1584.	1 t. 20 Diesel train ..	2·50	1·00

325. Cycling. 326. Flag, Rocket and Coastal Scene.

1984. Olympic Games, Los Angeles, Multicoloured.

1587.	20 m. Gymnastics (horiz.)	25	15
1588.	30 m. Type **325**	35	20
1589.	40 m. Weightlifting ..	45	25
1590.	50 m. Judo	55	30
1591.	60 m. Archery	65	35
1592.	80 m. Boxing	90	60
1593.	1 t. 20 High jumping (horiz.)	1·25	75

1984. 25th Anniv. of Cuban Revolution.

1595.	**326.** 60 m. multicoloured	80	40

328. "DC-10".

329. Speaker, Radio and Transmitter.

1984. Air. Civil Aviation. Multicoloured.

1597.	20 m. Type **328**	35	15
1598.	30 m. Airbus "A 300 B 2"	55	20
1599.	40 m. "Concorde" ..	70	30
1600.	50 m. Boeing "747" ..	85	35
1601.	60 m. "IL-62"	1·00	40
1602.	80 m. "TU-154"	1·40	70
1603.	1 t. 20 "IL-86"	1·75	85

1984. 50th Anniv. of Mongolian Broadcasting.

1605.	**329.** 60 m. multicoloured	75	40

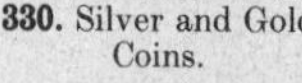

330. Silver and Gold Coins.

332. Sukhe Bator Statue.

331. Golden Harp.

1984. 60th Anniv. of State Bank.

1606.	**330.** 60 m. multicoloured	75	40

1984. Scenes from Walt Disney's "Mickey and the Beanstalk" (cartoon film). Multicoloured.

1607.	25 m. Type **331**	20	10
1608.	35 m. Mickey holding box of magic beans ..	30	15
1609.	45 m. Mickey about to eat bean	40	20
1610.	55 m. Mickey looking for magic bean	50	25
1611.	65 m. Goofy, Mickey and Donald at top of beanstalk	55	30
1612.	75 m. Giant holding Mickey	60	35
1613.	85 m. Giant threatening Mickey	80	40
1614.	140 m. Goofy, Mickey and Donald cutting down beanstalk ..	1·40	65
1615.	2 t. Goofy and Donald rescuing golden harp	1·60	75

1984. 60th Anniv. of Ulan Bator City.

1617.	**332.** 60 m. multicoloured	75	40

333. Arms, Flag and Landscape.

334. Rider carrying Flag.

1984. 60th Anniv. of Mongolian People's Republic.

1618.	**333.** 60 m. multicoloured	75	40

1984. 60th Anniv. of Mongolian People's Revolutionary Party.

1619.	**334.** 60 m. multicoloured	75	40

335. Gaetan Boucher (speed skating).

1984. Winter Olympic Gold Medal Winners. Multicoloured.

1620.	20 m. Type **335**	30	10
1621.	30 m. Eirik Kvalfoss (biathlon)	40	20
1622.	40 m. Marja-Liisa Hamalainen (cross-country skiing) ..	55	25
1623.	50 m. Max Julen (slalom)	70	35
1624.	60 m. Jens Weissflog (ski jumping) (vert.) ..	85	40
1625.	80 m. W. Hoppe and D. Schauerhammer (two-man bobsleigh) (vert.)	1·25	60
1626.	1 t. 20 J. Valova and O. Vassiliev (pairs figure skating) (vert.) ..	1·75	85

336 Donshy Mask

1984. Traditional Masks. Multicoloured.

1628	20 m. Type **336**	10	10
1629	30 m. Zamandi	10	10
1630	40 m. Ulaan-Yadam ..	15	10
1631	50 m. Lkham	20	10
1632	60 m. Damdinchoizhoo ..	25	10
1633	80 m. Ochirvaan ..	30	15
1634	1 t. 20 Namsrai	50	25

337 Collie

1984. Dogs. Multicoloured.

1636	20 m. Type **337**	10	10
1637	30 m. German shepherd ..	10	10
1638	40 m. Papillon	15	10
1639	50 m. Cocker spaniel ..	20	10
1640	60 m. Terrier puppy (diamond-shaped) ..	25	10
1641	80 m. Dalmatians (diamond-shaped) ..	30	15
1642	1 t. 20 Mongolian shepherd	50	25

338 Four Animals and Tree

1984. "The Four Friendly Animals" (fairy tale). Multicoloured.

1643	10 m. Type **338**	10	10
1644	20 m. Animals discussing who was the oldest ..	10	10
1645	30 m. Monkey and elephant beside tree ..	10	10
1646	40 m. Elephant as calf and young tree ..	15	10
1647	50 m. Monkey and young tree	20	10
1648	60 m. Hare and young tree	25	10
1649	70 m. Dove and sapling ..	30	15
1650	80 m. Animals around mature tree	30	15
1651	1 t. 20 Animals supporting each other so that dove could reach fruit ..	50	25

339 Fawn

1984. Red Deer. Multicoloured.

1653	50 m. Type **339**	20	10
1654	50 m. Stag	20	10
1655	50 m. Adults and fawn by river	20	10
1656	50 m. Doe in woodland ..	20	10

340 Flag and Pioneers

342 Black Stork

341 Shar Tarlan

1985. 60th Anniv of Mongolian Pioneer Organization.

1657	**340** 60 m. multicoloured ..	25	10

1985. Cattle. Multicoloured.

1658	20 m. Type **341**	10	10
1659	30 m. Bor khaliun ..	10	10
1660	40 m. Sarlag	15	10
1661	50 m. Dornod taliin bukh	20	10
1662	60 m. Char tarlan ..	25	15
1663	80 m. Nutgiin uulderiin unee	30	15
1664	1 t. 20 Tsagaan tolgoit ..	50	25

1985. Birds. Multicoloured.

1666	20 m. Type **342**	10	10
1667	30 m. White-tailed sea eagle	10	10
1668	40 m. Great white crane	15	10
1669	50 m. Heude's parrotbill	20	10
1670	60 m. Crane	25	15
1671	80 m. Japanese white-necked crane	30	15
1672	1 t. 20 Rough-legged buzzard	50	25

343 Footballers

344 Monument

1985. World Junior Football Championship, U.S.S.R.

1674	**343** 20 m. multicoloured	10	10
1675	– 30 m. multicoloured	10	10
1676	– 40 m. multicoloured	15	10
1677	– 50 m. multicoloured	20	10
1678	– 60 m. multicoloured	25	10
1679	– 80 m. multicoloured	30	15
1680	– 1 t. 20 multicoloured	50	25

DESIGNS: 30 m. to 1 t. 20, Different footballing scenes.

1985. 40th Anniv of Victory in Europe.

1682	**344** 60 m. multicoloured ..	25	15

345 Snow Leopards

1985. The Snow Leopard. Multicoloured.

1683	50 m. Type **345**	20	10
1684	50 m. Leopard	20	10
1685	50 m. Leopard on cliff ledge	20	10
1686	50 m. Mother and cubs ..	20	10

346 Moscow Kremlin and Girls of Different Races

347 Monument

1985. 12th World Youth and Students' Festival, Moscow.

1687	**346** 60 m. multicoloured ..	25	10

1985. 40th Anniv of Victory in Asia.

1688	**347** 60 m. multicoloured ..	25	10

348 "Rosa dahurica"

1985. Plants. Multicoloured.

1689	20 m. Type **348**	10	10
1690	30 m. False chamomile ..	10	10
1691	40 m. Dandelion ..	15	10
1692	50 m. "Saxzitraga nirculus"	20	10
1693	60 m. Cowberry	25	10
1694	80 m. "Sanguisorba officinalis"	30	15
1695	1 t. 20 "Plantago major"	50	25

See also Nos. 1719/25.

349 Camel

1985. The Bactrian Camel. Multicoloured.

1697	50 m. Type **349**	20	10
1698	50 m. Adults and calf ..	20	10
1699	50 m. Calf	20	10
1700	50 m. Adult	20	10

350 "Soyuz" Spacecraft

1985. Space. Multicoloured.
1701 20 m. Type **350** 10 10
1702 30 m. "Kosmos" satellite 10 10
1703 40 m. "Venera-9" satellite 15 10
1704 50 m. "Salyut" space station 20 10
1705 60 m. "Luna-9" landing vehicle 25 10
1706 80 m. "Soyuz" rocket on transporter 30 15
1707 1 t. 20 Dish aerial receiving transmission from "Soyuz" .. 50 25

352 U.N. and Mongolian Flags and U.N. Headquarters, New York

354 Congress Emblem

353 "Tricholoma mongolica"

1985. 40th Anniv of U. N. O.
1710 **352** 60 m. multicoloured .. 25 10

1985. Fungi. Multicoloured.
1711 20 m. Type **353** 10 10
1712 30 m. Chanterelle .. 10 10
1713 40 m. Boot-lace fungus .. 15 10
1714 50 m. Caesar's mushroom 20 10
1715 70 m. Chestnut mushroom 30 15
1716 80 m. Red-staining mushroom 30 15
1717 1 t. 20 Cep 50 25

1986. 19th Mongolian Revolutionary People's Party Congress.
1718 **354** 60 m. multicoloured .. 25 10

1986. Plants. As T **348**. Multicoloured.
1719 20 m. "Valeriana officinalis" 10 10
1720 30 m. "Hyoscymus niger" 10 10
1721 40 m. "Ephedra sinica" .. 15 10
1722 50 m. "Thymus gobica" 20 10
1723 60 m. "Paeonia anomalia" 25 10
1724 80 m. "Achilea millefolium" 30 15
1725 1 t. 20 "Rhododendron adamsii" 50 25

355 Scene from Play

1986. 80th Birth Anniv of D. Natsagdorj (writer).
1726 **355** 60 m. multicoloured .. 25 10

356 Thalmann

357 Man wearing Patterned Robe

1986. Birth Centenary of Ernst Thalmann (German politician).
1727 **356** 60 m. multicoloured .. 25 10

1986. Costumes. Multicoloured.
1728 60 m. Type **357** .. 25 10
1729 60 m. Man in blue robe and fur-lined hat with ear flaps 25 10
1730 60 m. Woman in black and yellow dress and bolero 25 10
1731 60 m. Woman in pink dress patterned with stars 25 10
1732 60 m. Man in cream robe with fur cuffs 25 10
1733 60 m. Man in brown robe and mauve and yellow tunic 25 10
1734 60 m. Woman in blue dress with with black, yellow and red overtunic 25 10

358 Footballers

1986. World Cup Football Championship, Mexico.
1735 **358** 20 m. multicoloured 10 10
1736 – 30 m. multicoloured 10 10
1737 – 40 m. mult (horiz) .. 15 10
1738 – 50 m. multicoloured 20 10
1739 – 60 m. multicoloured 25 10
1740 – 80 m. multicoloured 30 15
1741 – 1 t. 20 multicoloured 50 25
DESIGNS: 30 m. to 1 t. 20, Different footballing scenes.

359 Mink

1986. Mink. Multicoloured.
1743 60 m. Type **359** 25 10
1744 60 m. Mink on rock .. 25 10
1745 60 m. Mink on snow-covered branch .. 25 10
1746 60 m. Two mink 25 10
See also Nos. 1771/4, 1800/3, 1804/7, 1840/3 and 1844/7.

360 "Neptis coenobita"

361 Sukhe Bator Statue

1986. Butterflies and Moths. Multicoloured.
1747 20 m. Type **360** 10 10
1748 30 m. "Colias tycha" .. 10 10
1749 40 m. "Leptidea amurensis" 15 10
1750 50 m. "Oeneis tarpenledevi" 20 10
1751 60 m. "Mesoacidalia charlotta" 25 10
1752 80 m. Eyed hawk moth .. 30 15
1753 1 t. 20 Large tiger moth 50 25

1986. 65th Anniv of Independence.
1754 **361** 60 m. multicoloured .. 25 10

362 Yak and Goats Act

1986. Circus. Multicoloured.
1755 20 m. Type **362** 10 10
1756 30 m. Acrobat 10 10
1757 40 m. Yak act 15 10
1758 50 m. Acrobats (vert) .. 20 10
1759 60 m. High wire act (vert) 25 10
1760 80 m. Fire juggler on camel (vert) 30 15
1761 1 t. 20 Acrobats on camel-drawn cart (vert) .. 50 25

363 Morin Khuur

364 Flag and Emblem

1986. Musical Instruments. Multicoloured.
1762 20 m. Type **363** 10 10
1763 30 m. Bishguur (wind instrument) 10 10
1764 40 m. Ever buree (wind) 15 10
1765 50 m. Shudarga (string) .. 20 10
1766 60 m. Khiil (string) .. 25 10
1767 80 m. Janchir (string) (horiz) 30 15
1768 1 t. 20 Jatga (string) (horiz) 50 25

1986. International Peace Year.
1770 **364** 10 m. multicoloured .. 10 10

1986. Przewalski's Horse. As T **359**. Mult.
1771 50 m. Horses grazing on sparsely grassed plain 20 10
1772 50 m. Horses grazing on grassy plain .. 20 10
1773 50 m. Adults with foal .. 20 10
1774 50 m. Horses in snow .. 20 10

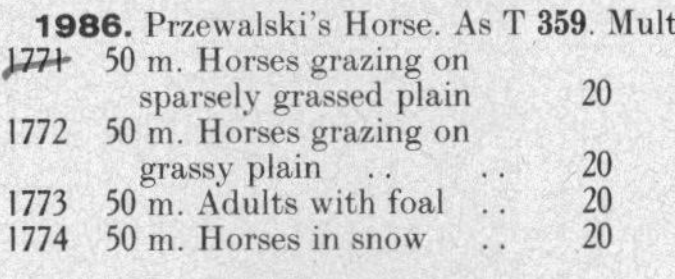

365 Temple

1986. Ancient Buildings. Multicoloured.
1775 60 m. Type **365** 25 10
1776 60 m. Temple with light green roof and white doors 25 10
1777 60 m. Temple with porch 25 10
1778 60 m. White building with three porches 25 10

366 Redhead ("Aythya americana")

1986. Birds. Multicoloured.
1779 60 m. Type **366** 25 10
1780 60 m. Ruffed grouse ("Bonasa umbellus") .. 25 10
1781 60 m. Whistling swan ("Olor columbianus") 25 10
1782 60 m. Rock pipit ("Anthus spinoletta") 25 10

367 Alfa Romeo "RL Sport", 1922

1986. Cars. Multicoloured.
1783 20 m. Type **367** 10 10
1784 30 m. Stutz "Bearcat", 1912 .. .. .. 10 10
1785 40 m. Mercedes "Simplex", 1902 .. 15 10
1786 50 m. Tatra "11", 1923 .. 20 10
1787 60 m. Ford Model "T", 1908 .. .. .. 25 10
1788 80 m. Vauxhall, 1905 .. 30 15
1789 1 t. 20 Russo-Balt "K", 1913 .. .. .. 50 25

368 Wilhelm Steinitz and Bardeleben Game, 1895

1986. World Chess Champions. Multicoloured.
1791 20 m. Type **368** 10 10
1792 30 m. Emanuel Lasker and Pilsberi game, 1895 10 10
1793 40 m. Alexander Alekhine and Retti game, 1925 .. 15 10
1794 50 m. Mikhail Botvinnik and Capablanca game, 1938 .. .. .. 20 10
1795 60 m. Anatoly Karpov and Untsiker game, 1975 .. .. .. 25 10
1796 80 m. Nona Gaprindashvili and Lasarevich game, 1961 .. .. 30 15
1797 1 t. 20 M. Chirburdanidze and Levitina game, 1984 50 25

1986. Saiga Antelope ("Saiga tatarica"). As T **359**. Multicoloured.
1800 60 m. Male 25 10
1801 60 m. Female with calf .. 25 10
1802 60 m. Male and female .. 25 10
1803 60 m. Male and female in snow 25 10

1986. Pelicans. As T **359**. Multicoloured.
1804 60 m. Dalmatian pelican ("Pelecanus crispus") 25 10
1805 60 m. Dalmatian pelican preening 25 10
1806 60 m. Eastern white pelican ("Pelecanus onocrotalus") 25 10
1807 60 m. Eastern white pelicans in flight .. 25 10

370 Siamese Fighting Fish

1987. Aquarium Fishes. Multicoloured.
1808 20 m. Type **370** 10 10
1809 30 m. Goldfish 10 10
1810 40 m. "Rasbora hengeli" 15 10
1811 50 m. "Aequidens sp." .. 20 10
1812 60 m. Moonfish 25 10
1813 80 m. Green swordtail .. 30 15
1814 1 t. 20 Angel fish (vert) .. 50 25

371 Lassooing Horse

1987. Traditional Equestrian Sports. Mult.

1816 20 m. Type **371** 10 10
1817 30 m. Breaking horse .. 10 10
1818 40 m. Mounted archer .. 15 10
1819 50 m. Race .. 20 10
1820 60 m. Horseman snatching flag from ground .. 25 10
1821 80 m. Tug of war .. 30 15
1822 1 t. 20 Racing wolf .. 50 25

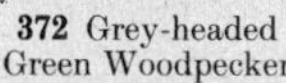

372 Grey-headed Green Woodpecker

373 Butterfly Hunting

1987. Woodpeckers. Multicoloured.

1823 20 m. Type **372** 10 10
1824 30 m. Wryneck 10 10
1825 40 m. Great spotted woodpecker 15 10
1826 50 m. White-backed woodpecker 20 10
1827 60 m. Lesser spotted woodpecker 25 10
1828 80 m. Black woodpecker 30 15
1829 1 t. 20 Three-toed woodpecker 50 25

1987. Children's Activities. Multicoloured.

1831 20 m. Type **373** 10 10
1832 30 m. Feeding calves .. 10 10
1833 40 m. Drawing on ground in chalk 15 10
1834 50 m. Football 20 10
1835 60 m. Go-carting .. 25 10
1836 80 m. Growing vegetables 30 15
1837 1 t. 20 Playing string instrument 50 25

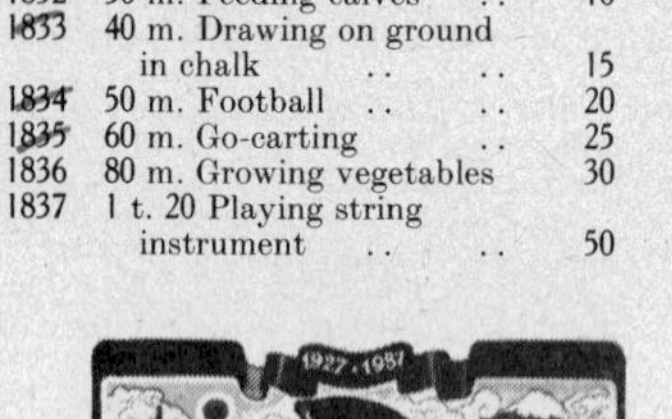

374 Industry and Agriculture

1987. 13th Congress and 60th Anniv of Mongolian Trade Union.

1838 **374** 60 m. multicoloured .. 25 10

375 Women in Traditional Costume

376 Flags of Member Countries

1987. 40th Anniv of Mongol–Soviet Friendship.

1839 **375** 60 m. multicoloured .. 25 10

1987. Argali ("Ovis ammon"). As T **359**. Multicoloured.

1840 60 m. On grassy rock (full face) 25 10
1841 60 m. On rock (three-quarter-face) .. 25 10
1842 60 m. Family 25 10
1843 60 m. Close-up of head and upper body .. 25 10

1987. Swans. As T **359**. Multicoloured.

1844 60 m. Mute swan ("Cygnus olor") in water 25 10
1845 60 m. Mute swan on land 25 10
1846 60 m. Whistling swan ("Cygnus bewickii") .. 25 10
1847 60 m. Whistling swan, "Cygnus gunus" and mute swan 25 10

1987. 25th Anniv of Membership of Council for Mutual Economic Aid.

1848 **376** 60 m. multicoloured .. 25 10

377 Sea Buckthorn

378 Couple in Traditional Costume

1987. Fruits. Multicoloured.

1849 20 m. Type **377** 10 10
1850 30 m. Blackcurrants .. 10 10
1851 40 m. Redcurrants .. 15 10
1852 50 m. Redcurrants .. 20 10
1853 60 m. Raspberries .. 25 10
1854 80 m. "Padus asiatica" .. 30 15
1855 1 t. 20 Strawberries .. 50 25

1987. Folk Art. Multicoloured.

1857 20 m. Type **378** 10 10
1858 30 m. Gold-inlaid baton and pouch 10 10
1859 40 m. Gold and jewelled ornaments 15 10
1860 50 m. Bag and dish .. 20 10
1861 60 m. Earrings 25 10
1862 80 m. Pipe, pouch and bottle 30 15
1863 1 t. 20 Decorative head-dress 50 25

379 Dancer

1987. Dances.

1864 **379** 20 m. multicoloured 10 10
1865 – 30 m. multicoloured 10 10
1866 – 40 m. multicoloured 15 10
1867 – 50 m. multicoloured 20 10
1868 – 60 m. multicoloured 25 10
1869 – 80 m. multicoloured 30 15
1870 – 1 t. 20 multicoloured 50 25

DESIGNS: 30 m. to 1 t. 20, Different dances.

381 Scottish Fold

1987. Cats. Multicoloured.

1872 20 m. Type **381** 10 10
1873 30 m. Grey 10 10
1874 40 m. Oriental 15 10
1875 50 m. Abyssinian (horiz) 20 10
1876 60 m. Manx (horiz) .. 25 10
1877 80 m. Black shorthair (horiz) 30 15
1878 1 t. 20 Spotted (horiz) .. 50 25

382 "B-12"

1987. Helicopters. Multicoloured.

1880 20 m. Type **382** 10 10
1881 30 m. Westland "WG-30" 15 10
1882 40 m. Bell "S-206 L" .. 20 10
1883 50 m. Kawasaki "369 HS" 25 10
1884 60 m. "KA-32" 30 10
1885 80 m. "MI-17" 35 15
1886 1 t. 20 "MI-10 K" .. 60 25

383 City Scene

384 Kremlin, Lenin and Revolutionaries

1987. 19th Mongolian People's Revolutionary Party Congress. Multicoloured.

1887 60 m. Type **383** 25 10
1888 60 m. Clothing and mining industries .. 25 10
1889 60 m. Agriculture .. 25 10
1890 60 m. Family 25 10
1891 60 m. Workers, factories and fields 25 10
1892 60 m. Building construction 25 10
1893 60 m. Scientist 25 10

1987. 70th Anniv of Russian October Revolution.

1894 **384** 60 m. multicoloured .. 25 10

385 Seven with One Blow

1987. Walt Disney Cartoons. Mult. (a) "The Brave Little Tailor" (Grimm Brothers)

1895 25 m. Type **385** 10 10
1896 35 m. Brought before the King 15 10
1897 45 m. Rewards for bravery 20 10
1898 55 m. Fight between Mickey and the giant .. 25 10
1899 2 t. Happy ending .. 80 40

(b) "The Celebrated Jumping Frog of Calaveras County" (Mark Twain)

1901 65 m. He'd bet on anything 25 10
1902 75 m. He never done nothing but...learn that frog to jump 30 15
1903 85 m. What might it be that you've got in that box? 35 15
1904 1 t. 40 He got the frog out and filled him full of quail shot 60 30

386 Head

1987. The Red Fox. Multicoloured.

1906 60 m. Type **386** 25 10
1907 60 m. Vixen and cubs .. 25 10
1908 60 m. Stalking 25 10
1909 60 m. In the snow .. 25 10

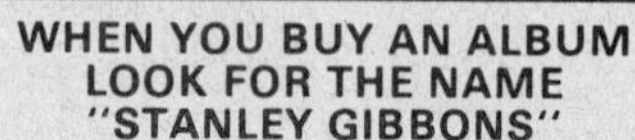

388 Bobsleighing

389 Sukhe Bator

1988. Air. Winter Olympic Games, Calgary. Multicoloured.

1911 20 m. Type **388** 10 10
1912 30 m. Ski jumping .. 10 10
1913 40 m. Skiing 15 10
1914 50 m. Biathlon 20 10
1915 60 m. Speed skating .. 25 10
1916 80 m. Figure skating .. 30 15
1917 1 t. 20 Ice hockey .. 50 25

1988. 95th Birth Anniv of Sukhe Bator.

1919 **389** 60 m. multicoloured .. 25 10

390 "Invitation"

1988. Roses. Multicoloured.

1920 20 m. Type **390** 10 10
1921 30 m. "Meilland" .. 10 10
1922 40 m. "Pascali" .. 15 10
1923 50 m. "Tropicana" .. 20 10
1924 60 m. "Wendy Cussons" 25 10
1925 80 m. "Rosa sp." (wrongly inscr "Blue Moon") 30 15
1926 1 t. 20 "Diorama" .. 50 25

391 "Ukhaant Ekhner"

1988. Puppets. Multicoloured.

1928 20 m. Type **391** 10 10
1929 30 m. "Altan Everte Mungun Turuut" .. 10 10
1930 40 m. "Aduuchyn Khuu" 15 10
1931 50 m. "Suulenkhuu" .. 20 10
1932 60 m. "Khonchyn Khuu" 25 10
1933 80 m. "Argat Byatskhan Baatar" 30 15
1934 1 t. 20 "Botgochyn Khuu" 50 25

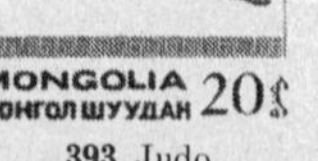

393 Judo

394 Marx

1988. Olympic Games, Seoul. Multicoloured.

1936 20 m. Type **393** 10 10
1937 30 m. Archery 10 10
1938 40 m. Weightlifting .. 15 10
1939 50 m. Gymnastics .. 20 10
1940 60 m. Cycling 25 10
1941 80 m. Running 30 15
1942 1 t. 20 Wrestling .. 50 25

1988. 170th Birth Anniv of Karl Marx.

1944 **394** 60 m. multicoloured .. 25 10

395 Couple and Congress Banner — **396** "Kosmos"

1988. 19th Revsomol Youth Congress.

1945	**395**	60 m. multicoloured . .	25	10

1988. Spacecraft and Satellites. Mult.

1946	20 m. Type **396**	10	10
1947	30 m. "Meteor"	10	10
1948	40 m. "Salyut"–"Soyuz" space complex . .	15	10
1949	50 m. "Prognoz-6" . .	20	10
1950	60 m. "Molniya-1" . .	25	10
1951	80 m. "Soyuz"	30	15
1952	1 t. 20 "Vostok" . .	50	25

397 Buddha — **398** Emblem

1988. Religious Sculptures

1954	**397**	20 m. multicoloured	10	10
1955	–	30 m. multicoloured	10	10
1956	–	40 m. multicoloured	15	10
1957	–	50 m. multicoloured	20	10
1958	–	60 m. multicoloured	25	10
1959	–	70 m. multicoloured	30	15
1960	–	80 m. multicoloured	30	15
1961	–	1 t. 20 multicoloured	50	25

DESIGNS: 30 m. to 1 t. 20, Different buddhas.

1988. 30th Anniv of Problems of "Peace and Socialism" (magazine).

1962	**398**	60 m. multicoloured . .	25	10

399 Eagle

1988. White-tailed Sea Eagle. Multicoloured.

1963	60 m. Type **399**	25	10
1964	60 m. Eagle on fallen branch and eagle landing . .	25	10
1965	60 m. Eagle on rock . .	25	10
1966	60 m. Eagle (horiz) . .	25	10

400 Ass

1988. Asiatic Wild Ass. Multicoloured.

1967	60 m. Type **400**	25	10
1968	60 m. Head of ass . .	25	10
1969	60 m. Two adults . .	25	10
1970	60 m. Mare and foal . .	25	10

401 Athlete — **403** U.S.S.R. (ice hockey)

1988. Traditional Sports. Multicoloured.

1971	10 m. Type **401**	10	10
1972	20 m. Horseman . .	10	10
1973	30 m. Archery	10	10
1974	40 m. Wrestling	15	10
1975	50 m. Archery (different)	20	10
1976	70 m. Horsemen (national holiday cavalcade) . .	30	15
1977	1 t. 20 Horsemen, wrestlers and archers . .	50	25

1988. Winter Olympic Games Gold Medal Winners. Multicoloured.

1979	1 t. 50 Type **403**	60	30
1980	1 t. 50 Bonnie Blair (speed skating)	60	30
1981	1 t. 50 Alberto Tomba (slalom)	60	30
1982	1 t. 50 Matti Nykanen (ski jumping) (horiz) . .	60	30

404 Brown Goat

1988. Goats. Multicoloured.

1984	20 m. Type **404**	10	10
1985	30 m. Black goat . .	10	10
1986	40 m. White long-haired goats	15	10
1987	50 m. Black long-haired goat	20	10
1988	60 m. White goat . .	25	10
1989	80 m. Black short-haired goat	30	15
1990	1 t. 20 Nanny and kid . .	50	25

405 Emblem

1989. 60th Anniv of Mongolian Writers' Association.

1992	**405**	60 m. multicoloured . .	25	10

406 Beaver gnawing Trees

1989. Eurasian Beaver. Multicoloured.

1993	60 m. Type **406**	25	10
1994	60 m. Beaver with young	25	10
1995	60 m. Beavers beside tree stump and in water . .	25	10
1996	60 m. Beaver rolling log	25	10

407 Dancers

1989. Ballet.

1997	**407**	20 m. multicoloured	10	10
1998	–	30 m. multicoloured	10	10
1999	–	40 m. mult (vert) . .	15	10
2000	–	50 m. multicoloured	20	10
2001	–	60 m. multicoloured	25	10
2002	–	80 m. mult (vert) . .	30	15
2003	–	1 t. 20 mult (vert) . .	50	25

DESIGNS: 30 m. to 1 t. 20, Different dancing scenes.

408 "Ursus pruinosis"

1989. Bears. Multicoloured.

2004	20 m. Type **408**	10	10
2005	30 m. Brown bear . .	10	10
2006	40 m. Asiatic black bear	15	10
2007	50 m. Polar bear . .	20	10
2008	60 m. Brown bear . .	25	10
2009	80 m. Giant panda . .	30	15
2010	1 t. 20 Brown bear . .	50	25

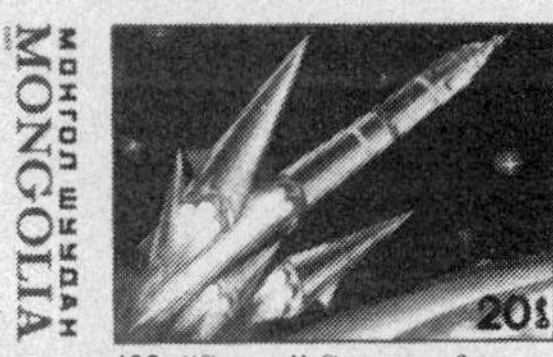

409 "Soyuz" Spacecraft

1989. Space. Multicoloured.

2012	20 m. Type **409**	10	10
2013	30 m. "Apollo"–"Soyuz" link	10	10
2014	40 m. "Columbia" space shuttle (vert) . .	15	10
2015	50 m. "Hermes" space-craft	20	10
2016	60 m. "Nippon" space-craft (vert) . .	25	10
2017	80 m. "Energy" rocket (vert)	30	15
2018	1 t. 20 "Buran" space shuttle (vert) . .	50	25

411 Nehru — **412** "Opuntia microdasys"

1989. Birth Centenary of Jawaharlal Nehru (Indian statesman).

2021	**411**	10 m. multicoloured . .	10	10

1989. Cacti. Multicoloured.

2022	20 m. Type **412**	10	10
2023	30 m. "Echinopsis multiplex"	10	10
2024	40 m. "Rebutia tephracanthus" . .	15	10
2025	50 m. "Brasilicactus haselbergii" . .	20	10
2026	60 m. "Gymnocalycium mihanovichii" . .	25	10
2027	80 m. "C. strausii" . .	30	15
2028	1 t. 20 "Horridocactus tuberisvicatus" . .	50	25

1989. 800th Anniv of Coronation of Genghis Khan. Nos. 291/4 optd **CHINGGIS KHAN CROWNATION 1 1 8 9**.

2030	**67**	20 m. multicoloured	10	10
2031	–	30 m. multicoloured	10	10
2032	–	50 m. black, brn & red	20	10
2033	–	60 m. buff, blue & brn	25	10

415 Citroen "BX"

1989. Motor Cars. Multicoloured.

2035	20 m. Type **415**	10	10
2036	30 m. Volvo "760 GLF"	10	10
2037	40 m. Honda "Civic" . .	15	10
2038	50 m. Volga	20	10
2039	60 m. Ford "Granada" . .	25	10
2040	80 m. Baz "21099" . .	30	15
2041	1 t. 20 Mercedes "190" . .	50	25

416 Monument — **417** Florence Griffith-Joyner (running)

1989. 50th Anniv of Battle of Khalka River.

2043	**416**	60 m. multicoloured . .	30	10

1989. Olympic Games Medal Winners. Mult.

2044	60 m. Type **417**	25	10
2045	60 m. Stefano Cerioni (fencing)	25	10
2046	60 m. Gintautas Umaras (cycling)	25	10
2047	60 m. Kristin Otto (swimming)	25	10

418 "Malchin Zaluus" (N. Sandagsuren)

1989. 30th Anniv of Co-operative Movement. Paintings. Multicoloured.

2049	20 m. Type **418**	10	10
2050	30 m. "Tsaatny Tukhai Dursamkh" (N. Sandagsuren) (vert)	10	10
2051	40 m. "Uul Shig Tushigtei" (D. Amgalan) . .	15	10
2052	50 m. "Goviin Egshig" (D. Amgalan) . .	20	10
2053	60 m. "Tsagaan Sar" (Ts. Dagvanyam) . .	25	10
2054	80 m. "Tumen Aduuny Bayar" (M. Butemkh) (vert)	30	15
2055	1 t. 20 "Bilcheer Deer" (N. Tsultem) . .	50	25

419 Four-man Bobsleighing — **420** Victory Medal

1989. Ice Sports. Multicoloured.

2057	20 m. Type **419**	10	10
2058	30 m. Luge	10	10
2059	40 m. Figure skating . .	15	10
2060	50 m. Two-man bob-sleighing	20	10
2061	60 m. Ice dancing . .	25	10
2062	80 m. Speed skating . .	30	15
2063	1 t. 20 Ice speedway . .	50	25

1989. Orders. Designs showing different badges and medals. Multicoloured, background colour given.

2065	420	60 m. blue	25	10
2066	–	60 m. orange . .	25	10
2067	–	60 m. mauve . .	25	10
2068	–	60 m. violet . .	25	10
2069	–	60 m. green . .	25	10
2070	–	60 m. blue	25	10
2071	–	60 m. red	25	10

422 Chu Lha

423 Sukhe Bator Statue

1989. Buddhas. Multicoloured.

2073	20 m. Damdin Sandub . .	10	10
2074	30 m. Pagwa Lama . .	10	10
2075	40 m. Type **422** . .	15	10
2076	50 m. Agwanglobsan . .	20	10
2077	60 m. Dorje Dags Dan . .	25	10
2078	80 m. Wangchikdorje . .	30	15
2079	1 t. 20 Buddha	50	25

1990. New Year.

2081	423	10 m. multicoloured . .	75	35

424 Newspapers and City

425 Emblem

1990. 70th Anniv of "Khuvisgalt Khevlel" (newspaper).

2082	424	60 m. multicoloured . .	65	30

1990. 20th Mongolian People's Revolutionary Party Congress.

2083	425	60 m. multicoloured . .	50	25

426 Male Character

1990. "Mandukhai the Wise" (film).

2084	426	20 m. multicoloured	20	10
2085	–	30 m. multicoloured	30	15
2086	–	40 m. multicoloured	45	20
2087	–	50 m. multicoloured	55	30
2088	–	60 m. multicoloured	75	35
2089	–	80 m. multicoloured	90	45
2090	–	1 t. 20 multicoloured	1·25	65

DESIGNS: 30 m. to 1 t. 20, Different characters from the film.

427 Trophy and Players

1990. World Cup Football Championship, Italy.

2092	427	20 m. multicoloured	20	10
2093	–	30 m. multicoloured	30	15
2094	–	40 m. multicoloured	40	20
2095	–	50 m. multicoloured	60	30
2096	–	60 m. multicoloured	70	35
2097	–	80 m. multicoloured	95	40
2098	–	1 t. 20 multicoloured	1·25	65

DESIGNS: 30 m. to 1 t. 20, Trophy and different players.

428 Lenin

1990. 120th Birth Anniv of Lenin.

2100	428	60 m. black, red & gold	65	30

429 Mother with Fawn

1990. Siberian Musk Deer. Multicoloured.

2101	60 m. Type **429**	65	30
2102	60 m. Deer in wood . .	65	30
2103	60 m. Deer on river bank	65	30
2104	60 m. Deer in winter landscape	65	30

433 Russian Victory Medal

434 Crane

1990. 45th Anniv of End of Second World War.

2108	433	60 m. multicoloured . .	65	30

1990. The Japanese White-necked Crane. Multicoloured.

2109	60 m. Type **434**	45	25
2110	60 m. Crane feeding (horiz)	45	25
2111	60 m. Cranes flying (horiz)	45	25
2112	60 m. Crane on river bank	45	25

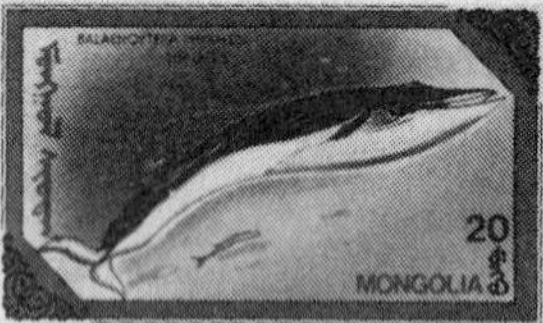

435 Fin Whale

1990. Marine Mammals. Multicoloured.

2113	20 m. Type **435**	15	10
2114	30 m. Humpback whale . .	25	10
2115	40 m. Narwhal	35	15
2116	50 m. Risso's dolphin . .	45	20
2117	60 m. Bottle-nosed dolphin	50	25
2118	80 m. Atlantic white-sided dolphin	70	35
2119	1 t. 20 Bowhead whale . .	90	45

436 Weapons and Black Standard

437 Panda

1990. 750th Anniv of "Secret History of the Mongols" (book). Multicoloured.

2121	10 m. Type **436** . .	10	10
2122	10 m. Weapons and white standard	10	10
2123	40 m. Brazier (17½ × 22 mm)	30	15
2124	60 m. Genghis Khan (17½ × 22 mm)	55	25
2125	60 m. Horses galloping . .	55	25
2126	60 m. Tartar camp . .	55	25
2127	80 m. Men kneeling to ruler	60	30
2128	80 m. Court	60	30

1990. The Giant Panda. Multicoloured.

2129	10 m. Type **437**	10	10
2130	20 m. Panda eating bamboo . .	15	10
2131	30 m. Adult eating bamboo, and cub . .	25	10
2132	40 m. Panda on tree branch (horiz) . .	35	15
2133	50 m. Adult and cub resting (horiz) . .	40	20
2134	60 m. Panda and mountains (horiz) . .	55	25
2135	80 m. Adult and cub playing (horiz) . .	60	30
2136	1 t. 20 Panda on snow-covered river bank (horiz)	1·25	60

438 Chasmosaurus

1990. Prehistoric Animals. Multicoloured.

2138	20 m. Type **438**	15	10
2139	30 m. Stegosaurus . .	25	10
2140	40 m. Probactrosaurus . .	35	15
2141	50 m. Opisthocoelicaudia	45	20
2142	60 m. Iguanodon (vert) . .	50	25
2143	80 m. Tarbosaurus . .	70	35
2144	1 t. 20 Mamenchisaurus (after Mark Hallett) (60 × 22 mm)	90	45

439 Lighthouse, Alexandria, Egypt

440 Parrot

1990. Seven Wonders of the World. Mult.

2146	20 m. Type **439**	15	10
2147	30 m. Pyramids of Egypt (horiz)	25	10
2148	40 m. Statue of Zeus, Olympia	35	15
2149	50 m. Colossus of Rhodes	45	25
2150	60 m. Mausoleum, Halicarnassus . .	50	25
2151	80 m. Temple of Artemis, Ephesus (horiz) . .	70	35
2152	1 t. 20 Hanging Gardens of Babylon	90	45

1990. Parrots.

2154	440	20 m. multicoloured	15	10
2155	–	30 m. multicoloured	25	10
2156	–	40 m. multicoloured	35	15
2157	–	50 m. multicoloured	45	20
2158	–	60 m. multicoloured	55	25
2159	–	80 m. multicoloured	75	35
2160	–	1 t. 20 multicoloured	90	45

DESIGNS: 30 m. to 1 t. 20, Different parrots.

441 Purple Bear Moth

1990. Moths and Butterflies. Multicoloured.

2162	20 m. Type **441**	15	10
2163	30 m. Great night peacock butterfly	25	10
2164	40 m. Moth	35	15
2165	50 m. Magpie moth . .	45	20
2166	60 m. Chequered moth . .	50	25
2167	80 m. Swallowtail . .	70	35
2168	1 t. 20 Butterfly . .	90	45

442 Jetsons in Flying Saucer

1991. The Jetsons (cartoon characters). Multicoloured.

2170	20 m. Type **442**	10	10
2171	25 m. Family walking on planet and dragon (horiz)	10	10
2172	30 m. Jane, George, Elroy and dog Astro . .	10	10
2173	40 m. George, Judy, Elroy and Astro crossing river	15	10
2174	50 m. Flying in saucer (horiz)	35	15
2175	60 m. Jetsons and Cosmo Spacely (horiz) . .	45	20
2176	70 m. George and Elroy flying with jetpacks . .		
2177	80 m. Elroy (horiz) . .	55	25
2178	1 t. 20 Judy and Astro watching Elroy doing acrobatics on tree . .	95	45

443 Dino and Bam-Bam meeting Mongolian Boy with Camel

1991. The Flintstones (cartoon characters). Multicoloured.

2180	25 m. Type **443**	10	10
2181	35 m. Bam-Bam and Dino posing with boy (vert)	15	10
2182	45 m. Mongolian mother greeting Betty Rubble, Wilma Flintstone and children	20	10
2183	55 m. Barney Rubble and Fred riding dinosaurs	25	10
2184	65 m. Flintstones and Rubbles by river . .	30	15
2185	75 m. Bam-Bam and Dino racing boy on camel . .	40	20
2186	85 m. Fred, Barney and Bam-Bam with Mongolian boy . .	55	25
2187	1 t. 40 Flintstones and Rubbles in car . .	90	45
2188	2 t. Fred and Barney taking refreshments with Mongolian . .	1·40	70

444 Party Emblem

445 Bird and Emblem

1991. 70th Anniv of Mongolian People's Revolutionary Party.

2190	444	60 m. multicoloured . .	50	25

1991. "Stamp World London 90" International Stamp Exhibition.

2191 **445** 25 m. multicoloured 10 10
2192 – 35 m. multicoloured 15 10
2193 – 45 m. multicoloured 20 10
2194 – 55 m. multicoloured 25 10
2195 – 65 m. multicoloured 30 10
2196 – 75 m. mult (horiz) .. 35 10
2197 – 85 m. multicoloured 45 15
2198 – 1 t. 40 multicoloured 85 40
2199 – 2 t. multicoloured .. 1·10 55

DESIGNS: 35 m. to 2 t. Different birds.

446 Black Grouse

1991. Birds. Multicoloured.

2201 20 m. Type **446** 15 10
2202 30 m. Common shelduck 25 10
2203 40 m. Ring-necked pheasant 35 15
2204 50 m. Long-tailed duck .. 50 25
2205 60 m. Hazel grouse .. 60 30
2206 80 m. Red-breasted merganser 80 40
2207 1 t. 20 Goldeneye .. 1·10 55

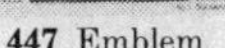

447 Emblem **448** Superb Pink

1991. 70th Anniv of Mongolian People's Army.

2209 **447** 60 m. multicoloured .. 50 25

1991. Flowers. Multicoloured.

2210 20 m. Type **448** 15 10
2211 30 m. "Gentiana pneumonanthe" (wrongly inscr "puenmonanthe") 25 10
2212 40 m. Dandelion .. 35 15
2213 50 m. Siberian iris .. 50 25
2214 60 m. Turk's-cap lily .. 60 30
2215 80 m. "Aster amellus" .. 80 40
2216 1 t. 20 "Ciszium rivulare" 1·10 55

449 Stag Beetle

1991. Beetles. Multicoloured.

2218 20 m. Type **449** 15 10
2219 30 m. "Chelorrhina polyphemus" 25 15
2220 40 m. "Coptolabrus coelestis" 35 15
2221 50 m. "Epepeotes togatus" 50 25
2222 60 m. Tiger beetle .. 60 30
2223 80 m. "Macrodontia cervicornis" 80 40
2224 1 t. 20 Hercules beetle .. 1·10 55

450 Defend

1991. Buddhas. Multicoloured.

2226 20 m. Type **450** 15 10
2227 30 m. Badmasanhava .. 25 10
2228 40 m. Avalokitecvara .. 35 15
2229 50 m. Buddha 50 25
2230 60 m. Mintugwa 60 30
2231 80 m. Shyamatara .. 70 35
2232 1 t. 20 Samvara .. .. 1·10 55

451 Zebras

1991. African Wildlife. Multicoloured.

2234 20 m. Type **451** 15 10
2235 30 m. Cheetah (wrongly inscr "Cheetan") .. 25 10
2236 40 m. Black rhinoceros .. 35 15
2237 50 m. Giraffe (vert) .. 50 25
2238 60 m. Gorilla 60 30
2239 80 m. Elephants .. 80 40
2240 1 t. 20 Lion (vert) .. 1·10 55

452 Communications

1991. Meiso Mizuhara Stamp Exhibition, Ulan-Bator.

2242 **452** 1 t. 20 multicoloured 55 25

453 Scotch Bonnet

1991. Fungi. Multicoloured.

2243 20 m. Type **453** 10 10
2244 30 m. Oak mushroom .. 15 10
2245 40 m. "Hygrophorus marzuelus" 20 10
2246 50 m. Chanterelle .. 30 15
2247 60 m. Field mushroom .. 40 20
2248 80 m. Bronze boletus .. 50 25
2249 1 t. 20 Caesar's mushroom 85 40
2250 2 t. "Tricholoma terreum" 1·50 75

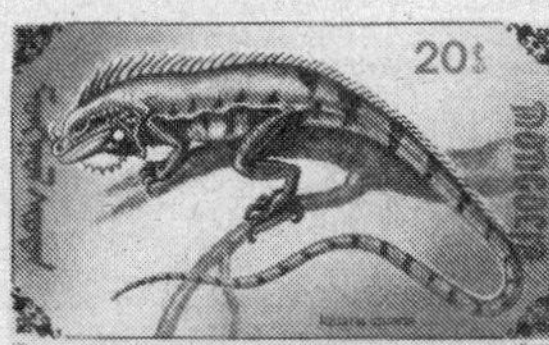

455 Green Iguana

1991. Reptiles. Multicoloured.

2253 20 m. Type **455** 15 10
2254 30 m. Flying gecko .. 30 15
2255 40 m. Frilled lizard .. 40 20
2256 50 m. Common cape lizard 50 25
2257 60 m. Common basilisk .. 60 30
2258 80 m. Common tegu .. 80 40
2259 1 t. 20 Marine iguana .. 1·25 65

456 Warrior

1991. Masked Costumes. Multicoloured.

2261 35 m. Type **456** 15 10
2262 45 m. Mask with fangs .. 25 10
2263 55 m. Bull mask .. 40 20
2264 65 m. Dragon mask .. 50 25
2265 85 m. Mask with beak .. 60 30
2266 1 t. 40 Old man .. .. 1·10 55
2267 2 t. Gold mask with ear-rings .. .. 1·25 60

457 German Shepherd

1991. Dogs. Multicoloured.

2269 20 m. Type **457** 15 10
2270 30 m. Dachshund (vert) .. 30 15
2271 40 m. Yorkshire terrier (vert) 40 20
2272 50 m. Standard poodle .. 50 25
2273 60 m. Springer spaniel .. 60 30
2274 80 m. Norfolk terrier .. 80 40
2275 1 t. 20 Keeshund .. 1·25 60

458 Siamese

1991. Cats. Multicoloured.

2277 20 m. Type **458** 15 10
2278 30 m. Black and white longhaired (vert) .. 30 15
2279 40 m. Ginger red .. 40 20
2280 50 m. Tabby (vert) .. 50 25
2281 60 m. Red and white (vert) 60 30
2282 80 m. Maine coon (vert) 80 40
2283 1 t. 20 Blue-eyed white persian (vert) .. .. 1·25 60

459 Pagoda **460** Butterfly

1991. "Phila Nippon '91" International Stamp Exhibition, Tokyo. Multicoloured.

2285 1 t. Type **459** 25 10
2286 2 t. Japanese woman .. 50 25
2287 3 t. Mongolian woman 80 40
2288 4 t. Temple .. .. 1·25 60

1991. Butterflies and Flowers. Multicoloured.

2289 20 m. Type **460** 10 10
2290 25 m. Yellow roses .. 15 10
2291 30 m. Butterfly .. 20 10
2292 40 m. Butterfly 25 10
2293 50 m. Butterfly 30 15
2294 60 m. Butterfly 35 15
2295 70 m. Red rose 40 20
2296 80 m. Margueritas .. 50 25
2297 1 t. 20 Lily 75 35

1991. "Expo '90" International Garden and Greenery Exhibition, Osaka. Nos. 2289/97 optd **EXPO '90** and symbol.

2298 20 m. multicoloured .. 10 10
2299 25 m. multicoloured .. 15 10
2300 30 m. multicoloured .. 20 10
2301 40 m. multicoloured .. 25 10
2302 50 m. multicoloured .. 30 15
2303 60 m. multicoloured .. 35 15
2304 70 m. multicoloured .. 40 20
2305 80 m. multicoloured .. 50 25
2306 1 t. 20 multicoloured .. 75 35

462 Poster for 1985 Digital Stereo Re-issue

1991. 50th Anniv (1990) of Original Release of Walt Disney's "Fantasia" (cartoon film). Multicoloured.

2308 1 t. 70 Type **462** 10 10
2309 2 t. 1940 poster for original release .. 15 10
2310 2 t. 30 Poster for 1982 digital re-issue .. 20 10
2311 2 t. 60 Poster for 1981 stereo re-issue .. 25 10
2312 4 t. 20 Poster for 1969 "Psychedelic Sixties" release 45 20
2313 10 t. 1941 poster for original release .. 1·50 75
2314 15 t. Mlle. Upanova (sketch by Campbell Grant) .. .. 1·75 85
2315 16 t. Mickey as the Sorcerer's Apprentice (original sketch) .. 2·10 1·00

MONG-TSEU (MENGTSZ) Pt. 17

An Indo-Chinese P.O. in Yunnan province, China, closed in 1922.

1903. 100 centimes = 1 franc.
1919. 100 cents = 1 piastre.

Stamps of Indo-China surcharged.

1903. "Tablet" key-type surch **MONGTZE** and value in Chinese.

No.	Type	Description		
1	D	1 c. black and red on blue	3·50	3·50
2		2 c. brown & blue on buff	2·25	2·25
3		4 c. brown & blue on grey	3·50	3·50
4		5 c. green and red	2·75	3·00
5		10 c. red and blue	4·00	4·00
6		15 c. grey and red	5·00	4·50
7		20 c. red & blue on green	5·25	5·25
8		25 c. blue and red	5·75	5·50
9		25 c. black & red on pink	£400	£400
10		30 c. brown & bl on drab	4·75	5·00
11		40 c. red & blue on yellow	38·00	38·00
12		50 c. red and blue on pink	£190	£190
13		50 c. brown & red on blue	60·00	60·00
14		75 c. brown & red on orge	60·00	60·00
15		1 f. green and red	60·00	60·00
16		5 f. mauve & blue on lilac	60·00	60·00

1906. Surch **Mong-Tseu** and value in Chinese.

No.	Type	Description		
17	8	1 c. green	90	85
18		2 c. purple on yellow	90	85
19		4 c. mauve on blue	90	85
20		5 c. green	90	85
21		10 c. pink	1·10	1·10
22		15 c. brown on blue	1·10	1·10
23		20 c. red on green	2·00	2·00
24		25 c. blue	2·25	2·25
25		30 c. brown on cream	3·50	3·50
26		35 c. black on yellow	2·50	2·50
27		40 c. black on grey	3·25	3·25
28		50 c. brown	9·50	9·50
29	D	75 c. brown & red on orge	23·00	23·00
30	8	1 f. green	11·00	11·00
31		2 f. brown on yellow	27·00	27·00
32	D	5 f. mauve & blue on lilac	60·00	60·00
34	8	10 f. red on green	80·00	80·00

1908 Surch **MONGTSEU** and value in Chinese.

No.	Type	Description		
35	10	1 c. black and brown	35	40
36		2 c. black and brown	40	45
37		4 c. black and blue	50	55
38		5 c. black and green	60	60
39		10 c. black and red	85	90
40		15 c. black and violet	95	95
41	11	20 c. black and violet	2·50	2·25
42		25 c. black and blue	3·25	3·25
43		30 c. black and brown	2·25	2·00
44		35 c. black and green	2·25	2·00
45		40 c. black and brown	2·25	2·25
46		50 c. black and red	2·25	2·25
47	12	75 c. black and orange	5·50	5·50
48	–	1 f. black and red	6·00	6·25
49	–	2 f. black and green	8·00	8·25
50	–	5 f. black and blue	55·00	60·00
51	–	10 f. black and violet	65·00	70·00

1919. Nos. 35/51 further surch in figures and words.

No.	Type	Description		
52	10	2/5 c. on 1 c. black & brn	45	45
53		4/5 c. on 2 c. black & brn	45	40
54		1 3/5 c. on 4 c. black & bl	90	90
55		2 c. on 5 c. black & green	55	55
56		4 c. on 10 c. black & red	1·10	1·00
57		6 c. on 15 c. black & vio	1·10	1·00
58	11	8 c. on 20 c. black & vio	2·00	2·00
59		10 c. on 25 c. black & bl	1·60	1·60
60		12 c. on 30 c. black & brn	1·60	1·60
61		14 c. on 35 c. black & grn	1·60	1·50
62		16 c. on 40 c. black & brn	2·00	2·00
63		20 c. on 50 c. black & red	2·25	2·00
64	12	30 c. on 75 c. blk & orge	2·00	2·00
65	–	40 c. on 1 f. black and red	4·25	4·25
66	–	80 c. on 2 f. black & green	2·75	2·75
67	–	2 p. on 5 f. black & blue	70·00	75·00
68	–	4 p. on 10 f. black & vio	13·00	13·00

MONTENEGRO Pt. 3

Formerly a monarchy on the Adriatic Sea and now part of Yugoslavia. In Italian and German occupation during 1939-45 war.

1874. 100 novcic = 1 florin.
1902. 100 heller = 1 krone.
1907. 100 para = 1 krone (1910 = 1 perper)

1. Prince Nicholas.

Прослава 1493 1893 Штампарије

(2.)

1874.

No.	Type	Description		
45.	1.	1 n. pale blue	10	12
38.		2 n. yellow	2·50	1·90
51.		2 n. green	10	12
39.		3 n. green	40	50
52.		3 n. red	10	12
40.		5 n. red	40	40
53.		5 n. orange	25	15
19.		7 n. mauve	29·00	19·00
41.		7 n. pink	40	40
54.		7 n. grey	15	20
42	1	10 n. blue	40	40
55		10 n. purple	15	10
56		15 n. brown	15	15
46		20 n. brown	10	12
7		25 n. purple	£225	£200
44		25 n. brown	40	1·50
57		25 n. blue	10	25
47		30 n. brown	10	15
48		50 n. blue	10	20
49		1 f. green	25	1·40
50		2 f. red	80	2·25

1893. 400th Anniv of Introduction of Printing into Montenegro. Optd with T 2.

No.	Type	Description		
81.	1.	2 n. yellow	20·00	2·50
82.		3 n. green	2·50	1·60
83.		5 n. red	1·90	90
84.		7 n. pink	3·25	1·50
86.		10 n. blue	3·25	2·50
87.		15 n. bistre	3·50	3·25
89.		25 n. brown	3·25	1·50

3. Monastery near Cetinje, Royal Mausoleum.

1896. Bicent. of Petrovich Niegush Dynasty.

No.	Type	Description		
90.	3.	1 n. brown and blue	10	80
91.		2 n. yellow and purple	10	80
92.		3 n. green and brown	10	80
93.		5 n. brown and green	10	80
94.		10 n. blue and yellow	10	80
95.		15 n. green and blue	10	80
96.		20 n. blue and green	10	80
97.		25 n. yellow and blue	10	80
98.		30 n. brown and purple	10	80
99.		50 n. slate and red	10	70
100.		1 f. slate and pink	15	1·25
101.		2 f. grey and brown	15	1·25

4.

УСТАВ Constitution Никољдан 1905

(5.)

7.

1902.

No.	Type	Description		
102.	4.	1 h. blue	15	12
103.		2 h. purple	20	15
104.		5 h. green	15	10
105.		10 h. red	20	10
106a.		25 h. blue	12	12
107.		50 h. green	35	30
108.		1 k. brown	30	30
109.		2 k. brown	35	35
110.		5 k. orange	50	90

1905. Granting of Constitution. Optd with T 5.

No.	Type	Description		
111.	4.	1 h. blue	12	15
112.		2 h. mauve	12	15
113.		5 h. green	12	15
114.		10 h. red	12	15
124.		25 h. blue	15	15
125.		50 h. green	12	15
126.		1 k. brown	12	15
127.		2 k. brown	12	15
119.		5 k. orange	50	1·50

1907.

No.	Type	Description		
129.	7.	1 p. yellow	10	20
130.		2 p. black	10	20
131.		5 p. green	65	10
132.		10 p. red	1·60	10
133.		15 p. blue	10	15
134.		20 p. orange	10	20
135.		25 p. blue	10	15
136.		35 p. brown	15	15
137.		50 p. lilac	30	35
138.		1 k. red	30	30
139.		2 k. green	35	30
140.		5 k. red	75	60

9. King Nicholas when a Youth.

10. King Nicholas and Queen Milena.

11. Prince Nicholas.

12. Nicholas I.

1910. Fiftieth Year of King's Reign.

No.	Type	Description		
141.	9.	1 p. black	15	8
142.	10.	2 p. purple	15	8
143.	–	5 p. green	10	5
144.	–	10 p. red	10	5
145.	–	15 p. blue	10	8
146.	10.	20 p. olive	20	12
147.	–	25 p. blue	15	10
148.	–	35 p. brown	50	40
149.	–	50 p. violet	20	20
150.	–	1 per. lake	30	30
151.	–	2 per. green	70	45
152.	11.	5 per. blue	75	75

DESIGNS—As Type 9: 5 p., 10 p., 25 p., 35 p. Nicholas I in 1910. 15 p. Nicholas I in 1878. 50 p., 1 per., 2 per. Nicholas I in 1890.

1913.

No.	Type	Description		
153.	12.	1 p. orange	10	10
154.		2 p. purple	10	10
155.		5 p. green	8	8
156.		10 p. red	8	8
157.		15 p. blue	15	15
158.		20 p. brown	15	15
159.		25 p. blue	15	15
160.		35 p. red	40	40
161.		50 p. blue	20	20
162.		1 per. brown	20	20
163.		2 per. lilac	40	40
164.		5 per. green	40	40

ITALIAN OCCUPATION

Montenegro
Црна Гора
17-IV-41-XIX
(1).

ЦРНА ГОРА
(2).

1941. Stamps of Yugoslavia optd. with T 1.

(a) Postage. On Nos. 414, etc.

No.	Type	Description		
1.	99.	25 p. black	10	45
2.		1 d. green	10	45
3.		1 d. 50 red	10	45
4.		2 d. mauve	10	45
5.		3 d. brown	10	45
6.		4 d. blue	10	45
7.		5 d. blue	1·25	2·25
8.		5 d. 50 violet	1·25	2·25
9.		6 d. blue	1·25	2·25
10.		8 d. brown	1·40	2·25
11.		12 d. violet	1·25	2·25
12.		16 d. purple	1·25	2·25
13.		20 d. blue	50·00	95·00
14.		30 d. pink	25·00	45·00

(b) Air. On Nos. 360/7.

No.	Type	Description		
15.	80.	50 p. brown	2·50	5·00
16.	–	1 d. green	1·75	3·25
17.	–	2 d. blue	1·75	3·25
18.	–	2 d. 50 red	2·50	5·00
19.	80.	5 d. violet	22·00	38·00
20.	–	10 d. red	16·00	32·00
21.	–	20 d. green	22·00	45·00
22.	–	30 d. blue	16·00	32·00

1941. Stamps of Italy optd. with T 2.

(a) On Postage stamps of 1929.

No.	Type	Description		
28.	98.	5 c. brown	10	35
29.	–	10 c. brown	10	35
30.	–	15 c. green	10	35
31.	99.	20 c. red	10	35
32.	–	25 c. green	10	35
33.	103.	30 c. brown	10	35
34.		50 c. violet	10	35
35.	–	75 c. red	10	35
36.	–	1 l. 25 blue	10	35

(b) On Air stamp of 1930.

No.	Type	Description		
37.	110.	50 c. brown	10	35

1942. Nos. 416, etc., of Yugoslavia optd. **Governatorato del Montenegro Valore LIRE.**

No.	Type	Description		
43.	99.	1 d. green	25	40
44.		1 d. 50 red	11·00	22·00
45.		3 d. brown	25	40
46.		4 d. blue	30	40
47.		5 d. 50 violet	30	40
48.		6 d. blue	30	40
49.		8 d. brown	30	40
50.		12 d. violet	30	40
51.		16 d. purple	30	40

1942. Air. Nos. 360/7 of Yugoslavia optd. **Governatorato/del/Montenegro/Valore in Lire.**

No.	Type	Description		
52.	80.	0. 50 l. brown	1·40	3·00
53.	–	1 l. green	1·40	3·00
54.	–	2 l. blue	1·40	3·00
55.	–	2. 50 l. red	1·40	3·00
56.	80.	5 l. violet	1·40	3·00
57.	–	10 l. brown	1·40	3·00
58.	–	20 l. green	55·00	£120
59.	–	30 l. blue	12·50	27·00

4. Prince Bishop Peter Njegos and View.

1943. National Poem Commemoratives. Each stamp has fragment of poetry inscr. at back.

No.	Type	Description		
60.	4.	5 c. violet	8	60
61.	–	10 c. green	8	60
62.	–	15 c. brown	8	60
63.	–	20 c. orange	8	60
64.	–	25 c. green	15	60
65.	–	50 c. mauve	15	60
66.	–	1 l. 25 blue	15	85
67.	–	2 l. green	30	1·25
68.	–	5 l. red on buff	1·75	4·75
69.	–	20 l. purple on grey	3·75	11·00

DESIGNS—HORIZ. 10 c. Meadow. 15 c. Country chapel. 20 c. Chiefs Meeting. 25 c., 50 c. Folk-dancing. 1 l. 25, Taking the Oath. 2 l. Procession. 5 l. Watch over wounded standard-bearer. VERT. 20 l. Portrait of Prince Bishop Peter Njegos.

5. Cetinje.

DESIGNS—HORIZ. 1 l. Coastline. 2 l. Budva. 5 l. Mt. Lovcen. 10 l. Lake of Scutari. VERT. 20 l. Mt. Durmitor.

1943. Air.

No.	Type	Description		
70.	5.	50 c. brown	10	70
71.	–	1 l. blue	15	70
72.	–	2 l. mauve	20	1·00
73.	–	5 l. green	45	1·90
74.	–	10 l. purple on buff	3·00	8·00
75.	–	20 l. blue on pink	5·00	13·00

GERMAN OCCUPATION

1943. Nos. 419/20 of Yugoslavia surch. **Deutsche Militaer-Verwaltung Montenegro** and new value in lire.

No.	Type	Description		
76.	99.	50 c. on 3 d. brown	3·00	18·00
77.		1 l. on 3 d. brown	3·00	18·00
78.		1 l. 50 on 3 d. brown	3·00	18·00
79.		2 l. on 3 d. brown	6·25	38·00
80.		4 l. on 3 d. brown	6·25	38·00
81.		5 l. on 4 d. blue	6·25	38·00
82.		8 l. on 4 d. blue	7·75	75·00
83.		10 l. on 4 d. blue	14·00	£120
84.		20 l. on 4 d. blue	25·00	£250

1943. Appointment of National Administrative Committee. Optd. **Nationaler Verwaltungsausschuss 10.XI.1943.**

(a) Postage. On Nos. 64/8.

No.	Type	Description		
85.		25 c. green	9·25	£140
86.		50 c. mauve	9·25	£140
87.		1 l. 25 blue	9·25	£140
88.		2 l. green	9·25	£140
89.		5 l. red on buff	£250	£1900

(b) Air. On Nos. 70/4.

No.	Type	Description		
90.	5.	50 c. brown	17·00	£160
91.		1 l. blue	17·00	£160
92.		2 l. mauve	17·00	£160
93.		5 l. green	17·00	£160
94.		10 l. purple on buff	£3250	£12000

1944. Refugees Fund. Surch. **Fluchtlingshilfe Montenegro** and new value in German currency.

(a) On Nos. 419/20 of Yugoslavia.

No.	Type	Description		
95.	99.	0.15+0.85 Rm. on 3 d.	9·25	£140
96.		0.15+0.85 Rm. on 4 d.	9·25	£140

(b) On Nos. 46/9.

No.	Type	Description		
97.	–	0.15+0.85 Rm. on 25 c.	9·25	£140
98.	–	0.15+1.35 Rm. on 50 c.	9·25	£140
99.	–	0.25+1.75 Rm. on 1 l. 25	9·25	£140
100.	–	0.25+1.75 Rm. on 2 l.	9·25	£140

(c) Air. On Nos. A 52/4.

No.	Type	Description		
101.	5.	0.15+0.85 Rm. on 50 c.	9·25	£140
102.	–	0.25+1.25 Rm. on 1 l.	9·25	£140
103.	–	0.50+1.50 Rm. on 2 l.	9·25	£140

1944. Red Cross. Surch. + **Crveni krst Montenegro** and new value in German currency.

(a) On Nos. 419/20 of Yugoslavia.

No.	Type	Description		
104.	99.	0.50+2.50 Rm. on 3 d.	9·25	£110
105.		0.50+2.50 Rm. on 4 d.	9·25	£110

(b) On Nos. 64/5.

No.	Type	Description		
106.	–	0.15+0.85 Rm. on 25 c.	9·25	£110
107.	–	0.15+1.35 Rm. on 50 c.	9·25	£110

(d) Air. On Nos. 70/2.

No.	Type	Description		
108.	5.	0.25+1.75 Rm. on 50 c.	10·50	£110
109.	–	0.25+2.75 Rm. on 1 l.	10·50	£110
110.	–	0.50+2 Rm. on 2 l.	10·50	£110

ACKNOWLEDGMENT OF RECEIPT STAMPS

A 3.

A 4.

1895.

No.	Type	Description		
A 90.	A 3.	10 n. blue and red	10	30

1902.

No.	Type	Description		
A 111.	A 4.	25 h. orange and red	40	40

1905. Optd. with T 5.

No.	Type	Description		
A 130.	A 4.	25 h. orange and red	10	15

1907. As T 7, but letters "A" and "R" in top corners.

No.	Type	Description		
A 141.	7.	25 p. olive	20	35

1913. As T 12, but letters "A" and "R" in top corners.

No.	Type	Description		
A 169.	12.	25 p. olive	20	35

POSTAGE DUE STAMPS

D 3.

D 4.

D 8.

1894.

D 90. D 3. 1 n. red .. .. 1·90 1·25
D 91. 2 n. green 15 15
D 92. 3 n. orange 15 15
D 93. 5 n. green 15 15
D 94. 10 n. purple 15 15
D 95. 20 n. blue 15 20
D 96. 30 n. green 15 20
D 97. 50 n. pale green .. 15 20

1902.

D 111. D 4. 5 h. orange .. 10 10
D 112. 10 h. olive .. 15 10
D 113. 25 h. purple .. 15 10
D 114. 50 h. green .. 15 10
D 115. 1 k. pale green .. 20 20

1905. Optd. with T 5.

D 120. D 4. 5 h. orange .. 25 25
D 129. 10 h. olive .. 15 20
D 122. 25 h. purple .. 25 25
D 123. 50 h. green .. 25 25
D 124. 1 k. pale green .. 40 40

1907.

D 141. D 8. 5 p. brown 12 12
D 142. 10 p. violet .. 12 12
D 143. 25 p. red 12 12
D 144. 50 p. green .. 12 12

1913. As T 12 but inscr. "HOPTOMAPKA" at top.

D 165. 5 p. grey 50 50
D 166. 10 p. violet 25 25
D 167. 25 p. blue 25 25
D 168. 50 p. red 40 35

ITALIAN OCCUPATION

1941. Postage Due stamps of Yugoslavia optd. **Montenegro Upha 17-IV-41-XIX.**

D 23. D 56. 50 p. violet .. 20 65
D 24. 1 d. mauve 20 65
D 25. 2 d. blue 20 65
D 26. 5 d. orange .. 9·25 18·00
D 27. 10 d. brown .. 1·60 3·25

1942. Postage Due stamps of Italy optd. **UPHATOPA.**

D 38. D141. 10 c. blue 5 80
D 39. 20 c. red 5 80
D 40. 30 c. orange 8 80
D 41. 50 c. violet 8 80
D 42. 1 l. orange 20 80

MOROCCO Pt. 13

An independent kingdom, established in 1956, comprising the former French and Spanish International Zones.

A. NORTHERN ZONE.
100 centimos = 1 peseta.

1. Sultan of Morocco. 2. Polytechnic.

1956.

1. 1. 10 c. brown 8 8
2. – 15 c. brown 8 8
3. 2. 25 c. violet 8 8
4. – 50 c. green 25 25
5. 1. 80 c. green 30 30
6. – 2 p. lilac .. .. 2·00 1·60
7. 2. 3 p. blue .. .. 4·00 2·75
8. – 10 p. green .. .. 14·00 11·00

DESIGNS—HORIZ. 15 c., 2 p. Villa Sanjurjo harbour. VERT. 50 c., 10 p. Cultural Delegation building, Tetuan.

3. "Constellation" over Lau Dam.

1956. Air.

9. 3. 25 c. purple 20 15
10. – 1 p. 40 mauve 35 25
11. 3. 3 p. 40 red .. .. 1·60 1·25
12. – 4 p. 80 purple .. 2·50 1·75

DESIGN: 1 p. 40, 4 p. 80, "Constellation" over Rio Nekor Bridge.

1957. 1st Anniv. of Independence. As T 7 but with Spanish inscriptions and currency.

13. 80 c. green 35 25
14. 1 p. 50 olive .. .. 1·25 80
15. 3 p. red .. .. 3·25 2·75

1957. As T 5 but with Spanish inscriptions and currency.

16. 30 c. indigo and blue .. 8 5
17. 70 c. purple and brown .. 20 5
18. 80 c. purple 80 15
19. 1 p. 50 lake and green .. 25 12
20. 3 p. green 35 15
21. 7 p. red .. .. 1·40 40

1957. Investiture of Prince Moulay el Hassan. As T 9 but with Spanish inscriptions and currency.

22. 80 c. blue 30 25
23. 1 p. 50 green .. .. 1·00 80
24. 3 p. red .. .. 2·40 2·25

1957. Nos. 17 and 19 surch.

25. 15 c. on 70 c. pur. & brown 30 30
26. 1 p. 20 on 1 p. 50 lake and green 65 30

1957. 30th Anniv. of Coronation of Sultan Sidi Mohammed ben Yusuf. As T 10 but with Spanish inscription and currency.

27. 1 p. 20 green and black .. 35 35
28. 1 p. 80 red and black .. 40 40
29. 3 p. violet and black .. 80 75

B. SOUTHERN ZONE
100 centimes = 1 franc.

5. Sultan of Morocco. 6. Classroom. 7. Sultan of Morocco.

1956.

30. 5. 5 f. indigo and blue .. 20 5
31. 10 f. sepia and brown .. 15 5
32. 15 f. lake and green .. 25 5
33. 25 f. purple 70 5
34. 30 f. green .. .. 1·40 5
35. 50 f. red .. .. 2·10 15
36. 70 f. brown and sepia .. 3·50 60

1956. Education Campaign.

37. – 10 f. violet and purple .. 1·50 85
38. – 15 f. lake and red .. 1·75 1·25
39. 6. 20 f. green and turquoise 1·90 2·00
40. – 30 f. red and lake .. 3·50 3·25
41. – 50 f. blue and indigo .. 6·00 4·00

DESIGNS: 10 f. Peasants reading book. 15 f. Two girls reading. 30 f. Child reading to old man. 50 f. Child teaching parents the alphabet.

1957. 1st Anniv. of Independence.

42. 7. 15 f. green .. .. 1·25 90
43. 25 f. olive .. .. 1·75 90
44. 30 f. red .. .. 3·25 1·40

7. Emblem over Casablanca. 9. Crown Prince Moulay el Hassan.

1957. Air. Int. Fair, Casablanca.

45. 8. 15 f. green and red .. 90 60
46. 25 f. turquoise .. .. 1·75 1·10
47. 30 f. brown .. .. 2·25 1·25

1957. Investiture of Crown Prince Moulay el Hassan.

48. 9. 15 f. blue .. .. 1·25 65
49. 25 f. green .. .. 1·25 1·00
50. 30 f. red .. .. 2·25 1·25

10. King Mohammed V. 11. Moroccan Pavilion.

1957. 30th Anniv. of Coronation of King Mohammed V.

51. 10. 15 f. green and black .. 60 50
52. 25 f. red and black .. 1·10 60
53. 30 f. violet and black .. 1·10 90

C. ISSUES FOR THE WHOLE OF MOROCCO.
1958. 100 centimes = 1 franc.
1962. 100 francs = 1 dirham.

1958. Brussels Int. Exn.

54. 11. 15 f. turquoise 25 20
55. 25 f. red 25 25
56. 30 f. blue 35 30

12. King Mohammed V and U.N.E.S.C.O. Headquarters, Paris.

1958. Inaug. of U.N.E.S.C.O. Headquarters Building, Paris.

57. 12. 15 f. green 25 20
58. 25 f. lake 25 25
59. 30 f. blue 35 30

13. Ben-Smine Sanatorium. 14. King Mohammed V on Horseback.

1959. "National Aid".

60. 13. 50 f. bistre, green and red 70 35

1959. King Mohammed V's 50th Birthday.

61. 14. 15 f. lake 40 30
62. 25 f. blue 70 35
63. 45 f. green 80 45

15. Princess Lalla Amina. 16.

1959. Children's Week.

64. 15. 15 f. blue 25 20
65. 25 f. green 30 25
66. 45 f. purple 35 30

1960. Meeting of U.N. African Economic Commission, Tangier.

67. 16. 45 f. green, brn. & violet 65 50

+10 f
اعانة ضحايا
الزيوت المسممة
أكتوبر 1959

(17.) 18. Arab Refugees.

1960. Adulterated Cooking Oil Victims Relief Fund. Surch. as T 17.

68. 5. 5 f. + 10 f. indigo and blue 35 30
69. 10 f. + 10 f. sepia & brown 45 45
70. 15 f. + 10 f. lake and green 95 60
71. 25 f. + 15 f. purple .. 1·10 70
72. 30 f. + 20 f. green .. 1·75 1·60

1960. World Refugee Year.

73. 18. 15 f. black, green & ochre 25 20
74. – 45 f. green and black .. 35 35

DESIGN: 45 f. "Uprooted tree" and Arab refugees.

19. Marrakesh. 20. Lantern.

1960. 900th Anniv. of Marrakesh.

75. 19. 100 f. grn., brown & blue 80 65

1960. 1100th Anniv. of Karaouiyne University.

76. 20. 15 f. purple 25 25
77. – 25 f. blue (Fountain) .. 35 25
78. – 30 f. brown (Minaret) .. 90 60
79. – 35 f. black (Frescoes) .. 1·10 80
80. – 45 f. green (Courtyard) .. 1·60 1·10

اسبوع
التضامن
1380
1960
+5f

21. Arab League Centre and King Mohammed V. (22.)

1960. Inaug. of Arab League Centre, Cairo.

81. 21. 15 f. black and green .. 20 20

1960. Solidarity Fund. Nos. 458/9 (Mahakma, Casablanca) of French Morocco surch. as T 22.

82. 106. 15 f. + 3 f. on 18 f. myrtle 55 55
83. +5 f. on 20 f. lake .. 80 80

23. Wrestling. 24. Runner.

1960. Olympic Games.

84. 23. 5 f. purple, green & violet 8 5
85. – 10 f. choc., blue & brown 15 8
86. – 15 f. brown, blue & green 20 15
87. – 20 f. purple, blue & bistre 25 20
88. – 30 f. brown, violet & red 30 25
89. – 40 f. brown, blue & violet 60 25
90. – 45 f. blue, green & purple 75 35
91. – 70 f. black, blue & brown 1·10 45

DESIGNS: 10 f. Gymnastics. 15 f. Cycling. 20 f. Weightlifting. 30 f. Running. 40 f. Boxing. 45 f. Sailing. 70 f. Fencing.

1961. 3rd Pan-Arab Games, Casablanca.

92. 24. 20 f. green 20 15
93. 30 f. lake 25 20
94. 50 f. blue 40 35

25. Post Office and Letters. 26. King Mohammed V and African Map. 27. Lumumba and Congo Map.

1961. African Postal and Telecommunications Conf., Tangier.

95. 25. 20 f. purple and mauve .. 35 30
96. – 30 f. turquoise and green 45 35
97. – 90 f. ultramarine & blue 85 60

DESIGNS—VERT. 30 f. Telephone operator. HORIZ. 90 f. "Caravelle" mail-plane over Tangier.

1962. 1st Anniv. of African Charter of Casablanca.

98. 26. 20 f. purple and buff .. 20 20
99. 30 f. indigo and blue .. 25 25

1962. Patrice Lumumba Commem.

100. 27. 20 f. black and bistre .. 20 20
101. 30 f. black and brown 30 25

28. King Hassan II. 29. "Pupils of the Nation".

1962. Air.

102. 28. 90 f. black 40 12
103. 1 d. red 90 15
104. 2 d. blue .. .. 1·10 45
105. 3 d. green .. .. 1·75 75
106. 5 d. violet .. .. 3·50 1·25

1962. Children's Education.

107. 29. 20 f. blue, red and green 35 25
108. 30 f. sepia, brown & grn. 40 35
109. 90 f. blue, purple & green 60 50

1962. Arab League Week. As T 76 of Libya.

110. 20 f. brown 20 15

30. King Hassan II. 31. Scout with Banner.

1962.

111. 30.	1 f. olive	5	5
112.	2 f. violet	5	5
113.	5 f. sepia	5	5
114.	10 f. brown	8	5
115.	15 f. turquoise	15	5
116.	20 f. purple (18 × 22 mm.)	20	5
116a.	20 f. pur. (17½ × 23½ mm.)	30	8
116b.	25 f. red	20	5
117.	30 f. green	25	5
117a.	35 f. slate	25	8
117b.	40 f. blue	30	5
118.	50 f. purple	40	5
118a.	60 f. purple	70	5
119.	70 f. blue	95	10
120.	80 f. lake	1·50	15

1962. 5th Arab Scout Jamboree, Rabat.
121 31 20 f. purple and blue .. 20 15

32. Campaign Emblem and Swamp.
33. Aquarium and Fish.

فيفانات
1963
≋ 20+5
(35.)

34. Mounted Postman and 1912 Sherifian Stamp.

1962. Malaria Eradication Campaign.
122. 32. 20 f. blue and green .. 20 15
123. – 50 f. lake and green .. 35 25
DESIGN—VERT. 50 f. Sword piercing mosquito.

1962. Casablanca Aquarium. Multicoloured.
124. 20 f. Type 33 .. .. 35 25
125. 30 f. Aquarium and eel .. 35 25

1962. First National Philatelic Exn., Rabat, and Stamp Day.
126. 34. 20 f. green and brown .. 40 35
127. – 30 f. black and red .. 50 40
128. – 50 f. bistre and blue .. 95 50
DESIGNS: 30 f. Postman and circular postmark. 50 f. Sultan Hassan I and octagonal postmark. (Both stamps commemorate 70th anniv. of Sherifian post.)

1963. Flood Relief Fund. Surch. as T 35.
129. 5. 20+5 f. on 5 f. indigo and blue .. 40 35
130. 30+10 f. on 50 f. red .. 50 50

36. King Moulay Ismail.
37. Ibn. Batota (voyager).

1963. 300th Anniv. of Meknes.
131. 36. 20 f. sepia 25 20

1963. "Famous Men of Maghreb".
132. 37. 20 f. purple 20 20
133. – 20 f. black 20 20
134. – 20 f. myrtle 25 25
134a. 37. 40 f. blue 30 10
PORTRAITS: No. 133, Ibn Khaldoun (historian). No. 134, Al Idrissi (geographer).

38. Sugar Beet and Refinery.
39. Isis (bas relief).

1963. Freedom from Hunger.
135. 38. 20 f. black, brown & grn. 25 20
136. – 50 f. black, brown & blue 65 35
DESIGN—VERT. 50 f. Fisherman and tunny.

1963. Nubian Monuments Preservation.
137. – 20 f. black and grey .. 20 15
138. 39. 30 f. violet 25 25
139. – 50 f. purple 60 35
DESIGNS—HORIZ. 20 f. Heads of Colossi, Abu Simbel. 50 f. Philae Temple.

40. Agadir, before Earthquake.

41. Plan of new Agadir Hospital.
42. Emblems of Morocco and Rabat.

1963. Reconstruction of Agadir.
140. 40. 20 f. red and blue .. 35 35
141. 30 f. red and blue .. 45 35
142. – 50 f. red and blue .. 80 40
DESIGNS: 30 f. is optd. with large red cross and date of earthquake, 29th February, 1960. 50 f. Reconstructed Agadir.

1963. Cent. of International Red Cross.
143. 41. 30 f. multicoloured .. 20 20

1963. Opening of Parliament.
144. 42. 20 f. multicoloured .. 20 20

43. Hands breaking Chain.
44. National Flag.

1963. 15th Anniv. of Declaration of Human Rights.
145. 43. 20 f. brn., sepia & grn. 20 20

1963. Evacuation of Foreign Troops from Morocco.
146. 44. 20 f. red, green & black 25 25

45. "Moulay Abdurrahman" (after Delacroix).

1964. 3rd Anniv. of King Hassan's Coronation.
147. 45. 1 d. multicoloured .. 2·25 1·60

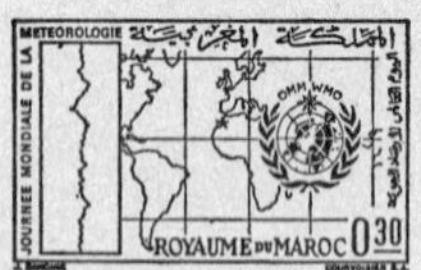

46. Map, Chart and W.M.O. Emblem.

1964. World Meteorological Day. Mult.
148. 20 f. African weather map (postage) (vert.) .. 25 20
149. 30 f. Type 46 .. .. 40 35
150. 90 f. Globe and weather vane (air) (vert.) .. 60 45

47. Fair Entrance.

1964. Air. 20th Anniv. of Casablanca Int. Fair.
151. 47. 1 d. red, drab and blue 70 60

48. Moroccan Pavilion at Fair.

1964. Air. New York World's Fair.
152. 48. 1 d. multicoloured .. 1·00 65

49. Children Playing in the Sun.
50. Olympic Torch.

1964. Postal Employees' Holiday Settlements.
153. 49. 20 f. multicoloured .. 25 20
154. – 30 f. multicoloured .. 35 25
DESIGN: 30 f. Boy, girl and holiday settlement.

1964. Olympic Games, Tokyo.
155. 50. 20 f. green, violet & red 25 25
156. 30 f. pur., blue and grn. 35 30
157. 50 f. red, blue and green 40 35

51. Lighthouse and Sultan Mohamed ben Abdurrahman (founder).
52. Tangier Iris.

1964. Cent. of Cape Spartel Lighthouse.
158. 51. 25 f. multicoloured .. 20 15

1965. Flowers. Multicoloured.
159. 25 f. Type 52 .. .. 70 45
160. 40 f. Gladiolus (vert.) .. 85 55
161. 60 f. Caper (horiz.) .. 1·50 1·00

53. Return of King Mohammed.
54. Early Telegraph Receiver.

1965. 10th Anniv. of Return of King Mohammed V from Exile.
162. 53. 25 f. green 25 20

1965. Cent. of I.T.U. Multicoloured.
163. 25 f. Type 54 .. .. 20 20
164. 40 f. "TIROS" weather satellite 35 30

55. I.C.Y. Emblem.
59. Corn.

1965. Int. Co-operation Year.
165. 55. 25 f. black and green .. 25 20
166. 60 f. lake 40 35

1965. Seashells. As T 52. Designs multi-coloured; background colours given.
167. 25 f. violet 25 20
168. 25 f. blue 25 20
169. 25 f. yellow 25 20
SEASHELLS: No. 167, "Charonia nodifera". No. 168, "Pitaria chione". No. 169, "Cymbium neptuni". Each value issued "tete-beche" horiz. in sheets.

1965. Shellfish. As T 52. Multicoloured.
170. 25 f. Helmet Crab .. 30 20
171. 40 f. Mantis shrimp .. 1·25 70
172. 1 d. Royal prawn (horiz.) .. 1·75 1·00

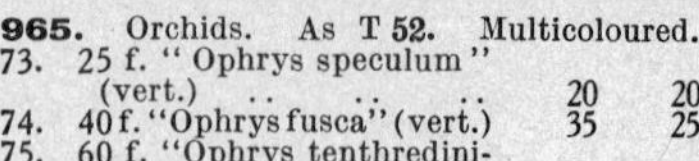

1965. Orchids. As T 52. Multicoloured.
173. 25 f. "Ophrys speculum" (vert.) 20 20
174. 40 f. "Ophrys fusca" (vert.) 35 25
175. 60 f. "Ophrys tenthredinifera" (horiz.) .. .. 1·25 90

1966. Agricultural Products (1st issue).
176. 59. 25 f. black and ochre 20 15
See also Nos. 188/9 and 211.

60. Flag, Map and Dove.

1966. 10th Anniv. of Independence.
177. 60. 25 f. red and green .. 20 15

61. King Hassan II and Crown.

1966. 5th Anniv. of King Hassan's Coronation.
178. 61. 25 f. blue, green and red 20 15

62. Cross-country Runner.

1966. 53rd "Cross des Nations" (Cross-country Race).
179. 62. 25 f. green 20 15

63. W.H.O. Building.

1966. Inaug. of W.H.O. Headquarters, Geneva.
180. 63. 25 f. black and purple .. 20 15
181. – 40 f. black and blue .. 25 20
DESIGN: 40 f. W.H.O. Building (different view).

64. King Hassan and Parachutist.
65. Brooch.

1966. 10th Anniv. of Royal Armed Forces.
182. 64. 25 f. black and gold .. 35 25
183. – 40 f. black and gold .. 35 25
DESIGN: 40 f. Crown Prince Hassan kissing hand of King Mohammed.

1966. Palestine Week. As No. 110 but inscr. "SEMAINE DE LA PALESTINE" at foot and dated "1966".
184. 25 f. blue 20 15

1966. Red Cross Seminar. Moroccan Jewellery. Multicoloured.
185. 25 f.+5 f. Type 65 .. 60 45
186. 40 f.+10 f. Pendant .. 90 55
See also Nos. 203/4, 246/7, 274/5, 287/8, 303/4, 324/5, 370/1, 397/8, 414/15, 450/1 and 493.

66. Rameses II, Abu Simbel.
67. Diesel Train.

1966. Air. 20th Anniv. of U.N.E.S.C.O.
187. 66. 1 d. red and yellow .. 70 50

1966. Agricultural Products (2nd and 3rd issue.) Designs as T 59.
188. 40 f. multicoloured .. 25 8
189. 60 f. multicoloured .. 35 20
DESIGNS—VERT. 40 f. Citrus fruits. HORIZ. 60 f. Olives.

1966. Moroccan Transport. Multicoloured.
(a) Postage. Size as T **67**.
190. 25 f. Type **67** 75 35
191. 40 f. Liner "Maroc" .. 55 15
192. 1 d. Tourist coach .. 50 20
(b) **Air.** Size 48×27½ mm.
193. 3 d. "Caravelle" of Royal Air Maroc .. .. 3·25 1·50

68. Shad.

1967. Fishes. Multicoloured.
194. 25 f. Type **68** 25 20
195. 40 f. Pale bonito 35 25
196. 1 d. Bluefish .. .. 1·40 90

69. Hilton Hotel, Ancient Ruin and Map.

1967. Opening of Hilton Hotel, Rabat.
197. **69.** 25 f. black and blue .. 20 15
198. 1 d. purple and blue .. 50 20

70. Ait Aadel Dam.

1967. Inaug. of Ait Aadel Dam.
199. 25 f. grey, blue and green 25 15
200. 40 f. bistre and blue .. 30 20

71. Moroccan Scene and Lions Emblem.

1967. 50th Anniv. of Lions Int.
201. **71.** 40 f. blue and gold .. 25 20
202. 1 d. green and gold .. 50 25

1967. Moroccan Red Cross. As T **65**. Mult.
203. 60 f.+5 f. Necklace .. 65 65
204. 1 d.+10 f. Two bracelets.. 1·40 1·40

72. Three Hands and Pickaxe. **73.** I.T.Y. Emblem.

1967. Communal Development Campaign.
205. **72.** 25 f. green 20 12

1967. Int. Tourist Year.
206. **73.** 1 d. blue and cobalt .. 50 35

74. Arrow and Map. **75.** Horse-jumping.

1967. Mediterranean Games, Tunis.
207. **74.** 25 f. multicoloured .. 25 20
208. 40 f. multicoloured .. 30 20

1967. Int. Horse Show.
209. **75.** 40 f. multicoloured .. 30 20
210. 1 d. multicoloured .. 50 35

1967. Agricultural Products (4th issue). As T **59**.
211. 40 f. mult. (Cotton plant) 25 15

76. Human Rights Emblem. **77.** Msouffa Woman.

1968. Human Rights Year.
212. **76.** 25 f. slate 20 20
213. 1 d. lake 35 25

1968. Moroccan Costumes. Multicoloured.
214. 10 f. Ait Moussa or Ali .. 40 25
215. 15 f. Ait Mouhad 60 30
216. 25 f. Barquemaster of Rabat-Sale 60 35
217. 25 f. Townsman 70 35
218. 40 f. Townswoman .. 70 45
219. 60 f. Royal Mokhazni .. 90 60
220. 1 d. Type **77** .. .. 1·10 70
221. 1 d. Riff .. .. 1·10 70
222. 1 d. Zemmour woman .. 1·25 85
223. 1 d. Meknassa .. .. 1·25 60

78. King Hassan. **79.** Red Crescent Nurse and Child.

1968.
224. **78.** 1 f. multicoloured .. 5 5
225. 2 f. multicoloured .. 5 5
226. 5 f. multicoloured .. 5 5
227. 10 f. multicoloured .. 8 5
228. 15 f. multicoloured .. 8 5
229. 20 f. multicoloured .. 10 5
230. 25 f. multicoloured .. 12 5
231. 30 f. multicoloured .. 12 5
232. 35 f. multicoloured .. 20 8
233. 40 f. multicoloured .. 20 10
234. 50 f. multicoloured .. 50 5
235. 60 f. multicoloured .. 50 5
236. 70 f. multicoloured .. 3·00 65
237. 75 f. multicoloured .. 70 12
238. 80 f. multicoloured .. 70 20
239. – 90 f. multicoloured .. 1·00 20
240. – 1 d. multicoloured .. 1·25 20
241. – 2 d. multicoloured .. 1·90 35
242. – 3 d. multicoloured .. 4·00 80
243. – 5 d. multicoloured .. 7·00 2·00
Nos. 239/43 bear a similar portrait of King Hassan, but are larger, 26½×40½ mm.

1968. 20th Anniv. of W.H.O.
244. **79.** 25 f. brown, red & blue 20 10
245. 40 f. brown, red & slate 25 15

1968. Red Crescent. Moroccan Jewellery. As T **65**. Multicoloured.
246. 25 f. Pendant brooch .. 40 15
247. 40 f. Bracelet 85 25

80. Rotary Emblem, Conference Building and Map.

1968. Rotary Int. District Conf., Casablanca.
248. **80.** 40 f. gold, blue & green 35 20
249. 1 d. gold, ultram. & blue 75 30

81. Belt Pattern. **82.** Princess Lalla Meryem.

1968. "The Belts of Fez". Designs showing ornamental patterns.
250. **81.** 25 f. multicoloured .. 1·50 70
251. – 40 f. multicoloured .. 1·75 85
252. – 60 f. multicoloured .. 2·75 1·25
253. – 1 d. multicoloured .. 4·75 2·75

1968. World Children's Day. Multicoloured.
254. 25 f. Type **82** 25 20
255. 40 f. Princess Lalla Asmaa 35 25
256. 1 d. Crown Prince Sidi Mohamed 45 55

83. Wrestling.

1968. Olympic Games, Mexico. Multicoloured.
257. 15 f. Type **83** 15 15
258. 20 f. Basketball 15 15
259. 25 f. Cycling 15 15
260. 40 f. Boxing 25 15
261. 60 f. Running 35 15
262. 1 d. Football 90 45

84. Silver Crown. **85.** Costumes of Zagora, South Morocco.

1968. Ancient Moroccan Coins.
263. **84.** 20 f. silver & pur. .. 20 20
264. – 25 f. gold and purple .. 25 25
265. – 40 f. silver and green .. 90 30
266. – 60 f. gold and red .. 1·25 65
COINS: 25 f. Gold dinar. 40 f. Silver dirham. 60 f. Gold piece.
See also Nos. 270/1.

1969. Traditional Women's Costumes. Mult.
267. 15 f. Type **85** (postage) .. 85 50
268. 25 f. Ait Adidou costumes 1·10 75
269. 1 d. Ait Ouaouzguit costumes (air) .. .. .. 1·75 85

1969. 8th Anniv. of Coronation of Hassan II. As T **84** (silver coins).
270. 1 d. silver and blue .. 3·25 95
271. 5 d. silver and violet .. 7·50 4·25
COINS: 1 d. One dirham coin of King Mohammed V. 5 d. One dirham coin of King Hassan II.

86. Hands "reading" Braille on Map.

1969. Protection of the Blind Week.
272. **86.** 25 f.+10 f. mult. .. 20 15

87. "Actor". **89.** King Hassan II.

1969. World Theatre Day.
273. **87.** 1 d. multicoloured .. 45 25

1969. 50th Anniv. of League of Red Cross Societies. Moroccan Jewellery as T **65**. Multicoloured.
274. 25 f.+5 f. Bracelets .. 60 45
275. 40 f.+10 f. Pendant .. 90 55

1969. King Hassan's 40th Birthday.
276. **89.** 1 d. multicoloured .. 90 35

مؤتمر القمة الاسلامي
الرباط ١٥ رجب 1389
(**90.**) **91.** Mahatma Gandhi.

1969. Islamic Summit Conf., Rabat (1st issue). No. 240 (King Hassan) optd. with T **90.**
278. 1 d. multicoloured .. 4·00 3·25

1969. Birth Cent. of Mahatma Gandhi.
279. **91.** 40 f. brown and lavender 20 15

92. I.L.O. Emblem.

1969. 50th Anniv. of I.L.O.
280. **92.** 50 f. multicoloured .. 25 20

93. King Hassan on Horseback.

1969. Islamic Summit Conference, Rabat (2nd issue).
281 **93** 1 d. multicoloured .. 85 35

94. "Spahi Horseman" (Haram al Glaoui).

1970. Moroccan Art.
282. **94.** 1 d. multicoloured .. 65 30

1970. Flood Victims Relief Fund. Nos. 227/8 surch.
283. **78.** 10 f.+25 f. multicoloured 2·75 2·75
284. 15 f.+25 f. multicoloured 2·75 2·75

96. Drainage System, Fez. **97.** "Dance of the Guedra" (P. Beaubrun).

1970. 50th Congress of Public and Municipal Health Officials, Rabat.
285. **96.** 60 f. multicoloured .. 35 20

1970. Folklore Festival, Marrakesh.
286. **97.** 40 f. multicoloured .. 25 20

1970. Red Crescent. Moroccan Jewellery as T **65**. Multicoloured.
287. 25 f.+5 f. Necklace .. 70 65
288. 50 f.+10 t. Pendant .. 1·25 1·00

1970. Population Census. No. 189 surch **1970 O,25** and Arabic inscr.
290 25 f. on 60 f. multicoloured 20 10

99. Dish Aerial, Souk el Arba des Sehoul Communications Station. **100.** Ruddy Shelduck.

1970. 17th Anniv. of Revolution.
291. **99.** 1 d. multicoloured .. 45 35

1970. Nature Protection, Wild Birds. Mult.
292. 25 f. Type **100** .. .. 1·00 35
293. 40 f. Houbara Bustard .. 1·60 35

101. I.E.Y. Emblem and Moroccan with Book.

1970. International Education Year.
294. **101.** 60 f. multicoloured .. 35 20

102. Symbols of U.N.

1970. 25th Anniv. of U.N.O.
295. **102.** 50 f. multicoloured .. 20 15

103. League Emblem, Map and Laurel.

1970. 25th Anniv. of Arab League.
296. **103.** 50 f. multicoloured .. 25 15

104. Olive Grove and Extraction Plant.

1970. World Olive-oil Production Year.
297. **104.** 50 f. blk., brn. & green 55 15

105. Es Sounna Mosque.

1971. Restoration of Es Sounna Mosque Rabat.
298. **105.** 60 f. multicoloured .. 25 15

106. "Heart" within Horse. **107.** King Hassan II and Dam.

1971. European and North African Heart Week.
299. **106.** 50 f. multicoloured .. 25 20

1971. 10th Anniv. of King Hassan's Accession.
300. **107.** 25 f. multicoloured .. 15 10

108. Palestine on Globe.

1971. Palestine Week.
302. **108.** 25 f. + 10 f. multicoloured 25 20

1971. Red Crescent. Moroccan Jewellery. As T **65**. Multicoloured.
303. 25 f. + 5 f. "Arrow-head" Brooch 50 50
304. 40 f. + 10 f. Square Pendant 75 65

109. Hands holding Peace Dove.

1971. Racial Equality Year.
305. **109.** 50 f. multicoloured .. 20 15

110. Musical Instrument.

1971. Protection of the Blind Week.
306. **110.** 40 f. + 10 f. mult. .. 20 20

111. Children at Play. **112.** Shah Mohammed Reza Pahlavi of Iran.

1971. International Children's Day.
307. **111.** 40 f. multicoloured .. 20 15

1971. 2,500th Anniv. of Persian Empire.
308. **112.** 1 d. multicoloured .. 40 30

113. Aerial View of Mausoleum.

1971. Mausoleum of Mohammed V. Mult.
309. 25 f. Type **113** 15 15
310. 50 f. Tomb of Mohammed V 20 20
311. 1 d. Interior of Mausoleum (vert.) 40 20

114. Football and Emblem. **116.** Sun and Landscape.

115. A.P.U. Emblem.

1971. Mediterranean Games, Izmir, Turkey. Multicoloured.
312. 40 f. Type **114** 20 15
313. 60 f. Athlete and emblem 25 20

1971. 25th Anniv. of Founding of Arab Postal Union at Sofar Conf.
314. **115.** 25 f. red, blue & light bl. 15 8

1971. 50th Anniv. of Sherifian Phosphates Office.
315. **116.** 70 f. multicoloured .. 30 20

117. Torch and Book Year Emblem. **118.** Lottery Symbol.

1972. Int. Book Year.
316. **117.** 1 d. multicoloured .. 40 25

1972. Creation of National Lottery.
317. **118.** 25 f. gold, blk. & brn. 15 10

119. Bridge of Sighs. **120.** Mizmar (double-horned flute).

1972. U.N.E.S.C.O. "Save Venice" Campaign. Multicoloured.
318. 25 f. Type **119** 15 15
319. 50 f. St Mark's Basilica (horiz.) 20 15
320. 1 d. Lion of St. Marks (horiz) 40 20

1972. Protection of the Blind Week.
321. **120.** 25 f. + 10 f. mult. .. 20 20

121. Bridge and Motorway.

1972. 2nd African Highways Conf., Rabat.
322. **121.** 75 f. multicoloured .. 25 20

122. Moroccan Stamp of 1969, and Postmark.

1972. Stamp Day.
323. **122.** 1 d. multicoloured .. 40 20

1972. Red Crescent. Moroccan Jewellery. As T **65**. Multicoloured.
324. 25 f. + 5 f. Jewelled bangles 50 50
325. 70 f. + 10 f. Filigree pendant 75 75

123. "Betrothal of Imilchil" (Tayeb Lahlou). **124.** Dove on African Map.

1972. Folklore Festival, Marrakesh.
326. **123.** 60 f. multicoloured .. 60 35

1972. 9th Organisation of African Unity Summit Conference, Rabat.
327. **124.** 25 f. multicoloured .. 15 15

125. Polluted Beach.

1972. U.N. Environmental Conservation Conf., Stockholm.
328. **125.** 50 f. multicoloured .. 25 20

126. Running. **127.** "Sonchus pinnatifidus".

1972. Olympic Games, Munich.
329. **126.** 25 f. red, pink & black 15 15
330. – 50 f. violet, lilac & blk. 20 15
331. – 75 f. grn., yell. and blk. 30 20
332. – 1 d. blue, light blue and black 35 25

DESIGNS: 50 f. Wrestling. 75 f. Football. 1 d. Cycling.

1972. Moroccan Flowers. (1st series). Mult.
333. 25 f. Type **127** 20 15
334. 40 f. "Amberboa crupinoides" 25 15

See also Nos. 375/6.

128. Sand Gazelle. **129.** Rabat Carpet.

1972. Nature Protection. Fauna. Mult.
335. 25 f. Type **128** 50 25
336. 40 f. Barbary sheep .. 60 25

1972. Moroccan Carpets (1st series). Mult.
337. 50 f. Type **129** 75 35
338. 75 f. Rabat carpet with "star-shaped" centre .. 1·00 50

See also Nos. 380/1, 406/7, 433/4, 485/7 and 513.

130. Mother and Child with U.N. Emblem. **132.** Global Weather Map.

131. "Postman" and "Stamp".

1972. International Children's Day.
339. **130.** 75 f. blue, yell. & grn. 35 30

1973. Stamp Day.
340. **131.** 25 f. multicoloured .. 15 8

1973. Cent. of W.M.O.
341. **132.** 70 f. multicoloured .. 35 20

133. King Hassan and Arms.

1973.
342. **133.** 1 f. multicoloured .. 5 5
343. 2 f. multicoloured .. 5 5
344. 5 f. multicoloured .. 5 5
345. 10 f. multicoloured .. 5 5
346. 15 f. multicoloured .. 5 5
347. 20 f. multicoloured .. 8 5
348. 25 f. multicoloured .. 10 5
349. 30 f. multicoloured .. 12 5
350. 35 f. multicoloured .. 12 10
351. 40 f. multicoloured .. 3·75 45
352. 50 f. multicoloured .. 20 10
353. 60 f. multicoloured .. 25 12

354. 70 f. multicoloured .. 25 12
355. 75 f. multicoloured .. 30 15
356. 80 f. multicoloured .. 30 20
357. 90 f. multicoloured .. 35 15
358. 1 d. multicoloured .. 1·50 20
359. 2 d. multicoloured .. 3·25 55
360. 3 d. multicoloured .. 4·25 75
361. 5 d. mult. (brown background) .. .. 3·25 75
361a. 5 d. mult. (pink background) .. .. 3·50 90

مناظرة
السياحة
1973
(134.)

1973. Nat. Tourist Conf. Nos. 324/5 surch. with T **134.**
362. **65.** 25 f. on 5 f. multicoloured 2·00 2·00
363. 70 f. on 10 f. mult. .. 2·00 2·00
On No. 363 the Arabic text is arranged in one line.

135. Tambours.

1973. Protection of the Blind Week.
364. **135.** 70 f.+10 f. multicoloured 40 30

136. Kaaba, Mecca, and Mosque, Rabat.

1973. Prophet Mohammed's Birthday.
365. **136.** 25 f. multicoloured .. 15 10

137. Roses and M'Gouna.

1973. M'Gouna Rose Festival.
366. **137.** 25 f. multicoloured .. 15 10

138. Handclasp and Torch. **139.** Folk-dancers.

1973. 10th Anniv. of Organization of African Unity.
367. **138.** 70 f. multicoloured .. 30 15

1973. Folklore Festival, Marrakesh. Mult.
368. 50 f. Type **139** 20 15
369. 1 d. Folk-musicians 40 25

1973. Red Crescent. Moroccan Jewellery. As T **65.** Multicoloured.
370. 25 f.+5 f. Locket 70 50
371. 70 f.+10 f. Bracelet inlaid with pearls 80 60

140. Solar System. **141.** Microscope.

1973. 500th Birth Anniv. of Nicholas Copernicus.
372. **140.** 70 f. multicoloured .. 35 20

1973. 25th Anniv. of W.H.O.
373. **141.** 70 f. multicoloured .. 25 20

INDEX

Countries can be quickly located by referring to the index at the end of this volume.

142. Interpol Emblem and Fingerprint.

1973. 50th Anniv. of International Criminal Police Organization (Interpol).
374. **142.** 70 f. multicoloured .. 30 25

1973. Moroccan Flowers. (2nd series). As T **127.** Multicoloured.
375. 25 f. "Chrysanthemum carinatum" (horiz.) .. 15 8
376. 1 d. "Amberboa muricata" 75 25

143. Striped Hyena.

1973. Nature Protection. Multicoloured.
377. 25 f. Type **143** 40 15
378. 50 f. Eleonora's Falcon (vert.) 1·75 35

144. Map and Arrows.

1973. Meeting of Maghreb Committee for Co-ordination of Posts and Telecommunications, Tunis.
379. **144.** 25 f. multicoloured .. 15 10

1973. Moroccan Carpets (2nd series). As T **129.** Multicoloured.
380. 25 f. Carpet from the High Atlas 60 25
381. 70 f. Tazenakht carpet .. 90 50

المؤتمر الاسلامي - لاهور
1394

145. Golf Club and Ball. (**146**).

1974. Int. "Hassan II Trophy" Golf Grand Prix, Rabat.
382. **145.** 70 f. multicoloured .. 2·25 1·25

1974. Islamic Summit Conf., Lahore, Pakistan. No. 281 optd. with T **146.**
383. 1 d. multicoloured .. 2·00 1·25

147. Human Rights Emblem. **148.** Vanadinite.

1974. 25th Anniv. (1973) of Declaration of Human Rights.
384. **147.** 70 f. multicoloured .. 25 20

1974. Moroccan Mineral Sources. Mult.
385. 25 f. Type **148** 25 15
386. 70 f. Erythrine 60 35

149. Marrakesh Minaret. **150.** U.P.U. Emblem and Congress Dates.

1974. 173rd District of Rotary Int. Annual Conf., Marrakesh.
387. **149.** 70 f. multicoloured .. 25 20

1974. Cent. of U.P.U.
388. **150.** 25 f. blk., red & green 15 10
389. – 1 d. multicoloured .. 40 25
DESIGN—HORIZ. 1 d. Commemorative scroll.

151. Drummers and Dancers.

1974. 15th Folklore Festival, Marrakesh. Multicoloured.
390. 25 f. Type **151** 35 15
391. 70 f. Juggler with woman 85 30

152. Environmental Emblem and Scenes. **154.** Flintlock Pistol.

1974. World Environmental Day.
392. **152.** 25 f multicoloured .. 20 15

1974. Red Crescent. Moroccan Firearms. Multicoloured.
397. 25 f.+5 f. Type **154** .. 50 50
398. 70 f.+10 f. Gunpowder box 75 75

الاحصاء الفلاحي
1.00

155. Stamps, Postmark and Magnifying Glass. (**156.**)

1974. Stamp Day.
399. **155.** 70 f. multicoloured .. 25 20

1974. No. D 393 surch. with T **156.**
400. 1 d. on 5 f. orge., grn. & blk. 1·50 95

157. World Cup Trophy. **158.** Erbab (two-string fiddle).

1974. World Cup Football Championship, West Germany.
401. **157.** 1 d. multicoloured .. 45 30

1974. Blind Week.
402. **158.** 70 f.+10 f. multicoloured 30 25
See also No. 423.

160. Double-spurred Francolin. **162.** Jasmine.

1974. Moroccan Animals. Multicoloured.
404. 25 f. Type **160** 90 25
405. 70 f. Leopard (horiz.) .. 60 40

1974. Moroccan Carpets (3rd series). As T **129.** Multicoloured.
406. 25 f. Zemmour carpet .. 25 10
407. 1 d. Beni M'Guild carpet .. 80 25

1975. Flowers (1st series). Mult.
408. 25 f. Type **162** 10 8
409. 35 f. Orange lilies 15 10
410. 70 f. Poppies 55 35
411. 90 f. Carnations 75 50
See also Nos. 417/20.

163. Aragonite. **165.** "The Water-carrier" (Feu Taieb-Lalou).

1975. Minerals. Multicoloured.
412. 50 f. Type **163** 20 15
413. 1 d. Agate 35 20
See also No. 543 and 563/4.

1975. Red Crescent. Moroccan Jewellery. As T **65.** Multicoloured.
414. 25 f. + 5 f. Pendant .. 50 50
415. 70 f. + 10 f. Earring .. 75 65

1975. "Moroccan Painters".
416. **165.** 1 d. multicoloured .. 75 30

1975. Flowers (2nd series). As T **162.** Mult.
417. 10 f. Daisies 10 10
418. 50 f. Pelargoniums .. 20 10
419. 60 f. Orange blossom .. 50 30
420. 1 d. Pansies 75 60

166. Collector with Stamp Album. **167.** Dancer with Rifle.

1975. Stamp Day.
421. **166.** 40 f. multicoloured .. 20 10

1975. 16th Nat. Folklore Festival, Marrakesh.
422. **167.** 1 d. multicoloured .. 65 30

168. "Animals in Forest" (child's drawing).

1975. Blind Week. As T **158.** Multicoloured.
423. 1 d. Mandolin 35 25

1975. Children's Week.
424. **168.** 25 f. multicoloured .. 15 8

169. Games Emblem and Athletes.

1975. 7th Mediterranean Games, Algiers.
425. **169.** 40 f. multicoloured .. 15 8

170. Waldrapp.

1975. Fauna. Multicoloured.
426. 40 f. Type **170** .. .. 1·50 40
427. 1 d. Caracal (vert.) .. 90 40
See also Nos. 470/71.

1975. "Green March" (1st issue). Nos. 370/1 optd. **1975** and Arabic inscr.
428. 25 f. (+5 f.) multicoloured 2·00 2·00
429. 70 f. (+10 f.) multicoloured 2·00 2·00
The premiums on the stamps are obliterated.

172. King Mohammed V greeting Crowd.

1975. 20th Anniv. of Independence. Mult.
430. 40 f. Type **172** 15 8
431. 1 d. King Hassan (vert.) .. 35 20
432. 1 d. King Hassan V wearing fez (vert.) 35 20

1975. Moroccan Carpets (4th series). As **T 129.** Multicoloured.
433. 25 f. Ouled Besseba carpet 60 35
434. 1 d. Ait Ouaouzguid carpet 90 45
See Nos. 485/7 and 513.

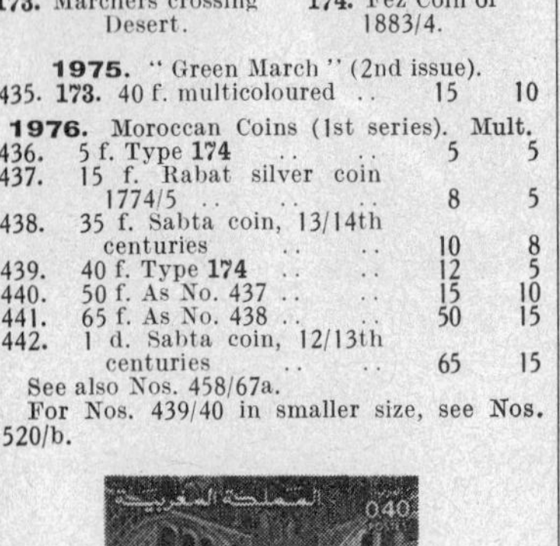

173. Marchers crossing Desert.  174. Fez Coin of 1883/4.

1975. "Green March" (2nd issue).
435. **173.** 40 f. multicoloured .. 15 10

1976. Moroccan Coins (1st series). Mult.
436. 5 f. Type **174** 5 5
437. 15 f. Rabat silver coin 1774/5 .. .. 8 5
438. 35 f. Sabta coin, 13/14th centuries 10 8
439. 40 f. Type **174** 12 5
440. 50 f. As No. 437 .. .. 15 10
441. 65 f. As No. 438 .. .. 50 15
442. 1 d. Sabta coin, 12/13th centuries 65 15
See also Nos. 458/67a.
For Nos. 439/40 in smaller size, see Nos. 520/b.

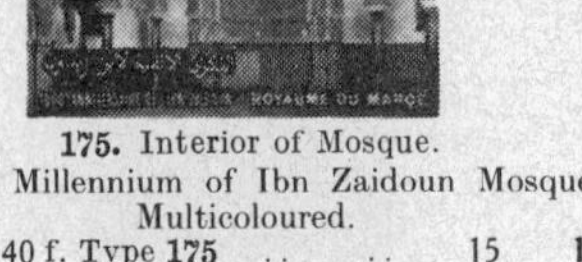

175. Interior of Mosque.

1976. Millennium of Ibn Zaidoun Mosque. Multicoloured.
443. 40 f. Type **175** 15 10
444. 65 f. Interior archways (vert.) 20 15

176. Moroccan Family.

1976. Family Planning.
445. **176.** 40 f. multicoloured .. 15 8

177. Bou Anania College, Fez.

1976. Moroccan Architecture.
446. **177.** 1 d. multicoloured .. 25 20

178. Temple Sculpture.

1976. Borobudur Temple Preservation Campaign. Multicoloured.
447. 40 f. Type **178** 15 15
448. 1 d. View of Temple .. 30 20

179. Dome of the Rock, Jerusalem.

1976. 6th Anniv. of Islamic Conference.
449. **179.** 1 d. multicoloured .. 30 20

1976. Red Crescent, Moroccan Jewellery. As **T 65.** Multicoloured.
450. 40 f. Jewelled purse .. 15 10
451. 1 d. Jewelled pectoral .. 65 25

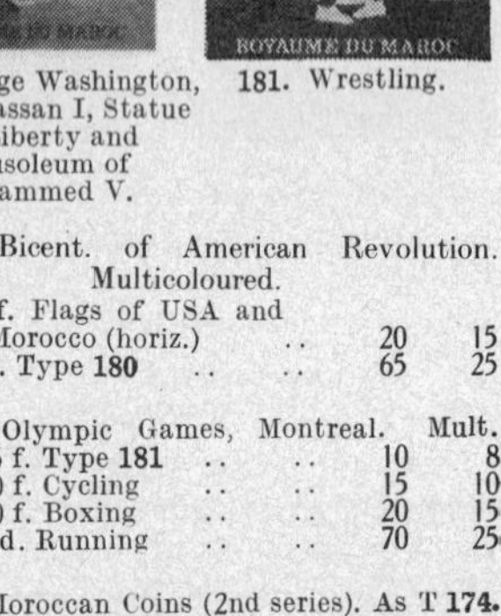

180. George Washington, King Hassan I, Statue of Liberty and Mausoleum of Mohammed V. 181. Wrestling.

1976. Bicent. of American Revolution. Multicoloured.
452. 40 f. Flags of USA and Morocco (horiz.) .. 20 15
453. 1 d. Type **180** 65 25

1976. Olympic Games, Montreal. Mult.
454. 35 f. Type **181** 10 8
455. 40 f. Cycling 15 10
456. 50 f. Boxing 20 15
457. 1 d. Running 70 25

1976. Moroccan Coins (2nd series). As **T 174.** Multicoloured.
458. 5 f. Medieval silver mohur 5 5
459. 10 f. Gold mohur 5 5
460. 15 f. Gold coin 8 5
461. 20 f. Gold coin (different) 10 5
461a. 25 f. As No. 437 .. .. 10 5
462. 30 f. As No. 459 .. .. 10 5
463. 35 f. Silver dinar 45 10
464. 60 f. As No. 458 .. .. 20 15
465. 70 f. Copper coin 55 15
466. 75 f. As No. 463 .. .. 25 15
466a. 80 f. As No. 460 .. .. 20 10
467. 75 f. As No. 465 .. .. 60 35
467a. 3 d. As No. 461 .. .. 60 50

182. Early and Modern Telephones with Dish Aerial.

1976. Telephone Centenary.
468. **182.** 1 d. multicoloured .. 35 25

183. Gold Medallion.

1976. Blind Week.
469. **183.** 50 f. multicoloured .. 20 10

1976. Birds. As **T 170.** Multicoloured.
470. 40 f. Dark Chanting Goshawk 1·10 35
471. 1 d. Purple Swamphen .. 1·60 70
Nos. 470/1 are vert. designs.

185. King Hassan, Emblems and Map.

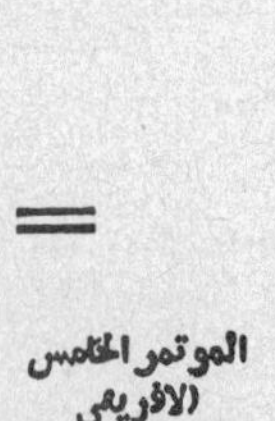

المؤتمر الخامس
الأفريقي
لداء السل
الرباط 1976

(186).

1976. 1st Anniv. of "Green March".
472. **185** 40 f. multicoloured .. 12 10

1976. Fifth African Tuberculosis Conference. Nos. 414/15 optd. with **T 186.**
473. 25 f. multicoloured .. 1·25 1·25
474. 70 f. multicoloured .. 1·50 1·50

187. Globe and Peace Dove.  188. African Nations Cup.

1976. Conference of Non-Aligned Countries Colombo.
475. **187.** 1 d. red, black and blue 30 20

1976. African Nations Football Championship.
476. **188.** 1 d. multicoloured .. 30 20

189. Letters encircling Globe.

1977. Stamp Day.
477. **189.** 40 f. multicoloured .. 12 8

190. "Aeonium arboreum".

1977. Flowers. Multicoloured.
478. 40 f. Type **190** 30 10
479. 50 f. "Malope trifida" (24 × 38 mm.) 50 30
480. 1 d. "Hesperolaburnum platyclarpum" .. 60 30

191. Ornamental Candle Lamps. 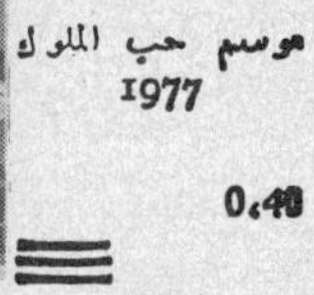 (192.)

1977. Procession of the Candles, Sale.
481. **191.** 40 f. multicoloured .. 12 8

1977. Cherry Festival. No. D 394 surch. with **T 192.**
482. 40 f. on 10 f. Cherries .. 40 30

193. Map and Emblem.

1977. Fifth Congress, Organization of Arab Towns.
483. **193.** 50 f. multicoloured .. 15 10

194. A.P.U. Emblem.

1977. 25th Anniv. of Arab Postal Union.
484. **194.** 1 d. multicoloured .. 30 20

1977. Carpets (5th series). As **T 129.** Mult.
485. 35 f. Marmoucha carpet .. 25 15
486. 40 f. Ait Haddou carpet .. 40 20
487. 1 d. Henbel rug, Sale .. 65 30

195. Zither.  196. Mohammed Ali Jinnah.

1977. Blind Week.
488. **195.** 1 d. multicoloured .. 35 25

1977. Birth Cent. of Mohammed Ali Jinnah.
489. **196.** 70 f. multicoloured .. 25 20

197. Marcher with Flag.

1977. 2nd Anniv. of "Green March".
490. **197.** 1 d. multicoloured .. 30 20

198. Assembly Hall.

1977. Opening of House of Representatives.
491. **198.** 1 d. multicoloured .. 30 20

199. Silver Brooch. 200. Bowl with Funnel.

1977. Red Crescent.
493. **199.** 1 d. multicoloured .. 60 20

1978. Moroccan Copperware. Multicoloured.
494. 40 f. Type **200** 10 8
495. 1 d. Bowl with cover .. 70 20

201. Development Emblem. 202. Decorative Pot with Lid.

1978. Sahara Development. Multicoloured.
496. 40 f. Type **201** 10 8
497. 1 d. Fishes in net and camels at oasis (horiz.) 30 20

1978. Blind Week. Multicoloured.
498. 1 d. Type **202** 60 30
499. 1 d. Decorative jar .. 60 30

203. Map and Red Cross within Red Crescent.

1978. Tenth Conference of Arab Red Crescent and Red Cross Societies.
500. **203.** 1 d. red and black .. 30 20

204. View of Fez.

205. Dome of the Rock.

1978. Rotary International Meeting, Fez.
501. **204.** 1 d. multicoloured .. 30 20

1978. Palestine Welfare.
502. **205.** 5 f. multicoloured .. 5 5
503. 10 f. multicoloured .. 5 5

206. Flautist and Folk Dancers.

1978. National Folklore Festival, Marrakesh.
504. **206.** 1 d. multicoloured .. 55 20

207. Sugar Field and Crushing Plant.

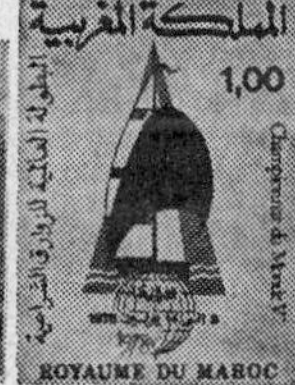

208. Yacht.

1978. Sugar Industry.
505. **207.** 40 f. multicoloured .. 15 8

1978. World Sailing Championships.
506. **208.** 1 d. multicoloured .. 60 20

209. Tree, Tent and Scout Emblem.

210. Moulay Idriss.

1978. Pan-Arab Scout Festival, Rabat.
507. **209.** 40 f. multicoloured .. 15 8

1978. Moulay Idriss Great Festival.
508. **210.** 40 f. multicoloured .. 15 8

211. Human Rights Emblem.

212. Houses in Agadir.

1978. 30th Anniv. of Declaration of Human Rights.
509. **211.** 1 d. multicoloured .. 30 20

1979. Southern Moroccan Architecture (1st series). Mult.
510. 40 f. Type **212** 12 8
511. 1 d. Old fort at Marrakesh 60 15
See also Nos. 536 and 562.

213. Player, Football and Cup.

1979. Mohammed V Football Cup.
512. **213.** 40 f. multicoloured .. 12 8

1979. Moroccan Carpets (6th series). As T **129**.
513. 40 f. Marmoucha carpet .. 40 15

214. Decorated Pot.

215. " Procession from a Mosque ".

1979. Blind Week.
514. **214.** 1 d. multicoloured .. 30 20

1979. Paintings by Mohamed Ben Ali Rbati. Multicoloured.
515. 40 f. Type **215** 12 8
516. 1 d. " Religious Ceremony in a Mosque " (horiz.) 55 20

216. Coffee Pot and Heater.

217. Costumed Girls.

1979. Red Crescent. Brassware. Multicoloured.
517. 40 f. Engraved Circular Boxes 25 15
518. 1 d. Type **216** 60 30

1979. National Folklore Festival, Marrakesh.
519. **217.** 40 f. multicoloured .. 12 8

1979. Booklet stamps. Moroccan Coins. As T **174**, but smaller, $17\frac{1}{2} \times 22\frac{1}{2}$ mm.
520. 40 f. multicoloured .. 10 5
520b. 50 f. multicoloured .. 10 10

218. Curved Dagger in Jewelled Sheath.

219. King Hassan II.

1979. Ancient weapons.
521. **218.** 1 d. black and yellow 30 20

1979. King Hassan's 50th Birthday.
522. **219.** 1 d. multicoloured .. 30 20

220. Festival Emblem.

221. King Hassan II.

1979. Fourth Arab Youth Festival, Rabat.
523. **220.** 1 d. multicoloured .. 30 20

1979. "25th Anniv of Revolution of King and People".
524 **221** 1 d. multicoloured .. 30 20

222. World Map superimposed on Open Book.

1979. 50th Anniv. of International Bureau of Education.
525. **222.** 1 d. brown and yellow 30 20

223. Pilgrims in Wuquf, Arafat.

1979. Pilgrimage to Mecca.
526. **223.** 1 d. multicoloured .. 30 20

استرجاع اقليم وادى الذهب
1979-8-14
(224.)

1979. Recovery of Oued Eddahab Province. Design as No. 497, with face value amended (40 f.), optd. with T **224**.
527. 40 f. multicoloured .. 12 8
528. 1 d. multicoloured .. 65 20

225. Centaurium.

226. Children around Globe.

1979. Flowers. Multicoloured.
529. 40 f. Type **225** 12 8
530. 1 d. " Leucanthemum catanance " 55 20

1979. International Year of the Child.
531. **226.** 40 f. multicoloured .. 60 25

227. European Otter.

228. Traffic Signs.

1979. Wildlife. Multicoloured.
532. 40 f. Type **227** 25 15
533. 1 d. Moussier's Redstart .. 1·10 40

1980. Road Safety. Multicoloured.
534. 40 f. Type **228** 12 8
535. 1 d. Children at crossing .. 30 20

229. Fortress.

1980. South Moroccan Architecture (2nd series).
536. **229.** 1 d. multicoloured .. 30 20

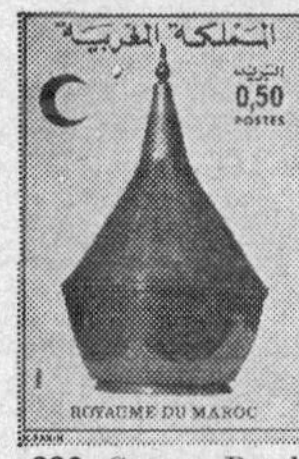

230. Copper Bowl with Lid.

231. Pot.

1980. Red Crescent. Multicoloured.
537. 50 f. Type **230** 15 12
538. 70 f. Copper kettle and brazier 35 20

1980. Blind Week.
539. **231.** 40 f. multicoloured .. 12 8

232. Mechanised Sorting Office, Rabat.

1980. Stamp Day.
540. **232.** 40 f. multicoloured .. 12 8

233. World Map and Rotary Emblem.

234. Leather Bag and Cloth.

1980. 75th Anniv. of Rotary International.
541. **233.** 1 d. multicoloured .. 30 20

1980. 4th Textile and Leather Exhibition, Casablanca.
542. **234.** 1 d. multicoloured .. 30 20

1980. Minerals (2nd series). As T **163**. Multicoloured.
543. 40 f. Gypsum 12 8

235. Peregrine Falcon.

236. Diagram of Blood Circulation and Heart.

1980. Hunting with Falcon.
544. **235.** 40 f. multicoloured .. 85 20

1980. Campaign against Cardio-vascular Diseases.
545. **236.** 1 d. multicoloured .. 30 20

237. Decade Emblem and Human Figures.

238. Harnessed Horse.

1980. Decade for Women.
546. **237.** 40 f. mauve and blue .. 12 8
547. – 1 d. multicoloured .. 30 20
DESIGN: 1 d. Decade and United Nations emblems.

1980. Ornamental Harnesses. Multicoloured.
548. 40 f. Harnessed horse (different) 12 8
549. 1 d. Type **238** 30 20

239. Satellite orbiting Earth and Dish Aerial.

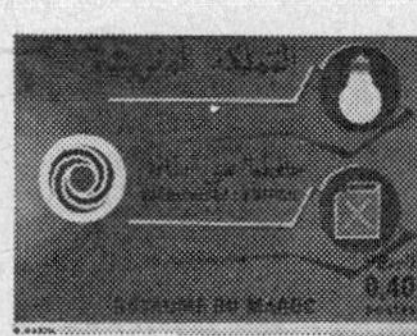

240. Light Bulb and Fuel Can.

1980. World Meteorological Day.
550. **239.** 40 f. multicoloured .. 12 8

1980. Energy Conservation. Multicoloured.
551. 40 f. Type **240** 12 8
552. 1 d. Hand holding petrol pump 30 20

241. Conference Emblem.

1980. World Tourism Conference, Manila.
553. **241.** 40 f. multicoloured .. 12 8

242. Tree bridging Straits of Gibraltar.

1980. European–African Liaison over the Straits of Gibraltar.
554. **242.** 1 d. multicoloured .. 60 20

243. Flame and Marchers.

1980. 5th Anniv. of "The Green March".
555. **243.** 1 d. multicoloured .. 30 20

244. Holy Kaaba, Mecca. **245.** " Senecio antheuphorbium ".

1980. Hegira. 1400th Anniv. Multicoloured.
556. 40 f. Type **244** 12 8
557. 1 d. Mosque, Mecca .. 30 20

1980. Flowers. Multicoloured.
558. 40 f. Type **245** 15 10
559. 1 d. " Periploca laevigata " 60 20

246. Painting by Aherdan. **247.** Nejjarine Fountain, Fez.

1980. Paintings.
560. – 40 f. bistre and brown 12 8
561. **246.** 1 d. multicoloured .. 30 20
DESIGN: 40 f. Composition of bird and feathers.

1981. Moroccan Architecture (3rd series).
562. **247.** 40 f. multicoloured .. 8 8

1981. Minerals. (3rd series). Vert designs as T **163**. Multicoloured.
563. 40 f. Onyx 25 10
564. 1 d. Malachite-azurite .. 55 25

248. King Hassan II. **249.** King Hassan II.

1981. 25th Anniv. of Independence. Mult.
565. 60 f. Type **248** 10 10
566. 60 f. Map, flags, broken chains and " 25 " .. 10 10
567. 60 f. King V. Mohammed 10 10

1981. 20th Anniv. of King Hassan's Coronation.
568. **249.** 1 d. 30 multicoloured 50 25

250. " Source " (Jillali Gharbaoul).

1981. Moroccan Painting.
569. **250.** 1 d. 30 multicoloured 50 25

251. " Anagalis monelli ". **252.** King Hassan as Major General.

1981. Flowers. Multicoloured.
570. 40 f. Type **251** 20 10
571. 70 f. " Bubonium intricatum " 40 15

1981. 25th Anniv. of Moroccan Armed Forces.
572. **252.** 60 f. lilac, gold and green 10 10
573. – 60 f. multicoloured .. 10 10
574. – 60 f. lilac, gold and green 10 10
DESIGNS: No. 573, Army badge. No. 574, King Mohamed V (founder).

253. Caduceus (Telecommunications and Health). **254.** Plate with Pattern.

1981. World Telecommunications Day.
575. **253.** 1 d. 30 multicoloured .. 20 20

1981. Blind Week. Multicoloured.
576. 50 f. Type **254** 8 8
577. 1 d. 30 Plate with ship pattern 20 20

255. Musicians and Dancers. **256.** " Seboula " Dagger.

1981. 22nd National Folklore Festival, Marrakesh.
578. **255.** 1 d. 30 multicoloured 50 25

1981. Ancient Weapons.
579. **256.** 1 d. 30 multicoloured 20 20

257. Pestle and Mortar. **258.** Hands holding I.Y.D.P. Emblem.

1981. Red Crescent. Moroccan Copperware. Multicoloured.
580. 60 f. Type **257** 25 15
581. 1 d. 30 Tripod brazier .. 55 25

1981. International Year of Disabled People.
582. **258.** 60 f. multicoloured .. 10 10

259. " Iphiclides feisthamelii Lotteri". **260.** King Hassan and Marchers.

1981. Butterflies (1st series). Multicoloured.
583. 60 f. Type **259** 50 25
584. 1 d. 30 " Zerynthina rumina africana " .. .. 1·25 60
See also Nos. 609/10.

1981. 6th Anniv. of "Green March".
585. **260.** 1 d. 30 multicoloured 20 20

261. Town Buildings and Congress Emblem.

1981. 10th International Twinned Towns Congress, Casablanca.
586. **261.** 1 d. 30 multicoloured .. 20 20

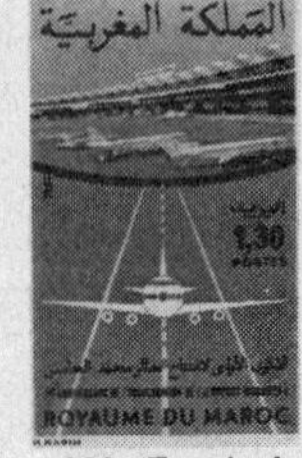

262. Dome of the Rock. **264.** Terminal Building and Runway.

1981. Palestinian Solidarity Day.
587. **262.** 60 f. multicoloured .. 10 10

1981. 12th Arab Summit Conference, Fez. No. 502/3 surch. **1981 0,40.**
588. **205.** 40 f. on 5 f. multicoloured .. 3·00 3·00
588a. 40 f. on 10 f. multicoloured .. 2·00 2·00

1981. 1st Anniv. of Mohammed V Airport.
589. **264.** 1 d. 30 multicoloured .. 20 20

265. Al Massira Dam. **266.** King Hassan II.

1981. Al Massira Dam.
590. **265.** 60 f. multicoloured .. 10 10

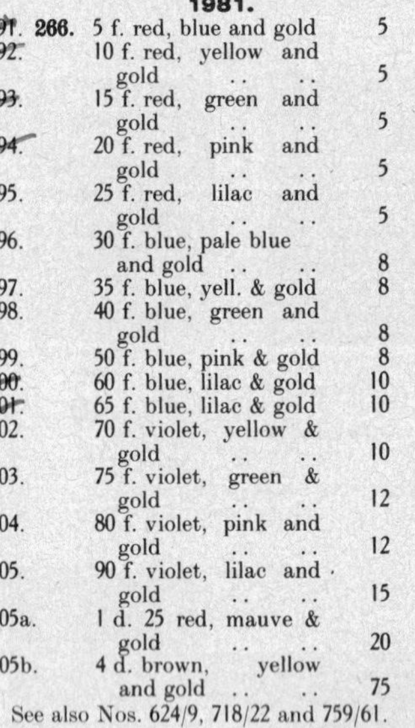

1981.
591. **266.** 5 f. red, blue and gold 5 5
592. 10 f. red, yellow and gold 5 5
593. 15 f. red, green and gold 5 5
594. 20 f. red, pink and gold 5 5
595. 25 f. red, lilac and gold 5 5
596. 30 f. blue, pale blue and gold 8 8
597. 35 f. blue, yell. & gold 8 8
598. 40 f. blue, green and gold 8 8
599. 50 f. blue, pink & gold 8 8
600. 60 f. blue, lilac & gold 10 10
601. 65 f. blue, lilac & gold 10 10
602. 70 f. violet, yellow & gold 10 10
603. 75 f. violet, green & gold 12 12
604. 80 f. violet, pink and gold 12 12
605. 90 f. violet, lilac and gold 15 15
605a. 1 d. 25 red, mauve & gold 20 15
605b. 4 d. brown, yellow and gold 75 55
See also Nos. 624/9, 718/22 and 759/61.

267. Horse Jumping. **268.** Ait Quaquzguit.

1981. Equestrian Sports.
606. **267.** 1 d. 30 multicoloured .. 50 25

1982. Carpets (1st series). Multicoloured.
607. 50 f. Type **268** 10 10
608. 1 d. 30 Ouled Besseba .. 30 30
See also Nos. 653/4.

1982. Butterflies and Moths (2nd series). As T **259**. Multicoloured.
609. 60 f. " Celerio oken lineata " 35 25
610. 1d. 30 " Mesoacidalia aglaja lyauteyi " 75 55

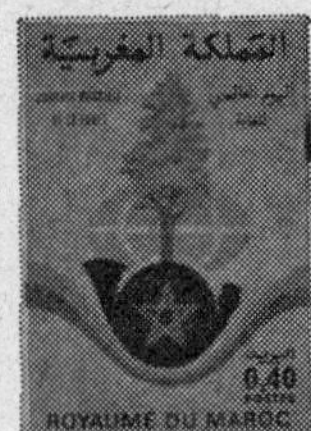

269. Tree and Emblem. **270.** Jug.

1982. World Forestry Day.
611. **269.** 40 f. Multicoloured .. 10 10

1982. Blind Week.
612. **270.** 1 d. multicoloured .. 25 25

271. Dancers. **272.** Candlestick.

1982. Popular Art.
613. **271.** 1 d. 40 multicoloured .. 35 35

1982. Red Crescent.
614. **272.** 1 d. 40 multicoloured .. 35 35

273. Painting by M. Mezian. **274.** Buildings and People on Graph.

1982. Moroccan Painting.
615. **273.** 1 d. 40 multicoloured .. 35 35

1982. Population and Housing Census.
616. **274.** 60 f. multicoloured .. 12 12

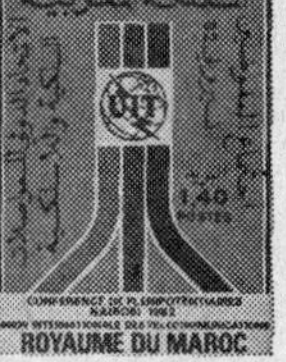

275. Dr. Koch, Lungs and Apparatus. **276.** I.T.U. Emblem.

1982. Centenary of Discovery of Tubercle Bacillus.
617. **275.** 1 d. 40 multicoloured 35 35

1982. I.T.U. Delegates' Conference, Nairobi.
618. **276.** 1 d. 40 multicoloured 35 35

277. Wheat, Globe, Sea and F.A.O. Emblem. **278.** Diesel Train and Route Map.

1982. World Food Day.
619. **277.** 60 f. multicoloured .. 12 12

1982. Unity Railway.
620. **278.** 1 d. 40 multicoloured 65 50

279. A.P.U. Emblem.

1982. 30th Anniv. of Arab Postal Union.
621 **279** 1 d. 40 multicoloured .. 40 15

280. Dome of the Rock and Map of Palestine. **281.** Red Coral.

1982. Palestinian Solidarity.
622. **280.** 1 d. 40 multicoloured 40 15

1982. Red Coral of Al Hoceima.
623. **281.** 1 d. 40 multicoloured 70 25

1983. As T 266 but inscribed "1982".
624. 1 d. maroon, blue and gold 25 10
625. 1 d. 40 brn., lt. brn. & gold 35 10
626. 2 d. maroon, green & gold 45 15
627. 3 d. brown, yellow & gold 65 25
628. 5 d. brown, green and gold 1·10 50
629. 10 d. brown, orange & gold 2·25 90

282. Moroccan Stamps. **283.** King Hassan II.

1983. Stamp Day.
630. **282.** 1 d. 40 multicoloured 25 20

1983.
631. **283.** 1 d. 40 multicoloured 25 20
632. 2 d. multicoloured .. 35 30
633. 3 d. multicoloured .. 55 50
634. 5 d. multicoloured .. 90 45
635. 10 d. multicoloured .. 2·25 85

284. Decorated Pot. **286.** Ornamental Stand.

285. Musicians.

1983. Blind Week.
636. **284.** 1 d. 40 multicoloured 25 20

1983. Popular Arts.
637. **285.** 1 d. 40 multicoloured 25 20

1983. Red Crescent.
638. **286.** 1 d. 40 multicoloured 25 20

287. Commission Emblem. **288.** "Tecoma sp".

1983. 25th Anniv. of Economic Commission for Africa.
639. **287.** 1 d. 40 multicoloured 25 20

1983. Flowers. Multicoloured.
640. 60 c. Type **288** 10 10
641. 1 d. 40 "Strelitzia sp." .. 25 20

289. King Hassan II, Map and Sultan of Morocco.

1983. 30th Anniv. of Revolution.
642. **289.** 80 c. multicoloured .. 20 20

290. Games Emblem and Stylized Sports. **291.** Ploughing.

1983. Ninth Mediterranean Games, Casablanca.
644. **290.** 80 c. blue, silver & gold 20 20
645. – 1 d. multicoloured .. 20 20
646. – 2 d. multicoloured .. 60 30
DESIGNS—VERT. 1 d. Games emblem. HORIZ. 2 d. Stylized runner.

1983. Touiza.
648. **291.** 80 c. multicoloured .. 20 20

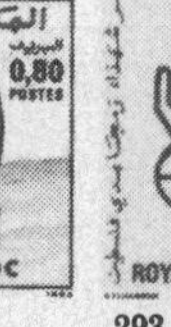

292. Symbol of "Green March". **293.** Palestinian formed from Map and Globe.

1983. 8th Anniv. of "Green March".
649. **292.** 80 f. multicoloured .. 20 15

1983. Palestinian Welfare.
650. **293.** 80 f. multicoloured .. 20 15

294. Ouzoud Waterfall. **295.** Children's Emblem.

1983. Ouzoud Waterfall.
651. **294.** 80 f. multicoloured .. 20 15

1983. Children's Day. Multicoloured.
652. **295.** 2 d. multicoloured .. 35 30

1983. Carpets (2nd series). As T **268**. Mult.
653. 60 f. Zemmouri 10 10
654. 1 d. 40 Zemmouri (different) 25 20

296. Transport and W.C.Y. Emblem.

1983. World Communications Year.
655. **296.** 2 d. multicoloured .. 1·25 50

297. Views of Jerusalem and Fez.

1984. Twinned Towns.
656. **297.** 2 d. multicoloured .. 40 20

298. Fennec Fox.

1984. Animals. Multicoloured.
657. 80 f. Type **298** 30 25
658. 2 d. Lesser Egyptian jerboa 60 35

299. Map of League Members and Emblem.

المهرجان
25
300.

1984. 39th Anniv. of League of Arab States.
659. **299.** 2 d. multicoloured .. 40 20

1984. 25th National Folklore Festival, Marrakesh. No. 578. optd. with T **300**.
660. **255.** 1 d. 30 multicoloured 20 15

301. "Metha viridis". **302.** Decorated Bowl.

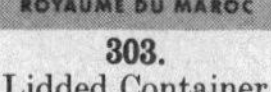

1984. Flowers. Multicoloured.
661. 80 f. Type **301** 20 15
662. 2 d. Aloe 40 30

1984. Blind Week.
663. **302.** 80 f. multicoloured .. 20 15

303. Lidded Container. **304.** Sports Pictograms.

1984. Red Crescent.
664. **303.** 2 d. multicoloured .. 40 30

1984. Olympic Games, Los Angeles.
665. **304.** 2 d. multicoloured .. 40 30

305. Dove carrying Children. **306.** U.P.U. Emblem and Ribbons.

1984. International Child Victims' Day.
666. **305.** 2 d. multicoloured .. 40 30

1984. Universal Postal Union Day.
667. **306.** 2 d. multicoloured .. 40 30

MINIMUM PRICE
The minimum price quoted is 5p which represents a handling charge rather than a basis for valuing common stamps. For further notes about prices see introductory pages.

307. Hands holding Ears of Wheat. **308.** Stylized Bird, Airplane and Emblem.

1984. World Food Day.
668. **307.** 80 f. multicoloured .. 20 15

1984. 40th Anniv. of I.C.A.O.
669. **308.** 2 d. multicoloured .. 40 30

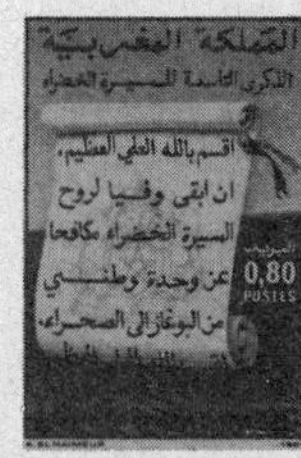

309. Inscribed Scroll.

1984. 9th Anniv. of "Green March".
670. **309.** 80 f. multicoloured .. 20 15

311. Flag and Dome of the Rock. **312.** Emblem and People.

1984. Palestinian Welfare.
672. **311.** 2 d. multicoloured .. 30 25

1984. 36th Anniv. of Human Rights Declaration.
673. **312.** 2 d. multicoloured .. 30 25

313. Aidi. **314.** Weighing Baby.

1984. Dogs. Multicoloured.
674. 80 f. Type **313** 12 10
675. 2 d. Sloughi 30 25

1985. Infant Survival Campaign.
676. **314.** 80 f. multicoloured .. 12 10

315. Children playing in Garden. **316.** Sherifian Mail Postal Cancellation, 1892.

1985. First Moroccan S.O.S. Children's Village.
677. **315.** 2 d. multicoloured .. 30 25

1985. Stamp Day.
678. **316.** 2 d. grey, pink and black 30 25

See also Nos. 698/9, 715/16, 757/8, 778/9, 796/7, 818/19 and 841/2.

317. Emblem, Birds, Landscape and Fish. **318.** Musicians.

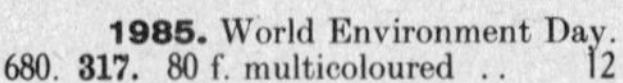

1985. World Environment Day.
680. **317.** 80 f. multicoloured .. 12 10

1985. National Folklore Festival, Marrakesh.
681. **318.** 2 d. multicoloured .. 75 25

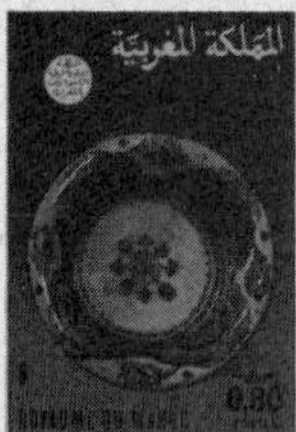

319. Decorated Plate. **320.** Bougainvillea.

1985. Blind Week.
682. **319.** 80 f. multicoloured .. 12 10

1985. Flowers. Multicoloured.
683. 80 f. Type **320** 12 10
684. 2 d. "Hibiscus rosa-sinensis 70 25

321. Woman in Headdress. **323.** Map and Emblem.

322. Musicians and Dancers.

1985. Red Crescent.
685. **321.** 2 d. multicoloured .. 65 25

1985. National Folklore Festival, Marrakesh.
686. **322.** 2 d. multicoloured. .. 30 25

1985. 6th Pan-Arab Games.
687. **323.** 2 d. multicoloured .. 30 25

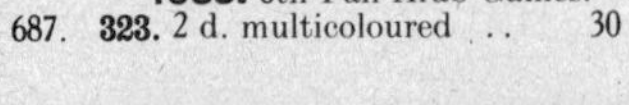

324. Emblem on Globe. **325.** Emblem.

1985. 40th Anniv. of U.N.O.
688. **324.** 2 d. multicoloured .. 30 25

1986. International Youth Year.
689. **325.** 2 d. multicoloured .. 30 25

326. Medal. **327.** Clasped Hands around Flag.

1985. 10th Anniv. of "Green March".
690. **326.** 2 d. multicoloured .. 30 25

1985. Palestinian Welfare.
691. **327.** 2 d. multicoloured .. 30 25

328. "Euphydryas desfontainii". **329.** Arms.

1985. Butterflies (1st series). Multicoloured.
692. 80 f. Type **328** 45 30
693. 2 d. "Colotis evagore" .. 95 55
See also Nos. 713/14.

1986. 25th Anniv. of King Hassan's Coronation. Multicoloured.
694. 80 f. Type **329** 12 10
695. 2 d. King Hassan II (horiz.) 30 25

330. Emblem. **331.** Vase.

1986. 26th International Military Medicine Congress.
697. **330.** 2 d. multicoloured .. 30 25

1986. Stamp Day. As T **316.**
698. 80 f. orange and black .. 12 10
699. 2 d. green and black .. 30 25
DESIGNS: 80 f. Sherifian postal seal of Maghzen-Safi. 2 d. Sherifian postal seal of Maghzen-Safi (different).

1986. Blind Week.
700. **331.** 1 d. multicoloured .. 15 10

332. Footballer and Emblem.

1986. World Cup Football Championship, Mexico. Multicoloured.
701. 1 d. Type **332** 15 10
702. 2 d. Cup, pictogram of footballer and emblem .. 30 25

333. Copper Coffee Pot. **334.** "Warionia saharae".

1986. Red Crescent.
703. **333.** 2 d. multicoloured .. 30 25

1986. Flowers. Multicoloured.
704. 1 d. Type **334** 15 10
705. 2 d. "Mandragora autumnalis" 30 25

335. Emblem. **336.** Dove and Olive Branch.

1986. 18th Parachute Championships.
706. **335.** 2 d. multicoloured .. 30 25

1986. International Peace Year.
707. **336.** 2 d. multicoloured .. 30 25

337. Horsemen. **338.** Book.

1986. Horse Week.
708. **337.** 1 d. light brown, pink and brown 15 10

1986. 11th Anniv. of "Green March".
709. **338.** 1 d. multicoloured .. 15 10

339. Stylized People and Wheat. **340.** Marrakesh.

1986. Fight against Hunger.
710. **339.** 2 d. multicoloured .. 30 25

1986. Aga Khan Architecture Prize.
711. **340.** 2 d. multicoloured .. 30 25

341. Hands holding Wheat.

الملتقى العالمي الاول
لخطباء الجمعة

(**342**).

1986. "1,000,000 Hectares of Grain".
712. **341.** 1 d. multicoloured .. 15 10

1986. Butterflies (2nd series). At T **328.** Multicoloured.
713. 1 d. "Elphinstonia charlonia" 65 35
714. 2 d. "Anthocharis belia" .. 90 85

1987. Stamp Day. As T **316.**
715. 1 d. blue and black .. 15 10
716. 2 d. red and black .. 30 25
DESIGNS: 1 d. Circular postal cancellation of Tetouan. 2 d. Octagonal postal cancellation of Tetouan.

1987. Air. 1st World Reunion of Friday Preachers. Optd. with T **342.**
717. **283.** 2 d. multicoloured .. 30 25

1987. Size 25 × 32 mm. Inscribed "1986".
718. **266.** 1 d. 60 red, brown and gold 25 20
719. 2 d. 50 red, grey and gold 35 25
720. 6 d. 50 red, brown and gold .. .. 1·25 35
721. 7 d. red, brown and gold .. .. 1·40 45
722. 8 d. 50 red, lilac and gold .. .. 1·60 50

343. Sidi Muhammad ben Yusuf addressing Crowd.

1987. 40th Anniv. of Tangier Conference. Each blue, silver and black.
723. 1 d. Type **343** 15 10
724. 1 d. King Hassan II making speech 15 10

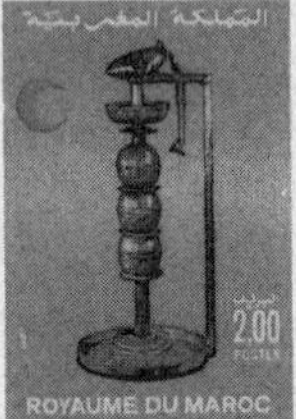

344. Copper Lamp. **345.** Woman with Baby and Packet of Salt being emptied into Beaker.

1987. Red Crescent.
726. **344.** 2 d. multicoloured .. 30 25

1987. U.N.I.C.E.F. Child Survival Campaign.
727. **345.** 1 d. multicoloured .. 15 10

346. Decorated Pottery Jug. **347.** "Zygophyllum fontanesii".

1987. Blind Week.
728. **346.** 1 d. multicoloured .. 15 10

1987. Flowers. Multicoloured.
729. 1 d. Type **347** 15 10
730. 2 d. "Otanthus maritimus" 30 25

348. Arabesque from Door, Dar Batha Palace, Fez. **349.** Map and King Hassan giving Blood.

1987. Bicentenary of Diplomatic Relations with United States of America.
731. **348.** 1 d. bl., red & blk. .. 15 10

1987. Blood Transfusion Service.
732. **349.** 2 d. multicoloured .. 30 25

350. Woman from Melhfa. **351.** Emblem and Irrigated Field.

1987. Sahara Costumes. Multicoloured.
733. 1 d. Type **350** 15 10
734. 2 d. Man from Derraa .. 30 25

1987. 13th International Irrigation and Drainage Congress.
735. **351.** 1 d. multicoloured .. 15 10

352. Baby on Hand and Syringe. **353.** Azurite.

1987. United Nations Children's Fund Child Survival Campaign.
736. **352.** 1 d. multicoloured . . 15 10

1987. Mineral Industries Congress, Marrakesh. Multicoloured.
737. 1 d. Type **353** 15 10
738. 2 d. Wulfenite 30 25

354. "12" on Scroll.

1987. 12th Anniv. of "Green March".
739. **354.** 1 d. multicoloured . . 15 10

355. Activities. **356.** Desert Sparrow.

1987. Armed Forces Social Services Month.
740. **355.** 1 d. multicoloured . . 15 10

1987. Birds. Multicoloured.
741. 1 d. Type **356** 45 20
742. 2 d. Barbary partridge . . 85 50

357. 1912 25 m. Stamp and Postmark.

1987. 75th Anniv. of Moroccan Stamps.
743. **357.** 3 d. mauve, black and green 80 40

358. "Cetiosaurus mogrebiensis".

1988. Dinosaur of Tilougguite.
744. **358.** 2 d. multicoloured . . 1·00 25

359. King Mohammed V. **360.** Map and Player in Arabesque Frame.

1988. International Conference on King Mohammed V, Rabat.
745. **359.** 2 d. multicoloured . . 30 25

1988. 16th African Nations Cup Football Competition.
746. **360.** 3 d. multicoloured . . 75 40

361 Boy with Horse

1988. Horse Week.
747 **361** 3 d. multicoloured . . 1·10 35

362 Pottery Flask **363** Anniversary Emblem

1988. Blind Week.
748 **362** 3 d. multicoloured . . 75 35

1988. 125th Anniv of Red Cross.
749 **363** 3 d. black, red and pink 75 35

364 "Citrullus colocynthis" **365** Breastfeeding Baby

1988. Flowers. Multicoloured.
750 3 d. 60 Type **364** 90 45
751 3 d. 60 "Calotropis procera" 90 45

1988. U.N.I.C.E.F. Child Survival Campaign.
752 **365** 3 d. multicoloured . . 40 35

366 Olympic Medals and Rings **367** Greater Bustard

1988. Olympic Games, Seoul.
753 **366** 2 d. multicoloured . . 30 25

1988. Birds. Multicoloured.
754 3 d. 60 Type **367** . . . . 1·40 45
755 3 d. 60 Greater flamingo . . 1·40 45

368 "13" on Scroll

اتحاد المغرب العربي

مراكش ـ فبراير 89

(**370**)

369 Housing of the Ksours and Csbaha

1988. 13th Anniv of "Green March".
756 **368** 2 d. multicoloured . . 30 25

1988. Stamp Day. As T **316**.
757 3 d. brown and black . . 40 35
758 3 d. violet and black . . 40 35
DESIGNS: No. 757, Octagonal postal cancellation of Maghzen el Jadida; 758, Circular postal cancellation of Maghzen el Jadida.

1988. Inscribed "1988".
759 **266** 1 d. 20 bl, lilac & gold 15 10
760 3 d. 60 red and gold . . 75 20
761 5 d. 20 brn, bis & gold 1·00 30

1989. Architecture.
762 **369** 2 d. multicoloured . . 30 25

1989. Union of Arab Maghreb. No. 631 optd with T **370**.
763 **283** 1 d. 40 multicoloured . . 20 15

371 King and Bishop with Chess Symbols

1989. 25th Anniv of Royal Moroccan Chess Federation.
764 **371** 2 d. multicoloured . . 30 25

372 Copper Vase **373** Ceramic Vase

1989. Red Crescent.
765 **372** 2 d. multicoloured . . 30 25

1989. Blind Week.
766 **373** 2 d. multicoloured . . 30 25

374 King Hassan **375** "Cerinthe major"

1989. 60th Birthday of King Hassan II. Mult.
767 2 d. Type **374** 30 25
768 2 d. King Hassan in robes 30 25

1989. Flowers. Multicoloured.
770 2 d. Type **375** 30 25
771 2 d. "Narcissus papyraceus" 30 25

376 Telephone Handset linking Landmarks

1989. World Telecommunications Day.
772 **376** 2 d. multicoloured . . 30 25

377 Gender Symbols forming Globe, Woman and Eggs

1989. 1st World Fertility and Sterility Congress.
773 **377** 2 d. multicoloured . . 30 25

378 Desert Wheatear

1989. Birds. Multicoloured.
774 2 d. Type **378** 60 25
775 3 d. Shore lark . . . . 1·50 35

379 House of Representatives

1989 Centenary of Interparliamentary Union.
776 **379** 2 d. multicoloured . . 30 25

380 Scroll

1989. 14th Anniv of "Green March".
777 **380** 3 d. multicoloured . . 70 35

1990. Stamp Day. As T **316**.
778 2 d. orange and black . . 25 20
779 3 d. green and black . . 70 35
DESIGNS: 2 d. Round postal cancellation of Casablanca; 3 d. Octagonal postal cancellation of Casablanca.

381 Flags forming Map

1990. 1st Anniv of Union of Arab Maghreb.
780 **381** 2 d. multicoloured . . 25 20

382 Oil Press

1990. 3rd World Olive Year. Multicoloured.
782 2 d. Type **382** 25 15
783 3 d. King Hassan and olives 40 25

383 Decorated Pot

1990. Blind Week.
784 **383** 2 d. multicoloured .. 25 15

384 Silver Teapot

1990. Red Crescent.
785 **384** 2 d. multicoloured .. 25 15

385 Arabic Script and Open Book

386 Turtle Dove

1990. International Literacy Year.
786 **385** 3 d. green, yellow & blk 40 25

1990. Birds. Multicoloured.
787 2 d. Type **386** 60 30
788 3 d. Hoopoe (horiz) .. 1·00 50

387 "15" on Scroll

388 "35", Sun's Rays and Flag

1990. 15th Anniv of "Green March".
789 **387** 3 d. multicoloured .. 40 25

1990. 35th Anniv of Independence.
790 **388** 3 d. multicoloured .. 40 25

389 Dam

1990.
791 **389** 3 d. multicoloured .. 40 25

390 Emblem

392 Projects and Emblem

391 Morse Code Apparatus

1990. 10th Anniv of Royal Academy of Morocco.
792 **390** 3 d. multicoloured .. 40 25

1990. 20th Anniv of National Postal Museum. Multicoloured.
793 2 d. Type **391** 25 15
794 3 d. Horse-drawn mail wagon, 1913 .. .. 40 25

1991. Stamp Day. As T **316**.
796 2 d. red and black .. 25 15
797 3 d. blue and black .. 40 25
DESIGNS: 2 d. Round postal cancellation of Rabat; 3 d. Octagonal postal cancellation of Rabat.

1991. 40th Anniv of United Nations Development Programme.
798 **392** 3 d. turq, yell & blk .. 40 25

393 King Hassan

394 Mining

1991. 30th Anniv of Enthronement of King Hassan II. Multicoloured.
799 3 d. Type **393** .. 40 25
800 3 d. King Hassan in robes 40 25

1991. 70th Anniv of Mineral Exploitation by Sherifian Phosphates Office.
802 **394** 3 d. multicoloured .. 40 25

395 Kettle on Stand

396 Lantern

1991. Blind Week.
803 **395** 3 d. multicoloured .. 40 25

1991. Red Crescent.
804 **396** 3 d. multicoloured .. 40 25

397 "Cynara humilis"

398 Man

1991. Flowers. Multicoloured.
805 3 d. Type **397** 40 25
806 3 d. "Pyrus mamorensis" 40 25

1991. Ouarzazate Costumes. Multicoloured.
807 3 d. Type **398** 45 20
808 3 d. Woman 45 20

1991. Inscribed "1991".
809 **266** 1 d. 35 red, green & gold 20 10

399 Road

400 Members' Flags and Map

1991. 19th World Roads Congress, Marrakesh.
810 **399** 3 d. multicoloured .. 45 20

1991. 4th Ordinary Session of Arab Maghreb Union Presidential Council, Casablanca.
811 **400** 3 d. multicoloured .. 45 20

401 "16" on Scroll

402 White Stork

1991. 16th Anniv of "Green March".
812 **401** 3 d. multicoloured .. 45 20

1991. Birds. Multicoloured.
813 3 d. Type **402** 45 20
814 3 d. European bee eater .. 45 20

403 Figures and Blood Splash

405 Zebra and Map of Africa

404 Emblem

1991. World AIDS Day.
815 **403** 3 d. multicoloured .. 45 20

1991. 20th Anniv of Islamic Conference Organization.
816 **404** 3 d. multicoloured .. 45 20

1991. African Tourism Year.
817 **405** 3 d. multicoloured .. 45 20

1992. Stamp Day. As T **316**.
818 3 d. green and black .. 45 20
819 3 d. violet and black .. 45 20
DESIGNS: No. 818, Circular postal cancellation of Essaouira; 819, Octagonal postal cancellation of Essaouira.

406 Satellites around Earth

407 Bottle

1992. International Space Year.
820 **406** 3 d. multicoloured .. 45 20

1992. Blind Week.
821 **407** 3 d. multicoloured .. 45 20

408 Brass Jug

409 Quartz

1992. Red Crescent.
822 **408** 3 d. multicoloured .. 45 20

1992. Minerals. Multicoloured.
823 1 d. 35 Type **409** 20 10
824 3 d. 40 Calcite 50 25

410 Woman

411 "Campanula afra"

1992. Tata Costumes. Multicoloured.
825 1 d. 35 Type **410** 20 10
826 3 d. 40 Man 50 25

1992. Flowers. Multicoloured.
827 1 d. 35 Type **411** 20 10
828 3 d. 40 "Thymus broussonetii" 50 20

412 Olympic Rings and Torch

414 La Koutoubia, La Giralda (cathedral bell-tower) and Exhibition Emblem

413 Map of Africa and Methods of Transport and Communication

1992. Olympic Games, Barcelona.
829 **412** 3 d. 40 multicoloured .. 50 20

1992. Decade of Transport and Communications in Africa.
830 **413** 3 d. 40 multicoloured .. 50 20

1992. "Expo '92" World's Fair, Seville.
831 **414** 3 d. 40 multicoloured .. 50 20

415 Columbus's Fleet and Route Map

1992. 500th Anniv of Discovery of America by Columbus.
832 **415** 3 d. 40 multicoloured .. 50 20

416 "Ganga cala"

1992. Birds. Multicoloured.
833 3 d. Type **416** 40 20
834 3 d. Griffon vulture ("Gyps fulvus") (vert) 40 20

417 "17" on Scroll

1992. 17th Anniv of "Green March".
835 **417** 3 d. 40 multicoloured .. 50 20

418 Postal Messenger, Route Map and Cancellations

1992. Centenary of Sherifian Post. Mult.
836 1 d. 35 Type **418** 20 10
837 3 d. 40 Postal cancellation, "100" on scroll and Sultan Mulay al-Hassan 50 20

419 Conference Emblem

1992. International Nutrition Conference, Rome.
839 **419** 3 d. 40 multicoloured .. 50 20

420 Planes on Runway

422 Satellite orbiting Earth

421 Dishes

1992. Al Massira Airport, Agadir.
840 **420** 3 d. 40 multicoloured .. 50 20

1993. Stamp Day. As T **316**.
841 1 d. 70 green and black .. 25 10
842 3 d. 80 orange and black .. 55 25
DESIGNS: 1 d. 70, Round postal cancellation of Tangier; 3 d. 80, Octagonal postal cancellation of Tangier.

1993. Blind Week.
843 **421** 4 d. 40 multicoloured .. 60 25

1993. World Meteorological Day.
844 **422** 4 d. 40 multicoloured .. 60 25

423 Kettle on Stand

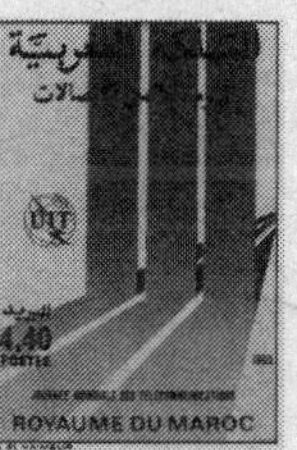

424 Emblem

1993. Red Crescent.
845 **423** 4 d. 40 multicoloured .. 60 25

1993. World Telecommunications Day.
846 **424** 4 d. 40 multicoloured .. 60 25

POSTAGE DUE STAMPS

D 53.

1965.
D 162. **D 53.** 5 f. green .. .. 1·50 75
D 163. 10 f. brown 50 25
~~D 164.~~ 20 f. red 50 25
D 165. 30 f. sepia .. .. 1·00 50

D 153. Peaches.

1974.
D393 – 5 f. orange, green and black .. 5 5
D394 – 10 f. green, red and black .. 8 5
D395 – 20 f. green & black 15 8
~~D396~~ **D 153** 30 f. orange, green & black .. 20 10
D397 – 40 f. green and black 15 8
D398 – 60 f. orange, green and black 20 15
D399 – 80 f. orange, green and black 25 20
D399a – 1 d. mult. 20 15
D400 – 1 d. 20 mult. .. 20 15
D401 – 1 d. 60 mult. .. 25 20
D402 – 2 d. mult. 30 25
DESIGNS: 60 f., 1d. 60, Peaches. VERT. 5 f. Oranges. 10 f, 1 d. 20, Cherries, 20 f. Raisins. 40 f. Grapes. 80 f. Oranges. 1 d. Apples. 2 d. Strawberries.

MOSUL Pt. 19

Stamps used by Indian forces in Mesopotamia (now Iraq) at the close of the 1914–18 war.

12 pies = 1 anna; 16 annas = 1 rupee.

1919. Turkish Fiscal stamps surch. **POSTAGE I.E.F. D and value in annas.**
1. $\frac{1}{2}$ a. on 1 pi. green and red .. 1·40 1·40
2. 1 a. on 20 pa. black on red .. 1·40 1·60
4. $2\frac{1}{2}$ a. on 1 pi. mauve & yellow 1·50 1·50
5. 3 a. on 20 pa. green .. 1·60 2·00
6. 3 a. on 20 pa. green & orange 24·00 38·00
7. 4 a. on 1 pi. violet .. .. 3·00 3·50
8. 8 a. on 10 pa. lake .. .. 4·25 5·00

MOZAMBIQUE Pt. 9; Pt. 13

Former Overseas Province of Portugal in East Africa, granted independence in 1975.

1876. 1000 reis = 1 milreis.
1913. 100 centavos = 1 escudo.
1980. 100 centavos = 1 metical.

1876. "Crown" key-type inscr. "MOCAMBIQUE".
1 P 5 r. black 60 50
11 10 r. yellow .. .. 2·00 1·75
19 10 r. green 50 30
3 20 r. bistre 60 35
20 20 r. red .. .. £140 90·00
4a 25 r. red 30 20
21 25 r. lilac .. .. 1·25 75
14 40 r. blue .. .. 5·50 3·00
22 40 r. buff 90 30
6 50 r. green .. .. 40·00 12·00
23 50 r. blue 45 30
7 100 r. lilac 40 25
17 200 r. orange .. .. 1·50 80
9 300 r. brown .. .. 1·25 75

1886. "Embossed" key-type inscr. "PROVINCIA DE MOCAMBIQUE".
30 Q 5 r. black 60 35
32 10 r. green 55 35
34 20 r. red 60 35
48 25 r. mauve .. .. 3·75 1·90
37 40 r. brown 60 35
38 50 r. blue 80 40
40 100 r. brown 60 35
42 200 r. violet .. .. 1·25 90
43 300 r. orange .. .. 1·75 1·00

1893. No. 37 surch. **PROVISORIO 5 5.**
53 Q. 5 on 40 r. brown .. 30·00 20·00

1894. "Figures" key-type inscr. "MOCAMBIQUE".
56. R. 5 r. orange 35 25
57. 10 r. mauve 35 25
58. 15 r. brown 45 30
59. 20 r. lilac 45 25
65. 25 r. green 40 15
60. 50 r. blue .. .. 1·25 35
67. 75 r. red 75 50
61. 80 r. green .. .. 1·25 70
62. 100 r. brown on buff .. 80 55
68. 150 r. red on rose .. 3·50 2·00
64. 200 r. blue on blue .. 1·25 95
69. 300 r. blue on brown .. 2·00 1·50

1895. "Embossed" key-type of Mozambique optd. **1195 CENTENARIO ANTONINO 1895.**
71. Q. 5 r. black .. .. 2·50 2·00
72. 10 r. green .. .. 2·50 2·25
73. 20 r. red .. .. 2·75 2·50
74. 25 r. mauve .. .. 2·75 2·50
75. 40 r. brown .. .. 2·75 2·75
76. 50 r. blue .. .. 2·75 2·75
77. 100 r. brown .. .. 2·75 2·75
78. 200 r. lilac .. .. 8·50 6·50
79. 300 r. orange .. .. 8·50 6·50

1897. No. 69 surch. **50 reis.**
82. R. 50 r. on 300 r. bl. on brn. 70·00 50·00

1898. Nos. 34 and 37 surch. **MOCAMBIQUE and value.**
84 Q $2\frac{1}{2}$ r. on 20 r. red .. 7·00 5·50
85 5 r. on 40 r. brown .. 6·00 5·50

1898. "King Carlos" key type inscr "MOCAMBIQUE",
86. S. $2\frac{1}{2}$ r. grey 15 15
87. 5 r. orange 15 15
88. 10 r. green 15 15
89. 15 r. brown .. .. 1·75 75
138. 15 r. green 50 40
90. 20 r. lilac 50 25
91. 25 r. green 50 25
139. 25 r. red 40 15
92. 50 r. blue 55 30
140. 50 r. brown .. .. 1·00 85
141. 65 r. blue .. .. 3·00 3·00
93. 75 r. red .. .. 2·75 1·50
142. 75 r. purple .. .. 1·00 85
94. 80 r. mauve .. .. 2·75 1·50
95. 100 r. blue on blue .. 1·25 60
143. 115 r. brown on pink .. 3·00 2·50
144. 130 r. brown on yellow 3·00 2·50
96. 150 r. brown on yellow 2·75 1·50
97. 200 r. purple on pink .. 1·00 70
98. 300 r. blue on pink .. 2·25 1·25
145. 400 r. blue on yellow .. 4·50 3·25
99. 500 r. black on blue .. 5·00 3·00
100. 700 r. mauve on yellow 6·00 3·50

1902. Various types surch.
146 S 50 r. on 65 r. blue .. 1·10 1·00
101 R 65 r. on 10 r. mauve .. 1·00 90
102 65 r. on 15 r. brown .. 1·00 90
105 Q 65 r. on 20 r. red .. 1·50 1·25
106 R 65 r. on 20 r. lilac .. 1·00 90
108 Q 65 r. on 40 r. brown .. 2·00 2·00
110 65 r. on 200 r. violet .. 1·75 1·25
111 V 115 r. on $2\frac{1}{2}$ r. brown .. 1·00 90
113 Q 115 r. on 5 r. black .. 75 60
114 R 115 r. on 5 r. orange .. 1·00 90
115 115 r. on 25 r. green .. 1·00 90
117 Q 115 r. on 50 r. blue .. 60 55
120 130 r. on 25 r. mauve 80 50
121 R 130 r. on 75 r. red .. 1·00 90
122 130 r. on 100 r. brown on buff .. .. 2·25 2·25
123 130 r. on 150 r. red on rose 1·25 1·10
124 130 r. on 200 r. bl. on bl. 2·00 2·00
126 Q 130 r. on 300 r. orange .. 80 50
128 400 r. on 10 r. green .. 2·00 2·00
129 R 400 r. on 50 r. blue .. 60 50
130 400 r. on 80 r. green .. 60 50
132 Q 400 r. on 100 r. brown .. 15·00 9·00
133 R 400 r. on 300 r. blue on brown 60 50

1903. "King Carlos" key-type of Mozambique optd. **PROVISORIO.**
134. S. 15 r. brown 75 40
135. 25 r. green 75 40
136. 50 r. blue .. .. 1·25 90
137. 75 r. red .. .. 2·00 1·25

1911. "King Carlos" key-type of Mozambique optd. **REPUBLICA.**
147. S. $2\frac{1}{2}$ r. grey 10 15
148. 5 r. orange 15 15
149. 10 r. green 40 25
150. 15 r. green 15 10
151. 20 r. lilac 40 20
152. 25 r. red 15 10
153. 50 r. brown 15 15
154. 75 r. purple 30 25
155. 100 r. blue on blue .. 30 25
156. 115 r. brown on pink .. 40 30
157. 130 r. brown on yellow 40 30
158. 200 r. purple on pink .. 80 45
159. 400 r. blue on yellow .. 70 45
160. 500 r. black on blue .. 70 45
161. 700 r. mauve on yellow 70 45

1912. "King Manoel" key-type inscr. "MOCAMBIQUE" with opt. **REPUBLICA.**
162. T. $2\frac{1}{2}$ r. lilac 10 10
163. 5 r. black 15 10
164. 10 r. green 15 10
165. 20 r. red 30 25
166. 25 r. brown 10 10
167. 50 r. blue 20 15
168. 75 r. brown 20 15
169. 100 r. brown on green 20 15
170. 200 r. green on pink .. 45 40
171. 300 r. black on blue .. 45 40
172. 500 r. brown and olive 85 75

1913. Surch. **REPUBLICA MOCAMBIQUE** and value on "Vasco da Gama" issues of

(a) **Portuguese Colonies.**
173. $\frac{1}{4}$ c. on $2\frac{1}{2}$ r. green 45 30
174. $\frac{1}{2}$ c. on 5 r. red 40 30
175. 1 c. on 10 r. purple .. 30 30
176. $2\frac{1}{2}$ c. on 25 r. green .. 30 30
177. 5 c. on 50 r. blue 40 30
178. $7\frac{1}{2}$ c. on 75 r. brown .. 75 60
179. 10 c. on 100 r. brown .. 50 45
180. 15 c. on 150 r. bistre .. 40 35

(b) **Macao.**
181. $\frac{1}{4}$ c. on $\frac{1}{2}$ a. green 60 50
182. $\frac{1}{2}$ c. on 1 a. red 50 50
183. 1 c. on 2 a. purple 35 30
184. $2\frac{1}{2}$ c. on 4 a. green .. 35 30
185. 5 c. on 8 a. blue .. .. 1·50 1·25
186. $7\frac{1}{2}$ c. on 12 a. brown .. 90 80
187. 10 c. on 16 a. brown .. 60 50
188. 15 c. on 24 a. bistre .. 60 45

(c) **Timor**
189. $\frac{1}{4}$ c. on $\frac{1}{2}$ a. green 60 50
190. $\frac{1}{2}$ c. on 1 a. red 60 50
191. 1 c. on 2 a. purple 35 30
192. $2\frac{1}{2}$ c. on 4 a. green .. 35 30
193. 5 c. on 8 a. blue 90 70
194. $7\frac{1}{2}$ c. on 12 a. brown .. 90 80
195. 10 c. on 16 a. brown .. 50 45
196. 15 c. on 24 a. bistre .. 60 45

1914. "Ceres" key-type inscr. "MOCAMBIQUE".
~~197~~ U $\frac{1}{4}$ c. olive 10 10
198 $\frac{1}{2}$ c. black 10 10
199 1 c. green 10 10
200 $1\frac{1}{2}$ c. brown 10 10
201 2 c. red 10 10
270 2 c. grey 10 10
202 $2\frac{1}{2}$ c. violet 10 10
255 3 c. orange 10 10
256 4 c. pink 10 10
257 $4\frac{1}{2}$ c. grey 10 10
203 5 c. blue 10 10
275 6 c. mauve 10 10
259 7 c. blue 10 10
260 $7\frac{1}{2}$ c. brown 10 10
278 8 c. grey 10 10
279 10 c. brown 10 10
280 12 c. brown 10 10
281 12 c. green 10 10
283 15 c. red 10 10
284 20 c. green 15 15
285 24 c. blue 15 15
286 25 c. brown 20 20
209 30 c. brown on green .. 70 50
287 30 c. green 15 15
295 30 c. lilac on red .. 70 55
210 40 c. brown on red .. 75 60
288 40 c. blue 35 15
211 50 c. orange on pink .. 1·50 1·00
289 50 c. mauve 15 10
297 60 c. brown on red .. 70 50
290 60 c. blue 40 25
291 60 c. red 40 35
298 80 c. brown on blue .. 65 40
293 80 c. red 40 20
299 1 e. green on blue .. 1·00 55
264 1 e. pink 50 30
301 1 e. blue 70 40
300 2 e. mauve on red .. 75 45
302 2 e. purple 40 25
303 5 e. bistre .. .. 4·00 1·75
304 10 e. pink .. .. 6·50 2·25
305 20 e. green .. .. 17·00 7·50

1915. Nos. 136/7 optd. **REPUBLICA.**
226. S. 50 r. blue 30 25
213. 75 r. red 70 40

1915. Provisional issues of 1902 optd. **REPUBLICA.**
227 S 50 r. on 65 r. blue .. 30 25
214 V 115 r. on 2½ r. brown .. 30 25
216 Q 115. r. on 5 r. black .. 11·00 11·00
229 R 115 r. on 5 r. orange .. 30 25
230 115 r. on 25 r. green .. 30 25
231 130 r. on 75 r. red .. 30 25
220 130 r. on 100 r. brown on buff 55 45
232 130 r. on 150 r. red on rose 30 25
233 130 r. on 200 r. bl. on bl. 30 25
223 400 r. on 50 r. blue .. 65 55
224 400 r. on 80 r. green .. 65 55
225 400 r. on 300 r. bl. on brn. 65 55

1918. Charity Tax stamp surch 2½ **CENTAVOS.** Roul or perf.
248 C 16 2½ c. on 5 c. red .. 40 25

1920. Charity Tax stamps surch. **CORREIOS** and value in figures.
306. C 15. 1 c. on 1 c. green .. 30 25
307. C 16. 1½ c. on 5 c. red .. 25 20

1920. Charity Tax stamp surch. **SEIS CENTAVOS.**
308. C 16. 6 c. on 5 c. red.. .. 35 30

1921. "Ceres" stamps of 1913 surch.
309 U 10 c. on ½ c. black .. 70 60
310 30 c. on 1½ c. brown .. 70 60
316 50 c. on 4 c. pink .. 50 30
311 60 c. on 2½ c. violet .. 85 70
328 70 c. on 2 e. purple .. 25 15
329 1 e. 40 c. on 2 e. purple 30 20

1922. "Ceres" key-type of Lourenco Marques surch.
312 U 10 c. on ½ c. black .. 40 30
314 30 c. on 1½ c. brown .. 40 30

1922. Charity Tax stamp surch **2$00.**
315 C 16 $2 on 5 c. red .. 60 35

1924. 4th Death Cent. of Vasco da Gama. "Ceres" key-type of Mozambique optd. **Vasco da Gama 1924.**
317. U. 80 c. pink 50 30

1925. Nos. 129 and 130 surch **Republica 40 C.**
318 R 40 c. on 400 r. on 50 r. .. 30 25
319 40 c. on 400 r. on 80 r. .. 35 30

1929. "Due" key-type inscr. "MOCAMBIQUE", optd. **CORREIOS.**
320. W. 50 c. lilac 50 40

23. Mousinho de Albuquerque.

25. "Portugal" and Camoens' "The Lusiads".

1930. Albuquerque's Victories Commem. Vignette in grey.
321. 23. 50 c. lake and red (Macontene) .. .. 3·00 3·00
322. 50 c. orange and red (Mujenga) .. .. 3·00 3·00
323. 50 c. mauve and brown (Coolela) .. .. 2·50 2·50
324. 50 c. grey and green (Chaimite) .. .. 3·00 3·00
325. 50 c. blue and indigo (Ibrahimo) .. .. 2·50 2·50
326. 50 c. blue and black (Mucuto-muno) .. 2·50 2·50
327. 50 c. violet and lilac (Naguema) .. .. 2·50 2·50

The above were for compulsory use throughout Mozambique in place of ordinary postage stamps on certain days in 1930 and 1931. They are not listed among the Charity Tax stamps as the revenue was not applied to any charitable fund.

1938. Value in black or red.
330. 25. 1 c. brown 10 10
331. 5 c. sepia 10 10
332. 10 c. mauve 10 10
333. 15 c. black 10 10
334. 20 c. grey 10 10
335. 30 c. green 10 10
336. 35 c. green .. .. 2·50 1·50
337. 40 c. red 10 10
338. 45 c. blue 20 20
339. 50 c. brown 15 15
340. 60 c. olive 20 10
341. 70 c. brown 20 10
342. 80 c. green 20 10
343. 85 c. red 50 35
344. 1 e. red 20 10
345. 1 e. 40 blue .. .. 3·50 1·25
346. 1 e. 75 blue .. .. 2·50 1·00
347. 2 e. mauve 75 20
348. 5 e. green .. .. 1·40 30
349. 10 e. brown .. .. 3·00 40
350. 20 e. orange .. .. 12·00 80

1938. As 1938 issue of Macao. Name and value in black.
351 54 1 c. olive (postage) .. 10 10
352 5 c. brown 10 10
353 10 c. red 10 10
354 15 c. purple 10 10
355 20 c. slate 10 10
356 – 30 c. purple 10 10
357 – 35 c. green 10 10
358 – 40 c. brown 10 10
359 – 50 c. mauve 10 10
360 – 60 c. black 15 10
361 – 70 c. violet 15 15
362 – 80 c. orange 15 15
363 – 1 e. red 25 15
364 – 1 e. 75 blue 80 20
365 – 2 e. red 90 35
366 – 5 e. olive.. .. 2·00 40
367 – 10 e. blue .. .. 4·50 50
368 – 20 e. brown .. .. 10·00 55
369 56 10 c. red (air) 10 10
370 20 c. violet 10 10
371 50 c. orange 15 10
372 1 e. blue 35 15
373 2 e. red 50 20
374 3 e. green 85 30
375 5 e. brown .. .. 1·50 40
376 9 e. red .. .. 2·25 60
377 10 e. mauve .. ..

DESIGNS: 30 to 50 c. Mousinho de Albuquerque. 60 c. to 1 e. Dam. 1 e. 75 to 5 e. Henry the Navigator. 10, 20 e. Afonso de Albuqerque.

1938. No. 338 surch **40 centavos.**
378 25 40 c. on 45 c. blue .. 1·60 1·40

26a. Route of President's Tour.

27. New Cathedral, Lourenco Marques.

1938. President Carmona's 2nd Colonial Tour.
379. 26a. 80 c. violet .. .. 1·25 85
380. 1 e. 75 blue .. .. 3·75 2·25
381. 3 e. green .. .. 5·50 3·00
382. 20 e. brown .. .. 27·00 18·00

1944. 400th Anniv of Lourenco Marques.
383 27 50 c. brown 60 30
384 50 c. green 60 30
385 – 1 e. 75 blue .. .. 3·50 80
386a – 20 e. black .. .. 2·50 25

DESIGNS—HORIZ. 1 e. 75, Lourenco Marques Central Railway Station. 20 e. Town Hall, Lourenco Marques.
See also No. 405.

1946. Nos. 354, 364 and 375 surch.
387. 10 c. on 15 c. purple (post.) 25 20
388. 60 c. on 1 c. 75 blue .. 35 20
389. 3 e. on 5 e. brown (air) .. 2·25 1·25

1947. No. 386a surch.
390 2 e. on 20 e. black .. 80 30

30.

1946. Air. Values in black.
391. 30. 1 e. 20 red 85 50
392. 1 e. 60 blue .. .. 1·00 55
393. 1 e. 70 purple .. .. 1·75 90
394. 2 e. 90 brown .. .. 2·75 1·75
395. 3 e. green .. .. 2·00 1·25

1947. Air. Optd **Taxe percue.** Values in red (50 c.) or black (others).
397. 30. 50 c. black 45 30
398. 1 e. pink 45 30
399. 3 e. green 75 30
400. 4 e. 50 green .. .. 1·50 80
401. 5 e. lake .. .. 1·50 80
402. 10 e. blue .. .. 5·75 1·60
403. 20 e. violet .. .. 10·50 4·00
404. 50 e. orange .. .. 18·00 7·25

1948. As T **27** but without commem. inscr.
405. 4 e. 50 red 90 25

31. Antonio Enes.

33. Lourenco Marques.

1948. Birth Cent. of Antonio Enes.
406. 31. 50 c. black and cream .. 50 15
407. 5 e. purple and cream .. 2·25 55

1948.
408. – 5 c. brown 15 25
409. – 10 c. purple 15 10
410. – 20 c. brown 15 10
411. – 30 c. purple 15 10
412. – 40 c. green 15 10
413. 33. 50 c. grey 15 10
414. – 60 c. red 30 10
415. 33. 80 c. violet 30 10
416. – 1 e. red 25 10
417. – 1 e. 20 grey 50 20
418. – 1 e. 50 violet 30 15
419. – 1 e. 75 blue 70 15
420. – 2 e. brown 45 10
421. – 2 e. 50 blue .. .. 1·75 15
422. – 3 e. olive 65 15
423. – 3 e. 50 olive .. .. 1·50 20
424. – 5 e. green .. .. 1·00 15
425. – 10 e. brown .. .. 2·50 3·00
426. – 15 e. red .. .. 7·00 1·00
427. – 20 e. orange .. .. 10·00 1·00

DESIGNS—VERT. 5 c., 30 c. Gogogo Peak. 20 c., 40 c. Zumbo River. 60 c., 3 e. 50, Nhanhangare Waterfall. HORIZ. 10 c., 1 e. 20, Bridge over Zambesi. 1 e., 5 e. Gathering coconuts. 1 e. 50, 2 e. River Pungue at Beira. 1 e. 75, 3 e. Polana beach, Lourenco Marques. 2 e. 50, 10 e. Bird's eye view of Lourenco Marques. 15 e., 20 e. Malema River.

1949. Honouring the Statue of Our Lady of Fatima. As T **62** of Macao.
428. 50 c. blue 65 35
429. 1 e. 20 mauve .. .. 1·75 1·00
430. 4 e. 50 green .. .. 6·50 2·00
431. 20 e. brown .. .. 13·00 2·75

35. Aircraft and Globe.

36. "Balistoides conspicillum".

1949. Air.
432. 35. 50 c. brown 15 10
433. 1 e. 20 violet 20 10
434. 4 e. 50 blue 40 15
435. 5 e. green 90 30
436. 20 e. brown .. .. 2·50 70

1949. 75th Anniv of U.P.U. As T **64** of Macao.
437 4 e. 50 blue 90 40

1950. Holy Year. As Nos. 425/6 of Macao.
438. 1 e. 50 orange 35 20
439. 3 e. blue 55 30

1951. Fishes. Multicoloured.
440 5 c. Type **36** 15 15
441 10 c. "Chaetodon aurigia" .. 10 10
442 15 c. "Chaetodon inula" .. 40 35
443 20 c. "Pterois volitans" .. 15 10
444 30 c. "Canthigaster margaritatus" 15 10
445 40 c. "Stephanolepis auratus" 15 10
446 50 c. "Teuthis nigrofuscus' 15 10
447 1 e. "Heniochus acuminatus" (vert) .. 15 10
448 1 e. 50 "Novaculichthys macrolepidotus" .. 15 10
449 2 e. "Gaterin schotaf" .. 15 10
450 2 e. 50 "Lutianus kasmira" 35 15
451 3 e. "Acauthurus triostegus" 35 15
452 3 e. 50 "Abalistes stellaris" 40 15
453 4 e. "Fistularia petimba" 60 30
454 4 e. 50 "Chaetodon vagabundus" 90 30
455 5 e. "Amblyapistus binotata" 70 10
456 6 e. "Platax pinnatus" (vert) 70 15
457 8 e. "Zanclus canescens" (vert) 90 25
458 9 e. "Tetrosomus concatenatus" 90 20
459 10 e. "Dactyloptena orientalis" .. .. 3·75 80
460 15 e. "Odonus niger" .. 16·00 5·50
461 20 e. "Rhinecanthus aculeatus" .. .. 8·00 2·50
462 30 e. "Lactoria cornutus" 8·00 2·75
463 50 e. "Lactoria fornasina" 15·00 6·00

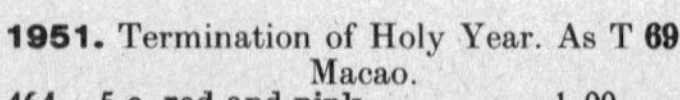

1951. Termination of Holy Year. As T **69** of Macao.
464. 5 e. red and pink .. .. 1·00 60

37. Victor Cordon (colonist).

39. Liner and Aeroplane.

1951. Birth Cent. of Cordon.
465. 37. 1 e. brown and orange .. 65 20
466. 5 e. black and blue .. 3·00 50

1952. 1st Tropical Medicine Congress. Lisbon. As T **71** of Macao.
467. 3 e. orange and blue .. 50 20
DESIGN: Miguela Bombarda Hospital.

1952. 4th African Tourist Congress.
468. 39. 1 e. 50 multicoloured .. 50 30

40. Missionary.

41. "Papilio demodocus".

1953. Missionary Art Exn.
469. 40. 10 c. lake and lilac .. 10 10
470. 1 e. lake and green .. 40 15
471. 5 e. black and blue .. 75 20

1953. Butterflies and Moths. Multicoloured.
472. 10 c. Type **41** 10 10
473. 15 c. "Amphicallia thelwalli" 10 10
474. 20 c. "Euxanthe wakefieldi" 10 10
475. 30 c. "Axiocerses harpax" 10 10
476. 40 c. "Teracolus omphale" 10 10
477. 50 c. "Papilio dardanus tibullus" 10 10
478. 80 c. "Nudaurelia hersilia dido" 15 15
479. 1 e. "Aigenia mimosae" .. 15 10
480. 1 e. 50 "Papilio antheus evombaroides" 15 10
481. 2 e. "Athletes ethica" .. 3·75 25
482. 2 e. 30 "Danais chrysippus" .. .. 2·50 20
483. 2 e. 50 "Papilio phorcas ansorgei" .. .. 6·00 20
484. 3 e. "Arniocera ericata" .. 75 10
485. 4 e. "Pseudaphelia pollinaris" 40 10
486. 4 e. 50 "Egybolis vaillantina" 40 10
487. 5 e. "Metarctia lateritia" 40 10
488. 6 e. "Xanthospilopteryx mozambica" 45 15
489. 7 e. 50 "Nyctemera leuconoe" .. .. 2·50 25
490. 10 e. "Charaxes azota" .. 6·00 80
491. 20 e. "Aegocera fervida" .. 8·50 80

42.

43. Map of Mozambique.

1953. Philatelic Exn., Lourenco Marques.
492 42 1 e. multicoloured .. 65 20
493 3 e. multicoloured .. 1·75 40

1953. Portuguese Postage Stamp Centenary. As T **75** of Macao.
494 50 c. multicoloured .. 30 25

1954. 4th Cent of Sao Paulo. As T **76** of Macao.
495 3 e. 50 multicoloured .. 20 10

1954. Multicoloured map; Mozambique territory in colours given.
496. 43. 10 c. lilac 10 10
497. 20 c. yellow 10 10
498. 50 c. violet 10 10
499. 1 e. orange 10 10
500. 2 e. 30 white 35 30
501. 4 e. salmon 35 15
502. 10 e. green .. .. 1·25 20
503. 20 e. brown .. .. 1·75 25

44. Arms of Beira.

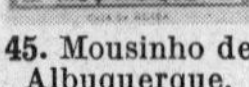

45. Mousinho de Albuquerque.

1954. 1st Philatelic Exn., Manica and Sofala.
504. 44. 1 e. 50 multicoloured.. 20 15
505. 3 e. 50 multicoloured.. 40 25

1955. Birth Cent of M. de Albuquerque.
506 45 2 e. black and grey .. 30 20
507 – 2 e. 50 black, blue & buff 70 40
DESIGN: 2 e. 50, Equestrian statue of Albuquerque.

46. Arms and Inhabitants. **47.** Beira.

1956. Visit of President to Mozambique. Multicoloured. Background in colours given.
508. **46.** 1 e. cream 15 10
509. 2 e. 50 blue 35 20

1957. 50th Anniv. of Beira.
510. **47.** 2 e. 50 multicoloured .. 40 15

1958. 6th Int. Congress of Tropical Medicine. As T **79** of Macao.
511. 1 e. 50 multicoloured .. 80 45
DESIGN: 1 e. 50, "Strophanthus grandiflorus" (plant).

1958. Brussels Int. Exn. As T **78** of Macao.
512. 3 e. 50 multicoloured .. 15 10

48. Caravel. **49.** "Arts and Crafts".

1960. 500th Death Anniv. of Prince Henry the Navigator.
513. **48.** 5 e. multicoloured .. 40 15

1960. 10th Anniv. of African Technical Co-operation Commission.
514. **49.** 3 e. multicoloured .. 25 15

50. Arms of Lourenco Marques. **51.** D.H. "Dragon Rapide" and Fokker "Friendship" over Route Map.

1961. Arms. Multicoloured.
515. 5 c. Type **50** 10 10
516. 15 c. Chibuto 10 10
517. 20 c. Nampula 10 10
518. 30 c. Inhambane 10 10
519. 50 c. Mozambique (city) .. 10 10
520. 1 e. Matola 15 10
521. 1 e. 50, Quelimane .. 15 10
522. 2 e. Mocuba 30 10
523. 2 e. 50, Antonio Enes .. 70 10
524. 3 e. Cabral 30 10
525. 4 e. Manica 30 15
526. 4 e. 50, Pery 30 15
527. 5 e. St. Tiago de Tete .. 35 15
528. 7 e. 50, Porto Amelia .. 55 25
529. 10 e. Chinde 90 25
530. 20 e. Joao Belo .. .. 2·00 35
531. 50 e. Beira .. .. 4·00 85

1962. Sports. As T **82** of Macao. Mult.
532 50 c. Water-skiing .. 10 10
533 1 e. Wrestling 50 15
534 1 e. 50 Gymnastics .. 25 10
535 2 e. 50 Hockey 60 10
536 4 e. 50 Netball 70 35
537 15 e. Outboard speedboat racing 90 70

1962. Malaria Eradication. Mosquito design as T **83** of Macao. Multicoloured.
538. 2 c. 50 "A. funestus" .. 30 20

1962. 25th Anniv. of D.E.T.A. (Mozambique Airline).
539. **51.** 3 e. multicoloured .. 30 15

52. Lourenco Marques in 1887 and 1962. **53.** Oil Refinery, Sonarep.

1962. 75th Anniv. of Lourenco Marques.
540. **52.** 1 e. multicoloured .. 25 15

1962. Air. Multicoloured.
541 1 e. 50 Type **53** 35 10
542 2 e. Salazar Academy .. 25 10
543 3 e. 50 Aerial view of Lourenco Marques Port 30 10
544 4 e. 50 Salazar Barrage .. 30 10
545 5 e. Trigo de Morais Bridge and Dam 35 10
546 20 e. Marcelo Caetano Bridge and Dam .. 1·25 35
Each design includes an aircraft in flight.

54. Arms of Mozambique and Statue of Vasco da Gama. **55.** Nef, 1430.

1963. Bicent. of City of Mozambique.
547. **54.** 3 e. multicoloured .. 25 15

1963. 10th Anniv. of T.A.P. Airline. As T **52** of Portuguese Guinea.
548. 2 e. 50 multicoloured .. 20 15

1963. Evolution of Sailing Ships. Mult.
549 10 c. Type **55** 10 10
550 20 c. Caravel, 1436 (vert) .. 10 10
551 30 c. Caravel, 1460 (vert) .. 10 10
552 50 c. Vasco da Gama's ship "Sao Gabriel", 1497 (vert) 10 10
553 1 e. Don Manuel's nau, 1498 (vert) 40 10
554 1 e. 50 Galleon, 1530 (vert) 40 10
555 2 e. Nau "Flor de la Mar", 1511 (vert) 40 10
556 2 e. 50 Caravel "Redonda", 1519 .. .. .. 40 10
557 3 e. 50 Nau, 1520 (vert) .. 45 10
558 4 e. Portuguese Indies galley, 1521 .. .. 50 10
559 4 e. 50 "Santa Tereza" (galleon), 1639 (vert) .. 50 20
560 5 e. Nau "N. Senhora da Conceicao", 1716 (vert) 9·75 20
561 6 e. Warship "N. Senhora do Bom Sucesso", 1764 65 20
562 7 e. 50 Bomb launch, 1788 90 30
563 8 e. Naval brigantine "Lebre", 1793 .. .. 90 30
564 10 e. Corvette "Andorinha", 1799 .. 95 30
565 12 e. 50 Naval schooner "Maria Teresa", 1820 .. 1·10 55
566 15 e. Warship "Vasco da Gama", 1841 .. .. 1·75 55
567 20 e. Sail frigate "Don Fernando II e Gloria", 1843 (vert) .. .. 2·25 65
568 30 e. Cadet barque "Sagres I", 1924 (vert) .. .. 3·50 1·10

1964. Centenary of National Overseas Bank. As T **84** of Macao but view of Bank building, Lourenco Marques.
569 1 e. 50 multicoloured .. 20 15

56. Pres. Tomas. **57.** State Barge of Joao V, 1728.

1964. Presidential Visit.
570. **56.** 2 e. 50 multicoloured .. 15 10

1964. Portuguese Marine, 18th and 19th Centuries. Multicoloured.
571 15 c. Type **57** 10 10
572 35 c. State barge of Jose I, 1753 .. .. .. 10 10
573 1 e. Barge of Alfandega, 1768 .. .. .. 30 10
574 1 e. 50 Oarsman of 1780 (vert) 25 10
575 2 e. 50 State barge "Pinto da Fonseca", 1780 .. 20 10
576 5 e. State barge of Carlota Joaquina, 1790 .. 25 15
577 9 e. Don Miguel's state barge, 1831 .. .. 45 30

1965. I.T.U. Cent. As T **85** of Macao.
578. 1 e. multicoloured .. 25 15

1966. 40th Anniv. of National Revolution. As T **86** of Macao, but showing different building. Multicoloured.
579. 1 e. Railway station, Beira and Antonio Enes Academy 30 30

58. Arquebusier, 1560. **59.** Luis de Camoens (poet).

1967. Portuguese Military Uniforms. Mult.
580. 20 c. Type **58** 10 10
581. 30 c. Arquebusier, 1640 .. 10 10
582. 40 c. Infantryman, 1777 15 10
583. 50 c. Infantry officer, 1777 15 10
584. 80 c. Drummer, 1777 .. 30 10
585. 1 e. Infantry sergeant, 1777 25 10
586. 2 e. Infantry major, 1784 20 10
587. 2 e. 50 Colonial officer, 1788 30 10
588. 3 e. Infantryman, 1789 .. 35 10
589. 5 e. Colonial bugler, 1801 40 20
590. 10 e. Colonial officer, 1807 55 25
591. 15 e. Infantryman, 1817 70 40

1967. Centenary of Military Naval Association. As T **88** of Macao. Multicoloured.
592 3 e. A. Coutinho and paddle-gunboat "Tete" 30 10
593 10 e. J. Roby and paddle-gunboat "Granada" .. 50 25

1967. 50th Anniv. of Fatima Apparitions. As T **89** of Macao.
594. 50 c. "Golden Crown" .. 10 10

1968. 500th Birth Anniv of Pedro Cabral (explorer). As T **90** of Macao.
595 1 e. Erecting the Cross at Porto Sequro (horiz) .. 10 10
596 1 e. 50 First mission service in Brazil (horiz) .. 20 10
597 3 e. Church of Grace, Santarem 30 15

1969. Birth Centenary of Admiral Gago Coutinho. As T **91** of Macao.
598 70 c. Admiral Gago Coutinho Airport, Lourenco Marques (horiz) 25 10

1969. 400th Anniv of Camoens' Visit to Mozambique. Multicoloured.
599 15 c. Type **59** 10 10
600 50 c. Nau (horiz) 10 10
601 1 e. 50 Map of Mozambique, 1554 .. 20 10
602 2 e. 50 Chapel of Our Lady of Baluarte (horiz) .. 15 15
603 5 e. Part of the "Lusiad" (poem) 30 20

1969. 500th Birth Anniv. of Vasco da Gama (explorer). As T **92** of Macao. Multicoloured.
604. 1 e. Route map of Da Gama's Voyage to India (horiz.) 15 10

1969. Cent. of Overseas Administrative Reforms. As T **93** of Macao.
605. 1 e. 50 multicoloured .. 10 10

1969. 500th Birth Anniv. of King Manoel I. As T **95** of Macao. Multicoloured.
606 80 c. Illuminated arms (horiz) 15 10

1970. Birth Cent. of Marshal Carmona. As T **96** of Macao.
607. 5 e. Portrait in ceremonial dress 15 10

60. Fossilized Fern.

1971. Rocks, Minerals and Fossils. Mult.
608. 15 c. Type **60** 15 10
609. 50 c. Fossilized snail .. 15 10
610. 1 e. Stibnite 20 10
611. 1 e. 50 Pink beryl 20 10
612. 2 e. Endothiodon and fossil skeleton 25 10
613. 3 e. Tantalocolumbite .. 30 10
614. 3 e. 50 Verdelite 35 10
615. 4 e. Zircon 45 30
616. 10 e. Petrified tree-stump 1·50 50

1972. 400th Anniv of Camoens' "The Lusiads" (epic poem). As T **98** of Macao. Multicoloured.
617 4 e. Mozambique Island in 16th century .. .. 1·25 30

1972. Olympic Games, Munich. As T **99** of Macao. Multicoloured.
618. 3 e. Hurdling and swimming 10 10

1972. 50th Anniv. of 1st Flight, Lisbon–Rio de Janeiro. As T **100** of Macao. Mult.
619. 1 e. Seaplane "Santa Cruz" at Recife 10 10

61. Racing Yachts.

1973. World Championships for "Vauriens" Class Yachts, Lourenco Marques.
620. **61.** 1 e. multicoloured .. 15 10
621. – 1 e. 50 multicoloured .. 15 10
622. – 3 e. multicoloured .. 25 15
DESIGNS: Nos. 621/2 similar to Type **61.**

1973. Centenary of I.M.O./W.M.O. As T **102** of Macao.
623 2 e. multicoloured .. 15 15

62 Dish Aerials.

1974. Inauguration of Satellite Communications Station Network.
624. **62.** 50 c. multicoloured .. 20 15

63. Bird with "Flag" Wings.

1975. Implementation of Lusaka Agreement.
625. **63.** 1 e. multicoloured .. 10 10
626. 1 e. 50 multicoloured .. 10 10
627. 2 e. multicoloured .. 15 10
628. 3 e. 50 multicoloured .. 20 10
629. 6 e. multicoloured .. 40 15

1975. Independence. Optd **INDEPENDENCIA 25 JUN 75.**
631. **43.** 10 c. mult. (postage) .. 25 25
632. – 40 c. mult. (No. 476) .. 10 10
633. **62.** 50 c. multicoloured .. 20 15
634. **61.** 1 e. multicoloured .. 30 25
635. – 1 e. 50 mult. (No. 621) 60 50
636. – 2 e. mult. (No. 623) .. 1·75 1·75
637. – 2 e. 50 mult. (No. 535) 35 30
638. – 3 e. mult. (No. 618) .. 40 35
639. – 3 e. mult. (No. 622) .. 45 40
640. – 3 e. 50 mult. (No. 614) 1·75 1·75
641. – 4 e. 50 mult. (No. 536) 2·00 1·10
642. – 7 e. 50 mult. (No. 489) 55 30
643. – 10 e. mult. (No. 616) .. 1·00 35
644. – 15 e. mult. (No. 537) .. 1·25 1·10
645. **43.** 20 e. multicoloured .. 1·25 1·10
646. – 3 e. 50 multicoloured (No. 543) (air) .. 35 25
647. – 4 e. 50 mult. (No. 544) 40 25
648. – 5 e. mult. (No. 545) .. 90 50
649. – 20 e. mult. (No. 546) .. 1·50 90

66. Workers, Farmers and Children. **67.** Farm Worker.

1975. "Vigilance, Unity, Work". Mult.
650. 20 c. Type **66** 10 10
651. 30 c. Type **66** 10 10
652. 50 c. Type **66** 10 10
653. 2 e. 50 Type **66** 15 10
654. 4 e. 50 Armed family, workers and dancers .. 25 15
655. 5 e. As No. 654 .. .. 35 15
656. 10 e. As No. 654 .. .. 70 30
657. 50 e. As No. 654 .. .. 3·00 1·50

1976. Women's Day.
659. **67.** 1 e. black and green .. 10 10
660. – 1 e. 50 black and brown 10 10
661. – 2 e. 50 black and blue .. 15 10
662. – 10 e. black and red .. 65 40
DESIGNS: 1 e. 50, Teaching. 2 e. 50, Nurse. 10 e. Mother.

1976. Pres. Kaunda's First Visit to Mozambique. Optd. **PRESIDENTE KENNETH KAUNDA PRIMEIRA VISITA 20/4/1976.**
663. **63.** 2 e. multicoloured .. 15 10
664. 3 e. 50 multicoloured .. 25 15
665. 6 e. multicoloured .. 50 30

MINIMUM PRICE

The minimum price quoted is 5p which represents a handling charge rather than a basis for valuing common stamps. For further notes about prices see introductory pages.

69. Arrival of President Machel. 70. Mozambique Stamp of 1876 and Emblem.

1976. 1st Anniv. of Independence. Mult.
666. 50 c. Type **69** 10 10
667. 1 e. Proclamation ceremony 10 10
668. 2 e. 50 Signing ceremony 15 10
669. 7 e. 50 Soldiers on parade 40 20
670. 20 e. Independence flame 1·10 80

1976. Stamp Cent.
671. **70.** 1 e. 50 multicoloured .. 10 10
672. 6 e. multicoloured .. 30 20

1976. "FACIM" Industrial Fair. Optd. **FACIM 1976.**
673. **66.** 2 e. 50 multicoloured .. 30 15

72. Weapons and Flag. 73. Thick-tailed Bush baby.

1976. Army Day.
674. **72.** 3 e. multicoloured .. 20 10

1977. Animals. Multicoloured.
675. 50 c. Type **73** 15 10
676. 1 e. Ratel (horiz.) 15 10
677. 1 e. 50 Temminck's ground pangolin 20 10
678. 2 e. Steenbok (horiz.) .. 20 10
679. 2 e. 50 Diademed monkey 25 10
680. 3 e. Hunting dog (horiz.) .. 25 10
681. 4 e. Cheetah (horiz.) .. 35 10
682. 5 e. Spotted hyena .. 50 15
683. 7 e. 50 Warthog (horiz.) .. 75 25
684. 8 e. Hippopotamus (horiz.) 80 30
685. 10 e. White rhinoceros (horiz.) 80 30
686. 15 e. Sable antelope .. 1·25 65

74. Congress Emblem. 75. "Women" (child's drawing).

1977. Third Frelimo Congress, Maputo. Multicoloured.
687. 3 e. Type **74** 15 10
688. 3 e. 50 Macheje Monument (site of 2nd Congress) (34 × 24 mm.) 20 10
689. 20 e. Maputo Monument (23 × 34 mm.) .. .. 1·10 50

1977. Mozambique Women's Day.
690. **75.** 5 e. multicoloured .. 25 10
691. 15 e. multicoloured .. 65 25

76. Labourer and Farmer. 77. Crowd with Arms and Crops.

1977. Labour Day.
692. **76.** 5 e. multicoloured .. 25 10

1977. 2nd Anniv. of Independence.
693. **77.** 50 c. multicoloured .. 10 10
694. 1 e. 50 multicoloured .. 10 10
695. 3 e. multicoloured .. 15 10
696. 15 e. multicoloured .. 60 25

78. "Encephalartos ferox". 79. "Chariesthes bella".

1978. Stamp Day. Nature Protection. Mult.
697. 1 e. Type **78** 10 10
698. 10 e. Nyala 50 20

1978. Beetles. Multicoloured.
699 50 c. Type **79** 10 10
700 1 e. "Tragocephalus variegata" 10 10
701 1 e. 50 "Monochamus leuconotus" 10 10
702 3 e. "Prosopocera lactator" 25 10
703 5 e. "Dinocephalus ornatus" 40 10
704 10 e. "Tragiscoschema nigroscriptus" .. 60 20

80. Violet-crested Turaco 81. Mother and Child.

1978. Birds. Multicoloured.
705. 50 c. Type **80** 25 10
706. 1 e. Lilac-breasted roller .. 35 10
707. 1 e. 50 Red-headed weaver 35 10
708. 2 e. 50 Violet starling .. 35 10
709. 3 e. Peters's twin-spot .. 60 10
710. 15 e. European bee eater .. 1·50 35

1978. Global Eradication of Smallpox.
711. **81.** 15 e. multicoloured .. 45 25

82. "Crinum delagoense". 83. First Stamps of Mozambique and Canada.

1978. Flowers. Multicoloured.
712. 50 c. Type **82** 10 10
713. 1 e. "Gloriosa superba" 10 10
714. 1 e. 50 "Eulophia speciosa" 10 10
715. 3 e. "Erithrina humeana" 15 10
716. 5 e. "Astripomoea malvacea" 40 15
717. 10 e. "Kigelia africana" 50 30

1978. "CAPEX '78" International Stamp Exhibition, Toronto.
718. **83.** 15 e. multicoloured .. 45 25

84. Mozambique Flag. 85. Boy with Books.

1978. 3rd Anniv. of Independence. Mult.
719. 1 e. Type **84** 10 10
720. 1 e. 50 Coat of Arms .. 10 10
721. 7 e. 50 People and Constitution 25 15
722. 10 e. Band and National Anthem 30 20

1978. 11th World Youth Festival, Havana. Multicoloured.
724. 2 e. 50 Type **85** 10 10
725. 3 e. Soldiers 15 10
726. 7 e. 50 Harvesting wheat .. 25 20

86. Czechoslovakian 50 h Stamp, 1919.

1978. "PRAGA '78" International Stamp Exhibition.
727. **86** 15 e. blue, ochre and red 45 30

87. Football.

1978. Stamp Day. Sports. Multicoloured.
729. 50 c. Type **87** 10 10
730. 1 e. 50 Putting the shot .. 10 10
731. 3 e. Hurdling 15 10
732. 7 e. 50 Basketball .. 35 20
733. 12 e. 50 Swimming .. 45 35
734. 25 e. Roller-skate hockey 95 60

88. U.P.U. Emblem and Dove.

1979. Membership of U.P.U.
735. **88.** 20 e. multicoloured .. 70 45

89. Eduardo Mondlane.

1979. 10th Death Anniv. of Eduardo Mondlane (founder of FRELIMO). Mult.
736. 1 e. Soldier handing gourd to woman 10 10
737. 3 e. FRELIMO soldiers .. 15 10
738. 7 e. 50 Children learning to write 30 20
739. 12 e. 50 Type **89** 40 30

90. Shaded Silver. 91. I.Y.C. Emblem.

1979. Domestic Cats. Multicoloured.
740. 50 c. Type **90** 10 10
741. 1 e. 50 Manx cat 10 10
742. 2 e. 50 British blue .. 15 10
743. 3 e. Turkish cat 20 10
744. 12 e. 50 Long-haired tabby 50 30
745. 20 e. African wild cat .. 85 55

1979. Obligatory Tax. International Year of the Child.
746. **91.** 50 c. red 15 10

92. Wrestling.

1979. Olympic Games, Moscow (1980). Multicoloured.
747. 1 e. Type **92** 10 10
748. 2 e. Running 10 10
749. 3 e. Horse jumping .. 15 10
750. 5 e. Canoeing 15 10
751. 10 e. High jump 30 20
752. 15 e. Archery 50 40

93. Flowers.

1979. International Year of the Child. Multicoloured.
754. 50 c. Type **93** 10 10
755. 1 e. 50 Dancers 10 10
756. 3 e. In the city 15 10
757. 5 e. Working in the country 15 10
758. 7 e. 50 Houses 25 15
759. 12 e. 50 Transport .. 90 35

94. Flight from Colonialism.

1979. 4th Anniv. of Independence. Mult.
760. 50 c. Type **94** 10 10
761. 2 e. Eduardo Mondlane (founder of FRELIMO) 10 10
762. 3 e. Armed struggle, death of Mondlane 15 10
763. 7 e. 50 Final fight for liberation 25 15
764. 15 e. President Samora Machel proclaims victory 45 35

95. "Scorpaena mossambica".

1979. Tropical Fish. Multicoloured.
766. 50 c. Type **95** 10 10
767. 1 e. 50 "Caraux speciosus" 15 10
768. 2 e. 50 "Gobius inhaca" .. 15 10
769. 3 e. "Acanthurus lineatus" 15 10
770. 10 e. "Gobuchthys lemayi" 40 20
771. 12 e. 50 "Variola louti" .. 60 30

96. Quartz.

1979. Minerals. Multicoloured.
772. 1 e. Type **96** 10 10
773. 1 e. 50 Beryl 10 10
774. 2 e. 50 Magnetite 15 10
775. 5 e. Tourmaline 30 10
776. 10 e. Euxenite 60 20
777. 20 e. Fluorite .. .. 1·10 45

97. Soldier handing out Guns.

1979. 15th Anniv. of Fight for Independence.
778. **97.** 5 e. multicoloured .. 25 15

98. Locomotive.

1979. Early Locomotives. Designs depicting various locomotives.

779. **98.** 50 c. multicoloured .. 10 10
780. – 1 e. 50 multicoloured .. 15 10
781. – 3 e. multicoloured .. 30 10
782. – 7 e. 50 multicoloured .. 50 15
783. – 12 e. 50 multicoloured 80 25
784. – 15 e. multicoloured .. 90 35

99. Dalmatian.

1979. Dogs. Multicoloured.

785. 50 c. Basenji (vert.) .. 10 10
786. 1 e. 50 Type **99** 15 10
787. 3 e. Boxer 15 10
788. 7 e. 50 Blue Gascon Pointer 35 15
789. 12 e. 50 English Cocker Spaniel 60 25
790. 15 e. Pointer 85 30

100. "Papilio nireus".

1979. Stamp Day. Butterflies. Multicoloured.

791 1 e. Type **100** 10 10
792 1 e. 50 "Amauris ochlea" 10 10
793 2 e. 50 "Pinacopterix eriphia" 15 10
794 5 e. "Junonia hierta" .. 35 10
795 10 e. "Nephronia argia" .. 60 20
796 20 e. "Catacroptera cloanthe" .. .. 1·25 55

101. "Dermacentor circumguttatus cunhasilvai" and African Elephant.

1980. Ticks. Multicoloured.

797 50 c. Type **101** 20 10
798 1 e. 50 "Dermacentor rhinocerinus" and black rhinoceros 30 10
799 2 e. 50 "Amblyomma hebraeum" and giraffe 40 15
800 3 e. "Amblyomma pomposum" amd eland 50 15
801 5 e. "Amblyomma theilerae" and cow 60 15
802 7 e. 50 "Amblyomma eburneum" and African buffalo 85 30

102. Ford "Hercules" Bus, 1950.

1980. Road Transport. Multicoloured.

803. 50 c. Type **102** 10 10
804. 1 e. 50 Scania "Marco-polo" bus, 1978 .. 10 10
805. 3 e. Bussing Nag Bus, 1936 15 10
806. 5 e. Ikarus articulated bus, 1978 .. .. 20 10
807. 7 e. 50 Ford Taxi, 1929 .. 40 15
808. 12 e. 50 Fiat "131" Taxi, 1978 .. .. 65 20

103. Soldier and Map of Southern Africa.

1980. Zimbabwe Independence.

809. **103.** 10 e. blue and brown .. 40 15

104. Marx, Engels and Lenin.

1980. International Workers' Day.

810. **104.** 10 e. multicoloured .. 40 15

105. "Market" (Moises Simbine).

1980. "London 1980" International Stamp Exhibition. Multicoloured.

811. 50 c. "Heads" (Malangatana) 10 10
812. 1 e. 50 Type **105** 10 10
813. 3 e. "Heads with Helmets" (Malangatana) 15 10
814. 5 e. "Women with Goods" (Machiana) 20 10
815. 7 e. 50 "Crowd with Masks" (Malangatana) 25 15
816. 12 e. 50 "Man and Woman with Spear" (Mankeu) 50 25

106. Telephone.

1980. World Telecommunications Day.

817. **106.** 15 e. multicoloured .. 60 25

107. Mueda Massacre.

108. Crowd waving Tools.

1980. 20th Anniv. of Mueda Massacre.

818. **107.** 15 e. grn., brn. and red 60 25

1980. 5th Anniv. of Independence.

819. – 1 e. black and red .. 10 10
820. **108.** 2 e. multicoloured .. 10 10
821. – 3 e. multicoloured .. 15 10
822. – 4 e. multicoloured .. 20 10
823. – 5 e. black, yellow and red 20 10
824. – 10 e. multicoloured .. 40 15

DESIGNS: As T **108**. 1 e. Crowd, doctor tending patient, soldier and workers tilling land. 3 e. Crowd with flags and tools. 4 e. Stylised figures raising right hand. 5 e. Hand grasping flags, book and plants. 10 e. Figures carrying banners each with year date. 55 × 37 mm. 30 e. Soldiers.

109. Gymnastics.

1980. Olympic Games, Moscow. Multicoloured.

826. 50 c. Type **109** 10 10
827. 1 e. 50 Football 10 10
828. 2 e. 50 Running 10 10
829. 3 e. Volleyball 20 10
830. 10 e. Cycling 40 15
831. 12 e. 50 Boxing 45 20

110. Narina Trogon.

1980. Birds Multicoloured.

832. 1 m. Type **110** 25 10
833. 1 m. 50 South African Crowned Crane 30 10
834. 2 m. 50 Bare-throated Francolin 30 10
835. 5 m. Ostrich 65 10
836. 7 m. 50 Spur-winged Goose 75 15
837. 12 m. 50 African Fish Eagle 90 25

111. Family and Census Officer.

1980. First General Census.

838. **111.** 3 m. 50 multicoloured 25 10

112. Animals fleeing from Fire.

1980. Campaign against Bush Fires.

839. **112.** 3 m. 50 multicoloured 25 10

113. "Harpa major".

1980. Stamp Day. Shells. Multicoloured.

840. 1 m. Type **113** 10 10
841. 1 m. 50 "Lambis chiragra" 10 10
842. 2 m. 50 Venus comb shell 15 10
843. 5 m. "Architectonia perspectiva" 25 10
844. 7 m. 50 "Murex ramosus" 35 15
845. 12 m. 50 "Strombus aurisdianae" 55 20

114. Pres. Machel, Electricity Pylons, Aircraft and Lorry.

1981. "Decade for Victory over Underdevelopment".

846. **114.** 3 m. 50 blue and red .. 1·00 25
847. – 7 m. 50 brown and green 25 15
848. – 12 m. 50 mauve & blue 50 30

DESIGNS: 7 m. 50, Pres. Machel and armed forces on parade. 12 m. 50, Pres. Machel and classroom scenes.

115. Footballer and Athletic de Bilbao Stadium.

1981. World Cup Football Championships, Spain (1982). Multicoloured.

849. 1 m. Type **115** 10 10
850. 1 m. 50 Valencia, C.F. .. 10 10
851. 2 m. 50 Oviedo C.F. .. 10 10
852. 5 m. R. Betis Balompie 20 10
853. 7 m. 50 Real Zaragoza .. 25 15
854. 12 m. 50 R. C.D. Espanol 50 25

116. Giraffe. 117. Chitende.

1981. Protected Animals. Multicoloured.

856. 50 c. Type **116** 10 10
857. 1 m. 50 Topi 10 10
858. 2 m. 50 Aardvark 10 10
859. 3 m. African Python .. 10 10
860. 5 m. Loggerhead Turtle .. 20 15
861. 10 m. Marabou Stork .. 50 30
862. 12 m. 50 Saddle-bill Stork 80 35
863. 15 m. Kori Bustard .. 95 45

1981. Musical Instruments. Multicoloured.

864. 50 c. Type **117** 10 10
865. 2 m. Pankwe (horiz.) .. 10 10
866. 2 m. 50 Kanyembe .. 10 10
867. 7 m. Nyanga (horiz.) .. 30 20
868. 10 m. Likuti and M'Petheni (horiz.) 70 25

118. Disabled Persons making Baskets.

1981. International Year of Disabled People.

869. **118.** 5 m. multicoloured .. 25 15

119. "Dragon Fly".

1981. Air. Mozambique Aviation History. Multicoloured.

870. 50 c. Type **119** 10 10
871. 1 m. 50 Junker "JU 52–3M" 10 10
872. 3 m. Lockheed "Loadstar" 20 15
873. 7 m. 50 De Haviland "Dove" 35 30
874. 10 m. Douglas "DC–3" 50 35
875. 12 m. 50 Fokker "Friendship" 75 50

120. Controlled Killing, Marromeu.

1981. World Hunting Exhibition, Plovdiv. Multicoloured.

876. 2 m. Type **120** 30 15
877. 5 m. Traditional hunting Cheringoma 20 15
878. 6 m. Tourist hunting, Save 40 30
879. 7 m. 60 Marksmanship Gorongosa 40 20
880. 12 m. 50 African elephants, Gorongosa .. .. 1·25 60
881. 20 m. Trap, Cabo Delgado 80 50

121. 50 Centavos Coin. 122. Sunflower.

1981. 1st Anniv. of New Currency. Mult.

883. 50 c. Type **121** 10 10
884. 1 m. One metical coin .. 10 10
885. 2 m. 50 Two meticals 50 coin 10 10
886. 5 m. Five meticals coin .. 20 15
887. 10 m. Ten meticals coin .. 50 25
888. 20 m. Twenty meticals coin 1·10 55

1981. Agricultural Resources.

890. 122. 50 c. orange and red .. 10 10
891. – 1 m. black and red .. 10 10
892. – 1 m. 50 blue and red .. 10 10
893. – 2 m. 50 yellow and red 10 10
894. – 3 m. 50 green and red 15 10
895. – 4 m. 50 grey and red .. 15 10
896. – 10 m. blue and red .. 40 15
897. – 12 m. 50 brown and red 50 20
898. – 15 m. brown and red .. 60 25
899. – 25 m. green and red .. 1·10 40
900. – 40 m. orange and red 1·60 60
901. – 60 m. brown and red .. 2·25 1·00

DESIGNS: 1 m. Cotton. 1 m. 50, Sisal. 2 m. 50, Cashew. 3 m. 50, Tea. 4 m. 50, Sugar cane. 10 m. Castor oil. 12 m. 50, Coconut. 15 m. Tobacco. 25 m. Rice. 40 m. Maize. 60 m. Groundnut.

123. Archaeological Excavation, Manyikeni.

1981. Archaeological Excavations. Mult.

902. 1 m. Type 123 .. .. 10 10
903. 1 m. 50 Hand-axe (Massingir Dam) 10 10
904. 2 m. 50 Ninth century bowl (Chibuene) 10 10
905. 7 m. 50 Ninth century pot (Chibuene) 30 20
906. 12 m. 50 Gold beads (Manyikeni) 50 30
907. 20 m. Gong (Manyikeni) 80 50

124. Mapiko Mask.

1981. Sculptures. Multicoloured.

908. 50 c. Type 124 .. .. 10 10
909. 1 m. Woman who suffers 10 10
910. 2 m. 50 Woman with a child 10 10
911. 3 m. 50 The man who makes fire 15 10
912. 5 m. Chietane 20 15
913. 12 m. 50 Chietane (different) 70 30

125. Broken Loaf on Globe.

1981. World Food Day.

914. 125. 10 m. multicoloured .. 45 25

126. Tanker "Matchedje".

1981. Mozambique Ships. Multicoloured.

915. 50 c. Type 126 .. .. 10 10
916. 1 m. 50 Tug "Macuti" .. 10 10
917. 3 m. Trawler "Vega 7" .. 20 10
918. 5 m. Freighter "Linde" .. 30 20
919. 7 m. 50 Freighter "Pemba" 50 30
920. 12 m. 50 Dredger "Rovuma" 95 55

127. " Portunus pelagicus ".

1981. Crustaceans. Multicoloured.

921. 50 c. Type 127 .. .. 10 10
922. 1 m. 50 " Scylla serrata " 10 10
923. 3 m. " Penaeus indicus " 15 10
924. 7 m. 50 " Palinurus delagoae " 35 20
925. 12 m. 50 " Lysiosquilla maculata " 55 35
926. 15 m. " Panulirus ornatus " 80 45

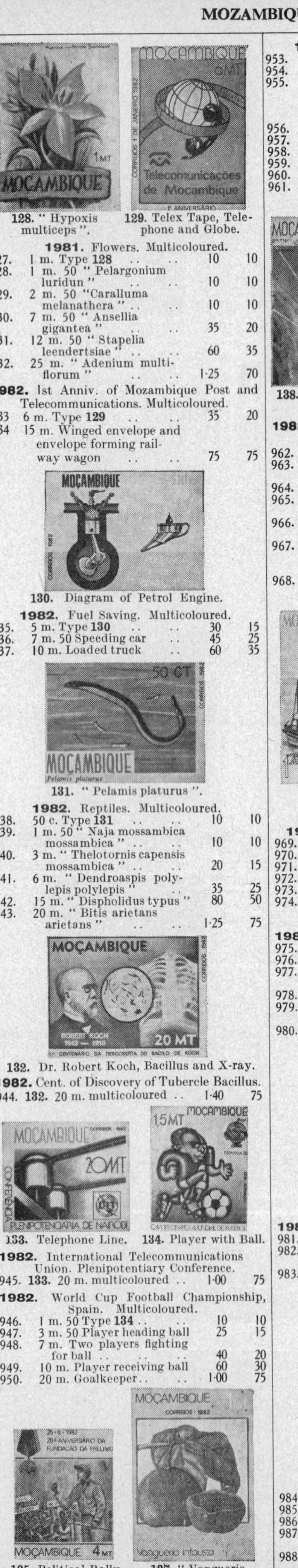

128. " Hypoxis multiceps ". 129. Telex Tape, Telephone and Globe.

1981. Flowers. Multicoloured.

927. 1 m. Type 128 .. .. 10 10
928. 1 m. 50 " Pelargonium luridun " 10 10
929. 2 m. 50 "Caralluma melanathera " 10 10
930. 7 m. 50 " Ansellia gigantea " 35 20
931. 12 m. 50 " Stapelia leendertsiae " 60 35
932. 25 m. " Adenium multiflorum " .. .. 1·25 70

1982. 1st Anniv. of Mozambique Post and Telecommunications. Multicoloured.

933 6 m. Type 129 .. .. 35 20
934 15 m. Winged envelope and envelope forming railway wagon 75 75

130. Diagram of Petrol Engine.

1982. Fuel Saving. Multicoloured.

935. 5 m. Type 130 .. .. 30 15
936. 7 m. 50 Speeding car .. 45 25
937. 10 m. Loaded truck .. 60 35

131. " Pelamis platurus ".

1982. Reptiles. Multicoloured.

938. 50 c. Type 131 .. .. 10 10
939. 1 m. 50 " Naja mossambica mossambica " 10 10
940. 3 m. " Thelotornis capensis mossambica " 20 15
941. 6 m. " Dendroaspis polylepis polylepis " .. 35 25
942. 15 m. " Dispholidus typus " 80 50
943. 20 m. " Bitis arietans arietans " .. .. 1·25 75

132. Dr. Robert Koch, Bacillus and X-ray.

1982. Cent. of Discovery of Tubercle Bacillus.

944. 132. 20 m. multicoloured .. 1·40 75

133. Telephone Line. 134. Player with Ball.

1982. International Telecommunications Union. Plenipotentiary Conference.

945. 133. 20 m. multicoloured .. 1·00 75

1982. World Cup Football Championship, Spain. Multicoloured.

946. 1 m. 50 Type 134 .. .. 10 10
947. 3 m. 50 Player heading ball 25 15
948. 7 m. Two players fighting for ball 40 20
949. 10 m. Player receiving ball 60 30
950. 20 m. Goalkeeper .. .. 1·00 75

135. Political Rally. 137. " Vangueria infausta ".

1982. 25th Anniv. of Frelimo. Mult.

953. 4 m. Type 135 .. .. 25 15
954. 8 m. Agriculture 45 25
955. 12 m. Marching workers .. 70 35

1982. Fruits. Multicoloured.

956. 1 m. Type 137 .. .. 10 10
957. 2 m. "Mimusops caffra" .. 10 10
958. 4 m. "Sclerocarya caffra" 25 15
959. 8 m. "Strychnos spinosa" 45 25
960. 12 m. "Salacia kraussi" .. 70 40
961. 32 m. "Trichilia emetica" 1·50 85

138. "Sputnik I". 139. Vigilantes.

1982. 25th Anniv. of First Artificial Satellite. Multicoloured.

962. 1 m. Type 138 .. .. 10 10
963. 2 m. First manned space flight 10 10
964. 4 m. First walk in space .. 25 15
965. 8 m. First manned flight to the moon 45 25
966. 16 m. "Soyuz"-"Apollo" mission .. .. .. 1·00 70
967. 20 m. "Intercosmos" rocket 1·25 70

1982. People's Surveillance Day.

968. 139. 4 m. multicoloured 25 15

140. Caique. 141. " Ophiomostix venosa ".

1982. Traditional Boats. Multicoloured.

969. 1 m. Type 140 .. .. 10 10
970. 2 m. Machua 15 10
971. 4 m. Calaua (horiz.) .. 30 15
972. 8 m. Chitatarro (horiz.) .. 60 25
973. 12 m. Cangaia (horiz.) .. 80 35
974. 16 m. Chata (horiz.) .. 1·40 60

1982. Starfishes and Sea Urchins. Mult.

975. 1 m. Type 141 .. .. 10 10
976. 2 m. " Protoreaster lincki " 10 10
977. 4 m. " Tropiometra carinata " 15 10
978. 8 m. " Holothuria scabra " 35 20
979. 12 m. " Prionocidaris baculosa " 60 35
980. 16 m. " Colobocentrotus atnatus " 80 40

142. Soldiers defending Mozambique.

1983. Fourth Frelimo Party Congress. Mult.

981. 4 m. Type 142 .. .. 15 10
982. 8 m. Crowd waving voting papers 30 20
983. 16 m. Agriculture, industry and education 65 40

143. " Codium duthierae ".

1983. Seaweeds. Multicoloured.

984. 1 m. Type 143 .. .. 10 10
985. 2 m. " Halimeda cunata " 10 10
986. 4 m. " Dictyota liturata " 15 10
987. 8 m. " Endorachne binghamiae " 40 20
988. 12 m. " Laurencia flexuosa " 60 30
989. 20 m. " Acrosorium sp. " .. 1·00 55

144. Diving and Swimming.

1983. Olympic Games, Los Angeles (1st issue). Multicoloured.

990. 1 m. Type 144 .. .. 10 10
991. 2 m. Boxing 10 10
992. 4 m. Basketball 20 10
993. 8 m. Handball 35 20
994. 12 m. Volleyball 55 30
995. 16 m. Running 65 40
996. 20 m. Yachting .. .. 1·00 65

See also Nos. 1029/34.

145. Mallet Type Locomotive.

1983. Steam Locomotives. Multicoloured.

998 1 m. Type 145 .. .. 10 10
999 2 m. Baldwin Series "200" 15 10
1000 4 m. Henschel Series "1600" 30 15
1001 8 m. Baldwin Series "05" 60 25
1002 16 m. Henschel Garratt type .. .. .. 1·10 50
1003 32 m. Henschel Series "50" .. .. .. 2·25 1·00

146. O.A.U. Emblem.

1983. 20th Anniv. of Organization of African Unity.

1004. 146. 4 m. multicoloured .. 20 15

147. Four-toed Elephant-shrew. 150. " Communications ".

148. Aiding Flood Victims.

1983. Mozambique Mammals. Multicoloured.

1005. 1 m. Type 147 .. .. 10 10
1006. 2 m. Four-striped grass mouse 15 10
1007. 4 m. Vincent's bush squirrel 25 15
1008. 8 m. Hottentot mole-rat 50 25
1009. 12 m. Natal red hare .. 75 40
1010. 16 m. Straw-coloured fruit bat 95 50

1983. 2nd Anniv. of Mozambique Red Cross. Multicoloured.

1011. 4 m. Type 148 .. .. 20 10
1012. 8 m. Red Cross lorry .. 40 20
1013. 16 m. First aid demonstration 75 40
1014. 32 m. Agricultural worker performing first aid .. 1·50 75

1983. World Communications Year.

1016. 150. 8 m. multicoloured .. 60 25

151. Line Fishing.

1983. Fishery Resources. Multicoloured.

1017. 50 . Type **151** 10 10
1018. 2 m. Chifonho (basket trap) 10 10
1019. 4 m. Spear fishing .. 20 15
1020. 8 m. Gamboa (fence trap) 40 25
1021. 16 m. Mono (basket trap) 1·00 40
1022. 20 m. Lema (basket trap) 1·25 55

152. Kudu Horn. **153.** Swimming.

1983. Stamp Day. Multicoloured.

1023. 50 c. Type **152** 10 10
1024. 1 m. Drum communication 10 10
1025. 4 m. Postal runners .. 20 15
1026. 8 m. Mail canoe 40 40
1027. 16 m. Mail van 75 40
1028. 20 m. Mail train .. .. 1·75 1·00

1984. Olympic Games, Los Angeles (2nd issue). Multicoloured.

1029. 50 c. Type **153** 10 10
1030. 4 m. Football 20 10
1031. 8 m. Hurdling 35 20
1032. 16 m. Basketball .. 90 50
1033. 32 m. Handball .. .. 1·50 80
1034. 60 m. Boxing .. .. 2·50 1·50

154. "Trichilia emetica".

1984. Indigenous Trees. Multicoloured.

1035. 50 c. Type **154** 10 10
1036. 2 m. "Brachystegia spiciformis" 10 10
1037. 4 m. "Androstachys johnsonii" 20 10
1038. 8 m. "Pterocarpus angolensis" 35 20
1039. 16 m. "Milletia stuhlmannii" 80 40
1040. 50 m. "Dalbergia melanoxylon" .. 2·25 1·40

155. Dove with Olive Sprig.

1984. Nkomati South Africa-Mozambique Non-aggression Pact.

1041. **155.** 4 m. multicoloured .. 25 10

156. State Arms.

1984. Emblems of the Republic. Mult.

1042. 4 m. Type **156** 20 10
1043. 8 m. State Flag 40 20

157. Makway Dance.

1984. "Lubrapex '84" Portuguese-Brazilian Stamp Exhibition, Lisbon. Traditional Mozambican dances. Multicoloured.

1044. 4 m. Type **157** 20 10
1045. 8 m. Mapiko dance .. 40 20
1046. 16 m. Wadjaba dance .. 1·10 50

158. Nampula Museum and Statuette of Woman with Water Jug.

1984. Museums. Multicoloured.

1047. 50 c. Type **158** 10 10
1048. 4 m. Natural History Museum and secretary bird 45 10
1049. 8 m. Revolution Museum and soldier carrying wounded comrade .. 35 20
1050. 16 m. Colonial History Museum and cannon .. 65 40
1051. 20 m. National Numismatic Museum and coins .. .. 1·00 65
1052. 30 m. St. Paul's Palace and antique chair .. 1·25 95

159. "Alestes imberi".

1984. Fishes. Multicoloured.

1053. 50 c. Type **159** 10 10
1054. 4 m. "Labeo congoro" .. 20 10
1055. 12 m. "Synodontis zambezensis" 60 35
1056. 16 m. "Notobranchius rachovii" 75 50
1057. 40 m. "Barbus paludinosus" .. .. 2·00 1·25
1058. 60 m. "Barilius zambezensis" .. .. 2·75 1·75

160. Badge and Laurels. **162.** Knife and Club.

161. Rural Landscape and Emblem.

1984. International Fair, Maputo.

1059. **160.** 16 m. multicoloured 70 50

1984. 20th Anniv. of African Development Bank.

1060. **161.** 4 m. multicoloured .. 30 10

1984. Traditional Weapons. Multicoloured.

1061. 50 c. Type **162** 10 10
1062. 4 m. Axes 20 10
1063. 8 m. Spear and shield .. 35 15
1064. 16 m. Bow and arrow .. 75 35
1065. 32 m. Rifle .. .. 1·50 95
1066. 50 m. Assegai and arrow 2·25 1·60

163. Workers and Emblem.

1984. 1st Anniv. of Organization of Mozambican Workers.

1067. **163.** 4 m. multicoloured .. 20 10

164. Barue 1902 Postmark.

1984. Stamp Day. Postmarks. Multicoloured.

1068. 4 m. Type **164** 15 10
1069. 8 m. Zumbo postmark and King Carlos 15 r. Mozambique "key type" stamp 35 20
1070. 12 m. Mozambique Company postmark and 1935 airmail stamp 55 30
1071. 16 m. Macequece postmark and 1937 2 e. Mozambique Company stamp 70 40

165. Keeper and Hive. **166.** Shot-putter and Emblem.

1985. Bee-keeping. Multicoloured.

1072. 4 m. Type **165** 15 10
1073. 8 m. Worker bee .. 45 20
1074. 16 m. Drone .. .. 1·00 40
1075. 20 m. Queen bee .. 1·40 60

1985. "Olymphilex 85" Olympic Stamps Exhibition, Lausanne.

1076. **166.** 16 m. bl., blk. & red 75 35

167. Forecasting Equipment and Desert.

1985. World Meteorology Day.

1077. **167.** 4 m. multicoloured .. 35 10

168. Map.

1985. 5th Anniv. of Southern African Development Co-ordination Conference. Multicoloured.

1078. 4 m. Type **168** 15 10
1079. 8 m. Map and pylon .. 45 20
1080. 16 m. Industry and transport .. .. 1·00 50
1081. 32 m. Member states' flags .. .. .. 1·60 95

169. Battle of Mujenga, 1896.

1985. 10th Anniv. of Independence. Mult.

1082. 1 m. Type **169** 10 10
1083. 4 m. Attack on Barue by Macombe, 1917 .. 25 10
1084. 8 m. Attack on Massangano, 1868 .. 55 20
1085. 16 m. Battle of Marracuene, 1895, and Gungunhana .. .. 1·25 50

170. U.N. Building, New York and Flag.

1985. 40th Anniv. of U.N.O.

1086. **170.** 16 m. multicoloured 80 50

171. Mathacuzana.

1985. Traditional Games and Sports. Multicoloured.

1087. 50 c. Type **171** 10 10
1088. 4 m. Mudzobo 20 10
1089. 8 m. Muravarava (board game) 40 20
1090. 16 m. N'tshuwa 90 50

172. "Rana angolensis".

1985. Frogs and Toads. Multicoloured.

1091. 50 c. Type **172** 10 10
1092. 1 m. "Hyperolius pictus" 10 10
1093. 4 m. "Ptychadena porosissima" 15 10
1094. 8 m. "Afrixalus formasinii" 50 20
1095. 16 m. "Bufo regularis" .. 95 50
1096. 32 m. "Hyperolius marmoratus .. .. 2·00 95

174. "Aloe ferox". **176.** Comet and "Giotto" Space Probe.

175. Mozambique Company, 1918 10 c. Stamp.

1985. Medicinal Plants. Multicoloured.
1099. 50 c. Type **174**. 10 10
1100. 1 m. "Boophone disticha" 10 10
1101. 3 m. 50 "Gloriosa superba" 15 10
1102. 4 m. "Cotyledon orbiculata" 15 10
1103. 8 m. "Homeria breyniana" 55 20
1104. 50 m. "Haemanthus coccineus" .. .. 3·00 1·50

1985. Stamp Day. Multicoloured.
1105. 1 m. Type **175** 10 10
1106. 4 m. Nyassa Co. 1911 25 r. stamp 15 10
1107. 8 m. Mozambique Co. 1918 ½ c. stamp .. 50 20
1108. 16 m. Nyassa Co. 1924 1 c. Postage Due stamp .. .. .. 1·10 50

1986. Appearance of Halley's Comet.
1109. **176.** 4 m. blue & light bl. 20 10
1110. – 8 m. vio. & light vio. 50 20
1111. – 16 m. multicoloured 95 50
1112. – 30 m. multicoloured. 2·00 95

DESIGNS: 8 m. Comet orbits. 16 m. Small and large telescopes, comet and space probe. 30 m. Comet, stars and globe.

177. Vicente.

1986. World Cup Football Championship, Mexico. Multicoloured.
1113. 3 m. Type **177** 15 10
1114. 4 m. Coluna 20 10
1115. 8 m. Costa Pereira .. 40 20
1116. 12 m. Hilario 65 35
1117. 16 m. Matateu 95 50
1118. 50 m. Eusebio .. .. 3·00 1·60

178. Dove and Emblem.

179. "Amanita muscaria".

1986. International Peace Year.
1119. **178.** 16 m. multicoloured 85 45

1986. Fungi. Multicoloured.
1120. 4 m. Type **179** 35 15
1121. 8 m. "Lactarius deliciosus" 65 25
1122. 16 m. "Amanita phaloides" .. .. 1·40 60
1123. 30 m. "Tricholoma nudum" .. .. 2·75 1·10

181. Spiky Style.

1986. Women's Hairstyles. Multicoloured.
1125. 1 m. Type **181** 10 10
1126. 4 m. Beaded plaits .. 25 10
1127. 8 m. Plaited tightly to head 50 20
1128. 16 m. Plaited tightly to head with ponytail .. 1·25 55

182. Dugong.

1986. Marine Mammals. Multicoloured.
1129. 1 m. Type **182** 10 10
1130. 8 m. Common dolphin .. 35 20
1131. 16 m. "Neobalena marginata" .. .. 1·25 50
1132. 50 m. Fin whale .. .. 3·50 1·75

183. Children Studying.

1986. 1st Anniv. of Continuadores Youth Organization.
1133. **183.** 4 m. multicoloured .. 30 15

184. 50 m. Notes.

1986. Savings. Multicoloured.
1134. 4 m. Type **184** 25 10
1135. 8 m. 100 m. notes .. 50 20
1136. 16 m. 500 m. notes .. 1·40 50
1137. 30 m. 1000 m. notes .. 2·50 1·25

185. Quelimane Post Office.

1986. Stamp Day. Post Offices. Mult.
1138. 3 m. Type **185** 20 10
1139. 4 m. Maputo 30 10
1140. 8 m. Beira 65 20
1141. 16 m. Nampula .. .. 1·40 50

186. Pyrite.

1987. Minerals. Multicoloured.
1142. 4 m. Type **186** 30 10
1143. 8 m. Emerald 60 20
1144. 12 m. Agate 85 40
1145. 16 m. Malachite .. .. 1·40 50
1146. 30 m. Garnet .. .. 2·25 1·25
1147. 50 m. Amethyst .. .. 3·75 1·75

187. Crowd beneath Flag.

1987. 10th Anniv. of Mozambique Liberation Front.
1148. **187.** 4 m. multicoloured .. 30 15

188. Little Libombos Dam.

1987.
1149. **188.** 16 m. multicoloured 1·40 60

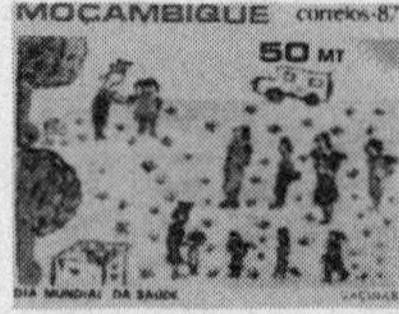

189 Children being Vaccinated

1987. World Health Day. Vaccination Campaign.
1150 **189** 50 m. multicoloured .. 1·60 1·50

190 Common Grenadier

191 Football

1987. Birds. Multicoloured.
1151 3 m. Type **190** 65 40
1152 4 m. Woodland kingfisher 65 40
1153 8 m. White-fronted bee eater 65 40
1154 12 m. Lesser seedcracker 65 40
1155 16 m. Broad-billed roller 65 40
1156 30 m. Neergaard's sunbird 65 40

1987. Olympic Games, Seoul (1988) (1st issue). Multicoloured.
1157 12 m. 50, Type **191** .. 10 10
1158 25 m. Running 20 10
1159 50 m. Handball 40 20
1160 75 m. Chess .. .. 1·25 30
1161 100 m. Basketball .. 1·25 35
1162 200 m. Swimming .. 1·75 65

See also 1176/81.

193 Work on Loom

1987. Weaving. Multicoloured.
1164 20 m. Type **193** 15 10
1165 40 m. Triangle and diamond design .. 40 10
1166 80 m. "Eye" design .. 70 20
1167 200 m. Red carpet .. 1·75 60

194 Piper "Navajo"

1987. Air. History of Aviation in Mozambique. Multicoloured.
1168 20 m. Type **194** 15 10
1169 40 m. De Havilland "Hornet" 25 10
1170 80 m. Boeing "737" .. 50 20
1171 120 m. Beechcraft King Air "C-90" 75 20
1172 160 m. Piper "Aztec" .. 1·00 35
1173 320 m. Douglas "DC-10" 2·00 75

195 Early Plan

1987. Centenary of Maputo as City.
1174 **195** 20 m. multicoloured .. 20 15

1987. No. 895 surch **4,00 MT**.
1175 4 m. on 4 m. 50 grey & red 15 10

197 Javelin throwing

198 "Boophane disticha"

1988. Olympic Games, Seoul (2nd issue). Mult.
1176 10 m. Type **197** 10 10
1177 20 m. Baseball 10 10
1178 40 m. Boxing 10 10
1179 80 m. Hockey 40 10
1180 100 m. Gymnastics .. 50 15
1181 400 m. Cycling .. .. 1·50 75

1988. Flowers. Multicoloured.
1182 10 m. "Heamanthus nelsonii" 10 10
1183 20 m. "Crinum polyphyllum" .. 15 10
1184 40 m. Type **198** .. 15 10
1185 80 m. "Cyrtanthus contractus" 35 10
1186 100 m. "Nerine angustifolia" 50 15
1187 400 m. "Cyrtanthus galpinnii" .. .. 1·75 75

199 Man refusing Cigarette

1988. 40th Anniv of W. H. O. Anti-smoking Campaign.
1188 **199** 20 m. multicoloured 20 10

201 Mat

1988. Basketry. Multicoloured.
1190 20 m. Type **201** 10 10
1191 25 m. Basket with lid .. 10 10
1192 80 m. Basket with handle 20 10
1193 100 m. Fan 30 10
1194 400 m. Dish .. .. 1·25 60
1195 500 m. Conical basket .. 1·60 85

203 Percheron

1988. Horses. Multicoloured.
1197 20 m. Type **203** 15 10
1198 40 m. Arab 20 10
1199 80 m. Pure blood .. 40 10
1200 100 m. Pony 50 15

204 Machel

1988. 2nd Death Anniv of Samora Machel (President 1975–86).
1201 **204** 20 m. multicoloured .. 15 10

205 Inhambane

1988. Ports. Multicoloured
1202 20 m. Type **205** 15 10
1203 50 m. Quelimane (vert) .. 10 10
1204 75 m. Pemba 15 10
1205 100 m. Beira 35 10
1206 250 m. Nacala (vert) .. 65 35
1207 500 m. Maputo .. 1·40 70

206 Mobile Post Office

1988. Stamp Day. Multicoloured.
1208 20 m. Type **206** 10 10
1209 40 m. Posting box (vert) 15 10

207 Maize

208 Mondlane

1989. 5th FRELIMO Congress. Multicoloured.
1210 25 m. Type **207** 10 10
1211 50 m. Hoe 10 10
1212 75 m. Abstract 10 10
1213 100 m. Cogwheels .. 20 10
1214 250 m. Right-half of cogwheel 50 25
Nos. 1210/14 were printed together, se-tenant, forming a composite design.

1989. 20th Anniv of Assassination of Pres. Mondlane.
1215 **208** 25 m. black, gold & red 15 10

209 "Storming the Bastille" (Thevenin)

1989. Bicent of French Revolution. Mult.
1216 100 m. Type **209** .. 25 10
1217 250 m. "Liberty guiding the People" (Delacroix) 60 35

MORE DETAILED LISTS
are given in the Stanley Gibbons Catalogues referred to in the country headings.
For lists of current volumes see Introduction.

210 "Pandinus sp"

1989. Venomous Animals. Multicoloured.
1219 25 m. Type **210** 10 10
1220 50 m. Egyptian cobra .. 10 10
1221 75 m. "Bombus sp." (bee) 15 10
1222 100 m. "Paraphysa sp." (spider) 25 10
1223 250 m. "Conus marmoreus" 65 35
1224 500 m. Devil firefish .. 1·40 70

211 "Acropora pulchra"

1989. Corals. Multicoloured.
1225 25 m. Type **210** 10 10
1226 50 m. "Eunicella papilosa" 15 10
1227 100 m. "Dendrophyla migrantus" 30 10
1228 250 m. "Favia fragum" .. 50 35

212 Footballers

213 Macuti Lighthouse

1989. World Cup Football Championship, Italy (1990). Designs showing various footballing scenes.
1229 **212** 30 m. multicoloured 10 10
1230 – 60 m. multicoloured 15 10
1231 – 125 m. multicoloured 30 10
1232 – 200 m. multicoloured 50 25
1233 – 250 m. multicoloured 65 35
1234 – 500 m. multicoloured 1·50 70

1989. Lighthouses. Multicoloured.
1235 30 m. Type **213** 15 10
1236 60 m. Pinda 15 10
1237 125 m. Cape Delgado .. 30 10
1238 200 m. Goa Island .. 60 25
1239 250 m. Caldeira Point .. 80 35
1240 500 m. Vilhena .. 1·50 70

214 Bracelet

1989. Silver Filgree Work.
1241 **214** 30 m. grey, red & blk 10 10
1242 – 60 m. grey, blue & blk 15 10
1243 – 125 m. grey, red & blk 25 10
1244 – 200 m. grey, bl & blk 40 25
1245 – 250 m. grey, purple and black .. 55 35
1246 – 500 m. grey, grn & blk 1·25 70
DESIGNS: 60 m. Flower belt; 125 m. Necklace; 200 m. Casket; 250 m. Spoons; 500 m. Butterfly.

215 Flag and Soldiers

216 Rain Gauge

1989. 25th Anniv of Fight for Independence.
1247 **215** 30 m. multicoloured .. 15 10

1989. Meteorological Instruments. Mult.
1248 30 m. Type **216** 10 10
1249 60 m. Radar graph .. 15 10
1250 125 m. Sheltered measuring instruments 30 10
1251 200 m. Computer terminal 55 25

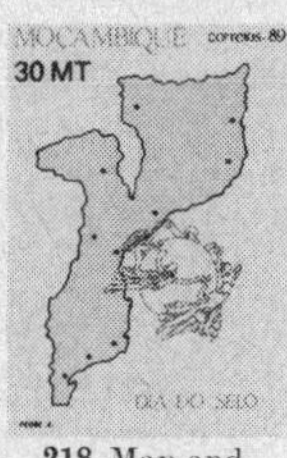

218 Map and U.P.U. Emblem

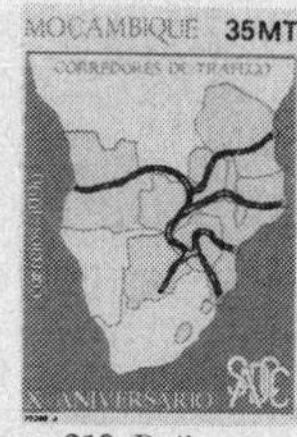

219 Railway Map

1989. Stamp Day.
1253 **218** 30 m. multicoloured 15 10
1254 – 60 m. black, grn & red 15 10
DESIGN: 60 m. Map and Mozambique postal emblem.

1990. 10th Anniv of Southern Africa Development Co-ordination Conference.
1255 **219** 35 m. multicoloured .. 20 10

220 Cloth and Woman wearing Dress

1990. Traditional Dresses. Designs showing women wearing different dresses and details of cloth used.
1256 **220** 42 m. multicoloured 10 10
1257 – 90 m. multicoloured 15 10
1258 – 150 m. multicoloured 20 10
1259 – 200 m. multicoloured 25 15
1260 – 400 m. multicoloured 55 40
1261 – 500 m. multicoloured 65 50

221 Sena Fortress, Sofala

1990. Fortresses.
1262 **221** 45 m. blue and black 10 10
1263 – 90 m. blue and black 15 10
1264 – 150 m. multicoloured 20 10
1265 – 200 m. multicoloured 30 15
1266 – 400 m. red and black 55 40
1267 – 500 m. red and black 70 40
DESIGNS: 90 m. Sto. Antonio, Ibo Island; 150 m. S. Sebastiao, Mozambique Island; 200 m. S. Caetano, Sofala; 400 m. Our Lady of Conception, Maputo; 500 m. S. Luis, Tete.

223 Obverse and Reverse of 50 m. Coin

1990. 15th Anniv of Bank of Mozambique.
1269 **223** 100 m. multicoloured 20 10

224 Statue of Eduardo Mondlane (founder of FRELIMO)

1990. 15th Anniv of Independence. Mult.
1270 42 m. 50 Type **224** .. 10 10
1271 150 m. Statue of Samora Machel (President, 1975–86) 25 15

225 White Rhinoceros

1990. Endangered Animals. Multicoloured.
1272 42 m. 50 Type **225** .. 15 10
1273 100 m. Dugong 20 10
1274 150 m. African elephant 35 15
1275 200 m. Cheetah 40 15
1276 400 m. Spotted-necked otter 70 40
1277 500 m. Hawksbill turtle .. 85 50

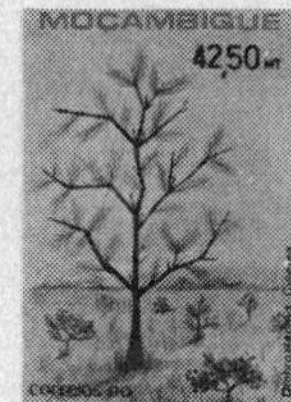

226 "Dichrostachys cinerea"

227 Pillar Box waving to Kurika

1990. Environmental Protection. Plants. Multicoloured.
1278 42 m. 50 Type **226** .. 10 10
1279 100 m. Forest fire .. 20 10
1280 150 m. Horsetail tree .. 25 10
1281 200 m. Mangrove .. 30 15
1282 400 m. "Estrato herbaceo" (grass) .. 65 40
1283 500 m. Pod mahogany .. 80 50

1990. Kurika (post mascot) at Work. Mult.
1284 42 m. 50 Type **227** .. 15 10
1285 42 m. 50 Hand cancelling envelopes 15 10
1286 42 m. 50 Leaping across hurdles 15 10
1287 42 m. 50 Delivering post to chicken 15 10

228 "10" and Posts Emblem

229 Bird-of-Paradise Flower

1991. 10th Anniv of National Posts and Telecommunications Enterprises, Mozambique.
1288 **228** 50 m. blue, red & blk 15 10
1289 – 50 m. brn, grn & blk 15 10
DESIGN: No. 1289, "10" and telecommunications emblem.

1991. Flowers. Multicoloured.
1290 50 m. Type **229** 15 10
1291 125 m. Flamingo lily .. 25 15
1292 250 m. Calla lily 50 30
1293 300 m. Canna lily .. 55 35

230 Two Hartebeest

231 Mpompine

1991. Lichtenstein's Hartebeest. Mult.
1294 50 m. Type **230** 15 10
1295 100 m. Alert hartebeest .. 20 10
1296 250 m. Hartebeest grazing 50 30
1297 500 m. Mother feeding young 90 60

1991. Maputo Drinking Fountains. Mult.
1298 50 m. Type **231** 10 10
1299 125 m. Chinhambanine .. 15 10
1300 250 m. S. Pedro-Zaza .. 25 10
1301 300 m. Xipamanine .. 35 15

232 Painting by Samate

233 Diving

1991. Paintings by Mozambican Artists. Mult.
1302 180 m. Type **232** .. 15 10
1303 250 m. Malangatana Ngwenya 20 15
1304 560 m. Malangatana Ngwenya (different) .. 40 30

1991. Olympic Games, Barcelona (1992). Mult.
1305 10 m. Type **233** 10 10
1306 50 m. Roller hockey .. 15 10
1307 100 m. Tennis .. 20 10
1308 200 m. Table tennis .. 30 10
1309 500 m. Running 50 20
1310 1000 m. Badminton .. 85 40

234 Proposed Boundaries in 1890 Treaty

236 Skipping

1991. Centenary of Settling of Mozambique Borders. Multicoloured.
1311 600 m. Type **234** .. 50 25
1312 800 m. Frontiers settled in English–Portuguese 1891 treaty 75 35

1991. Stamp Day. Children's Games. Mult.
1314 40 m. Type **236** 10 10
1315 150 m. Spinning top .. 10 10
1316 400 m. Marbles 20 10
1317 900 m. Hopscotch .. 45 20

237 "Christ"

238 "Rhisophora mucronata"

1992. Stained Glass Windows. Multicoloured.
1318 40 m. Type **237** 10 10
1319 150 m. "Faith" 10 10
1320 400 m. "IC XC" 20 10
1321 900 m. Window in three sections 45 20

1992. Marine Flowers. Multicoloured.
1322 300 m. Type **238** .. 15 10
1323 600 m. "Cymodocea ciliata" 30 15
1324 1000 m. "Sophora inhambanensis" 50 25

239 Spears

240 Amethyst Sunbird

1992. "Lubrapex 92" Brazilian–Portuguese Stamp Exhibition, Lisbon. Weapons. Mult.
1325 100 m. Type **239** .. 10 10
1326 300 m. Tridents 15 10
1327 500 m. Axe 25 10
1328 1000 m. Dagger 50 25

1992. Birds. Multicoloured.
1329 150 m. Type **240** .. 10 10
1330 200 m. Mosque swallow .. 10 10
1331 300 m. Red-capped robin chat 15 10
1332 400 m. "Lamprocolius chloropterus" 20 10
1333 500 m. Bush shrike .. 25 10
1334 800 m. African golden oriole 40 20

241 Emblem

242 Phiane

1992. 30th Anniv of Eduardo Mondlane University.
1335 **241** 150 m. green & brown 10 10

1992. "Genova '92" International Thematic Stamp Exn. Musical Instruments. Mult.
1336 200 m. Type **242** .. 10 10
1337 300 m. Xirupe (rattle) .. 15 10
1338 500 m. Ngulula (drum) .. 25 10
1339 1500 m. Malimba (drum) 75 35

243 Children Eating

244 Parachutist

1992. International Nutrition Conference, Rome.
1341 **243** 450 m. multicoloured 20 10

1992. Parachuting. Multicoloured.
1342 50 m. Type **244** 10 10
1343 400 m. Parachutist and buildings .. 20 10
1344 500 m. Airplane dropping parachutists 25 10
1345 1500 m. Parachutist (different) 70 35

1992. No. 890 optd **50MT**.
1346 **122** 50 m. on 50 c. orange and red 10 10

246 Order of Peace and Friendship

1993. Mozambique Decorations. Mult.
1347 400 m. Type **246** .. 20 10
1348 800 m. Bagamoyo Medal 40 20
1349 1000 m. Order of Eduardo Mondlane 50 25
1350 1500 m. Veteran of the Struggle for National Liberation Medal .. 70 35

247 Tree Stumps and Girl Carrying Wood

1993. Pollution. Multicoloured.
1351 200 m. Type **247** .. 10 10
1352 750 m. Chimneys smoking 35 15
1353 1000 m. Tanker sinking .. 50 25
1354 1500 m. Car exhaust fumes 70 35

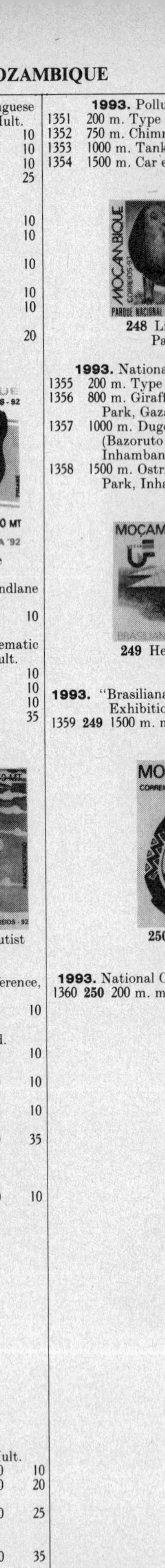

248 Lion (Gorongosa Park, Sofala)

1993. National Parks. Multicoloured.
1355 200 m. Type **248** .. 10 10
1356 800 m. Giraffes (Banhine Park, Gaza) 40 20
1357 1000 m. Dugongs (Bazoruto Park, Inhambane) 50 25
1358 1500 m. Ostriches (Zinave Park, Inhambane) .. 70 35

249 Heroes Monument, Maputo

1993. "Brasiliana 93" International Stamp Exhibition, Rio de Janeiro.
1359 **249** 1500 m. multicoloured 55 25

250 Conference Emblem

1993. National Culture Conference, Maputo.
1360 **250** 200 m. multicoloured 10 10

CHARITY TAX STAMPS

The notes under this heading in Portugal also apply here.

C **15.** Arms of Portugal and Mozambique and Allegorical Figures.

C **16.** Prow of Galley of Discoveries and Symbols of Declaration of War.

1916. War Tax Fund. Imperf. roul. or perf.
C 234. C **15.** 1 c. green 50 30
C 235. C **16.** 5 c. red 50 30

C **18.** "Charity".

C **22.** Society's Emblem.

1920. 280th Anniv. of Restoration of Portugal. Wounded Soldiers and Social Assistance Funds.
C 309. C **18.** ¼ c. olive 70 70
C 310. ½ c. black 80 80
C 311. 1 c. brown 80 80
C 312. 2 c. brown 80 80
C 313. 3 c. lilac 80 80
C 314. 4 c. green 80 80
C 315. – 5 c. green 90 90
C 316. – 6 c. blue 90 90
C 317. – 7½ c. brown .. 90 90
C 318. – 8 c. yellow 90 90
C 319. – 10 c. lilac 90 90
C 320. – 12 c. pink 90 90
C 321. – 18 c. red 90 90
C 322. – 24 c. brown .. 1·10 90
C 323. – 30 c. olive .. .. 1·10 90
C 324. – 40 c. red .. .. 1·10 90
C 325. – 50 c. yellow .. 1·10 90
C 326. – 1 e. blue .. .. 1·10 90

DESIGNS: 5 c. to 12 c. Wounded soldier and nurse. 18 c. to 1 e. Family scene.

1925. Marquis de Pombal stamps of Portugal, but inscr. "MOCAMBIQUE".
C 327. C **73.** 15 c. brown .. 20 20
C 328. – 15 c. brown 20 20
C 329. C **75.** 15 c. brown .. 20 20

1925. Red Cross. Surch. **50 CENTAVOS.**
C 330. C **22.** 50 c. yellow and grey 60 40

1926. Surch **CORREIOS** and value.
C 337. C **22.** 5 c. yellow and red.. 50 50
C 338. 10 c. yellow & green 60 60
C 339. 20 c. yellow and grey 75 60
C 340. 30 c. yellow and blue 75 60
C 331. 40 c. yellow and grey 80 60
C 341. 40 c. yellow & violet 75 60
C 332. 50 c. yellow and grey 80 60
C 342. 50 c. yellow and red 75 70
C 333. 60 c. yellow and grey 80 60
C 343. 60 c. yellow & brown 75 70
C 334. 80 c. yellow and grey 80 60
C 344. 80 c. yellow and blue 75 70
C 335. 1 e. yellow and grey 90 80
C 345. 1 e. yellow and olive 75 70
C 336. 2 e. yellow and grey 90 80
C 346. 2 e. yellow & brown 80 80

C **25.**

1928. Surch **CORREIOS** and value in black, as in Type C **25**.
C 347. C **25.** 5 c. yellow and green 1·00 1·00
C 348. 10 c. yellow and blue 1·00 1·00
C 349. 20 c. yellow & black 1·00 1·00
C 350. 30 c. yellow and red 1·00 1·00
C 351. 40 c. yellow and red 1·00 1·00
C 352. 50 c. yellow and red 1·00 1·00
C 353. 60 c. yellow & brown 1·00 1·00
C 354. 80 c. yellow & brown 1·00 1·00
C 355. 1 e. yellow and grey 1·00 1·00
C 356. 2 e. yellow and red.. 1·00 1·00

C 27.

C 29. Pelican.

C 28. "Charity".

1929. Value in black.

C 357.	C **27.**	40 c. red and blue ..	1·00	1·00
C 358.		40 c. violet and red	1·00	1·00
C 359.		40 c. violet and olive	1·00	1·00
C 360.		40 c. red and brown	1·00	1·00
C 361.		(No value) red & grn.	1·50	1·50
C 362.		40 c. blue and brown	1·00	1·00
C 363.		40 c. blue and orange	1·00	1·00
C 364.		40 c. red and green ..	1·00	1·00
C 365.		40 c. black & yellow	1·50	1·25
C 366.		40 c. black & brown	1·50	1·40

1942.

C 383.	C **28.**	50 c. red and black ..	2·50	1·00

1943. Inscr. "Colonia de Mocambique" Value in black.

C 384.	C **29.**	50 c. red	2·00	75
C 385.		50 c. blue	2·00	75
C 386.		50 c. violet	2·00	75
C 387.		50 c. brown ..	2·00	75
C 388.		50 c. bistre	2·00	75
C 389.		50 c. blue	2·00	75
C 393.		50 c. green	2·00	75

1952. Inscr "Provincia de Mocambique". Value in black.

C514	C **29**	30 c. yellow ..	75	50
C515		50 c. orange ..	75	50
C469		50 c. green ..	75	50
C470		50 c. brown ..	75	50

1957. No. C 470 surch.

C 511.	C **29.**	30 c. on 50 c. brown	40	30

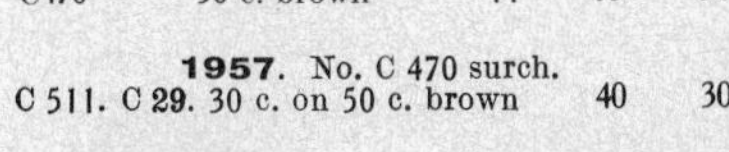

C 56. Women and Children.

C 58. Telegraph Poles and Map.

1963.

C 569.	C **56.**	30 c. grn., blk. & red	10	10
C 570.		50 c. blk., bistre & red	10	10
C 571.		50 c. blk., pink & red	20	10
C 572.		50 c. blk., green & red	20	10
C 573.		50 c. blk., blue & red	20	10
C 574.		50 c. blk., buff & red	20	10
C 575.		50 c. blk., grey & red	20	10
C 576.		50 c. blk., yell. & red	15	10
C 577.		1 e. grey, blk. & red	50	25
C 578.		1 e. blk., brn. & red	15	10
C 578a.		1 e. blk., mve. & red	15	10

1965. Mozambique Telecommunications Improvement. Inscr. "TELECOMUNICACOES".

C579	C **58**	30 c. blk, pink & vio	10	10
C580	–	50 c. black, brn & bl	10	10
C581	–	1 e. blk, orge & grn	15	10

DESIGN (19½ × 36 mm): 50 c. 1 e. Telegraph linesman.

A 2 e. 50 in Type C **58** was also issued for compulsory use on telegrams.

NEWSPAPER STAMPS

1893. "Embossed" key-type of Mozambique surch. **JORNAES 2½ 2½.**

N 53.	Q.	2½ r. on 40 r. brown ..	14·00	9·00

1893. "Embossed" key-type of Mozambique surch. **JORNAES 2½ REIS.**

N 54.	Q.	2½ r. on 40 r. brown ..	55·00	38·00
N 55.		5 r. on 40 r. brown ..	35·00	30·00

1893. "Newspaper" key-type inscr. "MOCAMBIQUE".

N 58.	V.	2½ r. brown	25	20

POSTAGE DUE STAMPS

1904. "Due" key-type inscr. "MOCAMBIQUE".

D 146.	W.	5 r green	20	20
D 147.		10 r. grey	20	20
D 148.		20 r. brown	20	20
D 149.		30 r. orange	35	20
D 150.		50 r. brown	35	20
D 151.		60 r. brown	1·25	75
D 152.		100 r. mauve	1·25	75
D 153.		130 r. blue	75	60
D 154.		200 r. red	1·10	60
D 155.		500 r. violet	1·25	60

1911. "Due" key-type of Mozambique optd. **REPUBLICA.**

D 162.	W.	5 r. green	20	20
D 163a.		10 r. green	20	20
D 164.		20 r. brown	25	20
D 165.		30 r. orange	25	20
D 166.		50 r. brown	25	20
D 167.		60 r. brown	35	20
D 168.		100 r. mauve	45	25
D 169.		130 r. blue	55	40
D 170.		200 r. red	65	55
D 171.		500 r. violet	85	60

1917. "Due" key-type of Mozambique, but currency changed.

D 246.	W.	½ c. green	20	20
D 247.		1 c. grey	20	20
D 248.		2 c. brown	20	20
D 249.		3 c. orange	20	20
D 250.		5 c. brown	20	20
D 251.		6 c. brown	20	20
D 252.		10 c. mauve	20	20
D 253.		13 c. blue	30	30
D 254.		20 c. red	30	30
D 255.		50 c. violet	30	30

1918. Charity Tax stamps. optd. **PORTEADO.**

D 256.	C **15.**	1 c. green	70	50
D 257.	C **16.**	5 c. red	70	50

1922. "Ceres" key-type of Lourenco Marques (½ c., 1½ c.) and of Mozambique (1 c., 2½ c., 4 c.) surch. **PORTEADO** and value and bar.

D 316.	U.	5 c. on ½ c. black ..	70	50
D 317.		6 c. on 1 c. green ..	70	50
D 318.		10 c. on 1½ c. brown ..	70	50
D 319.		20 c. on 2½ c. violet ..	70	50
D 320.		50 c. on 4 c. pink ..	70	50

1924. "Ceres" key-type of Mozambique surch **Porteado** and value.

D 321.	U.	20 c. on 30 c. green ..	40	30
D 323.		50 c. on 60 c. blue ..	60	40

1925. Marquis de Pombal tax stamps as Nos. C 24/6, optd. **MULTA.**

D 327.	C **73.**	30 c. brown ..	20	20
D 328.	–	30 c. brown ..	20	20
D 329.	C **75.**	30 c. brown ..	20	20

1952. As Type D **70** of Macao, but inscr. "MOCAMBIQUE". Numerals in red, name in black (except 50 c. in blue).

D 468.	10 c. red and green ..	10	10
D 469.	30 c. sepia and pink ..	10	10
D 470.	50 c. black, blue and grey	10	10
D 471.	1 e. blue and olive ..	10	10
D 472.	2 e. green and yellow ..	15	15
D 473.	5 e. brown and stone ..	25	15

MOZAMBIQUE COMPANY Pt. 9

The Mozambique Company was responsible until 1942 for the administration of Manica and Sofala territory in Portuguese E. Africa from 1891. Now part of Mozambique.

1899. 1000 reis = 1 milreis.
1913. 100 centavos = 1 escudo.

1892. "Embossed" key-type inscr. "PROVINCA DE MOCAMBIQUE" optd. **COMPA DE MOCAMBIQUE.**

10	Q	5 r. black	30	20
2		10 r. green	40	20
3		20 r. red	50	20
4		25 r. mauve	35	25
5		40 r. brown	35	20
6		50 r. blue	40	25
7		100 r. brown	35	25
8		200 r. violet	65	50
9		300 r. orange	65	50

2.

1895. Value in black or red (500, 1000 r.).

33	**2**	2½ r. yellow	10	10
114		2½ r. grey	50	25
17		5 r. orange	15	10
18		10 r. mauve	20	15
115		10 r. green	30	25
39		15 r. brown	20	15
116		15 r. green	30	25
20		20 r. lilac	25	15
45		25 r. green	20	15
117		25 r. red	40	20
46		50 r. blue	25	20
118		50 r. brown	40	30
109		65 r. blue	25	20
48		75 r. red	25	20
119		75 r. mauve	90	75
50		80 r. green	25	20
52		100 r. brown on buff ..	30	20
120		100 r. blue on blue ..	90	75
110		115 r. pink on rose ..	75	65
121		115 r. brown on rose ..	1·40	90
111		130 r. green on rose ..	75	65
122		130 r. brown on yellow ..	1·40	90
54		150 r. orange on rose ..	30	20
55		200 r. blue on blue ..	30	20
123		200 r. lilac on red ..	1·40	90
56		300 r. blue on brown ..	30	20
112		400 r. black on blue ..	75	65
124		400 r. blue on yellow ..	1·75	1·40
58		500 r. black	40	30
125		500 r. black on blue ..	1·75	40
126		700 r. mauve on yellow ..	1·90	1·60
59		1000 r. mauve	45	30

1895. Surch. **PROVISORIO 25.**

105.	**2.**	25 on 75 r. red	1·40	1·25
77.		25 on 80 r. green ..	7·00	5·00

1895. No. 6 optd. **PROVISORIO.**

78.	Q.	50 r. blue	1·75	1·50

1898. Vasco da Gama. Optd. **1498 Centenario da India 1898.**

80	**2**	2½ r. yellow	60	60
81		5 r. orange	75	65
82		10 r. mauve	75	60
84		15 r. brown	90	80
86		20 r. lilac	1·00	90
87		25 r. green	1·60	1·00
99		50 r. blue	95	90
89		75 r. red	1·60	1·40
91		80 r. green	1·60	1·25
101		100 r. brown on buff ..	1·75	1·50
102		150 r. orange on red ..	1·75	1·60
94		200 r. blue on blue ..	2·25	2·00
104		300 r. blue on brown ..	3·25	2·25

1900. Surch. **25 Reis** and bar.

106.	**2.**	25 r. on 5 r. orange ..	1·25	75

1900. Perforated through centre and surch. **50 REIS.**

108.	**2.**	50 r. on half of 20 r. lilac	40	35

1911. Optd. **REPUBLICA.**

145	**2**	2½ r. grey	15	10
147		5 r. orange	15	10
148		10 r. green	10	10
150		15 r. green	10	10
151		20 r. lilac	10	10
153		25 r. red	10	10
155		50 r. brown	10	10
156		75 r. mauve	15	10
157		100 r. blue on blue ..	20	10
159		115 r. brown on red ..	30	20
160		130 r. brown on yellow	30	20
161		200 r. lilac on red ..	30	15
162		400 r. blue on yellow ..	30	15
163		500 r. black on blue ..	30	15
164		700 r. purple on yellow	35	30

1916. Surch. **REPUBLICA** and value in figures.

166	**2**	¼ c. on 2½ r. grey ..	10	10
168		½ c. on 5 r. orange ..	10	10
170		1 c. on 10 r. green ..	15	15
173		1½ c. on 15 r. green ..	15	15
175		2 c. on 20 r. lilac	15	15
178		2½ c. on 25 r. red	15	15
180		5 c. on 50 r. brown ..	15	15
181		7½ c. on 75 r. mauve ..	25	15
182		10 c. on 100 r. blue on blue	25	15
183		11½ c. on 115 r. brn. on red	50	30
184		13 c. on 130 r. brn. on yell.	50	25
185		20 c. on 200 r. lilac on red	40	25
186		40 c. on 400 r. blue on yell.	40	25
187		50 c. on 500 r. blk. on blue	45	35
188		70 c. on 700 r. pur. on yell.	45	35

1917. Red Cross Fund. Optd **REPUBLICA,** red cross and **31.7.17.**

189.	**2.**	2½ r. grey	1·25	1·00
190.		10 r. green	1·50	1·25
191.		20 r. lilac	1·50	1·25
192.		50 r. brown	4·00	2·00
193.		75 r. mauve	10·00	8·50
194.		100 r. blue	12·00	9·00
195.		700 r. purple on yellow ..	40·00	28·00

1918. Surch. **REPUBLICA** and value.

196.	**2.**	½ c. on 700 r. pur. on yell.	70	65
197.		2½ c. on 500 r. blk. on bl.	70	65
198.		5 c. on 400 r. blue on yell.	70	65

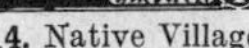

14. Native Village.

15. Ivory.

33.

36. Tea.

1918.

199	**14**	¼ c. green and brown ..	15	15
233		¼ c. black and olive ..	15	15
200	**15**	½ c. black	15	15
201	–	1 c. black & green ..	15	15
202	–	1½ c. green and black ..	15	15
203	–	2 c. black and red ..	15	15
235	–	2 c. black and grey ..	15	15
204	–	2½ c. black and lilac ..	15	15
236	–	3c. black and orange ..	15	15
205	–	4 c. brown and green ..	15	15
237	–	4 c. black and red ..	15	15
227	**14**	4½ c. black and grey ..	15	15
206	–	5 c. black and blue ..	15	15
207	–	6 c. blue and purple ..	25	20
238	–	6 c. black and mauve ..	15	15
228	–	7 c. black and blue ..	45	25
208	–	7½ c. green and orange	25	25
209	–	8 c. black and lilac ..	25	25
210	–	10 c. black and red ..	50	25
229	–	12 c. black and brown ..	65	40
241	–	12 c. black and green ..	25	20
211	–	15 c. black and red ..	50	25
212	–	20 c. black and green ..	20	15
251	**33**	24 c. black and blue ..	70	60
252	–	25 c. blue and brown ..	70	60
213	–	30 c. black and brown ..	30	25
244	–	30 c. black and green ..	35	25
214	–	40 c. black and green ..	25	15
246	**33**	40 c. black and blue ..	40	25
258	–	45 c. blue	1·50	70
215	–	50 c. black and orange	30	25
247	–	50 c. black and mauve .	55	25
230	–	60 c. brown and red ..	70	45
259	–	70 c. brown	1·25	45
231	–	80 c. brown and blue ..	1·10	50
248	–	80 c. black and red ..	75	40
253	–	85 c. black and red ..	55	40
216	–	1 e. black and green ..	65	45
249	–	1 e. black and blue ..	50	40
254	–	1 e. 40 black and blue ..	1·00	40
232	–	2 e. violet and red ..	1·50	75
250	–	2 e. black and lilac ..	1·00	40
255	–	5 e. blue and brown ..	75	30
256	**36**	10 e. black and red ..	80	35
257	–	20 e. black and green ..	1·00	40

DESIGNS—HORIZ. 1, 3 c. Maize field. 2 c. Sugar factory. 5 c., 2 e. Beira. 20 c. Law Court. 40 c. Mangrove swamp. 43 c. Ivory store. 20 e. R. Zambesi. VERT. 1½ c. India-rubber. 2½ c. River Buzi. 4 c. Tobacco bushes. 6 c. Coffee bushes. 7, 15 c. Steam train. 7½ c. Orange tree. 8, 12 c. Cotton plants. 10, 80 c. Sisal plantation. 25 c., 1 e. 40, Beira. 30 c. Coconut palm. 50, 60 c. Cattle-breeding. 70 c. Gold-mining. 1 e. Mozambique Co's Arms. 5 c. Tapping rubber.

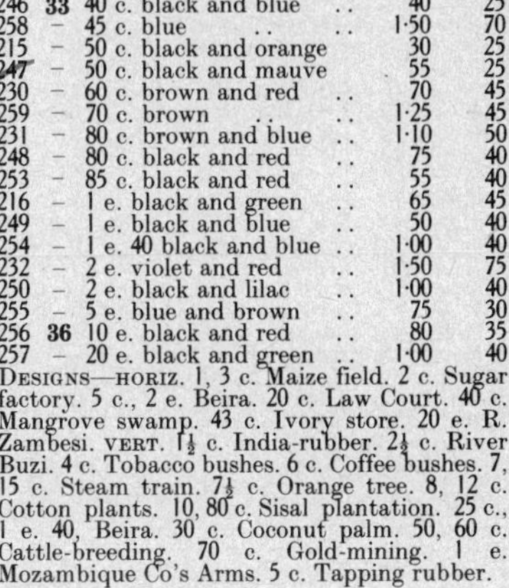

1920. Pictorial issue surch.

217.	½ c. on 30 c. (No. 213) ..	90	90
218.	½ c. on 1 e. (No. 216) ..	70	60
219.	1½ c. on 2½ c. (No. 204) ..	90	90
220.	1½ c. on 5 c. (No. 206) ..	1·10	70
221.	2 c. on 2½ c. (No. 204) ..	60	50
222.	4 c. on 20 c. (No. 212) ..	90	80
223.	4 c. on 40 c. (No. 214) ..	90	70
224.	6 c. on 8 c. (No. 209) ..	90	70
225.	6 c. on 50 c. (No. 215) ..	90	70

40. Zambesi Bridge.

1935. Opening of Zambesi Bridge.

260.	**40.**	1 e. black and blue ..	2·00	1·00

41. Armstrong-Whitworth "Atlanta" Airliner over Beira.

1935. Inauguration of Blantyre-Beira-Salisbury Air Route.

261.	**41.**	5 c. black and blue ..	35	25
262.		10 c. black and red ..	35	25
263.		15 c. black and red ..	35	25
264.		20 c. black and green ..	35	25
265.		30 c. black and green ..	35	25
266.		40 c. black and green ..	50	30
267.		45 c. black and blue ..	50	30
268.		50 c. black and purple ..	50	35
269.		60 c. brown and red ..	85	40
270.		80 c. black and red ..	85	40

42. Armstrong-Whitworth "Atlanta" Airliner over Beira.

1935. Air.

271.	**42.**	5 c. black and blue ..	10	10
272.		10 c. black and red ..	10	10
273.		15 c. black and red ..	10	10
274.		20 c. black and green ..	10	10
275.		30 c. black and green ..	10	10
276.		40 c. black and green ..	10	10
277.		45 c. black and blue ..	10	10
278.		50 c. black and purple ..	10	10
279.		60 c. brown and red ..	10	10
280.		80 c. black and red ..	10	10
281.		1 e. black and blue ..	15	20
282.		2 e. black and purple ..	30	20
283.		5 e. blue and brown ..	55	35
284.		10 e. black and red ..	60	35
285.		20 e. black and green ..	1·25	50

43. Dhow.

46. Palms at Beira.

45. Crocodile.

1937.

286. – 1 c. violet and green .. 10 10
287. – 5 c. green and blue .. 10 10
288. **43.** 10 c. blue and red .. 10 10
289. – 15 c. black and red .. 10 10
290. – 20 c. blue and green .. 10 10
291. – 30 c. blue and green .. 10 10
292. 40 c. black and green .. 15 10
293. – 45 c. brown and blue .. 10 10
294. **45.** 50 c. green and purple .. 10 10
295. – 60 c. blue and red .. 10 10
296. – 70 c. green and brown .. 10 10
297. – 80 c. green and red .. 15 10
298. – 85 c. black and brown .. 20 15
299. – 1 e. black and blue .. 15 15
300. **46.** 1 e. 40 c. green and blue 20 15
301. – 2 e. brown and lilac .. 50 15
302. – 5 e. blue and brown .. 60 20
303. – 10 e. black and red .. 50 30
304. – 20 e. purple and green .. 1·00 45

DESIGNS—VERT. (21 × 29 mm)—1 c. Giraffe. 20 c. Common zebra. 70 c. Native woman. (23 × 31mm)—10 e. Old Portuguese gate, Sena. 20 e. Arms. HORIZ. (29 × 21 mm)—5 c. Native huts. 15 c. Caetano fortress, Sofala. 60 c. Leopard. 80 c. Hippopotami (37 × 22 mm)—5 e. Railway bridge over River Zambesi. TRIANGALR: 30 c. Python. 40 c. White rhinoceros. 45 c. Lion. 85 c. Vasco da Gama's flagship "Sao Gabriel". 1 e. Native in dugout canoe. 2 e. Greater kudu.

1939. President Carmona's Colonial Tour. Optd. **28-VII-1939 Visita Presidencial.**

305. – 30 c. (No. 291) 60 45
306. – 40 c. (No. 292) 60 45
307. – 45 c. (No. 293) 60 45
308. **45.** 50 c. green and purple .. 60 45
309. – 85 c. (No. 298) 60 45
310. – 1 e. (No. 299) .. .. 1·00 60
311. – 2 e. (No. 301) .. .. 1·25 1·00

49. King Afonso Henriques. **51.** "Don John IV" after Alberto de Souza.

1940. 800th Anniv of Portuguese Independence.

312 **49** 1 e. 75 light blue & blue 65 35

1940. Tercentenary of Restoration of Independence.

313. **51.** 40 c. black and blue .. 20 15
314. 50 c. green and violet 20 15
315. 60 c. blue and red .. 20 15
316. 70 c. green and brown 20 15
317. 80 c. green and red .. 20 15
318. 1 e. black and blue .. 20 15

CHARITY TAX STAMPS

The notes under this heading in Portugal also apply here.

1932. No. 236 surch. **Assistencia Publica 2 Ctvos. 2.**

C260 2 c. on 3 c. black & orge 30 30

C **41.** "Charity". C **50.**

1934.

C 261. C **41.** 2 c. black and mauve 35 30

1940.

C313 C **50** 2 c. blue and black .. 2·75 2·25

C **52**

1941.

C319 C **52** 2 c. red and black .. 2·75 2·25

NEWSPAPER STAMP

1894. "Newspaper" key-type inscr. "MOCAMBIQUE" optd. **COMPA DE MOCAMBIQUE.**

N 15. V. 2½ r. brown 30 25

POSTAGE DUE STAMPS

D **9.**

D **32.**

1906.

D 114. D **9.** 5 r. green 20 20
D 115. 10 r. grey 20 20
D 116. 20 r. brown 20 20
D 117. 30 r. orange .. 30 25
D 118. 50 r. brown 30 25
D 119. 60 r. brown .. .. 1·60 1·50
D 120. 100 r. mauve .. 45 45
D 121. 130 r. blue .. .. 2·50 1·60
D 122. 200 r. red .. .. 1·00 65
D 123. 500 r. lilac .. .. 1·25 1·00

1911. Optd. **REPUBLICA.**

D 166. D **9.** 5 r. green 15 15
D 167. 10 r. grey 15 15
D 168. 20 r. brown 15 15
D 169. 30 r. orange .. 15 15
D 170. 50 r. brown 15 15
D 171. 60 r. brown 25 20
D 172. 100 r. mauve .. 25 20
D 173. 130 r. blue 65 65
D 174. 200 r. red 70 65
D 175. 500 r. lilac 80 70

1916. Currency changed.

D 189. D **9.** ½ c. green 10 10
D 190. 1 c. grey 10 10
D 191. 2 c. brown 10 10
D 192. 3 c. orange 10 10
D 193. 5 c. brown 10 10
D 194. 6 c. brown 15 15
D 195. 10 c. mauve .. 30 30
D 196. 13 c. blue 65 65
D 197. 20 c. red 65 65
D 198. 50 c. lilac 80 80

1919.

D 217. D **32.** ½ c. green 10 10
D 218. 1 c. black 10 10
D 219. 2 c. brown 10 10
D 220. 3 c. orange 10 10
D 221. 5 c. brown 10 10
D 222. 6 c. brown 25 25
D 223. 10 c. red 25 25
D 224. 13 c. blue 25 25
D 225. 20 c. red 40 20
D 226. 50 c. grey 25 20

MUSCAT AND OMAN Pt. 19

Independent Sultanate in Eastern Arabia. The title of the Sultanate was changed in 1971 to Oman.

1966. 64 baizas = 1 rupee.
1970. 1000 baizas = 1 rial saidi.

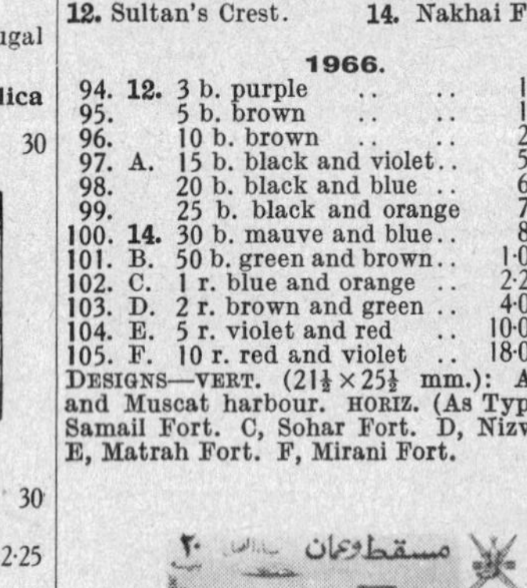

12. Sultan's Crest. **14.** Nakhai Fort.

1966.

94. **12.** 3 b. purple 10 15
95. 5 b. brown 15 10
96. 10 b. brown 20 10
97. A. 15 b. black and violet .. 50 15
98. 20 b. black and blue .. 60 15
99. 25 b. black and orange 75 20
100. **14.** 30 b. mauve and blue .. 80 25
101. B. 50 b. green and brown .. 1·00 30
102. C. 1 r. blue and orange .. 2·25 55
103. D. 2 r. brown and green .. 4·00 1·75
104. E. 5 r. violet and red .. 10·00 6·00
105. F. 10 r. red and violet .. 18·00 12·00

DESIGNS—VERT. (21½ × 25½ mm.): A, Crest and Muscat harbour. HORIZ. (As Type 14) B, Samail Fort. C, Sohar Fort. D, Nizwa Fort. E, Matrah Fort. F, Mirani Fort.

15. Mina el Fahal.

1969. 1st Oil Shipment (July 1967). Mult.

106 20 b. Type **15** 70 35
107 25 b. Storage tanks .. 1·00 50
108 40 b. Desert oil-rig .. 1·50 85
109 1 r. Aerial view from "Gemini 4" .. .. 3·50 2·25

1970. Designs as issue of 1966, but inscribed in new currency.

110. **12.** 5 b. purple 15 10
111. 10 b. brown 20 10
112. 20 b. brown 40 10
113. A. 25 b. black and violet .. 75 15
114. 30 b. black and blue .. 85 20
115. 40 b. black and orange .. 1·00 25
116. **14.** 50 b. mauve and blue .. 1·50 25
117. B. 75 b. green and brown .. 2·00 50
118. C. 100 b. blue and orange .. 2·50 60
119. D. ¼ r. brown and green .. 7·50 3·25
120. E. ½ r. violet and red .. 12·00 7·50
121. F. 1 r. red and violet .. 22·00 13·00

For later issues see **OMAN**.

MYANMAR Pt.21

Formerly known as Burma.

100 pyas = 1 kyat.

81 Fountain, National Assembly Park (½-size illustration, actual size 79 × 36 mm)

1990. State Law and Order Restoration Council.

312 **81** 1 k. multicoloured .. 20 15

1990. As Nos. 258/61 of Burma but inscr "UNION OF MYANMAR".

313 15 p. deep green and green 10 10
314 20 p. brown, black & blue 10 10
316 50 p. violet and brown .. 10 10
317 1 k. violet, black & mauve 20 15

82 Map and Emblem

83 Nawata Ruby

1990. 40th Anniv of United Nations Development Programme.

322 **82** 2 k. blue, yellow & black 35 20

1991. Gem Emporium.

323 **83** 50 p. multicoloured .. 10 10

84 "Grandfather recounting History" (statuette)

85 Emblem

1992. 44th Anniv of Independence. Mult.

324 50 p. Warrior defending personification of Myanmar and map .. 10 10
325 2 k. Type **84** 35 20

1992. National Sports Festival.

326 **85** 50 p. mutlicoloured .. 10 10

86 Campaign Emblem

87 Fish, Water Droplet and Leaf

1992. Anti-AIDS Campaign.

327 **86** 50 p. red 10 10

1992. International Nutrition Conference, Rome.

328 **87** 50 p. multicoloured .. 10 10
329 1 k. multicoloured .. 20 15
330 3 k. multicoloured .. 60 35
331 5 k. multicoloured .. 1·10 65

88 Statue

89 Hin Thar (legendary bird)

1993. National Convention for drafting of New Constitution.

332 **88** 50 p. multicoloured .. 10 10
333 3 k. multicoloured .. 60 35

1993. Statuettes. Multicoloured.

334 5 k. Type **89** .. .. 1·10 65
335 10 k. Lawkanat .. .. 2·10 1·25

90 Horseman aiming Spear at Target

1993. Festival of Traditional Equestrian Sports.

336 **90** 3 k. multicoloured .. 65 40

MINIMUM PRICE

The minimum price quoted is 5p which represents a handling charge rather than a basis for valuing common stamps. For further notes about prices see introductory pages.

NAKHICHEVAN Pt.10

An autonomous province of Azerbaijan, separated from the remainder of the republic by Armenian territory. Nos. 1 and 2 were issued during a period when the administration of Nakhichevan was in dispute with the central government.

100 qopik = 1 manat.

1 President Aliev

1993. 70th Birthday of President H. Aliev of Nakhichevan.

No.	Type	Description		
1	1	5 m. black and red		
2	–	5 m. multicoloured		

DESIGN: No. 2, Map of Nakhichevan.

NAPLES Pt. 8

A state on the S.W. coast of Central Italy, formerly part of the Kingdom of Sicily, but now part of Italy.

100 grana = 200 tornesi = 1 ducato.

1. Arms under Bourbon Dynasty. 4. Cross of Savoy.

1858. The frames differ in each value. Imperf.

No.	Type	Description		
8.	1.	½ t. blue	£12000	£8000
1.		½ g. lake	£650	£170
2.		1 g. lake	£180	15·00
3.		2 g. lake	£110	4·25
4.		5 g. lake	£900	18·00
5.		10 g. lake	£2000	65·00
6.		20 g. lake	£1700	£275
7.		50 g. lake	£42500	£2500

1860. Imperf.

No.	Type	Description		
9.	4.	½ t. blue	£20000	£3250

NEAPOLITAN PROVINCES Pt. 8

Temporary issues for Naples and other parts of S. Italy which adhered to the new Kingdom of Italy in 1860.

100 grana = 200 tornesi = 1 ducato.

1.

1861. Embossed. Imperf.

No.	Type	Description		
2.	1.	½ t. green	3·25	55·00
5.		½ g. brown	£110	80·00
9.		1 g. black	£200	5·00
10.		2 g. blue	45·00	3·75
15.		5 g. red	£130	40·00
18.		10 g. orange	£110	70·00
19.		20 g. yellow	£400	£700
23.		50 g. slate	5·00	£6000

NEPAL Pt. 21

An independent Kingdom in the Himalayas N. of India.

1881. 16 annas = 1 rupee.
1907. 64 pice = 1 rupee.
1954. 100 paisa = 1 rupee.

1. (1 a.). 2. (½ a.). 3. Siva Mahadeva (2 pice).

1881. Imperf. or pin-perf.

No.	Type	Description		
34.	2.	½ a. black	2·00	50
35.		½ a. orange	£190	95·00
10.	1.	1 a. blue	1·25	90
19.		1 a. green	18·00	14·50
11.		2 a. purple	1·75	1·25
40.		2 a. brown	3·00	1·50
12.		4 a. green	2·40	1·75

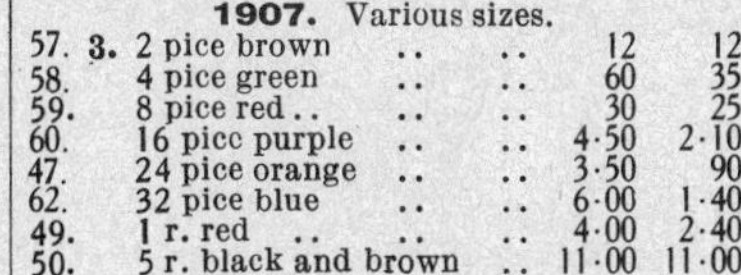

1907. Various sizes.

No.	Type	Description		
57.	3.	2 pice brown	12	12
58.		4 pice green	60	35
59.		8 pice red	30	25
60.		16 pice purple	4·50	2·10
47.		24 pice orange	3·50	90
62.		32 pice blue	6·00	1·40
49.		1 r. red	4·00	2·40
50.		5 r. black and brown	11·00	11·00

5. Swayambhunath Temple, Katmandu. 8. Sri Pashupati (Siva Mahadeva).

7. Guheswari Temple, Patan.

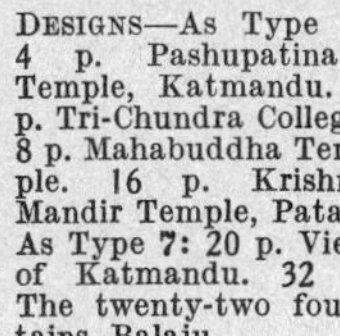

DESIGNS—As Type 5: 4 p. Pashupatinath Temple, Katmandu. 6 p. Tri-Chundra College. 8 p. Mahabuddha Temple. 16 p. Krishna Mandir Temple, Patan. As Type 7: 20 p. View of Katmandu. 32 p. The twenty-two fountains, Balaju.

1949.

No.	Type	Description		
64.	5.	2 p. brown	65	40
65.	–	4 p. green	65	40
66.	–	6 p. pink	1·40	40
67.	–	8 p. red	1·40	70
68.	–	16 p. purple	1·40	70
69.	–	20 p. blue	3·00	1·25
70.	7.	24 p. red	1·75	70
71.	–	32 p. blue	4·75	1·50
72.	8.	1 r. orange	18·00	8·00

9. King Tribhuvana. 10. Map of Nepal.

1954. (a) Size 18×22 mm.

No.	Type	Description		
73.	9.	2 p. brown	12	5
74.		4 p. green	12	8
75.		6 p. red	15	10
76.		8 p. lilac	20	10
77.		12 p. orange	40	20
		(b) Size 25½×29½ mm.		
78.	9.	16 p. brown	45	20
79.		20 p. red	50	25
80.		24 p. red	80	40
81.		32 p. blue	1·00	60
82.		50 p. mauve	1·25	70
83.		1 r. red	2·50	1·25
84.		2 r. brown	5·00	2·50
		(c) Size 30×18 mm.		
85.	10.	2 p. brown	35	5
86.		4 p. green	90	8
87.		6 p. red	1·10	12
88.		8 p. lilac	90	10
89.		12 p. orange	1·10	15
		(d) Size 38×21½ mm.		
90.	10.	16 p. brown	90	20
91.		20 p. red	1·00	25
92.		24 p. red	1·10	25
93.		32 p. blue	1·20	40
94.		50 p. mauve	4·00	1·25
95.		1 r. red	7·00	1·75
96.		2 r. brown	8·00	5·00

11. Mechanization of Agriculture. 13. Hanuman Dhoka, Katmandu.

1956. Coronation.

No.	Type	Description		
97.	11.	4 p. green	75	45
98.	–	6 p. red and orange	50	15
99.	–	8 p. violet	50	15
100.	13.	24 p. red	1·25	40
101.	–	1 r. brown	35·00	20·00

DESIGNS—VERT. As Type 11: 8 p. Processional elephant. As Type 13: 6 p. Throne. 1 r. King and Queen and mountains.

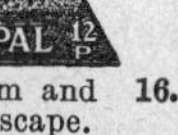

15. U.N. Emblem and Nepalese Landscape. 16. Nepalese Crown.

1956. 1st Anniv. of Admission into U.N.O.

No.	Type	Description		
102.	15.	12 p. blue and buff	1·50	1·10

1957. (a) Size 18×22 mm.

No.	Type	Description		
103.	16.	2 p. brown	40	25
104.		4 p. green	50	40
105.		6 p. red	40	25
106.		8 p. lilac	40	25
107.		12 p. red	2·00	60
		(b) Size 25½×29½ mm.		
108.	16.	16 p. brown	2·50	75
109.		20 p. red	4·00	1·10
110.		24 p. red	3·00	1·00
111.		32 p. blue	3·50	1·10
112.		50 p. red	7·50	3·00
113.		1 r. salmon	10·00	4·00
114.		2 r. orange	6·00	3·00

17. Gaunthali carrying Letter. 18. Temple of Lumbini.

1958. Air. Inauguration of Nepalese Internal Airmail Service.

No.	Type	Description		
115.	17.	10 p. blue	60	50

1958. Human Rights Day.

No.	Type	Description		
116.	18.	6 p. yellow	75	60

19. Nepalese Map and Flag.

1959. 1st Nepalese Elections.

No.	Type	Description		
117.	19.	6 p. red and green	25	20

20. Spinning Wheel. 21. King Mahendra.

1959. Cottage Industries.

No.	Type	Description		
118.	20.	2 p. brown	10	8

1959. Admission of Nepal to U.P.U.

No.	Type	Description		
119.	21.	12 p. blue	20	10

22. Vishnu. 23. Nyatopol Temple, Bhaktapur.

1959.

No.	Type	Description		
120.	22.	1 p. brown	10	8
121.	–	2 p. violet	10	8
122.	–	4 p. blue	25	12
123.	–	6 p. pink	20	10
124.	–	8 p. sepia	20	10
125.	–	12 p. grey	25	10
126.	23.	16 p. violet and brown	25	15
127.		20 p. lake and blue	50	40
128.		24 p. red and myrtle	45	40
129.		32 p. blue and lilac	45	35
130.		50 p. myrtle and red	75	50
131.	–	1 r. blue and brown	4·50	1·25
132.	–	2 r. blue and mauve	6·00	3·00
133.	–	5 r. red and violet	45·00	35·00

DESIGNS—As Type 22—HORIZ. 2 p. Krishna. 8 p. Siberian musk deer. 12 p. Indian rhinoceros. VERT. 4 p. Himalayas. 6 p. Gateway, Bhaktapur Palace. As Type 23—VERT. 1 r., 2 r. Himalayan monal pheasant. 5 r. Satyr tragopan.

24. King Mahendra opening Parliament. 25. Sri Pashupatinath.

1959. Opening of 1st Nepalese Parliament.

No.	Type	Description		
134.	24.	6 p. red	60	50

1959. Temple Renovation.

No.	Type	Description		
135.	25.	4 p. green (18×25 mm.)	50	40
136.		8 p. red (21×28½ mm.)	50	40
137.		1 r. blue (24½×33½ mm.)	6·50	4·00

26. Children, Pagoda and Mt. Everest. 27. King Mahendra.

1960. Children's Day.

No.	Type	Description		
137a.	26.	6 p. blue	10·00	6·00

1960. King Mahendra's 41st Birthday

No.	Type	Description		
138.	27.	1 r. purple	1·10	75

See also Nos. 163/4a.

28. Mt. Everest. 29. King Tribhuvana.

1960. Mountain Views.

No.	Type	Description		
139.	–	5 p. sepia and purple	15	8
140.	28.	10 p. purple and blue	40	25
141.	–	40 p. brown and violet	60	40

DESIGNS: 5 p. Machha Puchhre. 40 p. Manaslu (wrongly inscr. "MANSALU").

1961. 10th Democracy Day.

No.	Type	Description		
142.	29.	10 p. salmon and brown	10	10

30. Prince Gyanendra cancelling Children's Day Stamps of 1960. 31. King Mahendra.

1961. Children's Day.

No.	Type	Description		
143.	30.	12 p. orange	25·00	21·00

1961. King Mahendra's 42nd Birthday.

No.	Type	Description		
144.	31.	6 p. green	20	20
145.		12 p. blue	30	30
146.		50 p. red	60	50
147.		1 r. brown	85	75

32. Campaign Emblem and House. 33. King Mahendra on horseback.

1962. Malaria Eradication.

No.	Type	Description		
148.	32.	12 p. blue	25	25
149.	–	1 r. orange and red	60	60

DESIGN: 1 r. Emblem and Nepalese flag.

1962. King Mahendra's 43rd Birthday.

No.	Type	Description		
150.	33.	10 p. blue	12	12
151.		15 p. brown	20	20
152.		45 p. brown	35	35
153.		1 r. olive	70	70

34. Bhana Bhakta Acharya. 35. King Mahendra. 36.

1962. Nepalese Poets.
154. 34. 5 p. brown 12 12
155. – 10 p. turquoise 12 12
156. – 40 p. olive 25 25
PORTRAITS: 10 p. Moti Ram Bhakta. 40 p. Sambhu Prasad.

1962.
157. 35. 1 p. red 5 5
158. 2 p. blue 5 5
158a. 3 p. grey 25 25
159. 5 p. bistre 8 8
160. 36. 10 p. purple 15 15
161. 40 p. brown 35 35
162. 75 p. turquoise .. .. 6·00 6·00
162a. 35 75 p. turquoise 70 60
163. 27. 2 r. orange .. .. 1·00 85
164. 5 r. green .. .. 1·40 1·25
164a. 10 r. violet .. .. 6·00 5·50
No. 158a is smaller, 17½ × 20 mm.

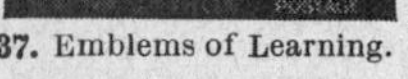

37. Emblems of Learning.

38. Hands holding Lamps.

39. Campaign Symbols. 40. Map of Nepal and Open Hand.

1963. U.N.E.S.C.O. "Education for All" Campaign.
165. 37. 10 p. black 12 12
166. 15 p. brown 20 20
167. 50 p. violet 45 40

1963. National Day.
168. 38. 5 p. blue 5 5
169. 10 p. brown 10 10
170. 50 p. mauve 25 25
171. 1 r. turquoise 45 45

1963. Freedom from Hunger.
172. 39. 10 p. orange 5 5
173. 15 p. blue 20 15
174. 50 p. green 45 40
175. 1 r. brown 75 70

1963. Rastruya Panchayat.
176. 40. 10 p. green 10 10
177. 15 p. purple 15 15
178. 50 p. slate 35 30
179. 1 r. violet 60 55

41. King Mahendra. 42. King Mahendra and Highway Map.

1963. King Mahendra's 44th Birthday.
180. 41. 5 p. violet 10 10
181. 10 p. brown 12 12
182. 15 p. green 15 15

1964. Inaug. of East–West Highway.
183. 42. 10 p. orange and blue .. 8 8
184. 15 p. orange and blue .. 10 10
185. 50 p. brown and green .. 25 20

43. King Mahendra at Microphone. 44. Crown Prince Birendra.

1964. King Mahendra's 45th Birthday.
186. 43. 1 p. brown 8 8
187. 2 p. slate 8 8
188. 2 r. brown 60 60

1964. Crown Prince's 19th Birthday.
189. 44. 10 p. green 50 45
190. 15 p. brown 45 35

45. Flag, Kukris, Rings and Torch. 46. Nepalese Family.

1964. Olympic Games, Tokyo.
191. 45. 10 p. blue, red and pink 35 30

1965. Land Reform.
192. – 2 p. black and green .. 15 15
193. – 5 p. brown and green .. 15 15
194. – 10 p. purple and grey .. 15 15
195. 46. 15 p. brown and yellow 20 20
DESIGNS: 2 p. Farmer and cattle. 5 p. Ears of corn. 10 p. Grain elevator.

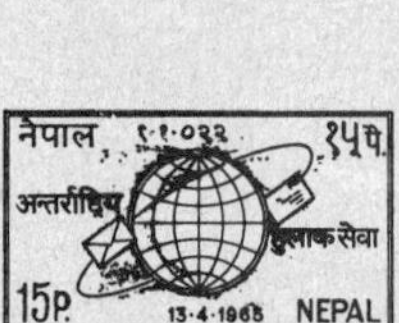

47. Globe and Letters. 48. King Mahendra.

1965. Introduction of International Insured and Parcel Service.
196. 47. 15 p. violet 20 15

1965. King Mahendra's 46th Birthday.
197. 48. 50 p. purple 55 45

49. Four Martyrs. 50. I.T.U. Emblem.

1965. "Nepalese Martyrs".
198. 49. 15 p. green 20 15

1965. I.T.U. Cent.
199. 50. 15 p. black and purple 20 15

51. I.C.Y. Emblem. 52. Devkota (poet).

1965. Int. Co-operation Year.
200. 51. 1 r. multicoloured .. 55 45

1965. Devkota Commem.
201. 52. 15 p. brown 20 15

54. Flag and King Mahendra.

1966. Democracy Day.
202. 54. 15 p. red and blue .. 55 25

55. Siva Parvati and Pashuvati Temple. 56. "Stamp" Emblem.

1966. Maha Siva-Ratri Festival.
203. 55. 15 p. violet 20 20

1966. Nepalese Philatelic Exn.
204. 56. 15 p. orange and green 25 25

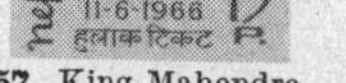

57. King Mahendra. 58. Queen Mother.

1966. King Mahendra's 47th Birthday.
205. 57. 15 p. brown and ochre .. 20 15

1966. Queen Mother's 60th Birthday.
206. 58. 15 p. brown 20 15

59. Queen Ratna. 60. Flute-player and Dancer.

1966. Children's Day.
207. 59. 15 p. brown and yellow 20 15

1966. Krishna Anniv.
208. 60. 15 p. violet and yellow 20 15

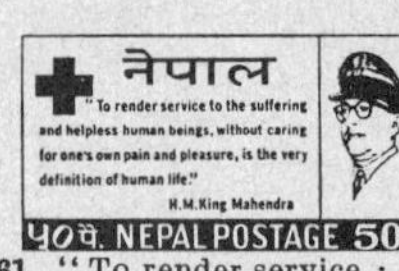

61. "To render service . . ."

1966. 1st Anniv. of Nepalese Red Cross.
209. 61. 50 p. red and green .. 2·00 60

62. W.H.O. Building on flag. 63. Paudyal.

1966. Inaug. of W.H.O. Headquarters Geneva.
210. 62. 1 r. violet 85 80

1966. Leknath Paudyal (poet) Commem.
211 63 15 p. blue 20 15

MORE DETAILED LISTS
are given in the Stanley Gibbons Catalogues referred to in the country headings.
For lists of current volumes see Introduction.

64. Rama and Sita. 65. Buddha.

1967. Rama Navami, 2024, birthday of Rama.
212. 64. 15 p. brown and yellow 20 15

1967. Buddha Jayanti, birthday of Buddha.
213. 65. 75 p. purple and orange 50 50

66. King Mahendra addressing Nepalese.

1967. King Mahendra's 48th Birthday.
214. 66. 15 p. brown and blue .. 20 20

67. Queen Ratna and Children. 68. Ama Dablam (mountain).

1967. Children's Day.
215. 67. 15 p. brown and cream 20 15

1967. Int. Tourist Year.
216. 68. 5 p. violet (postage) .. 12 12
217. – 65 p. brown 35 35
218. – 1 r. 80 red & blue (air) 85 80
DESIGNS (38 × 20 mm.): 65 p. Bhaktapur Durbar Square. (35½ × 25½ mm.). 1 r. 80, Plane over Kathmandu.

69. Open-air Class.

1967. Constitution Day. "Go to the Village" Educational Campaign.
219. 69. 15 p. multicoloured .. 20 15

70. Crown Prince Birendra, Camp-fire and Scout Emblem.

1967. Diamond Jubilee of World Scouting.
220 70 15 p. blue 25 15

71. Prithvi Narayan Shah (founder of Kingdom). 72. Arms of Nepal.

1968. Bicentenary of the Kingdom.
221. 71. 15 p. blue and red .. 35 30

1968. National Day.
222. 72. 15 p. blue and red .. 30 25

73. W.H.O. Emblem and Nepalese Flag.

1968. 20th Anniv. of W.H.O.
223. **73.** 1 r. 20 blue, red & yellow 1·25 1·00

74. Sita and Janaki Temple.

1968. Sita Jayanti.
224. **74.** 15 p. brown and violet 15 12

75. King Mahendra, Mountains and Himalayan Monal Pheasant.

1968. King Mahendra's 49th Birthday.
225. **75.** 15 p. multicoloured .. 75 30

76. Garuda and Airline Emblem.

1968. Air. 10th Anniv. of Royal Nepalese Airlines.
226. **76.** 15 p. brown and blue .. 15 15
227. – 65 p. blue 35 35
228. – 2 r. 50 blue and orange 1·50 1·10
DESIGNS—DIAMOND ($25\frac{1}{2} \times 25\frac{1}{2}$ mm.) 65 p. Route-map. HORIZ. (As Type **70**). 2 r. 50, Airliner over Mount Dhaulagiri.

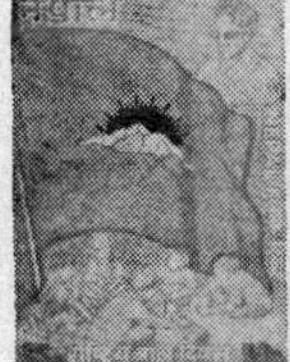

77. Flag, Queen Ratna and Children. **78.** Human Rights Emblem and Buddha.

1968. Children's Day and Queen Ratna's 41st Birthday.
229. **77.** 5 p. red, yellow & green 15 15

1968. Human Rights Year.
230. **78.** 1 r. red and green .. 1·10 80

79. Crown Prince Birendra and Dancers.

1968. Crown Prince Birendra's 24th Birthday, and National Youth Festival.
231. **79.** 25 p. blue 35 30

80. King Mahendra, Flags and U.N. Building, New York. **81.** Amsu Varma (7th-century ruler).

1969. Nepal's Election to U.N. Security Council.
232. **80.** 1 r. multicoloured .. 60 55

1969. Famous Nepalese.
233. **81.** 15 p. violet and green .. 35 30
234. – 25 p. turquoise 45 45
235. – 50 p. brown 55 45
236. – 1 r. purple and brown .. 50 45
DESIGNS—VERT. 25 p. Ram Shah (7th-century King of Gurkha). 50 p. Bhimsen Thapa (19th-century Prime Minister). HORIZ. 1 r. Bal Bhadra Kunwar (19th-century warrior).

82. I.L.O. Emblem.

1969. 50th Anniv. of I.L.O.
237. **82.** 1 r. brown and red .. 2·50 1·25

83. King Mahendra. **85.** Queen Ratna, and Child with Toy.

84. King Tribhuvana and Queens.

1969. King Mahendra's 50th Birthday.
238. **83.** 25 p. multicoloured .. 20 20

1969. 64th Birth Anniv. of King Tribhuvana.
239. **84.** 25 p. sepia and yellow .. 25 25

1969. National Children's Day.
240. **85.** 25 p. red and brown .. 20 20

86. Rhododendron. **87.** Durga, Goddess of Victory.

1969. Flowers. Multicoloured.
241. 25 p. Type **86** 25 20
242. 25 p. Narcissus 25 20
243. 25 p. Marigold 25 20
244. 25 p. Poinsettia 25 20

1969. Durga Pooja Festival.
245. **87.** 15 p. black and orange 15 15
246. 50 p. violet and brown 45 35

88. Crown Prince Birendra and Princess Aishwarya.

1970. Royal Wedding.
247. **88.** 25 p. multicoloured .. 20 15

89. Produce, Cow and Landscape.

1970. Agricultural Year.
248. **89.** 25 p. multicoloured .. 20 20

90. King Mahendra, Mt. Everest and Nepalese Crown.

1970. King Mahendra's 51st Birthday.
249. **90.** 50 p. multicoloured .. 30 25

91. Lake Gosainkunda.

1970. Nepalese Lakes. Multicoloured.
250. 5 p. Type **91** 12 12
251. 25 p. Lake Phewa Tal .. 30 30
252. 1 r. Lake Rara Daha .. 45 45

92. A.P.Y. Emblem.

1970. Asian Productivity Year.
253. **92.** 1 r. blue 45 35

93. Queen Ratna and Children's Palace, Taulihawa.

1970. National Children's Day.
254. **93.** 25 p. slate and brown .. 20 15

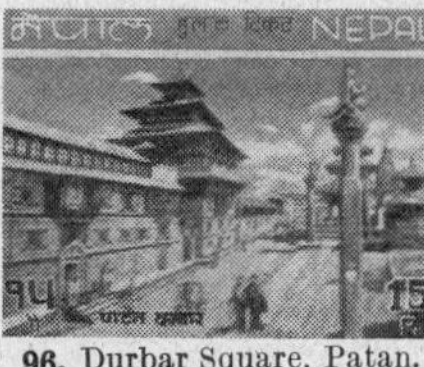

94. New Headquarters Building.

1970. New U.P.U. Headquarters, Berne.
255. **94.** 2 r. 50 brown 85 80

95. U.N. Flag.

1970. 25th Anniv. of United Nations.
256. **95.** 25 p. blue and purple .. 20 15

96. Durbar Square, Patan.

1970. Tourism. Multicoloured.
257. 15 p. Type **96** 12 10
258. 25 p. Boudhanath Stupa (temple) (vert.) .. 15 12
259. 1 r. Mt. Gauri Shankar .. 45 40

97. Statue of Harihar, Valmiki Ashram.

98. Torch within Spiral.

99. King Mahendra taking Salute. **100.** Sweta Bhairab.

1971. Nepalese Religious Art.
260. **97.** 25 p. black and brown 20 15

1971. Racial Equality Year.
261. **98.** 1 r. red and blue .. 60 50

1971. King Mahendra's 52nd Birthday.
262. **99.** 15 p. plum and blue .. 20 15

1971. Bhairab Images.
263. **100.** 15 p. brown and chest. 12 12
264. – 25 p. brown & green .. 20 20
265. – 50 p. brown and blue .. 30 30
DESIGNS: 25 p. Mahankal Bhairab. 50 p. Kal Bhairab.

101. Child presenting Queen Ratna with Garland.

1971. National Children's Day.
266. **101.** 25 p. multicoloured .. 15 12

102. Iranian and Nepalese Flags on Map of Iran.

1971. 2,500th Anniv. of Persian Empire.
267. **102.** 1 r. multicoloured .. 35 30

103 Mother and Child.

1971. 25th Anniv. of U.N.I.C.E.F.
268. **103.** 1 r. blue 40 35

104. Mt. Everest. **105.** Royal Standard.

1971. Himalayan Peaks. Multicoloured.
269. 25 p. Type **104** .. 12 12
270. 1 r. Mt. Kanchenjunga .. 35 30
271. 1 r. 80 Mt. Annapurna I .. 60 45

1972. National Day.
272. **105.** 25 p. black and red .. 15 12

106. Araniko and White Dagoba, Peking. **107.** Open Book.

1972. Araniko (13th-century architect). Commemoration.
273. **106.** 15 p. brown and blue .. 12 10

1972. Int. Book Year
274. **107.** 2 p. brown and buff .. 8 8
275. 5 p. black and brown 8 8
276. 1 r. black and blue .. 30 20

108. Human Heart.

1972. World Heart Month.
277. **108.** 25 p. red and green .. 15 12

109. King Mahendra. **110.** King Birendra.

1972. 1st Death Anniv. of King Mahendra.
278. **109.** 25 p. brown & black .. 15 12

1972. King Birendra's 28th Birthday.
279. **110.** 50 p. purple and brown 20 20

111. Northern Border Costumes. **112.** Sri Baburam Acharya.

1973. National Costumes. Multicoloured.
280. 25 p. Type **111** 12 10
281. 50 p. Hill-dwellers .. 15 12
282. 75 p. Katmandu Valley .. 20 15
283. 1 r. Inner Terai 25 20

1973. 85th Birth Anniv. of Sri Baburam Acharya (historian).
284. **112.** 25 p. drab and red .. 12 10

113. Nepalese Family.

1973. 25th Anniv. of W.H.O.
285. **113.** 1 r. blue and brown .. 30 25

114. Birthplace of Buddha, Lumbini.

1973. Tourism. Multicoloured.
286. 25 p. Type **114** 15 10
287. 75 p. Mt. Makalu .. 25 25
288. 1 r. Castle, Gurkha .. 30 25

115. Transplanting Rice.

1973. 10th Anniv. of World Food Programme.
289. **115.** 10 p. brown & violet .. 8 5

116. Interpol H.Q., Paris.

1973. 50th Anniv. of Int. Criminal Police Organization (Interpol).
290. **116.** 25 p. blue and brown 12 10

117. Shri Shom Nath Sigdyal. **118.** Cow.

1973. 1st Death Anniv. of Shri Shom Nath Sigdyal (scholar).
291. **117.** 1 r. 25 violet 45 35

1973. Domestic Animals. Multicoloured.
292. 2 p. Type **118** 8 8
293. 3 r. 25 Yak .. .. .. 1·50 1·50

119. King Birendra.

1974. King Birendra's 29th Birthday.
294. **119.** 5 p. brown and black 5 5
295. 15 p. brown and black 8 5
296. 1 r. brown and black 25 20

120. Text of National Anthem. **121.** King Janak seated on Throne.

1974. National Day.
297. **120.** 25 p. red 12 10
298. – 1 r. green 30 25
DESIGN: 1 r. Anthem musical score.

1974. King Janak Commemoration.
299. **121.** 2 r. 50 multicoloured 50 35

122. Emblem and Village.

1974. 25th Anniv. of SOS Children's Village International.
300. **122.** 25 p. blue and red .. 12 10

123. Football. **124.** W.P.Y. Emblem.

1974. Nepalese Games. Multicoloured.
301. 2 p. Type **123** .. 8 8
302. 2 r. 75 Baghchal (diagram) 60 50

1974. World Population Year.
303. **124.** 5 p. blue and brown .. 8 5

125. U.P.U. Monument, Berne. **126.** "Cethosia biblis".

1974. Cent. of U.P.U.
304. **125.** 1 r. black and green .. 30 20

1974. Napalese Butterflies. Multicoloured.
305 10 p. Type **126** 15 10
306 15 p. "Kallima inachus" .. 25 20
307 1 r. 25 As No. 306 .. 1·10 65
308 1 r. 75 "Delias thysbe" .. 1·25 1·00

127. King Birendra. **128.** Muktinath.

1974. King Birendra's 30th Birthday.
309. **127.** 25 p. black & green .. 12 10

1974. "Visit Nepal". Tourism. Multicoloured.
310. 25 p. Type **128** 12 8
311. 1 r. Peacock window, Bhaktapur (horiz.) 30 20

129. Guheswari Temple.

1975. Coronation of King Birendra. Mult.
312. 25 p. Type **129** 10 8
313. 50 p. Rara (lake view) .. 12 10
314. 1 r. Throne and sceptre .. 20 15
315. 1 r. 25 Royal Palace, Katmandu 75 25
316. 1 r. 75 Pashupatinath Temple 35 35
317. 2 r. 75 King Birendra and Queen Aishwarya .. 55 45
SIZES—HORIZ. 50 p. (37×30 mm.). 1 r., 1 r. 25 2 r. 75 (46×26 mm.). VERT. 1 r. 75 (25×31 mm.).

130. Tourism Year Emblem.

1975. South Asia Tourism Year. **Mult.**
319. 2 p. Type **130** 8 8
320. 25 p. Temple stupa (vert.) 20 8

131. Tiger.

1975. Wildlife Conservation. Multicoloured.
321. 2 p. Type **131** 35 30
322. 5 p. Swamp deer (vert.) .. 25 20
323. 1 r. Lesser panda 65 60

132. Queen Aishwarya and I.W.Y. Emblem.

1975. International Women's Year.
324. **132.** 1 r. multicoloured .. 20 15

133. Rupse Falls. **134.** King Birendra.

1975. Tourism. Multicoloured.
325. 2 p. Mt. Ganesh Himal (horiz.) 5 5
326. 25 p. Type **133** 10 5
327. 50 p. Kumari ("Living Goddess") 25 15

1975. King Birendra's 31st Birthday.
328. **134.** 25 p. violet and purple 5 5

136. Flag and Map. **138.** Flags of Nepal and Colombo Plan.

137. Transplanting Rice.

1976. Silver Jubilee of Nat. Democracy Day.
330. **136.** 2 r. 50 red and blue .. 35 25

1976. Agriculture Year.
331. **137.** 25 p. multicoloured .. 5 5

1976. 25th Anniv. of Colombo Plan.
332. **138.** 1 r. multicoloured .. 20 15

139. Running. **140.** "Dove of Peace".

1976. Olympic Games, Montreal.
333. **139.** 3 r. 25 black & blue .. 60 55

1976. 5th Non-aligned Countries' Summit Conference.
334. **140.** 5 r. blue, yell. and blk. 75 55

141. Lakhe Dance.

1976. Nepalese Dances. Multicoloured.
335. 10 p. Type **141** 5 5
336. 15 p. Maruni dance .. 5 5
337. 30 p. Jhangad dance .. 5 5
338. 1 r. Sebru dance 20 15

142. Nepalese Lily. **143.** King Birendra.

1976. Flowers. Multicoloured.
339. 30 p. Type **142** 10 5
340. 30 p. "Meconopsis grandis" 10 5
341. 30 p. "Cardiocrinum giganteum" (horiz.) .. 10 5
342. 30 p. "Megacodon stylophorus" (horiz.) .. 10 5

1976. King Birendra's 32nd Birthday.
343. **143.** 5 p. green 5 5
344. 30 p. lake, brn & yell. 5 5

144. Liberty Bell.

1976. Bicent. of American Revolution.
345. **144.** 10 r. multicoloured .. 1·40 1·25

145. Kaji Amarsingh Thapa.

1977. Thapa (19th-century warrior). Comm.
346. 145. 10 p. brn. & light brn. 5 5

146. Terracotta Figurine and Kapilavastu.

1977. Tourism.
347. 146. 30 p. violet 5 5
348. – 5 r. brown and green .. 55 45
DESIGN: 5 r. Ashokan pillar, Lumbini.

147. Great Indian Hornbill. 148. Tukuche Himal and Police Flag.

1977. Birds. Multicoloured.
349. 5 p. Type 147 .. .. 30 10
350. 15 p. Cheer pheasant (horiz.) 30 10
351. 1 r. Green magpie (horiz.) 1·10 30
352. 2 r. 30 Spiny babbler .. 2·25 65

1977. 1st Anniv. of Ascent of Tukuche Himal.
353. 148. 1 r. 25 multicoloured 15 12

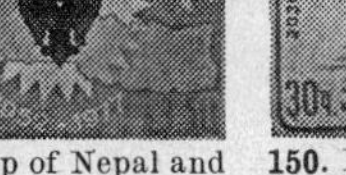

149. Map of Nepal and Scout Emblem. 150. Dhanwantari, the Health-giver.

1977. 25th Anniv. of Scouting in Nepal.
354. 149. 3 r. 50 multicoloured .. 35 30

1977. Dhanwantari Commemoration.
355. 150. 30 p. green 8 5

151. Map of Nepal and Flags. 152. King Birendra.

1977. Colombo Plan. 26th Consultative Committee Meeting, Katmandu.
356. 151. 1 r. multicoloured .. 15 12

1977. King Birendra's 33rd Birthday.
357. 152. 5 p. brown 5 5
358. 1 r. brown 15 12

153. General Post Office, Katmandu, and Seal.

1978. Cent. of Nepalese Post Office.
359. 153. 25 p. brown and black 5 5
360. – 75 p. ochre and black 12 10
DESIGN: 75 p. General Post Office, Katmandu, and early postmark.

154. South-west Face of Mount Everest.

1978. 25th Anniv. of Ascent of Mount Everest.
361. 154. 2 r. 30 slate and brown 30 35
362. – 4 r. blue and green .. 60 55
DESIGN: 4 r. South face of Mt. Everest.

155. Sun, Ankh and Landscape.

1978. World Environment Day.
363. 155. 1 r. orange and green .. 12 10

156. Queen Mother Ratna. 157. Rapids, Tripsuli River.

1978. Queen Mother's 50th Birthday.
364. 156. 2 r. 30 olive 35 25

1978. Tourism. Multicoloured.
365. 10 p. Type 157 .. .. 5 5
366. 50 p. Window, Nara Devi, Katmandu 5 5
367. 1 r. Mahakali dance (vert.) 15 10

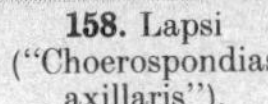

158. Lapsi ("Choerospondias axillaris"). 159. Lamp and U.N. Emblem.

1978. Fruits. Multicoloured.
368. 5 p. Type 158 .. .. 5 5
369. 1 r. Katus ("Castanopsis indica") (vert.) .. 15 12
370. 1 r. 25 Rudrakshya ("Elaeocarpus sphaericus") 20 15

1978. 30th Anniv. of Human Rights Declaration.
371. 159. 25 p. red and brown .. 5 5
372. 1 r. red and blue .. 15 10

160. "Flyer" and Jet. 161. King Birendra.

1978. Air. 75th Anniv. of First Powered Flight.
373. 160. 2 r. 30 blue and brown 45 20

1978. King Birendra's 34th Birthday.
374. 161. 30 p. blue and brown 5 5
375. 2 r. brown and violet 25 20

162. Red Machchhindranath and Kamroop and Patan Temples.

1979. Red Machchhindranath (guardian deity) Festival.
376. 162. 75 p. brown and green 15 10

163. "Buddha's Birth" (carving, Maya Devi Temple). 164. Planting a Sapling.

1979. Lumbini Year.
377. 163. 1 r. yellow and brown 15 10

1979. Tree Planting Festival.
378. 164. 2 r. 30 multicoloured 30 20

165. Chariot of Red Machchhindranath. 166. Nepalese Scouts and Guides.

1979. Bhoto Jatra (Vest Show Festival).
379. 165. 1 r. 25 multicoloured 20 15

1979. International Year of the Child.
380. 166. 1 r. yellow-brown .. 15 10

167. Mount Pabil. 168. Great Grey Shrike.

1979. Tourism.
381. 167. 30 p. green 5 5
382. – 50 p. red and blue .. 8 5
383. – 1 r. 25 multicoloured 20 15
DESIGNS: 50 p. Yajnashala, Swargadwari 1 r. 25, Shiva-Parbati (wood carving, Gaddi Baithak Temple).

1979. International World Pheasant Association Symposium, Katmandu. Multicoloured.
384. 10 p. Type 168 (postage) .. 15 10
385. 10 r. Fire-tailed sunbird .. 5·75 3·00
386. 3 r. 50 Himalayan monal pheasant (horiz.) (air) .. 2·10 1·10

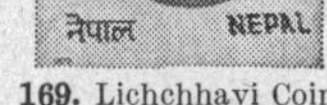

169. Lichchhavi Coin (obverse). 170. King Birendra.

1979. Coins.
387. 169. 5 p. pink and brown .. 5 5
388. – 5 p. pink and brown .. 5 5
389. – 15 p. blue and deep blue 5 5
390. – 15 p. blue and deep blue 15 12
391. – 1 r. blue and grey .. 15 12
392. – 1 r. blue and grey .. 45 30
DESIGNS: No. 388, Lichchhavi coin (reverse). No. 389, Malla coin (obverse). No. 390, Malla coin (reverse). No. 391, Prithvi Narayan Shah coin (obverse). No. 392, Prithvi Narayan Shah coin (reverse).

1979. King Birendra's 35th Birthday. Mult
393. 25 p. Type 170 .. .. 5 5
394. 2 r. 30 Reservoir 30 25

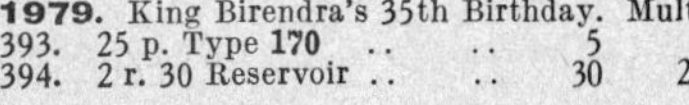

171. Samyak Pooja Festival. 172. Sacred Basil ("Ocimum sanctum").

1980. Samyak Pooja.
395. 171. 30 p. grey, brn. & mar. 5 5

1980. Nepalese Herbs. Multicoloured.
396. 5 p. Type 172 .. .. 5 5
397. 30 p. Valerian ("Valeriana jatamansi jones") .. 5 5
398. 1 r. Nepalese pepper ("Zanthoxylum armatum") 12 8
399. 2 r. 30 Himalayan rhubarb ("Rheum emodi wall") 25 15

173. Gyandil Das. 174. Everlasting Flame and Temple, Shirsasthan.

1980. Nepalese Writers.
400. 173. 5 p. lilac and ochre .. 5 5
401. – 30 p. maroon & brown 5 5
402. – 1 r. olive and blue .. 12 8
403. – 2 r. 30 blue and green 25 15
DESIGNS: 30 p. Siddhidas Amatya. 1 r. Pahalman Singh Swanr. 2 r. 30, Jay Prithvi Bahadur Singh.

1980. Tourism. Multicoloured.
404. 10 p. Type 174 .. .. 5 5
405. 1 r. Godavari Pond .. 15 8
406. 5 r. Mount Dhaulagiri .. 65 45

175. Bhairab Dancer. 176. King Birendra.

1980. World Tourism Conference, Manila.
407. 175. 25 r. multicoloured .. 3·25 2·50

1980. King Birendra's 36th Birthday.
408. 176. 1 r. multicoloured .. 15 8

177. I.Y.D.P. Emblem and Nepalese Flag.

1981. International Year of Disabled Persons.
409. 177. 5 r. multicoloured .. 85 50

178. Nepal Rastra Bank. 179. One Anna Stamp of 1881.

1981. 25th Anniv. of Nepal Rastra Bank.
410. 178. 1 r. 75 multicoloured 30 20

1981. Nepalese Postage Stamp Centenary.
411. 179. 10 p. blue, brn. and blk 8 5
412. – 40 p. pur., brn. and blk 8 5
413. – 3 r. 40 grn, brn. and blk 60 40
DESIGNS: 40p. 2 anna stamp of 1881. 3r. 40, 4a stamp of 1881.

180. Nepalese Flag and Association Emblem. **181.** Hand holding Stamp.

1981. International Hotel Association, Katmandu. 70th Council Meeting.
415. **180.** 1 r. 75 multicoloured 30 15

1981. "Nepal 81" Stamp Exhibition, Katmandu.
416. **181.** 40 p. multicoloured .. 10 8

182. King Birendra. **183.** Image of Hrishikesh, Ridi.

1981. King Birendra's 37th Birthday.
417. **182.** 1 r. multicoloured .. 15 10

1981. Tourism. Multicoloured.
418. 5 p. Type **183** 5 5
419. 25 p. Tripura Sundari Temple, Baitadi .. 5 5
420. 2 r. Mt Langtang Lirung .. 30 20

184. Academy Building. **185.** Balakrishna Sama.

1982. 25th Anniv. of Royal Nepal Academy.
421. **184.** 40 p. multicoloured .. 10 8

1982. 1st Death Anniv. of Balakrishna Sama (writer).
422. **185.** 1 r. multicoloured .. 20 10

186. "Intelsat V" and Dish Aerial. **187.** Mount Nuptse.

1982. Sagarmatha Satellite Earth Station, Balambu.
423. **186.** 5 r. multicoloured .. 85 50

1982. 50th Anniv. of Union of International Alpinist Associations. Multicoloured.
424. 25 p. Type **187** 5 5
425. 2 r. Mount Lhotse (31 × 31 mm.) 40 25
426. 3 r. Mount Everest (39 × 31 mm.) 55 40
Nos. 424/6 were issued together, se-tenant, forming a composite design.

188. Games Emblem and Weights. **189.** Indra Sarobar Lake.

1982. 9th Asian Games, New Delhi.
427. **188.** 3 r. 40 multicoloured .. 60 40

1982. Kulekhani Hydro-electric Project.
428. **189.** 2 r. multicoloured .. 35 25

190. King Birendra. **191.** N.I.D.C. Emblem.

1982. King Birendra's 38th Birthday.
429. **190.** 5 p. multicoloured .. 10 8

1983. 25th Anniv. of Nepal Industrial Development Corporation.
430. **191.** 50 p. multicoloured .. 12 8

192. Airliner over Himalayas.

1983. 25th Anniv. of Royal Nepal Airlines.
431. **192.** 1 r. multicoloured .. 40 15

193. W.C.Y. Emblem and Nepalese Flag. **194.** Sarangi.

1983. World Communications Year.
432. **193.** 10 p. multicoloured .. 8 5

1983. Musical Instruments. Multicoloured.
433. 5 p. Type **194** 5 5
434. 10 p. Kwota (drum) .. 5 5
435. 50 p. Narashinga (horn) .. 8 5
436. 1 r. Murchunga 20 10

195. Chakrapani Chalise. **196.** King Birendra and Doves.

1983. Birth Bicentenary of Chakrapani Chalise (poet).
437. **195.** 4 r. 50 multicoloured .. 75 40

1983. King Birendra's 39th Birthday.
438. **196.** 5 r. multicoloured .. 85 50

197. Barahkshetra Temple and Image of Barah.

1983. Tourism. Multicoloured.
439. 1 r. Type **197** 20 10
440. 2 r. 20 Temple, Triveni .. 35 20
441. 6 r. Mount Cho-oyu .. 1·00 70

198. Auditing Accounts. **199.** Antenna and Emblem.

1984. 25th Anniv. of Auditor General.
442. **198.** 25 p. multicoloured .. 8 5

1984. 20th Anniv. of Asia-Pacific Broadcasting Union.
443. **199.** 5 r. multicoloured .. 85 50

200. University Emblem. **201.** Boxing.

1984. 25th Anniv. of Tribhuvan University.
444. **200.** 50 p. multicoloured .. 12 8

1984. Olympic Games, Los Angeles.
445. **201.** 10 r. multicoloured .. 1·40 90

202. Family and Emblem. **203.** National Flag and Emblem.

1984. 25th Anniv. of Nepal Family Planning Association.
446. **202.** 1 r. multicoloured .. 20 10

1984. Social Service Day.
447. **203.** 5 p. multicoloured .. 5 5

204. Gharial. **205.** "Vishnu as Giant" (stone carving).

1984. Wildlife. Multicoloured.
448. 10 p. Type **204** 25 25
449. 25 p. Snow leopard .. 25 25
450. 50 p. Blackbuck 35 35

1984. Tourism. Multicoloured.
451. 10 p. Type **205** 5 5
452. 1 r. Temple of Chhinna Masta Bhagavati and sculpture (horiz.) .. 20 10
453. 5 r. Mt. Api 85 50

206. King Birendra.

1984. King Birendra's 40th Birthday.
454. **206.** 1 r. multicoloured .. 20 10

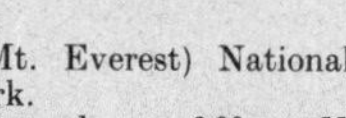

207. Animals and Mountains. **208.** Shiva.

1985. Sagarmatha (Mt. Everest) National Park.
455. **207.** 10 r. multicoloured .. 2·00 55

1985. Traditional Paintings. Details of cover of "Siva Dharma Purana". Multicoloured.
456. 50 p. Type **208** 5 5
457. 50 p. Multi-headed Shiva talking to woman .. 5 5
458. 50 p. Brahma and Vishnu making offering (15 × 22 mm.) 5 5
459. 50 p. Shiva (different) .. 5 5
460. 50 p. Shiva talking to woman 5 5
Nos. 456/60 were printed together, se-tenant, forming a composite design.

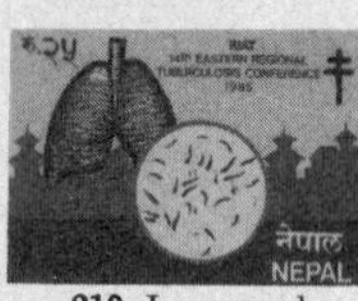

209. U.N. Flag. **210.** Lungs and Bacilli.

1985. 40th Anniv. of U.N.O.
461. **209.** 5 r. multicoloured .. 35 20

1985. 14th Eastern Regional Tuberculosis Conference.
462. **210.** 25 r. multicoloured .. 1·75 1·10

211. Flags of Member Countries.

1985. 1st South Asian Regional Co-operation Summit.
463. **211.** 5 r. multicoloured .. 35 20

212. Jaleshwar Temple. **213.** I.Y.Y. Emblem.

1985. Tourism. Multicoloured.
464. 10 p. Type **212** 5 5
465. 1 r. Temple of Goddess Shaileshwari 8 5
466. 2 r. Phoksundo Lake .. 12 8

1985. International Youth Year.
467. **213.** 1 r. multicoloured .. 8 5

214. King Birendra. **215.** Devi Ghat Hydro-electric Project.

1985. King Birendra's 41st Birthday.
468. **214.** 50 p. multicoloured .. 5 5

1985.
469. **215.** 2 r. multicoloured .. 12 8

216. Emblem. **217.** Royal Crown.

1986. 25th Anniv. of Panchayat System (partyless government).
470. **216.** 4 r. multicoloured .. 25 15

1986.
471. – 5 p. brown and deep brown 5 5
472. – 10 p. blue 5 5
474. – 50 p. blue 5 5
476. **217.** 1 r. brown and light brown 8 5

DESIGNS: 5, 50 p. Pashupati Temple. 10 r. Mayadevi Temple of Lumbini (Buddha's birthplace).

218. Pharping Hydro-electric Station.

1986. 75th Anniv. of Pharping Hydro-electric Power Station.
480. **218.** 15 p. multicoloured .. 5 5

219. Emblem and Map.

1986. 25th Anniv. of Asian Productivity Organization.
481. **219.** 1 r. multicoloured .. 8 5

220. Mt. Pumori, Himalayas. **221.** King Birendra.

1986. Tourism. Multicoloured.
482. 60 p. Budhanilkantha (statue), Katmandu Valley (38 × 22 mm.) .. 5 5
483. 8 r. Type **220** 50 35

1986. King Birendra's 42nd Birthday.
484. **221.** 1 r. multicoloured .. 8 5

223. Flag and Emblem.

1986. International Peace Year.
485. **222.** 10 r. multicoloured .. 60 40

1987. 10th Anniv. of National Social Service Co-ordination Council.
486. **223.** 1 r. multicoloured .. 8 5

224. Emblem and Forest.

1987. 1st Nepal Scout Jamboree, Katmandu.
487. **224.** 1 r. brn., orge. & bl. 8 5

225. Ashokan Pillar and Maya Devi.

1987. Lumbini, Buddha's Birthplace.
488. **225.** 4 r. multicoloured .. 20 12

226. Emblem. **227.** Emblem.

1987. 3rd South Asian Association for Regional Co-operation Summit, Katmandu.
489. **226.** 60 p. gold and red .. 5 5

1987. 25th Anniv. of Rastriya Samachar Samiti (news service).
490. **227.** 4 r. pur., bl. & red .. 20 12

228. Kashthamandap, Katmandu. **229.** Gyawali.

1987.
491. **228.** 25 p. multicoloured .. 5 5

1987. 89th Birth Anniv. of Surya Bikram Gyawali.
492. **229.** 60 p. multicoloured .. 5 5

230. Emblem. **231.** King Birendra.

1987. International Year of Shelter for the Homeless.
493. **230.** 5 r. multicoloured .. 30 20

1987. King Birendra's 43rd Birthday.
494. **231.** 25 p. multicoloured .. 5 5

232. Mt. Kanjiroba.

1987.
495. **232.** 10 r. multicoloured .. 55 40

233. Crown Prince Dipendra.

1988. Crown Prince Dipendra's 17th Birthday.
496. **233.** 1 r. multicoloured .. 5 5

234. Baby in Incubator.

1988. 25th Anniv. of Kanti Children's Hospital.
497. **234.** 60 p. multicoloured .. 5 5

235. Swamp Deer. **236.** Laxmi, Goddess of Wealth.

1988. 12th Anniv. of Royal Shukla Phanta Wildlife Reserve.
498. **235.** 60 p. multicoloured .. 5 5

1988. 50th Anniv. of Nepal Bank Ltd.
499. **136.** 2 r. multicoloured .. 10 5

237 Queen Mother **238** Hands protecting Blood Droplet

1988. 60th Birthday of Queen Mother.
500 **237** 5 r. multicoloured .. 25 15

1988. 25th Anniv of Nepal Red Cross Society.
501 **238** 1 r. red and brown .. 10 5

239 Temple and Statue

1988. Temple of Goddess Bindhyabasini, Pokhara.
502 **239** 15 p. multicoloured .. 5 5

240 King Birendra **241** Temple

1988. King Birendra's 44th Birthday.
503 **240** 4 r. multicoloured .. 20 10

1989. Pashupati Area Development Trust.
504 **241** 1 r. multicoloured .. 10 5

242 Emblem **243** S.A.A.R.C. Emblem

1989. 10th Anniv of Asia–Pacific Tele-community.
505 **242** 4 r. green, black & vio 25 15

1989. South Asian Association for Regional Co-operation Year against Drug Abuse and Trafficking.
506 **243** 60 p. multicoloured .. 5 5

INDEX

Countries can be quickly located by referring to the index at the end of this volume.

244 King Birendra **245** Child Survival Measures

1989. King Birendra's 45th Birthday.
507 **244** 2 r. multicoloured .. 12 5

1989. Child Survival Campaign.
508 **245** 1 r. multicoloured .. 5 5

246 Lake Rara **247** Mt. Amadablam

1989. Rara National Park.
509 **246** 4 r. multicoloured .. 20 10

1989.
510 **247** 5 r. multicoloured .. 25 15

248 Crown Prince Dipendra **249** Temple of Manakamana, Gorkha

1989. Crown Prince Dipendra's Coming-of-Age.
511 **248** 1 r. multicoloured .. 5 5

1990.
512 **249** 60 p. black and blue .. 5 5

250 Emblem and Children **251** Emblem

1990. 25th Anniv of Nepal Children's Organization.
513 **250** 1 r. multicoloured .. 5 5

1990. Centenary of Bir Hospital.
514 **251** 60 p. red, blue & yellow 5 5

252 Emblem **253** Goddess and Bageshwori Temple, Nepalgunj

1990. 20th Anniv of Asian-Pacific Postal Training Centre, Bangkok.
515 **252** 4 r. multicoloured .. 15 8

1990. Tourism. Multicoloured.
516 1 r. Type **253** 5 5
517 5 r. Mt. Saipal (36 × 27 mm) 20 10

254 Leisure Activities

1990. South Asian Association for Regional Co-operation Girls' Year.
518 **254** 4 r. 60 multicoloured .. 15 8

255 King Birendra — 256 Koirala

1990. King Birendra's 46th Birthday.
519 **255** 2 r. multicoloured .. 8 5

1990. 76th Birth Anniv of Bisweswar Prasad Koirala (Prime Minister, 1959–60).
520 **256** 60 p. black, orge & red 5 5

257 Indian Rhinoceros and Lake — 258 Flower and Crowd

1991. Royal Chitwan National Park.
521 **257** 4 r. multicoloured .. 15 8

1991. 1st Anniv of Abrogation of Ban on Political Parties.
522 **258** 1 r. multicoloured .. 5 5

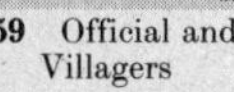

259 Official and Villagers — 260 Federation and Jubilee Emblems

1991. National Population Census.
523 **259** 60 p. multicoloured .. 5 5

1991. 25th Anniv of Federation of Nepalese Chambers of Commerce and Industry.
524 **260** 3 r. multicoloured .. 8 5

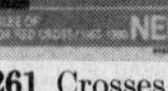

261 Crosses — 262 Delegates

1991. 25th Anniv (1990) of Nepal Junior Red Cross.
525 **261** 60 p. red and grey .. 5 5

1991. 1st Session of Revived Parliament.
526 **262** 1 r. multicoloured .. 5 5

263 King Birendra making Speech — 264 Rama and Janaki (statues) and Vivaha Mandap

1991. Constitution Day.
527 **263** 50 p. multicoloured .. 5 5

1991. 5th Anniv of Rebuilt Vivaha Mandap Pavilion, Janaki Temple.
528 **264** 1 r. multicoloured .. 5 5

265 Mt. Kumbhakarna — 266 King Birendra

1991.
529 **265** 4 r. 60 multicoloured .. 12 8

1991. King Birendra's 47th Birthday.
530 **266** 8 r. multicoloured .. 20 12

267 Houses — 268 Glass magnifying Society Emblem

1991. South Asian Association for Regional Co-operation Year of Shelter.
531 **267** 9 r. multicoloured .. 25 15

1992. 25th Anniv (1991) of Nepal Philatelic Society.
532 **268** 4 r. multicoloured .. 10 5

269 Rainbow over River and Trees

1992. Environmental Protection.
533 **269** 60 p. multicoloured .. 5 5

270 Nutrition, Education and Health Care

1992. Rights of the Child.
534 **270** 1 r. multicoloured .. 5 5

271 Thakurdwara Temple, Bardiya — 272 Bank Emblem

1992. Temples. Multicoloured.
535 75 p. Type **271** (postage) .. 5 5
536 1 r. Namo Buddha Temple, Kavre 5 5
537 2 r. Narijhowa Temple, Mustang 5 5
538 11 r. Dantakali Temple, Bijayapur (air) .. 35 20

1992. 25th Anniv of Agricultural Development Bank.
539 **272** 40 p. brown and green 5 5

273 Pin-tailed Green Pigeon

1992. Birds. Multicoloured.
540 1 r. Type **273** 5 5
541 3 r. Bohemian waxwing .. 10 5
542 25 r. Rufous-tailed desert lark 75 45

274 King Birendra exchanging Swords with Goddess Sree Bhadrakali — 275 Pandit Kulchandra Gautam

1992. King Birendra's 48th Birthday.
543 **274** 7 r. multicoloured .. 20 10

1992. Poets. Multicoloured, frame colour given in brackets.
544 1 r. Type **275** 5 5
545 1 r. Chittadhar Hridaya (drab) 5 5
546 1 r. Vidyapati (stone) .. 5 5
547 1 r. Teongsi Sirijunga (grey) 5 5

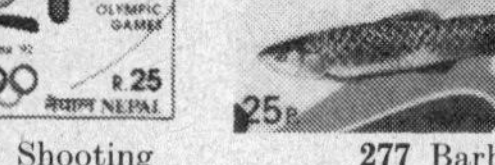

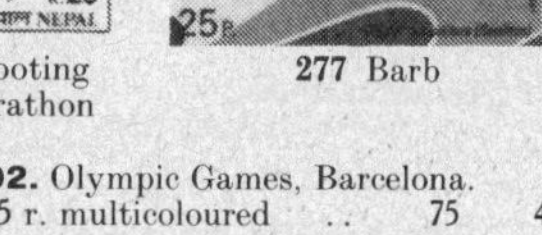

276 Shooting and Marathon — 277 Barb

1992. Olympic Games, Barcelona.
548 **276** 25 r. multicoloured .. 75 45

1993. Fishes. Multicoloured.
549 25 p. Type **277** 5 5
550 1 r. Marinka 5 5
551 5 r. Indian eel 15 5
552 10 r. "Psilorhynchus pseudecheneis" .. 30 15

278 Antibodies attacking Globe — 279 Tanka Prasad Acharya (Prime Minister, 1956–57)

1993. World AIDS Day.
554 **278** 1 r. multicoloured .. 5 5

1993. Death Anniversaries. Multicoloured.
555 25 p. Type **279** (1st anniv) 5 5
556 1 r. Sungdare Sherpa (mountaineer) (4th anniv) 5 5
557 7 r. Siddhi Charan Shrestha (poet) (1st anniv) 20 10
558 15 r. Falgunanda (religious leader) (44th anniv) .. 45 25

280 Bagh Bairab Temple, Kirtipur

1993. Holy Places. Multicoloured.
559 1 r. 50 Halesi Mahadev cave (hiding place of Shiva), Khotang .. 5 5
560 5 r. Devghat (gods' bathing place), Tanahun .. 15 5
561 8 r. Type **280** 25 15

281 Tushahity Fountain, Sundari Chowk, Patan — 282 King Birendra

1993. Tourism. Multicoloured.
562 5 r. Type **281** 5 5
563 8 r. White-water rafting .. 25 15

1993. King Birendra's 49th Birthday.
564 **282** 10 r. multicoloured .. 30 15

OFFICIAL STAMPS

O 25. Nepalese Arms and Soldiers. — काज सरकारी (O 28.)

1960. (a) Size 30 × 18 mm.
O 135. O **25.** 2 p. brown 8 5
O 136 4 p. green 10 8
O 137. 6 p. red 12 8
O 138. 8 p. violet 15 12
O 139. 12 p. orange 20 12

(b) Size 38 × 27 mm.
O 140. O **25.** 16 p. brown .. 30 35
O 141. 24 p. red 50 30
O 142. 32 p. purple .. 75 25
O 143. 50 p. blue .. .. 1·25 1·10
O 144. 1 r. red .. .. 2·50 2·00
O 145. 2 r. orange .. .. 5·00 3·75

1960. Optd. as Type O **28.**
O 146. **27.** 1 r. purple 40

1961. Optd with Type O 28.
O 148. **35.** 1 p. red .. .. 5 1·00
O 149. 2 p. blue .. .. 5 2·00
O 150. 5 p. brown .. .. 5 4·50

NETHERLANDS Pt. 4

A kingdom in the N.W. of Europe on the North Sea.

100 cents = 1 gulden (florin).

King William III.
1. 3. 4.

1852. Imperf.

1. 1. 5 c. blue .. .. .. £425 23·00
2. 10 c. red .. .. .. £600 32·00
3b. 15 c. orange .. .. £700 75·00

1864. Perf.

8. 3. 5 c. blue .. .. .. £300 12·00
9. 10 c. red .. .. .. £425 6·50
10. 15 c. orange .. .. £1200 60·00

1867.

47 4 5 c. blue .. .. .. 80·00 1·00
30 10 c. red .. .. .. £130 1·40
46 15 c. brown .. .. £600 26·00
50 20 c. green .. .. £550 20·00
15 25 c. purple .. .. £2250 80·00
16 50 c. gold £2500 £130

5. 6.

1869.

58. 5. ½ c. brown .. .. 23·00 2·50
53. 1 c. black .. .. £200 55·00
59. 1 c. green .. .. 11·00 1·00
60. 1½ c. red .. .. £140 80·00
61. 2 c. yellow .. .. 50·00 8·50
62. 2½ c. mauve .. .. £500 45·00

1872.

91 6 5 c. blue .. .. .. 8·00 15
92 7½ c. brown .. .. 35·00 17·00
112 10 c. red .. .. .. 50·00 65
113 12½ c. grey .. .. 60·00 1·25
95 15 c. brown .. .. £350 3·75
96 20 c. green .. .. £450 3·75
97 22½ c. green .. .. 65·00 38·00
98 25 c. lilac .. .. £600 2·50
100 50 c. bistre .. .. £700 8·00
101 1 g. violet .. .. £500 22·00
74 – 2 g. 50 blue and red .. £900 85·00

No. 74 is similar to Type **6** but larger and with value and country scrolls transposed.

8. 9. Queen Wilhelmina.

1876.

138d. 8. ½ c. red .. .. 2·75 10
140. 1 c. green .. .. 2·25 10
143. 2 c. yellow .. .. 35·00 2·50
145. 2½ c. mauve .. .. 14·00 15

1891.

147a 9 3 c. orange .. .. 6·00 1·10
148a 5 c. blue .. .. 4·00 10
149b 7½ c. brown .. .. 16·00 5·00
150b 10 c. red .. .. 23·00 55
151b 12½ c. grey .. .. 22·00 65
152a 15 c. brown .. .. 55·00 4·00
153b 20 c. green .. .. 55·00 2·00
154a 22½ c. green .. .. 32·00 11·00
155 25 c. mauve .. .. £110 3·00
156a 50 c. bistre .. .. £500 15·00
159 – 50 c. brown and green 70·00 7·50
157 9 1 g. violet .. .. £550 55·00
160 – 1 g. green and brown .. £180 21·00
161 – 2 g. 50 blue and red .. £425 £120
165 – 5 g. red and green .. £750 £350

Nos. 159, 160, 161 and 165 are as Type **9** but larger and with value and country scrolls transposed.

11. 12. 13.

1898. Nos. 174 and 176 also exist imperf.

167 12 ½ c. lilac 40 15
168 1 c. red .. .. 1·00 10
226 1½ c. blue .. .. 3·25 25
170 2 c. brown .. .. 3·75 10
171 2½ c. green .. .. 3·25 10
172 13 3 c. orange .. .. 14·00 2·50
173 3 c. green .. .. 1·25 10
227 4 c. purple .. .. 1·50 70
228 4½ c. mauve .. .. 3·75 4·00
174 5 c. red .. .. 1·50 10
187a 5 c. red and blue .. 5·00 80
175 7½ c. brown 60 10
176 10 c. grey .. .. 7·00 10
177 12½ c. blue .. .. 3·00 15
178 15 c. brown .. .. 80·00 3·25
179 15 c. red and blue .. 6·00 10
180 17½ c. mauve .. .. 50·00 12·00
181 17½ c. brown and blue 16·00 85
182 20 c. green £100 65
183 20 c. grey and green .. 10·00 30
184 22½ c. green and brown 9·50 40
185 25 c. blue and pink .. 9·50 10
230 30 c. purple and mauve 23·00 20
231 40 c. orange and green 38·00 75
186 50 c. red and green .. 75·00 90
232 50 c. violet and grey .. 70·00 60
233 60 c. green and olive .. 38·00 90
202 11 1 g. green .. .. 55·00 30
203 2½ g. lilac .. .. £100 2·50
201 5 g. red .. .. £225 4·25
198 10 g. red £700 £600

14.

1906. Society for the Prevention of Tuberculosis.

208 14 1 c. (+1 c.) red .. 2·50 2·50
209 3 c. (+3 c.) green .. 25·00 24·00
210 5 c. (+5 c.) violet .. 25·00 7·50

15. Admiral M. A. de Ruyter. 16. William I.

1907. Birth Tercent. of Admiral de Ruyter.

211. 15. ½ c. blue 70 80
212. 1 c. red .. .. .. 2·50 2·00
213. 2½ c. red .. .. 7·50 2·00

1913. Independence Centenary.

214. 16. 2½ c. green on green .. 60 50
215. – 3 c. yellow on cream .. 90 90
216. – 5 c. red on buff 90 40
217. – 10 c. grey .. .. 3·50 1·75
218. 16. 12½ c. blue on blue .. 2·50 1·50
219. – 20 c. brown .. .. 12·00 9·00
220. – 25 c. blue .. .. 13·00 7·50
221. – 50 c. green .. .. 32·00 30·00
222. 16. 1 g. red .. .. .. 45·00 15·00
223. – 2½ g. lilac .. .. £120 50·00
224. – 5 g. yellow on cream .. £250 38·00
225. – 10 g. orange £700 £700

DESIGNS: 3 c., 20 c., 2½ g. William II. 5 c., 25 c., 5 g. William III. 10 c., 50 c., 10 g. Queen Wilhelmina.

1919. Surch **Veertig Cent** (40 c.) or **Zestig Cent** (60 c.).

234 13 40 c. on 30 c. pur & mve 25·00 2·50
235 60 c. on 30 c. pur & mve 24·00 3·50

1920. Surch in figures.

238 13 4 c. on 4½ c. mauve .. 4·00 1·40
236 11 2.50 on 10 g. red .. £150 £120
237 – 2.50 on 10 g. red (225) .. £140 90·00

23. 24.

1921. Air.

239. 23. 10 c. red .. .. 1·75 1·25
240. 15 c. green .. .. 6·00 2·00
241. 60 c. blue .. .. 16·00 20

1921.

242. 24. 5 c. green .. .. 10·00 15
243. 12½ c. red .. .. 15·00 1·75
244. 20 c. blue .. .. 23·00 15

25. Lion in Dutch Garden and Orange Tree (emblematical of Netherlands). 26. 27.

1923.

248. 25. 1 c. violet 50 60
249. 2 c. orange .. .. 5·00 10
250. 26. 2½ c. green .. .. 1·75 70
251 27. 4 c. blue .. .. 1·25 45

1923. Surch.

252. 12. 2 c. on 1 c. red .. 45 20
253. 2 c. on 1½ c. blue .. 45 20
254. 13. 10 c. on 3 c. green .. 4·50 15
255. 10 c. on 5 c. red .. 8·50 55
256. 10 c. on 12½ c. blue .. 7·50 55
257a. 10 c. on 17½ c. brn. & bl. 3·00 3·50
258a. 10 c. on 22½ c. ol. & brn. 3·00 3·50

30. 31.

1923. 25th Anniv. of Queen's Accession.

259a. 31. 2 c. green 15 10
260a. 30. 5 c. green 25 10
261a. 31. 7½ c. red 40 10
262b. 10 c. red 30 10
263. 20 c. blue .. .. 3·50 55
264. 25 c. yellow .. .. 6·00 90
265b. 35 c. orange .. .. 5·50 2·50
266a. 50 c. black .. .. 16·00 20
267. 30. 1 g. red .. .. 30·00 5·00
268. 2½ g. black £225 £200
269. 5 g. blue £200 £190

1923. Surch **DIENST ZEGEL PORTEN AAN TEEKEN RECHT** and value.

270 13 10 c. on 3 c. green .. 90 1·00
271 1 g. on 17½ c. brown & bl 65·00 15·00

DESIGN: 10 c. Two women.

33.

1923. Culture Fund.

272. 33. 2 c.+5 c. blue on pink .. 17·00 17·00
273. – 10 c.+5 c. red on pink .. 17·00 17·00

35. Carrier Pigeon. 36. Queen Wilhelmina.

1924.

330 35 ½c. grey 40 25
423 1 c. red 10 10
332 1½ c. mauve 20 10
424a 1½ c. grey 10 10
425 2 c. orange 10 10
426a 2½ c. green 70 20
427 3 c. green 10 10
427a 4 c. blue 10 10
428 36 5 c. green 15 10
429 6 c. brown 15 10
279 7½ c. yellow 40 10
313 7½ c. violet .. .. 2·75 10
314 7½ c. red 20 10
279c 9 c. red and black .. 1·75 1·60
281 10 c. red .. .. 1·40 10
317 10 c. blue .. .. 2·00 10
282 12½ c. red .. .. 1·75 35
431 12½ c. blue 30 10
320 15 c. blue .. .. 7·00 15
432 15 c. yellow 80 10
433 20 c. blue .. .. 7·00 10
434 21 c. brown .. .. 24·00 90
323 22½ c. brown .. .. 7·00 2·50
434a 22½ c. orange .. .. 16·00 18·00
435 25 c. green .. .. 4·75 10
346 27½ c. grey .. .. 3·25 1·50
437 30 c. violet .. .. 6·00 10
286c 35 c. brown .. .. 32·00 6·50
437a 40 c. brown .. .. 12·00 15
329 50 c. green .. .. 5·00 15
289 60 c. violet .. .. 30·00 85
437c 60 c. black .. .. 27·00 90
301 1 g. blue (23 × 29 mm) 8·00 30
302 2½ g. red (23 × 29 mm) 85·00 4·00
303 5 g. black (23 × 29 mm) £170 2·50

For further stamps in Type **35**, see Nos. 546/57.

1924. Int. Philatelic Exn., The Hague.

290. 36. 10 c. green .. .. 40·00 45·00
291. 15 c. black .. .. 45·00 55·00
292. 35 c. red .. .. 40·00 45·00

37. 38. 39.

1924. Dutch Lifeboat Centenary.

293. 37. 2 c. brown .. .. 2·25 2·50
294. 38. 10 c. brown on yellow 7·00 2·00

1924. Child Welfare.

295. 39. 2 c.+2 c. green .. 90 1·60
296. 7½ c.+3½ c. brown .. 5·50 7·00
297. 10 c.+2½ c. red .. 5·50 1·50

40. Arms of South Holland. 46. Queen Wilhelmina. 47. Red Cross Allegory.

1925. Child Welfare. Arms as T **40**.

298. – 2 c.+2 c. grn. & yell... 80 80
299. – 7½ c.+3½ c. vio. & blue 4·00 4·00
300. 40. 10 c.+2½ c. red & yell. 3·25 40

ARMS: 2 c. North Brabant. 7½ c. Gelderland.

See also Nos. 350/3 and 359/62.

1926. Child Welfare. Arms as T **40**.

350. 2 c.+2 c. red and silver .. 40 40
351. 5 c.+3 c. green and blue .. 1·50 1·25
352. 10 c.+3 c. red and green .. 2·25 20
353. 15 c.+3 c. yellow & blue.. 6·00 6·00

ARMS: 2 c. Utrecht. 5 c. Zeeland. 10 c. North Holland. 15 c. Friesland.

1927. 60th Anniv. of Dutch Red Cross Society.

354a. 46. 2 c.+2 c. red .. .. 1·75 2·25
355. – 3 c.+2 c. green .. 6·00 8·50
356. – 5 c.+3 c. blue .. 70 55
357a. – 7½ c.+3½ c. blue .. 5·00 1·60
358. 47. 15 c.+5 c. red & blue 12·00 12·00

PORTRAITS: 2 c. King William III. 3 c. Queen Emma. 5 c. Henry, Prince Consort.

1927. Child Welfare. Arms as T **40**.

359. 2 c.+2 c. red and lilac .. 30 35
360. 5 c.+3 c. green & yellow.. 1·50 1·40
361. 7½ c.+3½ c. red and black 3·50 30
362. 15 c.+3 c. blue & brown.. 5·50 5·00

ARMS: 2 c. Drente. 5 c. Groningen. 7½ c. Limburg. 15 c. Overyssel.

48. Sculler. 49. Footballer.

1928. Olympic Games, Amsterdam.

363. 48. 1½ c.+1 c. green .. 1·25 70
364. – 2 c.+1 c. purple .. 2·00 1·10
365. 49. 3 c.+1 c. green.. .. 2·00 1·00
366. – 5 c.+1 c. blue .. .. 2·25 80
367. – 7½ c.+2½ c. orange .. 2·50 1·00
368. – 10 c.+2 c. red .. .. 7·00 5·50
369. – 15 c.+2 c. blue .. 6·50 3·50
370. – 30 c.+3 c. sepia .. 25·00 25·00

DESIGNS—HORIZ. 2 c. Fencer. VERT. 5 c. Yachting. 7½ c. Putting the weight. 10 c. Runner. 15 c. Horseman. 30 c. Boxer.

50. Lieut. Koppen.

DESIGN: 75 c. Van der Hoop.

1928. Air.

371. 50. 40 c. red 45 45
372. – 75 c. green 45 45

52. J. P. Minckelers. 53. Mercury.

1928. Child Welfare.

373. 52. 1½ c.+1½ c. violet .. 50 35
374. – 5 c.+3 c. green .. 80 65
375a. – 7½ c.+2½ c. red .. 3·00 25
376a. – 12½ c.+3½ c. blue .. 12·00 8·00

PORTRAITS: 5 c. Boerhaave. 7½ c. H. A. Lorentz. 12½ c. G. Huygens.

1929. Air.

377. 53. 1½ g. black .. .. 2·00 1·60
378. 4½ g. red .. .. 1·50 3·50
379. 7½ g. green .. .. 21·00 3·75

1929. Surch **21**.

380 36 21 c. on 22½ c. brown .. 23·00 1·40

55. " Friendship and Security ". 56. Rembrandt and "De Staalmeesters".

1929. Child Welfare.
381. 55. 1½ c.+1½ c. grey .. 1·50 40
382. 5 c.+3 c. green .. 2·50 65
383. 6 c.+4 c. red .. 1·75 30
384. 12½ c.+3½ c. blue .. 15·00 13·00

1930. Rembrandt Society.
385 56 5 c. (+5 c.) green .. 9·00 8·00
386 6 c. (+5 c.) black .. 4·50 1·50
387 12½ c. (+5 c.) blue .. 13·00 15·00

57. Spring. 58. 59. Queen Wilhelmina.

1930. Child Welfare.
388. 57. 1½ c.+1½ c. red .. 1·50 35
389. – 5 c.+3 c. green .. 2·25 65
390. – 6 c.+4 c. purple .. 2·25 25
391. – 12½ c.+3½ c. blue .. 18·00 10·00
DESIGNS (allegorical): 5 c. Summer, 6 c. Autumn. 12½ c. Winter.

1931. Gouda Church Restoration Fund.
392. 58. 1½ c.+1½ c. green .. 13·00 13·00
393. 6 c.+4 c. red .. .. 27·00 25·00

1931.
395. – 70 c. blue and red (post.) 26·00 45
395b. – 80 c. green and red .. 95·00 3·00
394. 59. 36 c. red and blue (air).. 14·00 40
DESIGNS: 70 c. Portrait and factory. 80 c. Portrait and shipyard.

61. Mentally Deficient Child. 62. Windmill and Dykes, Kinderdijk. 63. Gorse (Spring).

1931. Child Welfare.
396. – 1½ c.+1½c. red & blue.. 1·40 50
397. 61. 5 c.+3 c. green & pur... 2·25 1·25
398. – 6 c.+4 c. pur. & grn. .. 1·75 40
399. – 12½ c.+3½ c. bl. & red.. 28·00 24·00
DESIGNS: 1½ c. Deaf mute. 6 c. Blind girl. 12½ c. Sick child.

1932. Tourist Propaganda.
400. 62. 2½ c.+1½ c. grn. & blk. 5·50 2·50
401. – 6 c.+4 c. grey & black 9·00 2250
402. – 7½ c.+3½ c. red & blk... 32·00 23·00
403. – 12½ c.+2½ c. bl. & blk. 35·00 24·00
DESIGNS: 6 c. Aerial view of Town Hall, Zierikzee. 7½ c. Bridges at Schipluiden and Moerdijk. 12½ c. Tulips.

1932. Child Welfare.
404. 63. 1½ c.+1½ c. brn. & yell. 1·75 35
405. – 5 c.+3 c. blue & red .. 1·75 65
406. – 6 c.+4 c. grn. & orge... 1·75 30
407. – 12½ c.+3½ c. bl. & orge. 30·00 20·00
DESIGNS—Child and: 5 c. Cornflower (Summer). 6 c. Sunflower (Autumn). 12½ c. Christmas rose. (Winter).

64. Arms of House of Orange. 65. Portrait by Goltzius.

1933. 4th Birth Cent. of William I of Orange. T 64 and portraits of William I inscr. "1533", as T 65.
408. 64. 1½ c. black 55 15
409. 65. 5 c. green .. .. 1·75 20
410. – 6 c. purple .. .. 2·75 10
411. – 12½ c. blue .. .. 17·00 3·50
DESIGNS: 6 c. Portrait by Key. 12½ c. Portrait attributed to Moro.

68. Dove of Peace. 69. Projected Monument at Den Helder. 70. "De Hoop" (hospital ship).

1933. Peace Propaganda.
412. 68. 12½ c. blue .. .. 8·50 25

1933. Seamen's Fund.
413. 69. 1½ c.+1½ c. red.. .. 1·75 1·25
414. 70. 5 c.+3 c. green and red 12·00 2·50
415. – 6 c.+4 c. green.. .. 17·00 2·50
416. – 12½ c.+3½ c. blue .. 24·00 21·00
DESIGNS: 6 c. Lifeboat. 12½ c. Seaman and Seamen's Home.

73. Monoplane.

1933. Air. (Special Flights).
417. 73. 30 c. green 70 75

74. Child and Star of Epiphany. 75. Princess Juliana.

1933. Child Welfare.
418. 74. 1½ c.+1½ c. orge. & grey 1·50 45
419. 5 c.+3 c. yell. & brn. .. 2·25 60
420. 6 c.+4 c. gold & green.. 2·50 40
421. 12½ c.+3½ c. silver & bl. 24·00 20·00

1934. Crisis stamps.
438. – 5 c.+4 c. purple .. 10·00 2·75
439. 75. 6 c.+5 c. blue.. .. 11·00 5·50
DESIGN: 5 c. Queen Wilhelmina.

76. Dutch Warship. 77. Dowager Queen Emma.

1934. Tercent. of Curaçao.
440. – 6 c. black .. .. 4·00 10
441. 76. 12½ c. blue .. .. 26·00 2·75
DESIGN: 6 c. Willemstad Harbour.

1934. Anti-T.B Fund.
442. 77. 6 c.+2 c. blue .. .. 11·00 1·60

78. Destitute child. 79. H. D. Guyot.

1934. Child Welfare.
443. 78. 1½ c.+1½ c. brown .. 1·50 50
444. 5 c.+3 c. red .. .. 2·25 1·25
445. 6 c.+4 c. green .. 2·25 25
446. 12½ c.+3½ c. blue .. 26·00 20·00

1935. Cultural and Social Relief Fund.
447. 79. 1½c.+1½c. red.. .. 1·90 1·90
448. – 5 c.+3 c. brown .. 4·50 5·50
449. – 6 c.+4 c. green.. .. 6·00 30
450. – 12½ c.+3½ c. blue .. 30·00 6·00
PORTRAITS: 5 c. A. J. M. Diepenbrock. 6 c. F. C. Donders. 12½ c. J. P. Sweelinck.
See also Nos. 456/9, 469/72, 478/82 and 492/6.

80. Aerial map of Netherlands. 81. Child picking fruit.

1935. Air Fund.
451. 80. 6 c.+4 c. brown .. 24·00 11·00

1935. Child Welfare.
452. 81. 1½ c.+1½ c. red.. .. 60 30
453. 5 c.+3 c. green.. .. 1·75 1·25
454. 6 c.+4 c. brown .. 1·50 30
455. 12½ c.+3½ c. blue .. 24·00 9·00

1936. Cultural and Social Relief Fund. As T 79.
456. 1½ c.+1½ c. sepia.. .. 85 1·00
457. 5 c.+3 c. green .. 4·75 3·75
458. 6 c.+4 c. red .. .. 1·75 35
459. 12½ c.+3½ c. blue.. .. 17·00 3·25
PORTRAITS: 1½ c. H. Kamerlingh Onnes. 5 c. Dr. A. S. Talma. 6 c. Mgr. Dr. H. J. A. M. Schaepman. 12½ c. Desiderius Erasmus.

83. Pallas Athene.

1936. Tercentenary of Utrecht University Foundation.
460 83 6 c. red .. .. 1·50 20
461 – 12½ c. blue .. .. 5·00 4·50
DESIGN: 12½ c. Gisbertus Voetius.

84. Child Herald. 85. Scout Movement.

1936. Child Welfare.
462. 84. 1½ c.+1½ c. slate .. 50 25
463. 5 c.+3 c. green.. .. 2·25 75
464. 6 c.+4 c. brown .. 2·00 20
465. 12½ c.+3½ c. blue .. 16·00 5·00

1937. Scout Jamboree.
466. – 1½ c. black and green .. 15 10
467. 85. 6 c. brown and black .. 1·50 10
468. – 12½ c. black and blue .. 3·00 1·25
DESIGNS: 1½ c. Scout Tenderfoot Badge. 12½ c. Hermes.

1937. Cultural and Social Relief Fund Portraits as T 79.
469. 1½ c.+1½ c. sepia.. .. 60 60
470. 5 c.+3 c. green .. 4·75 4·00
471. 6 c.+4 c. purple .. .. 1·10 25
472. 12½ c.+3½ c. blue.. .. 9·00 1·00
PORTRAITS: 1½ c. Jacob Maris. 5 c. F. de la B. Sylvius. 6 c. J. van den Vondel. 12½ c. A van Leeuwenhoek.

86. "Laughing Child" by Frans Hals. 87. Queen Wilhelmina.

1937. Child Welfare.
473. 86. 1½ c.+1½ c. black .. 15 15
474. 3 c.+2 c. green .. 1·25 1·25
475. 4 c.+2 c. red 60 50
476. 5 c.+3 c. green .. 50 15
477. 12½ c.+3½ c. blue .. 7·50 1·75

1938. Cultural and Social Relief Fund. As T 79.
478. 1½ c.+1½ c. sepia.. .. 40 70
479. 3 c.+2 c. green .. 60 35
480. 4 c.+2 c. red .. .. 1·75 2·25
481. 5 c.+3 c. green .. 2·50 30
482. 12½ c.+3½ c. blue .. 9·00 1·25
PORTRAITS: 1½ c. M. van St. Aldegonde. 3 c. O. G. Heldring. 4 c. Maria Tesselschade. 5 c. Rembrandt. 12½ c. H. Boerhaave.

1938. 40th Anniv. of Coronation.
483. 87. 1½ c. black 20 10
484. 5 c. red 25 10
485. 12½ c. blue .. .. 3·25 1·40

88. Carrion Crow. 89. Boy with flute.

1938. Air. (Special Flights).
486. 88. 12½ c. blue and grey .. 70 65
790a. 25 c. blue and grey .. 4·50 1·90

1938. Child Welfare.
487. 89. 1½ c.+1½ c. black .. 15 20
488. 3 c.+2 c. brown .. 40 30
489. 4 c.+2 c. green.. .. 75 85
490. 5 c.+3 c. red 35 15
491. 12½ c.+3½ c. blue .. 9·00 2·00

1939. Cultural and Social Relief Fund. As T 79.
492. 1½ c.+1½ c. brown .. 60 60
493. 2½ c.+2½ c. green.. .. 3·75 2·75
494. 3 c.+3 c. red .. .. 80 1·25
495. 5 c.+3 c. green .. 2·75 30
496. 12½ c.+3½ c. blue.. .. 8·00 1·00
PORTRAITS: 1½ c. M. Maris. 2½ c. Anton Mauve. 3 c. Gerardus van Swieten. 5 c. Nicolaas Beets. 12½ c. Pieter Stuyvesant.

91. St. Willibrord's landing in the Netherlands. 92. Steam Locomotive "Der Arend". 93. Child and Cornucopia.

1939. 12th Death Cent. of St. Willibrord.
497. 91. 5 c. green 75 10
498. – 12½ c. blue .. .. 4·25 2·50
DESIGN: 12½ c. St. Willibrord as Bishop of Utrecht.

1939. Cent. of Netherlands Railway.
499. 92. 5 c. green 75 15
500. – 12½ c. blue .. .. 9·50 3·50
DESIGN: 12½ c. Modern electric locomotive.

1939. Child Welfare.
501. 93. 1½ c.+1½ c. black .. 15 20
502. 2½ c.+2½ c. green .. 4·50 2·75
503. 3 c.+3 c. red 60 25
504. 5 c.+3 c. green .. 1·00 10
505. 12½ c.+3½ c. blue .. 3·75 1·40

94. Queen Wilhelmina. 95. Vincent Van Gogh. 98. Girl with Dandelion.

1940.
506. 94. 5 c. green 10 10
506a. 6 c. brown 65 10
507. 7½ c. red 10 10
508. 10 c. purple 10 10
509. 12½ c. blue 10 10
510. 15 c. blue 15 10
510a. 17½ c. blue .. .. 1·40 80
511. 20 c. violet 20 10
512. 22½ c. olive 80 95
513. 25 c. red 20 10
514. 30 c. ochre 45 30
515. 40 c. green 95 85
515a. 50 c. orange .. .. 7·50 60
515b. 60 c. purple .. .. 6·50 2·50

1940. Cultural and Social Relief Fund.
516. 95. 1½ c.+1½ c. brown .. 1·10 35
517. – 2½ c.+2½ c. green .. 3·00 1·25
518. – 3 c.+3 c. red .. .. 2·00 1·00
519. – 5 c.+3 c. green.. .. 4·00 25
520. – 12½ c.+3½ c. blue .. 4·00 65
PORTRAITS: 2½ c. E. J. Potgieter. 3c. Petrus Camper. 5 c. Jan Steen. 12½ c. Joseph Scaliger.
See also Nos. 558/62 and 656/60.

1940. As No. 519, colour changed. Surch.
521. 7½ c.+2½ c. on 5 c.+3 c. red 35 25

1940. Surch. with large figures and network.
522. 35. 2½ on 3 c. red 85 25
523. 5 on 3 c. green .. 10 20
524. 7½ on 3 c. red 10 10
525. 10 on 3 c. green .. 10 15
526. 12½ on 3 c. blue .. 15 30
527. 17½ on 3 c. green .. 35 65
528. 20 on 3 c. green .. 15 15
529. 22½ on 3 c. green .. 50 1·10
530. 25 on 3 c. green .. 25 30
531. 30 on 3 c. green .. 30 50
532. 40 on 3 c. green .. 35 70
533. 50 on 3 c. green .. 50 60
534. 60 on 3 c. green .. 90 1·25
535. 70 on 3 c. green .. 2·00 3·00
536. 80 on 3 c. green .. 2·75 5·50
537. 100 on 3 c. green .. 24·00 35·00
538. 250 on 3 c. green .. 25·00 42·00
539. 500 on 3 c. green .. 25·00 40·00

1940. Child Welfare.
540. 98. 1½ c.+1½ c. violet .. 50 20
541. 2½ c.+2½ c. olive .. 1·75 90
542. 4 c.+3 c. blue .. .. 1·90 1·10
543. 5 c.+3 c. green.. .. 2·00 15
544. 7½ c.+3½ c. red.. .. 50 15

1941.
546. 35. 5 c. green 10 10
547. 7½ c. red 10 10
548. 10 c. violet 10 10
549. 12½ c. blue 10 30
550. 15 c. blue 20 35
551. 17½ c. red 10 15
552. 20 c. violet 15 15
553. 22½ c. olive 10 30
554. 25 c. lake 15 25
555. 30 c. brown .. .. 3·75 25
556. 40 c. green 15 30
557. 50 c. brown 10 15

1941. Cultural and Social Relief Fund. As T 95 but inscr. "ZOMERZEGEL 31.12.46".
558. 1½ c.+1½ c. brown .. 60 30
559. 2½ c.+2½ c. green .. 60 30
560. 4 c.+3 c. red 50 30
561. 5 c.+3 c. green .. 65 30
562. 7½ c.+3½ c. purple .. 65 30
PORTRAITS: 1½ c. Dr. A. Mathijsen. 2½ c. J. Ingenhousz. 4 c. Aagje Deken. 5 c. Johan Bosboom. 7½ c. A. C. W. Staring.

100. "Titus Rembrandt."
101. Legionary.

1941. Child Welfare.
563. 100. 1½ c.+1½ c. black .. 25 30
564. 2½ c.+2½ c. olive .. 25 30
565. 4 c.+3 c. blue .. 25 30
566. 5 c.+3 c. green .. 25 30
567. 7½ c.+3½ c. red .. 25 30

1942. Netherlands Legion Fund.
568. 101. 7½ c.+2½ c. red .. 25 50
569. – 12½ c.+87½ c. blue .. 3·75 7·00
DESIGN—HORIZ. 12½ c. Legionary with similar inscription.

1943. 1st European Postal Congress. As T 26 but larger (21×27½ mm) surch **EUROPEESCHE P T T VEREENIGING 19 OCTOBER 1942 10 CENT**.
570 26 10 c. on 2½ c. yellow .. 10 15

103. Seahorse.
104. Michiel A. de Ruyter.

1943. Old Germanic Symbols.
571. 103. 1 c. black 10 10
572. – 1½ c. red 10 10
573. – 2 c. blue 10 10
574. – 2½ c. green 10 10
575. – 3 c. red 10 10
576. – 4 c. brown 10 10
577. – 5 c. olive 10 10
DESIGNS—VERT. 1½ c. Triple crowned tree. 2½ c. Birds in ornamental tree. 4 c. Horse and rider. HORIZ. 2 c. Swans. 3 c. Trees and serpentine roots. 5 c. Prancing horses.

1943. Dutch Naval Heroes.
578. 104. 7½ c. red 10 10
579. – 10 c. green 10 10
580. – 12½ c. blue 10 15
581. – 15 c. violet 15 15
582. – 17½ c. grey 10 10
583. – 20 c. brown 10 10
584. – 22½ c. red 10 20
585. – 25 c. purple 25 50
586. – 30 c. blue 10 10
587. – 40 c. grey 10 15
PORTRAITS: 10 c. Johan Evertsen. 12½ c. Maarten H. Tromp. 15 c. Piet Hein. 17½ c. Wilhem Joseph van Gent. 20 c. Witte de With. 22½ c. Cornelis Evertsen. 25 c. Tjerk Hiddes de Fries. 30 c. Cornelis Tromp. 40 c. Cornelis Evertsen the younger.

105. Mail Cart.
106. Child and Doll's House.

1943. Stamp Day.
589. 105. 7½ c.+7½ c. red .. 10 10

1944. Child Welfare and Winter Help Funds. Inscr. "WINTERHULP" (1½ c. and 7½ c.) or "VOLKSDIENST" (others).
590. 106. 1½ c.+3½ c. black .. 10 20
591. – 4 c.+3½ c. brown .. 10 20
592. – 5 c.+5 c. green .. 10 20
593. – 7½ c.+7½ c. red .. 10 20
594. – 10 c.+40 c. blue .. 10 20
DESIGNS: 4 c. Mother and child. 5 c., 10 c. Mother and children. 7½ c. Child and wheat-sheaf.

107. Infantryman.
111. Queen Wilhelmina.

1944.
595. 107. 1½ c. black 10 10
596. – 2½ c. green 10 10
597. – 3 c. brown 10 10
598. – 5 c. blue 10 10
599. 111. 7½ c. red 10 10
600. 10 c. orange 10 10
601. 12½ c. blue 10 10
602. 15 c. red .. .. 1·75 1·75
603. 17½ c. green .. .. 1·00 1·40
604. 20 c. violet 25 20
605. 22½ c. red 75 90
606. 25 c. brown .. .. 2·25 2·00
607. 30 c. green 20 15
608. 40 c. purple .. .. 2·75 2·75
609. 50 c. mauve .. .. 1·50 1·25
DESIGNS—HORIZ. 2½ c. "Nieuw Amsterdam" (liner). 3 c. Airman. VERT. 5 c. "De Ruyter" (cruiser).

The above set was originally for use on Netherlands warships serving with the Allied Fleet, and was used after liberation in the Netherlands.

112. Lion and Dragon.
113.
114. Queen Wilhelmina.

1945. Liberation.
610. 112. 7½ c. orange .. 10 10

1945. Child Welfare.
611. 113. 1½ c.+2½ c. grey .. 30 25
612. 2½ c.+3½ c. green .. 30 25
613. 5 c.+5 c. brown .. 30 25
614. 7½ c.+4½ c. red .. 30 25
615. 12½ c.+5½ c. blue .. 30 25

1946.
616. 114. 1 g. blue 80 20
617. 2½ g. red .. .. £140 9·00
618. 5 g. green .. .. £140 30·00
619. 10 g. violet .. .. £140 28·00

115. Emblem of Abundance.
116. Princess Irene.
117. Boy on Roundabout.

1946. War Victims' Relief Fund.
620. 115. 1½ c.+3½ c. black .. 50 30
621. 2½ c.+5 c. green .. 60 60
622. 5 c.+10 c. violet .. 65 60
623. 7½ c.+15 c. red .. 45 20
624. 12½ c.+37½ c. blue .. 95 60

1946. Child Welfare.
625. 116. 1½ c.+1½ c. brown .. 50 50
626. – 2½ c.+1½ c. green .. 50 60
627. 116. 4 c.+2 c. red .. 65 65
628. – 5 c.+2 c. brown .. 65 65
629. – 7½ c.+2½ c. red .. 50 15
630. – 12½ c.+7½ c. blue .. 50 65
PORTRAITS: 2½ c., 5 c. Princess Margriet. 7½ c., 12½ c. Princess Beatrix.

1946. Child Welfare.
631. 117. 2 c.+2 c. violet .. 40 40
632. 4 c.+2 c. green .. 45 50
633. 7½ c.+2½ c. red .. 45 50
634. 10 c.+5 c. purple .. 60 15
635. 20 c.+5 c. blue .. 60 65

118. Numeral.
119. Queen Wilhelmina.
122. Children.

1946.
636 118 1 c. red 10 10
637 2 c. blue 10 10
638 2½ c. orange .. 8·50 1·75
638a 3 c. brown 10 10
639 4 c. green 20 10
639a 5 c. orange 10 10
639c 6 c. grey 45 10
639d 7 c. red 20 10
639f 8 c. mauve 20 10

1947.
640 119 5 c. green 65 10
641 6 c. black 15 10
642 6 c. blue 40 10
643 7½ c. red 15 20
644 10 c. purple 40 10
645 12½ c. red 60 40
646 15 c. violet .. .. 3·25 10
647 20 c. blue .. .. 5·00 10
648 22½ c. green 70 70
649 25 c. blue .. .. 13·00 10
650 30 c. orange .. .. 7·50 20
651 35 c. blue .. .. 6·50 50
652 40 c. brown .. .. 18·00 50
653 – 45 c. blue .. .. 23·00 12·00
654 – 50 c. brown .. .. 22·00 25
655 – 60 c. red .. .. 23·00 1·75
Nos. 653/5 are as Type **119** but have the inscriptions in colour on white ground.

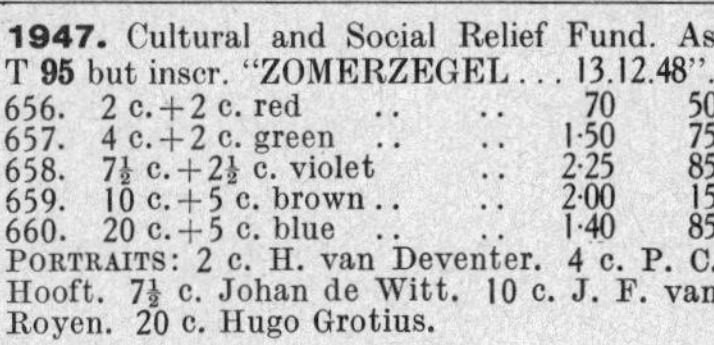

1947. Cultural and Social Relief Fund. As T **95** but inscr. "ZOMERZEGEL . . . 13.12.48".
656. 2 c.+2 c. red 70 50
657. 4 c.+2 c. green .. .. 1·50 75
658. 7½ c.+2½ c. violet .. 2·25 85
659. 10 c.+5 c. brown .. .. 2·00 15
660. 20 c.+5 c. blue .. .. 1·40 85
PORTRAITS: 2 c. H. van Deventer. 4 c. P. C. Hooft. 7½ c. Johan de Witt. 10 c. J. F. van Royen. 20 c. Hugo Grotius.

1947. Child Welfare.
661. 122. 2 c.+2 c. brown .. 20 10
662. – 4 c.+2 c. green .. 1·40 60
663. – 7½ c.+2½ c. brown .. 1·75 90
664. – 10 c.+5 c. lake .. 1·50 10
665. 122. 20 c.+5 c. blue .. 1·75 90
DESIGN: 4 c. to 10 c. Baby.

124. Ridderzaal, The Hague.
125. Queen Wilhelmina.

1948. Cultural and Social Relief Fund.
666. 124. 2 c.+2 c. brown .. 1·75 40
667. – 6 c.+4 c. green .. 2·00 40
668. – 10 c.+5 c. red .. 1·60 15
669. – 20 c.+5 c. blue .. 2·00 90
BUILDINGS: 6 c. Palace on the Dam. 10 c. Kneuterdijk Palace. 20 c. Nieuwe Kerk, Amsterdam.

1948. Queen Wilhelmina's Golden Jubilee.
670. 125. 10 c. red 10 10
671. 20 c. blue .. .. 2·50 1·60

126. Queen Juliana.
127. Boy in Canoe.

1948. Coronation.
672. 126. 10 c. brown .. .. 1·50 10
673. 20 c. blue .. .. 2·75 50

1948. Child Welfare.
674. 127. 2 c.+2 c. green .. 15 10
675. – 5 c.+3 c. green .. 2·75 80
676. – 6 c.+4 c. grey .. 1·40 15
677. – 10 c.+5 c. red .. 45 10
678. – 20 c.+8 c. blue .. 2·75 1·10
DESIGNS: 5 c. Girl swimming. 6 c. Boy on toboggan. 10 c. Girl on swing. 20 c. Boy skating.

128. Terrace near Beach.

DESIGNS: 5 c. Hikers in cornfield. 6 c. Campers by fire. 10 c. Gathering wheat. 20 c. Yachts.

1949. Cultural and Social Relief Fund.
679. 128. 2 c.+2 c. yell. & blue 1·50 20
680. – 5 c.+3 c. yell. & blue 2·50 2·00
681. – 6 c.+4 c. green .. 2·25 50
682. – 10 c.+5 c. yell. & blue 3·25 10
683. – 20 c.+5 c. blue .. 2·50 2·25

129. Queen Juliana.
130.
131. Hands reaching for Sunflower.

1949.
684 129 5 c. green 50 10
685 6 c. blue 40 10
686 10 c. yellow 30 10
687 12 c. red .. .. 1·75 1·75
688 15 c. olive .. .. 3·25 10
689 20 c. blue .. .. 3·00 10
690 25 c. brown .. .. 12·00 10
691 30 c. violet .. .. 7·00 10
692 35 c. blue .. .. 15·00 15
693 40 c. purple .. .. 28·00 20
694 45 c. orange .. .. 1·75 90
695 45 c. violet .. .. 35·00 30
696 50 c. green .. .. 6·50 15
697 60 c. brown .. .. 13·00 15
697a 75 c. red .. .. 75·00 1·25
698 130 1 g. red .. .. 3·50 10
699 2½ g. brown .. .. £180 2·00
700a 5 g. brown .. .. £400 3·00
701 10 g. violet .. .. £350 14·00

1949. Red Cross and Indonesian Relief Fund.
702. 131. 2 c.+3 c. yell. & grey 90 30
703. 6 c.+4 c. yell. & lake 65 40
704. 10 c.+5 c. yell. & bl. 3·75 25
705. 30 c.+10 c. yell. & brn. 10·00 3·00

132. Posthorns and Globe.
133. "Autumn".

1949. 75th Anniv. of U.P.U.
706. 132. 10 c. lake 55 10
707. 20 c. blue .. .. 8·00 2·25

1949. Child Welfare Fund. Inscr. "VOOR HET KIND".
708. 133. 2 c.+3 c. brown .. 20 10
709. 5 c.+3 c. red .. .. 6·00 1·75
710. – 6 c.+4 c. green .. 3·00 30
711. – 10 c.+5 c. grey .. 20 10
712. – 20 c.+7 c. blue .. 5·00 1·60
DESIGNS: 5 c. "Summer". 6 c. "Spring". 10 c. "Winter". 20 c. "New Year".

134. Resistance Monument.
135. Part of Moerdyk Bridge.

1950. Cultural and Social Relief Fund. Insc. "ZOMERZEGEL 1950".
713. 134. 2 c.+2 c. brown .. 1·40 1·25
714. – 4 c.+2 c. green .. 10·00 10·00
715. – 5 c.+3 c. grey .. 6·50 3·50
716. – 6 c.+4 c. violet .. 3·25 75
717. 135. 10 c.+5 c. slate .. 5·00 20
718. – 20 c.+5 c. blue .. 14·00 13·00
DESIGNS—VERT. 4 c. Sealing dykes. 5 c. Rotterdam skyscraper. HORIZ: 6 c. Harvesting. 20 c. "Overijssel" (canal freighter).

1950. Surch. with bold figure **6**.
719. 119. 6 c. on 7½ c. red .. 1·40 10

137. Good Samaritan and Bombed Church.
138. Janus Dousa.

1950. Bombed Churches Rebuilding Fund.
720. 137. 2 c.+2 c. olive .. 4·50 1·75
721. 5 c.+3 c. brown .. 14·00 14·00
722. 6 c.+4 c. green .. 10·00 2·00
723. 10 c.+5 c. red .. 12·00 35
724. 20 c.+5 c. blue .. 26·00 26·00

1950. 375th Anniv. of Leyden University.
725. 138. 10 c. olive .. .. 3·75 10
726. – 20 c. blue .. .. 3·75 1·40
PORTRAIT: 20 c. Jan van Hout.

139. Baby and Bees.
140. Bergh Castle.

1950. Child Welfare. Inscr. "VOOR HET KIND".
727. 139. 2 c.+3 c. red 20 10
728. – 5 c.+3 c. olive .. 8·00 3·50
729. – 6 c.+4 c. green .. 3·25 60
730. – 10 c.+5 c. purple .. 20 10
731. – 20 c.+7 c. blue .. 12·00 11·00
DESIGNS: 5 c. Boy and fowl. 6 c. Girl and birds. 10 c. Boy and fish. 20 c. Girl, butterfly and frog.

1951. Cultural and Social Relief Fund. Castles.
732. – 2 c.+2 c. violet .. 2·50 1·25
733. 140. 5 c.+3 c. red .. .. 8·50 8·00
734. – 6 c.+4 c. sepia .. 2·75 60
735. – 10 c.+5 c. green .. 6·00 25
736. – 20 c.+5 c. blue .. 6·00 8·00
DESIGNS—HORIZ. 2 c. Hillenraad. 6 c. Hernen. VERT. 10 c. Rechteren. 20 c. Moermond.

141. Girl and Windmill. 142. Gull. 143. Jan van Riebeeck.

1951. Child Welfare.
737. 141. 2 c.+3 c. green .. 30 10
738. – 5 c.+3 c. blue .. 4·50 4·50
739. – 6 c.+4 c. brown .. 4·25 60
740. – 10 c.+5 c. lake .. 20 10
741. – 20 c.+7 c. blue .. 6·50 6·50
DESIGNS—Each shows boy or girl: 5 c. Crane. 6 c. Fishing nets. 10 c. Factory chimneys. 20 c. Flats.

1951. Air.
742 142 15 g. brown £250 £120
743 25 g. black £275 £120

1952. Tercent. of Landing in South Africa and Van Riebeeck Monument Fund.
744. 143. 2 c.+3 c. violet .. 3·25 3·25
745. 6 c.+4 c. green .. 8·00 6·50
746. 10 c.+5 c. red .. 8·50 5·00
747. 20 c.+5 c. blue .. 5·50 3·00

144. Miner. 145. Wild Rose.

1952. 50th Anniv. of State Mines, Limburg.
748. 144. 10 c. blue .. .. 2·50 10

1952. Cultural and Social Relief Fund. Floral designs inscr. "ZOMERZEGEL 1952".
749. 145. 2 c.+2 c. grn. & red.. 75 50
750. – 5 c.+3 c. yell. & green 1·25 90
751. – 6 c.+4 c. green & red 1·50 55
752. – 10 c.+5 c. grn. & orge. 2·00 15
753. – 20 c.+5 c. grn. & blue 13·00 12·00
FLOWERS: 5 c. Marsh Marigold. 6 c. Tulip. 10c. Marguerite. 20 c. Cornflower.

146. Radio Masts 147. Boy Feeding Goat.

1952. Netherlands Stamp Cent. and Cent. of Telegraph Service.
754. – 2 c. violet 70 10
755. 146. 6 c. red 20 10
756. – 10 c. green 20 10
757. – 20 c. slate .. .. 5·00 2·00
DESIGNS: 2 c. Telegraph poles and train. 10 c. Postman delivering letters, 1852. 20 c. Postman delivering letters, 1952.

1952. Int. Postage Stamp Ex., Utrecht ("ITEP"). Nos. 754/7 but colours changed.
757a. – 2 c. brown .. .. 20·00 15·00
757b. 146. 6 c. blue .. .. 15·00 13·00
757c. – 10 c. lake .. .. 15·00 13·00
757d. – 20 c. blue .. .. 15·00 13·00
Nos. 757a/d were sold only in sets at the Exhibition at face + 1 g. entrance fee.

1952. Child Welfare.
758. 147. 2 c.+3 c.blk. & olive.. 15 10
759. – 5 c.+3 c. blk. & pink 1·00 80
760. – 6 c.+4 c. blk. & green 1·90 50
761. – 10 c.+5 c. blk. & orge. 20 10
762. – 20 c.+7 c. blk. & blue 6·50 6·50
DESIGNS: 5 c. Girl riding donkey. 6 c. Girl playing with dog. 10 c. Boy and cat. 20 c. Boy and rabbit.

1953. Flood Relief Fund. Surch **19 53 10 c +10 WATERSNOOD.**
763 129 10 c.+10 c. orange .. 65 10

149. Hyacinth. 150. Red Cross.

1953. Cultural and Social Relief Fund.
764. 149. 2 c.+2 c. grn. & violet 60 35
765. – 5 c.+3 c. grn. & orge. 1·00 1·10
766. – 6 c.+4 c. yell. & green 1·25 55
767. – 10 c.+5 c. grn. & red 2·25 15
768. – 20 c.+5 c. grn. & blue 12·00 12·00
FLOWERS: 5 c. African marigold. 6 c. Daffodil. 10 c. Anemone. 20 c. Dutch iris.

1953. Red Cross Fund. Inscr. "RODE KRUIS".
769. 150. 2 c.+3 c. red & sepia 40 45
770. – 6 c.+4 c. red & brown 2·75 2·75
771. – 7 c.+5 c. red & olive 75 50
772. – 10 c.+5 c. red .. 60 10
773. – 25 c.+8 c. red & blue 7·50 6·00
DESIGNS: 6 c. Man with lamp. 7 c. Rescue worker in flooded area. 10 c. Nurse giving blood transfusion. 25 c. Red Cross flags.

151. Queen Juliana. 152. Queen Juliana.

1953.
775 151 10 c. brown 10 10
776 12 c. turquoise .. 10 10
777 15 c. red 10 10
777b 18 c. turquoise .. 20 10
778 20 c. purple .. 15 10
778b 24 c. olive .. 40 20
779 25 c. blue .. 20 10
780a 30 c. orange .. 40 15
781 35 c. brown .. 90 10
781a 37 c. turquoise .. 85 20
782 40 c. slate .. 35 10
783 45 c. red .. 40 10
784 50 c. green .. 35 10
785 60 c. brown .. 50 10
785a 62 c. red .. 5·00 3·25
785b 70 c. blue .. 60 10
786 75 c. purple .. 50 10
786a 80 c. violet .. 75 15
786b 85 c. green .. 1·40 20
786c 95 c. brown .. 2·25 25
787 152 1 g. red .. 2·50 10
788 2½ g. green .. 9·00 10
789 5 g. black .. 3·50 15
790 10 g. blue .. 19·00 1·25

154. M. Nijhoff (poet). 153. Girl with Pigeon.

1953. Child Welfare. Inscr. "VOOR HET KIND".
791. – 2 c.+3 c. blue & yell. 10 10
792. – 5 c.+3 c. lake & green 75 85
793. 153. 7 c.+5 c. brn. & blue 3·00 80
794. – 10 c.+5 c. lilac & bis. 10 10
795. – 25 c.+8 c. turquoise and pink .. 11·00 12·00
DESIGNS: 2 c. Girl, bucket and spade. 5 c. Boy and apple. 10 c. Boy and tjalk (sailing boat). 25 c. Girl and tulip.

1954. Cultural and Social Relief Fund.
796. 154. 2 c.+3 c. blue .. 1·75 1·75
797. – 5 c.+3 c. brown .. 60 60
798. – 7 c.+5 c. red.. 2·00 1·40
799. – 10 c.+5 c. green .. 7·50 15
800. – 25 c.+8 c. purple .. 14·00 13·00
PORTRAITS: 5 c. W. Pijper (composer). 7 c. H. P. Berlage (architect). 10 c. J. Huizinga historian). 25 c. Vincent van Gogh (painter).

155. St. Boniface. 156. Boy and Model Aeroplane.

1954. 1200th Anniv. of Martyrdom of St. Boniface.
801. 155. 10 c. blue .. 1·75 10

1954. National Aviation Fund.
802. 156. 2 c.+2 c. green .. 75 90
803. – 10 c.+4 c. blue .. 2·25 50
PORTRAIT: 10 c. Dr. A. Plesman (aeronautical pioneer).

157. Making Paper-chains. 158. Queen Juliana.

1954. Child Welfare.
804. 157. 2 c.+3 c. brown .. 10 10
805. – 5 c.+3 c. olive .. 90 65
806. – 7c.+5c. blue.. 1·50 50
807. – 10c.+5c. red.. 10 10
808. – 25 c.+8 c. blue 9·50 8·00
DESIGNS—VERT. 5 c. Girl brushing her teeth. 7 c. Boy and toy boat. 10 c. Nurse and child. HORIZ. 25 c. Invalid boy drawing in bed.

1954. Ratification of Statute for the Kingdom.
809. 158 10 c. red 80 10

159. Factory, Rotterdam. 160. "The Victory of Peace".

1955. Cultural and Social Relief Fund.
810. 159. 2 c.+3 c. brown .. 1·25 1·25
811. – 5 c.+3 c. green .. 55 35
812. – 7 c.+5 c. red.. .. 1·25 1·25
813. – 10 c.+5 c. blue .. 1·75 15
814. – 25 c.+8 c. brown .. 13·00 11·00
DESIGNS—HORIZ. 5 c. Post Office, The Hague. 10 c. Town Hall, Hilversum. 25 c. Office Building, The Hague. VERT. 7 c Stock Exchange, Amsterdam.

1955. 10th Anniv. of Liberation.
815. 160. 10 c. red .. .. 1·25 10

161. Microscope and Emblem of Cancer. 162. "Willem van Loon" (D. Dircks).

1955. Queen Wilhelmina Anti-Cancer Fund.
816. 161. 2 c.+3 c. blk. & red.. 60 50
817. 5 c.+3 c. green & red 60 30
818. 7 c.+5 c. purple & red 85 70
819. 10 c.+5 c. blue and red 85 10
820. 25 c.+8 c. olive & red 9·00 7·00

1955. Child Welfare Fund.
821. 162. 2 c.+3 c. green .. 10 10
822. – 5 c.+3 c. red .. 65 60
823. – 7 c.+5 c. brown .. 3·25 80
824. – 10 c.+5 c. blue .. 10 10
825. – 25 c.+8 c. lilac .. 9·00 9·00
PORTRAITS: 5 c. "Portrait of a Boy" (J. A. Backer). 7 c. "Portrait of a Girl" (unknown). 10 c. "Philips Huygens" (A. Hanneman). 25 c. "Constantin Huygens" (A. Hanneman).

163. "Farmer".

PAINTINGS: 5 c. "Young Tobias with Angel". 7 c. "Persian wearing fur cap". 10 c. "Old Blind Tobias". 25 c. Self-portrait 1639.

1956. Cultural and Social Relief Fund and 350th Birth Anniv. of Rembrandt. Details from Rembrandt's paintings.
826. 163. 2 c.+3 c. slate .. 2·25 2·50
827. – 5 c.+3 c. olive .. 1·25 1·25
828. – 7 c.+5 c. brown .. 3·50 3·50
829. – 10 c.+5 c. green .. 10·00 25
830. – 25 c.+8 c. brown .. 13·00 15·00

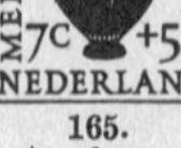

164. Yacht. 165. Amphora. 167. "Portrait of a Boy" (Van Scorel).

1956. 16th Olympic Games, Melbourne.
831. 164. 2 c.+3 c. blk. & blue 40 40
832. – 5 c.+3 c. blk. & yellow 40 40
833. 165. 7 c.+5 c. blk. & brown 1·50 1·25
834. – 10 c.+5 c. blk. & grey 3·50 40
835. – 25 c.+8 c. blk. & green 8·50 8·50
DESIGNS—As Type 164: 5 c. Runner. 10 c. Hockey player. 25 c. Water polo player.

1956. Europa. As T **110** of Luxembourg.
836. 10 c. black and lake .. 1·75 10
837. 25 c. black and blue .. 50·00 1·75

1956. Child Welfare Fund. 16th century Dutch Paintings.
838. 167. 2 c.+3 c. grey & cream 10 10
839. – 5 c.+3 c. ol. & cream 50 65
840. – 7 c.+5 c. pur. & cream 3·75 1·50
841. – 10 c.+5 c. red & cream 10 10
842. – 25 c.+8 c. bl. & cream 8·00 5·50
PAINTINGS: 5 c. "Portrait of a Boy". 7 c. "Portrait of a Girl". 10 c. "Portrait of a Girl". 25 c. "Portrait of Eechie Pieters".

168. "Curacao" (trawler) and Fish Barrels. 169. Admiral M. A. de Ruyter.

1957. Cultural and Social Relief Fund. Ships.
843. – 4 c.+3 c. blue .. 1·25 90
844. – 6 c.+4 c. lilac .. 1·00 60
845. – 7 c.+5 c. red .. .. 1·50 95
846. 168. 10 c.+8 c. green .. 3·75 15
847. – 30 c.+8 c. brown .. 7·50 7·00
DESIGNS: 4 c. "Gaasterland" (freighter). 6 c. Coaster. 7 c. "Willem Barendsz" (whale factory ship) and whale. 30 c. "Nieuw Amsterdam" (liner).

1957. 350th Birth Anniv. of M. A. de Ruyter.
848. 169. 10 c. orange 75 10
849. – 30 c. blue .. .. 5·00 1·75
DESIGN: 30 c. De Ruyter's flagship, "De Zeven Provincien".

170. Blood Donors' Emblem. 171. "Europa" Star.

1957. 90th Anniv. of Netherlands Red Cross Society and Red Cross Fund.
850. 170. 4 c.+3 c. blue & red .. 75 1·00
851. – 6 c.+4 c. grn. & red 65 65
852. – 7 c.+5 c. red & green 75 75
853. – 10 c.+8 c. red & ochre 90 10
854. – 30 c.+8 c. red & blue 3·50 3·75
DESIGNS: 6 c. "J. Henry Dunant" (hospital ship). 7 c. Red Cross. 10 c. Red Cross emblem. 30 c. Red Cross on globe.

1957. Europa.
855. 171. 10 c. black and blue .. 65 10
856. 30 c. green and blue .. 8·00 1·75

172. Portrait by B. J. Blommers. 173. Walcheren Costume.

1957. Child Fund Welfare. 19th/20th Century Paintings by Dutch Masters.
857. 172. 4 c.+4 c. red 10 10
858. – 6 c.+4 c. green .. 1·50 80
859. – 8 c.+4 c. sepia .. 2·25 1·75
860. – 12 c.+9 c. purple .. 10 10
861. – 30 c.+9 c. blue .. 6·50 8·00
PORTRAITS: Child paintings by: W. B. Tholen (6 c.); J. Sluyters (8 c.); M. Maris (12 c.); C. Kruseman (30 c.).

1958. Cultural and Social Relief Fund. Provincial Costumes.
862. 173. 4 c.+4 c. blue .. 80 60
863. – 6 c.+4 c. ochre .. 90 80
864. – 8 c.+4 c. red.. .. 5·00 1·75
865. – 12 c.+9 c. brown .. 2·00 15
866. – 30 c.+9 c. lilac .. 8·00 7·50
COSTUMES: 6 c. Marken. 8 c. Scheveningen. 12 c. Friesland. 30 c. Volendam.

1958. Surch **12 C.**
867 151 12 c. on 10 c. brown .. 80 10

1958. Europa. As T **119a** of Luxembourg.
868. 12 c. blue and red .. 20 10
869. 30 c. red and blue .. 90 70

176. Girl on Stilts and Boy on Tricycle. 177. Cranes.

1958. Child Welfare Fund. Children's Games.
870. 176. 4 c.+4 c. blue .. 10 10
871. – 6 c.+4 c. red .. 1·50 1·25
872. – 8 c.+4 c. green .. 1·50 1·25
873. – 12 c.+9 c. red .. 10 10
874. – 30 c.+9 c. blue .. 5·50 5·50
DESIGNS: 6 c. Boy and girl on scooters. 8 c. Boys playing leap-frog. 12 c. Boys on roller-skates. 30 c. Girl skipping and boy in toy car.

1959. 10th Anniv. of N.A.T.O. As T **123** of Luxembourg (N.A.T.O. emblem).
875. 12 c. blue and yellow .. 10 10
876. 30 c. blue and red .. 1·00 60

1959. Cultural and Social Relief Fund. Prevention of Sea Encroachment.
877. – 4 c.+4 c. blue on green 1·10 1·25
878. – 6 c.+4 c. brn. on grey 90 90
879. – 8 c.+4 c. violet on blue 2·25 1·75
880. **177.** 12 c.+9 c. grn. on yell. 3·75 15
881. – 30 c.+9 c. blk. on red 6·50 6·50
DESIGNS: 4 c. Tugs and caisson. 6 c. Dredger. 8 c. Labourers making fascine mattresses. 30 c. Sand-spouter and scoop.

1959. Europa. As T **123a** of Luxembourg.
882. 12 c. red 15 10
883. 30 c. green .. .. 2·50 1·50

178. Silhouette of Douglas DC-8 Airliner and World Map. **179.** Child in Play-pen.

1959. 40th Anniv. of K.L.M. (Royal Dutch Airlines).
884. **178.** 12 c. blue and red .. 20 10
885. – 30 c. blue and green 2·00 1·25
DESIGN: 30 c. Silhouette of Douglas DC-8 airliner.

1959. Child Welfare Fund.
886. **179.** 4 c.+4 c. blue & brown 10 10
887. – 6 c.+4 c. brn. & green 1·75 1·40
888. – 8 c.+4 c. blue & red.. 3·00 1·50
889. – 12 c.+9 c. red, black and blue 10 10
890. – 30 c.+9 c. turquoise and yellow .. 4·00 4·00
DESIGNS: 6 c. Boy as "Red Indian" with bow and arrow. 8 c. Boy feeding geese. 12 c. Traffic warden escorting children. 30 c. Girl doing homework.

180. Refugee Woman. **181.** White Water-lily.

1960. World Refugee Year.
891. **180.** 12 c.+8 c. purple .. 25 15
892. 30 c.+10 c. green .. 2·00 2·50

1960. Cultural and Social Relief Fund. Flowers.
893. – 4 c.+4 c. red, green and grey 80 65
894. – 6 c.+4 c. yellow, green and salmon.. .. 50 45
895. **181.** 8 c.+4 c. multicoloured 2·25 2·50
896. – 12 c.+8 c. red, green and buff .. .. 2·00 20
897. – 30 c.+10 c. blue, green and yellow.. .. 5·50 6·00
FLOWERS—VERT. 4 c. "The Princess" tulip. 6 c. Gorse. 12 c. Poppy. 30 c. Blue sea-holly.

182. J. van der Kolk. **183.** Marken Costume. **184.** Herring Gull.

1960. World Mental Health Year.
898. **182.** 12 c. red 50 10
899. – 30 c. blue (J. Wier) .. 4·00 2·25

1960. Europa. As T **113a** of Norway.
900. 12 c. yellow and red .. 25 10
901. 30 c. yellow and blue .. 2·75 2·00

1960. Child Welfare Fund. Costumes. Multicoloured portraits.
902 **183.** 4 c.+4 c. slate .. 30 10
903. – 6 c.+4 c. ochre .. 2·50 1·25
904. – 8 c.+4 c. turquoise .. 5·50 2·25
905. – 12 c.+9 c. violet .. 30 10
906. – 30 c.+9 c. grey .. 7·00 6·00
DESIGNS—Costumes of: 6 c. Volendam. 8 c. Bunschoten. 12 c. Hindeloopen. 30 c. Huizen.

1961. Cultural and Social Relief Fund. Beach and Meadow Birds.
907. **184.** 4 c.+4 c. slate & yell. 1·50 1·50
908. – 6 c.+4 c. sep. & brown 50 40
909. – 8 c.+4 c. brn. & olive 1·40 1·25
910. – 12 c.+8 c. blk. & blue 3·00 25
911. – 30 c.+10 c. blk. & green 5·50 4·00
BIRDS—HORIZ. 6 c. Oystercatcher. 12 c. Avocet. VERT. 8 c. Curlew. 30 c. Lapwing.

185. Doves. **186.** St. Nicholas.

1961. Europa.
912. **185.** 12 c. brown 10 10
913. 30 c. turquoise .. 30 30

1961. Child Welfare.
914. **186.** 4 c.+4 c. red 10 10
915. – 6 c.+4 c. blue .. 1·25 90
916. – 8 c.+4 c. bistre .. 1·25 1·25
917. – 12 c.+9 c. green .. 10 10
918. – 30 c.+9 c. orange .. 3·50 3·25
DESIGNS: 6 c. Epiphany. 8 c. Palm Sunday. 12 c. Whitsuntide. 30 c. Martinmas.

187. Queen Juliana and Prince Bernhard. **188.** Detail of "The Repast of the Officers of the St. Jorisdoelen" after Frans Hals.

1962. Silver Wedding.
919. **187.** 12 c. red 15 10
920. 30 c. green .. .. 1·50 60

1962. Cultural, Health and Social Welfare Funds.
921. – 4 c.+4 c. green .. 1·25 90
922. – 6 c.+4 c. black .. 65 65
923. – 8 c.+4 c. purple .. 1·50 1·50
924. – 12 c.+8 c. bistre .. 1·50 25
925. **188.** 30 c.+10 c. blue .. 2·00 2·00
DESIGNS—HORIZ. 4 c. Roman cat (sculpture). VERT. 6 c. Ammonite fossil. 8 c. Pendulum clock (after principle of Huygens). 12 c. Ship's figurehead.

189. Telephone Dial. **190.** Europa "Tree".

1962. Completion of Netherlands Automatic Telephone System. Inscr. "1962".
926. **189.** 4 c. red & black .. 10 10
927. – 12 c. drab and black.. 20 10
928. – 30 c. ochre, bl. & blk.. 2·75 1·40
DESIGNS—VERT. 12 c. Diagram of telephone network. HORIZ. 30 c. Arch and telephone dial.

1962. Europa.
929. **190.** 12 c. blk., yell. & bistre 10 10
930. 30 c. blk., yellow & bl. 90 60

191. "Polder" Landscape (reclaimed area). **192.** Children cooking Meal.

1962.
935 – 4 c. blue and blue .. 10 10
937 191 6 c. deep green & green 40 10
938 – 10 c. dp purple & pur 10 10
DESIGNS: 4 c. Cooling towers, State mines, Limburg. 10 c. Delta excavation works.

1962. Child Welfare.
940. **192.** 4 c.+4 c. red 10 10
941. – 6 c.+4 c. bistre .. 70 55
942. – 8 c.+4 c. blue .. 1·25 1·25
943. – 12 c.+9 c. green .. 10 10
944. – 30 c.+9 c. lake .. 2·25 2·75
DESIGNS—Children: 6 c. Cycling. 8 c. Watering flowers. 12 c. Feeding poultry. 30 c. Making music.

193. Ears of Wheat. **194.** "Gallery" Windmill.

1963. Freedom from Hunger.
945. **193.** 12 c. ochre and blue 10 10
946. 30 c. ochre and red .. 1·00 75

1963. Cultural, Health and Social Welfare Funds. Windmill types.
947. **194.** 4 c.+4 c. blue .. 1·00 1·00
948. – 6 c.+4 c. violet .. 1·00 1·00
949. – 8 c.+4 c. green .. 1·40 1·40
950. – 12 c.+8 c. brown .. 1·75 25
951. – 30 c.+10 c. red .. 2·00 2·00
WINDMILLS—VERT. 6 c. North Holland polder. 12 c. "Post". 30 c. "Wip". HORIZ. 8 c. South Holland polder.

195. **196.** Wayside First Aid Post.

1963. Paris Postal Conference Cent.
952. **195.** 30 c. blue, green & blk. 1·25 1·00

1963. Red Cross Fund and Cent. (8 c.).
953. **196.** 4 c.+4 c. blue and red 40 40
954. – 6 c.+4 c. violet and red 25 30
955. – 8 c.+4 c. red & black 90 75
956. – 12 c.+9 c. brn. & red.. 35 15
957. – 30 c.+9 c. grn. & red.. 1·25 1·60
DESIGNS: 6 c. "Books" collection-box. 8 c. Crosses. 12 c. "International Aid" (Negro children at meal). 30 c. First aid party tending casualty.

197. "Co-operation". **198.** "Auntie Luce sat on a goose . . .".

1963. Europa.
958. **197.** 12 c. orange and brown 10 10
959. 30 c. orange and green 1·25 1·00

1963. Child Welfare.
960. **198.** 4 c.+4 c. ult. & blue.. 10 10
961. – 6 c.+4 c. green & red.. 70 65
962. – 8 c.+4 c. brn. & green 90 65
963. – 12 c.+9 c. vio. & yell. 10 10
964. – 30 c.+8 c. bl. & pink.. 1·75 1·75
DESIGNS (Nursery rhymes): 6 c. "In the Hague there lives a count . . .". 8 c. "One day I passed a puppet's fair . . .". 12 c. "Storky, storky, Billy Spoon . . .". 30 c. "Ride on a little pram . . .".

199. William, Prince of Orange, landing at Scheveningen. **200.** Knights' Hall, The Hague.

1963. 150th Anniv of Kingdom of the Netherlands.
965 **199** 4 c. black, bistre & bl 10 10
966 5 c. black, red & green 10 10
967 – 12 c. bistre, blue & blk 10 10
968 – 30 c. red and black 50 50
DESIGNS: 12 c. Triumvirate: Van Hogendorp, Van Limburg, and Van der Duyn van Maasdam. 30 c. William I taking oath of allegiance.

1964. 500th Anniv. of 1st States-General Meeting.
969. **200.** 12 c. black and olive.. 15 10

DESIGNS: 8 c. Three red deer. 12 c. Three kittens. 30 c. European bison and calf.

201. Guide Dog for the Blind.

1964. Cultural, Health and Social Welfare Funds. Animals.
970. **201.** 5 c.+5 c. red, black and olive 60 50
971. – 8 c.+5 c. brown, black and red 30 30
972. – 12 c.+9 c. black, grey and bistre 55 15
973. – 30 c.+9 c. multicoloured 85 70

202. University Arms. **203.** Station Signal.

1964. 350th Anniv. of Groningen University.
974. **202.** 12 c. slate 10 10
975. – 30 c. brown 20 15
DESIGN: 30 c. "AG" monogram.

1964. 125th Anniv. of Netherlands Railways.
976. **203.** 15 c. black and green.. 20 10
977. – 40 c. black and yellow 90 70
DESIGN: 40 c. Electric train at speed.

204. Bible and Dove. **205.** Europa "Flower".

1964. 150th Anniv. of Netherlands Bible Society.
978. **204.** 15 c. brown 10 10

1964. Europa.
979. **205.** 15 c. green 15 10
980. 20 c. brown 35 25

1964. 20th Anniv. of "BENELUX" As T **150a** of Luxembourg, but smaller (35×22 mm.).
981. 15 c. violet and flesh .. 10 10

206. Young Artist. **207.** Queen Juliana.

1964. Child Welfare.
982. **206.** 7 c.+3 c. blue & green 40 50
983. – 10 c.+5 c. red, pink and green 35 40
984. – 15 c.+10 c. yellow, black and bistre .. 10 10
985. – 20 c.+10 c. red, sepia and mauve .. 45 45
986. – 40 c.+15 c. grn. & blue 75 70
DESIGNS: 10 c. Ballet-dancing. 15 c. Playing the recorder. 20 c. Masquerading. 40 c. Toy-making.

1964. 10th Anniv. of Statute for the Kingdom.
987. **207.** 15 c. green 10 10

208. "Killed in Action" (Waalwijk) and "Destroyed Town" (Rotterdam)(monuments). **209.** Medal of Knight (Class IV).

1965. "Resistance" Commem.
988. **208.** 7 c. black and red .. 10 10
989. – 15 c. black and olive.. 10 10
990. – 40 c. black and red .. 1·25 75
MONUMENTS: 15 c. "Docker" (Amsterdam) and "Killed in Action" (Waalwijk). 40 c. "Destroyed Town" (Rotterdam) and "Docker" (Amsterdam).

1965. 150th Anniv. of Military William Order.
991. **209.** 1 g. grey 90 55

210. I.T.U. Emblem and "Lines of Communication". **211.** Veere.

1965. Cent. of I.T.U.
992. **210.** 20 c. blue and drab .. 20 15
993. 40 c. brown and blue 65 50

1965. Cultural, Health and Social Welfare Funds.

994. 211. 8 c.+6 c. blk. & yell. 30 45
995. – 10 c.+6 c. blk. & turq. 45 40
996. – 18 c.+12 c. black and brown 35 15
997. – 20 c.+10 c. blk. & blue 45 40
998. – 40 c.+10 c. blk. & grn. 55 55

DESIGNS (Dutch towns): 10 c. Thorn. 18 c. Dordrecht. 20 c. Staveren. 40 c. Medemblik.

212. Europa "Sprig". 213. Girl's Head.

1965. Europa.

999. 212. 18 c. black, red & brn. 20 10
1000. 20 c. black, red & blue 30 25

1965. Child Welfare. Multicoloured.

1001. 8 c.+6 c. Type 213 .. 10 10
1002. 10 c.+6 c. Ship .. 50 50
1003. 18 c.+12 c. Boy (vert.) 10 10
1004. 20 c.+10 c. Duck-pond 65 60
1005. 40 c.+10 c. Tractor .. 1·25 80

214. Marines of 1665 and 1965. 215. "Help them to a safe Haven" (Queen Juliana).

1965. Tercentenary of Marine Corps.

1007. 214. 18 c. blue and red .. 10 10

1966. Intergovernmental Committee for European Migration (I.C.E.M.) Fund.

1008. 215. 18 c.+7 c. yell. & blk. 30 25
1009. 40 c.+20 c. red and blk. 30 15

216. Writing Materials. 217. Aircraft in Flight.

1966. Cultural, Health and Social Welfare Funds. Gysbert Japicx Commem. and 200th Anniv. of Netherlands Literary Society. Multicoloured.

1011. 10 c.+5 c. Type 216 .. 30 35
1012. 12 c.+8 c. Part of MS, Japicx's poem "Wobbelke" 30 35
1013. 20 c.+10 c. Part of miniature, "Knight Walewein" 40 35
1014. 25 c.+10 c. Initial "D" and part of MS, novel, "Ferguut" .. 50 65
1015. 40 c.+20 c. 16th-cent. printery (woodcut) 40 65

1966. Air (Special Flights).

1016. 217. 25 c. multicoloured 30 40

218. Europa "Ship". 219. Infant.

1966. Europa.

1017 218 20 c. green and yellow 15 10
1018 40 c. deep blue & blue 30 15

1966. Child Welfare.

1019. 219. 10 c.+5 c. red & blue 10 10
1020. – 12 c.+8 c. green & red 10 10
1021. – 20 c.+10 c. bl. & red 10 10
1022. – 25 c.+10 c. pur. & bl. 80 90
1023. – 40 c.+20 c. red & grn. 70 80

DESIGNS: 12 c. Young girl. 20 c. Boy in water. 25 c. Girl with moped. 40 c. Young man with horse.

220. Assembly Hall. 221. Whelk Eggs.

1967. 125th Anniv. of Delft Technological University.

1025. 220. 20 c. sepia and yellow 10 10

1967. Cultural, Health and Social Welfare Funds. Marine Fauna.

1026 221 12 c.+8 c. brn & grn 20 20
1027 – 15 c.+10 c. blue, light blue and deep blue 20 20
1028 – 20 c.+10 c. mult 20 15
1029 – 25 c.+10 c. purple, brown and bistre .. 45 50
1030 – 45 c.+20 c. mult 70 65

DESIGNS: 15 c. Whelk. 20 c. Mussel. 25 c. Jellyfish. 45 c. Crab.

222. Cogwheels. 223. Netherlands 5 c. Stamp of 1852.

1967. Europa.

1031 222 20 c. blue & light blue 40 10
1032 45 c. purple & lt pur 1·00 70

1967. "Amphilex 67" Stamp Exn., Amsterdam.

1035. 223. 20 c. blue and black .. 1·90 1·90
1036. – 25 c. red and black .. 1·90 1·90
1037. – 75 c. green and black 1·90 1·90

DESIGNS: 25 c. Netherlands 10 c. stamp of 1864. 75 c. Netherlands 20 c. stamp of 1867.

Nos. 1035/7 were sold at the Exhibition and at post offices at 3 g. 70, which included entrance fee to the Exhibition.

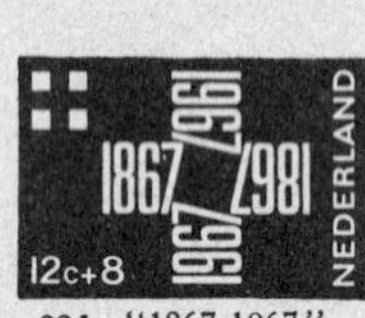

224. "1867-1967". 225. "Porcupine Lullaby".

1967. Centenary of Dutch Red Cross.

1038. 12 c.+8 c. blue and red 20 20
1039. 15 c.+10 c. red .. 35 35
1040. 20 c.+10 c. olive & red .. 20 15
1041. 25 c.+10 c. grn. & red .. 35 40
1042. 45 c.+20 c. grey & red .. 60 70

DESIGNS: 12 c. Type 224. 15 c. Red crosses. 20 c. "NRK" ("Nederlandsche Rood Kruis") in the form of a cross. 25 c. Maltese cross and "red" crosses. 45 c. "100" in the form of a cross.

1967. Child Welfare. Multicoloured.

1043. 12 c.+8 c. Type 225 .. 10 10
1044. 15 c.+10 c. "The Whistling Kettle" .. 10 10
1045. 20 c.+10 c. "Dikkertje Dap" (giraffe) .. 10 10
1046. 25 c.+10 c. "The Flowerseller" .. 70 80
1047. 45 c.+20 c. "Pippeloentje" (bear) 80 95

226. "Financial Automation".

1968. 50th Anniv. of Netherlands Postal Cheque and Clearing Service.

1049. 226. 20 c. red, black & yell. 15 10

227. St. Servatius' Bridge, Maastricht. 228. Europa "Key".

1968. Cultural, Health and Social Welfare Funds. Dutch Bridges.

1050. 227. 12 c.+8 c. green .. 40 50
1051. – 15 c.+10 c. brown .. 60 70
1052. – 20 c.+10 c. red .. 1·50 25
1053. – 25 c.+10 c. blue .. 40 50
1054. – 45 c.+20 c. blue .. 60 80

BRIDGES: 15 c. Magere ("Narrow"), Amsterdam. 20 c. Railway, Culemborg. 25 c. Van Brienenoord, Rotterdam. 45 c. Oosterschelde, Zeeland.

1968. Europa.

1055. 228. 20 c. blue 20 10
1056. 45 c. red 70 60

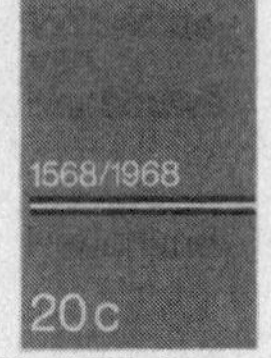

229. "Wilhelmus van Nassouwe". 230. "Wright" Biplane and Cessna Light Aircraft.

1968. 400th Anniv. of Dutch National Anthem, "Wilhelmus".

1057. 229. 20 c. multicoloured .. 20 10

1968. Dutch Aviation Anniversaries.

1058. 12 c. black, red & mauve 10 10
1059. 20 c. black, emerald & grn. 10 10
1060. 45 c. black, blue & green 1·25 1·25

DESIGNS AND EVENTS: 12 c. T 230 (60th anniv. (1967) of Royal Netherlands Aeronautical Assn.). 20 c. Fokker "F-2" and "F-29" "Fellowship" aircraft (50th anniv. (1969) of Royal Netherlands Aircraft Factories "Fokker"). 45 c. De Havilland "DH-9" and Douglas "DC-9" aircraft (50th anniv. (1969) of Royal Dutch Airlines "KLM").

231. "Goblin".

1968. Child Welfare.

1061. 231. 12 c.+8 c. pink, blk. and green .. 10 10
1062. – 15 c.+10 c. pink, blue and black .. 10 10
1063. – 20 c.+10 c. blue, green and black 10 10
1064. – 25 c.+10 c. red, yellow and black .. 1·50 1·50
1065. – 45 c.+20 c. yellow, orange & black .. 1·75 1·75

DESIGNS: 15 c. "Giant"; 20 c. "Witch"; 25 c. "Dragon"; 45 c. "Sorcerer".

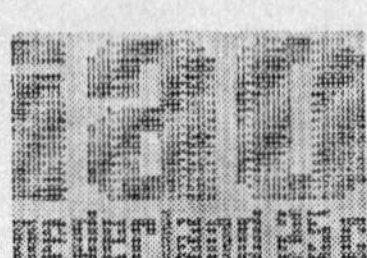

232. "I A O" (Internationale Arbeidsorganisatie).

1969. 50th Anniv. of I.L.O.

1067. 232. 25 c. red and black .. 35 10
1068. 45 c. blue and black 65 65

233. Queen Juliana. 234. Villa, Huis ter Heide (1915).

1969. (a) Type 233.

1069. 233. 25 c. red .. .. 1·75 10
1069c. 30 c. brown 15 10
1070a. 35 c. blue 20 10
1071a. 40 c. red 25 10
1072a. 45 c. blue 30 10
1073a. 50 c. purple 25 10
1073c. 55 c. red 20 10
1074a. 60 c. blue 20 10
1075. 70 c. brown 40 10
1076. 75 c. green 45 10
1077. 80 c. red 45 10
1077a. 90 c. grey 50 10

(b) Size 22 × 33 mm.

1078. – 1 g. green 50 10
1079. – 1 g. 25 lake 70 10
1080. – 1 g. 50 brown 80 10
1081. – 2 g. mauve 95 10
1082. – 2 g. 50 blue .. .. 1·25 10
1083. – 5 g. grey .. .. 3·50 10
1084. – 10 g. blue .. .. 4·50 80

DESIGNS: 1 g., 1 g. 25, 1 g. 50, 2 g., 2g. 50, 5 g. and 10 g. similar to Type 233.

1969. Cultural, Health and Social Welfare Funds. 20th-century Dutch Architecture.

1085. 234. 12 c.+8 c. blk. & brn. 70 70
1086. – 15 c.+10 c. black, red and blue .. 70 70
1087. – 20 c.+10 c. blk. & vio. 70 70
1088. – 25 c.+10 c. brn. & grn. 70 30
1089. – 45 c.+20 c. black, blue and yellow .. 70 70

DESIGNS: 15 c. Private House, Utrecht (1924). 20 c. Open-Air School, Amsterdam (1930). 25 c. Orphanage, Amsterdam (1960). 45 c. Congress Building, The Hague (1969).

235. Colonnade. 236. Stylised "Crab" (of Cancer).

1969. Europa.

1090. 235. 25 c. blue 40 10
1091. 45 c. red .. .. 1·25 1·10

1969. 20th Anniv. of Queen Wilhelmina Cancer Fund.

1092. 236. 12 c.+8 c. violet .. 75 75
1093. 25 c.+10 c. orange .. 1·00 30
1094. 45 c.+20 c. green .. 1·40 1·75

1969. 25th Anniv. of "BENELUX" Customs Union. As T 186 of Luxembourg.

1095. 25 c. multicoloured .. 30 10

238. Erasmus. 239. Child with Violin.

1969. 500th Birth Anniv. of Desiderius Erasmus.

1096. 238. 25 c. purple on green 30 10

1969. Child Welfare.

1097. – 12 c.+8 c. black, yellow and blue 10 10
1098. 239. 15 c.+10 c. black and red .. 10 10
1099. – 20 c.+10 c. black, yellow and red .. 1·90 2·00
1100. – 25 c.+10 c. black, red and yellow .. 10 10
1101. – 45 c.+20 c. black, red and green .. 1·90 2·00

DESIGNS—VERT. 12 c. Child with recorder. 20 c. Child with drum. HORIZ. 25 c. Three choristers. 45 c. Two dancers.

240. Queen Juliana and "Sunlit Road". 241. Prof. E. M. Meijers (author of "Burgerlijk Wetboek").

1969. 25th Anniv. of Statute for the Kingdom.

1103. 240. 25 c. multicoloured .. 30 10

1970. Introduction of New Netherlands Civil Code ("Burgerlijk Wetboek")

1104 241 25 c. ultramarine, green and blue .. 30 10

242. Netherlands Pavilion. 243. "Circle to Square".

1970. Expo 70, World Fair, Osaka, Japan.

1105. 242. 25 c. grey, blue & red 30 10

1970. Cultural, Health and Social Welfare Funds.

1106. 243. 12 c.+8 c. blk. on yell. 1·10 1·25
1107. – 15 c.+10 c. black on silver .. .. 1·10 1·25
1108. – 20 c.+10 c. black .. 1·10 1·25
1109. – 25 c.+10 c. blk. on bl. 1·10 70
1110. – 45 c.+20 c. white on grey .. .. 1·10 1·25

DESIGNS: 15 c. Parallel planes in cube. 20 c. Overlapping scales. 25 c. Concentric circles in transition. 45 c. Spirals.

244. "V" Symbol. **245.** "Flaming Sun".

1970. 25th Anniv. of Liberation.
1111. **244.** 12 c. red, blue & brown 40 10

1970. Europa.
1112. **245.** 25 c. red 40 10
1113. 45 c. blue .. .. 1·60 1·00

246. "Work and Co-operation". **247.** Globe on Plinth.

1970. Inter-Parliamentary Union Conf.
1114. **246.** 25 c. green, blk. & grey 40 10

1970. 25th Anniv. of United Nations.
1115. **247.** 45 c. blk., violet and bl. 75 70

248. Human Heart. **249.** Toy Block.

1970. Netherlands Heart Foundation.
1116. **248.** 12 c.+8 c. red, black and yellow .. 80 80
1117. 25 c.+10 c. red, black and mauve .. 80 65
1118. 45 c.+20 c. red, black and green .. 80 80

1970. Child Welfare. "The Child and the Cube".
1119. **249.** 12 c.+8 c. blue, violet and green 10 10
1120. – 15 c.+10 c. green, blue and yellow .. 1·60 1·60
1121. **249.** 20 c.+10 c. mauve, red and violet .. 1·60 1·60
1122. – 25 c.+10 c. red, yell. and mauve .. 15 10
1123. **249.** 45 c.+20 c. grey, cream and black .. .. 2·00 2·00
DESIGN: 15 c., 25 c. As Type **249**, but showing underside of block.

250. "Fourteenth Census 1971".

1971. 14th Netherlands Census.
1125. **250.** 15 c. purple 15 10

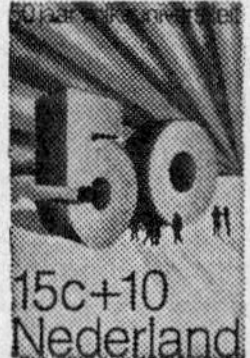

251. "50 years of Adult University Education". **252.** Europa Chain.

1971. Cultural, Health and Social Welfare Funds. Other designs show 15th-century wooden statues by unknown artists.
1126. **251.** 15 c. + 10 c. blk., red & yellow .. 1·50 1·50
1127. – 20 c. + 10 c. blk. & green on green 1·00 1·00
1128. – 25 c. + 10 c. blk. & orange on orge. 1·25 60
1129. – 30 c. + 15 c. blk. and blue on blue 1·50 1·50
1130. – 45 c. + 20 c. blk. & red on pink .. 1·50 1·50
STATUES: 20 c. "Apostle Paul". 25 c. "Joachim and Ann". 30 c. "John the Baptist and Scribes". 45 c. "Ann, Mary and Christ-Child" (detail).

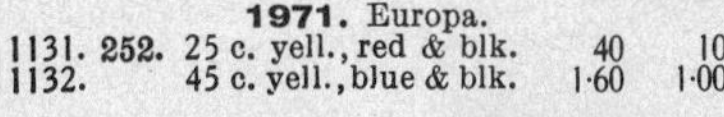
1971. Europa.
1131. **252.** 25 c. yell., red & blk. 40 10
1132. 45 c. yell., blue & blk. 1·60 1·00

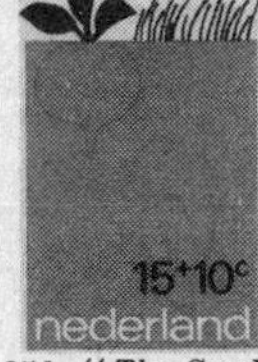

253. Carnation Symbol of Prince Bernhard Fund. **254.** "The Good Earth".

1971. Prince Bernhard's 60th Birthday.
1133. **253.** 15 c. yell., grey & blk. 15 10
1134. – 20 c. multicoloured .. 25 15
1135. – 25 c. multicoloured .. 25 10
1136. – 45 c.+20 c. blk., pur. and yellow .. 2·75 2·75
DESIGNS—HORIZ. 20 c. Panda symbol of World Wildlife Fund. VERT. 25 c. Prince Bernhard. 45 c. Statue, Borobudur Temple, Indonesia.

1971. Child Welfare.
1137. **254.** 15 c.+10 c. red, purple and black 10 10
1138. – 20 c.+10 c. mult. .. 30 15
1139. – 25 c.+10 c. mult. .. 15 10
1140. – 30 c.+15 c. bl., violet and black 85 70
1141. – 45 c.+20 c. blue, green and black .. 1·75 2·00
DESIGNS—VERT. 20 c. Butterfly. 45 c. Reflecting water. HORIZ. 25 c. Sun waving. 30 c. Moon winking.

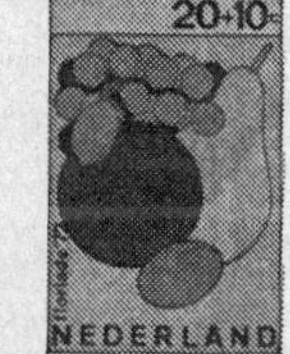

255. Delta Map. **256.** "Fruits".

1972. Delta Sea-Defences Plan.
1143. **255.** 20 c. multicoloured .. 30 10

1972. Cultural, Health and Social Welfare Funds. "Floriade Flower Show" (20 c., 25 c.) and "Holland Arts Festival" (30 c., 45 c.). Multicoloured.
1144. 20 c.+10 c. Type **256** .. 1·25 1·00
1145. 25 c.+10 c. "Flower" .. 1·25 1·00
1146. 30 c.+15 c. "Sunlit Landscape" .. .. 1·25 70
1147. 45 c.+25 c. "Music" .. 1·25 1·00

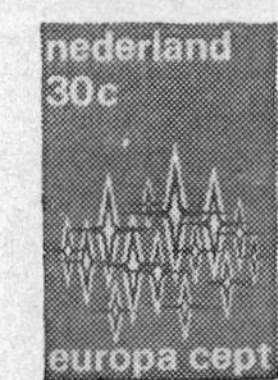

257. "Communications". **258.** "There is more to be done in the world than ever before" (Thorbecke).

1972. Europa.
1148. **257.** 30 c. brown and blue 85 10
1149. 45 c. brown and orge. 1·40 1·25

1972. Death Centenary of J. R. Thorbecke (statesman).
1150. **258.** 30 c. black and blue 30 10

259. Netherlands Flag. **260.** Hurdling.

1972. 400th Anniv. of Netherlands Flag.
1151. **259.** 20 c. multicoloured .. 60 15
1152. 25 c. multicoloured .. 1·40 10

1972. Olympic Games, Munich. Mult.
1153. 20 c. Type **260** 15 10
1154. 30 c. Diving 15 10
1155. 45 c. Cycling .. .. 1·00 1·25

261. Red Cross. **262.** Prince Willem-Alexander.

1972. Netherlands Red Cross.
1156. **261.** 5 c. red 10 10
1157. – 20 c.+10 c. red & pink 60 60
1158. – 25 c.+10 c. red & orge. 80 1·00
1159. – 30 c.+15 c. red & blk. 75 35
1160. – 45 c.+25 c. red & blue 85 95
DESIGNS: 20 c. Accident services. 25 c. Blood transfusion. 30 c. Refugee relief. 45 c. Child care.

1972. Child Welfare. Multicoloured.
1161. 25 c.+15 c. Type **262** .. 15 15
1162. 30 c.+10 c. Prince Johan Friso 70 80
1163. 35 c.+15 c. Prince Constantijn 70 10
1164. 50 c.+20 c. The Three Princes .. .. 2·00 2·50
Nos. 1162/4 are horiz.

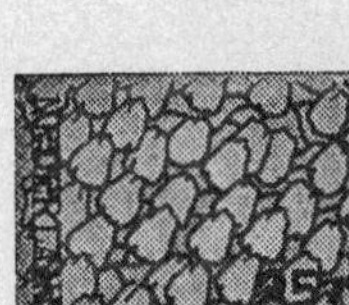

263. Tulips in Bloom. **264.** "De Zeven Provincien" (De Ruyter's flagship).

1973. Tulip Exports.
1166. **263.** 25 c. multicoloured .. 75 10

1973. Cultural, Health and Social Welfare Funds. Dutch Ships. Multicoloured.
1167 25 c.+15 c. Type **264** .. 1·25 1·50
1168 30 c.+10 c. "W.A. Scholten" (steamship) (horiz) .. .. 1·25 1·50
1169 35 c.+15 c. "Veendam" (liner) (horiz) .. .. 1·50 1·00
1170 50 c.+20 c. Fishing boat (from etching by R. Nooms) .. .. 1·50 1·50

265. Europa "Posthorn". **266.** Hockey-players.

1973. Europa.
1171. **265.** 35 c. light. bl. & bl. 45 40
1172. 50 c. blue and violet 80 75

1973. Events and Anniversaries. Mult.
1173. 25 c. Type **266** 25 10
1174. 30 c. Gymnastics .. 2·25 55
1175. 35 c. Dish aerial (vert.) 35 10
1176. 50 c. Rainbow 60 60
EVENTS—VERT. 25 c. 75th Anniv. of Royal Netherlands Hockey Assn. 30 c. World Gymnastics Championships, Rotterdam. HORIZ. 35 c. Opening of Satellite Station, Burum. 50 c. Centenary of World Meteorological Organization.

267. Queen Juliana. **268.** "Co-operation".

1973. Silver Jubilee of Queen Juliana's Accession.
1177. **267.** 40 c. multicoloured .. 50 10

1973. Int. Development Co-operation.
1178. **268.** 40 c. multicoloured .. 1·00 10

269. "Chess". **270.** Northern Goshawk.

1973. Child Welfare.
1179. **269.** 25 c.+15 c. red, yellow and black 65 15
1180. – 30 c.+10 c. green, mauve and black .. 1·00 70
1181. – 40 c.+20 c. yellow, green and black .. 80 10
1182. – 50 c.+20 c. blue, yellow and black .. 2·25 2·25
DESIGNS: 30 c. "Noughts and crosses". 40 c. "Maze". 50 c. "Dominoes".

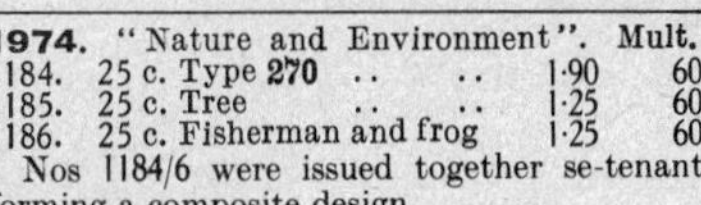
1974. "Nature and Environment". Mult.
1184. 25 c. Type **270** .. .. 1·90 60
1185. 25 c. Tree .. .. 1·25 60
1186. 25 c. Fisherman and frog 1·25 60
Nos 1184/6 were issued together se-tenant forming a composite design.

271. Bandsmen (World Band Contest, Kerkrade). **272.** Football on Pitch.

1974. Cultural, Health and Social Welfare Funds.
1187. **271.** 25 c.+15 c. mult. .. 90 90
1188. – 30 c.+10 c. mult. .. 90 90
1189. – 40 c.+20 c. brn., blk. and red 90 65
1190. – 50 c.+20 c. purple, black and red .. 90 90
DESIGNS: 30 c. Dancers and traffic-lights ("Modern Ballet"). 40 c. Herman Heijermans. 50 c. "Kniertje" (character from Heijermans' play "Op hoop van zegan"). The 40 c. and 50 c. commemorate the 50th Death Anniv. of the playwright.

1974. Sporting Events.
1191. **272.** 25 c. multicoloured .. 20 10
1192. 40 c. yell., red & mve. 30 10
DESIGNS AND EVENTS—HORIZ. 25 c. (World Cup Football Championships, West Germany). VERT. 40 c. Hand holding tennis ball (Royal Dutch Lawn Tennis Assn. 75th anniv.).

273. Netherlands Cattle. **274.** "BENELUX" (30th Anniv. of Benelux (Customs Union)).

1974. Anniversaries. Multicoloured.
1193 25 c. Type **273** .. .. 11·00 1·40
1194 25 c. "Cancer" .. 15 15
1195 40 c. "Suzanna" (lifeboat) seen through binoculars 20 10
EVENTS AND ANNIVERSARIES: No. 1193, Cent. of Netherlands Cattle Herdbook Society. No. 1194, 25th Anniv. of Queen Wilhelmina Cancer Research Fund. No. 1195. 150th Anniv. of Dutch Lifeboat Service.

1974. International Anniversaries.
1196 **274** 30 c. green, turq & bl 20 10
1197 – 45 c. dp bl, silver & bl 30 10
1198 – 45 c. yellow, bl & blk 30 10
DESIGNS—VERT. No. 1197, NATO emblem (25th anniv). 1198, Council of Europe emblem (25th anniv).

275. Hands with Letters. **276.** Boy with Hoop.

1974. Cent. of Universal Postal Union.
1199. **275.** 60 c. multicoloured .. 40 35

1974. 50th Anniv. of Child Welfare Issues. Early Photographs.
1200. **276.** 30 c.+15 c. brn. & blk. 15 15
1201. – 35 c.+20 c. brown .. 40 50
1202. – 45 c.+20 c. black .. 40 15
1203. – 60 c.+20 c. black .. 1·00 1·40
DESIGNS: 35 c. Child and baby. 45 c. Two young girls. 60 c. Girl sitting on balustrade.

277. Amsterdam. **278.** St. Hubertus Hunting Lodge, De Hoge Veluwe National Park.

1975. Anniversaries. Multicoloured.
1205. 30 c. Type **277** 20 10
1206. 30 c. Synagogue and map 40 15
1207. 35 c. Type **277** 35 10
1208. 45 c. "Window" in human brain 40 15

ANNIVERSARIES: Nos. 1205, 1207, Amsterdam (700th anniv.). No. 1206, Portuguese-Israelite Synagogue, Amsterdam (300th anniv.). No. 1208, Leyden University and university education (400th anniv.).

1975. Cultural, Health and Social Welfare Funds. National Monument Year. Preserved Monuments. Multicoloured.
1209 35 c.+20 c. Type **278** .. 50 50
1210 40 c.+15 c. Begijnhof (Beguinage), Amsterdam (vert) 50 50
1211 50 c.+20 c. "Kuiperspoort" (Cooper's gate), Middelburg (vert) .. 65 50
1212 60 c.+20 c. Orvelte village, Drenthe .. 75 90

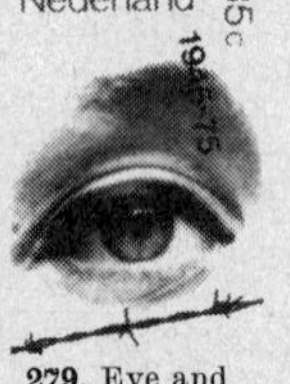

279. Eye and Barbed Wire. **280.** Company Emblem and "Stad Middleburg" (schooner).

1975. 30th Anniv. of Liberation.
1213. **279.** 35 c. black and red .. 30 10

1975. Cent. of Zeeland Shipping Company.
1214. **280.** 35 c. multicoloured .. 30 10

281. Dr. Albert Schweitzer crossing Lambarene River.

1975. Birth Cent. of Dr. Schweitzer.
1215. **281.** 50 c. multicoloured .. 40 10

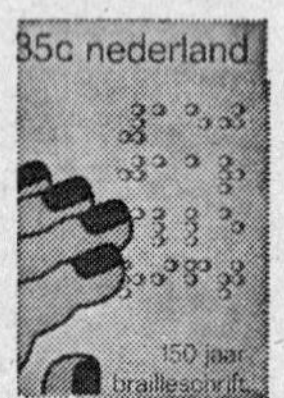

282. Man and Woman on "Playing-card". **283.** Braille Reading.

1975. International Events Multicoloured.
1216. 35 c. Type **282** (Int. Women's Year) .. 20 10
1217. 50 c. Metric scale (Metre Convention centenary) (horiz.) 30 10

1975. 150th Anniv. of Invention of Braille.
1218. **283** 35 c. multicoloured .. 30 10

284. Dutch 25c. Coins. **285.** "Four Orphans" (C. Simons), Torenstraat Orphanage, Medemblik.

1975. Savings Campaign.
1219. **284.** 50 c. grey, grn. & blue 35 10

1975. Child Welfare. Historic Ornamental Stones. Multicoloured.
1220. 35 c.+15 c. Type **285** .. 15 15
1221. 40 c.+15 c. "Milkmaid" Kooltuin Alkmaar .. 45 45
1222. 50 c.+25 c. "Four Sons of Aymon seated on Beyaert", Herengracht 30 10
1223. 60 c.+25 c. "Life at the Orphanage", Molenstraat Orphanage, Gorinchem 85 85

286. 18th-century Lottery Ticket. **287.** Numeral.

1976. 250th Anniv. of National Lottery.
1225. **286.** 35 c. multicoloured .. 30 10

1976.
1226 **287** 5 c. grey 10 10
1227 10 c. blue 10 10
1228 25 c. violet 10 10
1229 40 c. brown 15 10
1230 45 c. blue 30 10
1231 50 c. mauve 30 10
1232 55 c. green 45 10
1233 60 c. yellow 45 10
1234 65 c. brown 45 10
1235 70 c. violet 45 10
1236 80 c. mauve 50 10

288. West European Hedgehog.

1976. Cultural, Health and Social Welfare Funds. Nature Protection (1241, 1244) and Anniversaries. Multicoloured.
1241. 40 c.+20 c. Type **288** .. 60 60
1242. 45 c.+20 c. Open book (vert.) 60 60
1243. 55 c.+20 c. People and organization initials .. 70 25
1244. 75 c.+25 c. Frog and spawn (vert.) 85 85

ANNIVERSARIES: No. 1242, 175th Anniv. of Primary education and centenary of Agricultural education. No. 1245, 75th Anniv. of Social Security Bank and legislation.

289. Admiral Michiel de Ruyter (statue).

1976. 300th Death Anniv. of Admiral Michiel de Ruyter.
1245. **289.** 55 c. multicoloured .. 35 10

290. Guillaume Groen van Prinsterer.

1976. Death Centenary of Guillaume Groen van Prinsterer (statesman).
1246. **290.** 55 c. multicoloured .. 35 10

291. Detail of 18th Century Calendar.

1976. Bicent. of American Revolution.
1247. **291.** 75 c. multicoloured .. 50 35

292. Long-distance Marchers. **293.** The Art of Printing.

1976. Sport and Recreation Anniversaries. Multicoloured.
1248. 40 c. Type **292** 20 15
1249. 55 c. Runners "photo-finish" 60 15

ANNIVERSARIES: 40 c. 60th Nijmegen Long-Distance March. 55 c. Royal Dutch Athletics Society (75th anniv.).

1976. Anniversaries.
1250. **293.** 45 c. red and blue .. 25 10
1251. – 55 c.+25 c. mult. .. 45 45

DESIGNS AND EVENTS: 45 c. Type **293.** (75th Anniv. of Netherlands Printer's organization) 55 c. Rheumatic patient "Within Care" (50th Anniv. of Dutch Anti-Rheumatism Association).

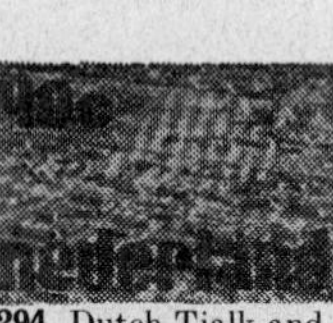

294. Dutch Tjalk and Reclaimed Land. **295.** Queen Wilhelmina 4½ c. Stamp, 1919.

1976. Zuider Zee Project—Reclamation and Urbanization. Multicoloured.
1252. **294.** 40 c. blue, olive & red 25 10
1253. – 75 c. yell, red & blue 50 35

DESIGN: 75 c. Duck flying over reclaimed land.

1976. "Amphilex '77" International Stamp Exhibition, Amsterdam (1977) (1st series). Stamp Portraits of Queen Wilhelmina. Multicoloured.
1254. – 55 c.+55 c. blue, deep grey and grey .. 70 75
1255. **295.** 55 c.+55 c. purple, deep grey and grey 70 75
1256. – 55 c.+55 c. brown, deep grey and grey 70 75
1257. – 75 c.+75 c. turq., deep grey and grey 70 75
1258. – 75 c.+75 c. blue, deep grey and grey .. 70 75

DESIGNS: No. 1254, 5 c. stamp, 1891. No. 1256, 25 c. stamp, 1924. No. 1257, 15 c. stamp, 1940. No. 1258, 25 c. stamp, 1947.
See also Nos. 1273/6.

296. "Football" (J. Raats).

1976. Child Welfare. Children's Paintings. Multicoloured.
1259. 40 c.+20 c. Type **296** .. 25 25
1260. 45 c.+20 c. "Boat" (L Jacobs) 25 25
1261. 55 c.+20 c. "Elephant" (M. Lugtenburg) .. 30 10
1262. 75 c.+25 c. "Caravan" (A. Seeleman) 65 80

297. Ballot-paper and Pencil.

1977. National Events. Multicoloured.
1264. 40 c. "Energy" (vert.) .. 30 10
1265. 45 c. Type **297** 40 10

EVENTS: 40 c. "Be wise with energy" campaign. 45 c. Elections to Lower House of States General.
See also No. 1268.

298. Spinoza. **299.** Early Type Faces and "a" on Bible Script.

1977. 300th Death Anniv. of Barach (Benedictus) de Spinoza (philosopher).
1266. **298.** 75 c. multicoloured .. 60 30

1977. 500th Anniv. of Printing of "Delft Bible".
1267. **299.** 55 c. multicoloured .. 40 30

1977. Elections to Lower House of States General. As T **297** but also inscribed "25 MEI '77".
1268 45 c. multicoloured .. 45 10

300. Altar of Goddess Nehalennia. **301.** "Kaleidoscope".

1977. Cultural, Health and Social Welfare Funds. Roman Archaeological Discoveries.
1269. – 40 c.+20 c. mult. .. 30 30
1270. **300.** 45 c.+20 c. black, stone and green .. 30 25
1271. – 55 c.+20 c. black, blue and red .. 30 20
1272. – 75 c.+25 c. black, grey and yellow .. 40 45

DESIGNS: 40 c. Baths, Heerlen. 55 c. Remains of Zwammerdam ship. 75 c. Parade helmet.

1977. "Amphilex 1977" International Stamp Exhibition, Amsterdam (2nd series). As T **295.**
1273. 55 c.+45 c. green, brown and grey 45 50
1274. 55 c.+45 c. blue, brown and grey 45 50
1275. 55 c.+45 c. blue, brown and grey 45 50
1276. 55 c.+45 c. red, brown and grey 45 50

DESIGNS: No. 1273, Queen Wilhelmina 1 g. stamp, 1898. No. 1274, Queen Wilhelmina 20 c. stamp, 1923. No. 1275, Queen Wilhelmina 12½ c. stamp, 1938, No. 1276, Queen Wilhelmina 10 c. stamp, 1948.

1977. Bicentenary of Netherlands Society for Industry and Commerce.
1278. **301.** 55 c. multicoloured .. 30 10

302. Man in Wheelchair and Maze of Steps. **303.** Risk of Drowning.

1977. Anniversaries.
1279 **302** 40 c. brown, grn & bl 20 10
1280 – 45 c. multicoloured .. 25 10
1281 – 55 c. multicoloured .. 35 10

DESIGNS—HORIZ. 40 c. Type **302** (50th anniv of A.V.O. Nederland). 45 c. Diagram of water current (50th anniv of Delft Hydraulic Laboratory). VERT. 55 c. Teeth (centenary of dentists' training in Netherlands).

1977. Child Welfare. Dangers to Children. Multicoloured.
1282. 40 c.+20 c. Type **303** 30 20
1283. 45 c.+20 c. Medicine cabinet (poisons) .. 30 25
1284. 55 c.+20 c. Balls in road (traffic) 30 20
1285. 75 c.+25 c. Matches (fire) 55 65

304. "Postcode". **305.** Makkum Dish.

1978. Introduction of Postcodes.
1287. **304.** 40 c. red and blue .. 20 10
1288. 45 c. red and blue .. 25 10

1978. Cultural, Health and Social Welfare Funds. Multicoloured.
1289 40 c.+20 c. Anna Maria van Schurman (writer) 30 30
1290 45 c.+20 c. Passage from letter by Belle de Zuylen (Mme. de Charriere) .. 30 25
1291 55 c.+20 c. Delft dish .. 30 25
1292 75 c.+25 c. Type **305** .. 40 45

306. "Human Rights" Treaty. **307.** Chess.

1978. European Series.
1293. **306.** 45 c. grey, black and blue 25 10
1294. – 55 c. black, stone and orange 35 10

DESIGN: 55 c. Haarlem Town Hall (Europa).

1978. Sports.
1295 **307** 40 c. multicoloured .. 50 15
1296 – 45 c. red and blue .. 50 15

DESIGN: 45 c. The word "Korfbal".

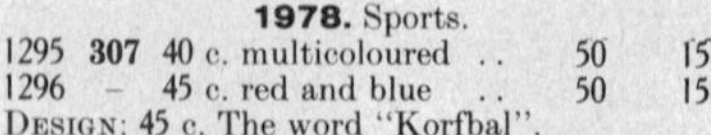

308. Kidney Donor. **309.** Epaulettes.

1978. Health Care. Multicoloured.
1297. **308.** 40 c. black, blue & red 25 10
1298. – 45 c. multicoloured .. 30 10
1299. – 55 c.+25 c. red, grey and black .. 45 50

DESIGNS—VERT: 45 c. Heart and torch. HORIZ: 55 c. Red crosses on world map.

1978. 150th Anniv of Royal Military Academy, Breda.

1301 309 55 c. multicoloured .. 30 10

310. Verkade as Hamlet.

1978. Birth Cent. of Eduard Rutger Verkade (actor and producer).

1302. 310. 45 c. multicoloured.. 30 10

311. Boy ringing Doorbell.

1978. Child Welfare. Multicoloured.

1303. 40 c.+20 c. Type 311 .. 30 20
1304. 45 c.+20 c. Child reading 30 20
1305. 55 c.+20 c. Boy writing (vert.) 30 15
1306. 75 c.+25 c. Girl and blackboard 40 60

312. Clasped Hands and Arrows. 313. Names of European Community Members.

1979. 400th Anniv. of Treaty of Utrecht.

1308. 312. 55 c. blue 35 10

1979. First Direct Elections to European Assembly.

1309. 313. 45 c. red, blue and black 40 10

314. Queen Juliana.

1979. Queen Juliana's 70th Birthday.

1310. 314. 55 c. multicoloured.. 40 10

315. Fragment of "Psalmen Trilogie". (J. Andriessen.) 316. Netherlands Stamps and Magnifying Glass.

1979. Cultural, Health and Social Welfare Funds.

1311. 315. 40 c.+20 c. grey and red 30 30
1312. – 45 c.+20 c. grey and red 30 25
1313. – 55 c.+20 c. mult. .. 30 20
1314. – 75 c.+25 c. mult. .. 40 45

DESIGNS AND EVENTS: 150th anniv of Musical Society— 45 c. Choir. Restoration of St. John's Church, Gouda (stained glass windows)— 55 c. Mary (detail, "Birth of Christ"). 75 c. William of Orange (detail, "Relief of Leyden").

1979. Europa and 75th Anniv. of Scheveningen Radio. Multicoloured.

1315. 55 c. Type 316 .. .. 35 10
1316. 75 c. Liner and Morse Key 50 35

317. Map of Chambers of Commerce. 318. Action Shot of Football Match.

1979. 175th Anniv. of First Dutch Chamber of Commerce, Maastricht.

1317. 317. 45 c. multicoloured.. 40 15

1979. Anniversaries. Multicoloured.

1318. 45 c. Type 318 (Cent. of organized football) .. 35 15
1319. 55 c. Women's suffrage meeting. (60th anniv. of Women's suffrage) (vert.) 45 10

319. Porch of Old Amsterdam Theatre.

1979. 300th Death Annivs. of Joost van den Vondel (poet) and Jan Steen (painter). Multicoloured.

1320. 40 c. Type 319 .. .. 20 10
1321. 45 c. "Gay Company" (detail) (Jan Steen) .. 25 10

320. Hindustani Girl on Father's Shoulder (The Right to Love).

1979. Child Welfare. International Year of the Child.

1322. 320. 40 c.+20 c. grey, red and yellow .. 35 20
1323. – 45 c.+20 c. grey, red and black 35 15
1324. – 55 c.+20 c. grey, black and yellow .. 35 15
1325. – 75 c.+25 c. black, blue and red 45 60

DESIGNS—HORIZ: 45 c. Chilean child from refugee camp (The Right to Medical Care). VERT: 55 c. Senegalese boy from Sahel area (The Right to Food). 75 c. Class from Albert Cuyp School, Amsterdam (The Right to Education).

321. A. F. de Savornin Lohman. 322. Dunes.

1980. Dutch Politicians. Multicoloured.

1327 45 c. Type 321 (Christian Historical Union) .. 25 10
1328 50 c. P. J. Troelstra (Socialist Party) .. 25 10
1329 60 c. P. J. Oud (Liberal Party) 35 10

1980. Cultural, Health and Social Welfare Funds. Multicoloured.

1330. 45 c.+20 c. Type 322 .. 40 30
1331. 50 c.+20 c. Country estate (vert.) 40 30
1332. 60 c.+25 c. Lake district 50 25
1333. 80 c.+35 c. Moorland .. 65 65

323. British Bomber dropping Food Parcels. 324. Queen Beatrix and New Church, Amsterdam.

1980. 35th Anniv. of Liberation. Mult.

1334. 45 c. Type 323 .. .. 40 15
1335. 60 c. Anne Frank (horiz.) 60 10

1980. Installation of Queen Beatrix.

1336. 324. 60 c. blue, red & yell. 45 10
1337. 65 c. blue, red & yell 55 10

325. Young Stamp Collectors. 326. "Flight".

1980. "Jupostex 1980" Stamp Exhibition, Eindhoven, and Dutch Society of Stamp Dealers Show, The Hague.

1338 325 50 c. multicoloured .. 30 20

1980. Air. (Special Flights).

1339. 326. 1 g. blue and black.. 45 45

327. Bridge Players and Cards. 328. Road Haulage.

1980. Sports Events. Multicoloured.

1340. 50 c. Type 327 (Bridge Olympiad, Valkenburg) 30 10
1341. 60 c.+25 c. Sportswoman in wheelchair (Olympics for the Disabled, Arnhem and Veenendaal .. 50 40

1980. Transport.

1342. 328. 50 c. multicoloured .. 25 10
1343. – 60 c. blue, brn. & blk. 40 10
1344. – 80 c. multicoloured .. 45 25

DESIGNS: 60 c. Rail transport. 80 c. Motorised canal barge.

329. Queen Wilhelmina.

1980. Europa.

1345. 329. 60 c. blk., red & blue 35 10
1346. – 80 c. blk., red & blue 40 20

DESIGN: 80 c. Sir Winston Churchill.

330. Abraham Kuyper (first rector) and University Seal.

1980. Cent. of Amsterdam Free University.

1347. 330. 50 c. multicoloured .. 30 10

331. "Pop-up" Book 332. Saltmarsh.

1980. Child Welfare. Multicoloured.

1348. 45 c.+20 c. Type 331 .. 35 20
1349. 50 c.+20 c. Child flying on a book (vert.) .. 35 35
1350. 60 c.+30 c. Boy reading "Kikkerkoning" (vert.) 45 20
1351. 80 c.+30 c. Dreaming in a book 60 65

1981. Cultural, Health and Social Welfare Funds. Multicoloured.

1353. 45 c.+20 c. Type 332 .. 30 30
1354. 55 c.+25 c. Dyke .. 30 30
1355. 60 c.+25 c. Drain .. 35 30
1356. 65 c.+30 c. Cultivated land 40 40

333. Parcel (Parcel Post).

1981. P.T.T. Centenaries. Multicoloured.

1357. 45 c. Type 333 .. .. 25 10
1358. 55 c. Telephone, dish aerial and telephone directory page (public telephone service) .. 30 10
1359. 65 c. Savings bank books, deposit transfer card and savings bank stamps (National Savings Bank) 35 10

INDEX

Countries can be quickly located by referring to the index at the end of this volume.

334. Huis ten Bosch Royal Palace, The Hague.

1981.

1361. 334. 55 c. multicoloured 35 10

335. Carillon.

1981. Europa. Multicoloured.

1362. 45 c. Type 335 .. .. 35 10
1363. 65 c. Barrel organ .. 55 10

336. Council of State Emblem and Maps of 1531 and 1981.

1981. 450th Anniv. of Council of State.

1364. 336. 65 c. orge, deep orge. and red 45 10

337. Marshalling Yard, Excavator and Ship's Screw.

1981. Industrial and Agricultural Exports. Multicoloured.

1365. 45 c. Type 337 .. .. 40 15
1366. 55 c. Inner port, cast-iron component and weighing machine 40 15
1367. 60 c. Airport, tomato and lettuce 45 40
1368. 65 c. Motorway interchange, egg and cheese 55 10

338. "Integration in Society".

1981. Child Welfare. Integration of Handicapped Children. Multicoloured.

1369 45 c.+25 c. Type 338 .. 40 20
1370 55 c.+20 c. "Integration in the Family" (vert) 45 45
1371 60 c+25 c. Child vaccinated against polio (Upper Volta project) (vert) 50 50
1372 65 c.+30 c. "Integration among Friends" .. 60 20

339. Queen Beatrix. 340. Agnieten Chapel and Banners.

1981.

1374 339 65 c. brown & black 40 10
1375 70 c. lilac and black .. 55 10
1376 75 c. pink and black 50 10
1377 90 c. green and black 1·25 10
1378 1 g. lilac and black .. 50 10
1379 1 g. 20 bistre & black 80 10
1380 1 g. 40 green & black 1·75 10
1381 1 g. 50 lilac & black .. 90 10
1382 2 g. bistre and black 1·10 10
1383 2 g. 50 orange & black 1·50 15
1384 3 g. blue and black .. 1·50 10
1385 4 g. green and black 2·25 10
1386 5 g. blue and black .. 2·75 10
1387 6 g. 50 lilac & black .. 5·00 15
1388 7 g. blue and black .. 4·00 10
1389 7 g. 50 green & black 4·25 30

For this design but on uncoloured background see Nos. 1594/1605.

1982. 350th Anniv. of University of Amsterdam.

1395. 340. 65 c. multicoloured .. 50 10

341. Skater. **342.** Apple Blossom.

1982. Centenary of Royal Dutch Skating Association.
1396. **341.** 45 c. multicoloured .. 40 20

1982. Cultural, Health and Social Welfare Funds. Multicoloured.
1397. 50 c. + 20 c. Type **342** .. 40 45
1398. 60 c. + 25 c. Anemones .. 50 45
1399. 65 c. + 25 c. Roses .. 50 45
1400. 70 c. + 30 c. African violets 70 75

343. Stripes in National Colours.

1982. Bicentenary of Netherlands–United States Diplomatic Relations.
1401 **343** 50 c. red, blue & black 40 10
1402 65 c. red, blue & black 60 20

344. Sandwich Tern and Eider. **345.** Zebra Crossing.

1982. Waddenzee. Multicoloured.
1403. 50 c. Type **344** 40 15
1404. 70 c. Barnacle Geese .. 60 15

1982. 50th Anniv. of Dutch Road Safety Organization.
1405. **345.** 60 c. multicoloured .. 55 15

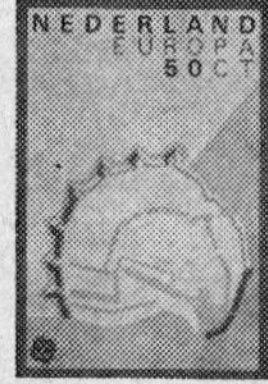

346. Ground Plan of Enkhuizen Fortifications. **347.** Aerial view of Palace and Liberation Monument.

1982. Europa. Multicoloured.
1406. 50 c. Type **346** 40 10
1407. 70 c. Part of ground plan of Coevorden fortifications 60 10

1982. Royal Palace, Dam Square, Amsterdam. Multicoloured.
1408. 50 c. Facade, ground plan and cross-section of Palace 40 10
1409. 60 c. Type **347** 45 10

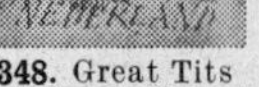

348. Great Tits and Child. **349.** Touring Club Activities.

1982. Child Welfare. Child and Animal. Mult.
1410. 50 c. + 30 c. Type **348** .. 60 30
1411. 60 c. + 20 c. Child arm-in-arm with cat 65 20
1412. 65 c. + 20 c. Child with drawing of rabbit .. 70 85
1413. 70 c. + 30 c. Child with palm cockatoo .. 1·00 95

1983. Cent. of Royal Dutch Touring Club.
1415. **349.** 70 c. multicoloured .. 65 10

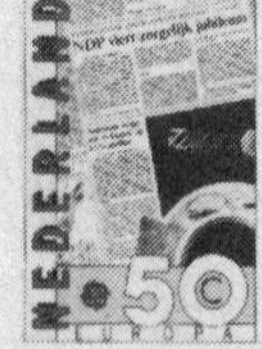

350. Johan van Oldenbarnevelt (statesman) (after J. Houbraken). **351.** Newspaper.

1983. Cultural, Health and Social Welfare Funds.
1416 **350** 50 c. + 20 c. pink, blue and black .. 50 40
1417 – 60 c. + 25 c. mult .. 60 40
1418 – 65 c. + 25 c. mult .. 75 60
1419 – 70 c. + 30 c. grey, black and gold .. 80 60

DESIGNS: 60 c. Willem Jansz Blaeu (cartographer) (after Thomas de Keijser). 65 c. Hugo de Groot (statesman) (after J. van Ravesteyn). 70 c. "Saskia van Uylenburch" (portrait of his wife by Rembrandt).

1983. Europa. Multicoloured.
1420. 50 c. Type **351** (75th anniv. of Netherlands Newspaper Publishers Assoc.) 40 10
1421. 70 c. European Communications Satellite and European Telecommunication Satellites Organization members' flags .. 60 10

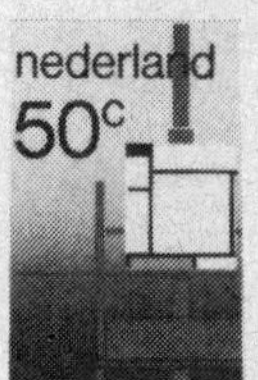

352. "Composition 1922" (P. Mondriaan). **353.** "Geneva Conventions".

1983. De Stijl Art Movement. Multicoloured.
1422. 50 c. Type **352** 40 10
1423. 65 c. Contra construction from "Maison Particuliere" (C. van Eesteren and T. van Doesburg) 60 20

1983. Red Cross.
1424. **353.** 50 c. + 25 c. mult. .. 45 45
1425. – 60 c. + 20 c. mult. .. 55 45
1426. – 65 c. + 25 c. mult. .. 70 45
1427. – 70 c. + 30 c. grey, black and red 80 70

DESIGNS: 60 c. Red Cross and text "charity, independence, impartiality". 65 c. "Sociomedical work". 70 c. Red Cross and text "For Peace".

354. Luther's Signature. **355.** Child looking at Donkey and Ox through Window.

1983. 500th Birth Anniv. of Martin Luther (Protestant Reformer).
1428. **354.** 70 c. multicoloured .. 40 10

1983. Child Welfare. Child and Christmas. Multicoloured.
1429. 50 c. + 10 c. Type **355** .. 50 50
1430. 50 c. + 25 c. Child riding flying snowman .. 60 20
1431. 60 c. + 30 c. Child in bed and star 75 75
1432. 70 c. + 30 c. Children dressed as the three kings 80 20

356. Parliament.

1984. Second Elections to European Parliament.
1434. **356.** 70 c. multicoloured .. 55 10

357. Lapwings. **358.** St. Servaas.

1984. Cultural, Health and Social Welfare Funds. Pasture Birds. Multicoloured.
1435. 50 c. + 20 c. Type **357** .. 50 35
1436. 60 c. + 25 c. Ruffs .. 70 35
1437. 65 c. + 25 c. Redshanks (vert.) 80 70
1438. 70 c. + 30 c. Black-tailed godwits (vert.) .. 85 80

1984. 1600th Death Anniv. of St. Servaas (Bishop of Tongeren and Maastricht).
1439. **358.** 60 c. multicoloured .. 50 10

359. Bridge.

1984. Europa. 25th Anniv. of European Post and Telecommunications Conference.
1440. **359.** 50 c. dp. blue & blue 40 10
1441. 70 c. green & lt green 70 10

360. Eye and Magnifying Glass.

1984. Centenary of Organized Philately in the Netherlands and "Filacento" International Stamp Exhibition, The Hague. Multicoloured.
1442. 50 c. + 20 c. Type **360** .. 40 40
1443. 60 c. + 25 c. 1909 cover .. 50 50
1444. 70 c. + 30 c. Stamp club meeting, 1949 .. .. 60 60

361. William of Orange (after Adriaen Thomaszoon Key).

1984. 400th Death Anniv. of William of Orange.
1446. **361.** 70 c. multicoloured .. 60 10

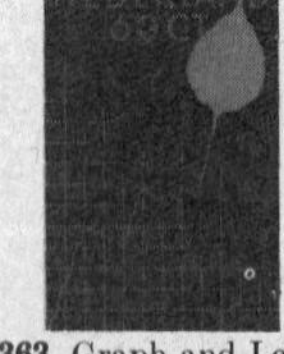

362. Giant Pandas and Globe. **363.** Graph and Leaf.

1984 World Wildlife Fund.
1447. **362.** 70 c. multicoloured .. 75 10

1984. 11th International Small Business Congress, Amsterdam.
1448. **363.** 60 c. multicoloured .. 55 10

364. Violin Lesson. **365.** Sunny, First Dutch Guide-Dog.

1984. Child Welfare. Strip Cartoons. Multicoloured.
1449. 50 c. + 25 c. Type **364** .. 40 25
1450. 60 c. + 20 c. At the dentist 75 55
1451. 65 c. + 20 c. The plumber 85 85
1452. 70 c. + 30 c. The king and money chest 65 35

1985. 50th Anniv. of Royal Dutch Guide-Dog Fund.
1454. **365.** 60 c. black, ochre and red 60 10

366. Plates and Cutlery on Place-mat. **367.** Saint Martin's Church, Zaltbommel.

1985. Tourism. Multicoloured.
1455. 50 c. Type **366** (Centenary of Travel and Holidays Association) 40 10
1456. 70 c. Kroller-Muller museum emblem, antlers and landscape (50th anniv. of De Hoge Veluwe National Park) 60 10

1985. Cultural, Health and Social Welfare Funds. Religious Buildings. Multicoloured.
1457. 50 c. + 20 c. Type **367** .. 60 45
1458. 60 c. + 25 c. Winterswijk synagogue and Holy Ark (horiz.) 65 55
1459. 65 c. + 25 c. Bolsward Baptist church .. 80 55
1460. 70 c. + 30 c. Saint John's Cathedral, 's-Hertogenbosch (horiz.) 85 35

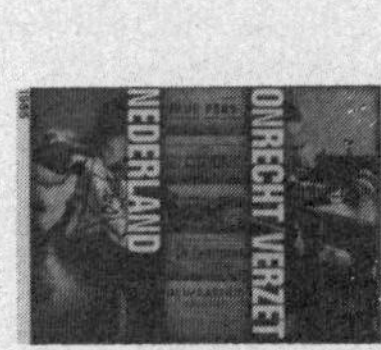

368. Star of David, Illegal Newspapers and Rifle Practice (Resistance Movement). **369.** Piano Keyboard.

1985. 40th Anniv of Liberation.
1461 **368** 50 c. blk, stone & red 50 10
1462 – 60 c. black, stone & bl 55 10
1463 – 65 c. blk, stone & orge 60 25
1464 – 70 c. blk, stone & grn 65 10

DESIGNS: 60 c. Airplanes over houses, "De Vliegende Hollander" (newspaper) and soldier (Allied Forces). 65 c. Soldiers and civilians, "Parool" (newspaper) and American war cemetery, Margraten (Liberation). 70 c. Women prisoners, prison money and Burma Railway (Dutch East Indies).

1985. Europa. Music Year. Multicoloured.
1465. 50 c. Type **369** 40 10
1466. 70 c. Organ 60 10

370. National Museum, Amsterdam (centenary).

1985. Anniversaries and Events. Mult.
1467. 50 c. Type **370** 45 10
1468. 60 c. Teacher with students (bicentenary of Amsterdam Nautical College 55 10
1469. 70 c. Ship's mast and rigging ("Sail '85", Amsterdam) 70 10

371. Porpoise and Graph.

1985. Endangered Animals.
1470. **371.** 50 c. blk., bl. & red 40 10
1471. – 70 c. blk., bl. & red 85 10
DESIGN: 70 c. Seal and PCB molecule structure.

372. Ignition Key and Framed Photograph ("Think of Me").

1985. Child Welfare. Road Safety. Mult.
1472. 50 c. + 25 c. Type **372** .. 60 30
1473. 60 c. + 20 c. Child holding target showing speeds 70 70
1474. 65 c. + 20 c. Girl holding red warning triangle .. 85 85
1475. 70 c. + 30 c. Boy holding "Children Crossing" sign 90 20

373. Penal Code Extract.

1986. Centenary of Penal Code.
1477. **373.** 50 c. black, yellow and purple .. 35 10

374. Surveyor with Pole and N.A.P. Water Gauge.

1986. 300th Anniv. of Height Gauging Marks at Amsterdam.
1478. **374.** 60 c. multicoloured .. 45 10

375. Windmill, Graph and Cloudy Sky.

1986. Inauguration of Windmill Test Station, Sexbierum.
1479. **375.** 70 c. multicoloured .. 60 10

376. Scales. **377.** Het Loo Palace Garden, Apeldoorn.

1986. Cultural, Health and Social Welfare Funds. Antique Measuring Instruments. Multicoloured.
1480. 50 c. + 20 c. Type **376** .. 45 30
1481. 60 c. + 25 c. Clock (vert.) 55 30
1482. 65 c. + 25 c. Barometer (vert.) 70 70
1483. 70 c. + 30 c. Jacob's staff 80 80

1986. Europa. Multicoloured.
1484. 50 c. Type **377** 40 10
1485. 70 c. Tree with discoloured crown .. 70 10

378. Cathedral. **379.** Drees at Binnenhof, 1947.

1986. Utrecht Events.
1486. **378.** 50 c. multicoloured .. 45 20
1487. – 60 c. blue, pink and black 65 20
1488. – 70 c. multicoloured .. 80 10
DESIGNS—VERT. 50 c. Type **378** (completion of interior restoration). 60 c. German House (75th anniv. of Heemschut Conservation Society). HORIZ. 70 c. Extract from foundation document (350th anniv. of Utrecht University).

1986. Birth Centenary of Dr. Willem Drees (politician).
1489. **379.** 55 c. multicoloured .. 60 10

380. Draughts as Biscuits in Saucer. **381.** Map of Flood Barrier.

1986. 75th Annivs. of Royal Dutch Draughts Association (1490) and Royal Dutch Billiards Association (1491). Multicoloured
1490. 75 c. Type **380** 90 15
1491. 75 c. Player in ball preparing to play .. 90 15

1986. Delta Project Completion. Mult.
1492. 65 c. Type **381** 70 20
1493. 75 c. Flood barrier .. 90 10

382. Children listening to Music (experiencing). **383.** Engagment Picture.

1986. Child Welfare. Child and Culture.
1494. 55 c. + 25 c. Type **382** .. 70 70
1495. 65 c. + 35 c. Boy drawing (achieving) 80 60
1496. 75 c. + 35 c. Children at theatre (understanding) 90 20

1987. Golden Wedding of Princess Juliana and Prince Bernhard.
1498. **383.** 75 c. orange, black and gold 75 10

384. Block of Flats and Hut.

1987. International Year of Shelter for the Homeless (65 c.) and Centenary of Netherlands Salvation Army (75 c.). Multicoloured.
1499. 65 c. Type **384** .. 60 20
1500. 75 c. Army officer, meeting and tramp .. 80 10

385. Eduard Douwes Dekker (Multatuli) and De Harmonie Club.

1987. Writers' Death Annivs. Multicoloured.
1501. 55 c. Type **385** (centenary) 55 20
1502. 75 c. Constantijn Huygens and Scheveningseweg, The Hague (300th anniv.) 85 10

386. Steam Pumping Station, Nijkerk.

1987. Cultural Health and Social Welfare Funds. Industrial Buildings.
1503. **386.** 55 c. + 30 c. red, grey and black 70 75
1504. – 65 c. + 35 c. grey, black and blue .. 85 85
1505. – 75 c. + 35 c. grey, yellow and black 90 60
DESIGNS: 65 c. Water tower, Deventer. 75 c. Brass foundry, Joure.

387. Dance Theatre, Scheveningen (Rem Koolhaas).

1987. Europa. Architecture. Multicoloured.
1506. 55 c. Type **387** 55 20
1507. 75 c. Montessori School, Amsterdam (Herman Hertzberger) 85 10

388. Auction at Broek op Langedijk.

1987. Centenary of Auction Sales (55, 75 c.) and 150th Anniv. of Groningen Agricultural Society (65 c.). Multicoloured.
1508 55 c. Type **388** 55 20
1509 65 c. Groningen landscape and founders' signatures 65 20
1510 75 c. Auction sale and clock 75 10

389. Telephone Care Circles. **390.** Map of Holland.

1987. Dutch Red Cross. Multicoloured.
1511. 55 c. + 30 c. Type **389** .. 60 60
1512. 65 c. + 35 c. Red cross and hands (Welfare work) 75 75
1513. 75 c. + 35 c. Red cross and drip (Blood transfusion) 85 45

1987. 75th Anniv. of Netherlands Municipalities Union.
1514. **390.** 75 c. multicoloured .. 65 10

391. Noordeinde Palace, The Hague. **392.** Woodcutter.

1987.
1515. **391.** 65 c. multicoloured .. 50 10

1987. Child Welfare. Child and Profession. Multicoloured.
1516. 55 c. + 25 c. Type **392** .. 60 60
1517. 65 c. + 35 c. Woman sailor 75 55
1518. 75 c. + 35 c. Woman pilot 85 25

393. Star. **394.** "Narcissus cyclamineus" "Peeping Tom" and Extract from "I Call You Flowers" (Jan Hanlo).

1987. Christmas.
1520. **393.** 50 c. red, blue and green 60 20
1521. 50 c. yellow, red and blue 60 20
1522. 50 c. red, blue and yellow 60 20
1523. 50 c. yellow, red and green 60 20
1524. 50 c. blue, green and red 60 20
The first colour described is that of the St. George's Cross.

1988. "Filacept" European Stamp Exhibition, The Hague. Flowers. Mult.
1525 55 c. + 55 c. Type **394** .. 90 80
1526 75 c. + 70 c. "Rosa gallica" "Versicolor" and "Roses" (Daan van Golden) .. .. 1·10 1·00
1527 75 c. + 70 c. Sea holly and 1270 map of The Hague 1·10 1·00

395. Quagga.

1988. Cultural, Health and Social Welfare Funds. 150th Anniv. of Natura Artis Magistra Zoological Society. Multicoloured.
1528. 55 c. + 30 c. Type **395** .. 70 70
1529. 65 c. + 35 c. American manatee 80 80
1530. 75 c. + 35 c. Orang-utan (vert.) 90 45

396 Man's Shoulder **397** Traffic Scene with Lead Symbol crossed Through

1988. 75th Anniv of Netherlands Cancer Institute.
1531 **396** 75 c. multicoloured .. 80 10

1988. Europa. Transport. Multicoloured.
1532 55 c. Type **397** (lead-free petrol) 50 20
1533 75 c. Cyclists reflected in car wing mirror (horiz) 75 10

398 Pendulum, Prism and Saturn

1988. 300th Anniv of England's Glorious Revolution. Multicoloured.
1534 65 c. Type **398** 50 20
1535 75 c. Queen Mary, King William III and 17th-century warship .. 60 10

399 "Cobra Cat" (Appel) **400** Sailing Ship and Map of Australia

1988. 40th Anniv of Founding of Cobra Painters Group. Multicoloured.
1536 55 c. Type **399** 50 50
1537 65 c. "Kite" (Corneille) .. 55 50
1538 75 c. "Stumbling Horse" (Constant) 60 20

1988. Bicentenary of Australian Settlement.
1539 **400** 75 c. multicoloured .. 70 10

401 Statue of Erasmus, Rotterdam

402 "Rain"

1988. 75th Anniv of Erasmus University, Rotterdam (1540) and Centenary of Concertgebouw Concert Hall and Orchestra (1541).
1540 **401** 75 c. dp green & green 65 20
1541 – 75 c. violet 65 20
DESIGN: No. 1541, Violin and Concertgebouw concert hall.

1988. Child Welfare. Centenary of Royal Netherlands Swimming Federation. Children's drawings. Multicoloured.
1543 55 c.+25 c. Type **402** .. 65 60
1544 65 c.+35 c. "Getting Ready for the Race" .. 85 50
1545 75 c.+35 c. "Swimming Test" 85 30

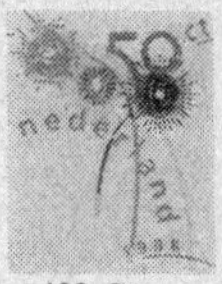

403 Stars

1988. Christmas.
1547 **403** 50 c. multicoloured .. 50 10

404 Postal and Telecommunications Services

1989. Privatization of Netherlands PTT.
1548 **404** 75 c. multicoloured .. 75 10

405 "Solidarity"

406 Members' Flags

1989. Trade Unions. Multicoloured.
1549 55 c. Type **405** 40 20
1550 75 c. Talking mouths on hands 50 10

1989. 40th Anniv of N.A.T.O.
1551 **406** 75 c. multicoloured .. 75 10

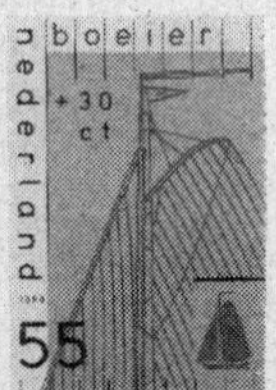

407 Boier

408 Boy with Homemade Telephone

1989. Cultural, Health and Social Welfare Funds. Old Sailing Vessels.
1552 **407** 55 c.+30 c. grn & blk 30 10
1553 – 65 c.+35 c. blue & blk 35 10
1554 – 75 c.+35 c. brn & blk 40 10
DESIGNS: 65 c. Fishing smack; 75 c. Clipper.

1989. Europa. Children's Games. Mult.
1555 55 c. Type **408** 50 20
1556 75 c. Girl with homemade telephone 75 10

409 Wheel on Rail

410 Boy with Ball and Diagram of Goal Scored in European Championship

1989. 150th Anniv of Netherlands' Railways. Multicoloured.
1557 55 c. Type **409** 60 20
1558 65 c. Locomotives .. 65 20
1559 75 c. Clock and "The Kiss" (sculpture by Rodin) .. 70 10

1989. Cent of Royal Dutch Football Assn.
1560 **410** 75 c. multicoloured .. 80 10

411 Map

412 Right to Housing

1989. 150th Anniv of Division of Limburg between Netherlands and Belgium.
1561 **411** 75 c. multicoloured .. 80 10

1989. Child Welfare. 30th Anniv of Declaration of Rights of the Child. Mult.
1562 55 c.+25 c. Type **412** .. 60 60
1563 65 c.+35 c. Right to food 80 50
1564 75 c.+35 c. Right to education 90 30

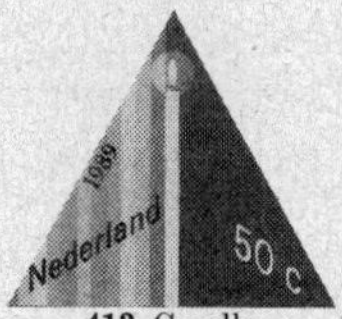

413 Candle

414 "Arms of Leiden" (tulip) and Plan of Gardens in 1601

1989. Christmas.
1566 **413** 50 c. multicoloured .. 60 10

1990. 400th Anniv of Hortus Botanicus (botanical gardens), Leiden.
1567 **414** 65 c. multicoloured .. 70 20

415 Pointer on Graduated Scale

416 "Self-portrait" (detail)

1990. Centenary of Labour Inspectorate.
1568 **415** 75 c. multicoloured .. 70 10

1990. Death Centenary of Vincent van Gogh (painter). Multicoloured.
1569 55 c. Type **416** 75 20
1570 75 c. "Green Vineyard" (detail) .. .. 1·25 10

417 Summer's Day

1990. Cultural, Health and Social Welfare Funds. The Weather. Multicoloured.
1571 55 c.+30 c. Type **417** .. 60 50
1572 65 c.+35 c. Clouds and isobars (vert) 75 65
1573 75 c.+35 c. Satellite weather picture (vert) 90 30

418 Zuiderkerk Ruins

1990. 50th Anniv of German Bombing of Rotterdam.
1574 **418** 55 c. deep brown, brown and black .. 55 20
1575 – 65 c. multicoloured .. 65 10
1576 – 75 c. multicoloured .. 85 10
DESIGNS: 65 c. City plan as stage; 75 c. Girder and plans for future construction.

419 Postal Headquarters, Groningen, and Veere Post Office

420 Construction of Indiaman and Wreck of "Amsterdam"

1990. Europa. Post Office Buidings.
1577 – 55 c. grey, mve & brn 55 20
1578 **419** 75 c. blue, grn & grey 85 10
DESIGN: 55 c. As Type **419** but inscr "Postkantoor Veere".

1990. 3rd Anniv of Dutch East India Company Ships Association (replica ship project) (1579) and "Sail 90", Amsterdam (1580). Multicoloured.
1579 65 c. Type **420** 65 20
1580 75 c. Crew manning yards on sailing ship .. 95 10

421 Queens Emma, Wilhelmina, Juliana and Beatrix

422 Flames, Telephone Handset and Number

1990. Netherlands Queens of the House of Orange.
1581 **421** 150 c. multicoloured .. 1·50 45

1990. Introduction of National Emergency Number.
1582 **422** 65 c. multicoloured .. 60 20

423 Girl riding Horse

424 Falling Snow

1990. Child Welfare. Hobbies. Multicoloured.
1583 55 c.+25 c. Type **423** .. 75 60
1584 65 c.+35 c. Girl at computer 85 50
1585 75 c.+35 c. Young philatelist 90 30

1990. Christmas.
1587 **424** 50 c. multicoloured .. 50 10

425 Industrial Chimneys, Exhaust Pipes and Aerosol Can (Air Pollution)

1991. Environmental Protection. Mult.
1588 55 c. Type **425** 55 20
1589 65 c. Outfall pipes and chemicals (sea pollution) 70 20
1590 75 c. Agricultural chemicals, leaking drums and household landfill waste (soil pollution) 90 10

426 German Raid on Amsterdam Jewish Quarter and Open Hand

1991. 50th Anniv of Amsterdam General Strike.
1591 **426** 75 c. multicoloured .. 75 10

427 Princess Beatrix and Prince Claus on Wedding Day

428 Queen Beatrix

1991. Royal Silver Wedding Anniversary. Multicoloured.
1592 75 c. Type **427** 95 35
1593 75 c. Queen Beatrix and Prince Claus on horseback 95 35

1991.
1594 **428** 75 c. dp green & grn 55 10
1595 80 c. brown & lt brn 60 10
1597 90 c. blue .. 70 10
1598 1 g. violet .. 75 10
1600 1 g. 30 blue & violet 1·00 10
1601 1 g. 40 green & olive 1·00 10
1602 1 g. 60 purple & mve 1·25 10
1603 2 g. brown .. 1·50 10
1603a 2 g. 50 purple 1·75 10
1604 3 g. blue .. 2·25 10
1605 5 g. red .. 3·75 10

429 "Meadow" Farm, Wartena, Friesland

430 Gerard Philips's Experiments with Carbon Filaments

1991. Cultural, Health and Social Welfare Funds. Traditional Farmhouses. Mult.
1610 55 c.+30 c. Type **429** .. 80 50
1611 65 c.+35 c. "T-house" farm, Kesteren, Gelderland 90 65
1612 75 c.+35 c. "Courtyard" farm, Nuth, Limburg 95 30

1991. 75th Anniv of Netherlands Standards Institute (65 c.) and Centenary of Philips Organization (others). Multicoloured.
1615 55 c. Type **430** 45 20
1616 65 c. Wiring to Standard NEN 1010 (horiz) .. 55 20
1617 75 c. Laser beams reading video disc 70 10

431 Man raising Hat to Space

432 Sticking Plaster over Medal

1991. Europa. Europe in Space. Mult.
1618 55 c. Type **431** 60 20
1619 75 c. Ladders stretching into space 80 10

1991. 75th Anniv of Nijmegen International Four Day Marches.
1620 **432** 80 c. multicoloured .. 65 10

433 Jacobus Hendericus van't Hoff

434 Children and Open Book

1991. Dutch Nobel Prize Winners. Mult.
1621 60 c. Type **433** (chemistry, 1901) 50 15
1622 70 c. Pieter Zeeman (physics, 1902) .. 60 20
1623 80 c. Tobias Michael Carel Asser (peace, 1911) .. 65 10

1991. Centenary (1992) of Public Libraries in the Netherlands.
1624 **434** 70 c. drab, blk & mve 60 20
1625 – 80 c. multicoloured .. 65 10
DESIGN: 80 c. Books on shelf.

435 Girls with Doll and Robot

436 "Greetings Cards keep People in Touch"

1991. Child Welfare. Outdoor Play. Mult.
1626 60 c.+30 c. Type **435** .. 75 50
1627 70 c.+35 c. Bicycle race 85 65
1628 80 c.+40 c. Hide and Seek 95 30

1991. Christmas.
1630 **436** 55 c. multicoloured .. 45 15

437 Artificial Lightning, Microchip and Oscilloscope

1992. 150th Anniv of Delft University of Technology.
1631 **437** 60 c. multicoloured .. 50 15

438 Extract from Code

440 Tulips ("Mondrian does not like Green")

1992. Implementation of Property Provisions of New Civil Code.
1632 **438** 80 c. multicoloured .. 65 10

1992. "Expo '92" World's Fair, Seville. Mult.
1634 70 c. Type **440** 60 20
1635 80 c. "Netherland Expo '92" 65 10

441 Tasman's Map of Staete Landt (New Zealand)

1992. 350th Anniv of Discovery of Tasmania and New Zealand by Abel Tasman.
1636 **441** 70 c. multicoloured .. 60 20

442 Yellow and Purple Flowers

443 Geometric Planes

1992. Cultural, Health and Social Welfare Funds. "Floriade" Flower Show, Zoetermeer. Multicoloured.
1637 60 c.+30 c. Water lilies .. 75 50
1638 70 c.+35 c. Orange and purple flowers .. 85 65
1639 80 c.+40 c. Type **442** .. 95 30

1992. 150th Anniv of Royal Association of Netherlands Architects (60 c.), and Inauguration of New States General Lower House (80 c.). Multicoloured.
1643 60 c. Type **443** 50 15
1644 80 c. Atrium and blue sky (symbolising sending of information into society) 65 10

444 Globe and Columbus

445 Moneta (Goddess of Money)

1992. Europa. 500th Anniv of Discovery of America by Columbus.
1645 **444** 60 c. multicoloured .. 50 15
1646 – 80 c. blk, mve & yell 65 10
DESIGN—VERT. 80 c. Galleon.

1992. Centenary of Royal Netherlands Numismatics Society.
1647 **445** 70 c. multicoloured .. 60 20

446 Teddy Bear wearing Stethoscope

447 List of Relatives and Friends

1992. Centenary of Netherlands Paediatrics Society.
1648 **446** 80 c. multicoloured .. 65 10

1992. 50th Anniv of Departure of First Deportation Train from Westerbork Concentration Camp.
1649 **447** 70 c. multicoloured .. 55 15

448 Cross

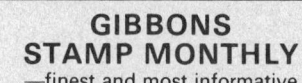

1992. 125th Anniv of Netherlands Red Cross. Multicoloured.
1650 60 c.+30 c. Type **448** .. 70 45
1651 70 c.+35 c. Supporting injured person .. 80 55
1652 80 c.+40 c. Red cross on dirty bandage .. 90 30

449 "United Europe" and European Community Flag

450 Queen Beatrix on Official Birthday, 1992, and at Investiture

1992. European Single Market.
1656 **449** 80 c. multicoloured .. 60 10

1992. $12\frac{1}{2}$ Years since Accession to the Throne of Queen Beatrix.
1657 **450** 80 c. multicoloured .. 60 10

451 Saxophone Player

452 Poinsettia

1992. Child Welfare. Child and Music. Mult.
1658 60 c.+30 c. Type **451** .. 70 45
1659 70 c.+35 c. Piano player 80 55
1660 80 c.+40 c. Double bass player 90 30

1992. Christmas.
1662 **452** 55 c. multicoloured (centre of flower silver) 40 10
1663 55 c. multicoloured (centre red) .. 40 10

453 Cycling

1993. Centenary of Netherlands Cycle and Motor Industry Association.
1664 **453** 70 c. multicoloured .. 55 15
1665 – 80 c. brn, grey & yell 60 10
DESIGN: 80 c. Car.

454 Collages

455 Mouth to Mouth Resuscitation

1993. Greetings Stamps. Multicoloured.
1666 70 c. Type **454** 55 10
1667 70 c. Collages (different) 55 10

1993. Anniversaries. Multicoloured.
1668 70 c. Type **455** (centenary of Royal Netherlands First Aid Association) 55 10
1669 80 c. Pests on leaf (75th anniv of Wageningen University of Agriculture) 55 10
1670 80 c. Lead driver and horses (bicentenary of Royal Horse Artillery) 60 10

456 Emblems

1993. 150th Anniv of Royal Dutch Notaries' Association. Each red and violet.
1671 80 c. Type **456** ("150 Jaar" reading up) .. 60 10
1672 80 c. As Type **456** but emblems inverted and "150 Jaar" reading down 60 10
Nos. 1671/2 were issued together in horizontal tete-beche pairs, each pair forming a composite design.

457 Large White

458 Elderly Couple

1993. Butterflies. Multicoloured.
1673 70 c. Pearl-bordered fritillary 55 15
1674 80 c. Large tortoiseshell 60 10
1675 90 c. Type **457** 70 20

1993. Cultural, Health and Social Welfare Funds. Senior Citizens' Independence.
1677 70 c.+35 c. Type **458** .. 75 50
1678 70 c.+35 c. Elderly man 75 50
1679 80 c.+40 c. Elderly woman with dog .. 75 25

459 Radio Orange

460 Sports Pictograms

1993. Radio Orange (Dutch broadcasts from London during Second World War). Mult.
1683 80 c. Type **459** 55 10
1684 80 c. Man listening to radio in secret .. 55 10

1993. 2nd European Youth Olympic Days. Multicoloured.
1685 70 c. Type **460** 50 10
1686 80 c. Sports pictograms (different) 55 10

461 "The Embodiment of Unity" (Wessel Couzijn)

462 Johannes Diderik van der Waals (Physics, 1910)

1993. Europa. Contemporary Art. Mult.
1687 70 c. Type **461** 50 10
1688 80 c. Architectonic sculpture (Per Kirkeby) 55 10
1689 160 c. Sculpture (Naum Gabo) (vert) .. .. 1·10 55

1993. Nobel Prize Winners.
1690 **462** 70 c. blue, black & red 50 10
1691 – 80 c. mauve, blk & red 55 10
1692 – 90 c. multicoloured .. 65 15
DESIGNS: 80 c. Willem Einthoven (medicine, 1924); 90 c. Christiaan Eijkman (medicine, 1929).

463 Pen and Pencils

1993. Letter Writing Campaign. Mult.
1693 80 c. Type **463** 55 10
1694 80 c. Envelope 55 10

464 "70"

1993. Stamp Day (70 c.) and Netherlands PTT (80 c.). Multicoloured.

1695	70 c. Type **464**	50	10
1696	80 c. Dish aerial and dove carrying letter ..	55	10

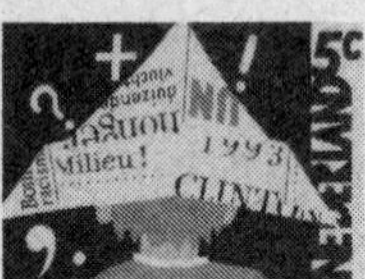

465 Child in Newspaper Hat

1993. Child Welfare. Child and the Media. Multicoloured.

1697	70 c.+35 c. Type **465** ..	75	50
1698	70 c.+35 c. Elephant listening to radio on headphones	75	50
1699	80 c.+40 c. Television ..	75	25

MARINE INSURANCE STAMPS

M 22.

1921.

M 238.	M **22.**	15 c. green ..	4·00	45·00
M 239.		60 c. red	5·00	65·00
M 240.		75 c. brown ..	7·00	70·00
M 241.	–	1 g. 50 blue ..	60·00	£500
M 242.	–	2 g. 25 brown ..	£120	£700
M 243.	–	4½ g. black ..	£170	£900
M 244.	–	7½ g. red	£300	£1400

Designs (inscr "DRIJVENDE BRANDKAST"): 1 g. 50, 2 g. 25, "Explosion". 4½ g., 7½ g. Lifebelt.

OFFICIAL STAMPS

1913. Stamps of 1898 optd. **ARMENWET.**

O214	**12**	1 c. red	3·50	1·75
O215		1½ c. blue	85	1·40
O216		2 c. brown	6·00	6·00
O217		2½ c. green	14·00	11·00
O218	**13**	3 c. green	3·50	65
O219		5 c. red	3·50	4·00
O220		10 c. grey	29·00	38·00

POSTAGE DUE STAMPS

D8.

D 9.

1870.

D 76.	D **8.**	5 c. brn. on yellow ..	65·00	10·00
D 77.		10 c. purple on blue ..	£150	13·00

For same stamps in other colours, see Netherlands Indies, Nos. D 1/5.

1881.

D208	D **9**	½ c. black and blue	15	15
D182		1 c. black and blue	1·25	15
D183		1½ c. black and blue	45	20
D184		2½ c. black and blue	1·40	15
D209		3 c. black and blue	1·50	1·00
D210		4 c. black and blue	1·50	1·75
D185		5 c. black and blue	10·00	10
D211		6½ c. black and blue	35·00	35·00
D212		7½ c. black and blue	1·25	40
D186		10 c. black and blue	27·00	25
D187		12½ c. black and blue	23·00	70
D188		15 c. black and blue	27·00	60
D189		20 c. black and blue	16·00	6·00
D190		25 c. black and blue	35·00	45
D181		1 g. red and blue ..	85·00	22·00

No. D181 is inscribed "EEN GULDEN".

1906. Surch.

D213	D **9**	3 c. on 1 g. red & bl	26·00	24·00
D215		4 on 6½ c. black & bl	4·00	5·50
D216		6½ on 20 c. black & bl	3·50	4·50
D214		50 c. on 1 g. red & bl	£130	£120

1907. De Ruyter Commem. stamps surch. **PORTZEGEL** and value.

D 217.	**15.**	½ c. on 1 c. red ..	1·25	1·25
D 218.		1 c. on 1 c. red ..	40	40
D 219.		1½ c. on 1 c. red ..	35	35
D 220.		2½ c. on 1 c. red ..	85	85
D 221.		5 c. on 2½ c. red ..	1·25	35
D 222.		6½ c. on 2½ c. red ..	3·00	3·00
D 223.		7½ c. on ½ c. blue ..	1·75	1·25
D 224.		10 c. on ½ c. blue ..	1·50	55
D 225.		12½ c. on ½ c. blue ..	4·50	4·50
D 226.		15 c. on 2½ c. red ..	6·00	3·00
D 227.		25 c. on ½ c. blue ..	8·00	6·50
D 228.		50 c. on ½ c. blue ..	35·00	32·00
D 229.		1 g. on ½ c. blue ..	55·00	48·00

1912. Re-issue of Type D **9** in one colour.

D230	D **9**	½ c. blue	10	10
D231		1 c. blue	10	10
D232		1½ c. blue	1·00	1·00
D233		2½ c. blue	10	10
D234		3 c. blue	35	35
D235		4 c. blue	10	15
D236		4½ c. blue	4·75	4·75
D237		5 c. blue	10	10
D238		5½ c. blue	4·50	4·50
D239		7 c. blue	2·00	2·25
D240		7½ c. blue	2·25	75
D241		10 c. blue	10	10
D242		12½ c. blue	20	15
D453		15 c. blue	20	10
D244		20 c. blue	20	10
D245		25 c. blue	65·00	60
D246		50 c. blue	40	15

D 25.

D 121.

1921.

D 442.	D **25.**	3 c. blue	10	15
D 445.		6 c. blue	10	15
D 446.		7 c. blue	15	15
D 447.		7½ c. blue	20	25
D 448.		8 c. blue	15	15
D 449.		9 c. blue	20	25
D 247.		11 c. blue	11·00	3·00
D 451.		12 c. blue	15	15
D 455.		25 c. blue	20	10
D 456.		30 c. blue	25	10
D 458.		1 g. red	60	10

1923. Surch. in white figures in black circle.

D 272.	D **9.**	1 c. on 3 c. blue ..	30	35
D 273.		2½ c. on 7 c. blue ..	35	25
D 274.		25 c. on 1½ c. blue ..	7·50	35
D 275.		25 c. on 7½ c. blue ..	7·50	25

1924. Stamps of 1898 surch. **TE BETALEN PORT** and value in white figures in black circle.

D295	**13**	4 c. on 3 c. green ..	1·25	1·50
D296	**12**	5 c. on 1 c. red ..	35	10
D297		10 c. on 1½ c. blue ..	75	15
D298	**13**	12½ c. on 5 c. red ..	80	15

1947.

D 656.	D **121.**	1 c. blue	10	10
D 657.		3 c. blue	10	15
D 658.		4 c. blue	13·00	80
D 659.		5 c. blue	10	10
D 660.		6 c. blue	35	35
D 661.		7 c. blue	15	15
D 662.		8 c. blue	15	15
D 663.		10 c. blue	15	10
D 664.		11 c. blue	35	35
D 665.		12 c. blue	55	80
D 666.		14 c. blue	75	70
D 667.		15 c. blue	30	10
D 668.		16 c. blue	85	85
D 669.		20 c. blue	30	10
D 670.		24 c. blue	1·25	1·25
D 671.		25 c. blue	30	10
D 672.		26 c. blue	1·60	1·75
D 673.		30 c. blue	65	10
D 674.		35 c. blue	70	10
D 675.		40 c. blue	75	10
D 676.		50 c. blue	85	10
D 677.		60 c. blue	1·00	25
D 678.	D **121.**	85 c. blue	17·00	35
D 679.		90 c. blue	3·50	40
D 680.		95 c. blue	3·50	35
D 681.		1 g. red	2·25	10
D 682.		1 g. 75 red ..	6·00	25

For stamps as Types D **121**, but in violet, see under Surinam.

INTERNATIONAL COURT OF JUSTICE

Stamps specially issued for use by the Headquarters of the Court of International Justice. Nos. J1 to J36 were not sold to the public in unused condition.

1934. Optd **COUR PER- MANENTE DE JUSTICE INTER- NATIONALE.**

J1	**35**	1½ c. mauve	—	40
J2		2½ c. green	—	40
J3	**36**	7½ c. red	—	80
J4	**68**	12½ c. blue	—	27·00
J7	**36**	12½ c. blue	—	13·00
J5		15 c. yellow	—	1·00
J6		3 c. purple	—	1·50

1940. Optd **COUR PER- MANANTE DE JUSTICE INTER- NATIONALE.**

J 9	**94**	7½ c. red	—	9·00
J10		12½ c. blue	—	9·00
J11		15 c. blue	—	9·00
J12		30 c. bistre	—	9·00

1947. Optd. **COUR INTERNATIONALE DE JUSTICE.**

J 13.	**94.**	7½ c. red	—	1·00
J 14.		10 c. purple	—	1·00
J 15.		12½ c. blue	—	1·00
J 16.		20 c. violet	—	1·00
J 17.		25 c. red	—	1·00

J 3.

J 4. Peace Palace, The Hague.

J 5. Queen Juliana.

1950.

J 18.	J **3.**	2 c. blue	—	7·00
J 19.		4 c. green	—	7·00

1951.

J 20.	J **4.**	2 c. lake	—	50
J 21.		3 c. blue	—	50
J 22.		4 c. green	—	50
J 23.		5 c. brown	—	50
J 24.	J **5.**	6 c. mauve	—	2·75
J 25.	J **4.**	6 c. green	—	85
J 26.		7 c. red	—	85
J 27.	J **5.**	10 c green	—	15
J 28.		12 c. red	—	1·75
J 29.		15 c. red	—	15
J 30.		20 c. blue	—	20
J 31.		25 c. brown	—	20
J 32.		30 c. purple	—	30
J 33.	J **4.**	40 c. blue	—	30
J 34.		45 c. red	—	35
J 35.		50 c. mauve	—	35
J 36.	J **5.**	1 g. grey	—	70

J **6** Olive Branch and Peace Palace, The Hague

1989.

J37	J **6**	5 c. black and yellow	10	10
J38		10 c. black and blue ..	10	10
J39		25 c. black and red ..	20	20
J41		50 c. black and green	40	40
J42		55 c. black and mauve	40	40
J43		60 c. black and bistre	45	45
J44		65 c. black and green	50	50
J45		70 c. black and blue ..	55	55
J46		75 c. black and yellow	55	55
J47		80 c. black and green	60	60
J49		1 g. black and orange	75	75
J50		1 g. 50 black and blue	1·10	1·10
J54	–	5 g. multicoloured ..	3·75	3·75
J56	–	7 g. multicoloured ..	5·25	5·25

DESIGNS: 5, 7 g. Olive branch and column.

NETHERLANDS ANTILLES Pt. 4

Curacao and other Netherlands islands in the Caribbean Sea. In December 1954 these were placed on an equal footing with Netherlands under the Crown.

100 cents = 1 gulden

48. Spanish Galleon. 49. Alonso de Ojeda.

1949. 450th Anniv. of Discovery of Curacao.
306. 48. 6 c. green .. .. 3·50 1·75
307. 49. 12½ c. red .. .. 3·75 3·50
308. 48. 15 c. blue .. .. 3·75 2·25

50. Posthorns and Globe. 51. Leap-frog.

1949. 75th Anniv. of U.P.U.
309. 50. 6 c. red .. .. 3·00 2·25
310. 25 c. blue .. .. 3·00 1·10

1950. As numeral and portrait types of Netherlands but inscr. "NED. ANTILLEN".

325	118	1 c. brown	10	10
326		1½ c. blue	10	10
327		2 c. orange	10	10
328		2½ c. green	80	15
329		3 c. violet	10	10
329a		4 c. green	45	35
330		5 c. red	10	10
310a	129	5 c. yellow	25	25
311		6 c. purple	85	10
311a		7½ c. brown	4·00	10
312a		10 c. red	30	30
313		12½ c. green	1·75	15
314a		15 c. blue	35	35
315a		20 c. orange	70	70
316		21 c. black	2·00	1·75
316a		22½ c. green	5·00	10
317a		25 c. violet	80	10
318		27½ c. brown	5·00	1·90
319a		30 c. sepia	80	80
319b		40 c. blue	80	80
320		50 c. olive	9·00	10
321	130	1½ g. green	32·00	20
322		2½ g. brown	30·00	70
323		5 g. red	50·00	8·50
324		10 g. purple	£200	50·00

1951. Child Welfare.
331. 51. 1½ c.+1 c. violet .. 1·75 2·25
332. – 5 c.+2½ c. brown .. 11·00 4·50
333. – 6 c.+2½ c. blue .. 11·00 4·50
334. – 12½ c.+5 c. red .. 11·00 4·50
335. – 25 c.+10 c. turquoise .. 11·00 4·50
DESIGNS: 5 c. Kite-flying. 6 c. Girl on swing. 12½ c. Girls playing "Oranges and Lemons". 25 c. Bowling hoops.

52. Gull over Ship. 54. Fort Beekenburg.

1952. Seamen's Welfare Fund. Inscr. "ZEEMANSWELVAREN".
336. 52. 1½ c.+1 c. green .. 1·50 75
337. – 6 c.+4 c. brown .. 8·00 3·50
338. – 12½ c.+7 c. mauve .. 8·00 3·75
339. – 15 c.+10 c. blue .. 10·00 4·00
340. – 25 c.+15 c. red .. 8·50 3·50
DESIGNS: 6 c. Sailor and lighthouse. 12½ c. Sailor on ship's prow. 15 c. Tanker in harbour. 25 c. Anchor and compass.

1953. Netherlands Flood Relief Fund No. 321 surch. **22½ Ct.+7½ Ct. WATERSNOOD NEDERLAND 1953.**
341. 130. 22½ c.+7½ c. on 1½ g... 1·10 1·10

1953. 250th Anniv. of Fort Beekenburg.
342. 54. 22½ c. brown .. .. 3·50 40

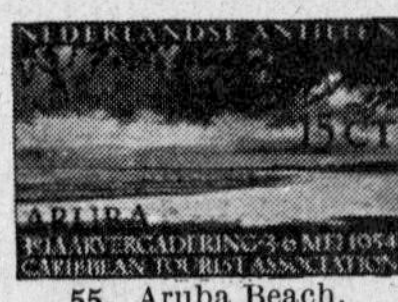

55. Aruba Beach.

1954. 3rd Caribbean Tourist Assn. Meeting.
343. 55. 15 c. blue and buff .. 3·50 2·50

1954. Ratification of Statute of the Kingdom. As No. 809 of Netherlands.
344 158 7½ c. green 70 65

56. "Anglo" Flower.

FLOWERS: 7½ c. White Cayenne., 15 c. "French" flower. 22½ c. Cactus. 25 c. Red Cayenne.

1955. Child Welfare.
345. 56. 1½ c.+1 c. blue, yellow & turquoise 40 50
346. – 7½ c.+5 c. red, yellow and violet .. .. 3·25 2·25
347. – 15 c.+5 c. red, grn. & olive 3·25 2·50
348. – 22½ c.+7½ c. red, yellow and blue .. .. 3·25 2·25
349. – 25 c.+10 c. red, yellow and grey .. .. 3·25 2·50

57. Prince Bernhard and Queen Juliana.

1955. Royal Visit.
350. 57. 7½ c.+2½ c. red 20 20
351. 22½ c.+7½ c. blue .. 95 95

59. Oil Refinery.

1955. 21st Meeting of Caribbean Commission.
352. – 15 c. blue, green & brown 2·50 2·00
353. 59. 25 c. blue, green & brown 4·00 2·50
DESIGN (rectangle, 36×25 mm): 15 c. Aruba Beach.

60. St. Anne Bay. 61. Lord Baden-Powell.

1956. 10th Anniv. of Caribbean Commission.
354. 60. 15 c. blue, red and black 30 25

1957. 50th Anniv. of Boy Scout Movement.
355. 61. 6 c.+1½ c. yellow .. 50 50
356. 7½ c.+2½ c. green .. 50 50
357. 15 c.+5 c. red .. 50 50

62. "Dawn of Health".

1957. 1st Caribbean Mental Health Congress, Aruba.
358. 62. 15 c. black and yellow.. 30 30

63. Saba.

1957. Tourist Publicity. Multicoloured.
359. 7½ c. Type 63 .. .. 35 35
360. 15 c. St. Maarten 35 35
361. 25 c. St. Eustatius 35 35

64. Footballer. 65. Curacao Intercontinental Hotel.

1957. 8th Central American and Caribbean Football Championships.
362. 64. 6 c.+2½ c. orange .. 50 70
363. – 7½ c.+5 c. red .. .. 1·00 1·10
364. – 15 c.+5 c. green .. 1·10 1·10
365. – 22½ c.+7½ c. blue .. 1·10 80
DESIGNS—HORIZ. 7½ c. Caribbean map. VERT. 15 c. Goalkeeper saving ball. 22½ c. Footballers with ball.

1957. Opening of Curacao Inter-continental Hotel.
366. 65. 15 c. blue 30 25

66. Map of Curacao. 67. American Kestrel.

1957. International Geophysical Year.
367 66 15 c. deep blue and blue 80 65

1958. Child Welfare. Bird design inscr. "VOOR HET KIND". Multicoloured.
368. 2½ c.+1 c. Type 67 .. 30 25
369. 7½ c.+1½ c. Yellow Oriole 85 65
370. 15 c.+2½ c. Scaly-breasted Ground Doves .. .. 1·10 80
371. 22½ c.+2½ c. Brown-throated Conure .. 1·25 70

68. Greater Flamingoes (Bonaire).

DESIGNS (33½×22 mm.): A. Dutch Colonial houses (Curacao). B. Mountain and palms (Saba). C. Town Hall (St. Maarten). D. Church tower Aruba). E. Memorial obelisk (St. Eustatius).

1958.

372	68	6 c. pink and green	7·50	10
373	A	7½ c. yellow & brown	10	10
374		8 c. yellow and blue	10	15
375	B	10 c. yellow and grey	10	10
376	C	12 c. grey and green	15	20
377	D	15 c. blue and green	15	10
377a		15 c. lilac and green	15	10
378	E	20 c. grey and red	20	10
379	A	25 c. green and blue	25	10
380	D	30 c. green and brown	30	10
381	E	35 c. pink and grey	35	20
382	C	40 c. green and mauve	40	10
383	B	45 c. blue and violet	50	20
384	68	50 c. pink and brown	50	10
385	E	55 c. green and red	65	25
386	68	65 c. pink and green	65	30
387	D	70 c. orange and purple	70	45
388	68	75 c. pink and violet	80	45
389	B	85 c. green and brown	85	60
390	E	90 c. orange and blue	85	70
391	C	95 c. yellow and orange	90	70
392	D	1 g. grey and red	1·00	15
393	A	1½ g. brown and violet	1·40	20
394	C	2½ g. yellow and blue	2·50	30
395	B	5 g. mauve and brown	4·75	85
396	68	10 g. pink and blue	8·50	4·00

For larger versions of some values see Nos. 653/6.

69. 70. Red Cross Flag and Antilles Map.

1958. 50th Anniv. of Neth. Antilles Radio & Telegraph Administration.
397. 69. 7½ c. lake and blue .. 15 15
398. 15 c. blue and red .. 30 30

1958. Neth. Antilles Red Cross Fund. Cross in red.
399. 70. 6 c.+2 c. brown .. 30 30
400. 7½ c.+2½ c. green .. 45 45
401. 15 c.+5 c. yellow .. 45 45
402. 22½ c.+7½ c. blue .. 45 45

71. Aruba Caribbean Hotel.

1959. Opening of Aruba Caribbean Hotel.
403. 71. 15 c. multicoloured .. 30 20

72. Zeeland.

1959. Curacao Monuments Preservation Fund. Multicoloured.
404. 6 c.+1½ c. Type 72 .. 80 80
405. 7½ c.+2½ c. Saba Island.. 80 90
406. 15 c.+5 c. Molenplein .. 80 90
407. 22½ c.+7½ c. Scharloobrug 80 90
408. 25 c.+7½ c. Brievengat.. 80 90
No. 406 is vert.

73. Water-distillation Plant. 74. Antilles Flag.

1959. Inauguration of Aruba Water-distillation Plant.
409 73 20 c. light blue and blue 35 35

1959. 5th Anniv of Ratification of Statute of the Kingdom.
410 74 10 c. red, blue & lt blue 25 25
411 20 c. red, blue & yellow 30 30
412 25 c. red, blue and green 30 30

75. Fokker plane "Snip" over Caribbean. 76. Mgr. Niewindt.

1959. 25th Anniv of K.L.M. Netherlands–Curacao Air Service. Each yellow, deep blue and blue.
413 10 c. Type 75 .. 40 30
414 20 c. Fokker F.XVIII "De Snip" over globe .. 40 30
415 25 c. Douglas DC-7C "Seven Seas" over Handelskade (bridge), Willemstad 40 15
416 35 c. Douglas DC-8 at Aruba Airport 40 40

1960. Death Cent. of Mgr. M. J. Niewindt.
417. 76. 10 c. purple 35 35
418. 20 c. violet 50 50
419. 25 c. olive 35 35

77. Flag and Oil-worker. 78. Frogman.

1960. Labour Day.
420. 77. 20 c. multicoloured .. 30 30

1960. Princess Wilhelmina Cancer Relief Fund. Inscr. "KANKERBESTRIJDING".
421. 78. 10 c.+2 c. blue .. 1·10 1·10
422. – 20 c.+3 c. multicoloured 1·40 1·25
423. – 25 c.+5 c. red, bl. & blk. 1·40 1·25
DESIGNS—HORIZ. 20 c., 25 c. Tropical fishes (different).

79. Child on Bed. 80. Governor's Salute to the American Naval Brig "Andrew Doria" at St. Eustatius.

1961. Child Welfare. Inscr. "voor het kind".
424. 6 c.+2 c. black and green 25 25
425. 10 c.+3 c. black and red.. 30 30
426. 20 c.+6 c. black & yellow 30 30
427. 25 c.+8 c. black & orange 35 35
DESIGNS: 6 c. Type 79. 10 c. Girl with doll. 20 c. Boy with bucket. 25 c. Children in classroom.

1961. 185th Anniv. of 1st Salute to the American Flag.
428. 80. 20 c. multicoloured .. 70 60

1962. Royal Silver Wedding. As T 187 of Netherlands.
429. 10 c. orange 15 15
430. 25 c. blue 30 20

81. Jaja (nursemaid) and Child. 82. Knight and World Map.

1962. Cultural Series.
431. – 6 c. brown and yellow .. 15 15
432. – 10 c. multicoloured .. 20 15
433. – 20 c. multicoloured .. 30 30
434. **81.** 25 c. brn., grn. and blk. 35 30
DESIGNS: 6 c. Corn-masher. 10 c. Benta player. 20 c. Petji kerchief.

1962. 5th International Candidates Chess Tournament, Curacao.
436. **82.** 10 c.+5 c. green .. 95 60
437. 20 c.+10 c. red .. 95 60
438. 25 c.+10 c. blue .. 95 60

1963. Freedom from Hunger. No. 378 surch. **TEGEN DE HONGER** wheat sprig and **+10 c.**
439. 20 c.+10 c. grey and red .. 50 50

84. Family Group.

1963. 4th Caribbean Mental Health Congress, Curacao.
440. **84.** 20 c. buff and blue .. 30 30
441. – 25 c. red and blue .. 30 30
DESIGN: 25 c. Egyptian Cross emblem.

85. "Freedom". 86. Hotel Bonaire.

1963. Centenary of Abolition of Slavery in Dutch West Indies.
442. **85.** 25 c. brown and yellow 25 25

1963. Opening of Hotel Bonaire.
443. **86.** 20 c. brown 20 20

87. Child and Flowers. 88. Test-tube and Flask.

1963. Child Welfare. Child Art. Mult.
444. 5 c.+2 c. Type **87** .. 25 35
445. 6 c.+3 c. Children and flowers 25 35
446. 10 c.+5 c. Girl with ball .. 30 35
447. 20 c.+10 c. Men with flags 30 35
448. 25 c.+12 c. Schoolboy .. 30 35
Nos. 445/7 are horiz.

1963. 150th Anniv. of Kingdom of the Netherlands. As No. 968 of Netherlands, but smaller, size 26×27 mm.
449 25 c. green, red and black 20 20

1963. Chemical Industry, Aruba.
450. **88.** 20 c. red, light green and green 45 40

89. Winged Letter.

1964. 35th Anniv of 1st U.S.-Curacao Flight. Multicoloured.
451 20 c. Type **89** 30 30
452 25 c. Route map, Sikorsky S-38 flying boat and Boeing 707 .. .. 40 30

90. Trinitaria.

1964. Child Welfare. Multicoloured.
453. 6 c.+3 c. Type **90** 20 20
454. 10 c.+5 c. Magdalena .. 25 25
455. 20 c.+10 c. Yellow kelki .. 30 30
456. 25 c.+11 c. Bellisima .. 30 30

91. Caribbean Map. 92. "Six Islands".

1964. 5th Caribbean Council Assembly.
457. **91.** 20 c. yellow, red & blue 30 20

1964. 10th Anniv. of Statute for the Kingdom.
458. **92.** 25 c. multicoloured .. 20 20

93. Princess Beatrix. 94. I.T.U. Emblem and Symbols.

1965. Visit of Princess Beatrix.
459. **93.** 25 c. red 35 30

1965. Centenary of I.T.U.
460. **94.** 10 c. deep blue and blue 15 15

95. "Asperalla" (tanker) at Curacao.

1965. 50th Anniv. of Curacao's Oil Industry. Multicoloured.
461. 10 c. Catalytic cracking plant (vert.) 20 15
462. 20 c. Type **95** 25 15
463. 25 c. Super fractionating plant (vert.) 25 20

96. Flag and Fruit Market, Curacao. 97. Cup Sponges.

1965.
464. **96.** 1 c. blue, red & green .. 10 10
465. – 2 c. blue, red and yellow 10 10
466. – 3 c. blue, red and cobalt 10 10
467. – 4 c. blue, red and orange 25 10
468. – 5 c. blue, red and blue .. 10 10
469. – 6 c. blue, red and pink .. 10 10
DESIGNS (Flag and): 2 c. Divi-divi tree. 3 c. Lace. 4 c. Greater Flamingoes. 5 c. Church. 6 c. Lobster. Each is inscr. with a different place-name.

1965. Child Welfare. Marine Life. Mult.
470. 6 c.+3c. Type **97** .. 15 15
471. 10 c. +5 c. Cup sponges (diff.) 20 20
472. 20 c.+10 c. Sea anemones on star coral 20 20
473. 25 c.+11 c. Basket sponge and "Brain" coral .. 30 35

98. Marine and Seascape. 99. Budgerigars and Wedding Rings.

1965. Tercent. of Marine Corps.
474. **98.** 25 c. multicoloured .. 20 15

1966. Intergovernmental Committee for European Migration (I.C.E.M.) Fund. As T **215** of Netherlands.
475. 35 c.+15 c. bistre & brown 20 25

1966. Marriage of Crown Princess Beatrix and Herr Claus von Amsberg.
476. **99.** 25 c. multicoloured .. 40 35

100. Admiral De Ruyter and Map.

1966. 300th Anniv. of Admiral De Ruyter's Visit to St. Eustatius.
477. **100.** 25 c. ochre, violet & blue 20 15

101. "Grammar". 102. Cooking.

1966. 25 years of Secondary Education.
478. **101.** 6 c. black, blue & yellow 10 10
479. – 10 c. black, red & green 10 10
480. – 20 c. black, blue & yellow 15 15
481. – 25 c. black red and green 20 20
DESIGNS—The "Free Arts", figures representing: 10 c. "Rhetoric" and "Dialect". 20 c. "Arithmetic" and "Geometry". 25 c. "Astronomy" and "Music".

1966. Child Welfare. Multicoloured.
482 6 c.+3 c. Type **102** .. 10 10
483 10 c.+5 c. Nursing .. 10 10
484 20 c.+10 c. Metal-work fitting 20 20
485 25 c.+11 c. Ironing .. 25 25

103. "Gelderland" (cruiser).

1967. 60th Anniv. of Royal Netherlands Navy League.
486. **103.** 6 c. bronze and green .. 10 10
487. – 10 c. ochre and yellow .. 15 15
488. – 20 c. brown and sepia .. 20 15
489. – 25 c. blue and indigo .. 20 20
SHIPS: 10 c. "Pioneer" (schooner). 20 c. "Oscilla" (tanker). 25 c. "Santa Rosa" (liner).

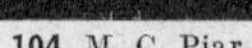
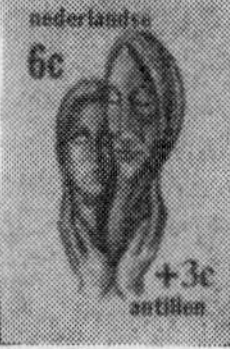

104. M. C. Piar. 105. "Heads in Hands".

1967. 150th Death Anniv. of Manuel Piar (patriot).
490. **104.** 20 c. brown and red .. 15 15

1967. Cultural and Social Relief Funds.
491. **105.** 6 c.+3 c. black & blue 10 10
492. – 10 c.+5 c. blk. & mve. 15 15
493. 20 c.+10 c. purple .. 15 15
494. 25 c.+11 c. blue .. 15 20

106. "The Turtle and the Monkey". 107. Olympic Flame and Rings.

1967. Child Welfare. "Nanzi" Fairy Tales. Multicoloured.
495. 6 c.+3 c. "Princess Long Nose" (vert.) .. 15 15
496. 10 c.+5 c. Type **106.** 20 15
497. 20 c.+10 c. "Nanzi (spider) and the Tiger" .. 25 15
498. 25 c.+11 c. "Shon Arey's Balloon" (vert.) .. 30 20

1968. Olympic Games, Mexico. Mult.
499. 10 c. Type **107** 20 20
500. 20 c. "Throwing the discus" (statue) 20 20
501. 25 c. Stadium and doves .. 20 20

108. "Dance of the Ribbons".

1968. Cultural and Social Relief Funds.
502. **108.** 10 c.+5 c. multicoloured 15 15
503. 15 c.+5 c. multicoloured 15 15
504. 20 c.+10 c. multicoloured 15 20
505. 25 c.+10 c. multicoloured 20 25

109. Boy with Goat.

1968. Child Welfare Fund. Multicoloured.
506. 6 c.+3 c. Type **109** .. 15 15
507. 10 c.+5 c. Girl with Dog 15 15
508. 20 c.+10 c. Boy with Cat 25 25
509. 25 c.+11 c. Girl with Duck 35 35

110. Friendship "500" Airliner. 111. Radio Pylon, "Waves" and Map.

1968. Dutch Antillean Airlines.
510. **110.** 10 c. blue, black & yell. 25 20
511. – 20 c. blue, black & brn. 25 20
512. – 25 c. blue, black & pink 25 20
DESIGNS: 20 c. Douglas "DC-9"; 25 c. Friendship "500" in flight and Douglas "DC-9" on ground.

1969. Opening of Broadcast Relay Station, Bonaire.
513 **111** 25 c. green, dp blue & bl 20 20

112. "Code of Laws". 113. "Carnival".

1969. Centenary of Netherlands Antilles' Court of Justice.
514. **112.** 20 c. grn., gold & lt. grn. 20 20
515. – 25 c. multicoloured .. 20 20
DESIGN: 25 c. "Scales of Justice".

1969. Cultural and Social Relief Funds. Antilles' Festivals. Multicoloured.
516. 10 c.+5 c. Type **113.** .. 30 30
517. 15 c.+5 c. "Harvest Festival" 30 30
518. 20 c.+10 c. "San Juan Day" 40 40
519. 25 c.+10 c. "New Years' Day" 40 40

114. I.L.O. Emblem, "Koenoekoe" House and Cacti. 115. Boy playing Guitar.

1969. 50th Anniv. of Int. Labour Organization.
520. **114.** 10 c. black and blue .. 15 15
521. 25 c. black and red .. 15 15

1969. Child Welfare.
522. **115.** 6 c.+3 c. violet & orge. 25 25
523. – 10 c.+5 c. grn. & yell. 35 35
524. – 20 c.+10 c. red and blue 40 40
525. – 25 c.+11 c. brn. & pink 50 50
DESIGNS: 10 c. Girl playing recorder. 20 c. Boy playing "marimula". 25 c. Girl playing piano.

1969. 15th Anniv. of Statute of the Kingdom. As T **240.** of the Netherlands, but inscr. "NEDERLANDSE ANTILLEN".
526. 25 c. multicoloured .. 25 20

HAVE YOU READ THE NOTES AT THE BEGINNING OF THIS CATALOGUE?

These often provide answers to the enquiries we receive.

117. Radio Station, Bonaire. **118.** St. Anna Church, Otrabanda, Curacao.

1970. 5th Anniv. of Trans-World Religious Radio Station, Bonaire. Multicoloured.

527. 10 c. Type **117** 15 15
528. 15 c. Trans-World Radio Emblem 15 15

1970. Churches of the Netherlands Antilles. Multicoloured.

529. 10 c. Type **118** 20 20
530. 20 c. "Mikve Israel-Emanuel" Synagogue, Punda, Curacao (horiz.) .. 20 20
531. 25 c. Pulpit Fort Church Curacao 20 20

119. "The Press". **120.** Mother and Child.

1970. Cultural and Social Relief Funds. "Mass-media". Multicoloured.

532. 10 c.+5 c. Type **119**. .. 40 40
533. 15 c.+5 c. "Films" .. 40 40
534. 20 c.+10 c. "Radio" .. 45 45
535. 25 c.+10 c. "Television" 45 45

1970. Child Welfare. Multicoloured.

536. 6 c.+3 c. Type **120**. .. 45 45
537. 10 c.+5 c. Child with piggy-bank 45 45
538. 20 c.+10 c. Children's Judo 45 45
539. 25 c.+11 c. "Pick-a-back" 45 45

121. St Theresia's Church, St. Nicolaas, Aruba. **122.** Lions Emblem.

1971. 40th Anniv. of St. Theresia Parish, Aruba.

540. **121.** 20 c. multicoloured .. 20 20

1971. 25th Anniv. of Curacao Lions Club.

541. **122.** 25 c. multicoloured .. 35 25

123. Charcoal Stove. **125.** Admiral Brion.

1971. Cultural and Social Relief Funds Household Utensils. Multicoloured.

542. 10 c.+5 c. Type **123** .. 45 45
543. 15 c.+5 c. Earthenware water vessel 45 45
544. 20 c.+10 c. Baking oven 45 45
545. 25 c.+10 c. Kitchen implements 45 45

1971. Prince Bernhard's 60th Birthday. Design as No. 1135 of Netherlands.

546. 45 c. multicoloured .. 45 40

1971. 150th Death Anniv. of Admiral Pedro Luis Brion.

547. **125.** 40 c. multicoloured .. 30 30

126. Bottle Doll. **127.** Queen Emma Bridge, Curacao.

1971. Child Welfare. Home-made Toys. Mult.

548 15 c.+5 c. Type **126** .. 60 60
549 20 c.+10 c. Simple cart .. 65 65
550 30 c.+15 c. Spinning-tops 65 65

1971. Views of the Islands. Multicoloured.

551 1 c. Type **127** 10 10
552 2 c. The Bottom, Saba .. 10 10
553 3 c. Greater flamingoes, Bonaire 30 10
554 4 c. Distillation plant, Aruba 10 10
555 5 c. Fort Amsterdam, St. Maarten 10 10
556 6 c. Fort Oranje, St. Eustatius 10 10

128. Ship in Dock. **129.** Steel Band.

1972. Inauguration of New Dry Dock Complex, Willemstad, Curacao.

557. **128.** 30 c. multicoloured .. 35 30

1972. Cultural and Social Relief Funds. Folklore. Multicoloured.

558. 15 c.+5 c. Type **129** .. 75 75
559. 20 c.+10 c. "Seu" festival 75 75
560. 30 c.+15 c. "Tambu" dance 75 75

130. J. E. Irausquin. **131.** Dr. M. F. da Costa Gomez.

1972. 10th Death Anniv. of Juan Enrique Irausquin (Antilles statesman).

561. **130.** 30 c. red 30 25

1972. 65th Birth Anniv. of Moises F. da Costa Gomez (statesman).

562. **131.** 30 c. black and green .. 30 25

132. Child playing with Earth. **133.** Pedestrian Crossing.

1972. Child Welfare. Multicoloured.

563. 15 c.+5 c. Type **132** .. 85 85
564. 20 c.+10 c. Child playing in water 85 85
565. 30 c.+15 c. Child throwing ball into the air .. 85 85

1973. Cultural and Social Relief Funds. Road Safety.

566. **133.** 12 c.+6 c. multicoloured 90 80
567. – 15 c.+7 c. grn., orge. & red 90 80
568. – 40 c.+20 c. multicoloured 90 80

DESIGNS: 15 c. Road-crossing patrol. 40 c. Traffic lights.

134. William III (portrait from stamp of 1873). **135.** Map of Aruba, Curacao and Bonaire.

1973. Stamp Centenary.

569. **134.** 15 c. lilac, mauve & gold 30 25
570. – 20 c. multicoloured .. 35 30
571. – 30 c. multicoloured .. 35 30

DESIGNS: 20 c. Antilles postman. 30 c. Postal Service emblem.

1973. Inauguration of Submarine Cable and Microwave Telecommunications Link. Mult.

572. 15 c. Type **135** 40 20
573. 30 c. Six stars ("The Antilles") 40 40
574. 45 c. Map of Saba, St. Maarten and St. Eustatius 40 40

136. Queen Juliana. **137.** Jan Eman.

1973. Silver Jubilee of Queen Juliana's Reign.

576. **136.** 15 c. multicoloured .. 45 45

1973. 16th Death Anniv. of Jan Eman (Aruba statesman).

577. **137.** 30 c. black and green .. 30 25

138. "1948–1973". **139.** L. B. Scott.

1973. Child Welfare Fund. 25th Anniv of 1st Child Welfare Stamps.

578. **138.** 15 c.+5 c. light green, green and blue .. 85 70
579. – 20 c.+10 c. brown, green and blue .. 85 75
580. – 30 c.+15 c. violet, blue and light blue .. 1·25 90

DESIGNS: No. 579, Three Children. No. 580, Mother and child.

1974. 8th Death Anniv. of Lionel B. Scott (St. Maarten statesman).

582. **139.** 30 c. multicoloured .. 30 30

140. Family Meal. **141.** Girl combing Hair.

1974. Family Planning Campaign. Mult.

583. 6 c. Type **140** 10 10
584. 12 c. Family at home .. 25 20
585. 15 c. Family in garden .. 30 20

1974. Cultural and Social Relief Funds. "The Younger Generation". Mult.

586. 12 c.+6 c. Type **141** .. 1·00 1·00
587. 15 c.+7 c. "Pop dancers" 1·00 1·00
588. 40 c.+20 c. Group drummer 1·00 1·00

142. Desulphurisation Plant.

1974. 50th Anniv. of Lago Oil Co., Aruba. Multicoloured.

589. 15 c. Type **142** 45 30
590. 30 c. Fractionating towers 45 30
591. 45 c Lago refinery at night 45 35

143. U.P.U. Emblem. **144.** "A Carpenter outranks a King".

1974. Cent. of Universal Postal Union.

592. **143.** 15 c. gold, grn. & blk. .. 40 35
593. 30 c. gold, blue & black 40 40

1974. Child Welfare. Children's Songs. Mult.

594. 15 c.+5 c. Type **144** .. 70 70
595. 20 c.+10 c. Footprints ("Let's Do a Ring-dance") 70 70
596. 30 c.+15 c. "Moon and Sun" 70 70

145. Queen Emma Bridge. **146.** Ornamental Ventilation Grid.

1975. Antillean Bridges. Multicoloured.

597 20 c. Type **145** 45 40
598 30 c. Queen Juliana Bridge 50 40
599 40 c. Queen Wilhelmina Bridge 65 50

1975. Cultural and Social Relief Funds.

600 **146** 12 c.+6 c. mult .. 65 65
601 – 15 c.+7 c. brn & stone 65 65
602 – 40 c.+20 c. mult .. 65 65

DESIGNS: 15 c. Knight accompanied by buglers (tombstone detail). 40 c. Foundation stone.

147. Sodium Chloride Molecules.

1975. Bonaire Salt Industry. Multicoloured.

603. 15 c. Type **147** 55 35
604. 20 c. Salt incrustation and blocks 55 45
605. 40 c. Map of salt area (vert.) 65 45

148. Fokker "F-18" and Old Control Tower.

1975. 40th Anniv. of Aruba Airport. Mult.

606. 15 c. Type **148** 45 25
607. 30 c. Douglas "DC-9" and modern control tower .. 45 30
608. 40 c. Tail of Boeing "727" and "Princess Beatrix" Airport buildings .. 45 45

149. I.W.Y. Emblem.

1975. International Women's Year. Mult.

609. 6 c. Type **149** 20 15
610. 12 c. "Social Development" 35 20
611. 20 c. "Equality of Sexes" .. 45 30

150. Children making Windmill.

1975. Child Welfare. Multicoloured.

612. 15 c. + 5 c. Type **150** .. 70 65
613. 20 c. + 10 c. Child modelling clay .. 70 65
614. 30 c. + 15 c. Children drawing pictures .. 70 65

151. Beach, Aruba. **152.** J. A. Abraham (statesman).

1976. Tourism. Multicoloured.

615. 40 c. Type **151** 60 50
616. 40 c. Fish Kiosk, Bonaire 60 50
617. 40 c. "Table Mountain", Curacao 60 50

1976. Abraham Commemoration.

618. **152.** 30 c. purple on brown 40 35

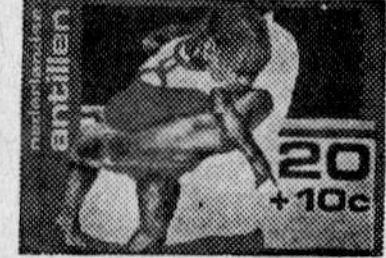

153. Dyke Produce. **154.** Arm holding Child.

1976. Agriculture, Animal Husbandry and Fisheries. Multicoloured.

619. 15 c. Type **153** 35 25
620. 35 c. Cattle 50 40
621. 45 c. Fishes 50 50

1976. Child Welfare. "Carrying the Child".
622. 154. 20 c.+10 c. mult. .. 60 60
623. – 25 c.+12 c. mult. .. 60 60
624. – 40 c.+18 c. mult. .. 60 60
DESIGNS—HORIZ. 25 c. VERT. 40 c. Both similar to Type 154 showing arm holding child.

155. "Andrew Doria" (naval brig) receiving Salute.
156. Carnival Costume.

1976. Bicentenary of American Revolution. Multicoloured.
625. 25 c. Flags and plaque, Fort Oranje 70 45
626. 40 c. Type 155 .. .. 70 45
627. 55 c. Johannes de Graaff, Governor of St. Eustatius 70 70

1977. Carnival.
628. – 25 c. multicoloured .. 45 35
629. 156. 35 c. multicoloured .. 45 35
630. – 40 c. multicoloured .. 45 35
DESIGNS: 25 c., 40 c. Women in Carnival costumes.

157. Tortoise (Bonaire).
158. "Ace" Playing Card.

1977. Rock Paintings. Multicoloured.
631. 25 c. Bird (Aruba) .. 60 35
632. 35 c. Abstract (Curacao) .. 60 45
633. 40 c. Type 157 .. .. 75 45

1977. Sixth Central American and Caribbean Bridge Championships. Multicoloured.
634. 158. 20 c.+10 c. red & black 50 35
635. – 25 c.+12 c. mult. .. 50 45
636. – 40 c.+18 c. mult. .. 65 60
DESIGNS—VERT. 25 c. "King" playing card. HORIZ. 40 c. Bridge hand.

159. "Cordia sebestena".
160. Bells outside Main Store.

1977. Flowers. Multicoloured.
639. 25 c. Type 159 .. .. 40 35
640. 40 c. "Albizzia lebbeck" (vert.) 50 45
641. 55 c. "Tamarindus indica" 60 55

1977. 50th Anniv of Spritzer and Fuhrmann (jewellers). Multicoloured.
642 20 c. Type 160 .. .. 40 30
643 40 c. Globe basking in sun 50 40
644 55 c. Antillean flag and diamond ring 60 60

161. Children with Toy Animal.

1977. Child Welfare. Multicoloured.
645 15 c.+15 c. Type 161 .. 35 25
646 20 c.+10 c. Children with toy rabbit 40 40
647 25 c.+12 c. Children with toy cat 50 45
648 40 c.+18 c. Children with toy beetle 55 55

162. "The Unspoiled Queen" (Saba).

1977. Tourism. Multicoloured.
650. 25 c. Type 162 .. .. 15 15
651. 35 c. "The Golden Rock" (St. Eustatius) .. 20 20
652. 40 c. "The Friendly Island" (St. Maarten) .. 25 25

1977. As Nos. 378, 381/2 and 385, but larger, 39×22 mm.
653. E. 20 c. grey and red .. 1·00 1·00
654. 35 c. pink and brown .. 2·50 3·00
655. C. 40 c. green and mauve 1·25 1·25
656. E. 55 c. green and red .. 1·50 1·50

163. 19th-century Chest.
164. Water-skiing.

1978. 150th Anniv. of Netherlands Antilles' Bank. Multicoloured.
657 163 15 c. blue & light blue 10 10
658 – 20 c. orange and gold 10 10
659 – 40 c. green & dp green 20 20
DESIGNS: 20 c. Bank emblem. 40 c. Strong-room door.

1978. Sports Funds. Multicoloured.
660 15 c.+5 c. Type 164 .. 10 10
661 20 c.+10 c. Yachting .. 15 15
662 25 c.+12 c. Football .. 20 20
663 40 c.+18 c. Baseball .. 35 35

165. "Erythrina velutina".
166. "Polythysana rubrescens".

1978. Flora of Netherlands Antilles. Mult.
664. 15 c. "Delconix regia" .. 20 15
665. 25 c. Type 165 .. .. 25 25
666. 50 c. "Guaiacum officinale" (horiz.) 35 30
667. 55 c. "Gilricidia sepium" (horiz.) 45 45

1978. Butterflies. Multicoloured.
668 15 c. Type 166 .. .. 25 15
669 25 c. "Caligo sp." .. 40 20
670 35 c. "Prepona praeneste" 55 35
671 40 c. "Morpho sp." .. 70 50

167. "Conserve Energy" (English).
168. Red Cross.

1978. Energy Conservation.
672. 167. 15 c. orange and black 15 15
673. – 20 c. green and black .. 20 20
674. – 40 c. red and black .. 40 40
DESIGNS: As No. 672 but text in Dutch (20 c.) or in Papiamento (40 c.).

1978. 150th Birth Anniv. of Henri Dunant (founder of Red Cross).
675. 168. 55 c.+25 c. red & blue 30 30

169. Curacao from Sea, and Punched Tape.
170. Boy Roller-skating.

1978. 70th Anniv. of Antilles Telecommunications Corporation (Landsradio). Mult.
677. 20 c. Type 169 .. .. 25 25
678. 40 c. Ship's bridge, punched tape and radio mast .. 35 35
679. 55 c. Satellite and aerial (vert.) 50 50

1978. Child Welfare. Multicoloured.
680. 15 c.+5 c. Type 170 .. 40 35
681. 20 c.+10 c. Boy and girl flying kite 50 40
682. 25 c.+12 c. Boy and girl playing marbles .. 50 45
683. 40 c.+18 c. Girl riding bicycle 60 55

171. Ca'i Awa (pumping station).
172. Aruba Coat of Arms (float).

1978. 80th Death Anniv. of Leonard Burlington Smith (entrepreneur and U.S. consul).
685. 171. 25 c. multicoloured .. 20 15
686. – 35 c. black, greenish yellow and yellow .. 25 20
687. – 40 c. multicoloured .. 35 30
DESIGNS—VERT. 35 c. Leonard Burlington Smith. HORIZ. 40 c. Opening ceremony of Queen Emma Bridge, 1888.

1979. 25th Aruba Carnival. Multicoloured.
688. 40 c.+10 c. Float representing heraldic fantasy .. 40 35
689. 75 c.+20 c. Type 172 .. 65 65

173. Goat and P.A.H.O. Emblem.
174. Yacht and Sun.

1979. 12th Inter-American Ministerial Meeting on Foot and Mouth Disease and Zoonosis Control, Curacao. Multicoloured.
690 50 c. Type 173 .. .. 30 30
691 75 c. Horse and conference emblem 45 45
692 150 c. Cows, flag and Pan-American Health Organization (P.A.H.O.) and W.H.O. emblems .. 1·00 1·00

1979. 12th International Sailing Regatta, Bonaire. Multicoloured.
694. 15 c.+5 c. Type 174 .. 15 15
695. 35 c.+25 c. Yachts .. 35 35
696. 40 c.+15 c. Yacht and globe (horiz.) 50 50
697. 55 c.+25 c. Yacht, sun and flamingo 60 60

175. Corps Members.
176. "Melochia tomentosa".

1979. 50th Anniv of Curacao Volunteer Corps.
699 175 15 c.+10 c. blue, red and ultramarine .. 25 20
700 – 40 c.+20 c. blue, violet and gold 45 40
701 – 1 g. multicoloured .. 70 65
DESIGNS: 40 c. Sentry in battle dress and emblem. 1 g. Corps emblem, flag and soldier in ceremonial uniform.

1979. Flowers. Multicoloured.
702. 25 c. "Casearia tremula" 20 15
703. 40 c. "Cordia cylindrostachya" 35 30
704. 1 g. 50 Type 176 .. .. 1·00 1·00

177. Girls reading Book.
178. Dove and Netherlands Flag.

1979. International Year of the Child.
705 177 20 c.+10 c. mult .. 25 25
706 – 25 c.+12 c. mult .. 35 30
707 – 35 c.+15 c. violet, brown and black .. 50 45
708 – 50 c.+20 c. mult .. 60 55
DESIGNS: 25 c. Toddler and cat. 35 c. Girls carrying basket. 50 c. Boy and girl dressing-up.

1979. 25th Anniv of Statute of the Kingdom. Multicoloured.
710 65 c. Type 178 .. .. 50 40
711 1 g. 50 Dove and Netherlands Antilles flag .. 80 90

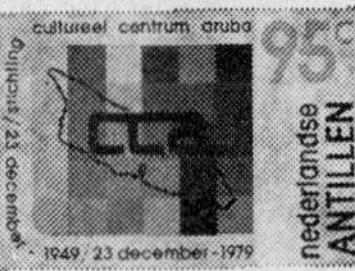

179. Map of Aruba and Foundation Emblem.

1979. 30th Anniv of Aruba Cultural Centre Foundation. Multicoloured.
712. 95 c. Type 179 .. .. 60 60
713. 1 g. Foundation headquarters 70 70

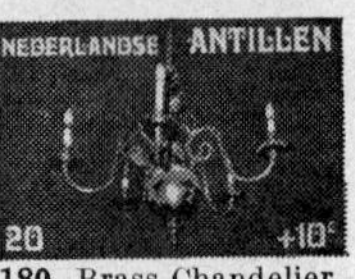

180. Brass Chandelier.

1980. 210th Anniv. of Fort Church, Curacao.
714. 180. 20 c.+10 c. yellow, black and brown .. 20 20
715. – 50 c.+25 c. mult. .. 50 50
716. – 100 c. multicoloured .. 65 65
DESIGNS: 50 c. Pipe organ. 100 c. Cupola tower, 1910.

181. Rotary Emblem and Cogwheel.

1980. 75th Anniv. of Rotary International. Multicoloured.
717 45 c. Rotary emblem .. 35 35
718 50 c. Globe and cogwheels 40 40
719 85 c. Type 181 .. .. 65 65

182. Savings Box.

1980. 75th Anniv. of Post Office Savings Bank. Multicoloured
721. 25 c. Type 182 .. .. 20 20
722. 150 c. Savings box (different) 1·00 1·00

183. Queen Juliana Accession Stamp.

1980. Accession of Queen Beatrix.
723. 183. 25 c. red, grn. and gold 20 20
724. – 60 c. grn. red and gold 40 40
DESIGN: 60 c. 1965 Royal Visit stamp.

184. Sir Rowland Hill.
185. Volleyball.

1980. "London 1980" International Stamp Exhibition.
725. 184. 45 c. black and green .. 35 35
726. – 60 c. black and red .. 40 40
727. – 1 g. red, black and blue 70 70
DESIGNS: 60 c. "London 1980" logo. 1 g. Airmail label.

1980. Sports Funds.
729 – 25 c.+10 c. red & black 25 25
730 – 40 c.+15 c. yell & blk 35 35
731 185 45 c.+20 c. pale green, green and black .. 50 50
732 – 60 c.+25 c. pink, orange and black .. 75 75
DESIGNS: 25 c. Gymnastics (beam exercise). 30 c. Gymnastics (horse vaulting). 60 c. Basketball.

186. White-fronted Dove.

1980. Birds. Multicoloured.
734. 25 c. Type 186 .. .. 25 20
735. 60 c. Tropical Mockingbird 65 45
736. 85 c. Bananaquit 80 70

187. " St. Maarten Landscape ".

188. Rudolf Theodorus Palm.

1980. Child Welfare. Children's Drawings. Multicoloured.

737 25 c.+10 c. Type **187** .. 30 30
738 30 c.+15 c. "Bonaire House" 35 40
739 40 c.+20 c. "Child writing on Board" 45 50
740 60 c.+25 c. "Dancing Couple" (vert) 60 65

1981. Birth Centenary (1980) of Rudolf Theodorus Palm (musician).

742 **188** 60 c. brown and yellow 50 45
743 – 1 g. buff and blue .. 1·00 85

DESIGN: 1 g. Musical score and hands playing piano.

189. Map of Aruba and TEAM Emblem.

190. Boy in Wheelchair.

1981. 50th Anniv of Evangelical Alliance Mission (TEAM) in Antilles. Multicoloured.

744 30 c. Type **189** 25 20
745 50 c. Map of Curacao and emblem 50 40
746 1 g. Map of Bonaire and emblem .. .. 1·00 85

1981. International Year of Disabled Persons. Multicoloured.

747 25 c.+10 c. Blind woman 35 35
748 30 c.+15 c. Type **190** .. 45 45
749 45 c.+20 c. Child in walking frame 70 70
750 60 c.+25 c. Deaf girl .. 80 80

191. Tennis.

192. Gateway.

1981. Sports Funds. Multicoloured.

751. 30 c.+15 c. Type **191** .. 50 50
752. 50 c.+20 c. Swimming .. 70 70
753. 70 c.+25 c. Boxing .. 90 90

1981. 125th Anniv. of St. Elisabeth's Hospital. Multicoloured.

755. 60 c. Type **192** 60 50
756. 1 g. 50 St. Elisabeth's Hospital .. .. 1·40 1·40

193. Marinus van der Maarel (promoter).

194. Mother and Child.

1981. 50th Anniv (1980) of Antillean Boy Scouts Association. Multicoloured.

757. 45 c.+20 c. Wolf Cub and leader 75 75
758. 70 c.+25 c. Type **193** .. 1·10 1·10
759. 1 g.+50 c. Headquarters, Ronde Klip .. .. 1·60 1·60

1981. Child Welfare. Multicoloured.

761. 35 c.+15 c. Type **194** .. 45 50
762. 45 c.+20 c. Boy and girl 55 60
763. 55 c.+25 c. Child with cat 70 75
764. 85 c.+40 c. Girl with Teddy bear .. .. 1·10 1·25

195. " Jatropha gossypifolia ".

196. Pilot Gig approaching Ship.

1981. Flowers. Multicoloured.

766. 45 c. " Cordia globosa ".. 35 35
767. 70 c. Type **195** 70 70
768. 100 c. " Croton flavens ".. 85 85

1982. Cent. of Pilotage Service. Mult.

769. 70 c. Type **196** 80 80
770. 85 c. Modern liner and map of Antilles .. 1·00 1·00
771. 1 g. Pilot boarding ship 1·10 1·10

197. Fencing.

198. Holy Ark.

1982. Sports Funds.

772. **197.** 35 c.+15 c. mauve and violet 65 50
773. – 45 c.+20 c. blue and deep blue 85 70
774. – 70 c.+35 c. multicoloured 1·25 95
775. – 85 c.+40 c. brown and deep brown .. 1·40 1·10

DESIGNS: 45 c. Judo. 70 c. Football. 85 c. Cycling.

1982. 250th Anniv of Dedication of Mikve Israel-Emanuel Synagogue, Curacao. Mult.

777. 75 c. Type **198** .. .. 1·25 90
778. 85 c. Synagogue facade .. 1·40 90
779. 150 c. Tebah (raised platform) .. .. .. 1·75 1·40

199. Peter Stuyvesant (Governor) and Flags of Netherlands, Netherlands Antilles and United States.

200. Airport Control Tower.

1982. Bicentenary of Netherlands-United States Diplomatic Relations.

780. **199.** 75 c. multicoloured .. 1·00 80

1982. International Federation of Air Traffic Controllers.

782 – 35 c. black, ultramarine and blue 50 35
783 **200** 75 c. black, green and light green .. .. 1·00 75
784 – 150 c. black, orange and salmon .. 1·50 1·25

DESIGNS: 35 c. Radar plot trace. 150 c. Radar aerials.

201. Mail Bag.

202. Brown Chromis.

1982. "Philexfrance 82" International Stamp Exhibition, Paris. Multicoloured.

785 45 c. Exhibition emblem .. 50 40
786 85 c. Type **201** 95 75
787 150 c. Netherlands Antilles and French flags .. 1·40 1·25

1982. Fishes. Multicoloured.

789 35 c. Type **202** 70 40
790 75 c. Spotted trunkfish .. 1·25 75
791 85 c. Blue tang .. .. 1·40 1·00
792 100 c. French angelfish .. 1·50 1·10

203. Girl playing Accordion.

1982. Child Welfare. Multicoloured.

793. 35 c.+15 c. Type **203** .. 80 60
794. 75 c.+35 c. Boy playing guitar .. .. .. 1·40 1·25
795. 85 c.+40 c. Boy playing violin .. .. .. 1·75 1·40

204. Saba House.

1982. Cultural and Social Relief Funds. Local Houses. Multicoloured.

797. 35 c.+15 c. Type **204** .. 70 45
798. 75 c.+35 c. Aruba House 1·25 95
799. 85 c.+40 c. Curacao House 1·40 1·25

205. High Jumping.

1983. Sports Funds. Multicoloured.

801. 35 c. + 15 c. Type **205** .. 65 50
802. 45 c. + 20 c. Weightlifting 1·00 85
803. 85 c. + 40 c. Wind-surfing 1·50 1·40

206. Natural Bridge, Aruba.

207. W.C.Y. Emblem and Means of Communication.

1983. Tourism. Multicoloured.

804. 35 c. Type **206** 60 50
805. 45 c. Lac Bay, Bonaire .. 75 55
806. 100 c. Willemstad, Curacao 1·25 1·10

1983. World Communications Year.

807. **207.** 1 g. multicoloured .. 1·25 1·10

208. "Curacao" (paddle-steamer) and Post Office Building.

209. Mango ("Mangifera indica").

1983. "Brasiliana 83" International Stamp Exhibition, Rio de Janeiro. Multicoloured.

809. 45 c. Type **208** 70 60
810. 55 c. Brazil flag, exhibition emblem and Netherlands Antilles flag and postal service emblem 75 65
811. 100 c. Governor's Palace, Netherlands Antilles, and Sugarloaf Mountain, Rio de Janeiro .. .. 1·25 1·00

1983. Flowers. Multicoloured.

813. 45 c. Type **209** 80 65
814. 55 c. " Malpighia punicifolia " 95 75
815. 100 c. " Citrus aurantifolia " .. .. .. 1·50 1·25

210. Boy and Lizard.

1983. Child Welfare. Multicoloured.

816. 45 c.+20 c. Type **210** .. 1·00 85
817. 55 c.+25 c. Girl watching ants .. .. .. 1·25 1·10
818. 100 c.+50 c. Girl feeding donkey .. .. .. 2·00 1·75

211. Aruba Water Jar.

212. Saba.

1983. Cultural and Social Relief Funds. Pre-Columbian Pottery.

820. **211.** 45 c.+20 c. light blue, blue and black .. 1·10 1·00
821. – 55 c.+25 c. pink, red and black .. .. 1·25 1·10
822. – 85 c.+40 c. stone, grn. and black .. .. 1·50 1·25
823. – 100 c.+50 c. light brn., brown and black .. 2·00 1·75

DESIGNS: 55 c. Aruba decorated bowl. 85 c. Curacao human figurine. 100 c. Fragment of Curacao female figurine.

1983. Local Government Buildings. Mult.

824 20 c. Type **212** 20 20
825 25 c. St. Eustatius .. 25 25
826 30 c. St. Maarten 30 30
827 35 c. Aruba .. .. 1·75 35
828 45 c. Bonaire 45 45
829 55 c. Curacao 55 55
830 60 c. Type **212** 60 60
831 65 c. As No. 825 .. .. 65 65
832 70 c. Type **212** 75 75
833 75 c. As No. 826 .. .. 75 75
834 85 c. As No. 827 .. .. 3·00 1·10
835 85 c. As No. 828 .. .. 85 85
836 90 c. As No. 828 .. .. 90 90
837 95 c. As No. 829 .. .. 95 95
838 1 g. Type **212** .. .. 1·00 1·00
839 1 g. 50 As No 825 .. .. 1·40 1·40
841 2 g. 50 As No. 826 .. 2·25 2·25
842 5 g. As No. 828 .. 4·25 4·25
843 10 g. As No. 829 .. .. 7·50 7·50
844 15 g. Type **212** .. .. 11·00 11·00

213. Note-taking, Type-setting and Front Page of " Amigoe ".

1984. Centenary of "Amigoe de Curacao" (newspaper). Multicoloured.

845. 45 c. Type **213** 65 55
846. 55 c. Printing press and newspapers 75 65
847. 85 c. Reading newspaper .. 1·25 1·10

214. W.I.A. and I.C.A.O. Emblems.

1984. 40th Anniv. of I.C.A.O.

848. **214.** 25 c. multicoloured .. 40 35
849. – 45 c. violet, blue & black 75 60
850. – 55 c. multicoloured .. 85 70
851. – 100 c multicoloured .. 1·40 1·25

DESIGNS: 45 c. I.C.A.O. anniversary emblem. 55 c. A.L.M. and I.C.A.O. emblems. 100 c. Early passenger airplane.

215. Fielder.

1984. Sports Funds. 50th Anniv. of Curacao Baseball Federation. Multicoloured.

852. 25 c.+10 c. Type **215** .. 80 60
853. 45 c.+20 c. Batter .. 1·25 1·10
854. 55 c.+25 c. Pitcher .. 1·50 1·25
855. 85 c.+40 c. Running for base .. .. .. 1·75 1·50

216. Microphones and Radio.

1984. Cultural and Social Relief Funds. Radio and Gramophone. Multicoloured.

857 45 c.+20 c. Type **216** .. 1·25 1·10
858 55 c.+25 c. Gramophones and record .. .. 1·50 1·40
859 100 c.+50 c. Gramophone with horn .. .. 1·90 1·75

217. Bonnet-maker.

1984. Centenary of Curacao Chamber of Commerce and Industry. Multicoloured.
860 45 c. Type **217** .. .. 1·10 85
861 55 c. Chamber emblem .. 1·10 90
862 1 g. "Southward" (liner) passing under bridge .. 1·50 1·25
No. 861 is an inverted triangle.

218. Black-faced Grassquit. **219.** Eleanor Roosevelt and Val-Kill, Hyde Park, New York.

1984. Birds. Multicoloured.
863. 45 c. Type **218** .. .. 1·10 75
864. 55 c. Rufous-collared sparrow .. .. .. 1·40 1·00
865. 150 c. Blue-tailed emerald 2·25 1·75

1984. Birth Centenary of Eleanor Roosevelt.
866. **219.** 45 c. multicoloured .. 70 65
867. – 85 c. blk., gold & bis. 1·00 1·00
868. – 100 c. blk., yell. & red 1·10 1·10
DESIGNS: 85 c. Portrait in oval frame; 100 c. Eleanor Roosevelt with children.

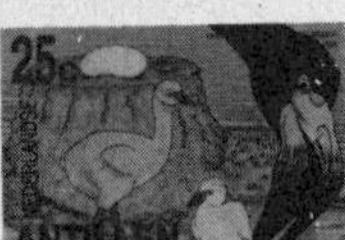

220. Child Reading. **221.** Adult Flamingo and Chicks.

1984. Child Welfare. Multicoloured.
869. 45 c.+20 c. Type **220** .. 1·10 1·10
870. 55 c.+25 c. Family reading 1·40 1·40
871. 100 c.+50 c. Family in church .. .. .. 1·75 1·75

1985. Greater Flamingoes. Multicoloured.
873. 25 c. Type **221** 85 60
874. 45 c. Young flamingoes .. 1·10 80
875. 55 c. Adult flamingoes .. 1·40 90
876. 100 c. Flamingoes in various flight positions .. .. 2·25 1·40

222. Symbols of Entered Apprentice. **223.** Players with Ball.

1985. Bicentenary of De Vergenoeging Masonic Lodge, Curacao. Multicoloured.
877. 45 c. Type **222** .. .. 1·10 75
878. 55 c. Symbols of the Fellow Craft .. .. .. 1·40 1·10
879. 100 c. Symbols of the Master Mason .. .. 2·50 1·60

1985. Sports Funds. Football. Multicoloured.
880. 10 c.+5 c. Type **223** .. 40 35
881. 15 c.+5 c. Dribbling ball .. 50 40
882. 45 c.+20 c. Running with ball .. .. .. 1·10 95
883. 55 c.+25 c. Tackling 1·40 1·25
884. 85 c.+40 c. Marking player with ball .. .. .. 1·75 1·60

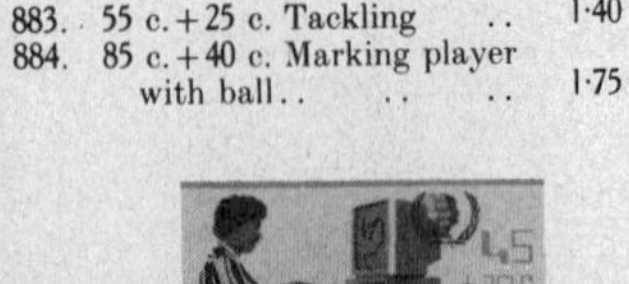

224. Boy using Computer.

1985. Cultural and Social Welfare Funds. International Youth Year. Multicoloured.
885. 45 c.+20 c. Type **224** .. 1·25 1·10
886. 55 c.+25 c. Girl listening to records .. .. 1·50 1·40
887. 100 c.+50 c. Boy break-dancing .. .. .. 2·25 2·00

225. U.N. Emblem.

1985. 40th Anniv. of U.N.O.
888. **225.** 55 c. multicoloured .. 1·00 85
889. 1 g. multicoloured .. 1·50 1·40

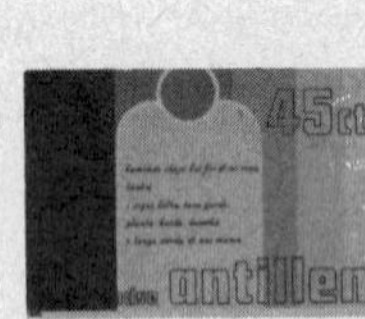

226. Pierre Lauffer and Poem. **227.** Eskimo.

1985. Papiamentu (Creole language). Mult.
890. 45 c. Type **226** 50 50
891. 55 c. Wave inscribed "Papiamentu" 75 75

1985. Child Welfare. Multicoloured.
892. 5 c.+5 c. Type **227** .. 35 20
893. 10 c.+5 c. African child .. 45 30
894. 25 c.+10 c. Chinese girl .. 65 50
895. 45 c.+20 c. Dutch girl .. 1·25 85
896. 55 c.+25 c. Red Indian girl 1·40 1·10

228. "Calotropis procera". **229.** Courthouse.

1985. Flowers. Multicoloured.
898. 5 c. Type **228** 20 10
899. 10 c. "Capparis flexuosa" 20 15
900. 20 c. "Mimosa distachya" 45 30
901. 45 c. "Ipomoea nil" .. 75 55
902. 55 c. "Heliotropium ternatum" 90 70
903. 150 c. "Ipomoea incarnata" .. .. 1·75 1·50

1986. 125th Anniv. of Curacao Courthouse. Multicoloured.
904. 5 c. Type **229** 15 10
905. 15 c. States room (vert.) .. 25 15
906. 25 c. Court room 45 35
907. 55 c. Entrance (vert.) .. 80 70

230. Sprinting. **231.** Girls watching Artist at work.

1986. Sports Funds. Multicoloured.
908. 15 c.+5 c. Type **230** .. 60 35
909. 25 c.+10 c. Horse racing .. 85 60
910. 45 c.+20 c. Motor racing .. 1·25 85
911. 55 c.+25 c. Football .. 1·40 1·25

1986. Curacao Youth Care Foundation. Multicoloured.
912. 30 c.+15 c. Type **231** .. 80 55
913. 45 c.+20 c. Children watching sculptor at work .. .. .. 1·10 75
914. 55 c.+25 c. Children watching potter at work 1·25 1·10

232. Chained Man.

1986. 25th Anniv. of Amnesty International. Multicoloured.
915. 45 c. Type **232** 80 55
916. 55 c. Dove behind bars .. 90 65
917. 100 c. Man behind bars .. 1·40 1·10

233. Post Office Mail Box. **234.** Boy playing Football.

1986. Mail Boxes. Multicoloured.
918. 10 c. Type **233** 15 10
919. 25 c. Street mail box on pole 30 25
920. 45 c. Street mail box in brick column 60 45
921. 55 c. Street mail box .. 75 65

1986. Child Welfare. Multicoloured.
922. 20 c.+10 c. Type **234** .. 50 40
923. 25 c.+15 c. Girl playing tennis 65 55
924. 45 c.+20 c. Boy practising judo 90 75
925. 55 c.+25 c. Boy playing baseball .. .. .. 1·25 1·10

235. Brothers' First House and Mauritius Vliegendehond. **236.** Engagement Picture.

1986. Centenary of Friars of Tilburg Mission. Multicoloured.
927. 10 c. Type **235** 25 15
928. 45 c. St. Thomas College and Mgr. Ferdinand E. C. Kieckens 80 55
929. 55 c. St. Thomas College courtyard and Fr. F. S. de Beer 90 70

1987. Golden Wedding of Princess Juliana and Prince Bernhard.
930. **236.** 1 g. 35 orange, black and gold .. .. 1·75 1·40

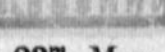

237. Map. **238.** Girls playing Instruments.

1987. 150th Anniv. of Maduro Holding Inc. Multicoloured.
932. 70 c. Type **237** 80 65
933. 85 c. Group activities .. 90 80
934. 1 g. 55 Saloman Elias Levy Maduro (founder) .. 1·75 1·50

1987. Cultural and Social Relief Funds.
935. **238.** 35 c.+15 c. mult. .. 70 60
936. – 45 c.+25 c. light green, green and blue .. 1·00 85
937. – 85 c.+40 c. mult. .. 1·40 1·25
DESIGNS: 45 c. Woman pushing man in wheelchair. 85 c. Bandstand.

239. Map and Emblem.

1987. 50th Anniv. of Curacao Rotary Club. Multicoloured.
938. 15 c. Type **239** 20 15
939. 50 c. Zeelandia country house (meeting venue) .. 65 55
940. 65 c. Emblem on map of Curacao 80 65

240. Octagon (house where Bolivar's sisters lived).

1987. 175th Anniv. of Simon Bolivar's Exile on Curacao (60, 80 c.) and 50th Anniv. of Bolivarian Society (70, 90 c.). Multicoloured.
941. 60 c. Type **240** 75 65
942. 70 c. Society headquarters, Willemstad, Curacao .. 80 70
943. 80 c. Room in Octagon .. 1·10 90
944. 90 c. Portraits of Manuel Carlos Piar, Simon Bolivar and Pedro Luis Brion .. .. .. 1·25 1·10

241. Baby.

1987. Child Welfare. Multicoloured.
945. 40 c.+15 c. Type **241** .. 80 70
946. 55 c.+25 c. Child .. .. 1·25 1·10
947. 115 c.+50 c. Youth .. 1·75 1·60

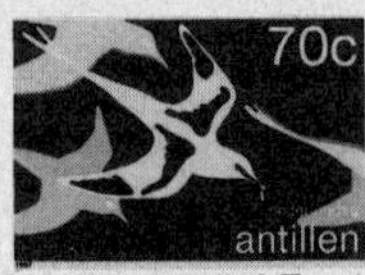

242. White-tailed Tropic Birds.

1987. 25th Anniv. of Netherlands Antilles National Parks Foundation. Multicoloured.
949. 70 c. Type **242** 80 60
950. 85 c. White-tailed deer .. 90 75
951. 155 c. Iguana .. .. 1·75 1·50

243. Printing Press and Type.

1987. 175th Anniv. of "De Curacaosche Courant" (periodical and printing shop). Multicoloured.
952. 55 c. Type **243** 65 55
953. 70 c. Keyboard and modern printing press .. 85 65

244. William Godden (founder).

1988. 75th Anniv. of Curacao Mining Company. Multicoloured.
954. 40 c. Type **244** 70 45
955. 105 c. Phosphate processing plant .. .. .. 1·50 1·10
956. 155 c. Tafelberg (source of phosphate) .. .. 2·25 1·60

245 Flags, Minutes and John Horris Sprockel (first President) **246** Bridge through "100"

1988. 50th Anniv of Netherlands Antilles Staten (legislative body). Multicoloured.
957 65 c. Type **245** 75 65
958 70 c. Ballot paper and schematic representation of extension of voting rights 75 65
959 155 c. Antilles and Netherlands flags and birds representing five Antilles islands and Aruba .. .. .. 1·50 1·40

1988. Cultural and Social Relief Funds. Cent of Queen Emma Bridge, Curacao. Mult.
960 55 c. + 25 c. Type **246** .. 70 65
961 115 c. + 55 c. Willemstad harbour (horiz) .. 1·40 1·25
962 190 c. + 60 c. Leonard B. Smith (engineer) and flags (horiz) .. .. 2·50 2·40

247 Broken Chain

1988. 125th Anniv of Abolition of Slavery. Multicoloured.
963 155 c. Type **247** .. .. 1·40 1·25
964 190 c. Breach in slave wall 1·60 1·50

248 Flags and Map

249 Charles Hellmund (Bonaire councillor)

1988. 3rd Inter-American Foundation of Cities "Let us Build Bridges" Conference, Curacao. Multicoloured.
965 80 c. Type **248** 90 70
966 155 c. Bridge and globe .. 1·40 1·25

1988. Celebrities. Multicoloured.
967 55 c. Type **249** 55 45
968 65 c. Atthelo Maud Edwards-Jackson (founder of Saba Electric Company) .. 60 55
969 90 c. Nicolaas Debrot (Governor of Antilles, 1962–69) .. .. 1·00 90
970 120 c. William Charles de la Try Ellis (lawyer and politican) .. .. 1·10 1·00

250 Child watching Television

251 "Cereus hexagonus"

1988. Child Welfare. Multicoloured.
971 55 c. + 25 c. Type **250** .. 80 60
972 65 c. + 30 c. Boy with radio 1·10 85
973 115 c. + 55 c. Girl using computer .. .. 1·50 1·25

1988. Cacti. Multicoloured.
975 55 c. Type **251** 70 45
976 115 c. Melocactus .. 1·10 85
977 125 c. "Opuntia wentiana" 1·25 1·00

252 Magnifying Glass over 1936 and 1980 Stamps

253 Crested Bobwhite

1989. Cultural and Social Relief Funds. 50th Anniv of Curacao Stamp Association. Mult.
978 30 c. + 10 c. Type **252** .. 60 40
979 55 c. + 20 c. Picking up stamp with tweezers (winning design by X. Rico in drawing competition) .. 85 75
980 80 c. + 30 c. Barn owl and stamp album .. .. 1·10 95
Nos. 978/80 were printed together, se-tenant, forming a composite design.

1989. 40th Anniv of Curacao Foundation for Prevention of Cruelty to Animals. Mult.
981 65 c. Type **253** 85 55
982 115 c. Dogs and cats .. 1·40 90

254 "Sun Viking" in Great Bay Harbour, St. Maarten

255 Paula Clementina Dorner (teacher)

1989. Tourism. Cruise Liners. Multicoloured.
983 70 c. Type **254** 70 55
984 155 c. "Eugenio C" entering harbour, St. Annabay, Curacao .. 1·40 1·25

1989. Celebrities. Multicoloured.
985 40 c. Type **255** 55 35
986 55 c. John Aniseto de Jongh (pharmacist and politician) 65 45
987 90 c. Jacobo Jesus Maria Palm (musician) .. 95 70
988 120 c. Abraham Mendes Chumaceiro (lawyer and social campaigner) .. 1·25 1·00

256 Boy and Girl under Tree

257 Hand holding "7"

1989. Child Welfare. Multicoloured.
989 40 c. + 15 c. Type **256** .. 75 60
990 65 c. + 30 c. Two children playing on shore .. 1·10 85
991 115 c. + 35 c. Adult carrying child .. .. 1·60 1·40

1989. 40th Anniv of Queen Wilhelmina Foundation for Cancer Care. Multicoloured.
993 30 c. Type **257** 40 25
994 60 c. Seated figure and figure receiving radiation treatment 65 55
995 80 c. Figure exercising and Foundation emblem .. 80 70

258 Fireworks

259 "Tephrosia cinerea"

1989. Christmas. Multicoloured.
997 30 c. Type **258** 40 25
998 100 c. Christmas tree decorations .. .. 1·10 85

1990. Flowers. Multicoloured.
999 30 c. Type **259** 35 30
1000 55 c. "Erithalis fruticosa" 60 50
1001 65 c. "Evolvulus antillanus" 70 60
1002 70 c. "Jacquinia arborea" 80 65
1003 125 c. "Tournefortia onaphalodes" .. .. 1·40 1·25
1004 155 c. "Sesuvium portulacastrum" .. .. 1·75 1·40

260 Girl Guides

261 Nun with Child, Flag and Map

1990. Cultural and Social Relief Funds. Mult.
1005 30 c. + 10 c. Type **260** (60th anniv) 50 50
1006 40 c. + 15 c. Totolika (care of mentally handicapped organization) (17th anniv) 65 65
1007 155 c. + 65 c. Boy scout (60th anniv) .. .. 2·50 2·50

1990. Centenary of Arrival of Dominican Nuns in Netherlands Antilles. Multicoloured.
1008 10 c. Type **261** 15 10
1009 55 c. St. Rose Hospital and St. Martin's Home, St. Maarten 65 55
1010 60 c. St. Joseph School, St. Maarten 70 60

262 Goal Net, Ball and Shield

263 Carlos Nicolaas-Perez (philologist and poet)

1990. Multicoloured.
1011 65 c + 30 c. Type **262** (65th anniv of Sport Unie Brion Trappers football club) .. .. 1·10 1·10
1012 115 c. + 55 c. Guiding addict from darkness towards sun (anti-drugs campaign) .. .. 2·25 2·25

1990. Meritorious Antilleans. Multicoloured.
1013 40 c. Type **263** 45 40
1014 60 c. Evert Kruythoff (writer) 65 55
1015 80 c. John de Pool (writer) 90 75
1016 150 c. Joseph Sickman Corsen (poet and composer) .. .. 1·75 1·40

264 Queen Emma

265 Isla Refinery

1990. Dutch Queens of the House of Orange. Multicoloured.
1017 100 c. Type **264** .. 1·10 90
1018 100 c. Queen Wilhelmina .. 1·10 90
1019 100 c. Queen Juliana .. 1·10 90
1020 100 c. Queen Beatrix .. 1·10 90

1990. 75th Anniv of Oil Refining on Curacao.
1022 **265** 100 c. multicoloured .. 1·40 1·25

266 Flower and Bees

267 Parcels

1990. Child Welfare. International Literacy Year. Designs illustrating letters of alphabet. Multicoloured.
1023 30 c. + 5 c. Type **266** .. 40 40
1024 55 c. + 10 c. Dolphins and sun 75 75
1025 65 c. + 15 c. Donkey with bicycle 95 95
1026 100 c. + 20 c. Goat dreaming of house .. .. 1·40 1·40
1027 115 c. + 25 c. Rabbit carrying food on yoke .. 1·60 1·60
1028 155 c. + 55 c. Lizard, moon and cactus .. .. 2·40 2·40

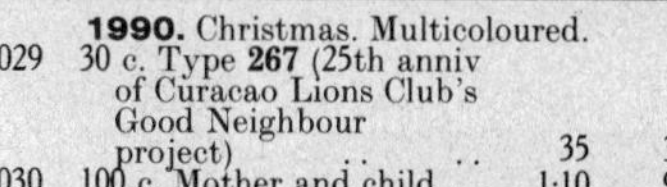
1990. Christmas. Multicoloured.
1029 30 c. Type **267** (25th anniv of Curacao Lions Club's Good Neighbour project) 35 30
1030 100 c. Mother and child .. 1·10 90

268 Flag, Map and Distribution of Mail

269 Scuba Diver and French Grunt

1991. 6th Anniv of Express Mail Service.
1031 **268** 20 g. multicoloured .. 18·00 14·00

1991. Fishes. Multicoloured.
1032 10 c. Type **269** 15 10
1033 40 c. Spotted trunkfish .. 50 40
1034 55 c. Coppersweepers .. 70 60
1035 75 c. Skindiver and yellow goatfishes 90 75
1036 100 c. Blackbar soldierfishes .. 1·25 1·00

270 Children and Stamps

1991. Cultural and Social Relief Funds. Mult.
1037 30 c. + 10 c. Type **270** (12th anniv of Philatelic Club of Curacao) .. 50 50
1038 65 c. + 25 c. St. Vincentius Brass Band (50th anniv) .. .. 1·10 1·10
1039 155 c. + 55 c. Games and leisure pursuits (30th anniv of FESEBAKO (Curacao community centres) .. .. 2·40 2·40

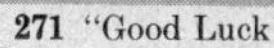
271 "Good Luck"

272 Westpoint Lighthouse, Curacao

1991. Greetings Stamps. Multicoloured.
1040 30 c. Type **271** 35 30
1041 30 c. "Thank You" .. 35 30
1042 30 c. Couple and family ("Love You") .. 35 30
1043 30 c. Song birds ("Happy Day") 35 30
1044 30 c. Greater flamingo and medicines ("Get Well Soon") 35 30
1045 30 c. Flowers and balloons ("Happy Birthday") .. 35 30

1991. Lighthouses. Multicoloured.
1046 30 c. Type **272** 45 40
1047 70 c. Willems Toren, Bonaire .. .. 1·00 80
1048 115 c. Klein Curacao lighthouse .. .. .. 1·90 1·60

273 Peter Stuyvesant College

1991. 50th Anniv of Secondary Education in Netherlands Antilles (65 c.) and "Espamer '91" Spain–Latin America Stamp Exhibition, Buenos Aires (125 c.). Multicoloured.
1049 65 c. Type **273** 75 60
1050 125 c. Dancers of Netherlands Antilles, Argentina and Portugal (vert) .. .. .. 1·40 1·25

274 Octopus with Letters and Numbers

275 Nativity

1991. Child Welfare. Multicoloured.

1051		40 c.+15 c. Type **274** ..	75	75
1052		65 c.+30 c. Parents teaching arithmetic ..	1·25	1·25
1053		155 c.+65 c. Bird and tortoise with clock ..	2·50	2·50

1991. Christmas. Multicoloured.

1055		30 c. Type **275**	35	30
1056		100 c. Angel appearing to shepherds	1·25	1·00

276 Joseph Alvarez Correa (founder) and Headquarters of S.E.L. Maduro and Sons

277 Fawn

1991. 75th Anniv of Maduro and Curiel's Bank. Multicoloured.

1057		30 c. Type **276**	40	35
1058		70 c. Lion rampant (bank's emblem) and "75"	75	60
1059		155 c. Isaac Haim Capriles (Managing Director, 1954–74) and Scharloo bank branch	1·60	1·40

1992. The White-tailed Deer. Multicoloured.

1060		5 c. Type **277** (postage) ..	10	10
1061		10 c. Young adults ..	10	10
1062		30 c. Stag	30	25
1063		40 c. Stag and hind in water	35	30
1064		200 c. Stag drinking (air)	1·75	1·40
1065		355 c. Stag calling ..	2·75	2·25

278 Windsurfer

280 "Santa Maria"

1992. Cultural and Social Relief Funds. Olympic Games, Barcelona. Multicoloured.

1066		30 c.+10 c. Type **278** (award of silver medal to Jan Boersma, 1988 Games)	35	35
1067		55 c.+25 c. Globe, national flag and Olympic rings	65	65
1068		115 c.+55 c. Emblem of National Olympic Committee (60th anniv)	1·40	1·40

Nos. 1066/8 were issued together, se-tenant, forming a composite design.

1992. "World Columbian Stamp Expo '92", Chicago. Multicoloured.

1070		250 c. Type **280**	2·00	1·60
1071		500 c. Chart and Columbus	4·00	3·25

281 View of Dock and Town

282 Angela de Lannoy-Willems

1992. Curacao Port Container Terminal. Mult.

1072		80 c. Type **281**	60	50
1073		125 c. Crane and ship ..	95	80

1992. Celebrities.

1074	**282**	30 c. black, brn & grn	35	20
1075	–	40 c. black, brn & bl	30	25
1076	–	55 c. black, brn & orge	40	35
1077	–	70 c. black, brn & red	55	45
1078	–	100 c. black, brn & bl	75	60

DESIGNS: 30 c. Type **282** (first woman Member of Parliament); 40 c. Lodewijk Daniel Gerharts (entrepreneur on Bonaire); 55 c. Cyrus Wilberforce Wathey (entrepreneur on St. Maarten); 70 c. Christiaan Winkel (Deputy Governor of Antilles); 100 c. Mother Joseph (founder of Roosendaal Congregation (Franciscan welfare sisterhood)).

283 Spaceship

284 Queen Beatrix and Prince Claus

1992. Child Welfare. Multicoloured.

1079		30 c.+10 c. Type **283** ..	30	30
1080		70 c.+30 c. Robot ..	75	75
1081		100 c.+40 c. Extra-terrestrial being ..	1·00	1·00

1992. 12½ Years since Accession to the Throne of Queen Beatrix (100 c.) and Royal Visit to Netherlands Antilles (others). Designs showing photos of previous visits to the Antilles. Multicoloured.

1083		70 c. Type **284**	55	45
1084		100 c. Queen Beatrix signing book ..	75	60
1085		175 c. Queen Beatrix and Prince Claus with girl	1·25	1·00

285 Crib

286 Hibiscus

1992. Christmas. Multicoloured.

1086		30 c. Type **285**	25	20
1087		100 c. Mary and Joseph searching for lodgings (vert)	75	60

1993. Flowers. Multicoloured.

1088		75 c. Type **286**	55	45
1089		90 c. Sunflower	70	60
1090		175 c. Ixora	1·25	1·00
1091		195 c. Rose	1·50	1·25

287 Airplane and Flight Paths

288 Pekingese

1993. Anniversaries. Multicoloured.

1092		65 c. Type **287** (50th anniv of Princess Juliana International Airport, St. Maarten) ..	50	40
1093		75 c. Laboratory worker and National Health Laboratory (75th anniv)	55	45
1094		90 c. Aircraft on runway at Princess Juliana International Airport	70	60
1095		175 c. White and yellow cross (50th anniv of Princess Margriet White and Yellow Cross Foundation for District Nursing)	1·25	1·00

1993. Dogs. Multicoloured.

1096		65 c. Type **288**	50	40
1097		90 c. Standard poodle ..	70	70
1098		100 c. Pomeranian ..	75	60
1099		175 c. Papillon ..	1·25	1·00

289 Cave Painting, Bonaire

290 "Sun and Sea"

1993. "Brasiliana '93" International Stamp Exhibition, Rio de Janeiro, and Admittance of Antilles to Postal Union of the Americas, Spain and Portugal. Multicoloured.

1100		150 c. Type **289** ..	1·10	90
1101		200 c. Exhibition emblem and Antilles flag ..	1·50	1·25
1102		250 c. Globe and hand signing U.P.A.E.P. agreement	1·90	1·60

1993. "Carib-Art" Exhibition, Curacao. Multicoloured.

1103		90 c. Type **290**	70	60
1104		150 c. "Heaven and Earth"	1·10	90

291 "Safety in the Home"

1993. Child Welfare. Child and Danger. Multicoloured.

1105		65 c.+25 c. Type **291** ..	70	70
1106		90 c.+35 c. Child using seat belt ("Safety in the Car") (vert) ..	95	95
1107		175 c.+75 c. Child wearing armbands ("Safety in the Water")	1·90	1·90

292 Consulate, Curacao

1993. Bicentenary of United States Consul General to the Antilles. Multicoloured.

1109		65 c. Type **292**	50	40
1110		90 c. Arms of Netherlands Antilles and U.S.A. ..	70	60
1111		175 c. American bald eagle	2·25	1·00

POSTAGE DUE STAMPS

1952. As Type D **121** of Netherlands but inscr "NEDERLANDSE ANTILLEN".

D 336.	1 c. green	10	10
D 337.	2½ c. green	60	60
D 338.	5 c. green	20	10
D 339.	6 c. green	65	50
D 340.	7 c. green	65	50
D 341.	8 c. green	65	50
D 342.	9 c. green	65	50
D 343.	10 c. green	30	15
D 344.	12½ c. green	30	15
D 345.	15 c. green	35	25
D 346.	20 c. green	35	45
D 347.	25 c. green	65	10
D 348.	30 c. green	1·25	1·50
D 349.	35 c. green	1·50	1·50
D 350.	40 c. green	1·25	1·50
D 351.	45 c. green	1·50	1·50
D 352.	50 c. green	1·25	1·25

NETHERLANDS INDIES Pt. 4

A former Dutch colony, consisting of numerous settlements in the East Indies, of which the islands of Java and Sumatra and parts of Borneo and New Guinea are the most important. Renamed Indonesia in 1948, Independence was granted during 1949. Netherlands New Guinea remained a Dutch possession until 1962 when it was placed under U.N. control, being incorporated with Indonesia in 1963.

100 cents = 1 gulden.

1. King William III. 2.

1864. Imperf.

1	**1.**	10 c. red	£170	75·00

1868. Perf.

2	**1.**	10 c. red	£650	£110

1870. Perf.

27	**2**	1 c. green	1·60	1·00
28		2 c. purple	£100	75·00
29		2 c. brown	4·50	3·25
30		2½ c. buff	32·00	18·00
12		5 c. green	50·00	3·25
32		10 c. brown	12·00	15
51		12½ c. drab	2·50	80
34		15 c. brown	18·00	50
5		20 c. blue	90·00	1·40
36		25 c. purple	17·00	50
55		30 c. green	28·00	2·25
17		50 c. red	15·00	85
38		2 g. green and purple ..	85·00	9·00

5. 6. Queen Wilhelmina.

1883.

89	**5**	1 c. green	50	10
90		2 c. brown	50	10
91		2½ c. buff	65	55
92		3 c. purple	75	10
88		5 c. green	24·00	15·00
93		5 c. blue	7·50	10

1892.

94	**6**	10 c. brown	3·50	15
95		12½ c. grey	7·00	11·00
96		15 c. brown	12·00	60
97		20 c. blue	26·00	65
98		25 c. purple	25·00	90
99		30 c. green	35·00	1·40
100		50 c. red	24·00	55
101		2 g. 50 blue and brown ..	£110	22·00

1900. Netherlands stamps of 1898 surch **NED.-INDIE** and value.

111	**13**	10 c. on 10 c. lilac ..	1·25	10
112		12½ c. on 12½ c. blue ..	1·75	45
113		15 c. on 15 c. brown ..	2·25	15
114		20 c. on 20 c. green ..	12·00	40
115		25 c. on 25 c. bl & pink	12·00	45
116		50 c. on 50 c. red & grn	22·00	55
117	**11**	2½ g. on 2½ g. lilac ..	38·00	8·50

1902. Surch.

118	**5**	½ on 2 c. brown	20	20
119		2½ on 3 c. purple ..	25	25

1902. As T **11/13** of Surinam but inscr. "NEDERLANDSCH-INDIE".

120.	½ c. lilac	30	10
121.	1 c. olive	30	10
122.	2 c. brown..	2·25	15
123.	2½ c. green	1·50	10
124.	3 c. orange	1·40	1·00
125.	4 c. blue	8·50	7·50
126.	5 c. red	3·75	10
127.	7½ c. grey	1·75	25
128.	10 c. slate	1·00	10
129.	12½ c. blue	1·40	10
130.	15 c. brown	6·50	1·50
131.	17½ c. bistre	2·25	15
132.	20 c. grey	1·40	1·40
133.	20 c. olive..	18·00	10
134.	22½ c. olive and brown ..	3·25	15
135.	25 c. mauve	7·00	10
136.	30 c. brown	23·00	10
137.	50 c. red	14·00	10
138.	1 g. lilac	40·00	20
206.	1 g. lilac on blue	40·00	4·50
139.	2½ g. grey	48·00	1·25
207.	2½ g. grey on blue ..	55·00	25·00

1902. No. 130 optd with horiz bars.

140	15 c. brown	1·10	55

1905. No. 132 surch **10 cent.**

141	10 c. on 20 c. grey ..	1·60	90

1908. Stamps of 1902 optd **JAVA.**

142. ½ c. lilac 15 20
143. 1 c. olive 15 15
144. 2 c. brown .. .. .. 1·40 1·40
145. 2½ c. green 65 10
146. 3 c. orange 50 65
147. 5 c. red .. .. .. 1·90 10
148. 7½ c. grey .. .. .. 1·75 1·50
149. 10 c. slate 45 10
150. 12½ c. blue .. .. .. 2·00 40
151. 15 c. brown .. .. .. 2·40 2·25
152. 17½ c. bistre .. .. .. 1·40 60
153. 20 c. olive .. .. .. 7·50 40
154. 22½ c. olive and brown .. 3·75 1·75
155. 25 c. mauve .. .. .. 3·25 15
156. 30 c. brown .. .. .. 22·00 1·60
157. 50 c. red .. .. .. 14·00 45
158. 1 g. lilac .. .. .. 38·00 2·00
159. 2½ g. grey .. .. .. 55·00 38·00

1908. Stamps of 1902 optd **BUITEN BEZIT.**

160. ½ c. lilac 20 20
161. 1 c. olive 25 15
162. 2 c. brown .. .. .. 1·25 1·90
163. 2½ c. green 55 15
164. 3 c. orange 45 90
165. 5 c. red .. .. .. 1·90 30
166. 7½ c. grey .. .. .. 2·00 2·25
167. 10 c. slate 45 10
168. 12½ c. blue .. .. .. 6·50 1·60
169. 15 c. brown .. .. .. 3·50 1·90
170. 17½ c. bistre .. .. .. 1·25 85
171. 20 c. olive .. .. .. 6·00 1·25
172. 22½ c. olive and brown .. 5·00 3·00
173. 25 c. mauve .. .. .. 3·75 25
174. 30 c. brown .. .. .. 14·00 1·60
175. 50 c. red .. .. .. 6·00 55
176. 1 g. lilac .. .. .. 45·00 2·25
177. 2½ g. grey .. .. .. 70·00 55·00

1912. As T **18/19** of Surinam, but inscr "NEDERLANDSCH-INDIE" (T **19**) or "NEDERL-INDIE" (T **20**).

208 **18** ½ c. lilac 10 10
209 1 c. green 15 10
210 2 c. brown 30 10
264 2 c. grey 30 10
211 2½ c. green .. .. .. 1·10 10
265 2½ c. pink 25 10
212 3 c. brown 30 10
266 3 c. green 65 10
213 4 c. blue 55 15
267 4 c. green .. .. .. 1·25 15
268 4 c. bistre .. .. .. 7·00 3·75
214 5 c. pink 70 10
269 5 c. green 85 10
270 5 c. blue 35 10
215 7½ c. brown 35 10
271 7½ c. bistre 35 10
216 **19** 10 c. red 50 10
272 **18** 10 c. lilac 90 10
217 **19** 12½ c. blue 80 10
273 12½ c. red 85 10
274 15 c. blue .. .. .. 6·50 10
218 17½ c. brown 80 10
219 20 c. green .. .. .. 1·40 10
275 20 c. blue .. .. .. 1·40 10
276 20 c. orange .. .. .. 12·00 10
220 22½ c. orange .. .. .. 1·25 50
221 25 c. mauve .. .. .. 1·40 10
222 30 c. grey .. .. .. 1·50 10
277 32½ c. violet and orange .. 1·40 15
278 35 c. brown .. .. .. 7·00 50
279 40 c. green .. .. .. 1·40 10

1913. As T **20** of Surinam but inscr "NED. INDIE".

223 50 c. green .. .. .. 2·50 10
280 60 c. blue .. .. .. 3·25 10
281 80 c. orange .. .. .. 3·75 10
224 1 g. brown .. .. .. 2·50 10
283 1 g. 75 lilac .. .. .. 14·00 1·75
225 2½ g. pink .. .. .. 9·50 35

1915. Red Cross. Stamps of 1912 surch **+5 cts.** and red cross.

243 1 c.+5 c. green .. .. 3·50 3·25
244 5 c.+5 c. pink .. .. 4·25 4·00
245 10 c.+5 c. red .. .. 6·50 6·50

1917. Stamps of 1902, 1912 and 1913 surch.

246. ½ c. on 2½ c. (No. 211) .. 20 20
247. 1 c. on 4 c. (No. 213) .. 45 45
250. 12½ c. on 17½ c. (No. 218) 25 10
251. 12½ c. on 22½ c. (No. 220) 35 10
248. 17½ c. on 22½ c. (No. 134) 70 35
252. 20 c. on 22½ c. (No. 220) .. 35 10
249. 30 c. on 1 g. (No. 138) .. 6·00 1·25
253. 32½ c. on 50 c. (No. 223) .. 1·25 10
254. 40 c. on 50 c. (No. 223) .. 3·50 40
255. 60 c. on 1 g. (No. 224) .. 5·50 30
256. 80 c. on 1 g. (No. 224) .. 6·50 75

1922. Bandoeng Industrial Fair. Stamps of 1912 and 1917 optd **3de N. I. JAARBEURS BANDOENG 1922.**

285 **18** 1 c. green .. .. .. 6·00 4·50
286 2 c. brown .. .. .. 6·00 4·50
287 2½ c. pink .. .. .. 50·00 60·00
288 3 c. yellow .. .. .. 6·00 5·50
289 4 c. blue .. .. .. 35·00 30·00
290 5 c. green .. .. .. 12·00 8·00
291 7½ c. brown .. .. .. 7·50 4·50
292 10 c. lilac .. .. .. 60·00 75·00
293 **19** 12½ c. on 22½ c. orange (No. 251) .. .. 6·00 6·00
294 17½ c. brown .. .. .. 3·75 4·50
295 20 c. blue .. .. .. 6·00 4·50

Nos. 285/95 were sold at a premium for 3, 4, 5, 6, 8, 9, 10, 12½, 15, 20 and 22 c. respectively.

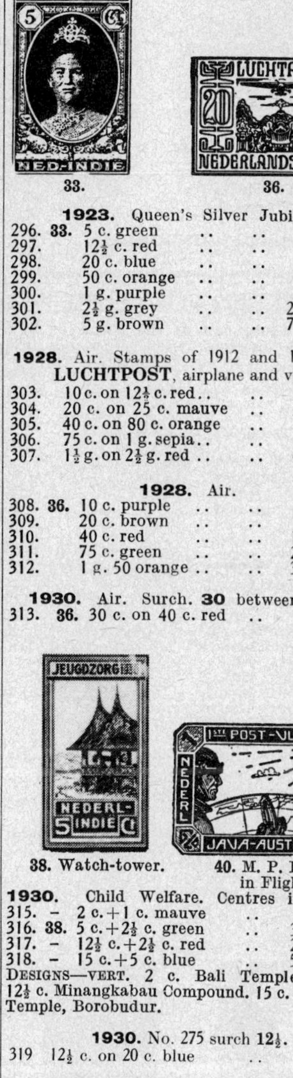

33. 36.

1923. Queen's Silver Jubilee.

296. **33.** 5 c. green 15 10
297. 12½ c. red 15 10
298. 20 c. blue 25 10
299. 50 c. orange .. .. 1·25 50
300. 1 g. purple .. .. 2·50 30
301. 2½ g. grey .. .. 23·00 14·00
302. 5 g. brown .. .. 75·00 95·00

1928. Air. Stamps of 1912 and 1913 surch **LUCHTPOST**, airplane and value.

303. 10 c. on 12½ c. red 90 90
304. 20 c. on 25 c. mauve .. 2·25 2·25
305. 40 c. on 80 c. orange .. 1·75 1·40
306. 75 c. on 1 g. sepia 85 50
307. 1½ g. on 2½ g. red .. .. 6·00 5·50

1928. Air.

308. **36.** 10 c. purple 30 15
309. 20 c. brown 75 50
310. 40 c. red .. .. 1·00 50
311. 75 c. green .. .. 2·00 15
312. 1 g. 50 orange .. .. 3·75 50

1930. Air. Surch. **30** between bars.

313. **36.** 30 c. on 40 c. red .. 75 15

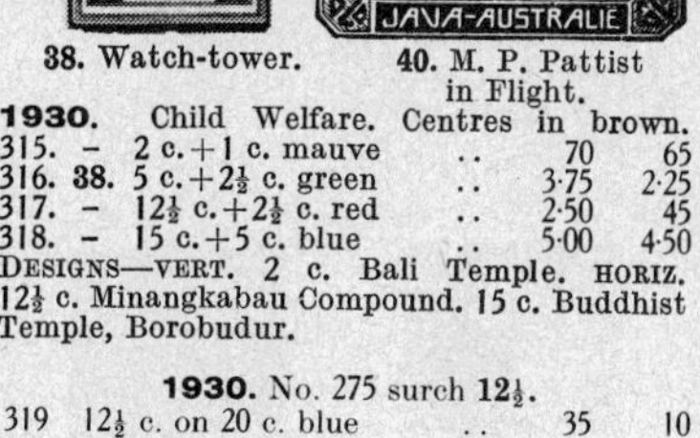

38. Watch-tower. 40. M. P. Pattist in Flight.

1930. Child Welfare. Centres in brown.

315. – 2 c.+1 c. mauve .. 70 65
316. **38.** 5 c.+2½ c. green .. 3·75 2·25
317. – 12½ c.+2½ c. red .. 2·50 45
318. – 15 c.+5 c. blue .. 5·00 4·50

DESIGNS—VERT. 2 c. Bali Temple. HORIZ. 12½ c. Minangkabau Compound. 15 c. Buddhist Temple, Borobudur.

1930. No. 275 surch **12½**.

319 12½ c. on 20 c. blue 35 10

1931. Air. 1st Java–Australia Mail.

320 **40** 1 g. brown and blue .. 10·00 10·00

41. 42. Ploughing.

1931. Air.

321. **41.** 30 c. red .. .. 2·25 10
322. 4½ g. blue .. .. 8·00 3·00
323. 7½ g. green .. .. 9·50 3·25

1931. Lepers' Colony.

324. **42.** 2 c.+1 c. brown .. 2·25 1·50
325. – 5 c.+2½ c. green .. 3·50 3·00
326. – 12½ c.+2½ c. red .. 2·25 45
327. – 15 c.+5 c. blue .. 8·00 6·50

DESIGNS: 5 c. Fishing. 12½ c. Native actors. 15 c. Native musicians.

1932. Air. Surch. with aeroplane and value.

328. **36.** 50 c. on 1 g. 50 c. orange 2·50 35

44. Plaiting Rattan. 45. William of Orange.

1932. Salvation Army. Centres in brown.

329. – 2 c.+1 c. purple .. 40 30
330. **44.** 5 c.+2½ c. green .. 2·75 2·00
331. – 12½ c.+2½ c. red .. 85 25
332. – 15 c.+5 c. blue .. 3·75 3·00

DESIGNS: 2 c. Weaving. 12½ c. Textile worker. 15 c. Metal worker.

1933. 400th Birth Anniv of William I of Orange.

333 **45** 12½ c. red .. .. 1·10 15

46. Rice Cultivation. 47. Queen Wilhelmina.

1933.

335 **46** 1 c. violet 20 10
397 2 c. purple 10 15
337 2½ c. bistre 20 10
338 3 c. green 20 15
339 3½ c. grey 15 15
340 4 c. green 75 10
401 5 c. blue 10 10
342 7½ c. violet .. .. 1·25 10
343 10 c. red .. .. 1·75 10
403 **47** 10 c. red 10 10
334 12½ c. brown .. .. 8·00 25
345 12½ c. red 25 10
404 15 c. blue 10 10
405 20 c. purple 20 10
348 25 c. green .. .. 1·60 10
349 30 c. blue .. .. 2·40 10
350 32½ c. bistre .. .. 7·00 6·00
408 35 c. violet .. .. 3·50 1·10
352 40 c. green .. .. 2·50 10
353 42½ c. yellow .. .. 2·50 20
354 50 c. blue .. .. 3·25 15
355 60 c. blue .. .. 4·00 40
356 80 c. red .. .. 4·50 60
357 1 g. violet .. .. 6·00 30
358 1 g. 75 green .. .. 14·00 13·00
414 2 g. green .. .. 25·00 13·00
359 2 g. 50 purple .. .. 17·00 1·10
415 5 g. bistre .. .. 25·00 5·50

The 50 c. to 5 g. are larger, 30 × 30 mm.

48.

1933. Air. Special Flights.

360. **48.** 30 c. blue .. .. 1·40 1·40

49. Woman and Lotus Blossom. 53. Cavalryman and Wounded Soldier.

1933. Y.M.C.A. Charity.

361. **49.** 2 c.+1 c. brn. & purple 70 1·25
362. – 5 c.+2½ c. brn. & green 2·25 1·75
363. – 12½ c.+2½ c. brn. & orge. 2·50 25
364. – 15 c.+5 c. brn. & blue 3·25 2·00

DESIGNS: 5 c. Symbolising the sea of life. 12½ c. Y.M.C.A. emblem. 15 c. Unemployed man.

1934. Surch.

365. **36.** 2 c. on 10 c. purple .. 25 45
366. 2 c. on 20 c. brown .. 20 20
367. **41.** 2 c. on 30 c. red .. 35 75
368. **36.** 42½ c. on 75 c. green .. 3·75 25
369. 42½ c. on 1 g. 50 orange 3·75 35

1934. Anti-Tuberculosis Fund. As T **77** of Netherlands.

370. 12½ c.+2½ c. brown .. 1·25 45

1935. Christian Military Home.

371. – 2 c.+1 c. brown & pur. 1·40 1·25
372. **53.** 5 c.+2½ c. brn. & grn. 3·50 2·75
373. – 12½ c.+2½ c. brn. & orge. 3·50 25
374. – 15 c.+5 c. brn. & blue 5·00 6·00

DESIGNS: 2 c. Engineer chopping wood. 12½ c. Artilleryman and volcano victim. 15 c. Infantry bugler.

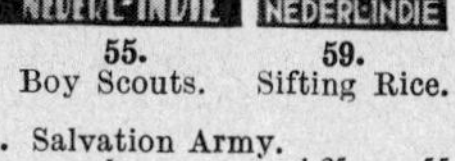

54. Dinner-time. 55. Boy Scouts. 59. Sifting Rice.

1936. Salvation Army.

375. **54.** 2 c.+1 c. purple .. 1·25 55
376. 5 c.+2½ c. blue .. 1·40 1·10
377. 7½ c.+2½ c. violet .. 1·40 1·40
378. 12½ c.+2½ c. orange .. 1·40 25
379. 15 c.+5 c. blue .. 2·40 1·90

Nos. 376/9 are larger, 30 × 27 mm.

1937. Scout's Jamboree.

380. **55.** 7½ c.+2½ c. green .. 1·25 1·10
381. 12½ c.+2½ c. red .. 1·25 50

1937. Nos. 222 and 277 surch. in figures.

382. 10 c. on 30 c. slate .. 2·40 25
383. 10 c. on 32½ c. vio. & orge. 2·40 25

1937. Relief Fund. Inscr. "A.S.I.B.".

385. **59.** 2 c.+1 c. sepia & orge. 1·25 80
386. – 3½ c.+1½ c. grey .. 1·25 80
387. – 7½ c.+2½ c. grn. & orge. 1·40 85
388. – 10 c.+2½ c. red & orge. 1·40 20
389. – 25 c.+5 c. blue .. 1·40 1·25

DESIGNS: 3½ c. Mother and children. 7½ c. Ox-team ploughing rice-field. 10 c. Ox-team and cart. 20 c. Man and woman.

1938. 40th Anniv of Coronation. As T **87** of Netherlands.

390. 2 c. violet 10 15
391. 10 c. red 15 10
392. 15 c. blue .. .. 1·40 65
393. 20 c. red 60 25

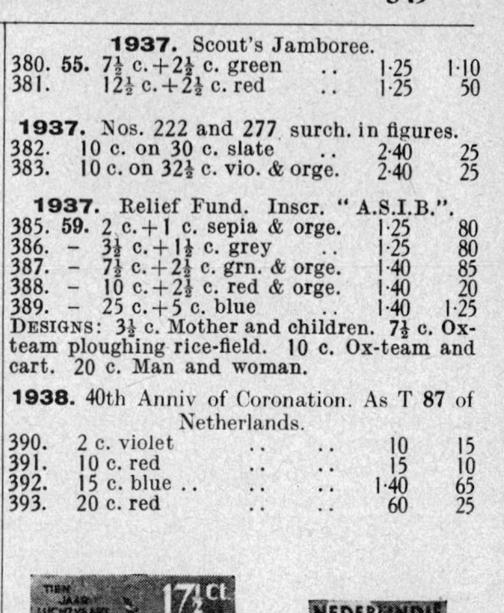

62. Douglas DC-2 Airliner. 63. Nurse and Child.

1938. Air Service Fund. 10th Anniv. of Royal Netherlands Indies Air Lines.

394. **62.** 17½ c.+5 c. brown .. 85 85
395. – 20 c.+5 c. slate .. 85 85

DESIGNS: 20 c. As Type **62**, but reverse side of airliner.

1938. Child Welfare. Inscr. "CENTRAAL MISSIE-BUREAU".

416. **63.** 2 c.+1 c. violet 65 40
417. – 3½ c.+1½ c. green .. 1·10 1·10
418. – 7½ c.+2½ c. red 80 70
419. – 10 c.+2½ c. red .. .. 1·00 20
420. – 20 c.+5 c. blue .. .. 1·25 80

DESIGNS—23 × 23 mm: Nurse with child suffering from injuries to eye (3½ c.), arm (7½ c.), head (20 c.) and nurse bathing a baby (10 c.).

63a. Group of Natives. 64. European nurse and Patient.

1939. Netherlands Indies Social Bureau and Protestant Church Funds.

421. – 2 c.+1 c. violet .. 25 15
422. – 3½ c.+1½ c. green .. 35 20
423. **63a.** 7½ c.+2½ c. brown .. 25 20
424. – 10 c.+2½ c. red .. 1·50 75
425. **64.** 10 c.+2½ c. red .. 1·50 75
426. 20 c.+5 c. blue .. 50 35

DESIGNS—VERT. 2 c. as Type **63a** but group in European clothes. HORIZ. 3½ c., 10 c. (No. 424) as Type **64**, but Native nurse and patient.

1940. Red Cross Fund. No. 345 surch **10+5 ct** and cross.

428 **47** 10 c.+5 c. on 12½ c. red 80 45

68. Queen Wilhelmina. 69. Netherlands Coat of Arms.

1941. As T **94** of Netherlands but inscr. "NED. INDIE" and T **68**

429. – 10 c. red 20 10
430. – 15 c. blue .. .. 1·10 1·10
431. – 17½ c. orange 35 55
432. – 20 c. mauve .. .. 16·00 27·00
433. – 25 c. green .. .. 23·00 38·00
434. – 30 c. brown .. .. 1·50 30
435. – 35 c. purple .. .. 80·00 £250
436. – 40 c. green .. .. 6·50 2·25
437. – 50 c. red .. .. 1·40 65
438. – 60 c. blue 85 50
439. – 80 c. red .. .. 1·00 75
440. – 1 g. violet .. .. 1·25 25
441. – 2 g. green .. .. 7·00 80
442. – 5 g. bistre £170 £475
443. – 10 g. green .. .. 23·00 17·00
444. **68.** 25 g. orange £150 £130

Nos 429/36 measure 18 × 23 mm., Nos. 437/43 20½ × 26 mm.

1941. Prince Bernhard Fund for Dutch Forces.

453. **69.** 5 c.+5 c. blue & orange 10 15
454. 10 c.+10 c. blue and red 15 15
455. 1 g.+1 g. blue and grey 7·50 11·00

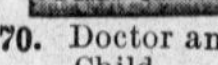

70. Doctor and Child. 71. Wayangwong Dancer.

1941. Indigent Mohammedans' Relief Fund.
456. 70. 2 c.+1 c. green .. 40 50
457. – 3½ c.+1½ c. brown .. 2·50 3·25
458. – 7½ c.+2½ c. violet .. 2·00 2·25
459. – 10 c.+2½ c. red .. 70 30
460. – 15 c.+5 c. blue .. 6·50 5·50
DESIGNS: 3½ c. Native eating rice. 7½ c. Nurse and patient. 10 c. Nurse and children. 15 c. Basket-weaver.

1941.
461 – 2 c. red 10 15
462 – 2½ c. purple 15 20
463 – 3 c. green 15 40
464 71 4 c. green 15 35
465 – 5 c. blue 10 10
466 – 7½ c. violet 40 10
DESIGNS (dancers): 2 c. Menari. 2½ c. Nias. 3 c. Legon. 5 c. Padjoge. 7½ c. Dyak.
See also Nos. 514/16.

72. Paddyfield. 73. Queen Wilhelmina.

1945.
467. 72. 1 c. green 20 15
468. – 2 c. mauve 20 30
469. – 2½ c. purple 20 15
470. – 5 c. blue 15 10
471. – 7½ c. olive 45 10
472. 73. 10 c. brown 10 10
473. 15 c. blue 10 10
474. 17½ c. red 15 15
475. 20 c. purple 15 10
476. 30 c. grey 25 10
477. – 60 c. grey 60 10
478. – 1 g. green .. .. 1·00 10
479. – 2½ g. orange .. .. 3·25 45
DESIGNS—As Type 72: 2 c. Lake in W. Java. 2½ c. Medical School, Batavia. 5 c. Seashore. 7½ c. Airplane over Bromo Volcano. 30×30mm: 60 c. to 2½ g. Portrait as Type 73 but different frame.

76. Railway Viaduct near Soekaboemi. 81. Queen Wilhelmina.

1946.
484. 76. 1 c. green 30 60
485. – 2 c. brown 10 10
486. – 2½ c. red 15 15
487. – 5 c. blue 10 10
488. – 7½ c. blue 15 10
DESIGNS: 2 c. Power station. 3 c. Minangkabau house. 5 c. Tondano scene (Celebes). 7½ c. Buddhist Stupas, Java.

1947. Surch. in figures.
502. – 3 c. on 2½ c. red (No. 486) 10 10
503. – 3 c. on 7½ c. bl. (No. 488) 10 10
504. 76. 4 c. on 1 c. green .. 45 1·50
505. – 45 c. on 60 c. blue (No. 355) .. .. .. 1·25 90
No. 505 has three bars.

1947. Optd 1947.
506 47 12½ c. red 10 10
507 25 c. green 20 10
508 – 40 c. green (No. 436) .. 30 10
509 47 50 c. blue 50 25
510 80 c. red 75 55
511 – 2 g. green (No. 441) .. 3·25 45
512 – 5 g. brown (No. 442) .. 9·50 6·50

1948. Relief for Victims of the Terror. Surch. **PELITA 15+10 Ct.** and lamp.
513. 47. 15 c.+10 c. on 10 c. red 10 10

1948. Dancers. As T 71.
514 3 c. red (Menari) 10 10
515 4 c. green (Legon) 10 10
516 7½ c. brown (Dyak) 55 55

1948.
517. 81. 15 c. orange 60 60
518. 20 c. blue 10 10
519. 25 c. green 15 10
520. 40 c. green 20 10
521. 45 c. mauve 35 45
522. 50 c. lake 25 10
523. 80 c. red 30 10
524. 1 g. violet 25 10
525. 10 g. green .. .. 27·00 8·50
526. 25 g. orange .. .. 65·00 55·00
Nos. 524/6 are larger (21×26 mm.).

1948. Queen Wilhelmina's Golden Jubilee. As T **81** but inscr. "1898 1948".
528. 15 c. orange 25 15
529. 20 c. blue 25 10

1948. As T **126** of Netherlands.
530. 15 c. red 30 15
531. 20 c. blue 30 10

MARINE INSURANCE STAMPS

1921. As Type M **22** of the Netherlands, but inscribed "NED. INDIE".
M 257. 15 c. green .. .. 1·75 30·00
M 258. 60 c. red .. .. 3·50 48·00
M 259. 75 c. brown .. .. 3·50 50·00
M 260. 1 g. 50 blue .. .. 24·00 £250
M 261. 2 g. 25 brown .. .. 30·00 £325
M 262. 4½ g. black .. .. 65·00 £650
M 263. 7½ g. red .. .. 85·00 £750

OFFICIAL STAMPS

1911. Stamps of 1892 optd **D** in white on a black circle.
O 178. 6. 10 c. brown .. .. 1·00 50
O 179. 12½ c. grey .. .. 2·25 3·75
O 180. 15 c. bistre .. .. 2·25 2·00
O 181. 20 c. blue .. .. 2·25 80
O 182. 25 c. mauve .. .. 8·00 7·00
O 183. 50 c. red .. .. 1·75 1·00
O 184. 2 g. 50, blue and brown 45·00 45·00

1911. Stamps of 1902 (except No. O 185) optd. **DIENST.**
O 186. ½ c. lilac 10 30
O 187. 1 c. olive 15 10
O 188. 2 c. brown 10 10
O 185. 2½ c. yellow (No. 91) .. 50 50
O 189. 2½ c. green .. .. 1·10 1·00
O 190. 3 c. orange 30 25
O 191. 4 c. blue 15 10
O 192. 5 c. red 55 55
O 193. 7½ c. grey .. .. 2·00 2·25
O 194. 10 c. slate 15 10
O 195. 12½ c. blue .. .. 1·60 1·75
O 196. 15 c. brown 50 50
O 197. 15 c. brown (No. 140) .. 26·00
O 198. 17½ c. bistre .. .. 2·25 1·75
O 199. 20 c. olive 50 40
O 200. 22½ c. olive and brown .. 3·00 2·25
O 201. 25 c. mauve .. .. 1·75 1·50
O 202. 30 c. brown 70 40
O 203. 50 c. red .. .. 11·00 6·00
O 204. 1 g. lilac .. .. 2·25 1·00
O 205. 2½ g. grey .. .. 26·00 28·00

POSTAGE DUE STAMPS

1874. As Postage Due stamps of Netherlands. Colours changed.
D 56. D 8. 5 c. yellow £250 £225
D 57. 10 c. green on yellow £110 75·00
D 59. 15 c. orange on yellow 16·00 13·00
D 60. 20 c. green on blue .. 28·00 9·00

1882. As Type D 2 of Surinam.
D68 2½ c. black and red .. 30 80
D69 5 c. black and red .. 20 35
D65 10 c. black and red .. 2·25 2·25
D70 15 c. black and red .. 2·50 2·25
D71 20 c. black and red .. 85·00 35
D82 30 c. black and red .. 1·60 1·90
D72 40 c. black and red .. 1·10 1·50
D73 50 c. black and pink .. 70 45
D74 75 c. black and red .. 45 45

1892. As Type D 9 of Netherlands.
D102 2½ c. black and pink .. 40 25
D103 5 c. black and pink .. 2·25 10
D104b 10 c. black and pink .. 2·25 1·75
D105 15 c. black and pink .. 11·00 1·40
D106b 20 c. black and pink .. 3·50 1·25
D107 30 c. black and pink .. 16·00 4·75
D108 40 c. black and pink .. 11·00 1·25
D109 50 c. black and pink .. 7·00 65
D110 75 c. black and pink .. 17·00 3·50

1913. As Type D 9 of Netherlands.
D226 1 c. orange 10 95
D227 2½ c. orange 10 10
D228 3½ c. orange 10 95
D229 5 c. orange 10 10
D230 7½ c. orange 10 10
D231 10 c. orange 10 10
D232 12½ c. orange .. .. 2·50 10
D448 15 c. orange 65 85
D234 20 c. orange 15 10
D235 25 c. orange 15 10
D236 30 c. orange 20 20
D237 37½ c. orange .. .. 15·00 13·00
D238 40 c. orange 20 15
D239 50 c. orange .. .. 1·25 10
D240 75 c. orange .. .. 2·25 15
D241 1 g. orange .. .. 4·50 4·75
D452 1 g. blue 45 55

1937. Surch. **20.**
D 384. D 5. 20 c. on 37½ c. red 25 25

1946. Optd. **TE BETALEN PORT** or surch. also.
D 480. 2½ c. on 10 c. red (No. 429) 45 45
D 481. 10 c. red (No. 429) .. 1·00 1·00
D 482. 20 c. mauve (No. 432) .. 2·25 2·25
D 483. 40 c. green (No. 436) .. 48·00 48·00

1946. As Type D **9** of Netherlands.
D489 1 c. violet 50 80
D527 2½ c. brown 45 75
D491 3½ c. blue 50 80
D493 7½ c. green 60 80
D494 10 c. lilac 60 80
D495 20 c. blue 60 90
D496 25 c. olive 75 90
D497 30 c. brown .. .. 80 1·00
D498 40 c. green .. .. 1·25 1·10
D499 50 c. yellow .. .. 1·40 1·25
D500 75 c. blue .. .. 1·40 1·25
D501 100 c. green .. .. 1·40 1·25

For later issues see **INDONESIA.**

NETHERLANDS NEW GUINEA Pt. 4

The Western half of the island of New Guinea was governed by the Netherlands until 1962, when control was transferred to the U.N. (see West New Guinea). The territory later became part of Indonesia as West Irian (q.v.).

100 cents = 1 gulden.

1950. As numeral and portrait types of Netherlands but inscr. "NIEUW GUINEA".
1. 118. 1 c. grey 15 15
2. 2 c. orange 15 15
3. 2½ c. olive 15 10
4. 3 c. mauve .. .. 1·50 1·25
5. 4 c. green .. .. 1·50 1·00
6. 5 c. blue .. .. 3·00 15
7. 7½ c. brown 35 15
8. 10 c. violet .. .. 1·75 15
9. 12½ c. red .. .. 1·75 1·40
10. 129. 15 c. brown .. .. 1·25 50
11. 20 c. blue 35 10
12. 25 c. red 35 10
13. 30 c. blue .. .. 6·50 25
14. 40 c. green 65 10
15. 45 c. brown .. .. 3·50 50
16. 50 c. orange 65 10
17. 55 c. grey .. .. 6·00 50
18. 80 c. purple .. .. 7·00 3·00
19. 130. 1 g. red .. .. 11·00 15
20. 2 g. brown .. .. 8·50 1·10
21. 5 g. green .. .. 12·00 1·00

1953. Netherlands Flood Relief Fund. Nos. 6, 10 and 12 surch **hulp nederland 1953** and premium.
22. 118. 5 c.+5 c. blue .. 8·00 8·50
23. 129. 15 c.+10 c. brown .. 8·00 8·50
24. 25 c.+10 c. red .. 8·00 8·50

5. Lesser Bird of Paradise. 6. Queen Juliana.

1954.
25 5 1 c. yellow and red .. 30 10
26 5 c. yellow and brown .. 35 10
27 – 10 c. brown and blue .. 40 10
28 – 15 c. brown and yellow .. 50 10
29 – 20 c. brown and green .. 90 35
DESIGN: 10, 15, 20 c. Greater bird of paradise.

1954.
30 6 25 c. red 20 10
31 30 c. blue 20 10
32 40 c. orange .. .. 1·75 2·00
33 45 c. green 60 85
34 55 c. turquoise 45 10
35 80 c. grey 85 30
36 85 c. brown 90 45
37 1 g. purple .. .. 4·50 1·75

1955. Red Cross. Nos. 26/8 surch with cross and premium.
38. 5. 5 c.+5 c. yellow and sepia 1·00 85
39. – 10 c.+10 c. brown & blue 1·00 85
40. – 15 c.+10 c. brown & lemon 1·00 85

8. Child and Native Hut. 10. Papuan Girl and Beach Scene.

1956. Anti-Leprosy Fund.
41. – 5 c.+5 c. green 90 85
42. 8. 10 c.+5 c. purple 90 85
43. – 25 c.+10 c. blue 90 85
44. 8. 30 c.+10 c. buff 90 85
DESIGN: 5 c., 25 c. Palm-trees and native hut.

1957. Child Welfare Fund.
51.10. 5 c.+5 c. lake 90 85
52. – 10 c.+5 c. green 90 85
53.10. 25 c.+10 c. brown 90 85
54. – 30 c.+10 c. blue 90 85
DESIGN: 10 c., 30 c. Papuan child and native hut.

11. Red Cross and Idol. 12. Papuan and Helicopter.

1958. Red Cross Fund.
55.11. 5 c+5 c. multicoloured .. 1·00 90
56. – 10 c.+5 c. multicoloured 1·00 90
57.11. 25 c.+10 c. multicoloured 1·00 90
58. – 30 c.+10 c. multicoloured 1·00 90
DESIGN: 10 c., 30 c. Red Cross and Asman-Papuan bowl in form of human figure.

1959. Stars Mountains Expedition, 1959.
59.12. 55 c. brown and blue .. 1·10 80

13. Blue-crowned Pigeon. 14. "Tecomanthe dendrophila".

1959.
60 13 7 c. purple, blue & brown 50 20
61 12 c. purple, blue & green 50 20
62 17 c. purple and blue .. 50 15

1959. Social Welfare. Inser. "SOCIALE ZORG".
63.14. 5 c.+5 c. red and green .. 65 45
64. – 10 c.+5 c. purple, yellow and olive 65 45
65. – 25 c.+10 c. yellow, green and red 65 45
66. – 30 c.+10 c. green & violet 65 45
DESIGNS: 10 c. "Dendrobium attenuatum Lindley". 25 c. "Rhododendron zoelleri Warburg". 30 c. "Boea cf. urvillei".

1960. World Refugee Year. As T **180** of Netherlands.
67. 25 c. blue 40 40
68. 30 c. ochre 40 70

16. Paradise Birdwing. 17. Council Building, Hollandia.

1960. Social Welfare Funds. **Butterflies.**
69. 16. 5 c.+5 c. multicoloured .. 80 65
70. – 10 c.+5 c. bl., blk. & salmon 80 65
71. – 25 c.+10 c. red, sep. & yell. 85 65
72. – 30 c.+10 c. multicoloured 85 65
BUTTERFLIES: 10 c. Large green-banded blue. 25 c. Red lacewing. 30 c. Catops owl butterfly.

1961. Opening of Netherlands New Guinea Council.
73.17. 25 c. turquoise 20 30
74. 30 c. red 20 30

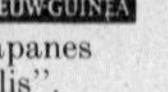

18. "Scapanes australis". 19. Children's Road Crossing.

1961. Social Welfare Funds. Beetles.
75. 18. 5 c.+5 c. multicoloured 20 25
76. – 10 c.+5 c. multicoloured 20 25
77. – 25 c.+10 c. multicoloured 25 30
78. – 30 c.+10 c. multicoloured 30 35
BEETLES: 10 c. Brenthid weevil. 25 c. "Neolamprima adolphinae" (stag beetle). 30 c. "Aspidomorpha aurata" (leaf beetle).

1962. Road Safety Campaign. Triangle in red.
79. 19. 25 c. blue 35 35
80. – 30 c. green (Adults at road crossing) .. 35 35

1962. Silver Wedding of Queen Juliana and Prince Bernhard. As T **187** of Netherlands.
81. 55 c. brown 30 35

21. Shadow of Palm on Beach. **22.** Lobster.

1962. 5th South Pacific Conf., Pago Pago Multicoloured.
82. 25 c. Type **21** 20 35
83. 30 c. Palms on beach .. 20 35

1962. Social Welfare Funds. Shellfish. Multicoloured.
84. 5 c.+5 c. Crab (horiz.) .. 20 20
85. 10 c.+5 c. Type **22** .. 20 20
86. 25 c.+10 c. Spiny lobster .. 25 25
87. 30 c.+10 c. Shrimp (horiz.) 25 30

POSTAGE DUE STAMPS

1957. As Type D **121** of Netherlands but inscr. "NEDERLANDS NIEUW GUINEA".
D 45. 1 c. red 10 20
D 46. 5 c. red .. .. .. 50 1·10
D 47. 10 c. red .. .. .. 1·50 2·25
D 48. 25 c. red .. .. .. 2·25 70
D 49. 40 c. red .. .. .. 2·25 85
D 50. 1 g. blue .. .. .. 3·00 3·75

For later issues see **WEST NEW GUINEA** and **WEST IRIAN.**

NEW CALEDONIA Pt. 6

A French Overseas Territory in the S. Pacific, E. of Australia, consisting of New Caledonia and a number of smaller islands.

100 centimes = 1 franc.

1. Napoleon III.

1860. Imperf.
1. **1.** 10 c. black £170

Nos. 5/35 are stamps of French Colonies optd or surch.

1881. "Peace and Commerce" type surch **N C E** and new value. Imperf.
5 H 05 on 40 c. red on yellow 17·00 16·00
8a 5 on 40 c. red on yellow 12·00 12·00
9 5 on 75 c. red .. .. 28·00 27·00
6a 25 on 35 c. black on orge £100 90·00
7 25 on 75 c. red £250 £190
On No. 8a the surcharge is inverted.

1886. "Peace and Commerce" (imperf) and "Commerce" types surch **N.C.E. 5c.**
10 J 5 c. on 1 f. green .. 11·00 11·00
11 H 5 c. on 1 f. green .. £7000 £7500

1891. "Peace and Commerce" (imperf) and "Commerce" types surch **N.-C.E. 10 c.** in ornamental frame.
13 H 10 c. on 40 c. red on yell 16·00 15·00
14 J 10 c. on 40 c. red on yell 8·25 7·75

1892. "Commerce" type surch **N.-C.E. 10 centimes** in ornamental frame.
15 J 10 c. on 30 c. brn on drab 8·00 8·00

1892. Optd **NLLE CALEDONIE.** (a) "Peace and Commerce" type. Imperf.
16 H 20 c. red on green .. £225 £250
17 35 c. black on orange .. 40·00 40·00
19 1 f. green £170 £170

(b) "Commerce" type.
20 J 5 c. green on green .. 9·00 7·50
21 10 c. black on lilac .. 85·00 42·00
22 15 c. blue .. .. 60·00 27·00
23 20 c. red on green .. 60·00 35·00
24 25 c. brown on yellow .. 11·00 8·75
25 25 c. black on pink .. 60·00 8·00
26 30 c. brown on drab .. 45·00 38·00
27 35 c. black on orange .. £160 £120
29 75 c. red on pink .. £120 90·00
30 1 f. green .. .. £100 85·00

1892. Surch **N-C-E** in ornamental scroll and new value. (a) "Peace and Commerce" type. Imperf.
31 H 10 on 1 f. green £3500 £2750

(b) "Commerce" type.
32 J 5 on 20 c. red on green .. 11·00 8·25
34 5 on 75 c. red on pink .. 7·50 4·75
35 10 on 1 f. green .. .. 7·50 5·00

1892. "Tablet" key-type inscr "NLLE CALEDONIE ET DEPENDANCES".
37 D 1 c. black and red on blue 35 30
38 2 c. brown & blue on buff 65 40
39 4 c. brown & blue on grey 90 1·00
55 5 c. green and red .. 85 50
41 10 c. black & blue on lilac 3·50 2·25
56 10 c. red and blue .. 4·00 70
42 15 c. blue and red .. 11·00 80
57 15 c. grey and red .. 6·00 65
43 20 c. red & blue on green 9·75 6·25
44 25 c. black & red on pink 10·00 3·00
58 25 c. blue and red .. 8·75 5·75
45 30 c. brown & bl on drab 10·00 6·00
46 40 c. red & blue on yellow 10·00 8·25
47 50 c. red and blue on pink 38·00 16·00
59 50 c. brown & red on blue 40·00 48·00
60 50 c. brown & blue on bl 38·00 35·00
48 75 c. brown & red on orge 19·00 12·50
49 1 f. green and red .. 22·00 13·50

1899. Stamps of 1892 surch. (a) **N-C-E** in ornamental scroll and **5.**
50 D 5 on 2 c. brn & bl on buff 11·00 8·75
51 5 on 4 c. brn & bl on grey 1·90 2·00

(b) **N.C.E.** and **15** in circle.
52 D 15 on 30 c. brown and blue on drab .. 2·50 2·75
53 15 on 75 c. brown and red on orange .. 8·50 6·25
54 15 on 1 f. green and red 13·50 12·50

1902. Surch **N.-C.E.** and value in figures.
61 D 5 on 30 c. brown and blue on drab .. .. 5·25 4·75
62 15 on 40 c. red and blue on yellow .. .. 4·00 3·75

1903. 50th Anniv of French Annexation. Optd **CINQUANTENAIRE 24 SEPTEMBRE 1853 1903** and eagle.
63 D 1 c. black and red on blue 95 75
64 2 c. brown & blue on buff 2·25 1·90
65 4 c. brown & blue on grey 3·50 2·00
66 5 c. green and red .. 2·75 2·50
69 10 c. black & blue on lilac 4·50 5·50
70 15 c. grey and red .. 6·50 3·25
71 20 c. red & blue on green 11·00 8·25
72 25 c. black & red on pink 11·00 9·75
73 30 c. brown & bl on drab 13·50 10·50
74 40 c. red & blue on yellow 20·00 13·50
75 50 c. red and blue on pink 35·00 21·00
76 75 c. brown & bl on orge 60·00 55·00
77 1 f. green and red .. 70·00 65·00

1903. Nos. 64 etc further surch with value in figures within the jubilee opt.
78 D 1 on 2 c. brn & bl on buff 50 45
79 2 on 4 c. brn & bl on grey 1·25 1·10
80 4 on 5 c. green and red .. 1·25 1·10
82 10 on 15 c. grey and red 1·60 1·75
83 15 on 20 c. red and blue on green .. .. 1·75 1·60
84 20 on 25 c. black and red on pink .. .. 3·00 2·75

15. Kagu. **16.**

17. "President Felix Faure" (barque).

1905.
85. **15.** 1 c. black on green .. 15 10
86. 2 c. brown 20 15
87. 4 c. blue on orange .. 20 25
88. 5 c. green 30 20
112. 5 c. blue 25 30
113. 10 c. green 50 45
114. 10 c. red 30 35
90. 15 c. lilac 40 25
91. **16.** 20 c. brown 30 25
92. 25 c. blue on green .. 45 20
115. 25 c. red on yellow .. 30 20
93. 30 c. brown on orange 30 40
116. 30 c. red 85 90
117. 30 c. orange 35 30
94. 35 c. black on yellow .. 25 30
95. 40 c. red on green .. 65 55
96. 45 c. red 40 45
97. 50 c. red on orange .. 1·50 1·00
118. 50 c. blue 90 85
119. 50 c. grey 40 35
120. 65 c. blue 35 35
98. 75 c. olive 35 35
121. 75 c. blue 30 40
122. 75 c. violet 60 50
99. **17.** 1 f. blue on green .. 50 45
123. 1 f. blue 90 95
100. 2 f. red on blue .. 1·40 1·10
101. 5 f. black on orange .. 4·00 3·75

1912. Stamps of 1892 surch.
102 D 05 on 15 c. grey and red 40 45
103 05 on 20 c. red and blue on green 40 55
104 05 on 30 c. brown and blue on drab .. 40 55
105 10 on 40 c. red and blue on yellow 90 95
106 10 on 50 c. brown and blue on blue .. .. 95 1·00

1915. Surch **NCE 5** and red cross.
107 **15** 10 c.+5 c. red 65 60

1915. Surch **5c** and red cross.
109 **15** 10 c.+5 c. red 40 50
110 15 c.+5 c. lilac .. 35 45

1918. Surch **5 CENTIMES.**
111 **15** 5 c. on 15 c. lilac .. 70 70

1922. Surch **0 05.**
124 **15** 0.05 on 15 c. lilac .. 25 45

1924. Types **15/17** (some colours changed) surch.
125 **15** 25 c. on 15 c. lilac .. 30 35
126 **17** 25 c. on 2 f. red on blue 40 50
127 25 c. on 5 f. blk on orge 40 50
128 **16** 60 on 75 c. green .. 25 35
129 65 on 45 c. purple .. 70 80
130 85 on 45 c. purple .. 90 1·00
131 90 on 75 c. red .. 35 45
132 **17** 1 f. 25 on 1 f. blue .. 30 35
133 1 f. 50 on 1 f. blue on bl 60 70
134 3 f. on 5 f. mauve .. 65 70
135 10 f. on 5 f. grn on mve 4·00 4·25
136 20 f. on 5 f. red on yell 8·50 8·50

22. Pointe des Paletuviers.

23. Chief's Hut.

24. La Perouse, De Bougainville and "L'Astrolabe".

1928.
137 **22** 1 c. blue and purple .. 10 20
138 2 c. green and brown .. 10 30
139 3 c. blue and red .. 15 25
140 4 c. blue and orange .. 15 35
141 5 c. brown and blue .. 15 35
142 10 c. brown and lilac .. 20 25
143 15 c. blue and brown .. 20 25
144 20 c. brown and red .. 20 35
145 25 c. brown and green .. 25 30
146 **23** 30 c. deep green & green 20 30
147 35 c. mauve and black 30 20
148 40 c. green and red .. 25 30
149 45 c. red and blue .. 50 60
150 45 c. green & deep green 40 50
151 50 c. brown and mauve 40 25
152 55 c. red and blue .. 1·90 95
153 60 c. red and blue .. 25 35
154 65 c. blue and brown .. 45 55
155 70 c. brown and mauve 30 40
156 75 c. drab and blue .. 80 60
157 80 c. green and purple 50 40
158 85 c. brown and green .. 75 55
159 90 c. pink and red .. 40 55
160 90 c. red and brown .. 50 60
161 **24** 1 f. pink and drab .. 3·75 2·00
162 1 f. carmine and red .. 65 75
163 1 f. green and red .. 40 50
164 1 f. 10 brown and green 8·75 7·50
165 1 f. 25 green and brown 55 65
166 1 f. 25 carmine and red 40 50
167 1 f. 40 red and blue .. 40 50
168 1 f. 50 light blue & blue 35 40
169 1 f. 60 brown and green 65 70
170 1 f. 75 orange and blue 45 45
171 1 f. 75 blue & ultram 45 50
172 2 f. brown and orange .. 45 50
173 2 f. 25 blue & ultram .. 45 50
174 2 f. 50 brown 65 70
175 3 f. brown and mauve .. 45 50
176 5 f. brown and blue .. 45 50
177 10 f. brn & pur on pink 80 80
178 20 f. brown & red on yell 1·40 1·10

1931. "Colonial Exhibition" key-types.
179 E 40 c. green and black 2·50 2·50
180 F 50 c. mauve and black 2·50 2·50
181 G 90 c. red and black .. 2·50 2·50
182 H 1 f. 50 blue and black 2·50 2·50

1932. Paris-Noumea Flight. Optd. with aeroplane and **PARIS-NOUMEA Verneilh-Dove-Munch 5 Avril 1932.**
183. **23.** 40 c. olive and red .. £300 £350
184. 50 c. brown and mauve £300 £350

1933. 1st Anniv of Paris–Noumea Flight. Optd **PARIS-NOUMEA Premiere liaison aerienne 5 Avril 1932** and airplane.
185 **22** 1 c. blue and purple .. 4·75 4·75
186 2 c. green and brown .. 4·75 4·75
187 4 c. blue and orange .. 4·75 4·75
188 5 c. brown and blue .. 4·75 4·75
189 10 c. brown and lilac .. 4·75 4·75
190 15 c. blue and brown .. 4·75 4·75
191 20 c. brown and red .. 4·75 4·75
192 25 c. brown and green .. 4·75 4·75
193 **23** 30 c. deep green & green 4·50 4·75
194 35 c. mauve and black 4·50 4·75
195 40 c. green and red .. 4·50 4·75
196 45 c. red and blue .. 4·50 4·75
197 50 c. brown and mauve 4·50 4·75
198 70 c. brown and mauve 5·25 5·50
199 75 c. drab and blue .. 5·25 5·50
200 85 c. brown and green 5·25 5·50
201 90 c. pink and red .. 5·25 5·50
202 **24** 1 f. pink and drab .. 5·25 5·50
203 1 f. 25 green and brown 5·25 5·50
204 1 f. 50 light blue & blue 5·25 5·50
205 1 f. 75 orange and blue 5·00 5·50
206 2 f. brown and orange .. 6·25 6·25
207 3 f. brown and mauve .. 5·75 6·25
208 5 f. brown and blue .. 5·75 6·25
209 10 f. brn & pur on pink 6·00 6·25
210 20 f. brown & red on yell 6·00 6·25

24a. Commerce.

27. Flying-boat over Noumea.

1937. International Exhibition, Paris.
211 **24a** 20 c. violet 60 80
212 – 30 c. green 65 85
213 – 40 c. red 60 80
214 – 50 c. brown and blue 60 75
215 – 90 c. red 60 85
216 – 1 f. 50 blue 60 80
Designs—horiz. 30 c. Sailing ships. 40 c. Berber, Negress and Annamite. 90 c. France extends torch of civilization. 1 f. 50, Diane de Poitiers. vert. 50 c. Agriculture.

1938. Air.
217. **27.** 65 c. violet 50 60
218. 4 f. 50 red 70 70
219. 7 f. green 50 50
220. 9 f. blue .. .. .. 1·40 1·50
221. 20 f. orange 85 85
222. 50 f. black .. .. 1·75 1·75

1938. Int. Anti-Cancer Fund. As T **22** of Mauritania.
223. 1 f. 75+50 c. blue .. .. 5·75 7·25

1939. New York World's Fair. As T **28** of Mauritania.
224. 1 f. 25 red 70 70
225. 2 f. 25 blue 60 70

1939. 150th Anniv of French Revolution. As T **29** of Mauritania.
226 45 c.+25 c. green and black (postage) .. 5·00 5·50
227 70 c.+30 c. brown & black 5·00 5·50
228 90 c.+35 c. orange & black 5·00 5·50
229 1 f. 25+1 f. red & black 5·00 5·50
230 2 f. 25+2 f. blue & black 5·50 5·00
231 4 f. 50+4 f. black and orange (air) .. .. 12·00 17·00

1941. Adherence to General de Gaulle. Optd **France Libre.**
232 **22** 1 c. blue and purple .. 12·50 12·50
233 2 c. green and brown .. 12·50 12·50
234 3 c. blue and red .. 12·00 12·50
235 4 c. blue and orange .. 12·50 12·50
236 5 c. brown and blue .. 11·50 12·50
237 10 c. brown and lilac .. 11·50 12·50
238 15 c. blue and brown .. 12·50 12·50
239 20 c. brown and red .. 12·50 12·50
240 25 c. brown and green .. 12·50 12·50
241 **23** 30 c. deep green & green 12·50 12·50
242 35 c. mauve and black 12·50 12·50
243 40 c. green and red .. 12·50 12·50
244 45 c. green & deep green 12·50 12·50
245 50 c. brown and mauve 12·50 12·50
246 55 c. red and blue .. 12·50 12·50
247 60 c. red and blue .. 12·50 12·50
248 65 c. blue and brown .. 12·50 12·50
249 70 c. brown and mauve 12·50 12·50
250 75 c. drab and blue .. 12·50 12·50
251 80 c. green and purple 12·50 12·50
252 85 c. brown and green .. 14·00 14·00
253 90 c. pink and red .. 14·00 14·00

No.	Type	Description	Unused	Used
254	24	1 f. carmine and red ..	14·00	14·00
255		1 f. 25 green and brown	14·00	14·00
256		1 f. 40 red and blue ..	14·00	14·00
257		1 f. 50 light blue & blue	14·00	14·00
258		1 f. 60 brown and green	14·00	14·00
259		1 f. 75 orange and blue	14·00	14·00
260		2 f. brown and orange ..	14·00	14·00
261		2 f. 25 blue & ultram ..	14·00	14·00
262		2 f. 50 brown	15·00	15·00
263		3 f. brown and mauve ..	15·00	15·00
264		5 f. brown and blue ..	15·00	15·00
265		10 f. brn & pur on pink	18·00	18·00
266		20 f. brown & red on yell	20·00	20·00

29. Kagu.

30. Airliner.

1942. Free French Issue (a) Postage.

No.	Type	Description	Unused	Used
267.	29.	5 c. brown	20	30
268.		10 c. blue	20	30
269.		25 c. green	20	30
270.		30 c. red	20	30
271.		40 c. green	40	30
272.		80 c. purple	40	30
273.		1 f. mauve	50	35
274.		1 f. 50 red	50	35
275.		2 f. black	60	60
276.		2 f. 50 blue	60	60
277.		4 f. violet	70	45
278.		5 f. yellow	80	60
279.		10 f. brown	1·25	85
280.		20 f. green	1·75	1·25

(b) Air.

No.	Type	Description	Unused	Used
281.	30.	1 f. orange	45	55
282.		1 f. 50 red	45	55
283.		5 f. purple	50	60
284.		10 f. black	70	70
285.		25 f. blue	70	70
286.		50 f. green	95	1·00
287.		100 f. red	1·40	1·25

31.

32. Felix Eboue.

1944. Mutual Aid and Red Cross Funds.

No.	Type	Description	Unused	Used
288.	31.	5 f. + 20 f. red	50	60

1945. Eboue.

No.	Type	Description	Unused	Used
289.	32.	2 f. black	40	50
290.		25 f. green	1·10	1·25

1945. Surch.

No.	Type	Description	Unused	Used
291.	29.	50 c. on 5 c. brown ..	55	70
292.		60 c. on 5 c. brown ..	55	70
293.		70 c. on 5 c. brown ..	70	80
294.		1 f. 20 on 5 c. brown ..	30	40
295.		2 f. 40 on 25 c. green ..	40	50
296.		3 f. on 25 c. green ..	40	50
297.		4 f. 50 on 25 c. green ..	60	70
298.		15 f. on 2 f. 50 blue ..	1·00	1·25

34. "Victory".

1946. Air. Victory.

No.	Type	Description	Unused	Used
299.	34.	8 f. blue	50	70

35. Legionaries by Lake Chad.

1946. Air. From Chad to the Rhine.

No.	Type	Description	Unused	Used
300	35	5 f. black	50	70
301	–	10 f. red	75	85
302	–	15 f. blue	70	85
303	–	20 f. brown	70	85
304	–	25 f. green	90	1·25
305	–	50 f. purple	90	1·75

DESIGNS: 10 f. Battle of Koufra. 15 f. Tank Battle, Mareth. 20 f. Normandy Landings. 25 f. Liberation of Paris. 50 f. Liberation of Strasbourg.

36. Two Kagus. 37. Airliners over landscape.

1948. (a) Postage.

No.	Type	Description	Unused	Used
306	36	10 c. purple and yellow	10	30
307		30 c. purple and green	15	30
308		40 c. purple and brown	15	30
309	–	50 c. purple and pink ..	15	35
310	–	60 c. brown and yellow	25	35
311	–	80 c. green & light green	25	35
312	–	1 f. violet and orange ..	25	35
313	–	1 f. 20 brown and blue	25	35
314	–	1 f. 50 blue and yellow	25	35
315	–	2 f. brown and green ..	30	25
316	–	2 f. 40 red and purple ..	40	35
317	–	3 f. violet and orange ..	3·50	1·00
318	–	4 f. indigo and blue ..	75	45
319	–	5 f. violet and red ..	90	60
320	–	6 f. brown and yellow ..	90	80
321	–	10 f. blue and orange ..	90	70
322	–	15 f. red and blue ..	1·00	1·00
323	–	20 f. violet and yellow	1·25	1·10
324	–	25 f. blue and orange ..	1·75	1·60

(b) Air.

No.	Type	Description	Unused	Used
325	–	50 f. purple and orange	3·00	3·00
326	37	100 f. blue and green ..	6·25	4·50
327	–	200 f. brown and yellow	10·00	8·00

DESIGNS—As T **36**: HORIZ. 50 c. to 80 c. Ducos Sanatorium. 1 f. 50, Porcupine Is. 2 f. to 4 f. Nickel foundry. 5 f. to 10 f. "The Towers of Notre Dame" Rocks. VERT. 15 f. to 25 f. Chief's hut. As T **37**: HORIZ. Sud Est Languedoc airliner over—50 f. St. Vincent Bay. 200 f. Noumea.

38. People of Five Races, Aircraft and Globe.

1949. Air. 75th Anniv. of U.P.U.

No.	Type	Description	Unused	Used
328.	38.	10 f. multicoloured ..	3·00	3·50

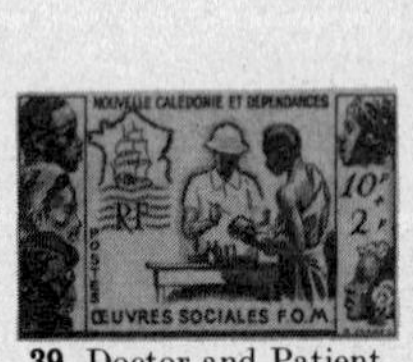

39. Doctor and Patient. 40.

1950. Colonial Welfare Fund.

No.	Type	Description	Unused	Used
329.	39.	10 f. + 2 f. pur. & brn.	2·25	2·75

1952. Military Medal Cent.

No.	Type	Description	Unused	Used
330.	40.	2 f. red, yell. & grn. ..	2·25	2·75

41. Admiral D'Entrecasteaux.

DESIGNS: 2 f. Mgr. Douarre and church. 6 f. Admiral D'Urville and map. 13 f. Admiral Despointes and view.

1953. French Administration Cent. Inscr. "1853 1953".

No.	Type	Description	Unused	Used
331.	41.	1 f. 50 lake and brown ..	4·25	3·75
332.	–	2 f. blue and turquoise ..	3·25	2·25
333.	–	6 f. brown, blue and red	7·00	4·50
334.	–	13 f. blue and green ..	7·50	5·25

42. Normandy Landings, 1944.

1954. Air. 10th Anniv. of Liberation.

No.	Type	Description	Unused	Used
335.	42.	3 f. blue and dark blue	4·00	3·50

43. Towers of Notre-Dame (rocks). 44. Coffee.

45. Transporting Nickel.

1955.

No.	Type	Description	Unused	Used
336.	43.	2 f. 50 c. blue, green and sepia (postage)	80	70
337.	–	3 f. blue, brown & grn.	5·25	3·00
338.	44.	9 f. deep blue and blue	1·40	75
339.	45.	14 f. blue & brown (air)	2·50	1·10

46. Dumbea Barrage. 47. "Xanthostemon".

1956. Economic and Social Development Fund.

No.	Type	Description	Unused	Used
340.	46.	3 f. green and blue ..	1·10	65

1958. Flowers.

No.	Type	Description	Unused	Used
341.	47.	4 f. multicoloured ..	1·60	65
342.	–	15 f. red, yell. & grn...	3·50	1·25

DESIGN: 15 f. "Hibiscus".

48. "Human Rights". 49. "Brachyrus zebra".

1958. 10th Anniv. of Declaration of Human Rights.

No.	Type	Description	Unused	Used
343.	48.	7 f. red and blue ..	1·25	95

1959.

No.	Type	Description	Unused	Used
344	49	1 f. brown and grey ..	60	45
345	–	2 f. blue, purple & green	70	40
346	–	3 f. red, blue and green	85	45
347	–	4 f. purple, red & green	70	50
348	–	5 f. bistre, blue & green	1·40	65
349	–	10 f. multicoloured ..	2·00	80
350	–	26 f. multicoloured ..	4·25	2·75

DESIGNS—HORIZ. 2 f. Outrigger canoes racing. 3 f. "Lienardella fasciata" (fish). 5 f. Sail Rock, Noumea. 26 f. Fluorescent corals. VERT. 4 f. Fisherman with spear. "Glaucus" and "Spirographe" (corals).

49a. The Carved Rock, Bourail.

1959. Air.

No.	Type	Description	Unused	Used
351	–	15 f. green, brn & red	3·50	1·50
352	–	20 f. brown and green	6·25	2·50
353	–	25 f. black, blue & pur	6·50	2·50
354	–	50 f. brown, green & bl	5·25	3·50
355	–	50 f. brown, green & bl	4·25	2·50
356	–	100 f. brown, grn & bl	17·00	9·00
357	49a	200 f. brown, grn & bl	28·00	13·00

DESIGNS—HORIZ. 15 f. Fisherman with net. 20 f. Nautilus shell. 25 f. Underwater swimmer shooting fish. 50 f. (No. 355), Isle of Pines. 100 f. Corbeille de Yate. VERT. 50 f. (No. 354), Yate barrage.

49b. Napoleon III. 49c. Port-de-France, 1859

1960. Postal Centenary.

No.	Type	Description	Unused	Used
358.	15.	4 f. red	75	50
359.	–	5 f. brown and lake ..	75	50
360.	–	9 f. brown and turquoise	90	60
361.	–	12 f. black and blue ..	90	75
362.	49b.	13 f. blue	2·50	1·60
363.	49c.	19 f. red, green & turq.	2·75	1·10
364.	–	33 f. red, green and blue	4·00	2·25

DESIGNS—As Type **49c**: HORIZ. 5 f. Girl operating cheque-writing machine. 12 f. Telephone receiver and exchange building. 33 f. As Type **49c** but without stamps in upper corners. VERT. 9 f. Letter-box on tree.

49d. Map of Pacific and Palms.

1962. 5th South Pacific Conference. Pago-Pago.

No.	Type	Description	Unused	Used
365.	49d.	15 f. multicoloured ..	2·00	1·25

49e. Map and Symbols of Meteorology.

1962. 3rd Regional Assembly of World Meteorological Association, Noumea.

No.	Type	Description	Unused	Used
366.	49e.	50 f. multicoloured ..	7·50	4·50

50. "Telstar" Satellite and part of Globe.

1962. Air. 1st Transatlantic TV Satellite Link.

No.	Type	Description	Unused	Used
367.	50.	200 f. turq., brn. & bl.	26·00	11·00

51. Emblem and Globe.

1963. Freedom from Hunger.

No.	Type	Description	Unused	Used
368.	51.	17 f. blue and purple ..	2·50	1·50

52. Relay-running. 53. Centenary Emblem.

1963. 1st South Pacific Games, Suva, Fiji.
369. **52.** 1 f. red and green .. 65 60
370. – 7 f. brown and blue .. 1·10 65
371. – 10 f. brown and green 1·75 1·00
372. – 27 f. blue & dp. pur. .. 4·00 2·25
DESIGNS: 7 f. Tennis. 10 f. Football. 27 f. Throwing the javelin.

1963. Red Cross Cent.
373. **53.** 37 f. red, grey and blue 5·50 4·00

54. Globe and Scales of Justice. 54a. "Bikkia fritillarioides".

1963. 15th Anniv. of Declaration of Human Rights.
374. **54.** 50 f. red and blue .. 5·50 5·00

1964. Flowers. Multicoloured.
375. 1 f. "Freycinettia" .. 60 40
376. 2 f. Type **54a** .. 60 40
377. 3 f. "Xanthostemon francii" 90 70
378. 4 f. "Psidiomyrtus locellatus" .. .. 1·40 80
379. 5 f. "Callistemon suberosum" .. .. 1·75 1·00
380. 7 f. "Montrouziera sphaeroidea" .. 4·75 1·40
381. 10 f. "Ixora collina" .. 4·75 1·40
382. 17 f. "Deplanchea speciosa" 6·75 3·50
The 7 f. and 10 f. are horiz.

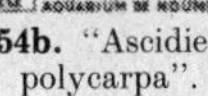

54b. "Ascidies polycarpa". 54c. "Philately".

1964. Corals and Marine Animals from Noumea Aquarium.
383 **54b** 7 f. red, brown and blue (postage) .. 1·10 80
384 – 10 f. red and blue .. 1·60 65
385 – 17 f. red, green & blue 3·50 2·00
388 – 13 f. bistre, black and orange (air) .. 2·50 1·10
389 – 15 f. green, olive & bl 3·75 1·25
390 – 25 f. blue and green .. 6·00 3·75
386 – 27 f. multicoloured .. 4·50 2·50
387 – 37 f. multicoloured .. 7·00 3·75
DESIGNS—As T **54b**: VERT. 10 f. "Alcyonium catalai" (coral). HORIZ. 17 f. "Hymenocera elegans" (crab). 48 × 28 mm: 27 f. Surgeon fish. 37 f. "Phyllobranchus" (sea slug). 48 × 27 mm: 13 f. "Coris angulata" (fish) (juvenile). 15 f. "Coris angulata". 25 f. "Coris angulata" (adult).

1964. "PHILATEC 1964" Int. Stamp Exn., Paris.
391. **54c.** 40 f. brn., grn. & vio. 6·00 5·50

54d. Houailou Mine.

1964. Air. Nickel Production at Houailou
392. **54d.** 30 f. multicoloured .. 3·50 2·50

54e. Ancient Greek Wrestling.

1964. Air. Olympic Games, Tokyo.
393. **54e.** 10 f. sepia, mauve & grn. 16·00 14·00

55. Weather Satellite. 56. "Syncom" Communications Satellite, Telegraph Poles and Morse Key.

1965. Air. World Meteorological Day.
394. **55.** 9 f. multicoloured .. 2·75 2·25

1965. Air. Cent. of I.T.U.
395. **56.** 40 f. pur., brn. & blue 10·00 7·50

56a. De Gaulle's Appeal of 18th June, 1940. 56b Amedee Lighthouse.

1965. 25th Anniv. of New Caledonia's Adherence to the Free French.
396. **56a.** 20 f. blk., red & blue 10·00 6·00

1965. Inaug. of Amedee Lighthouse.
397. **56b.** 8 f. bis., bl. & green 1·00 60

56c. Rocket "Diamant".

1966. Air. Launching of 1st French Satellite.
398. **56c.** 8 f. lake, bl. & turq. 3·00 1·50
399. – 12 f. lake, bl. & turq. 3·50 2·50
DESIGN: 12 f. Satellite "A1".

56d. Games Emblem.

1966. Publicity for 2nd South Pacific Games, Noumea.
400. **56d.** 8 f. black, red and blue 1·10 70

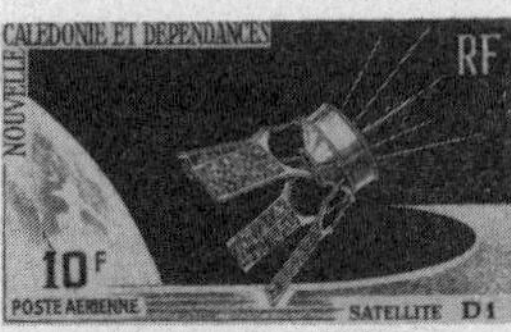

56e. Satellite "D1".

1966. Air. Launching of Satellite "D1".
401. **56e.** 10 f. brown, blue and buff .. .. .. 2·25 1·50

57. Noumea, 1866 (after Lebreton).

1966. Air. Centenary of Renaming of Port-de-France as Noumea.
402. **57.** 30 f. slate, red and blue 4·00 2·75

58. Red-throated Parrot Finch. 59. U.N.E.S.C.O. Allegory.

1966. Birds. Multicoloured.
403 1 f. Type **58** (postage) .. 1·50 75
404 1 f. New Caledonian grass warbler 85 60
405 2 f. New Caledonian whistler .. .. 1·10 70
406 3 f. New Caledonian pigeon ("Notou") .. .. 2·50 1·40
407 3 f. White-throated pigeon ("Collier blanc") .. 1·10 80
408 4 f. Kagu .. .. .. 2·40 1·10
409 5 f. Horned parakeet .. 4·25 1·50
410 10 f. Red-faced honeyeater 8·50 2·75
411 15 f. New Caledonian friar-bird .. .. .. 4·75 1·90
412 30 f. Sacred kingfisher .. 6·50 3·75
413 27 f. Horned parakeet (diff) (air) .. .. .. 5·00 3·00
414 37 f. Scarlet honeyeater .. 8·50 4·25
415 39 f. Emerald dove .. 7·75 2·75
416 50 f. Cloven-feathered dove 10·50 5·00
417 100 f. Whistling hawk .. 18·00 7·25
Nos. 413/14 are 26 × 45½ mm; Nos. 415/17 are 27½ × 48 mm.

1966. 20th Anniv. of U.N.E.S.C.O.
418. **59.** 16 f. purple, ochre and green .. .. 1·50 1·00

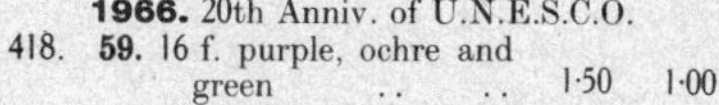

60. High-jumping.

1966. South Pacific Games, Noumea.
419. **60.** 17 f. violet, grn. & lake 1·75 1·10
420. – 20 f. green, purple & lake 3·00 1·50
421. – 40 f. green, violet & lake 3·50 2·25
422. – 100 f. pur., turq. & lake 7·50 4·50
DESIGNS: 20 f. Hurdling. 40 f. Running. 100 f. Swimming.

61. Lekine Cliffs.

1967.
424. **61.** 17 f. grey, green & blue 1·75 1·00

62. Ocean Racing Yachts.

1967. Air. 2nd Whangarei-Noumea Yacht Race.
425. **62.** 25 f. red, blue and green 4·50 3·00

63. Magenta Stadium.

1967. Sport Centres. Multicoloured.
426. 10 f. Type **63** .. .. 1·40 60
427. 20 f. Ouen-Toro swimming pool .. .. .. 2·50 1·10

64. New Caledonian Scenery.

1967. Int. Tourist Year.
428. **64.** 30 f. multicoloured .. 4·00 2·00

65. 19th-Cent. Postman.

1967. Stamp Day.
429. **65.** 7 f. red, green & turq... 1·40 1·00

66. "Papilio montrouzieri".

1967. Butterflies and Moths.
430. **66.** 7 f. blue, black & green (postage) .. .. 1·60 80
431. – 9 f. blue, brn. and mve. 2·50 1·10
432. – 13 f. violet, pur. & brn. 3·00 1·40
433. – 15 f. yell., purple & blue 5·00 2·50
434. – 19 f. orange, brown and green (air) .. .. 4·50 2·75
435. – 29 f. purple, red & blue 6·00 4·00
436. – 85 f. brown, red & yell. 14·00 6·75
BUTTERFLIES—As T **66**: 9 f. "Polyura clitarchus". 13 f. Common eggfly (male), and 15 f. (female). 48 × 27 mm: 19 f. Orange tiger. 29 f. Silver-striped hawk moth. 85 f. "Dellas elipsis".

67. Garnierite (mineral), Factory and Jules Garnier.

1967. Air. Cent. of Garnierite Industry.
437. **67.** 70 f. multicoloured .. 6·75 4·50

67a. Lifou Island.

1967. Air.
438. **67a.** 200 f. multicoloured .. 11·50 7·50

67b. Skier and Snow-crystal.

1967. Air. Winter Olympic Games, Grenoble.
439. **67b.** 100 f. brn., blue & grn. 12·00 7·50

68. Bouquet, Sun and W.H.O. Emblem. 69. Human Rights Emblem.

1968. 20th Anniv. of W.H.O.
440. **68.** 20 f. blue, red & violet 2·75 1·50

1968. Human Rights Year.
441. **69.** 12 f. red, green & yell. 1·40 1·00

70. Ferrying Mail-van across Tontouta River.

1968. Stamp Day.
442. **70.** 9 f. brown, blue & green 1·75 1·00

71. " Conus geographus ". 72. Dancers.

1968. Sea Shells.

443. –	1 f. brn., grey & grn. (post.)	80	45
444. –	1 f. purple and vio. ..	65	35
445. –	2 f. pur., red & blue ..	65	60
446. –	3 f. brown and green ..	90	45
447. –	5 f. red, brn. & violet ..	1·25	65
448. **71.**	10 f. brn., grey & bl. ..	2·00	1·10
449. –	10 f. yell., brn. & red ..	2·00	80
450. –	10 f. blk., brn. & orge.	1·60	65
451. –	15 f. red, grey & green	3·50	1·40
452. –	21 f. brn., sepia & green	3·75	1·25
453. –	22 f. red, brn. & bl. (air)	3·50	1·75
454. –	25 f. brown and red ..	3·50	2·00
455. –	33 f. brown and blue ..	4·50	2·50
456. –	34 f. vio., brn. & orge.	4·50	2·50
457. –	39 f. brn., grey & green	4·50	2·00
458. –	40 f. blk., brn. & red ..	4·50	2·00
459. –	50 f. red, pur. & green	6·00	3·00
460. –	60 f. brown and green	9·00	4·50
461. –	70 f. brn., grey & violet	10·00	4·00
462. –	100 f. brn., blk. & blue	17·00	8·50

DESIGNS—VERT. (22 × 36 mm.). 1 f. (No. 443) " Strombus epidromis ". 1 f. (No. 444) " Lambis scorpius ". 3 f. " Lambis lambis ". 10 f. (No. 450) " Strombus variabilis ". (27 × 48 mm.). 22 f. " Strombus sinuatus ". 25 f. " Lambis crocata ". 34 f. " Strombus vomer ". 50 f. " Lambis chiragra ". HORIZ. (36 × 22 mm.). 2 f. " Murex haustellum ". 5 f. " Murex triremis ". 10 f. (No. 449) " Cypraea cribaria ". 15 f. " Murex rameux ". 21 f. " Cypraea talpe ". (48 × 27 mm.). 33 f. " Cypraea argus ". 39 f. " Conus lienardi ". 40 f. " Conus cabriti ". 60 f. " Cypraea mappa ". 70 f. " Conux coccineus ". 100 f. " Murex noir ".

1968. Air.
463. **72.** 60 f. red, blue & green 6·50 4·00

73. Rally Car.

1968. 2nd New Caledonian Motor Safari.
464. **73.** 25 f. blue, red and green 4·50 2·00

74. Caudron C 600 "Eaglet" and Route-map.

1969. Air. Stamp Day. 30th Anniv. of 1st Noumea-Paris Flight by Martinet and Klein.
465. **74.** 29 f. red, blue & violet 3·50 2·00

75. "Concorde" in Flight.

1969. Air. 1st Flight of "Concorde".
466 **75** 100 f. green & light green 22·00 15·00

76. Cattle-dip.

1969. Cattle-breeding in New Caledonia.
467. **76.** 9 f. brown, green & blue (postage) 90 65
468. – 25 f. violet, brn. & grn. 2·50 1·00
469. – 50 f. pur., red & grn. (air) 4·00 2·75
DESIGNS: 25 f. Branding. LARGER (48 × 27 mm.). 50 f. Stockman with herd.

77. Judo.

1969. 3rd South Pacific Games, Port Moresby, Papua New Guinea.
470. **77.** 19 f. pur., blue & red (post.) 2·75 1·25
471. – 20 f. black, red & green 2·75 1·25
472. – 30 f. black & blue (air) 3·50 1·75
473. – 39 f. brn., grn. and blk. 5·50 2·50
DESIGNS—HORIZ. 20 f. Boxing. 30 f. Diving (48 × 27 mm.) VERT. 39 f. Putting the shot (27 × 48 mm.)

1969. Air. Birth Bicentenary of Napoleon Bonaparte. As T **114b** of Mauritania. Multicoloured.
474. 40 f. " Napoleon in Coronation Robes " (Gerard) (vert.) .. .. .. 15·00 8·50

78. Airliner over Outrigger Canoe.

1969. Air. 20th Anniv of Regular Noumea–Paris Air Service.
475 78 50 f. green, brown & blue 4·50 2·75

79. I.L.O. Building Geneva.

1969. 50th Anniv. of I.L.O.
476. **79.** 12 f. brown, violet & salmon .. .. 1·10 80

80. "French Wings around the World".

1970. Air. 10th Anniv. of French "Around the World" Air Service.
477. **80.** 200 f. brn., bl. & vio.. 15·00 8·50

81. New U.P.U. Building, Berne.

1970. Inaug. of New U.P.U. Headquarters Building, Berne.
478. **81.** 12 f. red, grey and brown .. .. 1·40 80

82. Packet Steamer "Natal", 1883.

1970. Stamp Day.
479. **82.** 9 f. black, green & blue 2·00 1·00

83. Cyclists on Map.

1970. Air. 4th "Tour de Nouvelle Caledonie" Cycle Race.
480. **83.** 40 f. brown, blue and light blue .. .. 3·50 2·25

84. Mt. Fuji and Japanese Express Train

1970. Air. "EXPO 70" World Fair, Osaka, Japan. Multicoloured.
481. 20 f. Type **84** .. .. 2·50 1·10
482. 45 f. "EXPO" emblem, map and Buddha .. 3·50 1·60

85. Racing Yachts.

1971. Air. One Ton Cup Yacht Race Auckland, New Zealand.
483. **85.** 20 f. green, red & black 2·50 1·25

86. Dumbea Mail Train.

1971. Stamp Day.
484. **86.** 10 f. black, green & red 2·50 1·25

87. Ocean Racing Yachts.

1971. 3rd Whangarei–Noumea Ocean Yacht Race.
485. **87.** 16 f. turquoise, green and blue .. .. 3·50 1·75

88. Lieut.-Col. Broche and Theatre Map.

1971. 30th Anniv. of French Pacific Battalion's Participation in Second World War Mediterranean Campaign.
486. **88.** 60 f. multicoloured .. 5·50 3·50

89. Early Tape Machine. 90. Weightlifting.

1971. World Telecommunications Day.
487. **89.** 19 f. orange, pur. & red 2·50 1·00

1971. 4th South Pacific Games, Papeete, French Polynesia.
488. **90.** 11 f. brn. & red (post.) 1·40 1·25
489. – 23 f. violet, red & blue 2·50 1·25
490. – 25 f. green & red (air).. 2·75 2·00
491. – 100 f. blue, green & red 6·50 4·00
DESIGNS—VERT. 23 f. Basketball. HORIZ. (48 × 27 mm.) 25 f. Pole-vaulting. 100 f. Archery.

91. Port de Plaisance, Noumea.

1971. Air.
492. **91.** 200 f. multicoloured .. 14·50 7·75

92. De Gaulle as President of French Republic, 1970. 93. Publicity Leaflet showing Aircraft.

1971. 1st Death Anniv of General De Gaulle.
493 **92** 34 f. black and purple .. 6·50 2·75
494 – 100 f. black and purple 13·00 6·00
DESIGN: 100 f. De Gaulle in uniform, 1940.

1971. Air. 40th Anniv. of 1st New Caledonia to Australia Flight.
495. **93.** 90 f. brn., blue & orge. 7·50 4·00

94. Downhill Skiing.

1972. Air. Winter Olympic Games, Sapporo, Japan.
496. **94.** 50 f. grn., red & blue.. 5·00 2·50

95. St. Mark's Basilica, Venice.

1972. Air. U.N.E.S.C.O. " Save Venice " Campaign.
497. **95.** 20 f. brn., grn. and blue 2·75 1·40

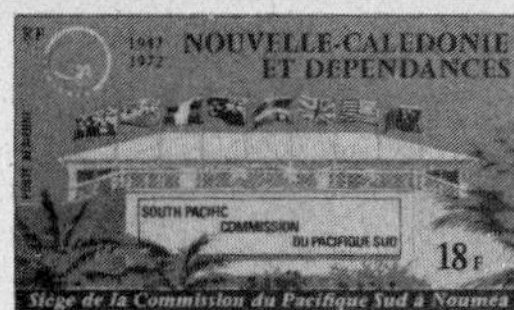

96. Commission Headquarters, Noumea.

1972. Air. 25th Anniv. of South Pacific Commission.
498. **96.** 18 f. multicoloured .. 1·50 1·00

97. Breguet Aircraft and Noumea Monument.

1972. Air. 40th Anniv. of 1st Paris-Noumea Flight.
499. **97.** 110 f. bl., pur. & grn. 10·00 6·75

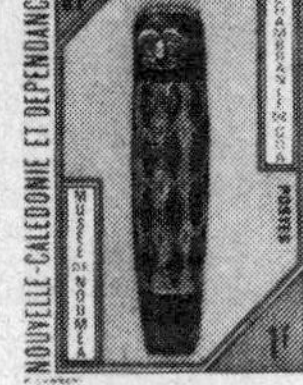

98. Pacific Island Dwelling. **99.** Goa Door-post.

1972. Air. South Pacific Arts Festival, Fiji.
500. **98.** 24 f. brn., blue & orange 2·75 1·50

1972. Exhibits from Noumea Museum.
501. **99.** 1 f. red, grn. & grey (post.) 75 30
502. – 2 f. blk., grn. & dull grn. 75 30
503. – 5 f. multicoloured .. 1·00 50
504. – 12 f. multicoloured .. 2·25 1·00
505. – 16 f. multicoloured (air) 1·50 1·00
506. – 40 f. multicoloured .. 3·00 1·50
DESIGNS: 2 f. Carved wooden pillow. 5 f. Monstrance. 12 f. Tchamba mask. 16 f. Ornamental arrowheads. 40 f. Portico, chief's house.

100. Hurdling over " H " of " MUNICH ".

1972. Air. Olympic Games, Munich.
507. **100.** 72 f. violet, pur. & blue 6·50 3·50

101. New Head Post Office Building, Noumea.

1972. Air.
508. **101.** 23 f. brn., blue & green 2·25 1·00

102. J.C.I. Emblem.

1972. 10th Anniv. of New Caledonia Junior Chamber of Commerce.
509. **102.** 12 f. multicoloured .. 1·25 80

103. Forest Scene.

1973. Air. Landscapes of the East Coast. Multicoloured.
510. 11 f. Type **103** .. .. 1·25 80
511. 18 f. Beach and palms (vert.) 2·50 1·25
512. 21 f. Waterfall and inlet (vert.) .. .. .. 3·00 1·40
See also Nos. 534/6.

104. Moliere and Characters.

1973. Air. 300th Death Anniv. of Moliere (playwright).
513. **104.** 50 f. multicoloured .. 5·50 2·50

105. Tchamba Mask.

1973.
514 **105** 12 f. purple (postage) 2·50 1·40
515 – 23 f. blue (air) .. 6·50 4·00
DESIGN: 23 f. "Concorde" in flight.

106. Liner "El Kantara" in Panama Canal.

1973. 50th Anniv of Marseilles–Noumea Shipping Service via Panama Canal.
516 **106** 60 f. black, brown & grn 5·50 3·00

107. Globe and Allegory of Weather.

1973. Air. Centenary of World Meteorological Organization.
517. **107.** 80 f. multicoloured .. 5·50 2·75

108. " DC-10 " in Flight.

1973. Air. Inauguration of Noumea–Paris "DC-10" Air Service.
518. **108.** 100 f. grn., brn. & blue 6·50 3·50

109. " Ovula ovum ".

1973. Marine Fauna from Noumea Aquarium. Multicoloured.
519. 8 f. " Chaetodon melanotus " (daylight) .. .. 1·40 70
520. 14 f. "Chaetodon melanotus" (nocturnal) .. .. 2·00 1·10
521. 3 f. Type **109** (air) .. 80 35
522. 32 f. " Acanthurus olivaceus " (adult and young) .. 4·00 1·75
523. 32 f. " Hydatina " .. 3·50 1·60
524. 37 f. " Dolium perdix " .. 3·50 1·60

111. Office Emblem.

1973. 10th Anniv of Central Schools Co-operation Office.
532 **111** 20 f. blue, yellow & grn 1·60 90

112. New Caledonia Mail-coach, 1880.

1973. Air. Stamp Day.
533. **112.** 15 f. multicoloured .. 1·75 1·10

1974. Air. Landscapes of the West Coast. As T **103**. Multicoloured.
534 8 f. Beach and palms (vert) 1·00 65
535 22 f. Trees and mountain 1·75 1·10
536 26 f. Trees growing in sea 2·75 1·25

113. Centre Building.

1974. Air. Opening of Scientific Studies Centre, Anse-Vata, Noumea.
537. **113.** 50 f. multicoloured .. 2·50 1·40

114. "Bird" embracing Flora.

1974. Nature Conservation.
538. **114.** 7 f. multicoloured .. 65 45

115. 18th-century French Sailor.

1974. Air. Discovery and Reconnaissance of New Caledonia and Loyalty Islands.
539. – 20 f. vio. red and blue 1·50 80
540. – 25 f. grn., brn. & red .. 1·50 1·00
541. **115.** 28 f. brn., bl. & grn. .. 1·60 1·00
542. – 30 f. bl., brn. & red .. 2·25 1·40
543. – 36 f. red, brn. & blue .. 3·50 2·00
DESIGNS—HORIZ. 20 f. Captain Cook, H.M.S. "Endeavour" and map of Grand Terre island. 25 f. La Perouse, "L'Astrolabe" and map of Grand Terre island (reconnaissance of west coast). 30 f. Entrecasteaux, ship and map of Grand Terre island (reconnaissance of west coast). 36 f. Dumont d'Urville, "L'Astrolabe" and map of Loyalty Islands.

116. "Telecommunications".

1974. Air. Centenary of U.P.U.
544. **116.** 95 f. orge., pur. & grey 5·00 3·00

117. "Art".

1974. Air. "Arphila 75" International Stamp Exhibition Paris (1975) (1st issue).
545. **117.** 80 f. multicoloured .. 3·50 2·50
See also No. 554.

118. Hotel Chateau-Royal.

1974. Air. Inauguration of Hotel Chateatu Royal, Noumea.
546. **118.** 22 f. multicoloured .. 1·40 80

118a. Animal Skull, Burnt Tree and Flaming Landscape.

1975. "Stop Bush Fires".
547 **118a** 20 f. multicoloured .. 1·00 65

119. " Cricket ".

1975. Air. Tourism. Multicoloured.
548 3 f. Type **119** 80 45
549 25 f. "Bougna" ceremony 1·50 80
550 31 f. "Pilou" native dance 2·25 1·00

120. "Calanthe veratrifolia". **121.** Global "Flower".

1975. New Caledonian Orchids. Mult.
551. 8 f. Type **120** (postage) .. 1·10 55
552. 11 f. "Lyperanthus gigas" 1·40 65
553. 42 f. "Eriaxis rigida" (air) 3·50 2·00

1975. Air. "Arphila 75" International Stamp Exhibition, Paris (2nd issue).
554. **121.** 105 f. purple, grn. & bl. 5·50 3·00

122. Throwing the Discus.

1975. Air. 5th South Pacific Games, Guam.
555. 24 f. Type **122** .. .. 1·50 1·00
556. 50 f. Volleyball .. .. 2·50 1·50

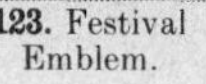

123. Festival Emblem. **124.** Birds in Flight.

1975. " Melanesia 2000 " Festival, Noumea.
557. **123.** 12 f. multicoloured .. 80 45

1975. 10th Anniv. of Noumea Ornithological Society.
558. **124.** 5 f. multicoloured .. 65 40

125. Pres. Pompidou. 127. Brown Booby.

126. " Concordes ".

1975. Pompidou Commemoration.
559. 125. 26 f. grey and green .. 1·60 80

1976. Air. First Commercial Flight of "Concorde".
560. 126. 147 f. blue and red .. 10·00 6·50

1976. Ocean Birds. Multicoloured.
561. 1 f. Type **127** 60 40
562. 2 f. Blue-faced booby .. 85 40
563. 8 f. Red-footed booby (vert.) .. .. .. 2·00 1·00

128. Festival Emblem.

1976. South Pacific Festival of Arts, Rotorua, New Zealand.
564. 128. 27 f. multicoloured .. 1·50 1·00

129. Lion and Lions' Emblem. 130. Early and Modern Telephones.

1976. 15th Anniv. of Lions Club. Noumea.
565. 129. 49 f. multicoloured .. 3·00 1·75

1976. Air. Telephone Centenary.
566. 130. 36 f. multicoloured .. 2·00 1·25

131. Capture of Penboscot.

1976. Air. Bicent. of American Revolution.
567. 131. 24 f. purple and brown 1·50 1·00

132. Bandstand.

1976. " Aspects of Old Noumea ". Mult.
568. 25 f. Type **132** .. .. 1·10 55
569. 30 f. Monumental fountain (vert.) .. .. .. 1·40 80

133. Athletes. 134. " Chick " with Magnifier.

1976. Air. Olympic Games, Montreal.
570. 133. 33 f. violet, red & purple 1·75 1·00

1976. Air. " Philately in Schools ", Stamp Exhibition, Noumea.
571. 134. 42 f. multicoloured .. 2·50 1·50

135. Dead Bird and Trees.

1976. Nature Protection.
572. 135. 20 f. multicoloured .. 1·40 65

136. South Pacific Heads.

1976. 16th South Pacific Commission Conference.
573. 136. 20 f. multicoloured .. 1·25 70

137. Old Town Hall, Noumea.

1976. Air. Old and New Town Halls, Noumea. Multicoloured.
574. 75 f. Type **137** .. .. 3·75 2·50
575. 125 f. New Town Hall .. 6·25 3·00

138. Water Carnival.

1977. Air. Summer Festival, Noumea.
576. 138. 11 f. multicoloured .. 80 40

139. "Pseudophyllanax imperialis" (cricket).

1977. Insects.
577 139 26 f. emer, grn & brn 1·25 1·00
578 – 31 f. brn, sepia & grn 2·00 1·00
DESIGN: 31 f. "Agrianome fairmairei" (long-horn beetle).

140. Miniature Roadway.

1977. Air. Road Safety.
579. 140. 50 f. multicoloured .. 2·50 1·25

141. Earth Station.

1977. Earth Satellite Station, Noumea.
580. 141. 29 f. multicoloured .. 1·40 80

142. " Phajus daenikeri ".

1977. Orchids. Multicoloured.
581. 22 f. Type **142** .. .. 1·25 80
582. 44 f. " Dendrobium finetianum " .. .. 2·50 1·25

143. Mask and Palms.

1977. La Perouse School Philatelic Exn.
583. 143. 35 f. multicoloured .. 1·40 1·00

144. Trees.

1977. Nature Protection.
584. 144. 20 f. multicoloured .. 1·00 65

145. Palm Tree and Emblem.

1977. French Junior Chambers of Commerce Congress.
585. 145. 200 f. multicoloured .. 7·75 5·00

146. Young Great Frigate Bird.

1977. Great Frigate Birds. Multicoloured.
586 16 f. Type **146** (postage) .. 1·10 65
587 42 f. Adult male bird (horiz) (air) .. .. 3·25 1·75

147. Magenta Airport and Map of Internal Air Network.

1977. Air. Airports. Multicoloured.
588. 24 f. Type **147** .. .. 1·00 65
589. 57 f. La Tontout International Airport, Noumea 2·50 1·50

1977. Air. 1st Commercial Flight of Concorde, Paris–New York. Optd **22.11.77 PARIS NEW-YORK.**
590 126 147 f. blue and red .. 11·00 9·00

149. Horse and Foal.

1977. 10th Anniv. of S.E.C.C. (Horse-breeding Society).
591. 149. 5 f. brn., grn. and blue 80 40

150. " Moselle Bay " (H. Didonna).

1977. Air. Views of Old Noumea (1st series).
592. 150. 41 f. multicoloured .. 2·50 1·50
593. – 42 f. purple and brown 2·50 1·50
DESIGN—49 × 27 mm. 42 f. "Settlers' Valley" (J. Kreber).

151. Black-naped Tern.

1978. Ocean Birds. Multicoloured.
594. 22 f. Type **151** .. .. 1·25 80
595. 40 f. Sooty tern .. .. 2·50 1·50

152. " Araucaria montana ". 153. " Halityle regularis ".

1978. Flora. Multicoloured.
596. 16 f. Type **152** (postage) .. 55 45
597. 42 f. " Amyema scandens " (horiz.) (air) .. .. 2·50 1·50

1978. Noumea Aquarium.
598. 153. 10 f. multicoloured .. 65 30

154. Turtle.

1978. Protection of the Turtle.
599. **154.** 30 f. multicoloured .. 1·25 80

155. New Caledonian Flying Fox.

1978. Nature Protection.
600. **155.** 20 f. multicoloured .. 1·10 65

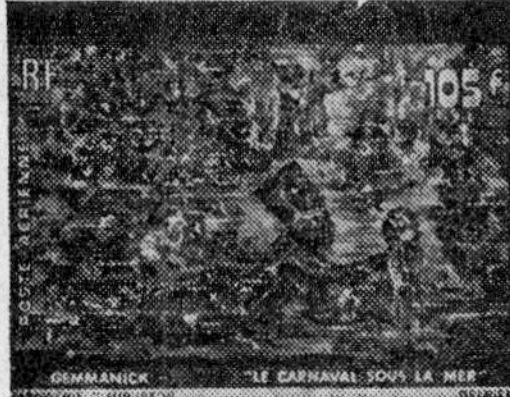

156. " Underwater Carnival ".

1978. Air. Aubusson Tapestry.
601. **156.** 105 f. multicoloured .. 4·25 2·50

157. Pastor Maurice Leenhardt.

1978. Birth Centenary of Pastor Maurice Leenhardt.
602. **157.** 37 f. sepia, grn. & orge. 1·50 1·10

158. Hare chasing " Stamp " Tortoise.

1978. School Philately (1st series).
603. **158.** 35 f. multicoloured .. 2·25 1·40

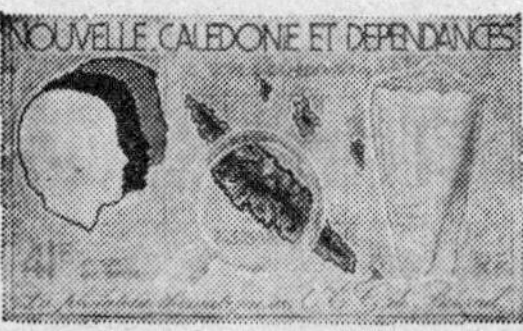

159. Heads, Map, Magnifying Glass and Shell.

1978. Air. Thematic Philately at Bourail.
604. **159.** 41 f. multicoloured .. 1·75 1·10

160. Candles.

161. Footballer and League Badge.

1978. Third New Caledonian Old People's Day.
605. **160.** 36 f. multicoloured .. 1·25 80

1978. 50th Anniv. of New Caledonian Football League.
606. **161.** 26 f. multicoloured .. 1·25 65

162. " Fauberg Blanchot " (after Lacouture).

1978. Air. Views of Old Noumea.
607 **162** 24 f. multicoloured .. 1·25 65

163. Map of Lifou, Solar Energy Panel and Transmitter Mast.

1978. Telecommunications through Solar Energy.
608. **163.** 33 f. multicoloured .. 1·40 80

164. Petroglyph, Mere Region.

165. Ouvea Island and Outrigger Canoe.

1979. Archaeological Sites.
609. **164** 10 f. red 65 45

1979. Islands. Multicoloured.
610. 11 f. Type **165** 60 40
611. 31 f. Mare Island and ornaments (horiz.) .. 85 60
See also Nos. 629 and 649.

166. Satellite Orbit of Earth.

167. 19th-century Barque and Modern Container Ship.

1979. Air. 1st World Survey of Global Atmosphere.
612. **166.** 53 f. multicoloured .. 1·50 1·00

1979. Air. Centenary of Chamber of Commerce and Industry.
613. **167.** 49 f. mauve, blue & brn. 1·50 80

168. Child's Drawing.

1979. Air. International Year of the Child.
614. **168.** 35 f. multicoloured .. 1·40 80

169. House at Artillery Point.

1979. Views of Old Noumea.
615 **169** 20 f. multicoloured .. 85 55

170. " Katsuwonus pelamis ".

1979. Air. Sea Fishes (1st series) Multicoloured.
616. 29 f. Type **170** .. .. 1·40 65
617. 30 f. " Makaira indica " .. 1·40 70
See also Nos. 632/3 and 647/8.

171. L. Tardy de Montravel (founder) and View of Port-de-France (Noumea).

1979. Air. 125th Anniv. of Noumea.
618. **171.** 75 f. multicoloured .. 2·75 1·50

172. The Eel Queen (Kanaka legend).

173. Auguste Escoffier.

1979. Air. Nature Protection.
619. **172.** 42 f. multicoloured .. 2·00 1·40

1979. Auguste Escoffier Hotel School.
620. **173.** 24 f. brown, green and turquoise 85 55

174. Games Emblem and Catamarans.

1979. Sixth South Pacific Games, Fiji.
621. **174.** 16 f. multicoloured .. 85 45

175. Children of Different Races, Map and Postmark.

1979. Air. Youth Philately.
622. **175.** 27 f. multicoloured .. 90 55

176. Aerial View of Centre.

1979. Air. Overseas Scientific and Technical Research Office (O.R.S.T.O.M.) Centre, Noumea.
623. **176.** 25 f. multicoloured .. 90 55

177. " Agathis ovata ".

1979. Trees. Multicoloured.
624. 5 f. Type **177** 50 20
625. 34 f. " Cyathea intermedia " 1·25 65

178. Rodeo Riding.

1979. Pouembout Rodeo.
626. **178.** 12 f. multicoloured .. 80 40

179. Hill, 1860 10 c. Stamp and Post Office.

1979. Air. Death Cent. of Sir Rowland Hill.
627. **179.** 150 f. blk., brn. & orge. 4·50 2·50

180. "Bantamia merleti".

1980. Noumea Aquarium. Fluorescent Corals (1st issue).
628 **180** 23 f. multicoloured .. 90 45
See also No. 646.

1980. Islands. As T **165**. Multicoloured.
629. 23 f. Map of Ile des Pins & ornaments (horiz.) .. 80 40

181. Outrigger Canoe.

1980. Air.
630 **181** 45 f. blue, turq & indigo 1·40 1·00

182. Globe, Rotary Emblem, Map and Carving.

1980. Air. 75th Anniv. of Rotary International.
631. **182.** 100 f. multicoloured .. 3·25 1·75

1980. Air. Sea Fishes (2nd series). As T **170**. Multicoloured.
632 34 f. Angler holding dolphin fish .. .. 1·25 80
633 39 f. Fishermen with sailfish (vert) .. .. 1·50 90

183. " Hibbertia virotii ".

184. High Jumper, Magnifying Glass, Albums and Plimsoll.

1980. Flowers. Multicoloured.
634. 11 f. Type **183** 60 40
635. 12 f. " Grevillea meisneri " 60 40

1980. School Philately.
636. **184.** 30 f. multicoloured .. 80 50

185. Aeroplane and Map.

1980. Air. Coral Sea Air Rally.
637. 185. 31 f. blue, grn. & brn. 1·00 80

186. Sailing Canoe.

1980. Air. South Pacific Arts Festival, Port Moresby.
638. 186. 27 f. multicoloured .. 80 65

187. Road Signs as Road-users.

1980. Road Safety.
639. 187. 15 f. multicoloured .. 60 25

188. " Parribacus caledonicus ".

1980. Noumea Aquarium. Marine Animals (1st series). Multicoloured.
640. 5 f. Type 188 .. .. 30 20
641. 8 f. " Panulirus versicolor " 40 20
See also Nos. 668/69.

189. Kiwanis Emblem.

1980. Air. 10th Anniv. of Noumea Kiwanis Club.
642. 189. 50 f. multicoloured .. 1·50 1·00

190. Sun, Tree and Solar Panel.

1980. Nature Protection. Solar Energy.
643. 190. 23 f. multicoloured .. 90 55

191. Old House, Poulou.

1980. Air. Views of Old Noumea (4th series).
644. 191. 33 f. multicoloured .. 90 65

192. Charles de Gaulle.

193. Manta Ray.

1980. Air. 10th Death Anniv. of Charles de Gaulle (French statesman).
645. 192. 120 f. green, olive & bl. 4·50 2·75

1981. Air. Noumea Aquarium. Fluorescent Corals (2nd series). As T 180. Mult.
646 60 f. "Trachyphyllia geoffroyi" .. .. 1·60 90

1981. Sea Fishes (3rd series). Multicoloured.
647. 23 f. Type 193 .. .. 70 50
648. 25 f. Grey Shark 75 50

1981. Islands. As T 165. Multicoloured.
649. 26 f. Map of Belep Archipelago and Diver (horiz.) 75 45

194. " Xeronema moorei ".

1981. Air. Flowers. Multicoloured.
650 38 f. Type 194 .. .. 90 55
651 51 f. "Geissois pruinosa" .. 1·25 75

195. Yuri Gagarin and " Vostok 1 ".

1981. Air. 20th Anniv. of First Men in Space. Multicoloured.
652. 64 f. Type 195 .. .. 1·50 1·25
653. 155 f. Alan Shepard and " Freedom 7 " .. .. 4·00 2·50

196. Liberation Cross, "Zealandia" (troopship) and Badge.

1981. Air. 40th Anniv. of Departure of Pacific Battalion for Middle East.
655. 196. 29 f. multicoloured .. 1·40 80

197. " Cymbiola rossiniana ".

198. Sail Corvette "Constantine".

1981. Shells. Multicoloured.
656. 1 f. Type 197 .. .. 15 10
657. 2 f. " Connus floccatus " 25 20
658. 13 f. " Cypraea stolida " (horiz.) 65 25

1981. Ships (1st series).
659. 198. 10 f. blue, brown & red 65 30
660. – 25 f. blue, brown & red 1·00 65
DESIGN: 25 f. Paddle-gunboat "Le Phoque", 1853.
See also Nos. 680/81 and 725/6.

199. " Echinometra mathaei ".

1981. Air. Water Plants. Multicoloured.
661. 38 f. Type 199 .. .. 90 55
662. 51 f. " Prionocidaris verticillata " .. .. .. 1·25 65

200. Broken-stemmed Rose and I.Y.D.P. Emblems.

1981. International Year of Disabled Persons.
663. 200. 45 f. multicoloured .. 1·40 80

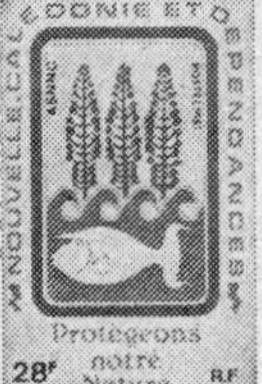
201. 25 c. Surcharged Stamp of 1881.

202. Latin Quarter.

1981. Air. Stamp Day.
664. 201. 41 f. multicoloured .. 1·10 65

1981. Air. Views of Old Noumea.
665 202 43 f. multicoloured .. 1·10 65

203. Trees and Fish.

204. Victor Roffey and "Golden Eagle".

1981. Nature Protection.
666. 203. 28 f. blue, green & brn. 1·10 65

1981. Air. 50th Anniv. of First New Caledonia-Australia Airmail Flight.
667. 204. 37 f. black, vio. and blue 90 60

1982. Noumea Aquarium. Marine Animals (2nd series). As T 188. Multicoloured.
668. 13 f. " Calappa calappa " 65 45
669. 25 f. " Etisus splendidus " 1·00 65

205. " La Rousette ".

1982. Air. New Caledonian Aircraft (1st series).
670. 205. 38 f. brown, red and green 90 55
671. – 51 f. brown, orange and green .. .. 1·10 65
DESIGN: 51 f. " Le Cagou ".
See also Nos. 712/3.

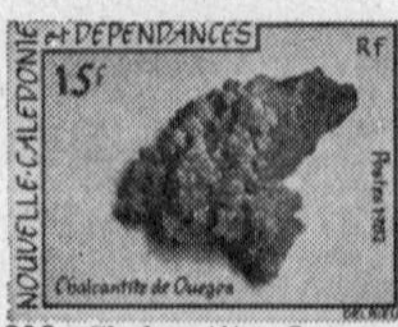
206. Chalcantite, Ouegoa.

1982. Rocks and Minerals (1st series). Multicoloured.
672. 15 f. Type 206 .. .. 90 65
673. 30 f. Anorthosite, Blue River .. .. .. 1·25 65
See also Nos. 688/9.

207. De Verneilh, Deve and Munch (air crew), Aeroplane " Le Biarritz " and Route Map.

1982. Air. 50th Anniv. of First Flight from Paris to Noumea.
674. 207. 250 f. mauve, blue and black .. .. 5·50 2·75

208. Scout and Guide Badges and Map.

1982. Air. 50th Anniv. of New Caledonian Scout Movement.
675. 208. 40 f. multicoloured .. 1·00 65

209. " The Rat and the Octopus " (Canaque legend).

1982. "Philexfrance 82" International Stamp Exhibition, Paris.
676. 209. 150 f. blue, mauve and deep blue .. .. 3·00 2·25

210. Footballer, Mascot and Badge.

1982. Air. World Cup Football Championship, Spain.
677. 210. 74 f. multicoloured .. 1·60 1·00

211. Savanna Trees at Niaoulis.

212. Islanders, Map and Kagu.

1982. Flora. Multicoloured.
678. 20 f. Type 211 .. .. 80 45
679. 29 f. " Melaleuca quinquenervia " (horiz.) .. 1·00 55

1982. Ships (2nd series). As T 198.
680. 44 f. blue, purple and brn. 1·00 65
681. 59 f. blue, light brown and brown .. .. .. 1·25 80
DESIGNS: 44 f. Naval transport barque "Le Cher". 59 f. Sloop "Kersaint", 1902.

1982. Air. Overseas Week.
682. 212. 100 f. brn., grn. & bl. 2·00 1·10

213. Ateou Tribal House.

214. Grey's Fruit Dove.

1982. Traditional Houses.
683. 213. 52 f. multicoloured .. 1·40 90

1982. Birds. Multicoloured.
684. 32 f. Type 214 .. .. 1·40 70
685. 35 f. Rainbow lory .. 1·40 70

215. Canoe.

1982. Central Office of Education Co-operation office.
686 215 48 f. multicoloured .. 1·25 65

216. Bernheim and Library.

1982. Bernheim Library, Noumea.
687. 216. 36 f. brn., purple and black 90 50

1983. Air. Rocks and Minerals (2nd series). As T **206**. Multicoloured.
688 44 f. Paya gypsum (vert) 1·10 80
689 59 f. Kone silica (vert) .. 1·40 90

217. "Dendrobium oppositifolium".

1983. Orchids. Multicoloured.
690. 10 f. Type **217** 30 10
691. 15 f. "Dendrobium munificum" 40 15
692. 29 f. "Dendrobium fractiflexum" 80 35

218. W.C.Y. Emblem, Map of New Caledonia and Globe.

1983. Air. World Communications Year.
693. 218. 170 f. multicoloured 3·50 2·00

219. "Crinum asiaticum".

1983. Flowers. Multicoloured.
694. 1 f. Type **219** 10 10
695. 2 f. "Xanthostemon aurantiacum" 10 10
696. 4 f. "Metrosideros demonstrans" (vert.) .. 10 10

220. Wall Telephone and Noumea Post Office, 1890. **221.** "Laticaudata laticaudata".

1983. 25th Anniv. of Post and Telecommunications Office. Multicoloured.
697. 30 f. Type **220** 70 30
698. 40 f. Telephone & Noumea Post Office, 1936 .. 80 30
699. 50 f. Push-button telephone and Noumea Post Office, 1972 .. 1·25 40

1983. Noumea Aquarium. Sea Snakes. Mult.
701. 31 f. Type **221** 80 40
702. 33 f. "Laticauda colubrina" .. .. 1·00 40

1983. Air. New Caledonian Aircraft (2nd series). As T **205**. Each red, mauve & brown.
712. 46 f. "Pou du Ciel" .. 1·00 65
713. 61 f. "L'Aiglon Caudron" 1·25 80

223. Bangkok Temples.

1983. Air. "Bangkok 1983" International Stamp Exhibition.
714. 223. 47 f. multicoloured .. 1·10 80

224. Volleyball.

1983. 7th South Pacific Games, Western Samoa.
715 224 16 f. purple, blue & red 65 40

225. Oueholle.

1983. Air.
716. 225. 76 f. multicoloured .. 1·50 1·00

226. Desert & Water Drop showing Fertile Land. **227.** Barn Owl.

1983. Water Resources.
717. 226. 56 f. multicoloured .. 1·40 90

1983. Birds of Prey. Multicoloured.
718. 34 f. Type **227** .. .. 1·50 80
719. 37 f. Osprey .. .. 1·75 95

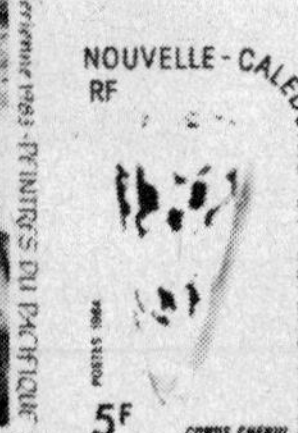

228. "Young Man on Beach" (R. Mascart). **229.** "Conus chenui".

1983. Air. Paintings. Multicoloured.
720. 100 f. Type **228** .. .. 2·25 1·50
721. 350 f. "Man with Guitar" (P. Nielly) .. .. 7·50 4·50

1984. Sea Shells (1st series). Multicoloured.
722. 5 f. Type **229** 30 10
723. 15 f. "Conus moluccensis" 40 15
724. 20 f. "Conus optimus" .. 75 40
See also Nos. 761/2 and 810/11.

230. "Saint Joseph" (freighter).

1984. Ships (3rd series). Each black, red and blue.
725 18 f. Type **230** 65 40
726 31 f. "Saint Antoine" (freighter) 75 60

231. "Amphiprion clarkii".

1984. Air. Noumea Aquarium. Fishes. Mult.
727. 46 f. Type **231** .. .. 1·10 65
728. 61 f. "Centropyge bicolor" 1·50 1·10

232. Arms of Noumea. **233.** "Araucaria columnaris".

1984.
729. 232. 35 f. multicoloured .. 80 45

1984. Air. Trees. Multicoloured.
730. 51 f. type **233** .. .. 1·25 65
731. 67 f. "Pritchardiopsis jeanneneyi" .. .. 1·40 80

234. Tourist Centres.

1984. Nature Protection.
732. 234. 65 f. multicoloured .. 1·50 80

235. Swimming.

1984. Air. Olympic Games, Los Angeles. Multicoloured.
733. 50 f. Type **235** .. .. 1·25 90
734. 83 f. Windsurfing .. .. 1·75 1·25
735. 200 f. Marathon .. .. 4·25 3·00

236. "Diplocaulobium ou-hinnae".

1984. Orchids. Multicoloured.
736. 16 f. Type **236** 65 40
737. 38 f. "Acianthus atepalus" 1·00 75

237. Royal Exhibition Hall, Melbourne.

1984. Air "Ausipex 84" International Stamp Exhibition, Melbourne.
738. 237. 150 f. green, brown and mauve .. 3·50 2·50

238. School and Arrow Sign-post. **239.** Anchor, Rope and Stars.

1984. Centenary of Public Education.
740. 238. 59 f. multicoloured .. 1·10 65

1984. Air. Armed Forces Day.
741. 239. 51 f. multicoloured .. 1·00 65

240. "Women looking for Crabs" (Mme. Bonnet de Larbogne).

1984. Air. Art. Multicoloured.
742. 120 f. Type **240** .. .. 2·50 1·50
743. 300 f. "Cook discovering New Caledonia" (tapestry by Pilioko) .. .. 6·00 4·00

241. Kagu.

1985.
744. **241.** 1 f. blue 10 10
745. 2 f. green 10 10
746. 3 f. orange 10 10
747. 4 f. green 15 15
748. 5 f. mauve 15 15
749. 35 f. red 80 45
750. 38 f. red 80 60
751. 40 f. red 90 35
For similar design but with "& DEPENDANCES" omitted, see Nos. 837/43.

1985. Sea Shells (2nd series). As T **229**. Multicoloured.
761. 55 f. "Conus bullatus" .. 1·25 80
762. 72 f. "Conus lamberti" .. 1·50 1·00

243. Weather Station transmitting Forecast to Airplane and Trawler.

1985. World Meteorology Day.
763. **243.** 17 f. multicoloured .. 45 25

244. Map and Hands holding Red Cross.

1985. International Medicines Campaign.
764. **244.** 41 f. multicoloured .. 90 45

245. Electronic Telephone Exchange.

1985. Inauguration of Electronic Telephone Equipment.
765. **245.** 70 f. multicoloured .. 1·50 80

246. Marguerite La Foa Suspension Bridge.

1985. Protection of Heritage.
766. **246.** 44 f. brn., red & blue 1·00 55

247. Kagu with Magnifying Glass and Stamp.

1985. "Le Cagou" Stamp Club.
767. **247.** 220 f. multicoloured .. 4·00 2·50

248. Festival Emblem.

1985. Fourth Pacific Arts Festival, Papeete. Multicoloured.
769. 55 f. Type **248** .. .. .. 1·25 80
770. 75 f. Girl blowing triton shell .. .. .. 1·50 1·00

249. Flowers, Barbed Wire and Starving Child.

1985. International Youth Year.
771. **249.** 59 f. multicoloured .. 1·10 55

250. "Amedee Lighthouse" (M. Hosken).

251. Tree and Seedling.

1985. Electrification of Amedee Lighthouse.
772. **250.** 89 f. multicoloured .. 1·75 1·00

1985. "Planting for the Future"
773. **251.** 100 f. multicoloured .. 2·00 1·00

252. Airplane and Route Map.

1985. Air. 30th Anniv. of First Regular Internal Air Service.
774. **252.** 80 f. multicoloured .. 1·50 1·00

253. Hands and U.N. Emblem.

1985. 40th Anniv. of U.N.O.
775. **253.** 250 f. multicoloured .. 4·50 2·50

254. School, Map and "Shell".

1985. Air. Jules Garnier High School.
776. **254.** 400 f. multicoloured .. 7·50 4·00

255. Purple Swamphen.

1985. Birds. Multicoloured.
777. 50 f. Type **255** .. .. 1·00 70
778. 60 f. Island thrush .. 1·25 90

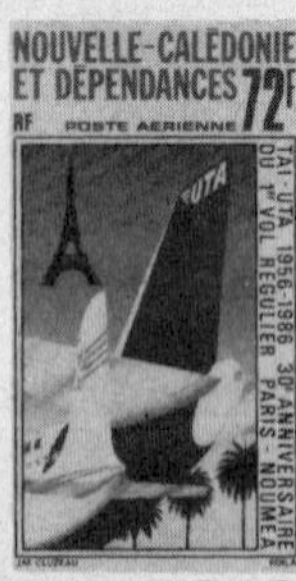

256. Aircraft Tail Fins and Eiffel Tower.

1986. Air. 30th Anniversary of Scheduled Paris–Noumea Flights.
779. **256.** 72 f. multicoloured .. 1·50 90

257. "Rhinopias aphanes".

1986. Noumea Aquarium. Multicoloured.
780. 10 f. "Pomacanthus imperator" 25 20
781. 17 f. Type **257** 35 25

258. Kanumera Bay, Isle of Pines.

1986. Landscapes (1st series). Multicoloured.
782. 50 f. Type **258** .. .. 1·00 55
783. 55 f. Inland village .. 1·10 55
See also Nos. 795/6 and 864/5.

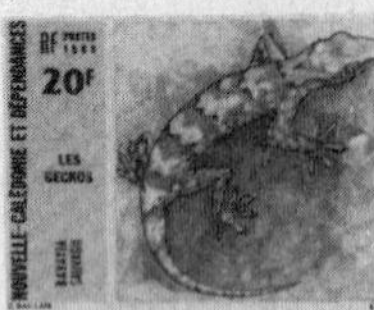

259. "Bavayia sauvagii".

1986. Geckos. Multicoloured.
784. 20 f. Type **259** 55 25
785. 45 f. "Rhacodactylus leachianus" .. .. 1·00 65

260. Players and Azteca Stadium.

1986. World Cup Football Championship, Mexico.
786. **260.** 60 f. multicoloured .. 1·10 90

261. Vivarium, Nou Island.

1986. Air. Protection of Heritage.
787. **261.** 230 f. deep brown, blue and brown .. 4·50 2·75

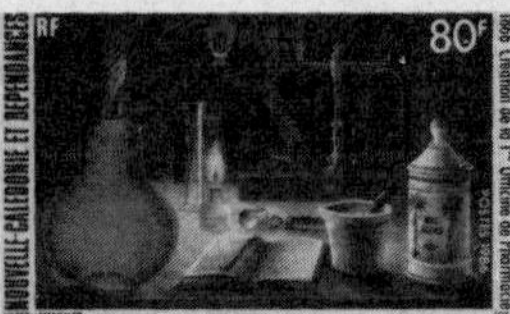

262. Pharmaceutical Equipment.

1986. 120th Anniv. of First Pharmacy.
788. **262.** 80 f. multicoloured .. 1·50 1·10

263. "Coelogynae licastioides".

1986. Orchids. Multicoloured.
789. 44 f. Type **263** .. .. 1·00 55
790. 58 f. "Calanthe langei" .. 1·25 80

264. Black-backed Magpie.

1986. "Stampex 86" National Stamp Exhibition, Adelaide.
791. **264.** 110 f. multicoloured .. 2·50 2·00

265. Airplane over New Caledonia.

1986. Air. Inaugural Flight of "ATR 42".
792. **265.** 18 f. multicoloured .. 35 25

266. Emblem and 1860 Stamp.

267. Arms of Mont Dore.

1986. Air. "Stockholmia 86" International Stamp Exhibition.
793. **266.** 108 f. black, red and lilac .. .. 2·00 1·50

1986.
794. **267.** 94 f. multicoloured .. 1·75 1·10

1986. Landscapes (2nd series). As T **258**. Multicoloured.
795. 40 f. West coast (vert.) .. 80 40
796. 76 f. South .. .. .. 1·50 90

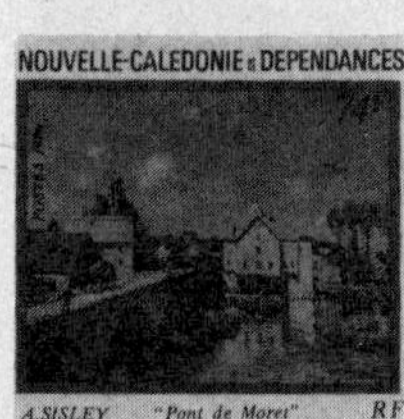

268. Wild Flowers. **269.** Club Banner.

1986. Association for Nature Protection.
797. **268.** 73 f. multicoloured .. 1·50 90

1986. 25th Anniv. of Noumea Lions Club.
798. **269.** 350 f. multicoloured .. 6·00 4·50

270. "Moret Bridge" (Alfred Sisley).

1986. Paintings. Multicoloured.
799. 74 f. Type **270** .. .. 1·50 90
800. 140 f. "Hunting Butterflies" (Berthe Morisot) .. 2·75 1·75

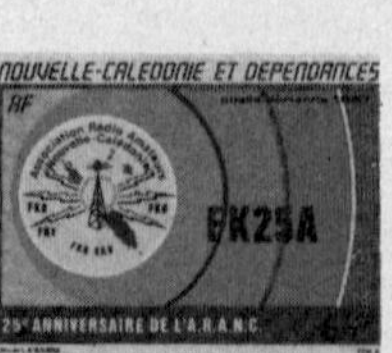

271. Emblem and Sound Waves.

272. "Challenge France".

1987. Air. 25th Anniv. of New Caledonia Amateur Radio Association.
801. **271.** 64 f. multicoloured .. 1·25 80

1987. America's Cup Yacht Race. Mult.
802. 30 f. Type **272** .. .. 1·00 55
803. 70 f. "French Kiss" .. 1·50 1·00

273. "Anona squamosa" and "Graphium gelon".

1987. Plants and Butterflies. Multicoloured.

804	46 f. Type **273**	1·00	65
805	54 f. "Abizzia granulosa" and "Polyura gamma"	1·25	80

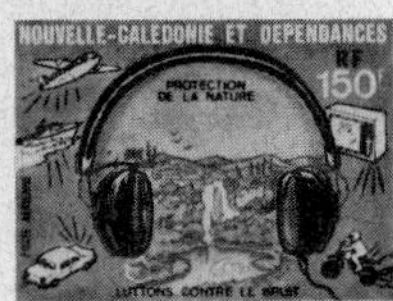
274. Peaceful Landscape, Earphones and Noisy Equipment.

1987. Air. Nature Protection. Campaign against Noise.

806. **274.** 150 f. multicoloured .. 3·00 1·50

275. Isle of Pines Canoe.

1987. Canoes. Each brown, green and blue.

807	72 f. Type **275**	1·40	90
808	90 f. Ouvea canoe ..	1·75	1·10

276. Town Hall.

1987. New Town Hall, Mont Dore.

809. **276.** 92 f. multicoloured .. 1·75 1·10

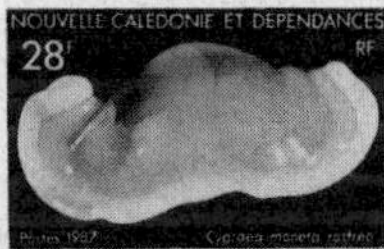
277. "Cypraea moneta".

1987. Sea Shells (3rd series). Multicoloured.

810.	28 f. Type **277**	55	45
811.	36 f. "Cypraea martini" ..	80	55

278. Games Emblem.

279. Emblem.

1987. 8th South Pacific Games. Noumea (1st issue).

812 **278** 40 f. multicoloured .. 80 55

See also Nos. 819/21.

1987. 13th Soroptimists International Convention, Melbourne.

813 **279** 270 f. multicoloured .. 5·00 3·25

280. New Caledonia White Eye.

1987. Birds. Multicoloured.

814	18 f. Type **280**	45	30
815	21 f. Peregrine falcon (vert)	45	30

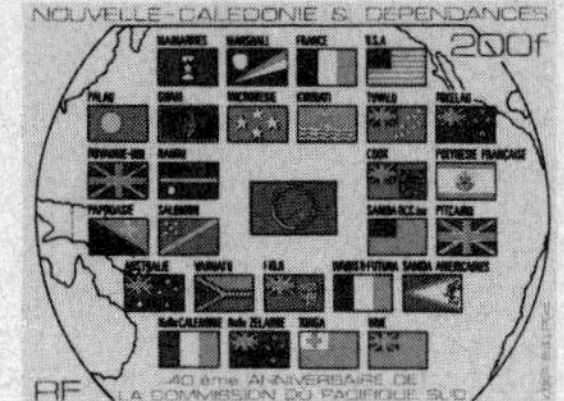
281. Flags on Globe.

1987. 40th Anniv of South Pacific Commission.

816 **281** 200 f. multicoloured .. 3·75 2·25

282. Globe and Magnifying Glass on Map of New Caledonia.

1987. Schools Philately.

817. **282.** 15 f. multicoloured .. 35 20

283. Cricketers.

1987. Air. French Cricket Federation.

818. **283.** 94 f. multicoloured .. 1·90 1·25

284. Golf.

1987. 8th South Pacific Games, Noumea (2nd issue). Multicoloured.

819.	20 f. Type **284**	40	20
820.	30 f. Rugby football ..	60	35
821.	100 f. Long jumping ..	1·75	1·10

285. Arms of Dumbea. 287. University.

286. Route Map, "L'Astrolabe", "La Boussole" and La Perouse.

1988. Air.

822. **285.** 76 f. multicoloured .. 1·40 90

1988. Bicentenary of Disappearance of La Perouse's Expedition.

823. **286.** 36 f. bl., brn. & red .. 80 45

1988. French University of South Pacific, Noumea and Papeete.

824. **287.** 400 f. multicoloured .. 7·25 4·50

288 Zebra Angelfish

289 Mwaringou House, Canala

1988. Noumea Aquarium. Fishes. Mult.

825	30 f. Type **288**	65	40
826	46 f. "Glyphidodontops cyaneus"	1·00	60

1988. Traditional Huts. Each brown, green and blue.

827	19 f. Type **289**	35	20
828	21 f. Nathalo house, Lifou (horiz)	35	20

290 Anniversary Emblem

1988. 125th Anniv of International Red Cross.

829 **290** 300 f. blue, green & red 6·00 3·25

291 "Ochrosia elliptica"

1988. Medicinal Plants. Multicoloured.

830	28 f. Type **291** (postage) ..	60	40
831	64 f. "Rauvolfia sevenetii" (air)	1·25	80

292 "Gymnocrinus richeri"

1988.

832 **292** 51 f. multicoloured .. 1·10 65

293 Furnished Room and Building Exterior

1988. Bourail Museum and Historical Association.

833 **293** 120 f. multicoloured .. 2·25 1·50

294 La Perouse sighting Phillip's Fleet in Botany Bay

1988. "Sydpex 88" Stamp Exhibition, Sydney. Multicoloured.

834	42 f. Type **294**	85	70
835	42 f. Phillip sighting "La Boussole" and "L'Astrolabe" ..	85	70

295 Kagu

297 Laboratory Assistant, Noumea Institute and Pasteur

296 Table Tennis

1988.

837	**295**	1 f. blue	10	10
838		2 f. green	10	10
839		3 f. orange	10	10
840		4 f. green	10	10
841		5 f. mauve	15	10
842		28 f. orange	50	20
843		40 f. red	65	20

1988. Olympic Games, Seoul.

846 **296** 150 f. multicoloured .. 2·75 1·60

1988. Centenary of Pasteur Institute, Paris.

847 **297** 100 f. red, black & blue 1·90 1·25

298 Georges Baudoux

1988. Writers.

848	**298**	72 f. brown, green and purple (postage) ..	1·40	80
849	–	73 f. brn, bl & blk (air)	1·40	90

DESIGN: 73 f. Jean Mariotti.

299 Map and Emblems

1988. Air. Rotary International Anti-Polio Campaign.

850 **299** 220 f. multicoloured .. 4·00 2·75

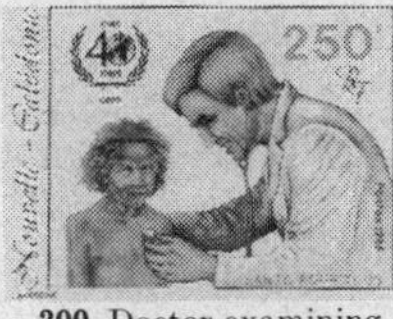
300 Doctor examining Child

1988. 40th Anniv of W.H.O.

851 **300** 250 f. multicoloured .. 4·50 2·50

301 "Terre des Hommes" (L. Bunckley)

1988. Paintings. Multicoloured.

852	54 f. Type **301**	1·25	80
853	92 f. "Latin Quarter" (Marik)	2·00	1·25

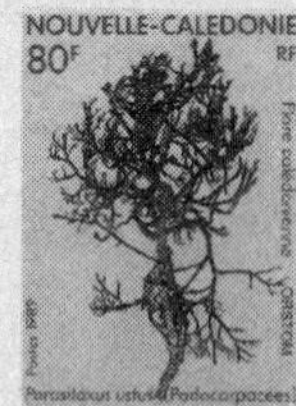
302 Arms of Koumac 303 "Parasitaxus ustus"

1989.
854 302 200 f. multicoloured .. 3·25 2·25

1989. Flowers. Multicoloured.
855 80 f. Type 303 .. .. 1·50 90
856 90 f. "Tristaniopsis guillainii" (horiz) .. 1·60 1·00

304 "Plesionika sp."

1989. Marine Life. Multicoloured.
857 18 f. Type 304 .. .. 45 20
858 66 f. Waspfish .. .. 1·10 80
859 110 f. "Latiaxis sp." .. 2·00 80

305 "Liberty" 306 Canoe and Diamond Decoration

1989. Bicentenary of French Revolution and "Philexfrance 89" International Stamp Exhibition, Paris. Multicoloured.
860 40 f. Type 305 (postage) .. 80 45
861 58 f. "Equality" (air) .. 1·10 65
862 76 f. "Fraternity" .. 1·40 90

1989. Landscapes (3rd series). As T 258. Mult.
684 180 f. Ouaieme ferry (post) 3·25 1·75
865 64 f. "The Broody Hen" (rocky islet), Hienghene (air) .. .. .. 1·25 65

1989. Bamboo Decorations by C. Ohlen. Each black, bistre and orange.
866 70 f. Type 306 (postage) .. 1·40 80
867 44 f. Animal design (air) .. 80 55

307 "Hobie Cat 14" Yachts

1989. 10th World "Hobie Cat" Class Catamaran Championship, Noumea.
868 307 350 f. multicoloured .. 6·00 3·50

308 Book Title Pages and Society Members

1989. 20th Anniv of Historical Studies Society.
869 308 74 f. black and brown 1·40 90

309 Fort Teremba

1989. Protection of Heritage.
870 309 100 f. green, brown & bl 1·75 1·10

310 "Rochefort's Escape" (Edouard Manet) 311 Fr. Patrick O'Reilly

1989. Paintings. Multicoloured.
871 130 f. Type 310 .. .. 2·50 1·50
872 270 f. "Self-portrait" (Gustave Courbet) .. 4·75 3·00

1990. Writers.
873 311 170 f. black and mauve 3·00 1·75

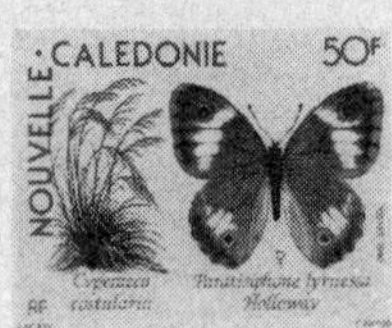
312 Grass and Female Butterfly

1990. "Cyperacea costularia" (grass) and "Paratisiphone lyrnessa" (butterfly). Mult.
874 50 f. Type 312 (postage) .. 90 55
875 18 f. Grass and female butterfly (different) (air) 35 20
876 94 f. Grass and male butterfly .. .. 1·60 1·00

313 "Maize" Stem with Face 314 Exhibit

1990. Kanaka Money.
877 313 85 f. olive, orge & grn 1·60 80
878 – 140 f. orange, blk & grn 2·50 1·40
DESIGN: 140 f. "Rope" stem with decorative end.

1990. Jade and Mother-of-pearl Exhibition.
879 314 230 f. multicoloured .. 4·00 2·40

315 "Phyllidia ocellata"

1990. Noumea Aquarium. Sea Slugs. Mult.
880 10 f. Type 315 .. .. 20 10
881 42 f. "Chromodoris kuniei" (vert) 80 45

316 Head of "David" (Michelangelo) and Footballers

1990. World Cup Football Championship, Italy.
882 316 240 f. multicoloured .. 4·00 2·40

317 De Gaulle

1990. Air. 50th Anniv of De Gaulle's Call to Resist.
883 317 160 f. multicoloured .. 2·75 1·90

318 Neounda Site

1990. Petroglyphs.
884 318 40 f. brown, green and red (postage) .. 65 45
885 – 58 f. black, brown and blue (air) .. .. 1·00 65
DESIGN—HORIZ. 58 f. Kassducou site.

319 Map and Pacific International Meeting Centre

1990.
886 319 320 f. multicoloured .. 5·00 2·40

320 New Zealand Cemetery, Bourail 321 Kagu

1990. Air. "New Zealand 1990" International Stamp Exhibition, Auckland. Multicoloured.
887 80 f. Type 320 .. .. 1·40 1·10
888 80 f. Brigadier William Walter Dove .. .. 1·40 1·10

1990.

890	321	1 f. blue	10	10
891		2 f. green	10	10
892		3 f. yellow	10	10
893		4 f. green	10	10
894		5 f. violet	10	10
895		9 f. grey	10	10
896		12 f. red	15	10
897		40 f. mauve	50	30
898		50 f. red	65	40
899		55 f. red	70	45

The 55 f. exists both perforated with ordinary gum and imperforate with self-adhesive gum.

322 "Munidopsis sp." 324 "Gardenia aubryi"

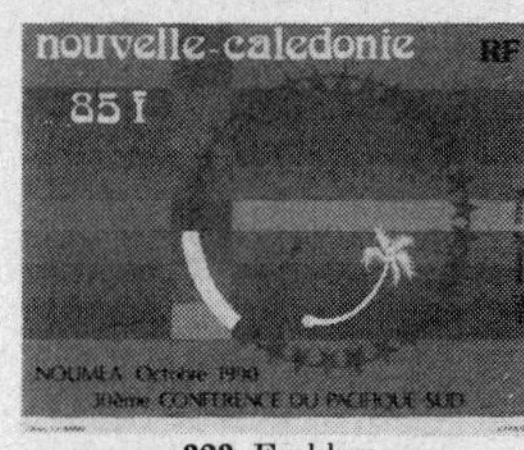
323 Emblem

1990. Air. Deep Sea Animals. Multicoloured.
900 30 f. Type 322 .. .. 55 35
901 60 f. "Lyreidius tridentatus" .. .. .. 1·00 55

1990. Air. 30th South Pacific Conference, Noumea.
902 323 85 f. multicoloured .. 1·40 90

1990. Flowers. Multicoloured.
903 105 f. Type 324 .. .. 1·60 1·10
904 130 f. "Hibbertia baudouinii" .. .. 2·00 1·40

325 De Gaulle

1990. Air. Birth Centenary of Charles de Gaulle (French statesman).
905 325 410 f. blue .. 6·75 2·75

326 "Mont Dore, Mountain of Jade" (C. Degroiselle)

1990. Air. Pacific Painters. Multicoloured.
906 365 f. Type 326 (postage) 5·75 3·25
907 110 f. "The Celieres House" (M. Petron) (air) .. 1·75 1·40

327 Fayawa-Ouvea Bay

1991. Air. Regional Landscapes. Mult.
908 36 f. Type 327 .. .. 65 45
909 90 f. Coastline of Mare .. 1·60 90

328 Louise Michel and Classroom

1991. Writers.
910 328 125 f. mauve & blue .. 2·00 1·25
911 – 125 f. blue & brown .. 2·00 1·25
DESIGN: No. 911, Charles B. Nething and photographer.

329 Houailou Hut   **330** Northern Province

1991. Melanesian Huts. Multicoloured.
912 12 f. Type **329** 20 10
913 35 f. Hienghene hut .. 55 35

1991. Provinces. Multicoloured.
914 45 f. Type **330** 65 55
915 45 f. Islands Province .. 65 55
916 45 f. Southern Province .. 65 55

331 "Dendrobium biflorum"

1991. Orchids. Multicoloured.
917 55 f. Type **331** 90 55
918 70 f. "Dendrobium closterium" .. .. 1·10 65

332 Pinecone Fish

1991. Fishes. Multicoloured.
919 60 f. Type **332** .. .. 1·00 55
920 100 f. "Tristigenys niphonia" .. .. 1·60 1·00

333 Research Equipment and Sites

1991. French Scientific Research Institute for Development and Co-operation.
921 **333** 170 f. multicoloured .. 2·75 1·40

334 Emblem   **336** Emblems

335 Map and Dragon

1991. 9th South Pacific Games, Papua New Guinea.
922 **334** 170 f. multicoloured .. 2·75 1·40

1991. Centenary of Vietnamese Settlement in New Caledonia.
923 **335** 300 f. multicoloured .. 4·50 2·75

1991. 30th Anniv of Lions International in New Caledonia.
924 **336** 192 f. multicoloured .. 3·00 1·60

337 Map, "Camden" (missionary brig), Capt. Robert Clark Morgan and Trees

1991. 150th Anniv of Discovery of Sandalwood.
925 **337** 200 f. blue, turq & grn 3·00 1·75

338 "Phillantus" and Common Grass Yellow

1991. "Phila Nippon '91" International Stamp Exhibition, Tokyo. Plants and Butterflies. Multicoloured.
926 8 f. Type **338** 10 10
927 15 f. "Pipturus incanus" and "Hypolimnas octocula" 20 10
928 20 f. "Stachytarpheta urticaefolia" and meadow argos 30 20
929 26 f. "Malaisia scandens" and "Cyrestis telamon" 40 20

339 Nickel Processing Plant and Dam

1991. 50th Anniv of Central Economic Co-operation Bank. Multicoloured.
931 76 f. Type **339** .. .. 1·25 75
932 76 f. Housing and hotels .. 1·25 75

340 "Caledonian Cricket" (Marcel Moutouh)

1991. Air. Pacific Painters. Multicoloured.
933 130 f. Type **340** .. .. 2·10 1·10
934 435 f. "Saint Louis" (Janine Goetz) .. .. 6·75 4·00

341 Blue River (½ size illustration)

1992. Air. Blue River National Park.
935 **341** 400 f. multicoloured .. 5·25 3·25

342 La Madeleine Falls

1992. Nature Protection.
937 **342** 15 f. multicoloured .. 20 15

343 Lapita Pot   **345** "Pinta"

344 Barqueta Bridge

1992. Air. Noumea Museum.
939 **343** 25 f. black and orange 30 20

1992. Air. "Expo '92" World's Fair, Seville.
940 **344** 10 f. multicoloured .. 15 10

1992. Air. "World Columbian Stamp Expo '92", Chicago. Multicoloured.
941 80 f. Type **345** .. .. 1·00 90
942 80 f. "Santa Maria" .. 1·00 90
943 80 f. "Nina" .. .. 1·00 90

346 Crane and Kagu within "100"

1992. Centenary of Arrival of First Japanese Immigrants. Multicoloured, background colours given.
945 **346** 95 f. yellow .. .. 1·25 75
946 95 f. grey .. .. 1·25 75

347 Synchronized Swimming

1992. Olympic Games, Barcelona.
947 **347** 260 f. multicoloured .. 3·25 2·00

348 Airplanes, Barrage Balloon, Harbour and Nissen Huts

1992. 50th Anniv of Arrival of American Forces in New Caledonia.
948 **348** 50 f. multicoloured .. 65 40

349 "Wahpa" (Paul Mascart)

1992. Air. Pacific Painters.
949 **349** 205 f. multicoloured .. 2·50 1·50

350 Australian Cattle Dog   **352** "Amalda fuscolingua"

351 Entrecasteaux and Fleet

1992. Air. Canine World Championships.
950 **350** 175 f. multicoloured .. 2·25 1·40

1992. Air. Navigators. Bicentenary of Landing of Admiral Bruni d'Entrecasteaux on West Coast of New Caledonia.
951 **351** 110 f. orange, bl & grn 1·50 90

1992. Air. Shells. Multicoloured.
952 30 f. Type **352** 40 25
953 50 f. "Cassis abbotti" .. 65 40

353 Deole

1992. Air. "La Brousse en Folie" (comic strip) by Bernard Berger. Multicoloured.
954 80 f. Type **353** .. .. 1·00 60
955 80 f. Tonton Marcel .. 1·00 60
956 80 f. Tathan .. .. 1·00 60
957 80 f. Joinville .. .. 1·00 60

354 Lagoon

1993. Lagoon Protection.
958 **354** 120 f. multicoloured .. 1·50 90

355 Harbour (Gaston Roullet)

1993. Air. Pacific Painters.
959 **355** 150 f. multicoloured .. 1·90 1·25

356 Symbols of New Caledonia

1993. School Philately. "Tourism my Friend".
960 **356** 25 f. multicoloured .. 30 20

357 Still and Plantation

1993. Air. Centenary of Production of Essence of Niaouli.
966 **357** 85 f. multicoloured .. 1·10 65

358 Planets and Copernicus

1993. Air. "Polska '93" International Stamp Exhibition, Poznan. 450th Death Anniv of Nicolas Copernicus (astronomer).
967 **358** 110 f. blue, turq & grey 1·40 85

359 Noumea Temple

1993. Air. Centenary of First Protestant Church in Noumea.
968 **359** 400 f. multicoloured .. 5·25 3·25

1993. No. 898 surch **55F**.
969 **321** 55 f. on 50 f. red .. 70 45

361 Malabou

1993. Air. Regional Landscapes.
970 **361** 85 f. multicoloured .. 1·10 65

362 Locomotive and Bridge

1993. Air. Centenary of Little Train of Thio.
971 **362** 115 f. red, green & lilac 1·50 90

363 Rochefort

364 "Megastylis paradoxa"

1993. Air. 80th Death Anniv of Henri Rochefort (journalist).
972 **363** 100 f. multicoloured .. 1·40 85

1993. Air. "Bangkok 1993" International Stamp Exhibition, Thailand. Mult.
973 30 f. Type **364** 40 25
974 30 f. "Vanda coerulea" .. 40 25

365 Route Map and Airplane

1993. Air. 10th Anniv of Aircalin (national airline).
976 **365** 85 f. multicoloured .. 1·10 65

366 "Le Francois Arago" (cable ship)

1993. Air. Centenary of New Caledonia–Australia Telecommunications Cable.
977 **366** 200 f. purple, bl & turq 2·50 1·50

367 "Oxypleurodon orbiculatus"

1993. Air. Deep-sea Life.
978 **367** 250 f. multicoloured .. 3·25 2·00

368 Aircraft, Engine and Hangar

1993. Air. 25th Anniv of Chamber of Commerce and Industry's Management of La Tontout Airport, Noumea.
979 **368** 90 f. multicoloured .. 1·25 75

369 First Christmas Mass, 1843 (stained glass window, Balade church)

1993. Air. Christmas.
980 **369** 120 f. multicoloured .. 1·60 1·00

OFFICIAL STAMPS

O **49**. Ancestor Pole.

O **110**. Carved Wooden Pillow (Noumea Museum).

1958. Inscr "OFFICIEL".
O 344. O **49**. 1 f. yellow 45 40
O 345. 3 f. green 45 40
O 346. 4 f. purple 45 50
O 347. 5 f. blue 60 50
O 348. 9 f. black 70 70
O 349. A. 10 f. violet 85 70
O 350. 13 f. green .. .. 1·00 80
O 351 15 f. blue .. .. 1·25 1·00
O 352. 24 f. mauve .. 1·40 1·10
O 353. 26 f. orange .. 1·50 1·25
O 354. B. 50 f. green .. .. 3·50 2·50
O 355. 100 f. brown .. 7·50 4·00
O 356. 200 f. red .. .. 15·00 9·00
DESIGNS: A, B, Different idols.

1973.
O 525. O **110**. 1 f. grn., blk. & yell. 20 20
O 526. 2 f. red, blk. & grn. 20 15
O 527. 3 f. grn., blk. & brn. 30 20
O 528. 4 f. grn., blk. & bl. 30 20
O 529. 5 f. grn., blk. & mve. 45 25
O 530. 9 f. grn., blk. & bl. 55 45
O 531. 10 f. green, black and orange .. 55 45
O 532. 11 f. grn., blk. & mve. 35 20
O 533. 12 f. green, black and turquoise .. 65 45
0 534. 15 f. green, black and light green 35 25
O 535. 20 f. grn., blk. & red 35 25
O 536. 23 f. grn., blk. & red 55 45
O 537. 24 f. grn., blk. & bl. 45 35
O 538. 25 f. grn. blk. & grey 65 45
O 539. 26 f. grn., blk. & yell. 55 35
O 540. 29 f. red, blk. & grn. 80 55
O 541. 31 f. red, blk. & yell. 65 45
O 542. 35 f. red, blk. & yell. 65 45
O 543. 36 f. grn., blk. & mve. 65 45
O 544. 38 f. red, blk. & brn. 65 45
O 545. 40 f. red, blk. & bl. 65 55
O 546. 42 f. grn., blk. & brn. 65 45
O 547. 50 f. grn., blk. & bl. 90 65
O 548. 58 f. bl., blk. & grn. 1·00 65
O 549. 65 f. red, blk. & mve. 1·10 65
O 549a. 76 f. red, black and yellow .. .. 1·40 75
O 550. 100 f. grn., blk. & red 1·75 1·25
O 551. 200 f. green, black and yellow .. 3·50 2·25

PARCEL POST STAMPS

1926. Optd **Colis Postaux** or surch also.
P137 **17** 50 c. on 5 f. green on mauve 60 90
P138 1 f. blue .. .. 90 1·00
P139 2 f. red on blue .. 1·25 1·40

1930. Optd **Colis Postaux**.
P179 **23** 50 c. brown and mauve 70 70
P180 **24** 1 f. pink and drab .. 85 85
P181 2 f. brown and orange 1·25 1·25

POSTAGE DUE STAMPS

1903. Postage Due stamps of French Colonies optd **CINQUANTENAIRE 24 SEPTEMBRE 1853 1903** and eagle. Imperf.
D78 U 5 c. blue .. .. 1·40 1·25
D79 10 c. brown .. .. 5·00 4·25
D80 15 c. green .. .. 14·00 5·50
D81 30 c. red .. .. 9·50 7·00
D82 50 c. purple .. .. 45·00 10·50
D83 60 c. brown on buff .. £160 40·00
D84 1 f. pink .. .. 21·00 9·75
D85 2 f. brown £600 £650

D **18**. Outrigger Canoe. D **25**. Sambar Stag. D **38**.

1906.
D102 D **18** 5 c. blue on blue .. 25 30
D103 10 c. brown on buff 35 50
D104 15 c. green .. 40 45
D105 20 c. black on yellow 40 45
D106 30 c. red 50 50
D107 50 c. blue on cream 80 85
D108 60 c. green on blue 75 80
D109 1 f. green on cream 1·10 1·10

1926. Surch.
D 137. D **18**. 2 f. on 1 f. mauve .. 1·90 2·00
D 138. 3 f. on 1 f. brown .. 1·90 2·00

1928.
D 179. D **25**. 2 c. brown and blue 15 30
D 180. 4 c. green and red .. 25 35
D 181. 5 c. grey and orange 25 35
D 182. 10 c. blue & mauve 20 35
D 183. 15 c. red and olive 25 35
D 184. 20 c. olive and red 40 60
D 185. 25 c. blue and brown 40 45
D 186. 30 c. olive and green 40 55
D 187. 50 c. red and brown 75 85
D 188. 60 c. red and mauve 80 80
D 189. 1 f. green and blue 95 1·00
D 190. 2 f. olive and red .. 1·10 1·10
D 191. 3 f. brown and violet 1·90 1·75

1948.
D 328. D **38**. 10 c. mauve .. 15 30
D 329. 30 c. brown .. 20 30
D 330. 50 c. green 30 35
D 331. 1 f. brown 30 35
D 332. 2 f. red 30 35
D 333. 3 f. brown 30 35
D 334. 4 f. blue 45 45
D 335. 5 f. red 55 60
D 336. 10 f. green 85 85
D 337. 20 f. blue .. .. 1·60 1·75

D **223**. New Caledonian Flying Fox.

1983.
D 703. D **223**. 1 f. multicoloured 10 10
D 704. 2 f. multicoloured 10 10
D 705. 3 f. multicoloured 10 10
D 706. 4 f. multicoloured 20 20
D 707. 5 f. multicoloured 20 20
D 708. 10 f. multicoloured 20 20
D 709. 20 f. multicoloured 40 40
D 710. 40 f. multicoloured 80 80
D 711. 50 f. multicoloured 90 90

NICARAGUA Pt. 15

A republic of Central America independent since 1821.

1862. 100 centavos = 1 peso (paper currency).
1912. 100 centavos de cordoba = 1 peso de cordoba (gold currency).
1925. 100 centavos = 1 cordoba.

2. Volcanoes. 5.

1862. Perf. or roul.

13. **2.** 1 c. brown 1·50 75
4. 2 c. blue 2·25 75
14. 5 c. black 6·00 1·25
18. 10 c. red 2·25 1·40
19. 25 c. green 2·25 2·40

1882.

20. **5.** 1 c. green 12 20
21. 2 c. red 12 20
22. 5 c. blue 12 15
23. 10 c. violet 15 60
24. 15 c. yellow 30 1·50
25. 20 c. grey 50 3·00
26. 50 c. violet 70 6·00

6. Locomotive and Telegraph Key. 7.

1890.

27. **6.** 1 c. brown 15 25
28. 2 c. red 15 25
29. 5 c. blue 15 15
30. 10 c. grey 15 20
31. 20 c. red 15 1·50
32. 50 c. violet 15 4·75
33. 1 p. brown 20 6·50
34. 2 p. green 20 8·50
35. 5 p. red 25 16·00
36. 10 p. orange 25 23·00

1891.

37. **7.** 1 c. brown 15 30
38. 2 c. red 15 30
39. 5 c. blue 15 25
40. 10 c. grey 15 35
41. 20 c. lake 15 1·75
42. 50 c. violet 15 3·00
43. 1 p. sepia 15 4·50
44. 2 p. green 15 5·00
45. 5 p. red 15 12·00
46. 10 p. orange 15 15·00

8. First sight of the New World. 9. Volcanoes. 10.

1892. Discovery of America.

47. **8.** 1 c. brown 15 25
48. 2 c. red 15 25
49. 5 c. blue 15 20
50. 10 c. grey 15 25
51. 20 c. red 15 1·75
52. 50 c. violet 15 4·25
53. 1 p. brown 15 4·25
54. 2 p. green 15 5·00
55. 5 p. red 15 14·00
56. 10 p. orange 15 18·00

1893.

57. **9.** 1 c. brown 15 25
58. 2 c. red 15 25
59. 5 c. blue 15 20
60. 10 c. grey 15 25
61. 20 c. brown 15 1·40
62. 50 c. violet 15 3·50
63. 1 p. brown 15 4·25
64. 2 p. green 15 5·00
65. 5 p. red 15 11·00
66. 10 p. orange 15 14·00

1894.

67. **10.** 1 c. brown 15 25
68. 2 c. red 15 25
69. 5 c. blue 15 20
70. 10 c. grey 15 25
71. 20 c. red 15 1·50
72. 50 c. violet 15 3·50
73. 1 p. brown 15 4·25
74. 2 p. green 15 7·50
75. 5 p. brown 15 9·00
76. 10 p. orange 15 12·00

11. 12. Map of Nicaragua. 13. Arms of Republic of Central America.

1895.

77. **11.** 1 c. brown 15 20
78. 2 c. red 15 20
79. 5 c. blue 15 15
80. 10 c. grey 15 20
81. 20 c. red 15 70
82. 50 c. violet 15 3·00
83. 1 p. brown 15 4·50
84. 2 p. green 15 4·75
85. 5 p. red 15 9·25
86. 10 p. orange 15 14·50

1896. Date "1896".

90. **12.** 1 c. violet 15 75
91. 2 c. green 15 50
92. 5 c. red 15 35
93. 10 c. blue 30 65
94. 20 c. brown 1·75 3·50
95. 50 c. grey 35 4·75
96. 1 p. black 35 6·50
97. 2 p. red 35 9·00
98. 5 p. blue 35 9·00

1897. As T **12**, dated "1897".

99. **12.** 1 c. violet 25 35
100. 2 c. green 25 35
101. 5 c. red 25 20
102. 10 c. blue 3·75 65
103. 20 c. brown 1·50 2·25
104. 50 c. grey 5·25 5·75
105. 1 p. black 5·25 8·75
106. 2 p. red 11·50 11·00
107. 5 p. blue 11·50 25·00

1898.

108. **13.** 1 c. brown 20 20
109. 2 c. grey 20 20
110. 4 c. lake 20 30
122. 5 c. olive 15·00 12
112 10 c. purple 8·75 40
113. 15 c. blue 25 1·00
114. 20 c. blue 6·00 1·00
115. 50 c. yellow 6·00 5·75
116. 1 p. blue 30 9·50
117. 2 p. brown 11·00 13·00
118. 5 p. orange 15·00 19·00

14. 15. Mt. Momotombo.

1899.

126. **14.** 1 c. green 8 25
127. 2 c. brown 8 25
128. 4 c. red 20 25
129. 5 c. blue 12 25
130. 10 c. orange 12 25
131. 15 c. brown 12 40
132. 20 c. green 20 70
133. 50 c. red 12 1·75
134. 1 p. orange 12 5·00
135. 2 p. violet 12 12·00
136. 5 p. blue 12 14·50

1900.

137. **15.** 1 c. red 30 10
138. 2 c. orange 60 15
139. 3 c. green 70 20
140. 4 c. olive 90 25
184. 5 c. red 75 25
185. 5 c. blue 55 15
142. 6 c. red 18·00 5·50
186. 10 c. mauve 55 10
144. 15 c. blue 9·50 35
145. 20 c. brown 8·50 30
146. 50 c. lake 8·50 1·50
147. 1 p. yellow 18·00 6·50
148. 2 p. red 7·50 75
149. 5 p. black 13·00 2·50

1901. Surch. **1901** and value.

151. **15.** 2 c. on 1 p. yellow 7·00 6·00
169. 3 c. on 6 c. red 6·50 3·75
163. 4 c. on 6 c. red 5·50 3·50
173. 5 c. on 1 p. yellow 9·00 4·25
168. 10 c. on 2 p. red 7·00 1·75
152. 10 c. on 5 p. black 12·50 10·00
153. 20 c. on 2 p. red 12·50 12·50
176. 20 c. on 5 p. black 4·75 3·75

1901 Postage Due stamps of 1900 optd **1901 Correos**.

177. D **16.** 1 c. red 60 30
178. 2 c. orange 45 30
179. 5 c. blue 55 45
180. 10 c. violet 55 45
181. 20 c. brown 75 1·00
182. 30 c. green 70 1·00
183. 50 c. lake 70 1·00

1902. Surch. **1902** and value.

187. **15.** 15 c. on 2 c. orange 2·50 1·00
188. 30 c. on 1 c. red 1·00 3·50

27. Pres. Santos Zelaya. 37. Arms.

1903. 10th Anniv. of Revolution against Sacaza. and 1st election of Pres. Zelaya.

189. **27.** 1 c. black and green 25 45
190. 2 c. black and red 50 45
191. 5 c. black and blue 25 45
192. 10 c. black and orange 25 70
193. 15 c. black and lake 45 1·40
194. 20 c. black and violet 45 1·40
195. 50 c. black and olive 45 3·00
196. 1 p. black and brown 45 3·50

1904. Surch.

205. **15.** 5 c. on 10 c. mauve 75 50
200. 15 c. on 10 c. mauve 5·75 3·00

1904. Surch. **Vale,** value and wavy lines.

203. **15.** 5 c. on 10 c. mauve 1·50 35
204. 15 c. on 10 c. mauve 40 30

1905.

206. **37.** 1 c. green 20 15
207. 2 c. red 20 15
208. 3 c. violet 25 20
280. 3 c. orange 25 15
209. 4 c. orange 25 20
281. 4 c. violet 25 15
282. 5 c. blue 25 15
211. 6 c. grey 45 30
283. 6 c. brown 1·75 1·10
212. 10 c. brown 55 20
284. 10 c. lake 60 10
213. 15 c. olive 55 25
285. 15 c. black 60 10
214. 20 c. lake 45 25
286. 20 c. olive 60 10
215. 50 c. orange 1·75 1·40
287. 50 c. green 70 35
216. 1 p. black 90 90
288. 1 p. yellow 70 35
217. 2 p. green 90 1·25
289. 2 p. red 70 35
218. 5 p. violet 1·00 1·50

1906. Surch. **Vale** (or **VALE**) and value in one line.

292 **37** 2 c. on 3 c. orange 90 75
293 5 c. on 20 c. olive 30 25
247 10 c. on 2 c. red 1·10 45
223 10 c. on 3 c. violet 30 12
248 10 c. on 4 c. orange 1·25 55
291 10 c. on 15 c. black 30 25
250 10 c. on 20 c. lake 1·90 85
252 10 c. on 50 c. orange 1·40 45
234 10 c. on 2 p. green 12·00 7·00
235 10 c. on 5 p. violet 60·00 42·00
226 15 c. on 1 c. green 30 20
229 20 c. on 2 c. red 40 25
230 20 c. on 5 c. blue 45 35
236 35 c. on 6 c. grey 1·60 1·60
232 50 c. on 6 c. grey 45 35
238 1p. on 5 p. violet 25·00 14·50

51. 50. 64.

1908. Fiscal stamps as T **51** optd. **CORREO —1908** or surch. **VALE** and value also.

260. **51.** 1 c. on 5 c. yellow 35 20
261. 2 c. on 5 c. yellow 35 25
262. 4 c. on 5 c. yellow 65 30
256. 5 c. yellow 45 35
257. 10 c. blue 35 20
263. 15 c. on 50 c. green 45 30
264. 35 c. on 50 c. green 2·50 65
258. 1 p. brown 20 1·40
259. 2 p. grey 20 1·50

1908. Fiscal stamps as T **50** optd **CORREOS—1908** or surch **VALE** and value also.

268. **50.** 2 c. orange 2·10 1·00
269. 4 c. on 2 c. orange 1·00 65
270. 5 c. on 2 c. orange 1·10 45
271. 10 c. on 2 c. orange 1·10 25

1909. Surch. **CORREOS—1909 VALE** and value.

273. **51.** 1 c. on 50 c. green 2·25 95
274. 2 c. on 50 c. green 4·00 1·75
275. 4 c. on 50 c. green 4·00 1·75
276. 5 c. on 50 c. green 2·25 1·10
277. 10 c. on 50 c. green 65 40

1910. Surch. **Vale** and value in two lines.

296. **37.** 2 c. on 3 c. orange 65 35
300. 2 c. on 4 c. violet 25 15
301. 5 c. on 20 c. olive 25 15
302. 10 c. on 15 c. black 30 15
303. 10 c. on 50 c. green 20 15
299. 10 c. on 1 p. yellow 65 35
305. 10 c. on 2 p. red 45 35

1911. Surch. **Correos 1911** (or **CORREOS 1911**) and value.

307. **51.** 2 c. on 5 p. blue 25 30
312. 5 c. on 2 p. grey 90 70
308. 5 c. on 10 p. pink 55 30
309. 10 c. on 25 c. lilac 30 20
310. 10 c. on 2 p. grey 30 20
311. 35 c. on 1 p. brown 30 25

1911. Surch. **VALE POSTAL de 1911** and value.

313. **51.** 5 c. on 25 c. lilac 90 70
314. 5 c. on 50 c. green 3·00 3·00
315. 5 c. on 5 p. blue 4·00 4·00
317 5 c. on 50 p. red 3·00 3·00
318. 10 c. on 50 c. green 70 45

1911. Railway stamps as T **64**, with fiscal surch. on the front, surch. on back **Vale— cts. CORREO DE 1911.**

319. **64.** 2 c. on 5 c. on 2 c. blue 55 65
320. 05 c. on 5 c. on 2 c. blue 30 40
321. 10 c. on 5 c. on 2 c. blue 30 40
322. 15 c. on 10 c. on 1 c. red 40 50

1911. Railway stamps, with fiscal surch. as last, further surch. on front **CORREO** and value.

323. **64.** 2 c. on 10 c. on 1 c. red 80 80
324. 20 c. on 10 c. on 1 c. red 4·00 4·00
325. 50 c. on 10 c. on 1 c. red 7·50 7·50

1911. Railway stamps, with fiscal surch. as last, surch. in addition on front **Correo Vale 1911** and value.

326. **64.** 2 c. on 10 c. on 1 c. red 15 12
328. 5 c. on 5 c. on 2 c. blue 90 80
327. 5 c. on 10 c. on 1 c. red 20 12
330. 10 c. on 10 c. on 1 c. red 70 50

1911. Railway stamps, with fiscal surch. on front, surch. in addition **Vale CORREO DE 1911** and value on back.

331. **64.** 5 c. on 10 c. on 1 c. red 18·00
332. 10 c. on 10 c. on 1 c. red 7·00

70. 71.

1912.

337. **70.** 1 c. green 25 12
338. 2 c. red 25 12
339. 3 c. brown 25 12
340. 4 c. purple 25 12
341. 5 c. black and blue 25 12
342. 6 c. brown 25 70
343. 10 c. brown 25 12
344. 15 c. violet 25 12
345. 20 c. brown 25 15
346. 25 c. black and green 25 15
347. **71.** 35 c. brown and green 1·10 1·10
348. **70.** 50 c. blue 65 30
349. 1 p. orange 90 1·40
350. 2 p. green 90 1·75
351. 5 p. black 1·60 2·10

1913. Surch. **Vale 15 cts Correos 1913.**

352. **71.** 15 c. on 35 c. brn. & grn. 30 20

1913. Surch. **VALE 1913** and value in "centavos de cordoba".

A. On stamps of 1912 issue.

353. **70.** ½ c. on 3 c. brown 35 25
354. ½ c. on 15 c. violet 20 15
355. ½ c. on 1 p. orange 20 15
356. 1 c. on 3 c. brown 55 45
357. 1 c. on 4 c. purple 20 15
358. 1 c. on 50 c. blue 20 15
359. 1 c. on 5 p. black 20 15
360. 2 c. on 4 c. purple 25 20
361. 2 c. on 20 c. brown 2·25 2·75
362. 2 c. on 25 c. blk. & grn. 25 15
363. **71.** 2 c. on 35 c. brn. & grn. 20 35
364. **70.** 2 c. on 50 c. blue 20 90
365. 2 c. on 2 p. green 15 12
366. 3 c. on 6 c. brown 15 10

B. On Silver Currency stamps of 1912 (Locomotive type).

367. Z **1.** ½ c. on 2 c. red 1·40 1·25
368. 1 c. on 3 c. brown 95 85
369. 1 c. on 4 c. red 95 85
370. 1 c. on 6 c. red 95 85
371. 1 c. on 20 c. blue 95 85
372. 1 c. on 25 c. blk. & grn. 95 85
384. 2 c. on 1 c. green 11·00 10·00
373. 2 c. on 25 c. blk. & grn. 5·00 4·50
374. 5 c. on 35 c. blk. & brn. 95 85
375. 5 c. on 50 c. olive 95 85
376. 6 c. on 1 p. orange 95 85
377. 10 c. on 2 p. brown 95 85
378. 1 p. on 5 p. green 95 85

1914. No. 352 surch. with new value and **Cordoba** and thick bar over old surch.

385. **71.** ½ c. on 15 c. on 35 c. 15 10
386. 1 c. on 15 c. on 35 c. 20 15

1914. Official stamps of 1913 surch. with new value and thick bar through "OFFICIAL".

387. **70.** 1 c. on 25 c. blue 30 20
388. **71.** 1 c. on 35 c. blue 30 20
389. **70.** 1 c. on 1 p. blue 20 15
391. 2 c. on 50 c. blue 30 15
392. 2 c. on 2 p. blue 20 15
393. 5 c. on 5 p. blue 20 15

79. National Palace, Managua. 80. Leon Cathedral.

1914. Various frames.

394. **79.** ½ c. blue 50 12
395. 1 c. green 50 12
396. **80.** 2 c. orange 50 12
397. **79.** 3 c. brown 80 25
398. **80.** 4 c. red 80 25
399. **79.** 5 c. grey 30 10
400. **80.** 6 c. sepia 5·25 3·25
401. 10 c. yellow 55 15
402. **79.** 15 c. violet 3·50 1·40
403. **80.** 20 c. grey 6·50 3·25
404. **79.** 25 c. orange 85 20
405. **80.** 50 c. blue 85 25

See also Nos. 465/72, 617/27 and 912/24.

1915. Surch. **VALE 5 cts. de Cordoba 1915.**

406. **80.** 5 c. on 6 c. sepia 1·10 35

1918. Stamps of 1914 surch. **Vale— centavos de cordoba.**

407. **80.** ½ c. on 6 c. sepia 2·00 75
408. ½ c. on 10 c. yellow 1·40 25
409. **79.** ½ c. on 15 c. violet 1·40 45
410. ½ c. on 25 c. orange 3·00 85
411. **80.** ½ c. on 50 c. blue 1·40 25
440. 1 c. on 2 c. orange 90 20
413. **79.** 1 c. on 3 c. brown 1·50 25
414. **80.** 1 c. on 6 c. sepia 7·00 2·10
415. 1 c. on 10 c. yellow 13·00 4·75
416. **79.** 1 c. on 15 c. violet 2·40 55
418. **80.** 1 c. on 20 c. grey 1·40 25
420. **79.** 1 c. on 25 c. orange 2·40 70
421. **80.** 1 c. on 50 c. blue 7·75 2·25
422. 2 c. on 4 c. red 1·75 25
423. 2 c. on 6 c. sepia 13·00 4·75
424. 2 c. on 10 c. yellow 13·00 2·50
425. 2 c. on 20 c. grey 7·00 2·10
426. **79.** 2 c. on 25 c. orange 3·00 30
427. **80.** 5 c. on 6 c. sepia 5·00 2·50
428. **79.** 5 c. on 15 c. violet 1·75 45

1919. Official stamps of 1915 surch. **Vale—centavo de cordoba** and with bar through "OFICIAL".
444. 80. ½ c. on 2 c. blue 30 15
445. ½ c. on 4 c. blue 70 15
446. 79. 1 c. on 3 c. blue 70 25
432. 1 c. on 25 c. blue 1·10 20
433. 80. 2 c. on 50 c. blue 1·10 20
443a. 10 c. on 20 c. blue 1·00 40

1921. Official stamps of 1913 optd. **Particular** and wavy lines through "OFICIAL".
441. 70. 1 c. blue 90 45
442. 5 c. blue 90 35

1921. No. 399 surch. **Vale medio centavo**
447. 79. ½ c. on 5 c. black 35 15

1921. Official stamp of 1915 optd. **Particular R de C** and bars.
448. 79. 1 c. blue 3·50 1·00

1921. Official stamps of 1915 surch. **Vale un centavo R de C** and bars.
449. 79. 1 c. on 5 c. blue 95 35
450. 80. 1 c. on 6 c. blue 50 20
451. 1 c. on 10 c. blue 65 20
452. 79. 1 c. on 15 c. blue 1·10 20

90. 91. Jose C. del Valle.

1921. Fiscal stamps as T 23 surch. **R. de C Vale** and new value.
453. 90. 1 c. on 1 c. red & black 10 8
454. 1 c. on 2 c. green & black 10 8
455. 1 c. on 4 c. orge. & black 10 8
456. 1 c. on 15 c. blue & black 10 8
No. 456 is inscr. "TIMBRE TELEGRAFICO".

1921. Independence Cent.
457. – ½ c. black and blue 30 25
458. 91. 1 c. black and green 30 25
459. – 2 c. black and red 30 25
460. – 5 c. black and violet 30 25
461. – 10 c. black and orange 20 25
462. – 25 c. black and yellow 30 25
463. – 50 c. black and violet 30 25
DESIGNS: ½ c. Arce. 2 c. Larreinaga. 5 c. F.Chamorro. 10 c. Jerez. 25 c. J. P. Chamorro 50 c. Dario.

1922. Surch. **Vale un centavo R. de C.**
464. 80. 1 c. on 10 c. yellow 10 8

1922. As Nos. 394, etc., but colours changed.
465. 79. ½ c. green 15 8
466. 1 c. violet 15 8
467. 80. 2 c. red 15 8
468. 79. 3 c. olive 25 12
469. 80. 6 c. brown 15 12
470. 79. 15 c. brown 25 15
471. 80. 20 c. brown 35 15
472. 1 cor. brown 65 35
Nos. 465/72 are size 27 × 22¾ mm.
For later issues of these types, see Nos. 617/27 and 912/24.

1922. Optd. **R. de C.**
473. 79. 1 c. violet 10 8

1922. Independence issue of 1921 surch. **R. de C. Vale un centavo.**
474. 91. 1 c. on 1 c. black & green 55 45
475. – 1 c. on 5 c. black & vio. 55 55
476. – 1 c. on 10 c. blk. & orge. 55 30
477. – 1 c. on 25 c. black & yell. 55 25
478. – 1 c. on 50 c. black & vio. 25 20

94. 99. F. Hernandez de Cordoba. 106.

1922. Surch. **Nicaragua R. de C. Vale un cent.**
479. 94. 1 c. yellow 10 8
480. 1 c. mauve 10 8
481. 1 c. blue 10 8

1922. Surch. thus: **Vale 0.01 de Cordoba** in two lines.
482. 80. 1 c. on 10 c. yellow 70 25
483. 2 c. on 10 c. yellow 70 20

1923. Surch. thus: **Vale 2 centavos de cordoba** in three lines.
484. 79. 1 c. on 5 c. black 70 15
485. 80. 2 c. on 10 c. yellow 70 15

1923. Optd. **Sello Postal.**
486. – ½ c. blk. & bl. (No. 457) 5·50 4·25
487. 91. 1 c. black and green 1·40 70

1923. Independence issue of 1921 surch. **R. de C. Vale un centavo de cordoba.**
488. 1 c. on 2 c. black and red 30 30
489. 1 c. on 5 c. black & violet 35 12
490. 1 c. on 10 c. black & orge. 15 15
491. 1 c. on 25 c. black & yellow 25 25
492. 1 c. on 50 c. black & violet 15 10

1923. Fiscal stamp optd. **R. de C.**
493. 90. 1 c. red and black 12 8

1924. Optd. **R. de C. 1924** in two lines.
494. 79. 1 c. violet 12 12

1924. 400th Anniv. of Foundation of Leon and Granada.
495. 99. 1 c. green 90 25
496. 2 c. red 90 25
497. 5 c. blue 65 25
498. 10 c. brown 65 45

1925. Optd. **R. de C. 1925** in two lines.
499. 79. 1 c. violet 12 8

1927. Optd. **Resello 1927.**
525. 79. ½ c. green 8 5
528. 1 c. violet (No. 466) 12 8
555. 1 c. violet (No. 473) 12 8
532. 80. 2 c. red 15 10
533. 79. 3 c. green 20 10
537. 80 4 c. red 9·50 8·00
539. 79. 5 c. grey 55 20
542. 80. 6 c. brown 7·75 6·50
543. 10 c. yellow 25 15
545. 79. 15 c. brown 55 25
547. 80. 20 c. brown 25 15
549. 79. 25 c. orange 30 15
551. 80. 50 c. blue 30 15
553. 1 cor. brown 35 15

1928. Optd. **Resello 1928.**
559. 79. ½ c. green 20 15
560. 1 c. violet 10 5
561. 80. 2 c. red 15 10
562. 79. 3 c. green 15 10
563. 80. 4 c. red 15 10
564. 79. 5 c. grey 15 10
565. 80. 6 c. brown 15 10
566. 10 c. yellow 20 10
567. 79. 15 c. brown 25 20
568. 80. 20 c. brown 35 20
569. 79. 25 c. orange 55 20
570. 80. 50 c. blue 90 10
571. 1 cor. brown 75 25

1928. Optd. **Correos 1928.**
574. 79. ½ c. green 12 10
575. 1 c. violet 10 5
576. 3 c. olive 55 20
577. 80. 4 c. red 25 10
578. 79. 5 c. grey 20 15
579. 80. 6 c. brown 30 15
580. 10 c. yellow 35 15
581. 79. 15 c. brown 1·00 15
582. 80. 20 c. brown 1·00 15
583. 79. 25 c. orange 1·00 20
584. 80. 50 c. blue 1·00 20
585. 1 cor. brown 3·00 1·50

1928. No. 577 surch. **Vale 2 cts.**
586. 80. 2 c. on 4 c. red 90 25

1928. Fiscal stamp as T 90. but inscr. "TIMBRE TELEGRAFICO" and surch. **Correos 1928 Vale** and new value.
587. 90. 1 c. on 5 c. blue & black 25 15
588. 2 c. on 5 c. blue & black 25 15
589. 3 c. on 5 c. blue & black 25 15

1928. Obligatory Tax. No. 587 additionally optd. **R. de T.**
590. 90. 1 c. on 5 c. blue & black 45 10

1928. As Nos. 465/72 but colours changed.
591. 79. ½ c. red 30 12
592. 1 c. orange 30 12
593. 80. 2 c. green 30 12
594. 79. 3 c. purple 30 20
595. 80. 4 c. brown 30 20
596. 79. 5 c. yellow 30 12
597. 80. 6 c. blue 30 20
598. 10 c. blue 65 20
599. 79. 15 c. red 85 35
600. 80. 20 c. green 85 35
601. 79. 25 c. purple 16·00 3·75
602. 80. 50 c. brown 1·90 70
603. 1 cor. violet 3·75 1·75
See also Nos. 617/27 and 912/24.

1928.
604. 106. 1 c. purple 20 8
647. 1 c. red 25 5
For 1 c. green see No. 925.

1929. Optd. **R. de C.**
605. 79. 1 c. orange 8 8
628. 1 c. olive 15 8

1929. Optd. **Correos 1929.**
606. 79. ½ c. green 20 15

1929. Optd. **Correos 1928.**
607. 99. 10 c. brown 55 45

1929. Fiscal stamps as T 90, but inscr. "TIMBRE TELEGRAFICO". A. Surch. **Correos 1929 R. de C. C$ 0.01** vert.
613. 90. 1 c. on 5 c. blue & black 10 12

B. Surch. **Correos 1929** and value.
611. 90. 1 c. on 10 c. green & blk. 20 15
612. 2 c. on 5 c. blue & black 20 10

C. Surch. **Correos 1929** and value vert. and **R. de C.** or **R. de T.** horiz.
608. 90. 1 c. on 5 c. blue and black (R. de T.) 20 15
609. 2 c. on 5 c. blue and black (R. de T.) 15 12
610. 2 c. on 5 c. blue and black (R. de C.) 13·00 70

1929. Air. Optd. **Correo Aereo 1929. P.A.A.**
614. 79. 25 c. sepia 1·40 1·40
615. 25 c. orange 1·00 1·00
616. 25 c. violet 90 70

1929. As Nos. 591/603 but colours changed.
617. 79. 1 c. green 10 5
618. 3 c. blue 25 12
619. 80. 4 c. blue 25 12
620. 79. 5 c. brown 30 12
621. 80. 6 c. drab 30 15
622. 10 c. brown 45 15
623. 79. 15 c. red 65 20
624. 80. 20 c. orange 80 25
625. 79. 25 c. violet 20 10
626. 80. 50 c. green 35 15
627. 1 cor. yellow 2·75 90
See also Nos. 912/24.

112. Mt. Momotombo. 114. G.P.O. Managua.

1929. Air.
629. 112. 15 c. purple 25 10
630. 20 c. green 70 45
631. 25 c. olive 50 30
632. 50 c. sepia 80 45
633. 1 cor. red 1·10 55
See also Nos. 926/30.

1930. Air. Surch. **Vale** and value.
634. 112. 15 c. on 25 c. olive 40 30
635. 20 c. on 25 c. olive 60 45

1930. Opening of the G.P.O., Managua.
636. 114. ½ c. sepia 80 60
637. 1 c. red 80 60
638. 2 c. orange 65 45
639. 3 c. orange 1·00 90
640. 4 c. yellow 1·00 90
641. 5 c. olive 1·60 1·10
642. 6 c. green 1·60 1·10
643. 10 c. black 1·60 1·00
644. 25 c. blue 3·25 2·40
645. 50 c. blue 5·25 3·50
646. 1 cor. violet 15·00 7·25

1931. Optd. **1931** and thick bar obliterating old overprint "1928".
648. 99. 10 c. brown (No. 607) 45 90

1931. No. 607 surch. **C $ 0.02.**
649. 99. 2 c. on 10 c. brown 55 45

1931. Optd. **1931** and thick bar.
650. 99. 2 c. on 10 c. brown (498) 55 1·75

1931. Air. Nos. 614/6 surch. **1931 Vale** and value.
651. 79. 15 c. on 25 c. sepia 90·00 90·00
652. 15 c. on 25 c. orange 45·00 45·00
653. 15 c. on 25 c. violet 9·00 9·00
654. 20 c. on 25 c. violet 9·00 9·00

1931. Optd. **1931.**
656. 79. ½ c. green 35 10
657. 1 c. olive 35 10
665. 1 c. orange (No. 605) 10 8
658. 80. 2 c. red 35 8
659. 79. 3 c. blue 35 12
660. 5 c. yellow 2·10 1·40
661. 5 c. sepia 65 20
662. 15 c. orange 70 45
663. 25 c. sepia 9·00 3·75
664. 25 c. violet 3·50 1·50

1931. Air. Surch. **1931** and value.
667. 80. 15 c. on 25 c. olive 4·75 4·75
668. 15 c. on 50 c. sepia 36·00 36·00
669. 15 c. on 1 cor. red 90·00 90·00
666. 15 c. on 20 c. on 25 c. olive (No. 635) 7·50 7·50

120. G.P.O. before and after the Earthquake.

1932. G.P.O. Reconstruction Fund.
670. 120. ½ c. green (postage) 90 90
671. 1 c. brown 1·25 1·25
672. 2 c. red 90 90
673. 3 c. blue 90 90
674. 4 c. blue 90 90
675. 5 c. brown 1·40 1·40
676. 6 c. brown 1·40 1·40
677. 10 c. brown 2·25 1·50
678. 15 c. red 3·50 2·25
679. 20 c. orange 2·10 2·10
680. 25 c. violet 2·25 2·25
681. 50 c. green 2·25 2·25
682. 1 cor. yellow 4·50 4·50
683. 15 c. mauve (air) 90 75
684. 20 c. green 1·10 1·10
685. 25 c. brown 5·50 5·50
686. 50 c. brown 7·00 7·00
687. 1 cor. red 10·50 10·50

1932. Air. Surch. **Vale** and value.
688. 112. 30 c. on 50 c. sepia 1·40 1·40
689. 35 c. on 50 c. sepia 1·40 1·40
690. 40 c. on 1 cor. red 1·60 1·60
691. 55 c. on 1 cor. red 1·60 1·60
For similar surcharges on these stamps in different colours see Nos. 791/4 and 931/4.

1932. Air. Int. Air Mail Week. Optd. **Semana Correo Aereo Internacional 11-17 Septiembre 1932.**
692. 112. 15 c. violet 40·00 40·00

1932. Air. Inaug. of Inland Airmail Service. Surch. **Inauguracion Interior 12 Octubre 1932 Vale C$0.08.**
693. 112. 8 c. on 1 cor. red 13·00 13·00

1932. Air. Optd. **Interior—1932** or surch. **Vale** and value also.
705. 120. 25 c. brown 4·75 4·75
706. 32 c. on 50 c. brown 5·50 5·50
707. 40 c. on 1 cor. red 4·25 4·25

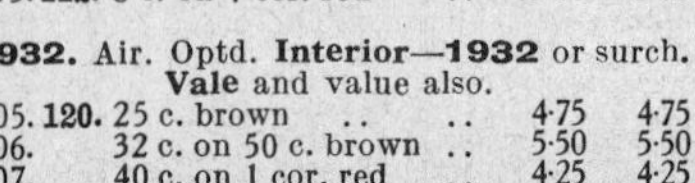

1932. Air. Nos. 671, etc., optd. **Correo Aereo Interior** in one line and **1932**, or surch. **Vale** and value also.
694. 120. 1 c. brown 12·00 12·00
695. 2 c. red 12·00 12·00
696. 3 c. blue 5·50 5·50
697. 4 c. blue 5·50 5·50
698. 5 c. brown 5·50 5·50
699. 6 c. brown 5·50 5·50
700. 8 c. on 10 c. brown 5·25 5·25
701. 16 c. on 20 c. orange 5·25 5·25
702. 24 c. on 25 c. violet 5·25 5·25
703. 50 c. green 5·25 5·25
704. 1 cor. yellow 5·50 5·50

1932. Air. Surch. **Correo Aereo Interior—1932** in two lines and **Vale** and value below.
710. 80. 1 c. on 2 c. red 40 40
711. 79. 2 c. on 3 c. blue 40 40
712. 80. 3 c. on 4 c. blue 40 40
713. 79. 4 c. on 5 c. sepia 40 40
714. 80. 5 c. on 6 c. brown 40 40
715. 6 c. on 10 c. brown 40 40
716. 79. 8 c. on 15 c. orange 40 40
717. 80. 16 c. on 20 c. orange 40 40
718. 79. 24 c. on 25 c. violet 85 60
719. 25 c. on 25 c. violet 85 60
720. 80. 32 c. on 50 c. green 85 75
721. 40 c. on 50 c. green 95 85
722. 50 c. on 1 cor. yellow 1·25 1·25
723. 100 c. on 1 cor. yellow 2·50 2·50

127. Wharf, Port San Jorge.

DESIGNS — HORIZ. 2 c. El Nacascolo Halt. 5 c. Rivas Station. 10 c. San Juan del Sur. 15 c. (No. 730), Arrival platform at Rivas. 20 c. El Nacascolo. 25 c. La Cuesta cutting. 50 c. San Juan del Sur Quay 1 cor. El El Estero.

128. La Chocolata Cutting.

1932. Opening of Rivas Railway.
726. 127. 1 c. yellow (postage) 17·00
727. – 2 c. red 17·00
728. – 5 c. sepia 17·00
729. – 10 c. brown 17·00
730. – 15 c. yellow 17·00
731. 128. 15 c. violet (air) 22·00
732. – 20 c. green 22·00
733. – 25 c. brown 22·00
734. – 50 c. sepia 22·00
735. – 1 cor. red 22·00

1932. Surch. **Vale** and value in words.
736. 79. 1 c. on 3 c. blue 35 15
737. 80. 2 c. on 4 c. blue 30 15

130. Railway Construction.

1932. Opening of Leon-Sauce Railway.
739. – 1 c. yellow (postage) 17·00
740. – 2 c. red 17·00
741. – 5 c. sepia 17·00
742. 130. 10 c. brown 17·00
743. – 15 c. yellow 17·00
744. – 15 c. violet (air) 22·00
745. – 20 c. green 22·00
746. – 25 c. brown 22·00
747. – 50 c. sepia 22·00
748. – 1 cor. red 22·00
DESIGNS—HORIZ. 1 c. El Sauce. 2 c., 15 c. (No. 744), Bridge at Santa Lucia. 5 c. Santa Lucia. 15 c. (No. 743) Santa Lucia cutting. 20 c. Santa Lucia River Halt. 25 c. Malpaicillo Station. 50 c. Railway panorama. 1 cor. San Andres.

1933. Surch. **Resello 1933 Vale** and value in words.
749. 79. 1 c. on 3 c. blue 20 12
750. 1 c. on 5 c. sepia 20 12
751. 80. 2 c. on 10 c. brown 20 15

133. Flag of the Race.

1933. 441st Anniv. of Columbus' Departure from Palos. Roul.

No.	Type	Description	Unused	Used
753.	**133.**	½ c. green (postage) ..	95	95
754.		1 c. green	80	80
755.		2 c. red	80	80
756.		3 c. red	80	80
757.		4 c. orange	80	80
758.		5 c. yellow	95	95
759.		10 c. brown	95	95
760.		15 c. brown	95	95
761.		20 c. blue	95	95
762.		25 c. blue	95	95
763.		30 c. violet	2·40	2·40
764.		50 c. purple	2·40	2·40
765.		1 cor. brown	2·40	2·40
766.		1 c. brown (air) ..	90	90
767.		2 c. purple	90	90
768.		4 c. violet	1·50	1·40
769.		5 c. blue	1·40	1·40
770.		6 c. blue	1·40	1·40
771.		8 c. brown	45	45
772.		15 c. brown	45	45
773.		20 c. yellow	1·40	1·40
774.		25 c. orange	1·40	1·40
775.		50 c. red	1·40	1·40
776.		1 cor. green	9·00	9·00

(**134.**) (Facsimile signatures of R. E. Deshon, Minister of Transport and J. R. Sevilla, P.M.G.).

1933. Optd. with T **134**.

No.	Type	Description	Unused	Used
777.	**79.**	½ c. green	30	12
778.		1 c. green	12	8
779.	**80.**	2 c. red	40	12
780.	**79.**	3 c. blue	15	8
781.	**80.**	4 c. blue	20	12
782.	**79.**	5 c. brown	20	8
783.	**80.**	6 c. drab	25	20
784.		10 c. brown	25	15
785.	**79.**	15 c. red	30	20
786.	**80.**	20 c. orange	40	30
787.	**79.**	25 c. violet	45	25
788.	**80.**	50 c. green	75	50
789.		1 cor. yellow	4·00	1·60

1933. No. 605 optd. with T **134**.

No.	Type	Description	Unused	Used
790.	**79.**	1 c. orange	25	12

1933. Air. Surch. **Vale** and value.

No.	Type	Description	Unused	Used
791.	**112.**	30 c. on 50 c. orange ..	35	15
792.		35 c. on 50 c. blue ..	45	20
793.		40 c. on 1 cor. yellow ..	70	15
794.		55 c. on 1 cor. green ..	70	30

135. Lake Xolotlan.

1933. Air. Int. Airmail Week.

No.	Type	Description	Unused	Used
795.	**135.**	10 c. brown	90	90
796.		15 c. violet	75	75
797.		25 c. red	85	85
798.		50 c. blue	90	90

Correo Aérea
Interior
Vale C 0.50

(**136.**)

1933. Air. Surch. as T **136**.

No.	Type	Description	Unused	Used
799.	**80.**	1 c. on 2 c. green ..	12	12
800.	**79.**	2 c. on 3 c. olive ..	12	12
801.	**80.**	3 c. on 4 c. red ..	12	12
802.	**79.**	4 c. on 5 c. blue ..	12	12
803.	**80.**	5 c. on 6 c. blue ..	15	15
804.		6 c. on 10 c. sepia ..	12	8
805.	**79.**	8 c. on 15 c. brown ..	20	15
806.	**80.**	16 c. on 20 c. brown ..	20	15
807.	**79.**	24 c. on 25 c. red ..	15	15
808.		25 c. on 25 c. orange ..	30	30
809.	**80.**	32 c. on 50 c. violet ..	30	25
810.		40 c. on 50 c. green ..	40	25
811.		50 c. on 1 cor. yellow	40	30
812.		1 cor. on 1 cor. red ..	95	80

1933. Obligatory Tax. As No. 647 optd. with T **134**. Colour changed.

No.	Type	Description	Unused	Used
813.	**106.**	1 c. orange	25	12

1934. Air. Surch. **Servicio Centroamericano Vale 10 centavos.**

No.	Type	Description	Unused	Used
814.	**112.**	10 c. on 20 c. green ..	35	35
815.		10 c. on 25 c. olive ..	35	35

See also No. 872.

1935. Optd. **Resello 1935.**

(a) Nos. 778/9.

No.	Type	Description	Unused	Used
816.	**79.**	1 c. green	10	5
817.	**80.**	2 c. red	12	5

(b) No. 813 but without T **134** opt.

No.	Type	Description	Unused	Used
818.	**106.**	1 c. orange	12	8

1935. No. 783 surch. **Vale Medio Centavo.**

No.	Type	Description	Unused	Used
819.	**80.**	½ c. on 6 c. brown ..	35	15

1935. Optd. with T **134** and **RESELLO-1935** in a box.

No.	Type	Description	Unused	Used
820.	**79.**	½ c. green	20	15
821.	**80.**	½ c. on 6 c. brown (No. 819)	15	10
822.	**79.**	1 c. green	25	10
823.	**80.**	2 c red	55	8
824.		2 c. red (No. 817) ..	30	8
825.	**79.**	3 c. blue	30	12
826.	**80.**	4 c. blue	30	15
827.	**79.**	5 c. brown	25	5
828.	**80.**	6 c. drab	30	10
829.		10 c. brown	55	20
830.	**79.**	15 c. red	15	8
831.	**80.**	20 c. orange	90	25
832.	**79.**	25 c. violet	30	15
833.	**80.**	50 c. green	35	25
834.		1 cor. yellow	45	35

1935. Obligatory Tax. No. 605 optd. with **RESELLO-1935** in a box.

No.	Type	Description	Unused	Used
835.	**79.**	1 c. orange	25·00	

1935. Obligatory Tax. Optd. **RESELLO-1935** in a box.

(a) No. 813 without T **134** opt.

No.	Type	Description	Unused	Used
836.	**106.**	1 c. orange	25	12

(b) No. 818.

No.	Type	Description	Unused	Used
868.	**106.**	1 c. orange	20	12

1935. Air. Nos. 799/812 optd. with **RESELLO-1935** in a box.

No.	Type	Description	Unused	Used
839.	**80.**	1 c. on 2 c. green ..	10	10
840.	**79.**	2 c. on 3 c. olive ..	20	20
879.	**80.**	3 c. on 4 c. red.. ..	12	12
880.	**79.**	4 c. on 5 c. blue ..	12	12
881.	**80.**	5 c. on 6 c. blue ..	12	12
882.		6 c. on 10 c. sepia ..	12	12
883.	**79.**	8 c. on 15 c. brown ..	15	15
884.	**80.**	16 c. on 20 c. brown ..	15	15
847.	**79.**	24 c. on 25 c. red ..	35	30
848.		25 c. on 25 c. orange ..	25	25
849.	**80.**	32 c. on 50 c. violet ..	20	20
850.		40 c. on 50 c. green ..	30	25
851.		50 c. on 1 cor. yellow ..	45	35
852.		1 cor. on 1 cor. red ..	85	40

1935. Air. Optd. with **RESELLO-1935** in a box.

(a) Nos. 629/33.

No.	Type	Description	Unused	Used
853	112	15 c. purple	30	10
873		20 c. green	40	30
855		25 c. green	40	35
856		50 c. sepia	40	35
857		1 cor. red	65	35

(b) Nos 791/4.

No.	Type	Description	Unused	Used
858.	**112.**	30 c. on 50 c. orange ..	40	35
859.		35 c. on 50 c. blue ..	40	25
860.		40 c. on 1 cor. yellow ..	40	35
861.		55 c. on 1 cor. green ..	40	30

(c) Nos. 814/5.

No.	Type	Description	Unused	Used
862.	**112.**	10 c. on 20 c. green ..	£300	£300
863.		10 c. on 25 c. olive ..	60	50

1935. Optd. with **RESELLO-1935** in a box.

No.	Type	Description	Unused	Used
864.	**79.**	½ c. green (No. 465) ..	15	8
865.		1 c. green (No. 617) ..	20	8
866.	**80.**	2 c. red (No. 467) ..	55	8
867.	**79.**	3 c. blue (No. 618) ..	20	15

1936. Surch. **Resello 1936 Vale** and value.

No.	Type	Description	Unused	Used
869.	**79.**	1 c. on 3 c. blue (No. 618)	15	10
870.		2 c. on 5 c. brown (No. 620)	15	10

1936. Air. Surch. **Servicio Centroamericano Vale diez centavos** and **RESELLO-1935** in a box.

No.	Type	Description	Unused	Used
871.	**112.**	10 c. on 25 c. olive ..	30	30

1936. Obligatory Tax. No. 818 optd. **1936.**

No.	Type	Description	Unused	Used
874.	**106.**	1 c. orange	50	20

1936. Obligatory Tax. No. 605 optd. with T **134** and **1936.**

No.	Type	Description	Unused	Used
875.	**79.**	1 c. orange	50	20

1936. Air. No. 622 optd. **Correo Aereo Centro-Americano Resello 1936.**

No.	Type	Description	Unused	Used
876.	**80.**	10 c. brown	20	20

1936. Air. Nos. 799/800 and 805 optd. **Resello 1936.**

No.	Type	Description	Unused	Used
885.	**80.**	1 c. on 2 c. green ..	25	20
886.	**79.**	2 c. on 3 c. olive ..	10	10
887.		8 c. on 15 c. brown ..	25	25

1936. Optd. with or without T **37**, surch. **1936 Vale** and value.

No.	Type	Description	Unused	Used
888.	**79.**	½ c. on 15 c. red ..	20	12
889.	**80.**	1 c. on 4 c. blue ..	25	15
890.	**79.**	1 c. on 5 c. brown ..	25	20
891.	**80.**	1 c. on 6 c. drab ..	45	20
892.	**79.**	1 c. on 15 c. red ..	25	20
893.	**80.**	1 c. on 20 c. orange ..	20	15
895.		2 c. on 10 c. brown ..	30	20
896.	**79.**	2 c. on 15 c. red ..	60	50
897.	**80.**	2 c. on 20 c. orange ..	55	45
898.	**79.**	2 c. on 25 c. violet ..	35	20
900.	**80.**	2 c. on 50 c. green ..	35	25
901.		2 c. on 1 cor. yellow ..	35	30
902.		3 c. on 4 c. blue ..	40	30

1936. Optd. **Resello 1936.**

No.	Type	Description	Unused	Used
903.	**79.**	3 c. blue (No. 618) ..	35	25
904.		5 c. brown (No. 620) ..	30	15
905.	**80.**	10 c. brown (No. 784)..	30	20

1936. Air. Surch. **1936 Vale** and value.

No.	Type	Description	Unused	Used
906.	**112.**	15 c. on 50 c. brown ..	30	25
907.		15 c. on 1 cor. red ..	30	25

1936. Fiscal stamps surch. **RECONSTRUCCION COMUNICACIONES 5 CENTAVOS DE CORDOBA** and further surch. **Vale dos centavos Resello 1936.**

No.	Type	Description	Unused	Used
908.	**90.**	1 c. on 5 c. green ..	25	8
909.		2 c. on 5 c. green ..	25	8

1936. Obligatory Tax. Fiscal stamps surch. **RECONSTRUCCION COMUNICACIONES 5 CENTAVOS DE CORDOBA** and further surch.

(a) **1936 R. de C. Vale Un Centavo.**

No.	Type	Description	Unused	Used
910.	**90.**	1 c. on 5 c. green ..	12	10

(b) **Vale un centavo R. de C. 1936.**

No.	Type	Description	Unused	Used
911.	**90.**	1 c. on 5 c. green ..	20	10

1937. Colours changed. Size 27 × 22¾ mm.

No.	Type	Description	Unused	Used
912.	**79.**	½ c. black	15	5
913.		1 c. red	15	5
914.	**80.**	2 c. blue	15	5
915.	**79.**	3 c. brown	15	8
916.	**80.**	4 c. yellow	20	10
917.	**79.**	5 c. red	15	10
918.	**80.**	6 c. violet	20	10
919.		10 c. green	20	10
920.	**79.**	15 c. green	15	10
921.	**80.**	20 c. brown	30	10
922.	**79.**	25 c. orange	30	10
923.	**80.**	50 c. brown	35	15
924.		1 cor. blue	40	25

1937. Obligatory Tax. Colour changed.

No.	Type	Description	Unused	Used
925.	**106.**	1 c. green	12	8

1937. Air. Colours changed.

No.	Type	Description	Unused	Used
926.	**112.**	15 c. orange	20	10
927.		20 c. red	20	15
928.		25 c. black	25	15
929.		50 c. violet	45	15
930.		1 cor. orange	65	15

1937. Air. Surch. **Vale** and value. Colours changed.

No.	Type	Description	Unused	Used
931.	**112.**	30 c. on 50 c. red ..	30	10
932.		35 c. on 50 c. olive ..	35	10
933.		40 c. on 1 cor. green ..	35	15
934.		55 c. on 1 cor. blue ..	35	30

1937. Air. Surch. **Servicio Centroamericano Vale Diez Centavos.**

No.	Type	Description	Unused	Used
949.	**112.**	10 c. on 1 cor. red ..	30	15

1937. Air. No. 805 (without T **134**) optd. **1937.**

No.	Type	Description	Unused	Used
950.	**79.**	8 c. on 15 c. brown ..	50	15

142. Baseball Player.

1937. Obligatory Tax. For 1937 Central American Olympic Games. Optd. with ball in red under "OLIMPICO".

No.	Type	Description	Unused	Used
951.	**142.**	1 c. red	35	15
952.		1 c. yellow	35	15
953.		1 c. blue	35	15
953a.		1 c. green	35	15

1937. Nos. 799/809 optd. **Habilitado 1937.**

No.	Type	Description	Unused	Used
954.	**80.**	1 c. on 2 c. green ..	8	5
955.	**79.**	2 c. on 3 c. olive ..	8	5
956.	**80.**	3 c. on 4 c. red ..	8	5
957.	**79.**	4 c. on 5 c. blue ..	8	8
658.	**80.**	5 c. on 6 c. blue ..	8	8
959.		6 c. on 10 c. brown ..	8	8
960.	**79.**	8 c. on 15 c. brown ..	8	8
661.	**80.**	16 c. on 20 c. brown ..	20	20
992.	**79.**	24 c. on 25 c. red ..	20	20
993.		25 c. on 25 c. orange ..	20	25
664.	**80.**	32 c. on 50 c. violet ..	20	25

144. Presidential Palace, Managua.

1937. Air. Inland.

No.	Type	Description	Unused	Used
965.	**144.**	1 c. red	15	10
966.		2 c. blue	15	10
967.		3 c. olive	15	10
968.		4 c. black	15	10
969.		5 c. purple	20	10
970.		6 c. brown	20	10
971.		8 c. violet	20	10
972.		16 c. orange	35	25
973.		24 c. yellow	20	15
974.		25 c. green	50	25

145. Nicaragua.

1937. Air. Abroad.

No.	Type	Description	Unused	Used
975.	**145.**	10 c. green	25	10
976.		15 c. blue	25	10
977.		20 c. yellow	30	25
978.		25 c. violet	30	25
979.		30 c. red	40	25
980.		50 c. orange	60	25
981.		1 cor. olive	65	45

146. Presidential Palace.

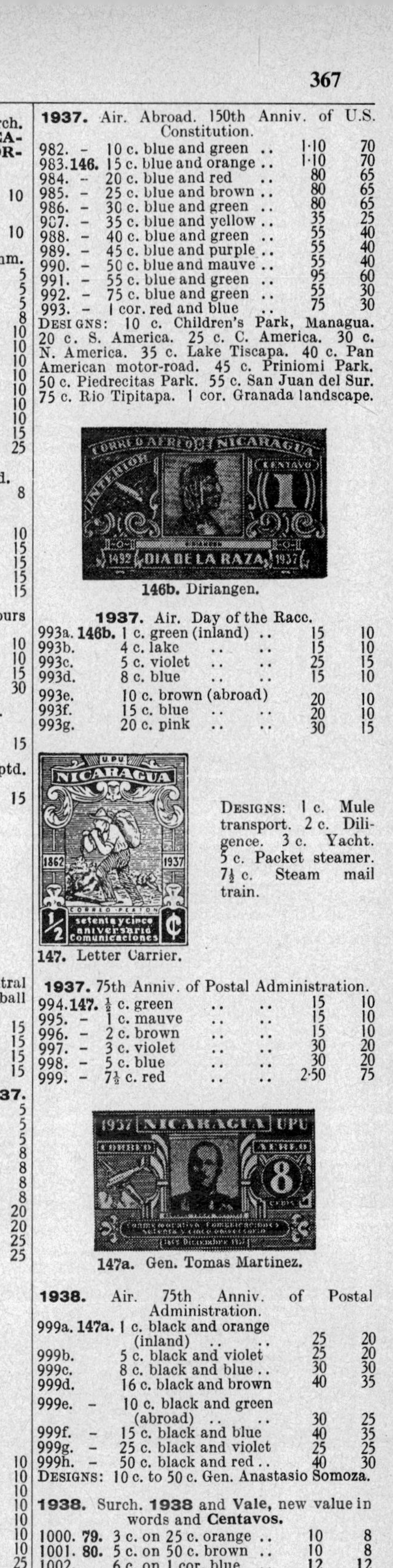

1937. Air. Abroad. 150th Anniv. of U.S. Constitution.

No.	Type	Description	Unused	Used
982.	–	10 c. blue and green ..	1·10	70
983.	**146.**	15 c. blue and orange ..	1·10	70
984.	–	20 c. blue and red ..	80	65
985.	–	25 c. blue and brown ..	80	65
986.	–	30 c. blue and green ..	80	65
987.	–	35 c. blue and yellow ..	35	25
988.	–	40 c. blue and green ..	55	40
989.	–	45 c. blue and purple ..	55	40
990.	–	50 c. blue and mauve ..	55	40
991.	–	55 c. blue and green ..	95	60
992.	–	75 c. blue and green ..	55	30
993.	–	1 cor. red and blue ..	75	30

DESIGNS: 10 c. Children's Park, Managua. 20 c. S. America. 25 c. C. America. 30 c. N. America. 35 c. Lake Tiscapa. 40 c. Pan American motor-road. 45 c. Priniomi Park. 50 c. Piedrecitas Park. 55 c. San Juan del Sur. 75 c. Rio Tipitapa. 1 cor. Granada landscape.

146b. Diriangen.

1937. Air. Day of the Race.

No.	Type	Description	Unused	Used
993a.	**146b.**	1 c. green (inland) ..	15	10
993b.		4 c. lake	15	10
993c.		5 c. violet	25	15
993d.		8 c. blue	15	10
993e.		10 c. brown (abroad)	20	10
993f.		15 c. blue	20	10
993g.		20 c. pink	30	15

147. Letter Carrier.

DESIGNS: 1 c. Mule transport. 2 c. Diligence. 3 c. Yacht. 5 c. Packet steamer. 7½ c. Steam mail train.

1937. 75th Anniv. of Postal Administration.

No.	Type	Description	Unused	Used
994.	**147.**	½ c. green	15	10
995.	–	1 c. mauve	15	10
996.	–	2 c. brown	15	10
997.	–	3 c. violet	30	20
998.	–	5 c. blue	30	20
999.	–	7½ c. red	2·50	75

147a. Gen. Tomas Martinez.

1938. Air. 75th Anniv. of Postal Administration.

No.	Type	Description	Unused	Used
999a.	**147a.**	1 c. black and orange (inland)	25	20
999b.		5 c. black and violet	25	20
999c.		8 c. black and blue ..	30	30
999d.		16 c. black and brown	40	35
999e.	–	10 c. black and green (abroad)	30	25
999f.	–	15 c. black and blue	40	35
999g.	–	25 c. black and violet	25	25
999h.	–	50 c. black and red ..	40	30

DESIGNS: 10 c. to 50 c. Gen. Anastasio Somoza.

1938. Surch. **1938** and **Vale,** new value in words and **Centavos.**

No.	Type	Description	Unused	Used
1000.	**79.**	3 c. on 25 c. orange ..	10	8
1001.	**80.**	5 c. on 50 c. brown ..	10	8
1002.		6 c. on 1 cor. blue ..	12	12

149. Dario Park.

150. Lake Managua. **151.** President Somoza.

1939.

No.	Type	Description	Unused	Used
1003.	**149.**	1½ c. green (postage)..	5	5
1004.		2 c. red	5	5
1005.		3 c. blue	5	5
1006.		6 c. brown	10	10
1007.		7½ c. green	10	8
1008.		10 c. brown	15	10
1009.		15 c. orange	15	10
1010.		25 c. violet	15	12
1011.		50 c. green	30	20
1012.		1 cor. yellow	60	45

1013.150. 2 c. blue (air: inland) 15 15
1014. 3 c. olive 15 15
1015. 8 c. mauve 15 15
1016. 16 c. orange 25 15
1017. 24 c. yellow 25 15
1018. 32 c. green 35 15
1019. 50 c. red 40 15
1020.151. 10 c. brown (air: abroad) 12 10
1021. 15 c. blue 12 10
1022. 20 c. yellow 15 20
1023. 25 c. violet 15 15
1024. 30 c. red 20 20
1025. 50 c. orange 30 20
1026. 1 cor. olive 45 35

1939. Nos. 920/1. Surch. **Vale un Centavo 1939.**

1027. 79. 1 c. on 15 c. green .. 10 10
1028. 80. 1 c. on 20 c. brown .. 10 10

153. Will Rogers and Managua Airport.

1939. Air. Will Rogers Commem. Inscr. "WILL ROGERS/1931/1939".

1029.153. 1 c. green 10 10
1030. – 2 c. red 10 10
1031. – 3 c. blue 10 10
1032. – 4 c. blue 15 10
1033. – 5 c. red 10 10

DESIGNS: 2 c. Rogers at Managua. 3 c. Rogers in P.A.A. hut. 4 c. Rogers and U.S. Marines. 5 c. Rogers and street in Managua.

156. Senate House and Pres. Somoza.

1940. Air. President's Visit to U.S.A. Inscr. "AEREO INTERIOR".

1034. – 4 c. brown 12 8
1035.156. 8 c. brown 10 5
1036. – 16 c. green 12 5
1037.156. 20 c. mauve 30 15
1038. – 32 c. red 20 20

(b) Inscr. "CORREO AEREO INTERNACIONAL".

1039. – 25 c. blue 20 12
1040. – 30 c. black 20 8
1041.156. 50 c. red 25 40
1042. – 60 c. green 30 35
1043. – 65 c. brown 30 20
1044. – 90 c. olive 40 35
1045. – 1 cor. violet 60 30

DESIGNS: 4 c., 16 c., 25 c., 30 c., 65 c., 90 c. Pres. Somoza addressing Senate. 32 c., 60 c., 1 cor. Portrait of Pres. Somoza between symbols of Nicaragua and New York World's Fair.

158. L. S. Rowe, Statue of Liberty and Union Flags.

1940. Air. 50th Anniv. of Pan-American Union.

1046.158. 1 cor. 25 multicoloured 40 35

159. First Issue of Nicaragua and Sir Rowland Hill.

1941. Air. Centenary of First Adhesive Postage stamps.

1047.159. 2 cor. brown .. .. 2·25 75
1048. 3 cor. blue .. .. 7·00 80
1049. 5 cor. red .. .. 20·00 2·10

1941. Surch. **Servicio ordinario/Vale Diez Centavos/de Cordoba.**

1050.153. 10 c. on 1 c. green .. 15 10

161. Ruben Dario.

1941. 25th Death Anniv. of Ruben Dario (poet).

1051. 161. 10 c. red (postage) .. 20 15
1052. 20 c. mauve (air) .. 25 15
1053. 35 c. green 30 20
1054. 40 c. orange 35 25
1055. 60 c. blue 40 35

1943. As No. 1050, but **de Cordoba** omitted.

1056. 153. 10 c. on 1 c. green .. 10 10

162. "V" for Victory.

163. Red Cross.

164. Red Cross Workers and Wounded.

1943. Victory.

1057.162. 10 c. red & violet (post.) 8 5
1058. 30 c. red and brown.. 12 8
1059. 40 c. red and green (air) 15 5
1060. 60 c. red and blue .. 20 5

1944. Air. 80th Anniv. of Int. Red Cross Society.

1061.163. 25 c. red 40 15
1062. – 50 c. bistre 65 35
1063.164. 1 cor. green .. .. 1·25 1·00

DESIGN—VERT. 50 c. Two Hemispheres.

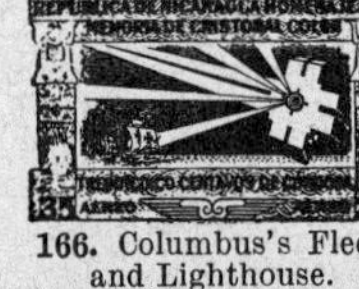

166. Columbus's Fleet and Lighthouse.

165. Columbus and Lighthouse.

168. Roosevelt as a Stamp Collector.

1945. Honouring Columbus's Discovery of America and Erection of Columbus Lighthouse near Trujillo City, Dominican Republic.

1064.165. 4 c. blk. & green (post.) 15 10
1065. 6 c. black and orange.. 20 10
1066. 8 c. black and red .. 20 15
1067. 10 c. black and blue.. 30 15
1068.166. 20 c. grey & green (air) 40 15
1069. 35 c. black and red .. 70 20
1070. 75 c. pink and green 1·25 40
1071. 90 c. blue and red .. 1·50 60
1072. 1 cor. blue and black.. 1·75 45
1073. 2 cor. 50 red and blue.. 4·50 2·25

1946. President Roosevelt Commem. Inscr. "HOMENAJE A ROOSEVELT".

1074.168. 4 c. green & black (post) 15 15
1075. – 8 c. violet and black .. 20 20
1076. – 10 c. blue and black .. 30 25
1077. – 16 c. red and black .. 40 30
1078. – 32 c. brown and black 50 25
1079. – 50 c. grey and black.. 50 25
1080. – 25 c. orge. & black (air) 20 10
1081. – 75 c. red and black .. 25 20
1082. – 1 cor. green and black 30 30
1083. – 3 cor. violet and black 2·25 2·25
1084. – 5 cor. blue and black.. 3·00 3·00

DESIGNS—portraying Roosevelt. HORIZ. 8 c., 25 c. with Churchill at the Atlantic Conference. 16 c., 1 cor. with Churchill, De Gaulle and Giraud at the Casablanca Conference. 32 c., 3 cor. with Churchill and Stalin at the Teheran Conference. VERT. 10 c., 75 c. Signing Declaration of War against Japan. 50 c., 5 cor. Head of Roosevelt.

171. Managua Cathedral.

172. G.P.O., Managua.

1947. Managua Cent. Frames in black.

1085.171. 4 c. red (postage) .. 10 8
1086. – 5 c. blue 15 8
1087. – 6 c. green 20 15
1088. – 10 c. olive 20 15
1089. – 75 c. brown 30 25
1090. – 5 c. violet (air) .. 8 8
1091.172. 20 c. green 12 12
1092. – 35 c. orange 15 12
1093. – 90 c. purple 30 20
1094. – 1 cor. brown 45 35
1095. – 2 cor. 50 purple .. 1·00 1·10

DESIGNS—POSTAGE (as Type 171): 5 c. Health Ministry. 6 c. Municipal Building. 10 c. College. 75 c. G.P.O., Managua. AIR (as Type 172): 5 c. College. 35 c. Health Ministry. 90 c. National Bank. 1 cor. Municipal Building. 2 cor. 50, National Palace.

173. San Cristobal Volcano.

174. Ruben Dario Monument, Managua.

1947. (a) Postage.

1096.173. 2 c. orange and black.. 8 5
1097. – 3 c. violet and black .. 10 5
1098. – 4 c. grey and black .. 10 8
1099. – 5 c. red and black .. 20 10
1100. – 6 c. green and black .. 12 10
1101. – 8 c. brown and black.. 15 10
1102. – 10 c. red and black .. 25 12
1103. – 20 c. blue and black .. 1·10 25
1104. – 30 c. purple and black 70 25
1105. – 50 c. red and black .. 1·90 70
1106. – 1 cor. brown and black 60 35

DESIGNS—as Type 173: 3 c. Lion on Ruben Dario's tomb, Leon Cathedral. 4 c. Race Stand. 5 c. Soldiers' Monument. 6 c. Sugar cane. 8 c. Tropical fruits. 10 c. Cotton. 20 c. Horses. 30 c. Coffee plant. 50 c. Prize bullock. 1 cor. Agricultural landscape.

(b) Air.

1107.174. 5 c. red and green .. 10 10
1108. – 6 c. orange and black.. 10 10
1109. – 8 c. brown and red .. 10 10
1110. – 10 c. blue and brown.. 15 10
1111. – 20 c. orange and blue.. 15 10
1112. – 25 c. green and red .. 20 15
1113. – 35 c. brown and black 30 15
1114. – 50 c. black and violet.. 20 10
1115. – 1 cor. red and black .. 45 25
1116. – 1 cor. 50 green & red.. 50 45
1117. – 5 cor. red and brown 3·75 3·75
1118. – 10 cor. brown and violet 3·00 3·00
1119. – 25 cor. yellow and green 6·00 6·00

DESIGNS—As Type 174: 6 c. Baird's Tapir. 8 c. Highway and Lake Managua. 10 c. Genizaro Dam. 20 c. Ruben Dario Monument, Managua. 25 c. Sulphur Lagoon, Nejapa. 35 c. Managua Airport. 50 c. Mouth of Rio Prinzapolka. 1 cor. Thermal Baths, Tipitapa. 1 cor. 50, Rio Tipitapa. 5 cor. Embassy building. 10 cor. Girl carrying basket of fruit. 25 cor. Franklin D. Roosevelt Monument, Managua.

175. Soft-ball.

176. Pole-vaulting.

177. Tennis.

178. National Stadium Managua.

1949. 10th World Amateur Baseball Championships.

(a) Postage as T 175/6.

1120. 175. 1 c. brown 10 10
1121. – 2 c. blue 50 15
1122.176. 3 c. green 25 10
1123. – 4 c. purple 15 15
1124. – 5 c. orange 40 15
1125. – 10 c. green 40 15
1126. – 15 c. red 50 15
1127. – 25 c. blue 50 20
1128. – 35 c. green 80 20
1129. – 40 c. violet .. .. 1·75 30
1130. – 60 c. black .. .. 1·40 35
1131. – 1 cor. red .. .. 1·50 90
1132. – 2 cor. purple .. .. 2·75 1·50

DESIGNS—VERT. 2 c. Scout. 5 c. Cycling. 25 c. Boxing. 35 c. Basket-ball. HORIZ. 4 c. Diving. 10 c. Stadium. 15 c. Baseball. 40 c. Yachting. 60 c. Table tennis. 1 cor. Football. 2 cor. Tennis.

(b) Air as T 177.

1133.177. 1 c. red 10 10
1134. – 2 c. black 10 10
1135. – 3 c. red 10 10
1136. – 4 c. black 10 10
1137. – 5 c. blue 35 15
1138. – 15 c. green 65 10
1139. – 25 c. purple .. .. 1·25 25
1140. – 30 c. brown .. .. 1·00 25
1141. – 40 c. violet 50 25
1142. – 75 c. mauve .. .. 2·50 1·60
1143. – 1 cor. blue .. .. 3·00 80
1144. – 2 cor. olive .. .. 1·25 1·00
1145. – 5 cor. green .. .. 2·10 2·10

DESIGNS—SQUARE: 2 c. Football. 3 c. Table tennis. 4 c. Stadium. 5 c. Yachting. 15 c. Basket-ball. 25 c. Boxing. 30 c. Baseball. 40 c. Cycling. 75 c. Diving. 1 cor. Pole-vaulting. 2 cor. Scout. 5 cor. Soft-ball.

1949. Obligatory Tax stamps. Stadium Construction Fund.

1146.178. 5 c. blue 20 5
1146a. 5 c. red 20 5

179. Rowland Hill.

180. Heinrich von Stephan.

1950. 75th Anniv. of U.P.U. Frames in black.

1147.179. 20 c. red (postage) .. 12 10
1148. – 25 c. green 15 10
1149. – 75 c. blue 50 50
1150. – 80 c. green 30 25
1151. – 4 cor. blue 85 80

DESIGNS—VERT. 25 c. Portrait as Type 180. 75 c. Monument, Berne. 80 c., 4 cor. Obverse and reverse of Congress Medal.

1152. – 16 c. red (air).. .. 12 10
1153.180. 20 c. orange 12 10
1154. – 25 c. black 15 15
1155. – 30 c. red 25 10
1156. – 85 c. green 55 50
1157. – 1 cor. 10 brown .. 50 35
1158. – 2 cor. 14 green .. 1·25 1·25

DESIGNS—HORIZ. 16 c. Rowland Hill. 25 c., 30 c. U.P.U. Offices, Berne. 85 c. Monument, Berne. 1 cor. 10, and 2 cor. 14, Obverse and reverse of Congress Medal.

181. Queen Isabella and Columbus's Fleet.

182. Isabella the Catholic.

1952. 500th Birth Anniv. of Isabella the Catholic.

1159. – 10 c. mauve (postage) 10 10
1160.181. 96 c. blue .. .. 1·00 55
1161. – 98 c. red .. .. 1·00 55
1162. – 1 cor. 20 brown .. 50 40
1163.182. 1 cor. 76 purple .. 60 60
1164. 2 cor. 30 red (air) .. 1·40 1·10
1165. – 2 cor. 80 orange .. 1·00 95
1166. – 3 cor. green .. .. 3·25 1·50
1167.181. 3 cor. 30 blue.. .. 3·25 1·75
1168. – 3 cor. 60 green .. 1·50 1·25

DESIGNS—VERT. 10 c., 3 cor. 60 Queen facing right. 98 c., 3 cor. Queen and "Santa Maria". 1 cor. 20, 2 cor. 80 Queen and Map of Americas.

183. O.D.E.C.A. Flag.

1953. Foundation of Organization of Central American States.
1169.**183.** 4 c. blue (postage) .. 5 5
1170. – 5 c. green 10 5
1171. – 6 c. brown 10 5
1172. – 15 c. olive 20 12
1173. – 50 c. sepia 25 15
1174. – 20 c. red (air) 10 10
1175.**183.** 25 c. blue 12 10
1176. – 30 c. brown 15 12
1177. – 60 c. green 25 20
1178. – 1 cor. purple 35 45
DESIGNS: 5 c., 1 cor. Map of C. America. 6 c., 20 c. Hands holding O.D.E.C.A. arms. 15 c., 30 c. Five Presidents of C. America. 50 c. 60 c. Charter and flags.

184. Pres. Solorzano. 185. Pres. Arguello.

1953. Presidential Series. Portraits in black.
(a) Postage. As T **184.**
1179.**184.** 4 c. red 5 5
1180. – 6 c. blue (D. M. Chamorro) 5 5
1181. – 8 c. brown (Diaz) .. 10 5
1182. – 15 c. red (Somoza) .. 15 10
1183. – 50 c. grn. (E. Chamorro) 20 15
(b) Air. As T **185.**
1184.**185.** 4 c. red 5 5
1185. – 5 c. orange (Moncada) 5 5
1186. – 20 c. blue (J. B. Sacasa) 8 5
1187. – 25 c. (Zelaya) 10 10
1188. – 30 c. lake (Somoza) .. 10 10
1189. – 35 c. green (Martinez) 20 20
1190. – 40 c. plum (Guzman) 20 20
1191. – 45 c. olive (Cuadra) .. 20 20
1192. – 50 c. red (P.J. Chamorro) .. 35 25
1193. – 60 c. blue (Zavala) .. 40 40
1194. – 85 c. brown (Cardenas) 40 40
1195. – 1 cor. 10 pur. (Carazo) 60 55
1196. – 1 cor. 20 bistre (R. Sacasa) 65 55

186. Sculptor and U.N. Emblem.

DESIGNS: A, Detail from Nicaragua's Coat of Arms. B, Globe. C, Candle and Nicaragua's Charter. D, Flags of Nicaragua and U.N. E, Torch. F, Trusting hands.

1954. U.N.O. Inscr. "HOMENAJE A LA ONU".
1197.**186.** 3 c. drab (postage) .. 10 5
1198. A. 4 c. green 12 5
1199. B. 5 c. green 20 8
1200. C. 15 c. green 55 20
1201. D. 1 cor. turquoise .. 45 40
1202. E. 3 c. red (air) 5 5
1203. F. 4 c. orange 5 5
1204. C. 5 c. red 12 5
1205. D. 30 c. pink 75 15
1206. B. 2 cor. red 80 70
1207. A. 3 cor. brown .. 1·50 1·00
1208.**186.** 5 cor. purple .. 1·75 1·40

187. Capt. D. L. Ray. 188. F-86 Sabre-Jet.

1954. National Air Force. Frames in black.
(a) Postage. Frames as T **187.**
1209.**187.** 1 c. black 10 10
1210. – 2 c. black (F-86 Sabre-Jet) 10 10
1211. – 3 c. myrtle (A-20 'plane) 10 10
1212. – 4 c. orge. (B-24 bomber) 15 10
1213. – 5 c. grn. (AT-6 trainer) 20 10
1214. – 15 c. turquoise (Pres. Somoza) 15 10
1215. – 1 cor. vio. (Emblem) .. 35 25
(b) Air. Frames as T **188.**
1216. – 10 c. black (D. L. Ray) 10 10
1217.**188.** 15 c. black 15 10
1218. – 20 c. mve. (Emblem) .. 15 10
1219. – 25 c. red (Hangars) .. 20 10
1220. – 30 c. blue (Pres. Somoza) 10 10
1221. – 50 c. bl. (AT-6 formation) 75 50
1222. – 1 cor. grn. (P-38 'plane) 65 35

189. Rotary Slogans. 190a.

1955. 50th Anniv. of Rotary Int.
1223.**189.** 15 c. orange (postage) 10 8
1224. A. 20 c. olive 12 12
1225. B. 35 c. violet 15 12
1226. C. 40 c. red 15 12
1227. D. 90 c. black 30 25
1228. D. 1 c. red (air) 5 5
1229. A. 2 c. blue 5 5
1230. C. 3 c. green 5 5
1231.**189.** 4 c. violet 5 5
1232. B. 5 c. brown 10 5
1233. 25 c. turquoise .. 15 15
1234.**189.** 30 c. black 12 10
1235. C. 45 c. mauve 30 25
1236. A. 50 c. green 25 20
1237. D. 1 cor. blue 45 30
DESIGNS—VERT. A, Clasped hands. B, Rotarian and Nicaraguan flags. D, Paul P. Harris. HORIZ. C, World map and winged emblem.

1956. National Exhibition. Surch. **Conmemoracion Exposicion Nacional Febrero 4-16, 1956** and value.
1238. 5 c. on 6 c. brown (No. 1171) postage 5 5
1239. 5 c. on 6 c. blk. & blue (1180) 5 5
1240. 5 c. on 8 c. brn. & blk. (1101) 5 5
1241. 15 c. on 35 c. violet (1225) 12 10
1242. 15 c. on 80 c. grn. & blk. (1150) 12 10
1243. 15 c. on 90 c. black (1227) 12 10
1244. 30 c. on 35 c. black & green (1189) (air) 5 15
1245. 30 c. on 45 c. blk. & ol. (1191) 25 15
1246. 30 c. on 45 c. mauve (1235) 25 15
1247. 2 cor. on 5 cor. purple (1208) 50 35

1956. Obligatory Tax. Social Welfare Fund.
1247a. **190a.** 5 c. blue 8 5

191. Gen. J. Dolores Estrada. 192. President Somoza.

1956. Cent. of War of 1856. Inscr. as in T **191.**
1248. – 5 c. brown (postage) .. 5 5
1249. – 10 c. lake 5 5
1250. – 15 c. grey 10 8
1251. – 25 c. red 15 12
1252. – 50 c. purple 30 20
1253.**191.** 30 c. red (air) .. 8 8
1254. – 60 c. brown 20 15
1255. – 1 cor. 50 green .. 20 35
1256. – 2 cor. 50 blue .. 30 30
1257. – 10 cor. oran e .. 1·90 1·75
DESIGNS—VERT. 5 c. Gen. M. Jerez. 10 c. Gen. F. Chamorro. 50 c. Gen. J. D. Estrada. 1 cor. 50, E. Mangalo. 10 cor. Commodore H. Paulding. HORIZ. 15 c. Battle of San Jocinto. 25 c. Granada in flames. 60 c. Bas-relief. 2 cor. 50, Battle of Rivas.

1957. Air. National Mourning for Pres. G. A. Somoza. Various frames. Inscr. as in T **192.** Centres in black.
1258. – 15 c. black 10 10
1259. – 30 c. blue 15 15
1260.**192.** 2 cor. violet 80 70
1261. – 3 cor. olive .. .. 1·25 1·10
1262. – 5 cor. sepia .. .. 1·90 1·90

193. Scout and Badge. 194. Clasped Hands, Badge and Globe.

1957. Birth Cent. of Lord Baden-Powell.
1263.**193.** 10 c. ol. & violet (post.) 10 5
1264. – 15 c. sepia and purple 12 12
1265. – 20 c. brown and blue .. 12 12
1266. – 25 c. brown & turquoise 15 12
1267. – 50 c. olive and red .. 35 35
1268.**194.** 3 c. olive and red (air) 12 12
1269. – 4 c. blue and brown .. 12 12
1270. – 5 c. brown and green .. 12 12
1271. – 6 c. drab and violet .. 12 12
1272. – 8 c. red and black .. 12 12
1273. – 30 c. black and green .. 15 15
1274. – 40 c. black and blue .. 15 15
1275. – 75 c. sepia and purple 35 35
1276. – 85 c. grey and red .. 40 40
1277. – 1 cor. brown and green 40 40
DESIGNS—VERT. 4 c. Scout badge. 5 c., 15 c. Wolf cub. 6 c. Badge and flags. 8 c. Badge and emblems of scouting. 20 c. Scout. 25 c. 1 cor. Lord Baden-Powell. 30 c., 50 c. Joseph A. Harrison. 75 c. Rover Scout. 85 c. Scout. HORIZ. 40 c. Presentation to Pres. Somoza.

195. Pres. Luis Somoza. 197. Archbishop of Managua.

196. Managua Cathedral.

1957. Election of Pres. Somoza. Portrait in brown. (a) Postage. Oval frame.
1278.**195.** 10 c. red 5 5
1279. 15 c. blue 5 5
1280. 35 c. purple 10 10
1281. 50 c. brown 15 15
1282. 75 c. green 40 40
(b) Air. Rectangular frame.
1283. – 20 c. blue 10 10
1284. – 25 c. mauve 12 10
1285. – 30 c. sepia 12 12
1286. – 40 c. turquoise .. 15 15
1287. – 2 cor. violet 95 95

1957. Churches and Priests. Centres in olive.
1288.**196.** 5 c. green (postage) .. 5 5
1289. – 10 c. purple 5 5
1290.**197.** 15 c. blue 10 5
1291. – 20 c. sepia 12 5
1292. – 50 c. green 20 15
1293. – 1 cor. violet 30 30
1294.**197.** 30 c. green (air) .. 10 10
1295.**196.** 60 c. brown 15 15
1296. – 75 c. blue 25 25
1297. – 90 c. red 30 30
1298. – 1 cor. 50 turquoise .. 35 35
1299. – 2 cor. purple 40 40
DESIGNS—HORIZ. As Type **196**: 20 c., 90 c. Leon Cathedral. 50 c., 1 cor. 50, La Merced, Granada Church. VERT. As Type **197**: 10 c., 75 c. Bishop of Nicaragua. 1 cor., 2 cor. Father Mariano Dubon.

198. "Honduras" (freighter). 199. Exhibition Emblem.

1957. Nicaraguan Merchant Marine Commemoration. Inscr. as in T **198.**
1300. **198.** 4 c. black, blue and myrtle (postage) .. 15 10
1301. – 5 c. vio., blue & brn. 15 10
1302. – 6 c. black, blue & red 15 10
1303. – 10 c. black, green and sepia 20 10
1304. – 15 c. brown, blue & red 30 10
1305. – 50 c. brown, blue & vio. 30 20
1306. – 25 c. purple, blue and ultramarine (air) .. 30 10
1307. – 30 c. grey, buff & brown 12 8
1308. – 50 c. bistre, blue & violet 20 20
1309. – 60 c. black, turquoise and purple .. 55 20
1310. – 1 cor. blk., blue & red 75 30
1311. – 2 cor. 50 brown, blue and black .. .. 1·75 1·00
DESIGNS: 5 c. Gen. A. Somoza, founder of Mamenic (National) Shipping Line, and "Guatemala" (freighter). 6 c. "Guatemala". 10 c. "Salvador" (freighter). 15 c. Freighter between hemispheres. 25 c. "Managua" (freighter). 30 c. Ship's wheel and world map. 50 c. (No. 1305), Hemispheres and ship. 50 c. (No. 1308), Mamenic Shipping Line flag. 60 c. "Costa Rica" (freighter). 1 cor. "Nicarao" (freighter). 2 cor. 50, Map, freighter and flag.

1958. Air. Brussels Int. Exn. Inscr. "EXPOSICION MUNDIAL DE BELGICA 1958".
1312.**199.** 25 c. blk., yell. & grn. 10 10
1313. – 30 c. multicoloured .. 12 12
1314. – 45 c. blk., ochre & blue 15 15
1315.**199.** 1 cor. black, blue and dull purple 25 25
1316. – 2 cor. multicoloured .. 25 25
1317. – 10 cor. sepia, purple and blue .. .. 1·40 1·00
DESIGNS—As Type **199**: 30 c., 20 cor. Arms of Nicaragua. 45 c., 10 cor. Nicaraguan Pavilion.

200. Emblems of C. American Republics. 201. Arms of La Salle.

1958. 17th Central American Lions Convention. Inscr. as in T **200.** Emblems (5 c., 60 c.) multicoloured; Lions badge (others) in blue, red, yellow (or orange and buff).
1318.**200.** 5 c. blue (postage) .. 5 5
1319. – 10 c. blue and orange 5 5
1320. – 20 c. blue and green .. 8 8
1321. – 50 c. blue and purple .. 15 15
1322. – 75 c. blue and mauve 30 25
1323. – 1 cor. 50, blue, salmon and drab 45 45
1324. – 30 c. blue & orge. (air) 10 10
1325.**200.** 60 c. blue and pink .. 20 15
1326. – 90 c. blue 25 20
1327. – 1 cor. 25 blue and olive 35 30
1328. – 2 cor. blue and green .. 60 50
1329. – 3 cor. blue, red & violet 95 90
DESIGNS—HORIZ. 10 c., 1 cor. 25, Melvin Jones. 20 c., 30 c. Dr. T. A. Arias. 50 c., 90 c. Edward G. Barry. 75 c., 2 cor. Lions emblem. 1 cor. 50, 3 cor. Map of C. American Isthmus.

1958. Brothers of the Nicaraguan Christian Schools Commem. Inscr. as in T **201.**
1330.**201.** 5 c. red, blue & yellow (postage) 5 5
1331. – 10 c. sepia, blue & grn. 5 5
1332. – 15 c. sepia, brn. & bis. 5 5
1333. – 20 c. black, red & bistre 8 8
1334. – 50 c. sepia, orge & bis. 12 12
1335. – 75 c. sepia, turq. & grn. 25 20
1336. – 1 cor. blk., vio. & bistre 40 30
1337.**201.** 30 c. blue, red & yellow (air) 10 8
1338. – 60 c. sepia, pur. & grey 25 20
1339. – 85 c. black, red & blue 30 25
1340. – 90 c. blk., grn. & ochre 35 35
1341. – 1 cor. 25 black, red and ochre 50 45
1342. – 1 cor. 50 sepia, green and grey 60 55
1343. – 1 cor. 75 black, brown and blue 65 55
1344. – 2 cor. sepia, grn. & grey 65 65
DESIGNS—HORIZ. 10 c., 60 c. Managua Teachers Institute. VERT. 15 c., 85 c. De La Salle (founder). 20 c., 90 c. Brother Carlos. 50 c. 1 cor. 50, Brother Antonio. 75 c., 1 cor. 25, Brother Julio. 1 cor., 1 cor. 75, Brother Argeo. 2 cor. Brother Eugenio.

202. U.N. Emblem. 203. 204.

1958. Inaug. of U.N.E.S.C.O. Headquarters Building, Paris. Inscr. as in T **202.**
1345.**202.** 10 c. blue & mve. (post.) 5 5
1346. – 15 c. mauve and blue .. 8 8
1347. – 25 c. brown and green 10 10
1348. – 40 c. black and red .. 15 15
1349. – 45 c. mauve and blue .. 20 20
1350.**202.** 50 c. green and brown 25 25
1351. – 60 c. blue & mve. (air) 25 15
1352. – 75 c. brown and green 25 20
1353. – 90 c. green and brown 30 25
1354. – 1 cor. mauve and blue 40 30
1355. – 3 cor. red and black .. 60 60
1356. – 5 cor. blue and mauve 1·00 85
DESIGNS—VERT. 15 c. Aerial view of H.Q. 25 c., 45 c. Facade composed of letters "UNESCO". 40 c. H.Q. and Eiffel Tower. In oval vignettes—60 c., As 15 c.; 75 c., 5 cor., As 25 c.; 90 c., 3 cor. As 40 c.; 1 cor., As Type **202.**

1959. Obligatory Tax. Consular Fiscal stamps surch. Serial Nos. in red.
1357.**203.** 5 c. on 50 c. blue .. 10 5
1358.**204.** 5 c. on 50 c. blue .. 10 5

205. 206. Cardinal Spellman with Pope John XXIII. 207. Abraham Lincoln.

1959. Obligatory Tax.
1359.**205.** 5 c. blue 12 5

1959. Cardinal Spellman Commem.

1360. **206.** 5 c. flesh & grn. (post.) 5 5
1361. A. 10 c. multicoloured .. 5 5
1362. B. 15 c. red, blk. and grn. 5 5
1363. C. 20 c. yellow and blue .. 8 5
1364. D. 25 c. red and blue .. 8 5

1365. E. 30 c. bl., red & yell. (air) 10 8
1366. **206.** 35 c. bronze and orange 10 10
1367. A. 1 cor. multicoloured .. 30 30
1368. B. 1 cor. 5, red and black 35 30
1369. C 1 cor. 50, yellow & blue 45 35
1370. D. 2 cor. blue, violet & red 55 45
1371. E. 5 cor. multicoloured .. 75 55

DESIGNS—VERT. A, Cardinal's Arms. B, Cardinal. D, Cardinal wearing sash. HORIZ. C, Cardinal and Cross. E, Flags of Nicaragua, Vatican City and U.S.A.

1960. 150th Birth Anniv. of Abraham Lincoln. Portrait in black.

1372. **207.** 5 c. red (postage) .. 5 5
1373. 10 c. green 5 5
1374. 15 c. orange 8 8
1375. 1 cor. purple 25 25
1376. 2 cor. blue 30 45

1377. 30 c. blue (air) .. 10 5
1378. 35 c. red 12 10
1379. 70 c. purple 20 20
1380. 1 cor. 5, green .. 35 35
1381. 1 cor. 50, violet .. 50 45
1382. – 5 cor. ochre and black 55 55

DESIGN—HORIZ. 5 cor. Scroll inscr. "Dar al que necesite—A. Lincoln".

1960. Air. 10th Anniv. of San Jose (Costa Rica) Philatelic Society. Optd. **X Aniversario Club Filatelico S. J.—C. R.**

1383. 2 cor. red (No. 1206) .. 70 60
1384. 2 cor. 50 blue (No. 1256) 75 75
1385. 3 cor. green (No. 1166) .. 1·40 90

1960. Red Cross Fund for Chilean Earthquake Relief Nos. 1372/82 optd. **Resello** and Maltese Cross. Portrait in black.

1386. **207.** 5 c. red (postage) .. 5 5
1387. 10 c. green 5 5
1388. 15 c. orange 5 5
1389. 1 cor. purple 25 25
1390. 2 cor. blue 30 25

1391. 30 c. blue (air) .. 25 20
1392. 35 c. red 20 20
1393. 70 c. purple 25 25
1394. 1 cor. 5 green 30 30
1395. 1 cor. 50 violet .. 40 35
1396. – 5 cor. ochre and black 1·00 1·00

210.

1961. Air. World Refugee Year. Inscr. "ANO MUNDIAL DEL REFUGIADO".

1397. – 2 cor. multicoloured 20 20
1398. **210.** 5 cor. ochre, bl. & grn. 60 60

DESIGN: 2 cor. Procession of refugees.

211. Pres. Roosevelt, Pres. Somoza and Officer.

1961. Air. 20th Anniv. of Nicaraguan Military Academy.

1399. **211.** 20 c. multicoloured .. 8 5
1400. – 25 c. red, blue & black 8 8
1401. – 30 c. multicoloured .. 10 10
1402. – 35 c. multicoloured .. 10 10
1403. – 40 c. multicoloured .. 10 10
1404. – 45 c. black, flesh & red 12 12
1405. **211.** 60 c. multicoloured .. 15 15
1406. – 70 c. multicoloured .. 20 20
1407. – 1 cor. 5 multicoloured 25 25
1408. – 1 cor. 50 multicoloured 35 35
1409. – 2 cor. multicoloured .. 50 50
1410. – 5 cor. blk., flesh & grey 70 60

DESIGNS—VERT. 25 c., 70 c. Flags. 35 c., 1 cor. 50, Standard bearers. 40 c. 2 cor. Pennant and emblem. HORIZ. 30 c., 1 cor. 5, Group of officers. 45 c., 5 cor. Pres. Somoza and Director of Academy.

1961. Air. Consular Fiscal stamps as T **203/4** with serial Nos. in red, surch. **Correo Aereo** and value.

1411. 20 c. on 50 c. blue .. 12 10
1412. 20 c. on 1 cor. olive .. 12 10
1413. 20 c. on 2 cor. green .. 12 10
1414. 20 c. on 3 cor. red .. 12 10
1415. 20 c. on 5 cor. red .. 12 10
1416. 20 c. on 10 cor. violet .. 12 10
1417. 20 c. on 20 cor. brown .. 12 10
1418. 20 c. on 50 cor. brown .. 12 10
1419. 20 c. on 100 cor. lake .. 12 10

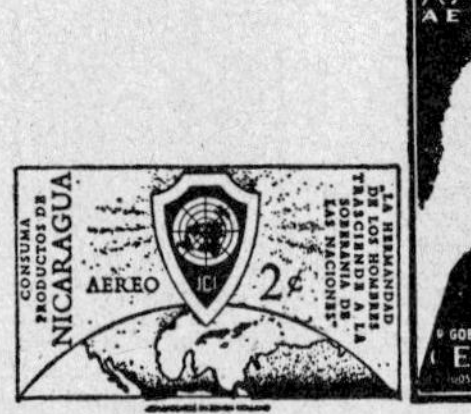

213. I.J.C. Emblem and Global Map of the Americas. **215.** R. Cabezas.

1961. Air. Junior Chamber of Commerce Congress.

1420. 2 c. multicoloured .. 5 5
1421. 3 c. black and yellow .. 5 5
1422. 4 c. multicoloured .. 5 5
1423. 5 c. black and red .. 5 5
1424. 6 c. multicoloured .. 5 5
1425. 10 c. multicoloured .. 5 5
1426. 15 c. black, green and blue 8 8
1427. 30 c. black and blue .. 12 10
1428. 35 c. multicoloured .. 12 10
1429. 70 c. black, red and yellow 20 20
1430. 1 cor. 5 multicoloured .. 35 30
1431. 5 cor. multicoloured .. 70 70

DESIGNS—HORIZ. 2 c., 15 c. Type **213**: 4 c., 35 c. "J.C.I." upon Globe. VERT. 3 c., 30 c. I.J.C. emblem. 5 c., 70 c. Scroll. 6 c., 1 cor. 5, Handclasp. 10 c., 5 cor. Regional map of Nicaragua.

1961. Air. 1st Central American Philatelic Convention, San Salvador. Optd. **Convencion Filatelica - Centro - America - Panama - San Salvador - 27 Julio 1961.**

1432. **158.** 1 cor. 25 multicoloured 25 25

1961. Air. Birth Cent. of Cabezas.

1433. **215.** 20 c. blue & orange .. 10 10
1434. – 40 c. purple and blue .. 15 15
1435. – 45 c. sepia and green .. 15 15
1436. – 70 c. green and brown 25 20
1437. – 2 cor. blue and pink .. 60 40
1438. – 10 cor. purple and turq. 1·50 1·50

DESIGNS—HORIZ. 40 c. Map and view of Cartago. 45 c. 1884 newspaper. 70 c. Assembly outside building. 2 cor. Scroll. 10 cor. Map and view of Masaya.

216. Official Gazettes. **219.** "Cattleya skinneri".

1961. Cent. of Regulation of Postal Rates.

1439. **216.** 5 c. brown & turquoise 5 5
1440. – 10 c. brown and green 5 5
1441. – 15 c. brown and red .. 8 5

DESIGNS: 10 c. Envelopes and postmarks. 15 c. Martinez and Somoza.

1961. Air. Dag Hammarskjold Commem. Nos. 1351/6 optd. **Homenaje a Hammarskjold Sept. 18-1961.**

1442. 60 c. blue and mauve .. 30 30
1443. 75 c. brown and green .. 35 35
1444. 90 c. green and brown .. 45 45
1445. 1 cor. mauve and blue .. 50 50
1446. 3 cor. red and black .. 80 80
1447. 5 cor. blue and mauve .. 1·50 1·50

1962. Air. Surch. **RESELLO C$ 1.00.**

1448. – 1 cor. on 1 cor. 10 brown (No. 1157) .. 30 25
1449. **207.** 1 cor. on 1 cor. 5 black and green .. 30 25

See also Nos. 1498/1500a, 1569/70, 1608/14, 1669/76 and 1748/62.

1962. Obligatory Tax. Nicaraguan Orchids. Multicoloured.

1450 5 c. Type **219** .. 5 5
1451 5 c. "Bletia roezlii" .. 5 5
1452 5 c. "Sobralia pleiantha" 5 5
1453 5 c. "Lycaste macrophylla" .. 5 5
1454 5 c. "Schomburgkia tibicinus" .. 5 5
1455 5 c. "Maxillaria tenuifolia" 5 5
1456 5 c. "Stanhopea ecornuta" 5 5
1457 5 c. "Oncidium ascendens" and "O. cebolleta" .. 5 5
1458 5 c. "Cycnoches egertonianum" .. 5 5
1459 5 c. "Hexisia bidentata" 5 5

220. U.N.E.S.C.O. "Audience".

NICARAGUA
CORREOS CORREOS
0.02 CENTAVOS 0.02
222. Arms of Nueva Segovia.

1962. Air. 15th Anniv. of U.N.E.S.C.O.

1460. **220.** 2 cor. multicoloured 15 15
1461. – 5 cor. multicoloured 80 80

DESIGN: 5 cor. U.N. and U.N.E.S.C.O. emblems.

1962. Air. Malaria Eradication. Nos. 1425, 1428/31 optd. with mosquito surrounded by **LUCHA CONTRA LA MALARIA.**

1462. – 10 c. 35 30
1463. – 35 c. 45 30
1464. – 70 c. 60 45
1465. – 1 cor. 5 .. .. 80 65
1466. – 5 cor. .. .. .. 1·00 1·25

1962. Urban and Provincial Arms. Arms mult.; inscr. black; background colours below.

1467. **222.** 2 c. mauve (postage) 5 5
1468. – 3 c. blue 5 5
1469. – 4 c. lilac 5 5
1470. – 5 c. yellow 5 5
1471. – 6 c. brown 5 5

1472. **222.** 30 c. red (air) .. 8 8
1473. – 50 c. orange .. 12 10
1474. – 1 cor. green .. 25 20
1475. – 2 cor. grey .. 45 40
1476. – 5 cor. blue .. 75 60

ARMS: 3 c., 50 c. Leon. 4 c., 1 cor. Managua. 5 c., 2 cor. Granada. 6 c., 5 cor. Rivas.

223. Liberty Bell. **224.** Blessing.

1963. Air. 150th Anniv. of Independence.

1477. **223.** 30 c. drab, blue & blk. 15 10

1963. Air. Death Tercentenary of St. Vincent de Paul and St Louise de Marillac.

1478. – 60 c. black and orange 15 10
1479. **224.** 1 cor. olive & orange 25 20
1480. – 2 cor. black and red .. 50 45

DESIGNS—VERT. 60 c. "Comfort" (St. Louise and woman). HORIZ. 2 cor. St. Vincent and St. Louise.

225. "Map Stamp". **226.** Cross on Globe.

1963. Air. Central American Philatelic Societies Federation Commemoration.

1481. **225.** 1 cor. blue and yellow 30 20

1963. Air. Ecumenical Council, Vatican City.

1482. **226.** 20 c. red and yellow 12 5

227. Ears of Wheat. **228.** Boxing.

1963. Air. Freedom from Hunger.

1483. **227.** 10 c. green & lt. green 8 5
1484. – 25 c. sepia & yellow 12 8

DESIGN: 25 c. Barren tree and campaign emblem.

1963. Air. Sports. Multicoloured.

1485. 2 c. Type **228** 5 5
1486. 3 c. Running 5 5
1487. 4 c. Underwater harpooning 8 5
1488. 5 c. Football 8 5
1489. 6 c. Baseball 12 5
1490. 10 c. Tennis 20 8
1491. 15 c. Cycling 20 10
1492. 20 c. Motor-cycling .. 20 10
1493. 35 c. Chess 30 12
1494. 60 c. Angling 35 20
1495. 1 cor. Table-tennis .. 55 35
1496. 2 cor. Basketball .. 75 55
1497. 5 cor. Golf .. .. 1·90 1·10

1964. Air. Surch. **Resello** or **RESELLO** (1500a) and value.

1498. – 5 c. on 6 c. (No. 1424) 35 8
1499. – 10 c. on 30 c. (No. 1365) 45 12
1500. **207.** 15 c. on 30 c. .. 70 20
1500a. **201.** 20 c. on 30 c. .. 15 8

See also Nos. 1448/9, 1569/70, 1608/14 and 1669/76.

1964. Optd. **CORREOS.**

1501. 5 c. mult. (No. 1451) 8 5

231. Flags. **232.** "Alliance Emblem".

1964. Air. "Centro America".

1502. **231.** 40 c. multicoloured .. 15 12

1964. Air. "Alliance for Progress". Mult.

1503. 5 c. Type **232** 10 10
1504. 10 c. Red Cross Post .. 10 10
1505. 15 c. Highway 10 10
1506. 20 c. Ploughing 10 10
1507. 25 c. Housing 15 10
1508. 30 c. Presidents Somoza and Kennedy and Eugene Black (World Bank) 15 10
1509. 35 c. School and adults 20 15
1510. 40 c. Chimneys 25 15

Nos. 1504/10 are horiz.

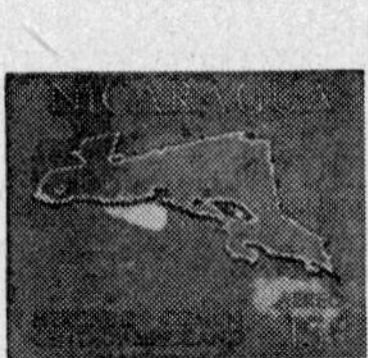

233. Map of Member Countries. **235.** Rescue of Wounded Soldier.

1964. Air. Central-American "Common Market". Multicoloured.

1511. 15 c. Type **233** 5 5
1512. 25 c. Ears of wheat .. 8 5
1513. 40 c. Cogwheels .. 12 8
1514. 50 c. Heads of cattle .. 15 10

1964. Air. Olympic Games, Tokyo. Nos. 1485/7, 1489 and 1495/6 optd. **OLIMPIADAS TOKYO-1964.**

1515. 2 c. Type **108** 5 5
1516. 3 c. Running 5 5
1517. 4 c. Underwater harpooning 5 5
1518. 6 c. Baseball 5 5
1519. 1 cor. Table-tennis .. 1·10 1·10
1520. 2 cor. Basketball .. 2·25 2·25

1965. Air. Red Cross Cent. Multicoloured.

1521. 20 c. Type **235** 8 5
1522. 25 c. Blood transfusion 12 10
1523. 40 c. Red Cross and snowbound town .. 15 12
1524. 10 cor. Red Cross and map of Nicaragua .. 1·50 1·50

236. Statuettes.

1965. Air. Nicaraguan Antiquities. Mult.

1525. 5 c. Type **236** 5 5
1526. 10 c. Totem 5 5
1527. 15 c. Carved dog .. 5 5
1528. 20 c. Composition of "objets d'art" .. 5 5
1529. 25 c. Dish and vase .. 5 5
1530. 30 c. Pestle and mortar .. 8 5
1531. 35 c. Statuettes (different) 8 5
1532. 40 c. Deity 12 8
1533. 50 c. Wine vessel and dish 15 10
1534. 60 c. Bowl and dish .. 20 10
1535. 1 cor. Urn 45 15

The 15, 25, 35 and 60 c. are horiz.

237. Pres. Kennedy. **238.** A. Bello.

1965. Air. Pres. Kennedy Commem.
1536. **237.** 35 c. black and green .. 15 10
1537. 75 c. black and mauve .. 25 15
1538. 1 cor. 10 black & blue .. 35 25
1539. 2 cor. black & brown .. 90 55

1965. Air. Death Centenary of Andres Bello (poet and writer).
1540. **238.** 10 c. black and brown .. 5 5
1541. 15 c. black and blue .. 5 5
1542. 45 c. black & purple .. 12 8
1543. 80 c. black and green .. 20 15
1544. 1 cor. black & yellow .. 25 20
1545. 2 cor. black and grey .. 45 45

1965. 9th Central-American Scout Camporee Nos. 1450/9 optd. with scout badge and **CAMPOREE SCOUT 1965.**
1546. 5 c. multicoloured .. 20 20
1547. 5 c. multicoloured .. 20 20
1548. 5 c. multicoloured .. 20 20
1549. 5 c. multicoloured .. 20 20
1550. 5 c. multicoloured .. 20 20
1551. 5 c. multicoloured .. 20 20
1552. 5 c. multicoloured .. 20 20
1553. 5 c. multicoloured .. 20 20
1554. 5 c. multicoloured .. 20 20
1555. 5 c. multicoloured .. 20 20

240. Sir Winston Churchill. **241.** Pope John XXIII.

1966. Air. Churchill Commem.
1556. **240.** 20 c. mauve & black .. 8 5
1557. – 35 c. green and black .. 12 8
1558. – 60 c. ochre and black .. 15 12
1559. – 75 c. red 20 20
1560. – 1 cor. purple 30 25
1561. **240.** 2 cor. vio., lilac & blk. 60 55
1562. – 3 cor. blue and black 65 60
DESIGNS—HORIZ. 35 c., 1 cor. Churchill broadcasting. VERT. 60 c., 3 cor. Churchill crossing the Rhine. 75 c. Churchill in Hussars' uniform.

1966. Air. Closure of Vatican Ecumenical Council. Multicoloured.
1564. 20 c. Type **241** 8 8
1565. 35 c. Pope Paul VI .. 12 12
1566. 1 cor. Archbishop Gonzalez y Robleto 30 25
1567. 2 cor. St. Peter's, Rome 30 25
1568. 3 cor. Papal arms .. 60 40

1967. Air. Nos. 1533/4 surch. **RESELLO** and value.
1569. 10 c. on 50 c. multicoloured 5 5
1570. 15 c. on 60 c. multicoloured 5 5
See also Nos. 1448/9, 1498/1500a, 1608/14 and 1669/76.

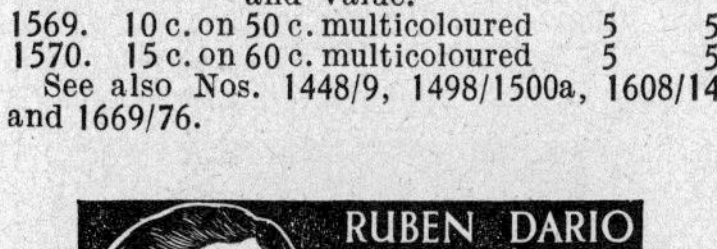

243. Dario and Birthplace.

1967. Air. Birth Cent. of Ruben Dario (poet). Designs showing Dario and view. Mult.
1571. 5 c. Type **243** 5 5
1572. 10 c. Monument, Managua 5 5
1573. 20 c. Leon Cathedral (site of Dario's tomb) .. 5 5
1574. 40 c. Allegory of the centaurs 15 10
1575. 75 c. Allegory of the swans 2·00 75
1576. 1 cor. Roman triumphal march 25 20
1577. 2 cor. St. Francis and the wolf 45 40
1578. 5 cor. "Faith" opposing "Death" 65 60

244. "Megalura peleus".

1967. Air. Butterflies. Multicoloured.
1580 5 c. "Heliconius petiveranua" 10 5
1581 10 c. "Colaenis julia" .. 10 5
1582 15 c. Type **244** 10 5
1583 20 c. "Ancyluris jurgensii" 10 5
1584 25 c. "Thecla regalis" .. 10 5
1585 30 c. "Doriana thia" .. 10 5
1586 35 c. "Lymnias pixae" .. 15 8
1587 40 c. "Metamorpho dido" 25 8
1588 50 c. "Papilio arcas" .. 25 12
1589 60 c. "Ananea cleomestra" 35 15
1590 1 cor. "Victorina epaphus" 60 30
1591 2 cor. "Prepona demophon" .. .. .. 1·10 50
The 5, 10, 30, 35, 50 c. and 1 cor. are vert.

245. McDivitt and White.

1967. Air. Space Flight of McDivitt and White. Multicoloured.
1592. 5 c. Type **245** 10 10
1593. 10 c. Astronauts and "Gemini 5" on launching pad 10 10
1594. 15 c. "Gemini 5" and White in Space .. 10 10
1595. 20 c. Recovery operation at sea 15 10
1596. 35 c. Type **245** 10 10
1597. 40 c. As 10 c. 15 10
1598. 75 c. As 15 c. 20 20
1599. 1 cor. As 20 c. 35 25

246. National Flower of Costa Rica.

1967. Air. 5th Year of Central American Economic Integration. Designs showing National Flowers of the Central-American Countries. Multicoloured.
1600. 40 c. Type **246** 15 8
1601. 40 c. Guatemala 15 8
1602. 40 c. Honduras 15 8
1603. 40 c. Nicaragua 15 8
1604. 40 c. El Salvador 15 8

247. Presidents Diaz and Somoza. **249.** Mangoes.

1968. Air. Visit of Pres. Diaz of Mexico.
1605. – 20 c. black 10 5
1606. **247.** 40 c. olive 20 8
1607. – 1 cor. brown 35 20
DESIGNS—VERT. 20 c. Pres. Somoza greeting Pres. Diaz. 1 cor. Pres. Diaz of Mexico.

1968. Surch. **RESELLO** and value.
1608. – 5 c. on 6 c. (No. 1180) (postage) 5 5
1609. – 5 c. on 6 c. (No. 1471) 5 5
1610. – 5 c. on 6 c. (No. 1424) (air) 5 5
1611. – 5 c. on 6 c. (No. 1489) 5 5
1612. **156.** 5 c. on 8 c. (No. 1035) 5 5
1614. – 1 cor. on 1 cor. 50 (No. 1369) 25 20
See also Nos. 1448/9, 1498/1500a, 1569/70 and 1669/76.

1968. Air. Nicaraguan Fruits. Multicoloured.
1615. 5 c. Type **249** 5 5
1616. 10 c. Pineapples 5 5
1617. 15 c. Oranges 5 5
1618. 20 c. Pawpaws 8 5
1619. 30 c. Bananas 8 8
1620. 35 c. Avocado pears .. 12 8
1621. 50 c. Water-melons .. 15 8
1622. 75 c. Cashews 25 15
1623. 1 cor. Sapodilla plums .. 35 20
1624. 2 cor. Cocoa beans .. 45 20

250. "The Crucifixion" (Fra Angelico).

1968. Air. Religious Paintings. Multicoloured.
1625. 10 c. Type **250**. 5 5
1626. 15 c. "The Last Judgement" (Michelangelo) 8 8
1627. 35 c. "The Beautiful Gardener" (Raphael) .. 12 12
1628. 2 cor. "The Spoliation of Christ" (El Greco) .. 45 30
1629. 3 cor. "The Conception" (Murillo) 60 45
Nos. 1626/9 are vert.

1968. Air. Pope Paul's Visit to Bogota. Nos. 1625/8 optd. **Visita de S. S. Paulo VI C. E. de Bogota 1968.**
1631. **250.** 10 c. multicoloured 5 5
1632. – 15 c. multicoloured 5 5
1633. – 35 c. multicoloured 10 8
1634. – 2 cor. multicoloured 30 20

252. Basketball.

1969. Air. Olympic Games, Mexico. Mult.
1635. 10 c. Type **252** 5 5
1636. 15 c. Fencing 5 5
1637. 20 c. High-diving 5 5
1638. 35 c. Running 8 5
1639. 50 c. Hurdling 12 8
1640. 75 c. Weightlifting .. 20 15
1641. 1 cor. Boxing 35 20
1642. 2 cor. Football 55 55
The 15 c., 50 c. and 1 cor. are horiz.

253. "Cichlasoma citrinellum".

1969. Air. Fishes. Multicoloured.
1644. 10 c. Type **253** 5 5
1645. 15 c. "Cichlasoma nicaraguensis" 5 5
1646. 20 c. "Cyprinus carpio" (Carp) 5 5
1647. 30 c. "Lepisosteus tropicus" (Gar) 10 5
1648. 35 c. "Xiphias gladius" (Swordfish) 10 5
1649. 50 c. "Phylipuns dormitor" (vert.) 15 8
1650. 75 c. "Tarpon atlanticus" (Tarpon) (vert.) .. 20 12
1651. 1 cor. "Eulamia nicaraguensis" (vert.) .. 30 15
1652. 2 cor. "Istiophorus albicans" (Sailfish) (vert.) 30 35
1653. 3 cor. "Pristis antiquorum" (Sawfish) (vert.) .. 60 40

1969. Air. Various stamps surch. **RESELLO** and value.
1655. 10 c. on 25 c. (No. 1507) .. 5 5
1656. 10 c. on 25 c. (No. 1512) .. 5 5
1657. 15 c. on 25 c. (No. 1529) .. 5 5
1658. 50 c. on 70 c. (No. 1379) .. 12 8

255. Scenery, Tower and Emblem. **258.** "Minerals".

1969. Air. "Hemisfair" (1968) Exn.
1659. **255.** 30 c. blue and red .. 8 5
1660. 35 c. purple and red .. 10 8
1661. 75 c. red and blue .. 15 10
1662. 1 cor. purple and black 30 20
1663. 2 cor. purple and green 55 40

1969. Various stamps, surch.
(a) Optd. **CORREO.**
1665. 5 c. (No. 1450) 5 5
1666. 5 c. (No. 1453) 5 5
1667. 5 c. (No. 1454) 5 5
1668. 5 c. (No. 1459) 5 5
(b) Optd. **RESELLO** and surch.
1670. 10 c. on 30 c. (No. 1324) .. 5 5
1671. 10 c. on 30 c. (No. 1427) .. 5 5
1669. 10 c. on 25 c. (No. 1529) .. 5 5
1672. 10 c. on 30 c. (No. 1530) .. 5 5
1673. 15 c. on 35 c. (No. 1531) .. 5 5
1674. 20 c. on 30 c. (No. 1307) .. 5 5
1675. 20 c. on 30 c. (No. 1401) .. 5 5
1676. 20 c. on 35 c. (No. 1509) .. 5 5

1969. Air. Nicaraguan Products. Mult.
1677. 5 c. Type **258** 5 5
1678. 10 c. "Fish" 5 5
1679. 15 c. "Bananas" 5 5
1680. 20 c. "Timber" 5 5
1681. 35 c. "Coffee" 10 5
1682. 40 c. "Sugar-cane" .. 12 8
1683. 60 c. "Cotton" 20 10
1684. 75 c. "Rice and Maize" .. 20 12
1685. 1 cor. "Tobacco" .. 30 20
1686. 2 cor. "Meat" 35 25

1969. 50th Anniv. of I.L.O. Obligatory tax stamps, Nos. 1450/9, optd., **O.I.T. 1919-1969.**
1687. 5 c. multicoloured .. 5 5
1688. 5 c. multicoloured .. 5 5
1689. 5 c. multicoloured .. 5 5
1690. 5 c. multicoloured .. 5 5
1691. 5 c. multicoloured .. 5 5
1692. 5 c. multicoloured .. 5 5
1693. 5 c. multicoloured .. 5 5
1694. 5 c. multicoloured .. 5 5
1695. 5 c. multicoloured .. 5 5
1696. 5 c. multicoloured .. 5 5

260. Girl carrying Tinaja. **261.** Pele (Brazil).

1970. Air. 8th Inter-American Savings and Loans Conf., Managua.
1697. **260.** 10 c. multicoloured .. 5 5
1698. 15 c. multicoloured .. 5 5
1699. 20 c. multicoloured .. 5 5
1700. 35 c. multicoloured .. 8 5
1701. 50 c. multicoloured .. 15 8
1702. 75 c. multicoloured .. 20 12
1703. 1 cor. multicoloured .. 30 20
1704. 2 cor. multicoloured .. 60 40

1970. World Football "Hall of Fame" Poll-winners. Multicoloured.
1705. 5 c. Type **261** (postage) .. 5 5
1706. 10 c. Puskas (Hungary) .. 5 5
1707. 15 c. Matthews (England) .. 5 5
1708. 40 c. Di Stefano (Argentina) 10 8
1709. 2 cor. Facchetti (Italy) .. 55 45
1710. 3 cor. Yashin (Russia) .. 70 65
1711. 5 cor. Beckenbauer (West Germany) 70 90
1712. 20 c. Santos (Brazil) (air) 10 8
1713. 80 c. Wright (England) .. 20 15
1714. 1 cor. Flags of 16 World Cup Finalists 25 20
1715. 4 cor. Bozsik (Hungary) .. 90 75
1716. 5 cor. Charlton (England) 1·10 90

262. Torii (Gate). **263.** Module and Astronauts on Moon.

1970. Air. EXPO 70, World Fair, Osaka, Japan.
1717. **262.** 25 c. multicoloured .. 5 5
1718. 30 c. multicoloured .. 10 5
1719. 35 c. multicoloured .. 10 5
1720. 75 c. multicoloured .. 25 12
1721. 1 cor. 50 multicoloured 35 30
1722. 3 cor. multicoloured 45 35

1970. Air. "Apollo 11" Moon Landing. Multicoloured.
1724. 35 c. Type **263** 10 5
1725. 40 c. Module landing on Moon 10 8
1726. 60 c. Astronauts with U.S. Flag 20 15
1727. 75 c. As 40 c. 25 15
1728. 1 cor. As 60 c. 35 20
1729. 2 cor. Type **263** 40 35

264. F. D. Roosevelt. **265.** "The Annunciation" (Grunewald).

1970. Air. 25th Death Anniv. of Franklin D. Roosevelt.

1730.	264. 10 c. black	5	5
1731.	– 15 c. brown and black	5	5
1732.	– 20 c. green & black	8	5
1733.	264. 35 c. purple & black	10	8
1734.	– 50 c. brown	12	10
1735.	264. 75 c. blue	20	12
1736.	– 1 cor. red	25	20
1737.	– 2 cor. black	30	35

PORTRAITS: 15 c., 1 cor. Roosevelt with stamp collection. 20 c., 50 c., 2 cor. Roosevelt (full-face).

1970. Air. Christmas. Paintings. Mult.

1738.	10 c. Type 265	5	5
1739.	10 c. "The Nativity" (detail, El Greco)	5	5
1740.	10 c. "The Adoration of the Magi" (detail, Durer)	5	5
1741.	10 c. "Virgin and Child" (J. van Hemessen)	5	5
1742.	10 c. "The Holy Shepherd" (Portuguese School, 16th cent.)	5	5
1743.	15 c. Type 265	5	5
1744.	20 c. As No. 1739	8	5
1745.	35 c. As No. 1740	12	8
1746.	75 c. As No. 1741	20	15
1747.	1 cor. As No. 1742	30	20

1971. Surch. **RESELLO** and new value.

1748.	30 c. on 90 c. black (No. 1227) (postage)	10·00	10·00
1749.	10 c. on 1 cor. 5 red, blk. & red (No. 1368) (air)	8	5
1750.	10 c. on 1 cor. 5 mult. (No. 1407)	8	5
1751.	10 c. on 1 cor. 5 mult. (No. 1430)	8	5
1752.	15 c. on 1 cor. 50 green and red (No. 1116)	10	5
1753.	15 c. on 1 cor. 50 green (No. 1255)	10	5
1754.	15 c. on 1 cor. 50 yellow and blue (No. 1369)	10	5
1755.	15 c. on 1 cor. 50 black and violet (No. 1381)	10	5
1756.	20 c. on 85 c. black and red (No. 1276)	12	8
1757.	20 c. on 85 c. black, red and blue (No. 1339)	12	8
1758.	25 c. on 90 c. black, green and ochre (No. 1440)	15	12
1759.	30 c. on 1 cor. 10 black and purple (No. 1195)	15	12
1760.	40 c. on 1 cor. 10 brown and black (No. 1157)	65	65
1761.	40 c. on 1 cor. 50 mult. (No. 1408)	65	65
1762.	1 cor. on 1 cor. 10 black and blue (No. 1538)	1·60	1·60

266. Basic Mathematical Equation.

1971. Scientific Formulae. "The Ten Mathematical Equations that changed the Face of the Earth". Multicoloured.

1763.	10 c. Type 266 (postage)	5	5
1764.	15 c. Newton's Law	5	5
1765.	20 c. Einstein's Law	8	8
1766.	1 cor. Tsiolkovsky's Law	25	25
1767.	2 cor. Maxwell's Law	90	75
1768.	25 c. Napier's Law (air)	8	5
1769.	30 c. Pythagoras' Law	10	8
1770.	40 c. Boltzmann's Law	12	10
1771.	1 cor. Broglie's Law	30	20
1772.	2 cor. Archimedes' Law	55	40

267. Peace Emblem.

1971. "Is There a Formula for Peace?".

1773.	267. 10 c. blue and black	5	5
1774.	15 c. blue, blk. & vio.	5	5
1775.	20 c. blue, blk. & brn.	5	5
1776.	40 c. blue, blk. & grn.	10	8
1777.	50 c. blue, blk. & pur.	12	10
1778.	80 c. blue, blk. & red	15	12
1779.	1 cor. blue, blk. & grn.	30	20
1780.	2 cor. blue, blk. & vio.	55	35

268. Montezuma Oropendola. **269.** "Moses with the Tablets of the Law" (Rembrandt).

1971. Air. Nicaraguan Birds. Multicoloured.

1781.	10 c. Type 268	35	15
1782.	15 c. Turquoise-browed Motmot	35	15
1783.	20 c. White-throated Magpie-Jay	45	15
1784.	25 c. Scissor-tailed Fly-catcher	45	15
1785.	30 c. Spotted-breasted Oriole (horiz.)	60	15
1786.	35 c. Rufous-naped Wren	70	15
1787.	40 c. Great Kiskadee	70	15
1788.	75 c. Red-legged Honey-creeper (horiz.)	1·25	35
1789.	1 cor. Great-tailed Grackle (horiz.)	1·50	45
1790.	2 cor. Belted Kingfisher	2·50	65

1971. "The Ten Commandments". Paintings. Multicoloured.

1791.	10 c. Type 269 (postage)	5	5
1792.	15 c. "Moses and the Burning Bush" (Botticelli) (1st Commandment)	5	5
1793.	20 c. "Jepthah's Daughter" (Degas) (2nd Commandment) (horiz.)	5	5
1794.	30 c. "St. Vincent Ferrer preaching in Verona" (Morone) (3rd Commandment) (horiz.)	8	5
1795.	35 c. "Noah's Drunkenness" (Michelangelo) (4th Commandment) (horiz.)	10	5
1796.	40 c. "Cain and Abel" (Trevisani) (5th Commandment) (horiz.)	10	8
1797.	50 c. "Joseph accused by Potiphar's Wife" (Rembrandt) (6th Commandment)	10	10
1798.	60 c. "Isaac blessing Jacob" (Eeckhout) (7th Commandment) (horiz.)	12	10
1799.	75 c. "Susannah and the Elders" (Rubens) (8th Commandment) (horiz.)	25	20
1800.	1 cor. "Bathsheba after her Bath" (Rembrandt) (9th Commandment) (air)	25	20
1801.	2 cor. "Naboth's Vineyard" (Smetham) (10th Commandment)	40	35

270. U Thant and Pres. Somoza.

1971. Air. 25th Anniv. of U.N.O.

1802.	270. 10 c. brown and red	5	5
1803.	15 c. green and emerald	5	5
1804.	20 c. blue & light blue	5	5
1805.	25 c. red and purple	8	5
1806.	30 c. brown & orange	8	5
1807.	40 c. green and grey	12	8
1808.	1 cor. green & sage	25	20
1809.	2 cor. brn. & light brn.	30	35

1972. Olympic Games, Munich. Nos. 1709, 1711, 1713 and 1716 surch. **OLIMPIADAS MUNICH 1972**, emblem and value or optd. only (5 cor.).

1810.	40 c. on 2 cor. multicoloured (postage)	10	10
1811.	50 c. on 3 cor. mult.	15	10
1812.	20 c. on 80 c. mult. (air)	5	5
1813.	60 c. on 4 cor. mult.	12	10
1814.	5 cor. multicoloured	65	65

272. Figurine and Apoyo Site on Map.

1972. Air. Pre-Columbian Art. A. H. Heller's Pottery Discoveries. Multicoloured.

1815.	10 c. Type 272	5	5
1816.	15 c. Cana Castilla	5	5
1817.	20 c. Catarina	8	5
1818.	25 c. Santa Helena	8	5
1819.	30 c. Mombacho	8	5
1820.	35 c. Tisma	8	5
1821.	40 c. El Menco	8	8
1822.	50 c. Los Placeres	12	8
1823.	60 c. Masaya	15	12
1824.	80 c. Granada	20	15
1825.	1 cor. Las Mercedes	30	20
1826.	2 cor. Nindiri	55	35

273. "Lord Peter Wimsey" (Dorothy Sayers).

1972. Air. 50th Anniv. of International Criminal Police Organization (INTERPOL). Famous Fictional Detectives. Mult.

1827.	5 c. Type 273	5	5
1828.	10 c. "Philip Marlow" (Raymond Chandler)	5	5
1829.	15 c. "Sam Spade" (D. Hammett)	4·50	10
1830.	20 c. "Perry Mason" (Erle Stanley Gardner)	5	5
1831.	25 c. "Nero Wolfe" (Rex Stout)	5	5
1832.	35 c. "C. Auguste Dupin" (Edgar Allen Poe)	8	5
1833.	40 c. "Ellery Queen" (F. Dannay and M. Lee)	8	8
1834.	50 c. "Father Brown" (G. K. Chesterton)	10	8
1835.	60 c. "Charlie Chan" (Earl D. Biggers)	12	10
1836.	80 c. "Inspector Maigret" (Georges Simenon)	25	15
1837.	1 cor. "Hercule Poirot" (Agatha Christie)	25	20
1838.	2 cor. "Sherlock Holmes" (A. Conan Doyle)	70	70

274. "The Shepherdess and her Brothers".

1972. Air. Christmas. Scenes from Legend of the Christmas Rose. Multicoloured.

1839.	10 c. Type 274	5	5
1840.	15 c. Adoration of the Wise Men	5	5
1841.	20 c. Shepherdess crying	5	5
1842.	35 c. Angel appears to Shepherdess	8	5
1843.	40 c. Christmas Rose	8	8
1844.	60 c. Shepherdess thanks angel for roses	12	10
1845.	80 c. Shepherdess takes roses to Holy Child	15	12
1846.	1 cor. Holy Child receiving roses	20	15
1847.	2 cor. Nativity Scene	45	35

275. Sir Walter Raleigh and Elizabethan Galleon.

1973. Air. Causes of the American Revolution. Multicoloured.

1849.	10 c. Type 275	30	10
1850.	15 c. Signing "Mayflower Compact"	10	10
1851.	20 c. Acquittal of Peter Zenger (vert.)	10	10
1852.	25 c. Acclaiming American resistance (vert.)	10	10
1853.	30 c. Revenue Stamp (vert.)	10	10
1854.	35 c. "Serpent" slogan—"Join or die"	10	10
1855.	40 c. Boston massacre (vert.)	10	10
1856.	50 c. Boston Tea-party	10	10
1857.	60 c. Patrick Henry on trial (vert.)	15	10
1858.	75 c. Battle of Bunker Hill	20	10
1859.	80 c. Declaration of Independence	20	15
1860.	1 cor. Liberty Bell	30	20
1861.	2 cor. US seal (vert.)	90	60

1973. Nos. 1450/54, 1456 and 1458/9 optd. **CORREO.**

1862.	219. 5 c. multicoloured	25	8
1863.	– 5 c. multicoloured	25	8
1864.	– 5 c. multicoloured	25	8
1865.	– 5 c. multicoloured	25	8
1866.	– 5 c. multicoloured	25	8
1867.	– 5 c. multicoloured	25	8
1868.	– 5 c. multicoloured	25	8
1869.	– 5 c. multicoloured	25	8

277. Baseball, Player and Map. **278.** Givenchy, Paris.

1973. Air. 20th Int. Baseball Championships, Managua (1972).

1870.	277. 15 c. multicoloured	5	5
1871.	20 c. multicoloured	5	5
1872.	40 c. multicoloured	8	8
1873.	10 cor. multicoloured	1·50	90

1973. World-famous Couturiers. Mannequins. Multicoloured.

1875.	1 cor. Type 278 (postage)	25	20
1876.	2 cor. Hartnell, London	40	40
1877.	5 cor. Balmain, Paris	1·00	90
1878.	10 c. Lourdes, Nicaragua (air)	5	5
1879.	15 c. Halston, New York	5	5
1880.	20 c. Pino Lancetti, Rome	5	5
1881.	35 c. Madame Gres, Paris	8	5
1882.	40 c. Irene Galitzine, Rome	8	8
1883.	80 c. Pedro Rodriguez, Barcelona	12	12

279. Diet Chart.

1973. Air. Child Welfare. Multicoloured.

1885.	5 c.+5 c. Type 279	5	5
1886.	10 c.+5 c. Senora Somoza with baby, and Children's Hospital	5	5
1887.	15 c.+5 c. "Childbirth"	5	5
1888.	20 c.+5 c. "Immunisation"	5	5
1889.	30 c.+5 c. Water purification	8	5
1890.	35 c.+5 c. As No. 1886	8	8
1891	50 c.+10 c. Alexander Fleming and "Antibiotics"	10	8
1892.	60 c.+15 c. Malaria control	12	10
1893.	70 c.+10 c. Laboratory analysis	12	12
1894.	80 c.+20 c. Gastro-enteritis	20	15
1895.	1 cor.+50 c. As No. 1886	30	25
1896.	2 cor. Pediatric surgery	45	35

280. Virginia and Father.

1973. Christmas. "Does Santa Claus exist?" (Virginia O'Hanlon's letter to American "Sun" newspaper). Multicoloured.

1897.	2 c. Type 280 (postage)	5	5
1898.	3 c. Text of letter	5	5
1899.	4 c. Reading the reply	5	5
1900.	5 c. Type 280	5	5
1901.	15 c. As 3 c.	5	5
1902.	20 c. As 4 c.	5	5
1903.	1 cor. Type 280 (air)	20	15
1904.	2 cor. As 3 c.	35	30
1905.	4 cor. As 4 c.	75	65

281. Churchill making Speech, 1936.

1974. Birth Cent. of Sir Winston Churchill.
1907. 281. 2 c. mult. (postage) .. 10 10
1908. – 3 c. blk., bl. & brn. .. 10 10
1909. – 4 c. multicoloured .. 10 10
1910. – 5 c. multicoloured .. 10 10
1911. – 10 c. brn., grn. & bl. 30 10
1912. – 5 cor. mult. (air) .. 90 80
1913. – 6 cor. blk. brn. & bl. 1·00 90
DESIGNS: 3 c. "The Four Churchills" (wartime cartoon). 4 c. Candle, cigar and "Action" stickers. 5 c. Churchill, Roosevelt and Stalin at Yalta. 10 c. Churchill landing in Normandy, 1944. 5 cor. Churchill giving "V" sign. 6 cor. "Bulldog Churchill" (cartoon).

282. Presentation of World Cup to Uruguay, 1930.

1974. World Cup Football Championships. Multicoloured.
1915. 1 c. Type 282 (postage) .. 5 5
1916. 2 c. Victorious Italian team, 1934 .. .. 5 5
1917. 3 c. Presentation of World Cup to Italy, 1938 .. 5 5
1918. 4 c. Uruguay's winning goal, 1950 .. .. 5 5
1919. 5 c. Victorious West German team, 1954 .. 5 5
1920. 10 c. Rejoicing Brazilian players, 1958 .. .. 5 5
1921. 15 c. Brazilian player holding World Cup, 1962 .. 5 5
1922. 20 c. Queen Elizabeth II presenting Cup to Bobby Moore, 1966 .. 5 5
1923. 25 c. Victorious Brazilian players, 1970 .. .. 5 5
1924. 10 cor. Football and flags of participating countries, 1974 (air) .. 1·75 1·75

283. "Malachra sp.".

284. Nicaraguan 7½ c. Stamp of 1937.

1974. Wild Flowers and Cacti. Multicoloured.
1926. 2 c. Type 283 (postage) .. 5 5
1927. 3 c. "Paguira insignis" .. 5 5
1928. 4 c. "Convolvulus sp." .. 5 5
1929. 5 c. "Pereschia autumnalis" 5 5
1930. 10 c. "Ipomea tuberosa" 5 5
1931. 15 c. "Hibiscus elatus" .. 5 5
1932. 20 c. "Plumeria acutifolia" 8 5
1933. 1 cor. "Centrosema sp." (air) 20 20
1934. 3 cor. "Hylocereus undatus" 60 55

1974. Cent. of U.P.U.
1935. 284. 2 c. red, grn. & blk. (post.) 10 15
1936. – 3 c. bl., grn. & blk. .. 10 10
1937. – 4 c. multicoloured .. 10 10
1938. – 5 c. brn., mve. & blk. 10 10
1939. – 10 c. red, brn. & blk. 10 10
1940. – 20 c. grn., bl. & blk. 10 10
1941. – 40 c. multicoloured (air) 10 10
1942. – 3 cor. grn., blk. & pink 50 40
1943. – 5 cor. bl., blk. & lilac 1·00 80
DESIGNS—VERT. 3 c. 5 c. stamp of 1937. 5c. 2 c. stamp of 1937. 10 c. 1 c. stamp of 1937. 20 c. ½ c. stamp of 1937. 40 c. 10 c. stamp of 1961. 5 cor. 4 cor. U.P.U. stamp of 1950. HORIZ. 4 c. 10 c. air stamp of 1934. 3 cor. 85 c. U.P.U. air stamp of 1950.

1974. Air. West Germany's Victory in World Cup Football Championships. No. 1924 optd. **TRIUMFADOR ALEMANIA OCCIDENTAL.**
1945. 10 cor. multicoloured .. 1·75 1·60

286. Tamandua.

1974. Nicaraguan Fauna. Multicoloured.
1947. 1 c. Type 286 (postage) .. 5 5
1948. 2 c. Puma 5 5
1949. 3 c. Common raccoon .. 5 5
1950. 4 c. Ocelot 5 5
1951. 5 c. Kinkajou 5 5
1952. 10 c. Coypu 10 10
1953. 15 c. Collared peccary .. 12 10
1954. 20 c. Baird's tapir .. 12 10
1955. 3 cor. Red brocket (air) .. 1·50 1·40
1956. 5 cor. Jaguar .. .. 2·40 2·00

287. "Prophet Zacharias".

288. Giovanni Martinelli ("Othello").

1975. Christmas. 500th Birth Anniv. of Michelangelo. Multicoloured.
1957. 1 c. Type 287 (postage) .. 5 5
1958. 2 c. "Christ amongst the Jews" 5 5
1959. 3 c. "The Creation of Man" (horiz.) .. 5 5
1960. 4 c. Interior of Sistine Chapel, Rome 5 5
1961. 5 c. "Moses" 5 5
1962. 10 c. "Mouscron Madonna" 5 5
1963. 15 c. "David" 5 5
1964. 20 c. "Doni Madonna" .. 5 5
1965. 40 c. "Madonna of the Steps" (air) 8 8
1966. 80 c. "Pitti Madonna" .. 15 12
1967. 2 cor. "Christ and Virgin Mary" 35 30
1968. 5 cor. "Michelangelo" (self-portrait) 75 75

1975. Great Opera Singers. Multicoloured.
1970. 1 c. Type 288 (postage) .. 5 5
1971. 2 c. Tito Gobbi ("Simone Boccaoegra") 5 5
1972. 3 c. Lotte Lehmann ("Der Rosenkavalier") .. 5 5
1973. 4 c. Lauritz Melchior ("Parsifal") 5 5
1974. 5 c. Nellie Melba ("La Traviata") 5 5
1975. 15 c. Jussi Bjoerling ("La Boheme") 5 5
1976. 20 c. Birgit Nilsson ("Turandot") 8 8
1977. 25 c. Rosa Ponselle ("Norma") (air) .. 5 5
1978. 35 c. Guiseppe de Luca ("Rigoletto") .. 8 5
1979. 40 c. Joan Sutherland ("La Figlia del Reggimiento") 8 8
1980. 50 c. Enzio Pinza ("Don Giovanni") 8 8
1981. 60 c. Kirsten Flagstad ("Tristan und Isolde") 12 10
1982. 80 c. Maria Callas ("Tosca") 15 12
1983. 2 cor. Fyodor Chaliapin ("Boris Godunov") .. 60 35
1984. 5 cor. Enrico Caruso ("La Juive") .. .. 1·10 60

289. The First Station.

290. "The Spirit of 76".

1975. Easter. The 14 Stations of the Cross.
1986. 289. 1 c. mult. (postage) .. 5 5
1987. – 2 c. multicoloured .. 5 5
1988. – 3 c. multicoloured .. 5 5
1989. – 4 c. multicoloured .. 5 5
1990. – 5 c. multicoloured .. 5 5
1991. – 15 c. multicoloured .. 5 5
1992. – 20 c. multicoloured .. 5 5
1993. – 25 c. multicoloured .. 5 5
1994. – 35 c. multicoloured .. 8 5
1995. – 40 c. mult. (air) .. 8 8
1996. – 50 c. multicoloured .. 8 8
1997. – 80 c. multicoloured .. 15 12
1998. – 1 cor. multicoloured 20 15
1999. – 5 cor. multicoloured 80 65
DESIGNS: 2 c. to 5 cor. Different Stations of the Cross.

1975. Bicentenary of American Independence (1st series). Multicoloured.
2000. 1 c. Type 290 (postage) .. 5 5
2001. 2 c. Pitt addressing Parliament 5 5
2002. 3 c. Paul Revere's Ride (horiz.) 5 5
2003. 4 c. Demolishing statue of George III (horiz.) .. 5 5
2004. 5 c. Boston Massacre .. 5 5
2005. 10 c. Tax stamp and George III 3d. coin (horiz.) 5 5
2006. 15 c. Boston Tea Party (horiz.) 5 5
2007. 20 c. Thomas Jefferson .. 5 5
2008. 25 c. Benjamin Franklin 5 5
2009. 30 c. Signing of Declaration of Independence (horiz.) 8 5
2010. 35 c. Surrender of Cornwallis at Yorktown (horiz.) 8 5
2011. 40 c. Washington's Farewell (horiz.) (air) .. 10 10
2012. 50 c. Washington addressing Congress (horiz.) .. 10 10
2013. 2 cor. Washington arriving for Presidential Inauguration (horiz.) .. 70 30
2014. 5 cor. Statue of Liberty & flags 75 45
See also Nos. 2056/71.

291. Saluting the Flag.

1975. "Nordjamb 75" World Scout Jamboree, Norway. Multicoloured.
2016. 1 c. Type 291 (postage) 10 10
2017. 2 c. Scout canoe .. 10 10
2018. 3 c. Scouts shaking hands 10 10
2019. 4 c. Scout preparing meal 10 10
2020. 5 c. Entrance to Nicaraguan camp .. 10 10
2021. 20 c. Scouts meeting .. 10 10
2022. 35 c. Aerial view of camp (air) 10 10
2023. 40 c. Scouts making music 10 10
2024. 1 cor. Camp-fire .. 20 15
2025. 10 cor. Lord Baden-Powell .. .. 1·25 1·10

292. President Somoza.

293. "Chess Players" (L. Carracci).

1975. President Somoza's New Term of Office, 1974-1981.
2027. 292. 20 c. mult. (postage) 5 5
2028. 40 c. multicoloured .. 8 8
2029. 1 cor. mult. (air) .. 20 20
2030. 10 cor. multicoloured 1·25 1·10
2031. 20 cor. multicoloured 3·25 2·75

1975. Chess. Multicoloured.
2032 1 c. Type 293 (postage) .. 5 5
2033 2 c. "Arabs playing Chess" (Delacroix) 5 5
2034 3 c. "Cardinals playing Chess" (V. Marais-Milton) .. 5 5
2035 4 c. "Duke Albrecht V of Bavaria and Anna of Austria at Chess" (H. Muelich) (vert) 5 5
2036 5 c. "Chess game" (14th-century Persian manuscript) .. 5 5
2037 10 c. "Origins of Chess" (India, 1602) .. 5 5
2038 15 c. "Napoleon playing Chess in Schonbrunn Palace in 1809" (A. Uniechowski) (vert) .. 5 5
2039 20 c. "The Chess Game in the House of Count Ingenheim" (J.E. Hummel) .. 5 5
2040 40 c. "The Chess-players" (T. Eakins) (air) .. 10 8
2041 2 cor. Fischer v Spassky match, Reykjavik, 1972 55 35
2042 5 cor. "William Shakespeare and Ben Jonson playing Chess" (K. van Mander) .. 60 50

294. Choir of King's College Cambridge.

1975. Christmas. Famous Choirs. Mult.
2044. 1 c. Type 294 (postage) .. 5 5
2045. 2 c. Abbey Choir, Einsiedeln 5 5
2046. 3 c. Regensburg Cathedral choir 5 5
2047. 4 c. Vienna Boys' choir .. 5 5
2048. 5 c. Sistine Chapel choir .. 5 5
2049. 15 c. Westminster Cathedral choir 5 5
2050. 20 c. Mormon Tabernacle choir 5 5
2051. 50 c. School choir, Montserrat (air) .. 8 8
2052. 1 cor. St. Florian children's choir 20 15
2053. 2 cor. "Little Singers of the Wooden Cross" (vert.) 45 35
2054. 5 cor. Pope with choristers of Pueri Cantores .. 60 50

295. "The Smoke Signal" (F. Remington).

1976. Bicent of American Revolution (2nd series). "200 Years of Progress". Mult.
2056 1 c. Type 295 (postage) .. 10 10
2057 1 c. Houston Space Centre 10 10
2058 2 c. Lighting candelabra, 1976 .. .. 10 10
2059 2 c. Edison's lamp and houses 10 10
2060 3 c. "Agriculture 1776" .. 10 10
2061 3 c. "Agriculture 1976" .. 10 10
2062 4 c. Harvard College, 1776 10 10
2063 4 c. Harvard University, 1976 .. .. 10 10
2064 5 c. Horse and carriage .. 15 10
2065 5 c. Boeing 747 airliner .. 15 10
2066 80 c. Philadelphia, 1776 (air) 25 15
2067 80 c. Washington, 1976 .. 25 15
2068 2 cor. 75 "Bonhomme Richard" (John Paul Jones's flagship) and H.M.S. "Serapis", Battle of Flamborough Head .. .. 1·50 70
2069 2 cor. 75 U.S.S. "Glenard Phipscomp" (nuclear submarine) .. .. 1·50 70
2070 4 cor. Wagon train .. 90 70
2071 4 cor. "Amtrak" express train .. .. 1·90 1·25

296. Italy, 1968.

1976. Olympic Games, Victors in Rowing and Sculling. Multicoloured.
2073. 1 c. Denmark 1964 (postage) 5 5
2074. 2 c. East Germany 1972 5 5
2075. 3 c. Type 296 .. .. 5 5
2076. 4 c. Great Britain 1936 .. 5 5
2077. 5 c. France 1952 (vert.) .. 5 5
2078. 35 c. U.S.A. 1920 (vert.) 10 8
2079. 55 c. Russia 1956 (vert.) (air) 20 8
2080. 70 c. New Zealand 1972 (vert.) 20 12
2081. 90 c. New Zealand 1968 .. 25 20
2082. 20 cor. U.S.A. 1956 .. 2·75 2·50

1976. Air. Olympic Games, Montreal. East German Victory in Rowing Events. No. 2082 optd. **REPUBLICA DEMOCRATICA ALEMANA VENCEDOR EN 1976.**
2084 20 cor. multicoloured .. 2·75 2·50

299. Mauritius 1847 2d. "Post Office".

1976. Rare and Famous Stamps. Mult.
2087. 1 c. Type 299 (postage) 10 10
2088. 2 c. Western Australia 1854 "Inverted Mute Swan" 30 10
2089. 3 c. Mauritius 1847 1d. "Post Office" 10 10
2090. 4 c. Jamaica 1920 1s. Inverted Frame .. 10 10
2091. 5 c. U.S. 1918 24 c. Inverted Aircraft .. 10 10
2092. 10 c. Swiss 1845 Basel "Dove" 10 10
2093. 25 c. Canada 1959 Seaway Inverted Centre 10 10
2094. 40 c. Hawaiian 1851 2 c. "Missionary" (air) .. 10 10
2095. 1 cor. G.B. 1840 "Penny Black" 20 20
2096. 2 cor. British Guiana 1850 1 c. Black on Magenta 40 35
2097. 5 cor. Honduras 1925 Airmail 25 c. on 10 c. .. 70 50
2098. 10 cor. Newfoundland 1919 "Hawker" Airmail stamp .. 1·25 1·10

300. Olga Nunez de Saballos (Member of Parliament).

1977. Air. International Women's Year. Multicoloured.

2100. 35 c. Type **300** 8 5
2101. 1 cor. Josefa Toledo de Aguerri (educator) .. 20 20
2102. 10 cor. Hope Portocarrco de Samoza (President's wife) .. .. .. 1·25 1·00

301. " Graf Zeppelin " in Hangar.

1977. 75th Anniv. of First Zeppelin Flight. Multicoloured.

2104. 1 c. Type **301** (postage) .. 10 10
2105. 2 c. " Graf Zeppelin " in flight 10 10
2106. 3 c. Giffard's steam-driven airship, 1852 .. .. 15 10
2107. 4 c. Zeppelin in mooring hangar 15 10
2108. 5 c. " Graf Zeppelin " on ground 15 10
2109. 35 c. Dirigible with inflatable ailerons (air) .. 35 15
2110. 70 c. " Schwaben " .. 40 20
2111. 3 cor. " Graf Zeppelin " over Lake Constance .. 1·00 65
2112. 10 cor. " Z 3 " on Lake Constance .. .. 3·75 2·25

302. Lindbergh and Map.

1977. 50th Anniv. of Lindbergh's Transatlantic Flight. Multicoloured.

2114. 1 c. Type **302** (postage) .. 10 10
2115. 2 c. Map and " Spirit of St. Louis " 10 10
2116. 3 c. Charles Lindbergh (vert.) 10 10
2117. 4 c. " Spirit of St. Louis " crossing Atlantic .. 10 10
2118. 5 c. Lindbergh standing by plane 10 10
2119. 20 c. Lindbergh, route and plane 20 15
2120. 55 c. Lindbergh landing in Nicaragua (1928) (air) 20 15
2121. 80 c. Plane and route-map 35 15
2122. 2 cor. " Spirit of St. Louis " flying along Nicaraguan coast 65 35
2123. 10 cor. Passing Momotombo (Nicaragua) .. 1·90 1·25

303. Christmas Festival.

1977. Christmas. Scenes from Tchaikovsky's "Nutcracker" Suite. Multicoloured.

2125. 1 c. Type **303** 5 5
2126. 2 c. Doll's dance .. 5 5
2127. 3 c. Clara and snowflakes 5 5
2128. 4 c. Snow fairy and Prince 5 5
2129. 5 c. Snow fairies .. 5 5
2130. 15 c. Sugar fairy and Prince 5 5
2131. 40 c. Waltz of the Flowers 8 5
2132. 90 c. Chinese dance .. 20 15
2133. 1 cor. Senora Bonbonierre 20 20
2134. 10 cor. Arabian dance .. 1·40 1·25

304. " Mr. and Mrs. Andrews ". (Gainsborough).

1978. Paintings. Multicoloured.

2136. 1 c. Type **304** (postage) .. 5 5
2137. 2 c. " Giovanna Bacelli " (Gainsborough) .. 5 5
2138. 3 c. " Blue Boy " (Gainsborough) 5 5
2139. 4 c. " Francis I " (Titian) 5 5
2140. 5 c. " Charles V at Battle of Muhlberg " (Titian) 5 5
2141. 25 c. " Sacred Love " (Titian) 5 5
2142. 5 cor. " Hippopotamus and Crocodile Hunt " (Rubens) (air) 60 50
2143. 10 cor. " Duke of Lerma on Horseback " (Rubens) 1·75 1·40

305. Gothic Portal with Rose Window, Small Basilica of St. Francis.

1978. 750th Anniv. of Canonisation of St. Francis of Assisi. Multicoloured.

2145. 1 c. Type **305** (postage) .. 5 5
2146. 2 c. St. Francis preaching to birds 5 5
2147. 3 c. Painting of St. Francis 5 5
2148. 4 c. Franciscan genealogical tree 5 5
2149. 5 c. Portiuncola .. 5 5
2150. 15 c. Autographed blessing 5 5
2151. 25 c. Windows of Large Basilica 5 5
2152. 80 c. St. Francis and wolf (air) 12 8
2153. 10 cor. St. Francis .. 1·60 1·50

306. Passenger and Freight Locomotive.

1978. Cent. of Railway. Mult.

2155. 1 c. Type **306** (postage) .. 10 5
2156. 2 c. Light-weight cargo locomotive 10 5
2157. 3 c. American locomotive 10 5
2158. 4 c. Baldwin heavy freight locomotive 10 5
2159. 5 c. Baldwin light freight and passenger locomotive 10 5
2160. 15 c. Presidential Pullman coach 10 5
2161. 35 c. Light-weight American locomotive (air) .. 20 5
2162. 4 cor. Baldwin locomotive 1·75 70
2163. 10 cor. Juniata locomotive 4·75 1·75

307. Mongol Warriors (" Michael Strogoff ").

1978. 150th Birth Anniv. of Jules Verne. Multicoloured.

2165. 1 c. Type **307** (postage) 10 10
2166. 2 c. Sea scene "The (Mysterious Island") .. 10 10
2167. 3 c. Sea monsters ("Journey to the Centre of the Earth") 10 10
2168. 4 c. Balloon and African elephant ("Five Weeks in a Balloon") .. 20 10
2169. 90 c. Submarine ("Twenty Thousand Leagues Under the Sea") (air) 30 20
2170. 10 cor. Balloon, Indian, steam locomotive and elephant ("Around the World in Eighty Days") .. .. 5·50 3·00

308. Icarus.

1978. 75th Anniv. of History of Aviation. First Powered Flight. Multicoloured.

2172. 1 c. Type **308** (postage) .. 10 10
2173. 2 c. Montgolfier balloon (vert.) 10 10
2174. 3 c. " Flyer I " 10 10
2175. 4 c. Orville Wright at controls of " Flyer " (vert.) 10 10
2176. 55 c. Early Sikorsky helicopter (air) .. 30 10
2177. 10 cor. Space shuttle .. 2·10 1·00

309. Ernst Ocwirk and Alfredo di Stefano. **310.** " St. Peter " (Goya).

1978. World Cup Football Championship, Argentina. Multicoloured.

2179. 20 c. Type **309**. (postage) 5 5
2180. 25 c. Ralf Edstrom and Oswaldo Piazza .. 5 5
2181. 50 c. Franz Beckenbauer and Dennis Law (air) .. 8 5
2182. 5 cor. Dino Zoff and Pele 65 50

1978. Christmas. Multicoloured.

2184. 10 c. Type **310** (postage) 8 8
2185. 15 c. " St. Gregory " (Goya) 8 8
2186. 3 cor. " The Apostles John and Peter " (Durer) (air) 40 30
2187. 10 cor. " The Apostles Paul and Mark " (Durer) 1·40 1·00

311. San Cristobal.

1978. Volcanoes and Lakes. Multicoloured.

2189. 5 c. Type **311** (postage) .. 5 5
2190. 5 c. Lake de Cosiguina .. 5 5
2191. 20 c. Telica 5 5
2192. 20 c. Lake Jiloa 5 5
2193. 35 c. Cerro Negro (air) .. 8 5
2194. 35 c. Lake Masaya .. 8 5
2195. 90 c. Momotombo .. 20 12
2196. 90 c. Lake Asososca .. 20 12
2197. 1 cor. Mombacho .. 20 15
2198. 1 cor. Lake Apoyo .. 20 15
2199. 10 cor. Concepcion .. 1·60 80
2200. 10 cor. Lake Tiscapa .. 1·60 80

312. General O'Higgins.

1979. Air. Birth Bicentenary of Bernardo O'Higgins (liberation hero).

2201 **312** 20 cor. multicoloured 3·75 1·90

313. Ginger Plant and Broad-tailed Hummingbird.

1979. Air. Flowers. Multicoloured.

2202 50 c. Type **313** .. .. 1·25 10
2203 55 c. Orchids 10 5
2204 70 c. Pionsettia 12 8
2205 80 c. "Poro poro" .. 15 10
2206 2 cor. "Morpho cypris" (butterfly) and Guayacan flowers .. 50 30
2207 4 cor. Iris 45 30

314. Children with football. **315.** Indian Postal Runner.

1980. Year of Liberation (1979) and Nicaragua's Participation in Olympic Games. Unissued stamps Overprinted.

(a). International Year of the Child. Multicoloured.

2208 20 c. Children on round-about (postage) .. 15 15
2209 90 c. Type **314** (air) .. 65 65
2210 2 cor. Children with stamps albums .. 1·50 1·50
2211 2 cor. 20 Children playing with train and airplanes .. .. .. 3·00 2·00
2212 10 cor. Baseball .. .. 7·50 7·50

(b) Death Centenary of Sir Rowland Hill. Multicoloured.

2214. 20 c. Type **315** (postage) 20 20
2215. 35 c. Pony express .. 40 40
2216. 1 cor. Pre-stamp letter (horiz.) .. .. 1·10 1·10
2217. 1 cor. 80 Sir Rowland Hill examining sheet of Penny Black stamps (air) .. 1·90 1·90
2218. 2 cor. 20 Penny Blacks (horiz.) .. .. 2·40 2·40
2219. 5 cor. Nicaraguan Zeppelin flight cover (horiz.) .. 5·50 5·50

316. Einstein and Albert Schweitzer.

(c) Birth Centenary of Albert Einstein (physicist). Multicoloured.

2221. 5 c. Type **316** (postage) 12 12
2222. 10 c. Einstein and equation 25 25
2223. 15 c. Einstein and 1939 World Fair pavilion .. 40 40
2224. 20 c. Einstein and Robert Oppenheimer 50 50
2225. 25 c. Einstein in Jerusalem 65 65
2226. 1 cor. Einstein and Nobel Prize medal (air) .. 2·50 2·50
2227. 2 cor. 75 Einstein and space exploration .. 7·00 7·00
2228. 10 cor. Einstein and Mahatma Gandhi .. 15·00 15·00

317. Loggerhead Turtle.

(d). Endangered Turtles. Multicoloured.

2230. 90 c. Type **317** 70 70
2231. 2 cor. Leatherback turtle 1·50 1·50
2232. 2 cor. 30 " Ridley turtle " 1·75 1·75
2233. 10 cor. Hawksbilled turtle 7·50 7·50

318. Rigoberto Lopez Perez and Crowds pulling down Statue.

1980. 1st Anniv. of the Revolution. Mult.

2235. 40 c. Type **318** 5 5
2236. 75 c. Street barricade .. 8 8
2237. 1 cor. " Learn to Read " emblem (vert.) .. 12 10
2238. 1 cor. 25 German Pomares Ordonez and jungle fighters 20 12
2239. 1 cor. 85 Victory celebrations (vert.) 25 15
2240. 2 cor. 50 Carlos Fonesca and camp-fire .. 35 35
2241. 5 cor. Gen. Augusto Sandino and flag (vert.) .. 70 55

1980. Literacy Year. Unissued stamps optd. **1980 ANO DE LA ALFABETIZACION.**

(a). International Year of the Child. As Nos. 2208/12. Multicoloured.

2243. – 20 c. Children on round-about (postage) .. 1·00 1·00
2244. **314.** 90 c. Children with football (air) .. 1·00 1·00
2245. – 2 cor. Children with stamp albums .. 1·00 1·00
2246. – 2 cor 20 Children playing with train and airplane .. .. 2·00 2·00
2247. – 10 cor. Baseball .. 4·50 4·50

(b) Death Centenary of Sir Rowland Hill. As Nos. 2214/6. additionally optd. with Olympic symbols 1980. Multicoloured.

2249. **315.** 20 c. Indian postal runner 70 70
2250. – 35 c. Pony express .. 70 70
2251. – 1 cor. Pre-stamp letter (horiz.) .. 70 70

(c) Birth Cent. of Albert Einstein (physicist). As Nos. 221/8. (additionally optd.) **PARTICIPACION NICARAGUA OLIMPIADAS 1980.** Multicoloured.

2253. 5 c. Optd. " **YURI GAGARIN/12/IV/1961/ LER HOMBRE EN EL ESPACIO** " (postage) 1·10 1·10
2254. 10 c. Optd. " **LURABA 1981** " and space shuttle 1·10 1·10
2255. 15 c. Optd. " **SPACE SHUTTLE** " and craft 1·10 1·10
2256. 20 c. Optd. **ANO DE LA ALFABETIZACION** 1·10 1·10
2257. 25 c. Optd. " **16/VII/1969/ LER HOMBRE A LA LUNA** " and " **APOLLO XI** " .. .. .. 1·10 1·10
2258. 1 cor. Optd. As No. 2256 (air) .. .. .. 1·10 1·10
2259. 2 cor. 75 Optd. As No. 2256 .. .. .. 1·10 1·10
2260. 10 cor. 75 Optd. " **LUNOJOD 1** " and vehicle .. 1·10 1·10

(d). Air. Endangered Species. Turtles. As Nos. 2230/3. Multicoloured.

2262. **317.** 90 c. Loggerhead turtle 1·00 1·00
2263. – 2 cor. Leatherback turtle .. .. 1·00 1·00
2264. – 2 cor. 20 Ridley turtle 1·00 1·00
2265. – 10 cor. Hawksbill turtle .. .. 1·00 1·00

321. Footballer and El Molinon Stadium.

1981. World Cup Football Championships, Spain. (1st issue). Venues. Multicoloured.

2268. 5 c. Type **321** 5 5
2269. 20 c. Sanchez Pizjuan, Seville 5 5
2270. 25 c. San Mames, Bilbao 5 5
2271. 30 c. Vincent Calderon, Madrid 5 5
2272. 50 c. R.C.D. Espanol, Barcelona 8 5
2273. 4 cor. New Stadium, Valladolid 55 35
2274. 5 cor. Balaidos, Vigo .. 55 35
2275. 10 cor. Santiago Bernabeu, Madrid .. .. 1·10 65

See also Nos. 2325/31.

322. Adult Education.

1981. 2nd Anniv. of Revolution. Mult.

2277. 50 c. Type **322** (postage) 10 10
2278. 2 cor. 10 Workers marching (air) 30 15
2279. 3 cor. Roadbuilding and container ship .. 65 30
2280. 6 cor. Medical services .. 50 25

323. Allegory of Revolution.

1981. 20th Anniv. of Sandinista National Liberation Front. Multicoloured.

2281. 50 c. Type **323** (postage) 8 5
2282. 4 cor. Sandinista guerrilla (air) 25 10

324. Postman.

1981. 12th Postal Union of the Americas and Spain Congress, Managua. Multicoloured.

2283. 50 c. Type **324** (postage) 8 5
2284. 2 cor. 10 Pony Express (air) 30 15
2285. 3 cor. Postal Headquarters Managua 45 25
2286. 6 cor. Government building, globe and flags of member countries .. 50 25

326. " Nymphaea capensis ".

1981. Water Lilies. Multicoloured.

2288. 50 c. Type **326.** (postage) 8 5
2289. 1 cor. " Nymphaea daubenyana " 15 8
2290. 1 cor. 20 " Nymphaea Marliacea Chromat " .. 20 10
2291. 1 cor. 80 " Nymphaea Dir. Geo. T. Moore " 25 15
2292. 2 cor. " Nymphaea lotus " .. 30 15
2293. 2 cor. 50 " Nymphaea B.G. Berry " 35 20
2294. 10 cor. " Nymphaea Gladstoniana " (air) .. 60 40

328. " Cheirodon axelrodi ".

1981. Tropical Fishes. Multicoloured.

2296. 50 c. Type **328** (postage) 8 5
2297. 1 cor. " Poecilia reticulata " 15 8
2298. 1 cor. 85 " Anostomus anostomus " 25 15
2299. 2 cor. 10 " Corydoras arculatus " 30 15
2300. 2 cor. 50 " Cynolebias nigripinnis " 35 20
2301. 3 cor. 50 " Petrolebias longipinnis " (air) .. 50 30
2302. 4 cor. " Xiphophorus helleri " 55 35

330. Lineated Woodpecker.

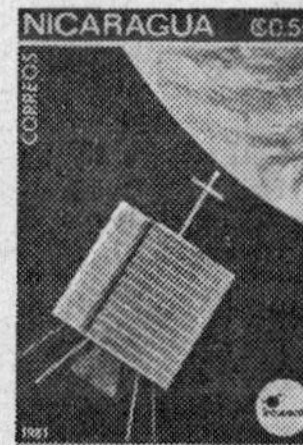

331. Satellite in Orbit.

1981. Birds. Multicoloured.

2304. 50 c. Type **330** (postage) 30 15
2305. 1 cor. 20 Keel-billed toucan (horiz.) .. 60 25
2306. 1 cor. 80 Finsch's conure (horiz.) 70 35
2307. 2 cor. Scarlet macaw .. 95 40
2308. 3 cor. Slaty-tailed trogon (air) .. .. .. 1·25 50
2309. 4 cor. Violet sabrewing (horiz.) .. .. 1·50 60
2310. 6 cor. Blue-crowned motmot .. .. 2·75 1·00

1981. Satellite Communications. Multicoloured.

2311. 50 c. Type **331** (postage) 8 5
2312. 1 cor. "Intelstat IVA" .. 15 8
2313. 1 cor. 50 " Intelstat V " moving into orbit .. 20 12
2314. 2 cor. Rocket releasing " Intelstat V " .. 30 20
2315. 3 cor. Satellite and Space Shuttle (air) 45 25
2316. 4 cor. " Intelstat V " and world maps 55 30
2317. 5 cor. Tracking stations .. 70 45

332. Locomotive "El 93" at Lago Granada.

1981. Locomotives. Multicoloured.

2318. 50 c. Type **332** (postage) 15 5
2319. 1 cor. Vulcan Iron Works 0-6-0 locomotive, 1946 30 5
2320. 1 cor. 20 Philadelphia Iron Works 0-6-0 locomotive 1911 .. .. .. 35 5
2321. 1 cor. 80 Steam hoist, 1909 50 5
2322. 2 cor. " U-10B ", 1956 .. 55 10
2323. 2 cor. 50 German railbus, 1954 .. .. .. 65 15
2324. 6 cor. Japanese railbus, 1967 (air) .. .. 1·75 35

333. Heading Ball.

1982. World Cup Football Championship, Spain (2nd issue). Multicoloured.

2325. 5 c. Type **333** (postage) .. 5 5
2326. 20 c. Running with ball .. 5 5
2327. 25 c. Running with ball (different) 5 5
2328. 2 cor. 50 Saving goal .. 35 20
2329. 3 cor 50 Goalkeeper diving for ball (horiz.) .. 50 30
2330. 4 cor. Kicking ball (air) .. 55 35
2331. 10 cor. Tackle (horiz.) .. 60 40

334. Cocker Spaniel.

1982. Pedigree Dogs. Multicoloured.

2333. 5 c. Type **334** (postage) .. 5 5
2334. 20 c. Alsatian 5 5
2335. 25 c. English setter .. 5 5
2336. 2 cor. 50 Brittany spaniel 35 20
2337. 3 cor. Boxer (air) .. 45 25
2338. 3 cor. 50 Pointer .. 50 30
2339. 6 cor. Collie 60 30

335. Satellite Communications.

1982. Air. I.T.U. Congress.

2340. **335.** 25 cor. multicoloured 2·10 1·50

336. " Dynamine myrrhina ".

1982. Butterflies. Multicoloured.

2341. 50 c. Type **336** (postage) 20 5
2342. 1 cor. 20 " Eunica alcmena 40 10
2343. 1 cor. 50 " Callizona acesta " 40 12
2344. 2 cor. " Adelpha leuceria " 60 20
2345. 3 cor. " Parides iphidamas " (air) .. .. .. 1·00 30
2346. 3 cor. 50 " Consul hippona " 1·10 35
2347. 4 cor. " Morpho peleides " 1·25 40

337. Dog and Russian Rocket.

1982. Space Exploration. Multicoloured.

2348. 5 c. Type **337** (postage) .. 5 5
2349. 15 c. Satellite (vert.) .. 5 5
2350. 50 c. " Apollo-Soyuz " link 8 5
2351. 1 cor. 50 Satellite .. 20 12
2352. 2 cor. 50 Docking in space 35 20
2353. 5 cor. Russian space station (air) 45 20
2354. 6 cor. Space shuttle " Columbia " (vert.) .. 60 30

338. Mailcoach.

1982. Centenary of U.P.U Membership. Multicoloured.

2355 50 c. Type **338** (postage) 10 10
2356 1 cor. 20 "Victoria" (packet steamer) .. 60 20
2357 3 cor. 50 Railway locomotive (air) .. .. 1·50 15
2358 10 cor. Jet airliner .. 1·50 1·10

339. Cyclists.

1982. 14th Central American and Caribbean Games. Multicoloured.

2359. 10 c. Type **339** (postage) 5 5
2360. 15 c. Swimming (horiz.) 5 5
2361. 25 c. Basketball .. 5 5
2362. 50 c. Weightlifting .. 8 5
2363. 2 cor. 50 Handball (air) .. 35 20
2364. 3 cor. Boxing (horiz.) .. 45 25
2365. 9 cor. Football (horiz.) .. 75 45

341. Washington passing through Trenton.

1982. 250th Birth Anniv of George Washington. Multicoloured.

2368. 50 c. Mount Vernon, Washington's house (39 × 49 mm.) (postage) 8 5
2369. 1 cor. Washington signing the Constitution (horiz.) 15 10
2370. 2 cor. Type **341** 30 20
2371. 2 cor. 50 Washington crossing the Delaware (horiz.) (air) 35 20
2372. 3 cor 50 Washington at Valley Forge (horiz.) .. 50 30
2373. 4 cor. Washington at the Battle of Trenton .. 55 35
2374. 6 cor. Washington at Princeton 60 55

342. Carlos Fonseca, Dove and Flags.

1982. 3rd Anniv. of Revolution. Mult.

2375. 50 c. Type **342** (postage) 8 5
2376. 2 cor. 50 Ribbons forming dove (vert.) (air) .. 35 20
2377. 1 cor. Augusto Sandino and dove (vert.) .. 55 30
2378. 6 cor. Dove 60 55

343. " Vase of Flowers " (R. Penalba).

1982. Paintings. Multicoloured.

2379. 25 c. Type **343** (postage) 5 5
2380. 50 c. " El Gueguense " (M. Garcia) (horiz.) .. 8 5
2381. 1 cor. " The Couple " (R. Perez) 15 8
2382. 1 cor. 20 " Canales Valley (A. Mejias) (horiz.) .. 20 10
2383. 1 cor. 85 " Portrait of Senora Castellon " (T. Jerez) 25 15
2384. 2 cor. " The Vendors " (L. Cerrato) 30 20
2385. 9 cor. " Sitting Woman " (A. Morales) (horiz.) (air) 55 35

344. Lenin and Dimitrov, Moscow, 1921.

1982. Birth Cent. of Georgi Dimitrov (Bulgarian statesman). Multicoloured.

2387. 50 c. Type **344** (postage) 8 5
2388. 2 cor. 50 Dimitrov & Todor Yikov, Sofia, 1946 (air) 35 20
2389. 4 cor. Dimitrov and flag 55 35

345. Ausberto Narvaez.

1982. 26th Anniv. of State of Resistance Movement. Multicoloured.

2390. 50 c. Type **345.** (postage) 8 5
2391. 2 cor. 50 Cornelio Silva .. 35 20
2392. 4 cor. Rigoberto Lopez Perez (air) 55 35
2393. 6 cor. Edwin Castro .. 60 55

346. Old Ruins at Leon.

1982. Tourism. Multicoloured.

2394. 50 c. Type **346** (postage) 8 5
2395. 1 cor. Ruben Dario Theatre and Park, Managua .. 15 8
2396. 1 cor. 20 Independence Square, Grenada .. 20 10
2397. 1 cor. 80 Corn Island .. 25 15
2398. 2 cor. Carter Santiago Volcano, Masaya .. 30 20
2399. 2 cor. 50 El Coyotepe Fortress, Masaya (air) 35 20
2400. 3 cor. 50 Luis A. Velazquez Park, Managua .. 50 30

347. Karl Marx and View of Trier.

1982. Death Cent. of Karl Marx. Mult.

2401. 1 cor. Type **347** (postage) 15 8
2402. 4 cor. Marx and grave in Highgate Cemetery (air) 55 35

348. Stacking Cane and Fruit.

1982. World Food Day. Multicoloured.

2403. 50 c. Picking Fruit (horiz.) 8 5
2404. 1 cor. Type **348** 15 8
2405. 2 cor. Cutting sugar cane (horiz.) 30 20
2406. 10 cor. F.A.O. and P.A.N. emblems (horiz.) .. 85 65

349. " Santa Maria ".

1982. 490th Anniv. of Discovery of America. Multicoloured.

2407. 50 c. Type **349** (postage) 50 15
2408. 1 cor. "Nina" .. .. 1·00 30
2409. 1 cor. 50 "Pinta" .. .. 1·40 35
2410. 2 cor. Columbus and fleet 1·60 55
2411. 2 cor. 50 Fleet and map of route (air) .. .. 1·75 55
2412. 4 cor. Arrival in America 55 35
2413. 7 cor. Death of Columbus 65 60

350. " Lobelia laxiflora ". **351.** "Micrurus lemniscatus".

1982. Woodland Flowers. Multicoloured.

2415. 50 c. Type **350** (postage) 8 5
2416. 1 cor. 20 " Bombacopsis quinata " 20 10
2417. 1 cor. 80 " Mimosa albida " 25 15
2418. 2 cor. " Epidendrum alatum " 30 20
2419. 2 cor. 50 Passion flower " Passiflora foetida " wrongly inscr. " Pasiflora " (air) 35 20
2420. 3 cor. 50 " Clitoria sp. " 50 30
2421. 5 cor. " Russelia sarmentosa " 70 45

1982. Reptiles. Multicoloured.

2422. 10 c. Type **351** (postage) 5 5
2423. 50 c. Common iguana " Iguana iguana " (horiz.) 8 5
2424. 2 cor. " Lachesis muta " (snake) (horiz.) .. 30 20
2425. 2 cor. 50 Hawksbill turtle " Eretmochelys imbricata " (horiz.) (air) .. 35 20
2426. 3 cor. Boa Constrictor " Constrictor constrictor " 45 25
2427. 3 cor. 50 American crocodile " Crocodilus acutus " (horiz.) 50 30
2428. 5 cor. Diamond-back rattlesnake " Sistrurus catenatus " (horiz.) .. 70 45

352. Tele-cor Building, Managua.

1982. Telecommunications Day. Multicoloured.

2429. 1 cor. Type **352** (postage) 15 8
2430. 50 c. Interior of radio transmission room (air) 8 5

353. Girl with Dove.

1983. Air. Non-Aligned States Conference.

2431. **353.** 4 cor. multicoloured 55 35

354. Jose Marti and Birthplace.

1983. 130th Birth Anniv. of Jose Marti. (Cuban revolutionary).

2432. **354.** 1 cor. multicoloured 15 8

355. Boxing. **356.** " Neomarica coerulea ".

1983. Olympic Games, Los Angeles (1st issue). Multicoloured.

2433. 50 c. Type **355** (postage) 8 5
2434. 1 cor. Gymnastics .. 15 8
2435. 1 cor. 50 Running .. 20 12
2436. 2 cor. Weightlifting .. 30 20
2437. 4 cor. Discus (air) .. 55 35
2438. 5 cor. Basketball .. 70 45
2439. 6 cor. Cycling 90 55

See also Nos. 2609/15.

1983. Flowers.

2441. **356.** 1 cor. blue 15 8
2442. – 1 cor. violet 15 8
2443. – 1 cor. mauve .. 15 8
2444. – 1 cor. brown 15 8
2445. – 1 cor. green 15 8
2446. – 1 cor. blue 15 8
2447. – 1 cor. green 15 8
2448. – 1 cor. green 15 8
2449. – 1 cor. mauve .. 15 8
2450. – 1 cor. red 15 8
2451. – 1 cor. grey 15 8
2452. – 1 cor. yellow 15 8
2453. – 1 cor. brown 15 8
2454. – 1 cor. purple 15 8
2455. – 1 cor. green 15 8
2456. – 1 cor. black 15 8

DESIGNS: No. 2442, " Tabebula ochraceae ". 2443, " Laella sp ". 2444, " Plumeria rubra ". 2445, " Brassavola nodosa ". 2446, " Stachytarpheta indica ". 2447, " Cochiospermum sp ". 2448, " Malvaviscus arboreus ". 2449, " Telecoma stans ". 2450, " Hibiscus rosa-sinensis ". 2451, " Cattleya lueddemanniana ". 2452, " Tagetes erecta ". 2453, " Senecio sp ". 2454, " Sobralia macrantha ". 2455, " Thumbergia alata ". 2456, " Bixa orellana ".

See also Nos. 2739/54 and 2838/53.

MINIMUM PRICE

The minimum price quoted is 5p which represents a handling charge rather than a basis for valuing common stamps. For further notes about prices see introductory pages.

357. Momotombo Geo-thermal Electrical Plant.

1983. Air. Energy.

2457. **357.** 2 cor. 50 mult. .. 35 20

358. Demonstrating Crowd.

1983. Papal Visit.

2458. **358.** 50 c. red, black and blue (postage) .. 8 5
2459. – 1 cor. multicoloured 15 8
2460. – 4 cor. mult. (air) .. 55 35
2461. – 7 cor. multicoloured 1·00 60

DESIGNS: 1 cor. Map of Nicaragua and girl picking coffee. 4 cor. Pres. Cordova Rivas and Pope John Paul II. 7 cor. Pope outside Managua Cathedral.

359. " Xilophanes chiron ".

1983. Moths. Multicoloured.

2463. 15 c. Type **359** (postage) 10 10
2464. 50 c. " Protoparce ochus " 15 10
2465. 65 c. " Pholus lasbruscae " 25 10
2466. 1 cor. " Amphypterus gannascus " 30 10
2467. 1 cor. 50 " Pholus licaon " 40 15
2468. 2 cor. " Agrius cingulata " 60 25
2469. 10 cor. " Rothschildia jurulla " (vert.) (air) .. 3·25 95

360. Subriava Church, Leon.

1983. Monuments. Multicoloured.

2470. 50 c. Type **360** (postage) 8 5
2471. 1 cor. " La Immaculada " Castle, Rio San Juan .. 15 8
2472. 2 cor. La Recoleccion Church, Leon (vert.) .. 30 20
2473. 4 cor. Ruben Dario Monument, Managua (vert.) (air) 55 35

361. Passenger Coach.

1983. Railway Wagons. Multicoloured.

2474. 15 c. Type **361** (postage) 10 5
2475. 65 c. Goods wagon .. 25 5
2476. 1 cor. Tanker .. 30 10
2477. 1 cor. 50 Ore hopper .. 40 15
2478. 4 cor. Passenger railcar (air) .. .. .. 1·10 50
2479. 5 cor. Tipper truck .. 1·25 60
2480. 7 cor. Railbus .. .. 1·90 75

362. Aiding Flood Victims.

1983. Red Cross. Multicoloured.

2481. 50 c. Type **362** (postage) 8 5
2482. 1 cor. Placing stretcher patient into ambulance 15 8
2483. 4 cor. Helping earthquake victim (vert.) (air) 55 35
2484. 5 cor. Doctor examining wounded soldier 70 45

363. Raising Telephone Pole.

1983. World Communications Year.

2485. **363.** 1 cor. multicoloured 15 8

365. Baseball.

1983. Ninth Pan-American Games. Mult.

2487. 15 c. Type **365** (postage) 5 5
2488. 50 c. Water polo 8 5
2489. 65 c. Running 12 5
2490. 1 cor. Basketball (vert.) 15 8
2491. 2 cor. Weightlifting (vert.) 30 20
2492. 7 cor. Fencing (air) 65 30
2493. 8 cor. Gymnastics 70 40

367. Container Ship being Unloaded.

1983. 4th Anniv. of Revolution. Mult.

2496. 1 cor. Type **367** 45 15
2497. 2 cor. Telcor building, Leon 30 20

368. Carlos Fonseca. **369.** Simon Bolivar on Horseback.

1983. Founders of Sandinista National Liberation Front. Multicoloured.

2498. 50 c. Escobar, Navarro, Ubeda, Pomares and Ruiz (postage) 8 5
2499. 1 cor. Santos Lopez, Borge, Buitrago and Mayorga 15 8
2500. 4 cor. Type **368** (air) 55 35

1983. Birth Bicentenary of Simon Bolivar. Multicoloured.

2501. 50 c. Bolivar and Sandinista guerrilla 8 5
2502. 1 cor. Type **369** 15 8

371. Movements of a Pawn.

1983. Chess. Multicoloured.

2504 15 c. Type 371 (postage) 5 5
2505 65 c. Knight's movements 12 5
2506 1 cor. Bishop's movements 15 8
2507 2 cor. Rook's movements 30 20
2508 4 cor. Queen's movements (air) 55 35
2509 5 cor. King's movements 70 45
2510 7 cor. Game in progress 75 60

372. Speed Skating.

1983. Winter Olympic Games, Sarajevo (1984) (1st issue). Multicoloured.

2511. 50 c. Type **372** (postage) 8 5
2512. 1 cor. Slalom 15 8
2513. 1 cor. 50 Luge 20 12
2514. 2 cor. Ski jumping 30 20
2515. 4 cor. Figure skating (air) 55 35
2516. 5 cor. Downhill skiing 70 45
2517. 6 cor. Biathlon 90 55

373. Soldiers with German Shepherd Dog. **374.** "Madonna of the Chair".

1983. Armed Forces.

2519. **373.** 4 cor. multicoloured 55 35

1983. 500th Birth Anniv. of Raphael. Mult.

2520. 50 c. Type **374** (postage) 8 5
2521. 1 cor. "Esterhazy Madonna" 15 8
2522. 1 cor. 50 "Sistine Madonna" 20 12
2523. 2 cor. "Madonna of the Linnet" 30 20
2524. 4 cor. "Madonna of the Meadow" (air) 55 35
2525. 5 cor. "Madonna of the Garden" 70 45
2526. 6 cor. "Adoration of the Kings" 90 55

375. Pottery Idol.

1983. Archaeological Finds. Multicoloured.

2528. 50 c. Type **375** (postage) 8 5
2529. 1 cor. Pottery dish with ornamental lid 15 8
2530. 2 cor. Vase with snake design 30 20
2531. 4 cor. Pottery dish (air) 55 35

376. Metal being poured into Moulds.

1983. Nationalization of Mines. Mult.

2532. 1 cor. Type **376** (postage) 15 8
2533. 4 cor. Workers and mine (air) 55 35

377. Radio Operator and Sinking Liner.

1983. "Fracap '83" Congress of Radio Amateurs of Central America and Panama. Multicoloured.

2534. 1 cor. Type **377** 45 15
2535. 4 cor. Congress emblem and town destroyed by earthquake 55 35

378. Tobacco.

1983. Agrarian Reform.

2536. **378.** 1 cor. green 15 8
2537. – 2 cor. orange 30 20
2538. – 4 cor. brown 35 35
2539. – 5 cor. blue 45 45
2540. – 6 cor. lavender 55 55
2541. – 7 cor. purple 60 60
2542. – 8 cor. purple 70 65
2543. – 10 cor. brown 90 90

DESIGNS: 2 cor. Cotton. 4 cor. Maize. 5 cor. Sugar. 6 cor. Cattle. 7 cor. Rice. 8 cor. Coffee. 10 cor. Bananas.

See also Nos. 2755/62 and 2854/61.

379. Fire Engine with Ladder.

1983. Fire Engines. Multicoloured.

2544. 50 c. Type **379** (postage) 8 5
2545. 1 cor. Water Tanker 15 8
2546. 6 cor. Crew vehicle, 1930 90 55
2547. 1 cor. 50 Pump with extension fire hoses (air) 20 12
2548. 2 cor. Pump with high-pressure tank 30 20
2548a. 4 cor. Water tanker 60 40
2549. 5 cor. Fire engine, 1910 70 45

380. Jose Marti and General Sandino.

1983. Nicaragua–Cuba Solidarity. Mult.

2550. 1 cor. Type **380** (postage) 15 8
2551. 4 cor. Teacher, doctor and welder 55 35

381. "Adoration of the Shepherds" (Hugo van der Gaes). **382.** Anniversary Emblem.

1983. Christmas. Multicoloured.

2552. 50 c. Type **381** (postage) 8 5
2553. 1 cor. "Adoration of the Kings" (Domenico Ghirlandaio) 15 8
2554. 2 cor. "Adoration of the Shepherds" (El Greco) 30 20
2555. 7 cor. "Adoration of the Kings" (Konrad von Soest) (air) 65 30

1984. Air. 25th Anniv. of Cuban Revolution.

2557. **382.** 4 cor. red, blue and black 45 20
2558. – 6 cor. multicoloured 55 30

DESIGN: 6 cor. Fidel Castro and Che Guevara.

383. Bobsleigh.

1984. Winter Olympic Games, Sarajevo. Multicoloured.

2559. 50 c. Type **383** (postage) 10 5
2560. 50 c. Biathlon 10 5
2561. 1 cor. Slalom 20 12
2562. 1 cor. Speed skating 20 12
2563. 4 cor. Skiing (air) 45 45
2564. 5 cor. Ice dancing 55 55
2565. 10 cor. Ski jumping 90 60

384. Chinchilla.

1984. Cats. Multicoloured.

2567. 50 c. Type **384** (postage) 10 5
2568. 50 c. Longhaired white 10 5
2569. 1 cor. Red tabby 20 12
2570. 2 core. Tortoiseshell 35 20
2571. 4 cor. Burmese 70 45
2572. 3 cor. Siamese (air) 50 35
2573. 7 cor. Longhaired silver 70 35

385. National Arms. **386.** Blanca Arauz.

1984. 50th Death Anniv. of Augusto Sandino. Multicoloured.

2574. 1 cor. Type **385** (postage) 20 12
2575. 4 cor. Augusto Sandino (air) 35 20

1984. International Women's Day.

2576. **386.** 1 cor. multicoloured 20 12

387. Sunflower. **388.** "Soyuz".

1984. Apicultural Flowers. Multicoloured.

2577 50 c. Type 387 (postage) 10 10
2578 50 c. "Poinsettia pulcherrima" 10 10
2579 1 cor. "Cassia alata" 20 15
2580 2 cor. "Antigonon leptopus" 35 20
2581 3 cor. "Bidens pilosa" (air) 50 35
2582 4 cor. "Althaea rosea" 70 45
2583 5 cor. "Rivea corymbosa" 85 55

1984. Space Anniversaries. Multicoloured.

2584. 50 c. Type **388** (15th anniv. of "Soyuz 6", "7" and "8" flights) (postage) 10 5
2585. 50 c. "Soyuz" (different) (15th anniv. of "Soyuz 6", "7" and "8" flights) 10 5
2586. 1 cor. "Apollo II" approaching Moon (15th anniv. of 1st manned landing) 20 12
2587. 2 cor. "Luna I" (25th anniv. of 1st Moon satellite) 35 20
2588. 3 cor. "Luna II" (25th anniv. of 1st Moon landing) (air) 50 35
2589. 4 cor. "Luna III" (25th anniv. of 1st photographs of far side of Moon) 70 45
2590. 9 cor. Rocket (50th anniv. of Korolev's book on space flight) 1·25 75

389. "Noli me Tangere" (detail). **390.** Daimler, 1886.

1984. 450th Death Anniv. of Correggio (artist). Multicoloured.

2591. 50 c. Type **389** (postage) 10 5
2592. 50 c. "Madonna of St. Jerome" (detail) .. 10 5
2593. 1 cor. "Allegory of Virtue" 20 12
2594. 2 cor. "Allegory of Pleasure" 35 20
2595. 3 cor. "Ganymedes" (detail) (air) 50 35
2596. 5 cor. "The Danae" (detail) 55 55
2597. 8 cor. "Leda and the Swan" (detail) .. 1·00 60

1984. 150th Birth Anniv. of Gottlieb Daimler (automobile designer). Multicoloured.

2599. 1 cor. Type **390** (postage) 10 5
2600. 1 cor. Abadal, 1914 (horiz.) 10 5
2601. 2 cor. Ford, 1903 .. 35 20
2602. 2 cor. Renault, 1899 .. 35 20
2603. 3 cor. Rolls Royce, 1910 (horiz.) (air) 50 35
2604. 4 cor. Metallurgique, 1907 (horiz.) .. 70 45
2605. 7 cor. Bugatti "Mod 40" (horiz.) 75 50

392. Mail Transport.

1984. Air. 19th Universal Postal Union Congress Philatelic Salon, Hamburg.

2607. **392.** 15 cor. multicoloured 4·00 2·10

393. Basketball.

1984. Olympic Games, Los Angeles (2nd issue). Multicoloured.

2609. 50 c. Type **393** (postage) 10 5
2610. 50 c. Volleyball 10 5
2611. 1 cor. Hockey 20 12
2612. 2 cor. Tennis (air) .. 35 20
2613. 3 cor. Football (horiz.) .. 50 35
2614. 4 cor. Water polo (horiz.) 70 45
2615. 9 cor. Soccer (horiz.) .. 1·10 75

395. Rural Construction Site.

1984. 5th Anniv. of Revolution. Mult.

2618. 5 c. Type **395** (postage) 5 5
2619. 1 cor. Pacific-Atlantic Railway locomotive .. 30 20
2620. 4 cor. Ploughing with oxen and tractor (Agrarian reform) (air) 40 20
2621. 7 cor. State Council building 75 35

396. "Children defending Nature" (Pablo Herrera Berrios).

1984. U.N.E.S.C.O. Environmental Protection Campaign. Multicoloured.

2622. 50 c. Type **396** (postage) 5 5
2623. 1 cor. Living and dead forests 20 12
2624. 2 cor. Fisherman and dried river bed .. 35 20
2625. 10 cor. Hands holding plants (vert.) (air) .. 85 75

397. Red Cross Airplane and Ambulance.

1984. 50th Anniv. of Nicaraguan Red Cross. Multicoloured.

2626. 1 cor. Type **397** (postage) 30 15
2627. 7 cor. Battle of Solferino (125th anniv.) (air) .. 90 45

399. Ventura Escalante and Dominican Republic Flag.

1984. Baseball. Multicoloured.

2629. 50 c. Type **399** (postage) 10 5
2630. 50 c. Danial Herrera and Mexican flag 10 5
2631. 1 cor. Adalberto Herrera and Venezuelan flag .. 20 12
2632. 1 cor. Roberto Clemente and Nicaraguan flag .. 20 12
2633. 3 cor. Carlos Colas and Cuban flag (air) .. 30 35
2634. 4 cor. Stanley Cayasso and Argentinian flag .. 45 45
2635. 5 cor. Babe Ruth and U.S.A. flag 55 55

400. Central American Tapir.

1984. Wildlife Protection. Multicoloured.

2636. 25 c. Type **400** (postage) 5 5
2637. 25 c. Young tapir .. 5 5
2638. 3 cor. Close-up of tapir (air) 15 10
2639. 4 cor. Mother and young 20 12

401. Football in 1314.

1985. World Cup Football Championship, Mexico (1986) (1st issue). Multicoloured.

2640. 50 c. Type **401** (postage) 5 5
2641. 50 c. Football in 1500 .. 5 5
2642. 1 cor. Football in 1872 .. 5 5
2643. 1 cor. Football in 1846 .. 5 5
2644. 2 cor. Football in 1883 (air) 10 5
2645. 4 cor. Football in 1890 .. 20 12
2646. 6 cor. Football in 1953.. 30 20

See also Nos. 2731/7 and 2812/18.

402. "Strobilomyces retisporus". **403.** Postal Runner and Map.

1985. Fungi. Multicoloured.

2648. 50 c. Type **402** (postage) 8 5
2649. 50 c. "Boletus calopus" 8 5
2650. 1 cor. "Boletus luridus .. 8 5
2651. 1 cor. "Xerocomus illudens" (air).. .. 8 5
2652. 4 cor. "Gyrodon merulioides" 25 12
2653. 5 cor. "Tylopilus plumbeoviolaceus".. .. 30 15
2654. 8 cor. "Gyroporus castaneus" 50 25

1985. 13th Postal Union of the Americas and Spain Congress. Multicoloured.

2655. 1 cor. Type **403** (postage) 10 10
2656. 7 cor. Mail airplane over map (air) 45 20

406. Early Steam Engine.

1985. 150th Anniv. of German Railway. Multicoloured.

2659 1 cor. Type **406** (postage) 12 5
2660 1 cor. Electric locomotive 12 5
2661 9 cor. Steam locomotive No. 88 (air) 50 12
2662 9 cor. Double deck tram 50 12
2663 15 cor. Steam passenger locomotive 75 20
2664 21 cor. Mountain steam locomotive .. .. 1·10 30

407. Douglas, 1928.

1985. Centenary of Motor Cycle. Mult.

2666 50 c. Type **407** (postage) 5 5
2667 50 c. FN, 1928 .. .. 5 5
2668 1 cor. Puch, 1938 .. 5 5
2669 2 cor. Wanderer, 1939 (air) 5 5
2670 4 cor. Honda, 1949 .. 8 5
2671 5 cor. BMW, 1984 .. 10 5
2672 7 cor. Honda, 1984 .. 40 8

408. "Matelea quirosii". **409.** "Capitulation of German Troops" (P. Krivonogov).

1985. Flowers. Multicoloured.

2673. 50 c. Type **408** (postage) 5 5
2674. 50 c. "Ipomea nil" .. 5 5
2675. 1 cor. "Lysichitum americanum" 5 5
2676. 2 cor. "Clusia sp." (air) 5 5
2677. 4 cor. "Vanilla planifolia" 8 5
2678. 7 cor. "Stemmadenia obovata" 75 40

1985. 40th Anniv. of End of World War II. Multicoloured.

2679. 9 cor. 50 Type **409** (postage) .. .. 1·00 50
2680. 28 cor. Woman behind barbed wire and Nuremberg trial (air) 3·00 1·50

410. Lenin and Red Flag. **413.** Ring-necked Pheasant.

412. Victoria de Julio Sugar Factory.

1985. 115th Birth Anniv. of Lenin. Multicoloured.

2681. 4 cor. Type **410** 8 5
2682. 21 cor. Lenin addressing crowd 45 30

1985. Air. 6th Anniv. of Revolution. Multicoloured.

2684. 9 cor. Type **412** 20 12
2685. 9 cor. Soldier and flag .. 20 12

1985. Domestic Birds. Multicoloured.

2686. 50 c. Type **413** 30 10
2687. 50 c. Hen 10 5
2688. 1 cor. Helmet guineafowl 30 10
2689. 2 cor. Goose 15 5
2690. 6 cor. Ocellated turkey.. 70 15
2691. 8 cor. Duck 20 8

414. Luis A. Delgadillo. **415.** Zeledon.

1985. International Music Year. Mult.

2692. 1 cor. Type **414** (postage) 5 5
2693. 1 cor. Masked dancer with floral headdress 5 5
2694. 9 cor. Masked procession (air) 65 40
2695. 9 cor. Crowd outside church 65 40
2696. 15 cor. Masked dancer in brimmed hat .. .. 1·10 55
2697. 21 cor. Procession resting 1·50 75

1985. Air. Birth Centenary of Benjamin Zeledon.

2698. **415.** 15 cor. multicoloured 1·00 55

416. Dunant and Lifeboat.

1985. 75th Death Anniv. of Henri Dunant (founder of Red Cross). Multicoloured.

2699. 3 cor. Type **416** 20 10
2700. 15 cor. Dunant and aircraft .. .. .. 1·25 55

417. Fire Engine.

1985. 6th Anniv. of SINACOI Fire Service. Multicoloured.

2701. 1 cor. Type **417** (postage) .. 5 5
2702. 1 cor. Fire station .. 5 5
2703. 1 cor. Engine with water jet 5 5
2704. 3 cor. Foam tender (air) 5 5
2705. 9 cor. Airport fire engine 50 12
2706. 15 cor. Engine at fire .. 85 45
2707. 21 cor. Fireman in protective clothing .. 1·10 75

418. Halley, Masaya Volcano and Comet.

1985. Appearance of Halley's Comet. Multicoloured.

2708. 1 cor. Type **418** (postage) 5 5
2709. 3 cor. Armillary sphere and 1910 trajectory .. 5 5
2710. 3 cor. "Venus" space probe and Tycho Brahe underground observatory 5 5
2711. 9 cor. Habermel's astrolabe and comet's path through solar system (air) 50 12
2712. 15 cor. Hale Telescope, Mt. Palomar, and Herschel's telescope .. 85 45
2713. 21 cor. Galileo's telescope and sections through telescopes of Newton, Cassegrain and Ritchey .. .. 1·25 60

419. Tapir eating.

1985. Protected Animals. Baird's Tapir. Multicoloured.

2714. 1 cor. Type **419** (postage) 5 5
2715. 3 cor. Tapir in water (air) 5 5
2716. 5 cor. Tapir in undergrowth 10 5
2717. 9 cor. Mother and calf .. 20 12

420. "Rosa spinosissima".

1986. Wild Roses. Multicoloured.

2718. 1 cor. Type **420** 5 5
2719. 1 cor. Dog rose ("R. canina") 5 5
2720. 3 cor. "R. eglanteria" .. 5 5
2721. 5 cor. "R. rubrifolia" .. 10 5
2722. 9 cor. "R. foetida" .. 20 12
2723. 100 cor. "R. rugosa" .. 2·00 1·10

421. Crimson Topaz. 422. Footballer and Statue.

1986. Birds. Multicoloured.

2724. 1 cor. Type **421** 10 10
2725. 3 cor. Orange-billed nightingale thrush .. 10 10
2726. 3 cor. Troupial 10 10
2727. 5 cor. Painted bunting .. 30 10
2728. 10 cor. Frantzius's nightingale thrush .. 65 30
2729. 21 cor. Great horned owl 1·25 75
2730. 75 cor. Great kiskadee .. 4·50 2·40

1986. World Cup Football Championship, Mexico (2nd issue). Multicoloured.

2731. 1 cor. Type **422** (postage) 5 5
2732. 1 cor. Footballer and sculptured head .. 5 5
2733. 3 cor. Footballer and water holder with man as stem (air) 5 5
2734. 3 cor. Footballer and sculpture 5 5
2735. 5 cor. Footballer and sculptured head (different) 10 5
2736. 9 cor. Footballer and sculpture (different) .. 20 12
2737. 100 cor. Footballer and sculptured snake's head .. .. .. 3·00 1·50

1986. (a) Flowers. As Nos. 2441/56 but values changed.

2739. 5 cor. blue 10 5
2740. 5 cor. violet 10 5
2741. 5 cor. purple 10 5
2742. 5 cor. orange 10 5
2743. 5 cor. green 10 5
2744. 5 cor. blue 10 5
2745. 5 cor. green 10 5
2746. 5 cor. green 10 5
2747. 5 cor. mauve 10 5
2748. 5 cor. red 10 5
2749. 5 cor. grey 10 5
2750. 5 cor. orange 10 5
2751. 5 cor. brown 10 5
2752. 5 cor. brown 10 5
2753. 5 cor. green 10 5
2754. 5 cor. black 10 5

DESIGNS: No. 2739, Type **356**; 2740, "Tabebula ochraceae". 2741, "Laella sp.". 2742, Frangipani ("Plumeria rubra"). 2743, "Brassavola nodosa". 2744, "Strachytarpheta indica". 2745, "Cochlospermum sp.". 2746, "Malvaviscus arboreus". 2747, "Tecoma stans". 2748, Chinese hibiscus ("Hibiscus rosa-sinensis"). 2749, "Cattleya lueddemanniana". 2750, African marigold ("Tagetes erecta"). 2751, "Senecio sp.". 2752, "Sobralia macrantha". 2753, "Thumbergia alata". 2754, "Bixa orellana".

(b) Agrarian Reform. As T **378**.

2755. 1 cor. brown 5 5
2756. 9 cor. violet 20 12
2757. 15 cor. purple 30 20
2758. 21 cor. red 45 30
2759. 33 cor. orange 65 45
2760. 42 cor. green 90 55
2761. 50 cor. brown .. .. 1·00 65
2762. 100 cor. blue .. .. 2·00 1·50

DESIGNS: 1 cor. Type **378**. 9 cor. Cotton. 15 cor. Maize. 21 cor. Sugar. 33 cor. Cattle. 42 cor. Rice. 50 cor. Coffee. 100 cor. Bananas.

423. Alfonso Cortes.

1986. National Libraries. Latin American Writers. Multicoloured.

2763. 1 cor. Type **423** (postage) 5 5
2764. 3 cor. Azarias H. Pallais 5 5
2765. 3 cor. Salomon de la Selva 5 5
2766. 5 cor. Ruben Dario .. 5 5
2767. 9 cor. Pablo Neruda .. 5 5
2768. 15 cor. Alfonso Reyes (air) 45 25
2769. 100 cor. Pedro Henriquez Urena .. .. .. 3·00 1·50

424. Great Britain Penny Black and Nicaragua 1929 25 c. Stamps.

1986. Air. 125th Anniv. of Nicaraguan Stamps. Designs showing G.B. Penny Black and Nicaragua stamps.

2770. **424.** 30 cor. multicoloured 90 45
2771. – 40 cor. brown, black and grey .. .. 1·25 60
2772. – 50 cor. red, black and grey .. .. 1·50 75
2773. – 100 cor. blue, black and grey .. .. 3·00 1·50

DESIGNS: 40 c. 1903 1 p. stamp. 50 c. 1892 5 p. stamp. 1 p. 1862 2 c. stamp.

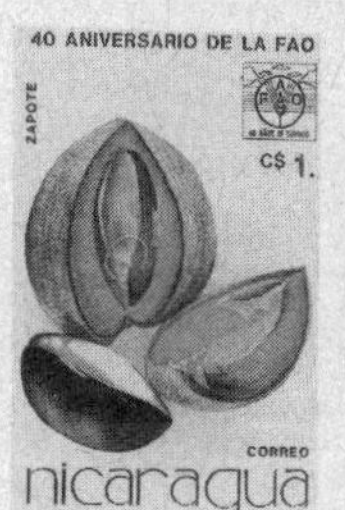

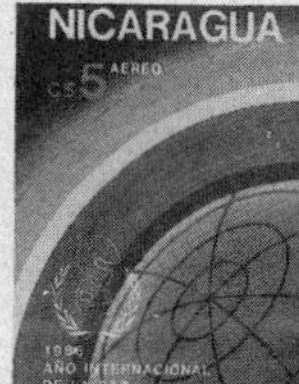

425. Sapodilla 426. Rainbow and Globe.

1986. 40th Anniv. of F.A.O. Multicoloured.

2774. 1 cor. Type **425** (postage) 5 5
2775. 1 cor. Maranon 5 5
2776. 3 cor. Tree-cactus .. 5 5
2777. 3 cor. Granadilla .. 5 5
2778. 5 cor. Custard-apple (air) 5 5
2779. 21 cor. Melocoton .. 65 35
2780. 100 cor. Mamey .. .. 3·00 1·50

1986. Air. International Peace Year. Mult.

2781. 5 cor. Type **426** 5 5
2782. 10 cor. Dove and globe .. 30 5

427. Lockheed "L-1011 TriStar".

1986. "Stockholmia 86" International Stamp Exhibition. Multicoloured.

2783. 1 cor. Type **427** (postage) 10 10
2784. 1 cor. Yak "40" 10 10
2785. 3 cor. B.A.C. "1-11" .. 10 10
2786. 3 cor. Boeing "747" .. 10 10
2787. 9 cor. "A-300" (air) .. 30 10
2788. 15 cor. "Tu-154" .. 45 10
2789. 100 cor. "Concorde" (vert.) .. .. .. 3·00 1·50

428. "Pinta" and 16th-century Map.

1986. 500th Anniv. (1992) of Discovery of America by Columbus (1st issue). Mult.

2791. 1 cor. Type **428** (postage) 45 20
2792. 1 cor. "Santa Maria" and "Nina" 45 20
2793. 9 cor. Juan de la Cosa (air) 30 10
2794. 9 cor. Christopher Columbus 30 10
2795. 21 cor. King and Queen of Spain 65 35
2796. 100 cor. Courtiers behind Columbus and Indians 3·00 1·50

The designs of the same value and Nos. 2795/6 were printed together in se-tenant pairs within their sheets, Nos. 2791/2 and 2795/6 forming composite designs.

See also Nos. 2903/8.

429. Fonseca and Flags.

1986. Air. 25th Anniv. of Sandinista Front and 10th Death Anniv. of Carlos Fonseca (co-founder).

2798. **429.** 15 cor. multicoloured 5 5

430. Rhinoceros. 431. "Theritas coronata".

1986. Air. Endangered Animals. Mult.

2799. 15 cor. Type **430** .. 45 5
2800. 15 cor. Zebra 45 5
2801. 25 cor. Elephant .. 75 40
2802. 25 cor. Giraffe 75 40
2803. 50 cor. Tiger .. .. 1·50 75
2804. 50 cor. Mandrill .. .. 1·50 75

1986. Butterflies. Multicoloured.

2805. 10 cor. Type **431** (post) 20 8
2806. 15 cor. "Salamis cacta" (air) 20 8
2807. 15 cor. "Charayes nitebis" 20 8
2808. 15 cor. "Papilio maacki" 20 8
2809. 25 cor. "Palaeochrysophonus hippothoe" .. 20 8
2810. 25 cor. "Euphaedro cyparissa" 20 8
2811. 30 cor. "Ritra aurea" .. 20 8

432. Player and French Flag. 433. Ernesto Mejia Sanchez.

1986. Air. World Cup Football Championship, Mexico (3rd issue). Finalists. Multicoloured. Designs showing footballers and national flags.

2812. 10 cor. Type **432** .. 5 5
2813. 10 cor. Argentina .. 5 5
2814. 10 cor. West Germany .. 5 5
2815. 15 cor. England 5 5
2816. 15 cor. Brazil 5 5
2817. 25 cor. Spain 5 5
2818. 50 cor. Belgium (horiz.) 5 5

1987. Ruben Dario Cultural Order of Independence. Multicoloured.

2820 10 cor. Type **433** (postage) 8 5
2821 10 cor. Fernando Gordillo 8 5
2822 10 cor. Francisco Perez Estrada 8 5
2823 15 cor. Order medal (air) 10 5
2824 30 cor. Julio Cortazar .. 20 20
2825 60 cor. Enrique Fernandez Morales 35 25

434 Ice Hockey

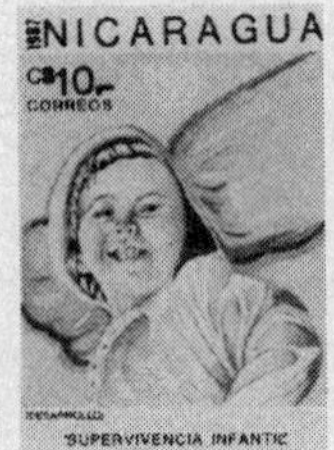

435 Development

1987. Winter Olympic Games, Calgary (1988). Multicoloured.

2826 10 cor. Type **434** (postage) 10 10
2827 10 cor. Speed skating .. 10 10
2828 15 cor. Downhill skiing (air) 10 10
2829 15 cor. Figure skating .. 10 10
2830 20 cor. Shooting 15 10
2831 30 cor. Slalom 20 10
2832 40 cor. Ski jumping .. 25 10

1987. U.N.I.C.E.F. Child Survival Campaign. Multicoloured.

2834 10 cor. Type **435** (postage) 10 10
2835 25 cor. Vaccination (air) 75 40
2836 30 cor. Oral rehydration therapy 90 45
2837 50 cor. Breastfeeding .. 1·50 75

1987. (a) Flowers. As Nos. 2441/56 and 2739/54 but values changed.

2838 10 cor. blue 5 5
2839 10 cor. violet 5 5
2840 10 cor. purple 5 5
2841 10 cor. red 5 5
2842 10 cor. green 5 5
2843 10 cor. blue 5 5
2844 10 cor. green 5 5
2845 10 cor. green 5 5
2846 10 cor. mauve 5 5
2847 10 cor. red 5 5
2848 10 cor. green 5 5
2849 10 cor. orange 5 5
2850 10 cor. brown 5 5
2851 10 cor. purple 5 5
2852 10 cor. turquoise 5 5
2853 10 cor. black 5 5

DESIGNS: No. 2838, Type **356**, 2839, "Tabebula ochraceae"; 2840, "Laella sp."; 2841, Frangipani; 2842, "Brassavola nodosa"; 2843, "Stachytarpheta indica"; 2844, "Cochlospermum sp."; 2845, "Malvaviscus arboreus"; 2846, "Tecoma stans"; 2847, Chinese hibiscus; 2848, "Cattleya lueddermanniana", 2849, African marigold; 2850, "Senecio sp." 2851, "Sobralla macrantha"; 2852, "Thumbergia alata"; 2853, "Bixa orellana".

(b) Agrarian Reform. As T **378**. Dated "1987".

2854 10 cor. brown 5 5
2855 10 cor. violet 5 5
2856 15 cor. purple 10 5
2857 25 cor. red 15 5
2858 30 cor. orange 20 10
2859 50 cor. brown 30 20
2860 60 cor. green 35 25
2861 100 cor. blue 65 45

DESIGNS: No. 2854, Type **378**; 2855, Cotton; 2856, Maize; 2857, Sugar; 2858, Cattle; 2859, Coffee; 2860, Rice; 2861, Bananas.

436 Flags and Buildings

438 Tennis Player

437 "Mammuthus columbi"

1987. 77th Interparliamentary Conference, Managua.

2862 **436** 10 cor. multicoloured 10 10

1987. Prehistoric Animals. Multicoloured.

2863 10 cor. Type **437** (postage) 10 10
2864 10 cor. Triceratops .. 10 10
2865 10 cor. Dimetrodon .. 10 10
2866 15 cor. Uintaterium (air) 10 10
2867 15 cor. Dinichthys .. 10 10
2868 30 cor. Pteranodon .. 60 35
2869 40 cor. Tilosaurus .. 85 45

1987. "Capex 87" International Stamp Exhibition, Toronto.

2870 10 cor. multicoloured (Type **438**) (postage) .. 10 10
2871 10 cor. multicoloured .. 10 10
2872 15 cor. multicoloured (male player) (air) .. 45 10
2873 15 cor. multicoloured (female player) .. 45 10
2874 20 cor. multicoloured .. 60 30
2875 30 cor. multicoloured .. 60 45
2876 40 cor. multicoloured .. 85 60

DESIGNS: Nos. 2871/6, Various tennis players.

439 Dobermann Pinscher

441 Levski

440 Modern Wooden Houses

1987. Dogs. Multicoloured.

2878 10 cor. Type **439** (postage) 10 10
2879 10 cor. Bull mastiff .. 10 10
2880 15 cor. Japanese spaniel (air) 45 10
2881 15 cor. Keeshond .. 45 10
2882 20 cor. Chihuahua .. 60 30
2883 30 cor. St. Bernard .. 90 45
2884 40 cor. West Gotha spitz 85 60

1987. Air. International Year of Shelter for the Homeless. Multicoloured.

2885 20 cor. Type **440** .. 15 10
2886 30 cor. Modern brick-built houses 20 10

1987. Air. 150th Birth Anniv of Vasil Levski (revolutionary).

2887 **441** 30 cor. multicoloured 20 10

442 "Opuntia acanthocarpa major"

1987. Cacti. Multicoloured.

2888 10 cor. Type **442** (postage) 10 10
2889 10 cor. "Lophocereus schottii" 10 10
2890 10 cor. "Echinocereus engelmanii 10 10
2891 20 cor. Saguaros (air) .. 60 30
2892 20 cor. "Lemaireocereus thurberi" 60 30
2893 30 cor. "Opuntia fulgida" 90 45
2894 50 cor. "Opuntia ficus indica" .. .. 1·50 75

443 High Jumping

1987. 10th Pan-American Games, Indiana. Multicoloured.

2895 10 cor. Type **443** (postage) 10 10
2896 10 cor. Handball .. 10 10
2897 15 cor. Running (air) .. 45 10
2898 15 cor. Gymnastics .. 45 10
2899 20 cor. Baseball 60 30
2900 30 cor. Synchronised swimming (vert) .. 90 45
2901 40 cor. Weightlifting (vert) .. .. .. 1·25 60

445 "Cosmos"

1987. Cosmonautics Day. Multicoloured.

2904 10 cor. Type **445** (postage) 10 10
2905 10 cor. "Sputnik" .. 10 10
2906 15 cor. "Proton" (air) .. 45 10
2907 25 cor. "Luna" 75 40
2908 25 cor. "Meteor" .. 75 40
2909 30 cor. "Electron" .. 90 45
2910 50 cor. "Mars-1" .. 1·50 75

446 Native Huts and Terraced Hillside

1987. Air. 50th Anniv (1992) of Discovery of America by Christopher Columbus (2nd issue). Multicoloured.

2911 15 cor. Type **446** .. 45 20
2912 15 cor. Columbus's fleet .. 65 20
2913 20 cor. Spanish soldiers in native village 60 30
2914 30 cor. Mounted soldiers killing natives .. 90 45
2915 40 cor. Spanish people and houses .. .. 1·25 60
2916 50 cor. Church and houses 1·50 75

447 "Atractoteus tropicus gaspar"

1987. World Food Day. Fishes. Multicoloured.

2917 10 cor. Type **447** (postage) 10 10
2918 10 cor. "Tarpon atlanticus" 10 10
2919 10 cor. Cichlid 10 10
2920 15 cor. "Astyana fasciatus" (air) .. 45 10
2921 15 cor. Midas cichlid .. 45 10
2922 20 cor. Cichlid (different) 60 30
2923 50 cor. "Carcharhinus nicaraguensis" .. 1·50 75

448 Lenin

449 "Nativity"

1987. 70th Anniv of Russian Revolution. Multicoloured.

2924 10 cor. Type **448** (postage) 10 10
2925 30 cor. "Aurora" (cruiser) (horiz) (air) 35 15
2926 50 cor. Russian arms .. 30 20

1987. Christmas. Details of Painting by L. Saenz. Multicoloured.

2927 10 cor. Type **449** .. 10 10
2928 20 cor. "Adoration of the Magi" 60 30
2929 25 cor. "Adoration of the Magi" (close-up detail) 75 40
2930 50 cor. "Nativity" (close-up detail) .. 1·50 75

1987. Surch.

2931 **435** 400 cor. on 10 cor. mult (postage) .. 30 15
2935 **440** 200 cor. on 20 cor. multicoloured (air) 15 10
2932 – 600 cor. on 50 cor. mult (No. 2837) .. 40 20
2933 – 1000 cor. on 25 cor. mult (No. 2835) .. 70 35
2936 – 3000 cor. on 30 cor. mult (No. 2886) .. 2·10 1·00
2934 – 5000 cor. on 30 cor. mult (No. 2836) .. 3·50 1·75

451 Cross-country Skiing

452 Flag around Globe

1988. Winter Olympic Games, Calgary. Mult.

2937 10 cor. Type **451** .. 10 10
2938 10 cor. Rifle-shooting (horiz) 10 10
2939 15 cor. Ice hockey .. 45 10
2940 20 cor. Ice skating .. 60 30
2941 25 cor. Downhill skiing .. 75 40
2942 30 cor. Ski jumping (horiz) 90 45
2943 40 cor. Slalom .. .. 1·25 60

1988. 10th Anniv of Nicaragua Journalists' Association. Mdulticoloured.

2945 1 cor. Type **452** (postage) 10 10
2946 5 cor. Churches of St. Francis Xavier, Sandino and Fatima, Managua, and speaker addressing journalists (42 × 27 mm) (air) .. 1·25 60

453 Basketball

1988. Olympic Games, Seoul. Multicoloured.

2947 10 cor. Type **453** .. 10 10
2948 10 cor. Gymnastics .. 10 10
2949 15 cor. Volleyball .. 45 10
2950 20 cor. Long jumping .. 60 30
2951 25 cor. Football .. 75 40
2952 30 cor. Water polo .. 90 45
2953 40 cor. Boxing .. .. 1·25 60

454 Brown Bear

1988. Mammals and their Young. Mult.

2955 10 c. Type **454** (postage) 10 10
2956 15 c. Lion 10 10
2957 25 c. Cocker spaniel .. 10 10
2958 50 c. Wild boar .. 15 10
2959 4 cor. Cheetah (air) .. 55 20
2960 7 cor. Spotted hyena .. 1·00 40
2961 8 cor. Red fox .. .. 1·25 50

455 Slide Tackle

1988. "Essen '88" International Stamp Fair and European Football Championship, Germany. Multicoloured.

2963	50 c. Type **455** (postage)	10	10
2964	1 cor. Footballers ..	15	10
2965	2 cor. Lining up shot (vert) (air) ..	30	10
2966	3 cor. Challenging for ball (vert)	50	20
2967	4 cor. Heading ball (vert)	65	25
2968	5 cor. Tackling (vert) ..	80	30
2969	6 cor. Opponent winning possession	1·00	40

456 "B-206B-JRIII" Helicopter

1988. "Finlandia 88" International Stamp Exhibition, Helsinki. Helicopters. Mult.

2971	4 cor. Type **456** (postage)	15	10
2972	12 cor. "BK-117A-3" (air)	20	10
2973	16 cor. "B-360"	30	10
2974	20 cor. "109-MR II" ..	40	10
2975	24 cor. "S-61"	55	20
2976	28 cor. "SA-365N-D2" ..	60	25
2977	56 cor. "S-76"	1·25	50

457 Flags and Map

458 Casimiro Sotelo Montenegro

1988. 9th Anniv of Revolution. Multicoloured.

2979	1 cor. Type **457** (postage)	20	10
2980	5 cor. Landscape and hands releasing dove (air)	80	30

1988. Revolutionaries.

2981	**458**	4 cor. blue (postage)	15	10
2982	–	12 cor. mauve (air) ..	20	10
2983	–	16 cor. green ..	30	10
2984	–	20 cor. red	45	15
2985	–	24 cor. brown ..	55	20
2986	–	28 cor. violet ..	65	25
2987	–	50 cor. red	1·25	45
2988	–	100 cor. purple ..	2·40	1·00

DESIGNS: 12 cor. Ricardo Morales Aviles; 16 cor. Silvio Mayorga Delgado; 20 cor. Pedro Arauz Palacios; 24 cor. Oscar A. Turcios Chavarrias; 28 cor. Julio C. Buitrago Urroz; 50 cor. Jose B. Escobar Perez; 100 cor. Eduardo E. Contreras Escobar.

459 "Acacia baileyana"

460 "Strombus pugilis"

1988. Flowers. Multicoloured.

2989	4 cor. Type **459** (postage)	15	10
2990	12 cor. "Anigozanthos manglesii" (air) ..	20	10
2991	16 cor. "Telopia speciosissima" ..	30	10
2992	20 cor. "Eucalyptus ficifolia"	45	15
2993	24 cor. "Boronia heterophylla"	60	25
2994	28 cor. "Callistemon speciosus"	70	30
2995	30 cor. "Nymphaea caerulea" (horiz) ..	80	35
2996	50 cor. "Clianthus formosus"	1·25	50

1988. Molluscs. Multicoloured.

2997	4 cor. Type **460** (postage)	15	10
2998	12 cor. "Polymita picta" (air)	20	10
2999	16 cor. "Architectonica maximum"	30	10
3000	20 cor. "Pectens laqueatus"	40	10
3001	24 cor. "Guildfordia triumphans"	55	20
3002	28 cor. "Ranella pustulosa"	60	25
3003	50 cor. "Trochus maculatus"	1·25	50

461 Zapotecan Funeral Urn

462 "Chrysina macropus"

1988. 500th Anniv (1992) of Discovery of America by Columbus (3rd issue). Mult.

3004	4 cor. Type **461** (postage)	15	10
3005	12 cor. Mochican ceramic seated figure (air) ..	20	10
3006	16 cor. Mochican ceramic head	30	10
3007	20 cor. Tainan ceramic vessel	45	10
3008	28 cor. Nazcan vessel (horiz)	65	20
3009	100 cor. Incan ritual pipe (horiz)	2·40	1·00

1988. Beetles. Multicoloured.

3011	4 cor. Type **462** (postage)	15	10
3012	12 cor. "Plusiotis victoriana" (air) ..	20	10
3013	16 cor. "Ceratotrupes bolivari"	30	10
3014	20 cor. "Gymnetosoma stellata"	50	15
3015	24 cor. "Euphoria lineoligera"	60	20
3016	28 cor. "Euphoria candezei"	70	30
3017	50 cor. "Sulcophanaeus chryseicollis"	1·25	50

463 Dario

1988. Air. Centenary of Publication of "Blue" by Ruben Dario.

3018	**463**	25 cor. multicoloured	60	20

464 Simon Bolivar, Jose Marti, Gen. Sandino and Fidel Castro

1989. Air. 30th Anniv of Cuban Revolution.

3019	**464**	20 cor. multicoloured	50	20

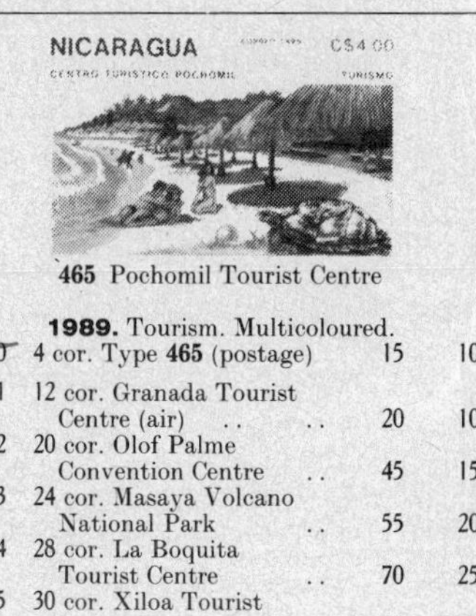

465 Pochomil Tourist Centre

1989. Tourism. Multicoloured.

3020	4 cor. Type **465** (postage)	15	10
3021	12 cor. Granada Tourist Centre (air)	20	10
3022	20 cor. Olof Palme Convention Centre ..	45	15
3023	24 cor. Masaya Volcano National Park ..	55	20
3024	28 cor. La Boquita Tourist Centre ..	70	25
3025	30 cor. Xiloa Tourist Centre	75	30
3026	50 cor. Managua Hotel ..	1·25	50

466 Footballers

467 Downhill Skiing

1989. Air. World Cup Football Championship, Italy (1990).

3028	**466**	100 cor. multicoloured	10	10
3029	–	200 cor. multicoloured	10	10
3030	–	600 cor. multicoloured	10	10
3031	–	1000 cor. mult ..	30	10
3032	–	2000 cor. mult ..	60	10
3033	–	3000 cor. mult ..	90	40
3034	–	5000 cor. mult ..	1·50	50

DESIGNS: 200 cor. to 5000 cor. Different footballers.

1989. Air. Winter Olympic Games, Albertville (1992). Multicoloured.

3036	50 cor. Type **467** ..	10	10
3037	300 cor. Ice hockey ..	10	10
3038	600 cor. Ski jumping ..	10	10
3039	1000 cor. Ice skating ..	30	10
3040	2000 cor. Biathlon ..	60	10
3041	3000 cor. Slalom	90	40
3042	5000 cor. Skiing	1·50	50

468 Water Polo

1989. Air. Olympic Games, Barcelona (1992). Multicoloured.

3044	100 cor. Type **468** ..	10	10
3045	200 cor. Running ..	10	10
3046	600 cor. Diving	10	10
3047	1000 cor. Gymnastics ..	30	10
3048	2000 cor. Weightlifting ..	60	10
3049	3000 cor. Volleyball ..	90	40
3050	5000 cor. Wrestling ..	1·50	50

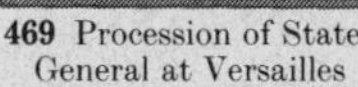

469 Procession of States General at Versailles

470 American Anhinga

1989. "Philexfrance 89" International Stamp Exhibition, Paris, and Bicentenary of French Revolution. Multicoloured.

3052	50 cor. Type **469** (postage)	15	10
3054	300 cor. Oath of the Tennis Court (36 × 28 mm) (air)	10	10
3055	600 cor. "The 14th of July" (29 × 40 mm) ..	10	10
3056	1000 cor. Tree of Liberty (36 × 28 mm)	30	10
3057	2000 cor. "Liberty guiding the People" (Eugene Delacroix) (29 × 40 mm)	60	10
3058	3000 cor. Storming the Bastille (36 × 28 mm) ..	90	40
3059	5000 cor. Lafayette taking oath (28 × 36 mm) ..	1·50	50

1989. Air. "Brasiliana 89" Int Stamp Exhibition, Rio de Janeiro. Birds. Mult.

3060	100 cor. Type **470** ..	10	10
3061	200 cor. Swallow-tailed kite	10	10
3062	600 cor. Turquoise-browed motmot	10	10
3063	1000 cor. "Setophaga picta"	30	10
3064	2000 cor. Great antshrike (horiz)	60	10
3065	3000 cor. Northern royal flycatcher	90	40
3066	5000 cor. White-flanked antwren (horiz) ..	1·50	50

471 Anniversary Emblem

472 Animal-shaped Vessel

1989. Air. 10th Anniv of Revolution.

3068	**471**	300 cor. multicoloured	10	10

1989. Air. America. Pre-Columbian Artefacts.

3070	**472**	2000 cor. multicoloured	60	10

NO ISSUES DATED 1990 EXCEPT! BIRDS ANIMALS.

MAY '96

SILVER CURRENCY

The following were for use in all places on the Atlantic coast of Nicaragua where the silver currency was in use. This curency was worth about 50 c. to the peso. Earlier issues (overprints on Nicaraguan stamps) were also issued for Zelaya. These are listed in the Stanley Gibbons Part 15 (Central America) Catalogue.

Z 1.

1912.

No.	Type	Description	Unused	Used
Z 1.	Z 1.	1 c. green	1·25	65
Z 2.		2 c. red	85	40
Z 3.		3 c. brown	1·25	60
Z 4.		4 c. lake	1·25	50
Z 5.		5 c. blue	1·25	50
Z 6.		6 c. red	6·75	3·50
Z 7.		10 c. grey	1·25	50
Z 8.		15 c. lilac	1·25	90
Z 9.		20 c. blue	1·25	90
Z 10.		25 c. black & green	1·60	1·25
Z 11.		35 c. black & brown	2·25	1·40
Z 12.		50 c. green	2·25	1·40
Z 13.		1 p. orange	3·50	2·25
Z 14.		2 p. brown	6·75	4·25
Z 15.		5 p. green	13·50	8·75

OFFICIAL STAMPS

Overprinted **FRANQUEO OFICIAL**.

1890. Stamps of 1890.

No.	Type	Description	Unused	Used
O 37.	6.	1 c. blue	15	35
O 38.		2 c. blue	15	35
O 39.		5 c. blue	15	40
O 40.		10 c. blue	15	45
O 41.		20 c. blue	15	55
O 42.		50 c. blue	15	75
O 43.		1 p. blue	20	1·10
O 44.		2 p. blue	20	1·60
O 45.		5 p. blue	20	3·50
O 46.		10 p. blue	20	6·75

1891. Stamps of 1891.

No.	Type	Description	Unused	Used
O 47.	7.	1 c. green	12	40
O 48.		2 c. green	12	40
O 49.		5 c. green	12	40
O 50.		10 c. green	12	40
O 51.		20 c. green	12	70
O 52.		50 c. green	12	75
O 53.		1 p. green	12	90
O 54.		2 p. green	12	90
O 55.		5 p. green	12	2·25
O 56.		10 p. green	12	3·50

1892. Stamps of 1892.

No.	Type	Description	Unused	Used
O 57.	8.	1 c. brown	12	30
O 58.		2 c. brown	12	30
O 59.		5 c. brown	12	30
O 60.		10 c. brown	12	30
O 61.		20 c. brown	12	50
O 62.		50 c. brown	12	70
O 63.		1 p. brown	12	1·10
O 64.		2 p. brown	12	1·75
O 65.		5 p. brown	12	2·75
O 66.		10 p. brown	12	3·50

1893. Stamps of 1893.

No.	Type	Description	Unused	Used
O 67.	9.	1 c. black	12	30
O 68.		2 c. black	12	30
O 69.		5 c. black	12	30
O 70.		10 c. black	12	30
O 71.		20 c. black	12	50
O 72.		25 c. black	12	65
O 73.		50 c. black	12	70
O 74.		1 p. black	12	1·00
O 75.		2 p. black	12	1·25
O 76.		5 p. black	12	2·75
O 77.		10 p. black	12	3·50

1894. Stamps of 1894.

No.	Type	Description	Unused	Used
O 78.	10.	1 c. orange	12	30
O 79.		2 c. orange	12	30
O 80.		5 c. orange	12	30
O 81.		10 c. orange	12	30
O 82.		20 c. orange	12	30
O 83.		50 c. orange	12	45
O 84.		1 p. orange	12	1·00
O 85.		2 p. orange	12	1·75
O 86.		5 p. orange	12	3·50
O 87.		10 p. orange	12	4·50

1895. Stamps of 1895.

No.	Type	Description	Unused	Used
O 88.	11.	1 c. green	12	30
O 89.		2 c. green	12	30
O 90.		5 c. green	12	30
O 91.		10 c. green	12	30
O 92.		20 c. green	12	50
O 93.		50 c. green	12	80
O 94.		1 p. green	12	80
O 95.		2 p. green	12	1·25
O 96.		5 p. green	12	1·90
O 97.		10 p. green	12	2·40

1896. Stamps of 1896, dated " 1896 ", optd. **FRANQUEO OFICIAL** in oval frame.

No.	Type	Description	Unused	Used
O 99.	12.	1 c. red	1·50	1·90
O 100.		2 c. red	1·50	1·90
O 101.		5 c. red	1·50	1·90
O 102.		10 c. red	1·50	1·90
O 103.		20 c. red	1·90	1·90
O 104.		50 c. red	3·00	3·00
O 105.		1 p. red	7·25	7·25
O 106.		2 p. red	7·25	7·25
O 107.		5 p. red	9·50	9·50

1896. Nos. D 99/103 handstamped **Franqueo Oficial.**

No.	Type	Description	Unused	Used
O 108.	D 13.	1 c. orange		4·25
O 109.		2 c. orange		4·25
O 110.		5 c. orange		3·00
O 111.		10 c. orange		3·00
O 112.		20 c. orange		3·00

1897. Stamps of 1897, dated "1897", optd. **FRANQUEO OFICIAL** in oval frame.

No.	Type	Description	Unused	Used
O 113.	12.	1 c. red	2·00	2·00
O 114.		2 c. red	2·00	2·00
O 115.		5 c. red	2·00	2·00
O 116.		10 c. red	1·90	2·10
O 117.		20 c. red	1·90	2·40
O 118.		50 c. red	3·00	3·00
O 119.		1 p. red	8·25	8·25
O 120.		2 p. red	9·75	9·75
O 121.		5 p. red	15·00	15·00

1898. Stamps of 1898 optd. **FRANQUEO OFICIAL** in oval frame.

No.	Type	Description	Unused	Used
O 124.	13.	1 c. red	2·00	2·00
O 125.		2 c. red	2·00	2·00
O 126.		4 c. red	2·00	2·00
O 127.		5 c. red	1·50	1·50
O 128.		10 c. red	2·40	2·40
O 129.		15 c. red	3·75	3·75
O 130.		20 c. red	3·75	3·75
O 131.		50 c. red	5·00	5·00
O 132.		1 p. red	6·50	6·50
O 133.		2 p. red	6·50	6·50
O 134.		5 p. red	6·50	6·50

1899. Stamps of 1899 optd. **FRANQUEO OFICIAL** in scroll.

No.	Type	Description	Unused	Used
O 137.	14.	1 c. green	12	60
O 138.		2 c. brown	12	60
O 139.		4 c. red	12	60
O 140.		5 c. blue	12	40
O 141.		10 c. orange	12	60
O 142.		15 c. brown	12	1·25
O 143.		20 c. green	12	2·00
O 144.		50 c. red	12	2·00
O 145.		1 p. orange	12	6·00
O 146.		2 p. violet	12	6·00
O 147.		5 p. blue	12	9·00

O 16. O 38.

1900.

No.	Type	Description	Unused	Used
O 148.	O 16.	1 c. purple	45	45
O 149.		2 c. orange	35	35
O 150.		4 c. olive	45	45
O 151.		5 c. blue	90	30
O 152.		10 c. violet	90	25
O 153.		20 c. brown	65	25
O 154.		50 c. lake	90	35
O 155.		1 p. blue	2·10	1·50
O 156.		2 p. orange	2·40	2·40
O 157.		5 p. black	3·00	3·00

1903. Stamps of 1900 surch. **OFICIAL** and value, with or without ornaments.

No.	Type	Description	Unused	Used
O 197.	15.	1 c. on 10 c. mauve	75	1·00
O 198.		2 c. on 3 c. green	1·00	1·25
O 199.		4 c. on 3 c. green	3·75	3·75
O 200.		4 c. on 10 c. mauve	3·75	3·75
O 201.		5 c. on 3 c. green	45	50

1903. Surch.

No.	Type	Description	Unused	Used
O 202.	O 16.	10 c. on 20 c. brown	15	15
O 203.		30 c. on 20 c. brown	15	15
O 204.		50 c. on 20 c. brown	35	25

1905.

No.	Type	Description	Unused	Used
O 219.	O 38.	1 c. green	20	20
O 220.		2 c. red	20	20
O 221.		5 c. blue	20	20
O 222.		10 c. brown	20	20
O 223.		20 c. orange	20	20
O 224.		50 c. olive	20	20
O 225.		1 p. lake	20	20
O 226.		2 p. violet	20	20
O 227.		5 p. black	20	20

1907. Surch. thus: **Vale 10 c.**

No.	Type	Description	Unused	Used
O 239.	O 38.	10 c. on 1 c. green	55	55
O 241.		10 c. on 2 c. red	15·00	11·50
O 243.		20 c. on 2 c. red	13·50	9·00
O 245.		50 c. on 1c. green	1·10	1·10
O 247.		50 c. on 2 c. red	13·50	6·50

1907. Surch. thus: **Vale 20 cts** or **Vale $1.00.**

No.	Type	Description	Unused	Used
O 249.	O 38.	20 c. on 1 c. green	70	70
O 250.		$1 on 2 c. red	1·10	1·10
O 251.		$2 on 2 c. red	1·10	1·10
O 252.		$3 on 2 c. red	1·10	1·10
O 253.		$4 on 5 c. blue	1·40	1·40

1907. No. 206 surch. **OFICIAL** and value.

No.	Type	Description	Unused	Used
O 256.	49.	10 c. on 1 c. green	9·00	7·75
O 257.		15 c. on 1 c. green	9·00	7·75
O 258.		20 c. on 1 c. green	9·00	7·75
O 259.		50 c. on 1 c. green	9·00	7·75
O 260.		1 p. on 1 c. green	8·25	7·75
O 261.		2 p. on 1 c. green	8·25	7·75

1907. Fiscal stamps as T 50 surch. thus: **10 cts. CORREOS 1907 OFICIAL 10 cts.**

No.	Type	Description	Unused	Used
O 262.	50.	10 c. on 2 c. orange	10	10
O 263.		35 c. on 1 c. blue	10	10
O 264.		70 c. on 1 c. blue	10	10
O 266.		1 p. on 2 c. orange	10	12
O 267.		2 p. on 2 c. orange	10	12
O 268.		3 p. on 5 c. brown	10	12
O 269.		4 p. on 5 c. brown	15	15
O 270.		5 p. on 5 c. brown	15	15

1908. Stamp of 1905 surch. **OFICIAL VALE** and value.

No.	Type	Description	Unused	Used
O 271.	37.	10 c. on 3 c. violet	9·00	7·75
O 272.		15 c. on 3 c. violet	9·00	7·75
O 273.		20 c. on 3 c. violet	9·00	7·75
O 274.		35 c. on 3 c. violet	9·00	7·75
O 275.		50 c. on 3 c. violet	9·00	7·75

1908. Fiscal stamps as T 50 surch. as last but dated **1908.**

No.	Type	Description	Unused	Used
O 276.	50.	10 c. on 1 c. blue	55	35
O 277.		10 c. on 2 c. orange	75	30
O 278.		35 c. on 1 c. blue	55	35
O 279.		35 c. on 2 c. orange	80	45
O 280.		50 c. on 1 c. blue	55	35
O 281.		50 c. on 2 c. orange	80	45
O 282.		70 c. on 2 c. orange	80	45
O 283.		1 p. on 1 c. blue	23·00	23·00
O 284.		1 p. on 2 c. orange	80	45
O 285.		2 p. on 1 c. blue	65	55
O 286.		2 p. on 2 c. orange	80	45

1909. Stamps of 1905 optd. **OFICIAL.**

No.	Type	Description	Unused	Used
O 290.	37.	10 c. lake	15	12
O 291.		15 c. black	45	35
O 292.		20 c. olive	70	55
O 293.		50 c. green	1·10	70
O 294.		1 p. yellow	1·25	90
O 295.		2 p. red	1·75	1·40

1911. Stamps of 1905 optd. **OFICIAL** and surch. **Vale** and value.

No.	Type	Description	Unused	Used
O 296.	37.	5 c. on 3 c. orange	3·75	3·75
O 297.		10 c. on 4 c. violet	3·00	3·00

1911. Railway coupon stamp surch. **Timbre Fiscal Vale 10 ctvs** further surch. **Correo oficial Vale** and new value. Printed in red.

No.	Type	Description	Unused	Used
O 334.	64.	10 c. on 10 c. on 1 c.	3·00	3·00
O 335.		15 c. on 10 c. on 1 c.	3·00	3·00
O 336.		20 c. on 10 c. on 1 c.	3·00	3·00
O 337.		50 c. on 10 c. on 1 c.	4·00	4·00
O 338.		$1 on 10 c. on 1 c.	4·75	7·25
O 339.		$2 on 10 c. on 1 c.	6·50	10·00

1911. Railway coupon stamp surch. **TIMBRE FISCAL VALE 10 ctvs.** further surch. **CORREO OFICIAL** and new value. Printed in red.

No.	Type	Description	Unused	Used
O 340.	64.	10 c. on 10 c. on 1 c.	22·00	17·00
O 341.		15 c. on 10 c. on 1 c.	22·00	17·00
O 342.		20 c. on 10 c. on 1 c.	22·00	18·00
O 343.		50 c. on 10 c. on 1 c.	18·00	15·00

1911. Railway stamp with value of postal surch. on back cancelled with thick bar, surch. on front **Correo Oficial Vale 1911** and new value. Printed in red.

No.	Type	Description	Unused	Used
O 344.	64.	5 c. on 10 c. on 1 c.	3·75	4·50
O 345.		10 c. on 10 c. on 1 c.	4·25	5·25
O 346.		15 c. on 10 c. on 1 c.	5·00	5·75
O 347.		20 c. on 10 c. on 1 c.	5·50	8·50
O 348.		50 c. on 10 c. on 1 c.	6·25	7·50

1912. Railway stamp with whole surch. on back cancelled with thick bar, surch on front **Correo Oficial 1912** and new value. Printed in red.

No.	Type	Description	Unused	Used
O 349.	64.	5 c. on 10 c. on 1 c.	5·50	4·75
O 350.		10 c. on 10 c. on 1 c.	5·50	4·75
O 351.		15 c. on 10 c. on 1 c.	5·50	4·75
O 352.		20 c. on 10 c. on 1 c.	5·50	4·75
O 353.		25 c. on 10 c. on 1 c.	5·50	4·75
O 354.		50 c. on 10 c. on 1 c.	5·50	4·75
O 355.		$1 on 10 c. on 1 c.	5·50	4·75

1913. Stamps of 1912 optd. **OFICIAL.**

No.	Type	Description	Unused	Used
O 356.	70.	1 c. blue	5	5
O 357.		2 c. blue	5	5
O 358.		3 c. blue	5	5
O 359.		4 c. blue	5	8
O 360.		5 c. blue	5	10
O 361.		6 c. blue	8	15
O 362.		10 c. blue	8	15
O 363.		15 c. blue	8	15
O 364.		20 c. blue	12	20
O 365.		25 c. blue	15	15
O 366.	71.	35 c. blue	20	20
O 367.	70.	50 c. blue	1·10	1·10
O 368.		1 p. blue	25	25
O 369.		2 p. blue	25	25
O 370.		5 p. blue	35	35

1915. Optd. **OFICIAL.**

No.	Type	Description	Unused	Used
O 406.	79.	1 c. blue	12	12
O 407.	80.	2 c. blue	12	12
O 408.	79.	3 c. blue	15	12
O 409.	80.	4 c. blue	12	12
O 410.	79.	5 c. blue	12	12
O 411.	80.	6 c. blue	12	12
O 412.		10 c. blue	15	15
O 413.	79.	15 c. blue	15	15
O 414.	80.	20 c. blue	15	15
O 415.	79.	25 c. blue	25	25
O 416.	80.	50 c. blue	45	45

1925. Optd. **Oficial** or **OFICIAL.**

No.	Type	Description	Unused	Used
O 513.	79.	½ c. green	5	5
O 514.		1 c. violet	5	5
O 515.	80.	2 c. red	5	5
O 516.	79.	3 c. olive	5	5
O 517.	80.	4 c. red	5	5
O 518.	79.	5 c. black	8	8
O 519.	80.	6 c. brown	8	8
O 520.		10 c. yellow	8	8
O 521.	79.	15 c. brown	8	8
O 522.	80.	20 c. brown	8	8
O 523.	79.	25 c. orange	40	40
O 524.	80.	50 c. blue	45	45

1929. Air. Official stamps of 1925 additionally optd. **Correo Aereo.**

No.	Type	Description	Unused	Used
O 618.	79.	25 c. orange	35	35
O 619.	80.	50 c. blue	55	55

1931. Stamp of 1924 surch. **OFICIAL C$ 0.05 Correos 1928.**

No.	Type	Description	Unused	Used
O 651.	99.	5 c. on 10 c. brown	25	25

1931. No. 648 additionally surch. **OFICIAL** and value.

No.	Type	Description	Unused	Used
O 652.	99.	5 c. on 10 c. brown	25	25

1931. Stamps of 1914 optd. **1931** (except 6 c., 10 c.), and also optd. **OFICIAL.**

No.	Type	Description	Unused	Used
O 670.	79.	1 c. olive (No. 762)	20	20
O 707.	80.	2 c. red	6·50	6·50
O 671.	79.	3 c. blue	20	20
O 672.		5 c. sepia	20	20
O 673.	80.	6 c. brown	25	25
O 675.		10 c. brown	25	25
O 674.		10 c. blue (No. 697)	1·10	1·10
O 710.	79.	15 c. orange	70	70
O 711.		25 c. sepia	70	70
O 712.		25 c. violet	1·75	1·75

1932. Air. Optd. **Correo Aereo OFICIAL** only.

No.	Type	Description	Unused	Used
O 688.	79.	15 c. orange	45	45
O 689.	80.	20 c. orange	50	50
O 690.	79.	25 c. violet	50	50
O 691.	80.	50 c. green	60	60
O 692.		1 cor. yellow	60	60

1932. Air. Optd. **1931. Correo Aereo OFICIAL.**

No.	Type	Description	Unused	Used
O 693.	79.	25 c. sepia	25·00	25·00

1932. Optd. **OFICIAL.**

No.	Type	Description	Unused	Used
O 694.	79.	1 c. olive	5	5
O 695.	80.	2 c. red	8	8
O 696.	79.	3 c. blue	12	8
O 697.	80.	4 c. blue	12	8
O 698.	79.	5 c. sepia	15	12
O 699.	80.	6 c. brown	20	8
O 700.		10 c. brown	30	25
O 701.	79.	15 c. orange	40	25
O 702.	80.	20 c. orange	40	30
O 703.	79.	25 c. violet	1·25	50
O 704.	80.	50 c. green	12	12
O 705.		1 cor. yellow	20	20

1933. 441st Anniv. of Columbus's Departure from Palos. As T 133, but inscr. "CORREO OFICIAL". Roul.

No.	Type	Description	Unused	Used
O 777.		1 c. yellow	60	60
O 778.		2 c. yellow	60	60
O 779.		3 c. brown	60	60
O 780.		4 c. brown	60	60
O 781.		5 c. brown	60	60
O 782.		6 c. blue	75	75
O 783.		10 c. violet	75	75
O 784.		15 c. purple	75	75
O 785.		20 c. green	75	75
O 786.		25 c. green	1·75	1·75
O 787.		50 c. red	2·25	2·25
O 788.		1 cor. red	3·50	3·50

1933. Optd. with T **134** and **OFICIAL.**

No.	Type	Description	Unused	Used
O 814.	79.	1 c. green	5	5
O 815.	80.	2 c. red	5	5
O 816.	79.	3 c. blue	8	8
O 817.	80.	4 c. blue	5	5
O 818.	79.	5 c. brown	5	5
O 819.	80.	6 c. grey	8	8
O 820.		10 c. brown	8	8
O 821.	79.	15 c. red	12	12
O 822.	80.	20 c. orange	12	12
O 823.	79.	25 c. violet	15	15
O 824.	80.	50 c. green	25	25
O 825.		1 cor. yellow	50	45

1933. Air. Optd. with T **134** and **CORREO Aereo OFICIAL.**

No.	Type	Description	Unused	Used
O 826.	79.	15 c. violet	20	20
O 827.	80.	20 c. green	20	20
O 828.	79.	25 c. olive	20	20
O 829.	80.	50 c. green	35	35
O 830.		1 cor. red	60	50

1935. Nos. O 814/25 optd. **RESELLO-1935** in a box.

No.	Type	Description	Unused	Used
O 864.	79.	1 c. green	5	5
O 865.	80.	2 c. red	5	5
O 866.	79.	3 c. blue	8	8
O 867.	80.	4 c. blue	8	8
O 868.	79.	5 c. brown	8	8
O 869.	80.	6 c. grey	10	10
O 870.		10 c. brown	10	10
O 871.	79.	15 c. red	15	15
O 872.	80.	20 c. orange	15	15
O 873.	79.	25 c. violet	12	12
O 874.	80.	50 c. green	20	20
O 875.		1 cor. yellow	35	35

1935. Air. Nos. O 826/30 optd. **RESELLO-1935** in a box.

No.	Type	Description	Unused	Used
O 877.	79.	15 c. violet	30	25
O 878.	80.	20 c. green	30	25
O 879.	79.	25 c. olive	30	30
O 880.	80.	50 c. green	90	90
O 881.		1 cor. red	90	90

(O 141.) O 151. Islets in the Great Lake.

1937. Nos. 913, etc., optd. with Type O 141.

No.	Type	Description	Unused	Used
O 935.	79.	1 c. red	25	15
O 936.	80.	2 c. blue	25	15
O 937.	79.	3 c. brown	30	25
O 938.		5 c. red	35	30
O 939.	80.	10 c. green	40	35
O 940.	79.	15 c. green	50	40
O 941.		25 c. orange	60	45
O 942.	80.	50 c. brown	85	50
O 943.		1 cor. blue	2·25	1·00

1937. Air. Nos. 926/30 optd. with Type O 141.

No.	Type	Description	Unused	Used
O 944.	112.	15 c. orange	50	35
O 945.		20 c. red	50	35
O 946.		25 c. black	50	45
O 947.		50 c. violet	50	45
O 948.		1 cor. orange	50	45

1939.

O 1020.	O 151.	2 c. red	12	12
O 1021.		3 c. blue ..	12	12
O 1022.		6 c. brown ..	12	12
O 1023.		7½ c. green ..	12	12
O 1024.		10 c. brown ..	12	12
O 1025.		15 c. orange ..	12	12
O 1026.		25 c. violet ..	30	30
O 1027.		50 c. green ..	45	45

O 152. Pres. Somoza.

1939. Air.

O 1028.	O 152.	10 c. brown ..	30	30
O 1029.		15 c. blue ..	30	30
O 1030.		20 c. yellow ..	30	30
O 1031.		25 c. violet ..	30	30
O 1032.		30 c. red ..	30	30
O 1033.		50 c. orange ..	40	40
O 1034.		1 cor. olive ..	75	75

O 175. Managua Airport.

1947. Air.

O 1120.	O 175.	5 c. brown & blk.	15	10
O 1121.	–	10 c. blue & blk.	15	15
O 1122.	–	15 c. vio. & blk.	15	10
O 1123.	–	20 c. orge. & blk.	20	10
O 1124.	–	25 c. blue & blk.	15	15
O 1125.	–	50 c. red & blk.	15	15
O 1126.	–	1 cor. grey & blk.	40	35
O 1127.	–	2 cor. 50 brown and black ..	75	90

DESIGNS: 10 c. Sulphur Lagoon, Nejapa. 15 c. Ruben Dario Monument, Managua. 20 c. Baird's tapir. 25 c. Genizaro Dam. 50 c. Thermal Baths, Tipitapa. 1 cor. Highway and Lake Managua. 2 cor. 50, Franklin D. Roosevelt Monument, Managua.

O 181. U.P.U. Offices, Berne.

1950. Air. 75th Anniv. of U.P.U. Inscr. as in Type O **181**. Frames in black.

O 1159.	–	5 c. purple ..	8	5
O 1160.	–	10 c. green ..	8	8
O 1161.	–	25 c. purple ..	10	10
O 1162.	O 181.	50 c. orange ..	15	10
O 1163.	–	1 cor. blue ..	35	30
O 1164.	–	2 cor. 60 black ..	2·10	1·75

DESIGNS—HORIZ. 5 c. Rowland Hill. 10 c. Heinrich von Stephan. 25 c. Standehaus, Berne. 1 cor. Monument, Berne. 2 cor. 60, Congress Medal.

1961. Air. Consular Fiscal stamps as T **203/4** with serial Nos. in red, surch. **Oficial** Aereo and value.

O 1448.	10 c. on 1 cor. olive ..	8	5
O 1449.	15 c. on 20 cor. brown	10	10
O 1450.	20 c. on 100 cor. lake ..	10	10
O 1451.	25 c. on 50 c. blue ..	12	8
O 1452.	35 c. on 50 cor. brown	12	12
O 1453.	50 c. on 3 cor. red ..	12	12
O 1454.	1 cor. on 2 cor. green ..	25	20
O 1455.	2 cor. on 5 cor. red ..	25	45
O 1456.	5 cor. on 10 cor. violet	60	60

POSTAGE DUE STAMPS

D 13.

D 16.

1896.

D 99.	D 13.	1 c. orange ..	45	1·10
D 100.		2 c. orange ..	45	1·10
D 101.		5 c. orange ..	45	1·10
D 102.		10 c. orange ..	45	1·10
D 103.		20 c. orange ..	45	1·10
D 104.		30 c. orange ..	45	1·10
D 105.		50 c. orange ..	45	1·40

1897.

D 108.	D 13.	1 c. violet	45	1·10
D 109.		2 c. violet	45	1·10
D 110.		5 c. violet	45	1·10
D 111.		10 c. violet ..	45	1·10
D 112.		20 c. violet ..	75	1·25
D 113.		30 c. violet ..	45	90
D 114.		50 c. violet ..	45	90

1898.

D 124.	D 13.	1 c. green	12	1·25
D 125.		2 c. green	12	1·25
D 126.		5 c. green	12	1·25
D 127.		10 c. green ..	12	1·25
D 128.		20 c. green ..	12	1·25
D 129.		30 c. green ..	12	1·25
D 130.		50 c. green ..	12	1·25

1899.

D 137.	D 13.	1 c. red	12	1·25
D 138.		2 c. red	12	1·25
D 139.		5 c. red	12	1·25
D 140.		10 c. red	12	1·25
D 141.		20 c. red	12	1·25
D 142.		50 c. red	12	1·25

1900.

D 146.	D 16.	1 c. red	70
D 147.		2 c. orange ..	70
D 148.		5 c. blue	70
D 149.		10 c. violet ..	70
D 150.		20 c. brown ..	70
D 151.		30 c. green ..	1·40
D 152.		50 c. lake	1·40

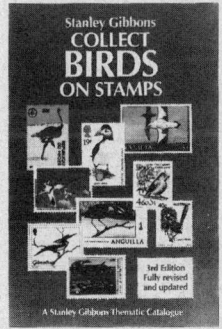

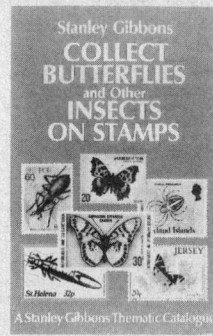

NIGER Pt. 6; Pt. 14

Area south of the Sahara. In 1920 was separated from Upper Senegal and Niger to form a separate colony. From 1944 to 1959 used the stamps of French West Africa.

In 1958 Niger became an autonomous republic within the French Community and on 3 August 1960 an independent republic.

100 centimes = 1 franc.

1921. Stamps of Upper Senegal and Niger optd **TERRITOIRE DU NIGER**.

1 **7** 1 c. violet and purple .. 10 30
2 2 c. purple and grey .. 10 30
3 4 c. blue and black .. 15 30
4 5 c. chocolate and brown 15 30
5 10 c. green and light green 50 75
25 10 c. pink on blue .. 10 30
6 15 c. yellow and brown .. 15 30
7 20 c. black and purple .. 15 30
8 25 c. green and black .. 15 30
9 30 c. carmine and red .. 50 65
26 30 c. red and green .. 30 50
10 35 c. violet and red .. 25 40
11 40 c. red and grey .. 35 50
12 45 c. brown and blue .. 35 50
13 50 c. blue and ultramarine 40 60
27 50 c. blue and grey .. 50 70
28 60 c. red 35 55
14 75 c. brown and yellow .. 45 85
15 1 f. purple and brown .. 60 80
16 2 f. blue and green .. 65 90
17 5 f. black and violet .. 1·25 1·40

1922. Stamps of 1921 surch.

18 **7** 25 c. on 15 c. yellow & brn 25 40
19 25 c. on 2 f. blue and green 25 45
20 25 c. on 5 f. black & violet 25 45
21 60 on 75 c. violet on pink 25 45
22 65 on 45 c. brown and blue 75 1·40
23 85 c. on 75 c. brown & yell 85 1·40
24 1 f. 25 on 1 f. lt blue & bl 60 85

3. Wells.

5. Zinder Fort.

4. Canoe on River Niger.

1926.

29 **3** 1 c. green and purple .. 10 25
30 2 c. red and grey .. 10 30
31 3 c. brown and mauve .. 10 30
32 4 c. black and brown .. 10 30
33 5 c. green and red .. 10 35
34 10 c. green and blue .. 10 20
35 15 c. light green and green 40 40
36 15 c. red and lilac .. 10 25
37 **4** 20 c. brown and blue .. 15 30
38 25 c. pink and black .. 15 30
39 30 c. light green and green 35 55
40 30 c. mauve and yellow .. 20 40
41 35 c. blue and red on blue 15 30
42 35 c. green and deep green 35 50
43 40 c. grey and purple .. 25 40
44 45 c. mauve and yellow .. 55 70
45 45 c. green & turquoise .. 35 55
46 50 c. green & red on green 25 30
47 55 c. brown and red .. 50 70
48 60 c. brown and red .. 40 65
49 65 c. red and green .. 25 45
50 70 c. red and green .. 55 70
51 75 c. mauve & grn on pink 70 90
52 80 c. green and purple .. 80 95
53 90 c. red and carmine .. 55 70
54 90 c. green and red .. 55 70
55 **5** 1 f. green and red .. 3·00 3·00
56 1 f. orange and red .. 65 60
57 1 f. red and green .. 40 55
58 1 f. 10 green and brown .. 2·25 2·00
59 1 f. 25 red and green .. 70 75
60 1 f. 25 orange and red .. 50 70
61 1 f. 40 brown and mauve 50 70
62 1 f. 50 light blue and blue 25 35
63 1 f. 60 green and brown .. 75 95
64 1 f. 75 brown and mauve 1·40 1·50
65 1 f. 75 ultramarine & blue 65 85
66 2 f. brown and orange .. 35 50
67 2 f. 25 ultramarine & blue 55 75
68 2 f. 50 brown 65 80
69 3 f. grey and mauve .. 35 45
70 5 f. black & pur on pink 50 65
71 10 f. mauve and lilac .. 75 80
72 20 f. orange and green .. 75 85

1931. "Colonial Exhibition" key types inscr. "NIGER".

73. E. 40 c. green .. .. 2·25 2·25
74. F. 50 c. mauve .. .. 2·00 2·25
75. G. 90 c. red .. .. 2·50 2·75
76. H. 1 f. 50 blue .. .. 2·50 2·75

1937. International Exhibition, Paris. As Nos. 168/73 of St.-Pierre et Miquelon.

77 20 c. violet 60 85
78 30 c. green 60 85
79 40 c. red 55 75
80 50 c. brown and agate .. 50 70
81 90 c. red 55 85
82 1 f. 50 blue 55 85

1938. Int. Anti-Cancer Fund. As T **22** of Mauritania.

83. 1 f. 75+50 c. blue .. 8·50 9·50

1939. Caille. As T **27** of Mauritania.

84. 90 c. orange 40 55
85. 2 f. violet 40 55
86. 2 f. 25 blue 40 55

1939. New York World's Fair. As T **28** of Mauritania.

87. 1 f. 25 red 50 60
88. 2 f. 25 blue 50 60

1939. 150th Anniv of French Revolution. As T **29** of Mauritania.

89 45 c.+25 c. green and black 4·50 5·00
90 70 c.+30 c. brown and black 4·50 5·00
91 90 c.+35 c. orange and black 4·75 5·00
92 1 f. 25+1 f. red and black 4·50 5·00
93 2 f. 25+2 f. blue and black 4·50 5·00

1940. Air. As T **30** of Mauritania.

94. 1 f. 90 blue 50 55
95. 2 f. 90 red 45 55
96. 4 f. 50 green 60 70
97. 4 f. 90 olive 50 60
98. 6 f. 90 orange 45 60

1941. National Defence Fund. Surch **SECOURS NATIONAL** and additional value.

98a **4** +1 f. on 50 c. green and red on green .. .. 2·00 2·00
98b +2 f. on 80 c. grn & pur 3·00 3·00
98c **5** +2 f. on 1 f. 50 lt bl & bl 4·25 4·25
98d +3 f. on 2 f. brn & orge 4·25 4·25

5a. Zinder Fort.

5c. "Vocation".

5b. Weighing Baby.

1942. Marshal Petain issue.

98e **5a** 1 f. green 10
98f 2 f. 50 blue 10

1942. Air. Colonial Child Welfare Fund.

98g – 1 f. 50+3 f. 50 green .. 20
98h – 2 f.+6 f. brown .. 15
98i **5b** 3 f.+9 f. red 15

DESIGNS—49×28 mm. 1 f. 50, Maternity Hospital, Dakar. 2 f. Dispensary, Mopti.

1942. Air. Imperial Fortnight.

98j **5c** 1 f. 20+1 f. 80 blue & red 10

1942. Air. As T **32** of Mauritania but inscr "NIGER" at foot.

98k 50 f. red and yellow .. 80 1·00

7. Giraffes.

8. Carmine Bee Eater.

1959. Wild Animals and Birds. Inscr. "PROTECTION DE LA FAUNE".

~~99.~~ – 50 c. turquoise, green and black (postage) .. 25 10
100. – 1 f. multicoloured .. 30 15
~~101.~~ – 2 f. multicoloured .. 30 15
102. – 5 f. mve., blk. and brn. 40 15
103. – 7 f. red, black and green 50 20
104. – 10 f. multicoloured .. 25 10
105. – 15 f. sepia and turquoise 25 10
106. – 20 f. black and violet .. 35 10
107. **7.** 25 f. multicoloured .. 45 10
108. 30 f. brn., bistre & green 50 20
109. – 50 f. blue and brown .. 4·00 80
110. 60 f. sepia and green .. 5·50 1·10
111. – 85 f. brown and bistre .. 2·50 85
112. – 100 f. bistre and green .. 3·25 85
113. **8.** 200 f. multicoloured (air) 18·00 5·50
114. – 500 f. grn., brn. and blue 8·50 6·00

DESIGNS—As Type **7**—HORIZ. 50 c., 10 f. African manatee. VERT. 1 f., 2 f. Crowned Cranes. 5 f., 7 f. Saddle-bill Stork. 15 f., 20 f. Barbary sheep. 50 f., 60 f. Ostriches. 85 f., 100 f. Lion. As Type **8**—VERT. 500 f. Game animals.

1960. 10th Anniv. of African Technical Co-operation Commission. As T **4** of Malagasy Republic.

115. 25 f. brown and ochre .. 50 40

9. Conseil de l'Entente Emblem.

11. Pres. Diori Hamani.

1960. 1st Anniv. of Conseil de l'Entente.

116. **9.** 25 f. multicoloured .. 50 40

1960. Independence. No. 112 surch. **200 F** and bars and **Independance 3-8-60.**

117. – 200 f. on 100 f. .. 9·00 9·00

1960.

118. **11.** 25 f. black and bistre .. 35 25

12. U.N. Emblem and Niger Flag.

1961. Air. 1st Anniv. of Admission into U.N.

119. **12.** 25 f. red, green & orange 40 25
120. 100 f. green, red & emer. 1·40 90

1962. Air. "Air Afrique" Airline. As T **42** of Mauritania.

121. 100 f. violet, black & brown 1·50 75

1962. Malaria Eradication. As T **43** of Mauritania.

122. 25 f.+5 f. brown 45 45

13. Athletics.

1962. Abidjan Games, 1961. Multicoloured.

123. 15 f. Boxing and cycling (vert.) 25 15
124. 25 f. Basketball and football (vert.) 35 20
125. 85 f. Type **13** .. .. 1·10 55

1962. 1st Anniv. of Union of African and Malagasy States. As T **45** of Mauritania.

126. **72.** 30 f. mauve 40 30

14. Pres. Hamani and Map.

15. Running.

1962. 4th Anniv. of Republic.

127. **14.** 25 f. multicoloured .. 35 25

1963. Freedom from Hunger. As T **51** of Mauritania.

128. 25 f.+5 f. pur., brn. & olive 55 55

1963. Dakar Games.

129. – 15 f. brown and blue .. 25 15
130. **15.** 25 f. red and brown .. 35 20
131. – 45 f. black and green .. 70 40

DESIGNS—HORIZ. 15 f. Swimming. VERT. 45 f. Volleyball.

16. Agadez Mosque.

1963. Air. 2nd Anniv. of Admission to U.P.U. Multicoloured.

132. 50 f Type **16** 75 40
133. 85 f. Gaya Bridge .. 1·25 60
134. 100 f. Presidential Palace, Niamey .. .. .. 1·25 70

17. Wood-carving.

1963. Traditional Crafts. Multicoloured.

135 5 f. Type **17** (postage) .. 15 15
136 10 f. Skin-tanning .. 20 15
137 25 f. Goldsmith 40 20
138 30 f. Mat-making 60 30
139 85 f. Potter .. .. 1·40 80
140 100 f. Canoe building (air) 2·00 1·10

The 10 f. and 30 f. are horiz. and the 100 f. larger (47×27 mm.).

1963. Air. African and Malagasy Posts and Telecommunications Union. As T **56** of Mauritania.

141. 85 f. multicoloured .. 95 55

1963. Air. Red Cross Centenary. Optd. with cross and **Centenaire de la Croix-Rouge** in red.

142. **12.** 25 f. red, green & orange 60 40
143. 100 f. green, red & emerald 1·40 85

19. Costume Museum.

1963. Opening of Costume Museum, Niamey. Vert. costume designs. Multicoloured.

144. 15 f. Berber woman .. 20 15
145. 20 f. Haussa woman .. 35 15
146. 25 f. Tuareg woman .. 45 20
147. 30 f. Tuareg man .. 55 20
148. 60 f. Djerma woman .. 1·25 50
149. 85 f. Type **19** .. .. 1·50 60

20. "Europafrique". 22. Man and Globe.

21. Groundnut Cultivation.

1963. Air. European–African Economic Convention.
150. **20.** 50 f. multicoloured .. 2·50 2·00

1963. Air. Groundnut Cultivation Campaign.
151. **21.** 20 f. blue, brn. & green 35 20
152. – 45 f. brn., blue & green 75 25
153. – 85 f. multicoloured .. 1·40 65
154. – 100 f. olive, brn. & blue 1·50 90
DESIGNS: 45 f. Camel transport. 85 f. Fastening sacks. 100 f. Dispatch of groundnuts by lorry.

1963. Air. 1st Anniv. of "Air Afrique" and "DC-8" Service Inauguration. As T **59** of Mauritania.
155. 50 f. multicoloured .. 70 45

1963. 15th Anniv. of Declaration of Human Rights.
156. **22.** 25 f. blue, brn. & green 45 25

23. "Telstar".

1964. Air. Space Telecommunications.
157. **23.** 25 f. olive and violet .. 40 20
158. – 100 f. green and purple 1·10 80
DESIGN: 100 f. "Relay".

24. "Parkinsonia aculeata". 25. Statue, Abu Simbel.

1964. Flowers. Multicoloured.
159. 5 f. Type **24** 60 30
160. 10 f. "Russelia equisetiformis" .. 50 30
161. 15 f. "Lantana Camara" 1·00 45
162. 20 f. "Agyreia nervosa" 1·00 45
163. 25 f. "Luffa Cylindrica" 1·00 45
164. 30 f. "Hibiscus rosa-sinensis" .. .. 1·40 60
165. 45 f. "Plumierai rubra" 2·00 1·25
166. 50 f. "Catharanthus roseus" .. .. 2·00 1·25
167. 60 f. "Caesalpinia pulcherrima" .. .. 3·50 1·50
Nos. 164/7 have "REPUBLIQUE DU NIGER" at the top and the value at bottom right.

1964. Air. Nubian Monuments Preservation.
168. **25.** 25 f. green and brown .. 65 45
169. 30 f. brown and blue .. 1·00 70
170. 50 f. blue and purple .. 2·00 1·25

26. Globe and "Tiros" Satellite.

1964. Air. World Meteorological Day.
171. **26.** 50 f. brn., blue and grn. 1·10 65

27. Sun Emblem and Solar Flares. 28. Convoy of Lorries.

1964. International Quiet Sun Years.
172. **27.** 30 f. red, violet & sepia 50 35

1964. O.M.N.E.S. (Nigerian Mobile Medical and Sanitary Organization) Commemoration.
173. **28.** 25 f. orge. olive & blue 40 20
174. – 30 f. multicoloured .. 50 20
175. – 50 f. multicoloured .. 80 30
176. – 60 f. purple, orge. & turq. 90 35
DESIGNS: 30 f. Tending children. 50 f. Tending women. 60 f. Open-air laboratory.

29. Rocket, Stars and Stamp Outline.

1964. Air. "PHILATEC 1964" Int. Stamp Exn., Paris.
177. **29.** 50 f. mauve and blue .. 85 60

30. European, African and Symbols of Agriculture and Industry. 31. Pres. Kennedy.

1964. Air. 1st Anniv. of European–African Economic Convention.
178. **30.** 50 f. multicoloured .. 65 40

1964. Air. Pres. Kennedy. Commem.
179. **31.** 100 f. multicoloured .. 1·25 1·10

32. Water-polo.

1964. Air. Olympic Games, Tokyo.
180. **32.** 60 f. brown, deep green and purple 60 50
181. – 85 f. brown, blue & red 1·00 60
182. – 100 f. blue, red & green 1·25 70
183. – 250 f. blue, brn. and grn. 2·50 1·75
DESIGNS—HORIZ. 85 f. Relay-racing. VERT. 100 f. Throwing the discus. 250 f. Athlete holding Olympic Torch.

1964. French, African and Malagasy Co-operation. As T **68** of Mauritania.
184. 50 f. brown, orge. & violet 65 40

33. Azawak Tuareg Encampment.

1964. Native Villages. Multicoloured.
185. 15 f. Type **33** 20 20
186. 20 f. Songhai hut .. 25 20
187. 25 f. Wogo and Kourtey tents 30 20
188. 30 f. Djerma hut 40 25
189. 60 f. Sorkawa fishermen's encampment 75 30
190. 85 f. Hausa urban house 1·25 50

34. Doctors and Patient and Microscope Slide. 35. Abraham Lincoln.

1964. Anti-Leprosy Campaign.
191. **34.** 50 f. multicoloured .. 50 45

1965. Death Cent. of Abraham Lincoln.
192. **35.** 50 f. multicoloured .. 60 50

36. Instruction by "Radio-Vision".

1965. "Human Progress". Inscr. as in T **36**.
193. **36.** 20 f. brn., yell. and blue 30 20
194. – 25 f. sepia, brown & grn. 35 20
195. – 30 f. purple, red & grn. 45 25
196. – 50 f. purple, blue & brn. 70 35
DESIGNS: 25 f. Student. 30 f. Adult class. 50 f. Five tribesmen ("Alphabetisation").

37. Ader's Telephone. 38. Pope John XXIII.

1965. I.T.U. Cent.
197. **37.** 25 f. black, lake & green 50 25
198. – 30 f. green, purple & red 60 30
199. – 50 f. green, purple & red 1·00 50
DESIGNS: 30 f. Wheatstone's telegraph. 50 f. "Telautographe".

1965. Air. Pope John Commem.
200. **38.** 100 f. multicoloured .. 1·40 75

39. Hurdling. 40. "Capture of Cancer" (the Crab).

1965. 1st African Games, Brazzaville.
201. **39.** 10 f. purple, grn. & brn. 20 15
202. – 15 f. red, brown and grey 30 15
203. – 20 f. purple, blue & grn. 40 20
204. – 30 f. purple, grn. & lake 50 25
DESIGNS—VERT. 15 f. Running. 30 f. Long-jumping. HORIZ. 20 f. Pole-vaulting.

1965. Air. Campaign against Cancer.
205. **40.** 100 f. brown, black & grn. 1·40 80

41. Sir Winston Churchill. 42. Interviewing.

1965. Air. Churchill Commemoration.
206 **41** 100 f. multicoloured .. 1·40 80

1965. Radio Club Promotion.
207. **42.** 30 f. brn., violet & grn. 30 15
208. – 45 f. red, black and buff 45 25
209. – 50 f. multicoloured .. 55 30
210. – 60 f. pur., blue & ochre 60 40
DESIGNS—VERT. 45 f. Recording. 50 f. Listening to broadcast. HORIZ. 60 f. Listeners debate.

43. "Agricultural and Industrial Workers". 44. Fair Scene and Flags.

1965. Air. Int. Co-operation Year.
211. **43.** 50 f. brn., blk. & bistre 70 35

1965. Air. Int. Fair, Niamey.
212. **44.** 100 f. multicoloured .. 1·10 70

45. Dr. Schweitzer and Diseased Hands.

1966. Air. Schweitzer Commem.
213. **45.** 50 f. multicoloured .. 80 45

46. "Water Distribution and Control".

1966. Int. Hydrological Decade Inaug.
214. **46.** 50 f. blue, orge. & violet 70 35

47. Weather Ship "France I".

1966. Air. 6th World Meteorological Day.
215. **47.** 50 f. green, purple & blue 1·25 55

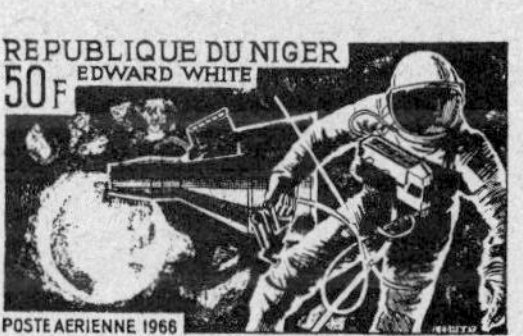
48. White and "Gemini" Capsule.

1966. Air. Cosmonauts.
216. **48.** 50 f. black, brn. & grn. 75 40
217. – 50 f. blue, violet & orge. 75 40
DESIGN: No. 217 Leonov and "Voskhod" capsule.

49. Head-dress and Carvings.

51. Goalkeeper saving ball. 50. "Diamant" Rocket and Gantry.

1966. World Festival of Negro Arts, Dakar.
218. **49.** 30 f. black, brown & grn. 45 25
219. – 50 f. violet, brown & blue 60 35
220. – 60 f. lake, violet & brn. 70 40
221. – 100 f. black, red & blue 1·25 70
DESIGNS: 50 f. Carved figures and mosaics. 60 f. Statuettes, drums and arch. 100 f. Handicrafts and church.

1966. Air. French Space Vehicles. Multicoloured designs each showing different Satellites.
222. 45 f. Type **50** 70 40
223. 60 f. "A 1" (horiz.) .. 80 45
224. 90 f. ' FR 1" (horiz.) .. 1·00 50
225. 100 f. "D 1" (horiz.) .. 1·50 75

1966. World Cup Football Championships.
226. – 30 f. red, brown & blue 55 25
227. **51.** 50 f. brn., blue & green 75 35
228. – 60 f. blue, purple & bistre 85 50
DESIGNS—VERT. 30 f. Player dribbling ball. 60 f. Player kicking ball.

53. Parachutist.

52. Cogwheel Emblem and Hemispheres. 54. Inoculating Cattle.

1966. Air. Europafrique.
229. **52.** 50 f. multicoloured .. 70 45

1966. 5th Anniv. of National Armed Forces. Multicoloured.
230. 20 f. Type **53** 35 15
231. 30 f. Soldiers with standard (vert.) 45 20
232. 45 f. Armoured patrol vehicle (horiz.) 70 30

1966. Air. Inauguration of "DC-8F" Air Services. As T **87** of Mauritania.
233. 30 f. olive, black and grey 60 25

1966. Campaign for Prevention of Cattle Plague.
234. **54.** 45 f. black, brn. & blue 1·00 50

55. "Voskhod 1". 56. U.N.E.S.C.O. "Tree".

1966. Air. Astronautics.
235. **55.** 50 f. blue, indigo and lake 65 35
236. – 100 f. violet, blue & lake 1·25 75
DESIGN—HORIZ. 100 f. "Gemini 6" and "7"

1966. 20th Anniv. of U.N.E.S.C.O.
237. **56.** 50 f. multicoloured .. 70 25

57. Japanese Gate, Atomic Symbol and Cancer ("The Crab"). 58. Furnace.

1966. Air. Int. Cancer Congress, Tokyo.
238. **57.** 100 f. multicoloured .. 1·40 75

1966. Malbaza Cement Works.
239. **58.** 10 f. blue, orange & brn. 15 10
240. – 20 f. blue and green .. 30 15
241. – 30 f. brown, grey & blue 45 20
242. – 50 f. indigo, brn. & blue 65 30
DESIGNS—HORIZ. 20 f. Electrical power-house. 30 f. Works and cement silos. 50 f. Installation for handling raw materials.

59. Niamey Mosque.

1967. Air.
243. **59.** 100 f. blue, green & grey 1·10 70

60. Durer (self-portrait).

1967. Air. Paintings. Multicoloured.
244. 50 f. Type **60** 80 60
245. 100 f. David (self-portrait) 1·50 90
246. 250 f. Delacroix (self-portrait) .. .. .. 3·00 2·00
See also Nos. 271/2 and 277/9.

61. Red-billed Hornbill. 62. Bob-sleigh Course, Villard-de-Lans.

1967. Birds.
247. **61.** 1 f. bistre, red and green (postage) 15 15
248. – 2 f. black, brn. & green 15 15
249. – 30 f. multicoloured .. 85 30
249a. – 40 f. purple, orange and green .. .. .. 1·00 50
250. – 45 f. brown, green & blue 1·25 30
250a. – 65 f. yell., brn. & purple 1·40 60
251. – 70 f. multicoloured .. 1·60 75
251a. – 250 f. blue, purple and green (air) (48 × 27 mm.) 4·75 1·75
BIRDS: 2 f. Lesser pied kingfishers. 30 f. Common gonolek. 40 f. Red bishop. 45 f., 65 f. Little masked weaver. 70 f. Chestnut-bellied sandgrouse. 250 f. Splendid glossy starlings.

1967. Grenoble—Winter Olympics Town (1968).
252. **62.** 30 f. brown, blue & grn. 40 25
253. – 45 f. brown, blue & grn. 60 30
254. – 60 f. brown, blue & grn. 80 50
255. – 90 f. brown, blue & grn. 1·10 65
DESIGNS: 45 f. Ski-jump, Autrans. 60 f. Ski-jump, St. Nizier du moucherotte. 90 f. Slalom course, Chamrousse.

63. Family and Lions Emblem. 64. Weather Ship.

1967. 50th Anniv. of Lions Int.
256. **63.** 50 f. blue, red and green 60 35

1967. Air. World Meteorological Day.
257. **64.** 50 f. red, black and blue 1·25 65

65. View of World Fair.

1967. Air. World Fair, Montreal.
258. **65.** 100 f. black, blue & pur. 1·10 50

66. I.T.Y. Emblem and Aircraft. 67. Scouts around Camp-fire.

1967. Int. Tourist Year.
259. **66.** 45 f. violet, grn. & pur. 45 35

1967. World Scout Jamboree, Idaho, U.S.A.
260. **67.** 30 f. brown, lake & blue 40 20
261. – 45 f. blue, brn. & orge. 60 30
262. – 80 f. lake, slate & bistre 1·25 50
DESIGNS—HORIZ. 45 f. Jamboree emblem and scouts. VERT. 80 f. Scout cooking meal.

68. Audio-Visual Centre.

1967. Air. National Audio-Visual Centre, Niamey.
263. **68.** 100 f. violet, blue & grn. 90 50

69. Carrying Patient. 70. "Europafrique".

1967. Nigerian Red Cross.
264. **69.** 45 f. black, red & green 60 20
265. – 50 f. black, red & green 75 25
266. – 60 f. black, red & green 1·00 35
DESIGNS: 50 f. Nurse with mother and child. 60 f. Doctor giving injection.

1967. Europafrique.
267. **70.** 50 f. multicoloured .. 60 30

71. Dr. Konrad Adenauer. 72. African Women.

1967. Air. Adenauer Commem.
268. **71.** 100 f. brown and blue 1·40 70

1967. Air. African and Malagasy Post and Telecommunications Union (U.A.M.P.T.). 5th Anniv. As T **101** of Mauritania.
270. 100 f. violet, green and red 1·10 60

1967. Air. Death Cent. of Jean Ingres (painter). Paintings by Ingres. As T **60.** Mult.
271. 100 f. "Jesus among the Doctors" (horiz.) .. 1·60 1·00
272. 150 f. "Jesus restoring the Keys to St. Peter" (vert.) 2·25 1·50

1967. U.N. Women's Rights Commission.
273. **72.** 50 f. brown, yellow & blue 60 35

1967. 5th Anniv. of West African Monetary Union. As T **103** of Mauritania.
274. 30 f. green and purple .. 35 20

73. Nigerian Children. 75. Allegory of Human Rights.

74. O.C.A.M. Emblem.

1967. Air. 21st Anniv. of U.N.I.C.E.F.
275. **73.** 100 f. brn., blue & grn. 1·25 95

1968. Air. O.C.A.M. Conf., Niamey.
276. **74.** 100 f. orange, green & blue 1·10 60

1968. Air. Paintings (self-portraits). As T **60.** Multicoloured.
277. 50 f. J.-B. Corot .. 70 40
278. 150 f. Goya .. .. 1·90 1·00
279. 200 f. Van Gogh .. .. 2·50 1·50

1968. Human Rights Year.
280. **75.** 50 f. indigo, brown & blue 60 30

76. Breguet "27" Biplane over Lake.

1968. Air. 35th Anniv. of 1st France–Niger Airmail Service.
281. **76.** 45 f. blue, green & mauve 95 35
282. – 80 f. slate, brown & blue 1·60 55
283. – 100 f. black, grn. & blue 2·50 75
DESIGNS: Potez "25 T.O.E." biplane. 80 f. On ground. 100 f. In flight.

77. "Joyous Health".

1968. 20th Anniv. of W.H.O.
284. **77.** 50 f. indigo, blue & brn. 60 35

78. Cyclists of 1818 and 1968.

1968. Air. 150th Anniv. of Bicycle.
285. **78.** 100 f. green and red .. 1·50 70

79. Beribboned Rope.

1968. Air. 5th Anniv. of Europa–Afrique.
286. **79.** 50 f. multicoloured .. 65 40

80. Fencing.

1968. Air. Olympic Games, Mexico.

287. **80.** 50 f. pur., violet & green .. 50 35
288. – 100 f. black, pur. & blue .. 85 50
289. – 150 f. purple and orange .. 1·25 70
290. – 200 f. blue, brn. & grn. .. 1·75 1·25

DESIGNS—VERT. 100 f. High-diving. 150 f. Weight-lifting. HORIZ. 200 f. Horse-jumping.

81. Woodland Kingfisher. **82.** Mahatma Gandhi.

1969. Birds. Dated "1968". Multicoloured.

292. 5 f. African Grey Hornbill (postage) 25 10
293. 10 f. Type **81** 30 10
294. 15 f. Senegal Coucal .. 65 25
295. 20 f. Rose-ringed Parakeets 75 40
296. 25 f. Abyssinian roller .. 1·10 50
297. 50 f. Cattle Egret .. .. 1·50 70
298. 100 f. Violet Starling (air) (27 × 49 mm.) .. 3·25 1·40

See also Nos. 372/7, 567/8 and 714/15.

1968. Air. "Apostles of Non-Violence".

299. **82.** 100 f. black & yellow .. 1·75 60
300. – 100 f. black & turquoise 1·00 50
301. – 100 f. black and grey .. 1·00 50
302. – 100 f. black & orange .. 1·00 50

PORTRAITS: No. 300, President Kennedy. No. 301, Martin Luther King. No. 302, Robert F. Kennedy.

1968. Air. "Philexafrique" Stamp Exn., Abidjan (Ivory Coast, 1969) (1st issue). As T **113a** of Mauritania. Multicoloured.

304. 100 f. "Pare, Minister of the Interior" (J. L. La Neuville) .. .. 1·60 1·60

83. Arms of the Republic.

1968. Air. 10th Anniv. of Republic.

305. **83.** 100 f. multicoloured .. 1·00 50

1969. Air. Napoleon Bonaparte. Birth Bicent. As T **114b** of Mauritania. Mult.

306. 50 f. "Napoleon as First Consul" (Ingres) .. 1·50 90
307. 100 f. "Napoleon visiting the plague victims of Jaffa" (Gros) .. .. 2·50 1·25
308. 150 f. "Napoleon Enthroned" (Ingres) .. 3·50 1·75
309. 200 f. "The French Campaign" (Meissonier) .. 5·00 2·50

1969. Air. "Philexafrique" Stamp Exn., Abidjan, Ivory Coast (2nd issue). As T **114a** of Mauritania.

310. 50 f. brown, blue & orange 1·25 1·00

DESIGN: 50 f. Giraffes and stamp of 1926.

84. Plane over Rain-cloud and Anemometer.

1969. Air. World Meteorological Day.

311. **84.** 50 f. blk., blue & green 90 35

85. Workers supporting Globe.

1969. 50th Anniv. of I.L.O.

312. **85.** 30 f. red and green .. 40 20
313. 50 f. green and red .. 50 35

86. Panhard and Levassor (1909).

1969. Air. Veteran Motor Cars.

314. **86.** 25 f. green 45 20
315. – 45 f. violet, blue & grey 55 25
316. – 50 f. brown, ochre & grey 1·10 35
317. – 70 f. purple, red & grey 1·50 45
318. – 100 f. green, brn. & grey 1·75 65

DESIGNS: 45 f. De Dion Bouton 8 (1904). 50 f. Opel "Doktor-wagen" (1909). 70 f. Daimler (1910). 100 f. Vermorel 12/16 (1912).

87. Mother and Child. **88.** Mouth and Ear.

1969. 50th Anniv. of League of Red Cross Societies.

319. **87.** 45 f. red, brown & blue 60 25
320. – 50 f. red, grey & green .. 70 25
321. – 70 f. red, brown & ochre 1·00 40

DESIGNS—VERT.: 70 f. Man with Red Cross parcel. HORIZ. 50 f. Symbolic Figures, Globe and Red Crosses.

1969. First French Language Cultural Conf., Niamey.

322. **88.** 100 f. multicoloured .. 1·25 60

89. School Building.

1969. National School of Administration.

323. **89.** 30 f. black, green & orge. 30 20

1969. Air. 1st Man on the Moon. No. 114 optd. **L'HOMME SUR LA LUNE JUILLET 1969 APOLLO 11** and moon module.

324. 500 f. grn., brn. & blue .. 6·50 6·50

91. "Apollo 8" and Rocket.

1969. Air. Moon Flight of "Apollo 8". Embossed on gold foil.

325. **91.** 1,000 f. gold .. .. 15·00 15·00

1969. 5th Anniv. of African Development Bank. As T **122a** of Mauritania.

326. 30 f. brown, green & violet 35 15

92. Child and Toys.

1969. Air. Int. Toy Fair, Nuremburg.

327. **92.** 100 f. blue, brown & green .. .. 1·50 50

93. Linked Squares.

1969. Air. "Europafrique".

328. **93.** 50 f. yellow, blk. & violet 55 30

94. Trucks crossing Sahara.

1969. Air. 45th Anniv. of "Croisiere Noire" Trans-Africa Expedition.

329. **94.** 50 f. brn., violet & mve. 75 35
330. – 100 f. violet, red & blue 1·50 65
331. – 150 f. multicoloured .. 2·00 1·25
332. – 200 f. grn., indigo & blue 3·00 1·50

DESIGNS: 100 f. Crossing the mountains. 150 f. African children and expedition at Lake Victoria. 200 f. Route Map, European greeting African and Citroen truck.

94a. Aircraft, Map and Airport.

1969. 10th Anniv. of Aerial Navigation Security Agency for Africa and Madagascar (A.S.E.C.N.A.).

333. **94a.** 100 f. red .. .. 1·50 70

95. Classical Pavilion.

1970. National Museum.

334. **95.** 30 f. blue, green & brown 30 15
335. – 45 f. blue, green & brown 45 25
336. – 50 f. blue, brown & green 50 25
337. – 70 f. brown, blue & green 70 40
338. – 100 f. brown, blue & grn. 1·10 60

DESIGNS: 45 f. Temporary Exhibition Pavilion. 50 f. Audio-visual Pavilion. 70 f. Local Musical Instruments Gallery. 100 f. Handicrafts Pavilion.

96. Niger Village and Japanese Pagodas. **97.** Hypodermic "Gun" and Map.

1970. Air "EXPO 70" World Fair, Osaka, Japan (1st issue).

339. **96.** 100 f. multicoloured .. 90 45

1970. One Hundred Million Smallpox Vaccinations in West Africa.

340. **97.** 50 f. blue, purple & green 70 30

98. Education Symbols.

1970. Air. Int. Education Year.

341. **98.** 100 f. slate, red & purple 1·00 45

99. Footballer.

1970. World Cup Football Competitions Mexico.

342. **99.** 40 f. green, brn. & purple 60 25
343. – 70 f. purple, brn. & blue 1·00 40
344. – 90 f. red and black .. 1·25 60

DESIGNS: 70 f. Football and Globe. 90 f. Two footballers.

100. Rotary Emblems.

1970. Air. 65th Anniv. of Rotary Int.

345. **100.** 100 f. multicoloured 1·25 55

101. Bay of Naples and Niger Stamp.

1970. Air. 10th "Europafrique" Stamp Exn., Naples.

346. **101.** 100 f. multicoloured .. 1·00 60

102. Clement Ader, Flying Machine and Modern Aircraft.

1970. Air. Aviation Pioneers.

347. **102.** 50 f. slate, blue & red .. 70 25
348. – 100 f. brn., slate & blue 1·50 60
349. – 150 f. ochre, brn. & grn. 1·50 75
350. – 200 f. red, bistre & violet 2·25 1·00
351. – 250 f. violet, slate & red 3·50 1·40

DESIGNS: 100 f. Montgolfier brothers, balloon and rocket. 150 f. Isaac Newton and gravity diagram. 200 f. Galileo and rocket in planetary system. 250 f. Leonardo da Vinci, flying machine and modern glider.

103. Cathode Ray Tube illuminating Books, Microscope and Globe.

1970. Air. World Telecommunications Day.

352. **103.** 100 f. brn., grn. and red 1·25 50

1970. New U.P.U. Headquarters Building, Berne. Inaug. As T **81** of New Caledonia.

353. 30 f. red, slate and brown 35 20
354. 60 f. violet, red and blue .. 60 30

1970. Air. Safe Return of "Apollo 13". Nos. 348 and 350 optd. **Solidarite Spatiale Apollo XIII 11-17 Avril 1970.**

355. 100 f. red, slate and blue .. 1·00 50
356. 200 f. red, bistre & violet .. 1·75 75

105. U.N. Emblem, Man, Woman and Doves.

1970. Air. 25th Anniv. of U.N.O.

357. **105.** 100 f. multicoloured .. 1·00 50
358. 150 f. multicoloured .. 1·50 75

106. Globe and Heads.

1970. Air. Int. French Language Conference, Niamey. Die-stamped on gold foil.

359. **106.** 250 f. gold and blue .. 2·50 2·50

107. European and African Women.

1970. Air. "Europafrique".

360. **107.** 50 f. red and green .. 55 30

108. Japanese Girls and "EXPO 70" Skyline.

1970. Air. "EXPO 70" World Fair, Osaka, Japan. (2nd issue).
361. **108.** 100 f. pur., orge. & grn. 90 40
362. – 150 f. blue, brn. & grn. 1·25 60
DESIGN: 150 f. "No" actor and "EXPO 70" by night.

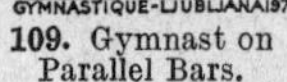

109. Gymnast on Parallel Bars. **111.** Beethoven, Keyboard and Manuscripts.

1970. Air. World Gymnastic Championships, Ljubljana.
363. **109.** 50 f. blue 50 30
364. – 100 f. green . . . . 1·10 55
365. – 150 f. purple . . . . 1·75 75
366. – 200 f. red . . . . 2·00 95
GYMNASTS—HORIZ. 100 f. Gymnast on vaulting-horse. 150 f. Gymnast in mid-air. VERT. 200 f. Gymnast on rings.

1970. Air. Moon Landing of "Luna 16". Surch. **LUNA 16–Sept. 1970 PREMIERS PRELEVEMENTS AUTOMATIQUES SUR LA LUNE** and value.
367. 100 f. on 150 f. (Nos. 349) 1·10 50
368. 200 f. on 250 f. (Nos. 351) 2·40 1·00

1970. Air. Birth Bicentenary of Beethoven. Multicoloured.
369. 100 f. Type **111** . . . . 1·40 55
370. 150 f. Beethoven and allegory, "Hymn of Joy" 2·25 85

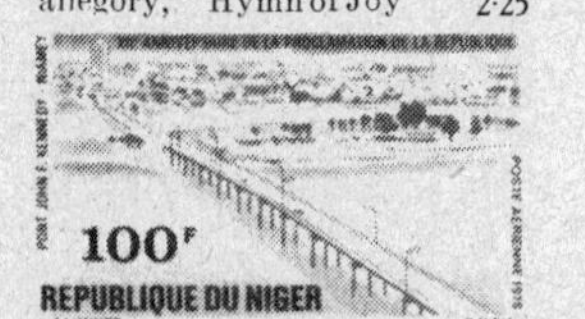

112. John F. Kennedy Bridge, Niamey.

1970. Air. 12th Anniv. of Republic.
371. **112.** 100 f. multicoloured . . 1·10 45

1971. Birds. Designs similar to T 81. Variously dated between 1970 and 1972. Mult.
372. 5 f. African grey hornbill 40 20
373. 10 f. Woodland kingfisher 50 20
374. 15 f. Senegal coucal . . 1·10 65
375. 20 f. Rose-ringed parakeet 1·25 65
376. 35 f. Broad-tailed paradise whydah . . . . 1·75 90
377. 50 f. Cattle egret . . . . 2·25 1·25
The Latin inscription on No. 377 is incorrect, reading "Bulbucus ibis" instead of "Bubulcus ibis".
See also Nos. 714/15.

114. Pres. Nasser.

1971. Air. Death of Pres. Gamal Nasser (Egyptian statesman). Multicoloured.
378. 100 f. Type **114** 75 40
379. 200 f. Nasser waving . . 1·50 75

115. Pres. De Gaulle.

1971. Air. De Gaulle Commemoration. Embossed on gold foil.
380. **115.** 1000 f. gold . . . . 38·00 38·00

116. "MUNICH" and Olympic Rings.

1971. Air. Publicity for 1972 Olympic Games, Munich.
381. **116.** 150 f. pur., blue & grn. 1·25 70

117. "Apollo 14" leaving Moon. **118.** Symbolic Masks.

1971. Air. Moon Mission of "Apollo 14".
382. **117.** 250 f. grn., orge. & blue 2·25 1·25

1971. Air. Racial Equality Year.
383. **118.** 100 f. red, green & blue 90 40
384. – 200 f. brn., grn. & blue 1·75 80
DESIGN: 200 f. "Peoples" and clover-leaf emblem.

119. Niamey on World Map.

1971. 1st Anniv. of French-speaking Countries Co-operative Agency.
385. **119.** 40 f. multicoloured . . 50 25

120. African Telecommunications Map.

1971. Air. Pan-African Telecommunications Network.
386. **120.** 100 f. multicoloured . . 75 40

121. African Mask and Japanese Stamp.

1971. Air. "PHILATOKYO 71" Int. Stamp Exhibition, Japan.
387. **121.** 50 f. olive, pur. & grn. 65 30
388. – 100 f. violet, red & grn. 1·10 45
DESIGN: 100 f. Japanese scroll painting and Niger stamp.

122. "Longwood House, St. Helena" (C. Vernet).

1971. Air. 150th Anniv. of Napoleon's Death. Paintings. Multicoloured.
389. 150 f. Type **122** . . 1·75 70
390. 200 f. "Napoleon's Body on his Camp-bed" (Marryat) . . . . 2·50 90

123. Satellite, Radio Waves, and Globe. **125.** Scout Badges and Mount Fuji.

124. Pierre de Coubertin and Discus-throwers.

1971. Air. World Telecommunications Day.
391. **123.** 100 f. multicoloured . . 1·10 50

1971. Air. 75th Anniv. of Modern Olympic Games.
392. **124.** 50 f. red and blue . . 50 25
393. – 100 f. multicoloured . . 90 40
394. – 150 f. blue and purple 1·40 65
DESIGNS—VERT. 100 f. Male and female athletes holding torch. HORIZ. 150 f. Start of race.

1971. 13th World Scout Jamboree, Asagiri, Japan.
395. **125.** 35 f. red, pur. & orge. 40 20
396. – 40 f. brown, plum & green 45 20
397. – 45 f. green, red & blue 60 25
398. – 50 f. grn., vio. and red 70 30
DESIGNS—VERT. 40 f. Scouts and badge. 45 f. Scouts converging on Japan. HORIZ. 50 f. "Jamboree" in rope, and marquee.

126. "Apollo 15" on Moon.

1971. Air. Moon Mission of "Apollo 15".
399. **126.** 150 f. blue, vio. & brn. 1·50 70

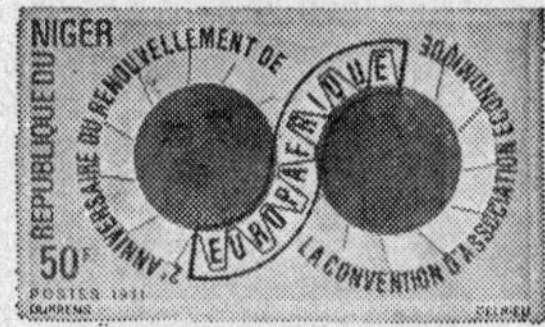

127. Linked Maps.

1971. 2nd Anniv. of Renewed "Europafrique" Convention, Niamey.
400. **127.** 50 f. multicoloured . . 60 30

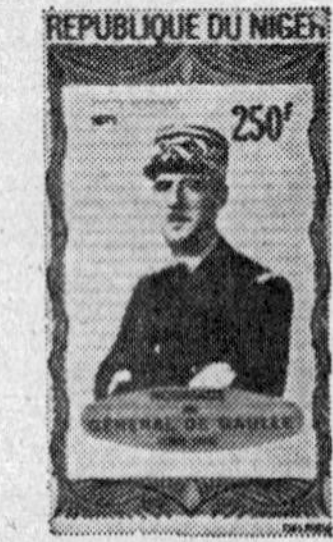

128. Gouroumi (Hausa). **129.** De Gaulle in Uniform.

1971. Musical Instruments.
401. **128.** 25 f. brn., grn. and red 30 10
402. – 30 f. brn., vio. and grn. 35 15
403. – 35 f. blue, grn. & pur. 35 25
404. – 40 f. brn., orge. & grn. 45 25
405. – 45 f. ochre, brn. & blue 55 35
406. – 50 f. brn., red and blk. 95 45
DESIGNS: 30 f. Molo (Djerma). 35 f. Garaya (Hausa). 40 f. Godjie (Djerma-Sonrai). 45 f. Inzad (Tuareg). 50 f. Kountigui (Sonrai).

1971. Air. 1st Death Anniv. of Gen. Charles De Gaulle (French statesman).
407. **129.** 250 f. multicoloured . . 5·00 4·00

1971. Air. 10th Anniv. of African and Malagasy Posts and Telecommunications Union. As T **139a** of Mauritania. Multicoloured.
408. 100 f. U.A.M.P.T. H.Q. and rural scene 90 45

130. "Audience with Al Hariri" (Baghdad, 1237).

1971. Air. Moslem Miniatures. Mult.
409. 100 f. Type **130** . . . . 1·00 45
410. 150 f. "Archangel Israfil" (Iraq, 14th-cent.) (vert.) 1·50 70
411. 200 f. "Horsemen" (Iraq, 1210) . . . . . . 2·25 1·25

131. Louis Armstrong. **132.** "Children of All Races".

1971. Air. Death of Louis Armstrong (American jazz musician). Multicoloured.
412. 100 f. Type **131** . . 1·50 55
413. 150 f. Armstrong playing trumpet . . . . 2·00 85

1971. 25th Anniv. of U.N.I.C.E.F.
414. **132.** 50 f. multicoloured . . 60 45

133. "Adoration of the Magi" (Di Bartolo).

1971. Air. Christmas. Paintings. Mult.
415. 100 f. Type **133** . . . . 1·00 45
416. 150 f. "The Nativity" (D. Ghirlandaio) (vert.) 1·50 70
417. 200 f. "Adoration of the Shepherds" (Perugino) 2·00 1·00

134. Presidents Pompidou and Hamani.

1972. Air. Visit of Pres. Pompidou of France.
418. **134.** 250 f. multicoloured . . 4·75 3·50

135. Ski "Gate" and Cherry Blossom.

1972. Air. Winter Olympic Games, Sapporo, Japan.
419. **135.** 100 f. violet, red & grn. 90 40
420. – 150 f. red, pur. & vio. 1·25 70
DESIGN—HORIZ. 150 f. Snow Crystals and Olympic flame.

1972. Air. U.N.E.S.C.O. "Save Venice" Campaign. As T **145** of Senegal.
422. 50 f. mult. (vert.) . . 50 25
423. 100 f. mult. (vert.) . . 1·00 45
424. 150 f. mult. (vert.) . . 1·50 70
425. 200 f. multicoloured . . 2·00 1·00
DESIGNS: Nos. 422/5 depict various details of Guardi's painting, "The Masked Ball".

136. Johannes Brahms and Music.

137. Saluting Hand.

1972. Air. 75th Death Anniv. of Johannes Brahms (composer).
426. **136.** 100 f. grn., myrtle & red 1·50 55

1972. Air. Int. Scout Seminar, Cotonou, Dahomey.
427. **137.** 150 f. vio., blue & orge. 1·50 60

138. Star Symbol and Open Book.

1972. Int. Book Year.
428. **138.** 35 f. purple and green 35 20
429. – 40 f. blue and lake .. 1·00 25
DESIGN: 40 f. Boy reading, galleon and early aircraft.

139. Heart Operation.

1972. Air. World Heart Month.
430 **139** 100 f. brown and red .. 1·50 55

140. Bleriot crossing the Channel, 1909.

1972. Air. Milestones in Aviation History.
431. **140.** 50 f. brn., blue & lake 1·10 50
432. – 75 f. grey, brn. & blue 1·75 60
433. – 100 f. ultram., blue and purple .. .. 3·25 1·40
DESIGNS: 75 f. Lindbergh crossing the Atlantic in "Spirit of St. Louis". 100 f. First flight of "Concorde", 1969.

141. Satellite and Universe.

1972. Air. World Telecommunications Day.
434. **141.** 100 f. brn., purple & red 1·10 45

142. Boxing.

1972. Air. Olympic Games, Munich. Sports and Munich Buildings.
435. **142.** 50 f. brown and blue 50 20
436. – 100 f. brn. and green 75 40
437. – 150 f. brown and red .. 1·25 60
438. – 200 f. brown & mauve 1·75 85
DESIGNS—VERT. 100 f. Long-jumping. 150 f. Football. HORIZ. 200 f. Running.

143. A. G. Bell and Telephone.

1972. Air. 50th Death Anniv. of Alexander Graham Bell (inventor of telephone).
440. **143.** 100 f. blue, pur. & red 1·10 55

144. "Europe on Africa" Map.

1972. Air. "Europafrique" Co-operation.
441. **144.** 50 f. red, green & blue 50 25

145. Herdsman and Cattle.

146. Lottery Wheel.

1972. Medicinal Salt-Ponds at In-Gall. Mult.
442. 35 f. Type **145**. 50 25
443. 40 f. Cattle in Salt-pond .. 60 25

1972. 6th Anniv. of National Lottery.
444. **146.** 35 f. multicoloured .. 35 25

147. Postal Runner.

1972. Air. U.P.U. Day. Postal Transport.
445. **147.** 50 f. brn., grn. & lake 60 25
446. – 100 f. grn., blue & lake 90 45
447. – 150 f. grn., violet & lake 1·75 70
DESIGNS: 100 f. Rural mail-van. 150 f. Loading mail-plane.

1972. 10th Anniv. of West African Monetary Union. As T **149** of Mauritania.
448. 40 f. grey, violet & brown 40 25

1972. Air. Gold Medal Winners. Munich Olympic Games. Nos. 435/8 optd. with events and names, etc.
449. **142.** 50 f. brown and blue .. 50 20
450. – 100 f. brown and green 85 40
451. – 150 f. brown and red .. 1·40 60
452. – 200 f. brown and mauve 1·75 80
OVERPRINTS: 50 f. **WELTER CORREA MEDAILLE D'OR.** 100 f. **TRIPLE SAUT SANEIEV MEDAILLE D'OR.** 150 f. **FOOTBALL POLOGNE MEDAILLE D'OR.** 200 f. **MARATHON SHORTER MEDAILLE D'OR.**

148. "The Raven and the Fox".

1972. Air. Fables of Jean de La Fontaine.
453. **148.** 25 f. blk., brn. and grn. 1·25 40
454. – 50 f. brn., grn. and pur. 60 25
455. – 75 f. brn., grn. & brn. 1·00 45
DESIGNS: 50 f. "The Lion and the Rat". 75 f. "The Monkey and the Leopard".

149. Astronauts on Moon.

1972. Air. Moon Flight of "Apollo 17".
456. **149.** 250 f. multicoloured .. 2·75 1·25

150. Dromedary Race. **151.** Pole-vaulting.

1972. Niger Sports.
457. **150.** 35 f. purple, red & blue 75 40
458. – 40 f. lake, brn. and grn. 1·00 60
DESIGN: 40 f. Horse race.

1973. 2nd African Games, Lagos, Nigeria. Multicoloured.
459. 35 f. Type **151** 30 25
460. 40 f. Basketball 35 25
461. 45 f. Boxing 45 25
462. 75 f. Football 70 45

152. "Young Athlete". **153.** Knight and Pawn.

1973. Air. Antique Art Treasures.
463. **152.** 50 f. red 50 25
464. – 100 f. violet .. .. 1·00 40
DESIGN: 100 f. "Head of Hermes".

1973. World Chess Championships, Reykjavik, Iceland.
465. **153.** 100 f. grn., blue & red 2·50 1·00

154. "Abutilon pannosum". **155.** Interpol Badge.

1973. Rare African Flowers. Multicoloured.
466. 30 f. Type **154** 70 30
467. 45 f. "Crotalaria barkae" 80 30
468. 60 f. "Dichrostachys cinerea" .. .. 1·40 45
469. 80 f. "Caralluma decaisneana" .. .. 1·60 55

1973. 50th Anniv. of International Criminal Police Organization (Interpol).
470. **155.** 50 f. multicoloured .. 85 30

156. Scout with Radio.

1973. Air. Scouting in Niger.
471. **156.** 25 f. brn., grn. & red .. 25 20
472. – 50 f. brn., green & red 55 25
473. – 100 f. brn., grn. & red 1·25 50
474. – 150 f. brn., grn. & red 1·60 70
DESIGNS: 50 f. First Aid. 100 f. Care of animals. 150 f. Care of the environment.

157. Hansen and Microscope. **158.** Nurse tending Child.

1973. Centenary of Dr. Hansen's Discovery of Leprosy Bacillus.
475. **157.** 50 f. brn., grn. & blue 85 35

1973. 25th Anniv. of W.H.O.
476. **158.** 50 f. brn., red & blue 65 25

159. "The Crucifixion" (Hugo van der Goes).

1973. Air. Easter. Paintings. Mult.
477. 50 f. Type **159** 55 25
478. 100 f. "The Deposition" (Cima de Conegliano) (horiz.) .. .. .. 1·10 50
479. 150 f. "Pieta" (Bellini) (horiz.) .. .. .. 1·60 65

160. Airliner and Mail-van.

1973. Air. Stamp Day.
480. **160.** 100 f. brn., red & green 1·50 55

161. W.M.O. Emblem and "Weather Conditions".

1973. Air. Cent. of W.M.O.
481. **161.** 100 f. brn., red and grn. 1·10 45

162. "Crouching Lioness" (Delacroix).

1973. Air. Paintings by Delacroix. Mult.
482. 130 f. Type **162** .. .. 2·00 1·00
483. 200 f. "Tigress and Cub" 3·25 1·50

163. Crocodile.

1973. Wild Animals from "Park W".
484. **163.** 25 f. multicoloured .. 45 20
485. – 35 f. grey, gold & blk. 75 30
486. – 40 f. multicoloured .. 75 30
487. – 80 f. multicoloured .. 1·25 50
DESIGNS: 35 f. African elephant. 40 f. Hippopotamus. 80 f. Warthog.

164. Eclipse over Mountain.

1973. Total Eclipse of the Sun.
488. **164.** 40 f. violet 60 30

1973. Air. 24th Int. Scouting Congress, Nairobi, Kenya. Nos. 473/4 optd. **24 Conference Mondiale du Scoutisme NAIROBI, 1973.**
489. 100 f. brn., grn. & red .. 1·00 40
490. 150 f. brn., grn. & red .. 1·50 60

166. Palomino.

1973. Horse-breeding. Multicoloured.

491. 50 f. Type **166** 90 30

492. 75 f. French trotter .. 1·40 40

493. 80 f. English thoroughbred 1·50 55

494. 100 f. Arab thoroughbred 2·00 65

1973. Pan-African Drought Relief. African Solidarity. No. 436 surch. **SECHERESSE SOLIDARITE AFRICAINE** and value.

495. **145.** 100 f. on 35 f. mult. .. 1·40 1·00

168. Rudolf Diesel and Engine.

1973. 60th Death Anniv. of Rudolf Diesel (engineer).

496. **168.** 25 f. bl., pur. & grey 55 35

497. – 50 f. grey, grn. & blue 95 50

498. – 75 f. blue, blk. & mve. 1·40 75

499. – 125 f. blue, red & grn. 2·40 90

DESIGNS: 50 f. Type "BB-610 ch" diesel locomotive. 75 f. Type "060-DB" diesel locomotive. 125 f. Type "CC-72004" diesel locomotive.

1973. African and Malagasy Posts and Telecommunications Union. As T **155a** of Mauritania.

509. 100 f. red, green & brown .. 75 50

168a. African Mask and Old Town Hall, Brussels **169.** T.V. Set and Class.

1973. Air. African Fortnight, Brussels.

501. **168a.** 100 f. purple, blue and red .. .. 1·00 50

1973. Schools Television Service.

502. **169.** 50 f. blk., red and blue 60 30

1973. 3rd Int. French Language and Culture Conf., Liege. No. 385 optd. **3e CONFERENCE DE LA FRANCOPHONIE LIEGE OCTOBRE 1973.**

503. **110.** 40 f. multicoloured .. 50 25

171. "Apollo". **172.** Bees and Honeycomb.

1973. Classical Sculptures.

504. **171.** 50 f. green and brown 60 30

505. – 50 f. black and brown 60 30

506. – 50 f. brown and red .. 60 30

507. – 50 f. purple and red .. 60 30

DESIGNS: No. 505, "Atlas". No. 506, "Hercules". No. 507, "Venus".

1973. World Savings Day.

508. **172.** 40 f. brn., red and blue 45 25

173. "Food for the World". **174.** Copernicus and "Sputnik 1".

1973. Air. 10th Anniversary of World Food Programme.

509. **173.** 50 f. violet, red and blue 60 30

1973. Air. 500th Birth Anniv. of Copernicus (astronomer).

510. **174.** 150 f. brn., blue and red 1·40 70

175. Pres. John Kennedy.

1973. Air. 10th Death Anniv. of U.S. President Kennedy.

511. **175.** 100 f. multicoloured .. 1·00 50

176. Kounta Songhai Blanket. **178.** Lenin.

177. Barges on River Niger.

1973. Niger Textiles. Multicoloured.

513. 35 f. Type **176** 50 30

514. 40 f. Tcherka Snghai blanket (horiz.) .. 70 40

1974. Air. 1st Anniv. of Ascent of Niger by "Fleet of Hope".

515. **177.** 50 f. blue, grn. & red .. 75 35

516. – 75 f. pur., blue & green 1·00 45

DESIGN: 75 f. "Barban Maza" (tug) and barge.

1974. Air. 50th Death Anniv. of Lenin.

517. **178.** 50 c. brown 50 30

179. Slalom Skiing.

1974. Air. 50th Anniv. of Winter Olympic Games.

518. **179.** 200 f. red, brn. & blue 2·50 1·00

180. Newly-born Baby.

1974. World Population Year.

519. **180.** 50 f. multicoloured .. 50 25

181. Footballers and "Global" Ball.

1974. Air. World Cup Football Championships, West Germany.

520. **181.** 75 f. vio., blk. and brn. 65 35

521. – 150 f. brn., grn. & turq. 1·40 55

522. – 200 f. blue, orge. & grn. 1·75 1·00

DESIGNS: 150 f., 200 f. Football scenes similar to Type **181.**

182. "The Crucifixion" (Grunewald).

1974. Air. Easter. Paintings. Multicoloured.

524. 50 f. Type **182** 50 25

525. 75 f. "Avignon Pieta" (attributed to E. Quarton) 75 35

526. 125 f. "The Entombment" (G. Isenmann) .. .. 1·25 65

183. Locomotive No. 230k (1948) and U.S.A. Loco No. 2222 (1938).

1974. Famous Railway Locomotives of the Steam Era.

527. **183.** 50 f. grn., blk. & violet 80 35

528. – 75 f. grn., blk. and brn. 1·25 45

529. – 100 f. multicoloured .. 1·75 70

530. – 150 f. brn., blk. & red 2·50 1·00

DESIGNS: 75 f. P.L.M. loco No. C 21 (1893). 100 f. U.S.A. "220" (1866) and British "231" (1939) class locomotives. 150 f. Seguin locomotive (1829) and Stephenson's "Rocket" (1829).

184. Map of Member Countries. **185.** Knights.

1974. 15th Anniv. of Conseil de l'Entente.

531. **184.** 40 f. multicoloured .. 40 20

1974. Air. 21st Chess Olympiad, Nice.

532 **185** 50 f. brown, blue & ind 1·25 65

533 – 75 f. purple, brn & grn 1·75 75

DESIGN: 75 f. Kings.

186. Marconi and "Elettra" (steam yacht).

1974. Birth Centenary of Guglielmo Marconi (radio pioneer).

534. **186.** 50 f. blue, brn. & mve. 50 30

187. Astronaut on Palm of Hand. **188.** Tree on Palm of Hand.

1974. Air. 5th Anniv. of 1st Landing on Moon.

535. **187.** 150 f. brn., bl. & ind... 1·25 60

1974. National Tree Week.

536. **188.** 35 f. turq., grn. & brn. 40 30

189. "The Rhinoceros" (Longhi). **190.** Camel Saddle.

1974. Air. Europafrique.

537. **189.** 250 f. multicoloured .. 5·00 3·00

1974. Handicrafts.

538. **190.** 40 f. red, bl. & brn. .. 45 20

539. – 50 f. bl., red & brn. .. 55 30

DESIGN: 50 f. Statuettes of horses.

192. Frederic Chopin.

1974. 125th Death Anniv. of Frederic Chopin.

541. **192.** 100 f. blk., red & blue 1·50 55

1974. Beethoven's Ninth Symphony Commemoration. As T **192.**

542. 100 f. lilac, blue & indigo .. 1·50 55

DESIGN: 100 f. Beethoven.

193. European Woman and Aircraft. **194.** "Skylab" over Africa.

1974. Air. Cent. of U.P.U.

543. **193.** 50 f. turq., grn. & pur. 50 25

544. – 100 f. blue, mve. & ultram 1·50 60

545. – 150 f. brn., bl. & indigo 1·50 80

546. – 200 f. brn., orge. & red 1·60 1·25

DESIGNS: 100 f. Japanese woman and electric locomotives. 150 f. American Indian woman and liner. 200 f. African woman and road vehicles.

1974. Air. "Skylab" Space Laboratory.

547. **194.** 100 f. vio., brn. & blue 1·00 45

195. Don-don Drum. **197.** "Virgin and Child" (Correggio).

196. Tree and Compass Rose.

1974.

548. **195.** 60 f. pur., grn. & red .. 90 45

1974. 1st Death Anniv. of Tenere Tree (desert landmark).

549. **196.** 50 f. brn., blue & ochre 2·00 1·00

1974. Air. Christmas. Multicoloured.
550. 100 f. Type **197** .. .. 1·00 35
551. 150 f. "Virgin and Child, and St. Hilary" (F. Lippi) 1·50 55
552. 200 f. "Virgin and Child" (Murillo) .. .. 2·00 95

198. "Apollo" Spacecraft. **199.** European and African Women.

1975. Air. "Apollo-Soyuz" Space Test Project.
553. **198.** 50 f. green, red & blue 50 25
554. – 100 f. grey, red & blue 80 40
555. – 150 f. pur., plum & bl. 1·25 60
DESIGNS: 100 f. "Apollo" and "Soyuz" docked. 150 f. "Soyuz" spacecraft.

1975. Air. Europafrique.
556. **199.** 250 f. brn., pur. & red 2·25 1·75

200. Communications Satellite and Weather Map.

1975. World Meteorological Day.
557. **200.** 40 f. red, black & blue 40 20

201. "Christ in the Garden of Olives". (Delacroix).

1975. Air. Easter. Multicoloured.
558. 75 Type **201** 65 35
559. 125 f. "The Crucifixion" (El Greco) (vert.) .. 1·10 50
560. 150 f. "The Resurrection" (Limousin) (vert.) .. 1·25 75

202. Lt-Col. S. Kountche, Head of State.

1975. Air. 1st Anniv. of Military Coup.
561. **202.** 100 f. multicoloured .. 1·00 50

203. "City of Truro" (G.W.R., England, 1903).

1975. Famous Locomotives. Multicoloured.
562. 50 f. Type **203** .. 85 35
563. 75 f. No. 5003 (Germany, 1937) .. .. 1·10 50
564. 100 f. "The General" (U.S.A., 1863) .. .. 1·75 75
565. 125 f. "BB-15000" Electric (France, 1971) .. 2·00 90

1975. Birds. As Nos. 296 and 298, but dated "1975". Multicoloured.
567. 25 f. Abyssinian Roller (postage) 85 20
568. 100 f. Violet Starlings (air) 1·90 60

205. "Zabira" Leather Bag. **206.** African Woman and Child.

1975. Niger Handicrafts. Multicoloured.
569. 35 f. Type **205** 30 20
570. 40 f. Chequered rug .. 45 25
571. 45 f. Flower pot 50 30
572. 60 f. Gourd 75 35

1975. International Women's Year.
573. **206.** 50 f. blue, brn. & red 75 50

207. Dr. Schweitzer and Lambarene Hospital.

1975. Birth Cent. of Dr. Albert Schweitzer.
574. **207.** 100 f. brn., grn. & blk. 1·00 55

208. Peugeot, 1892.

1975. Early Motor-cars.
575. **208.** 50 f. blue and mauve 60 30
576. – 75 f. purple and blue 1·00 40
577. – 100 f. mauve and green 1·40 60
578. – 125 f. green and red .. 1·50 70
DESIGNS: 75 f. Daimler, 1895. 100 f. Fiat, 1899. 125 f. Cadillac, 1903.

209. Tree and Sun. **211.** Leontini Tetradrachme.

210. Boxing.

1975. National Tree Week.
579. **209.** 40 f. grn., orge. and red 40 25

1975. Traditional Sports.
580. **210.** 35 f. brn., orge. & blk. 35 20
581. – 40 f. brn., grn. & blk. 40 20
582. – 45 f. brn., blue & blk. 50 25
583. – 50 f. brn., red and blk. 55 30
DESIGNS—VERT. 40 f. Boxing. 50 f. Wrestling. HORIZ. 45 f. Wrestling.

1975. Ancient Coins.
584. **211.** 50 f. grey, blue & red 60 20
585. – 75 f. grey, blue & mve. 85 30
586. – 100 f. grey, oran. & bl. 1·25 40
587. – 125 f. grey, pur. & grn. 1·50 60
COINS: 75 f. Athens tetradrachme. 100 f. Himer diadrachme. 125 f. Gela tetradrachme.

212. Putting the Shot.

1975. Air. "Pre-Olympic Year". Olympic Games, Montreal (1976).
588. **212.** 150 f. brown and red .. 1·10 55
589. – 200 f. red, chestnut and brown .. .. 1·50 85
DESIGN: 200 f. Gymnastics.

213. Starving Family.

1975. Pan-African Drought Relief.
590. **213.** 40 f. blue, brn. & orge. 55 30
591. – 45 f. brown and blue .. 1·10 50
592. – 60 f. blue, grn. & orge. 1·00 40
DESIGNS: 45 f. Animal skeletons. 60 f. Truck bringing supplies.

214. Trading Canoe crossing R. Niger.

1975. Tourism. Multicoloured.
593. 40 f. Type **214** 50 25
594. 45 f. Boubon Camp entrance 55 25
595. 50 f. Boubon Camp view .. 60 35

215. UN Emblem and Peace Dove.

1975. Air. 30th Anniv. of U.N.O.
596. **215.** 100 f. light blue & blue 85 40

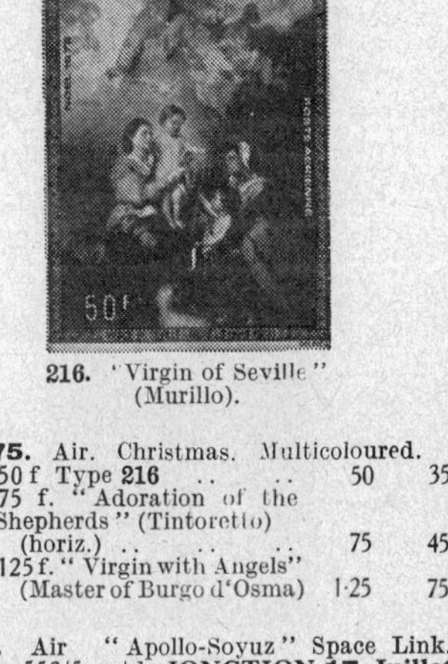

216. "Virgin of Seville" (Murillo).

1975. Air. Christmas. Multicoloured.
597. 50 f. Type **216** 50 35
598. 75 f. "Adoration of the Shepherds" (Tintoretto) (horiz.) 75 45
599. 125 f. "Virgin with Angels" (Master of Burgo d'Osma) 1·25 75

1975. Air "Apollo-Soyuz" Space Link. Nos. 553/5 optd. **JONCTION 17 Juillet 1975.**
600. **198.** 50 f. grn., red and blue 50 25
601. – 100 f. grey, red & blue 75 45
602. – 150 f purple, plum & bl. 1·25 75

218. "Ashak".

1976. Literacy Campaign. Mult.
603. 25 f. Type **218** 15 10
604. 30 f. "Kaska" 20 15
605. 40 f. "Iccee" 25 15
606. 50 f. "Tuuri-nya" 30 20
607. 60 f. "Lekki" 35 25

219. Ice-hockey.

1976. Winter Olympic Games, Innsbruck, Austria. Multicoloured.
608. 40 f. Type **219** (postage) .. 35 20
609. 50 f. Tobogganing .. 40 20
610. 150 f. Ski-jumping .. 1·25 50
611. 200 f. Figure-skating (air) 1·50 75
612. 300 f. Cross-country skiing 2·00 1·00

220. Early Telephone and Satellite.

1976. Telephone Centenary.
614. **220.** 100 f. orge., blue & grn. 85 50

221. Baby and Ambulance.

1976. World Health Day.
615. **221.** 50 f. red, brn. and pur. 50 25

222. Washington crossing the Delaware (after Leutze).

1976. Bicent. of American Revolution. Mult.
616. 40 f. Type **222** (postage) .. 30 15
617. 50 f. First soldiers of the Revolution 40 20
618. 150 f. Joseph Warren—martyr of Bunker Hill (air) .. .. .. 1·10 35
619. 200 f. John Paul Jones aboard the "Bonhomme Richard" .. .. 1·50 60
620. 300 f. Molly Pitcher—heroine of Monmouth .. 2·00 90

223. Distribution of Provisions. **225.** "Europafrique" Symbols.

224. Zeppelin "LZ-129" crossing Lake Constance.

1976. 2nd Anniv. of Military Coup. Mult.
622. 50 f. Type **223** 35 25
623. 100 f. Soldiers with bull-dozer (horiz.) .. .. 1·10 45

1976. Air. 75th Anniv. of Zeppelin Airships. Multicoloured.
624. 40 f. Type **224** 40 15
625. 50 f. " LZ–3 " over Wurzberg 50 25
626. 150 f. " L–9 " over Friedrichshafen .. .. 1·40 55
627. 200 f. " LZ–9 " over Rothenburg (vert.) .. .. 1·75 70
628. 300 f. " LZ–130 " over Essen .. .. 3·25 85

1976. " Europafrique ".
630. **225.** 100 f. multicoloured .. 1·40 50

226. Plant Cultivation.

1976. Communal Works. Multicoloured.
631. 25 f. Type **226** 15 10
632. 30 f. Harvesting rice .. 20 15

227. Boxing.

1976. Olympic Games, Montreal. Mult.
633. 40 f. Type **227** 25 15
634. 50 f. Basketball 40 20
635. 60 f. Football 45 25
636. 80 f. Cycling (horiz.) .. 60 20
637. 100 f. Judo (horiz.) .. 70 30

228. Motobecane ' 125 '.

1976. Motorcycles.
639. **228.** 50 f. violet, brn. & turq. 60 25
640. – 75 f. grn., red & turq. 85 35
641. – 100 f. brn., orge. & pur. 1·25 50
642. – 125 f. slate, olive & blk. 1·50 75
DESIGNS: 75 f. Norton " Challenge ". 100 f. B.M.W. " 903 ". 125 f. Kawasaki " 1000 ".

229. Cultivation Map.

1976. Operation " Sahel Vert ". Mult.
643. 40 f. Type **229** 30 15
644. 45 f. Tending plants (vert.) 35 20
645. 60 f. Planting sapling (vert.) 55 30

1976. International Literacy Day. Nos. 603/7 optd. **JOURNEE INTERNATIONALE DE L'ALPHABETISATION.**
646. **218.** 25 f. multicoloured .. 15 15
647. – 30 f. multicoloured .. 15 15
648. – 40 f. multicoloured .. 20 15
649. – 50 f. multicoloured .. 25 20
650. – 60 f. multicoloured .. 30 20

231. Basket Making.

1976. Niger Women's Association. Mult.
651. 40 f. Type **231** 35 20
652. 45 f. Hairdressing (horiz.) 40 25
653. 50 f. Making pottery .. 50 35

232. Wall Paintings.

1976. " Archaeology ". Multicoloured.
654. 40 f. Type **232** 45 25
655. 50 f. Neolithic statuettes 50 25
656. 60 f. Dinosaur skeleton .. 90 35

233. " The Nativity " (Rubens).

234. Benin Ivory Mask.

1976. Air. Christmas. Multicoloured.
657. 50 f. Type **233** 50 25
658. 100 f. " Holy Night " (Correggio) .. .. .. 1·10 45
659. 150 f. " Adoration of the Magi " (David) (horiz.) 1·50 90

1977. 2nd World Festival of Negro-African Arts, Lagos.
660. **234.** 40 f. brown 40 20
661. – 50 f. blue 60 30
DESIGNS—HORIZ. 50 f. Nigerian stick dance.

235. Students in Class.

236. Examining Patient.

1977. Alphabetisation Campaign.
662. **235.** 40 f. multicoloured .. 30 15
663. 50 f. multicoloured .. 40 20
664. 60 f. multicoloured .. 60 20

1977. Village Health. Multicoloured.
665. 40 f. Type **236** 50 20
666. 50 f. Examining baby .. 60 30

237. Rocket Launch.

1977. " Viking " Space Mission. Mult.
667. 50 f. Type **237** (postage) .. 45 15
668. 80 f. " Viking " approaching Mars (horiz.) .. 65 20
669. 100 f. " Viking " on Mars (horiz.) (air) 65 25
670. 150 f. Parachute descent .. 1·00 30
671. 200 f. Rocket in flight .. 1·40 45

238. Marabou Stork.

1977. Fauna Protection.
673. **238.** 80 f. sepia, bis. & red 1·50 75
674. – 90 f. brown and turq. 1·25 60
DESIGN: 90 f. Bushbuck.

239. Satellite and Weather Symbols.

1977. World Meteorological Day.
675. **239.** 100 f. blue, blk. & turq. 1·00 50

240. Gymnastic Exercise.

1977. 2nd Youth Festival, Tahoua. Mult.
676. 40 f. Type **240** 35 20
677. 50 f. High jumping .. 40 25
678. 80 f. Choral ensemble .. 70 35

241. Red Cross and Children playing.

1977. World Health Day. Child Immunisation Campaign.
679. **241.** 80 f. red, mauve & orge. 75 35

242. Fly, Dagger, and W.H.O. Emblem in Eye.

1977. Fight against Onchocerosis (blindness caused by worm infestation).
680. **242.** 100 f. blue, grey & red 1·40 55

243. Guirka Tahoua Dance.

1977. " Popular Arts and Traditions ". Multicoloured.
681. 40 f. Type **243** 45 25
682. 50 f. Maifilafili Gaya .. 50 20
683. 80 f. Naguihinayan Loga 80 45

244. Four Cavalrymen.

1977. Chief's Traditional Cavalry. Mult.
684. 40 f. Type **244** 55 25
685. 50 f. Chieftain at head of cavalry 65 30
686. 60 f. Chieftain and cavalry 90 45

245. Planting Crops.

1977. " Operation Green Sahel " (recovery of desert).
687. **245.** 40 f. multicoloured .. 50 25

INDEX

Countries can be quickly located by referring to the index at the end of this volume.

246. Albert John Luthuli (Peace, 1960).

1977. Nobel Prize Winners. Multicoloured.
688. 50 f. Type **246** 30 15
689. 80 f. Maurice Maeterlinck (Literature, 1911) .. 55 20
690. 100 f. Allan L. Hodgkin (Medicine, 1963) .. 70 25
691. 150 f. Albert Camus (Literature, 1957) .. 1·00 35
692. 200 f. Paul Ehrlich (Medicine, 1908) .. 1·50 40

247. Mao Tse-tung.

1977. 1st Death Anniv. of Mao Tse-tung (Chinese leader).
694. **247.** 100 f. black and red .. 80 50

248. Vittorio Pozzo (Italy).

1977. World Football Cup Elimination Rounds. Multicoloured.
695. 40 f. Type **248** 30 10
696. 50 f. Vincente Feola, Spain 35 15
697. 80 f. Aymore Moreira, Portugal 50 20
698. 100 f. Sir Alf Ramsey, England 75 25
699. 200 f. Helmut Schon, West Germany .. 1·40 45

249. Horse's Head and Parthenon.

1977. U.N.E.S.C.O. Commemoration.
701. **249.** 100 f. blue, red and pale blue .. .. 1·25 60

250. Carrying Water.

1977. Women's Work. Multicoloured.
702. 40 f. Type **250** 35 30
703. 50 f. Pounding maize .. 40 25

251. Crocodile Skull.

1977. Archaeology. Multicoloured.
704. 50 f. Type **251** 60 40
705. 80 f. Neolithic tools .. 90 60

252. Paul Follereau and Leper. 253. " The Assumption ".

1978. 25th Anniv. of World Leprosy Day.
706. **252.** 40 f. red, bl. & orge.. .. 30 15
707. – 50 f. blk., red & orge. 40 20
DESIGN—HORIZ. 50 f. Follereau and two lepers.

1978. 400th Birth Anniv. of Peter Paul Rubens. Paintings. Multicoloured.
708. 50 f. Type **253** 30 15
709. 70 f. " The Artist and His Friends " (horiz.) .. 40 20
710. 100 f. " History of Maria de Medici " 70 25
711. 150 f. " Alathea Talbot " 1·10 35
712. 200 f. " Portrait of the Marquise de Spinola " .. 1·50 40

1978. As Nos. 376/7 but redrawn and background colour of 35 f. changed to blue. 35 f. undated, 50 f. dated "1978".
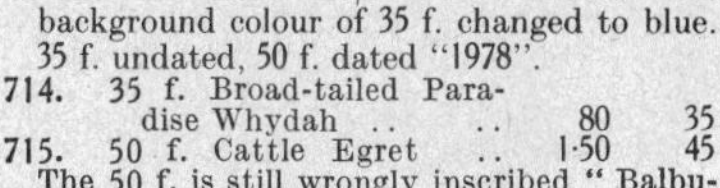
714. 35 f. Broad-tailed Paradise Whydah 80 35
715. 50 f. Cattle Egret .. 1·50 45
The 50 f. is still wrongly inscribed " Balbucus ".

254. Putting the Shot.

1978. National Schools and University Sports Championships. Multicoloured.
716. 40 f. Type **254** 20 15
717. 50 f. Volleyball 30 20
718. 60 f. Long-jumping .. 35 20
719. 100 f. Throwing the javelin 55 35

255. Nurse assisting Patient.

1978. Niger Red Cross.
720. **255.** 40 f. multicoloured .. 30 20

256. Station and Dish Aerial.

1978. Goudel Earth Receiving Station.
721. **256.** 100 f. multicoloured .. 65 40

257. Football and Flags of Competing Nations.

1978. World Cup Football Championship, Argentina. Multicoloured.
722. 40 f. Type **257** 25 10
723. 50 f. Football in net .. 35 15
724. 100 f. Globe and goal .. 75 25
725. 200 f. Tackling (horiz.) .. 1·40 55

258. " Fireworks ".

1978. Air. Third African Games, Algiers. Multicoloured.
727. 40 f. Type **258** 25 20
728. 150 f. Olympic rings emblem 1·00 60

259. Niamey Post Office.

1978. Niamey Post Office. Multicoloured.
729. 40 f. Type **259** 25 15
730. 60 f. Niamey Post Office (different) 35 25

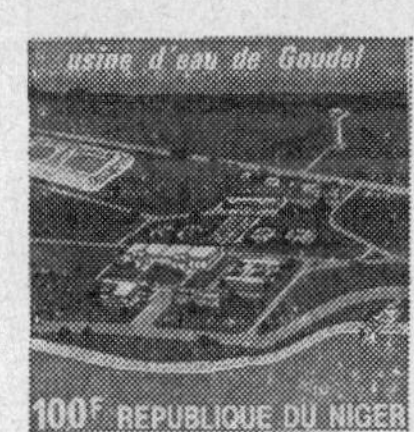

260. Aerial View of Water-works.

1978. Goudel Water-works.
731. **260.** 100 f. multicoloured .. 55 40

261. R. T. N. Emblem.

1978. Air. 20th Anniv. of Niger Broadcasting.
732. **261.** 150 f. multicoloured .. 90 60

262. Golden Eagle and Oldenburg 2 g. Stamp of 1859.

1978. Air. " Philexafrique " Stamp Exhibition, Libreville, Gabon (1st issue) and Int. Stamp Fair, Essen, West Germany. Mult.
733. 100 f. Type **262** .. .. 1·50 1·25
734. 100 f. Giraffes and Niger 1959 2 f. stamp.. .. 1·50 1·25

263. Giraffe. 265. Dome of the Rock, Jerusalem.

1978. Endangered Animals. Multicoloured.
735. 40 f. Type **263** 45 25
736. 50 f. Ostrich .. .. 1·25 30
737. 70 f. Cheetah 75 35
738. 150 f. Scimitar oryx (horiz.) 1·50 75
739. 200 f. Addax (horiz.) .. 2·00 95
740. 300 f. Hartebeest (horiz.).. 2·50 1·25

1978. World Cup Football Championship Finalists. Nos. 695/9 optd.
741. **248.** 40 f. multicoloured .. 30 20
742. – 50 f. multicoloured .. 40 20
743. – 80 f. multicoloured .. 55 25
744. – 100 f. multicoloured .. 65 40
745. – 200 f. multicoloured .. 1·40 75
OVERPRINTS: 40 f. **EQUIPE QUATRIEME: ITALIE.** 50 f. **EQUIPE TROISIEME: BRESIL.** 80 f. **EQUIPE SECONDE: PAYS BAS.** 100 f. **EQUIPE VAINQUEUR: ARGENTINE.** 200 f. **ARGENTINE - PAYS BAS 3 - 1.**

1978. Palestinian Welfare.
747. **265.** 40 f.+5 f. multicoloured 40 30

266. Laying Foundation Stone, and View of University.

1978. Air. Islamic University of Niger.
748. **266.** 100 f. multicoloured .. 60 40

267. Tinguizi. 268. " The Homecoming " (Daumier).

1978. Muscians. Multicoloured.
749. 100 f. Type **267** 75 40
750. 100 f. Chetima Ganga (horiz.) 75 40
751. 100 f. Dan Gourmou .. 75 40

1979. Paintings. Multicoloured.
752. 50 f. Type **268** 50 20
753. 100 f. " Virgin in Prayer " (Durer) 60 20
754. 150 f. " Virgin and Child " (Durer) 90 30
755. 200 f. " Virgin and Child " (Durer) (different) .. 1·25 40

269. Feeder Tanks.

1979. Solar Energy. Multicoloured.
757. 40 f. Type **269** 30 20
758. 50 f. Solar panels on house roofs (horiz.) 40 25

270. Langha Contestants.

1979. Traditional Sports. Multicoloured.
759. 40 f. Type **270** 25 15
760. 50 f. Langha contestants clasping hands.. .. 35 20

271. Children with Building Bricks.

1979. International Year of the Child. Multicoloured.
761. 40 f. Type **271** 25 15
762. 100 f. Children with book 60 25
763. 150 f. Children with model aeroplane .. .. 1·25 45

272. Rowland Hill, Peugeot Mail Van and French " Ceres " Stamp of 1849.

1979. Death Centenary of Sir Rowland Hill. Multicoloured.
764. 40 f. Type **272** 25 15
765. 100 f. Canoes and Austrian newspaper stamp, 1851 60 25
766. 150 f. "DC-3" aircraft & U.S. "Lincoln" stamp, 1869 .. .. .. 1·10 35
767. 200 f. British Advanced Passenger Train and Canada 7½d. stamp, 1857 1·90 50

273. Zabira Decorated Bag and Niger 45 f. Stamp, 1965.

1979. " Philexafrique 2 " Exhibition, Libreville.
769. **273.** 50 f. multicoloured .. 65 40
770. – 150 f. blue, red & carm. 1·60 1·10
DESIGNS: 150 f. Talking Heads, world map, satellite and U.P.U. emblem.

274. Alcock and Brown Statue, and Vickers " Vimy " aircraft.

1979. 60th Anniv. of First Transatlantic Flight.
771. **274.** 100 f. multicoloured .. 1·00 35

275. Djermakoye Palace.

1979. Historic Monuments.
772. **275.** 100 f. multicoloured .. 55 40

276. Bororos in Festive Headdress.

1979. Annual Bororo Festival. Multicoloured.
773. 45 f. Type **276** 30 20
774. 60 f. Bororo women in traditional costume (vert.).. 35 25

277. Boxing.

1979. Pre-Olympic Year.

775. 277. 45 f. multicoloured .. 30 15
776. – 100 f. multicoloured .. 55 25
777. – 150 f. multicoloured .. 85 35
778. – 250 f. multicoloured .. 1·25 45

DESIGNS: 100 f. to 250 f. Various boxing scenes.

278. Class of Learner-drivers.

1979. Driving School.

780. 278. 45 f. multicoloured .. 30 20

279. Aircraft over Map of Niger.

1979. Air. 20th Anniv. of ASECNA (African Air Safety Organization).

781. 279. 150 f. multicoloured .. 1·10 60

1979. " Apollo 11 " Moon Landing. Nos. 667/8, 670/1 optd. **alunissage apollo XI juillet 1969** and lunar module.

782. 50 f. Type **237** (postage).. 30 20
783. 80 f. " Viking " approaching Mars (horiz.) .. 50 35
784. 150 f. Parachute descent (air) 90 60
785. 200 f. Rocket in flight .. 1·25 80

281. Four-man Bobsleigh.

1979. Winter Olympic Games, Lake Placid (1980). Multicoloured.

787. 40 f. Type **281** 25 15
788. 60 f. Downhill skiing .. 35 15
789. 100 f. Speed skating .. 60 25
790. 150 f. Two-man bobsleigh 90 35
791. 200 f. Figure skating .. 1·10 45

282. Le Gaweye Hotel.

1980. Air.

793. 282. 100 f. multicoloured .. 60 40

283. Sultan and Court.

1980. Sultan of Zinder's Court. Mult.

794. 45 f. Type **283** 30 20
795. 60 f. Sultan and court (different) 40 20

284. Chain Smoker and Athlete. 285. Walking.

1980. World Health Day. Anti-Smoking Campaign.

796. 284. 100 f. multicoloured .. 65 40

1980. Olympic Games, Moscow. Mult.

797. 60 f. Throwing the javelin 35 15
798. 90 f. Type **285** 50 20
799. 100 f. High jump (horiz.) 55 25
800. 300 f. Running (horiz.) .. 1·50 55

1980. Winter Olympic Games Medal Winners. Nos. 787/91 optd.

802. 281. 40 f. **VAINQUEUR R.D.A.** 25 15
803. – 60 f. **VAINQUEUR STENMARK SUEDE** 30 20
804. – 100 f. **VAINQUEUR HEIDEN Etats-Unis** 60 30
805. – 150 f. **VAINQUEURS SCHERER-BENZ Suisse** 90 45
806. – 200 f. **VAINQUEUR COUSINS Grande Bretagne** .. .. 1·25 65

287. Village Scene.

1980. Health Year.

808. 287. 150 f. multicoloured .. 75 50

288. Shimbashi-Yokohama Steam Locomotive.

1980. Steam Locomotives. Multicoloured.

809. 45 f. Type **288** 50 15
810. 60 f. American locomotive 60 20
811. 90 f. German State Railway series 61 .. .. 1·00 25
812. 100 f. Prussian State Railway P2 .. .. 1·25 40
813. 130 f. " L'Aigle " .. .. 1·75 50

289. Steve Biko and Map of Africa. 292. U.A.P.T. Emblem.

291. Footballer.

1980. 4th Death Anniv. of Steve Biko (South African Anti-apartheid Worker).

815. 289. 150 f. multicoloured .. 80 60

1980. Olympic Medal Winners. Nos. 797/800 optd.

816. 285. 60 f. **KULA (URSS)** 35 15
817. – 90 f. **DAMILANO (IT)** 55 25
818. – 100 f. **WZSOLA (POL)** 60 30
819. – 300 f. **YIFTER (ETH)** 1·60 90

1980. World Cup Football Championship, Spain (1982). Various designs showing Football.

821. 291. 45 f. multicoloured 25 15
822. – 60 f. multicoloured .. 30 15
823. – 90 f. multicoloured .. 55 20
824. – 100 f. multicoloured 60 25
825. – 130 f. multicoloured .. 80 30

1980. 5th Anniv. of African Posts and Telecommunications Union.

827. 292. 100 f. multicoloured .. 55 40

293. Earthenware Statuettes.

1981. Kareygorou Culture Terracotta Statuettes. Multicoloured.

828. 45 f. Type **293** 25 20
829. 60 f. Head (vert.) .. 35 20
830. 90 f. Head (different) (vert.) 50 30
831. 150 f. Three heads .. 90 50

294. " Self-portrait ". 295. Ostrich.

1981. Paintings by Rembrandt. Multicoloured.

832. 60 f. Type **294** 40 15
833. 90 f. " Portrait of Hendrickje at the Window " .. 60 20
834. 100 f. " Portrait of an Old Man " 65 25
835. 130 f. " Maria Trip " .. 90 35
836. 200 f. " Self-portrait " (different) .. .. 1·25 45
837. 400 f. " Portrait of Saskia " 2·25 1·00

1981. Animals. Multicoloured.

839. 10 f. Type **295** 50 15
840. 20 f. Scimitar oryx .. 25 15
841. 25 f. Addra gazelle .. 20 15
842. 30 f. Arabian bustard .. 85 30
843. 60 f. Giraffe 50 20
844. 150 f. Addax .. .. 1·00 45

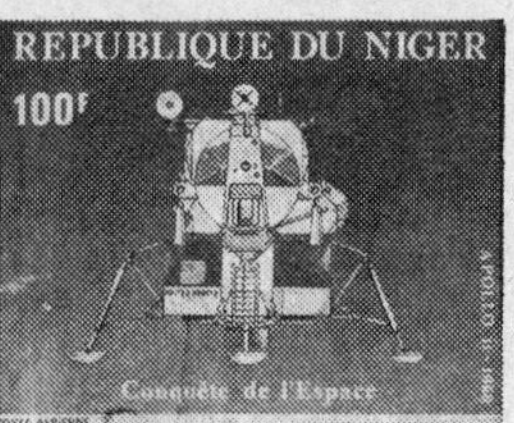

296. " Apollo 11 ".

1981. Air. Conquest of Space. Multicoloured.

845. 100 f. Type **296** 60 25
846. 150 f. Airplane carrying space shuttle. .. 1·00 40
847. 200 f. Rocket carrying space shuttle .. .. 1·25 40
848. 300 f. Space shuttle flying over planet .. .. 3·00 1·00

297. Tanks. 298. Disabled Archer.

1981. 7th Anniv. of Military Coup.

849. 297. 100 f. multicoloured .. 1·00 40

1981. International Year of Disabled People.

850. 298. 50 f. dp. brn., red & brn. 50 20
851. – 100 f. brn., red and grn. 75 40

DESIGN: 100 f. Disabled draughtsman.

299. Ballet Mahalba.

1981. Ballet Mahalba. Multicoloured.

852. 100 f. Type **299** 70 35
853. 100 f. Ballet Mahalba (different) 70 35

300. " Portrait of Olga in an Armchair ". 301. Mosque and Ka'aba.

1981. Air. Birth Centenary of Pablo Picasso (artist). Multicoloured.

854. 60 f. Type **300** 40 20
855. 90 f. " The Family of Acrobats " 55 25
856. 120 f. " The Three Musicians " 70 35
857. 200 f. " Paul on a Donkey " 1·10 55
858. 400 f. " Young Girl drawing in an Interior " (horiz.) 2·40 1·25

1981. 15th Centenary of Hejira.

859. 301. 100 f. multicoloured .. 60 35

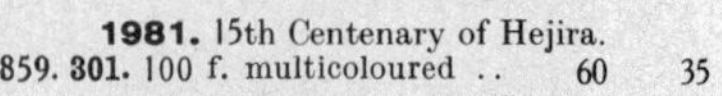

302. Carriage.

1981. British Royal Wedding.

860. 302. 150 f. multicoloured .. 60 35
861. – 200 f. multicoloured .. 1·00 55
862. – 300 f. multicoloured .. 1·25 1·00

DESIGNS: 200 f., 300 f. Similar designs showing carriages.

303. Sir Alexander Fleming. 305. Crops, Cattle and Fish.

304. Pen-nibs, Envelope, Flower and U.P.U. Emblem.

1981. Birth Centenary of Sir Alexander Fleming (discoverer of Penicillin).

864 303 150 f. blue, brown & grn 1·25 50

1981. International Letter Writing Week.

865. 304. 65 f. on 45 f. bl. and red 40 20
866. – 85 f. on 60 f. blue, orange and black .. 50 30

DESIGN: 85 f. Quill, hand holding pen and U.P.U. emblem.

1981. World Food Day.

867. 305. 100 f. multicoloured .. 60 35

306. Tackling.

1981. World Cup Football Championship, Spain (1982). Multicoloured.

868. 40 f. Type **306** 25 20
869. 65 f. Goal keeper fighting for ball 40 30
870. 85 f. Passing ball 55 35
871. 150 f. Running with ball.. 1·00 60
872. 300 f. Jumping for ball .. 2·25 1·10

307. Peugeot, 1912.

1981. 75th Anniv. of French Grand Prix Motor Race. Multicoloured.

874. 20 f. Type **307** 25 15
875. 40 f. Bugatti, 1924 .. 35 20
876. 65 f. Lotus-Climax, 1962.. 55 30
877. 85 f. Georges Boillot .. 75 35
878. 150 f. Phil Hill .. .. 1·10 60

308. " Madonna and Child " (Botticelli). **309.** Children watering Plants.

1981. Christmas, Various Madonna and Child Paintings by named artists. Mult.
880. 100 f. Type **308** 60 40
881. 200 f. Botticini .. .. 1·25 75
882. 300 f. Botticini (different) 2·00 1·10

1982. School Gardens. Multicoloured.
883. 65 f. Type **309** 50 30
884. 85 f. Tending plants and examining produce .. 60 35

310. Arturo Toscanini (conductor, 25th death anniv.).

1982. Celebrities' Anniversaries. Mult.
885. 120 f. Type **310** .. .. 1·00 45
886. 140 f. " Fruits on a Table " (Manet, 150th birth anniv.) (horiz.) 80 55
887. 200 f. " L'Estaque " (Braque, birth centenary) (horiz.) .. .. .. 1·25 60
888. 300 f. George Washington (250th birth anniv.) .. 2·00 90
889. 400 f. Goethe (poet, 150th death anniv.) .. .. 2·50 1·25
890. 500 f. Princess of Wales (21st birthday) .. 2·75 1·50

311. Palace of Congresses.

1982. Palace of Congresses.
892. **311.** 150 f. multicoloured .. 90 60

312. Martial Arts.

1982. Seventh Youth Festival, Agadez. Multicoloured.
893. 65 f. Type **312** 40 30
894. 100 f. Traditional wrestling 60 40

313. Planting a Tree.

1982. National Re-afforestation Campaign. Multicoloured.
895. 150 f. Type **313** .. .. 1·00 60
896. 200 f. Forest and desert .. 1·25 75

314. Scouts in Pirogue. **315.** Map of Africa showing Member States.

1982. 75th Anniv. of Boy Scout Movement. Multicoloured.
897. 65 f. Type **314** 55 30
898. 85 f. Scouts inflatable dinghy 65 30
899. 130 f. Scouts in canoe .. 1·25 45
900. 200 f. Scouts on raft .. 1·75 60

1982. Economic Community of West African States.
902. **315.** 200 f. yellow, black and blue .. .. 1·25 75

316. Casting Net.

318. Hands reaching towards Mosque. **319.** " Flautist ".

1982. Niger Fishermen. Multicoloured.
903. 65 f. Type **316** 55 30
904. 85 f. Net fishing 70 40

1982. Birth of Prince William of Wales. Nos. 860/2 optd. **NAISSANCE ROYALE 1982.**
905. **302.** 150 f. multicoloured .. 75 60
906. – 200 f. multicoloured .. 1·00 75
907. – 300 f. multicoloured .. 1·40 1·10

1982. 13th Islamic Foreign Ministers Meeting, Niamey.
909. **318.** 100 f. multicoloured .. 60 40

1982. Norman Rockwell Paintings. Multicoloured.
910. 65 f. Type **319** 40 25
911. 85 f. " Clerk " 50 25
912. 110 f. " Teacher and Pupil " 70 35
913. 150 f. " Girl Shopper " .. 90 50

320. World Map and Satellite.

1982. I.T.U. Delegates' Conference, Nairobi.
914. **320.** 130 f. blue, light blue and black .. .. 1·00 50

1982. World Cup Football Championship Winners. Nos. 868/72 optd.
915. 40 f. Type **306** 25 20
916. 65 f. Goal keeper fighting for ball 40 30
917. 85 f. Passing ball 45 25
918. 150 f. Running with ball 90 50
919. 300 f. Jumping for ball .. 1·75 1·10

OVERPRINTS: 40 f. **1966 VAINQUEUR GRANDE - BRETAGNE.** 65 f. " **1970 VAINQUEUR BRESIL** ". 85 f. " **1974 VAINQUEUR ALLEMAGNE (RFA)** ". 150 f. " **1978 VAINQUEUR ARGENTINE** " 300 f. " **1982 VAINQUEUR ITALIE** ".

322. Laboratory Workers with Microscopes.

1982. Laboratory Work. Multicoloured.
921. 65 f. Type **322** 60 40
922. 115 f. Laboratory workers 80 50

323. " Adoration of the Kings ".

1982. Air. Christmas. Paintings by Rubens. Multicoloured.
923. 200 f. Type **323** .. .. 1·25 50
924. 300 f. " Mystic Marriage of St. Catherine .. .. 2·00 75
925. 400 f. " Virgin and Child " 2·50 1·00

324. Mongolfier Hot-air Balloon.

1983. Air. Bicentenary of Manned Flight. Multicoloured.
926. 65 f. Type **324** 45 15
927. 85 f. Hydrogen balloon .. 60 20
928. 200 f. Zeppelin (horiz.) .. 1·25 60
929. 250 f. Farman biplane (horiz.) .. .. .. 1·50 70
930. 300 f. " Concorde " .. 3·00 1·40
931. 500 f. " Apollo 11 " .. 3·00 1·40

325. Harvesting Rice. **326.** E.C.A. Anniversary Emblem.

1983. Self-sufficiency in Food. Mult.
932. 65 f. Type **325** 60 30
933. 85 f. Planting Rice .. 80 40

1983. 25th Anniv. of Economic Commission for Africa.
934. **326.** 120 f. multicoloured .. 75 40
935. 200 f. multicoloured .. 1·25 70

327. " The Miraculous Draught of Fishes ".

1983. 500th Birth Anniv. of Raphael. Multicoloured.
936. 65 f. Type **327** 60 15
937. 85 f. " Grand Ducal Madonna " (vert.) .. 50 20
938. 100 f. " The Deliverance of St. Peter " 60 25
939. 150 f. " Sistine Madonna " (vert.) .. .. 1·00 45
940. 200 f. " The Fall on the Way to Calvary " (vert.) .. 1·10 60
941. 300 f. " The Entombment " 1·75 80
942. 400 f. " The Transfiguration " (vert.) .. .. 2·25 1·10
943. 500 f. " St. Michael fighting the Dragon " (vert.) .. 3·00 1·40

328. Surveying.

1983. The Army in the Service of Development. Multicoloured.
944. 85 f. Type **328** 60 25
945. 150 f. Road building .. 1·00 50

329. Palace of Justice.

1983. Palace of Justice, Agadez.
946. **329.** 65 f. multicoloured .. 40 20

330. Javelin.

1983. Air. Olympic Games, Los Angeles. Multicoloured.
947. 85 f. Type **330** 50 20
948. 200 f. Shotput .. .. 1·10 60
949. 250 f. Throwing the Hammer (vert.) .. 1·50 70
950. 300 f. Discus .. .. 1·75 80

331. Rural Post Vehicle. **332.** Dome of the Rock.

1983. Rural Post Service. Multicoloured.
952. 65 f. Type **331** 50 20
953. 100 f. Post vehicle and map 75 30

1983. Palestine.
954. **332.** 65 f. multicoloured .. 65 20

333. Class watching Television.

1983. International Literacy Day. Multicoloured.
955. 40 f. Type **333** 25 15
956. 65 f. Teacher at black-board (vert.) 40 25
957. 85 f. Learning weights (vert.) 55 30
958. 100 f. Outdoor class .. 60 35
959. 150 f. Woman reading magazine (vert.) .. 1·00 50

334. Three Dancers.

1983. Seventh Dosso Dance Festival. Multicoloured.
960. 65 f. Type **334** 50 25
961. 85 f. Four dancers .. 60 35
962. 120 f. Two dancers .. 90 50

335. Post Van. **336.** Television Antenna and Solar Panel.

1983. World Communications Year. Multicoloured.
963. 80 f. Type **335** 60 40
964. 120 f. Sorting letters .. 80 40
965. 150 f. W.C.Y. emblem (vert.) 1·00 50

1983. Solar Energy in the Service of Television. Multicoloured.
966. 85 f. Type **336** 60 30
967. 130 f. Land-rover and solar panel 90 45

337. " Hypolimnas misippus ".

1983. Butterflies. Multicoloured.
968. 75 f. Type **337** 70 35
969. 120 f. " Papilio demodocus " 1·10 50
970. 250 f. " Vanessa antiopa " 2·00 90
971. 350 f. " Charexes jasius " 2·75 1·40
972. 500 f. " Danaus chrisippus " 4·50 1·75

338. " Virgin and Child with Angels ". **339.** Samariya Emblem.

1983. Air. Christmas. Paintings by Botticelli. Multicoloured.
973. 120 f. Type **338** 75 40
974. 350 f. " Adoration of the Magi " (horiz.) .. .. 2·25 1·00
975. 500 f. " Virgin of the Pomegranate " .. .. 3·00 1·25

1984. Samariya.
976. **339.** 80 f. blk., orge. & grn. 50 30

340. Running.

1984. Air. Olympic Games, Los Angeles. Multicoloured.
977. 80 f. Type **340** 40 20
978. 120 f. Pole vault 60 30
979. 140 f. High jump 80 30
980. 200 f. Triple jump (vert.) .. 1·25 45
981. 350 f. Long jump (vert.) .. 2·00 1·00

341. " Alestes bouboni ".

1984. Fish.
983. **341.** 120 f. multicoloured .. 1·50 55

342. Obstacle Course.

1984. Military Pentathlon. Multicoloured.
984. 120 f. Type **342** 80 40
985. 140 f. Shooting 95 50

343. Radio Station.

1984. New Radio Station.
986. **343.** 120 f. multicoloured .. 85 40

344. Flags, Agriculture and Symbols and Unity and Growth.

1984. 25th Anniv. of Council of Unity.
987. **344.** 65 f. multicoloured .. 40 25
988. 85 f. multicoloured .. 50 40

345. "Paris" (early steamer).

1984. Ships. Multicoloured.
989 80 f. Type **345** 70 25
990 120 f. "Jacques Coeur" (full-rigged ship) .. 80 35
991 150 f. "Bosphorus" (full-rigged ship) .. 1·25 45
992 300 f. "Comet" (full-rigged ship) .. .. .. 2·25 85

346. Daimler.

1984. Motor Cars. Multicoloured.
993. 100 f. Type **346** 75 30
994. 140 f. Renault .. .. 1·10 45
995. 250 f. Delage "D 8" .. 1·75 70
996. 400 f. Maybach "Zeppelin" 2·75 90

347. "Rickmer Rickmers" (full-rigged ship).

1984. Universal Postal Union Congress, Hamburg.
997. **347.** 300 f. blue, brown and green .. .. 2·50 1·50

348. Cattle.

1984. Ayerou Market. Multicoloured.
998. 80 f. Type **348** 60 40
999. 120 f. View of market .. 90 60

349. Viper.

1984.
1000. **349.** 80 f. multicoloured .. 75 40

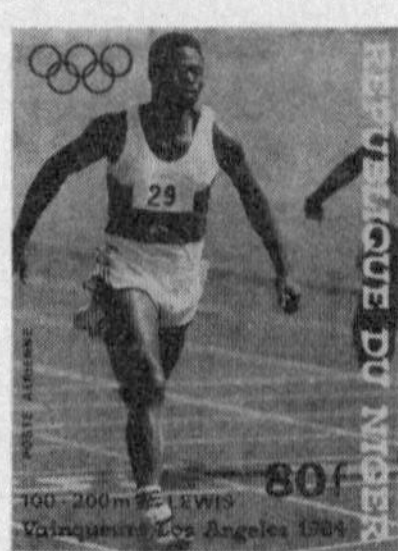

350. Carl Lewis (100 and 200 metres).

1984. Air. Olympic Games Medal Winners. Multicoloured.
1001. 80 f. Type **350** 50 20
1002. 120 f. J. Cruz (800 metres) 70 40
1003. 140 f. A. Cova (10,000 metres) 80 45
1004. 300 f. Al Joyner (Triple jump) .. .. .. 1·75 90

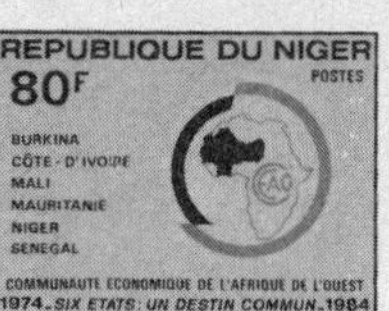

351. Emblem.

1984. 10th Anniv. of Economic Community of West Africa.
1006. **351.** 80 f. multicoloured .. 50 30

352. Emblem and Extract from General Kountche's Speech.

1984. United Nations Disarmament Decennials.
1007. **352.** 400 f. black & green 2·50 1·75
1008. 500 f. black and blue 3·00 1·75

353. Football.

1984. Air. Preliminary Rounds of World Cup Football Championship, Mexico.
1009. **353.** 150 f. multicoloured 1·00 45
1010. – 250 f. multicoloured 1·75 80
1011. – 450 f. multicoloured 2·50 1·25
1012. – 500 f. multicoloured 3·00 1·75
Designs: 250 to 500 f. Footballing scenes.

354. "The Visitation" (Ghirlandaio).

1984. Air. Christmas. Multicoloured.
1013. 100 f. Type **354** 60 30
1014. 200 f. "Virgin and Child" (Master of Saint Verdiana) .. .. 1·25 65
1015. 400 f. "Virgin and Child" (J. Koning) .. .. 2·50 1·25

1984. Drought Relief. Nos. 895/6 optd. **Aide au Sahel 84.**
1016. 150 f. multicoloured .. 1·00 80
1017. 200 f. multicoloured .. 1·25 1·10

356. Organization Emblem. **357.** Breast-feeding Baby.

1985. 10th Anniv. of World Tourism Organization.
1018. **356.** 100 f. black, orange and green 70 40

1985. Infant Survival Campaign. Mult.
1019. 85 f. Type **357** 70 30
1020. 110 f. Feeding baby and changing nappy .. 90 40

358. Black-necked Stilt.

1985. Air. Birth Bicentenary of John J. Audubon (ornithologist). Multicoloured.
1021. 110 f. Type **358** 70 60
1022. 140 f. Greater flamingo (vert.) .. .. .. 1·00 80
1023. 200 f. Atlantic puffin .. 1·40 1·25
1024. 350 f. Arctic tern (vert.) 2·50 1·75

360. Profile and Emblem.

1985. 15th Anniv. of Technical and Cultural Co-operation Agency.
1026. **360.** 110 f. brn., red & vio. 65 40

361. Dancers.

1985. Eighth Niamey Festival. Mult.
1027. 85 f. Type **361** 60 40
1028. 110 f. Four dancers (vert.) 70 50
1029. 150 f. Dancers (different) 1·00 65

362. Wolf ("White Fang") and Jack London.

1985. International Youth Year. Mult.
1030. 85 f. Type **362** 60 25
1031. 105 f. Woman with lion and Joseph Kessel .. 75 30
1032. 250 f. Capt. Ahab harpooning white whale ("Moby Dick") .. 1·75 90
1033. 450 f. Mowgli on elephant ("Jungle Book") .. 2·75 1·50

363. Two Children on Leaf.

1985. "Philexafrique" Stamp Exhibition, Lome, Togo (1st issue). Multicoloured.
1034. 200 f. Type **363** .. .. 1·25 1·00
1035. 200 f. Mining .. .. 1·25 1·00
See also Nos. 1064/5.

364. "Hugo with his Son Francois" (A. de Chatillon).

1985. Death Cent. of Victor Hugo (writer).
1036. **364.** 500 f. multicoloured 3·00 1·75

365. Diesel Train, Satellite and Airplane on Map.

1985. Europafrique.
1037. **365.** 110 f. multicoloured 1·25 55

366. Addax.

1985. Endangered Animals. Multicoloured.
1038. 50 f. Type **366** 40 15
1039. 60 f. Addax (different) (horiz.) 45 25
1040. 85 f. Two Scimitar oryxes (horiz.) .. 55 25
1041. 110 f. Oryx 75 35

367. "Oedaleus sp" on Millet.

368. Agadez Cross.

1985. Vegetation Protection. Multicoloured.
1042 85 f. Type **367** 55 20
1043 110 f. "Dysdercus volkeri" (beetle) 75 35
1044 150 f. Fungi attacking sorghum and millet (horiz) .. .. 1·00 50
1045 210 f. Sudan golden sparrows in tree .. 2·50 1·40
1046 390 f. Red-billed queleas in tree .. .. 4·00 2·50

1985.
1047. **368.** 85 f. green 45 15
1048. – 110 f. brown.. .. 55 15
DESIGN: 110 f. Girl carrying water jar on head.

369. Arms, Flags and Agriculture.

1985. 25th Anniv. of Independence.
1049. **369.** 110 f. multicoloured 70 40

370. Baobab.

371. Man watching Race.

1985. Protected Trees. Multicoloured.
1050. 110 f. Type **370** 80 50
1051. 210 f. "Acacia albida" .. 1·40 1·00
1052. 390 f. Baobab (different) 3·00 1·60

1985. Niamey–Bamako Powerboat Race. Multicoloured.
1053. 110 f. Type **371** 70 45
1054. 150 f. Helicopter and powerboat .. .. 1·60 85
1055. 250 f. Powerboat and map .. .. 1·75 1·25

1985. "Trees for Niger". As Nos. 1050/2 but new values and optd. **DES ARBRES POUR LE NIGER.**
1056. **370.** 30 f. multicoloured .. 25 20
1057. – 85 f. multicoloured .. 55 40
1058. – 110 f. multicoloured 70 55

373. "Boletus".

1985. Fungi. Multicoloured.
1059. 85 f. Type **373** 80 20
1060. 110 f. "Hypholoma fasciculare" .. .. 1·25 30
1061. 200 f. "Coprinus comatus" .. .. 1·75 70
1062. 300 f. "Agaricus arvensis" (horiz.) .. 2·75 1·00
1063. 400 f. "Geastrum fimbriatum" (horiz.) .. 3·50 1·40

374. First Village Water Pump.

1985. "Philexafrique" Stamp Exhibition, Lome, Togo (2nd issue). Multicoloured.
1064. 250 f. Type **374** .. .. 1·75 1·25
1065. 250 f. Handicapped youths playing dili (traditional game) .. 1·75 1·25

375. "Saving Ant" and Savings Bank Emblem.

376. Gouroumi.

1985. World Savings Day.
1066. **375.** 210 f. multicoloured 1·40 85

1985. Musical Instruments. Multicoloured.
1067. 150 f. Type **376** .. .. 1·10 60
1068. 210 f. Gassou (drums) (horiz.) .. .. 1·60 1·00
1069. 390 f. Algaita (flute) .. 2·75 1·50

377. "The Immaculate Conception".

379. National Identity Card.

378. Comet over Paris, 1910.

1985. Air. Christmas. Paintings by Murillo. Multicoloured.
1071. 110 f. "Madonna of the Rosary" 65 35
1072. 250 f. Type **377** .. .. 1·75 90
1073. 390 f. "Virgin of Seville" 2·50 1·25

1985. Air. Appearance of Halley's Comet. Multicoloured.
1074. 110 f. Type **378** 70 35
1075. 130 f. Comet over New York 85 40
1076. 200 f. "Giotto" satellite 1·50 70
1077. 300 f. "Vega" satellite .. 2·25 1·00
1078. 390 f. "Planet A" space probe .. .. .. 2·50 1·25

1986. Civil Statutes Reform. Each black, green and orange.
1079. 85 f. Type **379** 65 30
1080. 110 f. Civil registration emblem 75 40

380. Road Signs.

381. Oumarou Ganda (film producer).

1986. Road Safety Campaign.
1081. **380.** 85 f. blk, yell. & red 75 30
1082. – 110 f. blk, red & grn. 1·00 40
DESIGN: 110 f. Speed limit sign, road and speedometer ("Watch your speed").

1986. Honoured Artists. Multicoloured.
1083. 60 f. Type **381** 35 20
1084. 85 f. Idi Na Dadaou .. 50 30
1085. 100 f. Dan Gourmou .. 60 40
1086. 130 f. Koungoui (comedian) 80 45

382. Martin Luther King.

384. Statue and F. A. Bartholdi.

383. Footballer and 1970 40 f. Stamp.

1986. Air. 18th Death Anniv. of Martin Luther King (human rights activist).
1087. **382.** 500 f. multicoloured 3·25 1·90

1986. Air. World Cup Football Championship, Mexico. Multicoloured.
1088. 130 f. Type **383** .. .. 1·00 30
1089. 210 f. Footballer and 1970 70 f. stamp .. .. 1·25 45
1090. 390 f. Footballer and 1970 90 f. stamp .. .. 2·75 1·00
1091. 400 f. Footballer and Mexican figure on "stamp" .. .. 2·75 1·00

1986. Air. Centenary of Statue of Liberty.
1093. **384.** 300 f. multicoloured 2·25 1·10

385. Truck.

1986. "Trucks of Hope". Multicoloured.
1094. 85 f. Type **385** 75 30
1095. 110 f. Mother and baby (vert.) .. .. .. 1·00 40

386. Nelson Mandela and Walter Sisulu.

387. Food Co-operatives.

1986. International Solidarity with S. African and Namibian Political Prisoners Day. Multicoloured.
1096. 200 f. Type **386** .. .. 1·50 80
1097. 300 f. Nelson Mandela .. 2·25 1·00

1986. 40th Anniv. of F.A.O. Multicoloured.
1098. 50 f. Type **387** 30 20
1099. 60 f. Anti-desertification campaign 35 25
1100. 85 f. Irrigation 50 35
1101. 100 f. Rebuilding herds of live-stock 60 40
1102. 110 f. Reafforestation .. 75 45

388. Trees and Woman with Cooking Pots. **389.** "Sphodromantis sp".

1987. "For a Green Niger".
1103. 85 f. Type **388** 55 30
1104. 110 f. Trees, woman and cooking pots (different) 70 40

1987. Protection of Vegetation. Useful Insects. Multicoloured.
1105 85 f. Type **389** 60 40
1106 110 f. "Delta sp" 85 50
1107 120 f. "Cicindela sp" 95 65

390. Transmitter, Map and Woman using Telephone.

1987. Liptako–Gourma Telecommunications Network.
1108. **390.** 110 f. multicoloured 80 50

391. Morse Key and Operator, 19th-century.

1987. 150th Anniv. of Morse Telegraph. Multicoloured.
1109. 120 f. Type **391** 75 40
1110. 200 f. Samuel Morse (inventor) (vert.) 1·25 70
1111. 350 f. Morse transmitter and receiver 2·25 1·25

392. Tennis Player.

1987. Olympic Games, Seoul (1988). Mult.
1112. 85 f. Type **392** 50 40
1113. 110 f. Pole vaulter 70 40
1114. 250 f. Footballer 1·50 90

393. Ice Hockey.

1987. Winter Olympic Games, Calgary (1988) (1st issue). Multicoloured.
1116. 85 f. Type **393** 60 35
1117. 110 f. Speed skating 70 35
1118. 250 f. Figure skating (pairs) 1·75 90
See also Nos. 1146/9.

394. Long-distance Running.

1987. African Games, Nairobi. Multicoloured.
1120. 85 f. Type **394** 50 35
1121. 110 f. High jumping 60 35
1122. 200 f. Hurdling 1·25 70
1123. 400 f. Javelin throwing 2·50 1·40

395. Chief's Stool, Sceptre and Crown.

1987. 10th Anniv. of National Tourism Office. Multicoloured.
1124. 85 f. Type **395** 50 35
1125. 110 f. Nomad, caravan and sceptre handle 60 35
1126. 120 f. Houses 70 40
1127. 200 f. Bridge over River Niger 1·25 70

396. Yaama Mosque at Dawn.

1987. Aga Khan Prize. Designs Showing Yaama mosque at various times of day.
1128. **396.** 85 f. multicoloured 50 35
1129. 110 f. multicoloured 60 35
1130. 250 f. multicoloured 1·50 90

397. Court Building. **398.** "Holy Family of the Sheep" (Raphael).

1987. Appeal Court, Niamey. Multicoloured.
1131. 85 f. Type **397** 50 30
1132. 110 f. Front entrance 60 35
1133. 140 f. Side view 90 55

1987. Christmas.
1134. **398.** 110 f. multicoloured 65 40

399. Water Drainage.

1988. Health Care. Multicoloured.
1136. 85 f. Type **399** 70 40
1137. 110 f. Modern sanitation 80 40
1138. 165 f. Refuse collection 1·25 65

400. Singer and Band. **402.** New Great Market, Niamey.

1988. Award of Dan-Gourmou Music Prize.
1139. **400.** 85 f. multicoloured 80 50

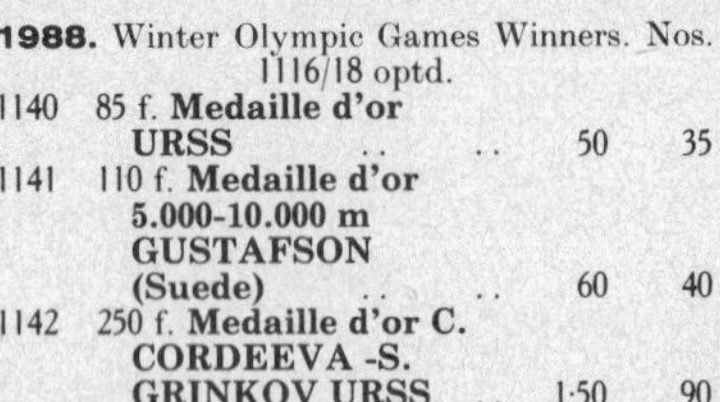

1988. Winter Olympic Games Winners. Nos. 1116/18 optd.
1140 85 f. **Medaille d'or URSS** 50 35
1141 110 f. **Medaille d'or 5.000-10.000 m GUSTAFSON (Suede)** 60 40
1142 250 f. **Medaille d'or C. CORDEEVA -S. GRINKOV URSS** 1·50 90

1988.
1143 **402** 85 f. multicoloured 60 40

403 Mother and Child

1988. U.N.I.C.E.F. Child Vaccination Campaign and 40th Anniv of W.H.O. Mult.
1144 85 f. Type **403** 70 40
1145 110 f. Doctor and villagers 90 50

404 Kayak **405** Emblem

1988. Air. Olympic Games, Seoul (2nd issue) and 125th Birth Anniv of Pierre de Coubertin (founder of modern Olympic Games). Mult.
1146 85 f. Type **404** 50 20
1147 165 f. Rowing (horiz) 90 50
1148 200 f. Two-man kayak (horiz) 1·25 70
1149 600 f. One-man kayak 3·50 2·00

1988. 25th Anniv of Organization of African Unity.
1151 **405** 85 f. multicoloured 50 30

406 Team working **407** Anniversary Emblem

1988. Dune Stabilisation.
1152 **406** 85 f. multicoloured 60 40

1988. 125th Anniv of International Red Cross.
1153 **407** 85 f. multicoloured 60 30
1154 110 f. multicoloured 80 40

409 Emblem **410** Couple, Globe and Laboratory Worker

1989. Niger Press Agency.
1159 **409** 85 f. black, orge & grn 45 30

1989. Campaign against AIDS.
1160 **410** 85 f. multicoloured 55 30
1161 110 f. multicoloured 85 40

411 Radar, Tanker and Signals **412** General Ali Seybou (Pres.)

1989. 30th Anniv of International Maritime Organization.
1162 **411** 100 f. multicoloured 1·25 60
1163 120 f. multicoloured 1·50 80

1989. 15th Anniv of Military Coup. Mult.
1164 85 f. Type **412** 45 25
1165 110 f. Soldiers erecting flag 65 35

413 Eiffel Tower

1989. "Philexfrance 89" International Stamp Exhibition, Paris. Multicoloured.
1166 100 f. Type **413** 60 40
1167 200 f. Flags on stamps 1·25 65

414 "Planting a Tree of Liberty"

1989. Bicentenary of French Revolution.
1168 **414** 250 f. multicoloured 1·50 1·00

415 Telephone Dial, Radio Mast, Map and Stamp **416** "Apollo 11" Launch

1989. 30th Anniv of West African Posts and Telecommunications Association.
1169 **415** 85 f. multicoloured 45 30

1989. Air. 20th Anniv of First Manned Landing on Moon. Multicoloured.
1170 200 f. Type **416** 1·25 65
1171 300 f. Crew 2·00 1·00
1172 350 f. Astronaut and module on lunar surface 2·25 1·25
1173 400 f. Astronaut and U.S. flag on lunar surface 2·50 1·25

417 Emblem

1989. 25th Anniv of African Development Bank.
1174 **417** 100 f. multicoloured .. 60 30

418 Before and After Attack, and "Schistocerca gregaria"

1989. Locusts.
1175 **418** 85 f. multicoloured .. 50 30

419 Auguste Lumiere and 1st Cine Performance, 1895

1989. 35th Death Anniv of Auguste Lumiere and 125th Birth Anniv of Louis Lumiere (photography pioneers). Multicoloured.
1176 150 f. Type **419** 90 55
1177 250 f. Louis Lumiere and first cine-camera, 1894 1·50 85
1178 400 f. Lumiere brothers and first colour cine-camera, 1920 .. .. 2·50 1·25

420 Tractor, Map and Pump

1989. 30th Anniv of Agriculture Development Council.
1179 **420** 75 f. multicoloured .. 45 30

421 Zinder Regional Museum
422 "Russelia" equisetiformis"

1989. Multicoloured.
1180 85 f. Type **421** 45 30
1182 165 f. Temet dunes .. 90 60

1989. Flowers. Multicoloured.
1183 10 f. Type **422** 15 10
1184 20 f. "Argyreia nervosa" 15 10
1185 30 f. "Hibiscus rosa-sinensis" 20 10
1186 50 f. "Catharanthus roseus" 35 20
1187 100 f. "Cymothoe sangaris" (horiz) .. 75 35

423 Emblem
424 Adults learning Alphabet

1990. 10th Anniv of Pan-African Postal Union.
1188 **423** 120 f. multicoloured .. 70 40

1990. International Literacy Year. Mult.
1189 85 f. Type **424** 45 25
1190 110 f. Adults learning arithmetic 65 35

425 Emblem
427 Leland and Child

426 Footballers and Florence

1990. 20th Anniv of Islamic Conference Organization.
1191 **425** 85 f. multicoloured .. 50 30

1990. Air. World Cup Football Championship, Italy. Multicoloured.
1192 130 f. Type **426** .. .. 1·00 40
1193 210 f. Footballers and Verona .. .. 1·40 75
1194 500 f. Footballers and Bari .. .. .. 3·25 1·75
1195 600 f. Footballers and Rome .. .. .. 3·75 2·00

1990. Mickey Leland (American Congressman) Commemoration.
1196 **427** 300 f. multicoloured .. 1·75 1·00
1197 500 f. multicoloured .. 3·00 1·75

428 Emblem
429 Flags and Envelopes on Map

1990. 1st Anniv of National Movement for the Development Society.
1198 **428** 85 f. multicoloured .. 50 30

1990. 20th Anniv of Multinational Postal Training School, Abidjan.
1199 **429** 85 f. multicoloured .. 65 30

430 Gymnastics

1990. Olympic Games, Barcelona (1992). Mult.
1200 85 f. Type **430** 40 25
1201 110 f. Hurding 60 35
1202 250 f. Running .. .. 1·50 90
1203 400 f. Show jumping .. 2·75 1·40
1204 500 f. Long jumping .. 3·00 1·75

431 Arms, Map and Flag
432 Emblem

1990. 30th Anniv of Independence.
1206 **431** 85 f. multicoloured .. 45 30
1207 110 f. multicoloured .. 65 40

1990. 40th Anniv of United Nations Development Programme.
1208 **432** 100 f. multicoloured .. 50 30

433 The Blusher
434 Christopher Columbus and "Santa Maria"

1991. Butterflies and Fungi. Multicoloured.
1209 85 f. Type **433** (postage) 55 20
1210 110 f. "Graphium pylades" (female) .. 75 25
1211 200 f. "Pseudacraea hostilia" .. .. 1·25 55
1212 250 f. Cracked green russula .. .. 1·50 75
1213 400 f. "Boletus impolitus" (air) .. .. .. 2·50 1·00
1214 500 f. "Precis octavia" 2·75 1·25

1991. 540th Birth Anniv of Christopher Columbus. Multicoloured.
1216 85 f. Type **434** 70 25
1217 110 f. 15th-century Portuguese caravel .. 1·00 30
1218 200 f. 16th-century four-masted caravel 1·60 65
1219 250 f. "Estremadura" (Spanish caravel), 1511 2·00 85
1220 400 f. "Vija" (Portuguese caravel), 1600 (air) .. 3·25 1·10
1221 500 f. "Pinta" .. .. 3·50 1·50

435 Speed Skating

1991. Winter Olympic Games, Albertville (1992). Multicoloured.
1223 110 f. Type **435** 60 25
1224 300 f. Ice-hockey .. 1·25 80
1225 500 f. Women's downhill skiing .. .. .. 2·50 1·25
1226 600 f. Two-man luge .. 2·75 1·25

436 Flag and Boy holding Stone
437 Hairstyle

1991. Palestinian "Intifada" Movement.
1227 **436** 110 f. multicoloured .. 75 30

1991. Traditional Hairstyles. Multicoloured.
1228 85 f. Type **437** 20 10
1229 110 f. Netted hairstyle .. 25 15
1230 165 f. Braided hairstyle .. 40 20
1231 200 f. Plaited hairstyle .. 45 25

438 Boubon Market

1991. African Tourism Year. Multicoloured.
1232 85 f. Type **438** 20 10
1233 110 f. Timia waterfalls (vert) 25 15
1234 130 f. Ruins at Assode .. 30 15
1235 200 f. Tourism Year emblem (vert) .. 45 25

439 Anatoly Karpov and Gary Kasparov

1991. Anniversaries and Events. Mult.
1236 85 f. Type **439** (World Chess Championship) (postage) 20 10
1237 110 f. Ayrton Senna and Alain Prost (World Formula 1 motor racing championship) .. 25 15
1238 200 f. Reading of Declaration of Human Rights and Comte de Mirabeau (bicentenary of French Revolution) 45 25
1239 250 f. Dwight D. Eisenhower, Winston Churchill and Field-Marshal Montgomery (50th anniv of America's entry into Second World War) .. 60 35
1240 400 f. Charles de Gaulle and Konrad Adenauer (28th anniv of Franco-German Co-operation Agreement) (air) .. 95 55
1241 500 f. Helmut Kohl and Brandenburg Gate (2nd anniv of German reunification) .. .. 1·10 60

440 Japanese "ERS-1" Satellite

1991. Satellites and Transport. Multicoloured.
1243 85 f. Type **440** (postage) 20 10
1244 110 f. Japanese satellite observing Aurora Borealis 25 15
1245 200 f. Louis Favre and "BB 415" diesel locomotive 45 25
1246 250 f. "BB-BB301" diesel locomotive 60 35
1247 400 f. "BB-BB302" diesel locomotive (air) .. 95 55
1248 500 f. "F 117" jet fighter and "Concorde" .. 1·10 60

441 Crowd and Emblem on Map
443 Couple adding Final Piece to Globe Jigsaw

442 Timberless House

1991. National Conference (to determine new constitution).

1250	441	85 f. multicoloured ..	20	10

1992.

1251	442	85 f. multicoloured ..	20	10

1992. World Population Day. Multicoloured.

1252	85 f. Type **443**	20	10
1253	110 f. Children flying globe kite (after Robert Parker)	25	15

444 Columbus and Fleet

1992. 500th Anniv of Discovery of America by Columbus.

1254	444	250 f. multicoloured ..	60	35

445 Zaleye

1992. 2nd Death Anniv of Hadjia Haqua Issa (Zaleye) (singer).

1255	445	150 f. multicoloured ..	35	20

446 Conference Emblem

447 College Emblem

1992. International Nutrition Conference, Rome.

1256	446	145 f. multicoloured ..	35	20
1257		350 f. multicoloured ..	80	45

1993. 30th Anniv of African Meteorology and Civil Aviation College.

1258	447	110 f. blue, black & grn	25	15

448 Girl planting Sapling

1993. Anti-desertification Campaign.

1259	448	85 f. multicoloured ..	20	10
1260		165 f. multicoloured ..	40	20

MORE DETAILED LISTS

are given in the Stanley Gibbons Catalogues referred to in the country headings.
For lists of current volumes see Introduction.

449 Aerosol spraying Globe (Patricia Charets)

1993. World Population Day. Children's Drawings. Multicoloured.

1261	85 f. Type **449**	20	10
1262	110 f. Tree and person with globe as head looking at high-rise tower blocks (Mathieu Chevrault)	25	15

OFFICIAL STAMPS

O 13. Djerma Woman.

1962. Figures of value in black.

O 121.	O 13.	1 f. violet	10	10
O 122.		2 f. green	10	10
O 123.		5 f. blue	15	10
O 124.		10 f. red	15	10
O 125.		20 f. blue	20	15
O 126.		25 f. orange ..	25	20
O 127.		30 f. blue	30	25
O 128.		35 f. green	35	30
O 129.		40 f. brown	35	35
O 130.		50 f. slate	40	40
O 131.		60 f. turquoise ..	50	45
O 132.		85 f. turquoise ..	70	40
O 133.		100 f. purple ..	85	40
O 134.		200 f. blue	1·50	80

1988. As Type O **13**, but figures of value in same colour as remainder of design.

O 1155	O 13	5 f. blue	10	10
O 1156		10 f. red	10	10
O 1157		15 f. yellow ..	10	10
O 1158		20 f. blue ..	20	10
O 1159		45 f. orange ..	25	20
O 1160		50 f. green ..	30	20

POSTAGE DUE STAMPS

1921. Postage Due stamps of Upper Senegal and Niger "Figure" key-type optd. **TERRITOIRE DU NIGER.**

D 18.	M.	5 c. green	15	50
D 19.		10 c. red	15	50
D 20.		15 c. grey	20	60
D 21.		20 c. brown	20	60
D 22.		30 c. blue	20	60
D 23.		50 c. black	25	65
D 24.		60 c. orange	30	1·00
D 25.		1 f. violet	50	1·10

D 6. Zinder Fort.

1927.

D 73.	D 6.	2 c. red and blue ..	10	25
D 74.		4 c. black and orange	10	25
D 75.		5 c. violet and yellow	15	25
D 76.		10 c. violet and red ..	15	30
D 77.		15 c. orange & green	15	40
D 78.		20 c. sepia and red ..	20	45
D 79.		25 c. sepia and black	35	50
D 80.		30 c. grey and violet	60	1·00
D 81.		50 c. red on green ..	60	80
D 82.		60 c. orange and lilac on blue	60	80
D 83		1 f. violet & blue on bl.	60	75
D 84.		2 f. mauve and red ..	60	80
D 85.		3 f. blue and brown ..	80	1·00

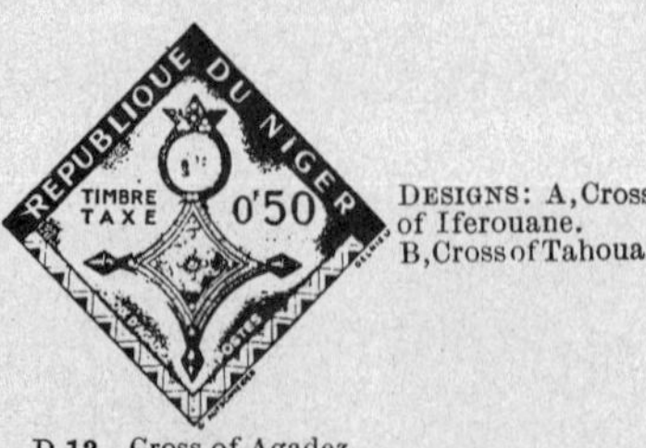

DESIGNS: A, Cross of Iferouane. B, Cross of Tahoua.

D 13. Cross of Agadez.

1962.

D 123.	D 13.	50 c. green	10	10
D 124.		1 f. violet	10	10
D 125.		2 f. myrtle	10	10
D 126.	A.	3 f. mauve	10	10
D 127.		5 f. green	15	15
D 128.		10 f. orange ..	15	15
D 129.	B.	15 f. blue	15	15
D 130.		20 f. red	20	20
D 131.		50 f. brown	40	40

D 450 Cross of Iferouane

1993.

D1263	D 450	5 f. multicoloured	10	10
D1264		10 f. orange & blk	10	10
D1265	–	15 f. mult ..	10	10
D1266	–	20 f. mauve, yellow & black	10	10
D1267	–	50 f. mult ..	10	10

DESIGN: 15 to 50 f. Cross of Tahoua.

NORTH GERMAN CONFEDERATION Pt. 7

The North German Confederation was set up on 1st January, 1868, and comprised the postal services of Bremen, Brunswick, Hamburg Lubeck, Mecklenburg (both), Oldenburg, Prussia (including Hanover, Schleswig-Holstein with Bergedorf and Thurn and Taxis) and Saxony.

The North German Confederation joined the German Reichspost on 4th May, 1871, and the stamps of Germany were brought into use on 1st January, 1872.

Northern District: 30 groschen = 1 thaler.
Southern District: 60 kreuzer = 1 gulden.

1.

3.

1868. Roul. or perf.

19.	1.	¼ g. mauve	15·00	12·00
22.		⅓ g. green	3·25	65
23.		½ g. orange	3·25	50
25.		1 g. red	2·40	30
27.		2 g. blue	3·25	40
29.		5 g. bistre	7·50	4·00
30.	–	1 k. green	10·00	6·50
13.	–	2 k. orange	30·00	35·00
33.	–	3 k. red	5·50	60
36.	–	7 k. blue	8·50	4·00
18.	–	18 k. bistre	26·00	65·00

The 1 k. to 18 k. have the figures in an oval.

1869. Perf.

38.	3.	10 g. grey	£275	50·00
39.	–	30 g. blue	£225	£100

The frame of the 30 g. is rectangular.

OFFICIAL STAMPS

O 5.

1870.

O 40	O 5.	¼ g. black and brown	22·00	45·00
O 41.		⅓ g. black and brown	14·00	17·00
O 42.		½ g. black and brown	2·00	2·50
O 43.		1 g. black and brown	2·50	35
O 44.		2 g. black and brown	5·00	2·75
O 45.		1 k. black and grey ..	32·00	£225
O 46.		2 k. black and grey ..	85·00	£800
O 47.		3 k. black and grey ..	28·00	35·00
O 48.		7 k. black and grey ..	38·00	£250

NORTH INGERMANLAND Pt. 10

Stamps issued during temporary independence of this Russian territory, which adjoins Finland.

100 pennia = 1 mark.

1. 18th century Arms of Ingermanland.

4. Gathering Crops.

1920.

1.	1.	5 p. green	2·25	3·75
2.		10 p. red	2·25	3·75
3.		25 p. brown	2·25	3·75
4.		50 p. blue	2·25	3·75
5.		1 m. black and red ..	20·00	27·00
6.		5 m. black and purple ..	65·00	£110
7.		10 m. black and brown ..	£130	£180

1920. Inscr. as in T **2**.

8.	–	10 p. blue and green ..	3·00	5·00
9.	–	30 p. green and brown ..	3·00	5·00
10.	–	50 p. brown and blue ..	3·00	5·00
11.	–	80 p. grey and red ..	3·00	5·00
12.	4.	1 m. grey and red ..	15·00	28·00
13.	–	5 m. red and violet ..	10·00	15·00
14.	–	10 m. violet and brown ..	11·00	17·00

DESIGNS—VERT. 10 p. Arms. 30 p. Reaper. 50 p. Ploughing. 80 p. Milking. HORIZ. 5 m. Burning church. 10 m. Zither players.

NORTH WEST RUSSIA Pt. 10

Issues made for use by the various Anti-bolshevist Armies during the Russian Civil War, 1918-20.

100 kopeks = 1 rouble.

NORTHERN ARMY

1. " OKCA " = Osobiy Korpus Severnoy Army.—(trans. " Special Corps, Northern Army ").

1919. As T 1 inscr. " OKCA ".

1. 1. 5 k. purple 10 25
2. 10 k. blue 10 25
3. 15 k. yellow 10 25
4. 20 k. red 10 25
5. 50 k. green 10 25

NORTH-WESTERN ARMY

Сѣв. Зап.
Армія

(2.)

1919. Arms types of Russia optd. as T 2. Imperf. or perf.

6. 22. 2 k. green .. .. 2·50 6·00
16. 3 k. red .. .. 1·75 5·50
7. 5 k. lilac .. .. 2·50 6·00
8. 23. 10 k. blue .. .. 3·50 8·00
9. 10. 15 k. blue and purple .. 3·25 6·00
10. 14. 20 k. red and blue .. 4·50 7·00
11. 10. 20 k. on 14 k. red & blue £200
12. 25 k. mauve and green .. 6·00 11·00
13. 14. 50 k. green and purple .. 6·00 11·00
14. 15. 1 r. orge. & brn. on brn. 12·00 22·00
17. 11. 3 r. 50 green and red .. 25·00 35·00
18. 22. 5 r. blue on green .. 14·00 22·00
19. 11. 7 r. pink and green .. 75·00 £140
15. 20. 10 r. grey and red on yell. 40·00 70·00

1919. No. 7 surch.

20. 22. 10 k. on 5 k. red .. 3·00 5·00

WESTERN ARMY

1919. Stamps of Lavtia optd. with Cross of Lorraine in circle with plain background. Imperf. (a) Postage stamps.

21. 1. 3 k. lilac .. .. .. 22·00 40·00
22. 5 k. red .. .. .. 22·00 40·00
23. 10 k. blue £110 £190
24. 20 k. orange .. .. .. 22·00 40·00
25. 25 k. grey .. .. .. 22·00 40·00
26. 35 k. brown .. .. .. 22·00 40·00
27. 50 k. violet .. .. .. 22·00 40·00
28. 75 k. green .. .. .. 24·00 55·00

(b) Liberation of Riga issue

29 4 5 k. red .. .. .. 15·00 35·00
30 15 k. green .. .. .. 15·00 35·00
31 35 k. brown .. .. .. 15·00 35·00

1919. Stamps of Latvia optd. with Cross of Lorraine in circle with burele background and characters **3. A** (=" Z. A."). Imperf.

(a) Postage stamps.

32. 1. 3 k. lilac .. .. .. 4·00 8·00
33. 5 k. red .. .. .. 4·00 8·00
34. 10 k. blue .. .. .. 90·00 £170
35. 20 k. orange .. .. .. 8·00 16·00
36. 25 k. grey .. .. .. 22·00 45·00
37. 35 k. brown .. .. .. 14·00 24·00
38. 50 k. violet .. .. .. 14·00 24·00
39. 75 k. green .. .. .. 14·00 24·00

(b) Liberation of Riga issue

40 4 5 k. red .. .. .. 2·75 6·50
41 15 k. green .. .. .. 2·75 6·50
42 35 k. brown .. .. .. 2·75 6·50

1919. Arms type of Russia surch. with Cross of Lorraine in ornamental frame and **LP** with value in curved frame. Imperf. or perf.

43. 22. 10 k. on 2 k. green .. 4·50 6·00
54. 20 k. on 3 k. red .. 48·00 75·00
44. 23. 30 k. on 4 k. red .. 4·50 7·00
45. 22. 40 k. on 5 k. red .. 4·50 7·00
46. 23. 50 k. on 10 k. blue .. 4·50 6·00
47. 10. 70 k. on 15 k. blue & pur. 4·50 6·00
48. 14. 90 k. on 20 k. red & blue 4·50 7·00
49. 10. 1 r. on 25 k. mve. & grn. 4·50 6·00
50. 1 r. 50 on 35 k. grn. & pur. 35·00 55·00
51. 14. 2 r. on 50 k. grn. & pur... 6·00 10·00
52. 10. 4 r. on 70 k. orge. & brn. 16·00 24·00
53. 15. 6 r. on 1 r. orge. & brown 16·00 25·00
56. 11. 10 r. on 3 r. 50 grn. & pur. 38·00 48·00

NORWAY Pt. 11

In 1814 Denmark ceded Norway to Sweden, from 1814 to 1905 the King of Sweden was also King of Norway after which Norway was an independent Kingdom.

1855. 120 skilling = 1 speciedaler.
1877. 100 ore = 1 krone.

1. 3. King Oscar I.

1855. Imperf.

1. 1. 4 s. blue .. .. .. £3500 90·00

1856. Perf.

4. 3. 2 s. yellow £350 £100
6. 3 s. lilac .. .. .. £225 60·00
7. 4 s. blue .. .. .. £130 10·50
11. 8 s. lake .. .. .. £700 26·00

4. 5.

1863.

12. 4. 2 s. yellow £450 £140
13. 3 s. lilac £400 £350
16. 4 s. blue .. .. 65·00 7·50
17. 8 s. pink .. .. £450 38·00
18. 24 s. brown .. .. 26·00 £100

1867.

21. 5. 1 s. black .. .. .. 60·00 32·00
23. 2 s. brown .. .. .. 13·00 35·00
26. 3 s. lilac .. .. .. £225 70·00
27. 4 s. blue .. .. .. 48·00 5·25
29. 8 s. red .. .. .. £275 25·00

6. A

1872. Value in " Skilling ".

33. 6. 1 s. green .. .. .. 7·00 26·00
35. 2 s. blue .. .. .. 8·75 50·00
39. 3 s. red .. .. .. 35·00 8·00
42. 4 s. mauve .. .. .. 8·75 45·00
44. 6 s. brown .. .. .. £300 35·00
45. 7 s. brown .. .. .. 35·00 45·00

1877. Letters without serifs as Type **A**. Value in " ore ".

47. 6. 1 ore grey .. .. .. 4·50 4·50
81. 1 ore brown .. .. .. 11·00 11·00
83. 2 ore brown .. .. .. 2·75 2·75
84c. 3 ore orange .. .. .. 40·00 3·50
51. 5 ore blue .. .. .. 45·00 6·25
85c. 5 ore green .. .. .. 30·00 1·10
86a. 10 ore red .. .. .. 35·00 1·10
55. 12 ore green .. .. .. 75·00 13·50
75b. 12 ore brown .. .. .. 18·00 13·00
76. 20 ore brown .. .. .. 70·00 8·25
87. 20 ore blue .. .. .. 60·00 2·25
88. 25 ore mauve .. .. .. 9·00 8·00
61. 35 ore green .. .. .. 12·50 8·75
62. 50 ore purple .. .. .. 32·00 7·50
63. 60 ore blue .. .. .. 28·00 7·50

9. King Oscar II.

1878.

68. 9. 1 k. green .. .. .. 22·00 5·75
69. 1 k. 50 blue .. .. .. 42·00 30·00
70. 2 k. brown and red .. .. 30·00 17·00

1888. Surch **2 Ore**.

89a 6 2 ore on 12 ore brown .. 1·40 1·40

12. With background shading. (D).

1893. Letters with serifs as Type D.

133. 12. 1 ore grey 15 20
134. 2 ore brown 15 15
135. 3 ore orange 20 10
136. 5 ore green .. .. .. 3·50 5
137. 5 ore mauve 30 5
138. 7 ore green 30 5
139. 10 ore red .. .. .. 3·50 5
140. 10 ore green .. .. .. 4·50 5
141. 12 ore violet 65 30
142a. 15 ore brown .. .. .. 3·50 10
143. 15 ore blue .. .. .. 3·50 10
144. 20 ore blue .. .. .. 5·00 5
145. 20 ore green .. .. .. 4·50 15
146. 25 ore mauve .. .. .. 32·00 15
147. 25 ore red .. .. .. 4·50 70
148. 30 ore grey .. .. .. 6·25 15
149. 30 ore blue .. .. .. 5·00 2·50
149. 35 ore green .. .. .. 8·75 4·00
150. 35 ore brown .. .. .. 7·00 20
151. 40 ore green .. .. .. 2·50 20
152. 40 ore blue .. .. .. 18·00 15
153. 50 ore red .. .. .. 14·00 20
154. 60 ore blue .. .. .. 18·00 20

See also Nos. 279, etc., 529 etc. and 1100/3.

1905. Surch.

122 5. 1 k. on 2 s. brown .. 26·00 26·00
123. 1 k. 50 on 2 s. brown .. 48·00 48·00
124. 2 k. on 2 s. brown .. 40·00 40·00

1906. Surch.

162. 12. 5 ore on 25 ore mauve .. 30 30
125. 6. 15 ore on 4 s. mauve .. 2·50 2·50
126. 30 ore on 7 s. brown .. 5·75 5·75

15. King Haakon VII. 16.

1907.

127. 15. 1 k. green .. .. 30·00 28·00
128. 1½ k. blue .. .. 70·00 £150
129. 2 k. red .. .. .. £100 95·00

1910.

155a. 16. 1 k. green 55 5
156. 1½ k. blue .. .. 1·25 25
157. 2 k. red .. .. 2·00 25
158. 5 k. violet .. .. 3·50 3·50

17. Constitutional Assembly (after O. Wergeland). 19.

1914. Cent. of Independence.

159. 17. 5 ore green 50 35
160. 10 ore red .. .. 1·40 15
161. 20 ore blue .. .. 7·00 4·75

1922.

163. 19. 10 ore green .. .. 7·00 10
164. 20 ore purple .. .. 10·50 5
165. 25 ore red .. .. 21·00 70
166. 45 ore blue .. .. 1·00 50

20. 21. 22.

1925. Air. Amundsen's Polar Flight.

167. 20. 2 ore brown .. .. 1·50 1·75
168. 3 ore orange .. .. 2·50 2·75
169. 5 ore mauve .. .. 4·50 5·50
170. 10 ore green .. .. 6·00 6·00
171. 15 ore blue .. .. 5·50 6·50
172. 20 ore mauve .. .. 9·00 10·00
173. 25 ore red .. .. 1·50 1·75

1925. Annexation of Spitzbergen.

183. 21. 10 ore green .. .. 4·25 4·25
184. 15 ore blue .. .. 3·75 3·75
185. 20 ore purple .. .. 5·00 85
186. 45 ore blue .. .. 4·00 4·25

1926. Size 16 × 19½ mm.

187. 22. 10 ore green 45 5
187a. 14 ore orange .. .. 1·75 1·75
188. 15 ore brown 55 5
189. 20 ore purple .. .. 18·00 5
189a. 20 ore red 55 5
190. 25 ore red .. .. 7·00 1·90
190a. 25 ore brown 85 10
190b. 30 ore blue .. .. 1·00 5
191. 35 ore brown .. .. 60·00 10
191a. 35 ore violet .. .. 1·50 10
192. 40 ore blue .. .. 3·50 85
193. 40 ore grey .. .. 1·90 5
194. 50 ore red .. .. 3·50 10
195. 60 ore blue .. .. 3·50 10

For stamps as Type **22** but size 17 × 21 mm., see Nos. 284, etc.

1927. Surcharged with new value and bar.

196. 22. 20 ore on 25 ore red .. 1·10 1·25
197. 19. 30 ore on 45 ore blue .. 8·00 1·25
198. 21. 30 ore on 45 ore blue .. 2·50 2·50

24. Akershus Castle. 25. Ibsen. 28. Abel.

1927. Air.

199a 24 45 ore blue (with frame-lines) .. .. 2·25 1·25
323 45 ore blue (without frame-lines) .. 40 15

1928. Ibsen Centenary.

200. 25. 10 ore green .. .. 4·50 1·75
201. 15 ore brown .. .. 2·40 2·40
202. 20 ore red .. .. 2·00 35
203. 30 ore blue .. .. 3·50 3·50

1929. Postage Due stamps optd. **Post Frimerke** or **POST** and thick bar.

204. D 12. 1 ore brown 20 25
205. 4 ore mve. (No. D96a) 20 20
206. 10 ore green .. .. 1·75 1·75
207. 15 ore brown .. .. 2·10 2·25
208. 20 ore purple 80 35
209. 40 ore blue .. .. 1·25 70
210. 50 ore purple .. .. 7·00 7·00
211. 100 ore yellow .. .. 2·50 1·50
212. 200 ore violet .. .. 4·50 3·00

1929. Death Cent. of N. H. Abel (mathematician).

213. 28. 10 ore green .. .. 1·25 85
214. 15 ore brown .. .. 1·50 1·50
215. 20 ore red 70 20
216. 30 ore blue .. .. 2·10 2·10

1929. Surch. **14 ORE 14.**

217. 4. 14 ore on 2 s. brown .. 2·10 2·10

30. St. Olaf (sculpture, Brunlanes Church). 31. Nidaros Trondhjem Cathedral.

32. Death of St. Olaf (after P. N. Arbo).

1930. 9th Death Cent. of St. Olaf.

219. 30. 10 ore green .. .. 7·50 20
220. 31. 15 ore sepia and brown 80 30
221. 30. 20 ore red 90 40
222. 32. 30 ore blue .. .. 2·50 3·00

33. North Cape and "Bergensfjord" (liner)

1930. Norwegian Tourist Assn. Fund. Size 35½ × 21½ mm.

223. 33. 15 ore + 25 ore brown .. 2·00 2·00
224. 20 ore + 25 ore red .. 18·00 22·00
225. 30 ore + 25 ore blue .. 70·00 75·00

For smaller stamps in this design see Nos. 349/51, 442/66 and 464/6.

34. Radium Hospital.

1931. Radium Hospital Fund.

226. 34. 20 ore + 10 ore red .. 5·25 3·75

35. Bjornson. 36. L. Holberg.

1932. Birth Cent. of Bjornstjerne Bjornson (writer).

227. 35. 10 ore green .. .. 6·00 20
228. 15 ore brown .. .. 1·25 1·25
229. 20 ore red 65 35
230. 30 ore blue .. .. 2·10 2·10

1934. 250th Birth Anniv. of Holberg (writer).

231. 36. 10 ore green .. .. 1·10 20
232. 15 ore brown 50 50
233. 20 ore red .. .. 8·75 15
234. 30 ore blue .. .. 2·25 2·25

37. Dr. Nansen. 38. No background shading. 38b. King Haakon VII.

1935. Nansen Refugee Fund.

235. 37. 10 ore + 10 ore green .. 2·10 2·10
236. 15 ore + 10 ore brown .. 7·75 7·75
237. 20 ore + 10 ore red .. 1·25 1·00
238. 30 ore + 10 ore blue .. 6·50 6·50

See also Nos. 275/8.

1937.

279. 38. 1 ore olive 10 10
280. 2 ore brown 10 10
281. 3 ore orange 12 10
282. 5 ore mauve 25 5
283. 7 ore green 30 5
413. 10 ore grey 30 5
285. 12 ore violet .. .. 70 1·10
414. 15 ore green .. .. 1·75 10
415. 15 ore brown 40 5
416. 20 ore brown .. .. 3·25 1·50
417. 20 ore green 40 5

1937. As T 22 but size 17 × 21 mm.

No.	Type	Description	Unused	Used
284.	22.	10 ore green	40	5
286.		14 ore orange	1·90	1·90
287.		15 ore olive	30	5
288a.		20 ore red	20	5
289.		25 ore brown	1·40	10
289a.		25 ore red	55	5
290.		30 ore blue	1·50	15
290a.		30 ore grey	8·75	20
291.		35 ore violet	1·50	10
292.		40 ore slate	1·50	5
292a.		40 ore blue	4·00	10
293.		50 ore red	1·40	5
293a.		55 ore orange	26·00	10
294.		60 ore blue	1·25	5
294a.		80 ore brown	22·00	10

1937.

No.	Type	Description	Unused	Used
255.	38b.	1 k. green	12	20
256.		1 k. 50 blue	70	2·10
257.		2 k. red	1·10	6·00
258.		5 k. purple	6·25	42·00

39. Reindeer. **41.** Joelster in Sunnfjord.

1938. Tourist Propaganda.

No.	Type	Description	Unused	Used
262.	39.	15 ore brown	50	30
263.	–	20 ore red	20	5
264.	41.	30 ore blue	25	10

DESIGN—VERT. 20 ore, Stave Church, Borgund.

1938. Norwegian Tourist Association Fund. As T 33, but reduced to 27 × 21 mm.

No.	Type	Description	Unused	Used
349.	33.	15 ore+25 ore brown	70	1·25
350.		20 ore+25 ore red	1·40	2·25
351.		30 ore+25 ore blue	1·50	2·25

42. Queen Maud. **43.** Lion Rampant. **44.** Dr. Nansen.

1939. Queen Maud Children's Fund.

No.	Type	Description	Unused	Used
267.	42.	10 ore+5 ore green	70	6·50
268.		15 ore+5 ore brown	70	6·50
269.		20 ore+5 ore red	70	5·50
270.		30 ore+5 ore blue	70	7·25

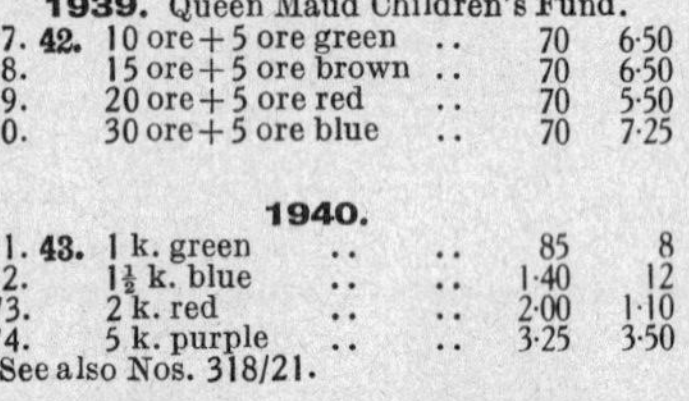

1940.

No.	Type	Description	Unused	Used
271.	43.	1 k. green	85	8
272.		1½ k. blue	1·40	12
273.		2 k. red	2·00	1·10
274.		5 k. purple	3·25	3·50

See also Nos. 318/21.

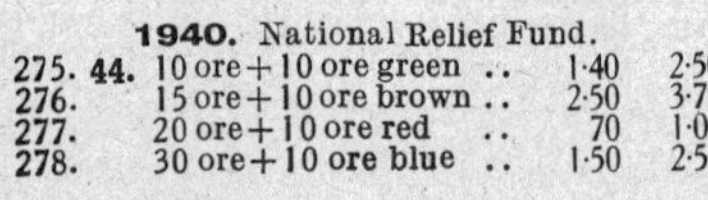

1940. National Relief Fund.

No.	Type	Description	Unused	Used
275.	44.	10 ore+10 ore green	1·40	2·50
276.		15 ore+10 ore brown	2·50	3·75
277.		20 ore+10 ore red	70	1·00
278.		30 ore+10 ore blue	1·50	2·50

46. Femboring (fishing boat) and Iceberg.

47. Colin Archer and "Colin Archer" (lifeboat).

1941. Haalogaland Exhibition and Fishermen's Families Relief Fund.

No.	Type	Description	Unused	Used
295.	46.	15 ore+10 ore blue	90	3·00

1941. 50th Anniv. of National Lifeboat Institution.

No.	Type	Description	Unused	Used
296.	47.	10 ore+10 ore green	1·00	1·40
297.		15 ore+10 ore brown	1·25	1·60
298.	–	20 ore+10 ore red	60	60
299.	–	30 ore+10 ore blue	2·75	3·50

DESIGN—VERT. 20 ore, 30 ore, "Osloskoyta" (lifeboat)

48. Soldier and Flags.

51. Oslo University.

1941. Norwegian Legion Support Fund.

No.	Type	Description	Unused	Used
300.	48.	20 ore+80 ore red	45·00	55·00

1941. Stamps of 1937 optd. V (= Victory).

No.	Type	Description	Unused	Used
301.	38.	1 ore green	12	1·75
302.		2 ore brown	12	2·25
303.		3 ore orange	12	1·75
304.		5 ore mauve	12	55
305.		7 ore green	40	2·50
306.	22.	10 ore green	15	15
307.	38.	12 ore violet	90	9·75
308.	22.	14 ore orange	1·10	8·75
309.		15 ore green	45	1·60
310.		20 ore red	15	10
311.		25 ore brown	15	30
312.		30 ore blue	65	1·10
313.		35 ore violet	70	90
314.		40 ore grey	65	90
315.		50 ore red	90	1·90
316.		60 ore blue	90	1·60
317.	43.	1 k. green	90	55
318.		1½ k. blue	3·50	10·50
319.		2 k. red	8·75	35·00
320.		5 k. purple	18·00	75·00

1941. As No. 413, but with "V" incorporated in the design.

No.	Type	Description	Unused	Used
321.		10 ore green	90	8·00

1941. Centenary of Foundation Oslo University Building.

No.	Type	Description	Unused	Used
322.	51.	1 k. green	27·00	38·00

52. Queen Ragnhild's Dream.

53. Stiklestad Battlefield.

1941. 700th Death Anniv. of Snorre Sturlason (historian).

No.	Type	Description	Unused	Used
324.	52.	10 ore green	15	10
325.	–	15 ore brown	40	50
326.	–	20 ore red	15	5
327.	–	30 ore blue	90	1·60
328.	–	50 ore violet	90	1·60
329.	53.	60 ore blue	1·10	1·75

DESIGNS—HORIZ. 15 ore Einar Tambarskjelve at Battle of Svolder. 30 ore King Olav sails to his wedding. 50 ore Svipdag's sons and their soldiers. VERT. 20 ore Snorre Sturlason.

55. Vidkun Quisling.

56. Rikard Nordraak.

57. Embarkation of the Viking Fleet.

DESIGN—As Type 57: 30 ore Mountains across sea and two lines of the National Anthem.

1942.

(a) Without opt.

No.	Type	Description	Unused	Used
330.	55.	20 ore+30 ore red	3·50	13·00

(b) Optd. 1-2 1942.

No.	Type	Description	Unused	Used
331.	55.	20 ore+30 ore red	3·50	13·00

1942. Birth Centenary of Rikard Nordraak (composer).

No.	Type	Description	Unused	Used
332.	56.	10 ore green	1·25	1·60
333.	57.	15 ore brown	1·25	1·60
334.	56.	20 ore red	1·25	1·60
335.	–	30 ore blue	1·25	1·60

1942. War Orphans' Relief Fund. As T 55 but inscr. "RIKSTINGET 1942".

No.	Type	Description	Unused	Used
336.		20 ore+30 ore red	20	3·25

58. J. H. Wessel.

59. Reproduction of Types 55 and 1.

1942. Birth Bicent. of Wessel (poet).

No.	Type	Description	Unused	Used
337.	58.	15 ore brown	10	15
338.		20 ore red	10	15

1942. Inaug. of European Postal Union, Vienna.

No.	Type	Description	Unused	Used
339.	59.	20 ore red	15	50
340.		30 ore blue	20	1·40

60. Destroyer "Sleipner".

61. Edvard Grieg.

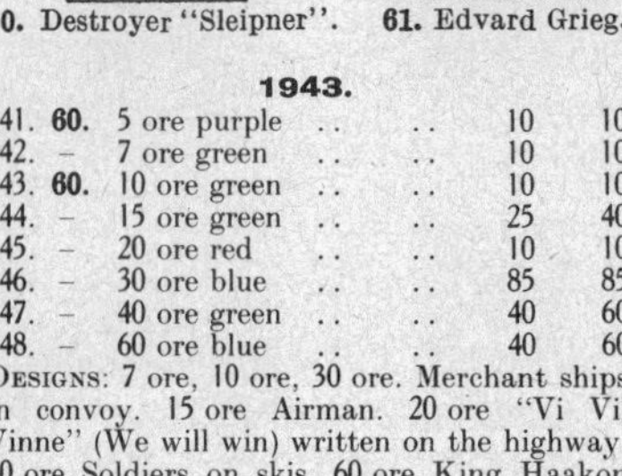

1943.

No.	Type	Description	Unused	Used
341.	60.	5 ore purple	10	10
342.	–	7 ore green	10	10
343.	60.	10 ore green	10	10
344.	–	15 ore green	25	40
345.	–	20 ore red	10	10
346.	–	30 ore blue	85	85
347.	–	40 ore green	40	60
348.	–	60 ore blue	40	60

DESIGNS: 7 ore, 10 ore, 30 ore. Merchant ships in convoy. 15 ore Airman. 20 ore "Vi Vil Vinne" (We will win) written on the highway. 40 ore Soldiers on skis. 60 ore King Haakon VII.

For use on correspondence posted at sea on Norwegian merchant ships and (in certain circumstances) from Norwegian camps in Gt. Britain during the German Occupation of Norway. After liberation all values were put on sale in Norway.

1943. Birth Cent. of Grieg (composer).

No.	Type	Description	Unused	Used
352.	61.	10 ore green	30	20
353.		20 ore red	30	20
354.		40 ore green	30	20
355.		60 ore blue	30	20

62. Soldier's Emblem.

63. Fishing Station.

1943. Soldiers' Relief Fund.

No.	Type	Description	Unused	Used
356.	62.	20 ore+30 ore red	30	3·25

1943. Winter Relief Fund.

No.	Type	Description	Unused	Used
357.	63.	10 ore+10 ore green	70	4·25
358.	–	20 ore+10 ore red	70	4·25
359.	–	40 ore+10 ore grey	70	4·25

DESIGNS: 20 ore Mountain scenery. 40 ore Winter landscape.

64. Sinking of "Baroy" (freighter).

65. First North Sea Flight.

1944. Shipwrecked Mariners' Relief Fund.

No.	Type	Description	Unused	Used
360.	64.	10 ore+10 ore green	70	4·25
361.	–	15 ore+10 ore brown	70	4·25
362.	–	20 ore+10 ore red	70	4·25

DESIGNS—HORIZ. 15 ore. Sinking of "Sanct Svithun" (cargo liner). VERT. 20 ore Sinking of "Irma" (freighter).

1944. 30th Anniv. of Tryggve Grans North Sea Flight.

No.	Type	Description	Unused	Used
363.	65.	40 ore blue	30	2·00

66. Girl Spinning. **67.** Arms. **68.** Henrik Wergeland.

1944. Winter Relief Fund. Inscr. as in T 66.

No.	Type	Description	Unused	Used
364.	66.	5 ore+10 ore mauve	55	3·50
365.	–	10 ore+10 ore green	55	3·50
366.	–	15 ore+10 ore purple	55	3·50
367.	–	20 ore+10 ore red	55	3·50

DESIGNS: 10 ore Ploughing. 15 ore Tree felling. 20 ore Mother and children.

1945.

No.	Type	Description	Unused	Used
368.	67.	1½ k. blue	1·40	40

1945. Death Cent. of Wergeland (poet).

No.	Type	Description	Unused	Used
369.	68.	10 ore green	30	20
370.		15 ore brown	1·00	1·00
371.		20 ore red	30	10

69. Red Cross Sister.

70. Folklore Museum Emblem.

1945. Red Cross Relief Fund and Norwegian Red Cross Jubilee.

No.	Type	Description	Unused	Used
372.	69.	20 ore+10 ore red	50	50

1945. 50th Anniv. of National Folklore Museum.

No.	Type	Description	Unused	Used
373.	70.	10 ore olive	60	20
374.		20 ore red	60	20

71. Crown Prince Olav.

72. "R.N.A.F.".

1946. National Relief Fund.

No.	Type	Description	Unused	Used
375.	71.	10 ore+10 ore green	30	30
376.		15 ore+10 ore brown	30	30
377.		20 ore+10 ore red	30	30
378.		30 ore+10 ore blue	1·40	1·25

1946. Honouring Norwegian Air Force Trained in Canada.

No.	Type	Description	Unused	Used
379.	72.	15 ore red	70	70

73. King Haakon VII.

74. Nansen Amundsen and "Fram".

1946.

No.	Type	Description	Unused	Used
380.	73.	1 k. green	1·60	5
381.		1½ k. blue	4·25	10
382.		2 k. brown	26·00	5
383.		5 k. violet	17·00	30

1947. Tercent. of Norwegian Post Office.

No.	Type	Description	Unused	Used
384.	–	5 ore mauve	30	10
385.	–	10 ore green	35	10
386.	–	15 ore brown	55	10
387.	–	25 ore red	30	10
388.	–	30 ore grey	1·10	30
389.	–	40 ore blue	1·60	15
390.	–	45 ore violet	2·50	50
391.	–	50 ore brown	2·50	15
392.	74.	55 ore orange	4·50	20
393.	–	60 ore grey	2·00	80
394.	–	80 ore brown	2·00	30

DESIGNS: 5 ore Hannibal Sehested (founder of postal service) and Akershus Castle. 10 ore "Postal-peasant". 15 ore Admiral Tordenskiold and 18th-century warship. 25 ore Christian M. Falsen. 30 ore Cleng Peerson and "Restaurationen" (emigrant sloop). 40 ore "Constitutionen" (paddle-steamer). 45 ore First Norwegian steam locomotive "Caroline". 50 ore Svend Foyn and "Spes et Fides" (whale catcher). 60 ore Coronation of King Haakon and Queen Maud in Nidaros Cathedral. 80 ore King Haakon and Oslo Town Hall.

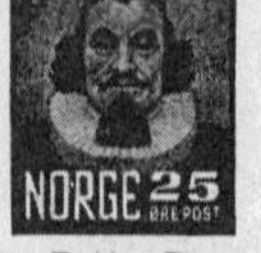

75. Petter Dass.

76. King Haakon VII.

1947. Birth Tercent. of Petter Dass (poet).

No.	Type	Description	Unused	Used
395.	75.	25 ore red	60	60

1947. 75th Birthday of King Haakon VII.

No.	Type	Description	Unused	Used
396.	76.	25 ore orange	60	60

MINIMUM PRICE

The minimum price quoted is 5p which represents a handling charge rather than a basis for valuing common stamps. For further notes about prices see introductory pages.

77. Axel Heiberg.

80. A. L. Kielland.

1948. 50th Anniv of Norwegian Forestry Society and Birth Centenary of Axel Heiberg (founder).

397. **77.** 25 ore red 85 30
398. 80 ore brown .. .. 1·75 20

1948. Red Cross. Surch. **25+5** and bars.

399. **69.** 25+5 ore on 20+10 ore red 60 60

1949. Stamps of 1937 surch.

400. **22.** 25 ore on 20 ore red .. 40 10
401. 45 ore on 40 ore blue .. 2·00 35

1949. Birth Centenary of Alexander L. Kielland (author).

402. **80.** 25 ore red .. .. 1·25 20
403. 40 ore blue .. .. 1·25 70
404. 80 ore brown .. .. 1·75 50

81. Symbolising Universe.

82. Pigeons and Globe.

1949. 75th Anniv. of U.P.U.

405. **81.** 10 ore green and purple 50 40
406. **82.** 25 ore red 60 15
407. – 40 ore blue 30 30

DESIGN—HORIZ. 40 ore Dove, globe and signpost.

84. King Harald Haardraade and Oslo Town Hall.

85. Child with Flowers.

1950. 900th Anniv. of Founding of Oslo.

408. **84.** 15 ore green 70 50
409. 25 ore red 70 15
410. 45 ore blue 60 60

1950. Infantile Paralysis Fund.

411. **85.** 25 ore+5 ore red .. 1·00 1·00
412. 45 ore+5 ore blue .. 4·25 4·25

87. King Haakon VII.

88. Arne Garborg (after O. Rusti).

1950.

418. **87.** 25 ore red 45 5
419. 25 ore grey .. .. 13·00 5
419a. 25 ore green 85 5
420. 30 ore grey .. .. 7·00 70
421. 30 ore red 50 5
422. 35 ore red .. .. 13·00 5
422a. 35 ore red .. .. 4·00 5
422b. 40 ore purple .. .. 1·50 10
423. 45 ore blue .. .. 1·90 1·50
424. 50 ore brown .. .. 1·75 5
425. 55 ore orange .. .. 1·75 1·10
426. 55 ore blue .. .. 1·00 60
427. 60 ore blue .. .. 10·50 5
427a. 65 ore blue .. .. 1·10 15
427b. 70 ore brown .. .. 10·50 10
428. 75 ore brown .. .. 1·90 5
429. 80 ore brown .. .. 2·10 10
430. 90 ore orange .. .. 1·10 10

1951. Birth Cent. Garborg (author).

431. **88.** 25 ore red 40 20
432. 45 ore blue .. .. 2·10 2·10
433. 80 ore brown .. .. 2·10 1·75

"NOREG" on the stamps was the spelling advocated by Arne Garborg.

89. Ice Skater.

92. King Haakon VII.

1951. 6th Winter Olympic Games. Inscr. "OSLO 1952".

434. **89.** 15 ore+5 ore green .. 1·40 1·40
435. – 30 ore+10 ore red .. 1·40 1·40
436. – 55 ore+20 ore blue .. 7·00 7·00

DESIGNS: 30 ore Ski-jumping. LONGER: 55 ore Winter landscape.

1951. Surch. in figures.

440. **38.** 20 ore on 15 ore green 40 15
437. **87.** 30 ore on 25 ore red .. 40 10

1952. 80th Birthday of King Haakon.

438. **92.** 30 ore red and pale red 20 15
439. 55 ore blue and grey .. 60 70

94. "Supplication".

95. Medieval Sculpture.

1953. Anti-Cancer Fund.

441. **94.** 30 ore+10 ore red and cream .. .. 1·50 1·50

1953. Norwegian Tourist Association Fund. As T **33** but smaller (27½ × 21 mm.).

442. **33.** 20 ore+10 ore green .. 8·75 8·75
464. 25 ore+10 ore green .. 4·25 4·25
443. 30 ore+15 ore red .. 8·75 8·75
465. 35 ore+15 ore red .. 5·25 5·25
444. 55 ore+25 ore blue .. 13·00 13·00
466. 65 ore+25 ore blue .. 3·50 3·50

1953. 8th Cent. of Archbishopric of Nidaros.

445. **95.** 30 ore red 30 20

96. 1st Railway Steam Locomotive "Caroline" and Horse-drawn Sledge.

97. C. T. Nielsen (first Director).

1954. Centenary of Norwegian Railways.

446. **96.** 20 ore green 80 30
447. – 30 ore red 80 15
448. – 55 ore blue .. .. 1·00 1·00

DESIGNS: 30 ore Diesel express train. 55 ore Engine driver.

1954. Cent. of Telegraph Service.

449. **97.** 20 ore black and green .. 30 20
450. – 30 ore red 30 10
451. – 55 ore blue .. .. 1·00 1·00

DESIGNS: 30 ore Radio masts at Tryvannshogda. 55 ore Telegraph linesman on skis.

98. "Posthorn" Type Stamp.

100. King Haakon and Queen Maud.

1955. Norwegian Stamp Cent.

452. – 20 ore blue and green 15 15
453. **98.** 30 ore deep red and red 15 10
454. – 55 ore blue & grey .. 70 70

DESIGNS: 20 ore Norway's first stamp. 55 ore "Lion" type stamp.

1955. Stamp Cent. and Int. Stamp Exn., Oslo. Nos. 452/4 with circular optd. **OSLO NORWEX.**

455. – 20 ore blue and green .. 9·50 9·50
456. **98.** 30 ore red & deep red .. 9·50 9·50
457. – 55 ore blue and grey .. 9·50 9·50

Nos. 455/7 were only on sale at the Exhibition P.O. at face+1 k. entrance fee.

1955. Golden Jubilee of King Haakon.

458. **100.** 30 ore red 30 10
459. 55 ore blue 40 40

101. Crown Princess Martha.

101a. Whooper Swans.

1956. Crown Princess Martha Memorial Fund.

460. **101.** 35 ore+10 ore red .. 1·00 1·00
461. 65 ore+10 ore blue .. 2·50 2·50

1956. Northern Countries' Day.

462. **101a.** 35 ore red .. .. 1·10 60
463. 65 ore blue .. .. 1·10 85

102. Jan Mayen Island (after aquarell, H. Mohn).

103. Map of Spitzbergen.

1957. Int. Geophysical Year. Inscr. "INTERN. GEOFYSISK AR 1957–1958".

467. **102.** 25 ore green 40 25
468. **103.** 35 ore red and grey .. 40 10
469. – 65 ore green and blue .. 50 40

DESIGN: 65 ore Map of Antarctica showing Queen Maud Land.

104. King Haakon VII.

105. King Olav V.

106.

1957. 85th Birthday of King Haakon.

470. **104.** 35 ore red 15 10
471. 65 ore blue 70 50

1958.

472. **105.** 25 ore light green .. 80 5
472a. 25 ore green .. .. 1·00 5
473. 30 ore violet .. .. 1·50 10
474. 35 ore red 70 5
474a. 35 ore green .. .. 3·00 5
475. 40 ore red .. .. 1·00 5
475a. 40 ore grey .. .. 2·50 85
476. 45 ore red .. .. 1·10 5
477. 50 ore brown .. .. 5·50 5
478. 50 ore red .. .. 6·00 5
479. 55 ore grey .. .. 2·00 30
480. 60 ore violet .. .. 3·75 40
481. 65 ore blue .. .. 2·00 35
482. 80 ore brown .. .. 8·75 50
483. 85 ore brown .. .. 1·75 15
484. 90 ore orange .. .. 1·00 10
485. **106.** 1 k. green 50 5
486. 1 k. 50 blue .. .. 2·00 5
487. 2 k. red .. .. 1·50 5
488. 5 k. purple .. .. 35·00 10
489. 10 k. orange .. .. 2·75 10

107. Asbjorn Kloster (founder).

108. Society's Centenary Medal.

1959. Cent. of Norwegian Temperance Movement.

490. **107.** 45 ore brown 25 15

1959. 150th Anniv. of Royal Norwegian Agricultural Society.

491. **108.** 45 ore brown and red 25 25
492. 90 ore grey and blue 1·75 1·75

109. Sower.

110. White Anemone.

1959. Centenary of Norwegian Royal College of Agriculture.

493. **109.** 45 ore black and ochre .. 70 50
494. – 90 ore black and blue .. 1·00 1·00

DESIGN—VERT. 90 ore Ears of Corn.

1960. Tuberculosis Relief Funds.

495. **110.** 45 ore+10 ore yellow, green and red .. 1·50 1·50
496. – 90 ore+10 ore orange, green and blue .. 4·25 4·25

DESIGN: 90 ore Blue anemone.

111. Society's Original Seal.

112. Refugee Mother and Child.

1960. Bicentenary of Royal Norwegian Society of Scientists.

497. **111.** 45 ore red on grey .. 70 40
498. 90 ore blue on grey .. 1·40 1·40

1960. World Refugee Year.

499. **112.** 45 ore+25 ore black and red .. .. 3·75 3·75
500. 90 ore + 25 ore black and blue .. .. 7·00 7·00

113. Viking Longship.

1960. Norwegian Ships.

501. **113.** 20 ore black and grey 80 60
502. – 25 ore black and green 80 60
503. – 45 ore black and red 80 10
504. – 55 ore black & brown 2·10 2·00
505. – 90 ore black and blue 1·25 1·00

SHIPS: 25 ore Hanse kogge. 45 ore "Skomvaer" (barque). 55 ore "Dalfon" (tanker). 90 ore "Bergensfjord" (liner).

113a. Conference Emblem.

113b. Douglas "DC8".

1960. Europa.

506. **113a.** 90 ore blue 60 60

1961. 10th Anniv. of Scandinavian airlines System (SAS).

507. **113b.** 90 ore blue 30 30

114. Throwing the Javelin.

115. Haakonshallen Barracks and Rosencrantz Tower.

1961. Norwegian Sport Centenary.

508. **114.** 20 ore brown 60 60
509. – 25 ore green 60 60
510. – 45 ore red 60 35
511. – 90 ore purple 70 80

DESIGNS: 25 ore Ice skating. 45 ore Ski jumping. 90 ore Sailing.

1961. 700th Anniv. of Haakonshallen.

512. **115.** 45 ore black and red 30 10
513. 1 k. black and green 40 20

116. Oslo University.

117. Nansen.

1961. 150th Anniv. of Oslo University.

514. **116.** 45 ore red 25 10
515. 1 k. 50 blue 45 20

1961. Birth Cent. of Nansen (polar explorer).

516. **117.** 45 ore black and red .. 25 15
517. 90 ore black and blue .. 50 45

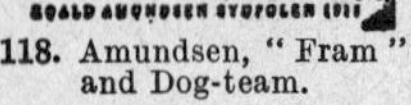

118. Amundsen, "Fram" and Dog-team.
119. Frederic Passy and Henri Dunant (Winners in 1901).

1961. 50th Anniv. of Amundsen's Arrival at South Pole.

518. **118.** 45 ore red and grey .. 50 15
519. – 90 ore deep blue & blue 90 75

DESIGN: 90 ore Amundsen's party and tent at South Pole.

1961. Nobel Peace Prize.

520. **119.** 45 ore red 30 10
521. 1 k. green 55 20

120. Prof. V. Bjerknes.
121. Rumpler Taube 'plane, "Start".

1962. Birth Centenary of Prof. Vilhelm Bjerknes (mathematician).

522. **120.** 45 ore black and red .. 25 10
523. 1 k. 50 black and blue 45 20

1962. 50th Anniv. of Norwegian Aviation.

524. **121.** 1 k. 50 brown and blue 70 40

122. Branch of Fir, and Cone.
123. Europa "Tree".

1962. Cent. of State Forestry Administration.

525. **122.** 45 ore grey, blk. & red 50 60
526. 1 k. grey, blk. & grn. 4·75 45

1962. Europa.

527. **123.** 50 ore red 30 10
528. 90 ore blue 90 90

125. Reef. Knot.
126. Camilla Collett.
127. Boatload of Wheat.

1962.

529. **12.** 5 ore red 5 5
529a. 10 ore slate 5 5
530. 15 ore orange 5 5
530a. 20 ore green 8 5
531. 25 ore blue 10 5
531ag. – 25 ore green 90 5
532. – 30 ore drab .. .. 2·25 2·25
532a. – 30 ore green 30 5
533. **125.** 35 ore green 40 5
533a. – 40 ore red .. .. 2·25 5
531aa. **12.** 40 ore green 10 5
534. – 40 ore green 30 5
534a. – 45 ore green 50 40
535. **125.** 50 ore red .. .. 3·50 5
535a. – 50 ore grey 30 5
531ab. **12.** 50 ore purple 10 5
536. – 55 ore brown 30 15
536a. **125.** 60 ore green .. .. 2·75 12
537. 60 ore red 50 5
531ac. **12.** 60 ore orange 10 5
537a. – 65 ore violet 55 5
538. **125.** 65 ore red 30 5
538a. – 70 ore brown 30 5
531ad. **12.** 70 ore yellow 20 10
539. – 75 ore green 30 5
539a. – 80 ore red .. .. 2·00 2·00
539b. – 80 ore brown 35 5
531ae. **12.** 80 ore brown 20 5
540. – 85 ore sepia 45 15
540a. – 85 ore buff 30 5
540b. – 90 ore blue 35 5
531af. **12.** 90 ore brown 20 10
541. – 100 ore violet 35 5
541a. – 100 ore red 50 5
542. – 110 ore red 35 5
542a. – 115 ore brown .. 70 20
543. – 120 ore blue 40 15
543a. – 125 ore red 30 5
544. – 140 ore blue 50 20
544a. – 750 ore brown .. 80 15

DESIGNS: 25, 40, 90, 100(2), 110, 120, 125 ore, Runic drawings. 30, 45, 55, 75, 85 ore, Ear of wheat and fish. 65, 80, 140 ore, "Stave" (wooden) church and Aurora Borealis. 115 ore, Fragment of Urnes stave-church. 750 ore, Sigurd the Dragon-killer testing sword.

For bicolour stamps as T **12** with face values in Kroners see Nos. 1100/3.

1963. 150th Birth Anniv. of Camilla Collett (author).

545. **126.** 50 ore red 20 10
546. 90 ore blue .. .. 1·00 1·00

1963. Freedom from Hunger.

547. **127.** 25 ore bistre 20 20
548. 35 ore green 70 70
549. – 50 ore red 40 40
550. – 90 ore blue .. .. 1·00 1·00

DESIGN—HORIZ. (37½ × 21 mm.): 50 ore, 90 ore, Birds carrying food on cloth.

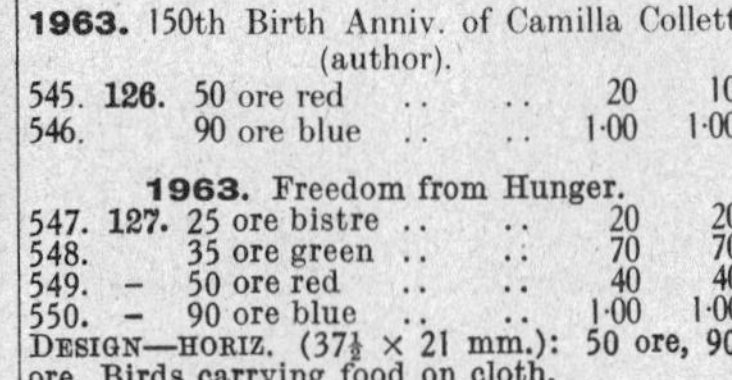

128. River Mail Boat.
129. Ivar Aasen.

1963. Tercentenary of Southern-Northern Norwegian Postal Services.

551. **128.** 50 ore red 65 50
552. – 90 ore blue .. .. 1·75 1·75

DESIGN: 90 ore, Northern femboring (sailing vessel).

1963. 150th Birth Anniv. of Ivar Aasen.

553. **129.** 50 ore red and grey .. 20 10
554. 90 ore blue and grey 85 80

The note after No. 433 re "NOREG" also applies here.

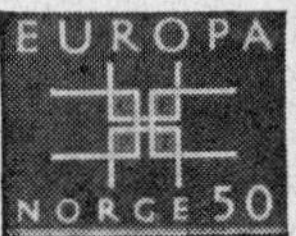

130. "Co-operation".
131. "Herringbone" Pattern.

1963. Europa.

555. **130.** 50 ore orange and red 30 10
556. 90 ore green and blue 1·50 1·50

1963. 150th Anniv. of Norwegian Textile Industry.

557. **131.** 25 ore green and bistre 30 30
558. 35 ore blue and turq... 85 85
559. 50 ore purple and red 60 50

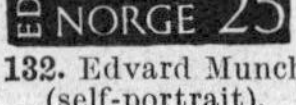

132. Edvard Munch (self-portrait).
133. Eilert Sundt (founder).

1963. Birth Centenary of Edvard Munch (painter and engraver).

560. **132.** 25 ore black 20 10
561. – 35 ore green 20 20
562. – 50 ore purple 20 10
563. – 90 ore blue & deep bl. 50 65

DESIGNS: (Woodcuts)—HORIZ. 35 ore "Fecundity". 50 ore, "The Solitaries". VERT. 90 ore. "The Girls on the Bridge".

1964. Centenary of Oslo Workers' Society.

564. **133.** 25 ore green 20 25
565. – 50 ore purple 20 10

DESIGN: 50 ore, Beehive emblem of O.W.S.

134. C. M. Guldberg and P. Waage (chemists).
135. Eidsvoll Manor.

1964. Centenary of Law of Mass Action.

566. **134.** 35 ore green 25 25
567. 55 ore ochre .. .. 1·25 1·25

1964. 150th Anniv. of Norwegian Constitution.

568. **135.** 50 ore grey and red .. 20 10
569. – 90 ore black and blue 60 60

DESIGN: 90 ore, Storting (Parliament House), Oslo.

On 1st June, 1964, a stamp depicting the U.N. refugee emblem and inscr. "PORTO BETALT . . . LYKKEBREVET 1964" was put on sale. It had a franking value of 50 ore but was sold for 2 k. 50, the balance being for the Refugee Fund. In addition, each stamp bore a serial number representing participation in a lottery which took place in September. The stamp was on sale until 15th July and had validity until 10th August.

136. Harbour Scene.
137. Europa "Flower".

1964. Cent. of Norwegian Seamen's Mission.

570. **136.** 25 ore green and yellow 30 25
571. 90 ore blue and cream 1·40 1·40

1964. Europa.

572. **137.** 90 ore lt. bl. & dp. bl. 1·75 1·75

138. H. Anker and O. Arvesen (founders).
139. "Radio-telephone".

1964. Cent. of Norwegian Folk High School.

573. **138.** 50 ore red 50 50
574. 90 ore blue .. .. 1·75 1·75

The note after No. 433 re "NOREG" also applies here.

1965. Cent. of I.T.U.

575. **139.** 60 ore purple 25 10
576. – 90 ore slate 75 75

DESIGN: 90 ore, "T.V. transmission".

DESIGN: 60 ore, Norwegian flags.

140. Dove of Peace and Broken Chain.

1965. 20th Anniv. of Liberation.

577. **140.** 30 ore + 10 ore brown, green and sepia .. 35 35
578. – 60 ore + 10 ore blue and red 35 25

141. Mountain Landscapes.
142. Europa "Sprig".

1965. Cent. of Norwegian Red Cross.

579. **141.** 60 ore brown and red 20 10
580. – 90 ore blue & red .. 2·10 2·10

DESIGN: 90 ore, Coastal view.

1965. Europa.

581. **142.** 60 ore red 25 10
582. 90 ore blue .. .. 1·10 1·10

143. St. Sunniva and Bergen Buildings.
144. Rondane Mountains (after H. Sohlberg).

1965. Bicentenary of Harmonien Philharmonic Society.

583. – 30 ore black and green 25 20
584. **143.** 90 ore black and blue 85 85

DESIGN—VERT. 30 ore, St. Sunniva.

1965. Rondane National Park.

585. **144.** 1 k. 50 blue .. .. 1·40 10

145. "Rodoy Skier" (rock carving).
146. "The Bible".

1966. World Skiing Championships, Oslo. Inscr. "VM OSLO 1966".

586. **145.** 40 ore brown 70 70
587. – 55 ore green .. .. 1·25 1·25
588. – 60 ore brown 25 10
589. – 90 ore blue .. .. 1·10 1·10

DESIGNS—HORIZ. 55 ore, Ski jumper. 60 ore, Cross-country skier. VERT. 90 ore, Holmenkollen ski jumping tower, Oslo.

1966. 150th Anniv. of Norwegian Bible Society.

590. **146.** 60 ore red 25 10
591. 90 ore blue 85 85

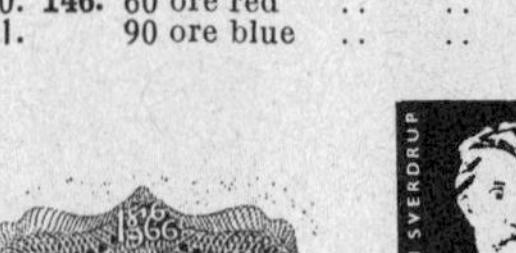

147. Guilloche Pattern.
148. J. Sverdrup (after C. Krohg).

1966. 150th Anniv. of Bank of Norway.

592. **147.** 30 ore green 20 20
593. – 60 ore red (Bank bldg.) 20 10

No. 593 is size 27½ × 21 mm.

1966. 150th Birth Anniv. of Johan Sverdrup (statesman).

594. **148.** 30 ore green 25 15
595. 60 ore purple 25 10

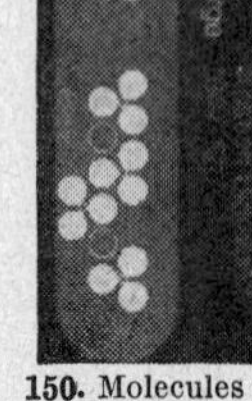

149. Europa "Ship".
150. Molecules in test-tube.

1966. Europa.

596. **149.** 60 ore red 20 10
597. 90 ore blue .. .. 1·00 85

1966. Birth Cents. of S. Eyde (industrialist) (1966) and K. Birkeland (scientist) (1967) founders of Norwegian Nitrogen Industry.

598. **150.** 40 ore indigo and blue 50 50
599. – 55 ore mauve and red 90 90

DESIGN: 55 ore, Ear of wheat and conical flask.

151. E.F.T.A. Emblem.
152. "Owl" and Three Swords.

1967. European Free Trade Assn.

600. **151.** 60 ore red 20 10
601. 90 ore blue .. .. 1·50 1·50

1967. 150th Anniv. of Higher Military Training.

602. **152.** 60 ore brown 40 20
603. 90 ore green .. .. 1·50 1·50

153. Cogwheels.
154. Johanne Dybwad.

1967. Europa.

604. **153.** 60 ore plum and green 25 10
605. 90 ore violet and blue 1·00 1·00

1967. Birth Cent. of J. Dybwad (actress).

606. **154.** 40 ore blue 20 20
607. 60 ore red 20 10

155. L. Skrefsrud (missionary and founder).
156. Climbers on Mountain-top.

1967. Cent. of Norwegian Santal Mission.

608. **155.** 60 ore brown 20 10
609. – 90 ore blue 50 50

DESIGN—HORIZ. 90 ore, Ebenezer Church, Benagaria, Santal, India.

1968. Centenary of Norwegian Mountain Touring Assn.

610. **156.** 40 ore brown 75 75
611. – 60 ore red 30 10
612. – 90 ore blue 70 80

DESIGNS: 60 ore Mountain cairn and scenery. 90 ore, Glitretind peak.

157. "The Blacksmiths".

158. A. O. Vinje.

1968. Norwegian Handicrafts.

613. **157.** 65 ore brn', blk. & red 25 10
614. 90 ore brn., blk. & blue 85 85

1968. 150th Birth Anniv. of Aasmund Vinje (poet).

615. **158.** 50 ore brown 20 20
616. 65 ore red 20 10

159. Cross and Heart.

160. Cathinka Guldberg (first deaconess).

1968. Centenary of Norwegian Lutheran Home Mission Society.

617. **159.** 40 ore red and green 2·25 1·40
618. 65 ore red and violet 50 25

1968. Cent. of Deaconess House, Oslo.

619. **160.** 50 ore blue 20 20
620. 65 ore red 20 10

161. K. P. Arnoldson and F. Bajer.

161a. Viking Ships (from old Swedish coin).

1968. Nobel Peace Prize Winners of 1908.

621. **161.** 65 ore brown 25 15
622. 90 ore blue 85 85

1969. 50th Anniv. of Northern Countries' Union.

623. **161a.** 65 ore red 15 10
624. 90 ore blue 85 85

162. Transport.

1969. Centenary of "Rutebok for Norge" ("Communications of Norway") and Road Safety Campaign.

625. **162.** 50 ore green 40 30
626. – 65 ore red and green .. 15 10

DESIGN: 65 ore Pedestrian-crossing.

163. Colonnade.

1969. Europa.

627. **163.** 65 ore black and red .. 25 10
628. 90 ore black and blue .. 85 85

164. J. Hjort and Fish Egg.

165. Traena Islands.

1969. Birth Centenary of Professor Johan Hjort (fisheries pioneer).

629. **164.** 40 ore brown and blue 40 60
630. – 90 ore blue and green 1·00 1·00

DESIGN: 90 ore J. Hjort and polyp.

1969.

631. **165.** 3 k. 50 black 85 5

166. King Olav V.

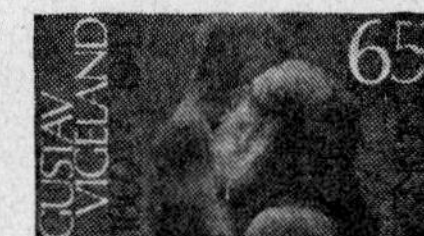
167. "Mother and Child".

1969.

632. **166.** 1 k. green 35 5
633. 1 k. 50 blue 40 5
634. 2 k. red 40 5
635. 5 k. blue 55 5
636. 10 k. brown 90 5
637. 20 k. brown .. .. 1·75 10
637a. 50 k. green .. .. 3·50 25

1969. Birth Centenary of Gustav Vigeland (sculptor).

638. **167.** 65 ore black and red .. 30 10
639. – 90 ore black and blue 70 70

DESIGN: 90 ore "Family" (sculpture).

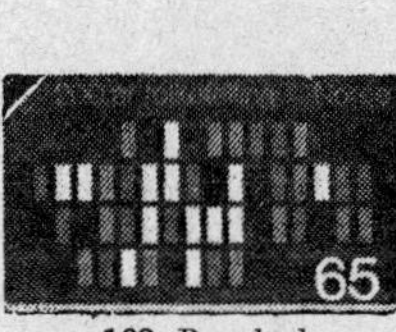
168. Punched Cards.

169. Queen Maud.

1969. Bicent. of 1st National Census. Mult.

640. 65 ore Type **168** 30 10
641. 90 ore "People" (diagram) 70 70

1969. Birth Cent. of Queen Maud.

642 **169** 65 ore purple 30 10
643 90 ore blue 70 70

170. Wolf.

171. "V" Symbol.

1970. Nature Conservation Year.

644. **170.** 40 ore brown and blue 80 70
645. – 60 ore grey and brown 1·10 1·10
646. – 70 ore brown and blue 1·00 60
647. – 100 ore brown and blue 2·25 1·00

DESIGNS—VERT. 60 ore Pale pasque flower. 70 ore Voringsfossen Falls. HORIZ. 100 ore. White-tailed sea eagle.

1970. 25th Anniv. of Liberation.

648. **171.** 70 ore red and violet .. 1·40 60
649. – 100 ore blue and green 1·40 1·25

DESIGN—HORIZ. 100 ore Merchant ships in convoy.

172. "Citizens".

173. Hands reaching for Globe.

1970. 900th Anniv. of Bergen.

650. **172.** 40 ore green .. .. 1·00 85
651. – 70 ore red .. .. 1·90 50
652. – 1 k blue .. .. 1·50 1·50

DESIGNS: 70 ore "City in the Mountains". 1 k. "Ships".

1970. 25th Anniv. of United Nations.

653. **173.** 70 ore red .. .. 1·90 60
654. 100 ore green .. 1·25 1·00

174. G.O. Sars.

175. Ball-game.

1970. Norwegian Zoologists.

655. **174.** 40 ore brown 85 85
656. – 50 ore violet 60 50
657. – 70 ore brown 70 50
658. – 100 ore blue 70 70

ZOOLOGISTS: 50 ore, Hans Strom. 70 ore, J. E Gunnerus. 100 ore, Michael Sars.

1970. Centenary of Central School of Gymnastics, Oslo.

659. **175.** 50 ore brown and blue 30 20
660. – 70 ore brown and red 50 10

DESIGN—HORIZ. 70 ore, "Leapfrog" exercise.

176. Tonsberg's Seal c. 1340.

1971. 1100th Anniv. of Tonsberg.

661. **176.** 70 ore red 30 10
662. 100 ore blue 50 70

177. Parliament House, Oslo.

1971. Centenary of Introduction of Annual Parliamentary Sessions.

663. **177.** 70 ore lilac and red .. 30 40
664. 100 ore green and blue 50 70

178. "Helping Hand".

1971. "Help for Refugees".

665. **178.** 50 ore green & black .. 30 20
666. 70 ore red & black .. 30 10

179. "Hauge addressing Followers" (A. Tidemand).

1971. Birth Centenary of Hans Nielson Hauge (church reformer).

667. **179.** 60 ore black 20 20
668. 70 ore brown 25 10

180. Bishop welcoming Worshippers.

1971. 900th Anniv. of Oslo Bishopric.

669. – 70 ore black and red .. 30 10
670. **180.** 1 k. black and blue .. 1·10 1·00

DESIGN—VERT. 70 ore, Masons building first church.

181. Roald Amundsen and Treaty Emblem.

182. "The Preacher and the King".

1971. 10th Anniv. of Antarctic Treaty.

671. **181.** 100 ore red and blue .. 2·10 1·90

1971. Norwegian Folk Tales. Drawings by Erik Werenskiold.

672. – 40 ore black & green .. 30 10
673. **182.** 50 ore black and blue 20 10
674. – 70 ore black and purple 50 10

DESIGNS—VERT. 40 ore, "The Farmer and the Woman". 70 ore, "The Troll and the Girl".

183. Anniversary Symbol.

184. 3s. "Posthorn" Stamp.

1972. 150th Anniv. of Norwegian Savings Banks.

675. **183.** 80 ore gold and red .. 30 10
676. 1 k. 20 gold and blue .. 40 30

1972. Centenary of Norwegian "Posthorn" Stamps.

677. **184.** 80 ore red and brown 30 10
678. 1 k. blue and violet .. 40 30

185. Alstad "Picture" Stone (detail).

186. King Haakon VII.

1972. 1,100th Anniv. of Norway's Unification.

680. **185.** 50 ore green 70 60
681. – 60 ore brown 85 85
682. – 80 ore red .. .. 1·00 50
683. – 1 k. 20 blue 85 70

DESIGNS: 60 ore, Portal, Hemsedal Church (detail). 80 ore, Figurehead of Oseberg Viking ship. 1 k. 20, Sword-hilt (Lodingen).

1972. Birth Cent. of King Haakon VII.

684. **186.** 80 ore red .. .. 1·25 40
685. 1 k. 20 blue 75 75

187. "Joy" (Ingrid Ekrem).

189. "Maud".

1972. "Youth and Leisure".

686. **187.** 80 ore mauve 60 35
687. – 1 k. 20 blue 75 75

DESIGN: 1 k. 20, "Solidarity" (Ole Instefjord).

1972. "Interjunex 1972" Stamp Exhib., Oslo. Nos. 686/7 optd. **INTERJUNEX 72.**

688. **187.** 80 ore mauve .. 2·00 2·10
689. – 1 k. 20 blue .. .. 2·00 2·10

1972. Norwegian Polar Ships.

690. **189.** 60 ore olive and green 70 60
691. – 80 ore red and black .. 1·00 10
692. – 1 k. 20 blue and red .. 85 80

DESIGNS: 80 ore, "Fram". 1 k. 20, "Gjoa".

190. "Little Man".

191. Dr. Hansen and Bacillus Diagram.

1972. Norwegian Folk Tales. Drawings of Trolls by Th. Kittelsen.

693. **190.** 50 ore black and green 30 10
694. – 60 ore black and blue 30 20
695. – 80 ore black and pink 30 10

TROLLS: 60 ore, "The troll who wonders how old he is". 80 ore, "Princess riding on a bear".

1973. Centenary of Hansen's Identification of Leprosy Bacillus.

696. **191.** 1 k. blue and red .. 40 10
697. – 1 k. 40 red and blue .. 70 70

DESIGN: 1 k. 40, As Type **191** but bacillus as seen in modern microscope.

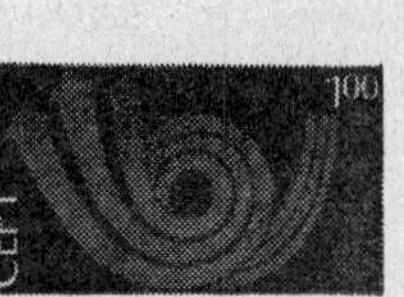
192. Europa "Posthorn".

193. King Olav V.

1973. Europa.

698. **192.** 1 k. orange, red and deep red .. .. 1·40 40
699. 1 k. 40 green, deep green and blue .. 75 70

1973. Nordic Countries Postal Co-operation. As T **214** of Sweden.

700. 1 k. multicoloured .. 85 40
701. 1 k. 40 multicoloured .. 70 70

1973. King Olav's 70th Birthday.

702. **193.** 1 k. brown and red .. 70 35
703. 1 k. 40 brown and blue 75 75

194. J. Aall.

195. Bone Carving.

1973. Birth Cent. of Jacob Aall (industrialist).

704. **194.** 1 k. purple 40 40
705. 1 k. 40 blue 75 75

1973. Lapp Handicrafts.
706. **195.** 75 ore brown & yellow .. 30 25
707. – 1 k. red and yellow .. 70 45
708. – 1 k. 40 black and blue .. 50 65
DESIGNS: 1 k. Detail of weaving. 1 k. 40, Detail of tin-ware.

196. Yellow Wood Violet.

197. Land Surveying.

1973. Mountain Flowers. Multicoloured.
709. 65 ore Type **196** 30 10
710. 70 ore Rock speedwell .. 40 30
711. 1 k. Mountain heath .. 40 10

1973. Bicentenary of Norwegian Geographical Survey.
712. **197.** 1 k. red 30 10
713. – 1 k. 40 blue 50 50
DESIGN: 1 k. 40, Old map of Hestbraepiggene (mountain range).

198. Lindesnes.

199. "Ferryboat, Hardanger Fjord" (A. Tidemand and H. Gude).

1974. Norwegian Capes.
714. **198.** 1 k. green 75 60
715. – 1 k. 40 blue .. .. 1·25 1·25
DESIGN: 1 k. 40, North Cape.

1974. Norwegian Paintings. Multicoloured.
716. 1 k. Type **199** 40 10
717. 1 k. 40 "Stugunoset from Filefjell" (J. Dahl) .. 50 50

200. Gulating Law Manuscript, 1325.

201. Trees and Saw Blade.

1974. 700th Anniv. of King Magnus Lagaboter's Legislation.
718. **200.** 1 k. red and brown .. 30 10
719. – 1 k. 40 blue and brown 35 35
DESIGN: 1 k. 40, King Magnus Lagaboter (sculpture in Stavanger Cathedral).

1974. Industrial Accident Prevention.
720. **201.** 85 ore light green to green and deep-green .. 1·25 1·25
721. – 1 k. light red, deep red and orange .. 1·00 50
DESIGN: 1 k. Flower and cogwheel.

202. J. H. L. Vogt.

203. Buildings of the World.

1974. Norwegian Geologists.
722. **202.** 65 ore brown & green 20 20
723. – 85 ore brown & purple 85 85
724. – 1 k. brown & orange 35 10
725. – 1 k. 40 brown & blue 50 50
Designs: 85 ore V. M. Goldschmidt. 1 k. Th. Kjerulf. 1 k. 40, W. C. Brogger.

1974. Cent. of Universal Postal Union.
726. **203.** 1 k. brown and green .. 30 10
727. – 1 k. 40 blue and brown 35 40
DESIGN: 1 k. 40, People of the World.

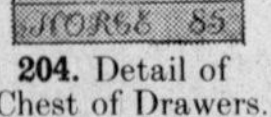
204. Detail of Chest of Drawers.

205. Woman Skier, 1900.

1974. Norwegian Folk Art. Rose Painting. Multicoloured.
728. 85 ore Type **204** 25 20
729. 1 k. Detail of cupboard .. 25 10

1975. Norwegian Skiing.
730. **205.** 1 k. red and green .. 50 15
731. – 1 k. 40 blue and brown 50 50
DESIGN: 1 k. 40, Skier making telemark turn.

206. "Three Women with Ivies" (wrought-iron gates, Vigeland Park).

207. Nusfjord Fishing Harbour, Lofoten Islands.

1975. International Women's Year.
732. **206.** 1 k. 25 violet & purple 50 10
733. 1 k. 40 blue and turq. 50 50

1975. European Architectural Heritage Year.
734. **207.** 1 k. green 50 20
735. – 1 k. 25 red 40 10
736. – 1 k. 40 blue 50 50
DESIGNS: 1 k. 25, Old Stavanger. 1 k. 40, Roros.

208. Norwegian 1-k. Coin, 1875.

1975. Centenary of Monetary and Metre Conventions.
737. **208.** 1 k. 25 red 30 10
738. – 1 k. 40 blue 50 50
DESIGN: 1 k. 40, O. J. Broch (original Director of the International Bureau of Weights and Measures).

209. Camping and Emblem.

1975. World Scout Jamboree, Lillehammer. Multicoloured.
739. 1 k. 25 Type **209** 70 40
740. 1 k. 40 Skiing and emblem 65 60

210. Colonist's Peat House.

1975. 150th Anniv. of First Emigrations to America.
741. **210.** 1 k. 25 brown.. .. 80 15
742. – 1 k. 40 blue 60 50
DESIGNS: 1 k. 40, C. Peerson and extract from letter to America, 1874.

211. "Templet" (Temple Mountain), Tempelfjord, Spitzbergen.

212. "Television Screen" (T. E. Johnsen).

1975. 50th Anniv. of Norwegian Administration of Spitzbergen.
743. **211.** 1 k. grey 50 20
744. – 1 k. 25 purple .. 50 10
745. – 1 k. 40 blue .. .. 1·50 1·50
DESIGNS: 1 k. 25, Miners leaving pit. 1 k. 40, Polar bear.

1975. 50th Anniv. of Norwegian Broadcasting System. Multicoloured.
746. 1 k. 25 Type **212** 30 10
747. 1 k. 40 Telecommunications antenna (N. Davidsen) (vert.) .. 50 35

213. "The Annunciation".

214. "Halling" (folk dance).

1975. Paintings from "Altaket" (wooden vault from "Al" (Stave Church), Hallingdal).
748. 80 ore Type **213** 30 10
749. 1 k. "The Visitation" .. 30 15
750. 1 k. 25 "The Nativity" (30 × 38 mm.).. .. 30 10
751. 1 k. 40 "The Adoration" (30 × 38 mm.) 50 40

1976. Norwegian Folk Dances. Multicoloured.
752. 80 ore Type **214** 30 20
753. 1 k. "Springar" 30 15
754. 1 k. 25 "Gangar" 30 10

215. Silver Sugar Caster, Stavanger, 1770.

217. "The Pulpit", Lyse Fjord.

216. Bishop's "Mitre" Bowl, 1760.

1976. Cent. of Oslo Museum of Applied Art.
755. **215.** 1 k. 25 brn., red & rose 50 10
756. – 1 k. 40 violet, blue and light blue 60 60
DESIGN: 1 k. 40, Goblet, Nostetangen Glass-works, 1770.

1976. Europa. Early Products of Herrebo Potteries, Halden.
757. **216.** 1 k. 25 mauve & purple 50 10
758. – 1 k. 40 deep blue & blue 60 60
DESIGN: 1 k. 40, Decorative plate, 1760.

1976. Norwegian Scenery. Multicoloured.
759 1 k. Type **217** 50 10
760 1 k. 25 Gulleplet peak, Balestrand, Sogne Fjord 70 10

218. Social Development Graph.

219. Olav Duun and Cairn, Dun Mountain, Joa Island, Namsen Fjord.

1976. Centenary of Norwegian Central Statistics Bureau.
761. **218.** 1 k. 25 red 50 10
762. – 2 k. blue 70 20
DESIGN: 2 k. National productivity graph.

1976. Birth Cent. of Olav Duun (novelist).
763. **219.** 1 k. 25 multicoloured 50 10
764. 1 k. 40 multicoloured 60 30

220. "Slindebirkin" (T. Fearnley).

221. Details of "April".

1976. Norwegian Paintings. Multicoloured.
765. 1 k. 25 Type **220** 50 10
766. 1 k. 40 "Gamle Furutraer" (L. Hertervig) 70 70

1976. Baldishol Stave Church Tapestry. Multicoloured.
767. 80 ore T **221** 20 10
768. 1 k. Detail of "May" .. 20 15
769. 1 k. 25 "April" and "May" section of tapestry (48 × 30 mm.) 20 15

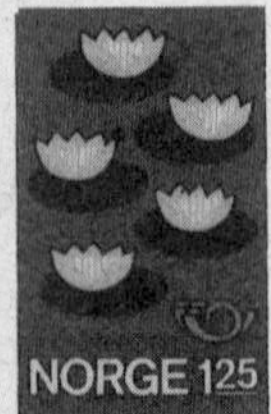

222. Five Water-lilies.

1977. Nordic Countries Co-operation in Nature Conservation and Environment Protection.
770. **222.** 1 k. 25 multicoloured 50 10
771. 1 k. 40 multicoloured 50 30

223. Akershus Castle, Oslo.

224. Hamnoy, Lofoten Islands.

1977.
772. – 1 k. green 15 5
773. – 1 k. 10 purple 20 10
774. **223.** 1 k. 25 red 20 10
775. – 1 k. 30 brown.. .. 20 10
776. – 1 k. 40 lilac 20 10
777. – 1 k. 50 red 20 10
778. – 1 k. 70 green 20 10
779. – 1 k. 75 green 20 10
780. – 1 k. 80 blue 30 20
781. – 2 k. red 25 25
782. – 2 k. 20 blue 30 40
783. – 2 k. 25 violet 30 25
784. – 2 k. 50 brown.. .. 30 5
785. – 2 k. 75 red 40 20
786. – 3 k. blue 40 10
787. – 3 k. 50 violet 40 15
DESIGNS—HORIZ. 1 k. Austraat Manor. 1 k. 10, Trondenes Church, Harstad. 1 k. 30, Steinviksholm Fortress, Asen Fjord, 1 k. 40, Ruins of Hamar Cathedral. 2 k. 20, Tromsdalen Church. 2 k. 50, Loghouse, Breiland. 2 k. 75, Damsgard Palace, Laksevag, near Bergen. 3 k. Ruins of Selje Monastery. 3 k. 50, Lindesnes lighthouse. VERT. 1 k. 50, Stavanger Cathedral. 1 k. 70, Rosenkrantz Tower, Bergen. 1 k. 75, Seamen's commemoration hall, Stavern. 1 k. 80, Torungen lighthouses, Arendal. 2 k. Tofte royal estate, Dovre. 2 k. 25, Oscarshall (royal residence), Oslofjord.

1977. Europa. Multicoloured.
795. 1 k. 25 Type **224** 85 10
796. 1 k. 80 Huldrefossen (vert.) 75 75

225. Spruce.

226. Paddle-Steamer "Constitutionen" at Arendal.

1977. Norwegian Trees.
797. **225.** 1 k. green 20 20
798. – 1 k. 25 brown.. .. 20 15
799. – 1 k. 80 black 30 30
DESIGNS: 1 k. 25, Fir. 1 k. 80, Birch.

1977. Norwegian Coastal Routes.
800. **226.** 1 k. brown 35 20
801. – 1 k. 25 red 50 10
802. – 1 k. 30 green .. .. 1·25 1·25
803. – 1 k. 80 blue 50 50
DESIGNS: 1 k. 25, "Vesteraalen" (freighter) off Bodo. 1 k. 30, Ferries "Kong Haakon" and "Dronningen" at Stavanger, 1893. 1 k. 80, "Nordstjernen" and "Harald Jarl" (ferries).

227. "From the Herring Fishery".

228. "Saturday Evening" (H. Egedius).

1977. Fishery Industry.
804. **227.** 1 k. 25 brown and pink 20 10
805. – 1 k. 80 blue & light blue 30 30
DESIGNS: 1 k. 80, Coley and fish hooks.

1977. Norwegian Paintings. Multicoloured.
806. 1 k. 25 Type **228** 20 10
807. 1 k. 80 "Forest Lake in Lower Telemark" (A. Cappelen) 30 30

229. "David with the Bells".

230. "Peer and the Buck Reindeer" (after drawing by P. Krohg for "Peer Gynt").

1977. Miniatures from the Bible of Aslak Bolt. Multicoloured.
808. 80 ore. Type **229** 20 10
809. 1 k. "Singing Friars" .. 20 15
810. 1 k. 25 "The Holy Virgin with the Child" (34 × 27 mm.) 20 10

1978. 150th Birth Anniv. of Henrik Ibsen (dramatist).
811. **230.** 1 k. 25 black and buff 20 10
812. – 1 k. 80 multicoloured .. 25 30
DESIGN: 1 k. 80, Ibsen (after E. Werenskiold).

231. Heddal Stave Church, Telemark. **232.** Lenangstindene and Jaegervasstindene, Troms.

1978. Europa.
813. **231.** 1 k. 25 brown & orange 50 10
814. – 1 k. 80 green and blue 70 70
DESIGN: 1 k. 80, Borgund stave church, Sogn.

1978. Norwegian Scenery. Multicoloured.
815. 1 k. Type **232** 70 10
816. 1 k. 25 Gaustatoppen, Telemark 70 10

233. King Olav in Sailing-boat.

1978. 75th Birthday of King Olav V.
817. **233.** 1 k. 25 brown.. .. 20 10
818. – 1 k. 80 violet 30 30
DESIGN—VERT. 1 k. 80, King Olav delivering royal speech, opening of Parliament.

234. Amundsen's Polar Flight Stamp of 1925.

1978. "Norwex 80" International Stamp Exhibition.
819. **234.** 1 k. 25 green and grey 85 90
820. **234.** 1 k. 25 blue and grey.. 85 90
821. – 1 k. 25 green and grey 85 90
822. – 1 k. 25 blue and grey.. 85 90
823. **234.** 1 k. 25 purple and grey 85 90
825. – 1 k. 25 purple and grey 85 90
824. **234.** 1 k. 25 red and grey.. 85 90
826. – 1 k. 25 blue and grey.. 85 90
DESIGNS: Nos. 821/2, 824, 826 Annexation of Spitzbergen stamps of 1925.
On Nos. 819/26 each design incorporates a different value of the 1925 issues.

235. Willow Pipe Player. **236.** Wooden Doll, c. 1830.

1978. Musical Instruments.
827. **235.** 1 k. green 20 10
828. – 1 k. 25 red 20 10
829. – 1 k. 80 blue 30 20
830. – 7 k. 50 grey .. .. 1·25 20
831. – 15 k. brown .. .. 2·50 25
DESIGNS: 1 k. 25, Norwegian violin. 1 k. 80, Norwegian zither. 7 k. 50, Ram's horn. 15 k, Jew's harp.

1978. Christmas Antique Toys from Norwegian Folk Museum. Multicoloured.
835. 80 ore Type **236** 20 10
836. 1 k. Toy town, 1896/7 .. 20 10
837. 1 k. 25 Wooden horse from Torpo, Hallingdal .. 20 10

237. Ski Jumping at Huseby, 1879. **238.** "Portrait of Girl" (Stoltenberg).

1979. Centenary of Skiing Competitions at Huseby and Holmenkollen.
838. **237.** 1 k. green 20 10
839. – 1 k. 25 red 20 10
840. – 1 k. 80 blue 30 30
DESIGNS: 1 k. 25, Crown Prince Olay ski jumping at Holmenkollen, 1922. 1 k. 80, Cross-country racing at Holmenkollen, 1976.

1979. International Year of the Child. Mult.
841. 1 k. 25 Type **238** 25 10
842. 1 k. 80 "Portrait of Boy" H. C. F. Hosenfelder) .. 30 30

239. Road to Briksdal Glacier. **240.** "Johan Falkberget" (Harold Dal).

1979. Norwegian Scenery. Multicoloured.
843. 1 k. Type **239** 20 10
844. 1 k. 25 Skjernoysund, near Mandal 20 10

1979. Birth Centenary of Johan Falkberget (novelist).
845. **240.** 1 k. 25 brown .. 20 10
846. – 1 k. 80 blue 25 30
DESIGN: 1 k. 80, "Ann-Magritt and the Hovi Bullock" (statue by Kristofer Leirdal).

242. Kylling Bridge, Verma, Romsdal. **243.** Glacier Buttercup.

1979. Norwegian Engineering.
848. **242.** 1 k. 25 black and brown 40 10
849. – 2 k. black and blue .. 35 20
850. – 10 k. brown and bistre 1·90 35
DESIGNS: 2 k. Vessingsjo Dam, Nea, Sor-Trondelag. 10 k. "Statfjord A" offshore oil drilling and production platform.

1979. Flowers. Multicoloured.
851. 80 ore Type **243** 20 8
852. 1 k. Alpine cinquefoil .. 25 20
853. 1 k. 25 Purple saxifrage .. 25 10

244. Leaf and Emblems. **245.** Oystercatcher Chick.

1980. Centenary of Norwegian Christian Youth Association. Multicoloured.
854. 1 k. Type **244** 15 8
855. 1 k. 80 Plant and emblems 20 25

1980. Birds (1st series). Multicoloured.
856. 1 k. Type **245** 35 10
857. 1 k. Mallard chick 35 10
858. 1 k. 25 Dipper 35 10
859. 1 k. 25 Great Tit 35 10
See also Nos. 869/72, 894/5 and 914/15.

246. Telephone and Dish Aerial.

1980. Centenary of Norwegian Telephone Service.
860. **246.** 1 k. 25 brn., red & blue 20 10
861. – 1 k. 80 multicoloured 30 30
DESIGN: 1 k. 80, Erecting a telephone pole.

248. "Vulcan as an Armourer" (Hassel Jerverk after Bech).

1980. Nordic Countries Co-operation. Cast-iron Stove Ornaments.
863. **248.** 1 k. 25 brown.. .. 15 10
864. – 1 k. 80 blue 20 25
DESIGN: 1 k. 80, "Hercules at a burning Altar" (Moss Jerverk after Henrich Bech).

249. "Jonsokbal" (N. Astrup).

1980. Norwegian Paintings. Multicoloured.
865. 1 k. 25 Type **249** 15 10
866. 1 k. 80 "Seljefloyten" (C. Skredsvig) 25 30

1980. Flowers. As T **243**. Multicoloured.
867. 80 o. Rowan berries 15 10
868. 1 k. Dog rose hips.. .. 15 10

1981. Birds (2nd series). As T **245**. Multicoloured.
869. 1 k. 30 Lesser white-fronted goose 30 10
870. 1 k. 30 Peregrine falcon .. 30 10
871. 1 k. 50 Atlantic puffin .. 50 10
872. 1 k. 50 Black guillemot .. 50 10

250. Cow. **251.** "The Mermaid" (painting by Kristen Aanstad on wooden dish from Hol).

1981. Centenary of Norwegian Milk Producers' National Association. Mult.
873. 1 k. 10 Type **250** 15 10
874. 1 k. 50 Goat 20 10

1981. Europa. Multicoloured.
875. 1 k. 50 Type **251** 30 10
876. 2 k. 20 "The Proposal" (painting by Ola Hansson on box from Nes) .. 40 40

252. Weighing Anchor. **253.** Paddle Steamer, "Skibladner".

1981. Sailing Ship Era.
877. **252.** 1 k. 30 green 20 20
878. – 1 k. 50 red 30 10
879. – 2 k. 20 blue 50 40
DESIGNS—VERT. 1 k. 50, Climbing the rigging. HORIZ. 2 k. 20, Cadet Ship "Christian Radich".

1981. Norwegian Lake Shipping.
880. **253.** 1 k. 10 brown 20 15
881. – 1 k. 30 green 20 20
882. – 1 k. 50 red 20 10
883. – 2 k. 30 blue 40 30
Designs: 1 k. 30, "Victoria (ferry). 1 k. 50, "Faemund II" (ferry). 2 k. 30, "Storegut" (train ferry).

254. Handicapped People as Part of Community.

1981. International Year of Disabled Persons.
884. **254.** 1 k. 50 pink, red & blue 20 10
885. – 2 k. 20 blue, deep blue and red 30 30
DESIGN: 2 k. 20, Handicapped and non-handicapped people walking together.

255. "Interior in Blue" (Harriet Backer). **256.** Hajalmar Branting and Christian Lange.

1981. Norwegian Paintings. Multicoloured.
886. 1 k. 50 Type **255** 20 10
887. 1 k. 70 "Peat Moor on Jaeren" (Kitty Lange Kielland) 30 30

1981. Nobel Peace Prize Winners of 1921.
888. **256.** 5 k. black .. .. 1·00 20

257. One of the Magi (detail from Skjak tapestry, 1625). **258.** Ski Sticks.

1981. Tapestries. Multicoloured.
889. 1 k. 10 Type **257** 20 10
890. 1 k. 30 "Adoration of Christ" (detail from Skjak tapestry, 1625) .. 20 10
891. 1 k. 50 "Marriage in Cana" (pillow slip from Storen, 18th century) (29 × 36 mm.) 20 10

1982. World Ski Championships, Oslo.
892. **258.** 2 k. red and blue .. 20 10
893. – 3 k. blue and red .. 40 25
DESIGN: 3 k. Skis.

1982. Birds (3rd series). As T **245**. Multicoloured.
894. 2 k. Bluethroat 45 25
895. 2 k. European robin .. 45 25

259. Nurse. **260.** King Haakon VII disembarking from "Heimdal" after Election, 1905.

1982. Anti-tuberculosis Campaign. Mult.
896. 2 k. Type **259** 25 10
897. 3 k. Microscope 35 25

1982. Europa.
898. **260.** 2 k. brown 25 10
899. – 3 k. blue 35 25
DESIGN: 3 k. Crown Prince Olav greeting King Haakon VII after liberation, 1945.

261. "Girls from Telemark" (Erik Werenskiold).

263. "Bjornstjerne Bjornson on the Balcony at Aulestad" (Erik Werenskiold). **262.** Consecration Ceremony, Nidaros Cathedral, Trondheim.

1982. Norwegian Paintings. Multicoloured.
900. 1 k. 75 Type **261** 25 20
901. 2 k. "Tone Veli by Fence" (Henrik Sorenson) .. 25 10

1982. 25th Anniv. of King Olav V's Reign.
902. **262.** 3 k. blue 70 60

1982. Writers' Anniversaries. Multicoloured.
903. 1 k. 75 Type **263** (150th birth anniv. 25 20
904. 2 k. "Sigrid Undset" (after A. C. Svarstad) (birth centenary) 25 10

264. Construction of Letter "A". **265.** Fridtjof Nansen.

1982. Cent. of Graphical Union of Norway.
905. **264.** 2 k. yellow, green and black 25 15
906. – 3 k. multicoloured .. 75 25
DESIGN: 3 k. Offset litho printing rollers.

1982. 1922 Nobel Peace Prize-Winner.
907. **265.** 3 k. blue 70 25

266. "Christmas Tradition" (Adolf Tidemand). **267.** Buhund (farm dog).

1982. Christmas.
908. **266.** 1 k. 75 multicoloured .. 25 15

1983. Norwegian Dogs. Multicoloured.
909. 2 k. Type **267** 25 15
910. 2 k. 50 Elk hound .. 30 10
911. 3 k. 50 Lundehund (puffin hunter) 40 30

268. Mountain Scenery.

269. Edvard Grieg with Concerto in A-minor.

1983. Nordic Countries' Postal Co-operation "Visit the North". Multicoloured.

912. 2 k. 50 Type 268 .. .. 25 10
913. 3 k. 50 Fjord scenery .. 35 25

1983. Birds. (4th series). As T **245**. Mult.

914. 2 k. 50 Barnacle goose .. 55 30
915. 2 k. 50 Little auk 55 30

1983. Europa.

916. **269.** 2 k. 50 red 85 10
917. – 3 k. 50 blue & green .. 35 25

DESIGN—VERT. 3 k. 50 Statue of Niels Henrik Abel (mathematician) by Gustav Vigeland.

270. Arrows forming Posthorn.

271. King Olav V and Royal Birch, Molde.

1983. World Communications Year. Multicoloured.

918. 2 k. 50 Type 270 .. .. 25 10
919. 3 k. 50 Arrows circling globe 35 25

1983. 80th Birthday of King Olav V.

920. **271.** 5 k. green 85 15

272. Lie.

273. Northern Femboring.

1983. 150th Birth Anniv. of Jonas Lie (author).

921. **272.** 2 k. 50 red 60 10

1983. North Norwegian Ships.

922. **273.** 2 k. blue and brown 25 10
923. – 3 k. brown and blue 70 50

DESIGNS: 3 k. Northern jekt (sailing vessel).

274. "The Sleigh Ride" (Axel Ender).

275. Post Office Counter.

1983. Christmas. Multicoloured.

924. 2 k. Type 274 .. .. 20 10
925. 2 k. 50 "The Guests are arriving" (Gustav Wendel) 25 10

1984. Postal Work. Multicoloured.

926. 2 k. Type 275 .. .. 50 15
927. 2 k. 50 Postal sorting .. 70 10
928. 3 k. 50 Postal delivery .. 85 30

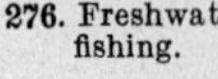

276. Freshwater fishing.

277. Magnetic Meridians and Parallels.

1984. Sport Fishing.

929. **276.** 2 k. 50 red 70 10
930. – 3 k. green 75 50
931. – 3 k. 50 blue 85 50

DESIGNS: 3 k. Salmon fishing. 3 k. 50 Sea fishing.

1984. Birth Bicentenary of Christopher Hansteen (astronomer and geophysicist).

932. **277.** 3 k. 50 blue 85 20
933. – 5 k. red .. .. 1·00 60

DESIGN: VERT. 5 k. Portrait of Hansteen by Johan Gorbitz.

278. Bridge.

279. Vegetables, Fruit and Herbs.

1984. Europa. 25th Anniv. of European Post and Telecommunications Conference.

934. **278.** 2 k. 50 multicoloured 70 10
935. – 3 k. 50 multicoloured 85 50

1984. Centenary of Norwegian Horticultural Society. Multicoloured.

936. 2 k. Type **279** 25 15
937. 2 k. 50 Rose and garland of flowers 30 10

280. "Apis mellifera".

281. Holberg (after J. M. Bernigeroth).

1984. Centenaries of Norwegian Beekeeping Society and Norwegian Poultry-breeding Society. Multicoloured.

938. 2 k. 50 Type **280** 30 10
939. 2 k. 50 Leghorn cock .. 30 10

1984. 300th Birth Anniv. of Ludvig Holberg (writer).

940. **281.** 2 k. 50 red 30 10

282. Children reading.

284. Karius and Baktus (tooth decay bacteria).

283. Entering Parliamentary Chamber, 2 July 1884.

1984. 150th Anniv. of "Norsk Penning-Magazin" (1st weekly magazine in Norway).

941. **282.** 2 k. 50 purple, blue and red 50 10
942. – 3 k. 50 yellow & vio. 85 20

DESIGN: 3 k. 50, 1st edition of "Norsk Penning-Magazin".

1984. Cent. of Norwegian Parliament.

943. **283.** 7 k. 50 brown .. 1·25 40

1984. Characters from Stories by Thorbjorn Egner. Multicoloured.

944. 2 k. Type **284** 40 10
945. 2 k. The tree shrew playing guitar 40 10
946. 2 k. 50 Kasper, Jesper and Jonatan (Rovers) in Kardemomme Town .. 50 25
947. 2 k. 50 Chief constable Bastian 50 10

285. Mount Sagbladet (Saw Blade).

286. Return of Crown Prince Olav, 1945.

1985. Antarctic Mountains. Multicoloured.

948. 2 k. 50 Type **285** 35 10
949. 3 k. 50 Mount Hoggestabben (Chopping Block) .. 75 20

1985. 40th Anniv. of Liberation.

950. **286.** 3 k. 50 red and blue .. 75 20

287. Kongsten Fort.

1985. 300th Anniv. of Kongsten Fort.

951. **287.** 2 k. 50 multicoloured 60 10

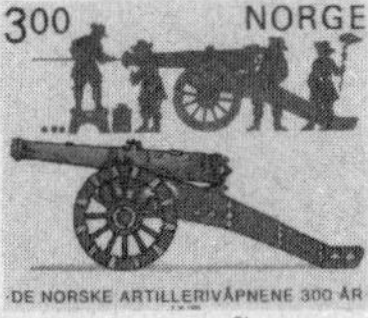

288. Bronze Cannon, 1596.

289. "Boy and Girl" (detail).

1985. Artillery Anniversaries. Multicoloured.

952. 3 k. Type **287** (300th anniv. of Artillery) 70 50
953. 4 k. Cannon on sledge carriage, 1758 (bicentenary of Artillery Officers Training School) 85 30

1985. International Youth Year. Sculptures in Vigeland Park. Mult.

954. 2 k. Type **289** 50 10
955. 3 k. 50 Bronze fountain (detail) 85 20

290. Torgeir Augundsson (violinist).

291. Workers at Glomfjord.

1985. Europa. Music Year.

956. **290.** 2 k. 50 red 70 10
957. – 3 k. 50 blue 85 50

DESIGN: 3 k. 50 Ole Bull (composer and violinist).

1985. Centenary of Electricity in Norway.

958. **291.** 2 k. 50 dp red & red .. 60 10
959. – 4 k. blue and green .. 85 30

DESIGN: 4 k. Men working on overhead cable.

293. Carl Deichman on Book Cover.

294. Wreath.

1985. Bicentenary of Public Libraries.

961. **293.** 2 k. 50 brown and red 35 10
962. – 10 k. green .. .. 1·75 50

DESIGN—HORIZ. 10 k. Library interior.

1985. Christmas. Multicoloured.

963. 2 k. Type **294** 25 10
964. 2 k. 50 Bullfinches 50 10

295. Dredger "Berghavn".

296. Sun.

1985. 250th Anniv. of Port Authorities and Hydrography in Norway.

965. **295.** 2 k. 50 pur., orge. & bl. 35 10
966. – 5 k. blue, gr. & brn.. 1·00 30

DESIGN: 5 k. Sextant and detail of chart No. 1 of Lt. F. C. Grove showing Trondheim sealane, 1791.

1986.

967. **296.** 2 k. 10 orange & brn. 25 10
968. – 2 k. 30 grey and blue 30 10
970. – 2 k. 70 pink and red 35 10
971. – 4 k. blue and green .. 85 50

DESIGNS: 2 k. 30, Fishes. 2 k. 70, Flowers. 4 k. Star ornaments.

297. Marksman in Prone Position.

1986. World Biathlon Championships. Mult.

977. 2 k. 50 Type **297** 35 10
978. 3 k. 50 Marksman standing to take aim 75 50

298. Industry and Countryside.

299. Stone Cutter.

1986. Europa. Multicoloured.

979. 2 k. 50 Type **298** 40 10
980. 3 k. 50 Dead and living forest, mountains and butterflies 85 70

1986. Centenary of Norwegian Craftsmen's Federation.

981. **299.** 2 k. 50 red and orange 35 10
982. – 7 k. blue and red .. 1·25 85

DESIGN: 7 k. Carpenter.

300. Moss.

1986. Nordic Countries' Postal Co-operation. Twinned Towns. Multicoloured.

983. 2 k. 50 Type **300** 35 10
984. 4 k. Alesund 85 60

301. Han Polson Egede (missionary) and Map.

303. "Olav Kyrre founds the Diocese in Nidaros".

1986. Birth Anniversaries.

985. **301.** 2 k. 10 brown and red 30 20
986. – 2 k. 50 red, grn. & bl. 35 10
987. – 3 k. brown and red .. 35 20
988. – 4 k. purple and lilac 45 25

DESIGNS: 2 k. 10, Type **301** (300th anniv.). 2 k. 50, Herman Vildenvey (poet) and poem carved in wall at Stavern centenary). 3 k. Tore Orjasaeter (poet) and old cupboard from Skjak (centenary). 4 k. Engebret Soot (engineer) and lock gates, Orje (centenary).

1986. Christmas. Stained Glass Windows by Gabriel Kielland from Nidaros Cathedral, Trondheim. Multicoloured.

990. 2 k. 10 Type **303** 50 15
991. 2 k. 50 "The King and the Peasant at Sul" .. 60 15

304. Doves.

305. Numeral.

1986. International Peace Year.

992. **304.** 15 k. red, bl. & grn. 2·50 1·25

1987.

993. **305.** 3 k. 50 yell., red & bl. 70 50
994. – 4 k. 50 bl., yell. & grn. 75 70

306. Wooden Building.

1987. Europa. Multicoloured.

1000. 2 k. 70 Type **306** .. 60 10
1001. 4 k. 50 Building of glass and stone 75 60

307. The Final Vote.

309. "Cantharellus tubaeformis".

1987. 150th Anniv. of Laws on Local Councils.

1002. **307.** 12 k. green .. .. 2·10 80

1987. Fungi (1st series) Multicoloured.

1004. 2 k. 70 Type **309** .. 35 10
1005. 2 k. 70 "Rozites caperata" 35 10

See also Nos. 1040/1 and 1052/3.

310. Bjornstad Farm from Vaga.

1987. Centenary of Sandvig Collections, Maihaugen.

1006. **310.** 2 k. 70 deep brown and brown .. 35 35
1007. – 3 k. 50 red and blue 70 60

DESIGN: 3 k. 50, "Horse and Rider" (wooden carving, Christen Erlandsen Listad).

311. Valevag Churchyard.

1987. Birth Centenary of Fartein Valen (composer).

1008. **311.** 2 k. 30 blue & grn. .. 30 35
1009. – 4 k. 50 brown .. 75 60

DESIGN—VERT. 4 k. 50, Fartein Valen.

312. "Storm at Sea" (Christian Krohg).

1987. Paintings. Multicoloured.

1010. 2 k. 70, Type **312** .. 35 40
1011. 5 k. "The Farm" (Gerhard Munthe) .. 90 70

314. Cat with Children making Decorations.

1987. Christmas. Multicoloured.

1013. 2 k. 30 Type **314** .. 35 10
1014. 2 k. 70 Dog with children making gingersnaps .. 45 15

315. Dales Pony.

316. Capercaillie.

1987. Native Ponies.

1015. **315.** 2 k. 30 deep brown, green and brown .. 50 40
1016. – 2 k. 70 buff, brown and blue 45 15
1017. – 4 k. 50 brown, red and blue 70 70

DESIGNS: 2 k. 70, Fjord pony. 4 k. 50, Nordland pony.

1988.

1017a – 2 k. 60 deep brown, brown and green 45 15
1018 **316** 2 k. 90 black, brown and green .. 45 15
1018a – 3 k. brn, grey & grn 45 15
1018b – 3 k. 20 blue, green and turquoise .. 55 20
1019 – 3 k. 80 brn, bl & blk 65 30
1020 – 4 k. brn, red & grn 70 35
1021 – 4 k. 50 brn, grn & bl 80 30
1023 – 5 k. 50 brown, grey and green .. 1·00 45
1025 – 6 k. 40 brown, black and green .. 1·10 50

DESIGNS: 2 k. 60, Fox; 3 k. Stoat; 3 k. 20, Mute swan; 3 k. 80, Reindeer; 4 k. Red squirrel; 4 k. 50, Beaver; 5 k. 50, Lynx; 6 k. 40, Tengmalm's owl.

317. Band.

1988. Centenary of Salvation Army in Norway. Multicoloured.

1035. 2 k. 90 Type **317** .. 45 15
1036. 4 k. 80 Othilie Tonning (early social worker) and Army nurse .. 80 40

318 Building Fortress

1988. Military Anniversaries.

1037 **318** 2 k. 50 green .. 40 15
1038 – 2 k. 90 brown .. 45 15
1039 – 4 k. 60 blue 75 35

DESIGNS: 2 k. 50, Type **318** (300th anniv of Defence Construction Service); 2 k. 90 Corps members in action (centenary of Army Signals corps); 4 k. 60, Making pontoon bridge (centenary of Engineer Corps).

1988. Fungi (2nd series). As T **309**. Mult.

1040 2 k. 90 Wood blewits .. 45 15
1041 2 k. 90 Saffron milkcaps 45 15

319 Globe

320 King Olav V

1988. European Campaign for Interdependence and Solidarity of North and South.

1042 **319** 25 k. multicoloured .. 4·00 3·00

1988. 85th Birthday of King Olav V.

1043 **320** 2 k. 90 multicoloured 45 15

321. "Prinds Gustav" (paddle-steamer).

322 King Christian IV

1988. Europa. Transport and Communications.

1045 **321** 2 k. 90 black, red & bl 45 15
1046 – 3 k. 80 bl, red & yell 65 25

DESIGN: 3 k. 80, Heroybrua Bridge.

1988. 400th Anniv of Christian IV's Accession to Danish and Norwegian Thrones.

1047 **322** 2 k. 50 blk, brn & vio 40 15
1048 – 10 k. multicoloured .. 1·60 1·40

DESIGN: 10 k. 1628 silver coin and extract from decree on mining in Norway.

324 Ludvig with Ski Stick

325 Start and Finish of Race

1988. Christmas. Multicoloured.

1050 2 k. 90 Type **324** .. 45 15
1051 2 k. 90 Ludvig reading letter 45 15

1989. Fungi (3rd series). As T **309**. Mult.

1052 3 k. Chanterelle 50 20
1053 3 k. Butter mushroom 50 20

1989. Cross-country Skiing World Championship, Stavanger.

1054 **325** 5 k. multicoloured .. 80 30

326 Vardo

327 Setesdal Woman

1989. Town Bicentenaries.

1055 **326** 3 k. blue, red & lt bl 50 20
1056 – 4 k. purple, bl & orge 65 25

DESIGN: 4 k. Hammerfest.

1989. Nordic Countries' Postal Co-operation. Traditional Costumes. Multicoloured.

1057 3 k. Type **327** 50 25
1058 4 k. Kautokeino man .. 65 25

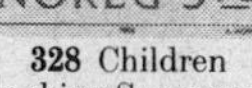

328 Children making Snowman

329 Rooster and Cover of First Reader

1989. Europa. Children's Games. Mult.

1059 3 k. 70 Type **328** .. 60 20
1060 5 k. Cat's cradle 85 35

1989. 250th Anniv of Primary Schools.

1061 **329** 2 k. 60 multicoloured 45 15
1062 – 3 k. brown 50 20

DESIGN: 3 k. Pocket calculator and child writing.

332 Arnulf Overland (centenary)

333 Star Decoration

1989. Writers' Birth Anniversaries.

1065 **332** 3 k. red and blue .. 50 20
1066 – 25 k. blue, orge & grn 4·50 4·50

DESIGN: 25 k. Hanna Winsnes (bicentenary).

1989. Christmas. Tree Decorations. Mult.

1067 3 k. Type **333** 50 20
1068 3 k. Bauble 50 20

334 Larvik Manor

335 Emblem

1989. Manor Houses.

1069 **334** 3 k. brown 50 50
1070 – 3 k. green 50 50

DESIGN: No. 1070, Rosendal Barony.

1990. Winter Cities Events, Tromso.

1071 **335** 5 k. multicoloured .. 85 35

336 "Dactylorhiza fuchsii"

337 Navy, Airforce, Home Guard, "Moses" (coastal gun) and Haakon VII's Monogram

1990. Orchids (1st series). Multicoloured.

1072 3 k. 20 Type **336** .. 50 20
1073 3 k. 20 "Epipactis atrorubens" 50 20

See also Nos. 1141/2.

1990. 50th Anniv of Norway's Entry into World War II. Multicoloured.

1074 3 k. 20 Type **337** .. 50 20
1075 4 k. Second Battle of Narvik, 1940 .. .. 65 25

339 Trondheim Post Office

340 "Tordenskiold" (after J. W. Tegner)

1990. Europa. Post Office Buildings. Mult.

1077 3 k. 20 Type **339** .. 55 20
1078 4 k. Longyearbyen Post Office .. 70 30

1990. 300th Birth Anniv of Admiral Tordenskiold (Peter Wessel). Multicoloured.

1079 3 k. 20 Type **340** .. 55 20
1080 5 k. Tordenskiold's coat-of-arms 90 45

341 Svendsen

343 "Children and Snowman" (Ragni Engstrom)

1990. 150th Birth Anniv of Johan Svendsen (composer and conductor).

1081 **341** 2 k. 70 black and red 45 15
1082 – 15 k. brown & yellow 2·75 1·50

DESIGN: 15 k. Svendsen Monument (Stinius Fredriksen), Oslo.

1990. Christmas. Children's Prizewinning Drawings. Multicoloured.

1084 3 k. 20 Type **343** .. 55 20
1085 3 k. 20 "Christmas Church" (Jorgen Ingier) 55 20

344 Nobel Medal and Soderblom

1990. 60th Anniv of Award of Nobel Peace Prize to Nathan Soderblom, Archbishop of Uppsala.
1086 **344** 30 k. brown, bl & red 5·25 2·75

345 Plan and Elevation of Container Ship and Propeller

346 Satellite transmitting to Tromso

1991. Centenaries of Federation of Engineering Industries (1989) and Union of Iron and Metal Workers.
1087 **345** 5 k. multicoloured .. 90 45

1991. Europa. Europe in Space. Mult.
1088 3 k. 20 Type **346** .. 55 20
1089 4 k. Rocket leaving Andoya rocket range .. 70 25

347 Christiansholm Fortress (late 17th-century)

348 Fountain, Vigeland Park, Oslo

1991. 350th Anniv of Kristiansand. Each black, blue and red.
1090 3 k. 20 Type **347** .. 55 20
1091 5 k. 50 Present day view of Christiansholm Fortress .. .. 1·10 55

1991. Nordic Countries' Postal Co-operation. Tourism. Multicoloured.
1092 3 k. 20 Type **348** .. 55 20
1093 4 k. Globe, North Cape Plateau 70 25

349 "Skomvaer III" (lifeboat)

352 Posthorn

1991. Centenary of Norwegian Society for Sea Rescue.
1094 **349** 3 k. 20 brn, blk & grn 55 20
1095 – 27 k. brn, grey & pur 4·75 2·40
DESIGNS—VERT. 27 k. "Colin Archer" (first lifeboat).

1991.
1098 **352** 1 k. black and orange 20 10
1099 2 k. red and green .. 40 20
1100 3 k. green and blue .. 60 30
1101 4 k. red and orange .. 80 40
1102 5 k. blue and green .. 1·00 50
1103 6 k. red and green .. 1·10 55
1104 7 k. blue and brown 1·25 65
1105 8 k. green and purple 1·40 70
1106 9 k. brown and blue 1·60 80

353 Guisers with Goat Head

1991. Christmas. Guising. Multicoloured.
1120 3 k. 20 Type **353** .. 55 20
1121 3 k. 20 Guisers with lantern 55 20

354 Queen Sonja

355 King Harald

356 King Harald

1992.
1122 **354** 2 k. 80 lake, pur & red 50 10
1123 3 k. green, deep green and turquoise .. 55 10
1124 **355** 3 k. 30 blue, ultram and light blue .. 60 10
1125 3 k. 50 black and grey 65 10
1128 5 k. 50 brown, sepia and black .. .. 1·00 25
1129 5 k. 60 orange, red and vermilion 1·00 25
1131 6 k. 50 emerald, green and turquoise 1·25 25
1132 6 k. 60 maroon, purple and brown .. 1·10 55
1135 **356** 10 k. green 90 45
1137 20 k. violet .. .. 3·75 85
1140 50 k. green .. .. 20·00 3·50

1992. Orchids (2nd series). As T **336**. Mult.
1141 3 k. 30 Lady's slipper orchid ("Cypripedium calceolus") .. 60 20
1142 3 k. 30 Fly orchid ("Ophrys insectifera") 60 20

358 "Restaurationen" (emigrant sloop)

1992. Europa. 500th Anniv of Discovery of America by Columbus. Transatlantic Ships. Multicoloured.
1144 3 k. 30 Type **358** .. 65 20
1145 4 k. 20 "Stavangerfjord" (liner) and American skyline .. 85 30

359 Norwegian Pavilion, Rainbow and Ship

360 Molde

1992. "Expo '92" World's Fair, Seville. Multicoloured.
1146 3 k. 30 Type **359** .. 65 20
1147 5 k. 20 Mountains, rainbow, fish and ship .. 1·00 50

1992. 250th Anniversaries of Molde and Kristiansund.
1148 **360** 3 k. 30 blue, grn & brn 65 20
1149 – 3 k. 30 bl, brn & lt bl 65 20
DESIGN: No. 1149, Kristiansund.

361 Banners and Lillehammer Buildings

363 Gnomes below Pillar Box

1992. Winter Olympic Games, Lillehammer (1994) (1st issue). Multicoloured.
1150 3 k. 30 Type **361** .. 65 20
1151 4 k. 20 Flags 85 30
See also Nos. 1169/70.

1992. Christmas. Designs showing Christmas card designs by Otto Moe. Multicoloured.
1153 3 k. 30 Type **363** .. 65 20
1154 3 k. 30 Gnome posting letter 65 20

364 Orange-tip

366 Grieg

1993. Butterflies. Multicoloured.
1155 3 k. 50 Type **364** .. 65 10
1156 3 k. 50 Small tortoiseshell 65 10

1993. 150th Birth Anniv of Edvard Grieg (composer). Multicoloured.
1158 3 k. 50 Type **366** .. 65 10
1159 5 k. 50 "Spring" .. 1·00 25

367 Two-man Kayak on Lake

368 Richard With (founder) and "Vesteraalen"

1993. Nordic Countries' Postal Co-operation. Tourist Activities. Multicoloured.
1160 4 k. Type **367** 75 45
1161 4 k. 50 White-water rafting 85 55

1993. Centenary of Express Coaster Service.
1162 **368** 3 k. 50 blue, vio & red 65 10
1163 – 4 k. 50 multicoloured 85 25
DESIGN: 4 k. 50, Modern vessel.

369 Handball

370 Johann Castberg (politician)

1993. Sports Events. Multicoloured.
1164 3 k. 50 Type **369** (women's World Championship, Norway) 65 10
1165 5 k. 50 Cycling (World Championships, Oslo and Hamar) .. .. 1·00 40

1993. Centenary of Workforce Protection Legislation.
1166 **370** 3 k. 50 brown & blue 65 10
1167 – 12 k. blue and brown 2·25 90
DESIGN: 12 k. Betzy Kjelsberg (first woman factory inspector).

372 Torch Bearer on Skis

373 Store Mangen Chapel

1993. Winter Olympic Games, Lillehammer (1994) (2nd issue). Morgedal–Lillehammer Torch Relay. Multicoloured.
1169 3 k. 50 Type **372** .. 65 10
1170 3 k. 50 Lillehammer .. 65 10
Nos. 1169/70 were issued together, se-tenant, forming a composite design.

1993. Christmas. Multicoloured.
1171 3 k. 50 Type **373** .. 65 10
1172 3 k. 50 Stamnes-church, Sandnessjoen 65 10

OFFICIAL STAMPS

O 22.

O 36.

1925.
O 187. O **22.** 5 ore mauve .. 80 80
O 188. 10 ore green 30 10
O 189. 15 ore blue .. .. 70 2·00
O 190. 20 ore purple .. 20 10
O 191. 30 ore slate .. .. 2·00 3·25
O 192. 40 ore blue 80 65
O 193. 60 ore blue .. .. 3·00 4·00

1929. Surch. **2** twice.
O 219. O **22.** 2 ore on 5 ore mauve 45 65

1933.
O 231. O **36.** 2 ore brown 30 90
O 243. 5 ore purple .. 90 1·25
O 244. 7 ore orange .. 6·00 3·75
O 245. 10 ore green .. 25 45
O 235. 15 ore olive .. 55 45
O 247. 20 ore red 25 10
O 237. 25 ore brown .. 40 30
O 238. 30 ore blue 40 20
O 248. 35 ore mauve .. 40 30
O 249. 40 ore grey 70 45
O 250. 60 ore blue 70 50
O 241. 70 ore brown .. 1·10 2·00
O 242. 100 ore violet .. 1·60 1·40

O 39.

O 58. Quisling Emblem.

1937.
O 267. O **39.** 5 ore mauve.. .. 40 10
O 256. 7 ore orange .. 20 70
O 257. 10 ore green .. 12 10
O 270. 15 ore olive .. 55 70
O 271. 20 ore red 10 5
O 260. 25 ore brown .. 80 50
O 273. 25 ore red 20 5
O 261. 30 ore blue 80 55
O 275. 30 ore grey 95 30
O 276. 35 ore purple .. 55 10
O 277. 40 ore grey 55 10
O 278. 40 ore blue .. .. 3·25 15
O 279. 50 ore lilac .. 70 10
O 280. 60 ore blue 65 10
O 281. 100 ore violet .. 70 10
O 282. 200 ore orange .. 2·75 55

1942.
O 336. O **58.** 5 ore mauve .. 45 1·25
O 337. 7 ore orange .. 45 1·25
O 338. 10 ore green .. 10 10
O 339. 15 ore brown .. 1·00 6·50
O 340. 20 ore red 10 10
O 341. 25 ore brown .. 2·75 9·75
O 342. 30 ore blue .. .. 1·75 11·00
O 343. 35 ore purple .. 1·75 9·75
O 344. 40 ore slate 15 15
O 345. 60 ore blue .. .. 1·75 6·50
O 346. 1 k. blue .. .. 1·75 8·00

1949. Surch. **25** and bar.
O 402. O **39.** 25 ore on 20 ore red .. 25 15

O 89.

O 99.

1951.
O 434. O **89.** 5 ore mauve .. 1·10 10
O 435. 10 ore grey 90 10
O 436. 15 ore brown .. 90 45
O 437. 30 ore red .. .. 1·10 5
O 438. 35 ore brown .. 1·10 40
O 439. 60 ore blue 90 10
O 440. 100 ore violet .. 1·60 20

1955.
O 458. O **99.** 5 ore purple .. 10 5
O 459. 10 ore grey .. 10 5
O 460. 15 ore brown .. 50 1·10
O 461. 20 ore green .. 10 5
O 462. 25 ore green .. 40 10
O 463. 30 ore red .. .. 1·25 80
O 464. 30 ore green .. 80 10
O 465. 35 ore red .. 55 5
O 466. 40 ore lilac .. 90 10
O 467. 40 ore green .. 25 10
O 468. 45 ore red 90 5
O 469. 50 ore brown .. 1·50 20
O 470. 50 ore red 90 5
O 471. 50 ore blue .. 25 10
O 738. 50 ore grey .. 15 10
O 739. 60 ore blue .. 80 1·10
O 473. 60 ore red .. 90 5
O 474. 60 ore green .. 1·75 1·75
O 475. 65 ore red 95 5

O 476.	70 ore brown	2·75	90
O 477.	70 ore red	30	5
O 478.	75 ore brown	8·50	8·50
O 479.	75 ore green	60	80
O 481.	80 ore brown	70	10
O 741.	80 ore red	25	10
O 482.	85 ore brown	60	1·10
O 483.	90 ore orange	90	10
O 484.	1 k. violet	90	5
O 485.	1 k. red	30	5
O 486.	1 k. 10 red	75	55
O 744.	1 k. 25 red	35	5
O 745.	1 k. 30 purple	70	90
O 746.	1 k. 50 red	45	5
O 747.	1 k. 75 green	1·10	90
O 749.	2 k. red	40	10
O 487.	2 k. green	2·25	10
O 750.	3 k. violet	90	20
O 488.	5 k. violet	4·50	1·10
O 752.	5 k. blue	1·25	25

POSTAGE DUE STAMPS

D 12.

1889. Inscr. "a betale" and "PORTOMAERKE".

D 95. D 12.	1 ore green	40	65
D 96a.	4 ore mauve	75	50
D 97.	10 ore red	2·25	30
D 98.	15 ore brown	75	65
D 99.	20 ore blue	1·50	30
D 94.	50 ore purple	2·25	1·75

1922. Inscr. "a betale" and "PORTOMERKE".

D 162. D 12.	4 ore mauve	4·00	4·50
D 163.	10 ore green	1·60	1·40
D 164.	20 ore purple	2·50	2·50
D 165.	40 ore blue	4·50	70
D 166.	100 ore yellow	17·00	7·00
D 167.	200 ore violet	45·00	13·50

NOSSI-BE Pt. 6

An island north-west of Madagascar, declared a French protectorate in 1840. In 1901 it became part of Madagascar and Dependencies.

100 centimes = 1 franc.

1889. Stamp of French Colonies, "Peace and Commerce" type, surch.

8 H	25 c. on 40 c. red on yellow	£1400	£500

1889. Stamps of French Colonies, "Commerce" type, surch.

4 J	5 c. on 10 c. black on lilac	£1600	£550
2	5 c. on 20 c. red on green	£1800	£700
6	15 on 20 c. red on green	£1500	£550
7	25 on 30 c. brown on drab	£1400	£425
9	25 on 40 c. red on yellow	£1400	£400

1890. Stamps of French Colonies, "Commerce" types, surch (a) **N S B 0 25.**

10 J	0 25 on 20 c. red on green	£225	£160
11	0 25 on 75 c. red on pink	£225	£160
12	0 25 on 1 f. green	£225	£160

(b) **N S B 25 c.**

13 J	25 c. on 20 c. red on green	£225	£160
14	25 c. on 75 c. red on pink	£225	£160
15	25 c. on 1 f. green	£225	£160

(c) **N S B 25** in frame.

16 J	25 on 20 c. red on green	£575	£375
17	25 on 75 c. red on pink	£575	£375
18	25 on 1 f. green	£575	£375

1893. Stamps of French Colonies, "Commerce" type, surch. **NOSSI-BE** and bar over value in figures.

36. J.	25 on 20 c. red on green	23·00	18·00
37.	50 on 10 c. black on lilac	25·00	18·00
38.	75 on 15 c. blue	£160	£120
39.	1 f. on 5 c. green	60·00	50·00

1893. Stamps of French Colonies, "Commerce" type, optd. **Nossi Be.**

40. J.	10 c. black on lilac	8·00	4·50
41.	15 c. blue	8·50	7·00
43.	20 c. red on green	60·00	30·00

1894. "Tablet" key-type inscr "NOSSI-BE" in red (1, 5, 15, 25, 75 c., 1 f.) or blue (others).

44 D	1 c. black on blue	60	60
45	2 c. brown on buff	85	75
46	4 c. brown on grey	1·25	75
47	5 c. green on green	1·40	85
48	10 c. black on lilac	3·00	1·90
49	15 c. blue	4·75	2·25
50	20 c. red on green	5·25	3·00
51	25 c. black on pink	6·00	4·25
52	30 c. brown on drab	8·25	5·00
53	40 c. red on yellow	9·00	7·75
54	50 c. red on pink	9·00	6·25
55	75 c. brown on orange	23·00	17·00
56	1 f. green	12·00	9·00

POSTAGE DUE STAMPS

1891. Stamps of French Colonies, "Commerce" type, surch **NOSSI-BE chiffre-taxe A PERCEVOIR** and value.

D19 J	0.20 on 1 c. black on blue	£210	£160
D20	0.30 on 2 c. brn on buff	£210	£160
D21	0.35 on 4 c. brn on grey	£225	£170
D22	0.35 on 20 c. red on green	£250	£170
D23	0.50 on 30 c. brn on drab	70·00	55·00
D24	1 f. on 35 c. blk on orge	£160	£110

1891. Stamps of French Colonies, "Commerce" type, surch **Nossi-Be A PERCEVOIR** and value.

D25 J	5 c. on 20 c. red on green	£160	£110
D26	10 c. on 15 c. blue on bl	£140	£140
D33	0.10 on 5 c. green	10·00	8·25
D27	15 c. on 10 c. blk on lilac	90·00	90·00
D34	0.15 on 20 c. red on green	12·50	11·00
D28	25 c. on 5 c. green on grn	90·00	90·00
D35	0.25 on 75 c. red on pink	£375	£350

NYASSA COMPANY Pt. 9

In 1894 Portugal granted a charter to the Nyassa Company to administer an area in the northern part of Mozambique, including the right to issue its own stamps. The lease was terminated in 1929 and the administration was transferred to Mozambique whose stamps were used there.

1898. 1000 reis = 1 milreis.
1913. 100 centavos = 1 escudo.

1898. "Figures" and "Newspaper" key-types inscr "MOCAMBIQUE" optd **NYASSA**.

1. V.	2½ r. brown	1·10	1·10
2. R.	5 r. orange	1·10	1·10
3.	10 r. mauve	1·10	1·10
4.	15 r. brown	1·10	1·10
5.	20 r. lilac	1·10	1·10
6.	25 r. green	1·10	1·10
7.	50 r. blue	1·10	1·10
8.	75 r. red	1·50	1·25
9.	80 r. green	1·50	1·40
10.	100 r. brown on buff	1·50	1·40
11.	150 r. red on rose	3·25	3·25
12.	200 r. blue on blue	2·25	2·25
13.	300 r. blue on brown	2·25	2·25

1898. "King Carlos" key-type inscr "MOCAMBIQUE" optd **NYASSA**.

14. S.	2½ r. grey	75	65
15.	5 r. orange	75	65
16.	10 r. green	75	65
17.	15 r. brown	90	75
18.	20 r. lilac	90	75
19.	25 r. green	90	75
20.	50 r. blue	90	75
21.	75 r. red	90	75
22.	80 r. mauve	1·25	1·10
23.	100 r. blue on blue	1·25	1·10
24.	150 r. brown on yellow	1·25	1·10
25.	200 r. purple on pink	1·25	1·10
26.	300 r. blue on pink	1·25	1·10

2. Giraffe. 3. Dromedaries.

1901.

27. 2.	2½ r. brown and black	60	30
28.	5 r. violet and black	60	30
29.	10 r. green and black	60	30
30.	15 r. brown and black	60	30
31.	20 r. red and black	60	40
32.	25 r. orange and black	60	40
33.	50 r. blue and black	60	40
34. 3.	75 r. red and black	70	50
35.	80 r. mauve and black	70	50
36.	100 r. brown and black	70	50
37.	150 r. brown and black	70	50
38.	200 r. green and black	75	55
39.	300 r. green and black	75	55

1903. Surch. in figures and words.

40. 3.	65 r. on 80 r. mauve & blk.	50	40
41.	115 r. on 150 r. brn. & blk.	50	40
42.	130 r. on 300 r. grn. & blk.	50	40

1903. Optd. **PROVISORIO.**

43. 2.	15 r. brown and black	55	45
44.	25 r. orange and black	55	45

1910. Optd. **PROVISORIO** and surch. in figures and words.

50. 2.	5 r. on 2½ r. brown & black	60	45
51. 3.	50 r. on 100 r. brn. & black	60	45

9. Dromedaries. 12. Vasco da Gama's Flagship. "Sao Gabriel".

1911. Optd. **REPUBLICA.**

53. 9.	2½ r. violet and black	50	30
54.	5 r. black	50	30
55.	10 r. green and black	50	30
56. –	20 r. red and black	50	30
57. –	25 r. brown and black	50	30
58. –	50 r. blue and black	50	30
59. –	75 r. brown and black	50	40
60. –	100 r. brn. & blk. on green	50	40
61. –	200 r. grn. & blk. on pink	60	60
62. 12.	300 r. black on blue	1·25	90
63.	400 r. brown and black	1·40	1·00
64.	500 r. violet and olive	1·75	1·40

DESIGNS—HORIZ. 20 r., 25 r., 50 r. Common zebra. VERT. 75 r., 100 r., 200 r. Giraffe.

1918. Surch. **REPUBLICA** and value in figures.

65. 2.	¼ c. on 2½ c. brown & black	20·00	13·00
66.	½ c. on 5 r. violet & black	20·00	13·00
67.	1 c. on 10 r. green & black	20·00	13·00
68.	1½ c. on 15 r. brn. & black	80	60
69.	2 c. on 20 r. red and black	60	50
70.	3½ c. on 25 r. orge. & black	60	50
71.	5 c. on 50 r. blue & black	60	50
72. 3.	7½ c. on 75 r. red & black	60	50
73.	8 c. on 80 r. mauve & black	60	50
74.	10 c. on 100 r. brn. & black	60	50
75.	15 c. on 150 r. brn. & blk.	75	65
76.	20 c. on 200 r. grn. & blk.	75	65
77.	30 c. on 300 r. grn. & blk.	95	80

1919. Nos. 43/4 and 40/2 surch. **REPUBLICA** and value in figures.

78. 2.	1½ c. on 15 r. brn. & black	2·00	1·50
79.	3½ c. on 25 r. orge. & blk.	70	50
80. 3.	40 c. on 65 r. on 80 r.	4·50	4·50
81.	50 c. on 115 r. on 150 r.	1·25	1·00
82.	1 c. on 130 r. on 300 r.	1·25	1·00

1921. Stamps of 1911 surch. in figures and words.

83. 9.	¼ c. on 2½ c. violet & black	80	80
85.	½ c. on 5 r. black	80	80
86.	1 c. on 10 r. green & black	80	80
87. 12.	1½ c. on 300 r. black on blue	80	80
88. –	2 c. on 20 r. red and black	80	80
89. –	2½ c. on 25 r. brown & blk.	80	80
90. 12.	3 c. on 400 r. brown & blk.	80	80
91. –	5 c. on 50 r. blue and black	80	80
92. –	7½ c. on 75 r. brown & blk.	80	80
93. –	10 c. on 100 r. brown and black on green	80	80
94. 12.	12 c. on 500 r. violet & olive	80	80
95. –	20 c. on 200 r. green and black on Pink	80	80

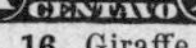

16. Giraffe. 19. Common Zebra.

1921.

96. 16.	¼ c. purple	50	40
97.	½ c. blue	50	40
98.	1 c. black and green	50	40
99.	1½ c. orange and black	50	40
100. –	2 c. black and red	55	40
101. –	2½ c. olive and black	55	40
102. –	4 c. red and black	55	40
103. –	5 c. black and blue	55	40
104. –	6 c. violet and black	55	40
105. –	7½ c. brown and black	55	40
106. –	8 c. olive and black	55	40
107. –	10 c. brown and black	55	40
108. –	15 c. red and black	55	40
109. –	20 c. blue and black	65	50
110. 19.	30 c. brown and black	90	50
111.	40 c. blue and black	90	50
112.	50 c. green and black	90	50
113.	1 e. brown and black	1·10	50
114. –	2 e. black and brown	2·00	1·25
115. –	5 e. brown and blue	1·60	1·10

DESIGNS—As Type 16: 2 c. to 6 c. Vasco da Gama. 7½ c. to 20 c. Vasco da Gama's flagship "Sao Gabriel". As Type 19: 2, 5 e. Native dhow.

CHARITY TAX STAMPS

The notes under this heading in Portugal also apply here.

1925. Marquis de Pombal Commem. Nos. C327/9 of Mozambique optd. **NYASSA.**

C 141. C 22.	15 c. brown	2·50	2·50
C 142. –	15 c. brown	2·50	2·50
C 143. C 25.	15 c. brown	2·50	2·50

POSTAGE DUE STAMPS

D 21. The "Sao Gabriel".

1924.

D 132. –	½ c. green	1·50	1·00
D 133. –	1 c. grey	1·50	1·00
D 134. –	2 c. red	1·50	1·00
D 135. –	3 c. orange	1·50	1·00
D 136. D 21.	5 c. brown	1·75	1·25
D 137.	6 c. brown	1·75	1·25
D 138.	10 c. purple	1·75	1·25
D 139. –	20 c. red	1·50	1·10
D 140. –	50 c. violet	1·50	1·25

DESIGNS: ½ c., 1 c. Giraffe. 2 c., 3 c. Common Zebra. 20 c., 50 c. Vasco da Gama.

1925. De Pombal stamps of Mozambique, Nos. D327/9 optd. **NYASSA.**

D 144. C 22.	30 c. brown	4·00	4·00
D 145. –	30 c. brown	4·00	4·00
D 146. C 25.	30 c. brown	4·00	4·00

OBOCK Pt. 6

A port and district on the Somali Coast. During 1894 the administration was moved to Djibouti, the capital of French Somali Coast, and the Obock post office was closed.

1892. Stamps of French Colonies, "Commerce" type, optd **OBOCK**.

1 J	1 c. black on blue	18·00	16·00
2	2 c. brown on buff	21·00	18·00
12	4 c. brown on grey	11·00	9·50
13	5 c. green on green	11·00	9·25
14	10 c. black on lilac	11·50	11·00
15	15 c. blue	12·00	10·50
16	20 c. red on green	25·00	20·00
17	25 c. black on pink	10·00	8·25
8	35 c. black on orange	£250	£250
18	40 c. red on buff	30·00	25·00
19	75 c. red on pink	£190	£160
20	1 f. green	40·00	35·00

1892. Nos. 14, 15, 17 and 20 surch.

39. J.	1 on 25 c. black on red	6·00	5·50
40.	2 on 10 c. black on lilac	40·00	25·00
41.	2 on 15 c. blue	6·25	6·75
42.	4 on 15 c. blue	7·00	6·75
43.	4 on 25 c. black on red	7·75	7·00
44.	5 on 25 c. black on red	11·00	8·25
45.	20 on 10 c. black on lilac	50·00	42·00
46.	30 on 10 c. black on lilac	65·00	55·00
47.	35 on 25 c. black on red	50·00	45·00
48.	75 on 1 f. olive	65·00	60·00
49.	5 f. on 1 f. olive	£525	£475

1892. "Tablet" key-type inscr "OBOCK" in red (1, 5, 15, 25, 75 c., 1 f.) or blue (others).

50 D	1 c. black on blue	1·40	1·25
51	2 c. brown on buff	60	65
52	4 c. brown on grey	1·50	1·25
53	5 c. green on green	2·25	1·50
54	10 c. black on lilac	3·75	2·25
55	15 c. blue	7·75	5·00
56	20 c. red on green	15·00	12·50
57	25 c. black on pink	14·00	12·50
58	30 c. brown on drab	11·00	9·00
59	40 c. red on yellow	11·00	8·00
60	50 c. red on pink	12·50	8·25
61	75 c. brown on orange	16·00	8·25
62	1 f. green	22·00	18·00

5.

1893.

63. 5.	2 f. grey	30·00	29·00
64.	5 f. red	80·00	75·00

The 5 f. stamp is larger than the 2 f.

6.

7.

1894.

65.	**6.**	1 c. black and red..	60	95
66.		2 c. red and green	90	95
67.		4 c. red and orange	50	1·00
68.		5 c. green and brown	1·00	85
69.		10 c. black and green	3·50	3·75
70.		15 c. blue and red	4·00	2·00
71.		20 c. orange and purple	4·50	2·25
72.		25 c. black and blue	5·00	3·00
73.		30 c. yellow and green	11·00	7·50
74.		40 c. orange and green	8·25	4·75
75.		50 c. red and blue	6·50	5·00
76.		75 c. lilac and orange	6·50	5·50
77.		1 f. olive and purple	7·50	6·00
78.	**7.**	2 f. orange and lilac	75·00	65·00
79.		5 f. red and blue	60·00	55·00
80.		10 f. lake and red	£100	90·00
81.		25 f. blue and brown	£575	£525
82.		50 f. green and lake	£625	£625

Length of sides of Type **7**: 2 f. 37 mm; 5 f. 42 mm; 10 f. 46 mm; 25, 50 f. 49 mm.

1892. Postage Due stamps of French Colonies optd **OBOCK**.

D 25.	**U 1.**	1 c. black	28·00	28·00
D 26.		2 c. black	22·00	22·00
D 27.		3 c. black	22·00	22·00
D 28.		4 c. black	15·00	16·00
D 29.		5 c. black	6·00	6·00
D 30.		10 c. black	16·00	16·00
D 31.		15 c. black	11·00	10·00
D 32.		20 c. black	14·00	14·00
D 33.		30 c. black	16·00	16·00
D 34.		40 c. black	28·00	28·00
D 35.		60 c. black	45·00	45·00
D 36.		1 f. brown	£130	£130
D 37.		2 f. brown	£130	£130
D 38.		5 f. brown	£275	£275

For later issues see **DJIBOUTI**.

OCEANIC SETTLEMENTS Pt. 6

Scattered French islands in the E. Pacific Ocean, including Tahiti and the Marquesas.

In 1957 the Oceanic Settlements were renamed French Polynesia.

1892. "Tablet" key-type.

1	D	1 c. black and red on blue	65	60
2		2 c. brown & blue on buff	90	85
3		4 c. brown & blue on grey	1·75	1·25
14		5 c. green and red	80	65
5		10 c. black & blue on lilac	12·00	5·00
15		10 c. red and blue	80	60
6		15 c. blue and red	10·50	4·75
16		15 c. grey and red	1·75	1·40
7		20 c. red & blue on green	9·25	4·00
8		25 c. black & red on pink	27·00	12·50
17		25 c. blue and red	7·50	3·25
9		30 c. brown & bl on drab	8·00	6·00
18		35 c. black & red on yell	2·50	2·00
10		40 c. red & blue on yellow	65·00	45·00
19		45 c. black & red on green	2·75	1·60
11		50 c. red and blue on pink	4·50	3·25
20		50 c. brown & red on blue	£140	£110
12		75 c. brown & red on orge	6·00	4·00
13		1 f. green and red	8·25	6·25

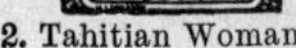

2. Tahitian Woman.

3. Kanakas.

4. Valley of Fautaua.

1913.

21	**2**	1 c. brown and violet	10	25
22		2 c. grey and brown	15	25
23		4 c. blue and orange	15	30
24		5 c. light green and green	30	45
46		5 c. black and blue	30	40
25		10 c. orange and red	40	50
47		10 c. light green & green	35	50
48		10 c. purple & red on bl	60	70
25a		15 c. black and orange	30	35
26		20 c. violet and black	25	35
49		20 c. green	35	50
50		20 c. brown and red	65	70
27	**3**	25 c. blue & ultramarine	45	50
51		25 c. red and violet	50	60
28		30 c. brown and grey	1·75	1·60
52		30 c. red and carmine	75	90
53		30 c. red and black	40	55
54		30 c. green and blue	65	80
29		35 c. red and green	35	40
30		40 c. green and black	40	45
31		45 c. red and orange	35	45
32		50 c. black and brown	7·25	5·50
55		50 c. blue & ultramarine	45	60
56		50 c. blue and grey	45	60
57		60 c. black and green	35	45
58		65 c. mauve and brown	1·25	1·40
33		75 c. violet and purple	1·00	85
59		90 c. mauve and red	8·25	8·25
34	**4**	1 f. black and red	1·40	1·00
60		1 f. 10 brown and mauve	85	85
61		1 f. 40 violet and brown	2·00	2·00
62		1 f. 50 light blue and blue	8·00	8·00
35		2 f. green and brown	2·25	2·00
36		5 f. blue and violet	5·00	5·00

1915. "Tablet" key-type optd. **E F O 1915** and bar.

37.	D.	10 c. red ..	1·90	1·90

1915. Red Cross. No. 37 surch **5c** and red cross.

38	D	10 c.+5 c. red	12·00	13·50

1915. Red Cross. Surch **5c** and red cross.

41	**2**	10 c.+5 c. orange and red	1·10	1·25

1916. Surch.

42	**2**	10 c. on 15 c. black & orge	70	75
67	**4**	25 c. on 2 f. green & brown	50	60
68		25 c. on 5 f. blue & violet	50	60
63	**3**	60 c. on 75 c. brown & blue	20	35
64	**4**	65 on 1 f. brown and blue	80	80
65		85 on 1 f. brown and blue	75	80
66	**3**	90 on 75 c. mauve and red	75	80
69	**4**	1 f. 25 on 1 f. ultram & bl	50	60
70		1 f. 50 on 1 f. lt blue & bl	1·00	1·25
71		20 f. on 5 f. mauve and red	12·50	10·00

1921. Surch **1921** and new value.

43	**2**	05 on 2 c. grey and brown	17·00	17·00
44	**3**	10 on 45 c. red and orange	17·00	17·00
45	**2**	25 on 15 c. black & orange	3·75	4·00

1924. Surch. **45 c. 1924.**

72.	**2.**	45 c. on 10 c. orange & red	95	95

1926. Surch. in words.

73.	**4.**	3 f. on 5 f. blue and grey..	1·10	90
74.		10 f. on 5 f. blk. and green	3·00	2·90

13. Papetoia Bay.

1929.

75.	**13.**	3 f. sepia and green	4·00	4·00
76.		5 f. sepia and blue	6·25	6·25
77.		10 f. sepia and red	18·00	20·00
78.		20 f. sepia and mauve	22·00	23·00

1931. "International Colonial Exhibition", Paris, key-types.

79	E	40 c. black and green	3·50	3·00
80	F	50 c. black and mauve	3·50	3·25
81	G	90 c. black and red	3·50	3·25
82	H	1 f. 50 black and blue	3·50	3·50

14. Spearing Fish.

15. Tahitian Girl.

16. Native Gods.

1934.

83.	**14.**	1 c. black	15	30
84.		2 c. red ..	15	30
85.		3 c. blue ..	15	30
86.		4 c. orange	15	35
87.		5 c. mauve	35	45
88.		10 c. brown	15	30
89.		15 c. green	25	35
90.		20 c. red ..	15	30
91.	**15.**	25 c. blue	35	45
92.		30 c. green	65	70
93.		30 c. orange	25	35
94.	**16.**	35 c. green	1·90	1·90
95.	**15.**	40 c. mauve	30	35
96.		45 c. red ..	4·75	4·50
97.		45 c. green	35	45
98.		50 c. violet	15	30
99.		55 c. blue	2·75	2·75
100.		60 c. black	25	35
101.		65 c. brown	1·60	1·60
102.		70 c. pink	40	45
103.		75 c. olive	4·00	4·00
104.		80 c. purple	70	65
105.		90 c. red ..	40	45
106.	**16.**	1 f. brown	40	50
107.		1 f. 25 purple	4·75	4·75
108.		1 f. 25 red	40	50
109.		1 f. 40 orange	40	50
110.		1 f. 50 blue	45	50
111.		1 f. 60 violet	40	50
112.		1 f. 75 green	3·25	3·00
113.		2 f. red ..	35	40
114.		2 f. 25 blue	40	50
115.		2 f. 50 black	55	60
116.		3 f. orange	50	60
117.		5 f. mauve	50	70
118.		10 f. green	1·50	1·60
119.		20 f. brown	2·00	2·00

17. Flying-boat.

1934. Air.

120.	**17.**	5 f. green	50	60

1937. International Exhibition, Paris. As Nos. 168/73 of St.-Pierre et Miquelon.

121.		20 c. violet	1·10	1·10
122.		30 c. green	1·10	1·10
123.		40 c. red	1·40	1·40
124.		50 c. brown	1·25	1·60
125.		90 c. red ..	1·40	1·90
126.		1 f. 50 blue	1·75	2·75

1938. Int. Anti-Cancer Fund. As T **33** of Mauritania.

127.		1 f. 75+50 c. blue	8·50	8·75

1939. New York World's Fair. As T **28** of Mauritania.

128.		1 f. 25 red..	1·10	1·10
129.		2 f. 25 blue	1·10	1·10

1939. 150th Anniv. of French Revolution. As T **29** of Mauritania.

130		45 c.+25 c. green and black (postage)	8·75	8·75
131		70 c.+30 c. brown & black	8·75	8·75
132		90 c.+35 c. orange & black	8·75	8·75
133		1 f. 25+1 f. red and black	8·75	8·75
134		2 f. 25+2 f. blue and black	8·75	8·75
135		5 f+4 f. black & orge (air)	17·00	17·00

1941. Adherence to General de Gaulle. Optd **FRANCE LIBRE**. (a) Nos. 75/8.

136	**13**	3 f. brown and green	3·25	
137		5 f. brown and blue	3·25	
138		10 f. brown and red	9·00	
139		20 f. brown and mauve	65·00	

(b) Nos. 106 and 115/19.

140	**16**	1 f. brown	2·25	2·75
141		2 f. 50 black	2·50	3·50
142		3 f. red	2·75	3·50
143		5 f. mauve	3·25	3·50
144		10 f. green	35·00	
145		20 f. brown	32·00	

(c) Air stamp of 1934.

146	**17**	5 f. green	1·90	1·90

19. Polynesian Travelling Canoe.

1942. Free French Issue. (a) Postage.

147.	**19.**	5 c. brown	15	30
148.		10 c. blue	15	30
149.		25 c. green	15	30
150.		30 c. red ..	15	30
151.		40 c. green	15	30
152.		80 c. purple	15	30
153.		1 f. mauve	20	35
154.		1 f. 50 red	25	35
155.		2 f. black	25	30
156.		2 f. 50 blue	60	1·10
157.		4 f. violet	40	55
158.		5 f. yellow	50	70
159.		10 f. brown	75	85
160.		20 f. green	90	90

(b) Air. As T **30** of New Caledonia.

161.		1 f. orange	40	50
162.		1 f. 50 red	40	50
163.		5 f. purple	50	60
164.		10 f. black	75	80
165.		25 f. blue	1·10	1·25
166.		50 f. green	1·10	1·25
167.		100 f. red	1·00	1·25

1944. Mutual Aid and Red Cross Funds. As T **31** of New Caledonia.

168.		5 f.+20 f. blue	65	80

1945. Surch. in figures.

169.	**19.**	50 c. on 5 c. brown	25	35
170.		60 c. on 5 c. brown	25	35
171.		70 c. on 5 c. brown	25	35
172.		1 f. 20 on 5 c. brown	25	35
173.		2 f. 40 on 25 c. green	60	70
174.		3 f. on 25 c. green	35	45
175.		4 f. 50 on 25 c. green	70	85
176.		15 f. on 2 f. 50 blue	95	1·10

1945. Eboue. As T **32** of New Caledonia.

177.		2 f. black ..	30	40
178.		25 f. green	95	1·10

1946. Air. Victory. As T **34** of New Caledonia.

179.		8 f. green ..	75	1·10

1946. Air. From Chad to the Rhine. As Nos. 300/5 of New Caledonia.

180.		5 f. red	1·00	1·10
181.		10 f. brown	1·00	1·10
182.		15 f. green	1·00	1·10
183.		20 f. red	1·50	1·50
184.		25 f. purple	1·60	1·90
185.		50 f. black	2·00	2·25

21. Moorea Coastline.

22. Tahitian Girl.

23. Wandering Albatross over Moorea.

1948. (a) Postage as T **21/22**.

186.	**21.**	10 c. brown	15	30
187.		30 c. green	15	30
188.		40 c. blue	15	30
189.	–	50 c. lake	30	40
190.	–	60 c. olive	30	40
191.	–	80 c. blue	30	40
192.	–	1 f. lake	30	40
193.	–	1 f. 20 blue	30	40
194.	–	1 f. 50 blue	30	40
195.	**22.**	2 f. brown	50	60
196.		2 f. 40 lake	65	70
197.		3 f. violet	5·00	1·50
198.		4 f. blue	65	65
199.	–	5 f. brown	75	70
200.	–	6 f. blue	90	75
201.	–	9 f. brown, black and red	6·00	5·00
202.	–	10 f. olive	2·75	1·25
203.	–	15 f. red	3·00	1·50
204.	–	20 f. blue	3·50	1·90
205.	–	25 f. brown	2·75	2·50

(b) Air. As T 23.

206.	–	13 f. light blue and deep blue	6·00	3·75
207.	**23.**	50 f. lake	13·50	8·75
208.	–	100 f. violet	8·50	5·50
209.	–	200 f. blue	25·00	16·00

DESIGNS—As T **22**: 50 c. to 80 c. Kanaka fishermen. 9 f. Bora-Bora girl. 1 f. to 1 f. 50, Faa village, 5 f., 6 f., 10 f. Bora-Bora and Pandanus pine. 15 f. to 25 f. Polynesian girls. As T **23**: 13 f. Pahia Peak and palms. 100 f. Airplane over Moorea. 200 f. Wandering albatross over Maupiti Island.

1949. Air. 75th Anniv. of U.P.U. As T **38** of New Caledonia.

210.		10 f. blue	7·50	9·00

1950. Colonial Welfare. As T **39** of New Caledonia.

211.		10 f.+2 f. green and blue	2·50	2·75

1952. Centenary of Military Medals. As T **40** of New Caledonia.

212.		3 f. violet, yellow & green	5·25	5·50

25. "Nafea" (after Gauguin). 26. Schooner in Dry Dock, Papeete.

1953. Air. 50th Death Anniv. of Gauguin (painter).

213.	25.	14 f. sepia, red and turq.	55·00	55·00

1954. Air. 10th Anniv. of Liberation. As T **42** of New Caledonia.

214.		3 f. green and turquoise	2·75	2·50

1956. Economic and Social Development Fund.

215.	26.	3 f. turquoise	1·40	1·00

POSTAGE DUE STAMPS

1926. Postage Due stamps of France surch **Etabts Francais de l'Oceanie 2 francs a percevoir** (No. D80) or optd **Etablissements Francais de l'Oceanie** (others).

D 73.	D 11.	5 c. blue	25	45
D 74.		10 c. brown	25	45
D 75.		20 c. olive	65	70
D 76.		30 c. red	65	70
D 77.		40 c. red	1·40	1·40
D 78.		60 c. green	1·40	1·40
D 79.		1 f. red on yellow	1·25	1·40
D 80.		2 f. on 1 f. red	1·90	1·90
D 81.		3 f. mauve	5·50	5·50

D 14. Fautaua Falls. D 24.

1929.

D 82.	D 14.	5 c. brown and blue	35	40
D 83.		10 c. green and orange	35	40
D 84.		30 c. red and brown	80	80
D 85.		50 c. brown and green	65	70
D 86.		60 c. green and violet	1·90	2·00
D 87.	–	1 f. mauve and blue	1·25	1·40
D 88.	–	2 f. brown and red	80	80
D 89.	–	3 f. green and blue	90	95

DESIGN: 1 to 3 f. Polynesian man.

1948.

D 210.	D 24.	10 c. green	15	30
D 211.		30 c. brown	25	30
D 212.		50 c. red	25	30
D 213.		1 f. blue	30	35
D 214.		2 f. green	50	55
D 215.		3 f. red	65	70
D 216.		4 f. violet	75	85
D 217.		5 f. mauve	1·10	1·25
D 218.		10 f. blue	2·00	2·25
D 219.		20 f. lake	2·50	2·75

For later issues see **FRENCH POLYNESIA.**

OLDENBURG Pt. 7

A former Grand Duchy in North Germany. In 1867 it joined the North German Federation.

72 grote = 1 thaler.

1. 2. 3.

1852. Imperf.

1	1	1/3 sgr. black on green	£1000	£900
2		1/30th. black on blue	£300	18·00
5		1/15th. black on red	£650	75·00
8		1/10th. black on yellow	£700	75·00

1859. Imperf.

17.	2.	1/4 g. orange	£225	£4500
10.		1/3 g. black on green	£1900	£2750
19.		1/3 g. green	£375	£750
21.		1/2 g. brown	£350	£425
11.		1 g. black on blue	£550	30·00
23.		1 g. blue	£180	£120
15.		2 g. black on red	£800	£550
26.		2 g. red	£375	£400
16.		3 g. black on yellow	£800	£500
28.		3 g. yellow	£375	£400

1862. Roul.

30	3	1/3 g. green	£190	£170
32		1/2 g. orange	£170	95·00
42		1 g. red	5·00	35·00
36		2 g. blue	£170	35·00
39		3 g. bistre	£170	40·00

OMAN (SULTANATE) Pt. 19

In Jan. 1971, the independent Sultanate of Muscat and Oman was renamed Sultanate of Oman.

NOTE. Labels inscribed "State of Oman" or "Oman Imamate State" are said to have been issued by a rebel administration under the Imam of Oman. There is no convincing evidence that these labels had any postal use within Oman and they are therefore omitted. They can be found, however, used on covers which appear to emanate from Amman and Baghdad.

1000 baizas = 1 rial saidi

1971. Nos. 110/21 of Muscat and Oman optd. **SULTANATE of OMAN** in English and Arabic.

122.	12.	5 b. purple	15	15
123.		10 b. brown	20	15
124.		20 b. brown	50	15
125.	A.	25 b. black and violet	80	20
126.		30 b. black and blue	90	25
127.		40 b. black and orange	1·00	25
128.	14.	50 b. mauve and blue	1·40	30
129.	B.	75 b. green and brown	1·75	70
130.	C.	100 b. blue and orange	2·25	70
131.	D.	1/4 r. brown and green	6·50	3·25
132.	E.	1/2 r. violet and red	11·00	1·50
133.	F.	1 r. red and violet	19·00	14·00

19. Sultan Qabus and Buildings ("Land Development").

1971. National Day. Multicoloured.

134.		10 b. Type **19**	40	15
135.		40 b. Sultan in military uniform, and Omanis ("Freedom")	1·40	60
136.		50 b. Doctors and patients ("Health Services")	1·50	65
137.		100 b. Children in class ("Education")	2·75	2·00

1971. No. 94 of Muscat and Oman, optd. with **SULTANATE of OMAN** in English and Arabic.

138.		5 b. on 3 b. purple	2·00	2·00

21. Child in Class.

1971. 25th Anniv. of U.N.I.C.E.F.

139.	21.	50 b. + 25 b. multicoloured	3·25	3·00

22. Book Year Emblem.

1972. Int. Book Year.

140.	22.	25 b. multicoloured	2·50	1·25

1972. Nos. 110/12 of Muscat and Oman optd with **SULTANATE of OMAN** in English and Arabic.

141.		5 b. purple	50	50
142.		10 b. brown	50	50
143.		20 b. brown	1·25	1·25

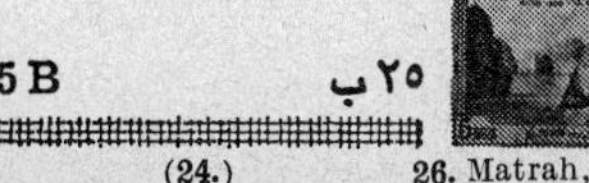

سلطنة عمان

25 B ٢٥ ب

(24.) 26. Matrah, 1809.

1972. Nos. 102 of Muscat and Oman and 127 of Oman optd. with T **24**.

144.		25 b. on 1 r.	5·00	3·75
145.		25 b. on 40 b.	5·00	3·75

1972.

158	26.	5 b. multicoloured	15	10
147		10 b. multicoloured	25	10
148		20 b. multicoloured	45	15
192		25 b. multicoloured	40	15
193	–	30 b. multicoloured	45	20
194	–	40 b. multicoloured	60	25
195	–	50 b. multicoloured	65	25
196	–	75 b. multicoloured	1·00	60
154	–	100 b. multicoloured	1·50	45
155	–	1/4 r. multicoloured	2·75	1·25
156	–	1/2 r. multicoloured	6·50	3·00
157	–	1 r. multicoloured	13·00	7·50

DESIGNS—(26 × 21 mm.) 30 b. to 75 b. Shinas, 1809. (42 × 25 mm.) 100 b. to 1 r. Muscat, 1809.

29. Government Buildings.

1973. Opening of Ministerial Complex.

170.	29.	25 b. multicoloured	65	35
171.		100 b. multicoloured	2·75	1·50

30. Oman Crafts (dhow building).

1973. National Day. Multicoloured.

172.		15 b. Type **30**	40	20
173.		50 b. Seeb International Airport	2·25	1·25
174.		65 b. Dhow and tanker	2·00	1·25
175.		100 b. "Ship of the Desert" (camel)	2·75	1·75

31. Aerial View of Port.

1974. Inaug. of Port Qabus.

176.	31.	100 b. multicoloured	3·00	2·25

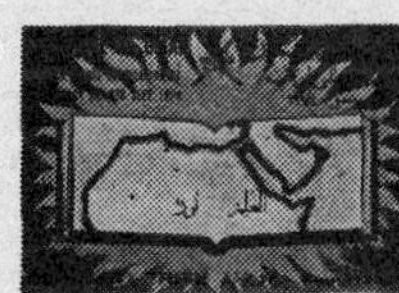

32. Map on Open Book.

1974. Illiteracy Eradication Campaign. **Mult.**

177.		25 b. Type **32**	50	30
178.		100 b. Hands reaching for open book (vert.)	2·25	1·75

33. Sultan Qabus bin Said and Emblems.

1974. Cent. of U.P.U.

179.	33.	100 b. multicoloured	1·00	1·25

MINIMUM PRICE

The minimum price quoted is 5p which represents a handling charge rather than a basis for valuing common stamps. For further notes about prices see introductory pages.

34. Arab Scribe.

1975. "Eradicate Illiteracy".

180.	34.	25 b. multicoloured	1·75	80

35. New Harbour, Mina Raysoot.

1975. National Day. Multicoloured.

181.		30 b. Type **35**	25	10
182.		50 b. Stadium and map	40	20
183.		75 b. Water Desalination Plant	65	50
184.		100 b. Television Station	85	70
185.		150 b. Satellite Earth Station and map	1·25	1·00
186.		250 b. Telecommunications symbols and map	2·00	2·00

36. Arab Woman and Child with Nurse.

1975. International Women's Year. **Mult.**

187.		75 b. Type **36**	55	45
188.		150 b. Mother and children (vert.)	1·00	1·00

37. Presenting Colours and Opening of Seeb-Nizwa Highway.

1976. National Day. Multicoloured.

201.		25 b. Type **37**	45	15
202.		40 b. Parachutists and harvesting	90	45
203.		75 b. Helicopters and Victory Day procession	1·75	90
204.		150 b. Road construction and Salalah T.V. Station	2·00	1·60

38. Great Bath, Moenjodaro.

1977. "Save Moenjodaro" Campaign.

205.	38.	125 b. multicoloured	2·50	1·75

39. A.P.U. Emblem. 40. Coffee Pots.

1977. 25th Anniv. of Arab Postal Union.

206.	39.	30 b. multicoloured	70	35
207.		75 b. multicoloured	1·90	1·10

1977. National Day. Multicoloured.

208. 40 b. Type **40** 40 30
209. 75 b. Earthenware pots .. 70 55
210. 100 b. Khor Rori inscriptions 85 65
211. 150 b. Silver jewellery .. 1·40 1·00

1978. Surch in English and Arabic.

212. 40 b. on 150 b. mult. (No. 185) .. .. .. 7·00 7·00
213. 50 b. on 150 b. mult. (No. 188) .. .. .. 8·50 8·50
214. 75 b. on 250 b. mult. (No. 186) .. .. .. 13·00 13·00

42. Mount Arafat Pilgrims and Kaaba.

1978. Pilgrimage to Mecca.

215. **42.** 40 b. multicoloured .. 1·40 75

43. Jalali Fort.

1978. National Day. Forts. Multicoloured.

216. 20 b. Type **43** 20 15
217. 25 b. Nizwa Fort 20 15
218. 40 b. Rostaq Fort .. 35 25
219. 50 b. Sohar Fort 40 40
220. 75 b. Bahla Fort 55 65
221. 100 b. Jibrin Fort .. 75 85

44. World Map, Koran and Symbols of Arab Achievements.

1979. The Arabs.

222. **44.** 40 b. multicoloured .. 45 35
223. 100 b. multicoloured .. 1·40 90

45. Child on Swing.

1979. International Year of the Child.

224. **45.** 40 b. multicoloured .. 1·50 1·00

46. Gas Plant.

1979. National Day. Multicoloured.

225 25 b. Type **46** 80 30
226 75 b. Dhow and modern trawler .. .. .. 1·25 1·10

47. Sultan Qabus on Horseback.

1979. Armed Forces Day. Multicoloured.

227. 40 b. Type **47** .. .. 2·25 75
228. 100 b. Soldier .. .. 2·50 1·75

48. Mosque, Mecca.

1980. 1400th Anniv of Hegira. Multicoloured.

229. 50 b. Type **48** 55 40
230. 150 b. Mosque and Kaaba 1·75 1·40

49. Bab Alkabir.

1980. National Day. Multicoloured.

231. 75 b. Type **49** 40 40
232. 100 b. Corniche 85 55
233. 250 b. Polo match .. 1·25 1·25
234. 500 b. Omani women .. 3·00 3·25

50. Sultan and Naval Patrol Boat.

1980. Armed Forces Day. Multicoloured.

235. 150 b. Type **50** .. .. 1·25 1·00
236. 750 b. Sultan and mounted soldiers .. .. 4·50 4·50

51. Policewoman helping Children across Road.

1981. National Police Day. Multicoloured.

237. 50 b. Type **51** 60 40
238. 100 b. Police bandsmen .. 1·00 80
239. 150 b. Mounted police .. 1·50 1·25
240. ½ r. Police Headquarters .. 4·50 3·50

1981. Nos. 231, 234 and 235/6 surch **POSTAGE** and new value in English and Arabic.

241. **50.** 20 b. on 150 b. mult. .. 50 30
242. – 30 b. on 750 b. mult. .. 80 45
243. **49.** 50 b. on 75 b. mult. .. 1·40 70
244. – 100 b. on 500 b. mult. .. 2·50 1·40

53. Sultan's Crest.

1981. Welfare of Blind.

245. **53.** 10 b. blk., blue and red 45 15

54. Palm Tree, Fishes and Wheat.

1981. World Food Day.

246. **54.** 50 b. multicoloured .. 1·40 60

55. Pilgrims at Prayer.

1981. Pilgrimage to Mecca.

247. **55.** 50 b. multicoloured .. 1·40 55

56. Al Razha.

1981. National Day. Multicoloured.

248. 160 b. Type **56** .. .. 1·25 1·25
249. 300 b. Sultan Qabus bin Said .. .. .. 2·00 2·00

57. Muscat Port, 1981.

1981. Retracing the Voyage of Sinbad. Mult.

250 50 b. Type **57** 50 50
251 100 b. "Sohar" (replica of medieval dhow) .. 1·00 1·00
252 130 b. Map showing route of voyage .. .. 1·25 1·25
253 200 b. Muscat Harbour, 1650 .. .. .. 1·75 1·75

58. Parachute-drop.

1981. Armed Forces Day. Multicoloured.

255. 100 b. Type **58** .. .. 1·40 85
256. 400 b. Missile-armed corvettes .. .. 3·25 3·25

59. Police Launch. **60.** "Nerium mascatense".

1982. National Police Day. Multicoloured.

257. 50 b. Type **59** .. .. 1·25 60
258. 100 b. Royal Oman Police Band at Cardiff .. 1·50 85

1982. Flora and Fauna. Multicoloured.

259. 5 b. Type **60** .. .. ·10 10
260. 10 b. "Dionysia mira" .. 10 10
261. 20 b. "Teucrium mascatense" 10 10
262. 25 b. "Geranium mascatense" 10 10
263. 30 b. "Cymatium boschi" (horiz.) 15 15
264. 40 b. "Acteon eloiseae" (horiz.) 15 15
265. 50 b. "Cypraea teulerei" (horiz.) 20 20
266. 75 b. "Cypraea pulchra" (horiz.) 30 30
267. 100 b. Arabian chukar (25 × 33 mm) .. .. 1·10 60
268. ½ r. Hoopoe (25 × 33 mm.) 2·50 2·00
269. ½ r. Arabian tahr (25 × 39 mm.) .. .. 2·50 2·50
270. 1 r. Arabian oryx (25 × 39 mm.) .. .. 5·00 5·00

Nos. 259/62 show flowers, Nos. 263/6 shells, Nos. 267/8 birds and Nos. 269/70 animals.

61. Palm Tree.

1982. Arab Palm Tree Day. Multicoloured.

271. 40 b. Type **61** 60 30
272. 100 b. Palm tree and nuts 1·40 80

62. I.T.U. Emblem.

1982. I.T.U. Delegates Conference, Nairobi.

273. **62.** 100 b. multicoloured .. 1·40 80

63. Emblem and Cups.

1982. Municipalities Week.

274. **63.** 40 b. multicoloured .. 90 50

64. State Consultative Council Inaugural Session.

1982. National Day. Multicoloured.

275. 40 b. Type **64** 45 30
276. 100 b. Petroleum refinery 1·75 80

65. Sultan meeting Troops.

1982. Armed Forces Day Multicoloured.

277. 50 b. Type **65** 85 35
278. 100 b. Mounted army band 1·90 90

66. Police Motorcyclist and Headquarters.

1983. National Police Day.

279. **66.** 50 b. multicoloured .. 1·25 60

INDEX

Countries can be quickly located by referring to the index at the end of this volume.

67. Satellite, W.C.Y. Emblem and Dish Aerial.

1983. World Communications Year.

280.	**67.**	50 b. multicoloured ..	1·25	60

68. Bee Hives.

1983. Bee-keeping. Multicoloured.

281.	50 b. Type **68**	1·10	95
282.	50 b. Bee collecting nectar	1·10	95

Nos. 281/2 were issued together in se-tenant pairs throughout the sheet, each pair forming a composite design.

69. Pilgrims at Mudhalfa.

1983. Pilgrimage to Mecca.

283.	**69.**	40 b. multicoloured ..	1·25	60

70. Emblem, Map and Sultan.

1983. Omani Youth Year.

284.	**70.**	50 b. multicoloured ..	1·00	55

71. Sohar Copper Mine.

1983. National Day. Multicoloured.

285.	50 b. Type **71**	85	40
286.	100 b. Sultan Qabus University & foundation stone	1·25	90

72. Machine Gun Post.

1983. Armed Forces Day.

287.	**72.**	100 b. multicoloured ..	2·25	1·25

73. Police Cadets Parade.

1984. National Police Day.

288.	**73.**	100 b. multicoloured ..	1·75	1·00

74. Footballers and Cup.

1984. Seventh Arabian Gulf Cup Football Tournament. Multicoloured.

289.	40 b. Type **74**	60	35
290.	50 b. Emblem and pictograms of footballers ..	80	45

75. Stoning the Devil.

1984. Pilgrimage to Mecca.

291.	**75.**	50 b. multicoloured ..	70	45

76. New Central Post Office and Automatic Sorting Machine.

1984. National Day. Multicoloured.

292.	130 b. Type **76**	90	85
293.	160 b. Map of Oman with telecommunications symbols	1·10	1·00

77. Scouts reading Map.

1984. 16th Arab Scouts Conference, Muscat. Multicoloured.

294.	50 b. Scouts pegging tent	35	30
295.	50b. Type **77**	35	30
296.	130 b. Scouts assembled around flag ..	95	85
297.	130 b. Scout, cub, guide, brownie and scout leaders	95	85

78. Sultan, Fighter Planes and "Al Munassir" (landing craft).

1984. Armed Forces Day.

298.	**78.**	100 b. multicoloured ..	1·50	85

79. Helicopter lifting Man from Tanker.

1985. National Police Day.

299.	**79.**	100 b. multicoloured ..	2·50	1·40

80. Al-Khaif Mosque and Tents, Mina.

1985. Pilgrimage to Mecca.

300.	**80.**	50 b. multicoloured ..	40	35

81. I.Y.Y. Emblem and Youth holding Olive Branches.

1985. International Youth Year. Mult.

301.	50 b. Type **81**	35	30
302.	100 b. Emblem and young people at various activities	75	60

82. Palace before and after Restoration.

1985. Restoration of Jabrin Palace. Mult.

303.	100 b. Type **82**	75	60
304.	250 b. Restored ceiling ..	2·75	2·50

83. Drummers.

1985. International Omani Traditional Music Symposium.

305.	**83.**	50 b. multicoloured ..	45	35

84. Scenes of Child Care and Emblem.

1985. United Nations Children's Fund Child Health Campaign.

306.	**84.**	50 b. multicoloured ..	45	35

85. Flags around Map of Gulf.

1985. 6th Supreme Council Session of Gulf Co-operation Council, Muscat. Multicoloured.

307.	40 b. Type **85**	40	30
308.	50 b. Portraits of rulers of Council member countries	45	35

86. Sultan Qabus University and Students.

1985. National Day. Multicoloured.

309.	20 b. Type **86**	20	15
310.	50 b. Tractor and Oxen ploughing field	45	35
311.	100 b. Port Qabus cement factory and Oman Chamber of Commerce ..	90	75
312.	200 b. Road bridge, airplane and communications centre	2·25	1·40
313.	250 b. Portrait of Sultan Qabus (vert.)	1·75	1·25

87. Military Exercise at Sea.

1985. Armed Forces Day.

314.	**87.**	100 b. multicoloured ..	1·50	85

88. "Chaetodon collaris".

1985. Marine Life. Multicoloured.

315	20 b. Type **88**	20	15
316	50 b. "Chaetodon melapterus"	45	35
317	100 b. "Chaetodon gardineri"	90	75
318	150 b. "Scomberomorus commerson" (horiz) ..	1·40	1·00
319	200 b. Lobster (horiz) ..	1·60	1·25

89. Frankincense Tree.

1985. Frankincense Production.

320.	**89.**	100 b. multicoloured ..	70	40
321.		3 r. multicoloured ..	12·00	8·00

90. Camel Corps Member

1986. National Police Day.

322.	**90.**	50 b. multicoloured ..	70	35

91. Cadet Barquentine "Shabab Oman", 1986.

1986. Participation of "Shabab Oman" in Statue of Liberty Centenary Celebrations. Multicoloured.

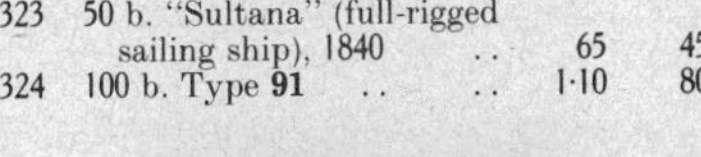

323	50 b. "Sultana" (full-rigged sailing ship), 1840 ..	65	45
324	100 b. Type **91**	1·10	80

92. Crowd around Holy Kaaba.

1986. Pilgrimage to Mecca.

326.	**92.**	50 b. multicoloured ..	70	35

93. Scouts erecting Tent.

1986. 17th Arab Scout Camp, Salalah. Multicoloured.

327.	50 b. Type **93**	50	30
328.	100 b. Scouts making survey	1·00	60

94. Sports Complex.

1986. Inauguration of Sultan Qabus Sports Complex.

329.	**94.**	100 b. multicoloured ..	80	60

95. Mother and Baby, Emblem and Tank on Globe.

1986. International Peace Year.

330.	**95.**	130 b. multicoloured ..	95	70

96. Al-Sahwa Tower.

1986. National Day. Multicoloured.

331	50 b. Type **96**	50	30
332	100 b. Sultan Qabus University (inauguration)	1·00	60
333	130 b. 1966 stamps and F.D.C. cancellation (20th anniv of first Oman stamp issue) (57 × 27 mm)	1·25	1·10

97. Camel Corps.

1987. National Police Day.

334.	**97.**	50 b. multicoloured ..	60	35

98. Family.

1987. Arabian Gulf Social Work Week.

335.	**98.**	50 b. multicoloured ..	45	35

99. Aqueduct.

101. Examples of Work and Hand holding Cup.

100. Crowd around Holy Kaaba.

1987. International Environment Day. Mult.

336	50 b. Greater flamingos ..	1·25	40
337	130 b. Type **99**	1·00	70

1987. Pilgrimage to Mecca. Multicoloured.

338.	50 b. Type **100**	45	40
339.	50 b. Al-Khaif Mosque and tents, Mina	45	40
340.	50 b. Stoning the Devil ..	45	40
341.	50 b. Pilgrims at Mudhalfa	45	40
342.	50 b. Pilgrims at prayer ..	45	40
343.	50 b. Mount Arafat, pilgrims and Kaaba ..	45	40

1987. 3rd Municipalities Month.

344.	**101.**	50 b. multicoloured ..	40	30

102. Marine Science and Fisheries Centre.

1987. National Day. Multicoloured.

345.	50 b. Type **102**	40	30
346.	130 b. Royal Hospital ..	1·00	80

103. Radio Operators.

1987. 15th Anniv. of Royal Omani Amateur Radio Society.

347.	**103.**	130 b. multicoloured	85	75

104 Weaver

1988. Traditional Crafts. Multicoloured.

348	50 b. Type **104**	30	25
349	100 b. Potter	55	50
350	150 b. Halwa maker ..	75	70
351	200 b. Silversmith ..	90	85

105 Showjumping

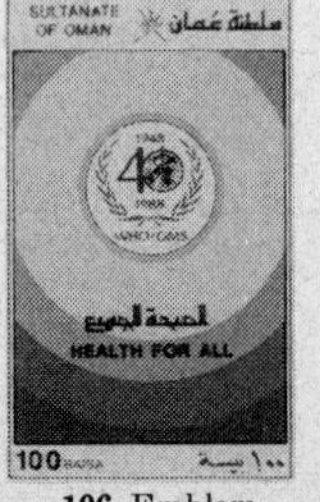

106 Emblem

1988. Olympic Games, Seoul. Multicoloured.

353	100 b. Type **105**	45	40
354	100 b. Hockey	45	40
355	100 b. Football	45	40
356	100 b. Running	45	40
357	100 b. Swimming	45	40
358	100 b. Shooting	45	40

1988. 40th Anniv of W.H.O. "Health for All".

359	**106**	100 b. multicoloured ..	45	40

107 Tending Land and Crops

1988. National Day. Agriculture Year. Mult.

360	100 b. Type **107**	45	40
361	100 b. Livestock	45	40

108 Dhahira Region (woman's)

1989. Costumes. Multicoloured.

363	30 b. Type **108**	15	10
364	40 b. Eastern region (woman's)	20	15
365	50 b. Batinah region (woman's)	25	20
366	100 b. Interior region (woman's)	45	40
367	130 b. Southern region (woman's)	60	50
368	150 b. Muscat region (woman's)	70	60
369	200 b. Dhahira region (man's)	90	85
370	¼ r. Dhahira region (man's)	1·00	90
371	½ r. Southern region (man's)	1·75	1·50
372	1 r. Muscat region (man's)	3·25	3·00

109 Fishing

1989. National Day. Agriculture Year. Mult.

375	100 b. Type **109**	45	40
376	100 b. Agriculture ..	45	40

110 Flags and Omani State Arms

1989. 10th Supreme Council Session of Arab Co-operation Council, Muscat. Multicoloured.

377	50 b. Type **110**	25	20
378	50 b. Council emblem and Sultan Qabus	25	20

111 Emblem and Map

1990. 5th Anniv (1989) of Gulf Investment Corporation.

379	**111**	50 b. multicoloured ..	25	20
380		130 b. multicoloured ..	50	45

112 Emblem and Airplane

113 Map

1990. 40th Anniv of Gulf Air.

381	**112**	80 b. multicoloured ..	50	30

1990. Omani Ophiolite Symposium, Muscat.

382	**113**	80 b. multicoloured ..	20	10
383		150 b. multicoloured ..	40	35

114 Ahmed bin Na'aman al-Ka'aby (envoy), "Sultana" and Said bin Sultan

1990. 150th Anniv of First Omani Envoy's Journey to U.S.A.

384	**114**	200 b. multicoloured ..	85	60

115 Sultan Qabus Rose

1990. 20th Anniv of Sultan Qabus's Accession.

385	**115**	200 b. multicoloured ..	55	45

116 National Day Emblem

1990. National Day.

386	**116**	100 b. red and green on gold foil	30	25
387	–	200 b. green and red on gold foil	55	45

DESIGN: 200 b. Sultan Qabus.

117 Donor and Recipient

118 Industrial Emblems

1991. Blood Donation.

389	**117**	50 b. multicoloured ..	15	10
390		200 b. multicoloured ..	60	50

1991. National Day and Industry Year. Mult.

391	100 b. Type **118**	30	25
392	200 b. Sultan Qabus ..	60	50

119 Weapons, Military Transport and Sultan Qabus

1991. Armed Forces Day.

394	119	100 b. multicoloured ..	60	35

120 Interior of Museum and National Flags

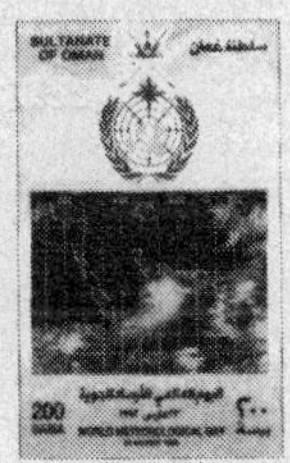

121 Satellite Picture of Asia

1992. Inauguration of Omani–French Museum, Muscat.

395	120	100 b. multicoloured ..	30	25

1992. World Meteorological Day.

397	121	220 b. multicoloured ..	80	65

122 Emblem

123 Emblem and Hands protecting Handicapped Child

1992. World Environment Day.

398	122	100 b. multicoloured ..	35	30

1992. Welfare of Handicapped Children.

399	123	70 b. multicoloured ..	25	20

124 Sultan Qabus and Books

1992. Publication of Sultan Qabus Encyclopedia of Arab Names.

400	124	100 b. multicoloured ..	35	30

125 Sultan Qabus, Factories and Industry Year Emblem

1992. National Day. Multicoloured.

401	100 b. Type **125**	35	30
402	200 b. Sultan Qabus and Majlis As'shura (Consultative Council) emblem	70	60

126 Mounted Policemen and Sultan Qabus

1993. National Police Day.

403	126	80 b. multicoloured ..	30	25

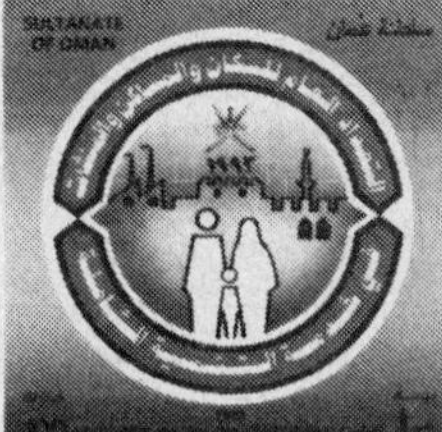

127 Census Emblem

1993. Population and Housing Census.

404	127	100 b. multicoloured ..	35	30

128 Frigate and Sultan Qabus presenting Colours

1993. Navy Day.

405	128	100 b. multicoloured ..	35	30

129 Youth Year Emblem

1993. National Day. Youth Year. Mult.

406	100 b. Type **129**	35	30
407	200 b. Sultan Qabus ..	70	60

130 Scout Headquarters and Emblem

1993. 61st Anniv of Scouting in Oman (408) and 10th Anniv of Sultan Qabus as Chief Scout (409). Multicoloured.

408	100 b. Type **130**	35	30
409	100 b. Scout camp and Sultan Qabus	35	30

Nos. 408/9 were issued together, se-tenant, forming a composite design.

131 Sei Whale and School of Dolphins

1993. Whales and Dolphins in Oman Waters. Multicoloured.

410	100 b. Type **131**	35	30
411	100 b. Sperm whale and dolphins	35	30

Nos. 410/11 were issued together, se-tenant, forming a composite design.

PAKHOI Pt. 17

An Indo-Chinese Post Office in China, closed in 1922.

1903. Stamps of Indo-China, "Tablet". key-type, surch. **PACKHOI** and value in Chinese.

1.	D.	1 c. black on blue ..	1·60	1·60
2.		2 c. brown on yellow ..	1·40	1·40
3.		4 c. red on grey	1·00	1·00
4.		5 c. green	1·00	1·00
5.		10 c. red	90	90
6.		15 c. grey	90	90
7.		20 c. red on green ..	1·60	1·60
8.		25 c. blue	1·60	1·60
9.		25 c. black on red ..	90	90
10.		30 c. brown	1·60	1·60
11.		40 c. red on yellow ..	12·00	12·00
12.		50 c. red on rose ..	£110	£110
13.		50 c. brown on blue ..	14·00	14·00
14.		75 c. brown on orange ..	15·00	15·00
15.		1 f. olive	22·00	22·00
16.		5 f. mauve on lilac ..	40·00	40·00

1906. Stamps of Indo-China surch. **PAK-HOI** and value in Chinese.

17.	**8.**	1 c. olive	40	40
18.		2 c. red on yellow ..	40	40
19.		4 c. purple on grey ..	40	40
20.		5 c. green	40	40
21.		10 c. red	40	40
22.		15 c. brown on blue ..	1·10	1·10
23.		20 c. red on green ..	80	80
24.		25 c. blue	80	80
25.		30 c. brown on cream ..	80	80
26.		35 c. black on yellow ..	80	80
27.		40 c. black on grey ..	85	85
28.		50 c. olive on green ..	1·40	1·40
29.	D.	75 c. brown on orange ..	12·00	12·00
30.	**8.**	1 f. green	7·00	7·00
31.		2 f. brown on yellow ..	10·00	10·00
32.	D.	5 f. mauve on lilac ..	32·00	32·00
33.	**8.**	10 f. red on green ..	42·00	42·00

1908. Stamps of Indo-China (Native types) surch. **PAKHOI** and value in Chinese.

34.	**10.**	1 c. black and olive ..	12	12
35.		2 c. black and brown ..	15	15
36.		4 c. black and blue ..	20	20
37.		5 c. black and green ..	25	25
38.		10 c. black and red ..	25	25
39.		15 c. black and violet ..	40	40
40.	**11.**	20 c. black and violet ..	40	40
41.		25 c. black and blue ..	40	40
42.		30 c. black and brown ..	65	65
43.		35 c. black and green ..	65	65
44.		40 c. black and brown ..	65	65
45.		50 c. black and red ..	65	65
46.	**12.**	75 c. black and orange ..	2·25	2·25
47.	–	1 f. black and red ..	1·60	1·60
48.	–	2 f. black and green ..	3·75	3·75
49.	–	5 f. black and blue ..	25·00	25·00
50.	–	10 f. black and violet ..	40·00	40·00

1919. As last surch. in addition in figures and words.

51.	**10.**	$\frac{2}{5}$ c. on 1 c. blk. & olive ..	20	20
52.		$\frac{4}{5}$ c. on 2 c. blk. & brn. ..	20	20
53.		$1\frac{3}{5}$ on 4 c. blk. & blue ..	20	20
54.		2 c. on 5 c. blk. & green ..	30	30
55.		4 c. on 10 c. black & red ..	65	65
56.		6 c. on 15 c. blk. & violet ..	20	20
57.	**11.**	8 c. on 20 c. blk. & violet ..	65	65
58.		10 c. on 25 c. blk. & bl. ..	80	80
59.		12 c. on 30 c. blk. & pur. ..	40	40
60.		14 c. on 35 c. blk. & grn. ..	20	20
61.		16 c. on 40 c. blk. & brn. ..	50	50
62.		20 c. on 50 c. blk. & red ..	35	35
63.	**12.**	30 c. on 75 c. blk. & orge.	40	40
64.	–	40 c. on 1 f. blk. & red ..	3·25	3·25
65.	–	80 c. on 2 f. blk. & grn. ..	1·00	1·00
66.	–	2 pi. on 5 f. blk. & blue ..	3·25	3·25
67.	–	4 pi. on 10 f. blk. & violet	5·50	5·50

PALAU Pt. 22

Formerly part of the United States Trust Territory of the Pacific Islands, Palau became a republic on 1 January 1981. Until 1983 it continued to use United States stamps.

100 cents = 1 dollar.

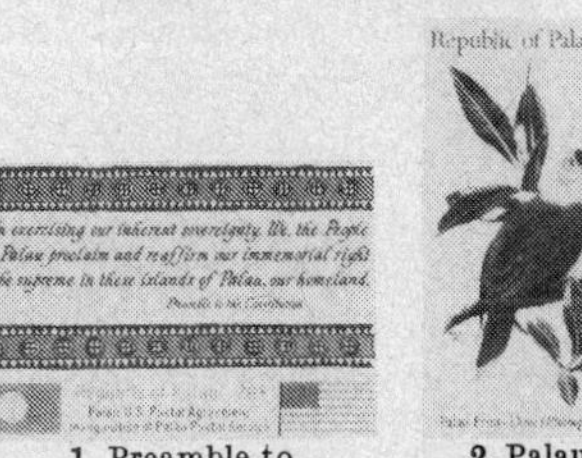

1. Preamble to Constitution. 2. Palau Fruit Dove.

1983. Inauguration of Postal Independence. Multicoloured.

1.	20 c. Type **1**	60	45
2.	20 c. Natives hunting (design from Koror meeting house)	60	45
3.	20 c. Preamble to Constitution (different)	60	45
4.	20 c. Three fishes (design from Koror meeting house)	60	45

1983. Birds. Multicoloured.

5.	20 c. Type **2**	55	40
6.	20 c. Morning bird	55	40
7.	20 c. Palau White eye (inscr. "Giant White-eye") ..	55	40
8.	20 c. Palau Fantail	55	40

3. Map Cowrie.

4. Humpback Whale.

1983. Marine Life. Multicoloured.

9	1 c. Sea fan	10	10
10	3 c. Type **3**	10	10
11	5 c. Jellyfish	15	10
12	10 c. Hawksbill turtle ..	20	10
13	13 c. Giant clam ..	25	15
14	14 c. Trumpet triton ..	30	25
15	20 c. Parrotfish	40	25
16	22 c. Bumphead parrotfish	40	30
17	25 c. Soft coral and damsel fish	40	30
17a	28 c. Chambered nautilus	55	40
18	30 c. Dappled sea cucumber	55	40
18a	33 c. Sea anemone and clownfish ..	55	40
19	37 c. Sea urchin	75	40
19a	39 c. Green sea turtle ..	75	60
19b	44 c. Pacific sailfish ..	85	70
20	50 c. Starfish	1·00	60
21	$1 Squid	2·00	1·00
22	$2 Dugong	3·75	2·25
23	$5 Pink sponge	8·50	5·50
24	$10 Spinner dolphin ..	15·00	11·00

1983. World Wildlife Fund. Whales. Mult

25	20 c. Type **4**	70	45
26	20 c. Blue whale	70	45
27	20 c. Fin whale	70	45
28	20 c. Sperm whale	70	45

5. "Spear fishing at New Moon".

6. King Abba Thulle.

1983. Christmas. Paintings by Charlie Gibbons. Multicoloured.

29.	20 c. Type **5**	55	35
30.	20 c. "Taro Gardening" ..	55	35
31.	20 c. "First Child Ceremony"	55	35
32.	20 c. "Traditional Feast at the Bai"	55	35
33.	20 c. "Spear Fishing from Red Canoe"	55	35

1983. Bicentenary of Captain Henry Wilson's Voyage to Palau.

34.	**6.**	20 c. brn., bl. & deep bl.	50	35
35.	–	20 c. brn., bl. & deep bl.	50	35
36.	–	20 c. brn., bl. & deep bl.	50	35
37.	–	20 c. brn., bl. & deep bl.	50	35
38.	–	20 c. brn., bl. & deep bl.	50	35
39.	–	20 c. brn., bl. & deep bl.	50	35
40.	–	20 c. brn., bl. & deep bl.	50	35
41.	–	20 c. brn., bl. & deep bl.	50	35

DESIGNS—VERT. No. 37, Ludee (King Abba Thulle's wife); 38, Capt. Henry Wilson; 41, Prince Lee Boo. HORIZ (47×20 mm). 35, Mooring in Koror; 36, Village scene in Pelew Islands; 39, Approaching Pelew; 40, Englishman's camp on Ulong.

7. Triton Trumpet.

1984. Sea Shells (1st series). Multicoloured.
42 20 c. Type **7** 50 40
43 20 c. Horned helmet 50 40
44 20 c. Giant clam 50 40
45 20 c. Laciniate conch 50 40
46 20 c. Royal cloak scallop 50 40
47 20 c. Triton trumpet (diff) 50 40
48 20 c. Horned helmet (diff) 50 40
49 20 c. Giant clam (different) 50 40
50 20 c. Laciniate conch (diff) 50 40
51 20 c. Royal cloak scallop (different) 50 40

Nos. 43/6 have mauve backgrounds, Nos. 48/51 blue backgrounds.

See also Nos. 145/9, 194/8, 231/5, 256/60 and 515/19.

8. White-tailed Tropic Bird.

1984. Air. Birds. Multicoloured.
52. 40 c. Type **8** 1·00 75
53. 40 c. White tern (inscr. "Fairy Tern") 1·00 75
54. 40 c. White-capped noddy (inscr. "Black Noddy") 1·00 75
55. 40 c. Black-naped tern 1·00 75

9. "Oroolong" (Wilson's schooner).

1984. 19th Universal Postal Union Congress Philatelic Salon, Hamburg. Multicoloured.
56 40 c. Type **9** 1·00 75
57 40 c. Missionary ship "Duff" 1·00 75
58 40 c. German expeditionary steamer "Peiho" 1·00 75
59 40 c. German gunboat "Albatros" 1·00 75

10. Spear Fishing.

1984. "Ausipex 84" International Stamp Exhibition, Melbourne. Fishing. Mult.
60. 20 c. Type **10** 55 35
61. 20 c. Kite fishing 55 35
62. 20 c. Underwater spear fishing 55 35
63. 20 c. Net fishing 55 35

11. Mountain Apple.

1984. Christmas. Multicoloured.
64. 20 c. Type **11** 55 35
65. 20 c. Beach morning glory 55 35
66. 20 c. Turmeric 55 35
67. 20 c. Plumeria 55 35

12. Chick.

1985. Birth Bicentenary of John J. Audubon (ornithologist). Designs showing Audubon's Shearwater. Multicoloured.
68 22 c. Type **12** (postage) 65 45
69 22 c. Head of shearwater 65 45
70 22 c. Shearwater flying 65 45
71 22 c. Shearwater on lake 65 45
72 44 c. "Audubon's Shearwater" (Audubon) (air) 1·00 70

13. Borotong (cargo canoe).

1985. Traditional Canoes and Rafts. Multicoloured.
73 22 c. Type **13** 60 45
74 22 c. Kabeki (war canoe) 60 45
75 22 c. Olechutel (bamboo raft) 60 45
76 22 c. Kaeb (racing/sailing canoe) 60 45

14. Boy with Guitar. **16.** Mother cuddling Child.

15. Raising German Flag at Palau, 1885, and German 1880 20 pf. Stamp.

1985. International Youth Year. Mult.
77. 44 c. Type **14** 80 60
78. 44 c. Boy with fishing rod 80 60
79. 44 c. Boy with baseball bat 80 60
80. 44 c. Boy with spade 80 60

Nos. 77/80 were issued together se-tenant, each block forming a composite design showing a ring of children of different races.

1985. Air. Centenary of Vatican Treaty (granting Germany trading privileges in Caroline Islands). Multicoloured.
81 44 c. Type **15** 1·00 75
82 44 c. Early German trading post, Angaur, and Marshall Islands 1899 5 pf. overprinted stamp 1·00 75
83 44 c. Abai (village meeting house) and Caroline Islands 1901 5 m. yacht stamp 1·00 75
84 44 c. "Cormoran" (German cruiser), 1914, and Caroline Islands 1901 40 pf. yacht stamp 1·00 75

1985. Christmas. Multicoloured.
85. 14 c. Mother with child on lap 30 15
86. 22 c. Type **16** 45 30
87. 33 c. Mother supporting child in arms 70 50
88. 44 c. Mother lifting child in air 80 70

17. "PBY-5A Catalina" Amphibian over Natural Bridge.

1985. Air. 50th Anniv. of First Trans-Pacific Airmail Flight. Multicoloured.
89. 44 c. Type **17** 1·00 65
90. 44 c. "DC-6B Super-Cloudmaster" approaching Airai-Koror Passage 1·00 65
91. 44 c. "SA-16 Albatross" over Airai Village 1·00 65
92. 44 c. Douglas "DC-4" landing at Airai 1·00 65

18. Comet and Kaeb, 1758.

1985. Appearance of Halley's Comet. Multicoloured.
94 44 c. Type **18** 1·10 75
95 44 c. Comet and U.S.S. "Vincennes", 1835 1·10 75
96 44 c. Comet and "Scharnhorst" (German cruiser), 1910 1·10 75
97 44 c. Comet and tourist cabin cruiser, 1986 1·10 75

19. Palau Myiagra Flycatchers.

1986. Songbirds. Multicoloured.
98. 44 c. Type **19** (inscr "Mangrove Flycatcher") 1·00 75
99. 44 c. Cardinal honeyeaters 1·00 75
100. 44 c. Blue-faced parrot finches 1·00 75
101. 44 c. Grey-brown white eye (inscr "Dusky White-eye") and bridled white eye 1·00 75

20. Spear Fisherman.

1986. "Ameripex '86" International Stamp Exhibition, Chicago. Sea and Reef World. Multicoloured.
102 14 c. Type **20** 90 55
103 14 c. Olechutel (native raft) 90 55
104 14 c. Kaebs (sailing canoes) 90 55
105 14 c. Rock islands and sailfish 90 55
106 14 c. Inter-island ferry and flying fishes 90 55
107 14 c. Bone fishes 90 55
108 14 c. Common jacks 90 55
109 14 c. Mackerel 90 55
110 14 c. Sailfishes 90 55
111 14 c. Barracuda 90 55
112 14 c. Trigger fishes 90 55
113 14 c. Dolphin fishes 90 55
114 14 c. Spear fisherman with grouper 90 55
115 14 c. Manta ray 90 55
116 14 c. Marlin 90 55
117 14 c. Parrotfishes 90 55
118 14 c. Wrasse 90 55
119 14 c. Red snappers 90 55
120 14 c. Herring 90 55
121 14 c. Dugongs 90 55
122 14 c. Surgeonfishes 90 55
123 14 c. Leopard ray 90 55
124 14 c. Hawksbill turtle 90 55
125 14 c. Needlefishes 90 55
126 14 c. Tuna 90 55
127 14 c. Octopus 90 55
128 14 c. Clown fishes 90 55
129 14 c. Squid 90 55
130 14 c. Groupers 90 55
131 14 c. Moorish idols 90 55
132 14 c. Queen conch and starfish 90 55
133 14 c. Squirrel fishes 90 55
134 14 c. Starfish and sting rays 90 55
135 14 c. Lion fish 90 55
136 14 c. Angel fishes 90 55
137 14 c. Butterfly fishes 90 55
138 14 c. Spiny lobster 90 55
139 14 c. Mangrove crab 90 55
140 14 c. Tridacna 90 55
141 14 c. Moray eel 90 55

Nos. 102/41 are each inscribed on the back (over the gum) with the name of the subject featured on the stamp.

Nos. 102/41 were printed together, se-tenant, forming a composite design.

21. Presidential Seal.

1986. Air. Haruo I. Remeliik (first President) Commemoration. Multicoloured.
142. 44 c. Type **21** 90 60
143. 44 c. Kabeki (war canoe) passing under Koror-Babeldaob Bridge 90 60
144. 44 c. Presidents Reagan and Remeliik 90 60

1986. Sea Shells (2nd series). As T **7**. Multicoloured.
145. 22 c. Commercial trochus 55 40
146. 22 c. Marble cone 55 40
147. 22 c. Fluted giant clam 55 40
148. 22 c. Bullmouth helmet 55 40
149. 22 c. Golden cowrie 55 40

23. Crab inhabiting Soldier's rusting Helmet.

1986. International Peace Year. Mult.
150. 22 c. Type **23** (postage) 55 40
151. 22 c. Marine life inhabiting airplane 55 40
152. 22 c. Rusting tank behind girl 55 40
153. 22 c. Abandoned assault landing craft, Airai 55 40
154. 44 c. Statue of Liberty, New York (centenary) (air) 1·00 70

24. Gecko.

1986. Reptiles. Multicoloured.
155. 22 c. Type **24** 60 45
156. 22 c. Emerald tree skink 60 45
157. 22 c. Estuarine crocodile 60 45
158. 22 c. Leatherback turtle 60 45

25. Girl with Guitar and Boy leading Child on Goat. **26.** Tailed Jay on Soursop.

1986. Christmas. Multicoloured.
159 22 c. Type **25** 45 35
160 22 c. Boys singing and girl carrying flowers 45 35
161 22 c. Mother holding baby 45 35
162 22 c. Children carrying baskets of fruit 45 35
163 22 c. Girl with white terns 45 35

Nos. 159/63 were issued together, se-tenant, forming a composite design.

1987. Butterflies (1st series). Multicoloured.
164 44 c. Type **26** 1·10 75
165 44 c. Common mormon on sweet orange 1·10 75
166 44 c. Common eggfly on swamp cabbage 1·10 75
167 44 c. Oleander butterfly on fig 1·10 75

See also Nos. 223/6.

27. Bat flying.

28. "Ixora casei".

1987. Air. Palau Fruit Bat. Multicoloured.
168. 44 c. Type **27** 95 70
169. 44 c. Bat hanging from branch 95 70
170. 44 c. Bat feeding 95 70
171. 44 c. Head of bat 95 70

1987. Flowers. Multicoloured.
172 1 c. Type **28** 10 10
173 3 c. "Lumnitzera littorea" 10 10
174 5 c. "Sonneratia alba" .. 10 10
175 10 c. Woody vine .. 15 10
176 14 c. "Bikkia palauensis" 20 10
177 15 c. "Limophila aromatica" 20 10
178 22 c. "Bruguiera gymnorhiza" 30 20
179 25 c. "Fragraea ksid" .. 30 20
180 36 c. "Ophiorrhiza palauensis" 45 35
181 39 c. "Cerbera manghas" 60 40
182 44 c. "Samadera indica" .. 65 45
183 45 c. "Maesa canfieldiae" 55 45
184 50 c. "Dolichandrone spathacea" 80 55
185 $1 "Barringtonia racemosa" .. .. .. 1·50 1·10
186 $2 "Nepenthes mirabilis 2·50 2·00
187 $5 Orchid .. .. 6·00 4·50
188 $10 Bouquet of mixed flowers .. .. .. 12·00 9·00

29. Babeldaob.

1987. "Capex'87" International Stamp Exhibition, Toronto. Multicoloured.
190. 22 c. Type **29** 40 30
191. 22 c. Floating Garden Islands 40 30
192. 22 c. Rock Island 40 30
193. 22 c. Koror 40 30

1987. Sea Shells (3rd series). As T **7**. Multicoloured.
194. 22 c. Black-striped triton 50 35
195. 22 c. Tapestry turban .. 50 35
196. 22 c. Adusta murex .. 50 35
197. 22 c. Little fox mitre .. 50 35
198. 22 c. Cardinal mitre .. 50 35

31. "The President shall be the chief executive . . .".

1987. Bicentenary of United States of America Constitution. Multicoloured.
199. 14 c. Type **31** 25 20
200. 14 c. Palau and U.S. Presidents' seals (24 × 37 mm.) 25 20
201. 14 c. "The executive power shall be vested . . ." .. 25 20
202. 22 c. "The legislative power of Palau . . ." .. 35 25
203. 22 c. Palau Olbiil Era Kelulau and U.S. Senate seals (24 × 37 mm.) .. 35 25
204. 22 c. "All legislative powers herein granted . . ." 35 25
205. 44 c. "The judicial power of Palau . . ." 70 60
206. 44 c. Palau and U.S. Supreme Court seals (24 × 37 mm.) 70 60
207. 44 c. "The judicial power of the United States . . ." 70 60

The three designs of the same value were printed together in se-tenant strips, the top stamp of each strip bearing extracts from the Palau Constitution and the bottom stamp extracts from the U.S. Constitution.

32. Japanese Mobile Post. Office and 1937 Japan ½ s. Stamp.

1987. Links with Japan. Multicoloured.
208 14 c. Type **32** 40 30
209 22 c. Phosphate mine and Japan 1942 5 s. stamp .. 70 50
210 33 c. Airplane flying over Badrulchau monuments and Japan 1937 2 s. + 2 s. stamp 85 60
211 44 c. Japanese Post Office, Koror, and Japan 1927 10 s. stamp .. .. 1·10 80

33. Huts, White Tern and Outrigger Canoes.

34. Snapping Shrimp and Goby.

1987. Christmas. Multicoloured.
213 22 c. Type **33** 45 35
214 22 c. Flying white tern carrying twig 45 35
215 22 c. Holy family in kaeb 45 35
216 22 c. Angel and kaeb .. 45 35
217 22 c. Outrigger canoes and hut 45 35

Nos. 213/17 were issued together, se-tenant, forming a composite design; each stamp bears a verse of the carol "I Saw Three Ships".

1987. 25th Anniv. of World Ecology Movement. Multicoloured.
218 22 c. Type **34** 50 40
219 22 c. Mauve vase sponge and sponge crab .. 50 40
220 22 c. Pope's damsel fish and cleaner wrasse .. 50 40
221 22 c. Clown anemone fishes and sea anemone .. 50 40
222 22 c. Four-coloured nudibranch and banded coral shrimp 50 40

1988. Butterflies (2nd series). As T **26**.
223 44 c. Orange tiger on "Tournefotia argentia" 65 55
224 44 c. Swallowtail on "Citrus reticulata" .. 65 55
225 44 c. Lemon migrant on "Crataeva speciosa" .. 65 55
226 44 c. "Appias ada" (wrongly inscr "Colias philodice") on "Crataeva speciosa" 65 55

35. Whimbrel.

37. Baseball.

1988. Ground-dwelling Birds. Multicoloured.
227. 44 c. Type **35** 65 55
228. 44 c. Chinese little bittern 65 55
229. 44 c. Rufous night heron .. 65 55
230. 44 c. Banded rail 65 55

1988. Sea Shells (4th series). As T **7**. Mult.
231 25 c. Striped engina .. 50 35
232 25 c. Ivory cone 50 35
233 25 c. Plaited mitre .. 50 35
234 25 c. Episcopal mitre .. 50 35
235 25 c. Isabelle cowrie .. 50 35

1988. Olympic Games, Seoul. Multicoloured.
237 25 c. + 5 c. Type **37** .. 45 40
238 25 c. + 5 c. Running .. 45 40
239 45 c. + 5 c. Diving .. 80 65
240 45 c. + 5 c. Swimming .. 80 65

39 Angel Violinist and Singing Cherubs

41 Nicobar Pigeon

1988. Christmas. Multicoloured.
242 25 c. Type **39** 40 30
243 25 c. Angels and children singing 40 30
244 25 c. Children adoring child 40 30
245 25 c. Angels and birds flying 40 30
246 25 c. Running children and angels playing trumpets 40 30

Nos. 242/6 were issued together, se-tenant, forming a composite design.

1989. Endangered Birds. Multicoloured.
248 45 c. Type **41** .. .. 1·10 75
249 45 c. Palau ground dove .. 1·10 75
250 45 c. Marianas scrub hen 1·10 75
251 45 c. Palau scops owl .. 1·10 75

42 Gilled Auricularia

1989. Fungi. Multicoloured.
252 45 c. Type **42** .. .. 1·10 75
253 45 c. Rock mushroom .. 1·10 75
254 45 c. Polyporous .. .. 1·10 75
255 45 c. Veiled stinkhorn .. 1·10 75

43 Robin Redbreast Triton

1989. Sea Shells (5th series). Mult.
256 25 c. Type **43** 55 40
257 25 c. Hebrew cone .. 55 40
258 25 c. Tadpole triton .. 55 40
259 25 c. Lettered cone .. 55 40
260 25 c. Rugose mitre .. 55 40

44 Cessna "207" Skywagon

46 Jettison of Third Stage

1989. Air. Airplanes. Multicoloured.
261 36 c. Type **44** 50 40
262 39 c. Embraer "EMB-110" Bandeirante 60 50
264 45 c. Boeing "727" .. 70 60

1989. 20th Anniv of First Manned Landing on Moon. Multicoloured.
267 25 c. Type **46** 40 30
268 25 c. Command Module adjusting position .. 40 30
269 25 c. Lunar Excursion Module "Eagle" docking 40 30
270 25 c. Space module docking 40 30
271 25 c. Propulsion for entry into lunar orbit .. 40 30
272 25 c. Third stage burn .. 40 30
273 25 c. Command Module orbiting Moon 40 30
274 25 c. Command Module and part of "Eagle" .. 40 30
275 25 c. Upper part of "Eagle" on Moon .. 40 30
276 25 c. Descent of "Eagle" .. 40 30
277 25 c. Nose of rocket .. 40 30
278 25 c. Reflection in Edwin "Buzz" Aldrin's visor .. 40 30
279 25 c. Neil Armstrong and flag on Moon 40 30
280 25 c. Footprints and astronaut's oxygen tank 40 30
281 25 c. Upper part of astronaut descending ladder 40 30
282 25 c. Launch tower and body of rocket 40 30
283 25 c. Survival equipment on Aldrin's space suit .. 40 30
284 25 c. Blast off from lunar surface 40 30
285 25 c. View of Earth and astronaut's legs .. 40 30
286 25 c. Leg on ladder .. 40 30
287 25 c. Lift off 40 30
288 25 c. Spectators at launch 40 30
289 25 c. Capsule parachuting into Pacific 40 30
290 25 c. Re-entry 40 30
291 25 c. Space Module jettison 40 30
292 $2.40 "Buzz" Aldrin on Moon (photo by Neil Armstrong) (34 × 47 mm) 3·50 2·50

Nos. 267/91 were issued together, se-tenant, forming a composite design.

47 Girl as Astronaut

48 Bridled Tern

1989. Year of the Young Reader. Mult.
293 25 c. Type **47** 45 35
294 25 c. Boy riding dolphin .. 45 35
295 25 c. Cheshire Cat in tree 45 35
296 25 c. Mother Goose .. 45 35
297 25 c. Baseball player .. 45 35
298 25 c. Girl reading .. 45 35
299 25 c. Boy reading .. 45 35
300 25 c. Mother reading to child 45 35
301 25 c. Girl holding flowers listening to story .. 45 35
302 25 c. Boy in baseball strip 45 35

1989. "World Stamp Expo '89" International Stamp Exhibition, Washington D.C. Stilt Mangrove. Multicoloured.
303 25 c. Type **48** 45 35
304 25 c. Lemon migrant (inscr "Sulphur Butterfly") .. 45 35
305 25 c. Palua myiagra flycatcher (inscr "Mangrove Flycatcher") 45 35
306 25 c. White-collard kingfisher 45 35
307 25 c. Fruit bat 45 35
308 25 c. Estuarine crocodile .. 45 35
309 25 c. Rufous night heron .. 45 35
310 25 c. Stilt mangrove .. 45 35
311 25 c. Bird's nest fern .. 45 35
312 25 c. Beach hibiscus tree .. 45 35
313 25 c. Common eggfly (butterfly) 45 35
314 25 c. Dog-faced watersnake 45 35
315 25 c. Jingle shell 45 35
316 25 c. Palau bark cricket .. 45 35
317 25 c. Periwinkle and mangrove oyster .. 45 35
318 25 c. Jellyfish 45 35
319 25 c. Striped mullet .. 45 35
320 25 c. Mussels, sea anemones and algae 45 35
321 25 c. Cardinalfish 45 35
322 25 c. Snappers 45 35

Nos. 303/22 are each inscribed on the back (over the gum) with the name of the subject featured on the stamp.

Nos. 303/22 were issued together, se-tenant, forming a composite design.

49 Angels, Sooty Tern and Audubon's Shearwater

50 Pink Coral

1989. Christmas. Carol of the Birds. Mult.
323 25 c. Type **49** 45 35
324 25 c. Palau fruit dove and angel 45 35
325 25 c. Madonna and child, cherub and birds .. 45 35
326 25 c. Angel, blue-faced parrot finch, Palau myiagra flycatcher and cardinal honeyeater .. 45 35
327 25 c. Angel, Palau myiagra flycatcher and black-headed gulls 45 35

Nos. 323/7 were printed together, se-tenant, forming a composite design.

1990. Soft Corals. Multicoloured.
328 25 c. Type **50** 50 35
329 25 c. Mauve coral 50 35
330 25 c. Yellow coral 50 35
331 25 c. Orange coral 50 35
See also Nos. 392/5.

51 Siberian Rubythroat

1990. Forest Birds. Multicoloured.
332 45 c. Type **51** 90 65
333 45 c. Palau bush warbler 90 65
334 45 c. Micronesian starling 90 65
335 45 c. Slender-billed greybird (inscr "Cicadabird") 90 65

52 Prince Lee Boo, Capt. Henry Wilson and H.M.S. "Victory"

1990. "Stamp World London 90" International Stamp Exhibition. Prince Lee Boo's Visit to England, 1784, and 150th Anniv of the Penny Black. Multicoloured.
336 25 c. Type **52** 30 20
337 25 c. St. James's Palace 30 20
338 25 c. Rotherhithe Docks 30 20
339 25 c. Oroolong House, Devon (Capt. Wilson's home) 30 20
340 25 c. Lunardi's hydrogen balloon 30 20
341 25 c. St. Paul's Cathedral 30 20
342 25 c. Prince Lee Boo's grave 30 20
343 25 c. St. Mary's Church, Rotherhithe 30 20
344 25 c. Memorial tablet to Prince Lee Boo 30 20

53 "Corymborkis veratrifolia"

55 White Tern, American Golden Plover and Sanderling

54 Plane Butterfly on Beach Sunflower

1990. "Expo 90" International Garden and Greenery Exposition, Osaka. Orchids. Mult.
346 45 c. Type **53** 55 40
347 45 c. "Malaxis setipes" 55 40
348 45 c. "Dipodium freycinetianum" 55 40
349 45 c. "Bulbophyllum micronesiacum" 55 40
350 45 c. "Vanda teres" 55 40

1990. Butterflies. Multicoloured.
351 45 c. Type **54** 70 55
352 45 c. Painted lady on coral tree 70 55
353 45 c. "Euploea nemertes" on sorcerer's flower 70 55
345 45 c. Meadow argus (inscr "Buckeye") on beach pea 70 55

1990. Lagoon Life. Multicoloured.
355 25 c. Type **55** 30 20
356 25 c. Bidekill fisherman 30 20
357 25 c. Yacht and insular halfbeaks 30 20
358 25 c. Palauan kaebs 30 20
359 25 c. White-tailed tropic-bird 30 20
360 25 c. Spotted eagle ray 30 20
361 25 c. Great barracudas 30 20
362 25 c. Reef needlefish 30 20
363 25 c. Reef blacktip shark 30 20
364 25 c. Hawksbill turtle 30 20
365 25 c. Sixfeeler treadfins and octopus 30 20
366 25 c. Batfish and sixfeeler threadfins 30 20
367 25 c. Lionfish and sixfeeler threadfins 30 20
368 25 c. Snowflake moray and sixfeeler threadfins 30 20
369 25 c. Inflated and uninflated porcupine fishes and sixfeeler threadfins 30 20
370 25 c. Regal angelfish, blue-streak cleaner wrasse, blue sea star and corals 30 20
371 25 c. Clown triggerfish and spotted garden eels 30 20
372 25 c. Spotted garden eels 30 20
373 25 c. Blue-lined sea bream, blue-green chromis and sapphire damselfish 30 20
374 25 c. Orangespine unicornfish and whitetipped soldierfish 30 20
375 25 c. Slatepencil sea urchin and leopard sea cucumber 30 20
376 25 c. Partridge tun shell 30 20
377 25 c. Mandarinfish 30 20
378 25 c. Tiger cowrie 30 20
379 25 c. Feather starfish and orange-fin anemone fish 30 20
Nos. 355/79 were printed together, se-tenant, forming a composite design.

56 "Delphin", 1890, and Card

1990. Pacifica. Mail Transport. Multicoloured.
380 45 c. Type **56** 55 45
381 45 c. Right-hand half of card flown on 1951 inaugural U.S. civilian airmail flight and forklift unloading mail from airplane 55 45
Nos. 380/1 were issued together, se-tenant, forming a composite design.

57 Girls singing and Boy with Butterfly

1990. Christmas. Multicoloured.
382 25 c. Type **57** 30 20
383 25 c. White terns perching on girl's songbook 30 20
384 25 c. Girl singing and boys playing flute and guitar 30 20
385 25 c. Couple with baby 30 20
386 25 c. Three girls singing 30 20

58 B-24 Bombers over Peleliu

1990. 46th Anniv of U.S. Action in Palau Islands during Second World War.
387 45 c. Type **58** 55 45
388 45 c. Landing craft firing rocket barrage 55 45
389 45 c. 1st Marine division attacking Peleliu 55 45
390 45 c. U.S. Infantryman and Palauan children 55 45

1991. Hard Corals. As T **50**.
392 30 c. Staghorn coral 40 30
393 30 c. Velvet leather coral 40 30
394 30 c. Van Gogh's cypress coral 40 30
395 30 c. Violet lace coral 40 30

59 Statue of Virgin Mary, Nkulangelul Point

1991. Angaur, The Phosphate Island. Mult.
396 30 c. Type **59** 40 30
397 30 c. Angaur Post Office opening day cancellation and kaeb (sailing canoe) (41 × 27 mm) 40 30
398 30 c. Swordfish and Caroline Islands 40 pf. "Yacht" stamp (41 × 27 mm) 40 30
399 30 c. Locomotive at phosphate mine 40 30
400 30 c. Lighthouse Hill and German copra freighter 40 30
401 30 c. Dolphins and map showing phosphate mines (41 × 27 mm) 40 30
402 30 c. Estuarine crocodile (41 × 27 mm) 40 30
403 30 c. Workers cyling to phosphate plant 40 30
404 30 c. Freighter loading phosphate 40 30
405 30 c. Hammerhead shark and German overseer (41 × 27 mm) 40 30
406 30 c. Angaur cancellation and Marshall Islands 10 pf. "Yacht" stamp (41 × 27 mm) 40 30
407 30 c. Rear Admiral Graf von Spee and "Scharnhorst" (German cruiser) 40 30
408 30 c. "Emden" (German cruiser) and Capt. Karl von Muller 40 30
409 30 c. Crab-eating macaque (41 × 27 mm) 40 30
410 30 c. Sperm whale (41 × 27 mm) 40 30
411 30 c. H.M.A.S. "Sydney" (cruiser) shelling radio tower 40 30
Nos. 396/411 were issued together, se-tenant, with the centre block of eight stamps forming a composite design of a map of the island.

60 Moorhen

61 Pope Leo XIII and 19th-century Spanish and German Flags

1991. Birds. Multicoloured.
412 1 c. Palau bush warbler 10 10
413 4 c. Type **60** 10 10
414 6 c. Banded rail 10 10
415 19 c. Palau fantail 25 15
416 20 c. Mangrove flycatcher 25 15
417 23 c. Purple swamphen 30 20
418 29 c. Palau fruit dove 40 30
420 35 c. Crested tern 45 30
421 40 c. Eastern reef herons (inscr "Pacific Reef-Heron") 55 40
422 45 c. Micronesian pigeon 60 45
423 50 c. Great frigate bird 65 45
424 52 c. Little pied cormorant 70 50
425 75 c. Jungle nightjar 1·00 75
426 95 c. Cattle egret 1·25 90
427 $1.34 Sulphur-crested cockatoo 1·75 1·25
429 $2 Blue-faced parrot finch 2·75 2·00
430 $5 Eclectus parrots 6·75 5·00
431 $10 Palau bush warblers feeding chicks (51 × 28 mm) 13·00 9·75

1991. Centenary of Christianity in Palau Islands. Multicoloured.
432 29 c. Type **61** 40 30
433 29 c. Ibedul Ilengelekei and Church of the Sacred Heart, Koror, 1920 40 30
434 29 c. Marino de la Hoz, Emilio Villar and Elias Fernandez (Jesuit priests executed in Second World War) 40 30
435 29 c. Centenary emblem and Fr. Edwin G. McManus (compiler of Palauan–English dictionary) 40 30
436 29 c. Present Church of the Sacred Heart, Koror 40 30
437 29 c. Pope John Paul II and Palau and Vatican flags 40 30

62 Pacific White-sided Dolphin

1991. Pacific Marine Life. Multicoloured.
438 29 c. Type **62** 40 30
439 29 c. Common dolphin 40 30
440 29 c. Rough-toothed dolphin 40 30
441 29 c. Bottle-nosed dolphin 40 30
442 29 c. Common (inscr "Harbor") porpoise 40 30
443 29 c. Head and body of killer whale 40 30
444 29 c. Tail of killer whale, spinner dolphin and yellowfin tuna 40 30
445 29 c. Dall's porpoise 40 30
446 29 c. Finless porpoise 40 30
447 29 c. Map of Palau Islands and bottle-nosed dolphin 40 30
448 29 c. Dusky dolphin 40 30
449 29 c. Southern right whale dolphin 40 30
450 29 c. Striped dolphin 40 30
451 29 c. Fraser's dolphin 40 30
452 29 c. Peale's dolphin 40 30
453 29 c. Spectacled porpoise 40 30
454 29 c. Spotted dolphin 40 30
455 29 c. Hourglass dolphin 40 30
456 29 c. Risso's dolphin 40 30
457 29 c. Hector's dolphin 40 30

63 McDonnell Douglas "Wild Weasel" Fighters

1991. Operation Desert Storm (liberation of Kuwait). Multicoloured.
458 20 c. Type **63** 25 20
459 20 c. Lockheed "Stealth" fighter-bomber 25 20
460 20 c. McDonnell Douglas "Apache" helicopter 25 20
461 20 c. "M-109 TOW" missile on "M998 HMMWV" vehicle 25 20
462 20 c. President Bush of U.S.A. 25 20
463 20 c. M2 "Bradley" tank 25 20
464 20 c. U.S.S. "Ranger" (aircraft carrier) 25 20
465 20 c. PHM-1 (patrol boat) 25 20
466 20 c. U.S.S. "Wisconsin" (battleship) 25 20
467 $2.90 Sun, dove and yellow ribbon 3·75 2·75

64 Bai Gable

66 "Silent Night, Holy Night!"

65 "Hippopus hippopus", "Hippopus porcellanus", "Tridacna squamosa" and "Tridacna derasa"

1991. 10th Anniv of Republic of Palau and Palau–Pacific Women's Conference, Koror. Bai (community building) Decorations. Multicoloured. Imperf (self-adhesive) (50 c), perf (others).

469 29 c. Type **64** (postage) .. 40 30
470 29 c. Interior of bai (left side) 32 × 48 mm) .. 40 30
471 29 c. Interior of bai (right side) (32 × 48 mm) .. 40 30
472 29 c. God of construction 40 30
473 29 c. Bubuu (spider) (value at left) (30 × 23 mm) .. 40 30
474 29 c. Delerrok, the money bird (facing right) (31 × 23 mm) 40 30
475 29 c. Delerrok (facing left) (31 × 23 mm) 40 30
476 29 c. Bubuu (value at right) (30 × 23 mm) .. 40 30
477 50 c. Bai gable (as in Type **64**) (24 × 51 mm) (air) .. 65 45

Nos. 469/76 were issued together, se-tenant, Nos. 470/1 forming a composite design.

1991. Conservation and Cultivation of Giant Clams. Multicoloured.

478 50 c. Type **65** 65 45
479 50 c. Symbiotic relationship between "Tridacna gigas" and "Symbiodinium microadriaticum" 65 45
480 50 c. Hatchery 65 45
481 50 c. Diver measuring clams in sea-bed nursery 65 45
482 50 c. Micronesian Mariculture Demonstration Center, Koror (108 × 16 mm) 65 45

1991. Christmas. Multicoloured.

483 29 c. Type **66** 40 30
484 29 c. "All is calm, all is bright;" 40 30
485 29 c. "Round yon virgin mother and child!" .. 40 30
486 29 c. "Holy Infant, so tender and mild," .. 40 30
487 29 c. "Sleep in heavenly peace." 40 30

Nos. 483/7 were issued together, se-tenant, forming a composite design.

67 Flag, Islands and Children

1991. 25th Anniv of Presence of United States Peace Corps in Palau. Children's paintings. Multicoloured.

488 29 c. Type **67** 40 30
489 29 c. Volunteers arriving by airplane 40 30
490 29 c. Health care 40 30
491 29 c. Fishing 40 30
492 29 c. Agriculture 40 30
493 29 c. Education 40 30

68 "Zuiho Maru" (trochus shell breeding and marine research)

1991. "Phila Nippon '91" International Stamp Exhibition, Tokyo. Japanese Heritage in Palau. Multicoloured.

494 29 c. Type **68** 40 30
495 29 c. Man carving story board (traditional arts) 40 30
496 29 c. Tending pineapple crop (agricultural training) 40 30
497 29 c. Klidm (stone carving), Koror (archaeological research) .. 40 30
498 29 c. Teaching carpentry and building design .. 40 30
499 29 c. "Mavis" flying boat (air transport) 40 30

69 Japanese Aircraft attacking Shipping at Pearl Harbor

70 "Troides criton"

1991. Pacific Theatre in Second World War (1st issue). Multicoloured.

501 29 c. Type **69** 40 30
502 29 c. U.S.S. "Nevada" underway from Pearl Harbor 40 30
503 29 c. U.S.S. "Shaw" exploding at Pearl Harbor 40 30
504 29 c. U.S. divebomber attacking Japanese carrier "Akagi" .. 40 30
505 29 c. U.S.S. "Wasp" sinking off Guadalcanal 40 30
506 29 c. Battle of Philippine Sea 40 30
507 29 c. Landing craft storming Saipan Beach 40 30
508 29 c. U.S. 1st Cavalry on Leyte 40 30
509 29 c. Battle of Bloody Nose Ridge, Peleliu 40 30
510 29 c. U.S. troops landing at Iwo Jima 40 30

See also Nos. 574/83 and 601/10.

1992. Butterflies. Multicoloured.

511 50 c. Type **70** 65 45
512 50 c. "Alcides zodiaca" .. 65 45
513 50 c. "Papilio poboroi" .. 65 45
514 50 c. "Vindula arsinoe" .. 65 45

71 Common Hairy Triton

73 "And darkness was upon the face of the deep..."

72 Christopher Columbus

1992. Sea Shells (6th series). Multicoloured.

515 29 c. Type **71** 40 30
516 29 c. Eglantine cowrie .. 40 30
517 29 c. Sulcate swamp cerith 40 30
518 29 c. Black-spined murex 40 30
519 29 c. Black-mouth moon .. 40 30

1992. Age of Discovery from Columbus to Drake. Multicoloured.

520 29 c. Type **72** 40 30
521 29 c. Ferdinand Magellan 40 30
522 29 c. Sir Francis Drake .. 40 30
523 29 c. Cloud blowing northerly wind .. 40 30
524 29 c. Compass rose .. 40 30
525 29 c. Dolphin and "Golden Hind" (Drake's ship) .. 40 30
526 29 c. Corn cobs and "Santa Maria" (Columbus's ship) 40 30
527 29 c. Mythical fishes .. 40 30
528 29 c. Betel palm, cloves and black pepper .. 40 30
529 29 c. "Vitoria" (Magellan's ship), Palau Islands, shearwater and crested tern 40 30
530 29 c. White-tailed tropic bird, bicolour parrotfish, pineapple and potatoes 40 30
531 29 c. Compass 40 30
532 29 c. Mythical sea monster 40 30
533 29 c. Paddles and astrolabe 40 30
534 29 c. Parallel ruler, divider and Inca gold treasure 40 30
535 29 c. Backstaff 40 30
536 29 c. Cloud blowing southerly wind 40 30
537 29 c. Amerigo Vespucci .. 40 30
538 29 c. Francisco Pizarro .. 40 30
539 29 c. Vasco Nunez de Balboa 40 30

With the exception of Nos. 523 and 536 each stamp is inscribed on the back (over the gum) with the name of the subject featured on the stamp.

Nos. 520/39 were issued together, se-tenant, the backgrounds forming a composite design of the hemispheres.

1992. 2nd U.N. Conference on Environment and Development, Rio de Janeiro. The Creation of the World from the Book of Genesis, Chapter 1. Multicoloured.

540 29 c. Type **73** 40 30
541 29 c. Sunlight 40 30
542 29 c. "Let there be a firmament in the midst of the waters, ..." .. 40 30
543 29 c. Sky and clouds .. 40 30
544 29 c. "Let the waters under the heaven..." 40 30
545 29 c. Tree 40 40
546 29 c. Waves and sunlight (no inscr) 40 30
547 29 c. Waves and sunlight ("... and it was good.") 40 30
548 29 c. Waves and clouds (no inscr) 40 30
549 29 c. Waves and clouds ("...and it was so.") .. 40 30
550 29 c. Plants on river bank (no inscr) 40 30
551 29 c. Plants on river bank ("...and it was good.") 40 30
552 29 c. "Let there be lights in the firmament..." .. 40 30
553 29 c. Comet, planet and clouds 40 30
554 29 c. "Let the waters bring forth abundantly the moving creature..." .. 40 30
555 29 c. Birds flying and parrot on branch .. 40 30
556 29 c. "Let the earth bring forth the living creature after his kind..." .. 40 30
557 29 c. Woman, man and rainbow 40 30
558 29 c. Mountains ("...and it was good") 40 30
559 29 c. Sun and hills .. 40 30
560 29 c. Whale and fishes .. 40 30
561 29 c. Fishes ("...and it was good.") 40 30
562 29 c. Elephants and squirrel 40 30
563 29 c. Orchard and cat ("...and it was very good.") 40 30

Nos. 540/63 were issued, together, se-tenant, forming six composite designs each covering four stamps.

75 Presley and Dove

1992. 15th Death Anniv of Elvis Presley (entertainer). Multicoloured.

565 29 c. Type **75** 40 30
566 29 c. Presley and dove's wing 40 30
567 29 c. Presley in yellow cape 40 30
568 29 c. Presley in white and red shirt (3/4 face) .. 40 30
569 29 c. Presley singing into microphone 40 30
570 29 c. Presley crying .. 40 30
571 29 c. Presley in red shirt (3/4 face) 40 30
572 29 c. Presley in purple shirt (full face) 40 30
573 29 c. Presley (left profile) 40 30

76 Grumman "TBF" Avenger

1992. Air. Pacific Theatre in Second World War (2nd issue). Aircraft. Multicoloured.

574 50 c. Type **76** 65 45
575 50 c. Curtiss "P-40 C" Flying Tigers 65 45
576 50 c. Mitsubishi "A6M" Zero-Sen 65 45
577 50 c. Hawker "Hurricane" 65 45
578 50 c. Consolidated "PBY Catalina" 65 45
579 50 c. Curtiss "Hawk 75" .. 65 45
580 50 c. Boeing "B-17 E" .. 65 45
581 50 c. Brewster "Buffalo" 65 45
582 50 c. Supermarine "Walrus" 65 45
583 50 c. Curtiss "P-40 E" .. 65 45

77 "Thus Every Beast"

1992. Christmas. "The Friendly Beasts" (carol). Multicoloured.

584 29 c. Type **77** 40 30
585 29 c. "By Some Good Spell" 40 30
586 29 c. "In the Stable Dark was Glad to Tell" .. 40 30
587 29 c. "of the Gift He Gave Emanuel" (angel on donkey) 40 30
588 29 c. "The Gift He Gave Emanuel" (Palauan fruit doves) 40 30

78 Dugong

1993. Animals. Multicoloured.

589 50 c. Type **78** 65 45
590 50 c. Blue-faced (inscr "Masked") booby .. 65 45
591 50 c. Crab-eating macaque 65 45
592 50 c. New Guinea crocodile 65 45

79 Giant Deepwater Crab

1993. Seafood. Multicoloured.

593 29 c. Type **79** 40 30
594 29 c. Scarlet shrimp .. 40 30
595 29 c. Smooth nylon shrimp 40 30
596 29 c. Armed nylon shrimp 40 30

80 Oceanic Whitetip Shark

1993. Sharks. Multicoloured.

597 50 c. Type **80** 65 45
598 50 c. Great hammerhead shark 65 45
599 50 c. Leopard shark .. 65 45
600 50 c. Reef blacktip shark 65 45

81 U.S.S. "Tranquillity" (hospital ship) 82 Girl with Goat

1993. Pacific Theatre in Second World War (3rd issue). Multicoloured.

601 29 c. Capture of Guadalcanal 40 30
602 29 c. Type **81** 40 30
603 29 c. New Guineans drilling 40 30
604 29 c. Americans land in New Georgia 40 30
605 29 c. U.S.S. "California" (battleship) 40 30
606 29 c. Dauntless bombers over Wake Island .. 40 30
607 29 c. Flame-throwers on Tarawa 40 30
608 29 c. American advance on Makin 40 30
609 29 c. B-25s bomb Simpson Harbour, Rabaul .. 40 30
610 29 c. Aerial bombardment of Kwajelein 40 30

1992. Christmas. Multicoloured.

611 29 c. Type **82** 40 30
612 29 c. Children with garlands and goats .. 40 30
613 29 c. Father Christmas .. 40 30
614 29 c. Musicians and singer 40 30
615 29 c. Family carrying food 40 30

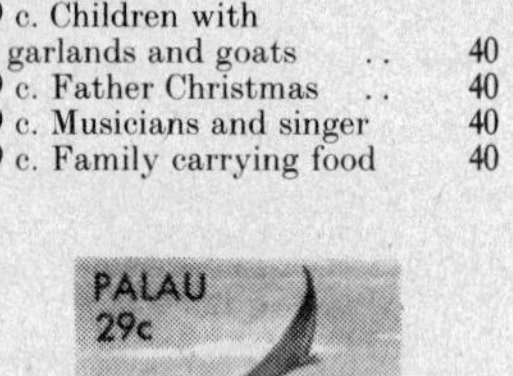

83 Pterosaur

1993. Monsters of the Pacific. Multicoloured.

616 29 c. Type **83** 40 30
617 29 c. Outrigger canoe .. 40 30
618 29 c. Head of plesiosaur .. 40 30
619 29 c. Pterosaur and neck of plesiosaur 40 30
620 29 c. Pterosaur (flying towards left) 40 30
621 29 c. Giant crab 40 30
622 29 c. Tentacles of kraken and two sharks .. 40 30
623 29 c. Hammerhead shark, tentacle of kraken and neck of plesiosaur .. 40 30
624 29 c. Head of lake serpent 40 30
625 29 c. Hammerhead shark and neck of serpent .. 40 30
626 29 c. Kraken 40 30
627 29 c. Ray, tentacles of kraken and body of plesiosaur 40 30
628 29 c. Three fishes and body of plesiosaur 40 30
629 29 c. Butterfly fishes and serpent's claw 40 30
630 29 c. Octopus and body of serpent 40 30
631 29 c. Giant nautilus and body of plesiosaur .. 40 30
632 29 c. Striped angel fishes .. 40 30
633 29 c. Lion fish 40 30
634 29 c. Squid 40 30
635 29 c. Shark and body of kronosaur 40 30
636 29 c. Striped shark and sea-bed 40 30
637 29 c. Squid and sea-bed .. 40 30
638 29 c. Giant nautilus and tail of serpent 40 30
639 29 c. Head of kronosaur .. 40 30
640 29 c. Lion fish, body of kronosaur and sea-bed 40 30

Nos. 616/40 were issued together, se-tenant, forming a composite design.

PANAMA Pt. 15

Country situated on the C. American isthmus. Formerly a State or Department of Colombia, Panama was proclaimed an independent republic in 1903.

1878. 100 centavos = 1 peso.
1906. 100 centesimos = 1 balboa.

1. Coat of Arms. 3. Map.

1878. Imperf. The 50 c. is larger.

1. **1.** 5 c. green .. .. .. 15·00 13·50
2. 10 c. blue .. .. .. 38·00 35·00
3. 20 c. red .. .. 24·00 21·00
4. 50 c. yellow .. .. 9·75

1887. Perf.

5. **3.** 1 c. black on green .. 50 65
6. 2 c. black on pink .. 1·25 1·00
7. 5 c. black on blue .. 90 35
7a. 5 c. black on grey .. 1·50 45
8. 10 c. black on yellow .. 90 45
9. 20 c. black on lilac .. 90 45
10. 50 c. brown .. .. 1·50 75

5. Map of Panama. 38.

1892.

12a.**5.** 1 c. green 15 15
12b. 2 c. red 20 20
12c. 5 c. blue 90 45
12d. 10 c. orange 20 20
12e. 20 c. violet 25 25
12f. 50 c. brown 30 25
12g. 1 p. lake .. .. .. 3·75 2·40

1894. Surch. **HABILITADO 1894** and value.

13. **5.** 1 c. on 2 c. red 35 35
15. **3.** 5 c. on 20 c. black on lilac 1·50 1·00
18. 10 c. on 50 c. brown .. 1·90 1·90

1903. Optd. **REPUBLICA DE PANAMA.**

70. **5.** 1 c. green .. .. .. 1·25 75
36. 2 c. red 55 55
37. 5 c. blue .. .. .. 1·25 55
38. 10 c. orange .. .. 1·25 1·25
39. 20 c. violet .. .. 2·40 2·40
75. **3.** 50 c. brown .. .. 14·00 14·00
40. **5.** 50 c. brown .. .. 6·00 4·25
41. 1 p. lake .. .. .. 29·00 24·00

1903. Optd. **PANAMA** twice.

53. **5.** 1 c. green 25 25
54. 2 c. red 25 25
55. 5 c. blue 30 30
56. 10 c. orange 30 30
64. 20 c. violet 90 90
65. 50 c. brown .. .. 1·50 1·50
66. 1 p. lake .. .. .. 3·50 2·75

1904. Optd. **Republica de Panama.**

94. **5.** 1 c. green 35 35
97. 2 c. red 45 45
98. 5 c. blue 45 45
99. 10 c. orange 45 45
100. 20 c. violet 45 45
103. **3.** 50 c. brown .. .. 1·75 1·75
104. **5.** 1 p. lake .. .. 9·50 8·25

1905.

151.**38.** ½ c. orange 55 45
136. 1 c. green 55 40
137. 2 c. red 70 55

1906. Surch. **PANAMA** twice and new value and thick bar.

138. **5.** 1 c. on 20 c. violet .. 25 25
139. 2 c. on 50 c. brown .. 25 25
140. 5 c. on 1 p. lake .. 55 45

41. Panamanian Flag. 42. Vasco Nunez de Balboa.

43. F. de Cordoba. 44. Arms of Panama.

45. J. Arosemena. 46. M. J. Hurtado. 47. J. de Obaldia.

1906.

142. **41.** ½ c. multicoloured .. 40 35
143. **42.** 1 c. black and green .. 40 35
144. **43.** 2 c. black and red .. 55 35
145. **44.** 2½ c. red 55 35
146. **45.** 5 c. black and blue .. 1·00 35
147. **46.** 8 c. black and purple .. 55 40
148. **47.** 10 c. black and violet .. 55 35
149. – 25 c. black and brown .. 1·50 60
150. – 50 c. black .. .. 3·75 2·10

DESIGNS: 25 c. Tomas Herrera. 50 c. Jose de Fabrega.

48. Balboa. 49. De Cordoba. 50. Arms.

51. Arosemena. 52. Hurtado. 53. Obaldia.

1909.

152. **48.** 1 c. black and green .. 65 50
153. **49.** 2 c. black and red .. 65 30
154. **50.** 2½ c. red 90 30
155. **51.** 5 c. black and blue .. 1·10 30
156. **52.** 8 c. black and purple .. 4·25 2·50
157. **53.** 10 c. black and purple .. 2·10 1·10

56. Balboa viewing Pacific Ocean. 57. Balboa reaches the Pacific.

1913. 400th Anniv. of Discovery of Pacific Ocean.

160. **56.** 2½ c. yellow and green .. 45 40

1915. Panama Exhibition and Opening of Canal.

161. – ½ c. black and olive .. 45 35
162. – 1 c. black and green .. 55 35
163. **57.** 2 c. black and red .. 65 35
164. – 2½ c. black and red .. 65 35
165. – 3 c. black and violet .. 1·00 35
166. – 5 c. black and blue .. 1·50 50
167. – 10 c. black and orange .. 1·50 50
168. – 20 c. black and brown .. 7·25 2·40

DESIGNS: ½ c. Chorrera Falls. 1 c. Relief Map of Panama Canal. 2½ c. Cathedral Ruins, Old Panama. 3 c. Palace of Arts, National Exhibition. 5 c. Gatun Locks. 10 c. Culebra Cut. 20 c. Archway, S. Domingo Monastery.

62. Balboa Docks.

1918. Views on Panama Canal.

178. – 12 c. black and violet .. 17·00 5·50
179. – 15 c. black and blue .. 10·00 2·75
180. – 24 c. black and brown .. 24·00 7·50
181. **62.** 50 c. black and orange .. 25·00 16·00
182. – 1 b. black and violet .. 35·00 19·00

DESIGNS: 12 c. "Panama" (cargo liner) in Gaillard Cut, north. 15 c. "Panama" in Gaillard Cut, south. 24 c. "Cristobal" (cargo liner) in Gatun Lock. 1 b. "Nereus" (U.S. Navy collier) in San Pedro Miguel Locks.

1919. 400th Anniv. of Founding of City of Panama. No. 164 surch. **1519 1919 2 CENTESIMOS 2.**

183. 2 c. on 2½ c. black and red 45 45

64. Arms of Panama. 65. Vallarino.

68. Bolivar's speech. 70. Hurtado.

1921. Independence Cent. Dated "1821 1921".

184. **64.** ½ c. orange 55 30
185. **65.** 1 c. green 55 25
186. – 2 c. red ("Land Gate", Panama City) .. 70 30
187. **65.** 2½ c. red (Bolivar) .. 95 75
188. – 3 c. violet (Cervantes Statue) 95 75
189. **68.** 5 c. blue 90 45
190. **65.** 8 c. olive (Carlos Ycaza) 3·50 2·10
191. – 10 c. violet (Government House 1821–1921) .. 2·40 85
192. – 15 c. blue (Balboa Stat.) 3·00 1·25
193. – 20 c. brown (Los Santos Church) .. .. 5·00 2·40
194. **65.** 24 c. sepia (Herrera) .. 5·00 3·00
195. – 50 c. black (Fabrega) .. 8·75 4·50

1921. Birth Centenary of Manuel Jose Hurtado (writer).

196 **70** 2 c. green 55 35

1923. No. 164 surch. **1923 2 CENTESIMOS 2.**

197. 2 c. on 2½ c. blk. & red 35 35

72. 73. Simon Bolivar.

74. Statue of Bolivar. 75. Congress Hall, Panama.

1924.

198. **72.** ½ c. orange 20 8
199. 1 c. green 20 8
200. 2 c. red 25 8
201. 5 c. blue 35 15
202. 10 c. violet 40 20
203. 12 c. olive 45 45
204. 15 c. blue 55 45
205. 24 c. brown .. .. 2·25 65
206. 50 c. orange .. .. 3·75 90
207. 1 b. black .. .. 5·50 2·25

1926. Bolivar Congress.

208. **73.** ½ c. orange 35 15
209. 1 c. green 35 15
210. 2 c. red 40 25
211. 4 c. grey 40 25
212. 5 c. blue 65 40
213. **74.** 8 c. purple 75 65
214. 10 c. violet 60 60
215. 12 c. olive 90 90
216. 15 c. blue .. .. 1·25 1·10
217. 20 c. brown .. .. 2·40 1·25
218. **75.** 24 c. slate .. .. 3·00 1·50
219. 50 c. black .. .. 7·00 3·50

78. "Spirit of St. Louis" over Map.

1928. Lindbergh's Flying Tour.

222. – 2 c. red on rose .. 55 35
223. **78.** 5 c. blue on green .. 75 55

DESIGN—VERT. 2 c. "Spirit of St. Louis" over Old Panama with opt. **HOMENAJE A LINDBERGH.**

1928. 25th Anniv. of Independence. Optd. **1903. NOV 3 BRE 1928.**

224. **70.** 2 c. green 30 20

1929. Air. Optd. **CORREO AEREO** or surch. also. With or without aeroplane.

238. E **81.** 5 c. on 10 c. orange .. 55 55
228. 10 c. orange .. 55 55
268. 10 c. on 20 c. brown .. 90 55
229. 15 c. on 10 c. orange .. 55 55
269. 20 c. brown 90 55
225. 25 c. on 10 c. orange 1·10 90
230. 25 c. on 20 c. brown .. 1·25 1·10
239. **62.** 1 b. violet (No. 182) 18·00 14·00

83.  **87.**

1930. Air.

231. **83.** 5 c. blue 20 10
232. 5 c. orange 35 10
233. 7 c. red 35 10
234. 8 c. black 35 10
235. 15 c. green 45 10
236. 20 c. red 50 10
237. 25 c. blue 55 55

1930. Air.

244. **87.** 5 c. blue 20 10
245. 10 c. orange 35 25
246. 30 c. violet .. .. 6·75 4·00
247. 50 c. red .. .. 1·25 35
248. 1 b. black .. .. 6·75 4·25

1930. Bolivar's Death Cent. Surch. **1830-1930 17 DE DICIEMBRE UN CENTESIMO.**

249. **73.** 1 c. on 4 c. grey .. 25 20

89. Seaplane over old Panama.  **92.** Manuel Amador Guerrero.

1931. Air. Opening of service between Panama City and western provinces.

250. **89.** 5 c. blue .. .. 1·00 90

1932. Optd. **HABILITADA** or surch. also.

251. **64.** ½ c. orange (postage) .. 35 20
252. **73.** ½ c. orange 20 20
253. 1 c. green 25 20
270. **68.** 1 c. on 5 c. blue .. 45 35
254. **73.** 2 c. red 20 20
255. 5 c. blue 45 30
256. – 10 c. violet (No. 191) .. 70 35
258. **74.** 10 c. on 12 c. olive .. 75 40
259. 10 c. on 15 c. blue .. 70 35
257. 20 c. brown .. .. 1·00 1·10
260. **83.** 20 c. on 25 c. blue (air) 4·00 55

1932. Birth Centenary of Dr. Guerrero (first president of republic).

261. **92.** 2 c. red 45 20

95. National Institute.  **(98.)**

1934. 25th Anniv. of National Institute.

262. – 1 c. green 55 55
263. 2 c. red 55 55
264. – 5 c. blue 75 60
265. **95.** 10 c. brown .. .. 2·10 1·00
266. – 12 c. green .. .. 3·50 1·50
267. – 15 c. blue .. .. 4·75 1·75

DESIGNS—VERT. 1 c. J. D. de Obaldia. 2 c. E. A. Morales. 5 c. Sphinx and Quotation from Emerson. HORIZ. 12 c. J. A. Facio. 15 c. P. Arosemena.

1936. Birth Cent. of Pablo Arosemena.

(a) Postage. Surch. as T **98,** but without **CORREO AEREO.**

271. **72.** 2 c. on 24 c. brown .. 55 45

(b) Air. Surch. with T **98.**

272. **72.** 5 c. on 50 c. orange .. 60 50

99. Custom House Ruins, Portobelo.  **100.** Urraca Monument.

1936. 4th Spanish-American Postal Congress (1st issue). Insc. "IV CONGRESO POSTAL AMERICO-ESPANOL".

273. **99.** ½ c. orange (postage) .. 40 25
274. – 1 c. green 40 25
275. – 2 c. red 40 25
276. – 5 c. blue 45 30
277. – 10 c. violet 75 45
278. – 15 c. blue 75 60
279. – 20 c. red .. .. 95 1·00
280. – 25 c. brown .. .. 1·50 1·40
281. – 50 c. orange .. .. 8·00 2·75
282. – 1 b. black .. .. 9·00 7·00

DESIGNS. 1 c. "Panama" (Old tree). 2 c. "La Pollera" (woman in costume). 5 c. Bolivar. 10 c. Ruins of Old Panama Cathedral. 15 c. Garcia y Santos. 20 c. Madden Dam. 25 c. Columbus. 50 c. "Resolute" (liner) in Gaillard Cut. 1 b. Panama Cathedral.

283. **100.** 5 c. blue (air) 70 40
284. – 10 c. orange 90 65
285. – 20 c. red .. .. 1·25 1·00
286. – 30 c. violet .. .. 2·10 1·90
287. – 50 c. red .. .. 22·00 15·00
288. – 1 b. black .. .. 9·00 6·50

DESIGNS— HORIZ. 10 c. "Man's Genius Uniting the Oceans". 20 c. Panama. 50 c. San Pedro Miguel Locks. 1 b. Courts of Justice. VERT. 10 c. Balboa Monument.

1937. 4th Spanish-American Postal Congress (2nd issue). Nos. 273/88 optd. **UPU.**

289. **99.** ½ c. orange (postage) .. 35 20
290. – 1 c. green 45 20
291. – 2 c. red 45 20
292. – 5 c. blue 45 30
293. – 10 c. violet 75 45
294. – 15 c. blue .. .. 4·75 2·40
295. – 20 c. red .. .. 1·10 1·10
296. – 25 c. brown .. .. 1·75 90
297. – 50 c. orange .. .. 7·00 4·25
298. – 1 b. black .. .. 8·75 7·50

299. **99.** 5 c. blue (air) 45 45
300. – 10 c. orange 70 55
301. – 20 c. red 95 75
302. – 30 c. violet .. .. 3·50 2·40
303. – 50 c. red .. .. 18·00 18·00
304. – 1 b. black .. .. 11·50 9·50

1937. Optd. **1937-38.**

305. **73.** ½ c. orange 50 45
306. **65.** 1 c. green 30 25
307. **73.** 1 c. green 30 25
308. **70.** 2 c. green 35 25
309. **73.** 2 c. red 35 30

1937. Surch. **1937-38** and value.

310. **73.** 2 c. on 4 c. grey .. 45 30
311. **78.** 2 c. on 8 c. olive .. 45 30
312. **74.** 2 c. on 8 c. purple .. 45 30
313. 2 c. on 10 c. violet .. 45 30
314. 2 c. on 12 c. olive .. 45 30
315. – 2 c. on 15 c. (No. 192) .. 45 30
316. **65.** 2 c. on 24 c. sepia .. 45 30
317. 2 c. on 50 c. black .. 45 30

1937. Air. Optd. **CORREO AEREO** or surch. also.

318. **73.** 5 c. blue 45 45
319. **74.** 5 c. on 15 c. blue .. 45 45
320. 5 c. on 20 c. brown .. 45 45
321. **75.** 5 c. on 24 c. slate .. 45 45
322. **62.** 5 c. on 1 b. blk. & violet 2·50 1·25
323. – 10 c. on 10 c. violet (191) 1·40 90
324. **75.** 10 c. on 50 c. black .. 1·40 90

105. Fire-Engine.

106. Firemen's Monument.  **107.** Fire-Brigade Badge.

1937. 50th Anniv. of Fire Brigade.

325. – ½ c. orange (postage) .. 45 25
326. – 1 c. green 45 25
327. – 2 c. red 45 30
328. **105.** 5 c. blue 65 30
329. **106.** 10 c. violet .. .. 1·10 65
330. – 12 c. green .. .. 1·50 1·10

331. **107.** 5 c. blue (air) 55 35
332. – 10 c. orange 70 45
333. – 20 c. red 90 55

DESIGNS—VERT. ½ c. R. Arango. 1 c. J. A. Guizado. 10 c. (No. 332), F. Arosemena. 12 c. D. H. Brandon. 20 c. J. G. Duque. HORIZ. 2 c. House on fire.

108. Basketball Player.  **111.** Old Panama Cathedral and Statue of Liberty.

1938. Air. C. American and Caribbean Olympic Games.

334. **108.** 1 c. red (Basket-ball) 80 30
335. – 2 c. green (Baseball player) 80 15
336. – 7 c. grey (Swimmer) .. 1·10 35
337. – 8 c. brown (Boxers) .. 1·10 35
338. – 15 c. blue (Footballer) 2·60 1·10

The 1 c. and 15 c. are vert., the rest horiz.

1938. Opening of Aguadulce Normal School, Santiago. Optd. **NORMAL DE SANTIAGO JUNIO 5 1938** or surch. also.

340. **72.** 2 c. red (postage) .. 30 25

341. **87.** 7 c. on 30 c. violet (air) 45 45
342. **83.** 8 c. on 15 c. green .. 45 45

1938. 150th Anniv. of U.S. Constitution. Flags in red, white and blue.

343. **111.** 1 c. blk. & grn. (post.) 45 20
344. 2 c. black and red .. 55 25
345. 5 c. black and blue .. 60 45
346. 12 c. black and olive .. 1·10 65
347. 15 c. black and blue .. 1·40 75

348. 7 c. black and grey (air) 50 30
349. 8 c. black and blue .. 70 30
350. 15 c. black and brown 90 70
351. 50 c. black and orange .. 12·00 9·00
352. 1 b. black .. .. 12·00 9·00

112. Pierre and Marie Curie.  **113.** Gatun Lock.

1939. Obligatory Tax. Cancer Research Fund. Dated "1939".

353. **112.** 1 c. red 55 15
354. 1 c. green 55 15
355. 1 c. orange 55 15
356. 1 c. blue 55 15

1939. 25th Anniv. of Opening of Panama Canal.

357. **113.** ½ c. yellow (postage) .. 1·25 1·25
358. – 1 c. green .. .. 1·50 1·50
359. – 2 c. red 55 15
360. – 5 c. blue .. .. 1·50 20
361. – 10 c. violet .. .. 2·00 50
362. – 12 c. olive 75 55
363. – 15 c. blue 75 70
364. – 50 c. orange .. .. 1·75 1·25
365. – 1 b. brown .. .. 3·50 2·25

DESIGNS: 1 c. "Santa Elena" (liner) in Pedro Miguel Locks. 2 c. Allegory of canal construction. 5 c. "Rangitata" (liner) in Culebra Cut. 10 c. Panama canal ferry. 12 c. Aerial view. 15 c. Gen. Gorgas. 50 c. M. A. Guerrero. 1 b. Woodrow Wilson.

366. – 1 c. red (air) 35 10
367. – 2 c. green 35 12
368. – 5 c. blue 55 20
369. – 10 c. violet 70 25
370. – 15 c. blue 95 35
371. – 20 c. red .. .. 2·50 95
372. – 50 c. brown .. .. 3·00 90
373. – 1 b. black .. .. 6·00 4·00

PORTRAITS: 1 c. B. Porras. 2 c. Wm. H. Taft. 5 c. P. J. Sosa. 10 c. L. B. Wise. 15 c. A. Reclus. 20 c. Gen. Goethals. 50 c. F. de Lesseps. 1 b. Theodore Roosevelt.

115. Flags of American Republics.  **120a.** "Liberty".

1940. Air. 50th Anniv. of Pan-American Union.

374. **115.** 15 c. blue 45 30

1940. Air. No. 370 surch. **55.**

375. 5 c. on 15 c. blue .. 25 25

No. 363 surch. **AEREO SIETE.**

376. 7 c. on 15 c. blue .. 40 30

No. 371 surch. **SIETE.**

377. 7 c. on 20 c. red .. 40 30

No. 374 surch **8—8.**

378. **115.** 8 c. on 15 c. blue .. 40 30

1941. Obligatory Tax. Cancer Research Fund. Optd. **LUCHA CONTRA EL CANCER.**

379. **72.** 1 c. green .. .. 1·40 1·10

1941. Enactment of New Constitution (a) Postage. Optd. **CONSTITUCION 1941**

380. **72.** ½ c. orange 35 20
381. 1 c. green 35 20
382. 2 c. red 35 25
383. 5 c. blue 45 20
384. 10 c. violet 65 45
385. 15 c. blue .. .. 1·00 65
386. 50 c. orange .. .. 5·50 2·50
387. 1 b. black .. .. 13·00 4·50

(b) Air. Surch. **CONSTITUCION 1941 AEREO** and value in figures.

388. E **81.** 7 c. on 10 c. orange .. 65 65
389. **72.** 15 c. on 24 c. brown .. 2·25 1·50

(c) Air. Optd. **CONSTITUCION 1941.**

390. **83.** 20 c. red .. .. 3·25 2·25
391. **87.** 50 c. red .. .. 7·50 4·25
392. 1 b. black .. .. 17·00 9·00

1941. Obligatory Tax. Cancer Research Fund. Dated "1940".

393. **112.** 1 c. red 45 10
394. 1 c. green 45 10
395. 1 c. orange 45 10
396. 1 c. blue 45 10

1942. Telegraph stamps as T **120a** optd. or surch. (a) Optd. **CORREOS 1942** and (No. 397) surch. **2c.**

397. 2 c. on 5 c. blue .. 70 55
398. 10 c. violet 90 70

(b) Air. Optd. **CORREO AEREO 1942.**

399. 20 c. brown .. .. 1·75 1·50

123. Flags of Panama and Costa Rica.

1942. 1st Anniv. of Revised Frontier Agreement between Panama and Costa Rica.

400. **123.** 2 c. red (postage) .. 30 25
401. 15 c. green (air) .. 60 15

1942. Obligatory Tax. Cancer Research Fund. Dated "1942".

402. **112.** 1 c. violet 45 15

127. Balboa reaches Pacific.

129. J. D. Arosemena Normal School.  **131.** A. G. Melendez

1942. (a) Postage stamps.

403. – ½ c. red, blue and violet 5 5
404. – ½ c. blue, orange and red 15 10
405. – 1 c. green 10 8
406. – 1 c. red 5 5
407. – 2 c. red ("ACARRERO") .. 20 8
408. – 2 c. red ("ACARREO") .. 45 10
409. – 2 c. black and red .. 15 8
410. **127.** 5 c. black and blue .. 20 8
411. – 5 c. blue 30 10
412. – 10 c. orange and red .. 45 20
413. – 10 c. orange and purple 35 20
414. – 15 c. black and blue .. 35 55
415. – 15 c. black 35 20
416. – 50 c. black and red .. 85 60
417. – 1 b. black .. .. 1·75 70

DESIGNS—VERT. ½ c. National flag. 1 c. Farm girl. 10 c. Golden Altar, Church of St. Jose. 50 c. San Blas Indian woman and child. HORIZ. 2 c. Oxen drawing sugar cart. 15 c. St. Thomas's Hospital. 1 b. National highway.

(b) Air.

418. – 2 c. red 45 10
419. – 7 c. red 55 20
420. – 8 c. black and brown .. 20 8
421. – 10 c. black and blue .. 20 15
422. – 15 c. violet 30 8
423. – 15 c. grey 35 15
424. **129.** 20 c. brown 35 8
425. 20 c. green 35 20
426. – 50 c. green .. .. 1·25 45
427. – 50 c. red .. .. 3·50 2·60
428. – 50 c. blue 60 40
429. – 1 b. orange, yell. & black 1·40 65

DESIGNS—HORIZ. 2 c., 7 c. Sword-fish. 8 c., 10 c. Gate of Glory, Portobelo. 15 c. Taboga Is. 50 c. Fire Brigade H.Q., Panama City. 1 b. Idol (Golden Beast).

1943. Obligatory Tax. Cancer Research Fund. Dated "1943".
433. **112.** 1 c. green 45 15
434. 1 c. red 45 15
435. 1 c. orange 45 15
436. 1 c. blue 45 15

1943. Air.
437. **131.** 3 b. grey .. .. 5·50 5·50
438. – 5 b. blue (T. Lefevre) .. 8·50 7·00

1945. Obligatory Tax. Cancer Research Fund. Dated "1945".
439. **112.** 1 c. red 45 20
440. 1 c. green 45 20
441. 1 c. orange 45 20
442. 1 c. blue 45 20

1946. Obligatory Tax. Cancer Research Fund. Surch. **CANCER B/.0.01 1947.**
443. **72.** 1 c. on ½ c. orange .. 55 15
444. 1 c. on 1 c. green .. 55 15
445. – 1 c. on ½ c. red, blue and violet (No. 403) .. 45 10
446. **72.** 1 c. on 12 c. olive .. 45 15
447. 1 c. on 24 c. brown .. 45 15

1947. Air. Surch. **AEREO 1947** and value.
448. – 5 c. on 7 c. red (No. 419) 20 20
449. **83.** 5 c. on 8 c. black .. 20 20
450. – 5 c. on 8 c. black and brown (No. 420) .. 20 20
451. **83.** 10 c. on 15 c. green .. 55 35
452. – 10 c. on 15 c. vio. (422) 30 25

134. Flag of Panama. **135.** National Theatre

1947. 2nd Anniv. of National Constitutional Assembly.
453. **134.** 2 c. red, deep red and blue (post.) .. 15 10
454. – 5 c. blue .. 20 20
455. **135.** 8 c. violet (air) .. 45 30
DESIGN—As Type **134**: 5 c. Arms of Panama.

1947. Cancer Research Fund. Dated "1947".
456. **112.** 1 c. red 45 8
457. 1 c. green 45 8
458. 1 c. orange 45 8
459. 1 c. blue 45 8

1947. Surch **HABILITADA CORREOS** and value.
460. **83.** ½ c. on 8 c. black .. 10 10
461. – ½ c. on 8c. black and brown (No. 420) .. 10 10
462. – 1 c. on 7 c. red (No. 419) 15 15
463. **135.** 2 c. on 8 c. violet .. 20 15

1947. Surch. **Habilitada CORREOS B/.0.50.**
464. **72.** 50 c. on 24 c. brown .. 65 65

138. J. A. Arango. **140.** Firemen's Monument.

1948. Air. Honouring members of the Revolutionary Junta of 1903.
465. – 3 c. black and blue .. 35 25
466. **138.** 5 c. black and brown .. 35 25
467. – 10 c. black and orange .. 35 25
468. – 15 c. black and red .. 35 55
469. – 20 c. black and red .. 40 40
470. – 50 c. black .. .. 1·75 70
471. – 1 b. black and green .. 3·00 2·75
472. – 2 b. black and yellow .. 7·00 6·00
PORTRAITS—HORIZ. 3 c. M. A. Guerrero. 10 c. F. Boyd. 15 c. R. Arias. VERT. 20 c. M. Espinosa. 50 c. C. C. Arosemena (engineer). 1 b. N. de Obarrio. 2 b. T. Arias.

1948. 50th Anniv. of Colon Fire Brigade.
473. **140.** 5 c. black and red .. 20 15
474. – 10 c. black and orange .. 35 20
475. – 20 c. black and blue .. 70 40
476. – 25 c. black and brown .. 70 55
477. – 50 c. black and violet .. 90 55
478. – 1 b. black and green .. 1·50 90
DESIGNS—HORIZ. 10 c. Fire engine. 20 c. Fire hose. 25 c. Fire Brigade Headquarters. VERT. 50 c. Commander Walker. 1 b. First Fire-Brigade Commander.

142. F. D. Roosevelt and J. D. Arosemena. **144.** Roosevelt Monument, Panama.

1948. Air. Homage to F. D. Roosevelt.
479. **142.** 5 c. black and red .. 20 15
480. – 10 c. orange 30 30
481. **144.** 20 c. green 35 35
482. – 50 c. black and blue .. 40 35
483. – 1 b. black 90 75
DESIGNS—HORIZ. 10 c. Woman with palm symbolizing "Four Freedoms". 50 c. Map of Panama Canal. VERT. 1 b. Portrait of Roosevelt.

147. Cervantes. **148.** Monument to Cervantes.

1948. 400th Birth Anniv. of Cervantes.
484. **147.** 2 c. black and red (post.) 30 15
485. **148.** 5 c. black and blue (air) 20 10
486. – 10 c. black and mauve .. 35 30
DESIGN—HORIZ. 10 c. Don Quixote and Sancho Panza (inscr. as Type **148**).

1949. Air. Jose Gabriel Duque (philanthropist). Birth Cent. No. 486 optd. **"CENTENARIO DE/JOSE GABRIEL DUQUE"/"18 de Enero de 1949".**
487. 10 c. blk. & mauve .. 40 40

1949. Obligatory Tax. Cancer Research Fund. Surch. **LUCHA CONTRA EL CANCER** and value.
488. **142.** 1 c. on 5 c. blk. and red 35 8
489. – 1 c. on 10 c. orange (No. 480) 35 8

1949. Incorporation of Chiriqui Province Cent. Stamps of 1930 and 1942 optd. **1849-1949 CHIRIQUI CENTENARIO.**
(a) On postage stamps as No. 407.
(i) Without surch.
491. – 2 c. red 20 10
(ii) Surch. **1 UN CENTESIMO 1** also
490. – 1 c. on 2 c. red .. 20 10
(b) Air.
492. – 2 c. red (No. 418) .. 20 20
493. **83.** 5 c. blue 30 30
494. – 15 c. grey (No. 423) .. 40 40
495. – 50 c. red (No. 427) .. 1·75 1·75

1949. 75th Anniv. of U.P.U. Stamps of 1930 and 1942/3 optd. **1874 1949 U.P.U.** No. 625 is also surch. **B/0.25.**
496. – 1 c. grn. (No. 405) (post.) 20 10
497. – 2 c. red (No. 407) .. 30 15
498. **127.** 5 c. blue 45 25
499. – 2 c. red (No. 418) (air) .. 20 20
500. **83.** 5 c. orange 55 35
501. – 10 c. black and blue (No. 421) 20 20
502. **131.** 25 c. on 3 b. grey .. 30 30
503. – 50 c. red (No. 427) .. 1·60 1·60

1949. Cancer Research Fund. Dated "1949".
504. **112.** 1 c. brown 45 8

153. Father Xavier. **154.** St. Xavier University.

1949. Bicentenary of Founding of St. Xavier University.
505. **153.** 2 c. blk. & red (postage) 25 15
506. **154.** 5 c. black & blue (air) .. 35 15

155. Dr. Carlos J. Finlay. **156.** "Aedes aegypti".

1950. Dr. Finlay (medical research worker).
507. **155.** 2 c. black & red (post.) 35 15
508. **156.** 5 c. black & blue (air) .. 85 40

1950. Death Cent. of San Martin. Optd. **CENTENARIO del General (or Gral.) Jose de San Martin 17 de Agosto de 1950** or surch. also. The 50 c. is optd. **AEREO** as well.
509. – 1 c. grn. (No. 405) (post.) 15 10
510. – 2 c. on ½ c. (No. 404) .. 20 10
511. **127.** 5 c. black and blue .. 25 20
512. – 2 c. red (No. 418) (air) .. 35 30
513. **83.** 5 c. orange 35 35
514. – 10 c. blk. & bl. (No. 421) 55 45
515. **83.** 25 c. blue 90 70
516. – 50 c. blk. & vio. (No. 477) 1·40 1·00

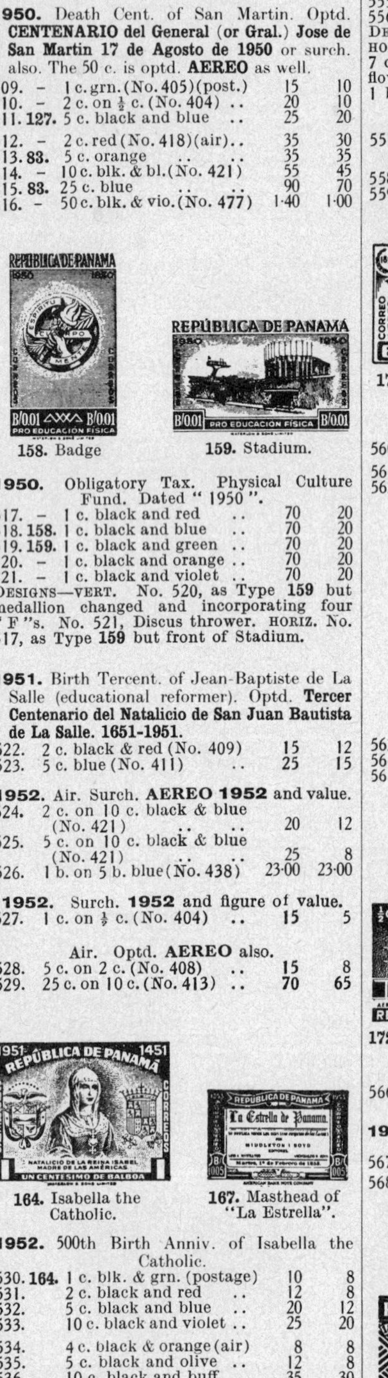

158. Badge **159.** Stadium.

1950. Obligatory Tax. Physical Culture Fund. Dated "1950".
517. – 1 c. black and red .. 70 20
518. **158.** 1 c. black and blue .. 70 20
519. **159.** 1 c. black and green .. 70 20
520. – 1 c. black and orange .. 70 20
521. – 1 c. black and violet .. 70 20
DESIGNS—VERT. No. 520, as Type **159** but medallion changed and incorporating four "F"s. No. 521, Discus thrower. HORIZ. No. 517, as Type **159** but front of Stadium.

1951. Birth Tercent. of Jean-Baptiste de La Salle (educational reformer). Optd. **Tercer Centenario del Natalicio de San Juan Bautista de La Salle. 1651-1951.**
522. 2 c. black & red (No. 409) 15 12
523. 5 c. blue (No. 411) .. 25 15

1952. Air. Surch. **AEREO 1952** and value.
524. 2 c. on 10 c. black & blue (No. 421) 20 12
525. 5 c. on 10 c. black & blue (No. 421) 25 8
526. 1 b. on 5 b. blue (No. 438) 23·00 23·00

1952. Surch. **1952** and figure of value.
527. 1 c. on ½ c. (No. 404) .. 15 5

Air. Optd. **AEREO** also.
528. 5 c. on 2 c. (No. 408) .. 15 8
529. 25 c. on 10 c. (No. 413) .. 70 65

164. Isabella the Catholic. **167.** Masthead of "La Estrella".

1952. 500th Birth Anniv. of Isabella the Catholic.
530. **164.** 1 c. blk. & grn. (postage) 10 8
531. 2 c. black and red .. 12 8
532. 5 c. black and blue .. 20 12
533. 10 c. black and violet .. 25 20
534. 4 c. black & orange (air) 8 8
535. 5 c. black and olive .. 12 8
536. 10 c. black and buff .. 35 30
537. 25 c. black and slate .. 55 35
538. 50 c. black and brown .. 75 45
539. 1 b. black .. .. 3·00 3·00

1953. Surch. **B/.0.01 1953.**
540. 1 c. on 10 c. (No. 413) .. 8 5
541. 1 c. on 15 c. blk. (No. 415) 15 5

1953. Air. No. 421 surch. **5 1953.**
542. 5 c. on 10 c. black & blue 35 10

1953. Air. Centenary of "La Estrella de Panama", Newspaper.
543. **167.** 5 c. red 20 15
544. 10 c. blue 25 25

168. Pres. and Senora Amador Guerrero.

1953. 50th Anniv. of Panama Republic.
545. – 2 c. violet (postage) .. 15 8
546. **168.** 5 c. orange 20 5
547. – 12 c. purple 35 15
548. – 20 c. indigo 65 25
549. – 50 c. yellow 90 65
550. – 1 b. blue .. .. 2·25 1·00
551. – 2 c. blue (air) 10 8
552. – 5 c. green 15 8
553. – 7 c. grey 20 15
554. – 25 c. black .. .. 1·40 70
555. – 50 c. brown 65 70
556. – 1 b. orange .. .. 2·25 1·00
DESIGNS—VERT. 2 c. Blessing the flag. 50 c. Old Town Hall. HORIZ. 12 c. J. A. Santos and J. De La Ossa. 20 c. Revolutionary council. 1 b. Obverse and reverse of coin.
DESIGNS—VERT. 2 c. Act of Independence. HORIZ. 5 c. Pres. and Senora Remon Cantera. 7 c. Girl in national costume. 25 c. National flower. 50 c. Salazar, Huertas and Domingo. 1 b. National dance.

1954. Surch. in figures.
557. – 3 c. on 1 c. red (No. 406) (postage) 8 5
558. **167.** 1 c. on 5 c. red (air) .. 8 5
559. 1 c. on 10 c. blue .. 8 5

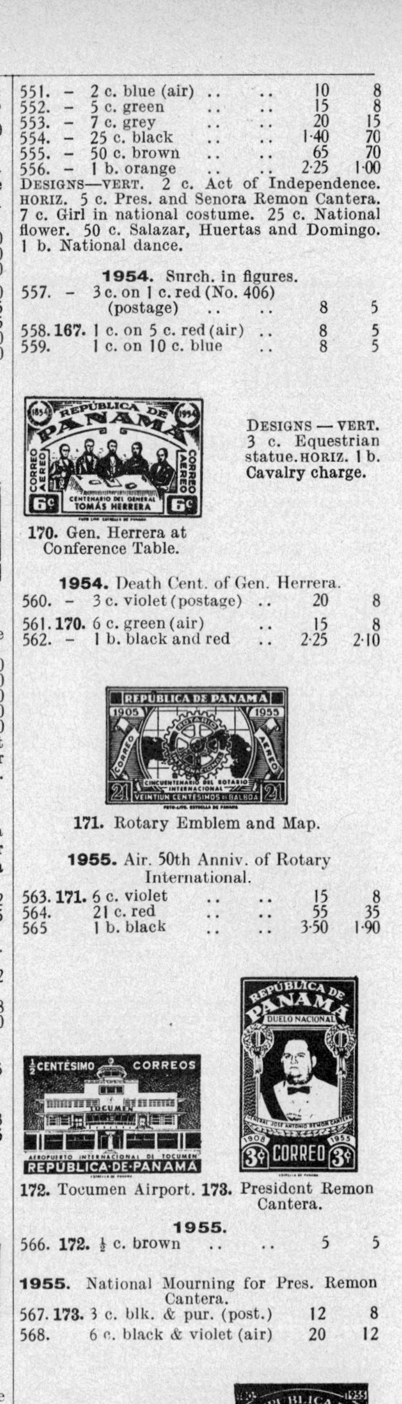

170. Gen. Herrera at Conference Table.

DESIGNS — VERT. 3 c. Equestrian statue. HORIZ. 1 b. Cavalry charge.

1954. Death Cent. of Gen. Herrera.
560. – 3 c. violet (postage) .. 20 8
561. **170.** 6 c. green (air) .. 15 8
562. – 1 b. black and red .. 2·25 2·10

171. Rotary Emblem and Map.

1955. Air. 50th Anniv. of Rotary International.
563. **171.** 6 c. violet 15 8
564. 21 c. red 55 35
565 1 b. black .. .. 3·50 1·90

172. Tocumen Airport. **173.** President Remon Cantera.

1955.
566. **172.** ½ c. brown 5 5

1955. National Mourning for Pres. Remon Cantera.
567. **173.** 3 c. blk. & pur. (post.) 12 8
568. 6 c. black & violet (air) 20 12

174. V. de la Guardia y Azala and M. Chiaria. **175.** F. de Lesseps.

1955. Cent. of Cocle Province.
569. **174.** 5 c. violet 20 8

1955. 150th Birth Anniv. of De Lesseps (engineer).
570. **175.** 3 c. lake on pink (post.) 30 8
571. – 25 c. blue on blue .. 2·25 1·25
572. – 50 c. violet on lilac .. 90 60
573. – 5 c. myrtle on green (air) 20 8
574. – 1 b. black & mauve .. 2·75 1·75
DESIGNS—VERT. 5 c. P. J. Sosa. 50 c. T. Roosevelt. HORIZ. 25 c. First excavations for Panama Canal. 1 b. "Ancon I" (first ship to pass through canal) and De Lesseps.

1955. Air. No. 564 surch.
575. **171.** 15 c. on 21 c. red .. 45 35

MINIMUM PRICE

The minimum price quoted is 5p which represents a handling charge rather than a basis for valuing common stamps. For further notes about prices see introductory pages.

177. Pres. Eisenhower (United States). **178.** Bolivar Statue.

1956. Air. Pan-American Congress, Panama and 30th Anniv. of First Congress.

576. – 6 c. black and blue .. 30 20
577. – 6 c. black and bistre .. 30 20
578. – 6 c. black and green .. 30 20
579. – 6 c. sepia and green .. 30 20
580. – 6 c. green and yellow .. 30 20
581. – 6 c. green and violet .. 30 20
582. – 6 c. blue and lilac .. 30 20
583. – 6 c. green and purple .. 30 20
584. – 6 c. blue and olive .. 30 20
585. – 6 c. sepia and yellow .. 30 20
586. – 6 c. blue and sepia .. 30 20
587. – 6 c. green and mauve .. 30 20
588. – 6 c. sepia and red .. 30 20
589. – 6 c. green and blue .. 30 20
590. – 6 c. sepia and blue .. 30 20
591. – 6 c. black and orange .. 30 20
592. – 6 c. sepia and grey .. 30 20
593. – 6 c. black and pink .. 30 20
594. **177.** 6 c. blue and red .. 70 35
595. – 6 c. blue and grey .. 30 20
596. – 6 c. green and brown .. 30 20
597. **178.** 20 c. grey 40 55
598. – 50 c. green 75 75
599. – 1 b. sepia .. .. 1·50 95

PRESIDENTIAL PORTRAITS as Type **177.** No. 576, Argentina. No. 577, Bolivia. No. 578, Brazil. No. 579, Chile. No. 580, Colombia. No. 581, Costa Rica. No. 582, Cuba. No. 583, Dominican Republic. No. 584, Ecuador. No. 585, Guatemala. No. 586, Haiti. No. 587, Honduras. No. 588, Mexico. No. 589, Nicaragua. No. 590, Panama. No. 591, Paraguay. No. 592, Peru. No. 593, Salvador. No. 595, Uruguay. No. 596, Venezuela. As Type **178**—HORIZ. No. 598, Bolivar Hall. VERT. No. 599, Bolivar Medallion.

179. Arms of Panama City. **180.** Pres. Carlos A. Mendoza.

1956. 6th Inter-American Congress of Municipalities, Panama City.

600. **179.** 3 c. green (postage) .. 12 5
601. – 25 c. red (air) .. 55 35
602. – 50 c. black 65 55

DESIGNS: 25 c. Stone bridge, Old Panama. 50 c. Town Hall, Panama.

1956. Birth Cent. of Pres. Carlos A. Mendoza.

604. **180.** 10 c. green and red .. 20 12

DESIGNS—HORIZ. 15 c. (No. 605) National Archives 15 c. (No. 608), St. Thomas's Hospital VERT. 5 c. Porras Monument.

182. Dr. Belisario Porras.

1956. Birth Cent. of Dr. Porras.

605. – 15 c. grey (postage) .. 45 20
606. **182.** 25 c. blue and red .. 65 45
607. – 5 c. green (air) .. 10 5
608. – 15 c. red 30 25

183. Isthmus Highway. **185.** Manuel E. Batista.

1957. 7th Pan-American Highway Congress.

609. **183.** 3 c. green (postage) .. 15 5
610. – 10 c. black (air) .. 20 15
611. – 20 c. black and blue .. 35 35
612. – 1 b. green .. .. 1·75 1·75

DESIGNS—VERT. 10 c. Highway under construction. 20 c. Darien Forest. 1 b. Map of Pan-American Highway.

1957. Air. Surch. **1957 X 10 ¢ X.**

614. **173.** 10 c. on 6 c. blk. & violet 20 20

1957. Birth Centenary of Manuel Espinosa Batista (independence leader).

615. **185.** 5 c. blue and green .. 15 8

186. Portobelo Castle. **189.** U.N. Emblem.

1957. Air. Buildings. Centres in black.

616. **186.** 10 c. grey 25 12
617. – 10 c. purple 25 12
618. – 10 c. violet 25 12
619. – 10 c. grey and green .. 25 12
620. – 10 c. blue 25 12
621. – 10 c. brown 25 12
622. – 10 c. orange 25 12
623. – 10 c. light blue 25 12
624. – 1 b. red .. .. .. 2·10 95

DESIGNS—HORIZ. No. 617, San Jeronimo Castle. No. 618, Portobelo Customs-house. No. 619, Panama Hotel. No. 620, Pres. Remon Cantera Stadium. No. 621, Palace of Justice. No. 622, Treasury. No. 623, San Lorenzo Castle. VERT. No. 624, Jose Remon Clinics.

1957. Surch. **1957** and value.

625. **172.** 1 c. on ½ c. brown .. 5 5
626. 3 c. on ½ c. brown .. 10 5

1958. Air. Surch. **1958** and value.

627. **170.** 5 c. on 6 c. green .. 20 8

1958. Air. 10th Anniv. of U.N.O.

628. **189.** 10 c. green 20 10
629. 21 c. blue 45 35
630. 50 c. orange 45 45
631. – 1 b. red, blue and grey 1·75 1·40

DESIGN: 1 b. Flags of Panama and United Nations.

1958. No. 547 surch. **3 c 1958.**

633. 3 c. on 12 c. purple .. 10 5

191. Flags Emblem. **192.** Brazilian Pavilion.

1958. 10th Anniv. of Organization of American States. Emblem (T **191**) multicoloured within yellow and black circular band; background colours given below.

634. **191.** 1 c. grey (postage) .. 8 5
635. 2 c. green 10 5
636. 3 c. red 15 5
637 7 c. blue 25 10
638. 5 c. blue (air.) .. 12 8
639. 10 c. red 20 12
640. – 50 c. black, yell. & grey 35 35
641. **191.** 1 b. black .. .. 1·75 1·40

DESIGN—VERT. 50 c. Headquarters building.

1958. Brussels. Int. Exn.

642. **192.** 1 c. green & yell. (post) 5 5
643. – 3 c. green and blue .. 12 5
644. – 5 c. slate and brown .. 15 10
645. – 10 c. brown and blue .. 20 20
646. – 15 c. violet & grey (air) 35 35
647. – 50 c. brown and slate .. 60 60
648. – 1 b. turquoise and lilac 1·25 1·25

DESIGNS—PAVILIONS—As Type **192**: 3 c. Argentina. 5 c. Venezuela. 10 c. Great Britain. 15 c. Vatican City. 50 c. United States. 1 b. Belgium.

193. Pope Pius XII. **194.** Children on Farm.

1959. Pope Pius XII Commem.

650. **193.** 3 c. brown (postage) .. 15 8
651. – 5 c. violet (air) 15 12
652. – 30 c. mauve 30 25
653. – 50 c. grey 75 60

PORTRAITS (Pope Pius XII): 5 c. when Cardinal. 30 c. wearing Papal tiara. 50 c. enthroned.

1959. Obligatory Tax. Youth Rehabilitation Institute. Size 35 × 24 mm.

655. **194.** 1 c. grey and red .. 12 5

195. U.N. Headquarters New York. **197.** J. A. Facio. **198.** Football.

1959. 10th Anniv. of Declaration of Human Rights.

656. **195.** 3 c. olive & brown (post.) 8 5
657. – 15 c. green and orange 35 25
658. – 5 c. blue and green (air) 12 8
659. – 10 c. brown and grey .. 20 12
660. – 20 c. slate and brown .. 35 35
661. – 50 c. blue and green .. 60 60
662. **195.** 1 b. blue and red .. 1·40 1·25

DESIGNS: 5 c., 15 c. Family looking towards light. 10 c., 20 c. U.N. emblem and torch. 50 c. U.N. flag.

1959. 8th Latin-American Economic Commission Congress. Nos. 656/61 optd. **8A REUNION C.E.P.A.L. MAYO 1959** or surch. also.

663. **195.** 3 c. olive and brown (post.) 10 8
664. – 15 c. green and orange 35 20
665. – 5 c. blue and green (air) 10 10
666. – 10 c. brown and grey .. 25 15
667. – 20 c. slate and brown .. 45 35
668. – 1 b. on 50 c. blue and green 1·60 1·60

1959. 50th Anniv. of National Institute.

670. – 3 c. red (postage) .. 8 5
671. – 13 c. green 30 15
672. – 21 c. blue 40 30
673. **197.** 5 c. black (air) .. 10 5
674. – 10 c. black 20 10

DESIGNS—VERT. 3 c. E. A. Morales (founder). 10 c. Ernesto de la Guardia, Jr. 13 c. A. Bravo. HORIZ. 21 c. National Institute Bldg.

1959. Obligatory Tax. Youth Rehabilitation Institute. As No. 655, but colours changed and inscr. "1959".

675. **194.** 1 c. green and black .. 8 5
676. 1 c. blue and black .. 8 5

See also No. 690.

1959. 3rd Pan-American Games, Chicago. Inscr. "III JUEGOS DEPORTIVOS PANAMERICANOS".

677. **198.** 1 c. green & grey (post.) 8 5
678. – 3 c. brown and blue .. 12 5
679. – 20 c. brown and green .. 50 45
680. – 5 c. brown & black (air) 12 10
681. – 10 c. brown and grey .. 25 20
682. – 50 c. brown and blue .. 45 40

DESIGNS: 3 c. Swimming. 5 c. Boxing. 10 c. Baseball. 20 c. Hurdling. 50 c. Basketball.

1960. Air. World Refugee Year. Nos. 554/6 optd. **NACIONES UNIDAS ANO MUNDIAL, REFUGIADOS. 1959-1960.**

683. 25 c. black 35 35
684. 50 c. brown 70 55
685. 1 b. orange .. .. 1·50 1·10

200. Administration Building. **202.** Fencing.

1960. Air. 25th Anniv. of National University.

686. **200.** 10 c. green 15 12
687. – 21 c. blue 30 20
688. – 25 c. blue 50 35
689. – 30 c. black 55 40

DESIGNS: 21 c. Faculty of Science. 25 c. Faculty of Medicine. 30 c. Statue of Dr. Octavio Mendez Pereira (first rector) and Faculty of Law.

1960. Obligatory Tax. Youth Rehabilitation Institute. As No. 655 but smaller (32 × 22 mm.) and inscr. "1960".

690. **194.** 1 c. grey and red .. 8 8

1960. Olympic Games.

691. **202.** 3 c. pur. & violet (post.) 10 5
692. – 5 c. green & turquoise .. 20 8
693. – 5 c. red and orange (air) 8 8
694. – 10 c. black and bistre .. 20 15
695. – 25 c. deep blue and blue 45 40
696. – 50 c. black and brown .. 60 45

DESIGNS—VERT. 5 c. (No. 692), Football. (No. 693), Basketball. 25 c. Javelin-throwing. 50 c. Runner with Olympic Flame. HORIZ. 10 c. Cycling.

DESIGN: 10 c. Two heads and map.

204. "Population".

1960. Air. 6th National Census (5 c.) and Central American Census.

698 **204.** 5 c. black 8 8
699. 10 c. brown 20 15

205. Boeing "707" Airliner.

1960. Air.

700. **205.** 5 c. blue 15 10
701. 10 c. green 40 20
702. 20 c. brown 85 40

206. Pastoral Scene. **207.** Helen Keller School.

1961. Agricultural Census. (16th April).

703. **206.** 3 c. turquoise 10 5

1961. 15th Anniv. of Lions Club.

705. – 3 c. blue (postage) .. 8 5
706. **207.** 5 c. black (air) .. 8 8
707. – 10 c. green 20 8
708. – 21 c. bl., red & yellow 40 30

DESIGNS: 3 c. Nino Hospital. 10 c. Children's Colony, Verano. 21 c. Lions emblem, arms and slogan.

1961. Air. Obligatory Tax. Youth Rehabilitation Fund. Surch. **1 c "Rehabilitacion de Menores".**

709. – 1 c. on 10 c. black and bistre (No. 694) .. 10 10
710. **205.** 1 c. on 10 c. green .. 10 10

1961. Air. Surch. **HABILITADA en** value.

712. **200.** 1 c. on 10 c. green .. 10 8
713. – 1 b. on 25 c. blue and blue (No. 695) .. 1·25 1·25

210. Flags of Costa Rica and Panama.

1961. Meeting of Presidents of Costa Rica and Panama.

715. **210.** 3 c. red & blue (post.) 12 8
716. – 1 b. black & gold (air) 1·25 75

DESIGN: 1 b. Pres. Chiari of Panama and Pres. Echandi of Costa Rica.

211. Girl using Sewing-machine. **212.** Campaign Emblem.

1961. Obligatory Tax. Youth Rehabilitation Fund.

717. **211.** 1 c. violet 8 5
718. 1 c. yellow 8 5
719. 1 c. green 8 5
720. 1 c. blue 8 5
721. 1 c. purple 8 5
722. – 1 c. mauve 8 5
723. – 1 c. grey 8 5
724. – 1 c. blue 8 5
725. – 1 c. orange 8 5
726. – 1 c. red 8 5

DESIGN: Nos. 722/6, Boy sawing wood.

1961. Air. Malaria Eradication.

727. **212.** 5 c. + 5 c. red .. 60 30
728. 10 c. + 10 c. blue .. 60 30
729. 15 c. + 15 c. green .. 60 30

213. Dag Hammarskjold. 214. Arms of Panama.

1961. Air. Death of Dag Hammarskjold.
730. 213. 10 c. black and grey .. 20 15

1962. Air. (a) Surch. "**Vale B/.0.15**".
731. 200. 15 c. on 10 c. green .. 30 20
(b) No. 810 surch. "**XX**" over old value and "**VALE B/.1.00**".
732. – 1 b. on 25 c. deep blue and blue .. .. 1·25 75

1962. 3rd Central American Inter-Municipal Co-operation Assembly.
733. 214. 3 c. red, yellow and blue (postage) .. 8 5
734. – 5 c. black & blue (air) 20 10
DESIGN—HORIZ. 5 c. City Hall, Colon.

215. Mercury on Cogwheel. 217. Social Security Hospital.

1962. 1st Industrial Census.
735. 215. 3 c. red 8 5

1962. Surch. **VALE** and value with old value obliterated.
736. 212. 10 c. on 5 c.+5 c. red .. 90 45
737. 20 c. on 10 c.+10 c. bl. 1·50 90

1962. Opening of Social Security Hospital, Panama City.
738. 217. 3 c. black and red .. 8 5

218. Colon Cathedral. 221. Col. Glenn and Capsule "Friendship".

220. Thatcher Ferry Bridge nearing completion.

1962. "Freedom of Worship". Inscr. "LIBERTAD DE CULTOS". Centres in black.
739. – 1 c. red and blue (post.) 5 5
740. – 2 c. red and cream .. 5 5
741. – 3 c. blue and cream .. 8 5
742. – 5 c. red and green .. 10 8
743. – 10 c. green and cream 20 12
744. – 10 c. mauve and blue 20 12
745. – 15 c. blue and green .. 30 20
746. 218. 20 c. red and pink .. 35 25
747. – 25 c. green and pink .. 45 35
748. – 50 c. blue and pink .. 60 55
749. – 1 b. violet and cream .. 1·75 1·40
DESIGNS—HORIZ. 1 c. San Francisco de Veraguas Church. 3 c. David Cathedral. 25 c. Orthodox Greek Temple. 1 b. Colon Protestant Church. VERT. 2 c. Panama Old Cathedral. 5 c. Nata Church. 10 c. Don Bosco Temple. 15 c. Virgin of Carmen Church. 50 c. Panama Cathedral.

750. – 5 c. violet and flesh (air) 8 8
751. – 7 c. lt. mauve & mauve 12 10
752. – 8 c. violet and blue .. 15 10
753. – 10 c. violet and salmon 20 10
754. – 10 c. green & light purple 20 20
755. – 15 c. red and orange .. 25 20
756. – 21 c. sepia and blue .. 35 30
757. – 25 c. blue and pink .. 45 35
758. – 30 c. mauve and blue 50 45
759. – 50 c. purple and green 70 70
760. – 1 b. blue and salmon .. 1·25 1·10
DESIGNS—HORIZ. 5 c. Cristo Rey Church. 7 c. San Miguel Church. 21 c. Canal Zone Synagogue. 25 c. Panama Synagogue. 50 c. Canal Zone Protestant Church. VERT. 8 c. Santuario Church. 10 c. Los Santos Church. 15 c. Santa Ana Church. 30 c. San Francisco Church. 1 b. Canal Zone Catholic Church.

1962. Air. 9th Central American and Caribbean Games, Jamaica. Nos. 693 and 695 optd. "**IX JUEGOS C.A. y DEL CARIBE KINGSTON - 1962**" or surch. also.
762. 5 c. red and orange .. 15 12
764. 10 c. on 25 c. dp. blue & blue 55 50
765. 15 c. on 25 c. dp. blue & blue 40 35
766. 20 c. on 25 c. dp. blue & blue 45 45
763. 25 c. dp. blue and blue .. 55 50

1962. Opening of Thatcher Ferry Bridge, Canal Zone.
767. 220. 3 c. black & red (post.) 8 5
768. – 10 c. black & blue (air) 20 15
DESIGN: 10 c. Completed bridge.

1962. Air. Col. Glenn's Space Flight.
769. 221. 5 c. red 10 10
770. – 10 c. yellow 20 20
771. – 31 c. blue 45 40
772. – 50 c. green 65 65
DESIGNS—HORIZ. "Friendship": 10 c. Over Earth. 31 c. In space. VERT. 50 c. Col Glenn.

222. U.P.A.E. Emblem. 225. F.A.O. Emblem.

223. Water Exercise.

1963. Air. 50th Anniv. of Postal Union of Americas and Spain.
774. 222. 10 c. multicoloured .. 20 12

1963. 75th Anniv. of Panama Fire Brigade.
775. 223. 1 c. blk. & green (post.) 5 5
776. – 3 c. black and blue .. 8 5
777. – 5 c. black and red .. 10 8
778. – 10 c. black & orge. (air) 15 15
779. – 15 c. black and purple 20 20
780. – 21 c. blue, gold and red 50 45
DESIGNS: 3 c. Brigade officers. 5 c. Brigade president and advisory council. 10 c. "China" pump in action, 1887. 15 c. "Cable 14" station and fire-engine. 21 c. Fire Brigade badge.

1963. Air. Red Cross Cent. (1st issue). Nos. 769/71 surch. with red cross **1863 1963** and premium.
781. 215. 5 c.+5 c. red .. .. 1·40 1·40
782. – 10 c.+10 c. yellow .. 2·75 2·75
783. – 31 c.+15 c. blue .. 2·75 2·75
See also No. 797.

1963. Air. Freedom from Hunger.
784. 225. 10 c. red and green .. 20 20
785. 15 c. red and blue .. 30 25

1963. Air. 22nd Central American Lions Convention. Optd. "**XXII Convencion. Leonistica Centroamericana Panama 18-21 Abril 1963**".
786. 207. 5 c. black 10 8

1963. Air. Surch. **HABILITADO Vale B/.0.04.**
789. 200. 4 c. in 10 c. green .. 8 5

1963. Air. Nos. 743 and 769 optd. **AEREO** vert.
790. 10 c. green and cream .. 20 15
791. 20 c. brown and green .. 30 25

1963. Air. Freedom of the Press. No. 693 optd. **LIBERTAD DE PRENSA 20-VIII-63.**
792. 5 c. red and orange .. 10 8

1963. Air. Visit of U.S. Astronauts to Panama. Optd. "**Visita Astronautas Glenn-Schirra Sheppard Cooper a Panama**" or surch. also.
793. 221. 5 c. red .. .. 2·50 2·50
794. 10 c. on 5 c. red .. 3·25 3·25

1963. Air. Surch. **HABILITADO 10 c.**
796. 221. 10 c. on 5 c. red .. 5·50 5·50

1963. Air. Red Cross Centenary (2nd issue). No. 781 surch. "**Centenario Cruz Roja Internacional 10 c.** with premium obliterated.
797. 221. 10 c. on 5 c.+5 c. red .. 6·00 6·00

1963. Surch. **VALE** and value.
798. 217. 4 c. on 3 c. black and red (postage) .. 15 5
799. – 4 c. on 3 c. black, blue and cream (No. 741) 15 5
800. 220. 4 c. on 3 c. blk. & red .. 15 5
801. – 4 c. on 3 c. black and blue (No. 776) .. 15 5
802. 182. 10 c. on 25 c. blue & red 35 15
803. – 10 c. on 25 c. blue (No. 688) (air) .. 20 15

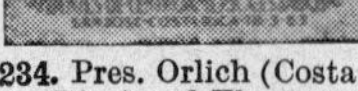

234. Pres. Orlich (Costa Rica) and Flags. 236. Vasco Nunez de Balboa.

235. Innsbruck.

1963. Presidential Reunion, San Jose (Costa Rica). Multicoloured. Presidents and flags of their countries.
804. 1 c. Type 234 (postage) .. 10 10
805. 2 c. Somoza (Nicaragua) .. 12 12
806. 3 c. Villeda (Honduras) .. 20 12
807. 4 c. Chiari (Panama) .. 25 20
808. 5 c. Rivera (El Salvador) (air) 30 30
809. 10 c. Ydigoras (Guatemala) 55 45
810. 21 c. Kennedy (U.S.A.) .. 1·60 1·40

1963. Winter Olympic Games, Innsbruck.
811. ½ c. red and blue (postage) 5 5
812. 1 c. red, brown & turquoise 8 5
813. 3 c. red and blue .. 25 15
814. 4 c. red, brown and green .. 35 20
815. 5 c. red, brn. & mve. (air) .. 45 25
816. 15 c. red, brown and blue .. 1·10 90
817. 21 c. red, brown and myrtle 2·25 1·90
818. 31 c. red, brown & blue .. 3·00 2·25
DESIGNS: ½ c. (expressed "B/0.005"), 3 c. Type 235. 1 c., 4 c. Speed-skating. 5 c. to 31 c. Skiing (slalom).

1964. 450th Anniv. of Discovery of Pacific Ocean.
820. 236. 4 c. grn. on flesh (post.) 10 5
821. 10 c. vio. on pink (air) 20 20

237. Boy Scout. 238. St. Paul's Cathedral, London.

1964. Olbigatory Tax for Youth Rehabilitation, Institute.
822. 237. 1 c. red 8 5
823. 1 c. grey 8 5
824. 1 c. light blue 8 5
825. 1 c. olive 8 5
826. 1 c. violet 8 5
827. – 1 c. brown 8 5
828. – 1 c. orange 8 5
829. – 1 c. turquoise 8 5
830. – 1 c. violet 8 5
831. – 1 c. yellow 8 5
DESIGN: Nos. 827/31, Girl guide.

1964. Air. Ecumenical Council, Vatican City (1st issue). Cathedrals. Centres in black.
832. 21 c. red (Type 238) .. 55 35
833. 21 c. blue (Kassa, Hungary) 55 35
834. 21 c. green (Milan) .. 55 35
835. 21 c. black (St. John's Poland) 55 35
836. 21 c. brown (St. Stephen's, Vienna) 55 35
837. 21 c. brown (Notre Dame, Paris) 55 35
838. 21 c. violet (Moscow) .. 55 35
839. 21 c. violet (Lima) .. 55 35
840. 21 c. red (Stockholm) .. 55 35
841. 21 c. mauve (Cologne) .. 55 35
842. 21 c. bistre (New Delhi) .. 55 35
843. 21 c. deep turq. (Basel) .. 55 35
844. 21 c. green (Toledo) .. 55 35
845. 21 c. red (Metropolitan, Athens) 55 35
846. 21 c. olive (St. Patrick's, New York) 55 35
847. 21 c. green (Lisbon) .. 55 35
848. 21 c. turquoise (Sofia) .. 55 35
849. 21 c. deep brown (New Church, Delft, Netherlands) 55 35
850. 21 c. deep sepia (St. George's Partriarchal Church, Istanbul) .. 55 35
851. 21 c. blue (Basilica, Guadalupe, Mexico) 55 35
852. 1 b. blue (Panama) 1·75 1·75
853. 2 b. green (St. Peter's, Rome) .. .. 3·00 3·00
See Nos. 882, etc.

1964. As Nos. 749 and 760 but colours changed and optd. **HABILITADA.**
855. 1 b. blk., red & blue (post.) 1·75 1·60
856. 1 b. blk., grn. & yell. (air) 1·75 1·25

1964. Air. No. 756 surch. **VALE B/.0.50**
857. 50 c. on 21 c. black, sepia and blue 65 40

241. Discus-thrower.

1964. Olympic Games, Tokyo.
858. ½ c. ("B/0.005") purple, red, brn. & grn. (post.) 5 5
859. 1 c. multicoloured .. 8 5
860. 5 c. black, red and olive (air) 35 25
861. 10 c. black, red and yellow 70 45
862. 21 c. multicoloured .. 1·40 90
863. 50 c. multicoloured .. 2·75 1·75
DESIGNS: ½ c. Type 241. 1 c. Runner with Olympic Flame. 5 c. to 50 c. Olympic Stadium, Tokyo, and Mt. Fuji.

1964. Air. Nos. 692 and 742 surch. **Aereo B/.0.10.**
865. 10 c. on 5 c. green & turq. 20 15
866. 10 c. on 5 c. black, red and green 20 15

243. Space Vehicles (Project "Apollo").

1964. Space Exploration. Multicoloured.
867. ½ c. ("B/0.005") Type 243 (postage) 10 8
868. 1 c. Rocket and capsule (Project "Gemini") .. 10 8
869. 5 c. W.M. Schirra (air) .. 20 20
870. 10 c. L. G. Cooper .. 30 30
871. 21 c. Schirra's capsule .. 75 75
872. 50 c. Cooper's capsule .. 3·25 3·00

1964. No. 687 surch. **Correos B/.0.10.**
874. 10 c. on 21 c. blue .. 15 12

245. Water-skiing.

1964. Aquatic Sports. Multicoloured.
875. ½ c. ("B/0.005") Type 245 (postage) 8 5
876. 1 c. Underwater-swimming 8 5
877. 5 c. Fishing (air) .. 20 10
878. 10 c. Sailing (vert.) .. 1·50 60
879. 21 c. Speedboat racing .. 2·75 1·50
880. 31 c. Water polo at Olympic Games, 1964 .. 3·50 1·75

1964. Air. Ecumenical Council, Vatican City (2nd issue). Stamps of 1st issue optd. **1964.** Centres in black.
882. 21 c. red (No. 832) .. 70 50
883. 21 c. green (No. 834) .. 70 50
884. 21 c. olive (No. 836) .. 70 50
885. 21 c. deep sepia (No. 850) 70 50
886. 1 b. blue (No. 852) .. 2·75 2·00
887. 2 b. green (No. 853) .. 5·50 4·50

247. General View. 248. Eleanor Roosevelt.

1964. Air. New York World's Fair.
889. 247. 5 c. black and yellow 30 25
890. – 10 c. black and red .. 75 60
891. – 15 c. black and green 1·25 80
892. – 21 c. black and blue .. 1·90 1·50
DESIGNS: 10 c., 15 c. Fair pavilions (different). 21 c. Unisphere.

1964. Mrs. Eleanor Roosevelt Commem.
894. 248. 4 c. black and red on yellow (postage) .. 12 8
895. 20 c. black and green on buff (air) .. 50 45

249. Dag Hammarskjold. 250. Pope John XXIII.

1964. Air. U.N. Day.
897. **249.** 21 c. black and blue .. 70 50
898. – 21 c. blue and black .. 70 50
DESIGN: No. 898, U.N. Emblem.

1964. Air. Pope John Commem.
900. **250.** 21 c. black and bistre 70 50
901. – 21 c. mult. (Papal Arms) 70 50

251. Slalom Skiing Medals.

1964. Winter Olympic Winners' Medals. Medals in gold, silver and bronze.
903. **251.** ½ c. (" B/0.005 ") turquoise (postage) 5 5
904. – 1 c. deep blue 8 5
905. – 2 c. brown 20 12
906. – 3 c. mauve 25 15
907. – 4 c. lake 35 20
908. – 5 c. violet (air) .. 45 25
909. – 6 c. blue 55 30
910. – 7 c. violet 65 35
911. – 10 c. green 90 50
912. – 21 c. red .. .. 1·40 95
913. – 31 c. blue .. .. 2·50 1·40
DESIGNS—Medals for: 1 c. 7 c. Speed-skating. 2 c., 21 c. Bobsleighing. 3 c., 10 c. Figure-skating. 4 c. Ski-jumping. 5 c., 6 c., 31 c. Cross-country skiing. Values in the same design show different medal-winners and country names.

252. Cuvier's Toucan.

1965. Birds. Multicoloured.
915. 1 c. Type **252** (postage) .. 40 10
916. 2 c. Scarlet Macaw .. 40 10
917. 3 c. Black-cheeked Woodpecker 65 10
918. 4 c. Blue-grey Tanager (horiz.) 65 15
919. 5 c. Troupial (horiz.) (air) 80 20
920. 10 c. Crimson-backed Tanager (horiz.) .. 1·60 30

253. Snapper.

1965. Marine Life. Multicoloured.
921. 1 c. Type **253** (postage) .. 5 5
922. 2 c. Dolphin 8 5
923. 8 c. Shrimp (air) 20 12
924. 12 c. Hammerhead .. 25 20
925. 13 c. Atlantic sailfish .. 30 25
926. 25 c. Seahorse (vert.) .. 30 25

254. Double Daisy and Emblem.

1966. Air. 50th Anniv. of Junior Chamber of Commerce. Flowers. Multicoloured: background colour given.
927. **254.** 30 c. mauve 55 45
928. – 30 c. flesh (Hibiscus) .. 55 45
929. – 30 c. olive (Mauve orchid) 55 45
930. – 40 c. green (Water lily) 60 55
931. – 40 c. blue (Gladiolus) 60 55
932. – 40 c. pink (White orchid) 60 55
Each design incorporates the Junior Chamber of Commerce Emblem.

1966. Surch. (a) Postage.
933. 13 c. on 25 c. (No. 747) .. 30 20
(b) Air.
934. 3 c. on 5 c. (No. 680) .. 8 8
935. 13 c. on 25 c. (No. 695) .. 30 25

256. Chicken.

1967. Domestic Animals. Multicoloured.
936. 1 c. Type **256** (postage) .. 5 5
937. 3 c. Cockerel 5 5
938. 5 c. Pig (horiz.) 10 5
939. 8 c. Cow (horiz.) 15 10
940. 10 c. Pekingese dog (air) .. 25 20
941. 13 c. Zebu (horiz.) .. 30 20
942. 30 c. Cat 60 50
943. 40 c. Horse (horiz.) .. 75 60

257. American Anhinga.

1967. Wild Birds. Multicoloured.
944. ½ c. Type **257** 35 10
945. 1 c. Resplendent quetzal .. 35 10
946. 3 c. Turquoise-browed motmot 45 10
947. 4 c. Red-necked aracari (horiz.) 55 15
948. 5 c. Chestnut-fronted macaw 70 15
949. 13 c. Belted kingfisher .. 1·50 35

258. " Deer " (F. Marc).

1967. Wild Animals. Paintings. Mult.
950. 1 c. Type **258** (postage) .. 5 5
951. 3 c. "Cougar" (F. Marc) .. 8 5
952. 5 c. "Monkeys" (F. Marc) 10 5
953. 8 c. "Fox" (F. Marc) 20 8
954. 10 c. "St. Jerome and the Lion" (Durer) (air) .. 20 15
955. 13 c. "The Hare" (Durer) 30 20
956. 20 c. "Lady with the Ermine" (Da Vinci) 45 25
957. 30 c. "The Hunt" (Delacroix) 65 45
The 3, 10, 13 and 20 are vert.

259. Map of Panama and People.

1969. National Population Census.
958. **259.** 5 c. blue 10 8
959. – 10 c. purple 20 15
DESIGN—VERT. 10 c. People and map of the Americas.

260. Cogwheel.

1969. 50th Anniv. of Rotary Int. in Panama.
960. **260.** 13 c. blk., yell. & blue 20 20

261. Cornucopia and Map. 262. Tower and Map.

1969. 1st Anniv. of 11 October Revolution.
961. **261.** 10 c. multicoloured .. 20 10

1969.
962. **262.** 3 c. black and orange 8 5
963. – 5 c. green 10 5
964. – 8 c. brown 20 15
965. – 13 c. black & green .. 25 15
966. – 20 c. brown 35 25
967. – 21 c. yellow 35 25
968. – 25 c. green 45 30
969. – 30 c. black 50 45
970. – 34 c. brown 55 45
971. – 38 c. blue 60 45
972. – 40 c. yellow 65 45
973. – 50 c. black and purple 85 65
974. – 59 c. purple .. .. 1·00 60
DESIGNS—HORIZ. 5 c. Peasants. 13 c. Hotel Continental. 25 c. Del Rey Bridge. 34 c. Panama Cathedral. 38 c. Municipal Palace. 40 c. French Plaza. 50 c. Thatcher Ferry Bridge. 59 c. National Theatre. VERT. 8 c. Nata Church. 20 c. Virgin of Carmen Church. 21 c. Altar, San Jose Church. 30 c. Dr. Arosemena statue.

263. Discus-thrower and Stadium.

1970. 11th Central American and Caribbean Games, Panama (1st series).
975. **263.** 1 c. multicoloured (post.) 5 5
976. 2 c. multicoloured .. 5 5
977. 3 c. multicoloured .. 5 5
978. 5 c. multicoloured .. 10 5
979. 10 c. multicoloured .. 20 12
980. 13 c. multicoloured .. 25 15
981. – 13 c. multicoloured .. 25 15
982. **263.** 25 c. multicoloured .. 45 35
983. 30 c. multicoloured .. 55 45
984. – 13 c. multicoloured (air) 70 20
985. – 30 c. multicoloured .. 60 45
DESIGNS—VERT. No. 981, " Flor del Espiritu Santo " (flowers). No. 985, Indian girl. HORIZ. No. 984, Thatcher Ferry Bridge and palm.
See also Nos. 986/94.

264. J. D. Arosemena and Stadium.

1970. Air. 11th Central American and Caribbean Games, Panama (2nd series). Multicoloured.
986. 1 c. Type **264** 5 5
987. 2 c. Type **264** 5 5
988. 3 c. Type **264** 5 5
989. 5 c. Type **264** 8 5
990. 13 c. Basketball 20 15
991. 13 c. New Gymnasium .. 20 15
992. 13 c. Revolution Stadium 20 15
993. 13 c. Panamanian couple in festive costume .. 20 15
994. 30 c. Eternal Flame and stadium 45 35

265. A. Tapia and M. Sosa (first comptrollers).

1971. 40th Anniv. of Panamanian Comptroller-General's Office. Multicoloured.
996. 3 c. Comptroller-General's Building (1970) (vert.) .. 8 5
997. 5 c. Type **265** 10 5
998. 8 c. Comptroller-General's emblem (vert.) 15 8
999. 13 c. Comptroller-General's Building (1955-70) .. 30 15

266. "Man and Alligator". 267. Map of Panama on I.E.Y. Emblem.

1971. Indian Handicrafts.
1000. **266.** 8 c. multicoloured .. 20 15

1971. Int. Education Year.
1001. **267.** 1 b. multicoloured .. 1·50 1·50

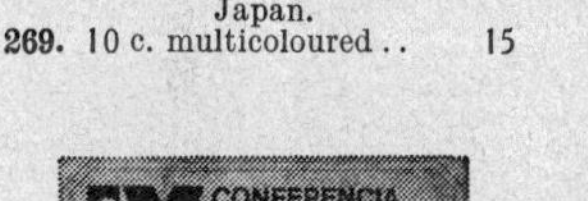

268. Astronaut on Moon. 269. Panama Pavilion.

1971. Air. "Apollo 11" and "Apollo 12" Moon Missions. Multicoloured.
1002. 13 c. Type **268** 35 25
1003. 13 c. "Apollo 12" astronauts 35 25

1971. Air. "EXPO 70", World Fair, Osaka, Japan.
1004. **269.** 10 c. multicoloured .. 15 15

270. Conference Text and Emblem.

1971. 9th Inter-American Loan and Savings Assn., Conf., Panama City.
1005. **270.** 25 c. multicoloured .. 60 35

271. Panama Flag.

1971. Air. American Tourist Year. Mult.
1006. 5 c. Type **271** 10 8
1007. 13 c. Map of Panama and Western Hemisphere .. 30 20

272. New U.P.U. H.Q. Building.

1971. Inauguration of New U.P.U. Headquarters Building, Berne. Multicoloured.
1008. 8 c. Type **272** 20 8
1009. 30 c. U.P.U. Monument, Berne (vert.) 60 35

273. Cow and Pig.

1971. 3rd Agricultural Census.
1010. **273.** 3 c. multicoloured .. 8 5

274. Map and "4S" Emblem.

1971. "4S" Programme for Rural Youth.
1011. **274.** 2 c. multicoloured .. 5 5

275. Gandhi. 276. Central American Flags.

1971. Air. Birth Centenary (1969) of Mahatma Gandhi.
1012. **275.** 10 c. multicoloured.. 20 15

1971. Air. 150th Anniv. of Central American States' Independence from Spain.
1013. **276.** 13 c. multicoloured .. 30 20

277. Early Panama Stamp. 278. Altar, Nata Church.

1971. Air. 2nd Nat., Philatelic and Numismatic Exhib., Panama.
1014. **277.** 8 c. blue, blk. & red .. 20 15

1972. Air. 450th Anniv. of Nata Church.
1015. **278.** 40 c. multicoloured .. 50 45

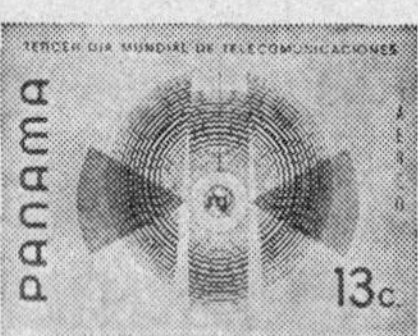

279. Telecommunications Emblem.

1972. Air. World Telecommunications Day.
1016. **279.** 13 c. blk., bl. & light bl. 20 15

280. "Apollo 14" Badge.

1972. Air. Moon Flight of "Apollo 14".
1017. **280.** 13 c. multicoloured.. 60 25

281. Children on See-saw.

1972. 25th Anniv. (1971) of U.N.I.C.E.F. Multicoloured.
1018. 1 c. Type **281** (postage) .. 5 5
1019. 5 c. Boy sitting by kerb (vert.) (air) .. 8 5
1020. 8 c. Indian mother and child (vert.) .. 15 8
1021. 50 c. U.N.I.C.E.F. emblem (vert.) 70 45

282. Tropical Fruits.

1972. Tourist Publicity. Multicoloured.
1023. 1 c. Type **282** (postage) .. 5 5
1024. 2 c. "Isle of Night" .. 5 5
1025. 3 c. Carnival float (vert.) 8 5
1026. 5 c. San Blas textile (air) 8 8
1027. 8 c. Chaquira (beaded collar) 20 8
1028. 25 c. Ruined fort, Portobello 35 30

283. Map and Flags. 284. Baseball Players.

1973. Obligatory Tax. Panama City Post Office Building Fund. 7th Bolivar Games.
1030. **283.** 1 c. black 5 5

1973. Air. 7th Bolivar Games.
1031. **284.** 8 c. red and yellow .. 15 10
1032. – 10 c. black & blue .. 20 12
1033. – 13 c. multicoloured.. 30 20
1034. – 25 c. blk., red & green 55 30
1035. – 50 c. multicoloured .. 1·25 55
1036. – 1 b. multicoloured .. 2·50 1·10

DESIGNS—VERT. 10 c. Basketball. 13 c. Flaming torch. HORIZ. 25 c. Boxing. 50 c. Panama map and flag, Games emblem and Bolivar. 1 b. Games' medals.

1973. U.N. Security Council Meeting, Panama City. Various stamps surch. **O.N.U.** in laurel leaf and **CONSEJO DE SEGURIDAD 15-21 Marzo 1973** and value.
1037. 8 c. on 59 c. (No. 974) (postage) 10 10
1038. 10 c. on 1 b. (No. 1001) .. 15 12
1039. 13 c. on 30 c. (No. 969) .. 20 15
1040. 13 c. on 40 c. (No. 1015) (air) 25 15

286. Farming Co-operative.

1973. Obligatory Tax. Post Office Building Fund.
1041. **286.** 1 c. green and red .. 8 5
1042. – 1 c. grey and red .. 8 5
1043. – 1 c. yellow and red .. 8 5
1044. – 1 c. orange and red .. 8 5
1045. – 1 c. blue and red .. 8 5

DESIGNS: No. 1042, Silver coins. No. 1043, V. Lorenzo. No. 1044, Cacique Urraca. No. 1045, Post Office building.

See also Nos. 1061/2.

287. J. D. Crespo (educator). 290. Women's upraised Hands.

1973. Famous Panamanians. Multicoloured.
1046. 3 c. Type **287** (postage) .. 8 5
1047. 5 c. Isabel Obaldia (educator) (air) .. 10 8
1048. 8 c. N. V. Jaen (educator) 20 12
1049. 10 c. "Forest Scene" (Roberto Lewis–painter) 20 15
1050. 13 c. R. Miro (poet) .. 35 20
1051. 13 c. "Portrait of a Lady" (M. E. Amador-painter) 35 20
1052. 20 c. "Self-Portrait" (Isaac Benitez–painter) 55 20
1053. 21 c. M. A. Guerrero (statesman) 55 25
1054. 25 c. Dr. B. Porras (statesman) 55 30
1055. 30 c. J. D. Arosemena (statesman) 70 35
1056. 34 c. Dr. O. M. Pereira (writer).. .. .. 90 45
1057. 38 c. Dr. R. J. Alfaro (writer) .. .. 1·10 50

1973. Air. 50th Anniv. of Isabel Obaldia Professional School. Nos. 1047, 1054 and 1056 optd. **1923, 1973 Bodas de Oro Eseuela Profesional Isabel Herrera Obaldia** and EP emblem.
1058. 5 c. multicoloured .. 15 8
1059. 25 c. multicoloured .. 55 30
1060. 34 c. multicoloured .. 60 55

1974. Obligatory Tax. Post Office Building Fund. As Nos. 1044/5.
1061. 1 c. orange 8 5
1062. 1 c. blue 8 5

1974. Surch. **VALE** and value.
1063. 5 c. on 30 c. black (No. 969) (postage) 10 8
1064. 10 c. on 34 c. brown (No. 970) 15 10
1065. 13 c. on 21 c. yellow (No. 967) 20 15
1066. 1 c. on 25 c. mult. (No. 1028) (air) 5 5
1067. 3 c. on 20 c. mult. (No. 1052) 5 5
1068. 8 c. on 38 c. mult. (No. 1057) 12 8
1069. 10 c. on 34 c. mult. (No. 1056) 15 12
1070. 13 c. on 21 c. mult. (No. 1053) 20 15

1975. Air. International Women's Year.
1071. **290.** 17 c. multicoloured.. 45 20

291. Bayano Dam.

1975. Air. 7th Anniv. of October 1968, Revolution.
1073. **291.** 17 c. blk., brn. & blue 20 15
1074. – 27 c. blue and green.. 30 25
1075. – 33 c. multicoloured .. 1·10 30

DESIGNS—VERT. 27 c. Victoria sugar plant, Veraguas, and sugar cane. HORIZ. 33 c. Tocumen International Airport.

1975. Obligatory Tax. Various stamps surch. **VALE PRO EDIFICIO** and value.
1076. – 1 c. on 30 c. black (No. 969) (postage) 8 5
1077. – 1 c. on 40 c. yellow (No. 972) .. 8 5
1078. – 1 c. on 50 c. black & purple (No. 973) .. 8 5
1079. – 1 c. on 30 c. mult. (No. 1009) .. 8 5
1080. **282.** 1 c. on 1 c. multicoloured 8 5
1081. – 1 c. on 2 c. multicoloured (No. 1024) .. 8 5
1082. **278.** 1 c. on 40 c. mult. (air) 8 5
1083. – 1 c. on 25 c. mult. (No. 1028) .. 8 5
1084. – 1 c. on 25 c. mult. (No. 1052) .. 8 5
1085. – 1 c. on 20 c. mult. (No. 1054) .. 8 5
1086. – 1 c. on 30 c. mult. (No. 1055) .. 8 5

1975. Obligatory Tax. Post Office Building Fund. As No. 1045.
1087. 1 c. red 10 5

294. Bolivar and Thatcher Ferry Bridge. 295. "Evibacus princeps".

1976. 150th Anniv. of Panama Congress (1st issue). Multicoloured.
1088. 6 c. Type **294** (postage).. 8 5
1089. 23 c. Bolivar Statue (air) 30 25
1090. 35 c. Bolivar Hall, Panama City (horiz.) 50 30
1091. 41 c. Bolivar and flag .. 60 40

1976. Marine Fauna. Multicoloured.
1092. 2 c. Type **295** (postage).. 5 5
1093. 3 c. "Ptitosarcus sinuosus" (vert.) 5 5
1094. 4 c. "Acanthaster planci" 5 5
1095. 7 c. "Oreaster reticulatus" 10 8
1096. 17 c. "Diodon hystrix" (vert.) (air) 25 15
1097. 27 c. "Pocillopora damicornis" 40 25

HAVE YOU READ THE NOTES AT THE BEGINNING OF THIS CATALOGUE?
These often provide answers to the enquiries we receive.

296. "Simon Bolivar".

1976. 150th Anniv. of Panama Congress (2nd issue). Designs showing details of Bolivar Monument or flags of Latin-American countries. Multicoloured.
1099. 20 c. Type **296** 30 20
1100. 20 c. Argentina 30 20
1101. 20 c. Bolivia 30 20
1102. 20 c. Brazil 30 20
1103. 20 c. Chile 30 20
1104. 20 c. "Battle scene" .. 30 20
1105. 20 c. Colombia 30 20
1106. 20 c. Costa Rica .. 30 20
1107. 20 c. Cuba 30 20
1108. 20 c. Ecuador 30 20
1109. 20 c. El Salvador .. 30 20
1110. 20 c. Guatemala .. 30 20
1111. 20 c. Guyana 30 20
1112. 20 c. Haiti 30 20
1113. 20 c. "Congress assembly" 30 20
1114. 20 c. "Liberated people" 30 20
1115. 20 c. Hondurus 30 20
1116. 20 c. Jamaica 30 20
1117. 20 c. Mexico 30 20
1118. 20 c. Nicaragua 30 20
1119. 20 c. Panama 30 20
1120. 20 c. Paraguay 30 20
1121. 20 c. Peru 30 20
1122. 20 c. Dominican Republic 30 20
1123. 20 c. "Bolivar and standard-bearer" 30 20
1124. 20 c. Surinam 30 20
1125. 20 c. Trinidad and Tobago 30 20
1126. 20 c. Uruguay 30 20
1127. 20 c. Venezuela 30 20
1128. 20 c. "Indian Delegation" 30 20

297. Nicanor Villalaz (designer of Panama Arms). 298. National Lottery Building, Panama City.

1976. Villalaz Commemoration.
1130. **297.** 5 c. blue 8 5

1976. "Progressive Panama".
1131. **298.** 6 c. multicoloured .. 8 5

299. Cerro Colorado, Copper Mine.

1976. Air.
1132. **299.** 23 c. multicoloured .. 30 20

300. Contadora Island.

1977. Tourism.
1133. **300.** 3 c. multicoloured .. 10 5

301 Secretary-General of Pan-American Union, A. Orfila. 302. Signing Ratification of Panama Canal Treaty.

1978. Signing of Panama–U.S.A. Treaty. Multicoloured.
1134. 3 c. Type **301** 5 5
1135. 23 c. Treaty signing scene (horiz.) 30 25
1136. 40 c. President Carter .. 55 30
1137. 50 c. Gen. O. Torrijos of Panama 70 50

Nos. 1134 and 1136/7 were issued together se-tenant in horizontal stamps of three showing Treaty signing as No. 1135.

1978. Ratification of Panama Canal Treaty.
1138. **302.** 3 c. multicoloured .. 5 5
1139. – 5 c. multicoloured .. 8 5
1140. – 35 c. multicoloured .. 50 25
1141. – 41 c. multicoloured .. 60 30
DESIGNS: 5 c., 35 c., 41 c. As Type **302**, but with the design of the Ratification Ceremony spread over the three stamps, issued as a se-tenant strip in the order 5 c. (29 × 39 mm.), 41 c. (44 × 39 mm.), 35 c. (29 × 39 mm.).

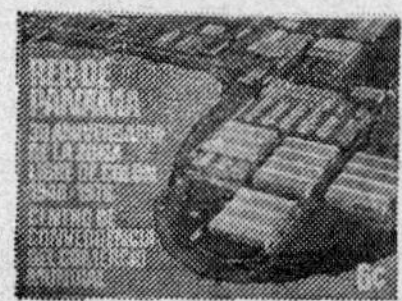

303. Colon Harbour and Warehouses.

1978. 30th Anniv. of Colon Free Zone.
1142. **303.** 6 c. multicoloured .. 8 5

304. Children's Home and Melvin Jones.

1978. Birth Centenary of Melvin Jones (founder of Lions International).
1143. **304.** 50 c. multicoloured .. 70 55

305. Pres. Torrijos, "Flavia" (liner) and Children.

1979. Return of Canal Zone. Multicoloured.
1144. 3 c. Type **305** 10 10
1145. 23 c. Presidents Torrijos and Carter, liner and flags of Panama and U.S.A. 40 20

306. " 75 " and Bank Emblem.

1979. 75th Anniv. of National Bank.
1146. **306.** 6 c. black, red & blue 8 5

307. Rotary Emblem. **308.** Children inside Heart.

1979. 75th Anniv. of Rotary International.
1147. **307.** 17 c. blue and yellow 25 20

1979. International Year of the Child.
1148. **308.** 50 c. multicoloured .. 70 45

309. U.P.U. Emblem and Globe. **310.** Colon Station.

1979. 18th Universal Postal Union Congress, Rio de Janeiro.
1149. **309.** 35 c. multicoloured .. 50 30

1980. Cent. of Trans-Panamanian Railway.
1150. **310.** 1 c. purple and lilac .. 10 25

311. Postal Headquarters, Balboa (inauguration). **318.** Boys in Children's Village.

1980. Anniversaries and Events.
1151. **311.** 3 c. multicoloured .. 5 5
1152. – 6 c. multicoloured .. 8 5
1153. – 17 c. multicoloured .. 25 20
1154. – 23 c. multicoloured .. 30 20
1155. – 35 c. blue, blk. & red 50 30
1156. – 41 c. pink and black .. 60 40
1157. – 50 c. multicoloured .. 70 45
DESIGNS—HORIZ. 17 c. Map of Central America and flags (census of the Americas). 23 c. Tourism and Convention Centre (opening). 35 c. Bank emblem (Inter-American Development Bank, 25th anniv.). 41 c. F. de Lesseps (Panama Canal cent.). 50 c. Olympic Stadium, Moscow (Olympic Games). VERT. 6 c. National flag (return of Canal Zone).

1980. Olympic Games, Lake Placid and Moscow.

(a) Optd. **1980 LAKE PLACID MOSCU** and venue emblems.
1158. 20 c. **LAKE PLACID MOSCU** (No. 1099) .. 80 80
1160. 20 c. As No. 1158 (1101) 80 80
1162. 20 c. As No. 1158 (1103) 80 80
1164. 20 c. As No. 1158 (1105) 80 80
1166. 20 c. As No. 1158 (1107) 80 80
1168. 20 c. As No. 1158 (1109) 80 80
1170. 20 c. As No. 1158 (1111) 80 80
1172. 20 c. As No. 1158 (1113) 80 80
1174. 20 c. As No. 1158 (1115) 80 80
1176. 20 c. As No. 1158 (1117) 80 80
1178. 20 c. As No. 1158 (1119) 80 80
1180. 20 c. As No. 1158 (1121) 80 80
1182. 20 c. As No. 1158 (1123) 80 80
1184. 20 c. As No. 1158 (1125) 80 80
1186. 20 c. As No. 1158 (1127) 80 80

(b) Optd. with Lake Placid Olympic emblems and medals total of country indicated.
1159. 20 c. **ALEMAMOA D.** (1101) 80 80
1161. 20 c. " **AUSTRIA** " (1102) 80 80
1163. 20 c. " **SUECIA** " (1104) 80 80
1165. 20 c. " **U.R.S.S.** " (1106) 80 80
1167. 20 c. " **ALEMANIA F.** " (1108) 80 80
1169. 20 c. " **ITALIA** " (1110) 80 80
1171. 20 c. " **U.S.A.** " (1112) .. 80 80
1173. 20 c. " **SUIZA** " (1114) 80 80
1175. 20 c. " **CANADA/GRAN BRETANA** " (1116) .. 80 80
1177. 20 c. " **NORUEGA** " (1118) 80 80
1179. 20 c. " **LICHTENSTEIN** " (1120) 80 80
1181. 20 c. " **HUNGRIA/BULGARIA** " (1122) 80 80
1183. 20 c. " **FINLANDIA** " (1124) 80 80
1185. 20 c. " **HOLANDA** " (1126) 80 80
1187. 20 c. " **CHECOSLOVAQUIA/FRANCIA** " (1128) 80 80
Footnote 1158 etc. occur on 1st, 3rd and 5th rows and Nos. 1160 etc. occur in other rows.

(a) Lake Placid and Moscow and venue with Olympic rings.
1188. 20 c. **LAKE PLACID MOSCU** (No. 1099) .. 80 80
1190. 20 c. As No. 1188 (1101) 80 80
1192. 20 c. As No. 1188 (1103) 80 80
1194. 20 c. As No. 1188 (1105) 80 80
1196. 20 c. As No. 1188 (1107) 80 80
1198. 20 c. As No. 1188 (1109) 80 80
1200. 20 c. As No. 1188 (1111) 80 80
1202. 20 c. As No. 1188 (1113) 80 80
1204. 20 c. As No. 1188 (1115) 80 80
1206. 20 c. As No. 1188 (1117) 80 80
1208. 20 c. As No. 1188 (1119) 80 80
1210. 20 c. As No. 1188 (1121) 80 80
1212. 20 c. As No. 1188 (1123) 80 80
1214. 20 c. As No. 1188 (1125) 80 80
1216. 20 c. As No. 1188 (1127) 80 80

(b) Optd. with country names as indicated.
1189. 20 c. " **RUSIA/ALEMANIA D.** " (1101) .. 80 80
1191. 20 c. " **SUECIA/FINLANDIA** " (1102) .. 80 80
1193. 20 c. " **GRECIA/BELGICA/INDIA** " (1104) 80 80
1195. 20 c. " **BULGARIA/CUBA** " (1106) .. 80 80
1197. 20 c. " **CHECOSLOVAQUIA/YUGOSLAVIA** " (1108) 80 80
1199. 20 c. " **ZIMBAWE/COREA DEL NORTE/MONGOLIA** " (1110) 80 80
1201. 20 c. " **ITALIA/HUNGRIA** " (1112) .. 80 80
1203. 20 c. " **AUSTRALIA/DINAMARCA** " (1114) 80 80
1205. 20 c. " **TANZANIA/MEXICO/HOLANDA** " (1116) 80 80
1207. 20 c. " **RUMANIA/FRANCIA** " (1118) .. 80 80
1209. 20 c. " **BRASIL/ETIOPIA** " (1120) 80 80
1211. 20 c. " **IRLANDA/UGANDA/VENEZUELA** " (1122) 80 80
1213. 20 c. " **GRAN BRETANA/POLONIA** " (1124) .. 80 80
1215. 20 c. " **SUIZA/ESPANA/AUSTRIA** .. (1126) .. 80 80
1217. 20 c. " **JAMAICA/LIBANO/GUYANA** " (1128) 80 80
Footnote Nos. 1188, etc., occur on 1st, 3rd and 5th rows and Nos. 1189 etc., on the others.

1980. Medal Winners at Winter Olympic Games, Lake Placid.

(a) Optd. with 1980, medals and venue emblems.
1219. 20 c. 1980 medals and venue and emblems (No. 1099) 80 80
1221. 20 c. As No. 1219 (1101) 80 80
1223. 20 c. As No. 1219 (1103) 80 80
1225. 20 c. As No. 1219 (1105) 80 80
1227. 20 c. As No. 1219 (1107) 80 80
1229. 20 c. As No. 1219 (1109) 80 80
1231. 20 c. As No. 1219 (1111) 80 80
1233. 20 c. As No. 1219 (1113) 80 80
1235. 20 c. As No. 1219 (1115) 80 80
1237. 20 c. As No. 1219 (1117) 80 80
1239. 20 c. As No. 1219 (1119) 80 80
1241. 20 c. As No. 1219 (1121) 80 80
1243. 20 c. As No. 1219 (1123) 80 80
1245. 20 c. As No. 1219 (1125) 80 80
1247. 20 c. As No. 1219 (1127) 80 80

(b) Optd. with 1980 medals and venue emblems and Olympic torch and country indicated.
1220. 20 c. " **ALEMANIA D.** " (1100) 80 80
1222. 20 c. " **AUSTRIA** " (1102) 80 80
1224. 20 c. " **SUECIA** " (1104) 80 80
1226. 20 c. " **U.R.S.S.** " (1106) 80 80
1228. 20 c. " **ALEMANIA F.** " (1108) 80 80
1230. 20 c. " **ITALIA** " (1110) 80 80
1232. 20 c. " **U.S.A.** " (1112) .. 80 80
1234. 20 c. " **SUIZA** " (1114) .. 80 80
1236. 20 c. " **CANADA/GRAN BRETANA** " (1116) .. 80 80
1238. 20 c. " **NORUEGA** " (1118) 80 80
1240. 20 c. " **LICHTENSTEIN** " (1120) 80 80
1242. 20 c. " **HUNGRIA/BULGARIA** " (1122) .. 80 80
1244. 20 c. " **FINLANDIA** " (1124) 80 80
1246. 20 c. " **HOLANDIA** " (1126) 80 80
1248. 20 c. " **CHECOSLOVAQUIA/FRANCIA** " (1128) 80 80
Footnote Nos. 1219, etc., occur in 1st, 3rd and 5th rows and Nos. 1220 occur in others.

1980. World Cup Football Championship, Argentina (1978) and Spain (1980). Optd. with
A. Football cup emblems.
B. " **ESPAMER 80** " and " Argentina '78 " emblems and inscriptions " **ESPANA '82/CAMPEONATO/MUNDIAL DE FUTBOL** ".
C. World Cup Trophy and " **ESPANA '82.** "
D. " **ESPANA '82/Football/Argentina '78/BESPAMER '80 MADRID** ".
E. FIFA globes emblem and " **ESPANA '82/ARGENTINA '78/ESPANA '82** ".
F. With ball and inscription as for B.
1249. 20 c. No. 1099 (A, C, E) .. 80 80
1250. 20 c. No. 1100 (B, D, F) .. 80 80
1251. 20 c. No. 1101 (A, C, E) .. 80 80
1252. 20 c. No. 1102 (B, D, F) .. 80 80
1253. 20 c. No. 1103 (A, C, E) .. 80 80
1254. 20 c. No. 1104 (B, D, F) .. 80 80
1255. 20 c. No. 1105 (A, C, E) .. 80 80
1256. 20 c. No. 1106 (B, D, F) .. 80 80
1257. 20 c. No. 1107 (A, C, E) .. 80 80
1258. 20 c. No. 1108 (B, D, F) .. 80 80
1259. 20 c. No. 1109 (A, C, E) .. 80 80
1260. 20 c. No. 1110 (B, D, F) .. 80 80
1261. 20 c. No. 1111 (A, C, E) .. 80 80
1262. 20 c. No. 1112 (B, D, F) .. 80 80
1263. 20 c. No. 1113 (A, C, E) .. 80 80
1264. 20 c. No. 1114 (B, D, F) .. 80 80
1265. 20 c. No. 1115 (A, C, E) .. 80 80
1266. 20 c. No. 1116 (B, D, F) .. 80 80
1267. 20 c. No. 1117 (A, C, E) .. 80 80
1268. 20 c. No. 1118 (B, D, F) .. 80 80
1269. 20 c. No. 1119 (A, C, E) .. 80 80
1270. 20 c. No. 1120 (B, D, F) .. 80 80
1271. 20 c. No. 1121 (A, C, E) .. 80 80
1272. 20 c. No. 1122 (B, D, F) .. 80 80
1273. 20 c. No. 1123 (A, C, E) .. 80 80
1274. 20 c. No. 1124 (B, D, F) .. 80 80
1275. 20 c. No. 1125 (A, C, E) .. 80 80
1276. 20 c. No. 1126 (B, D, F) .. 80 80
1277. 20 c. No. 1127 (A, C, E) .. 80 80
1278. 20 c. No. 1128 (B, D, F) .. 80 80

1980. Obligatory Tax. Children's Village. Multicoloured.
1280. 2 c. Type **318** 5 5
1281. 2 c. Boy with chicks .. 5 5
1282. 2 c. Working in the fields 5 5
1283. 2 c. Boys with pig .. 5 5

319. Jean Baptiste de la Salle and Map showing La Salle Schools. **320.** Louis Braille.

1981. Education in Panama by the Christian Schools.
1285. **319.** 17 c. bl., blk. and red 25 20

1981. International Year of Disabled People.
1286. **320.** 23 c. multicoloured 30 20

321. Statue of the Virgin.

1981. 150th Anniv. of Apparition of Miraculous Virgin to St. Catharine Laboure.
1287. **321.** 35 c. multicoloured 50 35

322. Crimson-backed Tanager.

1981. Birds. Multicoloured.
1288. 3 c. Type **322** 50 10
1289. 6 c. Chestnut-fronted Macaw (vert.) 60 25
1290. 41 c. Violet Sabrewing (vert.) .. .. .. 2·50 1·50
1291. 50 c. Keel-billed Toucan 3·25 1·75

323. " Boy feeding Donkey " (Ricardo Morales). **324.** Banner.

1981. Obligatory Tax. Christmas. Children's Village. Multicoloured.
1292. 2 c. Type **323** 5 5
1293. 2 c. " Nativity " (Enrique Daniel Austin) 5 5
1294. 2 c. " Bird in Tree " (Jorge Gonzalez) .. 5 5
1295. 2 c. " Church " (Eric Belgrane) 5 5

1981. National Reaffirmation.
1297. **324.** 3 c. multicoloured .. 5 5

325. General Herrera. **326.** Ricardo J. Alfaro.

1982. 1st Death Anniv. of General Omar Torrijos Herrera. Multicoloured.
1298. 5 c. Aerial view of Panama (postage) 10 10
1299. 6 c. Colecito army camp 10 10
1300. 17 c. Bayano river barrage 25 20
1301. 50 c. Felipillo engineering works 70 45
1302. 23 c. Type **325** (air) .. 35 25
1303. 35 c. Security Council reunion 50 30
1304. 41 c. Gen. Omar Torrijos airport .. .. .. 1·25 45

1982. Birth Centenary of Ricardo J. Alfaro (statesman).
1306. **326.** 3 c. black, mauve and blue (postage) .. 5 5
1307. – 17 c. black and mauve (air) 25 15
1308. – 23 c. multicoloured .. 30 20
DESIGNS: 17 c. Profile of Alfaro wearing spectacles (as humanist). 23 c. Portrait of Alfaro (as lawyer).

328. Pig Farming. **329.** Pele (Brazilian footballer).

1982. Obligatory tax. Christmas. Children's Village. Multicoloured.

1309. 2 c. Type **328** 5 5
1310. 2 c. Gardening 5 5
1311. 2 c. Metalwork (horiz.) .. 5 5
1312. 2 c. Bee-keeping (horiz.) 5 5

1982. World Cup Football Championship, Spain. Multicoloured.

1314. 50 c. Italian team (horiz.) (postage) 70 45
1315. 23 c. Football emblem and map of Panama (air) .. 30 20
1316. 35 c. Type **329** 50 30
1317. 41 c. World Cup Trophy 60 35

330. Chamber of Trade Emblem.

1983. "Expo Comer" Chamber of Trade Exhibition.

1319. **330.** 17 c. lt. bl., bl., & gold 25 15

331. Dr. Nicolas Solano. **332.** Pope John Paul II giving Blessing.

1983. Air. Birth Centenary (1982) of Dr. Nicolas Solano (anti-tuberculosis pioneer).

1320. **331.** 23 c. brown 35 20

1983. Papal Visit. Multicoloured.

1321. 6 c. Type **332** (postage) .. 8 5
1322. 17 c. Pope John Paul II 25 15
1323. 35 c. Pope and map of Panama (air) 50 30

333. Map of Americas and Sunburst. **334.** Simon Bolivar.

1983. 24th Assembly of Inter-American Development Bank Governors.

1324. **333.** 50 c. light blue, blue and gold 70 45

1983. Birth Bicent. of Simon Bolivar.

1325. **334.** 50 c. multicoloured .. 70 45

335. Postal Union of the Americas and Spain Emblem. **336.** Moslem Mosque.

1983. World Communications Day. Mult.

1327. 30 c. Type **335** 45 25
1328. 40 c. W.C.Y. Emblem .. 60 40
1329. 50 c. Universal Postal Union emblem .. 70 45
1330. 60 c. "Flying Dove" (Alfredo Sinclair) .. 85 55

1983. Freedom of Worship. Multicoloured.

1332. 3 c. Type **336** 5 5
1333. 5 c. Bahai temple .. 8 5
1334. 6 c. Church of St. Francis of the Mountains, Veraguas 8 5
1335. 17 c. Shevet Ahim synagogue 25 15

337. "The Annunciation" (Dagoberto Moran). **338.** Ricardo Miro (writer).

1983. Obligatory Tax. Christmas. Children's Village. Multicoloured.

1336. 2 c. Type **337** 5 5
1337. 2 c. Church and houses (Leonidas Molinar) (vert.) 5 5
1338. 2 c. Bethlehem and star (Colon Olmedo Zambrano) (vert.) 5 5
1339. 2 c. Flight into Egypt (Hector Ulises Velasquez) (vert.) 5 5

1983. Famous Panamanians. Multicoloured.

1341. 1 c. Type **338** 5 5
1342. 3 c. Richard Newman (educationalist) .. 5 5
1343. 5 c. Cristobal Rodriguez (politician) 8 5
1344. 6 c. Alcibiades Arosemena (politician) 8 5
1345. 35 c. Cirilo Martinez (educationalist) 50 30

339. "Rural Architecture" (Juan Manuel Cedero).

1983. Paintings. Multicoloured.

1346. 1 c. Type **339** 5 5
1347. 1 c. "Large Nude" (Manuel Chong Neto) .. 5 5
1348. 3 c. "On another Occasion" (Spiros Vamvas) 5 5
1349. 6 c. "Punta Chame" (Guillermo Trujillo) .. 8 5
1350. 28 c. "Neon Light" (Alfredo Sinclair) 30 20
1351. 35 c. "The Prophet" (Alfredo Sinclair) (vert.) .. 50 30
1352. 41 c. "Highland Girls" (Al Sprague) (vert.) .. 60 40
1353. 1 b. "One Morning" (Ignacio Mallol Pibernat) 1·40 75

340. Tonosi Double Jug.

1984. Archaeological Finds. Multicoloured.

1354. 30 c. Type **340** 35 10
1355. 40 c. Dish on stand .. 60 20
1356. 50 c. Jug decorated with human face (vert.) .. 70 25
1357. 60 c. Waisted bowl (vert.) 85 35

341. Boxing. **342.** Roberto Duran.

1984. Olympic Games, Los Angeles. Mult.

1359. 19 c. Type **341** 35 25
1360. 19 c. Baseball 35 25
1361. 19 c. Basketball (vert.) .. 35 25
1362. 19 c. Swimming (vert.) .. 35 25

1984. Roberto Duran (boxer) Comm.

1363. **342.** 26 c. multicoloured .. 45 30

343. Shooting.

1984. Olympic Games, Los Angeles (2nd series). Multicoloured.

1364. 6 c. Type **343** (postage) 12 8
1366. 30 c. Weightlifting (air) 50 30
1367. 37 c. Wrestling 65 45
1368. 1 b. Long jump .. .. 1·25 90

344. "Pensive Woman". (Manuel Chong Neto). **345.** Map, Pres. Torrijos Herrera and Liner in Canal Lock.

1984. Paintings. Multicoloured.

1369. 1 c. Type **344** 5 5
1370. 3 c. "The Child" (Alredo Sinclair) (horiz.) .. 5 5
1371. 6 c. "A Day in the Life of Rumalda" (Brooke Alfaro) (horiz.) .. 12 8
1372. 30 c. "Highlanders" (Al Sprague) 50 10
1373. 37 c. "Ballet Interval" (Roberto Sprague) (horiz.) 65 15
1374. 44 c. "Wood on Chame Head" (Guillermo Trujillo) (horiz.) .. 75 25
1375. 50 c. "La Plaza Azul" (Juan Manuel Cedeno) (horiz.) 60 25
1376. 1 b. "Ira" (Spiros Vamvas) (horiz.) .. 1·25 90

1984. 5th Anniv. of Canal Zone Postal Sovereignty.

1377. **345.** 19 c. multicoloured .. 25 25

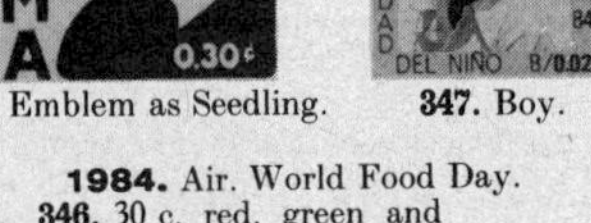

346. Emblem as Seedling. **347.** Boy.

1984. Air. World Food Day.

1378. **346.** 30 c. red, green and blue 50 45

1984. Obligatory Tax. Christmas. Children's Village. Multicoloured.

1379. 2 c. Type **347** 5 5
1380. 2 c. Boy in tee-shirt .. 5 5
1381. 2 c. Boy in checked shirt 5 5
1382. 2 c. Cub scout 5 5

348. American Manatee.

1984. Animals. Each in black.

1384. 3 c. Type **348** (postage) 8 5
1385. 30 c. "Tayra" (air) .. 60 25
1386. 44 c. Jaguarundi .. 85 40
1387. 50 c. White-lipped peccary 90 40

349. Copper One Centesimo Coins, 1935.

1985. Coins. Multicoloured.

1389. 3 c. Type **349** (postage) 5 5
1390. 3 c. Silver ten centesimo coins, 1904 .. .. 5 5
1391. 3 c. Silver five centesimo coins, 1916 .. .. 5 5
1392. 30 c. Silver 50 centesimo coins, 1904 (air) 50 30
1393. 37 c. Silver half balboa coins, 1962 .. .. 65 45
1394. 44 c. Silver balboa coins, 1953 .. .. .. 75 50

350. Figures on Map reaching for Dove. **351.** Tanker in Dock.

1985. Contadora Peace Movement.

1395. **350.** 10 c. multicoloured .. 15 8
1396. 20 c. multicoloured .. 30 20
1397. 30 c. multicoloured .. 40 25

1985. 70th Anniv. of Panama Canal.

1399. **351.** 19 c. multicoloured .. 70 20

352. Scouts with Statue of Christ. **354.** Boys in Cab of Crane.

353. "40" on Emblem.

1985. Obligatory Tax. Christmas. Children's Village. Multicoloured.

1400. 2 c. Type **352** 5 5
1401. 2 c. Children holding cards spelling "Feliz Navidad" 5 5
1402. 2 c. Children holding balloons 5 5
1403. 2 c. Group of cub scouts 5 5

1986. 40th Anniv. (1985) of U.N.O.

1405. **353.** 23 c. multicoloured .. 30 20

1986. International Youth Year (1985).

1406. **354.** 30 c. multicoloured .. 40 25

355. "Awaiting Her Turn" (Al Sprague). **356.** Atlapa Convention Centre.

1986. Paintings. Multicoloured.

1407. 3 c. Type **355** 5 5
1408. 5 c. "Aerobics" (Guillermo Trujillo) (horiz.) 8 5
1409. 19 c. "House of Cardboard" (Eduardo Augustine) 30 20
1410. 30 c. "Tierra Gate" (Juan Manuel Cedeno) (horiz.) .. 40 25
1411. 36 c. "Supper for Three" (Brood Alfaro) .. 50 30
1412. 42 c. "Tenderness" (Alfredo Sinclair) .. 60 40
1413. 50 c. "Lady of Character" (Manuel Chong Neto) .. 70 45
1414. 60 c. "Calla Lilies No. 1" (Maigualida de Diaz) (horiz.) 80 55

1986. Miss Universe Contest. Multicoloured.

1415. 23 c. Type **356** 30 20
1416. 60 c. Emblem 80 55

357. Comet and Globe.

358. Angels.

1986. Appearance of Halley's Comet.
1417. **357.** 23 c. multicoloured . . 25 15
1418. – 30 c. blue, brown and yellow 35 25
DESIGN: 30 c. Panama la Vieja Cathedral tower.

1986. Obligatory Tax. 20th Anniv. of Children's Village. Children's drawings. Multicoloured.
1420. 2 c. Type **358** 5 5
1421. 2 c. Cupids 5 5
1422. 2 c. Indians 5 5
1423. 2 c. Angels (different) . . 5 5

359. Basketball.

360. Argentina Player.

1986. 15th Central American and Caribbean Games, Santiago. Multicoloured.
1425. 20 c. Type **359** 20 10
1426. 23 c. Sports 25 15

1986. World Cup Football Championship, Mexico. Multicoloured.
1427. 23 c. Type **360** 25 15
1428. 30 c. West Germany player 35 25
1429. 37 c. West Germany and Argentina players . . 45 30

361. Crib.

362. Dove and Globe.

1986. Christmas. Multicoloured.
1431. 23 c. Type **361** 25 15
1432. 36 c. Tree and presents 40 25
1433. 42 c. As No. 1432 . . 45 30

1986. International Peace Year. Mult.
1434. 8 c. Type **362** 8 5
1435. 19 c. Profiles and emblem 20 10

363. Mask.

1987. Tropical Carnival. Multicoloured.
1436. 20 c. Type **363** 20 10
1437. 35 c. Sun with eye mask 40 25

364. Headquarters Building.

365. Mountain Rose.

1987. 50th Anniv. (1985) of Panama Lions Club.
1439. **364.** 37 c. multicoloured . . 45 30

1987. Flowers and Birds. Multicoloured.
1440. 3 c. Type **365** 5 5
1441. 5 c. Blue-grey tanager (horiz.) 30 10
1442. 8 c. Golden cup 8 5
1443. 15 c. Tropical kingbird (horiz.) 55 10
1444. 19 c. "Barleria micans" (flower) 20 10
1445. 23 c. Brown pelican (horiz.) 65 15
1446. 30 c. "Cordia dentata" (flower) 35 25
1447. 36 c. Rufous pigeon (horiz.) . . . . 1·10 25

366. Octavio Menendez Pereira (founder) and Anniversary Monument.

1987. 50th Anniv. (1986) of Panama University.
1448. **366.** 19 c. multicoloured . . 20 10

367. Emblem in "40".

368. Heinrich Schutz.

1987. 40th Anniv. (1985) of F.A.O.
1449. **367.** 10 c. brown, yellow and black 10 5
1450. 45 c. brown, green and black 50 30

1987. Composers and 75th Anniv. (1986) of National Theatre.
1451. **368.** 19 c. multicoloured . . 20 10
1452. – 30 c. green, mauve and brown . . 35 25
1453. – 37 c. brown, blue and deep blue 45 30
1454. – 60 c. green, yellow and black 70 45
DESIGNS—HORIZ. 30 c. National Theatre. VERT. 37 c. Johann Sebastian Bach. 60 c. Georg Friedrich Handel.

369. Development Projects.

370. Horse-drawn Fire Pump, 1887, and Modern Appliance.

1987. 25th Anniv. (1986) of Inter-American Development Bank.
1455. **369.** 23 c. multicoloured . . 25 15

1987. Centenary of Fire Service. Mult.
1456. 25 c. Type **370** 30 20
1457. 35 c. Fireman carrying boy 40 25

371. Wrestling.

372. "Adoration of the Magi" (Albrecht Nentz).

1987. 10th Pan-American Games, Indianapolis. Multicoloured.
1458. 15 c. Type **371** 20 10
1459. 23 c. Tennis (vert.) . . 25 15
1460. 30 c. Swimming 35 25
1461. 41 c. Basketball (vert.) . . 45 30
1462. 60 c. Cycling (vert.) . . 70 45

1987. Christmas. Multicoloured.
1464. 22 c. Type **372** 25 15
1465. 35 c. "The Virgin adored by Angels" (Matthias Grunewald) 40 25
1466. 37 c. "Virgin and Child" (Konrad Witz) . . 45 30

373. Distressed Family and Poor Housing.

374. Heart falling into Crack.

1987. International Year of Shelter for the Homeless. Multicoloured.
1467. 45 c. Type **373** 50 30
1468. 50 c. Happy family and stylized modern housing 50 30

1988. Anti-Drugs Campaign.
1469. **374.** 10 c. red and orange 10 5
1470. 17 c. red and green . . 20 10
1471. 25 c. red and blue . . 30 20

375. Hands and Sapling.

376. Breastfeeding.

1988. Reafforestation Campaign.
1472. **375.** 35 c. deep green and green 40 25
1473. 40 c. red and purple 45 30
1474. 45 c. brown & bistre 50 30

1988. U.N.I.C.E.F. Infant Survival Campaign. Multicoloured.
1475 20 c. Type **376** 25 15
1476 31 c. Vaccination . . 35 25
1477 45 c. Children playing by lake (vert) 50 30

377 Rock Beauty

1988. Fishes. Multicoloured.
1478 7 c. Type **377** 8 5
1479 35 c. French angelfish . . 40 25
1480 60 c. Black bar soldier fish 70 45
1481 1 b. Spotted drum fish 1·25 90

378 Emblem and Clasped Hands

379 "Virgin with Donors"

1988. 75th Anniv of Girl Guide Movement.
1482 **378** 35 c. multicoloured . . 35 25

1988. Christmas. Anonymous Paintings from Museum of Colonial Religious Art. Mult.
1483 17 c. Type **379** (postage) 20 10
1484 45 c. "Virgin of the Rosary with St. Dominic" 50 30
1485 35 c. "St. Joseph with the Child" (air) 35 25

380 Athletes and Silver Medal (Brazil)

381 St. John Bosco

1989. Seoul Olympic Games Medals. Mult.
1486 17 c. Type **380** (postage) 20 10
1487 25 c. Wrestlers and gold medal (Hungary) . . 30 20
1488 60 c. Weightlifter and gold medal (Turkey) 70 45
1490 35 c. Boxers and bronze medal (Colombia) (air) 35 25

1989. Death Centenary of St. John Bosco (founder of Salesian Brothers). Multicoloured.
1491 10 c. Type **381** 12 5
1492 20 c. Menor Basilica and St. John with people . . 25 15

382 Anniversary Emblem

383 "Ancon I" (first ship through Canal)

1989. 125th Anniv of Red Cross Movement.
1493 **382** 40 c. black and red . . 50 30
1494 – 1 b. multicoloured . . 1·50 90
DESIGN: 1 b. Red Cross workers putting patient in ambulance.

1989. Air. 75th Anniv of Panama Canal.
1495 **383** 35 c. red, black & yell 60 40
1496 – 60 c. multicoloured . . 1·00 85
DESIGN: 60 c. Modern tanker.

384 Barriles Ceremonial Statue

385 "March of the Women on Versailles' (engraving)

1989. America. Pre-Columbian Artefacts. Multicoloured.
1497 20 c. Type **384** 25 15
1498 35 c. Ceramic vase . . 45 30

1989. Bicent of French Revolution. Mult.
1499 25 c. Type **385** (postage) 30 20
1500 35 c. "Storming the Bastille" (air) 45 30
1501 45 c. Birds 55 35

386 "Holy Family"

1989. Christmas. Multicoloured.
1502 17 c. Type **386** 20 10
1503 35 c. 1988 crib in Cathedral 45 30
1504 45 c. "Nativity" 55 35
The 17 and 45 c. show children's paintings.

387 "Byrsonima crassifolia"   388 Sinan

1990. Fruit. Multicoloured.
1505 20 c. Type **387** 20 10
1506 35 c. "Bactris gasipaes" 40 25
1507 40 c. "Anacardium occidentale" .. 40 25

1990. 88th Birthday of Rogelio Sinan (writer).
1508 **388** 23 c. brown and blue 25 15

389 Pond Turtle

1990. Reptiles. Multicoloured.
1509 35 c. Type **389** 40 25
1510 45 c. Olive loggerhead turtle 50 35
1511 60 c. Red-footed tortoise 65 40

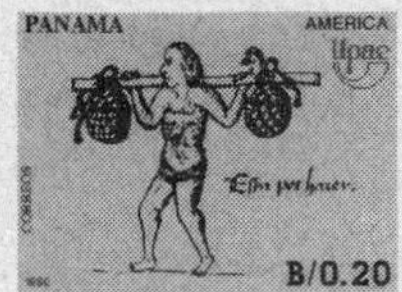

390 Carrying Goods on Yoke (after Oviedo)

1990. America.
1512 **390** 20 c. brown, light brown and gold .. 20 10
1513 – 35 c. multicoloured .. 70 50
DESIGN—VERT. 35 c. Warrior wearing gold chest ornament and armbands.

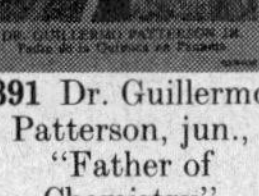

391 Dr. Guillermo Patterson, jun., "Father of Chemistry"   393 St. Ignatius

392 In Sight of Land

1990. Chemistry in Panama.
1514 **391** 25 c. black & turq .. 25 15
1515 – 35 c. multicoloured .. 40 25
1516 – 45 c. multicoloured .. 50 35
DESIGNS: 35 c. Evaporation experiment; 45 c. Books and laboratory equipment.

1991. America. 490th Anniv of Discovery of Panama Isthmus by Rodrigo Bastidas.
1517 **392** 35 c. multicoloured .. 50 35

1991. 450th Anniv of Society of Jesus and 500th Birth Anniv of St. Ignatius de Loyola (founder).
1518 **393** 20 c. multicoloured .. 30 20

394 Declaration of Women's Right to Vote

1991. 50th Anniv of First Presidency of Dr. Arnulfo Arias Madrid.
1519 **394** 10 c. brn, stone & gold 15 10
1520 – 10 c. brn, stone & gold 15 10
DESIGN: No. 1520, Department of Social Security headquarters.

395 "Glory to God..." (Luke 2:14) and Score of "Gloria in Excelsis"

1991. Christmas. Multicoloured.
1521 35 c. Type **395** 50 35
1522 35 c. Nativity 50 35

396 Adoration of the Kings

1992. Epiphany.
1523 **396** 10 c. multicoloured .. 15 10

397 Family and Housing Estate

1992. "New Lives" Housing Project.
1524 **397** 5 c. multicoloured .. 10 10

398 Costa Rican and Panamanian shaking Hands

1992. 50th Anniv (1991) of Border Agreement with Costa Rica. Multicoloured.
1525 20 c. Type **398** 30 20
1526 40 c. Map showing Costa Rica and Panama .. 55 35
1527 50 c. Presidents Calderon and Arias and national flags 70 45

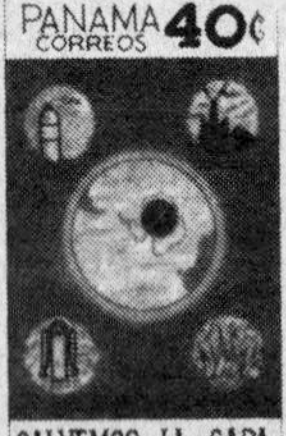

399 Pollutants and Hole over Antarctic

1992. "Save the Ozone Layer".
1528 **399** 40 c. multicoloured .. 55 35

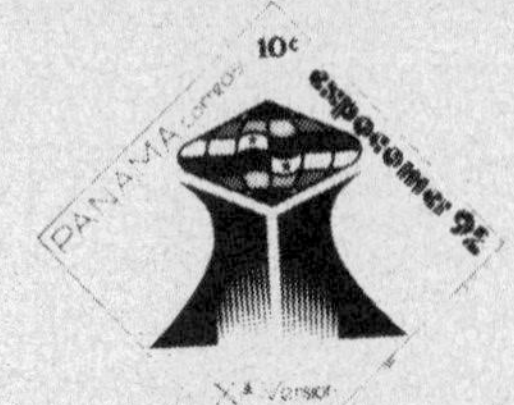

400 Exhibition Emblem

1992. "Expocomer 92" 10th International Trade Exhibition, Panama City.
1529 **400** 10 c. multicoloured .. 15 10

401 Portrait   402 Maria Olimpia de Obaldia

1992. 1st Death Anniv of Dame Margot Fonteyn (ballet dancer). Portraits by Pietro Annigoni. Multicoloured.
1530 35 c. Type **401** 50 35
1531 45 c. On stage 60 40

1992. Birth Centenary of Maria Olimpia de Obaldia (poet).
1532 **402** 10 c. multicoloured .. 15 10

403 Athletics Events and Map of Spain

1992. Olympic Games, Barcelona.
1533 **403** 10 c. multicoloured .. 15 10

404 Paca

1992. Endangered Animals.
1534 **404** 5 c. brn, stone & blk 10 10
1535 – 10 c. blk, brn & stone 15 10
1536 – 15 c. brn, blk & stone 20 15
1537 – 20 c. multicoloured .. 30 20
DESIGNS: 10 c. Harpy eagle; 15 c. Jaguar; 20 c. Iguana.

405 Zion Baptist Church, Bocas del Toro

1992. Cent of Baptist Church in Panama.
1538 **405** 20 c. multicoloured .. 30 20

406 Columbus's Fleet

1992. America. 500th Anniv of Discovery of America by Columbus. Multicoloured.
1539 20 c. Type **406** 30 20
1540 35 c. Columbus planting flag 50 35

407 Flag and Map of Europe   408 Mascot

1992. European Single Market.
1541 **407** 10 c. multicoloured .. 15 10

1992. "Expo '92" World's Fair, Seville.
1542 **408** 10 c. multicoloured .. 15 10

409 Occupations

1992. American Workers' Health Year.
1543 **409** 15 c. multicoloured .. 20 15

410 Angel and Shepherds

1992. Christmas. Multicoloured.
1544 20 c. Type **410** 30 20
1545 35 c. Mary and Joseph arriving at Bethlehem 50 35

411 Jesus lighting up the Americas

1993. 500th Anniv (1992) of Evangelization of the American Continent.
1546 **411** 10 c. multicoloured .. 15 10

412 Woman on Crutches and Wheelchair-bound Man   413 Herrera (bust)

1993. National Day of Disabled Persons.
1547 **412** 5 c. multicoloured .. 10 10

1993. 32nd Death Anniv of Dr. Jose de la Cruz Herrera (essayist).
1548 **413** 5 c. multicoloured .. 10 10

ACKNOWLEDGMENT OF RECEIPT STAMPS

1898. Handstamped **A. R. COLON COLOMBIA.**
AR24 5 5 c. blue .. .. 4·50 3·75
AR27 10 c. orange .. .. 8·00 8·00

1902. Handstamped **AR** in circle.
AR32 5 5 c. blue .. .. 3·00 3·00
AR33 10 c. orange .. .. 6·00 6·00

1903. No. AR169 of Colombia handstamped **AR** in circle.
AR34 AR 60 5 c. red .. .. 11·00 11·00

AR 37.

1904.
AR 135. AR 37. 5 c. blue .. 90 90

1916. Opt. **A.R.**
AR 177. 50. 2½ c. red 90 90

EXPRESS LETTER STAMPS

1926. Optd. **EXPRESO.**
E 220. 57. 10 c. black and orange 4·25 2·10
E 221. 20 c. black and brown 5·50 2·10

E 81. Cyclist Messenger.

1929.
E 226. E 81. 10 c. orange .. 90 70
E 227. 20 c. brown .. 1·75 1·10

INSURANCE STAMPS

1942. Surch. **SEGURO POSTAL HABILITADO** and value.
IN 430. 5 c. on 1 b. black (No. 373) 45 35
IN 431. 10 c. on 1 b. brown (No. 365) 70 55
IN 432. 25 c. on 50 c. brown (No. 372) .. .. 1·25 1·25

POSTAGE DUE STAMPS

D 58. San Geronimo Castle Gate, Portobelo.

1915.
D 169. D 58. 1 c. brown .. .. 1·90 30
D 170. – 2 c. brown .. .. 2·75 25
D 171. – 4 c. brown .. .. 3·75 55
D 172. – 10 c. brown .. .. 2·75 1·10

DESIGNS—VERT. 2 c. Statue of Columbus. HORIZ. 4 c. House of Deputies. VERT. 10 c. Pedro J. Sosa.

No. D 169, is wrongly inscr. "CASTILLO DE SAN LORENZO CHAGRES".

D 86.

1930.
D 240. D 86. 1 c. green 70 25
D 241. 2 c. red 70 20
D 242. 4 c. blue 75 30
D 243. 10 c. violet 75 40

REGISTRATION STAMPS

R 4.

1888.
R 12. R 4. 10 c. black on grey .. 6·00 4·00

1897. Handstamped **R COLON** in circle.
R 22. 5. 10 c. orange .. .. 4·25 4·00

R 15.

1900.
R 29. R 15. 10 c. black on blue .. 2·50 2·10
R 30. 10 c. red .. .. 18·00 15·00

1902. No. R 30 surch. by hand.
R 31. R 15. 20 c. on 10 c. red .. 15·00 12·00

1903. Type R 85 of Colombia. Optd. **REPUBLICA DE PANAMA.**
R 42. 20 c. red on blue .. 27·00
R 43. 20 c. blue on blue .. 27·00

1903. Nos. R 42/3 surch.
R 46. 10 c. on 20 c. red on blue 50·00 50·00
R 47. 10 c. on 20 c. blue on blue 50·00 50·00

1904. Optd. **PANAMA.**
R 60. 5. 10 c. orange .. .. 2·10 2·10

1904. Type R 6 of Colombia. Surch. **Panama 10** and bar.
R 67. 10 c. on 20 c. red on blue 38·00 35·00
R 68. 10 c. on 20 c. blue on blue 38·00 35·00

1904. Type R 85 of Colombia. Optd. **Republica de Panama.**
R 106. 20 c. red on blue .. 5·00 5·00

R 35.

1904.
R 133. R 35. 10 c. green .. 70 30

1916. Stamps of Panama surch. **R 5 cts.**
R 175. 46. 5 c. on 8 c. blk. & pur. 2·10 1·40
R 176. 52. 5 c. on 8 c. blk. & pur. 2·10 50

TOO LATE STAMPS

1903. Too Late stamp of Colombia optd. **REPUBLICA DE PANAMA.**
L 44. L. 86 5 c. violet on red .. 7·50 5·50

L 36.

1904.
L 134. L 36. 2½ c. red 70 40

1910. Typewritten optd. **Retardo.**
L 158. 50. 2½ c. red .. .. 75·00 75·00

1910. Optd. **RETARDO.**
L 159. 50. 2½ c. red .. .. 38·00 30·00

1916. Surch. **RETARDO UN CENTESIMO.**
L 174. 38. 1 c. on ½ c. orange .. 15·00 12·00

APPENDIX

The following stamps have either been issued in excess of postal needs or have not been available to the public in a reasonable quantities at face value. Such stamps may later be given full listing if there is evidence of regular postal use.

1964.

Satellites. Postage ½, 1 c.; Air 5, 10, 21, 50 c.

1965.

Tokyo Olympic Games Medal Winners. Postage ½, 1, 2, 3, 4 c.; Air 5, 6, 7, 10, 21, 31 c.

Space Research. Postage ½, 1, 2, 3 c.; Air 5, 10, 11, 31 c.

400th Birth Anniv. of Galileo. Air 10, 21 c.

Peaceful Uses of Atomic Energy. Postage ½, 1, 4 c.; Air 6, 10, 21 c.

Nobel Prize Medals. Air 10, 21 c.

Pres. John Kennedy. Postage ½, 1 c.; Air 10+5 c., 21+10 c., 31+15 c.

1966.

Pope Paul's Visit to U.N. in New York. Postage ½, 1 c.; Air 5, 10, 21, 31 c.

Famous Men. Postage ½ c.; Air 10, 31 c.

Famous Paintings. Postage ½ c.; Air 10, 31 c.

World Cup Football Championships. Postage ½, ½ c.; Air 10, 10, 21, 21 c.

Italian Space Research. Postage ½, 1 c.; Air 5, 10, 21 c.

Centenary of I.T.U. Air. 31 c.

World Cup Winners. Optd. on 1966 World Cup Issue. Postage ½, ½ c.; Air 10, 10, 21, 21 c.

Religious Paintings. Postage ½, 1, 2, 3 c.; Air 21, 21 c.

Churchill and Space Research. Postage ½ c.; Air 10, 31 c.

3rd Death Anniv. of Pres. John Kennedy. Postage ½, 1 c.; Air 10, 31 c.

Jules Verne and Space Research. Postage ½, 1 c.; Air 5, 10, 21, 31 c.

1967.

Religious Paintings. Postage ½, 1 c.; Air 5, 10, 21, 31 c.

Mexico Olympics. Postage ½, 1 c.; Air 5, 10, 21, 31 c.

Famous Paintings. Postage 5 c.×3; Air 21 c.×3.

Goya's Paintings. Postage 2, 3, 4 c.; Air 5, 8, 10, 13, 21 c.

1968.

Religious Paintings. Postage 1, 1, 3 c.; Air 4, 21, 21 c.

Mexican President's Visit. Air 50 c., 1 b.

Winter Olympic Games, Grenoble. Postage ½, 1 c.; Air 5, 10, 21, 31 c.

Butterflies. Postage ½, 1, 3, 4 c.; Air 5, 13 c.

Ship Paintings. Postage ½, 1, 3, 4 c.; Air 5, 13 c.

Fishes. Postage ½, 1, 3, 4 c.; Air 5, 13 c.

Winter Olympic Medal Winners. Postage 1, 2, 3, 4, 5, 6, 8 c.; Air 13, 30 c.

Paintings of Musicians. 5, 10, 15, 20, 25, 30 c.

Satellite Transmissions from Panama T.V. (a) Olympic Games, Mexico. Optd. on 1964 Satellites issue. Postage ½ c.; Air 50 c. (b) Pope Paul's Visit to Latin America. Postage ½ c.; Air 21 c. (c) Panama Satellite Transmissions. Inaug. (i) optd. on Space Research issue of 1965. Postage 5 c.; Air 31 c. (ii) optd. on Churchill and Space Research issue of 1966. Postage ½ c.; Air 10 c.

Hunting Paintings. Postage 1, 3, 5, 10 c.; Air 13, 30 c.

Horses and Jockeys. Postage 5, 10, 15, 20, 25, 30 c.

Mexico Olympics. Postage 1, 2, 3, 4, 5, 6, 8 c.; Air 13, 30 c.

1969.

1st Int. Philatelic and Numismatic Exhibition. Optd. on 1968 Issue of Mexican Presidents' Visit. Air 50 c., 1 b.

Telecommunications Satellites. Air 5, 10, 15, 20, 25, 30 c.

Provisionals. Surch. "Decreto No. 112 (de 6 de marzo de 1969)" and new values on No. 781 and 10 c.+5 c. and 21 c.+10 c. of 1965 Issue of 3rd Death Anniv. of Pres. John Kennedy. Air 5 c. on 5 c.+5 c., 5 c. on 10 c.+5 c., 10 c., on 21 c.+10 c.

Pope Paul VI. Visit to Latin America. Religious Paintings. Postage 1, 2, 3, 4, 5 c.; Air 6, 7, 8, 10 c.

PAPAL STATES Pt. 8

Parts of Italy under Papal rule till 1870 when they became part of the Kingdom of Italy.

1852. 100 bajocchi = 1 scudo.
1866. 100 centesimi = 1 lira.

1. 2.

1852. Papal insignia as in T 1 and 2 in various shapes and frames. Imperf.
1 ½ b. black on grey .. £225 50·00
5 ½ b. black on purple .. 13·00 £100
10 1 b. black on green .. 22·00 25·00
11 2 b. black on green .. 50·00 3·25
14 2 b. black on white .. 1·75 22·00
15 3 b. black on brown .. 85·00 17·00
16 3 b. black on yellow .. 7·50 80·00
17 4 b. black on brown .. £1700 30·00
19 4 b. black on yellow .. 80·00 30·00
21 5 b. black on pink .. £100 4·00
22 6 b. black on lilac .. 90·00 29·00
23 6 b. black on grey .. £250 15·00
25 7 b. black on blue .. £450 28·00
26 8 b. black on white .. £150 14·00
27 50 b. blue £7000 £1300
29 1 s. red £1300 £2500

1867. Same types. Imperf.
30 2 c. black on green .. 60·00 £130
32 3 c. black on grey .. £900 £1400
33 5 c. black on blue .. 70·00 £140
34 10 c. black on orange .. £450 20·00
35 20 c. black on red .. 60·00 21·00
36 40 c. black on yellow .. £100 £160
37 80 c. black on pink .. 90·00 £400

1868. Same types. Perf.
42 2 c. black on green .. 3·50 24·00
43 3 c. black on grey .. 18·00 £2500
45 5 c. black on blue .. 5·50 18·00
46 10 c. black on orange .. 1·25 6·00
50 20 c. black on red .. 1·25 10·00
49 20 c. black on mauve .. 2·00 10·00
52 40 c. black on yellow .. 1·75 60·00
55 80 c. black on pink .. 11·00 £250

PARAGUAY Pt. 20

A republic in the centre of S. America independent since 1811.

1870. 8 reales = 1 peso.
1878. 100 centavos = 1 peso.
1944. 100 centimos = 1 guarani.

1. 7.

1870. Various frames. Values in "reales". Imperf.
1. 1. 1 r. red .. .. .. 2·25 2·25
3. 2 r. blue .. .. .. 27·00 27·00
4. 3 r. black .. .. .. 65·00 65·00

1878. Handstamped with large **5.** Imperf.
5 1. 5 c. on 1 r. red .. .. 25·00 25·00
9 5 c. on 2 r. blue £120 £110
13 5 c. on 3 r. black .. .. 85·00 85·00

1879. Prepared for use but not issued (wrong currency). Values in "reales". Perf.
14. 7. 5 r. orange 40
15. 10 r. brown 50

1879. Values in "centavos". Perf.
16. 7. 5 c. brown 70 70
17. 10 c. green 95 95

1881. Handstamped with large figures.
18. 7. 1 on 10 c. green .. .. 3·50 3·50
19. 2 on 10 c. green .. .. 3·50 3·50

1881. As T 1 (various frames), but value in "centavos". Perf.
20. 1. 1 c. blue 40 40
21a. 2 c. red 30 40
22. 4 c. brown 40 50

1884. No. 1 handstamped with large **1.** Imperf.
23. 1. 1 c. on 1 r. red .. .. 1·50 1·40

13. 24.

1884. Perf.
24. 13. 1 c. green 30 15
25. 2 c. red 40 15
26. 5 c. blue 40 15

1887.
32 24 1 c. green 15 15
33a 2 c. red 15 15
34 5 c. blue 30 20
35 7 c. brown 30 25
36 10 c. mauve 45 30
37 15 c. orange 45 30
38 20 c. pink 45 30
50 40 c. blue .. .. 1·50 70
51 60 c. orange 60 30
52 80 c. blue 55 30
53 1 p. green 60 30

25. 27. C. Rivarola.

1889. Imperf. or perf.
40. 25. 15 c. purple 95 95

1892.
42. 27. 1 CENTAVOS grey .. 15 10
54. 1 CENTAVO grey .. 15 10
43. – 2 c. green 15 10
44. – 4 c. red 10 10
57. – 5 c. purple 15 10
46. – 10 c. violet 30 25
47. – 14 c. brown 30 30
48. – 20 c. red 50 30
49. – 30 c. green 75 30
84. – 1 p. blue 40 25

PORTRAITS: 2 c. S. Jovellano. 4 c. J. Bautista Gil. 5 c. H. Uriarte. 10 c. C. Barreiro. 14 c. Gen. B. Caballero. 20 c. Gen. P. Escobar. 30 c. J. Gonzales. 1 p. J.B. Egusquisa.

1892. 400th Anniv of Discovery of America. No. 46 optd **1492 12 DE OCTUBRE 1892** in oval.
41 10 c. violet .. .. 3·50 1·50

1895. Surch. **PROVISORIO 5.**
59. 24 5 c. on 7 c. brown .. 30 30

30. 39.

1896. Telegraph stamps as T 30 surch. **CORREOS 5 CENTAVOS** in oval.
60. 30. 5 c. on 2 c. brn., blk. & grey 45 20
61. 5 c. on 4 c. orge., blk. & grey 45 20

1898. Surch. **Provisorio 10 Centavos.**
63. 24. 10 c. on 15 c. orange .. 35 35
62. 10 c. on 40 c. blue .. 25 25

1900. Telegraph stamps as T 30 surch. with figures of value twice and bar.
64. 30. 5 c. on 30 c. green, black and grey 95 70
65. 10 c. on 50 c. lilac, black and grey .. .. 2·25 1·50

1900.

76 39 1 c. green 10 10
67 2 c. grey 10 10
73 2 c. pink 20 15
68 3 c. brown 10 10
78 4 c. blue 15 10
69 5 c. green 10 10
74 5 c. brown 20 10
79 5 c. lilac 25 10
80 8 c. brown 20 15
71 10 c. red 20 15
72 24 c. blue 45 20
82 28 c. orange 25 35
83 40 c. blue 25 10

1902. Surch. **Habilitado en** and new values.

88. – 1 c. on 14 c. brown (No. 47) 30 20
91. – 1 c. on 1 p. blue (No. 84) 20 15
86. 39. 5 c. on 8 c. brown (No. 80) 35 20
87. 5 c. on 28 c. orge. (No. 82) 20 30
89. 24. 5 c. on 60 c. orge. (No. 51) 20 25
90. 5 c. on 80 c. blue (No. 52) 30 25
85 39. 20 c. on 24 c. blue (No. 72) 35 20

46. 47. 48.

1903.

92 46. 1 c. grey 20 15
93 2 c. green 25 20
94a 5 c. blue 25 10
95 10 c. brown 45 20
96 20 c. red 45 25
97 30 c. blue 50 25
98 60 c. violet 75 30

1903.

99. 47. 1 c. green 15 10
100. 2 c. orange 15 10
101. 5 c. blue 20 15
102. 10 c. violet 30 20
103. 20 c. green 50 25
104. 30 c. blue 60 30
105. 60 c. brown 60 35

1904.

106. 48. 10 c. blue 35 20

1904. End of successful Revolt against Govt. (begun in August). Surch. **PAZ 12 Dic. 1904. 30 centavos.**

107. 48. 30 c. on 10 c. blue 50 35

50. 51. National Palace, Asuncion.

1905.

108 50 1 c. orange 15 10
109 1 c. red 15 10
110 1 c. blue 15 10
112 2 c. green 23·00
113 2 c. red 15 10
114 5 c. blue 15 10
116 5 c. yellow 15 10
117 10 c. brown 15 10
118 10 c. green 15 10
119 10 c. blue 15 10
120 20 c. lilac 45 35
121 20 c. brown 45 35
122 20 c. green 35 20
123 30 c. blue 45 20
124 30 c. grey 45 20
125 30 c. lilac 50 35
126 60 c. brown 35 25
128 60 c. pink 2·75 95
129 51 1 p. black and red 95 80
130 1 p. black and brown 35 35
131 1 p. black and green 35 35
132 2 p. black and blue 35 25
133 2 p. black and red 35 25
134 2 p. black and brown 40 30
135 5 p. black and red 60 35
136 5 p. black and blue 60 35
137 5 p. black and green 60 35
138 10 p. black and brown 55 35
139 10 p. black and blue 55 35
141 20 p. black and green 1·40 1·25
142 20 p. black and yellow 1·40 1·25
143 20 p. black and purple 1·40 1·25

1907. Surch **Habilitado en** and value and bars.

159 50 5 c. on 1 c. blue 10 10
160 5 c. on 2 c. red 15 10
145 5 c. on 2 c. green 40 25
172 39 5 c. on 28 c. orange 95 35
173 5 c. on 40 c. blue 30 25
163 50 5 c. on 60 c. brown 15 10
162 5 c. on 60 c. pink 20 15
175 20 c. on 1 c. blue 20 15
180 24 20 c. on 2 c. red 1·90 1·50
177 50 20 c. on 2 c. red 2·75 2·25
178 20 c. on 30 c. blue 1·10 1·10
179 20 c. on 30 c. lilac 30 30

1907. Official stamps surch **Habilitado en** and value and bars. Where not otherwise stated, the design is as T **50** but with "OFICIAL" below the lion.

164 – 5 c. on 10 c. green 30 20
149 – 5 c. on 10 c. brown 30 20
150 – 5 c. on 10 c. lilac 30 20
181 24 5 c. on 15 c. orange (No. O 63) 1·90 1·40
182 5 c. on 20 c. pink (No. O 64) 30·00 25·00
166 – 5 c. on 20 c. brown 30 25
151 – 5 c. on 20 c. green 30 20
167 – 5 c. on 20 c. pink 30 25
152 – 5 c. on 20 c. lilac 30 20
157 46 5 c. on 30 c. blue (No. O 104) 95 85
154 – 5 c. on 30 c. blue 50 50
169 – 5 c. on 30 c. yellow 10 10
168 – 5 c. on 30 c. grey 20 15
183 24 5 c. on 50 c. grey (No. O 65) 13·50 9·50
158 46 5 c. on 60 c. violet (No. O 105) 35 25
155 – 5 c. on 60 c. brown 20 15
171 – 5 c. on 60 c. blue 20 10
184 24 20 c. on 5 c. blue (No. O 60) 1·10 95
174 46 20 c. on 5 c. blue (No. O 101) 95 75

1907. Official stamps, as T **50** and **51** with "OFICIAL" added, optd **Habilitado** and one bar.

146 5 c. grey 30 20
148 5 c. blue 25 15
185 1 p. black and orange 35 35
186 1 p. black and red 30 25

1907. Official stamps, as T **51**. with "OFFICIAL" added, surch. **Habilitado. 1908 UN CENTAVO** and bar.

188 1 c. on 1 p. black and red 20 20
189 1 c. on 1 p. black & brown 70 50

1908. Optd **1908**.

190 50 1 c. green 10 10
191 5 c. yellow 10 10
192 10 c. brown 10 10
193 20 c. orange 10 10
194 30 c. red 40 30
195 60 c. mauve 30 30
196 51 1 p. blue 15 15

1909. Optd. **1909.**

197. 50. 1 c. blue 10 10
198. 1 c. red 10 10
199. 5 c. green 10 10
200. 5 c. orange 10 10
201. 10 c. red 20 15
202. 10 c. brown 20 15
203. 20 c. lilac 20 20
204. 20 c. yellow 10 10
205. 30 c. brown 45 30
206. 30 c. blue 45 30

62. 63. 65.

1910.

207. 62. 1 c. brown 10 10
208. 5 c. lilac 10 10
209. 5 c. green 10 10
210. 5 c. blue 10 10
211. 10 c. green 10 10
212. 10 c. violet 10 10
213. 10 c. red 10 10
214. 20 c. red 10 10
215. 50 c. red 45 20
216. 75 c. blue 15 10

1911. No. 216 perf. diagonally and each half used as 20 c.

217. 62. 20 c. (½ of 75 c.) blue 15 10

1911. Independence Cent.

218. 63. 1 c. black and olive 10 10
219. 2 c. black and blue 10 10
220. 5 c. black and red 20 10
221. 10 c. brown and blue 30 15
222. 20 c. blue and olive 30 15
223. 50 c. blue and lilac 45 30
224. 75 c. purple and olive 45 30

1912. Surch. **Habilitada en VEINTE** and thin bar.

225. 62. 20 c. on 50 c. red 10 10

1913.

226. 65. 1 c. black 10 10
227. 2 c. orange 10 10
228. 5 c. mauve 10 10
229. 10 c. green 10 10
230. 20 c. red 10 10
231. 40 c. red 10 10
232. 75 c. blue 10 10
233. 80 c. yellow 10 10
234. 1 p. blue 10 10
235. 1 p. 25 blue 30 10
236. 3 p. green 30 10

1918. No. D 242 surch. **HABILITADO EN 0.05 1918** and bar.

237. 5 c. on 40 c. brown 10 10

1918. Nos. D 239/42 optd. **HABILITADO 1918.**

238. 5 c. brown 10 10
239. 10 c. brown 10 10
240. 20 c. brown 10 10
241. 40 c. brown 15 10

1918. Surch. **HABILITADO EN 0.30 1918** and bar.

242. 65. 30 c. on 40 c. red 10 10

1920. Surch. **HABILITADO en,** value and **1920.**

243. 65. 50 c. on 80 c. yellow 15 10
244. 1 p. 75 on 3 p. green 60 50

1920. Nos. D 243/4 optd. **HABILITADO 1920** or surch. also.

245. 1 p. brown 20 10
246. 1 p. on 1 p. 50 brown 35 10

72. Parliament House, Asuncion. 75.

1920. Jubilee of Constitution.

247. 72. 50 c. black and red 30 20
248. 1 p. black and blue 50 40
249. 1 p. 75 black and blue 20 15
250. 3 p. black and yellow 75 25

1920. Surch. **50.**

251. 65. 50 on 75 c. blue 45 10

1921. Surch. **50** and two bars.

252. 62. 50 on 75 c. blue 10 10
253. 65. 50 on 75 c. blue 25 10

1922.

254. 75. 50 c. blue and red 10 10
255. 1 p. brown and blue 10 10

Between 1922 and 1936 many regular postage stamps were overprinted C (=Campana—country), these being used at post offices outside Asuncion but not for mail sent abroad. The prices quoted are for whichever is the cheapest.

77. Starting-point of Conspirators. 80. Map.

1922. Independence.

256. 77. 1 p. blue 20 10
258. 1 p. blue and red 30 10
259. 1 p. grey and purple 30 10
260. 1 p. grey and orange 30 10
257. 5 p. purple 30 25
261. 5 p. brown and blue 30 25
262. 5 p. black and green 30 25
263. 5 p. blue and red 30 25

1924. Surch. **Habilitado en** value and **1924.**

265. 65. 50 c. on 75 c. blue 10 10
266. $1 on 1 p. 25 blue 10 10
267. – $1 on 1 p. 50 brown (No. D 244) 10 10

1924.

268. 80. 1 p. blue 10 10
269. 2 p. red 15 10
270. 4 p. blue 30 10

81. Gen. Jose E. Diaz. 82. Columbus.

1925.

271. 81. 50 c. red 10 10
272. 1 p. blue 10 10
273. 1 p. green 10 10

1925.

274. 82. 1 p. blue 15 10

1926. Surch **Habilitado en** and new value.

275 62 1 c. on 5 c. blue 10 10
276 $0.02 on 5 c. blue 10 10
277 65 7 c. on 40 c. red 10 10
278 15 c. on 75 c. blue 10 10
279 50 $0.50 on 60 c. purple (No. 195) 10 10
280 – $0.50 on 75 c. blue (No. O 243) 10 10
281 – $1.50 on 1 p. 50 brown (No. D 244) 15 10
282 80 $1.50 on 4 p. blue 10 10

86. 87. P. J. Caballero. 88. Paraguay.

89. Cassel Tower, Asuncion. 90. Columbus.

1927.

283 86 1 c. red 10 10
284 2 c. orange 10 10
285 7 c. lilac 10 10
286 7 c. green 10 10
287 10 c. green 10 10
288 10 c. red 10 10
290 10 c. blue 10 10
291 20 c. blue 10 10
292 20 c. purple 10 10
293 20 c. violet 10 10
294 20 c. pink 10 10
295 50 c. blue 10 10
296 50 c. red 10 10
323 50 c. orange 10 10
326 50 c. green 10 10
299 50 c. mauve 10 10
300 50 c. pink 10 10
301 70 c. blue 10 10
328 87 1 p. green 10 10
329 1 p. red 10 10
330 1 p. purple 10 10
331 1 p. blue 10 10
304 1 p. orange 10 10
332 1 p. violet 10 10
333 88 1 p. 50 brown 10 10
334 1 p. 50 lilac 10 10
307 1 p. 50 pink 10 10
335 1 p. 50 blue 10 10
308 – 2 p. 50 bistre 10 10
337 – 2 p. 50 violet 10 10
338 – 3 p. grey 10 10
310 – 3 p. red 10 10
311 – 3 p. violet 10 10
312 89 5 p. brown 25 20
340 5 p. violet 10 10
314 5 p. orange 10 10
315 90 10 p. red 35 35
317 10 p. blue 35 35
318 88 20 p. red 1·10 85
319 20 p. green 1·10 85
320 20 p. purple 1·10 85

DESIGNS—As Type **87**. 2 p. 50, Fulgencio Yegros. 3 p. V. Ignacio Yturbe.

92. Arms of De Salazar de Espinosa, founder of Asuncion. 93. Pres. Hayes of U.S.A. and Villa Hayes.

1928. Foundation of Asuncion, 1537.

342. 92. 10 p. purple 95 70

1928. 50th Anniv. of Hayes's Decision to award Northern Chaco to Paraguay.

343. 93. 10 p. brown 2·50 1·10
344. 10 p. grey 2·50 1·10

1929. Air. Surch. **Correo Aereo Habilitado en** and value.

357 86 $0.95 on 7 c. lilac 20 20
358 $1.90 on 20 c. blue 20 20
345 – $2.85 on 5 c. purple (No. O 239) 60 70
348 – $3.40 on 3 p. grey (No. 338) 1·40 85
359 80 $3.40 on 4 p. blue 30 30
360 $4.75 on 4 p. blue 55 30
346 – $5.65 on 10 c. green (No. O 240) 35 45
361 – $6.80 on 3 p. grey (No. 338) 35 35
349 80 $6.80 on 4 p. blue 1·40 85
347 – $11.30 on 50 c. red (No. O 242) 60 50
350 89 $17 on 5 p. brown (A) 1·40 85
362 $17 on 5 p. brown (B) 1·10 1·10

On No. 350 (A) the surcharge is on four lines, and on No. 362 (B) it is in three lines.

95.

DESIGNS: 5.65 p. Carrier pigeon. 11.30 p. Stylized aeroplane.

1929. Air.

352	95	2.85 p. green	35	30
353	–	5.65 p. brown	60	30
354	–	5.65 p. red	40	35
355	–	11.30 p. purple	70	55
356	–	11.30 p. blue	35	35

1930. Air. Optd. **CORREO AEREO** or surch. also in words.

363	86	5 c. on 10 c. green	10	10
364		5 c. on 70 c. blue	10	10
365		10 c. green	10	10
366		20 c. blue	20	20
367	87	20 c. on 1 p. red	30	30
368	86	40 c. on 50 c. orange	15	10
369	87	1 p. green	35	35
370	–	3 p. grey (No. 338)	35	35
371	90	6 p. on 10 p. red	60	50
372	88	10 p. on 20 p. red	2·25	2·10
373		10 p. on 20 p. purple	2·25	2·10

101.

103.

1930. Air.

374.	101.	95 c. blue on blue	40	35
375.		95 c. red on pink	40	35
376.	–	1 p. 90 purple on blue	40	35
377.	–	1 p. 90 red on pink	40	35
378.	103.	6 p. 80 black on blue	40	35
379.		6 p. 80 green on pink	45	40

DESIGN: 1 p. 90, Asuncion Cathedral.

104. Declaration of Independence.

105.

1930. Air. Independence Day.

380.	104.	2 p. 85 blue	40	35
381.		3 p. 40 green	35	25
382.		4 p. 75 purple	35	25

1930. Red Cross Fund.

383.	105.	1 p. 50+50 c. blue	75	70
384.		1 p. 50+50 c. red	75	70
385.		1 p. 50+50 c. lilac	75	70

106. Portraits of Archbishop Bogarin.

1930. Consecration of Archbishop Bogarin.

386.	106.	1 p. 50 blue	75	60
387.		1 p. 50 red	75	60
388.		1 p. 50 violet	75	60

1930. Surch **Habilitado en CINCO.**

389.	86.	5 c. on 7 c. green	10	10

108. Planned Agricultural College at Ypacaraí.

1931. Agricultural College Fund.

390.	108.	1 p. 50+50 c. blue on red	30	30

109. Arms of Paraguay.

1931. 60th Anniv. of First Paraguay Postage Stamps.

391.	109.	10 p. brown	30	25
392.		10 p. red on blue	35	25
393.		10 p. blue on red	35	25
395.		10 p. grey	50	20
396.		10 p. blue	20	20

110. Gunboat "Paraguay".

1931. Air. 60th Anniv. of Constitution and Arrival of new Gunboats.

397	110	1 p. red	20	20
398		1 p. blue	20	20
399		2 p. orange	25	25
400		2 p. brown	25	25
401		3 p. green	50	40
402		3 p. blue	50	45
403		3 p. red	45	40
404		6 p. green	60	60
405		6 p. mauve	75	65
406		6 p. blue	55	50
407		10 p. red	1·60	1·40
408		10 p. green	2·00	1·90
409		10 p. blue	1·10	1·00
410		10 p. brown	1·75	1·60
411		10 p. pink	1·60	1·40

1931. As T **110**.

412.	–	1 p. 50 violet	70	35
413.	–	1 p. 50 blue	10	10

DESIGN: Gunboat "Humaita".

112. War Memorial.

113. Orange Tree and Yerba Mate.

114. Yerba Mate.

115. Palms.

116. Yellow-headed Caracara.

1931. Air.

414.	112.	5 c. blue	15	10
415.		5 c. green	15	10
416.		5 c. red	20	10
417.		5 c. purple	15	10
418.	113.	10 c. violet	10	10
419.		10 c. red	10	10
420.		10 c. brown	10	10
421.		10 c. blue	10	10
422.	114.	20 c. red	15	10
423.		20 c. blue	20	10
424.		20 c. green	20	15
425.		20 c. brown	15	10
426.	115.	40 c. green	20	10
426a.		40 c. blue	15	10
426b.		40 c. red	20	10
427.	116.	80 c. blue	50	15
428.		80 c. green	60	20
428a.		80 c. red	50	15

1931. Air. Optd. **Correo Aereo "Graf Zeppelin"** and airship or surch. also.

429.	80.	3 p. on 4 p. blue	4·50	3·75
430.		4 p. blue	3·50	3·00

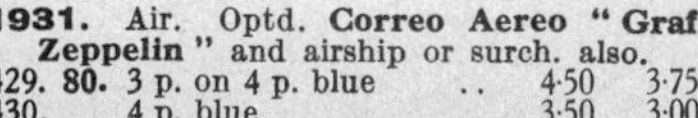

118. Farm Colony.

1931. 50th Anniv. of Foundation of San Bernardino.

431.	118.	1 p. green	35	20
432.		1 p. red	10	10

1931. New Year Optd. **FELIZ ANO NUEVO 1932.**

433.	106.	1 p. 50 blue	60	60
434.		1 p. 50 red	60	60

120. "Graf Zeppelin".

1932. Air.

435.	120.	4 p. blue	1·40	1·75
436.		8 p. red	2·40	2·00
437.		12 p. green	1·90	1·75
438.		16 p. purple	3·75	3·00
439.		20 p. brown	4·00	3·75

121. Red Cross H.Q.

122. (Trans: "Has been, is and will be").

1932. Red Cross Fund.

440.	121.	50 c.+50 c. pink	25	25

1932. Chaco Boundary Dispute.

441	122	1 p. purple	20	10
442		1 p. 50 pink	10	10
443		1 p. 50 brown	10	10
444		1 p. 50 green	10	10
445		1 p. 50 blue	10	10

Nos. 443/5 are optd with a large **C**.

1932. Surch. **CORREOS FELIZ ANO NUEVO 1933** (trans: "Happy New Year 1933") and value.

446.	120.	50 c. on 4 p. blue	35	30
447.		1 p. on 8 p. red	35	30
448.		1 p. 50 on 12 p. green	35	30
449.		2 p. on 16 p. purple	35	30
450.		5 p. on 20 p. brown	95	75

124. "Graf Zeppelin" over Paraguay.

125. "Graf Zeppelin" over Atlantic.

1933. Air. "Graf Zeppelin" issue.

451	124.	4 p. 50 blue	95	75
452.		9 p. red	1·90	1·50
453.		13 p. 50 green	1·90	1·50
454.	125.	22 p. 50 brown	4·75	3·75
455.		45 p. violet	6·75	6·75

126. Columbus's Fleet.

127. G.P.O., Asuncion.

1933. 441st Anniv. of Departure of Columbus from Palos. Maltese Crosses in violet.

456.	126.	10 c. olive and red	35	15
457.		20 c. blue and lake	35	15
458.		50 c. red and green	55	30
459.		1 p. brown and blue	40	35
460.		1 p. 50 green and blue	40	35
461.		2 p. green and sepia	1·25	65
462.		5 p. lake and olive	2·50	1·25
463.		10 p. sepia and blue	2·50	1·25

1934. Air.

464.	127.	33 p. 75 blue	1·10	95
468.		33 p. 75 red	95	95
466.		33 p. 75 green	1·10	95
467.		33 p. 75 brown	1·10	95

1934. Air. Optd. **1934.**

469.	124.	4 p. 50 blue	1·75	1·75
470.		9 p. red	2·25	2·25
471.		13 p. 50 green	6·50	6·50
472.	125.	22 p. 50 brown	5·25	5·25
473.		45 p. violet	11·00	11·00

1935. Air. Optd. **1935.**

474.	124.	4 p. 50 red	2·25	2·25
475.		9 p. green	3·25	3·25
476.		13 p. 50 brown	9·25	9·25
477.	125.	22 p. 50 purple	8·75	8·75
478.		45 p. blue	23·00	23·00

131. Tobacco Plant.

1935. Air.

479.	131.	17 p. brown	3·75	3·00
480.		17 p. red	6·75	5·50
481.		17 p. blue	4·25	3·50
482.		17 p. green	2·10	1·75

132. Church of the Incarnation.

1935. Air.

483.	132.	102 p. red	2·25	1·75
485.		102 p. blue	1·50	1·50
486.		102 p. brown	1·50	1·50
487.		102 p. violet	75	75
487a.		102 p. orange	65	65

1937. Air. Surch **Habilitado en** and value in figures.

488.	127.	$24 on 33 p. 75 blue	40	50
489.	132.	$65 on 102 p. grey	95	70
490.		$84 on 102 p. green	95	60

134. Arms of Asuncion.

135. Monstrance.

1937. 4th Cent. of Asuncion (1st issue).

491.	134.	50 c. purple and violet	10	10
492.		1 p. green and bistre	10	10
493.		3 p. blue and red	10	10
494.		10 p. yellow and red	15	10
495.		20 p. grey and blue	20	20

1937. First National Eucharistic Congress.

496.	135.	1 p. red, yellow & blue	10	10
497.		3 p. red, yellow & blue	10	10
498.		10 p. red, yellow & blue	15	10

136. Oratory of the Virgin of Asuncion.

137. Asuncion.

1938. Asuncion. 4th Cent. (2nd issue).

499.	136.	5 p. olive	25	10
500.		5 p. red	35	10
501.		11 p. brown	25	10

1939. Air.

502.	137.	3 p. 40 blue	75	45
503.		3 p. 40 green	75	45
504.		3 p. 40 brown	75	45

138. J. E. Diaz.

1939. Reburial in National Pantheon of Ashes of C. A. Lopez and J. E. Diaz.

505 138 2 p. brown and blue .. 25 15
506 – 2 p. brown and blue .. 25 15

DESIGN—VERT. No. 506, C. A. Lopez.

139. Pres. Caballero and Senator Decoud.

DESIGN: Nos. 507/9, Pres. Escobar and Dr. Zubizarreta.

1939. 50th Anniv. of Asuncion University.

507. – 50 c. blk. & orge. (post.) 10 10
508. – 1 p. black and blue .. 15 10
509. – 2 p. black and red .. 25 10
510. 139. 5 p. black and blue .. 35 20
511. 28 p. black & red (air) .. 2·50 2·50
512. 90 p. black & green .. 3·00 3·00

140. Coats of Arms. 141. Pres. Baldomir and Flags of Paraguay and Uruguay.

1939. Chaco Boundary Peace Conference, Buenos Aires (1st issue).

513. 140. 50 c. blue (postage) .. 15 10
514. 141. 1 p. olive 15 10
515. A. 2 p. green 20 10
516. B. 3 p. brown 35 25
517. C. 5 p. orange 25 20
518. D. 6 p. violet 40 30
519. E. 10 p. brown 50 35
520. F. 1 p. brown (air) .. 10 10
521. 140. 3 p. blue 10 10
522. E. 5 p. olive 10 15
523. D. 10 p. violet 15 15
524. C. 30 p. orange 25 15
525. B. 50 p. brown 15 25
526. A. 100 p. green 25 25
527. 141. 200 p. green .. .. 1·50 95
528. – 500 p. black .. .. 3·75 3·75

DESIGNS (flag on right is that of country named): A, Benavides (Peru). B, Eagle (U.S.A.). C, Alessandri (Chile). D, Vargas (Brazil). E, Ortiz (Argentina). F, Figure of "Peace" (Bolivia). 500 p. (30 × 40 mm), Map of Chaco frontiers.

See also Nos. 536/43.

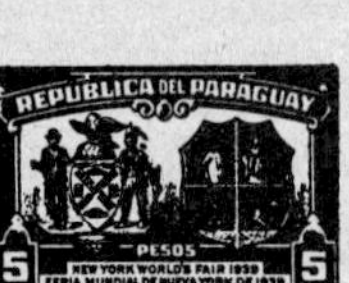

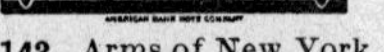

143. Arms of New York. 144. Asuncion-New York Air Route.

1939. New York World's Fair.

529. 143. 5 p. red (postage) .. 20 15
530. 10 p. blue 40 30
531. 11 p. green 25 45
532. 22 p. grey 35 30
533. 144. 30 p. brown (air) .. 1·50 1·10
534. 80 p. orange .. .. 1·75 1·75
535. 90 p. violet .. .. 3·00 3·00

145. Soldier. 147. Waterfall.

1940. Chaco Boundary Peace Conference, Buenos Aires (2nd issue). Inscr. "PAZ DEL CHACO".

536. 145. 50 c. orange 15 10
537. – 1 p. purple 15 15
538. – 3 p. green 25 20
539. – 5 p. brown 15 25
540. – 10 p. mauve 35 20
541. – 20 p. blue 30 25
542. – 50 p. green 70 35
543. 147. 100 p. black .. .. 1·50 1·10

DESIGNS as Type 145—VERT. 1 p. Water-carrier. 5 p. Ploughing with oxen. HORIZ. 3 p. Cattle Farming. As Type 147—VERT. 10 p. Fishing in the Paraguay River. HORIZ. 20 p. Bullock-cart. 50 p. Cattle-grazing.

148. Western Hemisphere. 149. Reproduction of Paraguay No. 1.

1940. 50th Anniv. of Pan-American Union.

544. 148. 50 c. orange (postage) 10 10
545. 1 p. green 10 10
546. 5 p. blue 25 10
547. 10 p. brown 30 30
548. 20 p. red (air) 35 25
549. 70 p. blue 35 30
550. 100 p. green 40 40
551. 500 p. violet .. .. 1·75 1·40

1940. Cent. of First Adhesive Postage Stamps. Inscr. "CENTENARIO DEL SELLO POSTAL 1940".

552. 149. 1 p. purple and green .. 40 35
553. – 5 p. brown and green .. 50 45
554. – 6 p. blue and brown .. 1·10 50
555. – 10 p. black and red .. 1·10 85

DESIGNS: 5 p. Sir Rowland Hill. 6 p., 10 p. Early Paraguayan stamps.

1940. National Mourning for Pres. Estigarribia. Surch. **7-IX-40/DUELO NACIONAL/5 PESOS** in black border.

556. 145. 5 p. on 50 c. orange .. 25 25

152. Dr. Francia. 154. Our Lady of Asuncion.

1940. Death Cent. of Dr. Francia (dictator).

557. 152. 50 c. red 15 10
558. – 50 c. purple 15 10
559. 152. 1 p. green 15 10
560. – 5 p. blue 15 10

PORTRAIT: Nos. 558 and 560, Dr. Francia seated in library.

1941. Visit of President Vargas of Brazil. Optd. **Visita al Paraguay/Agosto de 1941.**

560a. 6 p. violet (No. 518) .. 25 25

1941. Mothers' Fund.

561. 154. 7 p. + 3 p. brown .. 35 25
562. 7 p. + 3 p. violet .. 35 25
563. 7 p. + 3 p. red .. 35 25
564. 7 p. + 3 p. blue .. 35 25

1942. Nos. 520/2 optd. **Habilitado** and bar(s).

565. – 1 p. brown 15 10
566. 139. 3 p. blue 20 10
567. – 5 p. olive 25 10

156. Arms of Paraguay. 158. Irala's Vision.

1942.

568. 156. 1 p. green 10 10
569. 1 p. orange 10 10
570. 7 p. blue 10 10
571. 7 p. brown 10 10

For other values as Type 156 see Nos. 631, etc.

1942. 4th Cent. of Asuncion.

572. – 2 p. green (postage) .. 50 40
573. 158. 5 p. red 50 40
574. – 7 p. blue 50 35
575. – 20 p. purple (air) .. 40 30
576. 158. 70 p. brown .. .. 1·10 85
577. – 500 p. olive .. .. 3·00 2·75

DESIGNS—VERT. 2 p., 20 p. Indian hailing ships. 7 p., 500 p. Irala's Arms.

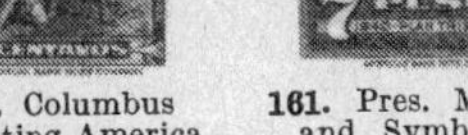

160. Columbus Sighting America. 161. Pres. Morinigo and Symbols of Progress.

1943. 450th Anniv of Discovery of America by Columbus.

578. 160. 50 c. violet 25 20
579. 1 p. brown 20 10
580. 5 p. green 35 20
581. 7 p. blue 35 10

1943. Three Year Plan.

582. 161. 7 p. blue 10 10

NOTE: From No. 583 onwards, the currency having been changed, the letter "c" in the value description indicates "centimos" instead of "centavos".

1944. St. Juan Earthquake Fund. Surch. **U.P.A.E. Adhesion victimas San Juan y Pueblo Argentino centimos** and bar.

583. – 10 c. on 10 p. brown (No. 519) 40 25

1944. No. 311 surch **Habilitado en un centimo.**

584 1 c. on 3 p. violet 10 10

1944. Surch. **1944/5 centimos 5.**

585. 160. 5 c. on 7 p. blue .. 15 10
586. 161. 5 c. on 7 p. blue .. 15 10

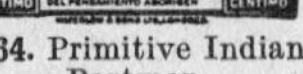

164. Primitive Indian Postmen. 181. Jesuit Relics of Colonial Paraguay.

1944.

587. 164. 1 c. black (postage) .. 10 10
588. – 2 c. brown 15 10
589. – 5 c. olive 20 10
590. – 7 c. blue 15 20
591. – 10 c. green .. .. 1·00 45
592. – 15 c. blue 40 25
593. – 50 c. black 35 35
594. – 1 g. red 70 40

DESIGNS—HORIZ. 2 c. Ruins of Humaita Church. 7 c. Marshal Francisco S. Lopez. 1 g. Ytororo Heroes' Monument. VERT. 5 c. First Paraguayan railway locomotive. 10 c. "Tacuary" (paddle-steamer). 15 c. Port of Asuncion. 50 c. Meeting place of Independence conspirators.

595. – 1 c. blue (air) 15 15
596. – 2 c. green 10 10
597. – 3 c. purple 50 20
598. – 5 c. green 20 10
599. – 10 c. violet 20 15
600. – 20 c. brown 15 10
601. – 30 c. blue 25 25
602. – 40 c. olive 15 15
603. – 70 c. red 25 20
604. 181. 1 g. orange 55 40
605. – 2 g. brown 65 55
606. – 5 g. brown .. .. 1·50 1·50
607. – 10 g. blue .. .. 3·50 3·50

DESIGNS—HORIZ. 1 c. Port of Asuncion. 2 c. First telegraphic apparatus in S. America. 3 c. Paddle-steamer "Tacuary". 5 c. Meeting Place of Independence Conspirators. 10 c. Antequera Monument. 20 c. First Paraguayan railway locomotive. 40 c. Government House. VERT. 30 c. Ytororo Heroes' Monument. 70 c. As Type 164 but vert. 2 g. Ruins of Humaita Church. 5 g. Oratory of the Virgin. 10 g. Marshal Francisco S. Lopez.

See also Nos. 640/51.

1945. No. 590 surch. with figures **5** over ornaments deleting old value.

608. 5 c. on 7 c. blue 10 10

186. Clasped Hands and Flags.

1945. President Morinigo's Goodwill Visits. Designs of different sizes inscr. "CONFRATERNIDAD" between crossed flags of Paraguay and another American country, mentioned in brackets. (a) Postage.

609. 186. 1 c. green (Panama) .. 10 10
610. 3 c. red (Venezuela) .. 10 10
611. 5 c. grey (Ecuador) .. 10 10
612. 2 g. brown (Peru) .. 85 60

(b) Air.

613. 186. 20 c. orange (Colombia) 10 30
614. 40 c. olive (Bolivia) .. 10 25
615. 70 c. red (Mexico) .. 10 10
616. 1 g. blue (Chile) .. 25 25
617. 2 g. violet (Brazil) .. 30 30
618. 5 g. green (Argentina) .. 45 45
619. 10 g. brown (U.S.A.) .. 2·25 2·25

The 5 and 10 g. are larger: 32 × 28 and 33½ × 30 mm respectively.

1945. Surch. **1945 5 Centimos 5.**

620. 160. 5 c. on 7 p. blue .. 25 20
621. 161. 5 c. on 7 p. blue .. 20 20
622. – 5 c. on 7 p. blue (No. 590) 10 20

1945. Surch. **1945** and value.

623. 154. 2 c. on 7 p. + 3 p. brown 10 10
624. 2 c. on 7 p. + 3 p. violet 10 10
625. 2 c. on 7 p. + 3 p. red .. 10 10
626. 2 c. on 7 p. + 3 p. blue 10 10
627. 5 c. on 7 p. + 3 p. brown 20 10
628. 5 c. on 7 p. + 3 p. violet 20 10
629. 5 c. on 7 p. + 3 p. red .. 20 10
630. 5 c. on 7 p. + 3 p. blue 20 10

1946. As T 156 but inscr "U.P.U." at foot.

631 156 5 c. grey 10 10
631a 5 c. pink 10 10
631b 5 c. brown 10 10
686 10 c. blue 10 10
687 10 c. pink 10 10
631c 30 c. green 10 10
631d 30 c. brown 10 10
775 45 c. green 10 10
631e 50 c. mauve 10 10
776 50 c. purple 10 10
858 70 c. brown 10 10
777 90 c. blue 10 10
778 1 g. violet 10 10
860 1 g. 50 mauve 10 10
814 2 g. ochre 10 10
780 2 g. 20 mauve 10 10
781 3 g. brown 10 10
782 4 g. 20 green 10 10
862 4 g. 50 blue 15 10
816 5 g. red 10 10
689 10 g. orange 20 30
784 10 g. green 20 15
818 12 g. 45 green 20 10
819 15 g. orange 25 15
786 20 g. blue 40 30
820 30 g. bistre 20 30
812 50 g. brown 30 25
821 100 g. blue 65 50

See also Nos. 1037/49.

1946. Surch. **1946 5 Centimos 5.**

632 154 5 c. on 7 p. + 3 p. brn 25 35
633 5 c. on 7 p. + 3 p. vio 25 35
634 5 c. on 7 p. + 3 p. red 25 35
635 5 c. on 7 p. + 3 p. blue 25 35

1946. Air. Surch. **1946 5 Centimos 5.**

636. 5 c. on 20 c. brown (No. 600) 30 30
637. 5 c. on 30 c. blue (No. 601) 30 30
638. 5 c. on 40 c. olive (No. 602) 30 30
639. 5 c. on 70 c. red (No. 603) .. 30 30

1946. As Nos. 587/607 but colours changed and some designs smaller.

640. – 1 c. red (postage) .. 15 15
641. – 2 c. violet 10 10
642. 164. 5 c. blue 10 10
643. – 10 c. orange 10 10
644 – 15 c. olive 15 15
645. 181. 50 c. green 25 30
646. – 1 g. blue 50 30

DESIGNS—VERT. 1 c. Paddle-steamer "Tacuary". 1 g. Meeting place of Independence Conspirators. HORIZ. 2 c. First telegraphic apparatus in S. America. 10 c. Antequera Monument. 15 c. Ytororo Heroes' Monument.

647. – 10 c. red (air) 10 10
648. – 20 c. green 40 20
649. – 1 g. brown 25 25
650. – 5 g. purple 70 70
651. – 10 g. red .. .. 1·90 1·90

DESIGNS—VERT. 10 c. Ruins of Humaita Church. HORIZ. 20 c. Port of Asuncion. 1 g. Govt. House. 5 g. Marshal Francisco S. Lopez. 10 g. Oratory of the Virgin.

189. Marshal Francisco S. Lopez. 190. Archbishop of Paraguay.

1947. Various frames.

652. 189. 1 c. violet (postage) .. 10 10
653. 2 c. red 10 10
654. 5 c. green 10 10
655. 15 c. blue 10 10
656. 50 c. green 40 40
657. 189. 32 c. red (air) .. 10 10
658. 64 c. brown 25 25
659. 1 g. blue 40 40
660. 5 g. purple and blue .. 60 60
661. 10 g. green and red .. 95 95

1947. 50th Anniv. of Archbishopric of Paraguay.

662. **190.** 2 c. grey (postage) .. 10 10
663. – 5 c. red 10 10
664. – 10 c. black 10 10
665. – 15 c. green 25 15
666. – 20 c. black (air) .. 10 10
667. – 30 c. grey 10 10
668. – 40 c. mauve 15 10
669. **190.** 70 c. red 25 25
670. – 1 g. lake 30 30
671. – 2 g. red 40 40
672. **190.** 5 g. slate and red .. 70 70
673. – 10 g. brown and green .. 95 95

DESIGNS: 5 c., 20 c., 10 g. Episcopal Arms. 10 c., 30 c., 1 g. Sacred Heart Monument. 15 c., 40 c., 2 g. Vision of projected monument.

194. Torchbearer. **195.** C. A. Lopez, J. N. Gonzalez and "Paraguari" (freighter).

1948. Honouring the "Barefeet" (political party). Badge in red and blue.

674. **194.** 5 c. red (postage) .. 10 10
675. 15 c. orange 15 10
676. 69 c. green (air) .. 40 40
677. 5 g. blue .. .. 1·50 1·50

1948. Cent. of Paraguay's Merchant Fleet. Centres in black, red and blue.

678. **195.** 2 c. orange 10 10
679. 5 c. blue 15 10
680. 10 c. black 20 10
681. 15 c. violet 30 10
682. 50 c. green 40 20
683. 1 g. red 60 25

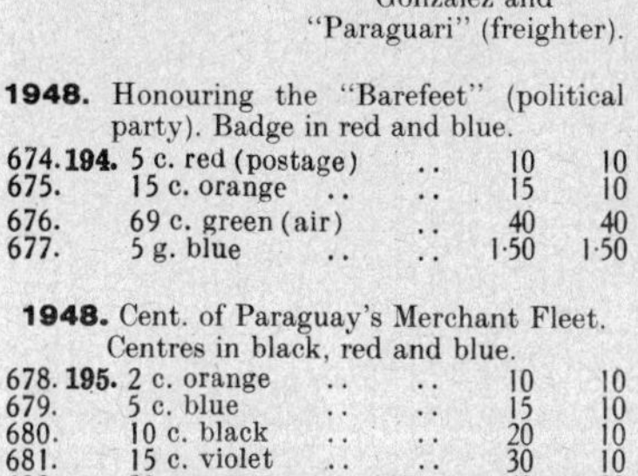

1949. Air. National Mourning for Archbishop of Paraguay. Surch. **DUELO NACIONAL 5 CENTIMOS 5.**

684. **190.** 5 c. on 70 c. red .. 15 15

1949. Air. Aid to victims of Ecuadorean Earthquake. No. 667 surch **AYUDA AL ECUADOR 5+5** and two crosses.

685. 5 c.+5 c. on 30 c. slate .. 10 10

198. "Postal Communications". **199.** President Roosevelt.

1950. Air. 75th Anniv. of U.P.U.

691. **198.** 20 c. violet and green .. 30 30
692. 30 c. brown and purple 10 10
693. 50 c. green and grey .. 10 10
694. 1 g. brown and blue 10 10
695. 5 g. black and red 10 30

1950. Air. Honouring F. D. Roosevelt. Flags in red and blue.

696. **199.** 20 c. orange 10 10
697. 30 c. black 10 10
698. 50 c. purple 15 10
699. 1 g. green 25 25
700. 5 g. blue 30 30

1951. First Economic Congress of Paraguay. Surch. **PRIMER CONGRESO DE ENTIDADES ECONOMICAS DEL PARAGUAY 18-IV-1951** and shield over a block of four stamps.

700a. **156.** 5 c. pink 20 10
700b. 10 c. blue 35 25
700c. 30 c. green 50 40

Prices are for single stamps. Prices for blocks of four, four times single prices.

200. Columbus Lighthouse.

201. Urn.

1952. Columbus Memorial Lighthouse.

701. **200.** 2 c. brown (postage) .. 10 10
702. 5 c. blue 10 10
703. 10 c. pink 10 10
704. 15 c. blue 10 10
705. 20 c. purple 10 10
706. 50 c. orange 15 10
707. 1 g. green 25 25
708. **201.** 10 c. blue (air) .. 10 10
709. 20 c. green 10 10
710. 30 c. purple 10 10
711. 40 c. pink 10 10
712. 50 c. bistre 10 10
713. 1 g. blue 15 10
714. 2 g. orange 25 20
715. 5 g. lake 25 40

202. Isabella the Catholic. **203.** S. Pettirossi (aviator).

1952. Air. 500th Birth Anniv. of Isabella the Catholic.

716. **202.** 1 g. blue 10 10
717. 2 g. brown 20 20
718. 5 g. green 40 40
719. 10 g. purple 40 40

1954. Pettirossi Commem.

720. **203.** 5 c. blue (postage) .. 10 10
721. 20 c. red 10 10
722. 50 c. purple 10 10
723. 60 c. violet 15 10
724. 40 c. brown (air) .. 10 10
725. 55 c. green 10 10
726. 80 c. blue 10 10
727. 1 g. 30 grey 35 35

204. San Roque Church, Asuncion.

1954. Air. San Roque Church Cent.

728. **204.** 20 c. red 10 10
729. 30 c. purple 10 10
730. 50 c. blue 10 10
731. 1 g. purple and brown .. 10 10
732. 1 g. black and brown .. 10 10
733. 1 g. green and brown .. 10 10
734. 1 g. orange and brown .. 10 10
735. 5 g. yellow and brown .. 20 20
736. 5 g. olive and brown .. 20 20
737. 5 g. violet and brown .. 20 20
738. 5 g. buff and brown .. 20 20

205. Marshal Lopez, C. A. Lopez and Gen. Caballero.

1954. National Heroes.

739. **205.** 5 c. violet (postage) .. 10 10
740. 20 c. blue 10 10
741. 50 c. mauve 10 10
742. 1 g. brown 10 10
743. 2 g. green 15 10
744. 5 g. violet (air) .. 20 15
745. 10 g. olive 35 35
746. 20 g. grey 35 30
747. 50 g. pink 75 75
748. 100 g. blue .. .. 2·50 2·50

206. Presidents Stroessner and Peron.

1955. Visit of President Peron. Flags in red and blue.

749. **206.** 5 c. brown & buff (post.) 10 10
750. 10 c. lake and buff .. 10 10
751. 50 c. grey 10 10
752. 1 g. 30 lilac and buff .. 10 10
753. 2 g. 20 blue and buff .. 20 10
754. **206.** 60 c. olive and buff (air) 10 10
755. 2 g. green 10 10
756. 3 g. red 20 10
757. 4 g. 10 mauve and buff 30 20

207. Trinidad Campanile.

1955. Sacerdotal Silver Jubilee of Mgr. Rodriguez.

758 **207** 5 c. brown (postage) .. 10 10
759 – 20 c. brown 10 10
760 – 50 c. brown 10 10
761 – 2 g. 50 green 10 10
762 – 5 g. brown 15 10
763 – 15 g. green 30 20
764 – 25 g. green 35 35
765 **207** 2 g. blue (air) .. 10 10
766 – 3 g. green 10 10
767 – 4 g. green 10 10
768 – 6 g. brown 10 10
769 – 10 g. red 20 10
770 – 20 g. brown 30 10
771 – 30 g. green 25 40
772 – 50 g. blue 25 25

DESIGNS—HORIZ. 20 c., 3 g. Cloisters in Trinidad. 5 g., 10 g. San Cosme Portico. 15 g., 20 g. Church of Jesus. VERT. 50 c., 4 g. Cornice in Santa Maria. 2 g. 50, 6 g. Santa Rosa Tower. 25 g., 30 g. Niche in Trinidad. 50 g. Trinidad Sacristy.

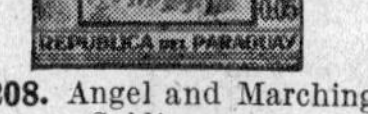

208. Angel and Marching Soldiers. **209.** Soldier and Flags.

1957. Chaco Heroes. Inscr. "HOMENAJE A LOS HEROES DEL CHACO". Flags in red, white and blue.

787. **208.** 5 c. green (postage) .. 10 10
788. 10 c. red 10 10
789. 15 c. blue 10 10
790. 20 c. purple 10 10
791. 25 c. black 10 10
792. – 30 c. blue 10 10
793. – 40 c. black 10 10
794. – 50 c. lake 10 10
795. – 1 g. turquoise 10 10
796. – 1 g. 30 blue 10 10
797. – 1 g. 50 purple 10 10
798. – 2 g. green 10 10
799. **209.** 10 c. blue (air) .. 10 10
800. 15 c. purple 10 10
801. 20 c. red 10 10
802. 25 c. blue 10 10
803. 50 c. turquoise 10 10
804. 1 g. red 10 10
805. – 1 g. 30 purple 10 10
806. – 1 g. 50 blue 10 10
807. – 2 g. green 10 10
808. – 4 g. 10 vermilion & red 10 10
809. – 5 g. black 10 10
810. – 10 g. turquoise 15 15
811. – 25 g. blue 40 15

DESIGNS—HORIZ. Nos. 792/8, Man, woman and flags. Nos. 805/11, "Paraguay" and kneeling soldier.

212. R. Gonzalez and St. Ignatius. **213.** President Stroessner.

1958. 4th Cent. of St. Ignatius of Loyola.

822. **212.** 50 c. green 10 10
823. – 50 c. brown 10 10
824. – 1 g. 50 violet 10 10
825. – 3 g. blue 10 10
826. **212.** 6 g. 25 red 15 10

DESIGNS—VERT. 50 c. brown, 3 g. Statue of St. Ignatius. HORIZ. 1 g. 50, Jesuit Fathers' house, Antigua.

See also Nos. 1074/81.

1958. Re-election of Pres. Stroessner. Portrait in black.

827. **213.** 10 c. red (postage) .. 10 10
828. 15 c. violet 10 10
829. 25 c. green 10 10
830. 30 c. lake 10 10
831. 50 c. mauve 10 10
832. 75 c. blue 10 10
833. 5 g. turquoise 10 10
834. 10 g. brown 10 15
835. 12 g. mauve (air) .. 40 35
836. 18 g. orange 25 40
837. 23 g. brown 40 40
838. 36 g. green 40 40
839. 50 g. olive 50 50
840. 65 g. grey 75 75

1959. Nos. 758/72 surch. with star enclosed by palm leaves and value.

841. 1 g. 50 c. on 5 c. ochre (post.) 10 10
842. 1 g. 50 c. on 20 c. brown .. 10 10
843. 1 g. 50 c. on 50 c. purple .. 10 10
844. 3 g. on 2 g. 50 c. olive .. 10 10
845. 6 g. 25 c. on 5 g. brown .. 10 10
846. 20 g. on 15 g. turquoise .. 35 35
847. 30 g. on 25 g. green .. 50 50
848. 4 g. on 2 g. blue (air) .. 10 10
849. 12 g. 45 c. on 3 g. olive .. 25 20
850. 18 g. 15 c. on 6 g. brown .. 35 30
851. 23 g. 40 c. on 10 g. red .. 25 35
852. 34 g. 80 c. on 20 g. bistre .. 40 50
853. 36 g. on 4 g. green 40 30
854. 43 g. 95 c. on 30 g. green .. 50 35
855. 100 g. on 50 g. blue .. 1·10 75

215. U.N. Emblem. **216.** U.N. Emblem and Map of Paraguay.

1959. Air. Visit of U.N. Secretary-General.

856. **215.** 5 g. blue and orange .. 40 30

1959. Air. U.N. Day.

857. **216.** 12 g. 45 orange & blue 25 20

217. Football. **218.** "Uprooted Tree".

1960. Olympic Games, Rome. Inscr. "1960".

863. **217.** 30 c. red & grn. (post.) 10 10
864. 50 c. purple and blue .. 10 10
865. 75 c. green and orange 10 10
866. 1 g. 50 violet and green 10 10
867. – 12 g. 45 blue & red (air) 25 25
868. – 18 g. 15 green & purple 35 35
869. – 36 g. red and green .. 30 30

DESIGN—AIR: Basketball.

1960. World Refugee Year (1st issue).

870. **218.** 25 c. pink & grn. (post.) 10 10
871. 50 c. green and red .. 10 10
872. 70 c. brown and mauve 30 25
873. 1 g. 50 blue & dp. blue 30 30
874. 3 g. grey and brown .. 40 35
875. – 4 g. pink & green (air) 35 50
876. – 12 g. 45 green and blue 70 50
877. – 18 g. 15 orange and red 95 60
878. – 23 g. 40 blue and red .. 95 1·10

DESIGN—AIR. As Type **218** but with "ANO MUNDIAL" inscr. below tree.

See also Nos. 971/7.

219. U.N. Emblem. **220.** U.N. Emblem and Flags.

1960. "Human Rights." Inscr. "DERECHOS HUMANOS".

879. **219.** 1 g. red & blue (post.) 10 10
880. – 3 g. orange and blue .. 10 10
881. – 6 g. orange and green .. 10 10
882. – 20 g. yellow and red .. 15 15
883. **219.** 40 g. blue and red (air) 30 30
884. – 60 g. red and green .. 40 40
885. – 100 g. red and blue .. 50 50

DESIGNS: 3 g., 60 g. Hand holding scales. 6 g. Hands breaking chain. 20 g., 100 g. "Freedom flame".

1960. U.N. Day. Flags and inscr. in blue and red.

886. **220.** 30 c. blue (postage) .. 10 10
887. 75 c. yellow 10 10
888. 90 c. mauve 10 10
889. 3 g. orange (air) .. 10 10
890. 4 g. green 10 10

INDEX

Countries can be quickly located by referring to the index at the end of this volume.

221. Bridge with Arms of Brazil and Paraguay.
222. Timber Truck.

1961. Inauguration of International Bridge between Brazil and Paraguay.

891. **221.** 15 c. green (postage).. 10 10
892. 30 c. blue 10 10
893. 50 c. orange 10 10
894. 75 c. blue 10 10
895. 1 g. violet 10 10
896. – 3 g. red (air) 15 10
897. – 12 g. 45 lake 30 25
898. – 18 g. 15 green .. 35 30
899. – 36 g. blue 30 25

DESIGN—HORIZ. Nos. 896/9, Aerial view of bridge.

1961. Paraguayan Progress. Inscr. "PARAGUAY EN MARCHA".

900. **222.** 25 c. red & grn. (post.) 10 10
901. – 90 c. yellow and blue.. 10 10
902. – 1 g. red and orange .. 10 10
903. – 2 g. green and pink .. 10 10
904. – 5 g. violet and green.. 15 10
905. **222.** 12 g. 45 bl. & buff (air) 40 25
906. – 18 g. 15 violet & buff 55 35
907. – 22 g. blue and orange 30 40
908. – 36 g. yell., grn. & blue 60 50

DESIGNS: 90 c. 2 g., 18 g., 15, Motorised timber barge. 1 g., 5., 22 g. Radio mast. 36 g. Boeing "707" jetliner.

223. P. J. Caballero, J. G. R. de Francia and F. Yegros.
224. "Chaco Peace".

1961. 150th Anniv. of Independence.

(a) 1st issue.

909. **223.** 30 c. green (postage).. 10 10
910. 50 c. mauve 10 10
911. 90 c. violet 10 10
912. 1 g. 50 blue 10 10
913. 3 g. bistre 10 10
914. 4 g. blue 10 10
915. 5 g. brown 10 10
916. – 12 g. 45 red (air) .. 20 15
917. – 18 g. 15 blue 30 25
918. – 23 g. 40 green .. 40 30
919. – 30 g. violet 45 35
920. – 36 g. red 30 50
921. – 44 g. brown 40 35

DESIGN: No. 916/21, Declaration of Independence.

(b) 2nd issue. Inscr. "PAZ DEL CHACO".

922. **224.** 25 c. red (postage) .. 10 10
923. 30 c. green 10 10
924. 50 c. brown 10 10
925. 1 g. violet 10 10
926. 2 g. blue 10 10
927. – 3 g. blue (air).. .. 20 15
928. – 4 g. purple 20 20
929. – 100 g. green 70 60

DESIGN: Nos. 927/9, Clasped hands.

225. Puma.
226. Arms of Paraguay.

(c) 3rd issue.

930. **225.** 75 c. violet (postage) 10 10
931. 1 g. 50 brown .. 10 10
932. 4 g. 50 green .. 15 10
933. 10 g. blue 25 20
934. – 12 g. 45 purple (air) .. 50 40
935. – 18 g. 15 blue 50 50
936. – 34 g. 80 brown .. 95 95

DESIGN: Nos. 934/6, Brazilian tapir.

(d) 4th issue.

937. **226.** 15 c. blue (postage) .. 10 10
938. 25 c. red 10 10
939. 75 c. green 10 10
940. 1 g. red 10 10
941. **226.** 3 g. brown (air) .. 10 10
942. 12 g. 45 mauve .. 25 25
943. 36 g. turquoise .. 30 30

The air stamps have a background pattern of horiz. lines.

227. Grand Hotel, Guarani.
228. Racquet, Net and Balls.

(e) 5th issue.

944. **227.** 50 c. grey (postage) .. 10 10
945. 1 g. green 10 10
946. 4 g. 50 violet 10 10
947. – 3 g. brown (air) .. 10 10
948. – 4 g. blue 10 10
949. – 18 g. 15 orange .. 40 35
950. – 36 g. red 30 50

The air stamps are similar to Type **227** but inscr. "HOTEL GUARANI" in upper left corner.

See also Nos. 978/85 and 997/1011.

1961. 28th South American Tennis Championships. Asuncion (1st issue). Centres multi-coloured; border colours given.

951. **228.** 35 c. pink (postage) .. 10 10
952. 75 c. yellow 10 10
953. 1 g. 50 blue 10 10
954. 2 g. 25 turquoise .. 10 10
955. 4 g. grey 15 10
956. 12 g. 45 orange (air) .. 40 40
957. 20 g. orange 35 70
958. 50 g. orange .. .. 75 1·75

See also Nos. 978/85.

229.

1961. "Europa".

959. **229.** 50 c. red, blue & mauve 10 10
960. 75 c. red, blue & green 10 10
961. 1 g. red, blue & brown 10 10
962. 1 g. 50 red, bl. & lt. bl. 10 10
963. 4 g. 50, red, bl. & yell. 20 20

230. Comm. Alan Shepard and Solar System.
231.

1961. Commander Shepard's Space Flight.

964 – 10 c. brn & blue (post) 10 10
965 – 25 c. mauve and blue 10 10
966 – 50 c. orange and blue 10 10
967 – 75 c. green and blue 10 10
968 **230** 18 g. 15 bl & grn (air) 4·50 3·25
969 36 g. blue and orange 4·50 3·25
970 50 g. blue and mauve 7·00 3·50

DESIGN—HORIZ. Nos. 964/7, Comm. Shepard.

1961. World Refugee Year (2nd issue).

971. **231.** 10 c. deep blue and blue (post.) 10 10
972. 25 c. purple and orange 10 10
973. 50 c. mauve and pink 10 10
974. 75 c. blue and green .. 10 10
975. – 18 g. 15 red & brn. (air) 25 25
976. – 36 g. green and red .. 55 55
977. – 50 g. orange and green 70 70

Nos. 975/7 have a different background and frame.

232. Tennis-player.
233. Scout Bugler.

1962. 150th Anniv of Independence (6th issue) and 28th South American Tennis Championships, Asuncion (2nd issue).

978. **232.** 35 c. blue (postage) .. 10 10
979. 75 c. violet 10 10
980. 1 g. 50 brown.. .. 10 10
981. 2 g. 25 green .. 10 10
982. – 4 g. red (air) 10 10
983. – 12 g. 45 purple .. 30 30
984. – 20 g. turquoise .. 25 25
985. – 50 g. brown 40 40

Nos. 982/5 show tennis-player using back-hand stroke.

1962. Boy Scouts Commem.

986. **233.** 10 c. grn. & pur. (post.) 10 10
987. 20 c. green and red .. 10 10
988. 25 c. green and brown 10 10
989. 30 c. green and emerald 10 10
990. 50 c. green and blue.. 10 10
991. – 12 g. 45 mve. & bl. (air) 20 40
992. – 36 g. mauve and green 60 90
993. – 50 g. mauve & yellow 75 90

DESIGN: Nos. 991/3, Lord Baden-Powell.

234. Pres. Stroessner and the Duke of Edinburgh.
235. Map of the Americas.

1962. Air. Visit of Duke of Edinburgh.

994. **234.** 12 g. 45 bl., buff & grn. 20 15
995. 18 g. 15 bl., pink & red 30 25
996. 36 g. blue, yell. & brn. 25 45

1962. 150th Anniv. of Independence (7th issue) and Day of the Americas.

997. **235.** 50 c. orange (post.).. 10 10
998. 75 c. blue 10 10
999. 1 g. violet 10 10
1000. 1 g. 50 green .. 10 10
1001. 4 g. 50 red 10 10
1002. – 20 g. mauve (air) .. 30 20
1003. – 50 g. orange 30 50

DESIGN: 20 g., 50 g. Hands supporting Globe.

236. U.N. Emblem.

1962. 150th Anniv. of Independence (8th issue).

1004. **236.** 50 c. brown (postage) 10 10
1005. 75 c. purple 10 10
1006. 1 g. blue 10 10
1007. 2 g. brown 10 10
1008. – 12 g. 45 violet (air).. 35 35
1009. – 18 g. 15 green .. 25 25
1010. – 23 g. 40 red 35 35
1011. – 30 g. red 40 40

DESIGN: Nos. 1008/11, U.N. Headquarters, New York.

237. Mosquito and W.H.O. Emblem.

1962. Malaria Eradication.

1012. **237.** 30 c. blk., blue & pink (postage) 10 10
1013. 50 c. blk., grn. & bistre 10 10
1014. – 75 c. blk., bistre & red 10 10
1015. – 1 g. blk., bistre & grn. 10 10
1016. – 1 g. 50 blk., bis. & brn. 10 10
1017. **237.** 3 g. blk., red & bl. (air) 10 10
1018. 4 g. blk., red & green 10 10
1019. – 12 g. 45 blk., green & brown 25 10
1020. – 18 g. 15 black, red and purple 50 15
1021. – 36 g. blk., blue & red 75 85

DESIGN: Nos. 1014/16, 1019/21, Mosquito on U.N. emblem, and microscope.

238. Football Stadium.
239. "Lago Ypoa" (freighter).

1962. World Football Championships, Chile.

1022. **238.** 15 c. brn. & yell. (post.) 10 10
1023. 25 c. brown and green 10 10
1024. 30 c. brown and violet 10 10
1025. 40 c. brown & orange 10 10
1026. 50 c. brown and green 10 10
1027. – 12 g. 45 black, red and violet (air) 50 25
1028. – 18 g. 15 blk., brn. & vio. 40 45
1029. – 36 g. blk., grey & brn. 85 80

DESIGN—HORIZ. Nos. 1027/9, Footballers and Globe.

1962. Paraguayan Merchant Marine Commemoration.

1030. **239.** 30 c. brown (postage) 10 10
1031. – 90 c. blue 10 10
1032. – 1 g. 50 purple .. 15 10
1033. – 2 g. green 25 15
1034. – 4 g. 20 blue 35 20
1035. – 12 g. 45 red (air) .. 30 15
1036. – 44 g. blue 30 45

DESIGNS—HORIZ. 90 c. Freighter. 1 g. 50, "Olympo" (freighter). 2 g. Freighter (different). 4 g. 20, "Rio Apa" (freighter). VERT. 12 g. 45, 44 g. Ship's wheel.

1962. As Nos. 631, etc., but with taller figures of value.

1037. **156.** 50 c. blue 10 10
1038. 70 c. lilac 10 10
1039. 1 g. 50 violet 10 10
1040. 3 g. blue 10 10
1041. 4 g. 50 brown.. .. 10 10
1042. 5 g. mauve 10 10
1043. 10 g. mauve 20 10
1044. 12 g. 45 blue 20 10
1045. 15 g. 45 red 25 10
1046. 18 g. 15 purple .. 10 15
1047. 20 g. brown 10 15
1048. 50 g. brown 25 30
1049. 100 g. grey 55 30

241. Gen. A. Stroessner.
242. Popes Paul VI, John XXIII and St. Peter's.

1963. Re-election of Pres. Stroessner to Third Term of Office.

1050. **241.** 50 c. brn. & drab (post.) 10 10
1051. 75 c. brown & pink.. 10 10
1052. 1 g. 50 brn. & mve.. 10 10
1053. 3 g. brown and green 10 10
1054. 12 g. 45 red & pink (air) 25 20
1055. 18 g. 15 grn. & pink 35 30
1056. 36 g. vio. and pink .. 60 40

1964. Popes Paul VI and John XXIII.

1057. **242.** 1 g. 50 yell. & red (post.) 10 10
1058. 3 g. green & red .. 10 10
1059. 4 g. brown & red .. 10 10
1060. – 12 g. 45 olive & grn. (air) 35 20
1061. – 18 g. 15 grn. & vio.. 20 30
1062. – 36 g. green & blue .. 75 60

DESIGNS: Nos. 1060/2, Cathedral, Asuncion.

243. Arms of Paraguay and France.
245. Map of the Americas.

1964. Visit of French President.

1063. **243.** 1 g. 50 brown (postage) 10 10
1064. – 3 g. blue 10 10
1065. **243.** 4 g. grey 10 10
1066. – 12 g. 45 violet (air).. 25 20
1067. **243.** 18 g. 15 green .. 40 30
1068. – 36 g. red 75 60

DESIGNS: 3 g., 12 g. 45, 36 g. Presidents Stroessner and De Gaulle.

1965. 6th Reunion of the Board of Governors of the Inter-American Development Bank. Optd. **Centenario de la Epopeya Nacional 1,864-1,870** as in T **245.**

1069. **245.** 1 g. 50 green (postage) 10 10
1070. 3 g. pink 10 10
1071. 4 g. blue 10 10
1072. **245.** 12 g. 45 brown (air) 20 10
1073. 36 g. violet 40 45

The overprint refers to the National Epic of 1864-70, the war with Argentina, Brazil and Uruguay and this inscription occurs on many other issues from 1965 onwards. Nos. 1069/73 without the overprint were not authorised.

246. R. Gonzalez and St. Ignatius.
247. Ruben Dario.

1966. 350th Anniv. of Founding of San Ignacio Guazu Monastery.
1074. **246.** 15 c. blue (postage) .. 10 10
1075. 25 c. blue 10 10
1076. 75 c. blue 10 10
1077. 90 c. blue 10 10
1078. – 3 g. brown (air) .. 10 10
1079. – 12 g. 45, brown .. 10 10
1080. – 18 g. 15, brown .. 20 10
1081. – 23 g. 40 brown .. 35 25
DESIGNS: Nos. 1078/81, Jesuit Fathers' house, Antigua.

For similar stamps with different inscriptions, see Nos. 822, 824 and 826.

1966. 50th Death Anniv. of Ruben Dario (poet).
1082. **247.** 50 c. blue 10 10
1083. 70 c. brown 10 10
1084. 1 g. 50 lake 10 10
1085. 3 g. violet 10 10
1086. 4 g. turquoise .. 10 10
1087. 5 g. black 10 10
1088. – 12 g. 45 blue (air) .. 10 10
1089. – 18 g. 15 violet .. 10 10
1090. – 23 g. 40 brown .. 35 10
1091. – 36 g. green 50 25
1092. – 50 g. red 30 25
DESIGNS: Nos. 1088/92, Open book inscr. "Paraguay de Fuego . . ." by Dario.

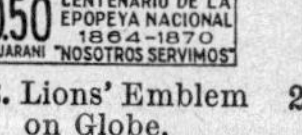

248. Lions' Emblem on Globe. **249.** W.H.O. Emblem.

1967. 50th Anniv. of Lions Int.
1093. **248.** 50 c. violet (postage) 10 10
1094. 70 c. blue 10 10
1095. – 1 g. 50 blue 10 10
1096. – 3 g. brown 10 10
1097. – 4 g. blue 10 10
1098. – 5 g. brown 10 10
1099. – 12 g. 45 brown (air) .. 10 10
1100. – 18 g. 15 violet .. 15 10
1101. – 23 g. 40 purple .. 20 10
1102. – 36 g. blue 25 25
1103. – 50 g. red 25 25
DESIGNS—VERT. 1 g. 50, 3 g. M. Jones. 4 g., 5 g. Lions headquarters, Chicago. HORIZ. 12 g. 45, 18 g. 15, Library—"Education". 23 g. 40, 36 g., 50 g. Medical laboratory—"Health".

1968. 20th Anniv. of W.H.O.
1104. **249.** 3 g. turquoise (postage) 10 10
1105. 4 g. purple 10 10
1106. 5 g. brown 10 10
1107. 10 g. violet 10 10
1108. – 36 g. brown (air) .. 40 25
1109. – 50 g. red 45 30
1110. – 100 g. blue 60 35
DESIGN—VERT. Nos. 1108/10, W.H.O. emblem on scroll.

250. **251.**

1969. World Friendship Week.
1111. **250.** 50 c. red 10 10
1112. 70 c. blue 10 10
1113. 1 g. 50 brown .. 10 10
1114. 3 g. mauve 10 10
1115. 4 g. green 10 10
1116. 5 g. violet 10 10
1117. 10 g. purple 20 10

1969. Air. Campaign for Houses for Teachers.
1118. **251.** 36 g. blue 40 45
1119. 50 g. brown 50 70
1120. 100 g. red .. .. 95 1·00

252. Pres. Lopez. **253.** Paraguay 2 r. Stamp of 1870.

1970. Death Cent. of Pres. F. Solano Lopez.
1121. **252.** 1 g. brown (postage) 10 10
1122. 2 g. violet 10 10
1123. 3 g. pink 10 10
1124. 4 g. red 10 10
1125. 5 g. blue 10 10
1126. 10 g. green 10 10
1127. 15 g. blue (air) .. 10 10
1128. 20 g. brown 20 10
1129. 30 g. green 30 20
1130. 40 g. purple 35 25

1970. Cent. of First Paraguayan Stamps.
1131. **253.** 1 g. red (postage) .. 10 10
1132. A. 2 g. blue 10 10
1133. B. 3 g. brown 10 10
1134. **253.** 5 g. violet 10 10
1135. A. 10 g. lilac 20 10
1136. B. 15 g. purple (air) .. 30 25
1137. **253.** 30 g. green 35 50
1138. A. 36 g. red 40 30
DESIGNS: First Paraguay stamps. A, 1 r. B, 3 r.

254. Teacher and Pupil. **255.** U.N.I.C.E.F. Emblem.

1971. Int Education Year—U.N.E.S.C.O.
1139. **254.** 3 g. blue (postage) .. 10 10
1140. 5 g. lilac 10 10
1141. 10 g. green 10 10
1142. 20 g. red (air) .. 20 10
1143. 25 g. mauve 25 15
1144. 30 g. brown 25 20
1145. 50 g. green 40 35

1972. 25th Annivof U.N.I.C.E.F.
1146. **255.** 1 g. brown (postage)
1147. 2 g. blue 10 10
1148. 3 g. red 10 10
1149. 4 g. purple 10 10
1150. 5 g. green 10 10
1151. 10 g. purple 10 10
1152. 20 g. blue (air) .. 20 10
1153. 25 g. green 25 15
1154. 30 g. brown 25 20

256. Acaray Dam.

1972. Tourist Year of the Americans.
1155. **256.** 1 g. brown (postage) 10 10
1156. – 2 g. brown 10 10
1157. – 3 g. blue 10 10
1158. – 5 g. red 10 10
1159. – 10 g. green 10 10
1160. – 20 g. red (air) .. 25 10
1161. – 25 g. grey 30 15
1162. – 50 g. lilac .. .. 1·00 45
1163. – 100 g. mauve .. 55 40
DESIGNS: 2 g. Statue of Lopez. 3 g. Friendship Bridge. 5 g. Rio Tebicuary Bridge. 10 g. Grand Hotel, Guarani. 20 g. Motor coach. 25 g. Social Service Institute Hospital. 50 g. Liner "Presidente Stroessner". 100 g. "Electra C" airliner.

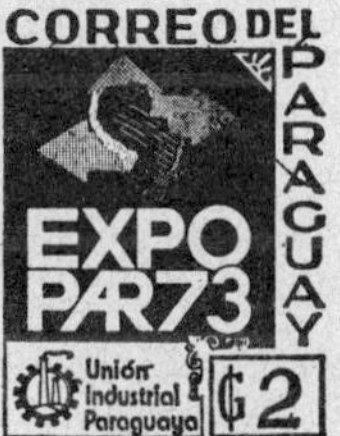

257. O.E.A. Emblem. **258.** Exhibition Emblem.

1973. 25th Anniv. of Organization of American States (O.E.A.).
1164. **257.** 1 g. mult. (postage) .. 10 10
1165. 2 g. multicoloured .. 10 10
1166. 3 g. multicoloured .. 10 10
1167. 4 g. multicoloured .. 10 10
1168. 5 g. multicoloured .. 10 10
1169. 10 g. multicoloured 10 10
1170. 20 g. multicoloured (air) 20 10
1171. 25 g. multicoloured .. 30 15
1172. 50 g. multicoloured .. 25 35
1173. 100 g. multicoloured 55 40

1973. Int. Industrial Exhibition, Paraguay.
1174. **258.** 1 g. brown (postage) 10 10
1175. 2 g. red 10 10
1176. 3 g. blue 10 10
1177. 4 g. green 10 10
1178. 5 g. lilac 10 10
1179. 20 g. mauve (air) .. 20 10
1180. 25 g. red 25 10

259. Carrier Pigeon with Letter.

1975. Cent. of U.P.U.
1181. **259.** 1 g. vio. & blk. (post.) 10 10
1182. 2 g. red & blk. .. 10 10
1183. 3 g. blue and black .. 10 10
1184. 5 g. blue and black .. 10 10
1185. 10 g. purple and black 10 10
1186. 20 g. brn. & blk. (air) 25 15
1187. 25 g. grn. and black .. 30 20

260. Institute Buildings.

1976. Inauguration (1974) of Institute of Higher Education.
1188. **260.** 5 g. violet, red and black (postage) .. 10 10
1189. 10 g. blue, red & black 10 10
1190. 30 g. brn., red & blk. (air) 25 15

261. Rotary Emblem.

1976. 70th Anniv. of Rotary International.
1191. **261.** 3 g. blue, bistre and black (postage) .. 10 10
1192. 4 g. blue, bistre and mauve 10 10
1193. 25 g. blue, bistre and green (air) .. 30 15

262. Woman and I.W.Y. Emblem.

1976. International Women's Year.
1194. **262.** 1 g. brn. & bl. (postage) 10 10
1195. 2 g. brown and red .. 10 10
1196. 20 g. brn. & grn. (air) 25 10

263. Black Palms.

1977. Flowering Plants and Trees. Mult.
1197. 2 g. Type **263** (postage) .. 10 10
1198. 3 g. Mburucuya flowers .. 10 10
1199. 20 g. Marsh rose (tree) (air) 35 25

MINIMUM PRICE

The minimum price quoted is 5p which represents a handling charge rather than a basis for valuing common stamps. For further notes about prices see introductory pages.

264. Nanduti Lace. **265.** F. S. Lopez.

1977. Multicoloured.
1200. 1 g. Type **264** (postage) 10 10
1201. 5 g. Nanduti weaver .. 10 10
1202. 25 g. Lady holding jar (air) 40 25

1977. 150th Birth Anniv. of Marshal Francisco Solano Lopez.
1203. **265.** 10 g. brown (postage) 10 10
1204. 50 g. blue (air) .. 40 50
1205. 100 g. green 75 60

266. General Bernardino Caballero National College.

1978. Cent. of National College of Asuncion.
1206. **266.** 3 g. red (postage) .. 10 10
1207. 4 g. blue 10 10
1208. 5 g. violet 10 10
1209. 20 g. brown (air) .. 20 15
1210. 25 g. purple 25 20
1211. 30 g. green 35 25

267. Marshal Jose F. Estigarribia, Trumpeter and Flag. **268.** Congress Emblem.

1978. "Salon de Bronce" Commem.
1212. **267.** 3 g. purple, blue & red (postage) .. 10 10
1213. 5 g. violet, blue & red 10 10
1214. 10 g. grey, blue & red 10 10
1215. 20 g. grn., bl. & red (air) 25 15
1216. 25 g. violet, blue & red 30 20
1217. 30 g. pur., blue & red 35 25

1979. 22nd Latin American Tourism Congress, Asuncion.
1218. **268.** 10 g. black, blue and red (postage) .. 10 10
1219. 50 g. black, bule and red (air) .. 30 40

269. Spanish Colonial House, Pilar.

1980. Bicentenary of Pilar City.
1220. **269.** 5 g. multicoloured (postage) 10 10
1221. 25 g. multicoloured (air) 30 20

270. Boeing "707".

1980. Inauguration of Paraguay Airlines Boeing "707" Service.
1222. **270.** 20 g. multicoloured (postage) .. 30 10
1223. 100 g. multicoloured (air) .. .. 1·40 70

271. Seminary, Communion Cup and Bible.

1981. Air. Centenary of Metropolitan Seminary, Asuncion.

1224. 271. 5 g. blue 10 10
1225. 10 g. brown 10 10
1226. 25 g. green 30 20
1227. 50 g. black 30 40

272. U.P.U. Monument, Berne.

1981. Centenary of Admission to U.P.U.

1228. 272. 5 g. red and black (postage) 10 10
1229. 10 g. mauve and black 10 10
1230. 20 g. green and black (air) 25 15
1231. 25 g. red and black .. 30 20
1232. 50 g. blue and black .. 30 40

273. St. Maria Mazzarello.

275. Sun and Map of Americas.

274. Stroessner and Bridge over River Itaipua.

1981. Air. Death Centenary of Mother Maria Mazzarello (founder of Daughters of Mary).

1233. 273. 20 g. green and black 25 15
1234. 25 g. red and black .. 30 20
1235. 50 g. violet and black 30 40

1983. 25th Anniv. of President Stroessner City.

1236. 274. 3 g. grn., bl. & blk. (postage) 10 10
1237. 5 g. red, blue and blk. 10 10
1238. 10 g. vio., blue & blk. 10 10
1239. 20 g. grey, bl. & blk. (air) 25 15
1240. 25 g. pur., bl. & blk. 30 20
1241. 50 g. bl., grey & blk. 30 40

1985. Air. 25th Anniv of Inter-American Development Bank.

1242. 275. 3 g. orge., yell. & pk. 10 10
1243. 5 g. orge., yell. & mauve 10 10
1244. 10 g. orge., yell. & mauve 10 10
1245. 50 g. orge., yell. & brown 10 10
1246. 65 g. orge., yell. & bl. 15 10
1247. 95 g. orge., yell. & green 20 15

276. U.N. Emblem.

277. 1886 1 c. Stamp.

1986. Air. 40th Anniv. of U.N.O.

1248. 276. 5 g. blue and brown 10 10
1249. 10 g. blue and grey .. 10 10
1250. 50 g. blue and black 10 10

1986. Centenary of First Official Stamp.

1251 277 5 g. deep blue, brown and blue (postage) 10 10
1252 15 g. deep blue, brown and blue 10 10
1253 40 g. deep blue, brown and blue 10 10
1254 – 65 g. blue, green and red (air) 15 15
1255 – 100 g. blue, green and red 25 25
1256 – 150 g. blue, green and red 40 40

DESIGN: 65, 100, 150 g. 1886 7 c. stamp.

278. Integration of the Nations Monument, Colmena.

1986. Air. 50th Anniv. of Japanese Immigration. Multicoloured.

1257 5 g. La Colmena vineyards (horiz) 10 10
1258 10 g. Flowers of cherry tree and lapacho (horiz) 10 10
1259 20 g. Type **278** 10 10

279 Caballero, Stroessner and Road

1987. Centenary of National Republican Association (Colorado Party).

1260 279 5 g. multicoloured (postage) 10 10
1261 10 g. multicoloured .. 10 10
1262 25 g. multicoloured .. 10 10
1263 – 150 g. multicoloured (air) 25 40
1264 – 170 g. multicoloured 30 20
1265 – 200 g. multicoloured 35 25

DESIGN: 150 to 200 g. Gen. Bernardino Caballero (President 1881–86 and founder of party), Pres. Alfredo Stroessner and electrification of countryside.

280 Emblem of Visit

281 Silver Mate

1988. Visit of Pope John Paul II.

1266 280 10 g. blue and black (postage) 10 10
1267 20 g. blue and black 10 10
1268 50 g. blue and black 15 10
1269 – 100 g. multicoloured (air) 30 20
1270 – 120 g. multicoloured 35 25
1271 – 150 g. multicoloured 45 35

DESIGN—HORIZ. 100 to 150 g. Pope and Caacupe Basilica.

1988. Air. Centenary of New Germany Colony. Multicoloured.

1272 90 g. Type **281** 25 10
1273 105 g. Mate ("Ilex paraguayensis") plantation 30 20
1274 120 g. As No. 1273 .. 35 25

1988. Air. 75th Anniv of Paraguay Philatelic Centre. No. 1249 optd. ***75o ANIVERSARIO DE FUNDACION CENTRO FILATELICO DEL PARAGUAY 15 JUNIO-1913 - 1988.**

1275 276 10 g. blue and grey .. 10 10

283 Pres. Stroessner and Government Palace

1988. Air. Re-election of President Stroessner.

1276 283 200 g. multicoloured 30 25
1277 500 g. multicoloured 75 90
1278 1000 g. multicoloured 1·50 1·50

1989. "Parafil 89" Stamp Exhibition. Nos. 1268 and 1270 optd **PARAFIL 89**.

1279 280 50 g. blue and black (postage) 15 10
1280 – 120 g. mult (air) .. 35 25

285 Green-winged Macaw

1989. Birds. Multicoloured.

1281 50 g. Type **285** (postage) 15 10
1282 100 g. Brazilian merganser (air) 15 10
1283 300 g. Greater rhea (horiz) 45 20
1284 500 g. Toco toucan (horiz) 70 45
1285 1000 g. Bare-faced curassow (horiz) .. 1·40 1·00
1286 2000 g. Caninde macaw and blue and yellow macaw .. .. 2·75 1·90

286 Anniversary Emblem

1990. Centenary of Organization of American States. Multicoloured.

1287 50 g. Type **286** 10 10
1288 100 g. Organization and anniversary emblems (vert) 10 10
1289 200 g. Map of Paraguay .. 45 15

287 Basket

288 Flags on Map

1990. America. Pre-Columbian Life. Mult.

1290 150 g. Type **287** (postage) 15 10
1291 500 g. Guarani post (air) 1·10 95

1990. Postal Union of the Americas and Spain Colloquium. Multicoloured.

1292 200 g. Type **288** 20 15
1293 250 g. First Paraguay stamp 25 15
1294 350 g. Paraguay 1990 America first day cover (horiz) 35 25

289 Planned Building

1990. Centenary of National University. Mult.

1295 300 g. Type **289** 70 55
1296 400 g. Present building .. 95 75
1297 600 g. Old building .. 1·40 1·10

290 Guarambare Church

1990. Franciscan Churches. Multicoloured.

1298 50 g. Type **290** 10 10
1299 100 g. Yaguaron Church 25 20
1300 200 g. Ita Church .. 45 35

1991. Visit of King and Queen of Spain. Nos. 1290/1 optd **Vista de sus Majestades Los Reyes de Espana 22–24 Octubre 1990.**

1301 287 150 g. mult (postage) 15 10
1302 – 500 g. mult (air) .. 1·10 95

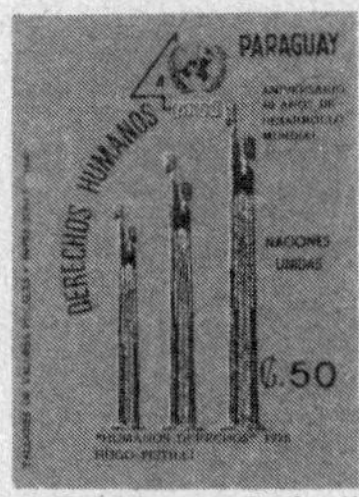

292 "Human Rights" (Hugo Pistilli)

1991. 40th Anniv of United Nations Development Programme. Multicoloured.

1303 50 g. Type **292** 10 10
1304 100 g. "United Nations" (sculpture, Hermann Guggiari) 10 20
1305 150 g. First Miguel de Cervantes prize, awarded to Augusto Roa Bastos, 1989 .. 15 10

294 Hands and Ballot Box (free elections)

1991. Democracy. Multicoloured.

1308 50 g. Type **294** (postage) 10 10
1309 100 g. Sun (State and Catholic Church) (vert) 10 10
1310 200 g. Arrows and male and female symbols (human rights) (vert) .. 15 10
1311 300 g. Dove and flag (freedom of the press) (vert) (air) .. 25 20
1312 500 g. Woman and child welcoming man (return of exiles) 35 25
1313 3000 g. Crowd with banners (democracy) .. 2·25 1·75

295 Julio Manuel Morales (gynaecologist)

1991. Medical Professors.
1314 295 50 g. mult (postage) 10 10
1315 – 100 g. multicoloured 10 10
1316 – 200 g. multicoloured 15 10
1317 – 300 g. brn, blk & grn 25 20
1318 – 350 g. brown, black and green (air) .. 25 20
1319 – 500 g. multicoloured 35 25
DESIGNS: 100 g. Carlos Gatti (surgeon); 200 g. Gustavo Gonzalez (symptomatologist); 300 g. Juan Max Boettner (physician and musician); 350 g. Juan Boggino (pathologist); 500 g. Andres Barbero (founder of Paraguayan Red Cross).

1991. "Espamer '91" Spain–Latin America Stamp Exhibition, Buenos Aires. Nos. 1298/1300 optd **ESPAMER 91 BUENOS AIRES 5 14 Jul** and Conquistador in oval.
1323 50 g. multicoloured .. 10 10
1324 100 g. multicoloured .. 10 10
1325 200 g. multicoloured .. 15 10

298 Ruy Diaz de Guzman (historian)

1991. Writers and Musicians. Multicoloured.
1326 50 g. Type **298** (postage) 10 10
1327 100 g. Maria Talavera (war chronicler) (vert) 10 10
1328 150 g. Augusto Roa Bastos (writer and 1989 winner of Miguel de Cervantes Prize) (vert) 10 10
1329 200 g. Jose Asuncion Flores (composer of "La Guarania") (vert) (air) 15 10
1330 250 g. Felix Perez Cardozo (harpist and composer) 20 15
1331 300 g. Juan Carlos Moreno Gonzalez (composer) .. 25 20

299 Battle of Tavare

300 "Compass of Life" (Alfredo Moraes)

1991. America. Voyages of Discovery. Mult.
1332 100 g. Type **299** (postage) 10 10
1333 300 g. Arrival of Domingo Martinez de Irala in Paraguay (air) .. 25 20

1991. Paintings. Multicoloured.
1334 50 g. Type **300** (postage) 10 10
1335 100 g. "Callejon Illuminated" (Michael Burt) 10 10
1336 150 g. "Arete" (Lucy Yegros) 10 10
1337 200 g. "Itinerants" (Hugo Bogado Barrios) (air) .. 15 10
1338 250 g. "Travellers without a Ship" (Bernardo Ismachoviez) 20 15
1339 300 g. "Guarani" (Lotte Schulz) 25 20

301 Chaco Peccary

302 Geometric Design, Franciscan Church, Caazapa

1992. Endangered Mammals. Multicoloured.
1340 50 g. Type **301** 10 10
1341 100 g. Ocelot (horiz) .. 10 10
1342 150 g. Brazilian tapir .. 10 10
1343 200 g. Maned wolf .. 15 10

1992. 500th Anniv of Discovery of America by Columbus (1st series). Church Roof Tiles. Multicoloured.
1344 50 g. Type **302** 10 10
1345 100 g. Church, Jesuit church, Trinidad .. 10 10
1346 150 g. Missionary ship, Jesuit church, Trinidad 10 10
1347 200 g. Plant, Franciscan church, Caazapa .. 15 10
See also Nos. 1367/71.

1992. "Granada '92" International Thematic Stamp Exhibition. Nos. 1344/7 optd **GRANADA '92** and emblem.
1348 50 g. multicoloured .. 10 10
1349 100 g. multicoloured .. 10 10
1350 150 g. multicoloured .. 10 10
1351 200 g. multicoloured .. 15 10

304 Malcolm L. Norment (founder) and Emblem

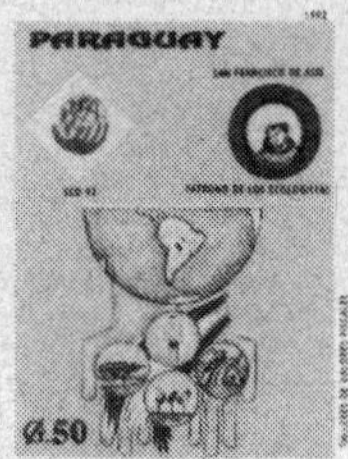

305 Southern Hemisphere and Ecology Symbols on Hands

1992. 68th Anniv of Paraguay Leprosy Foundation. Multicoloured.
1352 50 g. Type **304** 10 10
1353 250 g. Gerhard Hansen (discoverer of leprosy bacillus) 20 15

1992. 2nd United Nations Conference on Environment and Development, Rio de Janeiro. Multicoloured.
1354 50 g. Type **305** 10 10
1355 100 g. Butterfly and chimneys emitting smoke 10 10
1356 250 g. Tree and map of South America on globe 20 15

306 Factories and Cotton (economy)

1992. National Population and Housing Census. Multicoloured.
1357 50 g. Type **306** 10 10
1358 200 g. Houses (vert) .. 15 10
1359 250 g. Numbers and stylized people (population) (vert) .. 20 15
1360 300 g. Abacus (education) 25 20

307 Football

1992. Olympic Games, Barcelona. Mult.
1361 50 g. Type **307** 10 10
1362 100 g. Tennis 10 10
1363 150 g. Running 10 10
1364 200 g. Swimming (horiz) 15 10
1365 250 g. Judo 20 15
1366 350 g. Fencing (horiz) .. 25 20

308 Brother Luis Bolanos

1992. 500th Anniv of Discovery of America by Columbus (2nd series). Evangelists. Mult.
1367 50 g. Type **308** (translator of Catechism into Guarani and founder of Guarani Christian settlements) 10 10
1368 100 g. Brother Juan de San Bernardo (Franciscan and first Paraguayan martyr) .. 10 10
1369 150 g. St. Roque Gonzalez de Santa Cruz (Jesuit missionary and first Paraguayan saint) .. 10 10
1370 200 g. Fr. Amancio Gonzalez (founder of Melodia settlement) .. 15 10
1371 250 g. Mgr. Juan Sinforiano Bogarin (first Archbishop of Ascuncion) (vert) .. 20 15

309 Fleet approaching Shore

1992. America. 500th Anniv of Discovery of America by Columbus. Multicoloured.
1372 150 g. Type **309** (postage) 10 10
1373 350 g. Christopher Columbus (vert) (air) .. 25 20

1992. 30th Anniv of United Nations Information Centre in Paraguay. Nos. 1354/6 optd **NACIONES UNIDAS 1992 - 30 ANOS CENTRO INFORMACION OUN EN PARAGUAY**.
1374 50 g. multicoloured .. 10 10
1375 100 g. multicoloured .. 10 10
1376 250 g. multicoloured .. 20 15

1992. Christmas. Nos. 1367/9 optd **Navidad 92**.
1377 50 g. multicoloured .. 10 10
1378 100 g. multicoloured .. 10 10
1379 150 g. multicoloured .. 10 10

1992. "Parafil 92" Paraguay–Argentina Stamp Exhibition, Buenos Aires. Nos. 1372/3 optd **PARAFIL 92**.
1380 150 g. mult (postage) .. 10 10
1381 350 g. multicoloured (air) 25 20

313 Planting and Hoeing

1992. 50th Anniv of Pan-American Agricultural Institute. Multicoloured.
1382 50 g. Type **313** 10 10
1383 100 g. Test tubes .. 10 10
1384 200 g. Cotton plant in cupped hands 15 10
1385 250 g. Cattle and maize plant 20 15

314 Yolanda Bado de Artecona

1992. Centenary of Paraguayan Writers' College. Multicoloured.
1386 50 g. Type **314** 10 10
1387 100 g. Jose Ramon Silva 10 10
1388 150 g. Abelardo Brugada Valpy 10 10
1389 200 g. Tomas Varela .. 15 10
1390 250 g. Jose Livio Lezcano 20 15
1391 300 g. Francisco I. Fernandez 25 20

315 Members' Flags and Map of South America

316 Orange Flowers (Gilda Hellmers)

1993. 1st Anniv (1992) of Treaty of Ascuncion forming Mercosur (common market of Argentina, Brazil, Paraguay and Uruguay). Multicoloured.
1392 50 g. Type **315** 10 10
1393 350 g. Flags encircling globe showing map of South America .. 25 20

1993. 50th Anniv of St. Isabel Leprosy Association. Flower paintings by artists named. Multicoloured.
1394 50 g. Type **316** 10 10
1395 200 g. Luis Alberto Balmelli 15 10
1396 250 g. Lili del Monico .. 20 15
1397 350 g. Brunilde Guggiari 25 20

317 Goethe (after J. Lips) and Manuscript of Poem

1993. Centenary of Goethe College.
1398 317 50 g. brown, blk & bl 10 10
1399 – 200 g. multicoloured 15 10
DESIGN: 200 g. Goethe (after J. Tischbein).

OFFICIAL STAMPS

O 14. O 19.

O 20. O 37.

1886. Various types as **O 14, O 19,** and **O 20** optd. **OFICIAL.** (a) Imperf.

O 32.	1 c. orange	2·25	2·25
O 33.	2 c. violet	2·25	2·25
O 34.	5 c. orange	2·25	2·25
O 35.	7 c. green	2·25	2·25
O 36.	10 c. brown	2·25	2·25
O 37.	15 c. blue	2·25	2·25
O 38.	20 c. lake	2·25	2·25
	(b) New colours. Perf.		
O 39.	1 c. green	40	40
O 40.	2 c. red	40	40
O 41.	5 c. blue	40	40
O 42.	7 c. orange	40	40
O 43.	10 c. lake	40	40
O 44.	15 c. brown	40	40
O 45.	20 c. blue	40	40

1889. Stamp of 1889 surch. **OFICIAL** and value. Perf.

O 47. **25.**	1 on 15 c. purple ..	1·10	75
O 48.	2 on 15 c. purple ..	1·10	75

1889. Stamp of 1889 surch. **OFICIAL** and value. Imperf.

O 49. **25.**	3 on 15 c. purple ..	1·10	75
O 50.	5 on 15 c. brown ..	1·10	75

1890. Stamps of 1887 optd. **OFICIAL** or **Oficial.**

O 58 **24**	1 c. green	10	10
O 59	2 c. red	15	10
O 60	5 c. blue	15	10
O 61	7 c. brown	1·40	75
O 55	10 c. mauve	20	15
O 63	15 c. orange	20	15
O 64	20 c. pink	25	15
O 65	50 c. grey	15	15
O 86	1 p. green	10	10

1901.

O 73. O **37.**	1 c. blue	30	30
O 74.	2 c. red	10	10
O 75.	4 c. brown	10	10
O 76.	5 c. green	10	10
O 77.	8 c. brown	10	10
O 78.	10 c. red	10	10
O 79.	20 c. blue	20	15

1903. Stamps of 1903, optd. **OFICIAL.**

O 99. **46.**	1 c. grey	10	10
O 100.	2 c. green	10	10
O 101.	5 c. blue	15	10
O 102.	10 c. brown	10	10
O 103.	20 c. red	10	10
O 104.	30 c. blue	10	10
O 105.	60 c. violet	20	20

1904. As T **50,** but inscr. "OFICIAL".

O 106.	1 c. green	20	10
O 107.	1 c. olive	30	10
O 108.	1 c. orange	35	15
O 109.	1 c. red	30	20
O 110.	2 c. orange	20	10
O 111.	2 c. green	20	10
O 112.	2 c. red	60	40
O 113.	2 c. grey	50	30
O 114.	5 c. blue	25	20
O 116.	5 c. grey	1·10	75
O 117.	10 c. lilac	15	10
O 118.	20 c. lilac	50	30

1913. As T **65,** but inscr. "OFICIAL".

O 237.	1 c. grey	10	10
O 233.	2 c. orange	10	10
O 239.	5 c. purple	10	10
O 240.	10 c. green	10	10
O 241.	20 c. red	10	10
O 242.	50 c. red	10	10
O 243.	75 c. blue	10	10
O 244.	1 p. blue	10	10
O 245.	2 p. yellow	20	20

1935. Optd **OFICIAL.**

O 474 **86**	10 c. blue	10	10
O 475	50 c. mauve	10	10
O 476 **87**	1 p. orange	10	10
O 477 **122**	1 p. 50 green	10	10
O 478 –	2 p. 50 violet (No. 337)	10	10

1940. 50th Anniv of Asuncion University. As T **139**, inscr "SERVICIO OFICIAL", but portraits of Pres. Escobar and Dr. Zubizarreta.

O 513.	50 c. black and red ..	10	10
O 514.	1 p. black and red ..	10	10
O 515.	2 p. black and blue ..	10	10
O 516.	5 p. black and blue ..	10	10
O 517.	10 p. black and blue ..	10	10
O 518.	50 p. black and orange	40	10

POSTAGE DUE STAMPS

D 48.

1904.

D 106. **D 48.**	2 c. green	30	30
D 107.	4 c. green	30	30
D 108.	10 c. green ..	30	30
D 109.	20 c. green ..	30	30

1913. As T **65,** but inscr. "DEFICIENTE".

D 237.	1 c. brown	10	10
D 238.	2 c. brown	10	10
D 239.	5 c. brown	10	10
D 240.	10 c. brown	10	10
D 241.	20 c. brown	10	10
D 242.	40 c. brown	10	10
D 243.	1 p. brown	10	10
D 244.	1 p. 50 brown	10	10

APPENDIX

The following stamps have either been issued in excess of postal needs or have not been available to the public in a reasonable quantities at face value. Such stamps may later be given full listing if there is evidence of regular postal use.

1962.

Manned Spacecraft. Postage 15, 25, 30, 40, 50 c.; Air 12 g. 45, 18 g. 15, 36 g.

Previous Olympic Games. (First series). Vert. designs. Postage 15, 25, 30, 40, 50 c.; Air 12 g. 45, 18 g.15, 36 g.

Vatican Council. Postage 50, 70 c., 1 g. 50, 2, 3 g.; Air 5, 10 g., 12 g. 45, 18 g. 15, 23 g. 40, 36 g.

Europa. Postage 4 g.; Air 36 g.

Solar System. Postage 10, 20, 25, 30, 50 c.; Air 12 g. 45, 36 g., 50 g.

1963.

Previous Olympic Games. (Second series). Horiz. designs. Postage 15, 25, 30 40, 50 c.; Air 12 g. 45, 18 g. 15, 36 g.

Satellites and Space Flights. Vert designs. Postage 10, 20, 25, 30, 50 c.; Air 12 g. 45, 36 g., 50 g.

Previous Winter Olympic Games. Postage 10, 20, 25, 30, 50 c.; Air 12 g. 45, 36 g., 50 g.

Freedom from Hunger. Postage 10, 25, 50, 75 c.; Air 18 g. 15, 36 g., 50 g.

"Mercury" Space Flights. Postage 15, 25, 30, 40, 50 c.; Air 12 g. 45, 18 g. 15, 50 g.

Winter Olympic Games. Postage 15, 25, 30, 40, 50 c.; Air 12 g. 45, 18 g. 15, 50 g.

1964.

Tokyo Olympic Games. Postage 15, 25, 30, 40, 50 c.; Air 12 g. 45, 18 g. 15, 50 g.

Red Cross Cent. Postage 10, 25, 30, 50 c.; Air 18 g. 15, 36 g., 50 g.

"Gemini", "Telstar" and "Apollo" Projects. Postage 15, 25, 30, 40, 50 c.; Air 12 g. 45, 18 g. 15, 50 g.

Spacecraft Developments. Postage 15, 25, 30, 40, 50 c.; Air 12 g. 45, 18 g. 15, 50 g.

United Nations. Postage 15, 25, 30, 40, 50 c.; Air 12 g. 45, 18 g. 15, 50 g.

American Space Research. Postage 10, 15, 20, 30, 40 c.; Air 12 g. 45+6 g., 18 g. 15+9 g. 20 g.+10 g.

Eucharistic Conference. Postage 20 g.+10 g., 30 g.+15 g., 50 g.+25 g., 100 g.+50 g.

Pope John Memorial Issue. Postage 20 g.+10 g., 30 g.+15 g., 50 g.+25 g., 100 g.+50 g.

1965.

Scouts. Postage 10, 15, 20, 30, 50 c.; Air 12 g. 45, 18 g. 15, 36 g.

Tokyo Olympic Games Medals. Postage 15, 25, 30, 40, 50 c.; Air 12 g. 45, 18 g. 15, 50 g.

Famous Scientists. Postage 10, 15, 20, 30, 40 c.; Air 12 g. 45+6 g., 18 g. 15+9 g., 20 g.+10 g.

Orchids and Trees. Postage 20, 30, 90 c., 1 g. 50, 4 g. 50; Air 3 g., 4 g., 66 g.

Kennedy and Churchill. Postage 15, 25, 30, 40, 50 c.; Air 12 g. 45, 18 g. 15, 50 g.

I.T.U. Cent. Postage 10, 15, 20, 30, 40 c.; Air 12 g. 45+6 g., 18 g.+15+9 g., 20 g.+10 g.

Pope Paul VI. Visit to United Nations. Postage 10, 15, 20, 30, 50 c.; Air 12 g. 45, 18 g. 15, 36 g.

1966.

"Gemini" Space Project. Postage 15, 25, 30, 40, 50 c.; Air 12 g. 45, 18 g. 15, 50 g.

Events of 1965. Postage 10, 15, 20, 30, 50 c.; Air 12 g. 45, 18 g. 15, 36 g.

Mexico Olympic Games. Postage 10, 15, 20, 30, 50 c.; Air 12 g. 45, 18 g. 15, 36 g.

German Space Research. Postage 10, 15, 20, 30, 50 c.; Air 12 g. 45, 18 g. 15, 36 g.

Famous Writers. Postage 10, 15, 20, 30, 50 c.; Air 12 g. 45, 18 g. 15, 36 g.

Italian Space Research. Postage 10, 15, 20, 30, 50 c.; Air 12 g. 45, 18 g. 15, 36 g.

Moon Missions. Postage 10, 15, 20, 30, 50 c.; Air 12 g. 45, 18 g. 15, 36 g.

Sports Commemorative Issue. Postage 10, 15, 20, 30, 50 c.; Air 12 g. 45, 18 g. 15, 36 g.

3rd Death Anniv. of Pres. John Kennedy. Postage 10, 15, 20, 30, 50 c.; Air 12 g. 45, 18 g. 15, 36 g.

Famous Paintings. Postage 10, 15, 20, 30, 50 c.; Air 12 g. 45, 18 g. 15, 36 g.

1967.

Religious Paintings. Postage 10, 15, 20, 30, 50 c.; Air 12 g. 45, 18 g. 15, 36 g.

16th Cent. Religious Paintings. Postage 10, 15 20, 30, 50 c.; Air 12 g. 45, 18 g. 15, 36 g.

Impressionist Paintings. Postage 10, 15, 20, 30, 50 c.; Air 12 g. 45, 18 g. 15, 36 g.

European Paintings of 17th and 18th Cent. Postage 10, 15, 20, 25, 30, 50 c.; Air 12 g. 45, 18 g. 15, 36 g.

Birth Anniv. of Pres. John Kennedy. Postage 10, 15, 20, 25, 30, 50 c.; air 12 g. 45, 18 g. 15, 36 g.

Sculpture. Postage 10, 15, 20, 25, 30, 50 c.; Air 12 g. 45, 18 g. 15, 50 g.

Mexico Olympic Games. Archaeological Relics. Postage 10, 15, 20, 25, 30, 50 c.; Air 12 g. 45, 18 g. 15, 36 g.

1968.

Religious Paintings. Postage 10, 15, 20, 25, 30, 50 c.; Air 12 g. 45, 18 g. 15, 36 g.

Winter Olympic Games, Grenoble. Paintings. Postage 10, 15, 20, 25, 30, 50 c.; Air 12 g. 45, 18 g. 15, 36 g.

Paraguayan Stamps from 1870–1970. Postage 10, 15, 20, 25, 30, 50 c.; Air 12 g. 45, 18 g. 15, 36 g.

Mexico Olympic Games, Paintings of Children. Postage 10, 15, 20, 25, 30, 50 c.; Air 12 g. 45, 18 g. 15, 36 g. (Sailing ship and Olympic Rings).

Visit of Pope Paul VI to Eucharistic Congress. Religious Paintings. Postage 10, 15, 20, 25, 30, 50 c.; Air 12 g. 45, 18 g. 15, 36 g.

Important Events of 1968. Postage 10, 15, 20, 25, 30, 50 c.; Air 12 g. 45, 18 g. 15, 50 g.

1969.

Gold Medal Winners of 1968 Mexico Olympic Games. Postage 10, 15, 20, 25, 30, 50 c.; Air 12 g. 45, 18 g. 15, 50 g.

Int. Projects in Outer Space. Postage 10, 15, 20, 25, 30, 50 c.; Air 12 g. 45, 18 g. 15, 50 g.

Latin American Wildlife. Postage 10, 10, 15, 15, 20, 20, 25, 25, 30, 30, 50, 50, 75, 75 c.; Air 12 g. 45×2, 18 g. 15×2.

Gold Medal Winners in Olympic Football, 1900–1968. Postage 10, 15, 20, 25, 30, 50, 75 c.; Air 12 g. 45, 18 g. 15.

Paraguayan Football Champions, 1930–1966. Postage 10, 15, 20, 25, 30, 50, 75 c.; Air 12 g. 45, 18 g. 15.

Paintings by Goya. Postage 10, 15, 20, 25, 30, 50, 75 c.; Air 12 g. 45, 18 g. 15.

Christmas. Religious Paintings. Postage 10, 15, 20, 25, 30, 50, 75 c.; Air 12 g. 45, 18 g. 15.

1970.

Moon Walk. Postage 10, 15, 20, 25, 30, 50, 75 c.; Air 12 g. 45, 18 g. 15.

Easter. Paintings Postage 10, 15, 20, 25, 30, 50, 75 c.; Air 12 g. 45, 18 g. 15.

Munich, Olympic Games. Postage 10, 15, 20, 25, 30, 50, 75 c.; Air 12 g. 45, 18 g. 15.

Paintings from the Pinakothek Museum in Munich. Postage 10, 15, 20, 25, 30, 50, 75 c.; Air 12 g. 45, 18 g. 15.

"Apollo" Space Programme. Postage 10, 15, 20, 25, 30, 50, 75 c.; Air 12 g. 45, 18 g. 15.

Space Projects in the Future. Postage 10, 15, 20, 25, 30, 50, 75 c.; Air 12 g. 45, 18 g. 15.

"Expo 70" World Fair, Osaka, Japan. Japanese Paintings. Postage 10, 15, 20, 25, 30, 50, 75 c.; Air 12 g. 45, 18 g. 15, 50 g.

Flower Paintings. Postage 10, 15, 20, 25, 30, 50, 75 c.; Air 12 g. 45, 18 g. 15, 50 g.

Paintings from Prado Museum, Madrid. Postage 10, 15, 20, 25, 30, 50, 75 c.; Air 12 g. 45, 18 g. 15, 50 g.

Paintings by Durer. Postage 10, 15, 20, 25, 30, 50, 75 c.; Air 12 g. 45, 18 g. 15, 50 g.

1971.

Christmas 1970/71. Religious Paintings. Postage 10, 15, 20, 25, 30, 50, 75 c.; Air 12 g. 45, 18 g. 15, 50 g.

Munich Olympic Games 1972. Postage 10, 15, 20, 25, 30, 50, 75 c.; Air 12 g. 45, 18 g. 15, 50 g.

Paintings of Horses and Horsemen. Postage 10, 15, 20, 25, 30, 50, 75 c.; Air 12 g. 45, 18 g. 15, 50 g.

Famous Paintings from the Louvre, Paris. Postage 10, 15, 20, 25, 30, 50, 75 c.; Air 12 g. 45, 18 g. 15, 50 g.

Paintings in the National Museum, Asuncion. Postage 10, 15, 20, 25, 30, 50, 75 c.; Air 12 g. 45, 18 g. 15, 50 g.

Hunting Paintings. Postage 10, 15, 20, 25, 30, 50, 75 c.; Air 12 g. 45, 18 g. 15, 50 g.

Philatokyo '71, Stamp Exhibition, Tokyo. Japanese Paintings. Postage 10, 15, 20, 25, 30, 50, 75 c.; Air 12 g. 45, 18 g. 15, 50 g.

Winter Olympic Games, Sapporo 1972. Japanese Paintings. Postage 10, 15, 20, 25, 30, 50, 75 c.; Air 12 g. 45, 18 g. 15, 50 g.

150th Death Anniv. of Napoleon. Paintings. Postage 10, 15, 20, 25, 30, 50, 75 c.; Air 12 g. 45, 18 g. 15, 50 g.

Famous Paintings from the Dahlem Museum, Berlin. Postage 10, 15, 20, 25, 30, 50, 75 c.; Air 12 g. 45, 18 g. 15, 50 g.

1972.

Locomotives (1st series). Postage 10, 15, 20, 25, 30, 50, 75 c.; Air 12 g. 45, 18 g. 15, 50 g.

Winter Olympic Games, Sapporo. Postage 10, 15, 20, 25, 30, 50, 75 c.; Air 12 g. 45, 18 g. 15, 50 g.

Racing Cars. Postage 10, 15, 20, 25, 30, 50, 75 c.; Air 12 g. 45, 18 g. 15, 50 g.

Famous Sailing Ships. Postage 10, 15, 20, 25, 30, 50, 75 c.; Air 12 g. 45, 18 g. 15, 50 g.

Famous Paintings from the Vienna Museum. Postage 10, 15, 20, 25, 30, 50, 75 c.; Air 12 g. 45, 18 g. 15, 50 g.

Famous Paintings from the Asuncion Museum. Postage 10, 15, 20, 25, 30, 50, 75 c.; Air 12 g. 45, 18 g. 15, 50 g.

Visit of the Argentine President to Paraguay. Postage 10, 15, 20, 25, 30, 50, 75 c.; Air 12 g. 45, 18 g. 15.

Visit of President of Paraguay to Japan. Postage 10, 15, 20, 25, 30, 50, 75 c.; Air 12 g. 45, 18 g. 15.

Paintings of Animals and Birds. Postage 10, 15, 20, 25, 30, 50, 75 c.; Air 12 g. 45, 18 g. 15.

Locomotives (2nd series). Postage 10, 15, 20, 25, 30, 50, 75 c.; Air 12 g. 45, 18 g. 15.

South American Fauna. Postage 10, 15, 20, 25, 30, 50, 75 c.; Air 12 g. 45, 18 g. 15.

1973.

Famous Paintings from the Florence Museum Postage 10, 15, 20, 25, 30, 50, 75 c.; Air 5, 10 20 g.

South American Butterflies. Postage 10, 15, 20, 25, 30, 50, 75 c.; Air 5, 10, 20 g.

Cats. Postage 10, 15, 20, 25, 30, 50, 75 c.; Air 5, 10, 20 g.

Portraits of Women. Postage 10, 15, 20, 25, 30, 50, 75 c.; Air 5, 10, 20 g.

World Cup Football Championships, West Germany (1974) (1st issue). Postage 10, 15, 20, 25, 30, 50, 75 c.; Air 5, 10, 20 g.

Paintings of Women. Postage 10, 15, 20, 25, 30, 50, 75 c.; Air 5, 10, 20 g.

Birds. Postage 10, 15, 20, 25, 30, 50, 75 c.; Air 5, 10, 20 g.

"Apollo" Moon Missions and Future Space Projects. Postage 10, 15, 20, 25, 30, 50 75 c.; Air 5, 10, 20 g.

Visit of Pres. Stroessner to Europe and Morocco. Air 5, 10, 25, 50, 150 g.

Folk Costume. 25, 50, 75 c., 1 g., 1 g. 50, 1 g. 75, 2 g. 25.

Flowers. 10, 20, 25, 30, 40, 50, 75 c.

1974.

World Cup Football Championships, West Germany (2nd issue). Air 5, 10, 20 g.

Roses. 10, 15, 20, 25, 30, 50, 75 c.

Famous Paintings from the Gulbenkian Museum, New York. Postage 10, 15, 20, 25, 30, 50, 75 c.; Air 5, 10, 20 g.

U.P.U. Cent. Postage 10, 15, 20, 25, 30, 50, 75 c.; Air 5, 10, 20 g.

Famous Masterpieces. Postage 10, 15, 20, 25. 30, 50, 75 c.; Air 5, 10, 20 g.

Visit of Pres. Stroessner to France. Air 100 g.

World Cup Football Championships, West Germany (3rd issue). Air 4, 5, 10 g.

Ships. Postage 5, 10, 15, 20, 25, 35, 40, 50 c.

Events of 1974. Air 4 g. (U.P.U.), 5 g. (President of Chile's visit), 10 g. (Pres. Stroessners' visit to South Africa).

Centenary of U.P.U. Air 4, 5, 10, 20 g.

1975.

Paintings. 5, 10, 15, 20, 25, 35, 40, 50 c.

Christmas. (1974) 5, 10, 15, 20, 25, 35, 40, 50 c.

"Expo '75" Okinawa, Japan. Air 4, 5, 10 g.

Paintings from National Gallery, London. 5 10, 15, 20, 25, 35, 40, 50 c.

Dogs. 10, 15, 20, 25, 35, 40, 50 c.

South American Fauna. 5, 10, 15, 20, 25, 35, 40, 50 c.

"Espana '75". Air 4, 5, 10 g.

500th Birth Anniv. of Michelangelo. Postage 5, 10, 15, 20, 25, 35, 40, 50 c., Air 4, 5, 10 g.

Winter Olympic Games, Innsbruck (1976). Postage 1, 2, 3, 4, 5 g.; Air 10, 15, 20 g.

Olympic Games, Montreal (1976). Gold borders. Postage 1, 2, 3, 4, 5 g.; Air 10, 15, 20 g.

Various Commemorations. Air 4 g. (Zeppelin), 5 g. (1978 World Cup), 10 g. (Nordposta Exhibition).

Bicent. (1976) of American Revolution (1st issue). Paintings of Sailing Ships. 5, 10, 15, 20, 25, 35, 40, 50 c.

Bicent. (1976) of American Revolution (2nd issue). Paintings. 5, 10, 15, 20, 25, 35, 40, 50 c.

Bicent. (1976) of American Revolution (3rd issue). Lunar Rover and American Cars. Air 4, 5, 10 g.

Various Commemorations. Air 4 g. (Concorde) 5 g. (Lufthansa) 10 g. (" Exfilmo " and " Espamer " Stamp Exhibitions).

Paintings by Spanish Artists. Postage 1, 2, 3, 4, 5 g.; Air 10, 15, 20 g.

1976.

Holy Year. Air 4, 5, 10 g.

Cats. 5, 10, 15, 20, 25, 35, 40, 50 c.

Railway Locomotives. Postage 1, 2, 3, 4, 5 g.; Air 10, 15, 20 g.

Butterflies. 5, 10, 15, 20, 25, 35, 40, 50 c.

Domestic Animals. Postage 1, 2, 3, 4, 5 g.; Air 10, 15, 20 g.

Bicentenary of American Revolution (4th issue) and U.S. Postal Service. Postage 1, 2, 3, 4, 5 g.; Air 10, 15, 20 g.

"Paintings and Planets". Postage 1, 2, 3, 4, 5 g.; Air 10, 15, 20 g.

Ship Paintings. Postage 1, 2, 3, 4, 5 g.; Air 10, 15, 20 g.

German Ship Paintings (1st issue). Postage 1, 2, 3, 4, 5 g.; Air 10, 15, 20 g.

Bicentenary of American Revolution (5th issue). Paintings of Cowboys and Indians. Postage 1, 2, 3, 4, 5 g.; Air 10, 15, 20 g.

Gold Medal Winners. Olympic Games, Montreal. Postage 1, 2, 3, 4, 5 g.; Air 10, 15, 20 g.

Paintings by Titian. Postage 1, 2, 3, 4, 5 g.; Air 10, 15, 20 g.

History of the Olympics. Postage 1, 2, 3, 4, 5 g.; Air 10, 15, 20 g.

1977.

Paintings by Rubens (1st issue). Postage 1, 2, 3, 4, 5 g.; Air 10, 15, 20 g.

Bicentenary of American Revolution (6th issue). Astronautics. Postage 1, 2, 3, 4, 5 g.; Air 10, 15, 20 g.

"Luposta 77" Stamp Exhibition. Zeppelin and National Costumes. Postage 1, 2, 3, 4, 5 g.; Air 10, 15, 20 g.

History of Aviation. Postage 1, 2, 3, 4, 5 g.; Air 10, 15, 20 g.

Paintings. Postage 1, 2, 3, 4, 5 g.; Air 10, 15, 20 g.

German Ship Paintings (2nd issue). Postage 1, 2, 3, 4, 5 g.; Air 10, 15, 20 g.

Nobel Prize-winners for Literature. Postage 1, 2, 3, 4, 5 g.; Air 10, 15, 20 g.

History of World Cup (1st issue). Postage 1, 2, 3, 4, 5 g.; Air 10, 15, 20 g.

History of World Cup (2nd issue). Postage 1, 2, 3, 4, 5 g.; Air 10, 15, 20 g.

1978.

Paintings by Rubens (2nd issue). Postage 1, 2, 3, 4, 5 g.; Air 10, 15, 20 g.

23rd Chess Olympiad, Buenos Aries. Paintings of Chess Games. Postage 1, 2, 3, 4, 5 g.; Air 10, 15, 20 g.

Paintings by Jordaens. Postage 3, 4, 5, 6, 7, 8, 20 g.; Air 10, 25 g.

450th Death Anniv. of Durer (1st issue). Postage 3, 4, 5, 6, 7, 8, 20 g.; Air 10, 25 g.

Paintings by Goya. Postage 3, 4, 5, 6, 7, 8, 20 g.; Air 10, 25 g.

Astronautics of the Future. Postage 3, 4, 5, 6, 7, 8, 20 g.; Air 10, 25 g.

Racing Cars. Postage 3, 4, 5, 6, 7, 8, 20 g.; Air 10, 25 g.

Paintings by Rubens (3rd issue). Postage 3, 4, 5, 6, 7, 8, 20 g.; Air 10, 25 g.

25th Anniv. of Queen Elizabeth's Coronation (reproductions of stamps). Postage 3, 4, 5, 6, 7, 8, 20 g.; Air 10, 25 g.

Paintings and Stamp Exhibition Emblems. Postage 3, 4, 5, 6, 7, 8, 20 g.; Air 10, 25 g.

Various Commemorations. Air 75 g. (Satellite Earth Station), 500 g. (Coat of Arms), 1000 g. (Pres. Stroessner).

International Year of the Child (1st issue). Snow White and the Seven Dwarfs. Postage 3, 4, 5, 6, 7, 8, 20 g.; Air 10, 25 g.

Military Uniforms. Postage 3, 4, 5, 6, 7, 8, 20 g.; Air 10, 25 g.

1979.

World Cup Football Championship, Argentina. Postage 3, 4, 5, 6, 7, 8, 20 g.; Air 10, 25 g.

Christmas (1978) Paintings of Madonnas. Postage 3, 4, 5, 6, 7, 8, 20 g.; Air 10, 25 g.

History of Aviation. Postage 3, 4, 5, 6, 7, 8, 20 g.; Air 10, 25 g.

450th Death Anniv. of Durer (2nd issue). Postage 3, 4, 5, 6, 7, 8, 20 g.; Air 10, 25 g.

Death Centenary of Sir Rowland Hill (1st issue). Reproductions of Stamps. Postage 3, 4, 5, 6, 7, 8, 20 g.; Air 10, 25 g.

International Year of the Child (2nd issue) Cinderella. Postage 3, 4, 5, 6, 7, 8, 20 g.; Air 10, 25 g.

Winter Olympic Games, Lake Placid (1980). Postage 3, 4, 5, 6, 7, 8, 20 g.; Air 10, 25 g.

Sailing Ships. Postage 3, 4, 5, 6, 7, 8, 20 g.; Air 10, 25 g.

International Year of the Child (3rd issue). Cats. Postage 3, 4, 5, 6, 7, 8, 20 g.; Air 10, 25 g.

International Year of the Child (4th issue). Little Red Riding Hood. Postage 3, 4, 5, 6, 7, 8, 20 g.; Air 10, 25 g.

Olympic Games, Moscow (1980). Greek Athletes. Postages 3, 4, 5, 6, 7, 8, 20 g.; Air 10, 25 g.

Centenary of Electric Locomotives. Postage 3, 4, 5, 6, 7, 8, 20 g.; Air 10, 25 g.

1980.

Death Centenary of Sir Rowland Hill (2nd issue). Military Aircraft. Postage 3, 4, 5, 6, 7, 8, 20 g.; Air 10, 25 g.

Death Centenary of Sir Rowland Hill (3rd issue). Stamps. Postage 3, 4, 5, 6, 7, 8, 20 g.; Air 10, 25 g.

Winter Olympic Games Medal Winners (1st isue). Postage 3, 4, 5, 6, 7, 8, 20 g.; Air 10, 25 g.

Composers. Scenes from Ballets. Postage 3, 4, 5, 6, 7, 8, 20 g.; Air 10, 25 g.

International Year of the Child (1979) (5th issue). Christmas. Postage 3, 4, 5, 6, 7, 8, 20 g.; Air 10 ,25 g.

Exhibitions. Paintings of Ships. Postage 3, 4, 5, 6, 7, 8, 20 g.; Air 10, 25 g.

World Cup Football Championship, Spain(1982) (1st issue). Postage 3, 4, 5, 6, 7, 8, 20 g.; Air 10, 25 g.

World Chess Championship, Merano. Postage 3, 4, 5, 6, 7, 8, 20 g.; Air 10, 25 g.

1981.

Winter Olympic Games Medal Winners (2nd issue). Postage 25, 50 c., 1, 2, 3. 4, 5 g.; Air 5, 10, 30 g.

International Year of the Child (1979) (6th issue). Children and Flowers. Postage 10, 25, 50, 100, 200, 300, 400 g.; Air 75, 500, 1000 g.

"WIPA 1981" International Stamp Exhibition, Vienna. 1980 Composers stamp optd. Postage 4 g.; Air 10 g.

Wedding of Prince of Wales (1st issue). Postage 25, 50 c., 1, 2, 3, 4, 5 g.; Air 5, 10, 30 g.

Costumes and Treaty of Itaipu. 10, 25, 50, 100, 200, 300, 400 g.

Paintings by Rubens. 25, 50 c., 1, 2, 3, 4, 5 g.

Anniversaries and Events. Air 5 g. (250th birth anniv of George Washington), 10 g. (80th birthday of Queen Mother), 30 g. ("Philatokyo '81")

Flight of Space Shuttle. Air. 5, 10, 30 g.

Birth Bicentenary of Ingres. 25, 50 c., 1, 2, 3, 4, 5 g.

World Cup Football Championship, Spain (1982) (2nd issue). Air 5, 10, 30 g.

Birth Centenary of Picasso. 25, 50 c., 1, 2, 3, 4, 5 g.

"Philatelia '81" International Stamp Exhibition, Frankfurt. Picasso Stamps optd. 25, 50 c., 1, 2, 3, 4 g.

"Espamer '81" International Stamp Exhibition. Picasso stamps optd. 24, 50 c., 1, 2, 3, 4 g.

Wedding of Prince of Wales (2nd issue). Postage 25, 50 c., 1, 2, 3, 4, 5 g.; Air 5, 10, 30 g.

International Year of the Child (1979) (7th issue). Christmas. 25, 25 c., 1, 2, 3, 4, 5 g.

Christmas. Paintings. Air 5, 10, 30 g.

1982.

International Year of the Child (1979) (8th issue). Puss in Boots. 25, 50 c., 1, 2, 3, 4, 5 g.

World Cup Football Championship, Spain (3rd issue). Air 5, 10, 30 g.

75th Anniv. of Boy Scout Movement and 125th birth Anniv. of Lord Baden-Powell (founder). Postage 25, 50 c., 1, 2, 3, 4, 5 g.; Air 5, 10, 30 g.

"Essen 82" International Stamp Exhibition 1981 International Year of the Child (7th issue) Christmas stamps optd. 25, 50 c., 1, 2, 3, 4 g.

Cats. 25, 50 c., 1, 2, 3, 4, 5 g.

Chess paintings. Air 5, 10, 30 g.

"Philexfrance 82" International Stamp Exhibition. 1981 Ingres Stamps optd. 25, 50 c., 1, 2, 3 g.

World Cup Football Championship, Spain (4th issue). Postage 25, 50 c., 1, 2, 3, 4, 5 g.; Air 5, 10, 30 g.

"Philatelia 82" International Stamp Exhibition, Hanover. 1982 Cats issue optd. 25, 50 c., 1, 2, 3, 4, 5 g.

500th Birth Anniv. of Raphael (1st issue). 25, 50 c. 1, 2, 3, 4, 5 g.

500th Birth Anniv. of Raphael (2nd issue) and Christmas (1st issue). 25, 50 c., 1, 2, 3, 4, 5 g.

World Cup Football Championship Results. Air 5, 10, 30 g.

Christmas (2nd issue). Paintings by Rubens. Air 5, 10, 30 g.

Paintings by Durer. Life of Christ. 25, 50 c., 1, 2, 3, 4, 5 g.

500th Birth Anniv. of Raphael (3rd issue) and Christmas (3rd issue). Air 5, 10, 30 g.

1983.

Third International Railways Congress, Malaga (1982). 25, 50 c., 1, 2, 3, 4, 5 g.

Racing Cars. 25, 50 c., 1, 2, 3, 4, 5 g.

Paintings by Rembrandt. Air 5, 10, 30 g.

German Astronautics. Air 5, 10, 30 g.

Winter Olympic Games, Sarajevo (1984). 25, 50 c., 1, 2, 3, 4, 5 g.

Bicentenary of Manned Flight. Air 5, 10, 30 g.

Pope John Paul II, 25, 50 c., 1, 2, 3, 4, 5 g.

Olympic Games, Los Angeles (1984). Air 5, 10, 30 g.

Veteran Cars. Postage 25, 50 c., 1, 2, 3, 4, 5 g.; Air 5, 10, 30 g.

"Brasiliana '83" International Stamp Exhibition and 52nd F.I.P. Congress (1st issue). 1982 World Cup (4th issue) stamps optd. 25, 50 c., 1, 2, 3, 4, g.

"Brasiliana '83" International Stamp Exhibition and 52nd F.I.P. Congress (2nd issue). 1982 Raphael/Christmas stamps optd. 25, 50 c., 1, 2, 3, 4, g.

Aircraft Carriers. 25, 50 c., 1, 2, 3, 4, 5 g.

South American Flowers. Air 5, 10, 30 g.

South American Birds. 25, 50 c., 1, 2, 3, 4, 5 g.

25th Anniv. of International Maritime Organization. Air 5, 10, 30 g.

"Philatelia '83" International Stamp Exhibition, Dusseldorf. 1983 International Railway Congress stamps optd. 25, 50 c., 1, 2, 3, 4, g.

"Exfivia – 83" International Stamp Exhibition, Bolivia. 1982 Durer paintings optd. 25, 50 c., 1, 2, 3, 4 g.

Flowers 10, 25 g.; Chaco soldier 50 g.; Dams, Postage 75 g. Air 100 g.; President, Air 200 g.

1984

Bicentenary of Manned Flight. 25, 50 c., 1, 2, 3, 4, 5 g.

World Communications Year. Air 5, 10, 30 g.

Dogs. 25, 50 c., 1, 2, 3, 4, 5 g.

Olympic Games, Los Angeles. Air 5, 10, 30 g.

Animals. 10, 25, 50, 75 g.

1983 Anniversaries. Air 100 g. (birth bicentenary of Bolivar), 200 g. (76th anniv of boy scout movement)

Christmas (1983) and New Year. 25, 50 c., 1, 2, 3, 4, 5 g.

Winter Olympic Games, Sarajevo. Air 5, 10, 30 g.

Troubadour Knights. 25, 50 c., 1, 2, 3, 4, 5 g.

World Cup Football Championships, Spain (1982) and Mexico (1986). Air 5, 10, 30 g.

International Stamp Fair, Essen. 1983 Racing Cars stamps optd. 25, 50 c., 1, 2, 3, 4 g.

Extinct Animals. 25, 50 c., 1, 2, 3, 4, 5 g.

60th Anniv of International Chess Federation. Air 5, 10, 30 g.

19th Universal Postal Union Congress Stamp Exhibition, Hamburg (1st issue). Sailing Ships. 25, 50 c., 1, 2, 3, 4, 5 g.

19th Universal Postal Union Congress Stamp Exhibition, Hamburg (2nd issue). Troubadour Knights stamp optd. 5 g.

Leaders of the World. British Railway Locomotives. 25, 50 c., 1, 2, 3, 4, 5 g.

50th Anniv of First Lufthansa Europe–South America Direct Mail Flight. Air 5, 10, 30 g.

30th Anniv of Presidency of Alfredo Stroessner. Dam stamp optd. Air 100 g.

"Ausipex 84" International Stamp Exhibition, Melbourne. 1974 U.P.U. Centenary stamps optd. 10, 15, 20, 25, 30, 50, 75 c.

"Phila Korea 1984" International Stamp Exhibition, Seoul. Olympic Games, Los Angeles, and Extinct Animals stamps optd. Postage 5 g.; Air 30 g.

German National Football Championship and Sindelfingen Stamp Bourse. 1974 World Cup stamps (1st issue) optd. 10, 15, 20, 25, 30, 50, 75 c.

Cats. 25, 50 c., 1, 2, 3, 4, 5 g.

Winter Olympic Games Medal Winners. Air 5, 10, 30 g.

Centenary of Motor Cycle. Air 5, 10, 30 g.

1985

Olympic Games Medal Winners. 25, 50 c., 1, 2, 3, 4, 5 g.

Christmas (1984). Costumes. Air 5, 10, 30 g.

Fungi. 25, 50 c., 1, 2, 3, 4, 5 g.

Participation of Paraguay in Preliminary Rounds of World Cup Football Championship. Air 5, 10, 30 g.

"Interpex 1985" and "Stampex 1985" Stamp Exhibitions. 1981 Queen Mother's Birthday stamp optd. 10 g. x 2

International Federation of Aero-Philatelic Societies Congress, Stuttgart. 1984 Lufthansa Europe–South America Mail Flight stamp optd. Air 10 g.

Paraguayan Animals and Extinct Animals. 25, 50 c., 1, 2, 3, 4, 5 g.

"Olymphilex 85" Olympic Stamps Exhibition, Lausanne. 1984 Winter Olympic Games Medal Winners stamp optd. 10 g.

"Israphil 85" International Stamp Exhibition, Tel Aviv. 1982 Boy Scout Movement stamp optd. 5 g.

Music Year. Air 5, 10, 30 g.

Birth Bicentenary of John J. Audubon (ornithologist). Birds. 25, 50 c., 1, 2, 3, 4, 5 g.

Railway Locomotives. Air 5, 10, 30 g.

"Italia '85" International Stamp Exhibition, Rome (1st issue). 1983 Pope John Paul II stamp optd. 5 g.

50th Anniv of Chaco Peace (1st issue). 1972 Visit of Argentine President stamp optd. 30 c.

"Mophila 85" Stamp Exhibition, Hamburg. 1984 U.P.U. Congress Stamp Exhbition (1st issue) stamp optd. 5 g.

"Lupo 85" Stamp Exhibition, Lucerne. 1984 Bicentenary of Manned Flight stamp optd. 5 g.

"Expo 85" World's Fair, Tsukuba. 1981 "Philatokyo '81" stamp optd. Air 30 g.

International Youth Year. Mark Twain. 25, 50 c., 1, 2, 3, 4, 5 g.

75th Death Anniv of Henri Dunant (founder of Red Cross). Air 5, 10, 30 g.

150th Anniv of German Railways (1st issue). 25, 50 c., 1, 2, 3, 4, 5 g.

International Chess Federation Congress, Graz. Air 5, 10, 30 g.

50th Anniv of Chaco Peace (2nd issue) and Government Achievements. Postage 10, 25, 50, 75 g.; Air 100, 200 g.

Paintings by Rubens. 25, 50 c., 1, 2, 3, 4, 5 g.

Explorers and their Ships. Air 5, 10, 30 g.

"Italia '85" International Stamp Exhibition, Rome (2nd issue). Paintings. Air 5, 10, 30 g.

1986

Paintings by Titian. 25, 50 c., 1, 2, 3, 4, 5 g.

International Stamp Fair, Essen. 1985 German Railways stamps optd. 25, 50 c., 1, 2, 3, 4 g.

Fungi. 25, 50 c., 1, 2, 3, 4, 5 g.

"Ameripex '86" International Stamp Exhibition, Chicago. Air 5, 10, 30 g.

Lawn Tennis (1st issue). Inscriptions in black or red. Air 5, 10, 30 g.

Centenary of Motor Car. 25, 50 c., 1, 2, 3, 4, 5 g.

Appearance of Halley's Comet. Air 5, 10, 30 g.

Qualification of Paraguay for World Cup Football Championship Final Rounds, Mexico (1st issue). 25, 50 c., 1, 2, 3, 4, 5 g.

Tenth Pan-American Games, Indianapolis (1987). 1985 Olympic Games Medal Winners stamp optd. 5 g.

Maybach Cars. 25, 50 c., 1, 2, 3, 4, 5 g.

Freight Trains. Air 5, 10, 30 g.

Qualification of Paraguay for World Cup Football Championship Final Rounds (2nd issue). Air 5, 10, 30 g.

Winter Olympic Games, Calgary (1988) (1st issue). 1983 Winter Olympic Games stamp optd. 5 g.

Centenary of Statue of Liberty. 25, 50 c., 1, 2, 3, 4, 5 g.

Dogs. 25, 50 c., 1, 2, 3, 4, 5 g.

150th Anniv of German Railways (2nd issue). Air 5, 10, 30 g.

Lawn Tennis (2nd issue). 25, 50 c., 1, 2, 3, 4, 5 g.

Visit of Prince Hitachi of Japan. 1972 Visit of President of Paraguay to Japan stamps optd. 10, 15, 20, 25, 30, 50, 75 c.

International Peace Year. Paintings by Rubens. Air 5, 10, 30 g.

Olympic Games, Seoul (1988) (1st issue). 25, 50 c., 1, 2, 3, 4, 5 g.

27th Chess Olympiad, Dubai. 1982 Chess Paintings stamp optd. Air 10 g.

1987

World Cup Football Championships, Mexico (1986) and Italy (1990). Air 5, 10, 20, 25, 30 g.

12th Spanish American Stamp and Coin Exhibition, Madrid, and 500th Anniv of Discovery of America by Columbus. 1975 South American Fauna and 1983 25th Anniv of I.M.O. stamps optd. Postage 15, 20, 25, 35, 40 g.; Air 10 g.

Tennis as Olympic Sport. 1986 Lawn Tennis (1st issue) stamps optd. Air 10, 30 g.

Olympic Games, Barcelona (1992). 1985 Olympic Games Medal Winners stamps optd. 25, 50 c., 1, 2, 3, 4 g.

"Olymphilex '87" Olympic Stamps Exhibition, Rome. 1985 Olympic Games Medal Winners stamp optd. 5 g.

Cats. 1, 2, 3, 5, 60 g.

Paintings by Rubens (1st issue). 1, 2, 3, 5, 60 g.

Saloon Cars. Air 5, 10, 20, 25, 30 g.

National Topics. Postage 10 g. (steel plant), 25 g. (Franciscan monk), 50 g. (400th anniv of Ita and Yaguaron), 75 g. (450th Anniv of Asuncion); Air 100 g. (airliner), 200 g. (Pres. Stroessner)

"Capex 87" International Stamp Exhibition, Toronto. Cats stamps optd. 1, 2, 3, 5 g.

500th Anniv of Discovery of America by Columbus. 1, 2, 3, 5, 60 g.

Winter Olympic Games, Calgary (1988) (2nd issue). Air 5, 10, 20, 25, 30 g.

Centenary of Colorado Party. National Topics and 1978 Pres. Stroessner stamps optd. Air 200, 1000 g.

750th Anniv of Berlin (1st issue) and "Luposta '87" Air Stamps Exhibition, Berlin. 1, 2, 3, 5, 60 g.

Olympic Games, Seoul (1988) (2nd issue). Air 5, 10, 20, 25, 30 g.

Rally Cars. 1, 2, 3, 5, 60 g.

"Exfivia 87" Stamp Exhibition, Bolivia. National Topics stamps optd. Postage 75 g.; Air 100 g.

"Olymphilex '88" Olympic Stamps Exhbition, Seoul. 1986 Olympic Games, Seoul (1st issue) stamps optd. 2, 3, 4, 5 g.

"Philatelia '87" International Stamp Exhibiton, Cologne. 1986 Lawn Tennis (2nd issue) stamps optd. 25, 50 c., 1, 2, 3, 4 g.

Italy–Argentina Match at Zurich to Launch 1990 World Cup Football Championship, Italy. 1986 Paraguay Qualification (2nd issue) stamps optd. Air 10, 30 g.

"Exfilna '87" Stamp Exhibition, Gerona. 1986 Olympic Games, Seoul (1st issue) stamps optd. 25, 50 c.

Spanish Ships. 1, 2, 3, 5, 60 g.

Paintings by Rubens (2nd issue). Air 5, 10, 20, 25, 30 g.

Christmas. Air 5, 10, 20, 25, 30 g.

Winter Olympic Games, Calgary (1988) (3rd issue). 1, 2, 3, 5, 60 g.

1988

150th Anniv of Austrian Railways. Air 5, 10, 20, 25, 30 g.

"Aeropex 88" Air Stamps Exhibition, Adelaide. 1987 750th Anniv of Berlin and "Luposta '87" stamps optd. 1, 2, 3, 5 g.

"Olympex" Stamp Exhibition, Calgary. 1987 Winter Olympic Games (3rd issue) stamps optd. 1, 2, 3 g.

Olympic Games, Seoul (3rd issue). Equestrian Events. 1, 2, 3, 5, 60 g.

Space Projects. Air 5, 10, 20, 25, 30 g.

750th Anniv of Berlin (2nd issue). Paintings. 1, 2, 3, 5, 60 g.

Visit of Pope John Paul II. 1, 2, 3, 5, 60 g.

"Lupo Wien 88" Stamp Exhibition, Vienna. 1987 National Topics stamp optd. Air 100 g.

World Wildlife Fund. Extinct Animals. 1, 2, 3, 5 g.

Paintings in West Berlin State Museum. Air 5, 10, 20, 25, 30 g.

Bicentenary of Australian Settlement. 1981 Wedding of Prince of Wales (1st issue) optd. 25, 50 c., 1, 2 g.

History of World Cup Football Championship (1st issue). Air 5, 10, 20, 25, 30 g.

New Presidential Period, 1988-1993. 1985 Chaco Peace and Government Achievements issue optd. Postage 10, 25, 50 75 g.; Air 100, 200 g.

Olympic Games, Seoul (4th issue). Lawn Tennis and Medal. 1, 2, 3, 5, 60 g.

Calgary Winter Olympics Gold Medal Winners. Air 5, 10, 20, 25, 30 g.

History of World Cup Football Championship (2nd issue). Air 5, 10, 20, 25, 30 g.

"Prenfil '88" International Philatelic Press Exhibition, Buenos Aires. "Ameripex '86" stamp optd. Air 30 g.

"Philexfrance 89" International Stamp Exhibition, Paris. 1985 Explorers stamp optd. Air 30 g.

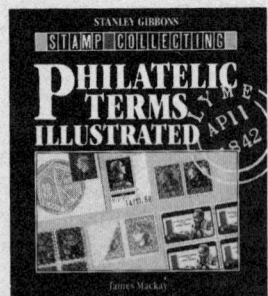

PARMA Pt. 8

A former Grand Duchy of N. Italy, united with Sardinia in 1860 and now part of Italy.

100 centesimi = 1 lira.

1. Bourbon "fleur-de-lis". 2. 3.

1852. Imperf.
1. 1. 5 c. black on yellow 38·00 65·00
11. 5 c. yellow £2750 £500
4. 10 c. black 38·00 65·00
6. 15 c. black on red £950 22·00
13. 15 c. red £3500 70·00
7. 25 c. black on purple £5500 90·00
14. 25 c. brown £6500 £150
9. 40 c. black on blue £950 £160

1857. Imperf.
17. 2. 15 c. red £100 £300
19. 25 c. purple £180 80·00
20. 40 c. blue 25·00 £300

1859. Imperf.
28. 3. 5 c. green £850 £2750
30. 10 c. brown £200 £375
31. 20 c. blue £400 £150
33. 40 c. red £300 £5500
35. 80 c. yellow £3250

NEWSPAPER STAMPS

1853. As T 3. Imperf.
N 1. 3. 6 c. black on red £170 £200
N 3. 9 c. black on blue 80·00 £16000

PERU Pt. 20

A republic on the N.W. coast of S. America independent since 1821.

1857. 8 reales = 1 peso.
1858. 100 centavos = 10 dineros = 5 pesetas = 1 peso.
1874. 100 centavos = 1 sol.
1985. 100 centimos = 1 inti.
1991. 100 centimos = 1 sol.

7. 8. 10. Vicuna.

1858. T 7 and similar designs with flags below arms. Imperf.
8. 7. 1 d. blue 75·00 5·00
13. 1 peseta red £100 19·00
5. ½ peso yellow £1300 £225

1862. Various frames. Imperf.
14. 8. 1 d. red 10·00 2·00
20. 1 d. green 8·25 1·75
16. 1 peseta, brown 55·00 17·00
22. 1 peseta, yellow 70·00 21·00

1866. Various frames. Perf.
17. 10. 5 c. green 5·00 60
18. – 10 c. red 5·00 1·10
19. – 20 c. brown 17·00 3·25
See also No. 316.

13. 14.

1871. 20th Anniv. of First Railway in Peru (Lima–Chorillos–Callao). Imperf.
21a. 13. 5 c. red £110 24·00

1873. Roul. by imperf.
23. 14. 2 c. blue 25·00 £200

15. Sun-god. 16.

20. 21.

1874. Various frames. Perf.
24 15 1 c. orange 40 40
25a 16 2 c. violet 40 40
26 5 c. blue 50 25
27 10 c. green 15 15
28 20 c. red 1·60 40
29 20 50 c. green 7·50 2·10
30 21 1 s. pink 1·25 1·25
For further stamps in these types, see Nos. 278, 279/84 and 314/5.

(24.) (27.) Arms of Chile.

1880. Optd. with T 24.
36. 15. 1 c. green 40 40
37. 16. 2 c. red 85 45
39. 5 c. blue 1·60 70
40. 20. 50 c. green 23·00 14·50
41. 21. 1 s. red 60·00 38·00

1881. Optd. as T 24. but inscr. "LIMA" at foot instead of "PERU".
42. 15. 1 c. green 60 30
43. 16. 2 c. red 11·50 7·50
44. 5 c. blue 1·25 45
286. 10 c. green 40 50
45. 20. 50 c. green £375 £200
46. 21. 1 s. red 70·00 45·00

1881. Optd. with T 27.
57. 15. 1 c. orange 30 85
58. 16. 2 c. violet 30 3·25
59. 2 c. red 1·40 15·00
60. 5 c. blue 45·00 50·00
61. 10 c. green 30 1·50
62. 20 c. red 65·00 £100

(28.) (28a.)

1882. Optd. with T 27 and 28.
63. 15. 1 c. green 45 65
64. 16. 5 c. blue 45 65
66. 20. 50 c. red 1·40 1·60
67. 21. 1 s. blue 2·75 3·75

1883. Optd. with T 28 only.
200. 15. 1 c. green 1·00 1·00
201. 16. 2 c. red 1·00 3·25
202. 5 c. blue 1·60 1·60
203. 20. 50 c. pink 48·00
204. 21. 1 s. blue 25·00

1883. Handstamped with T 28a only.
206. 15. 1 c. orange 65 65
210. 16. 5 c. blue 6·25 4·25
211. 10 c. green 65 65
216. 20. 50 c. green 5·75 3·00
220. 21. 1 s. red 8·25 5·00

1883. Optd. with T 24 and 28a, the inscription in oval reading "PERU".
223. 20. 50 c. green £100 50·00
225. 21. 1 s. red £120 75·00

1883. Optd with T 24 and 28a, the inscription in oval reading "LIMA".
227. 15. 1 c. green 3·25 3·25
229. 16. 2 c. red 3·25 3·25
232. 5 c. blue 5·50 5·00
234. 20. 50 c. green £120 75·00
236. 21. 1 s. red £130 £100

1883. Optd. with T 28 and 28a.
238. 15. 1 c. green 85 65
241. 16. 2 c red 85 60
246. 5 c. blue 1·00 65

1884. Optd. CORREOS LIMA and sun.
277. 16. 5 c. blue 35 25

1886. Re-issue of 1866 and 1874 types.
278. 15. 1 c. violet 25 20
314. 1 c. red 30 20
279. 16. 2 c. green 60 10
315. 2 c. blue 25 20
280. 5 c. orange 30 10
316. 10. 5 c. lake 1·00 35
281. 16. 10 c. black 12 8
317. – 10 c. orange (Llamas) 35 25
282. 16. 20 c. blue 4·25 35
318. – 20 c. blue (Llamas) 5·00 1·10
283. 20. 50 c. red 1·25 35
284. 21. 1 s. brown 1·00 35

(71. Pres. R. M. Bermudez.) 73.

1894. Optd. with T 71.
294 15. 1 c. orange 50 25
295 1 c. green 20 20
296c 16. 2 c. violet 15 15
297 2 c. red 25 20
298 5 c. blue 2·10 1·50
299 10 c. green 25 20
300 20. 50 c. green 1·10 1·00

1894. Optd. with T 28 and 71.
301. 16. 2 c. red 20 20
302. 5 c. blue 85 30
303. 20. 50 c. red 35·00 25·00
304. 21. 1 s. blue 85·00 75·00

1895. Installation of Pres. Nicolas de Pierola.
328. 73. 1 c. violet 1·00 75
329. 2 c. green 1·00 75
330. 5 c. yellow 1·00 75
331. 10 c. blue 1·00 75
332. – 20 c. orange 1·00 80
333. – 50 c. blue 6·00 3·75
334. – 1 s. lake 32·00 21·00
Nos. 332/4 are larger (30×36 mm.) and the central device is in a frame of laurel.
See also Nos. 352/4.

75. Atahualpa. 76. Pizarro.

77. General de la Mar.

1896.
335 75. 1 c. blue 25 15
336 1 c. green 25 5
337 2 c. blue 20 15
338 2 c. red 20 5
341 76. 5 c. blue 60 5
340 5 c. green 60 5
342 10 c. yellow 85 20
343 10 c. black 85 10
344 20 c. orange 1·60 25
345 77. 50 c. red 4·25 50
346 1 s. red 6·25 85
347 2 s. lake 1·90 65

1897. No. D 31 optd. FRANQUEO.
348. D 22. 1 c. brown 25 25

82. Suspension Bridge at Paucartambo. 83. Pres. D. Nicolas de Pierola.

1897. Opening of New Postal Building. Dated "1897".
349. 82. 1 c. blue 40 30
350. – 2 c. brown 40 25
351. 83. 5 c. red 85 30
DESIGN: 2 c. G.P.O. Lima.

1899. As Nos. 328/34, but vert. inscr. replaced by pearl ornaments.
352. 73. 22 c. green 30 15
353. – 5 s. red 1·40 1·40
354. – 10 s. green £350 £275

84. President Eduardo Lopez de Romana. 85. Admiral Grau.

1900.
357. 84. 22 c. black and green 6·75 70

1901. Advent of the Twentieth Cent.
358. 85. 1 c. black and green 70 25
359. – 2 c. black and red 70 25
360. – 5 c. black and lilac 1·00 25
PORTRAITS: 2 c. Col. Bolognesi. 5 c. Pres. Romana.

90. Municipal Board of Health Building.

1905.
361. 90. 12 c. black and blue 70 25

1907. Surch.
362. 90. 1 c. on 12 c. blk. & blue 25 20
363. 2 c. on 12 c. blk. & blue 50 35

97. Bolognesi Monument. 98. Admiral Grau.

99. Llama. 101. Exhibition Buildings.

103. G.P.O., Lima. 107. Columbus.

1907.
364. 97. 1 c. black and green 25 12
365. 98. 2 c. purple and red 25 12
366. 99. 4 c. olive 4·50 60
367. – 5 c. black and blue 40 10
368. 101. 10 c. black and brown 1·00 25
369. – 20 c. black and green 19·00 50
370. 103. 50 c. black 19·00 70
371. – 1 s. green and violet £100 2·10
372. – 2 s. black and blue £100 85·00
DESIGNS—VERT. As Type 98: 5 c. Statue of Bolivar. (24×33 mm.): 2 c. Columbus Monument. HORIZ. As Type 101: 20 c. Medical School, Lima. (33×24 mm.): 1 s. Grandstand, Santa Beatrice Race-course, Lima.

1909. Portraits.
373. – 1 c. grey (Manco Capac) 15 12
374. 107. 2 c. green 15 12
375. – 4 c. red (Pizarro) 40 15
376. – 5 c. purple (San Martin) 15 8
377. – 10 c. blue (Bolivar) 55 15
378. – 12 c. blue (de la Mar) 85 25
379. – 20 c. brown (Castilla) 90 40
380. – 50 c. orange (Grau) 4·25 30
381. – 1 s. black and lake (Bolognesi) 8·25 30
See also Nos. 406/13, 431/5, 439/40 and 484/9.

1913. Surch **UNION POSTAL 8 Cts. Sud Americana** in oval.
382 90 8 c. on 12 c. black & blue 55 20

1915. As 1896, 1905 and 1907, surch. **1915,** and value.
383. 75. 1 c. on 1 c. green 13·50 10·00
384. 97. 1 c. on 1 c. black & green 70 50
385. 98. 1 c. on 2 c. purple & red 1·00 85
386. 76. 1 c. on 10 c. black 85 60
387. 99. 1 c. on 4 c. green 1·60 1·40
388. 101. 1 c. on 10 c. blk. & brn. 35 20
389. 2 c. on 10 c. blk. & brn. 85·00 65·00
390. 90. 2 c. on 12 c. blk. & blue 25 15
391. – 2 c. on 20 c. black and green (No. 369) 11·50 10·00
392. 103. 2 c. on 50 c. black 1·60 1·60

1916. Surch. **VALE,** value and **1916.**
393. 1 c. on 12 c. blue (378) 15 12
394. 1 c. on 20 c. brown (379) 15 12
395. 1 c. on 50 c. orange (380) 15 12
396. 2 c. on 4 c. red (375) 15 12
397. 10 c. on 1 s. blk. & lake (381) 40 25

1916. Official stamps of 1909 optd. **FRANQUEO 1916** or surch. **VALE 2 Cts** also.
398. O 108. 1 c. red 12 12
399. 2 c. on 50 c. olive 15 15
400. 10 c. brown 20 12

1916. Postage Due stamps of 1909 surch. **FRANQUEO VALE 2 Cts. 1916.**
401. D 109. 2 c. on 1 c. brown 40 40
402. 2 c. on 5 c. brown 12 12
403. 2 c. on 10 c. brown 12 12
404. 2 c. on 50 c. brown 12 12

1917. Surch. **Un Centavo.**
405. 1 c. on 4 c. (No. (375) 20 15

1918. Portraits as T **107.**
406. 1 c. blk. & orge. (San Martin) 10 5
407. 2 c. blk. & green (Bolivar) 12 5
408. 4 c. blk. & red (Galvez) 25 8
409. 5 c. blk. & blue (Pardo) 15 5
410. 8 c. blk. & brown (Grau) 50 25
411. 10 c. blk. & blue (Bolognesi) 35 5
412. 12 c. blk. & lilac (Castilla) 70 15
413. 20 c. blk. & green (Caceres) 85 15

MINIMUM PRICE

The minimum price quoted is 5p which represents a handling charge rather than a basis for valuing common stamps. For further notes about prices see introductory pages.

126. Columbus at Salamanca University. 129. A. B. Leguia.

1918.
414 126 50 c. black and brown 4·25 35
415a – 1 s. black and green 10·00 50
416 – 2 s. black and blue . 18·00 55
DESIGNS: 1 s. Funeral of Atahualpa. 2 s. Battle of Arica.

1920. New Constitution.
417. 129. 5 c. black and blue .. 15 15
418. 5 c. black and brown .. 15 15

130. San Martin. 131. Oath of Independence.

132. Admiral Cochrane. 137. J. Olaya.

1921. Cent. of Independence.
419. 130. 1 c. brown (San Martin) 25 12
420. 2 c. green (Arenales) .. 25 15
421. 4 c. red (Las Heras) .. 85 50
422. 131. 5 c. brown 35 12
423. 132. 7 c. violet 70 35
424. 130. 10 c. blue (Guisse) .. 70 35
425. 12 c. black (Vidal) .. 2·00 40
426. 20 c. blk. & red (Leguia) 2·00 70
427. 50 c. violet and purple (S. Martin Monument) 6·00 2·00
428. 131. 1 s. green and red (San Martin and Leguia).. 10·00 3·00

1923. Surch. **CINCO Centavos 1923.**
429 5 c. on 8 c. black and brown (No. 410) .. 40 20

1924. Surch. **CUATRO Centavos 1924.**
430. 4 c. on 5 c. (No. 409) .. 25 15

1924. Portraits as T 107. Size 18½×23 mm.
431. 2 c. olive (Rivadeneyra) .. 10 5
432. 4 c. green (Melgar) .. 10 5
433. 8 c. black (Iturregui) .. 1·60 1·60
434. 10 c. red (A. B. Leguia) .. 15 5
435. 15 c. blue (De la Mar) .. 50 15
439. 1 s. brown (De Saco) .. 7·50 85
440. 2 s. blue (J. Leguia) .. 19·00 4·25

1924. Monuments.
436. 137. 20 c. blue 70 10
437. 20 c. yellow .. .. 1·25 15
438. – 50 c. purple (Bellido).. 4·25 35
See also Nos. 484/9.

139. Simon Bolivar. 140.

1924. Centenary of Battle of Ayacucho. Portraits of Bolivar.
441. – 2 c. olive 35 10
442. 139. 4 c. green 40 10
443. 5 c. black 85 10
444. 140. 10 c. red 40 10
445. – 20 c. blue 85 15
446. – 50 c. lilac .. .. 3·00 50
447. – 1 s. brown .. .. 8·25 2·00
448. – 2 s. blue .. .. 17·00 8·25

1925. Surch. **DOS Centavos 1925.**
449. 137. 2 c. on 20 c. blue .. 85 50

1925. Optd. **Plebiscito.**
450. 10 c. red (No. 434) .. 70 70

143. The Rock of Arica. 146.

1925. Obligatory Tax. Tacna-Arica Plebiscite.
451. 143. 2 c. orange 25 10
452. 5 c. blue.. .. .. 1·25 50
453. 5 c. red.. .. .. 65 40
454. 5 c. green 60 40
455. – 10 c. brown .. .. 2·50 85
456. – 50 c. green .. .. 16·00 7·50
DESIGNS—HORIZ. (39×30 mm.): 10 c. Soldiers with colours. VERT. (27×33 mm.): 50 c. Bolognesi Statue.

1927. Obligatory Tax. Figures of value not encircled.
457. 146. 2 c. orange 50 15
458. 2 c. brown 50 15
459. 2 c. blue.. .. .. 50 15
460. 2 c. violet 35 15
461. 2 c. green 35 15
462. 20 c. red .. .. 2·10 85

1927. Air. Optd **Servicio Aereo.**
463 9 50 c. purple (No. 438) .. 35·00 25·00

148. Pres. A. B. Leguia. 149. Rock of Arica.

1928. Air.
464. 148. 50 c. green 70 35

1928. Obligatory Tax. Plebiscite Fund.
465. 149. 2 c. mauve 15 10

1929. Surch. **Habilitada 2 Cts. 1929.**
466. – 2 c. on 8 c. (No. 410) .. 50 50
468. 137. 15 c. on 20 c. (No. 437) 70 70

1929. Surch. **Habilitada 2 centavos 1929.**
467. 2 c. on 8 c. (No. 410) .. 70 70

1930. Optd. **Habilitada Franqueo.**
469. 149. 2 c. mauve 30 30

1930. Surch. **Habilitada 2 Cts. 1930.**
470. 137. 2 c. on 20 c. yellow .. 25 25

1930. Surch. **Habilitada Franqueo 2 Cts. 1930.**
471. 148. 2 c. on 50 c. green .. 25 25

156. Arms of Peru. 157. Lima Cathedral.

1930. Sixth (inscribed "seventh") Pan-American Child Congress.
472. 156. 2 c. green 60 55
473. 157. 5 c. red .. .. 1·40 1·00
474. – 10 c. blue 90 85
475. – 50 c. brown .. .. 15·00 10·00
DESIGNS—HORIZ. 10 c. G.P.O., Lima. VERT. 50 c. Madonna and Child.

1930. Fall of Leguia Govt. No. 434 optd. with Arms of Peru or surch. with new value in four corners also.
477. 2 c. on 10 c. red 5 5
478. 4 c. on 10 c. red 20 20
479. 10 c. red 12 5
476. 15 c. on 10 c. red.. .. 20 15

159. Simon Bolivar. 161. Pizarro.

162. The Old Stone Bridge, Lima.

1930. Bolivar's Death Cent.
480. 159. 2 c. brown 35 20
481. 4 c. red 70 30
482. 10 c. green 35 25
483. 15 c. grey 70 50

1930. As T 107 and 137 but smaller (18×22 mm.).
484. – 2 c. olive (Rivadeneyra) 15 5
485. – 4 c. green (Melgar) .. 15 5
486. – 15 c. blue (De la Mar).. 50 8
487. 137. 20 c. yellow (Olaya) .. 1·00 20
488. – 50 c. purple (Bellido) .. 1·00 25
489. – 1 s. brown (De Saco) .. 1·60 35

1931. Obligatory Tax. Unemployment Fund. Surch. **Habilitada Pro Desocupados 2 Cts.**
490. 159. 2 c. on 4 c. red.. .. 70 35
491. 2 c. on 10 c. green .. 50 35
492. 2 c. on 15 c. grey .. 50 35

1931. 1st Peruvian Philatelic Exn.
493. 161. 2 c. slate .. .. 1·40 1·10
494. 4 c. brown .. .. 1·40 1·10
495. 162. 10 c. red .. .. 1·40 1·10
496. 10 c. green and mauve.. 1·40 1·10
497. 161. 15 c. green .. .. 1·40 1·10
498. 162. 15 c. red and grey .. 1·40 1·10
499. 15 c. blue and orange .. 1·40 1·10

163. Manco Capac. 164. Oil Well. 170.

1931.
500. 163. 2 c. olive 20 10
501. 164. 4 c. green 40 30
502. – 10 c. orange 85 10
503. – 15 c. blue .. .. 1·25 25
504. – 20 c. yellow .. .. 4·25 40
505. – 50 c. lilac .. .. 5·00 40
506. – 1 s. brown .. .. 11·00 85
DESIGNS—VERT. 10 c. Sugar Plantation. 15 c. Cotton Plantation. 50 c. Copper Mines. 1 s. Llamas. HORIZ. 20 c. Guano Islands.

1931. Obligatory Tax. Unemployment Fund.
507. 170. 2 c. green 8 5
508. 2 c. red 8 5

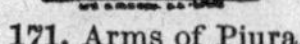

171. Arms of Piura. 172. Parakas.

1932. 4th Cent. of Piura.
509. 171. 10 c. blue (postage) .. 5·00 5·00
510. 15 c. violet .. .. 5·00 5·00
511. 50 c. red (air) .. .. 17·00 16·00

1932. 400th Anniv of Spanish Conquest of Peru. Native designs.
512. 172. 10 c. pur. (22×19½ mm.) 15 10
513. – 15 c. lake (25×19½ mm.) 35 10
514. – 50 c. brn. (19½×22 mm.) 75 15
DESIGNS: 15 c. Chimu. 50 c. Inca.

175. Arequipa and El Misti. 176. Pres. Sanchez Cerro.

1932. 1st Anniv. of Constitutional Govt.
515. 175. 2 c. blue 12 5
527. 2 c. black 15 5
528. 2 c. green 15 5
516. 4 c. brown 12 5
529. 4 c. orange 12 5
517. 176. 10 c. red .. .. 11·00 8·25
530. – 10 c. red 50 5
518. – 15 c. blue 35 5
531. – 15 c. mauve 35 10
519. – 20 c. lake 50 10
532. – 20 c. violet 50 15
520. – 50 c. green 70 15
521. – 1 s. orange .. .. 5·00 35
533. – 1 s. brown .. .. 6·25 40
DESIGNS—VERT. 10 c. (No. 530), Statue of Liberty. 15 c. to 1s. Bolivar Monument, Lima.

178. Blacksmith. 179. Monument of 2nd May to Battle of Callao.

1932. Obligatory Tax. Unemployment Fund.
522. 178. 2 c. grey 8 5
523. 2 c. violet 8 5

1933. Obligatory Tax. Unemployment Fund.
524. 179. 2 c. violet 12 5
525. 2 c. orange 12 5
526. 2 c. purple 12 5

181. Fairey Fighter. 184. F. Pizarro.

186. The Inca. 185. Coronation of Huascar.

1934. Air.
534. 181. 2 s. blue .. .. 4·50 35
535. 5 s. brown .. .. 9·50 70

1934. Obligatory Tax. Unemployment Fund. Optd. **Pro-Desocupados.** (a) In one line.
536. 176. 2 c. green 8 5
585. – 2 c. purple (No. 537) .. 8 5
(b) In two lines.
566. – 2 c. purple (No. 537) 8 5

1934.
537. – 2 c. purple 10 5
538. – 4 c. green 12 8
539. 184. 10 c. red 15 5
540. 15 c. blue 50 5
541. 185. 20 c. blue .. .. 1·00 12
542. 50 c. brown .. .. 1·00 12
543. 186. 1 s. violet .. .. 2·40 35
DESIGN: 2 c., 4 c. show the scene depicted in Type 189.

187. Lake of the Marvellous Cure. 188. Grapes.

1935. Tercent. of Founding of Ica.
544. – 4 c. black 65 65
545. 187. 5 c. red 25 65
546. 188. 10 c. mauve .. .. 2·75 1·40
547. 187. 20 c. green .. .. 1·00 1·00
548. – 35 c. red .. .. 5·50 3·25
549. – 50 c. brown & orange 3·75 3·25
550. – 1 s. red and violet .. 11·00 8·25
DESIGNS—HORIZ. 4 c. City of Ica. 50 c. Don Diego Lopez and King Philip IV of Spain. VERT. 35 c. Cotton blossom. 1 s. Supreme God of the Nazcas.

189. Pizarro and "The Thirteen".

192. Funeral of Atahualpa.

1935. 4th Cent. of Founding of Lima.
551. 189. 2 c. brown (postage) .. 35 20
552. – 4 c. violet 50 35
553. – 10 c. red 50 20
554. – 15 c. blue 85 40
555. 189. 20 c. grey .. .. 1·10 50
556. – 50 c. green .. .. 1·60 1·25
557. – 1 s. blue .. .. 3·75 2·40
558. – 2 s. brown .. .. 8·75 6·75
DESIGNS—HORIZ. 4 c. Lima Cathedral. VERT. 10 c., 50 c. Miss L. S. de Canevaro. 15 c., 2 s. Pizarro. 1 s. The "Tapada" (a veiled woman).

559. 192. 5 c. green (air) 35 20
560. – 35 c. brown 75 35
561. – 50 c. yellow .. .. 1·25 70
562. – 1 s. purple .. .. 1·75 75
563. – 2 s. orange .. .. 1·50 1·50
564. 192. 5 s. purple .. .. 6·25 4·25
565. 189. 10 s. blue .. .. 23·00 19·00
DESIGNS—HORIZ. 35 c. Aeroplane near San Cristobal Hill. 50 c., 1 s. Aeroplane over Avenue of Barefoot Friars. VERT. 2 s. Palace of Torre Tagle.

207. "San Cristobal" (caravel).

1936. Callao Cent.
567. 207. 2 c. black (postage) .. 90 20
568. – 4 c. green 45 15
569. – 5 c. brown 45 12
570. – 10 c. blue 45 20
571. – 15 c. green .. .. 1·40 25
572. – 20 c. brown 45 25
573. – 50 c. lilac 90 45
574. – 1 s. olive .. .. 18·00 1·60
575. – 2 s. purple .. .. 11·00 5·00
576. – 5 s. red .. .. .. 15·00 11·50
577. – 10 s. brown and red .. 38·00 29·00
578. – 35 c. slate (air) .. 2·10 2·10
DESIGNS—HORIZ. 4 c. La Punta Naval College. 5 c. Independence Square, Callao. 10 c. Aerial view of Callao. 15 c. "Reina del Pacifico" (liner) in Callao Docks and Custom House. 20 c. Plan of Callao, 1746. 35 c. "La Callao" (early locomotive). 1 s. Gunboat "Sacramento". 10 s. Real Felipe Fortifications. VERT. 50 c. D. Jose de la Mar. 2 s. Don Jose de Velasco. 5 s. Fort Maipo and miniature portraits of Galvez and Nunez.

1936. Obligatory Tax. St. Rosa de Lima Cathedral Construction Fund. Optd **"Ley 8310"**.
579.179. 2 c. purple 8 5

1936. Surch. **Habilitado** and value in figures and words.
580. – 2 c. on 4 c. green (No. 538) (postage) .. 10 10
581.185. 10 c. on 20 c. blue .. 15 15
582.186. 10 c. on 1 s. violet .. 20 20
583.181. 5 c. on 2 s. blue (air) .. 35 15
584. 25 c. on 5 s. brown .. 70 25

211. Guanay Cormorants. 217. Mail Steamer "Inca" on Lake Titicaca.

1936.
586 211 2 c. brown (postage) .. 1·50 15
616 2 c. green .. .. 1·25 15
587 – 4 c. brown 50 25
617 – 4 c. black 25 12
618 – 10 c. red 10 5
619 – 15 c. blue 20 8
590 – 20 c. black 70 15
620 – 20 c. brown 25 12
591 – 50 c. yellow .. .. 2·10 50
621 – 50 c. grey 70 15
592 – 1 s. purple .. .. 4·25 70
622 – 1 s. blue .. .. 1·40 35
593 – 2 s blue .. .. 9·00 2·00
623 – 2 s.violet .. .. 3·00 35
594 – 5 s. blue .. .. 9·00 3·00
595 – 10 s. brown and violet 50·00 19·00
DESIGNS—VERT. 4 c. Oil well. **10 c. Inca postal runner. 1 s. G.P.O., Lima. 2 s. M. de Amat y Junyent. 5 s. J. A. de Pando y Riva. 10 s. J. D. Condemarin. HORIZ. 15 c. Paseo de la Republica, Lima. 20 c. Municipal Palace and Natural History Museum. 50 c. University of San Marcos, Lima.**
See also Nos. 616/23.

596 – 5 c. green (air) .. 25 10
625 217 15 c. blue 70 15
598 – 20 c. grey 90 15
626 – 20 c. green 85 15
627 – 25 c. red 40 10
628 – 30 c. brown 80 15
600 – 35 c. brown .. .. 1·60 1·40
601 – 50 c. yellow 25 35
629 – 50 c. red 40 20
630 – 70 c. green .. .. 1·25 50
603 – 80 c. black .. .. 5·00 3·00
631 – 80 c. green .. .. 1·25 30
604 – 1 s. blue .. .. 9·50 1·50
632 – 1 s. brown .. .. 4·25 40
605 – 1 s. 50 brown .. .. 8·00 5·50
633 – 1 s. 50 orange .. .. 5·50 40
606 – 2 s. blue .. .. 15·00 6·50
634 – 2 s. green .. .. 11·00 70
607 – 5 s. green .. .. 20·00 3·25
608 – 10 s. brown and red .. 85·00 65·00
DESIGNS—HORIZ. 5 c. La Mar Park. 20 c. Native recorder player and llama. 30 c. Chuquibambilla ram. 25, 35 c. J. Chavez. 50 c. Mining Area. 70 c. Aeroplane over La Punta . 1 s. Steam train at La Cima. 1 s. 50, Aerodrome at Las Palmas, Lima. 2 s. Mail plane. 5 s. Valley of R. Inambari. VERT. 80 c. Infiernillo Canyon, Andes. 10 s. St. Rosa de Lima.

223. St. Rosa de Lima.

1937. Obligatory Tax. St. Rosa de Lima Construction Fund.
609.223. 2 c. red 12 5

1937. Surch. **Habilit.** and value in figures and words. (a) Postage.
610 1 s. on 2 s. blue (593) .. 2·10 2·10
(b) Air.
611 15 c. on 30 c. brown (599) 45 40
612 15 c. on 35 c. brown (600) 45 25
613 15 c. on 70 c. green (630) .. 2·75 2·25
614 25 c. on 80 c. black (603) .. 2·75 2·25
615 1 s. on 2 s. blue (606) .. 4·25 3·00

225. Bielovucic over Lima. 226. Jorge Chavez.

1937. Air. Pan-American Aviation Conf.
635. 225. 10 c. violet 40 10
636. 226. 15 c. green 50 10
637. – 25 c. brown 40 10
638. – 1 s. black .. .. 1·90 1·00
DESIGNS—As T 225. 25 c. Limatambo Airport. 1 s. Peruvian air routes.

229. "Protection" (by John Q. A. Ward). 230. Children's Holiday Camp.

1938. Obligatory Tax. Unemployment Fund
757c 229 2c. brown 5 5

1938. Designs as T **230**.
693 230 2 c. green 5 5
694 – 4 c. brown 5 5
642 – 10 c. red 20 5
696 – 15 c. blue 8 5
727 – 15 c. turquoise 5 5
644 – 20 c. purple 12 5
740 – 20 c. violet 8 5
698 – 50 c. blue 15 5
741 – 50 c. brown 12 5
699 – 1 s. purple 85 10
742 – 1 s. brown 25 8
700 – 2 s. green .. .. 2·50 10
731 – 2 s. blue 55 10
701 – 5 s. brown and violet 5·75 35
732 – 5 s. purple and blue .. 75 35
702 – 10 s. blue and black .. 10·00 50
733 – 10 s. black and green 2·50 70
DESIGNS—VERT. 4 c. Chavin pottery. 10 c. Automobile roads in Andes. 20 c. (2) Industrial Bank of Peru. 1 s. (2) Portrait of Toribio de Luzuriaga. 5 s. (2) Chavin Idol. HORIZ. 15 c. (2) Archaeological Museum, Lima. 50 c. (2) Labourers' homes at Lima. 2 s. (2) Fig Tree. 10 s. (2) Mt. Huascaran.

240. Monument on Junin Plains. 248. Seal of City of Lima.

1938. Air. As T **240**.
650 – 5 c. brown 15 10
743 – 5 c. green 10 10
651 240 15 c. brown 15 10
652 – 20 c. red 40 10
653 – 25 c. green 20 10
654 – 30 c. orange 20 10
735 – 30 c. red 12 10
655 – 50 c. green 35 30
736 – 70 c. blue .. .. 1·10 10
657 – 80 c. green 60 10
737 – 80 c. red 55 15
658 – 1 s. green .. .. 4·50 2·10
705 – 1 s. 50 violet 45 35
738 – 1 s. 50 purple .. 45 30
660 – 2 s. red and blue .. 1·60 50
661 – 5 s. purple .. .. 8·25 70
662 – 10 s. blue and green .. 32·00 20·00

DESIGNS—VERT. 20 c. Rear-Admiral M. Villar. 70 c. Infiernillo Canyon. 2 s. Stele from Chavin Temple. HORIZ. 5 c. People's restaurant, Callao. 25 c. View of Tarma. 30 c. Ica River irrigation system. 50 c. Port of Iquitos. 80 c. Mountain roadway. 1 s. Plaza San Martin, Lima. 1 s. 50, Nat. Radio Station, San Miguel. 5 s. Ministry of Public Works. 10 s. Heroe's Crypt, Lima.

1938. 8th Pan-American Congress, Lima.
663. – 10 c. grey (postage) .. 50 20
664.248. 15 c. gold, bl.,red & blk. 85 25
665. – 1 s. brown .. .. 1·60 85
DESIGNS (39×32½ mm.): 10 c. Palace and Square, 1864. 1 s. Palace, 1938.
666. – 25 c. blue (air) .. 55 50
667. – 1 s. 50 lake .. 1·50 1·25
668. – 2 s. black 90 45
DESIGNS—VERT. (26×37 mm.): 25 c. Torre Tagle Palace. HORIZ. (39×32½ mm.): 1 s. 50, National Congress Building, Lima. 2 s. Congress Presidents, Ferreyros, Paz Soldan and Arenas.

1940. No. 642 surch. **Habilitada 5 cts.**
669. 5 c. on 10 c. red 12 5

251. National Broadcasting Station.

1941. Optd. **FRANQUEO POSTAL.**
670.251. 50 c. yellow .. .. 1·60 15
671. 1 s. violet .. .. 1·60 20
672. 2 s. green .. .. 3·25 50
673. 5 s. brown .. .. 19·00 5·50
674. 10 s. mauve .. .. 29·00 4·25

1942. Air. No. 653 surch **Habilit 0.15.**
675 15 c. on 25 c. green .. 85 10

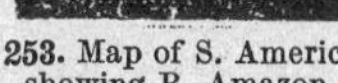

253. Map of S. America showing R. Amazon. 254. Francisco de Orellana.

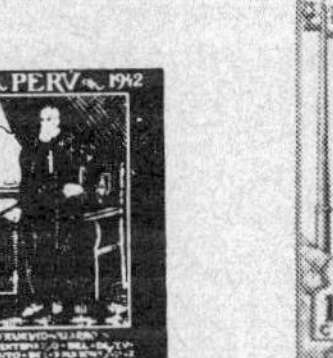

255. Francisco Pizarro. 257. Samuel Morse.

1943. 400th Anniv. of Discovery of R. Amazon.
676. – 2 c. red 8 5
677. 254. 4 c. grey 15 5
678. 255. 10 c. brown 20 8
679. 253. 15 c. blue 50 20
680. – 20 c. olive 20 12
681. – 25 c. orange .. .. 1·40 35
682. 254. 30 c. red 35 20
683. 253. 50 c. green 35 40
685. – 70 c. violet .. .. 2·00 70
686. – 80 c. blue .. .. 2·00 70
687. – 1 s. brown .. .. 3·25 70
688. 255. 5 s. black .. .. 6·75 3·25
DESIGNS. As Type **254**: 2 c., 70 c. Portraits of G. Pizarro and Orellana in medallion. 20 c., 80 c. G. Pizarro. As Type **253**: 25 c., 1 s. Orellana's Discovery of the R. Amazon.

1943. Surch. with Arms of Peru (as Nos. 483, etc) above **10 CTVS.**
689. 10 c. on 10 c. red (No. 642) 12 5

1944. Cent. of Invention of Telegraphy.
691. 257. 15 c. blue 15 12
692. 30 c. brown 50 20

1946. Surch. **Habilitada S/o 0.20.**
706. 20 c. on 1 s. purple (No 699) 25 10

259.

DESIGNS —VERT. 1 s. Mountain road. 1 s. 35, Forest road. HORIZ. 5s. Road and house.

261.

1947. 1st National Tourist Congress, Lima. Unissued designs inscr. "V Congreso Pan Americano de Carretas 1944" optd. **Habilitada I Congreso Nac. de Turismo Lima—1947.**
707. 259. 15 c. black and red .. 25 15
708. – 1 s. brown 35 20
709. – 1 s. 35 green 35 25
710. 261. 3 s. blue 85 50
711. – 5 s. green .. .. 1·75 1·25

1947. Air. 1st Peruvian Int. Airways Lima-New York Flight. Optd. with **PIA** badge and **PRIMER VUELO LIMA—NUEVA YORK.**
712. 5 c. brown (No. 650) .. 10 8
713. 50 c. green (No. 655) .. 15 10

263. Basketball Players.

1948. Air. Olympic Games.
714. – 1 s. blue .. .. 1·25 1·25
715. 263. 2 s. brown .. .. 1·60 1·60
716. – 5 s. green .. .. 2·75 2·75
717. – 10 s. yellow .. .. 3·25 3·25
No. 714 is inscr. "AEREO" and Nos. 715/7 are optd. **AEREO.**
DESIGNS: 1 s. Map showing air route from Peru to Great Britain. 5 s. Discus thrower. 10 s. Rifleman.
The above stamps exist overprinted **MELBOURNE 1956** but were only valid for postage on one day.

1948. Air. Nos. 653, 736 and 657 surch **Habilitada S/o.** and value.
722 5 c. on 25 c. green .. 10 10
723 10 c. on 25 c. green .. 10 10
718 10 c. on 70 c. blue .. 15 15
719 15 c. on 70 c. blue .. 15 15
720 20 c. on 70 c. blue .. 15 15
724 30 c. on 80 c. green .. 55 15
721 55 c. on 70 c. blue .. 15 15

263a. 263b.

1949. Anti-Tuberculosis Fund. Surch. **Decreto Ley No. 18** and value.
724a. 263a. 3 c. on 4 c. blue .. 55 5
724b. 263b. 3 c. in 10 c. blue .. 55 5

264. Statue of Admiral Grau. 264a. "Education".

1949.
726. 264. 10 c. blue and green .. 8 5

1950. Obligatory Tax. National Education Fund.
851 264a. 3 c. lake (16½×21 mm.) 8 5
897 3 c. lake (18×21½ mm.) 15 10

265. Park, Lima. 268. Obrero Hospital, Lima.

1951. Air. 75th Anniv of U.P.U. Unissued stamps inscr "VI CONGRESO DE LA UNION POSTAL DE LAS AMERICAS Y ESPANA-1949" optd **U.P.U. 1874-1949.**

745. **265.** 5 c. green 10 10
746. – 30 c. red and black .. 15 10
747. – 55 c. green 15 10
748. – 95 c. turquoise .. 20 15
749. – 1 s. 50 red 30 25
750. – 2 s. blue 35 30
751. – 5 s. red .. .. 2·10 2·10
752. – 10 s. violet .. .. 2·75 3·00
753. – 20 s. blue and brown 4·50 4·50

DESIGNS: 30 c. Peruvian flag. 55 c. Huancayo Hotel. 95 c. Ancash Mtns. 1 s. 50, Arequipa Hotel. 2 s. Coaling Jetty. 5 s. Town Hall, Miraflores. 10 s. Congressional Palace. 20 s. Pan-American flags.

1951. Air Surch. **HABILITADA S/O.O.25.**

754. 25 c. on 30 c. red (No. 735) 15 5

1951. Surch **HABILITADA S/.** and figures.

755 1 c. on 2 c. (No. 693) .. 5 5
756 5 c. on 15 c. (No. 727) .. 5 5
757 10 c. on 15 c. (No. 727) .. 5 5

1951. 5th Pan-American Highways Congress. Unissued "VI CONGRESO DE LA UNION POSTAL" stamps, optd. **V Congreso Panamericano de Carreteras 1951.**

758. – 2 c. green 5 5
759. **268.** 4 c. red 5 5
760. – 15 c. grey 8 5
761. – 20 c. brown 10 5
762. – 50 c. purple 15 5
763. – 1 s. blue 20 8
764. – 2 s. blue 30 10
765. – 5 s. red .. .. 1·00 1·00
766. – 10 s. brown .. .. 1·75 85

DESIGNS—HORIZ. 2 c. Aguas Promenade. 50 c. Archiepiscopal Palace, Lima. 1 s. National Judicial Palace. 2 s. Municipal Palace. 5 s. Lake Llanganuco, Ancash. VERT. 15 c. Inca postal runner. 20 c. Old P.O., Lima. 10 s. Machu-Picchu ruins.

269. Father Tomas de San Martin and Capt. J. de Aliaga.

1951. Air. 4th Cent. of S. Marcos University.

767. **269.** 30 c. black 10 5
768. – 40 c. blue 15 5
769. – 50 c. mauve 20 8
770. – 1 s. 20 green 30 15
771. – 2 s. grey 35 12
772. – 5 s. multicoloured .. 90 20

DESIGNS: 40 c. San Marcos University. 50 c. Santo Domingo Convent. 1 s. 20, P. de Peralto Barnuevo, Father Tomas de San Martin and Jose Baquijano. 2 s. Toribio Rodriguez, Jose Hipolito Unanue and Jose Cayetano Heredia. 5 s. University Arms in 1571 and 1735.

270. Engineer's School.

1952. (a) Postage.

774 – 2 c. purple 10 10
775 – 5 c. green 15 10
776 – 10 c. green 25 10
777 – 15 c. grey 10 10
777a – 15 c. brown 90 20
829 – 20 c. brown 20 10
779 **270** 25 c. red 15 10
779a 25 c. green 30 10
780 – 30 c. blue 10 10
780a – 30 c. red 15 10
830 – 30 c. mauve 15 10
924 – 50 c. green 15 10
831 – 50 c. purple 15 10
782 – 1 s. brown 30 10
782a – 1 s. blue 30 10
783 – 2 s. turquoise .. 40 15
783a – 2 s. grey 55 15

DESIGNS—As Type **270**: HORIZ. 2 c. Hotel, Tacna. 5 c. Tuna fishing boat and indigenous fish. 10 c. View of Matarani. 15 c. Steam train. 30 c. Public Health and Social Assistance. VERT. 20 c. Vicuna. Larger (35×25 mm.): HORIZ. 50 c. Inca maize terraces. 1 s. Inca ruins, Paramonga Fort. 2 s. Agriculture Monument, Lima.

(b) Air.

784 – 40 c. green 30 10
785 – 75 c. brown .. .. 1·50 25
834 – 80 c. red .. .. 1·25 10
786 – 1 s. 25 blue 25 10
787 – 1 s. 50 red 20 10
788 – 2 s. 20 blue 65 15
789 – 3 s. brown 75 25
835 – 3 s. green 50 30
836 – 3 s. 80 orange .. 85 35
790 – 5 s. brown 50 15
791 – 10 s. brown .. .. 1·50 35
838 – 10 s. red .. .. 1·00 45

DESIGNS—As Type **270**: HORIZ. 40 c. Gunboat "Maranon". 1 s. 50, Housing Complex. VERT. 75 c., 80 c. Colony Guanay Cormorants. Larger (25×25 mm): HORIZ. s. 25, Corpac-Limatambo Airport. 2 s. 20, 3 s. 80, Inca Observatory, Cuzco. 5 s. Garcilaso (portrait). VERT. 3 s. Tobacco plant, leaves and cigarettes. 10 s. Manco Capac Monument (25×37 mm).
See also Nos. 867, etc.

271. Isabella the Catholic.

272. "Santa Maria", "Pinta" and "Nina". **273.**

1953. Air. 500th Birth Anniv. of Isabella the Catholic.

792. **271.** 40 c. red 20 10
793. **272.** 1 s. 25 green .. .. 1·40 30
794. **271.** 2 s. 15 purple .. 35 25
795. **272.** 2 s. 20 black .. .. 3·25 55

1954. Obligatory Tax. National Marian Eucharistic Congress Fund. Roul.

796. **273.** 5 c. blue and red .. 25 5

274. Gen. M. Perez Jimenez. **275.** Arms of Lima and Bordeaux.

1956. Visit of President of Venezuela.

797. **274.** 25 c. brown 5 5

1957. Air. Exn. of French Products. Lima.

798. **275.** 40 c. lake, blue & green 10 10
799. – 50 c. blk., brn. & grn. 15 10
800. – 1 s. 25 c. deep blue, green and blue .. 1·25 35
801. – 2 s. 20 c. brown & blue 40 30

DESIGNS—HORIZ. 50 c. Eiffel Tower and Lima Cathedral. 1 s. 25 c. Admiral Dupetit-Thouars and frigate. "La Victorieuse". 2 s. 20 c. Exhibition building, Pres. Prado and Pres. Coty.

276. 1857 Stamp. **277.** Carlos Paz Soldan (founder).

1957. Air. Centenary of First Peruvian Postage Stamp.

802. – 5 c. black and grey .. 10 10
803. **276.** 10 c. turq. and mauve 10 10
804. – 15 c. brown and green 10 10
805. – 25 c. blue and yellow .. 10 10
806. – 30 c. brown & chocolate 10 10
807. – 40 c. ochre and black .. 15 10
808. – 1 s. 25 brown and blue 35 25
809. – 2 s. 20 red and blue .. 50 30
810. – 5 s. red and mauve .. 1·00 1·00
811. – 10 s. violet and green .. 1·60 1·50

DESIGNS: 5 c. Pre-stamp Postmarks. 15 c. 1857 2 r. stamp. 25 c. 1 d. 1858. 30 c. 1 p. 1858 stamp. 40 c. ½ peso 1858 stamp. 1 s. 25, J. Davila Condemarin, Director of Posts, 1857. 2 s. 20, Pres. Ramon Castilla. 5 s. Pres. D. M. Prado. 10 s. Various Peruvian stamps in shield.

1958. Air. Centenary of Lima-Callao Telegraph Service.

812. **277.** 40 c. brown and red .. 10 5
813. – 1 s. green 15 10
814. – 1 s. 25 blue and purple 25 15

DESIGNS—VERT. 1 s. Marshal Ramon Castilla. HORIZ. 1 s. 25, Pres. D. M. Prado and view of Callao. No. 814 also commemorates the political centenary of the Province of Callao.

278. Flags of France and Peru. **279.** Father Martin de Porras Velasquez.

1958. Air. "Treasures of Peru" Exn., Paris.

815. **278.** 50 c. red, bl. & deep bl. 8 5
816. – 65 c. multicoloured .. 10 8
817. – 1 s. 50 brn., pur. & blue 25 10
818. – 2 s. 50 purple, turq. and green 35 20

DESIGNS—HORIZ. 65 c. Lima Cathedral and girl in national costume. 1 s. 50, Caballero and ancient palace. VERT. 2 s. 50, Natural resources map of Peru.

1958. Air. Birth Centenary of D. A. Carrion Garcia (patriot).

819. **279.** 60 c. multicoloured .. 10 5
820. – 1 s. 20 multicoloured .. 15 8
821. – 1 s. 50 multicoloured .. 25 10
822. – 2 s. 20 black 30 20

DESIGNS—VERT. 1 s. 20, D. A. Carrion Garcia, 1 s. 50, J. H. Unanue Pavon. HORIZ. 2 s. 20, First Royal School of Medicine (now Ministry of Government, Police, Posts and Telecommunications).

280. Gen. Alvarez Thomas. **281.** Association Emblems.

1958. Air. Death Cent. of Gen. Thomas.

823. **280.** 1 s. 10 pur., red & bistre 20 12
824. 1 s. 20 blk., red & bistre 25 15

1958. Air. 150th Anniv. of Advocates' College Lima. Emblems in bistre and blue.

825. **281.** 80 c. green 10 5
826. 1 s. 10 red 12 10
827. 1 s. 20 blue 15 10
828. 1 s. 50 purple 20 10

282. Piura Arms and Congress Emblem. **283.**

1960. Obligatory Tax. 6th National Eucharistic Congress Fund.

839. **282.** 10 c. multicoloured .. 20 5
839a. 10 c. blue and red .. 20 10

1960. Air. World Refugee Year.

840. **283.** 80 c. multicoloured .. 30 30
841. 4 s. 30 multicoloured 50 50

284. Sea Bird bearing Map. **285.** Congress Emblem.

1960. Air. Int. Pacific Fair, Lima.

842. **284.** 1 s. multicoloured .. 40 12

1960. 6th National Eucharistic Congress, Piura.

843. **285.** 50 c. red, black & blue 12 10
844. – 1 s. mult. (Eucharistic symbols) 25 10

286. 1659 Coin.

1961. Air. 1st National Numismatic Exn. Lima. T **286** and similar design.

845. – 1 s. grey and brown .. 20 10
846. **286.** 2 s. grey and blue .. 25 15

287. "Amazonas". **288.** Globe, Moon and Stars.

1961. Air. Centenary of World Tour of Cadet Sailing Ship "Amazonas".

847. **287.** 50 c. green and brown 25 10
848. 80 c. red and purple .. 35 10
849. 1 s. black and green .. 50 10

1961. Air. I.G.Y.

850. **288.** 1 s. multicoloured .. 15 12

289. Olympic Torch. **290.** "Balloon".

1961. Air. Olympic Games, 1960.

852. **289.** 5 c. blue and black .. 40 35
853. 10 s. red and black .. 70 60

1961. Christmas and New Year.

854. **290.** 20 c. blue 30 8

291. Fair Emblem. **292.** Symbol of Eucharist.

1961. Air. 2nd Int. Pacific Fair, Lima.

855. **291.** 1 s. multicoloured .. 20 15

1962. Obligatory Tax. 7th National Eucharistic Congress Fund. Roul.

857. **292.** 10 c. blue and yellow .. 8 5

DESIGNS: 2 s. Tupac-Amaru and Hidalgo. 3s. Presidents Prado and Lopez.

293. Sculptures "Cahuide" and "Cuauhtemoc".

1962. Air. Peruvian Art Treasures Exn., Mexico. 1960. Flags red and green.

859. **293.** 1 s. red 15 8
860. – 2 s. turquoise .. 25 12
861. – 3 s. brown 30 15

294. Frontier Maps.

1962. Air. 20th Anniv. of Ecuador-Peru Border Agreement.
862. **294.** 1 s. 30 blk. & red on grey .. 25 15
863. 1 s. 50 multicoloured .. 25 15
864. 2 s. 50 multicoloured .. 30 30

295. The Cedar, Pomabamba. **296.** " Man ".

1962. Centenary of Pomabamba and Pallasca Ancash.
865. **295.** 1 s. green & red (post.) 35 12
866. – 1 s. black & grey (air) 10 8
DESIGN: No. 866, Agriculture, mining, etc., Pallasca Ancash (31½ × 22 mm.).

1962. As Nos. 774/91 but colours and some designs changed and new values.

(a) Postage.
867 20 c. purple 20 10
921 20 c. red 10 10
922 30 c. blue (as No. 776) .. 10 10
923 40 c. orange (as No. 784) .. 30 10
871 60 c. black (as No. 774) .. 25 10
925 1 s. red 10 10

(b) Air.
873 1 s. 30 ochre (as No. 785) .. 2·50 25
874 1 s. 50 purple 35 10
875 1 s. 80 blue (as No. 777) .. 45 15
876 2 s. green 40 15
926 2 s. 60 green (as No. 783) .. 30 15
877 3 s. purple 40 15
927 3 s. 60 purple (as No. 789) 45 20
878 4 s. 30 orange 55 30
928 4 s. 60 orange (as No. 788) 35 25
879 5 s. green 55 35
880 10 s. blue .. .. .. 1·00 40

1963. Air. Chavin Excavations Fund. Pottery.
881. – 1 s. + 50 c. grey & pink 15 15
882. – 1 s. 50 + 1 s. grey & blue 15 15
883. – 3 s. + 2 s. 50 grey & grn. 50 50
884. **296.** 4 s. 30 + 3 s. grey and green 85 65
885. – 6 s. + 4 s. grey & olive 95 85
FIGURES—HORIZ. 1 s. " Griffin ". 1 s. 50, " Eagle ". 3 s. " Cat ". VERT. 6 s. " Deity ".

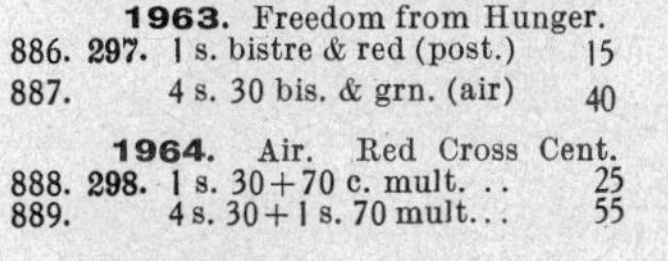

297. Campaign and Industrial Emblems. **298.** Henri Dunant and Centenary Emblem.

1963. Freedom from Hunger.
886. **297.** 1 s. bistre & red (post.) 15 8
887. 4 s. 30 bis. & grn. (air) 40 40

1964. Air. Red Cross Cent.
888. **298.** 1 s. 30 + 70 c. mult. .. 25 25
889. 4 s. 30 + 1 s. 70 mult. .. 55 55

299. Chavez and Wing. **300.** Alliance Emblem.

1964. Air. 50th Anniv. of Jorge Chavez's Trans-Alpine Flight.
890. **299.** 5 s. blue, purple & brn. 75 35

1964. " Alliance for Progress ". Emblem black, green and blue.
891. **300.** 40 c. blk. & yell. (post.) 5 5
892. – 1 s. 30 blk. & mve. (air) 15 10
893. **300.** 3 s. black and blue .. 30 25
DESIGN—HORIZ. 1 s. 30, As Type **300**, but with inscription at right.

301. Fair Poster. **302.** Net, Flag and Globe.

1965. Air. Third Int. Pacific Fair, Lima.
894. **301.** 1 s. multicoloured .. 10 8

1965. Air. Women's World Basketball Championships, Lima.
895. **302.** 1 s. 30 violet and red .. 30 15
896. 4 s. 30 bistre and red .. 45 30

303. St. Martin de Porras (anonymous). **304.** Fair Emblem.

1965. Air. Canonisation of St. Martin de Porras (1962). Paintings. Multicoloured.
898. 1 s. 30 Type **303** 15 8
899. 1 s. 80 " St. Martin and the Miracle of the Animals " (after painting by Camino Brent) 25 10
900. 4 s. 30 " St. Martin and the Angels " (after painting by Fausto Conti) .. 50 25
Porras is wrongly spelt " Porres " on the stamps.

1965. 4th Int. Pacific Fair, Lima.
901. **304.** 1 s. 50 multicoloured .. 12 8
902. 2 s. 50 multicoloured .. 20 10
903. 3 s. 50 multicoloured .. 30 20

305. Father Christmas and Postmarked Envelope. **312.** 2nd May Monument and Battle Scene.

1965. Christmas.
904. **305.** 20 c. black and red .. 12 5
905. 50 c. black and green .. 20 5
906. 1 s. black and blue .. 30 10
The above stamps were valid for postage only on November 2nd. They were subsequently used as postal employees' charity labels.

1966. Obligatory Tax. Journalists' Fund. (a) Surch **HABILITADO "Fondo del Periodista Peruano" Ley 16078 S/o. 0.10.**
907 **264a** 10 c. on 3 c. (No. 897) 65 5

(b) Surch **Habilitado "Fondo del Periodista Peruano" Ley 16078 S/. 0.10.**
909 **264a** 10 c. on 3 c. (No. 897) 25 5

1966. Obligatory Tax. Journalists' Fund. No. 857 optd **Periodista Peruano Ley 16078.**
910 **292** 10 c. blue and yellow .. 5 5

1966. Nos 757c, 851 and 897 surch **XX Habilitado S/. 0.10.**
911 **229** 10 c. on 2 c. brown 5 5
912 **264a** 10 c. on 3 c. lake (No. 897) .. 5 5
912b 10 c. on 3 c. lake (No. 851) .. 2·00 70

1966. Air. Cent. of Battle of Callao. Mult.
913. 1 s. 90 Type **312** .. 30 20
914. 3 s. 60 Monument and sculpture 45 30
915. 4 s. 60 Monument and Jose Galvez 50 40

313. Funerary Mask.

1966. Gold Objects of Chimu Culture. Multicoloured.
916. 1 s. 90 + 90 c. Type **313** .. 35 35
917. 2 s. 60 + 1 s. 30 Ceremonial knife (vert.) 40 40
918. 3 s. 60 + 1 s. 80 Ceremonial urn 60 60
919. 4 s. 60 + 2 s. 30 Goblet (vert.) 85 85
920. 20 s. + 10 s. Ear-ring .. 3·25 3·25

314. Civil Guard Emblem.

1966. Air. Civil Guard Cent. Multicoloured.
929. 90 c. Type **314** 8 8
930. 1 s. 90 Emblem and activities of Civil Guard .. 20 10

315. Map and Mountains. **316.** Globe.

1966. Opening of Huinco Hydro-electric Scheme.
931. **315.** 70 c. black, deep blue and blue (postage) .. 8 5
932. 1 s. 90 black, blue and violet (air) 20 12

1967. Air. Peruvian Photographic Exhibition, Lima.
933 – 2 s. 60 red and black 25 15
934 – 3 s. 60 black & blue 35 25
935 **316** 4 s. 60 multicoloured 40 30
DESIGNS: 2 s. 60, "Sun" carving. 3 s. 60, Map of Peru within spiral.

317. Symbol of Construction. **318.** "St. Rosa" (from painting by A. Medoro).

1967. Six-year Construction Plan.
936. **317.** 90 c. black, gold and mauve (postage) .. 8 5
937. 1 s. 90 black, gold and ochre (air) 15 12

1967. Air. 350th Death Anniv. of St. Rosa of Lima. Designs showing portraits of St. Rosa by artists given below. Multicoloured.
938. 1 s. 90 Type **318** .. 30 12
939. 2 s. 60 C. Maratta .. 40 15
940. 3 s. 60 Anon., Cusquena School 55 25

319. Vicuna within Figure " 5 ". **320.** Pen-nib made of Newspaper.

321. Wall Reliefs (fishes).

1967. 5th Int. Pacific Fair, Lima.
941. **319.** 1 s. black, green and gold (postage) .. 10 5
942. 1 s. purple, black and gold (air) 10 5

1967. Obligatory Tax. Journalists' Fund.
943. **320.** 10 c. black and red .. 8 5

1967. Obligatory Tax. Chan-Chan Excavation Fund.
944. **321.** 20 c. black and blue .. 8 8
945. – 20 c. black and mauve 8 8
946. – 20 c. black and brown 8 8
947. – 20 c. multicoloured .. 8 8
948. – 20 c. multicoloured .. 8 8
949. – 20 c. black and green .. 8 8
DESIGNS: No. 945, Ornamental pattern. No. 946, Carved " bird ". No. 947, Temple on hillside. No. 948, Corner of Temple. No. 949, Ornamental pattern (birds).

322. Lions' Emblem. **323.** Nazca Jug.

1967. Air. 50th Anniv. of Lions International.
950. **322.** 1 s. 60 violet, bl. & grey 15 10

1968. Air. Ceramic Treasures of Nazca Culture. Designs showing painted pottery jugs. Multicoloured.
951. 1 s. 90 Type **323** 15 12
952. 2 s. 60 Falcon 20 15
953. 3 s. 60 Round jug decorated with bird 25 20
954. 4 s. 60 Two-headed snake 30 25
955. 5 s. 60 Sea Bird 40 35

324. Alligator. **325.** "Antarqui" (Airline Symbol).

1968. Gold Sculptures of Mochica Culture. Multicoloured.
956. 1 s. 90 Type **324** 12 5
957. 2 s. 60 Bird 15 10
958. 3 s. 60 Lizard 25 12
959. 4 s. 60 Bird 30 15
960. 5 s. 60 Jaguar 35 20
Nos. 957 and 959 are vert.

1968. Air. 12th Anniv. of APSA (Peruvian Airlines).
961. **325.** 3 s. 60 multicoloured 30 12
962. – 5 s. 60 brown, blk. & red 45 20
DESIGN: 5 s. 60 Alpaca and aircraft symbol.

326. Human Rights Emblem. **327.** " The Discus-thrower".

1968. Air. Human Rights Year.
963. **326.** 6 s. 50 red, grn. & brn. 25 20

1968. Air. Olympic Games, Mexico.
964. **327.** 2 s. 30 brn., blue & yell. 12 8
965. 3 s. 50 blue, red & grn. 20 12
966. 5 s. black, blue & pink 25 15
967. 6 s. 50 pur., brn. & blue 35 20
968. 8 s. blue, mauve & lilac 40 25
969. 9 s. violet, grn. & orge. 45 30

328.

1968. Obligatory Tax. Unissued stamps surch. as in T **328**.
970. **328.** 20 c. on 50 c. violet, orange and black .. 40 40
971. 20 c. on 1 s. blue, orange and black .. 40 40

1968. Obligatory Tax. Journalists' Fund. No. 897 surch. **Habilitado Fondo Periodista Peruano Ley 17050 S/.** and value.
972. **264a.** 20 c. on 3 c. lake .. 8 5

1968. Christmas. No. 900 surch. **PRO NAVIDAD Veinte Centavos R.S. 5-11-68.**
973. 20 c. on 4 s. 30 multicoloured 25 20

331. Indian's Head and Wheat. **334.** Worker holding Flag and Oil Derrick.

333. First Peruvian Coin (obverse and reverse).

1969. Unissued Agrarian Reform stamps. Surch as in T **331**. Multicoloured.

974 2 s. 50 on 90 c. Type **331** (postage) 12 10
975 3 s. on 90 c. Man digging 15 15
976 4 s. on 90 c. As No. 975 .. 25 15
977 5 s. 50 on 1 s. 90 Corn-cob and hand scattering cobs (air) 30 15
978 6 s. 50 on 1 s. 90 As No. 977 40 20

1969. Air. 400th Anniv. of 1st Peruvian Coinage.

979. **333.** 5 s. black, grey and yellow 25 15
980. 5 s. black, grey & green 25 15

1969. Nationalization of Int. Petroleum Company's Oilfields and Refinery (9 October, 1968).

981. **334.** 2 s. 50 multicoloured .. 15 8
982. 3 s. multicoloured .. 20 10
983. 4 s. multicoloured .. 25 12
984. 5 s. 50 multicoloured .. 30 20

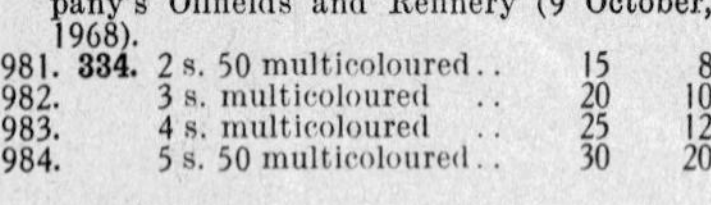

335. Castilla Monument.

336. Airliner, Globe, and "Kon Tiki" (replica of balsa raft).

1969. Air. Death Centenary of President Ramon Castilla.

985. **335.** 5 s. blue and green .. 30 15
986. – 10 s. brown and purple 70 30

DESIGN (21×37 mm.) 10 s. President Castilla.

1969. 1st A.P.S.A. (Peruvian Airlines) Flight to Europe.

987. **336.** 2 s. 50 mult. (postage) 20 10
988. 3 s. multicoloured (air) 30 10
989. 4 s. multicoloured .. 40 10
990. 5 s. 50 multicoloured .. 50 15
991. 6 s. 50 multicoloured .. 60 25

337. Dish Aerial, Satellite and Globe.

1969. Air. Inauguration of Lurin Satellite Telecommunications Station, Lima.

992. **337.** 20 s. multicoloured .. 1·00 60

338. Captain Jose A. Quinones Gonzales (military aviator).

1969. Quinones Gonzales Commem.

994. **338.** 20 s. mult. (postage) .. 1·00 70
995. 20 s. multicoloured (air) 1·00 45

339. W.H.O. Emblem.

1969. Air. 20th Anniv. (1968) of World Health Organization.

996. **339.** 5 s. multicoloured .. 15 12
997. 6 s. 50 multicoloured .. 20 15

340. Peasant breaking Chains.

341. Arms of the Inca Garcilaso de la Vega (historian).

1969. Agrarian Reform Decree.

998. **340.** 2 s. 50 deep blue, blue and red (post.) .. 10 5
999. 3 s. purple, lilac and black (air) 10 8
1000. 4 s. brn. & light brn. 12 10

1969. Air. Garcilaso De La Vega. Commem.

1001. **341.** 2 s. 40 blk., silver & grn. 10 8
1002. – 3 s. 50 black, buff & bl. 15 10
1003. – 5 s. multicoloured .. 20 12

DESIGNS: 3 s. 50, Title page, "Commentarios Reales", Lisbon, 1609. 5 s. Inca Garcilaso de la Vega.

342. Admiral Grau and Ironclad Warship "Huascar".

1969. Navy Day.

1005. **342.** 50 s. multicoloured .. 3·50 1·75

343. "6" and Fair Flags.

1969. 6th Int. Pacific Fair, Lima.

1006. **343.** 2 s. 50 mult. (postage) 10 5
1007. 3 s. multicoloured (air) 12 8
1008. 4 s. multicoloured .. 15 10

344. Father Christmas and Greetings Card.

345. Col. F. Bolognesi and Soldier.

1969. Christmas.

1009. **344.** 20 c. black and red 5 5
1010. 20 c. black & orange 5 5
1011. 20 c. black & brown 5 5

1969. Army Day.

1012. **345.** 1 s. 20 black, gold and blue (postage) .. 10 5
1013. 50 s. black, gold and brown (air) .. 2·50 1·10

346. Arms of Amazonas.

1970. Air. 150th Anniv. (1971) of Republic (1st issue).

1014. **346.** 10 s. multicoloured .. 35 30

See also Nos. 1066/70, 1076/80 and 1081/90.

347. I.L.O. Emblem on Map.

349. "Puma" Jug.

350. Ministry Building.

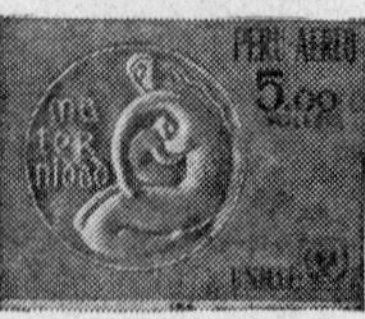

348. "Motherhood".

1970. Air. 50th Anniv. of I.L.O.

1015. **347.** 3 s. deep blue and blue 15 8

1970. Air. 24th Anniv of U.N.I.C.E.F.

1016. **348.** 5 s. black and yellow 25 12
1017. 6 s. 50 black and pink 35 20

1970. Vicus Culture. Ceramic Art. Mult.

1018. 2 s. 50 Type **349** (postage) 15 5
1019. 3 s. Squatting warrior (statuette) (air) .. 20 12
1020. 4 s. Animal jug 25 15
1021. 5 s. 50 Twin jugs .. 30 20
1022. 6 s. 50 Woman with jug (statuette) 40 25

1970. Ministry of Transport and Communications.

1023. **350.** 40 c. black and purple 5 5
1024. 40 c. black and yellow 5 5
1025. 40 c. black and grey .. 5 5
1026. 40 c. black and red .. 5 5
1027. 40 c. black and brown 5 5

351. Anchovy.

352. Telephone and Skyline.

1970. Fishes. Multicoloured.

1028. 2 s. 50 Type **351** (postage) 15 8
1029. 2 s. 50 Hake .. 15 8
1030. 3 s. Swordfish (air) .. 15 5
1031. 3s. Yellowfin tuna .. 15 8
1032. 5s. 50 Wolf-fish 40 15

1970. Air. Nationalization of Lima Telephone Service.

1033. **352.** 5 s. multicoloured .. 30 12
1034. 10 s. multicoloured .. 55 25

353. "Soldier and Farmer".

354. U.N. Headquarters and Dove.

1970. Unity of Armed Forces and People.

1035. **353.** 2 s. 50 multicoloured (postage) 15 8
1036. 3 s. multicoloured (air) 25 10
1037. 5 s. 50 multicoloured 35 15

1970. Air. 25th Anniv. of U.N.O.

1038. **354.** 3 s. blue & pale blue .. 12 8

355. Rotary Emblem.

1970. Air. 50th Anniv. of Lima Rotary Club.

1039. **355.** 10 s. gold, red & black 75 25

356. Military Parade (Army Staff College, Chorrillos).

1970. Military, Naval and Air Force Academies. Multicoloured.

1040. 2 s. 50 Type **356** 35 20
1041. 2 s. 50 Parade, Naval Academy, La Punta .. 35 20
1042. 2 s. 50 Parade, Air Force Officer Training School, Las Palmas 35 20

357. Puruchuco, Lima.

1970. Tourism. Multicoloured.

1043. 2 s. 50 Type **357** (postage) 15 8
1044. 3 s. Chan-Chan-Trujillo, La Libertad (air) .. 15 8
1045. 4 s. Sacsayhuaman, Cuzco 25 10
1046. 5 s. 50 Lake Titicaca, Pomata, Puno 30 15
1047. 10 s. Machu-Picchu, Cuzco 60 30

NOS. 1045/7 are vert.

358. Festival Procession.

1970. Air. October Festival, Lima. Mult.

1049. 3 s. Type **358** 15 5
1050. 4 s. "The Cock-fight" (T. Nunez Ureta) .. 25 10
1051. 5 s. 50 Altar, Nazarenas Shrine (vert.) 30 20
1052. 6 s. 50 "The Procession" (J. Vinatea Reinoso) .. 35 25
1053. 8 s. "The Procession" (Jose Sabogal) (vert.) .. 50 20

359. "The Nativity" (Cuzco School).

1970. Christmas. Paintings by Unknown Artists. Multicoloured.

1054. 1 s. 20 Type **359** .. 5 5
1055. 1 s. 50 "The Adoration of the Magi" (Cuzquena School) 5 5
1056. 1 s. 80 "The Adoration of the Shepherds" (Peruvian School) .. 10 5

360. "Close Embrace" (petroglyph).

1971. Air. "Gratitude for World Help in Earthquake of May 1970".

1057. **360.** 4 s. olive, black & red 25 12
1058. 5 s. 50 blue, flesh and red 35 15
1059. 6 s. 50 grey, blue and red 40 20

361. "St. Rosa de Lima" (F. Laso).

1971. 300th Anniv. of Canonisation of St. Rosa de Lima.

1060. **361.** 2 s. 50 multicoloured 15 10

362. Tiahuanaco Fabric.

1971. Ancient Peruvian Textiles.
1061. **362.** 1 s. 20 mult. (post.).. 15 5
1062. – 2 s. 50 multicoloured 25 8
1063. – 3 s. multicoloured (air) 30 8
1064. – 4 s. pink, grn. & dp. grn. 40 10
1065. – 5 s. 50 multicoloured 55 15
DESIGNS—HORIZ. 2 s. 50, Chancay fabric. 4 s. Chancay lace. VERT. 3 s. Chancay tapestry. 5 s. 50, Paracas fabric.

363. M. Garcia Pumacahua. **364.** "Cojinova" (Nazca Culture).

1971. 150th Anniv. of Independence (2nd issue). National Heroes.
1066. **363.** 1 s. 20 blk. & red (post.) 5 5
1067. – 2 s. 50 black & blue 12 8
1068. – 3 s. blk. & mve. (air) 12 10
1069. – 4 s. black & green .. 15 10
1070. – 5 s. 50 black & brown 25 15
DESIGNS: 2 s. 50 F. Antonio de Zela. 3 s. T. Rodriguez de Mendoza. 4 s. J. P. Viscardo y Guzman. 5 s. 50 J. G. Condorcanqui, Tupac Amani.
See also Nos. 1076/80 and Nos. 1081/90.

1971. "Traditional Fisheries of Peru". Piscatorial Ceramics. Multicoloured.
1071. 1 s. 50 Type **364** (post.) 15 5
1072. 3 s. 50 "Bonito" (Chimu Inca) (air) 30 10
1073. 4 s. "Anchoveta" (Mochica) 40 10
1074. 5 s. 50 "Merluza" (Chimu) 60 15
1075. 8 s. 50 "Machete" (Nazca) 80 25

1971. 150th Anniv. of Independence. National Heroes (3rd issue). As T **363**. Multicoloured.
1076. 1 s. 20 M. Melgar (postage) 5 5
1077. 2 s. 50 J. Baquijano y Carrillo 12 8
1078. 3 s. J. de la Riva Aguero (air) 15 10
1079. 4 s. H. Unanue 15 10
1080. 5 s. 50 F. J. de Luna Pizarro 25 15

366. Liberation Expedition Monument. **367.** R. Palma (author and poet).

1971. 150th Anniv. of Independence (4th issue). As T **366**. Multicoloured.
1081. 1 s. 50. M. Bastidas (post.) 8 5
1082. 2 s. J. F. Sanchez Carrion 8 5
1083. 2 s. 50 M. J. Guise .. 12 8
1084. 3 s. F. Vidal (air) .. 12 8
1085. 3 s. 50 J. de San Martin .. 15 12
1086. 4 s. 50 Type **366** .. 20 15
1087. 6 s. "Surrender of the 'Numancia Battalion'" (horiz.) (42 × 35 mm.) 30 12
1088. 7 s. 50 Alvarez de Arenales Monument (horiz.) (42 × 39 mm.) 35 20
1089. 9 s. Monument to Founders of the Republic, Lima (horiz.) (42 × 39 mm.) .. 40 20
1090. 10 s. "Proclamation of Independence" (horiz.) (46 × 35 mm.) .. 50 20

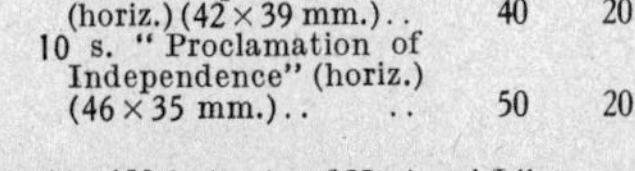

1971. Air. 150th Anniv of National Library.
1091. **367.** 7 s. 50 black and brn. 60 25

368. Weightlifting. **369.** "Gongora portentosa".

1971. Air. 25th World Weightlifting Championships, Huampani, Lima.
1092. **368.** 7 s. 50 black and blue 60 25

1971. Peruvian Flora (1st series). Orchids. Multicoloured.
1093. 1 s. 50 Type **369** 25 5
1094. 2 s. "Odontoglossum cristatum" 30 5
1095. 2 s. 50 "Mormolyca peruviana" 35 8
1096. 3 s. "Trichocentrum pulchrum" 45 12
1097. 3 s. 50 "Oncidium sanderae" 35 20
See also Nos. 1170/4 and 1206/10.

370. Family and Flag. **371.** Schooner "Sacramento" of 1821.

1971. Air. 3rd Anniv. of October 3rd Revolution.
1098. **370.** 7 s. 50 black, red & bl. 50 30

1971. Air. 150th Anniv. of Peruvian Navy and "Order of the Peruvian Sun".
1100. **371.** 7 s. 50 blue & new blue 1·00 30
1101. – 7 s. 50 multicoloured 50 25
DESIGN: No. 1101, Order of the Peruvian Sun.

372. "Development and Liberation" (detail).

1971. 2nd Ministerial Meeting of "The 77" Group.
1102. **372.** 1 s. 20 multicoloured (postage) 10 5
1103. – 3 s. 50 multicoloured 25 10
1104. – 50 s. mult. (air) .. 2·50 1·25
DESIGNS—As Type **372**. 3 s. 50, 50 s. Detail from the painting "Development and Liberation".

373. "Plaza de Armas, 1843" (J. Rugendas).

1971. "Exfilima" Stamp Exhib., Lima.
1105. **373.** 3 s. blk. & green .. 30 10
1106. – 3 s. 50 black & pink .. 40 15
DESIGN: 3 s. 50 "Plaza de Armas, 1971" (C. Zeiter).

374. Fair Emblem. **375.** Army Crest.

1971. Air. 7th Int. Pacific Fair, Lima.
1107. **374.** 4 s. 50 multicoloured 20 12

1971. 150th Anniv. of Peruvian Army.
1108. **375.** 8 s. 50 multicoloured 60 20

376. "The Flight into Egypt".

1971. Christmas. Multicoloured.
1109. 1 s. 80 Type **376** 20 5
1110. 2 s. 50 "The Magi" 25 8
1111. 3 s. "The Nativity" 35 10

377. "Fishermen" (J. Ugarte Elespuru). **378.** Chimu Idol.

1971. Social Reforms. Paintings. Mult.
1112. 3 s. 50 Type **377** 35 10
1113. 4 s. "Threshing Grain in Cajamarca" (Camilo Blas) 45 10
1114. 6 s. "Hand-spinning Huanca Native Women" (J. Sabogal) 60 15

1972. Peruvian Antiquities. Multicoloured.
1115. 3 s. 90 Type **378** .. 35 12
1116. 4 s. Chimu statuette .. 35 12
1117. 4 s. 50 Lambayeque idol 45 15
1118. 5 s. 40 Mochica collar .. 55 15
1119. 6 s. Lambayeque "spider" pendant 60 15

379. "Pseudopriacanthus serrula".

1972. Peruvian Fishes. Multicoloured.
1120. 1 s. 20 Type **379** (postage) 12 5
1121. 1 s. 50 "Trachichthys mento" 15 5
1122. 2 s. 50 "Trachurus symmetricus murphyi" 25 10
1123. 3 s. "Pontinus furcirhinus" (air) 30 10
1124. 5 s. 50 "Bodianus eclancheri 55 15

380. "Peruvian Family" (T. Nunez Ureta).

1972. Air. Educations Reforms.
1125. **380.** 6 s. 50 mult... .. 35 20

381. Mochica Warrior. **382.** White-tailed Trogon.

1972. Peruvian Art (1st series). Mochica Ceramics. Multicoloured.
1126. 1 s. 20 Type **381** .. 15 5
1127. 1 s. 50 Warrior's head .. 15 5
1128. 2 s. Kneeling deer .. 25 5
1129. 2 s. 50 Warrior's head (different) 35 10
1130. 3 s. Kneeling warrior .. 40 15
See also Nos. 1180/4.

1972. Air. Peruvian Birds. Multicoloured.
1131. 2 s. Type **382** 65 25
1132. 2 s. 50 Amazonian Umbrellabird 80 25
1133. 3 s. Andean Cock of the Rock 90 30
1134. 6 s. 50 Cuvier's Toucan .. 1·90 55
1135. 8 s. 50 Blue-Crowned Motmot .. .. 2·25 75

383. "The Harvest" (July). **384.** "Quipu" on Map.

1972. 400th Anniv of G. Poma de Ayala's "Inca Chronicles". Woodcuts.
1136. **383.** 2 s. 50 black & red .. 35 8
1137. – 3 s. black & green .. 60 8
1138. – 2 s. 50 black and pink 30 8
1139. – 3 s. black and blue .. 50 8
1140. – 2 s. 50 black & orange 50 8
1141. – 3 s. black and lilac .. 50 8
1142. – 2 s. 50 black & brown 35 8
1143. – 3 s. black & green .. 50 8
1144. – 2 s. 50 black & blue 35 8
1145. – 3 s. black & orange .. 50 8
1146. – 2 s. 50 black & mauve 35 8
1147. – 3 s. black & yellow .. 50 8
DESIGNS: No. 1137, "Land Purification" (August). No. 1138, "Sowing" (September). No. 1139, "Invocation of the Rains" (October). No. 1140, "Irrigation" (November). No. 1141, "Rite of the Nobility" (December). No. 1142, "Maize Cultivation Rites" (January). No. 1143, "Ripening of the Maize" (February). No. 1144, "Birds in the maize" (March). No. 1145, "Children as camp-guards" (April). No. 1146, "Gathering the harvest" (May). No. 1147, "Removing the harvest" (June).

1972. Air. "Exfibra 72" Stamp Exhib., Rio de Janeiro.
1148. **384.** 5 s. multicoloured .. 25 12

385. "The Messenger". **386.** Catacaos Woman.

1972. Air. Olympic Games, Munich.
1149. **385.** 8 s. multicoloured .. 55 20

1972. Air. Provincial Costumes (1st series). Multicoloured.
1150. 2 s. Tupe girl 15 5
1151. 3 s. 50 Type **386** 30 10
1152. 4 s. Conibo Indian .. 40 10
1153. 4 s. 50 Agricultural worker playing "quena" and drum 40 12
1154. 5 s. "Moche" (Trujillo) girl 40 12
1155. 6 s. 50 Ocongate (Cuzco) man and woman .. 55 40
1156. 8 s. "Chucupana" (Ayacucho) girl 60 50
1157. 8 s. 50 "Cotuncha" (Junin) girl 70 55
1158. 10 s. "Pandilla" dancer .. 60 60
See also Nos. 1248/9.

387. Ruins of Chavin (Ancash).

1972. Air. 25th Death Anniv. of Julio C. Tello (archaeologist). Multicoloured.
1159. 1 s. 50 "Stone of the 12 Angles", Cuzco (vert.) 15 5
1160. 3 s. 50 Type **387** 30 10
1161. 4 s. Burial-tower, Sillustani (Puno) (vert.) 30 10
1162. 5 s. Gateway, Chavin (Ancash) 45 15
1163. 8 s. "Wall of the 3 Windows", Machu Picchu (Cuzco) 55 25

388. "Territorial Waters".

1972. 4th Anniv. of Armed Forces Revolution. Multicoloured.
1164. 2 s. Agricultural Workers ("Agrarian Reform") (vert.) 10 5
1165. 2 s. 50 Type **388** .. 15 8
1166. 3 s. Oilrigs ("Nationalisation of Petroleum Industry") (vert.) .. 20 8

389. "The Holy Family". (wood-carving).

1972. Christmas. Multicoloured.

1167. 1 s. 50 Type **389** 12 5
1168. 2 s. "The Holy Family" (carved Huamanga stone) (horiz.) 15 5
1169. 2 s. 50 "The Holy Family" (carved Huamanga stone) .. 20 8

390. "Ipomoea purpurea". 391. Inca Poncho.

1972. Peruvian Flora (2nd series). Mult.

1170. 1 s. 50 Type **390** 15 5
1171. 2 s. 50 "Amaryllis ferreyrae" 20 10
1172. 3 s. "Liabum excelsum" .. 30 10
1173. 3 s. 50 "Bletia catenulata" 30 10
1174. 5 s. "Cantua buxifolia cantuta" 35 20

1973. Air. Ancient Inca Textiles.

1175. **391.** 2 s. multicoloured .. 15 5
1176. – 3 s. 50 multicoloured 25 10
1177. – 4 s. multicoloured .. 25 10
1178. – 5 s. multicoloured .. 30 12
1179. – 8 s. multicoloured .. 55 25

DESIGNS: Nos. 1176/9, similar to T **391**.

392. Mochica Cameo and Cups. 393. Andean Condor.

1973. Air. Peruvian Art (2nd series). Jewelled Antiquities. Multicoloured.

1180. 1 s. 50 Type **392** .. 10 5
1181. 2 s. 50 Gold-plated arms and hands (Lambayeque) 15 5
1182. 4 s. Bronze effigy (Mochica) 25 10
1183. 5 s. Gold pendants (Nazca) 30 12
1184. 8 s. Gold cat (Mochica) .. 60 25

1973. Air. Fauna Protection (1st series). Multicoloured.

1185. 2 s. 50 Lesser rhea .. 1·25 20
1186. 3 s. 50 Giant otter .. 45 10
1187. 4 s. Type **393** .. .. 1·75 30
1188. 5 s. Vicuna 60 15
1189. 6 s. Chilian flamingo .. 2·00 35
1190. 8 s. Spectacled bear .. 70 25
1191. 8 s. 50 Bush dog (horiz.) 60 25
1192. 10 s. Short-tailed chinchilla (horiz.) .. 75 30

See also Nos. 1245/6.

394. "The Macebearer" (J. Sabogal). 396. "Spanish Mayor on Horseback".

395. Basketball Net and Map.

1973. Air. Peruvian Paintings. Mult.

1193. 1 s. 50 Type **394** 5 5
1194. 8 s. "Yananacu Bridge" (E. C. Brent) (horiz.) .. 30 15
1195. 8 s. 50 "Portrait of a Lady" (D. Hernandez) 35 15
1196. 10 s. "Peruvian Birds" (T. N. Ureta) .. 2·25 30
1197. 20 s. "The Potter" (F. Laso) .. .. .. 1·10 40
1198. 50 s. "Reed Boats" (J. V. Reinoso) (horiz.) 2·75 1·00

1973. Air. 1st World Basketball Festival.

1199. **395.** 5 s. green 35 10
1200. 20 s. purple 90 40

1973. 170th Birth Anniv. of Pancho Fierro (painter). Multicoloured.

1201. 1 s. 50 Type **396** 10 5
1202. 2 s. "Peasants" 15 5
1203. 2 s. 50 "Father Abregu" 20 10
1204. 3 s. 50 "Dancers" .. 30 10
1205. 4 s. 50 "Esteban Arredondo on horseback" 45 20

1973. Air. Peruvian Flora (3rd series). Orchids. As T **390**. Multicoloured.

1206. 1 s. 50 "Lycaste reichenbachii" .. 20 5
1207. 2 s. 50 "Masdevallia amabilis" 30 5
1208. 3 s. "Sigmatostalix peruviana" 40 10
1209. 3 s. 50 "Porrogossum peruvianum" 40 10
1210. 8 s. "Oncidium incarum" 60 25

398. Fair Emblem (poster). 399. Symbol of Flight.

1973. Air. 8th International Pacific Fair, Lima.

1211. **398.** 8 s. red, black & grey 60 20

1973. Air. 50th Anniv. of Air Force Officers' School.

1212. **399.** 8 s. 50 multicoloured 60 15

400. "The Presentation of the Child".

1973. Christmas. Paintings of the Cuzco School. Multicoloured.

1213. 1 s. 50 Type **400** 10 5
1214. 2 s. "The Holy Family" (vert.) 12 5
1215. 2 s. 50 "The Adoration of the Kings" 15 8

401. Freighter "Ilo".

1973. Air. National Development. Mult.

1216. 1 s. 50 Type **401** 40 15
1217. 2 s. 50 Trawlers 60 15
1218. 8 s. "Aero Peru" jet aircraft and seagull .. 1·00 25

402. House of the Mulberry Tree, Arequipa.

1974. Air. "Landscapes and Cities". Mult.

1219. 1 s. 50 Type **402** 10 5
1220. 2 s. 50 El Misti (peak), Arequipa 15 5
1221. 5 s. Giant puya, Cordillera Blanca, Ancash (vert.) 30 12
1222. 6 s. Huascaran (peak), Cordillera Blanca, Ancash 35 15
1223. 8 s. Lake Querococha, Cordillera Blanca, Ancash 55 20

403. Peruvian 2 c. Stamp of 1873. 405. Church of San Jeronimo, Cuzco.

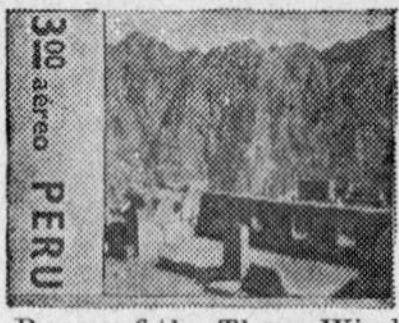

404. Room of the Three Windows, Machu Picchu.

1974. Stamp Day and 25th Anniv. of Peruvian Philatelic Association.

1224. **403.** 6 s. blue and grey .. 40 15

1974. Air. Archaeological Discoveries. Mult.

(a) Cuzco Relics.

1225. 3 s. Type **404** 15 10
1226. 5 s. Baths of Tampumacchay 25 15
1227. 10 s. "Kencco" 45 25

(b) Dr. Tello's Discoveries at Chavin de Huantar. Stone carvings.

1228. 3 s. Mythological jaguar 15 10
1229. 5 s. Rodent ("Vizcacha") 25 15
1230. 10 s. Chavin warrior .. 45 25

Nos. 1228/30 are vert. designs.

1974. Air. Architectural Treasures. Mult.

1231. 1 s. 50 Type **405** 10 5
1232. 3 s. 50 Cathedral of Santa Catalina, Cajamarca .. 20 5
1233. 5 s. Church of San Pedro, Zepita, Puno (horiz.) .. 25 10
1234. 6 s. Cuzco Cathedral .. 30 15
1235. 8 s. 50 Wall of the Coricancha, Cuzco 55 20

406. "Colombia" Bridge, Tarapoto-Juanjui Highway.

1974. "Structural Changes". Multicoloured.

1236. 2 s. Type **406** 12 5
1237. 8 s. Tayacaja hydro-electric scheme 40 20
1238. 10 s. Tablachaca dam .. 50 25

407. "Battle of Junin" (F. Yanez).

1974. 150th Anniv. of Battle of Junin.

1239. **407.** 1 s. 50 mult. (postage) 10 5
1240. 2 s. 50 multicoloured 10 8
1241. 6 s. multicoloured (air) 30 10

408. "Battle of Ayacucho" (F. Yanez).

1974. 150th Anniv. of Battle of Ayacucho.

1242. **408.** 2 s. mult. (postage).. 10 5
1243. 3 s. multicoloured .. 12 10
1244. 7 s. 50 mult. (air) .. 45 15

1974. Air. Fauna Protection (2nd series). As T **393**. Multicoloured.

1245. 8 s. Red uakari 50 15
1246. 20 s. As 8 s. 85 50

409. Chimu Gold Mask.

1974. Air. 8th World Mining Congress, Lima.

1247. **409.** 8 s. multicoloured .. 45 15

1974. Air. Provincial Costumes (2nd series). As T **386**. Multicoloured.

1248. 5 s. Horseman in "chalan" (Cajamarca) 35 12
1249. 8 s. 50 As 5 s. 60 15

410. Pedro Paulet and Spacecraft.

1974. Air. Cent. of U.P.U. and Birth Centenary of Pedro E. Paulet (aviation scientist).

1250. **410.** 8 s. violet and blue.. 40 15

411. Copper Smelter, La Oroya.

1974. Expropriation of Cerro de Pasco Mining Complex.

1251. **411.** 1 s. 50 blue & deep blue 8 5
1252. 3 s. red and brown .. 15 8
1253. 4 s. 50 green and grey 25 15

412. "Capitulation of Ayacucho" (D. Hernandez). 413. "Madonna and Child".

1974. Air. 150th Anniv. of Spanish Forces' Capitulation at Ayacucho.

1254. **412.** 3 s. 50 multicoloured 20 8
1255. 8 s. 50 multicoloured 60 20
1256. 10 s. multicoloured .. 55 25

1974. Christmas. Paintings of the Cuzco School. Multicoloured.

1257. 1 s. 50 Type **413** (postage) 10 5
1258. 6 s. 50 "Holy Family" (air) 30 12

414. "Andean Landscape" (T. Nunez Ureta). 415. Map and Civic Centre, Lima.

1974. Air. Andean Pact Communications Ministers' Meeting, Cali, Colombia.

1259. **414.** 6 s. 50 multicoloured 35 12

1975. Air. 2nd General Conference of U.N. Organization for Industrial Development.

1260. **415.** 6 s. black, red & grey 25 15

1975. Air. Various stamps surch.

1261. – 1 s. 50 on 3 s. 60 purple (No. 927) 10 5
1262. – 2 s. on 2 s. 60 green (No. 926) 15 5
1263. – 2 s. on 3 s. 60 purple (No. 927) 15 5
1263a. – 2 s. on 3 s. 60 black and blue (No. 934) 8 5
1264. – 2 s. on 4 s. 30 orange (No. 878) 10 5
1265. – 2 s. on 4 s. 30 multicoloured (No. 900) 15 5
1266. – 2 s. on 4 s. 60 orange (No. 928) 8 5
1267. – 2 s. 50 on 4 s. 60 orange (No. 928) .. 25 5
1268. – 3 s. on 2 s. 60 green (No. 926) 15 8
1294. – 3 s. 50 on 4 s. 60 orange (No. 928) 20 8
1269. – 4 s. on 2 s. 60 green (No. 926) 20 8
1270. – 4 s. on 3 s. 60 purple (No. 927) 20 8
1271. – 4 s. on 4 s. 60 orange (No. 928) 15 8
1295. – 4 s. 50 on 3 s. 80 orange (No. 836) 20 8

1272. – 5 s. on 3 s. 60 purple (No. 927) 20 10
1273. – 5 s. on 3 s. 80 orange (No. 836) 35 10
1296. – 5 s. on 4 s. 30 orange (No. 878) 30 10
1297. – 6 s. on 4 s. 60 orange (No. 928) 40 12
1277. **316.** 6 s. on 4 s. 60 multi-coloured (No. 935) 45 10
1278. – 7 s. on 4 s. 30 orange (No. 878) 40 12
1279. – 7 s. 50 on 3 s. 60 purple (No. 927) 50 15
1280. – 8 s. on 3 s. 60 purple (No. 927) 50 15
1281. **271.** 10 s. on 2 s. 15 purple (No. 794) 40 25
1298. – 10 s. on 2 s. 60 green (No. 926) 60 20
1282. – 10 s. on 3 s. 60 purple (No. 927) 60 25
1283. – 10 s. on 3 s. 60 multi-coloured (No. 940) 50 25
1284. – 10 s. on 4 s. 30 orange (No. 878) 25 25
1285. – 10 s. on 4 s. 60 orange (No. 928) 60 25
1286. – 20 s. on 3 s. 60 purple (No. 927) 40 12
1287. – 24 s. on 3 s. 60 multi-coloured (No. 953) 1·40 45
1288. – 28 s. on 4 s. 60 multi-coloured (No. 954) 85 55
1289. – 32 s. on 5 s. 60 multi-coloured (No. 955) 85 65
1290. – 50 s. on 2 s. 60 green (No. 926) .. .. 2·10 1·00
1299. – 50 s. on 3 s. 60 purple (No. 927) .. .. 1·60 1·50
1292. – 100 s. on 3 s. 80 orange (No. 836) .. .. 1·60 1·50

417. Lima on World Map.

1975. Air. Conference of Non-aligned Countries' Foreign Ministers, Lima.
1311. **417.** 6 s. 50 multicoloured 40 15

418. Maria Parado de Bellido.

1975. "Year of Peruvian Women" and International Women's Year. Multicoloured.
1312. 1 s. 50 Type **418** 12 5
1213. 2 s. Micaela Bastidas (vert.) 15 5
1314. 2 s. 50 Juana Alarco de Dammert 20 5
1315. 3 s. I.W.Y. emblem (vert.) 35 5

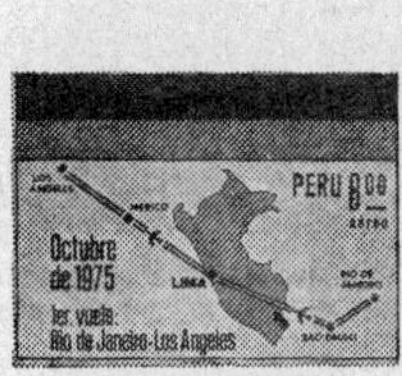

419. Route Map of Flight. **420.** San Juan Macias.

1975. Air. First "Aero-Peru" Flight, Rio de Janeiro–Lima–Los Angeles.
1316. **419.** 8 s. multicoloured .. 30 15

1975. Canonisation of St. Juan Macias.
1317. **420.** 5 s. multicoloured .. 30 10

421. Fair Poster. **422.** Col. F. Bolognesi.

1975. Air. 9th Int. Pacific Fair, Lima.
1318. **421.** 6 s. red, brn. & blk. 50 12

1975. Air. 159th Birth Anniv of Colonel Francisco Bolognesi.
1319 **422** 20 s. multicoloured .. 65 35

423. "Nativity". **424.** Louis Braille.

1976. Air. Christmas (1975).
1320. **423.** 6 s. multicoloured .. 35 12

1976. 150th Anniv. of Braille System for Blind.
1321. **424.** 4 s. 50 red, blk. & grey 30 10

426. Inca Postal Runner. **427.** Map on Riband.

1976. Air. 11th UPAE Congress, Lima.
1322. **426.** 5 s. black, brown & red 50 10

1976. Air. Re-incorporation of Tacna.
1323. **427.** 10 s. multicoloured .. 30 12

428. Peruvian Flag. **429.** Police Badge.

1976. 1st Anniv. of Second Phase of Revolution.
1324. **428.** 5 s. red, black & grey 15 10

1976. Air. 54th Anniv. of Peruvian Special Police.
1325. **429.** 20 s. multicoloured .. 55 40

430. "Tree of Badges". **431.** Chairman Pal Losonczi.

1976. Air. 10th Anniv. of Bogota Declaration.
1326. **430.** 10 s. multicoloured .. 30 20

1976. Air. Visit of Hungarian Head of State.
1327. **431.** 7 s. black and blue .. 40 15

432. "St. Francis of Assisi" (El Greco). **434.** "Nativity".

433. Map and National Colours.

1976. 750th Death Anniv. of St. Francis of Assisi.
1328. **432.** 5 s. brown and gold .. 35 10

1976. Air. Meeting of Presidents of Peru and Brazil.
1329. **433.** 10 s. multicoloured .. 30 20

1976. Christmas.
1330. **434.** 4 s. multicoloured .. 30 8

435. Military Monument and Symbols.

1977. Air. Army Day.
1331. **435.** 20 s. black, buff & red 40 40

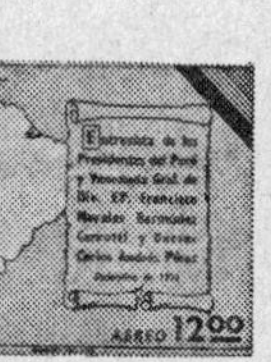

436. Map and Scroll. **437.** Printed Circuit.

1977. Air. Visit of Peruvian President to Venezuela.
1332. **436.** 12 s. multicoloured .. 60 25

1977. Air. World Telecommunications Day.
1333. **437.** 20 s. red, blk. & silver 55 40

438. Inca Postal Runner. **439.** Petrochemical Plant, Map and Tanker.

1977.
1334. **438.** 6 s. black and turq. (postage) 40 12
1335. 8 s. black and red .. 40 12
1336. 10 s. black and blue .. 55 25
1337. 12 s. black and green 55 35
1338. **438.** 24 s. black and red (air) 55 50
1339. 28 s. black and blue .. 1·10 50
1340. 32 s. black and brown 65 70

1977. Air. Bayovar Petrochemical Complex.
1341. **439.** 14 s. multicoloured .. 1·25 30

440. Arms of Arequipa. **441.** President Videla.

1977. Air. "Gold of Peru" Exhibition, Arequipa.
1342. **440.** 10 s. multicoloured .. 20 10

1977. Air. Visit of President Videla of Argentina.
1343. **441.** 36 s. multicoloured .. 75 25

1977. Various stamps surch **FRANQUEO** and new value.
1344. **325.** 6 s. on 3 s. 60 mult... 40 12
1345. 8 s. on 3 s. 60 mult... 45 15
1346. – 10 s. on 5 s. 60 brown, blk. & red (No. 962) 50 25
1347. **305.** 10 s. on 50 c. blk. & grn. 30 10
1348. 20 s. on 20 c. black and red 50 20
1349. 30 s. on 1 s. black and blue 70 35

444. Fair Emblem and Flags. **445.** Republican Guard Badge.

1977. 10th International Pacific Fair.
1350. **444.** 10 s. multicoloured .. 20 10

1977. 58th Anniv. of Republican Guard.
1351. **445.** 12 s. multicoloured .. 25 12

446. Admiral Miguel Grau. **447.** "The Holy Family".

1977. Air. Navy Day. Admiral Grau. Commemorative.
1352. **446.** 28 s. multicoloured .. 35 25

1977. Christmas. Multicoloured.
1353. 8 s. Type **447** (postage) .. 8 5
1354. 20 s. "The adoration of the Shepherds" (air) .. 50 20

448. Open Book of Flags. **449.** Inca Head.

1978. Air. 8th Meeting of Education Ministers.
1355. **448.** 30 s. multicoloured .. 40 25

1978.
1356 **449** 6 s. green (postage) .. 5 5
1357 10 s. red 12 8
1358 16 s. brown 20 20
1359 24 s. mauve (air) .. 30 25
1360 30 s. pink 40 30
1361 65 s. blue 90 70
1362 95 s. blue .. .. 1·00 1·00

450. Emblem and Flags of West Germany, Argentina, Austria and Brazil.

1978. World Cup Football Championship, Argentina (1st issue). Multicoloured.
1367. 10 s. Type **450** 20 10
1368. 10 s. Emblem and flags of Hungary, Iran, Italy and Mexico .. 20 10
1369. 10 s. Emblem and flags of Scotland, Spain, France and Netherlands .. 20 10
1370. 10 s. Emblem and flags of Peru, Poland, Sweden and Tunisia .. 20 10
See also Nos. 1412/15.

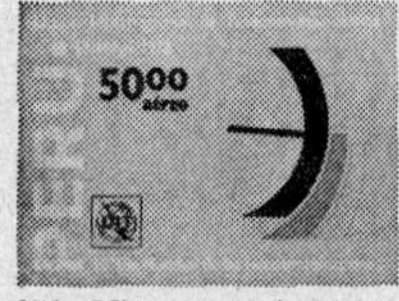

451. Microwave Antenna.

1978. Air. 10th World Telecommunications Day.
1371. **451.** 50 s. grey, deep blue and blue 75 50

1978. Various stamps surch. **Habilitado Dif.-Porte** and value (Nos. 1372/4), **Habilitado R.D. No. 0118** and value (Nos. 1377/8, 1381, 1384, 1390) or with value only (others).
1372. **229.** 2 s. on 2 c. brown (postage) 5 5
1373. 4 s. on 2 c. brown .. 8 5
1374. 5 s. on 2 c. brown .. 8 5
1375. **313.** 20 s. on 1 s. 90+90 c. multicoloured .. 75 60
1376. – 30 s. on 2 s. 60+1 s. 30 mult. (No. 917) .. 60 60
1377. **229.** 35 s. on 2 c. brown .. 25 20
1378. 50 s. on 2 c. brown .. 1·60 1·60
1379. – 55 s. on 3 s. 60+1 s. 80 mult. (No. 918) .. 85 85
1380. – 65 s. on 4 s. 60+2 s. 30 mult. (No. 919) .. 85 85
1381. – 80 s. on 5 s. 60 mult. (No. 960) 60 40
1382. – 85 s. on 20 s.+10 s. mult. (No. 920) .. 1·25 1·25
1383. – 25 s. on 4 s. 60 mult. (No. 954) (air) .. 20 15
1384. **316.** 34 s. on 4 s. 60 mult. 25 15
1385. **302.** 40 s. on 4 s. 30 bistre and red 50 20

1386. **449.** 45 s. on 28 s. green .. 45 25
1387. – 70 s. on 2 s. 60 green (No. 926) 50 40
1388. **449.** 75 s. on 28 s. green .. 75 40
1389. – 105 s. on 5 s. 60 mult. (No. 955) .. .. 1·00 85
1390. – 110 s. on 3 s. 60 purple (No. 927) 75 60
1391. – 265 s. on 4 s. 30 mult. (No. 900) .. .. 1·90 1·50

The 28 s. value as Type **449** was not issued without a surcharge.

1978. Surch. **SOBRE TASA OFICIAL** and value.
1400. **229.** 3 s. on 2 s. brown .. 5 5
1401. 6 s. on 2 c. brown .. 12 5

456. San Martin. **457.** Elmer Faucett and Aeroplanes.

1978. Air. Birth Bicentenary of General Jose de San Martin.
1410. **456.** 30 s. multicoloured .. 40 30

1978. 50th Anniv. of Faucett Aviation.
1411. **457.** 40 s. multicoloured .. 50 30

1978. World Cup Football Championship, Argentina (2nd issue). Multicoloured.
1412. 16 s. As Type **450** .. 15 5
1413. 16 s. As No. 1368 .. 15 5
1414. 16 s. As No. 1369 .. 15 5
1415. 16 s. As No. 1370 .. 15 5

458. Nazca Bowl. **459.** Peruvian Nativity.

1978.
1416. **458.** 16 s. blue 12 5
1417. 20 s. green 15 10
1418. 25 s. green 20 12
1419. 35 s. red 35 15
1420. 45 s. brown 40 25
1421. 50 s. black 50 25
1422. 55 s. mauve 50 25
1423. 70 s. mauve 60 35
1424. 75 s. blue 55 40
1425. 80 s. brown 55 40
1426. 200 s. violet .. .. 1·40 1·00

1978. Christmas.
1436. **459.** 16 s. multicoloured .. 12 5

460. Ministry of Education, Lima. **461.** Queen Sophia and King Juan Carlos.

1979. National Education.
1437. **460.** 16 s. multicoloured .. 12 5

1979. Air. Visit of King and Queen of Spain.
1438. **461.** 75 s. multicoloured .. 60 25

462. Red Cross Emblem.

1979. Centenary of Peruvian Red Cross Society.
1439. **462.** 16 s. multicoloured .. 10 5

HAVE YOU READ THE NOTES AT THE BEGINNING OF THIS CATALOGUE?
These often provide answers to the enquiries we receive.

463. "Naval Battle of Iquique" (E. Velarde).

1979. Pacific War Centenary. Mult.
1440. 14 s. Type **463** 20 10
1441. 25 s. "Col. Jose Joaquin Inclan" (vert.) .. 30 15
1442. 25 s. "Arica Blockade-runner Corvette "Union" 40 15
1443. 25 s. "Heroes of Angamos" 40 15
1444. 25 s. "Lt. Col. Pedro Ruiz Gallo" (vert.) .. 30 15
1445. 85 s. "Marshal Andres H. Caceres" (vert.) .. 45 40
1446. 100 s. "Battle of Angamos" (T. Castillo) .. 1·40 60
1447. 100 s. "Battle of Tarapaca" 55 45
1448. 115 s. "Admiral Miguel Grau" (vert.) .. 1·00 50
1449. 200 s. "Bolognesi's Reply" (Leppiani) .. .. 3·25 2·50
1450. 200 s. "Col. Francisco Bolognesi" (vert.) .. 1·00 85
1451. 200 s. "Col. Alfonso Ugarte" (Morizani) .. 1·00 85

A similar 200 s. value, showing the Crypt of the Fallen, was on sale for a very limited period only.

464. Billiard Balls and Cue. **465.** Arms of Cuzco.

1979. 34th World Billiards Championship, Lima.
1456. **464.** 34 s. multicoloured .. 30 15

1979. Inca Sun Festival, Cuzco.
1457. **465.** 50 s. multicoloured .. 35 20

466. Flag and Arch. **468.** Exposition Emblem.

1979. 50th Anniv. of Re-incorporation of Tacna into Peru.
1458. **466.** 16 s. multicoloured .. 12 5

1979. Surch. in figures only.
1459. **229.** 7 s. on 2 c. brown .. 5 5
1460. 9 s. on 2 c. brown .. 8 5
1461. 15 s. on 2 c. brown .. 12 5

1979. Third World Telecommunications Exhibition, Geneva.
1467. **468.** 15 s. orge. blue & grey 10 5

469. Caduceus. **470.** Fair Emblem on World Map.

1979. International Stomatology Congress, Lima, and 50th Anniv of Peruvian Academy of Stomatology.
1468. **469.** 25 s. gold, blk. & turq. 20 12

1979. 11th International Pacific Fair.
1469. **470.** 55 s. multicoloured .. 40 30

471. Regalia of Chimu Chief (Imperial period). **472.** Angel with Lute.

1979. Rafael Larco Herrera Museum of Archaeology.
1470. **471.** 85 s. multicoloured .. 60 40

1980. Christmas.
1471. **472.** 25 s. multicoloured .. 20 10

1980. Various stamps surch.
1472. **466.** 20 s. on 16 s. multicoloured (postage) 15 10
1473. **463.** 25 s. on 14 s. multicoloured 30 15
1474. **464.** 65 s. on 34 s. multicoloured 45 35
1475. **458.** 80 s. on 70 s. mauve 55 40
1476. **449.** 35 s. on 24 s. mauve (air) 25 15
1477. **438.** 45 s. on 32 s. black and brown .. 30 20

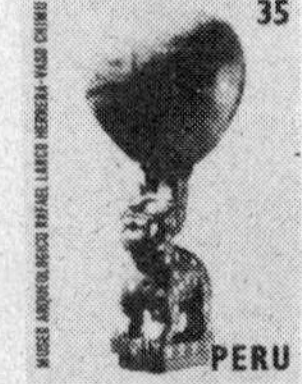
474. "Respect and Comply with the Constitution". **475.** Ceramic Vase (Chimu Culture).

1980. Citizens' Duties.
1478. **474.** 15 s. turquoise .. 10 8
1479. – 20 s. red 15 10
1480. – 25 s. blue 20 12
1481. – 30 s. mauve 20 15
1482. – 35 s. black 25 20
1483. – 45 s. green 30 25
1484. – 50 s. brown 35 25

INSCRIPTIONS: 20 s. "Honour your country and protect your interests". 25 s. "Comply with the elective process". 30 s. "Comply with your military service". 35 s. "Pay your taxes". 45 s. "Work and contribute to national progress". 50 s. "Respect the rights of others".

1980. Rafael Larco Herrera Archaeological Museum.
1485. **475.** 35 s. multicoloured .. 25 20

476. "Liberty" and Map of Peru.

1980. Return to Democracy.
1486. **476.** 25 s. black, buff & red 20 12
1487. – 35 s. black and red .. 25 20

DESIGN: 35 s. Handshake.

477. Machu Picchu. **478.** Rebellion Memorial Cuzco (Joaquin Ugarte).

1980. World Tourism Conference, Manila.
1488. **477.** 25 s. multicoloured .. 20 12

1980. Bicent. of Tupac Amaru Rebellion.
1489. **478.** 25 s. multicoloured .. 20 12

See also No. 1503.

479. Nativity.

1980. Christmas.
1490. **479.** 15 s. multicoloured 10 8

480. Bolivar and Flags. **482.** Presidential Badge of Office, Laurel Leaves and Open Book.

1981. 150th Death Anniv. of Simon Bolivar.
1491. **480.** 40 s. multicoloured .. 30 20

1981. Various stamps surch.
1492 – 25 s. on 35 s. black and red (No. 1487) 20 12
1493 **482** 40 s. on 25 s. mult .. 30 20
1494 **458** 85 s. on 200 s. violet 60 45
1495 – 100 s. on 115 s. mult (No. 1448) .. 70 50
1496 **482** 130 s. on 25 s. mult .. 25 15
1497 140 s. on 25 s. mult .. 25 15

1981. Re-establishment of Constitutional Government.
1498. **482.** 25 s. multicoloured .. 20 12

483. Stone Head, Pallasca.

1981.
1499. **483.** 30 s. violet 20 15
1500. – 40 s. blue 30 20
1501. – 100 s. mauve .. 70 45
1502. – 140 s. green 95 60

DESIGNS—VERT. 40 s. Stone head, Huamachuco. 100 s. Stone head (Chavin culture). HORIZ. 140 s. Stone puma head (Chavin culture).

484. Tupac Amaru and Micaela Bastidas (sculptures by Miguel Boca Rossi). **485.** Post Box, 1859.

1981. Bicentenary of Revolution of Tupac Amaru and Micaela Bastidas.
1503. **484.** 60 s. multicoloured .. 40 30

1981. 50th Anniv. of Postal and Philatelic Museum, Lima.
1504. **485.** 130 s. multicoloured 50 60

486. Map of Peru and I.Y.D.P. Emblem. **487.** Victor Raul Haya de la Torre (President of Constitutional Assembly).

1981. International Year of Disabled Persons.
1505. **486.** 100 s. violet, mauve and gold 70 45

1981. Constitution.
1506. **487.** 30 s. violet and grey . . 20 15

1981. No. 801 surch.
1507. 30 s. on 2 s. 20 brn. & blue 20 15
1508. 40 s. on 2 s. 20 brn. & blue 30 20

1981. 12th International Pacific Fair. No. 801 surch with **12 Feria Internacional del Pacifico 1981 140**.
1509. 140 s. on 2 s. 20 brn. & blue 95 70

490. Inca Messenger (drawing by Guaman Ponce de Ayala).
493. Inca Pot.

1981. Christmas.
1510. **490.** 30 s. black and mauve 20 10
1511. 40 s. black and red . . 30 10
1512. 130 s. black and green 40 35
1513. 140 s. black and blue 40 35
1514. 200 s. black and brown 60 55

1982. Various stamps surch **Habilitado Franq. Postal** and value (Nos. 1520/1) or with value only (others).
1515. **229.** 10 s. on 2 c. brown (postage) . . 15 5
1516. – 10 s. on 10 c. red (No. 642) . . 8 5
1517. **292.** 40 s. on 10 c. blue and yellow 15 10
1518. **273.** 70 s. on 5 c. blue and red 35 20
1519. **264a.** 80 s. on 3 c. lake . . 30 15
1520. D **109.** 80 s. on 10 c. green 30 15
1521. O **108.** 80 s. on 10 c. brown 30 15
1522. **292.** 100 s. on 10 c. blue and yellow . . 40 20
1523. – 140 s. on 50 c. brown, yellow and red . . 50 25
1524. – 140 s. on 1 s. mult. . . 50 25
1525. **264a.** 150 s. on 3 c. lake . . 40 20
1526. 180 s. on 3 c. lake . . 55 30
1527. 200 s. on 3 c. lake . . 40 40
1528. **273.** 280 s. on 5 c. blue and red 60 55
1529. – 40 s. on 1 s. 25 blue and purple (No. 814) (air) . . 30 15
1530. – 100 s. on 2 s. 20 brown and blue (No. 801) 40 20
1531. – 240 s. on 1 s. 25 blue and purple (No. 814) 50 60

Nos. 1523/4 are surcharged on labels for the Seventh Eucharistic Congress which previously had no postal validity.

1982. Indian Ceramics.
1532. **493.** 40 s. orange 30 15
1533. 80 s. lilac 50 25
1534. – 80 s. red 50 25
1535. **493.** 180 s. green . . . . 1·25 70
1536. – 240 s. blue 90 60
1537. – 280 s. violet . . . . 1·00 70

DESIGNS: 80 s., (No. 1534), 240 s., 280 s. Nazca fish ceramic.

494. Jorge Basadre (after Oscar Lopez Aliaga).

1982. Jorge Basadre (historian) Commemoration.
1538. **494.** 100 s. black and green 25 20

495. Julio C. Tello (bust, Victoria Macho).

1982. Birth Centenary of Julio C. Tello (archaeologist).
1539. **495.** 200 s. green and blue 45 30

496. Championship Emblem.
497. Disabled Person in Wheel-chair.

1982. 9th World Women's Volleyball Championship, Peru.
1540. **496.** 80 s. red and black . . 20 12

1982. Rights for the Disabled Year.
1541. **497.** 200 s. blue and red . . 50 30

498. Andres A. Caceres Medallion.

1982. Centenary of Brena Campaign.
1542. **498.** 70 s. brown and grey 20 12

499. Footballers.
500. Congress Emblem.

1982. World Cup Football Championship, Spain.
1543. **499.** 80 s. multicoloured . . 20 12

1982. 16th International Latin Notaries Congress, Lima.
1544. **500.** 500 s. black, gold and red 75 50

501. Bull (clay jar).
502. Pedro Vilcapaza.

1982. Handicrafts Year.
1545. **501.** 200 s. red, brown and black 50 30

1982. Death Bicentenary of Pedro Vilcapaza (Indian leader).
1546. **502.** 240 s. brown and black 35 35

503. Jose Davila Condemarin (after J. Y. Pastor).
504. " Nativity " (Hilario Mendivil).

1982. Death Cent. of Jose Davila Condemarin (Director General of Posts).
1547. **503.** 150 s. black & blue 40 25

1982. Christmas.
1548. **504.** 280 s. multicoloured 40 30

505. Centre Emblem and Hand holding Potatoes.

1982. 10th Anniv. of International Potato Centre.
1549. **505.** 240 s. brown & grey 35 35

506. Arms of Piura.

1982. 450th Anniv. of San Miguel de Piura.
1550. **506.** 280 s. multicoloured 40 40

507. Microscope.

1982. Centenary of Discovery of Tubercule Bacillus.
1551. **507.** 240 s. green . . 35 35

508. " St. Theresa of Avila " (Jose Espinoza de los Monteros).
509. Civil Defence Badge and Interlocked Hands.

1983. 400th Death Anniv. of St. Theresa of Avila.
1552. **508.** 100 s. multicoloured 25 15

1983. 10th Anniv. of Civil Defence System.
1553. **509.** 100 s. blue, orge. & blk. 25 15

510. Silver Shoe.

1983. " Peru, Land of Silver ".
1554. **510.** 250 s. silver, blk. & bl. 55 35

511. Map of Signatories and 200 Mile Zone.

1983. 30th Anniv. of Santiago Declaration.
1555. **511.** 280 s. brn., bl. & blk. 40 40

512. Boeing "747".
513. "75".

1983. 25th Anniv. of Lima–Bogota Airmail Service.
1556. **512.** 150 s. multicoloured 60 25

1983. 75th Anniv. of Lima and Callao State Lotteries.
1557. **513.** 100 s. blue and purple 20 12

514. Cruiser " Almirante Grau ".

1983. Peruvian Navy. Multicoloured.
1558. 150 s. Type **514** 75 20
1559. 350 s. Submarine " Ferre " 1·00 50

1983. Various stamps surch.
1560. **493.** 100 s. on 40 s. orange 20 12
1561. **498.** 100 s. on 70 s. brown and grey 20 12
1562. **496.** 100 s. on 80 s. red and black 20 12
1563. **502.** 100 s. on 240 s. brown and black 20 12
1564. **505.** 100 s. on 240 s. ochre, deep brown & brown 20 12
1565. **507.** 100 s. on 240 s. green 20 12
1566. **506.** 150 s. on 280 s. mult. 30 15
1567. **511.** 150 s. on 280 s. brown, blue and black . . 30 15
1568. **504.** 200 s. on 280 s. mult. 40 25
1569. **493.** 300 s. on 180 s. green 55 35
1570. 400 s. on 180 s. green 75 50
1571. **499.** 500 s. on 80 s. mult. . . 95 65

516. Simon Bolivar.
517. "Virgin and Child" (Cuzquena School).

1983. Birth Bicent. of Simon Bolivar.
1572. **516.** 100 s. blue and black 20 12

1983. Christmas.
1573. **517.** 100 s. multicoloured 20 10

518. Fair Emblem.
519. W.C.Y. Emblem.

1983. 14th International Pacific Fair.
1574. **518.** 350 s. multicoloured 65 40

1984. World Communications Year.
1575. **519.** 700 s. multicoloured 1·00 70

520. Leoncio Prado.
521. Container Ship at Wharf.

1984. Death Centenary (1983) of Colonel Leoncio Prado.
1576 **520** 150 s. bistre & brown 15 10

1984. Peruvian Industry.
1577. **521.** 200 s. purple 40 25
1578. – 300 s. blue 60 25

DESIGN: 300 s. Container ship.

522. Ricardo Palma
523. Pistol Shooting.

1984. 150th Birth Anniv (1983) of Ricardo Palma (writer).
1579. **522.** 200 s. violet 15 10

1984. Olympic Games, Los Angeles.
1580 **523** 500 s. mauve & black 45 25
1581 – 750 s. red and black . . 60 30

DESIGN: Hurdling.

INDEX

Countries can be quickly located by referring to the index at the end of this volume.

524. Arms of Callao. **525.** Water Jar.

1984. Town Arms.
1582. **524.** 350 s. grey 25 15
1583. – 400 s. brown . . 30 25
1584. – 500 s. brown . . 40 30
DESIGNS: 400 s. Cajamarca. 500 s. Ayacucho.

1984. Wari Ceramics (1st series).
1585. **525.** 100 s. brown . . 10 5
1586. – 150 s. brown . . 15 5
1587. – 200 s. brown . . 20 10
DESIGNS: 150 s. Llama. 200 s. Vase.
See also Nos. 1616/18.

526. Hendee's Woolly Monkeys. **527.** Signing Declaration of Independence.

1984. Fauna.
1588. **526.** 1000 s. multicoloured 45 40

1984. Declaration of Independence.
1589 **527** 350 s. black, brn & red 25 15

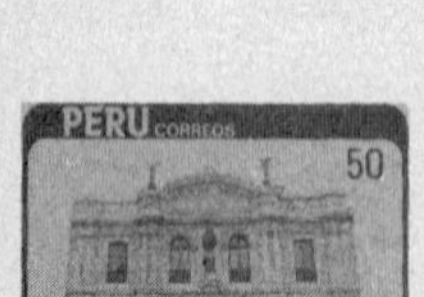

528. General Post Office, Lima. **529.** "Canna edulis"

1984. Postal Services.
1590. **528.** 50 s. olive 5 5

1984. Flora.
1591. **529.** 700 s. multicoloured 45 25

530. Grau (after Pablo Muniz). **531.** Hipolito Unanue.

1984. 150th Anniv. of Admiral Miguel Grau. Multicoloured.
1592. 600 s. Type **530** 35 20
1593. 600 s. Battle of Angamos (45 × 35 mm.) 70 30
1594. 600 s. Grau's seat, National Congress 35 20
1595. 600 s. "Battle of Iquique" (Guillermo Spier) (45 × 35 mm.) 70 30

1984. 150th Death Anniv (1983) of Hipolito Unanue (founder of School of Medicine).
1596 **531** 50 s. green . . 5 5

532. Destroyer "Almirante Guise".

1984. Peruvian Navy.
1597 **532** 250 s. blue 25 15
1598 – 400 s. turquoise & blue 55 20
DESIGN: 400 s. River gunboat "America".

533. "The Adoration of the Shepherds". **534.** Belaunde.

1984. Christmas.
1599. **533.** 1000 s. multicoloured 40 15

1984. Birth Centenary (1983) of Victor Andres Belaunde (diplomat).
1600 **534** 100 s. purple 15 10

535. Street in Cuzco. **536.** Fair Emblem.

1984. 450th Anniv. of Founding of Cuzco by the Spanish.
1601. **535.** 1000 s. multicoloured 40 25

1984. 15th International Pacific Fair, Lima.
1602. **536.** 1000 s. blue and red 40 25

537. "Foundation of Lima" (Francisco Gonzalez Gamarra). **538.** Pope John Paul II.

1985. 450th Anniv. of Lima.
1603. **537.** 1500 s. multicoloured 55 30

1985. Papal Visit.
1604. **538.** 2000 s. multicoloured 45 35

539. Dish Aerial, Huancayo. **540.** Jose Carlos Mariategui.

1985. 15th Anniv. (1984) of Entel Peru (National Telecommunications Enterprise).
1605. **539.** 1100 s. multicoloured 25 15

1985. 60th Death Anniv (1984) of Jose Carlos Mariategui (writer).
1606 **540** 800 s. red 20 12

541 Emblem.

1985. 25th Meeting of American Airforces Co-operation System.
1607. **541.** 400 s. multicoloured 15 10

542. Captain Quinones.

1985. 44th Death Anniv. of Jose Abelardo Quinones Gonzales (airforce captain).
1608. **542.** 1000 s. multicoloured 25 15

543. Arms of Huancavelica. **544.** Globe and Emblem.

1985.
1609 **543** 700 s. orange 15 15
See also Nos. 1628/9.

1985. 14th Latin–American Air and Space Regulations Days, Lima.
1610. **544.** 900 s. blue . . 25 15

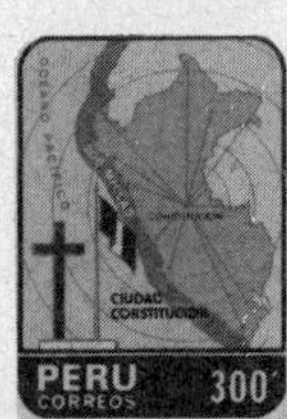

545. Francisco Garcia Calderon (head of 1881 Provisional Government). **546.** Cross, Flag and Map.

1985. Personalities.
1611 **545** 500 s. green 20 10
1612 – 800 s. green 35 15
DESIGN: 800 s. Oscar Miro Quesada (philosopher and jurist).

1985. 1st Anniv of Constitucion City.
1613 **546** 300 s. multicoloured . . 15 10

547. General Post Office Lima. **548.** Society Emblem, Satellite and Radio Equipment.

1985. Postal Services
1614 **547** 200 s. grey . . 10 5

1985. 55th Anniv of Peruvian Radio Club.
1615 **548** 1300 s. blue & orange 35 20

549. Robles Moqo Style Cat Vase. **550.** St. Francis's Monastry, Lima.

1985. Wari Ceramics (2nd series).
1616 **549** 500 s. brown . . 15 8
1617 – 500 s. brown . . 15 8
1618 – 500 s. brown . . 15 8
DESIGNS: No. 1617, Cat, Huaura Style. 1618, Llama's head, Robles Moqo style.

1985. Tourism Day.
1619 **550** 1300 s. multicoloured 30 15

551. Title Page of "Doctrina Christiana" **552.** Emblem and Curtiss "Jenny" Airplane.

1985. 400th Anniv of First Book printed in South America.
1620 **551** 300 s. black & stone . . 12 5

1985. 40th Anniv of I.C.A.O.
1621 **552** 1100 s. black, bl & red 40 15

553. Humboldt Penguin. **554.** "Virgin and Child" (Cuzquena School).

1985. Fauna.
1622 **553** 1500 s. multicoloured 90 30

1985. Christmas.
1623 **554** 2 i. 50 multicoloured 20 10

555. Postman lifting child. **556.** Cesar Vallejo.

1985. Postal Workers' Christmas and Children's Restaurant Funds.
1624 **555** 2 i. 50 multicoloured . . 30 20

1986. Poets.
1625 **556** 800 s. blue 20 10
1626 – 800 s. brown . . 20 10
DESIGN: No. 1626, Jose Santos Chocano.

557. Arms.

1986. 450th Anniv of Trujillo.
1627 **557** 3 i. multicoloured . . 30 15

1986. Town Arms. As T **543**.
1628 700 s. blue 15 10
1629 900 s. brown 25 15
DESIGNS: 700 s. Huanuco. 900 s. Puno.

558. Stone Carving of Fish.

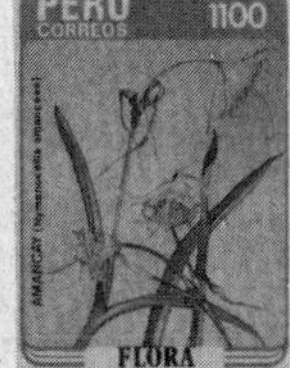

559. "Hymenocallis amancaes".

1986. Restoration of Chan-Chan.
1630 **558** 50 c. multicoloured .. 8 5

1986. Flora.
1631. **559.** 1100 s. multicoloured 25 15

560. Alpaca and Textiles.

561. St. Rosa de Lima (Daniel Hernandez).

1986. Peruvian Industry.
1632 **560** 1100 s. multicoloured 25 15

1986. 400th Birth Anniv. of St. Rosa de Lima.
1633. **561.** 7 i. multicoloured .. 70 40

562. Daniel Alcides Carrion.

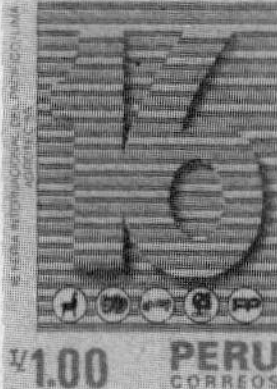

563. Emblems and "16".

1986. Death Centenary (1985) of Daniel Alcides Carrion.
1634. **562.** 50 c. brown 10 5

1986. 16th International Pacific Fair, Lima.
1635. **563.** 1 i. multicoloured .. 10 5

564. Woman Hand-spinning and Boy in Reed Canoe.

565. Pedro Vilcapaza.

1986. International Youth Year.
1636. **564.** 3 i. 50 multicoloured 55 20

1986. 205th Anniv. of Vilcapaza Rebellion.
1637. **565.** 50 c. brown 8 5

566. U.N. Building, New York.

567. Fernando and Justo Albujar Fayaque and Manuel Guarniz.

1986. 40th Anniv. (1985) of U.N.O.
1638. **566.** 3 i. 50 multicoloured 30 20

1986. National Heroes.
1639. **567.** 50 c. brown 5 5

568. Nasturtium.

569. Submarine "Casma (R-1)", 1926.

1986. Flora.
1640. **568.** 80 c. multicoloured.. 10 5

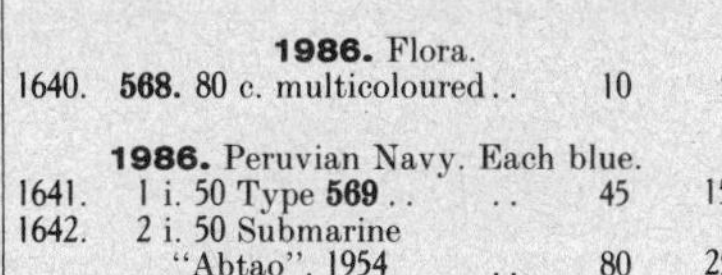

1986. Peruvian Navy. Each blue.
1641. 1 i. 50 Type **569** 45 15
1642. 2 i. 50 Submarine "Abtao", 1954 .. 80 25

570. Tinta Costumes, Canchis Province.

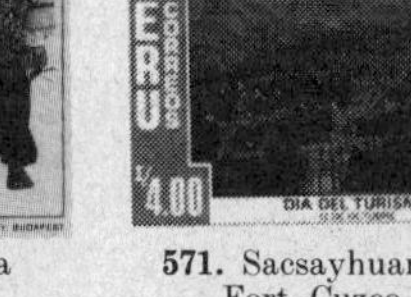

571. Sacsayhuaman Fort, Cuzco.

1986. Costumes.
1643 **570** 3 i. multicoloured .. 30 20

1986. Tourism Day (1st issue).
1644. **571.** 4 i. multicoloured .. 40 30
See also No. 1654.

572. La Tomilla Water Treatment Plant.

573. "Datura candida".

1986. 25th Anniv. of Inter-American Development Bank.
1645. **572.** 1 i. multicoloured .. 10 5

1986. Flora.
1646. **573.** 80 c. multicoloured.. 10 5

574. Pope John Paul and Sister Ana.

575. Chavez, Bleriot "XI" and Simplon Range.

1986. Beatification of Sister Ana of the Angels Monteagudo.
1647. **574.** 6 i. multicoloured .. 65 45

1986. 75th Anniv. of Trans-Alpine Flight by Jorge Chavez Dartnell.
1648. **575.** 5 i. multicoloured .. 75 35

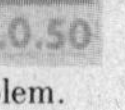

576. Emblem.

577. "Martyrs of Uchuraccay".

1986. National Vaccination Days.
1649. **576.** 50 c. blue 5 5

1986. Peruvian Journalists' Fund.
1650. **577.** 1 i. 50 black and blue 15 10

578. "Canis nudus".

579. Brigantine "Gamarra".

1986. Fauna.
1651. **578.** 2 i. multicoloured .. 20 15

1986. Navy Day.
1652. **579.** 1 i. blue & light blue 50 20
1653. – 1 i. blue and red .. 50 20
DESIGN: No 1653, Battleship "Manco Capac".

580. Intihuatana Cuzco.

1986. Tourism Day (2nd issue).
1654. **580.** 4 i. multicoloured .. 40 30

581. Institute Building.

1986. 35th Anniv (1985) of Institute of Higher Military Studies.
1655. **581.** 1 i. multicoloured .. 15 10

582. Children.

583. White-winged Guan.

1986. Postal Workers' Christmas and Children's Restaurant Funds.
1656 **582** 2 i 50 black and brown 30 20

1986. Fauna.
1657. **583.** 2 i. multicoloured .. 55 15

584. Galvez

585. "St. Joseph and Child" (Cuzquena School).

1986. Birth Centenary (1985) of Jose Galvez Barrenechea (poet).
1658 **584** 50 c. brown 5 5

1986. Christmas.
1659. **585.** 5 i. multicoloured .. 50 30

586. Flags, and Hands holding Cogwheel.

587. Shipibo Costumes.

1986. 25th Anniv of "Senati" (National Industrial Training Organization)
1660. **586.** 4 i. multicoloured .. 40 30

1987. Costumes.
1661. **587.** 3 i. multicoloured .. 30 25

588. Harvesting Mashua.

589. Dr. Reiche and Diagram of Nazca Lines.

1987. World Food Day.
1662 **588** 50 c. multicoloured .. 5 5

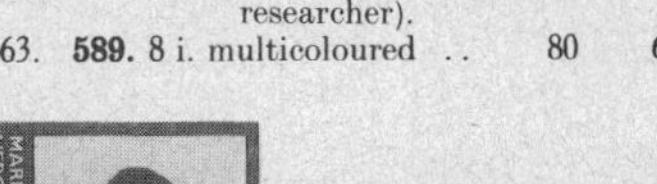

1987. Dr. Maria Reiche (Nazca Lines researcher).
1663. **589.** 8 i. multicoloured .. 80 60

590. Santos.

591. Showjumping.

1987. Mariano Santos (Hero of war of the Pacific).
1664. **590.** 50 c. violet 5 5

1987. 50th Anniv. of Peruvian Horse Club.
1665. **591.** 3 i. multicoloured .. 30 25

592. Salaverry.

1987. 150th Death Anniv (1986) of General Felipe Santiago Salaverry (President, 1835–36).
1666. **592.** 2 i. multicoloured .. 20 15

593. Colca Canyon.

594. 1857 1 & 2 r. Stamps.

1987. "Arequipa 87" National Stamp Exhibition.
1667. **593.** 6 i. multicoloured .. 50 30

1987. "Amifil 87" National Stamp Exhibition, Lima.
1668. **594.** 1 i. brown, blue and grey 10 10

595. Arguedas.

596. Carving, Emblem and Nasturtium.

1987. 75th Birth Anniv (1986) of Jose Maria Arguedas (writer).
1669. **595.** 50 c. brown 5 5

1987. Centenary of Arequipa Chamber of Commerce and Industry.
1670. **596.** 2 i. multicoloured .. 20 15

597. Vaccinating Child.

598. De la Riva Aguero.

1987. Child Vaccination Campaign.
1671. **597.** 50 c. red 5 5

1987. Birth Centenary (1985) of Jose de la Riva Aguero (historian).
1672. **598.** 80 c. brown 5 5

599. Porras Barrenechea.

600. Footballers.

1987. 90th Birth Anniv. of Raul Porras Barrenechea (historian).
1673. **599.** 80 c. brown 5 5

1987. World Cup Football Championship, Mexico (1986).
1674. **600.** 4 i. multicoloured .. 20 15

601. Stone Carving of Man.

1987. Restoration of Chan-Chan.
1675 **601** 50 c. multicoloured .. 5 5

602. Comet and "Giotto" Space Probe.

1987. Appearance of Halley's Comet (1986).
1676. **602.** 4 i. multicoloured .. 20 15

603. Chavez.

604. Osambela Palace.

1987. Birth Centenary of Jorge Chavez Dartnell (aviator).
1677 **603** 2 i. brn, ochre & gold 10 8

1987. 450th Anniv. of Lima.
1678. **604.** 2 i. 50 multicoloured 12 8

605. Machu Picchu.

1987. 75th Anniv (1986) of Discovery of Machu Picchu.
1679. **605.** 9 i. multicoloured .. 40 30

606. St. Francis's Church.

1987. Cajamarca, American Historical and Cultural Site.
1680. **606.** 2 i. multicoloured .. 10 8

607. National Team, Emblem and Olympic Rings.

1988. 50th Anniv (1986) of First Peruvian Participation in Olympic Games (at Berlin).
1681 **607** 1 i. 50 multicoloured .. 8 8

608. Children.

1988. 150th Anniv. of Ministry of Education.
1682. **608.** 1 i. multicoloured .. 5 5

609. Statue and Pope.

1988. Coronation of Virgin of Evangelization, Lima.
1683 **609** 10 i. multicoloured .. 40 30

610. Emblems.

611. Postman and Lima Cathedral.

1988. Rotary International Anti-Polio Campaign.
1684. **610.** 2 i. blue, gold & red 8 5

1988. Postal Workers' Christmas and Children's Restaurant Funds.
1685 **611** 9 i. blue 30 20

612 Flags

613 St. John Bosco

1988. 1st Meeting of Eight Latin American Presidents of Contadora and Lima Groups, Acapulco, Mexico.
1686 **612** 9 i. multicoloured .. 30 20

1988. Death Centenary of St. John Bosco (founder of Salesian Brothers).
1687 **613** 5 i. multicoloured .. 20 15

614 Supply Ship "Humboldt" and Globe

1988. 1st Peruvian Scientific Expedition to Antarctica.
1688 **614** 7 i. multicoloured .. 70 20

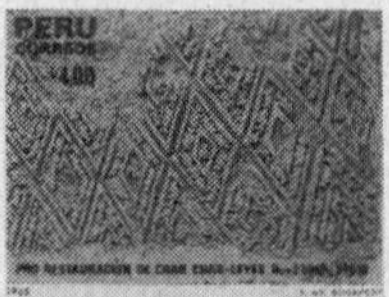

615 Clay Wall

1988. Restoration of Chan-Chan.
1689 **615** 4 i. brown and black 15 10

616 Vallejo (after Picasso)

617 Journalists at Work

1988. 50th Death Anniv of Cesar Vallejo (poet).
1690 **616** 25 i. black, yell & brn 50 40

1988. Peruvian Journalists' Fund.
1691 **617** 4 i. blue and brown .. 8 5

618 1908 2 s. Columbus Monument Stamp

619 "17" and Guanaco

1988. "Exfilima 88" Stamp Exhibition, Lima, and 500th Anniv of Discovery of America by Christopher Columbus.
1692 **618** 20 i. blue, pink & black 20 10

1988. 17th International Pacific Fair, Lima.
1693 **619** 4 i. multicoloured .. 5 5

620 "Village Band"

621 Dogs

1988. Birth Cent of Jose Sabogal (painter).
1694 **620** 12 i. multicoloured .. 15 10

1988. "Canino '88" International Dog Show, Lima.
1695 **621** 20 i. multicoloured .. 20 10

622 Silva and Score of "Splendour of Flowers"

623 Pope

1988. 50th Death Anniv (1987) of Alfonso de Silva (composer).
1696 **622** 20 i. grey, deep brown and brown .. 20 10

1988. 2nd Visit of Pope John Paul II.
1697 **623** 50 i. multicoloured .. 35 25

624 Volleyball

625 Volleyball

1988. Olympic Games, Seoul.
1698 **624** 25 i. multicoloured .. 20 10

1988. Postal Workers' Christmas and Children's Restaurant Funds. Unissued stamp surch as in T **625**.
1699 **625** 95 i. on 300 s. black and red 60 50

626 Ceramic Vase

627 Map

1988. Chavin Culture. Unissued stamps surch as in T **626**.
1700 **626** 40 i. on 100 s. red .. 30 20
1701 80 i. on 10 s. black .. 25 15

1989. Forest Boundary Road. Unissued stamp surch as in T **627**.
1702 **627** 70 i. on 80 s. green, black and blue .. 40 30

628 Arms

629 Huari Weaving

1989. Laws of the Indies. Unissued stamp surch as in T **628**.
1703 **628** 230 i. on 300 s. brown 40 15

1989. Centenary of Credit Bank of Peru.
1704 **629** 500 i. multicoloured .. 60 20

630 Special Postal Services Emblem

631 Newspaper Offices

1989. Postal Services.
1705 **630** 50 i. blue and green 5 5
1706 – 100 i. red and pink .. 5 5
DESIGN: 100 i. National Express Post emblem.

1989. 150th Anniv of "El Comercio" (newspaper).
1707 **631** 600 i. multicoloured .. 50 10

632 Garcilaso de la Vega

1989. 450th Birth Anniv of Garcilaso de la Vega (writer).
1708 **632** 300 i. multicoloured .. 8 5

633 Emblem

1989. Express Mail Service.
1709 **633** 100 i. red, blue & orge 5 5

634 Dr. Luis Loli Roca (founder of Journalists' Federation)

1989. Peruvian Journalists' Fund.
1710 **634** 100 i. blue, deep blue and black .. 5 5

635 Relief of Birds

1989. Restoration of Chan-Chan.
1711 **635** 400 i. multicoloured .. 35 5

636 Old Map of South America

1989. Cent of Lima Geographical Society.
1712 **636** 600 i. multicoloured .. 95 20

637 Painting

1989. 132nd Anniv of Society of Founders of Independence.
1713 **637** 300 i. multicoloured .. 8 5

638 Lake Huacachina

1989. 3rd Meeting of Latin American Presidents of Contadora and Lima Groups, Ica.
1714 **638** 1300 i. multicoloured 1·10 60

639 Children buying Stamps for Commemorative Envelopes

641 Vessel with Figure of Doctor examining Patient

640 "Corryocactus huincoensis"

1989. Postal Workers' Christmas and Children's Restaurant Funds.
1715 **639** 1200 i. multicoloured 30 20

1989. Cacti. Multicoloured
1716 500 i. Type **640** 12 5
1717 500 i. "Haageocereus clavispinus (vert) .. 12 5
1718 500 i. "Loxanthocereus acanthurus" 12 5
1719 500 i. "Matucana cereoides" (vert) .. 12 5
1720 500 i. "Trichocereus peruvianus" (vert) .. 12 5

1989. America. Pre-Columbian Ceramics. Multicoloured.
1721 5000 i. Type **641** .. .. 1·60 1·00
1722 5000 i. Vessel with figure of surgeon performing cranial operation .. 1·60 1·00

642 Bethlehem Church

1990. Cajamarca, American Historical and Cultural Site.
1723 **642** 600 i. multicoloured .. 15 10

643 Climber in Andes

644 Pope and Virgin of Evangelization

1990. Huascaran National Park. Mult.
1724 900 i. Type **643** 20 15
1725 900 i. Llanganuco Lake (horiz) 20 15
1726 1000 i. "Puya raimondi" (plant) 25 20
1727 1000 i. Snow-covered mountain peak (horiz) 25 20
1728 1100 i. Huascaran Mountain (horiz) .. 30 25
1729 1100 i. Andean condor over mountain slopes (horiz) 45 35

1990. 2nd Visit of Pope John Paul II.
1730 **644** 1250 i. multicoloured 30 25

645 "Agrias beata" (female)

1990. Butterflies. Multicoloured.
1731 1000 i. Type **645** 35 25
1732 1000 i. "Agrias beata" (male) 35 25
1733 1000 i. "Agrias amydon" (female) 35 25
1734 1000 i. "Agrias sardanapalus" (female) .. 35 25
1735 1000 i. "Agrias sardanapalus" (male) 35 25

646 Victor Raul Haya de la Torre (President of Constituent Assembly)

647 Emblem

1990. 10th Anniv of Political Constitution.
1736 **646** 2100 i. multicoloured 45 10

1990. 40th Anniv of Peruvian Philatelic Association.
1737 **647** 300 i. brn, blk & cream 10 10

648 Globe and Exhibition Emblem

1990. "Prenfil '88" International Philatelic Literature Exhibition, Buenos Aires.
1738 **648** 300 i. multicoloured .. 10 10

649 "Republic" (Antoine-Jean Gros)

1990. Bicentenary of French Revolution. Paintings. Multicoloured.
1739 2000 i. Type **649** 40 10
1740 2000 i. "Storming the Bastille" (Hubert Robert) 40 10
1741 2000 i. "La Fayette at the Festival of the Republic" (anon) .. 40 10
1742 2000 i. "Jean Jacques Rousseau and Symbols of the Revolution" (E. Jeaurat) 40 10

650 "Founding Arequipa" (Teodoro Nunez Ureta)

1990. 450th Anniv of Arequipa.
1743 **650** 50000 i. multicoloured 10 10

651 Pelado Island Lighthouse

1990. Peruvian Navy. Unissued stamps, each light blue and blue, surch as in T **651**.
1744 110000 i. on 200 i. Type **651** 40 25
1745 230000 i. on 400 i. "Morona" (hospital ship) .. 1·25 60

652 Games Mascot

653 1857 1 r. Stamp and Container Ship

1990. 4th South American Games (1st issue). Multicoloured.
1746 110000 i. Type **652** .. 25 20
1747 280000 i. Shooting .. 1·10 60
1748 290000 i. Athletics (horiz) 1·25 65
1749 300000 i. Football .. 1·25 65
See also Nos. 1753/6.

1990. 150th Anniv of Pacific Steam Navigation Company. Mult. Self-adhesive.
1750 250000 i. Type **653** .. 1·25 65
1751 350000 i. 1857 2 r. stamp and container ship .. 1·75 85

654 Postal Van

1990. Postal Workers' Christmas and Children's Restaurant Funds.
1752 **654** 310000 i. multicoloured 75 70

1991. 4th South American Games (2nd issue). As T **652**. Multicoloured.
1753 560000 i. Swimming .. 1·25 1·10
1754 580000 i. Show jumping (vert) .. .. 1·90 1·10
1755 600000 i. Yachting (vert) 2·00 1·25
1756 620000 i. Tennis (vert) .. 2·50 1·40
2·10 1·40

655 Maria Jesus Castaneda de Pardo

1991. Red Cross. Unissued stamp surch.
1757 **655** 0.15 i/m. on 2500 i. red 50 25

Note. " i/m" on No. 1757 onwards indicates face value in million intis.

656 Penguins, Scientist and Station

1991. 2nd Peruvian Scientific Expedition to Antartica. Unissued stamps surch. Mult.
1758 0.40 i/m. on 50000 i. Type **656** 20 10
1759 0.45 i/m. on 80000 i. Station and gull .. 20 10
1760 0.50 i/m. on 100000 i. Whale, map and station 1·60 10

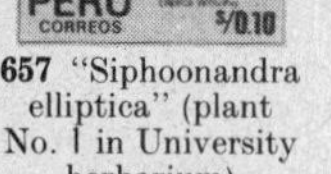

657 "Siphoonandra elliptica" (plant No. 1 in University herbarium)

658 "Virgin of the Milk"

1991. 300th Anniv of National University of St. Anthony Abad del Cusco. Mult.
1761 10 c. Type **657** 12 8
1762 20 c. Bishop Manuel de Mollinedo y Angulo (first Chancellor) .. 25 20
1763 1 s. University arms .. 2·00 1·00

1991. Postal Workers' Christmas and Children's Restaurant Funds. Paintings by unknown artists. Multicoloured.
1764 70 c. Type **658** .. .. 1·25 5
1765 70 c. "Divine Shepherdess" .. .. 1·25 5

659 Lake

1991. America (1990). The Natural World. Multicoloured.
1766 0.50 i/m. Type **659** .. 90 5
1767 0.50 i/m. Waterfall (vert) 90 5

660 Sir Rowland Hill and Penny Black

1992. 150th Anniv (1990) of the Penny Black.
1768 **660** 0.40 i/m. blk, grey & bl 70 5

661 Arms and College

662 Arms

1992. 150th Anniv (1990) of Our Lady of Guadalupe College.
1769 **661** 0.30 i/m. multicoloured 55 5

1992. 80th Anniv (1991) of Entre Nous Society, Lima (literature society for women).
1770 **662** 10 c. multicoloured .. 10 5

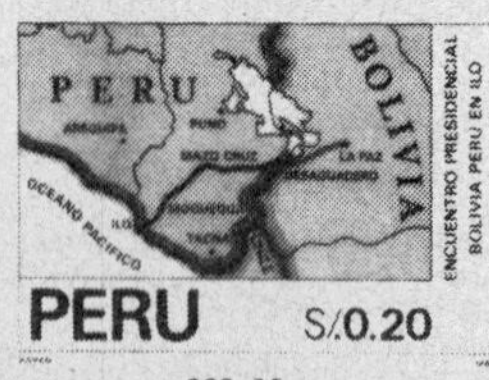

663 Map

1992. Bolivia–Peru Presidential Meeting, Ilo.
1771 **663** 20 c. multicoloured .. 15 10

664 Tacaynamo Idol

665 Raimondi

1992. Restoration of Chan-Chan.
1772 **664** 0.15 i/m. multicoloured 10 5
See note below No. 1757.

1992. Death Centenary of Jose Antonio Raimondi (naturalist).
1773 **665** 0.30 i/m. multicoloured 25 20
See note below No. 1757.

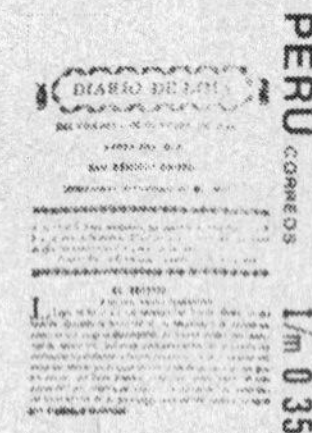

666 First Issue

1992. Bicentenary (1990) of "Diario de Lima" (newspaper).
1774 **666** 35 c. black and yellow 35 15

667 Melgar

1992. Birth Bicentenary (1990) of Mariano Melgar (poet).
1775 **667** 60 c. multicoloured .. 50 25

668 1568 Eight Silver Reales Coin

1992. First Peruvian Coinage.
1776 **668** 70 c. multicoloured 70 35

669 Emblem

1992. 75th Anniv of Catholic University of Peru.
1777 **669** 90 c. black and stone 70 35

670 Emblem

672 "Virgin of the Spindle" (painting, Santa Clara Monastery, Cuzco)

1992. 90th Anniv of Pan-American Health Organization. Self-adhesive. Imperf.
1778 **670** 3 s. multicoloured .. 2·40 1·10

1992. Various stamps surch.
1779 – 40 c. on 500 i. multicoloured (1717) 30 15
1780 – 40 c. on 500 i. multicoloured (1718) 30 15
1781 – 40 c. on 500 i. multicoloured (1719) 30 15
1782 – 40 c. on 500 i. multicoloured (1720) 30 15
1783 **493** 50 c. on 180 s. green .. 40 20
1784 **648** 50 c. on 300 i. mult .. 40 20
1785 **645** 50 c. on 1000 i. mult 40 20
1786 – 50 c. on 1000 i. multicoloured (1732) 40 20
1787 – 50 c. on 1000 i. multicoloured (1734) 40 20
1788 – 50 c. on 1000 i. multicoloured (1735) 40 20
1789 **647** 1 s. on 300 i. brown, black and cream .. 80 40
1790 **644** 1 s. on 1250 i. mult .. 80 40
1791 **638** 1 s. on 1300 i. mult .. 80 40

1993. Self-adhesive. Imperf.
1792 **672** 80 c. multicoloured .. 65 30

673 Gold Figures

1993. Sican Culture (1st series). Multicoloured. Self-adhesive. Imperf.
1793 2 s. Type **673** .. .. 1·60 80
1794 5 s. Gold foil figure (vert) 4·00 2·00
See also Nos. 1813/14.

674 Incan Gold Decoration and Crucifix on Chancay Robe

1993. 500th Anniv of Evangelization of Peru. Self-adhesive. Imperf.
1795 **674** 1 s. multicoloured .. 80 40

675 "The Marinera" (Monica Rojas)

676 "Madonna and Child" (statue)

1993. Paintings of Traditional Scenes. Multicoloured. Self-adhesive. Imperf.
1796 1 s. 50 Type **675** .. .. 1·25 60
1797 1 s. 50 "Fruit Sellers" (Angel Chavez) .. 1·25 60

1993. Centenary (1991) of Salesian Brothers in Peru. Self-adhesive. Imperf.
1798 **676** 70 c. multicoloured .. 55 25

677 Francisco Pizarro and Spanish Galleon

1993. America (1991). Voyages of Discovery. Multicoloured.
1799 90 c. Type **677** 55 25
1800 1 s. Spanish galleon and route map of Pizarro's second voyage .. 60 30
Nos. 1799/1800 were issued together, se-tenant, forming a composite design.

678 Gold Mask

1993. Jewels from Funerary Chamber of "Senor of Sipan".
1801 **678** 50 c. multicoloured .. 30 15

679 Escriva

680 Cherry Blossom and Nazca Lines Hummingbird

1993. 1st Anniv of Beatification of Josemaria Escriva (founder of Opus Dei). Self-adhesive. Imperf.
1802 **679** 30 c. multicoloured .. 20 10

1993. 120th Anniv of Diplomatic Relations and Peace, Friendship, Commerce and Navigation Treaty with Japan. Mult.
1803 1 s. 50 Type **680** 95 45
1804 1 s. 70 Peruvian and Japanese children and Mts. Huascaran (Peru) and Fuji (Japan) .. 1·10 55

681 Sea Lions

682 Delgado

1993. Stamp Exhibitions. Multicoloured.
1805 90 c. Type **681** ("Amifil '93" National Stamp Exhibition, Lima) .. 55 25
1806 1 s. Macaw ("Brasiliana '93" International Stamp Exhibition, Rio de Janeiro) (vert) .. 60 30

1993. Birth Centenary of Dr. Honorio Delgado (psychiatrist and neurologist). Self-adhesive. Imperf.
1807 **682** 50 c. brown 30 15

683 Morales Macedo

684 "The Sling" (Quechua Indians)

1993. Birth Centenary of Rosalia de Lavalle de Morales Macedo (founder of Society for Protection of Children and of Christian Co-operation Bank). Self-adhesive. Imperf.
1808 **683** 80 c. orange 50 25

1993. Ethnic Groups. Statuettes by Felipe Lettersten. Mult. Self-adhesive. Imperf.
1809 2 s. Type **684** .. .. 1·25 60
1810 3 s. 50 "Fire" (Orejon Indians) .. .. 2·25 1·10

685 "20" on Stamp

686 "Virgin of Loreta"

1993. 20th International Pacific Fair.
1811 685 1 s. 50 multicoloured 95 45

1993. Christmas.
1812 686 1 s. multicoloured .. 60 30

687 Artefacts from Tomb, Poma

688 Ceramic Figure

1993. Sican Culture (2nd series). Multicoloured. Self-adhesive. Imperf.
1813 2 s. 50 Type 687 .. .. 1·50 75
1814 4 s. Gold mask .. .. 2·50 1·25

1993. Chancay Culture. Multicoloured. Self-adhesive. Imperf.
1815 10 s. Type 688 .. .. 6·25 3·00
1816 20 s. Textile pattern (horiz) .. .. 12·50 6·25

689 "With AIDS There is No Tomorrow"

1993. International AIDS Day.
1817 689 1 s. 50 multicoloured 95 45

EXPRESS LETTER STAMPS

1908. Optd. **EXPRESO.**
E 373. 76. 10 c. black .. .. 17·00 12·50
E 382. – 10 c. blue (No. 377) 21·00 11·50
E 383. 101. 10 c. black and brown 11·50 10·00

OFFICIAL STAMPS

1890. Stamps of 1866 optd. **GOBIERNO** in frame.
O 287 15 1 c. violet .. .. 1·10 1·10
O 324 1 c. red .. .. 6·75 6·75
O 288 16 2 c. green .. .. 1·10 1·10
O 325 2 c. blue .. .. 6·75 6·75
O 289 5 c. orange .. .. 1·60 1·60
O 326 10 5 c. lake .. .. 5·50 5·50
O 290 16 10 c. black 85 45
O 291 20 c. blue .. .. 2·50 1·60
O 327 20 c. blue (as T 10) .. 5·50 5·50
O 292 20 50 c. red .. .. 3·25 1·40
O 293 21 1 s. brown .. .. 4·25 3·75

1894. Stamps of 1894 (with "Head" optd.) optd. **GOBIERNO** in frame.
O 305. 15. 1 c. orange (No. 294) 19·00 19·00
O 306. 1 c. green (No. 295) 1·10 1·10
O 307. 16. 2 c. violet (No. 296) 1·10 1·10
O 308. 2 c. red (No. 297) .. 90 90
O 309. 5 c. blue (No. 298) .. 8·25 7·50
O 310. 10 c. green (No. 299) 3·00 3·00
O 311. 20. 50 c. green (No. 300) 4·25 4·25

1894. Stamps of 1894 (with "Head" and "Horseshoe" optd.) optd. **GOBIERNO** in frame.
O 312. 16. 2 c. red (No. 301) .. 1·60 1·60
O 313. 5 c. blue (No. 302) .. 1·60 1·60

1896. Stamps of 1896 optd. **GOBIERNO.**
O 348. 75. 1 c. blue 8 5
O 349. 76. 10 c. yellow .. .. 1·00 25
O 350. 10 c. black 8 5
O 351. 77. 50 c. red 25 20

O 108.

1909.
O 382 O 108 1 c. red 10 8
O 572 10 c. brown .. 40 30
O 385 10 c. purple .. 15 10
O 573 50 c. green .. 35 20

1935. Optd. **Servicio Oficial.**
O 567. 184. 10 c. red 10 10

PARCEL POST STAMPS.

P 79

1896. Different frames.
P 348 P 79 1 c. purple .. 1·90 1·60
P 349 2 c. brown .. 2·10 1·90
P 350 5 c. blue .. .. 8·25 5·50
P 351 10 c. brown .. 11·50 8·25
P 352 20 c. pink .. 14·00 11·50
P 353 50 c. green .. 38·00 32·00

1903. Surch in words.
P 361 P 79 1 c. on 20 c. pink 10·00 8·25
P 362 1 c. on 50 c. green 10·00 8·25
P 363 5 c. on 10 c. brown 65·00 55·00

POSTAGE DUE STAMPS

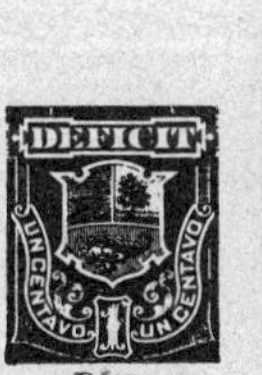

D 22.

D 23.

D 109.

1874.
D 31. D 22. 1 c. brown 10 10
D 32. D 23. 5 c. red 15 15
D 33. 10 c. orange 15 15
D 34. 20 c. blue 30 30
D 35. 50 c. brown .. .. 7·50 3·00

1881. Optd. with T 24 "LIMA" at foot instead of "PERU").
D 47. D 22. 1 c. brown .. .. 3·00 2·00
D 48. D 23. 5 c. red .. .. 5·50 5·00
D 49. 10 c. orange .. .. 5·50 5·50
D 50. 20 c. blue .. .. 21·00 17·00
D 51. 50 c. brown .. .. 45·00 42·00

1881. Optd. **LIMA CORREOS** in double-lined circle.
D 52. D 22. 1 c. brown .. .. 4·25 4·25
D 53. D 23. 5 c. red .. .. 5·50 5·00
D 54. 10 c. orange .. .. 6·75 5·50
D 55. 20 c. blue .. .. 21·00 17·00
D 56. 50 c. brown .. .. 65·00 55·00

1883. Optd. with T 24 (inscr. "LIMA" instead of "PERU") and also with T 28a.
D 247 D 22. 1 c. brown .. .. 4·25 3·00
D 250 D 23. 5 c. red .. .. 6·25 5·75
D 253 10 c. orange .. 6·25 5·75
D 256 20 c. blue £375 £375
D 258 50 c. brown .. .. 45·00 35·00

1884. Optd. with T 28a only.
D 259 D 22. 1 c. brown 40 40
D 262 D 23. 5 c. red 20 20
D 267. 10 c. orange 25 25
D 269. 20 c. blue 85 35
D 271. 50 c. brown .. .. 2·50 75

1894. Optd. **LIMA CORREOS** in double-lined circle and with T 28a.
D 275. D 22. 1 c. brown .. .. 10·50 9·25

1896. Optd. **DEFICIT.**
D 348. D 22. 1 c. brown (D 31) .. 15 15
D 349. D 23. 5 c. red (D 32) .. 15 15
D 350. 10 c. orange (D 33) 45 15
D 351. 20 c. blue (D 34) .. 55 20
D 352. 20. 50 c. red (283) .. 60 20
D 353. 21. 1 s. brown (284) .. 85 35

1899. As T 73, but inscr. "DEFICIT" instead of "FRANQUEO".
D 355. 5 s. green .. .. 85 4·25
D 356. 10 s. brown.. .. 60·00 60·00

1902. Surch **DEFICIT** and value in words.
D 361 1 c. on 10 s. (D 356) .. 85 50
D 362 5 c. on 10 s. (354) .. 50 40

1902. Surch. **DEFICIT** and value in words.
D 363. D 23. 1 c. on 20 c. (D 34) 50 40
D 364. 5 c. on 20 c. (D 34) 1·25 1·00

1909.
D 382. D 109. 1 c. brown .. 35 12
D 419. 1 c. purple .. 15 15
D 420. 2 c. purple .. 15 15
D 570. 2 c. brown .. 15 12
D 383. 5 c. brown .. 35 12
D 421. 5 c. purple .. 25 20
D 384. 10 c. brown .. 40 15
D 422. 10 c. purple .. 40 15
D 571. 10 c. green .. 40 15
D 385. 50 c. brown .. 60 20
D 423. 50 c. purple .. 1·40 50
D 424. 1 s. purple .. 10·00 3·00
D 425. 2 s. purple .. 19·00 6·75

1935. Optd. **Deficit.**
D 568. – 2 c. purple (No. 537) 40 40
D 569. 184. 10 c. red 50 40

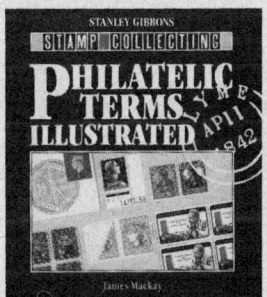

PHILIPPINES Pt. 9; Pt. 22; Pt. 21

A group of islands in the China Sea, E. of Asia, ceded by Spain to the United States after the war of 1898. Under Japanese Occupation from 1941 until 1945. The Philippines became fully independent in 1946. An independent Republic since 1946.

1854.	20 cuartos = 1 real. 8 reales = 1 peso plata fuerte.
1864.	100 centimos = 1 peso plata fuerte.
1871.	100 centimos = 1 escudo (= ½ peso).
1872.	100 centimos = 1 peseta (= ⅕ peso).
1876.	1000 milesimas = 100 centavos or centimos = 1 peso.
1899.	100 cents = 1 dollar.
1906.	100 centavos = 1 peso.
1962.	100 sentimos = 1 piso.

SPANISH ADMINISTRATION

1. 4. 5.
Queen Isabella II.

1854. Imperf.

1.	1.	5 c. orange	£1100	£190
3.		10 c. red	£325	£130
5.		1 r. blue	£350	£120
7a.		2 r. green	£475	£110

1859. Imperf.

13.	4.	5 c. orange	10·00	5·00
14.		10 c. pink	10·00	6·00

1861. Larger lettering. Imperf.

17.	5.	5 c. orange	18·00	6·50

7. 8. 13. King Amadeo.

1863. Imperf.

19.	7.	5 c. red	10·00	4·50
20.		10 c. red	25·00	13·00
21.		1 r. mauve	£375	£150
22.		2 r. blue	£325	£140

1863. Imperf.

25	8	1 r. green	75·00	28·00

1864. As T **12** of Spain, but value in "centimos de peso". Imperf.

26		3 1/8 c. black on buff	2·25	1·00
27		6 2/8 c. green on pink	2·25	80
28		12 4/8 c. blue on flesh	3·50	80
30		25 c. red	5·00	2·00

1868. Optd **HABILITADO POR LA NACION.**

(a) On 1854 to 1863 issues of Philippines

41	7	5 c. red	35·00	25·00
53	4	10 c. pink	65·00	30·00
36	8	1 r. green	35·00	10·00
42	7	1 r. mauve	£375	£225
52	1	1 r. blue	£1500	£700
43	7	2 r. blue	£325	£175

(b) On 1864 issues of Philippines

31		3 1/8 c. black on buff	10·00	2·75
32		6 2/8 c. green on pink	10·00	2·75
33		12 4/8 c. blue on flesh	32·00	15·00
34		25 c. red	13·00	9·00

(c) On Nos. 10/11 of Cuba (as T **9** of Spain but currency changed)

44		1 r. green	£110	55·00
45		2 r. red	£130	50·00

1871. As T **36** of Spain, but inscr "CORREOS" and currency altered. Perf.

37.		5 c. blue	25·00	2·25
38.		10 c. green	7·00	2·00
39.		20 c. brown	30·00	12·00
40.		40 c. red	35·00	6·00

1872.

46	13	12 c. red	7·00	2·00
47		16 c. blue	50·00	12·00
48a		25 c. grey	5·00	1·75
49		62 c. mauve	15·00	3·50
50a		1 p. 25 brown	28·00	8·50

1874. As T **42** of Spain, but inscr. "FILIPINAS".

54.		12 c. lilac	7·50	2·00
55.		25 c. blue	2·50	60
56.		62 c. red	20·00	1·50
57.		1 p. 25 brown	95·00	18·00

1875. As T **45** of Spain, but inscr. "FILIPINAS" between rosettes.

58.		2 c. red	1·25	40
59.		2 c. blue	85·00	35·00
60.		6 c. orange	5·50	1·10
61.		10 c. blue	2·00	45
62.		12 c. mauve	3·00	45
63.		20 c. brown	7·50	1·75
64.		25 c. green	5·50	45

1878. As T **45** of Spain, but inscr. "FILIPINAS" without rosettes.

65.		25 m. black	1·25	25
66.		25 m. green	27·00	12·00
67.		50 m. purple	13·00	3·50
68a.		(62½ m.) 0.0625 lilac	22·00	6·50
69.		100 m. red	42·00	14·00
70.		100 m. green	4·50	1·10
71.		125 m. blue	2·25	35
72.		200 m. red	13·00	2·75
74.		250 m. brown	5·00	1·25

1877. Surch. **HABILITADO 12 CS P.T.A.** in frame.

75.		12 c. on 2 c. red (No. 58)	30·00	9·00
76.		12 c. on 25 m. black (No. 65)	30·00	9·00

1879. Surch. **CONVENIO UNIVERSAL DE CORREOS HABILITADO** and value in figures and words.

78.		2 c. on 25 m. (No. 66)	23·00	6·00
79.		8 c. on 100 m. red (No. 69)	20·00	6·00

1880. "Alfonso XII" key-type inscr. "FILIPINAS".

97.	X.	1 c. green	30	10
82a.		2 c. red	20	15
83.		2½ c. brown	2·40	15
95.		2 4/8 c. blue	20	10
99.		50 m. brown	60	15
85.		5 c. lilac	25	15
100.		6 c. brown	6·00	1·25
87.		6 2/8 c. green	1·75	75
88.		8 c. brown	7·50	1·25
89a.		10 c. brown	1·00	10
90.		10 c. purple	2·00	1·00
91.		10 c. green	£150	80·00
92.		12 4/8 c. pink	50	15
93.		20 c. brown	1·25	15
94.		25 c. brown	1·50	20

1881. "Alfonso XII" key-type inscr "FILIPINAS" with circular surch **HABILITADO CORREOS** or **HABILITADO PA. U. POSTAL** and value in figures and words.

111	X	1 c. on 2 4/8 c. blue	60	40
101		2 c. on 2 1/8 c. brown	2·50	1·10
106		8 c. on 2 c. red	5·50	1·25
107		10 c. cuart. on 2 c. red	3·00	1·25
102		10 c. on 2 4/8 c. blue	5·50	1·00
112		16 cuart. on 2 4/8 c. blue	7·50	1·75
103		20 c. on 8 c. brown	7·50	2·25
113		1 r. on 2 c. red	5·00	1·75
109		1 r. on 5 c. lilac	4·50	2·00
110		1 r. on 8 c. brown	8·50	2·50
105		2 r. on 2 4/8 c. blue	4·50	1·25

25. 29. 30.

31. 34.

1881. Fiscal and telegraph stamps (a) with circular surch **HABILITADO CORREOS, HABILITADO PARA CORREOS** or **HABILITADO PA. U. POSTAL** and value in figures and words.

115	25	2 c. on 10 cuartos bistre	20·00	12·00
129	29	2 c. on 200 m. green	4·25	2·00
116	25	2 4/8 c. on 10 cuartos bistre	2·50	60
117		2 4/8 c. on 2 r. blue	£140	60·00
124		6 2/8 c. on 12 4/8 c. lilac	4·75	2·75
118		8 c. on 2 r. blue	7·50	2·00
119		8 c. on 10 c. brown	£150	£110
123		16 cmos. on 2 r. blue	5·00	2·00
137	31	20 c. on 150 m. blue	22·00	18·00
134		20 c. on 250 m. blue	85·00	70·00
127	25	1 r. on 10 cuartos bistre	9·00	3·00
121		1 r. on 12 4/8 c. lilac	6·00	2·50
130	29	1 r. on 200 m. green	55·00	32·00
131		1 r. on 1 peso green	25·00	12·00
132	30	1 r. on 10 pesetas bistre	35·00	18·00
133	31	2 r. on 250 m. blue	8·00	2·50

(b) With two circular surcharges as above, showing two different values

128	25	8 c. on 2 r. on 2 r. blue	17·00	10·00
136	31	1 r. on 20 c. on 250 m. bl	8·00	3·75

(c) Optd **HABILITADO PARA CORREOS** in straight lines

122	25	10 cuartos bistre	£140	60·00
126		1 r. green	85·00	55·00

1887. Various stamps with oval surch **UNION GRAL. POSTAL HABILITADO** (No. 142) or **HABILITADO PARA COMMUNICACIONES** and new value

(a) "Alfonso XII" key-type inscr "FILIPINAS"

138	X	2 4/8 c. on 1 c. green	1·40	40
139		2 4/8 c. on 5 c. lilac	1·00	40
140		2 4/8 c. on 50 m. brown	1·40	90
141		2 4/8 c. on 10 c. green	1·00	50
142		8 c. on 2 4/8 c. blue	60	30

(b) "Alfonso XII" key-type inscr "FILIPAS-IMPRESOS"

143	X	2 4/8 c. on 1/8 c. green	30	15

(c) Fiscal and telegraph stamps

144	29	2 4/8 c. on 200 m. green	2·75	1·00
145		2 4/8 c. on 20 c. brown	8·00	3·75
146	34	2 4/8 c. on 1 c. bistre	60	40

1889. Various stamps with oval surch **RECARGO DE CONSUMOS HABILITADO** and new value. (a) "Alfonso XII" key-type inscr "FILIPINAS".

147	X	2 4/8 c. on 1 c. green	15	15
148		2 4/8 c. on 2 c. red	10	10
149		2 4/8 c. on 2 4/8 c. blue	10	10
150		2 4/8 c. on 5 c. lilac	10	10
151		2 4/8 c. on 50 m. bistre	10	10
152		2 4/8 c. on 12 4/8 c. pink	50	50

(b) "Alfonso XII" key-type inscr "FILIPAS-IMPRESOS"

160	X	2 4/8 c. on 1/8 c. green	15	15

(c) Fiscal and telegraph stamps

153	34	2 4/8 c. on 1 c. bistre	25	25
154		2 4/8 c. on 2 c. red	25	25
155		2 4/8 c. on 2 4/8 c. brow	10	10
156		2 4/8 c. on 5 c. blue	10	10
157		2 4/8 c. on 10 c. green	10	10
158		2 4/8 c. on 10 c. mauve	50	60
159		2 4/8 c. on 20 c. mauve	20	20
161	25	17 4/8 c. on 5 p. green	60·00	

1890. "Baby" key-type inscr. "FILIPINAS".

176	Y	1 c. purple	50	20
188		1 c. red	2·50	1·40
197		1 c. green	1·10	40
162		2 c. red	10	10
177		2 c. purple	20	10
190		2 c. brown	15	10
198		2 c. blue	20	15
163		2 4/8 c. blue	30	10
178		2 4/8 c. grey	20	10
165		5 c. blue	30	10
191		5 c. green	20	20
199		5 c. brown	4·00	1·50
181		6 c. purple	20	10
192		6 c. red	40	25
166		8 c. green	20	10
182		8 c. blue	50	20
193		8 c. brown	20	10
167		10 c. green	1·00	20
194		10 c. red	20	10
202		10 c. brown	20	10
168		12 4/8 c. green	20	10
184		12 4/8 c. orange	50	10
185		15 c. brown	60	20
195		15 c. red	50	20
203		15 c. green	1·50	75
174		20 c. red	8·00	2·75
186		20 c. brown	1·25	25
196		20 c. purple	3·25	1·25
204		20 c. orange	2·00	75
170		25 c. brown	4·25	75
175		25 c. blue	1·25	25
205		40 c. purple	10·00	2·25
206		80 c. red	15·00	5·50

1897. "Baby" key-type inscr. "FILIPINAS" and surch. **HABILITADO CORREOS PARA 1897** and value in frame.

212.	Y.	5 c. on 5 c. green	2·00	1·00
208.		15 c. on 15 c. red	2·50	1·50
213.		15 c. on 15 c. brown	2·50	1·10
209.		20 c. on 20 c. purple	13·00	7·50
214.		20 c. on 20 c. brown	4·50	3·00
210.		20 c. on 25 c. brown	9·00	7·00

1897. No. 85 surch. **HABILITADO CORREOS PARA 1897 5 CENTS 1897** in frame.

215.	X.	5 c. on 5 c. lilac	3·25	2·00

1898. "Curly Head" key-type inscr. "FILIPNAS 1898 y 99".

217.	Z.	1 m. brown	10	10
218.		2 m. brown	10	10
219.		3 m. brown	15	10
220.		4 m. brown	3·25	65
221.		5 m. brown	10	10
222.		1 c. violet	10	10
223.		2 c. green	10	10
224.		3 c. brown	10	10
225.		4 c. orange	4·50	3·25
226.		5 c. red	15	10
227.		6 c. blue	50	25
228.		8 c. brown	25	15
229.		10 c. red	70	40
230.		15 c. olive	70	40
231.		20 c. red	70	50
232.		40 c. lilac	45	30
233.		60 c. black	2·25	1·00
234.		80 c. brown	2·25	1·00
235.		1 p. green	5·00	3·00
236.		2 p. blue	9·00	4·75

STAMPS FOR PRINTED MATTER

1886. "Alfonso XII" key-type inscr "FILIPAS-IMPRESOS".

P 138	X	1 m. red	20	10
P 139		1/8 c. green	20	10
P 140		2 m. blue	20	10
P 141		5 m. brown	25	10

1890. "Baby" key-type inscr. "FILIPAS-IMPRESOS".

P 171.	Y.	1 m. purple	10	10
P 172.		⅛ c. purple	10	10
P 173.		2 m. purple	10	10
P 174.		5 m. purple	10	10

1892. "Baby" key-type inscr. "FILIPAS-IMPRESOS".

P 192.	Y.	1 m. green	1·75	45
P 193.		⅛ c. green	70	30
P 194.		2 m. green	1·75	45
P 191.		5 m. green	80·00	18·00

1894. "Baby" key-type inscr. "FILIPAS-IMPRESOS".

P 197.	Y.	1 m. grey	15	10
P 198.		⅛ c. brown	15	10
P 199.		2 m. grey	15	10
P 200.		5 m. grey	15	10

1896. "Baby" key-type inscr. "FILIPAS-IMPRESOS".

P 205.	Y.	1 m. blue	20	10
P 206.		⅛ c. blue	20	10
P 207.		2 m. brown	25	10
P 208.		5 m. blue	1·50	60

UNITED STATES ADMINISTRATION

1899. United States stamps of 1894 (No. 267 etc) optd **PHILIPPINES.**

252	–	1 c. green	2·50	65
253	–	2 c. red	1·25	50
255	–	3 c. violet	4·00	1·60
256	–	4 c. brown	17·00	4·75
257	–	5 c. blue	4·00	1·00
258	–	6 c. purple	20·00	6·00
259	–	8 c. brown	22·00	6·00
260	–	10 c. brown	15·00	3·00
262	–	15 c. green	26·00	6·50
263	83	50 c. orange	90·00	38·00
264	–	$1 black	£325	£190
266	–	$2 blue	£500	£275
267	–	$5 green	£1200	£850

1903. United States stamps of 1902 optd. **PHILIPPINES.**

268.	103.	1 c. green	3·00	30
269.	104.	2 c. red	5·00	1·25
270.	105.	3 c. violet	55·00	14·00
271.	106.	4 c. brown	60·00	20·00
272.	107.	5 c. blue	8·50	70
273.	108.	6 c. lake	65·00	18·00
274.	109.	8 c. violet	28·00	12·00
275.	110.	10 c. brown	18·00	2·50
276.	111.	13 c. purple	23·00	13·00
277.	112.	15 c. olive	42·00	8·00
278.	113.	50 c. orange	£100	30·00
279.	114.	$1 black	£425	£200
280.	115.	$2 blue	£1300	£800
281.	116.	$5 green	£1500	£1000

1904. United States stamp of 1903 optd **PHILIPPINES.**

282	117	2 c. red	3·75	1·50

45. Rizal. 46. Arms of Manila.

1906. Various portraits as T **45** and T **46**.

337	45	2 c. green	10	10
338	–	4 c. red (McKinley)	10	10
339	–	6 c. violet (Magellan)	30	10
340	–	8 c. brown (Legaspi)	25	10
341	–	10 c. blue (Lawton)	20	10
288	–	12 c. red (Lincoln)	4·00	1·75
342	–	12 c. orange (Lincoln)	45	15
289	–	16 c. black (Sampson)	3·50	15
298	–	16 c. green (Sampson)	2·00	10
344	–	16 c. olive (Dewey)	1·00	15
290	–	20 c. brown (Washington)	3·50	20
345	–	20 c. yellow (Washington)	35	10
291	–	26 c. brown (Carriedo)	4·50	1·75
346	–	26 c. green (Carriedo)	65	30
292	–	30 c. green (Franklin)	4·75	90
313	–	30 c. blue (Franklin)	2·75	35
347	–	30 c. grey (Franklin)	45	10
293	46	1 p. orange	18·00	5·00
363a		1 p. violet	3·50	3·50
294		2 p. black	23·00	1·00
364		2 p. brown	9·00	9·00
350		4 p. blue	20·00	25
351		10 p. green	55·00	4·40

Nos. 288, 289, 298, 290, 291, 292, 313, 293 and 294 exist perf only, the other values perf or imperf.

1926. Air. Madrid-Manila Flight. Stamps as last, optd. **AIR MAIL 1926 MADRID-MANILA** and aeroplane propeller.
368 45 2 c. green .. .. 4·00 3·25
369 – 4 c. red .. .. 5·00 3·75
370 – 6 c. violet .. .. 25·00 8·00
371 – 8 c. brown .. .. 25·00 9·50
372 – 10 c. blue .. .. 25·50 9·50
373 – 12 c. orange .. .. 27·00 14·00
374 – 16 c. green (Sampson) .. £1100 £1000
375 – 16 c. olive (Dewey) .. 28·00 13·50
376 – 20 c. yellow .. .. 28·00 13·50
377 – 26 c. green .. .. 28·00 13·50
378 – 30 c. grey .. .. 28·00 13·50
383 46 1 p. violet .. .. £100 65·00
379 2 p. brown £250 £180
380 4 p. blue £425 £275
381 10 p. green £650 £450

49. Legislative Palace.

1926. Inauguration of Legislature Palace.
384. 49. 2 c. black and green .. 40 25
385. 4 c. black and red .. 40 30
386. 16 c. black and olive .. 60 50
387. 18 c. black and brown .. 1·00 55
388. 20 c. black and orange .. 1·25 80
389. 24 c. black and grey .. 1·00 50
390. 1 p. black and mauve .. 45·00 25·00

1928. Air. London–Orient Flight by British Squadron of Hydroplanes. Stamps of 1906 optd **L.O.F.** (= London Orient Flight) **1928** and aeroplane.
402 45 2 c. green 35 20
403 – 4 c. red 40 30
404 – 6 c. violet .. .. 2·40 1·60
405 – 8 c. brown .. .. 2·40 2·00
406 – 10 c. blue .. .. 2·40 2·00
407 – 12 c. orange .. .. 4·00 2·40
408 – 16 c. olive (Dewey) .. 3·75 2·40
409 – 20 c. yellow .. .. 4·00 2·40
410 – 26 c. green .. .. 7·50 5·50
411 – 30 c. grey .. .. 7·50 5·50
412 46 1 p. violet .. .. 32·00 32·00

54. Mayon Volcano.

57. Vernal Falls, Yosemite National Park, California, wrongly inscr "PAGSANJAN FALLS".

1932.
424. 54. 2 c. green 75 30
425. – 4 c. red 30 20
426. – 12 c. orange 60 50
427. 57. 18 c. red .. .. 24·00 7·00
428. – 20 c. yellow 70 45
429. – 24 c. violet .. .. 1·25 55
430. – 32 c. brown .. .. 1·25 65
DESIGNS—HORIZ. 4 c. Post Office, Manila. 12 c. Freighters at Pier No. 7, Manila Bay. 20 c. Rice plantation. 24 c. Rice terraces. 32 c. Baguio Zigzag.

1932. No. 350 surch. in words in double circle.
431. 46. 1 p. on 4 p. blue .. 1·50 30
432. 2 p. on 4 p. blue .. 3·00 55

1932. Air. Nos. 424/30 optd. with aeroplane and **ROUND-THE-WORLD FLIGHT VON GRONAU 1932.**
433. 2 c. green 30 30
434. 4 c. red 30 30
435. 12 c. orange 40 40
436. 18 c. red .. .. 3·00 2·50
437. 20 c. yellow .. .. 1·75 1·50
438. 24 c. violet .. .. 1·75 1·50
439. 32 c. brown .. .. 1·75 1·50

1933. Air. Stamps of 1906 optd. **F. REIN MADRID - MANILA FLIGHT - 1933** under propeller.
440 45 2 c. green 30 30
441 – 4 c. red 35 35
442 – 6 c. violet 60 60
443 – 8 c. brown .. .. 1·60 1·25
444 – 10 c. blue .. .. 1·40 90
445 – 12 c. orange .. .. 1·25 90
446 – 16 c. olive (Dewey) .. 1·25 90
447 – 20 c. orange .. .. 1·25 90
448 – 26 c. green .. .. 1·60 1·10
449 – 30 c. grey .. .. 2·00 1·25

1933. Air. Nos. 337 and 425/30 optd. with aeroplane with wings inscr. "**AIR MAIL**".
450. 2 c. green 40 30
451. 4 c. red 15 10
452. 12 c. orange 25 10
453. 20 c. yellow 25 15
454. 24 c. violet 35 15
455. 32 c. brown 40 25

66. Baseball.

1934. 10th Far Eastern Championship Games.
456 66 2 c. brown .. .. 1·50 60
457 – 6 c. blue 45 20
458 – 16 c. purple .. .. 1·25 80
DESIGNS—VERT. 6 c. Tennis. 16 c. Basketball.

69. Dr. J. Rizal.

72. Pearl Fishing.

1935. Designs as T 69/72 in various sizes. (Sizes in millimetres).
459. 2 c. red (19×22) 10 10
460. 4 c. green (34×22) .. 10 10
461. 6 c. brown (22½×28) .. 15 10
462. 8 c. violet (34×22) .. 20 15
463. 10 c. red (34×22) .. 30 15
464. 12 c. black (34×22) .. 25 20
465. 16 c. blue (34×22) .. 35 15
466. 20 c. bistre (19×22) .. 25 10
467. 26 c. blue (34×22) .. 40 20
468. 30 c. red (34×22) .. 40 30
469. 1 p. blk. & orge. (37×27) 2·40 90
470. 2 p. blk. & brn. (37×27) 4·00 1·25
471. 4 p. blk. & blue (37×27) 4·00 2·50
472. 5 p. black & grn. (27×37) 9·50 1·75
DESIGNS: 4 c. Woman, Carabao and Rice-stalks. 6 c. Filipino girl. 10 c. Fort Santiago. 12 c. Salt springs. 16 c. Magellan's landing. 20 c. "Juan de la Cruz". 26 c. Rice Terraces. 30 c. Blood Compact. 1 p. Barasoain Church. 2 p. Battle of Manila Bay. 4 p. Montalban Gorge. 5 p. George Washington (after painting by John Faed).

COMMONWEALTH OF THE PHILIPPINES

83. "Temples of Human Progress".

1935. Inauguration of Commonwealth of the Philippines.
483. 85. 2 c. red 15 15
484. 6 c. violet 20 15
485. 16 c. blue 20 15
486. 36 c. green 40 25
487. 50 c. brown 60 50

1935. Air. "China Clipper" Trans-Pacific Air Mail Flight. Optd **P.I.U.S. INITIAL FLIGHT December–1935** and aeroplane.
488. 10 c. red (No. 463) .. 25 20
489. 30 c. red (No. 468) .. 30 35

85. J. Rizal y Mercado.

89. Manuel L. Quezon.

1936. 75th Birth Anniv. of Rizal.
490. 85. 2 c. yellow 10 15
491. 6 c. blue 15 15
492. 36 c. brown 60 45

1936. Air. Manila–Madrid Flight by Arnaiz and Calvo. Stamps of 1906 surch **MANILA-MADRID ARNACAL FLIGHT—1936** and value.
493. 45. 2 c. on 4 c. red .. 10 10
494. 6 c. on 12 c. orange .. 15 10
495. 16 c. on 26 c. green .. 20 15

1936. Stamps of 1935 (Nos. 459/72) optd **COMMON- WEALTH** (2, 6, 20 c.) or **COMMONWEALTH** (others).
496 2 c. red 10 10
497 4 c. green 50 40
526 6 c. brown 10 10
527 8 c. violet 10 10
528 10 c. red 10 10
529 12 c. black 10 10
530 16 c. blue 20 10
531 20 c. bistre 20 10
532 26 c. blue 30 20
505 30 c. red 30 15
534 1 p. black and orange .. 50 15
535 2 p. black and brown .. 4·00 75
508 4 p. black and blue .. 17·00 2·50
509 5 p. black and green .. 2·40 1·25

1936. 1st Anniv. of Autonomous Government.
510. 89. 2 c. brown 10 10
511. 6 c. green 10 10
512. 12 c. blue 15 15

90. Philippine Is.

92. Arms of Manila.

1937. 33rd Int. Eucharistic Congress.
513. 90. 2 c. green 10 10
514. 6 c. brown 15 10
515. 12 c. blue 20 10
516. 20 c. orange 25 10
517. 36 c. violet 35 30
518. 50 c. red 45 25

1937.
522. 92. 10 p. grey .. .. 3·50 1·50
523. 20 p. brown .. .. 1·75 1·10

1939. Air. 1st Manila Air Mail Exhibition. Surch **FIRST AIR MAIL EXHIBITION Feb 17 to 19, 1939** and value.
548a. – 8 c. on 26 c. grn. (346) 60 35
549. 92. 1 p. on 10 p. grey .. 3·00 2·40

1939. 1st National Foreign Trade Week. Surch **FIRST FOREIGN TRADE WEEK MAY 21–27, 1939** and value.
551. – 2 c. on 4 c. green (460) 10 10
552a. 45. 6 c. on 26 c. grn. (346) 20 15
553. 92. 50 c. on 20 p. brown .. 90 85

101. Triumphal Arch.

102. Malacanan Palace.

103. Pres. Quezon taking Oath of Office.

1939. 4th Anniv. of Nat. Independence.
554. 101. 2 c. green 10 10
555. 6 c. red 15 10
556. 12 c. blue 20 10
557. 102. 2 c. green 10 10
558. 6 c. orange 15 10
559. 12 c. red 20 10
560. 103. 2 c. orange 10 10
561. 6 c. green 15 10
562. 12 c. violet 30 15

104. Jose Rizal.

105. Filipino Vinta and Clipper.

1941.
563 104 2 c. green 10 10
623 – 2 c. brown 10 10
In No. 623 the head faces to the right.

1941. Air.
566. 105. 8 c. red 80 75
567. 20 c. blue .. .. 1·00 50
568. 60 c. green .. .. 1·50 85
569. 1 p. sepia 75 60

For Japanese Occupation issues of 1941-45 see **JAPANESE OCCUPATION OF PHILIPPINE ISLANDS.**

1945. Victory issue. Nos. 496, 525/31, 505, 534 and 522/3 optd **VICTORY**.
610. 2 c. red 10 10
611. 4 c. green 10 10
612. 6 c. brown 15 10
613. 8 c. violet 20 15
614. 10 c. red 20 10
615. 12 c. black 25 15
616. 16 c. blue 40 15
617. 20 c. bistre 40 10
618. 30 c. red 70 50
619. 1 p. black and orange .. 1·40 30
620. 10 p. grey .. .. 40·00 14·00
621. 20 p. brown .. .. 35·00 16·00

INDEPENDENT REPUBLIC

111. "Independence".

113. Bonifacio Monument.

1946. Proclamation of Independence.
625. 111. 2 c. red 25 15
626. 6 c. green 45 25
627. 12 c. blue 50 45

1946. Optd. **PHILIPPINES** at top, **50TH ANNIVERSARY MARTYRDOM** in circle and **OF RIZAL 1896-1946** at foot.
628. 104. 2 c. brown (No. 623) .. 10 20

1947.
629. – 4 c. brown 20 5
630. 113. 10 c. red 25 5
631. – 12 c. blue 30 12
632. – 16 c. grey .. .. 1·25 75
633. – 20 c. brown 25 10
634. – 50 c. green .. .. 1·25 60
635. – 1 p. violet .. .. 1·90 45
DESIGNS—VERT. 4 c. Rizal Monument. 50 c. and 1 p. Avenue of Palm Trees. HORIZ. 12 c. Jones Bridge. 16 c. Santa Lucia Gate. 20 c. Mayon Volcano.

115. Manuel L. Quezon.

117. Presidents Quezon and Roosevelt.

116. Pres. Roxas taking Oath of Office.

1947.
636. 115. 1 c. green 20 12

1947. 1st Anniv. of Independence.
638. 116. 4 c. red 30 25
639. 6 c. green 45 30
640. 16 c. purple 90 60

1947. Air.
641. 117. 6 c. green 35 35
642. 40 c. orange 90 90
643. 80 c. blue .. .. 2·50 2·50

119. United Nations' Emblem.

121. General MacArthur.

1947. Conference of Economic Commission for Asia and Far East, Baguio. Imperf. or perf.
648. 119. 4 c. red and pink .. 1·25 1·10
649. 6 c. violet & pale violet 1·90 1·90
650. 12 c. bright blue & blue 2·10 2·10

1948. 3rd Anniv. of Liberation.
652. 121. 4 c. violet 45 25
653. 6 c. red 85 35
654. 16 c. blue .. .. 1·25 35

122. Threshing Rice.

125. Dr. Jose Rizal.

1948. United Nations' Food and Agriculture Organization Conference, Baguio.
655. 122. 2 c. grn. & yell. (postage) 60 45
656. 6 c. brown and yellow .. 85 60
657. 18 c. blue & pale blue .. 2·25 1·90
658. 40 c. red and pink (air) 12·00 7·00

1948.
662. 125. 2 c. green 15 8

126. Pres. Manuel Roxas. 127. Scout and Badge. 128. Sampaguita National Flower.

1948. President Roxas Mourning Issue.
663. **126.** 2 c. black 10 10
664. 4 c. black 15 10

1948. 25th Anniv. of Philippine Boy Scouts. Perf. or imperf.
665. **127.** 2 c. green and brown .. 45 25
666. 4 c. pink and brown .. 55 35

1948. Flower Day.
667. **128.** 3 c. green and black .. 45 35

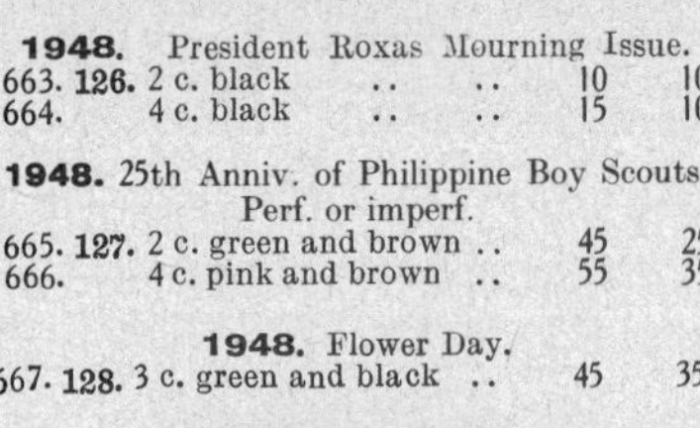

130. Santos, Tavera and Kalaw.

DESIGN—VERT. 18 c. Title page of Rizal's "Noli Me Tangere".

131. "Doctrina Christiana" (first book published in Philippines).

1949. Library Rebuilding Fund.
671. **130.** 4 c.+2 c. brown .. 75 45
672. **131.** 6 c.+4 c. violet .. 1·25 1·40
673. – 18 c.+7 c. blue .. 3·00 2·40

132. U.P.U. Monument, Berne.

1949. 75th Anniv. of U.P.U.
674. **132.** 4 c. green 20 10
675. 6 c. violet 25 12
676. 18 c. blue 40 35

133. General del Pilar at Tirad Pass. 134. Globe.

1949. 50th Death Anniv. of Gen. Gregorio del Pilar.
678. **133.** 2 c. brown 30 15
679. 4 c. green 50 30

1950. 5th Int. Congress of Junior Chamber of Commerce.
680. **134.** 2 c. violet (postage) .. 15 12
681. 6 c. green 25 15
682. 18 c. blue 45 15
683. 30 c. orange (air) .. 40 15
684. 50 c. red 60 15

135. Red Lauan Trees. 136. Franklin D. Roosevelt.

1950. 15th Anniv. of Forestry Service.
685. **135.** 2 c. green 20 10
686. 4 c. violet 25 20

1950. 25th Anniv. of Philatelic Assn.
687. **136.** 4 c. brown 20 15
688. 6 c. pink 25 20
689. 18 c. blue 80 45

137. Lions Emblem. 138. President Quirino taking Oath of Office.

1950. "Lions" Int. Convention, Manila.
691. **137.** 2 c. orange (postage) .. 40 35
692. 4 c. violet 55 50
693. 30 c. green (air) .. 60 45
694. 50 c. blue 70 55

1950. Pres. Quirino's Inaug.
696. **138.** 2 c. red 15 10
697. 4 c. purple 15 12
698. 6 c. green 15 15

1950. Surch. **ONE CENTAVO.**
699. **125.** 1 c. on 2 c. green .. 15 8

140. Dove and Map. 141. War Widow and Children.

1950. Baguio Conference.
701 **140** 5 c. green 35 25
702 6 c. red 35 25
703 18 c. blue 55 25

1950. Aid to War Victims.
704. **141.** 2 c.+2 c. red 15 10
705. – 4 c.+4 c. violet .. 45 35
DESIGN: 4 c. Disabled veteran.

142. Arms of Manila. 143. Soldier and Peasants.

1950. As T 142. Various arms and frames.

(a) Arms inscr. "MANILA".
706. 5 c. violet 40 40
707. 6 c. grey 40 35
708. 18 c. blue 40 40

(b) Arms inscr. "CEBU".
709. 5 c. red 40 40
710. 6 c. brown 40 35
711. 18 c. violet 40 40

(c) Arms inscr. "ZAMBOANGA".
712. 5 c. green 45 40
713. 6 c. brown 40 35
714. 18 c. blue 45 40

(d) Arms inscr. "ILOILO".
715. 5 c. green 55 40
716. 6 c. violet 40 35
717. 18 c. blue 55 40

1951. Guarding Peaceful Labour. Perf. or imperf.
718. **143.** 5 c. green 25 8
719. 6 c. brown 40 25
720. 18 c. blue 65 45

144. Philippines Flag and U.N. Emblem. 145. Statue of Liberty.

1951. U.N. Day.
721. **144.** 5 c. red 40 30
722. 6 c. green 45 25
723. 18 c. blue .. .. 1·00 45

1951. Human Rights Day.
724. **145.** 5 c. green 40 30
725. 6 c. orange 35 25
726. 18 c. blue 90 60

INDEX
Countries can be quickly located by referring to the index at the end of this volume.

146. Schoolchildren. 147. M. L. Quezon.

1952. 50th Anniv. of Philippine Educational System.
727. **146.** 5 c. orange 35 20

1952. Portraits.
728. **147.** 1 c. brown 5 5
729. – 2 c. black (J. Santos) 5 5
730. – 3 c. red (A. Mabini) .. 5 5
731. – 5 c. red (M. H. del Pilar) 8 5
842. – 6 c. blue (Dr. J. Rizal) 20 5
732. – 10 c. blue (Father J. Burgos) 25 5
733. – 20 c. red (Lapu-Lapu) 30 25
734. – 25 c. green (Gen. A. Luna) 40 30
735. – 50 c. red (C. Arellano) 60 20
736. – 60 c. red (A. Bonifacio) 75 20
737. – 2 p. violet (G. L. Jaena) .. .. 2·25 75

149. Aurora A. Quezon.

1952. Fruit Tree Memorial Fund.
742. **149.** 5 c.+1 c. blue 15 10
743. 6 c.+2 c. red 35 25
See also No. 925.

150. Milkfish and Map of Oceania. 151. "A Letter from Rizal".

1952. Indo-Pacific Fisheries Council.
744. **150.** 5 c. brown 85 50
745. 6 c. blue 85 35

1952. Pan-Asiatic Philatelic Exn., Manila.
746. **151.** 5 c. blue (postage) .. 25 10
747. 6 c. brown 25 20
748. 30 c. red (air) .. 75 65

152. Wright Park, Baguio City. 153. F. Baltazar (poet).

1952. 3rd Lions District Convention.
749. **152.** 5 c. orange 60 40
750. 6 c. green 85 65

1953. National Language Week.
751. **153.** 5 c. olive 40 40

154. "Gateway to the East". 155. Pres. Quirino and Pres. Sukarno.

1953. Int. Fair, Manila.
752. **154.** 5 c. turquoise 35 10
753. 6 c. red 45 20

1953. Visit of President to Indonesia. Flags in yellow, blue and red.
754. **155.** 5 c. blue, yellow & black 35 10
755. 6 c. green, yell. & black 35 25

156. Doctor examining patient.

1953. 50th Anniv. of Philippines Medical Association.
756. **156.** 5 c. mauve 40 30
757. 6 c. blue 50 40

1954. Optd. **FIRST NATIONAL BOY SCOUTS JAMBOREE APRIL 23-30 1954** or surch. also.
758. 5 c. red (No. 731) .. 1·25 95
759. 18 c. on 50 c. grn. (No. 634) 2·00 1·50

158. Stamp of 1854, Magellan and Manila P.O.

1954. 1st Philippines Postage Stamps Cent. Central stamp in orange.
760. **158.** 5 c. violet (postage) .. 45 20
761. 18 c. blue 90 75
762. 30 c. green .. .. 2·10 1·90
763. **158.** 10 c. brown (air) .. 90 25
764. 20 c. green .. .. 1·50 1·25
765. 50 c. red .. .. 3·25 2·90

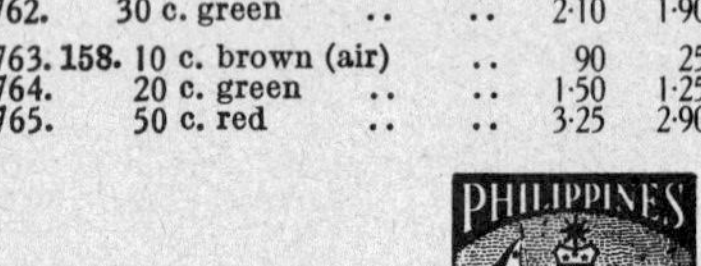

159. Diving. 161. "Independence".

1954. 2nd Asian Games, Manila.
766. – 5 c. blue (Discus) .. 70 45
767. **159.** 18 c. green .. .. 1·00 75
768. – 30 c. red (Boxing) .. 1·60 1·40

1954. Surch. **MANILA CONFERENCE OF 1954** and value.
769. **113.** 5 c. on 10 c. red 25 15
770. – 18 c. on 20 c. brown (No. 633) 35 35

1954. Independence. Commem.
771. **161.** 5 c. lake 15 25
772. 18 c. blue 60 25

162. "The Immaculate Conception" (Murillo). 163. Mayon Volcano and Filipino Vinta.

1954. Marian Year.
773. **162.** 5 c. blue 50 35

1955. 50th Anniv. of Rotary International.
774. **163.** 5 c. blue (postage) .. 35 15
775. 18 c. red .. .. 1·50 70
776. 50 c. green (air) .. 2·25 1·10

164. "Labour". 165. Pres. Magsaysay.

1955. Labour-Management Congress, Manila.
777. **164.** 5 c. brown .. .. 1·50 60

1955. 9th Anniv. of Republic.
778. **165.** 5 c. blue 20 15
779. 20 c. red 60 40
780. 30 c. green 75 75

166. Lt. J. Gozar.

1955. Air. Air Force Heroes.

781. **166.** 20 c. violet 65 20

782. – 30 c. red (Lt. C. F. Basa) 75 20

783. **166.** 50 c. green .. .. 1·60 30

784. – 70 c. bl. (Lt. C. F. Basa) 2·25 95

167. Liberty Well.

1956. Artesian Wells for Rural Areas.

785. **167.** 5 c. violet 35 30

786. 20 c. green 75 55

1956. 5th Conference of World Confederation of Organizations of the Teaching Profession. No. 731 optd. **WCOTP CONFERENCE MANILA.**

787. 5 c. red 55 30

169. Nurse and War Victims.  170. Monument (landing marker) in Leyte.

1956. 50th Anniv. of Philippines Red Cross.

788. **169.** 5 c. violet and red .. 25 20

789. 20 c. brown and red .. 35 20

1956. Liberation. Perf. or imperf.

790. **170.** 5 c. red 30 25

171. St. Thomas's University.  172. Statue of the Sacred Heart.

1956. University of St. Thomas.

791. **171.** 5 c. brown and lake .. 30 25

792. 60 c. brown and mauve 1·10 1·00

1956. 2nd National Eucharistic Congress and Cent. of the Feast of the Sacred Heart.

793. **172.** 5 c. olive 25 25

794. 20 c. red 55 55

1956. Surch.

795. 5 c. on 6 c. brown (No. 710) 40 20

796. 5 c. on 6 c. brn. (No. 713) 40 20

797. 5 c. on 6 c. violet (No. 716) 40 20

174. Girl Guide, Badge and Camp.  175. Pres. Ramon Magsaysay.

1957. Girl Guides' Pacific World Camp. Quezon City, and Cent. of Birth of Lord Baden-Powell. Perf. or imperf.

798. **174.** 5 c. blue 45 30

1957. Death of Pres. Magsaysay.

799. **175.** 5 c. black 15 10

176. Sergio Osmena (Speaker) and First Philippine Assembly.

1957. 50th Anniv. of First Philippine Assembly.

800. **176.** 5 c. green 20 10

177. "The Spoliarium" after Juan Luna.

1957. Birth Cent. of Juan Luna (painter).

801. **177.** 5 c. red 30 15

1957. Inaug. of President C. P. Garcia and Vice-President-elect D. Macapagal. Nos. 732/3 surch. **GARCIA-MACAPAGAL INAUGURATION DEC. 30, 1957** and value.

802. 5 c. on 10 c. blue 25 25

803. 10 c. on 20 c. red 35 35

179. University of the Philippines.

1958. Golden Jubilee of University of the Philippines.

804. **179.** 5 c. lake 35 15

180. Pres. Garcia.  181. Main Hospital Building, Quezon Institute.

1958. 12th Anniv. of Republic.

805. **180.** 5 c. multicoloured .. 10 15

806. 20 c. multicoloured .. 45 30

1958. Obligatory Tax. T.B. Relief Fund.

807. **181.** 5 c.+5 c. green and red 15 12

808. 10 c.+5 c. violet and red 40 30

182. The Immaculate Conception and Manila Cathedral.

1958. Inaug. of Manila Cathedral.

809. **182.** 5 c. multicoloured .. 30 15

1959. Surch. **One Centavo.**

810. 1 c. on 5 c. red (No. 731) 20 8

1959. 14th Anniv. of Liberation. Nos. 704/5 surch.

812. **141.** 1 c. on 2 c.+2 c. red .. 10 10

813. – 6 c. on 4 c.+4 c. violet 20 20

186. Philippines Flag.  187. Bulacan Seal.

1959. Philippines National Flag Commem.

814. **186.** 6 c. red, blue and yellow 15 8

815. 20 c. red, blue & yellow 35 25

1959. Bulacan Seal and 60th Anniv. of Malolos Constitution.

816. **187.** 6 c. green 15 8

817. 20 c. red 35 25

1959. Capiz Seal and 11th Death Anniv. of Pres. Roxas. As T **187** but with Capiz Seal.

818. 6 c. brown 15 8

819. 25 c. violet 30 25

The shield within the Capiz seal bears the inset portrait of Pres. Roxas.

1959. Bacolod Seal. As T **187** but with Bacolod Seal.

820. 6 c. green 15 10

821. 10 c. purple 45 30

188. Scout at Camp Fire.  190. Bohol Sanatorium.

1959. 10th World Scout Jamboree, Manila.

822. **188.** 6 c.+4 c. red on cream (postage) 15 12

823. 6 c.+4 c. red 15 15

824. – 25 c.+5 c. bl. on cream 30 25

825. – 25 c.+5 c. blue .. 40 40

826. – 30 c.+10 c. green (air) 30 30

827. – 70 c.+30 c. brown .. 60 60

828. – 80 c.+20 c. violet .. 85 85

DESIGNS: 25 c. Scout with bow and arrow. 30 c. Scout cycling. 70 c. Scout with model aeroplane. 80 c. Pres. Garcia with scout.

1959. Obligatory Tax. T.B. Relief Fund Nos. 807/8 surch. **HELP FIGHT T B** with Cross of Lorraine and value and new design (T 85).

830. **181.** 3 c.+5 c. on 5 c.+5 c. 20 15

831. 6 c.+5 c. on 10 c.+5 c. 30 15

832. **190.** 6 c.+5 c. green and red 15 15

833. 25 c.+5 c. blue and red 45 30

191. Pagoda and Gardens at Camp John Hay.

1959. 50th Anniv. of Baguio.

834. **191.** 6 c. green 20 15

835. 25 c. red 35 25

1959. U.N. Day. Surch. **6 ₵ UNITED NATIONS DAY.**

836. **132.** 6 c. on 18 c. blue .. 20 20

193. Maria Cristina Falls.

1959. World Tourist Conf., Manila.

837. **193.** 6 c. green and violet .. 15 8

838. 30 c. green and brown .. 50 35

1959. No. 629 surch. **One** and bars.

839. 1 c. on 4 c. brown .. 20 10

195.

1959. Cent. of Manila Athenaeum (school).

840. **195.** 6 c. blue 8 8

841. 30 c. red 50 35

197. Book of the Constitution.

1960. 25th Anniv. of Philippines Constitution.

844. **197.** 6 c. brn. & gold (post.) 20 15

845. 30 c. blue & silver (air) 40 25

198. Congress Building.

1960. 5th Anniv. of Manila Pact.

846. **198.** 6 c. green 15 8

847. 25 c. orange 40 30

199. Sunset, Manila Bay.

1960. World Refugee Year.

848. **199.** 6 c. multicoloured .. 10 10

849. 25 c. multicoloured .. 40 30

200. Fighter Planes of 1935 and 1960.  202. Lorraine Cross.

1960. Air. 25th Anniv. of Philippine Air Force.

850. **200.** 10 c. red 30 15

851. 20 c. blue 55 30

1960. Surch.

852. **134.** 1 c. on 18 c. blue .. 5 5

853. **161.** 5 c. on 18 c. blue .. 25 25

854. **163.** 5 c. on 18 c. red .. 25 25

855. **158.** 10 c. on 18 c. orge. & bl. 25 25

856. **140.** 10 c. on 18 c. blue .. 30 30

1960. 50th Anniv. of Philippine Tuberculosis Society. Lorraine Cross and wreath in red and gold.

857. **202.** 5 c. green 15 8

858. 6 c. blue 20 10

1960. Obligatory Tax. T.B. Relief Fund. Surch. **6+5** and bars and **HELP PREVENT TB.**

859. **181.** 6 c.+5 c. on 5 c.+5 c. green and red .. 25 25

204. Pres. Quezon.  205. Basketball.

1960.

860. **204.** 1 c. olive 10 5

1960. Olympic Games.

861. **205.** 6 c. brn. & grn. (post.) 15 8

862. – 10 c. brown and mauve 25 15

863. – 30 c. brn. and orge. (air) 25 20

864. – 70 c. purple and blue .. 75 65

DESIGNS: 10 c. Running. 30 c. Rifle-shooting. 70 c. Swimming.

206. Presidents Eisenhower and Garcia.

1960. Visit of President Eisenhower.

865. **206.** 6 c. multicoloured .. 25 20

866. 20 c. multicoloured .. 55 25

207. "Mercury" and Globe.

1961. Manila Postal Conf.

867. **207.** 6 c. multicoloured (post.) 20 8

868. 30 c. multicoloured (air) 45 30

1961. Surch.

869. 20 c. on 25 c. grn. (No. 734) 20 10

1961. 2nd National Scout Jamboree, Zamboanga. Nos. 822/5 surch. **2nd National Boy Scout Jamboree Pasonanca Park** and value.

870. 10 c. on 6 c.+4 c. red on cream 15 15

871. 10 c. on 6 c.+4 c. red .. 70 70

872. 30 c. on 25 c.+5 c. blue on cream 45 45

873. 30 c. on 25 c.+5 c. blue .. 45 45

210. La Salle College.

1961. 50th Anniv. of La Salle College.
874. 210. 6 c. multicoloured .. 8 5
875. 10 c. multicoloured .. 25 15

211. Rizal when student, School and University Buildings.

1961. Birth Cent. of Dr. Jose Rizal.
876. 211. 5 c. multicoloured .. 8 5
877. – 6 c. multicoloured .. 8 5
878. – 10 c. brown and green 25 20
879. – 20 c. turquoise & brown 30 25
880. – 30 c. multicoloured .. 45 35
DESIGNS: 6 c. Rizal and birthplace at Calamba, Laguna. 10 c. Rizal, mother and father. 20 c. Rizal extolling Luna and Hidalgo at Madrid. 30 c. Rizal's execution.

1961. 15th Anniv. of Republic. Optd. **IKA 15 KAARAWAN Republika ng Pilipinas Hulyo 4, 1961.**
881. 198. 6 c. green 15 15
882. 25 c. orange 20 20

213. Roxas Memorial T.B. Pavilion.
214. Globe, Plan Emblem and Supporting Hand.

1961. Obligatory Tax. T.B. Relief Fund.
883. 213. 6 c.+5 c. brown & red 30 20

1961. 7th Anniv. of Admission of Philippines to Colombo Plan.
884. 214. 5 c. multicoloured .. 8 8
885. 6 c. multicoloured .. 10 10

1961. Philippine Amateur Athletic Federation's Golden Jubilee. Surch. with P.A.A.F. monogram and **6 c. PAAF GOLDEN JUBILEE 1911 1961.**
886 200 6 c. on 10 c. red 25 20

216. Typist.

1961. Government Employees' Association Commemoration.
887. 216. 6 c. violet and brown .. 20 8
888. 10 c. blue and brown .. 40 85

1961. Inaug. of Pres. Macapagal and Vice Pres. Pelaez. Surch. **MACAPAGAL-PELAEZ DEC. 30, 1961 INAUGURATION 6 c.**
889. 6 c. on 25 c. vio. (No. 819) 25 15

1962. Cross obliterated by Arms and surch. **6 s** and bars.
890. 181. 6 c. on 5 c.+5 c. green and red 20 20

220. Waling Waling.
221. A. Mabini (statesman).

1962. Orchids in natural colours on blue background.
892. 5 c. Type **220** .. 10 10
893. 6 c. White Mariposa .. 15 12
894. 10 c. " Dendrobium sanderii " 20 15
895. 20 c. Sanggumay 30 25

1962. New Currency.
896. – 1 s. brown 5 5
897. 221. 3 s. red 5 5
898. – 5 s. red 5 5
899. – 6 s. brown 8 5
900. – 6 s. blue 8 5
901. – 10 s. purple 10 5
902. – 20 s. blue 20 5
903. – 30 s. red 20 8
904. – 50 s. violet 25 10
905. – 70 s. blue 45 30
906. – 1 p. green 90 25
907. – 1 p. orange 60 35
PORTRAITS: 1 s. M. L. Quezon. 5 s. M. H. del Pilar. 6 s. (2) J. Rizal (different). 10 s. Father J. Burgos. 20 s. Lapu-Lapu. 30 s. Rajah Soliman. 50 s. C. Arellano. 70 s. S. Osmena. 1 p. (No. 906) E. Jacinto. 1 p. (No. 907) J. M. Panganiban.

225. Pres. Macapagal taking Oath.

1962. Independence Day.
915. 225. 6 s. multicoloured .. 8 5
916. 10 s. multicoloured .. 15 8
917. 30 s. multicoloured .. 40 15

226. Valdes Memorial T.B. Pavilion.

1962. Obligatory Tax Stamps. T.B. Relief Fund. Cross in red.
918. 226. 6 s.+5 s. slate .. 20 15
919. 30 s.+5 s. blue .. 45 35
920. 70 s.+5 s. blue .. 1·10 90

227. Lake Taal.

1962. Malaria Eradication.
921. 227. 6 s. multicoloured .. 8 8
922. 10 s. multicoloured .. 15 8
923. 70 s. multicoloured .. 65 45

1962. Bicentenary of Diego Silang Revolt. No. 734 surch **1762 1962 BICENTENNIAL Diego Silang Revolt 20.**
924 20 s. on 25 c. green .. 30 25

1962. No. 742 with premium obliterated.
925. 53. 5 c. blue 25 10

230. Dr. Rizal playing Chess.

1962. Rizal Foundation Fund.
926. 230. 6 s.+4 s. green & mauve 25 20
927. – 30 s.+5 s. blue & pur. 55 45
DESIGN: 30 s. Dr. Rizal fencing.

1963. Surch.
928. 221. 1 s. on 3 s. red .. 10 5
929. – 5 s. on 6 s. brown (No. 899) 20 5

1963. Diego Silang Bicentenary Art and Philatelic Exn., G.P.O., Manila. No. 737 surch. **1763 1963 DIEGO SILANG BICENTENNIAL ARPHEX** and value.
930. 6 c. on 2 p. violet .. 15 8
931. 20 c. on 2 p. violet .. 30 25
932. 70 c. on 2 p. violet .. 90 65

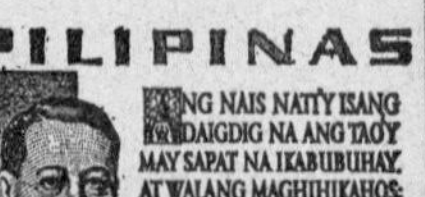

233. " We want to see . . ." (Pres. Roxas).
234. Lorraine Cross on Map.

1963. Presidential Sayings (1st issue).
933. 233. 6 s. blue and black .. 15 5
934. 30 s. brown and black 25 15
See also Nos. 959/60, 981/2, 1015/6, 1034/5, 1055/6, 1148/9 and 1292/3.

1963. Obligatory Tax. T.B. Relief Fund. Cross in red.
935. 234. 6 s.+5 s. pink & violet 10 5
936. 10 s.+5 s. pink & grn. 20 15
937. 50 s.+5 s. pink & brn. 70 45

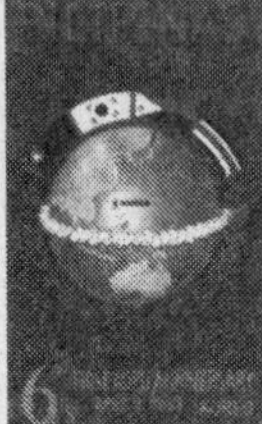

235. Globe and Flags.
236. Centenary Emblem.

1963. 1st Anniv. of Asian-Oceanic Postal Union.
938. 235. 6 s. multicoloured .. 5 5
939. 20 s. multicoloured .. 25 15

1963. Red Cross Centenary. Cross in red.
940. 236. 5 s. grey and violet .. 8 5
941. 6 s. grey and blue .. 8 5
942. 20 s. grey and green .. 30 20

237. Tinikling (dance).

1963. Folk Dances. Multicoloured.
943. 5 s. Type **237** 10 8
944. 6 s. Pandanggo sa Ilaw .. 15 10
945. 10 s. Itik-Itik 25 20
946. 20 s. Singkil 35 30

238. Pres. Macapagal and Philippine Family.

1963. President's Social-Economic Programme.
947. 238. 5 s. multicoloured .. 5 5
948. 6 s. multicoloured .. 10 5
949. 20 s. multicoloured .. 25 15

239. Presidents' Meeting.
240. Bonifacio and Flag.

1963. Visit of President Mateos of Mexico.
950. 239. 6 s. multicoloured .. 20 10
951. 30 s. multicoloured .. 40 20

1963. Birth Cent. of A. Bonifacio (patriot).
952. 240. 5 s. multicoloured .. 8 5
953. 6 s. multicoloured .. 8 5
954. 25 s. multicoloured .. 35 30

241. Harvester.
242. Bamboo Organ, Catholic Church, Las Pinas.

1963. Freedom from Hunger.
956. 241. 6 s. multicoloured (post.) 8 5
957. 30 s. multicoloured (air) 35 25
958. 50 s. multicoloured .. 45 45

1963. Presidential Sayings (2nd issue). As T **233** but with portrait and saying changed.
959. 6 s. black and mauve .. 15 5
960. 30 s. black and green .. 50 15
PORTRAIT AND SAYING: Pres. Magsaysay, "I believe . . .".

1964. Las Pinas Organ Commemoration.
961. 242. 5 s. multicoloured .. 10 8
962. 6 s. multicoloured .. 10 8
963. 20 s. multicoloured .. 25 20

243. A. Mabini (patriot).
245. S.E.A.T.O. Emblems and Flags.

244. Negros Oriental T.B. Pavilion.

1964. Birth Cent. of A. Mabini.
964. 243. 6 s. gold and violet .. 8 5
965. 10 s. gold and brown .. 15 8
966. 30 s. gold and green .. 30 25

1964. Obligatory Tax. T.B. Relief Fund. Cross in red.
967. 244. 5 s.+5 s. purple .. 8 5
968. 6 s.+5 s. blue .. 15 5
969. 30 s.+5 s. brown .. 45 35
970. 70 s.+5 s. green .. 90 80

1964. 10th Anniv. of S.E.A.T.O.
971. 245. 6 s. multicoloured .. 5 5
972. 10 s. multicoloured .. 15 8
973. 25 s. multicoloured .. 30 25

246. President Signing the Land Reform Code.
247. Basketball.

1964. Agricultural Land Reform Code. President and inscr. at foot; brown, red and sepia.
974. 246. 3 s. green (postage) .. 8 5
975. 6 s. blue 8 5
976. 30 s. brown (air) .. 30 25

1964. Olympic Games, Tokyo. Sport in chocolate. Perf. or imperf.
977. 247. 6 s. blue and gold .. 8 5
978. – 10 s. pink and gold .. 20 8
979. – 20 s. yellow and gold .. 30 20
980. – 30 s. green and gold .. 40 30
SPORTS: 10 s. Relay-racing. 20 s. Hurdling. 30 s. Football.

1965. Presidential Sayings (3rd issue). As T **233** but with portrait and saying changed.
981. 6 s. black and green .. 15 5
982. 30 s. black and purple .. 50 15
PORTRAIT AND SAYING: Pres. Quirino, " So live . . .".

248. Presidents Luebke and Macapagal.

1965. Visit of President of German Federal Republic.
983. 248. 6 s. multicoloured .. 5 5
984. 10 s. multicoloured .. 15 5
985. 25 s. multicoloured .. 25 25

249. Meteorological Emblems.
250. Pres. Kennedy.

1965. Centenary of Philippines Meteorological Services.
986. 249. 6 s. multicoloured .. 5 5
987. 20 s. multicoloured .. 15 5
988. 50 s. multicoloured .. 25 20

1965. 48th Birth Anniv. of Pres. Kennedy.
989. 250. 6 s. multicoloured .. 15 5
990. 10 s. multicoloured .. 20 8
991. 30 s. multicoloured .. 45 25

251. King Bhumibol and Queen Sirkit, Pres. Macapagal and Wife.

1965. Visit of King and Queen of Thailand.
992. **251.** 2 s. multicoloured .. 5 5
993. 6 s. multicoloured .. 15 5
994. 30 s. multicoloured .. 30 20

252. Princess Beatrix and Mrs. Macapagal.

1965. Visit of Princess Beatrix of the Netherlands.
995. **252.** 2 s. multicoloured .. 5 5
996. 6 s. multicoloured .. 8 5
997. 10 s. multicoloured .. 15 8

1965. Obligatory Tax. T.B. Relief Fund. Surch.
998. **244.** 1 s.+5 s. on 6 s.+5 s. 15 15
999. 3 s.+5 s. on 6 s.+5 s. 30 30

254. Hand holding Cross and Rosary.

256. Signing Agreement.

1965. 400th Anniv. of Philippines Christianisation. Multicoloured.
1000. 3 s. Type **254** (postage).. 8 5
1001. 6 s. Legaspi-Urdaneta, monument 15 5
1002. 30 s. Baptism of Filipinos by Father Urdaneta (air).. 30 20
1003. 70 s. "Way of the Cross"—ocean map of Christian voyagers' route, Spain to the Philippines .. 90 40
Nos. 1002/3 are horiz., 48 × 27 mm.

1965. "MAPILINDO" Conf., Manila.
1005. **256.** 6 s. blue, red & yellow 8 5
1006. 10 s. multicoloured .. 8 8
1007. 25 s. multicoloured .. 25 20
The above stamps depict Pres. Sukarno of Indonesia, former Pres. Macapagal of the Philippines and Prime Minister Tunku Abdul Rahman of Malaysia.

257. Cyclists and Globe.

259. Dr. A. Regidor.

1965. 2nd Asian Cycling Championships, Philippines.
1008. **257.** 6 s. multicoloured .. 15 5
1009. 10 s. multicoloured .. 20 8
1010. 25 s. multicoloured .. 25 25

1965. Inaug. of Pres. Marcos and Vice-Pres. Lopez. Nos. 926/7 surch. **MARCOS-LOPEZ INAUGURATION DEC. 30, 1965** with value and bars.
1011. **230.** 10 s. on 6 s.+4 s. .. 15 15
1012. – 30 s. on 30 s.+5 s. .. 35 35

1966. Regidor (patriot) Commem.
1013. **259.** 6 s. blue 10 5
1014. 30 s. brown 30 25

1966. Presidential Sayings (4th issue). As T **233** but with portrait and saying changed.
1015. 6 s. black and lake .. 15 5
1016. 30 s. black and blue .. 50 15
PORTRAIT AND SAYING: Pres. Aguinaldo, "Have faith . . .".

1966. Campaign Against Smuggling. No. 900 optd. **HELP ME STOP SMUGGLING Pres. MARCOS.**
1017. 6 s. blue 20 5

261. Girl Scout.

1966. Silver Jubilee of Philippines Girl Scouts.
1018. **261.** 3 s. multicoloured .. 15 8
1019. 6 s. multicoloured .. 15 8
1020. 20 s. multicoloured .. 40 20

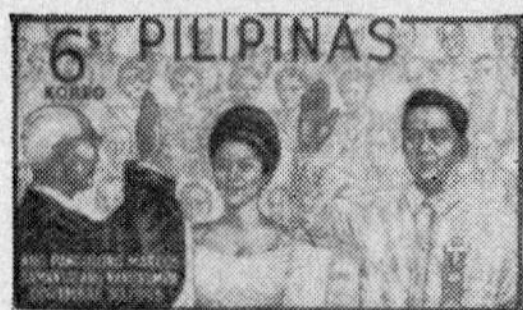

262. Pres. Marcos taking Oath.

1966. Inaug. (1965) of Pres. Marcos.
1021. **262.** 6 s. multicoloured .. 8 5
1022. 20 s. multicoloured .. 25 8
1023. 30 s. multicoloured .. 40 25

263. Manila Seal and Historical Scenes.

1966. Introduction of New Seal for Manila.
1024. **263.** 6 s. multicoloured .. 10 8
1025. 30 s. multicoloured .. 40 25

264. Bank Facade and 1-peso Coin.

1966. 50th Anniv. of Philippines National Bank. Multicoloured.
1026. 6 s. Type **264** 15 8
1027. 10 s. Old and new bank buildings 30 15

266. Bank Building.

1966. 60th Anniv. of Postal Savings Bank.
1029. **266.** 6 s. violet, yell. & grn. 5 5
1030. 10 s. red, yell. & grn. 10 8
1031. 20 s. blue, yell. & grn. 30 15

1966. Manila Summit Conf. Nos. 1021 and 1023 optd. **MANILA SUMMIT CONFERENCE 1966 7 NATIONS** and emblem.
1032. **262.** 6 s. multicoloured .. 8 8
1033. 30 s. multicoloured .. 20 20

1966. Presidential Sayings (5th issue). As T **233** but with portrait and saying changed.
1034. 6 s. black and brown .. 15 5
1035. 30 s. black and blue .. 20 15
PORTRAIT AND SAYING: Pres. Laurel. "No one can love the Filipinos better . . .".

1967. 50th Anniv. of Lions Int. Nos 977/80 optd. **50th ANNIVERSARY LIONS INTERNATIONAL 1967** and emblem. Imperf.
1036. **247.** 6 c. blue and gold .. 10 10
1037. – 10 c. pink and gold .. 25 25
1038. – 20 c. yellow and gold 35 35
1039. – 30 c. green and gold 45 45

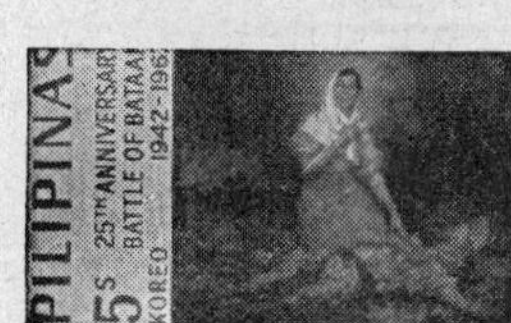

269. "Succour" (after painting by F. Amorsolo).

1967. 25th Anniv. of Battle of Bataan.
1040. **269.** 5 s. multicoloured .. 8 5
1041. 20 s. multicoloured .. 20 8
1042. 2 p. multicoloured .. 1·10 60

1967. Nos. 900 and 975 surch.
1043. 4 s. on 6 s. blue .. 10 10
1044. 5 s. on 6 s. blue .. 10 10

271. Stork-billed Kingfisher.

272. Gen. MacArthur and Paratroopers landing on Corregidor.

1967. Obligatory Tax. T.B. Relief Fund. Birds. Multicoloured.
1045. 1 s.+5 s. Type **271** .. 40 10
1046. 5 s.+5 s. Rufous hornbill 40 10
1047. 10 s.+5 s. Philippine eagle 90 25
1048. 30 s.+5 s. Great-billed parrot .. .. .. 1·90 65
See also Nos. 1113/6.

1967. 25th Anniv. of Battle of Corregidor.
1049. **272.** 6 s. multicoloured .. 10 15
1050. 5 p. multicoloured .. 3·00 2·00

273. Bureau of Posts Building, Manila.

1967. 65th Anniv. of Philippines Bureau of Posts.
1051. **273.** 4 s. multicoloured .. 20 15
1052. 20 s. multicoloured .. 20 10
1053. 50 s. multicoloured .. 45 30

274. Escaping from Eruption.

1967. Obligatory Tax. Taal Volcano Eruption (1965). (1st issue).
1054. **274.** 70 s. multicoloured .. 70 50
For compulsory use on foreign air mail where the rate exceeds 70 s. in aid of Taal Volcano Rehabilitation Committee.
See also No. 1071.

1967. Presidential Sayings (6th issue). As T **233** but with portrait and saying changed.
1055. 10 s. black and blue .. 15 5
1056. 30 s. black and violet .. 50 15
PORTRAIT AND SAYING: Pres. Quezon. "Social justice is far more beneficial . . .".

275. "The Holy Family" (Filipino version).

1967. Christmas.
1057. **275.** 10 s. multicoloured .. 20 15
1058. 40 s. multicoloured .. 40 30

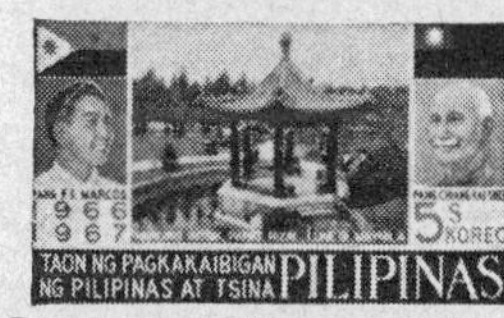

276. Pagoda, Pres. Marcos and Chiang Kai-shek.

1967. China-Philippines Friendship.
1059. **276.** 5 s. multicoloured .. 5 5
1060. – 10 s. multicoloured .. 10 8
1061. – 20 s. multicoloured .. 20 10
DESIGNS: (with portraits of Pres. Marcos and Chiang Kai-shek): 10 s. Gateway, Chinese Garden, Rizal Park, Luneta. 20 s. Chinese Garden, Rizal Park, Luneta.

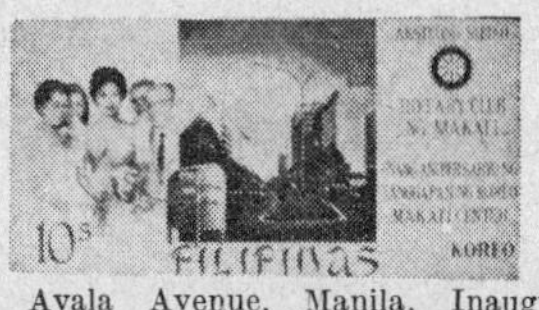

277. Ayala Avenue, Manila, Inaugural Ceremony and Rotary Badge.

1968. 1st Anniv. of Makati Centre Post Office, Manila.
1062. **277.** 10 s. multicoloured .. 10 10
1063. 20 s. multicoloured .. 25 25
1064. 40 s. multicoloured .. 40 40

1968. Surch.
1065. – 5 s. on 6 s. (No. 981) 12 8
1066. – 5 s. on 6 s. (No. 1034) 12 8
1067. **244.** 10 s. on 6 s.+5 s. .. 15 8

280. Calderon, Barasoain Church and Constitution.

1968. Birth Cent. of Felipe G. Calderon (lawyer and author of Malolos Constitution).
1068. **280.** 10 s. multicoloured .. 5 5
1069. 40 s. multicoloured .. 30 20
1070. 75 s. multicoloured .. 60 50

281. Eruption.

282. "Philcomsat", Earth Station and Globe.

1968. Taal Volcano Eruption (1965). (2nd issue).
1071. **281.** 70 s. multicoloured .. 70 60

Two issues were prepared by an American Agency under a contract signed with the Philippine postal authority but at the last moment this contract was cancelled by the Philippine Government. In the meanwhile the stamps had been on sale in the U.S.A. but they were never issued in the Philippines and they had no postal validity.

They comprise a set for the Mexican Olympic Games in the values 1, 2, 3 and 15 s. postage and 50, 75 s., 1, 2. p. airmail and a set in memory of J. F. Kennedy and Robert Kennedy in the values 1, 2, 3 s. postage and 5, 10 p. airmail.

1968. Inaug. of "Philcomsat"—POTC Earth Station, Tanay, Rizal, Luzon.
1072. **282.** 10 s. multicoloured .. 15 10
1073. 40 s. multicoloured .. 40 30
1074. 75 s. multicoloured .. 45 40

283. "Tobacco Production" (mural).

1968. Philippines Tobacco Industry.
1075. **283.** 10 s. multicoloured .. 8 5
1076. 40 s. multicoloured .. 30 25
1077. 70 s. multicoloured .. 55 45

284. "Kudyapi".

1968. St. Cecilia's Day. Musical Instruments. Multicoloured.
1078. 10 s. Type **284** 5 5
1079. 20 s. "Ludag" 15 10
1080. 30 s. "Kulintangan" .. 25 25
1081. 50 s. "Subing" 40 25

285. Concordia College.

286. Children singing Carols.

1968. Cent. of Concordia Women's College.
1082. **285.** 10 s. multicoloured .. 10 5
1083. 20 s. multicoloured .. 20 15
1084. 70 s. multicoloured .. 25 20

1968. Christmas.
1085. **286.** 10 s. multicoloured .. 8 5
1086. 40 s. multicoloured .. 35 30
1087. 75 s. multicoloured .. 45 40

287. Philippine Tarsier.

1969. Philippines Fauna. Multicoloured.
1088. 2 s. Type **287** 10 8
1089. 10 s. Tamarau 15 8
1090. 20 s. Water buffalo .. 30 25
1091. 75 s. Greater Malay chevrotain 85 70

288. President Aguinaldo and Cavite Building.

1969. Birth Centenary of President Amilio Aguinaldo.
1092. **288.** 10 s. multicoloured .. 15 8
1093. 40 s. multicoloured .. 40 25
1094. 70 s. multicoloured .. 45 40

289. Rotary Emblem and "Bastion of San Andres".

1969. 50th Anniv. of Manila Rotary Club.
1095. **289.** 10 s. multicoloured (post.) 10 5
1096. 40 s. multicoloured (air) 30 25
1097. 75 s. multicoloured .. 35 25

290. Senator C. M. Recto.

292. Jose Rizal College.

1969. Recto Commem.
1098. **290.** 10 s. purple 20 5

1969. Philatelic Week. No. 1051 optd. **PHILATELIC WEEK NOV. 24-30, 1968**, etc.
1099. 4 s. multicoloured .. 15 10

1969. Jose Rizal College, Mandaluyong, Rizal.
1100. **292.** 10 s. multicoloured .. 8 5
1101. 40 s. multicoloured .. 30 25
1102. 50 s. multicoloured .. 40 35

1969. 4th National Boy Scout Jamboree, Palayan City. No. 1019 surch. **4th NATIONAL BOY SCOUT JAMBOREE PALAYAN CITY - MAY, 1969** and value.
1103. **261.** 5 s. on 6 s. multicoloured 25 25

294. Red Cross Emblems and Map.

295. Pres. and Mrs. Marcos harvesting Rice.

1969. 50th Anniv. of League of Red Cross Societies.
1104. **294.** 10 s. red, blue & grey 8 5
1105. 40 s. red and blue .. 35 25
1106. 75 s. red, brn. & ochre 55 50

1969. "Rice for Progress".
1107. **295.** 10 s. multicoloured .. 8 5
1108. 40 s. multicoloured .. 20 15
1109. 75 s. multicoloured .. 35 30

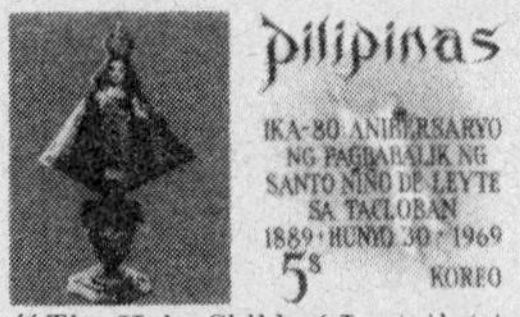

296. "The Holy Child of Leyte" (statue).

1969. 80th Anniv. of Return of the "Holy Child of Leyte" to Tacloban.
1110. **296.** 5 s. multicoloured (post.) 5 5
1111. 10 s. multicoloured .. 8 5
1112. 40 s. multicoloured (air) 35 25

1969. Obligatory Tax. T.B. Relief Fund. Birds, as T **271**.
1113. 1 s.+5 s. Golden-backed three-toed woodpecker 40 10
1114. 5 s.+5 s. Philippine trogon 65 20
1115. 10 s.+5 s. Johnstone's lorikeet .. .. 1·10 25
1116. 40 s.+5 s. Scarlet minivet .. .. 1·60 55

297. Bank Building.

1969. Inauguration of Philippines Development Bank, Makati, Rizal.
1117. **297.** 10 s. black, blue & grn. 12 5
1118. 40 s. black, red & grn. 65 25
1119. 75 s. black, brown & grn. 1·00 55

298. "Troides magellanus".

1969. Philippine Butterflies. Multicoloured.
1120 10 s. Type **298** 25 10
1121 20 s. "Graphium agamemnon" 45 15
1122 30 s. "Papilio helenus" .. 70 30
1123 40 s. "Trogonoptera trojana" 60 55

299. Children of the World.

1969. 15th Anniv. of Universal Children's Day.
1124. **299.** 10 s. multicoloured .. 5 5
1125. 20 s. multicoloured .. 15 10
1126. 30 s. multicoloured .. 25 20

300. Memorial and Outline of Landing.

1969. 25th Anniv. of U.S. Forces' Landing on Leyte.
1127. **300.** 5 s. multicoloured .. 5 5
1128. 10 s. multicoloured .. 15 5
1129. 40 s. multicoloured .. 40 25

301. Cultural Centre.

303. Melchora Aquino.

1969. Cultural Centre, Manila.
1130. **301.** 10 s. blue 8 5
1131. 30 s. purple 25 20

1969. Philatelic Week. Nos. 943/6 (Folk Dances) optd. **1969 PHILATELIC WEEK** or optd. and surch.
1132. 5 s. multicoloured .. 10 10
1133. 5 s. on 6 s. multicoloured 10 10
1134. 10 s. multicoloured .. 25 10
1135. 10 s. on 20 s. multicoloured 25 10

1969. 50th Death Anniv. of Melchora Aquino, "Tandang Sora" (Grand Old Woman of the Revolution).
1136. **303.** 10 s. multicoloured .. 5 5
1137. 20 s. multicoloured .. 15 8
1138. 30 s. multicoloured .. 25 15

1969. 2nd-term Inauguration of President Marcos. No. 1021 surch. **PASINAYA, IKA-2 PANUNUNGKULAN PANGULONG FERDINAND E. MARCOS DISYEMBRA 30, 1969.**
1139. **262.** 5 s. on 6 s. multicoloured 20 15

305. Ladle and Steel Mills.

1970. Iligan Integrated Steel Mills.
1140. **305.** 10 s. multicoloured .. 12 5
1141. 20 s. multicoloured .. 15 15
1142. 30 s. multicoloured .. 25 25

1970. Nos. 900, 962 and 964 surch.
1143. – 4 s. on 6 s. blue .. 10 8
1144. **242.** 5 s. on 6 s. multicoloured 10 8
1145. **243.** 5 s. on 6 s. multicoloured 10 8

307. New U.P.U. Headquarters Building.

1970. New U.P.U. Headquarters Building, Berne.
1146. **307.** 10 s. deep blue, yellow and blue 8 5
1147. 30 s. blue, yellow and green 30 15

1970. Presidential Sayings (7th issue). As T **233** but with portrait and saying changed.
1148. 10 s. black and purple .. 15 5
1149. 40 s. black and green .. 50 15
PORTRAIT AND SAYING: Pres. Osmena. "Ante todo el bien de nuestro pueblo".

308. Dona Julia V. de Ortigas and T.B. Society Headquarters.

1970. Obligatory Tax. T.B. Relief Fund.
1150. **308.** 1 s.+5 s. multicoloured 8 5
1151. 5 s.+5 s. multicoloured 15 8
1152. 30 s.+5 s. multicoloured 45 35
1153. 70 s.+5 s. multicoloured 60 40

309. I.C.S.W. Emblem.

1970. 15th Int. Conferenceon Social Welfare.
1154. **309.** 10 s. multicoloured .. 5 8
1155. 20 s. multicoloured .. 15 10
1156. 30 s. multicoloured .. 25 15

310. "Crab" (after sculpture by A. Calder).

1970. "Fight Cancer" Campaign.
1157. **310.** 10 s. multicoloured .. 10 8
1158. 40 s. multicoloured .. 30 20
1159. 50 s. multicoloured .. 45 25

311. Scaled Tridacna.

1970. Seashells. Multicoloured.
1160. 5 s. Type **311** 5 5
1161. 10 s. Royal spiny oyster 15 8
1162. 20 s. Venus comb .. 20 20
1163. 40 s. Glory-of-the-Sea cone 25 20

1970. Nos. 986, 1024 and 1026 surch. with new values in figures and letters.
1164. **249.** 4 s. on 6 s. 8 8
1165. **263.** 4 s. on 6 s. 8 8
1166. **264.** 4 s. on 6 s. 8 8

313. The "Hundred Islands" and Ox-cart.

1970. Tourism (1st series). Multicoloured.
1167. 10 s. Type **313** 10 10
1168. 20 s. Tree-house, Pasonanca Park, Zamboanga City 15 10
1169. 30 s. "Filipino" (statue) and sugar plantation, Negros Island 25 20
1170. 2 p. Calesa (horse-carriage) and Miagao Church, Iloilo 90 50
See also Nos. 1186/9, 1192/5 and 1196/9.

314. Map of the Philippines.

1970. Golden Jubilee of Philippine Pharmaceutical Association.
1171. **314.** 10 s. multicoloured .. 10 8
1172. 50 s. multicoloured .. 25 25

1970. U.P.U./A.O.P.U. Regional Seminar, Manila. No. 938 surch. **UPU-AOPU REGIONAL SEMINAR NOV. 23—DEC. 5, 1970,** and new value.
1173. **235** 10 s. on 6 s. multicoloured 20 10

1970. Philatelic Week. No. 977 surch. **1970 PHILATELIC WEEK** and new value.
1174. **247.** 10 s. on 6 s. brown, blue and gold .. 20 15

317. Pope Paul VI and Map.

1970. Pope Paul's Visit to the Philippines.
1175. **317.** 10 s. multicoloured (postage) 10 8
1176. 30 s. multicoloured .. 25 20
1177. 40 s. multicoloured (air) 35 25

318. Mariano Ponce.

320. P.A.T.A. Horse and Carriage.

1970.
1178. **318.** 10 s. red 10 5
1179. – 15 s. brown .. 15 5
1180. – 40 s. red .. 25 5
1181. – 1 p. blue .. 85 25
DESIGNS: 15 s. Josefa Llanes Escoda. 40 s. Gen. Miguel Malvar. 1 p. Julian Felipe.

1971. 20th P.A.T.A. Conference and Workshop, Manila.
1183. **320.** 5 s. multicoloured .. 5 5
1184. 10 s. multicoloured .. 15 5
1185. 70 s. multicoloured .. 40 30

1971. Tourism (2nd series). Views as T **313**. Multicoloured.
1186. 10 s. Nayong Pilipino resort 5 5
1187. 20 s. Fish farm, Iloilo .. 15 10
1188. 30 s. Pagsanjan Falls .. 25 20
1189. 5 p. Watch-tower, Punta Cruz .. .. .. 1·25 1·25

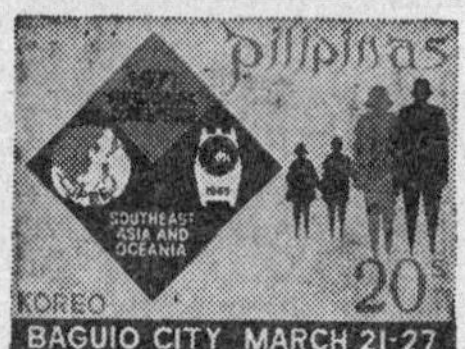

321. Emblem and Family.

1971. Regional Conference of Int. Planned Parenthood Federation for South-East Asia and Oceania.

No.	Type	Description		
1190.	321.	20 s. multicoloured	10	8
1191.		40 s. multicoloured	10	10

1971. Tourism (3rd series). As T **313**. Mult.

1192.	10 s. Aguinaldo pearl farm	5	5
1193.	20 s. Coral-diving, Davao	15	10
1194.	40 s. Taluksengay Mosque	25	20
1195.	1 p. Ifugao woman and Banaue rice-terraces	40	40

1971. Tourism (4th series). As T **313**. Mult.

1196	10 s. Cannon and Filipino vinta, Fort del Pilar	10	10
1197	30 s. Magellan's Cross, Cebu City	15	10
1198	50 s. "Big Jar", Calamba Laguna (Rizal's birth-place)	30	25
1199	70 s. Mayon Volcano and diesel train	1·75	50

1971. Surch in letters and figures.

No.	Type	Description		
1200.	264.	5 s. on 6 s. multicoloured	15	10

323. G. A. Malcolm (founder) and Law Symbols.

1971. 60th Anniv. of Philippines College of Law.

No.	Type	Description		
1201.	323.	15 s. mult. (post.)	10	5
1202.		1 p. multicoloured (air)	45	45

324. Commemorative Seal.

1971. 400th Anniv. of Manila.

No.	Type	Description		
1203.	324.	10 s. mult. (postage)	8	5
1204.		1 p. mult. (air)	40	30

325. Arms of Faculties.

1971. Centenaries of Faculties of Medicine and Surgery, and of Pharmacy, Santo Tomas University.

No.	Type	Description		
1205.	325.	5 s. mult. (postage)	5	5
1206.		2 p. mult. (air)	85	75

1971. University Presidents' World Congress, Manila. Surch. **CONGRESS OF UNIVERSITY PRESIDENTS**, emblems and value.

No.	Type	Description		
1207.	266.	5 s. on 6 s. violet, yellow and green	10	10

327. "Our Lady of Guia".

1971. 400th Anniv. of "Our Lady of Guia", Ermita, Manila.

No.	Type	Description		
1208.	327.	10 s. multicoloured	15	10
1209.		75 s. multicoloured	60	35

328. Bank and "Customers".

1971. 70th Anniv. of First National City Bank.

No.	Type	Description		
1210.	328.	10 s. multicoloured	10	10
1211.		30 s. multicoloured	45	20
1212.		1 p. multicoloured	50	20

1971. Surch. in letters and figure.

No.	Type	Description		
1213.	259.	4 s. on 6 s. blue	10	10
1214.		5 s. on 6 s. blue	15	15

1971. Philatelic Week. Surch. **1971-PHILATELIC WEEK** and new value in letters and figure.

No.	Type	Description		
1215.	266.	5 s. on 6 s. violet, yellow and green	10	10

331. Dish Aerial and Events.

1972. 6th Asian Electronics Conf., Manila (1971) and Related Events.

No.	Type	Description		
1216.	331.	5 s. multicoloured	5	5
1217.		40 s. multicoloured	20	20

332. Fathers Burgos, Gomez and Zamora.

1972. Centenary of Martyrdom of Fathers Burgos, Gomez and Zamora.

No.	Type	Description		
1218.	332.	5 s. multicoloured	5	5
1219.		60 s. multicoloured	35	25

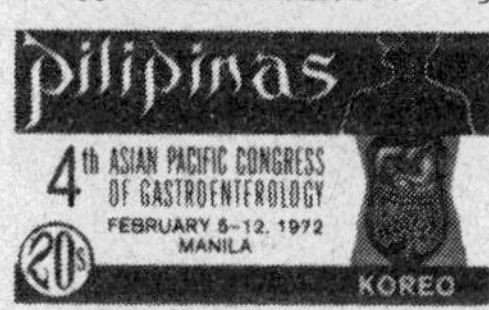

333. Human Organs.

1972. 4th Asian-Pacific Gastro-enterological Congress, Manila.

No.	Type	Description		
1220.	333.	20 s. mult. (postage)	15	10
1221.		40 s. mult. (air)	30	25

1972. Surch.

No.	Type	Description		
1222.	263.	5 s. on 6 s. mult.	15	10

1972. No. O 914 with opt. **G.O.** obliterated.

1223.	50 s. violet	25	15

1972. Surch.

No.	Type	Description		
1224.	245.	10 s. on 6 s. mult.	25	12
1225.	251.	10 s. on 6 s. mult.	25	12
1226.	–	10 s. on 6 s. black & red (No. 1015)	25	12

336. Memorial Gardens, Manila.

1972. Tourism. "Visit Asean Lands" Campaign.

No.	Type	Description		
1227.	336.	5 s. multicoloured	15	5
1228.		50 s. multicoloured	45	20
1229.		60 s. multicoloured	60	25

337. "KKK" Flag.

1972. Evolution of Philippines' Flag.

No.	Type	Description		
1230.	337.	30 s. red and blue	25	25
1231.	–	30 s. red and blue	25	25
1232.	–	30 s. red and blue	25	25
1233.	–	30 s. black and blue	25	25
1234.	–	30 s. red and blue	25	25
1235.	–	30 s. red and blue	25	25
1236.	–	30 s. red and blue	25	25
1237.	–	30 s. red and blue	25	25
1238.	–	30 s. blk., red and blue	25	25
1239.	–	30 s. yell., red & blue	25	25

FLAGS: No. 1231, Three "K"s in pyramid. **No.** 1232, Single "K". No. 1233, "K", skull and crossbones. No. 1234, Three "K"s and sun in triangle. No. 1235, Sun and three "K"s. No. 1236, Ancient Tagalog "K" within sun. No. 1237, Face in sun. No. 1238, Tricolor. No. 1239, Present national flag—sun and stars within triangle, two stripes.

338. Mabol, Santol and Papaya.

1972. Obligatory Tax. T.B. Relief Fund. Fruits. Multicoloured.

1240.	1 s.+5 s. Type **338**	5	5
1241.	10 s.+5 s. Bananas, balimbang and mangosteen	15	8
1242.	40 s.+5 s. Guava, mango, duhat and susongkalabac	50	30
1243.	1 p.+5 s. Orange, pineapple, lanzones and sirhuelas	1·10	65

339. "Scarus frenatus".

1972. Fishes. Multicoloured.

1244.	5 s. Type **339** (postage)	5	5
1245.	10 s. "Chaetodon kleini"	10	5
1246.	20 s. "Zanclus cornutus"	25	20
1247.	50 s. "Holacanthus bispinosus" (air)	25	20

340. Bank Headquarters.

1972. 25th Anniv. of Philippines Development Bank.

No.	Type	Description		
1248.	340.	10 s. multicoloured	5	5
1249.		20 s. multicoloured	15	8
1250.		60 s. multicoloured	20	20

341. Pope Paul VI.

1972. 1st Anniv. of Pope Paul's Visit to Philippines.

No.	Type	Description		
1251.	341.	10 s. mult. (postage)	5	5
1252.		50 s. multicoloured	35	25
1253.		60 s. multicoloured (air)	40	30

1972. Various stamps surch.

No.	Type	Description		
1254.	240.	10 s. on 6 s. (No. 953)	20	15
1255.	–	10 s. on 6 s. (No. 959)	20	15
1256.	250.	10 s. on 6 s. (No. 989)	20	15

343. "La Barca de Aqueronte" (Hidalgo).

1972. 25th Anniv. of Stamps and Philatelic Division, Philippines Bureau of Posts. Filipino Paintings. Multicoloured.

1257.	5 s. Type **343**	10	5
1258.	10 s. "Afternoon Meal of the Rice Workers" (Amorsolo)	15	5
1259.	30 s. "Espana y Filipinas" (Luna) (27×60 mm.)	20	15
1260.	70 s. "The Song of Maria Clara" (Amorsolo)	25	25

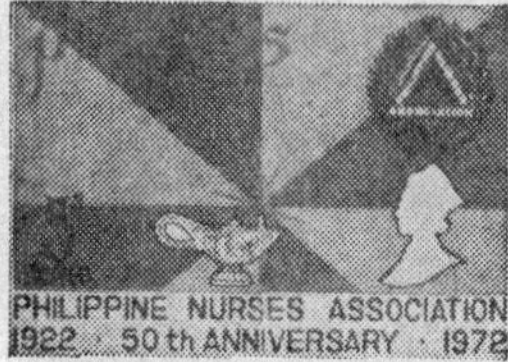

344. Lamp, Emblem and Nurse.

1972. 50th Anniv. of Philippine Nurses Assn.

No.	Type	Description		
1261.	344.	5 s. multicoloured	5	5
1262.		10 s. multicoloured	5	5
1263.		70 s. multicoloured	35	30

345. Heart on Map.

1972. World Heart Month.

No.	Type	Description		
1264.	345.	5 s. red, green & violet	10	5
1265.		10 s. red, green & blue	15	8
1266.		30 s. red, blue & green	15	15

346. "The First Mass" (C. V. Francisco).

1972. 450th Anniv. of 1st Mass in Limasawa (1971).

No.	Type	Description		
1267.	346.	10 s. mult. (postage)	10	5
1268.		60 s. multicoloured (air)	35	25

1972. Asia Pacific Scout Conference, Manila. Various stamps surch. **ASIA PACIFIC SCOUT CONFERENCE NOV. 1972,** and value.

No.	Type	Description		
1269.	233.	10 s. on 6 s. (No. 933)	15	15
1270.	240.	10 s. on 6 s. (No. 953)	15	15
1271.	–	10 s. on 6 s. (No. 981)	15	15

348. Olympic Emblems and Torch.

1972. Olympic Games, Munich.

No.	Type	Description		
1272.	348.	5 s. multicoloured	5	5
1273.		10 s. multicoloured	8	5
1274.		70 s. multicoloured	20	20

1972. Philatelic Week. Nos. 950 and 983 surch. **1972 PHILATELIC WEEK** and value.

No.	Type	Description		
1275.	239.	10 s. on 6 s. mult.	10	10
1276.	248.	10 s. on 6 s. mult.	10	10

350. Manunggul Burial Jar.

1972. Philippine Archaeological Discoveries. Multicoloured.

1277. 10 s. Type **350** 10 8
1278. 10 s. Ritual earthenware vessel 10 8
1279. 10 s. Metal pot 10 8
1280. 10 s. Earthenware vessel 10 8

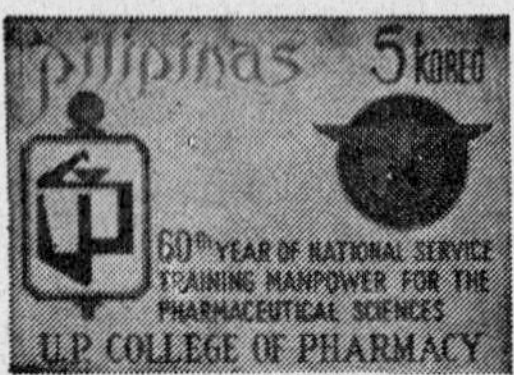

351. Emblems of Pharmacy and University of the Philippines.

1972. 60th Anniv. of Nat. Training for Pharmaceutical Sciences, University of the Philippines.

1281. **351.** 5 s. multicoloured .. 5 5
1282. 10 s. multicoloured 10 5
1283. 30 s. multicoloured 30 20

352. " The Lantern-makers " (J. Pineda).

1972. Christmas.

1284. **352.** 10 s. multicoloured.. 8 5
1285. 30 s. multicoloured.. 25 15
1286. 50 s. multicoloured.. 35 25

353. President Roxas and Wife.

1972. 25th Anniv. of Philippines' Red Cross.

1287. **353.** 5 s. multicoloured .. 5 5
1288. 20 s. multicoloured.. 10 15
1289. 30 s. multicoloured.. 25 20

1973. Nos. 948 and 1005 surch.

1290. **238.** 10 s. on 6 s. mult. .. 20 10
1291. **256.** 10 s. on 6 s. mult. .. 20 10

1973. Presidential Sayings (8th issue). As T **233**, but with portrait and saying changed.

1292. 10 s. black and yellow .. 15 5
1293. 30 s. black and mauve .. 50 15

PORTRAIT AND SAYING: 10 s., 30 s. **Pres. Garcia. "I would rather be right than successful".**

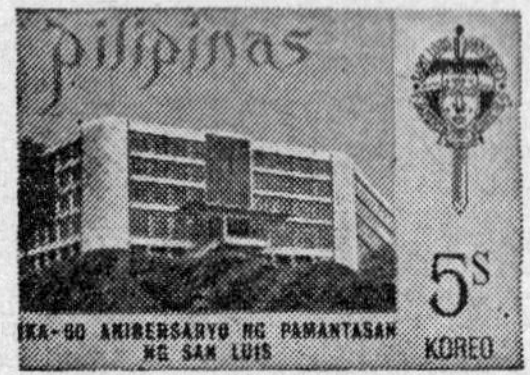

355. University Building.

1973. 60th Anniv. of St. Louis University, Baguio City.

1294. **355.** 5 s. multicoloured .. 5 5
1295. 10 s. multicoloured .. 5 5
1296. 75 s. multicoloured .. 40 35

1973. Villamor. Commem.

1297. **356.** 10 s. multicoloured .. 10 10
1298. 2 p. multicoloured .. 1·40 85

1973. Various stamps surch.

1299. **252.** 5 s. on 6 s. mult. .. 15 10
1300. **266.** 5 s. on 6 s. mult. .. 15 10
1301. **318.** 15 s. on 10 s. red & blk. 10 30

359. Actor and Stage Performance.

1973. 1st " Third-World " Theatre Festival, Manila.

1302. **359.** 5 s. multicoloured .. 5 5
1303. 10 s. multicoloured.. 10 5
1304. 50 s. multicoloured.. 30 20
1305. 70 s. multicoloured.. 40 25

1973. President Marcos' Anti-Smuggling Campaign. No. 1017. surch.

1306. 5 s. on 6 s. blue 20 10

1973. 10th Death Anniv. of John F. Kennedy. No. 989 surch.

1307. 5 s. on 6 s. multicoloured 20 10

1973. Compulsory Tax Stamps. T.B. Relief Fund. Nos. 1241/2 surch.

1308. 15 s.+5 s. on 10 s.+5 s. multicoloured 20 20
1309. 60 s.+5 s. on 40 s.+5 s. multicoloured 45 45

363. Proclamation Scenes.

1973. 75th Anniv. of Philippine Independence.

1310. **363.** 15 s. multicoloured.. 8 5
1311. 45 s. multicoloured.. 15 15
1312. 90 s. multicoloured.. 20 20

364. M. Agoncillo (maker of first national flag).

365. Imelda Marcos.

1973. Perf. or imperf.

1313. – 15 s. violet 10 5
1455. – 30 s. blue 15 5
1456. – 30 s. red 15 5
1314. **364.** 60 s. brown 30 10
1315. – 90 s. blue 40 20
1457. – 90 s. green 40 20
1316. – 1 p. 10 blue 25 25
1458. – 1 p. 20 red 15 10
1317. – 1 p. 50 red 45 25
1318. – 1 p. 50 brown .. 45 25
1319. – 1 p. 80 green .. 50 50
1320. – 5 p. blue .. .. 1·50 1·50

DESIGNS: 15 s. Gabriela Silang (revolutionary). 30 s. (No. 1455) Jose Rizal. 30 s. (No. 1456) Rajah Kalantiaw (Panay Chief). 90 s. (No. 1315) Teodoro Yangco (businessman). 90 s. (No. 1457) Lope K. Santos (father of grammar). 1 p. 10, Pio Valenzuela (physician). 1 p. 20, Gregoria de Jesus (patriot). 1 p. 50, (No. 1317) Pedro Paterno (revolutionary). 1 p. 50, (No. 1318) Teodora Alonso (mother of Jose Rizal). 1 p. 80, E. Evangelista (revolutionary). 5 p. F. M. Guerrero (writer).

1973. Projects Inaugurated by Sra Imelda Marcos.

1321. **365.** 15 s. multicoloured .. 8 8
1322. 50 s. multicoloured .. 30 25
1323. 60 s. multicoloured .. 40 30

366. Malakanyang Palace.

1973. Presidential Palace, Manila.

1324. **366.** 15 s. mult. (postage) 8 8
1325. 50 s. multicoloured .. 30 20
1326. 60 s. mult. (air) .. 40 25

367. Interpol Emblem.

368. Scouting Activities.

1973. 50th Anniv. of International Criminal Police Organization. (Interpol).

1327. **367.** 15 s. multicoloured .. 15 8
1328. 65 s. multicoloured .. 40 25

1973. Golden Jubilee of Philippine Boy Scouts. Perf. or imperf.

1329. **368.** 15 s. brown and green 10 8
1330. – 65 s. blue and brown 40 30

DESIGN: 65 s. Scouts reading brochure.

369. Bank Emblem, Urban and Agricultural Landscapes.

1974. 25th Anniv. of Central Bank of the Philippines. Multicoloured.

1331. 15 s. Type **369** 10 10
1332. 60 s. Bank building, 1949 25 15
1333. 1 p. 50 Bank complex, 1974 45 40

370. "Maria Clara" Costume.

373. Map of South-East Asia.

1974. U.P.U. Cent. Philippines' Costumes. Multicoloured.

1334. 15 s. Type **370** 10 5
1335. 60 s. "Balintawak" .. 30 20
1336. 80 s. "Malong" 40 25

1974. Philatelic Week (1973). No. 1303 surch. **1973 PHILATELIC WEEK** and value.

1337. **359.** 15 s. on 10 s. mult... 10 5

1974. 25th Anniv. of Philippine "Lionism". Nos. 1297 and 1180 surch. **PHILIPPINE LIONISM 1949-1974**, Lion emblem and value.

1338. **356.** 15 s. on 10 s. mult... 15 10
1339. – 45 s. on 40 s. red .. 35 20

1974. Asian Paediatrics Congress, Manila. Perf. or imperf.

1340. **373.** 30 s. red and blue .. 15 8
1341. 1 p. red and green .. 20 20

374. Gen. Valdes and Hospital.

1974. Obligatory Tax. T.B. Relief Fund. Perf. or imperf.

1342. **374.** 15 s.+5 s. grn. & red 8 8
1343. 1 p. 10+5 s. blue & red 50 35

1974. Nos. 974, 1024 and 1026 surch.

1344. **246.** 5 s. on 3 s. green .. 15 8
1345. **263.** 5 s. on 6 s. mult. .. 15 8
1346. **264.** 5 s. on 6 s. mult. .. 15 8

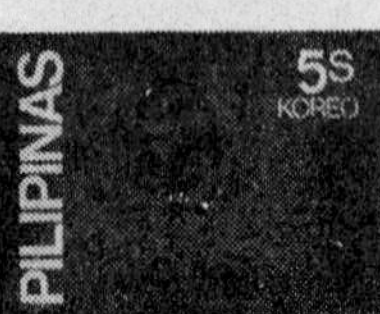

378. W.P.Y. Emblem.

1974. World Population Year. Perf. or imperf.

1347. **378.** 5 s. black and orange 5 5
1348. 2 p. blue & green .. 45 30

379. Red Feather Emblem.

1974. 25th Anniv. of Community Chest Movement in the Philippines. Perf. or imperf.

1349. **379.** 15 s. red and blue .. 8 5
1350. 40 s. red and green .. 25 15
1351. 45 s. red and brown 25 15

381. Sultan Mohammad Kudarat Map, Malayan Prau and Order.

1975. Sultan Kudarat of Mindanao Commem.

1352. **381.** 15 s. multicoloured .. 10 10

382. Association Emblem.

383. Rafael Palma.

1975. 25th Anniv. of Philippine Mental Health Association. Perf. or imperf.

1353. **382.** 45 s. green and orange 25 15
1354. 1 p. green and purple 40 25

1975. Birth Cent. of Rafael Palma (educationalist and statesman). Perf. or imperf.

1355. **383.** 15 s. green 15 5
1436. 30 s. brown 15 5

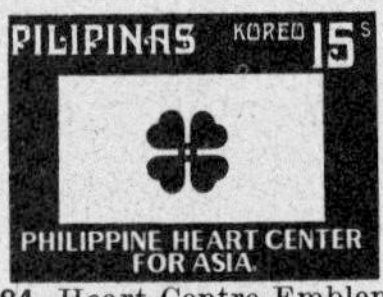

384. Heart Centre Emblem.

1975. Inaug. of Philippine Heart Centre for Asia, Quezon City. Perf. or imperf.

1356. **384.** 15 s. red and blue .. 5 5
1357. 50 s. red and green .. 20 15

385. Cadet in Full Dress, and Academy Building.

1975. 70th Anniv. of Philippine Military Academy.

1358. **385.** 15 s. multicoloured .. 15 8
1359. 45 s. multicoloured .. 35 25

386. " Helping the Disabled ".

397. Planting Sapling.

1975. 25th Anniv. (1974) of Philippines Orthopaedic Association.

1360. **386.** 45 s. green 20 10
1361. – 45 s. grn. (19 × 35 mm.) 20 10
1362. – 45 s. grn. (19 × 35 mm.) 20 10
1363. – 45 s. grn. (19 × 35 mm.) 20 10
1364. – 45 s. green 20 10
1365. – 45 s. green 20 10
1366. – 45 s. grn. (19 × 35 mm.) 20 10
1367. – 45 s. grn. (19 × 35 mm.) 20 10
1368. – 45 s. grn. (19 × 35 mm.) 20 10
1369. – 45 s. green 20 10

DESIGNS: Nos. 1361/9. Further details of the mural as Type **386**.

Nos. 1360/9 were issued together se-tenant in blocks of ten (5 × 2) forming a composite design within the sheet.

1975. Nos. 1153 and 1342/3 surch. with Cross of Lorraine and new value.
1370. **374.** 5 s. on 15 s.+5 s. green and red .. 10 5
1371. **308.** 60 s. on 70 s.+5 s. multicoloured .. 40 25
1372. **374.** 1 p. on 1 p. 10+5 s. blue and red 50 30

1975. Forest Conservation. Multicoloured.
1373. 45 s. Type **397** 20 15
1374. 45 s. Sapling and tree-trunks 20 15

398. Jade Vine. **399.** Imelda Marcos and I.W.Y. Emblem.

1975.
1375. **398.** 15 s. multicoloured .. 15 5

1975. International Women's Year.
1376. **399.** 15 s. blk., bl. & deep bl. 10 10
1377. 80 s. black, blue and pink 20 20

400. Commission Badge. **401.** Angat River Barrage.

1975. 75th Anniv. of Civil Service Commission.
1378. **400.** 15 s. multicoloured .. 8 5
1379. 50 s. multicoloured .. 20 15

1975. 25th Anniv. of International Irrigation and Drainage Commission.
1380. **401.** 40 s. blue and orange 15 15
1381. 1 p. 50 blue & mauve 25 20

402. "Welcome to Manila!" **403.** N. Romualdez (legislator and writer).

1975. Hong Kong and Shanghai Banking Corporation. Cent. of operations in the Philippines.
1382. **402.** 1 p. 50 multicoloured 1·25 35

1975. Birth Centenaries.
1383. **403.** 60 s. lilac 40 35
1384. – 90 s. mauve .. .. 1·00 35
DESIGN: 90 s. General G. del Pilar.

405. China Clipper, Boeing 747 and Flags.

1975. 40th Anniv. of First Trans-Pacific China Clipper Airmail Flight. San Francisco-Manila.
1385. **405.** 60 s. multicoloured .. 10 10
1386. 1 p. 50 multicoloured 25 20

1975. Airmail Exn. Nos. 1314 and 1318 optd. **AIRMAIL EXHIBITION NOV. 22-DEC. 9.**
1387. **364.** 60 s. brown 30 25
1388. – 1 p. 50 brown .. 30 25

407. APO Emblem. **408.** E. Jacinto.

1975. 25th Anniv. of APO Philatelic Society.
1389. **407.** 5 s. multicoloured .. 5 5
1390. 1 p. multicoloured .. 25 20

1975. Birth Centenary of Emilio Jacinto (military leader).
1391. **408.** 65 s. mauve.. .. 25 15

409. San Agustin Church. **410.** "Conducting" Hands.

1975. Holy Year. Churches.
1392. **409.** 20 s. turquoise .. 15 8
1393. – 30 s. black and yellow 20 10
1394. – 45 s. red and black .. 25 15
1395. – 60 s. brn., yell. & blk. 35 25
DESIGNS—HORIZ. 30 s. Morong Church. 45 s. Taal Basilica. VERT. 60 s. San Sebastian Church.

1976. 50th Anniv. of Manila Symphony Orchestra.
1396. **410.** 5 s. multicoloured .. 5 5
1397. 50 s. multicoloured .. 25 20

411. Philippines Airliners.

1976. 30th Anniv. of Philippines Airlines (P.A.L.).
1398. **411.** 60 s. multicoloured .. 40 15
1399. 1 p. 50 multicoloured 1·00 45

412. Felipe Agoncillo (statesman). **413.** University Building.

1976. Felipe Agoncillo. Commem.
1400. **412.** 1 p. 60 black .. 45 25

1976. 75th Anniv. of National University.
1401. **413.** 45 s. multicoloured .. 20 15
1402. 60 s. multicoloured .. 25 20

414. "Foresight Prevents Blindness". **415.** Emblem on Book.

1976. World Health Day.
1403. **414.** 15 s. multicoloured .. 20 8

1976. 75th Anniv. of National Archives.
1404. **415.** 1 p. 50 multicoloured 45 25

416. College Emblem and University Tower.

1976. 50th Anniv. of Colleges of Education and Science, Saint Thomas' University.
1405. **416.** 15 s. multicoloured.. 15 5
1406. 50 s. multicoloured.. 30 20

417. College Building.

1976. 50th Anniv. of Maryknoll College.
1407. **417.** 15 s. multicoloured .. 15 5
1408. 1 p. 50 multicoloured 40 20

1976. Olympic Games, Montreal. Surch. **Montreal 1976 21st OLYMPICS, CANADA.**
1409. **348.** 15 s. on 10 s. mult... 15 15

419. Constabulary Headquarters, Manila.

1976. 75th Anniv. of Philippine Constabulary.
1410. **419.** 15 s. multicoloured .. 15 5
1411. 60 s. multicoloured .. 35 20

420. Land and Aerial Surveying.

1976. 75th Anniv. of Lands Bureau.
1412. **420.** 80 s. multicoloured .. 20 15

422. Badges of Banking Organizations.

1976. Int. Monetary Fund and World Bank joint Board of Governors Annual Meeting, Manila.
1414. **422.** 60 s. multicoloured .. 25 20
1415. 1 p. 50 multicoloured 25 20

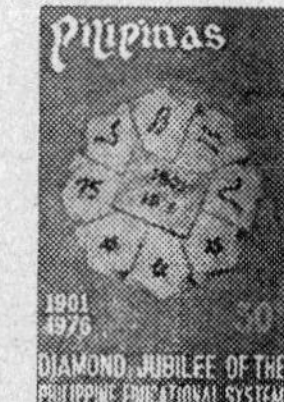

423. Virgin of Antipolo. **426.** Facets of Education.

425. "Going to Church".

1976. 350th Anniv. of "Virgin of Antipolo".
1416. **423.** 30 s. multicoloured .. 15 10
1417. 90 s. multicoloured .. 15 15

1976. Philatelic Week. Surch. **1976 PHILATELIC WEEK.**
1418. **355.** 30 s. on 10 s. mult... 20 10

1976. Christmas.
1419. **425.** 15 s. multicoloured .. 8 5
1420. 30 s. multicoloured .. 15 10

1976. 75th Anniv. of Philippine Educational System.
1421. **426.** 30 s. multicoloured .. 15 8
1422. 75 s. multicoloured .. 35 25

1977. Surch.
1423. 1 p. 20 on 1 p. 10 blue (No. 1316) 20 35
1424. 3 p. on 5 p. blue (No. 1320) 60 60

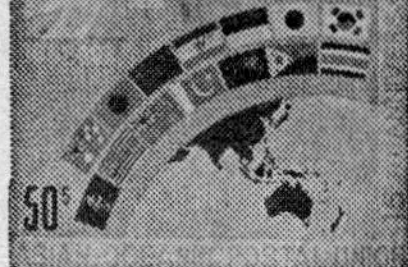

428. Jose Rizal. **429.** Flags, Map and Emblem.

1977. Famous Filipinos. Multicoloured.
1425. 30 s. Type **428** 10 5
1426. 2 p. 30 Dr. Galicano Apacible 55 25

1977. 15th Anniv. of Asian-Oceanic Postal Union.
1427. **429.** 50 s. multicoloured .. 20 8
1428. 1 p. 50 multicoloured 20 15

430. Worker and Cogwheels. **431.** Commission Emblem.

1977. 10th Anniv. of Asia Development Bank.
1429. **430.** 90 s. multicoloured .. 15 10
1430. 2 p. 30 multicoloured 45 25

1977. National Rural Credit Commission.
1431. **431.** 30 s. multicoloured .. 20 8

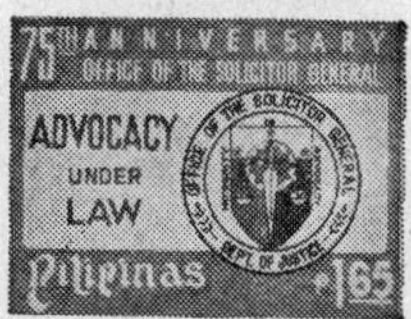

433. Solicitor-General's Emblem.

1977. 75th Anniv. of Office of Solicitor-General.
1433. **433.** 1 p. 65 multicoloured 20 20

434. Conference Emblem.

1977. World Law Conference, Manila.
1434. **434.** 2 p. 20 multicoloured 30 30

435. A.S.E.A.N. Emblem.

1977. 10th Anniv. of Association of South East Asian Nationals (A.S.E.A.N.).
1435. **435.** 1 p. 50 multicoloured 25 25

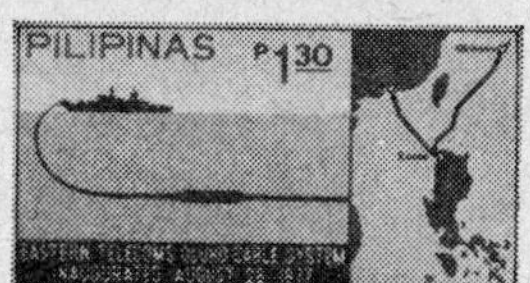

436. Cable Ship "Mercury" and Map.

1977. Inauguration of O.L.U.H.O. Cable.
1437. **436.** 1 p. 30 multicoloured 55 25

437. President Marcos.

1977. 60th Birthday of President Marcos.
1438. **437.** 30 s. multicoloured .. 15 5
1439. 2 p. 30 multicoloured 45 25

438. People raising Flag. **439.** Bishop Gregorio Aglipay (founder).

1977. 5th Anniv. of "New Society".
1440. **438.** 30 s. multicoloured .. 15 5
1441. 2 p. 30 multicoloured 45 25

1977. 75th Anniv. of Aglipayan Church.
1442. **439.** 30 s. multicoloured .. 15 5
1443. 90 s. multicoloured .. 30 20

441. Fokker "F-7" Trimotor and World Map.

1977. 50th Anniv. of Pan-Am International Air Service.
1445. **441.** 2 p. 30 multicoloured 65 20

442. Eight-pointed Star and Children.

1977. Christmas.
1446. **442.** 30 s. multicoloured .. 15 8
1447. 45 s. multicoloured .. 25 12

1977. Philatelic Week. Surch. **1977 PHILATELIC WEEK.**
1448. **407.** 90 s. on 1 p. mult. .. 35 20

444. Scouts and Map of Philippines.

1977. National Scout Jamboree.
1449. **444.** 30 s. multicoloured .. 20 10

445. University Badge. **446.** Sipa Player.

1978. 50th Anniv. of Far Eastern University.
1450. **445.** 30 s. multicoloured .. 10 5

1978. "Sipa" (Filipino ball game).
1451. **446.** 5 s. multicoloured .. 5 5
1452. – 10 s. multicoloured .. 5 5
1453. – 40 s. multicoloured .. 15 8
1454. – 75 s. multicoloured .. 35 15
DESIGNS: Nos. 1452/4, Different players.
Nos. 1451/4 were issued together se-tenant forming a composite design.

448. Arms of Meycauayan.

1978. 400th Anniv. of Meycauayan.
1459. **448.** 1 p. 05 multicoloured 35 15

449. Horse-drawn Mail Cart.

1978. "CAPEX 78" International Philatelic Exhibition, Toronto. Multicoloured.
1460 2 p. 50 Type **449** .. 1·75 1·40
1461 5 p. Filipino vinta (sailing canoe) .. .. 2·75 2·00

450. Andres Bonifacio Monument (G. Tolentino).

1978. Andres Bonifacio Monument.
1463. **450.** 30 s. multicoloured .. 20 10

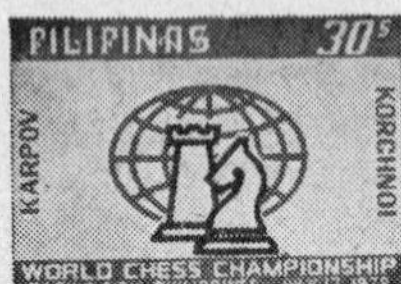

451. Knight, Rook and Globe.

1978. World Chess Championship, Baguio City.
1464 **451** 30 s. red and violet .. 8 5
1465 2 p. red and violet .. 60 40

452. Miner.

1978. 75th Anniv. of Benguet Consolidated Mining Company.
1466. **452.** 2 p. 30 multicoloured 1·25 50

453. Pres. Quezon. **455.** Pres. Osmena.

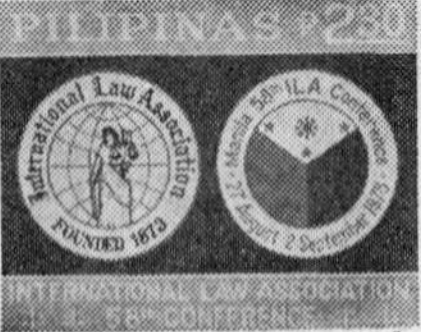

454. Law Association and Conference Emblems.

1978. Birth Centenary of Manuel L. Quezon (former President).
1467. **453.** 30 s. multicoloured .. 15 5
1468. 1 p. multicoloured .. 35 20

1978. 58th International Law Association Conference, Manila.
1469. **454.** 2 p. 30 multicoloured 45 20

1978. Birth Centenary of Sergio Osmena (former President).
1470. **455.** 30 s. multicoloured .. 15 5
1471. 1 p. multicoloured .. 15 15

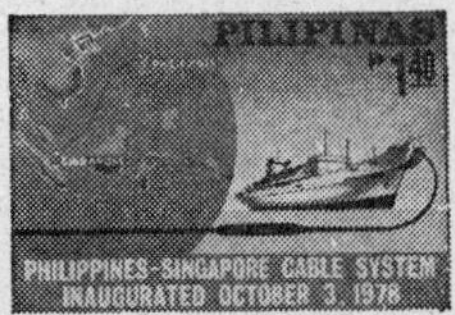

456. Map of Cable Route and Cable Ship "Mercury".

1978. Inauguration of Philippines-Singapore Submarine Cable.
1472. **456.** 1 p. 40 multicoloured 65 25

457. Basketball.

1978. 8th Men's World Basketball Championships.
1473. **457.** 30 s. multicoloured .. 15 5
1474. 2 p. 30 multicoloured 30 20

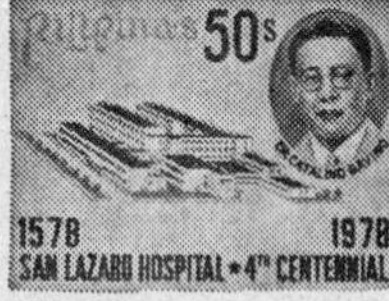

458. Dr. Catalino Gavino and Hospital.

1978. 400th Anniv. of San Lazaro Hospital.
1475. **458.** 50 s. multicoloured .. 20 10
1476. 90 s. multicoloured .. 35 15

459. Nurse vaccinating Child. **461.** Man making Telephone-call, Map and Satellite.

1978. Global Eradication of Smallpox.
1477. **459.** 30 s. multicoloured .. 20 10
1478. 1 p. 50 multicoloured 25 25

1978. Philatelic Week. No. 1391 surch **1978 PHILATELIC WEEK 60s**
1479. **408.** 60 s. on 65 s. mauve. 25 15

1978. 50th Anniv. of Philippines Long Distance Telephone Company. Multicoloured.
1480. 30 s. Type **461** 20 8
1481. 2 p. Woman on telephone and globe 25 20

462. Family travelling in Ox-drawn Cart.

1978. Decade of the Filipino Child.
1482. **462.** 30 s. multicoloured .. 8 5
1483. 1 p. 35 multicoloured 20 20

463. Spanish Colo· ial Church and Arms.

1978. 400th Anniv. of Agoo Town.
1484. **463.** 30 s. multicoloured .. 10 8
1485. 45 s. multicoloured .. 20 10

464. Church and Arms.

1978. 400th Anniv. of Balayan Town.
1486. **464.** 30 s. multicoloured .. 15 8
1487. 90 s. multicoloured .. 35 15

465. Family and Houses. **466.** Dr. Sison.

1978. 30th Anniv. of Declaration of Human Rights.
1488. **465.** 30 s. multicoloured .. 15 5
1489. 3 p. multicoloured .. 60 25

1978. Dr. Honoria Acosta Sison (first Filipino woman physician) Commem.
1490. **466.** 30 s. multicoloured .. 15 5

467. "Chaetodon trifasciatus".

1978. Fishes. Multicoloured.
1491. 30 s. Type **467** 20 10
1492. 1 p. 20 "Balistoides niger" 65 35
1493. 2 p. 20 "Rhinecanthus aculeatus" .. .. 1·00 50
1494. 2 p. 30 "Chelmon rostratus" .. .. 1·10 55
1495. 5 p. "Chaetodon mertensi" .. .. 2·00 1·00
1496. 5 p. "Euxiphipos xanthometapon" .. 2·00 1·00

468. Carlos P. Romulo.

1979. 80th Anniv. of Carlos P. Romulo (1st Asian President of U.N. General Assembly).
1497. **468.** 30 s. multicoloured .. 15 5
1498. 2 p. multicoloured .. 45 35

469. Cogwheel (Rotary Emblem). **470.** Rosa Sevilla de Alvero.

1979. 60th Anniv. of Manila Rotary Club.
1499. **469.** 30 s. multicoloured .. 15 5
1500. 2 p. 30 multicoloured 50 35

1979. Birth Centenary of Rosa Sevilla de Alvero (writer and educator).
1501. **470.** 30 s. mauve 10 5

471. Burning-off Gas and Map.

1979. 1st Philippine Oil Production, Nido Complex.
1502. **471.** 30 s. multicoloured .. 20 10
1503. 45 s. multicoloured .. 30 10

472. Merrill's Fruit Dove.

1979. Philippine Birds. Multicoloured.
1504. 30 s. Type **472** 25 15
1505 1 p. 20 Brown tit-babbler 75 40
1506. 2 p. 20 Mindoro zone-tailed pigeon .. .. 1·10 60
1507. 2 p. 30 Steere's pitta .. 1·25 65
1508. 5 p. Koch's pitta and red-breasted pitta .. 2·25 1·10
1509. 5 p. Great eared nightjar 2·25 1·10

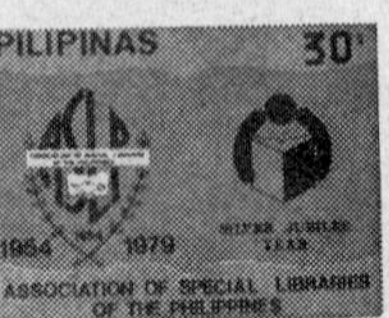

473. Association Emblem.

1979. 25th Anniv. of Association of Special Libraries of the Philippines.
1510. **473.** 30 s. grn., blk. & yell. 15 5
1511. 75 s. grn., blk. & yell. 30 10
1512. 1 p. grn., blk. & orge. 35 15

474. Conference Emblem.

1979. 5th U.N. Conference on Trade and Development, Manila.
1513. **474.** 1 p. 20 multicoloured 35 15
1514. 2 p. 30 multicoloured 45 25

475. Malay Civet.

1979. Philippine Animals. Multicoloured.
1515. 30 s. Type **475** 20 10
1516. 1 p. 20 Crab-eating macaque 65 35
1517. 2 p. 20 Jarvan pig .. 1·00 50
1518. 2 p. 30 Leopard cat .. 1·10 55
1519. 5 p. Oriental small-clawed otter .. .. 2·00 1·00
1520. 5 p. Malayan pangolin .. 2·00 1·00

476. Dish Aerial.

1979. World Telecommunications Day. Multicoloured.
1521. 90 s. Type **476** 10 8
1522. 1 p. 30 World Map .. 15 15

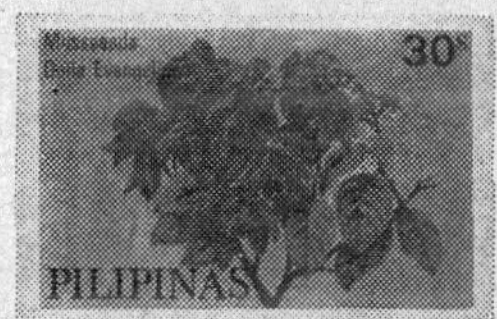

477. Mussaenda " Dona Evangelina ".

1979. Cultivated Mussaendas. Multicoloured.
1523. 30 s. Type **477** 10 10
1524. 1 p. 20 " Dona Esperanza " 15 10
1525. 2 p. 20 " Dona Hilaria " .. 40 25
1526. 2 p. 30 " Dona Aurora " 45 25
1527. 5 p. " Ginning Imelda " .. 90 55
1528. 5 p. " Dona Trining " .. 90 55

478. Manila Cathedral.

1979. 400th Anniv. of Archdiocese of Manila.
1529. **478.** 30 s. multicoloured .. 15 5
1530. 75 s. multicoloured .. 15 8
1531. 90 s. multicoloured .. 20 15

479. "Bagong Lakas" (patrol boat).

1979. Philippine Navy Foundation Day.
1532. **479.** 30 s. multicoloured .. 25 10
1533. 45 s. multicoloured .. 35 10

1979. Air. 1st Scout Philatelic Exhibition. 25th Anniv. of 1st National Jamboree. Surch. **1ST SCOUT PHILATELIC EXHIBITION, JULY 4.14.1979 QUEZON CITY AIRMAIL 90s.**
1534. **188.** 90 s. on 6 c. + 4 c. red on cream 30 25

481. Afghan Hound.

1979. Cats and Dogs. Multicoloured.
1536. 30 s. Type **481** 20 10
1537. 90 s. Striped tabby cat .. 65 35
1538. 1 p. 20 Dobermann pinscher .. .. 1·00 50
1539. 2 p. 20 Siamese cat .. 1·10 55
1540. 2 p. 30 Alsatian .. .. 2·00 1·00
1541. 5 p. Chinchilla cat .. 2·00 1·00

482. Drug Addict breaking Manacles.

483. Children flying Kites.

1979. " Fight Drug Abuse ".
1542. **482.** 30 s. multicoloured .. 15 5
1543. 90 s. multicoloured .. 35 15
1544. 1 p. 05 multicoloured 45 20

1979. International Year of the Child. Multicoloured.
1545. 15 s. Type **483** 10 5
1546. 20 s. Boys fighting with catapults 20 8
1547. 25 s. Girls dressing-up .. 25 12
1548. 1 p. 20 Boy playing policeman 35 15

484. Hands holding Emblems.

485. Anniversary Medal, and 1868 Coin.

1979. 80th Anniv. of Methodism in the Philippines.
1549. **484.** 30 s. multicoloured .. 15 8
1550. 1 p. 35 multicoloured 15 15

1979. 50th Anniv. of Philippine Numismatic and Antiquarian Society.
1551. **485.** 30 s. multicoloured .. 10 5

486. " Concorde " over Manila and Paris.

488. " 35 " and I.A.T.A. Emblem.

1979. 25th Anniv. of "Air France" Service to the Philippines. Multicoloured.
1552. 1 p. 05 Type **486** .. 75 30
1553. 2 p. 20 " Concorde " over monument .. .. 1·25 55

1979. Philatelic Week. Surch. **1979 PHILATELIC WEEK 90s.**
1554. **412.** 90 s. on 1 p. 60 black 35 20

1979. 35th Annual General Meeting of International Air Transport Association, Manila.
1555. **488.** 75 s. multicoloured .. 15 10
1556. 2 p. 30 multicoloured 45 45

489. Bureau of Local Government Emblem.

490. Christmas Greetings.

1979. Local Government Year.
1557. **489.** 30 s. multicoloured .. 10 5
1558. 45 s. multicoloured .. 15 10

1979. Christmas. Multicoloured.
1559. 30 s. Type **490** 15 5
1560. 90 s. Stars 15 15

491. Rheumatism Victim.

492. Birthplace, and MacArthur Memorial Foundation.

1980. Fourth Congress of Southeast Asia and Pacific Area League Against Rheumatism, Manila.
1561. **491.** 30 s. multicoloured .. 15 5
1562. 90 s. multicoloured .. 20 20

1980. Birth Centenary of General Douglas MacArthur. Multicoloured.
1563. 30 s. Type **492** 15 5
1564. 75 s. General MacArthur 30 15
1565. 2 p. 30 Hat, pipe and glasses 65 30

493. Columbus and Emblem.

495. Tirona, Benitez and University.

494. Soldiers and Academy Emblem.

1980. 75th Anniv. of Knights of Columbus Organization.
1567. **493.** 30 s. multicoloured .. 15 5
1568. 1 p. 35 multicoloured 45 35

1980. 75th Anniv. of Philippine Military Academy.
1569. **494.** 30 s. multicoloured .. 15 5
1570. 1 p. 20 multicoloured 25 25

1980. 60th Anniv. of Philippine Women's University.
1571. **495.** 30 s. multicoloured .. 15 5
1572. 1 p. 05 multicoloured 25 25

496. Boats and Burning City.

1980. 75th Anniv. of Rotary International. Different sections of the Francisco painting.
1573. **496.** 30 s. multicoloured .. 15 5
1574. – 30 s. multicoloured .. 15 5
1575. – 30 s. multicoloured .. 15 5
1576. – 30 s. multicoloured .. 15 5
1577. – 30 s. multicoloured .. 15 5
1578. **496.** 2 p. 30 multicoloured 75 25
1579. – 2 p. 30 multicoloured (As No. 1574) .. 75 25
1580. – 2 p. 30 multicoloured (As No. 1575) .. 75 25
1581. – 2 p. 30 multicoloured (As No. 1576) .. 75 25
1582. – 2 p. 30 multicoloured (As No. 1577) .. 75 25

Nos. 1573/7 and 1578/82 were issued together in se-tenant strips of five, each strip forming a composite design.

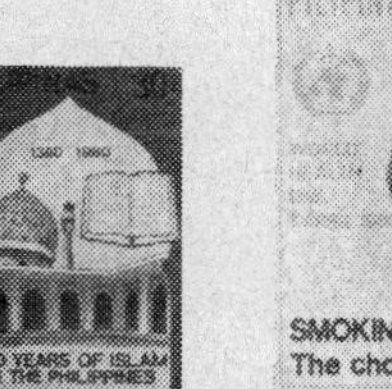

497. Mosque and Koran.

498. Hand stubbing out Cigarette.

1980. 600th Anniv. of Islam in the Philippines.
1583. **497.** 30 s. multicoloured .. 15 5
1584. 1 p. 30 multicoloured 45 25

1980. World Health Day. Anti-Smoking Campaign.
1585. **498.** 30 s. multicoloured .. 15 5
1586. 75 s. multicoloured .. 30 20

499. Scouting Activities and Badge.

1980. 40th Anniv. of Girl Scouting in the Philippines.
1587. **499.** 30 s. multicoloured .. 25 5
1588. 2 p. multicoloured .. 35 25

500. Jeepney.

501. Association Emblem.

1980. The Philippine Jeepney (decorated jeep). Multicoloured.
1589. 30 s. Type **500** 15 5
1590. 1 p. 20 Side view of Jeepney 25 25

1980. Seventh General Conference of International Association of Universities.
1591. **501.** 30 s. multicoloured .. 15 5
1592. 2 p. 30 multicoloured 75 45

1980. 82nd Anniv. of Independence. Surch. **Philippine Independence 82nd Anniversary 1898 1980.**
1593. **412.** 1 p. 35 on 1 p. 60 black 35 30
1594. 1 p. 50 on 1 p. 80 green (No. 1319) 40 35

503. Map and Emblems.

504. Filipinos and Emblem.

1980. 46th Congress of International Federation of Library Associations and Institutions.
1595. **503.** 30 s. green and black 15 5
1596. 75 s. blue and black .. 30 20
1597. 2 p. 30 red and black 85 30

1980. 5th Anniv. of Kabataang Barangay (New Society).
1598. **504.** 30 s. multicoloured .. 15 5
1599. 40 s. multicoloured .. 20 8
1600. 1 p. multicoloured .. 25 25

1980. Nos. 1433, 1501, 1542, 1557 and 1559. surch.
1601. **470.** 40 s. on 30 s. mauve .. 20 8
1602. **482.** 40 s. on 30 s. mult... 20 8
1603. **489.** 40 s. on 30 s. mult... 20 8
1604. **490.** 40 s. on 30 s. mult... 20 8
1605. **433.** 2 p. on 1 p. 65 mult. 75 25

506. Sunset, Filipino Vinta, and Conference Emblem.

1980. World Tourism Conference, Manila.
1606. **506.** 30 s. multicoloured .. 30 10
1607. 2 p. 30 multicoloured 1·25 80

507. Magnifying Glass and Stamps.

508. U.N. Headquarters and Philipines' Flag.

1980. Stamp Day.
1608. **507.** 40 s. multicoloured .. 20 8
1609. 1 p. multicoloured .. 25 25
1610. 2 p. multicoloured .. 75 25

1980. 35th Anniv. of U.N.O.
1611. 40 s. Type **508** 20 8
1612. 3p. 20 U.N. building, U.N. and Philippines' flags 1·00 75

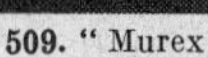

509. " Murex alabaster ".

510. Interpol Emblem on Globe.

1980. Shells. Multicoloured.

1613. 40 s. Type **509** 20 8
1614. 60 s. " Bursa bubo " .. 30 15
1615. 1 p. 20 " Homalocantha zamboi " 25 25
1616. 2 p. " Xenophora pallidula " 75 25

1980. 49th Session of Interpol General Assembly, Manila.

1617. **510.** 40 s. multicoloured .. 20 8
1618. 1 p. multicoloured .. 25 25
1619. 3 p. 20 multicoloured 1·10 75

511. University and Faculty Emblems.

513. Christmas Tree and Presents.

1980. 75th Anniv. of Central Philippine University. Mult., background colour given.

1620. **511.** 40 s. blue 20 8
1621. 3 p. 20 green .. 1·10 75

1980. Philatelic Week. No. 1377. surch. **1980 PHILATELIC WEEK pl. 20.**

1622. **399.** 1 p. 20 on 80 s. black, blue and pink .. 40 20

1980. Christmas.

1623. **513.** 40 s. multicoloured .. 20 8

1981. Various stamps surch.

1624. **244.** 10 s. on 6 s.+5 s. bl. 5 5
1625. **462.** 10 s. on 30 s. mult. .. 5 5
1626. **408.** 40 s. on 65 s. mauve 15 15
1627. **458.** 40 s. on 90 s. mult. .. 15 15
1628. **482.** 40 s. on 90 s. mult. .. 15 15
1629. – 40 s. on 90 s. mult. (No. 1560) 15 15
1630. **448.** 40 s. on 1 p. 05 mult. 40 15
1631. **462.** 40 s. on 1 p. 35 mult. 40 15
1632. **399.** 85 s. on 80 s. black, blue and pink (No. 1377) 40 15
1633. **408.** 1 p. on 65 s. mauve (No. 1391) 50 20
1634. **401.** 1 p. on 1 p. 50 blue and mauve .. 25 20
1635. **422.** 1 p. on 1 p. 50 mult. 50 20
1636. – 1 p. 20 on 1 p. 50 brown (No. 1318) 55 25
1637. **433.** 1 p. 20 on 1 p. 65 multicoloured .. 25 25
1638. – 1 p. 20 on 1 p. 80 grn. (No. 1319) 25 25
1639. **401.** 2 p. on 1 p. 50 blue and mauve .. 75 40
1640. **434.** 3 p. 20 on 2 p. 20 multicoloured .. 1·40 1·00

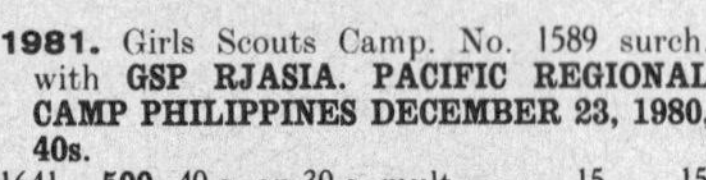

1981. Girls Scouts Camp. No. 1589 surch. with **GSP RJASIA. PACIFIC REGIONAL CAMP PHILIPPINES DECEMBER 23, 1980, 40s.**

1641. **500.** 40 s. on 30 s. mult. .. 15 15

1981. 30th Anniv. of APO Philatelic Society. Surch. **NOV. 30, 1980 APO PHILATELIC SOCIETY PEARL JUBILEE 40S.**

1642. **455.** 40 s. on 30 s. mult. .. 15 15

517. Von Stephan and U.P.U. Emblem.

1981. 150th Birth Anniv. of Heinrich von Stephan (founder of U.P.U.).

1643. **517.** 3 p. 20 multicoloured 1·10 40

518. Pope John Paul II.

519. Parliamentary Debate.

1981. Papal Visit. Multicoloured.

1644. 90 s. Type **518** 40 20
1645. 1 p. 20 Pope and cardinals 30 25
1646. 2 p. 30 Pope blessing crowd (horiz.) 85 45
1647. 3 p. Pope and Manila Cathedral (horiz.) .. 1·00 35

1981. Inter-parliamentary Union Meeting Manila.

1649. **519.** 2 p. multicoloured .. 50 40
1650. 3 p. 20 multicoloured 1·10 40

520. Monument.

521. President Aguinaldo's Car.

1981. Jose Rizal Monument, Luneta Park.

1651. **520.** 40 s. blk., yell. & brn. 20 8

1981. 50th Anniv. of Philippine Motor Association. Multicoloured.

1652. 40 s. Type **521** 20 8
1653. 40 s. 1930 model car .. 20 8
1654. 40 s. 1937 model car .. 20 8
1655. 40 s. 1937 model car different 20 8

522. Bubble Coral.

1981. Corals. Multicoloured.

1656. 40 s. Type **522** 20 8
1657. 40 s. Branching corals .. 20 8
1658. 40 s. Brain coral .. 20 8
1659. 40 s. Table coral .. 20 8

523. President Marcos and Flag.

1981. Inauguration of President Marcos.

1660. **523.** 40 s. multicoloured .. 20 8

524. St. Ignatius de Loyola (founder).

1981. 400th Anniv. of Jesuits in the Philippines. Multicoloured.

1662. 40 s. Type **524** 20 8
1663. 40 s. Dr. Jose P. Rizal and Intramuros Ateneo 20 8
1664. 40 s. Father Federico Faura (director) and Manila Observatory .. 20 8
1665. 40 s. Father Saturnino Urios (missionary) and map of Mindanao .. 20 8

525. F. R. Castro.

526. Pres. Ramon Magsaysay.

1981. Chief Justice F. R. Castro.

1667. **525.** 40 s. multicoloured .. 20 8

1981.

1668. – 1 p. brown and black 25 20
1669. **526.** 1 p. 20 brown and black 30 25
1670. – 2 p. red and black .. 75 40

DESIGNS: 1 p. General Gregorio del Pilar. 2 p. Ambrosio R. Bautista.

See also Nos. 1699/1704, 1807/15, 1889 and 2031/3.

527. Man in Wheelchair.

528. Early Filipino Writing.

1981. International Year of Disabled Persons.

1671. **527.** 40 s. multicoloured .. 20 8
1672. 3 p. 20 multicoloured 1·10 40

1981. 24th International Red Cross Conference.

1673. **528.** 40 s. black, red and brown 20 8
1674. 2 p. black and red .. 75 40
1675. 3 p. 20 black, red and lilac .. .. 1·10 40

529. Isabel II Gate, Manila.

1981.

1676. **529.** 40 s. black, red and brown 20 8

530. Concert in Park.

1981. Opening of Concert at Park 200.

1677. **530.** 40 s. multicoloured .. 20 8

1981. Philatelic Week. No. 1435 surch. **1981 PHILATELIC WEEK** and new value.

1678. **435.** 1 p. 20 on 1 p. 50 multicoloured .. 30 25

532. Running.

1981. 11th South-east Asian Games, Manila.

1679. **532.** 40 s. yell. grn. & brn. 20 8
1680. – 1 p. multicoloured .. 50 20
1681. – 2 p. multicoloured .. 85 40
1682. – 2 p. 30 multicoloured 85 25
1683. – 2 p. 80 multicoloured 1·00 30
1684. – 3 p. 20 violet & blue 1·10 40

DESIGNS: 1 p. Cycling. 2 p. President Marcos and Juan Antonio Samaranch (president of International Olympic Committee). 2 p. 30, Football. 2 p. 80, Shooting. 3 p. 20, Bowling.

533. Manila Film Centre.

1982. Manila International Film Festival. Multicoloured.

1685. 40 s. Type **533** 20 8
1686. 2 p. Front view of trophy 55 40
1687. 3 p. 20 Side view of trophy .. .. .. 1·10 40

534. Carriedo Fountain.

535. Lord Baden-Powell (founder).

1982. Centenary of Manila Metropolitan Waterworks and Sewerage System.

1688. **534.** 40 s. blue 20 8
1689. 1 p. 20 brown .. 30 25

1982. 75th Anniv. of Boy Scout Movement. Multicoloured.

1690. 40 s. Type **535** 20 8
1691. 2 p. Scout 85 25

536. Embroidered Banner.

1982. 25th Anniv. of Children's Museum and Library Inc. Multicoloured.

1692. 40 s. Type **536** 25 10
1693. 1 p. 20 Children playing 30 25

537. President Marcos presenting Sword of Honour.

1982. Military Academy.

1694. **537.** 40 s. multicoloured .. 20 8
1695. 1 p. multicoloured .. 50 25

538. Soldier and Memorial.

1982. Bataan Day. Multicoloured.

1696. 40 s. Type **538** 20 8
1697. 2 p. Doves and rifle .. 85 40

1982. Portraits. As T **526.**

1699. 40 s. blue 20 8
1700. 1 p. red 25 25
1701. 1 p. 20 brown 30 25
1702. 2 p. purple 75 40
1703. 2 p. 30 red 85 45
1704. 3 p. 20 blue .. .. 1·10 45

DESIGNS: 40 s. Isabelo de los Reyes (founder of first workers' union). 1 p. Aurora Aragon Quezon (social worker and former First Lady). 1 p. 20, Francisco Dagohoy. 2 p. Juan Sumulong (politician). 2 p. 30, Professor Nicanor Abelardo (composer). 3 p. 20, General Vicente Lim.

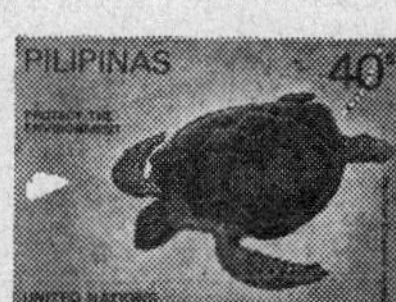

539. Worker with Tower Award. **541.** Green Turtle.

1982. Tower Awards (for "Blue Collar" Workers). Multicoloured.
1705. 40 s. Type **539** 20 8
1706. 1 p. 20 Cogwheel and tower award 30 25

1982. 10th Anniv. of U.N. Environmental Programme. Multicoloured.
1707. 40 s. Type **541** 20 8
1708. 3 p. 20 Philippine eagle 3·00 90

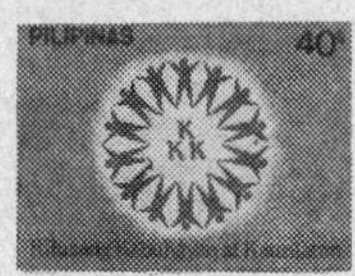

542. K.K.K. Emblem.

1982. Inaug. of Kilusang Kabuhayan at Kaunlaran (national livelihood movement).
1709. **542.** 40 s. green, light green and black 20 8

543. Chemistry Apparatus and Emblem.

1982. 50th Anniv. of Adamson University.
1710. **543.** 40 s. multicoloured .. 20 8
1711. 1 p. 20 multicoloured 30 25

544. Dr. Fernando G. Calderon and Emblems.

1982. 75th Anniv. of College of Medicine, University of the Philippines.
1712. **544.** 40 s. multicoloured .. 20 8
1713. 3 p. 20 multicoloured 1·10 40

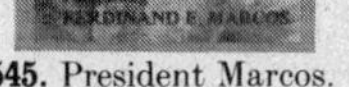

545. President Marcos. **546.** Hands supporting Family.

1982. 65th Birthday of President Marcos.
1714. **545.** 40 s. multicoloured .. 20 8
1715. 3 p. 20 multicoloured 1·10 40

1982. 25th Anniv. of Social Security System.
1717. **546.** 40 s. black, orange & blue 20 8
1718. 1 p. 20 black, orange & green 30 25

MINIMUM PRICE

The minimum price quoted is 5p which represents a handling charge rather than a basis for valuing common stamps. For further notes about prices see introductory pages.

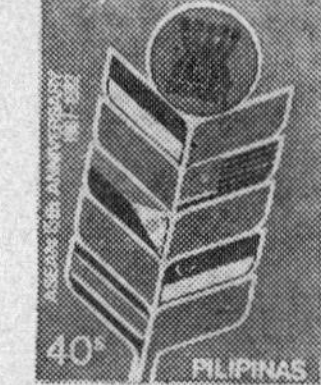

547. Emblem and Flags forming Ear of Wheat.

1982. 15th Anniv. of Association of South-East Asian Nations.
1719. **547.** 40 s. multicoloured .. 20 8

548. St. Theresa of Avila.

1982. 400th Death Anniv. of St. Theresa of Avila. Multicoloured.
1720. 40 s. Type **548** 20 8
1721. 1 p. 20 St. Theresa and map of Europe, Africa and Asia 45 25
1722. 2 p. As 1 p. 20 .. .. 75 35

549. St. Isabel College.

1982. 350th Anniv. of St. Isabel College.
1723. **549.** 40 s. multicoloured .. 20 8
1724. 1 p. multicoloured .. 40 20

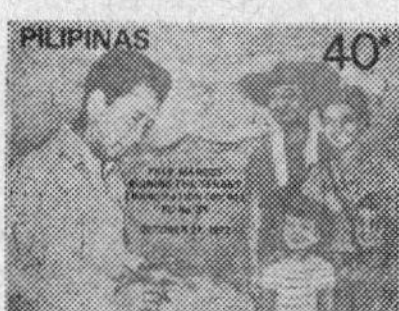

550. President Marcos signing Decree and Tenant Family.

1982. 10th Anniv. of Tenant Emancipation Decree.
1725. **550.** 40 s. grn., brn. & blk. 20 8

551. "Reading Tree".

1982. Literacy Campaign.
1727a. **551.** 40 s. multicoloured .. 25 12
1728a. 2 p. 30 multicoloured 55 45

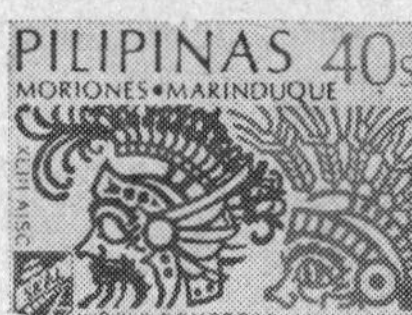

552. Moriones Marinduque (helmeted heads).

1982. 43rd World Congress of Skal Clubs, Manila.
1729a. 40 s. Type **552** 15 8
1730a. 2 p. Head in feathered headdress 55 40

553. Dancers with Parasols.

1982. 25th Anniv. of Bayanihan Folk Arts Centre. Multicoloured.
1731a. 40 s. Type **553** 15 8
1732. 2 p. 80 Dancers (different) 65 50

554. Dr. Robert Koch and Bacillus.

1982. Cent. of Discovery of Tubercule Bacillus.
1733. **554.** 40 s. red, bl. & blk. 15 8
1734. 2 p. 80 multicoloured 65 50

555. Father Christmas in Sleigh.

1982. Christmas.
1735. **555.** 40 s. multicoloured .. 15 8
1736a. 1 p. multicoloured .. 40 20

556. Presidential Couples and Flags.

1982. State Visit of Pres. Marcos to United States.
1737a. **556.** 40 s. multicoloured .. 15 8
1738a. 3 p. 20 multicoloured 75 50

557. Woman with Sewing Machine.

1982. U.N. World Assembly on Ageing.
1740a. **557.** 1 p. 20 grn. & orge. 40 20
1741a. – 2 p. red and blue .. 70 35
DESIGN: 2 p. Man with carpentry tools.

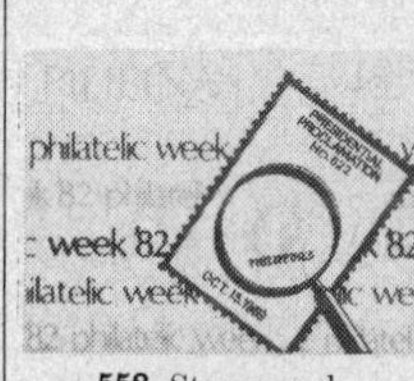

558. Stamp and Magnifying Glass. **559.** Eulogio Rodriguez.

1983. Philatellic Week.
1742. **558.** 40 s. multicoloured .. 15 8
1743. 1 p. multicoloured .. 40 20

1983. Birth Centenary of Eulogio Rodriguez (Former President of Senate).
1744a. **559.** 40 s. multicoloured 15 8
1745. 1 p. 20 multicoloured 45 25

560. Symbolic Figure and Film Frame.

1983. Manila International Film Festival.
1746a. **560.** 40 s. multicoloured 15 8
1747. 3 p. 20 multicoloured 1·10 60

561. Monument.

1983. 2nd Anniv. of Beatification of Lorenzo Ruiz.
1748. **561.** 40 s. yell., red & blk. 15 8
1749. 1 p. 20 multicoloured 45 25

562. Early Printing Press. **563.** Emblem and Ship.

1983. 390th Anniv. of First Local Printing Press.
1750. **562.** 40 s. green and black 15 8

1983. 25th Anniv. of International Maritime Organization.
1751. **563.** 40 s. red, blue & blk. 15 8

1983. Seventh National Scout Jamboree. No. 1709 optd. **7TH B S P NATIONAL JAMBOREE 1983.**
1752. **542.** 40 s. green, light green and black .. 15 8

1983. Nos. 1360/9 surch.
1753. **386.** 40 s. on 45 c. green .. 15 8
1754. – 40 s. on 45 c. green .. 15 8
1755. – 40 s. on 45 c. green .. 15 8
1756. – 40 s. on 45 c. green .. 15 8
1757. – 40 s. on 45 c. green .. 15 8
1758. – 40 s. on 45 c. green .. 15 8
1759. – 40 s. on 45 c. green .. 15 8
1760. – 40 s. on 45 c. green .. 15 8
1761. – 40 s. on 45 c. green .. 15 8
1762. – 40 s. on 45 c. green .. 15 8

566. Calculator Keys.

1983. 11th International Organization of Supreme Audit Institutions Congress.
1763. **566.** 40 s. deep blue, blue and silver 15 8
1764. – 2 p. 80 multicoloured 65 30
DESIGN: 2 p. 80 Congress emblem.

567. Smiling Children. **568.** Detail of Statue.

1983. 75th Anniv. of Philippine Dental Association.
1766. **567.** 40 s. grn., pur. & brn. 15 8

1983. 75th Anniv. of University of the Philippines.
1767. **568.** 40 s. brown & green 15 8
1768. – 1 p. 20 multicoloured 45 25
DESIGN: 1 p. 20, Statue and diamond.

569. Yasuhiro Nakasone and Pres. Marcos.

1983. Visit of Japanese Prime Minister.
1769. **569.** 40 s. multicoloured . . 15 8

570. Agriculture and Natural Resources.

1983. 25th Anniv. of National Science and Technology Authority. Multicoloured.
1770. 40 s. Type **570** 15 8
1771. 40 s. Heart and medical products and food (Health and nutrition) 15 8
1772. 40 s. Industrial complex and air (Industry and energy) 35 15
1773. 40 s. House, scientific equipment and book (Sciences and social science) 15 8

571. Globes and W.C.Y. Emblem.

1983. World Communications Year.
1774. **571.** 3 p. 20 multicoloured 75 50

572. Postman. **573.** Woman with Tambourine.

1983. Bicent. of Philippines Postal System.
1775. **572.** 40 s. multicoloured . . 15 8

1983. Christmas. Multicoloured.
1776. 40 s. Type **579** 15 8
1777. 40 s. Man turning spit (left side) 15 8
1778. 40 s. Pig on spit 15 8
1779. 40 s. Man turning spit (right side) 15 8
1780. 40 s. Man with guitar . . 15 8

Nos. 1776/80 were printed together in se-tenant strips of five within the sheet, each strip forming a composite design.

574. University Activities.

1983. 50th Anniv. of Xavier University.
1782. **574.** 40 s. multicoloured . . 15 8
1783. 60 s. multicoloured . . 20 10

575. Woman casting Vote. **576.** Workers.

1983. 50th Anniv. of Female Suffrage.
1784. **575.** 40 s. multicoloured . . 15 8
1785. 60 s. multicoloured . . 20 10

1983. 50th Anniv. of Ministry of Labour and Employment.
1786. **576.** 40 s. multicoloured . . 15 8
1787. 60 s. multicoloured . . 20 10

577. Cutting Stamp from Envelope. **578.** Red-vented Cockatoo.

1983. Philatelic Week. Multicoloured.
1788. 50 s. Type **577**. 20 10
1789. 50 s. Sorting stamps . . 20 10
1790. 50 s. Soaking stamps . . 20 10
1791. 50 s. Hinging stamp . . 20 10
1792. 50 s. Mounting stamp in album 20 10

1984. Parrots. Multicoloured.
1793. 40 s. Type **578** 10 10
1794. 2 p. 30 Guaiabero . . 70 30
1795. 2 p. 80 Mountain racket-tailed parrot 85 35
1796. 3 p. 20 Great-billed parrot 95 35
1797. 3 p. 60 Muller's parrot . . 1·10 45
1798. 5 p. Philippine hanging parrot . . . . . . 1·75 80

579. Princess Tarhata Kiram. **580.** Nun and Congregation.

1984. 5th Death Anniv. of Princess Tarhata Kiram.
1799. **579.** 3 p. deep green, green and red . . 45 25

1984. 300th Anniv. of Religious Congregation of the Virgin Mary.
1800. **580.** 40 s. multicoloured . . 5 5
1801. 60 s. multicoloured . . 10 8

581. Dona Concha Felix de Calderon. **583.** Manila

1984. Birth Centenary of Dona Concha Felix de Calderon.
1802. **581.** 60 s. green and black 10 8
1803. 3 p. 60 green and red 25 25

1984. Various stamps surch.
1804. **545.** 60 s. on 40 s. mult. . . 10 5
1805. **558.** 60 s. on 40 s. mult. . . 10 5
1806. – 3 p. 60 on 3 p. 20 blue (No. 1704) 25 25

1984. As Nos. 1700/4 but values changed, and new designs as T **526**.
1807. 60 s. brown and black . . 10 8
1808. 60 s. violet and black . . 10 8
1809. 60 s. black 10 8
1810. 60 s. blue 10 8
1811. 1 p. 80 blue 20 10
1812. 2 p. 40 red 35 15
1813. 3 p. brown 15 20
1814. 3 p. 60 red 20 20
1815. 4 p. 20 purple 25 25

DESIGNS: No. 1807, General Artemio Ricarte. 1808, Teodoro M. Kalaw (politician). 1809, Carlos P. Garcia (fourth President). 1810, Quintin Paredes (senator). 1811, General Vicente Lim. 1812, Professor Nicanor Abelardo. 1813, Francisco Dagohoy. 1814, Aurora Aragon Quezon. 1815, Juan Sumulong.

1984.
1816. **542.** 60 s. green, light green and black . . 10 8
1817. 60 s. green, red and black 10 8

1984. 150th Anniv. of Ayala Corporation.
1818. **583.** 70 s. multicoloured . . 10 5
1819. 3 p. 60 multicoloured 25 20

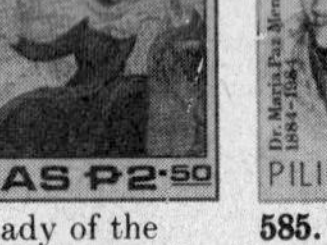

584. "Lady of the Most Holy Rosary with St. Dominic" (C. Francisco). **585.** Maria Paz Mendoza Guazon.

1984. "Espana 84" International Stamp Exhibition, Madrid. Multicoloured.
1820. 2 p. 50 Type **584** . . 35 20
1821. 5 p. "Spoliarum" (Juan Luna) 35 35

1984. Birth Centenary of Dr. Maria Paz Mendoza Guazon.
1823. **585.** 60 s. red and blue . . 10 8
1824. 65 s. red and black . . 10 8

586. "Adolias amlana".

1984. Butterflies. Multicoloured.
1825 60 s. Type **586** 15 10
1826 2 p. 40 "Papilio daedalus" 25 15
1827 3 p. "Prothoe franckii semperi" 75 25
1828 3 p. 60 "Troides magellanus" 85 30
1829 4 p. 20 "Yoma sabina vasuki" . . . . 1·10 35
1830 5 p. "Chilasa idaeoides" 1·40 50

1984. National Children's Book Day. Stamp from miniature sheet (The Monkey and the Turtle) surch. **7-17-84 NATIONAL CHILDREN'S BOOK DAY.**
1831. 7 p. 20 on 7 p. 50 mult. 85 40

1984. 420th Anniv. of Philippine–Mexican Friendship. Stamp from miniature sheet surch. **420TH PHIL-MEXICAN FRIENDSHIP 8.3.84.**
1832. 7 p. 20 on 7 p. 50 mult. . . 85 40

589. Running. **590.** The Mansion.

1984. Olympic Games, Los Angeles. Multicoloured.
1833. 60 s. Type **589** 10 8
1834. 2 p. 40 Boxing 30 12
1835. 6 p. Swimming 65 30
1836. 7 p. 20 Windsurfing . . 75 35
1837. 8 p. 40 Cycling 85 40
1838. 20 p. Running (woman athlete) . . . . 2·10 1·00

1984. 75th Anniv. of Baguio City.
1840. **590.** 1 p. 20 multicoloured 25 10

1984. 300th Anniv. of Our Lady of Holy Rosary Parish. Stamp from miniature sheet surch. **9-1-84 300th YR O.L. HOLY ROSARY PARISH.**
1841. 7 p. 20 on 7 p. 50 mult. . . 85 40

592. Electric Train on Viaduct.

1984. Light Railway Transit.
1842. **592.** 1 p. 20 multicoloured 20 8

593. Australian and Philippine Stamps and Koalas.

1984. "Ausipex 84" International Stamp Exhibition, Melbourne.
1843. **593.** 3 p. multicoloured . . 55 40
1844. 3 p. 60 multicoloured 70 60

1984. National Museum Week. Stamp from miniature sheet surch. **NATIONAL MUSEUM WEEK 10-5-84.**
1846. 7 p. 20 on 7 p. 50 mult. . . 85 40

1984. Asia Regional Conference of Rotary International. No. 1728 surch. **14-17 NOV. 84 R.I. ASIA REGIONAL CONFERENCE.**
1847. **551.** 1 p. 20 on 2 p. 30 multicoloured . . 20 8

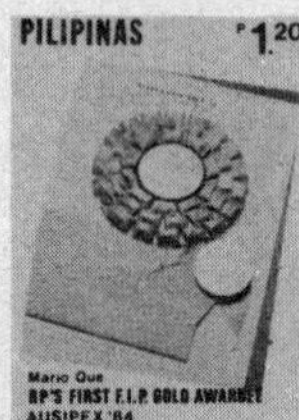

596. Gold Award.

1984. Philatelic Week. Gold Award at "Ausipex 84" to Mario Que. Multicoloured.
1848. 1 p. 20 Type **596** . . 20 8
1849. 3 p. Page of Que's exhibit 30 12

597. Caracao (canoes).

1984. Water Transport. Multicoloured.
1850. 60 s. Type **597** 10 10
1851. 1 p. 20 Junk 30 10
1852. 6 p. Spanish galleon . . 65 30
1853. 7 p. 20 Casco (Filipino cargo prau) 75 35
1854. 8 p. 40 Early paddle-steamer 85 40
1855. 20 p. Modern liner . . 2·10 1·00

599. Anniversary Emblem.

1984. 125th Anniv. of Ateneo de Manila University.
1857. **599.** 60 s. blue and gold . . 10 8
1858. 1 p. 20 bl. & silver . . 20 8

600. Virgin and Child. **602.** Abstract.

601. Manila-Dagupan Steam Locomotive, 1892.

1984. Christmas. Multicoloured.

1859.	60 s. Type **600**	10	8
1860.	1 p. 20 Holy Family	20	8

1984. Rail Transport. Multicoloured.

1861.	60 s. Type **601**	15	10
1862.	1 p. 20 Light Railway Transit train, 1984	35	15
1863.	6 p. Bicol express, 1955	80	40
1864.	7 p. 20 Electric tram 1905	90	45
1865.	8 p. 40 Commuter train, 1972	1·10	50
1866.	20 p. Horse-drawn tram, 1898	2·50	1·25

1984. 10th Anniv. of Philippine Jaycees' Ten Outstanding Men Awards. Multicoloured.

1867.	60 s. brown background in circle	10	8
1868.	60 s. Type **602**	10	8
1869.	60 s. red background	10	8
1870.	60 s. blue and purple background	10	8
1871.	60 s. orange and brown background	10	8
1872.	3 p. As No. 1867	35	15
1873.	3 p. Type **602**	35	15
1874.	3 p. As No. 1869	35	15
1875.	3 p. As No. 1870	35	15
1876.	3 p. As No. 1871	35	15

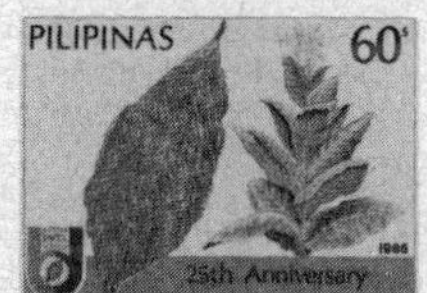

603. Tobacco Plant and Dried Leaf.

1985. 25th Anniv. of Philippine Virginia Tobacco Administration.

1877.	**603.** 60 s. multicoloured	10	8
1878.	3 p. multicoloured	35	15

1985. Philatelic Week, 1984. Nos. 1848/9 optd. **Philatelic Week, 1984.**

1879.	**596.** 1 p. 20 multicoloured	20	8
1880.	– 3 p. multicoloured	35	15

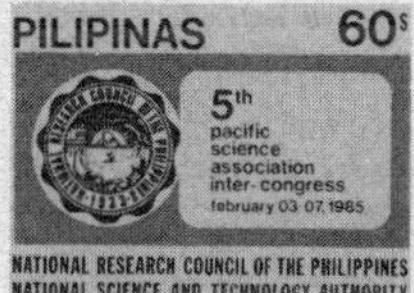

605. National Research Council Emblem.

1985. Fifth Pacific Science Association Congress.

1881.	**605.** 60 s. black, blue and light blue	10	8
1882.	1 p. 20 black, blue and orange	20	8

606. "Carmona retusa".

1985. Medicinal Plants. Multicoloured.

1883.	60 s. Type **606**	10	8
1884.	1 p. 20 "Orthosiphon aristatus"	20	8
1885.	2 p. 40 "Vitex negundo"	30	12
1886.	3 p. "Aloe barbadensis"	35	15
1887.	3 p. 60 "Quisqualis indica"	40	20
1888.	4 p. 20 "Blumea balsamifera	50	25

1985. As T **526**.

1889.	60 s. brown	10	8
1890.	60 s. red	5	5

DESIGNS: No. 1889 Dr. Deogracias V. Villadolid. No. 1890. Santiago Fonacier (former senator and army chaplain).

607. 'Early Bird' Satellite.

1985. 20th Anniv. of International Telecommunications Satellite Organization.

1896.	**607.** 60 s. multicoloured	10	8
1897.	3 p. multicoloured	35	15

608. Piebalds.

1985. Horses. Multicoloured.

1898.	60 s. Type **608**	10	8
1899.	1 p. 20 Palominos	20	8
1900.	6 p. Bays	65	30
1901.	7 p. 20 Browns	75	35
1902.	7 p. 40 Greys	85	40
1903.	20 p. Chestnuts	2·10	1·00

609. Emblem.

1985. 25th Anniv. of National Tax Research Centre.

1905.	**609.** 60 s. multicoloured	5	5

610. Transplanting Rice.

1985. 25th Anniv. of International Rice Research Institute, Los Banos. Multicoloured.

1906.	60 s. Type **610**	5	5
1907.	3 p. Paddy-fields	20	8

611. Image of Holy Child of Cebu.

1985. 420th Anniv. of Filipino–Spanish Treaty. Multicoloured.

1908.	1 p. 20 Type **611**	15	10
1909.	3 p. 60 Rajah Lupas and Miguel Lopez de Lagazpi signing treaty	40	10

613. Family Planting Tree.

1985. Tree Week. International Year of the Forest.

1911.	**613.** 1 p. 20 multicoloured	10	8

614. Battle of Bessang Pass. **615.** Vicente Orestes Romualdez.

1985. 40th Anniv. of Bessang Pass Campaign.

1912.	**614.** 1 p. 20 multicoloured	10	8

1985. Birth Centenary of Vicente Orestes Romualdez (lawyer).

1913.	**615.** 60 s. blue	5	5
1914.	2 p. mauve	12	8

616. Early Anti-TB Label.

1985. 75th Anniv. of Philippine Tuberculosis Society. Multicoloured.

1915.	60 s. Screening for TB, laboratory work, health education and inoculation	5	5
1916.	1 p. 20 Type **616**	10	8

1985. 45th Anniv. of Girl Scout Charter. No. 1409 surch. **45th ANNIVERSARY GIRL SCOUT CHARTER,** emblem and new value.

1921.	**348.** 2 p. 40 on 15 s. on 10 s. multicoloured	15	8
1922.	4 p. 20 on 15 s. on 10 s. multicoloured	30	12
1923.	7 p. 20 on 15 s. on 10 s. multicoloured	50	25

619. "Our Lady of Fatima".

1985. Marian Year. 2000th Birth Anniversary of Virgin Mary. Multicoloured.

1924.	1 p. 20 Type **619**	10	8
1925.	2 p. 40 "Our Lady of Beaterio" (Juan Bueno Silva)	15	8
1926.	3 p. "Our Lady of Penafrancia"	20	8
1927.	3 p. 60 "Our Lady of Guadalupe"	25	10

620. Fishing.

1985. International Youth Year. Children's paintings. Multicoloured.

1928.	2 p. 40 Type **620**	15	8
1929.	3 p. 60 Picnic	25	10

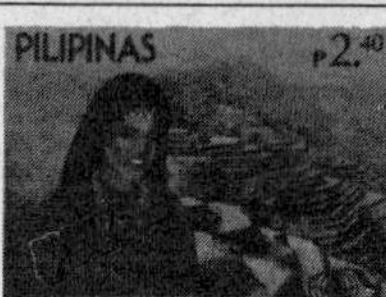

621. Local Girl, Banawe Rice Terraces and Emblem.

1985. World Tourism Organization Congress, Sofia.

1930.	**621.** 2 p. 40 multicoloured	15	8

622. Export Graph and Crane lifting Crate. **624.** Emblem, Doves and Olive Branch.

1985. Export Promotion Year.

1931.	**622.** 1 p. 20 multicoloured	10	8

1985. No. 1815 surch.

1932.	3 p. 60 on 4 p. 20 purple	25	10

1985. 40th Anniv. of U.N.O.

1933.	**624.** 3 p. 60 multicoloured	25	10

625. "China Clipper".

1985. 50th Anniv. of First Trans-Pacific Commercial Flight (San Francisco–Manila). Multicoloured.

1934.	3 p. Type **625**	35	15
1935.	3 p. 60 Map showing route, "China Clipper" and anniversary emblem	40	15

1985. Philatelic Week. Nos. 1863/4 surch. **PHILATELIC WEEK 1985,** No. 1937 further optd. **AIRMAIL.**

1936.	60 s. on 6 p. mult. (post.)	10	8
1937.	3 p. on 7 p. 20 mult. (air)	30	20

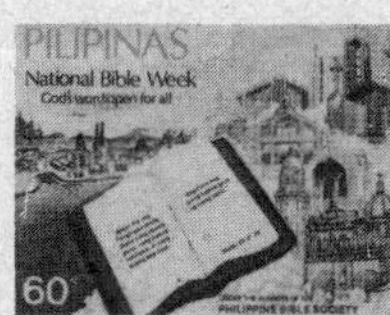

627. Bible and Churches.

1985. National Bible Week.

1938.	**627.** 60 s. multicoloured	5	5
1939.	3 p. multicoloured	20	8

628. Panuluyan (enactment of search for an inn).

1985. Christmas. Multicoloured.

1940.	60 s. Type **628**	5	5
1941.	3 p. Pagdalaw (nativity)	20	8

629. Justice holding Scales. **630.** Rizal and "Noli Me Tangere".

1986. 75th Anniv. of College of Law.
1942. **629.** 60 s. mauve & black 5 5
1943. 3 p. grn., red & blk. 20 8
See also No. 2009.

1986. Centenary of Publication of "Noli Me Tangere" (Jose Rizal's first book).
1944. **630.** 60 s. violet 5 5
1945. – 1 p. 20 green .. 10 5
1946. – 3 p. 60 brown .. 25 10
DESIGNS: 1 p. 20, 3 p. 60, Rizal, "To the Flowers of Heidelberg" and Heidelberg University.

631. Douglas "DC 3", 1946. **632.** Oil Refinery.

1986. 45th Anniv. of Philippine Airlines. Each red, black and blue.
1947. 60 s. Type **631** 10 10
1948. 60 s. Douglas "DC 4 Skymaster", 1946 .. 10 10
1949. 60 s. Douglas "DC 6", 1948 .. .. .. 10 10
1950. 60 s. Vickers "Viscount 784", 1957 .. .. 10 10
1951. 2 p. 40 Fokker "Friendship F 27" Mark 100, 1960 .. .. .. 30 10
1952. 2 p. 40 Douglas "DC 8" Series 50, 1962 .. 30 10
1953. 2 p. 40 BAC "111" Series 500, 1964 .. .. 30 10
1954. 2 p. 40 McDonnell Douglas "DC 10" Series 30, 1974 .. 30 10
1955. 3 p. 60 Beech "Model 18", 1941 .. .. 45 15
1956. 3 p. 60 Boeing "747", 1980 .. .. .. 45 15
See also No. 2013.

1986. 25th Anniv. of Bataan Refinery.
1957. **632.** 60 s. silver and green 5 5
1958. – 3 p. silver and blue 20 8
DESIGN—HORIZ. 3 p. Refinery (different).

633. Emblem.

1986. "Expo 86" World's Fair, Vancouver.
1959. **633.** 60 s. multicoloured .. 5 5
1960. 3 p. multicoloured .. 20 8

634. Emblem and Industrial and Agricultural Symbols.

1986. 25th Anniv. of Asian Productivity Organization.
1961. **634.** 60 s. blk., grn. & orge. 5 5
1962. 3 p. blk., grn. & orge. 20 8
1963. 3 p. brown (30 × 22 mm.) .. 20 8

635. 1906 2 c. Stamp. **637.** Corazon Aquino, Salvador Laurel and Hands.

1986. "Ameripex 86" International Stamp Exhibition, Chicago.
1964. **635.** 60 s. grn., blk. & yell. 5 5
1965. – 3 p. brn., blk. & grn. 20 8
DESIGN: 3 p. 1935 20 c. stamp.
See also No. 2006.

1986. "People Power". Multicoloured.
1966. 60 s. Type **637** 10 10
1967. 1 p. 20 Radio antennae, helicopter and people 30 10
1968. 2 p. 40 Religious procession 15 10
1969. 3 p. Crowds around soldiers in tanks .. 20 10

638. Monument and Paco and Taft Schools.

1986. 75th Anniv. of First La Salle School.
1971. **638.** 60 s. brown, lilac and green 5 5
1972. – 2 p. 40 brown, blue and green 15 8
1973. – 3 p. brn., yell. & grn. 20 8
DESIGNS: 2 p. 40, St. Miguel Febres Cordero and Paco school. 3 p. St. Benilde and Taft school. 7 p. 20, Founding brothers of Paco school.

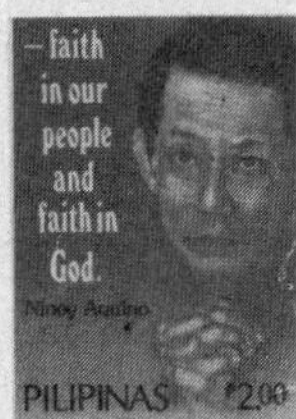

639. Aquino praying. **640.** "Vanda sanderiana".

1986. 3rd Death Anniv. of Benigno S. Aquino, jun.
1975. – 60 s. green 5 5
1976. **639.** 2 p. multicoloured .. 12 8
1977. – 3 p. 60 multicoloured 25 10
DESIGNS:—VERT. 60 s. Aquino. HORIZ. 3 p. 60, Aquino (different). 10 p. Crowd and Aquino.
See also No. 2007.

1986. Orchids. Multicoloured.
1979. 60 s. Type **640** 5 5
1980. 1 p. 20 "Epigeneium lyonii" 10 5
1981. 2 p. 40 "Paphiopedilum philippinense" .. 15 8
1982. 3 p. "Amesiella philippinense 20 8

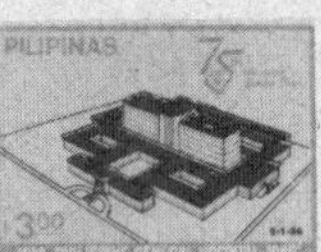

641. "Christ carrying the Cross". **642.** Hospital.

1986. 400th Anniv. of Quiapo District.
1983. **641.** 60 s. red, black and mauve 5 5
1984. – 3 p. 60 blue, black and green 25 10
DESIGN: 3 p. Quiapo Church.

1986. 75th Anniv. of Philippine General Hospital.
1985. **642.** 60 s. multicoloured .. 5 5
1986. 3 p. multicoloured .. 20 8
See also No. 2012.

643. Comet and Earth.

1986. Appearance of Halley's Comet. Multicoloured.
1987. 60 s. Type **643** 5 5
1988. 2 p. 40 Comet, Moon and Earth 15 8

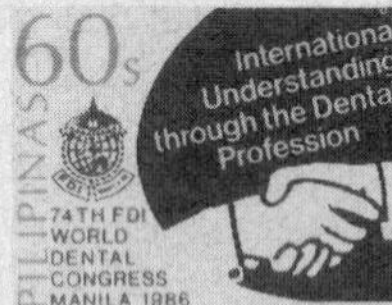

644. Handshake.

1986. 74th FDI World Dental Congress, Manila. Multicoloured.
1989. 60 s. Type **644** 5 5
1990. 3 p. Jeepney, Manila .. 20 8
See also Nos. 2008 and 2011.

645. Butterfly and Beetles. **646.** Emblem.

1986. Philatelic Week and International Peace Year.
1991. **645.** 60 s. multicoloured .. 10 10
1992. – 1 p. blue and black 5 5
1993. – 3 p. multicoloured .. 20 10
DESIGNS—VERT. 1 p. Peace Year emblem. HORIZ. 3 p. Dragonflies.

1986. 75th Anniv. of Manila Young Men's Christian Association.
1994. **646.** 2 p. blue 12 8
1995. 3 p. 60 red 25 10
See also No. 2010.

647. Old and New Buildings.

1986. 85th Anniv. of Philippine Normal College.
1996. – 60 s. multicoloured .. 5 5
1997. **647.** 3 p. 60 yellow, brown and blue 25 10
DESIGN: 60 s. Old and new buildings (different).

648. Mother and Child. **650.** Manila Hotel, 1912.

651. Emblem.

1986. Christmas. Multicoloured.
1998. 60 s. Type **648** 5 5
1999. 60 s. Nativity scene and cow 5 5
2000. 60 s. Mother and child with doves 5 5
2001. 1 p. Mother and child receiving gifts (horiz.) 5 5
2002. 1 p. Mother and child beneath arch (horiz.) 5 5
2003. 1 p. Nativity scene and sheep (horiz.) 5 5
2004. 1 p. Shepherds around child in manger (horiz.) 5 5

1987. No. 1944 surch.
2005. **630.** 1 p. on 60 s. violet .. 5 5

1987. As previous issues but smaller, 22 × 30 mm, 30 × 22 mm. or 32 × 22 mm. (5 p. 50), and values and colours changed.
2006. – 75 s. green (As No. 1965) 5 5
2007. – 1 p. blue (As No. 1975) 5 5
2008. **644.** 3 p. 25 green .. 20 8
2009. **629.** 3 p. 50 brown .. 20 8
2010. **646.** 4 p. blue 20 8
2011. – 4 p. 75 green (As No. 1990) 25 10
2012. **642.** 5 p. brown 30 15
2013. – 5 p. 50 blue (As No. 1956) 30 15

1987. 75th Anniv. of Manila Hotel.
2014. **650.** 1 p. brown and black 5 5
2015. – 4 p. multicoloured .. 20 8
2016. – 4 p. 75 multicoloured 25 10
2017. – 5 p. 50 multicoloured 30 15
DESIGNS: 4 p. Hotel. 4 p. 75, Lobby. 5 p. 50, Staff in ante-lobby.

1987. 50th Anniv. of International Eucharistic Congress, Manila. Multicoloured.
2018. 75 s. Type **651** 5 5
2019. 1 p. Emblem (different) 5 5

652. Pres. Cory Aquino taking Oath.

1987. Ratification of New Constitution.
2020. **652.** 1 p. multicoloured .. 5 5
2021. – 5 p. 50 bl. and brn. 30 15
DESIGN: 5 p. 50, Constitution on open book and dove.
See also No. 2060.

653. Dr. Jose P. Laurel (founder) and Tower.

1987. 35th Anniv. of Lyceum.
2022. **653.** 1 p. multicoloured .. 5 5
2023. 2 p. multicoloured .. 8 5

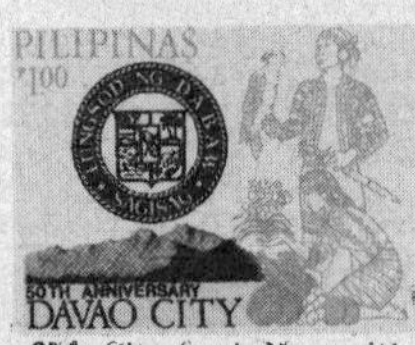

654. City Seal, Man with Hawk and Woman with Fruit.

1987. 50th Anniv. of Davao City.
2024. **654.** 1 p. multicoloured .. 35 10

655. Salary and Policy Loans. **656.** Emblem and People in Hand.

1987. 50th Anniv. of Government Service Insurance System. Multicoloured.
2025. 1 p. Type **655** 5 5
2026. 1 p. 25 Disability and medicare 5 5
2027. 2 p. Retirement benefits 8 5
2028. 3 p. 50 Survivorship benefits 20 8

1987. 50th Anniv. of Salvation Army in Philippines.
2029. **656.** 1 p. multicoloured .. 5 5

657. Woman, Ballot Box and Map.

659. Man with Outstretched Arm.

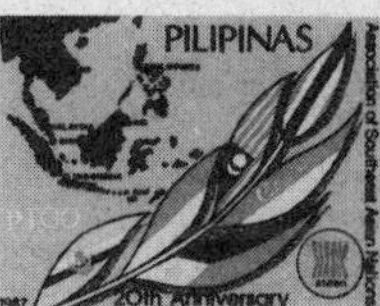

658. Map and Flags as Leaves.

1987. 50th Anniv. of League of Women Voters.

2030. **657.** 1 p. blue and mauve .. 5 5

1987. As T **526**.

2031. 1 p. green 5 5

2032. 1 p. blue 5 5

2033. 1 p. red 5 5

2034. 1 p. deep red and red .. 5 5

DESIGNS: No. 2031, Gen. Vicente Lukban. 2032. Wenceslao Z. Vinzons. 2033, Brigadier General Mateo M. Capinpin (birth centenary). 2034, Jesus Balmori.

1987. 20th Anniv. of Association of South-East Asian Nations.

2035. **658.** 1 p. multicoloured .. 5 5

1987. Exports.

2036. **659.** 1 p. multicoloured .. 5 5

2037. – 2 p. green, yellow and brown .. 8 5

DESIGN: 2 p. Man, cogwheel and factory.

See also No. 2059.

660. Nuns, People and Crucifix within flaming Heart.

661. Statue and Stained Glass Window.

1987. 125th Anniv. of Daughters of Charity in the Philippines.

2038. **660.** 1 p. blue, red and black 5 5

1987. Canonisation of Blessed Lorenzo Ruiz de Manila (first Filipino saint). Multicoloured.

2039. 1 p. Type **661** 5 5

2040. 5 p. 50 Lorenzo Ruiz praying before execution 30 15

1987. No. 2012 surch. **P4.75.**

2042. **642.** 4 p. 75 on 5 p. brown 30 15

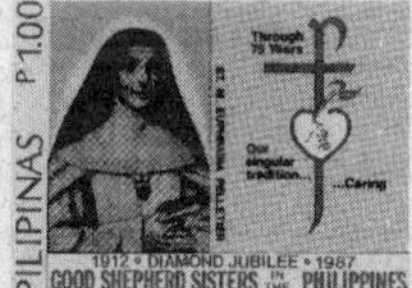

663. Nun and Emblem.

1987. 75th Anniv. of Good Shepherd Sisters in Philippines.

2043. **663.** 1 p. multicoloured .. 5 5

664. Founders.

1987. 50th Anniv. of Philippines Boy Scouts.

2044. **664.** 1 p. multicoloured .. 5 5

665. Family with Stamp Album.

1987. 50th Anniv. of Philippine Philatelic Club.

2045. **665.** 1 p. multicoloured .. 5 5

666. Monks, Church and Wrecked Galleon.

668. Dove and Letter.

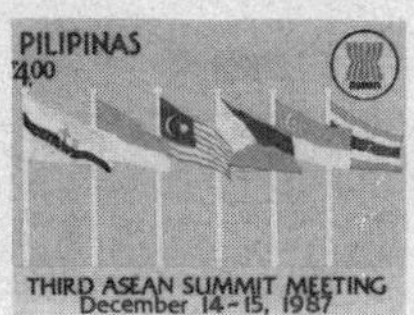

667. Flags.

1987. 400th Anniv. of Dominican Order in Philippines.

2046. **666.** 1 p. black, blue and orange 10 10

2047. – 4 p. 75 multicoloured 30 15

2048. – 5 p. 50 multicoloured 30 15

DESIGNS: 4 p. 75, J. A. Jeronimo Guerrero and Br. Diego de Sta. Maria and Letran Dominican college. 5 p. 50, Pope and monks.

1987. 3rd Association of South-east Asian Nations Summit Meeting.

2049. **667.** 4 p. multicoloured .. 20 10

1987. Christmas. Multicoloured.

2050. 1 p. Type **668** 5 5

2051. 1 p. People and star decoration 5 5

2052. 4 p. Crowd going to church 20 10

2053. 4 p. 75 Mother and children exchanging gifts 30 15

2054. 5 p. 50 Children and bamboo cannons .. 30 15

2055. 8 p. Children at table bearing festive fare .. 40 20

2056. 9 p. 50 Woman at table 60 30

2057. 11 p. Woman having Christmas meal .. 60 30

1987. As previous issues but new value (4 p. 75) or smaller, 22 × 32 mm (5 p. 50).

2059 4 p. 75 blue and grey (As No. 2036) 30 15

2060 5 p. 50 green and brown (As No. 2021) 30 15

669 Emblem, Headquarters and Dr. Rizal

1987. 75th Anniv of Philippines Grand Masonic Lodge.

2061 **669** 1 p. multicoloured .. 8 5

670 Foodstuffs in Split Globe

1987. 40th Anniv of U.N.O. Multicoloured.

2062 1 p. Type **670** (International Fund for Agricultural Development) 8 5

2063 1 p. Means of transport and communications (Asian and Pacific Transport and Communications Decade) 8 5

2064 1 p. People and hands holding houses (International Year of Shelter for the Homeless) .. 8 5

2065 1 p. Happy children playing musical instruments (World Health Day: U.N.I.C.E.F. child vaccination campaign) 8 5

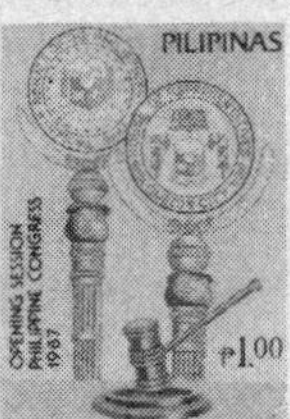

671 Official Seals and Gavel

1988. Opening Session of 1987 Congress. Multicoloured.

2066 1 p. Type **671** 8 5

2067 5 p. 50 Congress in session and gavel 30 15

672 Children and Bosco

1988. Death Centenary of St. John Bosco (founder of Salesian Brothers).

2068 **672** 1 p. multicoloured .. 8 5

2069 5 p. 50 multicoloured 30 15

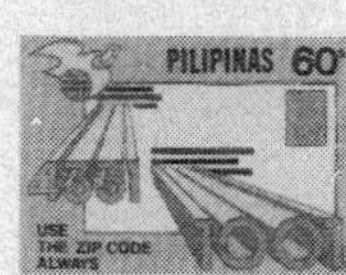

673 Emblem

675 Envelope with Coded Addresses

1988. Buy Philippine-Made Movement Month.

2070 **673** 1 p. multicoloured .. 8 5

1988. Various stamps surch **P 3.00**.

2071 – 3 p. on 3 p. 60 brown (No. 1946) .. 20 10

2072 **646** 3 p. on 3 p. 60 red .. 20 10

2073 – 3 p. on 3 p. 60 mult (No. 1977) .. 20 10

2074 – 3 p. on 3 p. 60 bl, blk & grn (No. 1984) .. 20 10

2075 **647** 3 p. on 3 p. 60 yellow, brown and blue .. 20 10

1988. Postal Codes.

2076 **675** 60 s. multicoloured .. 5 5

2077 1 p. multicoloured .. 8 5

676 "Vesbius purpureus"

677 Solar Eclipse

1988. Insect Predators. Multicoloured.

2078 1 p. Type **676** 15 10

2079 5 p. 50 "Campsomeris aurulenta" 45 20

1988.

2080 **677** 1 p. multicoloured .. 8 5

2081 5 p. 50 multicoloured 30 15

678 Teodoro

679 Emblem

1988. 101st Birth Anniv of Toribio M. Teodoro (industrialist).

2082 **678** 1 p. lt brn, brn & red 8 5

2083 1 p. 20 blue, brn & red 8 5

1988. 75th Anniv of College of Holy Spirit.

2084 **679** 1 p. brn, gold & blk 8 5

2085 – 4 p. brown, grn & blk 25 12

DESIGN: 4 p. Arnold Janssen (founder) and Sister Edelwina (director).

680 Emblem

681 Luna and Hidalgo

1988. Newly Restored Democracies International Conference.

2086 **680** 4 p. blue, dp bl & blk 25 12

1988. National Juan Luna and Felix Resurreccion Hidalgo Memorial Exhibition.

2087 **681** 1 p. black, yell & brn 8 5

2088 5 p. 50 black, light brown and brown 30 15

682 Magat Dam, Ramon, Isabela

1988. 25th Anniv of National Irrigation Administration.

2089 **682** 1 p. multicoloured .. 8 5

2090 5 p. 50 multicoloured 30 15

683 Scuba Diving, Siquijor

1988. Olympic Games, Seoul. Multicoloured.

2091 1 p. Type **683** .. 10 10

2092 1 p. 20 Big game fishing, Aparri, Cagayan .. 10 10

2093 4 p. Yachting, Manila Central 25 15

2094 5 p. 50 Mountain climbing, Mt. Apo, Davao 30 15

2095 8 p. Golfing, Cebu City, Cebu 45 25

2096 11 p. Cycling, Marawi City Tour of Mindanao .. 60 30

1988. Various stamps surch.

2097 1 p. 90 on 2 p. 40 mult (No. 1968) 10 5

2098 1 p. 90 on 2 p. 40 brown, blue & green (No. 1972) 10 5

2099 1 p. 90 on 2 p. 40 mult (No. 1981) 10 5

2100 1 p. 90 on 2 p. 40 mult (No. 1988) 10 5

685 Headquarters, Plaza Santa Cruz, Manila

686 Balagtas

1988. Banking Anniversaries. Multicoloured.
2101 1 p. Type **685** (50th anniv of Philippine Int. Commercial Bank) .. 8 5
2102 1 p. Family looking at factory and countryside (25th anniv of Land Bank) 8 5
2103 5 p. 50 Type **685** .. 30 15
2104 5 p. 50 As No. 2102 .. 30 15

1988. Birth Bicentenary of Francisco Balagtas Baltasco (writer). Each green, brown and yellow.
2105 1 p. Type **686** 8 5
2106 1 p. As Type **686** but details reversed .. 8 5

687 Hospital

688 Brown Mushroom

1988. 50th Anniv of Quezon Institute (tuberculosis hospital).
2107 **687** 1 p. multicoloured .. 8 5
2108 5 p. 50 multicoloured 30 15

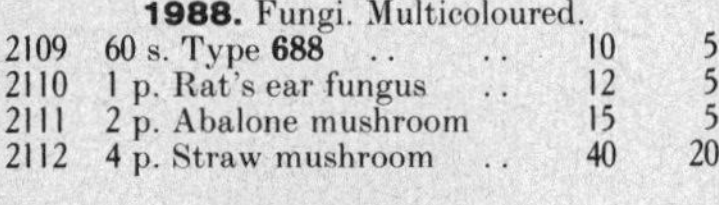

1988. Fungi. Multicoloured.
2109 60 s. Type **688** 10 5
2110 1 p. Rat's ear fungus .. 12 5
2111 2 p. Abalone mushroom 15 5
2112 4 p. Straw mushroom .. 40 20

689 Archery

1988. Olympic Games, Seoul. Multicoloured.
2113 1 p. Type **689** 5 5
2114 1 p. 20 Tennis 8 5
2115 4 p. Boxing 25 12
2116 5 p. 50 Athletics 30 15
2117 8 p. Swimming 45 25
2118 11 p. Cycling 60 30

690 Department of Justice

691 Red Cross Work

1988. Law and Justice Week.
2120 **690** 1 p. multicoloured .. 8 5

1988. 125th Anniv of Red Cross.
2121 **691** 1 p. multicoloured .. 8 5
2122 5 p. 50 multicoloured 30 15

692 Girl and Boy

693 Map and Shrimps

1988. 50th Anniv of Christian Children's Fund.
2123 **692** 1 p. multicoloured .. 8 5

1988. 50th Anniv of Bacolod City Charter.
2124 **693** 1 p. multicoloured .. 5 5

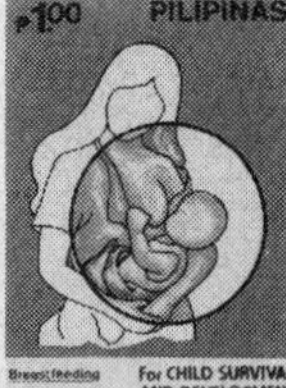

694 Breastfeeding

695 A. A. Quezon

1988. Child Survival Campaign. Mult.
2125 1 p. Type **694** 5 5
2126 1 p. Growth monitoring 5 5
2127 1 p. Immunization .. 5 5
2128 1 p. Oral rehydration .. 5 5
2129 1 p. Access for the disabled (U.N. Decade of Disabled Persons) .. 5 5

1988. Birth Cent of Aurora Aragon Quezon.
2130 **695** 1 p. multicoloured .. 5 5
2131 5 p. 50 multicoloured 30 15

696 Post Office

697 Aerials

1988. Philatelic Week. Multicoloured.
2132 1 p. Type **696** 5 5
2133 1 p. Stamp counter .. 5 5
2134 1 p. Fern and stamp displays 5 5
2135 1 p. People looking at stamp displays .. 5 5

1988. 10th Anniv of Long Distance Telephone Company.
2136 **697** 1 p. multicoloured .. 5 5

698 Clasped Hands and Dove

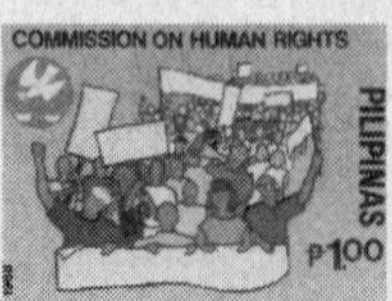

699 Crowd with Banners

1988. Christmas. Multicoloured
2137 75 s. Type **698** 5 5
2138 1 p. Children making decorations (horiz) .. 5 5
2139 2 p. Man carrying decorations on yoke (horiz) .. 10 5
2140 3 p. 50 Christmas tree .. 20 10
2141 4 p. 75 Candle and stars 25 12
2142 5 p. 50 Reflection of star forming heart (horiz) .. 30 15

1988. Commission on Human Rights (2143) and 40th Anniv of Universal Declaration of Human Rights (2144). Multicoloured.
2143 1 p. Type **699** 5 5
2144 1 p. Doves escaping from cage 5 5

700 Church, 1776

701 Statue and School

1988. 400th Anniv of Malate. Multicoloured.
2145 1 p. Type **700** 5 5
2146 1 p. Our Lady of Remedies Church anniversary emblem .. 5 5
2147 1 p. Church, 1880 .. 5 5
2148 1 p. Church, 1988 .. 5 5

1988. 50th Anniv of UST Graduate School.
2149 **701** 1 p. multicoloured .. 5 5

702 Order's Activities

703 Miguel Z. Ver

1989. 50th Anniv of Oblates of Mary Immaculate.
2150 **702** 1 p. multicoloured .. 5 5

1989. 47th Anniv of Guerrilla Action against Japanese. Multicoloured.
2151 1 p. Type **703** 5 5
2152 1 p. Eleuterio L. Adevoso 5 5

704 Foodstuffs and Gen. Santos

705 Sinulog

1989. 50th Anniv of General Santos City.
2153 **704** 1 p. multicoloured .. 5 5

1989. "Fiesta Islands '89" (1st series). Mult.
2154 4 p. 75 Type **705** .. 25 12
2155 5 p. 50 Cenaculo (Lenten festival) .. 30 15
2156 6 p. Vinta regatta, Iloilo Paraw 30 15
See also Nos. 2169/71, 2177/9, 2194/6 and 2210.

706 Tomas B. Mapua

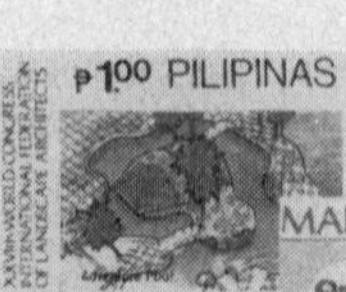

707 Adventure Pool

1989. Birth Centenaries. Multicoloured.
2157 1 p. Type **706** 5 5
2158 1 p. Camilo O. Osias .. 5 5
2159 1 p. Dr. Olivia D. Salamanca 5 5
2160 1 p. Dr. Francisco S. Santiago 5 5
2161 1 p. Leandro H. Fernandez 5 5

1989. 26th International Federation of Landscape Architects World Congress, Manila. Multicoloured.
2162 1 p. Type **707** 5 5
2163 1 p. Paco Park 5 5
2164 1 p. Street improvements in Malacanang area .. 5 5
2165 1 p. Erosion control on upland farm 5 5

708 Palawan Peacock Pheasant

709 Entrance and Statue of Justice

1989. Environment Month. Multicoloured.
2166 1 p. Type **708** 45 10
2167 1 p. Palawan bear cat .. 10 10

1989. Supreme Court.
2168 **709** 1 p. multicoloured .. 5 5

1989. "Fiesta Islands '89" (2nd series). As T **705**. Multicoloured.
2169 60 s. Turumba .. 5 5
2170 75 s. Pahiyas .. 5 5
2171 3 p. 50 Independence Day 20 10

710 Birds, Quill, "Noli Me Tangere" and Flags

1989. Bicentenary of French Revolution and Decade of Philippine Nationalism.
2172 **710** 1 p. multicoloured .. 5 5
2173 5 p. 50 multicoloured 30 15

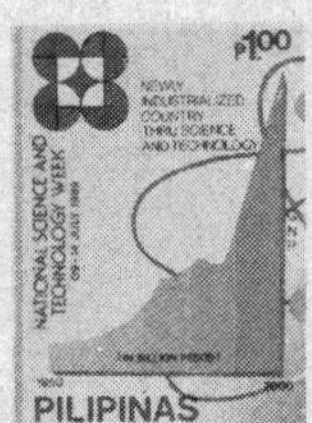

711 Graph

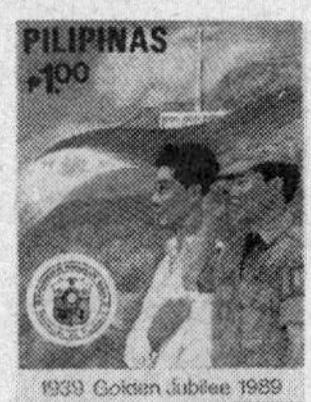

713 Monument, Flag, Civilian and Soldier

1989. National Science and Technology Week. Multicoloured.
2174 1 p. Type **711** 5 5
2175 1 p. "Man" (Leonardo da Vinci) and emblem of Philippine Science High School 5 5

1989. No. 2060 surch.
2176 4 p. 75 on 5 p. 50 grn & brn 25 12

1989. "Fiesta Island 89" (3rd series). As T **705**.
2177 1 p. Pagoda Sa Wawa .. 30 15
2178 4 p. 75 Cagayan de Oro Fiesta 25 10
2179 5 p. 50 Penafrancia Festival 30 15

1989. 50th Anniv of National Defence Department.
2180 **713** 1 p. multicoloured .. 5 5

714 Map and Satellite

715 Annunciation

1989. 10th Anniv of Asia-Pacific Telecommunity.
2181 **714** 1 p. multicoloured .. 5 5

1989. Christmas. Multicoloured.
2182 60 s. Type **715** 5 5
2183 75 s. Mary and Elizabeth 5 5
2184 1 p. Mary and Joseph travelling to Bethlehem 5 5
2185 2 p. Search for an inn .. 8 5
2186 4 p. Magi and star .. 15 8
2187 4 p. 75 Adoration of shepherds 20 10

716 Lighthouse, Liner and Lifebelt

1989. International Maritime Organization.
2188 **716** 1 p. multicoloured .. 10 10

717 Spanish Philippines 1854 5 c. and Revolutionary Govt 1898 2 c. Stamps

1989. "World Stamp Expo '89" International Stamp Exhibition, Washington D.C. Mult.
2189 1 p. Type **717** 5 5
2190 4 p. U.S. Administration 1899 50 c. and Commonwealth 1935 6 c. stamps 15 8
2191 5 p. 50 Japanese Occupation 1942 2 c. and Republic 1946 6 c. stamps 20 10

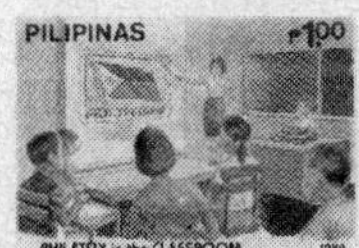

718 Teacher using Stamp as Teaching Aid

1989. Philatelic Week. Philately in the Classroom. Multicoloured.
2192 1 p. Type **718** 5 5
2193 1 p. Children working with stamps 5 5

1989. "Fiesta Islands '89" (4th series). As T **705**.
2194 1 p. Masked festival, Negros 5 5
2195 4 p. 75 Grand Canao, Baguio 20 5
2196 5 p. 50 Fireworks .. 20 10

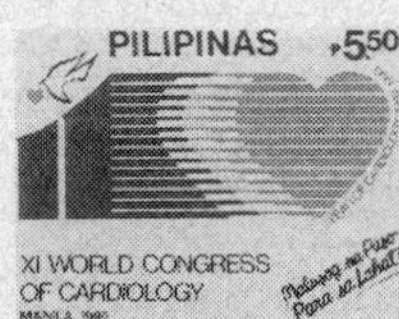

719 Heart

1990. 11th World Cardiology Congress, Manila.
2197 **719** 5 p. 50 red, blue & blk 20 10

720 Glasses of Beer

1990. Centenary of San Miguel Brewery.
2198 **720** 1 p. multicoloured .. 5 5
2199 5 p. 50 multicoloured 20 10

721 Houses and Family

1990. Population and Housing Census. Multicoloured. Colours of houses given.
2200 **721** 1 p. blue 5 5
2201 1 p. pink 5 5

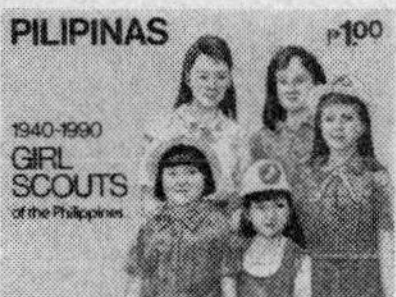

722 Scouts

723 Claro Recto (politician)

1990. 50th Anniv of Philippine Girl Scouts.
2202 **722** 1 p. multicoloured .. 5 5
2203 1 p. 20 multicoloured 5 5

1990. Birth Centenaries. Multicoloured.
2204 1 p. Type **723** 5 5
2205 1 p. Manuel Bernabe (poet) 5 5
2206 1 p. Guillermo Tolentino (sculptor) 5 5
2207 1 p. Elpidio Quirino (President 1948–53) .. 5 5
2208 1 p. Dr. Bienvenido Gonzalez (University President, 1937–51) .. 5 5

724 Badge in Globe

1990. 50th Anniv of Legion of Mary.
2209 **724** 1 p. multicoloured .. 5 5

1990. "Fiesta Islands '89" (5th series). As No. 2179 but new value.
2210 4 p. multicoloured .. 20 10

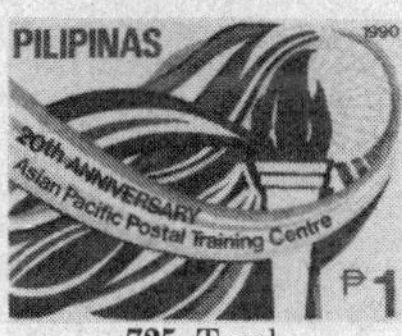

725 Torch

1990. 20th Anniv of Asian–Pacific Postal Training Centre.
2211 **725** 1 p. multicoloured .. 5 5
2212 4 p. multicoloured .. 20 10

726 Catechism Class

727 Waling Waling Flowers

1990. National Catechetical Year.
2213 **726** 1 p. multicoloured .. 5 5
2214 3 p. 50 multicoloured 15 8

1990. 29th Orient and South–East Asian Lions Forum, Manila. Multicoloured.
2215 1 p. Type **727** 5 5
2216 4 p. Sampaguita flowers 20 10

728 Areas for Improvement

1990. 40th Anniv of United Nations Development Programme.
2217 **728** 1 p. multicoloured .. 5 5
2218 5 p. 50 multicoloured 25 12

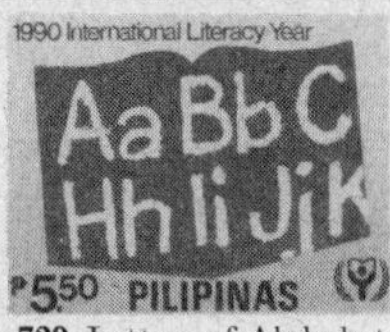

729 Letters of Alphabet

1990. International Literacy Year.
2219 **729** 1 p. green, orge & blk 5 5
2220 5 p. 50 grn, yell & blk 25 12

730 "Laughter" (A. Magsaysay-Ho)

1990. Philatelic Week. Multicoloured.
2221 1 p. "Family" (F. Amorsolo) (horiz) .. 5 5
2222 4 p. 75 "The Builders" (V. Edades) 20 10
2223 5 p. 50 Type **730** .. 25 12

731 Star

1990. Christmas. Multicoloured.
2224 1 p. Type **731** 5 5
2225 1 p. Stars within stars (Prussian blue background) 5 5
2226 1 p. Red and white star (royal blue background) 5 5
2227 1 p. Gold and red star (green background) .. 5 5
2228 5 p. 50 Geometric star .. 25 12

732 Figures

1990. International White Cane Safety Day.
2229 **732** 1 p. blk, yell & blue .. 5 5

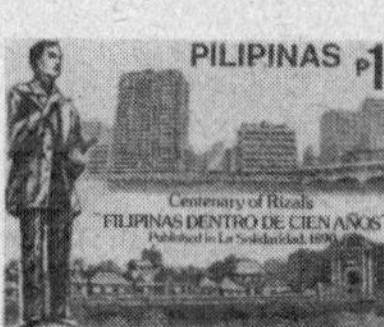

733 La Solidaridad in 1990 and 1890 and Statue of Rizal

1990. Centenary of Publication of "Filipinas Dentro de Cien Anos" by Jose Rizal.
2230 **733** 1 p. multicoloured .. 5 5

734 Crowd before Figure of Christ

735 Tailplane and Stewardess

1991. 2nd Plenary Council of the Philippines.
2231 **734** 1 p. multicoloured .. 5 5

1991. 50th Anniv of Philippine Airlines.
2232 **735** 1 p. mult (postage) .. 5 5
2233 5 p. 50 mult (air) .. 25 12

736 Gardenia

737 Sheepshank

1991. Flowers. Multicoloured.
2234 60 s. Type **736** 5 5
2235 75 s. Yellow bell .. 5 5
2236 1 p. Yellow plumeria .. 5 5
2237 1 p. Red plumeria .. 5 5
2238 1 p. Pink plumeria .. 5 5
2239 1 p. White plumeria .. 5 5
2240 1 p. 20 Nerium 5 5
2241 3 p. 25 Ylang-ylang .. 15 8
2242 4 p. Pink ixora 20 10
2243 4 p. White ixora .. 20 10
2244 4 p. Yellow ixora .. 20 10
2245 4 p. Red ixora 20 10
2246 4 p. 75 Orange bougainvillea 20 10
2247 4 p. 75 Purple bougainvillea 20 10
2248 4 p. 75 White bougainvillea 20 10
2249 4 p. 75 Red bougainvillea 20 10
2250 5 p. Canna 20 10
2251 5 p. 50 Red hibiscus .. 25 12
2252 5 p. 50 Yellow hibiscus .. 25 12
2253 5 p. 50 White hibiscus .. 25 12
2254 5 p. 50 Pink hibiscus .. 25 12
See also Nos. 2322/41.

1991. 12th Asia–Pacific and 9th National Boy Scouts Jamboree. Multicoloured.
2255 1 p. Reef knot 5 5
2256 4 p. Type **737** 20 10
2257 4 p. 75 Granny knot .. 20 10

738 Jorge Vargas

739 "Antipolo" (Carlos Francisco) and Score

1991. Birth Centenaries. Multicoloured.
2259 1 p. Type **738** 5 5
2260 1 p. Ricardo Paras .. 5 5
2261 1 p. Jose Laurel 5 5
2262 1 p. Vicente Fabella .. 5 5
2263 1 p. Maximo Kalaw .. 5 5

1991. 400th Anniv of Antipolo.
2264 **739** 1 p. multicoloured .. 5 5

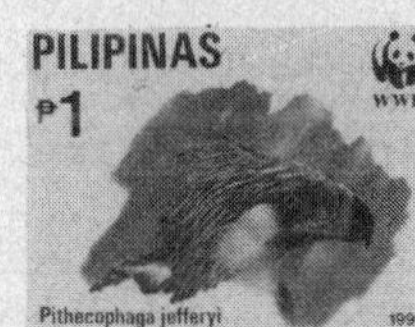

740 Philippine Eagle

1991. Endangered Species. Philippine Eagle. Multicoloured.
2265 1 p. Type **740** .. 10 10
2266 4 p. 75 Eagle on branch .. 40 20
2267 5 p. 50 Eagle in flight .. 50 25
2268 8 p. Eagle feeding chick 65 30

741 Emblem

1991. Centenary of Founding of Society of Lawyers (from 1904 Philippine Bar Association).
2269 **741** 1 p. multicoloured .. 5 5

742 Flags and Induction Ceremony

743 First Regular Division Emblem

1991. 50th Anniv of Induction of Philippine Reservists into United States Army Forces in the Far East. Background colours given where necessary in brackets.

2270 742 1 p. multicoloured .. 5 5
2272 743 2 p. red, black and yellow (1st Regular) 10 5
2273 – 2 p. multicoloured (yellow) (2nd Regular) 10 5
2274 – 2 p. multicoloured (yellow) (11th) .. 10 5
2275 – 2 p. blue, yellow and black (yellow) (21st) 10 5
2276 743 2 p. red and black (1st Regular) 10 5
2277 – 2 p. black, blue and red (2nd Regular) 10 5
2278 – 2 p. multicoloured (white) (11th) .. 10 5
2279 – 2 p. blue, yellow and black (white) (21st) 10 5
2280 – 2 p. multicoloured (yellow) (31st) .. 10 5
2281 – 2 p. multicoloured (yellow) (41st) .. 10 5
2282 – 2 p. multicoloured (yellow) (51st) .. 10 5
2283 – 2 p. multicoloured (yellow) (61st) .. 10 5
2284 – 2 p. red, blue and black (31st) .. 10 5
2285 – 2 p. multicoloured (white) (41st) .. 10 5
2286 – 2 p. blue, black and red (51st) 10 5
2287 – 2 p. multicoloured (white) (61st) .. 10 5
2288 – 2 p. multicoloured (yellow) (71st) .. 10 5
2289 – 2 p. multicoloured (yellow) (81st) .. 10 5
2290 – 2 p. multicoloured (yellow) (91st) .. 10 5
2291 – 2 p. multicoloured (yellow) (101st) .. 10 5
2292 – 2 p. multicoloured (white) (71st) .. 10 5
2293 – 2 p. multicoloured (white) (81st) .. 10 5
2294 – 2 p. multicoloured (white) (91st) .. 10 5
2295 – 2 p. multicoloured (white) (101st) .. 10 5
2296 – 2 p. blue, black & yell (Bataan Force) .. 10 5
2297 – 2 p. yellow, red & blk (yellow) (Philippine) 10 5
2298 – 2 p. multicoloured (yellow) (Air Corps) 10 5
2299 – 2 p. black, blue & yell (Offshore Patrol) .. 10 5
2300 – 2 p. blue and black (Bataan Force) .. 10 5
2301 – 2 p. yellow, red & blk (white) (Philippine) 10 5
2302 – 2 p. multicoloured (white) (Air Corps) 10 5
2303 – 2 p. black and blue (Offshore Patrol) .. 10 5

Nos. 2272/2303 show divsional emblems.

744 Basilio

745 St. John of the Cross

1991. Centenary of Publication of "El Filibusterismo" by Jose Rizal. Each red, green and black.

2304 1 p. Type 744 .. .. 5 5
2305 1 p. Simoun 5 5
2306 1 p. Father Florentino .. 5 5
2307 1 p. Juli 5 5

1991. 400th Death Anniv of St. John of the Cross.

2308 745 1 p. multicoloured .. 5 5

746 Faces (Children's Fund)

1991. United Nations Agencies.

2310 746 1 p. multicoloured .. 5 5
2311 – 4 p. multicoloured .. 20 10
2312 – 5 p. 50 black, red & bl 25 10

DESIGNS: 4 p. Hands supporting boatload of people (High Commissioner for Refugees); 5 p. 50, 1951 15 c. and 1954 3 c. U.N. stamps (40th anniv of Postal Administration).

747 "Bayanihan" (Carlos "Botong" Francisco)

1991. Philatelic Week. Multicoloured.

2313 2 p. Type 747 .. .. 10 5
2314 7 p. "Sari-Sari Vendor" (Mauro Malang Santos) 40 20
2315 8 p. "Give Us This Day" (Vicente Manansala) .. 45 20

748 Gymnastics

1991. 16th South-east Asian Games, Manila. Multicoloured.

2316 2 p. Type 748 .. .. 10 5
2317 2 p. Gymnastics (emblem at bottom) 10 5
2318 6 p. Arnis (martial arts) (emblem at left) (vert) 30 15
2319 6 p. Arnis (emblem at right) (vert) 30 15

Designs of the same value were issued together, se-tenant, each pair forming a composite design.

1991. Flowers. As T 736. Multicoloured.

2322 1 p. 50 Type 736 .. 10 5
2323 2 p. Yellow plumeria .. 10 5
2324 2 p. Red plumeria .. 10 5
2325 2 p. Pink plumeria .. 10 5
2326 2 p. White plumeria .. 10 5
2327 3 p. Nerium 15 5
2328 5 p. Ylang-ylang .. 30 15
2329 6 p. Pink ixora 30 15
2330 6 p. White ixora .. 30 15
2331 6 p. Yellow ixora .. 30 15
2332 6 p. Red ixora 30 15
2333 7 p. Orange bougainvillea 40 20
2334 7 p. Purple bougainvillea 40 20
2335 7 p. White bougainvillea 40 20
2336 7 p. Red bougainvillea .. 40 20
2337 8 p. Red hibiscus .. 45 20
2338 8 p. Yellow hibiscus .. 45 20
2339 8 p. White hibiscus .. 45 20
2340 8 p. Pink hibiscus .. 45 20
2341 10 p. Canna 55 25

750 Church

1991. Christmas. Children's Paintings. Mult.

2342 2 p. Type 750 .. .. 10 5
2343 6 p. Christmas present .. 30 15
2344 7 p. Santa Claus and tree 40 20
2345 8 p. Christmas tree and star 45 20

751 Basketball Player

752 Monkey firing Cannon

1991. Centenary of Basketball. Multicoloured.

2346 2 p. Type 751 .. .. 10 5
2347 6 p. Basketball player and map (issue of first basketball stamp, 1934) (horiz) 30 15
2348 7 p. Girls playing basketball (introduction of basketball in Philippines, 1904) (horiz) .. 40 20
2349 8 p. Basketball players .. 45 20

1991. New Year. Year of the Monkey.

2351 752 2 p. multicoloured .. 10 5
2352 6 p. multicoloured .. 30 15

753 Pres. Aquino and Mailing Centre Emblem

1992. Kabisig Community Projects Organization. Multicoloured.

2353 2 p. Type 753 .. .. 10 5
2354 6 p. Housing 30 15
2355 7 p. Livestock 40 20
2356 8 p. Handicrafts .. 45 20

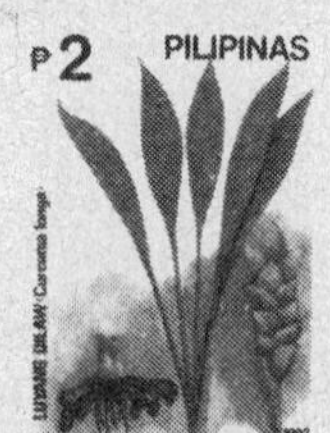

754 "Curcuma longa"

1992. Asian Medicinal Plants Symposium, Laguna. Multicoloured.

2357 2 p. Type 754 .. .. 10 5
2358 6 p. "Centella asiatica" .. 30 15
2359 7 p. "Cassia alata" .. 40 20
2360 8 p. "Ervatamia pandacaqui" 45 20

755 "Mahal Kita", Envelopes and Map

1992. Greetings Stamps. Multicoloured.

2361 2 p. Type 755 .. .. 10 5
2362 2 p. As No. 2361 but inscr "I Love You" .. 10 5
2363 6 p. Heart and doves ("Mahal Kita") .. 30 15
2364 6 p. As No. 2363 but inscr "I Love You" .. 30 15
2365 7 p. Basket of flowers ("Mahal Kita") .. 40 20
2366 7 p. As No. 2365 but inscr "I Love You" .. 40 20
2367 8 p. Cupid ("Mahal Kita") 45 20
2368 8 p. As No. 2367 but inscr "I Love You" .. 45 20

756 Philippine Pavilion and Couple Dancing

757 Our Lady of the Sun

1992. "Expo '92" World's Fair, Seville. Mult.

2369 2 p. Type 756 .. .. 10 5
2370 8 p. Pavilion, preacher and man holding globe 45 20

1992. 300th Anniv of Apparition of Our Lady of the Sun at Porta Vaga.

2372 757 2 p. multicoloured .. 10 5
2373 8 p. multicoloured .. 45 20

758 Fish Farming

1992. 75th Anniv of Department of Agriculture. Multicoloured.

2374 2 p. Type 758 .. .. 10 5
2375 2 p. Pig farming .. 10 5
2376 2 p. Sowing seeds .. 10 5

759 Race Horses and Emblem

760 Manuel Roxas (President, 1946-48)

1992. 125th Anniv of Manila Jockey Club.

2377 759 2 p. multicoloured .. 10 5

1992. Birth Centenaries. Multicoloured.

2379 2 p. Type 760 .. .. 10 5
2380 2 p. Natividad Almeda-Lopez (judge) 10 5
2381 2 p. Roman Ozaeta (judge) 10 5
2382 2 p. Engracia Cruz-Reyes (women's rights campaigner and environmentalist) .. 10 5
2383 2 p. Fernando Amorsolo (artist) 10 5

761 Queen, Bishop and 1978 30 s. Stamp

1992. 30th Chess Olympiad, Manila. Mult.

2384 2 p. Type 761 .. .. 10 5
2385 6 p. Queen, bishop and 1962 6 s. + 4 s. stamp .. 30 15

762 Bataan Cross

1992. 50th Anniv of Pacific Theatre in World War II. Multicoloured.

2387 2 p. Type 762 .. .. 10 5
2388 6 p. Map inside "W" .. 30 15
2389 8 p. Corregidor eternal flame 45 20

763 President Aquino and President-elect Ramos

1992. Election of Fidel Ramos to Presidency.
2391 **763** 2 p. multicoloured .. 10 5

764 "Dapitan Shrine" (Cesar Legaspi)

1992. Centenary of Dr. Jose Rizal's Exile to Dapitan. Multicoloured.
2392 2 p. Type **764** 10 5
2393 2 p. Portrait (after Juan Luna) (vert) 10 5

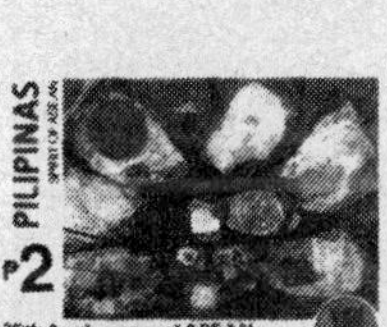

765 "Spirit of ASEAN" (Visit Asean Year) 766 Member of the Katipunan

1992. 25th Anniv of Association of South-East Asian Nations. Multicoloured.
2394 2 p. Type **765** 10 5
2395 2 p. "ASEAN Sea" (25th Ministerial Meeting and Postal Ministers' Conf) 10 5
2396 6 p. Type **765** 30 15
2397 6 p. As No. 2395 .. .. 30 15

1992. Centenary of Katipunan (revolutionary organization). Multicoloured.
2398 2 p. Type **766** 10 5
2399 2 p. Revolutionaries 10 5
2400 2 p. Plotting (horiz) .. 10 5
2401 2 p. Attacking (horiz) .. 10 5

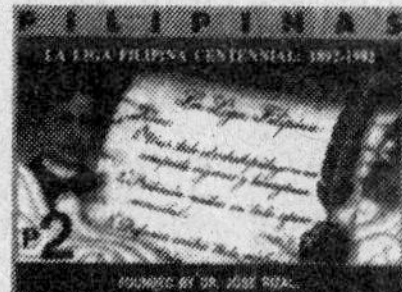

767 Dr. Jose Rizal, Text and Quill

1992. Centenary of La Liga Filipina.
2402 **767** 2 p. multicoloured .. 10 5

768 Swimming

1992. Olympic Games, Barcelona. Mult.
2403 2 p. Type **768** 10 5
2404 7 p. Boxing 40 20
2405 8 p. Hurdling 45 20

769 School, Emblem and Students

1992. Centenaries. Multicoloured.
2407 2 p. Type **769** (Sisters of the Assumption in the Philippines) 10 5
2408 2 p. San Sebastian's Basilica, Manila (centenary (1991) of blessing of fifth construction) (vert) .. 10 5

770 Masonic Symbols

1992. Centenary of Nilad Lodge (first Filipino Masonic Lodge).
2409 **770** 2 p. black and green 10 5
2410 – 6 p. multicoloured .. 30 15
2411 – 8 p. multicoloured .. 45 20
DESIGNS: 6 p. Antonio Luna and symbols; 8 p. Marcelo del Pilar ("Father of Philippine Masonry") and symbols.

771 Ramos taking Oath

1992. Swearing in of President Fidel Ramos. Multicoloured.
2412 2 p. Type **771** 10 5
2413 8 p. President taking oath in front of flag .. 45 20

772 Flamingo Guppy

1992. Freshwater Aquarium Fishes. Mult.
2414 1 p. 50 Type **772** .. 10 5
2415 1 p. 50 Neon tuxedo guppy 10 5
2416 1 p. 50 King cobra guppy 10 5
2417 1 p. 50 Red-tailed guppy 10 5
2418 1 p. 50 Tiger lacetail guppy 10 5
2419 2 p. Pearl scale goldfish .. 10 5
2420 2 p. Red-cap goldfish .. 10 5
2421 2 p. Lionhead goldfish .. 10 5
2422 2 p. Black moor 10 5
2423 2 p. Bubble-eye 10 5
2424 4 p. Delta topsail variatus 20 10
2425 4 p. Orange spotted hi-fin platy 20 10
2426 4 p. Red lyretail swordtail 20 10
2427 4 p. Bleeding heart hi-fin platy 20 10

774 Couple

1992. Greetings Stamps. "Happy Birthday". Multicoloured.
2430 2 p. Type **774** 10 5
2431 6 p. Type **774** 30 15
2432 7 p. Balloons and candles on birthday cake .. 35 15
2433 8 p. As No. 2432 .. .. 40 20

INDEX
Countries can be quickly located by referring to the index at the end of this volume.

775 Melon, Beans, Tomatoes and Potatoes

1992. 500th Anniv of Discovery of America by Columbus. Multicoloured.
2434 2 p. Type **775** 10 5
2435 6 p. Maize and sweet potatoes 30 15
2436 8 p. Pineapple, cashews, avocado and water melon 40 20

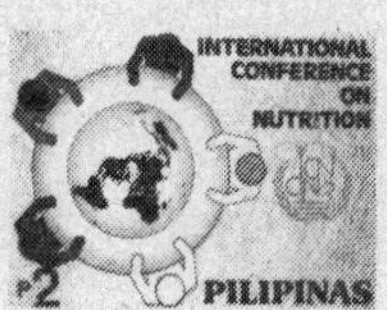

777 Figures around World Map

1992. International Nutrition Conference, Rome.
2438 **777** 2 p. multicoloured .. 10 5

778 Mother and Child 780 Family and Canoe

1992. Christmas.
2439 **778** 2 p. multicoloured .. 10 5
2440 – 6 p. multicoloured .. 30 15
2441 – 7 p. multicoloured .. 35 15
2442 – 8 p. multicoloured .. 40 20
DESIGNS: 6 p. to 8 p. Various designs showing mothers and children.

1992. Anti-drugs Campaign. Multicoloured.
2444 2 p. Type **780** 10 5
2445 8 p. Man carrying paddle, children and canoe .. 40 20

781 Damaged Trees 782 Labuyo (wild cock)

1992. Mt. Pinatubo Fund (for victims of volcanic eruption). Multicoloured.
2446 25 s. Type **781** 5 5
2447 1 p. Mt. Pinatubo erupting 5 5
2448 1 p. Cattle in ash-covered field 5 5
2449 1 p. Refugee settlement .. 5 5
2450 1 p. People shovelling ash 5 5

1992. New Year. Year of the Cock. Mult.
2451 2 p. Type **782** 10 5
2452 6 p. Maranao Sarimanok (mythical bird) .. 30 15

784 Badges of 61st and 71st Divisions, Cebu Area Command 785 "Family" (Cesar Legaspi) (family ties)

1992. Philippine Guerrilla Units of Second World War. Multicoloured.
2455 2 p. Type **784** 10 5
2456 2 p. Vinzon's Guerrillas and badges of 48th Chinese Guerrilla Squadron and 101st Division 10 5
2457 2 p. Anderson's Command, Luzon Guerrilla Army Forces and badge of Bulacan Military Area 10 5
2458 2 p. President Quezon's Own Guerrillas and badges of Marking's Fil-American Troops and Hunters ROTC Guerrillas 10 5

1992. Philatelic Week. Multicoloured.
2459 2 p. Type **785** 10 5
2460 6 p. "Pounding Rice" (Nena Saguil) (hard work and industry) .. 30 15
2461 7 p. "Fish Vendors" (Romeo Tabuena) (flexibility and adaptability) 35 15

786 Black Shama

1992. Endangered Birds. Multicoloured. (a) As T 786.
2462 2 p. Type **786** 10 5
2463 2 p. Blue-headed fantail 10 5
2464 2 p. Mindoro zone-tailed (inscr "Imperial") pigeon 10 5
2465 2 p. Sulu hornbill .. 10 5
2466 2 p. Red-vented (inscr "Philippine") cockatoo 10 5

(b) Size 29 × 39 mm.
2467 2 p. Philippine trogon .. 10 5
2468 2 p. Rufous hornbill .. 10 5
2469 2 p. White-bellied black woodpecker 10 5
2470 2 p. Spotted wood kingfisher 10 5

(c) Size 36 × 26½ mm.
2471 2 p. Brahminy kite .. 10 5
2472 2 p. Philippine falconet .. 10 5
2473 2 p. Eastern reef heron .. 10 5
2474 2 p. Philippine duck (inscr "Mallard") 10 5

JAN'95

OFFICIAL STAMPS

1926. Commemorative issue of 1926 optd **OFFICIAL**.
O 391. **49.** 2 c. black and green .. 1·50 80
O 392. 4 c. black and red .. 1·50 80
O 393. 18 c. black and brown 5·50 4·50
O 394. 20 c. black and orange 4·50 1·50

1931. Stamps of 1906 optd. **O.B.**
O 413. 2 c. green (No. 337) .. 10 10
O 414. 4 c. red (No. 338) .. 10 10
O 415. 6 c. violet (No. 339) .. 10 10
O 416. 8 c. brown (No. 340) .. 10 10
O 417. 10 c. blue (No. 341) .. 55 10
O 418. 12 c. orange (No. 342) 30 15
O 419. 16 c. olive (No. 344) .. 30 10
O 420. 20 c. orange (No. 345) 40 10
O 421. 26 c. green (No. 346) .. 50 40
O 422. 30 c. grey (No. 347) .. 40 30

1935. Nos. 459/68 optd. **O.B.**
O 473. 2 c. red 10 10
O 474. 4 c. green 10 10
O 475. 6 c. brown 10 10
O 476. 8 c. violet 15 15
O 477. 10 c. red 15 10
O 478. 12 c. black 20 15
O 479. 16 c. blue 20 15
O 480. 20 c. bistre 20 15
O 481. 26 c. blue 40 35
O 482. 30 c. red 45 40

1936. Stamps of 1935 (Nos. 459/68) optd **O. B. COMMONWEALTH** (2, 6, 20 c.) or **O. B. COMMONWEALTH** (others).
O 538. 2 c. red 10 10
O 539. 4 c. green 10 10
O 540. 6 c. brown 15 10
O 541. 8 c. violet 15 10
O 542. 10 c. red 15 10
O 543. 12 c. black 15 15
O 544. 16 c. blue 25 10
O 545. 20 c. bistre 40 40
O 546. 26 c. blue 45 45
O 547. 30 c. red 45 45

1941. Nos. 563 and 623 optd **O. B.**
O 565 **104** 2 c. green 10 10
O 624 – 2 c. brown 10 10

1948. Various stamps optd. **O.B.**

O 738. **147.** 1 c. brown 5 5
O 668. **125.** 2 c. green 40 5
O 659. – 4 c. brown (No. 629) 15 5
O 739. – 5 c. red (No. 731) .. 15 5
O 843. – 6 c. blue (No. 842) .. 25 5
O 660. **113.** 10 c. red 25 5
O 740. – 10 c. blue (No. 732) 25 10
O 661. – 16 c. slate (No. 632) 1·75 40
O 669. – 20 c. brown (No. 633) 70 15
O 741. – 20 c. red (No. 733) .. 55 10
O 670. – 50 c. green (No. 634) 1·10 70

1950. Surch. **ONE CENTAVO.**

O 700. **125.** 1 c. on 2 c. grn. (No. O 668) 8 5

1959. No. 810 optd. **O.B.**

O 811. 1 c. on 5 c. red.. .. 15 5

1962. Optd. **G.O.**

O 908. 5 s. red (No. 898) .. 5 5
O 909. 6 s. brown (No. 899) .. 5 5
O 910. 6 s. blue (No. 900) .. 5 5
O 911. 10 s. purple (No. 901).. 10 5
O 912. 20 s. blue (No. 902) .. 20 5
O 913. 30 s. red (No. 903) .. 20 15
O 914. 50 s. violet (No. 904).. 25 15

1970. Optd. **G.O.**

O 1182. **318.** 10 s. red 10 5

OFFICIAL SPECIAL DELIVERY STAMP

1931. No. E 353b optd **O.B.**

EO 423 20 c. violet 50 35

POSTAGE DUE STAMPS

1899. Postage Due stamps of United States of 1894 optd. **PHILIPPINES.**

D 268. **D 87.** 1 c. red .. .. 3·25 1·50
D 269. 2 c. red .. .. 3·25 1·25
D 270. 3 c. red .. .. 12·00 7·00
D 271. 5 c. red .. .. 8·00 2·50
D 272. 10 c. red .. .. 10·00 4·00
D 273. 30 c. red .. .. £180 85·00
D 274. 50 c. red .. .. £140 80·00

D 51. Post Office Clerk. **D 118.**

1928.

D 395. **D 51.** 4 c. red 15 15
D 396. 6 c. red 25 25
D 397. 8 c. red 25 25
D 398. 10 c. red 25 25
D 399. 12 c. red 25 25
D 400. 16 c. red 30 30
D 401. 20 c. red 25 25

1937. Surch. **3 CVOS. 3.**

D 521. **D 51.** 3 c. on 4 c. red .. 20 15

1947.

D 644. **D 118.** 3 c. red 20 20
D 645. 4 c. blue 20 15
D 646. 6 c. olive 25 25
D 647. 10 c. orange .. 30 30

SPECIAL DELIVERY STAMPS

1901. Special Delivery stamp of United States of 1888 optd. **PHILIPPINES.**

E 268. **E 46.** 10 c. blue (No. E 283) .. .. 85·00 90·00

1907. Special Delivery stamp of United States optd **PHILIPPINES.**

E29 **E 117** 10 c. blue £1500

E 47. Messenger running.

1919. Perf (E353), perf or imperf (E353b).

E 353. **E 47.** 20 c. blue 45 20
E 353b. 20 c. violet .. 45 15

1939. Optd **COMMONWEALTH.** Perf.

E550 E 47 20 c. violet .. 30 20

1945. Optd. **VICTORY.**

E 622. **E 47.** 20 c. vio. (No. E 550) 50 50

E 120. Cyclist Messenger and Post Office.

1947.

E 651. **E 120.** 20 c. purple .. 35 25

E 219. G.P.O. Manila.

1962.

E 891. **E 219.** 20 c. mauve .. 35 25

POLAND Pt. 5

A country lying between Russia and Germany, originally independent, but divided between Prussia, Austria and Russia in 1772/95. An independent republic since 1918. Occupied by Germany from 1939 to 1945.

1860. 100 kopeks = 1 rouble.
1918. 100 pfennig = 1 mark.
100 halerzy = 1 korona.
100 fenigow = 1 marka.
1924. 100 groszy = 1 zloty.

1. Russian Arms.

2. Sigismund III Vasa Column, Warsaw.

1860.

1b.	**1.**	10 k. blue and red	£650	£170

1918. Surch. **POCZTA POLSKA** and value in fen. as in T 2.

2.	**2.**	5 f. on 2 g. brown	75	60
3.	–	10 f. on 6 g. green	1·00	50
4.	–	25 f. on 10 g. red	2·40	1·25
5.	–	50 f. on 20 g. blue	5·25	4·00

DESIGNS: 6 g. Arms of Warsaw. 10 g. Polish eagle. 20 g. Jan III Sobieski Monument, Warsaw.

1918. Stamps of German Occupation of Poland optd. **Poczta Polska** or surch. also.

9	**10**	3 pf. brown	27·00	13·50
10		5 pf. green	65	40
6	**24**	5 on 2½ pf. grey	25	25
7	**10**	5 on 3 pf. brown	1·40	1·10
11		10 pf. red	15	15
12	**24**	15 pf. violet	20	15
13a	**10**	20 pf. blue	15	15
8	**24**	25 on 7½ pf. orange	40	30
14	**10**	30 pf. blk & orge on buff	15	15
15		40 pf. black and red	1·00	1·00
16		60 pf. mauve	65	65

1918. Stamps of Austro-Hungarian Military Post (Nos. 69/71) optd. **POLSKA POCZTA** and Polish eagle.

17.		10 h. green	6·75	6·75
18.		20 h. red	6·75	6·75
19.		45 h. blue	6·75	6·75

1918. As stamps of Austro-Hungarian Military Post of 1917 optd. **POLSKA POCZTA** and Polish eagle and (some) surch. also.

20.		3 h. on 3 h. olive	25·00	20·00
21.		3 h. on 15 h. red	3·25	2·75
22.		10 h. on 30 h. green	3·25	2·75
23.		25 h. on 40 h. olive	5·00	3·25
24.		45 h. on 60 h. red	4·25	3·25
25.		45 h. on 80 h. blue	4·75	4·00
28.		50 h. green	28·00	23·00
26.		50 h. on 60 h. red	4·75	4·00
29.		90 h. violet	5·00	3·25

1919. Stamps of Austria optd. **POCZTA POLSKA,** the 80 h. also surch. **25.**

30	**49**	3 h. violet	£180	£200
31		5 h. green	£225	£225
32		6 h. orange	20·00	20·00
33		10 h. purple	£180	£200
34		12 h. blue	17·00	15·00
35	**60**	15 h. red	5·00	5·75
36		20 h. green	85·00	95·00
37		25 h. blue	£850	£950
49	**51**	25 on 80 h. brown	2·40	2·40
38	**60**	30 h. violet	£170	£170
39	**51**	40 h. green	13·50	13·50
40		50 h. green	6·00	6·75
41		60 h. blue	4·00	4·00
42		80 h. brown	3·25	4·00
43		90 h. purple	£600	£650
44		1 k. red on yellow	6·75	6·75
45	**52**	2 k. blue	4·00	4·00
46		3 k. red	38·00	50·00
47		4 k. green	65·00	85·00
48a		10 k. violet	£3000	£4000

11.

1919. Imperf.

50.	**11.**	2 h. grey	30	30
51.		3 h. violet	30	30
52.		5 h. green	20	20
53.		6 h. orange	17·00	23·00
54.		10 h. red	20	20
55.		15 h. brown	20	20
56.		20 h. olive	30	30
57.		25 h. red	10	10
58.		50 h. blue	20	20
59.		70 h. blue	30	30
60.		1 k. red and grey	50	50

15.

16.

17. Agriculture.

18. Ploughing in peace.

19. Polish Uhlan.

1919. For Southern Poland. Value in "halerzy" or "kronen". Imperf. or perf.

68.	**15.**	3 h. brown	10	10
69.		5 h. green	10	10
70.		10 h. orange	10	10
71.		15 h. red	10	10
72.	**16.**	20 h. brown	10	10
85.		25 h. blue	10	10
86.		50 h. brown	10	10
87.	**17.**	1 k. green	10	10
88.		1 k. 50 brown	30	10
89.		2 k. blue	65	10
90.	**18.**	2 k. 50 purple	65	35
91.	**19.**	5 k. blue	1·00	35

1919. For Northern Poland. Imperf or perf.

104	**15**	3 f. brown	10	10
105		5 f. green	10	10
179		5 f. blue	10	10
106		10 f. purple	10	10
129		10 f. brown	10	10
107		15 f. red	10	10
108	**16**	20 f. blue	10	10
181		20 f. red	10	10
109		25 f. green	10	10
110		50 f. green	10	10
183		50 f. orange	10	10
137	**17**	1 m. violet	10	10
112		1 m. 50 green	30	10
138		2 m. brown	10	10
114	**18**	2 m. 50 brown	1·00	15
139		3 m. brown	10	10
140	**19**	5 m. purple	10	10
141		6 m. red	10	10
142		10 m. red	15	10
143		20 m. green	1·00	15

1919. 1st Polish Philatelic Exn. and Polish White Cross Fund. Surch. **1 POLSKA WYSTAWA MAREK,** cross and new value. Imperf. or perf.

116.	**15.**	5+5 f. green	10	10
117.		10+5 f. purple	55	10
118.		15+5 f. red	10	10
119.	**16.**	25+5 f. olive	15	10
120.		50+5 f. green	65	50

20.

21. Prime Minister Paderewski.

22. A. Trampczynski.

23. Eagle and Ship.

24.

1919. 1st Session of Parliament in Liberated Poland. Dated "1919".

121.	**20.**	10 f. mauve	15	10
122.	**21.**	15 f. red	15	10
123.	**22.**	20 f. brown	50	25
125.	–	25 f. green	30	10
126.	**23.**	50 f. blue	35	15
127.	–	1 m. violet	50	50

DESIGN—As Type **21:** 25 f. Gen. Pilsudski. As Type **23:** 1 m. Griffin and fasces.

1920. As T **22,** but smaller (17×20 mm.).

124.	**22.**	20 f. brown	1·25	1·40

1920.

146.	**24.**	40 f. violet	10	10
182.		40 f. brown	10	10
184.		75 f. green	10	10

1920. As T **15,** but value in marks ("Mk").

147.	**15.**	1 m. red	10	10
148.		2 m. green	10	10
149.		3 m. blue	10	10
150.		4 m. red	10	10
151.		5 m. purple	10	10
152.		8 m. brown	10	20

1921. Surch. **3 Mk.** and bars.

153.	**24.**	3 m. on 40 f violet	10	10

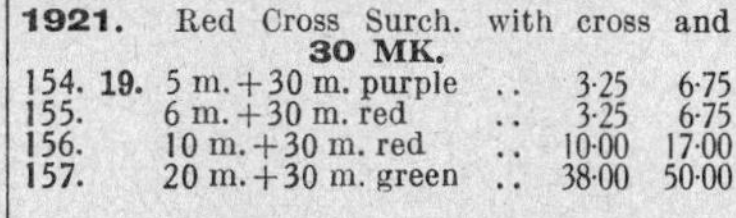

1921. Red Cross Surch. with cross and **30 MK.**

154.	**19.**	5 m.+30 m. purple	3·25	6·75
155.		6 m.+30 m. red	3·25	6·75
156.		10 m.+30 m. red	10·00	17·00
157.		20 m.+30 m. green	38·00	50·00

28. Sun of Peace.

29. Agriculture.

1921. New Constitution.

158.	**28.**	2 m. green	1·60	1·50
159.		3 m. blue	1·60	1·50
160.		4 m. red	1·00	35
161.	**29.**	6 m. red	1·00	35
162.		10 m. green	1·00	35
163.	–	25 m. violet	2·40	1·40
164.	–	50 m. green and buff	1·40	75

DESIGN: 25 m. 50 m. "Peace" (Seated woman.)

31. "Peace with Russia".

32.

1921.

165.	**31.**	10 m. blue	10	10
166.		15 m. brown	10	10
167.		20 m. red	10	10
170.	**32.**	25 m. violet and buff	10	10
171.		50 m. red and buff	10	10
172.		100 m. brown & orange	10	10
173.		200 m. pink and black	10	10
174.		300 m. green	10	10
175.		400 m. brown	10	10
176.		500 m. purple	10	10
177.		1000 m. orange	10	10
178.		2000 m. violet	10	10

33. Silesian Miner.

1922.

185.	**33.**	1 m. black	10	10
186.		1 m. 25 green	10	10
187.		2 m. red	10	10
188.		3 m. green	10	10
189.		4 m. blue	10	10
190.		5 m. brown	10	10
191.		6 m. orange	10	25
192.		10 m. brown	10	10
193.		20 m. purple	10	10
194.		50 m. olive	10	60
195.		80 m. red	25	1·60
196.		100 m. violet	55	1·60
197.		200 m. orange	1·00	2·75
198.		300 m. blue	1·40	5·00

34. Copernicus.

39.

1923. 450th Birth Anniv of Copernicus (astronomer) and 150th Death Anniv of Konarski (educationist).

199.	**34.**	1,000 m. slate	60	25
200.	–	3,000 m. brown	35	25
201.	**34.**	5,000 m. red	60	35

DESIGN: 3,000 m. Konarski.

1923. Surch.

202.	**32.**	10,000 m. on 25 m. violet and buff	10	10
206.	**15.**	20,000 m. on 2 m. green (No. 148)	25	15
204.	**31.**	25,000 m. on 20 m. red	10	10
205		50,000 m. on 10 m. grn.	10	10
207.	**15.**	100,000 m. on 5 m. purple (No. 151)	10	10

1924.

208.	**39.**	10,000 m. purple	25	30
209.		20,000 m. green	15	10
210.		30,000 m. red	1·00	30
211.		50,000 m. green	1·00	30
212.		100,000 m. brown	50	25
213.		200,000 m. blue	50	15
214.		300,000 m. mauve	50	30
215.		500,000 m. brown	50	2·75
216.		1,000,000 m. pink	50	5·00
217.		2,000,000 m. green	1·10	42·00

40.

41. President Wojciechowski.

42.

1924. New Currency.

218.	**40.**	1 g. brown	40	10
219.		2 g. brown	40	10
220.		3 g. orange	50	10
221.		5 g. green	1·00	10
222.		10 g. green	1·00	10
223.		15 g. red	1·00	10
224.		20 g. blue	4·25	10
225.		25 g. red	8·25	15
226.		30 g. violet	32·00	10
227.		40 g. blue	6·75	25
228.		50 g. purple	3·25	15
229.	**41.**	1 z. red	22·00	2·75

1925. National Fund.

230.	**42.**	1 g.+50 g. brown	13·50	20·00
231.		2 g.+50 g. brown	13·50	20·00
232.		3 g.+50 g. orange	13·50	20·00
233.		5 g.+50 g. green	13·50	20·00
234.		10 g.+50 g. green	13·50	20·00
235.		15 g.+50 g. red	13·50	20·00
236.		20 g.+50 g. blue	13·50	20·00
237.		25 g.+50 g. red	13·50	20·00
238.		30 g.+50 g. violet	13·50	20·00
239.		40 g.+50 g. blue	13·50	20·00
240.		50 g.+50 g. purple	13·50	20·00

43. Holy Gate, Vilna.

44. Town Hall, Poznan.

48. Galleon.

1925.

241.	**43.**	1 g. brown	15	10
242.	–	2 g. olive	50	20
243a.	–	3 g. blue	1·00	35
244a.	**44.**	5 g. green	1·00	10
245a.	–	10 g. violet	1·00	10
246.	–	15 g. red	1·00	10
247.	**48.**	20 g. red	3·00	10
248.	**43.**	24 g. blue	8·25	50
249.	–	30 g. blue	3·25	10
250.	–	40 g. blue	3·25	10
251.	**48.**	45 g. mauve	10·00	40

DESIGNS—VERT. As Type **43:** 2 g., 30 g. Sobieski Statue, Lwow. As Type **44:** 3 g., 10 g. King Sigismund Monument, Warsaw. HORIZ. 15 g., 40 g. Wawel Castle, Cracow.

49.

50. Chopin.

1925. Air.

252.	**49.**	1 g. blue	75	4·00
253.		2 g. orange	75	4·00
254.		3 g. brown	80	4·00
255.		5 g. brown	80	50
256.		10 g. green	2·40	60
257.		15 g. mauve	3·25	1·00
258.		20 g. olive	18·00	5·00
259.		30 g. red	9·75	1·75
260.		45 g. lilac	13·50	3·25

1927.

261.	**50.**	40 g. blue	17·00	1·90

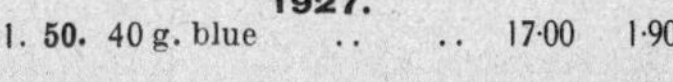

51. Marshal Pilsudski.

52. Pres. Moscicki.

53.

1927.

262.	**51.**	20 g. red	2·75	10
262a.		25 g. brown	2·50	10

1927.

263.	**52.**	20 g. red	6·75	85

1927. Educational Funds.

264.	**53.**	10 g.+5 g. pur. on grn.	13·50	11·50
265.		20 g.+5 g. blue on yell.	13·50	11·50

54. Dr. Karl Kaczkowki.

55. J. Slowacki (poet).

1927. 4th Int. Military Medical Congress, Warsaw.

266.	**54.**	10 g. green	3·25	2·75
267.		25 g. red	6·75	4·00
268.		40 g. blue	10·00	2·75

1927. Transfer of Slowacki's remains to Cracow.

269.	**55.**	20 g. red	6·75	85

56. Marshal Pilsudski. **57.** Pres. Moscicki. **58.** Gen. Joseph Bem.

1928.

272.	**56.**	50 g. grey	3·25	10
272a.		50 g. green	4·25	10
273.	**57.**	1 z. black on cream ..	10·00	10

1928.

271.	**58.**	25 g. red	3·25	15

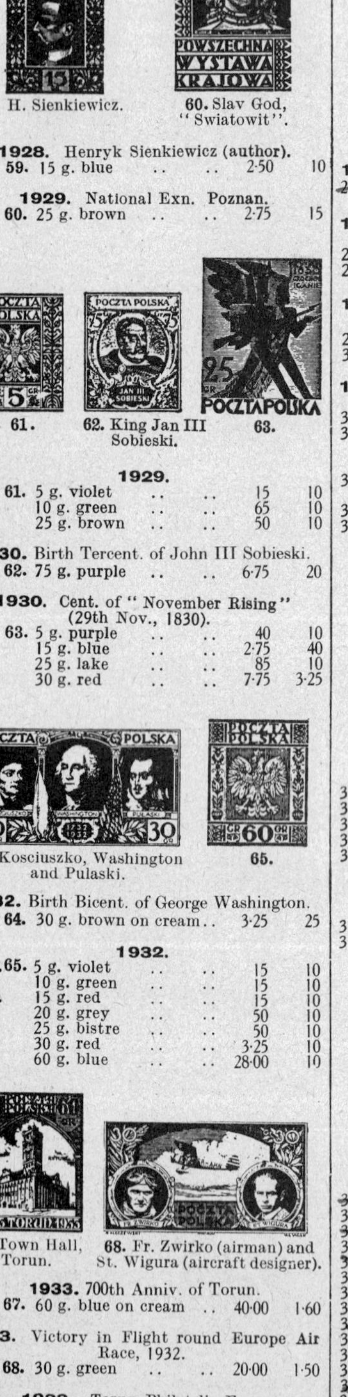

59. H. Sienkiewicz. **60.** Slav God, "Swiatowit".

1928. Henryk Sienkiewicz (author).

274.	**59.**	15 g. blue	2·50	10

1929. National Exn. Poznan.

275.	**60.**	25 g. brown	2·75	15

61. **62.** King Jan III Sobieski. **63.**

1929.

276.	**61.**	5 g. violet	15	10
277.		10 g. green	65	10
278.		25 g. brown	50	10

1930. Birth Tercent. of John III Sobieski.

279.	**62.**	75 g. purple	6·75	20

1930. Cent. of "November Rising" (29th Nov., 1830).

280.	**63.**	5 g. purple	40	10
281.		15 g. blue	2·75	40
282.		25 g. lake	85	10
283.		30 g. red	7·75	3·25

64. Kosciuszko, Washington and Pulaski. **65.**

1932. Birth Bicent. of George Washington.

284.	**64.**	30 g. brown on cream ..	3·25	25

1932.

284a.	**65.**	5 g. violet	15	10
285.		10 g. green	15	10
285a.		15 g. red	15	10
286.		20 g. grey	50	10
287.		25 g. bistre	50	10
288.		30 g. red	3·25	10
289.		60 g. blue	28·00	10

67. Town Hall, Torun. **68.** Fr. Zwirko (airman) and St. Wigura (aircraft designer).

1933. 700th Anniv. of Torun.

290.	**67.**	60 g. blue on cream ..	40·00	1·60

1933. Victory in Flight round Europe Air Race, 1932.

292.	**68.**	30 g. green	20·00	1·50

1933. Torun Philatelic Exn.

293.	**67.**	60 g. red on cream ..	23·00	13·50

69. Altar-piece, St. Mary's Church, Cracow

1933. 4th Death Cent. of Veit Stoss (sculptor).

294.	**69.**	80 g. brown on cream	17·00	1·50

70. " Liberation of Vienna " by J. Matejko.

1933. 250th Anniv. of Relief of Vienna.

295.	**70.**	1 z. 20 blue on cream ..	50·00	13·50

71. Cross of Independence. **73.** Marshal Pilsudski and Legion of Fusiliers Badge.

1933. 15th Anniv of Proclamation of Republic.

296	71	30 g. red	10·00	25

1934. Katowice Philatelic Exn. Optd. **Wyst. Filat. 1934 Katowice.**

297.	**65.**	20 g. grey	50·00	32·00
298.		30 g. red	50·00	32·00

1934. 20th Anniv of Formation of Polish Legion.

299.	**73.**	25 g. blue	1·50	25
300.		30 g. brown	2·75	25

1934. Int. Air Tournament. Optd. **Challenge 1934.**

301.	**49.**	20 g. olive	17·00	10·00
302.	**68.**	30 g. green ..	10·00	2·75

1934. Surch. in figures.

303.	**69.**	25 g. on 80 g. brown on cream	6·75	45
304.	**65.**	55 g. on 60 g. blue ..	5·00	25
305.	**70.**	1 z. on 1 z. 20 blue on cream	22·00	5·00

77. Marshal Pilsudski.

1935. Mourning Issue.

306.	**77.**	5 g. black	1·00	10
307.		15 g. black	1·00	25
308.		25 g. black	1·60	10
309.		45 g. black	5·00	1·50
310.		1 z. black	8·25	4·25

1935. Optd. **Kopiec Marszalka Pilsudskiego.**

311.	**65.**	15 g. red	1·40	70
312.	**73.**	25 g. blue	4·75	2·50

79. Pieskowa Skala (Dog's Rock).

80. Pres. Moscicki.

1935.

313.	**79.**	5 g. blue	65	10
317.	–	5 g. violet	15	10
314.	–	10 g. green	65	10
318.	–	10 g. green	75	10
315.	–	15 g. blue	3·25	10
319.	–	15 g. lake	30	10
316.	–	20 g. black	90	10
320.	–	20 g. orange	45	10
321a.	–	25 g. green	70	10
322.	–	30 g. red	2·10	10
323a.	–	45 g. mauve	1·90	10
324a.	–	50 g. black	3·00	10
325.	–	55 g. blue	6·75	25
326.	–	1 z. brown	5·75	70
327.	**80.**	3 z. brown	3·25	6·75

DESIGNS: 5 g. (No. 317) Monastery of Jasna Gora, Czestochowa. 10 g. (314) Lake Morskie Oko. 10 g. (318) "Batory" (liner) at sea passenger terminal, Gdynia. 15 g. (315) "Pilsudski" (liner). 15 g. (319) University, Lwow. 20 g. (316) Pieniny-Czorsztyn. 20 g. (320) Administrative Buildings, Katowice. 25 g. Belvedere Palace, Warsaw. 30 g. Castle at Mir. 45 g. Castle at Podhorce. 50 g. Cloth Hall, Cracow. 55 g. Raczynski Library, Poznan. 1 z. Vilna Cathedral.

1936. 10th Anniv of Moscicki Presidency. As T **57** but inscr "1926. 3. VI. 1936" below design.

328	**57**	1 z. blue	8·25	6·75

1936. Gordon-Bennett Balloon Race. Optd. **GORDON-BENNETT 30. VIII. 1936.**

329.		30 g. red (No. 322) ..	13·50	6·75
330.		55 g. blue (No. 325) ..	13·50	6·75

82. Marshal Smigly-Rydz.

83. Pres. Moscicki.

1937.

331.	**82.**	25 g. blue	35	10
332.		55 g. blue	50	10

For 25 g. brown see note after No. 273.

1938. President's 70th Birthday.

333.	**83.**	15 g. grey	15	10
334.		30 g. purple	35	10

84. Kosciuszko, Paine and Washington.

1938. 150th Anniv. of U.S. Constitution.

335.	**84.**	1 z. blue	2·00	1·60

85a.

86. Marshal Pilsudski.

1938. 20th Anniv. of Independence.

336.	–	5 g. orange	10	10
337.	–	10 g. green	10	10
338.	**85a.**	15 g. brown (A) ..	15	15
357.		15 g. brown (B) ..	25	10
339.	–	20 g. blue	35	55
340.	–	25 g. purple	10	10
341.	–	30 g. red	50	10
342.	–	45 g. black	1·00	1·00
343.	–	50 g. mauve	2·00	10
344.	–	55 g. blue	65	10
345.	–	75 g. green	3·00	1·25
346.	–	1 z. orange	3·25	1·25
347.	–	2 z. red	13·50	15·00
348.	**86.**	3 z. blue	10·00	15·00

DESIGNS—VERT. 5 g. Boleslaw the Brave. 10 g. Casimir the Great. 20 g. Casimir Jagiellon. 25 g. Sigismund August. 30 g. Stefan Batory. 45 g. Chodkiewicz and Zolkiewski. 50 g. John III Sobieski. 55 g. Symbol of Constitution of May 3rd, 1791. 75 g. Kosciuszko, Poniatowski and Dabrowski. 1 z. November Uprising 1830–31. 2 z. Romuald Traugutt.

(A) Type **85a.** (B) as Type **85a** but crossed swords omitted.

87. Teschen comes to Poland.

88. " Warmth ".

1938. Acquisition of Teschen.

349.	**87.**	25 g. purple	1·90	25

1938. Winter Relief Fund.

350.	**88.**	5 g. + 5 g. orange ..	40	1·60
351.		25 g. + 10 g. purple ..	85	2·50
352.		55 g. + 15 g. blue ..	1·90	4·25

89. Tatra Mountaineer.

1939. Int. Ski Championship, Zakopane.

353.	**89.**	15 g. brown	1·00	70
354.		25 g. purple	1·50	80
355.		30 g. red	2·40	1·50
356.		55 g. blue	10·00	5·00

90. Pilsudski and Polish Legionaries.

1939. 25th Anniv. of 1st Battles of Polish Legions.

358.	**90.**	25 g. purple	80	50

1939-1945. GERMAN OCCUPATION.

1939. T **94** of Germany surch. **Deutsche Post OSTEN** and value.

359.	**94.**	6 g. on 3 pf. brown ..	20	40
360.		8 g. on 4 pf. grey ..	20	30
361.		12 g. on 6 pf. green ..	20	25
362.		16 g. on 8 pf. orange ..	70	1·00
363.		20 g. on 10 pf. brown ..	25	20
364.		24 g. on 12 pf. red ..	25	20
365.		30 g. on 15 pf. red ..	1·00	85
366.		40 g. on 20 pf. blue ..	85	40
367.		50 g. on 25 pf. blue ..	85	50
368.		60 g. on 30 pf. olive ..	85	25
369.		80 g. on 40 pf. mauve ..	1·00	70
370.		1 z. on 50 pf. blk. & grn.	2·40	1·25
371.		2 z. on 100 pf. blk. & yell.	4·75	3·00

1940. Surch. **General Gouvernement** and Nazi emblem and value.

372.	–	2 g. on 5 g. orge. (No. 336)	20	30
373.	–	4 g. on 5 g. orge. (No. 336)	20	30
374.	–	6 g. on 10 g. grn. (No. 337)	20	30
375.	–	8 g. on 10 g. grn. (No. 337)	20	30
376.	–	10 g. on 10 g. green (No. 337)	20	30
377.	**107.**	12 g. on 15 g. brown (No. 338)	20	30
378.		16 g. on 15 g. brown (No. 338)	20	30
379.	**104.**	24 g. on 25 g. blue ..	2·75	2·75
380.	–	24 g. on 25 g. purple (No. 340)	35	35
381.	–	30 g. on 30 g. red (No. 341)	40	40
382.	**110.**	30 g. on 5 g. + 5 g. orge.	40	50
383.	**105.**	40 g. on 30 g. purple ..	1·00	1·00
384.	**110.**	40 g. on 25 g. + 10 g. pur.	40	40
385.	–	50 g. on 50 g. mauve (No. 343)	50	40
386.	**104.**	50 g. on 55 g. blue ..	40	40
386a.	D **88.**	50 g. on 20 g. green ..	2·00	2·00
386b.		50 g. on 25 g. green ..	18·00	11·50
386c.		50 g. on 30 g. green ..	50·00	32·00
386d.		50 g. on 50 g. green ..	2·00	1·60
386e.		50 g. on 1 z. green ..	3·25	1·60
387.	–	60 g. on 55 g. blue (No. 344)	17·00	8·25
388.	–	80 g. on 75 g. green (No. 345)	17·00	8·25
388a.	**110.**	1 z. on 55 g. + 15 g. blue	9·25	6·00
389.	–	1 z. on 1 z. orge. (No. 346)	17·00	8·25
390.	–	2 z. on 2 z. red (No. 347)	10·00	5·00
391.	**108.**	3 z. on 3 z. blue ..	11·50	5·00

Nos. 386a/e are all postage stamps.

93. Copernicus Memorial, Cracow.

95.

1940.

392.	–	6 g. brown	25	60
393.	–	8 g. brown	25	60
394.	–	8 g. black	25	40
395.	–	10 g. green	15	15
396.	**93.**	12 g. green	3·25	25
397.		12 g. violet	35	15
398.	–	20 g. brown	10	10
399.	–	24 g. red	10	10
400.	–	30 g. violet	10	15
401.	–	30 g. purple	20	30
402.	–	40 g. black	20	15
403.	–	48 g. brown	70	1·00
404.	–	50 g. blue	20	15
405.	–	60 g. olive	20	20
406.	–	80 g. violet	25	25
407.	–	1 z. purple	2·40	1·10
408.	–	1 z. green	45	35

DESIGNS: 6 g. Florian gate, Cracow. 8 g. Castle Keep, Cracow. 10 g. Cracow Gate, Lublin. 20 g. Church of the Dominicans, Cracow. 24 g. Wawel Castle, Cracow. 30 g. Old Church in Lublin. 40 g. Arcade, Cloth Hall, Cracow. 48 g. Town Hall, Sandomir. 50 g. Town Hall, Cracow. 60 g. Courtyard of Wawel Castle, Cracow. 80 g. St. Mary's Church, Cracow. 1 z. Bruhl Palace, Warsaw.

1940. Red Cross Fund. As last, new colours, surch. with Cross and premium in figures.

409.	12 g. + 8 g. olive	2·75	3·25
410.	24 g. + 16 g. olive ..	2·75	3·25
411.	50 g. + 50 g. olive ..	3·25	4·25
412.	80 g. + 80 g. olive ..	3·25	4·25

1940. 1st Anniv. of German Occupation.

413.	**95.**	12 g. + 38 g. green ..	2·00	2·75
414.	–	24 g. + 26 g. red ..	2·00	2·75
415.	–	30 g. + 20 g. violet ..	3·75	4·75

DESIGNS: 24 g. Woman with scarf. 30 g. Fur-capped peasant as Type **96**.

96.

1940. Winter Relief Fund.
416. 96. 12 g.+8 g. green .. 75 1·00
417. 24 g.+16 g. red .. 1·25 1·50
418. 30 g.+30 g. brown .. 1·60 2·10
419. 50 g.+50 g. blue .. 2·10 2·75

97. Cracow.

1941.
420. 97. 10 z. grey and red .. 1·50 2·00

98. The Rotunda, Cracow. 99. Adolf Hitler.

1941.
421. 98. 2 z. blue 30 35
422. – 4 z. green .. .. 65 1·00
DESIGN: 4 z. Tyniec Monastery.
See also Nos. 465/8.

1941.
423. 99. 2 g. grey 10 20
424. 6 g. brown 10 20
425. 8 g. blue 10 20
426. 10 g. green 10 10
427. 12 g. violet 10 10
428. 16 g. orange 15 40
429. 20 g. brown 10 15
430. 24 g. red 10 10
431. 30 g. purple 15 15
432. 32 g. green 15 35
433. 40 g. blue 10 15
434. 48 g. brown 20 40
435. 50 g. blue 40 50
436. 60 g. olive 40 50
437. 80 g. purple 40 50
441. 1 z. green 50 40
442. 1 z. 20 brown 60 45
443. 1 z. 60 blue 65 85

1942. Hitler's 53rd Birthday. As T 99, but premium inserted in design.
444. 30 g.+1 z. purple .. 25 35
445. 50 g.+1 z. blue .. 25 35
446. 1 z. 20+1 z. brown .. 25 35

DESIGN: 12 g., 50 g. Lublin, after an ancient engraving.
100. Modern Lublin.

1942. 600th Anniv. of Lublin.
447. – 12 g.+8 g. purple .. 10 15
448. 100. 24 g.+6 g. brown .. 10 15
449. – 50 g.+50 g. blue .. 15 25
450. 100. 1 z.+1 z. green .. 60 60

101. Copernicus. 102. Adolf Hitler.

1942. 3rd Anniv. of German Occupation.
451. – 12 g.+18 g. violet .. 10 15
452. – 24 g.+26 g. red .. 10 15
453. – 30 g.+30 g. purple .. 10 15
454. – 50 g.+50 g. blue .. 10 20
455. 101. 1 z.+1 z. green .. 45 35
DESIGNS: 12 g. Veit Stoss (Vit Stvosz). 24 g. Hans Durer. 30 g. J. Schuch. 50 g. J. Elsner.

1943. Hitler's 54th Birthday.
456. 102. 12 g.+1 z. violet .. 15 20
457. 24 g.+1 z. red .. 15 20
458. 84 g.+1 z. green .. 30 35

1943. 400th Death Anniv. of Copernicus. As No. 455, colour changed, optd. **24 MAI 1543** at left and **24 MAI 1943** at right.
459. 101. 1 z.+1 z. purple .. 60 85

103. Cracow Gate, Lublin. 104. Adolf Hitler.

1943. 3rd Anniv. of Nazi Party in German-occupied Poland.
460. 103. 12 g.+38 g. green .. 10 15
461. – 24 g.+76 g. red .. 10 15
462. – 30 g.+70 g. purple .. 10 15
463. – 50 g.+1 z. blue .. 10 15
464. – 1 z.+2 z. grey .. 15 25
DESIGNS: 24 g. Cloth Hall, Cracow. 30 g. Administrative Building, Radom. 50 g. Bruhl Palace, Warsaw. 1 z. Town hall, Lwow.

1943. As T 98, inscr. "DEUTSCHES REICH GENERALGOUVERNEMENT".
465. 98. 2 z. green 10 10
466. – 4 z. violet 15 20
467. – 6 z. brown 25 35
468. – 10 z. grey and brown .. 30 40
DESIGNS: 4 z. Tyniec Monastery. 6 z. Lwow 10 z. Cracow.

1944. Hitler's 55th Birthday.
469. 104. 12 z.+1 z. green .. 10 15
470. 24 z.+1 z brown .. 10 15
471. 84 z.+1 z. violet .. 15 20

105. Konrad Celtis. 105a. Cracow Castle.

1944. Culture Funds.
472. 105. 12 g.+18 g. green .. 10 10
473. – 24 g.+26 g. red .. 10 10
474. – 30 g.+30 g. purple .. 10 10
475. – 50 g.+50 g. blue .. 15 35
476. – 1 z.+1 z. brown .. 15 35
PORTRAITS: 24 g. A. Schluter. 30 g. H. Boner. 50 g. Augustus the Strong, 1 z. G. Pusch.

1944. 5th Anniv of German Occupation.
477a 105a 10 z.+10 z. blk & red 10·50 15·00

1941-45. ISSUES OF EXILED GOVERNMENT IN LONDON.
For correspondence on Polish sea-going vessels and, on certain days, from Polish Military camps in Great Britain.

106. Ruins of Ministry of Finance, Warsaw. 107. British Wellington & Hurricane Aeroplanes used by Poles in Great Britain.

1941.
478. – 5 g. violet .. .. 1·00 1·40
479. 106. 10 g. green .. .. 1·40 1·40
480. – 25 g. grey .. .. 1·60 2·00
481. – 55 g. blue .. .. 2·40 2·00
482. – 75 g. olive .. .. 6·00 6·75
483. – 80 g. red .. .. 6·00 6·75
484. 107. 1 z. blue .. .. 6·00 6·75
485. – 1 z. 50 brown .. .. 6·00 5·00
DESIGNS—VERT. 5 g. Ruins of U.S. Embassy, Warsaw. 25 g. Destruction of Mickiewicz Monument, Cracow. 1 z. 50, Polish submarine "Orzel". HORIZ. 55 g. Ruins of Warsaw. 75 g. Polish machine-gunners in Great Britain, 80 g. Polish tank in Great Britain.

108. Vickers-Armstrong Wellington and U-boat. 109. Merchant Navy.

1943.
486. 108. 5 g. red .. .. 1·00 85
487. 109. 10 g. green 60 90
488. – 25 g. violet .. .. 1·00 90
489. – 55 g. blue .. .. 1·40 1·25
490. – 75 g. brown .. .. 2·75 2·40
491. – 80 g. red .. .. 2·75 2·75
492. – 1 z. olive .. .. 2·75 2·75
493. – 1 z. 50 black .. .. 4·00 5·00
DESIGNS—VERT. 25 g. Anti-tank gun in France. 55 g. Poles at Narvik. 1 z. Saboteurs damaging railway line. HORIZ. 75 g. The Tobruk road. 80 g. Gen. Sikorski visiting Polish troops in Middle East. 1 z. 50, Underground newspaper office.

1944. Capture of Monte Casino. Nos. 482/5 surch. **MONTE CASSINO 18 V 1944** and value and bars.
494. – 45 g. on 75 g. olive .. 15·00 17·00
495. – 55 g. on 80 g. red .. 15·00 17·00
496. 107. 80 g. on 1 z. blue .. 15·00 17·00
497. – 1 z. 20 on 1 z. 50 brown 10·00 13·00

111. Polish Partisans.

1945. Relief Fund for Survivors of Warsaw Rising.
498 111 1 z.+2 z. green .. 8·25 10·00

1944. INDEPENDENT REPUBLIC.
IMPERF. STAMPS. Many Polish stamps from No. 499 onwards exist imperf. from limited printings.

PORTRAITS: 50 g. Kosciuszko. 1 z. H. Dabrowski.
112. Romuald Traugutt.

1944. National Heroes.
499. 112. 25 g. red .. .. 60·00 70·00
500. – 50 g. green .. .. 70·00 85·00
501. – 1 z. blue .. .. 60·00 70·00

113. White Eagle. 114. Grunwald Memorial, Cracow.

1944.
502. 113. 25 g. red 65 25
503. 114. 50 g. green 65 15

1944. No. 502 surch. with value **31.XII. 1943** or **1944** and **K.R.N., P.K.W.N.** or **R.T.R.P.**
504. 113. 1 z. on 25 g. red .. 2·40 2·75
505. 2 z. on 25 g. red .. 2·40 2·75
506. 3 z. on 25 g. red .. 2·40 2·75

1945. 82nd Anniv of 1863 Revolt against Russia. Surch with value and **22.I.1863.**
507 112 5 z. on 25 g. brown .. 40·00 55·00

1945. Liberation. No. 502 surch. **3 zl.** with town names and dates as indicated.
508. 3 z. on 25 g. Bydgoszcz 23.1.1945 .. .. 5·00 6·75
509. 3 z. on 25 g. Czestochowa 17.1.1945 .. .. 5·00 6·75
510. 3 z. on 25 g. Gniezno 22.1.1945 .. .. 5·00 6·75
511. 3 z. on 25 g. Kalisz 24.1.1945 5·00 6·75
512. 3 z. on 25 g. Kielce 15.1.1945 5·00 6·75
513. 3 z. on 25 g. Krakow 19.1.1945 .. .. 5·00 6·75
514. 3 z. on 25 g. Lodz 19.1.1945 5·00 6·75
515. 3 z. on 25 g. Radom 16.1.1945 .. .. 5·00 6·75
516. 3 z. on 25 g. Warszawa 17.1.1945 .. .. 13·50 13·50
517. 3 z. on 25 g. Zakopane 29.1.1945 .. .. 6·75 6·75

120. Flag-bearer and War Victim. 121. Lodz Factories. 123. Grunwald Memorial, Cracow.

1945. Liberation of Warsaw.
518. 120. 5 z. red .. .. 2·00 2·00

1945. Liberation of Lodz.
519. 121. 1 z. blue 65 20

1945. 151st Anniv. of Kosciuszko's Oath of Allegiance. No. 500 surch. **5 zl. 24.III.1794.**
520. 5 z. on 50 g. green.. .. 9·00 14·00

1945. Cracow Monuments. Inscr. "19.I.1945".
521. 123. 50 g. purple 15 10
522. – 1 z. brown 20 10
523. – 2 z. blue .. .. 1·00 15
524. – 3 z. violet 85 25
525. – 5 z. green .. .. 6·00 6·75
DESIGNS—VERT. 1 z. Kosciuszko Statue. 3 z. Copernicus Memorial. HORIZ. 2 z. Cloth Hall. 5 z. Wawel Castle.

125. H.M.S. "Dragon" (Cruiser).

1945. 25th Anniv. of Polish Maritime League.
526. 125. 50 g.+2 z. orange .. 8·50 6·50
527. – 1 z.+3 z. blue .. .. 4·50 6·50
528. – 2 z.+4 z. red .. .. 3·25 5·75
529. – 3 z.+5 z. olive.. .. 3·25 5·75
DESIGNS—VERT. 1 z. "Dar Pomorza" (full-rigged cadet ship). 2 z. Naval ensigns. HORIZ. 3 z. Crane and tower, Gdansk.

126. Town Hall, Poznan.

1945. Postal Employees Congress.
530. 126. 1 z.+5 z. green.. .. 22·00 30·00

127. Kosciuszko Memorial, Lodz. 128. Grunwald, 1410.

1945.
531. 127. 3 z. purple 70 25

1945. 535th Anniv of Battle of Grunwald.
532 128 5 z. blue .. .. 8·25 10·00

129. Eagle and Manifesto. 130. Westerplatte.

1945. 1st Anniv. of Liberation.
533. 129. 3 z. red .. .. 11·50 18·00

1945. 6th Anniv. of Defence of Westerplatte.
534. 130. 1 z.+9 z. slate.. .. 20·00 24·00

1945. Surch. with new value and heavy bars.
535. 114. 1 z. on 50 g. green .. 40 15
536a. 113. 1 z. 50 on 25 g. red .. 40 15

133. Crane Tower, Gdansk. 135. St. John's Cathedral.

1945. Liberation of Gdansk (Danzig). Perf. or imperf.
537. 133. 1 z. olive 10 10
538. – 2 z. blue 20 10
539. – 3 z. purple 35 15
DESIGNS—VERT. 2 z. Stock Exchange, Gdansk. HORIZ. 3 z. High Gate, Gdansk.

1945. "Warsaw, 1939–1945". Warsaw before and after destruction. Imperf.
540. – 1 z. 50 red 15 10
541. 135. 3 z. blue 25 10
542. – 3 z. 50 green .. .. 1·40 30
543. – 6 z. grey 25 15
544. – 8 z. brown .. .. 3·25 30
545. – 10 z. purple 60 20
DESIGNS: 1 z. 50 Royal Castle. 3 z. 50, City Hall, 6 z. G.P.O. 8 z. War Ministry. 10 z. Church of the Holy Cross.

136. United Workers.

1945. Trades' Union Congress.
546. 136. 1 z. 50+8 z. 50 grey.. 8·25 10·00

137. Soldiers of 1830 and Jan III Sobieski Statue. 139. Insurgent.

1945. 115th Anniv of 1830 Revolt against Russia.
547 137 10 z. grey .. .. 10·00 13·50

1946. 1st Anniv. of Warsaw Liberation. Nos. 540/5 optd. **WARSZAWA WOLNA 17 Styczen 1945-1946.** Imperf.

548. 1 z. 50 red .. .. .. 2·00 3·25
549. 3 z. blue .. .. .. 2·00 3·25
550. 3 z. 50 green .. .. 2·00 3·25
551. 6 z. grey .. .. .. 2·00 3·25
552. 8 z. brown .. .. 2·00 3·25
553. 10 z. purple .. .. 2·00 3·25

1946. 83rd Anniv. of 1863 Revolt.

554. **139.** 6 z. blue .. .. 8·25 10·00

140. Plane over ruins of Warsaw. **141.** Fighting in Spain.

1946. Air.

555. **140.** 5 z. grey 40 10
556. 10 z. purple 60 15
557. 15 z. blue .. .. 4·25 25
558. 20 z. purple .. .. 1·40 20
559. 25 z. green .. .. 2·50 40
560. 30 z. red .. .. 5·00 45

1946. Polish Legion in the Spanish Civil War.

561. **141.** 3 z.+5 z. red .. .. 4·00 4·75

142. Bydgoszcz. **143.** "Death" over Majdanek Concentration Camp.

1946. 600th Anniv. of City of Bydgoszcz.

562. **142.** 3 z.+2 z. grey .. 6·75 8·25

1946. Majdanek Concentration Camp.

563. **143.** 3 z.+5 z. green .. 2·75 3·25

144. Shield and Soldiers. **145.** Infantry.

1946. Uprisings in Upper Silesia (1919-23) and Silesian Campaign against the Germans (1939-45).

564. **144.** 3 z.+7 z. brown .. 1·00 85

1946. 1st Anniv. of Peace.

565. **145.** 3 z. brown 40 15

146. Polish Coastline. **148.** Bedzin Castle.

147. Pres. Bierut, Premier O. Morawski and Marshal Zymierski.

1946. Maritime Festival.

566. **146.** 3 z.+7 z. blue .. 2·75 3·25

1946. 2nd Anniv. of Polish Committee of National Liberation Manifesto.

567. **147.** 3 z. violet .. .. 4·00 5·00

1946. Imperf. (5 z., 10 z.) or perf. (6 z.).

568. **148.** 5 z. olive 15 10
568a. 5 z. brown 20 10
569. – 6 z. black 35 10
570. – 10 z. blue 70 10

DESIGNS—VERT. 6 z. Tombstone of Henry IV. HORIZ. 10 z. Castle at Lanckorona.

149. Crane, Monument and Crane Tower, Gdansk.

1946. The Fallen in Gdansk.

571. **149.** 3 z. + 12 z. grey 2·50 3·00

150. Schoolchildren at Desk.

1946. Polish Work for Education and Fund for Int. Bureau of Education.

571a. **150.** 3 z.+22 z. red .. 32·00 60·00
571b. – 6 z.+24 z. blue .. 32·00 60·00
571c. – 11 z.+19 z. green .. 32·00 60·00

DESIGNS: 6 z. Court of Jagiellonian University, Cracow. 11 z. Gregory Piramowicz (1735-1801), founder of the Education Commission.

152. Stojalowski, Bojko, Stapinski and Witos.

1946. 50th Anniv. of Peasant Movement and Relief Fund.

572. **152.** 5 z.+10 z. green .. 1·50 1·75
573. 5 z.+10 z. blue .. 1·50 1·75
574. 5 z.+10 z. olive .. 1·50 1·75

1947. Opening of Polish Parliament. Surch **+7 SEJM USTAWODAWCZY 19.1 1947.**

575 147 3 z.+7 z. violet 8·25 13·50

1947. National Ski Championships, Zakopane. Surch. **5+15 zl. XXII MISTRZOSTWA NARCIARSKIE POLSKI 1947.**

576. **113.** 5+15 z. on 25 g. red 3·25 5·00

1947. No. 569 surch. **5 ZL** in outlined figure and capital letters between stars.

577. 5 z. on 6 z. black 60 25

156. Home of Emil Zegadlowicz.

157. Frederic Chopin (musician).

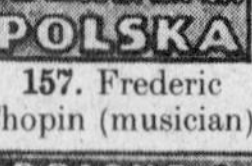

159. Wounded Soldier, Nurse and Child. **158.** Boguslawski, Modrzejewska and Jaracz (actors).

1947. Emil Zegadlowicz Commemoration.

578 156 5 z.+15 z. green .. 2·50 3·25

1947. Polish Culture. Imperf. or perf.

579. – 1 z. blue 20 15
580. – 1 z. grey 20 15
581. – 2 z. brown 20 15
582. – 2 z. orange 15 10
583. **157.** 3 z. green 80 15
584. 3 z. olive .. .. 1·10 20
585. **158.** 5 z. black 55 10
586. 5 z. brown 20 10
587. – 6 z. grey 80 20
588. – 6 z. red 35 10
589. – 10 z. grey .. .. 1·25 15
590. – 10 z. blue .. .. 1·40 25
591. – 15 z. violet .. .. 2·75 25
592. – 15 z. brown .. .. 1·00 35
593. – 20 z. black .. .. 3·25 40
594. – 20 z. purple .. .. 1·25 50

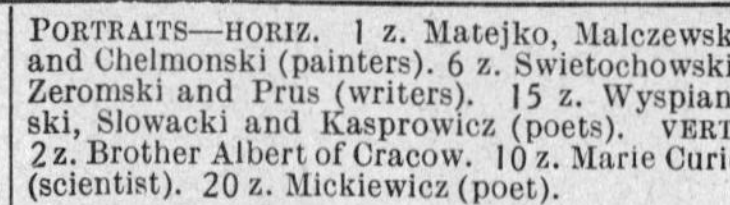

PORTRAITS—HORIZ. 1 z. Matejko, Malczewski and Chelmonski (painters). 6 z. Swietochowski, Zeromski and Prus (writers). 15 z. Wyspianski, Slowacki and Kasprowicz (poets). VERT. 2 z. Brother Albert of Cracow. 10 z. Marie Curie (scientist). 20 z. Mickiewicz (poet).

1947. Red Cross Fund.

595. **159.** 5 z.+5 z. grey and red 3·25 5·00

161. Steelworker. **163.** Brother Albert of Cracow.

1947. Occupations.

596. **161.** 5 z. lake .. .. 1·40 25
597. – 10 z. green 25 10
598. – 15 z. blue 55 20
599. – 20 z. black 90 25

DESIGNS: 10 z. Harvester. 15 z. Fisherman. 20 z. Miner.

1947. Air. Surch. **LOTNICZA** bars and value.

600 114 40 z. on 50 g. green .. 2·75 1·00
602 113 50 z. on 25 g. red .. 4·00 2·40

1947. Winter Relief Fund.

603. **163.** 2 z.+18 z. violet .. 1·40 4·00

164. Sagittarius. **165.** Chainbreaker.

1948. Air.

604. **164.** 15 z. violet .. .. 2·50 30
605. 25 z. blue .. .. 1·40 15
606. 30 z. brown .. .. 1·40 45
607. 50 z. green .. .. 3·00 50
608. 75 z. black .. .. 3·00 65
609. 100 z. orange .. .. 3·25 70

1948. Revolution Centenaries.

610. **165.** 15 z. brown 35 10
611. – 30 z. brown .. .. 1·25 30
612. – 35 z. green .. .. 3·25 50
613. – 60 z. red .. .. 1·60 55

PORTRAITS—HORIZ. 30 z. Generals H. Dembinski and J. Bem. 35 z. S. Worcell, P. Sciegienny and E. Dembowski. 60 z. F. Engels and K. Marx

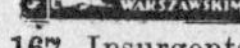

167. Insurgents. **168.** Wheel and Streamers.

1948. 5th Anniv. of Warsaw Ghetto Revolt.

614. **167** 15 z. black .. .. 2·40 3·25

1948. Warsaw—Prague Cycle Race.

615. **168.** 15 z. red and blue .. 3·25 1·25

169. Cycle Race. **170.** "Oliwa" under Construction.

1948. Seventh Circuit of Poland Cycle Race.

616. **169.** 3 z. black .. .. 2·00 2·75
617. 6 z. brown .. .. 2·00 3·25
618. 15 z. green .. .. 3·00 5·00

1948. Merchant Marine.

619. **170.** 6 z. violet .. .. 1·90 1·40
620. – 15 z. red .. .. 2·50 2·25
621. – 35 z. grey .. .. 3·50 3·50

DESIGNS—HORIZ. 15 z. Freighter at wharf. 35 z. "General M. Zaruski" (cadet ketch).

173. Firework Display. **174.** "Youth".

1948. Wroclaw Exn.

622. **173.** 6 z. blue 65 30
623. 15 z. red 65 20
624. 18 z. red .. .. 1·10 40
625. 35 z. brown .. .. 1·10 40

1948. Int. Youth Conf., Warsaw.

626. **174.** 15 z. blue 50 25

175. Roadway, St. Anne's Church and Palace. **176.** Torun Ramparts and Mail Coach.

1948. Warsaw Reconstruction Fund.

627. **175.** 15 z.+5 z. green .. 25 30

1948. Philatelic Congress, Torun.

628. **176.** 15 z. brown .. .. 1·40 65

177. Steam Locomotive, Clock and Winged Wheel. **178.** President Bierut.

1948. European Railway Conf.

629. **177.** 18 z. blue .. .. 7·00 17·00

1948.

629a. **178.** 2 z. orange 10 10
629b. 3 z. green 10 10
630. 5 z. brown 10 10
631. 6 z. black 90 10
631a. 10 z. violet 15 10
632. 15 z. red 50 10
633. 18 z. green 70 10
634. 30 z. blue .. .. 1·25 20
635. 35 z. purple .. .. 2·75 40

179. Workers and Flag.

1948. Workers' Class Unity Congress.

(a) Dated "8 XII 1948".

636. **179.** 5 z. red .. .. 1·00 60
637. – 15 z. violet .. .. 1·00 60
638. – 25 z. brown .. .. 1·00 60

(b) Dated "XII 1948".

639. **179.** 5 z. plum .. .. 2·25 1·60
640. – 15 z. blue .. .. 2·25 1·60
641. – 25 z. green .. .. 2·25 1·60

DESIGNS: 15 z. Flags and portraits of Engels, Marx, Lenin and Stalin. 25 z. Workers marching and portrait of L. Warynski.

180. Baby. **180a.** Pres. Franklin D Roosevelt.

1948. Anti-tuberculosis Fund. Portraits of babies as T **180.**

642. **180.** 3 z.+2 z. green .. 4·00 5·00
643. – 5 z.+5 z. brown .. 4·00 5·00
644. – 6 z.+4 z. purple .. 3·25 5·00
645. – 15 z.+10 z. red .. 2·00 5·00

1948. Air. Honouring Presidents Roosevelt, Pulaski and Kociuszko.

645a. **180a.** 80 z. violet .. 27·00 27·00
645b. – 100 z. purple (Pulaski) 28·00 28·00
645c. – 120 z. blue (Kosciusko) 28·00 28·00

181. Workers.

1949. Trades' Union Congress, Warsaw.

646. **181.** 3 z. red .. .. 1·10 1·10
647. – 5 z. blue .. .. 1·10 1·10
648. – 15 z. green .. .. 1·60 1·60

DESIGNS: 5 z. inscr. "PRACA" (Labour), Labourer and tractor. 15 z. inscr. "POKOJ" (Peace), Three labourers.

182. Banks of R. Vistula. **183.** Pres. Bierut.

1949. 5th Anniv. of National Liberation Committee.
649 182 10 z. black .. .. 2·40 1·60
650 183 15 z. mauve .. .. 2·40 1·60
651 – 35 z. blue .. .. 2·40 1·60
DESIGN—VERT. 35 z. Radio station, Raszyn.

184. Mail-coach and Map. **185.** Worker and Tractor.

1949. 75th Anniv. of U.P.U.
652. **184.** 6 z. violet .. .. 1·00 1·40
653. – 30 z. blue (liner) .. 1·75 1·60
654. – 80 z. green ('Plane) .. 4·75 4·75

1949. Congress of Peasant Movement.
655. **185.** 5 z. red .. .. 1·10 20
656. 10 z. red 20 10
657. 15 z. green 20 10
658. 35 z. brown .. .. 1·00 1·00

186. Frederic Chopin. **187.** Mickiewicz and Pushkin. **188.** Postman.

1949. National Celebrities.
659. – 10 z. purple .. .. 2·75 2·40
660. **186.** 15 z. red .. .. 2·75 2·40
661. – 35 z. blue .. .. 2·75 2·40
PORTRAITS: 10 z. Adam Mickiewicz. 35 z. Julius Slowacki.

1949. Polish-Russian Friendship Month.
662. **187.** 15 z. violet .. .. 4·00 4·00

1950. 3rd Congress of Postal Workers.
663 188 15 z. purple .. .. 2·00 2·75

189. Mechanic, Hanger and Aeroplane. **190.** President Bierut. **195a.**

1950. Air.
664. **189.** 500 z. lake .. .. 5·00 6·75

1950. (a) With frame.
665. **190.** 15 z. red 50 10

(b) Without frame. Values in "zloty".
673. **195a.** 5 z. green 10 10
674. 10 z. red 10 10
675. 15 z. blue .. .. 1·10 10
676. 20 z. violet 30 10
677. 25 z. brown 30 10
678. 30 z. red 45 10
679. 40 z. brown 65 10
680. 50 z. olive .. .. 1·60 10
For values in "groszy" see Nos. 687/94.

191. J. Marchlewski. **192.** Workers.

1950. 25th Death Anniv. of Julian Marchlewski (patriot).
666. **191.** 15 z. grey 65 40

1950. Reconstruction of Warsaw.
667 192 5 z. brown 10 10
See also No. 695.

193. Worker and Flag. **194.** Statue.

1950. 60th Anniv. of May Day Manifesto.
668. **193.** 10 z. mauve .. .. 2·00 30
669. – 15 z. olive .. .. 2·00 15
DESIGN—VERT. 15 z. Three workers and flag.

1950. 23rd International Fair, Poznan.
670. **194.** 15 z. brown 25 15

195. Dove and Globe. **196.** Industrial and Agricultural Workers.

1950. Int. Peace Conf.
671. **195.** 10 z. green .. .. 1·00 15
672. 15 z. brown 30 10

1950. Six Year Reconstruction Plan.
681a 196 15 zloty blue 15 10
See also Nos. 696/e.

197. Hibner, Kniewski, Rutkowski. **198.** Worker and Dove.

1950. 25th Anniv. of Revolutionaries' Execution.
682 197 15 z. grey .. .. 2·75 65

1950. 1st Polish Peace Congress.
683. **198.** 15 z. green 65 35

REVALUATION SURCHARGES. Following a revaluation of the Polish currency, a large number of definitive and commemorative stamps were locally overprinted "Groszy" or "gr". There are 37 known types of overprint and various colours of overprint. We do not list them as they had only local use, but the following is a list of the stamps which were duly authorised for overprinting:—Nos. 579/94, 596/615 and 619/58. Overprints on other stamps were not authorised.

Currency Revalued: 100 old zlotys = 1 new zloty.

199. Dove (after Picasso).

1950. 2nd World Peace Congress, Warsaw.
684. **199.** 40 g. blue .. .. 2·00 35
685a. 45 g. red 25 10

200. General Bem and Battle of Piski.

1950. Death Centenary of General Bem.
686 200 45 g. blue .. .. 2·75 2·00

1950. As T **195a.** Values in "groszy".
687. **195a.** 5 g. violet 10 10
688. 10 g. green 10 10
689. 15 g. olive 10 10
690. 25 g. red 15 10
691. 30 g. red 15 10
692. 40 g. orange 20 10
693. 45 g. blue .. .. 1·00 20
694. 75 g. brown 60 10

1950. As No. 667 but value in "groszy"
695 192 15 g. green 10 10

1950. As No. 681 but values in "groszy" or "zlotys".
696 196 45 g. blue 15 10
696b 75 g. brown 20 10
696d 1 z. 15 green 50 15
696e 1 z. 20 red 35 15

201. Woman and Doves. **202.** Battle Scene and J. Dabrowski.

1951. Women's League Congress.
697. **201.** 45 g. red 35 20

1951. 80th Anniv. of Paris Commune.
698. **202.** 45 g. green 30 10

1951. Surch. **45 gr.**
699. **199.** 45 g. on 15 z. red .. 60 20

204. Worker with Flag. **205.** Smelting Works.

1951. Labour Day.
700. **204.** 45 g. red 30 10

1951.
701 205 40 g. blue 15 10
702 45 g. black 15 10
702a 60 g. brown 20 10
702c 90 g. lake 85 10

206. Pioneer and Badge. **207.** St. Staszic.

1951. Int. Children's Day. Insc. "I-VI-51".
703. **206.** 30 g. olive .. .. 1·00 60
704. – 45 g. blue (Boy, girl and map) .. .. 6·75 60

1951. 1st Polish Scientific Congress. Inscr. "KONGRES NAUKI POLSKIEJ".
705. **207.** 25 g. red .. .. 4·00 2·50
706. – 40 g. blue 50 15
707. – 45 g. violet .. .. 9·25 1·50
708. – 60 g. green 50 15
709. – 1 z. 15 purple 80 45
710. – 1 z. 20 grey .. .. 1·50 15
DESIGNS—As Type **207**: 40 g. Marie Curie. 60 g. M. Nencki. 1 z. 15, Copernicus. 1 z. 20, Dove and book. HORIZ. (36×21 mm.): 45 g. Z. Wroblewski and Olszewski.

209. F. Dzerzhinsky. **210.** Pres. Bierut, Industry and Agriculture.

1951. 25th Death Anniv. of Dzerzhinsky (Russian politician).
711. **209.** 45 g. brown 20 10

1951. 7th Anniv. of People's Republic.
712. **210.** 45 g. red 45 15
713. 60 g. green .. .. 20·00 6·75
714. 90 g. blue .. .. 2·75 75

211. Young People and Globe. **213.** Sports Badge.

1951. 3rd World Youth Festival, Berlin.
715. **211.** 40 g. blue .. .. 1·10 15

1951. Surch. **45 gr.**
716. **195a.** 45 g. on 35 z. orange 20 10

1951. Spartacist Games.
717. **213.** 45 g. green .. .. 1·50 40

214. Stalin. **215.** Chopin and Moniuszko.

1951. Polish-Soviet Friendship.
718. **214.** 45 g. red 15 10
719. 90 g. black 35 20

1951. Polish Musical Festival.
720. **215.** 45 g. black 40 10
721. 90 g. red .. .. 1·50 50

216. Mining Machinery. **217.** Building Modern Flats.

1951. Six Year Plan (Mining).
722. **216.** 90 g. brown 25 10
723. 1 z. 20 blue 30 10
724. 1 z. 20+15 g. orange 25 15

1951. Six Year Plan (Reconstruction).
725. **217.** 30 g. green 10 10
726. 30 g.+15 g. red .. 10 10
727. 1 z. 15 purple 25 10

218. Installing Electric Cables. **219.** M. Nowotko. **220.** Women and Banner.

1951. Six Year Plan (Electrification).
728. **218.** 30 g. black 10 10
729. 45 g. red 15 10
730. 45 g.+15 g. brown .. 1·10 10

1952. 10th Anniv. of Polish Workers' Coalition.
731. **219.** 45 g.+15 g. lake .. 15 10
732. – 90 g. brown 30 15
733. – 1 z. 15 orange 65 15
PORTRAITS: 90 g. P. Finder. 1 z. 15, M. Fornalska.

1952. Int. Women's Day.
734. **220.** 45 g.+15 g. brown .. 30 10
735. 1 z. 20 red 65 20

221. Gen. Swierczewski. **222.** Aeroplane over Farm.

1952. 5th Death Anniv. of Gen. Swierczewski.
736. **221.** 45 g.+15 g. brown .. 30 10
737. 90 g. blue 40 25

1952. Air. Aeroplanes and views.
738 – 55 g. blue (Tug and freighters) 40 25
739 222 90 g. green 55 35
740 – 1 z. 40 pur (Warsaw) 80 35
741 – 5 z. black (Steelworks) 2·40 45

223. President Bierut. **224.** Cyclists and City Arms. **225.** Workers and Banner.

1952. Pres. Bierut's 60th Birthday.
742. **223.** 45 g.+15 g. red .. 30 25
743. 90 g. green .. .. 1·25 85
744. 1 z. 20+15 g. blue .. 70 25

1952. 5th Warsaw-Berlin-Prague Peace Cycle Race.
745. **224.** 40 g. blue .. .. 1·75 90

1952. Labour Day.
746. **225.** 45 g.+15 g. red .. 15 10
747. 75 g. green 85 60

226. J. I. Kraszewski. **227.** Maria Konopnicka.

1952. 140th Birth Anniv of Jozef Ignacy Kraszewski (writer).
748 226 25 g. purple 65 25

1952. 110th Birth Anniv. of Maria Konopnicka (poet).
749. **227.** 30 g.+15 g. green .. 65 15
750. 1 z. 15 brown .. 85 65

228. H. Kollataj. 229. Leonardo da Vinci. 231. N. V. Gogol.

230. President Bierut and Children.

1952. 140th Death Anniv of Hugo Kollataj (educationist and politician).
751. 228. 45 g.+15 g. brown .. 15 10
752. 1 z. green 25 15

1952. 500th Birth Anniv of Leonardo da Vinci (artist).
753. 229. 30 g.+15 g. blue .. 75 35

1952. Int. Children's Day.
754. 230. 45 g.+15 g. blue .. 2·75 65

1952. Death Centenary of Nikolai Gogol (Russian writer).
755 231 25 g. green .. .. 1·00 65

232. Cement Works. 233. Swimmers.

1952. Construction of Concrete Works, Wierzbica.
756. 232. 3 z. black .. .. 1·60 35
757. 10 z. red .. .. 1·40 30

1952. Sports Day.
758. 233. 30 g.+15 g. blue .. 5·00 1·00
759. – 45 g.+15 g. violet .. 1·50 15
760. – 1 z. 15 green .. .. 1·00 1·40
761. – 1 z. 20 red 75 85
Designs: 45 g. Footballers. 1 z. 15, Runners. 1 z. 20, Highjumper.

234. Yachts.

1952. Shipbuilders' Day.
762. 234. 30 g.+15 g. green .. 3·00 85
763. – 45 g.+15 g. blue .. 75 20
764. – 90 g. plum 75 75
Designs—vert. 45 g. Full-rigged cadet ship "Dar Pomorza". 90 g. Shipbuilding worker.

235. Young Workers. 236. " New Constitution".

1952. Youth Festival, Warsaw.
765. 235. 30 g.+15 g. green .. 35 25
766. – 45 g.+15 g. red .. 60 15
767. – 90 g. brown 35 30
Designs—horiz. 45 g. Girl and boy students. 90 g. Boy bugler.

1952. Adoption of New Constitution.
768. 236. 45 g.+15 g. grn. & brn. 1·40 20
769. 3 z. violet and brown 40 50

237. L. Warynski. 238. Jaworzno Power Station.

1952. 70th Anniv. of Party "Proletariat".
770. 237. 30 g.+15 g. red .. 50 15
771. 45 g.+15 g. brown 50 15

1952. Electricity Power Station, Jaworzno.
772. 238. 45 g.+15 g. red .. 85 10
773. 1 z. black 60 60
774. 1 z. 50 green .. 60 20

239. Frydman.

240. Pilot and Glider.

1952. Pieniny Mountain Resorts.
775. 239. 45 g.+15 g. purple .. 25 10
776. – 60 g. green (Grywald) 65 30
777. – 1 z. red (Niedzica) .. 1·00 10

1952. Aviation Day.
778. 240. 30 g.+15 g. green .. 1·40 20
779. – 45 g.+15 g. red .. 2·25 70
780. – 90 g. blue 40 30
Designs: 45 g. Pilot and aeroplane. 90 g. Parachutists descending.

241. Avicenna. 242. Victor Hugo. 243. Shipbuilding.

1952. Birth Millenary of Avicenna (Arab physician).
781. 241. 75 g. red 30 15

1952. 150th Birth Anniv. of Victor Hugo (French author).
782. 242. 90 g. brown 30 15

1952. Gdansk Shipyards.
783. 243. 5 g. green 15 10
784. 15 g. red 15 10

244. H. Sienkiewicz (author). 245. Assault on Winter Palace, Petrograd.

1952.
785. 244. 45 g.+15 g. brown .. 25 10

1952. 35th Anniv. of Russian Revolution. Perf. or imperf.
786. 245. 45 g.+15 g. red .. 1·00 20
787. 60 g. brown 55 40

246. Lenin. 247. Miner. 248. H. Wieniawski (violinist).

1952. Polish-Soviet Friendship Month.
788 246 30 g.+15 g. purple .. 30 15
789 45 g.+15 g. brown .. 85 25

1952. Miners' Day.
790. 247. 45 g.+15 g. black .. 20 10
791. 1 z. 20+15 g. brown.. 70 30

1952. 2nd Wieniawski Int. Violin Competition.
792. 248. 30 g.+15 g. green .. 65 70
793. 45 g.+15 g. violet .. 3·25 50

249. Car Factory, Zeran. 250. Dove of Peace.

1952.
800. – 30 g.+15 g. blue .. 20 10
794. 249. 45 g.+15 g. green .. 15 10
801. – 60 g.+20 g. purple .. 20 10
795. 249. 1 z. 15 brown .. 70 25
Design: 30 g., 60 g. Lorry factory, Lublin.

1952. Peace Congress, Vienna.
796. 250. 30 g. green 50 20
797. 60 g. blue .. .. 1·00 30

MINIMUM PRICE

The minimum price quoted is 5p which represents a handling charge rather than a basis for valuing common stamps. For further notes about prices see introductory pages.

251. Soldier and Flag. 253. Karl Marx. 254. Globe and Flag.

1952. 10th Anniv. of Battle of Stalingrad.
798. 251. 60 g. red and green .. 5·75 2·00
799. 80 g. red and grey .. 75 40

1953. 70th Death Anniv. of Marx.
802. 253. 60 g. blue .. .. 22·00 11·50
803. 80 g. brown .. .. 1·25 40

1953. Labour Day.
804. 254. 60 g. red .. .. 6·75 3·25
805. 80 g. red 40 10

255. Cyclists and Arms of Warsaw. 256. Boxer.

1953. 6th Int. Peace Cycle Race.
806. – 80 g. green .. .. 1·00 25
807. 255. 80 g. brown .. .. 1·00 25
808. – 80 g. red .. .. 15·00 10·00
Designs: As Type 255. but Arms of Berlin (No. 806) or Prague (No. 808).

1953. European Boxing Championship, Warsaw. Inscr. " 17–24. V. 1953".
809. 256. 40 g. lake 85 15
810. 80 g. orange .. .. 11·50 5·00
811. – 95 g. purple 85 30
Design: 95 g. Boxers in ring.

257. Copernicus (after Matejko). 258. "Dalmor" (trawler).

1953. 480th Birth Anniv. of Copernicus (astronomer).
812. 257. 20 g. brown .. .. 2·50 65
813. – 80 g. blue .. .. 17·00 15·00
Design—vert. 80 g. Copernicus and diagram.

1953. Merchant Navy Day.
814 258 80 g. green .. .. 2·00 10
815 – 1 z. 35 blue .. .. 1·50 3·00
Design: 1 z. 35, "Czech" (freighter).

259. Warsaw Market-place. 260. Students' Badge. 261. Nurse Feeding Baby.

1953. Polish National Day.
816. 259. 20 g. lake 15 10
817. 2 z. 35 blue .. .. 5·00 3·25

1953. 3rd World Students' Congress, Warsaw. Inscr. " III SWIATOWY KONGRES STUDENTOW". (a) Postage. Perf.
818. – 40 g. brown 15 10
819. 260. 1 z. 35 green 50 10
820. – 1 z. 50 blue .. .. 5·00 4·25

(b) Air. Imperf.
821. 260. 55 g. plum .. .. 1·50 40
822. 75 g. red .. .. 2·75 2·00
Designs—horiz. 40 g. Students and globe. vert. 1 z. 50, Woman and dove.

1953. Social Health Service.
823. 261. 80 g. red .. .. 10·00 6·00
824. – 1 z. 75 green 25 15
Design: 1 z. 75, Nurse, mother and baby.

262. M. Kalinowski. 263. J. Kochanowski.

1953. 10th Anniv. of Polish People's Army.
825. 262. 45 g. brown .. .. 5·00 3·25
826. – 80 g. red 50 10
827. – 1 g. 75 olive 50 10
Designs—horiz. 80 g. Russian and Polish soldiers. vert. 1 z. 75, R. Pazinski.

1953. " Renaissance" Commem. Inscr. " ROK ODRODZENIA ".
828. 263. 20 g. brown 10 10
829. – 80 g. purple 30 10
830. – 1 z. 35 blue .. .. 2·75 1·40
Designs—horiz. 80 g. Wawel Castle. vert. 1 z. 35, M. Bej.

264. Palace of Science and Culture. 265. Dunajec Canyon Pieniny Mts.

1953. Reconstruction of Warsaw. Inscr. " WARSZAWA ".
831. 264. 80 g. red .. .. 11·50 1·50
832. – 1 z. 75 blue .. .. 1·60 25
833. – 2 z. purple .. .. 5·00 3·25
Designs: 1 z. 75, Constitution Square. 2 z. Old City Market, Warsaw.

1953. Tourist Series.
834. – 20 g. lake and blue .. 15 10
835. – 80 g. lilac and green .. 3·25 1·75
836. 265. 1 z. 75 green & brown 85 15
837. – 2 z. black and red .. 1·00 10
Designs—horiz. 20 g. Krynica Spa. 2 z. Clechocinek Spa. vert. 80 g. Morskie Oko Lake, Tatra Mts.

266. Skiing. 267. Infants playing.

1953. Winter Sports.
838. – 80 g. blue .. .. 1·50 35
839. 266. 95 g. green .. .. 1·25 25
840. – 2 z. 85 red .. .. 4·00 2·25
Designs—vert. 80 g. Ice-skating. 2 z. 85, Ice-hockey.

1953. Children's Education.
841. 267. 10 g. violet 15 10
842. – 80 g. red 75 25
843. – 1 z. 50 green .. .. 7·50 3·00
Designs: 80 g. Girls and school. 1 z. 50, Two Schoolgirls writing.

268. Electric Locomotive. 269. Mill Girl.

1954. Electrification of Railways.
844 – 60 g. blue .. .. 8·25 5·00
845 268 80 g. brown 65 25
Design: 60 g. Electric commuter train.

1954. International Women's Day.
846. 269. 20 g. green .. .. 2·75 2·00
847. – 40 g. blue 50 10
848. – 80 g. brown 50 10
Designs: 40 g. Postwoman. 80 g. Woman driving tractor.

270. Flags and Mayflowers. 271. " Warsaw—Berlin—Prague".

272. Symbols of Labour. 273. Glider and Flags.

1954. Labour Day.
849. 270. 40 g. brown 55 25
850. 60 g. blue 55 15
851. 80 g. red 60 15

1954. 7th Int. Peace Cycle Race. Inscr. "2–17 MAJ 1954".
852. 271. 80 g. brown 75 10
853. – 80 g. blue (Dove and cycle wheel) .. 1·00 25

1954. 3rd Trades' Union Congress, Warsaw.
854. 272. 25 g. blue .. .. 1·40 65
855. 80 g. lake 20 10

1954. International Gliding Competition.
856 – 45 g. green 80 10
857 273 60 g. violet .. .. 2·00 85
858 60 g. brown .. .. 1·90 10
859a – 1 z. 35 blue .. .. 2·50 10
Designs: 45 g. Glider and clouds in frame. 1 z. 35, Glider and sky.

274. Aeroplane over Paczkow. **275.** Fencing.

1954. Air. Inscr. "POCZTA LOTNICZA".
860. **274.** 60 g. green 20 10
861. – 80 g. red 25 15
862. – 1 z. 15 black .. .. 1·90 1·50
863. – 1 z. 50 red 60 10
864. – 1 z. 55 blue 60 10
865. – 1 z. 95 brown .. .. 1·10 15
Designs: Aeroplane over—80 g. Kazimierz Dolny. 1 z. 15, Cracow. 1 z. 50, Wroclaw. 1 z. 55, Warsaw. 1 z. 95, Lublin.

1954. 2nd Spartacist Games (1st issue). Inscr. "II OGOLNOPOLSKA SPARTAKIADA".
866. **275.** 25 g. purple .. .. 1·50 40
867. – 60 g. turquoise .. .. 1·50 20
868. – 1 z. blue .. .. 2·25 85
Designs—vert. 60 g. Gymnastics. horiz. 1 z. Running.

276. Spartacist Games Badge. **277.** Battlefield.

1954. 2nd Spartacist Games (2nd issue).
869. **276.** 60 g. brown .. .. 1·25 25
870. 1 z. 55 grey .. .. 1·25 65

1954. 10th Anniv. of Liberation and Battle of Studzianki.
871. **277.** 60 g. green .. .. 2·00 45
872. – 1 z. blue .. .. 6·25 3·25
Design—horiz. 1 z. Soldier, airman and tank.

278. Steel Works.

1954. 10th Anniv of Second Republic.
873. – 10 g. sepia and brown 60 10
874. – 20 g. green and red .. 35 10
876. **278.** 25 g. black and buff .. 90 10
877. – 40 g. brown and yellow 50 10
878. – 45 g. purple and mauve 50 10
880. – 60 g. purple and green 55 10
881. – 1 z. 15 blk. & turquoise 1·60 20
882. – 1 z. 40 brown & orange 11·50 3·25
883. – 1 z. 55 blue and indigo 3·25 55
884. – 2 z. 10 blue and cobalt 3·25 1·50
Designs: 10 g. Coal mine. 20 g. Soldier and flag. 40g. Worker on holiday. 45 g. House-builders. 60 g. Tractor and binder. 1 z. 15, Lublin Castle. 1 z. 40, Customers in bookshop. 1 z. 55, "Soldek" (freighter) alongside wharf. 2 z. 10, Battle of Lenino.

279. Signal. **280.** Picking Apples.

1954. Railway Workers' Day.
885 279 40 g. blue .. .. 4·00 45
886 – 60 g. black .. .. 2·00 35
Design: 60 g. Night train.

1954. Polish–Russian Friendship.
887 280 40 g. violet .. .. 1·90 1·00
888 60 g. black 65 25

281. Elblag. **282.** Chopin and Grand Piano.

1954. 500th Anniv. of Return of Pomerania to Poland.
889. **281.** 20 g. red on blue .. 1·50 60
890. – 45 g. brown on yellow 15 10
891. – 60 g. green on yellow .. 20 10
892. – 1 z. 40 blue on pink .. 50 15
893. – 1 z. 55 brown on cream 75 10
Views: 45 g. Gdansk. 60 g. Torun. 1 z. 40, Malbork. 1 z. 55, Olsztyn.

1954. 5th Int. Chopin Piano Competition, Warsaw (1st issue).
894. **282.** 45 g. brown 45 10
895. 60 g. green 60 10
896. 1 z. blue .. .. 2·75 1·25
See also Nos. 906/7.

283. Battle Scene.

1954. 160th Anniv. of Kosciuszko's Insurrection.
897. **283.** 40 g. olive 55 15
898. – 60 g. brown 75 10
899. – 1 z. 40 black .. .. 1·75 1·10
Designs: 60 g. Kosciuszko on horseback, with insurgents. 1 z. 40, Street battle.

284. European Bison. **285.** "The Liberator".

1954. Polish Forest Animals.
900. **284.** 45 g. brown and green 55 15
901. – 60 g. brown and green 55 15
902. – 1 z. 90 brown and blue 1·00 15
903. – 3 z. brown & turquoise 1·50 60
Animals: 60 g. Elk. 1 z. 90, Chamois. 3 z. Eurasian beaver.

1955. 10th Anniv. of Liberation of Warsaw.
904. **285.** 40 g. brown .. .. 2·00 25
905. – 60 g. blue .. .. 2·00 1·00
Design: 60 g. "Spirit of Poland".

286. Bust of Chopin (after L. Isler). **287.** Mickiewicz Monument.

1955. 5th Int. Chopin Piano Competition (2nd issue).
906. **286.** 40 g. brown 45 10
907. 60 g. blue .. .. 1·25 65

1955. Warsaw Monuments
908. – 5 g. green on yellow .. 10 10
909. – 10 g. purple on yellow 10 10
910. – 15 g. brown on blue .. 10 10
911. – 20 g. blue on pink .. 10 10
912. – 40 g. violet on violet .. 30 10
913. – 45 g. brown on buff .. 1·00 15
914. **287.** 60 g. blue on stone .. 10 10
915. – 1 z. 55 turquoise on grey 3·25 65
Monuments: 5 g. "Siren". 10 g. Dzerzhinski Statue. 15 g. King Sigismund III Statue. 20 g. "Brotherhood in Arms". 40 g. Copernicus. 45 g. Marie Curie Statue. 1 z. 55, Kilinski Statue.

288. Flags and Tower. **289.**

1955. 10th Anniv. of Russo-Polish Treaty of Friendship.
916. **288.** 40 g. red 20 10
917. 40 g. brown .. .. 1·40 65
918. – 60 g. brown 20 10
919. – 60 g. turquoise 20 10
Design: 60 g. "Statue of Friendship".

1955. 8th Int. Peace Cycle Race.
920 289 40 g. brown 55 20
921 – 60 g. blue 30 10
Design: 60 g. "VIII" and doves.

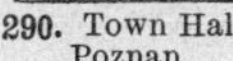

290. Town Hall, Poznan. **291.** Festival Emblem.

1955. 24th Int. Fair, Poznan.
922. **290.** 40 g. blue 25 10
923. 60 g. red 15 10

1955. Cracow Festival.
924. **291.** 20 g. multicoloured .. 50 20
925. – 40 g. multicoloured .. 25 15
926. **291.** 60 g. multicoloured .. 50 25
No. 925 is as T **291** but horiz. and inscr. "FESTIWAL SZTUKI", etc.

292 "Peace". **293.** Motor Cyclists. **294.**

1955. 5th Int. Youth Festival, Warsaw.
927 – 25 g. brn, pink & yell 20 10
928 – 40 g. grey and blue .. 20 10
929 – 45 g. red, mauve & yell 30 10
930 **292** 60 g. ultramarine & bl 30 10
931 – 60 g. black and orange 30 10
932 **292** 1 z. purple and blue .. 65 65
Designs: 25, 45 g. Pansies and dove. 40, 60 g. (No. 931) Dove and tower.

1955. 13th International Tatra Mountains Motor Cycle Race.
933 **293** 40 g. brown 40 10
934 60 g. green 20 10

1955. Polish National Day.
935. **294.** 60 g. blue 15 10
936. 60 g. grey 15 10
937. 75 g. green 50 20
938. 75 g. brown 50 20

295. Athletes. **296.** Szczecin. **297.** Peasants and Flag.

1955. 2nd Int. Games. Imperf. or perf.
939. **295.** 20 g. brown 15 10
940. – 40 g. purple 20 10
941. – 60 g. blue 35 10
942. – 1 z. red 70 10
943. – 1 z. 35 lilac 75 10
944. – 1 z. 55 green .. 1·75 65
Designs—vert. 40 g. Throwing the hammer. 1 z. Net-ball. 1 z. 35, Sculling. 1 z. 55, Swimming. horiz. 60 g. Stadium.

1955. 10th Anniv. of Return of Western Territories.
945. **296.** 25 g. green 15 10
946. – 40 g. red (Wroclaw) .. 25 10
947. – 60 g. bl. (Zielona Gora) 40 10
948. – 95 g. black (Opole) .. 1·50 85

1955. 50th Anniv. of 1905 Revolution.
949. **297.** 40 g. brown 25 15
950. 60 g. red 15 10

298. Mickiewicz. **299.** Statue.

1955. Death Cent of Adam Mickiewicz (poet).
951. **298.** 20 g. brown 15 10
952. **299.** 40 g. brown & orange .. 15 10
953. – 60 g. brown and green 25 10
954. – 95 g. black and red .. 1·60 75
Designs—As Type **299**: 60 g. Sculptured head. 95 g. Statue.

300. Teacher and Pupil. **301.** Rook and Hands. **302.** Ice Skates

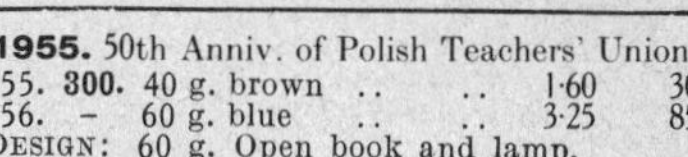

1955. 50th Anniv. of Polish Teachers' Union.
955. **300.** 40 g. brown .. .. 1·60 30
956. – 60 g. blue .. .. 3·25 85
Design: 60 g. Open book and lamp.

1956. 1st World Chess Championship for the Deaf and Dumb, Zakopane.
957 **301** 40 g. red .. .. 2·40 1·00
958 – 60 g. blue .. .. 1·40 10
Design: 60 g. Knight and hands.

1956. 11th World Students' Winter Sports Championship.
959. **302.** 20 g. black and blue 4·25 1·75
960. – 40 g. blue and green .. 1·00 10
961. – 60 g. red and mauve .. 1·00 10
Designs: 40 g. Ice-hockey sticks and puck. 60 g. Skis and ski sticks.

303. Officer and "Kilinski" (freighter). **304.** Racing Cyclist.

1956. Merchant Navy.
962 **303** 5 g. green 15 10
963 – 10 g. red 15 10
964 – 20 g. blue 30 10
965 – 45 g. brown 80 40
966 – 60 g. blue 45 10
Designs: 10 g. Tug and barges. 20 g. "Pokoj" (freighter) in dock. 45 g. Building "Marceli Nowatka" (freighter). 60 g. "Fryderyk Chopin" (freighter) and "Radunia" (trawler).

1956. 9th Int. Peace Cycle Race.
967. **304.** 40 g. blue .. .. 1·25 65
968. 60 g. green 30 10

305. Lodge, Tatra Mountains. **307.** Ghetto Heroes' Monument.

1956. Tourist Propaganda.
969. **305.** 30 g. green 15 10
970. – 40 g. brown 15 10
971. – 60 g. blue .. .. 1·50 70
972. – 1 z. 15 purple 60 10
Designs: 40 g. Compass, rucksack and map. 60 g. Canoe and map. 1 z. 15, Skis and mountains.

1956. No. 829 surch.
973. 10 g. on 80 g. purple .. 50 20
974. 40 g. on 80 g. purple .. 25 10
975. 60 g. on 80 g. purple .. 30 10
976. 1 z. 35 on 80 g. purple .. 1·50 1·10

1956. Warsaw Monuments.
977. **307.** 30 g. black 15 10
978. – 40 g. brown on green 1·40 50
979. – 1 z. 55 purple on pink 55 15
Statues: 40 g. Statue of King Jan III Sobieski. 1 z. 55, Statue of Prince Joseph Poniatowski.

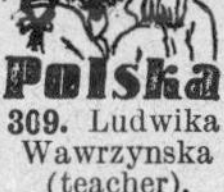

308. "Economic Co-operation". **309.** Ludwika Wawrzynska (teacher).

1956. Russo–Polish Friendship Month.
980. – 40 g. brown and pink 65 20
981. **308.** 60 g. red and bistre .. 25 10
Design: 40 g. Polish and Russian dancers.

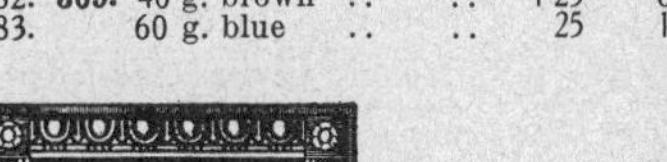

1956. Ludwika Wawrzynska Commem.
982. **309.** 40 g. brown .. .. 1·25 65
983. 60 g. blue 25 10

310. "Lady with a Weasel" (Leonardo da Vinci). **311.** "Apis mellifera" and Hive.

1956. Int. Campaign for Museums.
984. – 40 g. green .. .. 3·00 1·40
985. – 60 g. violet .. .. 1·25 15
986. **310.** 1 z. 55 brown .. .. 2·40 25
DESIGNS: 40 g. Niobe (bust). 60 g. Madonna (Vit Stvosz).

1956. 50th Death Anniv of Jan Dzierzon (agriculturalist)
987. **311.** 40 g. brown on yellow 1·40 30
988. – 60 g. brown on yellow 25 10
DESIGN: 60 g. Dr. J. Dzeirzon.

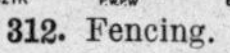

312. Fencing. **313.** 15th-century Postman.

1956. Olympic Games. Inscr. "MELBOURNE 1956".
989. **312.** 10 g. brown and grey .. 15 10
990. – 20 g. lilac and brown .. 20 10
991. – 25 g. black and blue .. 60 15
992. – 40 g. brown and green 30 10
993. – 60 g. brown and red .. 50 10
994. – 1 z. 55 brown & violet 3·00 1·00
995. – 1 z. 55 brown & orange 1·00 25
DESIGNS: No. 990, Boxing. No. 991, Rowing. No. 992, Steeplechase. No. 993, Javelin throwing. No. 994, Gymnastics. No. 995, Long jumping (inscr. "6,35 m").

1956. Re-opening of Postal Museum, Wroclaw.
996. **313.** 60 g. black on blue .. 2·75 2·00

314. Snow Crystals and Skier of 1907. **315.** Apple Tree and Globe.

1957. 50 Years of Skiing in Poland.
997. **314.** 40 g. blue 40 10
998. – 60 g. green 40 10
999. – 1 z. purple 55 15
DESIGNS (with snow crystals)—VERT. 60 g. Skier jumping. HORIZ. 1 z. Skier standing.

1957. U.N.O. Commem.
1000. **315.** 5 g. red & turquoise 25 15
1001. – 15 g. blue and grey .. 40 15
1002. – 40 g. green and grey .. 85 60
DESIGNS—VERT. 15 g. U.N.O. emblem. 40 g. U.N.O. Headquarters, New York.

316. Skier. **317.** Winged Letter.

1957. 12th Death Annivs. of Bronislaw Czech and Hanna Marusarzowna (skiers).
1003. **316.** 60 g. brown .. .. 1·10 50
1004. 60 g. blue 85 15

1957. Air. 7th Polish National Philatelic Exn., Warsaw.
1005. **317.** 4 z.+2 z. blue .. 4·25 4·25

318. Foil, Sword and Sabre on Map. **319.** Dr. S. Petrycy (philosopher).

1957. World Youth Fencing Championships, Warsaw.
1006. **318.** 40 g. purple 55 15
1007. – 60 g. red 20 10
1008. – 60 g. blue 20 10
DESIGNS: Nos. 1007/8 are arranged in se-tenant pairs in the sheet and together show two fencers duelling.

1957. Polish Doctors.
1009. **319.** 10 g. brown and blue 10 10
1010. – 20 g. lake and green .. 10 10
1011. – 40 g. black and red .. 10 10
1012. – 60 g. purple and blue 85 20
1013. – 1 z. blue and yellow .. 20 10
1014. – 1 z. 35 brown & green 15 10
1015. – 2 z. 50 violet and red 35 10
1016. – 3 z. brown and violet 45 10
PORTRAITS: 20 g. Dr. W. Oczko. 40 g. Dr. J. Sniadecki. 60 g. Dr. T. Chalubinski. 1 z. Dr. W. Bieganski. 1 z. 35, Dr. J. Dietl. 2 z. 50, Dr. B. Dybowski. 3 z. Dr. H. Jordan.

320. Cycle Wheel and Flower. **321.** Fair Emblem.

1957. 10th Int. Peace Cycle Race.
1017. **320.** 60 g. blue 40 10
1018. – 1 z. 50 red (Cyclist) .. 60 15

1957. 26th Int. Fair, Poznan.
1019. **321.** 60 g. blue 20 10
1020. 2 z. 50 green 20 10

322. Carline Thistle. **323.** Fireman.

1957. Wild Flowers.
1021. **322.** 60 g. yell., grn. & grey 45 10
1022. – 60 g. green and blue .. 45 10
1023. – 60 g. olive and grey .. 45 10
1024. – 60 g. yell., red & green 65 25
1025. – 60 g. purple & green .. 45 10
FLOWERS—VERT. No. 1022, Sea holly. No. 1023, Edelweiss. No. 1024, Lady's Slipper orchid. No. 1025, Turk's Cap lily.

1957. Int. Fire Brigades Conference, Warsaw. Inscr. "KONGRES C.T.I.F. WARSZAWA 1957".
1026. **323.** 40 g. black and red .. 15 10
1027. – 60 g. green and red .. 15 10
1028. – 2 z. 50 violet and red 60 20
DESIGNS: 60 g. Flames enveloping child. 2 z. 50, Ear of corn in flames.

324. Town Hall, Leipzig. **325.** "The Letter" (after Fragonard).

1957. 4th International Trade Union Congress, Leipzig.
1029. **324.** 60 g. violet 10 10

1957. Stamp Day.
1030. **325.** 2 z. 50 green .. 50 10

326. Red Banner. **327.** Karol Libelt (founder). **328.** H. Wieniawski (violinist).

1957. 40th Anniv. of Russian Revolution.
1031. **326.** 60 g. red and blue .. 10 10
1032. – 2 z. 50 brown & black 25 10
DESIGN: 2 z. 50, Lenin Monument, Poronin.

1957. Cent of Poznan Scientific Society.
1033. **327.** 60 g. red 10 10

1957. 3rd Wieniawski Int. Violin Competition.
1034. **328.** 2 z. 50 blue 50 15

329. Aeroplane over Steel Works. **330a.** J. A. Komensky (Comenius).

1957. Air.
1035. **329.** 90 g. black and pink .. 20 10
1036. – 1 z. 50 brown & salmon 20 10
1037. – 3 z. 40 sepia and buff 65 10
1038. – 3 z. 90 brown & yellow 1·25 55
1039. – 4 z. blue and green .. 65 10
1039a. – 5 z. lake and lavender 80 15
1039b. – 10 z. brown & turquoise 1·25 30
1040. – 15 z. violet and blue .. 2·25 35
1040a. – 20 z. violet & yellow 2·50 80
1040b. – 30 z. olive and buff .. 4·00 90
1040c. – 50 z. blue and drab .. 8·50 1·60
DESIGNS: Aeroplane over: 1 z. 50, Castle Square, Warsaw. 3 s. 40, Old Market, Cracow. 3 z. 90, Szczecin. 4 s. Karconosze Mountains. 5 z. Old Market, Gdansk. 10 z. Liw Castle. 15 z. Lublin. 20 z. Cable railway, Kasprowy Wierch. 30 z. Porabka Dam. 50 z. "Batory" (liner).
For stamp as No. 1039b, but printed in slate-purple only, see No. 1095.

1957. 300th Anniv. of Publication of Komensky's "Opera Didactica Omnia".
1041. **330a.** 2 z. 50 red 40 10

331. A. Strug. **332.** Joseph Conrad and sailing ship "Torrens".

1957. 20th Death Anniv. of Andrzej Strug (writer).
1042. **331.** 2 z. 50 brown .. 25 10

1957. Birth Centenary of Joseph Conrad (Korzeniowski) author.
1043. **332.** 60 g. brown on green 30 10
1044. 2 z. 50 blue on pink 1·10 10

333. Postman of 1558. **334.** Town Hall, Biecz.

1958. 400th Anniv. of Polish Postal Service (1st issue).
1045. **333.** 2 z. 50, purple & blue 25 10
For similar stamps see Nos. 1063/7.

1958. Ancient Polish Town Halls.
1046. **334.** 20 g. green .. 10 10
1047. – 40 g. brown (Wroclaw) 10 10
1048. – 60 g. blue (Tarnow) (horiz.) 10 10
1049. – 2 z. 10 lake (Gdansk) 15 10
1050. – 2 z. 50 vio. (Zamosc) 55 25

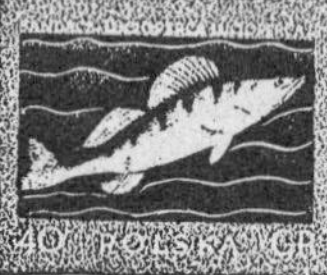

335. Perch. **336.** Warsaw University.

1958. Fishes.
1051. **335.** 40 g. yell., blk. & blue 15 10
1052. – 60 g. bl., indigo & grn. 25 10
1053. – 2 z. 10 multicoloured 55 10
1054. – 2 z. 50 green, black and violet .. 1·60 30
1055. – 6 z. 40 multicoloured 1·10 40
DESIGNS—VERT. 60 g. Salmon. 2 z. 10, Pike. 2 z. 50, Trout. HORIZ. 6 z. 40, Grayling.

1958. 140th Anniv. of Warsaw University.
1056. **336.** 2 z. 50 blue 25 10

337. Fair Emblem. **338.**

1958. 27th Int. Fair, Poznan.
1057. **337.** 2 z. 50 red and black 30 10

1958. 7th Int. Gliding Championships.
1058. **338.** 60 g. black and blue .. 10 10
1059. – 2 z. 50 black and grey 30 10
DESIGN: 2 z. 50, As Type **338** but design in reverse.

INDEX

Countries can be quickly located by referring to the index at the end of this volume.

339. Armed Postman. **340.** Polar Bear on Iceberg.

1958. 19th Anniv. of Defence of Gdansk Post Office.
1060. **339.** 60 g. blue 15 10

1958. I.G.Y. Inscr. as in T **340**.
1061. **340.** 60 g. black 15 10
1062. – 2 z. 50 blue 85 15
DESIGN: 2 z. 50, Sputnik and track of rocket.

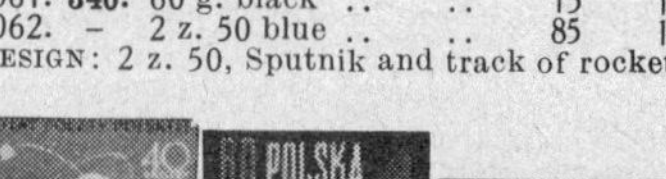

341. Tomb of Prosper Prowano (First Polish Postmaster). **342.** Envelope Quill and Postmark. **343.** Partisans' Cross.

1958. 400th Anniv. of Polish Postal Service (2nd issue).
1063. **341.** 40 g. purple and blue 40 10
1064. – 60 g. black and lilac .. 10 10
1065. – 95 g. violet and yellow 10 10
1066. – 2 z. 10 blue and grey 1·00 25
1067. – 3 z. 40 brown & turquoise 35 20
DESIGNS: 60 g. Mail coach and Church of Our Lady, Cracow. 95 g. Mail coach (rear view). 2 z. 10, 16th-century postman. 3 z. 40, Kogge. Nos. 1064/7 show various forms of modern transport in clear silhouette in the background.

1958. Stamp Day.
1068. **342.** 60 g. grn., red & blk. 50 50

1958. 15th Anniv of Polish People's Army. Polish decorations.
1069. **343.** 40 g. buff, black & grn. 15 10
1070. – 60 g. multicoloured .. 15 10
1071. – 2 z. 50 multicoloured 55 15
DESIGNS: 60 g. Virtuti Military Cross. 2 z. 50, Grunwald Cross.

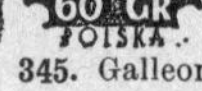

344. "Mail Coach in the Kielce District" (after painting by A. Kedzierskiego). **345.** Galleon.

1958. Polish Postal Service 400th Anniv Exhibition.
1072 **344** 2 z. 50 black on buff .. 1·40 1·00

1958. 350th Anniv. of Polish Emigration to America.
1073. **345.** 60 g. green 15 10
1074. – 2 z. 50 red (Polish emigrants) 65 15

346. U.N.E.S.C.O. Headquarters, Paris. **347.** S. Wyspianski (dramatist and painter).

1958. Inaug of U.N.E.S.C.O. Headquarters Building, Paris.
1075 **346** 2 z. 50 black and green 60 15

1958. Famous Poles.
1076. **347.** 60 g. violet 10 10
1077. – 2 z. 50 green 60 20
PORTRAIT: 2 z. 50, S. Moniuszko (composer).

348. "Human Rights". **349.** Party Flag. **350.** Yacht.

1958. 10th Anniv. of Declaration of Human Rights.
1078. **348.** 2 z. 50 g. lake & brn. 50 15

1958. 40th Anniv. of Polish Communist Party.
1079. **349.** 60 g. red and purple.. 10 10

1959. Sports.
1080. **350.** 40 g. ultram. & blue.. 35 10
1081. – 60 g. purple & salmon 35 10
1082. – 95 g. purple & green.. 70 10
1083. – 2 z. blue and green .. 35 10
DESIGNS: 60 g. Archer. 95 g. Footballers. 2 z. Horseman.

351. The "Guiding Hand". **352.** "Amanita phalloides".

1959. 3rd Polish United Workers' Party Congress.
1084. **351.** 40 g. blk., brown & red 10 10
1085. – 60 g. multicoloured.. 10 10
1086. – 1 z. 55 multicoloured 50 15
DESIGNS—HORIZ. 60 g. Hammer and ears of corn. VERT. 1 z. 55, Nowa Huta foundry.

1959. Mushrooms.
1087. **352.** 20 g. yell., brn. & grn. 1·60 25
1088. – 30 g. multicoloured.. 30 10
1089. – 40 g. multicoloured.. 65 10
1090. – 60 g. multicoloured.. 65 10
1091. – 1 z. multicoloured .. 1·00 10
1092. – 2 z. 50 brn., grn. & bl. 1·50 30
1093. – 3 z. 40 multicoloured 1·75 35
1094. – 5 z. 60 brown, green and yellow .. 4·50 1·50
MUSHROOMS: 30 g. "Boletus luteus". 40 g. "Boletus edulis". 60 g. "Lactarius deliciosus". 1 z. "Cantharellus cibarius". 2 z. 50, "Psalliota compestris". 3 z. 40, "Amanita muscaria". 5 z. 60, "Boletus scaber".

1959. Air. 65 Years of Philately in Poland and 6th Polish Philatelic Assn. Congress Warsaw. As No. 1039b but in one colour only.
1095. 10 z. purple .. .. 2·75 2·75

353. "Storks" (after Chelmonski). **354.** Miner.

1959. Polish Paintings.
1096. **353.** 40 g. green 15 10
1097. – 60 g. purple 30 10
1098. – 1 z. black 30 10
1099. – 1 z. 50 brown .. 80 25
1100. – 6 z. 40 blue .. .. 2·75 1·00
PAINTINGS—VERT. 60 g. "Motherhood" (Wyspianski). 1 z. "Madame de Romanet" (Rodakowski). 1 z. 50, "Death" (Malczewski). HORIZ. 6 z. 40, "The Sandmen" (Gierymski).

1959. 3rd Int. Miners' Congress, Katowice.
1101 354 2 z. 50 multicoloured 50 10

355. Sheaf of Wheat ("Agriculture"). **356.** Dr. L. Zamenhof. **357.** "Flowering Pink" (Map of Austria).

1959. 15th Anniv. of People's Republic.
1102. **355.** 40 g. green and black 10 10
1103. – 60 g. red and black.. 10 10
1104. – 1 z. 50 blue and black 20 10
DESIGNS: 60 g. Crane ("Building"). 1 z. 50, Corinthian column, and book ("Culture and Science").

1959. Int. Esperanto Congress, Warsaw and Birth Centenary of Dr. Ludwig Zamenhof (inventor of Esperanto).
1105 **356** 60 g. blk & grn on grn 15 10
1106 – 1 z. 50 green, red and violet on grey .. 1·40 65
DESIGN: 1 z. 50, Esperanto Star and globe.

1959. 7th World Youth Festival, Vienna.
1107. **357.** 60 g. multicoloured 10 10
1108. 2 z. 50 multicoloured 1·00 50

358. **359.** Parliament House, Warsaw.

1959. 30th Anniv. of Polish Airlines "LOT".
1109. **358.** 60 g. blue, vio. & black 15 10

1959. 48th Inter-Parliamentary Union Conf., Warsaw.
1110. **359.** 60 g. green, red & blk. 10 10
1111. 2 z. 50 pur., red & blk. 85 50

1959. Baltic States' International Philatelic Exhibition, Gdansk. No. 890 optd **BALPEX I-GDANSK 1959**.
1112 45 g. brown on lemon .. 65 70

361. Dove and Globe. **362.** Nurse with Bag.

1959. 10th Anniv. of World Peace Movement.
1113. **361.** 60 g. grey and blue.. 15 10

1959. 40th Anniv of Polish Red Cross. Cross in red.
1114. **362.** 40 g. black and green 15 10
1115. – 60 g. brown 15 10
1116. – 2 z. 50 black and red 1·40 60
DESIGNS—VERT. 60 g. Nurse with bottle and bandages. SQUARE (23×23 mm.): 2 z. 50, J. H. Dunant.

363. Emblem of Polish-Chinese Friendship Society. **364.**

1959. Polish-Chinese Friendship.
1117. **363.** 60 g. multicoloured.. 45 20
1118. 2 z. 50 multicoloured 30 10

1959. Stamp Day.
1119. **364.** 60 g. red, grn. & turq. 15 10
1120. 2 z. 50 bl., grn. & red 25 10

365. Sputnik "3".

1959. Cosmic Flights.
1121. **365.** 40 g. black and blue 15 10
1122. – 60 g. black and lake 30 10
1123. – 2 z. 50 blue and green 1·40 65
DESIGNS: 60 g. Rocket "Mieczta" encircling Sun. 2 z. 50, Moon rocket "Lunik 2".

366. Schoolgirl. **367.** Darwin.

1959. "1000 Schools for Polish Millennium". Inscr. as in T **366**.
1124. **366.** 40 g. brown and green 10 10
1125. – 60 g. red, black & blue 10 10
DESIGN: 60 g. Children going to school.

1959. Famous Scientists.
1126. **367.** 20 g. blue 10 10
1127. – 40 g. olive (Mendeleev) 10 10
1128. – 60 g. purple (Einstein) 15 10
1129. – 1 z. 50 brn. (Pasteur) 25 10
1130. – 1 z. 55 grn. (Newton) 55 10
1131. – 2 z. 50 violet (Copernicus) .. 1·40 65

368. Costumes of Rzeszow. **369.**

1959. Provincial Costumes (1st series).
1132. **368.** 20 g. black and green 10 10
1133. **369.** 20 g. black and green 10 10
1134. – 60 g. purple and pink 15 10
1135. – 60 g. purple and pink 15 10
1136. – 1 z. red and blue .. 25 10
1137. – 1 z. red and blue .. 25 10
1138. – 2 z. 50 green and lilac 50 10
1139. – 2 z. 50 green and lilac 50 10
1140. – 5 z. 60 blue & yellow 1·40 50
1141. – 5 z. 60 blue & yellow 1·40 50
DESIGNS—Male and female costumes of: Nos. 1134/5, Kurpie. Nos. 1136/7, Silesia. Nos. 1138/9, Mountain regions. Nos. 1140/1, Szamotuly.
See also Nos. 1150/9.

370. Piano. **371.** Polish 10 k. Stamp of 1860 and Postmark.

1960. 150th Birth Anniv. of Chopin and Chopin Music Competition, Warsaw.
1142. **370.** 60 g. black and violet 45 15
1143. – 1 z. 50 blk., red & blue 80 15
1144. – 2 z. 50 brown .. 2·40 1·25
DESIGNS—As Type **370**: 1 z. 50, Portion of Chopin's music, (25×39½ mm.): 2 z. 50, Portrait of Chopin.

1960. Stamp Centenary.
1145. **371.** 40 g. red, blue & black 15 10
1146. – 60 g. blue, blk. & vio. 20 10
1147. – 1 z. 35 blue, red & grey 50 35
1148. – 1 z. 55 red, blk. & grn. 1·00 20
1149. – 2 z. 50, grn., blk. & ol. 1·50 50
DESIGNS: 1 z. 35, Emblem inscr. "1860 1960". Reproductions of Polish stamps: 60 g. No. 356. 1 z. 55, No. 533. 2 z. 50, No. 1030. With appropriate postmarks.

1960. Provincial Costumes (2nd series). As T **368/69**.
1150 40 g. red and blue .. 10 10
1151. 40 g. red and blue .. 10 10
1152. 2 z. blue and yellow .. 30 10
1153. 2 z. blue and yellow .. 30 10
1154. 3 z. 10 turquoise & grn. 50 15
1155. 3 z. 10 turquoise & grn. 50 15
1156. 3 z. 40 brown & turquoise 65 20
1157. 3 z. 40 brown & turquoise 65 20
1158. 6 z. 50 violet & green .. 85 35
1159. 6 z. 50 violet & green .. 85 35
DESIGNS—Male and female costumes of: Nos. 1150/1, Cracow. Nos. 1152/3, Lowicz. Nos. 1154/5, Kujawy. Nos. 1156/7, Lublin, Nos. 1158/9, Lubusz.

372. Throwing the Discus. **373.** King Wladislaw Jagiello's Tomb, Wawel Castle.

1960. Olympic Games. Rings and inscr in black.
1160. 60 g. blue (T **372**) .. 10 10
1161. 60 g. mauve (Running).. 10 10
1162. 60 g. violet (Cycling) .. 10 10
1163. 60 g. turq. (Horse-jumping) 10 10
1164. 2 z. 30 blue (Trumpeters) 85 25
1165. 2 z. 50 brown (Boxing) .. 85 25
1166. 2 z. 50 red (Olympic Flame) 85 25
1167. 2 z. 50 grn. (Long-jump) 85 25
The designs all mark Polish successes in previous Olympic Games. The stamps in each denomination are arranged se-tenant in blocks of four (sheets of 60) to form a complete circuit of the stadium track.

1960. 550th Anniv. of Battle of Grunwald.
1168. **373.** 60 g. brown 25 15
1169. – 90 g. green 55 30
1170. – 2 z. 50 black.. .. 3·00 1·25
DESIGNS—As Type **373**: 90 g. Proposed Grunwald Monument. HORIZ. (78×35½ mm.): 2 z. 50, "Battle of Grunwald" (after Jan Matejko).

374. 1860 Stamp and Postmark. **375.** Lukasiewicz (inventor of petrol lamp).

1960. Int. Philatelic Exn., Warsaw.
1171. **374.** 10 z. + 10 z. red, black and blue .. .. 10·00 10·00

1960. Lukasiewicz Commem. and 5th Pharmaceutical Congress, Poznan.
1172. **375.** 60 g. black & yellow 15 10

376. "The Annunciation". **377.** Paderewski.

1960. Altar Wood Carvings of St. Mary's Church, Cracow, by Veit Stoss.
1173. **376.** 20 g. blue 20 10
1174. – 30 g. brown 15 10
1175. – 40 g. violet 20 10
1176. – 60 g. green 20 10
1177. – 2 z. 50 red 90 30
1178. – 5 z. 60 brown .. 7·00 4·00
DESIGNS: 30 g. "The Nativity". 40 g. "Homage of the Three Kings". 60 g. "The Resurrection". 2 z. 50, "The Ascension". 5 z. 60, "The Descent of the Holy Ghost".

1960. Birth Centenary of Paderewski.
1179. **377.** 2 z. 50 black .. 65 15

1960. Stamp Day. Optd. **DZIEN ZNACZKA 1960.**
1180. **371.** 40 g. red, blue & black 1·60 60

379. Gniezno. **380.** Great Bustard.

1960. Old Polish Towns as T **379**.
1181. 5 g. brown 10 10
1182. 10 g. turquoise 10 10
1183. 20 g. brown 10 10
1184. 40 g. red 10 10
1185. 50 g. violet 10 10
1186. 60 g. mauve 10 10
1187. 60 g. blue 10 10
1188. 80 g. blue 15 10
1189. 90 g. brown 15 10
1190. 95 g. black 30 10
1191. 1 z. red and pale lilac .. 15 10
1192. 1 z. 15 green and orange 30 10
1193. 1 z. 35 mauve & pale green 15 10
1194. 1 z. 50 bistre and pale blue 30 10
1195. 1 z. 55 red and pale yellow 30 10
1196. 2 z. blue and pale lilac .. 20 10
1197. 2 z. 10 brn. and pale yell. 25 10
1198. 2 z. 50 violet & pale green 30 10
1199. 3 z. 10 red and pale grey 35 20
1200. 5 z. 60 grey and green .. 1·90 25
TOWNS: 10 g. Cracow. 20 g. Warsaw. 40 g. Poznan. 50 g. Plock. 60 g. mauve, Kalisz. 60 g. blue, Tczew. 80 g. Frombork. 90 g. Torum. 95 g. Puck. 1 z. Slupsk. 1 z. 1, Gdansk. 1 z. 35, Wroclaw. 1 z. 50, Szczecin. 1 z. 55, Opole, 2 z. Kolobrzeg. 2 z. 10, Legnica, 2 z. 50, Katowice. 3 z. 10, Lodz. 5 z. 60, Walbrzych.

1960. Birds as T **380**. Multicoloured.
1201. 10 g. Type **380** 20 10
1202. 20 g. Raven 20 10
1203. 30 g. Common cormorant 20 10
1204. 40 g. Black stork .. 35 10
1205. 50 g. Eagle owl 65 10
1206. 60 g. White-tailed sea eagle 65 15
1207. 75 g. Golden eagle .. 70 15
1208. 90 g. Short-toed eagle .. 75 25
1209. 2 z. 50 Rock thrush .. 4·00 1·40
1210. 4 z. Common kingfisher 3·25 1·00
1211. 5 z. 60 Wallcreeper .. 5·75 1·10
1212. 6 z. 50 Common roller .. 8·25 2·00

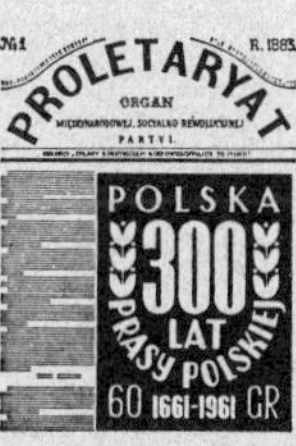

381. Front page of Newspaper "Proletaryat" (1883). **382.** Ice-hockey.

1961. 300th Anniv. of Polish Newspaper Press.
1213. – 40 g. grn., blue & blk. 50 25
1214. **381.** 60 g. yell., red & blk. 50 25
1215. – 2 z. 50 bl., vio. & blk. 3·75 3·25
DESIGNS—Newspaper front page: 40 g. "Mercuriusz" (first issue, 1661). 2 z. 50, "Rzeczpospolita" (1944).

1961. 1st Winter Military Spartakiad.
1216. **382.** 40 g. blk., yell. & lilac 40 10
1217. – 60 g. multicoloured .. 1·00 30
1218. – 1 z. multicoloured .. 6·75 2·50
1219. – 1 z. 50 black, yellow and turquoise .. 1·00 30
DESIGNS: 60 g. Ski jumping. 1 z. Rifle-shooting. 1 z. 50, Slalom.

383. Congress Emblem.

384. Yuri Gagarin.

1961. 4th Polish Engineers' Conf.
1220. **383.** 60 g. black and red 15 10

1961. World's First Manned Space Flight.
1221. **384.** 40 g. black, red and brown 75 15
1222. – 60 g. red., blk. & blue 75 25
DESIGN: 60 g. Globe and star.

385. Fair Emblem.

1961. 30th Int. Fair, Poznan.
1223 **385** 40 g. black, red & blue 10 10
1224 1 z. 50, black, bl & red 20 10

386. King Mieszko I.

1961. Famous Poles (1st issue).
1225. **386.** 60 g. black and blue .. 10 10
1226. – 60 g. black and red .. 10 10
1227. – 60 g. black and green 10 10
1228. – 60 g. black and violet 80 15
1229. – 60 g. black and brown 10 10
1230. – 60 g. black and olive 10 10
PORTRAITS: No. 1226, King Casimir the Great. No. 1227, King Casmir Jagiellon. No. 1228, Copernicus. No. 1229. A. F. Modrzewski. No. 1230, Kosciuszko.
See also Nos. 1301/6 and 1398/1401.

387. "Leskov" (trawler support ship).

1961. Shipbuilding Industry. Multicoloured.
1231. 60 g. Type **387** 25 10
1232. 1 z. 55 "Severodvinsk" (depot ship) 40 15
1233. 2 z. 50 "Rambutan" (coaster) 70 30
1234. 3 z. 40 "Krynica" (freighter) .. .. 1·00 30
1235. 4 z. "B 54" freighter .. 1·75 55
1236. 5 z. 60 "Bavsk" (tanker) 4·50 1·75
SIZES: 2 z. 50, As Type **387.** 5 z. 60, 108 × 21 mm. Rest, 81 × 21 mm.

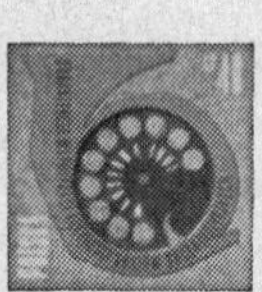
388. Posthorn and Telephone Dial.

389. Opole Seal.

1961. Communications Ministers' Conference, Warsaw.
1237. **388.** 40 g. red, grn. & blue 10 10
1238. – 60 g. violet, yellow & purple 15 10
1239. – 2 z. 50 ultram., blue and bistre 50 15
DESIGNS: 60 g. Posthorn and radar screen. 2 z. 50, Posthorn and conference emblem.

1961. Polish Western Provinces.
1240. 40 g. brown on buff .. 10 10
1241. 40 g. brown on buff .. 10 10
1242. 60 g. violet on pink .. 10 10
1243. 60 g. violet on pink .. 10 10
1243a. 95 g. green on blue .. 15 10
1243b. 95 g. green on blue .. 15 10
1244. 2 z. 50 sage on green .. 30 15
1245. 2 z. 50 sage on green .. 30 15
DESIGNS—VERT. No. 1240, Type **389.** No. 1242, Henry IV's tomb. No. 1243a, Seal of Conrad II. No. 1244, Prince Barnim's seal. HORIZ. No. 1241, Opole cement works. No. 1243, Wroclaw apartment-house. No. 1243b, Factory interior, Zielona Gora. No. 1245, Szczecin harbour.
See also Nos. 1308/13.

390. Beribboned Paddle.

391. Titov and Orbit within Star.

1961. 6th European Canoeing Championships. Multicoloured.
1246. 40 g. Two canoes within letter "E" 15 10
1247. 60 g. Two four-seater canoes at finishing post 15 10
1248. 2 z. 50 Type **390** .. 1·50 50
The 40 g. and 60 g. are horiz.

1961. 2nd Russian Manned Space Flight.
1249. **391.** 40 g. blk., red & pink 40 10
1250. – 60 g. blue and black 40 10
DESIGN: 60 g. Dove and spaceman's orbit around globe.

392. Monument.

393. P.K.O. Emblem and Ant.

1961. 40th Anniv. of 3rd Silesian Uprising.
1251. **392.** 60 g. grey and green 10 10
1252. – 1 z. 55 grey and blue 20 10
DESIGN: 1 z. 55, Cross of Silesian uprisers.

1961. Savings Month.
1253. – 40 g. red, yell. & blk. 15 10
1254. **393.** 60 g. brn., yell. & blk. 15 10
1255. – 60 g. blue, violet & pink 15 10
1256. – 60 g. grn., red & blk. 15 10
1257. – 2 z. 50 mve., grey & blk. 2·75 1·25
DESIGNS: No. 1253, Savings Bank motif. No. 1255, Bee. No. 1256, Squirrel. No. 1257, Savings Bank book.

394. "Mail Cart" (after J. Chelmonski).

1961. Stamp Day and 40th Anniv. of Postal Museum.
1258. **394.** 60 g. brown 35 10
1259. 60 g. green 35 10

395. Congress Emblem.

396. Emblem of Kopasyni Mining Family, 1284.

397. Child and Syringe.

398. Cogwheel and Wheat.

1961. 5th W.F.T.U. Congress, Moscow.
1260. **395.** 60 g. black 10 10

1961. Millenary of Polish Mining Industry.
1261. **396.** 40 g. purple & orange 15 10
1262. – 60 g. grey and blue .. 15 10
1263. – 2 z. 50 green and black 60 25
DESIGNS: 60 g. 14th-century seal of Bytom. 2 z. 50, Emblem of Int. Mine Constructors' Congress, Warsaw, 1958.

1961. 15th Anniv. of U.N.I.C.E.F.
1264. **397.** 40 g. black and blue .. 10 10
1265. – 60 g. black and orange 10 10
1266. – 2 z. 50 black & turq. 65 35
DESIGNS—HORIZ. 60 g. Children of three races. VERT. 2 z. 50, Mother and child, and feeding bottle.

1961. 15th Economic Co-operative Council Meeting, Warsaw.
1267. **398.** 40 g. red, yell. & blue 10 10
1268. – 60 g. red, bl. & ultram. 10 10
DESIGN: 60 g. Oil pipeline map, E. Europe.

399. "Calosoma sycophanta".

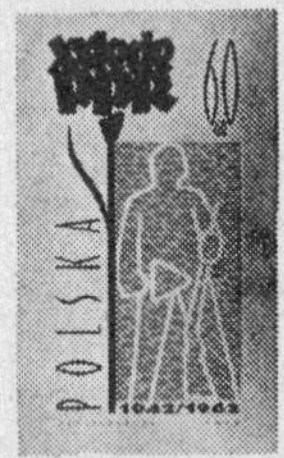

400. Worker with Flag and Dove.

1961. Insects. Multicoloured.
1269 20 g. Type **399** 20 10
1270 30 g. "Carabus violaceus" 20 10
1271 40 g. "Rosalia alpina" 20 10
1272 50 g. "Cerambyx cerdo" 20 10
1273 60 g. "Carabus auronitens" 20 10
1274 80 g. "Lucanus cervus" .. 35 10
1275 1 z. 15 "Parnassius mnemosyne" 70 15
1276 1 z. 35 "Acherontia atropos" 45 15
1277 1 z. 50 "Iphiclides podalirius" 90 15
1278 1 z. 55 "Parnassius apollo" 90 15
1279 2 z. 50 "Formica rufa" .. 1·50 40
1280 5 z. 60 "Bombus lucorum" 8·00 4·25
The 20 g. to 80 g. show beetles as Type **399** and the rest butterflies in square shape, size 36½ × 36½ mm.

1962. 20th Anniv. of Polish Worker's Coalition.
1281. **400.** 60 g. brn., blk. & red 10 10
1282. – 60 g. bistre, blk. & red 10 10
1283. – 60 g. blue, blk. & red 10 10
1284. – 60 g. grey, blk. & red 10 10
1285. – 60 g. blue, blk. & red 10 10
DESIGNS: No. 1282, Steersman. No. 1283, Worker with hammer. No. 1284, Soldier with weapon. No. 1285, Worker with trowel and rifle.

DESIGNS—HORIZ. 60 g. Skier racing. VERT. 1 z. 50, Ski-jumper.
401. Two Skiers Racing.

1962. F.I.S. Int. Ski Championships, Zakopane.
1286. **401.** 40 g. blue, grey & red 10 10
1287. 40 g. blue, brn. & red 1·00 35
1288. – 60 g. blue, grey & red 20 10
1289. – 60 g. blue, brn. & red 1·50 80
1290. – 1 z. 50 blue, grey & red 35 10
1291. – 1 z. 50 vio., grey & red 2·25 1·25

402. Majdanek Monument.

1962. Concentration Camp Monuments.
1292. – 40 g. blue 10 10
1293. **402.** 60 g. black .. 30 10
1294. – 1 z. 50 violet .. 40 15
DESIGNS—VERT. (20 × 31 mm.): 40 g. Broken carnations and portion of prison clothing (Auschwitz camp). 1 z. 50, Treblinka monument.

DESIGNS: (74½ × 22 mm.): 2 z. 50, Cyclists & "XV". As Type **403.** 3 z. 40, Arms of Berlin, Prague and Warsaw, and cycle wheel.
403. Racing Cyclist.

1962. 15th Int. Peace Cycle Race.
1295. **403.** 60 g. black and blue .. 20 10
1296. – 2 z. 50 black & yellow 60 15
1297. – 3 z. 40 black & violet 90 30

405. Lenin Walking.

406. Gen. K. Swierczewski-Walter (monument).

1962. 50th Anniv. of Lenin's Sojourn in Poland.
1298. **405.** 40 g. grn. & pale grn. 35 10
1299. – 60 g. lake and pink .. 15 10
1300. – 2 z. 50 brn. and yell. 65 10
DESIGNS: 60 g. Lenin. 2 z. 50, Lenin wearing cap, and St. Mary's Church, Cracow.

1962. Famous Poles (2nd issue). As T **386.**
1301. 60 g. black and green .. 10 10
1302. 60 g. black and brown .. 10 10
1303. 60 g. black and blue .. 15 10
1304. 60 g. black and bistre .. 10 10
1305. 60 g.lack and purple .. 10 10
1306. 60 g. black and turquoise 10 10
PORTRAITS: No. 1301, A. Mickiewicz (poet). 1302, J. Slowacki (poet). 1303, F. Chopin (composer). 1304, R. Traugutt (patriot). 1305, J. Dabrowski (revolutionary). 1306, Maria Konopnicka (poet).

1962. 15th Death Anniv. of Gen. K. Swierczewski-Walter (patriot).
1307. **406.** 60 g. black 10 10

1962. Polish Northern Provinces. As T **389.**
1308. 60 g. violet on blue .. 10 10
1309. 60 g. violet on blue .. 10 10
1310. 1 z. 55 brown on yellow .. 20 10
1311. 1 z. 55 brown on yellow .. 20 10
1312. 2 z. 50 blue on grey .. 55 15
1313. 2 z. 50 blue on grey .. 55 15
DESIGNS—VERT. No. 1308, Princess Elizabeth's seal. No. 1310, Gdansk Governor's seal. No. 1312, Frombork Cathedral. HORIZ. No. 1309, Insulators factory, Szczecinek. No. 1311, Gdansk shipyard. No. 1313, Laboratory of Agricultural College, Kortowo.

407. "Crocus scepusiensis" (Borb).

408. "The Poison Well", after J. Malczewski.

1962. Polish Protected Plants. Plants in natural colours.
1314. **407.** 60 g. yellow 20 10
1315. A. 60 g. brown 80 30
1316. B. 60 g. pink 20 10
1317. C. 90 g. green 25 10
1318. D. 90 g. olive 25 10
1319. E. 90 g. green 25 10
1320. F. 1 z. 50 blue 55 15
1321. G. 1 z. 50 green 55 15
1322. H. 1 z. 50 turquoise .. 55 15
1323. I. 2 z. 50 green .. .. 1·10 50
1324. J. 2 z. 50 turquoise .. 1·25 50
1325. K. 2 z. 50 blue .. .. 1·50 70
PLANTS: A, "Platanthera bifolia" (Rich). B, "Aconitum callibotryon" (Rchb.). C, "Gentiana clusii" (Perr. et Song). D, "Dictamnus albus" (L.) E, "Nymphaea alba" (L.). F, "Daphne mezereum" (L.). G, "Pulsatilla vulgaris" (Mill.). H, "Anemone silvestris" (L.). I, "Trollius europaeus" (L.). J, "Galanthus nivalis" (L.). K, "Adonis vernalis" (L.).

1962. F.I.P. Day ("Federation Internationale de Philatelie").
1326. **408.** 60 g. black on cream 15 10

409. Pole Vault.

1962. 7th European Athletic Championships, Belgrade. Multicoloured.
1327. 40 g. Type **409** .. 10 10
1328. 60 g. 400-metres relay .. 10 10
1329. 90 g. Throwing the javelin 10 10
1330. 1 z. Hurdling 10 10
1331. 1 z. 50 High-jumping .. 15 10
1332. 1 z. 55 Throwing the discus 15 10
1333. 2 z. 50 100-metres final .. 25 15
1334. 3 z. 40 Throwing the hammer .. .. 1·00 25

410. "Anopheles sp.".

411. Cosmonauts "in flight".

1962. Malaria Eradication.
1335. **410.** 60 g. brn. & turquoise 10 10
1336. – 1 z. 50 multicoloured 15 10
1337. – 2 z. 50 multicoloured 1·00 20
DESIGNS: 1 z. 50, Malaria parasites in blood. 2 z. 50, Cinchona plant.

1962. 1st "Team" Manned Space Flight.
1338. 411. 60 g. green, blk. & vio. 15 10
1339. – 2 z. 50 red, black and turquoise 55 10
DESIGN: 2 z. 50, Two stars (representing space-ships) in orbit.

412. "A Moment of Determination" (after painting by A. Kamienski).
413. Mazovian Princes' Mansion, Warsaw.

1962. Stamp Day.
1340. 412. 60 g. black .. 10 10
1341. 2 z. 50 brown .. 45 20

1962. 25th Anniv. of Polish Democratic Party.
1342. 413. 60 g. black on red .. 15 10

414. Cruiser "Aurora".

1962. 45th Anniv. of Russian Revolution.
1343. 414. 60 g. blue and red .. 30 10

415. J. Korczak (bust after Dunikowski).

DESIGNS: 60 g. to 5 z. 60, Illustrations from Korczak's children's books.

1962. 20th Death Anniv. of Janusz Korczak (child educator).
1344. 415. 50 g. sepia, bis. & brn. 15 10
1345. – 60 g. multicoloured .. 15 10
1346. – 90 g. multicoloured .. 45 15
1347. – 1 z. multicoloured .. 45 10
1348. – 2 z. 50 multicoloured 75 40
1349. – 5 z. 60 multicoloured 2·00 80

416. Old Town, Warsaw.

1962. 5th T.U. Congress, Warsaw.
1350. 416. 3 z. 40 multicoloured 85 15

417. Master Buncombe.
418. R. Traugutt (insurgent leader).

1962. Maria Konopnicka's Fairy Tale "The Dwarfs and Orphan Mary". Multicoloured.
1351. 40 g. Type 417 .. .. 50 15
1352. 60 g. Lardie the Fox and Master Buncombe .. 2·00 75
1353. 1 z. 50 Bluey the Frog making music 60 15
1354. 1 z. 55 Peter's kitchen .. 60 25
1355. 2 z. 50 Saraband's concert in Nightingale Valley 75 25
1356. 3 z. 40 Orphan Mary and Subearthy .. .. 2·40 1·75

1963. Cent. of January (1863) Rising.
1357. 418. 60 g. blk., pink & turq. 10 10

419. Tractor and Wheat.

DESIGNS: 60 g. Millet and hoeing. 2 z. 50, Rice and mechanical harvester.

1963. Freedom from Hunger.
1358. 419. 40 g. blk., ochre & bl. 10 10
1359. – 60 g. multicoloured .. 75 10
1360. – 2 z. 50 multicoloured 1·25 25

420. Cocker Spaniel.

1963. Dogs.
1361. 420. 20 g. red, blk. & lilac 20 10
1362. – 30 g. black and red .. 20 10
1363. – 40 g. ochre, blk. & lilac 25 10
1364. – 50 g. ochre, blk. & blue 25 10
1365. – 60 g. black and blue .. 35 10
1366. – 1 z. black and green .. 55 10
1367. – 2 z. 50 brn., yell. & blk. 1·00 40
1368. – 3 z. 40 black and red .. 2·50 1·00
1369. – 6 z. 50 black & yellow 7·00 4·75
DOGS—HORIZ. 30 g. Sheep-dog. 40 g. Boxer. 2 z. 50, Gun-dog "Ogar". 6 z. 50, Great Dane. VERT. 50 g. Airedale terrier. 60 g. French bulldog. 1 z. French poodle. 3 z. 40, Podhale sheep-dog.

421. Egyptian Galley (15th-century B.C.).
422. Insurgent.

1963. Sailing Ships (1st series).
1370. 421. 5 g. brown on bistre .. 15 10
1371. – 10 g. turquoise on grn. 15 10
1372. – 20 g. blue on grey .. 15 10
1373. – 30 g. black on olive .. 20 10
1374. – 40 g. blue on blue .. 20 10
1375. – 60 g. purple on brown 35 10
1376. – 1 z. black on blue .. 40 10
1377. – 1 z. 15 green on pink 60 10
SHIPS: 10 g. Phoenician merchantman (15th cent B.C.). 20 g. Greek trireme (5th cent B.C.). 30 g. Roman merchantman (3rd cent A.D.). 40 g. "Mora" (Norman ship) (1066). 60 g. Hanse kogge (14th cent). 1 z. Hulk (16 cent). 1 z. 15, Carrack (15th cent).
See also Nos. 1451/66.

1963. 20th Anniv of Warsaw Ghetto Uprising.
1378 422 2 z. 50 brown and blue 25 10

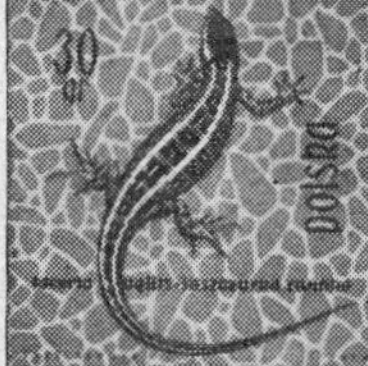

423. Centenary Emblem.
424. Lizard.

1963. Red Cross Cent.
1379. 423. 2 z. 50 red, blue & yell. 85 20

1963. Protected Reptiles and Amphibians. Reptiles in natural colours: inscr. in black: background colours given.
1380. 424. 30 g. green 10 10
1381. – 40 g. olive 10 10
1382. – 50 g. brown 15 10
1383. – 60 g. grey 15 10
1384. – 90 g. green 15 10
1385. – 1 z. 15 grey 20 10
1386. – 1 z. 35 blue 20 10
1387. – 1 z. 50 turquoise .. 25 10
1388. – 1 z. 55 pale blue .. 50 10
1389. – 2 z. 50 lavender .. 50 25
1390. – 3 z. green .. 1·25 30
1391. – 3 z. 40 purple .. 3·00 2·50
DESIGNS: 40 g. Copperhead (snake). 50 g. Marsh tortoise. 60 g. Grass snake. 90 g. Blindworm. 1 z. 15, Tree toad. 1 z. 35, Mountain newt. 1 z. 50, Crested newt. 1 z. 55, Green toad. 2 z. 50, "Bombina" toad, 3 z. Salamander. 3 z. 40, "Natterjack" (toad).

425. Epee, Foil, Sabre and Knight's Helmet.

1963. World Fencing Championships, Gdansk.
1392. 425. 20 g. yellow and brown 10 10
1393. – 40 g. light blue & blue 15 10
1394. – 60 g. vermilion & red 20 10
1395. – 1 z. 15 light grn. & grn. 35 10
1396. – 1 z. 55 red and violet 65 15
1397. – 6 z. 50 yellow, purple and bistre .. 1·90 90
DESIGNS—HORIZ. Fencers with background of: 40 g. Knights jousting. 60 g. Dragoons in sword-fight. 1 z. 15, 18th-century duellists. 1 z. 55, Old Gdansk. VERT. 6 z. 50, Inscription and Arms of Gdansk.

1963. Famous Poles (3rd issue). As T **386**.
1398. 60 g. black and brown .. 10 10
1399. 60 g. black and brown .. 10 10
1400. 60 g. black and turquoise 10 10
1401. 60 g. black and green .. 10 10
PORTRAITS: No. 1398, L. Warynski (patriot). No. 1399, L. Krzywicki (economist). No. 1400, M. Sklodowska-Curie (scientist). No. 1401, K. Swierczewski (patriot).

426. Bykovsky and "Vostok 5".

1963. 2nd "Team" Manned Space Flights.
1402. 426. 40 g. blk., green & blue 15 10
1403. – 60 g. black, blue & grn. 15 10
1404. – 6 z. 50 multicoloured 1·40 55
DESIGNS: 60 g. Tereshkova and "Vostok 6". 6 z. 50, "Vostoks 5 and 6" in orbit.

427. Basketball.

DESIGNS: 50 g. to 2 z. 50, As Type **427** but with ball, players and hands in various positions. 5 z. 60, Hands placing ball in net.

1963. 13th European (Men's) Basketball Championships, Wroclaw.
1405. 427. 40 g. multicoloured .. 10 10
1406. – 50 g. green, blk. & pink 10 10
1407. – 60 g. black, grn. & red 10 10
1408. – 90 g. multicoloured .. 10 10
1409. – 2 z. 50 multicoloured 35 10
1410. – 5 z. 60 multicoloured 1·75 40

428. Missile.

1963. 20th Anniv of Polish People's Army. Multicoloured.
1411 20 g. Type **428** 10 10
1412 40 g. "Blyskawica" (destroyer) 15 10
1413 60 g. Fighter plane .. 15 10
1414 1 z. 15 Radar scanner .. 20 10
1415 1 z. 35 Tank 30 10
1416 1 z. 55 Missile carrier .. 30 10
1417 2 z. 50 Amphibious troop carrier 40 10
1418 3 z. Ancient warrior, modern soldier and two swords 50 30

429. "A Love Letter" (after Czachorski).

1963. Stamp Day.
1419. 429. 60 g. brown 20 10

1963. Visit of Soviet Cosmonauts to Poland. Nos. 1402/4 optd. **23-28. X. 1963** and **w Polsce** together with Cosmonauts names.
1420. 426. 40 g. black, green & bl. 25 10
1421. – 60 g. black, blue & grn. 40 10
1422. – 6 z. 50 multicoloured 2·00 1·40

431. Tsiolkovsky's Rocket and Formula.
432. Mazurian Horses.

1963. "The Conquest of Space" Inscr. in black.
1423. 431. 30 g. turquoise .. 10 10
1424. – 40 g. olive 10 10
1425. – 50 g. violet 10 10
1426. – 60 g. brown 10 10
1427. – 1 z. turquoise .. 10 10
1428. – 1 z. 50 red 15 10
1429. – 1 z. 55 blue 15 10
1430. – 2 z. 50 purple .. 30 10
1431. – 5 z. 60 green 90 25
1432. – 6 z. 50 turquoise .. 1·50 40
DESIGNS: 40 g. "Sputnik 1". 50 g. "Explorer 1". 60 g. Banner carried by "Lunik 2". 1 z. "Lunik 3". 1 z. 50, "Vostok 1". 1 z. 55, "Friendship 7". 2 z. 50, "Vostoks 3 and 4" 5 z. 60, "Mariner 2". 6 z. 50, "Mars 1".

1963. Polish Horse-breeding. Multicoloured.
1433. 20 g. Arab stallion "Comet" 15 10
1434. 30 g. Wild horses .. 15 10
1435. 40 g. Sokolski horse .. 15 10
1436. 50 g. Arab mares and foals 15 10
1437. 60 g. Type **432** .. 15 10
1438. 90 g. Steeplechasers .. 20 10
1439. 1 z. 55 Arab stallion "Witez II" 60 10
1440. 2 z. 50 Head of Arab horse (facing right) .. 1·00 10
1441. 4 z. Mixed breeds .. 2·00 55
1442. 6 z. 50 Head of Arab horse (facing left) .. 2·75 2·10
SIZES — TRIANGULAR (55 × 27½ mm.): 20 g., 30 g., 40 g. HORIZ. (75×26 mm.): 50 g., 90 g., 4 z. VERT. as Type **432**: 1 z. 55, 2 z. 50, 6 z. 50.

433. Ice Hockey.

1964. Winter Olympic Games, Innsbruck. Multicoloured.
1443. 20 g. Type **433** 10 10
1444. 30 g. Slalom 10 10
1445. 40 g. Downhill skiing .. 10 10
1446. 60 g. Speed skating .. 10 10
1447. 1 z. Ski-jumping .. 20 10
1448. 2 z. 50 Tobogganing .. 50 10
1449. 5 z. 60 Cross-country skiing 1·00 50
1450. 6 z. 50 Pairs, figure skating 1·50 50

1964. Sailing Ships (2nd series). As T **421** but without coloured backgrounds. Some new designs.
1451. 421. 5 g. brown 15 10
1452. – 10 g. green 15 10
1453. – 20 g. blue 15 10
1454. – 30 g. bronze 20 10
1455. – 40 g. blue 20 10
1456. – 60 g. purple 20 10
1457. – 1 z. brown 40 10
1458. – 1 z. 15 brown .. 40 10
1459. – 1 z. 35 blue 40 10
1460. – 1 z. 50 purple .. 40 10
1461. – 1 z. 55 black 40 10
1462. – 2 z. violet 40 10
1463. – 2 z. 10 green 40 10
1464. – 2 z. 50 mauve .. 50 10
1465. – 3 z. olive 70 10
1466. – 3 z. 40 brown .. 1·00 10
SHIPS—HORIZ. 10 g. to 1 z. 15, As Nos. 1371/7. 1 z. 50, "Ark Royal" (English galleon, 1587). 2 z. 10, Ship of the line (18th cent). 2 z. 50, Sail frigate (19th cent). 3 z. "Flying Cloud" (sailing clipper). VERT. 1 z. 35, Columbus's "Santa Maria". 1 z. 55, "Wodnik" (Polish warship, 17th cent). 2 z. Dutch fleute (17th cent). 3 z. 40, "Dar Pomorza" (full-rigged cadet ship).

434. "Flourishing Tree".

DESIGN: No. 1468, Emblem composed of symbols of agriculture and industry.

1964. 20th Anniv. of People's Republic (1st issue).
1467. 434. 60 g. multicoloured 10 10
1468. – 60 g. black, yell. & red 10 10
See also Nos. 1497/1506.

435. European Cat.
436. Casimir the Great (founder).

1964. Domestic Cats. As T **435**.

1469. 30 g. black and yellow .. 30 10
1470. 40 g. multicoloured .. 30 10
1471. 50 g. black, turq. & yellow 30 10
1472. 60 g. multicoloured .. 30 10
1473. 90 g. multicoloured .. 40 10
1474. 1 z. 35 multicoloured .. 40 10
1475. 1 z. 55 multicoloured .. 45 10
1476. 2 z. 50 yell., blk. & violet 60 25
1477. 3 z. 40 multicoloured .. 2·75 65
1478. 6 z. 50 multicoloured .. 4·75 2·00

CATS—European: 30 g., 40 g., 60 g., 1 z. 55, 2 z. 50, 6 z. 50. Siamese: 50 g. Persian: 90 g., 1 z. 35, 3 z. 40. Nos. 1472/5 are horiz.

1964. 600th Anniv. of Jagiellonian University, Cracow.

1479. **436.** 40 g. purple 10 10
1480. – 40 g. green 10 10
1481. – 60 g. violet 10 10
1482. – 60 g. blue 70 10
1483. – 2 z. 50 sepia 40 15

PORTRAITS: No. 1480, Hugo Kollataj (educationist and politician). No. 1481, Jan Dlugosz (geographer and historian). No. 1482, Copernicus (astronomer). No. 1483 (36 × 37 mm.), King Wladislaw Jagiello and Queen Jadwiga.

437. Lapwing.

Nos. 1487/9 are vert. (35 × 48 mm.), the rest as Type **437**.

1964. Birds. Multicoloured.

1484. 30 g. Type **437** 15 10
1485. 40 g. Bluethroat .. 15 10
1486. 50 g. Black-tailed godwit 15 10
1487. 60 g. Osprey 25 10
1488. 90 g. Grey heron .. 35 10
1489. 1 z. 35 Little gull .. 60 10
1490. 1 z. 55 Common shoveler 60 15
1491. 5 z. 60 Black-throated diver .. .. .. 1·25 50
1492. 6 z. 50 Great crested grebe .. .. .. 1·75 70

438. Red Flag on Brick Wall.

1964. 4th Polish United Workers' Party Congress, Warsaw. Inscr. "PZPR". Multicoloured.

1493. 60 g. Type **438** 10 10
1494. 60 g. Beribboned hammer 10 10
1495. 60 g. Hands reaching for Red Flag 10 10
1496. 60 g. Hammer and corn emblems 10 10

439. Factory and Cogwheel.

441. Battle Scene.

440. Gdansk Shipyard.

1964. 20th Anniv. of People's Republic. (2nd issue).

1497. **439.** 60 g. black and blue .. 10 10
1498. – 60 g. black and green 10 10
1499. – 60 g. red and orange 10 10
1500. – 60 g. blue and grey .. 10 10
1501. **440.** 60 g. blue and green .. 10 10
1502. – 60 g. violet & mauve 10 10
1503. – 60 g. brown & violet 10 10
1504. – 60 g. bronze and green 10 10
1505. – 60 g. purple and red .. 10 10
1506. – 60 g. brown & yellow 10 10

DESIGNS—As Type **439**: No. 1498, Tractor and ear of wheat. No. 1499, Mask and symbols of the arts. No. 1500, Atomic symbol and book. As Type **440**: No. 1502, Lenin Foundry, Nowa Huta. No. 1503, Cement Works, Chelm. No. 1504, Turoszow power station. No. 1505, Petrochemical plant. Plock. No. 1506, Tarnobrzeg sulphur mine.

1964. 20th Anniv. of Warsaw Insurrection.

1507. **441.** 60 g. multicoloured .. 15 10

442. Relay-racing.

443. Congress Emblem.

1964. Olympic Games, Tokyo. Multicoloured.

1508. 20 g. Triple-jumping .. 10 10
1509. 40 g. Rowing 10 10
1510. 60 g. Weightlifting .. 10 10
1511. 90 g. Type **442** 10 10
1512. 1 z. Boxing 15 10
1513. 2 z. 50 Football 35 10
1514. 5 z. 60 High-jumping (women) .. .. 1·40 40
1515. 6 z. 50 High-diving .. 1·50 75

SIZES: DIAMOND—20 g. to 60 g. SQUARE—90 g. to 2 z. 50. VERT. ($23\frac{1}{2} \times 36$ mm.)—5 z. 60, 6 z. 50.

1964. 15th Int. Astronautical Congress, Warsaw.

1516. **443.** 2 z. 50 black & violet 40 15

444. Hand holding Hammer.

445. S. Zeromski.

1964. 3rd Congress of Fighters for Freedom and Democracy Association, Warsaw.

1517. **444.** 60 g. red, black & grn. 10 10

1964. Birth Cent. of Stefan Zeromski (writer).

1518. **445.** 60 g. brown 10 10

446. Globe and Red Flag.

448. Eleanor Roosevelt.

447. 18th-century Stage Coach (after J. Brodowski).

1964. Cent. of "First International".

1519. **446.** 60 g. black and red .. 10 10

1964. Stamp Day.

1520. **447.** 60 g. green 30 10
1521. 60 g. brown 30 10

1964. 80th Birth Anniv. of Eleanor Roosevelt.

1522. **448.** 2 z. 50 brown .. 25 10

449. Battle of Studzianki (after S. Zoltowski).

1964. "Poland's Struggle" (World War II) (1st issue).

1523. – 40 g. black 10 10
1524. – 40 g. violet 10 10
1525. – 60 g. blue 15 10
1526. – 60 g. green 15 10
1527. **449.** 60 g. bronze 15 10

DESIGNS—VERT. No. 1523, Virtuti Militari Cross. 1524, Westerplatte Memorial, Gdansk. 1527, Bydogoszcz Memorial. HORIZ. 1526, Soldiers crossing the Oder (after S. Zoltowski).

See also Nos. 1610/2.

450. Cyclamen.

451. Spacecraft of the Future.

1964. Garden Flowers. Multicoloured.

1528. 20 g. Type **450** 10 10
1529. 30 g. Freesia 10 10
1530. 40 g. Rose 10 10
1531. 50 g. Peony 10 10
1532. 60 g. Lily 10 10
1533. 90 g. Poppy 15 10
1534. 1 z. 35 Tulip 15 10
1535. 1 z. 50 Narcissus .. 70 25
1536. 1 z. 55 Begonia .. 25 10
1537. 2 z. 50 Carnation .. 75 15
1538. 3 z. 40 Iris .. .. 1·00 30
1539. 5 z. 60 Japanese camelia 1·90 85

Nos. 1534/9 are smaller, $26\frac{1}{2} \times 37$ mm.

1964. Space Research. Multicoloured.

1540. 20 g. Type **451** .. 10 10
1541. 30 g. Launching rocket 10 10
1542. 40 g. Dog "Laika" and rocket 10 10
1543. 60 g. "Lunik 3" and Moon 10 10
1544. 1 z. 55 Satellite 20 10
1545. 2 z. 50 "Elektron 2" .. 30 10
1546. 5 z. 60 "Mars 1" .. 90 20
1547. 6 z. 50+2 z. Gagarin seated in Capsule .. 1·40 65

452. "Siren of Warsaw".

1965. 20th Anniv. of Liberation of Warsaw.

1548. **452.** 60 g. green 10 10

453. Edaphosaurus.

1965. Prehistoric Animals (1st series). Multicoloured.

1549. 20 g. Type **453** 15 10
1550. 30 g. Cryptocleidus .. 15 10
1551. 40 g. Brontosaurus .. 15 10
1552. 60 g. Mesosaurus .. 15 10
1553. 90 g. Stegosaurus .. 15 10
1554. 1 z. 15 Brachiosaurus .. 20 10
1555. 1 z. 35 Styracosaurus .. 20 10
1556. 3 z. 40 Corythosaurus .. 70 20
1557. 5 z. 60 Rhamphorhynchus 1·40 50
1558. 6 z. 50 Tyrannosaurus .. 2·10 60

The 30 g., 60 g., 1 z. 15, 3 z. 40, and 5 z. 60, are vert.

See also Nos. 1639/47.

454. Petro-chemical Works, Plock, and Polish and Soviet Flags.

1965. 20th Anniv. of Polish-Soviet Friendship Treaty. Multicoloured.

1559. 60 g. Seal (vert., $27 \times 38\frac{1}{2}$ mm.) 10 10
1560. 60 g. Type **454** 10 10

455. Polish Eagle and Civic Arms.

1965. 20th Anniv. of Return of Western and Northern Territories to Poland.

1561. **455.** 60 g. red 10 10

456. Dove of Peace.

457. I.T.U. Emblem.

1965. 20th Anniv. of Victory.

1562. **456.** 60 g. red and black .. 10 10

1965. Centenary of I.T.U.

1563. **457.** 2 z. 50 blk. vio. & bl. 65 15

458. Clover-leaf Emblem and "The Friend of the People" (journal).

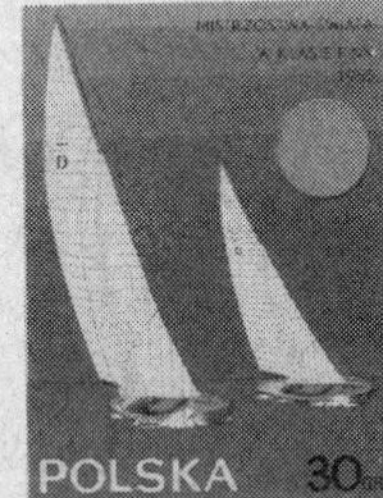

459. "Dragon" Class Yachts.

1965. 70th Anniv. of Peasant Movement. Multicoloured.

1564. 40 g. Type **458** 10 10
1565. 60 g. Ears of corn and industrial plant (horiz.). 10 10

1965. World Finn Class Sailing Championships, Gdynia. Multicoloured.

1566. 30 g. Type **459** 10 10
1567. 40 g. "5·5 m." class .. 10 10
1568. 50 g. "Finn" class .. 15 10
1569. 60 g. "V" class 15 10
1570. 1 z. 35 "Cadet" class .. 20 10
1571. 4 z. "Star" class .. 90 30
1572. 5 z. 60 "Flying Dutchman" class .. .. 1·50 60
1573. 6 z. 50 "Amethyst" class 2·25 75

The 50 g., 1 z. 35, 4 z. and 6 z. 50 are horiz.

460. Marx and Lenin.

461. 17th-Cent. Arms of Warsaw.

1965. Postal Minister's Congress, Peking.

1574. **460.** 60 g. black on red .. 15 10

1965. 700th Anniv. of Warsaw.

1575. **461.** 5 g. red 10 10
1576. – 10 g. green 10 10
1577. – 20 g. blue 10 10
1578. – 40 g. brown 10 10
1579. – 60 g. orange 10 10
1580. – 1 z. 50 black 15 10
1581. – 1 z. 55 blue 20 10
1582. – 2 z. 50 purple 35 10

DESIGNS—VERT. 10 g. 13th-cent. antiquities. HORIZ. 20 g. Tombstone of last Masovian dukes. 40 g. Old Town Hall. 60 g. Barbican. 1 z. 50, Arsenal. 1 z. 55, National Theatre. 2 z. 50, Staszic Palace.

463. I.Q.S.Y. Emblem.

464. "Odontoglossum grande".

1965. Int. Quiet Sun Year. Multicoloured. Background colours given.

1584. **463.** 60 g. blue 10 10
1585. 60 g. violet 10 10
1586. – 2 z. 50 red 35 10
1587. – 2 z. 50 brown .. 35 10
1588. – 3 z. 40 orange .. 55 20
1589. – 3 z. 40 olive 65 20

DESIGNS: 2 z. 50, Solar scanner. 3 z. 40, Solar System.

1965. Orchids. Multicoloured.

1590.	20 g. Type **464**	15	10
1591.	30 g. "Cypripedium hibridum"	15	10
1592.	40 g. "Lycaste skinneri"	15	10
1593.	50 g. "Cattleya warszewicza"	20	10
1594.	60 g. "Vanda sanderiana"	30	10
1595.	1 z. 35 "Cypripedium hibridum"	55	10
1596.	4 z. "Sobralia"	1·00	40
1597.	5 z. 60 "Disa grandiflora"	1·10	50
1598.	6 z. 50 "Cattleya labiata"	2·00	1·10

The 30 g. and 1 z. 35, are different designs.

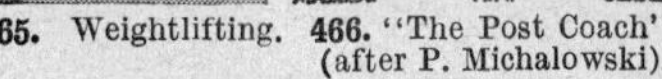

465. Weightlifting. **466.** "The Post Coach" (after P. Michalowski).

1965. Olympic Games, Tokyo. Polish Medal Winners. Multicoloured.

1599.	30 g. Type **465**	10	10
1600.	40 g. Boxing	10	10
1601.	50 g. Relay-racing	10	10
1602.	60 g. Fencing	10	10
1603.	90 g. Hurdling (women's 80 m.)	10	10
1604.	3 z. 40 Relay-racing (women's)	45	10
1605.	6 z. 50 "Hop, step and jump"	1·10	85
1606.	7 z. 10 Volleyball (women's)	1·40	30

1965. Stamp Day.

1607.	**466.** 60 g. brown	20	10
1608.	– 2 z. 50 green	30	10

DESIGN: 2 z. 50, "Coach about to leave" (after P. Michalowski).

467. U.N. Emblem. **468.** Memorial, Holy Cross Mountains.

1965. 20th Anniv of U.N.O.

1609	**467** 2 z. 50 blue	30	10

1965. "Poland's Struggle" (World War II) (2nd issue).

1610.	**468.** 60 g. brown	10	10
1611.	– 60 g. green	10	10
1612.	– 60 g. brown	10	10

DESIGNS—VERT. No. 1611, Memorial, Plaszow. HORIZ. No. 1612, Memorial, Chelm-on-Ner.

469. Wolf.

1965. Forest Animals. Multicoloured.

1613.	20 g. Type **469**	20	10
1614.	30 g. Lynx	20	10
1615.	40 g. Red fox	20	10
1616.	50 g. Eurasian badger	25	10
1617.	60 g. Brown bear	25	10
1618.	1 z. 50 Wild boar	60	30
1619.	2 z. 50 Red deer	35	15
1620.	5 z. 60 European bison	1·25	45
1621.	7 z. 10 Elk	2·10	65

470. Gig.

1965. Horse-drawn Carriages in Lancut Museum. Multicoloured.

1622.	20 g. Type **470**	10	10
1623.	40 g. Coupe	10	10
1624.	50g. Ladies' "basket" (trap)	10	10
1625.	60 g. "Vis-a-vis"	15	10
1626.	90 g. Cab	20	10
1627.	1 z. 15 Berlinka	25	10
1628.	2 z. 50 Hunting brake	65	10
1629.	6 z. 50 Barouche	1·50	45
1630.	7 z. 10 English brake	2·25	1·25

Nos. 1627/9 are 77×22 mm. and No. 1630 is 104×22 mm.

471. Congress Emblem and Industrial Products.

1966. 5th Polish Technicians' Congress, Katowice.

1631.	**471.** 60 g. multicoloured	15	10

1966. 20th Anniv. of Industrial Nationalisation. Designs similar to T471. Multicoloured.

1632.	60 g. Pithead gear (vert.)	15	10
1633.	60 g. Freighter	15	10
1634.	60 g. Petro-chemical works, Plock	15	10
1635.	60 g. Combine-harvester	15	10
1636.	60 g. Electric train	20	10
1637.	60 g. Exhibition Hall, 35th Poznan Fair	15	10
1638.	60 g. Crane (vert.)	15	10

1966. Prehistoric Animals (2nd series). As T **453**. Multicoloured.

1639.	20 g. Dinichthys	15	10
1640.	30 g. Eusthenopteron	15	10
1641.	40 g. Ichthyostega	20	10
1642.	50 g. Mastodonsaurus	20	10
1643.	60 g. Cynognathus	35	10
1644.	2 z. 50 Archaeopteryx (vert.)	40	10
1645.	3 z. 40 Brontotherium	80	10
1646.	6 z. 50 Machairodus	1·60	35
1647.	7 z. 10 Mammuthus	2·10	75

472. H. Sienkiewicz (novelist). **473.** Footballers (Montevideo, 1930).

1966. 50th Death Anniv. of Henryk Sienkiewicz.

1648.	**472.** 60 g black on buff	15	10

1966. World Cup Football Competition. Multicoloured.

1649.	20 g. Type **473**	10	10
1650.	40 g. Rome, 1934	10	10
1651.	60 g. Paris, 1938	10	10
1652.	90 g. Rio de Janeiro, 1950	10	10
1653.	1 z. 50 Berne, 1954	90	15
1654.	3 z. 40 Stockholm, 1958	85	15
1655.	6 z. 50 Santiago, 1962	1·40	50
1656.	7 z. 10 "London", 1966 (elimination match, Glasgow, 1965)	2·00	1·40

Football scenes represent World Cup finals played at the cities stated.

475. Soldier with Flag, and Dove of Peace. **476.** Women's Relay-racing.

1966. 21st Anniv. of Victory.

1658.	**475.** 60 g. red and black on silver	10	10

1966. 8th European Athletic Championships, Budapest. Multicoloured.

1659.	20 g. Runner starting race	10	10
1660.	40 g. Type **476**	10	10
1661.	60 g. Throwing the javelin	10	10
1662	90 g. Women's hurdles	10	10
1663.	1 z. 35 Throwing the discus	15	10
1664.	3 z. 40 Finish of race	55	10
1665.	6 z. 50 Throwing the hammer	90	35
1666.	7 z. 10 High-jumping	1·25	60

The 20 g., 60 g., 1 z. 35 and 6 z. 50 are vert.

478. White Eagle. **479.** Flowers and Produce.

1966. Polish Millenary (1st issue). Each red and black on gold.

1668.	60 g. Type **478**	10	10
1669.	60 g. Polish flag	10	10
1670.	2 z. 50 Type **478**	30	15
1671.	2 z. 50 Polish flag	30	15

See also Nos. 1717/18.

1966. Harvest Festival. Multicoloured.

1672.	40 g. Type **479**	25	10
1673.	60 g. Woman and loaf	25	10
1674.	3 z. 40 Festival bouquet	65	30

The 3 z. 40 is 49 × 48 mm.

480. Chrysanthemum. **481.** Tourist Map.

1966. Flowers. Multicoloured.

1675.	10 g. Type **480**	10	10
1676.	20 g. Poinsettia	10	10
1677.	30 g. Centaury	10	10
1678.	40 g. Rose	10	10
1679.	60 g. Zinnia	10	10
1680.	90 g. Nasturtium	15	10
1681.	5 z. 60 Dahlia	90	35
1682.	6 z. 50 Sunflower	1·25	45
1683.	7 z. 10 Magnolia	2·00	50

1966. Tourism.

1684.	**481.** 10 g. red	10	10
1685.	– 20 g. olive	10	10
1686.	– 40 g. blue	10	10
1687.	– 60 g. brown	10	10
1688.	– 60 g. black	10	10
1689.	– 1 z. 15 green	20	10
1690.	– 1 z. 35 red	25	10
1691.	– 1 z. 55 violet	30	10
1692.	– 2 z. green	45	10

DESIGNS: 20 g. Hela Lighthouse. 40 g. Yacht. 60 g. (No. 1687). Poniatowski Bridge, Warsaw. 60 g. (No. 1688), Mining Academy, Kielce. 1 z. 15, Dunajec Gorge. 1 z. 35, Old oaks, Rogalin. 1 z. 55, Silesian Planetarium. 2 z. "Batory" (liner).

482. Roman Capital.

1966. Polish Culture Congress.

1693.	**482.** 60 g. red & brown	10	10

DESIGN: 2 z. 50, Stablemen, with horses and dogs.

483. Stable-man with Percherons.

1966. Stamp Day.

1694.	**483.** 60 g. brown	15	10
1695.	– 2 z. 50 green	40	10

484. Soldier in Action.

1966. 30th Anniv. of Jaroslav Dabrowski Brigade.

1696.	**484.** 60 g. blk., grn. & red	20	10

485. Woodland Birds.

1966. Woodland Birds. Multicoloured.

1697.	10 g. Type **485**	25	10
1698.	20 g. Green woodpecker	25	10
1699.	30 g. Jay	25	10
1700.	40 g. Golden oriole	30	15
1701.	60 g. Hoopoe	30	15
1702.	2 z. 50 Redstart	65	40
1703.	4 z. Siskin	2·25	50
1704.	6 z. 50 Chaffinch	2·25	85
1705.	7 z. 10 Great tit	2·50	90

486. Ram (ritual statuette). **487.** "Vostok 1".

1966. Polish Archaeological Research.

1706.	**486.** 60 g. blue	15	10
1707.	– 60 g. green	15	10
1708.	– 60 g. brown	15	10

DESIGNS—VERT. No. 1707, Plan of Biskupin settlement. HORIZ. No. 1708, Brass implements and ornaments.

1966. Space Research. Multicoloured.

1709.	20 g. Type **487**	10	10
1710.	40 g. "Gemini"	10	10
1711.	60 g. "Ariel 2"	10	10
1712.	1 z. 35 "Progon 1"	15	10
1713.	1 z. 50 "FR 1"	25	10
1714.	3 z. 40 "Alouette"	40	10
1715.	6 z. 50 "San Marco 1"	1·25	25
1716.	7 z. 10 "Luna 9"	1·50	40

488. Polish Eagle and Hammer.

1966. Polish Millenary (2nd issue).

1717.	**488.** 40 g. pur., lilac & red	10	10
1718.	– 60 g. pur., grn. & red	10	10

DESIGN: 60 g. Polish eagle and agricultural and industrial symbols.

489. Dressage.

1967. 150th Anniv. of Racehorse Breeding in Poland. Multicoloured.

1719.	10 g. Type **489**	20	10
1720.	20 g. Cross-country racing	20	10
1721.	40 g. Horse-jumping	20	10
1722.	60 g. Jumping fence in open country	30	10
1723.	90 g. Horse-trotting	35	10
1724.	5 z. 90 Playing polo	1·00	45
1725.	6 z. 60 Stallion "Ofir"	1·75	80
1726.	7 z. Stallion "Skowronek"	2·75	90

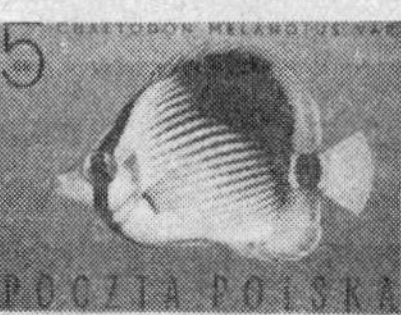

490. Striped Butterfly.

1967. Exotic Fishes. Multicoloured.

1727.	5 g. Type **490**	10	10
1728.	10 g. Imperial Angelfish	10	10
1729.	40 g. Banded Butterfly	10	10
1730.	60 g. Spotted Triggerfish	10	10
1731.	90 g. Undulate Triggerfish	15	10
1732.	1 z. 50 Picasso Fish	25	10
1733.	4 z. 50 Black Eyed Butterfly	1·25	15
1734.	6 z. 60 Blue Angelfish	1·50	1·00
1735.	7 z. Saddleback Butterfly	1·60	40

491. Auschwitz Memorial.

1967. Polish Martyrdom and Resistance, 1939–45.

1736.	**491.** 40 g. brown	10	10
1737.	– 40 g. black	10	10
1738.	– 40 g. violet	10	10

DESIGNS—VERT. No. 1737, Auschwitz-Monowitz Memorial. No. 1738, Memorial guide's emblem.

See also Nos. 1770/2, 1798/9 and 1865/9.

492. Cyclists.

1967. 20th International Peace Cycle Race.
1739. **492.** 60 g. multicoloured 20 10

493. Running. **495.** " Arnica montana ".

494. Socialist Symbols.

1967. Olympic Games (1968). Multicoloured.
1740. 20 g. Type **493**. 10 10
1741. 40 g. Horse-jumping .. 10 10
1742. 60 g. Relay-running .. 10 10
1743. 90 g. Weight-lifting .. 10 10
1744. 1 z. 35 Hurdling .. 10 10
1745. 3 z. 40 Gymnastics .. 45 15
1746. 6 z. 60 High-jumping .. 60 25
1747. 7 z. Boxing .. .. 1·40 50

1967. Polish Trade Unions Congress, Warsaw.
1749. **494** 60 g. multicoloured.. 10 10

1967. Protected Plants. Multicoloured.
1750. 40 g. Type **495** 10 10
1751. 60 g. "Aquilegia vulgaris" 10 10
1752. 3 z. 40 "Gentiana punctata" 40 10
1753. 4 s. 50 " Lycopodium clavatum" 45 10
1754. 5 z. "Iris sibirica" .. 65 15
1755. 10 z. "Azalea pontica" .. 1·25 20

496. Katowice Memorial. **497.** Marie Curie.

1967. Inaug. of Katowice Memorial.
1756. **496.** 60 g. multicoloured.. 10 10

1967. Birth Centenary of Marie Curie.
1757. **497.** 60 g. lake 15 10
1758. – 60 g. brown 15 10
1759. – 60 g. violet 15 10
DESIGNS: No. 1758, Marie Curie's Nobel Prize diploma. No. 1759, Statue of Marie Curie, Warsaw

498. " Fifth Congress of the Deaf". (sign language).

1967. 5th World Federation of the Deaf Congress, Warsaw.
1760. **498.** 60 g. black and blue 15 10

499. Bouquet.

1967. "Flowers of the Meadow". Mult.
1761 20 g. Type **499** 10 10
1762 40 g. Red poppy .. 10 10
1763 60 g. Field bindweed .. 10 10
1764 90 g. Wild pansy .. 15 10
1765 1 z. 15 Tansy 15 10
1766 2 z. 50 Corn cockle .. 30 10
1767 3 z. 40 Field scabious .. 60 25
1768 4 z. 50 Scarlet pimpernel 1·75 40
1769 7 z. 90 Chicory .. 2·00 65

1967. Polish Martyrdom and Resistance, 1939–45 (2nd series). As T **491**.
1770. 40 g. blue 10 10
1771. 40 g. green 10 10
1772. 40 g. black 10 10
DESIGNS—HORIZ. No. 1770, Stutthof Memorial. VERT. No. 1771, Walcz Memorial. No. 1772, Lodz-Radogoszcz Memorial.

500. " Wilanow Palace " (from painting by W. Kasprzycki).

1967. Stamp Day.
1773. **500.** 60 g. brown and blue 15 10

501. Cruiser " Aurora ".

1967. 50th Anniv. of October Revolution. Each black, grey and red.
1774. 60 g. Type **501** 30 10
1775. 60 g. Lenin 30 10
1776. 60 g. " Luna 10 " .. 30 10

502. "Inachis io". **503.** Kosciuszko.

1967. Butterflies. Multicoloured.
1777 10 g. Type **502** 15 10
1778 20 g. "Papilio machaon" 15 10
1779 40 g. "Aglais urticae" .. 15 10
1780 60 g. "Nymphalis antiopa" 20 10
1781 2 z. "Apatura iris" .. 35 10
1782 2 z. 50 "Vanessa atalanta" 45 10
1783 3 z. 40 "Colias hyale" .. 45 15
1784 4 z. 50 "Melanargia galathea" .. .. 2·00 80
1785 7 z. 90 "Maculinea arion" 2·25 80

1967. 150th Death Anniv. of Tadeusz Kosciuszko (national hero).
1786. **503.** 60 g. chocolate & brn. 10 10
1787. 2 z. 50 green and red 20 10

504. " The Lobster " (Jean de Heem).

1967. Famous Paintings.
1788. – 20 g. multicoloured .. 20 10
1789. – 40 g. multicoloured.. 10 10
1790. – 60 g. multicoloured.. 10 10
1791. – 2 z. multicoloured .. 25 15
1792. – 2 z. 50 multicoloured 30 20
1793. – 3 z. 40 multicoloured 55 15
1794. **504.** 4 z. 50 multicoloured 1·00 50
1795. – 6 z. 60 multicoloured 1·60 85
DESIGNS (Paintings from the National Museums, Warsaw and Cracow). VERT. 20 g. " Lady with a Weasel " (Leonardo da Vinci). 40 g. " The Polish Lady " (Watteau). 60 g. " Dog Fighting Heron " (A. Hondius). 2 z. " Fowler Tuning Guitar " (J.-B. Greuze). 2 z. 50, " The Tax Collectors " (M. van Reymerswaele). 3 z. 40, " Daria Fiodorowna " (F. S. Rokotov). HORIZ. 6 z. 60, " Parable of the Good Samaritan" (landscape, Rembrandt).

505. W. S. Reymont.

1967. Birth Centenary of W. S. Reymont (novelist).
1796. **505.** 60 g. brn., red & ochre 10 10

506. J. M. Ossolinski (medallion) Book and Flag.

1967. 150th Anniv. of Ossolineum Foundation.
1797. **506.** 60 g. brown, red & blue 10 10

1967. Polish Martyrdom and Resistance, 1939–45 (3rd series). As T **491**.
1798. 40 g. red 10 10
1799. 40 g. brown 10 10
DESIGNS—VERT. No. 1798, Zagan Memorial. HORIZ. No. 1799, Lambinowice Memorial.

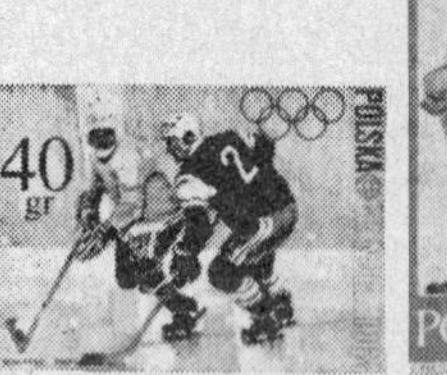

507. Ice Hockey. **508.** " Puss in Boots ".

1968. Winter Olympic Games, Grenoble. Multicoloured.
1800. 40 g. Type **507** .. 10 10
1801. 60 g. Ski-jumping .. 10 10
1802. 90 g. Slalom 15 10
1803. 1 z. 35 Speed-skating .. 15 10
1804. 1 z. 55 Ski-walking .. 15 10
1805. 2 z. Tobogganing .. 25 10
1806. 7 z. Rifle-shooting on skis 70 30
1807. 7 z. 90 Ski-jumping (different) .. .. .. 1·25 60

1968. Fairy Tales. Multicoloured.
1808. 20 g. Type **508** 10 10
1809. 40 g. "The Raven and the Fox" 10 10
1810. 60 g. " Mr. Twardowski " 15 10
1811. 2 z. " The Fisherman and the Fish " 35 10
1812. 2 z. 50 " Little Red Riding Hood " 40 10
1813. 3 z. 40 " Cinderella " .. 65 10
1814. 5 z. 50 " The Waif " .. 1·50 60
1815. 7 z. " Snow-White " .. 1·75 65

509. "Passiflora quadrangularis". **510.** " Peace " (poster by H. Tomaszewski).

1968. Flowers. Multicoloured.
1816 10 g. "Clianthus dampieri" 10 10
1817 20 g. Type **509** 10 10
1818 30 g. "Strelitzia reginae" 10 10
1819 40 g. "Coryphanta vivipara" 10 10
1820 60 g. "Odontonia" .. 10 10
1821 90 g. "Protea cyneroides" 15 10
1822 4 z. + 2 z. "Abutilon" .. 1·10 60
1823 8 z. + 4 z. "Rosa polyantha" .. .. 2·25 1·10

1968. 2nd Int. Poster Biennale, Warsaw. Multicoloured.
1824. 60 g. Type **510** 10 10
1825. 2 z. 50 Gounod's "Faust" (poster by Jan Lenica) 20 10

511. "Zephyr" Glider.

1968. 11th World Gliding Championships, Leszno. Gliders. Multicoloured.
1826. 60 g. Type **511** 10 10
1827. 90 g. " Stork " 10 10
1828. 1 z. 50 " Swallow " .. 20 10
1829. 3 z. 40 " Fly " 50 20
1830. 4 z. " Seal " .. .. 1·00 30
1831. 5 z. 50 " Pirate " .. 1·25 35

512. Child with " Stamp ". **513.** Part of Monument.

1968. " 75 years of Polish Philately". Multicoloured.
1832. 60 g. Type **512** 10 10
1833. 60 g. Balloon over Poznan 10 10

1968. Silesian Insurrection Monument, Sosnowiec.
1834. **513.** 60 g. black and purple 10 10

514. Relay-racing.

1968. Olympic Games, Mexico. Multicoloured.
1835. 30 g. Type **514** 10 10
1836. 40 g. Boxing 10 10
1837. 60 g. Basketball 10 10
1838. 90 g. Long-jumping .. 10 10
1839. 2 z. 50 Throwing the javelin 20 10
1840. 3 z. 40 Gymnastics .. 30 10
1841. 4 z. Cycling 40 30
1842. 7 z. 90 Fencing 95 30
1843. 10 z. + 5 z. Torch Runner and Aztec bas-relief .. 2·40 1·40
The 10 z. is larger, 56 × 45 mm.

515. " Knight on a Bay Horse" (P. Michalowski).

1968. Polish Paintings. Multicoloured.
1844. 40 g. Type **515** 10 10
1845. 60 g. " Fisherman " (L. Wyczolkowski).. .. 10 10
1846. 1 z. 15 " Jewish Woman with Lemons " (A. Gierymski) 10 10
1847. 1 z. 35 " Eliza Parenska " (S. Wyspianski) .. 20 10
1848. 1 z. 50 " Manifesto " (W. Weiss) 65 20
1849. 4 z. 50 " Stanczyk " (Jan Matejko) 45 30
1850. 5 z. " Children's Band " (T. Makowski) .. .. 1·00 20
1851. 7 z. " Feast II " (Z. Waliszewski) .. .. 1·40 50
The 4 z. 50, 5 z. and 7 z. are horiz.

516. "September, 1939" (Bylina).

1968. 25th Anniv. of Polish People's Army. Designs show paintings.
1852. 40 g. violet & olive on yell. 10 10
1853. 40 g. blue & violet on lilac 10 10
1854. 40 g. green & blue on grey 10 10
1855. 40 g. blk. & brn. on orge. 10 10
1856. 40 g. pur. & green on green 10 10
1857. 60 g. brn. & ultram. on bl. 15 10
1858. 60 g. pur. and grn. on grn. 15 10
1859. 60 g. olive & red on pink 15 10
1860. 60 g. green & brn. on red 30 10
1861. 60 g. blue & turq. on blue 20 10
PAINTINGS AND PAINTERS: No. 1852, Type **516**. 1853, "Partisans" (Maciag). 1854, "Lenino" (Bylina). 1855, "Monte Cassino" (Boratynski). 1856, "Tanks before Warsaw" (Garwatowski). 1857, "Neisse River" (Bylina). 1858, "On the Oder" (Mackiewicz). 1859, "In Berlin" (Bylina). 1860, "Blyskawica" (destroyer) (Mokwa). 1861, "Pursuit" (fighter planes) (Kulisiewicz).

517. " Party Members " (F. Kowarski).

1968. 5th Polish United Workers' Party Congress, Warsaw. Multicoloured designs showing paintings.

1862. 60 g. Type **517** 10 10
1863. 60 g. " Strike " (S. Lentz) 10 10
1864. 60 g. " Manifesto " (W. Weiss) 10 10
Nos. 1863/4 are vert.

1968. Polish Martyrdom and Resistance. 1939–45 (4th series). As T **491**.

1865. 40 g. grey 10 10
1866. 40 g. brown 10 10
1867. 40 g. brown 10 10
1868. 40 g. blue 10 10
1869. 40 g. brown 10 10

DESIGNS—HORIZ. No. 1865, Tomb of Unknown Soldier, Warsaw. No. 1866, Guerillas' Monument, Kartuzy. VERT. No. 1867, Insurgents' Monument, Poznan. No. 1868, People's Guard Insurgents' Monument, Polichno. No. 1869, Rotunda, Zamosc.

518. " Start of Hunt " (W. Kossak).

1968. Paintings. Hunting Scenes. Mult.

1870. 20 g. Type **518** 10 10
1871. 40 g. " Hunting with Falcon " (J. Kossak) .. 10 10
1872. 60 g. " Wolves' Raid " (A. Wierusz-Kowalski) 10 10
1873. 1 z. 50 " Home-coming with a Bear " (J. Falat) 40 10
1874. 2 z. 50 " The Fox-hunt " (T. Sutherland) .. 30 10
1875. 3 z. 40 " The Boar-hunt " (F. Snyders) 40 15
1876. 4 z. 50 " Hunters' Rest " (W. G. Pierow) .. 1·50 50
1877. 8 z. 50 " Hunting a Lion in Morocco " (Delacroix) .. 1·25 50

519. Maltese Terrier. **520.** House Sign.

1969. Pedigree Dogs. Multicoloured.

1878. 20 g. Type **519** 30 10
1879. 40 g. Wire-haired fox-terrier 40 15
1880. 60 g. Afghan hound .. 40 20
1881. 1 z. 50 Rough-haired terrier 40 20
1882. 2 z. 50 English setter .. 70 20
1883. 3 z. 40 Pekinese 85 20
1884. 4 z. 50 Alsatian .. .. 1·75 40
1885. 8 z. 50 Pointer .. .. 3·00 75
Nos. 1879, 1884 and 1885 are vert.

1969. 9th Polish Democratic Party Congress.

1886. **520.** 60 g. red, blk. & grey 10 10

521. " Dove " and Wheat-ears. **522.** Running.

1969. 5th Congress of United Peasant's Party.

1887. **521.** 60 g. multicoloured 10 10

1969. 75th Anniv. of Int. Olympic Committee and 50th Anniv. of Polish Olympic Committee. Multicoloured.

1888. 10 g. Type **522** 10 10
1889. 20 g. Gymnastics .. 10 10
1890. 40 g. Weightlifting .. 10 10
1891. 60 g. Throwing the javelin 10 10
1892. 2 z. 50+50 g. Throwing the discus 20 10
1893. 3 z. 40+1 z. Running .. 30 15
1894. 4 z.+1 z. 50 Wrestling .. 65 35
1895. 7 z.+2 z. Fencing .. 1·40 45

523. Pictorial Map of Swietokrzyski National Park.

1969. Tourism (1st series). Multicoloured.

1896. 40 g. Type **523** 10 10
1897. 60 g. Niedzica Castle (vert.) 10 10
1898. 1 z. 35 Kolobrzeg Lighthouse and yacht 30 10
1899. 1 z. 50 Szczecin Castle and Harbour 30 10
1900. 2 z. 50 Torun and Vistula River 25 10
1901. 3 z. 40 Klodzko, Silesia (vert.) 35 10
1902. 4 z. Sulejow 55 25
1903. 4 z. 50 Kazimierz Dolny market-place (vert.) .. 60 30
See also Nos. 1981/5.

524. Route Map and " Opty ".

1969. Leonid Teliga's World Voyage in Yacht " Opty ".

1904. **524.** 60 g. multicoloured .. 30 10

525. Copernicus (after woodcut by T. Stimer) and inscription. **526.** " Memory " Flame and Badge.

1969. 500th Birth Anniv. (1973) of Copernicus (1st issue).

1905. **525.** 40 g. brn., red & yellow 15 10
1906. – 60 g. blue, red & green 20 10
1907. – 2 z. 50 olive, red & pur. 55 20

DESIGNS: 60 g. Copernicus (after J. Falck) and 15th-century globe. 2 z. 50 Copernicus (after painting by J. Matejko) and diagram of heliocentric system.

See also Nos. 1995/7, 2069/72, 2167/70, 2213/14 and 2217/21.

1969. 5th National Alert of Polish Boy Scout Association.

1908. **526.** 60 g. black, red & blue 10 10
1909. – 60 g. red, black & green 10 10
1910. – 60 g. blk., grn. and red 10 10

DESIGN: No. 1909, " Defence " eagle and badge. No. 1910, " Labour " map and badge.

528. Coal-miner.

1969. 25th Anniv. of Polish People's Republic. Multicoloured.

1911. 60 g. Frontier Guard and Arms 10 10
1912. 60 g. Plock Petro-chemical Plant 10 10
1913. 60 g. Combine-harvester 10 10
1914. 60 g. Grand Theatre, Warsaw 10 10
1915. 60 g. Curie statue and University, Lublin .. 10 10
1916. 60 g. Type **528** 10 10
1917. 60 g. Sulphur-worker .. 10 10
1918. 60 g. Steel-worker .. 10 10
1919. 60 g. Ship-builder .. 10 10
Nos. 1911/5 are vert. and have white arms embossed in the top portion of the stamps.

529. Astronauts and Module on Moon.

1969. 1st Man on the Moon.

1920. **529.** 2 z. 50 multicoloured 75 45

530. " Motherhood " (S. Wyspiański).

1969. Polish Paintings. Multicoloured.

1921. 20 g. Type **530** 10 10
1922. 40 g. " Hamlet " (J. Malczewski) 10 10
1923. 60 g. " Indian Summer " (J. Chelmonski) .. 15 10
1924. 2 z. " Two Girls " (Olga Boznanska) (vert.) .. 25 10
1925. 2 z. 50 " The Sun of May " (J. Mehoffer) (vert.) .. 15 10
1926. 3 z. 40 " Woman combing her Hair " (W. Slewinski) 30 25
1927. 5 z. 50 " Still Life " (J. Pankiewicz) 65 35
1928. 7 z. " Abduction of the King's Daughter " (W. Wojtkiewicz) .. .. 1·25 40

531. " Nike " statue. **533.** Krzczonow (Lublin) Costumes.

532. Majdanek Memorial.

1969. 4th Congress of Fighters for Freedom and Democracy Association.

1929. **531.** 60 g. red, black & brn. 10 10

1969. Inaug of Majdanek Memorial.

1930 **532** 40 g. black and mauve 10 10

1969. Folk Dances. Multicoloured.

1931. 40 g. Type **533** 10 10
1932. 60 g. Lowicz (Lodz) .. 10 10
1933. 1 z. 15 Rozbark (Katowice) 15 10
1934. 1 z. 35 Lower Silesia (Wroclaw) 15 10
1935. 1 z. 50 Opoczno (Lodz) .. 35 10
1936. 4 z. 50 Sacz (Cracow) .. 70 15
1937. 5 z. Highlanders, Cracow 60 35
1938. 7 z. Kurpie (Warsaw) .. 1·00 40

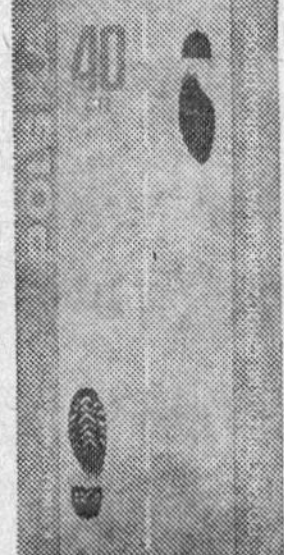

534. " Pedestrians Keep Left ". **535.** " Welding " and I.L.O. Emblem.

1969. Road Safety. Multicoloured.

1939. 40 g. Type **534** 10 10
1940. 60 g. " Drive Carefully " (horses on road) .. 10 10
1941. 2 z. 50 " Do Not Dazzle " (cars on road at night) 40 15

1969. 50th Anniv. of Int. Labour Organization.

1942. **535.** 2 z. 50 blue and gold 20 10

536. " The Bell-founder ". **537.** " Angel " (19th-century).

1969. Miniatures from Behem's Code of 1505. Multicoloured.

1943. 40 g. Type **536** 10 10
1944. 60 g. " The Painter " .. 10 10
1945. 1 z. 35 " The Woodcarver " 15 10
1946. 1 z. 55 " The Shoemaker " 20 10
1947. 2 z. 50 " The Cooper " .. 25 10
1948. 3 z. 40 " The Baker " .. 40 15
1949. 4 z. 50 " The Tailor " .. 65 35
1950. 7 z. " The Bowyer " .. 1·10 40

1969. Polish Folk Sculpture. Multicoloured.

1951. 20 g. Type **537** 10 10
1952. 40 g. " Sorrowful Christ " (19th-century) 10 10
1953. 60 g. " Sorrowful Christ " (19th-cent.) (diff.) .. 10 10
1954. 2 z. " Weeping Woman " (19th-century) 20 10
1955. 2 z. 50 " Adam and Eve " (F. Czajkowski) .. 20 10
1956. 3 z. 40 " Girl with Birds " (L. Kudla) 35 10
1957. 5 z. 50+1 z. 50 " Choir " (A. Zegadlo) 95 40
1958. 7 z.+1 z. " Organ-grinder " (Z. Skretowicz) .. 1·25 55
Nos. 1957/8 are larger, size 25 × 35 mm.

538. Leopold Staff.

1969. Modern Polish Writers.

1959. **538.** 40 g. blk., olive & grn. 10 10
1960. – 60 g. blk., red & pink 10 10
1961. – 1 z. 35 blk., dp. blue and blue 10 10
1962. – 1 z. 50 blk., vio. & lilac 10 10
1963. – 1 z. 55 blk., dp. green and green 15 10
1964. – 2 z. 50 blk., dp. blue and blue 20 10
1965. – 3 z. 40 blk., brn. and flesh 30 20

DESIGNS: 60 g. Wladyslaw Broniewski. 1 z. 35, Leon Kruczkowski. 1 z. 50, Julian Tuwim. 1 z. 55, Konstanty Ildefons Galczynski. 2 z. 50, Maria Dabrowska. 3 z. 40, Zofia Nalkowska.

539. Nike Monument.

1970. 25th Anniv. of Liberation of Warsaw.

1966. **539.** 60 g. multicoloured .. 20 10

540. Early Printing Works and Colour Dots. **541.** Mallard.

1970. Cent. of Printers' Trade Union.

1967. **540.** 60 g. multicoloured 10 10

1970. Game Birds. Multicoloured.

1968. 40 g. Type **541** 25 10
1969. 60 g. Ring-necked pheasant 45 10
1970. 1 z. 15 Woodcock .. 35 10
1971. 1 z. 35 Ruff 45 10
1972. 1 z. 50 Wood pigeon .. 45 20
1973. 3 z. 40 Black grouse .. 50 20
1974. 7 z. Grey partridge .. 3·00 1·10
1975. 8 z. 50 Capercaillie .. 3·25 1·10

542. Lenin at Desk.

1970. Birth Cent. of Lenin.

1976. **542.** 40 g. grey and red .. 10 10
1977. – 60 g. brown and red .. 10 10
1978. – 2 z. 50 black and red 20 10

DESIGNS: 60 g. Lenin addressing meeting. 2 z. 50, Lenin at Party conference.

543. Polish and Russian Soldiers in Berlin.

1970. 25th Anniv. of Liberation.
1980. **543.** 60 g. multicoloured .. 15 10

1970. Tourism (2nd series). As T **523**, but with imprint "PWPW 70". Multicoloured.
1981. 60 g. Town Hall, Wroclaw (vert.) 15 10
1982. 60 g. View of Opol .. 15 10
1983. 60 g. Legnica Castle .. 15 10
1984. 60 g. Bolkow Castle .. 15 10
1985. 60 g. Town Hall, Brzeg .. 15 10

544. Polish "Flower".

1970. 25th Anniv. of Return of Western Territories.
1986. **544.** 60 g. red, silver and green 10 10

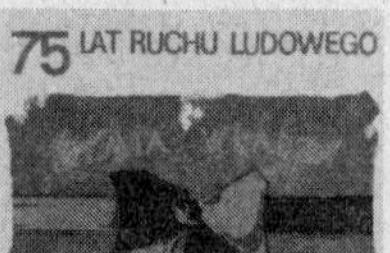

545. Movement Flag. **546.** U.P.U. Emblem and New Headquarters.

1970. 75th Anniv. of Peasant Movement.
1987. **545.** 60 g. multicoloured .. 10 10

1970. New U.P.U. Headquarters Building, Berne.
1988. **546.** 2 z. 50 blue and turq. 15 10

547. Footballers. **548.** Hand with "Lamp of Learning".

1970. Gornik Zabrze v. Manchester City, Final of European Cup-winners Cup Championship.
1989 **547** 60 g. multicoloured .. 20 10

1970. 150th Anniv. of Plock Scientific Society.
1990. **548.** 60 g. olive, red & black 10 10

549. "Olympic Runners" (from Greek amphora). **550.** Copernicus (after miniature by Bacciarelli) and Bologna.

1970. 10th Session of Int. Olympic Academy.
1991. **549.** 60 g. red, yell. & blk. 10 10
1992. – 60 g. violet, bl. & blk. 10 10
1993. – 60 g. multicoloured .. 10 10
DESIGNS: No. 1992, "The Archer". No. 1993, Modern runners.

1970. 500th Birth Anniv. (1973) of Copernicus. (2nd issue).
1995. **550.** 40 g. green, orge. & lilac 15 10
1996. – 60 g. lilac, grn. & yell. 15 10
1997. – 2 z. 50 brn., blue and green 55 15
DESIGNS: 60 g. Copernicus (after miniature by Lesseur) and Padua. 2 z. 50, Copernicus (by N. Zinck, after lost Goluchowska portrait) and Ferrara.

551. "Aleksander Orlowski" (self-portrait).

1970. Polish Miniatures. Multicoloured.
1998. 20 g. Type **551** 10 10
1999. 40 g. "Jan Matejko" (self-portrait) .. 10 10
2000. 60 g. "Stefan Batory" (unknown artist) .. 10 10
2001. 2 z. "Maria Leszczynska" (unknown artist) .. 15 10
2002. 2 z. 50 "Maria Walewska" (Marie-Victoire Jacquetot) 20 10
2003. 3 z. 40 "Tadeusz Kosciuszko" (Jan Rustem) 25 10
2004. 5 z. 50 "Samuel Linde" (G. Landolfi) 80 45
2005. 7 z. "Michal Oginski" (Nanette Windisch) .. 1·60 50

552. U.N. Emblem within "Eye".

1970. 25th Anniv. of United Nations.
2006. **552.** 2 z. 50 multicoloured 20 10

553. Piano Keyboard and Chopin's Signature. **554.** Population Pictograph.

1970. 8th Int. Chopin Piano Competition.
2007. **553.** 2 z. 50 black & violet 35 15

1970. National Census. Multicoloured.
2008. 40 g. Type **554** 10 10
2009. 60 g. Family in "house" 15 10

555. Destroyer "Piorun". (Illustration reduced. Actual size 77 × 23 mm.)

1970. Polish Warships, World War II.
2010. **555.** 40 g. brown 30 15
2011. – 60 g. black 35 15
2012. – 2 z. 50 brown 1·00 25
DESIGNS: 60 g. Submarine "Orzel". 2 z. 50 Destroyer "Garland".

556. "Expressions" (Maria Jarema).

1970. Stamp Day. Contemporary Polish Paintings. Multicoloured.
2013. 20 g. "The Violin-cellist" (J. Nowosielski) (vert.) 10 10
2014. 40 g. "View of Lodz" (B. Liberski) (vert.) .. 10 10
2015. 60 g. "Studio Concert" (W. Taranczewski) (vert.) 10 10
2016. 1 z. 50 "Still Life" (Z. Pronaszko) (vert.) .. 10 10
2017. 2 z. "Hanging-up Washing" (A. Wroblewski) (vert.) 15 10
2018. 3 z. 40 Type **556** 25 10
2019. 4 z. "Canal in the Forest" (P. Potworowski) .. 65 20
2020. 8 z. 50 "The Sun" W. Strzeminski) .. 1·25 55

557. "Luna 16" landing on Moon. **558.** "Stag" detail from "Daniel" tapestry).

1970. Moon Landing of "Luna 16".
2021. **557.** 2 z. 50 multicoloured 30 15

1970. Tapestries in Wawel Castle. Mult.
2022. 60 g. Type **558** 10 10
2023. 1 z. 15 "White Stork" (detail) 30 10
2024. 1 z. 35 "Panther fighting Dragon" 15 10
2025. 2 z. "Man's Head" (detail "Deluge" tapestry) .. 25 10
2026. 2 z. 50 "Child with Bird" (detail "Adam Tilling the Soil" tapestry) .. 30 10
2027. 4 z. "God, Adam and Eve" (detail "Happiness in Paradise" tapestry) .. 60 25
2028. 4 z. 50 Royal Monogram tapestry 90 40

559. Cadet ship "Dar Pomorza".

1971. Polish Ships. Multicoloured.
2030 40 g. Type **559** 15 10
2031 60 g. Liner "Stefan Batory" 15 10
2032 1 z. 15 Ice-breaker "Perkun" 25 10
2033 1 z. 35 Lifeboat "R-1" .. 30 10
2034 1 z. 50 Bulk carrier "Ziemia Szczecinska" 40 10
2035 2 z. 50 Tanker "Beskidy" 50 10
2036 5 z. Freighter "Hel" .. 1·10 20
2037 8 z. 50 Ferry "Gryf" .. 2·10 60

560. Checiny Castle.

1971. Polish Castles. Multicoloured.
2038. 20 g. Type **560** 10 10
2039. 40 g. Wisnicz 10 10
2040. 60 g. Bedzin 10 10
2041. 2 z. Ogrodzieniec .. 15 10
2042. 2 z. 50 Niedzica 20 10
2043. 3 z. 40 Kwidzyn .. 30 15
2044. 4 z. Pieskowa Skala .. 40 20
2045. 8 z. 50 Lidzbark Warminski 1·00 70

561. Battle of Pouilly, J. Dabrowski and W. Wroblewski.

1971. Centenary of Paris Commune.
2046. **561.** 60 g. brown, blue & red 20 10

562. Plantation. **563.** "Bishop Marianos".

1971. Forestry Management. Multicoloured.
2047. 40 g. Type **562** 10 10
2048. 60 g. Forest (27 × 47 mm.) 10 10
2049. 1 z. 50 Tree-felling .. 40 10

1971. Fresco Discoveries made by Polish Expedition at Faras, Nubia. Multicoloured.
2050. 40 g. Type **563** 10 10
2051. 60 g. "St. Anne" .. 10 10
2052. 1 z. 15 "Archangel Michael" 10 10
2053. 1 z. 35 "The Hermit, Anamon" 10 10
2054. 1 z. 50 "Head of Archangel Michael" 15 10
2055. 4 z. 50 "Evangelists' Cross" 50 15
2056. 5 z. "Christ protecting a nobleman" 60 30
2057. 7 z. "Archangel Michael" (half-length) 75 40

564. Revolutionaries.

1971. 50th Anniv. of Silesian Insurrection.
2058. **564.** 60 g. brown and gold 20 10

565. "Soldiers".

1971. 25th Anniv. of U.N.I.C.E.F. Children's Drawings. Multicoloured.
2060. 20 g. "Peacock" (vert.) 10 10
2061. 40 g. Type **565** 10 10
2062. 60 g. "Lady Spring" (vert.) 10 10
2063. 2 z. "Cat and Ball" .. 25 10
2064. 2 z. 50 "Flowers in Jug" (vert.) 30 10
2065. 3 z. 40 "Friendship" .. 35 15
2066. 5 z. 50 "Clown" (vert.) .. 80 35
2067. 7 z. "Strange Planet" .. 1·00 50

566. Fair Emblem. **567.** Copernicus's House, Torun.

1971. 40th Int. Fair, Poznan.
2068. **566.** 60 g. multicoloured .. 10 10

1971. 500th Birth Anniv. (1973) of Copernicus. (3rd issue). Multicoloured.
2069. 40 g. Type **567** 10 10
2070. 60 g. Collegium Naius, Jagiellonian University, Cracow (horiz.) .. 10 10
2071. 2 z. 50 Olsztyn Castle (horiz.) 40 10
2072. 4 z. Frombork Cathedral 50 30

568. Folk Art Pattern. **569.** "Head of Worker" (X. Dunikowski).

1971. Folk Art "Paper Cut-outs" showing various patterns.
2073. **568.** 20 g. blk., grn. & blue 10 10
2074. – 40 g. blue, grn. & cream 10 10
2075. – 60 g. brn., blue & grey 10 10
2076. – 1 z. 15 purple, brn. & buff 15 10
2077. – 1 z. 35 green, red and yellow 20 10

1971. Modern Polish Sculpture Mult.
2078. 40 g. Type **569** 10 10
2079. 40 g. "Foundryman" (X. Dunikowski) .. 10 10
2080. 60 g. "Miners" (M. Wiecek) 15 10
2081. 60 g. "Harvester" (S. Horno-Poplawski) .. 15 10

570. Congress Emblem and Computer Tapes.

1971. 6th Polish Technical Congress, Warsaw.
2083. **570.** 60 g. violet and red .. 10 10

571. "Angel" (J. Mehoffer). **573.** "P-11C" Fighters.

572. "Mrs. Fedorowicz" (W. Pruszkowski).

1971. Stained Glass Windows. Multicoloured.
2084. 20 g. Type **571** 10 10
2085. 40 g. "Lilies" (S. Wyspianski) 10 10
2086. 60 g. "Iris" (S. Wyspianski) 10 10
2087. 1 z. 35 "Apollo" (S. Wyspianski) 15 10
2088. 1 z. 55 "Two Wise Men" (14th-century) 15 10
2089. 3 z. 40 "The Flight into Egypt" (14th-century) 35 20
2090. 5 z. 50 "Jacob" (14th-century) 65 25
2091. 8 z. 50+4 z. "Madonna" (15th-century) .. .. 1·00 65

1971. Contemporary Art from National Museum, Cracow. Multicoloured.
2092. 40 g. Type **572** 10 10
2093. 50 g. "Woman with Book" (T. Czyzeski) 10 10
2094. 60 g. "Girl with Chrysanthemums" (O. Boznanska) 10 10
2095. 2 z. 50 "Girl in Red Dress" (J. Pankiewicz) (horiz.) 15 10
2096. 3 z. 40 "Reclining Nude" (L. Chwistek) (horiz.) .. 35 15
2097. 4 z. 50 "Strange Garden" (J. Mehoffer) 45 15
2098. 5 z. "Wife in White Hat" (Z. Pronaszko) 55 15
2099 7 z.+1 z. "Seated Nude" (W. Weiss) 75 60

1971. Polish Aircraft of World War II. Multicoloured.
2100. 90 g. Type **573** 25 10
2101. 1 z. 50 "Karas" fighter-bombers 70 10
2102. 3 z. 40 "Los" bomber .. 70 20

574. Royal Castle, Warsaw (pre-1939).

1971. Reconstruction of Royal Castle, Warsaw.
2103. **574.** 60 g. black, red & gold 10 10

575. Astronauts in Moon Rover. **576.** "Lunokhod 1".

1971. Moon Flight of "Apollo 15".
2104. **575.** 2 z. 50 multicoloured 45 15

1971. Moon Flight of "Lunik 17" and "Lunokhod 1".
2106. **576.** 2 z. 50 multicoloured 45 15

577. Worker at Wheel. **578.** Ship-building.

1971. 6th Polish United Workers' Party Congress (a) Party Posters.
2108. **577.** 60 g. red, blue & grey 10 10
2109. 60 g. red and grey (Worker's head) .. 10 10

(b) Industrial Development. Each in gold and red.
2110. 60 g. Type **578** 10 10
2111. 60 g. Building construction 10 10
2112. 60 g. Combine-harvester 10 10
2113. 60 g. Motor-car production 10 10
2114. 60 g. Pit-head 10 10
2115. 60 g. Petro-chemical plant 10 10

579. "Prunus cerasus".

1971. Flowers of Trees and Shrubs. Mult.
2117. 10 g. Type **579** 15 10
2118. 20 g. "Malusniedzwetzskyana" 15 10
2119. 40 g. "Pyrus L." .. 20 10
2120. 60 g. "Prunus persica" 20 10
2121. 1 z. 15 "Magnolia kobus" 20 10
2122. 1 z. 35 "Crataegus oxyacantha" 25 10
2123. 2 z. 50 "Malus M." .. 30 10
2124. 3 z. 40 "Aesculus carnea" 50 15
2125. 5 z. "Robinia pseudacacia" 85 35
2126. 8 z. 50 "Prunus avium" 1·60 80

580. "Worker" (sculpture, J. Januszkiewicz).

1972. 30th Anniv. of Polish Workers' Coalition.
2127. **580.** 60 g. black and red .. 10 10

581. Tobogganing.

1972. Winter Olympic Games, Sapporo, Japan. Multicoloured.
2128. 40 g. Type **581** .. 10 10
2129. 60 g. Slalom (vert.) .. 10 10
2130. 1 z. 65 Biathlon (vert.) .. 35 10
2131. 2 z. 50 Ski-jumping .. 50 20

582. "Heart" and Cardiogram Trace. **583.** Running.

1972. World Heart Month.
2133. **582.** 2 z. 50 multicoloured 40 10

1972. Olympic Games, Munich. Multicoloured.
2134. 20 g. Type **583** 10 10
2135. 30 g. Archery 10 10
2136. 40 g. Boxing 10 10
2137. 60 g. Fencing 10 10
2138. 2 z. 50 Wrestling .. 15 10
2139. 3 z. 40 Weightlifting .. 20 10
2140. 5 z. Cycling 65 30
2141. 8 z. 50 Shooting .. .. 1·40 45

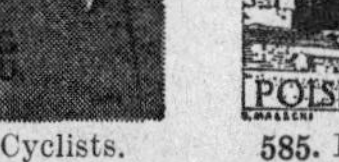

584. Cyclists. **585.** Polish War Memorial, Berlin.

1972. 25th International Peace Cycle Race.
2143. **584.** 60 g. multicoloured 20 10

1972. "Victory Day, 1945".
2144. **585** 60 g. green 10 10

586. "Rodlo" Emblem. **587.** Polish Knight of 972 A.D.

1972. 50th Anniv. of Polish Posts in Germany.
2145. **586.** 60 g. ochre, red & grn. 15 10

1972. Millenary of Battle of Cedynia.
2146 **587** 60 g. multicoloured .. 20 10

588. Cheetah.

1972. Zoo Animals. Multicoloured.
2147. 20 g. Type **588** 20 10
2148. 40 g. Giraffe (vert.) .. 20 10
2149. 60 g. Toco Toucan .. 30 10
2150. 1 z. 35 Chimpanzee .. 20 10
2151. 1 z. 65 Common gibbon 40 10
2152. 3 z. 40 Crocodile 55 10
2153. 4 z. Red kangaroo .. 1·00 15
2154. 4 z. 50 Tiger (vert.) .. 3·25 1·40
2155. 7 z. Mountain zebra .. 3·25 1·60

589. L. Warynski. (founder). **590.** F. Dzerzhinsky.

1972. 90th Anniv. of Proletarian Party.
2156. **589.** 60 g. multicoloured 10 10

1972. 95th Birth Anniv. of Feliks Dzerzhinsky (Russian politician).
2157. **590.** 60 g. black and red .. 10 10

591. Global Emblem. **592.** Scene from "In Barracks" (ballet).

1972. 25th International Co-operative Federation Congress.
2158. **591.** 60 g. multicoloured 10 10

1972. Death Centenary of Stanislaus Moniuszko (composer). Scenes from Works.
2159. **592.** 10 g. violet and gold 10 10
2160. – 20 g. black and gold .. 10 10
2161. – 40 g. green and gold .. 15 10
2162. – 60 g. blue and gold .. 20 10
2163. – 1 z. 15 blue and gold 25 10
2164. – 1 z. 35 blue and gold 30 10
2165. – 1 z. 55 green and gold 15 15
2166. – 2 z. 50 brown & gold 35 30

Designs: 20 g. "The Countess" (opera). 40 g. "The Haunted Manor" (opera). 60 g. "Halka" (opera). 1 z. 15, "New Don Quixote" (ballet). 1 z. 35, "Verbum Nobile". 1 z. 55, "Ideal" (operetta). 2 z. 50, "Pariah" (opera).

593. "Copernicus the Astronomer".

1972. 500th Birth Anniv. (1973) of Nicolas Copernicus. (4th issue).
2167. **593.** 40 g. black and blue .. 25 10
2168. – 60 g. black & orange 35 10
2169. – 2 z. 50 black and red 40 20
2170. – 3 z. 40 black & green 70 35

Designs: 60 g. Copernicus and Polish eagle. 2 z. 50, Copernicus and Medal. 3 z. 40, Copernicus and page of book.

594. "The Amazon" (P. Michalowski).

1972. Stamp Day. Polish Paintings. Mult.
2172. 30 g. Type **594** 10 10
2173. 40 g. "Ostafi Laszkiewicz" (J. Matejko) 10 10
2174. 60 g. "Summer Idyll" .. (W. Gerson) 10 10
2175. 2 z. "The Neapolitan Woman" (A. Kotsis) .. 15 10
2176. 2 z. 50 "Girl Bathing" (P. Szyndler) 20 10
2177. 3 z. 40 "The Princess of Thum" (A. Grottger) .. 30 10
2178. 4 z. "Rhapsody" (S. Wyspianski) .. .. 1·25 40
2179. 8 z. 50+4 z. "Young Woman" (J. Malczewski) (horiz.) .. 1·50 65

1972. Nos. 1578/9 surch.
2180. 50 g. on 40 g. brown .. 15 10
2181. 90 g. on 40 g. brown .. 30 10
2182. 1 z. on 40 g. brown .. 10 10
2183. 1 z. 50 on 60 g. orange .. 10 10
2184. 2 z. 70 on 40 g. brown .. 20 10
2185. 4 z. on 60 g. orange .. 55 10
2186. 4 z. 50 on 60 g. orange .. 55 10
2187. 4 z. 90 on 60 g. orange .. 60 15

596. "The Little Soldier" (E. Piwowarski).

1972. Children's Health Centre.
2188. **596.** 60 g. black & pink .. 20 10

597. "Royal Castle, Warsaw". (E. J. Dahlberg, 1656). **598.** Chalet, Chocholowska Valley.

1972. Restoration of Royal Castle, Warsaw.
2189. **597.** 60 g. black, vio. & bl. 20 10

1972. Tourism. Mountain Chalets. Mult.
2190. 40 g. Type **598** 10 10
2191. 60 g. Hala Ornak (horiz.) 10 10
2192. 1 z. 55 Hala Gasienicowa 20 10
2193. 1 z. 65 Valley of Five Lakes (horiz.) 25 10
2194. 2 z. 50 Morskie Oko .. 40 10

599. Trade Union Banners. **600.** Congress Emblem.

1972. 7th Polish Trade Union Congresses.
2195. **599.** 60 g. multicoloured .. 10 10

1972. 5th Socialist Youth Union Congress.
2196. **600.** 60 g. multicoloured .. 10 10

601. Japanese Azalea.

1972. Flowering Shrubs. **Multicoloured.**

2197. 40 g. Type **601** 10 10
2198. 50 g. Alpine rose 10 10
2199. 60 g. Pomeranian honeysuckle 10 10
2200. 1 z. 65 Chinese quince .. 15 10
2201. 2 z. 50 Korean cranberry 20 10
2202. 3 z. 40 Pontic azalea .. 35 10
2203. 4 z. Delavay's white syringa 1·00 25
2204. 8 z. 50 Common lilac ("Massena") .. .. 1·50 75

602. Piast Knight (10th-century).

603. Copernicus.

1972. Polish Cavalry Through the Ages. Multicoloured.

2205. 20 g. Type **602** 10 10
2206. 40 g. 13th-century knight 10 10
2207. 60 g. Knight of Wladyslaw Jagiello's Army (15th-century) (horiz.) 10 10
2208. 1 z. 35 17th-century hussar 25 10
2209. 4 z. Lancer of National Guard (18th-century) 75 15
2210. 4 z. 50 "Congress Kingdom" cavalry officer 85 20
2211. 5 z. Trooper of Light Cavalry (1939) (horiz.) 1·10 40
2212. 7 z. Trooper of People's Army (1945) .. 1·40 60

1972. 500th Birth Anniv. (1973) of Copernicus (5th issue).

2213. **603.** 1 z. brown 20 10
2214. 1 z. 50 ochre .. 30 10

604. Couple with Hammer and Sickle.

605. "Copernicus as Young Man" (Bacciarelli).

1972. 50th Anniv. of U.S.S.R. Mult.

2215. 40 g. Type **604** 10 10
2216. 60 g. Red star and globe 10 10

1973. 500th Birth Anniv. of Copernicus (6th issue). Multicoloured.

2217. 1 z. Type **605** 15 10
2218. 1 z. 50 "Copernicus" (anon) 20 10
2219. 2 z. 70 "Copernicus" (Zinck Nor) 50 15
2220. 4 z. "Copernicus" (from Strasbourg clock) .. 60 25
2221. 4 z. 90 "Copernicus" (Jan Matejko) (horiz.) .. 85 40

606. Coronation Sword.

607. Statue of Lenin.

1973. Polish Art. Multicoloured.

2222. 50 g. Type **606** 10 10
2223. 1 z. Kruzlowa Madonna (detail) 10 10
2224. 1 z. Armour of hussar .. 10 10
2225. 1 z. 50 Carved head from Wavel Castle 10 10
2226. 1 z. 50 Silver cockerel .. 15 10
2227. 2 z. 70 Armorial eagle .. 35 15
2228. 4 z. 90 Skarbimierz Madonna 80 40
2229. 8 z. 50 "Portrait of Tenczynski" (anon.) .. 1·25 60

1973. 50th Death Anniv. (1974) of Lenin.

2230. **607.** 1 z. multicoloured .. 15 10

608. Coded Letter.

1973. Introduction of Postal Codes.

2231. **608.** 1 z. multicoloured .. 20 10

609. Wolf.

1973. Game Animals. Multicoloured.

2232. 50 g. Type **609** 10 10
2233. 1 z. Mouflon 10 10
2234. 1 z. 50 Elk 15 10
2235. 2 z. 70 Capercaillie .. 30 10
2236. 3 z. Roe deer 30 10
2237. 4 z. 50 Lynx 70 20
2238. 4 z. 90 Red deer .. 2·10 60
2239. 5 z. Wild boar .. .. 2·40 50

610. "Salyut".

611. Open Book and Flame.

1973. Cosmic Research. Multicoloured.

2240. 4 z. 90 Type **610** 60 30
2241. 4 z. 90 "Copernicus" (U.S. satellite) 60 30

1973. 2nd Polish Science Congress, Warsaw.

2242. **611.** 1 z. 50 multicoloured 20 10

612. Ancient Seal of Poznan.

613. M. Nowotko.

1973. "Polska 73" Philatelic Exhibition, Poznan. Multicoloured.

2243 1 z. Type **612** 10 10
2244 1 z. 50 Tombstone of N. Tomicki 15 10
2245 2 z. 70 Kalisz paten .. 30 10
2246 4 z. Bronze gates, Gniezno Cathedral (horiz) .. 40 10

1973. 80th Birth Anniv. of Marceli Nowotko (party leader).

2249. **613.** 1 z. 50 black and red 15 10

614. Cherry Blossom.

1973. Protection of the Environment. **Mult.**

2250. 50 g. Type **614** 10 10
2251. 90 g. Cattle in meadow .. 10 10
2252. 1 z. White Stork on nest 50 10
2253. 1 z. 50 Pond life .. 20 10
2254. 2 z. 70 Meadow flora .. 25 10
2255. 4 z. 90 Ocean fauna .. 55 30
2256. 5 z. Forest life .. .. 2·75 45
2257. 6 z. 50 Agricultural produce 2·40 60

615. Motor-cyclist.

1973. World Speedway Race Championships, Chorzow.

2258. **615.** 1 z. 50 multicoloured 25 10

616. "Copernicus" (M. Bacciarelli).

1973. Stamp Day.

2259. **616.** 4 z. + 2 z. multicoloured 75 40

617. Tank.

1973. 30th Anniv. of Polish People's Army. Multicoloured.

2260. 1 z. Type **617** 15 10
2261. 1 z. Jet fighter 20 10
2262. 1 z. 50 Guided missile .. 30 15
2263. 1 z. 50 Missile boat .. 30 10

618. G. Piramowicz and Title Page.

1973. Bicent. of Nat. Educational Commission.

2264. **618.** 1 z. brown and yellow 10 10
2265. – 1 z. 50 grn. & pale grn. 20 10

DESIGN: 1 z. 50, J. Sniadecki, H. Kollataj and J. U. Niemcewicz.

619. Pawel Strzelecki (explorer) and Red Kangaroo.

1973. Polish Scientists. Multicoloured.

2266 1 z. Type **619** 15 10
2267 1 z. Henryk Arctowski (polar explorer) and Adelie penguins .. 35 10
2268 1 z. 50 Stefan Rogozinski (explorer) and "Lucy-Margaret" (schooner) .. 30 10
2269 1 z. 50 Benedykt Dybowski (zoologist) and sable, Lake Baikal 20 10
2270 2 z. Bronislaw Malinowski (anthropologist) and New Guinea dancers .. 25 10
2271 2 z. 70 Stefan Drzewiecki (oceanographer) and submarine 35 10
2272 3 z. Edward Strasburger (botanist) and classified plants 50 20
2273 8 z. Ignacy Domeyko (geologist) and Chilean desert landscape .. 1·25 50

620. Polish Flag.

621. Jelcz-Berliet Coach.

1973. 25th Anniv. of Polish United Workers' Party.

2274. **620.** 1 z. 40 red, blue & gold 15 10

1973. Polish Motor Vehicles. **Multicoloured.**

2275. 50 g. Type **621** 10 10
2276. 90 g. Jelcz "316" truck .. 10 10
2277. 1 z. Polski-Fiat "126p" saloon 10 10
2278. 1 z. 50 Polski-Fiat "125p" saloon and mileage records 15 10
2279. 4 z. Nysa "M-521" utility van 55 25
2280. 4 z. 50 Star "660" truck 65 45

622. Iris.

623. Cottage, Kurpie.

1974. Flowers. Drawings by S. Wyspianski.

2281. **622.** 50 g. purple 10 10
2282. – 1 z. green 15 10
2283. – 1 z. 50 red 20 10
2284. – 3 z. violet 35 10
2285. – 4 z. blue 55 15
2286. – 4 z. 50 green 65 25

FLOWERS: 1 z. Dandelion. 1 z. 50, Rose. 3 z. Thistle. 4 z. Cornflower. 4 z. 50, Clover.

1974. Wooden Architecture. Multicoloured.

2287. 1 z. Type **623** 10 10
2288. 1 z. 50 Church, Sekowa .. 10 10
2289. 4 z. Town Hall, Sulmierzyce 30 10
2290. 4 z. 50 Church, Lachowice 35 15
2291. 4 z. 90 Windmill, Sobienie Jeziory 55 30
2292. 5 z. Orthodox Church, Ulucz 65 35

624. 19th-century Mailcoach.

625. Cracow Motif.

1974. Centenary of Universal Postal Union.

2293. **624.** 1 z. 50 multicoloured 20 10

1974. "SOCPHILEX IV" Int., Stamp Exn., Katowice. Regional Floral Embroideries. Multicoloured.

2294. 50 g. Type **625** 10 10
2295. 1 z. 50 Lowicz motif .. 15 10
2296. 4 z. Silesian motif .. 35 15

626. Association Emblem.

627. Soldier and Dove.

1974. Fighters for Freedom and Democracy Association, Warsaw. 5th Congress.

2298. **626.** 1 z. 50 red 15 10

1974. 29th Anniv. of Victory over Fascism in Second World War.

2299. **627.** 1 z. 50 multicoloured 20 10

628. "Comecon" Headquarters, Moscow.

1974. 25th Anniv. of Council for Mutual Economic Aid.

2300 **628** 1 z. 50 brown, red & bl 15 10

629. World Cup Emblem.

1974. World Cup Football Championships, West Germany. Multicoloured.

2301. 4 z. 90 Type **629** 60 20
2302. 4 z. 90 Players and Olympic Gold Medal of 1972 .. 60 20

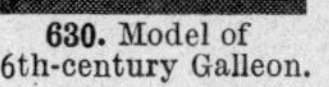

630. Model of 16th-century Galleon. **631.** Title page of "Chess" by J. Kochanowski.

1974. Gdansk Sailing Festival. Polish sailing ships. Multicoloured.

2304. 1 z Type **630** 20 10
2305. 1 z. 50 Sloop "Dal" (1934) 25 10
2306. 2 z. 70 Yacht "Opty" (Teliga's circum-navigation, 1969) .. 30 10
2307. 4 z. Cadet ship "Dar Pomorza", 1972 .. 65 25
2308. 4 z. 90 Yacht "Polonez" (Baranowski's circum-navigation, 1973 .. 1·10 35

1974. 10th International Chess Festival, Lublin. Multicoloured.

2309 1 z. Type **631** 30 10
2310 1 z. 50 "Education" (18th-century engraving, D. Chodowiecki) .. 45 10

632. Lazienkowska Road Junction.

1974. Opening of Lazienkowska Flyover.

2311. **632.** 1 z. 50 multicoloured 25 15

633. Face and Map of Poland. **634.** Strawberries.

1974. 30th Anniv. of Polish People's Republic.

2312. **633.** 1 z. 50 blk., gold & red 15 10
2313. – 1 z. 50 mult. (silver background) 15 10
2314. – 1 z. 50 mult. (red background) 15 10

Design—(31 × 43 mm.) Nos. 2313/14, Polish "Eagle".

1974. 19th Int. Horticultural Congress, Warsaw. Fruits, Vegetables and Flowers. Multicoloured.

2316. 50 g. Type **634** 10 10
2317. 90 g. Blackcurrants .. 15 10
2318. 1 z. Apples 15 10
2319. 1 z. 50 Cucumbers .. 20 10
2320. 2 z. 70 Tomatoes .. 25 10
2321. 4 z. 50 Green Peas .. 60 20
2322. 4 z. 90 Pansies .. 1·00 35
2323. 5 z. Nasturtiums .. 1·40 40

635. Civic Militia and Security Service Emblem. **636.** "Child in Polish Costume" (L. Orlowski).

1974. 30th Anniv. of Polish Civic Militia and Security Service.

2324. **635.** 1 z. 50 multicoloured 25 10

1974. Stamp Day. "The Child in Polish Painting". Multicoloured.

2325. 50 g. Type **636** 10 10
2326. 90 g. "Girl with Pigeon" (anon.) 10 10
2327. 1 z. "Portrait of a Girl" (S. Wyspianski) .. 10 10
2328. 1 z. 50 "The Orphan from Poronin" (W. Slewinski) 10 10
2329. 3 z. "Peasant Boy" (K. Sichulski) 30 10
2330. 4 z. 50 "Florence Page" (A. Gierymski) .. 45 10
2331. 4 z. 90 "Tadeusz and Dog" (P. Michalowski) .. 55 25
2332. 6 z. 50 "Boy with Doe" (A. Kotsis) 85 35

637. "The Crib", Cracow.

1974. Polish Art. Multicoloured.

2333 1 z. Type **637** 10 10
2334 1 z. 50 "The Flight to Egypt" (15th-century polyptych) 15 10
2335 2 z. "King Sigismund III Vasa" (16th-century miniature) 20 10
2336 4 z. "King Jan Olbracht" (16th-century title-page) 80 30

638. Angler and Fish. **639.** "Pablo Neruda" (O. Guayasamin).

1974. Polish Folklore. 16th-century Woodcuts. (1st series).

2337. **638.** 1 z. black 15 10
2338. – 1 z. 50 blue 20 10

Design: 1 z. 50, Hunter and wild animals.
See also Nos. 2525/6.

1974. 70th Birth Anniv. of Pablo Neruda (Chilean poet).

2339. **639.** 1 z. 50 multicoloured 20 10

640. "Nike" Memorial and National Opera House.

1975. 30th Anniv. of Warsaw Liberation.

2340. **640.** 1 z. 50 multicoloured 20 10

641. Male Lesser Kestrel. **642.** Broken Barbed Wire.

1975. Birds of Prey. Multicoloured.

2341. 1 z. Type **641** 25 10
2342. 1 z. Lesser kestrel (female) 25 10
2343. 1 z. 50 Red-footed falcon (male) 30 10
2344. 1 z. 50 Red-footed falcon (female) 30 10
2345. 2 z. European hobby .. 55 10
2346. 3 z. Common kestrel .. 85 10
2347. 4 z. Merlin .. .. 2·25 80
2348. 8 z. Peregrine falcon .. 3·25 1·60

1975. 30th Anniv. of Auschwitz Concentration Camp Liberation.

2349. **642.** 1 z. 50 black & red .. 25 10

643. Hurdling.

1975. 6th European Indoor Athletic Championships Katowice. Multicoloured.

2350. 1 z. Type **643** 10 10
2351. 1 z. 50 Pole vault .. 15 10
2352. 4 z. Triple jump .. 40 10
2353. 4 z. 90 Running 45 15

644. "St. Anne" (Veit Stoss).

1975. "Arphila 1975" International Stamp Exhibition, Paris.

2355. **644.** 1 z. 50 multicoloured 15 10

645. Globe and "Radio Waves".

1975. International Amateur Radio Union Conference, Warsaw.

2356. **645.** 1 z. 50 multicoloured 15 10

646. Stone, Pine and Tatra Mountains. **647.** Hands holding Tulips and Rifle.

1975. Cent. of Mountain Guides' Association. Multicoloured.

2357. 1 z. Type **646** 15 10
2358. 1 z. Gentians and Tatra Mountains 15 10
2359. 1 z. 50 Sudety Mountains (horiz.) 15 10
2360. 1 z. 50 Branch of yew (horiz.) 15 10
2361. 4 z. Beskidy Mountains .. 45 20
2362. 4 z. Arnica blossoms .. 45 20

1975. 30th Anniv. of Victory over Fascism.

2363. **647.** 1 z. 50 multicoloured 15 10

648. Flags of Member Countries.

1975. 20th Anniv. of Warsaw Treaty Organization.

2364. **648.** 1 z. 50 multicoloured 15 10

649. Hens.

1975. 26th European Zoo-technical Federation Congress, Warsaw. Multicoloured.

2365. 50 g. Type **649** 10 10
2366. 1 z. Geese 10 10
2367. 1 z. 50 Cattle 15 10
2368. 2 z. Cow 15 10
2369. 3 z. Wielkopolska horse .. 35 10
2370. 4 z. Pure-bred Arab horses 40 10
2371. 4 z. 50 Pigs .. .. 1·75 30
2372. 5 z. Sheep .. .. 2·00 40

650. "Apollo" and "Soyuz" Spacecraft linked. **651.** Organization Emblem.

1975. "Apollo-Soyuz" Space Project. Mult.

2373 1 z. 50 Type **650** 10 10
2374 4 z. 90 "Apollo" spacecraft 40 20
2375 4 z. 90 "Soyuz" spacecraft 40 20

1975. National Health Protection Fund.

2377. **651.** 1 z. 50 bl., blk. & silv. 20 10

652. U.N. Emblem.

1975. 30th Anniv. of U.N.O.

2378. **652.** 4 z. multicoloured .. 30 15

653. Polish Flag within "E" for Europe.

1975. European Security and Co-operation Conference, Helsinki.

2379. **653.** 4 z. red, blue & black 40 15

654. "Bolek and Lolek".

1975. Children's Television Characters. Multicoloured.

2380. 50 g. Type **654** 10 10
2381. 1 z. "Jacek" and "Agatka" 15 10
2382. 1 z. 50 "Reksio" (dog) 20 10
2383. 4 z. "Telesfor" (dragon) 70 15

655. Institute Emblem. **656.** Women's Faces.

1975. 40th Session of International Statistics Institute.

2384. **655.** 1 z. 50 multicoloured 15 10

1975. International Women's Year.

2385. **656.** 1 z. 50 multicoloured 15 10

657. "Albatros" Aeroplane.

1975. 50th Anniv. of First Polish Airmail Stamps. Multicoloured.

2386. 2 z. 40 Type **657** .. 40 15
2387. 4 z. 90 Tail of "Il-62" jetliner 85 20

658. " Mary and Margaret " and Polish Settlers. 659. Frederic Chopin.

1975. Bicent. of American Revolution. Poles in American Life. Multicoloured.

2388. 1 z. Type **658** 20 10
2389. 1 z. 50 Polish glass-worker Jamestown 15 10
2390. 2 z. 70 Helena Modrzejewska (actress) 20 10
2391. 4 z. General K. Pulaski .. 35 10
2392. 6 z. 40 Gen. T. Kosciuzko 55 35

1975. 9th International Chopin Piano Competition.

2394. **659.** 1 z. 50 blk., lilac & gold 25 10

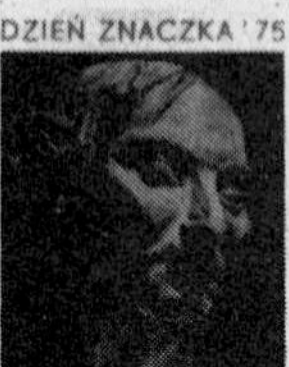

660. " Self-portrait ". 661. Market Place, Kazimierz Dolny.

1975. Stamp Day. Birth Cent. of Xawery Dunikowski (sculptor). Multicoloured.

2395. 50 g. Type **660** 10 10
2396. 1 z. " Breath " 10 10
2397. 1 z. 50 "Maternity" .. 15 10
2398. 8 z. + 4 z. " Silesian Insurrectionists " 90 45

1975. European Architectural Heritage Year.

2399. **661.** 1 z. green 10 10
2400. – 1 z. 50 brown .. 15 10

DESIGN—VERT. 1 z. 50, Town Hall, Zamosc.

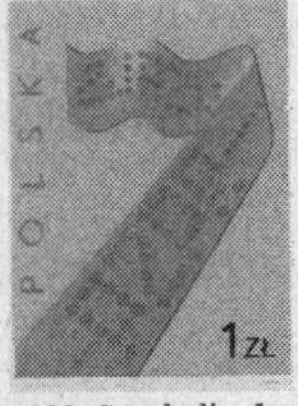

662. " Lodz " (W. Strzeminski). 664. Symbolised Figure " 7 ".

663. Henry IV's Eagle Gravestone Head (14th-century).

1975. " Lodz 75 " National Stamp Exhibition.

2401. **662.** 4 z. 50 multicoloured 30 15

1975. Piast Dynasty of Silesia.

2403. **663.** 1 z. green 10 10
2404. – 1 z. 50 brown .. 10 10
2405. – 4 z. violet 35 15

DESIGNS: 1 z. 50 Seal of Prince Boleslaw of Legnica. 4 z. Coin of last Prince, Jerzy Wilhelm.

1975. 7th Congress of Polish United Workers Party.

2406. **664.** 1 z. multicoloured .. 10 10
2407. – 1 z. 50 red, bl. & silver 15 10

DESIGN: 1 z. 50, Party initials " PZPR ".

665. Ski-jumping.

1976. Winter Olympic Games, Innsbruck. Multicoloured.

2408. 50 g. Type **665** 10 10
2409. 1 z. Ice-hockey 15 10
2410. 1 z. 50 Downhill skiing .. 20 10
2411. 2 z. Speed skating .. 20 10
2412. 4 z. Tobogganing .. 35 10
2413. 6 z. 40 Biathlon 50 25

666. R. Trevithick's Steam Railway Locomotive, 1803

1976. History of the Railway Locomotive. Multicoloured.

2414 50 g. Type **666** 15 10
2415 1 z. Murray and Blenkinsop's steam locomotive, 1810 .. .. .. 25 10
2416 1 z. 50 George Stephenson's locomotive "Rocket", 1829 .. 35 10
2417 1 z. 50 Polish "Universal" Type ET-22 electric locomotive, 1969 .. 35 10
2418 2 z. 70 Robert Stephenson's locomotive "North Star", 1837 .. 50 10
2419 3 z. Joseph Harrison's steam locomotive, 1840 60 10
2420 4 z. 50 Thomas Roger's steam locomotive, 1855 2·50 60
2421 4 z. 90 Polish Chrzanow Works steam locomotive, 1922 .. .. 2·50 60

667. Flags of Member Countries.

1976. 20th Anniv. of Institute for Nuclear Research (C.M.E.A.).

2422. **667.** 1 z. 50 multicoloured 15 10

668. Early Telephone, Satellite and Radar.

1976. Telephone Cent.

2423. **668.** 1 z. 50 multicoloured 15 10

669. " Jantar " Glider 670. Ice-hockey Player.

1976. Air. Contemporary Aviation.

2424. **669.** 5 z. blue 50 10
2425. – 10 z. brown 90 10
2425a. – 20 z. olive .. .. 1·90 15
2425b. – 50 z. lake .. .. 4·00 65

DESIGN: 10 z. " Mi-6 " transport helicopter. 20 z. PZL " 106 (Kruk) " light agricultural aircraft. 50 z. " TS-11 (Iskra) " jet trainer over Warsaw Castle.

1976. World Ice-hockey Championships, Katowice. Multicoloured.

2426. 1 z. Type **670** 15 10
2427. 1 z. 50 Type **670** reversed 25 10

671. Polish U.N. Soldier.

1976. Polish Troops in U.N. Sinai Force.

2428. **671.** 1 z. 50 multicoloured 20 10

672. " Glory to the Sappers " (S. Kulon). 673. " Interphil 76 ".

1976. War Memorials. Multicoloured.

2429 1 z. Type **672** 15 10
2430 1 z. 1st Polish Army Monument, Sandau, Laba (B. Koniuszy) .. 15 10

1976. " Interphil '76 " Int. Stamp Exn., Philadelphia.

2431. **673.** 8 z. 40 multicoloured 65 25

674. Wielkopolski Park and Tawny Owl.

1976. National Parks. Multicoloured.

2432. 90 g. Type **674** 40 15
2433. 1 z. Wolinski Park and White-tailed sea eagle 40 15
2434. 1 z. 50 Slowinski Park and seagull 50 15
2435. 4 z. 50 Bieszczadzki Park and lynx 50 20
2436. 5 z. Ojcowski Park and bat 50 30
2437. 6 z. Kampinoski Park and elk 75 35

675. Peace Dove within Globe.

1976. 25th Anniv. of U.N. Postal Administration.

2438. **675.** 8 z. 40 multicoloured 70 25

676. Fencing. 677. National Theatre.

1976. Olympic Games, Montreal. Mult.

2439. 50 g. Type **676** 10 10
2440. 1 z. Cycling 10 10
2441. 1 z. 50 Football 10 10
2442. 4 z. 20 Boxing 25 10
2443. 6 z. 90 Weightlifting .. 45 20
2444. 8 z. 40 Athletics 60 30

1976. Cent. of National Theatre, Poznan.

2446. **677.** 1 z. 50 green & orange 10 10

678. Aleksander Czekanowski and Baikal Landscape. 679. " Sphinx ".

1976. Death Cent of Aleksander Czekanowski (geologist).

2447 **678** 1 z. 50 multicoloured 15 10

1976. Stamp Day. Greek Corinthian Vases (7th century B.C.). Multicoloured.

2448. 1 z. Type **679** 10 10
2449. 1 z. 50 " Siren " (horiz.) .. 10 10
2450. 2 z. " Lion " (horiz.) .. 15 10
2451. 4 z. 20 " Bull " (horiz.) .. 30 10
2452. 4 z. 50 " Goat " (horiz.) .. 35 15
2453. 8 z. + 4 z. " Sphinx " (different) .. .. .. 1·10 40

680. Warszawa "M 20".

1976. 25th Anniv. of Zeran Motor-car Factory, Warsaw. Multicoloured.

2454. 1 z. Type **680** 10 10
2455. 1 z. 50 Warszawa " 223 " 15 10
2456. 2 z. Syrena " 104 " .. 20 10
2457. 4 z. 90 Polski - Fiat " 125 P " 40 20

681. Molten Steel Ladle.

1976. Huta Katowice Steel Works.

2459 **681** 1 z. 50 multicoloured 10 10

682. Congress Emblem. 683. " Wirzbieto Epitaph " (painting on wood, 1425).

1976. 8th Polish Trade Unions Congress.

2460. **682.** 1 z. 50 orange, bistre and brown .. 10 10

1976. Polish Art. Multicoloured.

2461. 1 z. Type **683** 10 10
2462. 6 z. " Madonna and Child " (painted carving, c. 1410) 40 15

684. Tanker " Zawrat " at Oil Terminal, Gdansk.

1976. Polish Ports. Multicoloured.

2463 1 z. Type **684** 20 10
2464 1 z. Ferry "Gryf" at Gdansk 20 10
2465 1 z. 50 Loading container ship "General Bem", Gdynia 35 10
2466 1 z. 50 Liner "Stefan Batory" leaving Gdynia 25 10
2467 2 z. Bulk carrier "Ziemia Szczecinska" loading at Szczecin 40 10
2468 4 z. 20 Loading coal, Swinoujscie 80 15
2469 6 z. 90 Pleasure craft, Kolobrzeg 95 25
2470 8 z. 40 Coastal map .. 1·50 35

685. Nurse and Patient. 686. Order of Civil Defence Service.

1977. Polish Red Cross.

2471. **685.** 1 z. 50 multicoloured 15 10

1977. Polish Civil Defence.

2472. **686.** 1 z. 50 multicoloured 15 10

687. Ball in Road.

1977. Child Road Safety Campaign.

2473. **687.** 1 z. 50 multicoloured 20 10

688. Dewberries "Rubus caesius". **689.** Computer Tape.

1977. Wild Fruits. Multicoloured.
2474. 50 g. Type **688** 10 10
2475. 90 g. Cowberries .. 10 10
2476. 1 z. Wild Strawberries .. 10 10
2477. 1 z. 50 Bilberries .. 15 10
2478. 2 z. Raspberries 20 10
2479. 4 z. 50 Sloes 45 15
2480. 6 z. Rose Hips 60 20
2481. 6 z. 90 Hazelnuts .. 1·10 35

1977. 30th Anniv. of Russian-Polish Technical Co-operation.
2482. **689.** 1 z. 50 multicoloured 20 10

690. Pendulum Traces and Emblem.

1977. Seventh Polish Congress of Technology.
2483. **690.** 1 z. 50 multicoloured 20 10

691. " Toilet of Venus ".

1977. 400th Birth Anniv. of Peter Paul Rubens. Multicoloured.
2484 1 z. Type **691** 10 10
2485 1 z. 50 "Bathsheba at the Fountain" 10 10
2486 5 z. "Helena Fourment with Fur Coat" .. 40 20
2487 6 z. "Self-portrait" .. 45 40

692. Dove. **694.** Wolf.

693. Cyclist.

1977. World Council of Peace Congress.
2489. **692.** 1 z. 50 blue, yell. & blk. 20 10

1977. 30th International Peace Cycle Race.
2490. **693.** 1 z. 50 multicoloured 20 10

1977. Endangered Animals. Multicoloured.
2491. 1 z. Type **694** 15 10
2492. 1 z. 50 Great bustard .. 40 15
2493. 1 z. 50 Common kestrel 40 15
2494. 6 z. European otter .. 70 25

695. " The Violinist " (J. Toornvliet). **697.** H. Wieniawski and Music Clef.

696. Midsummer's Day Bonfire.

1977. " Amphilex 77 " Stamp Exhibition, Amsterdam.
2495. **695.** 6 z. multicoloured .. 40 35

1977. Folk Customs. 19th-century Wood Engravings. Multicoloured.
2496 90 g. Type **696** 10 10
2497 1 z. Easter cock (vert) .. 10 10
2498 1 z. 50 "Smigus" (dousing of women on Easter Monday, Miechow district) (vert) .. 10 10
2499 3 z. Harvest Festival, Sandomierz district (vert) 25 10
2500 6 z. Children with Christmas crib (vert) .. 55 15
2501 8 z. 40 Mountain wedding dance 80 20

1977. Wieniawski International Music Competitions, Poznan.
2502. **697.** 1 z. 50 blk., red & gold 30 10

698. " Parnassius apollo ".

1977. Butterflies. Multicoloured.
2503. 1 z. Type **698** 20 10
2504. 1 z. " Nymphalis polychloros " 20 10
2505. 1 z. 50 " Nymphalis antiopa " .. 25 10
2506. 1 z. 50 " Papilio machaon " 25 10
2507. 5 z. " Fabriciana adippe " 65 20
2508. 6 z. 90 " Argynnis paphia " 1·40 70

699. Keyboard and Arms of Slupsk. **700.** Feliks Dzerzhinsky.

1977. Piano Festival, Slupsk.
2509 **699** 1 z. 50 mve, blk & grn 15 10

1977. Birth Cent. of Feliks Dzerzhinsky (Russian politician).
2510. **700.** 1 z. 50 brown & ochre 15 10

701. " Sputnik " circling Earth. **702.** Silver Dinar (11th century).

1977. 60th Anniv of Russian Revolution and 20th Anniv of 1st Artificial Satellite (1st issue).
2511 **701** 1 z. 50 red and blue .. 15 10
See also No. 2527.

1977. Stamp Day. Polish Coins. Mult.
2513 50 g. Type **702** 10 10
2514 1 z. Cracow grosz, 14th century 10 10
2515 1 z. 50 Legnica thaler, 17th century .. 15 10
2516 4 z. 20 Gdansk guilder, 18th century .. 40 10
2517 4 z. 50 Silver 5 z. coin, 1936 .. .. 40 10
2518 6 z. Millenary 100 z. coin, 1966 .. .. .. 65 25

703. Wolin Gate, Kamien Pomorski. **704.** " Sputnik 1 " and " Mercury " Capsule.

1977. Architectural Monuments. Mult.
2519 1 z. Type **703** 10 10
2520 1 z. Larch church, Debno 10 10
2521 1 z. 50 Monastery, Przasnysz (horiz) .. 10 10
2522 1 z. 50 Plock cathedral (horiz) 10 10
2523 6 z. Kornik castle (horiz) 40 15
2524 6 z. 90 Palace and garden, Wilanow (horiz) .. 45 25

1977. Polish Folklore. 16th Century woodcuts (2nd series). As T **638**.
2525. 4 z. sepia 25 10
2526. 4 z. 50 brown 30 10
DESIGNS: 4 z. Bird snaring. 4 z. 50, Bee-keeper and hives.

1977. 20th Anniv of 1st Space Satellite (2nd issue).
2527 **704** 6 z. 90 multicoloured 45 30

705. DN Category Iceboats.

1978. 6th World Ice Sailing Championships.
2528. **705.** 1 z. 50 blk., grey & bl. 15 10
2529. – 1 z. 50 blk., grey & bl. 15 10
DESIGN: No. 2529, Close-up of DN iceboat.

706. Electric Locomotive and Katowice Station.

1978. Railway Engines. Multicoloured.
2530. 50 g. Type **706** 15 10
2531. 1 z. Py 27 Steam locomotive (Znin-Gasawa narrow-gauge railway) 15 10
2532. 1 z. Pm 36 Steam locomotive and Cegielski's factory, Poznan .. 15 10
2533. 1 z. 50 Electric locomotive and Otwock station .. 20 10
2534. 1 z. 50 Steam locomotive and Warsaw Stalowa station 20 10
2535. 4 z. 50 Steam locomotive Ty 51 and Gdynia station 55 15
2536. 5 z. Tr 21 and steam locomotive factory, Chrzanow 60 15
2537. 6 z. Cockerill steam locomotive and Vienna station .. .. .. 1·00 60

707. Cz. Tanski and Glider. **708.** Tackle.

1978. Aviation History and 50th Anniv of Polish Aero Club. Multicoloured.
2538 50 g. Type **707** 10 10
2539 1 z. F. Zwirko and S. Wigura with "RWD-6" aircraft (vert) .. 10 10
2540 1 z. 50 S. Skarzynski and "RWD-5 bis" monoplane (vert) .. 20 10
2541 4 z. 20 "MI-2" helicopter (vert) 40 10
2542 6 z. 90 "PZL-104 Wilga 35" monoplane .. 1·40 25
2543 8 z. 45 "SZD-45 Ogar" powered glider .. 1·10 25

1978. World Cup Football Championship, Argentina. Multicoloured.
2544 1 z. 50 Type **708** 10 10
2545 6 z. 90 Ball on field (horiz) 45 30

709. Biennale Emblem.

1978. Seventh International Poster Biennale, Warsaw.
2546. **709.** 1 z. 50 mauve, yellow and violet 10 10

711. Polonez Saloon Car.

1978. Car Production.
2548. **711.** 1 z. 50 multicoloured 15 10

712. Fair Emblem. **713.** Miroslaw Hermaszewski.

1978. 50th International Fair, Poznan.
2549. **712.** 1 z. 50 multicoloured 10 10

1978. First Pole in Space. Multicoloured. With or without date.
2550. 1 z. 50 Type **713** 15 10
2551. 6 z. 90 M. Hermaszewski and globe 45 15

714. Globe containing Face.

1978. 11th World Youth and Students Festival, Havana.
2552. **714.** 1 z. 50 multicoloured 10 10

716. Mosquito and Malaria Organisms. **717.** Pedunculate Oak.

1978. 4th International Congress of Parasitologists, Warsaw and Cracow. Mult.
2554 1 z. 50 Type **716** 15 10
2555 6 z. Tsetse fly and sleeping sickness organism 55 30

1978. Environment Protection. Trees. Multicoloured.
2556. 50 g. Norway Maple .. 10 10
2557. 1 z. Type **717** 10 10
2558. 1 z. 50 White Poplar .. 15 10
2559. 4 z. 20 Scots Pine .. 40 10
2560. 4 z. 50 White Willow .. 40 10
2561. 6 z. Birch 60 25

719. Communications.

1978. 20th Anniv. of Socialist Countries' Communications Organization.
2563. **719.** 1 z. 50 red, lt. bl. & bl. 10 10

720. " Peace " (Andre Le Brun).

1978.

2564. 720. 1 z. violet 10 10
2565. 1 z. 50 turquoise .. 10 10
2565a. 2 z. brown 15 10
2565b. 2 z. 50 blue 20 10

721. Polish Unit of U.N. Middle East Force.

1978. 35th Anniv. of Polish People's Army. Multicoloured.

2566. 1 z. 50 Colour party of Tadeusz Kosciuszko 1st Warsaw Infantry Division 15 10
2567. 1 z. 50 Mechanised Unit colour party 15 10
2568. 1 z. 50 Type **721** 15 10

722. " Portrait of a Young Man " (Raphael).

1978. Stamp Day.

2569. **722.** 6 z. multicoloured .. 40 25

723. Janusz Korczak with Children. 724. Wojciech Boguslawski.

1978. Birth Centenary of Janusz Korczak (pioneer of children's education).

2570 **723** 1 z. 50 multicoloured 20 10

1978. Polish Dramatists. Multicoloured.

2571. 50 g. Type **724** 10 10
2572. 1 z. Aleksander Fredro .. 10 10
2573. 1 z. 50 Juliusz Slowacki 10 10
2574. 2 z. Adam Mickiewicz .. 15 10
2575. 4 z. 50 Stanislaw Wyspianski 30 10
2576. 6 z. Gabriela Zapolska .. 40 20

725. Polish Combatants' Monument and Eiffel Tower.

1978. Monument to Polish Combatants in France, Paris.

2577. **725.** 1 z. 50 brn., bl. & red 20 10

726. Przewalski Horses.

1978. 50th Anniv. of Warsaw Zoo. Mult.

2578. 50 g. Type **726** 10 10
2579. 1 z. Polar bears 20 10
2580. 1 z. 50 Indian Elephants 30 10
2581. 2 z. Jaguars 35 10
2582. 4 z. 20 Grey seals .. 45 10
2583. 4 z. 50 Hartebeests .. 45 15
2584. 6 z. Mandrills 70 25

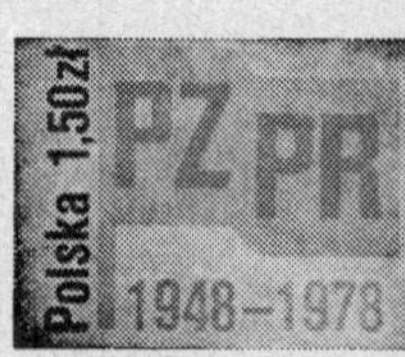

727. Party Flag. 728. Stanislaw Dubois.

1978. 30th Anniv. of Polish Workers' United Party.

2585. **727.** 1 z. 50 red, gold and blk 10 10

1978. Leaders of Polish Workers' Movement.

2586. **728.** 1 z. 50 blue and red .. 10 10
2587. – 1 z. 50 lilac and red .. 10 10
2588. – 1 z. 50 olive and red .. 10 10
2589. – 1 z. 50 brown and red 10 10

DESIGNS: No. 2587, Aleksander Zawadzki. No. 2588, Julian Lenski. No. 2589, Aldolf Warski.

729. Aircraft of 1929 and 1979.

1979. 50th Anniv. of LOT Polish Airlines.

2590. **729.** 6 z. 90 multicoloured 60 15

730. Train.

1979. International Year of the Child. Children's paintings. Multicoloured.

2591 50 g. Type **730** 15 10
2592 1 z. "Mother with Children" 10 10
2593 1 z. 50 Children playing .. 15 10
2594 6 z. Family Group .. 50 15

731. " Portrait of Artist's Wife with Foxgloves " (Karol Mondrala).

1979. Contemporary Graphics.

2595 – 50 g. lilac 10 10
2596 **731** 1 z. green 10 10
2597 – 1 z. 50 blue 10 10
2598 – 4 z. 50 brown .. 30 10

DESIGNS—HORIZ. 50 g. "Lightning" (Edmund Bartlomiejczyk). VERT. 1 z. 50, "The Musicians" (Tadeusz Kulisiewicz). 4 z. 50, "Head of a Young Man" (Wladyslaw Skoczylas).

732. A. Frycz Modrzewski (political writer), King Stefan Batory and Jan Zamoyski (chancellor).

1979. 400th Anniv. (1978) of Royal Tribunal in Piotrkow Trybunalski.

2599. **732.** 1 z. 50 brown and deep brown 20 10

733. Pole Vault.

1979. 60th Anniv. of Polish Olympic Committee. Multicoloured.

2600. 1 z. Type **733** 10 10
2601. 1 z. 50 High jump .. 10 10
2602. 6 z. Skiing 40 15
2603. 8 z. 40 Horse riding .. 60 25

734. Flounder.

1979. Centenary of Polish Angling. Mult.

2605. 50 g. Type **734** 10 10
2606. 90 g. Perch 15 10
2607. 1 z. Greyling 15 10
2608. 1 z. 50 Salmon 15 10
2609. 2 z. Trout 20 10
2610. 4 z. 50 Pike 40 10
2611. 5 z. Carp 45 15
2612. 6 z. Catfish 50 20

735. " 30 Years of RWPG ".

1979. 30th Anniv. of Council of Mutual Economic Aid.

2613. **735.** 1 z. 50 red, ultram. and blue 20 10

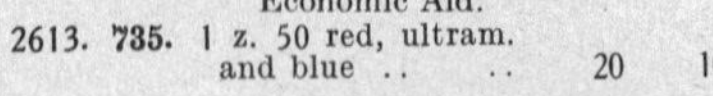

736. Soldier, Civilian and Congress Emblem. 738. Pope and Auschwitz Concentration Camp Memorial.

737. St. George's Church, Sofia.

1979. Sixth Congress of Association of Fighters for Liberty and Democracy.

2614. **736.** 1 z. 50 red and black 20 10

1979. " Philaserdica 79 " International Stamp Exhibition, Sofia, Bulgaria.

2615. **737.** 1 z. 50 orge., brn. & red 10 10

1979. Visit of Pope John Paul II. Mult.

2616. 1 z. 50 Pope and St. Mary's Church, Cracow .. 55 15
2617. 8 z. 40 Type **738** 85 35

739. River Paddle-steamer "Ksiaze Ksawery" and Old Warsaw.

1979. 150th Anniv of Vistula River Navigation. Multicoloured.

2619 1 z. Type **739** 25 10
2620 1 z. 50 River paddle-steamer "General Swierczewski" and Gdansk 30 10
2621 4 z. 50 River tug "Zubr" and Plock 85 10
2622 6 z. Passenger launch "Syrena" and modern Warsaw .. .. 1·10 20

740. Statue of Tadeusz Kosciuszko (Marian Konieczny). 741. Mining Machinery.

1979. Monument to Tadeusz Kosciuszko in Philadelphia.

2623 **740** 8 z. 40 multicoloured 60 25

1979. Wieliczka Salt Mine.

2624. **741.** 1 z. brown and black 10 10
2625. – 1 z. 50 turq. & black 15 10

DESIGN: 1 z. 50, Salt crystals.

742. Heraldic Eagle. 743. Rowland Hill and 1860 Stamp.

1979. 35th Anniv. of Polish People's Republic.

2626. – 1 z. 50 red, silver and black 15 10
2627. **742.** 1 z. 50 red, silver and blue 15 10

DESIGN: No. 2626, Girl and stylized flag.

1979. Death Cent. of Sir Rowland Hill.

2629. **743.** 6 z. blue, blk. & orge. 45 20

745. Wojciech Jastrzebowski. 746. Monument (Wincenty Kucma).

1979. 7th Congress of International Ergonomic Association, Warsaw.

2631 **745** 1 z. 50 multicoloured 15 10

1979. Unveiling of Monument to Defenders of Polish Post, Gdansk.

2632. **746.** 1 z. 50 multicoloured 15 10

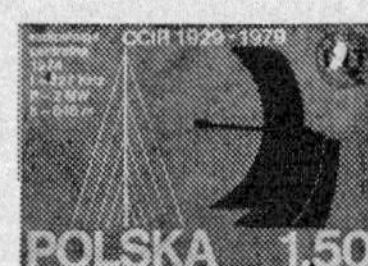

747. Radio Mast and Telecommunications Emblem.

1979. 50th Anniv. of International Radio Communication Advisory Committee.

2634. **747.** 1 z. 50 multicoloured 15 10

748. Violin.

1979. Wieniawski Young Violinists' Competition, Lublin.

2635 **748** 1 z. 50 blue, orge & grn 20 10

749. Statue of Kazimierz Pulaski, Buffalo (K. Danilewicz). 750. Franciszek Jozwiak (first Commander).

1979. Death Bicentenary of Kazimierz Pulaski (American Revolution Hero).

2636. **749.** 8 z. 40 multicoloured 60 25

1979. 35th Anniv. of Civic Militia and Security Force.

2637. **750.** 1 z. 50 blue and gold 20 10

751. Post Office in Rural Area.

1979. Stamp Day. Multicoloured.

2638	1 z. Type **751**	10	10
2639	1 z. 50 Parcel sorting machinery	15	10
2640	4 z. 50 Loading containers on train	45	10
2641	6 z. Mobile post office	60	30

752. " The Holy Family " (Ewelina Peksowa). 753. " Soyuz 30-Salyut 6 " Complex and Crystal.

1979. Polish Folk Art. Glass Paintings. Multicoloured.

2642.	2 z. Type **752**	15	10
2643.	6 z. 90 " The Nativity " (Zdzislaw Walczak)	55	25

1979. Space Achievements. Multicoloured.

2644	1 z. Type **753** (1st anniv of 1st Pole in space)	10	10
2645	1 z. 50 "Kopernik" and "Copernicus" satellites	15	10
2646	2 z. "Lunik 2" and "Ranger 7" spacecraft (20th anniv of 1st unmanned Moon landing)	15	10
2647	4 z. 50 Yuri Gagarin and "Vostok 1"	40	15
2648	6 z. 90 Neil Armstrong, lunar module and "Apollo 11" (10th anniv of first man on Moon)	50	20

754. Coach and Four. 755. Slogan on Map of Poland.

1980. 150th Anniv of Sierakow Stud Farm. Multicoloured.

2650	1 z. Type **754**	15	10
2651	2 z. Horse and groom	20	10
2652	2 z. 50 Sulky racing	25	10
2653	3 z. Hunting	25	20
2654	4 z. Horse-drawn sledge	30	20
2655	6 z. Haywain	50	20
2656	6 z. 50 Grooms exercising horses	55	20
2657	6 z. 90 Show jumping	60	25

1980. 8th Polish United Workers' Party Congress. Multicoloured.

2658	2 z. 50 Type **755**	20	10
2659	2 z. 50 Janusz Stann (26 × 46 mm)	20	10

756. Horse Jumping.

1980. Olympic Games, Moscow and Winter Olympic Games, Lake Placid. Multicoloured.

2660.	2 z. Type **756**	15	10
2661.	2 z. 50 Archery	20	10
2662.	6 z. 50 Skiing	45	15
2663.	8 z. 40 Volleyball	60	25

757. Town Plan and Old Town Hall.

1980. 400th Anniv. of Zamosc.

2665.	**757.** 2 z. 50 buff, grn. & brn.	20	10

759. Seals of Poland and Russia.

1980. 35th Anniv. of Soviet-Polish Friendship Treaty.

2667.	**759.** 2 z. 50 multicoloured	20	10

760. "Lenin in Cracow" (Zbigniew Pronaszko). 761. Workers with Red Flag.

1980. 110th Birth Anniv. of Lenin.

2668.	**760.** 2 z. 50 multicoloured	20	15

1980. 75th Anniv. of Revolution of 1905.

2669.	**761.** 2 z. 50 red, blk. & yell.	20	10

762. Dove. 763. Shield with Crests of Member Nations.

1980. 35th Anniv. of Liberation.

2670.	**762.** 2 z. 50 multicoloured	20	10

1980. 25th Anniv. of Warsaw Pact.

2671.	**763.** 2 z. grey and red	15	10

764. Speleological Expedition, Cuba.

1980. Polish Scientific Expeditions. Mult.

2672.	2 z. Type **764**	25	10
2673.	2 z. Antarctic	40	10
2674.	2 z. 50 Archaeology, Syria	30	10
2675.	2 z. 50 Ethnology, Mongolia	30	10
2676.	6 z. 50 Mountaineering, Nepal	70	20
2677.	8 z. 40 Paleontology, Mongolia	75	45

765. School and Arms. 766. " Clathrus ruber ".

1980. 800th Anniv of Malachowski School, Plock.

2678	**765** 2 z. green and black	15	10

1980. Mushrooms. Multicoloured.

2679.	2 z. Type **766**	25	10
2680.	2 z. " Xerocomus parasiticus "	25	10
2681.	2 z. 50 " Strobilomyces floccopus "	30	10
2682.	2 z. 50 " Phallus hadriani "	30	10
2683.	8 z. " Sparassis crispa "	75	15
2684.	10 z. 50 " Langermannia gigantea "	1·00	35

767. T. Ziolowski and "Lwow".

1980. Merchant Navy School Ships and Captains.

2685.	**767.** 2 z. black, mauve and violet	30	10
2686.	– 2 z. 50 black, light blue and blue	35	10
2687.	– 6 z. black, pale green and green	60	15
2688.	– 6 z. 50 black, yellow and grey	65	15
2689.	– 6 z. 90 black, grey and green	80	20
2690.	– 8 z. 40 black, blue and green	90	25

DESIGNS: 2 z. 50, A. Garmuszewski and "Antoni Garmuszewski". 6 z. A. Ledochowski and "Zenit". 6 z. 50, K. Porebski and "Jan Turleski". 6 z. 90, G. Kanski and "Horyzont". 8 z. 40, Maciejewicz and "Dar Pomorza".

768. Town Hall. 769. " Atropa belladonna ".

1980. Millenary of Sandomir.

2691.	**768.** 2 z. 50 brown & black	20	10

1980. Medicinal Plants. Multicoloured.

2692.	2 z. Type **769**	20	10
2693.	2 z. 50 " Datura innoxia "	25	10
2694.	3 z. 40 " Valeriana officinalis "	35	10
2695.	5 z. " Menta piperita "	45	10
2696.	6 z. 50 " Calendula officinalis "	55	15
2697.	8 z. " Salvia officinalis "	70	30

770. Jan Kochanowski. 771. U.N. General Assembly.

1980. 450th Birth Anniv. of Jan Kochanowski (poet).

2698.	**770.** 2 z. 50 multicoloured	20	10

1980. 35th Anniv. of U.N.O.

2703.	**771.** 8 z. 40 brn., blue & red	90	25

772. Chopin and Trees.

1980. 10th International Chopin Piano Competition, Warsaw.

2704.	**772.** 6 z. 90 multicoloured	80	25

773. Postman emptying Post Box.

1980. Stamp Day. Multicoloured.

2705.	2 z. Type **773**	20	10
2706.	2 z. 50 Mail sorting	25	10
2707.	6 z. Loading mail onto aircraft	50	15
2708.	6 z. 50 Letter boxes	55	15

774. Child embracing Dove.

1980. United Nations Declaration on the Preparation of Societies for Life in Peace.

2710.	**774.** 8 z. 40 multicoloured	60	25

775. "Battle of Olszynka Grochowska" (Wojciech Kossak).

1980. 150th Anniv. of Battle of Olszynka Grochowska.

2711.	**775.** 2 z. 50 multicoloured	30	15

776. Fire Engine.

1980. Warsaw Horse-drawn Vehicles. Mult.

2712	2 z. Type **776**	20	10
2713	2 z. 50 Omnibus	25	10
2714	3 z. Brewery dray	30	10
2715	5 z. Sledge-cab	50	10
2716	6 z. Tram	60	20
2717	6 z. 50 Droshky cab	70	30

777. " Honour to the Silesian Rebels " (statue by Jan Borowczak). 778. Picasso.

1981. 60th Anniv. of Silesian Rising.

2718.	**777.** 2 z. 50 green	20	10

1981. Birth Cent. of Pablo Picasso (artist).

2719.	**778.** 8 z. 40 multicoloured	80	25

779. Balloon of Pilatre de Rozier and Romain, 1785. 780. "Iphigenia" (Anton Maulbertsch).

1981. Balloons. Multicoloured.

2721.	2 z. Type **779**	30	10
2722.	2 z. Balloon of J. Blanchard and J. Jeffries, 1785	30	10
2723.	2 z. 50 F. Godard's balloon, 1850	35	10
2724.	3 z. F. Hynek and Z. Burzynski's " Kosciuszko ", 1933	40	10
2725.	6 z. Z. Burzynski and N. Wysocki's " Polonia II " 1935	80	15
2726.	6 z. 50 B. Abruzzo, M. Anderson and P. Newman's " Double Eagle II ", 1978	90	20

1981. " WIPA 1981 " International Stamp Exhibition, Vienna.

2728.	**780.** 10 z. 50 multicoloured	95	35

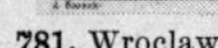

781. Wroclaw, 1493. **782.** Sikorski.

1981. Towns.

2729. – 4 z. violet 45 10
2730. – 5 z. green 55 15
2731. – 6 z. orange 70 15
2732. **781.** 6 z. 50 brown .. 70 20
2733. – 8 z. blue 85 20

DESIGNS—VERT. 4 z. Gdansk, 1652. 5 z. Cracow, 1493. HORIZ. 6 z. Legnica, 1744. 8 z. Warsaw, 1618.

1981. Birth Centenary of General Wladyslaw Sikorski (statesman).

2744. **782.** 6 z. 50 multicoloured 70 25

783. Faience Vase.

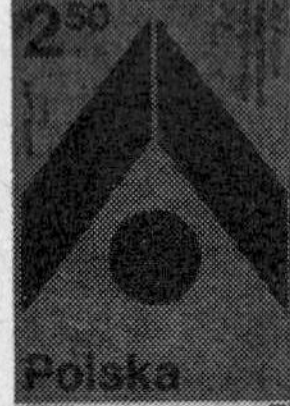

784. Congress Emblem.

1981. Pottery. Multicoloured.

2745 1 z. Type **783** 15 10
2746 2 z. Porcelain cup and saucer in "Baranowka" design 25 10
2747 2 z. 50 Porcelain jug, Korzec manufacture .. 25 10
2748 5 z. Faience plate with portrait of King Jan III Sobieski by Thiele 50 15
2749 6 z. 50 Faience "Secession" vase 65 20
2750 8 z. 40 Porcelain dish, Cmielow manufacture 80 30

1981. 14th International Architects' Union Congress, Warsaw.

2751. **784.** 2 z. yell., blk. and red 25 10

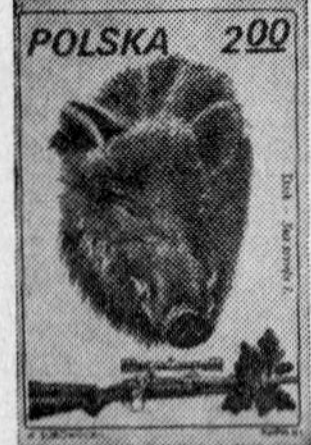

785. Wild Boar, Rifle and Oak Leaves.

786. European Bison.

1981. Game Shooting. Multicoloured.

2752 2 z. Type **785** 25 10
2753 2 z. Elk, rifle and fir twigs 25 10
2754 2 z. 50 Red fox, shotgun, cartridges and fir branches 30 10
2755 2 z. 50 Roe deer, feeding rack, rifle and fir branches 30 10
2756 6 z. 50 Mallard, shotgun, basket and reeds .. 1·10 30
2757 6 z. 50 Barnacle goose, shotgun and reeds (horiz) .. .. 1·10 30

1981. Protection of European Bison. Mult.

2758. 6 z. 50 Type **786** .. 90 35
2759. 6 z. 50 Two bison, one grazing 90 35
2760. 6 z. 50 Bison with calf 90 35
2761 6 z. 50 Calf Feeding .. 90 35
2762. 6 z. 50 Two bison, both looking towards right 90 35

787. Tennis Player.

1981. 60th Anniv. of Polish Tennis Federation.

2763. **787.** 6 z. 50 multicoloured 80 25

788. Boy with Model Aeroplane.

1981. Model Making. Multicoloured.

2764. 1 z. Type **788** 15 10
2765. 2 z. Model of "Atlas 2" tug 30 10
2766. 2 z. 50 Cars 25 10
2767. 4 z. 20 Man with gliders 45 15
2768. 6 z. 50 Racing cars .. 80 20
2769. 8 z. Boy with yacht .. 90 30

789. Disabled Pictogram.

1981. International Year of Disabled Persons.

2770. **789.** 8 z. 40 green, light green and black .. 1·00 30

790. 17th-cent. Flint-lock Pistol.

1981. Stamp Day. Antique Weapons. Mult.

2771. 2 z. 50 Type **790** .. 30 10
2772. 8 z. 40 17th-cent. gala sabre 95 30

792. Bronislaw Wesolowski.

791. H. Wieniawski and Violin Head. **793.** F.A.O. Emblem and Globe.

1981. Wieniawski Young Violinists' Competition.

2773. **791.** 2 z. 50 multicoloured 35 15

1981. Activists of Polish Workers' Movement.

2774. **792.** 50 g. green and black 10 10
2775. – 2 z. blue and black .. 15 10
2776. – 2 z. 50 brown and blk. 20 10
2777. – 6 z. 50 mauve and blk. 55 25

DESIGNS: 2 z. Malgorzata Fornalska. 2 z. 50, Maria Koszutska. 6 z. 50, Marcin Kasprzak.

1981. World Food Day.

2778. **793.** 6 z. 90 brown, orange and yellow .. 70 25

794. Helena Modrzejewska (actress).

1981. Bicentenary of Cracow Old Theatre.

2779. **794.** 2 z. pur., grey and vio. 20 10
2780. – 2 z. 50 bl., stone & brn. 30 10
2781. – 6 z. 50 vio., bl. and grn. 70 20
2782. – 8 z. brn., grn. and red 90 25

DESIGNS: 2 z. 50, Stanislaw Kozmian (politician, writer and theatre director). 6 z. 50, Konrad Swinarski (stage manager and scenographer). 8 z. Old Theatre building.

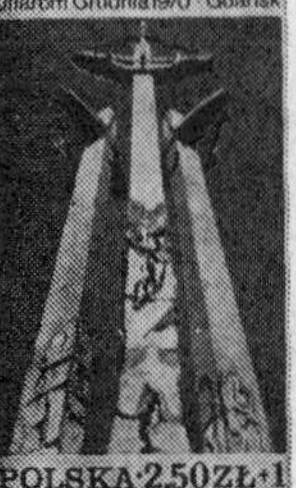

796. Gdansk Memorial.

797. "Epiphyllopsis gaertneri".

1981. Memorials to the Victims of the 1970 Uprisings.

2784. **796.** 2 z. 50+1 z. grey, black and red .. 35 15
2785. – 6 z. 50+1 z. grey, black and blue .. 75 25

DESIGN: 6 z. 50, Gdynia Memorial.

1981. Succulent Plants. Multicoloured.

2786. 90 g. Type **797** 15 10
2787. 1 z. "Cereus tonduzii" 15 10
2788. 2 z. "Cylindropuntia leptocaulis" 25 10
2789. 2 z. 50 "Cylindropuntia fulgida" 30 10
2790. 2 z. 50 "Coralluma lugardi" 30 10
2791. 6 z. 50 "Nopalea cochenillifera" .. 70 20
2792. 6 z. 50 "Lithops helmutii" 70 20
2793. 10 z. 50 "Cylindropuntia spinosior" .. .. 1·25 40

798. Writing on Wall.

799. Faience Plate.

1982. 40th Anniv. of Polish Workers' Coalition.

2794. **798.** 2 z. 50 pink, red and black 25 10

1982. Polish Ceramics. Multicoloured.

2795 1 z. Type **799** 15 10
2796 2 z. Porcelain cup and saucer, Korzec .. 25 10
2797 2 z. 50 Porcelain tureen and sauce-boat, Barnowka 30 10
2798 6 z. Porcelain inkpot, Horodnica 75 20
2799 8 z. Faience "Hunter's Tumbler", Lubartow .. 90 20
2800 10 z. 50 Faience figurine of nobleman, Biala Podlaska .. .. 1·25 50

800. Ignacy Lukasiewicz and Lamp.

801. Karol Szymanowski.

1982. Death Centenary of Ignacy Lukasiewicz (inventor of petroleum lamp).

2801. **800.** 1 z. multicoloured .. 15 10
2802. – 2 z. multicoloured .. 20 10
2803. – 2 z. 50 multicoloured 30 10
2804. – 3 z. 50 multicoloured 35 15
2805. – 9 z. multicoloured .. 1·00 25
2806. – 10 z. multicoloured .. 1·10 30

DESIGNS: 2 z. to 10 z. Different designs showing lamps.

1982. Birth Centenary of Karol Szymanowski (composer).

2807. **801.** 2 z. 50 brown and gold 30 10

802. "RWD 6" Aircraft, 1932.

1982. 50th Anniv. of Polish Victory in Tourist Aircraft Challenge Competition. Multicoloured.

2808 27 z. Type **802** .. .. 1·75 1·60
2809 31 z. "RWD 9" airplane (winner 1934 Challenge) 2·00 2·00

803. Henryk Sienkiewicz (literature, 1905).

804. Football as Globe.

1982. Polish Nobel Prize Winners.

2811. **803.** 3 z. green and black 20 10
2812. – 15 z. brown & black 75 25
2813. – 25 z. blue .. .. 1·50 30
2814. – 31 z. grey and black 1·75 70

DESIGNS: 15 z. Wladyslaw Reymont (literature, 1924). 25 z. Marie Curie (physics, 1903, and chemistry, 1911). 31 z. Czeslaw Milosz (literature, 1980).

1982. World Cup Football Championship, Spain. Multicoloured.

2815 25 z. Type **804** .. .. 1·50 40
2816 27 z. Bull and football (35 × 28 mm.) .. .. 1·50 60

806. Stanislaw Sierakowski and Boleslaw Domanski (former Association presidents).

807. Text around Globe.

1982. 60th Anniv. of Association of Poles in Germany.

2818. **806.** 4 z. 50 red and green 50 15

1982. 2nd U.N. Conference on the Exploration and Peaceful Uses of Outer Space, Vienna.

2819 **807** 31 z. multicoloured .. 1·25 30

1982. No. 2732 surch **10 °°**

2820 10 z. on 6 z. 50 brown .. 30 10

809. Father Augustyn Kordecki (prior).

810. Marchers with Banner.

1982. 600th Anniv of "Black Madonna" (icon) of Jasna Gora. Multicoloured.

2821 2 z. 50 Type **809** 10 10
2822 25 z. "Siege of Jasna Gora by Swedes, 1655" (detail) (horiz) .. 60 20
2823 65 z. "Black Madonna" .. 1·50 45

1982. Centenary of Proletarian Party.

2825. **810.** 6 z. multicoloured .. 30 10

811. Norbert Barlicki.

812. Dr. Robert Koch.

1982. Activists of Polish Workers' Movement.

2826. **811.** 5 z. light blue, blue and black 10 10
2827. – 6 z. deep green, green and black 15 10
2828. – 15 z. pink, red and black 30 10
2829. – 20 z. mauve, violet and black 45 10
2830. – 29 z. light brown, brown and black .. 60 15

DESIGNS: 6 z. Pawel Finder. 15 z. Marian Buczek. 20 z. Cezaryna Wojnarowska. 29 z. Ignacy Daszynski.

1982. Centenary of Discovery of Tubercle Bacillus. Multicoloured.
2831. 10 z. Type **812** 45 10
2832. 25 z. Dr. Odo Bujwid .. 1·25 30

813. Carved Head of Woman.

813a. Head of Ruler.

1982. Carved Heads from Wawel Castle.

2835	813a	3 z. 50 brown	15	10
2836	–	5 z. green	20	10
2837	–	5 z. red	20	10
2838	–	10 z. blue	35	10
2839	–	15 z. brown	15	10
2840	–	20 z. grey	55	15
2841	813a	20 z. blue	15	10
2842	–	40 z. brown ..	1·10	35
2833	813	60 z. orange & brn	1·60	50
2843	–	60 z. green	15	10
2834	–	100 z. ochre & brown	3·25	35
2843a	–	200 z. black ..	3·25	35

DESIGNS—As T **813**. 100 z. Man. As T **813a**. 5 z. (2836), Warrior. 5 (2837), 15 z. Woman wearing chaplet. 10 z. Man in cap. 20 z. (2840), Thinker. 40 z. Man in beret. 60 z. Young man. 200 z. Man.

814. Maximilian Kolbe (after M. Koscielniak).

815. Polar Research Station.

1982. Sanctification of Maximilian Kolbe (Franciscan concentration camp victim).
2844. **814.** 27 z. multicoloured .. 1·25 40

1982. 50th Anniv. of Polish Polar Research.
2845. **815.** 27 z. multicoloured .. 2·50 60

816. "Log Floats on Vistula River" (drawing by J. Telakowski).

817. Stanislaw Zaremba.

1982. Views of the Vistula River.
2846 **816** 12 z. blue 15 10
2847 – 17 z. blue 20 10
2848 – 25 z. blue 25 10
DESIGNS: 17 z. "Kazimierz Dolny" (engraving by Andriollo). 25 z. "Danzig" (18th-century engraving).

1982. Mathematicians.
2849. **817.** 5 z. lilac, blue and blk. 25 10
2850. – 6 z. orange, violet and black 30 10
2851. – 12 z. blue, brown and black 55 15
2852. – 15 z. yellow, brown and black 70 20
DESIGNS: 6 z. Waclaw Sierpinski. 12 z. Zygmunt Janiszewski. 15 z. Stefan Banach.

818. Military Council Medal.

1982. 1st Anniv. of Military Council.
2853 **818.** 2 z. 50 multicoloured 30 15

819. Deanery Gate.

820. Bernard Wapowski Map, 1526.

1982. Renovation of Cracow Monuments (1st series).
2854 **819** 15 z. blk, olive & grn 50 15
2855 – 25 z. black, pur & mve 75 25
DESIGN: 25 z. Gateway of Collegium.
See also Nos. 2904/5, 2968/9, 3029/30, 3116 and 3153.

1982. Polish Maps.
2857. **820.** 5 z. multicoloured .. 15 10
2858. – 6 z. brown, black and red 20 10
2859. – 8 z. multicoloured .. 25 10
2860. – 25 z. multicoloured .. 80 35
DESIGNS: 6 z. Map of Prague, 1839. 8 z. Map of Poland from Eugen Romer's Atlas, 1908. 25 z. Plan of Cracow by A. Buchowiecki, 1703, and Astrolabe.

821. "The Last of the Resistance" (Artur Grottger).

1983. 120th Anniv. of January Uprising.
2861. **821.** 6 z. brown 25 15

822. "Grand Theatre, Warsaw, 1838" (Maciej Zaleski).

1983. 150th Anniv of Grand Theatre, Warsaw.
2862 **822** 6 z. multicoloured .. 25 15

823. Wild Flowers.

824. Karol Kurpinski (composer).

1983. Environmental Protection. Mult.
2863. 5 z. Type **823** 20 10
2864. 6 z. Mute swan and river fishes 35 10
2865. 17 z. Hoopoe and trees .. 1·10 30
2866. 30 z. Sea fishes .. .. 1·10 45
2867. 31 z. European bison and roe deer .. .. 1·40 60
2868. 38 z. Fruit .. .. 1·40 70

1983. Celebrities.
2869. **824.** 5 z. light brn. & brn. 20 10
2870. – 6 z. purple & violet 25 10
2871. – 17 z. light grn. & grn. 65 25
2872. – 25 z. light brn. & brn. 80 25
2873. – 27 z. light bl. & bl. .. 90 30
2874. – 31 z. liliac & violet .. 1·00 30
DESIGNS: 6 z. Maria Jasnorzewska Pawlikowska (poetess). 17 z. Stanislaw Szober (linguist). 25 z. Tadeusz Banachiewicz (astronomer and mathematician). 27 z. Jaroslaw Iwaszkiewicz (writer). 31 z. Wladyslaw Tatarkiewicz (philosopher and historian).

825. 3000 Metres Steeplechase.

1983. Sports Achievements.
2875. **825.** 5 z. pink and violet .. 20 10
2876. – 6 z. pink, brn. & blk. 25 10
2877. – 15 z. yellow & green 55 20
2878. – 27 z. + 5 z. light blue, blue and black .. 1·10 40
DESIGNS: 6 z. Showjumping. 15 z. Football. 27 z. + 5 z. Pole Vault.

826. Ghetto Heroes Monument (Natan Rappaport).

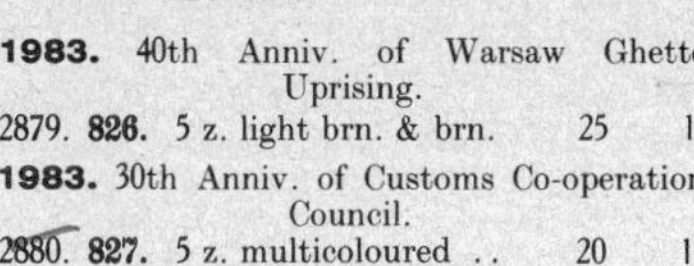

827. Customs Officer and Suitcases.

1983. 40th Anniv. of Warsaw Ghetto Uprising.
2879. **826.** 5 z. light brn. & brn. 25 15

1983. 30th Anniv. of Customs Co-operation Council.
2880. **827.** 5 z. multicoloured .. 20 15

828. John Paul II and Jasna Gora Sanctuary.

829. Dragoons.

1983. Papal Visit. Multicoloured.
2881 31 z. Type **828** .. .. 1·25 35
2882 65 z. Niepokalanow Church and John Paul holding crucifix .. 2·50 80

1983. 300th Anniv of Polish Relief of Vienna (1st issue). Troops of King Jan III Sobieski. Multicoloured.
2884. 5 z. Type **829** 20 10
2885. 5 z. Armoured cavalryman 20 10
2886. 6 z. Infantry non-commissioned officer and musketeer 25 10
2887. 15 z. Light cavalry lieutenant 55 30
2888. 27 z. "Winged" hussar and trooper with carbine .. .. 1·00 50
See also Nos. 2893/6.

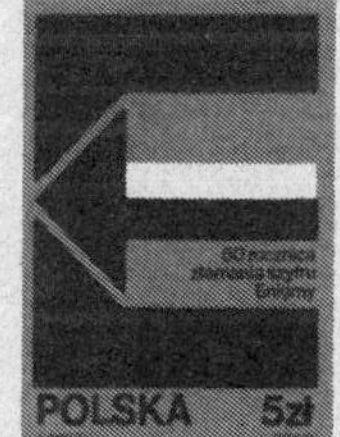

830. Arrow piercing "E".

1983. 50th Anniv. of Deciphering "Enigma" Machine Codes.
2889. **830.** 5 z. red, grey & black 20 15

831. Torun.

1983. 750th Anniv. of Torun.
2890. **831.** 6 z. multicoloured .. 30 15

832. Child's Painting.

833. King Jan III Sobieski.

1983. "Order of the Smile" (Politeness Publicity Campaign).
2892. **832.** 6 z. multicoloured .. 25 15

1983. 300th Anniv. of Relief of Vienna (2nd issue). Multicoloured.
2893 5 z. Type **833** 20 10
2894 6 z. King Jan III Sobieski (different) 25 10
2895 6 z. "King Jan III Sobieski on Horseback" (Francesco Trevisani) 25 10
2896 25 z. "King Jan III Sobieski" (Jerzy Eleuter) .. .. 1·10 45

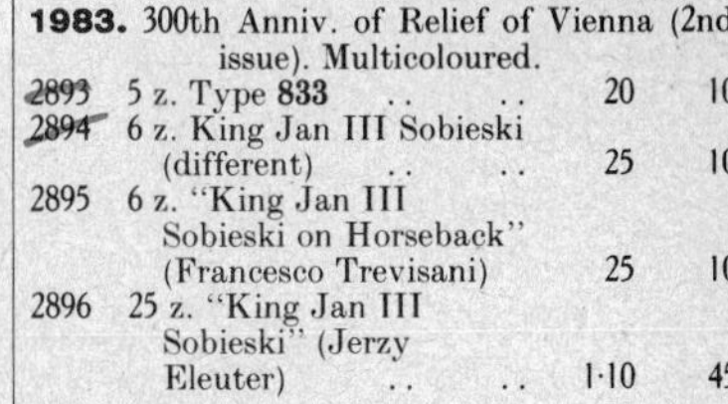

834. Wanda Wasilewska.

835. Profiles and W.C.Y. Emblem.

1983. 40th Anniv. of Polish People's Army. Multicoloured.
2898. **834.** 5 z. multicoloured .. 20 10
2899. – 5 z. deep green, green and black 20 10
2900. – 6 z. multicoloured .. 25 10
2091. – 6 z. multicoloured .. 25 10
DESIGNS—VERT. No. 2899, General Zygmunt Berling. 2900, "The Frontier Post" (S. Poznanski). HORIZ. No. 2901, "Taking the Oath" (S. Poznanski).

1983. World Communications Year.
2902. **835.** 15 z. multicoloured .. 60 20

836. Boxing.

1983. 60th Anniv. of Polish Boxing Federation.
2903. **836.** 6 z. multicoloured .. 25 10

1983. Renovation of Cracow Monuments (2nd series). As T **819**
2904. 5 z. brn., pur. & blk. .. 20 15
2905. 6 z. black, green and blue 25 20
DESIGNS—HORIZ: 5 z. Cloth Hall. VERT. 6 z. Town Hall tower.

837. Biskupiec Costume.

838. Hand with Sword (poster by Zakrzewski and Krolikowski, 1945).

1983. Women's Folk Costumes. Mult.
2906. 5 z. Type **837** 25 10
2907. 5 z. Rozbark 25 10
2908. 6 z. Warmia & Mazuria 30 10
2909. 6 z. Cieszyn 30 10
2910. 25 z. Kurpie .. .. 1·00 30
2911. 38 z. Lubusk .. .. 1·50 60

1983. 40th Anniv. of National People's Council.
2912. **838.** 6 z. multicoloured .. 25 15

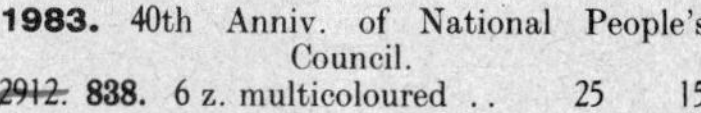

839. Badge of "General Bem" Brigade.

840. Dulcimer.

1983. 40th Anniv. of People's Army.
2913. **839.** 5 z. multicoloured .. 20 15

1984. Musical Instruments (1st series). Mult.

2914	5 z. Type **840**	20	10
2915	6 z. Kettle drum and tambourine	25	10
2916	10 z. Accordion	40	15
2917	15 z. Double bass ..	60	20
2918	17 z. Bagpipe	70	25
2919	29 z. Country band (wood carvings by Tadeusz Zak)	1·25	40

See also Nos. 2994/9.

841. Wincenty Witos.

842. "Clematis lanuginosa".

1984. 110th Birth Anniv. of Wincenty Witos (leader of Peasants' Movement).

2920.	**841.**	6 z. brown & green ..	25	10

1984. Clematis. Multicoloured.

2921.	5 z. Type **842**	20	10
2922.	6 z. "C. tangutica" ..	25	10
2923.	10 z. "C. texensis" ..	40	15
2924.	17 z. "C. alpina" ..	70	25
2925.	25 z. "C. vitalba" ..	1·00	40
2926.	27 z. "C. montana" ..	1·10	50

843. "The Ecstasy of St. Francis" (El Greco).

1984. "Espana 84" International Stamp Exhibition, Madrid.

2927.	**843.**	27 z. multicoloured ..	1·25	40

844. Handball.

1984. Olympic Games, Los Angeles, and Winter Olympics, Sarajevo. Mult.

2928	5 z. Type **844**	15	10
2929	6 z. Fencing	20	10
2930	15 z. Cycling	45	15
2931	16 z. Janusz Kusocinski winning 10,000 metres race, 1932 Olympics, Los Angeles	50	20
2932	17 z. Stanislawa Walasiewiczowna winning 100 metres race, 1932 Olympics, Los Angeles	50	20
2933	31 z. Women's slalom (Winter Olympics) ..	1·25	35

845. Monte Cassino Memorial Cross and Monastery.

846. "German Princess" (Lucas Cranach).

1984. 40th Anniv. of Battle of Monte Cassino.

2935.	**845.**	15 z. olive and red ..	65	20

1984. 19th Universal Postal Union Congress, Hamburg.

2936.	**846.**	27 z.+10 z. mult. ..	1·40	55

847. "Warsaw from the Praga Bank" (Canaletto).

1984. Paintings of Vistula River. Mult.

2937.	5 z. Type **847**	20	10
2938.	6 z. "Trumpet Festivity" (A. Gierymski) ..	25	10
2939.	25 z. "The Vistula near Bielany District" (J. Rapacki)	1·00	35
2940.	27 z. "Steamship Harbour in the Powisle District" (F. Kostrzewski) ..	1·25	50

848. Order of Grunwald Cross.

849. Group of Insurgents.

1984. 40th Anniv. of Polish People's Republic. Multicoloured.

2941.	5 z. Type **848**	20	10
2942.	6 z. Order of Revival of Poland	25	10
2943.	10 z. Order of Banner of Labour, First Class ..	40	15
2944.	16 z. Order of Builders of People's Poland ..	65	25

1984. 40th Anniv. of Warsaw Uprising. Multicoloured.

2946.	4 z. Type **849**	20	10
2947.	5 z. Insurgent on postal duty	25	10
2948.	6 z. Insurgents fighting	25	10
2949.	25 z. Tending wounded	1·00	45

850. Defence of Oksywie Holm and Col. Stanislaw Dabek.

1984. 45th Anniv. of German Invasion. Multicoloured.

2950.	5 z. Type **850**	25	10
2951.	6 z. Battle of Bzura River and Gen. Tadeusz Kutrzeba ..	35	10

See also Nos. 3004/5, 3062, 3126/8, 3172/4 and 3240/3.

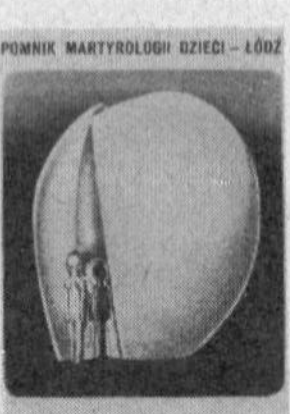

851. "Broken Heart" (monument. Lodz Concentration Camp).

1984. Child Martyrs.

2952.	**851.**	16 z. brown blue and deep brown ..	60	20

HAVE YOU READ THE NOTES AT THE BEGINNING OF THIS CATALOGUE?
These often provide answers to the enquiries we receive.

852. Militiaman and Ruins.

1984. 40th Anniv. of Security Force and Civil Militia. Multicoloured.

2953.	5 z. Type **852**	25	10
2954.	6 z. Militiaman in control centre	35	10

853. First Balloon Flight, 1784 (after Chostovski).

1984. Polish Aviation.

2955.	**853.**	5 z. blk., grn. & mve.	25	10
2956.	–	5 z. multicoloured ..	25	10
2957.	–	6 z. multicoloured ..	25	10
2958.	–	10 z. multicoloured ..	45	15
2959.	–	16 z. multicoloured ..	70	20
2960.	–	27 z. multicoloured ..	1·40	45
2961.	–	31 z. multicoloured ..	1·40	55

DESIGNS: No. 2956, Michal Scipio del Campo and biplane (first flight over Warsaw, 1911). 2957, "Polonez" balloon (winner, Gordon Bennett Cup, 1983). 2958. PWS "101" and "Jantar" gliders (Lilenthal Medal winners). 2959, "Wilga" airplane (world precise flight champion, 1983). 2960, Jan Nagorski and Farman airplane (Arctic zone flights, 1914). 2961, "Los" and PZL "P-7" airplanes.

854. Weasel.

1984. Fur-bearing Animals. Multicoloured.

2962.	4 z. Type **854**	25	10
2963.	5 z. Stoat	35	10
2964.	5 z. Beech marten ..	35	10
2965.	10 z. Eurasian beaver ..	35	15
2966.	10 z. Eurasian otter ..	35	15
2967.	65 z. Alpine marmot ..	2·50	1·10

1984. Renovation of Cracow Monuments (3rd series). At T **819**.

2968.	5 z. brown, black and green	20	10
2969.	15 z. blue, brown and black	50	15

DESIGNS—VERT. 5 z. Wawel cathedral. HORIZ. 15 z. Wawel castle (royal residence).

855. Protestant Church, Warsaw.

1984. Religious Architecture. Multicoloured.

2970.	5 z. Type **855**	15	10
2971.	10 z. Saint Andrew's Roman Catholic church, Krakow	30	10
2972.	15 z. Greek Catholic church, Rychwald ..	45	20
2973.	20 z. St. Maria Magdalena Orthodox church, Warsaw	60	20
2974.	25 z. Tykocin synagogue, Kaczorow (horiz.) ..	75	30
2975.	31 z. Tatar mosque Kruszyiany (horiz.) ..	95	45

856. Steam Fire Hose (late 19th century).

1985. Fire Engines. Multicoloured.

2976.	4 z. Type **856**	20	10
2977.	10 z. "Polski Fait", 1930s	40	10
2978.	12 z. "Jelcz 315" fire engine	50	15
2979.	15 z. Manual fire hose, 1899	60	15
2980.	20 z. "Magirus" fire ladder on "Jelcz" chassis	80	25
2981.	30 z. Manual fire hose (early 18th century) ..	1·10	45

857. "Battle of Raclawice" (Jan Styka and Wojciech Kossak)

1985.

2982.	**857.**	27 z. multicoloured ..	1·00	30

858. Wincenty Rzymowski.

859. Badge on Denim.

1985. 35th Death Anniv. of Wincenty Rzymowski (founder of Polish Democratic Party).

2983.	**858.**	10 z. violet and red	35	10

1985. International Youth Year.

2984.	**859.**	15 z. multicoloured ..	45	15

860. Boleslaw III, the Wry-mouthed, and Map.

1985. 40th Anniv. of Return of Western and Northern Territories to Poland. Multicoloured.

2985.	5 z. Type **860**.	15	10
2986.	10 z. Wladyslaw Gomulka (vice-president of first post-war government) and map	35	10
2987.	20 z. Piotr Zaremba (Governor of Szczecin) and map	60	20

861. "Victory, Berlin 1945" (Josef Mlynarski).

1985. 40th Anniv. of Victory over Fascism.

2988.	**861.**	5 z. multicoloured ..	20	10

862. Warsaw Arms and Flags of Member Countries.

864. Cadet Ship "Iskra".

863. Wolves in Winter.

1985. 30th Anniv. of Warsaw Pact.
2989. **862.** 5 z. multicoloured .. 15 10

1985. Protected Animals. The Wolf. Mult.
2990. 5 z. Type **863** 20 10
2991. 10 z. She-wolf with cubs 50 15
2992. 10 z. Close-up of wolf .. 50 15
2993. 20 z. Wolves in summer 60 40

1985. Musical Instruments (2nd series). As T **840**. Multicoloured.
2994. 5 z. Rattle and tarapata 20 10
2995. 10 z. Stick rattle and berlo 35 10
2996. 12 z. Clay whistles .. 40 15
2997. 20 z. Stringed instruments 60 20
2998. 25 z. Cow bells 85 30
2999. 31 z. Wind instruments 1·00 35

1985. 40th Anniv. of Polish Navy.
3000. **864.** 5 z. blue and yellow 40 10

865. Tomasz Nocznicki.

1985. Leaders of Peasants' Movement.
3001. **865.** 10 z. green 35 10
3002. – 20 z. brown 60 20
DESIGN: 20 z. Maciej Rataj.

866. Hockey Players.

1985. 60th Anniv. (1986) of Polish Field Hockey Association.
3003. **866.** 5 z. multicoloured .. 20 10

1985. 46th Anniv. of German Invasion. As T **850**. Multicoloured.
3004. 5 z. Defence of Wizna and Capt. Wladyslaw Raginis 20 10
3005. 10 z. Battle of Mlawa and Col. Wilhelm Liszka-Lawicz .. 60 15

867. Goods Wagon Type '20 K".

1985. PAFAWAG Railway Rolling Stock. Multicoloured.
3006. 5 z. Type **867** 20 10
3007. 10 z. Electric locomotive, type "201 E" 40 10
3008. 17 z. Two-axle coal car, type "OMMK" .. 65 20
3009. 20 z. Passenger car, type "111 A" 85 30

869. Green-winged Teal.

1985. Wild Ducks. Multicoloured.
3011. 5 z. Type **869** 20 10
3012. 5 z. Garganey duck .. 20 10
3013. 10 z. Tufted duck .. 40 10
3014. 15 z. Goldeneye 50 15
3015. 25 z. Eider 90 30
3016. 29 z. Red-crested pochard .. .. 1·25 40

870. U.N. Emblem and "Flags".

1985. 40th Anniv. of U.N.O.
3017. **870.** 27 z. multicoloured .. 1·00 35

871. Ballerina.

872. "Marysia and Burek in Ceylon".

1985. Bicentenary of Polish Ballet.
3018. **871.** 5 z. grn., orge. & red 15 10
3019. – 15 z. brn., vio. & orge. 45 10
DESIGN: 15 z. Male dancer.

1985. Birth Cent. of Stanislaw Ignacy Witkiewicz (artist). Multicoloured.
3020. 5 z. Type **872** 15 10
3021. 10 z. "Woman with Fox" (horiz.) 35 10
3022. 10 z. "Self-portrait" .. 35 10
3023. 20 z. "Compositions (1917–20)" 60 20
3024. 25 z. "Nena Stachurska" 85 30

874. Human Profile.

1986. Congress of Intellectuals for Defence of Peaceful Future of the World, Warsaw.
3026. **874.** 10 z. ultramarine, violet and blue .. 35 10

875. Michal Kamienski and Planetary and Comet's Orbits.

1986. Appearance of Halley's Comet.
3027. **875.** 25 z. blue and brown 80 25
3028. – 25 z. deep blue, blue and brown .. 80 25
DESIGN: No. 3028, "Vega", "Planet A", "Giotto" and "Ice" space probes and comet.

1986. Renovation of Cracow Monuments (4th series). As T **819**.
3029. 5 z. dp. brn., brn. & blk. 15 10
3030. 10 z. green, brn. & blk. 35 10
DESIGNS: 5 z. Collegium Maius (Jagiellonian University Museum). 10 z. Kazimierz Town Hall.

876. Sun.

877. Grey Partridge.

1986. International Peace Year.
3031. **876.** 25 z. yellow, light blue and blue .. 85 25

1986. Game. Multicoloured.
3032. 5 z. Type **877** 50 20
3033. 5 z. Common rabbit .. 15 10
3034. 10 z. Ring-necked pheasants (horiz.) .. 90 20
3035. 10 z. Fallow deer (horiz.) 30 10
3036. 20 z. Hare 60 20
3037. 40 z. Argali .. .. 1·25 45

878. Kulczynski.

880. Paderewski (composer).

879. "Warsaw Fire Brigade, 1871" (detail, Jozef Brodowski).

1986. 10th Death Anniv. (1985) of Stanislaw Kulczynski (politician).
3038. **878.** 10 z. light brown and brown 35 10

1986. 150th Anniv. of Warsaw Fire Brigade.
3039. **879.** 10 z. deep brown and brown 35 10

1986. "Ameripex '86" International Stamp Exhibition, Chicago.
3040. **880.** 65 z. bl., blk. & grey 1·75 55

881. Footballers.

1986. World Cup Football Championship, Mexico.
3041. **881.** 25 z. multicoloured .. 80 25

882. "Wilanow".

1986. Passenger Ferries. Multicoloured.
3042. 10 z. Type **882** 50 20
3043. 10 z. "Wawel" 50 20
3044. 15 z. "Pomerania" .. 75 30
3045. 25 z. "Rogalin" .. .. 1·25 50

883. A. B. Dobrowolski, Map and Research Vessel "Kopernik".

885. "The Paulinite Church on Skalka in Cracow" (detail), 1627.

884. Workers and Emblem.

1986. 25th Anniv. of Antarctic Agreement.
3047. **883.** 5 z. grn., blk. & red 40 20
3048. – 40 z. lavender, violet and orange .. 3·50 90
DESIGN: 40 z. H. Arctowski, map and research vessel "Professor Siedlecki".

1986. 10th Polish United Workers' Party Congress, Warsaw.
3049. **884.** 10 z. blue and red .. 35 10

1986. Treasures of Jasna Gora Monastery. Multicoloured.
3050 5 z. Type **885** 15 10
3051 5 z. "Tree of Jesse", 17th-century 15 10
3052 20 z. Chalice, 18th-century 60 20
3053 40 z. "Virgin Mary" (detail, chasuble column), 15th-century 1·25 40

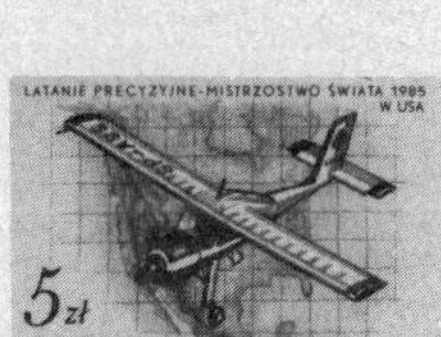

886. Precision Flying (Waclaw Nycz).

1986. 1985 Polish World Championship Successes. Multicoloured.
3054. 5 z. Type **886** 20 10
3055. 10 z. Windsurfing (Malgorzata Palasz-Piasecka) 50 10
3056. 10 z. Glider aerobatics (Jerzy Makula) .. 40 10
3057. 15 z. Wrestling (Bogdan Daras) 40 15
3058. 20 z. Individual road cycling (Lech Piasecki) 60 20
3059. 30 z. Women's pentathlon (Barbara Kotowska) 85 35

887. "Bird" in National Costume carrying Stamp.

888. Schweitzer.

1986. "Stockholmia '86" International Stamp Exhibition.
3060. **887.** 65 z. multicoloured .. 1·75 60

1986. 47th Anniv. of German Invasion. As T **850**. Multicoloured.
3062. 10 z. Battle of Jordanow and Col. Stanislaw Maczek 35 10

1986. 10th Death Anniv (1985) of Albert Schweitzer (medical missionary).
3063 888 5 z. brown, lt brn & bl 15 10

889. Airplane and Postal Messenger.

890. Basilisk.

1986. World Post Day.
3064. **889.** 40 z. brn., bl. & red 1·25 40

1986. Folk Tales. Multicoloured.
3066. 5 z. Type **890** 15 10
3067. 5 z. Duke Popiel (vert.) 15 10
3068. 10 z. Golden Duck 30 10
3069. 10 z. Boruta the Devil (vert.) 30 10
3070. 20 z. Janosik the Robber (vert.) 60 20
3071. 50 z. Lajkonik (vert.) 1·25 50

891. Kotarbinski.

892. 20th-century Windmill, Zygmuntow.

1986. Birth Centenary of Tadeusz Kotarbinski (philosopher).
3072. **891.** 10 z. deep brown and brown 30 10

1986. Wooden Architecture. Multicoloured.
3073 5 z. Type **892** 15 10
3074 5 z. 17th-century church, Baczal Dolny 15 10
3075 10 z. 19th-century Oravian cottage, Zubrzyca Gorna 30 10
3076 15 z. 18th-century Kashubian arcade cottage, Wdzydze 40 15
3077 25 z. 19th-century barn, Grzawa 80 25
3078 30 z. 19th-century watermill, Siolkowice Stare 75 35

893. Mieszko (Mieczyslaw) I.

1986. Polish Rulers (1st series). Drawings by Jan Matejko.
3079. **893.** 10 z. brown & green 30 10
3080. – 25 z. black and purple 75 25
DESIGN: 25 z. Queen Dobrawa (wife of Mieszko I).

See also Nos. 3144/5, 3193/4, 3251/2, 3341/2, 3351/2, 3387/8 and 3461/4.

894. Star.

1986. New Year.
3081. **894.** 25 z. multicoloured 75 25

895. Trip to Bielany, 1887.

1986. Centenary of Warsaw Cyclists' Society.
3082. **895.** 5 z. multicoloured 15 10
3083. – 5 z. brown, light brown and black 15 10
3084. – 10 z. multicoloured 30 10
3085. – 10 z. multicoloured 30 10
3086. – 30 z. multicoloured 80 25
3087. – 50 z. multicoloured 1·25 50
DESIGNS: No. 3083, Jan Stanislaw Skrodzki (1895 touring record holder). 3084, Dynasy (Society's headquarters, 1892–1937). 3085, Mieczyslaw Baranski (1896 Kingdom of Poland road cycling champion). 3086, Karolina Kociecka. 3087, Henryk Weiss (Race champion).

896. Lelewel.

1986. Birth Bicentary of Joachim Lelewel (historian).
3088 **896** 10 z. + 5 z. mult 45 15

897. Krill and "Antoni Garnuszewski" (cadet freighter).

1987. 10th Anniv of Henryk Arctowski Antarctic Station, King George Island, South Shetlands. Multicoloured.
3089 5 z. Type **897** 10 10
3090 5 z. "Nototenia marmurkowa", "Notothenia rossi" (fishes) and "Zulawy" (supply ship) 10 10
3091 10 z. Southern fulmar and "Pogoria" (cadet brigantine) 50 20
3092 10 z. Adelie penguin and "Gedania" (yacht) 50 20
3093 30 z. Fur seal and "Dziunia" (research vessel) 75 25
3094 40 z. Leopard seals and "Kapitan Ledochowski" (research vessel) 1·00 35

898. "Portrait of a Woman".

1987. 50th Death Anniv (1986) of Leon Wyczolkowski (artist). Multicoloured.
3095 5 z. "Cineraria Flowers" (horiz) 10 10
3096 10 z. Type **898** 25 10
3097 10 z. "Wooden Church" (horiz) 25 10
3098 25 z. "Beetroot Lifting" 55 20
3099 30 z. "Wading Fishermen" (horiz) 45 25
3100 40 z. "Self-portrait" (horiz) 60 35

899. "Ravage" (from "War Cycle") and Artur Grottger.

1987. 150th Birth Anniv. of Artur Grottger (artist).
3101. **899.** 15 z. brown & stone 30 10

900. Swierczewski.

901. Strzelecki.

1987. 90th Birth Anniv of General Karol Swierczewski.
3102 **900** 15 z. green and olive 30 10

1987. 190th Birth Anniv. of Pawel Edmund Strzelecki (scientist and explorer of Tasmania).
3103. **901.** 65 z. green 95 40

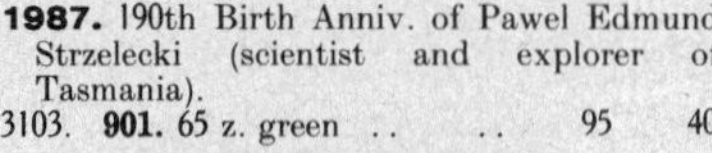

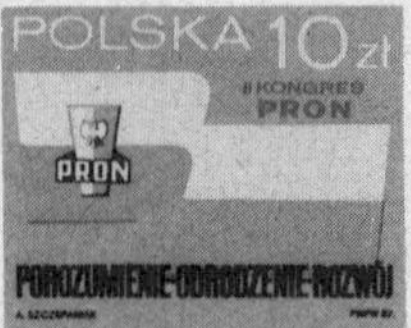

902. Emblem and Banner.

1987. 2nd Patriotic Movement for National Revival Congress.
3104. **902.** 10 z. red, blue and brown 20 10

903. CWS "T-1" Motor Car, 1928.

1987. Polish Motor Vehicles. Multicoloured.
3105 10 z. Type **903** 20 10
3106 10 z. Saurer-Zawrat bus, 1936 20 10
3107 15 z. Ursus-A lorry, 1928 30 10
3108 15 z. Lux-Sport motor car, 1936 30 10
3109 25 z. Podkowa "100" motor cycle, 1939 45 15
3110 45 z. Sokol "600 RT" motor cycle, 1935 65 30

904. Warsaw Old Town Hall.

1987.
3111. **904.** 50 z. multicoloured 75 35

905. Pope John Paul II.

1987. 3rd Papal Visit. Multicoloured.
3112. 15 z. Type **905** 30 10
3113. 45 z. Pope and signature 65 30

906. Polish Settler at Kasubia, Ontario.

1987. "Capex '87" International Stamp Exhibition, Toronto.
3115. **906.** 50 z. + 20 z. mult. 1·00 45

1987. Renovation of Cracow Monuments (5th series). As T **819**.
3116. 10 z. lilac, black & green 20 10
DESIGN: 10 z. Barbican.

907. Ludwig Zamenhof (inventor) and Star.

1987. Cent of Esperanto (invented language).
3117 **907** 5 z. brown, grn & blk 80 25

908. "Poznan Town Hall" (Stanislaw Wyspianski).

909. Queen Bee.

1987. "Poznan 87" National Stamp Exhibition.
3118. **908.** 15 z. brown & orange 30 10

1987. "Apimondia 87" International Bee Keeping Congress, Warsaw. Multicoloured.
3119. 10 z. Type **909** 20 10
3120. 10 z. Worker bee 20 10
3121. 15 z. Drone 30 10
3122. 15 z. Hive in orchard 30 10
3123. 40 z. Worker bee on clover flower 80 25
3124. 50 z. Forest bee keeper collecting honey 90 30

1987. 48th Anniv of German Invasion. As T **850**. Multicoloured.
3126 10 z. Battle of Mokra and Col. Julian Filipowicz 20 10
3127 10 z. Fighting at Oleszyce and Brig.-Gen. Jozef Rudolf Kustron 20 10
3128 15 z. Aircraft over Warsaw and Col. Stefan Pawlikowsi 40 15

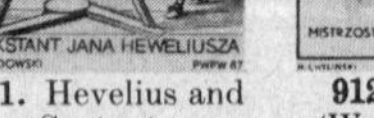

911. Hevelius and Sextant.

912. High Jump (World Acrobatics Championships, France).

1987. 300th Death Anniv. of Jan Hevelius (astronomer). Multicoloured.
3129 15 z. Type **911** 25 10
3130 40 z. Hevelius and map of constellations (horiz) 70 25

1987. 1986 Polish World Championship Successes. Multicoloured.
3131. 10 z. Type **912** 15 10
3132. 15 z. Two-man canoe (World Canoeing Championships, Canada) 25 10
3133. 20 z. Marksman (Free pistol event, World Marksmanship Championships, East Germany) 30 10
3134. 25 z. Wrestlers (World Wrestling Championships, Hungary) 40 15

914. Warsaw Post Office and Ignacy Franciszek Przebendowski (Postmaster General).

1987. World Post Day.
3136. **914.** 15 z. green and red . . 30 10

915. "The Little Mermaid". **916.** Col. Stanislaw Wieckowski (founder).

1987. "Hafnia 87" International Stamp Exhibition, Copenhagen. Hans Christian Andersen's Fairy Tales. Multicoloured.
3137. 10 z. Type **915** . . 15 10
3138. 10 z. "The Nightingale" 15 10
3139. 20 z. "The Wild Swans" 35 10
3140. 20 z. "The Little Match Girl" 35 10
3141. 30 z. "The Snow Queen" 60 20
3142. 40 z. "The Tin Soldier" 75 25

1987. 50th Anniv. of Democratic Clubs.
3143. **916.** 15 z. black and blue 30 10

1987. Polish Rulers (2nd series). As T **893.** Drawings by Jan Matejko.
3144 10 z. green and blue . . 15 10
3145 15 z. blue and ultramarine 25 10
DESIGNS: 10 z. Boleslaw I, the Brave. 15 z. Mieszko (Mieczyslaw) II.

917 Santa Claus with Christmas Trees

1987. New Year.
3146 **917** 15 z. multicoloured . . 30 10

918 "Anax imperator"

1988. Dragonflies. Multicoloured.
3147 10 z. Type **918** 20 10
3148 15 z. "Libellula quadrimaculata" (vert) 30 10
3149 15 z. "Calopteryx splendens" 30 10
3150 20 z. "Condulegaster annulatus" (vert) . . 35 10
3151 30 z. "Sympetrum pedemontanum" . . 60 15
3152 50 z. "Aeschna viridis" (vert) 90 25

1988. Renovation of Cracow Monuments (6th series). As T **819.**
3153 15 z. yellow, brown & blk 25 10
DESIGN: 15 z. Florianska Gate.

919 Composition

1988. International Year of Graphic Design.
3154 **919** 40 z. multicoloured . . 60 45

920 17th-century Friesian Wall Clock with Bracket Case

1988. Clocks and Watches. Multicoloured.
3155 10 z. Type **920** 15 10
3156 10 z. 20th-century annual clock (horiz) 15 10
3157 15 z. 18th-century carriage clock 25 10
3158 15 z. 18th-century French rococo bracket clock . . 25 10
3159 20 z. 19th-century pocket watch (horiz) 30 10
3160 40 z. 17th-cent tile-case clock from Gdansk by Benjamin Zoll (horiz) 65 20

921 Salmon and Reindeer

1988. "Finlandia 88" International Stamp Exhibition, Helsinki.
3161 **921** 45 z. + 20 z. mult . . 65 30

922 Triple Jump 924 Wheat as Graph on VDU

1988. Olympic Games, Seoul. Multicoloured.
3162 15 z. Type **922** 25 10
3163 20 z. Wrestling 30 10
3164 20 z. Canoeing 30 10
3165 25 z. Judo 40 15
3166 40 z. Shooting 40 20
3167 55 z. Swimming 55 30

1988. 16th European Conference of Food and Agriculture Organization, Cracow. Mult.
3169 15 z. Type **924** 20 10
3170 40 z. Factory in forest . . 40 20

925 "Elk"

1988. 70th Anniv of Polish Republic (1st issue). 60th Anniv of Polish State Aircraft Works.
3171 **925** 45 z. multicoloured . . 80 20
See also Nos. 3175, 3177, 3181/88 and 3190/2.

1988. 49th Anniv of German Invasion. As T **850.** Multicoloured.
3172 15 z. Battle of Modlin and Brig.-Gen. Wiktor Thommee 20 10
3173 20 z. Battle of Warsaw and Brig.-Gen. Walerian Czuma . . 20 10
3174 20 z. Battle of Tomaszow Lubelski and Brig.-Gen. Antoni Szylling . . 20 10

1988. 70th Anniv of Polish Republic (2nd issue). 50th Anniv of Stalowa Wola Ironworks. As T **925.** Multicoloured.
3175 15 z. View of plant . . 15 10

926 Postal Emblem and Tomasz Arciszewski (Postal Minister, 1918–19) 927 On the Field of Glory Medal

1988. World Post Day.
3176 **926** 20 z. multicoloured . . 20 10

1988. 70th Anniv of Polish Republic (3rd issue). 60th Anniv of Military Institute for Aviation Medicine. As T **925.** Multicoloured.
3177 20 z. Hanriot "XiV" hospital airplanes (38 × 28 mm) 30 10

1988. Polish People's Army Battle Medals (1st series). Multicoloured.
3178 20 z. Type **927** 20 10
3179 20 z. Battle of Lenino Cross 20 10
See also Nos. 3249/50.

928 "Stanislaw Malachowski" and "Kazimierz Nestor Sapieha"

1988. Bicentenary of Four Years Diet (political and social reforms). Paintings of Diet Presidents by Jozef Peszko.
3180 **928** 20 z. multicoloured . . 20 10

929 Ignacy Daszynski (politician) 930 Snowman

1988. 70th Anniv of Polish Republic (4th issue). Personalities.
3181 **929** 15 z. green, red & blk 10 10
3182 – 15 z. green, red & blk 10 10
3183 – 20 z. brown, red & blk 20 10
3184 – 20 z. brown, red & blk 20 10
3185 – 20 z. brown, red & blk 20 10
3186 – 200 z. pur, red & blk 2·00 65
3187 – 200 z. pur, red & blk 2·00 65
3188 – 200 z. pur, red & blk 2·00 65
DESIGNS: No. 3182, Wincenty Witos (politician); 3183, Julian Marchlewski (trade unionist and economist); 3184, Stanislaw Wojciechowski (politician); 3185, Wojciech Korfanty (politician); 3186, Ignacy Paderewski (musician and politician). 3187, Marshal Jozef Pilsudski; 3188, Gabriel Narutowicz (President, 1922).

1988. 70th Anniv of Polish Republic (5th issue). As T **925.** Multicoloured.
3190 15 z. Coal wharf, Gdynia Port (65th anniv) (38 × 28 mm) 10 10
3191 20 z. Hipolit Cegielski (founder) and steam locomotive (142nd anniv of H. Cegielski Metal Works, Poznan) (38 × 28 mm) 20 10
3192 40 z. Upper Silesia Tower (main entrance) (60th anniv of International Poznan Fair) 40 15

1988. Polish Rulers (3rd series). Drawings by Jan Matejko. As T **893.**
3193 10 z. deep brown & brown 10 10
3194 15 z. deep brown & brown 10 10
DESIGNS: 10 z. Queen Rycheza; 15 z. Kazimierz (Karol Odnowiciel) I.

1988. New Year.
3195 **930** 20 z. multicoloured . . 20 10

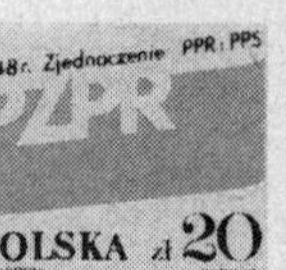

931 Flag 932 "Blysk"

1988. 40th Anniv of Polish United Workers' Party.
3196 **931** 20 z. red and black . . 20 10

1988. Fire Boats. Multicoloured.
3197 10 z. Type **932** 15 15
3198 15 z. "Plomien" 25 15
3199 15 z. "Zar" 25 15
3200 20 z. "Strazak II" . . 35 15
3201 20 z. "Strazak 4" . . 35 15
3202 45 z. "Strazak 25" . . 85 20

933 Ardennes 934 Wire-haired Dachshund

1989. Horses. Multicoloured.
3203 15 z. Lippizaner (horiz) . . 10 10
3204 15 z. Type **933** 10 10
3205 20 z. English thoroughbred (horiz) 15 15
3206 20 z. Arab 15 15
3207 30 z. Great Poland race-horse (horiz) . . 25 10
3208 70 z. Polish horse . . 65 20

1989. Hunting Dogs. Multicoloured.
3209 15 z. Type **934** 10 10
3210 15 z. Cocker spaniel . . 10 10
3211 20 z. Czech fousek pointer 15 10
3212 20 z. Welsh terrier . . 15 10
3213 25 z. English setter . . 20 10
3214 45 z. Pointer 40 15

935 Gen. Wladyslaw Anders and Plan of Battle 936 Marianne

1989. 45th Anniv of Battle of Monte Cassino.
3215 **935** 80 z. multicoloured . . 60 20
See also Nos. 3227, 3247, 3287 and 3327.

1989. Bicentenary of French Revolution.
3216 **936** 100 z. black, red & blue 50 25

937 Polonia House

1989. Opening of Polonia House (cultural centre), Pultusk.
3218 **937** 100 z. multicoloured . . 55 20

MINIMUM PRICE

The minimum price quoted is 5p which represents a handling charge rather than a basis for valuing common stamps. For further notes about prices see introductory pages.

938 Monument (Bohdan Chmielewski)

1989. 45th Anniv of Civic Militia and Security Force.
3219 **938** 35 z. blue and brown 20 10

939 Xaweri Dunikowski (artist)

941 Firemen

940 Astronaut

1989. Recipients of Order of Builders of the Republic of Poland. Multicoloured.
3220 35 z. Type **939** 20 10
3221 35 z. Stanislaw Mazur (farmer) 20 10
3222 35 z. Natalia Gasiorowska (historian) 20 10
3223 35 z. Wincenti Pstrowski (initiator of worker performance contests) 20 10

1989. 20th Anniv of First Manned Landing on Moon.
3224 **940** 100 z. multicoloured .. 55 20

1989. World Fire Fighting Congress, Warsaw.
3226 **941** 80 z. multicoloured .. 50 15

1989. 45th Anniv of Battle of Falaise. As T **935**. Multicoloured.
3227 165 z. Plan of battle and Gen. Stanislaw Maczek (horiz) 80 25

942 Daisy

943 Museum Emblem

1989. Plants. (a) Perf.
3229 **942** 40 z. green 10 10
3230 – 60 z. violet 10 10
3232 **942** 150 z. red 35 10
3234 – 500 z. mauve .. 1·10 40
3235 – 700 z. green 10 10
3237 – 1000 z. blue .. 2·10 85

(b) Self-adhesive. Imperf.
3297 – 2000 z. green .. 50 15
3298 – 5000 z. violet .. 1·00 35
DESIGNS: 60 z. Juniper. 500 z. Wild rose. 700 z. Lily of the valley. 1000 z. Blue cornflower. 2000 z. Water lily. 5000 z. Iris.

1989. 50th Anniv of German Invasion. As T **850**.
3240 25 z. grey, orange & black 10 10
3241 25 z. multicoloured .. 10 10
3242 35 z. multicoloured .. 20 10
3243 35 z. multicoloured .. 20 10
DESIGNS: No. 3240, Defence of Westerplatte and Captain Franciszek Dabrowski; 3241, Defence of Hel and Captain B. Przybyszewski; 3242, Battle of Kock and Brig.-Gen. Franciszek Kleeberg; 3243, Defence of Lwow and Brig.-Gen. Wladyslaw Langner.

1989. Caricature Museum.
3244 **943** 40 z. multicoloured .. 20 10

944 Rafal Czerwiakowski (founder of first university Surgery Department)

945 Emil Kalinski (Postal Minister, 1933–39)

1989. Polish Surgeons' Society Centenary Congress, Cracow.
3245 **944** 40 z. blue and black 20 10
3246 – 60 z. green and black 25 10
DESIGN: 60 z. Ludwik Rydygier (founder of Polish Surgeons' Society).

1989. 45th Anniv of Landing at Arnhem. As T **935**. Multicoloured.
3247 210 z. Gen. Stanislaw Sosabowski and plan of battle .. .. .. 1·00 25

1989. World Post Day.
3248 **945** 60 z. multicoloured .. 25 10

1989. Polish People's Army Battle Medals (2nd series). As T **927**. Multicoloured.
3249 60 z. "For Participation in the Struggle for the Rule of the People" .. 25 10
3250 60 z. Warsaw 1939–45 Medal 25 10

1989. Polish Rulers (4th series). As T **893**. Drawings by Jan Matejko.
3251 20 z. black and grey .. 10 10
3252 30 z. sepia and brown .. 10 10
DESIGNS: 20 z. Boleslaw II, the Bold; 30 z. Wladyslaw I Herman.

946 Stamps **947** Cross and Twig

1989. "World Stamp Expo '89" International Stamp Exhibition, Washington D.C.
3253 **946** 500 z. multicoloured .. 1·25 85

1989. 70th Anniv of Polish Red Cross.
3254 **947** 200 z. red, green & blk 65 20

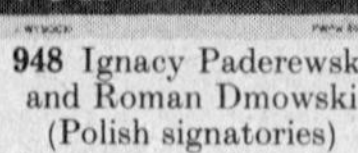

948 Ignacy Paderewski and Roman Dmowski (Polish signatories)

949 Photographer and Medal depicting Maksymilian Strasz

1989. 70th Anniv of Treaty of Versailles.
3255 **948** 350 z. multicoloured .. 75 35

1989. 150th Anniv of Photography. Mult.
3256 40 z. Type **949** 15 10
3257 60 z. Lens shutter as pupil of eye (horiz) 20 10

1989. No. 2729 surch **500**.
3258 500 z. on 4 z. violet .. 1·10 35

951 Painting by Jan Ciaglinski

1989. Flower Paintings by Artists Named. Multicoloured.
3259 25 z. Type **951** 10 10
3260 30 z. Wojciech Weiss .. 10 10
3261 35 z. Antoni Kolasinski .. 15 10
3262 50 z. Stefan Nacht-Samborski .. 15 10
3263 60 z. Jozef Pankiewicz .. 20 10
3264 85 z. Henryka Beyer .. 30 10
3265 110 z. Wladyslaw Slewinski 40 15
3266 190 z. Czeslaw Wdowiszewski .. 60 20

952 Christ

1989. Icons (1st series). Multicoloured.
3267 50 z. Type **952** 15 10
3268 60 z. Two saints with books 15 10
3269 90 z. Three saints with books 25 10
3270 150 z. Displaying scriptures (vert) .. 40 15
3271 200 z. Madonna and child (vert) 45 15
3272 350 z. Christ with saints and angels (vert) .. 75 15
See also Nos. 3345/50.

1990. No. 2839 surch **350 zl.**
3273 350 z. on 15 z. brown .. 75 10

954 Krystyna Jamroz

955 High Jumping

1990. Singers. Multicoloured.
3274 100 z. Type **954** 10 10
3275 150 z. Wanda Werminska 35 10
3276 350 z. Ada Sari 75 10
3277 500 z. Jan Kiepura .. 1·10 40

1990. Sports. Multicoloured.
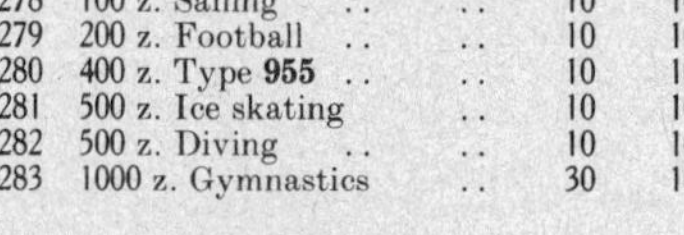
3278 100 z. Sailing 10 10
3279 200 z. Football 10 10
3280 400 z. Type **955** 10 10
3281 500 z. Ice skating .. 10 10
3282 500 z. Diving 10 10
3283 1000 z. Gymnastics .. 30 10

956 Kozlowski

1990. Birth Centenary (1989) of Roman Kozlowski (palaeontologist).
3284 **956** 500 z. brown and red 15 10

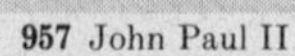

957 John Paul II

959 Ball and Colosseum

1990. 70th Birthday of Pope John Paul II.
3285 **957** 1000 z. multicoloured 30 10

1990. 50th Anniv of Battle of Narvik. As T **935**. Multicoloured.
3287 1500 z. Gen. Zygmunt Bohusz-Szyszko and plan of battle 40 10

1990. World Cup Football Championship, Italy.
3288 **959** 1000 z. multicoloured 30 10

1990. No. 3230 surch **700 zl.**
3289 700 z. on 60 z. violet .. 20 10

961 Memorial

963 Fresh-water Snail

962 People and "ZUS"

1990. 34th Anniv of 1956 Poznan Uprising.
3290 **961** 1500 z. multicoloured 40 15

1990. 70th Anniv of Social Insurance.
3291 **962** 1500 z. bl, mve & yell 40 15

1990. Shells. No value expressed.
3292 – B (500 z.) lilac .. 15 10
3293 **963** A (700 z.) green .. 20 10
DESIGN: B, Viviparous mussel.

964 Cross

1990. 50th Annniv of Katyn Massacre.
3294 **964** 1500 z. black and red 40 15

965 Weather Balloon

1990. Polish Hydrology and Meteorology Service. Multicoloured.
3295 500 z. Type **965** 15 10
3296 700 z. Water-height gauge 20 10

966 Women's Kayak Pairs

1990. 23rd World Canoeing Championships. Multicoloured.
3305 700 z. Type **966** 20 10
3306 1000 z. Men's kayak singles 30 10

967 Victory Sign

968 Jacob's Ladder

1990. 10th Anniv of Solidarity Trade Union.
3307 **967** 1500 z. grey, blk & red 40 15

1990. Flowers. Multicoloured.
3308 200 z. Type **968** 10 10
3309 700 z. Floating heart water fringe 10 10
3310 700 z. Dragonhead .. 10 10
3311 1000 z. "Helleborus purpurascens" .. 10 10
3312 1500 z. Daphne cneorum 15 10
3313 1700 z. Campion 20 10

969 Serving Dish, 1870-87

1990. Bicentenary of Cmieow Porcelain Works. Multicoloured.
3314 700 z. Type **969** 10 10
3315 800 z. Plate, 1887-90 (vert) 10 10
3316 1000 z. Cup and saucer, 1887 .. .. .. 10 10
3317 1000 z. Figurine of dancer, 1941-44 (vert) 10 10
3318 1500 z. Chocolate box, 1930-90 .. .. 15 10
3319 2000 z. Vase, 1979 (vert) 20 10

970 Little Owl

972 Collegiate Church, Tum (12th century)

971 Walesa

1990. Owls. Multicoloured.
3320 200 z. Type **970** 10 10
3321 500 z. Tawny owl .. 10 10
3322 500 z. Tawny owl (different) 10 10
3323 1000 z. Short-eared owl .. 35 30
3324 1500 z. Long-eared owl .. 55 30
3325 2000 z. Barn owl .. 70 30

1990. Lech Walesa, 1984 Nobel Peace Prize Winner and new President.
3326 **971** 1700 z. multicoloured 20 10

1990. 50th Anniv of Battle of Britain. As T **935**. Multicoloured.
3327 1500 z. Polish 303 Fighter Wing emblem and Hawker "Hurricane" .. 15 10

1990. Historic Architecture. Multicoloured.
3328 700 z. Tupe **972** 10 10
3329 800 z. Reszel castle (11th century) 10 10
3330 1500 z. Chelmno Town Hall (16th century) .. 15 10
3331 1700 z. Church of the Nuns of the Visitation, Warsaw (18th century) 20 10

973 "King Zygmunt II August" (anon)

974 Common Silver Fir

1991. Paintings. Multicoloured.
3332 500 z. Type **973** 10 10
3333 700 z. "Adoration of the Magi" (Pultusk Codex) 10 10
3334 1000 z. "St. Matthew" (Pultusk Codex) .. 10 10
3335 1500 z. "Expelling of Merchants from Temple" (Nikolai Haberschrack) .. 15 10
3336 1700 z. "The Annunciation" (miniature) .. 20 10
3337 2000 z. "Three Marys" (Nikolai Haberschrack) 20 10

1991. Cones. Multicoloured.
3338 700 z. Type **974** 10 10
3339 1500 z. Weymouth pine .. 15 10
See also Nos. 3483/4.

975 Radziwill Palace

977 Chmielowski

1991. Admission of Poland into C.E.P.T. (European Postal and Telecommunications Conference).
3340 **975** 1500 z. multicoloured 15 10

1991. Polish Rulers (5th series). Drawings by Jan Matejko. As T **893** but surch.
3341 1000 z. on 40 z. blk & grn 10 10
3342 1500 z. on 50 z. blk & red 15 10
DESIGNS: 1000 z. Boleslaw III, the Wry Mouthed; 1500 z. Wladyslaw II, the Exile.
Nos. 3341/2 were not issued unsurcharged.

1991. 75th Death Anniv of Adam Chmielowski ("Brother Albert") (founder of Albertine Sisters).
3343 **977** 2000 z. multicoloured 20 10

978 Battle (detail of miniature, Schlackenwerth Codex, 1350)

1991. 750th Anniv of Battle of Legnica.
3344 **978** 1500 z. multicoloured 15 10

1991. Icons (2nd series). As T **952**. Mult.
3345 500 z. Madonna and Child 10 10
3346 700 z. Christ 10 10
3347 1000 z. Madonna and Child with two saints .. 10 10
3348 1500 z. Madonna and Child 15 10
3349 2000 z. Christ holding figure of saint .. 20 10
3350 2200 z. Christ holding crystal box .. 25 10

1991. Polish Rulers (6th series). Drawings by Jan Matejko. As T **893**.
3351 1000 z. black and red .. 10 10
3352 1500 z. black and blue .. 15 10
DESIGNS: 1000 z. Boleslaw IV, the Curly; 1500 z. Mieszko (Mieczyslaw) III, the Old.

979 Title Page of Constitution

980 Satellite in Earth Orbit

1991. Bicentenary of 3rd May Constitution.
3353 **979** 2000 z. brn, buff & red 20 10
3354 – 2500 z. brown, stone & red 25 10
DESIGNS 2500 z. "Administration of Oath by Gustav Taubert" (detail, Johann Friedrich Bolt).

1991. Europa. Europe in Space.
3356 **980** 1000 z. multicoloured 10 10

981 Map and Battle Scene

1991. 50th Anniv of Participation of "Piorun" (destroyer) in Operation against "Bismarck" (German battleship).
3357 **981** 2000 z. multicoloured 35 15

982 Arms of Cracow

983 Pope John Paul II

1991. European Security and Co-operation Conference Cultural Heritage Symposium, Cracow.
3358 **982** 2000 z. purple and blue 20 10

1991. Papal Visit. Multicoloured.
3359 1000 z. Type **983** .. 10 10
3360 2000 z. Pope in white robes 20 10

984 Chinstrap Penguin

985 Making Paper

1991. 30th Anniv of Antarctic Treaty.
3361 **984** 2000 z. multicoloured 30 15

1991. 500th Anniv of Paper Making in Poland.
3362 **985** 2500 z. blue and red .. 25 10

986 Prisoner

1991. Commemoration of Victims of Stalin's Purges.
3363 **986** 2500 z. red and black 25 10

988 Ball and Basket

1991. Centenary of Basketball.
3365 **988** 2500 z. multicoloured 25 10

989 "Self-portrait" (Leon Wyczolkowski)

1991. "Bydgoszcz '91" National Stamp Exn.
3366 **989** 3000 z. green & brown 30 10

990 Twardowski

1991. 125th Birth Anniv of Kazimierz Twardowski (philosopher).
3368 **990** 2500 z. black and grey 25 10

991 Swallowtail

1991. Butterflies and Moths. Multicoloured.
3369 1000 z. Type **991** .. 10 10
3370 1000 z. Dark crimson underwing ("Mormonia sponsa") 10 10
3371 1500 z. Painted lady ("Vanessa cardui") .. 15 10
3372 1500 z. Scarce swallowtail ("Iphiclides podalirius") 15 10
3373 2500 z. Scarlet tiger moth ("Panaxia dominula") 30 10
3374 2500 z. Peacock ("Nymphalis io") .. 30 10

992 "The Shepherd's Bow" (Francesco Solimena)

1991. Christmas.
3376 **992** 1000 z. multicoloured 10 10

993 Gen. Stanislaw Kopanski and Battle Map

1991. 50th Anniv of Participation of Polish Troops in Battle of Tobruk.
3377 **993** 2000 z. multicoloured 20 10

994 Brig.-Gen. Michal Tokarzewski-Karaszewicz

995 Lord Baden-Powell (founder)

1991. World War II Polish Underground Army Commanders.
3378 **994** 2000 z. black and red 20 10
3379 – 2500 z. red and violet 25 10
3380 – 3000 z. blue & mauve 30 10
3381 – 5000 z. brown & green 50 20
3382 – 6500 z. dp brn & brn 70 25
DESIGNS: 2500 z. Gen. Broni Kazimierz Sosnkowski; 3000 z. Lt.-Gen. Stefan Rowecki; 5000 z. Lt.-Gen. Tadeusz Komorowski; 6500 z. Brig.-Gen. Leopold Okulicki.

1991. 80th Anniv of Scout Movement in Poland.
3383 **995** 1500 z. yellow & green 15 10
3384 – 2000 z. blue & yellow 20 10
3385 – 2500 z. violet & yellow 25 10
3386 – 3500 z. brown & yell 35 15
DESIGNS: 2000 z. Andrzej Malkowski (Polish founder); 2500 z. "Watch on the Vistula" (Wojciech Kossak); 3500 z. Polish scout in Warsaw Uprising, 1944.

1992. Polish Rulers (7th series). As T **893**.
3387 1500 z. brown and green 15 10
3388 2000 z. black and blue .. 20 10
DESIGNS: 1500 z. Kazimierz II, the Just; 2000 z. Leszek I, the White.

996 Sebastien Bourdon

1992. Self-portraits. Multicoloured.
3389 700 z. Type **996** 10 10
3390 1000 z. Sir Joshua Reynolds 10 10
3391 1500 z. Sir Godfrey Kneller 15 10
3392 2000 z. Bartolome Esteban Murillo 20 10
3393 2200 z. Peter Paul Rubens 25 10
3394 3000 z. Diego de Silva y Velazquez 30 10

997 Skiing

998 Manteuffel

1992. Winter Olympic Games, Albertville. Multicoloured.
3395 1500 z. Type **997** .. 15 10
3396 2500 z. Ice hockey .. 25 10

1992. 90th Birth Anniv of Tadeusz Manteuffel (historian).
3397 **998** 2500 z. brown .. 20 10

999 Nicolas Copernicus (astronomer)

1992. Famous Poles. Multicoloured.
3398 1500 z. Type **999** .. 15 10
3399 2000 z. Fryderyk Chopin (composer) 15 10
3400 2500 z. Henryk Sienkiewicz (writer) .. 20 10
3401 3500 z. Marie Curie (physicist) 30 10

1000 Columbus and Left-hand Detail of Map

1992. Europa. 500th Anniv of Discovery of America by Christopher Columbus. Mult.
3403 1500 z. Type **1000** .. 15 10
3404 3000 z. "Santa Maria" and right-hand detail of Juan de la Costa map, 1500 .. .. .. 45 15
Nos. 3403/4 were issued together, se-tenant, forming a composite design.

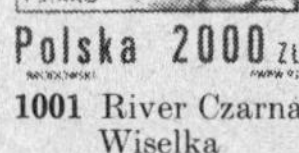

1001 River Czarna Wiselka

1003 Family and Heart

1002 Jozef Poniatowski

1992. River Cascades. Multicoloured.
3405 2000 z. Type **1001** .. 15 10
3406 2500 z. River Swider .. 20 10
3407 3000 z. River Tanew .. 25 10
3408 3500 z. Mickiewicz waterfall 30 10

1992. Bicentenary of Order of Military Virtue. Multicoloured.
3409 1500 z. Type **1002** .. 15 10
3410 3000 z. Marshal Jozef Pilsudski .. 25 10

1992. Children's Drawings. Multicoloured.
3412 1500 z. Type **1003** .. 15 10
3413 3000 z. Butterfly, sun, bird and dog 25 10

1004 Fencing

1992. Olympic Games, Barcelona. Mult.
3414 1500 z. Type **1004** .. 15 10
3415 2000 z. Boxing 15 10
3416 2500 z. Running 20 10
3417 3000 z. Cycling 25 10

1006 Statue of Korczak

1992. 50th Death Anniv of Janusz Korczak (educationist).
3419 **1006** 1500 z. blk, brn & yell 15 10

1007 Flag and "V"

1008 Wyszinski

1992. 5th Polish Veterans World Meeting.
3420 **1007** 3000 z. multicoloured 25 10

1992. 11th Death Anniv of Stefan Wyszinski (Primate of Poland) (3421) and 1st Anniv of World Youth Day (3422). Multicoloured.
3421 1500 z. Type **1008** .. 15 10
3422 3000 z. Pope John Paul II embracing youth .. 25 10

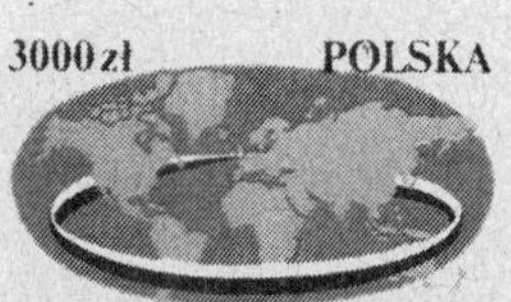

1009 National Colours encircling World Map

1992. World Meeting of Expatriate Poles.
3423 **1009** 3000 z. multicoloured 25 10

1010 House

1011 18th-century Post Office Sign, Slonim

1992. 150th Anniv of Polish Settlement at Adampol, Turkey.
3424 **1010** 3500 z. multicoloured 30 10

1992. World Post Day.
3425 **1011** 3500 z. multicoloured 30 10

1012 Portrait

1992. Birth Centenary of Bruno Schulz (writer).
3426 **1012** 3000 z. multicoloured 25 10

1013 "Seated Girl" (Henryk Wicinski)

1992. Polish Sculptures from the National Museum, Warsaw. Multicoloured.
3427 2000 z. Type **1013** .. 15 10
3428 2500 z. "Portrait of Tytus Czyzewski" (Zbigniew Pronaszko) 20 10
3429 3000 z. "Polish Nike" (Edward Wittig) .. 25 10
3430 3500 z. "The Nude" (August Zamoyski) .. 30 10

1014 "10th Theatrical Summer in Zamosc" (Jan Mlodozeniec)

1992. Poster Art. Multicoloured.
3432 1500 z. Type **1014** .. 15 10
3433 2000 z. "Red Art" (Franciszek Starowieyski) 15 10
3434 2500 z. "Circus" (Waldemar Swierzy) .. 20 10
3435 3500 z. "Mannequins" (Henryk Tomaszewski) 30 10

1015 Girl skipping with Snake

1992. "Polska '93" International Stamp Exn, Poznan (1st issue). Mult.
3436 1500 z. Type **1015** .. 15 10
3437 2000 z. Boy on rocking horse with upside-down runners 15 10
3438 2500 z. Boy firing bird from bow 20 10
3439 3500 z. Girl placing ladder against clockwork giraffe 30 10
See also Nos. 3452, 3453/6 and 3466/9.

1016 Medal and Soldiers

1992. Home Army Celebration Year. Mult.
3440 1500 z. Type **1016** .. 15 10
3441 3500 z. Soldiers 30 50

1017 Church and Star

1018 Wheat

1992. Christmas.
3443 **1017** 1000 z. multicoloured 10 10

1992. International Nutrition Conference, Rome. Multicoloured.
3444 1500 z. Type **1018** .. 15 10
3445 3500 z. Glass, bread, vegetables and jug on table 30 10

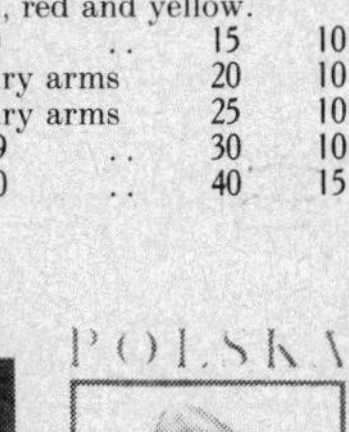

1019 Arms of Sovereign Military Order

1020 Arms, 1295

1992. Postal Agreement with Sovereign Military Order of Malta.
3446 **1019** 3000 z. multicoloured 25 10

1992. History of the White Eagle (Poland's arms). Each black, red and yellow.
3447 2000 z. Type **1020** .. 15 10
3448 2500 z. 15th-century arms 20 10
3449 3000 z. 18th-century arms 25 10
3450 3500 z. Arms, 1919 .. 30 10
3451 5000 z. Arms, 1990 .. 40 15

1021 Exhibition Emblem and Stylised Stamp

1022 Amber

1992. Centenary of Polish Philately and "Polska '93" International Stamp Exn, Poznan (2nd issue).
3452 **1021** 1500 z. multicoloured 15 10

1993. "Polska '93" International Stamp Exhibition, Poznan (3rd issue). Amber. Multicoloured.
3453 1500 z. Type **1022** .. 15 10
3454 2000 z. Pinkish amber .. 15 10
3455 2500 z. Amber in stone .. 20 10
3456 3000 z. Amber containing wasp 25 10

1023 Downhill Skier

1024 Flower-filled Heart

1993. Winter University Games, Zakopane.
3458 **1023** 3000 z. multicoloured 25 10

1993. Valentine's Day. Multicoloured.
3459 1500 z. Type **1024** .. 15 10
3460 3000 z. Heart in envelope 25 10

1993. Polish Rulers (8th series). As T **893** showing drawings by Jan Matejko.
3461 1500 z. brown and green 15 10
3462 2000 z. black & dp mauve 15 10
3463 2500 z. black and green .. 20 10
3464 3000 z. dp brown & brown 25 10
DESIGNS: 1500 z. Wladyslaw Laskonogi; 2000 z. Henryk I; 2500 z. Konrad I of Masovia; 3000 z. Boleslaw V, the Chaste.

1025 Arsenal

1993. 50th Anniv of Attack on Warsaw Arsenal by Szare Szeregi (formation of Polish Scouts in the Home Army).
3465 **1025** 1500 z. multicoloured 15 10

1026 Jousters with Lances

1993. "Polska '93" International Stamp Exhibition, Poznan (4th issue). Jousting at Golub Dobrzyn. Designs showing a modern and a medieval jouster. Multicoloured.
3466 1500 z. Type **1026** .. 15 10
3467 2000 z. Jousters 15 10
3468 2500 z. Jousters with swords 20 10
3469 3500 z. Officials 30 10

1027 Szczecin

1028 Jew and Ruins

1993. 750th Anniv of Granting of Town Charter to Szczecin.
3470 **1027** 1500 z. multicoloured 15 10

1993. 50th Anniv of Warsaw Ghetto Uprising.
3471 **1028** 4000 z. blk, yell & bl 25 10

1029 Works by A. Szapocznikow and J. Lebenstein

1993. Europa. Contemporary Art. Mult.
3472 1500 z. Type **1029** .. 10 10
3473 4000 z. Works by S. Gierowski and B. Linke 25 10

1030 King Alexander Jagiellonczyk and Parliament Session, 1505

1993. 500th Anniv of Parliament.
3474 **1030** 2000 z. multicoloured 10 10

1031 Nullo

1033 Cap

1993. 130th Death Anniv of Francesco Nullo (Italian volunteer in January 1863 Rising).
3475 **1031** 2500 z. multicoloured 15 10

1993. Cadets.
3477 **1033** 2000 z. multicoloured 10 10

HAVE YOU READ THE NOTES AT THE BEGINNING OF THIS CATALOGUE?
These often provide answers to the enquiries we receive.

1034 Copernicus and Solar System

1993. 450th Death Anniv of Nicolas Copernicus (astronomer).
3478 **1034** 2000 z. multicoloured 10 10

1035 Fiki Miki and Lion

1993. 40th Death Anniv of Kornel Makuszynski (writer of children's books). Multicoloured.
3479 1500 z. Type **1035** .. 10 10
3480 2000 z. Billy goat .. 10 10
3481 3000 z. Fiki Miki .. 20 10
3482 5000 z. Billy goat riding ostrich 30 10

1993. Cones. As T **974**. Multicoloured.
3483 10000 z. Arolla pine .. 60 20
3484 20000 z. Scots pine .. 1·25 45

1036 Tree Sparrow

1038 "Madonna and Child" (St. Mary's Basilica, Lesna Podlaska)

1037 Soldiers Marching

1993. Birds. Multicoloured.
3485 1500 z. Type **1036** .. 10 10
3486 2000 z. Pied wagtail .. 10 10
3487 3000 z. Syrian woodpecker 20 10
3488 4000 z. Goldfinch .. 25 10
3489 5000 z. Common starling 30 10
3490 6000 z. Bullfinch .. 35 15

1993. Bicentenary of Dabrowski's "Mazurka" (national anthem) (1st issue).
3491 **1037** 1500 z. multicoloured 10 10

1993. Sanctuaries to St. Mary. Multicoloured.
3492 1500 z. Type **1038** .. 10 10
3493 2000 z. "Madonna and Child" (St. Mary's Church, Swieta Lipka) 10 10

1039 Airplane and Parachutes

1993. 50th Anniv of Polish Rangers (paratroop regiment).
3494 **1039** 1500 z. multicoloured 10 10

1040 Trumpet Player

1993. "Jazz Jamboree '93" International Jazz Festival, Warsaw.
3495 **1040** 2000 z. multicoloured 10 10

1041 Postman

1042 St. Jadwiga (miniature, Schlackenwerther Codex)

1993. World Post Day.
3496 **1041** 2500 z. brown, grey and blue 15 10

1993. 750th Death Anniv of St. Jadwiga of Silesia.
3497 **1042** 2500 z. multicoloured 15 10

1044 Eagle and Crown

1045 St. Nicholas

1993. 75th Anniv of Republic.
3499 **1044** 4000 z. multicoloured 25 10

1993. Christmas.
3501 **1045** 1500 z. multicoloured 10 10

1046 "Come and see Polish mountains" (M. Urbaniec)

1993. Poster Art. Multicoloured.
3502 2000 z. Type **1046** .. 10 10
3503 5000 z. "Alban Berg Wozzeck" (J. Lenica) 30 10

MILITARY POST

I. Polish Corps in Russia, 1918.

1918. Stamps of Russia optd. **POCZTA. Pol. Korp.** and eagle. Perf. or imperf. (70 k.).

M 1. **22.** 3 k. red .. .. 50·00 32·00
M 2. **23.** 4 k. red .. .. 50·00 32·00
M 3. **22.** 5 k. red .. .. 17·00 13·50
M 4. **23.** 10 k. blue .. .. 17·00 13·50
M 5. **22.** 10 k. on 7 k. bl. (No. 151) £425 £500
M 6. **10.** 15 k. blue and purple 3·25 3·25
M 7. **14.** 20 k. red and blue .. 6·75 5·00
M 8. **10.** 25 k. mauve and green 85·00 70·00
M 9. 35 k. green and purple 3·25 3·25
M 10. **14.** 50 k. green and purple 13·50 10·00
M 11. **10.** 70 k. orange and brown (No. 166) £250 £200

1918. Stamps of Russia surch. **Pol. Korp.**, eagle and value. (a) Perf. on Nos. 92/4.

M 12A. **22.** 10 k. on 3 k. red .. 3·25 3·25
M 13A. 35 k. on 1 k. orange 50·00 50·00
M 14A. 50 k. on 2 k. green 3·25 3·25
M 15A. 1 r. on 3 k. red .. 60·00 60·00

(b) Imperf. on Nos. 155/7

M 12B. **22.** 10 k. on 3 k. red .. 1·10 1·10
M 13B. 35 k. on 1 k. orange 50 50
M 14B. 50 k. on 2 k. green 1·10 1·10
M 15B. 1 r. on 3 k. red .. 2·40 2·40

II. Polish Army in Russia, 1942.

M **3.** "We Shall Return".

1942.

M 16. M **3.** 50 k. brown £170 £400

NEWSPAPER STAMPS

1919. Newspaper stamps of Austria optd. **POCZTA POLSKA.** Imperf.

N 50. N **53.** 2 h. brown .. .. 10·00 10·00
N 51. 4 h. green .. .. 2·40 2·40
N 52. 6 h. blue .. .. 2·40 2·40
N 53. 10 h. orange .. 48·00 48·00
N 54. 30 h. red .. .. 5·25 5·25

OFFICIAL STAMPS

O 24. O 70.

1920.

O 128. O **24.** 3 f. red 10 10
O 129. 5 f. red 10 10
O 130. 10 f. red 10 10
O 131. 15 f. red 10 10
O 132. 25 f. red 10 10
O 123. 50 f. red 10 10
O 134. 100 f. red 10 10
O 135. 150 f. red 10 10
O 136. 200 f. red 10 10
O 137. 300 f. red 10 10
O 138. 600 f. red 10 10

1933. (a) Inscr. " ZWYCZAJNA ".

O 295. O **70.** (No value) mauve 10 10
O 306. (No value) blue .. 10 10

(b) Inscr. " POLECONA ".

O 307. O **70.** (No value) red .. 10 10

O 93.

1940. (a) Size 31 × 23 mm.

O 392. O **93.** 6 g. brown .. 1·50 1·50
O 393. 8 g. grey .. .. 1·50 1·50
O 394. 10 g. green .. 1·50 1·50
O 395. 12 g. green .. 1·50 2·00
O 396. 20 g. brown .. 1·50 3·25
O 397. 24 g. red .. .. 22·00 50
O 398. 30 g. red .. .. 2·00 3·00
O 399. 40 g. violet .. 2·00 4·75
O 400. 48 g. olive .. .. 7·50 5·00
O 401. 50 g. blue .. .. 1·60 3·00
O 402. 60 g. olive .. .. 1·40 2·00
O 403. 80 g. purple .. 1·40 2·00

(b) Size 35 × 26 mm.

O 404. 1 z. purple and grey 3·75 5·00
O 405. 3 z. brown and grey 3·75 5·00
O 406. 5 z. orge. and grey 5·00 6·75

1940. Size 21 × 16 mm.

O 407. O **93.** 6 g. brown .. 1·00 1·25
O 408. 8 g. grey .. .. 1·50 2·00
O 409. 10 g. green .. 2·75 2·40
O 410. 12 g. green .. 2·75 2·40
O 411. 20 g. brown .. 1·40 1·25
O 412. 24 g. red .. .. 1·00 1·40
O 413. 30 g. red .. .. 1·75 2·00
O 414. 40 g. violet .. 2·75 2·40
O 415. 50 g. blue .. .. 2·75 2·40

O 102. O 128. O 277.

1943.

O 456. O **102.** 6 g. brown .. 10 20
O 457. 8 g. blue 10 20
O 458. 10 g. green .. 10 20
O 459. 12 g. violet .. 25 20
O 460. 16 g. orange .. 10 30
O 461. 20 g. olive .. 15 20
O 462. 24 g. red 25 20
O 463. 30 g. purple .. 15 20
O 464. 40 g. blue .. 15 20
O 465. 60 g. olive .. 15 20
O 466. 80 g. purple .. 20 20
O 467. 100 g. grey .. 25 85

1945. No value.

The blue and indigo stamps are inscr. "ZWYKLA" (Ordinary) and the red stamps "POLECONA" (Registered).

(a) With control number below design. Perf or imperf.

O 534 O **128** (5 z.) blue .. 15 10
O 535 (10 z.) red .. 65 10

(b) Without control number below design. Perf.

O 748 O **128** (60 g.) pale blue .. 25 10
O 805 (60 g.) indigo .. 30 10
O 806 (1.55 z.) red .. 55 10

1954. No value.

O 871 O **277** (60 g.) blue .. 25 10
O 872 (1.55 z.) red ("POLECONA") 50 10

POSTAGE DUE STAMPS

1919. Postage Due stamps of Austria optd. **POCZTA POLSKA.**

D 50. D **55.** 5 h. red .. .. 8·00 6·75
D 51. 10 h. red £2000 £2000
D 52. 15 h. red .. .. 4·00 3·25
D 53. 20 h. red £500 £500
D 54. 25 h. red .. .. 20·00 17·00
D 55. 30 h. red £1300 £1300
D 56. 40 h. red £325 £325
D 57. D **56.** 1 k. blue £3000 £3250
D 58. 5 k. blue £3000 £3250
D 59. 10 k. blue £10000 £8000

1919. Postage Due Provisionals of Austria optd. **POCZTA POLSKA.**

D 60. **50.** 15 on 36 h. (No D 287) £325 £250
D 61. 50 on 42 h. (No. D 289) 32·00 32·00

D 20. D 28. D 63.

1919. Value in " halerzy ".

D 92. D **20.** 2 h. blue 10 10
D 93. 4 h. blue 10 10
D 94. 5 h. blue 10 10
D 95. 10 h. blue 10 10
D 96. 20 h. blue 10 10
D 97. 30 h. blue 10 10
D 98. 50 h. blue 10 10
D 145. 100 h. blue .. 10 65
D 147. 500 h. blue .. 75 1·60

1919. As Type D **20**, but value in " fenigow ".

D 128. D **20.** 2 f. red 25 25
D 129. 4 f. red 10 10
D 130. 5 f. red 10 10
D 131. 10 f. red 10 10
D 132. 20 f. red 10 10
D 133. 30 f. red 10 10
D 134. 50 f. red 10 10
D 135. 100 f. red 50 25
D 146. 200 f. blue .. 10 10
D 136. 500 f. red .. .. 1·40 60

1921. Stamps of 1919 surch. with new value and **doplata.** Imperf.

D 154. **11.** 6 m. on 15 h. brown 40 65
D 155. 6 m. on 25 h. red .. 40 45
D 156. 20 m. on 10 h. red 1·00 85
D 157. 20 m. on 50 h. blue 1·40 1·60
D 158. 35 m. on 70 h. blue 8·25 10·00

1921. Value in " marks ".

(a) Size 17 × 22 mm.

D 159. D **28.** 1 m. blue 10 10
D 160. 2 m. blue 10 10
D 161. 4 m. blue 10 10
D 162. 6 m. blue 10 10
D 163. 8 m. blue 10 10
D 164. 20 m. blue .. 10 10
D 165. 50 m. blue .. 10 10
D 166. 100 m. blue .. 10 10

(b) Size 19 × 24 mm.

D 199. D **28.** 50 m. blue .. 10 10
D 200. 100 m. blue .. 10 10
D 201. 200 m. blue .. 10 10
D 202. 500 m. blue .. 10 10
D 203. 1000 m. blue .. 10 10
D 204. 2000 m. blue .. 10 10
D 205. 10,000 m. blue .. 10 10
D 206. 20,000 m. blue .. 10 10
D 207. 30,000 m. blue .. 10 10
D 208. 50,000 m. blue .. 10 10
D 209. 100,000 m. blue .. 15 10
D 210. 200,000 m. blue .. 15 10
D 211. 300,000 m. blue .. 25 15
D 212. 500,000 m. blue .. 40 50
D 213. 1,000,000 m. blue 50 65
D 214. 2,000,000 m. blue 1·00 1·00
D 215. 3,000,000 m. blue 2·10 15

1923. Surch.

D 216. D **28.** 10,000 on 8 m. blue 10 10
D 217. 20,000 on 20 m. blue 10 20
D 218. 50,000 on 2 m. blue 30 50

1924. As Type D **28** but value in " groszy ", or " zloty ". (a) Size 20 × 25½ mm.

D 229. D **28.** 1 g. brown .. 10 10
D 230. 2 g. brown .. 15 10
D 231. 4 g. brown .. 15 10
D 232. 6 g. brown .. 15 10
D 233. 10 g. brown .. 3·25 10
D 234. 15 g. brown .. 2·75 10
D 235. 20 g. brown .. 6·75 10
D 236. 25 g. brown .. 4·75 10
D 237. 30 g. brown .. 75 10
D 238. 40 g. brown .. 90 10
D 239. 50 g. brown .. 90 10
D 240. 1 z. brown .. 75 10
D 241. 2 z. brown .. 75 10
D 242. 3 z. brown .. 90 25
D 243. 5 z. brown .. 90 10

(b) Size 19 × 24 mm.

D 290. D **28.** 1 g. brown .. 20 10
D 291. 2 g. brown .. 20 10
D 292. 10 g. brown .. 90 15
D 293. 15 g. brown .. 1·50 10
D 294. 20 g. brown .. 3·75 10
D 295. 25 g. brown .. 32·00 10

1930.

D 280. D **63.** 5 g. brown .. 20 10

1934. Nos. D 79/84 surch.

D 301. D **28.** 10 g. on 2 z. brown 15 10
D 302. 15 g. on 2 z. brown 15 10
D 303. 20 g. on 1 z. brown 15 10
D 304. 20 g. on 5 z. brown 1·90 10
D 305. 25 g. on 40 g. brown 60 15
D 306. 30 g. on 40 g. brown 55 15
D 307. 50 g. on 40 g. brown 55 15
D 308. 50 g. on 3 z. brown 1·90 20

1934. No. 273 surch. **DOPLATA** and value.

D 309. 10 g. on 1 z. blk. on cream 1·00 10
D 310. 20 g. on 1 z. blk. on cream 2·00 15
D 311. 25 g. on 1 z. blk. on cream 1·00 10

D 88. D 97.

1938.

D 350. D **88.** 5 g. green .. 15 10
D 351. 10 g. green .. 15 10
D 352. 15 g. green .. 15 10
D 353. 20 g. green .. 65 15
D 354. 25 g. green .. 15 15
D 355. 30 g. green .. 65 15
D 356. 50 g. green .. 85 40
D 357. 1 z. green .. 3·75 1·60

1940. German Occupation.

D 420. D **97.** 10 g. orange .. 50 85
D 421. 20 g. orange .. 50 1·00
D 422. 30 g. orange .. 50 1·00
D 423. 50 g. orange .. 1·40 2·40

D 126. D 190.

1945. Size 26 × 19½ mm. Perf.

D 530. D **126.** 1 z. brown .. 10 10
D 531. 2 z. brown .. 10 10
D 532. 3 z. brown .. 15 10
D 533. 5 z. brown .. 20 15

1946. Size 29 × 21½ mm. Perf or imperf.

D 646 D **126** 1 z. brown .. 10 10
D 647 2 z. brown .. 10 10
D 572 3 z. brown .. 10 10
D 573 5 z. brown .. 10 10
D 574 6 z. brown .. 10 10
D 575 10 z. brown .. 10 10
D 649 15 z. brown .. 10 10
D 577 25 z. brown .. 20 10
D 651 100 z. brown .. 50 15
D 652 150 z. brown .. 65 15

1950.

D 665. D **190.** 5 z. red 10 10
D 666. 10 z. red 10 10
D 667. 15 z. red 10 10
D 668. 20 z. red 10 10
D 669. 25 z. red 15 10
D 670. 50 z. red 25 10
D 671. 100 z. red .. 40 15

1951. Value in " groszy " or " zloty ".

D 701. D **190.** 5 g. red 10 10
D 702. 10 g. red 10 10
D 703. 15 g. red 10 10
D 704. 20 g. red 10 10
D 705. 25 g. red 10 10
D 706. 30 g. red 10 10
D 707. 50 g. red 10 10
D 708. 60 g. red 10 10
D 709. 90 g. red 15 10
D 710. 1 z. red 15 10
D 711. 2 z. red 30 10
D 712. 5 z. purple .. 90 15

1953. **As last but with larger figures of value and no imprint below design.**

D 804. D **190.** 5 g. brown .. 10 10
D 805. 10 g. brown .. 10 10
D 806. 15 g. brown .. 10 10
D 807. 20 g. brown .. 10 10
D 808. 25 g. brown .. 10 10
D 809. 30 g. brown .. 10 10
D 810. 50 g. brown .. 10 10
D 811. 60 g. brown .. 15 10
D 812. 90 g. brown .. 15 10
D 813. 1 z. brown .. 20 10
D 814. 2 z. brown .. 35 25

1980. As Type D **190** but redrawn without imprint.

D 2699. 1 z. red 10 10
D 2700. 2 z. drab 20 10
D 2701. 3 z. violet 30 10
D 2702. 5 z. brown 45 15

POLISH POST IN DANZIG Pt. 5

For Polish post in Danzig, the port through which Poland had access to the sea between the two Great Wars.

100 groszy = 1 zloty.

Stamps of Poland optd. **PORT GDANSK.**

1925. Issue of 1924.

R 1. **40.** 1 g. brown 35 1·50
R 2. 2 g. brown 40 3·00
R 3. 3 g. orange 40 1·50
R 4. 5 g. green 17·00 6·50
R 5. 10 g. green 6·00 3·00
R 6. 15 g. red 35·00 5·00
R 7. 20 g. blue 1·50 1·40
R 8. 25 g. red 1·50 1·40
R 9. 30 g. violet 1·75 1·40
R 10. 40 g. blue 1·75 1·40
R 11. 50 g. purple 5·50 1·50

1926. Issues of 1925-28.

R 14. **44.** 5 g. green 1·40 1·50
R 15. – 10 g. violet (No. 245a) 1·40 1·50
R 16. – 15 g. red (No. 246) 2·50 2·75
R 17. **48.** 20 g. red 2·00 1·75
R 18. **51.** 25 g. brown 4·50 1·50
R 19. **57.** 1 z. black and cream 32·00 30·00

1929. Issues of 1928/9.

R 21. **61.** 5 g. violet 1·50 1·60
R 22. 10 g. green 1·50 1·60
R 23. **59.** 15 g. blue 3·50 5·00
R 24. **61.** 25 g. brown 2·75 1·10

1933. Stamp of 1928 with **vert. opt.**

R 25. **57.** 1 z. black on cream 80·00 £100

1934. Issue of 1932.

R 26. **65.** 5 g. violet 3·75 3·50
R 27. 10 g. green 38·00 £110
R 28. 15 g. red 3·75 3·00

1936. Issue of 1935.

R 29. **79.** 5 g. blue (No. 313) 3·00 3·50
R 31. – 5 g. violet (No. 317) 80 1·50
R 30. – 15 g. blue (No. 315) 3·25 5·00
R 32. – 15 g. lake (No. 319) 80 1·50
R 33. – 25 g. green (No. 321a) 3·00 1·60

R 6. Port of Danzig.

1938. 20th Anniv. of Polish Independence.

R 34. **R 6.** 5 g. orange 60 1·00
R 35. 15 g. brown 60 1·00
R 36. 25 g. purple 60 1·25
R 37. 55 g. blue 1·25 3·00

POLISH POST OFFICE IN TURKEY Pt. 5

Stamps used for a short period for franking correspondence handed in at the Polish Consulate, Constantinople.

100 fenigow = 1 marka

1919. Stamps of Poland of 1919 optd. **LEVANT.** Perf.

1. **15.** 3 f. brown 1·75
2. 5 f. green 1·75
3. 10 f. purple 1·75
4. 15 f. red 1·75
5. 20 f. blue 1·75
6. 25 f. olive 1·75
7. 50 f. green 1·75
8. **17.** 1 m. violet 1·75
9. 1 m. 50 green 1·75
10. 2 m. brown 1·75
11. **18.** 2 m. 50 brown 1·75
12. **19.** 5 m. purple 1·75

PONTA DELGADA Pt. 9

A district of the Azores, whose stamps were used from 1868, and again after 1905.

1000 reis = 1 milreis.

1892. As T **26** of Portugal but inscr. "PONTA DELGADA".

6 5 r. orange 1·10 70
20 10 r. mauve 1·10 75
8 15 r. brown 1·40 1·25
9 20 r. lilac 1·50 1·10
10 25 r. green 2·40 75
24 50 r. blue 3·00 1·50
25 75 r. red 3·25 2·75
14 80 r. green 4·75 3·75
15 100 r. brown on yellow 5·00 2·75
28 150 r. red on rose 16·00 13·00
16 200 r. blue on blue 20·00 15·00
17 300 r. blue on brown 20·00 16·00

1897. "King Carlos" key-types inscr. "PONTA DELGADA".

29. S. 2½ r. grey 25 20
30. 5 r. orange 30 25
31. 10 r. green 30 25
32. 15 r. brown 3·50 2·75
45. 15 r. green 60 50
33. 20 r. lilac 65 45
34. 25 r. green 95 70
46. 25 r. red 40 20
35. 50 r. blue 1·10 70
48. 65 r. blue 40 35
36. 75 r. red 2·00 1·25
49. 75 r. brown on yellow 3·75 3·50
37. 80 r. mauve 40 35
38. 100 r. blue on blue 1·25 75
50. 115 r. brown on pink 70 65
51. 130 r. brown on yellow 70 65
39. 150 r. brown on yellow 70 65
52. 180 r. black on pink 70 65
40. 200 r. purple on pink 2·75 2·25
41. 300 r. blue on pink 2·75 2·25
42. 500 r. black on blue 5·00 3·75

PORT LAGOS Pt. 6

French Post Office in the Turkish Empire. Closed in 1898.

25 centimes = 1 piastre.

1893. Stamps of France optd **Port-Lagos** and the three higher values surch also in figures and words.

75 **10** 5 c. green 13·50 10·00
76 10 c. black on lilac 27·00 19·00
77 15 c. blue 55·00 45·00
78 1 p. on 25 black on pink 40·00 35·00
79 2 p. on 50 c. red £120 70·00
80 4 p. on 1 f. green 65·00 60·00

PORT SAID Pt. 6

French Post Office in Egypt. Closed 1931.

1902. 100 centimes = 1 franc.
1921. 10 milliemes = 1 piastre.

1899. Stamps of France optd **PORT-SAID.**

101 **10** 1 c. black on blue 40 50
102 2 c. brown on buff 50 60
103 3 c. grey 75 70
104 4 c. brown on grey 50 80
105 5 c. green 1·25 2·00
107 10 c. black on lilac 4·00 3·50
109 15 c. blue 2·50 4·00
110 20 c. red on green 3·25 4·50
111 25 c. black on pink 1·00 55
112 30 c. brown 4·75 5·00
113 40 c. red on yellow 7·25 4·50
115 50 c. red 9·50 6·00
116 1 f. green 13·00 7·75
117 2 f. brown on blue 42·00 35·00
118 5 f. mauve on lilac 65·00 50·00

1899. No. 107 surch.

(a) **25c VINGT- CINQ.**

119 **10** 25 c. on 10 c. blk on lilac £275 £110

(b) **VINGT- CINQ** only.

121 **10** 25 c. on 10 c. blk on lilac 75·00 14·50

1902. "Blanc", "Mouchon" and "Merson" key-types inscr "PORT SAID".

122 A 1 c. grey 10 40
123 2 c. purple 15 35
124 3 c. red 15 20
125 4 c. brown 20 20
126a 5 c. green 65 30
127 B 10 c. red 30 45
128 15 c. red 75 85
128a 15 c. orange 1·10 90
129 20 c. brown 35 60
130 25 c. blue 30 15
131 30 c. mauve 1·75 1·50
132 C 40 c. red and blue 1·25 2·00
133 50 c. brown and lilac 1·00 1·25
134 1 f. red and green 4·25 3·50
135 2 f. lilac and buff 3·75 6·00
136 5 f. blue and buff 14·00 15·00

1915. Red Cross. Surch **5c** and red cross.

137 B 10 c.+5 c. red 25 80

1921. Surch with value in figures and words (without bars).

151a A 1 m. on 1 c. grey 40 45
152 2 m. on 5 c. green 40 50
153 B 4 m. on 10 c. red 60 95
166a A 5 m. on 1 c. grey 4·00 4·50
167 5 m. on 2 c. purple 6·25 6·25
154 5 m. on 3 c. red 3·75 4·00
141 5 m. on 4 c. brown 4·75 4·75
155 B 6 m. on 15 c. orange 85 1·00
156 6 m. on 15 c. red 5·50 5·50
157 8 m. on 20 c. brown 75 90
168 A 10 m. on 2 c. purple 6·00 6·25
142 10 m. on 4 c. brown 9·50 9·50
158 B 10 m. on 25 c. blue 1·40 1·40
159 10 m. on 30 c. mauve 2·75 3·25
144 12 m. on 30 c. mauve 16·00 16·00
145 A 15 m. on 4 c. brown 3·50 3·75
169 B 15 m. on 15 c. red 27·00 27·00
170 15 m. on 20 c. brown 27·00 27·00
146 C 15 m. on 40 c. red & bl 25·00 25·00
160 15 m. on 50 c. brown and lilac 2·00 2·50
161 B 15 m. on 50 c. blue 2·50 2·00
171 C 30 m. on 50 c. brown and lilac £160 £160
162 30 m. on 1 f. red & grn 1·50 3·00
172 60 m. on 50 c. brown and lilac £170 £170
149 60 m. on 2 f. lilac & buff 48·00 48·00
164 60 m. on 2 f. red & grn 4·00 4·75
173 150 m. on 50 c. brown and lilac £200 £200
165 150 m. on 5 f. bl & buff 3·75 4·00

1925. Surch with value in figures and words and bars over old value.

174 A 1 m. on 1 c. grey 35 50
175 2 m. on 5 c. green 35 50
176 B 4 m. on 10 c. red 35 50
177 A 5 m. on 3 c. red 40 50
178 B 6 m. on 15 c. orange 60 70
179 8 m. on 20 c. brown 35 60
180 10 m. on 25 c. blue 60 70
181 15 m. on 50 c. blue 70 70
182 C 30 m. on 1 f. red & green 70 95
183 60 m. on 2 f. red & green 70 1·10
184 150 m. on 5 f. bl & buff 1·25 1·75

1927. Altered key-types. Inscr. "Mm" below value.

185. A. 3 m. orange 60 75
186. B. 15 m. blue 65 75
187. 20 m. mauve 90 1·00
188. C. 50 m. red and green 1·75 1·90
189. 100 m. blue and yellow 2·00 2·50
190. 250 m. green and red 4·00 4·25

1927. "French Sinking Fund" issue. As No. 186 (colour changed) surch **+5 Mm Caisse d'Amortissement.**

191 B 15 m.+5 m. orange 1·25 1·50
192 15 m.+5 m. mauve 1·25 1·50
193 15 m.+5 m. brown 1·25 1·50
194 15 m.+5 m. lilac 1·75 2·75

POSTAGE DUE STAMPS

1921. Postage Due stamps of France surch. in figures and words.

D 174. **D 11.** 2 m. on 5 c. blue 25·00 25·00
D 175. 4 m. on 10 c. brown 25·00 25·00
D 176. 10 m. on 30 c. red 25·00 25·00
D 166. 12 m. on 10 c. brn. 28·00 28·00
D 167. 15 m. on 5 c. blue 30·00 30·00
D 177. 15 m. on 50 c. pur. 35·00 35·00
D 168. 30 m. on 20 c. olive 35·00 35·00
D 169. 30 m. on 50 c. pur. £170 £170

For 1928 issue, see Alexandria.

PORTUGAL Pt. 9

A country on the S.W. coast of Europe, a kingdom till 1910, when it became a republic.

1853. 1000 reis = 1 milreis.
1912. 100 centavos = 1 escudo.

1. Queen Maria II. 5. King Pedro V. 9. King Luis.

1853. Various frames. Imperf.

1. **1.** 5 r. brown £900 £325
4. 25 r. blue £350 10·00
6. 50 r. green £1100 £300
8. 100 r. lilac £5500 £850

1855. Various frames. Imperf.

18 **5** 5 r. brown £118 14·00
21 25 r. blue £150 6·00
22 25 r. red £100 1·50
13 50 r. green £170 28·00
15 100 r. lilac £275 38·00

1862. Various frames. Imperf.

24. **9.** 5 r. brown 35·00 4·00
28. 10 r. yellow 60·00 14·00
30. 25 r. red 38·00 1·25
32. 50 r. green £225 27·00
34. 100 r. lilac £275 32·00

14. King Luis. 15.

1866. With curved value labels. Imperf.

35. **14.** 5 r. black 48·00 4·00
36. 10 r. yellow 85·00 32·00
38. 20 r. olive 70·00 25·00
39. 25 r. red 95·00 1·25
41. 50 r. green £110 26·00
43. 80 r. orange £110 26·00
45. 100 r. purple £110 35·00
46. 120 r. blue £120 22·00

1867. With curved value labels. Perf.

52. **14.** 5 r. black 55·00 12·00
54. 10 r. yellow £100 32·00
56. 20 r. olive £120 32·00
57. 25 r. red 28·00 1·25
60. 50 r. green £120 32·00
61. 80 r. orange £150 42·00
62. 100 r. lilac £130 40·00
64. 120 r. blue £130 25·00
67. 240 r. mauve £425 £160

1870. With straight value labels. Perf.

102 **15** 5 r. black 16·00 2·50
70 10 r. yellow 27·00 8·00
107 10 r. green 38·00 7·00
141 15 r. brown 28·00 4·00
142 20 r. olive 25·00 4·00
79 20 r. red 10·00 70
80 25 r. red 10·00 70
83 50 r. green 45·00 4·50
117 50 r. blue 85·00 12·00
146 80 r. orange 40·00 4·00
153 100 r. mauve 32·00 2·25
93 120 r. blue £110 28·00
95 150 r. blue £140 42·00
155 150 r. yellow 65·00 5·00
99 240 r. mauve £700 £400
156 300 r. mauve 45·00 10·00
128 1000 r. black £110 22·00

16. King Luis. 17.

1880. Various frames for T **16.**

185 **16** 5 r. black 7·50 1·00
188 25 r. grey 9·00 50
190 25 r. brown 9·00 50
180 **17** 25 r. grey £110 5·50
184 **16** 50 r. blue £100 5·00

19. King Luis. 26. King Carlos.

1882. Various frames.

229 **19** 5 r. black 2·25 50
231 10 r. green 10·00 80
232 20 r. red 18·00 5·00
194 25 r. brown 7·50 70
234 25 r. mauve 10·00 35
236 50 r. blue 16·00 90
216 500 r. black £200 £110
217 500 r. mauve £100 20·00

1892.

271 **26** 5 r. orange 2·50 45
239 10 r. mauve 7·50 90
256 15 r. brown 6·00 1·25
242 20 r. lilac 8·00 2·75
275 25 r. green 9·00 45
244 50 r. blue 12·00 3·00
245 75 r. red 24·00 1·25
262 80 r. green 25·00 15·00
248 100 r. brown on yellow 20·00 2·25
265 150 r. red on rose 55·00 15·00
252 200 r. blue on blue 50·00 13·00
267 300 r. blue on brown 65·00 18·00

1892. Optd. **PROVISORIO.**

284 **19** 5 r. black 3·50 3·25
285 10 r. green 5·00 2·50
295 **15** 15 r. brown 5·00 3·00
290 **19** 20 r. red 8·50 5·50
291 25 r. mauve 4·25 2·00
292 50 r. blue 25·00 20·00
293 **15** 80 r. orange 42·00 32·00

1893. Optd. **1893. PROVISORIO** or surch. also.

302. **19.** 5 r. black 7·50 4·50
303. 10 r. green 8·00 6·00
304. 20 r. red 15·00 13·00
309. 20 r. on 25 r. mauve 18·00 11·00
305. 25 r. mauve 40·00 32·00
306. 50 r. blue 40·00 32·00
310. **15.** 50 r. on 80 r. orange 32·00 42·00
312. 75 r. on 80 r. orange 32·00 25·00
308. 80 r. orange 40·00 32·00

32. Prince Henry in his Caravel and Family Motto.

DESIGNS: 25 r. to 100 r. Prince Henry's fleet. 150 r. to 1000 r. Prince Henry's studies.

1894. 500th Birth Anniv. of Prince Henry the Navigator.

314. **32.** 5 r. orange 1·25 1·00
315. 10 r. red 1·75 1·00
316. 15 r. brown 2·75 1·50
317. 20 r. violet 3·00 1·50
318. – 25 r. green 2·50 1·00
319. – 50 r. blue 6·00 2·00
320. – 75 r. red 12·00 4·00
321. – 80 r. green 15·00 4·50
322. – 100 r. brown on buff 9·00 2·50
323. – 150 r. red 22·00 10·00
324. – 300 r. blue on buff 30·00 10·00
325. – 500 r. purple 75·00 20·00
326. – 1000 r. black 95·00 35·00

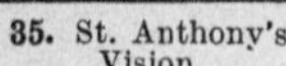

35. St. Anthony's Vision.

37. St. Anthony ascending into Heaven.

1895. 700th Birth Anniv. of St. Anthony (Patron Saint).

327. **35.** 2½ r. black .. .. 1·50 1·10
328. – 5 r. orange .. .. 1·75 1·10
329. – 10 r. mauve .. .. 4·00 2·50
330. – 15 r. brown .. .. 6·00 4·00
331. – 20 r. grey .. .. 6·00 4·00
332. – 25 r. purple and green .. 4·00 1·25
333. **37.** 50 r. brown and blue .. 14·00 10·00
334. 75 r. brown and red .. 20·00 15·00
335. 80 r. brown and green .. 25·00 20·00
336. 100 r. black and brown 25·00 13·00
337. – 150 r. red and brown .. 60·00 45·00
338. – 200 r. blue and brown .. 60·00 45·00
339. – 300 r. black and brown 85·00 55·00
340. – 500 r. brown and green £150 £120
341. – 1,000 r. lilac and green £225 £160

DESIGNS — HORIZ. 5 r. to 25 r. St. Anthony preaching to fishes. VERT. 150 r. to 1,000 r. St. Anthony from picture in Academy of Fine Arts Paris.

39. King Carlos.

1895. Numerals of value in black or red.

342 39 2½ r. grey 10 10
343 5 r. orange 20 10
344 10 r. green 20 10
345 15 r. green .. .. 18·00 1·00
346 15 r. brown .. .. 27·00 1·50
347 20 r. lilac 25 10
348 25 r. green .. .. 22·00 10
349 25 r. red 20 10
351 50 r. blue 25 10
352 65 r. blue 40 10
353 75 r. red .. .. 35·00 1·50
354 75 r. brown on yellow .. 50 20
355 80 r. mauve 80 25
356 100 r. blue on blue .. 40 10
357 115 r. brown on pink .. 2·00 1·00
358 130 r. brown on cream 1·50 65
359 150 r. brown on yellow 42·00 9·00
360 180 r. grey on pink .. 5·00 4·00
361 200 r. purple on pink .. 1·50 30
362 300 r. blue on pink .. 1·75 65
363 500 r. black on blue .. 3·00 2·00

40. Departure of Fleet.

DESIGNS—HORIZ. 5 r. Arrival at Calicut. 10 r. Embarkation at Rastello. 100 r. Flagship "Sao Gabriel". 150 r. Vasco da Gama. VERT. 75 r. Archangel Gabriel, Patron Saint of the Expedition.

43. Muse of History.

44. Da Gama and Camoens and "Sao Gabriel" (flagship).

1898. 4th Cent. of Discovery of Route to India by Vasco da Gama.

378. **40.** 2½ r. green 60 25
379. – 5 r. red 60 25
380. – 10 r. purple .. .. 3·50 1·25
381. **43.** 25 r. green .. .. 3·00 35
382. **44.** 50 r. blue .. .. 4·50 1·50
383. – 75 r. brown .. .. 13·00 5·50
384. – 100 r. brown .. .. 15·00 5·00
385. – 150 r. brown .. .. 25·00 14·00

48. King Manoel II. **49.**

1910.

390. **48.** 2½ r. violet 15 10
391. 5 r. black 15 10
392. 10 r. green 40 20
393. 15 r. brown .. .. 1·10 50
394. 20 r. red 65 35
395. 25 r. brown 40 10
396. 50 r. blue 65 35
397. 75 r. brown .. .. 4·25 2·00
398. 80 r. grey .. .. 1·50 1·25
399. 100 r. brown on green 5·50 2·00
400. 200 r. green on pink .. 2·25 1·75
401. 300 r. black on blue .. 3·25 2·25
402. **49.** 500 r. brown and olive .. 8·00 6·00
403. 1,000 r. black and blue 12·00 12·00

1910. Optd. **REPUBLICA.**

404. **48.** 2½ r. violet 20 10
405. 5 r. black 20 10
406. 10 r. green .. .. 1·25 40
407. 15 r. brown 40 30
408. 20 r. red .. .. 2·00 1·10
409. 25 r. brown 40 15
410. 50 r. blue .. .. 3·00 1·10
411. 75 r. brown .. .. 5·50 2·50
412. 80 r. grey .. .. 1·50 1·00
413. 100 r. brown on green .. 1·25 25
414. 200 r. green on pink .. 1·50 90
415. 300 r. black on blue .. 2·50 1·50
416. **49.** 500 r. brown and olive .. 5·50 4·50
417. 1,000 r. black and blue 10·00 10·00

1911. Optd. **REPUBLICA** or surch. also.

441. **40.** 2½ r. green 20 15
442a. D **48.** 5 r. black 10 10
443a. 10 r. mauve 10 10
444. – 15 r. on 5 r. red (379) 1·10 20
445a. D **48.** 20 r. orange 60 60
446. **43.** 25 r. green 50 25
447. **44.** 50 r. blue .. .. 2·00 1·75
448. – 75 r. brown (No. 383) 15·00 12·00
449. – 80 r. on 150 r. (385) .. 3·50 2·25
450. – 100 r. brown (No. 384) 2·50 1·50
451. D **48.** 200 r. brown on buff 25·00 22·00
452. 300 r. on 50 r. grey .. 20·00 16·00
453. 500 r. on 100 r. red .. 15·00 6·50
454. – 1,000 r. on 10 r. (380) 22·00 18·00

1911. Vasco da Gama stamps of Madeira optd. **REPUBLICA** or surch. also.

455. 2½ r. green .. .. 1·50 70
456. 15 r. on 5 r. red .. .. 1·50 1·00
457. 25 r. green .. .. 2·50 2·25
458. 50 r. blue .. .. .. 4·50 3·50
459. 75 r. brown .. .. 4·00 2·50
460. 80 r. on 150 r. brown .. 5·00 2·50
461. 100 r. brown .. .. 12·00 4·25
462. 1.000 r. on 10 r. purple .. 13·00 10·00

56. Ceres.

60. Presidents of Portugal and Brazil and Airmen G. Coutinho and S. Cabral.

1912.

484 **56** ¼ c. olive 10 10
485 ½ c. black 10 10
486 1 c. green 75 15
515 1 c. brown 10 10
488 1½ c. brown .. .. 2·75 75
516 1½ c. green 10 10
490 2 c. red .. .. 2·75 60
517 2 c. yellow 10 10
702 2 c. brown 10 10
492 2½ c. lilac 20 10
521 3 c. red 10 10
703 3 c. blue 10 10
495 3½ c. green 15 10
523 4 c. green 10 10
704 4 c. orange 10 10
497 5 c. blue .. .. 2·25 20
526 5 c. brown 10 10
499 6 c. purple 20 10
706 6 c. brown 10 10
815 6 c. red 10 10
500 7½ c. brown .. .. 3·50 50
529 7½ c. blue 10 10
530 8 c. grey 20 10
531 8 c. green 25 15
532 8 c. orange 30 15
503 10 c. brown .. .. 5·50 40
707 10 c. red 10 10
504 12 c. blue 90 35
534 12 c. green 25 15
535 13½ c. blue 45 25
481 14 c. blue on yellow .. 75 40
536 14 c. purple 35 15
505 15 c. purple .. .. 1·00 40
817 15 c. black 10 10
709 16 c. blue 20 15
474 20 c. brown on green .. 6·50 75
475 20 c. brown on buff .. 8·00 1·00
539 20 c. brown 35 10
540 20 c. green 35 15
541 20 c. grey 40 15
542 24 c. blue 30 15
543 25 c. pink 35 10
818 25 c. grey 20 10
819 25 c. green 20 10
476 30 c. brown on red .. 48·00 4·50
477 30 c. brown on yellow .. 2·50 50
545 30 c. brown 30 15
820 32 c. green 20 10
548 36 c. red 40 15
549 40 c. blue 45 20
550 40 c. brown 35 15
821 40 c. green 15 10
713 **56** 48 c. pink 60 50
478 50 c. orange on orange 5·50 75
553 50 c. yellow 50 25
824 50 c. red 50 40
554 60 c. blue 60 25
715 64 c. blue 60 45
826 75 c. red 75 25
510 80 c. pink 60 35
558 80 c. violet .. .. 1·00 45
827 80 c. green 85 25
559 90 c. blue .. .. 1·10 25
717 96 c. red .. .. 1·00 75
480 1 e. green on blue .. 7·00 1·00
561 1 e. lilac .. .. 2·50 50
565 1 e. blue .. .. 2·50 70
566 1 e. purple .. .. 1·00 25
829 1 e. red .. .. 2·00 35
562 1 e. 10 brown .. .. 2·75 50
563 1 e. 20 green .. .. 1·10 30
719 1 e. 20 ochre .. .. 4·50 35
830 1 e. 20 brown .. .. 1·25 35
831 1 e. 25 blue .. .. 1·00 30
568 1 e. 50 lilac .. .. 3·50 1·00
720 1 e. 60 blue .. .. 1·00 15
721 2 e. green .. .. 7·00 25
833 2 e. mauve .. .. 10·00 2·50
572 2 e. 40 green .. .. 55·00 45·00
573 3 e. pink .. .. 45·00 32·00
722 3 e. 20 green .. .. 2·50 45
723 4 e. 50 yellow .. .. 2·50 45
575 5 e. green .. .. 9·50 1·75
724 5 e. brown .. .. 42·00 75
725 10 e. red .. .. 3·25 55
577 20 e. blue .. .. £110 75·00

1923. Portugal–Brazil Trans-Atlantic Flight.

578. **60.** 1 c. brown 10 10
579. 2 c. orange 10 10
580. 3 c. blue 10 10
581. 4 c. green 15 15
582. 5 c. brown 15 15
583. 10 c. brown 15 15
584. 15 c. black 20 20
585. 20 c. green 20 20
586. 25 c. red 30 25
587. 30 c. brown .. .. 1·10 1·00
588. 40 c. brown 20 20
589. 50 c. yellow 30 20
590. 75 c. purple 35 25
591. 1 e. blue 45 35
592. 1 e. 50 grey 65 50
593. 2 e. green .. .. 1·10 1·00

62. Camoens at Ceuta.

63. Saving the "Lusiad".

1924. 4th Birth Centenary of Camoens (poet). Value in black.

600. **62.** 2 c. blue 20 20
601. 3 c. orange 20 20
602. 4 c. grey 20 20
603. 5 c. green 20 20
604. 6 c. red 20 20
605. **63.** 8 c. brown 20 20
606. 10 c. violet 20 20
607. 15 c. olive 20 20
608. 16 c. purple 20 20
609. 20 c. orange 20 20
610. – 25 c. mauve 25 25
611. – 30 c. brown 25 25
612. – 32 c. green 45 45
613. – 40 c. blue 40 40
614. – 48 c. purple 80 80
615. – 50 c. red 90 90
616. – 64 c. green 95 95
617. – 75 c. violet .. .. 1·00 1·00
618. – 80 c. brown .. .. 1·00 1·00
619. – 96 c. red .. .. 1·00 1·00
620. – 1 e. blue 90 90
621. – 1 e. 20 brown .. .. 1·25 1·25
622. – 1 e. 50 red .. .. 1·00 1·00
623. – 1 e. 60 blue .. .. 1·10 1·10
624. – 2 e. green .. .. 1·75 1·50
625. – 2 e. 40 green on green 2·50 2·25
626. – 3 e. blue on blue .. 2·25 2·00
627. – 3 e. 20 black on green 2·25 2·00
628. – 4 e. 50 black on yellow 2·50 2·25
629. – 10 e. brown on red .. 4·25 3·25
630. – 20 e. violet on mauve .. 5·50 4·50

DESIGNS—VERT. 25 c. to 48 c. Luis de Camoens. 50 c. to 96 c. 1st Edition of "Lusiad". 20 e. Monument to Camoens. HORIZ. 1 e. to 2 e. Death of Camoens. 2 e. 40 to 10 e. Tomb of Camoens.

65. Branco's House at S. Miguel de Seide.

67. Camilo Castelo Branco.

1925. Birth Centenary of Camilo Castelo Branco (novelist). Value in black.

631. **65.** 2 c. orange 25 25
632. 3 c. green 25 25
633. 4 c. blue 25 25
634. 5 c. red 25 25
635 6 c. purple 25 25
636. 8 c. brown 25 25
637. A. 10 c. blue 25 25
638. **67.** 15 c. olive 35 35
639. A. 16 c. orange 35 35
640. 20 c. violet 35 35
641. **67.** 25 c. red 35 10
642. A. 30 c. brown 35 10
643. 32 c. green 75 75
644. **67.** 40 c. black and green .. 45 45
645 A. 48 c. purple .. .. 1·25 1·25
646. B. 50 c. green .. .. 1·00 1·00
647. 64 c. brown .. .. 2·00 2·00
648. 75 c. grey .. .. 1·10 1·10
649. **67.** 80 c. brown .. .. 1·00 1·00
650. B. 96 c. red .. .. 1·25 1·25
651. 1 e. violet .. .. 1·25 1·25
652. 1 e. 20 green .. .. 1·25 1·25
653. C. 1 e. 50 blue on blue .. 6·50 6·50
654. **67.** 1 e. 60 blue .. .. 2·25 2·25
655. C. 2 e. green on green .. 3·50 3·25
656. 2 e. 40 red on orange .. 18·00 15·00
657. 3 e. red on blue .. 25·00 22·00
658. 3 e. 20 black on green .. 18·00 16·00
659. **67.** 4 e. 50 black and red .. 6·50 5·00
660. C. 10 e. brown on buff .. 7·50 4·50
661. D. 20 e. black on orange .. 11·00 2·50

DESIGNS—HORIZ. A, Branco's study. VERT. B, Teresa de Albuquerque. C, Mariana and Joao da Cruz. D, Simao de Botelho. Types B/D shows characters from Branco's "Amor de Peredicao".

76. Afonso I, first King of Portugal 1140.

80. Goncalo Mendes da Maia.

77. Battle of Aljubarrota.

1926. 1st Independence issue. Dated 1926. Centres in black.

671. **76.** 2 c. orange 20 20
672. – 3 c. blue 20 20
673. **76.** 4 c. green 20 20
674. – 5 c. brown 20 20
675. **76.** 6 c. orange 20 20
676. – 15 c. green 20 20
677. **76.** 16 c. blue 55 55
678. **77.** 20 c. violet 55 55
679. – 25 c. red 60 60
680. **77.** 32 c. green 60 60
681. – 40 c. brown 40 40
682. – 46 c. red .. .. 1·25 1·50
683. – 50 c. olive .. .. 1·50 1·75
684. – 64 c. green .. .. 2·00 2·75
685. – 75 c. red .. .. 2·25 2·50
686. – 96 c. red .. .. 3·00 3·75
687. – 1 e. violet .. .. 3·50 4·75
688. **77.** 1 e. 60 blue .. .. 4·75 6·50
689. – 3 e. purple .. .. 14·00 16·00
690. – 4 e. 50 green .. .. 14·00 20·00
691. **77.** 10 e. red .. .. 24·00 30·00

DESIGNS—VERT. 25, 40, 50, 75 c. Philippa de Vilhena arms her sons. 64 c., 1e. Don Joao IV, 1640. 96 c., 3 e., 4 e. 50, Independence Monument, Lisbon. HORIZ. 3, 5, 15, 46 c. Monastery of D. Joao I.

1926. 1st Independence issue surch. Centres in black.

692. 2 c. on 5 c. brown .. 60 60
693. 2 c. on 46 c. red 60 60
694. 2 c. on 64 c. green 60 60
695. 3 c. on 75 c. red 60 60
696. 3 c. on 96 c. red 60 80
697. 3 c. on 1 e. violet 60 60
698. 4 c. on 1 e. 60 blue .. .. 2·75 2·75
699. 4 c. on 3 e. purple .. 1·60 1·75
700. 6 c. on 4 e. 50 green .. 1·60 1·75
701. 6 c. on 10 e. red .. .. 1·75 1·75

1927. 2nd Independence issue. Dated 1927. Centres in black.

726. **80.** 2 c. brown 20 20
727. – 3 c. blue 20 20
728. **80.** 4 c. orange 20 20
729. – 5 c. brown 20 20
730. – 6 c. brown 20 20
731. – 15 c. brown 30 30
732. – 16 c. blue 45 45
733. **80.** 25 c. grey 45 45
734. – 32 c. green .. .. 1·25 1·10
735. – 40 c. green 45 45
736. **80.** 48 c. red .. .. 4·00 3·25
737. – 80 c. violet .. .. 3·75 3·25
738. – 96 c. red .. .. 5·50 4·75
739. – 1 e. 60 blue .. .. 5·50 6·00
740. – 4 e. 50 yellow .. .. 10·00 10·00

DESIGNS—HORIZ. 3 c., 15 c., 80 c. Guimaraes Castle. 6 c., 32 c. Battle of Montijo. VERT. 5 c., 16 c., 1 e. 60, Joao das Regras. 40 c., 96 c. Brites de Almeida. 4 e. 50, J. P. Ribeiro.

1928. Surch.

742	56	4 c. on 8 c. orange ..	25	25
743		4 c. on 30 c. brown ..	25	25
744		10 c. on ¼ c. olive ..	35	25
745		10 c. on ½ c. black ..	40	25
746		10 c. on 1 c. brown ..	35	15
747		10 c. on 4 c. green ..	25	25
748		10 c. on 4 c. orange ..	25	25
749		10 c. on 5 c. olive ..	25	25
751		15 c. on 16 c. blue ..	25	25
752		15 c. on 20 c. brown ..	13·00	13·00
753		15 c. on 20 c. grey ..	25	25
754		15 c. on 24 c. turquoise	1·10	40
755		15 c. on 25 c. pink ..	25	20
756		15 c. on 25 c. grey ..	25	20
757		16 c. on 32 c. green ..	50	40
758		40 c. on 2 c. yellow ..	25	25
760		40 c. on 2 c. brown ..	25	25
761		40 c. on 3 c. blue ..	25	25
762		40 c. on 50 c. yellow ..	25	25
763		40 c. on 60 c. blue ..	50	40
764		40 c. on 64 c. blue ..	60	50
765		40 c. on 75 c. pink ..	60	50
766		40 c. on 80 c. violet ..	40	30
767		40 c. on 90 c. blue ..	2·50	1·00
768		40 c. on 1 e. purple ..	45	35
769		40 c. on 1 e. 10 brown..	45	30
770		80 c. on 6 c. red ..	40	40
771		80 c. on 6 c. brown ..	40	30
772		80 c. on 48 c. pink ..	60	40
773		80 c. on 1 e. 50 lilac ..	75	50
774		96 c. on 1 e. 20 green ..	1·75	1·10
775		96 c. on 1 e. 20 ochre ..	1·75	1·25
777		1 $ 60 on 2 e. green ..	10·00	9·00
778		1 $ 60 on 3 e. 20 bronze	3·50	3·00
779		1 $ 60 on 20 e. blue ..	4·25	3·25

84. Storming of Santarem.

1928. 3rd Independence issue. Dated 1928. Centres in black.

780	–	2 c. blue	15	20
781	84	3 c. green	15	20
782	–	4 c. red	15	20
783	–	5 c. olive	15	20
784	–	6 c. brown	30	35
785	84	15 c. grey	40	45
786	–	16 c. purple	40	55
787	–	25 c. blue	50	55
788	–	32 c. green	95	1·25
789	–	40 c. brown	30	60
790	–	50 c. red	2·75	2·50
791	84	80 c. grey	3·25	3·75
792	–	96 c. red	6·00	7·50
793	–	1 e. mauve	12·00	13·00
794	–	1 e. 60 blue	5·00	6·00
795	–	4 e. 50 yellow	5·00	6·00

DESIGNS—VERT. 2 c., 25 c., 1 e. 60, G. Paes. 6 c., 32 c., 96 c. Joana de Gouveia. 4 e. 50, M. de Albuquerque. HORIZ. 4 c., 16 c., 50 c. Battle of Rolica. 5 c., 40 c., 1 e. Battle of Atoleiros.

1929. Optd. **Revalidado.**

805.	56.	10 c. red	25	15
806.		15 c. black	25	15
807.		40 c. brown	30	15
808.		40 c. green	25	15
810.		96 c. red	2·50	1·50
811.		1 e. 60 blue	6·50	4·00

1929. Telegraph stamp surch. **CORREIO 1 $ 60** and bars.

812.	–	1 $ 60 on 5 c. brown ..	5·00	3·25

88. Camoens' poem "Lusiads".

89. St. Anthony's Birthplace.

1931.

835.	88.	4 c. brown	10	10
836.		5 c. brown	10	10
837.		6 c. grey	15	10
838.		10 c. purple	10	10
839.		15 c. black	15	10
840.		16 c. blue	55	20
841.		25 c. green	1·75	10
841a.		25 c. blue	2·00	10
841b.		30 c. green	80	10
842.		40 c. red	4·25	10
843.		48 c. brown	40	15
844.		50 c. brown	20	10
845.		75 c. red	2·50	50
846.		80 c. green	25	10
846a.		95 c. red	6·50	2·00
847.		1 e. red	17·00	10
848.		1 e. 20 olive	1·10	60
849.		1 e. 25 blue	60	10
849a		1 e. 60 blue	13·00	1·40
849b		1 e. 75 blue	40	10
850.		2 e. violet	25	10
851.		4 e. 50 orange	50	10
852.		5 e. green	50	10

1931. 700th Death Anniv of St. Anthony.

853.	89.	15 c. purple	50	20
854.	–	25 c. green	50	20
855.	–	40 c. brown	75	20
856.	–	75 c. red	8·50	4·25
857.	–	1 e. 25 grey	16·00	8·50
858.	–	4 e. 50 purple	10·00	1·50

DESIGNS—VERT. 25 c. Saint's baptismal font. 40 c. Lisbon Cathedral. 75 c. St. Anthony. 1 e. 25, Santa Cruz Cathedral, Coimbra. HORIZ. 4 e. 50, Saint's tomb, Padua.

90. Don Nuno Alvares Pereira.

94. President Carmona.

1931. 5th Death Cent. of Pereira.

859.	90.	15 c. black	50	30
860.		25 c. green and black ..	50	35
861.		40 c. orange	75	35
862.		75 c. red	7·00	6·00
863.		1 e. 25 blue	11·00	8·00
864.		4 e. 50 green and brown	50·00	25·00

1933. Pereira issue of 1931 surch.

865.	90.	15 c. on 40 c. orange ..	35	30
866.		40 c. on 15 c. black ..	1·25	1·10
867.		40 c. on 25 c. grn. & blk.	40	35
868.		40 c. on 75 c. red ..	3·00	2·00
869.		40 c. on 1 e. 25 blue ..	3·00	2·00
870.		40 c. on 4 e. 50 green and brown	3·00	2·00

1933. St. Anthony issue of 1931 surch.

871.	–	15 c. on 40 c. brown ..	50	35
872.	89.	40 c. on 15 c. purple ..	75	40
873.	–	40 c. on 25 c. green ..	75	30
874.	–	40 c. on 75 c. red ..	3·00	2·00
875.	–	40 c. on 1 e. 25 grey ..	3·00	2·00
876.	–	40 c. on 4 e. 50 purple..	3·00	2·00

1934.

877.	94.	40 c. violet	5·50	10

95.

96. Queen Maria.

1934. Colonial Exhibition.

878.	95.	25 c. olive	2·00	45
879.		40 c. red	5·00	15
880.		1 e. 60 blue	13·00	4·25

1935. 1st Portuguese Philatelic Exhibition.

881.	96.	40 c. red	65	10

97. Temple of Diana at Evora.

98. Prince Henry the Navigator.

99. "All for the Nation".

100. Coimbra Cathedral.

1935.

882	97	4 c. black	20	10
883		5 c. blue	20	10
884		6 c. brown	20	10
885a	98	10 c. green	2·50	10
886		15 c. brown	15	10
887	99	25 c. blue	2·75	10
888		40 c. brown	60	10
889		1 e. red	1·50	15
890	100	1 e. 75 blue	28·00	1·25
890a	99	10 e. grey	6·00	75
890b		20 e. green	8·00	50

102. Shield and Propeller.

103. Symbol of Medicine.

1937. Air.

891.	102.	1 e. 50 blue	50	25
892.		1 e. 75 red	80	20
893.		2 e. 50 red	70	20
893a.		3 e. blue	5·00	2·50
893b.		4 e. green	9·00	6·50
894.		5 e red	1·00	20
895.		10 e. purple	2·50	20
895a.		15 e. orange	5·00	2·75
896.		20 e. brown	5·00	1·75
896a.		50 e. red	70·00	28·00

1937. Centenary of Medical and Surgical Colleges at Lisbon and Oporto.

897.	103.	25 c. blue	5·00	50

104. Gil Vicente.

106. Grapes.

107. Cross of Avis.

1937. 400th Death Anniv of Gil Vicente (poet).

898.	104.	40 c. brown	6·00	10
899.		1 e. red	1·00	10

1938. Wine and Raisin Congress.

900.	106.	15 c. violet	1·00	30
901.		25 c. brown	1·50	60
902.		40 c. mauve	4·50	15
903.		1 e. 75 blue	14·00	6·00

1940. Portuguese Legion.

904.	107.	5 c. yellow	25	10
905.		10 c. violet	35	10
906.		15 c. blue	35	10
907.		25 c. brown	7·00	25
908.		40 c. green	12·00	10
909.		80 c. green	1·00	20
910.		1 e. red	14·00	55
911.		1 e. 75 blue	3·75	65

109. Portuguese World Exhibition.

113. Sir Rowland Hill.

1940. Portuguese Centenaries.

912.	109.	10 c. red	10	10
913.	–	15 c. blue	10	10
914.	–	25 c. olive	35	15
915.	–	35 c. green	25	20
916.	–	40 c. brown	70	10
917.	109.	80 c. purple	1·75	15
918.	–	1 e. red	5·00	60
919.	–	1 e. 75 blue	2·50	90

DESIGNS—VERT. 15 c., 35 c. Statue of King Joao IV. 25 c., 1 e. Monument of Discoveries, Belem. 40 c., 1 e. 75, King Afonso Henriques.

1940. Cent of First Adhesive Postage Stamps.

920.	113.	15 c. purple	25	15
921.		25 c. red	25	15
922.		35 c. green	25	20
923.		40 c. purple	25	10
924.		50 c. green	4·50	2·00
925.		80 c. blue	50	60
926.		1 e. red	5·50	2·50
927.		1 e. 75 blue	2·50	1·25

114. Fish-woman of Nazare.

115. Caravel.

1941. Costumes.

932.	114.	4 c. green	15	10
933.	–	5 c. brown	15	10
934.	–	10 c. purple	1·25	30
935.	–	15 c. green	15	10
936.	–	25 c. purple	70	15
937.	–	40 c. green	15	10
938.	–	80 c. blue	1·00	80
939.	–	1 e. red	2·50	35
940.	–	1 e. 75 blue	2·50	1·25
941.	–	2 e. orange	13·00	8·50

DESIGNS: 5 c. Woman from Coimbra. 10 c. Vine-grower of Saloio. 15 c. Fish-woman of Lisbon. 25 c. Woman of Olhâo. 40 c. Woman of Aveiro. 80 c. Shepherdess of Madeira. 1 e. Spinner of Viana do Castelo. 1 e. 75, Horse-breeder of Ribatejo. 2 e. Reaper of Alentejo.

1943.

942.	115.	5 c. black	10	10
943.		10 c. red	10	10
944.		15 c. grey	10	10
945.		20 c. violet	10	10
946		30 c. brown	10	10
947.		35 c. green	10	10
948.		50 c. purple	10	10
948a.		80 c. green	1·25	20
949		1 e. red	1·75	10
949a.		1 e. lilac	90	10
949b.		1 e. 20 red	1·40	10
949c.		1 e. 50 olive	11·00	10
950.		1 e. 75 blue	7·00	25
950a.		1 e. 80 orange	12·50	1·40
951.		2 e. red	55	10
951a.		2 e. blue	1·75	10
952.		2 e. 50 red	90	10
953.		3 e. 50 blue	2·75	25
953a.		4 e. orange	14·00	90
954.		5 e. salmon	40	10
954a.		6 e. green	25·00	1·50
954b.		7 e. 50 green	7·50	1·50
955.		10 e. grey	60	10
956.		15 e. green	6·00	30
957.		20 e. olive	17·00	10
958.		50 e. orange	65·00	35

116. Labourer.

117. Mounted Postal Courier.

118. Felix Avellar Brotero.

1943. 1st Agricultural Science Congress.

959.	116.	10 c. blue	30	10
960.		50 c. red	40	10

1944. 3rd National Philatelic Exn., Lisbon.

961	117	10 c. brown	15	10
962		50 c. violet	15	10
963		1 e. red	1·25	25
964		1 e. 75 blue	1·25	75

1944. Birth Bicentenary of Avellar Brotero (botanist).

965.	118.	10 c. brown	25	10
966.	–	50 c. green	50	15
967.	–	1 e. red	1·75	30
968.	118.	1 e. 75 blue	1·50	50

DESIGN: 50 c., 1 e. Brotero's statue, Coimbra.

120. Vasco da Gama.

121. President Carmona.

1945. Portuguese Navigators.

969.	–	10 c. brown	15	10
970.	–	30 c. orange	15	10
971.	–	35 c. green	25	15
972.	120.	50 c. olive	40	10
973.	–	1 e. red	1·50	25
974.	–	1 e. 75 blue	1·75	70
975.	–	2 e. black	2·00	80
976.	–	3 e. 50 red	4·00	1·75

PORTRAITS: 10 c. Gil Eanes. 30 c. Joao Goncalves Zarco. 35 c. Bartolomeu Dias. 1 e. Pedro Alvares Cabral. 1 e. 75, Fernao de Magalhaes (Magellan). 2 e. Frey Goncalo Velho. 3 e. 50, Diogo Cao.

1945.

977.	121.	10 c. violet	10	10
978.		30 c. brown	10	10
979.		35 c. green	15	10
980.		50 c. olive	30	10
981.		1 e. red	2·75	15
982.		1 e. 75 blue	2·40	75
983.		2 e. purple	12·00	1·50
984.		3 e. 50 slate	7·00	2·75

122.

123. Almourol Castle.

1945. Naval School Cent.

985.	122.	10 c. brown	10	10
986.		50 c. green	15	10
987.		1 e. red	1·50	25
988.		1 e. 75 c. blue	1·60	1·10

1946. Portuguese Castles.

989.	–	10 c. purple	10	10
990.	–	30 c. brown	15	10
991.	–	35 c. olive	20	10
992.	–	50 c. grey	25	10
993.	123.	1 e. red	5·50	50
994.	–	1 e. 75 c. blue ..	4·50	1·00
995.	–	2 e. green	12·00	1·25
996.	–	3 e. 50 c. brown ..	7·00	2·25

DESIGNS: Castles at Silves (10 c.), Leiria (30 c.), Feira (35 c.), Guimaraes (50 c.), Lisbon (1 e. 75 c.), Braganza (2 e.) and Ourem (3 e. 50 c.).

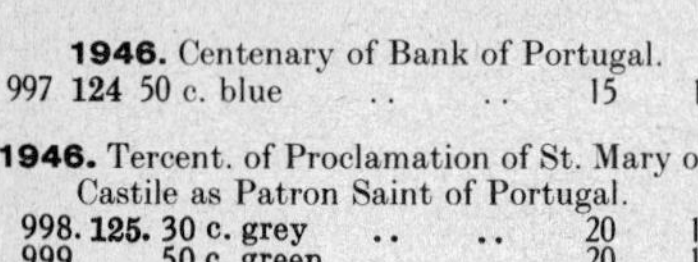

124. "Decree Founding National Bank". **125.** Madonna and Child.

1946. Centenary of Bank of Portugal.

997	124	50 c. blue	15	10

1946. Tercent. of Proclamation of St. Mary of Castile as Patron Saint of Portugal.

998.	125.	30 c. grey	20	15
999.		50 c. green	20	10
1000.		1 e. red	1·10	45
1001.		1 e. 75 blue	1·60	85

126. Caramulo Shepherdess. **127.** Surrender of the Keys of Lisbon.

1947. Regional Costumes.

1002.	126.	10 c. mauve	15	15
1003.	–	30 c. red	15	15
1004.	–	35 c. green	15	15
1005.	–	50 c. brown	20	10
1006.	–	1 e. red	4·25	40
1007.	–	1 e. 75 blue	4·00	1·00
1008.	–	2 e. blue	17·00	1·50
1009.	–	3 e. 50 green	10·00	2·25

COSTUMES: 30 c. Malpique timbrel player. 35 c. Monsanto flautist. 50 c. Woman of Avintes. 1 e. Maia field labourer. 1 e. 75, Woman of Algarve. 2 e. Miranda do Douro bastonet player. 3 e. 50, Woman of the Azores.

1947. 800th Anniv. of Recapture of Lisbon from the Moors.

1010.	127.	5 c. green	10	10
1011.		20 c. red	15	15
1012.		50 c. violet	25	10
1013.		1 e. 75 blue	2·00	1·60
1014.		2 e. 50 brown	3·00	3·00
1015.		3 e. 50 black	5·00	5·00

128. St. Joao de Brito.

1948. Birth Tercentenary of St. Joao de Brito.

1016.	128.	30 c. green	20	10
1017.	–	50 c. brown	20	10
1018.	128.	1 e. red	2·40	60
1019.	–	1 e. 75 blue	3·50	1·00

DESIGN: 50 c., 1 e. 75, St. Joao de Brito (different).

130. "Architecture and Engineering". **131.** King Joao I.

1948. Exhibition of Public Works, and National Congress of Engineering and Architecture.

1020.	130.	50 c. red	15	10

1949. Portraits.

1021	131	10 c. violet and buff	15	10
1022	–	30 c. green and buff	15	10
1023	–	35 c. green and olive	15	10
1024	–	50 c. blue & light blue	65	15
1025	–	1 e. lake and red	65	10
1026	–	1 e. 75 black and grey	6·00	2·75
1027	–	2 e. blue & light blue	3·00	75
1028	–	3 e. 50 chocolate & brn	11·00	7·50

PORTRAITS: 30 c. Queen Philippa. 35 c. Prince Fernando. 50 c. Prince Henry the Navigator. 1 e. Nun' Alvares. 1 e. 75, Joao da Regras. 2 e. Fernao Lopes. 3 e. 50, Afonso Domingues.

INDEX

Countries can be quickly located by referring to the index at the end of this volume.

132. Statue of Angel. **133.** Hands and Letter.

1949. 16th Congress of the History of Art.

1029	132	1 e. red	3·25	10
1030		5 e. brown	40	10

1949. 75th Anniv of U.P.U.

1031	133	1 e. lilac	15	10
1032		2 e. blue	35	15
1033		2 e. 50 green	1·50	40
1034		4 e. brown	4·50	2·00

134. Our Lady of Fatima. **135.** Saint and Invalid.

1950. Holy Year.

1035	134	50 c. green	35	20
1036		1 e. brown	1·50	10
1037		2 e. blue	2·00	60
1038		5 e. lilac	12·00	2·25

1950. 400th Death Anniv. of San Juan de Dios.

1039.	135.	20 c. violet	25	10
1040.		50 c. red	35	10
1041.		1 e. green	60	10
1042.		1 e. 50 c. orange	5·00	1·00
1043.		2 e. blue	3·25	55
1044.		4 e. brown	12·00	2·25

136. G. Junqueiro. **137.** Fisherman.

1951. Birth Cent. of Junqueiro (poet).

1045.	136.	50 c. brown	1·25	25
1046.		1 e. blue	30	10

1951. Fisheries Congress.

1047.	137.	50 c. green on buff	1·40	40
1048.		1 e. purple on buff	35	10

138. Dove and Olive Branch. **139.** 15th Century Colonists.

1951. Termination of Holy Year.

1049	138	20 c. brown and buff	20	10
1050		90 c. green and yellow	1·25	50
1051	–	1 e. purple and pink	1·10	10
1052	–	2 e. 30 green and blue	2·00	45

PORTRAIT: 1 e., 2 e. 30, Pope Pius XII.

1951. 500th Anniv. of Colonization of Terceira, Azores.

1053.	139.	50 c. blue	90	30
1054.		1 e. brown	90	30

140. Revolutionaries. **141.** Coach of King Joao VI.

1951. 25th Anniv. of National Revolution.

1055.	140.	1 e. purple	1·10	10
1056.		2 e. 30 blue	80	60

1952. National Coach Museum.

1057.	–	10 c. purple	15	10
1058.	141.	20 c. olive	15	10
1059.	–	50 c. green	25	10
1060.	–	90 c. green	1·00	90
1061.	–	1 e. orange	50	10
1062.	–	1 e. 40 red	2·25	2·25
1063.	141.	1 e. 50 brown	2·75	90
1064.	–	2 e. 30 blue	90	40

DESIGNS (coaches of): 10, 90 c. King Felippe II. 50 c., 1 e. 40, Papal Nuncio to Joao V. 1 e., 2 e. 30, King Jose.

142. "N.A.T.O." **143.** Hockey Players.

1952. 3rd Anniv. of N.A.T.O.

1065.	142.	1 e. green	5·00	50
1066.		3 e. 50 blue	95·00	12·00

1952. 8th World Roller-skating Hockey Championship.

1067.	143.	1 e. black and blue	2·25	15
1068.		3 e. 50 black & brown	3·75	1·40

144. Prof. G. Teixeira. **145.** Marshal Carmona Bridge.

1952. Birth Centenary of Prof. Gomes Teixeira (mathematician).

1069	144	1 e. purple and pink	40	10
1070		2 e. 30 dp blue & blue	2·75	2·00

1952. Cent. of Ministry of Public Works.

1071.	145.	1 e. brown on cream	40	10
1072.	–	1 e. 40 lilac on cream	3·50	2·50
1073.	–	2 e. green on cream	1·75	75
1074.	–	3 e. 50 blue on cream	3·75	1·25

DESIGNS: 1 e. 40, 28th May Stadium, Braga. 2 e. Coimbra University. 3 e. 50, Salazar Barrage.

146. St. Francis Xavier. **147.** Medieval Knight.

1952. 4th Death Cent of St. Francis Xavier.

1075	146	1 e. blue	35	10
1076		2 e. purple	45	15
1077		3 e. 50 blue	8·00	4·50
1078		5 e. lilac	14·00	1·90

1953.

1079	147	5 c. green on yellow	10	10
1080		10 c. grey on pink	10	10
1081		20 c. orange on yell	10	10
1081a		30 c. purple on buff	10	10
1082		50 c. black	10	10
1083		90 c. green on yellow	4·00	25
1084		1 e. brown on pink	10	10
1085		1 e. 40 red	4·00	40
1086		1 e. 50 red on yellow	15	10
1087		2 e. black	15	10
1088		2 e. 30 blue	7·00	25
1089		2 e. 50 black on pink	30	10
1089a		2 e. 50 green on yell	30	10
1090		5 e. purple on yellow	40	10
1091		10 e. blue on yellow	60	10
1091a		10 e. green on yellow	1·50	10
1092		20 e. brown on yell	2·00	10
1093		50 e. lilac	2·50	30

148. St. Martin of Dume. **149.** G. Gomes Fernandes.

1953. 14th Cent. of Landing of St. Martin of Dume on Iberian Peninsula.

1094.	148.	1 e. black and grey	50	15
1095.		3 e. 50 brown & yellow	3·75	2·75

1953. Birth Cent. of Fernandes (fire-brigade chief).

1096.	149.	1 e. purple and cream	70	10
1097.		2 e. 30 blue and cream	4·75	3·00

150. Club Emblems, 1903 and 1953. **151.** Princess St. Joan.

1953. 50th Anniv. of Portuguese Automobile Club.

1098.	150.	1 e. green	50	10
1099.		3 e. 50 brown	4·25	2·75

1953. 5th Cent of Birth of Princess St. Joan.

1100	151	1 e. black and green	75	15
1101		3 e. 50 dp blue & blue	4·50	3·00

152. Queen Maria II.

1953. Centenary of First Portuguese Stamps. Bottom panel in gold.

1102.	152.	50 c. lake	15	10
1103.		1 e. brown	15	10
1104.		1 e. 40 purple	80	70
1105.		2 e. 30 blue	1·75	1·00
1106.		3 e. 50 blue	1·75	1·25
1107.		4 e. 50 gold	1·25	90
1108.		5 e. olive	3·25	60
1109.		20 e. violet	20·00	2·00

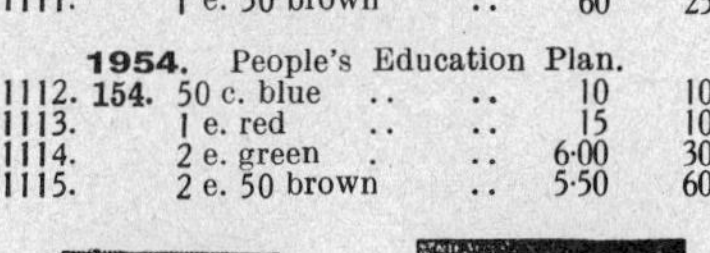

153. **154.**

1954. 150th Anniv. of Trade Secretariat.

1110.	153.	1 e. blue	30	10
1111.		1 e. 50 brown	60	25

1954. People's Education Plan.

1112.	154.	50 c. blue	10	10
1113.		1 e. red	15	10
1114.		2 e. green	6·00	30
1115.		2 e. 50 brown	5·50	60

155. Cadet and College Banner. **156.** Father Manuel da Nobrega.

1954. 150th Anniv. of Military College.

1116.	155.	1 e. brown and green	50	10
1117.		3 e. 50 blue and green	1·75	1·25

1954. 400th Anniv. of Sao Paulo.

1118.	156.	1 e. brown	35	10
1119.		2 e. 30 blue	10·00	6·50
1120.		3 e. 50 green	3·50	70
1121.		5 e. green	9·50	1·75

157. King Sancho I, 1154–1211. **158.** Telegraph Poles.

1955. Portuguese Kings.

1122.	–	10 c. purple	10	10
1123.	157.	20 c. green	15	10
1124.	–	50 c. turquoise	20	10
1125.	–	90 c. turquoise	70	70
1126.	–	1 e. brown	30	10
1127.	–	1 e. 40 red	2·00	1·75
1128.	–	1 e. 50 olive	1·00	55
1129.	–	2 e. salmon	2·50	1·50
1130.	–	2 e. 30 blue	2·50	1·25

KINGS: 10 c. Afonso I. 50 c. Afonso II. 90 c. Sancho II. 1 e. Afonso III. 1 e. 40, Diniz. 1 e. 50, Afonso IV. 2 e. Pedro I. 2 e. 30, Fernando.

1955. Centenary of Electric Telegraph System in Portugal.

1131.	158.	1 e. red and yellow	25	10
1132.		2 e. 30 blue and green	3·75	1·50
1133.		3 e. 50 green & yellow	3·75	1·10

159. A. J. Ferreira da Silva. **160.** Early Steam Locomotive.

1956. Birth Centenary of Ferreira da Silva (teacher).

1134	159	1 e. blue	20	10
1135		2 e. 30 green	2·25	1·75

1956. Centenary of Portuguese Railways.
1136 160 1 e. green & dp green 20 10
1137 – 1 e. 50 blue & turq .. 75 35
1138 – 2 e. brown and bistre 6·00 90
1139 160 2 e. 50 brown .. 7·00 1·40
DESIGN: 1 e. 50, 2 e. 1956 electric locomotive.

161. Madonna and Child. **162.** Almeida Garrett (after Barata Feyo).

1956. Mothers' Day.
1140. **161.** 1 e. sage and green .. 20 10
1141. 1 e. 50 olive & brown 40 15

1957. Almeida Garrett (writer) Commem.
1142. **162.** 1 e. brown 30 10
1143. 2 e. 30 violet .. 6·00 3·50
1144. 3 e. 50 green.. .. 1·00 55
1145. 5 e. red .. .. 8·00 4·00

163. Cesario Verde. **164.** Exhibition Emblem.

1957. Cesario Verde (poet). Commem.
1146. **163.** 1 e. brn., buff & olive 30 10
1147. 3 e. 30 blk., ol. & sage 60 45

1958. Brussels International Exhibition.
1148. **164.** 1 e. multicoloured .. 35 10
1149. 3 e. 30 multicoloured 90 70

165. St. Elizabeth. **166.** Institute of Tropical Medicine, Lisbon.

1958. St. Elizabeth and St. Teotonio Commem.
1150. **165.** 1 e. lake and cream .. 15 10
1151. – 2 e. green and cream 25 15
1152. **165.** 2 e. 50 violet & cream 1·00 20
1153. – 5 e. brown and cream 1·40 35
PORTRAIT: 2 e., 5 e. St. Teotonio.

1958. 6th Int. Congress of Tropical Medicine.
1154. **166.** 1 e. green and grey.. 50 10
1155. 2 e. 50 blue and grey 1·50 55

167. Liner.

168. Queen Leonora.

170. **169.** Arms of Aveiro.

1958. 2nd National Merchant Navy Congress.
1156. **167.** 1 e. brn., ochre & sepia 70 10
1157. 4 e. 50 vio., lav. & blue 80 60

1958. 500th Birth Anniv. of Queen Leonora. Frames and ornaments in bistre, inscriptions and value tablet in black.
1158. **168.** 1 e. blue and brown.. 20 10
1159. 1 e. 50 blue 90 30
1160. 2 e. 30 blue and green 80 30
1161. 4 e. 10 blue and grey 80 35

1959. Millenary of Aveiro.
1162. **169.** 1 e. multicoloured .. 35 10
1163. 5 e. multicoloured .. 1·90 55

1960. 10th Anniv. of N.A.T.O.
1164. **170.** 1 e. black and lilac .. 50 10
1165. 3 e. 50 black and grey 1·75 90

171. " Doorway to Peace ". **172.** Glider.

1960. World Refugee Year. Symbol in black.
1166. **171.** 20 c. yell., lemon & brn. 10 10
1167. 1 e. yell., green & blue 30 10
1168. 1 e. 80 yellow and green 30 30

1960. 50th Anniv. of Portuguese Aero Club. Multicoloured.
1169 1 e. Type **172** 15 10
1170 1 e. 50 Light monoplane 50 20
1171 2 e. Aircraft parachutes 80 30
1172 2 e. 50 Model aircraft .. 1·40 55

173. Padre Cruz (after M. Barata). **174.** University Seal.

1960. Death Cent. of Padre Cruz.
1173. **173.** 1 e. brown 25 10
1174. 4 e. 30 blue .. .. 2·25 2·00

1960. 400th Anniv. of Evora University.
1175. **174.** 50 c. blue 10 10
1176. 1 e. brown and yellow 15 10
1177. 1 e. 40 red 75 75

175. Prince Henry's Arms. **176.** Emblems of Prince Henry and Lisbon.

1960. 5th Death Centenary of Prince Henry the Navigator. Multicoloured.
1178 1 e. Type **175** 15 10
1179 2 e. 50 Caravel 55 25
1180 3 e. 50 Prince Henry the Navigator .. .. 1·25 65
1181 5 e. Motto .. .. 2·00 50
1182 8 e. Barketta 35 50
1183 10 e. Map showing Sagres 3·50 1·00

1960. Europa. As T **129a** of Luxembourg, but size 31 × 21 mm.
1184. 1 e. light blue and blue .. 25 10
1185. 3 e. 50 red and lake .. 1·75 1·25

1960. 5th National Philatelic Exn. Lisbon.
1186. **176.** 1 e. blue, black and green 30 10
1187. 3 e. 30 blue, black and olive .. .. 2·25 2·25

177. Portuguese Flag. **178.** King Pedro V.

1960. 50th Anniv. of Republic.
1188. **177.** 1 e. multicoloured .. 10 10

1961. Centenary of Lisbon University Faculty of Letters.
1189. **178.** 1 e. green and brown 30 10
1190. 6 e. 50 brown and blue 70 35

179. Arms of Setubal. **180.**

1961. Centenary of Setubal City.
1191. **179.** 1 e. multicoloured .. 25 10
1192. 4 e. 30 multicoloured 2·75 2·50

1961. Europa.
1193. **180.** 1 e. blue 20 10
1194. 1 e. 50 green .. 50 50
1195. 3 e. 50 pink and lake 80 80

181. Tomar Gateway. **182.** National Guardsman.

1961. 800th Anniv. of Tomar.
1196. – 1 e. multicoloured .. 30 10
1197. **181.** 3 e. 50 multicoloured 70 65
DESIGN: 1 e. As Type **181** but without ornamental background

1962. 50th Anniv. of National Republican Guard.
1198. **182.** 1 e. multicoloured .. 10 10
1199. 2 e. multicoloured .. 1·00 30
1200. 2 e. 50 multicoloured 90 20

183. St. Gabriel (Patron Saint of Telecommunications). **184.** Scout Badge and Tents.

1962. St. Gabriel Commem.
1201. **183.** 1 e. brn., grn. & olive 35 10
1202. 3 e. 50 grn., brn. & ol. 25 25

1962. 18th Int. Scout Conference (1961).
1203. **184.** 20 c. multicoloured.. 10 10
1204. 50 c. multicoloured.. 10 10
1205. 1 e. multicoloured 40 10
1206. 2 e. 50 multicoloured 1·40 15
1207. 3 e. 50 multicoloured 40 25
1208. 6 e. 50 multicoloured 65 40

185. Children with Ball. **186.** Europa " Honeycomb ".

1962. 10th Int. Paediatrics Congress, Lisbon. Centres in black.
1209. – 50 c. yellow & green 10 10
1210. – 1 e. yellow and grey.. 40 10
1211. **185.** 2 e. 80 yellow & brown 50 50
1212. – 3 e. 50 yellow & mauve 1·00 90
DESIGNS: 50 c. Children with book. 1 e. Inoculating child. 3 e. 50, Weighing baby.

1962. Europa. " EUROPA " in gold.
1213. **186.** 1 e. dp. blue & blue 20 10
1214. 1 e. 50 deep grn. & grn. 60 35
1215. 3 e. 50 brown & purple 70 40

187. St. Zenon (the Courier). **188.** Benfica Emblem and European Cup.

1962. Stamp Day. Saint in yellow and flesh.
1216. **187.** 1 e. black and purple 15 10
1217. 2 e. black and green.. 60 50
1218. 2 e. 80 black and bistre 1·00 1·00

1963. Benfica Club's Double Victory in European Football Cup Championships (1961-62).
1219. **188.** 1 e. multicoloured .. 70 10
1220. 4 e. 30 multicoloured 90 75

189. Campaign Emblem.

190. Mail Coach. **191.** St. Vincent de Paul.

1963. Freedom from Hunger.
1221. **189.** 1 e. multicoloured .. 20 10
1222. 3 e. 30 multicoloured 60 60
1223. 3 e. 50 multicoloured 75 55

1963. Cent. of Paris Postal Conference.
1224. **190.** 1 e. blue, light blue and grey 20 10
1225. 1 e. 50 multicoloured 60 10
1226. 5 e. brown, lilac & orge. 30 20

1963. 300th Death Anniv. of St. Vincent de Paul. Inscr. in gold.
1227. **191.** 20 c. ultram. and blue 10 10
1228. 1 e. blue and grey .. 15 10
1229. 2 e. 80 black and green 70 65
1230. 5 e. grey and mauve 65 55

192. Medieval Knight. **193.** Europa " Dove ".

1963. 800th Anniv. of Military Order of Avis.
1231. **192.** 1 e. multicoloured .. 15 10
1232. 1 e. 50 multicoloured 25 15
1233. 2 e. 50 multicoloured 75 45

1963. Europa.
1234. **193.** 1 e. grey, blue & black 15 10
1235. 2 e. 50 grey, grn. & blk. 85 40
1236. 3 e. 50 grey, red & blk. 1·40 90

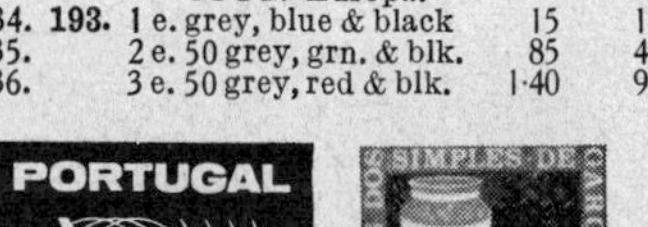

194. " Supersonic Flight ". **195.** Pharmacist's Jar.

1963. 10th Anniv. of T.A.P. Airline.
1237. **194.** 1 e. blue & deep blue 20 10
1238. 2 e. 50 green & black 60 30
1239. 3 e. 50 orange and red 70 60

1964. 400th Anniv. of Publication of " Coloquios dos Simples " (Dissertations on Indian herbs and drugs) by Dr. G. d'Orta.
1240. **195.** 50 c. brown, blk. & bis. 10 10
1241. 1 e. lake, black & brown 25 10
1242. 4 e. 30 blue, blk. & grey 2·00 2·25

196. Bank Emblem. **197.** Sameiro Shrine (Braga).

1964. Cent. of National Overseas Bank.
1243. **196.** 1 e. yellow, olive & blue 15 10
1244. 2 e. 50 yell., olive & grn. 85 35
1245. 3 e. 50 yell., olive & brn. 50 50

1964. Centenary of Sameiro Shrine.
1246. **197.** 1 e. yell., grey & brn. 15 10
1247. 2 e. yell., grey & brn. 60 35
1248. 5 e. yell., grn. & blue 80 70

198. Europa "Flower". **199.** Sun and Globe.

1964. Europa.
1249. **198.** 1 e. indigo, light blue and blue .. 20 10
1250. 3 e. 50 brown, orange and purple .. 80 40
1251. 4 e. 30 bronze, yellow and green .. 1·40 1·25

1964. International Quiet Sun Years.
1252. **199.** 1 e. multicoloured .. 20 10
1253. 8 e. multicoloured .. 70 50

200. Olympic " Rings ". **201.** E. Coelho (founder).

1964. Olympic Games, Tokyo.
1254. **200.** 20 c. multicoloured .. 10 10
1255. 1 e. multicoloured .. 15 10
1256. 1 e. 50 multicoloured 65 60
1257. 6 e. 50 multicoloured 1·00 1·25

1964. Centenary of "Diario de Noticias" (newspaper).
1258. **201.** 1 e. multicoloured .. 15 10
1259. 5 e. multicoloured .. 65 45

202. Traffic Signals.

203. Dom Fernando (second Duke of Braganza).

1965. 1st National Traffic Congress, Lisbon.
1260. **202.** 1 e. yellow, red & green 15 10
1261. 3 e. 30 green, red & yell. 1·75 1·75
1262. 3 e. 50 red, yell. & grn. 1·00 55

1965. 500th Anniv. of Braganza.
1263. **203.** 1 e. brown and black 10 10
1264. 10 e. green and black 75 45

204. Angel and Gateway.

205. I.T.U. Emblem.

1965. 900th Anniv. of Capture of Coimbra from the Moors.
1265. **204.** 1 e. multicoloured .. 10 10
1266. 2 e. 50 multicoloured 85 55
1267. 5 e. multicoloured .. 90 90

1965. Centenary of I.T.U.
1268. **205.** 1 e. olive and brown .. 15 10
1269. 3 e. 50 purple & green 70 50
1270. 6 e. 50 blue & green .. 60 55

206. C. Gulbenkian.

207. Red Cross Emblem.

1965. 10th Death Anniv. of Calouste Gulbenkian (oil industry pioneer and philanthropist).
1271. **206.** 1 e. multicoloured .. 30 10
1272. 8 e. multicoloured .. 45 40

1965. Cent. of Portuguese Red Cross.
1273. **207.** 1 e. red, green & black 15 10
1274. 4 e. red, olive and black 70 45
1275. 4 e. 30 red, brown & blk. 3·50 3·50

208. Europa "Sprig".

209. Fighter Aircraft.

1965. Europa.
1276. **208.** 1 e. turq., blk. & blue 15 10
1277. 3 e. 50 flesh, brn. & lake 85 55
1278. 4 e. 30 light green, black and green .. 2·40 2·50

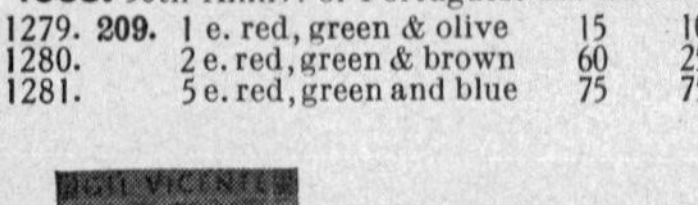

1965. 50th Anniv. of Portuguese Air Force.
1279. **209.** 1 e. red, green & olive 15 10
1280. 2 e. red, green & brown 60 25
1281. 5 e. red, green and blue 75 75

210.

211. Monogram of Christ.

1965. 500th Birth Anniv. of Gil Vicente (poet and dramatist). Designs depicting characters from Vicente's poems.
1282. **210.** 20 c. multicoloured .. 10 10
1283. – 1 e. multicoloured .. 15 10
1284. – 2 e. 50 multicoloured 1·00 20
1285. – 6 e. 50 multicoloured 45 45

1966. Int. Committee for the Defence of Christian Civilisation Congress, Lisbon.
1286. **211.** 1 e. violet, gold & bistre 20 10
1287. 3 e. 30 blk., gold & pur. 1·40 1·40
1288. 5 e. black, gold & lake 90 60

212. Emblems of Agriculture, Construction and Industry.

213. Giraldo the "Fearless".

1966. 40th Anniv. of National Revolution.
1289. **212.** 1 e. blk., blue & grey 10 10
1290. 3 e. 50 brown & bistre 75 60
1291. 4 e. pur., lake & pink 70 50

1966. 800th Anniv. of Reconquest of Evora.
1292. **213.** 1 e. multicoloured .. 25 10
1293. 8 e. multicoloured .. 50 40

214. Salazar Bridge.

215. Europa "Ship".

1966. Inaug. of Salazar Bridge, Lisbon.
1294. **214.** 1 e. red and gold .. 30 10
1295. 2 e. 50 blue & gold .. 1·00 30
1296. – 2 e. 80 blue & silver .. 1·10 85
1297. – 4 e. 30 green & silver 1·10 95
DESIGN—VERT. 2 e. 80, 4 e. 30, Salazar Bridge (different view).

1966. Europa.
1298. **215.** 1 e. multicoloured .. 10 10
1299. 3 e. 50 multicoloured 1·25 75
1300. 4 e. 50 multicoloured 1·25 1·00

216. C. Pestana (bacteriologist).

217. Bocage.

1966. Portuguese Scientists. Portraits in brown and bistre; background colours given.
1301. **216.** 20 c. green 10 10
1302. – 50 c. orange 10 10
1303. – 1 e. yellow 15 10
1304. – 1 e. 50 lt. brown .. 15 10
1305. – 2 e. brown 90 10
1306. – 2 e. 50 green .. .. 1·00 25
1307. – 2 e. 80 salmon .. 1·25 1·00
1308. – 4 e. 30 blue .. .. 1·60 1·40
SCIENTISTS: 50 c. E. Moniz (neurologist). 1 e. E. A. P. Coutinho (botanist). 1 e. 50, J. C. da Serra (botanist). 2 e. R. Jorge (hygienist and anthropologist). 2 e. 50, J. L. de Vasconcelos (ethnologist). 2 e. 80, M. Lemos (medical historian). 4 e. 30, J. A. Serrano (anatomist).

1966. Birth Bicent. (1965) of Manuel M. B. du Bocage (poet).
1309. **217.** 1 e. black, grn. & bistre 10 10
1310. 2 e. black, grn. & brn. 35 15
1311. 6 e. black, grn. & grey 55 40

218. Cogwheels.

219. Adoration of the Virgin.

1967. Europa.
1312. **218.** 1e. ultram., blk. & bl. 10 10
1313. 3 e. 50 brown, black and salmon .. 80 45
1314. 4 e. 30 bronze, black and green .. .. 1·40 1·25

1967. 50th Anniv. of Fatima Apparitions. Multicoloured.
1315. 1 e. Type **219** 10 10
1316. 2 e. 80 Fatima Church .. 50 50
1317. 3 e. 50 Virgin of Fatima .. 25 20
1318. 4 e. Chapel of the Apparitions 35 30

220. Roman Senators.

221. Lisnave Shipyard.

1967. New Civil Law Code.
1319. **220.** 1 e. lake and gold .. 10 10
1320. 2 e. 50 blue and gold 75 50
1321. 4 e. 30 green and gold 40 50

1967. Inaug. of Lisnave Shipyard, Lisbon.
1322. **221.** 1 e. multicoloured .. 10 10
1323. – 2 e. 80 multicoloured 35 30
1324. **221.** 3 e. 50 multicoloured 45 20
1325. – 4 e. 30 multicoloured 60 60
DESIGN: 2 e. 80, 4 e. 30, Section of ship's hull and location map.

222. Serpent Symbol.

223. Flags of EFTA Countries.

1967. 6th European Rheumatological Congress Lisbon.
1326. **222.** 1 e. multicoloured .. 10 10
1327. 2 e. multicoloured .. 55 20
1328. 5 e. multicoloured .. 90 80

1967. European Free Trade Assn.
1329. **223.** 1 e. multicoloured .. 10 10
1330. 3 e. 50 multicoloured 50 50
1331. 4 e. 30 multicoloured 1·75 2·00

224. Tombstones.

225. Bento de Goes.

1967. Centenary of Abolition of Death Penalty in Portugal.
1332. **224.** 1 e. olive 10 10
1333. 2 e. brown 50 20
1334. 5 e. green 75 75

1968. Bento de Goes Commem.
1335. **225.** 1 e. blue, pur. and grn. 25 10
1336. 8 e. purple, grn. & brn. 45 30

226. Europa "Key".

227. "Maternal Love".

1968. Europa.
1337. **226.** 1 e. multicoloured .. 10 10
1338. 3 e. 50 multicoloured 75 65
1339. 4 e. 30 multicoloured 1·60 1·75

1968. 30th Anniv. of Organization of Mothers for National Education (O.M.E.N.).
1340. **227.** 1 e. blk., orge. & grey 15 10
1341. 2 e. blk., orge. & pink 50 30
1342. 5 e. blk., orge. & blue 85 1·00

228. "Victory over Disease".

1968. 20th Anniv. of W.H.O.
1343. **228.** 1 e. multicoloured .. 15 10
1344. 3 e. 50 multicoloured 50 30
1345. 4 e. 30 multicoloured 2·75 3·00

229. Vineyard, Girao.

1968. "Lubrapex 1968" Stamp Exn. "Madeira—Pearl of the Atlantic". Mult.
1346. 50 c. Type **229** 10 10
1347. 1 e. Firework display .. 10 10
1348. 1 e. 50 Landscape .. 20 10
1349. 2 e. 80 J. Fernandes Vieira (liberator of Pernambuco) 90 90
1350. 3 e. 50 Embroidery .. 60 50
1351. 4 e. 30 J. Goncalves Zarco (navigator) .. .. 2·50 2·50
1352. 20 e. "Muschia aurea" 1·75 85
The 2 e. 80 to 20 e. are vert.

230. Pedro Alvares Cabral (from medallion).

1969. 500th Birth Anniv. of Pedro Alvares Cabral (explorer).
1353. **230.** 1 e. blue 20 10
1354. – 3 e. 50 purple .. 1·75 1·25
1355. – 6 e. 50 multicoloured 1·25 80
DESIGNS—VERT. 3 e. 50, Cabral's arms. HORIZ. 6 e. 50, Cabral's fleet (from contemporary documents).

231. Colonnade.

232. King Joseph I.

1969. Europa.
1356. **231.** 1 e. multicoloured .. 10 10
1357. 3 e. 50 multicoloured 90 70
1358. 4 e. 30 multicoloured 1·50 1·40

1969. Cent. of National Press.
1359. **232.** 1 e. multicoloured .. 10 10
1360. 2 e. multicoloured .. 65 20
1361. 8 e. multicoloured .. 60 60

233. I.L.O. Emblem.

234. J. R. Cabrilho (navigator and coloniser).

1969. 50th Anniv. of I.L.O.
1362. **233.** 1 e. multicoloured .. 10 10
1363. 3 e. 50 multicoloured 50 35
1364. 4 e. 30 multicoloured 75 75

1969. Bicent. of San Diego (California).
1365. **234.** 1 e. bronze, yell. & grn. 10 10
1366. 2 e. 50 brown & blue 70 20
1367. 6 e. 50 brown & green 55 70

235. Vianna da Motta (from painting by C. B. Pinheiro).

1969. Birth Cent. (1968) of Jose Vianna da Motta (concert pianist).
1368. **235.** 1 e. multicoloured .. 30 10
1369. 9 e. multicoloured .. 35 35

236. Coutinho and Seaplane.

1969. Birth Cent. of Gago Coutinho (aviator). Multicoloured.
1370. 1 e. Type **236** 15 10
1371. 2 e. 80 Coutinho & Sextant 75 75
1372. 3 e. 30 Type **236** .. .. 1·25 1·25
1373. 4 e. 30 As No. 1371 .. 1·25 1·25

237. Vasco da Gama.

1969. 500th Birth Anniv. of Vasco da Gama. Multicoloured.
1374. 1 e. Type **237** 15 10
1375. 2 e. 80 Arms of Vasco da Gama .. .. .. 1·60 1·60
1376. 3 e. 50 Route map (horiz.) 1·25 75
1377. 4 e. Vasca da Gama's fleet (horiz.) .. .. .. 1·00 40

238. " Flaming Sun ". **239.** Distillation Plant and Pipelines.

1970. Europa.
1378. **238.** 1 e. cream and blue.. 20 10
1379. 3 e. 50 cream and brn. 1·10 60
1380. 4 e. 30 cream & green 1·90 60

1970. Inaug. of Porto Oil Refinery.
1381. **239.** 1 e. blue 10 10
1382. – 2 e. 80 black & green 1·00 1·00
1383. **239.** 3 e. 30 olive .. 70 70
1384. – 6 e. brown 65 55
DESIGN: 2 e. 80, 6 e. Catalytic cracking plant and pipelines.

240. Marshal Carmona (from sculpture by L. de Almeida).

1970. Birth Cent. of Marshal Carmona.
1385. **240.** 1 e. green 10 10
1386. 2 e. 50 blue and red.. 80 30
1387. 7 e. blue 60 60

241. Station Badge. **242.** Emblem within Cultural Symbol.

1970. 25th Anniv. of Plant Breeding Station.
1388. **241.** 1 e. multicoloured .. 10 10
1389. 2 e. 50 multicoloured 55 25
1390. 5 e. multicoloured .. 70 45

1970. Expo 70. Multicoloured.
1391. 1 e. Compass (postage).. 10 10
1392. 5 e. Christian Symbol .. 45 35
1393. 6 e. 50 Symbolic initials 90 1·00
1394. 3 e. 50 Type **242** (air) .. 35 20

243. Wheel and Star.

1970. Cities' Centenaries. Multicoloured.
1395. 1 e. Type **243** (Covilha).. 10 10
1396. 2 e. 80 Ram and weaving frame .. .. .. 1·40 1·40
1397. 1 e. Castle (Santarem) .. 10 10
1398. 4 e. Two knights.. .. 65 40

244. "Great Eastern" laying Cable.

1970. Centenary of Portugal-England Submarine Telegraph Cable.
1399. **244.** 1 e. black, blue & grn. 15 10
1400. 2 e. 50 black, green and cream 80 25
1401. – 2 e. 80 multicoloured 1·40 1·40
1402. – 4 e. multicoloured .. 80 45
DESIGN: 2 e. 80, 4 e. Cable cross-section.

245. Harvesting Grapes. **246.** Mountain Windmill, Bussaco Hills.

1970. Port Wine Industry. Multicoloured.
1403. 50 c. Type **245** 10 10
1404. 1 e. Harvester and jug .. 10 10
1405. 3 e. 50 Wine-glass and wine barge 60 10
1406. 7 e. Wine-bottle and casks 60 30

1971. Portuguese Windmills.
1407. **246.** 20 c. red, blk. & brn. 10 10
1408. – 50 c. brn., blk. & blue 10 10
1409. – 1 e. pur., blk. and grey 10 10
1410. – 2 e. brn., blk. & mauve 50 10
1411. – 3 e. 30 brn., black & bistre .. .. 1·50 1·25
1412. – 5 e. brn., blk. & green 1·10 30
WINDMILLS: 50 c. Beira Litoral Province. 1 e. "Saloio" type, Estremadura Province. 2 e. St. Miguel, Azores. 3 e. 30, Porto Santo, Madeira. 5 e. Pico, Azores.

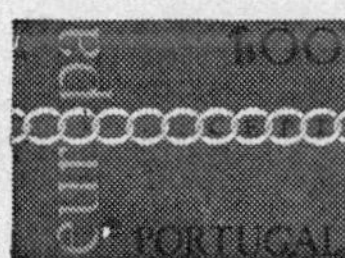

247. Europa Chain. **248.** F. Franco.

1971. Europa.
1413. **247.** 1 e. grn., blue & blk 15 10
1414. 3 e. 50 yell., brn. & blk. 95 15
1415. 7 e. 50 brn., grn. & blk. 1·50 1·25

1971. Portuguese Sculptors.
1416 **248** 20 c. black 10 10
1417 – 1 e. brown 10 10
1418 – 1 e. 50 brown .. 20 10
1419a – 2 e. 50 blue 50 10
1420 – 3 e. 50 red 55 15
1421 – 4 e. green .. .. 1·10 1·00
DESIGNS: 1 e. A. Lopes. 1 e. 50, A. de Costa Mota. 2 e. 50, R. Gameiro. 3 e. 50, J. Simoes de Almeida (the Younger). 4 e. F. dos Santos.

249. Pres. Salazar. **250.** Wolframite.

1971. Pres. Antonio Salazar Commemoration.
1422. **249.** 1 e. brn., green & orge. 10 10
1423. 5 e. brn., pur. & orge. 55 15
1424. 10 e. brn., blue & orge. 85 45

1971. 1st Spanish-Portuguese-American Congress of Economic Geology. Multicoloured.
1425. 1 e. Type **250** 15 10
1426. 2 e. 50 Arsenopyrite .. 1·25 35
1427. 3 e. 50 Beryllium .. 50 10
1428. 6 e. 50 Chalcopyrite .. 85 45

251. Town Gate. **252.** Weather Equipment.

1971. Bicent. of Castelo Branco. Mult.
1429. 1 e. Type **251** 10 10
1430. 3 e. Town square and monument 65 40
1431. 12 e. 50 Arms of Castelo Branco. (horiz.) .. 75 35

1971. 25th Anniv. of Portuguese Meteorological Services. Multicoloured.
1432. 1 e. Type **252** 10 10
1433. 4 e. Weather balloon .. 75 45
1434. 6 e. 50 Weather satellite 50 35

254. Man and his Habitat.
253. Drowning Missionaries. **255.** Clerigos Tower, Oporto.

1971. 400th Anniv. of Martyrdom of Brazil Missionaries.
1435. **253.** 1 e. blk., blue & grey 10 10
1436. 3 e. 30 blk., pur. & brn. 70 70
1437. 4 e. 80 blk., grn. & olive 75 75

1971. Nature Conservation. Multicoloured.
1438. 1 e. Type **254** 10 10
1439. 3 e. 30 Horses and trees (" Earth ") 25 25
1440. 3 e. 50 Birds (" The Atmosphere ") .. 35 10
1441. 4 e. 50 Fishes (" Water ") 1·10 80

1972. Buildings and Views.
1442 – 5 c. grey, blk & grn 10 5
1443 – 10 c. black, grn & bl 10 5
1444 – 30 c. sep, brn & yell 10 5
1445 – 50 c. blue, orge & blk 8 5
1446p **255** 1 e. black, brn & grn 30 10
1447 – 1 e. 50 brn, bl & blk 10 10
1448p – 2 e. blk, brn & pur 30 10
1449p – 2 e. 50 brown, light brown and grey .. 10 10
1450 – 3 e. yell, blk & brn 15 10
1451p – 3 e. 50 green, orange and brown .. 15 10
1452 – 4 e. black, yell & bl 40 10
1453 – 4 e. 50 blk, brn & grn 65 10
1454 – 5 e. green, brn & blk 3·50 10
1455 – 6 e. brown, grn & blk 1·60 20
1456 – 7 e. 50 black, orange and green .. 1·00 10
1457 – 8 e. bistre, blk & grn 1·50 15
1458 – 10 c. multicoloured 60 10
1459 – 20 e. multicoloured 2·25 10
1460 – 50 e. multicoloured 1·50 20
1461 – 100 e. multicoloured 2·25 50
DESIGNS: 5 c. Aguas Livres aqueduct, Lisbon. 10 c. Lima Bridge. 30 c. Monastery interior, Alcobaca. 50 c. Coimbra University. 1 e. 50, Belem Tower, Lisbon. 2 e. Domus Municipalis, Braganza. 2 e. 50, Castle, Vila de Feira. 3 e. Misericord House, Viana do Castelo. 3 e. 50, Window, Tomar Convent. 4 e. Gateway, Braga. 4 e. 50, Dolmen of Carrazeda. 5 e. Roman Temple, Evora. 6 e. Monastery, Leca do Balio. 7 e. 50 Almourol Castle. 8 e. Ducal Palace, Guimaraes. (31 × 22 mm). 10 e. Cape Girao, Madeira. 20 e. Episcopal Garden, Castelo Branco. 50 e. Town Hall, Sintra. 100 e. Seven Cities' Lake, Sao Miguel, Azores.

256. Arms of Pinhel. **257.** Heart and Pendulum.

1972. Bicentenary of Pinhel's Status as a City. Multicoloured.
1464. 1 e. Type **256** 10 10
1465. 2 e. 50 Balustrade (vert.) 60 15
1466. 7 e. 50 Lantern on pedestal (vert.) 50 35

1972. World Heart Month.
1467. **257.** 1 e. red and lilac .. 10 10
1468. – 4 e. red and green .. 1·25 65
1469. – 9 e. red and brown .. 50 30
DESIGNS: 4 e. Heart in spiral. 9 e. Heart and cardiogram trace.

258. "Communications". **259.** Container Truck.

1972. Europa.
1470. **258.** 1 e. multicoloured .. 10 10
1471. 3 e. 50 multicoloured 55 25
1472. 6 e. multicoloured 1·25 65

1972. 13th Int. Road Transport Union Congress, Estoril. Multicoloured.
1473. 1 e. Type **259** 15 10
1474. 4 e. 50 Roof of taxi-cab.. 1·00 55
1475. 8 e. Motor-coach.. .. 90 55

260. Football.

1972. Olympic Games, Munich. Mult.
1476 50 c. Type **260** 10 10
1477 1 e. Running 10 10
1478 1 e. 50 Show jumping .. 20 10
1479 3 e. 50 Swimming .. 30 15
1480 4 e. 50 Sailing 55 40
1481 5 e. Gymnastics 70 40

261. Marquis de Pombal. **262.** Tome de Sousa.

1972. Pombaline University Reforms. Multicoloured.
1482. 1 e. Type **261** 10 10
1483. 2 e. 50 " The Sciences " (emblems) 80 40
1484. 8 e. Arms of Coimbra University 80 65

1972. 150th Anniv of Brazilian Independence. Multicoloured.
1485. 1 e. Type **262** 10 10
1486. 2 e. 50 Jose Bonifacio .. 35 15
1487. 3 e. 50 Dom Pedro IV .. 40 15
1488. 6 e. Dove and globe .. 70 30

263. Cabral, Coutinho and Seaplane. **264.** Camoens.

1972. 50th Anniv. of 1st Lisbon-Rio de Janeiro Flight. Multicoloured.
1489. 1 e. Type **263** 15 10
1490. 2 e. 50 Route map .. 30 15
1491. 2 e. 80 Type **263** .. 45 40
1492. 3 e. 80 As 2 e. 50 .. 60 55

1972. 400th Anniv of Camoens' "Lusiads" (epic poem).
1493 **264** 1 e. yellow, brn & blk 10 10
1494 – 3 e. blue, green & blk 60 20
1495 – 10 e. brown, pur & blk 80 45
DESIGNS: 3 e. "Saved from the Sea". 10 e. "Encounter with Adamastor".

265. Graph and Computer Tapes.

1973. Portugese Productivity Conf., Lisbon. Multicoloured.
1496. 1 e. Type **265** 10 10
1497. 4 e. Computer scale .. 60 30
1498. 9 e. Graphs 55 25

266. Europa " Posthorn ". **268.** Child Running.

267. Pres. Medici and Arms.

1973. Europa.
1499. **266.** 1 e. multicoloured .. 10 10
1500. 4 e. multicoloured .. 1·25 35
1501. 6 e. multicoloured .. 1·75 70

1973. Visit of Pres. Medici of Brazil. Mult.

1502 1 e. Type **267** 10 10
1503 2 e. 80 Pres. Medici and globe 40 40
1504 3 e. 50 Type **267** 40 40
1505 4 e. 80 As No. 1503 .. 35 35

1973. "For the Child".

1506 **268** 1 e. dp blue, bl & brn 10 10
1507 4 e. purple, mve & brn 70 20
1508 7 e. 50 orange, ochre and brown .. 90 60

Designs: 4 e. Child running (to right). 7 e. 50, Child jumping.

269. Transport and Weather map. **270.** Child and Written Text.

1973. 25th Anniv. of Ministry of Communications. Multicoloured.

1509. 1 e. Type **269** 35 10
1510. 3 e. 80 "Telecommunications" 30 15
1511. 6 e. "Postal Services" .. 70 45

1973. Bicentenary of Primary State School Education. Multicoloured.

1512. 1 e. Type **270** 10 10
1513. 4 e. 50 Page of children's primer 55 20
1514. 5 e. 30 "Schooldays" (child's drawing) (horiz.) 60 35
1515. 8 e. "Teacher and children" (horiz.) 75 60

271. Early Tram-car. **272.** League Badge.

1973. Centenary of Oporto's Public Transport System. Multicoloured.

1516. 1 e. Horse-drawn tram-car 25 10
1517. 3 e. 50 Modern bus .. 90 50
1518. 7 e. 50 Type **271** .. 1·40 40

Nos. 1516/17 are $31\frac{1}{2} \times 31\frac{1}{2}$ mm.

1973. 50th Anniv. of Servicemen's League. Multicoloured.

1519. 1 e. Type **272** 10 10
1520. 2 e. 50 Servicemen .. 70 30
1521. 11 e. Awards and Medals 70 35

273. Death of Nuno Goncalves. **274.** Damiao de Gois (after Durer).

1973. 600th Anniv. of Defence of Faria Castle by the Alcaide, Nuno Goncalves.

1522. **273.** 1 e. green and yellow 10 10
1523. 10 e. purple and yellow 45 30

1974. 400th Death Anniv. of Damiao de Gois (scholar and diplomat). Multicoloured.

1524. 1 e. Type **274** 10 10
1525. 4 e. 50 Title-page of Chronicles of "Prince Dom Joao" 45 20
1526. 7 e. 50 Lute and "Dodecahordon" score .. 55 30

275. "The Exile" (A. Soares dos Reis). **276.** Light Emission.

1974. Europa.

1527. **275.** 1 e. green, blue & olive 10 10
1528. 4 e. green, red & yellow 2·00 40
1529. 6 e. dark grn., grn & blue 2·25 70

1974. Inauguration of Satellite Communications Station Network.

1530. **276.** 1 e. 50 green 10 10
1531. – 4 e. 50 blue 90 50
1532. – 5 e. 30 purple .. 50 30

Designs: 4 e. 50, Spiral Waves. 5 e. 30, Satellite and Earth.

277. "Diffusion of Hertzian Radio Waves".

1974. Birth Cent. of Guglielmo Marconi (radio pioneer). Multicoloured.

1533. 1 e. 50 Type **277** .. 10 10
1534. 3 e. 30 "Radio waves across Space" 60 35
1535. 10 e. "Radio waves for Navigation" .. .. 1·25 50

278. Early Post-boy and Modern Mail Van. **279.** Luisa Todi.

1974. Centenary of U.P.U. Multicoloured.

1536 1 e. 50 Type **278** 10 10
1537 2 e. Hand with letters .. 40 10
1538 3 e. 30 Sailing packet and modern liner 30 10
1539 4 e. 50 Dove and airliner 50 20
1540 5 e. 30 Hand with letter 40 30
1541 20 e. Early and modern railway locomotives .. 2·50 1·50

1974. Portuguese Musicians.

1543. **279.** 1 e. 50 purple .. 10 10
1544. – 2 e. red .. .. 1·25 10
1545. – 2 e. 50 brown .. 80 15
1546. – 3 e. blue 60 25
1547. – 5 e. 30 green 70 40
1548. – 11 e. purple 70 55

Portraits: 2 e. Joao Domingos Bomtempo. 2 e. 50, Carlos Seixas. 3 e. E. Duarte Lobo. 5 e. 30, Joao de Sousa Carvalho. 11 e. Marcos Portugal.

280. Arms of Beja.

1974. Bimillenary of Beja. Multicoloured.

1549. 1 e. 50 Type **280** .. 10 10
1550. 3 e 50 Beja's inhabitants through the ages .. 85 60
1551. 7 e. Moorish arches .. 1·40 70

281. "The Annunciation". **282.** Rainbow and Dove.

1974. Christmas. Multicoloured.

1552. 1 e. 50 Type **281** 10 10
1553. 4 e. 50 "The Nativity" .. 1·60 35
1554. 10 e. "The Flight into Egypt" .. .. .. 1·50 40

1974. Portuguese Armed Forces' Movement of 25 April.

1555. **282.** 1 e. 50 multicoloured 10 10
1556. 3 e. 50 multicoloured 1·60 90
1557. 5 e. multicoloured .. 1·50 35

283. Egas Moniz. **284.** Farmer and Soldier.

1974. Birth Centenary of Professor Egas Moniz (brain surgeon).

1558. **283.** 1 e. 50 brown & orge. 10 10
1559. – 3 e. 30 orge. & brown 35 20
1560. – 10 e. grey and blue .. 1·50 35

Designs: 3 e. 30, Nobel Medicine and Physiology Prize medal, 1949. 10 e. Cerebral angiograph (1927).

1975. Portuguese Cultural Progress and Citizens' Guidance Campaign.

1561. **284.** 1 e. 50 multicoloured 15 10
1562. 3 e. multicoloured .. 70 20
1563. 4 e. 50 multicoloured 90 50

285. Hands and Dove of Peace. **286.** "The Hand of God".

1975 1st Anniv of Portuguese Revoloution. Multicoloured.

1564 1 e. 50 Type **285** 10 10
1565 4 e. 50 Hands and dove .. 1·40 30
1566 10 e. Peace dove and emblem .. .. 1·50 50

1975. Holy Year. Multicoloured.

1567 1 e. 50 Type **286** 10 10
1568 4 e. 50 Hand with cross .. 1·50 40
1569 10 e. Peace dove .. 2·00 60

287. "The Horseman of the Apocalypse" (detail of 12th cent. manuscript). **288.** Assembly Building.

1975. Europa. Multicoloured.

1570. 1 e. 50 Type **287** .. 20 10
1571. 10 e. "Fernando Pessoa" (poet) (A. Negreiros) 2·50 50

1975. Opening of Portuguese Constituent Assembly.

1572 **288** 2 e. black, red & yell 15 10
1573 20 e. black, grn & yell 1·90 90

289. Hiking. **290.** Planting Tree.

1975. 36th International Camping and Caravanning Federation Rally. Mult.

1574. 2 e Type **289** 45 10
1575. 4 e. 50 Boating and swimming 80 40
1576. 5 e. 30 Caravanning .. 45 40

1975. 30th Anniv. of U.N.O. Mult.

1577. 2 e. Type **290** 20 10
1578. 4 e. 50 Releasing peace dove 80 20
1579. 20 e. Harvesting corn .. 1·50 60

291. Early Glider and Modern Space Rocket.

1975. 26th International Astronautical Federation Congress, Lisbon. Multicoloured.

1580 2 e. Type **291** 20 10
1581 4 e. 50 "Apollo"–"Soyuz" space link 80 40
1582 5 e. 30 R. H. Goddard, R. E. Pelterie, H. Oberth and K. E. Tsiolkovsky (space pioneers) .. 40 40
1583 10 e. Astronaut and space-ships (70 × 32 mm) .. 2·25 70

292. Surveying the Land.

1975. Centenary of National Geographical Society, Lisbon. Multicoloured.

1584. 2 e. Type **292** 20 10
1585. 8 e. Surveying the sea .. 1·00 50
1586. 10 e. Globe and people .. 1·75 60

293. Symbolic Arch. **294.** Nurse in Hospital Ward.

1975. European Architectural Heritage Year.

1587 **293** 2 e. grey, blue & dp bl 20 10
1588 – 8 e. grey and red .. 1·25 35
1589 – 10 e. multicoloured .. 1·50 60

Designs: 8 e. Stylized building plan. 10 e. Historical building being protected from development.

1975. International Women's Year. **Mult.**

1590. 50 c. Type **294** 10 10
1591. 2 e. Woman farm worker 65 10
1592. 3 e. 50 Woman office worker 75 30
1593. 8 e. Woman factory worker 80 75

295. Pen-nib as Plough Blade.

1976. 50th Anniv. of National Writers Society.

1595. **295.** 3 e. blue and red .. 25 10
1596. 20 e. red and blue .. 1·75 90

296. First Telephone Set.

1976. Telephone Centenary.

1597 **296** 3 e. blk, grn & dp grn 45 10
1598 – 10 e. 50 black, red and pink .. .. 1·75 55

Design: 10 e. 50 Alexander Graham Bell.

297. "Industrial Progress". **298.** Carved Olive-wood Spoons.

1976. Nat. Production Campaign.

1599. **297.** 50 c. brown 20 10
1600. – 1 e. green 30 10

Design: 1 e. Consumer goods.

1976. Europa. Multicoloured.

1601. 3 e. Type **298** 25 10
1602. 20 e. Gold ornaments .. 5·00 2·75

299. Stamp Designing.

1976. "Interphil '76". Int. Stamp Exn., Philadelphia. Multicoloured.

1603. 3 e. Type **299** 10 10
1604. 7 e. 50 Stamp being hand-cancelled 40 30
1605. 10 e. Stamp Printing .. 70 35

300. King Fernando promulgating Law.

1976. 600th Anniv. of Law of "Sesmarias" (uncultivated land). Multicoloured.

1606. 3 e. Type **300** 20 10
1607. 5 e. Plough and farmers repelling hunters .. 1·10 30
1608. 10 e. Corn harvesting .. 1·40 50

301. Athlete with Olympic Torch.

1976. Olympic Games, Montreal. Mult.

1610.	3 e. Type **301**	25	10
1611.	7 e. Women's relay ..	1·00	75
1612.	10 e. 50 Olympic flame ..	1·50	60

302. " Speaking in the Country ".

1976. Literacy Campaign. Multicoloured.

1613.	3 e. Type **302**	50	10
1614.	3 e. "Speaking at Sea" ..	50	10
1615.	3 e "Speaking in Town"	50	10
1616.	3 e. "Speaking at Work"	70	10

303. Azure-winged Magpie.

304. " Lubrapex " Emblem and Exhibition Hall.

1976. "Portucale '77". Thematic Stamp Exhibition, Oporto (1st issue). Mult.

1618.	3 e. Type **303**	40	10
1619.	5 e. Lynx	1·00	20
1620.	7 e. Portuguese laurel cherry and blue tit	1·25	45
1621.	10 e. 50 Little wild carnation and lizard ..	1·25	65

See also Nos 1673/8.

1976. "Lubrapex 1976" Luso–Brazilian Stamp Exhibition. Multicoloured.

1622	3 e. Type **304**	15	10
1623	20 e. "Lubrapex" emblem and "stamp"	1·90	85

305. Bank Emblem.

1976. Cent of National Trust Fund Bank.

1625.	**305.**	3 e. multicoloured ..	10	10
1626.		7 e. multicoloured ..	80	40
1627.		15 e. multicoloured ..	90	60

306. Sheep Grazing. **307.** " Liberty ".

1976. Water Conservation. Protection of Humid Zones. Multicoloured.

1628.	1 e. Type **306**	20	10
1629.	3 e. Marshland	45	10
1630.	5 e. Trout	85	25
1631.	10 e. Mallards	1·60	45

1976. Consolidation of Democratic Institutions.

1632.	**307.**	3 e. black, red & green	30	10

308. Examining Child's Eyes.

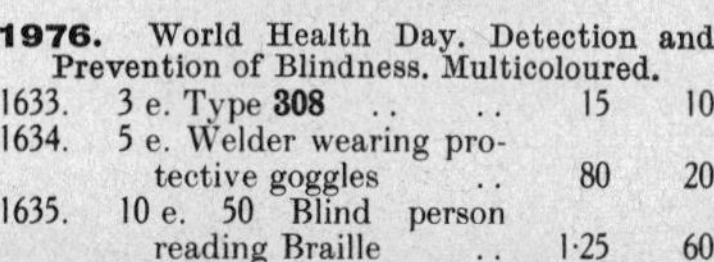

1976. World Health Day. Detection and Prevention of Blindness. Multicoloured.

1633.	3 e. Type **308**	15	10
1634.	5 e. Welder wearing protective goggles ..	80	20
1635.	10 e. 50 Blind person reading Braille ..	1·25	60

309. Hydro-electric Power.

1976. Uses of Natural Energy. Mult.

1636.	1 e. Type **309**	10	10
1637.	4 e. Fossil fuel (oil) ..	40	10
1638.	5 e. Geo-thermic sources	50	15
1639.	10 e. Wind power ..	75	35
1640.	15 e. Solar energy ..	1·25	55

310. Map of Member Countries.

311. Bottle inside Human Body.

1977. Admission of Portugal to the Council of Europe.

1641.	**310.**	8 e. 50 multicoloured	60	45
1642.		10 e. multicoloured ..	65	65

1977. 10th Anniv. of Portuguese Anti-Alcoholic Society. Multicoloured.

1643.	3 e. Type **311**	10	10
1644.	5 e. Broken body and bottle	45	15
1645.	15 e. Sun behind prison bars and bottle ..	1·00	55

312. Forest. **313.** Exercising.

1977. Natural Resources. Forests. Mult.

1646.	1 e. Type **312**	10	10
1647.	4 e. Cork oaks	30	15
1648.	7 e. Logs and trees ..	75	40
1649.	15 e. Trees by the sea ..	95	85

1977. International Rheumatism Year.

1650	–	4 e. orange, brn & blk	15	10
1651	**313**	6 e. ultramarine, blue and black	65	50
1652	–	10 e. red, mauve & blk	70	40

DESIGNS: 4 e. Rheumatism victim. 10 e. Group exercising.

314. Southern Plains. **315.** John XXI Enthroned.

1977. Europa. Multicoloured.

1653.	4 e. Type **314**	20	10
1654.	8 e. 50 Northern terraced mountains	80	55

1977. 7th Death Centenary of Pope John XXI. Multicoloured.

1656.	4 e. Type **315**	20	10
1657.	15 e. Pope as doctor ..	50	25

316. Compass.

1977. Camoes Day.

1658.	**316.**	4 e. multicoloured ..	15	10
1659.		8 e. 50 multicoloured	45	45

317. Child and Computer.

1977. Permanent Education. Multicoloured.

1660	4 e. Type **317**	25	10
1661	4 e. Flautist and dancers	25	10
1662	4 e. Farmer and tractor ..	25	10
1663	4 e. Students and atomic construction	25	10

318. Pyrite.

1977. Natural Resources. The Subsoil. Mult.

1665.	4 e. Type **318**	20	10
1666.	5 e. Marble	50	15
1667.	10 e. Iron ore	65	20
1668.	20 e. Uranium	1·75	75

319. Alexandre Herculano.

1977. Death Centenary of Alexandre Herculano (writer and politician).

1669.	**319.**	4 e. multicoloured ..	15	10
1670.		15 e. multicoloured ..	60	35

320. Early Locomotive and Peasant Cart (ceramic panel, J. Colaco).

1977. Centenary of Railway North of the River Douro. Multicoloured.

1671.	4 e. Type **320**	30	10
1672.	10 e. Maria Pia bridge (Eiffel)	1·50	1·00

321. Poviero (Northern coast).

1977. "Portucale 77" Thematic Stamp Exhibition, Oporto (2nd issue). Coastal Fishing Boats. Multicoloured.

1673	2 e. Type **321**	35	10
1674	3 e. Sea-going rowing boat, Furadouro	20	10
1675	4 e. Boat from Nazare ..	25	10
1676	7 e. Caique from Algarve	35	15
1677	10 e. Tunny fishing boat, Algarve	65	30
1678	15 e. Boat from Buarcos	1·00	45

322. " The Adoration " (Maria do Sameiro A. Santos).

1977. Christmas. Children's Paintings. Mult.

1680	4 e. Type **322**	15	10
1681	7 e. "Star over Bethlehem" (Paula Maria L. David)	55	15
1682	10 e. "The Holy Family" (Carla Maria M. Cruz) (vert)	60	20
1683	20 e. "Children following the Star" (Rosa Maria M. Cardoso) (vert) ..	1·75	75

323. Medical Equipment and Operating Theatre.

324. Mediterranean Soil.

1978.

(a) Size 22 × 17 mm.

1684.	**323.**	50 c. grn., blk. & red	10	10
1685.	–	1 e. blue, orange and black	10	10
1686.	–	2 e. blue, grn. & brn.	10	10
1687.	–	3 e. ochre, olive and black	10	10
1688.	–	4 e. grn., blue & brn.	10	10
1689.	–	5 e. blue, grn. & brn.	15	10
1690.	–	5 e. 50 brown, buff and olive	15	10
1691.	–	6 e. brn., yell & grn.	25	10
1692.	–	6 e. 50 blue, deep blue and olive ..	15	10
1693.	–	7 e. blk., grey & bl.	25	10
1694.	–	8 e. ochre, brown and grey	20	10
1694a	–	8 e. 50 brown, black and ochre ..	25	10
1695.	–	9 e. yell., brn. & blk.	20	10
1696.	–	10 e. ochre, black and green	25	10
1697.	–	12 e. 50 blue, brown and black	20	10
1698.	–	16 e. violet, brown and black	25	10

(b) Size 30 × 21 mm.

1699a	–	20 e. multicoloured ..	35	15
1700	–	30 e. multicoloured ..	50	20
1701	–	40 e. multicoloured ..	80	15
1702	–	50 e. multicoloured ..	90	15
1703	–	100 e. multicoloured	1·75	55
1703a	–	250 e. multicoloured	3·00	60

DESIGNS: 1 e. Old and modern kitchen equipment. 2 e. Telegraph key and masts, microwaves and dish aerial. 3 e. Dressmaking and ready-to-wear clothes. 4 e. Writing desk and computer. 5 e. Tunny fishing boats and modern trawler. 5 e. 50, Manual and mechanical weaver's looms. 6 e. Plough and tractor. 6 e. 50, Early airplane and modern commercial jet. 7 e. Hand press and modern printing press. 8 e. Carpenter's hand tools and mechanical tool. 8 e. 50, Potter's wheel and modern ceramic machinery. 9 e. Old cameras and modern cine and photo cameras. 10 e. Axe, saw and mechanical saw. 12 e. 50, Navigation and radar instruments. 16 e. Manual and automatic mail sorting. 20 e. Hand tools and building site. 30 e. Hammer, anvil, bellows and industrial complex. 40 e. Peasant cart and lorry. 50 e. Alembic, retorts and modern chemical plant. 100 e. Carpenter's shipyard, modern shipyard and tanker. 250 e. Survey instruments.

1978. Natural Resources. Soil. Mult.

1704.	4 e. Type **324**	20	10
1705.	5 e. Rock formation ..	30	10
1706.	10 e. Alluvial soil ..	40	25
1707.	20 e. Black soil	1·40	40

325. Pedestrian on Zebra Crossing.

1978. Road Safety.

1708.	**325.**	1 e. bl., blk. & orge...	10	10
1709.	–	2 e. bl., blk. & grn. ..	20	10
1710.	–	2 e. 50, bl., blk. & lt. bl.	30	10
1711.	–	5 e. bl., blk. & red ..	50	10
1712.	–	9 e. bl., blk. & bright blue	70	40
1713.	–	12 e. 50 bl., blk. & brn.	1·25	60

DESIGNS: 2 e. Motor cyclist. 2 e. 50, Children in back of car. 5 e. Driver in car. 9 e. View of road from driver's seat. 12 e. 50, Road victim ("Don't drink and drive.

326. Roman Tower of Centum Cellas, Belmonte.

327. Roman Bridge, Chaves.

1978. Europa. Multicoloured.

1714.	10 e. Type **326**	35	10
1715.	40 e. Belem Monastery, Lisbon	1·25	65

1978. 19th Centenary of Chaves (Aquae Flaviae). Multicoloured.

1717.	5 e. Type **327**	15	10
1718.	20 e. Inscribed tablet from bridge	90	60

328. Running.

1978. Sport for All. Multicoloured.

1719.	5 e. Type **328**	15	10
1720.	10 e. Cycling	30	15
1721.	12 e. 50 Swimming ..	60	60
1722.	15 e. Football	55	45

329. Pedro Nunes.

1978. 400th Death Anniv. of Pedro Nunes (cosmographer). Multicoloured.

1723. 5 e. Type **329** 20 10
1724. 20 e. Nonio (navigation instrument) and diagram .. .. .. 1·10 30

330. Trawler, Crates of Fish and Lorry.

1978. Natural Resources. Fish. Mult.

1725. 5 e. Type **329** 15 10
1726. 9 e. Trawler and dock-side cranes 25 15
1727. 12 e. 50 Trawler, radar and lecture 50 40
1728. 15 e. Trawler with echo-sounding equipment and laboratory .. 70 40

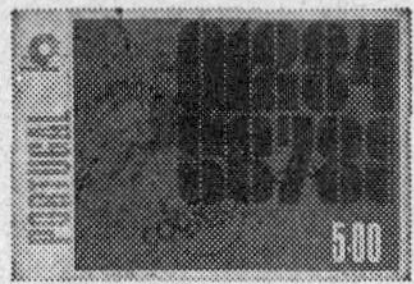

331. Post Rider.

1978. Introduction of Post Code. Mult.

1729. 5 e. Type **331** 25 10
1730. 5 e. Pigeon with letter .. 25 10
1731. 5 e. Sorting letters .. 25 10
1732. 5 e. Pen nib and post codes 25 10

332. Symbolic Figure.

1978. 30th Anniv. of Declaration of Human Rights. Multicoloured.

1733. 14 e. Type **332** 30 15
1734. 40 e. Similar symbolic figure, but facing right .. 80 55

333. Sebastiao Magalhaes Lima.

1978. 50th Death Anniv. of Magalhaes Lima (journalist and pacifist).

1736. **333.** 5 e. multicoloured .. 15 10

334. Portable Post Boxes and Letter Balance.

1978. Centenary of Post Museum. Mult.

1737 4 e. Type **334** 15 10
1738 5 e. Morse equipment .. 15 10
1739 10 e. Printing press and Portuguese stamps of 1853 (125th anniv) .. 30 15
1740 14 e. Books, bookcase and entrance to Postal Library (centenary) .. 55 65

335. Emigrant at Railway Station.

1979. Portuguese Emigrants. Multicoloured.

1742. 5 e. Type **335** 30 10
1743. 14 e. Emigrants at airport 35 20
1744. 17 e. Man greeting child at railway station .. 90 65

336. Traffic.

337. N.A.T.O. Emblem.

1979. Fight Against Noise. Multicoloured.

1745. 4 e. Type **336** 10 10
1746. 5 e. Pneumatic drill .. 15 10
1747. 14 e. Loud hailer .. 50 25

1979. 30th Anniv. of N.A.T.O.

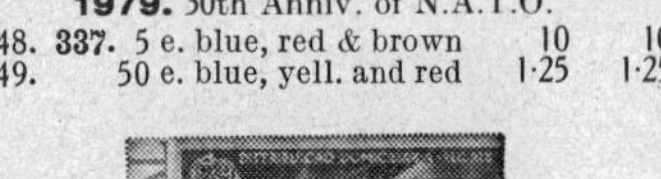

1748. **337.** 5 e. blue, red & brown 10 10
1749. 50 e. blue, yell. and red 1·25 1·25

338. Door-to-door Delivery.

1979. Europa. Multicoloured.

1751 14 e. Postal messenger delivering letter in cleft stick 30 15
1752 40 e. Type **338** 80 65

339. Children playing Ball.

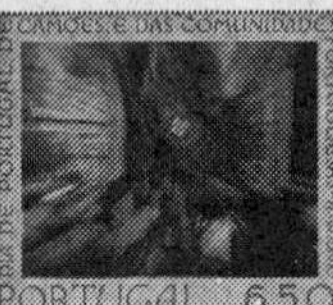

340. Saluting the Flag.

1979. International Year of the Child. Multicoloured.

1754. 5 e. 50 Type **339** 15 10
1755. 6 e. 50 Mother, baby and dove 15 10
1756. 10 e. Child eating .. 25 10
1757. 14 e. Children of different races 35 25

1979. Camoes Day.

1759. **340.** 6 e. 50 multicoloured 15 10

341. Pregnant Woman.

342. Children reading Book.

1979. The Mentally Handicapped. Mult.

1761. 6 e. 50 Type **341** .. 15 10
1762. 17 e. Boy sitting in cage 30 30
1763. 20 e. Face, and hands holding hammer and chisel 50 40

1979. 50th Anniv. of International Bureau of Education. Multicoloured.

1764. 6 e. 50 Type **342** 15 10
1765. 17 e. Teaching a deaf child 45 35

343. Water Cart, Caldas de Monchique.

1979. "Brasiliana 79" Philatelic Exhibitions. Portuguese Country Carts. Mult.

1766. 2 e. 50 Type **343** .. 10 10
1767. 5 e. 50 Wine sledge, Madeira 10 10
1768. 6 e. 50 Wine cart, Upper Douro 10 10
1769. 16 e. Covered cart, Alentejo 30 30
1770. 19 e. Cart, Mogadouro .. 40 40
1771. 20 e. Sand cart, Murtosa 40 30

344. Aircraft flying through Storm Cloud.

1979. 35th Anniv. of TAP National Airline. Multicoloured.

1772. 16 e. Type **344** 45 30
1773. 19 e. Aircraft and sunset 55 50

345. Antonio Jose de Almeida.

346. Family Group.

1979. Republican Personalities (1st series).

1774. **345.** 5 e. 50 mauve, grey and red 15 10
1775. – 6 e. 50 rose, grey & red 15 10
1776. – 10 e. brn., grey & red 20 10
1777. – 16 e. blue, grey & red 35 25
1778. – 19 e. 50 grn., grey & red 40 45
1779. – 20 e. claret, grey & red 40 20

DESIGNS: 6 e. Afonso Costa. 10 e. Teofilo Braga. 16 e. Bernardino Machado. 19 e. 50, Joao Chagas. 20 e. Elias Garcia.

See also Nos. 1787/92.

1979. Towards a National Health Service. Multicoloured.

1780. 6 e. 50 Type **346** .. 15 10
1781. 20 e. Doctor examining patient 55 30

347. " The Holy Family ".

1979. Christmas. Tile Pictures. Multicoloured.

1782. 5 e. 50 Type **347** .. 15 10
1783. 6 e. 50 " Adoration of the Shepherds " 15 10
1784. 16 e. " Flight into Egypt " 45 40

348. Rotary Emblem and Globe.

1980. 75th Anniv. of Rotary International. Multicoloured.

1785. 16 e. Type **348** 30 15
1786. 50 e. Rotary emblem and torch .. .. .. 1·00 80

349. Jaime Cortesao.

1980. Republican Personalities (2nd series).

1787 – 3 e. 50 orange & brn 10 10
1788 – 5 e. 50 grn, ol & brn 10 10
1789 – 6 e. 50 lilac & violet 15 10
1790 **349** 11 e. multicoloured .. 40 50
1791 – 16 e. ochre & brown 40 30
1792 – 20 e. green, bl & lt bl 50 20

DESIGNS: 3 e. 50, Alvaro de Castro. 5 e. 50, Antonio Sergio. 6 e. 50, Norton de Matos. 16 e. Teixeira Gomes. 20 e. Jose Domingues dos Santos.

350. Serpa Pinto.

1980. Europa. Multicoloured.

1793. 16 e. Type **350** 30 15
1794. 60 e. Vasco da Gama .. 1·00 75

351. Barn Owl.

1980. Protection of Species. Animals in Lisbon Zoo. Multicoloured.

1796. 6 e. 50 Type **351** .. 60 10
1797. 16 e. Red fox 70 30
1798. 19 e. 50 Wolf .. .. 1·10 45
1799. 20 e. Golden eagle .. 1·75 45

352. Luis Vaz de Camoes.

354. Lisbon and Statue of St. Vincent (Jeronimos Monastery).

353. Pinto in Japan.

1980. 400th Death Anniv of Luis Vaz de Camoes (poet).

1801 **352** 6 e. 50 multicoloured 15 10
1802 20 e. multicoloured .. 40 25

1980. 400th Anniv. of Fernao Mendes Pinto's "A Peregrinacao" (The Pilgrimage). Multicoloured.

1803. 6 e. 50 Type **353** .. 15 10
1804. 10 e. Sea battle .. 35 25

1980. World Tourism Conference, Manila, Philippines. Multicoloured.

1805. 6 e. 50 Type **354** .. 15 10
1806. 8 e. Lantern Tower, Evora Cathedral .. 20 15
1807. 11 e. Mountain Village and "Jesus with top-hat" (Mirando do Douro Cathedral) .. 30 20
1808. 16 e. Canicada dam and "Lady of the Milk" (Braga Cathedral) .. 55 30
1809. 19 e. 50 Aveiro River and pulpit from Santa Cruz Monastery, Coimbra .. 60 40
1810. 20 e. Rocha beach and ornamental chimney, Algarve 60 20

355. Caravel.

1980. "Lubrapex 80" Portuguese–Brazilian Stamp Exhibition, Lisbon. Mult.

1811 6 e. 50 Type **355** 20 10
1812 8 e. Nau 25 20
1813 16 e. Galleon 40 30
1814 19 e. 50 Early paddle-steamer with sails .. 50 40

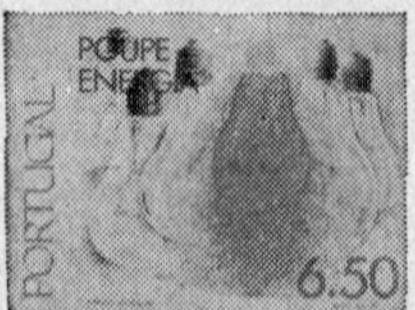

356. Lightbulbs.

1980. Energy Conservation. Multicoloured.

1816. 6 e. 50 Type **356** .. 15 10
1817. 16 e. Speeding car .. 50 25

357. Duke of Braganca and Open Book.

1980. Bicentenary of Academy of Sciences, Lisbon. Multicoloured.

1818. 6 e. 50 Type **357** .. 15 10
1819. 19 e. 50 Uniformed academician, Academy and sextant 60 40

358. Cigarette contaminating Lungs.

1980. Anti-Smoking Campaign. Mult.

1820. 6 e. 50 Type **358** .. 20 10
1821. 19 e. 50 Healthy figure pushing away hand with cigarette .. 60 40

359. Head and Computer Punch-card.

1981. National Census. Multicoloured.

1822. 6 e. 50 Type **359** .. 15 10
1823. 16 e. Houses and punch-card 50 40

360. Fragata, River Tejo.

361. "Rajola" Tile from Setubal Peninsula (15th century).

1981. River Boats. Multicoloured.

1824. 8 e. Type **380** 25 10
1825. 8 e. 50 Rabelo, River Douro 25 10
1826. 10 e. Moliceiro, Ria de Aveiro 35 10
1827. 16 e. Barco, River Lima 50 25
1828. 19 e. 50 Carocho, River Minho 70 35
1829. 20 e. Varino, River Tejo 70 20

1981. Tiles (1st issue).

1830. **361.** 8 e. 50 multicoloured 25 10

See also Nos. 1843, 1847, 1862, 1871, 1885, 1893, 1902, 1914, 1926, 1935, 1941, 1952, 1970, 1972, 1976, 1983, 1993, 2020 and 2031.

362. Agua Dog.

1981. 50th Anniv. of Kennel Club of Portugal. Multicoloured.

1832. 7 e. Type **362** 25 10
1833. 8 e. 50 Serra de Aires .. 30 10
1834. 15 e. Perdigueiro .. 45 20
1835. 22 e. Podengo 65 30
1836. 25 e. 50 Castro Laboreiro 75 60
1837. 33 e. 50 Serra de Estrella 1·00 50

363. " Agriculture ".

364. Dancer and Tapestry.

1981. May Day. Multicoloured.

1838. 8 e. Type **363** 15 10
1839. 25 e. 50 " Industry " .. 50 45

1981. Europa. Multicoloured.

1840. 22 e. Type **364** 40 30
1841. 48 e. Painted boat prow, painted plate and ship-wright with model boat 80 80

1981. Tiles (2nd issue). Horiz. design as **T 361**.

1843. 8 e. 50 multicoloured .. 25 10

DESIGN: 8 e. 50, Tracery-Pattern tile from Seville (16th century).

365. St. Anthony Writing.

1981. 750th Death Anniv. of St. Anthony of Lisbon. Multicoloured.

1845. 8 e. 50 Type **365** .. 15 10
1846. 70 e. St. Anthony giving blessing .. .. 1·40 90

1981. Tiles (3rd series). Vert design as **T 361**. Multicoloured.

1847 8 e. 50 Arms of Jaime, Duke of Braganca (Seville, 1510) 25 10

366. King Joao II and Caravels.

1981. 500th Anniv of King Joao II's Accession. Multicoloured.

1849 8 e. 50 Type **366** 30 10
1850 27 e. King Joao II on horseback 80 50

367. "Dom Luiz ", 1862.

1981. 125th Anniv of Portuguese Railways. Multicoloured.

1851 8 e. 50 Type **367** 30 10
1852 19 e. Pacific type steam locomotive, 1925 .. 70 50
1853 27 e. "Alco 1500" diesel locomotive, 1948 .. 1·00 40
1854 33 e. 50 Alsthom "BB 2600" electric loco-motive, 1974 .. 1·25 40

368. " Perrier " Pump, 1856.

369. "Virgin and Child"

1981. Portuguese Fire Engines. Mult.

1855. 7 e. Type **368** .. 20 15
1856. 8 e. 50 Ford fire engine, 1927 .. .. .. 30 25
1857. 27 e. Renault fire pump, 1914 .. .. .. 75 25
1858. 33 e. 50 Ford " Snorkel " combined hoist and pump, 1978 .. 1·00 75

1981. Christmas. Crib Figures. Multicoloured.

1859. 7 e. Type **369** .. 15 15
1860. 8 e. 50 "Nativity" .. 20 10
1861. 27 e. "Flight into Egypt" 50 50

1981. Tiles (4th issue). As **T 361**. Mult.

1862. 8 e. 50 " Pisana " tile, Lisbon (16th century) 20 10

370. St. Francis and Animals.

371. Flags of E.E.C. Members.

1982. 800th Birth Anniv. of St. Francis of Assisi. Multicoloured.

1865. 8 e. 50 Type **370** .. 15 10
1866. 27 e. St. Francis helping to build church .. 60 65

1982. 25th Anniv. of European Economic Community.

1867. **371.** 27 e. multicoloured .. 60 40

372. Fort St. Catherina, Lighthouse and Memorial Column.

1982. Centenary of Figuerira da Foz City. Multicoloured.

1869. 10 e. Type **372** 20 10
1870. 19 e. Tagus Bridge, ship-building yard and trawler 55 50

1982. Tiles (5th issue). As **T 361**. Mult.

1871. 10 e. Italo-Flemish pattern tile (17th century) .. 30 10

373. "Sagres I" (cadet barque).

374. Edison Gower Bell Telephone, 1883.

1982. Sporting Events. Multicoloured.

1873. 27 e. Type **373** (Lisbon sailing races) .. .. 1·00 40
1874. 33 e. 50 Roller hockey (25th World Championship) 90 80
1875. 50 e. "470 Class" racing yachts (World Championships) .. .. 1·75 85
1876. 75 e. Football (World Cup Football Championship Spain) .. 2·00 90

1982. Centenary of Public Telephone Service. Multicoloured.

1877. 10 e. Type **374** 20 10
1878. 27 e. Consolidated telephone, 1887 .. .. 50 50

375. Embassy of King Manuel to Pope Leo X.

1982. Europa.

1879. **375.** 33 e. 50 multicoloured 75 30

376. Pope John Paul II and Shrine of Fatima.

377. Dunlin.

1982. Papal Visit. Multicoloured.

1881. 10 e. Type **376** 20 10
1882. 27 e. Pope and Sameiro Sanctuary 65 50
1883. 33 e. 50 Pope and Lisbon Cathedral 85 65

1982. Tiles (6th issue). As **T 361**. Mult.

1885. 10 e. Altar front panel depicting oriental tapestry (17th century) .. 25 10

1982. "Philexfrance 82" International Stamp Exhibition, Paris. Birds. Mult.

1887. 10 e. Type **377** 35 15
1888. 19 e. Red-crested pochard 60 40
1889. 27 e. Greater flamingo .. 90 60
1890. 33 e. 50 Black-winged stilt .. .. .. 1·10 1·00

378. Dr. Robert Koch.

1982. Centenary of Discovery of Tubercle Bacillus. Multicoloured.

1891. 27 e. Type **378** 50 40
1892. 33 e. 50 Lungs 60 60

1982. Tiles (7th issue). As **T 361**. Mult.

1893. 10 e. Polychromatic quadrilobate pattern, 1630–40 .. .. 25 10

379. Wine Glass and Stop Sign.

1982. " Don't Drink and Drive ".

1895. **379.** 10 e. multicoloured .. 30 10

380. Fairey "III-D Mk 2" "Lusitania".

1982. "Lubrapex 82" Brazilian–Portuguese Stamp Exhibition, Curitiba. Multicoloured.

1896. 10 e. Type **380** 20 10
1897. 19 e. Dornier "Do Wal" "Argus" 35 30
1898. 33 e. 50 Douglas "DC-7C" "Seven Seas" 60 45
1899. 50 e. Boeing "747-282B" 90 55

381. Marquis de Pombal.

1982. Death Bicentenary of Marquis de Pombal (statesman and reformer).

1901. **381.** 10 e. multicoloured .. 30 10

1982. Tiles (8th issue). As **T 361. Mult.**

1902. 10 e. Monochrome quadrilobate pattern, 1670-90 25 10

382. Gallic Cock and Tricolour.

1983. Centenary of French Alliance (French language teaching association).

1905. **382.** 27 e. multicoloured .. 50 45

383. Lisnave Shipyard.

1983. 75th Anniv. of Port of Lisbon Administration.

1906. **383.** 10 e. multicoloured .. 45 15

384. Export Campaign Emblem.

1983. Export Promotion.

1907. **384.** 10 e. multicoloured .. 20 15

385. Midshipman, 1782, and Frigate "Vasco da Gama".

1983. Naval Uniforms. Multicoloured.

1908 12 e. 50 Type **385** .. 30 20
1909 25 e. Seaman and steam corvette "Estefania", 1845 .. .. 60 25
1910 30 e. Marine sergeant and cruiser "Adamastor", 1900 .. .. 75 40
1911 37 e. 50 Midshipman and frigate "Joao Belo", 1982 1·10 55

386. W.C.Y. Emblem.

1983. World Communications Year. Mult.

1912. 10 e. Type **386** 20 15
1913. 33 e. 50 W.C.Y. emblem (diff.) 70 60

1983. Tiles (9th issue). As T **361**. Mult.

1914. 12 e. 50 Hunter killing white bull (tile from Saldanha Palace, Lisbon, 17/18th Century) 30 10

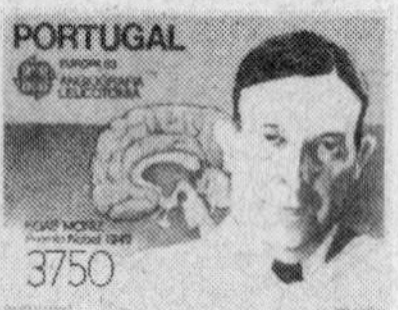

387. Portuguese Helmet (16th century).

1983. "Expo XVII" Council of Europe Exhibition. Multicoloured.

1916 11 e. Type **387** 20 15
1917 12 e. 50 Astrolabe (16th century) 30 10
1918 25 e. Portuguese caravels (from Flemish tapestry) (16th century) .. 65 35
1919 30 e. Carved capital (12th century) 60 35
1920 37 e. 50 Hour glass (16th century) 70 35
1921 40 e. Detail from Chinese panel painting (16th–17th century) 75 60

388. Egas Moniz (Nobel Prize Winner and brain surgeon).

1983. Europa.

1923. **388.** 37 e. 50 multicoloured 75 30

389. Passenger in Train.

1983. European Ministers of Transport Conference.

1925. **389.** 30 e. blue, deep blue and silver .. .. 1·25 60

1983. Tiles (10th issue). As T **361**. Mult.

1926. 12 e. 50 Tiles depicting birds (18th century) .. 30 10

390. Mediterranean Monk Seal.

1983. "Brasiliana 83" International Stamp Exhibition, Rio de Janeiro. Marine Life. Multicoloured.

1928. 12 e. 50 Type **390** .. 40 20
1929. 30 e. Common dolphin .. 75 60
1930. 37 e. 50 Killer whale .. 1·00 45
1931. 80 e. Humpback whale .. 2·25 1·00

391. Assassination of Spanish Administrator by Prince John.

1983. 600th Anniv. of Independence. Mult.

1933. 12 e. 50 Type **391** .. 30 15
1934. 30 e. Prince John proclaimed King of Portugal 60 50

1983. Tiles (11th issue). As T **361**. Mult.

1935. 12 e. 50 Flower pot by Gabriel del Barco (18th century) 30 10

392. Bartolomeu de Gusmao and Model Balloon, 1709.

393. "Adoration of the Magi".

1983. Bicent. of Manned Flight. Mult.

1937. 16 e. Type **392** 30 15
1938. 51 e. Montgolfier balloon, 1783 .. .. 95 65

1983. Christmas. Stained Glass Windows from Monastery of Our Lady of Victory, Batalha. Multicoloured.

1939. 12 e. 50 Type **393** .. 25 10
1940. 30 e. "The Flight into Egypt" 75 45

1983. Tiles (12th issue). As T **361**. Mult.

1941. 12 e. 50 Turkish horseman (18th century) .. 30 10

394. Siberian Tiger.

1983. Cent. of Lisbon Zoo. Multicoloured.

1944. 16 e. Type **394** 55 30
1945. 16 e. Cheetah 55 30
1946. 16 e. Blesbok 55 30
1947. 16 e. White rhino .. 55 30

395. Fighter Pilot and Hawker "Hurricane II", 1954.

1983. Air Force Uniforms. Multicoloured.

1948. 16 e. Type **395** 45 15
1949. 35 e. Pilot in summer uniform and Republic "F-84G" Thunderjet, 1960 .. .. .. 80 35
1950. 40 e. Paratrooper in walking-out uniform and Nord "250 1D Noratlas" military transport plane, 1966 95 45
1951. 51 e. Pilot in normal uniform and Vought "A-7P Corsair II", 1966 .. .. .. 1·10 60

1984. Tiles (13th issue). As T **361**. Mult.

1952 16 e. Coat of arms of King Jose I (late 18th cent) 30 15

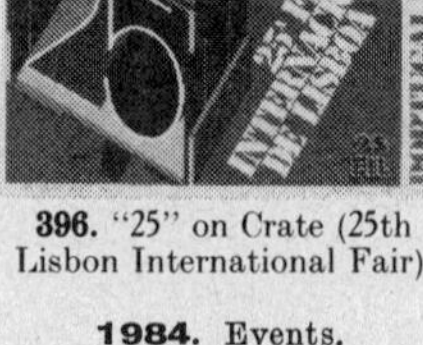

396. "25" on Crate (25th Lisbon International Fair).

1984. Events.

1954. 35 e. Type **396** 55 35
1955. 40 e. Wheat, rainbow and globe (World Food Day) 75 35
1956. 51 e. Hand holding stylised flower (15th International Rehabilitation Congress) (vert.) 1·00 60

397. National Flag.

1984. 10th Anniv. of Revolution.

1957. **397.** 16 e. multicoloured .. 30 15

398. Bridge.

1984. Europa.

1958 **398** 51 e. multicoloured .. 1·00 45

399. "Panel of St. Vincent".

1984. "Lubrapex 84" Portuguese–Brazilian Stamp Exhibition. Multicoloured.

1960 16 e. Type **399** 35 15
1961 40 e. "St. James" (altar panel) 60 45
1962 51 e. "View of Lisbon" (painting) 70 50
1963 66 e. "Head of Youth" (Domingos Sequeira) .. 1·10 65

400. Fencing

1984. Olympic Games, Los Angeles, and 75th Anniv of Portuguese Olympic Committee. Multicoloured.

1965 35 e. Type **400** 45 20
1966 40 e. Gymnastics .. 50 30
1967 51 e. Running 60 40
1968 80 e. Pole vaulting .. 75 60

1984. Tiles (14th issue). As T **361**. Multicoloured.

1970. 16 e. Pictorial tile from Pombal Palace, Lisbon (late 18th century) .. 30 10

1984. Tiles (15th issue). As T **361**. Multicoloured

1972. 16 e. Four art nouveau tiles (late 19th cent.) 30 10

401. Gil Eanes.

1984. Anniversaries. Multicoloured.

1974 16 e. Type **401** (550th anniv of rounding of Cape Bojador) .. 30 15
1975 51 e. King Pedro IV of Portugal and I of Brazil (150th death anniv) .. 90 60

1984. Tiles (16th issue). As T **361**. Multicoloured.

1976. 16 e. Grasshoppers and wheat (R. Bordallo Pinheiro, 19th century) 30 10

402. Infantry Grenadier, 1740, and Regiment in Formation.

1985. Army Uniforms. Multicoloured.

1979 20 e. Type **402** 35 15
1980 46 e. Officer, Fifth Cavalry, 1810, and cavalry charge .. 60 30
1981 60 e. Artillery corporal, 1891, and Krupp 9 mm. gun and crew 80 45
1982 100 e. Engineer in chemical protection suit, 1985, and bridge-laying armoured car .. 1·40 80

1985. Tiles (17th issue). As T **361**. Mult.

1983 20 e. Detail of panel by Jorge Barrados in Lisbon Faculty of Letters (20th century) 35 10

403. Calcada R. dos Santos Kiosk.

1985. Lisbon Kiosks. Multicoloured.

1985. 20 e. Type **403** 55 25
1986. 20 e. Tivoli kiosk, Avenida da Liberdade 55 25
1987. 20 e. Porto de Lisboa kiosk 55 25
1988. 20 e. Rua de Artilharia Um kiosk 55 25

404. Flags of Member Countries.

1985. 25th Anniv. of European Free Trade Association.

1989. **404.** 46 e. multicoloured .. 70 40

405. Profiles.

1985. International Youth Year.

1990. **405.** 60 e. multicoloured .. 85 50

406. Woman holding Adufe (tambourine).

1985. Europa.

1991 **406** 60 e. multicoloured .. 1·25 60

1985. Tiles (18th issue). As T **361**. Mult.

1993 20 e. Detail of panel by Maria Keil on Avenue Infante Santo (20th century) 35 10

407. Knight on Horseback.

1985. Anniversaries. Multicoloured.

1995. 20 e. Type **407** (600th anniv. of Battle of Aljubarrota) 30 15

1996. 46 e. Queen Leonor and hospital (500th anniv. of Caldas da Rainha thermal hospital) .. 60 35

1997. 60 e. Pedro Reinel (500th anniversary of first Portuguese sea-chart) 90 55

408. Farmhouse, Minho. **409.** Aquilino Ribeiro (writer).

1985. Architecture.

1998 – 50 c. black, bistre & bl 10 10

1999 – 1 e. black, yell & grn 10 10

2000 – 1 e. 50 black, green and emerald .. 10 10

2001 – 2 e. 50 brown, orange and blue 10 10

2002 – 10 e. blk, pur & pink 10 10

2003 **408** 20 e. brown, yellow and deep yellow .. 15 10

2004 – 22 e. 50 brown, blue and ochre 20 10

2005 – 25 e. brown, yell & grn 20 10

2006 – 27 e. black, yellow and light yellow .. 20 10

2007 – 29 e. black, yell & orge 20 10

2008 – 30 e. black, blue & brn 25 10

2009 – 40 e. black, yell & grn 30 10

2010 – 50 e. black, bl & ochre 40 10

2011 – 55 e. black, yell & grn 40 15

2012 – 60 e. black, orge & bl 45 15

2013 – 70 e. black, yell & orge 55 20

2014 – 80 e. brown, grn & red 60 35

2015 – 90 e. brown, yell & grn 70 35

2016 – 100 e. brown, yell & bl 80 35

2017 – 500 e. black, grey & bl 3·75 1·90

DESIGNS: 50 c. Saloia house, Estremadura. 1 e. Beria inland house. 1 e. 50 Ribatejo house. 2 e. 50 Tras-os-montes houses. 10 e. Minho and Douro coast house. 22 e. 50, Alentejo houses. 25 e. Sitio house, Algarve. 27 e. Beira inland house (different). 29 e. Tras-os-montes house. 30 e. Algarve house. 40 e. Beira inland house (different). 50 e. Beira coast house. 55 e. Tras-os-montes house (different). 60 e. Beira coast house (different). 70 e. South Estramadura and Alentejo house. 80 e. Estremadura house. 90 e. Minho house. 100 e. Monte house, Alentejo. 500 e. Terraced houses, East Algarve.

1985. Tiles (19th series). As T **361**. Mult.

2020. 20 e. Head of woman by Querubim Lapa (20th century) 35 10

1985. Anniversaries. Multicoloured.

2022. 20 e. Type **409** (birth centenary) 35 15

2023. 46 e. Fernando Pessoa (poet, 50th death anniv.) 95 40

410. Berlenga National Reserve.

1985. "Italia '85" International Stamp Exhibition, Rome. National Parks and Reserves. Multicoloured.

2024. 20 e. Type **410** 35 15

2025. 40 e. Estrela Mountains National Park .. 55 30

2026. 46 e. Boquilobo Marsh National Reserve .. 70 30

2027. 80 e. Formosa Lagoon National Reserve .. 1·25 65

411. "Nativity". **412.** Post Rider.

1985. Christmas. Illustrations from "Book of Hours of King Manoe I". Multicoloured.

2029 20 e. Type **411** 30 10

2030 46 e. "Adoration of the Three Wise Men" .. 80 35

1985. Tiles (20th issue). As T **361**. Mult.

2031. 20 e. Detail of panel by Manuel Cargaleiro (20th century) .. 35 10

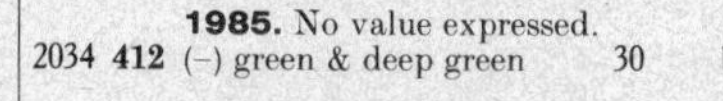

1985. No value expressed.

2034 **412** (–) green & deep green 30 10

413. Map and Flags of Member Countries.

1985. Admission of Portugal and Spain to European Economic Community. Mult.

2035. 20 e. Flags of Portugal and Spain joining flags of other members .. 35 10

2036. 57 e. 50 Type **413** .. 90 60

414. Feira Castle.

1986. Castles (1st series). Multicoloured.

2037. 22 e. 50 Type **414** .. 35 15

2038. 22 e. 50 Beja Castle .. 35 15

See also Nos. 2040/1, 2054/5, 2065/6, 2073/4, 2086/7, 2093/4, 2102/3 and 2108/9.

415. Globe and Dove.

1986. International Peace Year.

2039. **415.** 75 e. multicoloured .. 1·25 65

1986. Castles (2nd series). As T **414**. Mult.

2040. 22 e. 50 Braganca Castle 35 15

2041. 22 e. 50 Guimaraes Castle 35 15

416. Benz Motor Tricycle, 1886.

1986. Centenary of Motor Car. Multicoloured.

2042. 22 e. 50 Type **416** .. 45 20

2043. 22 e. 50 Daimler motor car, 1886 .. .. 45 20

417. Shad.

1986. Europa.

2044. **417.** 68 e. 50 multicoloured 90 40

418. Alter.

1986. "Ameripex '86" International Stamp Exhibition, Chicago. Thoroughbred Horses. Multicoloured.

2046. 22 e. 50 Type **418** .. 40 15

2047. 47 e. 50 Lusitano .. 70 45

2048. 52 e. 50 Garrano .. 80 45

2049. 68 e. 50 Sorraia .. .. 1·25 55

420. Diogo Cao (navigator) and Monument. **421.** Hand writing on Postcard.

1986. Anniversaries. Multicoloured.

2051 22 e. 50 Type **420** (500th anniv of 2nd expedition to Africa) 30 10

2052 52 e. 50 Passos Manuel (Director) and capital (150th anniv of National Academy of Fine Arts, Lisbon) .. 80 45

2053 52 e. 50 Joao Baptista Ribeiro (painter and Oporto Academy Director) and drawing (150th anniv of Portuguese Academy of Fine Arts, Oporto) .. 80 45

1986. Castles (3rd series). As T **414**. Mult.

2054. 22 e. 50 Belmonte Castle 35 15

2055. 22 e. 50 Montemor-o-Velho Castle 35 15

1986. Anniversaries. Multicoloured.

2057. 22 e. 50 Type **421** (centenary of first Portuguese postcard) 30 15

2058. 47 e. 50 Guardsman and houses (75th anniv. of National Republican Guard) 75 40

2059. 52 e. 50 Calipers, globe and banner (50th anniv. of Order of Engineers) 80 40

422. Seasonal Mill, Douro.

1986. "Luprapex '86" Portuguese–Brazilian Stamp Exhibition, Rio de Janeiro. Mult.

2060. 22 e. 50 Type **422** .. 35 15

2061. 47 e. 50 Seasonal mill, Coimbra 70 40

2062. 52 e. 50 Overshot bucket water mill, Gerez .. 80 40

2063. 90 e. Permanent stream mill, Braga .. .. 1·25 55

1987. Castles (4th series). As T **414**. Mult.

2065. 25 e. Silves Castle .. 35 15

2066. 25 e. Evora-Monte Castle 35 15

423. Houses on Stilts, Tocha.

1987. 75th Anniv (1986) of Organized Tourism. Multicoloured.

2067. 25 e. Type **423**. 35 15

2068. 57 e. Fishing boats, Espinho 75 45

2069. 98 e. Fountain, Arraiolos 1·10 70

424. Hand, Sun and Trees.

1987. European Enviroment Year. Mult.

2070 25 e. Type **424** 35 15

2071 57 e. Hands and flower on map of Europe .. 75 30

2072 74 e. 50 Hand, sea, shell, Moon and rainbow .. 1·00 50

1987. Castles (5th series). As T **414**. Mult.

2073. 25 e. Leiria Castle .. 25 10

2074. 25 e. Trancoso Castle .. 25 10

425. Bank Borges and Irmao Agency, Vila do Conde (Alvaro Siza).

1987. Europa. Architecture.

2075. **425.** 74 e. 50 multicoloured 90 40

426. Cape Mondego. **427.** Souzar-Cardoso (self-portrait).

1987. "Capex '87" International Stamp Exhibition, Toronto. Portuguese Lighthouses. Multicoloured.

2077. 25 e. Type **426** 40 15

2078. 25 e. Berlenga 40 15

2079. 25 e. Aveiro 40 15

2080. 25 e. Cape St. Vincent .. 40 15

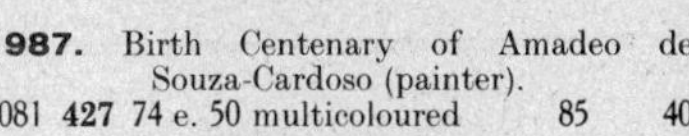

1987. Birth Centenary of Amadeo de Souza-Cardoso (painter).

2081 **427** 74 e. 50 multicoloured 85 40

428. Clipped 400 Reis Silver Coin.

1987. 300th Anniv. of Portuguese Paper Currency.

2082. **428.** 100 e. multicoloured 1·00 55

429. Dias's Fleet leaving Lisbon.

1987. 500th Anniv of Bartolomeu Dias's Voyages (1st issue). Multicoloured.

2083 25 e. Type **429** 35 20

2084 25 e. Ships off coast of Africa 35 20

Nos. 2083/4 were printed together, se-tenant, each pair forming a composite design.

See also Nos. 2099/2100.

430. Library.

1987. 150th Anniv of Portuguese Royal Library, Rio de Janeiro.

2085 **430** 125 e. multicoloured .. 1·10 70

1987. Castles (6th series). As T **414**. Mult.

2086. 25 e. Marvao Castle .. 25 10

2087. 25 e. St. George's Castle, Lisbon 25 10

432. Angels around Baby Jesus, Tree and Kings (Jose Manuel Coutinho).

1987. Christmas. Children's paintings. Mult.

2089 25 e. Type **432** 25 10

2090 57 e. Children dancing around sunburst (Rosa J. Leitao) 50 30

2091 74 e. 50 Santa Claus flying on dove (Sonya Alexandra Hilario) .. 75 55

1988. Castles (7th series). As T **414**. Mult.

2093. 27 e. Fernandine Walls, Oporto 25 10

2094. 27 e. Almourol Castle .. 25 10

433. Lynx.

1988. Iberian Lynx. Multicoloured.

2095. 27 e. Type **433** 50 20

2096. 27 e. Lynx carrying rabbit 50 20

2097. 27 e. Pair of lynxes .. 50 20

2098. 27 e. Mother with young 50 20

434. King Joao II sending Pero da Covilha on Expedition.

1988. 500th Anniv of Voyages of Bartolomeu Dias (2nd issue) (2099/2100) and Pero da Covilha (2101). Multicoloured.

2099 27 e. Dias's ships in storm off Cape of Good Hope 30 10

2100 27 e. Contemporary map 25 10

2101 105 e. Type **434** 95 50

Nos. 2099/2100 are as T **429**.

1988. Castles (8th series). As T **414**. Mult.

2102. 27 e. Palmela castle .. 25 10

2103. 27 e. Vila Nova de Cerveira castle .. 25 10

435. 19th-century Mail Coach.

1988. Europa. Transport and Communications.

2104. **435.** 80 e. multicoloured .. 75 35

436 Map of Europe and Monnet

1988. Birth Cent of Jean Monnet (statesman). "Europex 88" Stamp Exhibition.

2106 **436** 60 e. multicoloured .. 50 20

1988. Castles (9th series). As T **414**. Mult.

2108 27 e. Chaves Castle .. 25 10

2109 27 e. Penedono Castle .. 25 10

438 "Part of a Viola" (Amadeo de Souza-Cardoso)

1988. 20th-century Portuguese Paintings (1st series). Multicoloured.

2110 27 e. Type **438** 25 10

2111 60 e. "Acrobats" (Almada Negreiros) 50 20

2112 80 e. "Still Life with Viola" (Eduardo Viana) 70 30

See also Nos. 2121/3, 2131/3, 2148/50, 2166/8 and 2206/8.

439 Archery

1988. Olympic Games, Seoul (1st issue). Mult.

2114 27 e. Type **439** 25 10

2115 55 e. Weightlifting .. 45 20

2116 60 e. Judo 50 20

2117 80 e. Tennis 75 30

See also Nos. 2295/8.

440 "Winter" (House of the Fountains, Coimbra)

1988. Roman Mosaics of 3rd Century. Mult.

2119 27 e. Type **440** 25 10

2120 80 e. "Fish" (Baths, Faro) 70 30

1988. 20th Century Portuguese Paintings (2nd series). As T **438**. Multicoloured.

2121 27 e. "Internment" (Mario Eloy) 25 10

2122 60 e. "Lisbon Houses" (Carlos Botelho) .. 50 20

2123 80 e. "Avejao Lirico" (Antonoi Pedro) .. 70 30

441 Braga Cathedral

442 "Greetings"

1989. Anniversaries. Multicoloured.

2126 30 e. Type **441** (900th anniv) 25 10

2127 55 e. Caravel, parrot and Castle of Jorge da Mina (505th anniv) 60 20

2128 60 e. Sailor using astrolabe (500th anniv of South Atlantic voyages) 45 20

Nos. 2127/8 are inscribed for "India 89" stamp exhibition, New Delhi.

1989. Greetings Stamps. Multicoloured.

2129 29 e. Type **442** 25 10

2130 60 e. Airplane distributing envelopes inscribed "with Love" 45 20

1989. 20th-Century Portuguese Paintings (3rd series). As T **438**. Multicoloured.

2131 29 e. "Antithesis of Calm" (Antonio Dacosta) .. 25 10

2132 60 e. "Unskilled Mason's Lunch" (Julio Pomar) 45 20

2133 87 e. "Simumis" (Vespeira) .. 75 35

443 Flags in Ballot Box

444 Boy with Spinning Top

1989. 3rd Direct Elections to European Parliament.

2135 **443** 60 e. multicoloured .. 45 20

1989. Europa. Children's Games and Toys.

2136 **444** 80 e. multicoloured .. 65 30

445 Cable Railway

1989. Lisbon Transport. Multicoloured.

2138 29 e. Type **445** 25 10

2139 65 e. Electric tram-car .. 55 30

2140 87 e. Santa Justa lift .. 70 30

2141 100 e. Bus 80 35

446 Gyratory Mill, Ansiao

1989. Windmills. Multicoloured.

2143 29 e. Type **446** 25 10

2144 60 e. Stone mill, Santiago do Cacem 45 20

2145 87 e. Post mill, Afife .. 65 30

2146 100 e. Wooden mill, Caldas da Rainha .. 80 35

1989. 20th-Century Portuguese Paintings (4th series). As T **438**.

2148 29 e. blue, green and black 25 10

2149 60 e. multicoloured .. 45 20

2150 87 e. multicoloured .. 65 30

DESIGNS: 29 e. "046-72" (Fernando Lanhas); 60 e. "Spirals" (Nadir Afonso); 87 e. "Sim" (Carlos Calvet).

448 Luis I (death centenary) and Ajuda Palace, Lisbon

449 "Armeria pseudarmeria"

1989. National Palaces (1st series). Mult.

2153 29 e. Type **448** 20 10

2154 60 e. Queluz Palace .. 45 20

See also Nos. 2211/14.

1989. Wild Flowers. Multicoloured.

2155 29 e. Type **449** 20 10

2156 60 e. "Santolina impressa" 45 20

2157 87 e. "Linaria lamarckii" 65 30

2158 100 e. "Limonium multiflorum" 80 35

450 Blue and White Plate

1990. Portuguese Faience (1st series). Mult.

2159 33 e. Type **450** 25 10

2160 33 e. Blue and white plate with man in centre .. 25 10

2161 35 e. Vase decorated with flowers 25 10

2162 60 e. Fish-shaped jug .. 45 20

2163 60 e. Blue and white plate with arms in centre .. 45 20

2164 60 e. Blue and white dish with lid 45 20

See also Nos. 2221/6 and 2262/7.

1990. 20th-Century Portuguese Paintings (5th series). As T **438**. Multicoloured.

2166 32 e. "Aluenda-Tordesillas" (Joaquim Rodrigo) 25 10

2167 60 e. "Painting" (Noronha da Costa) 45 35

2168 95 e. "Painting" (Vasco Costa) 75 35

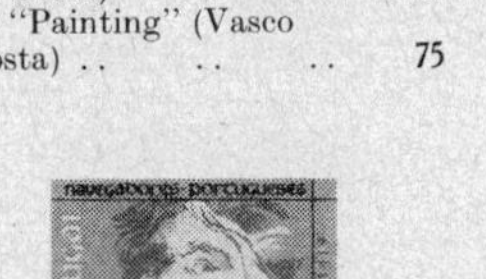

451 Joao Goncalves Zarco

1990. Portuguese Navigators.

2172 **451** 2 e. red, pink & blk 10 10

2174 – 4 e. purple, red & blk 10 10

2175 – 5 e. brn, grey & blk 10 10

2176 – 6 e. deep green, green and black .. 10 10

2180 – 32 e. grn, brn & blk 25 10

2181 – 35 e. pink, red & blk 25 10

2182 – 38 e. blue, lt bl & blk 35 15

2182a – 42 e. grn, grey & blk 30 15

2183 – 60 e. yell, pur & blk 45 20

2184 – 65 e. brn, grn & blk 60 30

2184a – 70 e. vio, mve & blk 55 25

2185 – 80 e. orge, brn & blk 60 30

2186 – 100 e. orge, red & blk 85 35

2187 – 200 e. grn, yell & blk 1·60 80

2188 – 250 e. green, bl & blk 1·90 95

2189 – 350 e. red, pink & blk 3·25 1·60

DESIGNS: 4 e. Duarto Pacheco Pereira; 5 e. Tristao Vaz Teixeira; 6 e. Pedro Alvares Cabral; 32 e. Bartolomeu Perestrelo; 35 e. Gil Eanes; 38 e. Vasco da Gama; 42 e. Joao de Lisboa; 60 e. Nuno Tristao; 65 e. Joao da Nova; 70 e. E. Fernao de Magalhaes (Magellan); 80 e. Diogo Gomes; 100 e. Diogo de Silves; 200 e. Estevao Gomes; 250 e. Diogo Cao; 350 e. Bartolomeu Dias.

452 Score and Singers

1990. Anniversaries. Multicoloured.
2191 32 e. Type **452** (centenary of "A Portuguesa" (national anthem)) .. 25 10
2192 70 e. Students and teacher (700th anniv of granting of charter to Lisbon University) (vert) .. 55 30

453 Santo Tirso Post Office

1990. Europa. Post Office Buildings. Mult.
2193 **453** 80 e. multicoloured .. 60 30

455 Street with Chairs under Trees

1990. Greetings Stamps. Multicoloured.
2196 60 e. Type **455** 45 20
2197 60 e. Hand holding bouquet out of car window 45 20
2198 60 e. Man with bouquet crossing street .. 45 20
2199 60 e. Woman with bouquet behind pillar box 45 20

456 Camilo Castelo Branco (writer)

1990. Death Anniversaries. Multicoloured.
2200 65 e. Type **456** (centenary) 50 25
2201 70 e. Brother Bartolomeu dos Martires (Bishop of Braga, 400th anniv) .. 55 30

457 Barketta

1990. 15th-century Explorers' Ships. Mult.
2202 32 e. Type **457** 30 10
2203 60 e. Carvel-built fishing boat 55 25
2204 70 e. Nau 70 40
2205 95 e. Caravel 95 45

1990. 20th-Century Portuguese Paintings (6th series). As T **438**. Multicoloured.
2206 32 e. "Dom Sebastiao" (Costa Pinheiro) .. 25 10
2207 60 e. "Domestic Scene with Green Dog" (Paula Rego) 45 20
2208 95 e. "Homage to Magritte" (Jose de Guimaraes) 75 35

458 Pena Palace

1990. National Palaces (2nd series). Mult.
2211 32 e. Type **458** 25 10
2212 60 e. Vila Palace .. 45 20
2213 70 e. Mafra Palace .. 55 30
2214 120 e. Guimaraes Palace 95 45

459 Carneiro

1990. 10th Death Anniv of Francisco Sa Carneiro (founder of Popular Democratic Party and Prime Minister, 1980).
2215 **459** 32 e. black and brown 25 10

460 Steam Locomotive No. 02, 1887

1990. Centenary of Rossio Railway Station, Lisbon. Multicoloured.
2216 32 e. Type **460** 25 10
2217 60 e. Steam locomotive No. 010, 1891 .. .. 45 20
2218 70 e. Steam locomotive No. 071, 1916 .. .. 55 30
2219 95 e. Electric locomotive, 1956 .. .. .. 75 35

1991. Portuguese Faience (2nd series). As T **450**. Multicoloured.
2221 35 e. Barrel of fish and plate (Rato factory, Lisbon) 25 10
2222 35 e. Floral vase (Bica do Sapato factory) .. 25 10
2223 35 e. Gargoyle (Costa Briozo factory, Coimbra) 25 10
2224 60 e. Dish with leaf pattern (Juncal factory) 45 20
2225 60 e. Coffee pot (Cavaquinho factory, Oporto) 45 20
2226 60 e. Mug (Massarelos factory, Oporto) .. 45 20

461 Greater Flamingoes

1991. European Tourism Year. Multicoloured.
2228 60 e. Type **461** 45 20
2229 110 e. European chameleon 85 40

462 "Eutelsat II" Satellite

1991. Europa. Europe in Space. Mult.
2231 **462** 80 e. multicoloured .. 65 30

463 Caravel

1991. 16th-century Explorers' Ships. Mult.
2233 35 e. Type **463** 25 15
2234 75 e. Port view of nau .. 45 35
2235 80 e. Stern view of nau .. 50 35
2236 110 e. Galleon 70 50

INDEX

Countries can be quickly located by referring to the index at the end of this volume.

465 Emerald and Diamond Bow

1991 "Royal Treasures" Exhibition, Ajuda Palace (1st issue). Multicoloured.
2238 35 e. Type **465** 30 15
2239 60 e. Royal sceptre .. 50 25
2240 70 e. Sash of the Grand Cross 55 25
2241 80 e. Hilt of sabre .. 65 30
2242 140 e. Crown .. .. 1·10 55
See also Nos 2270/4.

466 Antero de Quental (writer)

1991. Anniversaries. Multicoloured.
2243 35 e. Type **466** (death centenary) 30 15
2244 110 e. Arrival of expedition and baptism of Sonyo prince (500th anniv of first Portuguese missionary expedition to the Congo) .. .. 1·10 45

467 Faculty of Architecture, Oporto University (Siza Vieira)

1991. Architecture. Multicoloured.
2245 35 e. Type **467** 30 15
2246 60 e. Torre do Tombo (Arsenio Cordeiro Associates) 50 25
2247 80 e. River Douro railway bridge (Edgar Cardoso) and Donna Maria bridge 65 30
2248 110 e. Setubal–Braga highway 90 45

468 King Manuel I creating Public Post, 1520

1991. History of Communications in Portugal. Multicoloured.
2249 35 e. Type **468** 30 15
2250 60 e. Woman posting letter and telegraph operator (merging of posts and telegraph operations, 1881) .. 50 25
2251 80 e. Postman, mail van and switchboard operator (creation of Posts and Telecommunications administration, 1911) .. 65 30

469 Show Jumping

1991. Olympic Games, Barcelona (1992) (1st issue). Multicoloured.
2253 35 e. Type **469** 30 15
2254 60 e. Fencing 50 25
2255 80 e. Shooting 65 30
2256 110 e. Yachting .. 1·10 45
See also Nos. 2300/3.

470 Peugeot "19", 1899

1991. Caramulo Automobile Museum. Mult.
2257 35 e. Type **470** 30 15
2258 60 e. Rolls Royce "Silver Ghost", 1911 .. .. 50 25
2259 80 e. Bugatti "35B", 1930 65 30
2260 110 e. Ferrari "195 Inter", 1950 .. .. .. 90 45
See also Nos. 2275/8.

1992. Portuguese Faience (3rd series). As T **450**. Multicoloured.
2262 40 e. Jug (Viana do Castelo factory) .. 30 15
2263 40 e. Plate with flower design ("Ratinho" faience, Coimbra) .. 30 15
2264 40 e. Dish with lid (Estremoz factory) .. 30 15
2265 65 e. Decorated violin by Wescislau Cifka (Constancia factory, Lisbon) 30 15
2266 65 e. Figure of man seated on barrel (Calvaquinho factory, Oporto) .. 30 15
2267 65 e. Figure of woman (Fervenca factory, Oporto) 30 15

471 Astrolabe (Presidency emblem)

1992. Portuguese Presidency of European Community.
2269 **471** 65 e. multicoloured .. 50 20

1992. "Royal Treasures" Exhibition, Ajuda Palace (2nd issue). As T **465**. Multicoloured.
2270 38 e. Coral diadem .. 30 15
2271 65 e. Faberge clock .. 50 20
2272 70 e. Gold tobacco box studded with diamonds and emeralds by Jacqumin 50 25
2273 85 e. Royal sceptre with dragon supporting crown 70 35
2274 125 e. Necklace of diamond stars by Estevao de Sousa .. 90 45

1992. Oeiras Automobile Museum. As T **470**. Multicoloured.
2275 38 e. Citroen "Torpedo", 1922 .. .. .. 35 15
2276 65 e. Robert Schneider 12 H.P., 1914 .. .. 60 30
2277 85 e. Austin "Seven", 1933 80 40
2278 120 e. Mercedes Benz "770", 1938 .. .. 1·10 55

472 Portuguese Traders

1992. 450th Anniv of First Portuguese Contacts with Japan. Details of painting attributed to Kano Domi. Multicoloured.
2280 38 e. Type **472** 45 15
2281 120 e. Portuguese visitors with gifts .. .. 1·10 55

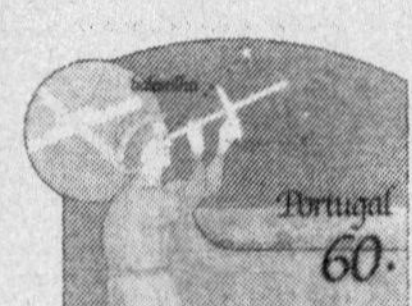

473 Portuguese Pavilion **474** Cross-staff

1992. "Expo '92" World's Fair, Seville.
2282 **473** 65 e. multicoloured .. 60 30

1992. Nautical Instruments (1st series). Mult.
2283 60 e. Type **474** 55 25
2284 70 e. Quadrant 65 30
2285 100 e. Astrolabe 90 45
2286 120 e. Compass .. .. 1·10 55
See also Nos. 2318/21.

475 Royal All Saints Hospital, Lisbon

1992. Anniversaries. Multicoloured.
2288 38 e. Type **475** (500th anniv of foundation) .. 35 15
2289 70 e. Lucia, Francisco and Jacinta (children) (75th anniv of apparition of Our Lady at Fatima) 65 30
2290 120 e. Crane and docks (centenary of Port of Leixoes) .. .. 1·10 55

476 Columbus with King Joao II

1992. Europa. 500th Anniv of Discovery of America by Columbus.
2291 **476** 85 e. multicoloured .. 80 40

478 Tern flying over contaminated River **479** Running

1992. 2nd United Nations Conference on Environment and Development, Rio de Janeiro. Multicoloured.
2293 70 e. Type **478** 65 30
2294 120 e. Kingfisher and butterfly beside clean river .. .. .. 1·10 55
Nos. 2293/4 were issued together, se-tenant, forming a composite design.

1992. Olympic Games, Barcelona (2nd issue). Multicoloured.
2295 38 e. Type **479** 35 15
2296 70 e. Football .. 65 30
2297 85 e. Hurdling 80 40
2298 120 e. Roller hockey .. 1·10 55

480 Bullfighter on Horse

1992. Centenary of Campo Pequeno Bull Ring, Lisbon. Multicoloured.
2300 38 e. Type **480** 35 15
2301 65 e. Bull charging at horse 60 30
2302 70 e. Bullfighter attacking bull 65 30
2303 155 e. Bullfighter flourishing hat .. 1·40 70

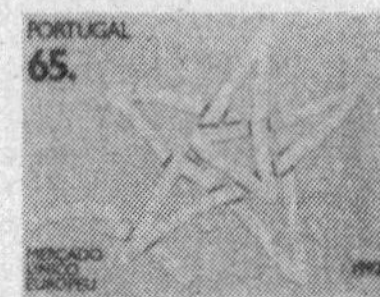

482 Star

1992. European Single Market.
2313 **482** 65 e. multicoloured .. 60 30

483 Industrial safety Equipment

1992. European Year of Health, Hygiene and Safety in the Workplace.
2314 **483** 120 e. multicoloured .. 1·10 55

484 Post Office Emblem **485** Graphic Poem

1993. No value expressed.
2315 **484** (–) red and black .. 35 15
No. 2315 was sold at the current first class inland letter rate. This was 42 e. at time of issue.

1993. Birth Centenary of Jose de Almada Negreiros (artist and poet). Multicoloured.
2316 40 e. Type **485** 30 15
2317 65 e. Ships (painting) .. 50 25

486 Sand Clock

1993. Nautical Instruments (2nd series). Multicoloured.
2318 42 e. Type **486** 30 15
2319 70 e. Nocturlabe .. 55 25
2320 90 e. Kamal 70 35
2321 130 e. Back-staff .. 1·00 50

487 View from Window

1993. Europa. Contemporary Art. Untitled painting by Jose Escada.
2322 **487** 90 e. multicoloured .. 70 35

488 Rossini and "The Barber of Seville"

1993. Bicentenary of San Carlos National Theatre, Lisbon. Multicoloured.
2324 42 e. Type **488** 30 15
2325 70 e. Verdi and "Rigoletto" 55 25
2326 90 e. Wagner and "Tristan and Isolde" .. 70 35
2327 130 e. Mozart and "The Magic Flute" .. .. 1·00 50

489 Fireman's Helmet

1993. 125th Anniv of Association of Volunteer Firemen of Lisbon.
2329 **489** 70 e. multicoloured .. 55 25

490 Santos-o-Velho, Lisbon **491** "Angel of the Annunciation"

1993. Union of Portuguese-speaking Capital Cities.
2330 **490** 130 e. multicoloured .. 1·00 50

1993. Sculptures. Multicoloured.
2332 42 e. Type **491** 30 15
2333 70 e. "St. Mark" (Cornelius de Holanda) (horiz) 55 25
2334 75 e. "Madonna and Child" 60 30
2335 90 e. "Archangel St. Michael" 70 35
2336 130 e. "Earl of Ferreira" (Soares dos Reis) .. 1·00 50
2337 170 e. "Construction" (Heldar Batista) .. 1·40 70

492 Road Tanker and Freight Train

1993. International Railways Congress, Lisbon. Multicoloured.
2339 90 e. Type **492** 70 35
2340 130 e. Train and traffic jam .. .. .. 1·00 50

493 Japanese Man with Musket

1993. 450th Anniv of First Portuguese Visit to Japan. Multicoloured.
2342 42 e. Type **493** 30 15
2343 130 e. Portuguese missionaries .. .. 1·00 50
2344 350 e. Traders carrying goods .. .. .. 2·75 1·25

494 Peniche Trawler **495** Rural Post Bag, 1800

1993. Trawlers. Multicoloured.
2345 42 e. Type **494** 30 15
2346 70 e. Peniche type trawler 55 25
2347 90 e. Germano 3o steam trawler 70 35
2348 130 e. Estrela 1o steam trawler .. .. 1·00 50

1993. Post Boxes. Multicoloured.
2349 42 e. Type **495** 30 15
2350 70 e. 19th-century wall-mounted box for railway travelling post office 55 25
2351 90 e. 19th-century pillar box 70 35
2352 130 e. Modern multi-function post box .. 1·00 50

496 Imperial Eagle **497** Knot

1993. Endangered Birds of Prey. Mult.
2354 42 e. Type **496** 30 15
2355 70 e. Eagle owl 55 25
2356 130 e. Peregrine falcon .. 1·00 50
2357 350 e. Hen harrier .. 2·75 1·25

1993. 40th Anniv of Brazil–Portugal Consultation and Friendship Treaty.
2358 **497** 130 e. multicoloured .. 1·00 50

499 Stylized Map of Member Nations

1994. 40th Anniv of Western European Union.
2360 **499** 85 e. multicoloured .. 65 30

500 Olympic Rings as Torch Flame

1993. Centenary of International Olympic Committee. Multicoloured.
2361 100 e. Type **500** 80 40
2362 100 e. "100" and rings .. 80 40

Aug '94
Sep '94
Oct '94

CHARITY TAX STAMPS

Used on certain days of the year as an additional postal tax on internal letters. Other values in some of the types were for use on telegrams only. The proceeds were devoted to public charities. If one was not affixed in addition to the ordinary postage, postage due stamps were used to collect the deficiency and the fine.

1911. Optd. **ASSISTENCIA.**

C 455.	**48.**	10 r. grn. (No. 406)	1·75	75
C 484.	**79.**	1 c. green (No. 486)	1·00	50

C 57. " Lisbon ".

C 58. " Charity ".

1913. Lisbon Fetes.

C 485.	C **57.**	1 c. green	25	20

1915. For poor people.

C 486.	C **58.**	1 c. red	15	15
C 669.		15 c. red	15	15

1924. Surch. **15 ctvs.**

C 594.	C **58.**	15 c. on 1 c. red ..	30	20

C **71.** Muse of History.

C **81.** Hurdler.

C **73.** Monument to de Pombal.

C **75.** Marquis de Pombal.

1925. Portuguese Army in Flanders, 1484 and 1918.

C 662.	**C 71.**	10 c. red	30	25
C 663.		10 c. green	30	25
C 664.		10 c. blue	30	25
C 665.		10 c. brown ..	30	25

1925. Marquis de Pombal Commemoration.

C666	C 73	15 c. blue and black	35	25
C667	–	15 c. blue and black	35	25
C668	C 75	15 c. blue and black	15	10

DESIGN: No. C677, Planning reconstruction of Lisbon.

1928. Olympic Games.

C741	C 81	15 c. black and red	3·00	2·25

NEWSPAPER STAMPS

N 16.

N 17.

1876.

N180	N 16	2 r. black	4·50	3·50
N178	N 17	2½ r. olive	2·50	45
N187		2½ r. bistre ..	3·50	15

OFFICIAL STAMPS

1938. Optd. **OFICIAL.**

O900	**99**	40 c.brown	10	10

O 144.

1952. No value.

O1069	O 144	(1 e.) blk & stone	10	10
O1070		(1 e.) blk & ochre	30	10

On No. O1069 "CORREIO DE PORTUGAL" is in stone on a black background, on No. O1070 it is in black on the ochre background.

PARCEL POST STAMPS

P 59.

1920.

P 578.	**P 59.**	1 c. brown ..	10	10
P 579.		2 c. orange ..	10	10
P 580.		5 c. brown ..	10	10
P 581.		10 c. brown ..	10	10
P 582.		20 c. blue ..	10	10
P 583.		40 c. red	20	10
P 584.		50 c. black ..	25	10
P 585.		60 c. blue ..	30	10
P 586.		70 c. brown ..	1·00	50
P 587.		80 c. blue ..	1·25	50
P 588.		90 c. violet ..	1·25	50
P 589.		1 e. green ..	1·40	35
P 591.		2 e. lilac	3·00	35
P 592.		3 e. olive ..	3·50	60
P 593.		4 e. blue	6·50	1·00
P 594.		5 e. lilac	8·00	80
P 595.		10 e. brown ..	25·00	2·25

P 101.

1936.

P 891.	**P 101.**	50 c. grey	25	10
P 892.		1 e. brown ..	25	10
P 893.		1 e. 50 violet ..	30	10
P 894.		2 e. red	65	10
P 895.		2 e. 50 olive ..	75	10
P 896.		4 e. 50 purple ..	1·90	10
P 897.		5 e. violet	2·25	20
P 898.		10 e. orange ..	3·75	40

POSTAGE DUE STAMPS

D **48.** Da Gama received by the Zamorin of Calicut.

D **49.**

1898.

D 386.	D **48.**	5 r. black	1·25	85
D 387.		10 r. mauve ..	1·75	1·10
D 388.		20 r. orange ..	3·50	1·75
D 389.		50 r. grey	10·00	4·00
D 390.		100 r. red	30·00	12·00
D 391.		200 r. brown ..	35·00	20·00

1904.

D 392.	D **49.**	5 r. brown	20	10
D 393.		10 r. orange ..	1·00	40
D 394.		20 r. mauve ..	3·25	1·50
D 395.		30 r. green	1·00	1·00
D 396.		40 r. lilac	1·10	1·00
D 397.		50 r. red	20·00	2·25
D 398.		100 r. blue	2·25	1·50

1911. Optd. **REPUBLICA.**

D 418.	D **49.**	5 r. brown	20	15
D 419.		10 r. orange ..	20	15
D 420.		20 r. mauve ..	40	15
D 421		30 r. green	20	15
D 422.		40 r. lilac	20	15
D 423.		50 r. red	2·25	1·25
D 424.		100 r. blue	2·50	1·50

1915. As Type **D 49,** but value in centavos.

D 491.	D **49.**	½ c. brown	10	10
D 498.		1 c. orange ..	10	15
D 493.		2 c. red	15	15
D 499.		3 c. green	30	30
D 500.		4 c. lilac	30	35
D 501.		5 c. red	35	35
D 497.		10 c. blue	30	30

1921.

D 578.	D **49.**	½ c. green	10	10
D 579.		4 c. green	10	10
D 580.		8 c. green	15	10
D 581.		10 c. green	15	10
D 582.		12 c. green	15	15
D 583.		16 c. green	10	10
D 584.		20 c. green	10	15
D 585.		24 c. green	10	15
D 586.		32 c. green	20	10
D 587.		36 c. green	20	15
D 588.		40 c. green	25	15
D 589.		48 c. green	25	15
D 590.		50 c. green	25	20
D 591.		60 c. green	25	20
D 592.		72 c. green	25	20
D 593.		80 c. green	2·25	1·25
D 594.		1 e. 20 green ..	1·25	1·00

D **72.**

D **82.**

1925. Great War Commemorative.

D 662.	D **72.**	20 c. brown ..	20	15

1925. De Pombal types optd. **MULTA.**

D 663.	C **73.**	30 c. blue	25	25
D 664.	–	30 c. blue	25	25
D 665.	C **75.**	30 c. blue	25	25

1928. Olympic Games.

D 741.	D **82.**	30 c. black and red ..	2·00	1·60

D **91.**

D **108.**

D **218.**

1932.

D 865.	D **91.**	5 c. buff	10	10
D 866.		10 c. blue	10	10
D 867.		20 c. pink	30	20
D 868.		30 c. blue	30	25
D 869.		40 c. green	35	30
D 870.		50 c. grey	40	40
D 871.		60 c. pink	85	75
D 872.		80 c. red	3·25	1·10
D 873.		1 e. 20 green ..	3·00	3·75

1940.

D912	D 108	5 c. brown ..	10	10
D913		10 c. lilac ..	10	10
D914		20 c. red	10	10
D925		30 c. violet ..	10	10
D916		40 c. mauve ..	10	10
D917		50 c. blue ..	10	10
D928		60 c. green ..	10	10
D929		80 c. red	10	10
D930		1 e. brown ..	25	10
D921		2 e. mauve ..	45	10
D922		5 e. orange ..	1·00	20

1967.

D 1312.	D **218.**	10 c. brown, yell. and orange ..	10	10
D 1313.		20 c. purple, yell. and ochre ..	10	10
D 1314.		30 c. brown, yell. and orange ..	10	10
D 1315.		40 c. purple, yell. and bistre ..	10	10
D 1316.		50 c. indigo, blue and light blue	10	10
D 1317.		60 c. olive, blue and turquoise	10	10
D 1318.		80 c. indigo, blue and light blue	10	10
D 1319.		1 e. indigo, blue and ult. ..	10	10
D 1320.		2 e. olive, light geeen & green	10	10
D 1321.		3 e. grey, green and yellow ..	10	10
D 1322.		4 e. grey, green and yellow	10	10
D 1323.		5 e. brn., mauve and red ..	10	10
D 1324.		9 e. grey, violet and mauve ..	10	10
D 1325.		10 e. grey, violet and lilac	10	10
D 1326.		20 e. brown, red and lilac ..	20	10
D 1327.		40 e. purple, lilac and mauve ..	35	25
D 1328.		50 e. red, lilac and purple ..	55	45

D 481

1992.

D2305	D 481	1 e. blue, deep blue and black	10	10
D2306		2 e. light green, green and black	10	10
D2307		5 e. yellow, brown and black ..	10	10
D2308		10 e. red, orange and black ..	10	10
D2309		20 e. green, violet and black ..	15	10
D2310		50 e. yellow, green and black	40	20
D2311		100 e. orange, red and black	80	40
D2312		200 e. mauve, violet & black	1·60	80

PORTUGUESE COLONIES Pt. 9

General issues for the Portuguese possessions in Africa: Angola, Cape Verde Islands, Guinea, Lourenco Marques, Mozambique, Congo, St. Thomas and Prince Islands, and Zambezia.

1898. 1000 reis = 1 milreis.
1919. 100 centavos = 1 escudo.

1898. 400th Anniv. of Vasco da Gama's Discovery of Route to India. As Nos. 378/85 of Portugal but inscr. "AFRICA".

1.	2½ r. green	40	30
2.	5 r. red	40	30
3.	10 r. purple	40	30
4.	25 r. green	35	30
5.	50 r. blue	40	40
6.	75 r. brown	2·00	1·25
7.	100 r. brown	1·50	1·00
8.	150 r. bistre	2·50	1·25

CHARITY TAX STAMP

C 1.

1919. Fiscal stamps optd. **TAXA DE GUERRA.**

C 1.	C **1.**	1 c. black and green ..	30	30
C 2.		5 c. green	30	30

POSTAGE DUE STAMPS

D 1.

1945. Value in black.

D 1.	D **1.**	10 c. red	10	10
D 2.		20 c. purple	10	10
D 3.		30 c. blue	10	10
D 4.		40 c. brown	15	15
D 5.		50 c. lilac	15	15
D 6.		1 e. brown	35	30
D 7.		2 c. green	75	75
D 8.		3 e. red	1·00	90
D 9.		5 e. yellow	1·90	1·60

PORTUGUESE CONGO Pt. 9

The area known as Portuguese Congo, now called Cabinda, was the part of Angola north of the River Congo. It issued its own stamps from 1894 until 1920.

1894. 1000 reis = 1 milreis.
1913. 100 centavos = 1 escudo.

1894. "Figures" key-type inscr. "CONGO".

8.	R.	5 r. orange	40	40
9.		10 r. mauve	75	45
10.		15 r. brown	1·25	95
12.		20 r. lilac	1·25	85
13.		25 r. green	60	30
22.		50 r. blue	1·25	75
5.		75 r. red	1·90	1·75
6.		80 r. green	3·00	2·75
7.		100 r. brown on yellow ..	2·25	1·75
17.		150 r. red on rose ..	4·00	3·75
18.		200 r. blue on blue ..	4·00	3·75
19.		300 r. blue on brown ..	5·00	4·25

1898. "King Carlos" key-type inscr. "CONGO".

24.	S.	2½ r. grey	10	15
25.		5 r. orange	15	15
26.		10 r. green	25	15
27.		15 r. brown	60	45
66.		15 r. green	45	30
28.		20 r. lilac	40	30
29.		25 r. green	55	30
67.		25 r. red	45	25
30.		50 r. blue	60	45
68.		50 r. brown	1·10	70
69.		65 r. blue	3·00	2·50
31.		75 r. red	1·25	90
70.		75 r. purple	1·25	1·00
32.		80 r. mauve	1·25	90
33.		100 r. blue on blue ..	90	80
71.		115 r. brown on pink ..	2·75	2·25
72.		130 r. brown on yellow ..	3·25	3·25
34.		150 r. brown on yellow ..	1·40	1·25
35.		200 r. purple on pink ..	1·75	1·50
36.		300 r. blue on pink ..	1·60	1·25
73.		400 r. blue on yellow ..	3·50	3·00
37.		500 r. black on blue ..	5·00	3·25
38.		700 r. mauve on yellow ..	8·00	5·50

1902. Surch.

74	S	50 r. on 65 r. blue ..	1·75	1·25
40	R	65 r. on 15 r. brown ..	1·60	1·00
41		65 r. on 20 r. lilac ..	1·60	1·00
44		65 r. on 25 r. green ..	1·50	1·25
46		65 r. on 300 r. blue on brn.	2·00	2·00
50	V	115 r. on 2½ r. brown ..	1·50	1·00
47	R	115 r. on 10 r. mauve ..	1·50	1·00
48		115 r. on 50 r. blue ..	1·50	1·00
53		130 r. on 5 r. orange ..	1·50	1·00
54		130 r. on 75 r. red ..	1·50	1·00
57		130 r. on 100 r. brown on yellow ..	1·50	1·00
58		400 r. on 80 r. green ..	55	45
60		400 r. on 150 r. red on rose	70	50
61		400 r. on 200 r. blue on blue	70	50

1902. "King Carlos" key-type of Portuguese Congo optd. **PROVISORIO.**

62. S. 15 r. brown 80 60
63. 25 r. green 80 60
64. 50 r. blue 80 60
65. 75 r. red 1·75 1·25

1911. "King Carlos" key-type of Angola, optd. **REPUBLICA** and **CONGO** with bar (200 r. also surch.).

75. S. 2½ r. grey 50 40
76. 5 r. orange 70 55
77. 10 r. green 70 50
78. 15 r. green 70 55
79. 25 r. on 200 r. purple on pink 1·10 90

1911. "King Carlos" key-type of Portuguese Congo optd. **REPUBLICA.**

80. S. 2½ r. grey 10 15
81. 5 r. orange 15 15
82. 10 r. green 15 15
83. 15 r. green 20 15
84. 20 r. lilac 20 15
85. 25 r. red 20 15
86. 50 r. brown 20 15
87. 75 r. purple 25 15
88. 100 r. blue on blue 25 15
89. 115 r. brown on pink 45 40
90. 130 r. brown on yellow 45 40
143. 200 r. purple on pink 60 55
92. 400 r. blue on yellow 1·00 75
93. 500 r. black on blue 1·60 80
94. 700 r. mauve on yellow 1·60 80

1913. Surch. **REPUBLICA CONGO** and value on "Vasco da Gama" stamps of

(a) Portuguese Colonies.

95. ¼ c. on 2½ r. green 50 45
96. ½ c. on 5 r. red 50 45
97. 1 c. on 10 r. purple 35 35
98. 2½ c. on 25 r. green 35 35
99. 5 c. on 50 r. blue 50 45
100. 7½ c. on 75 r. brown 80 65
101. 10 c. on 100 r. brown 50 45
102. 15 c. on 150 r. bistre 50 45

(b) Macao.

103. ¼ c. on ½ a. green 60 50
104. ½ c. on 1 a. red 60 50
105. 1 c. on 2 a. purple 45 40
106. 2½ c. on 4 a. green 45 40
107. 5 c. on 8 a. blue 60 50
108. 7½ c. on 12 a. brown 90 80
109. 10 c. on 16 a. brown 85 65
110. 15 c. on 24 a. bistre 65 45

(c) Timor.

111. ¼ c. on ½ a. green 70 60
112. ½ c. on 1 a. red 70 60
113. 1 c. on 2 a. purple 45 40
114. 2½ c. on 4 a. green 45 40
115. 5 c. on 8 a. blue 70 60
116. 7½ c. on 12 a. brown 90 80
117. 10 c. on 16 a. brown 90 60
118. 15 c. on 24 a. bistre 65 45

1914. "Ceres" key-type inscr. "CONGO".

135. U. ¼ c. olive 20 15
120. ½ c. black 30 20
121. 1 c. green 80 50
122. 1½ c. brown 70 35
136. 2 c. red 20 15
124. 2½ c. violet 20 15
125. 5 c. blue 30 20
126. 7½ c. brown 50 40
127. 8 c. black 50 40
128. 10 c. brown 50 40
129. 15 c. red 65 40
130. 20 c. green 65 50
131. 30 c. brown on green 1·00 80
132. 40 c. brown on rose 1·00 90
133. 50 c. orange on pink 1·25 90
134. 1 e. green on blue 1·90 1·10

1914. "King Carlos" key-type of Portuguese Congo optd. **PROVISORIO** and **REPUBLICA.**

146. S. 15 r. brown (No. 62) 25 25
147. 50 r. blue (No. 64) 25 25
140. 75 r. red (No. 65) 60 40

1914. Provisional stamps of 1902 optd. **REPUBLICA.**

148 S 50 r. on 65 r. blue 25 25
150 V 115 r. on 2½ r. brown 25 15
151 R 115 r. on 10 r. mauve 20 15
154 115 r. on 50 r. blue 20 15
156 130 r. on 5 r. orange 20 15
157 130 r. on 75 r. red 60 30
160 130 r. on 100 r. brown on yellow 30 20

NEWSPAPER STAMP

1894. "Newspaper" key-type inscr. "CONGO".

N 24. V 2½ r. brown 40 35

PORTUGUESE GUINEA Pt. 9

A former Portuguese territory, W. coast of Africa, with adjacent islands. Used stamps of Cape Verde from 1877 until 1881. In Sept. 1974 the territory became independent and was renamed Guinea-Bissau.

1881. 1000 reis = 1 milreis.
1913. 100 centavos = 1 escudo.

1881. "Crown" key-type inscr. "CABO VERDE" and optd. **GUINE.**

19 P 5 r. black 1·60 1·50
20 10 r. yellow 50·00 45·00
31 10 r. green 3·00 2·10
21 20 r. olive 1·40 90
32 20 r. red 3·00 2·10
13 25 r. red 90 65
28 25 r. lilac 1·50 65
23 40 r. blue 50·00 38·00
29 40 r. yellow 80 65
24 50 r. green 60·00 38·00
30 50 r. blue 2·25 1·00
16 100 r. lilac 2·75 2·00
17 200 r. orange 4·00 3·00
18 300 r. brown 5·50 4·50

1886. As T **19** of Portugal but inscr. "GUINE PORTUGUEZA".

35. 5 r. black 1·75 1·10
36. 10 r. green 2·50 1·60
37. 20 r. red 3·50 2·25
38. 25 r. mauve 3·50 2·50
46. 40 r. brown 2·50 2·25
40. 50 r. blue 6·00 2·00
47. 80 r. grey 5·00 4·00
48. 100 r. brown 5·00 4·00
43. 200 r. lilac 13·00 8·00
44. 300 r. orange 15·00 12·00

1893. "Figures" key-type inscr. "GUINE".

50. R. 5 r. yellow 60 50
51. 10 r. mauve 60 55
52. 15 r. brown 80 60
53. 20 r. lilac 80 60
54. 25 r. green 80 60
55. 50 r. blue 1·40 80
57. 75 r. red 3·50 3·00
58. 80 r. green 3·50 3·00
59. 100 r. brown on buff 3·75 3·00
60. 150 r. red on rose 4·50 4·00
61. 200 r. blue on blue 4·50 3·75
62. 300 r. blue on brown 6·00 5·50

1898. "King Carlos" key-type inscr. "GUINE".

65. S. 2½ r. grey 15 15
66. 5 r. orange 20 15
67. 10 r. green 20 15
68. 15 r. brown 1·10 90
114. 15 r. green 65 50
69. 20 r. lilac 30 20
70. 25 r. green 75 40
115. 25 r. red 40 25
71. 50 r. blue 1·10 50
116. 50 r. brown 75 60
117. 65 r. blue 3·00 2·50
72. 75 r. red 5·00 3·25
118. 75 r. purple 1·25 80
73. 80 r. mauve 1·10 75
74. 100 r. blue on blue 1·10 60
119. 115 r. brown on pink 3·00 2·25
120. 130 r. brown on yellow 3·00 3·25
75. 150 r. brown on yellow 3·00 1·50
76. 200 r. purple on pink 3·00 1·50
77. 300 r. blue on pink 2·75 1·75
121. 400 r. blue on yellow 3·00 2·25
78. 500 r. black on blue 4·00 3·00
79. 700 r. mauve on yellow 6·00 4·00

1902. Surch.

122 S 50 r. on 65 r. blue 1·50 90
81 – 65 r. on 10 r. grn. (No. 36) 2·50 1·50
84 R 65 r. on 10 r. mauve 2·50 1·40
85 65 r. on 15 r. brown 2·00 1·40
82 – 65 r. on 20 r. red (No. 37) 2·50 1·50
86 R 65 r. on 20 r. lilac 2·00 1·40
83 – 65 r. on 25 r. mve. (No. 38) 2·50 1·50
88 R 65 r. on 50 r. blue 1·10 90
97 V 115 r. on 2½ r. brown 1·75 1·25
93 R 115 r. on 5 r. yellow 1·75 1·25
95 115 r. on 25 r. green 2·00 1·25
89 – 115 r. on 40 r. brn. (No. 46) 2·00 1·50
91 – 115 r. on 50 r. blue (No. 40) 2·00 1·50
92 – 115 r. on 300 r. orange (No. 44) 2·75 2·25
98 – 130 r. on 80 r. grey (No. 47) 2·75 2·25
100 – 130 r. on 100 r. brown (No. 48) 2·75 2·25
102 R 130 r. on 150 r. red on rose 2·25 1·25
103 130 r. on 200 r. blue on blue 2·50 1·50
104 130 r. on 300 r. bl. on brn. 2·50 1·50
105 – 400 r. on 5 r. blk. (No. 35) 10·00 7·50
107 R 400 r. on 75 r. red 1·50 1·25
108 400 r. on 80 r. green 1·00 75
109 400 r. on 100 r. brn. on buff 1·00 75
106 400 r. on 200 r. lilac (No. 43) 4·50 3·25

1902. "King Carlos" key-type of Portuguese Guinea optd **PROVISORIO**.

110. S. 15 r. brown 1·00 60
111. 25 r. green 1·00 60
112. 50 r. blue 1·25 80
113. 75 r. red 1·75 1·60

1911. "King Carlos" key-type of Portuguese Guinea optd. **REPUBLICA.**

123. S. 2½ r. grey 15 20
124. 5 r. orange 20 20
125. 10 r. green 20 20
126. 15 r. green 20 20
127. 20 r. lilac 20 20
128. 25 r. red 20 20
129. 50 r. brown 20 25
130. 75 r. purple 25 25
131. 100 r. blue on blue 25 30
132. 115 r. brown on pink 55 30
133. 130 r. brown on yellow 55 30
134. 200 r. purple on pink 3·00 1·50
135. 400 r. blue on yellow 90 55
136. 500 r. black on blue 90 55
137. 700 r. mauve on yellow 1·50 90

1913. Surch. **REPUBLICA GUINE** and value on "Vasco da Gama" stamps of

(a) Portuguese Colonies.

138. ¼ c. on 2½ r. green 70 70
139. ½ c. on 5 r. red 70 70
140. 1 c. on 10 r. purple 40 40
141. 2½ c. on 25 r. green 40 40
142. 5 c. on 50 r. blue 70 70
143. 7½ c. on 75 r. brown 1·50 1·40
144. 10 c. on 100 r. brown 70 50
145. 15 c. on 150 r. bistre 1·60 1·60

(b) Macao.

146. ¼ c. on ½ a. green 80 70
147. ½ c. on 1 a. red 80 70
148. 1 c. on 2 a. purple 50 50
149. 2½ c. on 4 a. green 50 50
150. 5 c. on 8 a. blue 80 70
151. 7½ c. on 12 a. brown 1·40 1·10
152. 10 c. on 16 a. brown 1·25 1·10
153. 15 c. on 24 a. bistre 1·40 1·10

(c) Timor.

154. ¼ c. on ½ a. green 80 70
155. ½ c. on 1 a. red 80 70
156. 1 c. on 2 a. purple 50 50
157. 2½ c. on 4 a. green 50 50
158. 5 c. on 8 a. blue 80 70
159. 7½ c. on 12 a. brown 1·40 1·00
160. 10 c. on 16 a. brown 1·25 1·00
161 15 c. on 24 a. bistre 1·40 1·00

1913. "King Carlos" key-type of Portuguese Guinea optd. **PROVISORIO** and **REPUBLICA.**

184. S. 15 r. brown 35 30
185. 50 r. blue 35 30
164. 75 r. red 3·00 2·50

1914. "Ceres" key-type inscr. "GUINE".

204 U ¼ c. olive 10 10
209 ½ c. black 15 10
210 1 c. green 10 10
211 1½ c. brown 15 10
212 2 c. red 15 10
213 2 c. grey 10 10
214 2½ c. violet 15 10
215 3 c. orange 10 10
216 4 c. red 10 10
217 4½ c. grey 10 10
218 5 c. blue 10 10
219 6 c. mauve 10 10
220 7 c. blue 15 10
221 7½ c. brown 15 15
222 8 c. black 15 15
223 10 c. brown 15 10
224 12 c. green 25 15
225 15 c. red 25 10
226 20 c. green 15 10
227 24 c. blue 70 50
228 25 c. brown 70 50
180 30 c. brown on green 2·50 2·00
229 30 c. green 30 15
181 40 c. brown on rose 1·50 70
230 40 c. blue 30 15
182 50 c. orange on pink 1·50 70
231 50 c. mauve 70 35
232 60 c. blue 70 35
233 60 c. red 70 35
234 80 c. red 70 35
183 1 e. green on blue 1·75 90
236 1 c. pink 1·00 65
235 1 e. blue 1·00 65
237 2 e. purple 1·10 70
238 5 e. brown 5·50 4·00
239 10 e. pink 9·50 6·50
240 20 c. green 22·00 17·00

1915. Provisional stamps of 1902 optd. **REPUBLICA.**

186. S. 50 r. on 65 r. blue 35 30
187. V. 115 r. on 2½ r. brown 50 45
190. R. 115 r. on 5 r. yellow 35 30
191. 115 r. on 25 r. green 35 30
194. – 115 r. on 40 r. brown (89) 35 30
195. – 115 r. on 50 r. bl. (No. 91) 35 30
196. – 130 r. on 80 r. grey (98) 1·25 90
197. – 130 r. on 100 r. brn. (100) 80 65
199. R. 130 r. on 150 r. red on rose 35 35
200. 130 r. on 200 r. bl. on bl. 35 35
201. 130 r. on 300 r. bl. on brn. 35 35

1920. Surch.

241. U. 4 c. on ¼ c. olive 1·50 1·10
242. 6 c. on ½ c. black 1·50 1·10
243. S. 12 c. on 115 r. brown on pink (No. 132) 2·25 1·60

1925. Stamps of 1902 optd. **Republica** and surch.

244. R. 40 c. on 400 r. on 75 r. red 40 35
245. 40 c. on 400 r. on 80 r. grn. 40 35
246. 40 c. on 400 r. on 100 r. brown on buff 40 35

1931. "Ceres" key-type of Portuguese Guinea surch.

247. U. 50 c. on 60 c. red 80 60
248. 70 c. on 80 c. red 90 75
249. 1 e. 40 on 2 e. purple 2·00 1·75

24. Ceres.

31. Cacheu Castle.

1933.

251. 24. 1 c. brown 10 10
252. 5 c. brown 10 10
253. 10 c. mauve 10 10
254. 15 c. black 15 10
255. 20 c. grey 15 10
256. 30 c. green 15 10
257. 40 c. red 15 10
258. 45 c. blue 35 20
259. 50 c. brown 35 20
260. 60 c. olive 35 20
261. 70 c. brown 35 30
262. 80 c. green 40 30
263. 85 c. red 90 45
264. 1 e. red 45 30
265. 1 e. 40 blue 2·00 1·25
266. 2 e. mauve 90 60
267. 5 e. green 3·50 2·25
268. 10 e. bistre 6·00 4·25
269. 20 e. orange 20·00 12·00

1938. As T **54** and **56** of Macao but inscr. "GUINE".

270. 54. 1 c. olive (postage) 10 10
271. 5 c. brown 10 10
272. 10 c. red 10 10
273. 15 c. purple 10 10
274. 20 c. grey 15 10
275. – 30 c. purple 20 10
276. – 35 c. green 20 15
277. – 40 c. brown 20 15
278. – 50 c. mauve 20 15
279. – 60 c. black 25 20
280. – 70 c. violet 25 20
281. – 80 c. orange 35 25
282. – 1 e. red 35 25
283. – 1 e. 75 blue 60 30
284. – 2 e. red 1·50 45
285. – 5 e. olive 2·25 90
286. – 10 e. blue 4·00 1·00
287. – 20 e. brown 12·00 2·40
288. 56. 10 c. red (air) 15 10
289. 20 c. violet 15 10
290. 50 c. orange 15 10
291. 1 e. blue 30 20
292. 2 e. red 3·00 1·60
293. 3 e. green 60 35
294. 5 e. brown 1·75 50
295. 9 e. red 2·00 90
296. 10 e. mauve 4·00 1·25

DESIGNS (postage): 30 to 50 c. Mousinho de Albuquerque. 60 c. to 1 e. Dam. 1 e. 75 to 5 e. Prince Henry the Navigator. 10, 20 e. Afonso de Albuquerque.

1946. 500th Anniv. of Discovery of Port. Guinea.

297. 31. 30 c. black 40 30
298. – 50 c. green 20 20
299. 50 c. purple 20 20
300. – 1 e. 75 blue 1·25 1·50
301. – 3 e .50 red 2·00 80
302. – 5 e. brown 4·00 2·00
303. – 20 e. violet 6·50 3·00

DESIGNS—VERT. 50 c. Nuno Tristao. 1 e. 75, President Grant. 3 e. 50, Teixeiro Pinto. 5 e. Honorio Barreto. HORIZ. 20 e. Church at Bissau.

32. Native Huts.

34. Letter and Globe.

1948.

304. 32. 5 c. brown 10 10
305. – 10 c. purple 4·50 2·50
306. – 20 c. mauve 20 10
307. – 35 c. green 20 10
308. – 50 c. red 20 10
309. – 70 c. blue 20 15
310. – 80 c. green 25 15
311. – 1 c. red 40 15
312. – 1 e. 75 blue 5·00 90
313. – 2 e. blue 5·50 35
314. – 3 e. 50 brown 1·50 35
315. – 5 e. grey 2·50 60
316. – 20 e. violet 9·00 3·00

DESIGNS: 10 c. Crowned crane. 20 c., 3 e. 50 Youth. 35 c., 5 e. Woman. 50 c. Musician. 70 c. Man. 80 c., 20 e. Girl. 1 c., 2 e. Drummer. 1 e. 75, Bushbuck.

1948. Statue of Our Lady of Fatima. As T **62** of Macao.

317. 50 c. olive 1·25 1·00

1949. 75th Anniv. of U.P.U.

318. 34. 2 e orange 1·50 1·00

1950. Holy Year. As Nos. 425/6 of Macao.

319. 1 e. red 75 60
320. 3 e. green 1·10 80

1951. Termination of Holy Year. As T **69** of Macao.

321. 1 e. brown and buff 35 35

37. Doctor examining Patient.

39. Exhibition Entrance.

1952. 1st Tropical Medicine Congress, Lisbon.

322. 37. 50 c. brown and purple 25 20

1953. Missionary Art Exhibition.

323. 39. 10 c. lake and olive 10 10
324. 50 c. blue and ochre 35 20
325. 3 e black and salmon 90 55

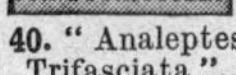

40. "Analeptes Trifasciata".

43. Arms of Cape Verde Islands and Portuguese Guinea.

1953. Insects. Multicoloured.

326.	5 c. Type **40**	10	10
327.	10 c. "Callidea panaethiopica kirk"	10	10
328.	30 c. "Craspedophorus brevicollis"	10	10
329.	50 c. "Anthia nimrod"	10	10
330.	70 c. "Platypria luctuosa"	20	10
331.	1 e. "Acanthophorus maculatus"	20	10
332.	2 e. "Cordylomera nitidipennis"	40	10
333.	3 e. "Lycus latissimus"	75	15
334.	5 e. "Cicindeia Brunet"	1·40	35
335.	10 e. "Colluris dimidiata"	2·00	80

1953. Portuguese Stamp Cent. As T **75** of Macao.

336.	50 c. grey and yellow	35	15

1954. 4th Cent. of Sao Paulo. As T **76** of Macao.

337.	1 e. blk., mauve & lavender	15	15

1955. Presidential Visit.

338. **43.**	1 c. multicoloured	20	15
339.	2 e. 50 multicoloured	30	20

44. Exhibition Emblem, Globe and Arms.

46. Statue of Barreto at Bissau.

1958. Brussels Int. Exn.

340. **44.**	2 e. 50 multicoloured	30	20

1958. 6th Int. Congress of Tropical Medicine. As T **79** of Macao.

341.	5 e. multicoloured	1·25	70

DESIGN: 5 e. "Maytenus senegalensis" (plant).

1959. Death Cent. of H. Barreto (statesman).

342. **46.**	2 e. 50 multicoloured	15	10

47. Astrolabe.

48. "Medical Services".

1960. 500th Death Anniv. of Prince Henry the Navigator.

343. **47.**	2 e. 50 multicoloured	20	10

1960. 10th Anniv. of African Technical Co-operation Commission.

344. **48.**	1 e. 50 multicoloured	20	10

1962. Sports. As T **82** of Macao. Mult.

345	50 c. Motor racing	10	10
346	1 e. Tennis	50	15
347	1 e. 50 Putting the shot	20	15
348	2 e. 50 Wrestling	30	20
349	3 e. 50 Shooting	30	20
350	15 e. Volleyball	1·25	80

1962. Malaria Eradication. Mosquito design as T **83** of Macao. Multicoloured.

351.	2 e. 50 "A. gambiae"	25	20

51. Common Spitting Cobra.

52. Map of Africa and Airliners.

1963. Snakes. Multicoloured.

352.	20 c. Type **51**	15	10
353.	35 c. African rock python	15	10
354.	70 c. Boomslang	40	10
355.	80 c. West African mamba	30	10
356.	1 e. 50 Symthe's water snake	40	10
357.	2 e. Common night adder	20	10
358.	2 e. 50 Green swamp-snake	1·10	10
359.	3 e. Brown house snake	30	15
360.	4 e. Spotted wolfsnake	40	20
361.	5 e. Common puff adder	50	20
362.	15 e. Striped beauty snake	1·25	35
363.	20 e. African egg-eating snake	1·75	50

The 2 e. and 20 e. are horiz, the rest vert.

1963. 10th Anniv. of T.A.P. Airline.

364. **52.**	2 e. 50 multicoloured	35	20

1964. National Overseas Bank Centenary. As T **84** of Macao but portrait of J. de A. Corvo.

365.	2 e. 50 multicoloured	30	20

1965. Cent. of I.T.U. As T **85** of Macao.

366.	2 e. 50 multicoloured	70	35

55. Soldier, 1548.

63. Pres. Tomas.

1966. Portuguese Military Uniforms. Multicoloured.

367.	25 c. Type **55**	10	10
368.	40 c. Arquebusier, 1578	15	10
369.	60 c. Arquebusier, 1640	20	10
370.	1 e. Grenadier, 1721	20	10
371.	2 e. 50 Captain of Fusiliers, 1740	45	10
372.	4 e. 50 Infantryman, 1740	1·00	40
373.	7 e. 50 Sergeant-major, 1762	1·40	55
374.	10 e. Engineer's officer, 1806	1·60	70

1966. 40th Anniv of Portuguese National Revolution. As T **86** of Macao but showing different buildings. Multicoloured.

375	2 e. 50 B. C. Lopes School and Bissau Hospital	25	20

1967. Cent. of Military Naval Assn. As T **88** of Macao. Multicoloured.

376.	50 c. O. Muzanty and cruiser "Republica"	15	10
377.	1 e. A. de Cerqueira and destroyer "Guadiana"	40	20

1967. 50th Anniv. of Fatima Apparitions. As T **89** of Macao.

378.	50 c. multicoloured	10	10

DESIGN: 50 c. Chapel of the Apparitions and Monument of the Holy Spirit.

1968. Visit of Pres. Tomas of Portugal.

396. **63.**	1 e. multicoloured	10	10

1968. 500th Birth Anniv. of Pedro Cabral (explorer). As T **90** of Macao. Multicoloured.

397.	2 e. 50 Cabral's arms (vert.)	25	15

1969. Birth Cent. of Admiral Gago Coutinho. As T **91** of Macao. Multicoloured.

409	1 e. Admiral Coutinho's astrolabe (horiz)	15	10

1969. 500th Birth Anniv. of Vasco da Gama (explorer). As T **92** of Macao. Mult.

410.	2 e. 50 Arms of Vasco da Gama (vert.)	15	10

1969. Centenary of Overseas Administrative Reforms. As T **93** of Macao.

411.	50 c. multicoloured	10	10

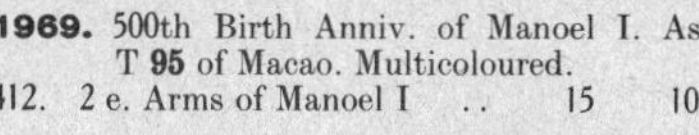

1969. 500th Birth Anniv. of Manoel I. As T **95** of Macao. Multicoloured.

412.	2 e. Arms of Manoel I	15	10

70. Ulysses Grant and Square, Bolama.

73. Camoens.

1970. Centenary of Arbitral Judgment on Sovereignty of Bolama.

413. **70.**	2 e. 50 multicoloured	20	15

1970. Birth Cent. of Marshal Carmona. As T **96** of Macao.

414.	1 e. 50 Portrait wearing cap and cloak	10	10

1972. 400th Anniv. of Camoens' "The Lusiads" (epic poem).

422. **73.**	50 c. multicoloured	15	10

74. Weightlifting and Hammer-throwing.

1972. Olympic Games, Munich.

423. **74.**	2 e. 50 multicoloured	15	10

75. Seaplane "Lusitania" taking-off from Lisbon.

1972. 50th Anniv. of 1st Lisbon-Rio de Janeiro Flight.

424. **75.**	1 e. multicoloured	15	10

1973. Centenary of I.M.O./W.M.O. As Type **102** of Macao.

425.	2 e. multicoloured	15	10

CHARITY TAX STAMPS

The notes under this heading in Portugal also apply here.

C 16

1919. Fiscal stamp optd. **REPUBLICA** and **TAXA DE GUERRA.**

C241 C 16	10 r. brn, buff & blk	11·00	9·00

1925. Marquis de Pombal Commem. stamps of Portugal, but inscr. "GUINE".

C 247. C **73.**	15 c. black and red	30	25
C 248. –	15 c. black and red	30	25
C 249. C **75.**	15 c. black and red	30	25

C 26.

C 59.

C 60.

C 29a.

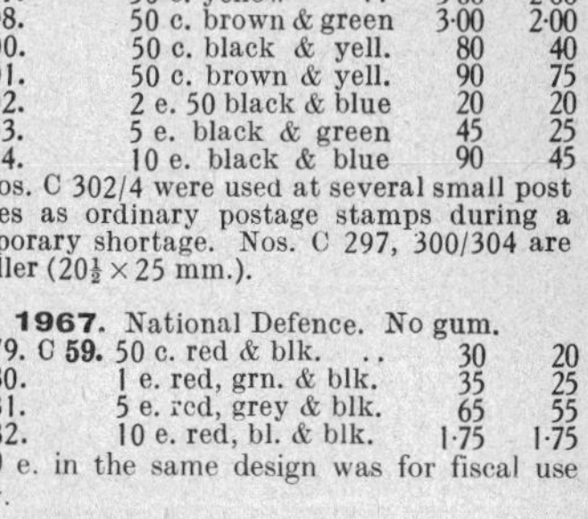

1934.

C 270. C **26.**	50 c. brn. & grn.	3·00	1·75

1938.

C 299. C **29a.**	30 c. black & purple	10	10
C 297.	50 c. yellow	3·00	2·00
C 298.	50 c. brown & green	3·00	2·00
C 300.	50 c. black & yell.	80	40
C 301.	50 c. brown & yell.	90	75
C 302.	2 e. 50 black & blue	20	20
C 303.	5 e. black & green	45	25
C 304.	10 e. black & blue	90	45

Nos. C 302/4 were used at several small post offices as ordinary postage stamps during a temporary shortage. Nos. C 297, 300/304 are smaller (20½ × 25 mm.).

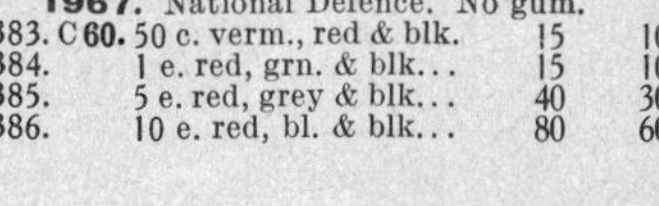

1967. National Defence. No gum.

C 379. C **59.**	50 c. red & blk.	30	20
C 380.	1 e. red, grn. & blk.	35	25
C 381.	5 e. red, grey & blk.	65	55
C 382.	10 e. red, bl. & blk.	1·75	1·75

50 e. in the same design was for fiscal use only.

1967. National Defence. No gum.

C 383. C **60.**	50 c. verm., red & blk.	15	10
C 384.	1 e. red, grn. & blk.	15	10
C 385.	5 e. red, grey & blk.	40	30
C 386.	10 e. red, bl. & blk.	80	60

C 61. Carved Statuette of Woman.

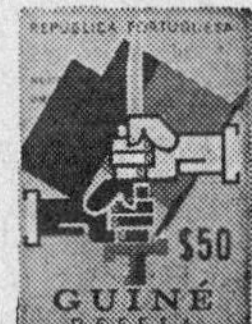

C 65. Hands grasping Sword.

1967. Guinean Artifacts from Bissau Museum. Multicoloured.

C 387.	50 c. Type C **61**	15	15
C 388.	1 e. "Tree of life" (carving)	15	15
C 389.	2 e. Cow-headed statuette	15	15
C 390.	2 e. 50 "The Magistrate" (statuette)	15	15
C 391.	5 e. "Kneeling Servant" (statuette)	30	30
C 392.	10 e. Stylized pelican (carving)	60	60

The 1 e. is horiz.

1968. No. C 389 but inscr. "TOCADOR DE BOMBOLON" surch.

C 394.	50 c. on 2 e. multicoloured	10	10
C 395.	1 e. on 2 e. multicoloured	15	15

1969. National Defence.

C 398. C **65.**	50 c. multicoloured	10	10
C 399.	1 e. multicoloured	10	10
C 400.	2 e. multicoloured	10	10
C 401.	2 e. 50 multicoloured	15	15
C 402.	3 e. multicoloured	15	15
C 403.	4 e. multicoloured	20	20
C 404.	5 e. multicoloured	25	25
C 405.	8 e. multicoloured	40	40
C 406.	9 e. multicoloured	45	45
C 407.	10 e. multicoloured	50	50
C 408.	15 e. multicoloured	80	80

NOTE—30, 50 and 100 e. stamps in the same design were for fiscal use only.

C 72. Mother and Children.

1971.

C 415. C **72.**	50 c. multicoloured	10	10
C 416.	1 e. multicoloured	10	10
C 417.	2 e. multicoloured	15	15
C 418.	3 e. multicoloured	15	15
C 419.	4 e. multicoloured	20	15
C 420.	5 e. multicoloured	30	15
C 421.	10 e. multicoloured	50	50

Higher values were intended for fiscal use.

NEWSPAPER STAMP

1893. "Newspaper" key-type inscr. "GUINE".

N 50. V.	2½ r. brown	35	30

POSTAGE DUE STAMPS

1904. "Due" key-type inscr. "GUINE".

D 122. W.	5 r. green	30	25
D 123.	10 r. grey	30	25
D 124.	20 r. brown	30	25
D 125.	30 r. orange	50	30
D 126.	50 r. brown	50	30
D 127.	60 r. brown	1·25	1·00
D 128.	100 r. mauve	1·25	1·00
D 129.	130 r. blue	1·25	1·00
D 130.	200 r. red	1·75	1·60
D 131.	500 r. lilac	4·50	2·50

1911. "Due" key-type of Portuguese Guinea optd. **REPUBLICA.**

D138 W 5 r. green 10 10
D139 10 r. grey 10 10
D140 20 r. brown 20 10
D141 30 r. orange 20 10
D142 50 r. brown 15 10
D143 60 r. brown 50 35
D208 100 r. mauve 65 55
D145 130 r. blue 85 70
D146 200 r. red 85 70
D147 500 r. lilac 60 55

1921. "Due" key-type of Portuguese Guinea. Currency changed.

D 244. W. ½ c. green 15 15
D 245. 1 c. grey 15 15
D 246. 2 c. brown 15 15
D 247. 3 c. orange 15 15
D 248. 5 c. brown 15 15
D 249. 6 c. brown 15 15
D 250. 10 c. mauve 20 20
D 251. 13 c. blue 20 20
D 252. 20 c. red 20 20
D 253. 50 c. grey 20 20

1925. Marquis de Pombal stamps, as Nos. C 247/9, optd. **MULTA.**

D 254. C 73. 30 c. red 30 35
D 255. – 30 c. red 30 25
D 256. C 75. 30 c. red 30 25

1952. As Type D 70 of Macao, but inscr. "GUINE PORTUGUESA". Numerals in red, name in black (except 2 e. in blue).

D 323. 10 c. green and pink .. 10 10
D 324. 30 c. violet and grey .. 10 10
D 325. 50 c. green and lemon .. 10 10
D 326. 1 e. blue and grey .. 10 10
D 327. 2 e. black and olive .. 20 20
D 328. 5 e. brown and orange 25 25

PORTUGUESE INDIA Pt. 9

Portuguese territories on the W. coast of India, consisting of Goa, Damao and Diu. Became part of India in December 1961.

1871. 1,000 reis = 1 milreis.
1882. 12 reis = 1 tanga. 16 tangas = 1 rupia.
1959. 100 centavos = 1 escudo.

1. 9.

1871. Perf.

35 1 10 r. black .. .. 3·00 2·50
33a 15 r. pink .. .. 5·00 4·50
26 20 r. red .. .. 5·00 4·00
21 40 r. blue .. .. 30·00 25·00
22 100 r. green .. .. 40·00 32·00
23 200 r. yellow .. .. £110 90·00
27 300 r. purple .. .. 60·00 50·00
28 600 r. purple .. .. 70·00 60·00
29 900 r. purple .. .. 70·00 65·00

1877. Star above value. Perf. or imperf.

241 9 1½ r. black 60 45
242 4½ r. olive .. .. 6·00 4·75
243 6 r. green .. .. 6·00 4·50
46 10 r. black .. .. 11·00 10·00
49 15 r. red .. .. 16·00 15·00
50 20 r. red .. .. 5·00 4·50
51 40 r. blue .. .. 9·00 6·50
52 100 r. green .. .. 40·00 35·00
53 200 r. yellow .. .. 45·00 38·00
54 300 r. purple .. .. 60·00 55·00
55 600 r. purple .. .. 60·00 55·00
56 900 r. purple .. .. 70·00 60·00

1877. "Crown" key-type inscr "INDIA PORTUGUEZA". Perf.

65 P 5 r. black .. .. 2·00 1·60
58 10 r. yellow .. .. 5·00 4·00
78 10 r. green .. .. 5·50 4·00
67 20 r. bistre .. .. 3·25 2·25
60 25 r. pink .. .. 5·00 4·00
79 25 r. grey .. .. 22·00 16·00
80 25 c. purple .. .. 15·00 12·00
69 40 r. blue .. .. 7·00 5·00
81 40 r. yellow .. .. 22·00 16·00
70 50 r. green .. .. 15·00 10·00
82 50 r. blue .. .. 10·00 8·50
71 100 r. lilac .. .. 6·00 5·00
64 200 r. orange .. .. 11·00 11·00
73 300 r. brown .. .. 12·00 12·00
See also Nos. 204/10.

1881. Surch. in figures.

213 1 1½ on 10 r. black .. — £140
89 1½ on 20 r. red .. .. 38·00 30·00
91 9 1½ on 20 r. red .. .. 70·00 50·00
219 1 4½ on 40 r. blue .. .. 10·00 10·00
223 4½ on 100 r. green .. 20·00 18·00
96 5 on 10 r. black .. 3·00 2·50
98 9 5 on 10 r. black .. 19·00 15·00
101 1 5 on 15 r. pink .. 1·00 1·00
106 5 on 20 r. red .. 1·00 1·00
108 9 5 on 20 r. red .. 2·50 2·50
224 1 6 on 20 r. red ..
228 6 on 100 r. green .. 85·00 70·00
231 6 on 200 r. yellow .. 65·00
233 9 6 on 200 r. yellow .. £250

1881. "Crown" key-type of Portuguese India surch. in figures.

109 P 1½ on 5 r. black .. 60 50
110 1½ on 10 r. green .. 70 50
111 1½ on 20 r. olive .. 5·50 4·00
157 1½ on 25 r. grey .. 16·00 12·00
158 1½ on 100 r. lilac .. 27·00 20·00
114 4½ on 5 r. black .. 3·75 3·00
115 4½ on 10 r. green .. 70·00 60·00
116 4½ on 20 r. olive .. 1·40 1·25
162 4½ on 25 r. purple .. 4·50 4·00
118 4½ on 100 r. lilac .. 50·00 40·00
164 6 on 10 r. yellow .. 22·00 17·00
120 6 on 10 r. green .. 3·75 3·00
121 6 on 20 r. olive .. 7·00 5·00
167 6 on 25 r. grey .. 13·00 9·50
168 6 on 25 r. purple .. 1·40 1·00
169 6 on 40 r. blue .. 45·00 35·00
170 6 on 40 r. yellow .. 17·00 14·00
171 6 on 50 r. green .. 23·00 18·00
127 6 on 50 r. blue .. 25·00 22·00
128 1 t. on 10 r. green .. 70·00 60·00
129 1 t. on 20 r. olive .. 21·00 19·00
175 1 t. on 25 r. grey .. 14·00 13·00
176 1 t. on 25 r. purple .. 4·50 3·25
132 1 t. on 40 r. blue .. 8·00 6·00
178 1 t. on 50 r. green .. 20·00 16·00
134 1 t. on 50 r. blue .. 10·00 8·50
136 1 t. on 100 r. lilac .. 8·00 6·00
137 1 t. on 200 r. orange .. 18·00 15·00
139 2 t. on 25 r. purple .. 6·00 4·50
182 2 t. on 25 r. grey .. 14·00 12·00
184 2 t. on 40 r. blue .. 17·00 15·00
141 2 t. on 40 r. yellow .. 18·00 16·00
186 2 t. on 50 r. green .. 7·50 5·00
187 2 t. on 50 r. blue .. 40·00 32·00
144 2 t. on 100 r. lilac .. 5·00 4·00
188 2 t. on 200 r. orange .. 14·00 12·00
189 2 t. on 300 r. brown .. 14·00 12·00
190 4 t. on 10 r. green .. 5·50 4·50
191 4 t. on 50 r. green .. 4·50 5·00
192 4 t. on 200 r. orange .. 18·00 15·00
193 8 t. on 20 r. olive .. 15·00 11·00
194 8 t. on 25 r. red .. 75·00 65·00
151 8 t. on 40 r. blue .. 20·00 15·00
196 8 t. on 100 r. lilac .. 20·00 16·00
197 8 t. on 200 r. orange .. 14·00 11·00
198 8 t. on 300 r. brown .. 17·00 15·00

1882. "Crown" key-type of Portuguese India.

204II. P. 1½ r. black 25 20
205I. 4½ r. olive 25 20
206I. 6 r. green 25 20
207I. 1 t. red 30 20
208I. 2 t. blue 30 20
209I. 4 t. purple .. .. 1·40 1·25
210I. 8 t. orange .. .. 1·40 1·25

1886. "Embossed" key-type inscr. "INDIA PORTUGUEZA".

244. Q. 1½ r. black 90 65
245. 4½ r. olive .. .. 1·00 75
246. 6 r. green .. .. 1·25 85
247. 1 t. red .. .. 1·75 1·25
248. 2 t. blue .. .. 3·50 2·00
249. 4 t. lilac .. .. 3·50 2·00
250. 8 t. orange .. .. 3·25 2·00

1895. "Figures" key-type inscr. "INDIA".

271. R. 1½ r. black 30 20
259. 4½ r. orange 45 25
273. 6 r. green 50 25
274. 9 r. lilac .. .. 1·75 1·50
260. 1 t. blue 70 45
261. 2 t. red 65 35
262. 4 t. blue 80 50
270. 8 t. lilac .. .. 1·60 80

1898. As Vasco da Gama stamps of Portugal T 40, etc., but inscr. "INDIA".

275. 1½ r. green 35 25
276. 4½ r. red 35 25
277. 6 r. purple 45 30
278. 9 r. green 60 40
279. 1 t. blue 75 55
280. 2 t. brown 80 70
281. 4 t. brown .. .. 1·00 75
282. 8 t. bistre .. .. 1·60 1·10

1898. "King Carlos" key-type inscr. "INDIA".

323. S. 1 r. grey 15 15
283. 1½ r. orange 15 15
324. 1½ r. grey 20 10
325. 2 r. orange 15 15
326. 2½ r. brown 20 15
327. 3 r. blue 20 15
284. 4½ r. green 50 30
285. 6 r. brown 50 30
328. 6 r. green 20 15
286. 9 r. lilac 50 30
287. 1 t. green 50 20
329. 1 t. red 20 15
288. 2 t. blue 50 20
330. 2 t. brown 80 40
331. 2½ t. blue .. .. 2·75 2·00
289. 4 t. blue on blue .. 1·25 55
332. 5 t. brown on yellow .. 1·00 60
290. 8 t. purple on pink .. 1·00 70
291. 12 t. blue on pink .. 1·40 1·00
334. 12 t. green on pink .. 2·25 1·25
292. 1 rp. black on blue .. 2·50 1·75
335. 1 rp. blue on yellow .. 5·00 2·25
293. 2 rp. mauve on yellow .. 4·50 2·50
336. 2 rp. black on yellow .. 7·50 8·00

1900. No. 288 surch. **1½ Reis.**

295. S. 1½ r. on 2 t. blue .. 80 50

1902. Surch.

299. R. 1 r. on 6 r. green .. 25 15
298. Q. 1 r. on 2 t. blue .. 30 20
300. 2 r. on 4½ r. olive .. 20 15
301. R. 2 r. on 8 t. lilac .. 25 15
302. Q. 2½ r. on 6 r. green .. 25 15
303. R. 2½ r. on 9 r. lilac .. 25 15
305. 3 r. on 4½ r. orange .. 60 40
304. Q. 3 r. on 1 t. red 20 15
306. R. 3 r. on 1 t. blue .. 50 50
337. S. 2 t. on 2½ t. blue .. 80 70
307. Q. 2½ t. on 1½ r. black .. 70 60
312. R. 2½ t. on 1½ r. black .. 70 40
309. Q. 2½ t. on 4 t. lilac .. 70 50
315. R. 5 t. on 2 t. red 70 50
317. 5 t. on 4 t. blue .. 70 50
314. Q. 5 t. on 8 t. orange .. 40 30

1902. Optd. **PROVISORIO.**

319. S. 6 r. brown (No. 285) .. 80 60
320. 1 t. green (No. 287) .. 80 60
321. 2 t. blue (No. 288) .. 80 60

1911. "King Carlos" key-type of Portuguese India, optd. **REPUBLICA**

338 S 1 r. grey 15 15
339 1½ r. grey 15 15
340 2 r. orange 15 15
341 2½ r. brown 20 15
342 3 r. blue 20 15
343 4½ r. green 20 15
344 6 r. green 15 15
345 9 r. lilac 20 15
346 1 t. red 30 15
347 2 t. brown 30 15
348 4 t. blue on blue .. 60 50
349 5 t. brown on yellow .. 70 50
350 8 t. purple on pink .. 2·00 1·10
402 12 t. green on rose .. 1·25 1·25
352 1 rp. blue on yellow .. 2·75 2·00
353 2 rp. black on yellow .. 3·75 3·00
404 2 rp. mauve on yellow .. 4·00 3·00

Both unused and used prices for the following three issues (Nos. 371 to 386) are for entire stamps showing both halves.

1911. "King Carlos" key-type of Portuguese India bisected by perforation, and each half surch.

371. S. 1 r. on 2 r. orange .. 15 15
372. 1 r. on 1 t. red .. 15 15
378. 1 r. on 5 t. brown on yell. 1·00 90
374. 1½ r. on 2½ r. brown .. 30 25
354. 1½ r. on 4½ r. green .. 6·00 3·00
355. 1½ r. on 9 r. lilac .. 25 20
356. 1½ r. on 4 t. blue on blue 25 20
375. 2 r. on 2½ r. brown .. 25 20
357. 2 r. on 4 t. blue on blue 40 25
376. 3 r. on 2½ r. brown .. 25 20
377. 3 r. on 2 t. brown .. 30 25
358. 6 r. on 4½ r. green .. 35 30
359d. 6 r. on 9 r. lilac .. 25 20
379. 6 r. on 8 t. purple on pink 60 45

1912. Stamps of 1902 bisected by perf., and each half surch.

360. S. 1 r. on 5 t. on 2 t. red .. 3·25 3·00
361. 1 r. on 5 t. on 4 t. blue .. 3·00 2·25
363. Q. 1 r. on 5 t. on 8 t. orange 1·00 75
364. 2 r. on 2½ r. on 6 r. green 1·25 1·00
365. R. 2 r. on 2½ r. on 9 r. lilac 7·00 7·00
366. 3 r. on 5 t. on 2 t. red .. 3·00 2·25
367. 3 r. on 5 t. on 4 t. blue .. 2·00 2·25
370. Q. 3 r. on 5 t. on 8 t. orange 80 60

1912 "King Carlos" key-type of Portuguese India, optd **REPUBLICA**, bisected by perf, and each half surch.

380 S 1 r. on 1 r. grey 15 15
381 1 r. on 2 r. orange .. 15 15
382 1 r. on 1 t. red 15 15
383 1 r. on 5 t. brown on yell 15 15
384 1½ r. on 4½ r. green .. 20 15
419 3 r. on 2 t. brown .. 1·10 90
420 6 r. on 4½ r. green .. 40 25
386 6 r. on 9 r. lilac 20 20
422 6 r. on 8 t. purple on pink 65 55

1913. Nos. 275/82 optd. **REPUBLICA.**

389. 1½ r. green 25 15
390. 4½ r. red 25 25
391. 6 r. purple 25 20
392. 9 r. green 25 20
393. 1 t. blue 40 20
394. 2 t. brown 80 15
395. 4 t. brown 50 25
396. 8 t. bistre 85 40

1914. Stamps of 1902 optd. **REPUBLICA.**

406 R 2 r. on 8 t. lilac .. 2·75 2·25
407 Q 2½ r. on 6 r. green .. 40 30
459 S 2 t. on 2½ t. blue .. 80 45
408 R 5 t. on 2 t. red .. .. 1·25 1·00
410 5 t. on 4 t. blue .. 1·25 1·00
460 Q 5 t. on 8 t. orange .. 85 70

1914. Nos. 320/1 optd. **REPUBLICA.**

415. S. 1 t. green .. .. 3·00 2·25
458. 2 t. blue 55 55

1914. "King Carlos" key-type of Portuguese India optd. **REPUBLICA** and surch.

423. S. 1½ r. on 4½ r. green .. 20 20
424. 1½ r. on 9 r. lilac .. 30 20
425. 1½ r. on 12 t. grn. on pink 40 25
426. 3 r. on 1 t. red .. 25 20
427. 3 r. on 2 t. brown .. 1·00 90
428. 3 r. on 8 t. purple on pink 70 60
429. 3 r. on 1 rp. blue on yellow 30 20
430. 3 r. on 2 rp. blk. on yellow 40 30

1914. Nos. 390 and 392/6 surch.

433. 1½ on 4½ r. red .. 20 20
434. 1½ r. on 9 r. green .. 25 20
435. 3 r. on 1 t. blue .. 25 20
436. 3 r. on 2 t. brown .. 40 30
437. 3 r. on 4 t. brown .. 20 15
438. 3 r. on 8 t. bistre .. 80 60

1914. "Ceres" key-type inscr. "INDIA".

439 U 1 r. olive 25 20
440 1½ r. green 25 20
441 2 r. black 25 20
442 2½ r. green 35 20
443 3 r. lilac 35 20
474 4 r. blue 70 60
444 4½ r. brown 35 20
445 5 r. green 35 20
446 6 r. brown 35 20
447 9 r. blue 35 20
448 10 r. red 45 25
468 1 t. violet 35 35
481 1½ t. green 70 40
469 2 t. blue 80 45
483 2½ t. blue 70 40
451 3 t. brown .. .. 1·25 35
484 3 t. 4 brown .. .. 2·25 2·00
452 4 t. grey 85 55
453 8 t. red .. .. 2·00 1·50
454 12 t. brown on green 2·00 1·50
455 1 rup. brown on red .. 7·00 6·50
487 1 rup. brown .. .. 9·00 7·00
456 2 rup. orange on pink .. 5·50 4·50
488 2 rup. yellow .. .. 9·00 7·00
457 3 rup. green on blue .. 6·00 4·00
489 3 rup. green .. .. 13·00 12·00
490 5 rup. red .. .. 14·00 13·00

1922. "Ceres" key-type of Portuguese India surch. with new value.

496. U. 1½ r. on 8 t. red .. 50 30
492. 1½ r. on 2 r. black .. 25 20
497. 2½ t. on 3 t. 4 brown .. 6·50 5·00

34. Vasco da Gama and Flagship "Sao Gabriel".

1925. 400th Death Anniv of Vasco da Gama. No gum.

493. 34. 6 r. brown .. .. 1·75 1·25
494. 1 t. purple .. .. 2·25 1·25

36. The Signature of Francis. 40. "Portugal" and "Galeasse".

1931. St. Francis Xavier Exhibition.

498. – 1 r. green 40 35
499. 36. 2 r. brown 40 35
500. – 6 r. purple 70 40
501. – 1½ t. brown .. .. 2·00 1·00
502. – 2 t. blue .. .. 3·50 2·25
503. – 2½ t. red .. .. 5·50 2·50

DESIGNS—VERT. 1 r. Monument to St. Francis. 6 r. St. Francis. 1½ t. St. Francis and Cross. 2½ t. St. Francis' Tomb. HORIZ. 2 t. Bom Jesus Church, Goa.

1933.

504. 40. 1 r. brown 15 10
505. 2 r. brown 15 10
506. 4 r. mauve 15 10
507. 6 r. green 15 10
508 8 r. black 20 15
509. 1 t. grey 20 20
510. 1½ t. red 20 15
511. 2 t. brown 20 25
512. 2½ t. blue 90 25
513. 3 t. blue 95 25
514. 5 t. orange .. .. 1·10 25
515. 1 rp. olive .. .. 2·75 1·10
516. 2 rp. red .. .. 5·25 2·50
517. 3 rp. orange .. .. 6·75 4·25
518. 5 rp. green .. .. 13·50 12·00

1938. As T 54 and 56 of Macao, but inscr. "ESTADO DA INDIA".

519. 54. 1 r. olive (postage) .. 15 15
520. 2 r. brown 15 15
521. 3 r. violet 15 15
522. 6 r. green 15 15
523. – 10 r. red 20 20
524. – 1 t. mauve 20 20
525. – 1½ t. red 20 20
526. – 2 t. orange 20 20
527. – 2½ t. blue 20 20
528. – 3 t. grey 40 20
529. – 5 t. purple 70 20
530. – 1 rp. red .. .. 1·60 35
531. – 2 rp. olive .. .. 3·00 1·40
532. – 3 rp. blue .. .. 5·00 2·75
533. – 5 rp. brown .. .. 11·00 3·50

DESIGNS: 2 t. to 3 t. Prince Henry the Navigator. 5 t. to 2 rp. Dam. 3, 5 rp. Alfonso de Albuquerque.

534. 56. 1 t. red (air) 20 15
535. 2½ t. violet 30 15
536. 3½ t. orange 30 15
537. 4½ t. blue 45 30
538. 7 t. red 45 30
539. 7½ t. green 80 35
540. 9 t. brown 2·00 85
541. 11 t. mauve 2·25 85

1942. Surch.
549. 40. 1 r. on 8 r. black 40 40
546. 1 r. on 5 t. orange 40 40
550. 2 r. on 8 r. black 40 30
547. 3 r. on 1½ t. red 40 30
551. 3 r. on 2 t. brown 40 80
552. 3 r. on 3 rp. orange 1·00 90
553. 6 r. on 2½ t. blue 1·25 1·00
554. 6 r. on 3 t. blue 1·25 1·00
542. 1 t. on 1½ t. red 1·40 1·25
548. 1 t. on 2 t. brown 1·40 1·25
543. 1 t. on 1 rp. olive 1·40 1·25
544. 1 t. on 2 rp. red 1·40 1·25
545. 1 t. on 5 rp. green 1·40 1·25

48. St. Francis Xavier. **50.** D. Joao de Castro. **53.** Our Lady of Fatima.

1946. Portraits and view.
555. 48. 1 r. black 15 15
556. – 2 r. red 15 15
557. – 6 r. bistre 15 15
558. – 7 r. violet 20 20
559. – 9 r. brown 50 20
560. – 1 t. green 50 20
561. – 3½ t. blue 60 45
562. – 1 rp. brown 1·50 50
DESIGNS: 2 r. Luis de Camoens. 6 r. Garcia de Orta. 7 r. Beato Joao Brito. 9 r. Viceregal Archway. 1 t. Afonso de Albuquerque. 3½ t. Vasco da Gama. 1 rp. D. Francisco de Almeida.

1948. Portraits.
564. 50. 3 r. blue 50 30
565. – 1 t. green 50 40
566. – 1½ t. violet 80 45
567. – 2½ t. red 1·25 90
568. – 7½ t. brown 1·75 1·40
PORTRAITS: 1 t. St. Francis Xavier. 1½ t. P. Jose Vaz. 2½ t. D. Luis de Ataide. 7½ t. Duarte Pacheco Pereira.

1948. Statue of Our Lady of Fatima. As T 62 of Macao.
570. 1 t. green 1·75 1·40

1949. Statue of Our Lady of Fatima.
571 53 1 r. blue 50 30
572 3 r. yellow 50 30
573 9 r. pink 1·75 30
574 2 t. green 2·50 30
575 9 t. orange 2·25 90
576 2 rp. brown 4·00 1·40
577 5 rp. olive and black 7·50 2·00
578 8 rp. violet and blue 16·00 6·50

1949. 75th Anniv. of U.P.U. As T 64 of Macao.
579. 2½ t. red 1·50 1·10

1950. Holy Year. As Nos. 425/6 of Macao.
580 65 1 r. bistre 40 20
588 1 r. red 10 10
589 2 r. green 20 15
590 – 3 r. brown 20 15
591 65 6 r. grey 20 15
592 – 9 r. mauve 40 30
593 65 1 t. blue 40 30
581 – 2 t. green 55 35
594 – 2 t. yellow 40 30
595 65 4 t. brown 40 30

1950. Nos. 523 and 527 surch.
582. 1 real on 10 r. red 15 10
583. 1 real on 2½ t. blue 15 15
584. 2 reis on 10 r. red 15 10
585. 3 reis on 2½ t. blue 15 15
586. 6 reis on 2½ t. blue 15 15
587. 1 tanga on 2½ t. blue 15 15

1951. Termination of Holy Year. As T 69 of Macao.
596. 1 rp. blue and lavender 80 60

59. Father Jose Vaz. **60.** Goa Medical School.

1951. 300th Birth Anniv. of Jose Vaz.
597. 59. 1 r. grey 10 10
598. – 2 r. orange and brown 10 10
599. 59. 3 r. black 25 15
600. – 1 t. blue and indigo 10 10
601. 59. 2 t. red 10 10
602. – 3 t. olive and black 20 10
603. 59. 9 t. blue and indigo 30 20
604. – 10 t. mauve 40 30
605. – 12 t. sepia and black 60 50
DESIGNS—Inscr. "1651 1951": 2 r., 1 t., 3 t., 10 t. Sancoale Church Ruins. 12 t. Veneravel Altar.

1952. 1st Tropical Medicine Congress, Lisbon.
606. 60. 4½ t. blue and black 1·40 1·25

1952. 4th Death Cent. of St. Francis Xavier. As Nos. 452/4 of Macao but without lined background.
607. 6 r. multicoloured 15 10
608. 2 t. multicoloured 75 30
609. 5 t. olive, silver and mauve 1·40 50

62. St. Francis Xavier. **63.** Stamp of 1871. **64.** The Virgin.

1952. Philatelic Exn., Goa.
612. 63. 3 t. black 4·00 4·00
613. 62. 5 t. black and lilac 4·00 4·00

1953. Missionary Art Exn.
614. 64. 6 r. black and blue 10 10
615. 1 t. brown and buff 35 20
616. 3 t. lilac and olive 1·00 80

1953. Portuguese Postage Stamp Cent. As T 75 of Macao.
617 1 t. multicoloured 35 30

66. Dr. Gama Pinto. **67.** Academy Buildings.

1954. Birth Cent. of Dr. Gama Pinto.
618. 66. 3 r. green and grey 10 10
619. 2 t. black and blue 15 15

1954. 4th Cent. of Sao Paulo. As T 76 of Macao.
620 2 t. multicoloured 20 20

1954. Centenary of Afonso de Albuquerque National Academy.
621. 67. 9 t. multicoloured 45 30

68. Mgr. Dalgado.

71. M. A. de Sousa.

73. Map of Becaim.

72. F. de Almeida.

1955. Birth Cent. of Mgr. Dalgado.
622. 68. 1 r. multicoloured 10 10
623. 1 t. multicoloured 20 10

1956. 450th Anniv. of Portuguese Settlements in India. Multicoloured.
(a) Famous Men. As T 71.
624. 6 r. M. A. de Sousa 15 15
625. 1½ t. F. N. Xavier 15 15
626. 4 t. A. V. Lourenco 15 15
627. 8 t. Father Jose Vaz 20 15
628. 9 t. M. G. de Heredia 25 15
629. 2 rp. A. C. Pacheco 75 60

(b) Viceroys. As T 72.
630. 3 r. F. de Almeida 10 10
631. 9 r. A. de Albuquerque 15 15
632. 1 t. Vasco da Gama 15 15
633. 3 t. N. da Cunha 20 15
634. 10 t. J. de Castro 20 15
635. 3 rp. C. de Braganca 90 60

(c) Settlements. As T 73.
636. 2 t. Bacaim 1·40 1·00
637. 2½ t. Mombaim 90 60
638. 3½ t. Damao 90 60
639. 5 t. Diu 35 25
640. 12 t. Cochim 50 45
641. 1 rp. Goa 1·25 1·00

74. Map of Damao. Dadra and Nagar Aveli Districts. **75.** Arms of Vasco da Gama.

1957. Centres multicoloured.
642. 74. 3 r. grey 10 10
643. 6 r. green 10 10
644. 3 t. pink 15 15
645. 6 t. blue 15 15
646. 11 t. bistre 35 25
647. 2 rp. lilac 65 50
648. 3 rp. yellow 90 75
649. 5 rp. red 1·40 1·00

1958. Heraldic Arms of Famous Men. Multicoloured designs.
650. 2 r. Type 75 10 10
651. 6 r. Lopo Soares de Albergaria 10 10
652. 9 r. D. Francisco de Almeida 10 10
653. 1 t. Garcia de Noronha 10 10
654. 4 t. D. Afonso de Albuquerque 15 15
655. 5 t. D. Joao de Castro 20 15
656. 11 t. D. Luis de Ataide 30 30
657. 1 rp. Nuno da Cunha 35 30

1958. 6th Int. Congress of Tropical Medicine. As T 79 of Macao.
658. 5 t. multicoloured 40 30
DESIGN: 5 t. "Holarrhena antidysenterica" (plant).

1958. Brussels Int. Exn. As T 78 of Macao.
659. 1 rp. multicoloured 20 20

1959. Surch. in new currency
660. – 5 c. on 2 r. (No. 650) 10 10
661. 74. 10 c. on 3 r. grey 10 10
662. – 15 c. on 6 r. (No. 651) 10 10
663. – 20 c. on 9 r. (No. 652) 10 10
664. – 30 c. on 1 t. (No. 653) 10 10
681. – 40 c. on 1½ t. (No. 566) 10 10
682. – 40 c. on 1½ t. (No. 625) 10 10
683. – 40 c. on 2 t. (No. 620) 25 15
665. – 40 c. on 2 t. (No. 636) 10 10
666. – 40 c. on 2½ t. (No. 637) 25 20
667. – 40 c. on 3½ t. (No. 638) 15 15
668. 74. 50 c. on 3 t. pink 15 15
684. 64. 80 c. on 3 t. lilac & olive 15 15
669. – 80 c. on 3 t. (No. 633) 15 15
685. – 80 c. on 3½ t. (No. 561) 15 15
686. – 80 c. on 5 t. (No. 658) 35 15
670. – 80 c. on 10 t. (No. 634) 20 20
687. – 80 c. on 1 rp. (No. 659) 85 40
671. – 80 c. on 3 rp. (No. 635) 35 20
672. – 1 e. on 4 t. (No. 654) 15 15
673. – 1 e. 50 on 5 t. (No. 655) 15 15
674. 74. 2 e. on 6 t. blue 15 15
675. 2 e. 50 on 11 t. bistre 20 10
676. – 4 e. on 11 t. (No. 656) 25 25
677. – 4 e. 50 on 1 rp. (No. 657) 35 30
678. 74. 5 e. on 2 rp. lilac 35 40
679. 10 e. on 3 rp. yellow 50 45
680. 30 e. on 5 rp. red 1·75 45

78. Coin of Manoel I. **79.** Prince Henry's Arms.

1959. Portuguese Indian Coins. Designs showing both sides of coins of various rulers. Multicoloured.
688 5 c. Type 78 10* 10
689 10 c. Joao III 10* 10
690 15 c. Sebastiao 10* 10
691 30 c. Filipe I 15 15
692 40 c. Filipe II 15 15
693 50 c. Filipe III 10 10
694 60 c. Joao IV 10 10
695 80 c. Afonso VI 10 10
696 1 e. Pedro II 10 10
697 1 e. 50 Joao V 10 10
698 2 e. Jose I 20 10
699 2 e. 50 Maria I 20 10
700 3 e. Prince Regent Joao 20 15
701 4 e. Pedro IV 25 20
702 4 e. 40 Miguel 25 20
703 5 e. Maria II 25 20
704 10 e. Pedro V 45 40
705 20 e. Luis 1·40 1·25
706 30 e. Carlos 1·75 1·60
707 50 e. Portuguese Republic 3·00 2·25

1960. 500th Death Anniv. of Prince Henry the Navigator.
708. 79. 3 e. multicoloured 25 25

The 1962 sports set and malaria eradication stamp similar to those for the other territories were ready for issue when Portuguese India was occupied but they were not put on sale there.

CHARITY TAX STAMPS

The notes under this heading in Portugal also apply here.

1919. Fiscal stamp. Type C 1 of Portuguese Africa optd. **TAXA DE GUERRA.**
C 491. Rps. 0:00:05, 48 green 1·25 1·00
C 492. Rps. 0:02:03, 43 green 2·25 1·75

1925. Marquis de Pombal Commem. stamps of Portugal, but inscr. "INDIA".
C 495. C 73. 6 r. red 20 20
C 496. – 6 r. red 20 20
C 497. C 75. 6 r. red 20 20

C 52. Mother and Child. **C 69.** Mother and Child.

1948. (a) Inscr. "ASSISTENCIA PUBLICA".
C571 C 52 6 r. green 1·25 75
C572 6 r. yellow 1·00 60
C573 1 t. red 1·25 75
C574 1 t. orange 1·10 60
C575 1 t. green 1·50 1·00
(b) Inscr. "PROVEDORIA DE ASSISTENCIA PUBLICA".
C607 C 52 1 t. grey 1·25 75

1951. Surch **1 tanga**.
C606 C 52 1 t. on 6 r. red 1·00 70

1953. Optd **"Revalidado" P.A.P.** and dotted line.
C617 C 52 1 t. red 3·00 1·75

1953. Surch as in Type C 69.
C624 C 69 1 t. on 4 t. blue 3·50 2·75

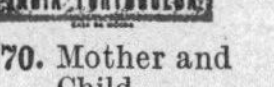

C 70. Mother and Child. **C 80.** Arms and People.

1956.
C 625. C 70. 1 t. black, green & red 30 20
C 626. 1 t. blue, salmon & grn. 30 20

1957. Surch.
C 650. C 70. 6 r. on 1 t. black, green and red 30 20

1959. Surch.
C 688. C 70. 20 c. on 1 t. blue, salmon and green 15 15
C 689. 40 c. on 1 t. blue, salmon and green 15 15

1960.
C 709. C 80. 20 c. brown and red 15 15

POSTAGE DUE STAMPS

1904. "Due" key-type inscr. "INDIA".
D 337. W. 2 r. green 25 25
D 338. 3 r. green 25 25
D 339. 4 r. orange 25 25
D 340. 5 r. black 25 25
D 341. 6 r. grey 25 25
D 342. 9 r. brown 25 25
D 343. 1 t. orange 30 25
D 344. 2 t. brown 65 45
D 345. 5 t. blue 1·40 1·25
D 346. 10 t. red 1·40 1·25
D 347. 1 rp. lilac 4·50 3·25

1911. Nos. D 337/47 optd. **REPUBLICA.**
D 354. W. 2 r. green 15 15
D 355. 3 r. green 15 15
D 356. 4 r. orange 15 15
D 357. 5 r. black 15 15
D 358. 6 r. grey 15 15
D 359. 9 r. brown 15 15
D 360. 1 t. orange 15 15
D 361. 2 t. brown 40 30
D 362. 5 t. blue 80 60
D 363. 10 t. red .. .. 1·25 1·10
D 364. 1 rp. lilac .. .. 3·50 1·50

1925. Marquis de Pombal stamps, as Nos. C 495/7, optd. **MULTA.**
D 495. C **73.** 1 t. red 20 20
D 496. – 1 t. red 20 20
D 497. C **75.** 1 t. red 20 20

1943. Stamps of 1933 surch. **Porteado** and new value.
D 549. **40.** 3 r. on 2½ t. blue .. 20 20
D 550. 6 r. on 3 t. blue .. 30 30
D 551. 1 t. on 5 t. orange .. 45 45

1945. As Type D 1 of Portuguese Colonies, but optd. **ESTADO DA INDIA.**
D 555. 2 r. red 40 40
D 556. 3 r. blue 40 40
D 557. 4 r. yellow 40 40
D 558. 6 r. green 40 40
D 559. 1 t. brown 40 40
D 560. 2 t. brown 40 40

1951. Surch. **Porteado** and new value and bar.
D 588. 2 rs. on 7 r. (No. 558) .. 20 20
D 589. 3 rs. on 7 r. (No. 558) .. 20 20
D 590. 1 t. on 1 rp. (No. 562) .. 20 20
D 591. 2 t. on 1 rp. (No. 562) .. 20 20

1952. As Type D **70** of Macao, but inscr. "INDIA PORTUGUESA". Numerals in red, name in black.
D 606. 2 r. olive and brown .. 10 10
D 607. 3 r. black and green .. 10 10
D 608. 6 r. blue and turquoise 10 10
D 609. 1 t. red and grey .. 15 15
D 610. 2 t. orange, green & grey 25 25
D 611. 10 t. blue, grn. & yellow 85 85

1959. Nos. D 606/8 and D 610/11 surch. in new currency.
D 688. 5 c. on 2 r. olive & brown 10 10
D 689. 10 c. on 3 r. blk. & grn. 10 10
D 690. 15 c. on 6 r. blue & turq. 15 15
D 691. 60 c. on 2 t. orge, green and grey 55 55
D 692. 60 c. on 10 t. blue, green and yellow .. .. 1·10 1·10

PRUSSIA Pt. 7

Formerly a kingdom in the N. of Germany. In 1867 it became part of the North German Confederation.

1850. 12 pfenige = 1 silbergroschen. 30 silbergroschen = 1 thaler.
1867. 60 kreuzer = 1 gulden.

1. Friedrich Wilhelm IV. 3. 4.

1850. Imperf.
14. **1.** 4 pf. green .. .. 65·00 24·00
4. 6 pf. red .. .. 70·00 38·00
5. 1 sgr. black on red .. 80·00 4·75
16. 1 sgr. red .. .. 35·00 1·50
6. 2 sgr. black on blue .. 85·00 10·00
18. 2 sgr. blue .. .. 90·00 11·00
8. 3 sgr. black on yellow .. 85·00 8·00
21. 3 sgr. yellow .. .. 70·00 11·00

1861. Roul.
24. **3.** 3 pf. lilac .. .. .. 17·00 30·00
26. 4 pf. green .. .. 8·00 5·50
28. 6 pf. orange .. .. 6·50 12·00
31. **4.** 1 sgr. red .. .. 3·25 30
35. 2 sgr. blue .. .. 7·00 80
36. 3 sgr. brown .. .. 7·00 1·25

5. 7.

1866. Printed in reverse on back of specially treated transparent paper. Roul.
38. **5.** 10 sgr. red .. .. 50·00 65·00
39. – 30 sgr. blue .. .. 70·00 £170
The 30 sgr. has the value in a square.

1867. Roul.
40. **7.** 1 k. green .. .. .. 17·00 38·00
42. 2 k. orange .. .. 38·00 85·00
43. 3 k. red .. .. 16·00 18·00
45. 6 k. blue .. .. 16·00 40·00
46. 9 k. bistre .. .. 20·00 45·00

PUERTO RICO Pt. 9; Pt. 22

A W. Indian island, ceded by Spain to the United States after the war of 1898. Until 1873 stamps of Cuba were in use. Now uses stamps of the U.S.A.

1873. 100 centimos = 1 peseta.
1881. 1000 milesimas = 100 centavos = 1 peso.
1898. 100 cents = 1 dollar.

A. SPANISH OCCUPATION

(2.)

1873. Nos. 53/5 of Cuba optd. with T **2.**
1. 25 c. de p. lilac .. .. 25·00 1·25
3. 50 c. de p. brown .. .. 60·00 5·00
4. 1 p. brown .. .. .. £110 12·00

1874. No. 57 of Cuba with opt. similar to T **2.** (Two separate characters.)
5. 25 c. de p. blue .. .. 20·00 2·00

1875. Nos. 61/3 of Cuba with opt. similar to T **2.** (Two separate characters.)
6. 25 c. de p. blue .. .. 13·00 1·75
7. 50 c. de p. green .. .. 20·00 2·50
8. 1 p. brown .. .. 75·00 8·00

1876. Nos. 65a/7 of Cuba with opt. similar to T **2.** (Two separate characters.)
9. 25 c. de p. lilac .. .. 2·75 1·25
10. 50 c. de p. blue .. .. 7·50 2·25
11. 1 p. black .. .. 25·00 6·00

1876. Nos. 65a and 67 of Cuba with opt. as last, but characters joined.
12. 25 c. de p. lilac .. .. 8·00 1·10
13. 1 p. black .. .. 27·00 6·00

1877. As T **45** of Spain, but inscr "PTO-RICO 1877".
14. 5 c. brown .. .. .. 3·50 1·50
15. 10 c. red .. .. .. 12·00 1·75
16. 15 c. green .. .. 18·00 7·50
17. 25 c. blue .. .. 7·00 1·10
18. 50 c. brown .. .. 12·00 2·50

1878. As T **45** of Spain, but inscr "PTO-RICO 1878".
19. 5 c. olive .. .. .. 10·00 10·00
20. 10 c. brown .. .. £110 45·00
21. 25 c. green .. .. 1·00 80
22. 50 c. blue .. .. 4·00 1·25
23a. 1 p. brown .. .. 7·00 3·75

1879. As T **45** of Spain, but inscr "PTO-RICO 1879".
24. 5 c. red .. .. .. 6·50 2·75
25. 10 c. brown .. .. 6·50 2·50
26. 15 c. black .. .. 6·50 2·75
27. 25 c. blue .. .. 2·00 95
28. 50 c. green .. .. 6·00 2·25
29. 1 p. grey .. .. 25·00 10·00

1880. "Alfonso XII" key-type inscr. "PUERTO-RICO 1880".
30. X. ¼ c. green .. .. 15·00 8·00
31. ½ c. red .. .. 4·00 1·25
32. 1 c. red .. .. 6·00 4·00
33. 2 c. grey .. .. 4·00 2·00
34. 3 c. orange .. .. 4·00 2·00
35. 4 c. black .. .. 4·00 2·00
36. 5 c. green .. .. 2·00 90
37. 10 c. red .. .. 2·50 1·25
38. 15 c. brown .. .. 4·00 1·60
39. 25 c. lilac .. .. 2·00 70
40. 40 c. grey .. .. 6·00 85
41. 50 c. brown .. .. 12·00 6·50
42. 1 p. olive .. .. 38·00 8·00

1881. "Alfonso XII" key-type inscr. "PUERTO-RICO 1881".
43. X. ⅛ m. red 20 10
45. 1 m. violet 25 10
46. 2 m. red 35 25
47. 4 m. green 60 20
48. 6 m. red 60 30
49. 8 m. blue .. .. 1·40 60
50. 1 c. green .. .. 2·25 1·10
51. 2 c. red .. .. 2·75 1·75
52. 3 c. brown .. .. 6·50 2·75
53. 5 c. lilac .. .. 2·25 20
54. 8 c. brown .. .. 3·50 60
55. 10 c. lilac .. .. 15·00 4·50
56. 20 c. olive .. .. 22·00 6·00

1882. "Alfonso XII" key-type inscr "PUERTO-RICO".
57 X ½ m. red 15 10
74 1 m. red 15 10
75 1 m. orange 15 10
59 2 m. mauve 20 15
60 4 m. purple 20 15
61 6 m. brown 25 15
62 8 m. green 25 15
63 1 c. green 15 15
64 2 c. red 80 15
65 3 c. yellow .. .. 2·25 1·00
76 3 c. brown .. .. 2·25 30
77 5 c. lilac .. .. 8·00 1·00
67 8 c. brown .. .. 2·75 10
68 10 c. green .. .. 2·75 20
69 20 c. grey .. .. 3·25 20
70 40 c. blue .. .. 22·00 7·00
71 80 c. brown .. .. 32·00 8·00

1890. "Baby" key-type inscr "PUERTO-RICO".
95 Y ½ m. black 10 10
111 ½ m. brown 10 10
124 ½ m. purple 10 10
81 1 m. green 25 10
96 1 m. purple 10 10
112 1 m. blue 10 10
125 1 m. brown 10 10
113 2 m. red 10 10
97 2 m. purple 10 10
126 2 m. green 10 10
83 4 m. black .. .. 8·00 4·00
98 4 m. blue 10 10
114 4 m. brown 10 10
127 4 m. green 60 25
84 6 m. brown .. .. 25·00 9·00
99 6 m. red 10 10
85 8 m. bistre .. .. 25·00 18·00
100 8 m. green 10 10
86 1 c. brown 20 10
101 1 c. green 40 10
115 1 c. purple .. .. 2·75 15
128 1 c. red 30 10
87 2 c. purple .. .. 1·00 50
102 2 c. pink 70 10
116 2 c. lilac .. .. 1·00 15
129 2 c. brown 30 10
88 3 c. blue .. .. 6·00 40
103 3 c. orange 70 10
117 3 c. grey .. .. 2·50 15
131 3 c. brown 20 10
89 5 c. purple .. .. 8·00 30
104 5 c. green 60 10
133 5 c. blue 20 10
120 6 c. orange 25 10
134 6 c. lilac 20 10
90 8 c. blue .. .. 11·00 1·25
105 8 c. brown 15 10
121 8 c. purple .. .. 5·50 1·50
135 8 c. red .. .. 1·25 50
106 10 c. red 70 10
122 20 c. red 75 15
107 20 c. lilac .. .. 1·00 20
136 20 c. grey .. .. 3·25 50
93 40 c. orange .. .. 65·00 22·00
108 40 c. blue .. .. 2·75 1·10
137 40 c. red .. .. 3·25 1·25
94 80 c. green .. .. £200 90·00
109 80 c. red .. .. 6·50 3·00
138 80 c. black .. .. 17·00 8·50

13. Landing of Columbus.

1893. 400th Anniv of Discovery of America by Columbus.
110 13 3 c. green .. .. £100 28·00

1898. "Curly Head" key-type inscr. "PTO. RICO 1898 y 99".
139. Z. 1 m. brown 10 10
140. 2 m. brown 10 10
141. 3 m. brown 10 10
142. 4 m. brown .. .. 1·10 50
143. 5 m. brown 10 10
144. 1 c. violet 10 10
145. 2 c. green 10 10
146. 3 c. brown 10 10
147. 4 c. orange .. .. 1·10 60
148. 5 c. red 10 10
149. 6 c. blue 15 10
150. 8 c. brown 15 10
151. 10 c. red 15 10
152. 15 c. olive 15 10
153. 20 c. red .. .. 1·25 40
154. 40 c. lilac 90 90
155. 60 c. black 90 90
156. 80 c. brown .. .. 3·00 3·00
157. 1 p. green .. .. 5·50 5·00
158. 2 p. blue .. .. 12·00 6·00

1898. "Baby" key-type inscr. "PUERTO RICO" and optd. **Habilitado PARA 1898 y '99.**
159. Y. ½ m. purple .. .. 9·00 4·25
160. 1 m. brown 30 15
161. 2 m. green 30 15
162. 4 m. green 30 15
163. 1 c. red 30 15
164. 2 c. brown 30 15
165. 3 c. blue .. .. 10·00 6·00
166. 3 c. brown 35 10
167. 4 c. grey 35 25
168. 4 c. blue .. .. 9·00 5·00
169. 5 c. blue 30 25
171. 5 c. green .. .. 7·50 5·00
172. 6 c. lilac 30 20
173a. 8 c. red 30 15
174. 20 c. grey 75 40
175. 40 c. red .. .. 2·00 50
176. 80 c. black .. .. 15·00 12·00

WAR TAX STAMPS

1898. "Baby' key-type inscr "PUERTO RICO" and "Curly Head" key-type inscr "PTO. RICO 1898 y 99", optd **IMPUESTO DE GUERRA** or surch also.
W 177 Y 1 m. blue .. .. 2·25 1·25
W 178 1 m. brown .. .. 6·00 3·75
W 179 2 m. red .. .. 10·00 6·00
W 180 2 m. green .. .. 5·50 4·00
W 181 4 m. green .. .. 8·00 7·00
W 182a 1 c. brown .. .. 4·75 2·75
W 183 1 c. red .. .. 9·00 7·00
W 184 2 c. purple 30 20
W 185 2 c. red 30 20
W 186 2 c. lilac 60 60
W 187 2 c. brown 35 20
W 192 2 c. on 2 m. red .. 25 15
W 193c 2 c. on 5 c. green .. 1·75 1·60
W 188 3 c. orange .. .. 10·00 8·00
W 194 3 c. on 10 c. red .. 10·00 7·00
W 195 4 c. on 20 c. red .. 10·00 7·00
W 189 5 c. green 25 15
W 196a 5 c. on ½ m. brown .. 5·00 3·00
W 197 5 c. on 1 m. purple .. 40 40
W 198 5 c. on 1 m. blue .. 30 30
W 199 Z 5 c. on 1 m. brown .. 6·50 3·50
W 200 Y 5 c. on 5 c. green .. 3·25 2·50
W 191 8 c. purple .. .. 15·00 12·00

B. UNITED STATES OCCUPATION

1899. 1894 stamps of United States (No. 267 etc) optd **PORTO RICO.**
202 1 c. green .. .. .. 6·00 1·25
203 2 c. red .. .. .. 5·50 1·00
204 5 c. blue .. .. .. 8·50 1·75
205 8 c. brown .. .. 25·00 12·00
206 10 c. brown .. .. 18·00 3·75

1900. 1894 stamps of United States (No. 267 etc) optd **PUERTO RICO.**
210 1 c. green .. .. .. 5·00 1·25
212 2 c. red .. .. .. 4·50 90

POSTAGE DUE STAMPS

1899. Postage Due stamps of United States of 1894 optd. **PORTO RICO.**
D 207. D **87.** 1 c. red .. .. 18·00 6·00
D 208. 2 c. red .. .. 14·00 4·50
D 209. 10 c. red .. .. £130 42·00

QATAR Pt. 19

An independent Arab Shaikhdom with British postal administration until May 23, 1963, issues for which are listed in Volume 3. Later issues by the Qatar Post Department.

1964. 100 naye paise = 1 rupee.
1966. 100 dirhams = 1 riyal.

1964. Olympic Games, Tokyo. Optd. **1964** Olympic Rings and Arabic inscr. or surch. also.
38. **9.** 50 n.p. brown .. .. 1·75 1·25
39. – 75 n.p. blue (No. 33) .. 2·50 1·75
40. – 1 r. on 10 r. black (No. 37) 3·50 2·50
41. **11.** 2 r. blue .. .. 5·00 2·75
42. 5 r. green (No. 36) .. 9·00 7·50

1964. Pres. Kennedy Commem. Optd. **John F. Kennedy 1917-1963** in English and Arabic or surch. also.
43. **9.** 50 n.p. brown .. .. 1·75 1·25
44. – 75 n.p. blue (No. 33) .. 2·50 1·75
45. – 1 r. on 10 r. black (No. 37) 3·50 2·50
46. **11.** 2 r. blue .. .. 5·00 3·75
47. – 5 r. green (No. 36) .. 9·00 7·50

15. Colonnade, Temple of Isis. 16. Scouts on Parade.

1965. Nubian Monuments Preservation. Mult.
48. 1 n.p. Type **15** 10 10
49. 2 n.p. Temple of Isis, Philae 10 10
50. 3 n.p. Trajan's Kiosk, Philae 10 10
51. 1 r. As 3 n.p. 40 60
52. 1 r. 50 As 2 n.p. .. .. 2·50 1·25
53. 2 r. Type **15** .. .. 3·00 2·00

1965. Qatar Scouts.
54. – 1 n.p. brown and green .. 10 10
55. – 2 n.p. blue and brown .. 10 10
56. – 3 n.p. blue and green .. 10 10
57. – 4 n.p. brown and blue .. 10 10
58. – 5 n.p. blue and turquoise 10 10
59. **16.** 30 n.p. multicoloured .. 75 30
60. 40 n.p. multicoloured .. 1·25 45
61. 1 r. multicoloured .. 2·25 1·00

DESIGNS—TRIANGULAR (60 × 30 mm.): 1 n.p., 4 n.p. Qatar Scout badge. 2 n.p., 3 n.p., 5 n.p. Ruler, badge, palms and camp.

17. "Telstar" and Eiffel Tower.

1965. I.T.U. Cent.
62. **17.** 1 n.p. brown and blue .. 10 10
63. – 2 n.p. brown and blue .. 10 10
64. – 3 n.p. violet and green .. 10 10
65. – 4 n.p. blue and brown .. 10 10
66. **17.** 5 n.p. ochre and violet .. 10 10
67. – 40 n.p. black and red .. 1·50 70
68. – 50 n.p. ochre and green .. 1·50 70
69. – 1 r. red and green .. 2·50 1·25

DESIGNS: 2 n.p., 1 r. "Syncom 3" and pagoda. 3, 40 n.p. "Relay" and radar scanner. 4, 50 n.p. Post Office Tower (London), globe and satellites.

18. Triggerfish.

1965. Fish of the Arabian Gulf. Mult.
70. 1 n.p. Type **18** 10 10
71. 2 n.p. Butterfly sweetlip .. 10 10
72. 3 n.p. Saddle-spot butterfly fish 10 10
73. 4 n.p. Threadfin butterfly fish 10 10
74. 5 n.p. Mahomet's lancet fish 10 10
75. 15 n.p. Paradise fish .. 30 10
76. 20 n.p. Sailfin tang 35 10
77. 30 n.p. Thousand-spotted grouper 45 10
78. 40 n.p. Regal angelfish .. 60 15
79. 50 n.p. As 2 n.p. 90 30
80. 75 n.p. Type **18** .. .. 1·50 35
81. 1 r. As 30 n.p. .. .. 2·25 35
82. 2 r. As 20 n.p. .. .. 4·50 90
83. 3 r. As 15 n.p. .. .. 6·50 1·75
84. 4 r. As 5 n.p. .. .. 7·50 2·25
85. 5 r. As 4 n.p. .. .. 8·50 2·50
86. 10 r. As 3 n.p. .. .. 14·00 3·00

19. Basketball.

1966. Pan-Arab Games, Cairo (1965).
87. **19.** 1 r. black, grey and red .. 1·25 80
88. – 1 r. brown and green .. 1·25 80
89. – 1 r. red and blue .. .. 1·25 80
90. – 1 r. green and blue .. 1·25 80
91. – 1 r. blue and brown .. 1·25 80

SPORTS: No. 88, Horse-jumping. No. 89, Running. No. 90, Football. No. 91, Weight-lifting.

1966. Space Rendezvous. Nos. 62/9 opted. **SPACE RENDEZVOUS 15th DECEMBER 1965** in English and Arabic and two space capsules.
92. **17.** 1 n.p. brown and blue .. 10 10
93. – 2 n.p. brown and blue .. 10 10
94. – 3 n.p. violet and green .. 10 10
95. – 4 n.p. blue and brown .. 10 10
96. **17.** 5 n.p. ochre and violet .. 10 10
97. – 40 m.p. black and red .. 75 30
98. – 50 n.p. ochre and green .. 1·25 35
99. – 1 r. red and green .. 2·75 1·25

21. Shaikh Ahmed.

1966. Gold and Silver Coinage. Circular designs, embossed on gold (G) or silver (S) foil, backed with "Walsall Security Paper" inscr. in English and Arabic. Imperf.

(a) Diameter $1\frac{7}{16}$ in.
101. **21.** 1 n.p. bistre & purple (S) 10 10
102. – 3 n.p. black & orange (S) 10 10
103. **21.** 4 n.p. violet and red (G) 10 10
104. – 5 n.p. green & red (G) .. 10 10

(b) Diameter $2\frac{3}{16}$ in.
105. **21.** 10 n.p. brown & violet (S) 20 10
106. – 40 n.p. red & bl. (S) .. 1·00 20
107. **21.** 70 n.p. blue & ultram. (G) 1·75 40
108. – 80 n.p. red & green (G) .. 2·00 50

(c) Diameter $2\frac{3}{8}$ in.
109. **21.** 1 r. mauve & black (S) .. 2·25 50
110. – 2 r. green and purple (S) 6·00 1·50
111. **21.** 5 r. purple & orange (G) 11·00 3·25
112. – 10 r. blue & red (G) .. 17·00 6·50

The 1, 4, 10, 70 n.p. and 1 and 5 r. each show the obverse side of the coins as Type **21.** The remainder show the reverse side of the coins (Shaikh's seal).

22. I.C.Y. and U.N. Emblems.

23. Pres. Kennedy and New York Skyline.

1966. Int. Co-operation Year.
113. **22.** 40 n.p. brn., violet & blue 1·50 70
114. A. 40 n.p. violet, brn. & turq. 1·50 70
115. B. 40 n.p. blue, brn. & violet 1·50 70
116. C. 40 n.p. turq., violet & bl. 1·50 70

DESIGNS: A, Pres. Kennedy, I.C.Y. emblem and U.N. Headquarters. B, Dag Hammarskjold and U.N. General Assembly. C, Nehru and dove.

Nos. 113/6 were issued together in blocks of four, each sheet containing four blocks separated by gutter margins. Subsequently the sheets were reissued perf. and imperf. with the opt. **U.N. 20TH ANNIVERSARY** on the stamps. The gutter margins were also printed in various designs, face values and opt.

1966. Pres. Kennedy Commem. Multicoloured.
118. 10 n.p. Type **23** 25 10
119. 30 n.p. Pres. Kennedy and Cape Kennedy 50 15
120. 60 n.p. Pres. Kennedy and Statue of Liberty .. 1·00 35
121. 70 n.p. Type **23** .. .. 1·25 40
122. 80 n.p. As 30 n.p... .. 1·40 50
123. 1 r. As 60 n.p. .. .. 1·60 60

24. Horse-jumping.

1966. Olympic Games Preparation (Mexico). Multicoloured.
125. 1 n.p. Type **24** 10 10
126. 4 n.p. Running 10 10
127. 5 n.p. Throwing the javelin 10 10
128. 70 n.p. Type **24** 75 40
129. 80 n.p. Running 90 55
130. 90 n.p. Throwing the javelin 1·10 80

25. J. A. Lovell and Capsule.

1966. American Astronauts. Each design showing space-craft and Astronaut. Mult.
132. 5 n.p. Type **25** 10 10
133. 10 n.p. T. P. Stafford .. 15 10
134. 15 n.p. A. B. Shepard .. 25 10
135. 20 n.p. J. H. Glenn .. 25 10
136. 30 n.p. M. Scott Carpenter 40 20
137. 40 n.p. W. M. Schirra .. 55 20
138. 50 n.p. V. I. Grissom .. 70 35
139. 60 n.p. L. G. Cooper .. 90 45

Nos. 132/4 are diamond-shaped as Type **25,** the remainder are horiz. designs (56 × 25 mm.).

1966. Various stamps with currency names changed to dirhams and riyals by overprinting in English and Arabic.

(i) Nos. 27/37 (Definitives).
141. 5 d. on 5 n.p. 10 10
142. 15 d. on 15 n.p. 25 10
143. 20 d. on 20 n.p. 25 10
144. 30 d. on 30 n.p. 45 15
145. 40 d. on 40 n.p. .. .. 1·00 20
146. 50 d. on 50 n.p. .. .. 1·25 30
147. 75 d. on 75 n.p. .. .. 1·50 45
148. 1 r. on 1 r. .. .. 1·75 40
149. 2 r. on 2 r. .. .. 3·75 1·50
150. 5 r. on 5 r. .. .. 8·50 5·00
151. 10 r. on 10 r. .. .. 14·00 7·50

(ii) Nos. 70/86 (Fish).
152. 1 d. on 1 n.p. 10 10
153. 2 d. on 2 n.p. 10 10
154. 3 d. on 3 n.p. 10 10
155. 4 d. on 4 n.p. 10 10
156. 5 d. on 5 n.p. 10 10
157. 15 d. on 15 n.p. 25 10
158. 20 d. on 20 n.p. 30 10
159. 30 d. on 30 n.p. 45 15
160. 40 d. on 40 n.p. 60 15
161. 50 d. on 50 n.p. 75 20
162. 75 d. on 75 n.p. .. .. 1·25 40
163. 1 r. on 1 r. .. .. 1·50 50
164. 2 r. on 2 r. .. .. 3·25 1·50
165. 3 r. on 3 r. .. .. 5·00 2·75
166. 4 r. on 4 r. .. .. 7·00 4·00
167. 5 r. on 5 r. .. .. 9·00 4·75
168. 10 r. on 10 r. .. .. 15·00 9·00

27. National Library, Doha.

1966. Education Day. Multicoloured.
169. 2 n.p. Type **27** 10 10
170. 3 n.p. School and playing field 10 10
171. 5 n.p. School and gardens 10 10
172. 1 r. Type **27** .. .. 1·50 65
173. 2 r. As 3 n.p. .. .. 2·50 1·25
174. 3 r. As 5 n.p. .. .. 3·50 1·75

28. Palace, Doha.

29. Hands holding Jules Rimet Trophy.

1966. Currency expressed in naye paise and rupees. Multicoloured.
175. 2 n.p. Type **28** 10 10
176. 3 n.p. Gulf Street, Shahra Al-Khalij 10 10
177. 10 n.p. Doha airport .. 30 10
178. 15 n.p. Garden, Rayan .. 35 10
179. 20 n.p. Head Post Office, Doha 45 10
180. 30 n.p. Mosque, Doha (vert.) 50 10
181. 40 n.p. Shaikh Ahmad .. 85 15
182. 50 n.p. Type **28** 95 20
183. 60 n.p. As 3 n.p. .. .. 1·25 40
184. 70 n.p. As 10 n.p... .. 2·00 50
185. 80 n.p. As 15 n.p... .. 1·75 60
186. 90 n.p. As 20 n.p... .. 2·00 90
187. 1 r. As 30 n.p. (vert.) .. 2·25 70
188. 2 r. As 40 n.p. .. .. 4·00 2·25

1966. World Football Cup Championships, England.
189. **29.** 60 n.p. mult. (postage) 80 65
190. – 70 n.p. multicoloured .. 1·00 80
191. – 80 n.p. multicoloured .. 1·25 1·00
192. – 90 n.p. multicoloured .. 1·40 1·10
193. – 1 n.p. blue (air) .. 15 15
194. – 2 n.p. blue 15 15
195. – 3 n.p. blue 20 20
196. – 4 n.p. blue 20 30

DESIGNS: No. 190, Jules Rimet Trophy and "football" globe. No. 191, Footballers and globe. No. 192, Wembley stadium. Nos. 193/6, Jules Rimet Trophy.

30. A.P.U. Emblem.

32. Traffic Lights.

31. Astronauts on Moon.

1967. Admission of Qatar to Arab Postal Union.
198. **30.** 70 d. brown & violet .. 1·25 60
199. 80 d. brown & blue .. 1·50 80

1967. U.S. "Apollo" Space Missions. Mult.
200. 5 d. Type **31** 15 10
201. 10 d. "Apollo" spacecraft 20 10
202. 20 d. Landing module on Moon 30 10
203. 30 d. Blast-off from Moon 35 15
204. 40 d. "Saturn 5" rocket .. 40 20
205. 70 d. Type **31** 65 40
206. 80 d. As 10 d. 80 50
207. 1 r. As 20 d. 95 60
208. 1 r. 20 As 30 d. .. .. 1·40 85
209. 2 r. As 40 d. .. .. 2·25 1·25

1967. Traffic Day.
211. **32.** 20 d. multicoloured .. 55 10
212. 30 d. multicoloured .. 95 25
213. 50 d. multicoloured .. 1·60 55
214. 1 r. multicoloured .. 3·50 1·50

33. Brownsea Island and Jamboree Camp, Idaho.

1967. Diamond Jubilee of Scout Movement and World Scout Jamboree, Idaho. Mult.
215. 1 d. Type **33** 10 10
216. 2 d. Lord Baden-Powell .. 10 10
217. 3 d. Pony-trekking .. 10 10
218. 5 d. Canoeing 15 10
219. 15 d. Swimming 55 20
220. 75 d. Rock-climbing .. 1·75 80
221. 2 r. World Jamboree emblem 5·00 2·50

34. Norman Ship (from Bayeux tapestry).

1967. Famous Navigators' Ships. Mult.
222 1 d. Type **34** 10 10
223 2 d. "Santa Maria" (Columbus) 10 10
224 3 d. "Sao Gabriel" (Vasco da Gama) 10 10
225 75 d. "Vitoria" (Magellan) 1·90 80
226 1 r. "Golden Hind" (Drake) .. .. 2·25 1·00
227 2 r. "Gipsy Moth IV" (Chichester) .. .. 5·50 2·25

35. Arab Scribe.

1968. 10th Anniv. of Qatar Postage Stamps. Multicoloured.
228. 1 d. Type **35** 10 10
229. 2 d. Pigeon post (vert.) .. 10 10
230. 3 d. Mounted postman .. 10 10
231. 60 d. Rowing boat postman (vert.) .. .. 1·25 55
232. 1 r. 25 Camel postman .. 2·50 1·50
233. 2 r. Letter-writing and Qatar 1 n.p. stamp of 1957 .. .. .. 3·75 1·50

36. Human Rights Emblem and Barbed Wire.

1968. Human Rights Year. Multicoloured designs embodying Human Rights emblem.
234. 1 d. Type **36** 10 10
235. 2 d. Arab refugees .. 10 10
236. 3 d. Scales of justice .. 10 10
237. 60 d. Opening doors .. 1·00 45
238. 1 r. 25 Family (vert.) .. 1·75 85
239. 2 r. Human figures .. 2·50 1·50

37. Shaikh Ahmed. 39.

38. Dhow.

1968.

240. **37.** 5 d. green and blue .. 15 10
241. 10 d. brown and blue .. 15 10
242. 20 d. red and black .. 30 10
243. 25 d. green and purple 40 10
244. **38.** 35 d. grn., blue and pink 1·00 20
245. – 40 d. purple, bl. & orge. 75 15
246. – 60 d. brown, bl. & violet 2·25 30
247. – 70 d. black, blue & green 1·25 40
248. – 1 r. blue, yellow & green 1·50 40
249. – 1 r. 25 blue and flesh .. 2·75 65
250. – 1 r. 50 grn., blue & pur. 4·50 85
251. **39.** 2 r. blue, brn. & lt. brn. 4·25 1·00
252. 5 r. purple and green .. 9·00 3·00
253. 10 r. brn., ultram. & blue 16·00 6·00

DESIGNS: As Type **38**. 40 d. Water purification plant. 60 d. Oil jetty. 70 d. Qatar mosque. 1 r. Palace, Doha. 1 r. 25, Doha fort. 1 r. 50, Peregrine Falcon.

41. Maternity Ward.

1968. 20th Anniv of W.H.O. Multicoloured.

258 1 d. Type **41** 10 10
259 2 d. Operating theatre .. 10 10
260 3 d. Dental surgery .. 10 10
261 60 d. X-ray examination table .. .. .. 1·50 60
262 1 r. 25 Laboratory .. 2·75 1·40
263 2 r. State Hospital, Qatar 4·00 2·50

42. Throwing the Discus.

1968. Olympic Games. Mexico. Mult.

264. 1 d. Type **42** 10 10
265. 2 d. Olympic Flame and runner 10 10
266. 3 d. "68" Rings and gymnast 10 10
267. 60 d. Weightlifting and Flame 65 40
268. 1 r. 25 "Flame" in mosaic pattern (vert.) .. .. 1·40 80
269. 2 r. "Cock" emblem .. 2·00 1·50

43. U.N. Emblem and Flags.

1968. United Nations Day. Multicoloured.

270. 1 d. Type **43** 10 10
271. 4 d. Dove of Peace and world map 10 10
272. 5 d. U.N. Headquarters and flags 10 10
273. 60 d. Teacher and class .. 85 50
274. 1 r. 50 Agricultural workers 1·75 95
275. 2 r. U Thant and U.N. Assembly .. .. 2·75 1·50

44. Trawler "Ross Rayyan".

1969. Progress in Qatar. Multicoloured.

276. 1 d. Type **44** 10 10
277. 4 d. Primary school .. 10 10
278. 5 d. Doha International Airport 10 10
279. 60 d. Cement factory and road-making .. .. 1·25 60
280. 1 r. 50 Power station and pylon .. .. 2·75 1·40
281. 2 r. Housing estate .. 3·25 2·00

45. Armoured Cars.

1969. Qatar Security Forces. Multicoloured.

282. 1 d. Type **45** 10 10
283. 2 d. Traffic control .. 10 10
284. 3 d. Trooping helicopter .. 10 10
285. 60 d. Section of military band .. .. .. 1·75 65
286. 1 r. 25 Field gun .. 3·25 1·25
287. 2 r. Mounted police .. 5·50 2·25

46. Tanker "Sivella" at Mooring.

1969. Qatar's Oil Industry. Multicoloured.

288 1 d. Type **46** 10 10
289 2 d. Training school .. 10 10
290 3 d. "Sea Shell" (oil rig) and "Shell Dolphin" (supply vessel) 10 10
291 60 d. Storage tanks, Halul 1·75 65
292 1 r. 50 Topping plant .. 4·00 1·50
293 2 r. Various tankers 1890–1968 .. .. 6·00 2·25

47. "Guest-house" and Dhow-building.

1969. 10th Scout Jamboree, Qatar. Mult.

294. 1 d. Type **47** 10 10
295. 2 d. Scouts at work .. 10 10
296. 3 d. Review and March Past 10 10
297. 60 d. Interior gateway .. 1·50 65
298. 1 r. 25 Camp Entrance .. 2·75 1·40
299. 2 r. Hoisting Flag, and Shaikh Ahmed .. .. 4·00 2·25

48. Neil Armstrong.

1969. 1st Man on the Moon. Multicoloured.

301. 1 d. Type **48** 10 10
302. 2 d. Edward Aldrin .. 10 10
303. 3 d. Michael Collins .. 10 10
304. 60 d. Astronaut on Moon 1·25 55
305. 1 r. 25 Take-off from Moon 2·50 1·25
306. 2 r. Splashdown (horiz.) .. 3·75 2·00

49. Airliner and Mail-van.

1970. Admission to U.P.U. Multicoloured.

307. 1 d. Type **49** 10 10
308. 2 d. Liner "Oriental Empress" 10 10
309. 3 d. Loading mail-van .. 10 10
310. 60 d. G.P.O. Doha .. 1·00 60
311. 1 r. 25 U.P.U. Building, Berne .. .. .. 2·25 1·40
312. 2 r. U.P.U. Monument, Berne (detail) .. .. 3·75 2·00

50. League Emblem, Flag and Map.

1970. Silver Jubilee of Arab League.

313. **50.** 35 d. multicoloured .. 40 20
314. 60 d. multicoloured .. 60 35
315. 1 r. 25 multicoloured .. 1·40 75
316. 1 r. 50 multicoloured .. 1·75 1·00

51. "VC–10" on Runway.

1970. 1st Gulf Aviation "VC–10" Flight, Doha–London. Multicoloured.

317. 1 d. Type **51** 10 10
318. 2 d. Peregrine Falcon and "VC–10" 65 10
319. 3 d. Tail view of "VC–10" 10 10
320. 60 d. Gulf Aviation emblem on map .. .. .. 1·25 60
321. 1 r. 25 "VC–10" over Doha 3·50 1·60
322. 2 r. Tail assembly of "VC–10" 4·50 2·25

52. "Space Achievements".

1970. Int. Education Year.

323. **52.** 35 d. multicoloured .. 55 25
324. 60 d. multicoloured .. 1·10 50

53. Freesias.

55. Globe, "25" and U.N. Emblem.

54. Toyahama Fishermen with Giant "Fish".

1970. Qatar Flowers. Multicoloured.

325. 1 d. Type **53** 10 10
326. 2 d. Azaleas 10 10
327. 3 d. Ixias 10 10
328. 60 d. Amaryllises .. .. 1·25 60
329. 1 r. 25 Cinerarias .. .. 2·75 1·40
330. 2 r. Roses .. .. .. 4·00 2·00

1970. "EXPO 70". World Fair, Osaka. Multicoloured.

331. 1 d. Type **54** 10 10
332. 2 d. Expo emblem and map of Japan 10 10
333. 3 d. Fisherman on Shikoku beach 10 10
334. 60 d. Expo emblem and Mt. Fuji 80 45
335. 1 r. 50 Gateway to Shinto Shrine .. .. 1·75 85
336. 2 r. Expo Tower and Mt. Fuji .. .. .. 2·50 2·00

Nos. 333, 334 and 336 are vert.

1970. 25th Anniv. of U.N.O. Mult.

337. 1 d. Type **55** 10 10
338. 2 d. Flowers in gun-barrel 10 10
339. 3 d. Anniversary cake .. 10 10
340. 35 d. "The U.N. Agencies" 40 25
341. 1 r. 50 "Trumpet fanfare" 1·50 90
342. 2 r. "World friendship" .. 2·00 1·25

56. Al Jahiz (philosopher), and Ancient Globe.

1971. Famous Men of Islam. Multicoloured.

343 1 d. Type **56** 10 10
344 2 d. Saladin (soldier), palace and weapons .. 10 10
345 3 d. Al Farabi (philosopher and musician), felucca and instruments .. 10 10
346 35 d. Ibn Al Haithum (scientist), palace and emblems 70 35
347 1 r. 50 Al Motanabbi (poet), symbols and desert .. .. .. 3·00 1·75
348 2 r. Ibn Sina (Avicenna) (physician and philosopher), medical instruments and ancient globe 3·75 2·00

57. Common Cormorant and Water Plants.

1971. Qatar Fauna and Flora. Multicoloured.

349. 1 d. Type **57** 40 10
350. 2 d. Lizard and prickly pear 5 5
351. 3 d. Greater Flamingoes and palms 40 10
352. 60 d. Arabian oryx and yucca .. .. .. 1·25 65
353. 1 r. 25 Mountain gazelle and desert dandelion .. 2·25 1·25
354. 2 r. Dromedary, palm and bronzed chenopod .. 3·50 1·50

58. Satellite Earth Station, Goonhilly.

1971. World Telecommunications Day. Multicoloured.

355. 1 d. Type **58** 10 10
356. 2 d. Cable ship "Ariel" .. 10 10
357. 3 d. Post Office Tower and T.V. control-room .. 10 10
358. 4 d. Modern telephones .. 10 10
359. 5 d. Video-phone equipment 10 10
360. 35 d. As 3 d. 55 30
361. 75 d. As 5 d. .. .. 1·25 80
362. 3 r. Telex machine .. 5·00 2·50

59. Arab Child reading Book.

60. A.P.U. Emblem.

1971. 10th Anniv. of Education Day.

363. **59.** 35 d. multicoloured .. 40 20
364. 55 d. multicoloured .. 65 30
365. 75 d. multicoloured .. 90 45

1971. 25th Anniv. of Arab Postal Union.

366. **60.** 35 d. multicoloured .. 40 15
367. 55 d. multicoloured .. 60 30
368. 75 d. multicoloured .. 95 55
369. 1 r. 25 multicoloured .. 1·40 1·00

61. "Hammering Racism".

1971. Racial Equality Year. Multicoloured.

370. 1 d. Type **61** 10 10
371. 2 d. "Pushing back racism" 10 10
372. 3 d. War-wounded .. 10 10
373. 4 d. Working together (vert.) 10 10
374. 5 d. Playing together (vert.) 10 10
375. 35 d. Racial "tidal-wave" 40 25
376. 75 d. Type **61** .. .. 1·00 65
377. 3 r. As 2 d. .. .. 3·25 2·25

62. Nurse and Child.

1971. 25th Anniv. of U.N.I.C.E.F. Mult.

378. 1 d. Mother and child (vert.) 10 10
379. 2 d. Child's face .. 10 10
380. 3 d. Child with book (vert.) 10 10
381. 4 d. Type **62** 10 10
382. 5 d. Mother and baby .. 10 10
383. 35 d. Child with daffodil (vert.) 40 25
384. 75 d. As 3 d. .. .. 1·00 65
385. 3 r. As 1 d. .. .. 3·25 2·25

63. Shaikh Ahmad, and Flags of Arab League and Qatar.

1971. Independence.

386. **63.** 35 d. multicoloured .. 40 15
387. – 75 d. multicoloured .. 90 45
388. – 1 r. 25 blk., pink & brn. 1·40 85
389. – 3 r. multicoloured .. 3·00 2·00

DESIGNS—HORIZ. 75 d. As Type **63**, but with U.N. flag in place of Arab League flag. VERT. 1 r. 25, Shaikh Ahmad. 3 r. Handclasp.

64. Common Roller. **66.** Shaikh Khalifa bin Hamad al-Thani.

1972. Birds. Multicoloured.

391. 1 d. Type **64** 10 10
392. 2 d. Common kingfisher .. 10 10
393. 3 d. Rock thrush 10 10
394. 4 d. Caspian tern 15 10
395. 5 d. Hoopoe 15 10
396. 35 d. European bee eater 70 25
397. 75 d. Golden oriole .. 1·75 70
398. 3 r. Peregrine falcon .. 6·00 2·50

1972. Provisionals. Nos. 328/30 surch. with value in English and Arabic.

399. 10 d. on 60 d. mult. .. 1·00 15
400. 1 r. on 1 r. 25 mult. .. 4·00 70
401. 5 r. on 2 r. multicoloured 8·00 3·50

1972.

402. **66.** 5 d. blue and violet .. 15 10
403. 10 d. red and brown .. 15 10
404. 35 d. green and orge. .. 55 10
405. 55 d. purple and grn... 90 20
406. 75 d. purple and blue 1·40 30
407. – 1 r. black & brown .. 1·75 35
408. – 1 r. 25 black and grn... 2·75 55
409. – 5 r. black and blue .. 10·00 2·75
410. – 10 r. black and red 17·00 5·00

The rupee values are larger, size 27 × 32 mm.

67. Book Year Emblem.

1972. Int. Book Year.

411. **67.** 35 d. black and blue .. 30 20
412. 55 d. black and brown 55 30
413. 75 d. black and green.. 75 85
414. 1 r. 25 black and lilac.. 1·25 85

68. Football.

1972. Olympic Games, Munich. Depicting sportsmen's hands or feet. Multicoloured.

415. 1 d. Type **68** 10 10
416. 2 d. Running (foot on starting block) 10 10
417. 3 d. Cycling (hand) .. 10 10
418. 4 d. Gymnastics (hand) .. 10 10
419. 5 d. Basketball (hand) .. 10 10
420. 35 d. Discus (hand) .. 35 20
421. 75 d. Type **68** 85 60
422. 3 r. As 2 d .. .. .. 2·75 2·25

69. Underwater Pipeline Construction.

1972. "Oil from the Sea". Multicoloured.

424. 1 d. Drilling (vert.) .. 10 10
425. 4 d. Type **69** 10 10
426. 5 d. Offshore rig "Sea Shell" 10 10
427. 35 d. Underwater "prospecting" for oil 80 30
428. 75 d. As 1 d. .. .. 1·75 80
429. 3 r. As 5 d... .. .. 7·50 3·75

70. Administrative Building.

1972. Independence Day. Multicoloured.

430. 10 d. Type **70** 20 10
431. 35 d. Handclasp and Arab League flag 50 20
432. 75 d. Handclasp and U.N. flag 90 50
433. 1 r. 25 Shaikh Khalifa .. 1·40 90

71. Dish Aerial, Satellite and Telephone (I.T.U.).

1972. United Nations Day. Multicoloured.

435. 1 d. Type **71** 10 10
436. 2 d. Archaeological team (U.N.E.S.C.O.) 10 10
437. 3 d. Tractor, produce and helicopter (F.A.O.) .. 10 10
438. 4 d. Children with books (U.N.I.C.E.F.) .. 10 10
439. 5 d. Weather satellite (W.M.O.) 10 10
440. 25 d. Construction workers (I.L.O.) 40 25
441. 55 d. Child care (W.H.O.).. 1·00 60
442. 1 r. Mail-plane and van (U.P.U.) .. .. 2·25 90

72. Emblem and Flags. **72a.** Shaikh Khalifa.

1972. 10th Session of Arab States Civil Aviation Council, Qatar.

443. **72.** 25 d. multicoloured .. 60 30
444. 30 d. multicoloured .. 80 45

1972. Coil Stamps.

444a. **72a.** 10 d. red and brown 60 50
444b. 25 d. green and purple 1·50 1·25

73 Shaikh Khalifa. **74.** Clock Tower, Doha.

1973.

445. **73.** 5 d. multicoloured .. 15 10
446. 10 d. multicoloured .. 15 10
447. 20 d. multicoloured .. 30 10
448. 25 d. multicoloured .. 25 10
449. 35 d. multicoloured .. 55 10
450. 55 d. multicoloured .. 90 20
451. **74.** 75 d. multicoloured .. 2·00 40
452. – 1 r. multicoloured .. 2·00 30
453. – 5 r. multicoloured .. 7·50 2·00
454 – 10 r. multicoloured .. 14·00 3·75

Nos. 452/4 are as Type **73**, but size 27 × 32 mm.

75. Housing Development.

1973. 1st Anniv. of Shaikh Khalifa's Accession. Multicoloured.

455. 2 d. Road construction .. 10 10
456. 3 d. Type **75** 10 10
457. 4 d. Hospital operating theatre 10 10
458. 5 d. Telephone exchange.. 10 10
459. 15 d. School classroom .. 20 10
460. 20 d. Television studio .. 25 10
461. 35 d. Shaikh Khalifa .. 45 15
462. 55 d. Gulf Hotel, Doha .. 90 40
463. 1 r. Industrial plant .. 1·40 70
464. 1 r. 35 Flour mills .. 2·00 1·25

76. Aerial Crop-spraying.

1973. 25th Anniv. of W.H.O. Mult.

465. 2 d. Type **76** 10 10
466. 3 d. Drugs and syringe .. 10 10
467. 4 d. Woman in wheelchair (Prevention of polio) .. 10 10
468. 5 d. Mosquito (Malaria control) 10 10
469. 55 d. Mental patient (Mental Health Research) .. 1·50 70
470. 1 r. Dead trees (Anti-pollution) .. .. 2·75 1·40

77. Weather Ship.

1973. Cent. of World Meteorological Organization. Multicoloured.

471. 2 d. Type **77** 10 10
472. 3 d. Launching radio-sonde balloon 10 10
473. 4 d. Weather plane .. 10 10
474. 5 d. Meteorological station 10 10
475. 10 d. Met. aircraft taking-off 20 10
476. 1 r. "Nimbus 1" .. .. 1·75 85
477. 1 r. 55 Rocket on launch-pad 3·00 1·50

78. Handclasp.

1973. 2nd Anniv. of Independence Day. Mult.

478. 15 d. Type **78** 10 10
479. 35 d. Agriculture 20 10
480. 55 d. Government building 55 20
481. 1 r. 35 View of Doha .. 1·25 65
482. 1 r. 55 Illuminated fountain 1·50 1·00

79. Child planting Sapling (UNESCO).

1973. United Nations Day. Multicoloured.

483. 2 d. Type **79** 10 10
484. 4 d. U.N. H.Q., New York and flags 10 10
485. 5 d. Building construction (I.L.O.) 10 10
486. 35 d. Nurses in dispensary (W.H.O.) 30 10
487. 1 r. 35 Radar control (I.T.U.) 1·50 85
488. 3 r. Inspection of wheat and cattle (F.A.O.) .. 3·50 2·25

80. "Open Gates".

1973. 25th Anniv. of Declaration of Human Rights. Multicoloured.

489. 2 d. Type **80** 10 10
490. 4 d. Freedom marchers .. 10 10
491. 5 d. "Equality of Man".. 10 10
492. 35 d. Primary education.. 25 10
493. 1 r. 35 General Assembly, U.N. .. .. .. 1·50 55
494. 3 r. Flame emblem (vert.) 3·50 2·00

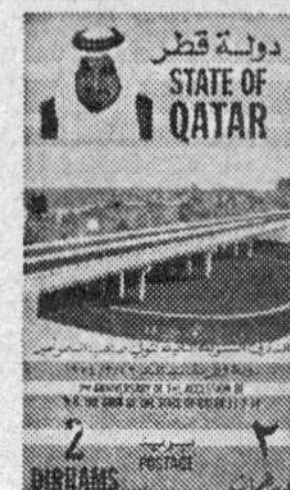

81. New Flyover, Doha.

1974. 2nd Anniv. of Shaikh Khalifa's Accession. Multicoloured.

495. 2 d. Type **81** 10 10
496. 3 d. Education symbol .. 10 10
497. 5 d. Gas plant 10 10
498. 35 d. Gulf Hotel, Doha .. 35 15
499. 1 r. 55 Space communications station .. .. 1·75 90
500. 2 r. 25 Shaikh Khalifa .. 2·75 1·60

82. Camel Caravan and Articulated Mail-van.

1974. Centenary of U.P.U. Multicoloured.

501 2 d. Type **82** 10 10
502 3 d. Early mail wagon and modern express train .. 10 20
503 10 d. "Hindoostan" (paddle-steamer) and "Iberia" (liner) .. 35 10
504 35 d. Early and modern mail planes 50 20
505 75 d. Manual and mechanised mail-sorting 95 55
506 1 r. 25 Early and modern P.O. sales counters .. 1·40 1·00

83. Doha Hospital.

1974. World Population Year. Multicoloured.

507. 5 d. Type **83** 10 10
508. 10 d. W.P.Y. emblem .. 15 10
509. 15 d. Emblem within wreath 15 10
510. 35 d. World population map 35 15
511. 1 r. 75 New-born infants and clock ("a birth every minute") .. .. 1·75 85
512. 2 r. 25 "Ideal Family" group 2·25 1·40

84. Television Station.

1974. Independence Day. Multicoloured.

513. 5 d. Type **84** 10 10
514. 10 d. Doha palace .. 15 10
515. 15 d. Teachers' College .. 20 10
516. 75 d. Clock tower and Mosque 80 35
517. 1 r. 55 Roundabout and surroundings .. .. 1·50 90
518. 2 r. Shaikh Khalifa .. 2·25 1·40

85. Operating Theatre (W.H.O.).

1974. United Nations Day.

519. **85.** 5 d. orge., mve. & blk... 10 10
520. – 10 d. orge., red & blk... 15 10
521. – 20 d. bl., grn. & blk. .. 20 10
522. – 25 d. bl., brn. & blk. .. 25 10
523. – 1 r. 75 bl., red & blk... 1·50 90
524. – 2 r. bl., orge. & blk. .. 2·00 1·25

DESIGNS: 10 d. Satellite earth station (I.T.U.). 20 d. Tractor (F.A.O.). 25 d. Classroom (U.N.E.S.C.O.). 1 r. 75, African open-air court ("Human Rights"). 2 r. U.P.U. and U.N. emblems (U.P.U.).

86. Gulf Aviation "VC-10" Airliner.

1974. Arab Civil Aviation Day.

525. 86. 20 d. multicoloured .. 35 15
526. – 25 d. bl., grn. & yellow 35 15
527. – 30 d. multicoloured .. 45 20
528. – 50 d. red, grn. & purple 75 45

DESIGNS: 25 d. Doha airport. 30 d., 50 d. Flags of Qatar and the Arab League.

87. Clock-tower, Qatar.

1974. Tourism. Multicoloured.

529. 5 d. Type 87 .. .. 15 10
530. 10 d. White-cheeked terns, hoopoes and Shara'o Island (horiz.) .. 1·40 20
531. 15 d. Fort Zubara (horiz.) 25 10
532. 35 d. Yachts and Gulf Hotel (horiz.) 45 15
533. 55 d. Qatar by night (horiz.) 75 20
534. 75 d. Arabian oryx (horiz.) 1·50 45
535. 1 r. 25 Khor al-Udeid (horiz.) .. .. .. 1·75 90
536. 1 r. 75 Ruins, Wakrah (horiz.) .. .. .. 2·00 1·40

88. Traffic Roundabout, Doha.

1975. 3rd Anniv. of Shaikh Khalifa's Accession. Multicoloured.

537. 10 d. Type 88 .. .. 20 10
538. 35 d. Oil pipelines .. 55 10
539. 55 d. Laying offshore pipelines 85 20
540. 1 r. Oil refinery .. .. 1·50 60
541. 1 r. 35 Shaikh Khalifa (vert.) .. .. .. 2·25 1·00
542. 1 r. 55 As 1 r. 35 .. 2·75 1·50

89. Flintlock Pistol.

1975. National Museum Opening. Mult.

543. 2 d. Type 89 .. .. 10 10
544. 3 d. Arabesque-pattern mosaic 10 10
545. 35 d. Museum buildings .. 55 15
546. 75 d. Museum archway (vert.) .. .. .. 1·40 60
547. 1 r. 25 Flint tools .. 2·00 1·00
548. 3 r. Gold necklace and pendant (vert.) .. 4·25 2·50

90. Policeman and Road Signs.

1975. Traffic Week. Multicoloured.

549. 5 d. Type 90 .. .. 20 10
550. 5 d. Traffic arrows and signal lights 50 15
551. 35 d. Type 90 .. .. 1·25 35
552. 55 d. As 15 d. .. .. 1·75 90

91. Flag and Emblem.

1975. 10th Anniv. of Arab Labour Charter and Constitution.

553. 91. 10 d. multicoloured .. 15 10
554. 35 d. multicoloured .. 45 15
555. 1 r. multicoloured .. 1·25 80

92. Government Building, Doha.

1975. 4th Anniv. of Independence. Mult.

556. 5 d. Type 92 .. .. 10 10
557. 15 d. Museum and clock tower, Doha .. 25 10
558. 35 d. Constitution-Arabic text (vert.) 40 10
559. 55 d. Ruler and flag (vert.) 60 25
560. 75 d. Constitution-English text (vert.) 80 50
561. 1 r. 25. As 55 d. .. 1·40 85

93. Telecommunications Satellite (I.T.U.).

1975. 30th Anniv. of U.N.O. Multicoloured.

562. 5 d. Type 93 .. .. 10 10
563. 15 d. U.N. Headquarters, New York 15 10
564. 35 d. U.P.U. emblem and map 35 10
565. 1 r. Doctors tending child (U.N.I.C.E.F.) .. 95 50
566. 1 r. 25 Bulldozer (I.L.O.) 1·50 90
567. 2 r. Students in class (U.N.E.S.C.O.) .. .. 2·50 1·50

94. Fertilizer Plant

1975. Qatar Industry. Multicoloured.

568. 5 d. Type 94 .. .. 15 10
569. 10 d. Flour Mills (vert.) .. 20 10
570. 35 d. Natural Gas plant .. 60 15
571. 75 d. Oil refinery .. .. 1·50 70
572. 1 r. 25 Cement works .. 1·90 1·25
573. 1 r. 55 Steel mills .. .. 2·25 1·50

95. Modern Building, Doha.

1976. 4th Anniv. of Shaikh Khalifa's Accession.

574. 95. 5 d. multicoloured .. 10 10
575. – 10 d. multicoloured .. 10 10
576. – 35 d. multicoloured .. 35 10
577. – 55 d. multicoloured .. 55 20
578. – 75 d. multicoloured .. 75 35
579. – 1 r. 55 multicoloured .. 1·50 1·00

DESIGNS: Nos. 575/6 and 579 show public buildings etc. Nos. 577/8 show Shaikh Khalifa with flag.

96. Tracking Aerial.

97. Early and Modern Telephones.

1976. Opening of Satellite Earth Station. Multicoloured.

580. 35 d. Type 96 .. .. 60 15
581. 55 d. "Intelsat" satellite 85 25
582. 75 d. Type 96 .. .. 1·40 60
583. 1 r. As 55 d. .. .. 1·75 80

1976. Telephone Centenary.

584. 97. 1 r. multicoloured .. 1·25 75
585. 1 r. 35 multicoloured .. 1·75 1·00

98. Tournament Emblem.

100. Football.

99. Qatar Dhows.

1976. 4th Arabian Gulf Football Cup Tournament. Multicoloured.

586. 5 d. Type 98 .. .. 10 10
587. 10 d. Qatar Stadium .. 10 10
588. 35 d. Type 98 .. .. 40 15
589. 55 d. Two players with ball 75 30
590. 75 d. Player with ball .. 1·00 50
591. 1 r. 25 As 10 d. .. .. 1·60 1·10

1976. Arab Dhows.

592. 99. 10 d. multicoloured .. 15 10
593. – 35 d. multicoloured .. 40 10
594. – 80 d. multicoloured .. 90 35
595. – 1 r. 25 multicoloured .. 1·40 30
596. – 1 r. 50 multicoloured .. 1·75 90
597. – 2 r. multicoloured .. 2·25 1·25

DESIGNS: As Type 99 showing local craft.

1976. Olympic Games, Montreal, Mult.

598 5 d. Type 100 .. .. 10 10
599 10 d. Sailing 15 10
600 35 d. Show jumping .. 30 10
601 80 d. Boxing 75 45
602 1 r. 25 Weightlifting .. 1·25 80
603 1 r. 50 Basketball .. 1·50 1·00

101. Urban Housing Development.

1976. U.N. Conf. on Human Settlements. Multicoloured.

604. 10 d. Type 101 .. .. 10 10
605. 35 d. U.N. and Conference emblems 25 10
606. 80 d. Communal housing development 70 45
607. 1 r. 25 Shaikh Khalifa .. 1·25 90

102. Kentish Plover.

1976. Birds. Multicoloured.

608. 5 d. Type 102 .. .. 20 10
609. 10 d. Common cormorant 20 10
610. 35 d. Osprey 95 25
611. 80 d. Greater flamingo (vert.) .. .. .. 2·00 55
612. 1 r. 25 Rock thrush (vert.) 2·75 80
613. 2 r. Saker falcon (vert.) .. 3·75 1·25

103. Shaikh Khalifa and Flag.

105. Shaikh Khalifa.

104. U.N. Emblem.

1976. 5th Anniv of Independence. Mult.

614 5 d. Type 103 .. .. 10 10
615 10 d. Type 103 .. .. 15 10
616 40 d. Doha buildings (horiz) 25 10
617 80 d. As 40 d. 45 20
618 1 r. 25 "Dana" (oil rig) (horiz) .. .. .. 1·25 65
619 1 r. 50 U.N. and Qatar emblems (horiz) .. 1·25 85

1976. United Nations Day.

620. 104. 2 r. multicoloured .. 1·75 1·25
621. 3 r. multicoloured .. 2·25 1·75

1977. 5th Anniv. of Amir's Accession.

622. 105. 20 d. multicoloured .. 20 10
623. 1 r. 80 multicoloured .. 1·90 1·40

106. Shaikh Khalifa. 107. Envelope and A.P.U. Emblem.

1977.

624. 106. 5 d. multicoloured .. 15 10
625. 10 d. multicoloured .. 20 10
626. 35 d. multicoloured .. 50 10
627. 80 d. multicoloured .. 90 20
628. 1 r. multicoloured .. 1·10 25
629. 5 r. multicoloured .. 5·00 2·25
630. 10 r. multicoloured .. 10·00 3·75

Nos. 628/30 are larger, 25×31 mm.

1977. 25th Anniv. of Arab Postal Union.

631. 107. 35 d. multicoloured .. 25 10
632. 1 r. 35 multicoloured . 1·25 90

108. Shaikh Khalifa and Sound Waves.

1977. International Telecommunications Day.

633. 108. 35 d. multicoloured .. 25 10
634. 1 r. 80 multicoloured .. 1·50 1·40

108a. Shaikh Khalifa. 109. Parliament Building, Doha.

1977. Booklet Stamps.

634a. 108a. 5 d. multicoloured .. 15 15
634c. 10 d. multicoloured .. 20 20
634d. 35 d. multicoloured .. 50 50
634e. 80 d. multicoloured .. 1·50 1·50

1977. 6th Anniv. of Independence. Mult.

635. 80 d. Type 109 .. .. 85 60
636. 80 d. Main business district, Doha 85 60
637. 80 d. Motorway, Doha .. 85 60

110. U.N. Emblem.

1977. United Nations Day.

638. 110. 20 d. multicoloured .. 15 10
639. 1 r. multicoloured .. 70 65

111. Steel Mill.

1978. 6th Anniv. of Amir's Accession. Mult.
640. 20 d. Type **111** 15 10
641. 80 d. Operating theatre .. 60 20
642. 1 r. Children's classroom 65 40
643. 5 r. Shaikh Khalifa .. 2·25 2·00

112. Oil Refinery.

1978. 7th Anniv. of Independence. Mult.
644. 35 d. Type **112** 30 10
645. 80 d. Apartment buildings 55 20
646. 1 r. 35 Town centre, Doha 85 65
647. 1 r. 80 Shaikh Khalifa .. 1·25 1·00

113. Man reading Alphabet.

1978. International Literacy Day.
648. **113.** 35 d. multicoloured .. 25 10
649. 80 d. multicoloured .. 75 55

114. U.N. Emblem and Qatar Flag.

1978. United Nations Day.
650. **114.** 35 d. multicoloured .. 25 10
651. 80 d. multicoloured .. 75 55

115. "Human Rights Flame".

116. I.Y.C. Emblem.

1978. 30th Anniv. of Declaration of Human Rights. Multicoloured.
652. 35 d. Type **115** 20 10
653. 80 d. Type **115** 40 25
654. 1 r. 25 Emblem and balance 70 60
655. 1 r. 80 As 1 r. 25 .. .. 70 85

1979. International Year of the Child.
656. **116.** 35 d. blue, mauve and black 25 10
657. 1 r. 80 blue, green and black 85 80

117. Shaikh Khalifa.

118. Shaikh Khalifa and Laurel Wreath.

1979.
658. **117.** 5 d. multicoloured .. 10 10
659. 10 d. multicoloured .. 10 10
660. 20 d. multicoloured .. 25 10
661. 25 d. multicoloured .. 25 10
662. 35 d. multicoloured .. 40 10
663. 60 d. multicoloured .. 70 10
664. 80 d. multicoloured .. 90 15
665. 1 r. multicoloured .. 1·00 15
666. 1 r. 25 multicoloured .. 1·25 25
667. 1 r. 35 multicoloured .. 1·50 30
668. 1 r. 80 multicoloured .. 1·75 45
669. 5 r. multicoloured .. 4·00 1·50
670. 10 r. multicoloured .. 7·00 2·25
Nos. 665/70 are larger, size 27 × 32½ mm.

1979. 7th Anniv. of Amir's Accession.
671. **118.** 35 d. multicoloured .. 25 10
672. 80 d. multicoloured .. 40 20
673. 1 r. multicoloured .. 60 45
674. 1 r.25 multicoloured .. 80 70

119. Wave Pattern and Television Screen.

1979. World Telecommunications Day.
675. **119.** 2 r. multicoloured .. 1·00 80
676. 2 r. 80 multicoloured .. 1·25 1·10

120. Two Children supporting Globe.

1979. 50th Anniv. of International Bureau of Education.
677. **120.** 35 d. multicoloured .. 25 10
678. 80 d. multicoloured .. 55 30

121. Rolling Mill.

122. U.N. Emblem and Flag of Qatar.

1979. 8th Anniv. of Independence. Mult.
679. 5 d. Type **121** 10 10
680. 10 d. Aerial view of Doha 10 10
681. 1 r. 25 Qatar flag 70 50
682. 2 r. Shaikh Khalifa .. 1·00 90

1979. United Nations Day.
683. **122.** 1 r. 25 multicoloured 75 45
684. 2 r. multicoloured .. 1·00 95

123. Mosque Minaret and Crescent Moon.

1979. Third World Conference on the Prophet's Seera and Sunna.
685. **123.** 35 d. multicoloured .. 25 10
686. 1 r. 80 multicoloured 1·00 90

124. Shaikh Khalifa.

1980. 8th Anniv. of Amir's Accession.
687. **124.** 20 d. multicoloured .. 15 10
688. 60 d. multicoloured .. 35 15
689. 1 r. 25 multicoloured 65 45
690. 2 r. multicoloured .. 90 90

125. Emblem.

1980. Sixth Congress of Arab Towns. Organization, Doha.
691. **125.** 2 r. 35 multicoloured .. 1·40 1·00
692. 2 r. 80 multicoloured .. 1·60 1·25

126. Oil Refinery.

1980. 9th Anniv. of Independence. Mult.
693. 10 d. Type **126** 15 10
694. 35 d. Doha 30 15
695. 2 r. Oil Rig .. .. 1·75 90
696. 2 r. 35 Hospital .. .. 2·25 1·40

127. Figures supporting O.P.E.C. Emblem.

1980. 20th Anniv. of Organization of Petroleum Exporting Countries.
697. **127.** 1 r. 35 multicoloured .. 75 45
698. 2 r. multicoloured .. 1·25 80

128. U.N. Emblem.

129. Mosque and Kaaba, Mecca.

1980. United Nations Day.
699. **128.** 1 r. 35 light blue, blue and mauve 65 45
700. 1 r. 80 grn., bl. and blk. 1·10 70

1980. 1400th Anniv. of Hegira.
701. **129.** 10 d. multicoloured .. 10 10
702. 35 d. multicoloured .. 30 15
703. 1 r. 25 multicoloured 75 55
704. 2 r. 80 multicoloured 1·40 1·25

130. I.Y.D.P. Emblem.

1981. International Year of Disabled Persons.
705. **130.** 2 r. multicoloured .. 1·60 1·10
706. 3 r. multicoloured .. 2·25 1·60

131. Student.

132. Shaikh Khalifa.

1981. 20th Anniv. of Education Day.
707. **131.** 2 r. multicoloured .. 1·50 1·00
708. 3 r. multicoloured .. 2·25 1·60

1981. 9th Anniv. of Amir's Accession.
709. **132.** 10 d. multicoloured .. 10 10
710. 35 d. multicoloured .. 35 20
711. 80 d. multicoloured .. 55 35
712. 5 r. multicoloured .. 2·75 2·00

133. I.T.U. and W.H.O. Emblems and Ribbons forming Caduceus.

134. Torch.

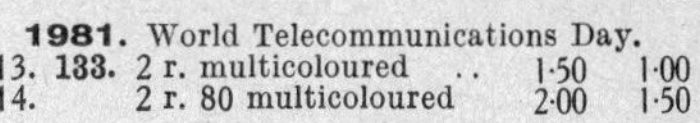

1981. World Telecommunications Day.
713. **133.** 2 r. multicoloured .. 1·50 1·00
714. 2 r. 80 multicoloured 2·00 1·50

1981. 30th International Military Football Championship.
715. **134.** 1 r. 25 multicoloured 1·50 75
716. 2 r. 80 multicoloured 3·00 2·00

135. Qatar Flag.

1981. 10th Anniv. of Independence.
717. **135.** 5 d. multicoloured .. 10 10
718. 60 d. multicoloured .. 60 25
719. 80 d. multicoloured .. 85 40
720. 5 r. multicoloured .. 4·00 2·75

136. Tractor gathering Crops.

1981. World Food Day.
721. **136.** 2 r. multicoloured .. 1·75 1·00
722. 2 r. 80 multicoloured 2·50 1·50

137. Red Crescent.

1982. Qatar Red Crescent.
723. **137.** 20 d. multicoloured .. 30 10
724. 2 r. 80 multicoloured 3·50 2·00

138. Shaikh Khalifa.

1982. 10th Anniv. of Amir's Accession.
725. **138.** 10 d. multicoloured .. 10 10
726. 20 d. multicoloured .. 20 10
727. 1 r. 25 multicoloured 1·00 60
728. 2 r. 80 multicoloured .. 2·50 1·50

139. Hamad General Hospital.

140. Shaikh Khalifa.

1982. Hamad General Hospital.
729. **139.** 10 d. multicoloured .. 10 10
730. 2 r. 35 multicoloured 2·00 1·50

1982.

731. **140** 5 d. multicoloured .. 10 10
732. 10 d. multicoloured .. 10 10
733. 15 d. multicoloured .. 25 10
734. 20 d. multicoloured .. 10 10
735. 25 d. multicoloured .. 15 10
736. 35 d. multicoloured .. 25 10
737. 60 d. multicoloured .. 35 10
738. 80 d. multicoloured .. 45 10
739. – 1 r. multicoloured .. 75 15
740. – 1 r. 25 multicoloured .. 75 20
741. – 2 r. multicoloured .. 1·00 50
742. – 5 r. multicoloured .. 3·00 1·25
743. – 10 r. multicoloured .. 6·00 2·50
744. – 15 r. multicoloured .. 8·00 3·50

DESIGNS—(25 × 32 mm.). 1 r. to 2 r. Oil refinery. 5 r. to 15 r. Doha clock tower.

142. Container Ship.

1982. 6th Anniv. of United Arab Shipping Company.

745. **142.** 20 d. multicoloured .. 25 15
746. 2 r. 35 multicoloured .. 2·50 1·75

143. A.P.U. Emblem. **144.** National Flag.

1982. 30th Anniv. of Arab Postal Union.

747. **143.** 35 d. multicoloured .. 40 10
748. 2 r. 80 multicoloured .. 2·25 1·75

1982. 11th Anniv. of Independence.

749. **144.** 10 d. multicoloured .. 10 10
750. 80 d. multicoloured .. 70 25
751. 1 r. 25 multicoloured .. 1·00 65
752. 2 r. 80 multicoloured .. 2·25 1·50

145. W.C.Y. Emblem. **147.** Arabic Script.

146. Conference Emblem.

1983. World Communications Year.

753. **145.** 35 d. multicoloured 45 10
754. – 2 r. 80 multicoloured 2·50 1·75

1983. Second Gulf Postal Organization Conference.

755. **146.** 1 r. multicoloured .. 1·00 35
756. 1 r. 35 multicoloured 1·50 65

1983. 12th Anniv. of Independence.

757. **147.** 10 d. multicoloured .. 10 10
758. 35 d. multicoloured .. 30 15
759. 80 d. multicoloured .. 65 30
760. 2 r. 80 multicoloured .. 2·25 1·75

148. Council Emblem.

1983. Fourth Session of Gulf Co-operation Supreme Council.

761. **148.** 35 d. multicoloured .. 35 15
762. 2 r. 80 multicoloured 2·00 1·50

149. Globe and Human Rights Emblem.

1983. 35th Anniv. of Declaration of Human Rights. Multicoloured.

763. 1 r. 25 Type **149** .. .. 1·40 60
764. 2 r. 80 Globe and emblem in balance .. .. 3·00 1·75

150. Harbour. **151.** Shaikh Khalifa.

1984.

765 **150** 15 d. multicoloured .. 10 10
765a **151** 25 d. multicoloured (22 × 27 mm) .. 15 10
766 **150** 40 d. multicoloured .. 25 15
767 50 d. multicoloured .. 25 15
767a **151** 75 d. multicoloured (2 × 27 mm) .. 40 25
768 1 r. multicoloured .. 55 25
769 1 r. 50 multicoloured 75 40
769a 2 r. multicoloured .. 1·10 80
770 2 r. 50 multicoloured 1·40 65
771 3 r. multicoloured .. 1·60 80
772 5 r. multicoloured .. 2·75 1·40
773 10 r. multicoloured .. 5·50 3·00

152. Flag and Shaikh Khalifa.

1984. 13th Anniv. of Independence.

774. **152.** 15 d. multicoloured .. 10 10
775. 1 r. multicoloured .. 70 25
776. 2 r. 50 multicoloured 1·60 90
777. 3 r. 50 multicoloured 2·25 1·50

153. Teacher and Blackboard. **154.** I.C.A.O. Emblem

1984. International Literacy Day. Multicoloured. Background colour behind board given.

778. **153.** 1 r. mauve 65 35
779. 1 r. orange 65 35

1984. 40th Anniv. of I.C.A.O.

780. **154.** 20 d. multicoloured .. 25 10
781. 3 r. 50 multicoloured 2·75 1·75

155. I.Y.Y. Emblem. **156.** Crossing the Road.

1985. International Youth Year.

782. **155.** 50 d. multicoloured .. 50 25
783. 1 r. multicoloured .. 1·10 40

1985. Traffic Week. Multicoloured, frame colour given.

784. **156.** 1 r. red 90 35
785. 1 r. blue 90 35

157. Emblem.

1985. 40th Anniv. of League of Arab States.

786. **157.** 50 d. multicoloured .. 30 15
787. 4 r. multicoloured .. 2·75 2·00

158. Doha.

1985. 14th Anniv. of Independence. Mult.

788. 40 d. Type **158** 25 15
789. 50 d. Dish aerials and microwave tower .. 30 15
790. 1 r. 50 Oil refinery .. 95 60
791. 4 r. Cement works .. 2·75 2·00

159. O.P.E.C. Emblem in "25".

1985. 25th Anniv. of Organization of Petroleum Exporting Countries. Multicoloured, background colours given.

792. **159.** 1 r. red 65 35
793. 1 r. green 65 35

160. U.N. Emblem.

1985. 40th Anniv. of U.N.O.

794. **160.** 1 r. multicoloured .. 55 30
795. 3 r. multicoloured .. 1·50 1·25

161. Emblem.

1986. Population and Housing Census.

796. **161.** 1 r. multicoloured .. 55 30
797. 3 r. multicoloured .. 1·50 1·25

162. "Qatari ibn al-Fuja'a" (container ship).

1986. 10th Anniv of United Arab Shipping Company. Multicoloured.

798 1 r. 50 Type **162** 90 50
799 4 r. "Al-Wajda" (container ship) .. .. .. 2·40 1·75

163. Flag and Shaikh Khalifa.

1986. 15th Anniv. of Independence.

800. **163.** 40 d. multicoloured .. 20 15
801. 50 d. multicoloured .. 30 15
802. 1 r. multicoloured .. 55 25
803. 4 r. multicoloured .. 2·25 2·00

164. Shaikh Khalifa. **165.** Palace.

1987.

804. **164.** 15 r. multicoloured .. 6·00 4·50
805. 20 r. multicoloured .. 8·00 6·50
806. 30 r. multicoloured .. 11·50 10·00

1987. 15th Anniv. of Amir's Accession.

807. **165.** 50 d. multicoloured .. 30 15
808. 1 r. multicoloured .. 55 25
809. 1 r. 50 multicoloured 75 60
810. 4 r. multicoloured .. 2·00 1·75

166. Emblem. **167.** Emblem.

1987. 35th Anniv. of Arab Postal Union.

811. **166.** 1 r. yellow, green and black 45 25
812. 1 r. 50 multicoloured 65 30

1987. Gulf Environment Day.

813. **167.** 1 r. multicoloured .. 55 40
814. 4 r. multicoloured .. 1·75 1·75

168. Modern Complex.

1987. 16th Anniv. of Independence.

815. 25 d. Type **168** 15 10
816. 75 d. Aerial view of city .. 40 25
817. 2 r. Modern building .. 1·10 80
818. 4 r. Oil refinery .. .. 1·90 1·75

169. Pens in Fist. **170.** Anniversary Emblem.

1987. International Literacy Day.

819. **169.** 1 r. 50 multicoloured 80 70
820. 4 r. multicoloured .. 1·90 1·50

1988. 40th Anniv of W.H.O.

821 **170** 1 r. 50 yell, blk & bl 80 70
822 2 r. yellow, blk & red 1·10 80

171 State Arms, Shaikh Khalifa and Flag

1988. 17th Anniv of Independence.

823 **171** 50 d. multicoloured .. 20 15
824 75 d. multicoloured .. 30 20
825 1 r. 50 multicoloured 60 50
826 2 r. multicoloured .. 75 60

172 Post Office

1988. Opening of New Doha General Post Office.

827	172	1 r. 50 multicoloured	60	50
828		4 r. multicoloured ..	1·50	1·25

173 Housing Development

1988. Arab Housing Day.

829	173	1 r. 50 multicoloured	60	50
830		4 r. multicoloured ..	1·50	1·25

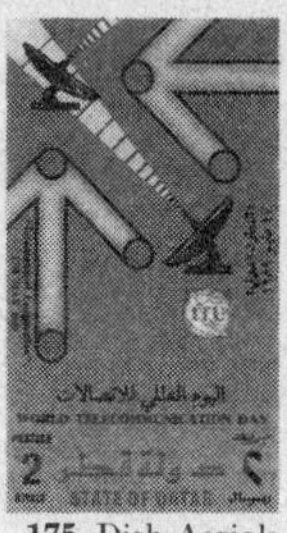

174 Hands shielding Flame
175 Dish Aerials and Arrows

1988. 40th Anniv of Declaration of Human Rights.

831	174	1 r. 50 multicoloured	60	50
832		2 r. multicoloured ..	75	60

1989. World Telecommunications Day.

833	175	2 r. multicoloured ..	75	60
834		4 r. multicoloured ..	1·50	1·25

176 Headquarters

1989. 10th Anniv of Qatar Red Crescent Society.

835	176	4 r. multicoloured ..	1·50	1·25

177 Palace

1989. 18th Anniv of Independence.

836	177	75 d. multicoloured ..	30	20
837		1 r. multicoloured ..	50	40
838		1 r. 50 multicoloured	60	50
839		2 r. multicoloured ..	75	60

178 Anniversary Emblem

1990. 40th Anniv of Gulf Air.

840	178	50 d. multicoloured ..	15	10
841		75 d. multicoloured ..	20	20
842		4 r. multicoloured ..	1·25	1·00

179 Map and Rising Sun

1990. 19th Anniv of Independence. Mult.

843	50 d. Type **179**	15	10
844	75 d. Map and sunburst ..	25	20
845	1 r. 50 Musicians and sword dancer	50	40
846	2 r. As No. 845	65	50

180 Anniversary Emblem
181 Emblem and Dhow

1990. 30th Anniv of Organization of Petroleum Exporting Countries. Mult.

847	50 d. Type **180**	15	10
848	1 r. 50 Flags of member nations	50	40

1990. 11th Session of Supreme Council of Gulf Co-operation Council. Multicoloured.

849	50 d. Type **181**	20	15
850	1 r. Council heads of state and emblem ..	35	30
851	1 r. 50 State flag and Council emblem ..	55	45
852	2 r. State and Council emblems	75	60

182 "Glossonema edule"
183 Emblem

1991. Plants. Multicoloured.

853	10 d. Type **182**	10	10
854	25 d. "Lycium shawii" ..	10	10
855	50 d. "Acacia tortilis" ..	20	15
856	75 d. "Acacia ehrenbergiana" ..	30	25
857	1 r. "Capparis spinosa" ..	35	30
858	4 r. "Cymhopogon parkeri"	1·50	1·25

1991. 20th Anniv of Independence. Mult.

859	25 d. Type **183**	10	10
860	75 d. Type **183**	30	25
861	1 r. View of Doha (35 × 32 mm)	35	30
862	1 r. 50 Palace (35 × 32 mm)	55	45

184 Fish
185 Shaikh Khalifa

1991. Fishes.

863	184	10 d. multicoloured ..	10	10
864	–	15 d. multicoloured ..	10	10
865	–	25 d. multicoloured ..	10	10
866	–	50 d. multicoloured ..	20	15
867	–	75 d. multicoloured ..	30	25
868	–	1 r. multicoloured ..	35	30
869	–	1 r. 50 multicoloured ..	55	45
870	–	2 r. multicoloured ..	75	60

DESIGNS: 15 d. to 2 r. Different fishes.

1992. Multicoloured. (a) Size 22 × 27 mm.

871	10 d. Type **185**	10	10
872	25 d. North Field gas project	10	10
873	50 d. Map of Qatar ..	20	15
874	75 d. Petrochemical factory	30	25
875	1 r. Petrol refinery ..	35	30

(b) Size 25 × 32 mm.

876	1 r. 50 As No. 872 ..	55	45
877	2 r. As No. 873	75	60
878	3 r. As No. 874	1·10	90
879	4 r. As No. 875	1·50	1·25
880	5 r. As No. 873	1·90	1·50
881	10 r. As No. 875	3·75	3·00
882	15 r. Shaikh Khalifa (different frame) ..	5·50	4·50
883	20 r. As No. 882	7·50	6·00
884	30 r. As No. 882	11·50	9·25

186 Shaikh Khalifa and Gateway
187 Heart in Centre of Flower

1992. 20th Anniv of Shaikh Khalifa's Accession. Multicoloured.

885	25 d. Type **186**	10	10
886	50 d. Type **186**	20	15
887	75 d. Archway and "20" ..	30	25
888	1 r. 50 As No. 887 ..	55	45

1992. World Health Day. "Heartbeat, the Rhythm of Health". Multicoloured.

889	50 d. Type **187**	20	15
890	1 r. 50 Heart on clockface and cardiograph (horiz)	55	45

188 Women Dancing

1992. Children's Paintings. Multicoloured.

891	25 d. Type **188**	10	10
892	50 d. Children's playground	20	15
893	75 d. Boat race	30	25
894	1 r. 50 Fishing fleet ..	55	45

189 Runner and Emblems

1992. Olympic Games, Barcelona. Mult.

896	50 d. Type **189**	20	15
897	1 r. 50 Footballer and emblems	55	45

190 Shaikh Khalifa and Script

1992. 21st Anniv of Independence. Mult.

898	50 d. Type **190**	20	15
899	50 d. Shaikh Khalifa and "21" in English and Arabic	20	15
900	1 r. Oil well, pen and dhow (42 × 42 mm) ..	35	30
901	1 r. Dhow in harbour (42 × 42 mm) ..	35	30

191 Ball, Flag and Emblem

1992. 11th Arabian Gulf Football Championship. Multicoloured.

902	50 d. Type **191**	20	15
903	1 r. Ball bursting goal net (vert)	35	30

192 Emblems and Globe
193 Mosque

1992. International Nutrition Conference, Rome. Multicoloured.

904	50 d. Type **192**	20	15
905	1 r. Cornucopia (horiz) ..	35	30

1993. Old Mosques. Each sepia, yellow and brown.

906	1 r. Type **193**	35	30
907	1 r. Mosque (minaret without balcony) ..	35	30
908	1 r. Mosque (minaret with wide balcony) ..	35	30
909	1 r. Mosque (minaret with narrow balcony) ..	35	30

194 Presenter and Dish Aerial

1993. 25th Anniv of Qatar Broadcasting. Mult.

910	25 d. Type **194**	10	10
911	50 d. Rocket and satellite	20	15
912	75 d. Broadcasting House	30	25
913	1 r. Journalists	35	30

195 Oil Refinery and Sea
196 Scroll, Quill and Paper

1993. 22nd Anniv of Independence. Mult.

915	25 d. Type **195**	10	10
916	50 d. Flag and clock tower, Doha	20	15
917	75 d. "22" in English and Arabic	30	25
918	1 r. 50 Flag and fort ..	55	45

1993. International Literacy Day. Mult.

919	25 d. Type **196**	10	10
920	50 d. Fountain pen and flags spelling "Qatar" ..	20	10
921	75 d. Fountain pen and Arabic characters ..	30	25
922	1 r. 50 Arabic text on scroll and fountain pen ..	55	45

POSTAGE DUE STAMPS

D 40.

1968.

D 254.	D 40.	5 d. blue	12·00	10·00
D 255.		10 d. red	15·00	12·00
D 256.		20 d. green ..	17·00	15·00
D 257.		30 d. lilac	18·00	17·00

QUELIMANE Pt. 9

A district of Portuguese E. Africa, now part of Mozambique, whose stamps it now uses.

100 centavos = 1 escudo.

1913. Surch. **REPUBLICA QUELIMANE** and new value on "Vasco da Gama" stamps of (a) Portuguese Colonies.

No.	Description	Unused	Used
1.	¼ c. on 2½ r. green	40	30
2.	½ c. on 5 r. red	40	30
3.	1 c. on 10 r. purple	40	30
4.	2½ c. on 25 r. green	40	30
5.	5 c. on 50 r. blue	40	30
6.	7½ c. on 75 r. brown	80	70
7.	10 c. on 100 r. brown	45	35
8.	15 c. on 150 r. bistre	45	35

(b) Macao.

No.	Description	Unused	Used
9.	¼ c. on ½ a. green	40	30
10.	½ c. on 1 a. red	40	30
11.	1 c. on 2 a. purple	40	30
12.	2½ c. on 4 a. green	40	30
13.	5 c. on 8 a. blue	40	30
14.	7½ c. on 12 a. brown	80	70
15.	10 c. on 16 a. brown	45	35
16.	15 c. on 24 a. bistre	45	35

(c) Timor.

No.	Description	Unused	Used
17.	¼ c. on ½ a. green	40	30
18.	½ c. on 1 a. red	40	30
19.	1 c. on 2 a. purple	40	30
20.	2½ c. on 2 a. green	40	30
21.	5 c. on 8 a. blue	40	30
22.	7½ c. on 12 a. brown	80	70
23.	10 c. on 16 a. brown	40	35
24.	15 c. on 24 a. bistre	45	35

1914. "Ceres" key-type inscr. "QUELIMANE".

No.	Description	Unused	Used
25. U.	¼ c. olive	20	20
26.	½ c. black	60	40
42.	1 c. green	50	45
28.	1½ c. brown	70	50
29.	2 c. red	70	60
30.	2½ c. violet	25	20
31.	5 c. blue	50	40
43.	7½ c. brown	50	45
33.	8 c. black	60	50
44.	10 c. brown	50	45
35.	15 c. red	95	70
45.	20 c. green	50	45
37.	30 c. brown on green	1·25	90
38.	40 c. brown on red	1·25	90
39.	50 c. orange on pink	1·25	90
40.	1 e. green on blue	1·25	90

RAS AL KHAIMA Pt. 19

Arab Shaikhdom in the Arabian Gulf.

Ras al Khaima joined the United Arab Emirates in February, 1972. U.A.E. stamps were used in the shaikhdom from 1st January, 1973.

1964. 100 naye paise = 1 rupee.
1966. 100 dirhams = 1 riyal.

1. Shaikh Saqr bin Mohamed al-Qasimi.

3. Dhow.

1964.

No.	Description	Unused	Used
1. 1.	5 n.p. brown and black	10	10
2.	15 n.p. blue and black	15	10
3. –	30 n.p. yellow and black	40	10
4. –	40 n.p. blue and black	60	15
5. –	75 n.p. red and black	1·00	30
6. 3.	1 r. brown and green	1·50	45
7.	2 r. brown and violet	2·50	1·25
8.	5 r. brown and slate	5·50	3·00

DESIGNS: As Type 1—VERT. 30 n.p. to 75 n.p. Seven palms.

3a. Pres. Kennedy inspecting "Friendship 7".

1965. Pres. Kennedy Commem.

No.	Description	Unused	Used
9. 3a.	2 r. blue and ochre	1·00	60
10. –	3 r. blue and ochre	1·25	80
11. –	4 r. blue and ochre	1·75	1·25

DESIGNS—HORIZ. 3 r. Kennedy and wife. VERT. 4 r. Kennedy and flame of remembrance.

4. Sir Winston Churchill and Houses of Parliament.

1965. Churchill Commem.

No.	Description	Unused	Used
12. 4.	2 r. blue and ochre	1·25	60
13. –	3 r. blue and ochre	1·40	80
14. –	4 r. blue and ochre	2·25	1·25

DESIGNS—HORIZ. 3 r. Churchill and Pres. Roosevelt. 4 r. Churchill, and Heads of State at his funeral.

1965. Olympic Games, Tokyo (1964). Optd. **OLYMPIC TOKYO 1964** in English and Arabic, and Olympic "rings".

No.	Description	Unused	Used
15. 3.	1 r. brown and green	50	35
16.	2 r. brown and violet	1·00	80
17.	5 r. brown and grey	2·50	2·25

1965. Death Cent. of Abraham Lincoln. Optd. **ABRAHAM LINCOLN 1809-1865** in English and Arabic.

No.	Description	Unused	Used
18. 3.	1 r. brown and green	50	35
19.	2 r. brown and violet	1·00	80
20.	5 r. brown and slate	2·50	2·25

1965. 20th Death Anniv. of Pres. Roosevelt. Optd. **FRANKLIN D. ROOSEVELT 1882-1945.** in English and Arabic.

No.	Description	Unused	Used
21. 3.	1 r. brown and green	50	35
22.	2 r. brown and violet	1·00	80
23.	5 r. brown and grey	2·50	2·25

8. Satellite and Tracking Station.

1966. I.T.U. Cent. Multicoloured.

No.	Description	Unused	Used
24.	15 n.p. Type 8	20	10
25.	50 n.p. Post Office Tower, London, "Telstar" and tracking gantry	55	30
26.	85 n.p. Rocket on launching-pad and "Relay"	1·00	50
27.	1 r. Type 8	1·25	60
28.	2 r. As 50 n.p.	2·00	90
29.	3 r. As 85 n.p.	2·50	1·10

9. Swimming.

10. Carpenter.

1966. Pan-Arab Games, Cairo (1965).

No.	Description	Unused	Used
31. A.	1 n.p. brown, pink & grn.	10	10
32. B.	2 n.p. black, grey & green	10	10
33. C.	3 n.p. brown, pink & green	10	10
34. D.	4 n.p. brown, pink & pur.	10	10
35. A.	5 n.p. black, grey & orge.	10	10
36. 9.	10 n.p. brown, pink & blue	10	10
37. B.	25 n.p. brn., pink & lt. brn.	10	10
38. C.	50 n.p. black, grey & violet	20	15
39. D.	75 n.p. black, grey & blue	35	15
40. 9.	1 r. black, grey & turquoise	45	25

DESIGNS: A, Running. B, Boxing. C, Football. D, Fencing.

1966. American Astronauts.

No.	Description	Unused	Used
42. 10.	25 n.p. black, gold & purple	15	10
43. –	50 n.p. black, silver & brn.	25	10
44. –	75 n.p. blk., silver & turq.	30	15
45. –	1 r. black, silver & bistre	45	20
46. –	2 r. black, silver & mauve	75	40
47. –	3 r. black, gold and green	1·25	60
48. –	4 r. black, gold and red	1·50	80
49. –	5 r. black, gold and blue	1·90	95

ASTRONAUTS: 50 n.p. Glenn. 75 n.p. Shepard. 1 r. Cooper. 2 r. Grissom. 3 r. Schirra. 4 r. Stafford. 5 r. Lovell.

11. Shaikh Sabah of Kuwait and Shaikh Saqr of Ras al Khaima.

1966. Int. Co-operation Year.

No.	Description	Unused	Used
51. 11.	1 r. black and brown	80	30
52. A.	1 r. black and lilac	80	30
53. B.	1 r. black and red	80	30
54. C.	1 r. black and turquoise	80	30
55. D.	1 r. black and olive	80	30
56. E.	1 r. black and yellow	80	30
57. F.	1 r. black and orange	80	30
58. G.	1 r. black and blue	80	30

SHAIKH SAQR AND WORLD LEADERS: A, Shaikh Ahmad of Qatar. B, Pres. Nasser. C, King Hussein. D, Pres. Johnson. E, Pres. De Gaulle. F, Pope Paul VI. G, Prime Minister Harold Wilson.

NEW CURRENCY SURCHARGES. During the latter half of 1966 various issues appeared surcharged in dirhams and riyals. The 1964 definitives with this surcharge are listed below as there is considerable evidence of their postal use. Nos. 24/58 also exist with these surcharges.

In August 1966 Nos. 1/14, 24/9 and 51/8 appeared surcharged in fils and rupees. As Ras Al Khaima did not adopt this currency their status is uncertain.

1966. Nos. 1/8 with currency names changed to dirhams and riyals by overprinting in English and Arabic.

No.	Description	Unused	Used
60 1.	5 d. on 5 n.p. black and brown	15	10
60a –	5 d. on 75 n.p. red & black	15	10
~~64b~~ 3.	5 d. on 5 r. brn. & grey	15	10
61 1.	15 d. on 15 n.p. blue and black	25	10
62 –	30 d. on 30 n.p. black and yellow	40	15
63 –	40 d. on 40 n.p. blue and black	55	20
64 –	75 d. on 75 n.p. red & black	65	25
65 3.	1 r. on 1 r. brn. & green	75	30
66	2 r. on 2 r. brn. & vio.	1·50	1·25
67	5 r. on 5 r. brown & grey	3·50	2·25

15. W.H.O. Building and Flowers.

1966. Inaug. of W.H.O. Headquarters, Geneva.

No.	Description	Unused	Used
68. 15.	15 d. multicoloured (post.)	20	10
69. –	35 d. multicoloured	60	20
70. 15.	50 d. multicoloured (air)	75	30
71. –	3 r. multicoloured	2·00	70

DESIGN: 35 d., 3 r. As Type 15 but with red instead of yellow flowers at left.

16. Queen Elizabeth II presenting Jules Rimet Cup to Bobby Moore, Captain of England Team.

1966. Air. England's Victory in World Cup Football Championships. Multicoloured.

No.	Description	Unused	Used
73.	1 r. Wembley Stadium	70	25
74.	2 r. Goalkeeper saving ball	1·25	45
75.	3 r. Footballers with ball	1·75	70
76.	4 r. Type 16	2·25	1·25

For later issues see **UNITED ARAB EMIRATES.**

APPENDIX

The following stamps have either been issued in excess of postal needs or have not been available to the public in a reasonable quantities at face value. Such stamps may later be given full listing if there is evidence of regular postal use.

1967.

"The Arabian Nights". Paintings. Air 30, 70 d., 1, 2, 3 r.

Cats. Postage 1, 2, 3, 4, 5d.; Air 3 r.

Arab Paintings. 1, 2, 3, 4, 10, 20, 30 d.

European Paintings. Air 60, 70 d., 1, 2, 3, 5, 10 r.

50th Birth Anniv. of Pres. John F. Kennedy. Optd. on 1965 Pres. Kennedy Commem. 2, 3, 4 r.

World Scout Jamboree, Idaho. Postage 1, 2, 3, 4 d.; Air 35, 75 d., 1 r.

U.S. "Apollo" Disaster. Optd. on 1968 American Astronauts issue. 25 d. on 25 n.p., 50 d. on 50 n.p., 75 d. on 75 n.p., 1, 2, 3, 4, 5 r.

Summer Olympics Preparation, Mexico 1968. Postage 10, 20, 30, 40 d.; Air 1, 2 r.

Winter Olympics Preparation, Grenoble 1968. Postage 1, 2, 3, 4, 5, d.; Air 85 d., 2, 3 r.

1968.

Mothers' Day. Paintings. Postage 20, 30 40, 50 d.; Air 1, 2, 3, 4 r.

Int. Human Rights Year. 2 r.×3.

Int. Museum Campaign. Paintings. 15, 15, 20, 25, 35, 40, 45, 60, 70, 80, 90 d., 1, 1 r. 25, 1 r. 50, 2 r. 50, 2 r. 75.

Winter Olympic Medal Winners, Grenoble. 50 d., 1, 1 r. 50, 2, 2 r. 50, 3 r.

Olympic Games, Mexico. Air 1, 2, 2, 3, 3, 4 r.

5th Death Anniv. of Pres. John F. Kennedy. Air 2, 3 r.

Christmas. Religious Paintings. Postage 20, 30, 40, 50, 60 d., 1 r.; Air 2, 3, 4 r.

1969.

Famous Composers (1st series). Paintings. 25, 50, 75 d., 1 r. 50, 2 r. 50.

Famous Operas. 20, 40, 60, 80 d., 1, 2 r.

Famous Men. Postage 20, 30, 50 d.; Air 1 r. 50, 2, 3, 4, 5 r.

Int. Philatelic Exhib., Mexico 1968 (EFIMEX). Postage 10, 10, 25, 35, 40, 50, 60, 70 d.; Air 1, 2, 3, 5, 5 r.

Int. Co-operation in Olympics. 1, 2, 3, 4 r.

Int. Co-operation in Space. Air 1 r. 50, 2 r. 50, 3 r. 50, 4 r. 50.

Birth Bicentenary of Napoleon. Paintings. Postage 1 r. 75, 2 r. 75, 3 r. 75; Air 75 d.

"Apollo" Moon Missions. Air 2, 2 r. 50, 3, 3 r. 50, 4, 4 r. 50, 5, 5 r. 50.

"Apollo 11" Astronauts. Air 2 r. 25, 3 r. 25, 4 r. 25, 5 r. 25.

"Apollo 12" Astronauts. Air 60 d., 2 r. 60, 3 r. 60, 4 r. 60, 5 r. 60.

1970.

Christmas 1969. Religious Paintings. Postage 50 d.; Air 3, 3 r. 50.

World Cup, Mexico. Air 1, 2, 3, 4, 5, 6 r.

Easter. Religious Paintings. Postage 50 d.; Air 3, 3 r. 50.

Paintings by Titian and Tiepolo. Postage 50, 50 d.; Air 3, 3, 3 r. 50, 3 r. 50.

Winter Olympics, Sapporo 1972. Air 1, 2, 3, 4, 5, 6 r.

Olympic Games, Munich 1972. Air 1, 2, 3, 4, 5, 6 r.

Paul Gauguin's Paintings. Postage 50 d.; Air 3, 3 r. 50.

Christmas. Religious Paintings. Postage 50 d.; Air 3, 3 r. 50.

"World Cup Champions, Brazil". Optd. on Mexico World Cup issue. Air 1, 2, 3, 4, 5, 6 r.

"EXPO 70" World Fair, Osaka, Japan (1st issue). Postage 40, 45, 50, 55, 60, 65, 70, 75 d.; Air 80, 85, 90, 95 d., 1 r. 60, 1 r. 65, 1 r. 85, 2 r.

"EXPO 70" World Fair, Osaka, Japan (2nd issue). Postage 55, 65, 75 d.; Air 25, 85, 95 d., 1 r. 50, 1 r. 75.

Space Programmes. Air 1 r.×6, 2 r.×6, 4 r.×6.

Famous Frenchmen. Air 1 r.×4, 2 r.×4, 2 r. 50×2, 3 r.×2, 4 r.×4, 5 r. 50×2.

Int. Philatelic Exhib. (Philympia '70). Air 1 r.×4, 1 r. 50×4, 2 r. 50×4, 3 r.×4, 4 r.×4.

Events in the Life of Christ. Religious Paintings. 5, 10, 25, 50 d., 1, 2, 5 r.

"Stages of the Cross". Religious Paintings. 10, 20, 30, 40, 50, 60, 70, 80 d., 1, 1 r. 50, 2, 2 r. 50, 3, 3 r. 50.

The Life of Mary. Religious Paintings. 10, 15, 30, 60, 75 d., 3, 4 r.

1971.

Easter. "Stages of the Cross" (1970) but with additional inscr. "EASTER". 10, 20, 30, 40, 50, 60, 70, 80 d., 1, 1 r. 50, 2, 2 r. 50, 3, 3 r. 50.

Charles de Gaulle Memorial. Postage 50 d.; Air 1, 1 r. 50, 2, 3, 4 r.

Safe return of "Apollo 14". Postage 50 d.; Air 1, 1 r. 50, 2, 3, 4 r.

U.S.A.—Japan Baseball Friendship. Postage 10, 25, 30, 80 d.; Air 50, 70 d., 1, 1 r. 50.

Munich Olympics, 1972. Postage 50 d.; Air 1, 1 r. 50, 2, 3, 4 r.

Cats. 35, 60, 65, 110, 120, 160 d.

13th World Jamboree, Japan. Postage 30, 50, 60, 75 d.; Air 1, 1 r. 50, 3, 4 r.

Sapporo Olympic Gold Medal Winners. Optd. on 1970 Winter Olympics, Sapporo 1972, issue, Air 1, 2, 3, 4, 5, 6 r.

Munich Olympic Medal Winners, Optd. on 1970 Summer Olympics, Munich 1972, issue. Air 1, 2, 3, 4, 5, 6 r.

Japanese Locomotives. Postage 30, 35, 75 d.; Air 90 d., 1, 1 r. 75.

"Soyuz 11" Russian Cosmonauts Memorial. Air 1, 2, 3, 4 r.

"Apollo 15". Postage 50 d.; Air 1, 1 r. 50, 2, 3, 4 r.

Dogs. 5, 20, 75, 85, 185, 200 d.

Durer's Paintings. Postage 50 d.; Air 1, 1 r. 50 2, 3, 4 r.

Famous Composers (2nd series). Postage 50 d;. Air 1, 1 r. 50, 2, 3, 4 r.

"Soyuz 11" and "Salyut" Space Projects. Postage 50 d.; Air 1, 1 r. 50, 2, 3, 4 r.

Butterflies. Postage 15, 20, 70 d.; Air 1 r. 25, 1 r. 50, 1 r. 70.

Wild Animals. 10, 40, 80 d., 1 r. 15, 1 r. 30, 1 r. 65.

Fishes. 30, 50, 60, 90 d., 1 r. 45, 1 r. 55.

Ludwig Van Beethoven. Portraits. Postage 50 d.; Air 1, 1 r. 50, 2, 3, 4 r.

1972.

Birds. 50, 55, 80, 100, 105, 190 d.

Winter Olympics, Sapporo (1st issue). Postage 20, 30, 50 d.; Air 70, 90 d., 2 r. 50.

Winter Olympics, Sapporo (2nd issue). Postage 5, 60, 80, 90 d.; Air 1 r. 10, 1 r. 75.

Mozart. Portraits. Postage 50 d.; Air 1, 1 r. 50, 2, 3, 4 r.

Olympic Games, Munich. Postage 50 d.; Air 1, 1 r. 50, 2, 3, 4 r.

" In Memory of Charles de Gaulle ". Optd. on 1971 Charles de Gaulle memorial issue. Postage 50 d.; Air 1, 1 r. 50, 2, 3, 4 r.

Winter Olympics, Sapporo (3rd issue). Postage 15, 45 d.; Air 65, 75 d., 1 r. 20, 1 r. 25.

Horses. Postage 10, 25, 30 d.; Air 1 r. 40, 1 r. 80, 1 r. 95.

Parrots. 40, 45, 70, 95 d., 1 r. 35, 1 r. 75.

"Apollo 16". Postage 50 d.; Air 1, 1 r. 50, 2, 3, 4 r.

European Footballers. Postage 50 d.; Air 1, 1 r. 50, 2, 3, 4 r.

A number of issues on gold or silver foil also exist, but it is understood that these were mainly for presentation purposes, although valid for postage.

In common with the other states of the United Arab Emirates the Ras al Khaima stamp contract was terminated on 1st August 1972, and any further new issues released after that date were unauthorised.

REUNION Pt. 6

An island in the Indian Ocean, E. of Madagascar, now an overseas department of France.

100 centimes = 1 franc.

1.

1852. Imperf. No gum.

1	1	15 c. black on blue ..	£20000	£11000
2		30 c. black on blue ..	£20000	£11000

1885. Stamps of French Colonies surch **R** and value in figures. Imperf.

5	D	5 c. on 30 c. brown ..	30·00	28·00
7	H	5 c. on 30 c. brown ..	3·50	4·50
3	A	5 c. on 40 c. orange ..	£225	£200
6	F	5 c. on 40 c. orange ..	26·00	18·00
8	H	5 c. on 40 c. red on yellow	65·00	55·00
9		10 c. on 40 c. red on yell	6·50	4·50
10		20 c. on 30 c. brown ..	42·00	35·00
4	A	25 c. on 40 c. orange ..	30·00	25·00

1891. Stamps of French Colonies optd **REUNION**. Imperf (Types F and H) or perf (Type J).

17	J	1 c. black on blue ..	1·40	1·60
18		2 c. brown on buff ..	2·25	1·00
19		4 c. brown on grey ..	3·00	3·00
20		5 c. green on green ..	4·50	2·25
21		10 c. black on lilac ..	19·00	1·75
22		15 c. blue on blue ..	28·00	1·75
23		20 c. red on green ..	18·00	2·50
24		25 c. black on pink ..	20·00	2·50
13	H	30 c. brown	23·00	21·00
25	J	35 c. black on yellow ..	16·00	11·50
11	F	40 c. orange	£300	£290
14	H	40 c. red on yellow ..	17·00	14·00
26	J	40 c. red on buff ..	45·00	35·00
15	H	75 c. red	£225	£225
27	J	75 c. red on pink ..	£400	£325
12	F	80 c. pink	35·00	30·00
16	H	1 f. green	25·00	23·00
28	J	1 f. green	£300	£300

1891. Stamps of French Colonies surch **REUNION** and new value.

29	J	02 c. on 20 c. red on green	4·50	3·75
31		2 on 20 c. red on green ..	1·75	1·75
30		15 c. on 20 c. red on green	5·50	5·00

1892. "Tablet" key-type inscr "REUNION".

34	D	1 c. black and red on blue	50	50
35		2 c. brown & blue on buff	50	45
36		4 c. brown & blue on grey	1·10	60
50		5 c. green and red ..	70	40
38		10 c. black & blue on lilac	4·00	1·00
51		10 c. red and blue ..	80	35
39		15 c. blue and red ..	11·50	75
52		15 c. grey and red ..	2·75	35
40		20 c. red & blue on green	4·50	5·00
41		25 c. black & red on pink	8·25	1·00
53		25 c. blue and red ..	9·75	9·50
42		30 c. brown & bl on drab	9·25	4·75
43		40 c. red & blue on yellow	14·00	9·00
44		50 c. red and blue on pink	42·00	21·00
54		50 c. brown & red on blue	23·00	21·00
55		50 c. brown & blue on bl	30·00	26·00
45		75 c. brown & red on orge	38·00	24·00
46		1 f. green and red ..	28·00	15·00

1893. Stamp of French Colonies, "Commerce" type, surch **2 c.**

47	J	2 c. on 20 c. red on green	1·00	95

1901. "Tablet" key-type surch in figures.

56	D	5 c. on 40 c. red and blue on yellow	1·25	2·25
57		5 c. on 50 c. red and blue on pink	2·75	2·75
58		15 c. on 75 c. brown and red on orange ..	8·00	8·00
59		15 c. on 1 f. green and red	7·00	7·00

16. Map of Reunion.

17. View of Saint-Denis and Arms of the Colony.

18. View of St. Pierre and Crater Dolomieu.

1907.

60	16	1 c. red and lilac ..	10	10
61		2 c. blue and brown ..	10	10
62		4 c. red and green ..	10	10
63		5 c. red and green ..	25	10
92		5 c. violet and yellow ..	20	15
64		10 c. green and red ..	90	10
93		10 c. turquoise and green	20	15
94		10 c. red & lake on blue	35	15
65		15 c. blue and black ..	30	10
95		15 c. turquoise and green	20	25
96		15 c. red and blue ..	25	35
66	17	20 c. green and olive ..	25	25
67		25 c. brown and blue ..	1·40	50
97		25 c. blue and brown ..	20	10
68		30 c. green and brown ..	35	55
98		30 c. pink and red ..	30	50
99		30 c. red and grey ..	15	25
100		30 c. light green & green	55	70
69		35 c. blue and brown ..	35	35
101		40 c. brown and green ..	35	15
70		45 c. pink and violet ..	55	70
102		45 c. red and purple ..	35	50
103		45 c. red and mauve ..	90	1·25
71		50 c. blue and brown ..	1·40	75
104		50 c. ultramarine & blue	25	25
105		50 c. violet and yellow ..	20	15
106		60 c. brown and blue ..	15	30
107		65 c. blue and violet ..	55	70
72		75 c. pink and red ..	45	35
108		75 c. purple and brown ..	1·00	1·00
109		90 c. pink and red ..	3·50	3·50
73	18	1 f. blue and brown ..	40	45
110		1 f. blue	50	65
111		1 f. lilac and brown ..	50	50
112		1 f. 10 mauve and brown	55	60
113		1 f. 50 lt blue & bl on bl	6·00	4·50
74		2 f. green and red ..	2·25	1·60
114		3 f. mauve on pink ..	6·25	4·75
75		5 f. brown and pink ..	3·50	3·00

1912. "Tablet" key-type surch.

76	D	05 on 2 c. brown and red on buff	20	25
77		05 on 15 c. grey and red	40	50
78		05 on 20 c. red and blue on green	65	75
79		05 on 25 c. black and red on pink	35	60
80		05 on 30 c. brown and blue on drab	35	55
81		10 on 40 c. red and blue on yellow	30	50
82		10 on 50 c. brown and blue on blue	75	1·60
83		10 on 75 c. brown and red on orange	2·50	5·00

1915. Red Cross. Surch **5c** and red cross.

90	16	10 c.+5 c. green and red	50	80

1917. Surch in figures.

91	16	0,01 on 4 c. red & green	70	70
124	18	25 c. on 5 f. brown & red	40	60
115	17	40 on 20 c. yellow & grn	30	40
116		50 on 45 c. red & purple	50	65
117		50 on 45 c. red & mauve	£160	£160
118		50 on 65 c. blue & violet	45	60
119		60 on 75 c. carmine and red	25	25
120	16	65 on 15 c. blue & black	65	75
121		85 on 15 c. blue & black	60	75
122	17	85 on 75 c. pink and red	70	85
123		90 on 75 c. pink & red	85	90
125	18	1 f. 25 on 1 f. blue ..	35	45
126		1 f. 50 on 1 f. light blue and blue on blue ..	35	35
127		3 f. on 5 f. blue and red	1·25	1·25
128		10 f. on 5 f. red & green	8·75	7·25
129		20 f. on 5 f. pink & brn	11·00	9·00

1931. "Colonial Exhibition" key-types inscr "REUNION".

130	E	40 c. green and black ..	1·50	1·60
131	F	50 c. mauve and black ..	1·90	2·00
132	G	90 c. red and black ..	2·00	2·00
133	H	1 f. 50 blue and black ..	2·00	2·00

30. Cascade, Salazie.

31. Anchain Peak, Salazie.

32. Leon Dierx Museum.

34.

1933.

134.	30.	1 c. purple	10	30
135.		2 c. brown	10	20
136.		3 c. mauve	10	25
137.		4 c. olive	10	30
138.		5 c. orange	10	20
139.		10 c. blue	10	25
140.		15 c. black	10	15
141.		20 c. blue	20	25
142.		25 c. brown	15	25
143.		30 c. green	15	20
144.	31.	35 c. green	30	40
145.		40 c. blue	25	35
146.		40 c. brown	20	35
147.		45 c. mauve	45	55
148.		45 c. green	25	35
149.		50 c. red	25	15
150.		55 c. orange	55	55
151.		60 c. blue	20	35
152.		65 c. olive	70	65
153.		70 c. olive	35	40
154.		75 c. brown	2·50	2·25
155.		80 c. black	35	50
156.		90 c. red	1·25	1·00
157.		90 c. purple	50	45
158.		1 f. green	1·00	65
159.		1 f. red	65	60
160.		1 f. black	25	35
161.	32.	1 f. 25 brown	35	50
162.		1 f. 25 red	50	50
163.	30.	1 f. 40 blue	50	45
164.	32.	1 f. 50 blue	15	15
165.	30.	1 f. 60 red	45	45
166.	32.	1 f. 75 olive	35	35
167.	30.	1 f. 75 blue	45	55
168.	32.	2 f. red	25	40
169.	30.	2 f. 25 blue	85	80
170.		2 f. 50 brown	55	55
171.	32.	3 f. violet	30	30
172.		5 f. mauve	30	35
173.		10 f. blue	40	45
174.		20 f. brown	70	75

1937. Air. Pioneer Flight from Reunion to France by Laurent, Lenier and Touge. Optd. **REUNION - FRANCE par avion "ROLAND GARROS".**

174a.	31.	50 c. red	£170	£160

1937. International Exhibition, Paris. As Nos. 168/73 of St.-Pierre et Miquelon.

175		20 c. violet	85	95
176		30 c. green	95	1·10
177		40 c. red	90	1·10
178		50 c. brown and agate ..	90	1·10
179		90 c. red	95	1·10
180		1 f. 50 blue	95	1·25

1938. Air.

181.	34.	3 f. 65 blue and red ..	60	85
182.		6 f. 65 brown and red ..	60	85
183.		9 f. 65 red and blue ..	60	85
184.		12 f. 65 brown and green	1·00	1·40

1938. Int. Anti-Cancer Fund. As T **22** of Mauritania.

185.		1 f. 75+50 c. blue ..	5·50	7·50

1939. New York World's Fair. As T **28** of Mauritania.

186.		1 f. 25 red	50	60
187.		2 f. 25 blue	55	60

1939. 150th Anniv of French Revolution. As T **29** of Mauritania.

188		45 c.+25 c. green and black (postage) ..	4·75	5·00
189		70 c.+30 c. brown & black	4·75	5·00
190		90 c.+35 c. orange & black	4·50	5·00
191		1 f. 25+1 f. red and black	4·75	5·00
192		2 f. 25+2 f. blue and black	4·75	5·00
193		3 f. 65+4 f. black and orange (air)	9·50	11·50

1943. Surch **1f.**

194	31	1 f. on 65 c. green ..	55	55

1943. Optd **France Libre**.

198	30	1 c. purple (postage) ..	50	55
199		2 c. brown	40	55
200		3 c. purple	40	55
195	16	4 c. red and green ..	1·25	1·90
201	30	4 c. green	40	55
202		5 c. red	40	55
203		10 c. blue	40	55
204		15 c. black	40	55
205		20 c. blue	40	55
206		25 c. brown	40	55
207		30 c. green	40	55
208	31	35 c. green	35	55
209		40 c. blue	40	55
210		40 c. brown	40	55
211		45 c. mauve	40	55
212		45 c. green	40	55
213		50 c. red	45	65
214		55 c. orange	40	55
215		60 c. blue	1·40	1·40
216		65 c. green	40	55
217		70 c. green	85	90
196	17	75 c. pink and red ..	65	70
218	31	75 c. brown	1·50	1·60
219		80 c. black	40	55
220		90 c. purple	40	55
221		1 f. green	40	55
222		1 f. red	40	55
223		1 f. black	95	1·00
240		1 f. on 65 c. green (No. 194)	65	75
224	32	1 f. 25 brown	40	55
225		1 f. 25 red	85	90
238	–	1 f. 25 red (No. 186) ..	1·25	1·40
226	30	1 f. 40 blue	75	90
227	32	1 f. 50 blue	35	55
228	30	1 f. 60 red	85	1·00
229	32	1 f. 75 green	40	55
230	30	1 f. 75 blue	2·00	2·25
231	32	2 f. red	35	55
239	–	2 f. 25 blue (No. 187) ..	1·40	1·40
232	30	2 f. 25 blue	85	90
233		2 f. 50 brown	3·00	3·00
234	32	3 f. violet	45	55
197	18	5 f. brown and pink ..	27·00	27·00
235	32	5 f. mauve	85	90
236		10 f. blue	3·50	3·75
237		20 f. brown	5·75	5·75
241	34	3 f. 65 blue and red (air)	2·00	2·00
242		6 f. 65 brown and red ..	2·00	2·00
243		9 f. 65 red and blue ..	2·00	2·00
244		12 f. 65 brown and green	2·00	2·00

37. Chief Products.

1943. Free French Issue.

245	37	5 c. brown	10	25
246a		10 c. blue	20	25
247		25 c. green	10	25
248		30 c. red	10	25
249		40 c. green	10	25
250		80 c. mauve	10	30
251		1 f. purple	15	30
252		1 f. 50 red	15	35
253		2 f. black	20	35
254		2 f. 50 blue	25	40
255		4 f. violet	15	30
256		5 f. yellow	20	30
257		10 f. brown	25	70
258		20 f. green	30	80

1944. Air. Free French Administration. As T **30** of New Caledonia.

259.		1 f. orange	20	30
260.		1 f. 50 red	30	35
261.		5 f. purple	30	35
262.		10 f. black	40	45
263.		25 f. blue	40	45
264.		50 f. green	40	50
265.		100 f. red	60	70

1944. Mutual Air and Red Cross Funds. As T **31** of New Caledonia.

266.		5 f.+20 f. black	55	55

1945. Eboue. As T **32** of New Caledonia.

267.		2 f. black	45	45
268.		25 f. green	55	55

1945. Surch.

269. **37.** 50 c. on 5 c. brown .. 25 35
270. 60 c. on 5 c. brown .. 25 35
271. 70 c. on 5 c. brown .. 25 35
272. 1 f. 20 on 5 c. brown .. 35 50
273. 2 f. 40 on 25 c. green .. 35 50
274. 3 f. on 25 c. green .. 35 50
275. 4 f. 50 on 25 c. green .. 45 60
276. 15 f. on 2 f. 50 blue .. 45 65

1946. Air. Victory. As T **34** of New Caledonia.

277. 8 f. grey 40 55

1946. Air. From Chad to the Rhine. As Nos. 300/305 of New Caledonia.

278. 5 f. red 60 85
279. 10 f. violet 60 85
280. 15 f. black 60 80
281. 20 f. red 70 90
282. 25 f. blue 70 85
283. 50 f. green 70 90

39. Cliffs.

40. Banana Tree and Cliff.

41. Mountain Landscape.

42. Shadow of Aeroplane over Coast.

1947.

284 **39** 10 c. orange & grn (post) 10 30
285 30 c. orange and blue .. 10 30
286 40 c. orange and brown 10 30
287 – 50 c. brown and green 15 30
288 – 60 c. brown and blue .. 15 10
289 – 80 c. green and brown 15 40
290 – 1 f. purple and blue .. 30 20
291 – 1 f. 20 grey and green .. 35 50
292 – 1 f. 50 purple & orange 35 50
293 **40** 2 f. blue and green .. 25 30
294 3 f. purple and green .. 35 55
295 3 f. 60 pink and red .. 35 55
296 4 f. blue and brown .. 35 55
297 **41** 5 f. mauve and brown 35 50
298 6 f. blue and brown .. 50 60
299 10 f. orange and blue .. 80 85
300 – 15 f. purple and blue .. 1·75 1·90
301 – 20 f. blue and orange .. 2·25 2·25
302 – 25 f. brown and mauve 2·75 2·75
303 **42** 50 f. green and grey (air) 3·75 3·75
304 – 100 f. orange and brown 5·75 5·75
305 – 200 f. blue and orange 7·50 7·75

DESIGNS—20 × 37 mm: 50 c. to 80 c. Cutting sugar cane. 1 f. to 1 f. 50, Cascade. 28 × 50 mm: 100 f. Douglas DC-4 Skymaster over Reunion. 37 × 20 mm: 15 f. to 25 f. "Ville de Strasbourg" (liner) approaching Reunion. 50 × 28 mm: 200 f. Reunion from the air.

1949. Stamps of France surch **CFA** and value.
(a) Postage. (i) Ceres

306 **218** 50 c. on 1 f. red .. 15 30
307 60 c. on 2 f. green .. 2·25 1·40

(ii) Nos. 972/3 (Arms)

308 10 c. on 30 c. black, red and yellow (Alsace) 10 30
309 30 c. on 50 c. brown, yellow and red (Lorraine) .. 25 40

(iii) Nos. 981, 979 and 982/a (Views)

310 5 f. on 20 f. blue (Finistere) 1·75 50
311 7 f. on 12 f. red (Luxembourg Palace) .. .. 2·50 1·25
312 8 f. on 25 f. blue (Nancy) 6·00 1·90
313 10 f. on 25 f. brn (Nancy) 1·00 70

(iv) Marianne

314 **219** 1 f. on 3 f. mauve .. 40 30
315 2 f. on 4 f. green .. 75 50
316 2 f. on 5 f. green .. 3·25 3·25
317 2 f. on 5 f. violet .. 60 50
318 2 f. 50 on 5 f. blue .. 7·50 6·75
319 3 f. on 6 f. red .. 90 30
320 3 f. on 6 f. green .. 1·60 1·40
321 4 f. on 10 f. violet .. 85 40
322 6 f. on 12 f. blue .. 2·25 75
323 6 f. on 12 f. orange .. 1·90 1·25
324 9 f. on 18 f. red .. 2·75 2·75

(v) Conques Abbey

325 **263** 11 f. on 18 f. blue .. 2·00 1·90

(b) Air. (i) Nos. 967/70 (Mythology)

326 – 20 f. on 40 f. green .. 1·50 1·00
327 **236** 25 f. on 50 f. pink .. 1·75 80
328 **237** 50 f. on 100 f. blue .. 3·75 2·50
329 – 100 f. on 200 f. red .. 25·00 12·50

(ii) Nos. 1056 and 1058/9 (Cities)

330 100 f. on 200 f. green (Bordeaux) .. .. 65·00 28·00
331 200 f. on 500 f. red (Marseilles) .. .. 24·00 16·00
332 500 f. on 1000 f. purple and black on blue (Paris) .. £170 £130

1950. Stamps of France surch **CFA** and value.
(a) Nos. 1050 and 1052 (Arms)

342 10 c. on 50 c. yellow, red and blue (Guyenne) .. 15 30
343 1 f. on 2 f. red, yellow & green (Auvergne) .. 3·00 2·50

(b) On Nos. 1067/8 and 1068b (Views)

344 – 5 f. on 20 f. red (Comminges) .. 2·75 50
345 **284** 8 f. on 25 f. blue (Wandrille) .. 1·60 50
346 – 15 f. on 30 f. blue (Arbois) 85 60

1951. Nos. 1123/4 of France (Arms) surch **CFA** and value.

347 50 c. on 1 f. red, yellow and blue (Bearn) 30 35
348 1 f. on 2 f. yellow, blue and red (Touraine) 35 35

1952. Nos. 1138 and 1144 of France surch **CFA** and value.

349 **323** 5 f. on 20 f. violet (Chambord) .. 60 50
350 **317** 8 f. on 40 f. violet (Bigorre) .. 2·75 35

1953. Stamps of France surch **CFA** and value.
(a) Nos. 1162, 1168 and 1170 (Literary Figures and National Industries).

351 3 f. on 6 f. lake and red (Gargantua) 40 35
352 8 f. on 40 f. brown and chocolate (Porcelain) .. 1·50 25
353 20 f. on 75 f. red and carmine (Flowers) .. 1·50 50

(b) Nos. 1181/2 (Arms)

354 50 c. on 1 f. yellow, red and black (Poitou) 45 60
355 1 f. on 2 f. yellow, blue and brown (Champagne) .. 60 55

1954. Stamps of France surch **CFA** and value.
(a) Postage. (i) Nos. 1188 and 1190 (Sports)

356 8 f. on 40 f. blue and brown (Canoeing) .. .. 10·00 5·00
357 20 f. on 75 f. red and orange (Horse jumping) 35·00 23·00

(ii) Nos. 1205/8 and 1210/11 (Views)

358 2 f. on 6 f. indigo, blue and green (Lourdes) .. 45 45
359 3 f. on 8 f. green and blue (Andelys) 50 55
360 4 f. on 10 f. brown and blue (Royan) 65 70
361 6 f. on 12 f. lilac and violet (Quimper) 90 80
362 9 f. on 18 f. indigo, blue and green (Cheverny) .. 2·25 2·75
363 10 f. on 20 f. brown, chestnut & bl (Ajaccio) 1·60 90

(iii) No. 1229 (Arms)

364 1 f. on 2 f. yellow, red and black (Angoumois) .. 30 30

(b) Air. Nos. 1194/7 (Aircraft)

365 50 f. on 100 f. brown and blue (Mystere IV) .. 1·00 75
366 100 f. on 200 f. purple and blue (Noratlas) .. 2·00 1·25
367 200 f. on 500 f. red and orange (Magister) .. 10·00 9·25
368 500 f. on 1000 f. indigo, purple & blue (Provence) 11·00 8·25

1955. Stamps of France surch **CFA** and value.
(a) Nos. 1262/5, 1266, 1268 and 1268b (Views)

369 2 f. on 6 f. red (Bordeaux) 70 65
370 3 f. on 8 f. blue (Marseilles) 80 80
371 4 f. on 10 f. blue (Nice) .. 55 50
372 5 f. on 12 f. brown and grey (Cahors) 60 50
373 6 f. on 18 f. blue and green (Uzerche) 60 50
374 10 f. on 25 f. brown and chestnut (Brouage) .. 65 50
375 17 f. on 70 f. black and green (Cahors) .. 2·75 2·00

(b) No. 1273 (Arms)

376 50 c. on 1 f. yellow, red and blue (Comtat Venaissin) 20 25

1956. Nos. 1297/1300 of France (Sports) surch **CFA** and value.

377 8 f. on 30 f. black and grey (Basketball) .. .. 1·25 45
378 9 f. on 40 f. purple and brown (Pelota) .. 1·90 1·10
379 15 f. on 50 f. violet and purple (Rugby) .. 2·75 1·25
380 20 f. on 75 f. green, black and blue (Climbing) .. 1·90 1·25

1957. Stamps of France surch **CFA** and value.
(a) Postage. (i) Harvester.

381 **344** 2 f. on 6 f. brown .. 25 15
382 4 f. on 12 f. purple .. 1·75 65
383 5 f. on 10 f. green .. 1·25 55

(ii) "France".

384 **362** 10 f. on 20 f. blue .. 55 15
385 12 f. on 25 f. red .. 2·00 30

(iii) No. 1335 (Le Quesnoy)

386 7 f. on 15 f. black & green 80 40

(iv) Nos. 1351, 1352/3, 1354/5 and 1356a (Tourist Publicity)

387 3 f. on 10 f. chocolate and brown (Elysee) .. 55 20
388 6 f. on 18 f. brown and blue (Beynac) 65 55
389 9 f. on 25 f. brown and grey (Valencay) .. 70 60
390 17 f. on 35 f. mauve and red (Rouen) .. .. 1·60 1·00
391 20 f. on 50 f. brown and green (St. Remy) .. 80 40
392 25 f. on 85 f. purple (Evian-les-Bains) .. 2·25 1·00

(b) Air. Nos. 1319/20 (Aircraft).

393 200 f. on 500 f. black and blue (Caravelle) .. 10·50 6·00
394 500 f. on 1000 f. black, violet & brn (L'Alouette) 15·00 8·75

1960. Nos. 1461, 1464 and 1467 of France (Tourist Publicity) surch **CFA** and value.

395 7 f. on 15 c. indigo and blue (Laon) 65 45
396 20 f. on 50 c. purple and green (Tlemcen) .. 12·00 3·25
397 50 f. on 1 f. violet, green and blue (Cilaos) .. 1·60 55

1961. Harvester and Sower stamps of France (in new currency) surch **CFA** and value.

398 **344** 5 f. on 10 c. green .. 30 20
400 **453** 10 f. on 20 c. red and turquoise 20 10

1961. "Marianne" stamp of France surch **12fCFA**.

401 **463** 12 f. on 25 c. grey & pur 20 10

1961. Nos. 1457, 1457b and 1459/60 of France (Aircraft) surch **CFA** and value.

402 100 f. on 2 f. purple and blue (Noratlas) .. 3·50 1·00
403 100 f. on 2 f. indigo and blue (Mystere 20) .. 1·25 50
404 200 f. on 5 f. black and blue (Caravelle) .. 4·50 2·00
405 500 f. on 10 f. black, violet and brown (L'Alouette) 11·50 4·00

1962. Red Cross stamps of France (Nos. 1593/4) surch. **CFA and value.**

409. 10 f. + 5 f. on 20 c. + 10 c... 1·75 1·50
410. 12 f. + 5 f. on 25 c. + 10 c... 1·75 1·50

1962. Satellite Link stamps of France surch. **CFA and value.**

411. 12 f. on 25 c. (No. 1587) .. 60 50
412. 25 f. on 50 c. (No. 1588) .. 60 50

1963. Nos. 1541 and 1545 of France (Tourist Publicity) surch **CFA** and value.

413 7 f. on 15 c. grey, purple and blue (St. Paul) .. 20 15
414 20 f. on 45 c. brown, green and blue (Sully) .. 80 30

1963. Nos. 1498b/9b and 1499e/f of France (Arms) surch **CFA** and value.

415 1 f. on 2 c. yellow, green and blue (Gueret) .. 10 10
416 2 f. on 5 c. mult (Oran) .. 10 10
417 2 f. on 5 c. red, yellow and blue (Armiens) 10 10
418 5 f. on 10 c. blue, yellow and red (Troyes) .. 10 10
419 6 f. on 18 c. multicoloured (St. Denis) 15 15
420 15 f. on 30 c. red and blue (Paris) 20 10

1963. Red Cross stamps of France. (Nos. 1627/8) surch. **CFA and value.**

421. 10 f. + 5 f. on 20 c. + 10 c... 2·50 2·25
422. 12 f. + 5 f. on 25 c. + 10 c... 2·50 2·25

1964. "PHILATEC 1964" Int. Stamp Exhibition stamp of France surch. **CFA** and value.

423. 12 f. on 25 c. (No. 1629) .. 85 60

1964. Nos. 1654/5 of France (Tourist Publicity) surch **CFA** and value.

431 20 f. on 40 c. chocolate, green & brn (Ronchamp) 60 45
432 35 f. on 70 c. purple, green and blue (Provins) .. 80 65

1964. Red Cross stamps of France. (Nos. 1665/6) surch. **CFA and value.**

433. 10 f. + 5 f. on 20 c. + 10 c. 1·10 1·00
434. 12 f. + 5 f. on 25 c. + 10 c. 1·10 1·00

1965. No. 1621 of France (Saint Flour) surch **3FCFA**.

435 30 f. on 60 c. red, grn & bl 80 65

1965. Nos. 1684/5 and 1688 of France (Tourist Publicity) surch **CFA** and value.

436 25 f. on 50 c. blue, green and bistre (St. Marie) .. 50 25
437 30 f. on 60 c. brown and blue (Aix les Bains) .. 65 45
438 50 f. on 1 f. grey, green and brown (Carnac) .. 1·10 90

1965. Colonisation of Reunion. Tercent. As No. 1692 of France, but additionally inscr. "CFA".

439. 15 f. blue and red 45 30

1965. Red Cross stamps of France (Nos. 1698/9) surch. **CFA** and value.

440. 12 f. + 5 f. on 25 c. + 10 c... 1·00 1·00
441. 15 f. + 5 f. on 30 c. + 10 c... 1·00 1·00

1966. "Marianne" stamp of France surch **10f CFA**.

442 **476** 10 f. on 20 c. red & blue 1·00 50

1966. Launching of 1st French Satellite. Nos. 1696/7 (plus se-tenant label) of France surch. **CFA** and value.

443. 15 f. on 30 c. blue, turquoise and lt. blue 60 50
444. 30 f. on 60 c. blue, turquoise and lt. blue 80 70

1966. Red Cross stamps of France (Nos. 1733/4) surch. **CFA** and value.

445. 12 f. + 5 f. on 25 c. + 10 c. 90 70
446. 15 f. + 5 f. on 30 c. + 10 c. 90 70

1967. World Fair, Montreal. No. 1747 of France surch. **CFA** and value.

447. 30 f. on 60 c. 90 65

1967. No. 1700 of France (Arms of Auch) surch **2f CFA**.

448 2 f. on 5 c. red and blue .. 15 10

1967. 50th Anniv. of Lions Int. No. 1766 of France surch. **CFA** and value.

449. 20 f. on 40 c. .. .. 1·10 90

1967. Red Cross. Nos. 1772/3 of France surch. **CFA** and value.

450. 12 f. + 5 f. on 25 c. + 10 c... 2·50 2·50
451. 15 f. + 5 f. on 30 c. + 10 c... 2·50 2·50

1968. French Polar Exploration. No. 1806 of France surch. **CFA** and value.

452. 20 f. on 40 c. 75 65

1968. Red Cross stamps of France (Nos. 1812/3) surch. **CFA** and value.

453. 12 f. + 5 f. on 25 c. + 10 c. 1·25 1·10
454. 15 f. + 5 f. on 30 c. + 10 c. 1·25 1·10

1969. Stamp Day. No. 1824 of France, surch. **CFA** and value.

455. 15 f. + 5 f. on 30 c. + 10 c. 80 80

1969. "Republique" stamps of France surch **CFA** and value.

456 **604** 15 f. on 30 c. green .. 45 35
457 20 f. on 40 c. mauve .. 45 25

1969. No. 1735 of France (Arms of Saint-Lo) surch **10F CFA**.

458 10 f. on 20 c. multicoloured 25 25

1969. Birth Bicent. of Napoleon Bonaparte. No. 1845 of France surch. **CFA** and value.

459. 35 f. on 70 c. green, violet and blue .. .. .. 1·10 90

1969. Red Cross stamps of France (Nos. 1853/4) surch. **CFA** and value.

460. 20 f. + 7 f. on 40 c. + 15 c... 1·00 1·00
461. 20 f. + 7 f. on 40 c. + 15 c... 1·00 1·00

1970. Stamp Day. No. 1866 of France surch **CFA** and value.

462. 20 f. + 5 f. on 40 c. + 10 c. 90 65

1970. Red Cross. Nos. 1902/3 of France surch. **CFA** and value.

463. 20 f. + 7 f. on 40 c. + 15 c. 2·25 1·75
464. 20 f. + 7 f. on 40 c. + 15 c. 2·25 1·75

1971. "Marianne" stamp of France surch **25f CFA**.

465 **668** 25 f. on 50 c. mauve .. 45 10

1971. Stamp Day. No. 1919 of France surch. **CFA** and value.

466. 25 f. + 5 f. on 50 c. + 10 c. 90 35

1971. "Antoinette". No. 1920 of France surch. **CFA** and value.

467. 40 f. on 80 c. .. .. 1·10 90

1971. No. 1928 of France (Rural Aid) surch. **CFA** and value.

468. **678.** 15 f. on 40 c. 55 45

1971. Nos. 1931/2 of France (Tourist Publicity) surch **CFA** and value.

469 45 f. on 90 c. brown, green and ochre (Riquewihr) 65 45
470 50 f. on 1 f. 10 brown, blue and green (Sedan) .. 90 55

1971. 40th Anniv. of 1st Meeting of Crafts Guilds Association. No. 1935 of France surch. **CFA** and value.

471. **680.** 45c. on 90c. purple & red 80 60

63. Reunion Chameleon.

65. King Penguin, Map and Exploration Ships.

1971. Nature Protection.

472. **63.** 25 f. grn., brn. & yellow 80 55

1971. De Gaulle Commem. As T **92** of New Caledonia, but with face value in CFA francs.

473. 25 f. black .. .. .. 1·10 1·10
474. 25 f. blue .. .. .. 1·10 1·00
475. 25 f. red .. .. .. 1·10 1·10
476. 25 f. black .. .. .. 1·10 1·10

DESIGNS: No. 473, De Gaulle in uniform (June, 1940). No. 474, De Gaulle at Brazzaville, 1944. No. 475, De Gaulle in Paris, 1944. No. 476, De Gaulle as President of the French Republic, 1970 (T **92**).

1971. Nos. 1942/3 of France (Red Cross Fund) surch. **CFA** and value.

477. 15 f.+5 f. on 30 c.+10 c. 90 90
478. 25 f.+5 f. on 50 c.+10 c... 90 90

1972. Bicentenary of Discovery of Crozet Islands and Kerguelen (French Southern and Antarctic Territories).

479. **65.** 45 f. blk., blue & brown 1·75 1·50

1972. No. 1956 of France, surch. **CFA** and value.

480. **688.** 25 f.+5 f. on 50 c.+10 c. blue, drab & yell. .. 65 65

1972. No. 1966 of France (Blood Donors) surch. **CFA** and value.

481. **692.** 15 f. on 40 c. red .. 45 30

1972. Air. No. 1890 of France (Daurat and Vanier) surch **CFA** and value.

482. **662.** 200 f. on 5 f. brn., grn. and blue .. .. 3·50 1·50

1972. Postal Codes. Nos. 1969/70 of France surch. **CFA** and value.

483. **695.** 15 f. on 30 c. red, black and green 40 25
484. 25 f. on 50 c. yellow, black and red .. 40 25

1972. Red Cross Fund. Nos. 1979/80 of France surch **CFA** and value.

485. **701.** 15 f.+5 f. on 30 c.+10 c. 75 75
486. 25 f.+5 f. on 50 c.+10 c. 90 90

1973. Stamp Day. No. 1996 of France surch. **CFA** and value.

487. **707.** 25 f.+5 f. on 50 c.+10 c. 1·10 90

1973. No. 2011 of France surch. **CFA** and value.

488. **714.** 45 f. on 90 c. green, violet and blue .. 1·25 1·00

1973. No. 2008 of France surch. **CFA** and value.

489. 50 f. on 1 f. grn., brn. & bl. 75 55

1973. No. 1960 of France surch. **CFA** and value.

490. 100 f. on 2 f. pur. & green 1·50 90

1973. No. 2021/2 of France surch. **CFA** and value.

491. **721.** 15 f.+ 5f. on 30 c.+ 10 c. green and red 1·00 1·00
492. 25 f.+5 f. on 50 c.+ 10 c. red and black.. 1·10 1·10

1973. No. 2026 of France surch. **CFA** and value.

494. **725.** 25 f. on 50 c. brown, blue and purple .. 55 35

1974. Stamp Day. No. 2031 surch **FCFA** and value.

495. **727.** 25 f.+5 f. on 50 c.+ 10 c.. .. .. 55 55

1974. French Art. No. 2033/6 surch. **FCFA** and value.

496. 100 f. on 2 f. multicoloured 1·75 1·50
497. 100 f. on 2 f. multicoloured 1·75 1·50
498. 100 f. on 2 f. brown and blue .. .. 2·00 1·50
499. 100 f. on 2 f. multicoloured 2·00 1·50

1974. French Lifeboat Service. No. 2040 surch. **FCFA** and value.

500. **731.** 45 f. on 90 c. blue, red and brown .. .. 1·10 90

1974. Centenary of Universal Postal Union. No. 2057 surch. **FCFA** and value.

501. **741.** 60 f. on 1 f. 20 grn., red and blue .. 1·10 1·00

1974. "Marianne" stamps of France surch **FCFA** and value.

502 **668** 30 f. on 60 c. green .. 1·40 1·25
503 40 f. on 80 c. red .. 1·60 1·40

1974. Red Cross Fund. "The Seasons" Nos. 2059/60 surch. **FCFA** and value.

504. **743.** 30 f.+7 f. on 60 c.+ 15 c. .. .. 1·00 1·00
505. – 40 f.+7 f. on 80 c.+ 15 c. .. .. 1·10 1·10

From 1st January 1975 the CFA franc was replaced by the French Metropolitan franc, and Reunion subsequently used unsurcharged stamps of France.

PARCEL POST STAMPS

P 5. P 20.

1890.

P11 P 5 10 c. black on yellow (black frame) .. £200 £120
P13 10 c. black on yellow (blue frame) .. 14·50 12·50

1907. Receipt stamps surch as in Type P **20**.

P76 **P 20** 10 c. brown and black 9·00 6·50
P77 10 c. brown and red 9·00 10·00

POSTAGE DUE STAMPS

D 4. D 19.

1889. Imperf.

D11 D 4 5 c. black .. 11·50 5·50
D12 10 c. black .. 14·50 4·75
D13 15 c. black .. 29·00 17·00
D14 20 c. black .. 25·00 9·00
D15 30 c. black .. 23·00 9·00

1907.

D76 D 19 5 c. red on yellow .. 10 20
D77 10 c. blue on blue .. 15 25
D78 15 c. black on grey .. 15 40
D79 20 c. pink .. 15 35
D80 30 c. green on green 20 65
D81 50 c. red on green .. 20 75
D82 60 c. pink on blue .. 25 75
D83 1 f. lilac .. 75 1·40

1927. Surch.

D 130. D **19.** 2 f. on 1 f. red .. 3·25 5·00
D 131. 3 f. on 1 f. brown .. 3·25 5·00

D 33. Arms of Reunion. D 43.

1933.

D 175. D **33.** 5 c. purple 10 25
D 176. 10 c. green 10 25
D 177. 15 c. brown .. 10 25
D 178. 20 c. orange .. 15 25
D 179. 30 c. olive 15 30
D 180. 50 c. blue 20 45
D 181. 60 c. brown .. 25 45
D 182. 1 f. violet 20 40
D 183. 2 f. blue 25 40
D 184. 3 f. red 25 45

1947.

D 306. D **43.** 10 c. mauve .. 10 30
D 307. 30 c. brown .. 10 25
D 308. 50 c. green 10 30
D 309. 1 f. brown 15 30
D 310. 2 f. red 20 30
D 311. 3 f. brown 20 30
D 312. 4 f. blue 20 60
D 313. 5 f. red 20 60
D 314. 10 f. green 25 60
D 315. 20 f. blue 30 75

1949. As Type D **250** of France, but inscr. "TIMBRE TAXE" surch. **CFA** and value.

D 333. 10 c. on 1 f. blue .. 10 30
D 334. 50 c. on 2 f. blue .. 10 30
D 335. 1 f. on 3 f. red 30 50
D 336. 2 f. on 4 f. violet .. 60 80
D 337. 3 f. on 5 f. pink .. 1·50 1·75
D 338. 5 f. on 10 f. red .. 85 1·00
D 339. 10 f. on 20 f. brown .. 1·25 1·50
D 340. 20 f. on 50 f. green .. 3·25 2·75
D 341. 50 f. on 100 f. green .. 11·00 9·50

1962. Wheat Sheaves Type of France surch **CFA** and value.

D 406. D **457.** 1 f. on 5 c. mauve 1·00 75
D 407. 10 f. on 20 c. brn. 2·50 1·50
D 408. 20 f. on 50 c. grn. 15·00 10·00

1964. Nos. D 1650/4 and D 1656/7 of France surch. **CFA** and value.

D 424. – 1 f. on 5 c. .. 10 10
D 425. – 5 f. on 10 c. .. 10 10
D 426. D **539.** 7 f. on 15 c. .. 20 20
D 427. – 10 f. on 20 c. .. 1·25 60
D 428. – 15 f. on 30 c. .. 35 30
D 429. – 20 f. on 50 c. .. 45 40
D 430. – 50 f. on 1 f. .. 1·25 1·00

RIAU-LINGGA ARCHIPELAGO Pt. 21

A group of islands E. of Sumatra and S. of Singapore. Part of Indonesia.

100 cents or sen = 1 rupiah.

1954. Optd. **RIAU** in double-lined letters.

A. On stamps of Indonesia.

1. **96.** 5 s. red .. .. .. 32·00 20·00
2. 7½ s. green 60 60
3. 10 s. blue .. .. 20·00 25·00
4. 15 s. violet .. .. 60 1·00
5. 20 s. red .. .. 75 1·00
6. 25 s. green .. .. 55·00 45·00
7. **97.** 30 s. red 50 75
8. 35 s. violet 50 75
9. 40 s. green 50 75
10. 45 s. purple .. .. 75 1·00
11. 50 s. brown £190 £110
12. **98.** 60 s. brown 50 75
13. 70 s. grey .. .. 1·75 1·50
14. 75 s. blue .. .. 2·50 3·00
15. 80 s. purple .. .. 1·50 1·90
16. 90 s. green .. .. 1·50 2·00

B. On Netherlands Indies Nos. 566/71.

17. – 1 r. violet .. .. 10·00 5·00
18. – 2 r. green .. .. 1·75 5·00
19. – 3 r. purple .. .. 2·50 3·75
20. – 5 r. brown .. .. 2·50 3·75
21. – 10 r. black .. .. 3·75 6·00
22. – 25 r. brown .. .. 3·75 6·00
Set of 22 .. .. £300 £225

Stamps of Indonesia overprinted.

1957. Optd. **RIAU** in bold letters.

23. **115.** 10 s. brown .. .. 3·75 5·00
24. – 25 s. purple (No. 717) .. 11·00 15·00
25. – 50 s. bistre (No. 722) .. 3·75 5·00

1958. Optd. **RIAU** in double-lined letters.

26. **115.** 5 s. blue 20 35
27. 10 s. brown (No. 714) .. 20 35
28. 15 s. purple (No. 715) .. 60 1·50
29. – 20 s. green (No. 716) .. 20 35
30. – 25 s. purple (No. 717) .. 20 35
31. – 30 s. orange (No. 718) .. 20 35
32. – 50 s. bistre (No. 722) .. 20 35
Set of 7 .. .. 1·60 3·50

1960. Optd. **RIAU** in double-lined letters.

33. **99.** 1 r. 25 orange 25 75
34. 1 r. 50 brown 25 75
35. 2 r. 50 lake .. .. 25 1·10
36. 4 r. olive .. .. 35 1·10
37. 6 r. purple .. .. 35 1·10
38. 15 r. yellow .. .. 35 1·50
39. 20 r. grey .. .. 35 3·00
40. 40 r. green .. .. 45 4·25
41. 50 r. violet .. .. 45 5·00
Set of 9 .. .. 2·75 17·00

RIO DE ORO Pt. 9

A Spanish territory on the W. Coast of N. Africa, renamed Spanish Sahara in 1924.

100 centimos = 1 peseta.

1905. "Curly Head" key-type inscr. "COLONIA DE RIO DE ORO".

1. Z. 1 c. green .. .. 2·50 1·25
2. 2 c. red .. .. 2·50 1·25
3. 3 c. black .. .. 2·50 1·25
4. 4 c. brown .. .. 2·50 1·25
5. 5 c. red .. .. 2·50 1·25
6. 10 c. grey .. .. 2·50 1·25
7. 15 c. brown .. .. 2·50 1·25
8. 25 c. blue .. .. 48·00 15·00
9. 50 c. green .. .. 25·00 6·00
10. 75 c. violet .. .. 25·00 9·00
11. 1 p. brown .. .. 18·00 3·75
12. 2 p. orange .. .. 50·00 20·00
13. 3 p. lilac .. .. 35·00 9·00
14. 4 p. green .. .. 35·00 8·50
15. 5 p. blue .. .. 50·00 17·00
16. 10 p. red .. .. £110 42·00

1906. "Curly Head" key-type surch. **HABILITADO PARA 15 CENTS** in circle.

17. Z. 15 c. on 25 c. blue .. £130 38·00

3. 7. 11.

1907.

18. **3.** 1 c. red .. .. .. 2·25 1·25
19. 2 c. black .. .. .. 2·25 1·25
20. 3 c. brown .. .. .. 2·25 1·25
21. 4 c. red .. .. .. 2·25 1·25
22. 5 c. brown .. .. .. 2·25 1·25
23. 10 c. brown .. .. .. 2·25 1·25
24. 15 c. blue .. .. .. 2·25 1·25
25. 25 c. green .. .. .. 6·00 1·50
26. 50 c. purple .. .. .. 6·00 1·50
27. 75 c. brown .. .. .. 6·00 1·50
28. 1 p. orange .. .. .. 10·00 1·50
29. 2 p. lilac .. .. .. 4·25 1·50
30. 3 p. green .. .. .. 4·25 1·50
31. 4 p. blue .. .. .. 7·50 3·25
32. 5 p. red .. .. .. 7·50 3·25
33. 10 p. green .. .. .. 7·50 8·00

1907. Nos. 9/10 surch. **1907 10 Cens.**

34. Z. 10 c. on 50 c. green .. 40·00 13·00
35. 10 c. on 75 c. violet .. 40·00 13·00

1908. Nos. 12 and 26 surch **1908** and value.

36. Z. 2 c. on 2 p. orange .. 35·00 12·00
37. **3.** 10 c. on 50 c. purple .. 25·00 6·50

1908. Surch. **HABILITADO PARA 15 CENTS** in circle.

38 **3** 15 c. on 25 c. green .. 25·00 5·00
39 15 c. on 75 c. brown .. 30·00 6·50
40 15 c. on 1 p. orange .. 30·00 6·00
71 15 c. on 3 p. green .. 85·00 8·00
72 15 c. on 5 p. red .. .. 7·50 3·50

1908. Large Fiscal stamp inscr. "TERRITORIOS ESPANOLES DEL AFRICA OCCIDENTAL" surch. **HABILITADO PARA CORREOS RIO DE ORO 5 CENS.** Imperf.

45. 5 c. on 50 c. green .. .. 65·00 25·00

1909.

47. **7.** 1 c. red 40 30
48. 2 c. orange 40 30
49. 5 c. green 40 30
50. 10 c. red 40 30
51. 15 c. green 40 30
52. 20 c. purple .. .. .. 1·00 40
53. 25 c. blue .. .. .. 1·00 40
54. 30 c. red .. .. .. 1·00 40
55. 40 c. brown .. .. .. 1·00 40
56. 50 c. purple .. .. .. 2·00 75
57. 1 p. brown .. .. .. 2·75 2·50
58. 4 p. red .. .. .. 3·50 3·00
59. 10 p. red .. .. .. 6·50 4·50

1910. Nos. 13/16 surch. **1910** and value.

60. Z. 10 c. on 5 p. blue .. 10·00 9·00
62. 10 c. on 10 p. red .. 10·00 8·50
65. 15 c. on 3 p. lilac .. 11·00 8·50
66. 15 c. on 4 p. green .. 11·00 8·50

1911. Surch with value in figures and words.

67 **3** 2 c. on 4 p. blue .. .. 8·50 2·75
68 5 c. on 10 p. green .. 18·00 2·75
69 10 c. on 2 p. lilac .. 9·00 2·75
70 10 c. on 3 p. green .. 95·00 12·00

1912.

73. **11.** 1 c. red 20 10
74. 2 c. lilac 20 10
75. 5 c. green 20 10
76. 10 c. red 20 10
77. 15 c. brown 20 10
78. 20 c. brown 20 10
79. 25 c. blue 20 10
80. 30 c. lilac 20 10
81. 40 c. green 20 10
82. 50 c. red 20 10
83. 1 p. red .. .. .. 1·75 40
84. 4 p. red .. .. .. 4·00 2·00
85. 10 p. brown .. .. .. 5·50 2·75

12. 14. 15.

1914.

86. **12.** 1 c. brown 20 10
87. 2 c. purple 20 10
88. 5 c. green 20 10
89. 10 c. red 20 10
90. 15 c. orange 20 10
91. 20 c. red 20 10
92. 25 c. blue 20 10
93. 30 c. green 20 10
94. 40 c. orange 20 10
95. 50 c. brown 20 10
96. 1 p. lilac .. .. 1·75 1·75
97. 4 p. red .. .. 4·25 1·75
98. 10 p. violet .. .. 5·50 4·50

1917. Nos. 73/85 optd **1917**.

99	**11**	1 c. red	6·50	1·00
100		2 c. lilac	6·50	1·00
101		5 c. green	2·50	50
102		10 c. red	2·50	50
103		15 c. brown	2·50	50
104		20 c. brown	2·50	50
105		25 c. blue	2·50	50
106		30 c. lilac	2·50	50
107		40 c. green	2·50	50
108		50 c. red	2·50	50
109		1 p. red	10·00	2·75
110		4 p. red	15·00	3·75
111		10 p. brown	28·00	8·00

1919.

112.	**14.**	1 c. brown	55	35
113.		2 c. purple	55	35
114.		5 c. green	55	35
115.		10 c. red	55	35
116.		15 c. orange	55	35
117.		20 c. orange	55	35
118.		25 c. blue	55	35
119.		30 c. green	55	35
120.		40 c. orange	55	35
121.		50 c. brown	55	35
122.		1 p. lilac	4·75	2·50
123.		4 p. red	8·00	4·50
124.		10 p. violet	12·00	5·00

1920.

125.	**15.**	1 c. purple	55	35
126.		2 c. red	55	35
127.		5 c. red	55	35
128.		10 c. purple	55	35
129.		15 c. brown	55	35
130.		20 c. green	55	35
131.		25 c. orange	55	35
132.		30 c. blue	3·25	2·50
133.		40 c. orange	2·50	1·10
134.		50 c. purple	2·75	1·25
135.		1 p. green	2·75	1·40
136.		4 p. red	4·50	2·75
137.		10 p. brown	11·00	5·50

1921. As T **2** of La Aguera, but inscr. "RIO DE ORO".

138.	1 c. yellow	55	35
139.	2 c. brown	55	35
140.	5 c. green	55	35
141.	10 c. red	55	35
142.	15 c. green	55	35
143.	20 c. blue	55	35
144.	25 c. blue	55	35
145.	30 c. red	1·40	1·10
146.	40 c. violet	1·40	1·10
147.	50 c. orange	1·40	1·10
148.	1 p. mauve	3·75	2·25
149.	4 p. red	6·50	3·75
150.	10 p. brown	11·00	6·50

For later issues see **SPANISH SAHARA.**

RIO MUNI Pt. 9

A coastal settlement between Cameroun and Gabon, formerly using the stamps of Spanish Guinea. On 12 October 1968 became independent and joined Fernando Poo to become Equatorial Guinea.

100 centimos = 1 peseta.

1. Native Boy reading Book. 2. Cactus. 3. Bishop Juan de Ribera.

1960.

1	1	25 c. grey	10	10
2		50 c. brown	10	10
3		75 c. purple	10	10
4		1 p. red	10	10
5		1 p. 50 green	10	10
6		2 p. purple	15	10
7		3 p. blue	30	10
8		5 p. brown	80	10
9		10 p. green	1·50	20

1960. Child Welfare Fund.

10	2	10 c.+5 c. purple	10	10
11	–	15 c.+5 c. brown	10	10
12	–	35 c. green	10	10
13	2	80 c. green	10	10

DESIGNS: 15 c. Sprig with berries. 35 c. Star-shaped flowers.

1960. Stamp Day.

14	3	10 c.+5 c. red	10	10
15	–	20 c.+5 c. green	10	10
16	–	30 c.+10 c.brown	10	10
17	3	50 c.+20 c. brown	10	10

DESIGNS: 20 c. Portrait of man (after Velazquez). 30 c. Statue.

4. Mandrill with Banana.

DESIGN—VERT. 25 c. African Elephant.

1961. Child Welfare. Inscr. "PRO-INFANCIA 1961".

18.	4.	10 c.+5 c. lake	15	10
19.	–	25 c.+10 c. violet	25	10
20.	4.	80 c.+20 c. green	15	10

5. 6. Statuette.

1961. 25th Anniv. of Gen. Franco as Head of State.

21.	–	25 c. grey	30	10
22.	5.	50 c. brown	10	10
23.	–	70 c. green	10	10
24.	5.	1 p. orange	10	10

DESIGNS: 25 c. Map. 70 c. Govt. building.

1961. Stamp Day. Inscr. "DIA DEL SELLO 1961".

25.	6.	10 c.+5 c. lake	5	5
26.	–	25 c.+10 c. purple	5	5
27.	6.	30 c.+10 c. brown	5	5
28.	–	1 p.+10 c. orange	8	5

DESIGN: 25 c., 1 p. Figure holding offering.

7. Girl wearing Headdress. 8. African Buffalo.

1962. Child Welfare. Inscr. "PRO-INFANCIA 1962".

29.	7.	25 c. violet	10	10
30.	–	50 c. green	10	10
31.	7.	1 p. brown	15	10

DESIGN: 50 c. Native mask.

1962. Stamp Day. Inscr. "DIA DEL SELLO 1962".

32.	8.	15 c. olive	10	10
33.	–	35 c. purple	10	10
34.	8.	1 p. red	15	10

DESIGN—VERT. 35 c. Gorilla.

9. Statuette. 10. "Blessing". 11. Child at Prayer.

1963. Seville Flood Relief.

35	9	50 c. green	10	10
36		1 p. brown	10	10

1963. Child Welfare. Inscr. "PRO-INFANCIA 1963".

37.	–	25 c. violet	10	10
38.	10.	50 c. olive	10	10
39.	–	1 p. red	10	10

DESIGN: 25 c., 1 p. Priest.

1963. "For Barcelona".

40.	11.	50 c. turquoise	10	10
41.		1 p. brown	10	10

MINIMUM PRICE

The minimum price quoted is 5p which represents a handling charge rather than a basis for valuing common stamps. For further notes about prices see introductory pages.

12. Copal Flower. 13. Giant Ground Pangolin.

1964. Stamp Day. Inscr. "DIA DEL SELLO 1963".

42.	12.	25 c. violet	10	10
43.	–	50 c. turquoise	10	10
44.	12.	1 p. red	10	10

FLOWER—HORIZ. 50 c. Cinchona blossom.

1964. Child Welfare. Inscr. "PRO-INFANCIA 1964".

45.	13.	25 c. violet	10	10
46.	–	50 c. olive (Chameleon)	15	10
47.	13.	1 p. brown	20	10

1964. Wild Life. As T **13** but without "PRO INFANCIA" inscription.

48.	15 c. bistre	10	10
49.	25 c. violet	10	10
50.	50 c. olive	10	10
51.	70 c. green	15	10
52.	1 p. brown	65	10
53.	1 p. 50 turquoise	65	10
54.	3 p. blue	1·10	10
55.	5 p. brown	2·75	40
56.	10 p. green	6·00	85

ANIMALS: 15 c., 70 c., 3 p. Crocodile. 25 c., 1 p., 5 p. Leopard. 50 c., 1 p. 50, 10 p. Black rhinoceros.

14. "Goliath" Frog. 15. Woman.

1964. Stamp Day.

57.	14.	50 c. bronze	20	10
58.	–	1 p. lake	45	10
59.	14.	1 p. 50 green	25	10

DESIGN—VERT. 1 p. Helmet Guineafowl.

1965. 25th Anniv. of End of Spanish Civil War.

60.	15.	50 c. green	10	10
61.	–	1 p. red	10	10
62.	–	1 p. 50 turquoise	10	10

DESIGNS: 1 p. Nurse. 1 p. 50, Logging.

16. "Goliathus goliathus".

1965. Child Welfare. Insects.

63.	16.	50 c. green	15	10
64.	–	1 p. brown	15	10
65.	16.	1 p. 50 black	15	10

DESIGN: 1 p. "Acridoxena hewaniana".

17. Leopard and Arms of Rio Muni.

1965. Stamp Day.

66.	–	50 c. grey	50	10
67.	17.	1 p. brown	55	10
68.	–	2 p. 50 violet	2·50	50

DESIGN—VERT. 50 c., 2 p. 50, Ring-necked Pheasant.

18. African Elephant and Grey Parrot.

1966. Child Welfare.

69.	18.	50 c. brown	30	10
70.		1 p. lilac	30	10
71.	–	1 p. 50 blue	25	10

DESIGN: 1 p. 50, African and lion.

19. Water Chevrotain. 20. Floss Flowers.

1966. Stamp Day.

72.	19.	10 c. brown and ochre	10	10
73.	–	40 c. brown and yellow	15	10
74.	19.	1 p. 50 violet and red	15	10
75.	–	4 p. blue and green	30	10

DESIGN—VERT. 40 c., 4 p. Giant ground pangolin.

1967. Child Welfare. Similar Floral designs.

76.	20.	10 c. yellow, olive & green	15	10
77.	–	40 c. green, blk. & mve.	15	10
78.	20.	1 p. 50 red and blue	25	10
79.	–	4 p. black and green	35	10

DESIGNS: 40 c., 4 p. Ylang-ylang.

21. Bush Pig.

1967. Stamp Day.

80.	21.	1 p. chestnut and brown	25	10
81.	–	1 p. 50 brown and green	35	10
82.	–	3 p. 50 brown and green	40	15

DESIGNS—VERT. 1 p. 50, Potto. HORIZ. 3 p. 50, African golden cat.

1968. Child Welfare. Signs of the Zodiac. As T **56a** of Spanish Sahara.

83.	1 p. mauve on yellow	30	10
84.	1 p. 50 brown on pink	40	10
85.	2 p. 50 violet on yellow	45	10

DESIGNS: 1 p. Cancer (crab). 1 p. 50, Taurus (bull). 2 p. 50, Gemini (twins).

ROMAGNA Pt. 8

One of the Papal states, now part of Italy. Stamps issued prior to the annexation by Sardinia.

100 bajocchi = 1 scudo.

1.

1859. Imperf.

2	1	½ b. black on yellow	10·00	£275
3		1 b. black on grey	10·00	£110
4		2 b. black on buff	16·00	£110
5		3 b. black on green	21·00	£275
6		4 b. black on brown	£475	£110
7		5 b. black on lilac	26·00	£325
8		6 b. black on green	£250	£7500
9		8 b. black on pink	£200	£1700
10		20 b. black on green	£160	£2500

ROUAD ISLAND (ARWAD) Pt. 6

An island in the E. Mediterranean off the coast of Syria. A French P.O. was established there during 1916.

25 centimes = 1 piastre.

1916. "Blanc" and "Mouchon" key-types inscr. "LEVANT" and optd. **ILE ROUAD** vert.

1.	A.	5 c. green	£300	£130
2.	B.	10 c. red	£300	£130
3.		1 pi. on 25 c. blue	£300	£130

1916. "Blanc," "Mouchon" and "Merson" key-types inscr. "LEVANT" and optd. **ILE ROUAD** horiz.

4	A	1 c grey	30	30
5		2 c. purple	30	35
6		3 c. red	30	35
7		5 c. green	35	40
8	B	10 c. red	40	40
9		15 c. red	60	70
10		20 c. brown	1·00	1·00
11		1 p. on 25 c. blue	1·00	1·00
12		30 c. lilac	1·00	1·00
13	C	40 c. red and blue	2·00	2·00
14		2 p. on 50 c. brown & lav	3·25	3·25
15		4 p. on 1 f. red and yellow	4·75	5·50
16		20 p. on 5 f. blue & yellow	17·00	20·00

RUANDA-URUNDI Pt. 4

Part of German E. Africa, including Ruanda and Urundi, occupied by Belgian forces during the war of 1914-18 and a Trust Territory administered by Belgium until 1 July 1962. The territory then became two separate independent states, named Rwanda and Burundi.

100 centimes = 1 franc.

1916. Nos. 70/77 of Belgian Congo optd.

(a) **RUANDA.**

1. **32.** 5 c. black and green .. 15·00
2. **33.** 10 c. black and red .. 15·00
3. **13.** 15 c. black and green .. 26·00
4. **34.** 25 c. black and blue .. 15·00
5. **14.** 40 c. black and red .. 15·00
6. – 50 c. black and red .. 18·00
7. – 1 f. black and brown .. 55·00
7a. – 5 f. black and orange .. £2000

(b) **URUNDI.**

8. **32.** 5 c. black and green .. 15·00
9. **33.** 10 c. black and red .. 15·00
10. **13.** 15 c. black and green .. 26·00
11. **34.** 25 c. black and blue .. 15·00
12. **14.** 40 c. black and red .. 15·00
13. – 50 c. black and red .. 18·00
14. – 1 f. black and brown .. 55·00
14a. – 5 f. black and orange .. £2000

1916. Stamps of Belgian Congo of 1915 optd **EST AFRICAIN ALLEMAND OCCUPATION BELGE. DUITSCH OOST AFRIKA BELIGISCHE BEZETTING.**

15 **32** 5 c. black and green .. 25 20
16 **33** 10 c. black and red .. 40 30
17 **13** 15 c. black and green .. 30 20
18 **34** 25 c. black and blue .. 1·75 95
19 **14** 40 c. black and lake .. 5·00 4·00
20 – 50 c. black and lake .. 5·50 4·00
21 – 1 f. black and olive .. 60 40
22 – 5 f. black and orange .. 85 75

1918. Belgian Congo Red Cross stamps of 1918 optd. **A. O.**

23 **32** 5 c.+10 c. blue & green 20 20
24 **33** 10 c.+15 c. blue and red 20 20
25 **13** 15 c.+20 c. blue & green 20 20
26 **34** 25 c.+25 c. blue.. .. 20 20
27 **14** 40 c.+40 c. blue and lake 25 25
28 – 50 c.+50 c. blue and lake 50 1·50
29 – 1 f.+1 f. blue and olive.. 1·25 1·25
30 – 5 f.+5 f. blue and orange 6·00 6·00
31 – 10 f.+10 f. blue & green 50·00 60·00

1922. Stamps of 1916 surch.

32 – 5 c. on 50 c. blk. & lake 35 1·50
33 **32** 10 c. on 5 c. blk. & grn. 30 20
34a **14** 25 c. on 40 c. black & lake .. .. 2·00 90
35 **33** 30 c. on 10 c. blk. & red 30 20
36 **34** 50 c. on 25 c. blk. & bl. 30 20

1924. Belgian Congo stamps of 1923 optd **RUANDA URUNDI.**

37 A 5 c. yellow 15 15
38 B 10 c. green 15 15
39 C 15 c. brown 15 15
40 D 20 c. green 15 15
41 E 20 c. green 15 15
42 F 25 c. brown 25 15
43 **46** 30 c. pink 20 20
44 30 c. green 15 15
66 35 c. green 20 15
45 D 40 c. purple 25 25
46 G 50 c. blue 25 20
47 50 c. orange 25 20
48 E 75 c. orange 25 25
49 75 c. blue 35 25
67 **46** 75 c. pink 30 25
50 H 1 f. brown 40 50
51 1 f. blue 45 20
68 1 f. pink 45 30
69 D 1 f. 50 blue 50 35
71 1 f. 75 blue 95 60
52 I 3 f. brown .. .. 2·50 1·90
53 J 5 f. grey .. .. 5·00 4·00
54 K 10 f. black .. .. 19·00 10·00

1925. Stamp of Belgian Congo, optd. **RUANDA-URUNDI.** Inscriptions in French or in Flemish.

61. **55.** 25 c.+25 c. black and red 20 30

1925. Native cattle type of Belgian Congo optd **RUANDA-URUNDI.**

62 **56** 45 c. purple 30 30
63 60 c. red 35 30

1927. Belgian Congo stamps of 1923 optd. **RUANDA URUNDI** in two lines, wide apart.

64. B. 10 c. green 20 20
65. C. 15 c. brown 80 60
66. **46.** 35 c. green 20 15
67. 75 c. red.. .. .. 30 25
68. H. 1 f. red 45 30
69. D. 1 f. 25 blue 50 40
70. 1 f. 50 blue 50 35
71. 1 f. 75 blue 95 60

1927. No. 144 of Belgian Congo optd. **RUANDA URUNDI.**

72. 1 f. 75 on 1 f. 50 blue .. 50 35

1930. Native Fund stamps of Belgian Congo (Nos. 160/8), optd. **RUANDA URUNDI.**

73. 10 c.+5 c. red 30 30
74. 20 c.+10 c. brown .. 65 65
75. 35 c.+15 c. green .. 1·25 1·25
76. 60 c.+30 c. purple .. 1·50 1·50
77. 1 f.+50 c. red .. .. 2·10 2·10
78. 1 f. 75+75 c. blue .. 2·50 2·50
79. 3 f. 50+1 f. 50 lake .. 5·00 5·00
80. 5 f.+2 f. 50 brown .. 4·00 4·00
81. 10 f.+5 f. black.. .. 4·75 4·75

1931. Nos. 68 and 71 surch.

82. H. 1 f. 25 on 1 f. red.. .. 2·25 1·25
83. D. 2 f. on 1 f. 75 blue .. 3·00 1·75

10. Mountain Scenery. **11.** King Albert I.

1931.

84. – 5 c. red 10 10
85. **10.** 10 c. grey 10 10
86. – 15 c. red 15 15
87. – 25 c. purple 10 10
88. – 40 c. green 30 30
89. – 50 c. violet 15 10
90. – 60 c. red 10 10
91. – 75 c. black 10 10
92. – 1 f. red 10 10
93. – 1 f. 25 brown 15 10
94. – 1 f. 50 purple 20 15
95. – 2 f. blue 20 15
96. – 2 f. 50 blue 20 20
97. – 3 f. 25 purple 20 15
98. – 4 f. red 30 30
99. – 5 f. grey 35 35
100. – 10 f. purple 70 45
101. – 20 f. brown .. .. 2·00 1·75

Designs—horiz. 15 c. Warrior. 25 c. Chieftain's kraal. 50 c. Head of African buffalo. 1 f. Wives of Urundi chiefs. 1 f. 50, 2 f. Wooden pot hewer. 2 f. 50, 3 f. 25, Workers making tissues from ficus bark. 4 f. Hutu Potter. vert. 5 c., 60 c. Native porter. 40 c. Two cowherds. 75 c. Native greeting. 1 f. 25, Mother and child. 5 f. Ruanda dancer. 10 f. Warriors. 20 f. Native prince of Urundi.

1934. King Albert Mourning stamps.

102. **11.** 1 f. 50 black 50 50

11a. Queen Astrid and Children. **14a.** "Belgium shall rise Again".

1936. Charity. Queen Astrid Fund.

103. **11a.** 1 f. 25+5 c. brown .. 50 50
104. 1 f. 50+10 c. red .. 50 50
105. 2 f. 50+25 c. blue .. 70 70

1941. Stamps of Belgian Congo optd. **RUANDA URUNDI.**

106. **78.** 10 c. grey .. .. 5·50 5·50
107. 1 f. 75 orange .. .. 3·75 3·75
108. 2 f. 75 blue .. .. 3·75 3·75

1941. Ruanda-Urundi stamps of 1931 surch.

109. – 5 c. on 40 c. green .. 3·00 3·00
110. – 60 c. on 50 c. violet .. 2·00 2·00
111. – 2 f. 50 on 1 f. 50 purple 2·00 2·00
112. – 3 f. 25 on 2 f. blue .. 9·00 9·00

1941. Stamps of Belgian Congo optd. **RUANDA URUNDI** and surch. also.

113. – 5 c. on 1 f. 50 black and brown (No. 222) .. 10 10
114. – 75 c. on 90 c. brown and red (No. 221) .. 90 75
115. **78.** 2 f. 50 on 10 f. red .. 1·50 1·25

1942. War Relief.

116. **14a.** 10 f.+40 f. red .. 1·75 1·75
117. 10 f.+40 f. blue .. 1·75 1·75

On No. 116 the French slogan is above the Flemish, on No. 117 vice versa.

1942. Nos. 107/8 of Ruanda-Urundi surch.

118. **78.** 75 c. on 1 f. 75 orange 85 85
119. 2 f. 50 on 2 f. 75 blue 3·25 3·25

15a. Head of Warrior.

17. Seated Figure.

1942.

120 A 5 c. red 10 10
121 10 c. green 10 10
122 15 c. brown 10 10
123 20 c. blue 10 10
124 25 c. purple 10 10
125 30 c. blue 10 10
126 50 c. green 10 10
127 60 c. brown 10 10
128 **15a** 75 c. black & lilac 15 10
129 1 f. black and brown 15 10
130 1 f. 25 black and red .. 20 15
131 B 1 f. 75 brown 75 45
132 2 f. orange 75 30
133 2 f. 50 red 75 15
134 C 3 f. 50 green 40 25
135 5 f. orange 40 25
136 6 f. blue 40 25
137 7 f. black 40 30
138 10 f. brown 65 40
139 – 20 f. black and brown 1·50 95
140 – 50 f. black and red .. 1·75 1·10
141 – 100 f. black and green 3·50 2·75

Designs— As Type **15a** (various frames): A, Oil palms. C, Askari sentry. 20 f. Head of zebra. 35×24 mm: B, Leopard. 29×34 mm: 50 f. Askari sentry. 100 f. Head of warrior.

1944. Red Cross Fund. Nos. 126, 130, 131 and 134 surch **Au profit de la Croix Rouge Ten voordeele van het Roode Kruis** (50 c., 1 f. 75) or with Flemish and French reversed (others) and premium.

147 50 c.+50 f. green 75 90
148 1 f. 25+100 f. black & red 1·10 1·40
149 1 f. 75+100 f. brown .. 75 90
150 3 f. 50+100 f. green .. 1·10 1·40

1948. Native Carvings.

151 **17** 10 c. orange 10 10
152 A 15 c. blue 10 10
153 B 20 c. blue 20 10
154 C 25 c. red 40 15
155 D 40 c. purple 20 10
156 **17** 50 c. brown 20 10
157 A 70 c. green 20 10
158 B 75 c. purple 25 15
159 C 1 f. purple and orange 25 10
160 D 1 f. 25 red and blue .. 25 15
161 E 1 f. 50 red and green .. 90 40
162 **17** 2 f. red and vermilion .. 30 10
163 A 2 f. 50 green and brown 30 10
164 B 3 f. 50 green and blue .. 40 20
165 C 5 f. red and bistre .. 85 20
166 D 6 f. green and orange .. 85 15
167 E 10 f. brown and violet .. 1·25 20
168 F 20 f. brown and red .. 1·90 35
169 E 50 f. black and brown .. 3·75 1·00
170 F 100 f. black and red .. 6·00 2·50

Designs: A, Seated figure (different). B, Kneeling figure. C, Double mask. D, Mask. E, Mask with tassels. F, Mask with horns.

1949. Surch.

171. 3 f. on 2 f. 50 (No. 163) .. 40 15
172. 4 f. on 6 f. (No. 166) .. 40 15
173. 6 f. 50 on 6 f. (No. 166) .. 40 25

18a. St Francis Xavier.

19. "Dissotis".

1953. 400th Death Anniv. of St. Francis Xavier.

174. **18a.** 1 f. 50, black and blue 40 40

1953. Flowers. Multicoloured.

175 10 c. Type **19** 15 10
176 15 c. "Protea" 15 10
177 20 c. "Vellozia" 15 10
178 25 c. "Littonia" 15 10
179 40 c. "Ipomoea" 15 10
180 50 c. "Angraecum" .. 15 10
181 60 c. "Euphorbia" .. 15 10
182 75 c. "Ochna" 15 10
183 1 f. "Hibiscus" 25 10
184 1 f. 25 "Protea" 90 40
185 1 f. 50 "Schizoglossum" .. 20 10
186 2 f. "Ansellia" .. .. 2·25 20
187 3 f. "Costus" 55 10
188 4 f. "Nymphaea" .. 55 15
189 5 f. "Thunbergia" .. 80 15
190 7 f. "Gerbera" 95 30
191 8 f. "Gloriosa" .. .. 1·40 45
192 10 f. "Silene" .. .. 2·50 35
193 20 f. "Aristolochia" .. 5·00 60

20. King Baudouin and Mountains.

20a. Mozart when a Child.

1955.

194. **20.** 1 f. 50 black and red .. 50 15
195. – 3 f. black and green .. 40 15
196. – 4 f. 50 black and blue 50 20
197. – 6 f. 50 black and purple 60 30

Designs: 3 f. Forest. 4 f. 50, River. 6 f. 50, Grassland.

1956. Birth Bicent. of Mozart.

198. **20a.** 4 f. 50+1 f. 50 violet 1·50 1·00
199. – 6 f. 50+2 f. 50 purple 4·50 2·00

Design—52×36 mm. 6 f. 50, Queen Elizabeth and Mozart Sonata.

20b. Nurse with Children.

21. Gorilla.

1957. Red Cross Fund.

200. **20b.** 3 f.+50 c. blue .. 55 20
201. – 4 f. 50 c.+50 c. green 70 30
202. – 6 f. 50 c.+50 c. brown 95 50

Designs: 4 f. 50, Doctor inoculating patient. 6 f. 50, Nurse in tropical kit bandaging patient.

1959. Fauna.

203. 10 c. black, red and brown 10 10
204. 20 c. black and green .. 10 10
205. 40 c. black, olive & mauve 10 10
206. 50 c. brown, yellow & green 10 10
207. 1 f. black, blue and brown 10 10
208. 1 f. 50 black and orange .. 15 10
209. 2 f. black, brown & turquoise 20 10
210. 3 f. black, red and brown.. 40 10
211. 5 f. multicoloured 40 15
212. 6 f. 50 brown, yell. & red.. 25 10
213. 8 f. black, mauve & blue .. 70 30
214. 10 f. multicoloured .. 70 20

Designs—vert. 10 c., 1 f. Type **21**. 40 c., 2 f. Eastern Black-and-white colobus. horiz. 20 c., 1 f. 50, African buffaloes. 50 c., 6 f. 50, Impala. 3 f., 8 f. African elephants. 5 f., 10 f. Eland and Common zebras.

22. African Resources.

1960. 10th Anniv. of African Technical Co-operation Commission. Inscr. in French or Flemish.

222. **22.** 3 f. salmon and blue .. 20 15

23. High Jumping.

1960. Child Welfare Fund. Olympic Games, Rome.

223. 50 c.+25 c. blue & red .. 10 10
224. 1 f. 50+50 c. lake & black 15 15
225. 2 f.+1 f. black and red .. 15 15
226. 3 f.+1 f. 25 red & green .. 95 85
227. 6 f. 50+3 f. 50 green & red 95 85

Designs: 50 c. Type **23.** 1 f. 50, Hurdling. 2 f. Football. 3 f. Throwing the javelin. 6 f. 50, Throwing the discus.

1960. No. 210 surch.
228. 3 f. 50 on 3 f. black, red and brown 30 10

25. Leopard.

DESIGN: 50 f. Lion and lioness.

1961.
229. 25. 20 f. multicoloured .. 85 35
230. – 50 f. multicoloured .. 1·90 85

26. Usumbura Cathedral.

DESIGNS: 1 f., 5 f. Side view of Cathedral. 1 f. 50, 6 f. 50, Stained glass windows.

1961. Usumbura Cathedral Fund.
231 26 50 c.+25 c. brn & buff 10 10
232 – 1 f.+50 c. dp grn & grn 10 10
233 – 1 f. 50+75 c. mult 10 10
234 26 3 f. 50+1 f. 50 bl & lt bl 10 10
235 – 5 f.+2 f. red and orange 20 20
236 – 6 f. 50+3 f. mult .. 40 30

POSTAGE DUE STAMPS

1924. Postage Due stamps of Belgian Congo optd. **RUANDA URUNDI.**
D 55. D 54. 5 c. brown 15 15
D 55. 10 c. red 15 15
D 57. 15 c. violet 20 20
D 58. 30 c. green 30 30
D 59. 50 c. blue 40 35
D 60. 1 f. grey 45 50

1943. Postage Due stamps of Belgian Congo optd. **RUANDA URUNDI.**
D 142. D 86. 10 c. olive .. 10 10
D 143. 20 c. blue .. 10 10
D 144. 50 c. green .. 10 10
D 145. 1 f. brown .. 20 20
D 146. 2 f. orange .. 25 25

1959. Postage Due stamps of Belgian Congo optd. **RUANDA URUNDI.**
D 215. D 99. 10 c. brown .. 10 10
D 216. 20 c. purple .. 10 10
D 217. 50 c. green .. 10 10
D 218. 1 f. blue .. 15 15
D 219. 2 f. red .. 20 20
D 220. 4 f. violet .. 50 40
D 221. 6 f. blue .. 60 50

For later issues see **BURUNDI** and **RWANDA.**

RUMANIA Pt. 3

A republic in S.E. Europe, bordering on the Black Sea, originally a kingdom formed by the union of Moldavia and Wallachia.

1858. 40 parale = 1 piastre.
1867. 100 bani = 1 leu.

MOLDAVIA

1. 2.

1858. Imperf.
1. 1. 27 p. black on red .. £12000 £4250
2. 54 p. blue on green .. £4500 £2000
3. 81 p. blue on blue .. £12000 £13000
4. 108 p. blue on pink .. £8000 £4000

1858. Imperf.
15. 2. 5 p. black £110
13. 40 p. blue £100 £100
14. 80 p. red £325 £170

RUMANIA

4.

1862. Imperf.
29. 4. 3 p. yellow .. .. 48·00 £140
30. 6 p. red .. .. 40·00 £100
31. 30 p. blue .. .. 35·00 35·00

5. Prince Alexander Cuza. 6. Prince Carol. 7.

1865. Imperf.
49a. 5. 2 p. orange .. .. 28·00 £130
46. 5 p. blue .. .. 23·00 £160
48. 20 p. red .. .. 15·00 21·00

1866. Imperf.
60. 6. 2 p. black on yellow .. 15·00 55·00
61. 5 p. black on blue .. 30·00 £325
62. 20 p. black on red .. 12·00 12·00

1868. Imperf.
71. 7. 2 b. orange .. .. 21·00 17·00
72. 3 b. mauve .. .. 30·00 26·00
66c. 4 b. blue .. .. 32·00 21·00
67. 18 b. red .. .. £140 14·00

8. 9. 10.

1869. Without beard. Imperf.
74. 8. 5 b. orange .. .. 50·00 27·00
75. 10 b. blue .. .. 24·00 17·00
76d. 15 b. red .. .. 24·00 17·00
77c. 25 b. blue and orange .. 24·00 17·00
78. 50 b. red and blue .. £120 29·00

1871. Witn beard. Imperf.
83. 9. 5 b. red .. .. 24·00 17·00
84. 10 b. orange .. .. 42·00 21·00
99. 10 b. blue .. .. 29·00 32·00
86. 15 b. red £100 £110
87. 25 b. brown .. .. 26·00 26·00
100. 50 b. red and blue .. £110 £140

1872. Perf.
93. 9. 5 b. red .. .. 45·00 29·00
94. 10 b. blue .. .. 40·00 30·00
95. 25 b. brown .. .. 24·00 30·00

1872. Perf.
112. 10. 1½ b. green .. .. 4·50 1·50
124. 1½ b. black .. .. 4·50 90
105. 3 b. green .. .. 18·00 2·50
125. 3 b. olive .. .. 9·00 5·50
106. 5 b. bistre .. .. 12·00 1·25
126. 5 b. green .. .. 3·00 1·25
107. 10 b. blue .. .. 10·50 1·75
127c. 10 b. red .. .. 7·50 1·25
115. 15 b. brown .. .. 42·00 4·50
128a. 15 b. red .. .. 21·00 7·50
110. 25 b. orange .. .. 65·00 10·50
130. 25 b. blue .. .. 90·00 10·50
116. 30 b. red .. .. £110 30·00
111. 50 b. red .. .. 75·00 27·00
131. 50 b. bistre .. .. 60·00 13·50

11. King Carol. 12. 14.

1880.
146a. 11. 15 b. brown .. .. 7·50 70
147. 25 b. blue .. .. 14·00 1·60

1885. On white or coloured papers.
161 12 1½ b. black .. .. 2·00 1·00
163 3 b. green .. .. 3·50 1·00
165a 3 b. violet .. .. 3·50 1·00
166 5 b. green .. .. 3·50 1·00
168 10 b. red .. .. 3·50 1·10
169 15 b. brown .. .. 10·50 1·50
171 25 b. blue .. .. 10·50 2·10
186 50 b. brown .. .. 48·00 10·50

1890.
271. 14. 1½ b. lake .. .. 1·00 30
272a. 3 b. mauve 75 30
273. 5 b. green .. .. 1·50 40
254. 10 b. red .. .. 7·50 1·00
255. 15 b. brown .. .. 9·00 60
306. 25 b. blue .. .. 4·75 95
307. 50 b. orange .. .. 20·00 7·50

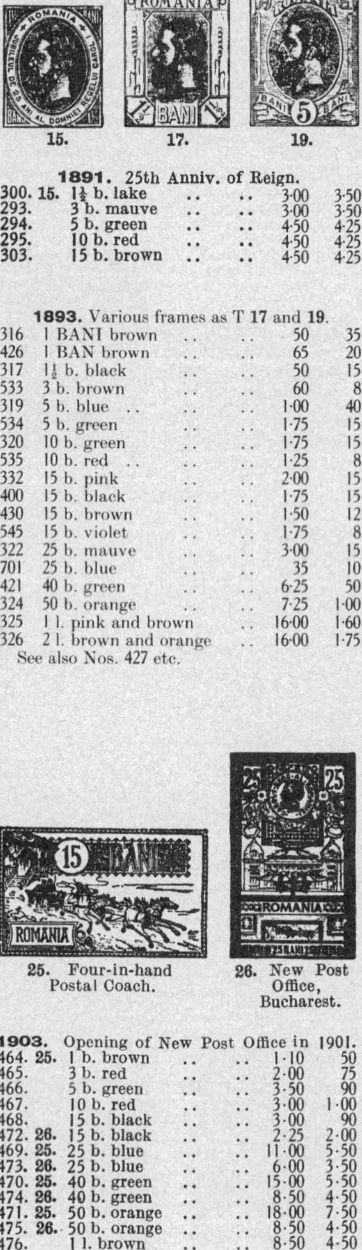

15. 17. 19.

1891. 25th Anniv. of Reign.
300. 15. 1½ b. lake .. .. 3·00 3·50
293. 3 b. mauve .. .. 3·00 3·50
294. 5 b. green .. .. 4·50 4·25
295. 10 b. red .. .. 4·50 4·25
303. 15 b. brown .. .. 4·50 4·25

1893. Various frames as T 17 and 19.
316 1 BANI brown 50 35
426 1 BAN brown 65 20
317 1½ b. black 50 15
533 3 b. brown 60 8
319 5 b. blue .. .. 1·00 40
534 5 b. green .. .. 1·75 15
320 10 b. green .. .. 1·75 15
535 10 b. red .. .. 1·25 8
332 15 b. pink .. .. 2·00 15
400 15 b. black .. .. 1·75 15
430 15 b. brown .. .. 1·50 12
545 15 b. violet .. .. 1·75 8
322 25 b. mauve .. .. 3·00 15
701 25 b. blue 35 10
421 40 b. green .. .. 6·25 50
324 50 b. orange .. .. 7·25 1·00
325 1 l. pink and brown .. 16·00 1·60
326 2 l. brown and orange .. 16·00 1·75

See also Nos. 427 etc.

25. Four-in-hand Postal Coach. 26. New Post Office, Bucharest.

1903. Opening of New Post Office in 1901.
464. 25. 1 b. brown .. .. 1·10 50
465. 3 b. red .. .. 2·00 75
466. 5 b. green .. .. 3·50 90
467. 10 b. red .. .. 3·00 1·00
468. 15 b. black .. .. 3·00 90
472. 26. 15 b. black .. .. 2·25 2·00
469. 25. 25 b. blue .. .. 11·00 5·50
473. 26. 25 b. blue .. .. 6·00 3·50
470. 25. 40 b. green .. .. 15·00 5·50
474. 26. 40 b. green .. .. 8·50 4·50
471. 25. 50 b. orange .. .. 18·00 7·50
475. 26. 50 b. orange .. .. 8·50 4·50
476. 1 l. brown .. .. 8·50 4·50
477. 2 l. red .. .. 55·00 35·00
478. 5 l. lilac .. .. 80·00 55·00

See also No. 1275.

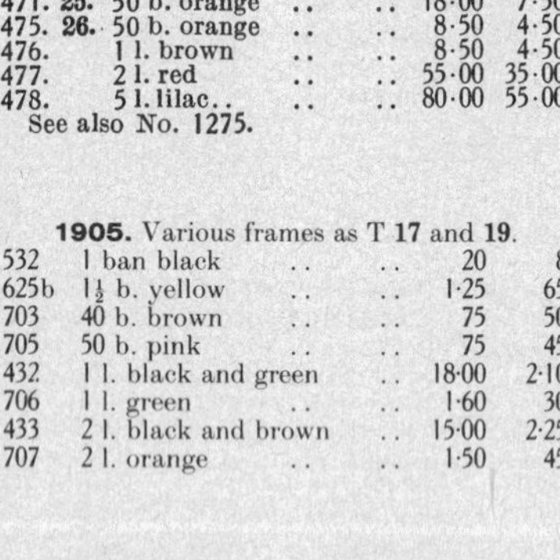

1905. Various frames as T 17 and 19.
532 1 ban black 20 8
625b 1½ b. yellow .. .. 1·25 65
703 40 b. brown 75 50
705 50 b. pink 75 45
432 1 l. black and green .. 18·00 2·10
706 1 l. green .. .. 1·60 30
433 2 l. black and brown .. 15·00 2·25
707 2 l. orange .. .. 1·50 45

27. Queen of Rumania spinning. 28. Queen of Rumania weaving.

1906. Welfare Fund.
481. 27. 3 b. (+7) brown .. 2·50 2·00
482. 5 b. (+10) green .. 2·50 2·00
483. 10 b. (+10) red .. 10·00 7·50
484. 15 b. (+10) purple .. 7·50 3·50

1906. Welfare Fund.
485. 28. 3 b. (+7) brown .. 4·50 2·25
486. 5 b. (+10) green .. 4·50 2·25
487. 10 b. (+10) red .. 24·00 8·50
488. 15 b. (+10) lilac .. 15·00 4·00

29. Queen of Rumania nursing wounded Soldier. 30.

1906. Welfare Fund.
489. 29. 3 b. (+7) brown .. 4·50 2·25
490. 5 b. (+10) green .. 4·40 2·25
491. 10 b. (+10) red .. 24·00 8·50
492. 15 b. (+10) purple .. 15·00 4·40

1906. 25th Anniv. of Kingdom.
493. 30. 1 b. black and bistre .. 25 25
494. 3 b. black and brown .. 1·00 30
495. 5 b. black and green .. 65 25
496. 10 b. black and red .. 65 25
497. 15 b. black and violet .. 75 25
498. 25 b. black and blue .. 7·50 3·50
499. 40 b. black and brown .. 1·50 80
500. 50 b. black and brown .. 1·50 75
501. 1 l. black and red .. 1·50 80
502. 2 l. black and orange .. 1·50 80

31. Prince Carol at Battle of Calafat. 32.

1906. 40 Years' Rule of Prince and King Dated "1906".
503. – 1 b. black and bistre .. 20 25
504. – 3 b. black and brown .. 40 30
505. 31. 5 b. black and green .. 75 25
506. – 10 b. black and red .. 30 15
507. – 15 b. black and violet .. 30 15
508. – 25 b. black and blue .. 3·50 3·00
508a. – 25 b. black and green .. 4·00 4·75
509. – 40 b. black and brown .. 70 70
510. – 50 b. black and brown .. 75 70
511. – 1 l. black and red .. 1·00 75
512. – 2 l. black and orange .. 1·00 1·00

DESIGNS—HORIZ. 1 b. Prince Carol taking oath of allegiance in 1866. 3 b. Prince in carriage. 10 b. Meeting of Prince and Osman Pasha, 1878. 15 b. Carol when Prince in 1866 and King in 1906. 25 b. Rumanian Army crossing Danube, 1877. 40 b. Triumphal entry into Bucharest, 1878. 50 b. Prince at head of Army in 1877. 1 l. King Carol at Cathedral in 1896. 2 l. King at shrine of S. Nicholas, 1904.

1906. Charity.
513. 32. 3 b. (+7) brown, bistre and blue .. 1·40 1·25
514. 5 b. (+10) green, red and bistre .. 1·40 1·25
515. 10 b. (+10) red, bistre and blue .. 2·50 2·25
516. 15 b. (+10) violet, bistre and blue .. 7·50 3·00

33. Peasant ploughing and Angel.

1906. Jubilee Exhibition, Bucharest.
517. 33. 5 b. black and green .. 2·40 70
518. 10 b. black and red .. 2·40 70
519. – 15 b. black and violet .. 3·75 1·25
520. – 25 b. black and blue .. 3·75 1·25
521. – 30 b. brown and red .. 4·50 1·25
522. – 40 b. brown and green .. 5·50 1·40
523. – 50 b. black and orange 4·75 1·75
524. – 75 b. sepia and brown .. 4·75 1·75
525. – 1 l. 50 brown & mauve .. 40·00 22·00
526. – 2 l. 50 brown and yellow 19·00 12·00
527. – 3 l. brown and orange .. 13·00 11·00

DESIGNS—HORIZ. 15 b., 25 b. Exhibition Building. VERT. 30 b., 40 b. Farmhouse. 50 b., 75 b. (different), Royal Family pavilion. 1 l. 50, 2 l. 50, King Carol on horseback. 3 l. Queen Elisabeth (Carmen Sylva).

34. Princess Maria and her Children receiving Poor Family conducted by an Angel.

1907. Welfare Fund.
528. 34. 3 b. (+7) brown .. 4·50 4·75
529. 5 b. (+10) brown & grn. 2·50 1·25
530. 10 b. (+10) brown & red 2·00 1·25
531. 15 b. (+10) brown & bl. 1·75 1·25

35. 37.

1908.

575.	**35.**	5 b. green	1·00	20
562.		10 b. red	30	5
577.		15 b. violet	6·75	1·75
564.		25 b. blue	75	8
579.		40 b. green	40	15
702.		40 b. brown	3·00	1·75
566.		50 b. orange	40	5
705.		50 b. red	1·25	45
581.		1 l. brown	1·10	25
582.		2 l. red	6·00	1·75

1908.

583.	**37.**	1 b. black	15	5
590.		3 b. brown	50	5
585.		5 b. green	20	5
592.		10 b. red	35	5
599.		15 b. violet	9·00	7·50
594.		15 b. olive	45	5
692.		15 b. brown	50	30

38.

39. Troops crossing Danube.

1913. Acquisition of Southern Dobruja.

626.	–	1 b. black	40	25
627.	**38.**	3 b. brown and grey ..	1·25	50
628.	**39.**	5 b. black and green ..	1·00	15
629.	–	10 b. black and orange	55	15
630.	–	15 b. violet and brown	1·00	40
631.	–	25 b. brown and blue ..	1·25	65
632.	**39.**	40 b. red and brown ..	2·50	70
633.	**38.**	50 b. blue and yellow ..	3·00	2·40
634.		1 l. brown and blue ..	7·50	6·00
635.		2 l. red and red ..	10·00	7·50

DESIGNS—VERT. (As Type **38**): 16 b. "Dobruja" holding flag. HORIZ. (As Type **39**): 10 b. Town of Constanza. 25 b. Church and School in Dobruja. (24×16 mm.). 15 b. "Mircea the Great and King Carol".

1918. Surch. **25. BANI.**

657.	**37.**	25 b. on 1 b. black ..	35	30

1918. Optd. **1918.**

662.	**37.**	5 b. green	40	25
663.		10 b. red	45	25

TRANSYLVANIA

The Eastern portion of Hungary. Union with Rumania proclaimed in December 1918, and the final frontiers settled by the Treaty of Trianon, 4th June, 1920.

The following issues for Transylvania (Nos. 747/858) were valid throughout Rumania.

(42.)

(43.)

(The "F" stands for King Ferdinand and "P.T.T." for Posts, Telegraphs and Telephones).

The values "BANI", "LEU" or "LEI" appear above or below the monogram.

A. Issues for Cluj (Kolozsvar or Klausenburg).

1919. Various stamps of Hungary optd. as T **42.**

(a) Flood Relief Charity stamps of 1913.

747.	**7.**	1 l. on 1 f grey ..	10·50	10·50
748.		1 l. on 2 f. yellow ..	45·00	45·00
749.		1 l. on 3 f. orange ..	24·00	24·00
750.		1 l. on 5 f. green ..	75	75
751.		1 l. on 10 f. red ..	75	75
752.		1 l. on 12 f. lilac on yell.	3·25	3·25
753.		1 l. on 16 f. green ..	1·75	1·75
754.		1 l. on 25 f. blue ..	24·00	24·00
755.		1 l. on 35 f. purple ..	1·50	1·75
756.	**8.**	1 l. on 1 k. red	30·00	30·00

(b) War Charity stamps of 1916.

757.	**20.**	10 (+2) b. red	15	15
758.	–	15 (+2) b. violet ..	15	15
759.	**22.**	40 (+2) b. lake ..	15	15

(c) Harvesters and Parliament Types.

760.	**18.**	2 b. brown	12	12
761.		3 b. red	12	12
762.		5 b. green	12	12
763.		6 b. blue	12	12
764.		10 b. red	60·00	60·00
765.		15 b. violet (No. 244)	2·25	2·25
766.		15 b. violet	12	12
767.		25 b. blue	12	12
768.		35 b. brown	12	12
769.		40 b. olive	12	12
770.	**19.**	50 b. purple	12	12
771.		75 b. blue	12	12
772.		80 b. green	12	12
773.		1 l. lake	12	12
774.		2 l. brown	20	20
775.		3 l. grey and violet ..	1·50	1·50
776.		5 l. brown	1·00	1·00
777.		10 l. lilac and brown ..	1·50	1·50

(d) Karl and Zita stamps.

778.	**27.**	10 b. red	12·00	12·00
779.		15 b. violet	4·50	4·50
780.		20 b. brown	12	12
781.		25 b. blue	30	30
782.	**28.**	40 b. olive	15	15

B. Issues for Oradea (Nagyvarad, Grosswardein).

1919. Various stamps of Hungary optd. as T **43.**

(a) "Turul" Type.

794.	**7.**	2 b. yellow	2·40	2·40
795.		3 b. orange	4·25	4·25
796.		6 b. drab	25	25
797.		16 b. green	7·50	7·50
798.		50 b. lake on blue ..	40	40
799.		70 b. brown and green	9·00	9·00

(b) Flood Relief Charity stamps of 1913.

800.	**7.**	1 l. on 1 f. grey ..	40	40
801.		1 l. on 2 f. yellow ..	1·50	1·50
802.		1 l. on 3 f. orange ..	45	45
803.		1 l. on 5 l. green ..	15	15
804.		1 l. on 6 f. drab ..	40	40
805.		1 l. on 10 f. red ..	15	15
806.		1 l. on 12 f. lilac on yell.	21·00	21·00
807.		1 l. on 16 f. green ..	50	50
808.		1 l. on 20 f. brown ..	2·75	2·75
809.		1 l. on 25 f. blue ..	1·50	1·50
810.		1 l. on 35 f. purple ..	1·50	1·50

(c) War Charity stamp of 1915.

811.	**7.**	5+2 b. green (No. 173) ..	3·75	3·75

(d) War Charity stamps of 1916.

812.	**20.**	10 (+2) b. red	20	20
813.	–	15 (+2) b. violet ..	15	15
814.	**22.**	40 (+2) b. lake	15	15

(e) Harvesters and Parliament Types.

815.	**18.**	2 b. brown	12	12
816.		3 b. red	12	12
817.		5 b. green	12	12
818.		6 b. blue	35	35
819.		10 b. red	40	40
820.		15 b. violet (No. 244) ..	60·00	60·00
821.		15 b. violet	12	12
822.		20 b. brown	5·50	5·50
823.		25 b. blue	15	15
824.		35 b. brown	15	15
825.		40 b. olive	12	12
826.	**19.**	50 b. purple	15	15
827.		75 b. blue	12	12
828.		80 b. green	12	12
829.		1 l. lake	20	20
830.		2 l. brown	15	15
831.		3 l. grey and violet ..	1·50	1·50
832.		5 l. brown	2·40	2·40
833.		10 l. lilac and brown ..	75	75

(f) Charles and Zita stamps.

834.	**27.**	10 b. red	1·00	1·00
835.		20 b. brown	15	15
836.		25 b. blue	20	20
837.	**28.**	40 b. olive	25	25

The following (Nos. 838/58) are also optd. **KOZTARSASAG.**

(g) Harvesters and Parliament Types.

838.	**18.**	2 b. brown	75	75
839.		3 b. red	15	15
840.		4 b. grey	15	15
841.		5 b. green	15	15
842.		6 b. blue	70	70
843.		10 b. red	7·50	7·50
844.		20 b. brown	60	60
845.		40 b. olive	15	15
846.	**19.**	1 l. lake	15	15
847.		3 l. grey and violet ..	35	35
848.		5 l. brown	2·10	2·10

(h) Charles and Zita stamps.

849.	**27.**	10 b. red	70·00	70·00
850.		20 b. brown	1·00	1·00
851.		25 b. blue	20	20
852.	**28.**	50 b. purple	15	15

(k) Harvesters and Parliament Types inscr. "MAGYAR POSTA".

853.	**18.**	5 b. green	12	12
854.		10 b. red	12	12
855.		20 b. brown	15	15
856.		25 b. blue	25	25
857.		40 b. olive	40	40
858.	**19.**	5 l. brown	3·50	3·50

(44.) King Ferdinand's Monogram.

45. King Ferdinand. 46.

1919. Recovery of Transylvania and Return of King of Rumania to Bucharest. Optd. with T **44.**

873.	**37.**	1 b. black	20	12
874.		5 b. green	30	20
878a.		10 b. red	10	8

1920.

891.	**45.**	1 b. black	10	5
892.		5 b. green	8	5
893.		10 b. red	8	5
882.		15 b. brown	30	12
895.		25 b. blue	20	10
896.		25 b. brown	20	10
910.		40 b. brown	45	20
898.		50 b. pink	20	10
887.		1 l. green	40	10
900.		1 l. red	30	10
889.		2 l. orange	45	25
902.		2 l. blue	45	10
903.		2 l. red	1·75	1·10

1922.

923.	**46.**	3 b. black	12	5
924.		5 b. black	5	5
925.		10 b. green	5	5
926.		25 b. brown	8	5
927.		25 b. red	12	5
928.		30 b. violet	12	5
929.		50 b. yellow	8	5
930.		60 b. green	75	40
931.		1 l. violet	15	5
932.		2 l. red	55	5
933a.		2 l. green	20	5
934.		3 l. blue	75	30
935a.		3 l. brown	75	10
937.		3 l. red	35	5
936a.		3 l. pink	25	5
938.		5 l. green	1·50	30
939b.		5 l. brown	20	5
940.		6 l. blue	1·75	70
941.		6 l. red	4·25	2·40
942.		6 l. olive	1·75	45
943.		7 l. 50 blue	1·50	25
944.		10 l. blue	1·50	20

47. Cathedral of Alba Julia.

48. King Ferdinand.

49. State Arms.

51. Michael the Brave and King Ferdinand.

1922. Coronation.

1032.	**47.**	5 b. black	12	15
1033	**48.**	25 b. brown	75	20
1034.	**49.**	50 b. green	75	50
1035.	–	1 l. olive	90	60
1036.	**51.**	2 l. red	90	60
1037.	–	3 l. blue	1·75	75
1050.	–	6 l. violet	6·50	5·50

DESIGNS—As Type **48**: 1 l. Queen Marie as a nurse. 3 l. Portrait of King, but rectangular frame. Larger (21×33 mm.) 6 l. Queen Marie in coronation robes.

54. King Ferdinand.

55. Map of Rumania.

1926. King's 60th Birthday. Imperf. or perf.

1051.	**54.**	10 b. green	20	20
1052.		25 b. orange	15	15
1053.		50 b. brown	15	15
1054.		1 l. violet	15	15
1055.		2 l. green	15	15
1056.		3 l. red	15	15
1057.		5 l. brown	15	15
1058.		6 l. olive	15	15
1059.		9 l. grey	15	15
1060.		10 l. blue	15	15

1927. 50th Anniv. of Rumanian Geographical Society.

1061.	**55.**	1+9 l. violet	1·75	1·00
1062.	–	2+8 l. green ..	1·75	1·00
1063.	–	3+7 l. red	1·75	1·00
1064.	–	5+5 l. blue	1·75	1·00
1065.	–	6+4 l. olive ..	4·75	1·75

DESIGNS: 2 l. Stephen the Great. 3 l. Michael the Brave. 5 l. Carol and Ferdinand. 6 l. Adam Clisi Monument.

60. King Carol and King Ferdinand.

DESIGNS—HORIZ. 30 b., 2 l., 3 l., 5 l. King Ferdinand. VERT. 50 b., 4 l., 4 l. 50, 6 l. King Ferdinand as in Type **60.**

1927. 50th Anniv. of Independence.

1066.	**60.**	25 b. red	25	12
1067.	–	30 b. black	20	15
1068.	–	50 b. green	25	15
1069.	**60.**	1 l. blue	20	15
1070.	–	2 l. green	20	20
1071.	–	3 l. purple	20	25
1072.	–	4 l. brown	45	30
1073.	–	4 l. 50 brown	1·60	1·25
1074.	–	5 l. brown	30	25
1075.	–	6 l. red	80	80
1076.	**60.**	7 l. 50 blue	30	25
1077.		10 l. blue	1·60	50

63. King Michael. 64.

1928.

1080.	**63.**	25 b. black	20	5
1081.		30 b. pink	50	8
1082.		50 b. olive	20	5

(a) Size 19×25 mm.

1083.	**64.**	1 l. purple	20	5
1084.		2 l. green	40	5
1085.		3 l. red	50	5
1086.		5 l. brown	1·00	5
1087.		7 l. 50 blue	4·75	45
1088.		10 l. blue	4·25	15

(b) Size 18×23 mm.

1129.	**64.**	1 l. purple	25	5
1130.		2 l. green	35	12
1131.		3 l. red	80	10
1132.		7 l. 50 blue	1·25	75
1133.		10 l. blue	4·00	3·75

65. Bessarabian Parliament House.

DESIGNS: 3 l., 5 l., 20 l. Hotin Fortress. 7 l. 50, 10 l. Alba Fortress.

1928. 10th Anniv. of Annexation of Bessarabia.

1092.	**65.**	1 l. green	1·10	40
1093.		2 l. brown	1·10	40
1094.	–	3 l. sepia	1·10	40
1095.	–	5 l. lake	1·50	45
1096.	–	7 l. 50 blue	1·50	50
1097.	–	10 l. blue	3·50	1·75
1098.	–	20 l. violet	4·75	2·40

66. Spad S 33 Biplane.

1928. Air.

1099.	**66.**	1 l. brown	5·50	2·50
1100.		2 l. blue	5·50	2·50
1101.		5 l. red	5·50	2·75

67. King Carol and King Michael.

DESIGNS: 2 l. Constanza Harbour and Carol Lighthouse. 5 l., 7 l. 50, Adam Clisi Monument. 10 l., 20 l. Cernavoda Bridge over the Danube.

1928. 50th Anniv. of Acquisition of Northern Dobruja.

1102.	**67.**	1 l. green	55	30
1103.	–	2 l. brown	75	30
1104.	**67.**	3 l. grey	80	30
1105.	–	5 l. mauve	85	35
1106.	–	7 l. 50 blue	1·00	50
1107.	–	10 l. blue	3·25	75
1108.	–	20 l. red	4·50	75

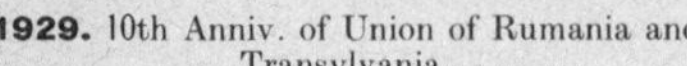

68. 69. The Union.

1929. 10th Anniv. of Union of Rumania and Transylvania.

1109.	68.	1 l. purple	80	80
1110.	69.	2 l. green	80	80
1111.	–	3 l. brown	90	80
1112.	–	4 l. red	80	80
1113.	–	5 l. orange	1·10	90
1114.	–	10 l. blue	1·50	2·00

DESIGNS—HORIZ. 1 l. Ferdinand I, Stephen the Great, Michael the Brave, Hunyadi and Brancoveanu. 10 l. Ferdinand I. VERT. 2 l. Union. 3 l. Avram Jancu. 4 l. King Michael the Brave. 5 l. Bran Castle.

1930. Stamps of King Michael optd. **8 IUNIE 1930.** (Accession of Carol II.)

1134.	63.	25 b. black (postage) ..	12	5
1135.		30 b. pink	25	5
1136.		50 b. olive	20	5
1142.	64.	1 l. purple (No. 1129)	20	5
1143.		2 l. green (No. 1130) ..	20	5
1144.		3 l. red (No. 1131)	25	5
1137.		5 l. brown	35	5
1140.		7 l. 50 blue (No. 1087)	1·50	75
1145.		7 l. 50 blue (No. 1132)	80	30
1138.		10 l. blue (No. 1088) ..	2·00	75
1146.		10 l. blue (No. 1133) ..	70	25
1147.	66.	1 l. brown (air)	10·00	5·00
1148.		2 l. blue	10·00	5·00
1149.		5 l. red ..	10·00	5·00

72. 73. King Carol II. 76.

1930.

1172.	72.	25 b. black	25	5
1173.		50 b. brown	60	30
1174.		1 l. violet	30	5
1175.		2 l. green	50	5
1176.	73.	3 l. red	1·10	5
1177.		4 l. orange	1·25	5
1178.		6 l. red	1·40	5
1179.		7 l. 50 blue	1·60	15
1180.	–	10 l. blue	2·75	10
1181.	–	16 l. green	6·00	15
1182.	–	20 l. yellow	7·50	40

DESIGN: 10 l. to 20 l. Portrait as Type **72**, but in plain circle, with "ROMANIA" at top.

1930. Air.

1183.	76.	1 l. violet on blue	2·00	1·25
1184.		2 l. green on blue	2·40	1·50
1185.		5 l. brown on blue	4·50	2·00
1186.		10 l. blue on blue	8·00	4·00

77. Map of Rumania. 78. Woman with Census Paper. 79. King Carol II.

1930. National Census.

1187.	77.	1 l. violet	65	30
1188.	78.	2 l. green	75	35
1189.		4 l. orange	1·00	30
1190.		6 l. red	2·75	35

1931.

1191.	79.	30 l. blue and olive ..	1·10	50
1192.		50 l. blue and red	2·40	90
1193.		100 l. blue and green	4·50	2·10

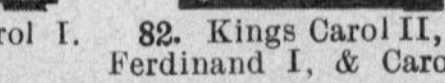

80. King Carol II.

81. King Carol I. 82. Kings Carol II, Ferdinand I, & Carol I.

1931. 50th Anniv. of Rumanian Monarchy.

1200.	80.	1 l. violet	2·00	1·00
1201.	81.	2 l. green	2·75	1·25
1202.	–	6 l. red	5·00	1·75
1203.	82.	10 l. blue	9·00	3·50
1204.	–	20 l. orange	9·50	4·50

DESIGNS—As Type **80**: 6 l. King Carol II, facing right. As Type **81**: 20 l. King Ferdinand I.

83. Naval Cadet Ship "Mircea".

1931. 50th Anniv. of Rumanian Navy.

1205.	83.	6 l. red	4·50	2·50
1206.	–	10 l. blue	5·50	2·75
1207.	–	12 l. green	20·00	3·00
1208.	–	20 l. orange	8·75	5·50

DESIGNS: 10 l. Monitors "Lascar Catargiu" and "Mihail Kogaliniceaunu". 16 l. Monitor "Ardeal". 20 l. Destroyer "Regele Ferdinand".

84. Bayonet Attack. 87. King Carol I.

88. Infantry Attack. 89. King Ferdinand I.

1931. Rumanian Army Cent.

1209.	84.	25 b. black	1·25	80
1210.	–	50 b. brown	1·90	1·10
1211.	–	1 l. violet	2·00	1·25
1212.	87.	2 l. green	3·25	1·50
1213.	88.	3 l. red	8·00	4·25
1214.	89.	7 l. 50 blue	8·50	11·00
1215.	–	16 l. green	10·00	4·25

DESIGNS: 50 b. Infantryman, 1870. (20×33 mm.). 1 l. Infantry and drummer, 1830 (23×36 mm.). 16 l. King Carol II in uniform with plumed helmet. (21×34 mm.).

91. Scouts' Encampment. 92a. Farman.

1931. Rumanian Boy Scouts' Exn. Fund.

1221.	91.	1 l.+1 l. red ..	2·25	2·10
1222.	–	2 l.+2 l. green	2·50	3·00
1223.	–	3 l.+3 l. blue	4·00	3·25
1224.	–	4 l.+4 l. brown	5·50	4·50
1225.	–	6 l.+6 l. brown	8·00	5·00

DESIGNS—VERT. As Type **91**. 3 l. Recruiting (22×37½ mm.): 2 l. Rescue work. (22×41½ mm.): 4 l. Prince Nicholas. 6 l. King Carol II in Scoutmaster's uniform.

1931. Air.

1226.	92a.	2 l. green	1·25	65
1227.	–	3 l. red	1·50	90
1228.	–	5 l. brown	2·25	1·10
1229.	–	10 l. blue	6·00	2·50
1230.	–	20 l. violet	13·50	3·75

DESIGNS: 3 l. Farman III. 5 l. Farman F 60 "Goliath". 10 l. Farman III.

The 20 l. is smaller and shows three aeroplanes.

95. Kings Carol II, Ferdinand I, and Carol I. 96. Alexander the Good.

1931.

1231.	95.	16 l. green	12·00	50

1932. 500th Death Cent. of Alexander I, Prince of Moldavia.

1232.	96.	6 l. red	7·00	6·00

97. King Carol II. 98. Semaphore signaller.

1932.

1248.	97.	10 l. blue	9·00	30

1932. Boy Scouts' Jamboree Fund.

1256.	–	25 b.+25 b. green ..	2·75	2·25
1257.	98.	50 b.+50 b. blue	2·75	2·50
1258.	–	1 l.+1 l. green	3·50	3·25
1259.	–	2 l.+2 l. red ..	6·50	5·25
1260.	–	3 l.+3 l. blue ..	18·00	10·50
1261.	–	6 l.+6 l. brown	19·00	14·00

DESIGNS—VERT. (As Type **98**). 25 b. Scouts in camp. 1 l. On the trail. 3. l King Carol II 6 l. King Carol and King Michael when a Prince. HORIZ. (20×15 mm.). 2 l. Camp fire.

99. Cantacuzino and Gregory Chika.

1932. 9th Int. Medical Congress.

1262.	99.	1 l. red	5·50	5·00
1263.	–	6 l. orange	16·00	7·50
1264.	–	10 l. blue	26·00	13·00

DESIGNS: 6 l. Congress in session. 10 l. Hygeia and Æsculapius.

100. Tuberculosis Sanatorium.

1932. Postal Employees' Fund.

1265.	100.	4 l.+1 l. green	3·25	2·25
1266.	–	6 l.+1 l. brown	4·50	2·75
1267.	–	10 l.+1 l. blue	7·50	4·25

DESIGNS—VERT. 6 l. War Memorial Tablet. HORIZ. 10 l. Convalescent Home.

102. "Bull's head". 103. Dolphins. 104. Arms.

1932. 75th Anniv. of First Moldavian Stamps. Imperf.

1268.	102.	25 b. black	50	20
1269.	–	1 l. purple	60	40
1270.	103.	2 l. green	85	55
1271.	–	3 l. red	95	70
1272.	104.	6 l. red	1·10	85
1273.	–	7 l. 50 blue	2·40	1·00
1274.	–	10 l. blue	3·25	1·75

DESIGNS—As Type **103**. 1 l. Lion rampant and bridge. 3 l. Eagle and castles. 7 l. 50, Eagle. 10 l. Bull's head.

1932. 30th Anniv. of Opening of G.P.O., Bucharest. As T **25**, but smaller.

1275.		16 l. green	7·50	5·25

DESIGNS: 50 b. Trajan at the completion of bridge over the Danube. 1 l. Arrival of Prince Carol at Turnu-Severin. 2 l. Trajan's Bridge.

105. Ruins of Trajan's Bridge: Arms of Turnu-Severin and Towers of Severus.

1933. Cent. of Founding of Turnu-Severin.

1279.	105.	25 b. green ..	20	20
1280.	–	50 b. blue ..	40	30
1281.	–	1 l. brown ..	50	45
1282.	–	2 l. green ..	1·75	75

107. Carmen Sylva and Carol I.

DESIGNS: 3 l. Eagle and medallion portraits of Kings Carol I, Ferdinand I and Carol II. 6 l. Pelesch Castle.

1933. 50th Anniv. of Construction of Pelesch Castle, Sinaia.

1283.	107.	1 l. violet	2·10	1·25
1284.	–	3 l. brown	2·40	1·50
1285.	–	6 l. red	3·00	2·10

108. Wayside Shrine. 110. King Carol II.

1934. Rumanian Women's Exhibition. Inscr. "L.N.F.R. MUNCA NOASTRA ROMANEASC".

1286.	108.	1 l.+1 l. brown ..	1·25	90
1287.	–	2 l.+1 l. blue ..	1·75	1·25
1288.	–	3 l.+1 l. green ..	2·10	1·75

DESIGNS—HORIZ. 2 l. Weaver. VERT. 3 l. Spinner.

1934. Mamaia Jamboree Fund. Nos. 1256/61. Optd. **MAMAIA 1934** and Arms of Constanza.

1289.	–	25 b.+25 b. green ..	2·75	2·75
1290.	98.	50 b.+50 b. blue ..	3·50	3·25
1291.	–	1 l.+1 l. green ..	4·50	4·75
1292.	–	2 l.+2 l. red ..	6·25	6·50
1293.	–	3 l.+3 l. blue ..	13·00	11·00
1294.	–	6 l.+6 l. brown ..	15·00	14·00

1934.

1295.	–	50 b. brown ..	50	30
1296.	110.	2 l. green ..	1·00	30
1297.		4 l. orange ..	1·00	45
1298.	–	6 l. lake ..	3·00	30

DESIGNS: 50 b. Profile portrait of King Carol II in civilian clothes. 6 l. King Carol in plumed helmet.

112. "Grapes for Health". 113. Crisan, Horia and Closca.

114. Boy Scouts.

1934. Bucharest Fruit Exhibition.

1299.	112.	1 l. green ..	2·25	2·00
1300.	–	2 l. brown ..	2·25	2·00

DESIGN: 2 l. Woman with fruit.

1935. 150th Anniv. of Death of Three Rumanian Martyrs. Portraits inscr. "MARTIR AL NEAMULUI 1785".

1301.	113.	1 l. violet ..	50	30
1302.	–	2 l. green (Crisan)	1·00	45
1303.	–	6 l. brown (Closca) ..	2·75	85
1304.	–	10 l. blue (Horia) ..	4·50	2·10

1935. 5th Anniv. of Accession of Carol II.

1305.	–	25 b. black	2·75	2·00
1306.	–	1 l. violet	4·25	3·50
1307.	**114.**	2 l. green	5·50	5·00
1308.	–	6 l.+1 l. brown ..	6·50	6·50
1309.	–	10 l.+2 l. blue ..	14·00	15·00

DESIGNS—VERT. 25 b. Scout saluting. 1 l. Bugler. 6 l. King Carol II. HORIZ. 10 l. Colour party.

1935. Portraits as T **110** but additionally inscr. "POSTA".

1310.	–	25 b. black	10	5
1311.	–	50 b. brown	10	5
1312.	–	1 l. violet	15	5
1313.	**110.**	2 l. green	35	5
1315.	–	3 l. red	70	12
1316.	–	3 l. blue	90	15
1317.	**110.**	4 l. orange	75	10
1318.	–	5 l. red	75	55
1319.	–	6 l. lake	95	5
1320.	–	7 l. 50 blue	1·25	35
1321.	–	8 l. purple	1·25	35
1322.	**110.**	9 l. blue	1·90	65
1323.	–	10 l. blue	85	20
1324.	–	12 l. blue	1·25	85
1325.	–	15 l. brown	1·25	50
1326.	–	16 l. green	1·50	30
1327.	–	20 l. orange ..	95	40
1328.	–	24 l. red	1·90	50

PORTRAITS—IN PROFILE: 25 b., 15 l. In naval uniform. 50 b., 3 l., 8 l., 10 l. In civilian clothes. THREE-QUARTER FACE: 1 l., 5 l., 7 l. 50. In civilian clothes. FULL FACE: 6 l., 12 l., 16 l., 20 l., 24 l. In plumed helmet.

118. King Carol II.

119. Oltenia Peasant Girl.

1936. Bucharest Exn. and 70th Anniv. of Hohenzollern-Sigmaringen Dynasty.

1329.	**118.**	6 l.+1 l. red	75	50

1936. 6th Anniv. of Accession of Carol II. Inscr. "O.E.T.R. 8 IUNIE 1936".

1330.	**119.**	50 b.+50 b. brown ..	1·00	50
1331.	–	1 l.+1 l. violet ..	75	55
1332.	–	2 l.+1 l. green ..	70	60
1333.	–	3 l.+1 l. red	1·00	75
1334.	–	4 l.+2 l. red	1·25	80
1335.	–	6 l.+3 l. grey ..	1·75	1·00
1336.	–	10 l.+5 l. blue ..	2·50	2·00

DESIGNS (costumes of following districts)—VERT. 1 l. Banat. 4 l. Gorj. 6 l. Neamz. HORIZ. 2 l. Saliste. 3 l. Hateg. 10 l. Suceava (Bukovina).

120. Brasov Jamboree Badge.

121. Liner "Transylvania".

1936. National Scout Jamboree, Brasov.

1337.	–	1 l.+1 l. blue ..	4·00	2·50
1338.	–	3 l.+3 l. grey ..	6·00	3·50
1339.	**120.**	6 l.+6 l. red	8·00	4·50

DESIGNS: 1 l. National Scout Badge. 3 l. Tenderfoot Badge.

1936. First Marine Exhibition, Bucharest.

1343.	–	1 l.+1 l. violet ..	5·25	3·00
1344.	–	3 l.+2 l. blue ..	5·25	3·25
1345.	**121.**	6 l.+3 l. red	6·25	4·75

DESIGNS: 1 l. Submarine "Delfinul". 3 l. Naval Cadet Ship "Mircea".

1936. 18th Anniv. of Annexation of Transylvania and 16th Anniv. of Foundation of "Little Entente" Nos. 1320 and 1323 optd. **CEHOSLOVACIA YUGOSLAVIA 1920-1936.**

1346.		7 l. 50 blue	2·75	3·25
1347.		10 l. blue	2·75	3·25

123. Creanga's Birthplace.

1937. Birth Cent. of Ion Creanga (poet).

1348.	**123.**	2 l. green	75	50
1349.	–	3 l. red	80	55
1350.	**123.**	4 l. violet	1·10	70
1351.	–	6 l. brown	1·75	1·60

DESIGN: 3 l., 6 l. Portrait of Creanga (37 × 22 mm.).

124. Footballers.

1937. 7th Anniv. of Accession of Carol II.

1352.	**124.**	25 b.+25 b. olive ..	30	20
1353.	–	50 b.+50 b. brown ..	35	25
1354.	–	1 l.+50 b. violet ..	55	40
1355.	–	2 l.+1 l. green ..	80	45
1356.	–	3 l.+1 l. red ..	1·00	50
1357.	–	4 l.+1 l. red	1·25	60
1358.	–	6 l.+2 l. brown ..	1·40	85
1359.	–	10 l.+4 l. blue ..	2·00	1·25

DESIGNS—HORIZ. 50 b. Swimmer. 3 l. King Carol II hunting. 10 l. U.F.S.R. Inaugural Meeting. VERT. 1 l. Javelin thrower. 2 l. Skier. 4 l. Rowing. 6 l. Steeplechaser.

Premium in aid of the Federation of Rumanian Sports Clubs (U.F.S.R.).

127. Curtea de Arges Cathedral.

128. Hurdling.

1937. "Little Entente".

1360.	**127.**	7 l. 50 blue	1·75	80
1361.		10 l. blue	2·40	45

1937. 8th Balkan Games, Bucharest. Inscr. as in T **115.**

1362.	–	1 l.+1 l. violet ..	85	65
1363.	–	2 l.+1 l. green ..	95	90
1364.	**128.**	4 l.+1 l. red	1·00	1·25
1365.	–	6 l.+1 l. brown ..	1·40	1·25
1366.	–	10 l.+1 l. blue ..	4·00	2·25

DESIGNS: 1 l. Sprinting. 2 l. Throwing the javelin. 6 l. Breasting the tape. 10 l. High-jumping.

129. Arms of Rumania, Greece, Turkey and Yugoslavia.

130. King Carol II.

132. Dimitrie Cantemir.

131. King Carol II and Provincial Arms.

1938. Balkan Entente.

1368.	**129.**	7 l. 50 blue	1·00	60
1369.		10 l. blue	1·60	40

1938. New Constitution. Profile portraits of King inscr. "27 FEBRUARIE 1938". 6 l. shows Arms also.

1370.	**130.**	3 l. red	30	25
1371.	–	6 l. brown	40	25
1372.	–	10 l. blue	65	45

1938. Fund for Bucharest Exhibition celebrating 20th Anniv. of Union of Provinces.

1373.	**131.**	6 l.+1 l. mauve ..	35	35

1938. Boy Scouts' Fund. 8th Anniv. of Accession of Carol II. Inscr. "STRAJA TARII 8 IUNIE 1938".

1374.	**132.**	25 b.+25 b. olive ..	35	20
1375.	–	50 b.+50 b. brown ..	40	20
1376.	–	1 l.+1 l. violet ..	50	25
1377.	–	2 l.+2 l. green ..	60	25
1378.	–	3 l.+2 l. mauve ..	60	30
1379.	–	4 l.+2 l. red	65	35
1380.	–	6 l.+2 l. brown ..	75	40
1381.	–	7 l. 50 blue	85	40
1382.	–	10 l. blue	90	50
1383.	–	16 l. green	1·50	1·00
1384.	–	20 l. red	2·25	1·25

PORTRAITS: 50 b. Maria Doamna. 1 l. Mircea the Great. 2 l. Constantin Brancoveanu. 3 l. Stephen the Great. 4 l. Prince Cuza. 6 l. Michael the Brave. 7 l. 50, Queen Elisabeth. 10 l. King Carol II. 16 l. King Ferdinand I. 20 l. King Carol I.

134. "The Spring".

135. Prince Carol in Royal Carriage.

1938. Birth Centenary of Nicholas Grigorescu (painter).

1385.	**134.**	1 l.+1 l. blue ..	90	50
1386.	–	2 l.+1 l. green ..	1·50	80
1387.	–	4 l.+1 l. red	1·75	90
1388.	–	6 l.+1 l. red	1·90	1·25
1389.	–	10 l.+1 l. blue ..	2·25	1·75

DESIGNS—HORIZ. 2 l. "Escorting Prisoners" (Russo-Turkish War 1877-78). 4 l. "Returning from Market". VERT. 6 l. "Rodica, the Water Carrier". 10 l. Self portrait.

1939. Birth Centenary of King Carol I.

1390.	**135.**	25 b. black	5	5
1391.	–	50 b. brown	5	5
1392.	–	1 l. violet	20	8
1393.	–	1 l. 50 green ..	5	5
1394.	–	2 l. blue	8	5
1395.	–	3 l. red	8	5
1396.	–	4 l. red	10	5
1397.	–	5 l. black	10	5
1398.	–	7 l. black	10	5
1399.	–	8 l. blue	25	15
1400.	–	10 l. mauve	30	15
1401.	–	12 l. blue	30	20
1402.	–	15 l. blue	35	15
1403.	–	16 l. green	75	45

DESIGNS—HORIZ. 50 b. Prince Carol at Battle of Calafat. 1 l. 50, Sigmaringen and Pelesch Castles. 15 l. Carol I, Queen Elizabeth and Arms of Rumania. VERT. 1 l. Examining plans for restoring Curtea de Arges Monastery. 2 l. Carol I and Queen Elizabeth. 3 l. Carol I at age of 8. 4 l. In 1866. 5 l. in 1877. 7 l. Equestrian Statue. 8 l. Leading troops in 1878. 10 l. In General's uniform. 12 l. Bust. 16 l. Restored Monastery of Curtea de Arges.

136. Rumanian Pavilion. N.Y. World's Fair.

137. Michael Eminescu, after painting by Joano Basarab.

1939. New York World's Fair.

1407.	**136.**	6 l. lake	25	30
1408.	–	12 l. blue	25	30

DESIGN: 12 l. Another view of Pavilion.

1939. 50th Death Anniv. of Michael Eminescu (poet).

1409.	**137.**	5 l. black	30	40
1410	–	7 l. red	30	40

DESIGN: 7 l. Eminescu in later years.

138. St. George and Dragon.

139. Railway Locomotives of 1869 and 1939.

1939. 9th Anniv. of Accession of Carol II and Boy Scouts' Fund.

1411.	**138.**	25 b.+25 b. grey ..	60	35
1412.		50 b.+50 b. brown	60	35
1413.		1 l.+1 l. blue ..	65	35
1414.		2 l.+2 l. green ..	75	35
1415.		3 l.+2 l. purple ..	90	35
1416.		4 l.+2 l. orange ..	1·10	45
1417.		6 l.+2 l. red	1·25	45
1418.		8 l. grey	1·50	50
1419.		10 l. blue	1·60	50
1420.		12 l. blue	2·00	1·10
1421.		16 l. green	2·40	1·50

1939. 70th Anniv. of Rumanian Railways.

1422.	**139.**	1 l. violet	95	55
1423.	–	4 l. red	1·00	65
1424.	–	5 l. grey	1·10	85
1425.	–	7 l. mauve	1·40	90
1426.	–	12 l. blue	2·00	1·25
1427.	–	15 l. green	3·00	2·00

DESIGNS—HORIZ. 4 l. Steam train crossing railway-bridge. 15 l. Railway Headquarters, Budapest. VERT. 5 l., 7 l. Steam train leaving station. 12 l. Diesel train crossing railway bridge.

1940. Balkan Entente. As T **103** of Yugoslavia, but with Arms rearranged.

1428.		12 l. blue	55	45
1429.		16 l. blue	55	45

141. King Carol II.

142. King Carol II.

1940. Aviation Fund.

1430.	**141.**	1 l.+50 b. green ..	20	15
1431.		2 l. 50+50 b. green ..	25	20
1432.		3 l.+1 l. red	35	25
1433.		3 l. 50+50 b. brown ..	35	30
1434.		4 l.+1 l. orange ..	45	35
1435.		6 l.+1 l. blue ..	65	20
1436.		9 l.+1 l. blue ..	80	70
1437.		14 l.+1 l. green ..	1·00	85

1940. 10th Anniv. of Carol II, and Aviation fund. Royal portraits.

1438.	**142.**	1 l.+50 b. purple ..	30	25
1439.		4 l.+1 l. brown ..	35	35
1440.	–	6 l.+1 l. blue ..	40	45
1441.	–	8 l. red	60	60
1442.	–	16 l. blue	70	75
1443.	–	32 l. brown	2·10	1·75

PORTRAITS: 6 l., 16 l. in steel helmet. 8 l. in military uniform. 32 l. in flying helmet.

144. The Iron Gates of the Danube.

1940. Charity. 10th Anniv. of Accession of Carol II and Boy Scouts' Fund. Inscr. "STRAJA TARII 8 IUNIE 1940".

1444.	**144.**	1 l.+1 l. violet ..	35	40
1445.	–	2 l.+1 l. brown ..	40	45
1446.	–	3 l.+1 l. green ..	40	50
1447.	–	4 l.+1 l. black ..	50	55
1448.	–	5 l.+1 l. orange ..	60	65
1449.	–	8 l.+1 l. red ..	60	70
1450.	–	12 l.+2 l. blue ..	70	75
1451.	–	16 l.+2 l. grey ..	2·25	1·75

DESIGNS—HORIZ. 3 l. Hotin Fortress. 4 l. Hurez Monastery. VERT. 2 l. Greco-Roman ruins. 5 l. Church in Suceava. 8 l. Alba Julia Cathedral. 12 l. Village Church, Transylvania. 16 l. Triumphal Arch, Bucharest.

145. King Michael. **146.**

1940.

1455.	**145.**	25 b. green	5	5
1456.		50 b. olive	5	5
1457.		1 l. violet	5	5
1458.		2 l. orange	5	5
1608.		3 l. brown	5	5
1609.		3 l. 50 brown ..	5	5
1459.		4 l. grey	5	5
1611.		4 l. 50 brown ..	5	5
1460.		5 l. pink	5	5
1613.		6 l. 50 violet	5	5
1461.		7 l. blue	5	5
1615.		10 l. mauve	5	5
1616.		11 l. blue	5	5
1463.		12 l. blue	5	5
1464.		13 l. purple	8	5
1618.		15 l. blue	5	5
1619.		16 l. blue	5	5
1620.		20 l. brown	5	5
1621.		29 l. blue	60	70
1467.		30 l. green	15	5
1468.		50 l. brown	15	5
1469.		100 l. brown ..	30	5

1940. Aviation Fund.

1470.	**146.**	1 l.+50 b. green ..	5	5
1471.		2 l.+50 b. green ..	5	5
1472.		2 l. 50+50 b. green ..	5	5
1473.		3 l.+1 l. violet ..	5	5
1474.		3 l. 50+50 b. pink ..	15	15
1475.		4 l.+50 b. red ..	5	5
1476.		4 l.+1 l. brown ..	5	5
1477.		5 l.+1 l. red	55	25
1478.		6 l.+1 l. blue ..	5	5
1479.		7 l.+1 l. green ..	20	10
1480.		8 l.+1 l. violet ..	15	5
1481.		12 l.+1 l. brown ..	20	10
1482.		14 l.+1 l. blue ..	25	12
1483.		19 l.+1 l. mauve ..	50	20

147. Codreanu (founder) **148.**

1940. "Iron Guard" Fund.

1484.	**147.**	7 l.+30 l. grn. (post.)	3·00	2·75
1485.	**148.**	20 l.+5 l. green (air)	80	70

149. Ion Mota.

150. Library.

1941. Marin and Mota (legionaries killed in Spain).

1486. – 7 l.+7 l. red.. .. 40 60
1487. 149. 15 l.+15 l. blue .. 1·25 1·75
PORTRAIT: 7 l. Vasile Marin.

1941. Carol I Endowment Fund. Inscr. "1891 1941".

1488. – 1 l. 50+43 l. 50 violet 1·10 1·00
1489. 150. 2 l.+43 l. red .. 1·10 1·00
1490. – 7 l.+38 l. red .. 1·10 1·00
1491. – 10 l.+35 l. green .. 1·10 1·10
1492. – 16 l.+29 l. brown .. 1·10 1·25
DESIGNS. 1 l. 50, Ex-libris. 7 l. Foundation building and equestrian statue. 10 l. Foundation stone. 16 l. Kings Michael and Carol I.

1941. Occupation of Cernauti. Nos. 1488/92 optd. **CERNAUTI 5 Iulie 1941.**

1493. – 1 l. 50+43 l. 50 violet 1·50 2·25
1494 150. 2 l.+43 l. red .. 1·50 2·25
1495. – 7 l.+38 l. red .. 1·50 2·25
1496. – 10 l.+35 l. green .. 1·50 2·40
1497. – 16 l.+29 l. brown .. 1·75 2·50

1941. Occupation of Chisinau. Nos. 1488/92 optd. **CHISINAU 16 Iulie 1941.**

1498. – 1 l. 50+43 l. 50 violet 1·50 2·25
1499. 150. 2 l.+43 l. red .. 1·50 2·25
1500. – 7 l.+38 l. red .. 1·50 2·25
1501. – 10 l.+35 l. green .. 1·50 2·40
1502. – 16 l.+29 l. brown .. 1·75 2·50

153. "Charity". 154. Prince Voda.

1941. Red Cross Fund. Cross in red.

1503. 153. 1 l. 50+38 l. 50 vio. 60 75
1504. 2 l.+38 l. red .. 60 75
1505. 5 l.+35 l. olive .. 60 75
1506. 7 l.+33 l. brown .. 60 75
1507. 10 l.+30 l. blue .. 1·25 1·40

1941. Conquest of Transdniestria.

1572. 154. 3 l. orange 5 8
1509. 6 l. brown 8 5
1510. 12 l. violet 12 8
1511. 24 l. blue 20 20

155. King Michael and Stephen the Great. 157. Hotin.

1941. Anti-Bolshevik Crusade. Inscr. "RAZBOIUL SFANT CONTRA BOLSEVISMULUI".

1512. 155. 10 l.+30 l. blue .. 1·10 1·50
1513. – 12 l.+28 l. red .. 1·10 1·50
1514. – 16 l.+24 l. brown .. 1·50 1·75
1515. – 20 l.+20 l. violet .. 1·50 1·75
DESIGNS: 12 l. Hotin and Akkerman Fortresses. 16 l. Arms and helmeted soldiers. 20 l. Bayonet charge and Arms of Rumania.

1941. Fall of Odessa. Nos. 1512/15 optd. **ODESA/16 Oct. 1941.**

1517. 155. 10 l.+30 l. blue .. 1·10 1·50
1518. – 12 l.+28 l. red .. 1·10 1·50
1519. – 16 l.+24 l. brown .. 1·50 1·75
1520. – 20 l.+20 l. violet .. 1·50 1·75

1941. Restoration of Bessarabia and Bukovina (Suceava). Inscr. "BASARABIA" or "BUCOVINA".

1522. – 25 b. red 5 5
1523. 157. 50 b. brown 5 5
1524. – 1 l. violet 5 5
1525. – 1 l. 50 green 5 5
1526. – 2 l. brown 10 8
1527. – 3 l. olive 12 10
1528. – 5 l. olive 20 10
1529. – 5 l. 50 brown 20 12
1530. – 6 l. 50 mauve 50 40
1531. 157. 9 l. 50 grey 50 50
1532. – 10 l. purple 35 12
1533. – 13 l. blue 50 20
1534. – 17 l. brown 60 15
1535. – 26 l. green 70 30
1536. – 39 l. blue .. .. 1·40 40
1537. – 130 l. yellow .. .. 4·50 3·00
VIEWS—VERT. 25 b., 5 l. Paraclis Hotin. 3 l. Dragomirna. 13 l. Milisauti. HORIZ. 1l., 17 l. Sucevita. 1 l. 50, Soroca. 2 l., 5 l. 50, Tighina. 6 l. 50, Cetatea Alba. 10 l., 130 l. Putna. 26 l. St. Nicolae, Suceava. 39 l. Monastery, Rughi.

1941. Winter Relief Fund. Inscr. "BASARABIA" or "BUCOVINA".

1538. – 3 l.+50 b. red .. 20 20
1539. – 5 l. 50+50 b. orange 30 30
1540. – 5 l. 50+1 l. black .. 30 30
1541. – 6 l. 50+1 l. brown .. 35 40
1542. – 8 l.+1 l. blue .. 30 25
1543. – 9 l. 50+1 l. blue .. 50 45
1544. – 10 l. 50+1 l. blue .. 50 25
1545. – 16 l.+1 l. mauve .. 60 55
1546. 157. 25 l.+1 l. grey .. 80 60
VIEWS—HORIZ. 3 l. Sucevita. 5 l. 50 (1539), Monastery, Rughi. 5 l. 50 (1540), Tighina. 6 l. 50, Soroca. 8 l. St Nicolae, Suceava. 10 l. 50, Putna. 16 l. Cetatea Alba. VERT. 9 l. 50, Milisauti.

158. Titu Maiorescu.

159. Coat-of-Arms of Bukovina.

1942. Prisoners of War Relief Fund through International Education Office, Geneva.

1549. 158. 9 l.+11 l. violet .. 50 65
1550. 20 l.+20 l. brown .. 1·50 1·50
1551. 20 l.+30 l. blue .. 1·75 1·75

1942. 1st Anniv. of Liberation of Bukovina.

1553. 159. 9 l.+41 l. red .. 1·25 1·50
1554. – 18 l.+32 l. blue .. 1·25 1·50
1555. – 20 l.+30 l. red .. 1·25 1·50
ARMORIAL DESIGNS: 18 l. Castle. 20 l. Mounds and crosses.

160. Map of Bessarabia, King Michael, Antonescu, Hitler and Mussolini.

161. Statue of Miron Costin.

1942. 1st Anniv. of Liberation of Bessarabia.

1556. 160. 9 l.+41 l. brown .. 90 1·40
1557. – 18 l.+32 l. olive .. 90 1·40
1558. – 20 l.+30 l. blue .. 90 1·40
DESIGNS—VERT. 18 l. King Michael and Marshal Antonescu below miniature of King Stephen. HORIZ. 20 l. Marching soldiers and miniature of Marshal Antonescu.

1942. 1st Anniv. of Incorporation of Transdniestria.

1559. 161. 6 l.+44 l. brown .. 90 1·40
1560. 12 l.+38 l. violet .. 90 1·40
1561. 24 l.+26 l. blue .. 90 1·40

162. Andrei Muresanu.

164. Nurse and wounded Soldier.

163. Statue of Avram Iancu. 165. Sword and Shield.

1942. 80th Death Anniv. of A. Muresanu (novelist).

1562. 162. 5 l.+5 l. violet .. 90 90

1943. Fund for Statue of Iancu (national hero).

1563. 163. 16 l.+4 l. brown .. 90 1·00

1943. Red Cross Charity. Cross in red

1564. 164. 12 l.+88 l. red .. 75 75
1565. 16 l.+84 l. blue .. 75 75
1566. 20 l.+80 l. olive .. 75 75

1943. Charity. 2nd Year of War. Inscr. "22 JUNIE 1941 22 JUNIE 1943".

1568. 165. 36 l.+164 l. brown .. 2·10 2·10
1569. – 62 l.+138 l. blue .. 2·10 2·10
1570. – 76 l.+124 l. red .. 2·10 2·10
DESIGNS: 62 l. Sword severing chain. 76 l. Angel protecting soldier and family.

167. P. Maior.

169. King Michael and Marshal Antonescu.

1943. Transylvanian Refugees' Fund (1st issue).

1576. 167. 16 l.+134 l. red .. 40 40
1577. – 32 l.+118 l. blue .. 40 40
1578. – 36 l.+114 l. purple 40 40
1579. – 62 l.+138 l. red .. 40 40
1580. – 91 l.+109 l. brown .. 40 40
PORTRAITS—VERT. 32 l. C. Sincai. 36 l. T. Cipariu. 91 l. G. Cosbuc. HORIZ. 62 l. Horia, Closca and Crisan.
See also Nos. 1584/8.

1943. 3rd Anniv. of King Michael's Reign.

1581. 169. 16 l.+24 l. blue .. 1·50 1·50

170. Sports Shield. 171. Calafat, 1877.

1943. Charity. Sports Week.

1582. 170. 16 l.+24 l. blue .. 45 45
1583. 16 l.+24 l. brown .. 45 45

1943. Transylvanian Refugees' Fund (2nd issue). Portraits as T **167.**

1584. 16 l.+134 l. mauve .. 40 40
1585. 51 l.+99 l. orange .. 40 40
1586. 56 l.+144 l. red 40 40
1587. 76 l.+124 l. blue .. 40 40
1588. 77 l.+123 l. brown .. 40 40
PORTRAITS—VERT. 16 l. S. Micu. 51 l. G. Lazar. 56 l. O. Goga. 76 l. S. Barnutiu. 77 l. A. Sarguna.

1943. Centenary of National Artillery.

1596. 171. 1 l.+1 l. brown .. 30 30
1597. – 2 l.+2 l. violet .. 30 30
1598. – 3 l. 50+3 l. 50 blue 30 30
1599. – 4 l.+4 l. mauve .. 30 30
1600. – 5 l.+5 l. orange .. 50 50
1601. – 6 l. 50+6 l. 50 blue 50 50
1602. – 7 l.+7 l. purple .. 75 75
1603. – 20 l.+20 l. red .. 1·25 1·25
DESIGNS—HORIZ.: (1 l. to 7 l. inscr. battle scenes): 2 l. "1916-1918". 3 l. 50, Stalingrad. 4 l. Crossing R. Tisza. 5 l. Odessa. 6 l. 50, Caucasus. 7 l. Sevastopol. 20 l. Bibescu and King Michael.

172. Association Insignia.

1943. 25th Anniv. of National Engineers' Assn.

1624. 172. 21 l.+29 l. brown .. 1·00 60

173. Motor-cycle and Delivery Van.

1944. Postal Employees' Relief Fund and Bicent. 200th Anniv. of National Postal Service.

(a) Without opt.

1625. 173. 1 l.+49 l. red .. 2·00 2·00
1626. – 2 l.+48 l. mauve .. 2·00 2·00
1627. – 4 l.+46 l. blue .. 2·00 2·00
1628. – 10 l.+40 l. purple .. 2·00 2·00

(b) Optd. **1744 1944.**

1631. 173. 1 l.+49 l. red .. 3·75 3·75
1632. – 2 l.+48 l. mauve .. 3·75 3·75
1633. – 4 l.+46 l. blue .. 3·75 3·75
1634. – 10 l.+40 l. purple .. 3·75 3·75
DESIGNS—HORIZ. 2 l. Mail van and eight horses. 4 l. Chariot. VERT. 10 l. Horseman and Globe.

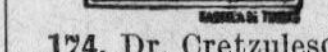
174. Dr. Cretzulescu.

175. Rugby Player.

1944. Cent. of Medicinal Teaching in Rumania.

1637. 174. 35 l.+65 l. blue .. 90 90

1944. 30th Anniv. of Foundation of National Rugby Football Association.

1638. 175. 16 l.+184 l. red .. 3·00 4·00

176. Stefan Tomsa Church, Radaseni.

177. Fruit Pickers.

1944. Cultural Fund. Town of Radaseni Inscr. "RADASENI".

1639. 176. 5 l.+145 l. blue .. 40 60
1640. – 12 l.+138 l. red .. 40 60
1641. 177. 15 l.+135 l. orange .. 40 60
1642. – 32 l.+118 l. brown .. 40 60
DESIGNS—HORIZ. 12 l. Agricultural Institution. 32 l. School.

178. Queen Helen.

179. King Michael and Carol I Foundation, Bucharest.

1945. Red Cross Relief Fund. Portrait in black on yellow and Cross in red.

1643. 178. 4 l. 50+5 l. 50 violet 15 20
1644. 10 l.+40 l. brown .. 25 30
1645. 15 l.+75 l. blue .. 40 50
1646. 20 l.+80 l. red .. 95 75

1945. King Carol I Foundation Fund.

1647. 179. 20 l.+180 l. orange .. 25 30
1648. 25 l.+175 l. slate .. 25 30
1649. 35 l.+165 l. brown .. 25 30
1650. 76 l.+125 l. violet .. 25 30

180. A. Saguna.

181. A. Muresanu.

1945. Liberation of Northern Transylvania. Inscr. "1944".

1652. 180. 25 b. red 50 50
1653. 181. 50 b. orange 15 15
1654. – 4 l. 50 brown .. 20 20
1655. – 11 l. blue 20 20
1656. – 15 l. green 20 20
1657. – 31 l. violet 20 20
1658. – 35 l. grey 20 20
1659. – 41 l. olive .. .. 1·00 1·00
1660. – 55 l. brown 20 20
1661. – 61 l. mauve 20 20
1662. – 75 l.+75 l. brown .. 40 40
DESIGNS—HORIZ. 4 l. 50, Samuel Micu. 31 l. George Lazar. 55 l. Three Heroes. 61 l. Petru Maior. 75 l. King Ferdinand and King Michael. VERT. 11 l. George Sincai, 15 l. Michael the Brave. 35 l. Avram Lancu. 41 l. Simeon Barnutiu.

182. King Michael. 183.

184. King Michael. 185.

1945.

1663. 182. 50 b. grey 10 10
1664. 183. 1 l. brown 10 10
1665. 2 l. violet 10 10
1666. 182. 2 l. brown 10 10
1667. 183. 4 l. green 10 10
1668. 184. 5 l. mauve 10 10
1669. 182. 10 l. blue 10 10
1670. 10 l. brown 10 10
1671. 183. 10 l. brown 10 10
1672. 182. 15 l. mauve 10 10
1673. 20 l. blue 10 10
1674. 20 l. lilac 10 10

1675. **184.** 20 l. purple 10 10
1676. 25 l. red 10 10
1677. 35 l. brown 10 10
1678. 40 l. red 10 10
1679. **183.** 50 l. blue 10 10
1680. 55 l. red 10 10
1681. **184.** 75 l. green 10 10
1682. **185.** 80 l. orange 10 10
1683. 80 l. blue 10 10
1684. **182.** 80 l. blue 10 10
1685. **185.** 100 l. brown .. 10 10
1686. **182.** 137 l. green 15 10
1687. **185.** 160 l. green 10 10
1688. 160 l. violet 10 10
1689. 200 l. green .. 20 15
1690. 200 l. red 10 10
1691. **183.** 200 l. red 10 10
1692. **185.** 300 l. blue 10 10
1693. 360 l. brown .. 15 10
1694. 400 l. violet 10 10
1695. **183.** 400 l. red 10 10
1696. **185.** 480 l. brown 15 10
1697. **182.** 500 l. mauve .. 15 10
1698. **185.** 600 l. green 10 10
1699. **184.** 860 l. brown 20 15
1700. **185.** 1000 l. green .. 10 10
1701. **182.** 1500 l. green .. 10 10
1702. **185.** 2400 l. lilac 25 10
1703. **183.** 2500 l. blue 15 10
1704. **185.** 3700 l. blue 25 10
1705. **182.** 5000 l. grey 10 10
1706. 8000 l. green .. 25 10
1707. **185.** 10000 l. brown .. 40 20

186. N. Jorga. **187.** Books and Torch.

1945. War Victims' Relief Fund.
1708. – 12 l. + 188 l. blue .. 65 65
1709. – 16 l. + 184 l. brown .. 65 65
1710. **186.** 20 l. + 180 l. brown .. 65 65
1711. – 32 l. + 168 l. red .. 65 65
1712. – 35 l. + 165 l. blue .. 65 65
1713. – 36 l. + 164 l. violet .. 70 80
PORTRAITS: 12 l. I. G. Duca. 16 l. Virgil Madgearu. 32 l. Ilie Pintilie. 35 l. Bernath Andrei. 36 l. Filimon Sarbu.

1945. Charity. First Rumanian-Soviet Congress Fund. Inscr. "ARLUS".
1715. **187.** 20 l. + 80 l. olive .. 30 30
1716. – 35 l. + 165 l. red .. 30 30
1717. – 75 l. + 225 l. blue .. 30 30
1718. – 80 l. + 420 l. brown .. 30 30
DESIGNS: 35 l. Soviet and Rumanian flags. 75 l. Drawn curtain revealing Kremlin. 80 l. T. Vladimirescu and A. Nevsky.

188. Karl Marx. **189.** Postman.

1945. Trade Union Congress, Bucharest. Perf. or Imperf.
1720. **188.** 75 l. + 425 l. red .. 3·00 3·00
1723. 75 l. + 425 l. blue .. 8·50 8·50
1721. – 120 l. + 380 l. blue .. 3·00 3·00
1724. – 120 l. + 380 l. brown .. 8·50 8·50
1722. – 155 l. + 445 l. brown .. 3·00 3·00
1725. – 155 l. + 445 l. red .. 8·50 8·50
PORTRAITS: 120 l. Engels. 155 l. Lenin.

1945. Postal Employees. Inscr. "MUNCA P.T.T.".
1726. **189.** 100 l. brown 50 50
1727. 100 l. olive 50 50
1728. – 150 l. brown .. 1·00 1·00
1729. – 150 l. red .. 1·00 1·00
1730. – 250 l. olive .. 1·60 1·60
1731. – 250 l. blue .. 1·60 1·60
1732. – 500 l. mauve .. 13·50 13·50
DESIGNS: 150 l. Telegraphist. 250 l. Lineman. 500 l. Post Office, Bucharest.

190. Discus Throwing. **192.** Agricultural and Industrial Workers.

1945. Charity. With shield inscr. "O.S.P.". Perf. or imperf.
1733. **190.** 12 l. + 188 l. olive (post.) 2·50 2·40
1738. – 12 l. + 188 l. orange .. 2·50 2·40
1734. – 16 l. + 184 l. blue .. 2·50 2·40
1739. – 16 l. + 184 l. purple 2·50 2·40
1735. – 20 l. + 180 l. green .. 2·50 2·40
1740. – 20 l. + 180 l. violet 2·50 2·40
1736. – 32 l. + 168 l. mauve .. 2·50 2·40
1741. – 32 l. + 168 l. green .. 2·50 2·40
1737. – 35 l. + 165 l. blue .. 2·50 2·40
1742. – 35 l. + 165 l. olive .. 2·50 2·40
1743. – 200 l. + 1000 l. bl. (air) 13·00 15·00
DESIGNS: 16 l. Diving. 20 l. Skiing. 32 l. Volleyball. 35 l. "Sport and work". Larger design—200 l. Mail-plane and bird.

1945. 1st Anniv of Rumanian Armistice with Russia.
1744. **192.** 100 l. + 400 l. red .. 75 60
1745. – 200 l. + 800 l. blue .. 75 60
DESIGN: 200 l. King Michael, "Agriculture" and "Industry".

193. T. Vladimirescu. **194.** Destitute Children.

1945. Charity. Patriotic Defence Fund Inscr. "APARAREA PATRIOTICA."
1746. – 20 l. + 580 l. brown 10·00 12·50
1747. – 20 l. + 580 l. mauve .. 10·00 12·50
1748. – 40 l. + 560 l. blue .. 10·00 12·50
1749. – 40 l. + 560 l. green .. 10·00 12·50
1750. – 55 l. + 545 l. red .. 10·00 12·50
1751. – 55 l. + 545 l. brown 10·00 12·50
1752. **193.** 60 l. + 540 l. blue .. 10·00 12·50
1753. 60 l. + 540 l. brown 10·00 12·50
1754. – 80 l. + 520 l. red .. 10·00 12·50
1755. – 80 l. + 520 l. mauve .. 10·00 12·50
1756. – 100 l. + 500 l. green 10·00 12·50
1757. – 100 l. + 500 l. brown 10·00 12·50
DESIGNS—HORIZ. 20 l. "Political Amnesty". 40 l. "Military Amnesty". 55 l. "Agrarian Amnesty". 100 l. King Michael and "Reconstruction". VERT. 80 l. Nicholas Horia.

1945. Child Welfare Fund.
1758. **194.** 40 l. blue 20 15

195. I. Ionescu, G. Titeica, A. G. Idachimescu and V. Cristescu.

1945. 50th Anniv. of Founding of Journal of Mathematics.
1759. **195.** 2 l. brown 10 10
1760. – 80 l. grey 60 60
DESIGN: 80 l. Allegory of Learning.

196. Cernavoda Bridge.

1945. 50th Anniv. of Cernavoda Bridge.
1761. **196.** 80 l. black 35 25

197. German Electric Train.

DESIGNS—HORIZ. As Type **197**: 20 l. Coats of arms. 25 l. Arterial road. 55 l. Oil wells. 100 l. "Agriculture".

198.

1945. Charity. 16th Congress of Rumanian Engineers. Perf. or imperf. (a) Postage.
1762. **197.** 10 l. + 490 l. olive .. 1·40 1·50
1763. 10 l. + 490 l. blue .. 1·40 1·50
1764. – 20 l. + 480 l. brown 65 65
1765. – 20 l. + 480 l. violet 65 65
1766. – 25 l. + 475 l. purple 65 65
1767. – 25 l. + 475 l. green .. 90 1·25
1768. – 55 l. + 445 l. blue .. 65 65
1769. – 55 l. + 445 l. grey .. 65 65
1770. – 100 l. + 400 l. brown 65 65
1771. – 100 l. + 400 l. mauve 65 65
(b) Air. Symbolical design as T **198**. Imperf.
1772. **198.** 80 l. + 420 l. grey .. 1·50 1·50
1773. 200 l. + 800 l. blue .. 1·50 1·50

199. Globe and Clasped Hands.

DESIGNS: 160 l. Globe and Dove of Peace. 320 l. Hand and hammer. 440 l. Scaffolding and flags.

1945. Charity. World Trade Union Congress, Paris. Symbolical designs inscr. "CONFERINTA MONDIALA SINDICALA DIN PARIS 25 SEPTEMVRE 1945".
1776. **199.** 80 l. + 920 l. mauve .. 17·00 17·00
1777. – 160 l. + 1840 l. brown 17·00 17·00
1778. – 320 l. + 1680 l. violet 17·00 17·00
1779. – 440 l. + 2560 l. green 17·00 17·00

1946. Nos. 1444/5 surch. in figures.
1780. 10 l. + 90 l. on 100 l. + 400 l. 95 1·90
1781. 10 l. + 90 l. on 200 l. + 800 l. 95 1·90
1782. 20 l. + 80 l. on 100 l. + 400 l. 95 1·90
1783. 20 l. + 80 l. on 200 l. + 800 l. 95 1·90
1784. 80 l. + 120 l. on 100 l. + 400 l. 95 1·90
1785. 80 l. + 120 l. on 200 l. + 800 l. 95 1·90
1786. 100 l. + 150 l. on 100 l. + 400 l. 95 1·90
1787. 100 l. + 150 l. on 200 l. + 800 l. 95 1·90

200. Sower.

201. Distribution of Title Deeds. **202.**

1946. Agrarian Reform. Inscr. "REFORMA AGRARA".
1788. – 80 l. blue 20 20
1789. **200.** 50 l. + 450 l. red .. 20 20
1790. **201.** 100 l. + 900 l. purple 20 20
1791. – 200 l. + 800 l. orange 20 20
1792. – 400 l. + 1600 l. green 25 25
DESIGNS—VERT. 80 l. Blacksmith and ploughman. HORIZ. 200 l. Ox-drawn farm wagon. 400 l. Plough and tractor.

1946. 25th Anniv. of Philharmonic Orchestra.
1794. **202.** 10 l. blue 10 10
1795. – 20 l. brown 10 10
1796. – 55 l. green 10 10
1797. – 80 l. violet 20 15
1798. – 160 l. orange .. 10 10
1799. **202.** 200 l. + 800 l. red .. 1·00 1·00
1800. – 350 l. + 1650 l. blue .. 1·25 1·25
DESIGNS: 20 l., 55 l., 160 l. "XXV" and musical score. 80 l., 350 l. G. Enescu.

203. Building worker. **205.** Sower.

1946. Labour Day. Designs of workers inscr. "ZIUA MUNCII".
1803. **203.** 10 l. red 10 10
1804. 10 l. green 40 50
1805. 20 l. blue 40 50
1806. 20 l. brown 10 10
1807. 200 l. red 15 15

1946. Youth Issue.
1809. **205.** 10 l. + 100 l. red & brn. 10 10
1810. – 10 l. + 200 l. pur. & blue 1·50 1·50
1811. – 80 l. + 200 l. brn. & pur. 10 10
1812. – 80 l. + 300 l. mve. & brn. 10 10
1813. – 200 l. + 400 l. red & grn. 15 15
DESIGNS: No. 1810, Hurdling. 1811, Student. 1812, Worker and factory. 1813, Marching with flag.

206. Aviator and Aeroplanes. **207.** Football.

1946. Air. Youth Issue.
1814. – 200 l. blue and green 3·00 3·00
1815. **206.** 500 l. blue and orange 3·00 3·00
DESIGN: 200 l. Aeroplane grounded.

1946. Sports, designs inscr. "O.S.P." Perf. or imperf.
1816. **207.** 10 l. blue (postage) .. 30 30
1817. – 20 l. red 30 30
1818. – 50 l. violet 30 30
1819. – 80 l. brown 30 30
1820. – 160 l. + 1340 l. green .. 30 30
1821. – 300 l. red (air) .. 90 1·50
1822. – 300 l. + 1200 l. blue .. 90 1·50
DESIGNS: 20 l. Diving. 50 l. Running. 80 l. Mountaineering. 160 l. Ski-jumping. 300 l., 300 l. + 1.200 l. Flying.

208. "Traditional Ties" **209.** Banat Girl holding Distaff.

1946. Rumanian–Soviet Friendship Pact.
1824. **208.** 80 l. brown 10 10
1825. – 100 l. blue 10 10
1826. – 300 l. grey 10 10
1827. – 300 l. + 1200 l. red .. 60 60
DESIGNS: 100 l. "Cultural ties". 300 l. "Economic ties". 300 l. + 1,200 l. Dove.
No. 1827 also exists imperf.

1946. Charity. Women's Democratic Federation.
1829. – 80 l. olive 10 10
1830. **209.** 80 l. + 320 l. red .. 15 15
1831. – 140 l. + 360 l. orange 15 15
1832. – 300 l. + 450 l. green .. 20 20
1833. – 600 l. + 900 l. blue .. 35 30
DESIGNS: 80 l. Girl and handloom. 140 l. Wallachian girl and wheatsheaf. 300 l. Transylvanian horsewoman. 600 l. Moldavian girl carrying water.

211. King Michael and Food Transport.

1947. Social Relief Fund.
1845. – 300 l. olive .. 15 15
1846. **211.** 600 l. mauve .. 20 20
1847. – 1500 l. + 3500 l. orge. 20 20
1848. – 3700 l. + 5300 l. violet 20 20
DESIGNS—VERT: 300 l. Loaf of bread and hungry child. 1500 l. Angel bringing food and clothing to destitute people. 3700 l. Loaf of bread and starving family.

213. King Michael and Chariot. **214.** Symbols of Labour and Clasped Hands.

1947. Peace.
1850. **213.** 300 l. purple 20 20
1851. – 600 l. brown .. 20 20
1852. – 3000 l. blue .. 20 20
1853. – 7200 l. green .. 20 20
DESIGNS—VERT. 600 l. Winged figure of Peace. 3000 l. Flags of four Allied Nations. 7200 l. Dove of Peace.

1947. Trades Union Congress.
1854. **214.** 200 l. blue (postage) .. 45 45
1855. 300 l. orange .. 45 45
1856. 600 l. red 45 45
1857. – 1100 l. blue (air) .. 85 85
DESIGN (22 × 37 mm.): 1100 l. as Type **214** with aeroplane at top.

216. Worker and Torch. **219.** King Michael.

1947. Air. Trades Union Congress. Imperf.
1858. **216.** 3000 l. + 7000 l. brn. 85 85

1947.
1865. **219.** 1000 l. blue .. 15 10
1869. 3000 l. blue .. 20 10
1866. 5500 l. green .. 25 10
1870. 7200 l. mauve .. 20 10
1871. 15000 l. blue .. 30 10
1867. 20000 l. brown .. 40 20
1872. 21000 l. mauve .. 30 20
1873. 36000 l. violet .. 60 25
1868. 50000 l. orange .. 70 25
Nos. 1865/8 are size 18 × 21½ mm. and Nos. 1869/73 are 25 × 30 mm.

218. Symbolical of "Learning".

1947. Charity. People's Culture.

1859. – 200 l.+200 l. blue .. 10 15
1860. – 300 l.+300 l. brown 10 15
1861. – 600 l.+600 l. green.. 10 15
1862. – 1200 l.+1200 l. blue 10 15
1863. **218.** 1500 l.+1500 l. red.. 10 15

DESIGNS—HORIZ. 200 l. Boys' reading class. 300 l. Girls' school. 600 l. Engineering classroom. 1200 l. School building.

220. N. Grigorescu.

221. Douglas DC3 over Land.

1947. Charity. Institute of Rumanian-Soviet Studies.

1874. – 1500 l.+1500 l. pur. (postage) 20 20
1875. – 1500 l.+1500 l. orge. 20 20
1876. – 1500 l.+1500 l. green 20 20
1877. **220.** 1500 l.+1500 l. blue 20 20
1878. – 1500 l.+1500 l. blue 20 20
1879. – 1500 l.+1500 l. lake 20 20
1880. – 1500 l.+1500 l. red.. 20 20
1881. – 1500 l.+1500 l. brn. 20 20
1882. **221.** 15000 l.+15000 l. green (air) 60 75

PORTRAITS: No. 1874, Petru Movila. No. 1875, V. Babes. No. 1876, M. Eminescu. No. 1878, P. Tchaikovsky. No. 1879, M. Lomonosov. No. 1880, A. Pushkin. No. 1881, L. Y. Repin. No. 1882 is imperf.

222. Miner.

224. Douglas DC4 over Black Sea.

1947. Charity. Labour Day.

1883. **222.** 1000 l.+1000 l. olive 25 30
1884. – 1500 l.+1500 l. brown 20 25
1885. – 2000 l.+2000 l. blue 20 25
1886. – 2500 l.+2500 l. mve. 20 25
1887. – 3000 l.+3000 l. red.. 25 30

DESIGNS: 1500 l. Peasant. 2000 l. Peasant woman. 2500 l. Intellectual. 3000 l. Factory worker.

1947. Air. Labour Day.

1888. – 3000 l. red 30 25
1889. – 3000 l. green .. 30 25
1890. – 3000 l. brown .. 30 25
1891. **224.** 3000 l.+12,000 l. bl. 30 25

DESIGNS—(24½ × 30 mm.): No. 1888, Four parachutes. No. 1889, Air Force Monument. No. 1890, Aeroplane over landscape.

(New currency 1 (new) leu = 100 (old) lei.)

225. King Michael and Timber Barges.

227.

1947. Designs with medallion portrait of King Michael.

1892. – 50 b. orange .. 10 10
1893. **225.** 1 l. brown .. 10 10
1894. – 2 l. blue .. 10 10
1895. – 3 l. red .. 20 10
1896. – 5 l. blue .. 20 10
1897. – 10 l. blue .. 40 10
1898. – 12 l. violet .. 60 20
1899. – 15 l. blue .. 1·00 20
1900. – 20 l. brown .. 1·60 25
1901. – 32 l. brown.. .. 4·75 2·25
1902. – 36 l. lake .. 4·00 1·60

DESIGNS: 50 b. Harvesting. 2 l. River Danube. 3 l. Reshitza Industries. 5 l. Curtea de Arges Cathedral. 10 l. Royal Palace, Bucharest. 12 l., 36 l. Cernavoda Bridge. 15 l., 32 l. Port of Constantza. 20 l. Oil Wells, Prahova.

1947. Balkan Games. Surch **2+3 LEI C.B.A. 1947** and bar.

1903. **219.** 2+3 l. on 36,000 l. vio. 90 90

1947. 17th Congress of General Assn. of Rumanian Engineers. With monogram as in T **227.**

1904. **227.** 1 l.+1 l. red (post.).. 10 10
1905. – 2 l.+2 l. brown .. 10 10
1906. – 3 l.+3 l. violet .. 20 20
1907. – 4 l.+4 l. olive .. 20 20
1908. – 5 l.+5 l. blue (air) .. 55 55

DESIGNS: 2 l. Sawmill. 3 l. Refinery. 4 l. Steel mill. 5 l. Aeroplanes over mountains.

1947. Charity. Soviet–Rumanian Amity. As No. 1896 surch **ARLUS 1-7.XI 1947 +5.** Imperf.

1909. 5 l.+5 l. blue 85 50

229. Beehive.

230. Food Convoy.

1947. Savings Day.

1910. **229.** 12 l. red .. 15 15

1947. Patriotic Defence.

1911. **230.** 1 l.+1 l. blue .. 15 15
1912. – 2 l.+2 l. brown .. 15 15
1913. – 3 l.+3 l. red.. .. 15 15
1914. – 4 l.+4 l. blue .. 20 20
1915. – 5 l.+5 l. red.. .. 35 35

SYMBOLIC DESIGNS—HORIZ. 2 l. Soldiers' parcels. 3 l. Modern hospital. 4 l. Hungry children. VERT. 5 l. Manacled wrist and flag.

231. Allegory of Work.

DESIGNS—HORIZ. 2 l. Industrial and Agricultural workers. 11 l. Aeroplane over demonstration.

1947. Charity. Trades Union Congress, Bucharest. Inscr. "C.G.M. 1947".

1916. – 2 l.+10 l. red (post).. 15 15
1917. **231.** 7 l.+10 l. black .. 20 20
1918. – 11 l. red and blue (air) 40 40

233. Map of Rumania.

1948. Census of 1948.

1925. **233.** 12 l. blue 25 15

234. Printing Works and Press.

235. Discus Thrower.

1948. 75th Anniv. of Rumanian State Stamp Printing Works.

1926. **234.** 6 l. violet .. .. 1·25 75
1927. 7 l. 50 green .. 65 10

1948. Balkan Games, 1947. Inscr. as in T **203.** Imperf. or perf.

1928. **235.** 1 l.+1 l. brown (post.) 50 50
1929. – 2 l.+2 l. red .. 65 65
1930. – 5 l.+5 l. blue .. 1·00 1·00
1931. – 7 l.+7 l. violet (air) 1·00 75
1932. – 10 l.+10 l. green .. 1·50 1·00

DESIGNS: 2 l. Runner. 5 l. Heads of two young athletes. 7 l., 10 l. Aeroplane over running track.

1948. Nos. 1892/1902 optd. **RPR** (Republica Populara Romana).

1933. 50 b. orange 25 20
1934. 1 l. brown 15 10
1935. 2 l. blue 70 15
1936. 3 l. red 85 15
1937. 5 l. blue .. .. 1·40 15
1938. 10 l. blue .. .. 1·60 15
1939. 12 l. violet .. .. 2·00 30
1940. 15 l. blue .. .. 2·00 40
1941. 20 l. brown .. .. 1·75 30
1942. 32 l. brown .. .. 8·50 3·75
1943. 36 l. lake .. .. 6·50 2·50

MINIMUM PRICE

The minimum price quoted is 5p which represents a handling charge rather than a basis for valuing common stamps. For further notes about prices see introductory pages.

237. Industrial Worker.

DESIGNS: As Type **237.** 3 l. Peasant girl and wheatsheaf. 5 l. Student and book. TRIANGULAR: 8 l. Youths bearing Filimon Sarbu banner. HORIZ. (larger): 12 l. Aeroplane and swallows.

1948. Young Workers' Union. Imperf. or perf.

1954. **237.** 2 l.+2 l. blue (post.) 40 40
1955. – 3 l.+3 l. green .. 35 25
1956. – 5 l.+5 l. brown .. 40 30
1957. – 8 l.+8 l. red .. 45 40
1958. – 12 l.+12 l. blue (air) 1·40 90

240. "Friendship".

241. "New Constitution".

243. Aviator and Aeroplane.

242. Globe and Banner.

1948. Rumanian-Bulgarian Amity.

1959. **240.** 32 l. brown .. .. 1·00 20

1948. New Constitution.

1960. **241.** 1 l. red 30 20
1961. 2 l. orange 65 50
1962. 12 l. blue .. .. 2·00 80

1948. Labour Day.

1963. **242.** 8 l.+8 l. red (postage) 1·50 2·50
1964. – 10 l.+10 l. green .. 2·50 3·25
1965. – 12 l.+12 l. brown .. 3·25 4·25
1966. **243.** 20 l.+20 l. blue (air) 5·25 5·75

DESIGNS—HORIZ. 10 l. Peasants and mountains VERT. 12 l. Worker and factory.

244. Barbed Wire Entanglement.

246. Proclamation of Islaz.

245. Five Portraits.

247. Emblem of Republic.

1948. Army Day.

1967. – 1 l. 50+1 l. 50 red (postage) 35 35
1968. **244.** 2 l.+2 l. purple .. 35 35
1969. – 4 l.+4 l. brown .. 70 70
1970. – 7 l. 50+7 l. 50 black 1·40 1·40
1971. – 8 l.+8 l. violet .. 1·50 1·50
1972. – 3 l.+3 l. blue (air) .. 5·50 5·50
1973. – 5 l.+5 l. blue .. 8·00 8·00

DESIGNS—VERT. 1 l. 50, Infantry. 3 l. Fighter aircraft. 5 l. Bomber aircraft. HORIZ. 4 l. Artillery. 7 l. 50, Tank. 8 l. Destroyer.

1948. Cent. of 1848 Revolution. Dated "1848 1948".

1974. – 2 l.+2 l. purple .. 35 30
1975. **245.** 5 l.+5 l. violet .. 45 40
1976. **246.** 11 l. red .. 60 15
1977. – 10 l.+10 l. green .. 60 60
1978. – 36 l.+18 l. blue .. 1·90 1·50

DESIGNS—22 × 38 mm. HORIZ. 10 l. Balcescu, Petofi, Iancu Barnutiu, Baritiu, and Murcu. VERT. 2 l. Nicolas Balcescu. 36 l. Balcescu, Kogalnicanu, Alecsandri and Cuza.

1948.

2023. **247.** 50 b. red 50 50
1980. 0.50 l. red 40 40
1981. 1 l. brown 15 10
1982. 2 l. green 20 10
1983. 3 l. grey 35 10
1984. 4 l. brown 30 10
1985. 5 l. blue 30 10
2028. 5 l. violet 60 10
1986. 10 l. blue .. .. 1·40 15

No. 2023 is inscribed "BANI 0.50" (=½ bani) and in No. 1980 this was corrected to "LEI 0.50".

248. Glider Meeting.

249. Yachts.

1948. Air Force and Navy Day. (a) Air Force (vert.).

1987. **248.** 2 l.+2 l. blue .. 1·25 1·25
1988. – 5 l.+5 l. violet .. 1·25 1·25
1989. – 8 l.+8 l. red.. .. 1·90 1·90
1990. – 10 l.+10 l. brown .. 2·50 2·50

(b) Navy (horiz.).

1991. **249.** 2 l.+2 l. green .. 1·25 1·25
1992. – 5 l.+5 l. grey .. 1·25 1·25
1993. – 8 l.+8 l. blue .. 1·90 1·90
1994. – 10 l.+10 l. red .. 2·50 2·50

DESIGNS—AIR FORCE: 5 l. Early aircraft. 8 l. 'Plane and tractor. 10 l. Transport 'plane. NAVY: 5 l. Cadet ship, "Mircea", 1882. 8 l. "Romana Mare" (Danube river steamer). 10 l. Liner "Transylvania".

1948. Surch.

1995. **240.** 31 l. on 32 l. brown 60 20

251. Newspapers and Torch.

252. Soviet Soldiers' Monument.

1948. Press week. Imperf. or perf.

1996. **251.** 5 l.+5 l. red 20 10
1997. 10 l. brown 65 65
1998. – 10 l.+10 l. violet .. 1·00 1·00
1999. – 15 l.+15 l. blue .. 1·40 1·40

DESIGNS—HORIZ. 10 l. (No. 1998), Flag, torch and ink-well. VERT. 15 l. Alexander Sahia (journalist).

1948. Rumanian-Russian Amity.

2000. **252.** 10 l. red (postage) .. 65 65
2001. – 10 l.+10 l. green .. 2·75 2·75
2002. – 15 l.+15 l. blue .. 3·25 3·25
2003. – 20 l.+20 l. blue (air) 9·75 6·00

DESIGNS—VERT. 10 l. (No. 2001), Badge of Arlus. 15 l. Kremlin. HORIZ. 20 l. Twin-engined aircraft.

255. Emblem of Republic.

DESIGNS: 50 l. Workers in a field. 100 l. Forms of transport (steam train, liner, etc.).

1948. Air. Designs showing aircraft.

2004. **255.** 30 l. red 50 10
2005. – 50 l. green 75 25
2006. – 100 l. blue .. .. 4·00 3·25

256. Lorry.

DESIGNS: 1 l. Dockers loading freighter. 11 l. Aeroplane. 15 l. Steam train.

1948. Work on Communications.

2007. – 1 l.+1 l. black & grn. 60 60
2008. **256.** 3 l.+3 l. black & brn. 70 60
2009. – 11 l.+11 l. blk. & blue 2·75 2·10
2010. – 15 l.+15 l. blk. & red 5·50 3·75

257. Nicolas Balcescu.

258. Hands Breaking Chain.

1948.

2012. **257.** 20 l. red 65 15

1948. 1st Anniv. of People's Republic.

2013. **258.** 5 l. red 25 15

259. Runners.

260. Lenin.

1948. National Sport Organization. Imperf. or perf.

2014. **259.** 5 l.+5 l. green (post.) 3·25 3·25
2017. 5 l.+5 l. brown .. 3·25 3·25
2015. – 10 l.+10 l. violet .. 5·00 5·00
2018. – 10 l.+10 l. red .. 5·00 5·00
2016. – 20 l.+20 l. blue (air) 17·00 17·00
2019. – 20 l.+20 l. green .. 17·00 17·00

DESIGNS—HORIZ. 10 l. Parade of athletes with flags. VERT. 20 l. Boy flying model aeroplane.

1949. 25th Death Anniv. of Lenin. Perf. or Imperf.

2020. **260.** 20 l. black 30 15

261. Dancers.

262. I. C. Frimu and Revolutionaries.

263. A. S. Pushkin.

1949. 90th Anniv. of Union of Rumanian Principalities.

2021. **261.** 10 l. blue 40 15

1949. 30th Death Anniv. of I. C. Frimu. Perf. or imperf.

2022. **262.** 20 l. red 30 15

1949. 150th Birth Anniv. of A. S. Pushkin (Russian poet).

2030. **263.** 11 l. red 75 15
2031. 30 l. green 90 25

264. Globe and Posthorn.

265. Forms of Transport.

1949. 75th Anniv. of U.P.U.

2032. **264.** 20 l. brown .. .. 1·75 1·75
2033. **265.** 30 l. blue .. .. 3·25 3·25

266. Russians entering Bucharest.

1949. Russian Army's Entry into Bucharest. 5th Anniv. Perf. or imperf.

2034. **266.** 50 l. brown on green 85 60

267. " Rumanian-Soviet Amity ".

1949. Rumanian-Soviet Friendship Week. Perf. or imperf.

2035. **267.** 20 l. red 65 40

268. Forms of Transport.

269. Joseph Stalin.

1949. Int. Congress of Transport Unions. Perf. or imperf.

2036. **268.** 11 l. blue .. .. 1·10 1·00
2037. 20 l. red .. .. 1·40 1·25

1949. Stalin's 70th Birthday. Perf. or imperf.

2038. **269.** 31 l. black 35 15

270. "The Third Letter".

271. Michael Eminescu.

1950. Birth Cent. of Eminescu (poet).

2040. **270.** 11 l. green .. .. 1·00 20
2041. – 11 l. brown .. .. 1·75 45
2042. – 11 l. red .. .. 1·00 20
2043. – 11 l. violet .. .. 1·00 20
2044. **271.** 11 l. blue .. .. 1·00 25

DESIGNS (scenes representing poems): No. 2041, " Angel and Demon ". No. 2042, " Ruler and Proletariat ". No. 2043, " Life ".

272. " Dragaica Fair ".

1950. Birth Cent. of Andreescu (painter). Inscr. "I. Andreescu".

(a) Perf.

2045. **272.** 5 l. olive .. .. 1·00 50
2047. – 20 l. brown .. .. 1·75 90

(b) Perf. or imperf.

2046. – 11 l. blue .. .. 1·50 65

DESIGNS—VERT. 11 l. I. Andreescu. HORIZ. 20 l. "The Village Well".

273. Factory and Graph.

274. Worker and Flag.

1950. State Plan, 1950. Inscr. "PLANUL DU STAT 1950".

2048. **273.** 11 l. red 30 15
2049. – 31 l. violet .. .. 1·00 50

DESIGN: 31 l. Tractor and factories. No. 2048 exists imperf.

1950. Labour Day. Perf. or imperf.

2050. **274.** 31 l. orange 35 10

275. Emblem of Republic.

276. Trumpeter and Drummer.

1950.

2051. **275.** 50 b. black 20 15
2052. 1 l. red 10 10
2053. 2 l. grey 10 10
2054. 3 l. purple 15 10
2055. 4 l. mauve 10 10
2056. 5 l. red 15 10
2057. 6 l. green 15 10
2058. 7 l. brown 20 10
2059. 7 l. 50 blue 25 10
2060. 10 l. brown 65 10
2061. 11 l. red 65 10
2062. 15 l. blue 35 10
2063. 20 l. green 35 10
2064. 31 l. green 50 10
2065. 36 l. brown .. .. 1·40 45

For stamps as Type **275** but with inscriptions in white, see Nos. 2240, etc., and Nos. 2277/8.

1950. 1st Anniv. of Rumanian Pioneers Organization.

2074. **276.** 8 l. blue .. .. 1·40 45
2075. – 11 l. purple .. .. 1·75 1·00
2076. – 31 l. red .. .. 3·00 2·00

DESIGNS: 11 l. Children reading. 31 l. Youth parade.

278. A. Vlaicu and Aeroplane.

277. Engineer.

279. Mother and Child.

1950. Industrial Nationalization.

2077. **277.** 11 l. red 35 25
2078. 11 l. blue 80 15
2079. 11 l. brown 80 25
2080. 11 l. olive 35 10

1950. 40th Anniv. of 1st Flight by A. Vlaicu.

2081. **278.** 3 l. green 45 10
2082. 6 l. blue 50 15
2083. 8 l. blue 60 20

1950. Peace Congress, Bucharest.

2084. **279.** 11 l. red 20 15
2085. – 20 l. brown 25 15

DESIGN: 20 l. Lathe operator.

280. Statue and Flags.

282. Young People and Badge.

1950. Rumanian-Soviet Amity.

2086. **280.** 30 l. brown 65 15

1950. Rumanian-Hungarian Amity. Optd. **TRAIASCA PREITENIA ROMANO-MAGHIARAL.**

2087. **275.** 15 l. blue 85 20

1950. G.M.A. Complex Sports Facilities. Designs incorporating badge.

2088. – 3 l. red .. .. 1·40 1·40
2089. **282.** 5 l. brown .. .. 1·00 1·00
2090. – 5 l. blue .. .. 1·00 1·00
2091. – 11 l. green .. .. 1·00 1·00
2092. – 31 l. olive .. .. 2·40 2·40

DESIGNS: 3 l. Agriculture and Industry. 11 l. Runners. 31 l. Gymnasts.

283.

284. Ski-jumper.

1950. 3rd Congress of "ARLUS".

2093. **283.** 11 l. red 30 20
2094. 11 l. blue 30 20

1951. Winter Sports.

2095. **284.** 4 l. brown .. .. 1·00 15
2096. – 5 l. red .. .. 1·40 25
2097. – 11 l. blue .. .. 2·00 25
2098. – 20 l. brown .. .. 2·00 1·40
2099. – 31 l. green .. .. 3·25 1·50

DESIGNS: 5 l. Skater. 11 l. Skier. 20 l. Ice-hockey. 31 l. Tobogganing.

286. Peasant and Tractor.

DESIGN — VERT. 11 l. Engineer and machine.

1951. Agricultural and Industrial Exhibition.

2100. – 11 l. brown 20 10
2101. **286.** 31 l. blue 65 20

287. Star of the Republic.

288. Youth Camp.

1951. Orders and Medals. Perf. or imperf.

2102. – 2 l. grey 20 15
2103. – 4 l. blue 25 20
2104. – 11 l. red 40 30
2105. **287.** 35 l. brown 60 45

DESIGNS: 2 l. Medal of Work. 4 l. As Type **287** but with different centre to star and with ribbon at top. 11 l. Order of Work.

1951. 2nd Anniv. of Rumanian Pioneer Organization.

2106. **288.** 1 l. green .. .. 1·00 65
2107. – 11 l. blue .. .. 1·00 65
2108. – 35 l. red .. .. 1·40 1·00

DESIGNS—VERT. 11 l. Children meeting Stalin. HORIZ. 35 l. Decorating boy on parade.

289. Woman and Flags.

290. Ion Negulici.

1951. Int. Women's Day. Perf. or imperf.

2109. **289.** 11 l. brown 25 10

1951. Death Cent. of Negulici (painter).

2110. **290.** 35 l. red .. .. 3·00 2·40

291. Cyclists.

292. F. Sarbu.

1951. Rumanian Cycle Race.

2111. **291.** 11 l. brown .. .. 1·90 75

1951. 10th Death Anniv. of Sarbu (patriot).

2112. **292.** 11 l. brown 30 15

293. " Revolutionary Rumania ".

294. Students.

1951. Death Cent. of Rosenthal (painter).

2113 **293** 11 l. green .. .. 1·60 50
2114 – 11 l. orange .. .. 1·60 65
2115 – 11 l. brown .. .. 1·60 50
2116 – 11 l. violet .. .. 1·60 65

DESIGN—VERT. Nos. 2115/16, Portrait of a woman.

1951. 3rd World Youth Festival, Berlin.

2117. **294.** 1 l. red 35 20
2118. – 5 l. blue 65 20
2119. – 11 l. purple 95 45

DESIGNS; 5 l. Girl, boy and flag. 11 l. Young people around globe.

295. "Scanteia" Building.

296. Soldier and Pithead.

1951. 20th Anniv. of "Scanteia" (Communist newspaper).

2120. **295.** 11 l. blue 65 20

1951. Miners' Day.

2121. **296.** 5 l. blue 40 20
2122. – 11 l. mauve 75 15

DESIGN: 11 l. Miner and pithead.

297. Order of Defence.

298. Oil Refinery.

1951. Liberation Day.
2123. **297.** 10 l. red 35 20

1951. Five Year Plan. Dated "1951 1955".
2124. **298.** 1 l. olive (postage) .. 20 10
2125. – 2 l. red 30 15
2126. – 3 l. red 55 25
2127. – 4 l. brown 35 15
2128. – 5 l. green 55 10
2129. – 6 l. blue .. .. 1·60 1·00
2130. – 7 l. green .. .. 1·00 35
2131. – 8 l. brown 65 25
2132. – 11 l. blue 75 10
2133. – 35 l. violet 80 45
2134. – 30 l. green (air) .. 3·25 2·75
2135. – 50 l. brown .. .. 5·00 3·50
DESIGNS: 2 l. Miner and pithead. 3 l. Soldier and pylons. 4 l. Steel furnace. 5 l. Combine-harvester. 6 l. Canal construction. 7 l. Threshing machine. 8 l. Sanatorium. 11 l. Dam and pylons. 30 l. Potato planting. 35 l. Factory. 50 l. Liner, loco and 'plane.

299. Orchestra and Dancers.

300. Soldier and Arms.

1951. Music Festival.
2136. **299.** 11 l. brown 45 20
2137. – 11 l. blue (Mixed Choir) 60 40
2138. – 11 l. mauve (Lyre and dove) (vert.) .. 45 25

1951. Army Day.
2139. **300.** 11 l. blue 40 10

301. Arms of U.S.S.R. and Rumania.

302. P. Tcancenco.

1951. Rumanian-Soviet Friendship.
2140. **301.** 4 l. brown on buff .. 20 20
2141. 35 l. orange .. 65 65

1951. 25th Death Anniv. of Tcancenco (revolutionary).
2142. **302.** 10 l. olive 65 15

303. Open Book "1907".

304. I. L. Caragiale.

1952. Birth Cent. of Caragiale (writer).
(a) Unissued values surch.
2143. **303.** 20 b. on 11 l. red .. 1·10 60
2144. – 55 b. on 11 l. green .. 1·50 75
2145. **304.** 75 b. on 11 l. blue .. 2·50 90
(b) Without surch.
2146. **303.** 55 b. red .. .. 2·75 40
2147. – 55 b. green .. .. 2·75 40
2148. **304.** 55 b. blue .. .. 2·75 40
2149. – 1 l. brown .. .. 4·00 1·60
DESIGNS—HORIZ. Nos. 2144, 2147, Profile of Caragiale. 1 l. Caragiale addressing assembly.

1952. Currency revalued. Surch.
2174. **275.** 3 b. on 1 l. red .. 1·50 75
2175. 3 b. on 2 l. grey .. 1·25 65
2176. 3 b. on 4 l. mauve .. 1·50 75
2177. 3 b. on 5 l. red .. 1·25 65
2178. 3 b. on 7 l. 50 blue 1·25 75
2179. 3 b. on 10 l. brown 1·25 65
2157a. **255.** 3 b. on 30 l. red .. 3·75 2·75
2158. – 3 b. on 50 l. (2005) 1·50 75
2159. – 3 b. on 100 l. (2006) 4·00 3·00
2191. **278.** 10 b. on 3 l. green .. 2·40 75
2218. **301.** 10 b. on 4 l. brown on buff .. .. 2·10 1·10
2192. **278.** 10 b. on 6 l. blue .. 2·40 75
2193. 10 b. on 8 l. blue .. 2·40 75
2220. **302.** 10 b. on 10 l. olive .. 2·10 75
2160. **263.** 10 b. on 11 l. red .. 3·75 1·50
2164. **270.** 10 b. on 11 l. green 3·75 1·50
2165. – 10 b. on 11 l. (2041) 2·75 1·90
2166. – 10 b. on 11 l. (2042) 2·75 1·90
2167. – 10 b. on 11 l. (2043) 2·75 1·90
2168. **271.** 10 b. on 11 l. blue .. 2·75 1·90
2161. **263.** 10 b. on 30 l. green 3·75 1·50
2219. **301.** 10 b. on 35 l. orange 2·10 1·10
2199. – 20 b. on 2 l. (2102) .. 4·25 2·10
2200. – 20 b. on 4 l. (2103) 4·25 2·10
2171. **273.** 20 b. on 11 l. red .. 4·25 2·10
2201. – 20 b. on 11 l. (2104) 4·25 2·10
2194. – 20 b. on 20 l. (2085) 3·00 1·50
2172. – 20 b. on 31 l. (2049) 3·25 1·25
2202. **287.** 20 b. on 35 l. brown .. 2·75 1·50
2206. **298.** 35 b. on 1 l. olive .. 1·90 65
2207. – 35 b. on 2 l. (2125) 3·00 3·00
2208. – 35 b. on 3 l. (2126) 3·75 1·90
2209. – 35 b. on 4 l. (2127) 3·00 1·50
2210. – 35 b. on 5 l. (2128) .. 3·75 3·75
2151. **241.** 50 b. on 12 l. blue .. 1·90 1·25
2180. **275.** 55 b. on 50 b. black 5·00 1·25
2181. 55 b. on 3 l. purple 5·00 1·25
2195. – 55 b. on 3 l. (2088) 17·00 11·00
2169. **272.** 55 b. on 5 l. olive .. 9·25 3·00
2204. **295.** 55 b. on 5 l. blue .. 3·00 2·50
2182. **275.** 55 b. on 6 l. green .. 5·00 1·25
2183. 55 b. on 7 l. brown .. 5·00 1·25
2188. **276.** 55 b. on 8 l. blue .. 7·50 3·75
2205. **297.** 55 b. on 10 l. red .. 5·00 2·50
2170. – 55 b. on 11 l. bl. (2046) 9·25 3·00
2189. – 55 b. on 11 l. (2075) 5·00 2·50
2150. **233.** 55 b. on 12 l. blue .. 3·75 1·25
2184. **275.** 55 b. on 15 l. blue .. 7·50 1·25
2185. 55 b. on 20 l. green 5·00 1·25
2196. – 55 b. on 20 l. (2098) 30·00 13·50
2186. **275.** 55 b. on 31 l. green 5·00 1·25
2173. **274.** 55 b. on 31 l. orange 4·50 3·00
2190. – 55 b. on 31 l. (2076) 5·00 3·25
2197. – 55 b. on 31 l. (2099) 30·00 13·50
2198. **286.** 55 b. on 31 l. blue .. 5·00 3·25
2203. – 55 b. on 35 l. (2108) 7·50 4·25
2187. **275.** 55 b. on 36 l. brown 7·50 1·25
2211. – 1 l. on 6 l. (No. 2129) 5·50 2·10
2212. – 1 l. on 7 l. (No. 2130) 5·50 5·50
2213. – 1 l. on 8 l. (No. 2131) 5·50 4·25
2214. – 1 l. on 11 l. (No. 2132) 5·50 2·75
2216. – 1 l. on 30 l. (No. 2134) 9·25 2·10
2215. – 1 l. on 35 l. (No. 2133) 7·50 2·10
2217. – 1 l. on 50 l. (No. 2135) 8·50 4·50
2152. – 1 l. 75 on 2 l.+2 l. purple (No. 1974) 13·50 4·50
2153. **245.** 1 l. 75 on 5 l.+5 l. violet .. .. 13·50 4·50
2154. **246.** 1 l. 75 on 11 l. red .. 13·50 4·50
2155. – 1 l. 75 on 10 l.+10 l. (No. 1977) .. 13·50 4·50
2156. – 1 l. 75 on 36 l.+18 l. (No. 1978) .. 13·50 4·50

Air. Surch. with aeroplane, **AERIANA** and value.
2162. **264.** 3 l. on 20 l. brown .. 25·00 18·00
2163. **265.** 5 l. on 30 l. blue .. 32·00 23·00

307. Railwayman.

308. Gogol and character from "Taras Bulba".

1952. Railway Day.
2229. **307.** 55 b. brown .. .. 2·40 30

1952. Death Cent of Gogol (Russian writer).
2230 **308** 55 b. blue .. .. 1·75 15
2231 – 1 l. 75 green .. .. 3·00 40
DESIGN—VERT. 1 l. 75, Gogol and open book.

309. Maternity Medal.

310. I. P. Pavlov.

1952. Int. Women's Day.
2232. **309.** 20 b. blue and purple 85 15
2233. – 55 b. brn. & chestnut 1·50 20
2234. – 1 l. 75 brown and red 4·25 40
MEDALS: 55 b. "Glory of Maternity" medal. 1 l. 75, "Mother Heroine" medal.

1952. Rumanian-Soviet Medical Congress.
2235. **310.** 11 l. brown .. .. 2·75 15

311. Hammer and Sickle Medal.

312. Boy and Girl Pioneers.

1952. Labour Day.
2236. **311.** 55 b. brown .. .. 2·40 15

1952. 3rd Anniv. of Rumanian Pioneers Organization.
2237. **312.** 20 b. brown .. .. 1·40 10
2238. – 55 b. green .. .. 3·25 15
2239. – 1 l. 75 blue .. .. 6·75 30
DESIGNS—VERT. 55 b. Pioneer nature-study group. HORIZ. 1 l. 75, Worker and pioneers.

1952. As T **275** but with figures and inscriptions in white. Bani values size $20\frac{1}{2} \times 24\frac{1}{2}$ mm., lei values size $24\frac{1}{2} \times 29\frac{1}{2}$ mm.
2240. **275.** 3 b. orange 40 20
2241. 5 b. red 60 10
2242. 7 b. green 65 25
2243. 10 b. brown 85 10
2244. 20 b. blue .. .. 1·25 10
2245. 35 b. brown .. .. 2·40 10
2246. 50 b. green .. .. 2·50 10
2247. 55 b. violet .. .. 6·00 10
2248. 1 l. 10 brown .. 5·00 20
2249. 1 l. 75 violet .. .. 22·00 35
2250. 2 l. olive .. .. 5·75 25
2251. 2 l. 35 brown .. 6·75 35
2252. 2 l. 55 orange .. 8·25 40
2253. 3 l. green .. .. 8·75 35
2254. 5 l. red .. .. 11·00 85
For similar stamps with star added at top of emblem, see Nos. 2277/8.

314. "Smirdan" (after Grigorescu).

315. Leonardo da Vinci.

1952. 75th Anniv. of Independence.
2255. **314.** 50 b. lake .. .. 1·00 10
2256. – 1 l. 10 b. blue .. 1·40 30
DESIGN—HORIZ. 1 l. 10 b. Rumanian and Russian soldiers.

1952. 500th Anniv. of Birth of Leonardo da Vinci.
2257. **315.** 55 b. violet .. .. 4·75 25

316. Miner.

317. Students' Union Badge.

1952. Miners' Day.
2258. **316.** 20 b. red .. .. 2·00 25
2259. 55 b. violet .. .. 2·00 20

1952. Int. Students' Union Council. Bucharest.
2260. **317.** 10 b. blue 25 10
2261. – 20 b. orange .. .. 2·75 20
2262. – 55 b. green .. .. 2·75 15
2263. – 1 l. 75 red .. .. 5·00 1·00
DESIGNS—HORIZ. 20 b. Student in laboratory ($35\frac{1}{2} \times 22$ mm.). 1 l. 75, Six students dancing (30×24 mm.). VERT. 55 b. Students playing football (24×30 mm.).

318. Soldier, Sailor and Airman.

319. Statue and Flags.

320. Workers and Views of Russia and Rumania (after N. Parlius).

1952. Army Day.
2264. **318.** 55 b. blue .. .. 1·60 15

1952. Rumanian-Soviet Friendship.
2265. **319.** 55 b. red .. .. 1·10 10
2266. **320.** 1 l. 75 brown .. 3·00 30

321. Rowing.

322. N. Balcescu (after C. Tattarescu).

1952. Physical Culture.
2267. **321.** 20 b. blue .. .. 4·00 20
2268. – 1 l. 75 red (Athletes) 9·25 90

1952. Death Cent. of Balcescu (revolutionary).
2269. **322.** 55 b. grey .. .. 3·25 10
2270. 1 l. 75 olive .. .. 8·25 90

323. Emblem and Flags.

324.

1952. New Constitution.
2271. **323.** 55 b. green .. .. 1·60 15

1952. 5th Anniv. of People's Republic.
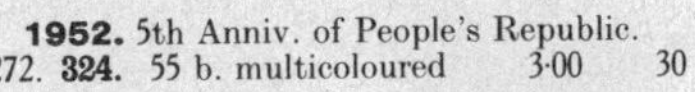
2272. **324.** 55 b. multicoloured 3·00 30

325. Millo, Caragiale and Mme. Romanescu.

326. Foundry Worker.

1953. Cent. of Caragiale National Theatre.
2273. **325.** 55 b. blue .. .. 3·25 15

1953. 3rd Industrial and Agricultural Congress.
2274. **326.** 55 b. green .. .. 1·00 15
2275. – 55 b. orange 90 30
2276. – 55 b. brown .. .. 1·40 15
DESIGNS—HORIZ. No. 2275, Farm workers and tractor. No. 2276, Workman, refinery and oil wells.

1953. As Nos. 2240, etc., but with star added at top of emblem.
2277. **275.** 5 b. red 70 10
2278. 55 b. purple .. .. 1·40 10

327. "The Strikers of Grivitsa" (after Nazarev).

1953. 20th Anniv. of Grivitsa Strike.
2279. **327.** 55 b. brown .. .. 2·75 15

328.

1953. 5th Anniv. of Treaty of Friendship with Russia.
2280. **328.** 55 b. brown on blue 2·75 20

329. Table Tennis Badge.

330. Oltenian Carpet.

1953. 20th World Table Tennis Championship, Bucharest.

2281 **329.** 55 b. green .. .. 6·75 1·00
2282. 55 b. brown .. .. 6·75 1·00

1953. Rumanian Art.

2283. – 10 b. green .. .. 1·40 10
2284. – 20 b. brown .. .. 2·00 10
2285. – 35 b. violet .. .. 2·40 15
2286. – 55 b. blue .. .. 4·25 10
2287. **330.** 1 l. purple .. .. 8·25 25

DESIGNS—VERT. 10 b. Pottery. 20 b. Campulung peasant girl. 55 b. Apuseni Mountains peasant girl. HORIZ. 35 b. National dance.

331. Karl Marx. **332.** Pioneers Planting Tree.

1953. 70th Death Anniv. of Karl Marx.

2288. **331.** 1 l. 55 brown .. 3·25 25

1953. 4th Anniv of Rumanian Pioneer Organization.

2289. **332.** 35 b. green .. .. 1·60 15
2290. – 55 b. blue .. .. 2·00 15
2291. – 1 l. 75 brown .. 4·75 40

DESIGNS—VERT. 55 b. Boy and girl flying model gliders. HORIZ. 1 l. 75, Pioneers and instructor.

333. Women and Flags.

1953. 3rd World Congress of Women.

2292. **333.** 55 b. brown .. .. 2·00 15

334. **335.** Cornfield and Forest.

1953. 4th World Youth Festival.

2293. **334.** 20 b. orange .. .. 1·00 10
2294. – 55 b. blue .. .. 1·60 10
2295. – 65 b. red .. .. 2·40 30
2296. – 1 l. 75 purple .. 6·75 45

DESIGNS—VERT. 55 b. Students releasing dove over globe. HORIZ. 65 b. Girl presenting bouquet. 1 l. 75, Folk dancers.

1953. Forestry Month.

2297. – 20 b. blue .. .. 1·00 15
2298. **335.** 38 b. green .. .. 3·25 90
2299. – 55 b. brown .. .. 4·00 15

DESIGNS—VERT. 20 b. Waterfall and trees. 55 b. Forestry worker.

336. V. V. Mayakovsky. **337.** Miner.

1953. 60th Birth Anniv. of Mayakovsky (Russian poet).

2300. **336.** 55 b. brown .. .. 2·40 20

1953. Miners' Day.

2301. **337.** 1 l. 55 black .. .. 3·75 20

338. Telephonist, G.P.O. and P.O. Worker. **339.**

1953. 50th Anniv. of Construction of G.P.O.

2302. **338.** 20 b. brown 25 10
2303. – 55 b. olive 45 10
2304. – 1 l. blue .. .. 1·60 15
2305. – 1 l. 55 lake .. .. 2·40 35

DESIGNS: 55 b. Postwoman and G.P.O. 1 l. G.P.O., radio-transmitter and map. 1 l. 55, Telegraphist, G.P.O. and teletypist.

1953. 9th Anniv. of Liberation.

2306. **339.** 55 b. brown .. .. 1·00 15

340. Soldier and Flag. **341.** Girl and Model Glider.

1953. Army Day.

2307. **340.** 55 b. olive .. .. 1·60 15

1953. Aerial Sports.

2308. **341.** 10 b. green & orange 2·75 25
2309. – 20 b. olive & brown .. 5·50 15
2310. – 55 b. purple and red 10·00 35
2311. – 1 l. 75 brown & pur. 12·00 75

DESIGNS: 20 b. Parachutists. 55 b. Glider and pilot. 1 l. 75, Monoplane.

342. Workman, Girl and Flags. **343.** "Unity".

1953. Rumanian-Soviet Friendship.

2312. **342.** 55 b. brown 70 15
2313. – 1 l. 55 lake .. .. 2·00 25

DESIGN: 1 l. 55, Spasski Tower and Volga-Don canal.

1953. 3rd World Trades' Union Congress.

2314. **343.** 55 b. olive 85 15
2315. – 1 l. 25 red .. .. 2·00 30

DESIGN—VERT. 1 l. 25, Workers, flags and globe.

344. C. Porumbescu. **345.** Agricultural Machinery.

1953. Birth Cent. of Porumbescu (composer).

2316. **344.** 55 b. lilac .. .. 8·25 20

1953. Agricultural designs.

2317. **345.** 10 b. olive 25 10
2318. – 35 b. green 40 10
2319. – 2 l. 55 brown .. 4·00 70

DESIGNS: 35 b. Tractor drawing disc harrows, 2 l. 55, Cows grazing.

346. A. Vlaicu. **347.** Lenin.

1953. 40th Death Anniv. of Vlaicu (pioneer aviator).

2320. **346.** 50 b. blue .. .. 1·75 20

1954. 30th Death Anniv. of Lenin.

2321. **347.** 55 b. brown .. .. 2·00 15

348. Red Deer. **349.** Calimanesti.

1954. Forestry Month.

2322. **348.** 20 b. brown on yellow 3·25 45
2323. – 55 b. violet on yellow 2·75 45
2324. – 1 l. 75 blue on yellow 4·00 85

DESIGNS: 55 b. Pioneers planting tree. 1 l. 75, Forest.

1954. Workers' Rest Homes.

2325. **349.** 5 b. black on yellow .. 40 10
2326. – 1 l. 55 black on blue .. 2·00 15
2327. – 2 l. green on pink .. 3·25 20
2328. – 2 l. 35 brown on green 3·00 1·00
2329. – 2 l. 55 brown on green 4·25 1·40

DESIGNS: 1 l. 55, Siniai. 2 l. Predeal. 2 l. 35, Tusnad. 2 l. 55, Govora.

350. O. Bancila. **351.** Child and Dove of Peace.

1954. 10th Death Anniv. of Bancila (painter).

2330. **350.** 55 b. green and brown 4·00 2·00

1954. Int. Children's Day.

2331. **351.** 55 b. brown .. .. 1·60 15

352. Girl Pioneer feeding Calf. **353.** Stephen the Great.

1954. 5th Anniv. of Rumanian Pioneer Organization.

2332. **352.** 20 b. black 30 15
2333. – 55 b. blue 85 15
2334. – 1 l. 75 red .. .. 2·75 65

DESIGNS: 55 b. Girl Pioneers harvesting. 1 l. 75, Young Pioneers examining globe.

1954. 450th Death Anniv. of Stephen the Great.

2335. **353.** 55 b. brown .. .. 2·75 20

354. Miner operating Coal-cutter. **355.** Dr. V. Babes.

1954. Miners' Day.

2336. **354.** 1 l. 75 black .. .. 2·75 40

1954. Birth Cent. of Babes (pathologist).

2337. **355.** 55 b. red .. .. 1·75 15

356. Sailor and Flag. **357.** Dedication Tablet.

1954. Navy Day.

2338. **356.** 55 b. blue .. .. 1·75 20

1954. 5th Anniv. of Mutual Aid Organization.

2339. – 20 b. violet 35 15
2340. **357.** 55 b. brown 85 15

DESIGN: 20 b. Man receiving money from counter clerk.

358. Liberation Monument. **359.** Recreation Centre.

1954. 10th Anniv. of Liberation.

2341. **358.** 55 b. lilac and red .. 1·40 15

1954. Liberation Anniv. Celebrations.

2342. **359.** 20 b. blue 30 10
2343. – 38 b. violet 90 25
2344. – 55 b. purple .. .. 1·00 10
2345. – 1 l. 55 brown .. 2·40 30

DESIGNS—(38×22 mm.): 55 b. "Scanteia" offices. (24½×29½ mm.): 38 b. Opera House, Bucharest. 1 l. 55, Radio Station.

360. Airman. **361.** Chemical Plant and Oil Derricks.

1954. Aviation Day.

2346. **360.** 55 b. blue .. .. 2·00 15

1954. Int. Chemical and Petroleum Workers Conference, Bucharest.

2347. **361.** 55 b. black .. .. 2·40 30

362. Dragon Pillar, Peking. **363.** T. Neculuta.

1954. Chinese Culture Week.

2348. **362.** 55 b. black on yellow 2·40 30

1954. 50th Death Anniv. of Neculuta (poet).

2349. **363.** 55 b. violet .. .. 2·00 15

364. ARLUS Badge. **365.** Friendship.

1954. 10th Anniv. of "ARLUS" and Rumanian-Russian Friendship.

2350. **364.** 55 b. red 65 15
2351 **365.** 65 b. purple .. .. 1·00 20

366. G. Tattarescu. **367.** B. Iscovescu.

1954. 60th Death Anniv. of Tattarescu (painter).

2352. **366.** 55 b. red .. .. 2·50 15

1954. Death Cent. of Iscovescu (painter).

2353. **367.** 1 l. 75 brown .. 3·25 45

368. Teleprinter. **369.** Wild Boar.

1954. Cent. of Telecommunications in Rumania.

2354. **368.** 50 b. lilac .. .. 1·50 20

1955. Forestry Month. Inscr. "LUNA PADURII 1955".

2355. **369.** 35 b. brown .. .. 1·60 20
2356. – 65 b. blue .. .. 2·10 25
2357. – 1 l. 20 red .. .. 4·75 50

DESIGNS: 65 b. Tree planting. 1 l. 20, Logging.

370. Airman.

371. Clasped Hands.

1955. Occupations.

2358. – 3 b. blue 25 10
2359. – 5 b. violet 15 10
2360. **370.** 10 b. brown 30 10
2361. – 20 b. mauve 40 10
2362. – 30 b. blue .. .. 1·00 10
2363. – 35 b. turquoise .. 60 10
2364. – 40 b. blue .. .. 1·40 15
2365. – 55 b. olive .. .. 1·40 10
2366. – 1 l. violet .. .. 2·00 10
2367. – 1 l. 55 lake .. .. 3·25 10
2368. – 2 l. 35 buff .. .. 4·75 60
2369. – 2 l. 55 green .. .. 6·75 40

DESIGNS: 3 b. Scientist. 5 b. Foundryman. 20 b. Miner. 30 b. Tractor driver. 35 b. Schoolboy. 40 b. Girl student. 55 b. Bricklayer. 1 l. Sailor. 1 l. 55, Millgirl. 2 l. 35, Soldier. 2 l. 55, Telegraph linesman.

1955. Int. Conference of Postal Municipal Workers, Vienna.

2370. **371.** 25 b. red 65 20

372. Lenin. **373.** Dove and Globe.

1955. 85th Birth Anniv. of Lenin. Portraits of Lenin.

2371. **372.** 20 b. brown and bistre 65 15
2372. – 55 b. brown (full-face) 1·40 20
2373. – 1 l. lake and red (half length) .. .. 2·00 25

1955. Peace Congress, Helsinki.

2374. **373.** 55 b. blue .. .. 1·60 15

374. War Memorial, Berlin. **375.** Children and Dove.

1955. 10th Anniv. of Victory over Germany.

2375. **374.** 55 b. blue .. .. 1·40 15

1955. Int. Children's Day.

2376. **375.** 55 b. brown .. .. 1·50 15

376. "Service". **377.** People's Art Museum.

1955. European Volley-ball Championships.

2377. – 55 b. purple on pink 5·00 1·00
2378. **376.** 1 l. 75 red on yellow .. 11·50 1·00

DESIGN: 55 b. Volley-ball players.

1955. Bucharest Museums.

2379. – 20 b. mauve 25 15
2380. – 55 b. brown 50 15
2381. **377.** 1 l. 20 black .. .. 1·60 50
2382. – 1 l. 75 green .. .. 2·75 50
2383. – 2 l. 55 purple .. .. 4·75 65

MUSEUMS—(30 × 24½ mm.): 20 b. Theodor Aman. 2 l. 55, Simu. (34 × 23 mm.): 55 b. Lenin-Stalin. 1 l. 75, Republican Art.

378. Mother and Child. **379.** "Nature Study".

1955. 1st World Mothers' Congress, Lausanne.

2384. **378.** 55 b. blue .. .. 1·60 20

1955. 5th Anniv. of Pioneer Headquarters, Bucharest.

2385. – 10 b. blue 60 10
2386. **379.** 20 b. green .. .. 1·40 10
2387. – 55 b. purple .. .. 3·00 20

DESIGNS: 10 b. Model railway. 55 b. Headquarters building.

380. Coxed Four. **381.** A. Pann.

1955. Women's European Rowing Championships, Snagov.

2388. **380.** 55 b. green .. .. 8·25 1·00
2389. – 1 l. blue (Woman sculler) .. .. 13·00 1·00

1955. Rumanian Writers.

2390. – 55 b. blue .. .. 1·40 25
2391. – 55 b. grey .. .. 1·40 25
2392. **381.** 55 b. olive .. .. 1·40 25
2393. – 55 b. violet .. .. 1·40 25
2394. – 55 b. purple .. .. 1·40 25

PORTRAITS—No. 2390, D. Cantemir. 2391, M. Dosoftei. 2393, S. C. Cantacuzino. 2394, E. Vacarescu.

382. Marksman. **383.** Fire Engine.

1955. European Sharpshooting Championships, Bucharest.

2395. **382.** 1 l. brn. & light brn. 6·00 65

1955. Firemen's Day.

2396. **383.** 55 b. red .. .. 1·90 25

384. **385.** Spraying Fruit Trees.

1955. 10th Anniv. of W.F.T.U.

2397. **384.** 55 b. olive 50 10
2398. – 1 l. blue 85 25

DESIGN: 1 l. Workers and flag.

1955. Fruit and Vegetable Cultivation.

2399. **385.** 10 b. green 40 15
2400. – 20 b. red 50 35
2401. – 55 b. blue .. .. 1·60 45
2402. – 1 l. lake .. .. 3·75 1·10

DESIGNS: 20 b. Fruit picking. 55 b. Harvesting grapes. 1 l. Gathering vegetables.

386. **387.** Michurin.

1955. 4th ARLUS Congress.

2403. **386.** 20 b. blue and buff .. 1·00 15

1955. Birth Centenary of Michurin (Russian botanist).

2404. **387.** 55 b. blue .. .. 1·60 20

388. Cotton. **389.** Sheep and Shepherd blowing Bucium.

1955.

2405. – 10 b. pur. (Sugar beet) 45 15
2406. **388.** 20 b. grey 85 15
2407. – 55 b. blue (Linseed) .. 2·10 60
2408. – 1 l. 55 brown (Sunflower) .. .. 4·25 1·10

1955.

2409. **389.** 5 b. brown & green .. 1·00 15
2410. – 10 b. violet and bistre 1·40 15
2411. – 35 b. brown & salmon 2·75 45
2412. – 55 b. brown & bistre 5·00 75

DESIGNS: 10 b. Pigs and farm girl. 35 b. Cows and dairy maid. 55 b. Horses and groom.

390. Schiller. **391.** Bank and Book.

1955. Famous Writers.

2413. – 20 b. blue 25 10
2414. – 55 b. blue .. .. 1·10 15
2415. **390.** 1 l. grey .. .. 2·00 20
2416. – 1 l. 55 brown .. 4·00 1·00
2417. – 1 l. 75 violet .. .. 5·00 1·00
2418. – 2 l. lake .. .. 5·75 1·60

PORTRAITS: 20 b. Hans Andersen. 55 b. Mickiewicz. 1 l. 55, Montesquieu. 1 l. 75, Walt Whitman. 2 l. Cervantes.

1955. Savings Bank.

2419. **391.** 55 b. blue .. .. 2·00 25
2420. 55 b. violet .. .. 6·75 4·00

392. Family. **393.** Brown Hare.

1956. National Census.

2421. – 55 b. orange 30 10
2422. **392.** 1 l. 75 brown & green 2·00 65

DESIGN: 55 b. "21 FEBRUARIE 1956" in circle.

1956. Wild Life.

2423. **393.** 20 b. black and green 2·00 2·00
2424. – 20 b. black and olive 2·00 2·00
2425. – 35 b. black and blue .. 2·00 2·00
2426. – 50 b. brown and blue 2·00 2·00
2427. – 55 b. green and bistre 2·50 2·00
2428. – 55 b. brown & turq. .. 2·50 2·00
2429. – 1 l. lake and green .. 4·00 4·00
2430. – 1 l. 55 lake and blue .. 4·50 4·50
2431. – 1 l. 75 brown and green 5·00 5·00
2432. – 2 l. brown and blue 20·00 20·00
2433. – 3 l. 25 black & green .. 20·00 20·00
2434. – 4 l. 25 brn. & salmon 20·00 20·00

DESIGNS—VERT. No. 2424, Great Bustard. 35 b. Trout. 1 l. 55 Eurasian red squirrel. 1 l. 75, Capercaillie 4 l. 25, Red deer. HORIZ. 50 b. Wild boar. No. 2427, Ringed-necked Pheasant, No. 2428, Brown bear. 1 l. Lynx. 2 l. Chamois. 3 l. 25 Pintail

See also Nos. 2474/85.

394. Insurgents. **395.** Boy and Globe.

1956. 85th Anniv. of Paris Commune.

2435. **394.** 55 b. red .. .. 1·60 50

1956. Int. Children's Day.

2436. **395.** 55 b. violet .. .. 1·90 20

396. Red Cross Nurse. **397.** Tree.

1956. 2nd Rumanian Red Cross Congress.

2437. **396.** 55 b. olive and red .. 2·75 20

1956. Forestry Month.

2438. **397.** 20 b. grey on green .. 1·40 20
2439. – 55 b. black on green .. 4·00 30

DESIGN: 55 b. Lumber train.

398. Woman Speaking. **399.** Academy Buildings.

1956. Int. Women's Congress, Bucharest.

2440. **398.** 55 b. green .. .. 1·60 20

1956. 90th Anniv. of Rumanian People's Academy.

2441. **399.** 55 b. green and buff 1·60 20

400. T. Vuia and Early and Modern Aeroplanes.

1956. 50th Anniv. of 1st Flight by Vuia (pioneer airman).

2442. **400.** 55 b. brn. & ol. 2·00 35

401. Georgescu and Statues. **402.** Farm Girl.

1956. Birth Cent. of Georgescu (sculptor).

2443. **401.** 55 b. grn. & brn. .. 2·75 20

1956. Collective Farming.

(a) Inscr. "1951-1956".

2444. **402.** 55 b. plum .. .. 10·00 10·00

(b) Inscr. "1949–1956".

2445. **402.** 55 b. plum .. .. 1·50 20

403. "Aporia crataegi". **404.** Striker.

1956. Insect Pests.

2446. **403.** 10 b. cream, black and violet .. .. 3·25 30
2447. – 55 b. orange & brown 5·00 60
2448. – 1 l. 75 lake and olive 13·50 10·00
2449. – 1 l. 75 brown & olive 10·50 1·10

PESTS: 55 b. "Leptinotarsa decemlineata". 1 l. 75 (2) "Melontha melontha".

1956. 50th Anniv. of Dockers Strike at Galatz.

2450. **404.** 55 b. brown on pink 1·60 20

405. **406.** Maxim Gorky.

1956. 25th Anniv. of Newspaper "Scanteia".

2451. **405.** 55 b. blue .. .. 1·40 20

1956. 20th Death Anniv. of Maxim Gorky.

2452. **406.** 55 b. brown .. .. 1·40 20

407. T. Aman. **408.** Snowdrops and Polyanthus.

1956. 125th Birth Anniv. of Aman (painter).

2453. **407.** 55 b. grey .. .. 2·75 65

1956. Flowers. Designs multicoloured. Colours of backgrounds given.

2454. **408.** 5 b. blue 55 15
2455. – 55 b. black .. .. 2·75 60
2456. – 1 l. 75 blue .. .. 6·75 85
2457. – 3 l. green .. .. 10·00 1·25

FLOWERS: 55 b. Daffodil and violets. 1 l. 75, Antirrhinums and campanulas. 3 l. Poppies and lilies of the valley.

409. Janos Hunyadi. **410.** Olympic Flame.

1956. 500th Death Anniv. of Hunyadi.

2458. **409.** 55 b. violet .. .. 2·00 25

1956. Olympic Games.

2459. **410.** 20 b. red 65 15
2460. – 55 b. blue .. .. 1·00 20
2461. – 1 l. mauve .. .. 2·40 25
2462. – 1 l. 55 turquoise .. 3·25 30
2463. – 1 l. 75 violet .. .. 4·25 65

DESIGNS: 55 b. Water-polo. 1 l. Ice-skating. 1 l. 55, Canoeing. 1 l. 75, High-jumping.

411. George Bernard Shaw.
412. Aeroplane over City.

1956. Cultural Anniversaries.
2464. – 20 b. blue (Franklin) 30 10
2465. – 35 b. red (Toyo Oda) 40 15
2466. **411.** 40 b. brown 45 15
2467. – 50 b. brown (I. Franko) 55 10
2468. – 55 b. olive (Curie) .. 95 10
2469. – 1 l. turquoise (Ibsen) 1·50 15
2470. – 1 l. 55 violet (Dostoevsky) .. 2·10 15
2471. – 1 l. 75 blue (Heine).. 2·75 15
2472. – 2 l. 55 pur. (Mozart).. 3·75 25
2473. – 3 l. 25 blue (Rembrandt) .. 4·00 65

1956. Wild Life. As Nos. 2423/34 but colours changed. Imperf.
2474. 20 b. brown and green.. 5·00 5·00
2475. 20 b. black and blue .. 5·00 5·00
2476. 35 b. black and blue .. 5·00 5·00
2477. 50 b. black and brown.. 5·00 5·00
2478. 55 b. black and violet .. 5·00 5·00
2479. 55 b. brown and green.. 5·00 5·00
2480. 1 l. brown and blue .. 5·00 5·00
2481. 1 l. 55 brown and bistre.. 5·00 5·00
2482. 1 l. 75 purple & green .. 5·00 5·00
2483. 2 l. black and blue .. 5·00 5·00
2484. 3 l. 25 brown and green.. 8·00 8·00
2485. 4 l. 25 brown and violet.. 10·00 10·00

1956. Air. Multicoloured designs embodying aeroplanes and views.
2486. 20 b. Type **412** 45 20
2487. 55 b. Mountains.. .. 95 15
2488. 1 l. 75 Cornfield.. .. 3·00 25
2489. 2 l. 55 Seashore .. .. 4·00 75

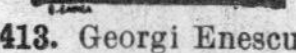

413. Georgi Enescu.
414. "Rebels" (after O. Bancila).

1956. 75th Birth Anniv. of Enescu (musician).
2490. – 55 b. blue .. .. 1·25 20
2491. **413.** 1 l. 75 purple .. 2·75 30
DESIGN: 55 b. Enescu when a child, holding violin.

1957. 50th Anniv. of Peasant Revolt.
2492. **414.** 55 b. slate .. .. 1·60 20

415. Stephen the Great.
416. Dr. G. Marinescu and Institute of Medicine.

1957. 500th Anniv. of Accession of Stephen the Great.
2493. **415.** 55 b. brown .. .. 1·40 25
2494. 55 b. olive .. .. 1·40 25

1957. National Congress of Medical Sciences, Bucharest and Cent. of Medical and Pharmaceutical Teaching in Bucharest (1 l. 75).
2495. **416.** 20 b. green 40 15
2496. – 35 b. brown 50 20
2497. – 55 b. purple .. .. 1·00 50
2498. – 1 l. 75 red and blue.. 4·25 1·60
DESIGNS: 35 b. Dr. I. Cantacuzino and Cantacuzino Institute. 55 b. Dr. V. Babes and Babes Institute. 1 l. 75, (66 × 23 mm.), Drs. N. Kretzulescu and C. Dairla, and Faculty of Medicine, Bucharest.

417. Gymnast and Spectator.
418. Emblems of Atomic Energy.

1957. 1st European Women's Gymnastic Championships, Bucharest.
2499. **417.** 20 b. green 65 15
2500. – 35 b. red .. .. 1·00 15
2501. – 55 b. blue .. .. 2·00 50
2502. – 1 l. 75 purple .. 5·75 85
DESIGNS—HORIZ. 35 h. On asymmetric bars. 55 h. Vaulting over horse. VERT. 1 l. 75, On beam.

1957. 2nd A.S.I.T. Congress.
2503. **418.** 55 b. brown .. .. 1·40 15
2504. 55 b. blue .. .. 1·60 20

419. Dove and Handlebars.
420. Rhododendron.

1957. 10th Int. Cycle Race.
2505. **419.** 20 b. blue 50 15
2506. – 55 b. brown .. .. 1·40 20
DESIGN: 55 b. Racing cyclist.

1957. Flowers of the Carpathian Mountains.
2513. **420.** 5 b. red and grey .. 35 10
2514. – 10 b. green and grey 50 10
2515. – 20 b. orange and grey 60 10
2516. – 35 b. olive and grey.. 90 15
2517. – 55 b. blue and grey.. 1·25 15
2518. – 1 l. red and grey .. 3·75 30
2519. – 1 l. 55 yellow and grey 3·75 35
2520. – 1 l. 75 violet and grey 6·75 35
FLOWERS: 10 b. Daphne. 20 b. Lily. 35 b. Edelweiss. 55 b. Gentian. 1 l. Dianthus. 1 l. 55, Primula. 1 l. 75, Anemone.

DESIGNS—HORIZ. 20 b. Country scene. 1 l. 75, Battle scene.

421. N. Grigorescu.

1957. 50th Death Anniv. of Grigorescu (painter).
2521. – 20 b. green .. .. 1·00 10
2522. **421.** 55 b. brown .. .. 2·40 20
2523. – 1 l. 75 blue .. .. 6·75 85

422. Festival Visitors. **423.** Festival Emblem.

1957. 6th World Youth Festival, Moscow.
2524. **422.** 20 b. purple 15 10
2525. – 55 b. green 45 10
2526. **423.** 1 l. orange .. .. 1·10 40
2527. – 1 l. 75 blue .. .. 2·00 20
DESIGNS: 55 b. Girl with flags. (22 × 38 mm.). 1 l. 75 Dancers (49 × 20 mm.).

424. Destroyer "Stalingrad".
425. "The Trumpeter" (after N. Grigorescu).

1957. Navy Day.
2528. **424.** 1 l. 75 blue .. .. 1·75 20

1957. 80th Anniv. of War of Independence.
2529. **425.** 20 b. violet .. .. 1·60 15

426. Soldiers Advancing.
427. Child with Dove.

1957. 40th Anniv. of Battle of Marasesti.
2530. **426.** 1 l. 75 brown .. 2·00 20

1957. Red Cross.
2531. **427.** 55 b. green and red.. 1·60 20

428. Sprinter and Bird.
429. Ovid.

1957. Int. Athletic Championships, Bucharest.
2532. **428.** 20 b. black and blue.. 65 10
2533. – 55 b. black and yellow 1·40 15
2534. – 1 l. 75 black and red.. 4·75 60
DESIGNS: 55 b. Javelin-thrower and bull. 1 l. 75, Runner and stag.

1957. Birth Bimillenary of Ovid (Latin poet).
2535. **429.** 1 l. 75 blue .. .. 3·25 65

430. Congress Emblem.
431. Oil Refinery, 1957.

1957. 4th W.F.T.U. Congress, Leipzig.
2536. **430.** 55 b. blue 90 15

1957. Cent. of Rumanian Petroleum Industry.
2537. **431.** 20 b. brown 35 10
2538. 20 b. blue 35 10
2539. – 55 b. purple 85 30
DESIGN: 55 b. Oil production, 1857: horse-operated borer.

432. Lenin, Youth and Girl.
433. Artificial Satellite encircling Globe.

1957. 40th Anniv. of Russian Revolution.
2540. **432.** 10 b. red 20 10
2541. – 35 b. purple 65 10
2542. – 55 b. brown .. .. 1·00 20
DESIGNS—HORIZ. 35 b. Lenin and flags. 55 b. Statue of Lenin.

1957. Air. Launching of Artificial Satellite by Russia. Inscr. "SATELITII ARTIFICIALI".
2543. **433.** 25 b. green 35 15
2545. 25 b. blue 35 15
2544. – 3 l. 75 green.. .. 3·25 35
2546. – 3 l. 75 blue .. .. 3·25 35
DESIGN: 3 l. 75 (2), Satellite's orbit around Globe.
See also Nos. 2593/6.

434. Peasant Soldiers.
435. Endre Ady.

1957. 520th Anniv. of Bobilna Revolution.
2547. **434.** 50 b. purple 35 15
2548. – 55 b. grey 45 20
DESIGN—VERT. 55 b. Bobilna Memorial.

1957. 80th Birth Anniv. of Endre Ady (Hungarian poet).
2549. **435.** 55 b. olive .. .. 1·40 15

436. "Laika" & Satellite. **437.** Black-winged Stilt.

1957. Launching of Dog "Laika" in artificial satellite.
2550. **436.** 1 l. 20 brown & green 4·75 85
2551. 1 l. 20 brown and blue 4·75 85

1957. Fauna of the Danube Delta.
2552. **437.** 5 b. grey & brn. (post.) 40 10
2553. – 10 b. orange and green 50 10
2554. – 20 b. orange and red 75 15
2555. – 50 b. orange and green 65 10
2556. – 55 b. blue and purple 1·00 10
2557. – 1 l. 30 orange & violet 2·50 20
2558. – 3 l. 30 grey & bl. (air) 4·75 90
2559. – 5 l. orange and red .. 6·00 1·40
DESIGNS—VERT. 10 b. Great Egret. 20 b. White Spoonbill. 50 b. Fish. HORIZ. 55 b. Stoat. 1 l. 30, Eastern White Pelican. 3 l. 30, Black-headed Gull 5 l. White-tailed Sea Eagle.

438. Emblem of Republic and Flags.

1957. 10th Anniv. of People's Republic.
2560. **438.** 25 b. buff, red & blue 20 10
2561. – 55 b. yellow .. 75 25
2562. – 1 l. 20 red .. .. 1·40 35
DESIGNS: 55 b. Emblem, Industry and Agriculture. 1 l. 20, Emblem, the Arts and Sport.

439. Republican Flag.
440. "Telecommunications".

1958. 25th Anniv. of Strike at Grivita.
2563. **439.** 1 l. red & brn. on buff 1·00 20
2564. 1 l. red & blue on buff 1·00 20

1958. Communist Postal Conference, Moscow.
2565. **440.** 55 b. violet 35 20
2566. – 1 l. 75 purple .. 1·10 15
DESIGN: 1 l. 75, Telegraph pole and pylons carrying lines.

441. N. Balcescu.
442. Fencer.

1958. Rumanian Writers.
2567. **441.** 5 b. blue 30 15
2568. – 10 b. black (Ion Creanga) 35 15
2569. – 35 b. blue (Vlahuta).. 40 15
2570. – 55 b. brown (Eminescu) 75 15
2571. – 1 l. 75 brown (Alecsandri) .. 1·10 30
2572. – 2 l. myrtle (Delavrancea) .. 2·75 30

1958. World Youth Fencing Championships, Bucharest.
2573. **442.** 1 l. 75 mauve .. 2·00 20

443. Symbols of Medicine and Sport.
444.

1958. 25th Anniv. of Sports Doctors' Service.
2574. **443.** 1 l. 20 red and green 2·00 20

1958. 4th Int. Congress of Democratic Women.
2575. **444.** 55 b. blue .. .. 1·10 15

445. Linnaeus.
446. "Lepiota procera".

1958. Cultural Celebrities. Inscr. "MARILE ANIVERSARI CULTURALE 1957".
2576. **445.** 10 b. green 20 10
2577. – 20 b. brown (Comte) 35 10
2578. – 40 b. purple (Blake) 50 15
2579. – 55 b. blue (Glinka) 1·25 10
2580. – 1 l. plum (Longfellow) 1·50 20
2581. – 1 l. 75 bl. (Goldoni).. 2·25 25
2582. – 2 l. brown (Comenius) 4·00 30

1958. Mushrooms. As T **446**.

2583. **446.** 5 b. brn., light brn. & blue 10 10
2584. – 10 b. brown, buff and bronze 15 10
2585. – 20 b. red, yell. & grey 35 10
2586. – 30 b. brown, orge and green 45 20
2587. – 35 b. brn., light brn. and blue 50 10
2588. – 55 b. brn., red & grn. 85 10
2589. – 1 l. brn., buff & turq. 1·50 15
2590. – 1 l. 55 pink, drab & grey .. .. 2·50 25
2591. – 1 l. 75 brown, buff and green .. .. 3·75 35
2592. – 2 l. yellow, brown and turquoise .. .. 4·50 40

MUSHROOMS: 10 b. "Clavaria aurea". 20 b. "Amanita caesarea". 30 b. "Lactarius deliciosus". 35 b. "Armillaria mellea". 55 b. "Coprinus comatus". 1 l. "Morchella conica". 1 l. 55, "Psalliota campestris". 1 l. 75, "Boletus edulis". 2 l. "Cantharellus cibarius".

1958. Brussels International Exhibition. Nos. 2543/4 and 2545/6 optd. **EXPOZITIA BRUXELLES 1958** and star or with star only.

2593 **433** 25 b. green .. .. 3·25 2·00
2594 25 b. blue .. .. 20·00 11·50
2595 – 3 l. 75 green .. .. 3·25 2·00
2596 – 3 l. 75 blue .. .. 20·00 11·50

448. Emil Racovita (scientist), Antarctic Map and "Belgica".

1958. Racovita Commem. Inscr. "1868 1947".

2597. **448.** 55 b. indigo and blue 3·25 40
2598. – 1 l. 20 violet and olive 2·75 30

DESIGN: 1 l. 20, Racovita and grotto.

449. Sputnik encircling Globe. 450. Servicemen's Statue.

1958. Air. Launching of Third Artificial Satellite by Russia.

2599. **449.** 3 l. 25 buff and blue .. 5·00 1·40

1958. Army Day.

2600. **450.** 55 b. brown (postage) 25 10
2601. – 75 b. purple 45 15
2602. – 1 l. 75 blue .. .. 1·10 20
2603. – 3 l. 30 violet (air) .. 2·00 65

DESIGNS: 75 b. Soldier guarding industrial plant. 1 l. 75, Sailor hoisting flag. 3 l. 30, Pilot and aircraft.

451. Costumes of Oltenia. 452.

1958. Provincial Costumes. Female and male costumes as T **451/2**.

2604. **451.** 35 b. red and black on yellow 30 15
2605. **452.** 35 b. red and black on yellow 30 15
2606. – 40 b. red and brown on grey 40 20
2607. – 40 b. red and brown on grey 40 20
2608. – 50 b. red and brown on lilac 45 15
2609. – 50 b. red and brown on lilac 45 15
2610. – 55 b. red and brown on grey 55 15
2611. – 55 b. red and brown on grey 55 15
2612. – 1 l. red & brn. on pink 1·50 20
2613. – 1 l. red & brn. on pink 1·50 20
2614. – 1 l. 75 red and brown on blue .. .. 2·00 35
2615. – 1 l. 75 red and brown on blue .. .. 2·00 35

PROVINCES: Nos. 2606/7, Tara Oasului. Nos. 2608/9, Transylvania. Nos. 2610/11, Muntenia. Nos. 2612/3, Banat. Nos. 2614/5, Moldova.

453. Stamp Printer. 454. Runner.

1958. Rumanian Stamp Centenary. Inscr. "1858 1958".

2617. **453.** 35 b. blue 35 10
2618. – 55 b. brown 45 10
2619. – 1 l. 20 blue .. .. 1·40 25
2620. – 1 l. 30 plum .. .. 1·50 40
2621. – 1 l. 55 brown .. 2·00 20
2622. – 1 l. 75 red .. .. 2·40 25
2623. – 2 l. violet .. .. 3·00 65
2624. – 3 l. 30 brown .. 5·00 1·00

DESIGNS: 55 b. Scissors and Moldavian stamps of 1858. 1 l. 20, Driver with whip and mail coach. 1 l. 30, Postman with horn and mounted courier. 1 l. 55 to 3 l. 30, Moldavian stamps of 1858 (Nos. 1/4).

1958. 3rd Youth Spartacist Games.

2627. **454.** 1 l. brown .. .. 1·40 20

455. Revolutionary Emblem. 456. Boy Bugler.

1958. 40th Anniv. of Workers' Revolution.

2628. **455.** 55 b. red 85 15

1958. 10th Anniv. of Education Reform.

2629. **456.** 55 b. red 65 15

457. Alexander Cuza. 458. First Cosmic Rocket.

1959. Cent. of Union of Rumanian Provinces.

2630. **457.** 1 l. 75 b. blue .. 1·60 15

1959. Air. Launching of 1st Cosmic Rocket.

2631. **458.** 3 l. 25 b. blue on salmon .. .. 13·50 1·50

459. Charles Darwin. 460. Maize.

1959. Cultural Anniversaries.

2633. **459.** 55 b. black (postage) 55 10
2634. – 55 b. blue (Robert Burns) 55 15
2635. – 55 b. red (Popov) .. 55 10
2636. – 55 b. purple (Sholem Aleichem) 55 10
2637. – 55 b. brown (Handel) 55 15
2638. – 3 l. 25 b. blue (Joliot-Curie) (air) .. 4·75 50

1959. 10th Anniv. of Collective Farming in Rumania.

2639. **460.** 55 b. green 35 10
2640. – 55 b. orange 35 20
2641. – 55 b. purple 35 20
2642. – 55 b. olive 35 20
2643. – 55 b. brown 35 20
2644. – 55 b. bistre 35 20
2645. – 55 b. blue 35 20
2646. – 55 b. bistre 35 20
2647. – 5 l. red .. .. 5·00 75

DESIGNS—VERT. No. 2640, Sunflower with bee. No. 2641, Sugar beet. HORIZ. No. 2642, Sheep. No. 2643, Cattle. No. 2644, Rooster and hens. No. 2645, Farm tractor. No. 2646, Farm wagon and horses. No. 2647 (38 × 26½ mm.), Farmer and wife, and wheatfield within figure "10".

461. Rock Thrush. 462.

1959. Air. Birds in natural colours. Inscriptions in grey. Colours of value tablets and backgrounds given.

2648. **461.** 10 b. grey on buff .. 20 15
2649. – 20 b. grey on grey .. 20 15
2650. – 35 b. grey on dp. grey 25 15
2651. – 40 b. red on pink .. 40 40
2652. – 55 b. grey on green .. 50 15
2653. – 55 b. grey on cream .. 50 15
2654. – 55 b. green on azure .. 50 15
2655. – 1 l. red on yellow .. 1·60 35
2656. – 1 l. 55 red on pink .. 2·10 35
2657. – 5 l. grey on green .. 8·25 2·00

BIRDS—HORIZ. No. 2649, Golden oriole. No. 2656, Long-tailed tit. No. 2657, Wallcreeper. VERT. No. 2650, Lapwing. No. 2651, Barn swallow. No. 2652, Great spotted woodpecker. No. 2653, Goldfinch. No. 2654, Great tit. No. 2655, Bullfinch.

1959. 7th World Youth Festival, Vienna. Inscr. "26 VII–4 VIII 1959".

2658. **462.** 1 l. blue 85 20
2659. – 1 l. 60 red 90 20

DESIGN. 1 l. 60, Folk-dancer in national costume.

463. Workers and Banners. (466.)

1959. 15th Anniv. of Liberation.

2660. **463.** 55 b. multicoloured 45 15

1959. Air. Landing of Russian Rocket on the Moon. Surch. **h. 00.02'.24" 14-IX-1959. PRIMA RACHETA COSMICA IN LUNA 5 LEI** in red.

2662. **458.** 5 l. on 3 l. 25 blue on salmon .. .. 17·00 4·00

1959. 8th Balkan Games. Optd. with T **466** in silver.

2663. **454.** 1 l. brown .. .. 17·00 17·00

467. Prince Vlad Tepes and Charter.

1959. 500th Anniv. of Bucharest.

2664. **467.** 20 b. black and blue .. 1·00 20
2665. – 40 b. black and brown 1·75 25
2666. – 55 b. black and bistre 2·40 25
2667. – 55 b. black and purple 2·75 25
2668. – 1 l. 55 black and lilac 6·00 1·10
2669. – 1 l. 75 black & turquoise 6·75 1·40

DESIGNS—HORIZ. 40 b. Peace Building, Bucharest. 55 b. (No. 2666), Athanaeum. 55 b. (No. 2667), "Scanteia" Printing House. 1 l. 55, Opera House. 1 l. 75, "23 August" Stadium.

468. Football. 469. Atomic Icebreaker "Lenin".

1959. International Sport. Multicoloured.

2671. 20 b. Type **468** (postage) 25 15
2672. 35 b. Motor-cycle racing 35 10
2673. 40 b. Ice-hockey 45 15
2674. 55 b. Handball 50 10
2675. 1 l. Horse-jumping .. 1·00 10
2676. 1 l. 50 Boxing .. .. 2·00 15
2677. 1 l. 55 Rugby football .. 2·10 10
2678. 1 l. 60 Tennis .. .. 2·50 25
2679. 2 l. 80 Hydroplaning (air) 3·00 90

The 35 b., 40 b., 1 l. 55, 1 l. 60 and 2 l. 80 values are horizontal designs.

1959. Launching of Atomic Icebreaker "Lenin".

2680. **469.** 1 l. 75 violet .. .. 2·50 30

470. Stamp Album and Magnifier.

1959. Stamp Day.

2681. **470.** 1 l. 60 (+40 b.) blue 1·60 1·00

471. Foxglove. 472. Cuza University.

1959. Medicinal Flowers. Multicoloured.

2682. 20 b. Type **471** 25 10
2683. 40 b. Peppermint .. 40 20
2684. 55 b. Camomile .. 55 10
2685. 55 b. Cornflower .. 65 15
2686. 1 l. Autumn crocus .. 85 15
2687. 1 l. 20 Monk's-hood .. 1·10 20
2688. 1 l. 55 Red poppy .. 1·40 25
2689. 1 l. 60 Linden .. .. 1·90 30
2690. 1 l. 75 Wild rose .. 2·00 35
2691. 3 l. 20 Adonis .. .. 4·00 45

1959. Cent. of Cuza University, Jassy.

2692. **472.** 55 b. brown 65 20

473. Rocket, Dog and Rabbit. 474. G. Cosbuc.

1959. Air. Cosmic Rocket Flight.

2693. **473.** 1 l. 55 blue .. .. 4·00 30
2694. – 1 l. 60 blue on cream 5·00 40
2695. – 1 l. 75 blue .. .. 5·00 45

DESIGNS—HORIZ. (52 × 29½ mm.): 1 l. 60, Picture of "invisible" side of the Moon, with lists of place-names in Rumanian and Russian. VERT. (as Type **473**): 1 l. 75, Lunik III's trajectory around the Moon.

1960. Rumanian Authors.

2696. **474.** 20 b. blue 20 15
2697. – 40 b. purple 65 20
2698. – 50 b. brown 85 15
2699. – 55 b. purple 85 15
2700. – 1 l. violet .. .. 1·50 20
2701. – 1 l. 55 blue .. .. 2·50 35

PORTRAITS: 40 b. I. L. Caragiale. 50 b. G. Alexandrescu. 55 b. A. Donici. 1 l. C. Negruzzi. 1 l. 55, D. Bolintineanu.

475. Huchen (Danube salmon). 476.

1960. Rumanian Fauna.

2702. **475.** 20 b. blue (postage) .. 30 10
2703. – 55 b. brn. (Tortoise) 55 10
2704. – 1 l. 20 lilac (Common Shelduck) .. 2·00 35
2705. – 1 l. 30 blue (Golden Eagle) (air) .. 2·50 35
2706. – 1 l. 75 grn. (Black Grouse) .. .. 2·75 35
2707. 2 l. red (Lammergeier) 3·00 50

1960. 50th Anniv. of Int. Women's Day.

2708. **476.** 55 b. blue .. .. 1·00 50

477. Lenin (after painting by M. A. Gerasimov). 478. "Victory".

1960. 90th Birth Anniv. of Lenin.
2709. **477.** 40 b. purple 45 15
2710. – 55 b. blue (Statue of Lenin by Boris Curogea) 60 15

1960. 15th Anniv. of Victory.
2712. **478.** 40 b. blue 50 10
2714. 40 b. purple 3·75 4·00
2713. – 55 b. blue 50 10
2715. – 55 b. purple 3·75 4·00
DESIGN: 55 b. Statue of soldier with flag.

479. Rocket Flight.

1960. Air. Launching of Soviet Rocket.
2716. **479.** 55 b. blue 3·75 25

480. Diving. **481.** Gymnastics.

1960. Olympic Games, Rome (1st issue). Multicoloured.
2717. 40 b. Type **480** 2·00 2·00
2718. 55 b. Gymnastics 2·00 2·00
2719. 1 l. 20 High-jumping 2·00 2·00
2720. 1 l. 60 Boxing 3·25 3·25
2721. 2 l. 45 Canoeing 3·25 3·25
2722. 3 l. 70 Canoeing 6·75 4·00
Nos. 2717/9 and 2720/1 are arranged together in "brickwork" fashion, se tenant in sheets, forming complete overall patterns of the Olympic rings.
No. 2722 is imperf.

1960. Olympic Games, Rome (2nd issue).
2723. – 20 b. blue 20 15
2724. **481.** 40 b. purple 65 15
2725. – 55 b. blue 1·00 15
2726. – 1 l. red 1·40 10
2727. – 1 l. 60 purple 2·00 30
2728. – 2 l. lilac 3·00 65
DESIGNS: 20 b. Diving. 55 b. High-jumping. 1 l. Boxing. 1 l. 60, Canoeing. 2 l. Football.

482. Industrial Scholars. **483.** Vlaicu and Aeroplane.

484. Ambulance 'Plane. **485.** Pilot and Planes.

1960.
2731. **482.** 3 b. mauve (post.) 10 10
2732. – 5 b. brown 25 10
2733. – 10 b. purple 10 10
2734. – 20 b. blue 15 10
2735. – 30 b. red 20 10
2736. – 35 b. red 20 10
2737. – 40 b. bistre 25 10
2738. – 50 b. violet 25 10
2739. – 55 b. blue 30 10
2740. – 60 b. green 30 10
2741. – 75 b. olive 50 10
2742. – 1 l. red 70 10
2743. – 1 l. 20 black 55 10
2744. – 1 l. 50 purple 75 10
2745. – 1 l. 55 turquoise 90 10
2746. – 1 l. 60 blue 80 10
2747. – 1 l. 75 brown 1·00 10
2748. – 2 l. brown 1·40 20
2749. – 2 l. 40 violet 1·50 15
2750. – 3 l. blue 1·50 15
2751. – 3 l. 20 blue (air) 3·25 10
DESIGNS—VERT. 5 b. Diesel train. 10 b. Dam. 20 b. Miner. 30 b. Doctor. 35 b. Textile worker. 50 b. Children at play. 55 b. Timber tractor. 1 l. Atomic reactor. 1 l. 20, Petroleum refinery. 1 l. 50, Iron-works. 1 l. 75, Mason. 2 l. Road-roller. 2 l. 40, Chemist. 3 l. Radio communications and television. HORIZ. 40 b. Grand piano and books. 60 b. Combine harvester. 75 b. Cattle-shed. 1 l. 55, Dock scene. 1 l. 60, Runner. 3 l. 20, Baneasa Airport, Bucharest.

1960. 50th Anniv. of 1st Flight by A. Vlaicu. and Aviation Day.
2752. **483.** 10 b. brown & yellow 20 10
2753. – 20 b. brown & orange 30 10
2754. **484.** 35 b. red 35 10
2755. – 40 b. violet 55 10
2756. **485.** 55 b. blue 70 10
2757. – 1 l. 60 multicoloured 1·75 50
2758. – 1 l. 75 multicoloured 2·25 55
DESIGNS—HORIZ. 20 b. Vlaicu in flying helmet and aeroplane. 40 b. Aeroplane spraying crops. (59×22 mm.). 1 l. 60, Ilyushin "IL-18" airliner and airport control tower. 1 l. 75, Parachute descents.

486. Worker and Emblem.

1960. 3rd Workers' Party Congress.
2759. **486.** 55 b. orange and red 1·00 15

487. Tolstoy. **488.** Tomis (Constantza).

1960. Cultural Anniversaries.
2760. 10 b. purple (T **487**) 10 10
2761. 20 b. olive (Mark Twain) 15 10
2762. 35 b. blue (K. Hokusai) 20 10
2763. 40 b. green (De Musset) 25 15
2764. 55 b. brown (Defoe) 45 10
2765. 1 l. turquoise (J. Bolyai) 1·40 20
2766. 1 l. 20 red (Chekhov) 1·50 10
2767. 1 l. 55 grey (R. Koch) 2·00 15
2768. 1 l. 75 brown (Chopin) 2·75 30

1960. Black Sea Resorts. Multicoloured.
2769. 20 b. Type **488** (postage) 20 10
2770. 35 b. Constantza 40 10
2771. 40 b. Vasile Roaita 45 10
2772. 55 b. Mangalia 85 10
2773. 1 l. Eforie 1·40 25
2774. 1 l. 60 Eforie (different) 1·50 20
2775. 2 l. Mamaia (air) 2·75 65

489. Globe and Flags. **490.** "Saturnia pyri" (moth).

1960. Int. Puppet Theatre Festival, Bucharest. Designs (24×28½ mm., except 20 b.) show puppets. Multicoloured.
2776. 20 b. Type **489** 25 10
2777. 40 b. Petrushka 30 10
2778. 55 b. Punch 40 10
2779. 1 l. Kaspar 60 15
2780. 1 l. 20 Tindarica 80 20
2781. 1 l. 75 Vasilache 1·25 15

1960. Air. Butterflies and Moths. Mult.
2782. 10 b. Type **490** 30 10
2783. 20 b. "Limenitus Populi" 35 10
2784. 40 b. "Chrisophanus virgaureae" 40 10
2785. 55 b. "Papilio machaon" 70 15
2786. 1 l. 60 "Acherontia atropus" 2·10 30
2787. 1 l. 75 "Apatura iris" 2·75 30
SIZES—Triangular (36½×21½ mm.). 20 b., 40 b. VERT. (23½×34 mm.). 55 b., 1 l. 60. HORIZ. (34×23½ mm.). 1 l. 75.

491. Children tobogganing.

1960. Village Children's Games. Multicoloured.
2788. 20 b. Type **491** 15 10
2789. 35 b. "Oina" (ball-game) 20 10
2790. 55 b. Ice-skating 30 10
2791. 1 l. Running 65 15
2792. 1 l. 75 Swimming 1·75 20
The 20 b. and 1 l. are vert. and the rest horiz.

492. Striker and Flag.

1960. 40th Anniv. of General Strike.
2793. **492.** 55 b. red and lake 65 25

493. Compass Points and Airliner.

1960. Air. Stamp Day.
2794. **493.** 55 b. (+45 b.) blue 85 25

494. "XV", Globe and "Peace" Riband. **496.** Woman tending Vine (Cotnari).

495. Herrings.

1960. 15th Anniv. of World Democratic Youth Federation.
2795. **494.** 55 b. yellow and blue 65 10

1960. Fish Culture. Fish in actual colours. Background colours given.
2796. – 10 b. turquoise 15 10
2797. – 20 b. blue 25 10
2798. – 40 b. yellow 45 10
2799. **495.** 55 b. grey 85 10
2800. – 1 l. red 1·50 15
2801. – 1 l. 20 blue 2·00 20
2802. – 1 l. 60 olive 2·75 25
FISHES: 10 b. Carp. 20 b. Coal-fish. 40 b. Turbot. 1 l. Silurus. 1 l. 20, Sturgeon. 1 l. 60, Cod.

1960. Rumanian Vineyards. Multicoloured.
2803. 20 b. Dragasani 15 10
2804. 30 b. Dealul Mare (horiz.) 25 10
2805. 40 b. Odobesti (horiz.) 40 10
2806. 55 b. Type **496** 65 10
2807. 75 b. Tirnave 1·40 15
2808. 1 l. Minis 2·10 25
2809. 1 l. 20 Murfatlar 2·75 40

497. "Furnaceman" (after I. Irimescu). **498.** Slalom Racer.

1961. Rumanian Sculptures.
2811. **497.** 5 b. red 10 10
2812. – 10 b. violet 15 10
2813. – 20 b. black 20 10
2814. – 40 b. bistre 25 10
2815. – 50 b. brown 40 10
2816. – 55 b. red 75 10
2817. – 1 l. purple 1·10 15
2818. – 1 l. 55 blue 1·75 15
2819. – 1 l. 75 green 2·40 20
SCULPTURES—VERT. 10 b. "Gh. Doja" (I. Vlad). 20 b. "Reunion" (B. Caragea). 40 b. "Enescu" (G. Anghel). 50 b. "Eminescu" (C. Baraschi). 1 l. "Peace" (I. Jalea). 1 l. 55, "Constructive Socialism" (C. Medrea). 1 l. 75, "Birth of an Idea" (A. Szobotka). HORIZ. 55 b. "Peasant Uprising, 1907" (M. Constantinescu).

1961. Air. 50th Anniv. of Rumanian Winter Sports.
2820. – 10 b. olive and grey 20 10
2821. **498.** 20 b. red and grey 25 10
2822. – 25 b. turquoise & grey 40 10
2823. – 40 b. violet and grey 50 10
2824. – 55 b. blue and grey 65 15
2825. – 1 l. red and grey 1·25 15
2826. – 1 l. 55 brown and grey 2·25 20

(b) Imperf.
2827. – 10 b. blue and grey 10 10
2828. **498.** 20 b. brown and grey 20 10
2829. – 25 b. olive and grey 30 15
2830. – 40 b. red and grey 65 25
2831. – 55 b. turquoise & grey 90 70
2832. – 1 l. violet and grey 1·40 1·25
2833. – 1 l. 55 red and grey 2·40 2·25
DESIGNS—HORIZ. Skier: racing (10 b.), jumping (55 b.), walking (1 l. 55). VERT. 25 b. Skiers climbing slope, 40 b. Toboggan. 1 l. Rock-climber.

499. P. Poni (chemist). **500.** Yuri Gagarin in Capsule.

1961. Rumanian Scientist. Inscr. "1961". Portraits in sepia.
2834. **499.** 10 b. brown and pink 10 10
2835. – 20 b. purple and yell. 25 10
2836. – 55 b. red and blue 40 10
2837. – 1 l. 55 vio. & orge. 1·60 30
PORTRAITS: 20 b. A. Saligny (engineer). 55 b. C. Budeanu (electrical engineer). 1 l. 55, G. Titeica (mathematician).

1961. Air. World's First Manned Space Flight. Inscr. "12.IV.1961". (a) Perf.
2838. – 1 l. 35 blue 1·00 20
2839. **500.** 3 l. 20 blue 2·40 70
(b) Imperf.
2840. **500.** 3 l. 20 red 8·50 2·75
DESIGN—VERT. 1 l. 35, Yuri Gagarin.

501. Freighter "Galati".

1961. Merchant Navy. Multicoloured.
2841. 20 b. Type **501** 35 10
2842. 40 b. Danube passenger vessel "Oltenita" 60 10
2843. 55 b. Hydrofoil "Tomis" 60 10
2844. 1 l. Freighter "Arad" 1·00 15
2845. 1 l. 55 Tug "N. Cristea" 1·60 15
2846. 1 l. 75 Freighter "Dobrogea" 1·90 25

502. Red Flag with Marx, Engels and Lenin.

1961. 40th Anniv. of Rumanian Communist Party.
2847. **502.** 35 b. multicoloured 65 10
2848. – 55 b. multicoloured 1·00 10
DESIGN: 55 b. Two bill-posters.

503. Eclipse over Scanteia Building, and Observatory. **504.** Roe Deer.

1961. Air. Solar Eclipse.
2850. – 1 l. 60 blue 1·50 15
2851. **503.** 1 l. 75 blue 1·75 15
DESIGN: 1 l. 60, Eclipse over Palace Square, Bucharest.

1961. Forest Animals. Inscr. "1961". Multicoloured.
2852. 10 b. Type **504** 15 15
2853. 20 b. Lynx (horiz.) 20 15
2854. 35 b. Wild boar (horiz.) 40 15
2855. 40 b. Brown bear (horiz.) 70 25
2856. 55 b. Red deer 90 25
2857. 75 b. Red fox (horiz.) 1·10 20
2858. 1 l. Chamois 1·50 25
2859. 1 l. 55 Brown hare 2·10 35
2860. 1 l. 75 Eurasian badger 2·50 45
2861. 2 l. Roe deer 3·75 70

505. George Enescu.

1961. 2nd Int. George Enescu Festival.
2862. 505. 3 l. lavender & brown 2·40 35

506. Gagarin and Titov. 507. Iris.

1961. Air. 2nd Soviet Space Flight.
2863. – 55 b. blue 50 10
2864. – 1 l. 35 violet.. .. 90 25
2865. 506. 1 l. 75 red .. .. 1·75 30
DESIGNS—VERT. 55 b. "Vostok-2" in flight. 1 l. 35, G. S. Titov.

1961. Cent of Bucharest Botanical Gardens. Flowers in natural colours. Background and inscription colours given. Perf or imperf.
2866. – 10 b. yellow & brown 15 10
2867. – 20 b. green and red.. 15 10
2868. – 25 b. blue, grn. & red 20 10
2869. – 35 b. lilac and grey.. 30 10
2870. 507. 40 b. yellow & violet 40 10
2871. – 55 b. blue & ultram.. 60 10
2872. – 1 l. orange and blue.. 1·40 10
2873. – 1 l. 20 blue & brown.. 1·50 10
2874. – 1 l. 55 brown & lake.. 2·00 15
FLOWERS—HORIZ. 10 b. Primula. 35 b. Opuntia. 1 l. Hepatica. VERT. 20 b. Dianthus. 25 b. Peony. 55 b. Ranunculus. 1 l. 20, Poppy. 1 l. 55, Gentian.

508. Cobza Player. 509. Heraclides.

1961. Musicians. Multicoloured.
2876. 10 b. Pan piper .. 10 10
2877. 20 b. Alpenhorn player 15 10
2878. 40 b. Flautist 40 10
2879. 55 b. Type 508 .. .. 60 10
2880. 60 b. Bagpiper 80 10
2881. 1 l. Cembalo player .. 1·40 20
The 20 b. is horiz. and the rest vert.

1961. Cultural Anniversaries.
2882. 10 b. purple (T 509) .. 30 25
2883. 20 b. brown (Sir Francis Bacon) 30 25
2884. 40 b. green (Tagore) .. 35 25
2885. 55 b. red (Sarmiento) .. 55 25
2886. 1 l. 35 blue (Von Kleist) 85 25
2887. 1 l. 75 vio. (Lomonosov) 1·40 25

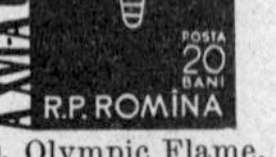
510. Olympic Flame. 512. Tower Building, Republic Palace Square, Bucharest.

511. "Stamps Round the World".

1961. Olympic Games 1960. Gold Medal Awards. Inscr. "MELBOURNE 1956" or "ROMA 1960". Perf. or imperf.
2888. – 10 b. turq. & ochre 20 10
2889. 510. 20 b. red 25 10
2890. – 20 b. grey 25 10
2891. – 35 b. brown and ochre 35 10
2892. – 40 b. purple & ochre 40 10
2893. – 55 b. blue 50 15
2894. – 55 b. blue 50 15
2895. – 55 b. red and ochre.. 50 15
2896. – 1 l. 35 blue and ochre 1·90 15
2897. – 1 l. 75 red and ochre 2·75 20
DESIGNS (Medals)—DIAMOND: 10 b. Boxing. 35 b. Pistol-shooting. 40 b. Rifle-shooting. 55 b. (No. 2895), Wrestling. 1 l. 35, High-Jumping. VERT. as Type 510: 20 b. (No. 2890), Diving. 55 b. (No. 2893), Water-polo. 55 b. (No. 2894), Women's high-jumping. HORIZ. (45×33 mm.): 1 l. 75, Canoeing.

1961. Air. Stamp Day.
2899. 511. 55 b. (+45 b.) blue, brown and red .. 1·60 65

1961. Air. Modern Rumanian Architecture. Multicoloured.
2900. 20 b. Type 512 .. .. 30 10
2901. 40 b. Constantza Railway Station .. .. 1·00 15
2902. 55 b. Congress Hall, Republic Palace, Bucharest 50 10
2903. 75 b. Rolling mill, Hunedoara 55 10
2904. 1 l. Apartment blocks, Bucharest 75 15
2905. 1 l. 20 Circus Building, Bucharest 80 30
2906. 1 l. 75 Workers' Club, Mangalia .. .. 1·50 20
The 40 b. to 1 l. 75 are horiz.

513. U.N. Emblem. 514. Workers with Flags.

1961. 15th Anniv. of U.N.O. Perf. or imperf.
2907. – 20 b. multicoloured .. 20 10
2908. – 40 b. multicoloured .. 65 15
2909. 513. 55 b. multicoloured .. 1·00 20
DESIGNS (bearing U.N. emblem): 20 b. Peace dove over Eastern Europe. 40 b. Peace dove and youths of three races.

1961. 5th W.F.T.U. Congress, Moscow.
2910. 514. 55 b. red .. .. 1·00 15

515. Cock and Savings Book. 516. Footballer.

1962. Savings Day. Inscr. "1962". Mult.
2911. 40 b. Type 515 .. .. 25 10
2912. 55 b. Savings Bank book, bee and honeycombs.. 65 15

1962. European Junior Football Competition, Bucharest.
2913. 516. 55 b. brown and green 1·40 20

517. Ear of Corn Map and Tractor. 518. Handball-player.

1962. Completion of Agricultural Collectivisation Project. Inscr. "1962".
2914. 517. 40 b. red and orange 20 10
2915. – 55 b. lake and yellow 25 10
2916. – 1 l. 55 yell., red & bl. 65 20
DESIGNS: 55 b. Commemorative medal. 1 l. 55, Wheatsheaf, and hammer and sickle emblem.

1962. Women's World Handball Championships, Bucharest.
2917. 518. 55 b. violet and yellow 1·40 20

519. Canoe Race. 520. J. J. Rousseau.

1962. Boating and Sailing. Inscr. "1962".

(a) Perf.

2918. 519. 10 b. blue & mauve .. 20 10
2919. – 20 b. blue and olive.. 25 10
2920. – 40 b. blue and brown 30 10
2921. – 55 b. bl. & ultramarine 40 12
2922. – 1 l. blue and red .. 1·00 15
2923. – 1 l. 20 blue & purple 1·25 15
2924. – 1 l. 55 blue & orange 1·50 15
2925. – 3 l. blue and violet .. 2·50 30

(b) Imperf. Colours changed.

2926. 519. 10 b. blue & ultram. 25 15
2927. – 20 b. blue & mauve 30 20
2928. – 40 b. blue & orange 50 30
2929. – 55 b. blue and olive 65 45
2930. – 1 l. blue and brown.. 1·40 60
2931. – 1 l. 20 blue & violet 1·50 1·00
2932. – 1 l. 55 blue and red.. 1·90 1·10
2933. – 3 l. blue and purple 4·00 1·90
DESIGNS: 20 b. Kayak. 40 b. Racing "eight". 55 b. Sculling. 1 l. Yachting. 1 l. 20, Motor-boats. 1 l. 55, Sailing. 3 l. Canoe slalom.

1962. Cultural Anniversaries (writers).
2934. 520. 40 b. olive 20 10
2935. – 55 b. lake 25 15
2936. – 1 l. 75 blue 95 15
WRITERS: 55 b. I. L. Caragiale. 1 l. 75, A. I. Herzen.

521. Flags and Globes. 522. T. Vuia (aviator).

1962. World Youth Festival. Helsinki.
2938. 521. 55 b. multicoloured .. 1·00 15

1962. Rumanian Celebrities.
2939. 522. 15 b. brown 15 10
2940. – 20 b. red 20 10
2941. – 35 b. purple 25 10
2942. – 40 b. blue 35 15
2943. – 55 b. blue 40 10
2944. – 1 l. blue .. .. 1·00 10
2945. – 1 l. 20 red .. .. 1·25 20
2946. – 1 l. 35 turquoise .. 1·40 20
2947. – 1 l. 55 violet.. .. 1·50 15
PORTRAITS: 20 b. A. Davila (writer). 35 b. V. Pirvan (archaeologist). 40 b. I. Negulici (painter). 55 b. G. Cobilcescu (geologist). 1 l. Dr. G. Marinescu. 1 l. 20, Dr. I. Cantacuzino. 1 l. 35, Dr. V. Babes. 1 l. 55, Dr. C. Levaditi.

523. Anglers by Pond.

1962. Fishing Sport. Multicoloured.
2948. 10 b. Rod-fishing in fishing punts 10 10
2949. 25 b. Line-fishing in mountain pool .. 15 10
2950. 40 b. Type 523 .. .. 25 10
2951. 55 b. Anglers on beach.. 35 10
2952. 75 b. Line-fishing in mountain stream .. 50 10
2953. 1 l. Shore-fishing .. 60 20
2954. 1 l. 75 Freshwater-fishing 1·25 15
2955. 3 l. 25 Fishing in Danube delta .. .. .. 2·10 20

524. Dove and "Space" Stamps of 1957/58. 527. "Vostok 3" and "4" in Orbit.

1962. Air. Cosmic Flights.
2956. 524. 35 b. brown 20 10
2957. – 55 b. green 30 10
2958. – 1 l. 35 blue 90 10
2959. – 1 l. 75 red .. .. 1·40 25
DESIGNS—Dove and: 55 b. "Space" stamps of 1959. 1 l. 35, "Space" stamps of 1957 ("Laika"), 1959 and 1960. 1 l. 75, "Spacemen" stamps of 1961.

1962. Rumanian Victory in European Junior Football Competition, Bucharest. Surch. **1962. Campioana Europeana 2 lei.**
2961. 516. 2 l. on 55 b. brn. & grn. 2·00 2·25

1962. Rumanian Victory in Women's World Handball Championships, Bucharest. Surch. **Campioana Mondiala 5 lei.**
2962. 518. 5 l. on 55 b. violet and yellow .. .. 7·50 5·00

1962. Air. 1st "Team" Manned Space Flight.
2963. – 55 b. violet 50 10
2964. 527. 1 l. 60 blue .. .. 1·50 25
2965. – 1 l. 75 purple.. .. 1·90 30
DESIGNS: 55 b. Cosmonaut Nikolaev. 1 l. 75, Cosmonaut Popovich.

528. Child and Butterfly. 529. Pottery.

1962. Children.
2966. 528. 20 b. blue, brown & red 20 10
2967. – 30 b. yell., bl. & red.. 25 10
2968. – 40 b. blue, red & turq. 30 10
2969. – 55 b. olive, blue & red 60 10
2970. – 1 l. 20 red, brn. & blue 1·25 20
2971. – 1 l. 55 ochre, bl. & red 2·10 20
DESIGNS—VERT. 30 b. Girl feeding dove. 40 b. Boy with model yacht. 1 l. 20, Boy violinist and girl pianist. HORIZ. 55 b. Girl teaching boy to write. 1 l. 55, Pioneers around camp-fire.

1962. 4th Sample Fair, Bucharest. Inscr. "AL IV—LEA PAVILION DE MOSTRE —BUCURESTI 1962". Multicoloured.
2972. 5 b. Type 529 (post.) .. 35 15
2973. 10 b. Preserved foodstuffs 40 15
2974. 20 b. Chemical products 40 15
2975. 40 b. Ceramics 50 10
2976. 55 b. Leather goods .. 70 10
2977. 75 b. Textiles 85 10
2978. 1 l. Furniture and fabrics 1·40 10
2979. 1 l. 20 Office equipment.. 1·75 10
2980. 1 l. 55 Needlework .. 2·10 10
2981. 1 l. 60 Fair pavilion (air) 2·75 15
The 1 l. 60 is horiz., the rest vert.

530. Lenin and Red Flag.

1962. 45th Anniv. of Russian Revolution.
2982. 530. 55 b. brown, red & blue 1·00 15

531. "The Coachmen" (after Szatmay).

1962. Air. Stamp Day and Centenary of 1st Rumanian Stamps.
2983. 531. 55 b. (+45 b.) black and blue .. .. 1·50 35

DESIGNS — HORIZ. 40 b. Ram. 1 l. 55, Heifer. 1 l. 75, Sows. VERT. 55 b. Bull. 1 l. Pig. 1 l. 35, Cow.

532. Lamb.

1962. Prime Farm Stock.
2984. 532. 20 b. black and blue 15 10
2985. – 40 b. brn., yell. & blue 15 10
2986. – 55 b. green, buff and orange 30 10
2987. – 1 l. brown, buff & grey 40 10
2988. – 1 l. 35 brn., blk. & grn. 60 15
2989. – 1 l. 55 brn., black & red 70 20
2990. – 1 l. 75 brown, cream & blue .. .. 1·40 35

534. Strikers.

533. Arms, Industry and Agriculture. 535. Tractor-driver.

1962. 15th Anniv. of People's Republic.
2991. 533. 1 l. 55 multicoloured 1·60 20

1963. 30th Anniv. of Grivitsa Strike.
2992. 534. 1 l. 75 multicoloured 1·75 30

1963. Freedom from Hunger.
2993. **535.** 40 b. blue 20 10
2994. – 55 b. brown 35 10
2995. – 1 l. 55 red .. .. 1·00 15
2996. – 1 l. 75 green .. .. 1·25 20
DESIGNS (each with F.A.O. emblem): 55 b. Girl harvester. 1 l. 55, Child with beaker of milk. 1 l. 75, Girl vintager.

1963. Air. Rumanian Philatelists' Conference, Bucharest. No. 2983, optd. **A.F.R.** surrounded by **CONFERINTA PE TARA BUCCURESTI 30-III-1963** in diamond shape.
2997. **531.** 55 b. (+45 b.) black and blue .. .. 5·00 4·00
The opt. is applied in the middle of the se-tenant pair—stamp and 45 b. label.

537. Sighisoara Glass Factory. **538.** Tomatoes.

1963. Air. "Socialist Achievements".
2998. **537.** 30 b. blue and red .. 30 10
2999. – 40 b. green & violet 40 15
3000. – 55 b. red and blue .. 65 15
3001. – 1 l. violet and brown 95 15
3002. – 1 l. 55 red and blue .. 1·25 15
3003. – 1 l. 75 blue and purple 1·25 15
DESIGNS: 40 b. Govora soda works. 55 b. Tirgul-Jiu wood factory. 1 l. Savinesti chemical works. 1 l. 55, Hunedoara metal works. 1 l. 75, Brazi thermic power station.

1963. Vegetable Culture. Multicoloured.
3004. 35 b. Type **538** 20 10
3005. 40 b. Hot peppers .. 35 10
3006. 55 b. Radishes 40 10
3007. 75 b. Aubergines .. 60 15
3008. 1 l. 20 Mild peppers .. 85 15
3009. 3 l. 25 Cucumbers (horiz.) 2·00 25

539. Moon Rocket "Luna 4". **540.** Chick.

1963. Air. Launching of Soviet Moon Rocket "Luna 4". The 1 l. 75 is imperf.
3010. **539.** 55 b. red and blue .. 35 15
3011. 1 l. 75 red and violet 1·40 10

1963. Domestic Poultry.
3012. **540.** 20 b. yellow and blue 20 10
3013. – 30 b. red, blue & brn. 25 10
3014. – 40 b. blue, orange and brown 35 10
3015. – 55 b. multicoloured .. 40 10
3016. – 70 b. blue, red & pur. 45 10
3017. – 1 l. red, grey and blue 50 10
3018. – 1 l. 35 red, blue & ochre 60 10
3019. – 3 l. 20 multicoloured 1·50 25
POULTRY: 30 b. Cockerel. 40 b. Duck. 55 b. White Leghorn. 70 b. Goose. 1 l. Rooster. 1 l. 35, Turkey (cock). 3 l. 20, Turkey (hen).

541. Diving.

542. Congress Emblem.

1963. Swimming. Bodies in drab.
3020. **541.** 25 b. green and brown 15 10
3021. – 30 b. yellow and olive 20 10
3022. – 55 b. red & turquoise 25 10
3023. – 1 l. red and green .. 45 10
3024. – 1 l. 35 mauve & blue 55 10
3025. – 1 l. 55 orange & violet 1·25 10
3026. – 2 l. yellow and mauve 1·25 15
DESIGNS—HORIZ. 30 b. Crawl. 55 b. Butterfly. 1 l. Back-stroke. 1 l. 35, Breast-stroke. VERT. 1 l. 55, Swallow-diving. 2 l. Water-polo.

1963. Int. Women's Congress, Moscow.
3027. **542.** 55 b. blue 65 15

DESIGN: 1 l. 75, Tereshkova and globe.

543. Bykovsky and Globe.

1963. Air. 2nd "Team" Manned Space Flights.
3028. **543.** 55 b. blue 35 15
3029. – 1 l. 75 red .. .. 1·60 25

544. Steam Locomotive. **545.** W. M. Thackeray (writer).

1963. Air. Transport. Multicoloured.
3031. 40 b. Type **544** 65 15
3032. 55 b. Diesel freight locomotive 65 15
3033. 75 b. Trolley bus .. 65 25
3034. 1 l. 35 "Oltenita" (Danube passenger vessel) .. 1·90 30
3035. 1 l. 75 Airliner .. .. 1·75 20

1963. Cultural Anniversaries. Inscr. "MARILE ANNIVERSARI CULTURALE 1963".
3036. **545.** 40 b. black and lilac 20 15
3037. – 50 b. black and brown 35 15
3038. – 55 b. black and olive 50 15
3039. – 1 l. 55 black and red 1·10 15
3040. – 1 l. 75 black and blue 1·25 20
PORTRAITS: 50 b. E. Delacroix (painter). 55 b. G. Marinescu (physician). 1 l. 55, G. Verdi (composer). 1 l. 75, K. Stanislavsky (theatrical producer).

546. Walnuts.

548. Volleyball.

1963. Fruits and Nuts. Multicoloured.
3041. 10 b. Type **546** .. 30 15
3042. 20 b. Plums 30 10
3043. 40 b. Peaches 60 10
3044. 55 b. Strawberries .. 70 10
3045. 1 l. Grapes 80 10
3046. 1 l. 55 Apples .. .. 1·40 15
3047. 1 l. 60 Cherries .. .. 1·40 15
3048. 1 l. 75 Pears .. .. 2·00 20

1963. Air. 50th Death Anniv. of Aurel Vlaicu (aviation pioneer). No. 2752 surch. **1913-1963. 50 ani de la moarte 1,75 lei.**
3049. **483.** 1 l. 75 on 10 b. brown and yellow .. 3·00 1·10

1963. European Volleyball Championships.
3050. **548.** 5 b. mauve & grey .. 20 10
3051. – 40 b. blue and grey .. 20 10
3052. – 55 b. turquoise & grey 65 10
3053. – 1 l. 75 brown & grey .. 1·40 15
3054. – 3 l. 20 violet and grey 2·00 25
DESIGNS: 40 b. to 1 l. 75, Various scenes of play at net. 3 l. 20, European Cup.

549. Rumanian 1 l. 55 "Centenary" stamp of 1958.

1963. Air. Stamp Day and 15th U.P.U. Congress. Inscr. "AL XV-LEA CONGRESS", etc.
3055. **549.** 20 b. brown & light bl. 15 10
3056. – 40 b. blue & mauve .. 20 10
3057. – 55 b. lake and blue .. 25 10
3058. – 1 l. 20 violet and buff 50 15
3059. – 1 l. 55 olive and red .. 70 15
3060. – 1 l. 60+50 b. mult .. 1·60 40
DESIGNS (Rumanian stamps): 40 b. (1 l. 20) "Laika", 1957 (blue). 55 b. (3 l. 20) "Gagarin" 1961. 1 l. 20 (55 b.) "Nikolaev" and (1 l. 75) "Popovich", 1962. 1 l. 55 (55 b.) "Postwoman", 1953. 1 l. 60, U.P.U. Monument, Berne, Globe, map of Rumania and aircraft (76×27 mm.).

551. Ski-jumping.

1963. Winter Olympic Games, Innsbruck, 1964. (a) Perf.
3061. **551.** 10 b. blue and red .. 50 15
3062. – 20 b. brown and blue 65 15
3063. – 40 b. brown and green 85 10
3064. – 55 b. brown & violet 1·00 10
3065. – 60 b. blue & brown .. 1·40 15
3066. – 75 b. blue and mauve 1·50 20
3067. – 1 l. blue and ochre .. 2·00 20
3068. – 1 l. 20 blue & turq. .. 2·75 35

(b) Imperf. Colours changed.
3069. **551.** 10 b. brown and green 1·50 1·25
3070. – 20 b. brown and violet 1·50 1·25
3071. – 40 b. blue and red .. 1·50 1·25
3072. – 55 b. brown and blue 1·50 1·25
3073. – 60 b. blue & turq. .. 1·50 1·25
3074. – 75 b. blue and ochre .. 1·50 1·25
3075. – 1 l. blue and mauve .. 1·50 1·25
3076. – 1 l. 20 blue & brn. .. 1·50 1·25
DESIGNS: 20 b. Ice-skating. 40 b. Ice-hockey. 55 b. Figure-skating. 60 b. Slalom. 75 b. Rifle-shooting on skis. 1 l. Bobsleigh. 1 l. 20, Skiing.

552. Cone, Fern and Conifer. **553.** Silkworm Moth.

1963. 18th Anniv. of Reafforestation Campaign.
3078. **552.** 55 b. green 20 10
3079. – 1 l. 75 blue 65 15
DESIGN: 1 l. 75, Chestnut trees.

1963. Bee-keeping and Silkworm-breeding. Multicoloured.
3080. 10 b. Type **553** 25 10
3081. 20 b. Moth emerging from chrysalis 35 10
3082. 40 b. Silkworm 45 10
3083. 55 b. Bee 85 10
3084. 60 b. } Bee extracting 1·00 20
3085. 1 l. 20 } nectar from 1·40 25
3086. 1 l. 35 } various flowers 1·60 35
3087. 1 l. 60 } (diff. designs) 2·00 40
The 55 b. to 1 l. 60 are horiz.

554. Carved Pillar.

556. G. Stephanescu.

555. Gagarin.

1963. Village Museum, Bucharest.
3088. **554.** 20 b. purple 25 10
3089. – 40 b. blue 30 10
3090. – 55 b. violet 40 10
3091. – 75 b. green 50 10
3092. – 1 l. red and brown .. 1·00 10
3093. – 1 l. 20 green .. .. 1·25 10
3094. – 1 l. 75 blue and brown 2·00 10
DESIGNS: Various Rumanian peasant houses. The 40 b. and 55 b. are horiz., the rest vert.

1964. Air. "Space Navigation". Soviet flag, red and yellow; U.S. flag, red and blue; backgrounds, light blue; portrait and inscription colours below. (a) Perf.
3095. **555.** 5 b. blue 25 10
3096. – 10 b. violet 35 10
3097. – 20 b. bronze 40 10
3098. – 35 b. grey 45 10
3099. – 40 b. violet 50 15
3100. – 55 b. violet 65 15
3101. – 60 b. brown 65 20
3102. – 75 b. blue 75 20
3103. – 1 l. purple .. .. 1·00 25
3104. – 1 l. 40 purple .. 1·50 50

(b) Imperf. Colours changed.
3105. **555.** 5 b. violet 10 10
3106. – 10 b. blue 15 10
3107. – 20 b. grey 30 15
3108. – 35 b. bronze 60 35
3109. – 40 b. purple 85 40
3110. – 55 b. purple .. .. 1·10 50
3111. – 60 b. blue .. .. 1·10 75
3112. – 75 b. brown .. .. 1·50 1·00
3113. – 1 l. violet .. .. 1·75 1·25
3114. – 1 l. 40 violet .. .. 2·40 1·90
PORTRAITS (with flags of their countries)—As Type **555**: 10 b. G. Titov. 20 b. J. Glenn. 35 b. S. Carpenter. 60 b. W. Schirra. 75 b. G. Cooper. SQUARE (35×34 mm.): 40 b. A. Nikolaev. 55 b. P. Popovich. 1 l. V. Bykovsky. 1 l. 40, V. Tereshkova.

1964. Rumanian Opera Singers and their stage roles. Portraits in brown.
3116. **556.** 10 b. olive 35 10
3117. – 20 b. blue 45 10
3118. – 35 b. green 50 10
3119. – 40 b. light blue .. 55 10
3120. – 55 b. mauve 65 10
3121. – 75 b. violet 70 10
3122. – 1 l. blue 80 10
3123. – 1 l. 35 violet 90 15
3124. – 1 l. 55 red .. .. 1·40 20
SINGERS: 20 b. Elena Teodorini. 35 b. I. Bajenaru. 40 b. D. Popovici. 55 b. Hariclea Darclee. 75 b. G. Folescu. 1 l. J. Athanasiu. 1 l. 35, T. Grosavescu. 1 l. 55, N. Leonard.

557. Prof. G. M. Murgoci.

558. "Ascalaphus macaronius" (moth).

1964. 8th Int. Soil Congress, Bucharest.
3125. **557.** 1 l. 60 indigo, ochre and blue .. .. 1·00 20

1964. Rumanian Insects. Multicoloured.
3126. 5 b. Type **558** 20 10
3127. 10 b. "Ammophila sabulosa" (flying ant) .. 25 10
3128. 35 b. "Scolia maculata" (wasp) 30 10
3129. 40 b. "Rhyparioides metelkana" (moth) .. 45 10
3130. 55 b. "Lymantria dispar" (moth) 60 10
3131. 1 l. 20 "Kanetisa circe" (butterfly) 85 15
3132. 1 l. 55 "C. Fabriciimalachiticus" (beetle) .. 90 20
3133. 1 l. 75 "Procerus gigas" (horned beetle) .. 1·50 20

559. "Nicotiana alata".

560. Cross Country.

1964. Rumanian Flowers. Multicoloured.
3134. 10 b. Type **559** 25 10
3135. 20 b. "Pelargonium" .. 25 10
3136. 40 b. "Fuchsia gracilis" 35 15
3137. 55 b. "Chrysanthemum indicum" 40 10
3138. 75 b. "Dahlia hybrida" 45 10
3139. 1 l. "Lilium croceum" .. 75 10
3140. 1 l. 25 "Hosta ovata" .. 90 20
3141. 1 l. 55 "Tagetes erectus" 1·40 15

1964. Horsemanship.
3142. – 40 b. multicoloured .. 30 10
3143. **560.** 55 b. brn., red & lilac 40 10
3144. – 1 l. 35 brn., red & grn. 1·00 15
3145. – 1 l. 55 mve., bl. & bis. 1·60 20
DESIGNS—HORIZ. 40 b. Dressage. 1 l. 55, Horse-race. VERT. 1 l. 35 Show jumping.

561. Scorpionfish.

562. M. Eminescu (poet).

1964. Constantza Aquarium. Fish designs. Multicoloured.
3146. 5 b. Type **561** .. 10 10
3147. 10 b. Blenny .. 10 10
3148. 20 b. Mackerel .. 15 10
3149. 40 b. Nisetru Sturgeon .. 30 10
3150. 50 b. Seahorse .. 40 10
3151. 55 b. Gurnard .. 50 10
3152. 1 l. Bekuga Sturgeon .. 70 10
3153. 3 l. 20 Sting Ray .. 2·75 25

1964. Cultural Anniversaries. Portraits in brown.
3154. 5 b. green (Type **562**) .. 10 10
3155. 20 b. lake (I. Creanga) .. 15 10
3156. 35 b. red (E. Girleanu) .. 25 10
3157. 55 b. bistre (Michelangelo) 30 10
3158. 1 l. 20 blue (Galileo) .. 85 15
3159. 1 l. 75 violet (Shakespeare) 1·40 20
Nos. 3154/5 commemorate 75th anniv. of death. No. 3156, 50th anniv. of death. No. 3157, 400th anniv. of death. Nos. 3158/9 400th anniv. of birth. Creanga and Girleanu were writers.

563. Cheile Bicazului (gorge).

564. High-jumping.

1964. Mountain resorts.
3160. 563. 40 b. lake 25 10
3161. – 55 b. blue 40 10
3162. – 1 l. purple 55 10
3163. – 1 l. 35 brown 65 10
3164. – 1 l. 75 green .. .. 1·40 10
DESIGNS—VERT. 55 b. Cabin on Lake Bilea. 1 l. Poiana Brasov ski-lift. 1 l. 75, Alpine Hotel. HORIZ. 1 l. 35, Lake Bicaz.

1964. Balkan Games. Multicoloured.
3165. 30 b. Type 564 .. 15 10
3166. 40 b. Throwing the javelin 15 10
3167. 55 b. Running .. 30 10
3168. 1 l. Throwing the discus 60 10
3169. 1 l. 20 Hurdling .. 60 10
3170. 1 l. 55 Flags of competing countries (24×44 mm.) 70 15

565. Arms and Flag.

1964. 20th Anniv. of Liberation. Mult.
3171. 55 b. Type 565 .. .. 25 10
3172. 60 b. Industrial plant .. 25 10
3173. 75 b. Harvest scene .. 35 15
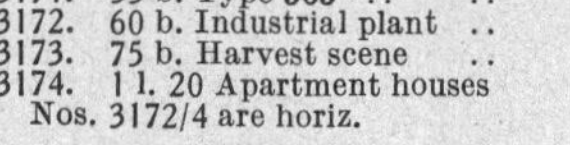
3174. 1 l. 20 Apartment houses 60 15
Nos. 3172/4 are horiz.

566. High-jumping.

1964. Olympic Games, Tokyo. Multicoloured.
(a) Perf.
3176. 20 b. Type 566 .. .. 25 10
3177. 30 b. Wrestling 40 15
3178. 35 b. Volley-ball 45 20
3179. 40 b. Canoeing 50 25
3180. 55 b. Fencing .. .. 1·00 15
3181. 1 l. 20 Gymnastics .. 1·40 25
3182. 1 l. 35 Football .. .. 1·60 40
3183. 1 l. 55 Rifle-shooting .. 2·00 75

(b) Imperf. Colours changed and new values.
3184. 20 b. Type 566 .. .. 45 10
3185. 30 b. Wrestling 50 20
3186. 35 b. Volley-ball 85 20
3187. 40 b. Canoeing 85 20
3188. 55 b. Fencing .. .. 1·40 50
3189. 1 l. 60 Gymnastics .. 3·00 1·25
3190. 2 l. Football .. .. 3·50 1·75
3191. 2 l. 40 Rifle-shooting .. 4·25 2·50

567. George Enescu.

568. Python.

1964. 3rd Int. George Enescu Festival.
3193. 567. 10 b. green 25 10
3194. – 55 b. purple 40 10
3195. – 1 l. 60 purple .. 1·00 35
3196. – 1 l. 75 blue .. .. 1·60 20
DESIGNS (Portraits of Enescu): 55 b. At piano. 1 l. 60, Medallion. 1 l. 75, When an old man.

1964. Bucharest Zoo. Multicoloured.
3197. 5 b. Type 568 .. .. 10 10
3198. 10 b. Black swans .. 45 10
3199. 35 b. Ostriches 60 10
3200. 40 b. Crowned cranes .. 75 15
3201. 55 b. Tigers 75 15
3202. 1 l. Lions .. .. 1·10 20
3203. 1 l. 55 Grevy's zebras .. 1·60 20
3204. 2 l. Bactrian camels .. 2·40 30

569. Brincoveanu, Cantacuzino, Lazar and Academy.

570. Soldier.

1964. Anniversaries. Multicoloured.
3205. 20 b. Type 569 .. .. 10 10
3206. 40 b. Cuza and seal .. 15 10
3207. 55 b. Emblems and the Arts (vert.) 25 10
3208. 75 b. Laboratory workers and class 30 10
3209. 1 l. Savings Bank building 50 25
Events, etc.: 20 b. 270th Anniv. of Domneasca Academy. 40 b. and 75 b. Bucharest University Cent. 55 b. "Fine Arts" Cent. (emblems are masks, curtains, piano keyboard, harp, palette and brushes). 1 l. Savings Bank Cent.

1964. Centenary of Army Day.
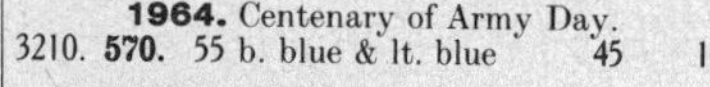
3210. 570. 55 b. blue & lt. blue 45 15

571. Post Offices of 19th and 20th Centuries.

No. 3211 is a two-part design, the two parts being arranged vert. imperf. between.

1964. Air. Stamp Day.
3211. 571. 1 l. 60+40 b. blue red and yellow .. 1·60 25

572. Canoeing Medal (1956).

573. Strawberries.

1964. Olympic Games—Rumanian Gold Medal Awards. Medals in brown and bistre (Nos. 3218/19 and 3226/7 in sepia and gold). (a) Perf.
3212. 572. 20 b. red and blue .. 50 15
3213. – 30 b. green and blue 65 20
3214. – 35 b. turquoise & blue 75 25
3215. – 40 b. lilac and blue .. 90 35
3216. – 55 b. orange and blue 1·10 20
3217. – 1 l. 20 green and blue 1·40 35
3218. – 1 l. 35 brown and blue 2·00 45
3219. – 1 l. 55 mauve and blue 2·40 50

(b) Imperf. Colours changed and new values.
3220. 572. 20 b. orange and blue 15 20
3221. – 30 b. turquoise & blue 40 30
3222. – 35 b. green and blue 40 30
3223. – 40 b. green and blue 50 40
3224. – 55 b. red and blue .. 1·10 50
3225. – 1 l. 60 lilac and blue .. 2·50 2·00
3226. – 2 l. mauve and blue .. 3·75 2·75
3227. – 2 l. 40 brown and blue 4·50 3·50
MEDALS: 30 b. Boxing (1956). 35 b. Pistol-shooting (1956). 40 b. High-jumping (1960). 55 b. Wrestling (1960). 1 l. 20, 1 l. 60, Rifle-shooting (1960). 1 l. 35, 2 l. High-jumping (1964). 1 l. 55, 2 l. 40, Throwing the javelin (1964).

1964. Forest Fruits. Multicoloured.
3229. 5 b. Type 573 .. .. 15 10
3230. 35 b. Blackberries .. 25 10
3231. 40 b. Raspberries .. 30 10
3232. 55 b. Rosehips 40 10
3233. 1 l. 20 Blueberries .. 75 15
3234. 1 l. 35 Cornelian cherries 85 15
3235. 1 l. 55 Hazel nuts .. 1·25 10
3236. 2 l. 55 Cherries .. .. 1·40 20

MINIMUM PRICE

The minimum price quoted is 5p which represents a handling charge rather than a basis for valuing common stamps. For further notes about prices see introductory pages.

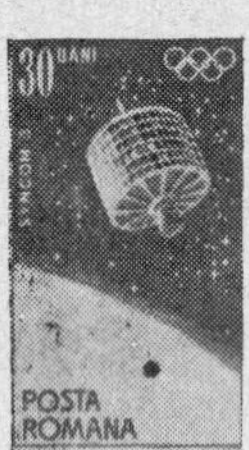

574. "Syncom 3".

575. U.N. Headquarters, New York.

1965. Space Navigation. Multicoloured.
3237. 30 b. Type 574 .. .. 20 10
3238. 40 b. "Syncom 3" (different view) .. 25 10
3239. 55 b. "Ranger 7" .. 45 10
3240. 1 l. "Ranger 7" (different view) .. 50 15
3241. 1 l. 20 "Voskhod 1" .. 90 10
3242. 5 l. Feoktistov, Komarov and Yegorov, and "Voskhod 1" (52½×29½ mm.) 2·75 75
Nos. 3239/42 are horiz.

1965. 20th Anniv. of U.N.O.
3243. 575. 55 b. gold, blue & red 30 10
3244. – 1 l. 60 multicoloured 1·00 20
DESIGN: 1 l. 60, Arms and U.N. emblem on Rumanian flag.

576. Tortoise ("Testudo graeca").

1965. Reptiles. Multicoloured.
3245. 5 b. Type 576 .. .. 15 10
3246. 10 b. "Lacerta taurica" 15 10
3247. 20 b. "Lacerta trilineata" 20 10
3248. 40 b. "Alepharus kitalbelii" .. 25 10
3249. 55 b. "Anguis fragilis" 30 10
3250. 60 b. "Vipera ammodytes" 45 10
3251. 1 l. "Eremias arguta" .. 55 10
3252. 1 l. 20 "Vipera ursinii" 65 10
3253. 1 l. 35 "Coluber jugularis" .. 85 15
3254. 3 l. 25 "Elaphe quatuorlineata" .. 2·75 40

577. Tabby Cat.

579. Ion Bianu (philologist).

1965. Domestic Cats. Multicoloured.
3255. 5 b. Type 577 .. .. 10 10
3256. 10 b. Ginger tomcat .. 15 10
3257. 40 b. White Persians .. 25 10
3258. 55 b. Kittens with shoe .. 40 10
3259. 60 b. Kitten with ball of wool 60 10
3260. 75 b. Cat and two kittens 75 10
3261. 1 l. 35, Siamese .. .. 1·40 15
3262. 3 l. 25, Heads of three cats (62×29 mm.) .. 3·00 40
Nos. 3257/61 are vert.

1965. Space Flight of "Ranger 9" (24.3.65). No. 3240 surch. **RANGER 9 24-3-1965 5 Lei** and floral emblem over old value.
3263. 5 l. on 1 l. multicoloured 29·00 29·00

1965. Cultural Anniversaries. Portraits in sepia.
3264. 579. 40 l. blue 15 10
3265. – 55 b. ochre 20 10
3266. – 60 b. purple 25 10
3267. – 1 l. red 60 15
3268. – 1 l. 35 olive 50 20
3269. – 1 l. 75 red 80 25
PORTRAITS, etc.: 40 b. (30th death anniv.). 55 b. A. Bacalbasa (writer: birth cent.). 60 b. V. Conta (philosopher: 120th birth anniv.). 1 l. Jean Sibelius (composer: birth cent.). 1 l. 35, Horace (poet: birth bimillenary). 1 l. 75, Dante (poet: 700th birth anniv.).

580. I.T.U. Emblem and Symbols.

1965. Cent. of I.T.U.
3270. 580. 1 l. 75 blue .. .. 1·25 20

581. Derdap Gorge (The Iron Gate).

1965. Inaug. of Derdap Hydro-Electric Project.
3271. 581. 30 b. (25 d.) green and grey 15 10
3272. – 55 b. (50 d.) red & grey 30 10
DESIGN: 55 b. Derdap Dam.
Nos. 3271/72 were issued simultaneously in Yugoslavia.

582. Rifleman.

583. "Fat-Frumos and the Beast".

1965. European Shooting Championships, Bucharest. Multicoloured.
(a) Perf.
3274. 20 b. Type 582 .. .. 15 10
3275. 40 b. Prone rifleman .. 25 10
3276. 55 b. Pistol-shooting .. 30 10
3277. 1 l. "Free" pistol-shooting 60 10
3278. 1 l. 60 Standing rifleman 85 15
3279. 2 l. Various marksmen .. 1·40 35

(b) Imperf. Colours changed and new values.
3280. 40 b. Prone rifleman .. 20 10
3281. 55 b. Pistol-shooting .. 25 15
3282. 1 l. "Free" pistol-shooting 45 25
3283. 1 l. 60 Standing rifleman 65 50
3284. 3 l. 25 Type 582 .. .. 1·60 90
3285. 5 l. Various marksmen .. 2·75 1·00
Apart from Type 582 the designs are horiz., the 2 l. and 5 l. being larger (51¼×28½ mm.).

1965. Rumanian Fairy Tales. Multicoloured.
3286. 20 b. Type 583 .. .. 25 10
3287. 40 b. "Fat-Frumos and Ileana Cosinzeana" .. 25 10
3288. 55 b. "Harap Alb" (horseman and bear) .. 30 10
3289. 1 l. "The Moralist Wolf" 60 10
3290. 1 l. 35 "The Ox and the Calf" 90 10
3291. 2 l. "The Bear and the Wolf" (drawing a sledge) 1·25 25

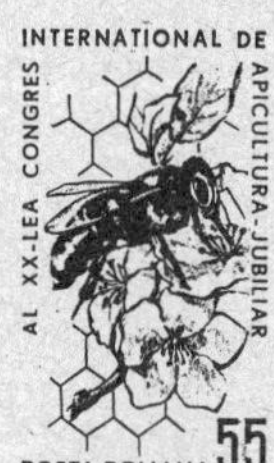

584. Bee on Flowers.

585. Beliaiev, Leonov, "Voskhod 2" and Leonov in Space.

1965. 20th Int. Bee-keeping Associations Federation ("Apimondia") Congress, Bucharest.
3292. 584. 55 b. black, red & yell. 35 10
3293. – 1 l. 60 multicoloured 1·25 15
DESIGN—HORIZ. 1 l. 60, Congress Hall.

1965. Space Achievements. Multicoloured.
3294. 5 b. "Proton 1" 15 10
3295. 10 b. "Sonda 3" (horiz.) 20 15
3296. 15 b. "Molnia 1" .. 25 20
3297. 1 l. 75 Type 585 .. 1·10 15
3298. 2 l. 40 "Early Bird" satellite .. .. 1·60 20
3299. 3 l. 20 "Gemini 3" and astronauts in capsule .. 3·00 25
3300. 3 l. 25 "Mariner 4" .. 3·75 40
3301. 5 l. "Gemini 5" (horiz.) 5·75 1·40

586. Marx and Lenin.

588. V. Alecsandri.

587. Common Quail.

1965. Postal Ministers' Congress, Peking.
3302. **586.** 55 b. multicoloured .. 50 15

1965. Migratory Birds. Multicoloured.
3303. 5 b. Type **587** 15 10
3304. 10 b. Woodcock 25 10
3305. 20 b. Common Snipe .. 35 10
3306. 40 b. Turtle Dove .. 35 15
3307. 55 b. Mallard 45 15
3308. 60 b. White-fronted Goose 55 15
3309. 1 l. Common Crane .. 75 20
3310. 1 l. 20 Glossy Ibis .. 1·00 20
3311. 1 l. 25 Mute Swan .. 1·25 20
3312. 3 l. 25, Eastern White Pelican .. .. 3·75 60
The 3 l. 25, is vert., 32 × 73 mm.

1965. 75th Death Anniv. of Vasile Alecsandri (poet).
3313. **588.** 55 b. multicoloured 50 15

589. " Nymphaea zanzibariensis ".

1965. Cluj Botanical Gardens. Multicoloured.
3314. 5 b. " Strelitzia reginae " (crane flower) 10 10
3315. 10 b. " Stanhopea tigrina " (orchid) 15 10
3316. 20 b. " Paphiopedilum insigne " (orchid) .. 15 10
3317. 30 b. Type **589** 30 10
3318. 40 b. " Ferocactus glaucescens " (cactus) .. 40 10
3319. 55 b. " Gossypium arboreum " 35 10
3320. 1 l. " Hibiscus rosa sinensis " 50 15
3321. 1 l. 35 " Gloxinia hibrida " 1·00 15
3322. 1 l. 75 "Victoria amazonica" (Victoria Regis lily) .. 1·60 15
3323. 2 l. 30 Hibiscus, crane flower, water lily and botanical building (52 × 29½ mm.) .. .. 2·00 40
The 5 b., 10 b., 20 b. and 1 l. 35 are vert.

590. Running. 592. Pigeon on TV Aerial.

591. Pigeon and Horseman.

1965. Spartacist Games. Multicoloured.
3324. 55 b. Type **590** 25 15
3325. 1 l. 55 Football .. .. 1·00 20
3326. 1 l. 75 Diving .. .. 1·00 20
3327. 2 l. Mountaineering (inscr. " TURISM ") .. .. 1·40 25
3328. 5 l. Canoeing (inscr. "CAMPIONATELE EUROPENE 1965 ") (horiz.) .. .. 3·00 50

1965. Stamp Day.
3329. **591.** 55 b. + 45 b. blue and mauve 40 10
3330. **592.** 1 l. brown & green .. 40 20
3331. – 1 l. 75 brn. and green 1·40 25
DESIGN: As Type **592.** 1 l. 75, Pigeon in flight. No. 3329 is a two-part design arranged horiz. imperf. between.

593. Chamois.

1965. " Hunting Trophies ".
3332. **593.** 55 b. brn., yell. & mve. 50 15
3333. – 1 l. brown, grn. & red 90 15
3334. – 1 l. 60 brn., bl. & orge. 1·75 30
3335. – 1 l. 75 brn., red & grn. 2·25 35
3336. – 3 l. 20 multicoloured 3·00 75
DESIGNS—(37 × 23 mm.) 1 l. Brown bear. 1 l. 60, Roe deer. 1 l. 75, Wild boar. (49 × 37½ mm.). 3 l. 20, Trophy and antlers.

594. Dachshund.

1965. Hunting Dogs. Multicoloured.
3337. 5 b. Type **594** 10 10
3338. 10 b. Spaniel 10 10
3339. 40 b. Retriever with Wood cock 60 10
3340. 55 b. Fox terrier 40 10
3341. 60 b. Red setter 55 10
3342. 75 b. White setter .. 1·00 15
3343. 1 l. 55 Pointers .. .. 2·00 20
3344. 3 l. 25 Duck-shooting with retriever .. .. 3·75 1·50
SIZES—DIAMOND (47½ × 47½ mm.): 10 b. to 75 b. HORIZ. (43½ × 29 mm.): 1 l. 55, 3 l. 25.

595. Pawn and Globe. 596. Tractor, Corn and Sun.

1966. 17th Chess Olympiad, Havana. Mult.
3345 20 b. Type **595** 35 10
3346 40 b. Jester and bishop (chess piece) 45 10
3347 55 b. Knight on horseback and rook (chess piece) 70 10
3348 1 l. As No. 3347 .. .. 95 10
3349 1 l. 60 Type **595** .. .. 2·00 20
3350 3 l. 25 As No. 3346 .. 4·00 1·50

1966. Co-operative Farming Union Congress.
3351. **596.** 55 b. green and yellow 45 15

597. G. Gheorghiu-Dej. 598. Congress Emblem.

1966. Death Anniv. of G. Gheorghiu-Dej (Head of State).
3352. **597.** 55 b. black and gold 40 15

1966. Communist Youth Union Congress.
3354. **598.** 55 b. red and yellow 40 15

599. Dance of Moldova.

1966. Rumanian Folk-dancing.
3355. **599.** 30 b. black and purple 30 10
3356. – 40 b. black and red .. 50 20
3357. – 55 b. black & turquoise 65 10
3358. – 1 l. black and lake .. 85 10
3359. – 1 l. 60 black and blue 1·25 15
3360. – 2 l. black and green .. 3·00 1·60
DANCES OF: 40 b. Oltenia. 55 b. Maramures. 1 l. Muntenia. 1 l. 60, Banat. 2 l. Transylvania.

600. Footballers. 601. " Agriculture and Industry ".

1966. World Cup Football Championships.
3361. **600.** 5 b. multicoloured .. 15 10
3362. – 10 b. multicoloured .. 25 10
3363. – 15 b. multicoloured .. 35 10
3364. – 55 b. multicoloured .. 95 10
3365. – 1 l. 75 multicoloured 2·25 25
3366. – 4 l. multicoloured .. 5·00 3·25
DESIGNS: 10 b. to 1 l. 75 Various footballers as Type **600.** 4 l. Jules Rimet Cup.

1966. Trade Union Congress, Bucharest.
3368. **601.** 55 b. multicoloured .. 35 15

602. Red-breasted Flycatcher. 603. " Venus 3 ".

1966. Song Birds. Multicoloured.
3369. 5 b. Type **602** 25 10
3370. 10 b. Red crossbill .. 35 10
3371. 15 b. Great reed warbler 60 10
3372. 20 b. Redstart 65 10
3373. 55 b. European robin .. 1·00 10
3374. 1 l. 20 Bluethroat .. 1·40 15
3375. 1 l. 55 Yellow wagtail .. 2·25 20
3376. 3 l. 20 Penduline tit .. 3·50 2·00

1966. Space Achievements. Multicoloured.
3377. 10 b. Type **603** 25 10
3378. 20 b. " FR 1 " satellite .. 30 10
3379. 1 l. 60 " Luna 9 " .. 2·00 20
3380. 5 l. "Gemini 6" and "7" 4·75 1·60

604. U. Nestor (birth cent.). 606. " Hottonia palustris ".

605. " House " (after Petrascu).

1966. Cultural Annivs.
3381. – 5 b. blue, blk. & grn. 10 10
3382. – 10 b. grn., blk. & red 15 10
3383. **604.** 20 b. pur., blk. & grn. 10 10
3384. – 40 b. brn., blk. & blue 15 10
3385. – 55 b. grn., blk. & brn. 20 10
3386. – 1 l. vio., blk. & bistre 45 15
3387. – 1 l. 35 olive., blk. & bl. 70 20
3388. – 1 l. 60 pur., blk. & grn. 1·50 45
3389. – 1 l. 75 pur., blk. & orge. 95 20
3390. – 3 l. 25 lake, blk. & bl. 1·60 40
PORTRAITS: 5 b. G. Cosbuc (birth cent). 10 b. G. Sincai (150th death anniv). 40 b. A. Pumnul (death cent). 55 b. S. Luchian (50th death anniv). 1 l. Sun Yat-sen (birth cent). 1 l. 35, G. W. Leibnitz (250th death anniv). 1 l. 60, R. Rolland (birth cent). 1 l. 75, I. Ghica (150th birth anniv). 3 l. 25, S. C. Cantacuzino (250th death anniv).

1966. Paintings in National Gallery, Bucharest. Multicoloured.
3391. 5 b. Type **605** 20 10
3392. 10 b. "Peasant Girl" (Grigorescu) 25 10
3393. 20 b. "Midday Rest" (Rescu) 40 15
3394. 55 b. "Portrait of a Man" (Van Eyck) .. .. 1·40 25
3395. 1 l. 55 "The 2nd Class Compartment" (Daumier) .. .. 5·25 60
3396. 3 l. 25 "The Blessing" (El Greco) .. .. 7·50 5·25
The 10 b., 55 b. and 3 l. 25 are vert.

1966. Aquatic Flora. Multicoloured.
3397. 5 b. Type **606** 15 10
3398. 10 b. "Ceratophyllum submersum" 20 10
3399. 20 b. "Aldrovanda vesiculosa" 25 10
3400. 40 b. "Callitriche verna" 35 10
3401. 55 b. "Vallisneria spiralis" 45 10
3402. 1 l. "Elodea canadensis" 1·25 15
3403. 1 l. 55 "Hippuris vulgaris" .. .. 1·50 20
3404. 3 l. 25 "Myriophyllum spicatum" (28 × 49½ mm.) 3·25 1·60

607. Diagram showing one metre in relation to quadrant of Earth. 608. Putna Monastery.

1966. Cent. of Metric System in Rumania.
3405. **607.** 55 b. blue & brown .. 30 10
3406. – 1 l. violet and green .. 50 20
DESIGN: 1 l. Metric abbreviations and globe.

1966. 500th Anniv. of Putna Monastery.
3407. **608.** 2 l. multicoloured .. 1·40 30

609. " Medicine ".

1966. Cent. of Rumanian Academy.
3408. **609.** 40 b. multicoloured .. 20 10
3409. – 55 b. multicoloured .. 25 10
3410. – 1 l. brn., gold & blue 40 10
3411. – 3 l. brn., gold & yell. 1·75 1·00
DESIGNS—As Type **609.** 55 b. " Science " (formula). VERT. (22½ × 33½): 1 l. Gold medal. HORIZ. (67 × 27 mm.): 3 l. I. Radulescu, M. Kogalniceanu and T. Savulescu.

610. Crayfish.

1966. Crustaceans and Molluscs. Mult.
3412 5 b. Type **610** 15 10
3413 10 b. Netted dog whelk (vert) 20 10
3414 20 b. Marbled rock crab 25 10
3415 40 b. Lapidary snail .. 30 10
3416 55 b. Brown lipped snail 50 10
3417 1 l. 35 Mediterranean mussel .. .. 1·25 15
3418 1 l. 75 Pond snail .. 1·50 20
3419 3 l. 25 Swan mussel .. 3·25 1·60

611. Bucharest and Mail-coach.

1966. Stamp Day.
3420. **611.** 55 b. + 45 b. mult. .. 1·00 25
No. 3420 is a two-part design arranged horiz. imperf. between.

612. "Ursus spelaeus".

1966. Prehistoric Animals.
3421. **612.** 5 b. blue, brn. & grn. 20 10
3422. – 10 b. violet, bis. & grn. 20 10
3423. – 15 b. brn., pur. & grn. 25 10
3424. – 55 b. vio., bistre & grn. 70 10
3425. – 1 l. 55 blue, brn. & grn. 2·00 15
3426. – 4 l. mve., bistre & grn. 3·75 1·75
ANIMALS: 10 b. " Mamuthus trogontherii ". 15 b. "Bison priscus". 55 b. "Archidiscodon". 1 l. 55, "Megaceros eurycerus" (43 × 27 mm.). 4 l. "Deinotherium gigantissimum".

613. "Sputnik 1" orbiting Globe.

1967. 10 years of Space Achievements. Multicoloured.

3427. 10 b. Type **613** (postage) 15 10
3428. 20 b. Gagarin and "Vostok 1" 15 10
3429. 25 b. Tereshkova ("Vostok 6") 20 10
3430. 40 b. Nikolaiev and Popovich ("Vostok 3" and "4") 35 10
3431. 55 b. Leonov in space ("Voskhod 2") .. 45 10
3432. 1 l. 20 "Early Bird" (air) 1·25 15
3433. 1 l. 55 Photo transmission ("Mariner 4") .. 1·60 20
3434. 3 l. 25 Space rendezvous ("Gemini 6" and "7") 2·25 40
3435. 5 l. Space link-up ("Gemini 8") .. .. 3·25 2·75

614. Barn Owl.

1967. Birds of Prey. Multicoloured.

3442. 10 b. Type **614** 45 10
3443. 20 b. Eagle Owl 70 10
3444. 40 b. Saker Falcon .. 65 10
3445. 55 b. Egyptian Vulture.. 80 10
3446. 75 b. Osprey 95 15
3447. 1 l. Griffon Vulture .. 1·40 15
3448. 1 l. 20 Lammergeier .. 2·40 25
3449. 1 l. 75 European Black Vulture .. .. 2·75 1·90

615. "Washerwomen" (after I. Steriadi).

1967. Paintings.

3450. – 10 b. blue, gold & red 20 10
3451. **615.** 20 b. grn., gold & ochre 25 15
3452. – 40 b. red, gold & blue 40 20
3453. – 1 l. 55 pur., gold & blue 95 30
3454. – 3 l. 20 brn., gold & grn. 3·25 40
3455. – 5 l. brn., gold & orge. 4·75 2·75

PAINTINGS—VERT. 10 b. "Model in Fancy Dress" (I. Andreescu). 40 b. "Peasants Weaving" (S. Dimitrescu). 1 l. 55, "Venus and Cupid" (L. Cranach). 5 l. "Haman beseeching Esther" (Rembrandt). HORIZ. 3 l. 20, "Hercules and the Lion" (Rubens).

616. Woman's Head. **618.** "Infantryman" (after Grigorescu).

617. Copper and Silver Coins of 1867.

1967. 10th Anniv. of C. Brancusi (sculptor). Sculptures.

3456. **616.** 5 b. brown, yell. & red 15 10
3457. – 10 b. blk., grn. & violet 20 10
3458. – 20 b. black, green & red 20 10
3459. – 40 b. black, red & grn. 25 10
3460. – 55 b. blk., olive & blue 50 20
3461. – 1 l. 20 brown, violet and orange .. 1·75 20
3462. – 3 l. 25 black, green and mauve .. 3·25 1·75

DESIGNS—HORIZ. 10 b. Sleeping muse. 40 b. "The Kiss". 3 l. 25 Gate of Kisses, Targujiu. VERT. 20 b. "The Endless Column". 55 b. Seated woman. 1 l. 20 "Miss Pogany".

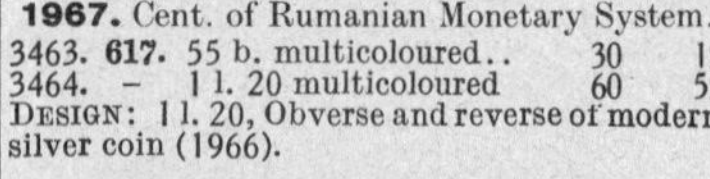

1967. Cent. of Rumanian Monetary System.

3463. **617.** 55 b. multicoloured.. 30 15
3464. – 1 l. 20 multicoloured 60 55

DESIGN: 1 l. 20, Obverse and reverse of modern silver coin (1966).

1967. 90th Anniv. of Independence.

3465. **618.** 55 b. multicoloured.. 1·60 1·60

619. Peasants attacking (after O. Bancila). **620.** "Centaurea pinnatifida".

1967. 60th Anniv. of Peasant Rising.

3466. **619.** 40 b. multicoloured.. 50 70
3467. – 1 l. 55 multicoloured 1·40 1·40

DESIGN—HORIZ. 1 l. 55, Peasants marching (after S. Luchian).

1967. Carpathian Flora. Multicoloured.

3468. 20 b. Type **620** 15 10
3469. 40 b. "Erysimum transsilvanicum" 20 10
3470. 55 b. "Aquilegia transsilvanica" 25 10
3471. 1 l. 20 "Viola alpina" .. 1·00 10
3472. 1 l. 75 "Campanula carpatica" .. .. 1·10 10
3473. 4 l. "Dryas octopetala" (horiz.) .. .. .. 3·25 1·60

621. Towers, Sibiu.

1967. Historic Monuments and Int. Tourist Year. Multicoloured.

3474. 20 b. Type **621** .. 20 10
3475. 40 b. Castle at Cris .. 25 10
3476. 55 b. Wooden church, Plopis 50 10
3477. 1 l. 60 Ruins, Neamtului 85 20
3478. 1 l. 75 Mogosoaia Palace, Bucharest .. .. 1·40 20
3479. 2 l. 25 Church, Voronet.. 2·00 1·40

No. 3479 is horiz., 48½ × 36 mm.

623. "The Marasesti Attack" (from painting by E. Stoica).

1967. 50th Anniv. of Battles of Marasesti, Marasti and Oituz.

3481. **623.** 55 b. brn., bl. & grey 70 25

624. D. Lipatti (composer and pianist: 50th birth anniv.). **625.** Wrestling.

1967. Cultural Annivs.

3482. **624.** 10 b. vio., bl. & black 15 10
3483. – 20 b. blue, brn. & blk. 15 10
3484. – 40 b. brn., turq. & blk. 15 10
3485. – 55 b. brown, red & blk. 25 10
3486. – 1 l. 20 brn., olive & blk. 40 15
3487. – 1 l. 75 grn., bl. & blk. 1·00 1·00

DESIGNS: 20 b. A. Orascu (architect: 150th birth anniv.). 40 b. G. Antipa (zoologist: birth cent.). 55 b. M. Kogalniceanu (politician: 150th birth anniv.). 1 l. 20, Jonathan Swift (300th birth anniv.). 1 l. 75, Marie Curie (birth cent.).

1967. World Wrestling Championships, Bucharest. Designs showing wrestlers and globes.

3488. **625.** 10 b. multicoloured.. 10 10
3489. – 20 b. mult. (horiz.) .. 15 10
3490. – 55 b. multicoloured.. 25 10
3491. – 1 l. 20 multicoloured 1·00 15
3492. – 2 l. mult. (horiz.) .. 1·60 80

626. Inscription on Globe.

1967. Int. Linguists' Congress, Bucharest.

3493. **626.** 1 l. 60 ultramarine, red and blue .. 1·40 20

627. Academy.

1967. Cent. of Book Academy, Bucharest.

3494. **627.** 55 b. grey, brn. & bl. 1·00 20

628. Dancing on Ice. **629.** Curtea de Arges Monastery.

1967. Winter Olympic Games, Grenoble. Multicoloured.

3495. 20 b. Type **628** 10 10
3496. 40 b. Skiing 15 10
3497. 55 b. Bobsleighing .. 25 10
3498. 1 l. Downhill skiing .. 45 15
3499. 1 l. 55 Ice-hockey .. 70 15
3500. 2 l. Games emblem .. 90 25
3501. 2 l. 30 Ski-jumping .. 1·60 1·00

1967. 450th Anniv. of Curtea de Arges Monastery.

3503. **629.** 55 b. multicoloured 65 20

630. Karl Marx and Title Page. **631.** Lenin.

1967. Cent. of Karl Marx's "Das Kapital".

3504. **630.** 40 b. blk., yell. & red 30 15

1967. 50th Anniv. of October Revolution.

3505. **631.** 1 l. 20 blk., gold & red 60 15

632. Arms of Rumania. **633.** Telephone Dial and Map.

1967. (a) T **632**.

3506. **632.** 40 b. blue 30 10
3507. 55 b. yellow 40 10
3508. 1 l. 60 red .. .. 1·00 10

(b) T **633** and similar designs.

3509. – 5 b. green 10 10
3510. – 10 b. red 10 10
3511. – 20 b. grey 40 10
3512. – 35 b. blue 20 10
3513. – 40 b. blue 20 10
3514. – 50 b. orange.. .. 25 10
3515. – 55 b. red 40 10
3516. – 60 b. brown 40 10
3517. – 1 l. green 40 10
3518. – 1 l. 20 violet.. .. 45 10
3519. – 1 l. 35 blue 75 10
3520. – 1 l. 50 red 70 10
3521. – 1 l. 55 brown .. 75 10
3522. – 1 l. 75 green.. .. 85 10
3523. – 2 l. yellow 90 10
3524. – 2 l. 40 blue 95 10
3525. **633.** 3 l. turquoise .. 1·10 10
3526. – 3 l. 20 ochre.. .. 1·50 10
3527. – 3 l. 25 blue .. .. 1·75 10
3528. – 4 l. mauve .. .. 2·50 15
3529. – 5 l. violet .. .. 2·00 15

DESIGNS—HORIZ. (23 × 17 mm.). 5 b. "Carpati" lorry. 20 b. Railway T.P.O. coach. 35 b. Light aircraft. 60 b. Electric parcels truck. As Type **633** (29 × 23 mm.). 1 l. 20, Motor-coach. 1 l. 35, Helicopter. 1 l. 75, Lakeside highway. 2 l. Postal van. 3 l. 20, Tarom airliner. 4 l. Electric train. 5 l. Telex instrument and world. map. VERT. (17 × 23 mm.). 10 b. Posthorn and telephone emblem. 40 b. Power Pylons. 50 b. Telephone handset. 55 b. Dam. (23 × 29 mm.). 1 l. Diesel train. 1 l. 50, Trolley-bus. 1 l. 55, Radio Station. 2 l. 40, T.V. relay station. 3 l. 25, Liner "Transylvania".

No. 3525 also commemorates the 40th anniv of the automatic telephone service.

For Nos. 3517/29 in smaller format see Nos. 3842/57.

634. "Crossing the River Buzau" (lithograph by Raffet) (actual size 93 × 30 mm.)

1967. Stamp Day.

3530. **634.** 55 b. + 45 b. blue and ochre .. .. 1·00 30

635. Monorail Train and Globe. **636.** Arms and Industrial Scene.

1967. World Fair, Montreal. Multicoloured.

3531. 55 b. Type **635** 30 10
3532. 1 l. Expo emblem within atomic symbol.. .. 35 10
3533. 1 l. 60 Gold cup and world map 70 15
3534. 2 l. Expo emblem .. 1·10 75

1967. 20th Anniv. of Republic. Mult.

3535. 40 b. Type **636** 15 10
3536. 55 b. Arms of Rumania .. 15 10
3537. 1 l. 60 Rumanian flag .. 40 15
3538. 1 l. 75 Arms and cultural emblems .. .. 1·40 75

The 1 l. 60, is 34 × 48 mm.

637. Flying Ambulance.

1968. Air. Rumanian Aviation.

3539. – 40 b. multicoloured.. 15 10
3540. **637.** 55 b. multicoloured.. 35 10
3541. – 1 l. multicoloured .. 40 10
3542. – 2 l. 40 multicoloured 1·10 55

DESIGNS—VERT. 40 b. Crop-spraying aircraft. 1 l. "Aviasan" emblem and aircraft. 2 l. 40, M. Zorileanu (pioneer aviator) and biplane.

638. "Angelica and Medor" (S. Ricci).

1968. Paintings in Rumanian Galleries. Multicoloured.

3543. 40 b. "Young Woman" (Misu Pop) 40 20
3544. 55 b. "Little Girl in Red Scarf" (N. Grigorescu) 55 25
3545. 1 l. "Old Nicholas, the Cobza-player" (S. Luchian) 1·25 30
3546. 1 l. 60 "Man with Skull" (Dierick Bouts) .. 1·60 35
3547. 2 l. 40 Type **638** .. .. 2·10 50
3548. 3 l. 20 "Ecce Homo" (Titian) .. .. 6·75 6·00

Nos. 3543/6 and 3548 are vert.

See also Nos. **3583/8**, **3631/6**, **3658/63**, **3756/61** and **3779/84**.

640. Human Rights Emblem. **641.** W.H.O. Emblem.

1968. Human Rights Year.
3551. 640. 1 l. multicoloured .. 1·00 15

1968. 20th Anniv. of W.H.O.
3552. 641. 1 l. 60 multicoloured 1·40 15

642. "The Hunter" (after N. Grigorescu).

1968. Hunting Congress, Mamaia.
3553. 642. 1 l. 60 multicoloured 1·60 25

643. Pioneers and Liberation Monument.

1968. Young Pioneers. Multicoloured.
3554. 5 b. Type 643 .. .. 10 10
3555. 40 b. Receiving scarves .. 15 10
3556. 55 b. With models .. 25 10
3557. 1 l. Operating radio sets 40 10
3558. 1 l. 60 Folk-dancing .. 70 15
3559. 2 l. 40 In camp .. .. 1·10 45

644. Prince Mircea. 645. Ion Ionescu de la Brad (scholar).

1968. 550th Death Anniv. of Prince Mircea (the Old).
3560. 644. 1 l. 60 multicoloured 1·40 25

1968. Cultural Annivs.
3561. 645. 40 b. multicoloured .. 15 15
3562. – 55 b. multicoloured .. 30 15
Portraits and Annivs.: 40 b. Type 645 (150th Birth Anniv.). 55 b. Emil Racovita (scientist: Birth Cent.).

646. "Pelargonium zonale, Ait". 648. Throwing the Javelin.

647. "Nicolae Balcescu" (G. Tattarescu).

1968. Garden Geraniums. Multicoloured.
3563. 10 b. Type 646 .. .. 15 10
3564. 20 b. "Pelargonium zonale Ait" 15 10
3565. 40 b. "Pelargonium zonale Ait" 20 10
3566. 55 b. "Pelargonium zonale Ait" 20 10
3567. 60 b. "Pelargonium grandiflorum Hort" .. 35 10
3568. 1 l. 20 "Pelargonium peltatum Hort" .. 40 10
3569. 1 l. 35 "Pelargonium peltatum Hort" .. 50 15
3570. 1 l. 60 "Pelargonium grandiflorum Hort" .. 1·00 50
Nos. 3563/6, 3567 and 3570, 3568/9 respectively are different varieties of the same species.

1968. 120th Anniv. of 1848 Revolution. Paintings. Multicoloured.
3571. 55 b. Type 647 .. .. 30 10
3572. 1 l. 20 "Avram Iancu" (B. Iscovescu) .. 35 15
3573. 1 l. 60 "Vasile Alecsandri" (N. Livaditti) .. 1·60 85

1968. Olympic Games, Mexico. Mult.
3574. 10 b. Type 648 .. .. 10 10
3575. 20 b. Diving 15 10
3576. 40 b. Volleyball 15 10
3577. 55 b. Boxing 25 10
3578. 60 b. Wrestling 25 10
3579. 1 l. 20 Fencing 65 15
3580. 1 l. 35 Punting 85 15
3581. 1 l. 60 Football .. .. 1·40 1·00

1968. Paintings in the Fine Arts Museum Bucarest. Multicoloured. As T 638.
3583. 10 b. "The Awakening of Rumania" (G. Tattarescu) (28×49 mm.) .. 10 10
3584. 20 b. "Composition" (Teodorescu Sionion) .. 15 10
3585. 35 b. "The Judgment of Paris" (H. van Balen) 20 10
3586. 60 b. "The Mystical Betrothal of St. Catherine" (L. Sustris) .. 35 15
3587. 1 l. 75 "Mary with the Child Jesus" (J. van Bylert) .. .. 1·40 25
3588. 3 l. "The Summer" (J. Jordaens) .. 3·25 1·60

649. F.I.A.P. Emblem within "Lens". 650. Academy and Harp.

1968. 20th Anniv. of International Federation of Photographic Art (F.I.A.P.).
3589. 649. 1 l. 60 multicoloured 1·40 20

1968. Centenary of Georges Enescu Philharmonic Academy.
3590. 650. 55 b. multicoloured 70 15

651. Triumph of Trajan. (Roman metope).

1968. Historic Monuments.
3591. 651. 10 b. grn., blue & red 10 10
3592. – 40 b. bl., brn. & red 20 10
3593. – 55 b. vio., brn. & grn. 25 10
3594. – 1 l. 20 purple, grey and ochre .. 45 15
3595. – 1 l. 55 bl., grn. & pur. 1·00 20
3596. – 1 l. 75 brown, bistre and orange .. 1·40 50
DESIGNS—HORIZ. 40 b. Monastery Church, Moldovita. 55 b. Monastery Church, Cezia. 1 l. 20, Tower and Church, Tirgoviste. 1 l. 55, Palace of Culture, Jassy. 1 l. 75, Corvinus Castle, Hunedoara.

652. Old Bucharest (18th-century painting). (Actual size 76×28 mm.).

1968. Stamp Day.
3597. 652. 55 b.+45 b. mult. .. 1·40 70

653. Mute Swan. 655. Neamtz Costume (female).

654. "Entry of Michael the Brave into Alba Julia" (E. Stoica).

1968. Fauna of Nature Reservations. Mult.
3598. 10 b. Type 653 .. .. 40 10
3599. 20 b. Black-winged Stilt 50 10
3600. 40 b. Common Shelduck 60 10
3601. 55 b. Great Egret .. 70 10
3602. 60 b. Golden Eagle .. 80 15
3603. 1 l. 20 Great Bustard .. 1·00 30
3604. 1 l. 35 Chamois 80 25
3605. 1 l. 60 European bison .. 1·00 40

1968. 50th Anniv. of Union of Transylvania with Rumania. Multicoloured.
3606. 55 b. Type 654 .. .. 25 10
3607. 1 l. "Union Dance" (T. Aman) 40 10
3608. 1 l. 75 "Alba Julia Assembly" .. .. 1·00 30

1968. Provincial Costumes (1st series). Multicoloured.
3610. 5 b. Type 655 .. .. 10 10
3611. 40 b. Neamtz (male) .. 20 10
3612. 55 b. Hunedoara (female) 30 10
3613. 1 l. Hunedoara (male) .. 50 10
3614. 1 l. 60 Brasov (female) .. 80 20
3615. 2 l. 40 Brasov (male) .. 1·25 1·00
See also Nos. 3617/22.

656. Earth, Moon and Orbital Track of "Apollo 8". 657. Fencing.

1969. Air. Flight of "Apollo 8" around the Moon.
3616. 656. 3 l. 30 blk., silver & bl. 2·75 2·75

1969. Provincial Costumes (2nd series). As T 655. Multicoloured.
3617. 5 b. Doli (female) .. 10 10
3618. 40 b. Doli (male) .. 20 10
3619. 55 b. Arges (female) .. 30 10
3620. 1 l. Arges (male) .. 50 20
3621. 1 l. 60 Timisoara (female) 80 25
3622. 2 l. 40 Timisoara (male) .. 1·25 1·00

1969. Sports.
3623. 657. 10 b. grey, blk. & brn. 10 10
3624. – 20 b. grey, blk. & vio. 10 10
3625. – 40 b. grey, blk. & blue 10 10
3626. – 55 b. grey, blk. & red 20 10
3627. – 1 l. grey, blk. & green 30 10
3628. – 1 l. 20 grey, blk. & bl. 35 10
3629. – 1 l. 60 grey, blk. & red 1·40 20
3630. – 2 l. 40 grey, blk. & grn. 1·00 50
DESIGNS: 20 b. Throwing the javelin. 40 b. Canoeing. 55 b. Boxing. 1 l. Volleyball. 1 l. 20, Swimming. 1 l. 60, Wrestling. 2 l. 40, Football.

1969. Nude Paintings in the National Gallery. As T 638. Multicoloured.
3631. 10 b. "Nude" 10 10
3632. 20 b. "Nude" (T. Pallady) 10 10
3633. 35 b. "Nude" (N. Tonitza) 15 10
3634. 60 b. "Venus and Cupid" (Flemish School) .. 40 10
3635. 1 l. 75 "Diana and Endymion" (M. Liberi) .. 1·60 65
3636. 3 l. "The Three Graces" (J. H. von Achen) .. 3·25 1·60
SIZES: VERT. (36 × 49 mm.)—10 b., 35 b., 60 b., 1 l. 75. (27 × 49 mm.)—3 l. HORIZ. 49 × 36 mm.)—20 b.

658. "Soyuz 4" and "Soyuz 5". 659. I.L.O. Emblem.

1969. Air. Space Link-up of "Soyuz 4" and "Soyuz 5".
3638. 658. 3 l. 30 multicoloured 2·75 2·75

1969. 50th Anniv. of Int. Labour Office.
3639. 659. 55 b. multicoloured 65 15

660. Stylised Head. 662. Referee introducing Boxers.

661. Posthorn.

1969. Inter-European Cultural and Economic Co-operation.
3640. 660. 55 b. multicoloured .. 65 65
3641. 1 l. 50 multicoloured 1·40 1·40

1969. Postal Ministers' Conf., Bucharest.
3642. 661. 55 b. dp. blue and blue 35 15

1969. European Boxing Championships, Bucharest. Multicoloured.
3643. 35 b. Type 662 .. .. 15 10
3644. 40 b. Sparring 20 10
3645. 55 b. Leading with Punch 30 10
3646. 1 l. 75 Declaring the Winner 1·40 50

663. "Apollo 9" and Module over Earth.

1969. Air. "Apollo" Moon Flights. Mult.
3647. 60 b. Type 663 .. .. 15 10
3648. 2 l. 40 "Apollo 10" and module approaching Moon (vert.) .. .. 1·40 15

664. "Apatura ilia". 665. Astronaut and Module on Moon.

1969. Butterflies. Multicoloured.
3649. 5 b. Type 664 .. .. 10 10
3650. 10 b. "Prosperpinus prosperina" 10 10
3651. 20 b. "Colias erate" .. 15 10
3652. 40 b. "Pericallia matronula" 20 10
3653. 55 b. "Argynnis laodice" 30 10
3654. 1 l. "Callimorpha quadripunctaria" 65 10
3655. 1 l. 20 "Anthocaris cardamines" 85 20
3656. 2 l. 40 "Meleageria daphnis" 1·75 1·00

1969. Air. 1st Man on the Moon.
3657. 665. 3 l. 30 multicoloured 2·00 2·00

1969. Paintings in the National Gallery, Bucharest. Multicoloured. As T 638.
3658. 10 b. "Venetian Senator" (School of Tintoretto) .. 10 10
3659. 20 b. "Sofia Kretzulescu" (G. Tattarescu) .. 10 10
3660. 35 b. "Philip IV" (Velasquez) 20 10
3661. 60 b. "Man Reading" (Memling) 40 10
3662. 1 l. 75 "Lady D'Aguesseau" (Vigee-Lebrun) .. 1·00 20
3663. 3 l. "Portrait of a Woman" (Rembrandt) .. .. 2·40 1·40

666. Communist Flag. 667. Symbols of Learning.

1969. 10th Rumanian Communist Party Congress.
3665. 666. 55 b. multicoloured .. 60 15

1969. National "Economic Achievements" Exn., Bucharest. Multicoloured.
3666. 35 b. Type 667 .. .. 10 10
3667. 40 b. Symbols of Agriculture and Science 15 10
3668. 1 l. 75 Symbols of Industry 1·00 15

668. Liberation Emblem. 669. Juggling on Trick-cycle.

1969. 25th Anniv. of Liberation. Mult.
3669. 10 b. Type 668 .. .. 10 10
3670. 55 b. Crane and Trowel .. 15 10
3671. 60 b. Flags on scaffolding 25 10

1969. Rumanian State Circus. Multicoloured.
3672. 10 b. Type **669** 10 10
3673. 20 b. Clown 10 10
3674. 35 b. Trapeze artists .. 25 10
3675. 60 b. Equestrian act .. 35 10
3676. 1 l. 75 High-wire act .. 65 10
3677. 3 l. Performing tiger .. 1·60 60

670. Forces Memorial.

1969. "Army Day" and 25th Anniv. of People's Army.
3678. **670.** 55 b. black, gold & red 40 15

671. Trains of 1869 and 1969.

1969. Cent. of Rumanian Railways.
3679. **671.** 55 b. multicoloured .. 60 15

672. "Courtyard" (M. Bouquet).

1969. Stamp Day.
3680. **672.** 55 b.+45 b. mult... 75 65

673. Branesti Mask.

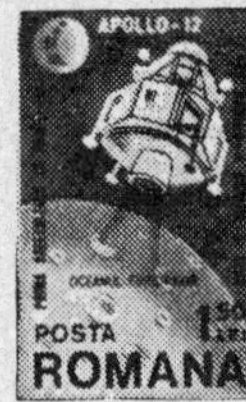

674. "Apollo 12" above Moon.

1969. Folklore Masks. Multicoloured.
3681. 40 b. Type **673** 15 10
3682. 55 b. Tudora mask .. 20 10
3683. 1 l. 55 Birsesti mask .. 50 10
3684. 1 l. 75 Rudaria mask .. 65 40

1969. Moon landing of "Apollo 12".
3685. **674.** 1 l. 50 multicoloured 1·10 75

675. "Three Kings" (Voronet Monastery).

1969. Frescoes from Northern Moldavian Monasteries (1st series). Multicoloured.
3686. 10 b. Type **675** 10 10
3687. 20 b. "Three Kings" (Sucevita) 15 10
3688. 35 b. "Holy Child in Manger" (Voronet) .. 20 10
3689. 60 b. "Ship" (Sucevita).. 35 10
3690. 1 l. 75 "Walled City" (Moldovita) .. .. 1·25 20
3691. 3 l. "Pastoral Scene" (Voronet) .. .. 2·40 1·40
The 60 b. and 3 l. are vert.
See also Nos. 3736/42 and 3872/8.

676. "Old Mother Goose", Capra.

1969. New Year Children's Celebrations. Multicoloured.
3692. 40 b. Type **676** 15 10
3693. 55 b. Decorated tree, Sorcova 20 10
3694. 1 l. 50 Drummers, Buhaiul 75 10
3695. 2 l. 40 Singer and bell-ringer, Plugusorol .. 1·00 45

677. Hockey-players and Emblem.

678. "Pulsatilla pratensis".

1970. World Ice-hockey Championships. Multicoloured.
3696. 20 b. Type **677** 10 10
3697. 55 b. Goalkeeper .. 15 10
3698. 1 l. 20 Two players .. 45 10
3699. 2 l. 40 Goal-mouth melee 1·00 40

1970. Flowers. Multicoloured.
3700. 5 b. Type **678** 10 10
3701. 10 b. "Adonis vernalis" 10 10
3702. 20 b. "Carduus nutans" 10 10
3703. 40 b. "Amygdalus nana" 10 10
3704. 55 b. "Iris pumilla" .. 10 10
3705. 1 l. "Linum hirsutum" 25 10
3706. 1 l. 20 "Salvia aethiopis" 40 10
3707. 2 l. 40 "Paeonia tenuifolia" 3·00 80

679. Japanese Woodcut.

681. Lenin.

680. BAC "1-11" in flight.

1970. World Fair, Osaka, Japan. Expo 70. Multicoloured.
3714. 20 b. Type **679** 20 10
3715. 1 l. Japanese pagoda (29×92 mm) .. .. 1·00 65

1970. 50th Anniv. of Rumanian Civil Aviation. Multicoloured.
3717. 60 b. Type **680** 25 10
3718. 2 l. Tail of BAC "1-11" 75 25

1970. Birth Centenary of Lenin.
3719. **681.** 40 b. multicoloured .. 40 10

682. "Camille" (Monet) and Maximum Card.

683. "Prince Alexander Cuza" (Szathmary).

1970. Maximafila Franco-Rumanian Philatelic Exn., Bucharest.
3720. **682.** 1 l. 50 multicoloured 1·40 30

1970. 150th Birth Anniv. of Prince Alexander Cuza.
3721. **683.** 55 b. multicoloured .. 55 15

684. "Co-operation" Map.

685. Victory Monument, Bucharest.

1970. Inter-European Cultural and Economic Co-operation.
3722. **684.** 40 b. grn., brn. & blk. 45 45
3723. 1 l. 50 blue, brn. & blk. 1·40 1·40

1970. 25th Anniv. of Liberation.
3724. **685.** 55 b. multicoloured 65 15

686. Greek Silver Drachma. 5th-cent B.C.

1970. Ancient Coins.
3725. **686.** 10 b. black and blue .. 15 10
3726. – 20 b. black and red .. 20 10
3727. – 35 b. bronze and green 25 10
3728. – 60 b. black and brown 35 10
3729. – 1 l. 75 black and blue 85 10
3730. – 3 l. blk. and red .. 2·00 1·00
DESIGNS—HORIZ. 20 b. Getic-Dacian silver didrachm, 2nd-1st-cent B.C. 35 b. Copper sestertius of Trajan, 106 A.D. 60 b. Mircea ducat, 1400, 1 l. 75, Silver groschen of Stephen the Great. 1460. VERT. 3 l. Brasov klippe-thaler, 1601.

687. Footballers and Ball.

1970. World Cup Football Championships, Mexico.
3731. **687.** 40 b. multicoloured .. 15 10
3732. – 55 b. multicoloured .. 20 10
3733. – 1 l. 75 multicoloured .. 70 15
3734. – 3 l. 30 multicoloured 1·60 50
DESIGNS: Nos. 3732/4, various football scenes as Type **687**.

688. "Apollo 13" Splashdown.

689. Engels.

1970. Frescoes from Northern Moldavian Monasteries (2nd series). As T **675**. Mult.
3736. 10 b. "Prince Petru Rares and Family" (Moldovita) 10 10
3737. 20 p. "Metropolitan Grigore Rosca" (Voronet) 15 10
3738. 40 b. "Alexander the Good and Family" (Sucevita) 20 10
3739. 55 b. } Scenes from "The Last Judgement" (Voronet) 35 10
3740. 1 l. 75 } 90 20
3741. 3 l. "St. Anthony" (Voronet) .. .. 2·50 1·40
The 20 b. is smaller, 28×48 mm.

1970. Air. Space Flight of "Apollo 13".
3743. **688.** 1 l. 50 multicoloured 65 65

1970. 150th Birth Anniv. of Friedrich Engels.
3744. **689.** 1 l. 50 multicoloured 1·00 15

690. Exhibition Hall.

1970. National Events. Multicoloured.
3745. 35 b. "Iron Gates" Dam 15 10
3746. 55 b. Freighter and flag .. 45 10
3747. 1 l. 50 Type **690**.. .. 85 15
EVENTS: 35 b. Danube navigation projects. 55 b. 75th Anniv. of Rumanian Merchant Marine. 1 l. 50, 1st International Fair, Bucharest.

691. New Headquarters Building.

1970. New U.P.U. Headquarters Building, Berne.
3748. **691.** 1 l. 50 green and blue 1·10 15

692. Education Year Emblem.

693. "Iceberg".

1970. Int. Education Year.
3749. **692.** 55 b. plum, blk. & red 65 15

1970. Roses. Multicoloured.
3750. 20 b. Type **693** 10 10
3751. 35 b. "Wiener Charme" 10 10
3752. 55 b. "Pink Lustre" .. 20 10
3753. 1 l. "Piccadilly" .. 60 10
3754. 1 l. 50 "Orange Delbard" 75 10
3755. 2 l. 40 "Sibelius" .. 1·50 55

694. "Spaniel and Pheasant" (J. B. Oudry).

695. Refugee Woman and Child.

1970. Paintings in Rumanian Galleries. Multicoloured. Sizes in millimetres.
3756. 10 b. "The Hunt" (D. Brandi) (38×50) .. 10 10
3757. 20 b. Type **694** 10 10
3758. 35 b. "The Hunt" (Jan Fyt) (38×50) 15 10
3759. 60 b. "After the Chase" (Jordaens) (As T **694**).. 40 10
3760. 1 l. 75 "The Game Dealer" (F. Snyders) (50×38).. 90 20
3761. 3 l. "The Hunt" (A. de Gryeff) (As T **694**) 2·40 1·40

1970. Danube Flood Victims (1st issue).
3763. **695.** 55 b. blk., blue & grn. (postage) 25 10
3764. – 1 l. 50 multicoloured 60 15
3765. – 1 l. 75 multicoloured 90 65
3766. – 60 b. black, drab and blue (air) 50 10
DESIGNS: 60 b. Helicopter rescue. 1 l. 50, Red Cross post. 1 l. 75, Building reconstruction.
See also No. 3777.

696. U.N. Emblem.

698. Beethoven.

697. Arab Horse.

1970. 25th Anniv. of United Nations.
3767. **696.** 1 l. 50 multicoloured 1·10 15

1970. Horses. Multicoloured.
3768. 20 b. Type **697** 10 10
3769. 35 b. American trotter .. 10 10
3770. 55 b. Ghidran .. 15 10
3771. 1 l. Hutul .. 50 10
3772. 1 l. 50 Thoroughbred .. 75 15
3773. 2 l. 40 Lippizaner .. 2·25 1·40

1970. Birth Bicent. of Beethoven.
3774. **698.** 55 b. multicoloured 1·25 15

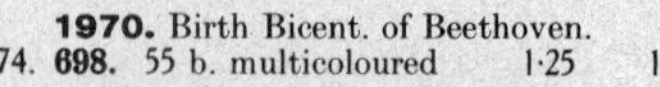

699. "Mail-cart in the Snow" (E. Volkers). (Illustration reduced. Actual size 75×33 mm.)

1970. Stamp Day.
3775. **699.** 55 b.+45 b. mult. 1·40 1·00

700. Coanda's Model Aircraft.

1970. Air. 60th Anniv. of 1st Experimental Rocket-powered Flight.
3776. 700. 60 b. multicoloured .. 75 15

701. "The Flood" (abstract, Joan Miro).

1970. Danube Flood Victims (2nd issue).
3777. 701. 3 l. multicoloured .. 3·25 3·25

702. "Sight" (G. Coques).

1970. Paintings from the Bruckenthal Museum, Sibiu. Multicoloured.
3779. 10 b. Type **702** 10 10
3780. 20 b. "Hearing" .. 10 10
3781. 35 b. "Smell" 15 10
3782. 60 b. "Taste" 25 10
3783. 1 l. 75 "Touch" 50 10
3784. 3 l. Bruckenthal Museum 1·60 85
Nos. 3779/84 show a series of pictures by Coques entitled "The Five Senses".

703. T. Vladimirescu (T. Aman). 705. Alsatian.

704. "Three Races".

1971. 150th Death Anniv. of Tudor Vladimirescu (Wallachian revolutionary).
3786. 703. 1 l. 50 multicoloured 90 15

1971. Racial Equality Year.
3787. 704. 1 l. 50 multicoloured 1·10 15

1971. Dogs. Multicoloured.
3788. 20 b. Type **705** 10 10
3789. 35 b. Bulldog 15 10
3790. 55 b. Fox terrier.. .. 20 10
3791. 1 l. Setter 50 10
3792. 1 l. 50 Cocker spaniel .. 75 20
3793. 2 l. 40 Poodle .. .. 3·25 1·60

706. "Luna 16" leaving Moon. 707. Proclamation of the Commune.

1971. Air. Moon Missions of "Luna 16" and "Luna 17". Multicoloured.
3794. 3 l. 30 Type **706** .. .. 1·60 1·60
3795. 3 l. 30 "Lunokhod 1" on Moon .. .. .. 1·60 1·60

1971. Centenary of Paris Commune.
3796. 707. 40 b. multicoloured 50 15

708. Astronaut and Moon Trolley.

710. "Toadstool" Rocks, Babele. 709. "Three Fists" Emblem and Flags.

1971. Air. Moon Mission of "Apollo 14".
3797. 708. 3 l. 30 multicoloured 1·60 1·60

1971. Trade Union Congress, Bucharest.
3798. 709. 55 b. multicoloured .. 65 15

1971. Tourism. Multicoloured.
3799 10 b. Gorge, Cheile Bicazului (vert) .. 10 10
3800 40 b. Type **710** 10 10
3801 55 b. Winter resort, Poiana Brasov .. 15 10
3802 1 l. Holiday scene, Danube delta 45 10
3803 1 l. 50 Hotel, Baile Sovata 85 15
3804 2 l. 40 Venus, Jupiter and Neptune Hotels, Black Sea (77 × 29 mm) .. 1·25 85

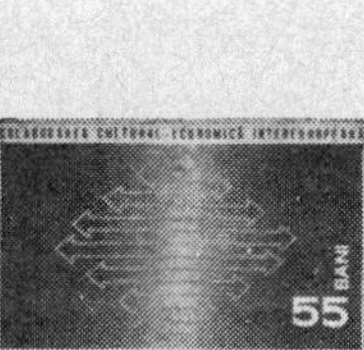

711. "Arrows". 712. Museum Building.

1971. Inter-European Cultural and Economic Co-operation. Multicoloured.
3805. 55 b. Type **711** .. .. 1·50 1·50
3806. 1 l. 75 Stylised map of Europe .. .. 2·75 2·40

1971. Historical Museum, Bucharest.
3807. 712. 55 b. multicoloured .. 40 10

713. "The Secret Printing-press" (S. Szonyi). 714. "Motra Tone" (K. Idromeno).

1971. 50th Anniv. of Rumanian Communist Party. Multicoloured.
3808. 35 b. Type **713** 10 10
3809. 40 b. Emblem and red flags (horiz.) 15 10
3810. 55 b. "The Builders" (A. Anastasiu) 25 15

1971. "Balkanfila III". Int. Stamp Exhib., Bucharest. Multicoloured.
3811. 1 l. 20+60 b. Type **714**.. 1·25 1·25
3812. 1 l. 20+60 b. "Maid" (V. Dimitrov-Maystora) 1·25 1·25
3813. 1 l. 20+60 b. "Rosa Botzaris" (J. Stieler).. 1·25 1·25
3814. 1 l. 20+60 b. "Portrait of a Lady" (K. Ivanovic) 1·25 1·25
3815. 1 l. 20+60 b. "Argeseanca" (C. Popp de Szathmary) 1·25 1·25
3816. 1 l. 20+60 b. "Woman in Modern Dress" (C. Ibrahim) .. .. 1·25 1·25

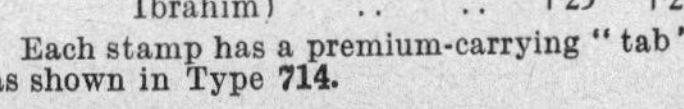
Each stamp has a premium-carrying "tab" as shown in Type **714**.

715. "Punica granatum".

1971. Flowers. Multicoloured.
3818. 20 b. Type **715** 10 10
3819. 35 b. "Calceolus speciosum" 10 10
3820. 55 b. "Life jagra" .. 10 10
3821. 1 l. "Mimulus luteus" .. 40 10
3822. 1 l. 50 "Convolvulus tricolor" 60 20
3823. 2 l. 40 "Phyllocactus phyllanthoides" (horiz.) .. 1·75 20

716. "Nude" (J. Iser).

1971. Paintings of Nudes. Multicoloured.
3824. 10 b. Type **716** 10 10
3825. 20 b. "Nude" (C. Ressu) 10 10
3826. 35 b. "Nude" (N. Grigorescu) 10 10
3827. 60 b. "Odalisque" (Delacroix) (horiz.) 10 10
3828. 1 l. 75 "Nude in Landscape" (Renoir) .. 1·00 20
3829. 3 l. "Venus and Cupid" (Il Vechio) (horiz.) .. 2·00 1·00
The 20 b. is smaller, 29 × 50 mm.

718. Astronauts and Lunar Rover on Moon.

1971. Air Moon Flight of "Apollo 15".
3833. 718. 1 l. 50 multicoloured (blue background) 2·40 2·40
No. 3833 also exists imperforate, with background colour changed to green, from a restricted printing.

719. "Fishing-Boats" (M. W. Arnold).

1971. Marine Paintings. Multicoloured.
3835. 10 b. "Coastal Storm" (B. Peters) 10 10
3836. 20 b. "Seascape" (I. Backhuysen) 10 10
3837. 35 b. "Boat in Stormy Seas" (A. van de Eertvelt) 15 10
3838. 60 b. Type **719** 25 10
3839. 1 l. 75 "Seascape" (I. K. Aivazovsky) 65 20
3840. 3 l. "Fishing-boats, Braila" (J. A. Steriadi) .. .. 1·75 40

1971. As Nos. 3517/29 and three new designs but in smaller format, 17 × 23 or 23 × 17 mm.
3842. 1 l. green 45 10
3843. 1 l. 20 violet 40 10
3844. 1 l. 35 blue 75 10
3845. 1 l. 50 red 50 10
3846. 1 l. 55 brown 50 10
3847. 1 l. 75 green 55 10
3848. 2 l. green 65 10
3849. 2 l. 40 blue 75 10
3850. 3 l. blue 95 10
3851. 3 l. 20 brown .. .. 1·50 10
3852. 3 l. 25 blue .. .. 1·50 10
3853. 3 l. 60 blue .. .. 1·25 10
3854. 4 l. mauve .. .. 1·50 10
3855. 4 l. 80 blue .. .. 1·50 10
3856. 5 l. violet .. .. 1·75 10
3857. 6 l. mauve .. .. 1·90 10
New designs—vert. 3 l. 60, Clearing letter-box. 4 l. 80, Postman on round. 6 l. Postal Ministry, Bucharest.

720. "Neagoe Basarab" (fresco, Curtea de Arges). 721. "T. Pallady" (self portrait).

1971. 450th Death Anniv. of Prince Neagoe Basarab, Regent of Wallachia.
3858. 720. 60 b. multicoloured.. 45 15

1971. Artists Anniversaries.
3859. 721. 40 b. multicoloured.. 10 10
3860. – 55 b. blk., stone & gold 15 10
3861. – 1 l. 50 blk. stone & gold 40 10
3862. – 2 l. 40 multicoloured 1·10 25
Designs: 40 b. (Birth centenary). 55 b. "B. Cellini" (400th Death anniv.), 1 l. 50, "Watteau" (self-portrait) (250th Death anniv.). 2 l. 40, "Durer" (self-portrait) (500th Birth anniv.)

722. Persian Text and Seal. 723. Figure-skating.

1971. 2500th Anniv. of Persian Empire.
3863. 722. 55 b. multicoloured.. 50 10

1971. Winter Olympic Games, Sapporo, Japan (1972). Multicoloured.
3864. 10 b. Type **723** 10 10
3865. 20 b. Ice-hockey 10 10
3866. 40 b. Biathlon 10 10
3867. 55 b. Bobsleighing .. 10 10
3868. 1 l. 75 Downhill skiing .. 65 20
3869. 3 l. Games emblem .. 1·60 1·00

724. "Lady with Letter" (Sava Hentia).

1971. Stamp Day.
3871. 724. 1 l. 10+90 b. mult. 1·50 1·00

1971. Frescoes from Northern Moldavian Monasteries (3rd series). As T **675**. Mult.
3872. 10 b. "St. George and The Dragon" (Moldovita) (vert.) 10 10
3873. 20 b. "Three Kings and Angel" (Moldovita) (vert.) 10 10
3874. 40 b. "The Crucifixion" (Moldovita) (vert.) .. 10 10
3875. 55 b. "Trial" (Voronet) (vert.) 15 10
3876. 1 l. 75 "Death of a Martyr" (Voronet) (vert.).. 1·00 20
3877. 3 l. "King and Court" (Arborea) .. .. 2·00 1·40

725. Matei Millo (dramatist, 75th Death Anniv.).
726. Magellan and Ships (450th Death Anniv.).

1971. Famous Rumanians. Multicoloured.
3879 55 b. Type **725** 20 10
3880 1 l. Nicolae Lorga (historian, birth cent) 35 15

1971. Scientific Annivs.
3881. **726.** 40 b. mauve, bl. & grn. 40 10
3882. – 55 b. blue, grn. & lilac 20 10
3883. – 1 l. multicoloured .. 50 10
3884. – 1 l. 50 grn., bl. & brn. 65 20
Designs and Anniversaries: 55 b. Kepler and observatory (400th Birth Anniv.). 1 l. Gagarin, rocket and Globe (10th anniv. of first manned space flight). 1 l. 50, Lord Rutherford and atomic symbol (Birth cent.).

727. Lynx Cubs.

1972. Young Wild Animals. Multicoloured.
3885. 20 b. Type **727** 10 10
3886. 35 b. Red fox cubs .. 10 10
3887. 55 b. Roe deer fawns .. 20 10
3888. 1 l. Wild piglets 50 20
3889. 1 l. 50 Wolf cubs .. 85 20
3890. 2 l. 40 Brown bear cubs 2·75 1·00

728. U.T.C. Emblem.
730. Stylised Map of Europe.

729. Wrestling.

1972. 50th Anniv. of Communist Youth Union (U.T.C.).
3891. **728.** 55 b. multicoloured 30 15

1972. Olympic Games, Munich (1st issue). Multicoloured.
3892. 10 b. Type **729** 10 10
3893. 20 b. Canoeing 10 10
3894. 55 b. Football 15 10
3895. 1 l. 55 High-jumping .. 45 10
3896. 2 l. 90 Boxing .. .. 1·10 15
3897. 6 l. 70 Volleyball .. 2·75 1·50
See also Nos. 3914/19 and 3926.

1972. Inter-European Cultural and Economic Co-operation.
3899. **730.** 1 l. 75 gold, blk. & pur. 1·40 1·40
3900. – 2 l. 90 gold, blk. & grn. 2·50 2·00
Design: 2 l. 90 " Crossed arrows " symbol.

731. Astronauts in Lunar Rover.
732. Modern Trains and Symbol.

1972. Air. Moon Flight of " Apollo 16 ".
3901. **731.** 3 l. blue, grn. & pink 2·00 2·00

1972. 50th Anniv. of Int. Railway Union.
3902. **732.** 55 b. multicoloured 70 15

734. " Paeonia romanica ".

1972. Scarce Rumanian Flowers.
3904. **734.** 20 b. multicoloured .. 10 10
3905. – 40 b. pur., grn. & brn. 15 10
3906. – 55 b. brown and blue 25 10
3907. – 60 b. red, green and bright green .. 30 10
3908. – 1 l. 35 multicoloured 65 15
3909. – 2 l. 90 multicoloured 1·50 35
Designs: 40 b. " Dianthus callizonus ". 55 b. Leontopodium alpinum ". 60 b. " Nigritella rubra ". 1 l. 35, " Narcissus stellaris". 2 l. 90, " Cypripedium calceolus ".

735. Saligny Bridge, Cernavoda.

1972. Danube Bridges. Multicoloured.
3910. 1 l. 35 Type **735** 80 10
3911. 1 l. 75 Giurgeni Bridge, Vadul Oii 85 20
3912. 2 l. 75 Prieteniei Bridge, Giurgiu-Russe .. .. 2·75 60

736. North Railway Station, Bucharest, 1872.

1972. Centenary of North Railway Station, Bucharest.
3913. **736.** 55 b. multicoloured 70 15

737. Water-polo.

1972. Olympic Games, Munich. (2nd issue). Multicoloured.
3914. 10 b. Type **737** 10 10
3915. 20 b. Pistol-shooting .. 15 10
3916. 55 b. Throwing the discus 15 10
3917. 1 l. 55 Gymnastics .. 45 10
3918. 2 l. 75 Canoeing .. .. 1·40 15
3919. 6 l. 40 Fencing .. .. 2·75 1·40

738. Rotary stamp-printing Press.
739. " E. Stoenescu " (S. Popescu).

1972. Cent. of State Stamp-printing Works.
3921. **738.** 55 b. multicoloured 50 10

1972. Rumanian Art. Portraits and Self-portraits. Multicoloured.
3922. 55 b. Type **739** 10 10
3923. 1 l. 75 " O. Bancila " (self-portrait) 30 10
3924. 2 l. 90 " Gh. Petrascu " (self-portrait) 60 10
3925. 6 l. 50 " I. Andreescu " (self-portrait) .. .. 2·00 35

740. Runner with Torch.
741. Aurel Vlaicu and Flying-Machine.

1972. Olympic Games, Munich (3rd issue). Olympic Flame.
3926. **740.** 55 b. pur. & blue on silver 1·00 45

1972. Air. Rumanian Aviation Pioneers. Multicoloured.
3927. 60 b. Type **741** 20 10
3928. 3 l. Traian Vuja and flying-machine .. .. 1·25 45

742. Cluj Cathedral.
743. Satu Mare.

1972.
3929 **742** 1 l. 85 violet (postage) 35 10
3930 – 2 l. 75 grey 45 10
3931 – 3 l. 35 red 55 10
3932 – 3 l. 45 green 65 10
3933 – 5 l. 15 blue 90 10
3934 – 5 l. 60 blue 95 10
3935 – 6 l. 20 mauve .. .. 1·00 10
3936 – 6 l. 40 brown .. .. 1·25 10
3937 – 6 l. 80 red .. .. 1·25 10
3938 – 7 l. 05 black .. .. 1·10 10
3939 – 8 l. 45 red .. .. 1·50 10
3940 – 9 l. 05 green .. .. 1·40 10
3941 – 9 l. 10 blue .. .. 1·40 15
3942 – 9 l. 85 green .. .. 1·40 15
3943 – 10 l. brown .. .. 1·50 20
3944 – 11 l. 90 blue .. .. 2·00 20
3945 – 12 l. 75 violet .. .. 1·90 25
3946 – 13 l. 30 red .. .. 2·00 25
3947 – 16 l. 20 green .. .. 2·40 25
3948 – 14 l. 60 blue (air) .. 3·50 25
Designs—horiz. (As Type **742**). 2 l. 75, Sphinx Rock, Mt. Bucegi. 3 l. 45, Sinaia Castle. 5 l. 15, Hydro-electric power station, Arges. 6 l. 40, Hunidoara Castle. 6 l. 80, Polytechnic complex. 9 l. 05, Coliseum, Sarmisegetuza. 9 l. 10, Hydro-electric power station, Iron Gates. (29×21 mm.). 11 l. 90, Palace of the Republic, Bucharest. 13 l. 30, City Gate, Alba Julia. 14 l. 60, Otopeni Airport. vert. (As Type **742**). 3 l. 35, Heroes' Monument, Bucharest. 5 l. 60, Iasi-Biserica. 6 l. 20, Bran Castle. 7 l. 05, Black Church, Brasova. 8 l. 45, Roman building, Bucharest. 9 l. 85, Decebal's statue, Cetatea Deva. (20×30 mm.). 10 l. City Hall Tower, Sibiu. 12 l. 75, T.V. Building, Bucharest. 16 l. 20, Clock Tower, Sighisoara.

1972. Satu Mare. Millenium.
3949. **743.** 55 b. multicoloured .. 50 10

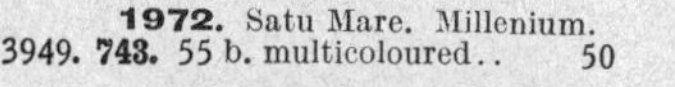

744. Davis Cup on Racquet.

1972. Final of Davis Cup Championships 1972, Bucharest.
3950. **744.** 2 l. 75 multicoloured 1·50 40

745. " Venice " (G. Petrascu).

1972. Paintings of Venice. Multicoloured.
3951. 10 b. Type **745** 10 10
3952. 20b. " Marina " (Darascu) 10 10
3953. 55 b. " Moliberi Palace " (Petrascu) 15 10
3954. 1 l. 55 " Venice " (Bunescu) 45 10
3955. 2 l. 75 " Venetian Palace " (Darascu) .. .. 1·10 15
3956. 6 l. 40 " Venice " (Bunesca) (different) .. 2·75 1·40

746. Fencing and Bronze Medal.
748. Flags and " 25 ".

747. " Travelling Romanies " (E. Volkers).

1972. Munich Olympic Games' Medals.
3958. **746.** 10 b. multicoloured .. 10 10
3959. – 20 b. multicoloured .. 15 10
3960. – 35 b. multicoloured .. 20 10
3961. – 1 l. 45 grey, pur. & pink 50 10
3962. – 2 l. 75 grey, brn. & ochre 1·25 15
3963. – 6 l. 20 multicoloured 3·75 1·50
Designs: 20 b. Handball and bronze medal. 35 b. Boxing and silver medal. 1 l. 45, Hurdling and silver medal. 2 l. 75, Pistol-shooting, silver and bronze medals. 6 l. 20, Wrestling and two gold medals.

1972. Stamp Day.
3965. **747.** 1 l. 10+90 b. mult... 1·60 1·00

1972. 25th Anniv. of Proclamation of Republic. Multicoloured.
3966. 55 b. Type **748** 20 10
3967. 1 l. 20 Arms and " 25 " .. 30 10
3968. 1 l. 75 Industrial scene and " 25 " 75 20

749. " Apollo 1, 2, 3 ".
750. European Bee Eater.

1972. " Apollo " Moon Flights. Mult.
3969. 10 b. Type **749** .. 10 10
3970. 35 b. Grissom, Chaffee and White 10 10
3971. 40 b. " Apollo 4, 5, 6 " .. 15 10
3972. 55 b. " Apollo 7, 8 " .. 20 10
3973. 1 l. " Apollo 9, 10 " .. 30 10
3974. 1 l. 20 " Apollo 11, 12 " .. 40 10
3975. 1 l. 85 " Apollo 13, 14 " .. 50 15
3976. 2 l. 75 " Apollo 15, 16 " .. 90 15
3977. 3 l. 60 " Apollo 17 " .. 2·00 1·40

1973. Protection of Nature. Multicoloured.
(a) Birds.
3979. 1 l. 40 Type **750** .. 75 15
3980. 1 l. 85 Red-breasted Goose 1·00 20
3981. 2 l. 75 Penduline Tit .. 1·75 40
(b) Flowers.
3982 1 l. 40 Marsh marigold .. 40 10
3983 1 l. 85 Martagon lily .. 50 12
3984 2 l. 75 Gentian 75 25

751. Copernicus.
752. Suceava Costume (female).

1973. 500th Birth Anniv. of Copernicus.
3985. **751.** 2 l. 75 multicoloured 1·40 35

1973. Regional Costumes. Multicoloured.
3986. 10 b. Type **752** 10 10
3987. 40 b. Suceava (male) .. 10 10
3988. 55 b. Harghila (female) 15 10
3989. 1 l. 75 Harghila (male) .. 45 10
3990. 2 l. 75 Gorj (female) .. 75 15
3991. 6 l. 40 Gorj (male) .. 1·50 1·00

753. D. Paciurea (sculptor).

754. Map of Europe.

1973. Cultural Celebrities. Multicoloured.

3992.	10 b. Type **753**	10	10
3993.	40 b. I. Slavici (writer) ..	10	10
3994.	55 b. G. Lazar (writer) ..	15	10
3995.	6 l. 40 A. Flechtenmacher (composer)	2·00	1·00

1973. Inter-European Cultural and Economic Co-operation.

3996. **754.**	3 l. 35 gold, blue & pur.	1·40	1·40
3997. –	3 l. 60 gold & purple	2·50	2·00

DESIGN: 3 l. 60, Symbol of collaboration.

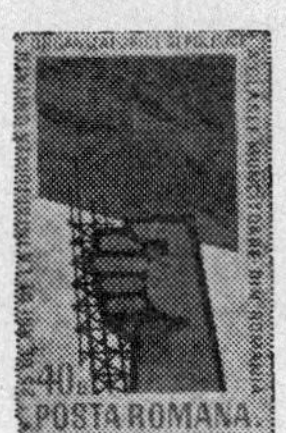

756. Hand with Hammer and Sickle.

757. W.M.O. Emblem and Weather Satellite.

1973. Anniversaries. Multicoloured.

3999.	40 b. Type **756** ..	30	10
4000.	55 b. Flags and bayonets	40	10
4001.	1 l. 75 Prince Cuza ..	1·00	15

EVENTS: 40 b. Rumanian Workers and Peasants Party. 25th Anniv. 55 b. National Anti-Fascist Committee. 40th Anniv. 1 l. 75, Prince Alexander Cuza. Death Cent.

1973. Centenary of I.M.O./W.M.O.

4002. **757.**	2 l. multicoloured ..	90	20

758. "Dimitri Ralet" (anon).

759. Prince Dimitri Cantemir.

1973. "Socfilex III" Stamp Exhibition, Bucharest. Portrait Paintings. Mult.

4003.	40 b. Type **758** ..	10	10
4004.	60 b. "Enacheta Vacarescu" (A. Chladek) ..	15	10
4005.	1 l. 55 "Dimitri Aman" (C. Lecca) ..	30	10
4006.	4 l.+2 l. "Barbat at his Desk" (B. Iscovescu)	2·00	1·00

1973. 300th Birth Anniv. of Dimitri Cantemir, Prince of Moldavia (writer). Mult.

4008. **759.**	1 l. 75 multicoloured	1·00	20

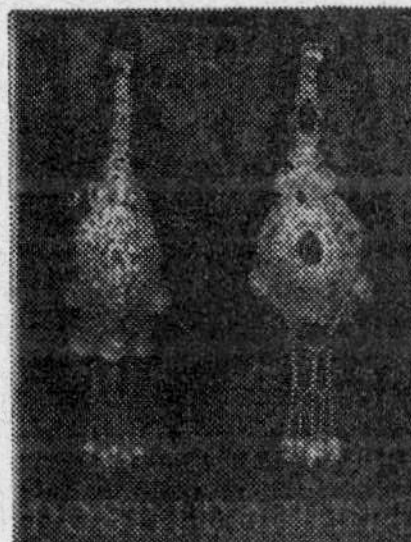
760. Fibular Brooches.

1973. Treasures of Pietrosa. Multicoloured.

4010.	10 b. Type **760** ..	10	10
4011.	20 b. Golden figurine and bowl (horiz.) ..	10	10
4012.	55 b. Gold oil flask	15	10
4013.	1 l. 55 Brooch and bracelets (horiz.) ..	60	10
4014.	2 l. 75 Gold platter	90	10
4015.	6 l. 80 Filgree cup-holder (horiz.) ..	2·40	1·00

MINIMUM PRICE

The minimum price quoted is 5p which represents a handling charge rather than a basis for valuing common stamps. For further notes about prices see introductory pages.

762. Oboga Jar.

763. "Postilion" (A. Verona).

1973. Rumanian Ceramics. Multicoloured.

4018.	10 b. Type **762**	10	10
4019.	20 b. Vama dish and jug ..	10	10
4020.	55 b. Maginea bowl ..	10	10
4021.	1 l. 55 Sibiu Saschiz jug and dish	60	10
4022.	2 l. 75 Pisc pot and dish ..	85	15
4023.	6 l. 80 Oboga "bird" vessel	2·10	45

1973. Stamp Day.

4024. **763.**	1 l. 10+90 b. mult. ..	1·10	1·10

764. "Textile Workers" (G. Saru).

765. Town Hall, Craiova.

1973. Paintings showing Workers. Mult.

4025.	10 b. Type **764**	10	10
4026.	20 b. "Construction Site" (M. Bunescu) (horiz.) ..	10	10
4027.	55 b. "Shipyard Workers" (H. Catargi) (horiz.) ..	15	10
4028.	1 l. 55 "Working Man" (H. Catargi)	40	10
4029.	2 l. 75 "Miners" (A. Phoebus)	1·00	15
4030.	6 l. 80 "The Spinner" (N. Grigorescu)	2·00	85

1974.

(a) Buildings.

4032.	**765.**	5 b. red	10	10
4033.	–	10 b. blue	10	10
4034.	–	20 b. orange ..	10	10
4035.	–	35 b. green	10	10
4036.	–	40 b. violet	10	10
4037.	–	50 b. blue	10	10
4038.	–	55 b. brown	10	10
4039.	–	60 b. red	10	10
4040.	–	1 l. blue	15	10
4041.	–	1 l. 20 green ..	20	10

(b) Ships.

4042.	–	1 l. 35 black	30	10
4043.	–	1 l. 45 blue	30	10
4044.	–	1 l. 50 red	30	10
4045.	–	1 l. 55 blue	40	10
4046.	–	1 l. 75 green	50	10
4047.	–	2 l. 20 blue	55	10
4048.	–	3 l. 65 lilac	80	10
4049.	–	4 l. 70 purple	1·25	15

DESIGNS—VERT. 10 b. "Column of Infinity", Tirgu Jiu. 40 b. Romanesque church, Densus. 50 b. Reformed Church, Dej. 1 l. Curtea de Arges Monastery. HORIZ. 20 b. Heroes' Monument, Merasesti. 35 b. Citadel, Risnov. 55 b. Castle, Maldarasti. 60 b. National Theatre, Jassy. 1 l. 20, Fortress and church, Tirgu Mures. 1 l. 35, Danube tug "Impingator". 1 l. 45, Freighter "Dimbovita". 1 l. 50, Danube passenger vessel "Muntenia". 1 l. 55, Cadet barque "Mircea". 1 l. 75, Liner "Transylvania". 2 l. 20, Bulk carrier "Oltul". 3 l. 65, Trawler "Mures". 4 l. 70, Tanker "Arges".

767. "Boats at Honfleur" (Monet).

1974. Impressionist Paintings. Multicoloured.

4056.	20 b. Type **767** ..	10	10
4057.	40 b. "Moret Church" (Sisley) (vert.)	10	10
4058.	55 b. "Orchard in Blossom" (Pissarro) ..	15	10
4059.	1 l. 75 "Jeanne" (Pissarro) (vert.)	35	10
4060.	2 l. 75 "Landscape" (Renoir)	60	15
4061.	3 l. 60 "Portrait of a Girl" (Cezanne) (vert.) ..	1·60	35

768. Trotting with Sulky.

769. Nicolas Titulescu (Rumanian League of Nations Delegate).

1974. Cent. of Horse-racing in Rumania. Multicoloured.

4063.	40 b. Type **768**	10	10
4064.	55 b. Three horses racing	15	10
4065.	60 b. Horse galloping ..	20	10
4066.	1 l. 55 Two trotters racing	40	10
4067.	2 l. 75 Three trotters racing	75	10
4068.	3 c. 45 Two horses racing	1·25	35

1974. Interparliamentary Congress Session, Bucharest.

4069. **769.**	1 l. 75 multicoloured	50	20

771. "Anniversary Parade" (Pepene Cornelia).

1974. 25th Anniv. of Young Pioneers Organization.

4071. **771.**	55 b. multicoloured	50	10

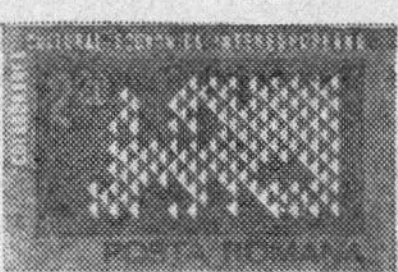
772. "Europe".

1974. Inter-European Cultural and Economic Co-operation. Multicoloured.

4072.	2 l. 20 Type **772**	1·50	1·50
4073.	3 l. 45 Satellite over Europe	2·40	2·00

1974. Rumania's Victory in World Handball Championships. No. 3959 surch. **ROMANIA CAMPIOANA MONDIALA 1974** and value.

4074.	1 l. 75 on 20 b. mult. ..	3·25	2·25

774. Postal Motor Boat.

1974. U.P.U. Cent. Multicoloured.

4075.	20 b. Type **774**	10	10
4076.	40 b. Loading mail-train	40	10
4077.	55 b. Loading mail-plane	10	10
4078.	1 l. 75 Rural postman delivering letter ..	45	10
4079.	2 l. 75 Town postman delivering letter ..	50	15
4080.	3 l. 60 Young stamp collectors	90	25

775. Footballers.

776. Anniversary Emblem.

1974. World Cup Football Championships, West Germany.

4082.	**775.**	20 b. multicoloured ..	10	10
4083.	–	40 b. multicoloured ..	10	10
4084.	–	55 b. multicoloured ..	10	10
4085.	–	1 l. 75 multicoloured	30	10
4086.	–	2 l. 75 multicoloured	65	15
4087.	–	3 l. 60 multicoloured	90	20

DESIGNS: Nos. 4083/7, Football scenes similar to Type **775**.

1974. Council for Mutual Economic Aid. 25th Anniv.

4089. **776.**	55 b. multicoloured ..	45	15

777. U.N. and World Population Emblems.

778. Emblem on Map of Europe.

1974. World Population Year Conference, Bucharest.

4090. **777.**	2 l. multicoloured ..	65	15

1974. "Euromax" Exhibition, Bucharest.

4091. **778.**	4 l.+3 l. yell., bl. & red	2·40	35

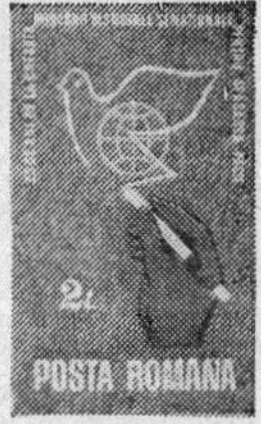

779. Hand drawing Peace Dove.

780. Prince John of Wallachia (400th birth anniv.).

1974. 25th Anniv. of World Peace Movement.

4092. **779.**	2 l. multicoloured ..	50	10

1974. Anniversaries.

4093.	**780.**	20 b. blue	10	10
4094.	–	55 b. red	10	10
4095.	–	1 l. blue	25	10
4096.	–	1 l. 10 brown ..	20	10
4097.	–	1 l. 30 purple ..	35	10
4098.	–	1 l. 40 violet	40	10

DESIGNS AND ANNIVERSARIES—VERT. 1 l. Iron and Steel Works, Hunedoara (220th anniv.). 1 l. 10, Avram Iancu (150th birth anniv.). 1 l. 30, Dr. C. I. Parhon (birth cent.). 1 l. 40, Dosoftei (savant) (350th birth anniv.). HORIZ. 55 b. Soldier and Installations (Rumanian Army Day. 30th anniv.).

781. Rumanian and Soviet Flags as "XXX".

783. "Centaurea nervosa".

1974. 30th Anniv. of Liberation. Mult.

4099.	40 b. Type **781**	15	10
4100.	55 b. Citizens and flags (horiz.)	15	10

1974. "Save Nature". Wild Flowers. Mult.

4102.	20 b. Type **783**	10	10
4103.	40 b. "Fritillaria montana"	10	10
4104.	55 b. "Taxus baccata" ..	20	10
4105.	1 l. 75 "Rhododendron kotschyi"	40	10
4106.	2 l. 75 "Eritrichium nanum"	55	20
4107.	3 l. 60 "Dianthus spiculifolius"	85	25

784. Bust of Isis.

1974. Rumanian Archaeological Finds. Sculpture. Multicoloured.
4108. 20 b. Type **784** 10 10
4109. 40 b. Glykon serpent (sculpture) 15 10
4110. 55 b. Head of Emperor Decius (bronze) .. 15 10
4111. 1 l. 75 Rumanian Woman (statue).. .. .. 30 10
4112. 2 l. 75 Mithras (sculptured relief) 50 15
4113. 3 l. 60 Rumanian senator (statue).. .. .. 1·10 25

785. Sibiu Market Place.

1974. Stamp Day.
4114. **785.** 2 l. 10+1 l. 90 mult. 1·50 35

1974. "Nationala 74" Stamp Exhibition. No. 4114 optd. **EXPOZITIA FILATELICA "NATIONALA '74" 15-24 noiembrie Bucuresti.**
4115. **785.** 2 l. 10+1 l. 90 mult. 2·75 2·75

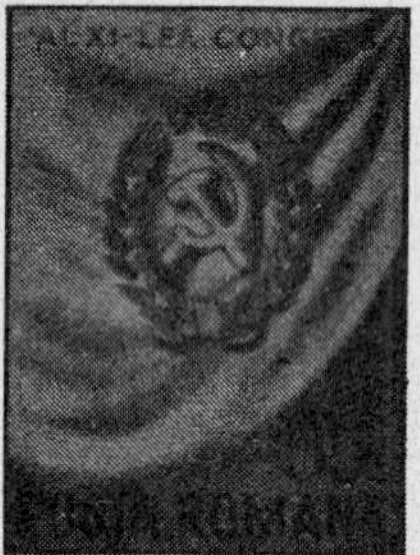
787. Party Emblem.

1974. 11th Rumanian Communist Party Congress, Bucharest.
4116. **787.** 55 b. multicoloured.. 10 10
4117. – 1 l. multicoloured .. 15 10
DESIGN: 1 l. Similar to Type **787**, showing party emblem and curtain.

788. "The Discus-thrower" (Myron).

1974. 60th Anniv. of Rumanian Olympic Committee.
4118. **788.** 2 l. multicoloured .. 1·00 25

789. "Skylab". **790.** Dr. Albert Schweitzer.

1974. "Skylab" Space Laboratory.
4119. **789.** 2 l. 50 multicoloured 1·25 1·10

1974. Birth Cent. of Dr. Albert Schweitzer.
4120. **790.** 40 b. brown 25 10

791. Handball. **793.** Torch and Inscription.

HAVE YOU READ THE NOTES AT THE BEGINNING OF THIS CATALOGUE?
These often provide answers to the enquiries we receive.

792. "Rocks and Birches".

1975. World Universities Handball Championships, Rumania.
4121. **791.** 55 b. multicoloured.. 15 10
4122. – 1 l. 75 multicoloured (vert.) 30 10
4123. – 2 l. 20 multicoloured 55 20
DESIGNS: 1 l. 75, 2 l. 20, similar designs to Type **791.**

1975. Paintings by Ion Andreescu. Mult.
4124. 20 b. Type **792** 10 10
4125. 40 b. "Peasant Woman with Green Kerchief".. 10 10
4126. 55 b. "Winter in the Forest".. .. .. 15 10
4127. 1 l. 75 "Winter in Barbizon" (horiz.).. .. 35 10
4128. 2 l. 75 Self-portrait 60 20
4129. 3 l. 50 "Main Road" (horiz.) 1·40 35

1975. 10th Anniv. of Socialist Republic.
4130. **793.** 40 b. multicoloured.. 25 10

794. "Battle of the High Bridge" (O. Obedeanu).

1975. 500th Anniv. of Victory over the Ottomans at High Bridge.
4131. **794.** 55 b. multicoloured 40 10

795. "Peasant Woman Spinning" (N. Grigorescu). **796.** "Self-portrait".

1975. International Women's Year.
4132. **795.** 55 b multicoloured.. 30 10

1975. 500th Birth Anniv. of Michelangelo.
4133. **796.** 5 l. multicoloured .. 1·60 25

798. Mitsui Children's Science Pavilion, Okinawa.

1975. International Exposition, Okinawa.
4135. **798.** 4 l. multicoloured .. 1·50 30

799. "Peonies" (N. Tonitza).

1975. Inter-European Cultural and Economic Co-operation. Multicoloured.
4136. 2 l. 20 Type **799** .. 1·50 1·50
4137. 3 l. 45 "Chrysanthemums" (St. Luchian) 2·00 2·00

800. Dove with Coded Letter.

1975. Introduction of Postal Coding.
4138. **800.** 55 b. multicoloured.. 30 10

801. Convention Emblem on "Globe".

1975. Centenary of International Metre Convention.
4139. **801.** 1 l. 85 multicoloured 85 20

802. Mihail Eminescu and Museum.

1975. 125th Birth Anniv. of Mihail Eminescu (poet).
4140. **802.** 55 b. multicoloured.. 30 10

803. Roman Coins and Stone Inscription. **805.** Ana Ipatescu.

1975. Bimillenary of Alba Julia.
4141. **803.** 55 b. multicoloured.. 30 10

1975. Death Centenary of Ana Ipatescu (revolutionary).
4143. **805.** 55 b. mauve.. .. 30 10

806. Turnu-Severin.

1975. European Architectural Heritage Year. Roman Antiquities.
4144. – 55 b. black & brown 10 10
4145. – 1 l. 20 black, pale blue and blue 25 15
4146. – 1 l. 55 black & green 50 15
4147. – 1 l. 75 black and red.. 60 20
4148. **806.** 2 l. black and ochre.. 70 25
4149. – 2 l. 25 black and blue 90 55
DESIGNS—VERT. 55 b. Emperor Trajan. 1 l. 20, Trajan's Column, Rome. 1 l. 55, Decebalus (sculpture). 10 l. Roman remains, Gradiste. HORIZ. 1 l. 75, Imperial monument, Adam Clissi. 2 l. 25, Trajan's Bridge.

807. "Apollo" and "Soyuz" Spacecraft.

1975. Air. "Apollo-Soyuz" Space Link. Multicoloured.
4151. 1 l. 75 Type **807** .. 1·40 1·40
4152. 3 l. 25 "Apollo" and "Soyuz" linked together .. .. 1·60 1·60

808. "Michael the Brave" (A. Sadeler).

1975. 375th Anniv. of First Political Union of Rumanian States. Multicoloured.
4153. 55 b. Type **808** 10 10
4154. 1 l. 20 "Ottoman Envoys bringing gifts to Michael the Brave" (T. Aman) (horiz.) 25 10
4155. 2 l. 75 "Michael the Brave at Calugareni" (T. Aman).. .. .. 55 20

810. "Delphinium consolida". **812.** Policeman using Walkie-talkie.

1975. Flowers. Multicoloured.
4157. 20 b. Type **810**.. .. 10 10
4158. 40 b. "Papaver dubium" 10 10
4159. 55 b. "Xeranthemum annuum" 15 10
4160. 1 l. 75 "Helianthemum nummularium" .. 35 10
4161. 2 l. 75 "Salvia pratensis" 65 15
4162. 3 l. 60 "Cichorium intybus" 85 25

1975. International Philatelic Fair, Riccione (Italy). Optd. **Riccione—Italia 23-25 August 1975.**
4163. **796.** 5 l. multicoloured .. 5·00 5·00

1975. Road Safety.
4164. **812.** 55 b. blue 40 10

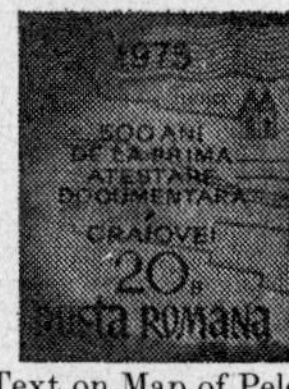

813. Text on Map of Pelendava.

1975. 1750th Anniv. of First Documentary Attestations of Daco-Getian Settlements of Pelendava and 500th Anniv. of Craiova. Multicoloured.
4165. 20 b. Type **813** 10 10
4166. 55 b. Map showing location of Pelendava and Craiova (horiz.) .. 15 10
4167. 1 l. Text on map of Pelendava 25 10

814. Muntenia Carpet.

1975. Rumanian Carpets. Multicoloured.
4168. 20 b. Type **814** 10 10
4169. 40 b. Banat 10 10
4170. 55 b. Oltenia 15 10
4171. 1 l. 75 Moldova 50 10
4172. 2 l. 75 Oltenia (different) 65 20
4173. 3 l. 60 Maramures .. 80 30

815. T.V. "12 M" Minibus.

1975. Rumanian Motor Vehicles. Mult.
4174. 20 b. Type **815** 10 10
4175. 40 b. L.K.W. "19 A.L.P." Oil tanker 15 10
4176. 55 b. A.R.O. "240" Field car 15 10
4177. 1 l. 75 L.K.W. "R 8135 F" Truck 50 10
4178. 2 l. 75 P.K.W. "Dacia 1300" Saloon car .. 65 20
4179. 3 l. 60 L.K.W. "R 19215 D.F.K." Tipper truck 85 35

816. Postal Transit Centre, Bucharest.

1975. Stamp Day. Multicoloured.
4180. 1 l. 50+1 l. 50 Type **816** 1·40 60
4181. 2 l. 10+1 l. 90 Aerial view of P.T.C. .. .. 2·40 85

818. Toboganning.

1976. Winter Olympic Games, Innsbruck. Multicoloured.

4183. 20 b. Type **818** 10 10
4184. 40 b. Rifle-shooting (biathlon) (vert.) 15 10
4185. 55 b. Downhill skiing (slalom) 25 10
4186. 1 l. 75 Ski-jumping .. 45 20
4187. 2 l. 75 Figure-skating (women's) 70 30
4188. 3 l. 60 Ice-hockey .. 1·25 60

819. " Washington at Valley Forge " (W. Trego).

1976. Bicent. of American Revolution. Mult.

4190. 20 b. Type **819** 10 10
4191. 40 b. " Washington at Trenton " (Trumbull) (vert.) 10 10
4192. 55 b. " Washington crossing the Delaware " (Leutze) 25 10
4193. 1 l. 75 " Capture of the Hessians " (Trumbull) 55 20
4194. 2 l. 75 " Jefferson " (Sully) (vert.) 85 25
4195. 3 l. 60 " Surrender of Cornwallis at Yorktown " (Trumbull) .. .. 1·25 40

820. " Prayer ".

1976. Birth Centenary of C. Brancusi (sculptor). Multicoloured.

4197. 55 b. Type **820** 15 10
4198. 1 l. 75 Architectural Assembly, Tg. Jiu .. 35 15
4199. 3 l. 60 C. Brancusi .. 90 35

821. Anton Davidoglu (mathematician) (birth cent.). **823.** Dr. Carol Davila.

822. Inscribed Tablets, Tibiscum (Banat).

1976. Anniversaries. Multicoloured.

4200. 40 b. Type **821** 10 10
4201. 55 b. Prince Vlad Tepes (500th death anniv.) .. 15 10
4202. 1 l. 20 Costache Negri (patriot-death centenary) 25 10
4203. 1 l. 75 Gallery, Archives Museum (50th anniv.) 30 20

1976. Daco-Roman Archaeological Finds. Multicoloured.

4204. 20 b. Type **822** 10 10
4205. 40 b. Roman sculptures 15 10
4206. 55 b. Dacian coins and pottery 25 10
4207. 1 l. 75 Dacian pottery .. 50 10
4208. 2 l. 75 Roman Altar and spears 65 15
4209. 3 l. 60 Vase and spears .. 95 35

1976. Centenary of Rumanian Red Cross. Multicoloured.

4211. 55 b. Type **823** (postage) 10 10
4212. 1 l. 75 Nurse and patient 30 10
4213. 2 l. 20 First aid 40 10
4214. 3 l. 35 Blood donors (air) 75 25

824. King Decebalus Vase. **825.** Rumanian Arms.

1976. Inter-European Cultural and Economic Collaboration. Multicoloured.

4215. 2 l. 20 Type **824** 65 75
4216. 3 l. 45 Vase with portrait of King Michael the Brave 2·00 2·00

1976.

4217. **825.** 1 l. 75 multicoloured 65 10

826. De Havilland " DH-9".

1976. 50th Anniv. of TAROM (State airline).

4218. 20 b. Type **826** 10 10
4219. 40 b. I.C.A R. " Commercial " monoplane .. 20 10
4220. 60 b. Douglas " DC "-3 .. 30 10
4221. 1 l. 75 Antonov " AN "-24 70 10
4222. 2 l. 75 Ilyushin " IL "-62 90 15
4223. 3 l. 60 Boeing " 707 " .. 1·40 45

827. Gymnastics. **828.** Spiru Haret.

1976. Olympic Games, Montreal. Mult.

4224. 20 b. Type **827** 10 10
4225. 40 b. Boxing 15 10
4226. 55 b. Handball 30 10
4227. 1 l. 75 Rowing (horiz.) .. 45 15
4228. 2 l. 75 Gymnastics (different) (horiz.) 70 20
4229. 3 l. 60 Canoeing (horiz.) .. 1·25 30

1976. 125th Birth Anniv. of Spiru Haret (mathematician).

4231. **828.** 20 b. brn., orge. & blue 25 10

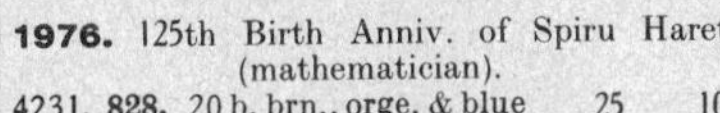

829. Daco-Getian Sculpture on Map of Buzau.

1976. 1600th Anniv. of Buzau State.

4232. **829.** 55 b. multicoloured .. 30 10

1976. Philatelic Exhibition, Bucharest. No. 4199 surch. **+1.80 EXPOZITIA FILATELICA BUCURESTI. 12-19 IX 1976.**

4233. 3 l. 60+1 l. 80 mult. .. 8·25 8·25

831. Red Deer.

1976. Endangered Animals. Multicoloured.

4234. 20 b. Type **831** 10 10
4235. 40 b. Brown Bear .. 20 10
4236. 55 b. Chamois 35 10
4237. 1 l. 75 Wild boar .. 50 10
4238. 2 l. 75 Red fox 95 25
4239. 3 l. 60 Lynx .. .. 1·25 35

832. Cathedral, Milan.

1976. " Italia '76 " International Philatelic Exhibition, Milan.

4240. **832.** 4 l. 75 multicoloured 1·50 35

833. D. Grecu (gymnast) and Bronze Medal.

1976. Olympic Games, Montreal. Rumanian Medal Winners. Multicoloured.

4241. 20 b. Type **833** 10 10
4242. 40 b. Fencing (Bronze Medal) 15 10
4243. 55 b. Javelin (Bronze Medal) 20 10
4244. 1 l. 75 Handball (Silver Medal) 35 10
4245. 2 l. 75 Boxing (Silver and Bronze Medals) (horiz.) 60 20
4246. 3 l. 60 Wrestling (Silver and Bronze Medals) (horiz.) .. .. 1·10 30
4247. 5 l. 70 Nadia Comaneci (gymnastics – 3 Gold, 1 Silver and 1 Bronze Medals) (27×42 mm.) 3·25 1·50

834. " Carnations and Oranges ".

1976. Floral Paintings by Stefan Luchian. Multicoloured.

4249. 20 b. Type **834** 10 10
4250. 40 b. " Flower Arrangement " 10 10
4251. 55 b. " Immortelles " .. 10 10
4252. 1 l. 75 " Roses in Vase " 35 15
4253. 2 l. 75 " Cornflowers " .. 45 15
4254. 3 l. 60 " Carnations in Vase " 90 35

835. " Elena Cuza " (T. Aman). **836.** Arms of Alba.

1976. Stamp Day.

4255. **835.** 2 l. 10+1 l. 90 mult. 1·90 1·50

1976. Rumanian Districts' Coats of Arms (1st series). Multicoloured.

4256. 55 b. Type **836** 15 10
4257. 55 b. Arad 15 10
4258. 55 b. Arges 15 10
4259. 55 b. Bacau 15 10
4260. 55 b. Bihor 15 10
4261. 55 b. Bisitrita Nasaud .. 15 10
4262. 55 b. Botosani 15 10
4263. 55 b. Brasov 15 10
4264. 55 b. Braila 15 10
4265. 55 b. Buzau 15 10
4266. 55 b. Caras-Severin .. 15 10
4267. 55 b. Cluj 15 10
4268. 55 b. Constanta 15 10
4269. 55 b. Covasna 15 10
4270. 55 b. Dimbovita 15 10

See also Nos. 4307/31, 4496/520 and 4542/63.

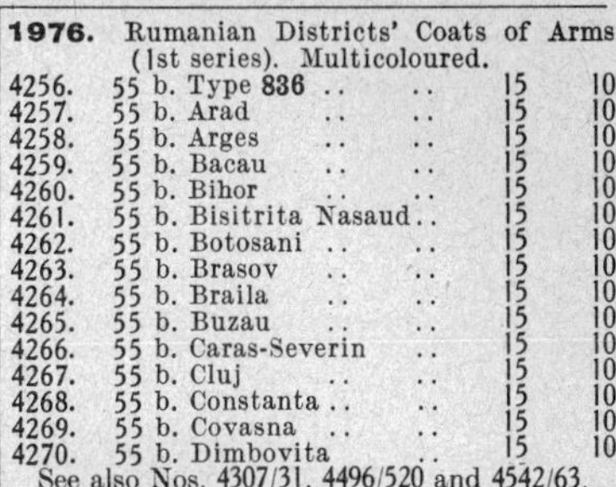

837. Ox Cart.

1977. Paintings by Nicola Grigorescu. Multicoloured.

4271. 55 b. Type **837** 15 10
4272. 1 l. Self portrait (vert.) .. 20 10
4273. 1 l. 50 " Shepherdess " .. 30 10
4274. 2 l. 15 " Girl with distaff " 40 15
4275. 3 l. 40 " Shepherd " (vert.) 50 25
4276. 4 l. 80 " Halt at the Well " 1·00 40

838. Telecommunications Station, Cheia.

1977.

4277. **838.** 55 b. multicoloured .. 20 10

839. I.C.A.R. " 1 ".

1977. Rumanian Gliders. Multicoloured.

4278. 20 b. Type **839** 10 10
4279. 40 b. I.S. " 3d " 15 10
4280. 55 b. R.G. " 5 " 20 10
4281. 1 l. 50 I.S. " 11 " .. 40 10
4282. 3 l. I.S. " 29D " 65 15
4283. 3 l. 40 " 28B " .. .. 1·10 40

840. Red Deer.

1977. Protected Animals. Multicoloured.

4284. 55 b. Type **840** 20 10
4285. 1 l. Mute swan 40 15
4286. 1 l. 50 Egyptian vulture 70 25
4287. 2 l. 15 European bison .. 60 10
4288. 3 l. 40 White-headed duck .. .. .. 1·40 35
4289. 4 l. 80 Common kingfisher .. .. 1·60 50

841. " The Infantryman " (O. Obedeanu).

1977. Cent. of Independence. Paintings. Multicoloured.
4290. 55 b. Type **841** 15 10
4291. 1 l. " Artillery Battery at Calafat " (S. Hentia) (horiz.) 20 10
4292. 1 l. 50 " Soldiers Attacking (S. Luchian) 30 10
4293. 2 l. 15 " Battle of Plevna " (N. Grigorescu) (horiz.) 45 10
4294. 3 l. 40 " The Artillerymen " (N. Grigorescu) (horiz.) 65 20
4295. 4 l. 80+2 l. " Battle of Rahova " (horiz.) .. 1·75 65

842. Sinaia, Carpathians.

843. Petro Rares (monarch) (450th birth Anniv.).

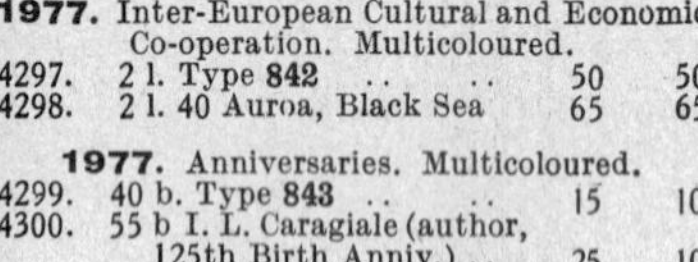

1977. Inter-European Cultural and Economic Co-operation. Multicoloured.
4297. 2 l. Type **842** 50 50
4298. 2 l. 40 Auroa, Black Sea 65 65

1977. Anniversaries. Multicoloured.
4299. 40 b. Type **843** 15 10
4300. 55 b I. L. Caragiale (author, 125th Birth Anniv.) .. 25 10

844. Nurse with Children and Emblems.

1977. 23rd International Red Cross Conference, Bucharest.
4301. **844.** 1 l. 50 multicoloured 40 15

845. Triumphal Arch, Bucharest.

1977. 60th Anniv. of Battles of Marasti, Marasesti and Oituz.
4302. **845.** 2 l. 15 Multicoloured 70 30

847. Postwoman and letters.

1977. Air.
4304. 20 l. Type **847** .. .. 5·00 1·40
4305. 30 l. Airliner and mail .. 7·50 2·00

848. Mount Titano Castle, San Marino.

1977. Cent. of San Marino Postage Stamps.
4306. **848.** 4 l. multicoloured .. 1·40 25

1977. Rumanian District Coats of Arms (2nd series). As T **836.** Multicoloured.
4307. 55 b. Dolj 15 10
4308. 55 b. Galati 15 10
4309. 55 b. Gorj 15 10
4310. 55 b. Harghita 15 10
4311. 55 b. Hunedoara 15 10
4312. 55 b. Ialomita 15 10
4313. 55 b. Iasi 15 10
4314. 55 b. Ilfov 15 10
4315. 55 b. Maramures 15 10
4316. 55 b. Mehedinti 15 10
4317. 55 b. Mures 15 10
4318. 55 b. Neamt 15 10
4319. 55 b. Olt 15 10
4320. 55 b. Prahova 15 10
4321. 55 b. Salaj 15 10
4322. 55 b. Satu Mare 15 10
4323. 55 b. Sibiu 15 10
4324. 55 b. Suceava 15 10
4325. 55 b. Teleorman 15 10
4326. 55 b. Timis 15 10
4327. 55 b. Tulcea 15 10
4328. 55 b. Vaslui 15 10
4329. 55 b. Vilcea 15 10
4330. 55 b. Vrancea 15 10
4331. 55 b. Rumanian postal emblem 15 10

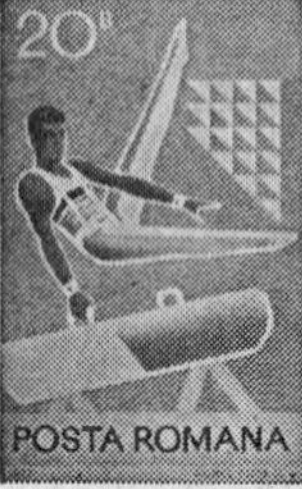

849. Gymnast on Vaulting Horse.

850. Dispatch Rider and Army Officer.

1977. Gymnastics. Multicoloured.
4332. 20 b. Type **849** 10 10
4333. 40 b. Floor exercise .. 10 10
4334. 55 b. Gymnast on parallel bars 15 10
4335. 1 l. Somersault on bar .. 25 10
4336. 2 l. 15 Gymnast on rings 40 15
4337. 4 l. 80 Gymnastic exercise 1·60 55

1977. Stamp Day.
4338. **850.** 2 l. 10+1 l. 90 mult. 1·40 1·25

851. Two Dancers with Sticks.

1977. Calusarii Folk Dance. Multicoloured.
4339. 20 b. Type **851** 10 10
4340. 40 b. Leaping dancer with stick 10 10
4341. 55 b. Two dancers .. 20 10
4342. 1 l. Dancer with stick .. 30 10
4343. 2 l. 15 Leaping dancers .. 50 15
4344. 4 l. 80 Leaping dancer .. 1·60 1·10

852. "Carpati" at Cazane.

1977. European Navigation on the Danube. Multicoloured.
4346 55 b. Type **852** 30 10
4347 1 l. Passenger vessel "Mircesti" near Orsova 40 10
4348 1 l. 50 Passenger vessel "Oltenita" near Calafat 60 15
4349 2 l. 15 Hydrofoil at Giurgiu port 65 25
4350 3 l. Passenger vessel "Herculani" at Tulcea 80 30
4351 3 l. 40 Passenger vessel "Muntenia" at Sulina 95 35
4352 4 l. 80 Map of Danube delta .. .. .. 2·00 80

853. Arms and Flag of Rumania.

1977. 30th Anniv. of Rumanian Republic. Multicoloured.
4354. 55 b. Type **853** 10 10
4355. 1 l. 20 Rumanian built computers 20 10
4356. 1 l. 75 National Theatre, Craiova 35 20

854. Firiza Dam.

1978. Rumanian Dams and Hydro-electric Installations. Multicoloured.
4357. 20 b. Type **854** 10 10
4358. 40 b. Negovanu dam .. 15 10
4359. 55 b. Piatra Neamt power station 25 10
4360. 1 l. Izvorul Montelui-Bicaz dam 30 10
4361. 2 l. 15 Vidraru dam .. 45 15
4362. 4 l. 80 Danube barrage and navigation system, Iron Gates 90 40

855. " LZ–1 " over Lake Constance.

1978. Air. Airships. Multicoloured.
4363. 60 b. Type **855** 15 10
4364. 1 l. Santos Dumont dirigible over Paris 25 10
4365. 1 l. 50 " R34 " over Manhattan Island 35 10
4366. 2 l. 15 " Italia " at North Pole 50 10
4367. 3 l. 40 " Graf Zeppelin " over Brasov 70 15
4368. 4 l. 80 " Graf Zeppelin " over Sibiu .. .. 1·40 45

856. Footballers and Emblem.

1978. World Cup Football Championship, Argentina.
4370. **856.** 55 b. blue 10 10
4371. – 1 l. orange 15 10
4372. – 1 l. 50 yellow .. 25 10
4373. – 2 l. 15 red 40 10
4374. – 3 l. 40 green 65 15
4375. – 4 l. 80 mauve .. .. 1·40 25

DESIGNS: Nos. 4371/5, Footballers and emblem, similar to Type **856**.

857. King Decebalus of Dacia.

858. Worker and Factory.

1978. Inter-European Cultural and Economic Co-operation. Multicoloured.
4377. 1 l. 30 Type **857** 65 75
4378. 3 l. 40 Prince Mircea the Elder .. .. .. 2·75 2·75

1978. 30th Anniv of Nationalization of Industry.
4379 **858** 55 b. multicoloured .. 20 10

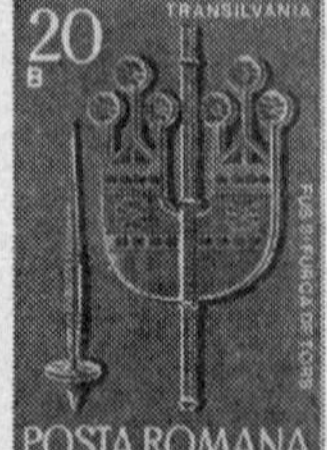

859. Spindle and Fork Handle, Transylvania.

1978. Woodcarving. Multicoloured.
4380. 20 b. Type **859** 10 10
4381. 40 b. Cheese mould, Muntenia 15 10
4382. 55 b. Spoons, Oltenia .. 20 10
4383. 1 l. Barrel, Moldavia .. 25 10
4384. 2 l. 15 Ladle and mug, Transylvania 40 10
4385. 4 l. 80 Water bucket, Oltenia 80 35

860. Danube Delta.

1978. Tourism. Multicoloured.
4386. 55 b. Type **860** 60 15
4387. 1 l. Bran Castle (vert.) .. 20 10
4388. 1 l. 50 Moldavian village 25 10
4389. 2 l. 15 Muierii caves .. 45 10
4390. 3 l. 40 Cable car at Boiana Brasov 60 15
4391. 4 l. 80 Mangalia (Black Sea resort) 90 30

861. MC–6 Electron Microscope.

862. Polovraci Cave.

1978. Rumanian Industry. Multicoloured.
4393. 20 b. Type **861** 10 10
4394. 40 b. Hydraulic excavator 10 10
4395. 55 b. Power station control room 15 10
4396. 1 l. 50 Oil drillheads .. 25 10
4397. 3 l. C–12 combine harvester (horiz.) 45 15
4398. 3 l. 40 Petro-chemical combine, Pitesti .. 55 25

1978. Caves and Caverns. Multicoloured.
4399. 55 b. Type **862** 10 10
4400. 1 l. Topolnita 20 10
4401. 1 l. 50 Ponoare 25 10
4402. 2 l. 15 Ratei 35 10
4403. 3 l. 40 Closani 60 15
4404. 4 l. 80 Epuran .. .. 1·10 30

863. Gymnastics.

865. Symbols of Equality.

864. Zoomorphic Gold Plate.

1978. " Daciada " Rumanian Games. Multicoloured.
4405. 55 b. Type **863** 10 10
4406. 1 l. Running 15 10
4407. 1 l. 50 Skiing 20 10
4408. 2 l. 15 Horse jumping .. 30 10
4409. 3 l. 40 Football 55 15
4410. 4 l. 80 Handball .. .. 1·10 25

1978. Daco-Roman Archaeology. Mult.
4411. 20 b. Type **864** 10 10
4412. 40 b. Gold torque .. 10 10
4413. 55 b. Gold cameo ring .. 15 10
4414. 1 l. Silver bowl 25 10
4415. 2 l. 15 Bronze eagle (vert.) 45 15
4416. 4 l. 80 Silver bracelet .. 55 30

1978. International Anti-Apartheid Year.
4418. **865.** 3 l. 40 blk., yell. & red 65 60

867. Ptolemaic Map of Dacia (2000th anniv. of first record of Ziridava).

1978. Anniversaries in the History of Arad. Multicoloured.
4420. 40 b. Type **867** 10 10
4421. 55 b. Meeting place of National Council (60th anniv. of unified Rumania) 10 10
4422. 1 l. 75 Ceramic pots (950th anniv. of first documentary evidence of Arad) 25 15

868. Dacian Warrior.

1978. Stamp Day.

4423. 868. 6 l.+3 l. multicoloured 2·00 1·40

No. 4423 was issued se-tenant with a premium-carrying tab as shown in Type 868.

869. Assembly at Alba Julia. 871. Dacian Warrior.

870. Wright Brothers and "Flyer 1".

1979. 60th Anniv. of National Unity. Mult.

4424. 55 b. Type 869 .. .. 10 10
4425. 1 l. Open book, flag and sculpture 20 10

1979. Air. Pioneers of Aviation. Multicoloured.

4426. 55 b. Type 870 .. 15 10
4427. 1 l. Bleriot and monoplane 25 10
4428. 1 l. 50 Fokker and "F VII Trimotor" 30 10
4429. 2 l. 15 Tupolev and "ANT-25" 50 10
4430. 3 l. Lilienthal and glider 55 15
4431. 3 l. 40 Trajan Vuia and aircraft 70 15
4432. 4 l. 80 Aurel Vlaicu and first Rumanian aeroplane 90 30

1979. 2050th Anniv. of Independent Centralised Dacian State. Multicoloured.

4434. 5 b. Type 871 .. .. 15 10
4435. 1 l. 50 Dacian warrior on horseback 25 20

872. "The Heroes from Vaslui". 873. Championship Emblem.

1979. International Year of the Child (1st issue). Children's Paintings. Multicoloured.

4436. 55 b. Type 872 .. .. 10 10
4437. 1 l. "Tica's Folk Music Band" 15 10
4438. 1 l. 50 "Building-site" 20 10
4439. 2 l. 15 "Industrial Landscape" (horiz.) .. 30 10
4440. 3 l. 40 "Winter Holiday" (horiz.) 45 15
4441. 4 l. 80 "Pioneers' Celebration" (horiz.) .. 65 25

See also Nos. 4453/6.

1979. European Junior, Miercurea-Ciuc and World Championship, Ice Hockey Championship Galati. Multicoloured.

4442. 1 l. 30 Type 873 .. .. 25 10
4443. 3 l. 40 Championship emblem (different) .. 45 15

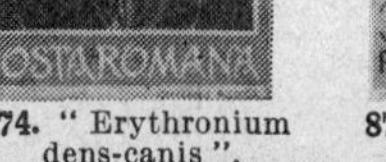

874. "Erythronium dens-canis". 876. Oil Derrick.

875. Street with Mail-coach and Post-rider.

1979. Protected Flowers. Multicoloured.

4444. 55 b. Type 874 .. .. 10 10
4445. 1 l. "Viola alpina" .. 15 10
4446. 1 l. 50 "Linum borzaeanum" 20 10
4447. 2 l. 15 "Convolvulus persicus" 30 10
4448. 3 l. 40 "Primula auricula serratifolia" 45 15
4449. 4 l. 80 "Aquilegia transsylvanica" 65 25

1979. Inter-European Cultural and Economic Co-operation.

4450. 1 l. 30 Type 875 (postage) 45 45
4451. 3 l. 40 Aircraft and motorcycle postman (air) .. 55 55

1979. International Petroleum Congress, Bucharest.

4452. 876. 3 l. 40 multicoloured 50 15

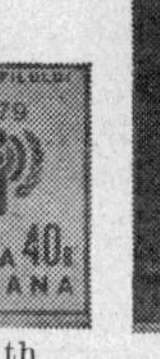

877. Children with Flowers. 878. Young Pioneer.

1979. Int. Year of the Child (2nd issue). Multicoloured.

4453. 40 b. Type 877 .. .. 10 10
4454. 1 l. Children at creative play 20 10
4455. 2 l. Children with hare .. 35 10
4456. 4 l. 60 Young pioneers .. 70 20

1979. 30th Anniv. of Young Pioneers.

4457. 878. 55 b. multicoloured 10 10

879. "Woman in Garden". 881. Stefan Gheorghiu.

880. Brasov University.

1979. Paintings by G. Tattarescu. Multicoloured.

4458. 20 b. Type 879 .. .. 10 10
4459. 40 b. "Muntenian Woman" 10 10
4460. 55 b. "Muntenian Man" 10 10
4461. 1 l. "General G. Magheru" 20 10
4462. 2 l. 15 "The Artist's Daughter" 40 10
4463. 4 l. 80 "Self-portrait" .. 1·00 20

1979. Contemporary Architecture. Mult.

4464. 20 b. State Theatre, Tirgu Mures 10 10
4465. 40 b. Type 880 .. .. 10 10
4466. 55 b. Administration Centre, Baia Mare 10 10
4467. 1 l. Stefan Gheorghiu Acadamy, Bucharest .. 15 10
4468. 2 l. 15 Administration Centre, Botosani .. 30 10
4469. 4 l. 80 House of Culture, Tirgoviste 70 20

1979. Anniversaries and Events. Multicoloured.

4470. 40 b. Type 881 (birth cent.) 10 10
4471. 55 b. Statue of Gheroghe Lazar (poet) (Birth bicent.) 10 10
4472. 2 l. 15 Fallen Workers monument (Strike at Lupeni. 50th anniv.) 30 10

882. Moldavian and Wallachian Women and Monument to Union. 883. Party and National Flags.

1979. 120th Anniv. of Union of Moldavia and Wallachia.

4473. 882. 4 l. 60 multicoloured 1·00 25

1979. Liberation. 25th Anniv. Multicoloured.

4474. 55 b. Type 883 .. .. 10 10
4475. 1 l. "Workers' Militia" (L. Suhar) (horiz.) .. 20 10

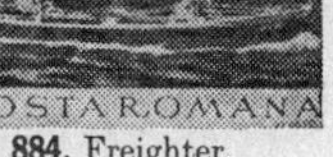

884. Freighter "Galati". 885. "Snapdragons".

1979. Ships. Multicoloured.

4476. 55 b. Type 884 .. .. 15 10
4477. 1 l. Freighter "Bucuresti" 20 10
4478. 1 l. 50 Bulk carrier "Resita" 30 10
4479. 2 l. 15 Bulk carrier "Tomis" 35 15
4480. 3 l. 40 Tanker "Dacia" .. 55 20
4481. 4 l. 80 Tanker "Independenta" 75 40

1979. "Socfilex 79" Stamp Exhibition, Bucharest. Flower Paintings by Stefan Luchian. Multicoloured.

4482. 40 b. Type 885 .. .. 10 10
4483. 60 b. "Carnations" .. 10 10
4484. 1 l. 55 "Flowers on a Stairway" 25 10
4485. 4 l.+2 l. "Flowers of the Field" .. .. 1·10 1·10

888. Olympic Stadium, Melbourne (1956 Games).

1979. Olympic Games, Moscow (1980). Olympic Stadia. Multicoloured.

4489. 55 h. Type 888 .. .. 10 10
4490. 1 l. Rome (1960) 15 10
4491. 1 l. 50 Tokyo (1964) .. 25 10
4492. 2 l. 15 Mexico City (1968) 30 10
4493. 3 l. 40 Munich (1972) .. 45 10
4494. 4 l. 80 Montreal (1978) .. 70 25

1979. Municipal Coats of Arms. As T 836. Multicoloured.

4496 1 l. 20 Alba Julia .. 20 10
4497 1 l. 20 Arad 20 10
4498 1 l. 20 Bacau 20 10
4499 1 l. 20 Baia Mare .. 20 10
4500 1 l. 20 Birland 20 10
4501 1 l. 20 Botosani 20 10
4502 1 l. 20 Brasov 20 10
4503 1 l. 20 Braila 20 10
4504 1 l. 20 Buzau 20 10
4505 1 l. 20 Calarasi 20 10
4506 1 l. 20 Cluj 20 10
4507 1 l. 20 Constanta .. 20 10
4508 1 l. 20 Craiova 20 10
4509 1 l. 20 Dej 20 10
4510 1 l. 20 Deva 20 10
4511 1 l. 20 Drobeta Turnu Severin 20 10
4512 1 l. 20 Focsani 20 10
4513 1 l. 20 Galati 20 10
4514 1 l. 20 Gheorghe Gheorghiu Dej .. 20 10
4515 1 l. 20 Giurgiu 20 10
4516 1 l. 20 Hunedoara .. 20 10
4517 1 l. 20 Iasi 20 10
4518 1 l. 20 Lugoj 20 10
4519 1 l. 20 Medias 20 10
4520 1 l. 20 Odorheiu Secuiesc 20 10

889. Costumes of Maramures (female). 891. Figure Skating.

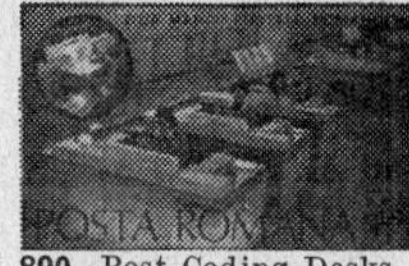

890. Post Coding Desks.

1979. National Costumes. Multicoloured.

4521. 20 b. Type 889 .. .. 10 10
4522. 40 b. Maramures (male) .. 15 10
4523. 55. b. Vrancea (female) .. 15 10
4524. 1 l. 50 Vrancea (male) .. 30 10
4525. 3 l. Padureni (female) .. 55 15
4526. 3 l. 40 Padureni (male) .. 60 30

1979. Stamp Day.

4527. 890. 2 l. 10+1 l. 90 mult. 75 30

1979. Winter Olympic Games, Lake Placid (1980). Multicoloured.

4528. 55 b. Type 891 .. .. 10 10
4529. 1 l. Downhill skiing .. 10 10
4530. 1 l. 50 Biathlon 15 10
4531. 2 l. 15 Bobsleighing .. 30 10
4532. 3 l. 40 Speed skating .. 50 10
4533. 4 l. 80 Ice hockey .. 70 20

892. Locomotive No. 43 "Calugareni". 893. Dacian Warrior.

1979. International Transport Exhibition, Hamburg. Multicoloured.

4535 55 b. Type 892 .. .. 15 10
4536 1 l. Locomotive No. 458 "Orleans" 35 10
4537 1 l. 50 Locomotive No. 1059 .. .. .. 40 10
4538 2 l. 15 Locomotive No. 15021 .. .. .. 55 15
4539 3 l. 40 Locomotive No. 231085 "Pacific" type .. 90 15
4540 4 l. 80 Electric locomotive "060-EA" .. .. 1·90 25

1980. Arms (4th series). As T 836. Multicoloured.

4542. 1 l. 20 Oradea 20 10
4543. 1 l. 20 Petrosani 20 10
4544. 1 l. 20 Piatra Neamt .. 20 10
4545. 1 l. 20 Pitesti 20 10
4546. 1 l. 20 Ploiesti 20 10
4547. 1 l. 20 Resita 20 10
4548. 1 l. 20 Rimnicu Vilcea 20 10
4549. 1 l. 20 Roman 20 10
4550. 1 l. 20 Satu Mare .. 20 10
4551. 1 l. 20 Sibiu 20 10
4552. 1 l. 20 Sighetu Marmatiei 20 10
4553. 1 l. 20 Sighisoara .. 20 10
4554. 1 l. 20 Suceava 20 10
4555. 1 l. 20 Tecuci 20 10
4556. 1 l. 20 Timisoara .. 20 10
4557. 1 l. 20 Tirgoviste .. 20 10
4558. 1 l. 20 Tirgu Jiu .. 20 10
4559. 1 l. 20 Tirgu Mures .. 20 10
4560. 1 l. 20 Tulcea 20 10
4561. 1 l. 20 Turda 20 10
4562. 1 l. 20 Turnu Magurele 20 10
4563. 1 l. 20 Bucharest .. 20 10

1980. 2050th Anniv. of Independent Centralised Dacian State under Burebista.

4564. 55 b. Type 893 .. .. 10 10
4565. 1 l. 50 Dacian fighters with flag 20 10

894. Common Kingfisher.

1980. European Nature Protection Year. Multicoloured.

4566. 55 b. Type 894 .. .. 45 15
4567. 1 l. Great egret (vert.) .. 60 15
4468. 1 l. 50 Red-breasted goose 75 25
4569. 2 l. 15 Red deer (vert.) .. 45 15
4570. 3 l. 40 Roe deer fawn .. 70 20
4571. 4 l. 80 European bison (vert.) .. .. .. 1·10 30

895. " Vallota purpurea ". **896.** Tudor Vladimirescu.

1980. Exotic Flowers from Bucharest Botanical Gardens. Multicoloured.

4573. 55 b. Type **895** 10 10
4574. 1 l. " Eichhornia crasipes " 20 10
4575. 1 l. 50 " Sprekelia formosissima " .. 25 10
4576. 2 l. 15 " Hypericum calycinum " 35 10
4577. 3 l. 40 " Camellia japonica " 45 25
4578. 4 l. 80 " Nelumbo nucifera " 70 25

1980. Anniversaries. Multicoloured.

4579. 40 b. Type **896** (revolutionary leader, birth bicent.) 10 10
4580. 55 b. Mihail Sadoveanu (writer—birth cent.) .. 10 10
4581. 1 l. 50 Battle of Posada (650th anniv.) 25 10
4582. 2 l. 15 Tudor Arghezi (poet—birth cent.) .. 35 10
4583. 3 l. Horea (leader, Transylvanian uprising—250th birth anniv.) .. 50 15

898. Dacian Fruit Dish. **899.** Throwing the Javelin.

1980. Bimillenary of Dacian Fortress Petrodava (now Piatra Neamt).

4585. **898.** 1 l. multicoloured .. 15 10

1980. Olympic Games, Moscow. Multicoloured.

4586. 55 b. Type **899** 10 10
4587. 1 l. Fencing 15 10
4588. 1 l. 50 Pistol shooting .. 20 10
4589. 2 l. 15 Single kayak .. 30 10
4590. 3 l. 40 Wrestling .. 45 10
4591. 4 l. 80 Single skiff .. 90 15

901. Congress Emblem. **902.** Fireman carrying Child.

1980. 15th International Congress of Historical Sciences.

4594. **901.** 55 b. deep blue & blue 10 10

1980. Firemen's Day.

4595. **902.** 55 b. multicoloured .. 10 10

903. Chinese and Rumanian Stamp Collectors. **906.** Dacian Warrior.

905. Rooks and Chessboard.

1980. Rumanian-Chinese Stamp Exhibition, Bucharest.

4596. **903.** 1 l. multicoloured .. 15 10

1980. 24th Chess Olympiad, Malta. Mult.

4598 55 b. Knights and chessboard 15 10
4599 1 l. Type **905** 25 10
4600 2 l. 15 Male head and chessboard 50 15
4601 4 l. 80 Female head and chessboard 95 35

1980. Military Uniforms. Multicoloured.

4602 20 b. Type **906** 10 10
4603 40 b. Moldavian soldier (15th century) .. 10 10
4604 55 b. Wallachian horseman (17th cent) .. 15 10
4605 1 l. Standard bearer (19th century) 20 10
4606 1 l. 50 Infantryman (19th century) 25 10
4607 2 l. 15 Lancer (19th cent) 35 15
4608 4 l. 80 Hussar (19th cent) 90 20

907. Burebista (sculpture, P. Mercea). **908.** George Oprescu.

1980. Stamp Day.

4609. **907.** 2 l. multicoloured .. 25 10

1981. Celebrities' Birth Anniversaries. Multicoloured.

4610. 1 l. 50 Type **908** (historian and art critic, centenary) .. 25 10
4611. 2 l. 15 Marius Bunescu (painter, centenary) .. 35 10
4612. 3 l. 40 Ion Georgescu (sculptor, 12th anniv.) 55 25

909. St. Bernard.

1981. Dogs. Multicoloured.

4613. 40 b. Mountain Sheepdog (horiz.) 10 10
4614. 55 b. Type **909** 15 10
4615. 1 l. Fox terrier (horiz.) .. 20 10
4616. 1 l. 50 Alsatian (horiz.) .. 30 10
4617. 2 l. 15 Boxer (horiz.) .. 45 10
4618. 3 l. 40 Dalmatian (horiz.) 65 15
4619. 4 l. 80 Poodle 85 30

910. Paddle-steamer "Stefan cel Mare".

1981. 125th Anniv of European Danube Committee. Multicoloured.

4620 55 b. Type **910** 20 10
4621 1 l. Danube Commission steam launch 30 15
4622 1 l. 50 Paddle-steamer "Tudor Vladimirescu" 45 15
4623 2 l. 15 Dredger "Sulina" 55 25
4624 3 l. 40 Paddle-steamer "Republica Populara Romana" 80 30
4625 4 l. 80 Freighter in Sulina Channel .. .. 1·00 40

911. Bare-neck Pigeon. **912.** Party Flag and Oak Leaves.

1981. Pigeons. Multicoloured.

4627. 40 b. Type **911** 15 10
4628. 55 b. Orbetan pigeon .. 10 10
4629. 1 l. Craiova chestnut pigeon 20 10
4630. 1 l. 50 Timisoara pigeon 30 10
4631. 2 l. 15 Homing pigeon .. 45 15
4632. 3 l. 40 Salonta giant pigeon 70 40

1981. 60th Anniv. of Rumanian Communist Party.

4633. **912.** 1 l. multicoloured .. 15 10

914. " Soyuz 40 ".

1981. Air. Soviet-Rumanian Space Flight. Multicoloured.

4635. 55 b. Type **914** 15 10
4636. 3 l. 40 " Soyuz "–" Salyut " link-up 55 15

915. Sun and Mercury. **916.** Industrial Symbols.

1981. The Planets. Multicoloured.

4638. 55 b. Type **915** 15 10
4639. 1 l. Venus, Earth and Mars 25 15
4640. 1 l. 50 Jupiter 35 20
4641. 2 l. 15 Saturn 50 25
4642. 3 l. 40 Uranus 75 30
4643. 4 l. 80 Neptune and Pluto 1·10 45

1981. " Singing Rumania " National Festival. Multicoloured.

4645. 55 b. Type **916** 15 10
4646. 1 l. 50 Science 30 10
4647. 2 l. 15 Agriculture .. 40 15
4648. 3 l. 40 Culture 65 30

917. Book and Flag. **918.** " Woman in an Interior ".

1981. " Universiada " Games, Bucharest. Multicoloured.

4649. 1 l. Type **917** 20 10
4650. 2 l. 15 Games emblem .. 40 20
4651. 4 l. 80 Stadium (horiz.) .. 1·00 1·00

1981. 150th Birth Anniv. of Theodore Aman (painter). Multicoloured.

4652. 40 b. " Self-portrait " .. 10 10
4653. 55 b. " Battle of Giurgiu " (horiz.) 15 10
4654. 1 l. " Family Picnic " (horiz.) 20 10
4655. 1 l. 50 " The Painter's studio " (horiz.) .. 30 10
4656. 2 l. 15 Type **918** 40 15
4657. 3 l. 10 Aman Museum, Bucharest (horiz.) .. 60 35

919. " The Thinker of Cernavoda " (polished stone sculpture). **920.** Blood Donation.

1981. 16th Science History Congress, Bucharest.

4658. **919.** 3 l. 40 multicoloured 65 65

1981. Blood Donor Publicity.

4659. **920.** 55 b. multicoloured .. 20 15

921. Central Military Hospital.

1981. 150th Anniv. of Central Military Hospital, Bucharest.

4660. **849.** 55 b. multicoloured 15 10

922. Paul Constantinescu. **923.** Children at Stamp Exhibition.

1981. Rumanian Musicians. Multicoloured.

4661. 40 b. George Enescu .. 15 10
4662. 55 b. Type **922** 15 10
4663. 1 l. Dinu Lipatti 25 10
4664. 1 l. 50 Ionel Perlea .. 35 10
4665. 2 l. 15 Ciprian Porumbescu 45 15
4666. 3 l. 40 Mihail Jora .. 70 40

1981. Stamp Day.

4667. **923.** 2 l. multicoloured .. 35 15

924. Hopscotch. **925.** Football Players.

1981. Children's Games and Activities. Multicoloured.

4668. 40 b. Type **924** (postage) 10 10
4669. 55 b. Football 15 10
4670. 1 l. Children with balloons and hobby horse .. 20 15
4671. 1 l. 50 Fishing 30 15
4672. 2 l. 15 Dog looking through school window at child 45 15
4673. 3 l. Child on stilts .. 55 20
4674. 4 l. Child tending sick dog 75 25
4675. 4 l. 80 Children with model aircraft (air) .. 1·00 75

Nos. 4671/5 are from illustrations by Norman Rockwell.

1981. World Cup Football Championship, Spain (1982). Multicoloured.

4676. 55 b. Type **925** 15 10
4677. 1 l. Goalkeeper saving ball 20 10
4678. 1 l. 50 Player heading ball 30 15
4679. 2 l. 15 Player kicking ball over head 40 20
4680. 3 l. 40 Goalkeeper catching ball 65 65
4681. 4 l. 80 Player kicking ball 90 90

926. Alexander the Good, Prince of Moldavia **927.** Entrance to Union Square Station.

1982. Anniversaries. Multicoloured.

4683 1 l. Type **926** (550th death anniv) 20 10
4684 1 l. 50 Bogdan P. Hasdeu (historian, 75th death anniv) 30 10
4685 2 l. 15 Nicolae Titulescu (diplomat and politician, birth centenary) .. 50 25

1982. Inauguration of Bucharest Underground Railway. Multicoloured.

4686. 60 b. Type **927** 15 10
4687. 2 l. 40 Platforms and train at Heroes' Square station 75 25

928. Dog rescuing Child from Sea.

1982. Dog, Friend of Mankind. Mult.

4688.	55 b. Type **928**	15	10
4689.	1 l. Shepherd and sheepdog (vert.)	20	10
4690.	3 l. Gundog (vert.)	55	15
4691.	3 l. 40 Huskies	65	20
4692.	4 l. Dog carrying woman's basket (vert.)	75	20
4693.	4 l. 80 Dog guiding blind person (vert.)	85	35
4694.	5 l. Dalmatian and Child with doll (vert.)	90	40
4695.	6 l. St. Bernard	1·10	55

929. Dove, Banner and Crowd.

1982. 60th Anniv. of Communist Youth Union.

4696.	1 l. Type **929**	20	10
4697.	1 l. 20 Construction worker	25	10
4698.	1 l. 50 Farm workers	30	15
4699.	2 l. Laboratory worker and students	40	15
4700.	2 l. 50 Labourers	55	20
4701.	3 l. Choir, musicians and dancers	65	25

932. Harvesting Wheat.

1982. 20th Anniv. of Agricultural Co-operatives. Multicoloured.

4704.	50 b. Type **932** (postage)	15	10
4705.	1 l. Cows and milking equipment	25	10
4706.	1 l. 50 Watering apple trees	30	15
4707.	2 l. 50 Cultivator in vineyard	55	20
4708.	3 l. Watering vegetables	65	25
4709.	4 l. Helicopter spraying cereal crop (air)	1·00	40

933. "Standard I" Hang-glider.

1982. Air. Hang-gliders. Multicoloured.

4711.	50 b. Type **933**	15	10
4712.	1 l. "Excelsior D"	35	10
4713.	1 l. 50 "Dedal I"	40	15
4714.	2 l. 50 "Entuziast"	75	25
4715.	4 l. "AK-22"	1·10	50
4716.	5 l. "Grifrom"	1·40	50

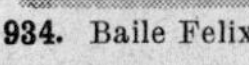

934. Baile Felix.

936. Vlaicu Monument, Banesti-Prahova.

935. "Legend".

1982. Spas and Health Resorts. Mult.

4717.	50 b. Type **934**	15	10
4718.	1 l. Perdeal (horiz.)	25	10
4719.	1 l. 50 Baile Herculane	30	15
4720.	2 l. 50 Eforie Nord (horiz.)	55	20
4721.	3 l. Olimp (horiz.)	65	20
4722.	5 l. Neptun (horiz.)	1·00	40

1982. Paintings by Sabin Balasa. Mult.

4723.	1 l. Type **935**	25	10
4724.	1 l. 50 "Contrarieties"	35	15
4725.	2 l. 50 "Peace Relay"	75	30
4726.	4 l. "Genesis of the Rumanian People" (vert.)	85	35

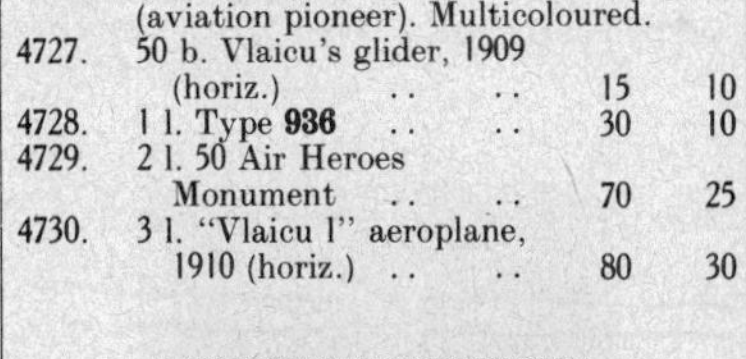

1982. Air. Birth Centenary of Aurel Vlaicu (aviation pioneer). Multicoloured.

4727.	50 b. Vlaicu's glider, 1909 (horiz.)	15	10
4728.	1 l. Type **936**	30	10
4729.	2 l. 50 Air Heroes Monument	70	25
4730.	3 l. "Vlaicu I" aeroplane, 1910 (horiz.)	80	30

938. Central Exhibition Pavilion.

1982. "Tib '82" International Fair, Bucharest.

4732. **938.**	2 l. multicoloured	45	10

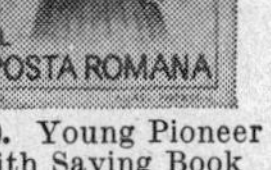

939. Young Pioneer with Saving Book and Books.

940. Postwoman delivering Letters.

1982. Saving Week. Multicoloured.

4733.	1 l. Type **939**	25	10
4734.	2 l. Savings Bank advertisement (Calin Popovici)	45	10

1982. Stamp Day. Multicoloured.

4735.	1 l. Type **940**	25	10
4736.	2 l. Postman	40	15

941. "Brave Young Man and the Golden Apples" (Petre Ispirescu).

942. Symbols of Industry, Party Emblem and Programme.

1982. Fairy Tales. Multicoloured.

4737.	50 b. Type **941**	15	10
4738.	1 l. "Bear tricked by the Fox" (Ion Creanga)	25	10
4739.	1 l. 50 Warrior fighting bird ("Prince of Tears" (Mihai Eminescu))	35	10
4740.	2 l. 50 Hen with bag ("Bag with Two Coins" (Ion Creanga))	55	20
4741.	3 l. Rider fighting three-headed dragon ("Ileana Simziana" (Petre Ispirescu))	65	25
4742.	5 l. Man riding devil ("Danila Prepeleac" (Ion Creanga))	1·10	35

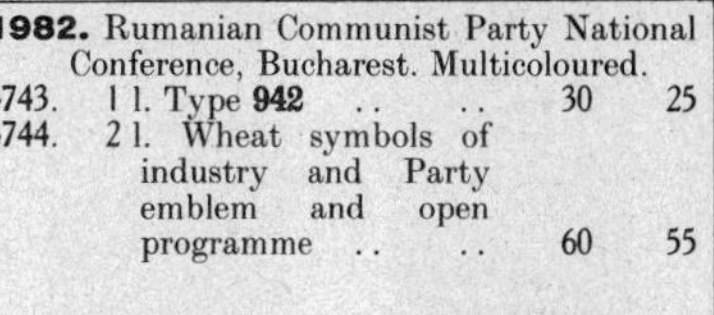

1982. Rumanian Communist Party National Conference, Bucharest. Multicoloured.

4743.	1 l. Type **942**	30	25
4744.	2 l. Wheat symbols of industry and Party emblem and open programme	60	55

943. Wooden Canteen from Suceava.

944. Wheat, Cogwheel, Flask and Electricity Emblem.

1982. Household Utensils.

4745. **943.**	50 b. red	10	10
4746. –	1 l. blue	20	10
4747. –	1 l. 50 orange	35	10
4748. –	2 l. blue	45	10
4749. –	3 l. green	65	10
4750. –	3 l. 50 green	75	10
4751. –	4 l. brown	90	10
4752. –	5 l. blue	1·10	10
4753. –	6 l. blue	1·40	10
4754. –	7 l. purple	1·50	10
4755. –	7 l. 50 mauve	1·60	10
4756. –	8 l. green	1·75	10
4757. –	10 l. red	2·10	10
4758. –	20 l. violet	4·25	15
4759. –	30 l. blue	6·50	15
4760. –	50 l. brown	10·50	15

DESIGNS: As T **943**—VERT. 1 l. Ceramic plates from Radauti. 2 l. Jug and plate from Vama-Maramures. 3 l. Wooden churn and pail from North Moldavia. 4 l. Wooden spoons and ceramic plate from Cluj. 5 l. Ceramic bowl and pot from Marginea-Suceava. HORIZ. 1 l. 50, Wooden dipper from Valea Mare. 3 l. 50, Ceramic plates from Leheceni-Crisana. 29 × 23 mm.—10 l. Wooden tubs from Hunedoara and Suceava. 30 l. Wooden spoons from Alba. 23 × 29 mm.—6 l. Ceramic pot and jug from Bihor. 7 l. Distaff and spindle from Transylvania. 7 l. 50, Double wooden pail from Suceava. 8 l. Pitcher and ceramic plate from Oboga and Horezu. 20 l. Wooden canteen and six glasses from Horezu. 50 l. Ceramic plates from Horezu.

1982. 35th Anniv. of People's Republic. Multicoloured.

4767.	1 l. Type **944**	25	10
4768.	2 l. National flag and oakleaves	45	15

945. H. Coanda and Diagram of Jet Engine.

1983. Air. 25 Years of Space Exploration. Multicoloured.

4769.	50 b. Type **945**	15	10
4770.	1 l. H. Oberth and diagram of rocket	25	10
4771.	1 l. 50 "Sputnik I", 1957 (first artificial satellite)	40	15
4772.	2 l. 50 "Vostok I", (first manned flight)	70	15
4773.	4 l. "Apollo 11, 1969 (first Moon landing)	1·10	30
4774.	5 l. Space shuttle "Columbia"	1·40	50

946. Rombac "1-11" Airliner.

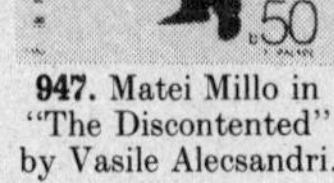

947. Matei Millo in "The Discontented" by Vasile Alecsandri.

1983. Air. First Rumanian-built Jet Airliner.

4776. **946.**	11 l. blue	3·50	15

1983. Rumanian Actors.

4777. **947.**	50 b. red and black	15	10
4778. –	1 l. green and black	30	10
4779. –	1 l. 50 violet & blk.	40	10
4780. –	2 l. brown & black	55	15
4781. –	2 l. 50 green & blk.	70	20
4782. –	3 l. blue and black	80	25
4783. –	4 l. green and black	1·10	30
4784. –	5 l. lilac and black	1·40	35

DESIGNS: 1 l. Mihail Pascaly in "Director Millo" by Vasile Alecsandri. 1 l. 50, Aristizza Romanescu in "The Dogs" by H. Lecca. 2 l. C. I. Nottara in "Blizzard" by B. S. Delavrancea. 2 l. 50, Grigore Manolescu in "Hamlet" by William Shakespeare. 3 l. Agatha Birsescu in "Medea" by Lebouvet. 4 l. Ion Brezeanu in "The Lost Letter" by I. L. Caragiale. 5 l. Aristide Demetriad in "The Despotic Prince" by Vasile Alecsandri.

948. Hugo Grotius.

949. Aro "10".

1983. 400th Birth Anniv. of Hugo Grotius (Dutch Jurist).

4785. **948.**	2 l. brown	55	15

1983. Rumanian-built Vehicles. Mult.

4786.	50 b. Type **949**	15	10
4787.	1 l. Dacia Break "1300"	30	10
4788.	1 l. 50 Aro "242"	45	10
4789.	2 l. 50 Aro "244"	70	20
4790.	4 l. Dacia "1310"	1·10	30
4791.	5 l. Oltcit "Club"	1·40	35

951. National and Communist Party Flags.

1983. 50th Anniv. of 1933 Workers' Revolution.

4793. **951.**	2 l. multicoloured	55	15

952. Loading Mail.

953. Bluethroat.

1983. Air. World Communications Year.

4794. **952.**	2 l. multicoloured	75	15

1983. Birds of the Danube Delta. Mult.

4795.	50 b. Type **953**	20	10
4796.	1 l. Rose-coloured starling	45	25
4797.	1 l. 50 Common roller	55	30
4798.	2 l. 50 European bee eater	1·00	50
4799.	4 l. Reed bunting	1·60	90
4800.	5 l. Lesser grey shrike	1·90	1·10

954. Kayak.

1983. Water Sports. Multicoloured.

4801.	50 b. Type **954**	15	10
4802.	1 l. Water polo	30	10
4803.	1 l. 50 Canoeing	40	15
4804.	2 l. 50 Diving	70	20
4805.	4 l. Rowing	1·10	35
4806.	5 l. Swimming (start of race)	1·40	50

955. Postman on Bicycle.

1983. Stamp Day. Multicoloured.

4807. 1 l. Type **955** 30 10
4808. 3 l. 50 (+3 l.) National flag as stamp .. .. 1·75 1·75

No. 4808 was issued with premium-carrying label attached.

956. "Geum reptans".

1983. European Flora and Fauna. Mult.

4810. 1 l. Type **956** 40 25
4811. 1 l. "Papaver dubium" 40 25
4812. 1 l. "Carlina acaulis" .. 40 25
4813. 1 l. "Paeonia peregrina" 40 25
4814. 1 l. "Gentiana excisa" .. 40 25
4815. 1 l. Eurasian red squirrel 40 25
4816. 1 l. "Grammia quenselii" (butterfly) 60 30
4817. 1 l. Middle spotted woodpecker 90 30
4818. 1 l. Lynx 40 25
4819. 1 l. Wallcreeper 90 30

957. "Girl with Feather." **958.** Flag and Oak Leaves.

1983. Paintings by C. Baba. Multicoloured.

4820. 1 l. Type **957** 30 10
4821. 2 l. "Congregation" .. 55 15
4822. 3 l. "Farm Workers" .. 80 25
4823. 4 l. "Rest in the Fields" (horiz.) .. .. 1·10 35

1983. 65th Anniv. of Union of Transylvania and Rumania. Multicoloured.

4824. 1 l. Type **958** 30 10
4825. 2 l. National and Communist Party Flags and Parliament building, Bucharest .. 55 15

959. Postman and Post Office. **961.** Cross-country Skiing.

1983. "Balkanfila IX '83" Stamp Exhibition, Bucharest. Multicoloured.

4826. 1 l. Type **959** 30 10
4827. 2 l. Postwoman and Athenaeum Concert Hall 55 15

1984. Winter Olympic Games, Sarajevo. Multicoloured.

4830. 50 b. Type **961** 15 10
4831. 1 l. Biathlon 25 20
4832. 1 l. 50 Ice skating .. 40 30
4833. 2 l. Speed skating .. 50 40
4834. 3 l. Ice hockey 75 65
4835. 3 l. 50 Bobsleighing .. 90 80
4836. 4 l. Luge .. .. .. 1·00 90
4837. 5 l. Downhill skiing .. 1·25 1·10

963. Palace of Udriste Nasturel (Chancery official). **967.** Flowering Rush.

966. Sunflower.

1984. 1983 Anniversaries.

4839. 50 b. grn., pink & silver 15 10
4840. 1 l. violet, grn. & silver 30 10
4841. 1 l. 50 multicoloured .. 40 15
4842. 2 l. brown, bl. & silver .. 65 15
4843. 3 l. 50 multicoloured .. 95 30
4844. 4 l. multicoloured .. 1·10 35

DESIGNS: 50 b. Type **963** (325th death anniv.). 1 l. Miron Costin (poet, 350th birth anniv.). 1 l. 50, Crisan (Giurgiu Marcu) (leader of peasant revolt, 250th birth anniv.). 2 l. Simion Barnutiu (scientist, 175th birth anniv.). 3 l. 50, Diuliu Zamfirescu (writer, 125th birth anniv.). 4 l. Nicolae Milescu at Great Wall of China (explorer, 275th death anniv.).

1984. Protection of Environment. Mult.

4847. 1 l. Type **966** 30 10
4848. 2 l. Red deer 55 20
4849. 3 l. Fish 80 25
4850. 4 l. Jay .. .. .. 1·90 45

1984. Flowers of the Danube. Multicoloured.

4851. 50 b. Arrowhead .. 15 10
4852. 1 l. Yellow iris 30 10
4853. 1 l. 50 Type **967** .. 40 15
4854. 3 l. White water-lily .. 80 25
4855. 4 l. Fringed water-lily (horiz.) .. .. 1·10 35
4856. 5 l. Yellow water-lily (horiz.) .. .. 1·40 50

968. Crowd with Banners. **970.** Congress Emblem.

969. High Jumping.

1984. 45th Anniv. of Anti-Fascist Demonstration.

4857. **968.** 2 l. multicoloured .. 55 15

1984. Olympic Games, Los Angeles (1st issue). Multicoloured.

4858. 50 b. Type **969** 15 10
4859. 1 l. Swimming 25 20
4860. 1 l. 50 Running 40 30
4861. 3 l. Handball 75 65
4862. 4 l. Rowing .. .. 1·00 90
4863. 5 l. Canoeing .. .. 1·25 1·10

See also Nos. 4866/73.

1984. 25th Ear, Nose and Throat Association Congress, Bucharest.

4864. **970.** 2 l. multicoloured .. 55 15

1984. Olympic Games, Los Angeles (2nd issue). As T **969**. Multicoloured.

4866. 50 b. Boxing 15 10
4867. 1 l. Rowing 25 20
4868. 1 l. Handball 40 30
4869. 2 l. Judo 50 40
4870. 3 l. Wrestling 75 65
4871. 3 l. 50 Fencing 90 80
4872. 4 l. Kayak .. .. 1·00 90
4873. 5 l. Swimming .. .. 1·25 1·10

972. Mihai Ciuca (bacteriologist, cent.). **974.** Flags, Flame and Power Station.

973. Lockheed "L-14".

1984. Birth Anniversaries. Dated "1983".

4874. **972.** 1 l. purple, blue and silver 30 10
4875. – 2 l. brown and silver 55 15
4876. – 3 l. green, brown and silver 80 25
4877. – 4 l. violet, green and silver .. .. 1·10 35

DESIGNS: 2 l. Petre S. Aurelian (agronomist, 150th anniv.). 3 l. Alexandru Vlahuta (writer, 125th anniv.). 4 l. Dimitrie Leonida (engineer, centenary).

1984. Air. 40th Anniv. of International Civil Aviation Organization. Multicoloured.

4878. 50 b. Type **973** 15 10
4879. 1 l. 50 "BN-2 Islander" 50 15
4880. 3 l. "Rombac" "1-11" .. 1·00 35
4881. 6 l. Boeing "707" .. 2·00 80

1984. 40th Anniv. of Liberation.

4882. **974.** 2 l. multicoloured .. 55 15

975. Lippizaner.

1984. Horses. Multicoloured.

4883. 50 b. Type **975** 15 10
4884. 1 l. Hutul 30 10
4885. 1 l. 50 Bukovina .. 40 15
4886. 2 l. 50 Nonius 70 20
4887. 4 l. Arab .. .. .. 1·10 35
4888. 5 l. Rumanian halfbreed 1·40 50

977. Memorial, Alba Julia. **978.** "Portrait of a Child". (Th. Aman).

1984. Bicentenary of Horea, Closa and Crisan Uprisings.

4890. **977.** 2 l. multicoloured .. 55 15

1984. Paintings of Children. Multicoloured.

4891. 50 b. Type **978** 15 10
4892. 1 l. "The Little Shepherd" (N. Grigorescu) .. 30 15
4893. 2 l. "Lica with an Orange" (St. Luchian) 55 15
4894. 3 l. "Portrait of a Child" (N. Tonitza) 80 25
4895. 4 l. "Portrait of a Boy" (S. Popp) .. .. 1·10 35
4896. 5 l. "Portrait of Young Girl" (I. Tuculescu) .. 1·40 50

979. Stage Coach and Rumanian Philatelic Association Emblem.

1984. Stamp Day.

4897. **979.** 2 l. (+1 l.) mult. .. 80 65

No. 4897 was issued with premium-carrying label attached.

981. Dalmatian Pelicans. **982.** Dr. Petru Groz (former President).

1984. Protected Animals. Dalmatian Pelicans. Multicoloured.

4899. 50 b. Type **981** 25 15
4900. 1 l. Pelican on nest .. 55 25
4901. 1 l. Pelicans on lake .. 55 25
4902. 2 l. Pelicans roosting .. 95 65

1984. Anniversaries. Mult.

4903. 50 b. Type **982** (birth centenary) 15 10
4904. 1 l. Alexandru Odobescu (writer) (150th birth anniv.) 30 10
4905. 2 l. Dr. Carol Davila (physician) (death centenary) 55 15
4906. 3 l. Dr. Nicolae Gh. Lupu (physician) (birth centenary) 80 25
4907. 4 l. Dr. Daniel Danielopolu (physician) (birth centenary) .. .. 1·10 35
4908. 5 l. Panait Istrati (writer) (birth centenary) .. 1·40 50

983. Generator. **985.** August Treboniu Laurian (linguist and historian).

1984. Centenary of Power Station and Electric Street Lighting in Timisoara. Mult.

4909. 1 l. Type **983** 30 10
4910. 2 l. Street lamp 55 15

1985. Anniversaries. Mult.

4912. 50 b. Type **985** (175th birth anniv.) 15 10
4913. 1 l. Grigore Alexandrescu (writer) (death cent.) 30 10
4914. 1 l. 50 Gheorghe Pop de Basesti (politician) (150th birth anniv.) .. 40 15
4915. 2 l. Mateiu Caragiale (writer) (birth cent.) .. 55 15
4916. 3 l. Gheorghe Ionescu-Sosesti (scientist) (birth centenary) .. 80 25
4917. 4 l. Liviu Rebreanu (writer) (birth cent.) .. 1·10 35

986. Students in Science Laboratory. **987.** Racoon Dog.

1985. International Youth Year. Mult.

No.	Description	Unused	Used
4918.	1 l. Type **986**	30	10
4919.	2 l. Students on construction site	55	15

1985. Protected Animals. Multicoloured.

No.	Description	Unused	Used
4921.	50 b. Type **987**	15	10
4922.	1 l. Grey partridge ..	80	10
4923.	1 l. 50 Snowy owl ..	1·40	30
4924.	2 l. Pine marten	55	15
4925.	3 l. Eurasian badger ..	80	25
4926.	3 l. 50 Eurasian otter ..	90	30
4927.	4 l. Capercaillie	3·00	65
4928.	5 l. Great bustard ..	3·25	80

988. Flags and Victory Monument, Bucharest. **989.** Union Emblem.

1985. 40th Anniv. of Victory in Europe Day.

No.	Description	Unused	Used
4929. **988.**	2 l. multicoloured ..	55	15

1985. Communist Youth Union Congress.

No.	Description	Unused	Used
4930. **989.**	2 l. multicoloured ..	55	15

990. Route Map and Canal.

1985. Danube-Black Sea Canal. Mult.

No.	Description	Unused	Used
4931.	1 l. type **990**	30	10
4932.	2 l. Canal and bridge, Cernavoda	70	25
4933.	3 l. Road over Canal, Medgidia	90	25
4934.	4 l. Canal control tower, Agigea	1·25	35

991. Brown Pelican. **992.** "Fire".

1985. Birth Bicentenary of John J. Audubon (ornithologist). Multicoloured.

No.	Description	Unused	Used
4936.	50 b. American robin (horiz.)	20	10
4937.	1 l. Type **991**	40	15
4938.	1 l. 50 Yellow-crowned night heron	70	30
4939.	2 l. Northern oriole ..	90	35
4940.	3 l. Red-necked grebe ..	1·40	50
4941.	4 l. Mallard (horiz.) ..	1·90	65

1985. Paintings by Ion Tuculescu. Mult.

No.	Description	Unused	Used
4942.	1 l. Type **992**	30	10
4943.	2 l. "Circulation" ..	55	15
4944.	3 l. "Interior of Peasant's Home" (horiz.)	80	25
4945.	4 l. "Sunset" (horiz.) ..	1·10	35

993. "Inachis io".

1985. Butterflies and Moths. Multicoloured.

No.	Description	Unused	Used
4946	50 b. Type **933**	20	10
4947	1 l. "Papilio machaon" ..	45	10
4948	2 l. "Vanessa atalanta" ..	70	20
4949	3 l. "Eudia pavonia" ..	1·00	30
4950	4 l. "Ammobiota festuva"	1·40	45
4951	5 l. "Smerinthus ocellata"	1·75	60

994. Transfagarasan Mountain Road.

1985. 20th Anniv. of Election of General Secretary Nicolae Ceausescu and 9th Communist Party Congress. Multicoloured.

No.	Description	Unused	Used
4952.	1 l. Type **994**	30	10
4953.	2 l. Danube-Black Sea Canal	55	15
4954.	3 l. Bucharest underground railway ..	80	25
4955.	4 l. Irrigating fields ..	1·10	35

995. Rumanian Crest, Symbols of Agriculture and "XX". **997.** "Senecio glaberrimus".

1985. 20th Anniv. of Rumanian Socialist Republic. Multicoloured.

No.	Description	Unused	Used
4956.	1 l. Type **995**	30	10
4957.	2 l. Crest, symbols of industry and "XX" ..	55	15

1985. 50th Anniv. of Retezat National Park. Multicoloured.

No.	Description	Unused	Used
4959.	50 b. Type **997**	15	15
4960.	1 l. Chamois	30	10
4961.	2 l. "Centaurea retezatensis"	55	15
4962.	3 l. Violet	80	25
4963.	4 l. Alpine marmot ..	1·10	35
4964.	5 l. Golden eagle ..	3·00	75

998. Universal "530 DTC".

1985. Rumanian Tractors. Multicoloured.

No.	Description	Unused	Used
4966.	50 b. Type **998**	15	10
4967.	1 l. Universal "550 M HC"	30	10
4968.	1 l. 50 Universal "650 Super"	40	15
4969.	2 l. Universal "850" ..	55	15
4970.	3 l. Universal "S 1801 IF" tracked front loader	80	25
4971.	4 l. Universal "A 3602 IF" front loader ..	1·10	35

999. Costume of Muscel (female).

1985. Costumes (1st series). Multicoloured.

No.	Description	Unused	Used
4972.	50 b. Type **999**	15	10
4973.	50 b. Muscel (male) ..	15	10
4974.	1 l. 50 Bistrita-Nasaud (female)	40	15
4975.	1 l. 50 Bistrita-Nasaud (male)	40	15
4976.	2 l. Vrancea (female) ..	55	15
4977.	2 l. Vrancea (male) ..	55	15
4978.	3 l. Vilcea (female) ..	80	25
4979.	3 l. Vilcea (male) ..	80	25

See also Nos. 5143/5150.

1000. Footballer attacking Goal.

1985. World Cup Football Championship, Mexico (1986) (1st issue). Multicoloured.

No.	Description	Unused	Used
4980.	50 b. Type **1000**	15	10
4981.	1 l. Player capturing ball	30	10
4982.	1 l. 50 Player heading ball	40	15
4983.	2 l. Player about to tackle	55	15
4984.	3 l. Player heading ball and goal keeper ..	80	25
4985.	4 l. Player kicking ball over head	1·10	35

See also Nos. 5038/43.

1001. U.N. Emblem and "40". **1002.** Copper.

1985. 40th Anniv. of U.N.O. (4986) and 30th Anniv. of Rumanian Membership (4987).

No.	Description	Unused	Used
4986.	2 l. Type **1001**	55	15
4987.	2 l. U.N. building, New York, U.N. emblem and Rumanian crest ..	55	15

1985. Minerals. Multicoloured.

No.	Description	Unused	Used
4988.	50 b. Quartz and calcite	15	10
4989.	1 l. Type **1002**	30	10
4990.	2 l. Gypsum	55	15
4991.	3 l. Quartz	80	25
4992.	4 l. Stibium	1·10	35
4993.	5 l. Tetrahedrite ..	1·40	50

1003. Posthorn.

1985. Stamp Day.

No.	Description	Unused	Used
4994. **1003.**	2 l. (+1 l.) mult. ..	80	70

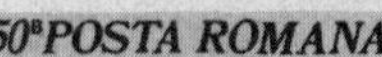

1004. Goofy as Hank waking to find himself at Camelot.

1985. 150th Birth Anniv. of Mark Twain (writer). Scences from "A Connecticut Yankee in King Arthur's Court" (film). Multicoloured.

No.	Description	Unused	Used
4995.	50 b. Type **1004**	2·00	2·00
4996.	50 b. Hank at the stake and Merlin (Mickey Mouse)	2·00	2·00
4997.	50 b. Hank being hoisted onto horseback in full armour	2·00	2·00
4998.	50 b. Pete as Sir Sagramoor on horseback	2·00	2·00

1985. Birth Bicentenaries of Grimm Brothers (folklorists). Scenes from "The Three Brothers". As T **1004**. Multicoloured.

No.	Description	Unused	Used
5000.	1 l. Father (Donald Duck) bidding farewell to the brothers (Huey, Louie and Dewey) ..	4·25	4·25
5001.	1 l. Louie as fencing master brother ..	4·25	4·25
5002.	1 l. Louie keeping rain off his father with sword	4·25	4·25
5003.	1 l. Huey as blacksmith brother shoeing galloping horse ..	4·25	4·25
5004.	1 l. Dewey as barber brother shaving Brer Rabbit on the run ..	4·25	4·25

1005. Wright Brothers (aviation pioneers).

1985. Explorers and Pioneers. Multicoloured.

No.	Description	Unused	Used
5006.	1 l. Type **1005**	35	10
5007.	1 l. 50 Jacques Yves Cousteau (undersea explorer)	60	15
5008.	2 l. Amelia Earhart Putnam (first woman trans-Atlantic flyer) ..	70	15
5009.	3 l. Charles Lindbergh (first solo trans-Atlantic flyer) ..	90	25
5010.	3 l. 50 Sir Edmund Hillary (first man to reach summit of Everest)	90	30
5011.	4 l. Robert Edwin Peary and Emil Racovita (polar explorers) ..	1·10	35
5012.	5 l. Richard Evelyn Byrd (polar explorer and aviator)	2·00	55
5013.	6 l. Neil A. Armstrong (first man on Moon) ..	1·40	50

1006. Edmond Halley and Comet.

1986. Air. Appearance of Halley's Comet.

No.	Description	Unused	Used
5014.	2 l. Type **1006**	55	15
5015.	4 l. Comet, orbit and space probes	1·10	35

No. 5014 is wrongly inscr "Edmund".

1007. "Nina in Green". **1010.** Hotel Diana, Baile Herculane.

1009. Goofy playing Clarinet.

1986. Paintings by Nicolae Tonitza. Multicoloured.

5016. 1 l. Type **1007** 25 10
5017. 2 l. "Irina" 55 20
5018. 3 l. "Forester's Daughter" 80 35
5019. 4 l. "Woman on Veranda" .. .. 1·10 55

1986. 50th Anniv. of Colour Animation. Scenes from "Band Concert" (cartoon film). Multicoloured.

5021. 50 b. Type **1009** .. .. 2·00 2·00
5022. 50 b. Clarabelle playing flute .. .. .. 2·00 2·00
5023. 50 b. Mickey Mouse conducting .. .. 2·00 2·00
5024. 50 b. Paddy and Peter Pig playing euphonium and trumpet .. .. 2·00 2·00
5025. 1 l. Conductor Mickey and flautist Donald Duck .. .. .. 4·25 4·25
5026. 1 l. Donald caught in trombone slide .. 4·25 4·25
5027. 1 l. Horace playing drums .. .. .. 4·25 4·25
5028. 1 l. Donald selling ice cream .. .. .. 4·25 4·25
5029. 1 l. Mickey and euphonium caught in tornado .. .. 4·25 4·25

1986. Spa Hotels. Multicoloured.

5031. 50 b. Type **1010** 15 10
5032. 1 l. Hotel Termal, Baile Felix 25 10
5033. 2 l. Hotels Delfin, Meduza and Steaua de Mare, North Eforie .. 55 15
5034. 3 l. Hotel Caciulata, Calimanesti-Caciulata 80 25
5035. 4 l. Villa Palas, Moldova 1·10 35
5036. 5 l. Hotel Bradet, Sovata 1·25 45

1011. Ceaucescu and Red Flag.

1986. 65th Anniv. of Rumanian Communist Party.

5037. **1011.** 2 l. multicoloured .. 55 15

1012. Italy v. Bulgaria.

1986. World Cup Football Championship, Mexico (2nd issue). Multicoloured.

5038. 50 b. Type **1012** 15 10
5039. 1 l. Mexico v. Belgium .. 25 10
5040. 2 l. Canada v. France .. 55 15
5041. 3 l. Brazil v. Spain .. 80 25
5042. 4 l. Uruguay v. W. Germany .. .. 1·10 35
5043. 5 l. Morocco v. Poland .. 1·25 45

1014. "Tulipa gesneriana".

1986. Flowers. Multicoloured.

5045. 50 b. Type **1014** 15 10
5046. 1 l. "Iris hispanica" .. 25 10
5047. 2 l. "Rosa hybrida" .. 55 15
5048. 3 l. "Anemone coronaria" 80 25
5049. 4 l. "Freesia refracta" .. 1·10 35
5050. 5 l. "Chrysanthemum indicum" .. .. 1·25 45

1015. Mircea the Old and Horsemen.

1986. 600th Anniv. of Mircea the Great's Accession.

5051. **1015.** 2 l. multicoloured .. 55 15

1016. Thatched House with Veranda, Alba.

1986. 50th Anniv. of Museum of Historic Dwellings, Bucharest. Multicoloured.

5052. 50 b. Type **1016** 15 10
5053. 1 l. Stone built house, Arges 25 10
5054. 2 l. House with veranda, Constanta 55 15
5055. 3 l. House with tiled roof and steps, Timis 80 25
5056. 4 l. House with ramp to veranda, Neamt .. 1·10 35
5057. 5 l. Two storey house with first floor veranda, Gorj .. 1·25 45

1017. Julius Popper (Tierra del Fuego, 1886–93).

1986. Polar Research. Multicoloured.

5058. 50 b. Type **1017** 15 10
5059. 1 l. Brazil Gh. Assan (Spitzbergen, 1896) .. 40 10
5060. 2 l. Emil Racovita (Antarctic, 1897–99) .. 75 15
5061. 3 l. Constantin Dumbrava (Greenland, 1927–28) .. 80 25
5062. 4 l. Rumanian participation in 17th Soviet Antarctic Expedition, 1971–72 .. 1·75 40
5063. 5 l. 1977 "Sinoe" and 1979–80 "Tirnava" krill fishing expeditions .. 1·50 45

1019. The Blusher. **1020.** Group of Cyclists.

1986. Fungi. Multicoloured.

5065. 50 b. Type **1019** 25 10
5066. 1 l. "Boletus luridus" .. 35 10
5067. 2 l. "Lactarius piperatus" 70 20
5068. 3 l. "Lepiota clypeolaria" 95 30
5069. 4 l. "Russula cyanoxantha" .. .. 1·50 40
5079. 5 l. "Tremiscus helvelloides" .. .. .. 1·75 55

1986. Cycle Tour of Rumania. Multicoloured.

5071. 1 l. Type **1020** 25 10
5072. 2 l. Motor cycle following cyclist 55 15
5073. 3 l. Jeep following cyclists 80 25
5074. 4 l. Winner .. .. 1·10 35

1021. Emblem. **1022.** Petru Maior (historian) (225th birth anniv.).

1986. 40th Anniv. of U.N. and 30th Anniv. of Rumanian Membership.

5076. **1021.** 4 l. multicoloured .. 1·10 35

1986. Birth Anniversaries.

5077. **1022.** 50 b. purple, gold and green .. 15 10
5078. – 1 b. green, gold and mauve 25 10
5079. – 2 l. red, gold and blue 55 15
5080. – 3 l. blue, gold and brown 80 25

DESIGNS: 1 l. George Topirceanu (writer, centenary). 2 l. Henri Coanda (engineer, centenary). 3 l. Constantin Budeanu (engineer, centenary).

1023. Coach and Horses. **1024.** F 300 Oil Drilling Rigs.

1986. Stamp Day.

5081. **1023.** 2 l. (+1 l.) mult. .. 80 25

No. 5081 was issued se-tenant with premium-carrying tab.

1986. Industry. Multicoloured.

5082. 50 b. Type **1024** 15 10
5083. 1 l. "Promex" excavator (horiz.) 25 10
5084. 2 l. Petrochemical refinery, Pitesti .. 55 15
5085. 3 l. Tipper "110 t" (horiz.) 80 25
5086. 4 l. "Coral" computer .. 1·10 35
5087. 5 l. 350 m.w. turbine (horiz.) .. .. 1·25 45

1025. "Goat". **1026.** Tin Can and Motor Car ("re-cycle metals").

1986. Folk Customs. Multicoloured.

5088. 50 b. Type **1025** 15 10
5089. 1 l. Sorcova 25 10
5090. 2 l. Plugusorul 55 15
5091. 3 l. Buhaiul 80 25
5092. 4 l. Caiutii .. .. 1·10 35
5093. 5 l. Uratorii .. .. 1·25 45

1986. "Save Waste Materials".

5094. **1026.** 1 l. red and orange 25 10
5095. – 2 l. light green and green 55 15

DESIGN: 2 l. Trees and hand with newspaper ("re-cycle waste paper").

1027. Flags and Young People. **1028.** Anniversary Emblem.

1987. 65th Anniv. of Communist Youth Union. Multicoloured.

5096. 1 l. Type **1027** 15 10
5097. 2 l. Anniversary emblem 20 10
5098. 3 l. Flags and young people (different) .. 40 10

1987. 25th Anniv. of Agricultural Co-operatives.

5099. **1028.** 2 l. multicoloured .. 20 10

1030. "Birch Trees by Lake" (I. Andreescu).

1987. Paintings. Multicoloured.

5101. 50 b. Type **1030** 10 10
5102. 1 l. "Young Peasant Girls spinning" (N. Grigorescu) 25 10
5103. 2 l. "Washerwoman" (St. Luchian) 55 10
5104. 3 l. "Interior" (St. Dimitrescu) 80 10
5105. 4 l. "Winter Landscape" (Al. Ciucurencu) .. 1·10 15
5106. 5 l. "Winter in Bucharest" (N. Tonitza) (vert.) .. 1·40 20

1031. "1907" and Peasants.

1987. 80th Anniv. of Peasant Uprising.

5107. **1031.** 2 l. multicoloured .. 55 10

1032. Players.

1033. 1 Leu Coin.

1987. 10th Men's World Handball Championship. Various match scenes.

5108. **1032.** 50 b. multicoloured 10 10
5109. – 1 l. mult. (horiz.) .. 10 10
5110. – 2 l. multicoloured .. 55 10
5111. – 3 l. mult. (horiz.) .. 80 10
5112. – 4 l. multicoloured .. 1·10 15
5113. – 5 l. mult. (horiz.) .. 1·40 20

1987. Currency.

5114. **1033.** 1 l. multicoloured 10 10

1034. Pelicans in the Danube Delta.

1987. Tourism. Multicoloured.

5116. 50 b. Type **1034** 10 10
5117. 1 l. Cable car above Transfagarasan mountain road 30 10
5118. 2 l. Cheile Bicazului .. 55 10
5119. 3 l. Ceahlau mountains .. 80 10
5120. 4 l. Lake Capra, Fagaras, mountains .. .. 1·10 15
5121. 5 l. Borsa orchards .. 1·40 20

1035. Henri August's Glider, 1909.

1987. Air. Gliders. Multicoloured.

5122. 50 b. Type **1035** 15 10
5123. 1 l. Sky-diver jumping from glider "IS-Z882" 20 10
5124. 2 l. "IS-29 D2" 35 10
5125. 3 l. "IS-32" 65 15
5126. 4 l. "IAR-35" 90 25
5127. 5 l. "IS-28 M2" .. .. 1·10 30

1036. Youth on Winged Horse.

1987. Fairy Tales by Petre Ispirescu. Mult.

5128. 50 b. Type **1036** 10 10
5129. 1 l. King and princesses ("Salt in the Food") .. 30 10
5130. 2 l. Girl on horse fighting lion ("Ileana Simziana") 20 10
5131. 3 l. Youth with bow and arrow aiming at bird ("The Youth and the Golden Apples") .. 80 10
5132. 4 l. "George the Brave" 1·10 15
5133. 5 l. Girl looking at sleeping youth ("The Enchanted Pig") .. 1·40 20

1037. Class "L 45H" Diesel Shunter.

1987. Railway Locomotives. Multicoloured.

5135 50 b. Type **1037** 15 10
5136 1 l. Class "LDE 125" .. 20 10
5137 2 l. Class "LDH 70" .. 30 10
5138 3 l. Class "LDE 2100" .. 65 10
5139 4 l. Class "LDE 3000" .. 90 15
5140 5 l. Class "LE 5100" .. 1·10 20

The 5 l. is an electric locomotive the rest are diesel.

1987. Costumes (2nd series). As T **999**. Multicoloured.

5143. 1 l. Tirnave (female) .. 30 10
5144. 1 l. Tirnave (male) .. 30 10
5145. 2 l. Buzau (female) .. 50 10
5146. 2 l. Buzau (male) .. 50 10
5147. 3 l. Dobrogea (female) .. 70 10
5148. 3 l. Dobrogea (male) .. 70 10
5149. 4 l. Ilfov (female) .. 95 15
5150. 4 l. Ilfov (male) 95 15

1040. Postal Services. (Illustration reduced. Actual size 78 × 23 mm.).

1987. Stamp Day.

5151. **1040.** 2 l. (+1 l.) mult. .. 75 10

No. 5151 was issued se-tenant with premium-carrying tab.

1041. Bee on Flower.

1987. Bee-keeping. Multicoloured.

5152. 1 l. Type **1041** 15 10
5153. 2 l. Bee, sunflowers and hives 60 10
5154. 3 l. Hives in Danube delta 70 10
5155. 4 l. Apiculture Complex, Bucharest 95 15

1042 Car behind Boy on Bicycle

1987. Road Safety. Multicoloured.

5156 50 b. Type **1042** 10 10
5157 1 l. Children using school crossing 10 10
5158 2 l. Driver carelessly opening car door .. 25 10
5159 3 l. Hand holding crossing sign and children using zebra crossing .. 70 10
5160 4 l. Speedometer and crashed car 95 15
5161 5 l. Child's face and speeding car .. .. 1·10 25

1043 Red Flag and Lenin

1987. 70th Anniv of Russian Revolution.

5162 **1043** 2 l. multicoloured .. 55 10

1044 Biathlon

1045 Crest and National Colours

1987. Winter Olympic Games, Calgary (1988). Multicoloured.

5163 50 b. Type **1044** 10 10
5164 1 l. Slalom 25 10
5165 1 l. 50 Ice hockey .. 20 10
5166 2 l. Luge 25 10
5167 3 l. Speed skating .. 40 10
5168 3 l. 50 Figure skating .. 80 10
5169 4 l. Downhill skiing .. 90 15
5170 5 l. Two-man bobsleigh .. 1·10 25

1987. 40th Anniv of People's Republic.

5171 **1045** 2 l. multicoloured .. 55 10

1046 Pres. Ceausescu and Flags

1988. 70th Birthday and 55 Years of Revolutionary Activity of Pres. Ceausescu.

5172 **1046** 2 l. multicoloured .. 55 10

1047 Wide-necked Pot, Marginea

1988. Pottery. Multicoloured.

5173 50 b. Type **1047** 10 10
5174 1 l. Flask, Oboga .. 15 10
5175 2 l. Jug and saucer, Horezu 25 10
5176 3 l. Narrow-necked pot, Curtea de Arges .. 70 10
5177 4 l. Jug, Birsa 95 15
5178 5 l. Jug and plate, Vama 1·10 25

1049 Ceramic Clock

1051 Constantin Brincoveanu

1988. Clocks in Ploiesti Museum. Mult.

5180 50 b. Type **1049** 10 10
5181 1 l. 50 Gilt clock with sun at base 20 10
5182 2 l. Clock with pastoral figure 25 10
5183 3 l. Gilt clock surmounted by figure 70 10
5184 4 l. Vase-shaped clock .. 95 15
5185 5 l. Clock surmounted by porcelain figures .. 1·10 25

1988. 300th Anniv of Election of Constantin Brincoveanu as Ruler of Wallachia.

5187 **1051** 2 l. multicoloured .. 55 10

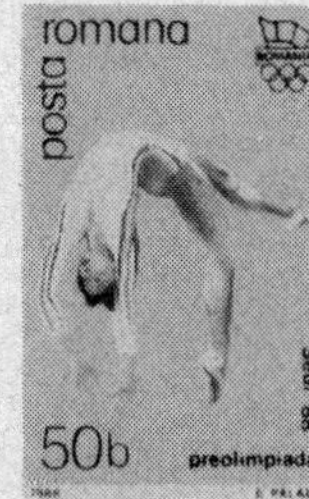

1052 Gymnastics

1988. Olympic Games, Seoul (1st issue). Mult.

5188 50 b. Type **1052** 10 10
5189 1 l. 50 Boxing 20 10
5190 2 l. Lawn tennis 25 10
5191 3 l. Judo 70 10
5192 4 l. Running 95 15
5193 5 l. Rowing .. .. 1·10 25

See also Nos. 5197/5204.

1053 Emblems and Roses

1988. Rumanian-Chinese Stamp Exhibition.

5194 **1053** 2 l. multicoloured .. 55 10

1056 Running

1988. Olympic Games, Seoul (2nd issue). Mult.

5197 50 b. Type **1056** 10 10
5198 1 l. Canoeing 25 10
5199 1 l. 50 Gymnastics .. 20 10
5200 2 l. Double kayak .. 25 10
5201 3 l. Weightlifting .. 70 10
5202 3 l. 50 Swimming .. 80 10
5203 4 l. Fencing 90 15
5204 5 l. Rowing .. .. 1·10 25

1058 Past and Present Postal Services (Illustration reduced, actual size 79 × 23 mm)

1988. Stamp Day.

5206 **1058** 2 l. (+1 l.) mult .. 70 10

No. 5206 was issued with se-tenant premium-carrying label, as shown in T **1058**.

MINIMUM PRICE

The minimum price quoted is 5p which represents a handling charge rather than a basis for valuing common stamps. For further notes about prices see introductory pages.

1060 State Arms

1988. 70th Anniv of Union of Transylvania and Rumania.
5208 **1060** 2 l. multicoloured .. 55 10

1061 Athenaeum Concert Hall, Bucharest (centenary)

1988. Rumanian History. Multicoloured.
5209 50 b. Type **1061** 15 10
5210 1 l. 50 Roman coin showing Drobeta Bridge 20 10
5211 2 l. Ruins (600th anniv of Suceava as capital of Moldavian feudal state) 25 10
5212 3 l. Scroll, arms and town (600th anniv of first documentary reference to Pitesti) 70 10
5213 4 l. Dacian warriors from Trajan's Column .. 95 15
5214 5 l. Thracian gold helmet from Cotofenesti-Prahova .. .. 1·10 25

1062 Zapodeni, 17th-century

1989. Traditional House Architecture. Mult.
5215 50 b. Type **1062** 15 10
5216 1 l. 50 Berbesti, 18th-century 20 10
5217 2 l. Voitinel, 18th-century 30 10
5218 3 l. Chiojdu Mic, 18th-century 70 10
5219 4 l. Cimpanii de Sus, 19th-century 95 15
5220 5 l. Naruja, 19th-century 1·10 25

1063 Red Cross Worker

1989. Life-saving Services. Multicoloured.
5221 50 b. Type **1063** 15 10
5222 1 l. Red Cross orderlies giving first aid to girl (horiz) 15 10
5223 1 l. 50 Fireman carrying child 20 10
5224 2 l. Rescuing child from earthquake-damaged building 30 10
5225 3 l. Mountain rescue team transporting casualty on sledge (horiz) .. 70 10
5226 3 l. 50 Rescuing climber from cliff face .. 85 15
5227 4 l. Rescuing child from river 95 15
5228 5 l. Life-guard in boat and children playing in sea (horiz) .. .. 1·10 25

1064 Tasca Bicaz Cement Factory

1989. Industrial Achievements. Mult.
5229 50 b. Type **1064** 15 10
5230 1 l. 50 Railway bridge, Cernavoda 20 10
5231 2 l. Synchronous motor, Resita 30 10
5232 3 l. Bucharest underground 40 10
5233 4 l. Mangalia–Constanta ferry 95 15
5234 5 l. "Gloria" oil drilling platform .. .. 1·10 25

1065 Flags and Symbols of Industry and Agriculture

1989. 50th Anniv of Anti-Fascist Demonstration.
5235 **1065** 2 l. multicoloured 55 10

1068 Ion Creanga (writer, death centenary)

1989. Anniversaries. Multicoloured.
5239 1 l. Type **1068** 15 10
5240 2 l. Mihai Eminescu (poet, death centenary) .. 30 10
5241 3 l. Nicolae Teclu (150th birth anniv) 75 10

1069 Flags and Symbols of Industry and Agriculture

1989. 45th Anniv of Liberation.
5242 **1069** 2 l. multicoloured .. 55 10

1070 "Pin-Pin"

1989. Rumanian Cartoon Films. Mult.
5243 50 b. Type **1070** 10 10
5244 1 l. "Maria" 15 10
5245 1 l. 50 "Gore and Grigore" 20 10
5246 2 l. "Pisoiul, Balanel, Manole, Monk" .. 30 10
5247 3 l. "Gruia lui Novac" .. 75 10
5248 3 l. 50 "Mihaela" .. 90 15
5249 4 l. "Harap Alb" .. 1·00 15
5250 5 l. "Homo Sapiens" .. 1·25 25

1071 Globe, Letter and Houses (illustration, ½ size)

1989. Stamp Day.
5251 **1071** 2 l. (+1 l.) mult .. 75 10
No. 521 was issued se-tenant with premium carrying tab as illustrated in T **1071**.

1072 Storming of the Bastille

1989. Bicent of French Revolution. Mult.
5252 50 b. Type **1072** 15 10
5253 1 l. 50 Street boy and Marianne 20 10
5254 2 l. Robespierre .. 30 10
5255 3 l. Rouget de Lisle singing "Marseillaise" 75 10
5256 4 l. Diderot (writer) .. 1·00 15
5257 5 l. Crowd .. .. 1·25 25

1073 Conrad Haas and Diagram

1989. Air. Space Pioneers. Multicoloured.
5259 50 b. Type **1073** 10 10
5260 1 l. 50 K. Tsiolkovski and diagram 40 10
5261 2 l. Hermann Oberth and equation 55 10
5262 3 l. Robert Goddard and diagram 80 10
5263 4 l. Sergei Pavlovich Korolev, Earth and satellite .. .. 1·10 10
5264 5 l. Wernher von Braun and landing module .. 1·40 10

1075 Flags and Emblem

1076 Date, Flag, Victory Sign and Candles

1989. 14th Communist Party Congress.
5266 **1075** 2 l. multicoloured .. 55 10

1990. Popular Uprising (1st issue).
5268 **1076** 2 l. multicoloured .. 55 10
See also Nos. 5294/5301.

1077 Flags and Footballers

1990. World Cup Football Championship, Italy (1st issue). Designs showing flags and footballers.
5269 **1077** 50 b. multicoloured 15 10
5270 – 1 l. 50 multicoloured 40 10
5271 – 2 l. multicoloured .. 55 10
5272 – 3 l. multicoloured .. 80 15
5273 – 4 l. multicoloured .. 1·10 25
5274 – 5 l. multicoloured .. 1·40 25
See also Nos. 5276/83

1079 Footballers

1990. World Cup Football Championship, Italy (2nd issue).
5276 **1079** 50 b. multicoloured 15 10
5277 – 1 l. multicoloured .. 25 10
5278 – 1 l. 50 multicoloured 40 10
5279 – 2 l. multicoloured .. 55 10
5280 – 3 l. multicoloured .. 80 15
5281 – 3 l. 50 multicoloured 95 20
5282 – 4 l. multicoloured .. 1·10 25
5283 – 5 l. multicoloured .. 1·40 25
DESIGNS: 1 to 5 l. Different football scenes.

1080 German Shepherds

1990. International Dog Show, Brno. Mult.
5284 50 b. Type **1080** 10 10
5285 1 l. English setter .. 25 10
5286 1 l. 50 Boxers 35 10
5287 2 l. Beagles 45 10
5288 3 l. Dobermann pinschers 70 15
5289 3 l. 50 Great danes .. 80 15
5290 4 l. Afghan hounds .. 90 15
5291 5 l. Yorkshire terriers .. 1·10 20

1081 Fountain

1990. "Riccione '90" International Stamp Fair.
5292 **1081** 2 l. multicoloured .. 45 10

1082 Bucharest Athenaeum and Chinese Temple

1990. Rumanian–Chinese Stamp Exhibition, Bucharest.
5293 **1082** 2 l. multicoloured .. 45 10

1083 Republic Palace ablaze, Bucharest

1990. Popular Uprising (2nd issue). Mult.
5294 50 b.+50 b. Type **1083** .. 25 10
5295 1 l.+1 l. Crowd in Opera Square, Timisoara .. 45 10
5296 1 l. 50+1 l. Soldiers joining crowd in Town Hall Square, Tirgu Mures 60 10
5297 2 l.+1 l. Soldiers and crowd before television headquarters, Bucharest (vert) 70 10
5298 3 l.+1 l. Mourners at funeral, Timisoara .. 90 10
5299 3 l. 50+1 l. Crowd celebrating, Brasov (vert) .. .. .. 1·00 15
5300 4 l.+1 l. Crowd, Sibiu .. 1·00 15
5301 5 l.+2 l. Cemetery, Bucharest .. .. 1·60 20

1084 "Nicolae Cobzarul" (St. Luchian)

1990. Paintings. Multicoloured.
5303 50 b. Type **1084** 10 10
5304 1 l. 50 "Woman in White" (I. Andreescu) .. 35 10
5305 2 l. "Florist" (St. Luchian) 45 10
5306 3 l. "Vase of Flowers" (Jan Brueghel, the elder) 70 15
5307 4 l. "Spring" (Pieter Brueghel, the elder) (horiz) 95 15
5308 5 l. "Madonna and Child" (G. B. Paggi) .. .. 1·10 20

1085 Flag Stamps encircling Globe

1990. Stamp Day.
5309 **1085** 2 l. (+1 l.) mult .. 70 30
No. 5309 was issued with se-tenant premium-carrying label.

1086 Prince Constantin Cantacuzino (350th birth anniv)

1087 Column of Infinity

1990. Anniversaries.
5310 **1086** 50 b. brown and blue 10 10
5311 – 1 l. 50 green & mauve 35 10
5312 – 2 l. red and blue .. 45 10
5313 – 3 l. blue and brown 65 10
5314 – 4 l. brown and blue 90 15
5315 – 5 l. violet and green 1·10 20
DESIGNS: 1 l. 50, Ienachita Vacarescu (annalist, 250th birth anniv); 2 l. Titu Maiorescu (writer, 150th birth anniv); 3 l. Nicolae Iorga (historian, 50th death anniv); 4 l. Martha Bibescu (birth centenary); 5 l. Stefan Procupiu (scientist, birth centenary).

1990. National Day.
5316 **1087** 2 l. multicoloured .. 45 10

1990. 1st Anniv of Popular Uprising. No. 5268 surch **L4 UN AN DE LA VICTORIA REVOLUTIEI.**
5317 **1076** 4 l. on 2 l. mult .. 90 10

1089 "Irises"

1991. Death Centenary of Vincent van Gogh (painter). Multicoloured.
5318 50 b. Type **1089** 10 10
5319 2 l. "The Artist's Room" 10 10
5320 3 l. "Illuminated Coffee Terrace" (vert) .. 25 10
5321 3 l. 50 "Orchard in Blossom" 30 10
5322 5 l. "Sunflowers" (vert) .. 40 10

1090 Great Black-backed Gull

1091 Crucifixion

1991. Water Birds.
5323 **1090** 50 b. blue 10 10
5324 – 1 l. green 10 10
5325 – 1 l. 50 bistre .. 10 10
5326 – 2 l. blue 10 10
5327 – 3 l. green 10 10
5328 – 3 l. 50 green .. 10 10
5329 – 4 l. violet 20 10
5330 – 5 l. brown 25 10
5331 – 6 l. brown 25 10
5332 – 7 l. blue 35 10
DESIGNS: 1 l. Common tern; 1 l. 50, Avocet; 2 l. Pomarine skua; 3 l. Lapwing; 3 l. 50, Red-breasted merganser; 4 l. Little egret; 5 l. Dunlin; 6 l. Black-tailed godwit; 7 l. Whiskered tern.

1991. Easter.
5333 **1091** 4 l. multicoloured .. 30 10

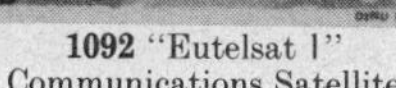
1092 "Eutelsat 1" Communications Satellite

1093 Posthorn

1991. Europa. Europe in Space.
5334 **1092** 4 l. 50 multicoloured 35 10

1991.
5335 **1093** 4 l. 50 blue 35 10

1094 Rings Exercise

1095 Curtea de Arges Monastery

1991. Gymnastics. Multicoloured.
5336 1 l. Type **1094** 10 10
5337 1 l. Parallel bars .. 10 10
5338 4 l. 50 Vaulting 40 10
5339 4 l. 50 Asymmetric bars .. 40 10
5340 8 l. Floor exercises .. 65 10
5341 9 l. Beam 75 10

1991. Monasteries. Multicoloured.
5342 1 l. Type **1095** 10 10
5343 1 l. Putna 10 10
5344 4 l. 50 Varatec 40 10
5345 4 l. 50 Agapia (horiz) .. 40 10
5346 8 l. Golia (horiz) .. 65 10
5347 9 l. Sucevita (horiz) .. 75 10

1096 Hotel Continental, Timisoara

1097 Gull and Sea Shore

1991. Hotels.
5349 **1096** 1 l. blue 10 10
5350 – 2 l. green 15 10
5352 – 4 l. red 25 10
5353 – 5 l. violet 40 10
5354 – 6 l. brown 35 10
5356 – 8 l. brown 45 10
5357 – 9 l. red 75 10
5358 – 10 l. green 85 10
5360 – 18 l. red .. .. 1·00 10
5361 – 20 l. orange .. 1·10 10
5362 – 25 l. blue .. .. 1·40 10
5363 – 30 l. purple .. .. 1·60 10
5365 – 45 l. blue .. .. 2·50 10
5367 – 60 l. green .. .. 3·25 10
5369 – 80 l. violet .. .. 4·50 10
5371 – 120 l. blue and grey 2·75 10
5372 – 160 l. red and pink .. 3·75 10
5374 – 250 l. blue and grey 5·50 10
5376 – 400 l. brown & ochre 9·00 10
5377 – 500 l. dp green & grn 11·00 10
5379 – 800 l. mauve & pink 18·00 10
DESIGNS—As T **1096**. HORIZ. 2 l. Valea Caprei Chalet, Mt. Fagaras; 5 l. Hotel Lebada, Crisan; 6 l. Muntele Rosu Chalet, Mt. Ciucas; 8 l. Transsilvania Hotel, Cluj-Napoca; 9 l. Hotel Orizont, Predeal; 20 l. Alpin Hotel, Poiana Bra, Psov; 25 l. Constanta Casino; 30 l. Miorita Chalet, Mt. Bucegi; 45 l. Sura Dacilor Chalet, Poiana Brasov; 60 l. Valea Draganului Tourist Complex; 80 l. Hotel Florica, Venus. VERT: 4 l. Intercontinental Hotel, Bucharest; 10 l. Hotel Roman, Baile Herculcane; 18 l. Rarau Chalet, Mt. Rarau. 26×40 mm: 120 l. International Complex, Baile Felix; 160 l. Hotel Egreta, Tulcea. 40×26 mm: 250 l. Valea de Pesti Motel, Jiului Valley; 400 l. Baisoara Tourist Complex; 500 l. Bradul Hotel, Covasna; 800 l. Gorj Hotel, Jiu.
Nos. 5367/79 have no frame.

1991. "Riccione '91" Stamp Exhibition, Italy.
5381 **1097** 4 l. multicoloured .. 10 10

1098 Vase

1099 Emblem

1991. Rumanian–Chinese Stamp Exhibition. Multicoloured.
5382 5 l. Type **1098** 40 10
5383 5 l. Vase with peony decoration 40 10

1991. 125th Anniv of Rumanian Academy.
5384 **1099** 1 l. blue 10 10

1100 "Flowers" (Nicu Enea)

1102 Map with House and People

1991. "Balcanfila '91" Stamp Exhibition, Bacau. Multicoloured.
5385 4 l. Type **1100** 35 10
5386 5 l. (+2 l.) "Peasant Girl of Vlasca" (Georghe Tattarescu) 60 15

1991. Population and Housing Census.
5389 **1102** 5 l. multicoloured .. 40 10

1103 Bridge

1991. "Phila Nippon '91" International Stamp Exhibition, Tokyo.
5390 **1103** 10 l. ochre, brn & red 10 10
5391 – 10 l. multicoloured .. 10 10
DESIGN: No. 5391, Junk.

1105 Running

1991. World Athletics Championships, Tokyo. Multicoloured.
5393 1 l. Type **1105** 10 10
5394 4 l. Long jumping .. 35 10
5395 5 l. High jumping .. 45 10
5396 5 l. Athlete in starting blocks 45 10
5397 9 l. Hurdling 75 10
5398 10 l. Throwing the javelin 85 10

1106 Mihail Kogalniceanu (politician, death cent)

1991. Anniversaries.
5399 **1106** 1 l. brown, bl & dp bl 10 10
5400 – 4 l. green, lilac & vio 35 10
5401 – 5 l. brown, dp bl & bl 45 10
5402 – 5 l. blue, brn & red 45 10
5403 – 9 l. red, blue & dp bl 75 10
5404 – 10 l. blk, lt brn & brn 85 10
DESIGNS: No. 5400, Nicolae Titulescu (politician, 50th death anniv); 5401, Andrei Mureseanu (writer, 175th birth anniv); 5402, Aron Pumnul (writer, 125th death anniv); 5403, George Bacovia (writer, 110th birth anniv); 5404, Perpessicius (literature critic, birth centenary).

1107 Library Building

1991. Centenary of Central University Library.
5405 **1107** 8 l. brown 65 10

1108 Coach and Horses

1991. Stamp Day.
5406 **1108** 8 l. (+2 l.) mult .. 85 15
No. 5406 was issued se-tenant with premium-carrying label as illustrated in Type **1108**.

1109 "Nativity" (17th-century icon) 1110 Shooting (biathlon)

1991. Christmas.

5407 **1109** 8 l. multicoloured .. 65 10

1992. Winter Olympic Games, Albertville. Multicoloured.

5408 4 l. Type **1110** 10 10
5409 5 l. Downhill skiing .. 15 10
5410 8 l. Cross-country skiing 25 10
5411 10 l. Two-man luge .. 30 10
5412 20 l. Speed skating .. 55 10
5413 25 l. Ski jumping .. 70 10
5414 30 l. Ice hockey 85 10
5415 45 l. Men's figure skating 1·25 10

1112 Jug, Plate, Tray and Bowl

1992. Rumanaian Porcelain. Multicoloured.

5419 4 l. Type **1112** 10 10
5420 5 l. Tea set 10 10
5421 8 l. Jug and goblet (vert) 10 10
5422 30 l. Tea set (different) .. 65 10
5423 45 l. Vase (vert) .. .. 1·00 10

1113 Mackerels

1992. Fishes. Multicoloured.

5424 4 l. Type **1113** 10 10
5425 5 l. Tench 10 10
5426 8 l. Speckled trout .. 10 10
5427 10 l. Riffle perch .. 10 10
5428 30 l. Undermouth .. 65 10
5429 45 l. Blunt-snouted mullet 1·00 10

1114 Vase 1115 Gymnast on Beam

1992. Apollo Art Gallery. Unissued stamp surch.

5430 **1114** 90 l. on 5 l. mult .. 2·10 10

1992. Individual Gymnastic Championships, Paris. Unissued stamp surch.

5431 **1115** 90 l. on 5 l. mult .. 2·10 10

1116 Dressage 1118 "Descent into Hell" (icon)

1992. Horses. Multicoloured.

5432 6 l. Type **1116** 15 10
5433 7 l. Racing (horiz) .. 15 10
5434 10 l. Rearing 20 10
5435 25 l. Jumping gate .. 55 10
5436 30 l. Stamping foot (horiz) 65 10
5437 50 l. Winged horse .. 1·10 10

1992. Easter.

5440 **1118** 10 l. multicoloured .. 25 10

1120 Tower and Hand Pump

1992. Centenary of Bucharest Fire Tower.

5441 **1120** 10 l. multicoloured .. 25 10

1121 Filipino Vinta and Rook

1992. 30th Chess Olympiad, Manila. Mult.

5442 10 l. Type **1121** 25 10
5443 10 l. Exterior of venue and chessmen 25 10

1122 Post Rider approaching Town

1992. Stamp Day.

5445 **1122** 10 l.+4 l. pink, violet and blue .. 15 10

1123 Pistol Shooting 1124 Ion Bratianu

1992. Olympic Games, Barcelona. Mult.

5446 6 l. Type **1123** 10 10
5447 7 l. Weightlifting .. 10 10
5448 9 l. Two-man kayak racing (horiz) 10 10
5449 10 l. Handball 10 10
5450 25 l. Wrestling (horiz) .. 30 10
5451 30 l. Fencing (horiz) .. 35 10
5452 50 l. Running 60 10
5453 55 l. Boxing (horiz) .. 65 10

1992. 130th Anniv of Foreign Ministry. Designs showing former Ministers.

5455 **1124** 10 l. violet, green and deep green .. 10 10
5456 – 25 l. pur, bl & dp bl 20 10
5457 – 30 l. blue, pur & brn 25 10

DESIGNS: 25 l. Ion Duca; 30 l. Grigore Gafencu.

1125 Sculpture

1992. "Expo 92" World's Fair, Seville. "Era of Discovery". Multicoloured.

5458 6 l. Type **1125** 10 10
5459 7 l. Roman bridge, Turnu-Severin .. 10 10
5460 10 l. House on stilts .. 10 10
5461 25 l. Railway bridge, Cernavoda 10 10
5462 30 l. Vuia No. 1 (airplane) 20 10
5463 55 l. Rocket 35 15

1126 Doves posting Letters in Globe

1992. World Post Day.

5465 **1126** 10 l. multicoloured .. 10 10

1127 "Santa Maria" and Bust of Columbus

1992. 500th Anniv of Discovery of America by Columbus. Multicoloured.

5466 6 l. Type **1127** 10 10
5467 10 l. "Nina" 10 10
5468 25 l. "Pinta" 20 10
5469 55 l. Columbus claiming New World 40 10

1128 Post Office Emblem

1992. 1st Anniv of Establishment of R.A. Posta Romana (postal organization).

5471 **1128** 10 l. multicoloured .. 10 10

1129 Jacob Negruzzi (writer, 150th birth anniv) 1130 American Bald Eagle

1992. Anniversaries.

5472 **1129** 6 l. green and violet 10 10
5473 – 7 l. mauve, purple and green .. 10 10
5474 – 9 l. blue and mauve 10 10
5475 – 10 l. lt brown, brown and ultramarine .. 10 10
5476 – 25 l. blue and brown 15 10
5477 – 30 l. green and blue 20 10

DESIGNS: 7 l. Grigore Antipa (zoologist, 125th birth anniv); 9 l. Alexe Mateevici (poet, 75th death anniv); 10 l. Cezar Petrescu (writer, birth centenary); 25 l. Octav Onicescu (mathematician, birth centenary); 30 l. Ecaterina Teodoroiu (first world war fighter, 75th death anniv).

1992. Animals. Multicoloured.

5478 6 l. Type **1130** 10 10
5479 7 l. Spotted owl 10 10
5480 9 l. Brown bear 10 10
5481 10 l. American black oystercatcher (horiz) .. 10 10
5482 25 l. Wolf (horiz) .. 20 10
5483 30 l. White-tailed deer (horiz) 20 10
5484 55 l. Elk (horiz) 40 10

1131 Arms 1133 Nativity

1132 Buildings and Street, Galea Victoriei

1992. New State Arms.

5486 **1131** 15 l. multicoloured .. 10 10

1992. Anniversaries. Multicoloured.

5487 7 l. Type **1132** (300th anniv) 10 10
5488 9 l. College building and statue, Roman (600th anniv) 10 10
5489 10 l. Prince Basarai, monastery and Princess Despina (475th anniv of Curtea de Arges monastery) 10 10
5490 25 l. Bucharest School of Architecture (80th anniv) 10 10

1992. Christmas.

5491 **1133** 15 l. multicoloured .. 10 10

1134 Globe and Key-pad on Telephone

1992. New Telephone Number System.

5492 **1134** 15 l. black, red & blue 10 10

1136 Mihai Voda Monastery

1993. Bucharest Buildings. Multicoloured.

5494 10 l. Type **1136** 10 10
5495 15 l. Vacaresti Monastery 10 10
5496 25 l. Unirii Hall 15 10
5497 30 l. Mina Minovici Medico-legal Institute 20 10

1137 "Draken", 1903

1993. Air Balloons. Multicoloured.

5498 30 l. Type **1137** 20 10
5499 90 l. "Caquot", 1917 .. 55 10

1138 Crucifixion 1139 Hawthorn

1993. Easter.

5500	1138	15 l. multicoloured ..	10	10

1993. Medicinal Plants. Multicoloured.

5501	10 l. Type 1139	10	10
5502	15 l. Gentian	10	10
5503	25 l. Sea buckthorn ..	15	10
5504	30 l. Bilberry	20	10
5505	50 l. Arnica	30	10
5506	90 l. Dog rose	55	15

1140 Stanescu

1141 Mounted Courier

1993. 60th Birth Anniv of Nichita Stanescu (poet).

5507	1140	15 l. multicoloured ..	10	10

1993. Stamp Day.

5508	1141	15 l. + 10 l. mult ..	10	10

1143 Magpie

1993. Birds.

5510	1143	5 l. black and green	10	10
5511	–	10 l. black and red ..	10	10
5512	–	15 l. black and red ..	10	10
5513	–	20 l. black and brown	10	10
5514	–	25 l. black and red ..	15	10
5515	–	50 l. black and yellow	30	10
5516	–	65 l. black and red ..	40	10
5517	–	90 l. black and red ..	55	15
5518	–	160 l. black and blue	95	30
5519	–	250 l. black & mauve	1·50	50

DESIGNS—HORIZ. 10 l. Golden eagle. VERT. 15 l. Bullfinch; 20 l. Hoopoe; 25 l. Great spotted woodpecker; 50 l. Golden oriole; 65 l. White-winged crossbill; 90 l. Barn swallows; 160 l. Azure tit; 250 l. Rose-coloured starling.

1144 Long-hair

1147 Pine Marten

1146 Adder

1993. Cats. Multicoloured.

5520	10 l. Type 1144	10	10
5521	15 l. Tabby-point long-hair	10	10
5522	30 l. Red long-hair ..	15	10
5523	90 l. Blue Persian ..	40	10
5524	135 l. Tabby	60	20
5525	160 l. Long-haired white Persian	70	20

1993. Protected Animals. Multicoloured.

5527	10 l. Type 1146	10	10
5528	15 l. Lynx (vert) ..	10	10
5529	25 l. Common shelduck ..	10	10
5530	75 l. Danube salmon ..	25	10
5531	105 l. Poplar admiral ..	35	10
5532	280 l. Alpine longhorn beetle	1·00	30

1993. Mammals.

5533	1147	10 l. black and yellow	10	10
5534	–	15 l. black and brown	10	10
5535	–	20 l. red and black ..	10	10
5536	–	25 l. black and brown	10	10
5537	–	30 l. black and red ..	10	10
5538	–	40 l. black and red ..	15	10
5539	–	75 l. black and yellow	25	10
5540	–	105 l. black & brown	35	10
5541	–	150 l. black & orange	50	15
5542	–	280 l. black & yellow	95	30

DESIGNS—HORIZ. 15 l. Common rabbit; 30 l. Red fox; 150 l. Stoat; 280 l. Egyptian mongoose. VERT. 20 l. Eurasian red squirrel; 25 l. Chamois; 40 l. Argali; 75 l. Small-spotted genet; 105 l. Garden dormouse.

1148 Brontosaurus

1993. Prehistoric Animals. Multicoloured.

5543	29 l. Type 1148	10	10
5544	46 l. Plesiosaurus ..	15	10
5545	85 l. Triceratops ..	30	10
5546	171 l. Stegosaurus ..	60	20
5547	216 l. Tyrannosaurus ..	75	20
5548	319 l. Archaeopteryx ..	1·10	35

1150 Stefan the Great, Prince of Moldavia

1151 Mounted Officers

1993. Icons. Multicoloured.

5550	75 l. Type 1150	10	10
5551	171 l. Prince Constantin Brancoveanu of Wallachia with his sons Constantin, Stefan, Radu and Matei and adviser Ianache Vacarescu	30	10
5552	216 l. St. Antim Ivireanul, Metropolitan of Wallachia	70	20

1993. Centenary of Rural Gendarmerie Law.

5553	1151	29 l. multicoloured ..	10	10

1993. "Riccione '93" International Stamp Fair. No. 5292 surch **Riccione '93 3–5 septembrie 171 L.**

5554	1081	171 l. on 2 l. mult ..	70	20

1154 George Baritiu

1993. Anniversaries.

5556	1154	29 l. flesh, blk & lilac	10	10
5557	–	46 l. flesh, black & bl	15	10
5558	–	85 l. flesh, blk & grn	30	10
5559	–	171 l. flesh, blk & pur	60	20
5560	–	216 l. flesh, blk & bl	75	25
5561	–	319 l. flesh, black and grey	1·10	35

DESIGNS: 29 l. Type 1154 (politician and journalist, death centenary); 46 l. Horia Creanga (architect, 50th death anniv); 85 l. Armand Calinescu (leader of Peasant National Party, birth centenary); 171 l. Dr. Dumitru Bagdasar (neuro-surgeon, birth centenary); 216 l. Constantin Brailoiu (musician, birth centenary); 319 l. Iuliu Maniu (politician, 40th death anniv).

EXPRESS LETTER STAMPS

1919. Transylvania. Cluj Issue. No. E 245 of Hungary optd. as T **42.**

E 784.	E **18.**	2 b. olive and red	12	12

1919. Transylvania. Oradea Issue. No. E 245 of Hungary optd. as T **43.**

E 860.	E **18.**	2 b. olive and red ..	15	15

NEWSPAPER STAMPS

1919. Transylvania. Cluj Issue. No. N 136 of Hungary optd. as T **42.**

N 783.	N **9.**	2 b. orange ..	12	12

1919. Transylvania. Oradea Issue. No. 136 of Hungary optd. as T **43.**

N 859.	N **9.**	2 b. orange ..	15	15

OFFICIAL STAMPS

O **71.** Rumanian Eagle and National Flag. O **80.**

1929.

O 1115.	O **71.**	25 b. orange ..	10	10
O 1116.		50 b. brown ..	10	12
O 1117.		1 l. violet	10	5
O 1118.		2 l. green	10	5
O 1119.		3 l. red	30	5
O 1120.		4 l. olive	25	12
O 1121.		6 l. blue	95	20
O 1122.		10 l. blue	35	25
O 1123.		25 l. red	1·50	90
O 1124.		50 l. violet ..	4·50	2·40

1930. Optd. **8 IUNIE 1930.**

O 1150.	O **71.**	25 b. orange ..	15	5
O 1151.		50 b. brown ..	15	5
O 1152.		1 l. violet	8	5
O 1153.		2 l. green	8	5
O 1165.	O **71.**	3 l. red	40	12
O 1154.		4 l. olive	40	12
O 1160.		6 l. blue	30	20
O 1161.		10 l. blue	50	12
O 1156.		25 l. red	2·10	75
O 1157.		50 l. violet ..	3·50	2·25

1931.

O 1194.	O **80.**	25 b. black ..	12	10
O 1195.		1 l. purple.. ..	20	15
O 1196.		2 l. green	30	20
O 1197.		3 l. red	35	25
O 1247.		6 l. red	75	40

PARCEL POST STAMPS

1895. As Type D12 but inscr. at top "TAXA DE FACTAGIU".

P 353.	25 b. brown	9·00	1·50
P 479.	25 b. red	7·00	75

1928. Surch. **FACTAJ 5 LEI.**

P 1078.	**46.**	5 l. on 10 b. green	75	25

POSTAGE DUE STAMPS

A. Ordinary Postage Due Stamps.

D **12.**

D **38.**

1881.

D 152.	D **12.**	2 b. brown ..	3·00	1·50
D 153.		5 b. brown ..	15·00	2·40
D 200.		10 b. brown ..	18·00	1·50
D 201.		30 b. brown ..	21·00	1·50
D 156.		50 b. brown ..	12·00	3·00
D 157.		60 b. brown ..	15·00	3·50

1887.

D 448.	D **12.**	2 b. green	1·10	45
D 551.		5 b. green	60	45
D 558.		10 b. green ..	90	45
D 553.		30 b. green ..	1·50	45
D 452.		50 b. green ..	4·75	90
D 245.		60 b. green ..	6·75	3·00

1911.

D 617.	D **38.**	2 b. blue on yellow	12	8
D 618.		5 b. blue on yellow	12	8
D 619.		10 b. blue on yellow	12	5
D 604.		15 b. blue on yellow	20	5
D 621.		20 b. blue on yellow	15	10
D 622.		30 b. blue on yellow	40	10
D 623.		50 b. blue on yellow	50	12
D 624.		60 b. blue on yellow	55	12
D 609.		2 l. blue on yellow	75	50

1918. Optd. **TAXA DE PLATA.**

D 675.	**37.**	5 b. green	1·10	40
D 676.		10 b. red	1·10	40

1918. Re-issue of Type D **38.** On greenish or white paper.

D 1001.	D **38.**	5 b. black ..	5	5
D 722.		10 b. black ..	10	5
D 734a.		20 b. black ..	12	10
D 735.		30 b. black ..	15	12
D 736.		50 b. black ..	25	35
D 998.		60 b. black ..	12	5
D 1007.		1 l. black.. ..	25	5
D 1010.		2 l. black.. ..	30	5
D 991.		3 l. black.. ..	15	5
D 992.		6 l. black.. ..	25	5
D 1547.		50 l. black ..	20	12
D 1548.		100 l. black ..	30	20

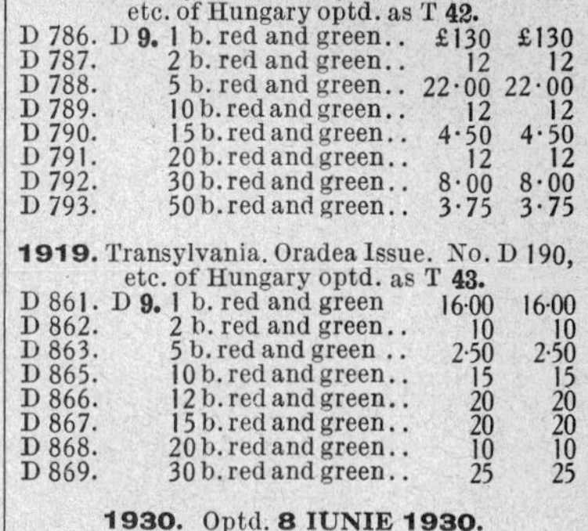

1919. Transylvania. Cluj Issue. No. D 190 etc. of Hungary optd. as T **42.**

D 786.	D **9.**	1 b. red and green..	£130	£130
D 787.		2 b. red and green..	12	12
D 788.		5 b. red and green..	22·00	22·00
D 789.		10 b. red and green..	12	12
D 790.		15 b. red and green..	4·50	4·50
D 791.		20 b. red and green..	12	12
D 792.		30 b. red and green..	8·00	8·00
D 793.		50 b. red and green..	3·75	3·75

1919. Transylvania. Oradea Issue. No. D 190, etc. of Hungary optd. as T **43.**

D 861.	D **9.**	1 b. red and green	16·00	16·00
D 862.		2 b. red and green..	10	10
D 863.		5 b. red and green ..	2·50	2·50
D 865.		10 b. red and green..	15	15
D 866.		12 b. red and green..	20	20
D 867.		15 b. red and green..	20	20
D 868.		20 b. red and green..	10	10
D 869.		30 b. red and green..	25	25

1930. Optd. **8 IUNIE 1930.**

D 1168.	D **38.**	1 l. black.. ..	12	5
D 1169.		2 l. black.. ..	20	10
D 1170.		3 l. black.. ..	25	12
D 1171.		6 l. black.. ..	40	25

D **98.**

D **233.**

1932.

D 1249.	D **98.**	1 l. black.. ..	5	5
D 1250.		2 l. black.. ..	5	5
D 1251.		3 l. black.. ..	10	5
D 1252.		6 l. black.. ..	12	8
D 1835.		20 l. black ..	10	5
D 1839.		50 l. black ..	12	5
D 1840.		80 l. black ..	25	12
D 1841.		100 l. black ..	35	20
D 1842.		200 l. black ..	55	35
D 1843.		500 l. black ..	80	50
D 1844.		5000 l. black ..	1·40	75

1947. Type D **233** perforated down centre (without opt.).

		Un. pair.
D 1919.	2 l. red	25
D 1920.	4 l. blue	40
D 1921.	5 l. black ..	1·00
D 1922.	10 l. brown ..	1·60

The left half of Nos. D 1919/22, showing Crown, served as a receipt and was stuck in the postman's book and so does not come postally used.

1948. Nos. D 1919/22, optd. as in Type D **233.**

		Un. pair.	Us. pair.
D 1944.	2 l. red..	20	15
D 1945.	4 l. blue	30	20
D 1946.	5 l. black	50	30
D 1947.	10 l. brown	1·40	45

D **276.**
Badge. Postwoman.

1950.

			Un. pair.	Us. pair.
D 2066.	D **276.**	2 l. red	40	40
D 2067.		4 l. blue.. ..	50	50
D 2068.		5 l. green ..	1·00	1·00
D 2069.		10 l. brown ..	1·40	1·40

1952. Currency revalued. Nos. D 2066/9 surch. thus: **4 Bani** on each half.

			Un. pair.	Us. pair.
D 2221.	D **276.**	4 b. on 2 l. red..	35	35
D 2222.		10 b. on 4 l. blue	35	35
D 2223.		20 b. on 5 l. grn.	75	75
D 2224.		50 b. on 10 l. brn.	85	85

D **420.**
G.P.O. Bucharest. Posthorn.

1957.

			Un. pair.	Us. pair.
D 2507.	D **420.**	3 b. black ..	15	10
D 2508.		5 b. orange ..	15	10
D 2509.		10 b. purple ..	15	10
D 2510.		20 b. red ..	15	10
D 2511.		40 b. green ..	40	20
D 2512.		1 l. blue.. ..	1·50	25

D 614.

1967.

No.	Type	Description	Un. pair.	Us. pair.
D 3436.	D 614.	3 b. green ..	10	10
D 3437.		5 b. blue ..	10	10
D 3438.		10 b. mauve ..	10	10
D 3439.		20 b. red ..	15	10
D 3440.		40 b. brown ..	20	10
D 3441.		1 l. violet ..	40	15

D 766. Postal Emblems and Postman.

1974.

No.	Type	Description	Un. pair.	Us. pair.
D 4050.	D 766.	5 b. blue ..	10	10
D 4051.		10 b. green ..	10	10
D 4052.	–	20 b. red ..	10	10
D 4053.	–	40 b. violet ..	15	10
D 4054.	–	50 b. brown ..	30	10
D 4055.	–	1 l. orange ..	40	10

DESIGNS: 20 b., 40 b. Dove with letter and Hermes with posthorn. 50 b., 1 l. G.P.O., Bucharest and emblem with mail-van.

1982. As Type D 766.

No.	Type	Description	Un.	Us.
D 4761.	–	25 b. violet ..	10	10
D 4762.	D 766.	50 b. yellow ..	15	10
D 4763.	–	1 l. red	25	10
D 4764.	–	2 l. green ..	45	10
D 4765.	D 766.	3 l. brown ..	65	15
D 4766.	–	4 l. blue.. ..	90	15

DESIGNS: 25 b., 1 l. Dove with letter and Hermes with posthorn. 2, 4 l. G.P.O., Bucharest, and emblem with mail-van.

D 1111

1992.

No.	Type	Description	Un.	Us.
D5417	D 1111	4 l. red	10	10
D5418		8 l. blue ..	10	10

B. Postal Tax Due Stamps.

1915. Optd. **TIMBRU DE AJUTOR.**

No.	Type	Description	Un.	Us.
TD 643.	D 38.	5 b. blue on yellow	35	12
TD 644.		10 b. blue on yellow	30	12

TD 42.

TD 106.

1917. Green or white paper.

No.	Type	Description	Un.	Us.
TD 655.	TD 42.	5 b. brown ..	55	25
TD 743.		5 b. red ..	12	12
TD 654.		10 b. red ..	35	25
TD 741.		10 b. brown ..	25	30

1918. Optd. **TAXA DE PLATA.**

No.	Type	Description	Un.	Us.
TD 680.	TD 42.	5 b. black ..	25	25
TD 681.		10 b. brown ..	25	25

1922. As Type TD 42, but inscr. "ASSISTENTA SOCIALA". On green or white paper.

No.	Type	Description	Un.	Us.
TD 1028.		10 b. brown	8	8
TD 1029.		20 b. brown	8	8
TD 1030.		25 b. brown	5	5
TD 1031.		50 b. brown	8	8

1931. Aviation Fund. Optd. **TIMBRUL AVIATIEI.**

No.	Type	Description	Un.	Us.
TD 1219.	D 38.	1 l. black ..	8	5
TD 1220.		2 l. black ..	8	5

1932.

No.	Type	Description	Un.	Us.
TD 1278.	TD 106.	3 l. black ..	80	60

POSTAL TAX STAMPS

The following stamps were for compulsory use at certain times on inland mail to raise money for various funds. In some instances where the stamps were not applied the appropriate Postal Tax Postage Due stamps were applied.

Other denominations exist but these were purely for revenue purposes and were not applied to postal matter.

Soldiers Families Fund.

1915. Optd. **TIMBRU DE AJUTOR.**

No.	Type	Description	Un.	Us.
T 638.	37.	5 b. green	20	12
T 639.		10 b. red	30	15

T 41. The Queen Weaving. T 47. "Charity".

1916.

No.	Type	Description	Un.	Us.
T 649.	T 41.	5 b. black	20	12
T 710.		5 b. green	50	15
T 650.		10 b. brown ..	25	15
T 711.		10 b. black	50	15

The 50 b. and 1, 2, 5 and 50 l. in similar designs were only used fiscally.

1918. Optd. **1918.**

No.	Type	Description	Un.	Us.
T 671.	37.	5 b. green (No. T 638)	30·00	30·00
T 667.	T 41.	5 b. black	50	35
T 672.	37.	10 b. red (No. T 639)	30·00	30·00
T 668.	T 41.	10 b. brown ..	75	30

1921. Social Welfare.

No.	Type	Description	Un.	Us.
T 978.	T 47.	10 b. green ..	5	5
T 979.		25 b. black ..	5	5

Aviation Fund.

T 91.

T 98.

1931.

No.	Type	Description	Un.	Us.
T 1216.	T 91.	50 b. green ..	30	10
T 1217.		1 l. brown ..	60	10
T 1218.		2 l. blue	75	20

1932.

No.	Type	Description	Un.	Us.
T 1253.	T 98.	50 b. green ..	15	10
T 1254.		1 l. purple.. ..	20	10
T 1255.		2 l. blue	30	10

Stamps as Type **98** but inscr. "FONDUL AVIATIEI" were only for fiscal use. Nos. T 1253/4 could only be used fiscally after 1937.

T 105.

T 121.
"Aviation".

1932. Cultural Fund.

No.	Type	Description	Un.	Us.
T 1276.	T 105.	2 l. blue	50	40
T 1277.		2 l. brown ..	45	30

These were for compulsory use on postcards.

1936.

No.	Type	Description	Un.	Us.
T 1340.	T 121.	50 b. green ..	15	10
T 1341.		1 l. brown ..	15	10
T 1342.		2 l. blue	25	10

Other stamps inscr. "FONDUL AVIATIEI" were only for fiscal use.

T 171. King Michael.

1943.

No.	Type	Description	Un.	Us.
T 1589.	T 171.	50 b. orange ..	10	10
T 1590.		1 l. lilac	10	10
T 1591.		2 l. brown ..	10	10
T 1592.		4 l. blue	10	10
T 1593		5 l. violet	10	10
T 1594.		8 l. green ..	10	10
T 1595.		10 l. brown ..	10	10

1947. Fiscal stamps (22 × 18½ mm.), perf. vert. through centre surch. **IOVR** and value.

No.	Type	Description	Un.	Us.
T 1923.		1 l. on 2 l. red.. ..	15	15
T 1924.		5 l. on 1 l. green ..	50	45

1948. Vert. designs (approx. 18½ × 22 mm.) inscr. "I.O.V.R.".

No.	Type	Description	Un.	Us.
T 1948.		1 l. red	15	20
T 1949.		1 l. violet	40	30
T 1950.		2 l. blue	60	40
T 1951.		5 l. yellow	3·00	2·00

SAVINGS BANK STAMPS

1919. Transylvania. Cluj Issue. No. B 199 of Hungary optd. as T **42.**

No.	Type	Description	Un.	Us.
B 785.	B 17.	10 b. purple ..	15	15

1919. Transylvania. Oradea Issue. No. B 199 of Hungary optd. as T **43.**

No.	Type	Description	Un.	Us.
B 861.	B 17.	10 b. purple ..	15	15

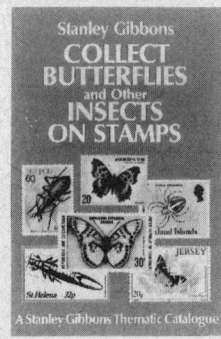

RUMANIAN OCCUPATION OF HUNGARY Pt. 2

BANAT BACSKA

The following stamps were issued by the Temesvar postal authorities between the period of the Serbian evacuation and the Rumanian occupation. This area was later divided, the Western part going to Yugoslavia and the Eastern part going to Rumania.

100 filler = 1 korona.

1919. Stamps of Hungary optd. **Banat Bacska 1919.**

(a) "Turul" Type.

1. **7.** 50 f. lake on blue .. 6·00 6·00

(b) War Charity stamps of 1916.

2. **20.** 10 f. (+2 f.) red 15 15
3. – 15 f. (+2 f.) violet .. 15 15
4. **22.** 40 f. (+2 f.) red 15 15

(c) Harvesters and Parliament Types.

5. **18.** 2 f. brown 15 15
6. 3 f. red 15 15
7. 5 f. green 15 15
8. 6 f. blue 15 15
9. 15 f. violet 15 15
10. 35 f. brown .. .. 5·00 5·00
11. **19.** 50 f. purple .. .. 4·00 4·00
12. 75 f. blue 15 15
13. 80 f. green 15 15
14. 1 k. red 15 15
15. 2 k. brown 15 15
16. 3 k. grey and violet .. 5·50 5·50
17. 5 k. brown 25 25
18. 10 k. lilac and brown .. 1·25 1·25

(d) Karl and Zita stamps.

19. **27.** 10 f. red 15 15
20. 20 f. brown 15 15
21. 25 f. blue 15 15
22. **28.** 40 f. green 15 15
23. 50 f. purple 15 15

(e) Harvesters Type inscr. "MAGYAR POSTA".

24. **18.** 10 f. red .. .. .. 3·00 3·00
25. 20 f. brown .. .. 2·75 2·75
26. 25 f. blue .. .. .. 4·00 4·00

The following (Nos. 27/39 are also optd. **KOZTARSASAG.**

(f) Harvesters and Parliament Types.

27. **18.** 4 f. grey 15 15
28. 5 f. green 15 15
29. 6 f. blue 15 15
30. 10 f. red .. .. .. 2·50 2·50
31. 20 f. brown .. .. 2·50 2·50
32. 40 f. green 15 15
33. **19.** 1 k. red 15 15
34. 2 k. brown .. .. 2·75 2·75
35. 3 k. grey and violet .. 2·75 2·75
36. 5 k. brown .. .. 2·75 2·75
37. 10 k. lilac and brown .. 2·75 2·75

(g) Karl portrait stamps.

38. **27.** 15 f. violet .. .. 1·75 1·75
39. 25 f. blue .. .. .. 1·25 1·75

(h) Serbian Occupation of Temesvar stamps.

40. **18.** 10 f. on 2 f. brown .. 25 25
41. **20.** 45 f. on 10 f. (+2 f.) red 25 25
42. **18.** 1 k. 50 in 15 f. violet .. 25 25

EXPRESS LETTER STAMP

1919. No. E 245 optd. as above, and surch.

E 44. E **18.** 30 f. on 2 f. olive & red 1·00 1·00

NEWSPAPER STAMP

1919. No. N 136 optd. **Banat Bacska 1919.**

N 43. N **9.** (2 f.) orange 25 25

POSTAGE DUE STAMPS

1919. Nos. D 191 etc. optd. as above.

D 46. D **9.** 2 f. red and green .. 30 30
D 47. 10 f. red and green .. 30 30
D 48. 15 f. red and green .. 4·25 4·25
D 49. 20 f. red and green 30 30
D 50. 30 f. red and green .. 2·75 2·75
D 51. 50 f. black and green 4·00 4·00

SAVINGS BANK STAMP

1919. No. B 199 optd. as above, and surch.

B 45. B **17.** 50 f. on 10 f. purple 1·00 1·00

DEBRECEN

This area was later returned to Hungary.

100 filler = 1 korona.

(1.)

1919. Stamps of Hungary optd. with T **1**, or surch. in addition.

(a) "Turul" Type.

1. **7.** 2 f. yellow .. .. 7·00 7·00
2. 3 f. orange .. .. 15·00 15·00
3. 6 f. brown .. .. 3·00 3·00

(b) War Charity stamps of 1915.

4. **7.** 2 f.+2 f. yellow (No. 171) .. 15·00 15·00
5. 3 f.+2 f. orange (No. 172) .. 15·00 15·00

(c) War Charity stamps of 1916.

6. **20.** 10 f. (+2 f.) red 25 25
7. – 15 f. (+2 f.) violet .. 40 40
8. **22.** 40 f. (+2 f.) red 30 30

(d) Harvesters and Parliament Types.

9. **18.** 2 f. brown 20 5
10. 3 f. red 20 10
11. 5 f. green 20 20
12. 6 f. blue 20 20
13. 10 f. red (No. 243) .. 7·00 7·00
14. 15 f. violet (No. 244) .. 5·00 5·00
15. 15 f. violet 15 15
16. 20 f. brown .. .. 4·50 4·50
17. 25 f. blue 45 45
18. 35 f. brown .. .. 3·50 3·50
19. 35 f. on 3 f. red 25 25
20. 40 f. olive 30 30
21. 45 f. on 2 f. brown .. 15 15
22. **19.** 50 f. purple 35 35
23. 75 f. blue 20 20
24. 80 f. green 30 30
25. 1 k. red 40 40
26. 2 k. brown 20 20
27. 3 k. grey and violet .. 2·50 2·50
28. 3 k. on 75 f. blue .. 1·10 1·10
29. 5 k. brown .. .. 2·00 2·00
30. 5 k. on 75 f. blue .. 50 50
31. 10 k. lilac and brown .. 12·00 12·00
32. 10 k. on 80 f. green .. 1·00 1·00

(e) Karl and Zita stamps.

33. **27.** 10 f. red .. .. .. 3·00 3·00
34. 15 f. violet .. .. 5·00 5·00
35. 20 f. brown 35 35
36. 25 f. blue 35 35
37. **28.** 40 f. olive 20 20
38. 50 f. purple .. .. 2·25 2·25

(f) Harvesters and Parliament Types inscr. "MAGYAR POSTA".

39. **18.** 5 f. green 10 10
40. 6 f. blue 65 65
41. 10 f. red 10 10
42. 20 f. brown 10 10
43. 25 f. blue 10 10
44. 45 f. orange .. .. 1·00 1·00
45. **19.** 5 k. brown £325

The following (Nos. 46/64) are also optd. **KOZTARSASAG.**

(g) Harvesters and Parliament Types.

46. **18.** 2 f. brown 20 20
47. 3 f. red 90 90
48. 4 f. grey 12 12
49. 5 f. green 10 10
50. 10 f. red .. .. .. 1·25 1·25
51. 20 f. brown 30 30
52. 40 f. olive 15 15
53. **19.** 1 k. lake 15 15
54. 2 k. brown .. .. 3·50 3·50
55. 3 k. grey and violet .. 80 80
56. 5 k. brown .. .. 38·00 38·00

(h) War Charity stamps of 1916.

57. **20.** 10 f. (+2 f.) red .. 1·00 1·00
58. – 15 f. (+2 f.) violet .. 11·00 11·00
59. **22.** 40 f. (+2 f.) lake .. 1·00 1·00

(k) Karl and Zita stamps.

60. **27.** 10 f. red 85 85
61. 15 f. violet .. .. 2·25 2·25
62. 20 f. brown .. .. 1·75 1·75
63. 25 f. blue 25 25
64. **28.** 50 f. purple 15 15

2.

4.

1920. Types **2** and **4** and similar design, optd. with inscr. as T **1** but in circle.

65. **2.** 2 f. brown 15 15
66. 3 f. brown 15 15
67. 4 f. violet 15 15
68. 5 f. green 10 10
69. 6 f. grey 15 15
70. 10 f. red 10 10
71. 15 f. violet 20 20
72. 20 f. brown 10 10
73. – 25 f. blue 15 15
74. – 30 f. ochre 15 15
75. – 35 f. red 15 15
76. – 40 f. green 15 15
77. – 45 f. red 15 15
78. – 50 f. mauve 15 15
79. – 60 f. green 15 15
80. – 75 f. blue 15 15
81. **4.** 80 f. green 15 15
82. 1 k. red 20 20
83. 1 k. 20 orange .. 3·75 3·75
84. 2 k. brown 30 30
85. 3 k. brown 45 45
86. 5 k. brown 45 45
87. 10 k. puple 55 55

DESIGN: Nos. 73/80, Horseman using lasso.

5.

1920. War Charity. Type **5** with circular opt., and "Segely belyeg" at top.

88. **5.** 20 f. green 20 20
89. 20 f. green on blue .. 40 40
90. 50 f. brown 20 20
91. 50 brown on mauve .. 25 25
92. 1 k. green 25 25
93. 1 k. green on green .. 20 20
94. 2 k. green 30 30

EXPRESS LETTER STAMP

1919. No. E 245 optd. with T **1.**

E 66. E **18.** 2 f. olive and red .. 20 20

NEWSPAPER STAMP

1919. No. N 136 optd. with T **1.**

N 65. N **9.** 2 f. orange 15 15

POSTAGE DUE STAMPS

1919. Nos. D 190 etc. optd. with T **1.**

D 68. D **9.** 1 f. red and green 3·50 3·50
D 69. 2 f. red and green . 10 10
D 70. 5 f. red and green .. 50·00 50·00
D 71. 6 f. red and green .. 4·50 4·50
D 72. 10 f. red and green .. 10 10
D 73. 12 f. red and green 18·00 18·00
D 74. 15 f. red and green .. 85 85
D 75. 20 f. red and green .. 85 85
D 76. 30 f. red and green .. 85 85

The following (Nos. D 77/82) are also optd. **KOZTARSASAG.**

D 77. D **9.** 2 f. red and green .. 1·00 1·00
D 78. 3 f. red and green .. 1·00 1·00
D 79. 10 f. red and green .. 1·00 1·00
D 80. 20 f. red and green .. 1·00 1·00
D 81. 40 f. red and green .. 1·00 1·00
D 82. 50 f. red and green .. 1·00 1·00

D 6.

1920.

D 95. D **6.** 5 f. green 15 15
D 96. 10 f. green 15 15
D 97. 20 f. green 15 15
D 98. 30 f. green 15 15
D 99. 40 f. green 15 15

SAVINGS BANK STAMP

1919. No. B 199 optd. with T **1.**

B 67. B **17.** 10 f. purple .. 3·75 3·75

TEMESVAR

After being occupied by Serbia this area was then occupied by Rumania. It later became part of Rumania and was renamed Timisoara.

100 filler = 1 korona.

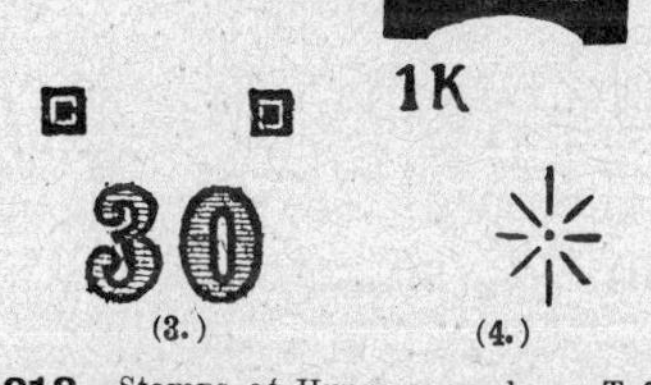

(3.) (4.)

1919. Stamps of Hungary surch. as T **3/4** (Nos. 6 and 7), with value only (Nos. 8 and 9) or with **KORONA** and value (No. 10).

(a) Harvesters Type.

6. **18.** 30 on 2 f. brown .. 10 10
7. 1 k. on 4 f. slate (optd. **KOZTARSASAG**) .. 10 10
8. 150 on 3 f. red 10 10
9. 150 on 5 f. green 15 15

(b) Express Letter Stamp.

10. E **18.** 3 KORONA on 2 f. olive and red .. 20 20

POSTAGE DUE STAMPS

1919. Charity stamp surch. **PORTO** and value.

D 11. – 40 PORTO on 15 + (2 f.) violet (No. 265) .. 15 15

(D 8.)

1919. Postage Due stamps surch. with T **D 8.**

D 12. D **9.** 60 on 2 f. red and reen 25 25
D 13. 60 on 10 f. red and green 25 25

RUMANIAN POST OFFICES ABROAD Pt. 16

Rumanian P.O.s in the Turkish Empire including Constantinople. Now closed.

I. IN TURKISH EMPIRE

40 paras = 1 piastre.

1896. Stamps of Rumania of 1893 surch in "PARAS".

9 10 pa. on 5 b. blue (No. 319) 10·00 10·00
10 20 pa. on 10 b. grn (No. 320) 10·00 10·00
11 1 pi. on 25 b. mve (No. 322) 10·00 10·00

II. IN CONSTANTINOPLE

100 bani = 1 leu.

(1.)

1919. Stamps of Rumania of 1893–1908 optd. with T **1.**

10 **37** 5 b. green 30 35
6 10 b. red 40 50
7 15 b. brown 50 55
13 – 25 b. blue (No. 701) .. 55 75
14 – 40 b. brown (No. 703) .. 1·75 1·75

1919. 1916 Postal Tax stamp of Rumania optd with T **1.**

16 T **41** 5 b. green .. .. 1·00 1·00

RUSSIA Pt. 10

A country in the E. of Europe and N. Asia. An empire until 1917 when the Russian Socialist Federal Soviet Republic was formed. In 1923 this became the Union of Soviet Socialist Republics (U.S.S.R.), eventually comprising 15 constituent republics.

In 1991 the U.S.S.R was dissolved and subsequent issues were used in the Russian Federation only.

100 kopeks = 1 rouble.

1.

5.

8.

9.

10.

11.

1858. Imperf.

1. **1.** 10 k. blue and brown .. £4000 £400

1858. Perf.

21. **1.** 10 k. blue and brown .. 32·00 25
22. 20 k. orange and blue .. 55·00 5·50
23. 30 k. green and red .. 75·00 25·00

1863.

8. **5.** 5 k. black and blue .. 20·00 80·00

No. 8 was first issued as a local but was later authorised for general use.

1864.

18 **9** 1 k. black and yellow .. 3·00 35
30 2 k. black and red .. 5·00 40
19b 3 k. black and green .. 4·00 45
20 5 k. black and lilac .. 7·50 25

1875.

31. **8.** 7 k. red and grey .. 4·50 15
32. 8 k. red and grey .. 7·50 25
33. 10 k. blue and brown .. 25·00 2·00
34. 20 k. orange and blue .. 30·00 1·75

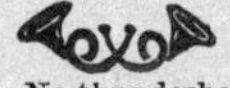

12. No thunderbolts.

1883. Posthorns in design without thunderbolts, as T **12.**

38 **9** 1 k. orange .. .. 2·50 35
40 2 k. green .. .. 3·00 30
41 3 k. red .. .. 3·50 20
42b 5 k. purple .. .. 2·75 15
43c 7 k. blue .. .. 3·00 15
44b **10** 14 k. red and blue .. 7·00 25
45 35 k. green and purple .. 12·00 1·75
46 70 k. orange and brown .. 22·00 1·75
47 **11** 3 r. 50 k. grey and black .. £300 £250
48 7 r. yellow and black .. £300 £300

14.

15.

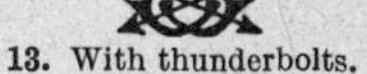

13. With thunderbolts.

1889. Posthorns in design with thunderbolts as T **13** Perf.

50	**9**	1 k. orange	20	10
51a		2 k. green	20	10
52		3 k. red	20	10
53	**14**	4 k. red	30	10
54	**9**	5 k. purple	60	10
55		7 k. blue	30	10
56	**14**	10 k. blue	60	10
114	**10**	14 k. red and blue ..	10	10
100		15 k. blue and purple	10	10
116	**14**	20 k. red and blue ..	10	10
102	**10**	25 k. violet and green	10	10
103		35 k. green and purple	10	10
119	**14**	50 k. green & purple..	10	10
120	**10**	70 k. orange & brown	10	10
121A	**15**	1 r. orange & brown ..	10	10
79	**11**	3 r. 50 grey and black	8·00	2·00
122A		3 r. 50 green and red..	20	30
80		7 r. yellow and black..	6·50	3·50
124bA		7 r. pink and green ..	20	50

For imperf. stamps, see Nos. 107B/125aB.

16. Monument to Admiral Kornilov at Sevastopol.

DESIGNS: 5 (8) k. Monument to Minin and Pozharsky, Moscow. 7(10) k. Statue of Peter the Great, St. Petersberg. 10 (13) k. Moscow Kremlin.

1905. War Orphans Fund (Russo-Japanese War).

88	**16**	3 (6) k. brown, red & grn	2·00	2·00
82	–	5 (8) k. purple and yellow	2·50	2·50
83	–	7 (10) k. blue, lt bl & pink	3·00	3·00
87	–	10 (13) k. bl, lt bl & yell	3·50	3·50

22.

23.

20.

1906.

107	**22**	1 k. orange	10	10
93		2 k. green	10	10
94		3 k. red	10	10
95	**23**	4 k. red	10	10
96	**22**	5 k. red	10	10
97		7 k. blue	10	10
98a	**23**	10 k. blue	10	10
123aA	**20**	5 r. blue and green ..	30	30
125aA		10 r. grey, red & yellow	60	65

For imperf. stamps, see Nos. 107B/125aB.

25. Nicholas II.

26. Elizabeth.

27. The Kremlin.

DESIGNS—HORIZ. 2 r. Winter Palace. 3 r. Castle Romanov. VERT. 5 r. Nicholas II (23 × 29 mm.).

1913. Tercent. of Romanov Dynasty. Views as T **27** and portraits as T **25/26**.

126.	1 k. orange (Peter I) ..	30	15
127.	2 k. green (Alexander II) ..	40	15
128.	3 k. red (Alexander III) ..	40	15
129.	4 k. red (Peter I)	40	15
130.	7 k. brown (Type **25**) ..	40	15
131.	10 k. blue (Nicholas II) ..	50	15
132.	14 k. green (Katherine II)..	50	15
133.	15 k. brown (Nicholas I) ..	75	25
134.	20 k. olive (Alexander I) ..	1·00	25
135.	25 k. red (Alexei Michaelovich)	1·50	40
136.	35 k. green & violet (Paul I)	1·50	50
137.	50 k. grey and brown (T **26**)	3·00	50
138.	70 k. brown and green (Michael Feodorovich) ..	3·00	1·00
139.	1 r. green (Type **27**) ..	7·50	2·00
140.	2 r. brown	8·50	3·00
141.	3 r. violet	20·00	6·00
142.	5 r. brown	25·00	12·00

31. Russian hero, Ilya Muromets.

DESIGNS: 3 k. Cossack shaking girl's hand. 7 k. Symbolical of Russia surrounded by her children. 10 k. St. George and Dragon.

1914. War Charity.

143.	**31.**	1 (2) k. grn. & red on yell.	25	1·00
144.	–	3 (4) k. grn. & red on red	25	1·00
145.	–	7 (8) k. green and brown on buff	25	2·00
161.	–	10 (11) k. brown and blue on blue	85	3·75

1915. As last. Colours changed.

155	**31**	1 (2) k. grey and brown	45	2·00
156	–	3 (4) k. black and red ..	40	2·50
158	–	10 (11) k. brown & blue	40	2·00

Имѣетъ хожденіе наравнѣ съ разменной серебряной монетой.

35.

КОП. 1 КОП. Имѣетъ хожденіе наравнѣ съ мѣдной монетой.

39.

1 КОПѢЙКА. Имѣетъ хожденіе наравнѣ съ мѣдной монетой.

41.

45. Cutting the fetters.

1915. Nos. 131, 133 and 134 printed on card with inscription on back as T **35.**

165.	10 k. blue	75	5·00
166.	15 k. brown	75	5·00
167	20 k. olive	75	5·00

1916. Various types surch.

168.	–	10 k. on 7 k. brown (No. 130)	30	15
170.	**22.**	10 k. on 7 k. blue ..	30	15
169.	–	20 k. on 14 k. green (No. 132)	30	20
171.	**10.**	20 k. on 14 k. red and blue	30	15

1917. Various earlier types, but imperf.

107B	**22**	1 k. orange	10	10
108bB		2 k. green	10	10
109B		3 k. red	10	10
110B	**23**	4 k. red	15	25
111B	**22**	5 k. lilac	10	10
113B	**23**	10 k. blue	10·00	27·00
115dB	**10**	15 k. blue & pur (100)	10	10
116B	**14**	20 k. red and blue ..	15	30
117dB	**10**	25 k. vio & grn (102)	50	1·00
118B		35 k. grn & pur (103)	15	25
119B	**14**	50 k. green & purple	15	25
120B	**10**	70 k. orange and brown (No. 120) ..	10	30
121B	**15**	1 r. orange and brown	10	10
122B	**11**	3 r. 50 k. green & red	20	30
123aB	**20**	5 r. blue and green ..	30	60
124aB	**11**	7 r. pink and green ..	50	1·40
125aB	**20**	10 r. grey, red & yell	22·00	30·00

1916. Types of 1913 printed on card with surch on back as T **39** or **41**, or optd with figure "1" or "2" in addition on front.

172	**39**	1 k. orange (No. 126) ..	20·00	35·00
175		1 on 1 k. orange (126) ..	1·00	5·00
177	**41**	1 on 1 k. orange (126) ..	75	4·50
173	**39**	2 k. green (No. 127) ..	40·00	45·00
176		2 on 2 k. green (127) ..	1·00	5·00
178	**41**	2 on 2 k. green (127) ..	75	4·75
174	**39**	3 k. red (No. 128) ..	1·00	4·00
179	**41**	3 k. red (No. 128) ..	75	4·50

1917.

187.	**45.**	35 k. blue	80	1·00
188.		70 k. brown	80	1·50

46. Agriculture and Industry.

47. Triumph of Revolution.

48. Agriculture.

49. Industry.

55. Science and Arts.

56.

64. Industry.

1921. Imperf.

195	**48**	1 r. orange	75	6·00
196		2 r. brown	75	6·00
197	**49**	5 r. blue	75	6·00
198	**46**	20 r. blue	1·75	4·00
199a	**47**	40 r. blue	1·50	3·25
214	**48**	100 r. yellow	10	10
215		200 r. brown	10	25
216	**55**	250 r. lilac	10	10
217	**48**	300 r. green	15	40
218	**49**	500 r. blue	15	45
219		1000 r. red	10	10
256	**64**	5000 r. violet	40	85
257	**46**	7500 r. blue	20	30
259		7500 r. blue on buff ..	20	35
258	**64**	10,000 r. blue	4·00	10·00
260		22,500 r. purple on buff	35	50

1921. 4th Anniv. of October Revolution. Imperf.

227.	**56.**	100 r. yellow	50	2·00
228.		250 r. violet	50	2·00
229.		1000 r. red	50	2·00

57. Famine Relief Work.

58.

Р. С. Ф. С. Р.
ГОЛОДАЮЩИМ
250 р.+250 р.
(62.)

1921. Charity. Volga Famine. Imperf.

230.	**57.**	2250 r. green	3·00	6·50
231.		2250 r. red	2·50	8·00
232.		2250 r. brown ..	3·50	11·00
233.	**58.**	2250 r. blue	10·00	15·00

1922. Surch. Imperf.

234	**48**	5000 r. on 1 r. orange ..	75	2·00
240		5000 r. on 2 r. brown ..	70	2·00
236	**49**	5000 r. on 5 r. blue ..	60	2·00
242	**46**	5000 r. on 20 r. blue ..	1·25	2·50
243	**47**	10,000 r. on 40 r. blue ..	1·00	2·50

1922. Famine Relief. Surch. as T **62.** Perf.

245.	**45.**	100 r.+100 r. on 70 k. brown	35	1·25
247.		250 r.+250 r. on 25 k. bl.	35	1·25

1922. Surch. with new value and diagonally. Imperf.

РУБ.

250.	**55.**	7500 r. on 250 r. lilac ..	10	10
251.		100,000 r. on 250 r. lilac	10	20

65.

1922. Obligatory Tax. Rostov-on-Don issue. Famine Relief. Various sizes. Without gum. Imperf.

261.	**65.**	2 T. (2000 r.) green ..	15·00	£120
262.	–	2 T. (2000 r.) red ..	18·00	£120
263.	–	4 T. (4000 r.) red ..	27·00	£130
264.	–	6 T. (6000 r. green ..	18·00	£120

DESIGNS: 2 T. red, Worker and family (35 × 42 mm.). 4 T. Clasped hands (triangular, 57 mm. each side). 6 T Sower (29 × 59 mm.)

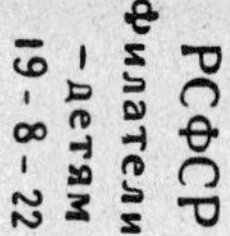

(**70.** "Philately—for the children".)

1922. Optd. with T **70.** Perf. or Imperf.

278.	**22.**	1 k. orange	£140	£250
274.		2 k. green	7·50	15·00
275.		3 k. red	5·00	12·00
276.		5 k. red	5·00	12·00
277.	**23.**	10 k. blue	5·00	15·00

71.

73.

1922. 5th Anniv. of October Revolution. Imperf.

279.	**71.**	5 r. black and yellow ..	50	45
280.		10 r. black and brown..	50	45
281.		25 r. black and purple..	2·00	1·75
282.		27 r. black and red ..	5·00	5·50
283.		45 r. black and blue ..	3·75	5·00

1922. Air. Optd. with aeroplane. Imperf.

284.	**71.**	45 r. black and green ..	18·00	45·00

1922. Famine Relief. Imperf.

285.	**73.**	20 r.+5 r. mauve ..	30	2·00
286.	–	20 r.+5 r. violet ..	40	2·00
287.	–	20 r.+5 r. blue ..	50	2·00
288.	–	20 r.+5 r. blue.. ..	3·00	15·00

DESIGNS—HORIZ. No. 286. Freighter. No. 287, Steam train. VERT. No. 288, Aeroplane.

Р.40Р.
(77.)

78. Worker.

79. Soldier.

1922. Surch as T **77**. Imperf or perf.

289	**14**	5 r. on 20 k. red & blue	1·75	8·00
290	**10**	20 r. on 15 k. bl & pur	2·00	4·00
291		20 r. on 70 k. orange and brown	15	30
292a	**14**	30 r. on 50 k. grn & pur	35	35
293	**10**	40 r. on 15 k. bl & pur	15	15
294		100 r. on 15 k. bl & pur	15	20
295		200 r. on 15 k. bl & pur	15	20

1922. Imperf or perf.

303	**78**	10 r. blue	10	10
304	**79**	50 r. brown	10	10
305		70 r. purple	10	10
310		100 r. red	15	15

1 мая
1923 г. Филателия—
Трудящимся,
1 р.+1 р.
(80.)

1923. Charity. Surch as T **80**. Imperf.

315	**71**	1 r.+1 r. on 10 r. black and brown	17·00	25·00
317b	**55**	2 r.+2 r. on 250 r. vio	16·00	25·00
318	**64**	4 r.+4 r. on 5000 r. vio	25·00	30·00

83. Worker.

84. Peasant.

85. Soldier

1923. Perf.

320.	**85.**	3 r. red	10	10
321.	**83.**	4 r. brown	10	10
322.	**84.**	5 r. blue	10	10
323.	**85.**	10 r. grey	15	15
324.		20 r. purple	25	25

86. Reaper.

88. Tractor.

1923. Agricultural Exn., Moscow. Imperf. or perf.

325.	**86.**	1 r. brown	90	3·75
326.	–	2 r. green	90	3·75
327.	**88.**	5 r. blue	1·60	3·75
328.	–	7 r. red	1·60	3·75

DESIGNS—As Type **86**: 2 r. Sower. 7 r. Exhibition buildings.

90. Worker. **91.** Peasant. **92.** Soldier. **93.**

94. **95.**

1923. Perf. (some values also imperf.).

335	**90**	1 k. yellow	30	15
359	**91**	2 k. green	30	15
360	**92**	3 k. brown	35	15
361	**90**	4 k. red	35	15
434		5 k. purple	55	15
363	**91**	6 k. blue	55	15
364	**92**	7 k. brown	55	15
437	**90**	8 k. olive	90	15
366	**91**	9 k. red	70	40
341	**92**	10 k. blue	55	15
385	**90**	14 k. grey	1·00	20
386	**91**	15 k. yellow	1·25	90
442	**92**	18 k. violet	1·75	55
443	**90**	20 k. green	2·00	30
444	**91**	30 k. violet	2·75	40
445	**92**	40 k. grey	4·00	60
343	**91**	50 k. brown	4·50	60
447	**92**	1 r. red and brown ..	4·75	80
375	**93**	2 r. green and red ..	5·50	2·00
449	**94**	3 r. green and brown ..	14·00	4·00
450	**95**	5 r. brown and blue ..	17·00	5·00

96. Lenin. **97.**

1924. Lenin Mourning. Imperf. or perf.

413	**96**	3 k. black and red ..	1·75	1·10
414		6 k. black and red ..	1·75	1·10
411		12 k. black and red ..	2·25	75
412		20 k. black and red ..	2·25	85

1924. Air. Surch. Imperf.

417.	**97.**	5 k. on 3 r. blue ..	2·00	1·50
418.		10 k. on 5 r. green ..	2·00	1·50
419.		15 k. on 1 r. brown ..	1·75	1·25
420.		20 k. on 10 r. red ..	1·75	1·10

О.С.С.Р.
пострадавшему
от наводнения
Ленинграду.
3 к. + 10 к.

(**99.** Trans. "For the victims of the flood in Leningrad".) **102.** Lenin Mausoleum, Moscow.

1924. Leningrad Flood Relief. Surch. as T **99**. Imperf.

421.	**48.**	3+10 k. on 100 r. yell.	80	1·40
422.		7+20 k. on 200 r. brown	90	1·75
423.		14+30 k. on 300 r. grn.	1·10	2·00
424.	**49.**	12+40 k. on 500 r. blue	1·90	2·75
425.		20+50 k. on 1000 r. red	1·75	2·75

1925. 1st Death Anniv. of Lenin. Imperf. or perf.

426.	**102.**	7 k. blue	3·00	2·50
427.		14 k. olive	3·75	3·50
428.		20 k. red	3·75	3·50
429.		40 k. brown	3·75	3·50

104. Lenin. **106.** Prof. Lomonosov and Academy of Sciences, Leningrad.

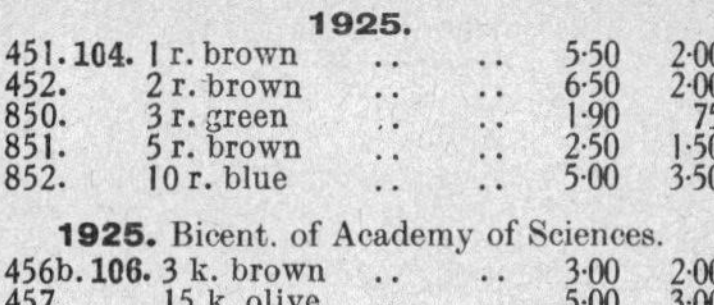

1925.

451.	**104.**	1 r. brown	5·50	2·00
452.		2 r. brown	6·50	2·00
850.		3 r. green	1·90	75
851.		5 r. brown	2·50	1·50
852.		10 r. blue	5·00	3·50

1925. Bicent. of Academy of Sciences.

456b.	**106.**	3 k. brown	3·00	2·00
457.		15 k. olive	5·00	3·00

107. A. S. Popov. **110.** Moscow Barricade.

1925. 30th Anniv. of Popov's Radio Discoveries.

458.	**107.**	7 k. blue	2·25	1·40
459.		14 k. olive	3·00	2·25

1925. 20th Anniv. of 1905 Rebellion. Imperf. or perf.

463b	–	3 k. green	2·00	1·75
464c	–	7 k. brown	2·75	1·75
465a	**110**	14 k. red	2·25	2·25

DESIGNS—VERT. 3 k. Postal rioters. 7 k. Orator and mob.

111. Decembrist Exiles. **112.** Senate Square, St. Petersburg, 1825.

1925. Centenary of Decembrist Rebellion. Imperf or perf.

466	**111**	3 k. green	2·00	2·25
467	**112**	7 k. brown	2·75	3·25
468	–	14 k. red	2·75	3·50

DESIGN—VERT. 14 k. Medallion with heads of Pestel, Ryleev, Bestuzhev-Ryumin, Muravev-Apostol and Kakhovsky.

114.

1926. 6th International Proletarian Esperanto Congress.

471.	**114.**	7 k. red and green ..	3·50	3·00
472.		14 k. violet and green ..	4·50	1·75

ПОЧТОВАЯ
МАРКА
КОП. 8 КОП.

115. Waifs. **116.** Lenin when a Child. (**117.**)

1926. Child Welfare.

473.	**115.**	10 k. brown	75	45
474.	**116.**	20 k. blue	1·75	95

1927. Same type with new inscriptions.

475.	**115.**	8 k.+2 k. green ..	40	35
476.	**116.**	18 k.+2 k. red ..	90	65

1927. Postage Due stamps surch. with T **117.**

491	D **104**	8 k. on 1 k. red ..	1·00	2·25
492		8 k. on 2 k. violet ..	1·00	2·25
493		8 k. on 3 k. blue ..	1·00	2·25
494		8 k. on 7 k. yellow ..	1·00	2·25
494b		8 k. on 8 k. green ..	1·00	2·25
494d		8 k. on 10 k. blue ..	1·00	2·25
494f		8 k. on 14 k. brown	1·00	2·25

1927. Various types of 7 k. surch (some values imperf or perf).

495	**92**	8 k. on 7 k. brown ..	6·00	6·00
523	**107**	8 k. on 7 k. blue ..	2·50	3·25
524	–	8 k. on 7 k. brown (No. 464c)	3·75	5·00
527	**112**	8 k. on 7 k. brown ..	3·75	6·50
526	**114**	8 k. on 7 k. red & green	11·00	14·00

119. Dr. Zamenhof.

1927. 40th Anniv of Publication of Zamenhof's "Langue Internationale" (Esperanto).

498	**119**	14 k. green and brown	3·00	1·75

120.

1927. 1st Int. Air Post Congress, The Hague.

499.	**120.**	10 k. blue and brown ..	12·00	4·75
500.		15 k. red and olive ..	13·00	6·00

121. Worker, Soldier and Peasant. **124.** Sailor and Worker.

122. Allegory of Revolution.

1927. 10th Anniv. of October Revolution.

501.	**121.**	3 k. red	2·25	75
502.	**122.**	5 k. brown	6·00	2·00
503.	–	7 k. green	8·00	2·50
504.	**124.**	8 k. black and brown ..	4·00	85
505.	–	14 k. red and blue ..	6·00	1·25
506.	–	18 k. blue	4·00	1·00
507.	–	28 k. brown	13·00	8·00

DESIGNS—HORIZ. (as Type **122**). 7 k. Smolny Institute. 14 k. Map of Russia inscr. "C.C.C.P.". 18 k. Various Russian races. 28 k. Worker, soldier and peasant.

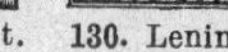

128. Worker. **129.** Peasant. **130.** Lenin.

1927.

508.	**128.**	1 k. orange	90	50
509.	**129.**	2 k. green	90	20
510.	**128.**	4 k. blue	90	20
511.	**129.**	5 k. brown	90	20
512.		7 k. red	4·50	1·00
513.	**128.**	8 k. green	2·50	20
514.		10 k. brown	2·00	20
515.	**130.**	14 k. green	2·25	45
516.		18 k. olive	3·00	40
517.		18 k. blue	4·50	70
518.	**129.**	20 k. olive	2·50	35
519.	**128.**	40 k. red	5·00	60
520.	**129.**	50 k. blue	7·00	1·00
521.	**128.**	70 k. olive	11·00	1·40
522.	**129.**	80 k. orange	22·00	5·00

131. Infantryman, Lenin Mausoleum and Kremlin.

DESIGNS: 14 k. Sailor and cruiser "Aurora". 18 k. Cavalryman. 28 k. Airman.

1928. 10th Anniv. of Red Army.

529.	**131.**	8 k. brown	1·40	45
530.	–	14 k. blue	2·25	50
531.	–	18 k. red	2·50	1·25
532.	–	28 k. green	4·00	4·00

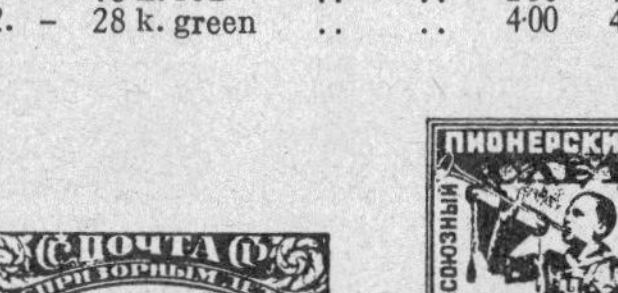

135. Young Factory Workers. **137.** Trumpeter sounding the Assembly.

1929. Child Welfare.

536.	**135.**	10 k.+2 k. brn. & sepia	1·50	1·10
537.	–	20 k.+2 k. blue & brown	1·50	1·25

DESIGN: 20 k. Children in harvest field.

See also Nos. 567/8.

1929. First All-Union Gathering of Pioneers.

538	**137**	10 k. brown	8·00	6·50
539		14 k. blue	6·00	4·00

138. Worker. **139.** Factory Girl. **140.** Peasant. **141.** Farm Girl.

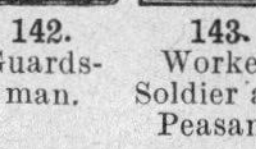

142. Guardsman. **143.** Worker, Soldier and Peasant. **144.** Lenin. **242a.** Miner.

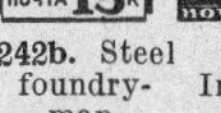

242b. Steel foundryman. **242c.** Infantryman. **242d.** Airman. **242e.** Arms of U.S.S.R.

744. Furnaceman. **743a.** Farm Girl. **149.** Central Telegraph Office, Moscow.

743b. Architect. **150.** Lenin Hydro-electric Power Station.

1929. Perf, but some values exist imperf.

541	**138**	1 k. yellow ..	40	15
542	**139**	2 k. green ..	60	10
543	**140**	3 k. blue	60	10
544	**141**	4 k. mauve ..	85	15
545	**142**	5 k. brown ..	90	10
847a	**242a**	5 k. red	20	10
546	**143**	7 k. red	1·75	50
547	**138**	10 k. grey ..	1·40	10
727f	**139**	10 k. blue ..	60	15
1214b		10 k. black ..	80	15
554	**144**	14 k. blue ..	1·40	55
548	**143**	15 k. olive ..	1·75	10
847b	**242b**	15 k. blue ..	1·50	30
847c	**242c**	15 k. green ..	50	15
549	**140**	20 k. green & blue	2·25	20
727h	**141**	20 k. green ..	70	25
2252a	**743a**	20 k. olive ..	80	30
2252b	**743b**	25 k. brown ..	1·10	45
550	**139**	30 k. violet & lilac	3·50	50
847d	**242d**	30 k. blue ..	90	20
727l	**144**	40 k. blue ..	1·10	40
727m	**141**	50 k. brown & buff	1·25	40
847f	**242e**	60 k. red	1·25	30
2253	**744**	60 k. red	1·00	20
2253a		60 k. blue ..	2·25	40
552	**142**	70 k. red and pink	6·00	1·40
553	**140**	80 k. brown & yell	6·00	1·25
561	**149**	1 r. blue	1·60	40
562	**150**	3 r. brown & green	18·00	6·00

Nos. 727f, 1214b and 550 show the factory girl without factory in background. Nos. 549, 727m, 552, 553 have designs like those shown but with unshaded background.

151. Industry. **153.** "More metal, more machines".

1929. Industrial Loan Propaganda.

563.	**151.**	5 k. brown	1·60	1·25
564.	–	10 k. olive	2·00	2·00
565.	**153.**	20 k. green	6·00	3·25
566.	–	28 k. violet	4·00	3·25

DESIGNS—HORIZ. 10 k. Tractors. VERT. 28 k. Blast Furnace and graph of Pig-iron output.

1930. Child Welfare.

567.	**135.**	10 k.+2 k. olive ..	80	1·00
568.	–	20 k.+2 k. green (as No. 537)	1·10	1·50

155.

DESIGNS — Dated "1919 1929": 5 k. Cavalry charge. 10 k. Cavalry charging. 14 k. (not dated) Cavalry and map.

1930. 10th Anniv. of 1st Red Cavalry.
569. **155.** 2 k. green .. .. 2·50 1·40
570. – 5 k. brown .. .. 2·50 1·40
571. – 10 k. olive .. .. 5·00 3·00
572. – 14 k. blue and red .. 2·50 2·50

159. Group of Soviet Pupils.

1930. Educational Exhibition, Leningrad.
573. **159.** 10 k. olive .. .. 1·40 1·00

160.

1930. Air. "Graf-Zeppelin". Flight to Moscow.
574. **160.** 40 k. blue .. .. 24·00 18·00
575. 80 k. red .. .. 18·00 13·00

162. "Potemkin".

1930. 25th Anniv. of 1905 Rebellion. Imperf. or perf.
576. **162.** 3 k. red .. .. 1·75 50
577. – 5 k. blue .. .. 1·50 60
578. – 10 k. red and green .. 2·75 1·10
DESIGNS—HORIZ. 5 k. Barricade and rebels. VERT. 10 k. Red Flag at Presnya barricade.

165. From the Tundra (reindeer) to the Steppes (camel).

DESIGNS—As Type **166**: 50 k. Above the North Pole. As Type **165**: 1 r. Airship construction. VERT. 20 k. Zeppelin above Lenin's Mausoleum.

166. Above Dnieprostroi Dam.

1931. Airship Construction Fund. Imperf. or perf.
579 **165** 10 k. violet .. .. 7·00 3·50
580 **166** 15 k. blue .. .. 17·00 12·00
581a – 20 k. red .. .. 8·00 3·00
582b – 50 k. brown .. .. 7·00 7·00
583 – 1 r. green .. .. 7·50 5·50
See also No. E592.

170. Ice breaker "Malygin".

1931. Air. "Graf Zeppelin" North Pole Flight. Imperf. or perf.
584. **170.** 30 k. purple .. .. 24·00 13·00
585. 35 k. green .. .. 24·00 13·00
586. 1 r. black .. .. 26·00 13·00
587. 2 r. blue .. .. 26·00 13·00

171. Polar Region and Ice-breaker "Sibiriakov".

1932. Air. 2nd Int. Polar Year and Franz Joseph's Land to Archangel Flight.
588 **171** 50 k. red .. .. 38·00 15·00
589a 1 r. green .. .. 38·00 20·00

172. Maksim Gorky.

173. Storming the Winter Palace.

1932. 40th Anniv. of Publication of "Makar Chadra".
590. **172.** 15 k. brown .. .. 4·00 2·50
591. 35 k. blue .. .. 14·00 8·00

1932. 15th Anniv. of October Revolution.
593. – 3 k. violet 90 50
594. **173.** 5 k. brown 90 50
595. – 10 k. blue .. .. 2·75 1·25
596. – 15 k. green .. .. 1·60 1·25
597. – 20 k. red .. .. 5·50 1·75
598. – 30 k. grey .. .. 6·00 1·90
599. – 35 k. brown .. .. 60·00 45·00
DESIGNS—HORIZ. 10 k. Dnieper Dam. 15 k. Harvesting with combines. 20 k. Industrial Works, Magnitogorsk. 30 k. Siberians listening to Moscow broadcast. VERT. 3 k. Lenin's arrival in Petrograd. 35 k. People of the World hailing Lenin.

175. "Liberation".

1932. 10th Anniv. of Int. Revolutionaries' Relief Organization.
600. **175.** 50 k. red .. .. 10·00 5·00

176. Museum of Fine Arts.

1932. 1st All-Union Philatelic Exn., Moscow.
601. **176.** 15 k. brown .. .. 18·00 13·00
602. 35 k. blue .. .. 35·00 20·00

177. Trier, Marx's Birthplace.

DESIGNS-VERT. 10 k. Marx's grave, Highgate Cemetery. 35 k. Marx.

1933. 50th Death Anniv. of Marx.
603. **177.** 3 k. green .. .. 3·50 90
604. – 10 k. brown .. .. 6·00 1·40
605. – 35 k. purple .. .. 9·50 8·50

1933. Leningrad Philatelic Exn. Surch. **LENINGRAD 1933** in Russian characters and premium.
606. **176.** 15 k.+30 k. blk. & brn. 65·00 30·00
607. 35 k.+70 k. blue .. 85·00 40·00

182.

183.

1933. Ethnographical Issue. Racial types.
608. – 1 k. brown (Kazakhs) 1·50 40
609. **183.** 2 k. blue (Lesgins) .. 1·50 40
610. – 3 k. green (Crimean Tatars) .. 1·25 40
611. – 4 k. brown (Jews of Birobidzhan) .. 90 60
612. – 5 k. red (Tungusians) 1·00 40
613. – 6 k. blue (Buryats) .. 90 40
614. – 7 k. brown (Chechens) 90 40
615. – 8 k. red (Abkhazians) 1·25 55
616. – 9 k. blue (Georgians) 2·50 60
617. – 10 k. brn. (Samoyedes) 4·00 1·50
618. – 14 k. green (Yakuts) 2·50 40
619. – 15 k. purple (Ukrainians) .. 4·00 1·25
620. – 15 k. black (Uzbeks) 3·50 80
621. – 15 k. blue (Tadzhiks) 3·50 75
622. – 15 k. brown (Transcaucasians) .. 2·50 75
623. – 15 k. green (Byelorussians) .. 2·50 60
624. – 15 k. orange (Great Russians) .. .. 2·50 80
625. – 15 k. red (Turkmens) 3·00 1·00
626. – 20 k. blue (Koryaks) 6·00 1·60
627. – 30 k. red (Bashkirs) .. 7·00 1·75
628. **182.** 35 k. brn. (Chuvashes) 11·00 2·25
SIZES: Nos. 608, 610/11, 614/17, 626/7, As T **182**. Nos. 612/13, 618, As T **183**. Nos. 619/24, 48 × 22 mm. No. 625, 22 × 48 mm.

186. V. V. Vorovsky.

1933. Communist Party Activists. Dated "1933", "1934" or "1935".
629 **186** 1 k. green 65 50
718 – 2 k. violet .. .. 4·00 25
630 – 3 k. blue .. .. 1·25 60
719 – 4 k. purple .. .. 3·25 2·00
631 – 5 k. brown .. .. 2·50 1·90
632 – 10 k. blue .. .. 12·00 5·00
633 – 15 k. red .. .. 30·00 20·00
720 – 40 k. brown .. .. 7·00 4·00
DESIGNS: 2 k. M. Frunze. 3 k. V. M. Volodarsky. 4 k. N. E. Bauman. 5 k. M. S. Uritsky. 10 k. Iacov M. Sverdlov. 15 k. Viktor P. Nogin. 40 k. S. M. Kirov.

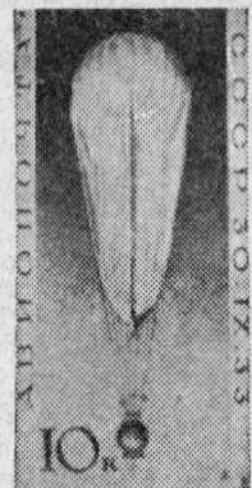
187. Stratostat "U.S.S.R." over Moscow.

188. Massed Standard Bearers.

1933. Air. Stratosphere record (19,000 metres).
634. **187.** 5 k. blue .. .. 75·00 19·00
635. 10 k. red .. .. 48·00 9·00
636. 20 k. violet .. .. 23·00 5·00

1933. 15th Anniv. of Order of Red Banner.
637. **188.** 20 k. red, yellow & blk. 2·25 1·50

189. Commissar Shaumyan.

190. Aeroplane over Oilfield.

1934. 15th Death Anniv. of 26 Baku Commissars.
638. **189.** 4 k. brown .. .. 3·50 1·25
639. – 5 k. black .. .. 3·50 1·25
640. – 20 k. violet .. .. 2·50 85
641. – 35 k. blue .. .. 18·00 4·00
642. – 40 k. red .. .. 12·00 4·00
DESIGNS: 5 k. Commissar Dzhaparidze. HORIZ. 20 k. The 26 condemned commissars. 35 k. Monument in Baku. 40 k. Workman, peasant and soldier dipping flags in salute.

1934. Air. 10th Anniv. of Soviet Civil Aviation and U.S.S.R. Airmail Service.
643. – 5 k. blue .. .. 7·00 2·25
644. **190.** 10 k. green .. .. 7·00 2·25
645. – 20 k. red .. .. 15·00 3·75
646. – 50 k. blue .. .. 25·00 9·25
647. – 80 k. violet .. .. 13·00 4·75
DESIGNS: Tupolev ANT-9 PS9 airplane over:—5 k. Furnaces at Kuznetsk. 20 k. Harvesters. 50 k. Volga-Moscow Canal. 80 k. Ice-breaker "Ob" in the Arctic.

191. New Lenin Mausoleum. 192. Fedorov Monument. Moscow, between Hand and Rotary Presses.

1934. 10th Death Anniv. of Lenin.
648. **191.** 5 k. brown .. .. 1·60 50
649. 10 k. blue .. .. 5·00 2·00
650. 15 k. red .. .. 4·50 2·00
651. 20 k. green .. .. 1·75 50
652. 35 k. brown .. .. 5·00 2·25

1934. 350th Death Anniv of Ivan Fedorov (first Russian printer).
653 **192** 20 k. red .. .. 8·00 3·75
654 40 k. blue .. .. 8·00 3·00

194. Dmitri Mendeleev.

195. A. V. Vasenko and Stratostat "Osoviachim".

1934. Birth Centenary of Dmitri Mendeleev (chemist).
655 – 5 k. green .. .. 3·25 1·10
656 **194** 10 k. brown .. .. 12·00 4·50
657 15 k. red .. .. 13·00 4·50
658 – 20 k. blue .. .. 5·00 2·25
DESIGN—VERT. 5 k., 20 k. Mendeleev seated.

1934. Air. Stratosphere Disaster Victims.
659. – 5 k. purple .. .. 19·00 4·00
660. **195.** 10 k. brown .. .. 45·00 4·00
661. – 20 k. violet .. .. 50·00 4·00
1042. – 1 r. green .. .. 8·50 1·75
1043. **195.** 1 r. green .. .. 8·50 1·75
1044. – 1 r. blue .. .. 8·50 1·75
DESIGNS: 5 k., 1 r. (No. 1042). N. D. Usyskin. 20 k., 1 r. (No. 1044), P. O. Fedoseenko.
The 1 r. values, issued in 1944, commemorated the 10th anniversary of the disaster.

196. Airship "Pravda".

1934. Air. Airship Travel Propaganda.
662. **196.** 5 k. red .. .. 13·00 2·25
663. – 10 k. lake .. .. 13·00 2·75
664. – 15 k. brown .. .. 17·00 8·00
665. – 20 k. black .. .. 18·00 5·50
666. – 30 k. blue .. .. 50·00 23·00
DESIGNS—HORIZ. 10 k. Airship landing. 15 k. Airship "Voroshilov". 30 k. Airship "Lenin" and route map. VERT. 20 k. Airship's gondolas and mooring mast.

DESIGN—VERT. 1 k. Lenin aged 3.3 k. Lenin as student. 5 k. Lenin as man. 10 k. Lenin as orator. HORIZ. 20 k. Red demonstration, Lenin Mausoleum.

199. Stalin and Marchers inspired by Lenin.

200. "War Clouds".

1934. "Ten years without Lenin". Portraits inscr. "1924-1934".
667. – 1 k. black and blue .. 1·50 75
668. – 3 k. black and blue .. 1·50 80
669. – 5 k. black and blue .. 3·50 1·40
670. – 10 k. black and blue .. 2·25 2·00
671. – 20 k. blue and orange 6·00 3·25
672. **199.** 30 k. red and orange .. 24·00 6·00

1935. Anti-War. Inscr. "1914-1934".
673. **200.** 5 k. black .. .. 4·50 90
674. – 10 k. blue .. .. 7·50 3·75
675. – 15 k. green .. .. 13·00 5·00
676. – 20 k. brown .. .. 10·00 2·75
677. – 35 k. red .. .. 22·00 13·00
DESIGNS: 10 k. "Flight from a burning village". 15 k. "Before war and afterwards". 20 k. "Ploughing with the sword". 35 k. "Fraternisation".

202. Capt. Voronin and "Chelyuskin".

1935. Air. Rescue of "Chelyuskin" Expedition.

678.	202.	1 k. orange	4·25	1·00
679.	–	3 k. red	5·00	1·40
680.	–	5 k. green	4·75	1·40
681.	–	10 k. brown	6·75	1·75
682.	–	15 k. black	8·50	2·50
683.	–	20 k. purple	13·50	2·50
684.	–	25 k. blue	40·00	11·00
685.	–	30 k. green	50·00	13·00
686.	–	40 k. violet	28·00	3·75
687.	202.	50 k. blue	40·00	9·00

DESIGNS—HORIZ. 3 k. Prof. Schmidt and Schmidt Camp. 50 k. Schmidt Camp dserted. VERT. 5 k. A. V. Lyapidevsky. 10 k. S. A. Levanevsky. 15 k. M. G. Slepnev. 20 k. I. V. Doronin. 25 k. M. V. Vodopyanov. 30 k. V. S. Molokov. 40 k. N. P. Kamanin.

205. Underground Station.

DESIGNS–HORIZ. as Type 205: 5 k. Excavating tunnel. 10 k. Section of roadway, escalator and station. 20 k. (48½ × 23 mm.) Train in station.

1935. Opening of Moscow Underground.

688.	–	5 k. orange	8·00	3·25
689.	–	10 k. blue	9·00	3·25
690.	205.	15 k. red	70·00	24·00
691.	–	20 k. green	15·00	9·00

207. Rowing.

1935. Spartacist Games.

692.	–	1 k. blue and orange	2·50	80
693.	–	2 k. blue and black	2·50	80
694.	207.	3 k. brown and green	4·50	1·50
695.	–	4 k. blue and red	2·75	90
696.	–	5 k. brown and violet	2·75	1·00
697.	–	10 k. purple and red	14·00	3·00
698.	–	15 k. brown and black	26·00	8·00
699.	–	20 k. blue and brown	15·00	3·25
700.	–	35 k. brown and blue	27·00	13·00
701.	–	40 k. red and brown	22·00	6·00

DESIGNS: 1 k. Running. 2 k. Diving. 4 k. Football. 5 k. Skiing. 10 k. Cycling. 15 k. Lawn tennis. 20 k. Skating. 35 k. Hurdling. 40 k. Parade of athletes.

208. Friedrich Engels.

210. A "Lion Hunt" from a Sassanian Silver Plate.

1935. 40th Death Anniv. of F. Engels.

702.	208.	5 k. red	4·50	45
703.		10 k. green	8·00	2·00
704.		15 k. blue	7·00	2·75
705.		20 k. black	3·25	2·50

1935. Air. Moscow - San Francisco via North Pole Flight. Surch. in Russian characters.

706.	1 r. on 10 k. brown (No. 681)	£200	£350

1935. 3rd International Congress of Persian Art and Archaeology, Leningrad.

707	210	5 k. orange	5·00	1·00
708		10 k. green	5·00	1·75
709		15 k. purple	6·50	3·00
710		35 k. brown	13·00	5·50

211. M. I. Kalinin.

212. Tolstoi.

1935. Pres. Kalinin's 60th Birthday. Autographed portraits inscr. "1875-1935".

711.	–	3 k. purple	75	20
712.	–	5 k. green	1·25	25
713.	–	10 k. blue	1·25	60
714.	211.	20 k. brown	1·60	70

DESIGNS: 3 k. Kalinin as machine worker. 5 k. Harvester. 10 k. Orator.
See also No. 1189.

1935. 25th Death Anniv of Tolstoi (writer).

715	–	3 k. violet and black	65	25
716	212	10 k. brown and blue	1·40	45
717	–	20 k. brown and green	3·00	1·75

DESIGNS: 3 k. Tolstoi in 1860. 20 k. Monument in Moscow.

213. Pioneers securing Letter-box.

DESIGNS: 3 k., 5 k. Pioneer preventing another from throwing stones. 10 k. Pioneers disentangling kite-line from telegraph wires. 15 k. Girl pioneer saluting

1936. Pioneer Movement.

721.	213.	1 k. green	1·10	30
722.		2 k. red	1·00	70
723.	–	3 k. blue	1·25	1·60
724.	–	5 k. red	1·25	55
725.	–	10 k. blue	2·00	2·50
726.	–	15 k. brown	6·50	3·00

214. N. A. Dobrolyubov. 215. A. S. Pushkin.

1936. Birth Cent. of Dobrolyubov (author and critic).

727.	214.	10 k. purple	3·25	80

1937. Death Cent. of A. S. Pushkin (poet).

728	215	10 k. brown	55	30
729		20 k. green	60	30
730		40 k. red	1·25	50
731	–	50 k. blue	2·00	35
732a	–	80 k. red	2·25	1·00
733a	–	1 r. green	3·25	1·00

DESIGN: 50 k. to 1 r., Pushkin's Monument.

217. Meyerhold Theatre. 218. F. E. Dzerzhinsky.

1937. 1st Soviet Architectural Congress.

734.	217.	3 k. red	1·00	20
735.	–	5 k. lake	1·00	20
736.	217.	10 k. brown	1·40	25
737.	–	15 k. black	1·75	25
738.	–	20 k. olive	1·10	40
739.	–	30 k. black	1·50	70
740.	–	40 k. violet	2·00	1·25
741.	–	50 k. brown	3·50	1·50

DESIGNS—As T 217: 5 k., 15 k. G.P.O. 20 k., 50 k. Red Army Theatre. 45 × 27 mm: 30 k. Hotel Moscow. 40 k. Palace of Soviets.

1937. 10th Death Anniv. of F. E. Dzerzhinsky.

742.	218.	10 k. brown	40	20
743.		20 k. green	55	35
744.		40 k. red	1·50	55
745.		80 k. red	2·00	70

219. Yakovlev Ya-7.

1937. Air. Air Force Exhibition.

746	173	10 k. black and brown	1·50	30
747	–	20 k. black and green	1·50	30
748	–	30 k. black and brown	2·50	30
749	–	40 k. black and purple	3·75	80
750	–	50 k. black and violet	5·50	1·00
751	–	80 k. brown and blue	6·50	1·75
752	–	1 r. black, orge & brn	10·00	2·25

DESIGNS—As T 173: 20 k. Tupolev ANT-9. 30 k. Tupolev ANT-6. 40 k. O.S.G.A. 101 flying boat. 50 k. Tupolev ANT-4 TB1. 60 × 26 mm: 80 k. Tupolev ANT-20 "Maksim Gorky". 1 r. Tupolev ANT-14 "Pravada".

220. Arms of Ukraine.

221. Arms of U.S.S.R.

1937. New U.S.S.R. Constitution. Arms of Constituent Republics.

753.	–	20 k. blue (Armenia)	1·25	40
754.	–	20 k. purple (Azerbaijan)	1·25	40
755.	–	20 k. brown (Byelorussia)	1·25	40
756.	–	20 k. red (Georgia)	1·25	40
757.	–	20 k. grn. (Kazakhstan)	1·25	40
758.	–	20 k. green (Kirghizia)	1·25	40
759.	–	20 k. red (Tadzhikistan)	1·25	40
760.	–	20 k. red (Turkmenistan)	1·25	40
761.	220.	20 k. red (Ukraine)	1·25	40
762.	–	20 k. orge. (Uzbekistan)	1·25	40
763.	–	20 k. blue (R.S.F.S.R.)	1·25	40
764.	221.	40 k. red	3·00	1·25

222. Sculptured group on Pavilion. 223. Russian Pavilion, Paris Exhibition. 224. Shota Rustaveli.

1938. Paris Int. Exn.

765.	222.	5 k. red	1·00	40
766.	223.	20 k. red	1·10	40
767.	222.	50 k. blue	2·75	1·00

1938. 750th Anniv. of Poem "Knight in Tiger Skin".

768.	224.	20 k. green	1·10	30

225. Route of North Pole Flight. 227. Infantryman.

1938. North Pole Flight.

769	225	10 k. black and brown	2·75	30
770		20 k. black and grey	3·75	30
771	–	40 k. red and green	7·50	1·25
772	–	80 k. red and deep red	2·75	90

DESIGN: 40 k., 80 k. Soviet Flag at North Pole.

1938. 20th Anniv. of Red Army.

773	227	10 k. black and red	50	20
774	–	20 k. black and red	85	25
775	–	30 k. black, red & blue	1·25	25
776	–	40 k. black, red & blue	1·75	75
777	–	50 k. black and red	2·25	75
778a	–	80 k. black and red	4·75	75
779	–	1 r. black and red	2·75	75

DESIGNS—VERT. 20 k. Tank driver. 30 k. Sailor. 40 k. Airman. 50 k. Artilleryman. HORIZ. 80 k. Stalin reviewing cavalry. 1 r. Machine-gunners.

229. Polar Flight Heroes. 230.

1938. 1st Polar Flight.

780.	229.	10 k. red and black	2·10	50
781.		20 k. red and black	2·25	70
782.		40 k. red and brown	4·00	1·10
783.		50 k. red and purple	7·25	1·50

1938. 2nd Polar Flight.

784.	230.	10 k. purple	3·50	45
785.		20 k. black	4·50	90
786.		50 k. purple	7·50	1·25

231. Ice-breaker "Murman" approaching survivors.

1938. Rescue of Papanin's North Pole Meteorological Party.

787.	231.	10 k. purple	4·00	50
788.		20 k. blue	4·00	70
789.	–	30 k. brown	7·00	1·25
790.	–	50 k. blue	8·00	1·50

DESIGN—VERT. 30, 50 k. Papanin survivors.

233. Nurse weighing Baby.

234. Children visiting Statue of Lenin.

1938. Soviet Union Children.

791.	233.	10 k. blue	1·25	30
792.	234.	15 k. blue	1·25	35
793.	–	20 k. purple	1·50	35
794.	–	30 k. red	1·90	45
795.	–	40 k. brown	2·40	55
796.	–	50 k. blue	4·50	85
797.	–	80 k. green	5·50	1·00

DESIGNS—HORIZ. 20 k., 40 k. Biology class. 30 k. Health camp. 50 k., 80 k. Young inventors at play.

235. Crimean Landscape.

1938. Views of Crimea and Caucasus.

798.	235.	5 k. black	80	40
799.	A.	5 k. brown	80	40
800.	B.	10 k. green	1·60	45
801.	C.	10 k. brown	1·60	45
802.	D.	15 k. black	2·50	50
803.	A.	15 k. black	2·50	50
804.	E.	20 k. brown	3·00	50
805.	C.	30 k. black	3·00	60
806.	F.	40 k. brown	3·75	80
807.	G.	50 k. green	3·75	1·25
808.	H.	80 k. brown	5·00	1·50
809.	I.	1 r. green	7·50	4·50

DESIGNS—HORIZ. A, Yalta (two views). B, Georgian military road. E, Crimean resthouse. F, Alupka. H, Crimea. I, Swallows' Nest Castle. VERT. C, Crimea (two views). D, Swallows' Nest Castle. G, Gurzuf Park.

236. Schoolchildren and Model Aeroplane. 237. Underground Railway.

1938. Aviation.

810.	236.	5 k. purple	1·75	60
811.	–	10 k. brown	1·75	60
812.	–	15 k. red	2·00	60
813.	–	20 k. blue	2·00	60
814.	–	30 k. red	3·50	90
815.	–	40 k. blue	6·00	90
816.	–	50 k. green	11·00	1·40
817.	–	80 k. brown	7·50	3·25
818.	–	1 r. green	13·00	2·50

DESIGNS—HORIZ. 10 k. Glider in flight. 40 k. Seaplane landing. 1 r. Transport aeroplane. VERT. 15 k. Captive observation balloon. 20 k. Airship over Kremlin. 30 k. Parachutists. 50 k. Balloon in flight. 80 k. Stratospheric balloon.

1938. Moscow Underground Railway. Extension.

819.	–	10 k. violet	2·00	60
820.	–	15 k. brown	2·50	60
821.	–	20 k. black	3·00	50
822.	–	30 k. violet	3·25	1·00
823.	237.	40 k. black	3·50	1·10
824.	–	50 k. brown	4·50	1·90

DESIGNS—VERT. 10 k. Mayakovsky Square station. 15 k. Sokol Terminus station. 20 k. Kiev station. HORIZ. 30 k. Dynamo Stadium station. 50 k. Revolution Square station.

238. Miner and Pneumatic Drill.

239. Diving.

1938. 20th Anniv. of Federation of Young Lenin Communists.

825	–	20 k. blue	80	30
826	238	30 k. purple	1·50	30
827	–	40 k. purple	1·25	30
828	–	50 k. red	1·50	90
829	–	80 k. blue	5·50	1·25

DESIGNS—VERT. 20 k. Girl parachutist. 50 k. Students and University. HORIZ. 40 k. Harvesting. 80 k. Airman, sailor and battleship "Marat".

1938. Soviet Sports.

830.	239.	5 k. red	1·75	30
831.	–	10 k. black	2·00	50
832.	–	15 k. brown	3·50	85
833.	–	20 k. green	3·50	80
834.	–	30 k. purple	7·50	1·25
835.	–	40 k. green	7·50	80
836.	–	50 k. blue	7·00	2·25
837.	–	80 k. blue	6·50	3·50

DESIGNS: 10 k. Discus throwing. 15 k. Tennis. 20 k. Motor cycling. 30 k. Skiing. 40 k. Sprinting. 50 k. Football. 80 k. Athletic parade.

241. Council of People's Commissars Headquarters and Hotel Moscow.

1939. New Moscow. Architectural designs as T **241**.

838.	–	10 k. brown	60	40
839.	241.	20 k. green	75	35
840.	–	30 k. purple	1·00	60
841.	–	40 k. blue	2·75	80
842.	–	50 k. red	3·50	1·25
843.	–	80 k. olive	4·50	1·75
844.	–	1 r. blue	9·50	2·25

DESIGNS—HORIZ. 10 k. Gorky Avenue. 30 k. Lenin Library. 40 k. Suspension and 50 k. Arched Bridges over River Moskva. 80 k. Khimki River Station. VERT. 1 r. Dynamo Underground Station.

242. Paulina Osipenko. 243. Russian Pavilion, N.Y. World's Fair.

1939. Women's Moscow-Far East Flight.

845.	242.	15 k. green	2·10	80
846.	–	30 k. purple	2·10	1·00
847.	–	60 k. red	3·50	1·50

PORTRAITS: 30 k. Marina Raskova. 60 k. Valentina Grisodubova.

1939. New York World's Fair.

848.	–	30 k. red and black ..	1·00	50
849.	243.	50 k. brown and blue	1·60	85

DESIGN—VERT. (26×41½ mm.): 30 k. Statue over Russian pavilion.

244. T. G. Shevchenko in early Manhood. 245. Milkmaid.

1939. 125th Birth Anniv. of Shevchenko (Ukrainian poet and painter).

853.	244.	15 k. black and brown	1·40	50
854.	–	30 k. black and red ..	2·00	70
855.	–	60 k. brown and green	3·25	1·50

DESIGNS: 30 k. Last portrait of Shevchenko. 60 k. Monument to Shevchenko, Kharkov.

1939. All Union Agricultural Fair.

856	245	10 k. red	60	25
857	–	15 k. red	60	15
858a	–	20 k. grey	70	15
859	–	30 k. orange	65	25
860	–	30 k. violet	65	25
861	–	45 k. green	1·40	35
862	–	50 k. brown	2·25	40
863a	–	60 k. violet	2·50	60
864	–	80 k. violet	2·50	60
865	–	1 r. blue	4·75	1·25

DESIGNS—HORIZ. 15 k. Harvesting. 20 k. Sheep farming. 30 k. (No. 860) Agricultural Fair Pavilion. VERT. 30 k. (No. 859) Agricultural Fair Emblem. 45 k. Gathering cotton. 50 k. Thoroughbred horses. 60 k. "Agricultural Wealth". 80 k. Girl with sugar-beet 1 r. Trapper.

18 АВГУСТА
ДЕНЬ АВИАЦИИ СССР
(247.)

1939. Aviation Day. As Nos. 811, 814/16 and 818 (colours changed) optd with T **247**.

866.	236.	10 k. red	2·00	55
867.		30 k. blue	2·00	55
868.		40 k. green	3·25	55
869.		50 k. violet	4·25	1·25
870.		1 r. brown	8·00	4·00

1939. Surch.

871.	141.	30 k. on 4 k. mauve ..	13·00	10·00

249. Saltykov-Schedrin. 250. Kislovodsk Sanatorium.

1939. 50th Death Anniv. of M. E. Saltykov-Schedrin (writer and satirist).

872.	249.	15 k. red	60	15
873.	–	30 k. green	80	20
874.	249.	45 k. brown	1·00	35
875.	–	60 k. blue	1·50	70

DESIGN: 30 k., 60 k. Saltykov-Schedrin in later years.

1939. Caucasian Health Resorts.

876.	250.	5 k. brown	40	15
877.	–	10 k. red	45	20
878.	–	15 k. green	50	30
879.	–	20 k. green	85	30
880.	–	30 k. blue	90	30
881.	–	50 k. black	1·75	35
882.	–	60 k. purple	1·75	90
883.	–	80 k. red	2·75	1·10

DESIGNS: 10 k., 15 k., 30 k., 50 k., 80 k. Sochi Convalescent Homes. 20 k. Abkhazia Sanatorium. 60 k. Sukumi Rest Home.

251. M. Yu. Lermontov. 252. N. G. Chernyshevsky.

1939. 125th Birth Anniv. of Lermontov (poet and novelist).

884.	251.	15 k. brown and blue ..	1·10	30
885.	–	30 k. black and green	2·75	55
886.	–	45 k. blue and red ..	2·50	95

1939. 50th Death Anniv. of N. G. Chernyshevsky (writer and politician).

887.	252.	15 k. green	50	30
888.		30 k. violet	90	40
889.		60 k. green	2·00	50

253. A. P. Chekhov. 254. Welcoming Soviet Troops.

1940. 80th Birth Anniv of Chekhov (writer).

890.	253.	10 k. green	30	15
891.		15 k. blue	30	15
892.	–	20 k. violet	60	30
893.	–	30 k. brown	1·40	55

DESIGN: 20 k., 30 k. Chekhov with hat on.

1940. Occupation of Eastern Poland.

893a.	254.	10 k. red	80	35
894.	–	30 k. green	80	35
895.	–	50 k. black	1·25	55
896.	–	60 k. blue	1·50	1·00
897.	–	1 r. red	4·00	1·75

DESIGNS: 30 k. Villagers welcoming tank crew. 50 k., 60 k. Soldier distributing newspapers to crowd. 1 r. People waving to column of tanks.

255. Ice-breaker "Georgy Sedov" and Badigin and Trofimov. 256. V. V. Mayakovsky.

1940. Polar research.

898.	–	15 k. green	2·25	40
899.	255.	30 k. violet	3·00	70
900.	–	50 k. brown	4·00	1·75
901.	–	1 r. blue	8·50	2·25

DESIGNS: 15 k. Ice-breaker "Iosif Stalin" and portraits of Papanin and Belousov. 50 k. Badigin and Papanin meeting. LARGER (46×26 mm.): 1 r. Route of drift of "Georgy Sedov".

1940. 10th Death Anniv. of Mayakovsky (poet).

902.	256.	15 k. red	30	15
903.		30 k. brown	55	20
904.	–	60 k. violet	1·00	45
905.	–	80 k. blue	80	45

DESIGN—VERT. 60 k., 80 k. Mayakovsky in profile wearing a cap.

257. Timiryazev. 258. Relay Runner.

1940. 20th Death Anniv of K. A. Timiryazev (scientist).

906.	–	10 k. blue	45	20
907.	–	15 k. violet	45	25
908.	257.	30 k. brown	70	30
909.	–	60 k. green	1·75	1·10

DESIGNS—HORIZ. 10 k. Miniature of Timiryazev and Academy of Agricultural Sciences, Moscow. 15 k. Timiryazev in laboratory. VERT. 60 k. Timiryazev's statue (by S. Merkurov), Moscow.

1940. 2nd All Union Physical Culture Festival.

910	258	15 k. red	90	35
911a	–	30 k. purple	1·60	30
912a	–	50 k. blue	2·50	55
913	–	60 k. blue	4·00	60
914	–	1 r. green	5·50	1·40

DESIGNS—HORIZ. 30 k. Girls' parade. 60 k. Skiing. 1 r. Grenade-throwing. VERT. 50 k. Children and sports badges.

259. Tchaikovsky and Passage from his "Fourth Symphony". 260. Central Regions Pavilion.

1940. Birth Cent. of Tchaikovsky (composer).

915.	–	15 k. green	1·10	20
916.	259.	20 k. brown	1·25	20
917.		30 k. blue	1·40	35
918.	–	50 k. red	2·00	60
919.	–	60 k. red	2·50	85

DESIGNS: 15 k., 50 k. Tchaikovsky's house at Klin. 60 k. Tchaikovsky and excerpt from "Eugene Onegin".

920. ПАВИЛЬОН «ПОВОЛЖЬЕ»
921. ПАВИЛЬОН «ДАЛЬНИЙ ВОСТОК»
922. ПОРТАЛ ПАВИЛЬОНА „ЛЕНИНГРАД И СЕВЕРО-ВОСТОК РСФСР"
923. ПАВИЛЬОН МОСКОВСКОЙ, РЯЗАНСКОЙ И ТУЛЬСКОЙ ОБЛ.
924. ПАВИЛЬОН УКРАИНСКОЙ ССР
925. ПАВИЛЬОН БЕЛОРУССКОЙ ССР
926. ПАВИЛЬОН АЗЕРБАЙДЖАНСКОЙ ССР
927. ПАВИЛЬОН ГРУЗИНСКОЙ ССР
928. ПАВИЛЬОН АРМЯНСКОЙ ССР
929. ВХОДА В ПАВИЛЬОН УЗБЕКСКОЙ ССР
930. ПАВИЛЬОН ТУРКМЕНСКОЙ ССР
931. ПАВИЛЬОН ТАДЖИКСКОЙ ССР
932. ПАВИЛЬОН КИРГИЗСКОЙ ССР
933. ПАВИЛЬОН КАРЕЛО-ФИНСКОЙ ССР
934. ПАВИЛЬОН КАЗАХСКОЙ ССР
935. ГЛАВНЫЙ ПАВИЛЬОН
936. ПАВИЛЬОН МЕХАНИЗАЦИИ

(211a.)

1940. All-Union Agricultural Fair. Coloured reproductions of Soviet Pavilions in green frames as T **260**. Inscriptions at foot as illustrated.

920	10 k. Volga Provinces (RSFSR) (horiz) ..	1·40	70
921	15 k. Far East	1·40	70
922	30 k. Leningrad and North East RSFSR ..	1·40	75
923	30 k. Three Central Regions (RSFSR) ..	1·40	80
924	30 k. Ukranian SSR ..	1·40	80
925	30 k. Byelorussian SSR ..	1·40	80
926	30 k. Azerbaijan SSR ..	1·40	80
927	30 k. Georgian SSR (horiz)	1·40	80
928	30 k. Armenian SSR ..	1·40	80
929	30 k. Uzbek SSR	1·40	80
930	30 k. Turkmen SSR (horiz)	1·40	80
931	30 k. Tadzhik SSR ..	1·40	80
932	30 k. Kirgiz SSR ..	1·40	80
933	30 k. Karelo-Finnish SSR	2·75	80
934	30 k. Kazakh SSR ..	1·40	80
935	50 k. Main Pavalion ..	2·25	1·75
936	60 k. Mechanization Pavilion and the statue of Stalin	8·00	1·90

261. Grenade Thrower. 262. Railway Bridge and Moscow-Volga Canal.

1940. 20th Anniv. of Wrangel's Defeat at Perekop (Crimea). Perf. or imperf.

937.	–	10 k. green	85	30
938.	261.	15 k. red	45	15
939.	–	30 k. brown and red ..	45	30
940.	–	50 k. purple	50	50
941.	–	60 k. blue	1·40	65
942.	–	1 r. black	2·25	1·40

DESIGNS—VERT. 10 k. Red Army Heroes Monument. 30 k. Map of Perekop and portrait of M. V. Frunze. 1 r. Victorious soldier. HORIZ.: 50 k. Soldiers crossing R. Sivash. 60 k. Army H.Q. at Stroganovka.

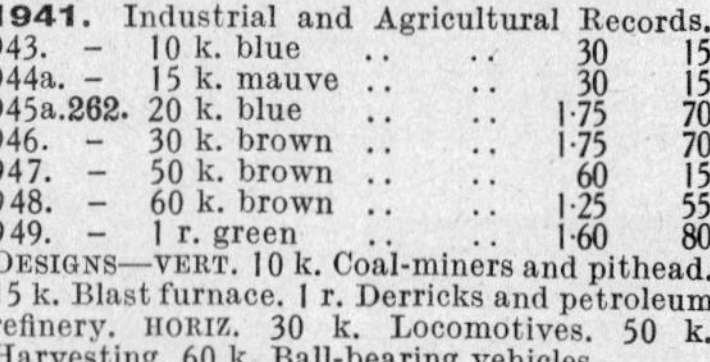

1941. Industrial and Agricultural Records.

943.	–	10 k. blue	30	15
944a.	–	15 k. mauve	30	15
945a.	262.	20 k. blue	1·75	70
946.	–	30 k. brown	1·75	70
947.	–	50 k. brown	60	15
948.	–	60 k. brown	1·25	55
949.	–	1 r. green	1·60	80

DESIGNS—VERT. 10 k. Coal-miners and pithead. 15 k. Blast furnace. 1 r. Derricks and petroleum refinery. HORIZ. 30 k. Locomotives. 50 k. Harvesting. 60 k. Ball-bearing vehicles.

263. Red Army Ski Corps. 264. N. E. Zhukovsky and Air Force Academy.

1941. 23rd Anniv. of Red Army. Designs with Hammer, Sickle and Star Symbol.

950a.	263.	5 k. violet	1·60	15
951.	–	10 k. blue	1·25	15
952.	–	15 k. green	45	15
953a.	–	20 k. red	45	15
954a.	–	30 k. brown	45	15
955a.	–	45 k. green	1·90	70
956.	–	50 k. blue	70	75
957.	–	1 r. green	1·00	80
957b.	–	3 r. green	6·50	3·00

DESIGNS—VERT. 10 k. Sailor. 20 k. Cavalry. 30 k. Automatic Rifle Squad. 50 k. Airman. 1 r., 3 r. Marshal's star. HORIZ. 15 k. Artillery. 45 k. Clearing a hurdle.

1941. 20th Death Anniv. of Zhukovsky (scientist).

958.	–	15 k. blue	50	20
959.	264.	30 k. red	1·10	30
960.	–	50 k. red	1·25	55

DESIGNS—VERT. 15 k. Zhukovsky. 50 k. Zhukovsky lecturing.

265. Thoroughbred Horses. 266. Arms of Karelo-Finnish S.S.R.

1941. 15th Anniv of Kirgiz S.S.R.

961	265	15 k. brown ..	3·00	50
962a	–	30 k. violet ..	4·00	75

DESIGN: 30 k. Coal-miner and colliery.

1941. 1st Anniv. of Karelo-Finnish Republic.

963.	266.	30 k. red	70	35
964.		45 k. green	85	60

267. Marshal Suvorov. 268. Spassky Tower, Kremlin.

1941. 150th Anniv of Battle of Izmail.

965	–	10 k. green	75	30
966	–	15 k. red	75	40
967	267	30 k. blue	1·75	35
968		1 r. brown	2·25	1·10

DESIGN: 10, 15 k. Storming of Izmail.

1941.

970.	268.	1 r. red	1·60	55
971.	–	2 r. orange ..	3·25	1·10

DESIGN—HORIZ. 2 r. Kremlin Palace.

269. "Razin on the Volga".

1941. 25th Death Anniv. of Surikov (artist).

972.	–	20 k. black	1·25	80
973.	269.	30 k. red	2·75	70
974.	–	50 k. purple	4·00	1·75
975.	269.	1 r. green	8·00	2·50
976.	–	2 r. brown	14·00	3·00

DESIGNS—VERT. 20 k., 50 k. "Suvorov's march through Alps, 1799". 2 r. Surikov.

270. Lenin Museum (interior).

271. Lermontov.

1941. 5th Anniv. of Lenin Museum.
977. 270. 15 k. red .. .. 2·50 1·25
978. – 30 k. violet on mauve 22·00 11·00
979. 270. 45 k. green .. .. 3·25 1·25
980. – 1 r. red on rose .. 8·00 5·00
DESIGN: 30 k., 1 r. Exterior of Lenin Museum.

1941. Death Centenary of M. Yu. Lermontov (poet and novelist).
981 271 15 k. green .. .. 3·50 2·50
982 30 k. violet .. .. 5·00 3·00

272. Reproduction of Poster.

273. Mass Enlistment.

1941. Mobilization.
983a. 272. 30 k. red .. .. 15·00 20·00

1941. National Defence.
984. 273. 30 k. blue .. .. 48·00 45·00

274. Alishir Navoi.

275. Lt. Talalikhin Ramming Enemy Aeroplane.

289a. Five Heroes.

276. Anti-tank Gun.

1942. 5th Centenary of Uzbek poet Mir Ali Shir (Alishir Navoi).
985 274 30 k. brown .. .. 8·00 6·00
986 1 r. purple .. .. 13·00 15·00

1942. Russian Heroes. (1st issue).
987. 275. 20 k. blue 50 15
988. A. 30 k. grey 60 25
989. B. 30 k. black 60 15
990. C. 30 k. black 60 15
991. D. 30 k. black 60 30
~~1048c~~. 275. 30 k. grey .. .. 1·00 30
1048d. A. 30 k. blue .. .. 1·00 30
1048e. C. 30 k. green .. .. 1·00 30
1048f. D. 30 k. purple .. .. 1·00 30
1048g. 289a. 30 k. blue .. .. 1·00 30
992. C. 1 r. green .. .. 4·00 2·75
993. D. 2 r. green .. .. 7·50 3·50
DESIGNS: A, Capt. Gastello and burning aeroplane diving into enemy petrol tanks. B, Maj-Gen. Dovator and Cossack cavalry in action. C, Shura Chekalin guerilla fighting. D, Zoya Kosmodemyanskaya being led to death.
See also Nos. 1072/6.

1942. War Episodes (1st series).
994. 276. 20 k. brown .. .. 1·25 50
995. – 30 k. blue .. .. 1·25 50
996. – 30 k. green .. .. 1·25 50
997. – 30 k. red .. .. 1·25 50
998. – 60 k. grey .. .. 1·75 1·50
999. – 1 r. brown .. .. 3·75 3·75
DESIGNS—HORIZ. 30 k. (No. 996), Guerrillas attacking train. 30 k. (No. 997), Munition-worker. 1 r. Machine gunners. VERT. 30 k. (No. 995), Signallers. 60 k. Defenders of Leningrad.

277. Distributing Gifts to Soldiers.

278. Munition Worker.

1942. War Episodes (2nd series).
1000. 277. 20 k. blue .. .. 1·50 50
1001. – 20 k. purple .. .. 1·75 50
1002. – 30 k. purple .. .. 1·75 45
1003. – 45 k. red .. .. 3·75 2·25
1004. – 45 k. blue .. .. 4·00 2·75
DESIGNS—VERT. No. 1001, Aeroplane destroying tank. No. 1002, Food packers. No. 1003, Woman sewing. No. 1004, Anti-aircraft gun.
See also Nos. 1013/17.

1943. 25th Anniv. of Russian Revolution.
1005. 278. 5 k. brown 55 25
1006. – 10 k. brown 80 15
1007. – 15 k. blue 65 20
1008. – 20 k. blue 65 20
1009. – 30 k. brown 85 20
1010. – 60 k. brown .. .. 1·40 45
1011. – 1 r. red .. .. 2·00 1·25
1012. – 2 r. brown .. .. 3·25 1·50
DESIGNS: 10 k. Lorry convoy. 15 k. Troops supporting Lenin's banner. 20 k. Leningrad seen through an archway. 30 k. Spassky Tower, Lenin and Stalin. 60 k. Tank parade. 1 r. Lenin speaking. 2 r. Star of Order of Lenin.

279. Nurses and Wounded Soldier.

280. Routes of Bering's Voyages.

1943. War Episodes (3rd series).
1013. 279. 30 k. green .. .. 1·25 65
1014. – 30 k. green (Scouts) 1·25 65
1015. – 30 k. brown (Mine-thrower) .. .. 1·25 65
1016. – 60 k. green (Anti-tank troops) .. .. 2·25 65
1017. – 60 k. blue (Sniper) .. 2·25 65

1943. Death Bicent of Vitus Bering (explorer).
1018 – 30 k. blue .. .. 1·60 15
1019 280 60 k. grey .. .. 3·25 30
1020 – 1 r. green .. .. 4·50 75
1021 280 2 r. brown .. .. 7·50 1·00
DESIGN: 30 k., 1 r. Mt. St. Ilya.

281. Gorky.

1943. 75th Birth Anniv of Maksim Gorky (novelist).
1022. 281. 30 k. green 75 15
1023. 60 k. blue .. .. 1·00 15

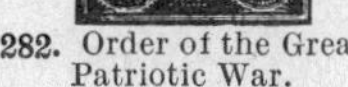

282. Order of the Great Patriotic War.

a. Order of Suvorov.

1943. War Orders and Medals (1st series), Medals with ribbon attached.
1024. 282. 1 r. black .. .. 1·25 1·00
1025. a. 10 r. olive .. .. 6·00 4·50
See also Nos. 1051/8, 1089/94, 1097/99a, 1172/86, 1197/1204 and 1776/80a.

283. Karl Marx.

284. Naval Landing Party.

1943. 125th Birth Anniv. of Marx.
1026. 283. 30 k. blue 85 20
1027. 60 k. green .. .. 1·40 35

1943. 25th Anniv of Red Army and Navy.
1028. 284. 20 k. brown 30 20
1029. – 30 k. green 35 15
1030. – 60 k. green .. .. 1·25 40
1031. 284. 3 r. blue .. .. 2·75 90
DESIGNS: 30 k. Sailors and anti-aircraft gun. 60 k. Tanks and infantry.

285. Ivan Turgenev.

286. Loading a Gun.

1943. 125th Birth Anniv of Ivan Turgenev (novelist).
1032 285 30 k. green .. .. 8·00 7·00
1032a 60 k. violet .. .. 12·00 11·00

1943. 25th Anniv. of Young Communist League.
1033. 286. 15 k. blue 55 15
1034. – 20 k. orange 55 15
1035. – 30 k. brown and red .. 70 15
1036. – 1 r. green .. .. 1·00 35
1037. – 2 r. green .. .. 2·25 75
DESIGNS—As T 286: 20 k. Tank and banner. 1 r. Infantrymen. 2 r. Grenade thrower. $22\frac{1}{2} \times 28\frac{1}{2}$ mm: 30 k. Bayonet fighter and flag.

287. V. V. Mayakovsky.

288. Memorial Tablet and Allied Flags.

1943. 50th Birth Anniv. of Mayakovsky (poet).
1038. 287. 30 k. orange 65 10
1039. 60 k. blue 95 20

1943. Teheran Three Power Conf. and 26th Anniv. of Revolution.
1040. 288. 30 k. black 80 50
1041. 3 r. blue .. .. 3·00 1·25

289. Defence of Odessa.

АВИАПОЧТА
1944 г.
1 РУБЛЬ
(290.)

1944. Liberation of Russian Towns.
1045. – 30 k. brown and red 65 25
1046. – 30 k. blue 65 25
1047. – 30 k. green 65 25
1048. 289. 30 k. green 65 25
DESIGNS: No. 1045, Stalingrad. No. 1046, Sevastopol. No. 1047, Leningrad.

1944. Air. Surch with T 290.
1049 275 1 r. on 30 k. grey .. 1·25 30
1050 A 1 r. on 30 k. blue (No. 1048d) .. .. 1·25 30

291. Order of Kutusov.

b. Order of Patriotic War. c. Order of Alexander Nevsky. d. Order of Suvorov. e. Order of Kutusov.

1944. War Orders and Medals (2nd series). Various Stars without ribbons showing as Types b to e. Perf. or imperf.
(a) Frames as T 291.
1051. b. 15 k. red 50 15
1052. c. 20 k. blue 50 15
1053. d. 30 k. green .. .. 1·00 25
1054. e. 60 k. red .. .. 1·50 40
(b) Frames as T 282.
1055. b. 1 r. black 80 30
1056. c. 3 r. blue .. .. 3·25 1·60
1057. e. 5 r. green .. .. 4·00 1·00
1058. d. 10 r. red .. .. 4·00 1·50

293. Lenin Mausoleum and Red Square, Moscow.

1944. "Twenty Years without Lenin". As Nos. 667/72, but inscr. "1924–1944", and T 293.
1059. – 30 k. black and blue 40 10
1060. 199. 30 k. red and orange 40 10
1061. – 45 k. black and blue 60 15
1062. – 50 k. black and blue 70 15
1063. – 60 k. black and blue 1·40 20
1064. 293. 1 r. brown and blue 1·75 45
1065. 199. 3 r. black and orange 3·50 1·40
DESIGNS—VERT. Lenin at 3 years of age. (No. 1059); at school (45 k.); as man (50 k.); as orator (60 k.).

INDEX

Countries can be quickly located by referring to the index at the end of this volume.

294. Allied Flags.

295. Rimsky-Korsakov and Bolshoi Theatre.

1944. 14 June (Allied Nations' Day).
1066. 294. 60 k. black, red & blue 1·00 35
1067. 3 r. blue and red .. 5·00 1·40

1944. Birth Centenary of Rimsky-Korsakov (composer). Imperf or perf.
1068 295 30 k. grey 40 10
1069 60 k. green 60 10
1070 1 r. green .. .. 1·25 20
1071 3 r. violet .. .. 2·50 50

296. Nuradilov and Machine-gun.

297. Polivanova and Kovshova.

1944. War Heroes (3rd issue)
1072. 296. 30 k. green 45 15
1073. – 60 k. violet 85 15
1074. – 60 k. blue 85 15
1075. 297. 60 k. green .. .. 1·50 45
1076. – 60 k. black .. .. 1·75 45
DESIGNS—HORIZ. No. 1073, Matrosov defending a snow-trench. No. 1074, Luzak hurling a hand-grenade. VERT. No. 1076, B. Safonev, medals and aerial battle over the sea.

298. S. A. Chaplygin.

299. V. I. Chapaev.

1944. 75th Birth Anniv. of S. A. Chaplygin (scientist).
1077. 298. 30 k. grey 30 10
1078. 1 r. brown 80 30

1944. Heroes of 1918 Civil War.
1079. 299. 30 k. green .. .. 1·00 25
1080. – 30 k. black (N. Shchors) 1·00 25
1081. – 30 k. green (S. Lazo) 1·00 25
For 40 k. stamp as Type 299, see No. 1531.
See also Nos. 1349/51.

300. Ilya Yenmovich Repin.

301. "Reply of the Cossacks to Sultan Mahmoud IV".

1944. Birth Cent. of I. Y. Repin (artist). Imperf. or perf.
1082. 300. 30 k. green 75 20
1083. 301. 50 k. green 75 20
1084. 60 k. blue 75 20
1085. 300. 1 r. brown .. .. 1·00 40
1086. 301. 2 r. violet .. .. 2·00 80

302. I. A. Krylov.

1944. Death Cent. of Krylov (fabulist).
1087. 302. 30 k. brown 25 10
1088. 1 r. blue 65 25

f. Partisans' Medal.

g. Medal for Bravery.

h. Order of Bogdan Chmielnitsky.

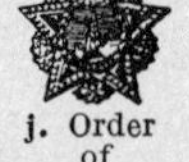

j. Order of Victory.

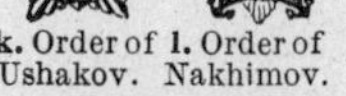

k. Order of Ushakov. l. Order of Nakhimov.

1945. War Orders and Medals (3rd series). Frame as T **291** with various centres as Types **f** to **l**. Perf. or imperf.

1089. **f.** 15 k. black 40 15
1090. **g.** 30 k. blue .. .. 1·50 20
1091. **h.** 45 k. blue .. .. 1·50 40
1092. **j.** 60 k. red .. .. 1·50 45
1093. **k.** 1 r. blue .. .. 2·50 1·00
1094. **l.** 1 r. green .. .. 2·50 1·00

303. Griboedov (after P. Karatygin). **305.** Soldier.

1945. 150th Birth Anniv of Aleksandr S. Griboedov (author).

1095 **303** 30 k. green .. .. 1·50 10
1096 60 k. brown .. .. 2·00 25

1945. War Orders and Medals (4th series) Frames as T **282**. Various centres.

1097. **g.** 1 r. black .. .. 1·00 40
1098. **h.** 2 r. black .. .. 5·00 1·75
1098a. 2 r. purple .. .. 40·00 12·00
1098b. 2 r. olive .. .. 7·00 2·50
1099. **j.** 3 r. red .. .. 4·00 1·00
1099a. 3 r. purple .. .. 5·50 3·00

1945. Relief of Stalingrad.

1100. **305.** 60 k. black and red .. 1·00 55
1101. 3 r. black and red .. 3·00 1·10

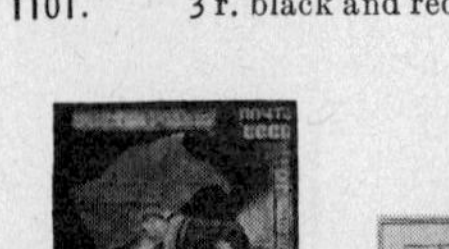

306. Standard-Bearer. **308.** Attack.

1945. Red Army Victories.

1102. **306.** 20 k. green, red & black 40 15
1103. – 30 k. black and red .. 40 15
1104. – 1 r. green and red .. 1·75 1·00

DESIGN—HORIZ. 30 k. Infantry v. Tank. 1 r. Infantry charge.

1945. Liberation of Russian Soil.

1105. **308.** 30 k. blue 40 15
1106. – 60 k. red 70 45
1107. – 1 r. green .. .. 1·75 1·00

DESIGNS: 60 k. Welcoming troops. 1 r. Grenade thrower.

309. Badge and Guns. **310.** Barricade.

1945. Red Guards Commem.

1108. **309.** 60 k. red .. .. 2·50 40

1945. Battle of Moscow.

1109. – 30 k. blue 40 20
1110. **310.** 60 k. black 80 20
1111. – 1 r. black .. .. 1·50 45

DESIGNS: 30 k. Tanks in Red Square, Moscow. 1 r. Aerial battle and searchlights.

311. Prof. Lomonosov and Academy of Sciences, Leningrad. **312.** Popov.

1945. 220th Anniv. of Academy of Sciences.

1112. – 30 k. blue 75 25
1113. **311.** 2 r. black .. .. 2·50 80

DESIGN—VERT. 30 k. Moscow Academy, inscr. "1725-1945".

1945. 50th Anniv. of Popov's Radio Discoveries.

1114. **312.** 30 k. blue 35 15
1115. 60 k. red .. .. 1·00 25
1116. – 1 r. brown (Popov) .. 1·75 65

314. Motherhood Medal. **315.**

1945. Orders and Medals of Motherhood. Imperf. or perf.

1117. **314.** 20 k. brown on blue .. 30 20
1118. – 30 k. brown on green 45 20
1119. – 60 k. red 95 70
1120. **315.** 1 r. black on green .. 1·00 20
1121. – 2 r. blue .. .. 2·00 30
1122. – 3 r. red on blue .. 2·75 90

DESIGNS: 30 k., 2 r. Order of Motherhood Glory. 60 k., 3 r. Order of Heroine-Mother.

316. Petlyakov-Pe2 Dive Bombers. **317.** Ilyushin-2 Bombers.

318. Petlyakov-PC8 Bombers.

1945. Air. Aviation Day.

1123. **316.** 1 r. brown .. .. 3·00 50
1124. **317.** 1 r. brown .. .. 3·00 50
1125. – 1 r. red .. .. 3·00 50
1126. – 1 r. black .. .. 3·00 50
1127. – 1 r. blue .. .. 3·00 50
1128. – 1 r. green .. .. 3·00 50
1129. **318.** 1 r. grey .. .. 3·00 50
1130. – 1 r. brown .. .. 3·00 50
1131. – 1 r. red .. .. 3·00 50

DESIGNS—As Type **317**: No. 1125, Lavocnkin-7 fighter shooting tail off enemy plane. No. 1126 Ilyushin-4 bomber dropping bombs. No. 1127, Tupolev-2 bombers in flight. No. 1128, Polikarpov-2 biplane. As Type **318**: No. 1130, Yakovlev-3 fighter destroying enemy fighter. No. 1131, Yakovlev-9 fighter destroying twin-engined plane.

See also Nos. 1163/71.

ПРАЗДНИК
ПОБЕДЫ

9 мая
1945 года

(**319.**)

1945. VE Day. No. 1099 optd. with T **319.**

1132. – 3 r. red .. .. 2·75 1·25

320. Lenin. **321.**

1945. 75th Birth Anniv. of Lenin.

1133. **320.** 30 k. blue 50 20
1134. – 50 k. brown .. .. 1·25 20
1135. – 60 k. red .. .. 1·25 30
1136. **321.** 1 r. black 20 35
1137. – 3 r. brown .. .. 6·00 1·75

DESIGNS—VERT. (inscr. "1870–1945"): 50 k. Lenin at desk. 60 k. Lenin making a speech. 3 r. Portrait of Lenin.

322. Kutuzov (after R. Volkov). **323.** A. I. Herzen.

1945. Birth Bicentenary of Mikhail Kutuzov (military leader).

1138. **322.** 30 k. blue 80 15
1139. 60 k. brown .. .. 1·50 30

1945. 75th Death Anniv. of Herzen (author and critic).

1140. **323.** 30 k. brown 70 15
1141. 2 r. black .. .. 1·90 35

324. I. I. Mechnikov. **325.** Friedrich Engels.

1945. Birth Cent. of Mechnikov (biologist).

1142. **324.** 30 k. brown 50 15
1143. 1 r. black .. .. 1·00 30

1945. 125th Birth Anniv. of Engels.

1144. **325.** 30 k. brown 80 15
1145. 60 k. green .. .. 1·25 25

326. Observer and Guns. **327.** Heavy Guns.

1945. Artillery Day.

1146. **326.** 30 k. brown .. .. 1·10 1·00
1147. **327.** 60 k. black .. .. 3·25 2·50

328. Tank Production.

DESIGNS: 30 k. Harvesting. 60 k. Aeroplane designing. 1 r. Firework display.

1945. Home Front.

1148. **328.** 20 k. blue and brown 1·75 35
1149. – 30 k. black and brown 1·50 40
1150. – 60 k. brown and green 2·00 60
1151. – 1 r. blue and brown .. 3·00 1·25

329. Victory Medal. **330.** Soldier with Victory Flag.

1946. Victory Issue.

1152. **329.** 30 k. violet 30 15
1153. 30 k. brown 30 15
1154. 60 k. black 55 20
1155. 60 k. brown 55 20
1156. **330.** 60 k. black and red .. 1·75 1·50

331. Arms of U.S.S.R. **332.** Kremlin, Moscow.

1946. Supreme Soviet Elections.

1157. **331.** 30 k. red 30 10
1158. **332.** 45 k. red 50 30
1159. **331.** 60 k. green .. .. 1·75 30

333. Tank Parade.

334. Infantry Parade.

1946. 28th Anniv. of Red Army and Navy.

1160. **333.** 60 k. brown .. .. 1·00 15
1161. 2 r. violet .. .. 2·00 50
1162. **334.** 3 r. black and red .. 4·25 1·00

1946. Air. As Nos. 1123/31.

1163. – 5 k. violet (as No. 1130) 70 60
1164. **316.** 10 k. red 70 60
1165. **317.** 15 k. red 70 60
1166. **318.** 15 k. green 70 60
1167. – 20 k. black (as No. 1127) 70 60
1168. – 30 k. vio. (as No. 1126) 1·40 75
1169. – 30 k. brown (as No. 1128) 1·40 75
1170. – 50 k. blue (as No. 1125) 2·10 1·50
1171. – 60 k. blue (as No. 1131) 3·75 2·25

A B C D

E F G H

J K L M

N O P

1946. War Orders with Medals (5th series). Frames as T **291** with various centres as Types A to P.

1172. A. 60 k. red .. .. 1·00 1·00
1173. B. 60 k. red .. .. 1·00 1·00
1174. C. 60 k. green .. .. 1·00 1·00
1175. D. 60 k. green .. .. 1·00 1·00
1176. E. 60 k. green .. .. 1·00 1·00
1177. F. 60 k. blue .. .. 1·00 1·00
1178. G. 60 k. blue .. .. 1·00 1·00
1179. H. 60 k. violet .. .. 1·00 1·00
1180. J. 60 k. purple .. .. 1·00 1·00
1181. K. 60 k. brown .. .. 1·00 1·00
1182. L. 60 k. brown .. .. 1·00 1·00
1183. M. 60 k. purple .. .. 1·00 1·00
1184. N. 60 k. red .. .. 1·00 1·00
1185. O. 60 k. blue .. .. 1·00 1·00
1186. P. 60 k. purple .. .. 1·00 1·00

336. P. L. Chebyshev. **337.** Gorky.

1946. 125th Birth Anniv. of Chebyshev (mathematician).

1187. **336.** 30 k. brown 50 20
1188. 60 k. black 75 30

1946. Death of President Kalinin. As T **211**, but inscr. "3-VI-1946".

1189. 20 k. black .. .. 1·00 35

1946. 10th Death Anniv of Maksim Gorky (novelist).

1190 **337** 30 k. brown 40 10
1191 – 60 k. green 70 20

DESIGN: 60 k. Gorky and laurel leaves.

338. Gagry.

DESIGNS—HORIZ. 15 k. Sukumi. 45 k. New Athos. VERT. 30 k. (No. 1194) Sochi.

1946. Health Resorts.

1192. – 15 k. brown 40 15
1193. **338.** 30 k. green 60 15
1194. – 30 k. green 70 15
1195. – 45 k. brown 70 35

339. Stalin and Parade of Athletes. **R.**

1946. Sports Festival.

1196. **339.** 30 k. green .. .. 8·00 5·00

1946. War Medals (6th series). Frames as T **282.** with various centres.

1197. R. 1 r. red .. .. 1·40 65
1198. B. 1 r. green .. .. 1·40 65
1199. C. 1 r. brown .. .. 1·45 65
1200. D. 1 r. blue .. .. 1·45 65
1201. G. 1 r. grey .. .. 1·40 65
1202. H. 1 r. red .. .. 1·40 65
1203. K. 1 r. purple .. .. 1·40 65
1204. L. 1 r. red .. .. 1·40 65

341. Moscow Opera House. **342.** Tanks in Red Square.

1946. Moscow Buildings.

1205. – 5 k. brown 30 15
1206. **341.** 10 k. grey 35 15
1207. – 15 k. brown 30 15
1208. – 20 k. brown 60 20
1209. – 45 k. green 70 30
1210. – 50 k. brown 80 35
1211. – 60 k. violet .. .. 1·00 45
1212. – 1 r. brown .. .. 1·50 1·25

DESIGNS—VERT. 5 k. Church of Ivan the Great and Kremlin. 1 r. Spassky Tower (larger). HORIZ. 15 k. Hotel Moscow. 20 k. Theatre and Sverdlov Square. 45 k. As 5 k. but horiz. 50 k. Lenin Museum. 60 k. St. Basil's Cathedral and Spassky Tower (larger).

1946. Heroes of Tank Engagements.

1213. **342.** 30 k. green .. .. 2·00 1·50
1214. 60 k. brown .. .. 3·25 2·00

343. "Iron". **345.** Lenin and Stalin.

344. Soviet Postage Stamps.

1946. 4th Stalin "Five-Year Reconstruction Plan". Agriculture and Industry.

1215. – 5 k. olive 30 10
1216. – 10 k. green 30 10
1217. – 15 k. brown 50 10
1218. – 20 k. violet 80 10
1219. **343.** 30 k. brown .. .. 1·00 25

DESIGNS—HORIZ. 5 k. "Agriculture". 15 k. "Coal". VERT. 10 k. "Oil". 20 k. "Steel".

1946. 25th Anniv. of Soviet Postal Services.

1220. – 15 k. black and red .. 1·50 40
1221. – 30 k. brown and green 2·00 1·00
1222. **344.** 60 k. black and green 3·25 1·60

DESIGNS: 15 k. (48½ × 23 mm.) Stamps on map of U.S.S.R. 30 k. (33 × 22½ mm.) Reproduction of Type **47.**

1946. 29th Anniv. of Russian Revolution. Imperf. or perf.

1223. **345.** 30 k. orange.. .. 2·50 2·50
1224. 30 k. green .. .. 2·50 2·50

346. N. A. Nekrasov. **347.** Stalin Prize Medal.

1946. 125th Birth Anniv. of Nekrasov (poet).

1225. **346.** 30 k. black 85 10
1226. 60 k. brown 95 25

1946. Stalin Prize.

1227. **347.** 30 k. brown .. .. 1·75 1·00

348. Dnieperprostroi Dam.

1946. Restoration of Dnieperprostroi Hydro-Electric Power Station.

1228. **348.** 30 k. black .. .. 1·50 30
1229. 60 k. blue .. .. 2·75 70

349. A. Karpinsky. **350.** N. E. Zhukovsky.

1947. Birth Cent. of Karpinsky (geologist).

1230. **349.** 30 k. green 80 35
1231. 50 k. black .. .. 3·00 90

1947. Birth Cent. of Zhukovsky (scientist).

1232. **350.** 30 k. black .. .. 1·50 30
1233. 60 k. blue .. .. 3·00 1·25

351. Lenin Mausoleum. **352.** Lenin.

1947. 23rd Death Anniv. of Lenin.

1234. **351.** 30 k. green 65 25
1235. 30 k. blue 65 25
1236. **352.** 50 k. brown .. .. 2·50 75

For similar designs inscr. "1924/1948" see Nos. 1334/6.

353. Nikolai M. Przhevalsky. **354.** Arms of R.S.F.S.R.

356. Arms of U.S.S.R.

1947. Cent. of Soviet Geographical Society.

1237. – 20 k. brown .. .. 2·00 50
1238. – 20 k. blue .. .. 2·00 50
1239. **353.** 60 k. olive .. .. 3·50 1·40
1240. 60 k. brown .. .. 3·50 1·40

DESIGN: 20 k. Miniature portrait of F. P. Lutke and full-rigged ship "Senyavin".

1947. Supreme Soviet Elections. Arms of Constituent Republics. As T **354.**

1241 **354** 30 k. red (Russian Federation) .. 75 65
1242 – 30 k. brown (Armenia) 75 65
1243 – 30 k. bistre (Azerbaijan) 75 65
1244 – 30 k. green (Byelorussia) 75 65
1245 – 30 k. grey (Estonia) .. 75 65
1246 – 30 k. brown (Georgia) 75 65
1247 – 30 k. purple (Karelo-Finnish S.S.R.) .. 75 65
1248 – 30 k. orange (Kazakhstan) 75 65
1249 – 30 k. purple (Kirgizia) 75 65
1250 – 30 k. brown (Latvia) 75 65
1251 – 30 k. green (Lithuania) 75 65
1252 – 30 k. purple (Moldavia) 75 65
1253 – 30 k. green (Tadzhikistan) 75 65
1254 – 30 k. black (Turkmenistan) 75 65
1255 – 30 k. blue (Ukraine) 75 65
1256 – 30 k. brown (Uzbekistan) 75 65
1257 **356** 1 r. multicoloured .. 3·25 85

A Hammer and Sickle in the centre of No. 1247 and at the base of No. 1249 should assist identification.

357. Russian Soldier. **359.** A. S. Pushkin.

1947. 29th Anniv. of Soviet Army. Perf. or imperf.

1258. **357.** 20 k. black 45 10
1259. – 30 k. blue 50 15
1260. – 30 k. brown 55 15

DESIGNS—VERT. No. 1259, Military cadet. HORIZ. No. 1260, Soldier, Sailor and Airman.

1947. 110th Death Anniv. of Pushkin (poet).

1261. **359.** 30 k. black 65 30
1262. 50 k. green .. .. 1·00 75

360. Schoolroom.

1947. Int. Women's Day.

1263. **360.** 15 k. blue .. .. 3·00 1·00
1264. – 30 k. red .. .. 6·00 2·00

DESIGN—26½ × 39½ mm. 30 k. Women students and banner.

362. Moscow Council Building. **364.** Soviet Aircraft and Flag.

363. May Day Procession.

1947. 30th Anniv. of Moscow Soviet. Perf. or imperf.

1265. **362.** 30 k. red, blue & blk. 2·00 1·25

1947. May Day.

1266. **363.** 30 k. red .. .. 1·75 80
1267. 1 r. green .. .. 3·75 2·50

1947. Air Force Day.

1268. **364.** 30 k. violet 80 15
1269. 1 r. blue .. .. 2·00 40

365. Yakhromsky Lock.

1947. 10th Anniv. of Volga-Moscow Canal.

1270. – 30 k. black 70 10
1271. **365.** 30 k. lake 70 10
1272. – 45 k. red 90 25
1273. – 50 k. blue .. .. 1·25 30
1274. – 60 k. red .. .. 1·25 30
1275. – 1 r. violet .. .. 2·50 60

DESIGNS—HORIZ. 30 k. (No. 1270), Karamyshevsky Dam. 45 k. Yakhromsky Pumping Station. 50 k. Khimki Pier. 1 r. Lock No. 8. VERT. 60 k. Map of Volga-Moscow Canal.

800 лет Москвы
1147—1947 гг.
(**366**).

367. Izmailovsky Station.

1947. 800th Anniv. of Moscow (1st issue). Opt. as T **366.**

1276. 20 k. brown (No. 1208) 55 15
1277. 50 k. brown (No. 1210) 90 35
1278. 60 k. violet (No. 1211) 1·40 85
1279. 1 r. brown (No. 1212) 3·50 1·75

See also Nos. 1286/1300.

1947. Opening of New Moscow Underground Stations. Inscr. "M".

1280. **367.** 30 k. blue 60 15
1281. – 30 k. brown 60 15
1282. – 45 k. brown .. .. 1·25 35
1283. – 45 k. violet .. .. 1·25 35
1284. – 60 k. green .. .. 2·00 50
1285. – 60 k. red .. .. 2·00 50

DESIGNS—HORIZ. No. 1281, Power House. No. 1282, Falcon Station. No. 1283, Stalinsky Station. No. 1284, Kiev Station. VERT. No. 1285, Mayakovsky Station.

368. Crimea Bridge, Moscow.

1947. 800th Anniv of Moscow (2nd issue).

1286. **368.** 5 k. brown and blue.. 50 10
1287. – 10 k. black and brown 30 10
1288. – 30 k. grey .. .. 1·25 25
1289. – 30 k. blue .. .. 1·25 25
1290. – 30 k. brown 55 25
1291. – 30 k. green 55 25
1292. – 30 k. green 55 25
1293. – 50 k. green .. .. 1·25 70
1294. – 60 k. blue .. .. 1·40 55
1295. – 60 k. black and brown 1·75 55
1296. – 1 r. purple .. .. 2·75 80

Centre in yellow, red and blue.

1297. – 1 r. blue .. .. 4·50 50
1298. – 2 r. red .. .. 8·00 1·75
1299. – 3 r. blue .. .. 12·00 2·75
1300. – 5 r. blue .. .. 23·00 5·50

DESIGNS—VERT. 10 k. Gorky Street, Moscow. 30 k. (No. 1292). Pushkin Place. 60 k. (No. 1294), 2 r. Kremlin. 1 r. (No. 1296), "Old Moscow" after A. M. Vasnetsov. 1 r. (No. 1297), St. Basil Cathedral. HORIZ. 30 k. (No. 1288), Kiev railway station. 30 k. (No. 1289), Kazan railway station. 30 k. (No. 1290), Central Telegraph Offices. 30 k. (No. 1291), Kaluga Street. 50 k. Kremlin. 3 r. Kremlin. 5 r. Government Buildings. (54½ × 24½ mm). 60 k. (No. 1295) Bridge and Kremlin.

369. "Ritz", Gagry. **370.** "Zapadugol", Sochi.

1947. U.S.S.R. Health Resorts.

(a) Vertical.

1301 **369** 30 k. green 55 15
1302 – 30 k. green (Sukhumi) 55 15

(b) Horizontal.

1303 **370** 30 k. black 55 15
1304 – 30 k. brown ("New Riveria", Sochi) .. 55 15
1305 – 30 k. purple ("Voroshilov", Sochi) .. 55 15
1306 – 30 k. violet ("Gulripsh", Sukhumi) .. 55 15
1307 – 30 k. blue ("Kemeri", Riga) 55 15
1308 – 30 k. brown ("Abkhazia", Novy Afon) 55 15
1309 – 30 k. bistre ("Krestyansky", Livadia) 55 15
1310 – 30 k. blue ("Kirov", Kislovodsk) .. 55 15

371. 1917 Revolution.

1947. 30th Anniv. of Revolution. Perf. or imperf.

1311. **371.** 30 k. black and red.. 30 15
1312. – 50 k. blue and red .. 1·25 20
1313. **371.** 60 k. black and red .. 1·00 30
1314. – 60 k. brown and red .. 1·00 30
1315. – 1 r. black and red .. 2·25 50
1316. – 2 r. green and red .. 3·00 1·00

DESIGNS: 50 k., 1 r. "Industry". 60 k. (No. 1314) 2 r. "Agriculture".

372. Metallurgical Works. **373.** Spassky Tower, Kremlin.

1947. Post-War Five Year Plan. Horiz. industrial designs. All dated "1947" except No. 1324. Perf. or imperf.

1317. **372.** 15 k. brown 40 20
1318. – 20 k. brown (Foundry) 50 30
1319. **372.** 30 k. purple .. .. 1·00 30
1320. – 30 k. green (Harvesting machines) .. 75 50
1321. – 30 k. brown (Tractor) 1·00 30
1322. – 30 k. brown (Tractors) 75 30
1323. – 60 k. bistre (Harvesting machines) .. 1·10 50
1324. – 60 k. purple (Builders) 1·10 50
1325. – 1 r. orange (Foundry) 2·50 1·25
1326. – 1 r. red (Tractor) .. 3·00 1·25
1327. – 1 r. violet (Tractors) 2·50 1·25

1947.

1328. 373. 60 k. red .. .. 4·00 1·40
1329a. 1 r. red .. .. 1·10 10

374. Peter I Monument.

376. Government Building, Kiev.

1948. 4th Anniv of Relief of Leningrad.

1330. – 30 k. violet 50 15
1331. 374. 50 k. green 70 30
1332. – 60 k. black .. .. 1·25 50
1333. – 1 r. violet .. .. 1·60 80

DESIGNS—HORIZ. 30 k. Winter Palace. 60 k. Peter and Paul Fortress. 1 r. Smolny Institute.

1948. 24th Death Anniv. of Lenin. As issue of 1947, but dated "1924 1948".

1334. 351. 30 k. violet 65 20
1335. 60 k. blue 90 25
1336. 352. 60 k. green .. .. 1·50 75

1948. 30th Anniversary of Ukrainian S.S.R. Various designs inscr. "XXX" and "1917-1947".

1337. 376. 30 k. blue 55 15
1338. – 50 k. violet 85 40
1339. – 60 k. brown .. .. 1·00 40
1340. – 1 r. brown .. .. 3·50 1·25

DESIGNS: 50 k. Dnieper hydro-electric power station. 60 k. Wheatfield and granary. 1 r. Metallurgical works and colliery.

377. Vasily I. Surikov.

378. Skiing.

1948. Birth Cent. of Surikov (artist).

1341. 377. 30 k. brown 85 35
1342. 60 k. green .. .. 1·25 75

1948. R.S.F.S.R. Games. Various designs.

1343. 378. 15 k. blue .. .. 2·50 25
1344. – 20 k. blue .. .. 3·00 50

DESIGN—VERT. 20 k. Motor cyclist crossing stream.

379. Artillery.

381. Karl Marx and Friedrich Engels.

380. Bulganin and Military School.

1948. 30th Anniv. of Founding of Soviet Defence Forces and of Civil War.

(a) Various designs with arms and inscr. "1918 XXX 1948".

1345. 379. 30 k. brown .. .. 1·25 35
1346. – 30 k. grey .. .. 1·25 35
1347. – 30 k. blue .. .. 1·60 35
1348. 380. 60 k. brown .. .. 2·40 55

DESIGNS—VERT.: No. 1346, Navy. HORIZ. No. 1347, Air Force.

(b) Portraits of Civil War Heroes as Nos. 1079/81.

1349 299 60 k. brown (Chapaev) 1·25 1·00
1350 – 60 k. green (Shchors) 1·25 1·00
1351 – 60 k. blue (Lazo) .. 1·25 1·00

1948. Centenary of Publication of "Communist Manifesto".

1352. 381. 30 k. black 40 25
1353. 50 k. brown 60 25

382. Miner.

384b. Arms of U.S.S.R.

384d. Spassky Tower, Kremlin.

1948.

1354 382 5 k. black .. 1·50 80
1355 – 10 k. vio (Sailor) 1·50 80
1356 – 15 k. bl (Airman) 5·00 1·60
1361i 382 15 k. black .. 20 10
1357 – 20 k. brown (Farm Girl) .. 5·00 1·60
1361j – 20 k. green (Farm Girl) .. .. 1·25 10
1361ka – 25 k. bl (Airman) 50 10
1358 384b 30 k. brown .. 6·50 2·75
1361l – 30 k. brown (Scientist) .. 60 10
1361m 384b 40 k. red .. 1·50 10
1359 – 45 k. violet (Scientist) .. 10·00 4·00
1361f 384d 50 k. blue .. 8·00 6·50
1361 – 60 k. grn (Soldier) 20·00 10·00

385. Parade of Workers.

1948. May Day.

1362. 385. 30 k. red 80 25
1363. 60 k. blue .. .. 1·75 70

386. Belinsky (after K. Gorbunov).

1948. Death Cent of Vissarion Grigorievich Belinsky (literary critic and journalist).

1364. 386. 30 k. brown .. .. 1·00 15
1365. 50 k. green .. .. 2·50 90
1366. 60 k. violet .. .. 2·50 80

387. A. N. Ostrovsky. 388.

1948. 125th Birth Anniv. of Ostrovsky (dramatist).

1367. 387. 30 k. green 75 25
1368. 388. 60 k. brown .. .. 1·00 55
1369. 1 r. violet .. .. 2·25 90

389. I. I. Shishkin (after I. Kramskoi).

391. Factories.

390. "Rye Field".

1948. 50th Death Anniv. of Shishkin (landscape painter).

1370. 389. 30 k. brown & green 1·25 20
1371. 390. 50 k. yell., red & blue 2·00 35
1372. – 60 k. multicoloured .. 3·00 60
1373. 389. 1 r. blue and brown .. 4·50 1·50

DESIGN—HORIZ. 60 k. "Morning in the Forest".

1948. Leningrad Workers' Four Year Plan.

1374. 391. 15 k. brown and red 2·50 1·00
1375. – 30 k. black and red .. 1·25 80
1376. 391. 60 k. brown and red 6·50 1·75

DESIGN—HORIZ. (40×22 mm.): 30 k. Proclamation to Leningrad workers.

392. Arms and People of the U.S.S.R.

(394.)

393. Caterpillar drawing Seed Drills.

1948. 25th Anniv. of U.S.S.R.

1377. 392. 30 k. black and red .. 1·10 45
1378. 60 k. olive and red .. 2·25 1·25

1948. Five Year Agricultural Plan.

1379. 393. 30 k. red 55 20
1380. 30 k. green 65 20
1381. – 45 k. brown .. .. 1·00 60
1382. 393. 50 k. black .. .. 2·75 1·50
1383. – 60 k. green .. .. 1·25 35
1384. – 60 k. green .. .. 1·25 35
1385. – 1 r. violet .. .. 4·75 2·25

DEIGNS: 30 k. (No. 1380), 1 r. Harvesting sugar beet. 45 k., 60 k. (No. 1383), Gathering cotton. 60 k. (No. 1384), Harvesting machine.

1948. Air Force Day. Optd. with T 394.

1386. 364. 30 k. violet .. .. 4·50 2·00
1387. 1 r. blue .. .. 4·50 2·00

395. Miners.

396. A. A. Zhdanov.

1948. Miners' Day.

1388. 395. 30 k. blue 70 15
1389. – 60 k. violet .. .. 1·75 25
1390. – 1 r. green .. .. 4·00 1·50

DESIGNS: 60 k. Inside a coal mine. 1 r. Miner's emblem.

1948. Death of A. A. Zhdanov (statesman).

1391. 396. 40 k. blue .. .. 3·50 1·00

397. Sailor.

398. Football.

1948. Navy Day.

1392. 397. 30 k. green .. .. 2·00 75
1393. 60 k. blue .. .. 6·00 1·50

1948. Sports.

1394 – 15 k. violet .. 1·25 15
1395 398 30 k. brown .. 2·00 15
1396 – 45 k. brown .. 2·00 35
1397a – 50 k. blue .. .. 3·50 35

DESIGNS—VERT. 15 k. Running. 50 k. Diving. HORIZ. 45 k. Power boat racing.

399. Tank and Drivers.

400. Horses and Groom.

1948. Tank Drivers' Day.

1398. 399. 30 k. black .. .. 2·50 1·25
1399. – 1 r. red .. .. 4·00 1·50

DESIGN: 1 r. Parade of tanks.

1948. Five Year Livestock Development Plan.

1400. 400. 30 k. black .. .. 2·25 70
1401. – 60 k. green .. .. 3·75 1·00
1402. 400. 1 r. brown .. .. 6·00 1·25

DESIGN: 60 k. Dairy farming.

401. Steam and Electric Locomotives.

402. Iron Pipe Manufacture.

1948. Five Year Transport Plan.

1403. 401. 30 k. brown .. .. 2·75 60
1404. 50 k. green .. .. 4·50 1·25
1405. – 60 k. blue .. .. 4·00 2·00
1406. – 1 r. violet .. .. 6·50 5·00

DESIGNS: 60 k. Road traffic. 1 r. Liner "Vyacheslav Molotov".

1948. Five Year Rolled-iron, Steel and Machine-building Plan.

1407. – 30 k. violet .. .. 1·75 90
1408. – 30 k. purple .. .. 1·75 90
1409. – 50 k. brown .. .. 2·50 1·40
1410. – 50 k. black .. .. 2·50 1·40
1411. – 60 k. brown .. .. 3·00 1·50
1412. 402. 60 k. red .. .. 3·00 3·00
1413. 1 r. blue .. .. 3·00 1·75

DESIGNS—HORIZ. Nos. 1407, 1410, Foundry. Nos. 1408/9, Pouring molten metal. No. 1411, Group of machines.

403. Abovyan.

404. Miner.

1948. Death Centenary of Khachatur Abovyan (writer).

1414. 403. 40 k. purple .. .. 2·00 1·50
1415. 50 k. green .. .. 6·00 3·00

1948. Five Year Coal-mining and Oil Extraction Plan.

1416. 404. 30 k. black .. .. 3·00 1·00
1417. 60 k. brown .. .. 8·00 2·00
1418. – 60 k. brown .. .. 11·00 4·00
1419. – 1 r. green .. .. 11·00 3·00

DESIGN: Nos. 1418/9, Oil wells and tanker train.

405. Farkhadsk Power Station.

406. Flying Model Aeroplanes.

1948. Five Year Electrification Plan.

1420. 405. 30 k. green .. .. 1·25 1·00
1421. – 60 k. red .. .. 3·00 1·75
1422. 405. 1 r. red .. .. 3·00 1·50

DESIGN: 60 k. Zuevsk Power Station.

1948. Government Care of School Children's Summer Vacation.

1423. 406. 30 k. green .. .. 3·25 95
1424. – 45 k. red .. .. 6·00 5·00
1425. – 45 k. violet .. .. 3·25 2·00
1426. – 60 k. blue .. .. 8·00 5·00
1427. – 1 r. blue .. .. 15·00 3·50

DESIGNS—VERT. No. 1424, Boy and girl saluting. 60 k. Boy trumpeter. HORIZ. No. 1425, Children marching. 1 r. Children round camp fire.

407. Children in School.

408. Flag of U.S.S.R.

1948. 30th Anniv of Lenin's Young Communist League.

1428. – 20 k. purple .. .. 2·75 70
1429. – 25 k. red .. .. 1·50 85
1430. – 40 k. brown and red .. 2·75 1·25
1431. 407. 50 k. green .. .. 3·75 1·75
1432. 408. 1 r. multicoloured .. 8·00 4·00
1433. – 2 r. violet .. .. 15·00 12·00

DESIGNS—HORIZ. 20 k. Youth parade. VERT. 25 k. Peasant girl. 40 k. Young people and flag. 2 r. Industrial worker.

409. Interior of Theatre.

410. Searchlights over Moscow.

1948. 50th Anniv. of Moscow Arts Theatre.

1434. 409. 50 k. blue .. .. 2·00 2·50
1435. – 1 r. purple .. .. 4·50 4·75

DESIGN: 1 r. Stanislavsky and Dantchenko.

1948. 31st Anniv. of October Revolution.

1436. 410. 40 k. red .. .. 1·25 1·50
1437. 1 r. green .. .. 4·00 4·25

411. Artillery Barrage.

412. Trade Union Building (venue).

1948. Artillery Day.
1438. **411.** 30 k. blue .. .. 2·25 2·75
1439. 1 r. red .. .. 3·50 3·50

1948. 16th World Chess Championship, Moscow.
1440 **412** 30 k. blue .. .. 4·00 1·00
1441 – 40 k. violet .. .. 9·00 55
1442 **412** 50 k. brown .. .. 9·00 1·75
DESIGN—VERT. 40 k. Players badge showing chessboard and rook.

413. Stasov and Building.

1948. Death Cent. of Stasov (architect).
1443. – 40 k. brown .. .. 1·00 1·25
1444. **413.** 1 r. black .. .. 3·00 4·75
DESIGN—VERT. 40 k. Portrait of Stasov.

414. Aeroplane and Flag.

415. Statue of Ya. M. Sverdlov.

1948. Air Force Day.
1445. **414.** 1 r. blue .. .. 6·50 1·00

1948. 225th Anniv. of Sverdlovsk City. Imperf. or perf.
1446. **415.** 30 k. blue 60 40
1447. – 40 k. purple .. .. 1·00 40
1448. **415.** 1 r. green .. .. 1·75 1·25
DESIGN: 40 k. View of Sverdlovsk.

416. Sukhumi

417. State Emblem.

1948. Views of Crimea and Caucasus.
1449. **416.** 40 k. green 70 30
1450. – 40 k. violet 70 30
1451. – 40 k. mauve 70 30
1452. – 40 k. brown 70 30
1453. – 40 k. purple 70 30
1454. – 40 k. green 70 30
1455. – 40 k. blue 70 30
1456. – 40 k. green 70 30
DESIGNS—VERT. No. 1450, Gardens, Sochi. No. 1451, Eagle-topped monument, Pyatigorsk. No. 1452, Cliffs, Crimea. HORIZ. No. 1453, Terraced gardens, Sochi. No. 1454, Roadside garden, Sochi. No. 1455, Colonnade, Kislovodsk. No. 1456, Sea and palms, Gagry.

1949. 30th Anniv. of Byelorussian Soviet Republic.
1457. **417.** 40 k. red .. .. 2·50 1·00
1458. 1 r. green .. .. 5·00 2·00

418. M. V. Lomonosov.

419. Lenin Mausoleum.

1949. Establishment of Lomonosov Museum of Academy of Science.
1459. **418.** 40 k. brown .. .. 1·50 75
1460. 50 k. green .. .. 2·00 1·00
1461. – 1 r. blue .. .. 4·50 2·00
DESIGN—HORIZ. 1 r. Museum.

1949. 25th Death Anniv of Lenin.
1462 **419** 40 k. brown and green 3·50 4·00
1463 1 r. brown & dp brn 4·50 7·00

420. Dezhnev's ship.

1949. Tercentenary of Dezhnev's Exploration of Bering Strait.
1464. – 40 k. olive .. .. 10·00 5·00
1465. **420.** 1 r. black .. .. 20·00 7·00
DESIGN: 40 k. Cape Dezhnev.

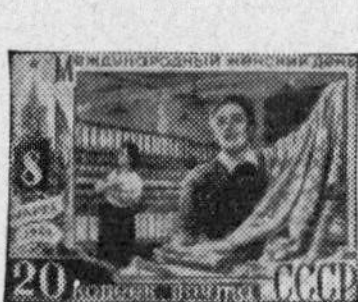

421. "Women in Industry".

422. Admiral S. O. Makarov.

1949. Int. Women's Day.
1466. **421.** 20 k. violet 30 10
1467. – 25 k. blue 35 10
1468. – 40 k. red 50 10
1469. – 50 k. grey 80 30
1470. – 50 k. brown 80 30
1471. – 1 r. green .. .. 2·50 40
1472. – 2 r. red .. .. 3·00 65
DESIGNS—HORIZ. 25 k. Kindergarten. 50 k. grey, Woman teacher. 50 k. brown, Women in field. 1 r. Women sports champions. VERT. 40 k., 2 r. Woman broadcasting.

1949. Birth Cent. of Admiral S. O. Makarov (naval scientist).
1473. **422.** 40 k. blue .. .. 1·75 70
1474. 1 r. red .. .. 4·25 2·25

425. Soldier.

424. Kirov Military Medical Academy.

1949. 31st Anniv. of Soviet Army.
1475. **423.** 40 k. red .. .. 7·50 7·50

1949. 150th Anniv. of Kirov Military Medical Academy.
1476 **424** 40 k. red .. .. 1·25 1·10
1477 – 50 k. blue .. .. 1·75 1·60
1478 **424** 1 r. green .. .. 3·00 3·00
DESIGN: 50 k. Professors Botkin, Pirogov and Sechenov and Kirov Academy.

425. V. R. Williams.

425a. Three Russians with Flag.

1949. Agricultural Reform.
1479. **425.** 25 k. green .. .. 3·00 2·00
1480. 50 k. brown .. .. 4·50 4·00

1949. Labour Day.
1481. **425a.** 40 k. red .. .. 1·00 80
1482. 1 r. green .. .. 2·75 1·60

426. Newspapers and Books.

427. A. S. Popov and Radio Equipment.

1949. Press Day. Inscr. "5 MAR 1949".
1483. **426.** 40 k. red .. .. 2·50 3·00
1484. – 1 r. violet .. .. 2·50 6·00
DESIGN: 1 r. Man and boy reading newspaper.

1949. Radio Day.
1485. **427.** 40 k. violet .. .. 1·60 1·10
1486. – 50 k. brown .. .. 2·50 2·50
1487. **427.** 1 r. green .. .. 5·00 4·00
DESIGN—HORIZ. 50 k. Popov demonstrating receiver to Admiral Makarov.

428. A. S. Pushkin.

429. "Pushkin reading Poems to Southern Society" (D. Kardovsky)

1949. 150th Birth Anniv. of Pushkin (poet).
1488. **428.** 25 k. black and grey 1·00 50
1489. – 40 k. black and brown 1·40 1·50
1490. **429.** 40 k. purple and red 1·40 1·50
1491. – 1 r. grey and brown .. 3·00 5·00
1492. **429.** 2 r. blue and brown .. 6·50 7·00
DESIGNS—VERT. No. 1489, Pushkin portrait after Kiprensky. HORIZ. 1 r. Pushkin museum, Boldino.

430. Tug "Boksirni Typlokod".

431. I. V. Michurin.

1949. Cent of Krasnoe Sormovo Machine-building and Ship-building Plant, Gorky.
1493. **430.** 40 k. blue .. .. 6·00 3·50
1494. – 1 r. brown .. .. 8·50 8·50
DESIGN: 1 r. Tanker "Bolshaya Volga".

1949. Agricultural Reform.
1495. **431.** 40 k. blue .. .. 1·50 75
1496. 1 r. green .. .. 4·00 2·25

432. Yachting. 433. V. V. Dokuchaev.

1949. National Sports.
1497. **432.** 20 k. blue .. .. 1·25 10
1498. – 25 k. green .. .. 1·25 15
1499. – 30 k. violet .. .. 1·50 15
1500. – 40 k. brown .. .. 2·00 25
1501. – 40 k. green .. .. 2·00 25
1502. – 50 k. grey .. .. 1·75 80
1503. – 1 r. red .. .. 4·50 1·50
1504. – 2 r. black .. .. 8·00 1·50
DESIGNS: 25 k. Canoeing. 30 k. Swimming. 40 k. (No. 1500), Cycling. 40 k. (No. 1501), Football. 50 k. Mountaineering. 1 r. Parachuting. 2 r. High jumping.

1949. Soil Research.
1505. **433.** 40 k. brown .. .. 1·25 20
1506. 1 r. green .. .. 2·00 50

434. V. I. Bazhenov.

435. A. N. Radischev.

1949. 150th Death Anniv. of V. I. Bazhenov (architect).
1507. **434.** 40 k. violet .. .. 1·00 30
1508. 1 r. brown .. .. 3·00 70

1949. Birth Bicent. of A. N. Radischev (writer).
1509. **435.** 40 k. green .. .. 1·50 1·10
1510. 1 r. black .. .. 4·50 2·00

436. Green Cape Sanatorium, Makhindzhauri.

437. I. P. Pavlov.

1949. State Sanatoria. Designs showing various buildings.
1511 **436** 40 k. green 50 15
1512 – 40 k. green 50 15
1513 – 40 k. blue 50 15
1514 – 40 k. violet 50 15
1515 – 40 k. red 50 15
1516 – 40 k. orange 50 15
1517 – 40 k. brown 50 15
1518 – 40 k. brown 50 15
1519 – 40 k. black 50 15
1520 – 40 k. black 50 15
DESIGNS—HORIZ. No. 1512, VTsSPS No. 41, Zheleznovodsk. No. 1513, Energetics, Hosta. No. 1514, VTs SPS No. 3, Kislovodsk. No. 1515, VTs SPS No. 3, Hosta. No. 1516, State Theatre, Sochi. No. 1517, Clinical, Tskhaltubo. No. 1518, Frunze, Sochi. No. 1519, VTs SPS No. 1, Kislovodsk. No. 1520, Communication, Hosta.

1949. Birth Cent of I. P. Pavlov (scientist).
1521. **437.** 40 k. brown .. .. 1·00 20
1522. 1 r. black .. .. 2·25 60

438. Globe and Letters.

1949. 75th Anniv. of U.P.U. Perf. or Imperf.
1523. **438.** 40 k. blue and brown 2·25 25
1524. 50 k. violet and blue 2·25 75

439. Tree-planting Machines.

440. Map of S.W. Russia.

1949. Forestry and Field Conservancy.
1525 **439** 25 k. green 75 25
1526 – 40 k. violet 90 25
1527 **440** 40 k. green and black 90 55
1528 – 50 k. blue .. .. 1·40 1·00
1529 **439** 1 r. black .. .. 4·50 2·00
1530 – 2 r. brown .. .. 6·50 4·50
DESIGNS ($33 \times 22\frac{1}{2}$ mm.): 40 k. violet, Harvesters. 50 k. River scene. ($33 \times 19\frac{1}{2}$ mm.): 2 r. Old man and children.

1949. 30th Death Anniv of V. I. Chapaev (military strategist).
1531 **299** 40 k. orange .. 10·00 8·50

442. I. S. Nikitin.

443. Malyi Theatre, Moscow.

1949. 125th Birth Anniv. of Nikitin (poet).
1532. **442.** 40 k. brown 80 20
1533. 1 r. blue .. .. 1·75 60

1949. 125th Anniv of Malyi Theatre, Moscow.
1534 **443** 40 k. green .. .. 1·00 20
1535 50 k. orange .. .. 1·50 25
1536 – 1 r. brown .. .. 3·00 1·25
DESIGN: 1 r. Five portraits and theatre.

444. Crowd with Banner.

1949. 32nd Anniv. of October Revolution.
1537. **444.** 40 k. red .. .. 1·75 1·60
1538. 1 r. green .. .. 4·50 4·00

445. Sheep and Cows.

446. Lenin Hydro-electric Station, Caucasus.

447. Aeroplanes and Map.

1949. Cattle-breeding Collective Farm.
1539. 445. 40 k. brown .. .. 1·50 20
1540. 1 r. violet .. .. 3·00 80

1949. Air. Aerial views and map.
1541. 446. 50 k. brown on yellow 1·90 1·00
1542. – 60 k. brown on buff .. 2·00 80
1543. – 1 r. orange on yellow 6·00 1·90
1544. – 1 r. brown on buff .. 5·50 1·90
1545. – 1 r. blue on buff .. 5·50 1·90
1546. 447. 1 r. blue, red and grey 10·00 3·50
1547. – 2 r. red on blue .. 12·00 5·00
1548. – 3 r. green on blue .. 23·00 8·00
DESIGNS (Lisunov Li-2 airplane over)—HORIZ. No. 1542, Farm. 1543, Sochi. VERT. 1544, Leningrad. 1545, Aleppo. 1547, Moscow. 1548, Arctic.

448. Ski Jumping.

449. Diesel Train.

1949. National Sports.
1549. 448. 20 k. green 80 15
1550. – 40 k. orange .. 1·40 20
1551. – 50 k. blue .. .. 2·50 45
1552. – 1 r. red .. .. 4·50 45
1553. – 2 r. violet .. .. 8·50 1·00
DESIGNS: 40 k. Girl gymnast. 50 k. Ice hockey. 1 r. Weightlifting. 2 r. Shooting wolves.

1949. Modern Railway Development.
1554. – 25 k. red .. .. 2·00 35
1555. 449. 40 k. violet .. 2·50 45
1556. – 50 k. brown .. .. 3·50 60
1557. 449. 1 r. green .. .. 9·00 2·75
DESIGNS: 25 k. Electric tram. 50 k. Steam train.

450. Arms of U.S.S.R.

451. Government Buildings, Dushanbe.

1949. Constitution Day.
1558. 450. 40 k. red .. .. 6·00 3·00

1949. 20th Anniv. of Republic of Tadzhikstan.
1559. – 20 k. blue 75 10
1560. – 25 k. green 70 10
1561. 451. 40 k. red 80 20
1562. – 50 k. violet .. .. 1·25 20
1563. 451. 1 r. black .. .. 2·00 75
DESIGNS: 20 k. Textile mills. 25 k. Irrigation canal. 50 k. Medical University.

452. People with Flag.

453. Worker and Globe.

1949. 10th Anniv of Incorporation of West Ukraine and West Byelorussia in U.S.S.R.
1564. 452. 40 k. red .. .. 6·50 8·00
1565. – 40 k. orange .. .. 6·50 8·00
DESIGN—VERT. No. 1565, Ukrainians and flag.

1949. Peace Propaganda.
1566. 453. 40 k. red 80 20
1567. 50 k. blue .. .. 1·25 30

454. Government Buildings, Tashkent.

1950. 25th Anniv of Uzbek S.S.R.
1568 – 20 k. blue 35 20
1569 – 25 k. black 35 20
1570 454 40 k. red 65 20
1571 – 40 k. violet 90 30
1572 – 1 r. green .. .. 2·25 70
1573 – 2 r. brown .. .. 4·00 1·40
DESIGNS: 20 k. Teachers' College. 25 k. Opera and Ballet House, Tashkent. 40 k. (violet) Navotz Street, Tashkent. 1 r. Map of Fergana Canal. 2 r. Lock, Fergana Canal.

455. Dam.

456. Statue of Lenin.

1950. 25th Anniv of Turkmen S.S.R.
1574 – 25 k. black .. .. 2·00 2·50
1575 455 40 k. brown .. .. 1·75 1·25
1576 – 50 k. green .. .. 3·50 3·50
1577 455 1 r. violet .. .. 5·50 5·50
DESIGNS: 25 k. Textile factory, Ashkhabad. 50 k. Carpet-making.

1950. 26th Death Anniv. of Lenin.
1578. 456. 40 k. brown and grey 65 15
1579. – 50 k. red, brn. & grn. 1·10 35
1580. – 1 r. buff, green & brn. 2·25 75
DESIGNS—HORIZ. 50 k. Lenin's Office, Kremlin. 1 r. Lenin Museum.

457. Film Show.

458. Voter.

1950. 30th Anniv. of Soviet Film Industry.
1581. 457. 25 k. brown .. .. 11·00 7·50

1950. Supreme Soviet Elections. Inscr. "12 МАРТА 1950".
1582. 458. 40 k. green on yellow 2·50 2·50
1583. – 1 r. red .. .. 3·25 3·75
DESIGN: 1 r. Kremlin and flags.

459. Statue of Morozov.

460. Lenin Central Museum.

1950. Unveiling of Monument to Pavlik Morozov (model Soviet youth).
1584. 459. 40 k. black and red .. 3·50 1·75
1585. 1 r. green and red .. 6·00 3·50

1950. Moscow Museums. Buildings inscr. "МОСКВА 1949".
1586. 460. 40 k. olive .. .. 1·25 25
1587. – 40 k. red .. .. 1·25 25
1588. – 40 k. turquoise .. 1·25 25
1589. – 40 k. brown .. .. 1·25 25
1590. – 40 k. mauve .. .. 1·25 25
1591. – 40 k. blue (no tree) .. 1·25 25
1592. – 40 k. brown .. .. 1·25 25
1593. – 40 k. blue (with tree) 1·25 25
1594. – 40 k. red .. .. 1·25 25
DESIGNS—HORIZ. ($33\frac{1}{2} \times 23\frac{1}{2}$ mm). No. 1587, Revolution Museum. No. 1588, Tretyakov Gallery. No. 1589, Timiryazev Biological Museum. No. 1591, Polytechnic Museum. No. 1593, Oriental Museum. ($39\frac{1}{2} \times 26\frac{1}{2}$ mm). No. 1590, Pushkin Pictorial Arts Museum. VERT. ($22\frac{1}{2} \times 33\frac{1}{2}$ mm). No. 1592, Historical Museum. No. 1594, Zoological Museum.

461. Hemispheres and Wireless Mast.

1950 Int. Congress of P.T.T. and Radio Trade Unions, London.
1595. 461. 40 k. green on blue .. 2·50 1·75
1596. 50 k. blue on blue .. 3·50 4·00

462. Three Workers.

463. A. S. Shcherbakov.

1950. Labour Day.
1597. 462. 40 k. red and black .. 2·25 1·75
1598. – 1 r. red and black .. 3·00 3·50
DESIGN—HORIZ. 1 r. Four Russians and banner.

1950. 5th Death Anniv. of Shcherbakov (statesman).
1599. 463. 40 k. black 80 65
1600. 1 r. green on pink .. 1·75 1·25

464. Marshal Suvorov.

465. Statue.

1950. 150th Death Anniv of Suvorov.
1601. 464. 40 k. blue on pink .. 2·25 75
1602. – 50 k. brown on pink .. 3·25 2·00
1603. – 60 k. black on blue .. 3·25 2·00
1604. 464. 1 r. brown on yellow 5·50 2·75
1605. – 2 r. green .. .. 8·00 6·00
DESIGNS—VERT. 50 k. Battle ($32\frac{1}{2} \times 47$ mm). 60 k. Order of Suvorov and military parade ($24\frac{1}{2} \times 39\frac{1}{2}$ mm). 2 r. Suvorov in cloak ($19\frac{1}{2} \times 33\frac{1}{2}$ mm).

1950. 5th Anniv. of Victory over Germany.
1606. 465. 40 k. red and brown .. 3·00 2·00
1607. – 1 r. red .. .. 3·50 2·00
DESIGN ($22\frac{1}{2} \times 33$ mm.): 1 r. Order of Stalin.

466. Sowing on Collective Farm.

1950. Agricultural Workers.
1608. – 40 k. green on blue .. 2·25 1·00
1609. 466. 40 k. brown on buff .. 2·25 1·00
1610. 1 r. blue on yellow .. 3·00 2·50
DESIGN: No. 1608, Collective farmers, studying.

467. G. M. Dimitrov.

468. Baku Opera House.

1950. 1st Death Anniv of Bulgarian Premier, Dimitrov.
1611. 467. 40 k. black on yellow 1·25 75
1612. 1 r. black on red .. 3·25 2·50

1950. 30th Anniv. of Azerbaijan S.S.R.
1613. 468. 25 k. green on yellow 1·40 1·40
1614. – 40 k. brown on red .. 2·00 1·10
1615. – 1 r. black on buff .. 4·00 4·50
DESIGNS: 40 k. Science Academy. 1 r. Stalin Avenue, Baku.

469. Lenin Street, Stalingrad.

470. Kaluzhskaya Station.

1950. Stalingrad Reconstruction.
1616. – 20 k. blue 80 65
1617. 469. 40 k. green .. .. 1·25 50
1618. – 50 k. orange .. .. 2·50 2·50
1619. – 1 r. black .. .. 3·50 3·00
DESIGNS—VERT. 20 k. Pobeda Cinema. HORIZ. 50 k. Gorky Theatre. 1 r. Pavlov House and Tank Memorial.

1950. Underground Railway Stations.
1620. 470. 40 k. green on buff .. 1·00 35
1621. A. 40 k. red .. .. 1·00 35
1622. B. 40 k. blue on buff .. 1·00 35
1623. C. 1 r. brown on yellow 3·00 1·10
1624. D. 1 r. violet on blue .. 3·00 1·10
1625. A. 1 r. green on yellow .. 3·00 1·10
1626. E. 1 r. black on buff .. 3·00 1·10
DESIGNS—HORIZ. ($34 \times 22\frac{1}{2}$ mm.): A, Culture Park. B, Taganskaya. C, Kurskaya. D, Paveletskaya. ($34 \times 18\frac{1}{2}$ mm.): E, Taganskaya.

471. National Flags and Civilians.

1950. Unconquerable Democracy. Flags in red, blue and yellow.
1627. 471. 40 k. black 75 15
1628. 50 k. brown .. .. 1·00 25
1629. 1 r. green .. .. 1·90 30

472. Trade Union Building.

473. Marite Melnikaite.

1950. 10th Anniv. of Latvian S.S.R.
1630. 472. 25 k. brown 70 40
1631. – 40 k. red 85 35
1632. – 50 k. green .. .. 1·25 70
1633. – 60 k. blue .. .. 1·25 80
1634. – 1 r. violet .. .. 3·00 2·75
1635. – 2 r. brown .. .. 4·00 2·75
DESIGNS—VERT. 40 k. Cabinet Council Offices. 50 k. Monument to Jan Rainis (poet). 2 r. Academy of Sciences. HORIZ. 60 k. Theatre, Riga. 1 r. State University, Riga.

1950. 10th Anniv. of Lithuanian S.S.R.
1636. – 25 k. blue 75 60
1637. 473. 40 k. brown .. .. 1·50 75
1638. – 1 r. red .. .. 5·00 3·25
DESIGNS—HORIZ. 25 k. Academy of Sciences. 1 r. Cabinet Council Offices.

474. Stalingrad Square, Tallinn.

475. Signing Peace Appeal.

1950. 10th Anniv. of Estonian S.S.R.
1639. 474. 25 k. green 85 45
1640. – 40 k. red 95 55
1641. – 50 k. blue on yellow .. 1·50 1·50
1642. – 1 r. brown on blue .. 3·00 3·50
DESIGNS—HORIZ. 40 k. Government building. 50 k. Opera and Ballet Theatre, Tallin. VERT. 1 r. Victor Kingisepp (revolutionary).

1950. Peace Conf.
1643. 475. 40 k. red on buff .. 1·25 45
1644. – 40 k. black .. .. 1·25 80
1645. – 50 k. red .. .. 2·00 1·60
1646. 475. 1 r. brown on buff .. 3·25 3·25
DESIGNS—VERT. 40 k. black, Children and teacher. 50 k. Young people with banner.

476. Bellingshausan, Lazarev and Globe.

477. M. V. Frunze.

1950. 130th Anniv. of 1st Antarctic Expedition.
1647. 476. 40 k. red on blue .. 17·00 7·00
1648. – 1 r. violet on blue .. 32·00 10·00
DESIGN—VERT. 1 r. "Mirnyi" and "Vostok" (ships) and map of Antarctica.

1950. 25th Death Anniv. of Frunze (military strategist).
1649. 477. 40 k. blue on buff .. 2·50 1·60
1650. 1 r. brown on blue .. 5·50 4·00

478. M. I. Kalinin.

479. Picking Grapes.

1950. 75th Birth Anniv. of Kalinin (statesman).
1651. **478.** 40 k. green 75 35
1652. 1 r. brown .. .. 1·50 90
1653. 5 r. violet .. .. 6·50 8·00

1950. 30th Anniv. of Armenian S.S.R.
1654. **479.** 20 k. blue on buff .. 1·00 70
1655. – 40 k. orange on blue .. 1·75 85
1656. – 1 r. black on yellow .. 3·25 3·25
DESIGNS—HORIZ. (33 × 16 mm.): 40 k. Government Offices. VERT ($21\frac{1}{2}$ × 33 mm.): 1 r. G.M. Sundukian (dramatist).

480. Kotelnicheskaya Quay.

481. Spassky Tower, Kremlin.

1950. Moscow Building Projects.
1657. **480.** 1 r. brown on buff .. 22·00 15·00
1658. – 1 r. black on buff .. 22·00 15·00
1659. – 1 r. brown on blue .. 22·00 15·00
1660. – 1 r. green on yellow .. 22·00 15·00
1661. – 1 r. blue on buff .. 22·00 15·00
1662. – 1 r. black .. .. 22·00 15·00
1663. – 1 r. orange .. .. 22·00 15·00
1664. – 1 r. green on blue .. 22·00 15·00
DESIGNS—HORIZ. No. 1659, Vosstaniya Square. No. 1660, Moscow University. No. 1662, Dorogomilovskaya Quay. No. 1664, Smolenskaya Sq. VERT. No. 1658, Krasnye Vorota. No. 1661, Komsomolskaya Sq. No. 1663, Zariadie.

1950. 33rd Anniv. of October Revolution.
1665. **481.** 1 r. red, yell. & green 10·00 8·50

482. "Golden Autumn".

PORTRAIT: 50 k. Levitan seated.

1950. 50th Death Anniv. of Levitan (painter).
1666. **482.** 40 k. multicoloured 3·25 65
1667. – 50 k. brown .. .. 3·75 65

483. Aivazovsky (after A. Tyranov).

484. Newspapers "Iskra" and "Pravda".

1950. 50th Death Anniv. of Aivazovsky (painter). Multicoloured centres.
1668. – 40 k. brown .. .. 2·75 30
1669. – 50 k. brown .. .. 3·50 70
1670. **483.** 1 r. blue .. .. 5·00 1·00
PAINTINGS—HORIZ. 40 k. "Black Sea". 50 k. "Ninth Wave".

1950. 50th Anniv. of Newspaper "Iskra".
1671. – 40 k. red and black .. 7·00 5·50
1672. **484.** 1 r. red and black .. 9·00 8·00
DESIGN: 40 k. Newspapers and banners.

485. Government Offices.

DESIGN: 1 r. Opera House, Alma-Ata.

1950. 30th Anniv. of Kazakh S.S.R.
1673. **485.** 40 k. black on blue .. 2·00 1·50
1674. – 1 r. brown on yellow 5·50 2·75

486. Decembrists and Senate Square, St. Petersburg.

1950. 125th Anniv of Decembrist Rising.
1675 **486** 1 r. brown on yellow 5·50 4·00

487. Govt. Offices, Tirana.

488. Greeting Soviet Troops.

1951. Friendship with Albania.
1676. **487.** 40 k. green on blue .. 11·00 9·00

1951. Friendship with Bulgaria.
1677. **488.** 25 k. black on blue .. 2·25 1·75
1678. – 40 k. orange on pink 4·00 2·50
1679. – 60 k. brown on pink .. 5·00 3·50
DESIGNS: 40 k. Lenin Square, Sofia. 60 k. Monument to Soviet fighters, Kolarovgrad.

489. Lenin at Razliv.

1951. 27th Death Anniv. of Lenin. Multicoloured centres.
1680. **489.** 40 k. green .. .. 2·00 40
1681. – 1 r. blue .. .. 3·50 85
DESIGN: 1 r. Lenin talking to young Communists.

490. Horses.
490a. Gathering Lemons.

1951. 25th Anniv. of Kirghiz S.S.R.
1682. **490.** 25 k. brown on blue .. 4·50 3·75
1683. – 40 k. green on blue .. 6·00 5·50
DESIGN ($33 \times 22\frac{1}{2}$ mm.): 40 k. Government Offices, Frunze.

1951. 30th Anniv. of Georgia S.S.R.
1683a. – 20 k. grn. on yellow 1·50 1·00
1683b. **490a.** 25 k. orange & pur. 2·00 1·50
1683c. – 40 k. brn. on blue 3·50 1·50
1683d. – 1 r. green & brown 6·00 4·00
DESIGNS—VERT. 20 k. Theatre, Tiflis. HORIZ. 40 k. Main thoroughfare, Tiflis. 1 r. Plucking tea.

491. University, Ulan-Bator.

1951. Friendship with Mongolia.
1684. **491.** 25 k. violet on pink .. 1·40 1·00
1685. – 40 k. orange on yellow 2·25 4·00
1686. – 1 r. multicoloured .. 6·00 4·00
DESIGNS—HORIZ. ($37\frac{1}{2}$ × 25 mm): 40 k. State Theatre, Ulan-Bator. VERT. (22 × 33 mm.): 1 r. State Emblem and Mongolian Flag.

492. D. A. Furmanov.
493. Soviet Soldiers Memorial, Berlin.

1951. 25th Death Anniv. of D. A. Furmanov (writer).
1687. **492.** 40 k. brown on blue .. 1·25 85
1688. – 1 r. black on pink .. 3·00 2·50
DESIGN—HORIZ. 1 r. Furmanov writing.

1951. Stockholm Peace Appeal.
1689. **493.** 40 k. green and red .. 3·50 2·50
1690. 1 r. black and red .. 6·50 5·00

494. Factories.

1951. 150th Anniv of Kirov Machine-building Factory, Leningrad.
1691 **494** 40 k. brown on yellow 4·00 2·75

495. Bolshoi State Theatre.

1951. 175th Anniv. of State Theatre.
1692. **495** 40 k. multicoloured .. 5·00 45
1693. – 1 r. multicoloured .. 6·50 1·00
DESIGN: 1 r. Medallion portraits of Glinka, Tchaikovsky, Moussorgsky, Rimsky-Korsakov, Borodin and theatre.

496. National Museum, Budapest.

497. Harvesting.

1951. Hungarian Peoples' Republic. Buildings in Budapest.
1694. – 25 k. green 80 75
1695. – 40 k. blue 90 75
1696. **496.** 60 k. black .. .. 1·25 90
1697. – 1 r. black on pink .. 2·75 2·50
DESIGNS—HORIZ. 25 k. Liberty Bridge. 40 k. Parliament bldgs. VERT. Liberation Monument.

1951. Agricultural scenes.
1698. **497.** 25 k. green 60 40
1699. – 40 k. green on blue 90 40
1700. – 1 r. brown on yellow 2·00 1·25
1701. – 2 r. green on pink .. 3·25 3·25
DESIGNS: 40 k. Apiary. 1 r. Gathering citrus fruit. 2 r. Harvesting cotton.

498. M. I. Kalinin.

499. F. E. Dzerzhinsky.

1951. 5th Death Anniv. of Pres. Kalinin.
1702. – 20 k. sepia and brown 55 20
1703. **498.** 40 k. brown and green 1·00 35
1704. – 1 r. black and blue .. 2·00 75
DESIGNS—HORIZ. 20 k. Kalinin Museum. VERT. 1 r. Kalinin Statue.

1951. 25th Death Anniv. of Dzerzhinsky (founder of Cheka).
1705. **499.** 40 k. red .. .. 1·75 40
1706. – 1 r. black (portrait in uniform) .. .. 3·00 1·10

500. P. K. Kozlov.

501. Kalinnikov.

1951. Russian Scientists.
1707. **500.** 40 k. orange .. .. 1·25 25
1708. – 40 k. orange on pink 1·25 25
1709. – 40 k. orange on blue 4·50 1·50
1710. – 40 k. brown .. .. 1·25 25
1711. – 40 k. brown on pink (facing left) .. 1·25 25
1712. – 40 k. brown on pink (facing right) .. 1·25 25
1713. – 40 k. grey .. .. 1·25 25
1714. – 40 k. grey on pink .. 1·25 25
1715. – 40 k. grey on blue .. 4·50 1·50
1716. – 40 k. green .. .. 1·25 25
1717. – 40 k. green on pink .. 1·25 25
1718. – 40 k. blue .. .. 1·25 25
1719. – 40 k. deep blue on pink 1·25 25
1720. – 40 k. blue on blue .. 1·25 25
1721. – 40 k. violet .. .. 1·25 25
1722. – 40 k. violet on pink 1·25 25
PORTRAITS: No. 1708, N. N. Miklukho-Makai. No. 1709, A. M. Butlerov. No. 1710, N. I. Lobachevsky. No. 1711, K. A. Timiryazev. No. 1712, N. S. Kurnakov. No. 1713, P. N. Yablochkov. No. 1714, A. N. Severtsov. No. 1715, K. E. Tsiolkovsky. No. 1716, A. N. Lodygin. No. 1717, A. G. Stoletov. No. 1718, P. N. Lebedev. No. 1719, A. O. Kovalevsky. No. 1720, D. I. Mendeleev. No. 1721, S. P. Krasheninnikov. No. 1722, S. V. Kovalevskaya.

1951. Russian Composers.
1723. **501.** 40 k. grey on pink .. 11·00 5·00
1724. – 40 k. brown on pink .. 11·00 5·00
PORTRAIT: No. 1724, Aliabiev and bar of music.

502. Aviation Society Badge.

503. V. M. Vasnetsov.

1951. Aviation Development.
1725. **502.** 40 k. multicoloured .. 1·00 15
1726. – 60 k. multicoloured .. 1·50 20
1727. – 1 r. multicoloured .. 2·50 50
1728. – 2 r. multicoloured .. 5·00 1·25
DESIGNS—VERT. 60 k. Boys and model gliders. 1 r. Parachutists descending. HORIZ. (45 × 25 mm) 2 r. Flight of Yakovlev Yak-18U trainers.

1951. 25th Death Anniv. of Vasnetsov (painter).
1729. **503.** 40 k. brown and blue 3·00 60
1730. – 1 r. grn. & yell. (frame) 4·00 90
DESIGN—(47 × 33 mm.): 1 r. Multicoloured painting—"Three Heroes".

504. Lenin, Stalin and Dnieperprostroi Dam.

DESIGN: 1 r. Lenin, Stalin and Spassky Tower.

1951. 34th Anniv. of October Revolution.
1731. **504.** 40 k. blue and red .. 4·00 2·00
1732. – 1 r. brown and red .. 6·00 3·75

505. Volga-Don Canal.

1951. Construction of Hydro-electric Power Stations.
1733. – 20 k. multicoloured .. 1·40 1·25
1734. **505.** 30 k. multicoloured .. 2·50 2·00
1735. – 40 k. multicoloured .. 3·50 2·00
1736. – 60 k. multicoloured .. 4·00 2·25
1737. – 1 r. multicoloured .. 7·50 4·50
DESIGNS—VERT. (32 × 47 mm.): 20 k. Khakhovsky power station. HORIZ. (47 × 32 mm.): 40 k. Stalingrad dam. 60 k. Excavator and map of Turkmen canal. 1 r. Kuibyshev power station.

506. Signing Peace Petition.

507. M. V. Ostrogradsky.

1951. 3rd U.S.S.R. Peace Conf.
1738. **506.** 40 k. red and brown .. 6·50 5·00

1951. 150th Birth Anniv. of Ostrogradsky (mathematician).
1739. **507.** 40 k. brown on pink .. 6·00 3·25

508. Zhizka Monument, Prague.

509. Volkhovsky Hydro-electric Station and Lenin Monument.

1951. Friendship with Czechoslovakia.
1740. **508.** 20 k. blue on pink .. 1·50 1·25
1741. – 25 k. red on lemon .. 4·00 4·00
1742. – 40 k. orange on orange 1·50 70
1743. – 60 k. grey .. .. 3·00 2·00
1744. – 1 r. grey .. .. 3·50 2·50
DESIGNS—VERT. 25 k. Soviet Army Monument, Ostrava. 40 k. J. Fucik. 60 k. Smetana Museum, Prague. HORIZ. 1 r. Soviet Soldiers Monument, Prague.

1951. 25th Anniv. of Lenin Volkhovsky Hydro-electric Station.
1745a **509** 40 k. yellow and blue 85 25
1746 1 r. yellow and violet 1·75 35

510. Lenin when a Student.

511. P. P. Semenov-Tian-Shansky.

1952. 28th Death Anniv. of Lenin. Multicoloured centres.
1747. **510.** 40 k. green .. .. 1·75 70
1748. – 60 k. blue .. .. 2·50 1·50
1749. – 1 r. brown .. .. 2·50 1·10
DESIGNS—HORIZ. 60 k. Lenin and children. 1 r. Lenin talking to peasants.

1952. 125th Birth Anniv. of Semenov-Tian-Shansky (scientist).
1750. **511.** 1 r. brown on blue .. 2·75 2·25

512. Skaters.

513. V. O. Kovalevsky.

1952. Winter Sports.
1751. **512.** 40 k. multicoloured .. 2·25 35
1752. – 60 k. mult. (skiers) .. 3·00 75

1952. Birth Cent. of Kovalevsky (scientist).
1753. **513.** 40 k. brown on yellow 3·25 1·75

514. Gogol and character from "Taras Bulba".

1952. Death Cent of Nikolai Gogol (writer).
1754 **514** 40 k. black on blue .. 1·25 20
1755 – 60 k. orange and black 1·75 30
1756 – 1 r. multicoloured .. 3·50 1·00
DESIGNS: 60 k. Gogol and Belinsky. 1 r. Gogol and Ukrainian peasants.

515. G. K. Ordzhonikidze.

516. Workers and Flag.

1952. 15th Death Anniv. of Ordzhonikidze (statesman).
1757. **515.** 40 k. green on pink .. 2·75 3·25
1758. 1 r. black on blue .. 4·00 3·25

1952. 15th Anniv. of Stalin Constitution.
1759. **516.** 40 k. red and black on cream .. .. 3·00 3·00
1760. – 40 k. red and green on green .. .. 3·00 3·00
1761. – 40 k. red and brown on blue .. .. 3·00 3·00
1762. – 40 k. red and black .. 3·00 3·00
DESIGNS—HORIZ. No. 1760, Recreation centre. No. 1761, Old people and banners. VERT. No. 1762, Schoolgirl and Spassky Tower Kremlin.

517. Novikov-Priboy and Battleship "Orel".

518. Victor Hugo.

1952. 75th Birth Anniv. of Novikov-Priboy (writer).
1763. **517.** 40 k. grey, yell. & grn. 3·25 80

1952. 150th Birth Anniv. of Victor Hugo (French writer).
1764. **518.** 40 k. blk., bl. & brn. 1·40 30

519. Salavat Yulaev.

520. G. Ya Sedov.

1952. Birth Bicent. of Yulaev (Bashkirian hero).
1765. **519.** 40 k. red on pink .. 1·40 30

1952. 75th Birth Anniv. of Sedov (Arctic explorer).
1766. **520.** 40 k. brn., bl. & grn. 9·00 4·50

521. Arms and Flag of Rumania.
522. V. A. Zhukovsky.
523. K. P. Bryullov.

1952. Friendship with Rumania.
1767. **521.** 40 k. multicoloured .. 1·75 75
1768. – 60 k. green on pink .. 2·50 1·75
1769. – 1 r. blue .. .. 4·00 3·00
DESIGNS—VERT. 60 k. Soviet Soldiers' Monument, Bucharest. HORIZ. 1 r. University Square, Bucharest.

1952. Death Cent. of Zhukovsky (poet).
1770. **522.** 40 k. black on blue .. 1·00 30

1952. Death Cent. of Bryullov (artist).
1771. **523.** 40 k. green on blue .. 1·00 30

524. N. P. Ogarev.

525. G. I. Uspensky.

1952. 75th Death Anniv. of Ogarev (revolutionary writer).
1772. **524.** 40 k. green 70 20

1952. 50th Death Anniv. of Uspensky (writer).
1773. **525.** 40 k. brown and blue 90 60

HAVE YOU READ THE NOTES AT THE BEGINNING OF THIS CATALOGUE?
These often provide answers to the enquiries we receive.

526. Admiral Nakhimov and "Rotislav".

527. Tartu University.

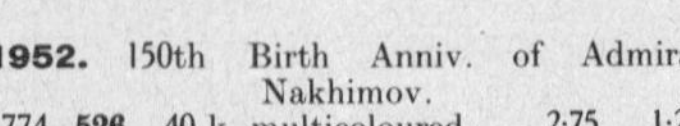

1952. 150th Birth Anniv. of Admiral Nakhimov.
1774. **526.** 40 k. multicoloured 2·75 1·25

1952. 150th Anniv. of Extension of Tartu University.
1775. **527.** 40 k. black on salmon 1·75 1·25

1952. War Orders and Medals (7th series). Frame as T 282 with various centres.
1776. F. 1 r. brown .. .. 10·00 7·50
1777. P. 2 r. red 60 40
1778. J. 3 r. violet 60 40
1779a. A. 5 r. lake 70 60
1780. E. 10 r. red 70 60

528. Kayum Nasyri.

529. A. N. Radishchev.

1952. 50th Death Anniv. of Nasyri (educationist).
1781. **528.** 40 k. brn. on yell. .. 1·75 1·25

1952. 150th Death Anniv. of Radishchev (writer).
1782. **529.** 40 k. black and red 1·25 45

530. Entrance to Volga-Don Canal.

531. P. A. Fedotov.

1952. 35th Anniv of Russian Revolution.
1783. **530.** 40 k. multicoloured .. 2·50 1·75
1784. – 1 r. yell., red & brn... 4·50 2·75
DESIGN: 1 r. Lenin, Stalin, Spassky Tower and flags.

1952. Death Cent. of Fedotov (painter).
1785. **531.** 40 k. brown and lake 1·60 45

532. V. D. Polenov.

534. Odoevsky (after N. Bestuzhev).

533. "Moscow Courtyard" (painting).

1952. 25th Death Anniv. of Polenov (painter).
1786. **532.** 40 k. lake and buff .. 1·50 30
1787. **533.** 1 r. blue and grey .. 3·50 1·00

1952. 150th Birth Anniv of A. I. Odoevsky (poet).
1788. **534.** 40 k. black and red .. 1·40 30

535. Mamin-Sibiryak.

536. V. M. Bekhterev.

1952. Birth Centenary of D. N. Mamin-Sibiryak (writer).
1789 **535** 40 k. green on yellow 1·10 20

1952. 25th Death Anniv. of Bekhterev (psychiatrist).
1790. **536.** 40 k. blk., grey & bl. 1·10 30

537. Komsomolskaya Koltsevaya Station.

1952. Underground stations. Multicoloured centres.
1791. – 40 k. violet .. .. 1·75 55
1792. – 40 k. blue .. .. 1·75 55
1793. – 40 k. grey .. .. 1·75 55
1794. **537.** 40 k. green .. .. 1·75 55
STATIONS: No. 1791, Byelorussia Koltsevaya. No. 1792, Botanical Gardens. No. 1793, Novoslobodskaya.

538. U.S.S.R. Arms and Flags.

539. Lenin and Flags.

1952. 30th Anniv. of U.S.S.R.
1795. **583.** 1 r. brn., red & grn. 3·50 2·25

1953. 29th Death Anniv. of Lenin.
1796. **539.** 40 l k. multicoloured 4·00 2·50

540. Peace Prize Medal.

541. V. V. Kuibyshev.

1953. Stalin Peace Prize.
1797. **540.** 40 k. yell., blue & brn. 3·75 2·50

1953. 65th Birth Anniv. of Kuibyshev (statesman).
1798. **541.** 40 k. black and lake 1·60 1·00

542. V. V. Mayakovsky.

543. N. G. Chernyshevsky.

1953. 60th Birth Anniv. of Mayakovsky (poet).
1799. **542.** 40 k. black and red 2·00 1·90

1953. 125th Birth Anniv. of Chernyshevsky (writer).
1800. **543.** 40 k. brown and buff 2·00 1·90

544. R. Volga Lighthouse.

1953. Views of Volga–Don Canal. Mult.

1801	40 k. Type **544**	1·50	60
1802	40 k. Lock No. 9	1·50	60
1803	40 k. Lock No. 13	1·50	60
1804	40 k. Lock No. 15	1·50	60
1805	40 k. Tsymlyanskaya hydro-electric station	1·50	60
1806	1 r. "Iosif Stalin" (river vessel)	2·50	1·40

545. V. G. Korolenko.

546. Tolstoi (after N. Ge).

1953. Birth Cent. of Korolenko (writer).
1807. **545.** 40 k. brown .. .. 1·10 20

1953. 125th Birth Anniv of Leo Tolstoi (writer).
1808 **546** 1 r. brown .. .. 4·50 2·00

547. Lomonosov University and Students.

548. Peoples of the U.S.S.R.

1953. 35th Anniv of "Komsomol" (Russian Youth Organization). Multicoloured.

1809	40 k. Type **547**	1·40	1·25
1810	1 r. Four medals and "Komsomol" badge	3·00	3·75

1953. 36th Anniv of Russian Revolution. Multicoloured.

1811	40 k. Type **548**	5·50	4·50
1812	60 k. Lenin and Stalin in Smolny Institute, 1917	8·50	7·50

549. Lenin Medallion.

550. Lenin Statue

551. Peter I Monument.

1953. 50th Anniv. of Communist Party.
1813. **549.** 40 k. multicoloured .. 2·75 1·90

1953. Views of Leningrad as T **550/1.**

1814.	**550.**	40 k. black on yellow	1·75	1·00
1815.		40 k. brown on pink ..	1·75	80
1816.	–	40 k. brown on yellow	90	35
1817.	–	40 k. black on buff ..	90	35
1818.	**551.**	1 r. brown on blue ..	2·75	1·10
1819.		1 r. violet on yellow ..	2·75	1·10
1820.	–	1 r. green on pink ..	2·75	1·10
1821.	–	1 r. brown on blue ..	2·75	1·10

DESIGNS—As Type **550**: Nos. 1816/7, Admiralty. As Type **551**: 1820/1, Smolny Institute.

552. Lenin and Book "What is to be Done?".

553. Pioneers and Moscow University Model.

1953. 50th Anniv. of 2nd Social Democratic Workers' Party Congress.
1822. **552.** 1 r. brown and red .. 5·50 3·75

1953. Peace Propaganda.
1823. **553.** 40 k. black, olive and grey .. .. 3·25 2·50

554. Griboedov (after I. Kramskoi).

555. Kremlin.

1954. 125th Death Anniv of A. S. Griboedov (author).

1824	**554**	40 k. purple on buff	1·25	30
1825a		1 r. black on green	1·60	60

1954. General Election.
1826. **555.** 40 k. grey and red .. 2·00 1·00

556. V. P. Chkalov.

557. Lenin in Smolny Institute.

1954. 50th Birthday of Chkalov (aviator).
1827. **556.** 1 r. brn., blue & grey 3·00 1·10

1954. 30th Death Anniv. of Lenin. Multicoloured.

1828.	40 k. Lenin (vert.)	1·75	75
1829.	40 k. Type **557**	1·75	75
1830.	40 k. Cottage Museum, Ulyunovsk	1·75	75
1831.	40 k. Lenin addressing revolutionaries	1·75	75
1832.	40 k. Lenin at Kazan University ..	1·75	75

Nos. 1829/30 are 38 × 26 mm. and 1831/2 48 × 35 mm.

558. Stalin.

559. Supreme Soviet Buildings in Kiev and Moscow.

1954. 1st Death Anniv. of Stalin.
1833. **558.** 40 k. brown .. .. 1·60 55

1954. Tercentenary of Reunion of Ukraine with Russia. Multicoloured. (a) Designs as T **559** inscr. "1654-1954".

1834.	40 k. Type **559**	80	40
1835.	40 k. Shevchenko Memorial, Kharkhov (vert.)	80	25
1836.	40 k. State Opera House, Kiev	80	25
1837.	40 k. Shevchenko University, Kiev	80	25
1838.	40 k. Academy of Sciences, Kiev	80	25
1839.	60 k. Bogdan Chmielnitsky Memorial, Kiev (vert.)	80	25
1840.	1 r. Flags of R.S.F.S.R. and Ukrainian S.S.R. (vert.)	2·50	55
1841.	1 r. Shevchenko Monument, Kanev (vert.) ..	2·00	35
1842.	1 r. Pereyaslavskaya Rada	2·50	35

(b) No. 1098b optd. with five lines of Cyrillic characters as inscr. at top of T **559**.
1843. **h.** 2 r. green .. .. 5·50 1·75

561. Running.

1954. Sports. Frames in brown.

1844.	**561.**	40 k. black and stone	1·25	20
1845.	–	40 k. black and blue	1·25	20
1846.	–	40 k. brown and buff	1·25	20
1847.	–	40 k. black and blue	1·25	20
1848.	–	40 k. black ..	1·25	20
1849.	–	1 r. grey and blue ..	5·00	1·50
1850.	–	1 r. black and blue ..	5·00	1·50
1851.	–	1 r. brown and drab	5·00	1·50

DESIGNS—HORIZ. No. 1845, Yachting. 1846, Cycling. 1847, Swimming. 1848, Hurdling. 1849, Mountaineering. 1850, Skiing. VERT. No. 1851, Basketball.

562. Cattle.

563. A. P. Chekhov.

1954. Agriculture.

1852.	**562.**	40 k. blue, brown & cream	1·40	35
1853.	–	40 k. grn., brn. & buff	1·40	35
1854.	–	40 k. black, blue and green	1·40	35

DESIGNS: No. 1853, Potato cultivation. No. 1854, Collective-farm hydro-electric station.

1954. 50th Death Anniv. of Chekhov (writer).
1855. **563.** 40 k. brown & green .. 1·10 30

564. Bredikhin, Struve, Belopolsky and Observatory.

565. M. I. Glinka.

1954. Rebuilding of Pulkov Observatory.
1856. **564.** 40 k. blk., bl. & violet 8·00 1·25

1954. 150th Birth Anniv. of Glinka (composer).

1857.	**565.**	40 k. brn., pink & red	2·25	35
1858.	–	60 k. multicoloured ..	3·25	65

DESIGN—HORIZ. (38 × 25½ mm): 60 k. "Glinka playing piano for Pushkin and Zhukovsky" (V. Artamonov).

566. Exhibition Emblem.

567. N. A. Ostrovsky.

1954. Agricultural Exhibition. Multicoloured.

1859.	40 k. Type **566**	55	30
1860.	40 k. Agricultural Pavilion	55	30
1861.	40 k. Cattle-breeding Pavilion	55	30
1862.	40 k. Mechanization Pavilion	55	30
1863.	1 r. Exhibition Entrance	1·90	75
1864.	1 r. Main Pavilion	1·90	85

Nos. 1860/3 are horiz., 1860/1 being 41 × 30½ mm., 1862 40 × 30 mm. and 1863 41 × 33 mm. No. 1864 is vert., 29 × 41 mm.

1954. 50th Birth Anniv. of Ostrovsky (writer).
1865. **567.** 40 k. multicoloured .. 1·25 40

568. Monument.

569. Marx, Engels, Lenin and Stalin.

1954. Cent. of Defence of Sevastopol.

1866.	**568.**	40 k. blk., brn. & grn.	1·00	30
1867.	–	60 k. blk., brn. & buff	1·50	50
1868.	–	1 r. multicoloured ..	2·75	90

DESIGNS—HORIZ. 60 k. Defenders of Sevastopol. VERT. 1 r. Admiral Nakhimov.

1954. 37th Anniv. of October Revolution.
1869. **569.** 1 r. brown, red & orge. 6·00 2·50

570. Kazan University.

1954. 150th Anniv. of Kazan University.

1870.	**570.**	40 k. blue on blue ..	80	30
1871.		60 k. red ..	1·40	55

571. Salomea Neris.

1954. 50th Birth Anniv. of Salomea Neris (poetess).
1872. **571.** 40 k. multicoloured .. 1·00 25

572. Cultivating Vegetables.

573. Stalin.

1954. Agriculture. Multicoloured.

1873	40 k. Type **572**	1·00	30
1874	40 k. Tractor and plough	1·00	30
1875	40 k. Harvesting flax (49 × 25½ mm)	1·00	30
1876	60 k. Harvesting sunflowers (49 × 25½ mm) ..	2·00	40

1954. 75th Birth Anniv. of Stalin.

1877.	**573.**	40 k. purple ..	1·50	50
1878.		1 r. blue ..	3·50	1·40

574. Rubinstein.

575. V. M. Garshin.

1954. 125th Birth Anniv. of Rubinstein (composer).
1879. **574.** 40 k. black & purple 2·00 40

1955. Birth Cent. of Garshin (writer).
1880. **575.** 40 k. blk., brn. & grn. 1·10 35

576. Aeroplane over Landscape.

577. K. A. Savitsky and "Construction of Railway".

1955. Air.

1881.	–	1 r. multicoloured ..	1·75	30
1882.	**576.**	2 r. black and green ..	3·25	50

DESIGN: 1 r. Aeroplane over coastline.

1955. 50th Death Anniv. of Savitsky (painter).
1883. **577.** 40 k. brown .. .. 1·50 20

578. Clasped Hands. 579. Pushkin and Mickiewicz.

1955. Int Conference of Postal and Municipal Workers, Vienna.
1884. 578. 50 k. multicoloured .. 80 20

1955. 10th Anniv. of Russo-Polish Friendship Agreement.
1885. 579. 40 k. multicoloured .. 2·10 30
1886. – 40 k. black .. .. 2·10 30
1887. – 1 r. multicoloured .. 3·50 75
1888. – 1 r. multicoloured .. 5·50 1·00
DESIGNS: No. 1886, " Brotherhood in Arms " Monument, Warsaw (26½ × 39 mm.). No. 1887, Palace of Science, Warsaw (37½ × 25½ mm.). No. 1888, Copernicus and Matejko (39 × 26½ mm.).

580. Lenin at Shushenskoe. 581. Schiller.

1955. 85th Birth Anniv. of Lenin. Multicoloured centres.
1889. 580. 60 k. red .. .. 2·00 30
1890. – 1 r. red .. .. 3·75 60
1891. – 1 r. red .. .. 3·75 60
DESIGNS: No. 1890, Lenin in secret printing house (26½ × 39 mm.). As Type 580: No. 1891, Lenin and Krupskaya at Gorky.

1955. 150th Death Anniv. of Schiller (poet).
1892. 581. 40 k. brown .. .. 1·10 55

582. Aeroplane over Globe. 583. V. Mayakovsky.

1955. Air.
1893. 582. 2 r. brown .. .. 4·50 80
1894. 2 r. blue .. .. 3·50 55

1955. 25th Death Anniv. of Mayakovsky (poet).
1895. 583. 40 k. multicoloured .. 1·40 30

584. Tadzhik S.S.R. Pavilion.

1955. Agricultural Exhibition. Soviet Pavilion. Multicoloured designs with green frames.
1896 40 k. R.S.F.S.R. .. 65 30
1897 40 k. Byelorussian S.S.R. 65 30
1898 40 k. Type 584 .. .. 65 30
1899 40 k. Azerbaijan S.S.R. .. 65 30
1900 40 k. Latvian S.S.R. .. 65 30
1901 40 k. Lithuanian S.S.R. .. 65 30
1902 40 k. Karelo-Finnish S.S.R. 65 30
1903 40 k. Estonian S.S.R. .. 65 30
1904 40 k. Armenian S.S.R. .. 65 30
1905 40 k. Ukrainian S.S.R .. 65 30
1906 40 k. Georgian S.S.R. .. 65 30
1907 40 k. Kazakh S.S.R. .. 65 30
1908 40 k. Turkmen S.S.R. .. 65 30
1909 40 k. Kirgiz S.S.R. .. 65 30
1910 40 k. Uzbek S.S.R. .. 65 30
1911 40 k. Moldavian S.S.R. .. 65 30

585. M. V. Lomonosov and Building.

1955. Bicentenary of Lomonosov University. Multicoloured.
1912. 40 k. Type 585 .. .. 1·10 30
1913. 1 r. Lomonosov University 1·90 55

586. A. G. Venetsianov and " The Labours of Spring ".

1955. 175th Birth Anniv. of Venetsianov (painter). Multicoloured centre.
1914. 586. 1 r. black .. .. 2·75 55

587. A. Lyadov.

1955. Birth Cent of Lyadov (composer).
1915 587 40 k. multicoloured .. 2·25 30

588. A. S. Popov. 589. Lenin.

590. Revolution Scene.

1955. 60th Anniv. of Popov's Radio Discoveries. Multicoloured centres.
1916. 588. 40 k. blue .. .. 1·25 20
1917. 1 r. brown .. .. 2·00 40

1955. 38th Anniv of Russian Revolution.
1918 589 40 k. multicoloured .. 1·40 1·00
1919 590 40 k. multicoloured .. 1·40 1·00
1920 – 1 r. multicoloured .. 3·50 2·00
DESIGN—As T 590. 1 r. Lenin speaking to revolutionaries.

„Сев. полюс"
— Москва
1955 г.
(591.)

592. Magnitogorsk.

1955. Air. Opening of North Pole Scientific Stations. Nos. 1881/2 optd. with T 591.
1921. – 1 r. multicoloured .. 9·00 6·00
1922. 576. 2 r. black and green .. 11·00 6·50

1955. 25th Anniv. of Magnitogorsk.
1923. 592. 40 k. multicoloured .. 1·25 20

593. Helicopter over Station. 594. F. I. Shubin.

1955. North Pole Scientific Stations.
1924. 593. 40 k. multicoloured .. 3·25 30
1925. 60 k. multicoloured .. 3·50 40
1926. – 1 r. multicoloured .. 5·50 70
DESIGN: 1 r. Meteorologist taking observations.

1955. 150th Death Anniv. of Shubin (sculptor).
1927. 594. 40 k. multicoloured .. 80 20
1928. 1 r. multicoloured .. 1·10 30

595. A. N. Krylov. 596. Racing.

1956. 10th Death Anniv. of Krylov (scientist).
1929. 595. 40 k. multicoloured .. 80 20

1956. International Horse Racing.
1930 596 40 k. sepia and brown 1·25 25
1931 60 k. blue and green 1·50 30
1932 – 1 r. purple and blue .. 2·75 55
DESIGN—HORIZ. 1 r. Trotting.

597. Badge and Stadium. 598. Atomic Power Station.

1956. 5th Spartacist Games.
1933. 597. 1 r. green and purple 1·50 35

1956. Foundation of Atomic Power Station of Russian Academy of Sciences.
1934. 598. 25 k. multicoloured .. 85 15
1935. – 60 k. yell., turq. & brn. 1·60 25
1936. 598. 1 r. yell., red & blue .. 2·50 45
DESIGN: 60 k. Top of atomic reactor.

599. Statue of Lenin.

1956. 20th Communist Party Congress.
1937. 599. 40 k. multicoloured .. 75 20
1938. 1 r. multicoloured .. 1·25 40

600. Kh. Abovyan. 601. Revolutionaries.

1956. 150th Birth Anniv. of Khatchatur Abovyan (Armenian writer).
1939. 600. 40 k. black on blue .. 1·10 20

1956. 50th Anniv. of 1905 Revolution.
1940. 601. 40 k. multicoloured .. 2·75 1·40

602.

1941. ПАВИЛЬОН «УРАЛ»
1942. ПАВИЛЬОН СЕВЕРО-ВОСТОЧНЫХ ОБЛАСТЕЙ
1943. ПАВИЛЬОН ЦЕНТРАЛЬНЫХ ЧЕРНОЗЕМНЫХ ОБЛАСТЕЙ
1944. ПАВИЛЬОН «ЛЕНИНГРАД • СЕВЕРО-ЗАПАД»
1945. ПАВИЛЬОН МОСКОВСКОЙ, ТУЛЬСКОЙ, КАЛУЖСКОЙ, РЯЗАНСКОЙ И БРЯНСКОЙ ОБЛАСТЕЙ
1946. ПАВИЛЬОН БАШКИРСКОЙ АССР
1947. ПАВИЛЬОН ДАЛЬНЕГО ВОСТОКА
1948. ПАВИЛЬОН ТАТАРСКОЙ АССР
1949. ПАВИЛЬОН ЦЕНТРАЛЬНЫХ ОБЛАСТЕЙ
1950. ПАВИЛЬОН ЮНЫХ НАТУРАЛИСТОВ
1951. ПАВИЛЬОН СЕВЕРНОГО КАВКАЗА
1952. ПАВИЛЬОН «СИБИРЬ»
1953. ПАВИЛЬОН «ПОВОЛЖЬЕ»

Inscr. at foot as shown above.

1956. Agricultural Exn. Multicoloured. Views of Pavilions of U.S.S.R. regions as T 602. Inscr. "ВСХВ".
1941. 1 r. Ural .. .. .. 1·50 40
1942. 1 r. North East .. .. 1·50 40
1943. 1 r. Central Black Soil Region .. .. 1·50 40
1944. 1 r. Leningrad .. .. 1·50 40
1945. 1 r. Moscow-Tula-Kaluga-Ryazan-Bryansk .. 1·50 40
1946. 1 r. Bashkhir .. .. 1·50 40
1947. 1 r. Far East .. .. 1·50 40
1948. 1 r. Tatar .. .. 1·50 40
1949. 1 r. Central Regions .. 1·50 40
1950. 1 r. Young Naturalists .. 1·50 40
1951. 1 r. North Caucasus .. 1·50 40
1952. 1 r. Siberia .. .. 1·50 40
1953. 1 r. Volga .. .. 1·50 40

603. N. A. Kasatkin (painter). 604. A. E. Arkhipov and painting "On the Oka River".

1956. Kasatkin Commemoration.
1954. 603. 40 k. red 70 15

1956. Arkhipov Commemoration.
1955. 604. 40 k. multicoloured .. 1·75 20
1956. 1 r. multicoloured .. 2·75 45

605. I. P. Kulibin. 606. " Fowler " (after Perov).

1956. 220th Birth Anniv. of Kulibin (inventor).
1957. 605. 40 k. multicoloured .. 1·10 30

1956. Perov Commemoration. Inscr. " 1956 ". Multicoloured centres.
1958. – 40 k. green .. .. 2·00 25
1959. 606. 1 r. brown .. .. 3·75 50
1960. – 1 r. brown .. .. 3·75 55
DESIGNS—VERT. No. 1958, V. G. Perov. HORIZ. No. 1960, " Hunters Resting " (after Perov).

607. Lenin speaking. 608. N. I. Lobachevsky.

1956. 86th Birth Anniv. of Lenin.
1961. 607. 40 k. multicoloured 60 3·25

1956. Death Centenary of Lobachevsky (mathematician).
1962. 608. 40 k. brown 80 15

609. Student Nurses.

DESIGNS — (37½ × 25½ mm.),: No. 1964, Nurse and textile factory.

1956. Red Cross.
1963. 609. 40 k. red, blue & brn. 1·00 30
1964. – 40 k. red, olive & turq. 1·00 30

610. 611. I. M. Sechenov (scientist).

1956. Air. Opening of North Pole Scientific Station No. 6.
1965. 610. 1 r. multicoloured .. 4·25 1·40

1956. Sechenov Commemoration.
1966. 611. 40 k. multicoloured .. 1·40 30

612. Arsenev. 613. I. V. Michurin.

1956. V. K. Arsenev (writer).
1967 612 40 k. black, vio & pink 1·75 55

1956. Birth Cent. of Michurin (naturalist). Multicoloured centres.
1968. 613. 25 k. brown 45 15
1969. – 60 k. green .. .. 1·10 25
1970. 613. 1 r. blue .. .. 1·75 45
DESIGN (47½ × 26½ mm.): 60 k. Michurin and children.

614. A. K. Savrasov (painter). 615. N. K. Krupskaya (Lenin's wife).

1956. Savrasov Commemoration.
1971. 614. 1 r. brown and yellow 1·40 50

1956. Krupskaya Commemoration.
1972 615 40 k. brown, blk & bl 1·25 20
For similar stamps see Nos. 2005, 2027, 2115 and 2169.

616. S. M. Kirov. 617. A. A. Blok (poet).

1956. 70th Birth Anniv. of Kirov (statesman).
1973. 616. 40 k. multicoloured .. 65 15

1956. Blok Commemoration.
1974. 617. 40 k. brn., blk. & olive 80 15

618. N. S. Leskov. 619. Factory Building.

1956. 125th Birth Anniv. of Leskov (writer).
1975. 618. 40 k. multicoloured .. 65 15
1976. 1 r. multicoloured .. 1·40 40

1956. 25th Anniv. of Rostov Agricultural Machinery Works.
1977. 619. 40 k. multicoloured .. 75 20

620. G. N. Fedotova (actress).

1956. Fedotova Commemoration.
1978 620 40 k. multicoloured .. 65 20
For similar stamp see No. 2159.

621. P. M. Tretyakov and Art Gallery.

DESIGN — VERT No. 1980 "Rooks have arrived" (painting by Savrasov).

1956. Cent. of Tretyakov Art Gallery.
1979. 621. 40 k. multicoloured 1·75 45
1980. – 40 k. multicoloured 1·75 45

622. Relay-race.

1956. Spartacist Games.
1981 622 10 k. red 30 10
1982 – 25 k. brown 40 10
1983 – 25 k. multicoloured .. 40 15
1984 – 25 k. blue 65 15
1985 – 40 k. blue 65 15
1986 – 40 k. green 65 15
1987 – 40 k. brown and green 65 15
1988 – 40 k. deep brown, brown and green .. 65 15
1989 – 40 k. red, green and light green .. 65 15
1990 – 40 k. brown 65 15
1991 – 40 k. multicoloured .. 65 15
1992 – 60 k. violet .. .. 1·25 25
1993 – 60 k. violet .. .. 1·25 25
1994 – 1 r. brown .. .. 2·50 55
DESIGNS—VERT. No. 1982, Volleyball. 1983, Swimming. 1984, Rowing. 1985, Diving. 1989, Flag and stadium. 1990, Tennis. 1991, Medal. 1993, Boxing. HORIZ. No. 1986, Cycle racing. 1987, Fencing. 1988, Football. 1992, Gymnastics. 1994, Netball.

623. Parachutist Landing. 624. Construction Work.

1956. 3rd World Parachute-jumping Competition.
1995. 623. 40 k. multicoloured .. 1·00 25

1956. Builders' Day.
1996a 624 40 k. orange .. 65 25
1997 – 60 k. brown .. 80 30
1998 – 1 r. blue .. .. 2·50 50
DESIGNS: 60 k. Plant construction. 1 r. Dam construction.

625. I. E. Repin and "Volga River Boatmen" (painting).

626. "Reply of the Cossacks to Sultan Mahmoud IV" (painting).

1956. Repin Commemoration (painter).
1999. 625. 40 k. multicoloured .. 3·00 45
2000. 626. 1 r. multicoloured .. 5·50 70

627. Robert Burns. 628. Ivan Franko.

1956. 160th Death Anniv. of Burns (Scots poet).
2001. 627. 40 k. brown .. .. 5·00 3·50
2002. 40 k. brown and blue 4·00 2·25

1956. Birth Cent of Franko (writer) (1st issue).
2003. 628. 40 k. purple 65 20
2004. 1 r. blue .. .. 1·25 30
See also No. 2037.

1956. Lesya Ukrainka Commemoration. As T 615, but portrait of Ukrainka (author).
2005 40 k. black, brown & grn 65 40

629. M. Aivazov (farmer.) 630. Statue of Nestor.

1956. 148th Birthday of Aivazov.
(a) Wrongly inscr. "Muhamed" (7 characters).
2006. 629. 40 k. green .. .. 20·00 18·00
(b) Corrected to "Makmud" (6 characters).
2006a. 629. 40 k. green .. .. 9·00 6·50

1956. 900th Birth Anniv. of Nestor (historian).
2007. 630. 40 k. multicoloured .. 1·00 20
2008. 1 r. multicoloured .. 1·75 40

631. A. A. Ivanov. 632. Feeding Poultry.

1956. 150th Birth Anniv. of Ivanov (painter).
2009. 631. 40 k. brown and grey 65 20

1956. Agriculture. Multicoloured.
2010. 10 k. Type 632 .. .. 35 10
2011. 10 k. Harvesting 35 10
2012. 25 k. Gathering maize .. 40 20
2013. 40 k. Maize field 80 20
2014. 40 k. Tractor station .. 80 20
2015. 40 k. Cattle grazing .. 80 20
2016. 40 k. "Agriculture and industry" 80 20
SIZES: Nos. 2010, 2014/5, 37 × 25½ mm. Nos. 2011/3, 37 × 28 mm. No. 2016, 37 × 21 mm.

633. Mozart. 634 Mirnyi Base and Supply Ship "Lena".

1956. Cultural Anniversaries.
2017 40 k. blue (Type 633) .. 3·00 40
2018 40 k. green (Curie) .. 3·00 40
2019 40 k. lilac (Heine) .. 1·40 40
2020 40 k. brown (Ibsen) .. 1·40 40
2021 40 k. green (Dostoevsky) 1·40 40
2022 40 k. brown (Franklin) .. 1·40 40
2023 40 k. black (Shaw) .. 2·50 40
2024 40 k. orange (Sesshu-Toyo Oda) .. .. .. 1·40 40
2025 40 k. black (Rembrandt) 1·40 40
Nos. 2022/5 are larger (25 × 38 mm).

1956. Soviet Scientific Antarctic Expedition.
2026. 634. 40 k. turq., red & grey 5·50 80

1956. Julia Zhemaite Commemoration. As T 615, but portrait of Zhemaite (author).
2027 40 k. green, brown & sepia 80 20

635. F. A. Bredikhin. 636. G. I. Kotovsky.

1956. 125th Birth Anniv. of Bredikhin (astronomer).
2028. 635. 40 k. multicoloured 5·00 1·00

1956. 75th Birth Anniv. of Kotovsky (military leader).
2029. 636. 40 k. mauve .. .. 1·40 40

637. Shatura Electric Power Station. 638. Marshal Suvorov.

1956. 30th Anniv. of Shatura Electric Power Station.
2030. 637. 40 k. multicoloured 75 20

1956. 225th Birth Anniv. of Marshal Suvorov.
2031. 638. 40 k. lake and orge. 60 20
2032. 1 r. brown and olive 1·25 45
2033. 3 r. black and brown 3·50 1·10

639. Kryakutni's Ascent.

1956. 225th Anniv. of First Balloon Flight by Kryakutni.
2034. 639. 40 k. multicoloured .. 1·75 40

640. "Dawn at the Voskresenski Gate".

1956. 30th Death Anniv. of A. M. Vasnetsov (artist).
2035. 640. 40 k. multicoloured .. 1·40 55

641. Y. M. Shokalsky. 642. Ivan Franko.

1956. Birth Cent. of Shokalsky (oceanographer).
2036. 641. 40 k. brown and blue 2·25 50

1956. Birth Cent. of Franko (writer) (2nd issue).
2037. 642. 40 k. green 55 20

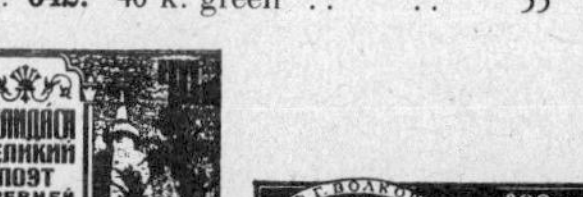

643. Indian Temple and Books. 644. F. G. Volkov (actor) and State Theatre.

1956. Kalidasa (Indian poet) Commem.
2038 643 40 k. red 55 20

1956. Bicent. of Leningrad State Theatre.
2039. 644. 40 k. blk., red & yell. 60 20

645. Lomonosov and St. Petersburg University.

1956. Russian Writers.
2040. 645. 40 k. multicoloured .. 80 25
2041. – 40 k. multicoloured .. 80 25
2042. – 40 k. brown and blue 80 25
2043. – 40 k. olive, brn. & blk. 80 25
2044. – 40 k. brown and turq. 80 25
2045. – 40 k. purple & brown 80 25
2046. – 40 k. olive and blue .. 80 25
DESIGNS: No. 2041, Gorky and scene from "Mother" (novel). No. 2042, Pushkin and "Bronze Horseman" (statue). No. 2043, Rustavely and episode from "The Knight in the Tiger Skin" (poem). No. 2044, Tolstoy and scene from "War and Peace" (novel). No. 2045, V. G. Belinsky and titles of literary works. No. 2046, M. Y. Lermontov and Daryal Pass
See also Nos. 2076, 2089/90, 2256, 2316/22 and 2458.

646. Vitus Bering and Routes of his Voyages.

647. Mendeleev.

1956. 275th Birth Anniv. of Bering (explorer).

2047.	**646.**	40 k. multicoloured	3·00	35

1957. 50th Death Anniv of Dmitri Mendeleev (chemist).

2048	**647**	40 k. brn, grey & blk	1·60	40

648. M. I. Glinka.

649. Youth Festival Emblem.

1957. Death Cent of Glinka (composer). Mult.

2049a	40 k. Type **648**	1·50	20
2050a	1 r. Scene from "Ivan Susanin"	3·00	55

1957. All-Union Festival of Soviet Youth.

2051.	**649.**	40 k. multicoloured ..	40	15

650. Ice Hockey Player.

651. Youth Festival Emblem and Pigeon

1957. 23rd World and 35th European Ice-Hockey Championships, Moscow.

2052.	–	25 k. violet	90	15
2053.	**650.**	40 k. blue	1·00	15
2054.	–	60 k. green	1·00	30

DESIGNS: 25 k. Championship emblem. 60 k. Goal-keeper.

1957. 6th World Youth Festival, Moscow. (1st issue). Perf. or imperf.

2055.	**651.**	40 k. multicoloured ..	70	15
2056.		60 k. multicoloured ..	1·10	20

See also Nos. 2084/7 and 2108/11.

652. Factory Plant.

653. Sika Deer.

1957. Cent. of "Red Proletariat" Plant, Moscow.

2057.	**652.**	40 k. multicoloured ..	70	25

1957. Russian Wildlife. Multicoloured.

2057a.	10 k. Grey Partridge ..	1·00	30
2058.	15 k. Black Grouse ..	1·00	15
2058a.	15 k. Polar bear ..	70	15
2059.	20 k. Type **653** ..	75	15
2059a.	20 k. Brown hare ..	60	25
2059b.	25 k. Tiger	75	25
2059c.	25 k. Wild horse ..	75	25
2060.	30 k. Mallard	1·25	25
2061.	30 k. European bison	75	20
2062.	40 k. Elk	1·50	35
2063.	40 k. Sable	1·50	35
2063a.	40 k. Eurasian red squirrel	80	30
2063b.	40 k. Yellow-throated marten	80	30
2063c.	60 k. Hazel Grouse ..	2·75	55
2063d.	1 r. Mute Swan ..	3·75	1·00

Nos. 2058/a, 2059a/62, 2063a/b and 2063d, are horiz.

See also Nos. 2534/6.

654. Vologda Lace-making.

655. G. V. Plekhanov.

1957. Regional Handicrafts. Multicoloured.

2064.	40 k. Moscow wood-carving	1·25	25
2065.	40 k. Woman engraving vase	1·25	25
2066.	40 k. Type **654** ..	1·25	25
2067.	40 k. Northern bone-carving	1·25	25
2067a.	40 k. Wood-block engraving	1·25	25
2067b.	40 k. Turkmen carpet-weaving	1·25	25

1957. Birth Cent. of Plekhanov (politician).

2068.	**655.**	40 k. plum	65	20

656. A. N. Bakh.

657. L. Euler.

1957. Birth Cent. of Bakh (biochemist).

2069.	**656.**	40 k. multicoloured	1·10	25

1957. 250th Birth Anniv. of Euler (mathematician).

2070.	**657.**	40 k. black and purple	1·75	30

658. Lenin in Meditation.

659. Dr. William Harvey.

1957. 87th Birth Anniv. of Lenin. Mult.

2071.	40 k. Type **658** ..	80	20
2072.	40 k. Lenin carrying pole	80	20
2073.	40 k. Talking with soldier and sailor	80	20

1957. 300th Death Anniv of Dr. William Harvey (discoverer of circulation of blood).

2074	**659**	40 k. brown ..	75	15

660. M. A. Balakirev.

661. 12th-Century Narrator.

1957. 120th Birth Anniv. of Balakirev (composer).

2075.	**660.**	40 k. black ..	1·25	20

1957. "The Tale of the Host of Igor".

2076.	**661.**	40 k. multicoloured ..	80	20

662. Agricultural Medal.

663. A. I. Herzen and N. P. Ogarev (writers).

1957. Cultivation of Virgin Soil.

2077.	**662.**	40 k. multicoloured ..	80	25

1957. Centenary of Publication of Magazine "Kolokol".

2078.	**663.**	40 k. brn., blk. & blue	80	25

664. Monument.

250 лет
Ленинграда
(665.)

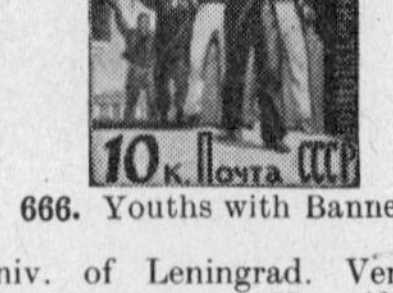

666. Youths with Banner.

1957. 250th Anniv. of Leningrad. Vert. designs as T **664** and stamps as Nos. 1818 and 1820 optd. as T **665**.

2079.	**664.**	40 k. green	50	15
2080.	–	40 k. violet	50	15
2081.	–	40 k. brown	50	15
2082.	**551.**	1 r. brown on green ..	1·40	25
2083.	–	1 r. green on salmon	1·40	25

DESIGNS: No. 2080, Nevsky Prospect, Leningrad. No. 2081, Lenin Statue.

1957. 6th World Youth Festival, Moscow (2nd issue). Multicoloured. Perf. or imperf.

2084.	10 k. Type **666** ..	25	10
2084a.	20 k. Sculptor with statue	40	15
2085.	25 k. Type **666**	80	15
2086.	40 k. Dancers	55	15
2087.	1 r. Festival emblem and fireworks over Moscow State University ..	1·10	30

667. A. M. Lyapunov.

668. T. G. Shevchenko (after I. Repin) and Scene from "Katharina".

1957. Birth Centenary of Lyapunov (mathematician).

2088	**667**	40 k. brown	5·00	2·25

1957. 19th-Century Writers. Multicoloured.

2089	40 k. Type **668**	65	20
2090	40 k. N. G. Chernyshevsky and scene from "What is to be Done?"	65	20

669. Henry Fielding.

670. Racing Cyclists.

1957. 250th Birth Anniv. of Fielding (novelist).

2091.	**669.**	40 k. multicoloured ..	45	15

1957. 10th Int. Cycle Race.

2092.	**670.**	40 k. multicoloured ..	1·25	25

671. Interior of Observatory.

1957. Int. Geophysical Year (1st issue).

2093.	**671.**	40 k. brown, yellow and blue	2·00	40
2094.	–	40 k. indigo, yellow and blue ..	2·75	40
2095.	–	40 k. vio. & lavender	2·50	40
2095a.	–	40 k. blue	2·50	30
2095b.	–	40 k. green	2·50	40
2095c.	–	40 k. yellow and blue	2·50	30

DESIGNS—As T **671**: No. 2094, Meteor in sky. 2095a, Malakhit radar scanner and balloon (meteorology). 2059b, "Zarya" (non-magnetic research schooner) (geo-magnetism). 2095c, Northern Lights and C-180 camera. 15 × 21 mm: No. 2095, Rocket.

See also Nos. 2371/3a.

672. Gymnast.

1957. 3rd Int. Youth Games.

2096.	**672.**	20 k. brown and blue	20	10
2097.	–	25 k. red and green ..	25	10
2098.	–	40 k. violet and red ..	30	20
2099.	–	40 k. olive, red & grn.	30	20
2100.	–	60 k. brown and blue	60	40

DESIGNS—As Type **672**: No. 2097, Wrestlers. No. 2098, Young athletes. No. 2099, Moscow Stadium. No. 2100, Javelin-thrower.

673. Football.

674. Yanka Kupala.

1957. Russian Successes at Olympic Games, Melbourne.

2101.	–	20 k. brn., blue & blk.	30	10
2102.	–	20 k. red and green ..	30	10
2103.	–	25 k. blue and orange	30	15
2104.	**673.**	40 k. multicoloured ..	50	15
2105.	–	40 k. brown & purple	50	15
2106.	–	60 k. brown and violet	80	40

DESIGNS—VERT. No. 2101, Throwing the javelin. 2102, Running. 2103, Gymnastics. 2105, Boxing. 2106, Weightlifting.

1957. 75th Birth Anniv. of Kupala (poet).

2107.	**674.**	40 k. brown	2·75	1·40

675. Moscow State University.

676. Lenin Library.

1957. 6th World Youth Festival (3rd issue), Moscow Views.

2108.	–	40 k. black and brown	55	15
2109.	–	40 k. black and purple	55	15
2110.	–	1 r. black and blue ..	1·10	30
2111.	**675.**	1 r. black and red ..	1·10	30

DESIGNS—HORIZ. No. 2108, Kremlin. No. 2109, Stadium. No. 2110, Bolshoi State Theatre.

1957. Int. Philatelic Exn., Moscow. Perf. or imperf.

2112.	**676.**	40 k. turquoise ..	45	20

677. Dove of Peace encircling Globe.

678. P. Beranger.

1957. "Defence of Peace".

2113.	**677.**	40 k. multicoloured ..	80	40
2114.		1 r. multicoloured ..	1·40	85

1957. Birth Cent of Clara Zetkin (German revolutionary). As T **615** but portrait of Zetkin.

2115	40 k. multicoloured ..	70	20

1957. Death Cent. of Beranger (French poet).

2116.	**678.**	40 k. green	70	20

679. Krengholm Factory, Narva.

680. Factory Plant and Statue of Lenin.

1957. Centenary of Krengholm Textile Factory, Narva, Estonia.

2117.	**679.**	40 k. brown	65	20

1957. Centenary of Krasny Vyborzhetz Plant, Leningrad.

2118	**680**	40 k. blue	50	25

681. V. V. Stasov

682. Pigeon with Letter.

1957. 50th Death Anniv. of Stasov (art critic).
2119. **681.** 40 k. brown 55 15
2120. 1 r. blue .. .. 1·40 20

1957. Int. Correspondence Week.
2121. **682.** 40 k. blue 35 20
2122. 60 k. purple 55 25

683. K. E. Tsiolkovsky.

684. Congress Emblem.

1957. Birth Cent. of Tsiolkovsky (scientist).
2123. **683.** 40 k. multicoloured .. 4·00 70

1957. 4th World T.U.C., Leipzig.
2124. **684.** 40 k. blue on blue .. 45 20

685. Students.

686. Workers and Emblem (Ukraine). 687. Lenin.

1957. 40th Anniv. of Russian Revolution (a) 1st issue. As T **685**. Multicoloured. Perf. or imperf.
2125 10 k. Type **685** 20 10
2126 40 k. Railway worker (horiz) .. 50 30
2127 40 k. Portrait of Lenin on banner 30 10
2128 40 k. Lenin and workers with banners .. 1·25 25
2129 60 k. Harvester (horiz) 1·75 60

(b) 2nd issue. As T **686**, designs representing the Soviet Republics. Multicoloured.
2130. **686.** 40 k. Ukraine .. 55 30
2131. – 40 k. Estonia .. 55 30
2132. – 40 k. Uzbekistan .. 55 30
2133. – 40 k. R.S.F.S.R. .. 75 30
2134. – 40 k. Byelorussia .. 55 30
2135. – 40 k. Lithuania .. 55 30
2136. – 40 k. Armenia .. 55 30
2137. – 40 k. Azerbaijan .. 55 30
2138. – 40 k. Georgia .. 55 30
2139. – 40 k. Kirghizia .. 55 30
2140. – 40 k. Turkmenistan 55 30
2141. – 40 k. Tadzhikistan .. 55 30
2142. – 40 k. Kazakhstan .. 55 30
2143. – 40 k. Latvia .. 55 30
2144. – 40 k. Moldavia .. 55 30

(c) 3rd Issue. As T **687**.
2145. **687.** 40 k. blue .. .. 1·50 50
2146. – 60 k. red .. .. 2·25 80
DESIGN—HORIZ. 60 k. Lenin at desk.

688. Satellite encircling Globe.

689. Meteor Falling.

1957. Launching of 1st Artificial Satellite.
2147. **688.** 40 k. indigo on blue 3·00 45
2148. 40 k. blue .. .. 3·00 45

1957. Sikhote-Alin Meteor.
2149. **689.** 40 k. multicoloured .. 3·00 75

4/X-57 г. Первый в мире искусств. спутник Земли
(691.)

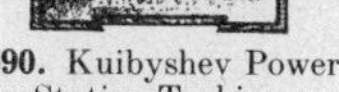
690. Kuibyshev Power Station Turbine.

692. Soviet War Memorial, Berlin.

1957. All-Union Industrial Exhibition (1st issue).
2150. **690.** 40 k. brown 60 20
See also Nos. 2168.

1957. First Artificial Satellite of the World. Optd. with T **691**.
2151. **683.** 40 k. multicoloured .. 24·00 19·00

1957. Bicent. of Academy of Arts, Moscow.
2152. – 40 k. black on salmon 25 10
2153. **692.** 60 k. black 50 15
2154. – 1 r. black on pink .. 1·00 30
DESIGNS—($25\frac{1}{2} \times 37\frac{1}{2}$ mm.): 40 k. Academy and portraits of Bryullov, Repin and Surikov. ($21\frac{1}{2} \times 32$ mm.): 1 r. Worker and Peasant Memorial, Moscow.

693. Arms of Ukraine.

694. Garibaldi.

1957. 40th Anniv. of Ukraine S.S.R.
2155. **693.** 40 k. multicoloured 55 15

1957. 150th Birth Anniv of Garibaldi.
2156 **694** 40 k. purple, maroon and green 65 15

695. Edvard Grieg. 696. Borovikovsky.

1957. 50th Death Anniv. of Grieg (composer).
2157. **695.** 40 k. black on salmon 1·25 20

1957. Birth Bicent. of Borovikovsky (painter).
2158. **696.** 40 k. brown 65 15

1957. M. N. Ermolova (actress). Commemoration. As T **620** but portrait of Ermolova.
2159 40 k. brown and violet .. 65 15

698. Y. Kolas.

699. U. N. Kapsukas.

700. G. Z. Bashindzhagian.

1957. 75th Birth Anniv of Kolas (poet).
2160 **698** 40 k. black .. .. 1·60 90

1957. Kapsukas (Communist Party leader) Commem.
2161. **699.** 40 k. brown .. .. 1·60 90

1957. Bashindzhagian (artist) Commem.
2162. **700.** 40 k. brown .. .. 1·60 90

701. Kuibyshev Hydro-electric Station.

702. Allegory of Progress.

1957. 40th Anniv of Kuibyshev Hydro-electric Station.
2163 **701** 40 k. blue on flesh .. 90 20

1957. Launching of 2nd Artificial Satellite.
2164. **702.** 20 k. red and black .. 55 10
2165. 40 k. green and black 90 15
2166. 60 k. brown & black 1·25 15
2167. 1 r. blue and black .. 1·75 45

703. Allegory of Industry.

704. Tsi Bai-Shi.

1958. All-Union Industrial Exn. (2nd issue).
2168. **703.** 60 k. red, blk. & lav. 75 20

1958. Rosa Luxemburg Commemoration. As T **615**, but portrait of Luxemburg (German revolutionary).
2169 40 k. brown and blue .. 75 20

1958. Tsi Bai-Shi (Chinese artist) Commem.
2170. **704.** 40 k. violet 75 20

705. Linnaeus (Carl von Linne).

706. Tolstoi.

1958. 250th Birth Anniv. of Linnaeus.
2171. **705.** 40 k. brown .. .. 1·90 75

1958. 75th Birth Anniv of A. N. Tolstoi (writer).
2172 **706** 40 k. bistre 65 20

707. Soldier, Sailor and Airman.

708. E. Charents. 709. Henry W. Longfellow.

1958. 40th Anniv. of Red Army. Mult.
2173. 25 k. Battle of Narva, 1918 40 15
2174. 40 k. Type **707** 60 20
2175. 40 k. Soldier and blast-furn aceman (vert.) .. 60 20
2176. 40 k. Soldier and sailor (vert.) 60 20
2177. 60 k. Storming the Reich-stag, 1945 .. .. 1·75 1·40

1958. Charents (Armenian poet) Commem.
2178. **708.** 40 k. brown .. .. 1·60 1·40

1958. 150th Birth Anniv. of Longfellow.
2179. **709.** 40 k. black .. .. 1·60 1·40

710. William Blake. 711. Tchaikovsky.

712 Admiral Rudnev and Cruiser "Varyag".

1958. Birth Bicent. of William Blake (poet).
2180. **710.** 40 k. black .. .. 1·75 1·40

1958. Tchaikovsky International Music Competition, Moscow.
2181 **711** 40 k. multicoloured 1·25 30
2181 – 40 k. multicoloured 1·25 30
2183a – 1 r. purple and green 3·50 75
DESIGNS—HORIZ. No. 2182, Scene from "Swan Lake" ballet. VERT. No. 2183, Pianist, violinist and inset portrait of Tchaikovsky.

1958. 45th Death Anniv. of Admiral Rudnev.
2184. **712.** 40 k. multicoloured .. 1·90 45

713. Gorky (writer).

714. Congress Emblem and Spassky Tower, Kremlin.

1958. Gorky Commem.
2185. **713.** 40 k. multicoloured .. 75 20

1958. 13th Young Communists' League Congress, Moscow.
2186. **714.** 40 k. violet on pink .. 55 15
2187. 60 k. red on flesh .. 80 20

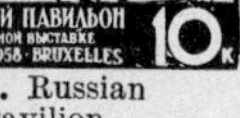
715. Russian Pavilion.

716. J. A. Komensky ("Comenius").

1958. Brussels Int. Exn. Perf or imperf.
2188. **715.** 10 k. multicoloured .. 15 10
2189. 40 k. multicoloured .. 30 15

1958. Komensky Commem.
2190. **716.** 40 k. green .. .. 2·50 90

717. Lenin.

200 лет Академии художеств СССР. 1957
(718.)

1958. Lenin Commem.
2191. **717.** 40 k. blue 45 10
2192. 60 k. red 55 25
2193. 1 r. brown .. .. 1·25 45

1958. Bicent. of Russian Academy of Artists. Optd. with T **718**.
2194. **557.** 40 k. multicoloured .. 4·25 1·75

719. C. Goldoni. 720. Lenin Prize Medal. 721. Karl Marx.

1958. 250th Birth Anniv. of C. Goldoni (Italian dramatist).
2195. **719.** 40 k. brown and blue 75 15

1958. Lenin Prize Medal.
2196. **720.** 40 k. red, yellow & brn. 65 15

1958. Karl Marx Commem.
2197. **721.** 40 k. brown 65 15
2198. 60 k. blue 80 25
2199. 1 r. red .. .. 1·60 35

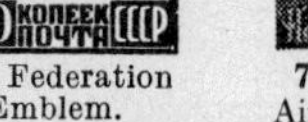
722. Federation Emblem.

723. Radio Beacon, Airliner and Freighter.

1958. 4th Int. Women's Federation Congress.
2200. **722.** 40 k. blue and black 45 15
2201. 60 k. blue and black 65 20

1958. Radio Day.
2202. **723.** 40 k. green and red .. 2·25 30

724. Chavchavadze.

725. Flags of Communist Countries.

1958. Chavchavadze (Georgian poet). Commem.
2203. **724.** 40 k. black and blue 65 15

1958. Socialist Countries' Postal Ministers Conference, Moscow.
2204. **725.** 40 k. multicoloured (A) 21·00 7·00
2205. 40 k. multicoloured (B) 14·00 6·00
Central flag to left of inscription is in red, white and mauve. (A) has red at top and white at foot, (B) is vice versa.

726. Camp Bugler. **727.** Negro, European and Chinese Children.

1958. "Pioneers" Day. Inscr. "1958".
2206. **726.** 10 k. multicoloured.. 20 10
2207. – 25 k. multicoloured.. 50 20
DESIGN: 25 k. Pioneer with model aircraft.

1958. Int. Children's Day. Inscr. "1958".
2208. **727.** 40 k. multicoloured.. 65 20
2209. – 40 k. multicoloured.. 65 20
DESIGN: No. 2209, Child with toys, and atomic bomb.

728. Footballers and Globe. **729.** Rimsky-Korsakov. **730.** Athlete.

1958. World Cup Football Championship, Sweden. Perf or imperf.
2210. **728.** 40 k. multicoloured.. 60 20
2211. 60 k. multicoloured.. 90 40

1958. Rimsky-Korsakov (composer). Commemoration.
2212 **729** 40 k. brown and blue 1·50 20

1958. 14th World Gymnastic Championships, Moscow. Inscr. "XIV". Mult.
2213. 40 k. Type **730** 60 15
2214. 40 k. Gymnast 60 15

731. Young Construction Workers.

1958. Russian Youth Day.
2215. **731.** 40 k. orange and blue 50 15
2216. 60 k. orange and green 60 20

732. Atomic Bomb, Globe, Sputniks, Atomic Symbol and "Lenin" (atomic ice-breaker). **733.** Rifleman and Gun crew.

1958. Int. Disarmament Conf., Stockholm.
2217. **732.** 60 k. black, orange and blue .. .. 3·00 40

1958. 40th Anniv. of Ukrainian Communist Party.
2218. **733.** 40 k. violet and red 65 30

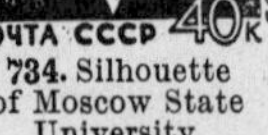

734. Silhouette of Moscow State University. **735.** Sadruddin Aini.

1958. 5th Int. Architects Union Congress, Moscow.
2219. **734.** 40 k. blue and red .. 60 15
2220. – 60 k. multicoloured.. 80 25
DESIGN—VERT. 60 k. "U.I.A. Moscou 1958" in square panel of bricks and "V" in background.

1958. 80th Birth Anniv. of Sadruddin Aini (Tadzhik writer).
2221. **735.** 40 k. red, black & buff 55 15

736. Third Artificial Satellite. **737.** Conference Emblem.

1958. Launching of 3rd Artificial Satellite.
2222. **736.** 40 k. red, blue & grn. 1·25 20

1958. 1st World T.U. Young Workers' Conf., Prague.
2223. **737.** 40 k. blue and purple 30 20

738. Tu-110 Jet Airliner. **739.** L. A. Kulik (scientist).

1958. Civil Aviation. Perf. or imperf.
2224. – 20 k. blk., red & blue 50 10
2225. – 40 k. blk., red & grn. 65 15
2226. – 40 k. blk., red & blue 65 15
2227. – 60 k. red, buff & blue 65 20
2228. **738.** 60 k. black and red.. 65 20
2229. – 1 r. blk., red & orange 1·50 30
2230. – 2 r. blk., red & purple 2·00 45
DESIGNS: 60 k. (No. 2227), Global air routes. Russian aircraft flying across globe: 20 k. Il-14 airliner. 40 k. (No. 2225), Tu-104 jet airliner. 40 k. (No. 2226), Tu-114 turbo-prop airliner. 1 r. An-10 "Ukraina" turbo-prop airliner. 2 r. Il-18 turbo-prop airliner.

1958. 50th Aniv. of Tunguz Meteor.
2231. **739.** 40 k. multicoloured.. 2·25 40

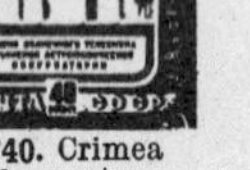

740. Crimea Observatory. **741.** 15th-century Scribe.

1958. 10th Int. Astronomical Union Congress, Moscow.
2232. **740.** 40 k. turq. & brown.. 1·00 30
2233. – 60 k. yell., vio. & blue 1·60 30
2234. – 1 r. brown and blue.. 2·25 50
DESIGNS—HORIZ. 60 k. Moscow University. VERT. 1 r. Telescope of Moscow Observatory.

1958. Cent. of 1st Russian Postage Stamp.
2235. **741.** 10 k. multicoloured.. 15 10
2236. – 10 k. multicoloured.. 15 10
2237. – 25 k. blue, blk. & grn. 30 10
2238. – 25 k. black and blue.. 30 10
2239. – 40 k. brn., pur. & sep. 40 15
2240. – 40 k. lake and brown 40 15
2241. – 40 k. black, orange and red 40 15
2242. – 60 k. turq., blk. & vio. 1·50 25
2243. – 60 k. black, turquoise and purple .. 80 25
2244. – 1 r. multicoloured .. 1·40 40
2245. – 1 r. purple, black and orange .. .. 1·40 40
DESIGNS—HORIZ. No. 2236, 16th-century courier. No. 2237, Ordin-Nastchokin (17th-century postal administrator) and postal sleigh coach. No. 2238, 18th-century mail coach. No. 2239, Reproduction of Lenin portrait stamp of 1947. No. 2240, 19th-century postal troika (three horse sleigh). No. 2241, Russian Tu-104 jet airliner. No. 2242, Parcel post train. No. 2243, V. L. Podbielsky (postal administrator, 1918–20) and postal scenes. No. 2244, Parcel post aircraft. No. 2245, Globe and modern forms of mail transport.

741a. Facade of Exhibition Building. **742.** Vladimir Gateway.

1958. Stamp Cent. Philatelic Exhibition, Leningrad.
2246. **741a.** 40 k. brn. & light brn. 40 20

1958. 850th Anniv of Town of Vladimir. Mult.
2247. 40 k. Type **742** 30 15
2248. 60 k. Street scene in Vladimir .. 50 20

743. M. Chigorin. **745.** Red Cross Nurse and Patient.

1958. 50th Death Anniv. of Chigorin (chess player).
2249. **743.** 40 k. green and black 1·75 20

1958. 40th Anniv. of Red Cross and Crescent Societies.
2254. **745.** 40 k. multicoloured 55 20
2255. – 40 k. red, yellow and bistre 55 20
DESIGN: No. 2255, Convalescent home.

746. Saltykov-Shchedrin (after I. Kramskoi) and Scene from his Works. **747.** V. Kapnist.

1958. 69th Death Anniv of Mikhail Saltykov-Shchedrin (writer).
2256 **746** 40 k. black and purple 50 15
For similar stamps see Nos. 2316/22 and 2458.

1958. Birth Bicent. of V. Kapnist (poet).
2257. **747.** 40 k. black and blue.. 55 15

748. Yerevan, Armenia.

1958. Republican Capitals.

2258	40 k. brown (T **748**) ..	55	20
2259	40 k. violet (Baku, Azerbaijan) ..	55	20
2260	40 k. brown (Minsk, Byelorussia) ..	55	20
2261	40 k. blue (Tblisi, Georgia)	55	20
2262	40 k. green (Tallin, Estonia) ..	55	20
2263	40 k. green (Alma-Ata, Kazakhstan) ..	55	20
2264	40 k. blue (Frunze, Kirgizia) ..	55	20
2265	40 k. brown (Riga, Latvia) ..	55	20
2266	40 k. red (Vilnius, Lithuania) ..	55	20
2267	40 k. bistre (Kishinev, Moldavia) ..	55	20
2268	40 k. violet (Moscow, R.S.F.S.R.) ..	55	20
2269	40 k. blue (Stalinabad, Tadzhikistan) ..	55	20
2270	40 k. green (Ashkhabad, Turkmenistan)	55	20
2271	40 k. mauve (Kiev, Ukraine) ..	55	20
2272	40 k. black (Tashkent, Uzbekistan) ..	55	20

See also No. 2940.

749. Open Book, Torch, Lyre and Flowers. **750.** Rudaki.

1958. Asian-African Writers' Conf., Tashkent.
2273. **749.** 40 k. orange, black and olive .. 60 15

1958. 1100th Birth Anniv. of Rudaki (Tadzhik poet and musician).
2274. **750.** 40 k. multicoloured.. 60 15

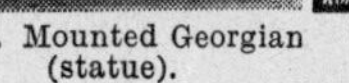

751. Mounted Georgian (statue). **752.** Chelyabinsk Tractor Plant.

1958. 1500th Anniv of Founding of Tbilisi (Georgian Capital).
2275 **751** 40 k. multicoloured .. 1·00 20

1958. 25th Anniv. of Industrial Plants.
2276. **752.** 40 k. green & yellow 80 20
2277. – 40 k. blue & pale blue 55 20
2278. – 40 k. lake & pale orge. 80 20
DESIGNS: No. 2277, Ural machine-construction plant. No. 2278, Zaporozhe foundry plant.

753. Young Revolutionary. **754.** Marx and Lenin (bas-relief).

1958. 40th Anniv. of Young Communists League. Multicoloured.
2279. 10 k. Type **753** 15 10
2280. 20 k. Riveters 30 10
2281. 25 k. Soldier 35 15
2282. 40 k. Harvester.. .. 50 15
2283. 60 k. Builder .. 80 20
2284. 1 r. Students .. .. 1·50 75

1958. 41st Anniv. of October Revolution.
2285. **754.** 40 k. blk., yell. & red 65 20
2286. – 1 r. multicoloured .. 80 25
DESIGN—HORIZ. 1 r. Lenin with student, peasant and miner.

755. "Human Rights". **756.** Yesenin.

1958. 10th Anniv. of Declaration of Human Rights.
2287. **755.** 60 k. blue, blk. & buff 30 15

1958. 30th Death Anniv of Sergei Yesenin (poet).
2288. **756.** 40 k. multicoloured.. 30 15

757. Kuan Han-Ching. **758.** G. K. Ordzhonikidze. **759.** John Milton.

1958. Kuan Han-Ching (Chinese playwright). Commem.
2289. **757.** 40 k. black and blue.. 35 15

1958. 21st Death Anniv. of Ordzhonikidze (statesman).
2290. **758.** 40 k. multicoloured.. 35 15

1958. 350th Birth Anniv. of John Milton (poet).
2291. **759.** 40 k. brown 60 15

760. Lenin's Statue, Minsk. **761.** Fuzuli **762.** Census Emblem.

1958. 40th Anniv of Byelorussian Republic.
2292 **760** 40 k. brn, grey & red 50 15

1958. Fuzuli (Azerbaijan poet). Commem.
2293. **761.** 40 k. bistre & turquoise 50 15

1958. All-Union Census, 1959. Multicoloured.
2294. 40 k. Type **762** 25 15
2295. 40 k. Census official with worker's family 25 15

763. Eleonora Duse.

764. Rule.

1958. Birth Centenary of Eleonora Duse (Italian actress).
2296. **763.** 40 k. blk., grey & grn. 70 20

1958. Death Cent of K. F. Rule (naturalist).
2297 **764** 40 k. black and blue .. 65 20

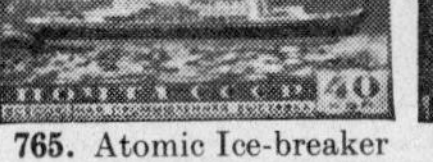
765. Atomic Ice-breaker "Lenin".

766. Moon Rocket and Sputniks.

1958. All-Union Industrial Exn. Mult.
2298. 40 k. Type **765** .. .. 2·50 65
2299. 60 k. "TE 3" Diesel loco 5·50 85

1959. 21st Communist Party Congress, Moscow.
2300. – 40 k. multicoloured .. 55 25
2301. – 60 k. multicoloured .. 65 40
2302. **766.** 1 r. multicoloured .. 2·25 1·40
DESIGNS: 40 k. Lenin, Red Banner and Kremlin view. 60 k. Workers beside Lenin hydro-electric plant, Volga River.

767. E. Torricelli.

768. Ice Skater.

769. Charles Darwin.

1959. 350th Birth Anniv. of Torricelli (physicist).
2303. **767.** 40 k. black and green 80 20

1959. Women's World Ice Skating Championships, Sverdlovsk.
2304. **768.** 25 k. multicoloured .. 40 10
2305. 40 k. black, bl. & grey 60 20

1959. 150th Birth Anniv. of Charles Darwin (naturalist).
2306. **769.** 40 k. brown and blue 75 15

770. N. Gamaleya.

771. Sholem Aleichem.

Победа баскетбольной команды СССР. Чили 1959 г.
(772.)

1959. Birth Cent. of Gamaleya (microbiologist).
2307. **770.** 40 k. black and red .. 75 15

1959. Birth Cent. of Aleichem (Jewish writer).
2308. **771.** 40 k. brown 70 15

1959. Russian (Unofficial) Victory in World Basketball Championships, Chile. No. 1851 optd. with T **772.**
2309. – 1 r. brown and drab .. 6·00 6·00

1959. Birth Bicent. of Robert Burns. Optd. **1759 1959.**
2310. **627.** 40 k. brown and blue 14·00 10·00

774. Selma Lagerlof.

775. P. Cvirka.

776. F. Joliot-Curie (scientist).

1959. Birth Centenary of Selma Lagerlof (Swedish writer).
2311. **774.** 40 k. black, brown and cream 55 15

1959. 50th Birth Anniv. of Cvirka (Lithuanian poet).
2312. **775.** 40 k. black and red on yellow 45 15

1959. Joliot-Curie Commem.
2313. **776.** 40 k. black and turq. 1·25 30

777. Popov and Polar Rescue by "Ermak".

778. Saadi (Persian poet).

1959. Birth Centenary of A. S. Popov (radio pioneer).
2314. **777.** 40 k. brn., blk. & blue 1·00 30
2315. – 60 k. multicoloured .. 1·25 55
DESIGN: 60 k. Popov and radio tower.

1959. Writers as T **746.** Inscr. "1959".
2316. 40 k. grey, black and red 90 20
2317. 40 k. brown, sepia & yell. 90 20
2318. 40 k. brown and violet .. 90 20
2319. 40 k. multicoloured .. 90 20
2320. 40 k. black, olive & yellow 90 20
2321. 40 k. multicoloured .. 90 20
2322. 40 k. slate and violet .. 90 20
PORTRAITS (with scene from works): No. 2316, Anton Chekhov. 2317, Ivan Krylov (after K. Bryullov). 2318, Aleksandr Ostrovsky. 2319, Aleksandr Griboedov (after I. Kramskoi). 2320, Nikolai Gogol (after F. Moller). 2321, Sergei Aksakov (after I. Kramskoi). 2322, Aleksei Koltsov (after K. Gorbunov).

1959. Saadi Commem.
2323. **778.** 40 k. black and blue .. 45 15

779. Orbeliani (Georgian writer).

780. Ogata Korin.

1959. Orbeliani Commem.
2324. **779.** 40 k. black and red .. 45 15

1959. Birth Tercentenary of Ogata Korin (Japanese artist).
2325. **780.** 40 k. multicoloured .. 2·50 1·25

781. "Rossiya" on Odessa-Batum Service.

1959. Russian Liners. Multicoloured.
2326 10 k. "Sovetsky Soyuz" on Vladivostok–Kamchatka service .. 30 15
2327 20 k. "Feliks Dzerzhinsky" on Odessa–Latakia service .. 45 15
2328 40 k. Type **781** .. 70 15
2329 40 k. "Kooperatsiya" on Murmansk–Tyksi service 70 15
2330 60 k. "Mikhail Kalinin" leaving Leningrad .. 90 15
2331 1 r. "Baltika" on Leningrad–London service .. .. 1·25 30

782. Trajectory of Moon Rocket.

783. Lenin.

1959. Launching of Moon Rocket. Inscr. "2-1-1959".
2332. **782.** 40 k. brown and pink 65 20
2333. – 40 k. blue & light blue 65 20
DESIGN: No. 2333, Preliminary route of moon rocket after launching.

1959. 89th Birth Anniv. of Lenin.
2334. **783.** 40 k. brown 50 20

784. M. Cachin.

785. Youths with Banner.

786. A. von Humboldt.

1959. 90th Birth Anniv. of Marcel Cachin (French communist leader).
2335. **784.** 60 k. brown 40 20

1959. 10th Anniv. of World Peace Movement.
2336. **785.** 40 k. multicoloured .. 55 20

1959. Death Cent. of Alexander von Humboldt (German naturalist).
2337. **786.** 40 k. brown and violet 55 15

787. Haydn.

788. Mountain-Climbing.

1959. 150th Death Anniv. of Haydn (Austrian composer).
2338. **787.** 40 k. brown and blue 1·25 20

1959. Tourist Publicity. Multicoloured.
2339 40 k. Type **788** 65 20
2340 40 k. Map-reading .. 65 20
2341 40 k. Cross-country skiing 65 20
2342 40 k. Canoeing (horiz) .. 65 20

789. Exhibition Emblem and New York Coliseum.

790. Statue of Repin (painter).

1959. Russian Scientific, Technological and Cultural Exn., New York.
2343. **789.** 20 k. multicoloured .. 30 15
2344. 40 k. multicoloured .. 50 15

1959. Cultural Celebrities. Inscr. "1959". Statues in black.
2345. **790.** 10 k. ochre 15 10
2346. – 10 k. red 15 10
2347. – 20 k. lilac 25 10
2348. – 25 k. turquoise .. 35 10
2349. – 60 k. green 40 10
2350. – 1 r. blue 70 15
STATUES: 10 k. (No. 2346), Lenin. 20 k. V. Mayakovsky (poet). 25 k. Pushkin. 60 k. Gorky. 1 r. Tchaikovsky.

791. Sturgeon.

792. Louis Braille.

1959. Fisheries Protection.
2350a. – 20 k. black & blue .. 30 10
2350b. – 25 k. brown & lilac .. 50 10
2351. **791.** 40 k. black & turq. .. 55 15
2351a. – 40 k. purple & mauve 70 15
2352. – 60 k. black and blue 85 30
DESIGNS: 20 k. Perch. 25 k. Northern fur seals. 40 k. (No. 2351a), Salmon. 60 k. Salmon and map.

1959. 150th Birth Anniv. of Braille (inventor of Braille).
2353. **792.** 60 k. brn., yell. & turq. 65 20

793. Musa Djalil (Tatar poet).

794. Vaulting.

1959. Djalil Commem.
2354. **793.** 40 k. black & violet .. 40 15

1959. 2nd Russian Spartakiad. Inscr. "1959".
2355. **794.** 15 k. grey and purple 20 10
2356. – 25 k. grey, brn. & grn. 30 10
2357. – 30 k. olive and red .. 30 10
2358. – 60 k. grey, blue & yell. 55 15
DESIGNS—HORIZ. 25 k. Running. 60 k. Water-polo. VERT. 30 k. Athletes supporting Spartakiad emblem.

795.

796. Steel Worker.

1959. 2nd Int. T. U. Conference, Leipzig.
2359. **795.** 40 k. red, blue & yell. 35 15

1959. Seven Year Plan.
2360. – 10 k. red, blue & vio. 10 10
2361. – 10 k. light red, deep red and yellow .. 10 10
2362. – 15 k. red, yell. & brn. 10 10
2363. – 15 k. brn., grn. & bistre 10 10
2364. – 20 k. red, yell. & grn. 15 10
2365. – 20 k. multicoloured .. 15 10
2366. – 30 k. red, flesh & pur. 30 10
2366a. – 30 k. multicoloured .. 30 10
2367. **796.** 40 k. orge., yell. & bl. 35 10
2368. – 40 k. red, pink & blue 35 10
2369. – 60 k. red, blue & yell. 80 25
2370. – 60 k. red, buff & blue 80 25
DESIGNS: No. 2360, Chemist. No. 2361, Spassky Tower, hammer and sickle. No. 2362, Builder's labourer. No. 2363, Farm girl. No. 2364, Machine-minder. No. 2365, Tractor-driver. No. 2366, Oil technician. No. 2366a, Cloth production. No. 2368, Coal miner. No. 2369, Iron moulder. No. 2370, Power station.

797. Glaciologist.

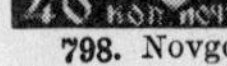

798. Novgorod.

1959. Int Geophysical Year (2nd issue).
2371. **797.** 10 k. turquoise .. 60 15
2372. – 25 k. red and blue .. 1·25 15
2373. – 40 k. red and blue .. 2·75 30
2373a. – 1 r. blue and yellow .. 3·00 75
DESIGNS: 25 k. Oceanographic survey ship "Vityaz". 40 k. Antarctic map, camp and emperor penguin. 1 r. Observatory and rocket.

1959. 11th Cent. of Novgorod.
2374. **798.** 40 k. red, brown & blue 40 15

799. Schoolboys in Workshop.

800. Exhibition Emblem.

1959. Industrial Training Scheme for School-leavers. Inscr. "1959".
2375. **799.** 40 k. violet .. . 30 10
2376. – 1 r. blue 60 30
DESIGN: 1 r. Children at night-school.

1959. All-Union Exhibition.
2377. **800.** 40 k. multicoloured .. 30 20

801. Russian and Chinese Students.

DESIGN: 40 k. Russian miner and Chinese foundryman.

1959. 10th Anniv. of Chinese Peoples' Republic.
2378. **801.** 20 k. multicoloured .. 20 15
2379. – 40 k. multicoloured .. 50 20

802. Postwoman.

803. Mahtumkuli.

1959. Int. Correspondence Week.
2380. **802.** 40 k. multicoloured .. 40 15
2381. 60 k. multicoloured .. 70 20

1959. 225th Birth Anniv. of Mahtumkuli (Turkestan writer).
2382. **803.** 40 k. brown 40 15

804. Arms and workers of the German Democratic Republic.

805. Lunik 3's trajectory around the Moon.

1959. 10th Anniv. of German Democratic Republic.
2383. **804.** 40 k. multicoloured .. 35 10
2384. – 60 k. purple & cream 40 15
DESIGN—VERT. 60 k. Town Hall, East Berlin.

1959. Launching of "Lunik 3" Rocket.
2385 **805** 40 k. violet .. .. 1·25 20

806. Republican Arms and Emblems.

807. Red Square, Moscow.

1959. 30th Anniv. of Tadzhikistan Republic.
2386. **806.** 40 k. multicoloured .. 45 15

1959. 42nd Anniv. of October Revolution.
2387. **807.** 40 k. red 40 15

808. Capitol, Washington and Kremlin, Moscow.

1959. Visit of Russian Prime Minister to U.S.A.
2388. **808.** 60 k. blue and yellow 65 25

809. Helicopter.

1959. Military Sports.
2389. **809.** 10 k. red and violet .. 30 10
2390. – 25 k. brown and blue 40 10
2391. – 40 k. blue and brown 60 15
2392. – 60 k. bistre and blue 90 25
DESIGNS: 25 k. Skin diver. 40 k. Racing motor cyclist. 60 k. Parachutist.

810. Track of Moon Rocket.

811. Statue and aerial view of Budapest.

1959. Landing of Russian Rocket on Moon Inscr. "14.IX.1959". Multicoloured.
2393. 40 k. Type **810** .. 65 20
2394. 40 k. Diagram of flight trajectory 65 20

1959. Hungarian Republic Commem. Mult.
2395. 20 k. Petofi (Hungarian poet) (horiz.) 25 15
2396. 40 k. Type **811** 45 20

812. Manolis Glezos (Greek Communist).

1959. Glezos Commem.
2397. **812.** 40 k. brown and blue 11·00 8·50

813. A. Voskresensky (chemist).

814. River Chusovaya.

1959. Voskresensky Commem.
2398. **813.** 40 k. brown and blue 50 20

1959. Tourist Publicity. Inscr. "1959".
2399. **814.** 10 k. violet 15 10
2400. – 10 k. mauve 15 10
2401. – 25 k. blue 30 10
2402. – 25 k. red 30 10
2403. – 25 k. olive 30 10
2404. – 40 k. red 50 10
2405. – 60 k. turquoise .. 65 15
2406. – 1 r. green .. .. 2·25 60
2407. – 1 r. orange .. .. 2·25 60
DESIGNS: No. 2400, Riza Lake, Caucasus. No. 2401, River Lena. No. 2402, Iskanderkuly Lake. No. 2403, Coastal region. No. 2404, Lake Baikal. No. 2405, Beluha Mountains, Altay. No. 2406, Hibinsky Mountain. No. 2407, Gursuff region, Crimea.

815. "The Trumpeters of the First Horse Army" (after Grekov).

1959. 40th Anniv. of Russian Cavalry.
2408. **815.** 40 k. multicoloured .. 85 20

816. A. P. Chekhov and Moscow Residence.

817. M. V. Frunze.

1960. Birth Cent. of Chekhov (writer).
2409. **816.** 20 k. red, brown and violet 25 10
2410. – 40 k. brn., bl. & sepia 50 15
DESIGN: 40 k. Chekhov and Yalta residence.

1960. 75th Birth Anniv. of M. V. Frunze (military leader).
2411. **817.** 40 k. brown 55 15

818. G. N. Gabrichevsky.

819. Vera Komissarzhevskaya.

1960. Birth Centenary of G. N. Gabrichevsky (microbiologist).
2412. **818.** 40 k. brown & violet 55 15

1960. 50th Death Anniv. of V. F. Komissarzhevskaya (actress).
2413. **819.** 40 k. brown 50 15

820. Free-skating.

1960. Winter Olympic Games.
2414. – 10 k. blue and orange 20 10
2415. – 25 k. multicoloured .. 35 10
2416. – 40 k. orge., bl. & pur. 60 10
2417. **820.** 60 k. viol., brn. & grn. 70 20
2418. – 1 r. blue, red & green 1·25 35
DESIGNS: 10 k. Ice hockey. 25 k. Ic skating. 40 k. Skiing. 1 r. Ski jumping.

821. Timur Frunze (fighter pilot) and Air Battle.

822. Helicopter over Kremlin.

1960. War Heroes. Multicoloured.
2419. 40 k. Type **821** .. .. 1·25 20
2420. 1 r. Gen. Cherniakovksy and battle scene .. 1·40 40

1960. Air.
2421. **822.** 60 k. blue .. .. 1·25 20

823. Women of various Races.

824. "Swords into Ploughshares".

1960. 50th Anniv. of Int. Women's Day.
2422. **823.** 40 k. multicoloured .. 50 20

1960. Presentation of Statue by Russia to U.N.
2423. **824.** 40 k. yellow, bistre and blue 40 15

15 лет
освобождения
Венгрии
(825.)

826. Lenin when a Child.

1960. 15th Anniv. of Liberation of Hungary. Optd. with T **825**.
2424. **811.** 40 k. multicoloured .. 3·25 2·50

1960. 90th Birth Anniv of Lenin. Portraits of Lenin. Multicoloured.
2425 **826** 10 k. multicoloured .. 10 10
2426 – 20 k. multicoloured .. 15 10
2427 – 30 k. multicoloured .. 25 15
2428 – 40 k. multicoloured .. 30 15
2429 – 60 k. multicoloured .. 1·10 25
2430 – 1 r. brown, blue & red 1·00 90
DESIGNS—Lenin: 20 k. holding child. 30 k. and revolutionary scenes. 40 k. with party banners. 60 k. and industrial scenes. 1 r. with globe and rejoicing people.

827. Lunik 3 photographing Moon.

828. Government House, Baku.

1960. Flight of Lunik 3. Inscr. "7.X.1959".
2431. **827.** 40 k. yellow and blue 90 25
2432. – 60 k. yell., blue & ind. 90 25
DESIGN: 60 k. Lunar map.

1960. 40th Anniv. of Azerbaijan Republic.
2433. **828.** 40 k. brn., bis. & yell. 50 15

829. "Fraternization" (after Pokorny).

830. Furnaceman.

1960. 15th Anniv. of Czechoslovak Republic.
2434. **829.** 40 k. black and blue 30 10
2435. – 60 k. brown & yellow 45 15
DESIGN: 60 k. Charles Bridge, Prague.

1960. Completion of First Year of Seven Year Plan.
2436. **830.** 40 k. brown and red .. 30 15

831. Popov Museum, Leningrad.

1960. Radio Day.
2437. **831.** 40 k. multicoloured .. 50 15

832. Robert Schumann.

833. Sverdlov.

1960. 150th Birth Anniv. of Schumann (composer).
2438. **832.** 40 k. black and blue .. 85 15

1960. 75th Birth Anniv of Ya. M. Sverdlov (statesman).
2439 **833** 40 k. sepia and brown 45 10

834. Magnifier and Stamp.

1960. Philatelists' Day.
2440. **834.** 60 k. multicoloured .. 50 15

835. Petrozavodsk (Karelian Republic).

1960. Capitals of Autonomous Republic (1st issue).
2441. **835.** 40 k. turquoise .. 60 20
2442. – 40 k. blue 60 20
2443. – 40 k. green 60 20
2444. – 40 k. purple 60 20
2445. – 40 k. red 60 20
2446. – 40 k. blue 60 20
2447. – 40 k. brown 90 20
2448. – 40 k. brown 60 20
2449. – 40 k. red 60 20
2450. – 40 k. brown 60 20
CAPITALS: Nos. 2442, Batumi (Adzharian). No. 2443, Izhevsk (Udmurt). No. 2444, Grozny (Chechen-Ingush). No. 2445, Cheboksary (Chuvash). No. 2446, Yakutsk (Yakut). No. 2447, Ordzhonikidze (North Ossetian). No. 2448, Nukus (Kara-Kalpak). No. 2449, Makhachkala (Daghestan). No. 2450, Yoshkar-Ola (Mari).

See also Nos. 2586/92 and 2703/5.

836. Children of Different Races.

838. Rocket.

1960. International Children's Day. Mult.
2451 10 k. Type **836** 15 10
2452 20 k. Children on farm (vert) 25 15
2453 25 k. Children with snowman 40 15
2454 40 k. Children in zoo gardens 65 20

1960. Karelian Autonomous Republic. 40th Anniv. Optd. **40 лет КАССР 8.VI.1960.**
2455. **835.** 40 k. turquoise .. 2·25 90

1960. Launching of Cosmic Rocket "Spacecraft 1" (first "Vostok" type spacecraft).
2456. **838.** 40 k. red and blue .. 1·40 35

839. I.F.A.C. Emblem.

1960. 1st Int. Automation Control Federation Congress, Moscow.
2457. **839.** 60 k. brown & yellow 2·00 30

1960. Kosta Hetagurov Commem. As T **746**. Inscr. " 1960 ".
2458. 40 k. brown and blue .. 50 15
DESIGN: 40 k. Portrait of Hetagurov and scene from his works.

840. Cement Works, Belgorod.

1960. First Plant Construction of Seven Year Plan.
2459 **840** 25 k. black and blue 25 10
2460 – 40 k. black and red .. 40 10
DESIGN: 40 k. Metal works, Novokrivorog.

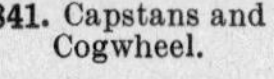

841. Capstans and Cogwheel. **842.** Vilnius (Lithuania).

1960. Industrial Mass-Production Plant.
2461. **841.** 40 k. turquoise .. 40 10
2462. – 40 k. purple (Factory plant) 40 10

1960. 20th Anniv of Soviet Baltic Republics. Multicoloured.
2463 40 k. Type **842** 45 10
2464 40 k. Riga (Latvia) .. 45 10
2465 40 k. Tallin (Estonia) .. 45 10

843. Running.

Международная ярмарка в Риччоне
(844.)

1960. Olympic Games. Inscr. " 1960 ". Multicoloured.
2466. 5 k. Type **843** 15 10
2467. 10 k. Wrestling 20 10
2468. 15 k. Basketball .. 35 10
2469. 20 k. Weightlifting .. 35 10
2470. 25 k. Boxing 35 10
2471. 40 k. High-diving .. 50 15
2472. 40 k. Fencing 50 15
2473. 40 k. Gymnastics .. 50 15
2474. 60 k. Canoeing 80 20
2475. 1 r. Horse-jumping .. 2·25 1·35

1960. 20th Anniv. of Moldavian Republic. As T **842**.
2476. 40 k. multicoloured .. 45 10
DESIGN: 40 k. Kishinev (capital).

1960. Int. Exhibition, Riccione. No. 2471 optd. with T **844**.
2477. 40 k. multicoloured .. 14·00 9·00

845. " Agriculture and Industry ". **846.** G. H. Minkh.

1960. 15th Anniv. of Vietnam Democratic Republic.
2478 40 k. Type **845** 40 15
2479 60 k. Book Museum, Hanoi (vert) 60 20

1960. 125th Birth Anniv. of G. H. Minkh. (epidemiologist).
2480. **846.** 60 k. brown and bistre 70 15

847. " March " (after I. Levitan).

1960. Birth Cent. of I. Levitan (painter).
2481. **847.** 40 k. black and olive 80 15

848. " Forest " (after Shishkin).

1960. 5th World Forestry Congress, Seattle.
2482. **848.** 1 r. brown .. .. 2·00 45

849. Addressing Letter.

1960. Int. Correspondence Week.
2483. **849.** 40 k. multicoloured .. 40 10
2484. 60 k. multicoloured .. 70 20

850. Kremlin, Dogs " Belka " and " Strelka ", and Rocket Trajectory.

1960. Second Cosmic Rocket Flight.
2485. **850.** 40 k. purple & yellow 80 15
2486. 1 r. blue and orange .. 1·40 25

851. Globes. **852.** People of Kazakhstan.

1960. 15th Anniv. of W.F.T.U.
2487. **851.** 60 k. bl., drab & lilac 50 15

1960. 40th Anniv. of Kazakh Soviet Republic.
2488. **852.** 40 k. multicoloured .. 50 10

853. " Karl Marx ". **854.** A. N. Voronikhin and Leningrad Cathedral.

1960. River Boats. Multicoloured.
2489 25 k. Type **853** 45 10
2490 40 k. "Lenin" 65 15
2491 60 k. "Raketa" (hydrofoil) .. .. 1·10 25

1960. Birth Bicentenary of A. N. Voronikhin (architect).
2492. **854.** 40 k. black and grey 45 10

855. Motor Coach. **856.** J. S. Gogebashvily.

1960. Russian Motor Industry.
2493. – 25 k. black and blue 40 10
2494. – 40 k. blue and olive 55 15
2495. – 60 k. red & turquoise 1·10 20
2496. **855.** 1 r. multicoloured .. 1·75 35
DESIGNS: 25 k. Lorry. 40 k. "Volga" car. 60 k. "Moskvich" car.

1960. 120th Birth Anniv. of J. S. Gogebashvily (Georgian teacher).
2497. **856.** 40 k. black and lake 45 10

857. Industrial Plant and Power Plant. **858.** Federation Emblem.

1960. 43rd Anniv. of October Revolution.
2498. **857.** 40 k. multicoloured .. 55 15

1960. 15th Anniv. of International Federation of Democratic Women.
2499. **858.** 60 k. red and grey .. 55 15

859. Youth of Three Races.

40 лет Удмуртской АССР 4/XI 1960.
(860.)

1960. 15th Anniv of World Democratic Youth Federation.
2500 **859** 60 k. multicoloured .. 55 15

1960. 40th Anniv. of Udmurt Autonomous Republic. No. 2443 optd. with T **860**.
2501 40 k. green .. .. 2·25 90

861. Tolstoi and his Moscow Residence. **862.** Government House, Yerevan.

1960. 50th Death Anniv of Leo Tolstoi (writer).
2502 **861** 20 k. multicoloured .. 25 15
2503 – 40 k. brn, sepia & bl 40 15
2504 – 60 k. multicoloured .. 1·00 25
DESIGNS—HORIZ. 40 k. Tolstoi and his country estate. VERT. 60 k. Full-face portrait.

1960. 40th Anniv. of Armenian Republic.
2505. **862.** 40 k. multicoloured .. 45 10

863. Students and University. **864.** Tulip.

1960. Opening of Friendship University, Moscow.
2506. **863.** 40 k. purple 45 10

1960. Russian Flowers. Multicoloured.
2507. 20 k. Type **864** 30 10
2508. 20 k. Autumn crocus .. 30 10
2509. 25 k. Marsh marigold .. 30 10
2510. 40 k. Tulip 40 10
2511. 40 k. Panax 40 10
2512. 60 k. Hypericum .. 75 25
2513. 60 k. Iris 75 25
2514. 1 r. Wild Rose .. 1·50 40

865. Engels. **866.** Mark Twain.

1960. 140th Birth Anniv. of Engels.
2515. **865.** 60 k. grey 90 20

1960. 125th Birth Anniv. of Mark Twain.
2516. **866.** 40 k. bistre & orange 2·25 1·10

867. N. Pirogov. **868.** Chopin.

1960. 150th Birth Anniv. of N. Pirogov (surgeon).
2517. **867.** 40 k. brown & green .. 45 10

1960. 150th Birth Anniv. of Chopin.
2518. **868.** 40 k. bistre and buff 1·50 20

869. North Korean Flag and Emblem. **870.** Lithuanian Costumes.

1960. 15th Anniv. of Korean Liberation.
2519. **869.** 40 k. multicoloured .. 70 15

1960. Provincial Costumes (1st issue). Inscr. " 1960 ". Multicoloured.
2520. 10 k. Type **870** 35 15
2521. 60 k. Uzbek costumes .. 1·40 25
See also Nos. 2537/45, 2796 and 2835/8.

871. A. Tseretely.

1960. 120th Birth Anniv. of A. Tseretely (Georgian poet).
2522. **871.** 40 k. purple and lilac 65 10

Currency Revalued.
10 (old) Kopeks = 1 (new) Kopek

872. Worker. **873.** "Ruslan and Lyudmila".

1961. Inscr. " 1961 ".
2531 **872** 1 k. bistre 40 10
2524 – 2 k. green 25 10
2525 – 3 k. violet .. .. 2·00 10
2526 – 4 k. red 45 10
2526a – 4 k. brown .. .. 3·00 1·40
2527 – 6 k. red .. .. 2·00 30
2528 – 6 k. claret .. .. 1·00 10
2529 – 10 k. orange .. .. 1·25 10
2533 – 12 k. purple .. .. 1·40 10
2530 – 16 k. blue .. .. 2·75 15
DESIGNS: 2 k. Combine-harvester. 3 k. Cosmic rocket. 4 k. Soviet Arms and Flag. 6 k. Spassky Tower and Kremlin. 10 k. Workers' Statue. 12 k. Monument and Spassky Tower. 16 k. Aircraft over power-station.

1961. Russian Wild Life. As T **653** but inscr. "1961". Centres in natural colours. Frame colours given.
2534. 1 k. sepia (Brown bear) 25 15
2535. 6 k. black (Eurasian beaver) .. .. 1·00 20
2536. 10 k. black (Roe deer) .. 1·25 55
The 1 k. is vert. and the rest horiz.

1961. Provincial Costumes (2nd issue). As T **870** but inscr. " 1961 ".
2537. 2 k. red, brown & stone .. 40 10
2538. 2 k. multicoloured .. 45 10
2539. 3 k. multicoloured .. 85 15
2540. 3 k. multicoloured .. 90 15
2541. 3 k. multicoloured .. 90 15
2542. 4 k. multicoloured .. 1·10 15
2543. 6 k. multicoloured .. 1·40 15
2544. 10 k. multicoloured .. 2·50 15
2545. 12 k. multicoloured .. 4·75 45
COSTUMES: No. 2537, Moldavia. No. 2538, Georgia. No. 2539, Ukraine. No. 2540, Byelorussia. No. 2541, Kazakhs. No. 2542, Koryaks. No. 2543, Russia. No. 2544, Armenia. No. 2545, Estonia.

1961. Scenes from Russian Fairy Tales. Multicoloured.
2546. 1 k. "Geese-Swans" .. 35 10
2547. 3 k. "The Fox, the Hare and the Cock" .. 55 15
2548. 4 k. "The Little Hump-backed Horse" .. 75 15
2549. 6 k. "The Muzhik and the Bear" .. .. .. 1·00 20
2550. 10 k. Type **873** .. .. 3·75 40

874. Lenin, Map and Power Station.

1961. 40th Anniv. of State Electricity Plan.
2551. **874.** 4 k. brn., yell. & blue 60 15
2552. 10 k. black, purple and salmon .. .. 1·25 25

875. Tractor. **876.** N. A. Dobrolyubov.

1961. Soviet Agricultural Achievements Inscr. "1961".
2553. – 3 k. mauve and blue 30 15
2554. **875.** 4 k. black and green 30 10
2555. – 6 k. brown and blue .. 45 25
2556. – 10 k. purple and olive 70 15
DESIGNS: 3 k. Dairy herd. 6 k. Agricultural machinery. 10 k. Fruit Picking.

1961. 125th Birth Anniv. of N. A. Dobrolyubov (writer).
2557. **876.** 4 k. buff, blk. & blue 45 15

877. N. D. Zelinsky.

1961. Birth Cent. of N. D. Zelinsky (chemist).
2558. **877.** 4 k. purple and mauve 45 15

878. Georgian Republic Flag.

1961. 40th Anniv. of Georgian Republic.
2559. **878.** 4 k. multicoloured .. 30 10

879. Sgt. Miroshnichenko and Battle.

1961. War Hero.
2560. **879.** 4 k. blue & purple .. 55 10
See also Nos. 2664/5.

880. T. G. Shevchenko and Birthplace. **881.** A. Rublev.

1961. Death Centenary of T. G. Shevchenko (Ukrainian Poet and painter).
2561. **880.** 3 k. brown and violet 20 10
2562. – 6 k. purple and green 55 15
DESIGN: 6 k. Portrait of Shevchenko in old age, pen, book and candle.
See also No. 2956/62.

1961. 600th Birth Anniv. of Rublev (painter).
2563. **881.** 4 k. multicoloured .. 60 20

882. Statue of Shevchenko (poet). **883.** N. V. Sklifosovsky.

1961. Cultural Celebrities.
2564. – 2 k. brown and blue .. 25 10
2565. **882.** 4 k. brown & black .. 20 15
2566. – 4 k. brown and purple 30 15
DESIGNS: 2 k. Shchors Monument, Kiev. 4 k. (No. 2566), Kotovsky Monument, Kishinev.

1961. 125th Birth Anniv. of N. V. Sklifosovsky (surgeon).
2567. **883.** 4 k. black and blue .. 45 10

884. Robert Koch. **885.** Zither-player and Folk Dancers.

1961. 50th Death Anniv. of Robert Koch (German microbiologist).
2568. **884.** 6 k. brown 70 20

1961. 50th Anniv. of Russian National Choir.
2569. **885.** 4 k. multicoloured 45 10

886. "Popular Science".

1961. Centenary of "Vokrug Sveta" (science magazine).
2570. **886.** 6 k. brown, blue and deep blue 90 30

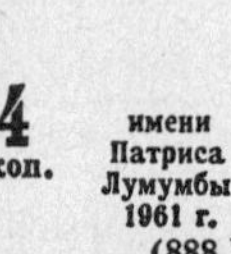

887. Venus Rocket. **(888.)**

1961. Launching of Venus Rocket.
2571. **887.** 6 k. orange and blue 1·25 20
2572. – 10 k. blue and yellow 1·75 40
DESIGN: 10 k. Capsule and flight route.

1961. Patrice Lumumba (Conglese politician) Commem (1st issue). Surch with T **888.**
2573 **863** 4 k. on 40 k. purple .. 75 85
See also No. 2593.

889. African breaking Chains.

1961. Africa Freedom Day. Inscr. "1961".
2574. **889.** 4 k. multicoloured .. 20 10
2575. – 6 k. pur., orge. & blue 35 20
DESIGN: 6 k. Hands clasping torch of freedom, and map.

891. Yuri Gagarin. **892.** Lenin.

1961. World's First Manned Space Flight. Inscr. "12-IV-1961". Perf. or imperf.
2576. **891.** 3 k. blue 45 10
2577. – 6 k. blue, vio. & red 55 20
2578. – 10 k. red, grn. & brn. 1·00 30
DESIGNS: (37×26 mm.): 6 k. Rocket and Spassky Tower. 10 k. Rocket, Gagarin and Kremlin.

1961. 91st Birth Anniv. of Lenin.
2579. **892.** 4 k. blk., salm. & red 30 10

893. Rabindranath Tagore. **894.** Garibaldi.

1961. Birth Cent. of Tagore (Indian writer).
2580. **893.** 6 k. blk., bistre & red 40 15

1961. Int. Labour Exhibition, Turin.
2581. – 4 k. salmon and red .. 40 10
2582. **894.** 6 k. salmon and lilac 55 15
DESIGN: 4 k. Statue.

895. Lenin. **896.** Patrice Lumumba.

1961.
2583. **895.** 20 k. green and brown 1·10 50
2584. – 30 k. blue and brown 1·90 1·10
2585. – 50 k. red and brown .. 2·75 1·75
PORTRAITS (Lenin): 30 k. In cap. 50 k. Profile.

1961. Capitals of Autonomous Republics (2nd issue). As T **835.**
2586. 4 k. deep violet 55 15
2587. 4 k. blue 55 15
2588. 4 k. orange 55 15
2589. 4 k. black 55 15
2590. 4 k. lake 55 15
2591. 4 k. green 55 15
2592. 4 k. deep purple 55 15
CAPITALS: No. 2586, Nalchik (Kabardino-Balkar). No. 2587, Ulan-Ude (Buryat). No. 2588, Sukhumi (Abkhazia). No. 2589, Syktyvkar (Komi). No. 2590, Nakhichevan (Nakhichevan). No. 2591, Rodina Cinema, Elista (Kalmyk). No. 2592, Ufa (Bashkir).

1961. Lumumba Commeoration (2nd issue).
2593. **896.** 2 k. multicoloured .. 15 10

897. Kindergarten. **898.** Chernushka and Rocket.

1961. Int. Children's Day.
2594. **897.** 2 k. blue and orange 15 10
2595. – 3 k. violet and ochre 25 10
2596. – 4 k. drab and red .. 40 15
DESIGNS—HORIZ. 3 k. Children in Pioneer camp. VERT. 4 k. Children with toys and pets.

1961. 4th and 5th "Spacecraft" Flights.
2597. – 2 k. blk., blue & vio. 35 15
2598. **898.** 4 k. turquoise & blue 65 15
DESIGN—HORIZ. 2 k. Dog "Zvezdochka", rocket and Controller (inscr. "25.III.1961").

899. Belinsky (after I. Astafev). **900.**

1961. 150th Birth Anniv of Vissarion Grigorievich Belinsky (literary critic and journalist).
2599 **899** 4 k. black and red .. 30 15

1961. 40th Anniv. of Soviet Hydro-metereological Service.
2600. **900.** 6 k. multicoloured .. 90 25

INDEX

Countries can be quickly located by referring to the index at the end of this volume.

901. D. M. Karbyshev. **902.** Glider.

1961. Lieut.-Gen. Karbyshev (war hero).
2601. **901.** 4 k. black, red & yell. 30 10

1961. Soviet Spartakiad.
2602. **902.** 4 k. red and grey .. 30 10
2603. – 6 k. red and grey .. 45 15
2604. – 10 k. red and grey .. 85 35
DESIGNS: 6 k. Inflatable motor boat. 10 k. Motor cyclist.

903. Sukhe Bator Monument and Govt. Buildings, Ulan Bator. **904.** S. I. Vavilov.

1961. 40th Anniv. of Revolution in Mongolia.
2605. **903.** 4 k. multicoloured .. 50 15

1961. 70th Birthday of Vavilov (scientist).
2606. **904.** 4 k. brown, bis. & grn. 30 15

905. V. Pshavela. **906.** "Youth Activities".

1961. Birth Cent. of Pshavela (Georgian poet).
2607. **905.** 4 k. brown and cream 25 10

1961. World Youth Forum.
2608. – 2 k. brown and orange 20 10
2609. – 4 k. green and lilac .. 65 10
2610. **906.** 6 k. blue and ochre .. 70 25
DESIGNS—HORIZ. 2 k. Youths pushing tank into river. VERT. 4 k. "Youths and progress".

907. **908.**

1961. 5th Int. Biochemical Congress, Moscow.
2611. **907.** 6 k. multicoloured .. 65 15

1961. Cent. of "Kalevipoeg" (Estonian Saga).
2612. **908.** 4 k. yell., turq. & blk. 25 10

909. Javelin Thrower.

1961. 7th Soviet Trade Union Sports.
2613. **909.** 6 k. red 40 15

910. A. D. Zakharov.

1961. Birth Bicent. of Zakharov (architect).
2614. **910.** 4 k. buff, brown & blue 40 15

911. Counter-attack.

912. Union Emblem.

1961. War of 1941-45 (1st issue). Inscr. "1961".
2615. 911. 4 k. multicoloured .. 65 15
2616. – 4 k. multicoloured .. 65 15
2617. – 4 k. indigo and brown 65 15
DESIGNS: No. 2616, Sailor with bayonet. No. 2617, Soldier with tommy-gun.
See also Nos. 2717 and 2851/5.

1961. 15th Anniv. of Int. Union of Students.
2617a. 912. 6 k. violet and red .. 35 10

913. Stamps Commemorating Industry.

1961. 40th Anniv. of First Soviet Stamp. Centres multicoloured.
2618. 913. 2 k. ochre and brown 30 15
2619. – 4 k. blue and indigo .. 45 15
2620. – 6 k. green and olive .. 70 15
2621. – 10 k. buff and brown 1·10 45
DESIGNS (Stamps commemorating): 4 k. Electrification. 6 k. Peace. 10 k. Atomic energy.

914. Titov and "Vostok 2".

1961. 2nd Manned Space Flight. Perf. or imperf.
2622. – 4 k. blue and purple 30 10
2623. 914. 6 k. orge., grn. & brn. 55 20
DESIGN: 4 k. Space pilot and globe.

915. Angara River Bridge.

1961. Tercent. of Irkutsk, Siberia.
2624. 915. 4 k. black, lilac & bis. 40 10

916. Letters and Mail Transport.

1961. International Correspondence Week.
2625. 916. 4 k. black and mauve 55 10

917. Workers and Banners.

1961. 22nd Communist Party Congress (1st issue).
2626. 917. 2 k. brn., yell. & red 15 10
2627. – 3 k. blue and orange 60 15
2628. – 4 k. red, buff & purple 25 10
2629. – 4 k. orge., blk. & pur. 40 10
2630. – 4 k. sepia, brn. & red 25 15
DESIGNS: No. 2627, Moscow University and obelisk. No. 2628, Combine-harvester. No. 2629, Workmen and machinery. No. 2630, Worker and slogan.
See also No. 2636.

MINIMUM PRICE

The minimum price quoted is 5p which represents a handling charge rather than a basis for valuing common stamps. For further notes about prices see introductory pages.

918. Soviet Monument, Berlin.

919. Adult Education.

1961. 10th Anniv of International Federation of Resistance Fighters.
2631 918 4 k. grey and red .. 25 10

1961. Communist Labour Teams.
2632. – 2 k. pur. & red on buff 12 5
2633. 919. 3 k. brn. & red on buff 15 5
2634. – 4 k. bl. & red on cream 35 5
DESIGNS: 2 k. Worker at machine. 4 k. Workers around piano.

920. Rocket and Globes.

1961. Cosmic Flights. Aluminium-surfaced paper.
2635. 920. 1 r. red & blk. on silver 13·00 13·00

922. A. Imanov (Kazakh leader).

XXII съезд КПСС (921.)

923. Liszt, Piano and Music.

1961. 22nd Communist Party Congress (2nd issue). Optd. with T 921.
2636. 920. 1 r. red & blk. on silver 13·00 15·00

1961. Imanov Commem.
2637. 922. 4 k. sepia, brn. & grn. 20 10

1961. 150th Birth Anniv. of Liszt.
2638. 923. 4 k. brown, pur. & yell. 75 15

924. Flags, Rocket and Skyline.

1961. 44th Anniv. of October Revolution.
2639. 924. 4 k. red, pur. and yell. 50 15

925. Congress Emblem.

926. M. V. Lomonosov and Lomonosov University.

1961. 5th W.F.T.U. Congress, Moscow. Inscr. "МОСКВА 1961".
2640. 925. 2 k. red and bistre .. 25 10
2641. – 2 k. violet and grey .. 25 10
2642. – 4 k. brn., pur. & bl. .. 45 10
2643. – 4 k. red, blue & violet 45 10
2644. 925. 6 k. red, bistre & grn. 70 15
2645. – 6 k. blue, pur. & bis. 70 15
DESIGNS—HORIZ. Nos. 2641, 2645, Negro breaking chains. VERT. No. 2642, Hand holding hammer. No. 2643, Hands holding globe.

1961. 250th Birth Anniv. of Lomonosov (scientist).
2646. 926. 4 k. brn., grn. & blue 30 15
2647. – 6 k. blue, buff & grn. 50 20
2648. – 10 k. brn., blue & pur. 1·00 40
DESIGNS—VERT. 6 k. Lomonosov at desk. HORIZ. 10 k. Lomonosov, his birthplace, and Leningrad Academy of Science.

927. Power Workers.

928. Scene from "Romeo and Juliet".

1961. Young Builders of Seven Year Plan. Inscr. "1961".
2649. 927. 3 k. grey, brn. & red 35 15
2650. – 4 k. brown, blue & red 45 15
2651. – 6 k. grey, brn. & red 75 20
DESIGNS: 4 k. Welders. 6 k. Engineer with theodolite.

1961. Russian Ballet (1st issue). Inscr. "1961". Multicoloured.
2652. 6 k. Type 928 .. .. 1·00 15
2653. 10 k. Scene from "Swan Lake" .. .. .. 1·40 25
See also Nos. 2666/7.

929. Hammer and Sickle.

930. A. Pumpur.

1961. 25th Anniv. of Soviet Constitution.
2654. 929. 4 k. lake, yell. & red .. 30 10

1961. 120th Birth Anniv. of Pumpur (Lettish poet).
2655. 930. 4 k. purple and grey 25 10

1961. Air. Surch. **1961 r. 6 kon.** and bars.
2656. 822. 6 k. on 60 k. blue .. 90 20

932. "Bulgarian Achievements".

1961. 15th Anniv. of Bulgarian Republic.
2657. 923. 4 k. multicoloured .. 25 10

933. Nansen and "Fram".

1961. Birth Cent. of Nansen (explorer).
2658. 933. 6 k. brown, blue & blk. 1·75 15

934. M. Dolivo-Dobrovolsky.

935. A. S. Pushkin.

1962. Birth Cent. of Dolivo-Dobrovolsky (electrical engineer).
2659. 934. 4 k. blue and bistre .. 25 10

1962. 125th Death Anniv. of Pushkin (poet).
2660. 935. 4 k. black, red & buff 20 10

936. Soviet Woman.

1962. Soviet Women.
2661 936 4 k. black, bis & orge 25 10

937. People's Dancers.

1962. 25th Anniv. of Soviet People's Dance Ensemble.
2662. 937. 4 k. brown and red .. 35 10

938. Skaters.

СОВЕТСКИЕ КОНЬКОБЕЖЦЫ–ЧЕМПИОНЫ МИРА (939.)

1962. Ice Skating Championships, Moscow.
2663 938 4 k. blue and orange 40 10

1962. War Heroes. As T 879 but inscr. "1962".
2664. 4 k. brown and blue .. 75 15
2665. 6 k. turquoise and brown 1·00 20
DESIGNS: 4 k. Lieut. Shalandin, tanks and 'planes. 6 k. Capt. Gadzhiev, "K-3" submarine and sinking ship.

1962. Russian Ballet (2nd issue). As T 928 but inscr. "1962".
2666. 2 k. multicoloured .. 60 15
2667. 3 k. multicoloured .. 65 15
DESIGNS: Scenes from—2 k. "Red Flower" (Glier). 3 k. "Paris Flame" (Prokofiev).

1962. Soviet Victory in Ice Skating Championships. Optd with T 939.
2668. 938. 4 k. blue and orange 2·50 1·50

940. Skiing.

1962. 1st People's Winter Games, Sverdlovsk.
2669. 940. 4 k. violet and red .. 45 15
2670. – 6 k. turquoise & pur. 1·00 20
2671. – 10 k. red, black & bl. 1·25 30
DESIGN: 6 k. Ice hockey. 10 k. Figure skating.

941. A. I. Herzen.

942. Lenin on Banner.

1962. 150th Birth Anniv. of A. I. Herzen (writer).
2672. 941. 4 k. flesh, black & bl. 25 10

1962. 14th Leninist Young Communist League Congress. Inscr. "1962".
2673. 942. 4 k. red, yell. & purple 20 10
2674. – 6 k. pur., orge. & blue 25 10
DESIGN—HORIZ. 6 k. Lenin on flag.

943. Rocket and Globe.

944. Tchaikovsky (after sculpture by Z. M. Vilensky).

1962. 1st Anniv. of World's First Manned Space Flight. Perf. or Imperf.
2675. 943. 10 k. multicoloured .. 45 20

1962. 2nd Int. Tchaikovsky Music Competition.
2676. 944. 4 k. drab, black & bl. 40 10

945. Youth of Three Races.

946. The Ulyanov (Lenin's) Family.

1962. Int. Day of "Solidarity of Youth against Colonialism".
2677. **945.** 6 k. multicoloured .. 30 10

1962. 92nd Birth Anniv of Lenin.
2678 **946** 4 k. brown, grey & red 25 15
2679 – 10 k. purple, red & blk 75 30
DESIGN: 10 k. Lenin.

947. "Cosmos 3". **948.** Charles Dickens.

1962. Cosmic Research.
2680 **947** 6 k. black, violet & bl 50 15

1962. 150th Birth Anniv. of Charles Dickens.
2681. **948.** 6 k. purple, turquoise and olive .. 50 15

949. J. J. Rousseau. **950.** Karl Marx Monument, Moscow.

1962. 250th Birth Anniv. of Rousseau.
2682. **949.** 6 k. bistre, grey & pur. 50 15

1962. Karl Marx Commem.
2683. **950.** 4 k. grey and blue .. 20 10

951. Lenin reading "Pravda". **952.** Mosquito and Campaign Emblem.

1962. 50th Anniv. of "Pravda" Newspaper.
2684. **951.** 4 k. purple, red & buff 25 15
2685. – 4 k. multicoloured .. 25 15
2686. – 4 k. multicoloured .. 25 15
DESIGNS (25×38 mm.): No. 2685, Statuary and front page of first issue of "Pravda". No. 2686, Lenin and modern front page of "Pravda".

1962. Malaria Eradication. Perf. (6 k. also imperf.).
2687. **952.** 4 k. black, turq. & red 20 10
2688. 6 k. black, grn. & red 25 10

953. Model Rocket Construction.

1962. 40th Anniv. of All-Union Lenin Pioneer Organization. Designs embody Pioneer badge. Multicoloured.
2689. 2 k. Lenin and Pioneers giving Oath 25 10
2690. 3 k. L. Golikov and V. Kotik (pioneer heroes) 25 10
2691. 4 k. Type **953** 35 10
2692. 4 k. Hygiene education .. 40 20
2693. 6 k. Pioneers marching .. 70 25

954. M. Mashtotz. **955.** Ski Jumping.

957. Cycle Racing. **956.** I. Goncharov.

1962. 1600th Birth Anniv. of Mesrop Mashtotz (author of Armenian Alphabet).
2694. **954.** 4 k. brown and yellow 25 10

1962. F.I.S. Int. Ski Championships, Zakopane (Poland).
2695. **955.** 2 k. red, brn. & blue 20 10
2696. – 10 k. blue, black & red 80 35
DESIGN—VERT. 10 k. Skier.

1962. 150th Birth Anniv. of I. Goncharov (writer).
2697. **956.** 4 k. brown and grey 35 10

1962. Summer Sports Championships.
2698. **957.** 2 k. blk., red & brown 40 10
2699. – 4 k. blk., yell. & brn. 75 20
2700. – 10 k. blk., lemon & bl. 80 30
2701. – 12 k. brn., yell. & blue 95 40
2702. – 16 k. multicoloured .. 1·50 50
DESIGN—VERT. 4 k. Volleyball. 10 k. Rowing. 16 k. Horse-jumping. HORIZ. 12 k. Football (goal-keeper).

1962. Capitals of Autonomous Republics. 3rd issue. As T **835**.
2703. 4 k. black 50 15
2704. 4 k. purple 50 15
2705. 4 k. green 50 15
CAPITALS: No. 2703, Kazan (Tatar). No. 2704, Kyzyl (Tuva). No. 2705, Saransk (Mordovian).

958. Lenin Library, 1862.

DESIGN: No. 2707, Modern library building.

1962. Centenary of Lenin Library.
2706. **958.** 4 k. black and grey .. 35 15
2707. – 4 k. black and grey .. 35 15

959. Fur Bourse, Leningrad, and Ermine.

1962. Fur Bourse Commem.
2708. **959.** 6 k. multicoloured .. 55 20

960. Pasteur. **961.** Youth and Girl with Book.

1962. Cent. of Pasteur's Sterilisation Process.
2709. **960.** 6 k. brown and black 60 15

1962. Communist Party Programme. Mult.
2710. 2 k. Type **961** 15 10
2711. 4 k. Workers of three races and dove .. 25 10

962. Hands breaking Bomb. **963.** Y. Kupala and Y. Kolas.

1962. World Peace Congress, Moscow.
2712. **962.** 6 k. bistre, blk. & blue 30 15

1962. Byelorussian Poets Commem.
2713. **963.** 4 k. brown and yellow 25 10

964. Sabir. **965.** Congress Emblem.

1962. Birth Cent. of Sabir (Azerbaijan poet).
2714. **964.** 4 k. brn., buff & blue 25 10

1962. 8th Anti-Cancer Congress, Moscow.
2715. **965.** 6 k. red, black & blue 45 15

966. N. N. Zinin. **967.** M. V. Nesterov (painter).

1962. 150th Birth Anniv. of N. N. Zinin (chemist).
2716. **966.** 4 k. brown and violet 25 10

1962. War of 1941-45 (2nd issue). As T **911** inscr. "1962".
2717. 4 k. multicoloured .. 55 15
DESIGN: Sailor throwing petrol bomb.

1962. Russian Artists Commemoration.
2718. **967.** 4 k. multicoloured .. 30 15
2719. – 4 k. brn., pur. & grey 30 15
2720. – 4 k. black and brown 30 15
PORTRAITS—VERT. No. 2719, I. N. Kramskoi (painter). HORIZ. No. 2220, I. D. Shadr (sculptor).

968. "Vostok-2". **969.** Nikolaev and "Vostok 3".

1962. 1st Anniv. of Titov's Space Flight. Perf. or imperf.
2721 **968** 10 k. purple, blk & bl 40 25
2722 10 k. orange, blk & bl 40 25

1962. 1st "Team" Manned Space Flight. Perf. or imperf.
2723. **969.** 4 k. brown, red & blue 50 15
2724. – 4 k. brown, red & blue 50 15
2725. – 6 k. multicoloured .. 65 20
DESIGNS: No. 2724, As Type **969** but with Popovich and "Vostok-4". No. 2725 (47×28½ mm.), Cosmonauts in flight.

970. House of Friendship.

1962. People's House of Friendship, Moscow.
2726. **970.** 6 k. grey and blue .. 30 10

971. Lomonosov University and Atomic Symbols.

1962. "Atoms for Peace".
2727. **971.** 4 k. multicoloured .. 35 10
2728. – 6 k. multicoloured .. 50 20
DESIGN: 6 k. Map of Russia, Atomic symbol and "Peace" in ten languages.

972. Sazan and Bream. **973.** F. E. Dzerzhinsky.

1962. Fish Preservation Campaign.
2729. **972.** 4 k. yell., vio. & blue 30 10
2730. – 6 k. blue, black & orge. 50 20
DESIGN: 6 k. Freshwater salmon.

1962. 85th Birth Anniv of Feliks Dzerzhinsky (founder of Cheka).
2731 **973** 4 k. blue and green .. 25 10

974. O. Henry.

1962. Birth Cent. of O. Henry (American writer).
2732. **974.** 6 k. blk., brn. & yell. 35 10

975. Field-Marshals Barclay de Tolly, Kutuzov and Bagration.

1962. 150th Anniv. of Patriotic War of 1812.
2733. **975.** 3 k. brown 55 10
2734. – 4 k. blue 65 15
2735. – 6 k. slate 75 20
2736. – 10 k. violet .. .. 1·10 25
DESIGNS: 4 k. Davidov and partisans. 6 k. Battle of Borodino. 10 k. Partisans escorting French prisoners-of-war.

976. Vinnitsa.

977. Transport, "Stamp" and "Postmark". **978.** Cedar.

1962. 600th Anniv. of Vinnitsa.
2737. **976.** 4 k. black and bistre 30 10

1962. Int. Correspondence Week.
2738. **977.** 4 k. blk., pur. & turq. 30 10

1962. 150th Anniv. of Nikitsky Botanical Gardens. Multicoloured.
2739. 3 k. Type **978** 35 10
2740. 4 k. "Vostok-2" canna (plant) 55 10
2741. 6 k. Strawberry tree (arbutus) 70 15
2742. 10 k. "Road to the Stars" chrysanthemum .. 95 25

979. Builder. **980.** "Sputnik 1".

982. Harvester. **981.** Akhundov.

1962. "The Russian People". Multicoloured.
2743. 4 k. Type **979** 30 15
2744. 4 k. Textile worker .. 30 15
2745. 4 k. Surgeon 30 15
2746. 4 k. Farm girl 30 15
2747. 4 k. P.T. instructor .. 30 15
2748. 4 k. Housewife 30 15
2749. 4 k. Rambler 30 15

1962. 5th Anniv. of Launching of "Sputnik 1".
2750. **980.** 10 k. multicoloured .. 75 30

1962. 150th Birth Anniv of M. F. Akhundov (poet).
2751 **981** 4 k. brown and green 20 10

1962. "Settlers on Virgin Lands". Mult.
2752 4 k. Type **982** 50 20
2753 4 k. Surveyors, tractors and map 50 20
2754 4 k. Pioneers with flag .. 50 20

983. N. N. Burdenko.

1962. Soviet Scientists. Inscr. "1962". Multicoloured.
2755. 4 k. Type **983** 25 10
2756. 4 k. V. P. Filatov (wearing beret) .. 25 10

984. Lenin Mausoleum.

1962. 92nd Birth Anniv of Lenin.
2757 984 4 k. multicoloured .. 25 10

985. Worker with Banner.

986. "Towards the Stars".

ЗЕМЛЯ—МАРС
1.XI.
(987.)

1962. 45th Anniv. of October Revolution.
2758. 985. 4 k. multicoloured .. 20 10

1962. Space Flights Commem. Perf. or imperf.
2759. 986. 6 k. black, brn. & blue 35 10
2760. 10 k. ult., bis. & violet 45 20

1962. Launching of Rocket to Mars (1st issue). Optd. with T 987.
2761. 986. 10 k. bl., bis. & violet 2·00 1·75
See also No. 2765.

988. T. Moldo (Kirghiz poet).

989. Hammer and Sickle.

1962. Poet's Anniversaries.
2762. 988. 4 k. black and red .. 30 10
2763. – 4 k. black and blue .. 30 10
DESIGN: No. 2763, Sayat-Nova (Armenian poet) with musical instrument.

1962. 40th Anniv of U.S.S.R.
2764 989 4 k. yellow, red and crimson 20 10

990. Mars Rocket in Space. (Actual size $73\frac{1}{2} \times 27\frac{1}{2}$ mm.).

1962. Launching of Rocket to Mars (2nd issue).
2765. 990. 10 k. violet and red .. 90 30

991. Chemical Industry and Statistics.

1962. 22nd Communist Party Congress. "Achievements of the People". Multicoloured.
2766. 4 k. Type 991 .. .. 55 20
2767. 4 k. Engineering (machinery and atomic symbol) .. 55 20
2768. 4 k. Hydro-electric power 55 20
2769. 4 k. Agriculture (harvester) 55 20
2770. 4 k. Engineering (surveyor and welder) .. 55 20
2771. 4 k. Communications (telephone installation) 55 20
2772. 4 k. Heavy industry (furnace) 55 20
2773. 4 k. Transport (signalman, etc.) 65 20
2774. 4 k. Dairy-farming (milk-maid, etc.) 55 20
All the designs show production targets relating to 1980.

992. Chessmen.

994. V. K. Blucher (military commander).

993. Four Soviet Cosmonauts (actual size 151 × 70 mm.).

1962. 30th Soviet Chess Championships, Yerevan.
2775 992 4 k. black and ochre .. 75 20

1962. Soviet Cosmonauts Commem. Perf. or imperf.
2776. 993. 1 r. black and blue .. 10·00 6·00

1962. V. K. Blucher Commem.
2777. 994. 4 k. multicoloured .. 30 10

995. V. N. Podbelsky.

996. A. Gaidar.

1962. 75th Birth Anniv. of V. N. Podbelsky (statesman).
2778. 995. 4 k. violet and brown 20 10

1962. Soviet Writers.
2779. 996. 4 k. buff, blk. & blue 20 10
2780. – 4 k. multicoloured .. 20 10
DESIGN: No. 2780, A. S. Makharenko.

997. Dove and Christmas Tree.

1962. New Year. Perf. or imperf.
2781. 997. 4 k. multicoloured .. 20 10

998. D. N. Pryanishnikov. (agricultural chemist).

999. Rose-coloured Starlings.

1962. D. N. Pryanishnikov Commem.
2782. 999. 4 k. multicoloured .. 20 10

1962. Birds.
2783. 999. 3 k. black, red & grn. 45 10
2784. – 4 k. blk., brn. & orge. 55 10
2785. – 6 k. blue, black & red 65 15
2786. – 10 k. blue, blk. & red 1·10 30
2787. – 16 k. red, blue & blk. 1·60 50
BIRDS: 4 k. Red-breasted Geese. 6 k. Snow Geese. 10 k. Great White Cranes. 16 k. Greater Flamingoes.

1000. F.I.R. Emblem and Handclasp.

1001. Badge and Yak Fighter 'Planes.

1962. 4th Int. Federation of Resistance Heroes Congress.
2788. 1000. 4 k. violet and red .. 20 10
2789. 6 k. turquoise and red 25 15

1962. 20th Anniv. of French Air Force "Normandy-Niemen" Unit.
2790. 1001. 6 k. red, green & buff 45 15

1002. Map and Savings Book.

DESIGN: 6 k. As Type 1002 but with people and figure "53" in place of symbols and "70" within map.

1962. 40th Anniv. of Soviet Savings Banks.
2791. 1002. 4 k. multicoloured .. 20 10
2792. – 6 k. multicoloured .. 35 15

1003. Fertilizer Plant, Rustavi, Georgia.

1962. Heavy Industries.
2793. 1003. 4 k. black, pale blue and blue 30 15
2794. – 4 k. black, turquoise and green .. 30 15
2795. – 4 k. black, light blue and grey .. 30 15
DESIGNS: No. 2794, Construction of Bratsk hydro-electric station. No. 2795, Volzhskaya hydro-electric station, Volgograd.

1962. Provincial Costumes (3rd issue). As T 870. Inscr. "1962".
2796. 3 k. red, brown and drab 40 15
COSTUME: 3 k. Latvia.

1004. K. S. Stanislavsky.

1005. A. S. Serafimovich.

1963. Russian Stage Celebrities.
2797. 1004. 4 k. grn. on pale grn. 30 10
2798. – 4 k. brown 30 10
2799. – 4 k. brown 30 10
PORTRAITS AND ANNIVERSARIES: No. 2797 Type 1004 (actor, birth cent). 2798, M. S. Shchepkin (actor, death cent). 2799, V. D. Durov (animal trainer and circus artiste, birth cent).

1963. Russian Writers and Poets.
2800. 1005. 4 k. brn., sepia & mve. 30 10
2801. – 4 k. brown and pur. 30 10
2802. – 4 k. brn., red & buff 30 10
2803. – 4 k. brown & green .. 30 10
2804. – 4 k. brn., sepia & mve. 30 10
2805. – 4 k. multicoloured .. 30 10
PORTRAITS AND ANNIVERSARIES: No. 2800 (birth cent.). No. 2801, D. Bednii (80th birth anniv.). No. 2802, G. I. Uspensky (120th birth anniv.). No. 2803, N. P. Ogarev (150th birth anniv.). No. 2804, V. J. Bryusov (90th birth anniv.). No. 2805, F. V. Gladkov (80th birth anniv.).

1006. Children in Nursery.

1007. Dolls and Toys.

1963. Child Welfare.
2806. 1006. 4 k. black and orange 25 10
2807. – 4 k. pur., blue & orge. 25 10
2808. – 4 k. bistre, red & grn. 25 10
2809. – 4 k. purple, red & orge. 25 10
DESIGNS: No. 2807, Children with nurse. No. 2808, Young pioneers. No. 2809, Students at desk and trainee at lathe.

1963. Decorative Arts. Multicoloured.
2810. 4 k. Type 1007 .. .. 25 10
2811. 6 k. Pottery 35 15
2812. 10 k. Books 60 20
2813. 12 k. Porcelain 85 30

1008. Ilyushin Il-62 Airliner.

DESIGNS: 12 k. "Aeroflot" emblem. 16 k. Tu-104 airliner.

1962. 40th Anniv. of "Aeroflot" Airline.
2814. 1008. 10 k. blk., brn. & red 55 15
2815. – 12 k. multicoloured .. 75 30
2816. – 16 k. red, blk. & blue 1·10 60

1009. M. N. Tukhachevsky.

1010. M. A. Pavlov (scientist).

1963. 45th Anniv. of Red Army and War Heroes.
2817. 1009. 4 k. green & turquoise 30 10
2818. – 4 k. black & brown .. 30 10
2819. – 4 k. brown and blue .. 30 10
2820. – 4 k. black and red .. 30 10
2821. – 4 k. violet & mauve .. 30 10
DESIGNS (Army heroes and battle scenes): No. 2817, Type 1009 (70th birth anniv). No. 2818, U. M. Avetisyan. No. 2819, A. M. Matrosov. No. 2820, I. V. Panflov. No. 2821, Ya. F. Fabricius.

1963. Academy of Sciences Members.
2822. 1010. 4 k. blue, grey & brn. 25 10
2823. – 4 k. brown and green 25 10
2824. – 4 k. multicoloured .. 25 10
2825. – 4 k. brn., red & blue 25 10
2826. – 4 k. multicoloured .. 25 10
PORTRAITS: No. 2823, I. V. Kurchatov. No. 2824, V. I. Vernadsky. LARGER. ($23\frac{1}{2} \times 30$ mm.). No. 2825, A. Krylov. No. 2826, V. Obroutchev. All commemorate birth centenaries except No. 2823 (60th anniv. of birth).

1011. Games Emblem.

Советские хоккеисты-чемпионы мира и Европы. Стокгольм. 1963 г.
(1012.)

1963. 5th Soviet T.U. Winter Sports.
2827. 1011. 4 k. orge., blk. & blue 30 10

1963. Soviet Victory in Swedish Ice Hockey Championships. No. 2670 optd. with T 1012.
2828. 6 k. turquoise and purple 2·00 60

1013. V. Kingisepp.

1014. R. M. Blauman.

1963. 75th Birth Anniv. of Victor Kingisepp (Estonian Communist Party leader).
2829. 1013. 4 k. brown and blue .. 25 10

1963. Birth Centenary of Rudolf Blauman (Latvian writer).
2830. 1014. 4 k. purple and blue .. 25 10

1015. Globe and Flowers.

1016. Lenin.

1963. "World without Arms and Wars". Perf. or imperf.
2831. 1015. 4 k. green, blue & red 25 10
2832. – 6 k. lilac, green & red 30 10
2833. – 10 k. violet, blue & red 50 25
DESIGNS: 6 k. Atomic emblem and pylon. 10 k. Sun and rocket.

1963. 93rd Birth Anniv. of Lenin.
2834. 1016. 4 k. brown and red .. 2·50 85

1963. Provincial Costumes (4th issue). As T 870. Inscr. "1963". Multicoloured.
2835 3 k. Tadzhikistan .. 40 15
2836 4 k. Azerbaijan 55 15
2837 4 k. Kirgizia 55 15
2838 4 k. Turkmenistan .. 55 15

1017. "Luna 4" Rocket.

1018. Woman and Lido.

1963. Launching of "Luna 4" Space Rocket. Perf. or imperf.
2839. 1017. 6 k. red, black & blue 30 15
See also No. 3250.

1963. 5th Anniv. of World Health Day. Mult.
2840. 2 k. Type **1018** 15 10
2841. 4 k. Man and stadium .. 25 20
2842. 10 k. Child and school .. 60 20

1019. Sputniks and Globe.

1963. "Cosmonautics Day".
2843. **1019.** 10 k. blue, blk. & pur. 50 15
2844. – 10 k. purple, blk. & bl. 50 15
2845. – 10 k. red, black & yell. 50 15
DESIGNS: No. 2844, "Vostok-1" and Moon. No. 2845, Space rocket and Sun.

1021. Cuban Horsemen with Flag.

1963. Cuban-Soviet Friendship.
2846. **1021.** 4 k. black, red & blue 40 10
2847. – 6 k. black, blue & red 50 10
2848. – 10 k. blue, red & black 65 20
DESIGNS: 6 k. Hands, weapon, book and flag. 10 k. Crane, hoisting tractor and flags.

1022. J. Hasek.

1023. Karl Marx.

1963. 40th Death Anniv. of Jaroslav Hasek (writer).
2849. **1022.** 4 k. black 20 10

1963. 80th Death Anniv. of Karl Marx.
2850. **1023.** 4 k. black and brown 20 10

1963. War of 1941-45 (3rd issue). As T **911** inscr. "1963".
2851. 4 k. multicoloured .. 45 15
2852. 4 k. multicoloured .. 45 15
2853. 4 k. multicoloured .. 45 15
2854. 4 k. sepia and red .. 45 15
2855. 6 k. olive, black and red 1·00 20
DESIGNS: No. 2851, Woman making shells (Defence of Leningrad, 1942). No. 2852, Soldier in winter kit with tommy-gun (20th anniv. of Battle of the Volga). No. 2853, Soldiers attacking (Liberation of Kiev, 1943). No. 2854, Tanks and map indicating Battle of Kursk, 1943. No. 2855, Tank commander and tanks.

1024. International P.O. Building.

1026. Wagner.

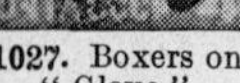

1027. Boxers on "Glove".

1025. Medal and Chessmen.

1963. Opening of Int. Post Office, Moscow.
2856. **1024.** 6 k. brown and blue 40 10

1963. World Chess Champion, Moscow. Perf or imperf.
2857 **1025** 4 k. multicoloured .. 65 15
2858 – 6 k. blue, mauve and ultramarine .. 70 20
2859 – 16 k. blk, mve & pur 1·50 50
DESIGNS: 6 k. Chessboard and pieces. 16 k. Venue and pieces.

1963. 150th Birth Anniv. of Wagner and Verdi (composers).
2860. **1026.** 4 k. black and red .. 50 15
2861. – 4 k. purple and red .. 50 15
DESIGN: No. 2861, Verdi.

1963. 15th European Boxing Championships, Moscow. Multicoloured.
2862. 4 k. Type **1027** 20 10
2863. 6 k. Referee and winning boxer on "glove" .. 30 15

1028. Bykovsky and "Vostok 5".

Всемирный конгресс женщин.

(**1029.**)

1963. Second "Team" Manned Space Flights (1st issue). Perf. or imperf.
2864. **1028.** 6 k. brown and purple 30 20
2865. – 6 k. red and green .. 30 20
2866. – 10 k. red and blue .. 60 30
DESIGNS: No. 2865, Tereshkova and "Vostok 6". No. 2866. Allegory—"Man and Woman in Space".
See also Nos. 2875/7.

1963. Int. Women's Congress, Moscow. Optd. with T **1029.**
2867. **1015.** 4 k. green, blue & red 40 25

1030. Cycling.

1031. Globe, Film and Camera.

1963. 3rd People's Spartakiad. Multicoloured. Perf or imperf.
2868. 3 k. Type **1030** 25 10
2869. 4 k. Athletics 30 10
2870. 6 k. Swimming (horiz.) .. 35 15
2871. 12 k. Basketball 75 30
2872. 16 k. Football .. .. 1·00 40

1963. Int. Film Festival, Moscow.
2873. **1031.** 4 k. blue, black & brn. 30 10

1032. V. V. Mayakovsky.

1033. Tereshkova.

1963. 70th Birth Anniv. of Mayakovsky (poet).
2874. **1032.** 4 k. brown 25 15

1963. 2nd "Team" Manned Space Flights (2nd issue). Multicoloured.
2875 4 k. Bykovsky (horiz) .. 30 20
2876 4 k. Tereshkova (horiz) .. 30 20
2877 10 k. Type **1033** .. .. 1·25 35

1034. Ice Hockey Player.

1035. Lenin.

1963. Russian Ice Hockey Championships.
2878. **1034.** 6 k. grey-blue and red 75 20

1963. 60th Anniv. of 1st Socialist Party Congress.
2879. **1035.** 4 k. black and red .. 30 10

1036. Freighter and Crate.

1037. Guibozo (polo).

1963. Red Cross Cent.
2880. **1036.** 6 k. red and green .. 60 15
2881. – 12 k. red and blue .. 90 30
DESIGN: 12 k. Centenary emblem.

1963. Regional Sports.
2882. – 3 k. multicoloured .. 25 10
2883. **1037.** 4 k. black, red & ochre 30 10
2884. – 6 k. red, brn. & yell. 55 15
2885. – 10 k. blk., brn. & olive 75 25
DESIGNS—HORIZ. 3 k. Lapp reindeer-racing. 6 k. Buryat archery. VERT. 10 k. Armenian wrestling.

1038. A. F. Mozhaisky and Model Aeroplane.

1963. Aviation Celebrities.
2886. **1038.** 6 k. black and blue 50 10
2887. – 10 k. black and blue 75 15
2888. – 16 k. black and blue 90 35
DESIGNS: 10 k. P. N. Nesterov and "looping the loop". 16 k. N. E. Zhukovsky and "aerodynamics".

1039. S. S. Gulak-Artemovsky (poet) (150th birth anniv.).

1040. Olga Kobilyanska (writer) (birth centenary).

1963. Celebrities.
2889. **1039.** 4 k. black and red .. 45 15
2890. – 4 k. brown & purple 45 15
2891. – 4 k. brown and violet 45 15
2892. **1040.** 4 k. mauve & brown 45 15
2893. – 4 k. mauve and green 45 15
DESIGNS AND ANNIVERSARIES—As Type **1039:** No. 2983, M. I. Petraskas (Lithuanian composer) and scene from one of works (90th birth anniv.). As Type **1040:** No. 2890, G. D. Eristavi (writer, death cent., 1964). No. 2891, A. S. Dargomizhsky (composer, 150th birth anniv.).

1041. Antactic Map and Supply Ship "Ob".

1043. E. O. Paton.

1042. Letters and Transport.

1963. Arctic and Antarctic Research. Mult.
2894 3 k. Type **1041** .. .. 2·00 30
2895 4 k. Convoy of snow tractors and map .. 1·00 30
2896 6 k. Globe and aircraft at polar base .. .. 1·75 30
2897 12 k. "Sovetskaya Ukraina" (whale factory ship), whale-catcher and whale .. 4·00 50

1963. Int. Correspondence Week.
2898. **1042.** 4 k. vio., orge. & blk. 35 10

1963. 10th Death Anniv. of Paton (engineer).
2899. **1043.** 4 k. black, red & blue 20 10

1045. D. Diderot.

1046. "Peace and Progress".

1963. 250th Birth Anniv. of Denis Diderot (French philosopher).
2900. **1045.** 4 k. brn., blue & bistre 20 10

1963. "Peace – Brotherhood – Liberty – Labour". All black, red and lake.
2901. 4 k. Type **1046.** 20 15
2902. 4 k. "The Plan" 20 15
2903. 4 k. "Intellectual Work" .. 20 15
2904. 4 k. "Peoples' Union" .. 20 15
2905. 4 k. "Nations' Elite" .. 20 15
2906. 4 k. "The Family" 20 15

1047. Academy of Sciences, Frunze.

1963. Cent of Union of Kirgizia and Russia.
2907 **1047** 4 k. blue, yell & red 20 10

1049. Lenin and Congress Building.

1050. Menchnikov.

1963. 13th Soviet Trade Unions Congress, Moscow.
2908. **1049.** 4 k. red and black .. 15 10
2909. – 4 k. red and black .. 15 10
DESIGN: No. 2909, Lenin with man and woman workers.

1963. 75th Anniv. of Pasteur Institute, Paris.
2910. **1050.** 4 k. green and bistre 25 10
2911. – 6 k. violet and bistre 45 15
2912. – 12 k. blue and bistre 65 30
PORTRAITS: 6 k. Pasteur. 12 k. Calmette.

1051. Cruiser "Aurora" and Rockets.

1052. Gur Emi Mausoleum.

1963. 46th Anniv. of October Revolution.
2913. **1051.** 4 k. blk., orge. & lake 30 10
2914. 4 k. blk., red & lake 50 30

1963. Ancient Samarkand Buildings. Mult.
2915. 4 k. Type **1052** 40 10
2916. 4 k. Shachi-Zinda Mosque 40 10
2917. 6 k. Registan Square (55 × 28½ mm.) 55 20

1053. Inscription, Globe and Kremlin.

1054. Pushkin Monument, Kiev.

1963. Signing of Nuclear Test-ban Treaty, Moscow.
2918. **1053.** 6 k. violet and pale blue 45 15

1963.
2919. **1054.** 4 k. brown 20 10

1056. V. G. Shukhov, and Tower.

1057. Y. M. Steklov and "Izvestia".

1963. 110th Birth Anniv. of Shukhov (engineer).
2920. **1056.** 4 k. black and green 20 10

1963. 90th Birth Anniv. of Steklov (first editor of "Izvestia").
2921. **1057.** 4 k. black and mauve 20 10

1058. Buildings and Emblems of Moscow (and U.S.S.R.) and Prague (and Czechoslovakia).

1963. 20th Anniv. of Soviet-Czech Friendship Treaty.

2922. **1058.** 6 k. red, bistre & blue 35 10

1059. F. A. Poletaev (soldier) and Medals.

1963. Poletaev Commem.

2923. **1059.** 4 k. multicoloured .. 30 10

1062. J. Grimau (Spanish Communist). **1063.** Rockets.

1963. Grimau Commem.

2924. **1062.** 6 k. violet, red and cream 45 10

1963. New Year (1st issue).

2925. **1063.** 6 k. multicoloured .. 25 10

1064. "Happy New Year". **1067.** Topaz.

1963. New Year (2nd issue).

2926. **1064.** 4 k. red, blue & grn. 30 10

2927. 6 k. red, blue and green 35 10

1963. "Precious Stones of the Urals". Multicoloured.

2928. 2 k. Type **1067** 25 10

2929. 4 k. Jasper 50 10

2930. 6 k. Amethyst 70 15

2931. 10 k. Emerald .. .. 1·25 25

2932. 12 k. Ruby .. .. 1·50 45

2933. 16 k. Malachite .. .. 2·00 55

1068. Sputnik 7. **1071.** Flame and Rainbow.

1069. Dushanbe (formerly "Stalinabad" 1929–62), Tadzhikistan.

1963. "First in Space". Gold, vermilion and grey.

2934. 10 k. Type **1068** 50 30

2935. 10 k. Moon-landing .. 50 30

2936. 10 k. Back of Moon .. 50 30

2937. 10 k. Vostok 7 .. .. 50 30

2938. 10 k. Twin flight 50 30

2939. 10 k. Seagull (first woman in space) .. 50 30

1963. Dushanbe Commem.

2940. **1069.** 4 k. blue 30 10

1963. 15th Anniv. of Declaration of Human Rights.

2941. **1071.** 6 k. multicoloured .. 30 10

1072. F. A. Sergeev ("Artyem").

1073. Sun and Globe. **1074.** K. Donelaitis.

1963. 80th Birth Anniv. of Sergeev (revolutionary).

2942. **1072.** 4 k. brown and red .. 20 10

1964. International Quiet Sun Year.

2943. – 4 k. blk., orge. & mve. 30 10

2944. **1073.** 6 k. blue, yell. & red 35 10

2945. – 10 k. violet, red & blue 40 20

Designs—horiz. 4 k. Giant telescope and sun. 10 k. Globe and Sun.

1964. 250th Birth Anniv. of K. Donelaitis (Lithuanian poet).

2946. **1074.** 4 k. black & myrtle 20 10

1075. Speed Skating.

1964 Winter Olympic Games, Innsbruck.

2947 **1075** 2 k. black, mve & bl 20 10

2948 – 4 k. black, bl & mve 35 10

2949 – 6 k. red, black & blue 40 15

2950 – 10 k. blk, mve & grn 70 25

2951 – 12 k. blk, grn & mve 95 35

Designs: 4 k. Skiing. 6 k. Games emblem. 10 k. Rifle shooting (biathlon). 12 k. Figure skating (pairs).

See also Nos. 2969/73.

1076. A. S. Golubkina and Statue. **1077.** "Agriculture".

150 pokів з дня народження. 1964 p.

1079. Shevchenko's Statue, Kiev (M. Manizer). (**1078.**)

1964. Birth Cent. of A. Golubkina (sculptress).

2952. **1076.** 4 k. sepia and grey 20 10

1964. Heavy Chemical Industries. Mult.

2953. 4 k. Type **1077** 20 10

2954. 4 k. "Textiles" 20 10

2955. 4 k. "Tyre Production" 20 10

1964. 150th Birth Anniv. of T. G. Shevchenko (Ukrainian poet and painter). No. 2561 optd. with T **1078** and designs as T **1079**.

2956. **880.** 4 k. brown & violet 25 10

2959. **1079.** 4 k. green 25 10

2960. 4 k. red 25 10

2961. – 6 k. blue 30 10

2962. – 6 k. brown 30 10

2957. – 10 k. violet & brown 55 30

2958. – 10 k. brown & bistre 55 30

Designs: Nos. 2957/8, Portrait of Shevchenko by I. Repin. 2961/2, Self-portrait.

1080. K. S. Zaslonov.

1964. War Heroes.

2963. **1080.** 4 k. sepia and brown 40 15

2964. – 4 k. purple and blue 40 15

2965. – 4 k. blue and red .. 40 15

2966. – 4 k. brown and blue 40 15

Portraits: No. 2964, N. A. Vilkov. No. 2965, Yu. V. Smirnov. No. 2966, V. Z. Khoruzhaya.

1081. Federov printing the first Russian book, "Apostle".

1964. 400th Anniv. of First Russian Printed Book. Multicoloured.

2967. 4 k. Type **1081** 20 10

2968. 6 k. Federov statue, books and newspapers .. 30 20

Слава советским спортсменам— победителям IX зимней Олимпиады!

(**1082.**)

1083. Ice Hockey Player.

1964. Winter Olympic Games, Soviet Medal Winners. (a) Nos. 2947/51 optd with T **1082** or similarly.

2969. 2 k. black, mauve & blue 20 10

2970. 4 k. black, blue & mauve 30 10

2971. 6 k. red, black and blue .. 30 15

2972. 10 k. black, mauve & grn. 55 25

2973. 12 k. black, green & mve. 60 30

(b) New designs.

2974. **1083.** 3 k. red, black & turq. 30 10

2975. – 16 k. orange & brown 90 40

Design: 16 k. Gold medal and inscr.—"Triumph of Soviet Sport—11 Gold, 8 Silver, 6 Bronze Medals".

1084. Militiaman and Factory Guard. **1085.** Lighthouse, Odessa, and Sailor.

1964. "Public Security".

2976. **1084** 4 k. blue, red & black 20 10

1964. 20th Anniv. of Liberation of Odessa and Leningrad. Multicoloured.

2977. 4 k. Type **1085** 50 10

2978. 4 k. Lenin, Statue, Leningrad 25 10

1086. Sputniks. **1087.** N. I. Kibalchich.

1964. "The Way to the Stars". Imperf. or perf.

(a) Cosmonautics. As T **1086**.

2979. 4 k. green, black and red 30 10

2980. 6 k. black, blue and red .. 40 10

2981. 12 k. turq., brown & black 80 30

Designs: 6 k. "Mars I" space station. 12 k. Gagarin and space capsule.

(b) Rocket Construction Pioneers. As T **1087**.

2982. 10 k. black, grn. & violet 65 20

2983. 10 k. black, turq. and red 65 20

2984. 10 k. black turq. and red 65 20

2985. 10 k. black and blue .. 65 25

Designs: No. 2982, Type **1087**. No. 2983, F. A. Zander. No. 2984, K. E. Tsiolkovsky. No. 2985, Pioneers' medallion and Saransk memorial.

1088. Lenin.

1964. 94th Birth Anniv. of Lenin.

2986a **1088** 4 k. black, bl & mve 3·00 2·25

1089. Shakespeare (400th Birth Anniv.).

1964. Cultural Annivs.

2987 – 6 k. yell., brn. & sepia 60 15

2988 **1089** 10 k. brown and olive 70 25

2989 – 12 k. green and brown 1·25 35

Designs and anniversaries: 6 k. Michelangelo (400th death anniv.). 12 k. Galileo (400th birth anniv.)

1090. Crop-watering Machine and Produce.

1964. "Irrigation".

2990. **1090.** 4 k. multicoloured .. 20 10

1091. Gamarnik.

1964. 70th Birth Anniv of Ya. B. Gamarnik (Soviet Army Commander).

2991 **1091** 4 k. brown, bl & blk 20 10

1092. D. I. Gulia (Abhazian poet).

1964. Cultural Annivs.

2992. **1092.** 4 k. black, green and light green 30 15

2993. – 4 k. blk., verm. & red 30 15

2994. – 4 k. blk., brn. & bistre 30 15

2995. – 4 k. blk., yell. & brn. 30 15

2996. – 4 k. multicoloured .. 30 15

2997. – 4 k. blk., yell. & brn. 30 15

Designs: No. 2993, Nijazi (Uzbek writer, composer and painter). No. 2994, S. Seifullin (Kazakh poet). No. 2995, M. M. Kotsyubinsky (writer). No. 2996, S. Nazaryan (Armenian writer). No. 2997, T. Satylganov (Kirghiz poet).

1093. A. Gaidar.

1964. 60th Birth Annivs. of Writers A. P. Gaider and N. A. Ostrovsky.

2998 **1093** 4 k. red and blue .. 25 10

2999 – 4 k. green and red .. 35 10

Design: No. 2999, N. Ostrovsky and battle scene.

150 лет вхождения
в состав России
1964

4
коп.

1094. Indian Elephant. (1095.)

1964. Moscow Zoo Cent. Multicoloured. Imperf. or perf.

3000. 1 k. Type **1094** 10 10
3001. 2k. Giant Panda .. 15 10
3002. 4 k. Polar bear 35 10
3003. 6 k. Elk 45 10
3004. 10 k. Eastern White Pelican .. .. 1·25 25
3005. 12 k. Tiger .. .. 1·25 30
3006. 16 k. Lammergeier .. 2·25 50

The 2 k. and 12 k. are horiz.; the 4 k. and 10 k. are "square", approx. 26½×28 mm.

1964. 150th Anniv. of Union of Azerbaijan and Russia. Surch. with T **1095**.

3007. **328.** 4 k. on 40 k. brown, bistre and yellow 1·00 1·25

1096. Rumanian Woman and Emblems on Map. **1097.** Maize.

1964. 20th Anniv. of Rumanian-Soviet Friendship Treaty.

3008. **1096.** 6 k. multicoloured .. 40 15

1964. Agricultural Crops. Multicoloured. Imperf. or perf.

3009. 2 k. Type **1097** 15 10
3010. 3 k. Wheat 20 10
3011. 4 k. Potatoes 30 10
3012. 6 k. Peas 25 20
3013. 10 k. Sugar beet .. 55 25
3014. 12 k. Cotton 75 30
3015. 16 k. Flax .. .. 1·00 40

1098. Flag and Obelisk. **1099.** Leningrad G.P.O.

1964. 20th Anniv. of Liberation of Byelorussia.

3016. **1098.** 4 k. multicoloured .. 20 10

1964. 250th Anniv. of Leningrad's Postal Service.

3017. **1099.** 4 k. blk., bistre & red 20 10

1100. Map of Poland and Emblems.

1964. 20th Anniv. of Polish People's Republic.

3018. **1100.** 6 k. multicoloured .. 35 10

1101. Horse-jumping. **1102.** M. Thorez (French Communist leader).

1964. Olympic Games, Tokyo. Imperf. or perf.

3019. 3 k. multicoloured .. 10 10
3020. 4 k. red, black & yellow 15 10
3021. 6 k. red, black and blue 25 10
3022. 10 k. red, blk. & turq. 40 15
3023. 12 k. black and grey .. 45 20
3024. 16 k. violet, red and blue 80 25

DESIGNS: 3 k. Type **1101**. 4 k. Weightlifting. 6 k. Pole-vaulting. 10 k. Canoeing. 12 k. Gymnastics. 16 k. Fencing.

1964. Maurice Thorez Commem.

3025. **1102.** 4 k. black and red .. 55 20

1103. Three Races. **1104.** Jawaharlal Nehru.

1964. Int. Anthropologists and Ethnographers Congress, Moscow.

3026. **1103.** 6 k. black and yellow 35 10

1964. Nehru Commem.

3027. **1104.** 4 k. brown and grey 35 10

1105. Globe and Banner. **1106.** A. V. Vishnevsky (surgeon).

1964. Cent. of "First International".

3028. 4 k. red, bistre and blue 20 10
3029. 4 k. red, olive and black 20 10
3030. 4 k. drab, red and lake .. 20 10
3031. 4 k. red, black and blue .. 20 10
3032. 4 k. multicoloured 20 10

DESIGNS: No. 3028, Type **1105**. No. 3029, Communist Party manifesto. No. 3030, Marx and Engels. No. 3031, Chain-breaker. No. 3032, Lenin.

1964. "Outstanding Soviet Physicians".

3033. 4 k. brown and pur. .. 40 15
3034. 4 k. brown, red & yellow 40 15
3035. 4 k. brown, blue & bistre 40 15

DESIGNS: No. 3033, Type **1106**. No. 3034, N. A. Semashko (public health pioneer). Both are 90th birth anniversaries. No. 3035, D. I. Ivanovsky and siphon (25×32 mm.)

1107. Bulgarian Flag, Rose and Emblems. **1108.** P. Togliatti (Italian Communist leader).

1964. 20th Anniv. of Bulgarian People's Republic.

3036. **1107.** 6 k. red, green & drab 30 15

1964. Togliatti Commem.

3037. **1108.** 4 k. black and red .. 30 10

1110. Globe and Letters.

1964. Int. Correspondence Week.

3038. **1110.** 4 k. mauve, bl. & brn. 30 10

1111. Soviet and Yugoslav Soldiers. **1112.** East German Arms, Industrial Plants, Freighter "Havel" and Goods Train.

1964. 20th Anniv. of Liberation of Belgrade.

3039. **1111.** 6 k. multicoloured .. 45 15

1964. 15th Anniv. of German Democratic Republic.

3040. **1112.** 6 k. multicoloured .. 45 15

1113. Woman holding Bowl of Produce (Moldavian Republic).

40 лет Советскому Таджикистану
1964 год

(1115.)

1964. 40th Anniv of Soviet Republic. (a) As T **1113**.

3041 **1113** 4 k. brown, grn & red 20 10
3042 – 4 k. multicoloured .. 30 10
3043 – 4 k. red, pur & yell 30 10

(b) Optd with T **1115**.

3044 **1069** 4 k. blue 70 60

DESIGNS—VERT. No. 3042, Woman holding Arms (Turkmenistan). No. 3043, Man and woman holding produce (Uzbekistan). No. 3044, commemorates the Tadzhikistan Republic.

1116. Yegorov.

1964. Three-manned Space Flight.

(a) Portraits in black, orange and turquoise.

3045. 4 k. Type **1116** 30 10
3046. 4 k. Feoktistov 30 10
3047. 4 k. Komarov 30 10

These can be identified by the close proximation of the Russian names on the stamps to the English versions.

(b) Designs 73½×22½ mm.

3048. 6 k. purple and violet .. 45 15
3049. 10 k. violet and blue .. 65 30

DESIGNS: 6 k. The three cosmonauts. 10 k. Spaceship "Voskhod I".

1117. Soldier and Flags. **1119.** Lermontov's Birthplace.

1964. 20th Anniv. of Liberation of Ukraine.

3050. **1117.** 4 k. multicoloured .. 20 10

1964. 150th Birth Anniv. of M. Lermontov (poet).

3051. **1119.** 4 k. violet 20 10
3052. – 6 k. black 30 10
3053. – 10k. brown and flesh 50 25

DESIGNS: 6 k. Lermontov. 10 k. Lermontov talking with Belinsky.

1120. Hammer and Sickle. **1121.** N. K. Krupskaya (Lenin's wife).

1964. 47th Anniv. of October Revolution.

3054. **1120.** 4 k. multicoloured .. 20 10

1964. Birth Anniversaries.

3055. **1121.** 4 k. multicoloured .. 20 10
3056. – 4 k. multicoloured .. 20 10

DESIGNS, etc.: No. 3055 (95th anniv.). No. 3056, A. I. Yelizarova-Ulianova (Lenin's sister) (cent.).

1122. Mongolian Woman and Lamb. **1124.** "Suillus luteus".

1964. 40th Anniv. of Mongolian People's Republic.

3057. **1122.** 4 k. multicoloured .. 30 15

1964. Mushrooms. Multicoloured.

3058 2 k. Type **1124** 30 10
3059 4 k. "Cantharellus cibarius" 50 10
3060 6 k. "Boletus edulis" .. 65 15
3061 10 k. "Leccinum aurantiacum" .. .. 1·00 30
3062 12 k. "Lactarius deliciosus" .. .. 1·25 40

1125. A. P. Dovzhenko. **1126.** Christmas Tree, Star and Globe.

1127. Struve. **1128.** S. V. Ivanov and Skiers.

1964. 70th Birth Anniv. of Dovzhenko (film producer).

3063. **1125.** 4 k. blue and grey .. 30 10

1964. New Year.

3064. **1126.** 4 k. multicoloured .. 40 15

1964. Death Cent of V. Ya. Struve (scientist).

3065 **1127** 4 k. brown and blue 60 15

1964. Birth Cent of S. V. Ivanov (painter).

3066 **1128** 4 k. brown and black 65 15

1129. Scene from Film.

1964. 30th Anniv of Film "Chapaev".

3067 **1129** 6 k. black and green 35 15

1130. Test-tubes, Jar and Agricultural Scenes.

1964. Chemistry for the National Economy.

3068. **1130.** 4 k. purple and olive 20 15
3069. – 6 k. black and blue .. 35 10

DESIGN: 6 k. Chemical plant.

1131. Cranberries. **1132.** Library.

1964. Woodland Fruits. Multicoloured.

3070 1 k. Type **1131** 10 10
3071 3 k. Bilberries 15 10
3072 4 k. Rowanberries .. 20 10
3073 10 k. Blackberries .. 55 20
3074 16 k. Red bilberries .. 85 40

1964. 250th Anniv. of Academy of Sciences Library, Leningrad.

3075. **1132.** 4 k. black, grn. & red 20 10

1133. Congress Palace and Spassky Tower. 1134. Mt. Khan-Tengri.

1964.
3076. 1133. 1 r. blue .. .. 7·50 1·25

1964. Mountaineering. Multicoloured.
3077. 4 k. Type 1134 .. .. 20 10
3078. 6 k. Mt. Kazbeck (horiz.) 40 15
3079. 12 k. Mt. Ushba 80 30

1136. Bowl.

1964. Kremlin Treasures. Multicoloured.
3080. 4 k. Helmet 70 15
3081. 6 k. Quiver 90 20
3082. 10 k. Coronation headgear 1·10 35
3083. 12 k. Ladle .. .. 1·50 45
3084. 16 k. Type 1136 .. .. 1·75 80

1137. I. M. Sivko. 1138. Dante.

1965. War Heroes.
3085. 1137. 4 k. black & violet .. 40 15
3086. – 4 k. brown and blue .. 40 15
DESIGN: No. 3086, General I. S. Polbin.

1965. 700th Birth Anniv. of Dante.
3087. 1138. 4 k. black, bistre and purple 45 10

1139. Blood Donor. 1140. N. P. Kravkov.

1965. Blood Donors. Multicoloured.
3088. 4 k. Type 1139 .. .. 35 15
3089. 4 k. Hand holding red carnation 35 15

1965. Birth Cent. of N. Kravkov (pharmacologist).
3090. 1140. 4 k. multicoloured .. 25 10

1141. Figure Skaters. 1142. Alsatian.

1965. European Figure Skating Championships, Moscow.
3091 1141 6 k. red, black & grn 40 15
See also No. 3108.

1965. World Ice Hockey Championships, Moscow. Designs similar to T 1141 but depicting ice hockey players.
3092 4 k. red, blue and bistre 30 15

1965. Hunting and Service Dogs.
3093 – 1 k. black, yell & red 15 10
3097 – 2 k. brown, bl & blk 20 10
3098 1142 3 k. black, red & yell 20 10
3099 – 4 k. black, brn & grn 30 10
3100 – 4 k. black, orge & grn 30 10
3101 – 6 k. black, brn & bl 40 15
3102 – 6 k. black, red & blue 40 15
3094 – 10 k. multicoloured 65 20
3095 – 12 k. blk, brn & vio 85 30
3096 – 16 k. multicoloured 1·25 35
DESIGNS—HORIZ. 1 k. Hound. 2 k. Setter. 4 k. (3099) (value in green) Fox terrier. 4 k. (3100) (value in orange) Pointer. 6 k. (3101) Borzoi. 12 k. Husky. VERT. 6 k. (3102) Sheepdog. 10 k. Collie. 16 k. Caucasion sheepdog.

1143. R. Sorge.

1965. Richard Sorge (Soviet secret agent) Commem.
3103. 1143. 4 k. black and red .. 55 15

1144. I.T.U. Emblem and Telecommunications Symbols.

1965. Cent. of I.T.U.
3104. 1144. 6 k. violet and blue 55 15

1145. Leonov in Space.

1965. Space Flight of "Voskhod 2" 1st issue). Imperf. or perf.
3105. 1145. 10 k. orge., blk. & bl. 1·00 30
See also Nos. 3138/9.

1965. Ice Hockey Championships. Optd ТАМПЕРЕ 1965 г.
3107 1034 6 k. blue and red .. 1·00 40

Советские фигуристы— чемпионы мира в парном катании

(1147.)

1148. Soldier and Woman.

1965. Soviet Victory in European Figure Skating Championships. Optd with T 1147.
3108 1141 6 k. red, black & grn 75 40

1965. 20th Anniversaries.
3109. 1148. 6 k. multicoloured .. 40 15
3110. – 6 k. multicoloured .. 40 15
3111. – 6 k. ochre and red .. 40 15
3112. – 6 k. multicoloured .. 40 15
3113. – 6 k. multicoloured .. 40 15
DESIGNS: No. 3109, Type 1148 (Czech Liberation). No. 3110, Statue and emblems of development (Friendship with Hungary). No. 3111, Polish and Soviet arms (Polish-Soviet Friendship Treaty). No. 3112, Viennese buildings and Russian soldier (Freeing of Vienna). No. 3113, Liberation medal, Polish flag and building reconstruction (Freeing of Warsaw).
See also Nos. 3182 and 3232.

1149. Statue, Rockets and Globe. 1150. Rockets and Radio-telescope.

1965. National Cosmonautics Day. Nos. 3117/18 on aluminium-surfaced paper.
3114. 1149. 4 k. grn., blk. & red 25 10
3115. – 12 k. pur., red & blue 40 15
3116. – 16 k. multicoloured 50 30
3117. 1150. 20 k. red, black and green on silver .. 6·50 4·00
3118. – 20 k. red, black and blue on silver .. 6·50 4·00
DESIGNS: 12 k. Statue and Globe. 16 k. Rockets and Globe. No. 3118, Globe, satellite and cosmonauts.

1151. Lenin.

1965. Lenin's 95th Birth Anniv.
3119. 1151. 10 k. blue, blk. & brn. 55 15

1152. Poppies. 1153. Red Flag, Reichstag Building and Broken Swastika.

1965. Flowers.
3120. 1152. 1 k. red, lake & grn. 10 10
3121. – 3 k. yell., brn. & grn. 20 10
3122. – 4 k. lilac, blk. & grn. 30 10
3123. – 6 k. red, deep green and green .. 40 10
3124. – 10 k. yell., pur. & grn. 75 25
FLOWERS: 3 k. Marguerite. 4 k. Peony. 6 k. Carnation. 10 k. Tulips.

1965. 20th Anniv. of Victory.
3125. 1153. 1 k. blk., gold & red 20 10
3126. – 2 k. red, black & gold 25 15
3127. – 3 k. blue and gold .. 40 15
3128. – 4 k. violet and gold 55 15
3129. – 4 k. green and gold .. 60 15
3130. – 6 k. pur., grn. & gold 1·25 20
3131. – 10 k. pur., brn. & gold 1·75 25
3132. – 12 k. blk., red & gold 2·25 30
3133. – 16 k. red and gold .. 2·50 40
3134. – 20 k. blk., red & gold 3·00 75
DESIGNS: 2 k. Soviet mother holding manifesto (poster by I. Toidze). 3 k. "The Battle for Moscow" (V. Bogatkin). 4 k. (No. 3128), "Partisan Mother" (from S. Gerasimov's film). 4 k. (No. 3129), "Red Army Soldiers and Partisans" (from Yu. Neprintsev's film). 6 k. Soldiers and flag (poster by V. Ivanov). 10 k. "Mourning the Fallen Hero" (from F. Bogorodsky's film). 12 k. Soldier and worker holding bomb (poster by V. Koretsky). 16 k. Victory celebrations, Red Square, Moscow (from K. Yuon's film). 20 k. Soldier and machines of war.

1154. Marx and Lenin.

No. 3136 is similar in design to those issued by China and Hungary for the Postal Ministers' Congress, Peking, but this event is not mentioned on the stamp or in the Soviet philatelic bulletins.

1965. Marxism and Leninism.
3136. 1154. 6 k. black and red .. 30 10

1155. Bolshoi Theatre.

1965. Int. Theatre Day.
3137. 1155. 6 k. ochre, blk. & turq. 35 15

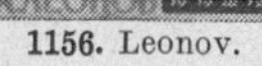

1156. Leonov. 1157. Yakov Sverdlov (revolutionary).

1965. "Voskhod 2" Space Flight (2nd issue).
3138. 1156. 6 k. violet and silver 30 15
3139. – 6 k. purple and silver 30 15
DESIGN: No. 3139, Belyaev.

1965. 80th Birth Anniversaries.
3140. 1157. 4 k. black and brown 20 10
3141. – 4 k. black and violet 20 10
PORTRAIT: No. 3141, J. Akhunbabaev (statesman).

1158. Otto Grotewohl (1st death anniv.). 1159. Telecommunications Satellites.

1965. Annivs. of Grotewohl and Thorez (Communist leaders).
3142. 1158. 4 k. black & purple 20 10
3143. – 6 k. brown and red 40 15
DESIGN: 6 k. Maurice Thorez (65th birth anniv.).

1965. Int. Co-operation Year. Multicoloured.
3144. 3 k. Type 1159. .. .. 20 10
3145. 6 k. Star and sputnik .. 40 15
3146. 6 k. Foundry ladle, iron works and map of India 40 15
No. 3145 signifies peaceful uses of atomic energy and No. 3146 co-operation with India.

1160. Conf. Emblem, Chemical Plant and Symbols.

1162. V. Ivanov and Armoured Train. 1161. V. A. Serov.

1965. 20th International Congress of Pure and Applied Chemistry, Moscow.
3147 1160 4 k. red, black & blue 25 10

1965. Birth Cent. of V. A. Serov (painter).
3148. 1161. 4 k. black, brown and pale stone .. 80 20
3149. – 6 k. black and drab 1·10 25
DESIGN: 6 k. Full length portrait of Chaliapin (singer) by Serov.

1965. Famous Writers.
3150. 1162. 4 k. black and purple 40 15
3151. – 4 k. black and violet 40 15
3152. – 4 k. black and blue .. 40 15
3153. – 4 k. black and grey .. 40 15
3154. – 4 k. blk., red & green 40 15
3155. – 4 k. black and brown 40 15
WRITERS AND ANNIVERSARIES: No. 3150, (70th birth anniv.). No. 3151, A. Kunanbaev and military parade. No. 3152, J. Rainis (Lettish poet: 90th birth anniv.). No. 3153, E. J. Vilde (Estonian author): 90th birth anniv.). No. 3154, M. Ch. Abegjan (Armenian writer and critic: 90th birth anniv.). No. 3155, M. L. Kropivnitsky and scene from play (Ukrainian playwright).

1163. Festival Emblem.

1965. Film Festival, Moscow.
3156. 1163. 6 k. blk., gold & blue 30 10

1164. Concert Arena, Tallinn. 1165. Hand holding "Peace Flower".

1965. 25th Anniv. of Incorporation of Estonia, Lithuania and Latvia in the U.S.S.R.
3157. 1164. 4k. multicoloured .. 30 10
3158. – 4 k. brown and red .. 30 10
3159. – 4 k. brn., red & blue 30 10
DESIGNS—VERT. No. 3158, Lithuanian girl and Arms. HORIZ. No. 3159, Latvian Flag and Arms.

1965. Peace Issue.
3160. 1165. 6 k. yell., blk. & blue 30 10

1167. "Potemkin" Sailors' Monument, Odessa.

1965. 60th Anniv. of 1905 Rebellion.
3161. 1167. 4 k. blue and red .. 20 15
3162. – 4 k. grn., blk. & red 20 15
3163. – 4 k. grn., blk. & red 20 15
3164. – 4 k. brn., blk. & red 20 15
DESIGNS: No. 3162, Demonstrator up lamp-post. No. 3163, Defeated rebels. No. 3164, Troops at street barricade.

1168. G. Gheorgi-Dej (Rumanian Communist). **1169.** Power Station.

1965. G. Gheorgi-Dej Commem.
3165. **1168.** 4 k. black and red .. 25 10

1965. Industrial Progress.
3166. **1169.** 1 k. multicoloured .. 10 10
3167. – 2 k. blk., orge. & yell. 10 10
3168. – 3 k. violet, yellow and ochre .. 15 10
3169. – 4 k. deep blue, blue and red .. 20 10
3170. – 6 k. blue and bistre 30 10
3171. – 10 k. brown, yellow and orange .. 60 20
3172. – 12 k. turquoise & red 90 20
3173. – 16 k. pur., blue & blk. 1·00 40
DESIGNS: 2 k. Steel works. 3 k. Chemical works and formula. 4 k. Machine tools production. 6 k. Building construction. 10 k. Agriculture. 12 k. Communications and transport. 16 k. Scientific research.

1170. Relay Racing. **1171.** Gymnastics.

1965. Trade Unions Spartakiad. Mult.
3174. 4 k. Type **1170** 25 15
3175. 4 k. Gymnastics 25 15
3176. 4 k. Cycling 25 15

1965. Schoolchildren's Spartakiad.
3177. **1171.** 4 k. red and blue .. 20 10
3178. – 6 k. red, brn. & turq. 35 15
DESIGN: 6 k. Cycle-racing.

1172. Throwing the Javelin and Running. **1173.** Star, Palms and Lotus.

1965. American-Soviet Athletic Meeting, Kiev.
3179. **1172.** 4 k. red, brn. & lilac 15 10
3180. – 6 k. red, brown & grn. 25 10
3181. – 10 k. red, brn. & grey 40 15
DESIGNS: 6 k. High jumping and putting the shot. 10 k. Throwing the hammer and hurdling.

1965. 20th Anniv. of North Vietnamese People's Republic.
3182. **1173.** 6 k. multicoloured .. 30 15

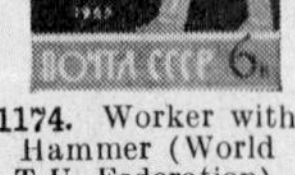

1174. Worker with Hammer (World T.U. Federation). **1176.** P. K. Sternberg (astronomer: birth cent.).

1965. 20th Anniv. of Int. Organizations.
3183. **1174.** 6 k. drab and plum 20 15
3184. – 6 k. brown, red & blue 20 15
3185. – 6 k. light brn. & turq. 20 15
DESIGNS: No. 3184, Torch and heads of three races (World Democratic Youth Federation). No. 3185, Woman holding dove (Int. Democratic Women's Federation).

1965. Scientists' Annivs.
3186. **1176.** 4 k. brown and blue 60 15
3187. – 4 k. black and purple 60 15
3188. – 4 k. blk., pur. & yell. 65 15
PORTRAITS: No. 3187, Ch. Valikhanov (scientific writer: death cent.). No. 3188, V. A. Kistyakovsky (scientist: birth cent.).

1177. "Battleship "Potemkin" ".

1965. "Soviet Cinema Art". Designs showing scenes from films. Multicoloured.
3189. 4 k. Type **1177** 30 10
3190. 6 k. "Young Guard" .. 40 15
3191. 12 k. "A Soldier's Ballad" 85 25

1178. Mounted Postman and Map.

1965. History of the Russian Post Office.
3192. **1178.** 1 k. grn., brown & vio. 20 10
3193. – 1 k. brn., ochre & grey 20 10
3194. – 2 k. brn., bl. & lilac 20 10
3195. – 4 k. blk., ochre & pur. 45 10
3196. – 6 k. blk., grn. & brn. 65 15
3197. – 12 k. sepia, brn. & bl. 1·00 25
3198. – 16 k. plum, red & grey 1·25 45
DESIGNS: No. 3193, Mail coach and map. 2 k. Early steam train and medieval kogge. 4 k. Mail lorry and map. 6 k. Diesel train and various transports. 12 k. Moscow Post Office—electronic facing, sorting and cancelling machines. 16 k. Airport and Lenin.

1179 "Vostok" and "Mirnyi" (Antarctic exploration vessels).

1965. Polar Research Annivs.
3199. – 4 k. black, orge. & bl. 90 15
3200. – 4 k. black, orge. & bl. 90 15
3201. – 6 k. sepia and violet 1·00 25
3202. **1179.** 10 k. blk., drab & red 1·25 35
3203. – 16 k. blk., viol. & brn. 1·75 65
DESIGNS—HORIZ. ($37\frac{1}{2} \times 25\frac{1}{2}$ mm): No. 3199, Ice-breakers "Taimyr" and "Vaigach" in Arctic (50th anniv). No. 3200, Atomic ice-breaker "Lenin". No. 3201, Dikson settlement (50th anniv). No. 3203, Vostok Antarctic station. SQUARE. No. 3202, (145th anniv of Lazarez-Bellingshausen Expedition).

Nos. 3199/3200 were issued together, se-tenant, forming a composite design.

1181. Agricultural Academy.

1965. Centenary Academy of Agricultural Sciences, Moscow.
3205. **1181.** 4 k. vio., red & drab 30 15

1183. N. Poussin (self-portrait). **1184.** Kremlin.

1965. 300th Death Anniv. of Nicolas Poussin (French painter).
3207. **1183.** 4 k. multicoloured .. 50 10

1965. New Year.
3208. **1184.** 4 k. red, silver & blk. 25 10

1185. M. I. Kalinin.

1965. 90th Birth Anniv. of Kalinin (statesman).
3209. **1185.** 4 k. lake and red .. 15 10

1186. Klyuchevski Volcano.

1965. Soviet Volcanoes. Multicoloured.
3210. 4 k. Type **1186** 40 15
3211. 12 k. Karumski Volcano (vert.) .. .. 1·00 30
3212. 16 k. Koryakski Volcano 1·40 45

1187. Oktyabrskaya Station, Moscow.

1965. Soviet Metro Stations.
3213. **1187.** 6 k. blue 40 15
3214. – 6 k. brown 40 15
3215. – 6 k. brown 40 15
3216. – 6 k. green 40 15
STATIONS: No. 3214, Leninsky Prospekt, Moscow. No. 3215, Moskovian Gate, Leningrad. No. 3216, Bolshevik Factory, Kiev.

1188. Common Buzzard. **1189.** "Red Star" (medal) and Scenes of Odessa.

1965. Birds of Prey. Birds in black.
3217. **1188.** 1 k. grey 35 10
3218. – 2 k. brown 45 10
3219. – 3 k. olive 55 10
3220. – 4 k. drab 65 10
3221. – 10 k. brown .. 1·25 20
3222. – 12 k. blue .. 1·50 35
3223. – 14 k. blue .. 1·75 40
3224. – 16 k. purple .. 2·00 50
BIRDS—VERT. 2 k. Common Kestrel. 3 k. Tawny Eagle. 4 k. Red Kite. 10 k. Peregrine Falcon. 16 k. Gyrfalcon. HORIZ. 12 k. Golden Eagle. 14 k. Lammergeier.

1965. Heroic Soviet Towns. Multicoloured.
3225. 10 k. Type **1189** 40 25
3226. 10 k. Leningrad 40 25
3227. 10 k. Kiev 40 25
3228. 10 k. Moscow 40 25
3229. 10 k. Brest-Litovak .. 40 25
3230. 10 k. Volgograd 40 25
3231. 10 k. Sevastopol 40 25

1190. Flag, Map and Parliament Building, Belgrade.

1965. 20th Anniv. of Yugoslavia Republic.
3232. **1190.** 6 k. multicoloured .. 20 10

1191. Tu-134 Jet-Airliner.

1965. Soviet Civil Aviation. Multicoloured.
3233. 6 k. Type **1191** 50 10
3234. 10 k. An-24 .. .. 70 15
3235. 12 k. Mi-10 (helicopter) .. 80 25
3236. 16 k. Be-10 (flying-boat) 1·10 40
3237. 20 k. "Antey" turboprop 1·40 45

1192. "The Proposal of Marriage", after P. Fedotov (150th Birth Anniv.).

1965. Soviet Painters' Annivs.
3238. – 12 k. black and red 1·50 35
3239. **1192.** 16 k. blue and red 2·00 60
DESIGN—VERT. 12 k. "A Collective Farm Watchman" (after S. Gerasimov: 80th Birth Anniv.).

1193. Crystallography Congress Emblem.

1966. Int. Congresses, Moscow.
3240. **1193.** 6 k. blk., bl. & bistre 25 15
3241. – 6 k. blk., red & blue 25 15
3242. – 6 k. pur., grey & blk. 25 15
3243. – 6 k. black and blue .. 25 15
3244. – 6 k. blk., red & yell. 25 15
CONGRESS EMBLEMS: No. 3241, Microbiology. No. 3242, Poultry-raising. No. 3243, Oceanography. No. 3244, Mathematics.

1194. 19th-cent. Statuettes.

1966. Bicentenary of Dmitrov Ceramic Works. Multicoloured.
3245. 6 k. Type **1194** 30 15
3246. 10 k. Modern tea-set .. 65 25

1195. Rolland and Scene from Novel. **1196.** Mongol Horseman.

1966. Birth Centenary of Romain Rolland (French writer) and 150th Birth Anniv. of Eugene Potier (French poet).
3247. **1195.** 4 k. brown and blue 30 15
3248. – 4 k. brn., red and blk. 30 15
DESIGN: No. 3248, Potier and revolutionary scene.

1966. 20th Anniv. of Soviet-Mongolian Treaty.
3249. **1196.** 4 k. multicoloured .. 25 10

„ЛУНА-9"—НА ЛУНЕ!
3.2.1966
(**1197.**)

1966. Landing of "Luna 9" Rocket on Moon. Optd. with T **1197.**
3250. **1017.** 6 k. red, black & blue 4·50 4·50

1198. Supply Ship "Ob".

1966. 10th Anniv. of Soviet Antarctic Expedition.
3251. **1198.** 10 k. lake and silver 2·00 50
3252. – 10 k. lake, silver & bl. 2·00 50
3253. – 10 k. lake, silver & bl. 2·00 50
DESIGNS—TRIANGULAR: No. 3252, Snow vehicle. DIAMOND: No. 3253, Antarctic Map. This stamp is partly perf. across the centre.

1199. Mussa Dyalil and Scene from Poem.

1966. Writers.
3254. **1199.** 4 k. black and brn. 30 10
3255. – 4 k. black and grn. 30 10
3256. – 4 k. black & green 30 10
WRITERS: No. 3254 (Azerbaijan writer: 60th birth anniv.). No. 3255, Akob Akopyan (Armenian poet: birth cent.). No. 3256, Djalil Mamedkulizade (Azerbaijan writer: birth cent.).

1200. Lenin (after bust by Kibalnikov).

1966. Lenin's 96th Birth Anniv.

3257. **1200.** 10 k. gold and green 80 25
3258. 10 k. silver and red 80 25

1201. N. Ilin.

1202. Scene from "Alive and Dead".

1966. War Heroes.

3259. **1201.** 4 k. violet and red .. 30 15
3260. – 4 k. lilac and blue .. 30 15
3261. – 4 k. brown and green 30 15

PORTRAITS: No. 3260, G. P. Kravchenko. No. 3261, A. Uglovsky.

1966. Soviet Cinema Art.

3262. **1202.** 4 k. blk., grn. & red 25 10
3263. – 10 k. black and blue 60 20

DESIGN: 10 k. Scene from "Hamlet".

1203. Kremlin and Inscription.

Учредительная конференция
Всесоюзного общества
филателистов. 1966

(1204.)

1966. 23rd Soviet Comunist Party Congress, Moscow (1st issue).

3264 **1203** 4 k. gold, red & blue 20 10

See also Nos. 3337/41.

1966. Philatelists All-Union Society Conf. No. 3198 optd. with T **1204**.

3265. 16 k. plum, red and grey 1·75 75

1205. Ice Skating.

1966. 2nd People's Winter Spartakiad.

3266. **1205.** 4 k. blue, red & olive 25 15
3267. – 6 k. red, lake & lilac 35 20
3268. – 10 k. lake, red & blue 60 30

DESIGNS: Inscription emblem and—6 k. Ice hockey. 10 k. Skiing.

Nos. 3266/8 are each perf across the centre.

1206. Liner "Aleksandr Pushkin".

1207. Government Building, Frunze.

1966. Soviet Transport.

3269. – 4 k. multicoloured .. 55 10
3270. – 6 k. multicoloured .. 45 10
3271. – 10 k. multicoloured 65 20
3272. **1206.** 12 k. multicoloured 1·00 20
3273. – 16 k. multicoloured 1·00 25

DESIGNS—HORIZ. 4 k. Electric train. 6 k. Map of Lenin Volga-Baltic canal system. 16 k. Silhouette of liner on Globe. VERT. 10 k. Canal lock. Nos. 3271/3 Commemorates the Inaug. of Leningrad-Montreal Sea Service.

1966. 40th Anniv of Kirgizia.

3274 **1207** 4 k. red 20 10

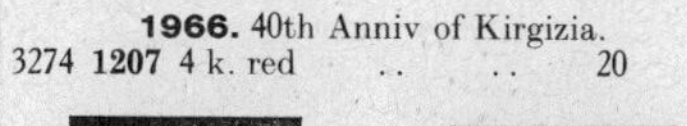

1208. S. M. Kirov (80th Birth Anniv.)

1210. A. Fersman (mineralogist).

1966. Soviet Personalities.

3275. **1208.** 4 k. brown 20 10
3276. – 4 k. green 20 10
3277. – 4 k. violet 20 10

PORTRAITS: No. 3276, G. I. Ordzhonikidze (80th birth anniv.). No. 3277, Ion Yakir (military commander, 70th birth anniv.).

1966. Soviet Scientists. Multicoloured. Colours of name-panels below.

3279. **1210**. 4 k. blue 60 15
3280. – 4 k. brown 60 15
3281. – 4 k. violet 60 15
3282. – 4 k. brown & blue .. 60 15

POTRAITS: No. 3280, Zabolotnyi (microbiologist). No. 3281, M. A. Shatelen (electrical engineer). No. 3282, O. Yu. Shmidt (arctic explorer).

„Луна-10"—XXIII съезду КПСС

(1211.)

1966. Launching of "Luna 10". As No. 3284, but imperf., optd with T **1211**.

3283. **1212.** 10 k. multicoloured 3·00 2·25

1212. Arrowheads, "Luna 9" and Orbit.

1966. Cosmonautics Day. Multicoloured.

3284. 10 k. Type **1212** 60 25
3285. 12 k. Rocket-launching and different orbit .. 65 30

1213. "Molniya 1" in Orbit.

1214. Ernst Thalmann (80th birth anniv.)

1966. Launching of "Molniya 1" Telecommunications Satellite.

3286. **1213.** 10 k. multicoloured 55 20

1966. Prominent Leaders.

3287. **1214.** 6 k. red 30 10
3288. – 6 k. violet 30 10
3289. – 6 k. brown 30 10

PORTRAITS: No. 3288, W. Pieck (90th birth anniv.). No. 3289, Sun Yat-sen (birth cent.).

1216. Spaceman and Soldier.

1966. 15th Young Communist League Congress.

3290. **1216.** 4 k. black and red .. 15 10

1217. Ice Hockey Player.

1966. Soviet Victory in World Ice Hockey Championships.

3291 **1217** 10 k. multicoloured .. 60 25

1218. N. I. Kuznetsov.

1219. Tchaikovsky.

1966. War Heroes. Guerilla Fighters.

3292. **1218.** 4 k. black and green 20 10
3293. – 4 k. black and yellow 20 10
3294. – 4 k. black and blue .. 20 10
3295. – 4 k. black and purple 20 10
3296. – 4 k. black and violet 20 10

PORTRAITS: No. 3293, I. Y. Sudmalis. No. 3294, A. A. Morozova. No 3295, F. E. Strelets. No. 3296, T. P. Bumazhkov.

1966. 3rd Int. Tchaikovsky Music Competition, Moscow.

3297. – 4 k. black red & yell. 35 10
3298. **1219.** 6 k. black, red & yell. 55 10
3299. – 16 k. blk., red & blue 1·40 35

DESIGNS: 4 k. Moscow State Conservatoire of Music. 16 k. Tchaikovsky's house and museum, Klin.

1220. Running.

1966. Sports Events.

3300. **1220.** 4 k. brn., olive & grn. 15 15
3301. – 6 k. blk., bis. & orge. 30 15
3302. – 12 k. blk., bistre & bl. 45 25

DESIGNS: 6 k. Weightlifting. 12 k. Wrestling.

1222. Gold Medal and Chess Pieces.

1966. World Chess Championship, Moscow.

3303 **1222** 6 k. multicoloured .. 75 20

1223. Jules Rimet Cup and Football.

1966. World Cup Football Championships and World Fencing Championships.

3304. **1223.** 4 k. blk., gold & red 20 10
3305. – 6 k. multicoloured .. 30 10
3306. – 12 k. multicoloured 60 20
3307. – 16 k. multicoloured 90 40

DESIGNS: 6 k. Footballers. 12 k. Fencers. 16 k. Fencer and fencing emblems.

1224. Sable, Lake Baikal and Animals (Reduced size illustration. Actual size 80 × 26 mm.).

1966. Barguzin Nature Reserve.

3308. **1224.** 4 k. black and blue .. 50 15
3309. – 6 k. black & purple 75 25

DESIGN: 6 k. Map of Reserve, and brown bear.

1225. Lotus Plants.

1226. "Venus 3"—Medal, Globe and Flight Trajectory.

1966. 125th Anniv. of Sukhumi Botanical Gardens.

3310. **1225.** 3 k. red, yell. & grn. 15 10
3311. – 6 k. bistre, brn. & bl. 30 10
3312. – 12 k. red, grn. & turq. 50 30

DESIGNS: 6 k. Palms and cypresses. 12 k. Water-lilies.

1966. Space Achievements.

3313. **1226.** 6 k. blk., silver & red 40 15
3314. – 6 k. deep blue, blue and brown .. 40 15
3315. – 6 k. ochre and blue 40 15
3316. – 6 k. multicoloured .. 45 15
3317. – 6 k. pink, mve. & blk. 45 15

DESIGNS: No. 3314, Spacedogs, Ugolek and Veterok. No. 3315, "Luna 10". No. 3316, "Molniya 1". No. 3317, "Luna 2's" pennant, Earth and Moon.

1227. Itkol.

1966. Tourist Resorts. Multicoloured.

3318. 1 k. Type **1227** 10 10
3319. 4 k. Cruise ship on the Volga 30 10
3320. 6 k. Archway, Leningrad 25 10
3321. 10 k. Kislovodsk .. 45 20
3322. 12 k. Ismail Samani Mausoleum Bokhara .. 65 15
3323. 16 k. Sochi (Black Sea) .. 80 30

The 6 k. is $27\frac{1}{2} \times 28$ mm.

1230. Congress Emblem.

1231. Peace Dove and Japanese Crane.

1966. 7th Consumers' Co-operative Societies' Congress, Moscow.

3325. **1230.** 4 k. yellow & brown 15 10

1966. Soviet-Japanese Meeting, Khabarovsk.

3326. **1231.** 6 k. black and red .. 30 15

1232. "Avtandil at a Mountain Spring", after engraving by S. Kabulazde.

1966. 800th Birth Anniv. of Shota Rustaveli (Georgian poet).

3327. – 3 k. black on green 25 10
3328. – 4 k. brn. on yellow .. 30 10
3329. **1232.** 6 k. black on blue .. 40 15

DESIGNS: 3 k. Scene from poem "The Knight in the Tiger's Skin", after I. Toidze. 4 k. Rustaveli, after bas-relief by Y. Nikoladze.

1234. Arms, Moscow Skyline and Fireworks.

1235. Trawler, Net and Map of Lake Baikal.

1966. 49th Anniv. of October Revolution.

3331. **1234.** 4 k. multicoloured .. 15 10

1966. Fish Resources of Lake Baikal. Mult.

3332.		2 k. Grayling	15	10
3333.		4 k. Sturgeon	20	10
3334.		6 k. Type 1235	30	10
3335.		10 k. " Omul "	50	20
3336.		12 k. " Sig " (salmon) ..	65	25

The 2, 4, 10 and 12 k. are horiz.

1236. " Agriculture and Industry ".

1966. 23rd Soviet Communist Party Congress, Moscow (3rd issue).

3337.	1236.	4 k. silver and brown	20	10
3338.	–	4 k. silver and blue ..	20	10
3339.	–	4 k. silver and red ..	20	10
3340.	–	4 k. silver and red ..	20	10
3341.	–	4 k. silver and green	20	10

DESIGN (MAP AS Type **1236** with SYMBOLS OF): No. 3338, " Communications and Transport ". No. 3339, " Education and Technology ". No. 3340, " Increased Productivity ". No. 3341, " Power Resources ".

1237. Government Buildings, Kishinev.

1966. 500th Anniv. of Kishinev (Moldavian Republic).

3342.	1237.	4 k. multicoloured ..	15	10

1238. Clouds, Rain and Decade Emblem.

1239. Nikitin Monument, Map and Ship.

1966. Int. Hydrological Decade.

3343.	1238.	6 k. multicoloured ..	30	10

1966. Nikitin's Voyage to India.

3344.	1239.	4 k. blk., grn. & yell.	20	10

1240. Scene from "Nargiz" (Muslim Magomaev).

1966. Azerbaijan Operas.

3345.	1240.	4 k. ochre and black	35	15
3346.	–	4 k. green and black	35	15

DESIGN: No. 3346, Scene from "Kehzoglu" (Uzeir Gadshibekov).

1241. " Luna 9 " and Moon.

1242. Agricultural and Chemical Symbols.

1966.

3347	–	1 k. brown	10	10
3348	1241	2 k. violet	10	10
3349	–	3 k. purple	20	10
3350	–	4 k. red ..	20	10
3351	–	6 k. blue	60	10
3563	–	10 k. olive	50	10
3353	–	12 k. brown ..	70	10
3354	–	16 k. blue	90	15
3355	–	20 k. red, blue & drab	80	20
3566	–	20 k. red	1·00	40
3356	1242	30 k. green	1·75	40
3357	–	50 k. ult., blue & grey	3·50	50
3568	–	50 k. blue	4·00	65
3358	–	1 r. brown and red ..	4·75	1·10
3569	–	1 r. brown and black	4·75	1·40

DESIGNS. As Type **1241**: 1 k. Palace of Congresses, Kremlin. 3 k. Youth, girl and Lenin emblem. 4 k. Arms and hammer and sickle emblem. 6 k. "Communications"—airliner and sputnik. 10 k. Soldier and star emblem. 12 k. Furnaceman. 16 k. Girl with dove. As Type **1242**. 20 k. Worker's demonstration and flower. 50 k. "Postal communications". 1 r. Lenin and Industrial emblems.

1243. " Presenting Arms ".

1245. Campaign Meeting.

1966. 25th Anniv. of People's Voluntary Corps.

3359.	1243.	4 k. brown and red ..	15	10

1966. " Hands off Vietnam ".

3360.	1245.	6 k. multicoloured ..	20	10

1246. Servicemen.

1966. 30th Anniv. of Spanish Civil War.

3361.	1246.	6 k. blk., red & ochre	20	10

1247. Ostankino TV Tower, "Molniya 1" (satellite) and "1967".

1249. Statue, Tank and Medal.

1250. Cervantes and Don Quixote.

1248. Flight Diagram.

1966. New Year and "50th Year of October Revolution".

3362.	1247.	4 k. multicoloured ..	30	10

1966. Space Flight and Moon landing of " Luna 9 ".

3363.	1248.	10 k. black & silver	55	25
3364.	–	10 k. red and silver	55	25
3365.	–	10 k. black and silver	55	25

DESIGNS—SQUARE (25 × 25 mm.). No. 3364, Arms of Russia and Lunar pennant. HORIZ. No. 3365, " Lunar 9 " on Moon's surface.

1966. 25th Anniv. of Battle of Moscow.

3366.	–	4 k. brown	30	10
3367.	1249.	6 k. ochre and sepia	30	15
3368.	–	10 k. yellow & brown	60	20

DESIGNS—HORIZ. (60 × 28 mm.): 4 k. Soviet troops advancing. 10 k. " Moscow at peace "—Kremlin, Sun and " Defence of Moscow " medal.

1966. 350th Death Anniv. of Cervantes.

3369.	1250.	6 k. brown, green and deep green ..	30	10

1252. Bering's Ship "Sv. Pyotr" and Map of Komandor Islands.

1966. Soviet Far Eastern Territories. Mult.

3370.		1 k. Type **1252**	40	10
3371.		2 k. Medny Island and map	45	10
3372.		4 k. Petropavlovsk Harbour, Kamchatka	65	10
3373.		6 k. Geyser, Kamchatka (vert.)	80	10
3374.		10 k. Avatchinskaya Bay, Kamchatka ..	1·00	15
3375.		12 k. Northern fur seals, Bering Is.	1·00	35
3376.		16 k. Common Guillemot colony, Kurile Islands	2·50	65

1254. " The Lute Player " (Caravaggio).

1966. Art Treasures of the Hermitage Museum, Leningrad.

3377.	–	4 k. black on yellow	20	10
3378.	–	6 k. black on grey	40	10
3379.	–	10 k. black on lilac ..	65	15
3380.	–	12 k. black on green	85	20
3381.	1254.	16 k. black on buff ..	1·10	35

DESIGNS—HORIZ. 4 k. " Golden Stag " (from Scythian battle-shield (6th cent. B.C.). VERT. 6 k. Persian silver jug (5th cent. A.D.). 10 k. Statue of Voltaire (Houdon, 1781). 12 k. Malachite vase (Urals, 1840).

1255. Sea-water Distilling Apparatus.

1967. World Fair, Montreal.

3382.	1255.	4 k. blk., silver & grn.	15	10
3383.	–	6 k. multicoloured ..	25	15
3384.	–	10 k. multicoloured	45	20

DESIGNS—VERT. 6 k. " Atomic Energy " (explosion and symbol). HORIZ. 10 k. Space-station " Proton I ".

1256. Lieut. B. I. Sizov.

1258. Cine-camera and Film " Flower ".

1257. Woman's Face and Pavlov Shawl.

1967. War Heroes.

3386.	1256.	4 k. brown on yellow	20	10
3387.	–	4 k. brown on drab ..	20	10

DESIGN: No. 3387, Private V. V. Khodyrev.

1967. Int. Women's Day.

3388.	1257.	4 k. red, violet & grn.	20	10

1967. 5th Int. Film Festival, Moscow.

3389.	1258.	6 k. multicoloured ..	30	10

1259. Factory Ship "Cheryashevsky".

1967. Soviet Fishing Industry. Multicoloured.

3390		6 k. Type **1259**	45	15
3391		6 k. Refrigerated trawler	45	15
3392		6 k. Crab-canning ship ..	45	15
3393		6 k. Trawler	45	15
3394		6 k. Seine-fishing boat, Black Sea	45	15

1260. Newspaper Cuttings, Hammer and Sickle.

1261. I.S.O. Congress Emblem.

1967. 50th Anniv. of Newspaper "Isvestia".

3395.	1260.	4 k. multicoloured ..	15	10

1967. Moscow Congresses.

3396.		6 k. turq., black & blue ..	20	10
3397.		6 k. red, black and blue ..	20	10

DESIGNS: No. 3396, Type **1261** (7th Congress of Int. Standards Assn. " I.S.O. "). No. **3397**, " V " emblem of 5th Int. Mining Congress.

1262. I.T.Y. Emblem.

1967. Int. Tourist Year.

3398.	1262.	4 k. blk., silver & blue	15	10

Вена-1967

(1263.)

1265. " Lenin as Schoolboy " (V. Tsigal).

1264. A. A. Leonov in Space.

1967. Victory in World Ice Hockey Championship No. 3291 optd with T **1263**.

3399	1217	10 k. multicoloured ..	2·00	1·40

1967. Cosmonautics Day. Multicoloured.

3400.		4 k. Type **1264**	20	10
3401.		10 k. Rocket and Earth	45	15
3402.		16 k. "Luna 10" over Moon	60	35

1967. Lenin's 97th Birth Anniv.

3403.	1265.	2 k. brn., yell. & grn.	20	10
3404.	–	3 k. brown and lake	35	10
3405.	–	4 k. green, yellow and olive ..	45	10
3406.		6 k. silver, blk. & bl.	50	10
3407.	–	10 k. bl., blk. & silver	1·10	30
3408.	–	10 k. black and gold	65	30

SCULPTURES—VERT. 3 k. Lenin's monument, Ulyanovsk. 6 k. Bust of Lenin (G. and Yu. Neroda). 10 k. (both) "Lenin as Leader" (Andreev). HORIZ. 4 k. "Lenin at Razliv" (Pinchuk).

1266. M. F. Shmyrev.

1268. Marshal Biryuzov.

1267. Transport crossing Ice on Lake Ladoga.

1967. War Heroes.

3409.	1266.	4 k. sepia and brown	20	10
3410.	–	4 k. brown and blue	20	10
3411.	–	4 k. brown and violet	20	10

DESIGNS: No. 3410, Major-General S. V. Rudney. 3411, First Lieut. M. S. Kharchenko.

1967. Siege of Leningrad, 1941-42.

3412.	1267.	4 k. grey, red & cream	20	10

1967. Biryuzov Commem.

3413.	1268.	4 k. green and yellow	15	10

1269. Minsk Old and New.

1270. Red Cross and Tulip.

1967. 900th Anniv. of Minsk.
3414. **1269.** 4 k. green and black 15 10

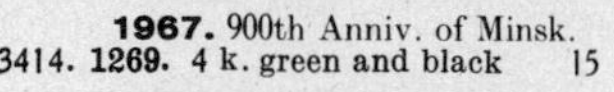

1967. Cent. of Russian Red Cross.
3415. **1270.** 4 k. red and ochre .. 15 10

1271 Russian Stamps of 1918 and 1967.

1967. "50th Anniv. of U.S.S.R.". Philatelic Exn., Moscow.
3416. **1271.** 20 k green and blue 60 40

1272. Komsomolsk-on-Amur and Map.

1273. Motor Cyclist (International Motor Rally, Moscow).

1967. 35th Anniv. of Komsomolsk-on-Amur.
3418. **1272.** 4 k. brown and red .. 25 10

1967. Sports and Pastimes. Int. Events.
3419. – 1 k. brn., bistre & grn. 20 10
3420. – 2 k. brown 20 10
3421. – 3 k. blue 20 10
3422. – 4 k. turquoise .. 20 10
3423. – 6 k. purple and bistre 30 10
3424. **1273.** 10 k. purple and lilac 75 30
DESIGNS AND EVENTS: 1 k. Draughts-board and players (World Draughts Championships). 2 k. Throwing the javelin. 3 k. Running. 4 k. Long jumping (all preliminary events for Europa Cup Games). 6 k. Gymnast (World Gymnastics Championships).

1275. G. D. Gai (soldier).

1276. Games Emblem and Cup.

1967. Commander G. D. Gai Commem.
3426. **1275.** 4 k. black and red .. 15 10

1967. All-Union Schoolchildren's Spartakiad.
3427. **1276.** 4 k. red, blk. & silver 10 10

1277. Spartakiad Emblem and Cup.

1967. 4th People's Spartakiad.
3428. 4 k. black, red and silver 15 10
3429. 4 k. black, red and silver 15 10
3430. 4 k. black, red and silver 15 10
3431. 4 k. black, red and silver 15 10
DESIGNS: Each with Cup. No. 3428, Type **1277**. No. 3429, Gymnastics. No. 3430, Diving. No. 3431, Cycling.

1278. V. G. Klochkov (Soviet hero).

1967. Klochkov Commem.
3432. **1278.** 4 k. black and red .. 15 10

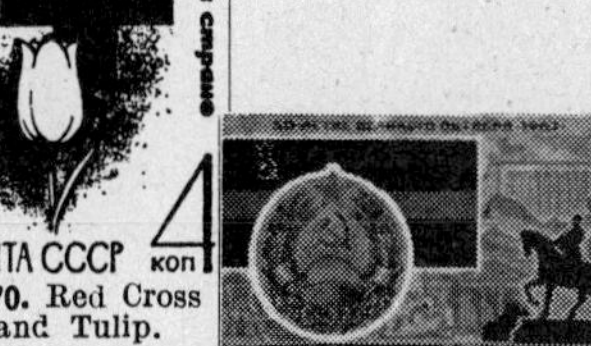
1279. Crest, Flag and Capital of Moldavia.

1280. Telecommunications Symbols.

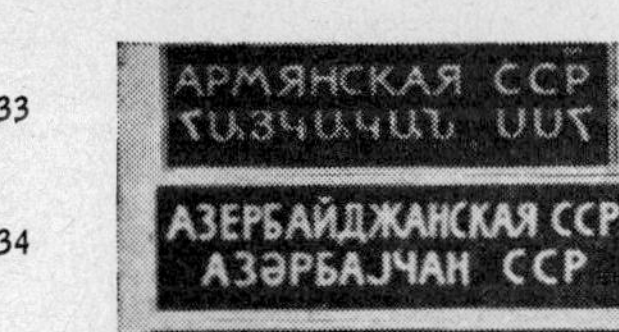

Inscr. at foot as shown above.

1967. 50th Anniv. of October Revolution. (1st issue.) Designs showing crests, flags and capitals of the Soviet Republics. Mult.
3433. 4 k. Armenia 15 10
3434. 4 k. Azerbaijan 15 10
3435. 4 k. Byelorussia 15 10
3436. 4 k. Estonia 15 10
3437. 4 k. Georgia 15 10
3438. 4 k. Kazakhstan .. 15 10
3439. 4 k. Kirghizia 15 10
3440. 4 k. Latvia 15 10
3441. 4 k. Lithuania 15 10
3442. 4 k. Type **1279** 15 10
3443. 4 k. Russia 15 10
3444. 4 k. Tadzhikistan .. 15 10
3445. 4 k. Turkmenistan .. 15 10
3446. 4 k. Ukraine 15 10
3447. 4 k. Uzbekistan 15 10
3448. 4 k. Soviet Arms .. 15 10
No. 3448 is size 47 × 32 mm.
See also Nos. 3473/82.

1967. "Progress of Communism".
3449. **1280.** 4 k. red, pur. & silver 2·50 1·40

1281. Manchurian Crane and Dove.

1967. Soviet-Japanese Friendship.
3450. **1281.** 16 k. brn., blk. & red 65 35

1282. Karl Marx and Title Page.

1967. Cent. of Karl Marx's "Das Kapital".
3451. **1282.** 4 k. brown and red .. 25 10

1283. Arctic Fox.

1285. Krasnodon Memorial.

1284. Ice Skating.

1967. Fur-bearing Animals.
3452. **1283.** 2 k. blue, blk. & brn. 15 10
3453. – 4 k. blue, blk. & drab 20 10
3454. – 6 k. ochre, blk. & grn. 35 10
3455. – 10 k. brn., blk. & grn. 50 15
3456. – 12 k. black, ochre and violet 55 25
3457. – 16 k. brn., blk. & yell. 70 35
3458. – 20 k. brown, black & turquoise 90 50
DESIGNS—VERT. 4 k. Red fox. 12 k. Stoat. 16 k. Sable. HORIZ. 6 k. Red fox. 10 k. Muskrat. 20 k. European mink.

1967. Winter Olympic Games, Grenoble (1968). Multicoloured.
3459 2 k. Type **1284** 10 10
3460 3 k. Ski jumping .. 15 10
3461 4 k. Games emblem (vert) 15 10
3462 10 k. Ice hockey .. 55 15
3463 12 k. Skiing 65 30

1967. 25th Anniv. of Krasnodon Defence.
3464. **1285.** 4 k. blk., yell. & pur. 15 10

1285a. Map and Snow Leopard. (Reduced size illustration. Actual size 80 × 26 mm.).

1967. Cedar Fall Nature Reserve.
3465. **1285a.** 10 k. black and bistre 75 30

1286. Badge and Fighter Aircraft.

1288. Cosmonauts in Space.

1287. Militiaman and Soviet Crest.

1967. 25th Anniv. of French "Normandie-Niemen" Fighter Squadron.
3466. **1286.** 6 k. red, blue & gold 35 15

1967. 50th Anniv. of Soviet Militia.
3467. **1287.** 4 k. red and blue .. 20 10

1967. Space Fantasies. Multicoloured.
3468. 4 k. Type **1288** 15 10
3469. 6 k. Men on the Moon (horiz.) 20 10
3470. 10 k. Cosmic vehicle .. 45 15
3471. 12 k. Planetary landscape (horiz.) 50 20
3472. 16 k. Imaginary spacecraft 60 30

1289. Red Star and Soviet Crest.

1967. 50th Anniv. of October Revolution (2nd issue.) "50 Heroic Years". Designs showing paintings and Soviet Arms. Multicoloured.
3473 4 k. Type **1289** 25 15
3474 4 k. "Lenin addressing Congress" (Serov—1955) 25 15
3475 4 k. "Lenin explaining the GOELRO map" (Schmatko—1957) .. 25 15
3476 4 k. "The First Cavalry" (Grekov—1924) .. 25 15
3477 4 k. "Students" (Yoganson—1928) .. 25 15
3478 4 k. "People's Friendship" (Karpov—1924) .. 25 15
3479 4 k. "Dawn of the Five-Year Plan" (construction work, Romas—1934) .. 35 15
3480 4 k. "Farmers' Holiday" (Gerasimov—1937) .. 25 15
3481 4 k. "Victory in World War II" (Korolev—1965) 25 15
3482 4 k. "Builders of Communism" (Merpert and Skripkov—1965) .. 25 15

1290. S. Katayama.

1292. T.V. Tower, Moscow.

1967. Katayama (founder of Japanese Communist Party) Commemoration.
3484. **1290.** 6 k. green 15 10

1967. Opening of Ostankino T.V. Tower, Moscow.
3486. **1292.** 16 k. black, silver and orange .. 50 20

1293. Narva-Joesuu (Estonia).

1967. Baltic Health Resorts. Multicoloured.
3487 4 k. Yurmala (Latvia) .. 10 10
3488 6 k. Type **1293** .. 20 10
3489 10 k. Druskininkai (Lithuania) 30 15
3490 12 k. Zelenogradsk (Kaliningrad) (vert) .. 40 20
3491 16 k. Svetlogorsk (Kaliningrad) (vert) .. 50 25

1294. K.G.B. Emblem.

1295. Moscow View.

1967. 50th Anniv. of State Security Commission (K.G.B.).
3492. **1294.** 4 k. red, silver & blue 15 10

1967. New Year.
3493. **1295.** 4 k. brown, pink and silver 20 10

1296. Revolutionaries at Kharkov, and Monument.

1967. 50th Anniv. of Ukraine Republic.
3494. **1296.** 4 k. multicoloured .. 15 10
3495. – 6 k. multicoloured .. 30 10
3496. – 10 k. multicoloured 30 15
DESIGNS: 6 k. Hammer and sickle and industrial and agricultural scenes. 10 k. Unknown Soldier's monument, Kiev, and young Ukrainians with welcoming bread and salt.

1297. Armoury, Commandant and Trinity Towers.

1299. Unknown Soldiers' Tomb, Kremlin.

1298. Moscow Badge, Lenin's Tomb and Rockets.

1967. Kremlin Buildings.

3497.	1297.	4 k. brn., pur. & grn.	15	10
3498.	–	6 k. brn., grn. & yell.	25	10
3499.	–	10 k. brown and grey	30	15
3500.	–	12 k. green, violet and cream ..	40	30
3501.	–	16 k. brown, red & lt. brown.. ..	50	30

DESIGNS—HORIZ. 6 k. Cathedral of the Annunciation. VERT. 10 k. Konstantino-Yelenin, Alarm and Spassky Towers. 12 k. Ivan the Great's bell-tower. 16 k. Kutafya and Trinity Towers.

1967. "50 Years of Communist Development".

3502.	1298.	4 k. lake	20	10
3503.	–	4 k. brown	20	10
3504.	–	4 k. green	20	10
3505.	–	4 k. blue	20	10
3506.	–	4 k. blue	20	10

DESIGNS—HORIZ. No. 3503, Computer-tape, cogwheel and industrial scene. No. 3504, Ear of wheat and grain silo. No. 3505, Microscope, radar antennae and Moscow University. VERT. No. 3506, T.V. Tower, liner, railway bridge and jetliner.

1967. "Unknown Soldier" Commem.

3507.	1299.	4 k. red	15	10

1300. "The Interrogation of Communists" (Yoganson).

1967. Paintings in the Tretyakov Gallery, Moscow. Multicoloured.

3508	3 k. Type 1300	15	10
3509	4 k. "The Sea-shore" (Aivazovsky)	25	10
3510	4 k. "The Lace-maker (Tropinin) (vert) ..	25	10
3511	6 k. "The Bakery" (Yablonskaya) ..	30	10
3512	6 k. "Alexander Nevsky" (part of triptych by Korin) (vert) ..	30	10
3513	6 k. "Boyarynya Morozova" (Surikov) ..	30	10
3514	10 k. "The Swan Maiden" (Vroubel) (vert) ..	50	20
3515	10 k. "The Arrest of a Propagandist" (Repin)	50	20
3516	16 k. "Moscow Suburb in February" (Nissky) ..	1·50	45

Nos. 3511/13 are larger (60 × 34 mm or 34 × 60 mm).

1301. Congress Emblem.

1302. Lieut. S. G. Bajkov.

1968. 14th Soviet Trade Unions Congress, Moscow.

3517.	1301.	6 k. red and green ..	15	10

1968. War Heroes.

3518.	1302.	4 k. black and blue ..	20	10
3519.	–	4 k. blue and green ..	20	10
3520.	–	4 k. black and red ..	20	10

PORTRAITS: No. 3519, Lieut. P. L. Guchenko. No. 3520, A. A. Pokaltchuk.

1303. Racehorses.

1304. M. Ulyanova.

1968. Soviet Horse-Breeding.

3521.	1303.	4 k. blk., pur. & blue	25	10
3522.	–	6 k. black, blue & red	35	10
3523.	–	10 k. blk., brn. & turq.	60	15
3524.	–	12 k. blk., grn. & brn.	65	20
3525.	–	16 k. blk., red & grn.	90	30

DESIGNS (each with horse's head and horses "in the field"). VERT. 6 k. Show horses. 12 k. Show-jumpers. HORIZ. 10 k. Trotters. 16 k. Hunters.

1968. 90th Birth Anniv. of M. I. Ulyanova (Lenin's sister).

3526.	1304.	4 k. blue and green ..	10	10

1305. Red Star and Forces' Flags.

1968. 50th Anniv. of Soviet Armed Forces. Multicoloured.

3527.	4 k. Type 1305	30	15
3528.	4 k. Lenin addressing recruits	30	15
3529.	4 k. Recruiting poster and volunteers ..	30	15
3530.	4 k. Red Army entering Vladivostok, 1922, and monument ..	30	15
3531.	4 k. Dnieper Dam and statue "On Guard" ..	30	15
3532.	4 k. "Liberators" poster and tanks in the Ukraine ..	30	15
3533.	4 k. "To the East" poster and retreating Germans fording river ..	30	15
3534.	4 k. Stalingrad battle monument and German prisoners-of-war ..	30	15
3535.	4 k. Victory parade, Red Square, Moscow, and monument, Treptow (Berlin) ..	30	15
3536.	4 k. Rockets, tank, warships and Red Flag ..	30	15

Nos. 3527 and 3536 are vert. The rest are horiz.

1306. Gorky (after Serov).

1307. Fireman and Appliances.

1968. Birth Cent of Maksim Gorky (writer).

3538	1306	4 k. brown and drab	15	10

1968. 50th Anniv. of Soviet Fire Services.

3539.	1307.	4 k. black and red ..	20	10

1308. Linked Satellites.

1309. N. N. Popudrenko.

1968. Space Link of "Cosmos" Satellites.

3540.	1308.	6 k. blk., gold & pur.	20	10

1968. War Heroes.

3541.	1309.	4 k. black and green	20	10
3542.	–	4 k. black and lilac ..	20	10

DESIGN: No. 3542, P. P. Vershigora.

1310. Protective Hand.

1312. Lenin.

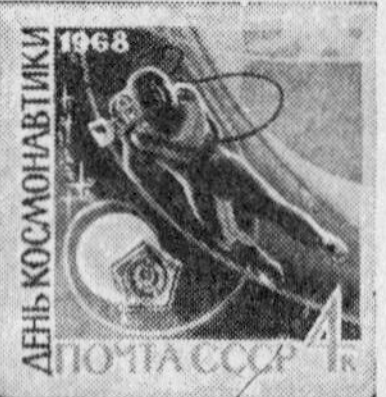

1311. Leonov filming in Space.

1968. "Solidarity with Vietnam".

3543.	1310.	6 k. multicoloured ..	15	10

1968. Cosmonautics Day. Multicoloured.

3544	4 k. Type 1311	25	15
3545	6 k. "Kosmos 186" and "Kosmos 188" linking in space	35	15
3546	10 k. "Venera 4" space probe	50	15

1968. Lenin's 98th Birth Anniv.

3547.	1312.	4 k. multicoloured ..	40	15
3548.	–	4 k. blk., red & gold	40	15
3549.	–	4 k. brn., red & gold	40	15

DESIGNS: No. 3548, Lenin speaking in Red Square. No. 3549, Lenin in peaked cap speaking from lorry during parade.

1313. A. Navoi.

1314. Karl Marx.

1968. 525th Birth Anniv. of Alisher Navoi (Uzbek poet).

3550.	1313.	4 k. brown	10	10

1968. 150th Birth Anniv. of Karl Marx.

3551.	1314.	4 k. black and red ..	15	10

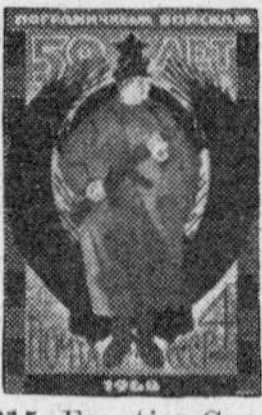

1315. Frontier Guard.

1316. Gem and Congress Emblem.

1968. 50th Anniv. of Soviet Frontier Guards. Multicoloured.

3552.	4 k. Type 1315	15	10
3553.	6 k. Jubilee badge ..	20	10

1968. "Int. Congresses and Assemblies".

3554	1249	6 k. deep blue, new blue and green ..	25	15
3555	–	6 k. gold, orge & brn	25	15
3556	–	6 k. gold, black & red	25	15
3557	–	6 k. orge, blk & mve	25	15

DESIGNS: No. 3554, Type 1316 (8th Enriched Minerals Congress). No. 3555, Power stations, pylon and emblem (7th World Power Conference). No. 3556, Beetle and emblem (13th Entomological Congress). No. 3557, Roses and emblem (4th Congress on Volatile Oils).

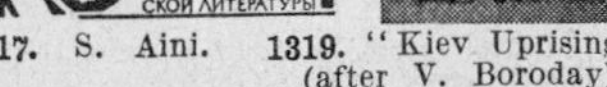

1317. S. Aini.

1319. "Kiev Uprising" (after V. Boroday).

1318. Congress Emblem and Postrider.

1968. 90th Birth Anniv. of Sadriddin Aini (Tadzhik writer).

3570.	1317.	4 k. purple and bistre	10	10

1968. Meeting of UPU Consultative Commission, Moscow.

3571.	1318.	6 k. red and grey ..	20	10
3572.	–	6 k. red and yellow	30	10

DESIGN: No. 3572, Emblem and transport.

1968. 50th Anniv. of Ukraine Communist Party.

3573.	1319.	4 k. red, pur. & gold	10	10

1320. Athletes and "50".

1321. Handball.

1968. Young Communist League's Games. 50th Anniv.

3574.	1320.	4 k. red, drab & yell.	10	10

1968. Various Sports Events.

3575.	1321.	2 k. multicoloured ..	15	10
3576.	–	4 k. multicoloured ..	25	10
3577.	–	6 k. multicoloured ..	30	10
3578.	–	10 k. red, blk. & bistre	30	20
3579.	–	12 k. multicoloured	35	25

DESIGNS AND EVENTS—VERT. Type 1321 (World Handball Games, Moscow). 6 k. Yachting (20th Baltic Regatta). 10 k. Football (70th anniv of Russian soccer). HORIZ. 4 k. Table tennis (All-European Juvenile Competitions). 12 k. Underwater swimming (European Underwater Sports Championships, Alushta, Ukraine).

1322. Girl Gymnasts.

1323. Gediminas Tower, Vilnius (Vilna).

1968. Olympic Games, Mexico. Backgrounds in gold.

3580.	1322.	4 k. turq. and blue ..	15	10
3581.	–	6 k. violet and red ..	15	10
3582.	–	10 k. green and turq.	25	10
3583.	–	12 k. brown & orge.	30	15
3584.	–	16 k. blue and pink	40	30

DESIGNS: 6 k. Weightlifting. 10 k. Rowing. 12 k. Women's Hurdles. 16 k. Fencing match.

1968. 50th Anniv. of Soviet Lithuania.

3586.	1323.	4 k. red, drab & pur.	10	10

1324. Tbilisi University.

1325. "Death of Laocoon and his sons" (from sculpture by Agesandre, Polidor and Asinodor).

1968. 50th Anniv. of Tbilisi University.

3587.	1324.	4 k. beige and green	10	10

1968. "Promote Solidarity with the Greek Democrats".

3588.	1325.	6 k. drab, purple and brown	2·50	2·75

1326. Cavalryman.

1968. 50th Anniv of Leninist Young Communist League (Komsomol) (1st issue). Multicoloured.

3589.	2 k. Type 1326	10	10
3590.	3 k. Young workers ..	10	10
3591.	4 k. Army officer ..	10	10
3592.	6 k. Construction workers	15	10
3593.	10 k. Agricultural workers	20	20

See also No. 3654.

1327. Institute and Molecular Structure.

1968. 50 Anniv. of N. S. Kurnakov Institute of Chemistry.

3595. **1327.** 4 k. purple, black and blue 10 10

1328. Letter.

1968. Int. Correspondence Week and Stamp Day.

3596. **1328.** 4 k. brn., red & lake 15 10
3597. – 4 k. blue, ochre and deep blue .. 15 10

DESIGN: No. 3597, Russian stamps.

1329. "The 26 Baku Commissars" (statue by Makarov). **1330.** T. Antikainen.

1968. 50th Anniv. of Execution of 26 Baku Commissars.

3598. **1329.** 4 k. multicoloured.. 10 10

1968. 70th Birthday of T. Antikainen (Finnish Communist leader).

3599. **1330.** 6 k. brown and grey 15 10

1331. Liner, "Ivan Franko". **1333.** P. P. Postyshev (1887–1940).

1332. Order of the October Revolution.

1968. Soviet Merchant Marine.

3600. **1331.** 6 k. red, deep blue and blue 25 10

1968. 51st Anniv. of October Revolution.

3601. **1332.** 4 k. multicoloured.. 10 10

1968. Soviet Personalities.

3602. **1333.** 4 k. black 15 10
3603. – 4 k. black 15 10
3604. – 4 k. black 15 10

DESIGNS: No. 3603, S. G. Shaumian (1878-1918). No. 3604, A. Ikramov (1898–1938).

1334. Statuette of Warrior and Ararat Mountains. **1335.** I. S. Turgenev.

1968. 2,750th Anniv of Yerevan (Armenian capital).

3605. **1334.** 4 k. black and brown on grey 15 10
3606. – 12 k. brown & sepia on yellow .. 45 25

DESIGN: 12 k. Sasunsky Monument.

1968. 150th Birth Anniv. of Ivan Turgenev (writer).

3607. **1335.** 4 k. green 15 10

1336. American Bison and Common Zebra.

1968. Fauna. Soviet Wildlife Reservations. Multicoloured.

3608. 4 k. Type **1336** 25 10
3609. 4 k. Purple swamphen and lotus 30 10
3610. 6 k. Great egrets (vert.) 40 15
3511. 6 k. Ostrich and golden pheasant (vert.) .. 40 15
3612. 10 k. Eland and guanaco 50 25
3613. 10 k. Glossy ibis and white spoonbill .. 60 30

1337. Building and Equipment.

1968. 50th Anniv. of Lenin Radio-laboratory, Gorky.

3614. **1337.** 4 k. blue and ochre 15 10

1338. Prospecting for Minerals. **1339.** Djety-Oguz, Kirgizia.

1968. Geology Day. Multicoloured.

3615. 4 k. Type **1338** 30 10
3616. 6 k. "Tracking down" metals 30 20
3617. 10 k. Oil derrick.. .. 85 20

1968. Central Asian Spas. Multicoloured.

3618 4 k. Type **1339** 15 10
3619 4 k. Borovoe, Kazakhstan (horiz) 15 10
3620 6 k. Issyk-kul, Kirgizia (horiz) 25 15
3621 6 k. Borovoe, Kazakhstan 25 15

1340. Silver Medal, "Philatec", Paris, 1964.

1968. Awards to Soviet Post Office at Foreign Stamp Exns.

3622. 4 k. black, silver and pur. 20 10
3623. 6 k. black, gold and blue 25 10
3624. 10 k. black, gold & blue.. 30 15
3625. 12 k. blk., silver & turq. 45 15
3626. 16 k. blk., gold and red.. 45 30
3627. 20 k. black, gold and blue 50 40
3628. 30 k. blk., gold & brown 70 55

DESIGNS: 4 k. Type **1340**. 6 k. Plaque, "Debria", Berlin, 1959. 10 k. Cup and medals, Riccione, 1952, 1968. 12 k. Diploma and medal, "Thematic Biennale", Buenos Aires, 1965. 16 k. Trophies and medals, Rome, 1952, 1954. 20 k. Medals and plaques, "Wipa", Vienna, 1966. 30 k. Glass trophies, Prague, 1950, 1955, 1962.

1341. V. K. Lebedinsky. **1342.** Soldier with Flag.

1968. Birth Cent. of Lebedinsky (physicist).

3629. **1341.** 4 k. multicoloured.. 10 10

1968. 50th Anniv. of Estonian Workers' Commune.

3630. **1342.** 4 k. black and red.. 10 10

1344. Moscow Buildings and Fir Branch.

1968. New Year.

3632. **1344.** 4 k. multicoloured.. 10 10

1345. G. Beregovoi (cosmonaut). **1346.** Electric Train, Map and Emblem.

1968. Flight of "Soyuz 3".

3633. **1345.** 10 k. blk., red & blue 30 10

1968. Soviet Railways.

3634. **1346.** 4 k. orange & mauve 25 15
3635. – 10 k. brown & green 65 25

DESIGN: 10 k. Track-laying train.

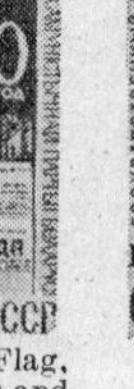

1347. Red Flag, Newspapers and Monument. **1348.** "The Reapers" (Venetsianov).

1968. 50th Anniv. of Byelorussian Communist Party.

3636. **1347.** 4 k. black, brn. & red 15 10

1968. Paintings in State Museum, Leningrad. Multicoloured.

3637. 1 k. Type **1348** 15 10
3638. 2 k. "The Last Days of Pompeii" (Bryullov) .. 20 10
3639. 3 k. "A Knight at the Cross-roads" (Vaznetzov) .. 25 10
3640. 4 k. "Conquering a Town in Winter" (Surikov).. 30 10
3641. 6 k. "The Lake" (Levitan) 45 10
3642. 10 k. "The Year 1919: Alarm" (Petrov-Vodkin) 50 15
3643. 16 k. "The Defence of Sevastopol" (Deineka) 60 20
3644. 20 k. "Homer's Bust" (Korzhev) 65 25
3645. 30 k. "The Celebration in Uritsky Square" (Kustodiev) 80 30
3646. 50 k. "The Duel between Peresvet and Chelumbey" (Avilov).. .. 1·10 80

Nos. 3638/41, 3643, 3645/6 are horiz. designs, size 61 × 28 mm.

1349. House, Onega Region, **1351.** "Declaration of Republic".

1350. Flags and Order of October Revolution.

1968. Soviet Architecture.

3647. **1349.** 3 k. brown on buff 20 10
3648. – 4 k. green on yellow 30 10
3649. – 6 k. violet on grey 35 10
3650. – 10 k. blue on green 40 25
3651. – 12 k. red on drab .. 55 40
3652. – 16 k. black on yellow 70 45

DESIGNS: 4 k. Farmhouse door, Gorky region. 6 k. Wooden Church, Kishi. 10 k. Citadel, Rostov-Yaroslavl. 12 k. Entrance gate, Tsaritzino. 16 k. Master-builder Rossi's Street, Leningrad.

1968. 50th Death Anniv. of N. G. Markin (1893–1918) (revolutionary). As T **1333**.

3653. 4 k. black 15 10

1968. 50th Anniv of Leninist Young Communist League (Komsomol) (2nd issue).

3654 **1350** 12 k. multicoloured .. 30 15

1969. 50th Anniv. of Byelorussian Republic. Multicoloured.

3655. 2 k. Type **1351** 10 10
3656. 4 k. Partisans at war, 1941–45 .. .. 10 10
3657. 6 k. Reconstruction workers 15 10

1352. Red Guards in Riga (statue). **1354.** University Building.

1969. 50th Anniv. of Soviet Revolution in Latvia.

3658. **1352.** 4 k. red and orange 10 10

1969. 150th Anniv. of Leningrad University.

3660. **1354.** 10 k. black and lake 20 10

1355. I. A. Krylov. **1356.** N. D. Filchenkov.

1969. Birth Bicent. of Ivan Krylov (fabulist).

3661. **1355.** 4 k. multicoloured.. 10 10

1969. War Heroes.

3662. **1356.** 4 k. brown and red.. 15 10
3663. – 4 k. brown and green 15 10

DESIGN: No. 3663, A. A. Kosmodemiansky.

1357. "The Wheel Turns Round Again" (sculpture, Z. Kisfaludi-Strobl).

1969. 50th Anniv. of 1st Hungarian Soviet Republic.

3664. **1357.** 6 k. blk., red & green 15 10

1358. Crest and Symbols of Petro-chemical Industry.

1969. 50th Anniv of Bashkir Autonomous Soviet Socialist Republic.

3665 **1358** 4 k. multicoloured .. 15 10

1359. "Vostok 1" on Launching-pad.

1969. Cosmonautics, Day. Multicoloured.

3666. 10 k. Type **1359** 40 15
3667. 10 k. "Zond 5" in Lunar orbit (horiz.) 40 15
3668. 10 k. Sergei Pavlovich Korolev (space scientist) (horiz.) .. 40 15

1360. Lenin University, Kazan.

1969. Buildings connected with Lenin. Mult.

3670. 4 k. Type **1360** 15 10
3671. 4 k. Lenin Museum, Kuibyshev 15 10
3672. 4 k. Lenin Museum, Pskov 15 10
3673. 4 k. Hunting-lodge, Shushenskaya 15 10
3674. 4 k. "Hay Hut", Razliv.. 15 10
3675. 4 k. Lenin Museum, Gorky Park, Leningrad .. 15 10
3676. 4 k. Smolny Institute, Leningrad 15 10
3677. 4 k. Lenin's Office, Kremlin 15 10

3678. 4 k. Library, Ulyanovsk (wrongly inscr " Lenin Museum ") 15 10
3679. 4 k. Lenin Museum, Ulyanovsk 15 10

1361. Telephone and Radio Set.

1969. 50th Anniv. of VEF Electrical Works, Riga.

3680. **1361.** 10 k. brown and red 20 15

1362. I.L.O. Emblem.

1969. 50th Anniv. of Int. Labour Organization.

3681. **1362.** 6 k. gold and red .. 15 10

1363. Otakar Jaros. 1364. P. E. Dybenko.

1969. Otakar Jaros (Czech war hero). Commem.

3682. **1363.** 4 k. black and blue .. 15 10

1969. Soviet Personalities. (80th Birth Annivs.)

3683. **1364.** 4 k. red 15 10
3684. – 4 k. blue 15 10

DESIGN: No. 3684, S. V. Kosior (1889-1939).

1365. Suleiman Stalsky.

1969. Birth Cent. of Suleiman Stalsky (Dagestan poet).

3685. **1365.** 4 k. grn. & brown .. 15 10

1366. " Clear Glade " Rose. 1367. Scientific Centre.

1969. 50th Anniv. of Ukraine Academy of Sciences, Kiev.

3686. 2 k. Type **1366** .. 10 10
3687. 4 k. " Slender lily " .. 15 10
3688. 10 k. " Cattleya hybr" orchid 35 10
3689. 12 k. " Leaves' Fall " dahlia 40 15
3690. 14 k. " Ural Girl " gladiolus 60 30

1969. 50th Anniv. of Ukraine Academy of Sciences, Kiev.

3691. **1367.** 4 k. purple & yellow 15 10

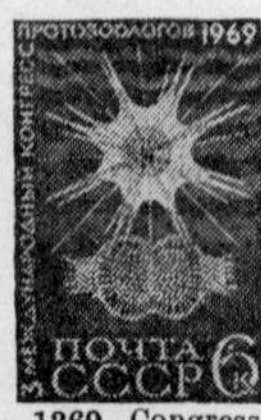

1368. Gold Medal within Film " Flower ". 1369. Congress Emblem.

1969. Cine and Ballet Events, Moscow. Multicoloured.

3692 6 k. Type **1368** (6th Int. Cinema Festival) .. 30 15
3693 6 k. Ballet dancers (1st Int. Ballet Competitions) 30 15

1969. 3rd Int. Protozoologists Congress, Leningrad.

3694. **1369.** 6 k. multicoloured .. 1·25 15

1370. Estonian Singer.

1969. Cent. of Estonian Choir Festival.

3695. **1370.** 4 k. red and ochre .. 20 10

1371. Mendeleev and Formula.

1969. Centenary of Mendeleev's Periodic Law of Elements.

3696. **1371.** 6 k. brown and red 40 20

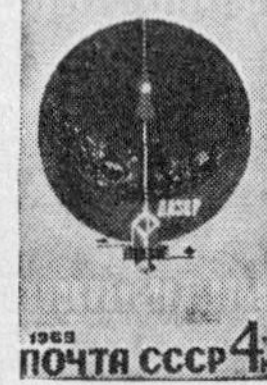

1372. Peace Banner and World Landmarks. 1373. Rocket on Laser Beam, and Moon.

1969. 20th Anniv. of World Peace Movement.

3698. **1372.** 10 k. multicoloured 20 15

1969. " 50 Years of Soviet Inventions ".

3699. **1373.** 4 k. red, black & silver 10 10

Стокгольм. 1969

1374. Kotlyarevsky. (1375.)

1969. Birth Bicentenary of Ivan Kotlyarevsky (Ukrainian writer).

3700 **1374** 4 k. black, brn & grn 10 10

1969. Soviet Ice Hockey Victory in World Championships, Stockholm. No. 2828 further optd with T **1375**.

3701 6 k. turquoise and purple 2·25 2·00

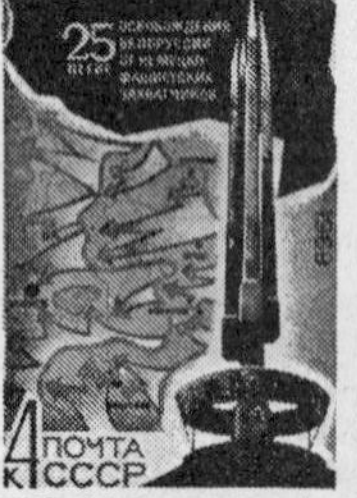

1376. Monument and Campaign map. 1377. Hands holding Torch, and Bulgarian Arms.

1969. 25th Anniv. of Byelorussian Liberation.

3702. **1376.** 4 k. red, purple & olive 15 10

1969. 25th Anniv. of Bulgarian and Polish Peoples' Republics.

3703. **1377.** 6 k. multicoloured .. 20 10
3704. – 6 k. red and ochre .. 20 10

DESIGN: No. 3704, Polish map, flag and arms.

1378. Registan Square, Samarkand.

1969. 2,500th Anniv. of Samarkand. Mult.

3705. 4 k. Type **1378** 15 10
3706. 6 k. Intourist Hotel, Samarkand 20 15

1379. Liberation Monument, Nikolaev. 1380. Volleyball. (European Junior Championships).

1969. 25th Anniv. of Liberation of Nikolaev.

3707. **1379.** 4 k. red, violet & blk. 15 10

1969. Int. Sporting Events.

3708. **1380.** 4 k. red, brn. & orge. 20 10
3709. – 6 k. multicoloured .. 30 10

DESIGN: 6 k. Canoeing (European Championships).

1381. M. Munkacsy and detail of painting, "Peasant Woman churning Butter". 1382. Miner's Statue, Donetsk.

1969. 125th Birth Anniv. of Mihaly Munkacsy (Hungarian painter).

3710. **1381.** 6 k. blk., orge. & brn. 15 10

1969. Centenary of Donetsk.

3711. **1382.** 4 k. mauve and grey 10 10

1383. " Horse-drawn Machine-guns " (M. Grekov).

1969. 50th Anniv. of 1st Cavalry Army.

3712. **1383.** 4 k. brown and red 25 10

1384. Ilya Repin (self-portrait). 1385. Running.

1969. 125th Birth Anniv. of Ilya Repin (painter). Multicoloured.

3713. 4 k. " Barge-haulers on the Volga " .. 20 10
3714. 6 k. " Unexpected " .. 25 15
3715. 10 k. Type **1384** .. 30 15
3716. 12 k. " The Refusal of Confession " .. 40 20
3717. 16 k. " Dnieper Cossacks " 50 30

1969. 9th Trade Unions' Games, Moscow.

3718. **1385.** 4 k. blk., grn. & red 10 10
3719. – 10 k. blk., blue & grn. 25 10

DESIGN: 10 k. Gymnastics.

1386. V. L. Komarov. 1387. O. Tumanyan and Landscape.

1969. Birth Cent. of V. L. Komarov (botanist).

3721. **1386.** 4 k. brown and olive 15 10

1969. Birth Cent. of O. Tumanyan (Armenian poet).

3722. **1387.** 10 k. black and blue 20 15

1388. Turkoman Drinking-horn (2nd-cent. B.C.). 1389. Mahatma Gandhi.

1969. Oriental Art Treasures, State Museum of Oriental Art, Moscow. Multicoloured.

3723. 4 k. Type **1388** .. 15 10
3724. 6 k. Simurg vessel, Persia (13th-cent.) 20 10
3725. 12 k. Statuette, Korea (8th-cent.) 35 15
3726. 16 k. Bodhisatva statuette, Tibet (7th-cent.) .. 45 20
3727. 20 k. Ebisu statuette, Japan (17th-cent.) .. 60 45

1969. Birth Cent. of Mahatma Gandhi.

3728 **1389** 6 k. brown 45 15

1390. Black Stork at Nest.

1969. Belovezhaskaya Pushcha State Reserve. Multicoloured.

3729. 4 k. Type **1390** 35 10
3730. 6 k. Red deer and fawn 40 15
3731. 10 k. European bison fighting 65 20
3732. 12 k. Lynx and cubs .. 75 20
3733. 16 k. Wild boar and young 90 35

No. 3731 is larger, 76 × 24 mm.

1391. " Komitas " and Rural Scene.

1969. Birth Cent. of "Komitas" (S. Sogomonyan, Armenian composer).

3734. **1391.** 6 k. black, flesh & grey 25 10

1392. Sergei Gritsevets (fighter pilot). 1393. I. Pavlov (after portrait by A. Yar-Kravchenko).

1969. Soviet War Heroes.

3735. **1392.** 4 k. black and grn. 30 10
3736. – 4 k. brn., red & yell. 20 10
3737. – 4 k. brown and green 20 10

DESIGNS: As Type **1392**. No. 3737, Lisa Chaikina (partisan). (35½ × 24 mm.): No. 3736, A. Cheponis, Y. Alexonis and G. Boris (Kaunas resistance fighters).

1969. 120th Birth Anniv. of Ivan P. Pavlov (physiologist).

3738. **1393.** 4 k. multicoloured .. 20 10

1394. DDR Arms and Berlin Landmarks. 1395 A. V. Koltsov (from portrait by A. Yar-Kravchenko.)

1969. 20th Anniv. of German Democratic Republic.

3739. **1394.** 6 k. multicoloured .. 15 10

1969. 160th Birth Anniv. of A. V. Koltzov (poet).

3740. **1395.** 4 k. brown and blue 10 10

1396. Arms of Ukraine and Memorial. 1397. Kremlin, and Hammer and Sickle

1969. 25th Anniv. of Ukraine Liberation.
3741. **1396.** 4 k. red and gold .. 15 10

1969. 52nd Anniv. of October Revolution.
3742. **1397.** 4 k. multicoloured.. 10 10

1398. G. Shonin and V. Kubasov (" Soyuz 6 ").

1969. Triple Space Flights.
3744 **1398** 10 k. green and gold 30 15
3745 – 10 k. green and gold 30 15
3746 – 10 k. green and gold 30 15
DESIGNS: No. 3745, A. Filipchenko, V. Volkov and V. Gorbatko ("Soyuz 7"). No. 3746, V. Shatalov and A. Yeliseev ("Soyuz 8").

1399. Lenin when a Youth, and Emblems. 1400. Corps Emblem on Red Star.

1969. U.S.S.R. Youth Philatelic Exn. to commemorate Lenin's Birth Centenary, Kiev.
3747. **1399.** 4 k. lake and pink.. 10 10

1969. 50th Anniv. of Red Army Communications Corps.
3748. **1400.** 4 k. red, brn. & bistre 10 10

1401. "Male and Female Farmworkers" (sculptured group, V. Mukhina), and Title-page.

1969. 3rd Soviet Collective Farmers' Congress, Moscow.
3749 **1401** 4 k. brown and gold 10 10

1402. "Vasilisa, the Beauty" (folk tale).

1969. Russian Fairy Tales. Multicoloured.
3750 4 k. Type **1402** 30 25
3751 10 k. "Maria Morevna" (folk tale) 75 45
3752 16 k. "The Golden Cockerel" (Pushkin) (horiz) 1·00 60
3753 20 k. "Finist, the Fine Fellow" (folk tale) .. 1·10 85
3754 50 k. "Tale of the Tsar Saltan" (Pushkin) .. 1·90 1·50

1403. Venus Plaque and Radio-telescope.

1969. Space Exploration.
3755. **1403.** 4 k. red, brn. & blk. 20 10
3756. – 6 k. pur., grey & blk. 30 15
3757. – 10 k. multicoloured 55 20
DESIGNS: 6 k. Space station and capsule in orbit. 10 k. Photograph of the Earth taken by "Zond 7".

1404. Soviet and Afghan Flags. 1405. Red Star and Arms.

1969. 50th Anniv. of U.S.S.R.-Afghanistan Diplomatic Relations.
3759. **1404.** 6 k. red, blk. & grn. 10 10

1969. Coil Stamp.
3760. **1405** 4 k. red .. .. 1·50 40

1406. "MIG" Fighters of 1940 and 1969.

1969. "30 Years of MIG Aircraft".
3761. **1406.** 6 k. blk., grey & red 70 15

1407. Lenin.

1969. New Year.
3762. **1407.** 4 k. multicoloured.. 10 10

1408. ANT-2" Aircraft.

1969. Development of Soviet Civil Aviation.
3763. **1408.** 2 k. multicoloured.. 20 10
3764. – 3 k. multicoloured.. 25 10
3765. – 4 k. multicoloured.. 25 10
3766. – 6 k. blk., red & pur. 25 10
3767. – 10 k. multicoloured 55 15
3768. – 12 k. multicoloured 60 15
3769. – 16 k. multicoloured 80 20
3770. – 20 k. multicoloured 95 30
AIRCRAFT: 3 k. "PO-2 (U-2)". 4 k. "ANT-9". 6 k. "ZAGI 1-EA" helicopter. 10 k. "ANT-20 Maxim Gorky". 12 k. "TU-104". 16 k. "MI-10" helicopter. 20 k. "Il-62".

1409. Model Aircraft.

1969. Technical Sports.
3772. **1409.** 3 k. purple 15 10
3773. – 4 k. green 15 10
3774. – 6 k. brown.. .. 25 10
DESIGNS: 4 k. Speed boat racing. 6 k. Parachuting.

1410. Rumanian Arms and Soviet Memorial, Bucharest. 1411. TV Tower, Ostankino.

1969. 25th Anniv. Rumanian Liberation.
3775. **1410.** 6 k. red and brown 15 10

1969. Television Tower, Ostankino, Moscow.
3776. **1411.** 10 k. multicoloured 20 15

1412. "Lenin" (after sculpture by N. Andreiev).

1970. Birth Cent. of V. I. Lenin (1st issue). Multicoloured.
3777. 4 k. Type **1412** 15 10
3778. 4 k. "Marxist meeting, Petrograd" (A. Moravov) 15 10
3779. 4 k. "Second RSDRP Congress" (Y. Vinogradov) 15 10
3780. 4 k. "First day of Soviet Power" (F. Morodov).. 15 10
3781. 4 k. "Visiting Lenin" (F. Morodov) 15 10
3782. 4 k. "Conversation with Ilyich" (A. Shirokov).. 15 10
3783. 4 k. "May Day 1920" (I. Brodsky) 15 10
3784. 4 k. "With Lenin" (V. Serov) 15 10
3785. 4 k. "Conquerors of the Cosmos" (A. Deyneka) 15 10
3786. 4 k. "Communism Builders" (A. Korentsov, J. Merkoulov, V. Bourakov) 15 10
See also Nos. 3812/21.

1413. F. V. Sychkov and painting "Tobogganing".

1970. Birth Cent. of F. V. Sychkov (artist).
3787. **1413.** 4 k. blue and brown 20 10

1414. "Vostok", "Mirnyi" and Antarctic Map. 1415. V. I. Peshekhonov.

1970. 150th Anniv. of Antarctic Expedition by Bellinghausen and Lazarev.
3788. **1414.** 4 k. turq., mve. & blue 2·00 25
3789. – 16 k. red, grn. & pur. 2·50 55
DESIGN: 16 k. Modern polar-station and map.

1970. Soviet War Heroes.
3790. **1415.** 4 k. pur. & black 15 10
3791. – 4 k. brown & olive 15 10
DESIGN: No. 3791, V. B. Borshoev (1906-1945).

1416. Geographical Society Emblem. 1417. "The Torch of Peace" (A. Dumpe).

1970. 125th Anniv. of Russian Geographical Society.
3792. **1416.** 6 k. multicoloured.. 15 10

1970. 60th Anniv. of Int. Women's Solidarity Day.
3793. **1417.** 6 k. drab and turq. 10 10

1418. Ivan Bazhov (folk hero) and Crafts. 1419. Lenin.

1970. World Fair "Expo 70", Osaka, Japan.
3794. **1418.** 4 k. blk., red and grn. 15 10
3795. – 6 k. silver, red & blk. 20 10
3796. – 10 k. multicoloured 25 15
DESIGNS: 6 k. U.S.S.R. Pavilion. 10 k. Boy and model toys.

1970. Lenin Birth Cent. All-Union Philatelic Exhib., Moscow.
3798. **1419.** 4 k. blk., gold & red 10 10

1420. Friendship Tree.

1970. Friendship Tree, Sochi.
3800. **1420.** 10 k. multicoloured 30 15

1421. Ice Hockey Players.

1970. World Ice Hockey Championships, Stockholm, Sweden.
3801 **1421** 6 k. green and blue .. 65 15

1422. Hammer, Sickle and Azerbaijan Emblems.

1970. 50th Anniv. of Soviet Republics.
3802. **1422.** 4 k. red and gold .. 15 10
3803. – 4 k. brown & silver.. 15 10
3804. – 4 k. purple and gold 15 10
DESIGNS: No. 3803, Woman and motifs of Armenia. No. 3804, Woman and emblem of Kazakh Republic.

1423. Worker and Book. 1424. D. N. Medvedev.

1970. U.N.E.S.C.O. "Lenin Centenary" Symposium.
3805. **1423.** 6 k. ochre and lake.. 10 10

1970. War Heroes.
3806. **1424.** 4 k. brown 15 10
3807. – 4 k. brown 15 10
PORTRAIT: No. 3807, K. P. Orlovsky.

(1425.) 1426. Hungarian Arms and Budapest View.

1970. Russian Victory in World Ice Hockey Championships, Stockholm. No. 3801 optd with T **1425**.

3808 **1421** 6 k. green and blue .. 50 15

1970. 25th Anniv. of Hungarian and Czech Liberation. Multicoloured.

3809. 6 k. Type **1426** 15 10
3810. 6 k. Czech Arms and Prague view 15 10

1427. Cosmonauts' Emblem. **1428.** Lenin, 1890.

1970. Cosmonautics Day.

3811. **1427.** 6 k. multicoloured .. 10 10

1970. Lenin. Birth Cent. (2nd issue).

3812. **1428.** 2 k. green 10 10
3813. – 2 k. olive 10 10
3814. – 4 k. blue 10 10
3815. – 4 k. lake 10 10
3816. – 6 k. brown 15 10
3817. – 6 k. lake 15 10
3818. – 10 k. purple .. 25 15
3819. – 10 k. brown .. 25 15
3820. – 12 k. black and silver 30 20
3821. – 12 k. red and gold .. 30 20

PORTRAITS OF LENIN: No. 3813, Period, 1893-1900. No. 3814, Period, 1900-03. No. 3815, In 1916, No. 3816, In 1917. No. 3817, Period of Revolurion. No. 3818, In 1918. No. 3819, In 1920. No. 3820, Sculptured head by J. Kolesnikov. No. 3821, Sculptured head by N. Andreiev.

1429. Order of Victory. **1430.** Komsomol Badge.

1970. 25th Anniv. of Victory in Second World War.

3823. **1429.** 1 k. gold, grey & pur. 10 10
3824. – 2 k. pur., brn. & gold 10 10
3825. – 3 k. red, blk. & gold 10 10
3826. – 4 k. red, brn. & gold 15 10
3827. – 10 k. gold, red & pur. 30 20

DESIGNS: 2 k. Eternal Flame. 3 k. Treptow Monument, Berlin. 4 k. Home Defence Order. 10 k. Hero of the Soviet Union and Hero of Socialist Labour medals.

1970. 16th Congress of Leninist Young Communist League (Komsomol).

3829 **1430** 4 k. multicoloured .. 10 10

1431. Sculptured Head of Lenin.

1970. World Youth Meeting for Lenin Birth Centenary.

3830 **1431** 6 k. red 10 10

1432. "Young Workers" and Federation Emblem.

1970. 25th Anniv. of World Democratic Youth Federation.

3831. **1432.** 6 k. black and blue .. 10 10

1433. Arms and Government Building, Kazan.

1970. 50th Anniv of Russian Federation Autonomous Soviet Socialist Republics.

3832 **1433** 4 k. blue 15 10
3833 – 4 k. green 15 10
3834 – 4 k. red 15 10
3835 – 4 k. brown 15 10
3836 – 4 k. green 15 10
3837 – 4 k. brown 15 10

DESIGNS: Arms and Government Buildings. No. 3832, (Tatar Republic). 3833, Petrozavodzk (Karelian Republic). 3834, Cheboksary (Chuvash Republic). 3835, Elista (Kalmyk Republic). 3836, Izhevsk (Udmurt Republic). 3837, Ioshkar-Ola (Mari Republic).

See also Nos. 3903/7, 4052/3, 4175, 4253, 4298, 4367 and 4955.

1434. Gymnast on Bar (World Championships, Yugoslavia). **1435.** "Swords into Ploughshares" (sculpture by E. Vuchetich).

1970. Int. Sporting Events.

3838. **1434.** 10 k. red and drab .. 20 15
3839. – 16 k. brown & green 40 20

DESIGN: 16 k. Three footballers (World Cup Championships, Mexico).

1970. 25th Anniv. of United Nations.

3840. **1435.** 12 k. purple and green 25 10

1436. Cosmonauts and Soyuz 9". **1437.** Engels.

1970. Space Flight by "Soyuz 9".

3841. **1436.** 10 k. black, red & pur. 20 10

1970. 150th Birth Anniv. of Friedrich Engels.

3842. **1437.** 4 k. brown and red .. 15 10

1438. Cruiser "Aurora".

1970. Soviet Warships.

3843. **1438.** 3 k. pink, lilac & blk. 30 10
3844. – 4 k. black and yellow 35 10
3845. – 10 k. blue and mauve 80 15
3846. – 12 k. brown and buff 90 20
3847. – 20 k. pur., blue & turq. 1·40 40

DESIGNS: 4 k. Missile cruiser "Groznyi". 10 k. Cruiser "Oktyabrskaya Revolyutsiya". 12 k. Missile cruiser "Varyag". 20 k. Nuclear submarine "Leninsky Komsomol".

MORE DETAILED LISTS
are given in the Stanley Gibbons Catalogues referred to in the country headings.
For lists of current volumes see Introduction.

1439. Soviet and Polish Workers. **1440.** Allegory of the Sciences.

1970. 25th Anniv. of Soviet-Polish Friendship Treaty.

3848. **1439.** 6 k. red and blue .. 10 10

1970. 13th Int. Historical Sciences Congress, Moscow.

3849. **1440.** 4 k. multicoloured .. 10 10

1441. Mandarins. **1442.** Magnifying Glass, "Stamp" and Covers.

1970. Fauna of Sikhote-Alin Nature Reserve. Multicoloured.

3850. 4 k. Type **1441** 40 10
3851. 6 k. Yellow-throated marten 45 15
3852. 10 k. Asiatic black bear (vert.) 60 15
3853. 16 k. Red deer 70 25
3854. 20 k. Tiger .. .. 1·00 35

1970. 2nd U.S.S.R. Philatelic Society Congress, Moscow.

3855. **1442.** 4 k. silver and red .. 15 10

1443. V. I. Kikvidze. **1444.** University Building.

1970. 75th Birth Anniv. of V. J. Kikvidze (Civil War hero).

3856. **1443.** 4 k. brown 10 10

1970. 50th Anniv of Yerevan University.

3857 **1444** 4 k. red and blue .. 10 10

1445. Lenin Badge. **1446.** Library Book-plate.

1970. Pioneer Organization.

3858. **1445.** 1 k. gold, red & grey 10 10
3859. – 2 k. grey and brown 10 10
3860. – 4 k. multicoloured .. 10 10

DESIGNS: 2 k. "Lenin with Children" (sculpture). 4 k. Red Star, Pioneer emblem.

1970. 400th Anniv. of Vilnius (Vilna) University Library (Lithuania).

3861. **1446.** 4 k. blk., grey & silver 10 10

1447. Woman with Bouquet.

1970. 25th Anniv. of Int. Democratic Women's Federation.

3862. **1447.** 6 k. brown and blue 10 10

1448. Milkmaid and Cows. ("Livestock").

1970. Soviet Agricultural. Multicoloured.

3863. 4 k. Type **1448** .. 10 10
3864. 4 k. Driver, tractor and harvester ("Mechanisation") 10 10
3865. 4 k. Lock-operator and canal ("Irrigation and Chemical Research") .. 10 10

1449. Lenin addressing Meeting.

1970. 53rd Anniv. of October Revolution.

3866. **1449.** 4. k. gold and red .. 10 10

50 лет
пенинономy ппану
ГОЭЛРО • 1970
(**1450.**)

1970. 50th Anniv. of GOELRO Electrification Plan. No. 3475 optd. with T **1450**.

3868. 4 k multicoloured .. 40 30

1451. Spassky Tower, Kremlin. **1452.** A. A. Baikov.

1970. New Year.

3869. **1451.** 6 k. multicoloured .. 10 10

1970. Birth Cent. of A. A. Baikov (metallurgic scientist).

3870. **1452.** 4 k. black and brown 10 10

1453. A. D. Tsyurupa. **1454.** St. Basil's Cathedral, Red Square, Moscow.

1970. Birth Cent. of A. D. Tsyurupa (Vice-Chairman of Soviet People's Commissars).

3871. **1453.** 4 k. brown and yellow 10 10

1970. Tourism.

3872. **1454.** 4 k. multicoloured .. 15 10
3873. – 6 k. blue, indigo & brn. 30 10
3874. – 10 k. brown and green 35 15
3875. – 12 k. multicoloured 40 15
3876. – 14 k. blue, red & brn. 45 20
3877. – 16 k. multicoloured 60 25

DESIGNS: 6 k. Scene from "Swan Lake". 10 k. Sika deer. 12 k. Souvenir handicrafts. 14 k. "Swords into Ploughshares" (sculpture by E. Vuchetich). 16 k. Tourist and camera.

1455. Camomile.

1970. Flowers. Multicoloured.
3878. 4 k. Type **1455** 15 10
3879. 6 k. Dahlia 25 10
3880. 10 k. Phlox 35 10
3881. 12 k. Aster 40 20
3882. 16 k. Clematis 60 30

1456. African Woman and Child. **1457.** Beethoven.

1970. 10th Anniv. of U.N. Declaration on Colonial Independence.
3883. **1456.** 10 k. brown and blue 20 10

1970. Birth Bicent of Beethoven (composer).
3884 **1457** 10 k. purple and pink 75 20

1458. "Luna 16" in Flight. **1459.** Speed Skating.

1970. Flight of "Luna 16".
3885. **1458.** 10 k. green .. 35 15
3886. – 10 k. purple .. 35 15
3887. – 10 k. green 35 15
DESIGNS: No. 3886, "Luna 16" on Moon's surface. No. 3887, Parachute descent.

1970. Trade-Unions' Winter Games (1971).
3889. **1459.** 4 k. blue, red & grey 15 10
3890. – 10 k. grn., brn. & grey 45 15
DESIGN: 10 k. Cross-country skiing.

1460. "The Conestabile Madonna" (Raphael).

1970. Foreign Paintings in Soviet Galleries. Multicoloured.
3891. 3 k. Type **1460** 15 10
3892. 4 k. "Saints Peter and Paul" (El Greco) .. 20 10
3893. 10 k. "Perseus and Andromeda" (Rubens) horiz.) 35 15
3894. 12 k. "The Return of the Prodigal Son" (Rembrandt) 35 15
3895. 16 k. "Family Portrait" (Van Dyck) 55 25
3896. 20 k. "The Actress Jeanne Samary" (Renoir) 65 35
3897. 30 k. "Woman with Fruit" (Gauguin) .. 90 50

1461. Harry Pollitt and Freighter "Jolly George". **1462.** "75" Emblem.

1970. 80th Birth Anniv. of H. Pollitt (British Communist).
3899. **1461.** 10 k. brn. & purple 35 15

1970. 75th Anniv. of Int. Co-operative Alliance.
3900. **1462.** 12 k. red and green 30 10

1463. Sculptured Head of Lenin.

1971. 24th Soviet Union Communist Party Congress.
3901. **1463.** 4 k. red and gold .. 10 10

1464. "50", State Emblem and Flag. **1465.** Genua Fortress and Cranes.

1971. 50th Anniv. of Georgian Soviet Republic.
3902. **1464.** 4 k. multicoloured .. 15 10

1971. 50th Anniv of Soviet Republics. Similar designs to T **1433**, but dated "1971".
3903. 4 k. turquoise 15 10
3904. 4 k. red 15 10
3905. 4 k. red 15 10
3906. 4 k. blue 15 10
3907. 4 k. green 15 10
DESIGNS: No. 3903, Russian Federation Arms and Supreme Soviet building (Dagestan Republic). No. 3904, National emblem and symbols of agriculture and industry (Abkhazian Republic). No. 3905, Arms produce and industry (Adjarian Republic). No. 3906, Arms and State building (Kabardino-Balkar Republic). No. 3907, Arms, industrial products and Government building (Komi Republic).

1971. 2,500th Anniv. of Feodosia (Crimean city).
3908. **1465.** 10 k. multicoloured 25 15

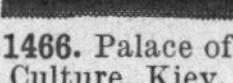

1466. Palace of Culture, Kiev. **1467.** "Features of National Economy".

1971. 24th Ukraine Communist Party Congress, Kiev.
3909. **1466.** 4 k. multicoloured .. 10 10

1971. 50th Anniv. of Soviet State Planning Organization.
3910. **1467.** 6 k. red and brown .. 10 10

1468. N. Gubin, I. Chernykh and S. Kosinov (dive-bomber crew).

1971. Soviet Air Force Heroes.
3911. **1468.** 4 k. brown & green .. 15 10

1469. Gipsy Dance.

1971. State Folk-dance Ensemble. Mult.
3912. 10 k. Type **1469** 40 15
3913. 10 k. Russian "Summer" dance (women in circle) 40 15
3914. 10 k. Ukraine "Gopak" dance (dancer leaping) 40 15
3915. 10 k. Adjar "Khorumi" dance (with drummer) 40 15
3916. 10 k. "On the Ice" (ballet) 40 15

1470. L. Ukrainka. **1472.** Fighting at the Barricades.

1471. "Luna 17" Module on Moon.

1971. Birth Cent. of Lesya Ukrainka (Ukrainian writer).
3917. **1470.** 4 k. red and brown 10 10

1971. Soviet Moon Exploration.
3918. **1471.** 10 k. brown and vio. 35 15
3919. – 12 k. brown & blue 40 20
3920. – 12 k. brown & blue 40 20
3921. – 16 k. brown & violet 65 30
DESIGNS: No. 3919, Control room and radio-telescope. No. 3920, Moon trench. No. 3921, "Lunokhod 1" Moon-vehicle.

1971. Centenary of Paris Commune.
3923. **1472.** 6 k. blk., brn. & red 10 10

1473. Hammer, Sickle and Development Emblems. **1475.** E. Birznieks-Upitis.

1474. Gagarin Medal, Spaceships and Planets.

1971. 24th Soviet Communist Party Congress, Moscow.
3924. **1473.** 6 k. red, bistre & brn. 10 10

1971. 10th Anniv. of First Manned Space Flight (1st issue), and Cosmonauts' Day.
3925. **1474.** 10 k. ol., yell. & brn. 35 15
3926. – 12 k. pur., bl. & grey 45 20
DESIGN: 12 k. Spaceship over Globe and economic symbols.
See also No. 3974.

1971. Birth Centenary of E. Birznieks-Upitis (Lithuanian writer).
3927. **1475.** 4 k. red and green .. 10 10

1476. Bee on Flower.

1971. 23rd Int. Bee-keeping Congress, Moscow.
3928. **1476.** 6 k. multicoloured .. 30 15

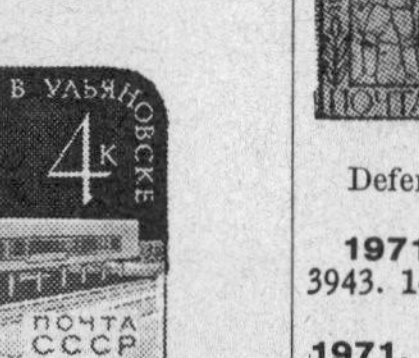

1478. Memorial Building.

1971. Lenin Memorial Building, Ulyanovsk.
3930. **1478.** 4 k. olive and red .. 10 10

1479. Lieut-Col. N.I. Vlasov. **1480.** Khafiz Shirazi.

1971. 26th Anniv. of Victory in 2nd World War.
3931. **1479.** 4 k. brown & green 10 10

1971. 650th Birth Anniv. of Khafiz Shirazi (Tadzhik writer).
3932. **1480.** 4 k. multicoloured .. 10 10

1481. "GAZ-66" Truck.

1971. Soviet Motor Vehicles.
3933. **1481.** 2 k. multicoloured .. 15 10
3934. – 3 k. multicoloured .. 15 10
3935. – 4 k. blue, blk. & lilac 20 10
3936. – 4 k. grn., purple & drab 20 10
3937. – 10 k. red, blk. & lilac 5 15
DESIGNS: 3 k. "BelAZ-540" tipper-truck. 4 k. (3935) "Moskvitch-412" 4-door saloon. 4 k. (3936) "Zaporozhez ZAZ-968" 2-door saloon. 10 k. "Volga GAZ-24" saloon.

1482. A. A. Bogomolets. **1483.** Commemorative Scroll.

1971. 90th Birth Anniv. of A. A. Bogomolets (medical scientist).
3938. **1482.** 4 k. blk., pink & orge. 15 10

1971. Int. Moscow Congresses.
3939. **1483.** 6 k. brown & green .. 25 15
3940. – 6 k. multicoloured .. 25 15
3941. – 6 k. multicoloured .. 25 15
DESIGNS AND EVENTS—HORIZ. No. 3939, (13th Science History Congress). No. 3940, Oil derrick and symbols (8th World Oil Congress). VERT. No. 3941, Satellite over Globe (15th General Assembly of Geodesics and Geophysics Union).

1484. Sukhe Bator Statue, Ulan Bator.

1971. 50th Anniv. of Revolution in Mongolia.
3942. **1484.** 6 k. grey, gold & red 20 10

1485. Defence Monument. **1486.** Treaty Emblem.

1971. 30th Anniv. of Defence of Liepaja.
3943. **1485.** 4 k. brn., blk. & grey 10 10

1971. 10th Anniv. of Antarctic Treaty and 50th Anniv. of Soviet Hydrometeorological Service.
3944. **1486.** 6 k. deep blue, black and blue .. .. 1·50 30
3945. – 10 k. violet, blk. & red 1·00 35
DESIGNS: 10 k. Hydrometeorological map.

1487. "Motherland" (sculpture by E. Vuchetich). 1488. Throwing the Discus.

1971. 20th Anniv. of "Federation Internationale des Resistants".

3946. **1487.** 6 k. green and red .. 15 10

1971. 5th Summer Spartakiad.

3947. **1488.** 3 k. blue on pink .. 10 10
3948. – 4 k. green on flesh .. 15 10
3949. – 6 k. brown on green 30 10
3950. – 10 k. purple on blue 55 20
3951. – 12 k. brown on yell. 60 20

DESIGNS: 4 k. Archery. 6 k. Horse-riding (dressage). 10 k. Basketball. 12 k. Wrestling.

1489. "Benois Madonna" (Leonardo da Vinci).

1971. Foreign Paintings in Russian Museums. Multicoloured.

3952 2 k. Type **1489** 10 10
3953 4 k. "Mary Magdalene confesses her Sins" (Titian) 15 10
3954 10 k. "The Washer-woman" (Chardin) (horiz) 35 15
3955 12 k. "Young Man with Glove" (Hals) .. 45 20
3956 14 k. "Tancred and Erminia" (Poussin) (horiz) 50 20
3957 16 k. "Girl Fruit Seller" (Murillo) 55 35
3958 20 k. "Child on ball" (Picasso) 90 50

1490. Lenin Badge and Kazakh Flag.

1971. 50th Anniv. of Kazakh Communist Youth Association.

3959. **1490.** 4 k. brown, red & bl. 10 10

1491. Posthorn within Star. 1492. A. Spendiarov (Armenian composer) (after M. Saryan).

1971. Int. Correspondence Week.

3960. **1491.** 4 k. black, blue & grn. 15 10

1971. Birth Anniversaries. Multicoloured.

3961 4 k. Type **1492** (cent) .. 20 10
3962 4 k. Nikolai Nekrasov (after I. Kramskoi) (poet, 150th anniv) .. 20 10
3963 10 k. Fyodor Dostoevsky (after V. Perov) (writer, 150th anniv) 50 25

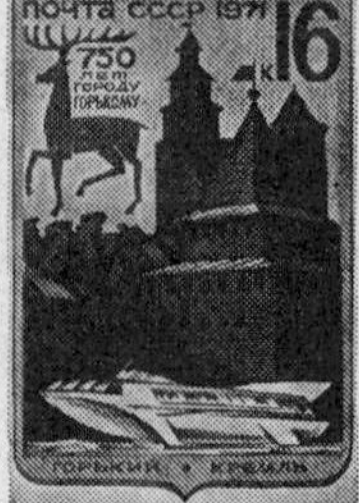

1493. Z. Paliashvili. 1494. Emblem, Gorky Kremlin and Hydrofoil.

1971. Birth Cent. of Z. Paliashvili (Georgian composer).

3964. **1493.** 4 k. brown 20 10

1971. 750th Anniv. of Gorky (formerly Nizhini-Novgorod). (1st issue).

3965. **1494.** 16 k. multicoloured 50 20

See also No. 3974.

1495. Students and Globe.

1971. 25th Anniv. of Int. Students' Federation.

3966. **1495.** 6 k. blue, red and brn. 10 10

1496. Atlantic white-sided Dolphins.

1497. Star and Miners' Order.

1499. Maksim Gorky Statue and View. 1498. Lord Rutherford and Atomic Formula.

1971. Marine Fauna. Multicoloured.

3967. 4 k. Type **1496** 25 10
3968. 6 k. Sea otter 35 10
3969. 10 k. Narwhals 45 15
3970. 12 k. Walrus 60 20
3971. 14 k. Ribbon seals .. 65 45

1971. 250th Anniv. of Coal Discovery in Donetz Basin.

3972. **1497.** 4 k. red, brown & blk. 20 10

1971. Birth Cent. of Lord Rutherford (physicist).

3973. **1498.** 6 k. brown & purple 30 15

1971. 750th Anniv. of Gorky (formerly Nizhini-Novgorod). (2nd issue).

3974. **1499.** 4 k. multicoloured .. 15 10

1500. Santa Claus in Troika.

1971. New Year.

3975. **1500.** 10 k. red, gold & blk. 25 10

1501. Workers and Marx Books. ("Int. Socialist Solidarity").

1971. 24th Soviet Union Communist Party Congress Resolutions.

3976. **1501.** 4 k. blue, ultram. & red 15 10
3977. – 4 k. red, yell. & brn. 15 10
3978. – 4 k. lilac, blk. & red 15 10
3979. – 4 k. bistre, brn. & red 15 10
3980. – 4 k. red, grn. & yellow 15 10

DESIGNS: No. 3977, Farmworkers and wheat-field ("Agricultural Production"). No. 3978, Factory production line ("Increased Productivity"). No. 3979, Heavy industry ("Industrial Expansion"). No. 3980, Family in department store ("National Welfare").

1502. "Meeting" (V. Makovsky). 1503. V. V. Vorovsky.

1971. Russian Paintings. Multicoloured.

3982. 2 k. Type **1502** 15 10
3983. 4 k. "Girl Student" (N. Yaroshenko) 20 10
3984. 6 k. "Woman Miner" (N. Kasatkin) 30 10
3985. 10 k. "Harvesters" (G. Myasoyedov) (horiz.) 50 15
3986. 16 k. "Country Road" (A. Savrasov) 70 30
3987. 20 k. "Pine Forest" (I. Shishkin) (horiz.) .. 95 40

See also Nos. 4064/70.

1971. Birth Centenary of V. V. Vorovsky (diplomat).

3989. **1503.** 4 k. brown 10 10

1504. Dobrovolsky, Volkov and Patsaev.

1971. "Soyuz II" Cosmonauts Commem.

3990. **1504.** 4 k. black, pur. & orge. 20 10

1505. Order of the Revolution and Building Construction.

1971. 54th Anniv. of October Revolution.

3991. **1505.** 4 k. multicoloured .. 10 10

1506. E. Vakhtangov (founder) and characters from "Princess Turandot". 1507. "Dzhambul Dzhabaiev" (A. Yar-Kravchenko).

1971. 50th Anniv. of Vakhtangov Theatre, Moscow.

3992. **1506.** 10 k. red and lake .. 30 15
3993. – 10 k. yell. & brown 30 15
3994. – 10 k. orange & brn. 30 15

DESIGNS—HORIZ. No. 3993, B. Shchukin (actor) and scene from "The Man with a Riffe". No. 3994, R. Simonov (director) and scene from "Cyrano de Bergerac".

1971. 125th Anniv. of Dzhambul Dzhabaiev (Kazakh poet).

3995. **1507.** 4 k. brn., yell. & orge. 10 10

1508. Pskov Kremlin.

1971. Historical Buildings. Multicoloured.

3996. 3 k. Type **1508** 15 10
3997. 4 k. Novgorod kremlin .. 15 10
3998. 6 k. Smolensk fortress and Liberation Monument 20 10
3999. 10 k. Kolomna kremlin 35 15

1509. William Foster.

1971. 90th Birth Anniv. of Foster (American communist).

4001. **1509.** 10 k. black & brown 12·00 15·00
4002. 10 k. black & brown 35 15

No. 4001 shows the incorrect date of **death "1964"**. No. 4002 shows the **correct date, "1961"**.

1510. Fadeev and Scene from "The Rout" (novel).

1971. 70th Birth Anniv of Aleksandr Fadeev (writer).

4003 **1510** 4 k. orange and blue 15 10

1511. Sapphire Brooch.

1971. Diamonds and Jewels. Multicoloured.

4004. 10 k. Type **1511** .. 60 15
4005. 10 k. "Shah" diamond 60 15
4006. 10 k. "Narcissi" diamond brooch 60 15
4007. 20 k. Amethyst pendant 1·25 40
4008. 20 k. "Rose" platinum and diamond brooch .. 1·25 40
4009. 30 k. Pearl and diamond pendant .. .. .. 1·75 60

1512. Vanda Orchid. 1514. Ice Hockey Players.

1513. Peter the Great's Imperial Barge, 1723.

1971. Tropical Flowers. Multicoloured.

4010 1 k. Type **1512** .. 20 10
4011 2 k. "Anthurium scherzerium" .. 20 10
4012 4 k. "Cactus epiphyllum" 30 10
4013 12 k. Amaryllis 90 20
4014 14 k. "Medinilla magnifica" .. .. 1·25 30

1971. History of the Russian Navy (1st series). Multicoloured.
4016 1 k. Type **1513** 15 10
4017 4 k. Galleon "Orel", 1668 (vert) 30 10
4018 10 k. Ship of the line "Poltava", 1712 (vert) 75 15
4019 12 k. Ship of the line "Ingermanland", 1715 (vert) 95 25
4020 16 k. Steam frigate "Vladimir", 1848 .. 1·25 40
See also Nos. 4117/21, 4209/13 and 4303/6.

1971. 25th Anniv of Soviet Ice Hockey.
4021 **1514** 6 k. multicoloured .. 50 10

1515. Baku Oil. Installations.
1516. G. M. Krzhizhanovsky.

1971. Baku Oil Industry.
4022. **1515.** 4 k. blk., red and blue 25 10

1972. Birth Centenary of G. M. Krzhizhanovsky (scientist).
4023. **1516.** 4 k. brown 15 10

1517. Alexander Scriabin.
1518. Red-faced Cormorant.

1972. Birth Centenary of Alexander Scriabin (composer).
4024. **1517.** 4 k. blue and green 30 10

1972. Sea Birds. Multicoloured.
4025. 4 k. Type **1518** 45 10
4026. 6 k. Ross's Gull (horiz.) 65 10
4027. 10 k. Pair of Barnacle geese 80 15
4028. 12 k. Pair of Spectacled Eiders (horiz.) .. .. 1·10 25
4029. 16 k. Mediterranean Gull 1·50 30

1519. Speed Skating.
1520. Heart Emblem.

1972. Winter Olympic Games, Sapporo, Japan. Multicoloured.
4030 4 k. Type **1519** 15 10
4031 6 k. Figure skating .. 20 10
4032 10 k. Ice hockey .. 50 15
4033 12 k. Ski jumping .. 65 20
4034 16 k. Cross-country skiing 75 30

1972. World Heart Month.
4036. **1520.** 4 k. red and green.. 15 10

1521. Fair Emblem.
1522. Labour Emblems.

1972. 50th Anniv. of Soviet Participation in Leipzig Fair.
4037. **1521.** 16 k. gold and red.. 35 30

1972. 15th Soviet Trade Unions Congress, Moscow.
4038. **1522.** 4 k. brn., red & pink 15 10

1523. " Aloe arborescens ".
1524. Alexandra Kollonai (diplomat) (Birth Cent.).

1972. Medicinal Plants. Multicoloured.
4039 1 k. Type **1523** 10 10
4040 2 k. Yellow horned-poppy 10 10
4041 4 k. Groundsel 20 10
4042 6 k. Nephrite tea .. 30 10
4043 10 k. Kangaroo apple .. 55 15

1972. Birth Anniversaries.
4044. **1524.** 4 k. brown 15 10
4045. – 4 k. lake 15 10
4046. – 4 k. bistre 15 10
Celebrities: No. 4045, G. Chicherin (Foreign Affairs Commissar) (Birth cent.). No. 4046, " Kamo " (S.A. Ter-Petrosyan—revolutionary). (90th birth anniv.)

1526. "Salyut" Space-station and "Soyuz" Spacecraft.

1972. Cosmonautics Day. Multicoloured.
4048. 6 k. Type **1526** 30 20
4049. 6 k. "Mars 2" approaching Mars 30 20
4050. 16 k. Capsule, "Mars 3" .. 75 30

1527. Factory and Products.

1972. 250th Anniv of Izhora Factory.
4051 **1527** 4 k. purple and silver 20 10

1972. 50th Anniv of Russin Federation Autonomous Soviet Socialist Republics. Designs similar to T **1433**, but dated "1972".
4052 4 k. blue 25 10
4053 4 k. mauve 25 10
Designs: No. 4052, Arms, natural resources and industry (Yakut Republic). No. 4053, Arms, agriculture and industry (Checheno-Ingush Republic).

1528. L. Sobinov and scene from " Eugene Onegin ".

1972. Birth Cent. of L. Sobinov (singer).
4054. **1528.** 10 k. brown.. .. 50 15

1529. Symbol of Knowledge and Children reading Books.

1972. Int. Book Year.
4055. **1529.** 6 k. multicoloured.. 25 15

1530. P. Morosov (pioneer) and Pioneers Saluting.

1972. 50th Anniv. of Pioneer Organization.
4056. **1530.** 1 k. multicoloured.. 10 10
4057. – 2 k. pur., red & grn. 10 10
4058. – 3 k. blue, red & brn. 15 10
4059. – 4 k. red, blue & grn. 15 10
Designs: 2 k. Girl laboratory worker and Pioneers with book. 3 k. Pioneer Palace, Chukotka, and Pioneers at work. 4 k. Pioneer parade.

1531. Pioneer Trumpeter.

1972. "50th Anniv of Pioneer Organization" Youth Philatelic Exhibition, Minsk.
4061 **1531** 4 k. purple, red & yell 15 10

1532. " World Security ".

1972. European Security Conference, Brussels.
4062. **1532.** 6 k. blue, turq. & gold 75 55

1533. M. S. Ordubady.
1534. G. Dimitrov.

1972. Birth Centenary of M. S. Ordubady (Azerbaijan writer).
4063. **1533.** 4 k. pur. & orange.. 15 10

1972. Russian Paintings. As T **1502**, but dated "1972". Multicoloured.
4064. 2 k. " Cossack Hetman " (I. Nikitin) 10 10
4065. 4 k. " F. Volkov " (A. Lossenko) 15 10
4066. 6 k. " V. Majkov " (F. Rokotov) 20 10
4067. 10 k. " N. Novikov " (D. Levitsky) 35 10
4068. 12 k. " G. Derzhavin " (V. Borovikovsky) .. 40 15
4069. 16 k. " Peasants' Dinner " (M. Shibanov) (horiz.) .. 55 25
4070. 20 k. " Moscow View " (F. Alexeiev) (horiz.) .. 75 45

1972. 90th Birth Anniv. of Georgi Dimitrov (Bulgarian statesman).
4071. **1534.** 6 k. brn. & bistre .. 20 10

1535. Congress Building and Emblem.

1972. 9th Int. Gerontology Congress, Kiev.
4072. **1535.** 6 k. brown and blue 20 10

1536. Fencing.

1972. Olympic Games, Munich.
4073. **1536.** 4 k. purple & gold.. 15 10
4074. – 6 k. green and gold 20 10
4075. – 10 k. blue and gold 30 10
4076. – 14 k. blue and gold 45 20
4077. – 16 k. red and gold.. 55 35
Designs: 6 k. Gymnastics. 10 k. Canoeing. 14 k. Boxing. 16 k. Running.

1537. Amundsen, Airship "Norge" and Northern Lights.
1538. Market-place, Lvov (Lemberg).

1972. Birth Cent. of Roald Amundsen (Polar explorer).
4079 **1537** 6 k. blue and brown 1·50 30

1972. Ukraine's Architectural Monuments. Multicoloured.
4080. 4 k. Type **1538** 15 10
4081. 6 k. 17th-century house, Tchernigov (horiz.) .. 20 15
4082. 10 k. Kovnirovsky building, Kiev (horiz.) .. 35 20
4083. 16 k. Kamenetz-Podolsk Castle 50 30

1539. Indian Flag and Asokan Capital.
1540. Liberation Monument, Vladivostok, and Cavalry.

1972. 25th Anniv. of India's Independence.
4084. **1539.** 6 k. red, blue & green 20 10

1972. 50th Anniv. of Liberation of Far Eastern Territories.
4085. **1540.** 3 k. grey, orge. & red 15 10
4086. – 4 k. grey, yell. & ochre 15 10
4087. – 6 k. grey, pink & red 30 15
Designs: 4 k. Labour Heroes Monument, Khabarovsk, and industrial scene. 6 k. Naval statue, Vladivostok, cruiser and aircraft.

1541. Miners' Day Emblem.

1972. 25th Anniv. of Miners' Day.
4088. **1541.** 4 k. red, blk. & violet 20 10

1542. " Boy with Dog " (Murillo).

1972. Paintings by Foreign Artists in Hermitage Gallery, Leningrad. Multicoloured.
4089. 4 k. " Breakfast " (Velasquez) (horiz.) .. 20 10
4090. 6 k. " The Milk Seller's Family " (Le Nain) (horiz.) 25 10
4091. 10 k. Type **1542** .. 45 20
4092. 16 k. " The Capricious Girl " (Watteau) .. 70 35
4093. 20 k. " Moroccan with Horse " (Delacroix) .. 85 45

1543. " Sputnik I ".

1972. 15th Anniv of "Cosmic Era". Mult.
4095 6 k. Type **1543** 35 15
4096 6 k. Launch of "Vostok 1" 35 15
4097 6 k. "Lunokhod" vehicle on moon 35 15
4098 6 k. "Man in space" .. 35 15
4099 6 k. "Mars 3" module on Mars 35 15
4100 6 k. Touch-down of "Venera 7" on Venus .. 35 15

1544. Konstantin Mardjanishevili.
1545. Museum Emblem.

1972. Birth Centenary of K. Mardjanishevili (Georgian actor).
4101. **1544.** 4 k. green 15 10

1972. Centenary of Popov Central Communications Museum.
4102 **1545** 4 k. blue, pur & grn 15 10

1546. Exhibition Labels.

1972. "50th Anniv. of U.S.S.R." Philatelic Exhibition.
4103. 1546. 4 k. red & blk. on yell. 15 10

1547. Lenin.

1972. 55th Anniv. of October Revolution.
4104. 1547. 4 k. red and gold .. 15 10

1548. Militia Badge and Soviet Flag. 1549. Arms of U.S.S.R.

1972. 55th Anniv of Soviet Militia.
4105 1548 4 k. gold, red & brn 15 10

1972. 50th Anniv. of U.S.S.R.
4106. 1549. 4 k. gold, purple & red 15 10
4107. – 4 k. gold, red & brn. 15 10
4108. – 4 k. gold, purple & grn. 15 10
4109. – 4 k. gold, pur. & grey 15 10
4110. – 4 k. gold, purple & grey 15 10
DESIGNS: No. 4107, Lenin and banner. No. 4108, Arms and Kremlin. No. 4109, Arms and industrial scenes. No. 4110, Arms, worker and open book "U.S.S.R. Constitution".

1550. Emblem of U.S.S.R. 1552. Savings Book.

1972. U.S.S.R. Victories in Olympic Games, Munich. Multicoloured.
4112. 20 k. Type 1550 .. .. 65 30
4113. 30 k. Olympic Medals .. 95 55

1972. "50 Years of Soviet Savings Bank".
4115. 1552. 4 k. blue and purple 15 10

1553. Kremlin and Snowflakes. 1555. "G. Skovoroda" (P. Mesheryakov).

1554. Battleship "Pyotr Veliky".

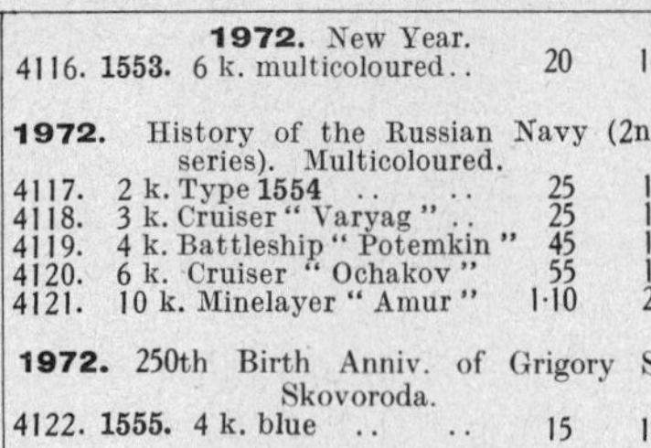

1972. New Year.
4116. 1553. 6 k. multicoloured .. 20 10

1972. History of the Russian Navy (2nd series). Multicoloured.
4117. 2 k. Type 1554 .. .. 25 10
4118. 3 k. Cruiser " Varyag " .. 25 10
4119. 4 k. Battleship " Potemkin " 45 10
4120. 6 k. Cruiser " Ochakov " 55 10
4121. 10 k. Minelayer " Amur " 1·10 25

1972. 250th Birth Anniv. of Grigory S. Skovoroda.
4122. 1555. 4 k. blue 15 10

1556. " Pioneer Girl with Books " (N. A. Kasatkin).

1972. "History of Russian Painting". Mult.
4123 2 k. "Meeting of Village Party Members" (E. M. Cheptsov) (horiz) .. 10 10
4124 4 k. Type 1556 .. 15 15
4125 6 k. "Party Delegate" (G. G. Ryazhsky) 25 15
4126 10 k. "End of Winter—Midday" (K. F. Yuon) (horiz) 35 20
4127 16 k. "Partisan Lunev" (N. I. Strunnikov) .. 55 35
4128 20 k. "Self-portrait in Fur Coat" (I. E. Grabar) .. 75 50

1557. Child reading Safety Code. 1558. Emblem of Technology.

1972. Road Safety Campaign.
4130. 1557. 4 k. black, blue & red 30 10

1972. Cent of Polytechnic Museum, Moscow.
4131 1558 4 k. red, yellow & grn 15 10

1559. " Venus 8 " and Parachute.

1972. Space Research.
4132. 1559. 6 k. blue, blk. & pur. 20 10

1560. Solidarity Emblem.

1973. 15th Anniv. of Asian and African People's Solidarity Organization.
4134. 1560. 10 k. bl., red & brn. 25 15

1561. Town and Gediminas Tower. 1562. I. V. Babushkin.

1973. 650th Anniv. of Vilnius (Vilna).
4135. 1561. 10 k. red, black & grn. 25 15

1973. Birth Cent. of I. V. Babushkin (revolutionary).
4136. 1562. 4 k. black 15 10

1563. "Tu-154" Jetliner.

1973. 50th Anniv. of Soviet Civil Aviation.
4137. 1563. 6 k. multicoloured .. 40 15

1564. " 30 " and Admiralty Spire, Leningrad. 1565. Portrait and Masks (Mayakovsky Theatre).

1973. 30th Anniv. of Relief of Leningrad Blockade.
4138. 1564. 4 k. blk., orange & brn. 20 10

1973. 50th Anniv. of Moscow Theatres.
4139. 1565. 10 k. multicoloured 25 10
4140. – 10 k. red and blue .. 25 10
DESIGN: No. 4140, Commemorative panel (Mossoviet Theatre).

1566. M. Prishvin.

1973. Birth Cent. of Mikhail Prishvin (writer).
4141. 1566. 4 k. multicoloured .. 10 10

1567. Heroes' Square, Volgograd.

1973. 30th Anniv. of Stalingrad Victory. Detail from Heroes' Memorial.
4142. – 3 k. black, yellow and orange .. 20 10
4143. 1567. 4 k. yellow and black 20 10
4144. – 10 k. multicoloured 40 15
4145. – 12 k. black, light red and red 60 20
DESIGNS—VERT. 3 k. Soldier and Allegory. 12 k. Hand with torch. HORIZ. 10 k. Mother mourning for child.

1568. Copernicus and Planetary Chart.

1973. 500th Birth Anniv. of Copernicus.
4147. 1568. 10 k. brown and blue 55 15

MINIMUM PRICE

The minimum price quoted is 5p which represents a handling charge rather than a basis for valuing common stamps. For further notes about prices see introductory pages.

1569. " Chaliapin " (K. Korovin).

1973. Birth Centenary of F. Chaliapin (opera singer).
4148. 1569. 10 k. multicoloured 60 15

1570. Ice Hockey Players. 1571. Athletes.

1973. World Ice Hockey Championships, Moscow.
4149 1570 10 k. brn, bl & gold 35 15

1973. 50th Anniv. of Central Red Army Sports Club.
4151. 1571. 4 k. multicoloured .. 15 10

1572. Red Star, Tank, and Map. 1573. N. E. Bauman.

1973. 30th Anniv. of Battle of Kursk.
4152. 1572. 4 k. black, red and grey 20 10

1973. Birth Centenary of Nikolai Bauman (revolutionary).
4153. 1573. 4 k. brown 15 10

1574. Red Cross and Red Crescent.

1973. International Co-operation.
4154. 1574. 4 k. red, blk. & grn. 15 10
4155. – 6 k. light blue, red and blue 20 10
4156. – 16 k. green, red and mauve 65 25
DESIGNS AND EVENTS: 4 k. (Soviet Red Cross and Red Crescent Societies Union. 50th Anniv.). 6 k. Mask, emblem and theatre curtain (15th Int., Theatre Institution Congress). 16 k. Floral emblem (10th World Festival of Youth, Berlin).

1575. " A. N. Ostrovsky " (V. Perov). 1576. Satellites.

1973. 150th Birth Anniv of Aleksandr Ostrovsky (writer).
4157 1575 4 k. multicoloured .. 15 10

1973. Cosmonauts Day. Multicoloured.
4158. 6 k. Type **1576** 20 15
4159. 6 k. " Lunokhod 2" .. 20 15

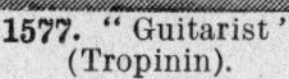

1577. " Guitarist " (Tropinin). **1578.** Athlete and Emblems.

1973. "History of Russian Painting". Mult.
4162 2 k. Type **1577** 15 10
4163 4 k. "The Young Widow" (Fedotov) 20 10
4164 6 k. "Self-portrait" (Kiprensky) 25 10
4165 10 k. "An Afternoon in Italy" (Brullov) .. 30 20
4166 12 k. "That's My Father's Dinner!" (boy with dog) (Venetsianov) 40 30
4167 16 k. "Lower Gallery of Albano" (A. A. Ivanov) (horiz) 55 35
4168 20 k. "Ermak conquering Siberia" (Surikov) (horiz) 75 50

1973. 50th Anniv. of Dynamo Sports Club.
4169. **1578.** 4 k. multicoloured .. 15 10

1580. Liner "Mikhail Lermontov". **1582.** Sports.

1581. E. T. Krenkel and Polar Scenes.

1973. Inauguration of Leningrad-New York Trans-Atlantic Service.
4171. **1580.** 16 k. multicoloured 70 30

1973. 70th Birth Anniv. of E. T. Krenkel (Polar explorer).
4172. **1581.** 4 k. brown and blue 55 10

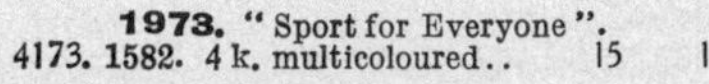

1973. " Sport for Everyone ".
4173. **1582.** 4 k. multicoloured .. 15 10

1583. Girls' Choir.

1973. Centenary of Latvian Singing Festival.
4174. **1583.** 10 k. multicoloured 35 10

1973. 50th Anniv of Russian Federation Autonomous Soviet Socialist Republics. Design similar to T **1433**, but dated "1973".
4175 4 k. blue 20 10
DESIGN: No. 4175, Arms and industries of Buryat Republic.

1584. Throwing the Hammer.

1973. Universiade Games, Moscow. Mult.
4176. 2 k. Type **1584** 10 10
4177. 3 k. Gymnastics .. 10 10
4178. 4 k. Swimming .. 15 10
4179. 16 k. Fencing 65 25

1586. European Bison.

1973. Caucasus and Voronezh Nature Reserves. Multicoloured.
4182 1 k. Type **1586** 10 10
4183 3 k. Ibex 15 10
4184 4 k. Caucasian snowcocks 50 15
4185 6 k. Eurasian beaver with young 35 10
4186 10 k. Red deer with fawns 55 20

1587. Lenin, Banner and Membership Card.

1973. 70th Anniv. of 2nd Soviet Social Democratic Workers' Party Congress.
4187. **1587.** 4 k. multicoloured .. 15 10

1588. A. R. al-Biruni. **1590.** " The Sculpture " (P. D. Korin).

1589. Schaumburg Palace, Bonn and Spassky Tower, Moscow.

1973. Millennium of Abu Reihan al-Biruni (astronomer and mathematician).
4188. **1588.** 6 k. brown 30 15

1973. General Secretary Leonid Brezhnev's Visits to West Germany, France and U.S.A. Multicoloured.
4189 **1589** 10 k. mve, brn & buff 30 15
4190 – 10 k. brown, ochre and yellow .. 30 15
4191 – 10 k. red, grey & brn 30 15
DESIGNS: No. 4190, Eiffel Tower, Paris, and Spassky Tower. 4191, White House, Washington, and Spassky Tower.
See also Nos. 4245 and 4257.

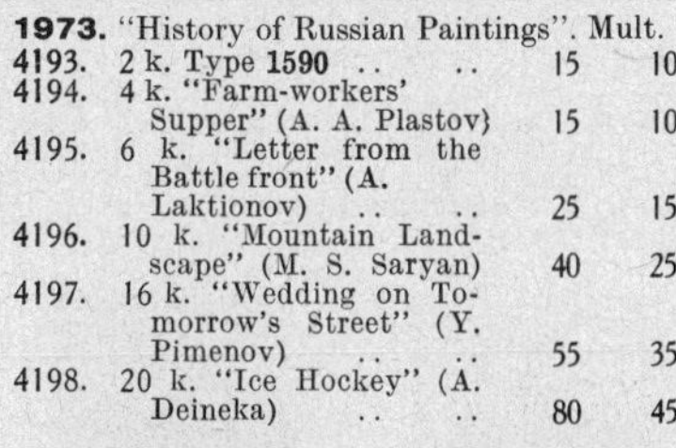

1973. "History of Russian Paintings". Mult.
4193. 2 k. Type **1590** 15 10
4194. 4 k. "Farm-workers' Supper" (A. A. Plastov) 15 10
4195. 6 k. "Letter from the Battle front" (A. Laktionov) 25 15
4196. 10 k. "Mountain Landscape" (M. S. Saryan) 40 25
4197. 16 k. "Wedding on Tomorrow's Street" (Y. Pimenov) 55 35
4198. 20 k. "Ice Hockey" (A. Deineka) 80 45

1591. Lenin Museum. **1592.** Y. Steklov.

1973. Inaug. of Lenin Museum, Tashkent.
4200. **1591.** 4 k. multicoloured 10 10

1973. Birth Cent. of Y. Steklov (statesman).
4201. **1592.** 4 k. brn., red & pink 10 10

1593. " The Eternal Pen " **1594.** " Oplopanax elatum ".

1973. Afro-Asian Writers' Conf., Alma-Ata.
4202. **1593.** 6 k. multicoloured .. 15 10

1973. Medicinal Plants. Multicoloured.
4203 1 k. Type **1594** 20 10
4204 2 k. Ginseng 25 10
4205 4 k. Spotted orchid .. 30 10
4206 10 k. Arnica 60 25
4207 12 k. Lily of the valley .. 1·10 35

1595. I. Nasimi.

1973. 600th Birth Anniv of Imadeddin Nasimi (Azerbaijan poet).
4208 **1595** 4 k. brown 10 10

1596. Cruiser "Kirov".

1973. History of Russian Navy (3rd series). Multicoloured.
4209 3 k. Type **1596** 20 10
4210 4 k. Battleship "Oktyabrskaya Revolyutsiya" .. 25 10
4211 6 k. Submarine "Krasnogvardeets" .. 30 10
4212 10 k. Destroyer "Soobrazitelnyi" .. 60 25
4213 16 k. Cruiser "Krasnyi Kavkaz" .. .. 1·10 35

1597. Pugachev and Battle Scene.

1973. Bicent. of Peasant War.
4214. **1597.** 4 k. multicoloured .. 15 10

1598. Red Flag encircling Globe.

1973. 15th Anniv. of Magazine "Problems of Peace and Socialism".
4215. **1598.** 6 k. red, gold & green 15 10

1599. Leningrad Mining Institute.

1973. Bicent. of Leningrad Mining Institute.
4216. **1599.** 4 k. multicoloured .. 15 10

1600. Laurel and Hemispheres. **1601.** Elena Stasova.

1973. World Congress of "Peaceful Forces", Moscow.
4217 **1600** 6 k. multicoloured 15 10

1973. Birth Centenary of Elena Stasova (party official).
4218. **1601.** 4 k. mauve 10 10

1602. Order of People's Friendship. **1603.** Marshal Malinovsky.

1973. Foundation of Order of People's Friendship.
4219. **1602.** 4 k. multicoloured .. 10 10

1973. 75th Birth Anniv. of Marshal R. Malinovsky.
4220. **1603.** 4 k. grey 15 10

1604. Workers and Red Guard. **1605.** D. Cantemir.

1973. 250th Anniv. of Sverdlovsk.
4221. **1604.** 4 k. blk., gold & red 10 10

1973. 300th Birth Anniv. of Dmitri Cantemir (Moldavian scientist and encyclopaedist).
4222. **1605.** 4 k. red 10 10

1606. Pres. Allende of Chile.

1973. Allende Commemoration.
4223. **1606.** 6 k. black and brn. 30 10

1607. Kremlin. **1608.** N. Narimanov.

1973. New Year.
4224. **1607.** 6 k. multicoloured .. 15 10

1973. Birth Centenary (1970) of Nariman Narimanov (Azerbaijan politician).
4225 **1608** 4 k. green 10 10

1609. "Russobalt" Touring Car (1909).

1973. History of Soviet Motor Industry (1st series). Multicoloured.
4226. 2 k. Type **1609** 15 10
4227. 3 k. "AMO-F15" lorry (1924) 15 10
4228. 4 k. Spartak "NAMI-1" tourer (1927) 20 10
4229. 12 k. Yaroslavsky "Ya-6" bus (1929) 55 20
4230. 16 k. Gorkovsky "GAZ-A" tourer (1932) 75 40
See also Nos. 4293/7, 4397/401 and 4512/16.

1610. "Game and Lobster" (Sneiders).

1973. Foreign Paintings in Soviet Galleries. Multicoloured.
4231 4 k. Type **1610** 15 10
4232 6 k. "Young Woman with Ear-rings" (Rembrandt) (vert) .. 20 10
4233 10 k. "Sick Woman and Physician" (Steen) (vert) 35 15
4234 12 k. "Attributes of Art" (Chardin) 45 20
4235 14 k. "Lady in a Garden" (Monet) 50 25
4236 16 k. "Village Lovers" (Bastien-Lepage) (vert) 60 30
4237 20 k. "Girl with Fan" (Renoir) (vert) .. 75 40

1611. Great Sea Gate, Tallin. **1612.** Picasso.

1973. Historical Buildings of Estonia, Latvia and Lithuania.
4239 **1611** 4 k. black, red & grn 10 10
4240 – 4 k. brown, red & grn 10 10
4241 – 4 k. multicoloured .. 10 10
4242 – 10 k. multicoloured 35 15
Designs: No. 4240, Organ-pipes and Dome Cathedral, Riga. 4241, Traku Castle, Lithuania. 4242, Town Hall and weather-vane, Tallin.

1973. Pablo Picasso Commemoration.
4243 **1612** 6 k. green, red & gold 25 10

1613. I. G. Petrovsky (mathematician and Rector of Moscow University).

1973. Petrovsky Commemoration.
4244. **1613.** 4 k. multicoloured .. 15 10

1973. Brezhnev's Visit to India. As T **1589,** but showing Kremlin, Red Fort, Delhi and flags.
4245. 4 k. multicoloured .. 10 10

1614. Soviet Soldier and Title Page. **1616.** Oil Workers.

1615. Siege Monument and Peter the Great Statue, Leningrad.

1974. 50th Anniv. of "Red Star" Newspaper.
4246. **1614.** 4 k. blk., red & gold 15 10

1974. 30th Anniv. of Soviet Victory in Battle for Leningrad.
4247. **1615.** 4 k. multicoloured 25 10

1974. 10th Anniv of Tyumen Oil-fields.
4248 **1616** 4 k. black, red & blue 30 10

1617. "Comecon" Headquarters, Moscow. **1618.** Skaters and Stadium.

1974. 25th Anniv of Concil for Mutual Economic Aid.
4249 **1617** 16 k. grn, red & brn 45 20

1974. European Women's Ice Skating Championships, Medeo, Alma-Ata.
4250 **1618** 6 k. red, blue & slate 20 10

1619. Kunstkammer Museum, Leningrad, Text and Academy. **1620.** L. A. Artsimovich.

1974. 250th Anniv. of Russian Academy of Sciences.
4251. **1619.** 10 k. multicoloured 25 10

1974. 1st Death Anniv. of Academician L. A. Artsimovich (physicist).
4252. **1620.** 4 k. brown and green 15 10

1974. 50th Anniv of Autonomous Soviet Socialist Republics. Design similar to T **1433**, but dated "1974".
4253 4 k. brown 15 10
Design: No. 4253, Arms and industries of Nakhichevan ASSR (Azerbaijan).

1621. K. D. Ushinsky. **1622.** M. D. Millionshchikov.

1974. 150th Birth Anniv. of K. D. Ushinsky (educationalist).
4254. **1621.** 4 k. brown and grn. 10 10

1974. 1st Death Anniv. of M. D. Millionshchikov (scientist).
4255. **1622.** 4 k. brown, pink & grn. 10 10

1623. Spartakiad Emblem. **1624.** Young Workers and Emblem.

1974. 3rd Winter Spartakiad Games.
4256. **1623.** 10 k. multicoloured 15 15

1974. General Secretary Leonid Brezhnev's Visit to Cuba. As Type **1589** but showing Kremlin, Revolution Square, Havana and Flags.
4257. 4 k. multicoloured .. 10 10

1974. Scientific and Technical Youth Work Review.
4258. **1624.** 4 k. multicoloured .. 10 10

1625. Theatre Facade. **1626.** Globe and Meteorological Activities.

1974. Cent. of Azerbaijan Drama Theatre, Baku.
4259. **1625.** 6 k. brown, red & orge. 15 10

1974. Cosmonautics Day.
4260. **1626.** 6 k. blue, red & vio. 20 10
4261. – 10 k. brn., red & blue 35 15
4262. – 10 k. blk. red & yell. 35 15
Designs: No. 4261, V. G. Lazarev and O. G. Makarov, and launch of "Soyuz 12". No. 4262, P. I. Klimuk and V. V. Lebedev, and "Soyuz 13".

1627. "Odessa by Moonlight" (Aivazovsky).

1974. Marine Paintings by Ivan Aivazovsky. Multicoloured.
4263. 2 k. Type **1627** 10 10
4264. 4 k. "Battle of Chesma" (vert.) 15 10
4265. 6 k. "St. George's Monastery" 20 10
4266. 10 k. "Storm at Sea" .. 35 15
4267. 12 k. "Rainbow" .. 40 20
4268. 16 k. "Shipwreck" .. 55 30

1628. Young Communists.

1974. 17th Leninist Young Communist League (Komsomol) Congress (4270) and 50th Anniv of Naming League after Lenin (4271). Mult.
4270 4 k. Type **1628** 10 10
4271 4 k. "Lenin" (from sculpture by V. Tsigal) 10 10

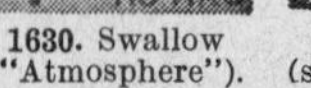

1630. Swallow ("Atmosphere"). **1631.** "Cobble-stone" (sculpture, I. D. Shadr).

1974. "EXPO 74" World Fair, Spokane, U.S.A. "Preserve the Environment".
4273. **1630.** 4 k. blk., red & lilac 15 10
4274. – 6 k. yell., blk. & blue 20 10
4275. – 10 k. blk., vio. & red 40 15
4276. – 16 k. bl., grn. & blk. 55 20
4277. – 20 k. blk., brn. & orge. 75 40
Designs: 6 k. Fish and globe ("The Sea"). 10 k. Crystals ("The Earth"). 16 k. Rose bush ("Flora"). 20 k. Young red deer. ("Fauna").

1974. 50th Anniv. of Central Museum of the Revolution.
4279. **1631.** 4 k. grn., red & gold 10 10

1632. Congress Emblem within Lucerne Grass. **1634.** Tchaikovsky and Competition Emblem.

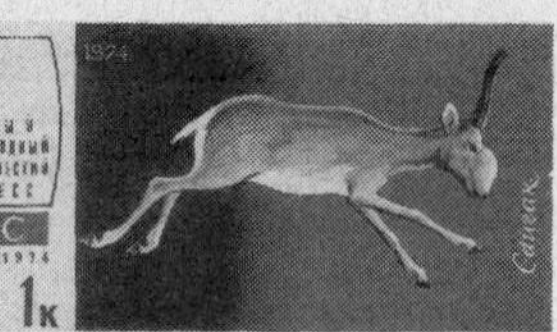

1633. Saiga.

1974. 12th Int. Congress of Meadow Cultivation, Moscow
4280. **1632.** 4 k. red, grn. & dark-grn. 10 10

1974. 1st Int. Theriological Congress, Moscow. Fauna. Multicoloured.
4281. 1 k. Type **1633** 10 10
4282. 3 k. Asiatic wild ass .. 15 10
4283. 4 k. Russian desman .. 20 10
4284. 6 k. Northern fur seal .. 25 10
4285. 10 k. Bowhead whale .. 60 20

1974. 5th Int. Tchaikovsky Music Competition.
4286. **1634.** 6 k blk., vio. & grn. 30 10

1636. Marshal F. I. Tolbukhin. **1638.** Runner and Emblem.

1637. K. Stanislavsky, V. Nemirovich-Danchenko and Theatre Curtain.

1974. 80th Birth Anniv. of Marshal F. I. Tolbukhin.
4288. **1636.** 4 k. green 15 10

1974. 75th Anniv. of Moscow Arts Festival.
4289. **1637.** 10 k. multicoloured 25 15

1974. 13th Soviet Schools Spartakiad, Alma Ata.
4290. **1638.** 4 k. multicoloured .. 15 10

1639. Modern Passenger Coach. **1640.** Shield and Monument on Battle Map.

1974. Centenary of Egorov Railway Wagon Works, Leningrad.
4291. **1639.** 4 k. multicoloured .. 30 10

1974. 30th Anniv. of Liberation of Byelorussia.
4292. **1640.** 4 k. multicoloured .. 10 10
See also No. 4301.

1974. History of Soviet Motor Industry (2nd series). As T **1609**. Multicoloured.
4293. 2 k. Gorkovsky "GAZ-AA" lorry (1932) 15 10
4294. 3 k. Gorkovsky "GAZ-03-30" bus (1933) 15 10
4295. 4 k. Moscow Auto Works "ZIS-5" lorry (1933) .. 15 10
4296. 14 k. Moscow Auto Works "ZIS-8" bus (1934) .. 55 15
4297. 16 k. Moscow Auto Works "ZIS-101" saloon car (1936) 65 25

1974. 50th Anniv. of Soviet Republics. As T **1433**, dated "1974".
4298. 4 k. red 15 10
DESIGN: 4 k. Arms and industries of North Ossetian Republic.
No. 4298 also commemorates the 200th anniv. of Ossetia's merger with Russia.

1641. Liberation Monument and Skyline. **1644.** Admiral Isakov.

1642. Warsaw Monument and Flag.

1974. 800th Anniv. of Poltava.
4299. **1641.** 4 k. red and brown 10 10

1974. 30th Anniv. of Polish People's Republic.
4300. **1642.** 6 k. brown and red 15 10

1974. 30th Anniv. of Liberation of Ukraine. As T **1640**, but background details and colours changed.
4301. 4 k. multicoloured .. 15 10

1974. 80th Birth Anniv. of Admiral I. S. Isakov.
4302. **1644.** 4 k. blue 15 10

1645. Minesweeper.

1974. History of the Russian Navy (4th series). Modern Warships. Multicoloured.
4303 3 k. Type **1645** 25 10
4304 4 k. Landing ship .. 25 10
4305 6 k. Helicopter carrier .. 45 15
4306 16 k. Destroyer "Otvazhny" .. .. 1·00 25

1646. Pentathlon Sports. **1647.** D. Ulyanov.

1974. World Modern Pentathlon Championships, Moscow.
4307. **1646.** 16 k. brn., gold & blue 35 20

1974. Birth Centenary of D. Ulyanov (Lenin's brother).
4308. **1647.** 4 k. green 15 10

1648. V. Menzhinsky. **1650.** S. M. Budennyi.

1649. "Lilac" (P. P. Konchalovsky).

1974. Birth Cent. of V. Menzhinsky (statesman).
4309. **1648.** 4 k. maroon .. 10 10

1974. Soviet Paintings. Multicoloured.
4310. 4 k. Type **1649** 15 10
4311. 6 k. "Towards the Wind" (sailing) (E. Kalnins) .. 20 15
4312. 10 k. "Spring" (young woman) (O. Zardarjan) 40 20
4313. 16 k. "Northern Harbour" (G. Nissky) .. 65 30
4314. 20 k. "Daughter of the Soviet Kirghiz" (S. Tchnikov) (vert.) .. 75 35

1974. Marshal S. M. Budennyi Commem.
4315 **1650** 4 k. green 15 10

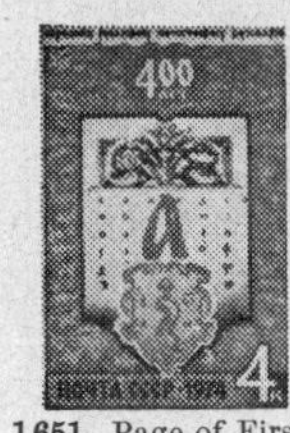

1651. Page of First Russian Dictionary. **1652.** Soviet War Memorial, Bucharest, and Flags.

1974. 400th Anniv. of First Russian Primer.
4316. **1651.** 4 k. red, blk. & gold 10 10

1974. 30th Anniv. of Rumanian Liberation.
4317. **1652.** 6 k. blue, yell. & red 15 10

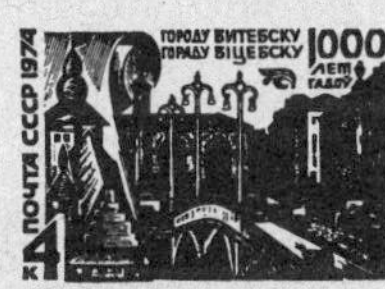

1653. Vitebsk.

1974. Millenary of Vitebsk.
4318. **1653.** 4 k. red and green.. 15 10

1654. Kirgizia. **1655.** Bulgarian Crest and Flags.

1974. 50th Anniv. of Soviet Republics. Flags, Agricultural and Industrial Emblems. Multicoloured. Background colours given.
4319. **1654.** 4 k. blue 15 10
4320. – 4 k. purple 15 10
4321. – 4 k. light blue .. 15 10
4322. – 4 k. yellow 15 10
4323. – 4 k. green 15 10
DESIGNS: No. 4320, Moldavia. 4321, Tadzhikistan. 4322, Turkmenistan. 4323, Uzbekistan.

1974. 30th Anniv. of Bulgarian Revolution.
4324. **1655.** 6 k. multicoloured.. 15 10

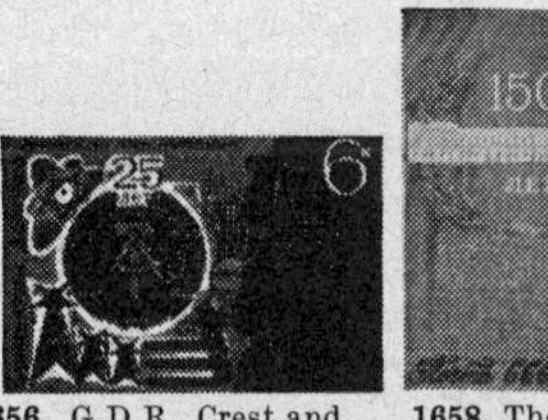

1656. G.D.R. Crest and Soviet War Memorial, Treptow, Berlin. **1658.** Theatre and Laurel Wreath.

1974. 25th Anniv. of German Democratic Republic.
4325. **1656.** 6 k. multicoloured 15 10

1974. 150th Anniv. of Maly State Theatre, Moscow.
4327. **1658.** 4 k. gold, red & blk. 10 10

1659. "Guests from Overseas".

1974. Birth Centenary of Nikolai K. Rorich (painter).
4328. **1659.** 6 k. multicoloured.. 20 10

1660. Soviet Crest and U.P.U. Monument, Berne.

1974. Centenary of U.P.U. Mult.
4329. 10 k. Type **1660** 30 15
4330. 10 k. Ukraine crest, U.P.U. Emblem and U.P.U. H.Q., Berne 30 15
4331. 10 k. Byelorussia crest, U.P.U. emblem and mail transport 30 15

1661. Order of Labour Glory.

1974. 57th Anniv. of October Revolution. Multicoloured.
4333. 4 k. Type **1661**. 15 10
4334. 4 k. Kamaz truck (vert.) 15 10
4335. 4 k. Hydro-electric power station, Nurek (vert.).. 15 10

1662. Soviet "Space Stations" over Mars.

1974. Soviet Space Exploration. Mult.
4336. 6 k. Type **1662** 20 10
4337. 10 k. P. R. Popovich and Y. P. Artchunin (" Soyuz 14 " cosmonauts) .. 30 15
4338. 10 k. I. V. Sarafanov and L. S. Demin (" Soyuz 15 " cosmonauts) .. 30 15
SIZES—VERT. No. 4337, 28 × 40 mm. HORIZ. No. 4338, 40 × 28 mm.

1663. Mongolian Crest Flag. **1664.** Commemorative Inscription.

1974. 50th Anniv. of Mongolian People's Republic.
4339. **1663.** 6 k. multicoloured.. 20 10

1974. 30th Anniv. of Estonian Liberation.
4340. **1664.** 4 k. multicoloured.. 15 10

1665. Liner "Aleksandr Pushkin", Freighter and Tanker.

1974. 50th Anniv. of Soviet Merchant Navy.
4341. **1665.** 4 k. multicoloured.. 25 10

1666. Spassky Clock-tower, Kremlin, Moscow.

1974. New Year.
4342. **1666.** 4 k. multicoloured.. 15 10

1667. "The Market Place" (Beuckelaar).

1974. Foreign Paintings in Soviet Galleries. Multicoloured.
4343. 4 k. Type **1667** 15 10
4344. 6 k. "Woman selling Fish" (Pieters) 25 10
4345. 10 k. "A Goblet of Lemonade" (Terborsh) 35 15
4346. 14 k. "Girl at Work" (Metsu) 50 20
4347. 16 k. " Saying Grace " (Chardin) 55 30
4348. 20 k. " The Spoilt Child " (Greuze) 80 35
Nos. 4344/8 are vertical designs.

1668. " Ostrowskia magnifica ". **1669.** I. S. Nikitin.

1974. Flowers. Multicoloured.
4350. 1 k. Type **1668** 10 10
4351. 2 k. "Paeonia intermedia" 10 10
4352. 4 k. "Roemeria refracta" 20 10
4353. 10 k. "Tulipia dasystemon" 40 15
4354. 12 k. "Dianthus versicolor" 45 20

1974. 150th Birth Anniv. of I. S. Nikitin (poet).
4355. **1669.** 4 k. blk., grn. & ol. 15 10

1670. Leningrad Mint Building.

1974. 250th Anniv. of Leningrad Mint.
4356. **1670.** 6 k. multicoloured 20 10

1671. Mozhaisky's Aeroplane, 1882.

1974. Early Russian Aircraft (1st series). Multicoloured.
4357. 6 k. Type **1671** 30 15
4358. 6 k. Grizidubov "No. 2" aeroplane, 1910 .. 30 15
4359. 6 k. Sikorsky "A" aeroplane, 1910 .. .. 30 15
4360. 6 k. Sikorsky "Vityaz" aeroplane, 1913 .. 30 15
4361. 6 k. Grigorovich flying-boat, 1914 .. .. 30 15
See also Nos. 4580/4, 4661/6 and 4791/6.

1673. Komsomol Emblem and Rotary Press ("Komsomolskaya Pravda").

1975. 50th Anniv of Children's Newspapers.
4363 1673 4 k. red, black & blue .. 10 10
4364 – 4 k. red, black & sil .. 10 10
DESIGN—VERT. No. 4364, Pioneer emblem and newspaper sheet ("Pionerskaya Pravda").

1674. Emblem and Skiers (8th Trade Unions' Games).

1975. Winter Spartakiads.
4365 1674 4 k. orange, blk & bl .. 10 10
4366 – 16 k. bistre, blk & bl .. 55 20
DESIGN—HORIZ. 16 k. Emblem, ice hockey player and skier (5th Friendly Forces Military Games).

1975. 50th Anniv of Autonomous Soviet Socialist Republics. Design similar to T **1433**, but dated "1975".
4367 4 k. green 15 10
DESIGN: No. 4367, Arms, industries and produce of Karakalpak ASSR (Uzbekistan).

1675. "David".

1975. 500th Birth Anniv of Michelangelo.
4368 1675 4 k. dp green & green .. 20 15
4369 – 6 k. brown and ochre .. 25 15
4370 – 10 k. dp green & grn .. 35 15
4371 – 14 k. brown & ochre .. 55 30
4372 – 20 k. dp green & grn .. 65 30
4373 – 30 k. brown & ochre .. 75 30
DESIGNS: 6 k. "Crouching Boy". 10 k. "Rebellious Slave". 14 k. "Creation of Adam" (detail Sistine Chapel ceiling). 20 k. Staircase of Laurentiana Library, Florence. 30 k. Christ and the Virgin (detail of "The Last Judgement", Sistine Chapel).

1676. A. F. Mozhaisky and Aircraft.

1975. 150th Birth Anniv. of A. F. Mozhaisky (aircraft designer).
4375. 1676. 6 k. brown and blue .. 40 10

1677. Convention Emblem.

1975. Cent. of International Metre Convention.
4376 1677 6 k. multicoloured .. 15 10

1678. Games Emblem.

1975. 6th Summer Spartakiad.
4377 1678 6 k. multicoloured .. 15 10

1679. Towers of Charles Bridge, Prague (Czechoslovakia).

1975. 30th Anniv. of Liberation. Mult.
4378. 6 k. Type **1679** 15 10
4379. 6 k. Liberation Monument and Parliament Buildings, Budapest (Hungary) 15 10

1680. French and Soviet Flags.

1681. Yuri Gagarin.

1975. 50th Anniv. of Franco-Soviet Diplomatic Relations.
4380. 1680. 6 k. multicoloured .. 15 10

1975. Cosmonautics Day.
4381. 1681. 6 k. red, silver and blue 15 10
4382. – 10 k. red, blk. and bl. 30 15
4383. – 16 k. multicoloured 50 20
DESIGNS—HORIZ. 10 k. A. A. Gubarev, G. M. Grechko ("Soyuz 17") and "Salyut 4". 16 k. A. V. Filipchenko, N. N. Rukavishnikov and "Soyuz 16".

1682. Treaty Emblem.

1684. Lenin.

1683. Emblem and Exhibition Hall, Sokolniki, Moscow.

1975. 20th Anniv. of Warsaw Treaty.
4384. 1682. 6 k. multicoloured .. 15 10

1975. "Communication 75" International Exhibition, Moscow.
4385. 1683. 6 k. red, silver and blue 15 10

1975. 30th Anniv. of Victory in Second World War. Multicoloured.
4386. 4 k. Type **1684** 15 10
4387. 4 k. Eternal flame and Guard of Honour .. 15 10
4388. 4 k. Woman in ammunition factory 15 10
4389. 4 k. Partisans 15 10
4390. 4 k. "Destruction of the enemy" 15 10
4391. 4 k. Soviet forces .. 15 10

1685. "Lenin" (V. G. Tsiplakov).

1686. Victory Emblems.

1975. 105th Birth Anniv. of Lenin.
4393. 1685. 4 k. multicoloured .. 15 10

1975. "Sozfilex 75" International Stamp Exhibition.
4394 1686 6 k. multicoloured .. 20 10

1687. "Apollo – Soyuz" Space Link.

1975. "Apollo-Soyuz" Space Project.
4396. 1687. 20 k. multicoloured 40 25

1975. History of Soviet Motor Industry (3rd series). As T **1609**.
4397 2 k. black, orange &d blue 15 10
4398 3 k. black, brown & green 15 10
4399 4 k. black, blue and green 15 10
4400 12 k. black, buff & purple 45 20
4401 16 k. black, green & olive 60 25
DESIGNS: 2 k. Gorkovsky "GAZ-M-1" saloon, 1936. 3 k. Yaroslavsky "YAG-6" truck, 1936. 4 k. Moscow Auto Works "ZIS-16" bus, 1938. 12 k. Moscow KIM Works "KIM-10" saloon, 1940. 16 k. Gorkovsky "GAZ-67B" field car, 1943.

1688. Irrigation Canal and Emblem.

1689. Flags and Crests of Poland and Soviet Union.

1975. Ninth International Irrigation Congress, Moscow.
4402. 1688. 6 k. multicoloured .. 15 10

1975. 30th Anniv. of Soviet-Polish Friendship.
4403. 1689. 6 k. multicoloured .. 15 10

1690. A. A. Leonov in Space. **1691.** Ya. M. Sverdlov.

1975. 10th Anniv. of First Space Walk by A. A. Leonov.
4404. 1690. 6 k. multicoloured 20 10

1975. 90th Birth Anniv. of Ya. M. Sverdlov (statesman).
4405. 1691. 4 k. brown, buff & silver 10 10

1692. Congress Emblem.

1975. 8th International Plant Conservation Congress, Moscow.
4406. 1692. 6 k. multicoloured .. 15 10

1693. Emblem and Flowers.

1975. 12th International Botanical Congress, Leningrad.
4407. 1693. 6 k. multicoloured .. 30 10

1695. Festival Emblem.

1975. 9th International Film Festival, Moscow.
4409. 1695. 6 k. multicoloured .. 15 10

1696. Crews of "Apollo" and "Soyuz".

1975. "Apollo"–"Soyuz" Space Link. Mult.
4410 10 k. Type **1696** 30 10
4411 12 k. "Apollo" and "Soyuz 19" in docking procedure 35 20
4412 12 k. "Apollo" and "Soyuz 19" linked together 35 20
4413 16 k. Launch of "Soyuz 19" (vert) 45 20

1697. Sturgeon.

1975. International Exposition, Okinawa. Marine Life.
4415 1697 3 k. bistre, blk & bl 15 10
4416 – 4 k. lilac, black & bl 20 10
4417 – 6 k. purple, blk & grn 25 10
4418 – 10 k. brown, blk & bl 90 15
4419 – 16 k. grn, blk & pur 60 25
4420 – 20 k. bl, pur & stone 65 30
DESIGNS: 4 k. Shell-fish. 6 k. Eel. 10 k. Long-tailed duck. 16 k. Crab. 20 k. Chrisipther.

1698. "Parade in Red Square, Moscow" (K. F. Yuon).

1975. Birth Centenaries of Soviet Painters. Multicoloured.
4422 1 k. Type **1698** 10 10
4423 2 k. "Winter morning in Industrial Moscow" (K. F. Yuon) 10 10
4424 6 k. "Soldiers with captured Guns" (E. E. Lansere) 25 10
4425 10 k. "Excavating the Metro Tunnel" (E. E. Lansere) 60 20
4426 16 k. "A. A. Pushkin and N. N. Pushkina at Palace Ball" (N. P. Ulyanov) (vert) .. 60 30
4427 20 k. "Lauriston at Kutuzov's Headquarters" (N. P. Ulyanov) 80 40

1699. Conference Emblem. **1700.** A. Isaakjan.

1975. European Security and Co-operation Conference, Helsinki.
4428. **1699.** 6 k. blk., gold & blue 15 10

1975. Birth Centenary of Avetic Isaakjan (Armenian poet).
4429 **1700** 4 k. multicoloured .. 10 10

1701. M. K. Cirurlionis. **1702.** J. Duclos.

1975. Birth Centenary of M. K. Ciurlionis (Lithuanian composer).
4430 **1701** 4 k. gold, green & yell 15 10

1975. Jacques Duclos (French communist leader). Commemoration.
4431. **1702.** 6 k. purple and silver 15 10

1703. Al Farabi. **1704.** Ruffs.

1975. 1100th Birth Anniv of Al Farabi (Persian philosopher).
4432 **1703** 6 k. multicoloured .. 15 10

1975. 50th Anniv. of Berezinsky and Stolby Nature Reserves. Multicoloured.
4433. 1 k. Type **1704** 30 10
4434. 4 k. Siberian musk deer 30 10
4435. 6 k. Sable 30 10
4436. 10 k. Capercaillie .. 55 20
4437. 16 k. Eurasian badger .. 60 55

1705. Korean Crest with Soviet and Korean Flags (Korean Liberation). **1707.** S. A. Esenin.

1706. Cosmonauts, " Soyuz 18 " and " Salyut 4 " Linked.

1975. 30th Anniversaries. Multicoloured.
4438. 6 k. Type **1705** .. 15 10
4439. 6 k. Vietnamese crest, Soviet and Vietnamese flags (Vietnam Democratic Republic) .. 15 10

1975. Space Flight of " Soyuz 18—Salyut 4 " by Cosmonauts P. Klimuk and V. Sevastyanov.
4440 **1706** 10 k. black, red & bl 25 10

1975. 80th Birth Anniv. of S. A. Esenin (poet).
4441 **1707** 6 k. brn, yell & grey 15 10

1708. Standardisation Emblems.

1975. 50th Anniv. of Soviet Communications Standardisation Committee.
4442. **1708.** 4 k. multicoloured .. 10 10

1709. Astrakhan Lamb. **1710.** M. P. Konchalovsky.

1975. 3rd International Astrakhan Lamb Breeding Symposium, Samarkand.
4443 **1709** 6 k. blk, grn & stone 20 10

1975. Birth Centenary of M. P. Konchalovsky (therapeutist).
4444. **1710.** 4 k. brown and red 15 10

1711. Exhibition Emblem. **1712.** I.W.Y. Emblem and Rose.

1975. 3rd All-Union Youth Philatelic Exhibition, Yerevan.
4445 **1711** 4 k. red, brown & bl 10 10

1975. International Women's Year.
4446. **1712.** 6 k. red, blue & turq. 20 10

1713. Parliament Buildings, Belgrade. **1714.** Title-page of 1938 Edition.

1975. 30th Anniv of Yugoslav Republic.
4447 **1713** 6 k. blue, red & gold 15 10

1975. 175th Anniv of Publication of "Tale of the Host of Igor".
4448 **1714** 4 k. red, grey & bistre 10 10

1715. M. I. Kalinin. (statesman).

1975. Celebrities' Birth Cents.
4449. **1715.** 4 k. brown 10 10
4450. – 4 k. brown 10 10
DESIGN. No. 4450. A. V. Lunacharsky. (politician).

1716. Torch and Inscription.

1975. 70th Anniv. of Russian 1905 Revolution.
4451. **1716.** 4 k. red and brown 10 10

1717. Track-laying Machine and Baikal-Amur Railway. **1719.** Star of Spassky Tower.

1718. " Decembrists in Senate Square " (D. N. Kardovsky).
(Illustration reduced. Actual size 70×33 mm.)

1975. 58th Anniv. of October Revolution. Multicoloured.
4452. 4 k. Type **1717** 35 10
4453. 4 k. Rolling mill, Novolipetsk steel plant (vert.) 35 10
4454. 4 k. Formula and ammonia plant, Nevynomyssk chemical works (vert.) 35 10

1975. 150th Anniv of Decembrist Rising.
4455 **1718** 4 k. multicoloured .. 20 10

1975. New Year.
4456. **1719.** 4 k. multicoloured .. 10 10

1720. "Village Street".

1975. 125th Birth Anniv of F. A. Vasilev (painter). Multicoloured.
4457. 2 k. Type **1720** 10 10
4458. 5 k. " Forest Path " .. 15 10
4459. 6 k. " After the Thunder-storm " .. 20 10
4460. 10 k. " Forest Marsh " (horiz.) .. 35 15
4461. 12 k. " In the Crimean Mountains " 45 20
4462. 16 k. " Wet Meadow " (horiz.) 60 30

1721. " Venus " Spacecraft.

1975. Space Flights of " Venus 9 " and " Venus 10 ".
4464. **1721.** 10 k. multicoloured 60 30

1722. G. Sundukyan.

1975. 150th Birth Anniv. of G. Sundukyan (Armenian playwright).
4465. **1722.** 4 k. multicoloured .. 10 10

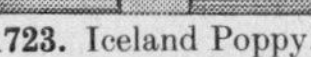

1723. Iceland Poppy. **1724.** A. L. Mints.

1975. Flowers (1st series). Multicoloured.
4466 4 k. Type **1723** 20 10
4467 6 k. Globe flower .. 25 10
4468 10 k. Yellow anemone .. 35 15
4469 12 k. Snowdrop wind-flower 40 20
4470 16 k. "Eminium lehemannii" 50 30
See also Nos. 4585/9.

1975. A. L. Mints (scientist) Commemoration.
4471. **1724.** 4 k. brown and gold 10 10

1725. " Demon " (A. Kochupalov). **1726.** Pieck.

1975. Miniatures from Palekh Village (1st series). Multicoloured.
4472 4 k. Type **1725** 20 10
4473 6 k. "Vasilisa the Beautiful" (I. Vakurov) .. 30 10
4474 10 k. "The Snow Maiden" (T. Zubkova) 40 15
4475 16 k. "Summer" (K. Kukulieva) 55 25
4476 20 k. "Fisherman and Goldfish" (I. Vakurov) (horiz) 60 30
See also Nos. 4561/5.

1975. Birth Centenary of Wilhelm Pieck (President of German Democratic Republic).
4477. **1726.** 6 k. black 15 10

1727. M. E. Saltykov-Shchedrin. **1728.** Congress Emblem.

1976. 150th Birth Anniv. of M. Saltykov-Shchedrin (writer).
4478. **1727.** 4 k. multicoloured .. 15 10

1976. 25th Communist Party Congress, Moscow (1st issue).
4479 **1728** 4 k. gold, brn & red 10 10
See also Nos. 4489 and 4556/60.

1729. Lenin (statue), Kiev. **1730.** Ice Hockey.

1976. 25th Ukraine Communist Party Congress, Kiev.
4481. **1729.** 4 k. black, red & blue 10 10

1976. Winter Olympic Games, Innsbruck (1st series). Multicoloured.
4482 2 k. Type **1730** 15 10
4483 4 k. Skiing 20 10
4484 6 k. Figure skating .. 25 10
4485 10 k. Speed skating .. 35 15
4486 20 k. Tobogganing .. 75 35

1731. Marshal C. E. Voroshilov. **1732.** Congress Hall and Red Banner.

1976. 95th Birth Anniv. of Marshal C. E. Voroshilov.

4488. **1731.** 4 k. green 15 10

1976. 25th Communist Party Congress, Moscow (2nd issue).

4489 **1732** 20 k. orge, red & grn 3·00 2·25

1733. " Lenin on Red Square " (P. Vasiliev).

1976. 106th Birth Anniv. of Lenin.

4490. **1733.** 4 k. multicoloured .. 15 10

1734. Atomic Symbol and Institute Emblem.

1976. 20th Anniv. of Joint Institute of Nuclear Research, Dubna.

4491. **1734.** 6 k. multicoloured .. 20 10

1736. Bolshoi Theatre.

1976. Bicentenary of Bolshoi Theatre.

4493 **1736** 10 k. bl, brn & ochre 30 20

1737. " Back from the Fair ".

1976. Birth Centenary of P. P. Konchalovsky (painter). Multicoloured.

4494. 1 k. Type **1737** 10 10
4495. 2 k. " The Green Glass " 10 10
4496. 6 k. " Peaches " 20 10
4497. 16 k. " Meat, Game and Vegetables by the Window " 55 30
4498. 20 k. Self-portrait (vert.) 75 35

1738. " Vostok ", " Salyut ", and " Soyuz " Spacecraft.

1976. 15th Anniv of First Manned Space Flight by Yuri Gagarin.

4499 4 k. Type **1738** 15 10
4500 6 k. "Meteor" and "Molniya" satellites .. 20 10
4501 10 k. Cosmonauts on board "Salyut" space-station 35 15
4502 12 k. "Interkosmos" satellite and "Apollo"–"Soyuz" space link .. 45 20

1739. I. A. Dzhavakhishvili. **1740.** S. Vurgun.

1976. Birth Centenary of I. A. Dzhavakhishvili (scientist).

4504. **1739.** 4 k. black, stone and green .. 10 10

1976. 70th Birth Anniv. of Samed Vurgun (Azerbaijan poet).

4505. **1740.** 4 k. black, brown and green .. 10 10

1741. Festival Emblem. **1742.** F.I.P. Emblem.

1976. First All-Union Amateur Art Festival.

4506. **1741.** 4 k. multicoloured .. 10 10

1976. 50th Anniv of International Philatelic Federation.

4507 **1742** 6 k. red and blue .. 15 10

1744. Dnepropetrovsk Crest. **1745.** N. N. Burdenko.

1976. Bicentenary of Dnepropetrovsk.

4509. **1744.** 4 k. multicoloured 15 10

1976. Birth Centenary of N. N. Burdenko (neurologist).

4510. **1745.** 4 k. brown and red 15 10

1746. K. A. Trenev. **1748.** Electric Railway Train.

1747. Canoeing.

1976. Birth Cent. of K. A. Trenev (playwright).

4511. **1746.** 4 k. multicoloured .. 10 10

1976. History of Soviet Motor Industry (4th series). As T **1609**.

4512 2 k. black, red and green 10 10
4513 3 k. black, orange & bistre 15 10
4514 4 k. black, buff and blue 15 10
4515 12 k. black, green & brn 45 15
4516 16 k. black, red & yellow 65 25

DESIGNS: 2 k. Moscow Auto Works "ZIS-110" saloon, 1945. 3 k. Gorkovsky "GAZ-51" truck, 1946. 4 k. Gorkovsky "GAZ-M20 (Pobeda)" saloon, 1946. 12 k. Moscow Auto Works "ZIS-150" truck, 1947. 16 k. Moscow Auto Works "ZIS-154" bus, 1947.

1976. Olympic Games, Montreal. Mult.

4517. 4 k. Type **1747** 10 10
4518. 6 k. Basketball (vert.) .. 20 10
4519. 10 k. Graeco-Roman wrestling 25 15
4520. 14 k. Discus-throwing (vert.) 30 15
4521. 16 k. Rifle-shooting .. 35 20

1976. 50th Anniv. of Soviet Railway Electrification.

4523. **1748.** 4 k. black, red and green 30 10

1749. L. M. Pavlichenko. **1750.** L. E. Rekabarren.

1976. 60th Birth Anniv. of L. M. Pavlichenko (war heroine).

4524. **1749.** 4 k. brown, yellow and silver .. 15 10

1976. Birth Centenary of Luis Rekabarren (founder of Chilean Communist Party).

4525. **1750.** 6 k. blk., red & gold 15 10

1751. " Fresh Partner ".

1976. Russian Art. Paintings by P. A. Fedotov. Mult.

4526. 2 k. Type **1751** 10 10
4527. 4 k. " Fastidious Fiancee " (horiz.) 15 10
4528. 6 k. " Aristocrat's Breakfast " 20 10
4529. 10 k. " The Gamblers " (horiz.) 35 20
4530. 16 k. " The Outing " .. 50 30

1752. S. S. Nametkin. **1753.** Soviet Armed Forces Order.

1754. Marx and Lenin (sculpture, Ye Belostotsky and E. Fridman).

1976. Birth Centenary of Sergei S. Nametkin (chemist).

4532 **1752** 4 k. black, yell & blue 15 10

1976.

(a) As T **1753**.

4533 1 k. olive 10 10
4670 2 k. mauve 10 10
4671 3 k. red 10 10
4672 4 k. red 10 10
4673 6 k. blue 15 10
4674 10 k. green 25 10
4675 12 k. blue 25 10
4676 15 k. blue 50 10
4677 16 k. green 35 15

(b) As T **1754**.

4678 20 k. red 50 10
4679 30 k. red 70 20
4680 32 k. blue 90 30
4681 50 k. brown .. .. 1·10 40
4682 1 r. blue .. .. .. 2·25 1·00

DESIGNS: 2 k. Gold Star (military) and Hammer and Sickle (labour) decorations. 3 k. "Worker and Farmer" (sculpture). 4 k. Soviet crest. 6 k. Globe and Tupolev Tu-154 aircraft (Soviet postal communications). 10 k. Soviet Reputation for Work order. 12 k. Yuri Gagarin and rocket (space exploration). 15 k. Ostankino T.V. tower and globe. 16 k. International Lenin Prize medal (international peace and security). 30 k. Council for Mutual Economic Aid building. 32 k. "Tu-114" aircraft and compass rose. 50 k. Lenin (after P. Zhukov). 1 r. Satellites orbiting globe.

The 6 and 32 k. are airmail stamps.

1755. Cattle Egret. **1756.** Peace Dove with Laurel.

1976. Water Birds. Multicoloured.

4545. 1 k. Type **1755** 20 15
4546. 3 k. Black-throated Diver 25 15
4547. 4 k. Common Coot .. 40 15
4548. 6 k. Atlantic Puffin .. 65 20
4549. 10 k. Slender-billed Gull 1·10 30

1976. 2nd Stockholm World Peace Appeal.

4550. **1756.** 4 kl blue, yell. & gold 10 10

1757. Federation Emblem.

1976. 25th Anniv. of International Resistance Movement Federation.

4551. **1757.** 6 k. blk., gold & bl. 15 10

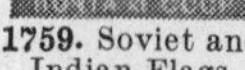

1759. Soviet and Indian Flags. **1761.** UNESCO Emblem.

1760. B. V. Volynov and V. M. Zholobov.

1976. Soviet–Indian Friendship.

4553. **1759.** 4 k. multicoloured .. 10 10

1976. Space Flight of " Soyuz 21 ".

4554. **1760.** 10 k. blk., bl. & brn. 30 15

1976. 30th Anniv. of UNESCO.

4555. **1761.** 16 k. brn., bistre & bl. 40 20

1762. " Industry ".

1976. 25th Communist Pary Congress (3rd issue).

4556 **1762** 4 k. brn, red & yell 15 10
4557 – 4 k. green, red & orge 15 10
4558 – 4 k. vio, red & pink 15 10
4559 – 4 k. deep red, red and grey 15 10
4560 – 4 k. violet, red & bl 15 10

DESIGNS: No. 4557, "Agriculture". 4558, "Science and Technology". 4559, "Transport and Communications". 4560, "International Co-operation".

1763. " The Ploughman " (I. Golikov).

1976. Miniatures from Palekh Art Museum (2nd series). Multicoloured.

4561.	2 k. Type **1763**	10	10
4562.	4 k. " The Search " (I. Markichev) (vert.) ..	15	10
4563.	12 k. " The Firebird " (A. Kotuchin)	40	20
4564.	14 k. " Folk Festival " (A. Vatagin) (vert.) ..	45	25
4565.	20 k. " Victory " (I. Vakurov) (vert.) ..	70	35

1764. Shostakovich and part of 7th Symphony. 1765. G. K. Zhukov.

1976. 70th Birth Anniv of Dmitri Shostakovich (composer).

4566	**1764**	6 k. blue	30	10

1976. 80th Birth Anniversaries of Soviet Marshals.

4567.	**1765.**	4 k. green	15	10
4568.	–	4 k. brown	15	10

DESIGN: No. 4568, K. K. Rokossovsky.

1766. " Interkosmos 14 " Satellite. 1767. V. I. Dal.

1976. International Co-operation in Space Research.

4569	**1766**	6 k. blue, gold & blk	20	10
4570	–	10 k. vio, gold & blk	25	10
4571	–	12 k. pur, gold & blk	35	15
4572	–	16 k. grn, gold & blk	40	15
4573	–	20 k. mve, gold & blk	50	20

DESIGNS: 10 k. "Aryabhata" (Indian satellite). 12 k. "Apollo"–"Soyuz" space link. 16 k. "Aureole" (French satellite). 20 k. Globe and spacecraft.

1976. 175th Birth Anniv. of V. I. Dal (scholar).

4574.	**1767.**	4 k. green	15	10

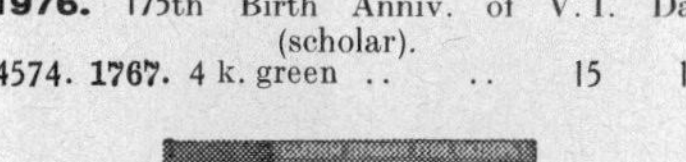

1768. Electric Power Station.

1976. 59th Anniv. of October Revolution. Multicoloured.

4575.	4 k. Type **1768**	15	10
4576.	4 k. Balashovo fabrics factory	15	10
4577.	4 k. Irrigation ditch construction	15	10

1769. Medicine Emblem. 1770. M. A. Novinsky (oncologist).

1976. 50th Anniv. of Petrov Institute of Cancer Research.

4578	**1769**	4 k. lilac, gold & blue	20	10

1976. Cent. of Cancer Research.

4579.	**1770.**	4 k. brn., bl. & buff	20	10

1771. " Gakkel VII ", 1911.

1976. Early Russian Aircraft (2nd series). Multicoloured.

4580.	3 k. Type **1771**	10	10
4581.	6 k. Gakkel "IX", 1912	20	10
4582.	12 k. Steglau's "No. 2", 1912	35	15
4583.	14 k. Dybovsky's "Dolphin", 1913	50	15
4584.	16 k. Dybovsky's "Il'ya Muromets", 1914 ..	55	25

See also Nos. 4661/6 and 4791/6.

1976. Flowers (2nd series). As T **1723**. Mult.

4585	1 k. Safflower	10	10
4586	2 k. Anemone	10	10
4587	3 k. Gentian	10	10
4588	4 k. Columbine	15	10
4589	6 k. Fitillaria	20	10

1772. New Year Greeting.

1976. New Year.

4590.	**1772.**	4 k. multicoloured ..	10	10

1773. " Parable of the Vineyard."

1976. 370th Birth Anniv. of Rembrandt. Multicoloured.

4591.	4 k. Type **1773**	15	10
4592.	6 k. " Danae "	20	10
4593.	10 k. " David and Jonathan " (vert.) ..	30	10
4594.	14 k. " The Holy Family " (vert.)	45	15
4595.	20 k. " Adrian " (vert.) ..	65	25

1774. " Luna 24 " and Emblem.

1976. "Luna 24" Unmanned Space Flight to Moon

4597.	**1774.**	10 k. brown, yellow and blue	30	15

1775. "Pailot".

1976. Russian Ice-breakers (1st series). Mult.

4598.	4 k. Type **1775** ..	40	10
4599.	6 k. "Ermak" (vert.) ..	50	10
4600.	10 k. "Fedor Litke" ..	70	15
4601.	16 k. "Vladmir Ilich" (vert.)	95	25
4602.	20 k. "Krasin"	1·25	45

See also Nos. 4654/60, 4843/8 and 5147.

1776. " Raduga " Experiment and Cosmonauts.

1976. "Soyuz 22" Space Flight by V. F. Bykovsky and V. V. Aksenov.

4603	**1776**	10 k. green, bl & red	30	15

1777. Olympic Torch.

1976. Olympic Games, Moscow (1980).

4604	**1777**	4 k.+2 k. black, red and blue	15	10
4605	–	10 k.+5 k. black, blue and red ..	45	25
4606	–	16 k.+6 k. black, mauve and yellow	60	40

DESIGNS: 10, 16 k. Games emblem.

1778. Society Emblem and " Red Star ". 1779. S. P. Korolev Memorial Medallion.

1977. 50th Anniv. of Red Banner (Forces Voluntary Society).

4608.	**1778.**	4 k. multicoloured	15	10

1977. 70th Birth Anniv, of S.P. Korolev (scientist and rocket pioneer).

4609.	**1779.**	4 k. gold, blk. & bl.	15	10

1780. Congress Emblem.

1977. World Peace Congress, Moscow.

4610.	**1780.**	4 k. gold. utram. & bl.	10	10

1781. Sedov and "Sv. Foka".

1977. Birth Cent. of G. Y. Sedov (polar explorer).

4611.	**1781.**	4 k. multicoloured	1·10	20

1782. Working Class Monument, Red Flag and Newspaper Cover. 1783. Ship on Globe.

1977. 60th Anniv. of Newspaper "Izvestiya".

4612.	**1728.**	4 k. blk., red & sil.	10	10

1977. 24th International Navigation Congress, Leningrad.

4613.	**1783.**	6 k. blue, blk. & gold	20	10

1784. Kremlin Palace of Congresses, Moscow. 1785. L. A. Govorov.

1977. 16th Soviet Trade Unions Congress.

4614.	**1784.**	4 k. gold, blk. & red	10	10

1977. 80th Birth Anniv. of Marshal L. A. Govorov.

4615.	**1785.**	4 k. brown	15	10

1786. Academy Emblem, Text and Building.

1977. 150th Anniv. of Grechko Naval Academy, Leningrad.

4616.	**1786.**	6 k. multicoloured ..	15	10

1787. J. Labourbe. 1788. Chess Pieces.

1977. Birth Centenary of Jeanne Labourbe (French communist).

4617.	**1787.**	4 k. blk., bl. & red	10	10

1977. Sixth European Chess Team Championship, Moscow.

4618.	**1788.**	6 k. multicoloured ..	50	10

1789. " Soyuz 23 " and Cosmonauts.

1977. " Soyuz 23 " Space Flight by V. D. Zudov and V. I. Rozhdestvensky.

4619	**1789**	10 k. red, blk & brn	30	15

1790. Novikov-Priboi. 1791. " Welcome " (N. M. Soloninkin).

1977. Birth Centenary of Aleksei Novikov-Priboi (writer).

4620	**1790**	4 k. black, orge & bl	10	10

1977. Folk Paintings from Fedoskino Village. Multicoloured.

4621.	4 k. Type **1791** ..	15	10
4622.	6 k. " Along the Street " (V. D. Antonov) (horiz.)	20	10
4623.	10 k. " Northern Song " (J. V. Karapaev) ..	30	15
4624.	12 k. " Fairy Tale about Tzar Saltan " (A. I. Kozlov) ..	30	15
4625.	14 k. " Summer Troika " (V. A. Nalimov) (horiz.)	40	20
4626.	16 k. " Red Flower " (V. D. Lipitsky) ..	45	25

1792. Congress Emblem.

1977. World Electronics Congress, Moscow.

4627	**1792**	6 k. red, grey & blue	15	10

1793. "In Red Square" (K. V. Filatov).

1977. 107th Birth Anniv. of Lenin.
4628. **1793.** 4 k. multicoloured 15 10

1794. Yuri Gagarin and Spacecraft.

1977. Cosmonautics Day.
4629. **1794.** 6 k. blue, lilac and purple 25 15

1295. N. I. Vavilov. **1796.** F. E. Dzerzhinsky.

1977. 90th Birth Anniv. of N. I. Vavilov (biologist).
4630. **1795.** 4 k. black and brown 10 10

1977. Birth Centenary of Feliks Dzerzhinsky (founder of Cheka).
4631 **1796** 4 k. black 10 10

1797. Mountain Saxifrage. **1798.** V. V. Gorbatko and Yu. N. Glazkov (cosmonauts).

1977. Flowers. Multicoloured.
4632 2 k. Type **1797** 10 10
4633 3 k. Pinks 10 10
4634 4 k. "Novosieversia glacialis" 15 10
4635 6 k. "Cerastium maximum" 20 10
4636 16 k. "Rhododendron aureum" 60 25

1977. "Soyuz 24-Salyut 5" Space Project.
4637. **1798.** 10 k. blk., red & blue 50 15

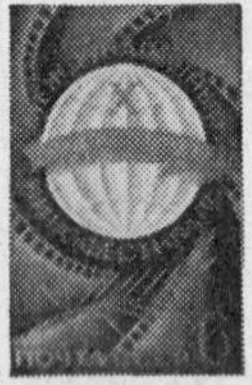

1799. I. S. Konev. **1800.** Festival Emblem.

1977. 80th Birth Anniv. of Soviet Marshals.
4638. **1799.** 4 k. green 15 10
4639. – 4 k. black 15 10
4640. – 4 k. brown 15 10
DESIGNS: No. 4639, V. D. Sokolovsky. No. 4640, K. A. Meretskov.

1977. 10th International Film Festival, Moscow.
4641. **1800.** 6 k. gold, red & lake 15 10

1801. Greco-Roman Wrestling.

1977. Olympic Sports (1st series).
4642. **1801.** 4 k. + 2 k. black, ochre and gold .. 15 10
4643. – 6 k. + 3 k. black, green and gold .. 20 10
4644. – 10 k. + 5 k. black, mauve and gold 35 20
4645. – 16 k. + 6 k. black, blue and gold .. 55 30
4646. – 20 k. + 10 k. black, brown and gold .. 1·25 65
DESIGNS: 6 k. Free-style wrestling. 10 k. Judo. 16 k. Boxing. 20 k. Weightlifting.
See also Nos. 4684/9, 4749/53, 4820/4, 4870/4, 4896/4900, 4962/6 and 4973/7.

1802. "Portrait of a Chambermaid". **1804.** Stamps and Emblem.

1977. 400th Birth Anniv. of Rubens. Mult.
4647. 4 k. Type **1802** 15 10
4648. 6 k. "The Lion Hunt" (horiz.) 20 10
4649. 10 k. "Stone Carriers" (horiz.) 25 10
4650. 12 k. "Water and Earth Alliance" 40 15
4651. 20 k. "Landscape with Rainbow" (horiz.) .. 60 35

1977. Soviet Ice-breakers (2nd series). As T **1775**. Multicoloured.
4654 4 k. "Aleksandr Sibiryakov" .. 25 10
4655 6 k. "Georgy Sedov" .. 30 10
4656 10 k. "Sadko" 55 10
4657 12 k. "Dezhnev" 65 15
4658 14 k. "Sibir" 75 20
4659 16 k. "Lena" 90 30
4660 20 k. "Amguema" .. 1·10 40

1977. Air. Early Soviet Aircraft (3rd series). As T **1771**, but dated 1977.
4661. 4 k. blk., brn. and blue .. 15 10
4662. 6 k. blk., orge. and grn. .. 25 10
4663. 10 k. blk., mauve & blue 30 10
4664. 12 k. black, blue & red .. 35 15
4665. 16 k. multicoloured .. 50 15
4666. 20 k. black, green & blue 70 20
DESIGNS: 4 k. "P–IV–BIS" aeroplane, 1917. 6 k. "AK–1" aeroplane, 1924. 10 k. "R–3 (ANT–3)" aeroplane, 1925. 12 k. "TB–1 (ANT–4)" aeroplane, 1925. 16 k. "R–5" aeroplane, 1929. 20 k. "SH–2" flying-boat, 1930.

1977. "60th Anniv. of October Revolution" Philatelic Exhibition, Moscow.
4667. **1804.** 4 k. red, blue and brn. 10 10

1805. Buildings and Arms, Stavropol. **1807.** Yuri Gargarin and "Vostok" Spacecraft.

1977. Bicentenary of Stavropol.
4668. **1805.** 6 k. gold, red & grn. 15 10

1977. Olympic Sports (2nd series). As T **1801**.
4684. 4 k. + 2 k. blk., gold & red 20 10
4685. 6 k. + 3 k. blk., gold & blue 20 15
4686. 10 k. + 5 k. blk., gold & grn. 30 20
4687. 16 k. + 6 k. blk., gold & olive 50 30
4688. 20 k. + 10 k. blk., gold & pur. 1·10 65
DESIGNS—HORIZ. 4 k. Cycling. 10 k. Rifle-shooting. 16 k. Horse-jumping. 20 k. Fencing. VERT. 6 k. Archery.

1977. 20th Anniv. of Space Exploration.
4690. **1807.** 10 k. red, blue & brn. 30 15
4691. – 10 k. brn., blue & vio. 30 15
4692. – 10 k. red, pur. & grn. 30 15
4693. – 20 k. grn., brn. & red 55 25
4694. – 20 k. pur., red & blue 55 25
4695. – 20 k. red, blue & grn. 55 25
DESIGNS: No. 4691, Space walking. No. 4692, "Soyuz" spacecraft and "Salyut" space-station linked. No. 4693, "Proton 4" satellite. No. 4694, "Luna, Venus" and "Mars" space-stations. No. 4695, "Intercosmos 10" satellite and "Apollo" and "Soyuz" spacecraft linked.

1808. Carving from St. Dmitri Cathedral, Vladimir (12th-cent.).

1977. Russian Art. Multicoloured.
4697. 4 k. Type **1808** 15 10
4698. 6 k. Bracelet, Ryazan (12th-cent.) 20 15
4699. 10 k. Detail of Golden Gate from Nativity Cathedral, Suzdal (13th-cent.) .. 30 15
4700. 12 k. Detail from "Archangel Michael" (icon) (A. Rublev) (15th-cent.) 30 15
4701. 16 k. Gold and marble chalice made by I. Fomin (15th-cent.) 45 20
4702. 20 k. St. Basil's Cathedral, Moscow, (16th cent.) .. 55 20

1809. "Snow-flake" and Fir Twig. **1810.** Cruiser "Aurora".

1977. New Year.
4703. **1809.** 4 k. multicoloured .. 10 10

1977. 60th Anniv. of October Revolution.
4704. **1810.** 4 k. multicoloured .. 15 10
4705. – 4 k. black, red & gold 15 10
4706. – 4 k. black, red & gold 15 10
4707. – 4 k. multicoloured .. 15 10
DESIGNS: No. 4705, Statue of Lenin. No. 4706, Page of "Izvestiya", book by Brezhnev and crowd. No. 4707, Kremlin spire, star and fireworks.

1811. First Clause of U.S.S.R. Constitution.

1977. New Constitution.
4709 **1811** 4 k. yell, red & brn 10 10
4710 – 4 k. multicoloured .. 10 10
DESIGN: No. 4710, People of the U.S.S.R. welcoming new constitution.

1813. Postwoman and Post Code.

1977. Postal Communications. Mult.
4713. 4 k. Type **1813** 15 10
4714. 4 k. Letter collection .. 15 10
4715. 4 k. "Map-0" automatic sorting machine .. 15 10
4716. 4 k. Mail transport .. 15 10
4717. 4 k. Delivering the mail .. 15 10

1814. Red Fort, Delhi and Asokan Capital. **1815.** Monument, Kharkov.

1977. 30th Anniv. of Indian Independence.
4718. **1814.** 6 k. gold, pur. & red 20 10

1977. 60th Anniv. of Establishment of Soviet Power in the Ukraine.
4719. **1815.** 6 k. multicoloured 15 10

1816. Adder.

1977. Snakes and Protected Animals. Mult.
4720 1 k. Type **1816** 10 10
4721 4 k. Levantine viper .. 15 10
4722 6 k. Saw-scaled viper .. 20 10
4723 10 k. Central Asian viper 30 15
4724 12 k. Central Asian cobra 30 15
4725 16 k. Polar bear and cub 40 25
4726 20 k. Walrus and young 55 25
4727 30 k. Tiger and cub .. 60 30

1817. Olympic Emblem and Arms of Vladimir.

1977. 1980 Olympics. "Tourism around the Golden Ring" (1st issue). Multicoloured.
4728. 1 r. + 50 k. Type **1817** .. 3·00 2·00
4729. 1 r. + 50 k. Vladimir Hotel 3·00 2·00
4730. 1 r. + 50 k. Arms of Suzdal 3·00 2·00
4731. 1 r. + 50 k. Pozharsky monument .. 3·00 2·00
4732. 1 r. + 50 k. Arms of Ivanovo and Frunze monument 3·00 2·00
4733. 1 r. + 50 k. Monument to Revolutionary Fighters 3·00 2·00
See also Nos. 4828/31, 4850/3, 4914/17, 4928/9, 4968/9, 4981/2 and 4990/5.

1818. Combine Harvester. **1819.** Kremlin Palace of Congresses.

1978. 50th Anniv of "Gigant" Collective Farm, Rostov.
4734 **1818** 4 k. brown, red & yell 10 10

1978. 18th Leninist Young Communist League (Komsomol) Congress.
4735 **1819** 4 k. multicoloured .. 10 10

1820. Globe, Obelisk and Emblem.

1978. Eighth International Federation of Resistance Fighters Congress, Minsk.
4736. **1820.** 6 k. red, blue & blk. 15 10

1821. Red Army Detachment and Modern Sailor, Airman and Soldier.

1978. 60th Anniv. of Soviet Military Forces. Multicoloured.
4737. 4 k. Type **1821** 15 10
4738. 4 k. Defenders of Moscow monument (detail), Lenin banner and Order of Patriotic War 15 10
4739. 4 k. Soviet soldier .. 15 10

1822. " Celebration in a Village ".

1978. Birth Centenary of Boris M. Kustodiev (artist). Multicoloured.
4740 4 k. Type **1822** 15 10
4741 6 k. "Shrovetide" .. 20 10
4742 10 k. "Morning" (50×36 mm) 30 15
4743 12 k. "Merchant's Wife drinking Tea" (50×36 mm) 40 15
4744 20 k. "Bolshevik" (50×36 mm) 55 25

1823. Gubarev and Remek at Launch Pad. **1824.** " Soyuz " Capsules linked to " Salyut " Space Station.

1978. Soviet-Czech Space Flight. Mult.
4746. 6 k. Type **1823** 15 10
4747. 15 k. " Soyuz-28 " docking with " Salyut-6 " space station 35 15
4748. 32 k. Splashdown .. 75 35

1978. Olympic Sports (3rd series). As T **1801**. Multicoloured.
4749. 4 k.+2 k. Swimmer at start 15 10
4750. 6 k.+3 k. Diving (vert.) 20 10
4751. 10 k.+5 k. Water polo .. 40 15
4752. 16 k.+6 k. Canoeist .. 40 20
4753. 20 k.+10 k. Single sculls 1·10 70

1978. Cosmonautics Day.
4755. **1824.** 6 k. gold, blue and deep blue .. 15 10

1825. Shield and Luarel Wreath. **1826.** First Russian Locomotive and Designers.

1978. 9th World Congress of Trade Unions.
4756. **1825.** 6 k. multicoloured.. 15 10

1978. Russian Locomotives (1st series). Mult.
4757 1 k. Type **1826** 20 10
4758 2 k. "D series" freight train, 1845 .. .. 20 10
4759 3 k. First passenger locomotive, 1845 .. 20 10
4760 16 k. "Gv series" locomotive, 1863–7 .. 90 20
4761 20 k. "Bv series" passenger locomotive, 1863–7 .. .. .. 1·10 30
Nos. 4758/61 are horizontal designs.
See also Nos. 4861/5.

1828. " XI " and Laurel Branch. **1830.** I.M.C.O. Emblem.

1829. Tulip " Bolshoi Theatre ".

1978. 11th World Youth ad Students Festival, Havana.
4763 **1828** 4 k. multicoloured .. 10 10

1978. Moscow Flowers. Multicoloured.
4764. 1 k. Type **1829** 10 10
4765. 2 k. Rose " Moscow Morning " 10 10
4766. 4 k. Dahlia " Red Star " 10 10
4467. 10 k. Gladiolus " Moscovite " 35 15
4768. 12 k. Iris " To Il'ich's Anniversary " .. 45 15

1978. 20th Anniv of Intergovernment Maritime Consultative Organization, and World Maritime Day.
4769 **1830** 6 k. multicoloured .. 10 10

1831. " Salyut–6 " Space Station performing Survey Work. **1832.** " Space Meteorology ".

1978. " Salyut–6 " Space Station. Mult.
4770. 15 k. Type **1831**.. .. 40 30
4771. 15 k. Yu. V. Romanenko and G. M. Grechko .. 40 30
Nos. 4770/1 were issued in se-tenant pairs forming a composite design.

1978. Space Research. Multicoloured.
4772 10 k. Type **1832** 30 15
4773 10 k. "Soyuz" orbiting globe ("Natural resources") 30 15
4774 10 k. Radio waves, ground station and "Molniya" satellite ("Communication") 30 15
4775 10 k. Human figure, "Vostok" orbiting Earth ("Medicine and biology") 30 15

1833. Transporting Rocket to Launch-site.

1978. Soviet–Polish Space Flight. Mult.
4777. 6 k. Type **1833** 15 10
4778. 15 k. Crystal (Sirena experiment) 40 15
4779. 32 k. Space station, map and scientific research ship " Cosmonaut Vladimir Komarov " 95 35

1834. Komsomol Awards. **1835.** M. V. Zakharov.

1978. 60th Anniv of Leninist Young Communist League (Komsomol). Mult.
4780. 4 k. Type **1834** 10 10
4781. 4 k. Products of agriculture and industry .. 20 10

1978. 80th Birth Anniv. of Marshal M. V. Zakharov.
4782. **1835.** 4 k. brown 15 10

1836. N. G. Chernyshevsky.

1978. 150th Birth Anniv of Nikolai G. Chernyshevsky (revolutionary).
4783 **1836** 4 k. brown and yellow 10 10

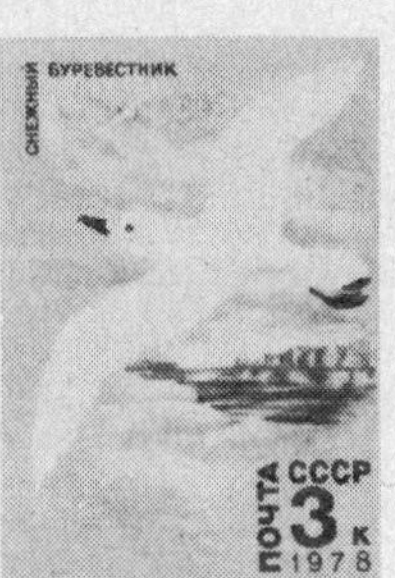

1837. Snow Petrel.

1978. Antarctic Fauna. Multicoloured.
4784. 1 k. Snares Island penguin (horiz.) .. 50 15
4785. 3 k. Type **1837** 65 15
4786. 4 k. Emperor penguin .. 80 15
4787. 6 k. White-blood pikes .. 70 10
4788. 10 k. Southern elephant-seal (horiz.) .. .. 1·25 15

1838. Torch and Flags. **1839.** William Harvey.

1978. Construction of Orenburg–U.S.S.R. Western Frontier Gas Pipe-line.
4789. **1838.** 4 k. multicoloured.. 10 10

1978. 400th Birth Anniv. of William Harvey (discoverer of blood circulation).
4790. **1839.** 6 k. grn., blk. & blue 15 10

1978. Air. Early Russian Aircraft (3rd series). As T **1771**.
4791 4 k. green, brown & black 15 10
4792 6 k. multicoloured .. 20 10
4793 10 k. yellow, blue & black 35 15
4794 12 k. orange, blue & black 40 15
4795 16 k. blue, dp blue & blk 50 15
4796 20 k. multicoloured .. 65 20
DESIGNS: 4 k. "U-2" biplane. 6 k. "K-5" airplane. 10 k. "TB-3 (Ant-6)" airplane. 12 k. "Stal-2" airplane. 16 k. "MBR-2" hydroplane. 20 k. "I-16" airplane.

1840. " Bathing of Red Horse ".

1978. Birth Centenary of K. S. Petrov-Vodkin (painter). Multicoloured.
4797 4 k. Type **1840** 10 10
4798 6 k. "Petrograd, 1918" .. 15 10
4799 10 k. "Commissar's Death" 25 15
4800 12 k. "Rose Still Life" .. 30 15
4801 16 k. "Morning Still Life" 40 15

1841. Assembling " Soyuz 31 ".

1978. Soviet-East German Space Flight. Multicoloured.
4803. 6 k. Type **1841** 15 10
4804. 15 k. Space photograph of Pamir mountains .. 35 15
4805. 32 k. Undocking from space station 80 35

1842. " Molniya 1 " Satellite, " Orbita " Ground Station and Aircraft.

1978. "PRAGA 78" International Stamp Exhibition.
4806. **1842.** 6 k. multicoloured.. 15 10

1843. Tolstoi.

1978. 150th Birth Anniv of Leo Tolstoi (novelist).
4807 **1843** 4 k. green 15 10

1844. Union Emblem. **1845.** Bronze Figure, Erebuni Fortress.

1978. 14th General Assembly of International Union for the Protection of Nature and Natural Resources, Ashkabad.
4808 **1844** 4 k. multicoloured .. 15 10

1978. Armenian Architecture. Multicoloured.
4809 4 k. Type **1845** 10 10
4810 6 k. Echmiadzin Cathedral 15 10
4811 10 k. Khachkary (carved stones) 25 15
4812 12 k. Matenadaran building (repository of manuscripts) (horiz) .. 35 15
4813 16 k. Lenin Square, Yerevan (horiz) .. 45 20

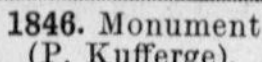

1846. Monument (P. Kufferge).

1847. Emblem, Ostankino TV Tower and Hammer and Sickle.

1978. 70th Anniv. of Russian Aid to Messina Earthquake Victims.
4814. **1846.** 6 k. multicoloured . . 20 10

1978. 20th Anniv. of Organization for Communication Co-operation.
4815. **1847.** 4 k. multicoloured . . 10 10

ФИЛВЫСТАВКА „60 лет ВЛКСМ"

МОСКВА. 1978

(1848.)

1978. "60th Anniv. of Komsomol" Philatelic Exhibition. Optd. with T **1848.**
4816. **1834.** 4 k. multicoloured . . 55 50

1851. Stepan Georgievich Shaumyan.

1852. "Star" Class Yacht.

1978. Birth Centenary of S. G. Shaumyan (Commissar).
4819. **1851.** 4 k. green 10 10

1978. Olympic Sports (4th series). Sailing Regatta, Tallin. Multicoloured.
4820. 4 k.+2 k. Type **1852** . . 20 10
4821. 6 k.+3 k. "Soling" class yacht 30 10
4822. 10 k.+5 k. "470" class yacht 40 15
4823. 16 k.+6 k. "Finn" class yacht 60 25
4824. 20 k.+10 k. "Flying Dutchman" class yacht . . 1·10 50

1853. Industrial Structures and Flag.

1854. Black Sea Ferry.

1978. 61st Anniv. of October Revolution.
4826. **1853.** 4 k. multicoloured . . 15 10

1978. Inauguration of Il'ichevsk–Varna, Bulgaria, Ferry Service.
4827. **1854.** 6 k. multicoloured . . 15 10

1855. Zagorsk.

1978. 1980 Olympics. "Tourism around the Golden Ring" (2nd issue). Multicoloured.
4828. 1 r.+50 k. Type **1855** . . 2·75 2·00
4829. 1 r.+50 k. Palace of Culture, Zagorsk . . . . 2·75 2·00
4830. 1 r.+50 k. Kremlin Rostov-Veliki . . . . 2·75 2·00
4831. 1 r.+50 k. View of Rostov-Veliki . . . . . . 2·75 2·00

1856. Church of the Intercession on River Nerl.

1978. "Masterpieces of Old Russian Culture". Multicoloured.
4832 6 k. Golden crater (horiz) 15 10
4833 10 k. Type **1856** 25 15
4834 12 k. "St. George and the Dragon" (15th-century icon) 30 15
4835 16 k. Tsar Cannon (horiz) 35 20

1857. Cup with Snake and Institute.

1859. Spasskky Tower, Kremlin.

1858. Nestor Pechersky and "Chronicle of Past Days".

1978. 75th Anniv of Herzen Oncology Research Institute, Moscow.
4836 **1857** 4 k. gold, pur & blk 15 10

1978. History of the Russian Posts. Mult.
4837. 4 k. Type **1858** 10 10
4838. 6 k. Birch-bark letter . . 15 10
4839. 10 k. Messenger with trumpet 25 15
4840. 12 k. Mail sledges . . 30 15
4841. 16 k. Interior of Prikaz Post Office 35 20

1978. New Year.
4842. **1859.** 4 k. multicoloured . . 10 10

1978. Soviet Ice-breakers (3rd series). As T **1775.** Multicoloured.
4843 4 k. "Vasily Pronchishchev" 20 10
4844 6 k. "Kapitan Belousov" (vert) 25 10
4845 10 k. "Moskva" 30 15
4846 12 k. "Admiral Makarov" 45 15
4847 16 k. "Lenin" atomic ice-breaker (vert) 65 20
4848 20 k. "Arktika" atomic ice-breaker 80 25

1860. V. Kovalenok and A. Ivanchenkov.

1978. "140 Days in Space".
4849. **1860.** 10 k. multicoloured 20 15

1978. 1980 Olympics. "Tourism around the Golden Ring" (3rd issue). As T **1855.** Multicoloured.
4850. 1 r.+50 k. Alexander Nevsky Monument, Pereslavl-Zalessky . . 2·75 2·00
4851. 1 r.+50 k. Peter I Monument, Pereslavl-Zalessky 2·75 2·00
4852. 1 r.+50 k. Monastery of the Transfiguration, Yaroslavl . . . . 2·75 2·00
4853. 1 r.+50 k. Ferry terminal and Eternal Glory Monument, Yaroslavl . . 2·75 2·00

1862. Cuban Flags.

1863. Government Building, Minsk.

1979. 20th Anniv. of Cuban Revolution.
4855. **1862.** 6 k. multicoloured . . 15 10

1979. 60th Anniv. of Byelorussian Soviet Socialist Republic and Communist Party.
4856. **1863.** 4 k. multicoloured . . 10 10

1864. Flags and Reunion Monument.

1866. Exhibition Hall and First Bulgarian Stamp.

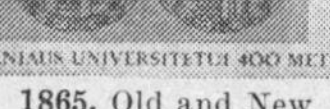

1865. Old and New University Buildings.

1867. Satellites "Radio 1" and "Radio 2".

1979. 325th Anniv. of Reunion of Ukraine with Russia.
4857. **1864.** 4 k. multicoloured 10 10

1979. 400th Anniv. of Vilnius University.
4858. **1865.** 4 k. black and pink 10 10

1979. "Philaserdica 79" International Stamp Exhibition, Sofia.
4859. **1866.** 15 k. multicoloured 30 15

1979. Launching of "Radio" Satellites.
4860. **1867.** 4 k. multicoloured . . 10 10

1868. "A" Series Passenger Locomotive.

1979. Railway Locomotives (2nd series). Multicoloured.
4861. 2 k. Type **1868** 15 10
4862. 3 k. "Shch" series locomotive 15 10
4863. 4 k. "L-Putilov" series locomotive 20 10
4864. 6 k. "Su" series locomotive 35 15
4865. 15 k. "L" series locomotive . . . . . . 1·00 35

1870. "Venera 12" over Venus.

1871. Albert Einstein.

1979. "Venera" Flights to Venus.
4867. **1870.** 10 k. red, lilac and purple 30 10

1979. Birth Centenary of Albert Einstein (physicist).
4868. **1871.** 6 k. multicoloured . . 20 10

1872. Congress Emblem.

1873. Free Exercise.

1979. 21st World Veterinary Congress, Moscow.
4869. **1872.** 6 k. multicoloured . . 15 10

1979. Olympic Sports (5th series). Gymnastics.
4870 **1873** 4 k.+2 k. brown, stone and orange 15 10
4871 – 6 k.+3 k. blue, grey and violet . . 20 10
4872 – 10 k.+5 k. red, stone and brown . . 30 15
4873 – 16 k.+6 k. mauve, grey and purple . . 40 15
4874 – 20 k.+10 k. red, stone and brown 75 65

DESIGNS: 6 k. Parallel bars. 10 k. Horizontal bar. 16 k. Beam. 20 k. Asymmetric bars.

1874. "To Arms" (poster by R. Beren).

1875. Cosmonauts at Yuri Gagarin Training Centre.

1979. 60th Anniv. of First Hungarian Socialist Republic.
4876. **1874.** 4 k. multicoloured . . 10 10

1979. Soviet-Bulgarian Space Flight Multicoloured.
4877. 6 k. Type **1875** . . 20 10
4878. 32 k. Landing of cosmonauts 75 35

1876. "Intercosmos".

1979. Cosmonautics Day.
4879. **1876.** 15 k. multicoloured 30 15

1878. Exhibition Emblem.

1979. U.S.S.R. Exhibition, London.
4881. **1878.** 15 k. multicoloured 25 15

1880. "AN-28" Short-haul Aircraft.

1979. Air. Soviet Aircraft. Multicoloured.

4883.	2 k. Type **1880**	10	10
4884.	3 k. "YAK–42" tri-jet	15	10
4885.	10 k. "TU–145" turbo-jet	35	15
4886.	15 k. "IL–76" cargo jet	50	20
4887.	32 k. "IL–86" widebody jet	85	35

1882. "Tent" Monument, Mining Institute, Pushkin Theatre and Blast Furnace.

1883. Child and Apple Blossom.

1979. 50th Anniv. of Magnitogorsk City.

4889. **1882.**	4 k. multicoloured ..	15	10

1979. International Year of the Child (1st issue).

4890. **1883.**	4 k. multicoloured ..	15	10

See also Nos. 4918/21.

1884. Bogorodsk Wood-carvings.

1979. Folk Crafts. Multicoloured.

4891.	2 k. Type **1884**	10	10
4892.	3 k. Khokhloma painted dish and jars	10	10
4893.	4 k. Zhostovo painted tray	15	10
4894.	6 k. Kholmogory bone-carvings	25	10
4895.	15 k. Vologda lace ..	45	35

1885. Football.

1979. Olympic Sports (6th series). Mult.

4896	**1885**	4 k.+2 k. blue, grey and orange ..	30	10
4897	–	6 k.+3 k. yellow, orange and blue ..	40	10
4898	–	10 k.+5 k. green, red and mauve ..	50	15
4899	–	16 k.+6 k. purple, blue and green ..	60	25
4900	–	20 k.+10 k. yellow, red and green ..	1·00	60

DESIGNS—VERT. 6 k. Basketball. 10 k. Volleyball. HORIZ. 16 k. Handball. 20 k. Hockey.

1886. Lenin Square Underground Station.

1979. Tashkent Underground Railway.

4901. **1886.**	4 k. multicoloured ..	20	10

1887. V. A. Dzhanibekov and O. G. Makarov.

1888. Council Building and Flags of Member Countries.

1979. "Soyuz 27–Salyut 6–Soyuz 26" Orbital Complex.

4902. **1887.**	4 k. multicoloured ..	20	10

1979. 30th Anniv. of Council of Mutual Economic Aid.

4903. **1888.**	16 k. multicoloured	30	15

1889. Scene from "Battleship Potemkin".

1892. Exhibition Hall and Film Still.

1979. 60th Anniv of Soviet Films (1st issue) and 11th International Film Festival, Moscow.

4904 **1889**	15 k. multicoloured ..	35	15

See also No. 4907.

1979. 60th Anniv of Soviet Films (2nd issue).

4907 **1892**	4 k. multicoloured ..	15	10

1893. "Lilac" (K. A. Korovin).

1894. John McClean.

1979. Flower Paintings. Multicoloured.

4908.	1 k. "Flowers and Fruits" (I. F. Khrutsky) (horiz.)	10	10
4909.	2 k. "Phloxes" (I. N. Kramskoi)	15	10
4910.	3 k. Type **1893**	15	10
4911.	15 k. "Bluebells" (S. V. Gerasimov)	40	20
4912.	32 k. "Roses" (P. P. Konchalovsky) (horiz.)	85	40

1979. Birth Centenary of John McClean (first Soviet consul for Scotland).

4913 **1894**	4 k. black and red ..	15	10

1979. 1980 Olympics. "Tourism around the Golden Ring" (4th issue). As T **1855**. Multicoloured.

4914.	1 r.+50 k. Narikaly Fortress, Tbilisi ..	3·00	2·10
4915.	1 r.+50 k. Georgian Philharmonic Society Concert Hall and "Muse" (sculpture), Tbilisi	3·00	2·10
4916.	1 r.+50 k. Chir-Dor Mosque, Samarkand ..	3·00	2·10
4917.	1 r.+50 k. People's Friendship Museum and "Courage" monument, Tashkent ..	3·00	2·10

1895. "Friendship" (Liberda Lena).

1979. Int. Year of the Child (2nd issue). Children's Paintings. Multicoloured.

4918.	2 k. Type **1895**	10	10
4919.	3 k. "After Rain" (Akhmetshina Dania)	10	10
4920.	4 k. "Dance of Friendship" (Elistratova Lilia)	15	10
4921.	15 k. "On the Excursion" (Smalyuk Vika) ..	35	20

1896. Golden Oriole.

1979. Birds. Multicoloured.

4922.	2 k. Type **1896**	25	10
4923.	3 k. Lesser Spotted Woodpecker	30	10
4924.	4 k. Crested Tit	35	10
4925.	10 k. Barn Owl	80	25
4926.	15 k. European Nightjar	1·10	40

1897. Soviet Circus Emblem.

1898. Marx, Engels, Lenin and View of Berlin.

1979. 60th Anniv. of Soviet Circus.

4927. **1897.**	4 k. multicoloured	20	10

1979. 1980 Olympics. "Tourism around the Golden Ring" (5th issue). As T **1855**. Multicoloured.

4928	1 r.+50 k. Relics of Yerevan's origin ..	3·00	2·10
4929	1 r.+50 k. Armenian State Opera and Ballet Theatre, Yerevan ..	3·00	2·10

1979. 30th Anniv. of German Democratic Republic.

4930 **1898**	6 k. multicoloured ..	20	10

1899. V. A. Lyakhov, V. V. Ryumin and "Salyut 6".

1979. Lyakhov and Ryumin's 175 Days in Space. Multicoloured.

4931	15 k. Type **1899**	30	20
4932	15 k. Radio-telescope mounted on "Salyut 6"	30	20

Nos. 4931/2 were issued together, se-tenant, forming a composite design.

1900. Hammer and Sickle.

1901. Communications Equipment and Signal Corps Emblem.

1979. 62nd Anniv. of October Revolution.

4933. **1900.**	4 k. multicoloured	15	10

1979. 60th Anniv. of Signal Corps.

4934. **1901.**	4 k. multicoloured	20	10

1902. "Katherine" (T. G. Shevchenko).

1903. Shabolovka Radio Mast, Moscow.

1979. Ukrainian Paintings. Multicoloured.

4935	2 k. Type **1902**	10	10
4936	3 k. "Into Service" (K. K. Kostandi)	15	10
4937	4 k. "To Petrograd" (A. M. Lopukhov) ..	30	10
4938	10 k. "Return" (V. N. Kostetsky) ..	30	15
4939	15 k. "Working Morning" (M. G. Belsky) ..	40	20

1979. 50th Anniv. of Radio Moscow.

4940. **1903.**	32 k. multicoloured	50	30

1904. Misha (Olympic mascot).

1905. "Peace" and Hammer and Sickle.

1979. New Year.

4941. **1904.**	4 k. multicoloured ..	15	10

1979. "Peace Programme in Action". Multicoloured.

4942.	4 k. Type **1905**	15	10
4943.	4 k. Hand holding demand for peace	15	10
4944.	4 k. Hands supporting emblems of peace ..	15	10

1906. Traffic Policeman.

1909. Industrial Landscape.

1907. "Vulkanolog".

1979. Road Safety. Multicoloured.

4945.	3 k. Type **1906**	20	10
4946.	4 k. Child playing in road	20	10
4947.	6 k. Speeding car out of control	35	10

1979. Soviet Scientific Research Ships. Multicoloured.

4948	1 k. Type **1907**	10	10
4949	2 k. "Professor Bogorov"	10	10
4950	4 k. "Ernst Krenkel" ..	15	10
4951	6 k. "Kosmonavt Vladislav Volkov" ..	30	10
4952	10 k. "Kosmonavt Yury Gagarin"	60	20
4953	15 k. "Akademik Kurchatov"	85	35

1980. 50th Anniv of Mordovian ASSR of Russian Federation.

4955 **1909**	4 k. red ..	15	10

1910. Speed Skating.

1911. Running.

1980. Winter Olympic Games, Lake Placid.

4956.	**1910.**	4 k. bl., brt. bl. & orge.	15	10
4957.	–	6 k. vio., bl. & orge.	15	10
4958.	–	10 k. red, bl. & gold	40	15
4959.	–	15 k. brn., bl. & turq.	50	15
4960.	–	20 k. turq., bl. & red	60	25

DESIGNS—HORIZ. 6 k. Figure skating (pairs). 10 k. Ice hockey. 15 k. Downhill skiing. VERT. 20 k. Luge.

1980. Olympic Sports (7th series). Athletics. Multicoloured.

4962.	4 k.+2 k. Type **1911** ..	20	10
4963.	6 k.+3 k. Hurdling ..	20	10
4964.	10 k.+5 k. Walking (vert.)	30	20
4965.	16 k.+6 k. High jumping	45	20
4966.	20 k.+10 k. Long jumping	80	60

1912. N. I. Podvoisky. 1915. Georg Ots.

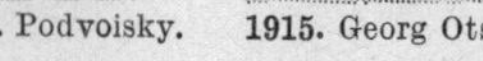

1913. " Rainbow " (A. K. Savrasov).
(Illustration Reduced. Actual size 74×38 mm.).

1980. Birth Centenary of Nikolai Ilich Podvoisky (revolutionary).
4967 1912 4 k. brown 15 10

1980. 1980 Olympics. "Tourism around the Golden Ring" (6th issue). As T **1855**. Multicoloured.
4968. 1 r.+50 k. Kremlin, Moscow .. .. 3·00 2·00
4969. 1 r.+50 k. Kalinin Prospect, Moscow .. .. 3·00 2·00

1980. Birth Anniversaries of Soviet Artists. Multicoloured.
4970 6 k. "Harvest-Summer" (A. G. Venetsianov, bicent) (vert) 15 10
4971 6 k. Type **1913** (150th anniv) 15 10
4972 6 k. "Old Yerevan" (M. S. Saryan, centenary) .. 15 10

1980. Olympic Sports (8th series). Athletics. As T **1911**. Multicoloured.
4973. 4 k.+2 k. Pole vaulting 20 10
4974. 6 k.+3 k. Discus throwing 20 10
4975. 10 k.+5 k. Javelin throwing 30 10
4976. 16 k.+6 k. Hammer throwing 45 20
4977. 20 k.+10 k. Putting the shot 80 45

1980. 60th Birth Anniv of Georg K. Ots (artist).
4980 1915 4 k. blue 10 10

1980. 1980 Olympics. "Tourism around the Golden Ring" (7th issue). As T **1855**. Multicoloured.
4981. 1 r.+50 k. St. Isaac's Cathedral, Leningrad 3·00 2·00
4982. 1 r.+50 k. Monument to the Defenders of Leningrad .. .. 3·00 2·00

1916. Order of Lenin. 1919. " Motherland " (detail of Heroes Monument, Volgograd).

1980. 50th Anniv. of Order of Lenin.
4983. **1916.** 4 k. multicoloured 10 10

1980. 35th Anniv. of World War II Victory. Multicoloured.
4986. 4 k. Type **1919** 15 10
4987. 4 k. Victory Monument, Treptow Park, Berlin 15 10
4988. 4 k. Victory Parade, Red Square, Moscow .. 15 10

1920. Government House, Arms and Flag of Azerbaijan. 1921. Monument, Ivanovo.

1980. 60th Anniv. of Azerbaijan Soviet Republic.
4989. **1920.** 4 k. multicoloured 10 10

1980. 1980 Olympics. "Tourism around the Golden Ring" (8th issue). As T **1855**. Multicoloured.
4990 1 r.+50 k. Bogdan Khmelnitsky Monument and St. Sophia Monastery, Kiev .. 2·50 2·00
4991 1 r.+50 k. Metro bridge over Dnieper, Kiev .. 2·50 2·00
4992 1 r.+50 k. Sports Palace and War Memorial, Minsk .. .. .. 2·50 2·00
4993 1 r.+50 k. House of Cinematography, Minsk 2·50 2·00
4994 1 r.+50 k. Old City, Tallin .. .. .. 2·50 2·00
4995 1 r.+50 k. Hotel Viru, Tallin .. .. .. 2·50 2·00

1980. 75th Anniv. of First Soviet of Workers' Deputies, Ivanovo.
4996. **1921.** 4 k. multicoloured .. 10 10

1922. Shield and Industrial Complexes. 1924. Title Page of Book.

1923. " YAK–24 " Helicopter.

1980. 25th Anniv. of Warsaw Treaty.
4997. **1922.** 32 k. multicoloured 65 30

1980. Helicopters. Multicoloured.
4998. 1 k. Type **1923** 10 10
4999. 2 k. " MI–8 " 10 10
5000. 3 k. " KA–26 " 20 10
5001. 6 k. " MI–6 " 30 10
5002. 15 k. " MI–10K " .. 80 20
5003. 32 k. " V–12 " .. .. 1·90 40

1980. 1500th Birth Anniv. of David Anacht (Armenian philosopher).
5004. **1924.** 4 k. multicoloured .. 10 10

1925. Medical Check-up of Cosmonauts. 1926. Red Fox.

1980. Soviet-Hungarian Space Flight. Multicoloured.
5005 6 k. Type **1925** 15 10
5006 15 k. Crew meeting on "Salyut-6" space station 35 15
5007 32 k. Press Conference .. 75 35

1980. Fur-bearing Animals. Multicoloured.
5008. 2 k. Type **1926** 10 10
5009. 4 k. Artic fox (horiz.) .. 15 10
5010. 6 k. European mink (horiz.) 20 10
5011. 10 k. Coypu 30 15
5012. 15 k. Sable (horiz.) .. 40 25

1927. Kazan. 1928. College and Emblem.

1980. 60th Anniv. of Tatar Republic.
5013. **1927.** 4 k. multicoloured 10 10

1980. 150th Anniv. of Bauman Technical College, Moscow.
5014. **1928.** 4 k. multicoloured 10 10

1929. Ho Chi Minh. 1930. Arms, Monument and Modern Buildings.

1980. 90th Birth Anniv. of Ho Chi Minh (Vietnamese leader).
5015. **1929.** 6 k. multicoloured 20 10

1980. 40th Anniv. of Soviet Socialist Republics of Lithuania, Latvia and Estonia. Multicoloured
5016. **1930.** 4 k. Lithuania .. 10 10
5017. – 4 k. Latvia 10 10
5018. – 4 k. Estonia .. 10 10

1933. Crew of "Soyuz 27" at launching site. 1934. Avicenna.

1980. Soviet–Vietnamese Space Flight. Multicoloured.
5019. 6 k. Type **1933** 15 10
5020. 15 k. Cosmonauts at work in space 40 20
5021. 32 k. Cosmonauts returning to Earth .. .. 1·40 60

1980. Birth Millenary of Avicenna (Arab philosopher and physician).
5022. **1934.** 4 k. multicoloured .. 10 10

1935. " Khadi-7 " Gas-turbine Car.

1980. Racing Cars designed by Kharkov Automobile and Road-building Institute. Multicoloured.
5023. 2 k. Type **1935** 10 10
5024. 6 k. " Khadi–10 " piston-engined car 20 10
5025. 15 k. " Khadi–11 E " electric car 55 20
5026. 32 k. " Khadi–13 E " electric car .. .. 1·00 40

1936. Arms, Flags, Government House and Industrial Complex.

1980. 60th Anniv. of Kazakh Soviet Socialist Republic.
5027. **1936.** 4 k. multicoloured .. 15 10

1937. " Self-portrait " and " The Spring ".

1980. Birth Bicentenary of Jean Ingres (French painter).
5028. **1937.** 32 k. multicoloured 65 35

1938. " Morning on Kulikovo Field " (A. Bubnov).

1980. 600th Anniv. of Battle of Kulikovo.
5029. **1938.** 4 k. multicoloured .. 15 10

1939. Town Hall. 1940. Yuri V. Malyshev and Valdimir V. Aksenov.

1980. 950th Anniv. of Tartu, Estonia.
5030. **1939.** 4 k. multicoloured .. 10 10

1980. " Soyuz T–2 " Space Flight.
5031. **1940.** 10 k. multicoloured 25 15

1941. Theoretical Training. 1942. Crew Training.

1980. 20th Anniv. of Gagarin Cosmonaut Training Centre. Multicoloured.
5032. 6 k. Type **1941** 15 10
5033. 15 k. Practical training .. 35 15
5034. 32 k. Physical endurance tests 65 40

1980. Soviet-Cuban Space Flight. Mult.
5035. 6 k. Type **1942** 15 10
5036. 15 k. Physical exercise on board space complex 30 15
5037. 32 k. Returned cosmonauts and space capsule 55 40

1943. " Bargaining " (Nevrev).
(Illustration reduced. Actual size 69×32 mm.).

1980. 150th Birth Anniv. of N. V. Nevrev and K. D. Flavitzky (painters). Multicoloured.
5038. 6 k. Type **1943** 20 10
5039. 6 k. " Princess Tarakanova " (Flavitzky) .. 20 10

1944. Vasilevsky. 1945. Banner.

1980. 85th Birth Anniv of Marshal A. M. Vasilevsky.
5040 1944 4 k. green 15 10

1980. 63rd Anniv. of October Revolution.
5041. **1945.** 4 k. red, gold & pur. 10 10

1946. Guramishvili. **1947.** Ioffe.

1980. 275th Birth Anniv. of David Guramishvili (Georgian poet).

5042. **1946.** 4 k. green, silver and black .. 10 10

1980. Birth Cent. of A. F. Ioffe (physicist).

5043. **1947.** 4 k. brown and buff 15 10

1948. Siberian Cedar.

1980. Trees. Multicoloured.

5044. 2 k. Type **1948** 10 10
5045. 4 k. Pedunculate oak .. 10 10
5046. 6 k. Lime (vert.) 10 10
5047. 10 k. Sea buckthorn .. 25 15
5048. 15 k. Ash 40 20

1950. Suvorov.

1980. 250th Birth Anniv. of Field Marshal A. V. Suvorov.

5050. **1950.** 4 k. blue 15 10

1951. State Emblem and Republican Government House. **1952.** Blok (after K. Somov).

1980. 60th Anniv. of Armenian Soviet Socialist Republic.

5051. **1951.** 4 k. multicoloured 10 10

1980. Birth Centenary of Aleksandr Aleksandrovich Blok (poet).

5052 **1952** 4 k. multicoloured .. 10 10

1980. Soviet Scientific Research Ships (2nd series). As T **1907**. Multicoloured.

5053 2 k. "Ayu-dag" 10 10
5054 3 k. "Valerian Uryvaev" 10 10
5055 4 k. "Mikhail Somov" .. 25 10
5056 6 k. "Akademik Sergei Korolev" 25 10
5057 10 k. "Otto Schmidt" .. 40 15
5058 15 k. "Akademik Mstislav Keldysh" 60 20

1953. Spassky Tower and Kremlin Palace of Congresses. **1955.** Sable in Cedar.

1980. New Year.

5059. **1953.** 4 k. multicoloured 10 10

1980. Perf or imperf (2 r.), perf (others).

5060 – 3 k. orange .. 10 10
5061 – 5 k. blue 15 10
5063 **1955** 35 k. olive .. 1·00 35
5064 – 45 k. brown .. 1·40 35
5066 – 50 k. green .. 1·50 70
5067 – 2 r. black .. .. 5·50 2·00
5068 – 3 r. black .. .. 6·50 3·00
5068a – 3 r. green .. .. 6·00 3·00
5069 – 5 r. blue .. .. 11·00 5·00

DESIGNS—14×22 mm. 3 k. State flag. 5 k. Forms of transport. 22×33 mm. 45 k. Spassky Tower. 50 k. Vodovzodny Tower and Grand Palace, Moscow Kremlin. 2 r. Atomic ice-breaker. 3 r. Globe, child and olive branch. 5 r. Globe and feather ("Peace").

1957. Institute Building.

1980. 50th Anniv. of Institute for Advanced Training of Doctors.

5075. **1957.** 4 k. multicoloured 15 10

1958. Lenin Monument, Leningrad, and Dneproges Hydro-electric Station. **1959.** Nesmeyanov.

1980. 60th Anniv. of GOELRO (electrification plan).

5076. **1958.** 4 k. multicoloured 10 10

1980. Academician A.N. Nesmeyanov (organic chemist) Commemoration.

5077. **1959.** 4 k. multicoloured 10 10

1960. Nagatinsky Bridge.

1980. Moscow Bridges. Multicoloured.

5078. 4 k. Type **1960** 15 10
5079. 6 k. Luzhniki underground railway bridge 25 10
5080. 15 k. Kalininsky bridge 45 20

1961. Timoshenko. **1962.** Indian and Russian Flags with Government House, New Delhi.

1980. 10th Death Anniv. of Marshal S. K. Timoshenko.

5081. **1961.** 4 k. purple 10 10

1980. President Brezhnev's Visit to India.

5082. **1962.** 4 k. multicoloured 10 10

MINIMUM PRICE

The minimum price quoted is 5p which represents a handling charge rather than a basis for valuing common stamps. For further notes about prices see introductory pages.

1963. Antarctic Research Station. **1964.** Arms and Symbols of Agriculture and Industry.

1981. Antarctic Exploration. Multicoloured.

5083. 4 k. Type **1963** 25 10
5084. 6 k. Antennae, rocket, weather balloon and tracked vehicle (Meteorological research) 50 10
5085. 15 k. Map of Soviet bases and supply ship .. 2·25 40

1981. 60th Anniv. of Dagestan Autonomous Soviet Socialist Republic.

5086. **1964.** 4 k. multicoloured 10 10

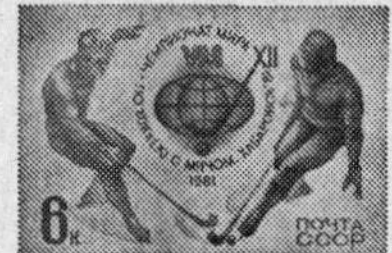

1965. Hockey Players and Emblem.

1981. 12th World Hockey Championships, Khabarovsk.

5087. **1965.** 6 k. multicoloured 15 10

1966. Banner and Star.

1981. 26th Soviet Communist Party Congress. Multicoloured.

5088. 4 k. Type **1966** 10 10
5089. 20 k. Kremlin Palace of Congresses and Lenin (51×36 mm.) .. 65 60

1967. Lenin and Congress Building. **1968.** Keldysh.

1981. 26th Ukraine Communist Party Congress.

5090. **1967.** 4 k. multicoloured 10 10

1981. 70th Birth Anniv of Academician Mstislav Vsevolodovich Keldysh (mathematician).

5091 **1968** 4 k. multicoloured .. 10 10

1970. Baikal-Amur Railway.

1981. Construction Projects of the 10th Five Year Plan. Multicoloured.

5093. 4 k. Type **1970** 20 10
5094. 4 k. Urengoi gas field .. 20 10
5095. 4 k. Sayano-Shushenskaya hydro-electric dam 20 10
5096. 4 k. Atommash Volga-Don atomic reactor .. 20 10
5097. 4 k. Syktyvkar paper mill 20 10
5098. 4 k. Giant excavator, Ekibastuz 20 10

1971. Freighter and Russian and Indian Flags.

1981. 25th Anniv. of Soviet-Indian Shipping Line.

5099. **1971.** 15 k. multicoloured 40 20

1972. Arms, Monument and Building.

1981. 60th Anniv. of Georgian Soviet Socialist Republic.

5100. **1972.** 4 k. multicoloured 10 10

1973. Arms and Abkhazian Scenes. **1974.** Institute Building.

1981. 60th Anniv. of Abkhazian Autonomous Soviet Socialist Republic.

5101. **1973.** 4 k. multicoloured 10 10

1981. 60th Anniv. of Moscow Electro-technical Institute of Communications.

5102. **1974.** 4 k. multicoloured 10 10

1975. Communications Equipment and Satellite. **1976.** L. I. Popov and V. V. Ryumin.

1981. 30th All-Union Amateur Radio Exhibition.

5103. **1975.** 4 k. multicoloured 10 10

1981. 185 Days in Space of Cosmonauts Popov and Ryumin. Multicoloured.

5104 15 k. Type **1976** .. 35 20
5105 15 k. "Salyut 6"–"Soyuz" complex 35 20

1977. O. G. Makarov, L. D. Kizim and G. M. Strekalov.

1981. "Soyuz T–3" Space Flight.

5106. **1977.** 10 k. multicoloured 30 15

1978. Rocket Launch.

1981. Soviet-Mongolian Space Flight. Multicoloured.

5107. 6 k. Type **1978** 20 10
5108. 15 k. Mongolians watching space flight on television 40 15
5109. 32 k. Re-entry stages .. 75 40

1979. Bering. **1980.** Yuri Gagarin and Globe.

1981. 300th Birth Anniv. of Vitus Bering (navigator).

5110. **1979.** 4 k. blue 25 10

1981. 20th Anniv. of First Manned Space Flight. Multicoloured.

5111. 6 k. Type **1980** 20 10
5112. 15 k. S. P. Korolev (spaceship designer) .. 40 15
5113. 32 k. Statue of Gagarin and "Interkosmos" emblem 75 40

1981. "Salyut" Orbital Space Station. **1983.** Prokofiev.

1981. 10th Anniv. of First Manned Space Station.

5115. **1981.** 32 k. multicoloured 75 40

1981. 90th Birth Anniv. of S. S. Prokofiev (composer).

5117. **1983.** 4 k. lilac 30 10

1984. New Hofburg Palace, Vienna. **1985.** Arms, Industrial Complex and Docks.

1981. "WIPA 1981" International Stamp Exhibition, Vienna.

5118. **1984.** 15 k. multicoloured 30 20

1981. 60th Anniv. of Adzharskian Autonomous Soviet Socialist Republic.

5119. **1985.** 4 k. multicoloured 10 10

1986. N. N. Benardos. **1987.** Congress Emblem.

1981. Cent. of Invention of Welding.

5120. **1986.** 6 k. multicoloured 15 10

1981. 14th Congress of International Union of Architects, Warsaw.

5121. **1987.** 15 k. multicoloured 30 20

1988. "Albanian Girl in Doorway". (A. A. Ivanov).

1981. Paintings. Multicoloured.

5122. 10 k. Type **1988** 30 15
5123. 10 k. "Sunset over Sea at Livorno" (N. N. Ge) (horiz.) 30 15
5124. 10 k. "Demon" (M. A. Vrubel) (horiz.) .. 30 15
5125. 10 k. "Horseman" (F. A. Rubo) 30 15

1989. Flight Simulator.

1981. Soviet-Rumanian Space Flight. Multicoloured.

5126. 6 k. Type **1989** 15 10
5127. 15 k. "Salyut"–"Soyuz" space complex .. 35 20
5128. 32 k. Cosmonauts greeting journalists after return 80 40

1990. "Primula minima".

1981. Flowers of the Carpathians. Mult.

5129. 4 k. Type **1990** 15 10
5130. 6 k. "Carlina acaulis" .. 20 10
5131. 10 k. "Parageum montanum" 35 15
5132. 15 k. "Atragene alpina" 50 20
5133. 32 k. "Rhododendron kotschyi" .. .. 1·00 50

1991. Gyandzhevi. **1992.** Longo.

1981. 840th Birth Anniv. of Nizami Gyandzhevi (poet and philosopher).

5134. **1991.** 4 k. brn., yell. & grn. 10 10

1981. Luigi Longo (Italian politician) Commemoration.

5135. **1992.** 6 k. multicoloured 15 10

1993. Running. **1994.** Flag and Arms of Mongolia.

1981. Sports. Multicoloured.

5136 4 k. Type **1993** 15 10
5137 6 k. Football 15 10
5138 10 k. Throwing the discus 25 15
5139 15 k. Boxing 40 20
5140 32 k. Swimmer on block 85 40

1981. 60th Anniv. of Revolution in Mongolia.

5141. **1994.** 6 k. multicoloured 15 10

1995. Spassky Tower and Film encircling Globe. **1996.** "Lenin".

1981. 12th International Film Festival, Moscow.

5142. **1995.** 15 k. multicoloured 35 15

1981. River Ships. Multicoloured.

5143 4 k. Type **1996** 20 10
5144 6 k. "Kosmonavt Gagarin" (tourist ship) 25 10
5145 15 k. "Valerian Kuibyshev" (tourist ship) 60 20
5146 32 k. "Baltysky" (tanker) 1·40 55

1981. Russian Ice-breakers (4th issue). As T **1775**. Multicoloured.

5147. 15 k. "Malygin" 65 15

1997. Industry.

1981. Resolutions of the 26th Party Congress. Multicoloured.

5148. 4 k. Type **1997** 15 10
5149. 4 k. Agriculture 15 10
5150. 4 k. Energy 15 10
5151. 4 k. Transport and communications 15 10
5152. 4 k. Arts and science .. 15 10
5153. 4 k. International co-operation 15 10

1998. Ulyanov. **2000.** Brushes, Palette and Gerasimov.

1999. Facade of Theatre.

1981. 150th Birth Anniv. of I. N. Ulyanov (Lenin's father).

5154. **1998.** 4 k. brn., blk. & grn. 10 10

1981. 225th Anniv. of Pushkin Drama Theatre, Leningrad.

5155. **1999.** 6 k. multicoloured 15 10

1981. Birth Centenary of A. M. Gerasimov (artist).

5156. **2000.** 4 k. multicoloured 10 10

2001. Institute Building.

1981. 50th Anniv. of Institute of Physical Chemistry, Academy of Sciences, Moscow.

5157. **2001.** 4 k. multicoloured 10 10

2002. Severtzov's Tit Warbler.

1981. Song Birds. Multicoloured.

5158. 6 k. Type **2002** 25 10
5159. 10 k. Asiatic paradise flycatcher (vert.) .. 25 15
5160. 15 k. Jankowski's bunting 60 30
5161. 20 k. Vinous-throated parrotbill (vert.) .. 75 40
5162. 32 k. Hodgson's bushchat (vert.) .. 1·40 60

2003. Arms and Industrial Scenes.

1981. 60th Anniv. of Komi A.S.S.R.

5163. **2003.** 4 k. multicoloured 30 10

2004. Orbiting Satellite and Exhibition Emblem.

1981. "Svyaz 81" Communications Exhibition.

5164. **2004.** 4 k. multicoloured 15 10

2005. Buildings, Arms and Monument. **2006.** Soviet Soldier (monument, Treptow Park, Berlin).

1981. 60th Anniv. of Kabardino-Balkar A.S.S.R.

5165. **2005.** 4 k. multicoloured 10 10

1981. 25th Anniv. of Soviet War Veterans Committee.

5166. **2006.** 4 k. multicoloured 10 10

2007. Four-masted Barque "Tovarishch".

1981. Cadet Sailing Ships. Multicoloured.

5167	4 k. Type **2007**	15	10
5168	6 k. Barquentine "Vega"	25	10
5169	10 k. Schooner "Kodor" (vert)	35	15
5170	15 k. Three-masted barque "Tovarishch" ..	50	20
5171	20 k. Four-masted barque "Kruzenshtern" ..	75	25
5172	32 k. Four-masted barque "Sedov" (vert) ..	1·10	50

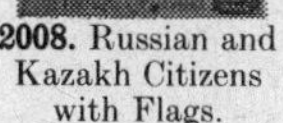

2008. Russian and Kazakh Citizens with Flags.

2209. Lavrentev.

1981. 250th Anniv. of Unification of Russia and Kazakhstan.

5173.	**2008.** 4 k. multicoloured	10	10

1981. Academician Mikhail Alekseevich Lavrentev (mathematician) Commemoration.

5174.	**2009.** 4 k. multicoloured	10	10

2010. Kremlin Palace of Congresses, Moscow, and Arch of the General Staff, Leningrad.

1981. 64th Anniv. of October Revolution.

5175.	**2010.** 4 k. multicoloured	10	10

2011. Transmitter, Dish Aerial and "Ekran" Satellite.

1981. "Ekran" Television Satellite.

5176.	**2011.** 4 k. multicoloured	10	10

2012. V. V. Kovalyonok and V. P. Savinykh.

2014. Merkurov.

1981. "Soyuz T-4"–"Salyut 6" Space Complex. Multicoloured.

5177.	10 k. Type **2012**	25	15
5178.	10 k. Microscope slide, crystal and text ..	25	15

1981. Birth Centenary of Sergei Dmitrievich Merkurov (sculptor).

5180.	**2012.** 4 k. brn., grn. & bis.	10	10

2015. "Autumn" (Nino A. Piromanashvili).

2016. Arms and Saviour Tower. Moscow.

1981. Paintings by Georgian Artists. Mult.

5181.	4 k. Type **2015**	15	10
5182.	6 k. "Gurian Woman" (Sh. G. Kikodze) ..	15	10
5183.	10 k. "Travelling Companions" (U. M. Dzhaparidze) (horiz.)	25	15
5184.	15 k. "Shota Rustaveli" (S. S. Kobuladze) ..	45	25
5185.	32 k. "Tea Pickers" (V. D. Gudiashvili) (horiz.)	90	45

1981. New Year.

5186.	**2016.** 4 k. multicoloured	10	10

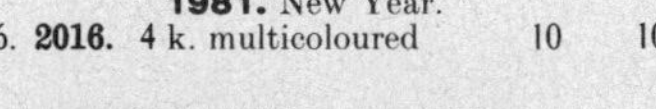

2017. Horse-drawn Sleigh (19th century).

1981. Moscow Municipal Transport.

5187.	**2017.** 4 k. brn. & silver	15	10
5188.	– 6 k. green and silver	20	10
5189.	– 10 k. lilac and silver	30	15
5190.	– 15 k. blk. & silver	45	20
5191.	– 20 k. brn. & silver	60	30
5192.	– 32 k. red and silver	90	50

DESIGNS: 6 k. Horse-drawn tram (19th century). 10 k. Horse-drawn cab (19th century) 15 k. Taxi, 1926. 20 k. British Leyland bus, 1926. 32 k. Electric tram, 1912.

2019. Modern Kiev.

1982. 1500th Anniv. of Kiev.

5194.	**2019.** 10 k. multicoloured	35	15

2020. S. P. Korolev.

2021. Arms and Industrial Complexes.

1982. 75th Birth Anniv. of Academician S. P. Korolev (spaceship designer).

5195.	**2020.** 4 k. multicoloured	15	10

1982. 60th Anniv. of Checheno-Ingush A.S.S.R.

5196.	**2021.** 4 k. multicoloured	15	10

2022. Arms and Construction Sites.

2023. Hikmet.

1982. 60th Anniv. of Yakut A.S.S.R.

5197.	**2022.** 4 k. multicoloured	15	10

1982. 80th Birth Anniv. of Nazim Hikmet (Turkish poet).

5198.	**2023.** 6 k. multicoloured	25	10

2024. "The Oaks".

1982. 150th Birth Anniv. of I. I. Shishkin (artist).

5199.	**2024.** 6 k. multicoloured	25	10

2025. Trade Unionists and World Map.

1982. Tenth World Trade Unions Congress, Havana.

5200.	**2025.** 15 k. multicoloured	40	20

2026. Kremlin Palace of Congresses and Flag.

2027. "Self-portrait".

1982. 17th Soviet Trade Unions Congress.

5201.	**2026.** 4 k. multicoloured	10	10

1982. 150th Birth Anniv. of Edouard Manet (artist).

5202.	**2027.** 32 k. multicoloured	80	40

2028. Show Jumping.

2029. Tito.

1982. Soviet Horse-breeding. Multicoloured.

5203.	4 k. Type **2028**	30	10
5204.	6 k. Dressage	30	10
5205.	15 k. Racing	60	25

1982. President Tito of Yugoslavia Commemoration.

5206.	**2029.** 6 k. brown & black	15	10

2030. University, Book and Monument.

1982. 350th Anniv. of University of Tartu.

5207.	**2030.** 4 k. multicoloured	10	10

2031. Heart on Globe. **2033.** Blackberry.

1982. Ninth International Cardiologists' Conference, Moscow.

5208.	**2031.** 15 k. multicoloured	45	20

1982. Wild Berries. Multicoloured.

5210.	4 k. Type **2033**	15	10
5211.	6 k. Blueberries	20	10
5212.	10 k. Cranberry	30	15
5213.	15 k. Cherry	45	25
5214.	32 k. Strawberry ..	1·10	55

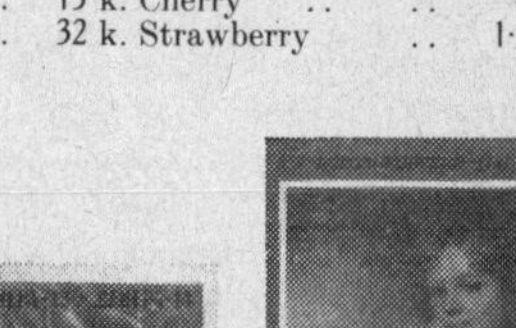

2034. "Venera 13" and "14".

2035. "M.I. Lopukhina" (V. L. Borovikovsky).

1982. "Venera" Space Flights to Venus.

5215	**2034** 10 k. multicoloured ..	30	15

1982. Paintings. Multicoloured.

5216.	6 k. Type **2035**	20	10
5217.	6 k. "E. V. Davydov" (O. A. Kiprensky) ..	20	10
5218.	6 k. "The Unequal Marriage" (V. V. Pukirev)	20	10

2036. Chukovsky.

2039. Solovev-Sedoi.

2037. Rocket, "Soyuz" Spaceship, Globe and Space Station.

1982. Birth Cent. of K. I. Chukovsky (author).

5219.	**2036.** 4 k. black and grey	15	10

1982. Cosmonautics Day.

5220.	**2037.** 6 k. multicoloured	20	10

1982. 75th Birth Anniv. of V. P. Solovev-Sedoi (composer).

5222.	**2039.** 4 k. brown	20	10

2040. Dimitrov.

2041. Masthead.

1982. Birth Centenary of Georgi Dimitrov (Bulgarian statesman).

5223.	**2040.** 6 k. green	15	10

1982. 70th Anniv. of "Pravda" (Communist Party newspaper).

5224.	**2041.** 4 k. multicoloured	15	10

2042. Congress Emblem and Ribbons.

2043. Globe and Hands holding Seedling.

1982. 19th Congress of Leninist Young Communist League (Komsomol).
5225. **2042.** 4 k. multicoloured .. 15 10

1982. 10th Anniv. of U.N. Environment Programme.
5226. **2043.** 6 k. multicoloured .. 15 10

2044. Pioneers.

2045. I.T.U. Emblem, Satellite and Receiving Station.

1982. 60th Anniv. of Pioneer Organization.
5227. **2044.** 4 k. multicoloured .. 10 10

1982. I.T.U. Delegates' Conference, Nairobi.
5228. **2045.** 15 k. multicoloured .. 40 20

2046. "VL80T" Electric Locomotive.

1982. Locomotives. Multicoloured.
5229. 4 k. Type **2046** 20 10
5230. 6 k. "TEP-75" diesel .. 25 10
5231. 10 k. "TEM-7" diesel .. 50 20
5232. 15 k. "VL82M" electric .. 75 30
5233. 32 k. "EP200" electric .. 1·75 60

2047. Players with Trophy and Football.

1982. World Cup Football Championship, Spain.
5234. **2047.** 20 k. lilac, yellow and brown .. 65 30

2048. Hooded Crane.

1982. 18th International Ornithological Congress, Moscow. Multicoloured.
5235. 2 k. Type **2048** 15 15
5236. 4 k. Steller's Sea Eagle .. 30 15
5237. 6 k. Spoon-billed Sand-piper 35 15
5238. 10 k. Bar-headed Goose 60 20
5239. 15 k. Sociable Plover .. 90 35
5240. 32 k. White Stork .. 2·10 75

2049. Buildings and Workers with Picks.

2051. U.N. Flag.

2050. "The Cart".

1982. 50th Anniv. of Komomolsk-on-Amur.
5241. **2049.** 4 k. multicoloured .. 15 10

1982. Birth Cent. of M. B. Grekov (artist).
5242. **2050.** 6 k. multicoloured .. 20 10

1982. Second U.N. Conference on the Exploration and Peaceful Uses of Outer Space, Vienna.
5243. **2051.** 15 k. multicoloured .. 40 20

2052. Scientific Research in Space.

1982. Soviet-French Space Flight. Mult.
5244. 6 k. Type **2052** 15 10
5245. 20 k. Rocket and trajectory 60 30
5246. 45 k. Satellites and globe 1·40 75

2053. "Legend of the Golden Cockerel" (P. I. Sosin).

1982. Lacquerware Paintings. Multicoloured.
5248. 6 k. Type **2053** 20 10
5249. 10 k. "Minin's Appeal to Count Pozharsky" (I. A. Fomichev) .. 30 20
5250. 15 k. "Two Peasants" (A. F. Kotyagin) .. 45 25
5251. 20 k. "The Fisherman" (N. P. Klykov) .. 60 35
5252. 32 k. "Arrest of the Propagandists" (N. I. Shishakov) 90 55

2054. Early Telephone, Moscow, Leningrad, Odessa and Riga.

2055. P. Schilling (inventor).

1982. Telephone Centenary.
5253. **2054.** 4 k. multicoloured .. 15 10

1982. 150th Anniv. of Electro-magnetic Telegraph in Russia.
5254. **2055.** 6 k. multicoloured .. 20 10

2056. Gymnast and Television Screen.

1982. Intervision Cup Gymnastics Contest.
5255. **2056.** 15 k. multicoloured 40 20

2057. "Mastyazhart" Glider.

2058. Garibaldi.

1982. Gliders (1st series). Multicoloured.
5256. 4 k. Type **2057** 20 10
5257. 6 k. "Red Star" 20 10
5258. 10 k. "Tsagi-2" 40 15
5259. 20 k. "Stakhanovets" (60 × 27 mm.) 90 35
5260. 32 k. "Gr-29" (60 × 27 mm.) .. .. 1·40 55
See Nos. 5301/5.

1982. 175th Birth Anniv of Giuseppe Garibaldi.
5261 **2058** 6 k. multicoloured .. 15 10

2059. Emblem.

2060. F.I.D.E. Emblem, Chess Symbol for Queen and Equestrian Statue.

1982. 25th Anniv. of International Atomic Energy Agency.
5262. **2059.** 20 k. multicoloured 50 30

1982. World Chess Championship Interzone Tournaments for Women (Tbilisi) and Men (Moscow). Multicoloured.
5263. 6 k. Type **2060** .. 35 15
5264. 6 k. F.I.D.E. emblem, chess symbol for King and Kremlin tower .. 35 15

2061. Shaposhnikov.

2062. Clenched Fist.

1982. Birth Centenary of Marshal B. M. Shaposhnikov.
5265. **2061.** 4 k. brown 15 10

1982. 70th Anniv. of African National Congress.
5266. **2062.** 6 k. multicoloured 20 10

2063. Botkin.

А. КАРПОВ — обладатель восьми „Шахматных Оскаров"

(**2065.**)

1982. 150th Birth Anniv. of S. P. Botkin (therapeutist).
5267. **2063.** 4 k. green 15 10

1982. A. Karpov's Victory in World Chess Championship. No. 5264 optd. with T **2065.**
5269. 6 k. multicoloured .. 50 35

2066. Submarine "S-56".

1982. Soviet Naval Ships. Multicoloured.
5270 4 k. Type **2066** 20 10
5271 6 k. Minelayer "Gremyashschy" .. 20 10
5272 15 k. Minesweeper "Gafel" 65 25
5273 20 k. Cruiser "Krasnyi Krim" 90 40
5274 45 k. Battleship "Sevastopol" .. .. 1·90 80

2067. Flag and Arms.

1982. 65th Anniv. of October Revolution.
5275. **2067.** 4 k. multicoloured 15 10

2068. House of the Soviets, Moscow.

1982. 60th Anniv. of U.S.S.R. Multicoloured.
5276. 10 k. Type **2068.** .. 30 20
5277. 10 k. Dneiper Dam and statue 30 20
5278. 10 k. Soviet war memorial and resistance poster .. 30 20
5279. 10 k. Newspaper, worker holding peace text, and sun illuminating city 30 20
5280. 10 k. Workers' Monument, Moscow, rocket, jet and factories 30 20
5281. 10 k. Soviet arms and Kremlin tower 30 20

Всесоюзная филателистическая выставка

(**2069.**)

1982. All-Union Stamp Exhibition, Moscow. No. 5280 optd. with T **2069.**
5282. 10 k. multicoloured .. 40 30

2070. "Portrait of an Actor" (Domenico Fetti).

2072. Hammer and Sickle, Clock and Date.

1982. Italian Paintings in the Hermitage Museum, Leningrad. Multicoloured.

5283	4 k. Type **2070**	15	10
5284	10 k. "St. Sebastian" (Pietro Perugino)	30	15
5285	20 k. "Danae" (Titian) (horiz)	60	30
5286	45 k. "Portrait of a Woman" (Correggio)	1·25	75
5287	50 k. "Portrait of a Young Man" (Capriolo)	1·40	85

1982. New Year.

5289. **2072.** 4 k. multicoloured 10 10

2075. Kherson Lighthouse, Black Sea.

2076. F. P. Tolstoi.

1982. Lighthouses (1st series). Multicoloured.

5292.	6 k. Type **2075**	40	15
5293.	6 k. Vorontsov lighthouse, Odessa, Black Sea	40	15
5294.	6 k. Temryuk lighthouse, Sea of Azov	40	15
5295.	6 k. Novorossiisk lighthouse, Black Sea	40	15
5296.	6 k. Dneiper harbour light	40	15

See also Nos. 5362/6 and 5449/53.

1983. Birth Bicentenary of Fyodor Petrovich Tolstoi (artist).

5297 **2076** 4 k. multicoloured 15 10

2077. Masthead of "Iskra".

2078. Army Star and Flag.

1983. 80th Anniv. of 2nd Social Democratic Workers' Congress.

5298. **2077.** 4 k. multicoloured 15 10

1983. 65th Anniv. of U.S.S.R. Armed Forces.

5299. **2078.** 4 k. multicoloured 15 10

1983. Gliders (2nd series). As T **2057.** Multicoloured.

5301.	2 k. "A-9" glider (1948)	10	10
5302.	4 k. "KAI-12" (1957)	15	10
5303.	6 k. "A-15" (1960)	20	10
5304.	20 k. "SA-7" (1970)	70	35
5305.	45 k. "LAK-12" (1979)	1·50	75

2080. "The Holy Family".

2081. B. N. Petrov.

1983. 500th Birth Anniv. of Raphael (artist).

5306. **2080.** 50 k. multicoloured 1·10 75

1983. 70th Birth Anniv. of Academician B. N. Petrov (chairman of Interkosmos).

5307. **2081.** 4 k. multicoloured 15 10

2082. Tashkent Buildings.

1983. 2000th Anniv. of Tashkent.

5308. **2082.** 4 k. multicoloured 15 10

2083. Popov, Serebrov and Savitskaya.

1983. "Soyuz T-7"—"Salyut 7"—"Soyuz T-5" Space Flight.

5309. **2083.** 10 k. multicoloured 30 15

2085. Aleksandrov and Bars of Music.

1983. Birth Centenary of A. V. Aleksandrov (composer).

5311. **2085.** 4 k. multicoloured 30 10

2086. "Portrait of an Old Woman".

1983. Rembrandt Paintings in Hermitage Museum, Leningrad. Multicoloured.

5312.	4 k. Type **2086**	15	10
5313.	10 k. "Portrait of a Learned Man"	30	15
5314.	20 k. "Old Warrior"	65	30
5315.	45 k. "Portrait of Mrs B. Martens Doomer"	1·25	75
5316.	50 k. "Sacrifice of Abraham"	1·40	85

2089. A.N. Berezovoi and V.V. Lebedev.

1983. 211 Days in Space of Berezovoi and Lebedev. Multicoloured.

5320.	10 k. Type **2089**	30	20
5321.	10 k. "Salyut 7"—"Soyuz T" space complex	30	20

2090. Marx.

1983. Death Centenary of Karl Marx.

5322. **2090.** 4 k. multicoloured 15 10

2091. Memorial, Building and Hydrofoil.

1983. Rostov-on-Don.

5323. **2091.** 4 k. multicoloured 15 10

2092. Kirov Theatre.

1983. Bicentenary of Kirov Opera and Ballet Theatre, Leningrad.

5324. **2092.** 4 k. blk., bl. & gold 30 10

2093. Arms, Communications and Industrial Complex.

1983. 60th Anniv. of Buryat A.S.S.R.

5325. **2093.** 4 k. multicoloured 20 10

2094. Sports Vignettes.

1983. Eight Summer Spartakiad.

5326. **2094.** 6 k. multicoloured 15 10

2095. Khachaturyan.

1983. 80th Birth Anniv. of Aram I. Khachaturyan (composer).

5327. **2095.** 4 k. brown 30 10

2096. Tractor and Factory.

1983. 50th Anniv. of Lenin Tractor Factory, Chelyabinsk.

5328. **2096.** 4 k. multicoloured 15 10

2097. Simon Bolivar.

1983. Birth Bicent. of Simon Bolivar.

5329. **2097.** 6 k. deep brown, brown and black 15 10

2098. 18th-century Warship and modern Missile Cruiser.

1983. Bicentenary of Sevastopol.

5330. **2098.** 5 k. multicoloured 40 15

2099. Snowdrops.

2101. P. N. Posepelov.

2100. "Vostok 6" and Tereshkova.

1983. Spring Flowers. Multicoloured.

5331	4 k. Type **2099**	15	10
5332	6 k. Siberian squills	20	10
5333	10 k. "Anemone hepatica"	35	15
5334	15 k. Cyclamen	50	25
5335	20 k. Yellow star of Bethlehem	90	45

1983. 20th Anniv. of First Woman Cosmonaut Valentina V. Tereshkova's Space Flight.

5336. **2100.** 10 k. multicoloured 30 15

1983. 85th Birth Anniv. of Pyotr Nicolaievich Pospelov (scientist).

5337. **2101.** 4 k. multicoloured 15 10

2102. Congress Emblem.

2103. Film around Globe and Festival Emblem.

1983. 10th European Rheumatologists' Congress, Moscow.

5338. **2102.** 4 k. multicoloured 20 10

1983. 13th International Film Festival, Moscow.

5339. **2103.** 20 k. multicoloured 70 30

2104. Vakhtangov.

1983. Birth Centenary of Ye. B. Vakhtangov (producer and actor).

5340. **2104.** 5 k. multicoloured 20 10

2105. Coastal Trawlers.

1983. Fishing Vessels. Multicoloured.

5341	4 k. Type **2105**	20	10
5342	6 k. Refrigerated trawler	25	10
5343	10 k. "Pulkovsky Meridian" (deep-sea trawler)	45	15
5344	15 k. Refrigerated freighter	60	25
5345	20 k. "50 let SSR" (factory ship)	1·00	50

2106. "SSSR-1".

2107. Red salmon.

1983. 50th Anniv. of Stratospheric Balloon's Record Altitude Flight.

5346. **2106.**	20 k. multicoloured	60	30

1983. Fishes. Multicoloured.

5347.	4 k. Type **2107**	15	10
5348.	6 k. Smarida	20	10
5349.	15 k. Spotted perch ..	50	20
5350.	20 k. Goby	65	30
5351.	45 k. Starry flounder ..	1·40	70

2108. Exhibition Emblem.

2110. S.W.A.P.O. Flag and Emblem.

1983. "Sozphilex 83" Stamp Exhibition, Moscow.

5352. **2108.**	6 k. multicoloured	15	10

1983. Namibia Day.

5355. **2110.**	5 k. multicoloured	20	10

2111. Palestinian with Flag.

2112. Emblem and Ostankino TV Tower, Moscow.

1983. Palestinian Solidarity.

5356. **2111.**	5 k. multicoloured	30	10

1983. 1st European Radio-telegraphy Championship, Moscow.

5357. **2112.**	6 k. multicoloured	20	10

2113. Council Session Emblem.

2114. Mohammed al-Khorezmi.

1983. 4th U.N.E.S.C.O. International Communications Development Programme Council Session, Tashkent.

5358. **2113.**	10 k. blue, mauve & black	30	15

1983. 1200th Birth Anniv of Mohammed al-Khorezmi (astronomer and mathematician).

5359 **2114**	4 k. multicoloured ..	20	10

2115. Yegorov.

2116. Treaty.

1983. Birth Cent. of Marshal A. I. Yegorov.

5360. **2115.**	4 k. purple	15	10

1983. Bicentenary of First Russian–Georgian Friendship Treaty.

5361. **2116.**	6 k. multicoloured	15	10

1983. Lighthouses (2nd series). As Type **2075**. Multicoloured.

5362	1 k. Kipu lighthouse, Baltic Sea	10	10
5363	5 k. Keri lighthouse, Gulf of Finland	25	10
5364	10 k. Stirsudden lighthouse, Gulf of Finland	40	15
5365	12 k. Takhkun lighthouse, Baltic Sea	55	30
5366	20 k. Tallin lighthouse, Gulf of Finland ..	75	45

2117. "Wife's Portrait with Flowers". (I. F. Khrutsky).

1983. Byelorussian Paintings. Multicoloured.

5367.	4 k. Type **2117**	15	10
5368.	6 k. "Early spring" (V. K. Byalynitsky-Birulya)	20	10
5369.	15 k. "Young Partisan" (E.A. Zaitsev) (vert.)	45	20
5370.	20 k. "Partisan Madonna" (M.A. Savitsky) (vert.) ..	60	30
5371.	45 k. "Corn Harvest" (V.K. Tsvirko) ..	1·40	65

2118. Steel Mill.

1983. Centenary of Hammer and Sickle Steel Mill.

5372. **2118.**	4 k. multicoloured	15	10

2119. Grain Production.

2120. Banner and Symbols of Economic Growth.

1983. Food Programme. Multicoloured.

5373.	5 k. Type **2119**	15	10
5374.	5 k. Cattle breeding ..	15	10
5375.	5 k. Fruit and vegetable production	15	10

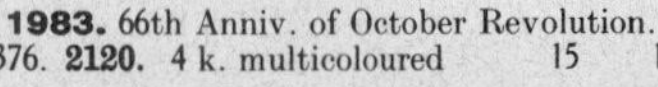
1983. 66th Anniv. of October Revolution.

5376. **2120.**	4 k. multicoloured	15	10

2121. Ivan Fyodorov.

1983. 400th Death Anniv of Ivan Fyodorov (printer) and 420th Anniv of Publication of "The Apostle" (first Russian printed book).

5377 **2121**	4 k. black	15	10

2122. Pipeline Construction.

1983. Inauguration of Urengoi-Uzhgorod Gas Pipeline.

5378. **2122.**	5 k. multicoloured	25	10

2123. Sidorenko.

2124. Marchers pushing Nuclear Weapons off Globe.

1983. Academician A. V. Sidorenko (geologist) commemoration.

5379. **2123.**	4 k. multicoloured	20	10

1983. Nuclear Disarmament.

5380. **2124.**	5 k. multicoloured	20	10

2125. Makhtumkuli.

2126. "Madonna and Child under Apple Tree" (Cranach the Elder).

1983. 250th Birth Anniv. of Makhtumkuli (Turkmen poet).

5381. **2125.**	5 k. multicoloured	20	10

1983. German Paintings in the Hermitage Museum. Multicoloured.

5382.	4 k. Type **2126**	15	10
5383.	10 k. "Self-portrait" (Anton Raphael Mengs)	30	15
5384.	20 k. "Self-portrait" (Jurgens Ovens) ..	60	30
5385.	45 k. "On Board a Sailing Vessel" (Casper David Friedrich) ..	1·25	60
5386.	50 k. "Rape of the Sabine Women" (Johann Schonfeld) (horiz.)	1·40	80

2127. Sukhe Bator.

2128. Globe and Hand holding Baby.

1983. 90th Birth Anniv. of Sukhe Bator (Mongolian statesman).

5388. **2127.**	5 k. multicoloured	15	10

1983. International Association of Physicians against Nuclear War.

5389. **2128.**	5 k. multicoloured	15	10

2129. Moscow Kremlin Tower Star.

1983. New Year.

5390. **2129.**	5 k. multicoloured	15	10

2130. Children's Music Theatre.

1983. New Buildings in Moscow.

5391. **2130.**	3 k. green	10	10
5392. –	4 k. blue	15	10
5393. –	6 k. brown	15	10
5394. –	20 k. green	60	30
5395. –	45 k. green	1·40	65

DESIGNS—VERT. 4 k. Hotel and Tourist Centre. HORIZ. 6 k. Russian Federation parliament building. 20 k. Hotel Izmailovo. 45 k. Novosti News and Press Agency.

2132. Cuban Flag.

2133. Broadcasting Station.

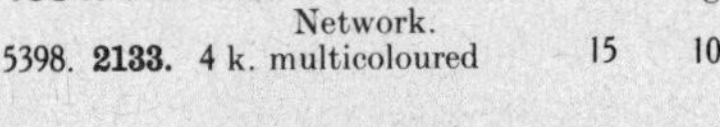
1984. 25th Anniv. of Cuban Revolution.

5397. **2132.**	5 k. multicoloured	15	10

1984. 50th Anniv. of Moscow Broadcasting Network.

5398. **2133.**	4 k. multicoloured	15	10

2134. Speed Skating.

1984. Women's European Skating Championship. Alma-Ata.

5399. **2134.**	5 k. multicoloured	15	10

2135. "T-34" Medium Tank.

1984. World War II Armoured Vehicles. Multicoloured.

5400.	10 k. Type **2135**	40	20
5401.	10 k. "KV" heavy tank	40	20
5402.	10 k. "IS-2" heavy tank	40	20
5403.	10 k. "SU-100" self-propelled gun	40	20
5304.	10 k. "ISU-152" heavy self-propelled gun ..	40	20

2136. Biathlon.

1984. Winter Olympic Games, Sarajevo. Multicoloured.
5405. 5 k. Type **2136** 15 10
5406. 10 k. Speed skating .. 35 15
5407. 20 k. Ice hockey .. 65 30
5408. 45 k. Figure skating .. 1·25 60

2137. Mandrill.

1984. 120th Anniv. of Moscow Zoo. Mult.
5409. 2 k. Type **2137** 10 10
5410. 3 k. Blesbok 10 10
5411. 4 k. Snow leopard .. 15 10
5412. 5 k. South African crowned crane .. 30 10
5413. 20 k. Blue and yellow macaw 70 20

2138. Yuri Gagarin.

1984. 50th Birth Anniv of Yuri Alekseevich Gagarin (first man in Space).
5414 **2138** 15 k. blue 40 20

2140. "E. K. Vorontsova" (George Hayter).

2141. Ilyushin.

1984. English Paintings in Hermitage Museum, Leningrad. Multicoloured.
5416. 4 k. Type **2140** 15 10
5417. 10 k. "Portrait of Mrs. Harriet Greer" (George Romney) .. 30 15
5418. 20 k. "Approaching Storm" (George Morland) (horiz.) .. 60 25
5419. 45 k. "Portrait of an Unknown Man" (Marcus Gheeraerts, the younger) .. .. 1·25 60
5420. 50 k. "Cupid untying the Robe of Venus" (Joshua Reynolds) .. 1·40 70

1984. 90th Birth Anniv. of Academician S. V. Ilyushin (aircraft designer).
5422. **2134.** 5 k. light brown, brown and black .. 15 10

2142. Bubnov.

2143. Launching Site of "M-100" Meteorological Station.

1984. Birth Centenary of Andrei Sergeevich Bubnov (Communist Party Leader).
5423. **2142.** 5 k. light brown, brown and black 15 10

1984. Soviet-Indian Space Co-operation. Multicoloured.
5424. 5 k. Type **2143** 15 10
5425. 20 k. Satellite and observatory (space geoclesy) 60 30
5426. 45 k. Rocket, satellites and dish aerials (Soviet-Indian space flight) .. .. .. 1·40 65

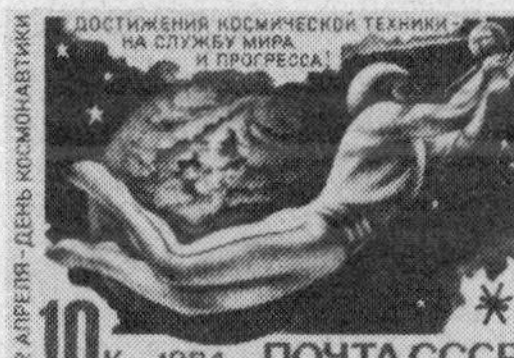

2144. Globe and Cosmonaut.

1984. Cosmonautics Day.
5428. **2144.** 10 k. multicoloured 30 15

2145. "Chelyuskin" (ice-breaker) and Route Map.

1984. 50th Anniv of Murmansk–Vladivostok Voyage of "Chelyuskin". Multicoloured.
5429. 6 k. Type **2145** 25 10
5430. 15 k. Evacuation of sinking ship 60 25
5431. 45 k. Air rescue of crew 1·75 75

2148. Lotus.

2149. Globe and Peace March. (left).

1984. Aquatic Flowers. Multicoloured.
5434. 1 k. Type **2148** 10 10
5435. 2 k. Euriala 10 10
5436. 3 k. Yellow water lilies (horiz.) 15 10
5437. 10 k. White water lilies (horiz.) 35 20
5438. 20 k. Marshflowers (horiz.) 70 30

1984. Peace.
5439. **2149.** 5 k. multicoloured 15 10
5440. – 5 k. red, gold and black 15 10
5441. – 5 k. multicoloured 15 10
Designs: No. 5440, Hammer and sickle and text. 5441, Globe and peace march (right).

2150. Welder.

2151. Communications Emblem.

1984. 50th Anniv. of E. O. Paton Institute of Electric Welding, Kiev.
5442. **2150.** 10 k. multicoloured 25 15

1984. 25th Conference of Community for Mutual Economic Aid Electrical and Postal Communications Standing Committee Cracow.
5443. **2151.** 10 k. multicoloured 25 15

2152. Emblem and Symbols of Match Venues.

2153. Maurice Bishop.

1984. European Youth Football Championship.
5444. **2152.** 15 k. multicoloured 45 20

1984. 40th Birth Anniv of Maurice Bishop (former Prime Minister of Grenada).
5445 **2153** 5 k. brown 20 10

2154. Lenin and Museum.

2155. Freighter, Monument and Aurora Borealis.

1984. 60th Anniv. of Lenin Central Museum, Moscow.
5446. **2154.** 5 k. multicoloured 15 10

1984. 400th Anniv. of Archangel.
5447. **2155.** 5 k. multicoloured 15 10

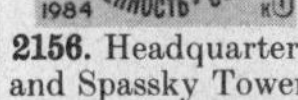

2156. Headquarters and Spassky Tower, Moscow.

2158. Liner.

2157. Vladimir A. Lyakhov and Aleksandr Aleksandrov.

1984. Council of Mutual Economic Aid Conference, Moscow.
5448. **2156.** 5 k. blue, red and black 15 10

1984. Lighthouses (3rd series). As T **2075.** Multicoloured.
5449. 1 k. Petropavlovsk lighthouse, Kamchatka .. 10 10
5450. 2 k. Tokarev lighthouse, Sea of Japan 10 10
5451. 4 k. Basargin lighthouse, Sea of Japan 20 10
5452. 5 k. Kronotsky lighthouse, Kamchatka .. 20 10
5453. 10 k. Marekan lighthouse, Sea of Okhotsk 35 15

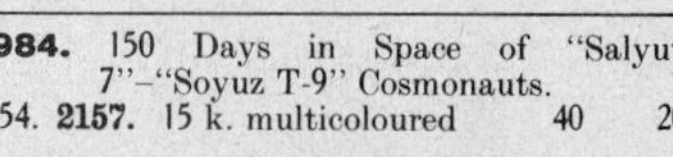
1984. 150 Days in Space of "Salyut 7"–"Soyuz T-9" Cosmonauts.
5454. **2157.** 15 k. multicoloured 40 20

1984. 60th Anniv. of Morflot (Soviet merchant fleet).
5455. **2158.** 10 k. multicoloured 35 15

2159. Komsomol Badge and Banner.

1984. 60th Anniv of Naming of Young Communist League (Komsomol) after Lenin.
5456 **2159** 5 k. multicoloured .. 15 10

2160. Memorial, Minsk.

1984. 40th Anniv. of Byelorussian Liberation.
5457. **2160.** 5 k. multicoloured 15 10

2161. Congress Emblem.

2162. Polish Arms and Flag.

1984. 27th International Geological Congress, Moscow.
5458. **2161.** 5 k. blue, gold and deep blue .. 20 10

1984. 40th Anniv. of Republic of Poland.
5459. **2162.** 5 k. multicoloured 15 10

2163. Asafev.

1984. Birth Centenary of Boris Vladimirovich Asafev (composer).
5460. **2163.** 5 k. green 20 10

2164. Russian and Mexican Flags and Scroll.

1984. 60th Anniv. of U.S.S.R.–Mexico Diplomatic Relations.
5461. **2164.** 5 k. multicoloured 15 10

2165. Title Page of "The Princess-Frog".

1984. Folk Tales. Illustrations by I. Bilibin. Multicoloured.

5462.	5 k. Type **2165**	20	15
5463.	5 k. Hunter and frog in marshland	20	15
5464.	5 k. Old man and hunter in forest	20	15
5465.	5 k. Crowd and mute swans	20	15
5466.	5 k. Title page of "Ivan the Tsarevich, the fire-bird and the Grey Wolf"	20	15
5467.	5 k. Ivan and the fire-bird	20	15
5468.	5 k. Grave and Ivan on horse	20	15
5469.	5 k. Ivan and princess ..	20	15
5470.	5 k. Title page of "Vasilisa the Beautiful"	20	15
5471.	5 k. Knight on horse ..	20	15
5472.	5 k. Tree-man in forest	20	15
5473.	5 k. Vasalisa and skulls	20	15

2166. Basketball.

1984. "Friendship 84" Sports Meetings. Multicoloured.

5474	1 k. Type **2166**	10	10
5475	5 k. Gymnastics (vert) ..	15	10
5476	10 k. Weightlifting ..	30	10
5477	15 k. Wrestling	45	20
5478	20 k. High jumping ..	60	30

2167. Flag and Soviet Soldier's Monument, Bucharest.

2168. Emblem, Chess Symbol for Queen and Motherland Statue.

1984. 40th Anniv. of Rumania's Liberation.
5479. **2167.** 5 k. multicoloured 15 10

1984. World Chess Championship Finals for Women (Volgograd) and Men (Moscow).

5480. **2168.**	15 k. gold, red and black	70	25
5481. –	15 k. multicoloured	70	25

DESIGN: No. 5481, Emblem, chess symbol for king and Spassky tower, Moscow Kremlin.

2169. Party House and Soviet Army Monument, Sofia, and State Emblem.

2170. Arms and Flag.

1984. 40th Anniv. of Bulgarian Revolution.
5482. **2169.** 5 k. multicoloured 15 10

1984. 10th Anniv. of Ethiopian Revolution.
5483. **2170.** 5 k. multicoloured 15 10

2171. Excavator.

1984. 50th Anniv. of Lenin Machine-building Plant, Novokramatorsk.
5484. **2171.** 5 k. multicoloured 15 10

2172. Arms and Symbols of Industry and Agriculture.

1984. 60th Anniv. of Nakhichevan A.S.S.R.
5485. **2172.** 5 k. multicoloured 15 10

2174. "Luna-3" photographing Moon.

1984. 25th Anniv. of Photography in Space. Multicoloured.

5487.	5 k. Type **2174**	15	10
5488.	20 k. "Venera-9" and control centre ..	60	25
5489.	45 k. "Meteor" meteorological satellite and Earth	1·40	60

2175. Arms and Flag.

1984. 35th Anniv. of German Democratic Republic.
5491. **2175.** 5 k. multicoloured 15 10

2176. Arms and Motherland Statue, Kiev.

1984. 40th Anniv. of Liberation of the Ukraine.
5492. **2176.** 5 k. multicoloured 15 10

2177. Town, Arms and Countryside.

1984. 60th Anniv. of Moldavian Soviet Socialist Republic.
5493. **2177.** 5 k. multicoloured 15 10

2178. Arms, Power Station and Mountains.

1984. 60th Anniv. of Kirgizia Soviet Socialist Republic.
5494. **2178.** 5 k. multicoloured 15 10

2179. Arms and Symbols of Industry and Agriculture.

2180. Flags and Spassky Tower.

1984. 60th Anniv. of Tadzhikistan Soviet Socialist Republic.
5495. **2179.** 5 k. multicoloured 15 10

1984. 67th Anniv. of October Revolution.
5496. **2180.** 5 k. multicoloured 15 10

2181. Arms, State Building and Dam.

1984. 60th Anniv. of Uzbekistan Soviet Socialist Republic.
5497. **2181.** 5 k. multicoloured 15 10

2182. Arms, Flag and State Building.

1984. 60th Anniv. of Turkmenistan Soviet Socialist Republic.
5498. **2182.** 5 k. multicoloured 15 10

2183. Medal, Workers, Diesel Train and Map of Route.

2184. "Il-86" Airplane, Rocket, "Soyuz"–"Salyut" Complex and Museum.

1984. Completion of Baikal–Amur Railway.
5499 **2183** 5 k. multicoloured .. 30 10

1984. 60th Anniv of M. V. Frunze Central House of Aviation and Cosmonautics, Moscow.
5500 **2184** 5 k. multicoloured .. 15 10

2185. Girl in Hat" (Jean-Louis Voile).

2186. Mongolian Arms and Flag.

1984. French Paintings in Hermitage Museum, Leningrad. Multicoloured.

5501.	4 k. Type **2185**	15	10
5502.	10 k. "The Stolen Kiss" (Jean-Honore Fragonard) (horiz.) ..	30	15
5503.	20 k. "Woman at her Toilette" (Edgar Degas)	60	30
5504.	45 k. "Pygmalion and Galatea (Francois Boucher) (horiz.) ..	1·25	60
5505.	50 k. "Landscape with Polyphemus" (Nicolas Poussin) (horiz.) ..	1·40	85

1984. 60th Anniv. of Mongolian People's Republic.
5507. **2186.** 5 k. multicoloured 15 10

2187. Spassky Tower and Snowflakes.

1984. New Year.
5508. **2187.** 5 k. multicoloured 15 10

2189. Horse-drawn Crew Wagon (19th century).

1984. Fire Engines (1st series). Multicoloured.

5510.	3 k. Type **2189**	15	10
5511.	5 k. 19th-century horse-drawn steam pump ..	25	10
5512.	10 k. "Freze" fire engine, 1904	45	15
5513.	15 k. "Lessner" fire engine 1904	75	25
5514.	20 k. "Russo-Balt" fire engine, 1913	1·00	30

See also Nos. 5608/12.

2190. Space Observatory and Flight Trajectory.

1984. International Venus-Halley's Comet Space Project. (1st issue).
5515. **2190.** 15 k. multicoloured 45 20
See also Nos. 5562 and 5630.

2191. Indira Gandhi.

2192. Heroes of December Revolution Monument, Moscow.

1984. Indira Gandhi (Indian Prime Minister) Commemoration.
5516 **2191** 5 k. lt brown & brn 30 10

1985. 80th Anniv. of 1905 Revolution.
5517. **2192.** 5 k. multicoloured 15 10

2193. Jubilee Emblem.

2194. Frunze.

1985. 25th Anniv. of Patrice Lumumba University, Moscow.
5518. **2193.** 5 k. multicoloured 15 10

1985. Birth Centenary of Mikhail Vasilievich Frunze (military strategist).
5519. **2194.** 5 k. stone, black and blue 15 10

2195. Arms and Industrial Landscape.

2196. Ice Hockey Player.

1985. 60th Anniv. of Karakalpak A.S.S.R.
5520. **2195.** 5 k. multicoloured 15 10

1985. 10th Friendly Armies Winter Spartakiad.
5521. **2196.** 5 k. multicoloured 15 10

2197. Dulcimer Player and Title Page.

2198. Pioneer Badge.

1985. 150th Anniv of "Kalevala" (Karelian poems collected by Elino Lonnrot).
5522 **2197** 5 k. brown, bl & blk 20 10

1985. 60th Anniv. of "Pionerskaya Pravda" (children's newspaper).
5523. **2198.** 5 k. multicoloured 20 10

2199. Maria Aleksandrovna Ulyanova.

2200. "Young Madonna Praying" (Francisco de Zurbaran).

1985. 150th Birth Anniv. of Maria Aleksandrovna Ulyanova (Lenin's mother).
5524. **2199.** 5 k. black 20 10

1985. Spanish Paintings in Hermitage Museum, Leningrad. Multicoloured.
5525. 4 k. Type **2200** 15 10
5526. 10 k. "Still Life" (Antonio Pereda) (horiz.) 30 15
5527. 20 k. "The Immaculate Conception" (Bartolome Esteban Murillo) 65 30
5528. 45 k. "The Grinder" (Antonio Puga) (horiz.) .. 1·50 70
5529. 50 k. "Count Olivares" (Diego Velazquez) .. 1·75 85

2201. Cosmonauts and Globe.

2203. Hungarian Arms and Budapest.

1985. "Expo '85" World's Fair, Tsukuba, Japan. Multicoloured.
5531. 5 k. Type **2201** 15 10
5532. 10 k. "Molniya-I" communications satellite .. 30 15
5533. 20 k. Energy sources of the future 65 30
5534. 45 k. Futuristic city .. 1·40 60

1985. 40th Anniv. of Hungary's Liberation.
5537. **2203.** 5 k. multicoloured 20 10

2204. Emblem and Text.

2206. Young People of Different Races.

2205. Cosmonautics, "Soyuz T" Training Model and Gagarin.

1985. 60th Anniv. of Union of Soviet Societies of Friendship and Cultural Relations with Foreign Countries.
5538. **2204.** 15 k. multicoloured 45 30

1985. Cosmonauts Day. 25th Anniv of Yuri A. Gagarin Cosmonauts Training Centre.
5539 **2205** 15 k. multicoloured .. 45 30

1985. 12th World Youth and Students' Festival, Moscow. Multicoloured.
5540 1 k. Type **2206** 10 10
5541 3 k. Girl with festival emblem in hair .. 10 10
5542 5 k. Rainbow and girl .. 15 10
5543 20 k. Youth holding camera 60 25
5544 45 k. Festival emblem .. 1·25 60

2207. Soviet Memorial, Berlin-Treptow.

Всесоюзная филатели-стическая выставка
„40 лет Великой Победы"
(**2209.**)

2208. Lenin and Paris Flat.

1985. 40th Anniv of Victory in Second World War (1st issue). Multicoloured.
5545 5 k. Type **2207** 20 15
5546 5 k. Partisans 20 15
5547 5 k. Lenin, soldier and Moscow Kremlin 20 15
5548 5 k. Soldiers and military equipment 20 15
5549 5 k. Woman worker, tank, tractor and aircraft assembly 20 15
See also No. 5555.

1985. 115th Birth Anniv. of Lenin. Mult.
5551. 5 k. Type **2208** 20 15
5552. 5 k. Lenin and Lenin Museum, Tampere, Finland 20 15

1985. "Second World War Victory" Philatelic Exhibition. No. 5545 optd with T **2209**.
5554 **2207** 5 k. multicoloured .. 20 20

2210. Victory Order. (½-size illustration).

1985. 40th Anniv. of Victory in Second World War. (2nd issue).
5555. **2210.** 20 k. multicoloured 65 45

2211. Czechoslovakian arms and Prague Buildings.

2212. Members' Flags on Shield.

1985. 40th Anniv. of Czechoslovakia's Liberation.
5556. **2211.** 5 k. multicoloured 20 10

1985. 30th Anniv. of Warsaw Pact Organization.
5557. **2212.** 5 k. multicoloured 20 10

2213. Sholokhov and Books.

2214. Sverdlov.

1985. 80th Birth Anniv. of Mikhail Aleksandrovich Sholokhov (writer).
5558. **2213.** 5 k. multicoloured 20 15
5559. – 5 k. multicoloured 20 15
5560. – 5 k. black, gold and brown 20 15
DESIGNS—As T **2213**. No. 5559, Sholokhov and books (different). 36 × 51 mm. 5560, Sholokhov.

1985. Birth Centenary of Ya. M. Sverdlov (Communist Party leader).
5561. **2214.** 5 k. brown and red 20 10

1985. International Venus-Halley's Comet Space Project (2nd issue). As T **2190**. Mult.
5562. 15 k. "Vega" space probe and Venus 55 30

2215. Battleship "Potemkin".

1985. 80th Anniv. of Mutiny on Battleship "Potemkin".
5563. **2215.** 5 k. black, red and gold 20 10

2216. "VL80R" Electric Locomotive.

1985. Locomotives and Rolling Stock.
5564. **2216.** 10 k. green 45 25
5565. – 10 k. brown .. 45 25
5566. – 10 k. blue 45 25
5567. – 10 k. brown .. 45 25
5568. – 10 k. blue 45 25
5569. – 10 k. blue 45 25
5570. – 10 k. brown .. 45 25
5571. – 10 k. green 45 25
DESIGNS: No. 5565, Coal wagon. 5566, Oil tanker wagon. 5567, Goods wagon. 5568, Refrigerated wagon. 5569, "TEM 2" diesel locomotive. 5570, "Sv" passenger carriage. 5571, Mail van.

2217. Camp and Pioneer Badge.

1985. 60th Anniv. of Artek Pioneer Camp.
5572. **2217.** 4 k. multicoloured 20 10

2218. Leonid Kizim, Vladimir Solovyov and Oleg Atkov.

1985. "237 Days in Space".
5573. **2218.** 15 k. multicoloured 50 20

2219. Youths of different Races.

2220. "Beating Swords into Ploughshares" (sculpture) and U.N. Emblem.

1985. International Youth Year.
5574. **2219.** 10 k. multicoloured 30 15

1985. 40th Anniv. of U.N.O. (1st issue).
5575. **2220.** 45 k. blue and gold 1·25 60
See also No. 5601.

2222. Larkspur.

2224. Cecilienhof Palace and Flags.

2223. V. A. Dzhanibekov, S. E. Savitskaya and I. P. Volk.

1985. Plants of Siberia. Multicoloured.
5577. 2 k. Type **2222** 10 10
5578. 3 k. "Thermopsis lanceolata" 10 10
5579. 5 k. Rose 20 10
5580. 20 k. Cornflower .. 70 30
5581. 45 k. Bergenia .. .. 1·40 65

1985. 1st Anniv. of First Space-walk by Woman Cosmonaut.
5582. **2223.** 10 k. multicoloured 30 15

1985. 40th Anniv. of Potsdam Conference.
5583. **2224.** 15 k. multicoloured 40 20

2225. Finland Palace.

2226. Russian and N. Korean Flags and Monument.

1985. 10th Anniv. of European Security and Co-operation Conference Helsinki.
5584. **2225.** 20 k. multicoloured 75 35

1985. 40th Anniv. of Liberation of Korea.
5585. **2226.** 5 k. multicoloured 20 10

2227. Pamir Shrew.

2228. A. G. Stakhanov and Industrial Scenes.

1985. Protected Animals. Multicoloured.

5586 2 k. Type **2227** 10 10
5587 3 k. Satunin's jerboa (horiz) 10 10
5588 5 k. Desert dormouse .. 15 10
5589 20 k. Caracal (47 × 32 mm) 60 30
5590 45 k. Goitred gazelle (47 × 32 mm) .. .. 1·40 65

1985. 50th Anniv. of Stakhanov Movement (for high labour productivity).

5592. **2228.** 5 k. yellow, red and black 15 10

2229. Cup, Football, F.I.F.A. Emblem and Kremlin Tower.

2230. Chess Pieces.

1985. World Junior Football Championship, Moscow.

5593. **2229.** 5 k. multicoloured 20 10

1985. World Chess Championship Final between Anatoly Karpov and Gary Kasparov.

5594. **2230.** 10 k. multicoloured 55 20

2231. Vietnam State Emblem.

2232. Immortality Monument and Buildings.

1985. 40th Anniv. of Vietnamese Independence.

5595. **2231.** 5 k. multicoloured 20 10

1985. Millenary of Bryansk.

5596. **2232.** 5 k. multicoloured 20 10

2233. Title Page.

1985. 800th Anniv. of "Song of Igor's Campaigns".

5597. **2233.** 10 k. multicoloured 35 20

2234. Lutsk Castle.

2235. Gerasimov.

1985. 900th Anniv. of Lutsk.

5598. **2234.** 5 k. multicoloured 20 10

1985. Birth Centenary of Sergei Vasilievich Gerasimov (artist).

5599. **2235.** 5 k. multicoloured 20 10

2236. Globe, "Aurora" and "1917".

2237. Headquarters, New York, and Flag.

1985. 68th Anniv. of October Revolution.

5600. **2236.** 5 k. multicoloured 20 10

1985. 40th Anniv. of U.N.O. (2nd issue).

5601. **2237.** 15 k. green, blue and black .. 45 20

2238. Krishjanis Baron.

1985. 150th Birth Anniv. of Krishjanis Baron (writer).

5602. **2238.** 5 k. black & brown 20 10

2239. Lenin and Worker breaking Chains.

1985. 90th Anniv. of Petersburg Union of Struggle for Liberating the Working Class.

5603. **2239.** 5 k. multicoloured 20 10

2240. Telescope.

1985. 10th Anniv. of World's Largest Telescope.

5604. **2240.** 10 k. blue 55 20

2241. Angolan Arms and Flag.

2242. Yugoslav Arms, Flag and Parliament Building.

1985. 10th Anniv of Independence of Angola.

5605 **2241** 5 k. multicoloured .. 20 10

1985. 40th Anniv. of Federal People's Republic of Yugoslavia.

5606. **2242.** 5 k. multicoloured 20 10

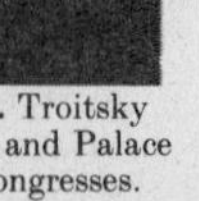

2243. Troitsky Tower and Palace of Congresses.

2244. Samantha Smith.

1985. New Year.

5607. **2243.** 5 k. multicoloured 15 10

1985. Fire Engines (2nd series). As T **2189.** Multicoloured.

5608. 3 k. "AMO-F15", 1926 .. 15 10
5609. 5 k. "PMZ-1", 1933 .. 25 10
5610. 10 k. "ATs-40", 1977 .. 45 15
5611. 20 k. "Al-30" with automatic ladder, 1970 .. 80 30
5612. 45 k. "AA-60", 1978 .. 1·60 60

1985. Samantha Smith (American schoolgirl peace campaigner) Commemoration.

5613. **2244.** 5 k. brn., bl. & red 40 10

2245. N.M. Emanuel

2246. Family and Places of Entertainment.

1985. Academician N. M. Emanual (chemist) Commemoration.

5614 **2245.** 5 k. multicoloured 20 10

1985. Anti-alcoholism Campaign. Mult.

5615. 5 k. Type **2246** 25 10
5616. 5 k. Sports centre and family 25 10

2247. Emblem.

2248. Banners and Kremlin Palace of Congresses.

1986. International Peace Year.

5617. **2247.** 20 k. bl., grn. & sil. 60 30

1986. 27th Soviet Communist Party Congress.

5618. **2248.** 5 k. multicoloured 15 10
5619. – 20 k. multicoloured 60 30

Designs—(36 × 51 mm). 20 k. Palace of Congresses, Spassky Tower and Lenin.

2249. 1896 Olympics Medal.

2250. Tulips.

1986. 90th Anniv. of First Modern Olympic Games.

5621. **2249.** 15 k. multicoloured 45 20

1986. Plants of Russian Steppes. Mult.

5622. 4 k. Type **2250** 15 10
5623. 5 k. Grass (horiz.) .. 20 10
5624. 10 k. Iris 35 15
5625. 15 k. Violets 55 25
5626. 20 k. Cornflower .. 70 30

2251. Voronezh and Arms.

2252. Bela Kun.

1986. 400th Anniv. of Voronezh.

5627. **2251.** 5 k. multicoloured 20 10

1986. Birth Centenary of Bela Kun (Hungarian Communist Party leader).

5628. **2252.** 10 k. blue 30 15

2253. Pozela.

2255. "Utetheisa pulchella.

1986. 90th Birth Anniv. of Karolis Pozela (founder of Lithuanian Communist Party).

5629. **2253.** 5 k. grey 20 10

1986. International Venus–Halley's Comet Space Project (3rd issue). As T **2190.** Multicoloured.

5630. 15 k. "Vega 1" and Halley's Comet .. 55 30

1986. Butterflies listed in U.S.S.R. Red Book. (1st series). Multicoloured.

5632. 4 k. Type **2255** 15 10
5633. 5 k. "Allancastria caucasica" 20 10
5634. 10 k. "Zegris eupheme" 45 15
5635. 15 k. "Catocala sponsa" 75 25
5636. 20 k. "Satyrus bischoffi" 95 35

See also Nos. 5726/30.

2256. Globe and Model of Space Complex.

2257. Kirov.

1986. "Expo '86" World's Fair, Vancouver.

5637. **2256.** 20 k, multicoloured 60 30

1986. Birth Centenary of S. M. Kirov (Communist Party Secretary).

5638. **2257.** 5 k. black 20 10

2258. Tsiolkovsky.

1986. Cosmonautics Day. Multicoloured.

5639. 5 k. Type **2258** 15 10
5640. 10 k. Sergei Pavlovich Korolev (rocket designer) and "Vostok" rocket (vert.) 30 15
5641. 15 k. Yuri Gagarin, "Vega", sputnik and globe (25th anniv. of first man in space) .. 55 25

2259. Ice Hockey Player.

2260. Thalmann.

1986. World Ice Hockey Championship, Moscow.

5642. **2259.** 15 k. multicoloured 60 20

1986. Birth Centenary of Ernst Thalmann (German politician).

5643. **2260.** 10 k. brown 30 15

2261. Lenin Museum, Leipzig.

1986. 116th Birth Anniv. of Lenin.

5645. **2261.** 5 k. multicoloured 20 10
5646. – 5 k. ol., brn. & blk. 20 10
5647. – 5 k. multicoloured 20 10

DESIGNS: No. 5646, Lenin Museum, Prague. 5647, Lenin Museum, Poronine, Poland.

2262. Tambov and Arms.

1986. 350th Anniv. of Tambov.

5648. **2262.** 5 k. multicoloured 20 10

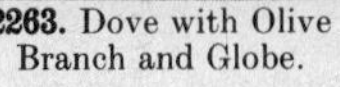

2263. Dove with Olive Branch and Globe.
2264. Emblem and Cyclists.

1986. 25th Anniv. of Soviet Peace Fund.

5649. **2263.** 10 k. multicoloured 35 20

1986. 39th Peace Cycle Race.

5650. **2264.** 10 k. multicoloured 45 20

2265. "Amanita phalloides".
2266. Globe and Wildlife.

1986. Fungi. Multicoloured.

5651. 4 k. Type **2256** 15 10
5652. 5 k. "Amanita muscaria" 25 10
5653. 10 k. "Amanita pantherina" 45 15
5654. 15 k. "Tylopilus felleus" 75 25
5655. 20 k. "Hypholoma fasciculare" 95 40

1986. U.N.E.S.C.O. Man and Biosphere Programme.

5656. **2266.** 10 k. multicoloured 40 15

2267. Torch and Runner.
2268. Kuibyshev.

1986. 9th People's Spartakiad.

5657. **2267.** 10 k. multicoloured 35 15

1986. 400th Anniv. of Kuibyshev (formerly Samara).

5658. **2268.** 5 k. multicoloured 20 10

No. 5658 depicts the Lenin Museum, Eternal Glory and V. I. Chapaev monuments and Gorky State Theatre.

2269. Ostankino T. V. Tower.
2270. Footballers.

1986. "Communication 86" International Exhibition, Moscow.

5659. **2269.** 5 k. multicoloured 20 10

1986. World Cup Football Championship, Mexico. Multicoloured.

5660. 5 k. Type **2270** 20 10
5661. 10 k. Footballers (different) 40 15
5662. 15 k. Championship medal 75 25

2271. "Lane in Albano" (M. I. Lebedev).
2272. Arms and City.

1986. Russian Paintings in Tretyakov Gallery, Moscow. Multicoloured.

5663. 4 k. Type **2271** 15 10
5664. 5 k. "View of the Kremlin in foul Weather" (A. K. Savrasov) (horiz.) .. 20 10
5665. 10 k. "Sunlit Pine Trees" (I. I. Shishkin) .. 30 15
5666. 15 k. "Reverse" (A. E. Arkhipov) (69 × 33 mm.) 50 25
5667. 45 k. "Wedding Procession in Moscow" (A. P. Ryabushkin) (69 × 33 mm.) .. .. 1·50 70

1986. 300th Anniv. of Irkutsk City Status.

5668. **2272.** 5 k. multicoloured 20 10

2273. World Map, Stadium and Runners.
2274. Globe, Punched Tape and Keyboard.

1986. International Goodwill Games, Moscow.

5669. **2273.** 10 k. blue, brown and black .. 30 15

1986. U.N.E.S.C.O. Programmes in U.S.S.R. Multicoloured.

5671 5 k. Type **2274** (information science) .. 20 10
5672 10 k. Landscape and geological section (geological correlation) 35 15
5673 15 k. Oceanographic research vessel, albatross and ocean (Intergovernmental Oceanographic Commission) 55 30
5674 35 k. Fluvial drainage (International Hydrological Programme) .. 1·40 60

2275. Arms and Town Buildings.

1986. 400th Anniv of Tyumen, Siberia.

5675 **2275** 5 k. multicoloured .. 20 10

2276. Olof Palme.
2277. Hands, Ball and Basket.

1986. Olof Palme (Swedish Prime Minister) Commemoration.

5676. **2276.** 10 k. bl., blk. & brn. 35 15

1986. 10th Women's Basketball Championship.

5677. **2277.** 15 k. brn., blk. & red 60 25

2278. "Ural-375D".

1986. Lorries. Multicoloured.

5678. 4 k. Type **2278** 15 10
5679. 5 k. "GAZ-53A" 20 10
5680. 10 k. "KrAZ-256B" .. 35 15
5681. 15 k. "MAZ-515B" .. 55 25
5682. 20 k. "ZIL-133GYa" .. 70 30

2279. Lenin Peak.

1986. U.S.S.R. Sports Committee's International Mountaineers' Camps (1st series). Multicoloured.

5683 4 k. Type **2279** 15 10
5684 5 k. E. Korzhenevskaya Peak 20 10
5685 10 k. Belukha Peak .. 30 15
5686 15 k. Communism Peak .. 55 25
5687 30 k. Elbrus Peak 95 50

See also Nos. 5732/5.

2281. Lenin Monument and Drama Theatre.
2282. Ferry, Maps and Flags.

1986. 250th Anniv. of Chelyabinsk City.

5689. **2281.** 5 k. multicoloured 20 10

1986. Opening of Mukran (East Germany)–Klaipeda (U.S.S.R.) Railway Ferry.

5690 **2282** 15 k. multicoloured .. 75 25

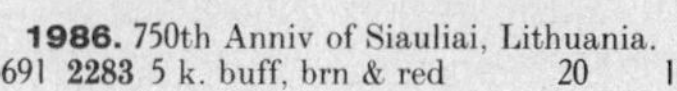

2283. Victory Monument and Buildings.
2284. Lenin Monument and Moscow Kremlin.

1986. 750th Anniv of Siauliai, Lithuania.

5691 **2283** 5 k. buff, brn & red 20 10

1986. 69th Anniv. of October Revolution.

5692. **2284.** 5 k. multicoloured 25 10

2285. Ice-breaker "Vladivostok", Mil Mi-4 Helicopter, Satellite and Map.

15.III–26.VII.1985
Дрейф во льдах Антарктики
(**2286**).

1986. Antarctic Drift of "Mikhail Somov" (ice-breaker).

(a) As Type **2285**.

5693. 5 k. blue, black and red 25 10
5694. 10 k. multicoloured .. 50 20

(b) No. 5055 optd. with T **2286**.

5696. 4 k. multicoloured .. 20 10

DESIGN: As T **2285**. 10 k. Map and "Mikhail Somov".

Nos. 5693/4 were printed together, se-tenant, forming a composite design.

2287. Class "Зu" No. EU 684-37, Slavyansk.

1986. Steam Locomotives as Monuments. Multicoloured.

5697 4 k. Type **2287** .. 20 10
5698 5 k. Class "FD" No. 21–3000, Novosibirsk .. 20 10
5699 10 k. Class "Ov" No. 5109, Volgograd 40 15
5700 20 k. Class "SO" No. 17–1613, Dnepropetrovsk 75 30
5701 30 k. Class "FDp" No. 20–578, Kiev .. .. 1·00 50

2288. G. K. Ordzhonikidze.
2289. Novikov and Score.

1986. Birth Centenary of Grigory Konstantinovich Ordzhonikidze (revolutionary).

5702 **2288** 5 k. grey .. 20 10

1986. 90th Birth Anniv of Anatoli Novikov (composer).

5703 **2289** 5 k. brown 30 10

2290. U.N. and U.N.E.S.C.O. Emblems.
2291. Sun Yat-sen.

1986. 40th Anniv. of U.N.E.S.C.O.

5704. **2290.** 10 k. silver and blue 40 15

1986. 120th Birth Anniv. of Sun Yat-sen (first President of Chinese Republic).

5705. **2291.** 5 k. black and grey 25 10

2292. Lomonosov.

1986. 275th Birth Anniv. of Mikhail Vasilievich Lomonosov (scientist).

5706. **2292.** 5 k. brown 20 10

2293. "Ya-1", 1927.

1986. Sports Aircraft designed by Aleksandr Yakovlev. Multicoloured.

5707 4 k. Type **2293** 15 10
5708 5 k. "Ut-2" trainer, 1935 15 10
5709 10 k. "Yak-18", 1946 .. 30 15
5710 20 k. "Yak-50", 1972 .. 60 30
5711 30 k. "Yak-55", 1981 .. 95 50

2294. Spassky, Senate and Nikolsky Towers, Kremlin.

2295. Computer and Terminal.

1986. New Year.

5712. **2294.** 5 k. multicoloured 20 10

1986. Resolutions of 27th Communist Party Congress. Multicoloured.

5713 5 k. Type **2295** (scientific and technical progress) 20 10
5714 5 k. Construction engineer and building project .. 20 10
5715 5 k. City (welfare of people) 20 10
5716 5 k. Peace demonstration at Council for Mutual Economic Aid building (peace) 20 10
5717 5 k. Spassky Tower and Kremlin Palace, Moscow Kremlin (unity of party and people) .. 20 10

2296. Parkhomeko.

2297. Machel.

1986. Birth Cent of Aleksandr Parkhomenko (revolutionary).

5718 **2296** 5 k. black 20 10

1986. Samora Moizes Machel (President of Mozambique) Commemoration.

5719. **2297.** 5 k. brown & blk. 25 10

2298. Russian State Museum (Mikhailovsky Palace).

1986. Palace Museums of Lenningrad.

5720. **2298.** 5 k. brown & grn. 20 15
5721. – 10 k. green and blue 30 15
5722. – 15 k. blue and green 50 20
5723. – 20 k. green & brn. 60 30
5724. – 50 k. brown & bl. 1·50 70

DESIGNS: 10 k. Hermitage Museum (Winter Palace). 15 k. Grand Palace Museum (Petrodvorets). 20 k. Catherine Palace Museum (Pushkin). 50 k. Palace Museum (Pavlovsk).

2299. Couple and Industrial Landscape.

2300. "Atrophaneura alcinous".

1987. 18th Soviet Trades Union Congress, Moscow.

5725. **2299.** 5 k. multicoloured 20 10

1987. Butterflies listed in U.S.S.R. Red Book (2nd series). Multicoloured.

5726. 4 k. Type **2300** 20 10
5727. 5 k. "Papilio machaon" 20 10
5728. 10 k. "Papilio alexanor" 35 15
5729. 15 k. "Papilio maackii" 60 25
5730. 30 k. "Iphiclides podalirius" 95 50

2301. Karlis Miesnieks.

2302. Stasys Simkus.

1987. Birth Centenary of Karlis Miesnieks (Latvian artist).

5731. **2301.** 5 k. multicoloured 20 10

1987. U.S.S.R. Sports Committee's International Mountaineers' Camps (2nd series). As T **2279.** Multicoloured.

5732 4 k. Chimbulak Gorge .. 15 10
5733 10 k. Shavla Gorge .. 30 15
5734 20 k. Donguz-Orun and Nakra-Dau, Caucasus 70 30
5735 35 k. Kazbek, Caucasus .. 1·25 60

1987. Birth Centenary of Stasys Simkus (Lithuanian composer).

5736 **2302** 5 k. purple & yellow 30 10

2303. V. I. Chapaev.

2304. Lenin.

1987. Birth Centenary of Vasily Ivanovich Chapaev (revolutionary).

5737. **2303.** 5 k. brown 20 10

1987. 20th Leninist Young Communist League (Komsomol) Congress, Moscow.

5738 **2304** 5 k. multicoloured .. 20 10

MINIMUM PRICE

The minimum price quoted is 5p which represents a handling charge rather than a basis for valuing common stamps. For further notes about prices see introductory pages.

2305. Heino Eller.

2306. Orbeli.

1987. Birth Centenary of Heino Eller (Estonian composer).

5740. **2305.** 5 k. lt. brn. & brn. 30 10

1987. Birth Centenary of Academician Iosif Abgarovich Orbeli (first President of Armenian Academy of Sciences).

5741. **2306.** 5 k. brown and pink 20 10

2307. Bears in and out of Water.

1987. Polar Bears. Multicoloured.

5742. 5 k. Type **2307** 20 10
5743. 10 k. Mother and cubs .. 40 15
5744. 20 k. Mother and cubs (different) 75 30
5745. 35 k. Bears .. .. 1·25 55

2308. "Sputnik 1" and Globe.

2309. Emblem and Headquarters, Bangkok.

1987. Cosmonautics Day. Multicoloured.

5746 10 k. Type **2308** (30th anniv of launching of first artificial satellite) 35 15
5747 10 k. "Vostok-3" "Vostok-4" and globe (25th anniv of first group space flight) .. 35 15
5748 10 k. "Mars-1" and globe (25th anniv of launching of automatic interplanetary station) .. 35 15

1987. 40th Anniv. of U.N. Economic and Social Commission for Asia and the Pacific Ocean.

5749. **2309.** 10 k. multicoloured 35 15

2310. "Birthday" (N. A. Sysoev).

1987. 117th Birth Anniv. of Lenin. Mult.

5750. 5 k. Type **2310** 20 10
5751. 5 k. "V. I. Lenin with Delegates to the Third Congress of the Young Communist League" (P. P. Belousov) .. 20 10

2311. Gymnast on Rings.

2312. Cyclists and "40".

1987. European Gymnastics Championships, Moscow.

5753 **2311** 10 k. multicoloured .. 40 15

1987. 40th Peace Cycle Race.

5754. **2312.** 10 k. multicoloured 50 15

2313. Menzbir's Marmot

2315. "Portrait of a Woman" (Lucas Cranach the Elder).

2314. "Maksim Gorky".

1987. Mammals listed in U.S.S.R. Red Book. Multicoloured.

5755. 5 k. Type **2313** 20 10
5756. 10 k. Ratel (horiz.) .. 35 15
5757. 15 k. Snow leopard (32 × 47 mm.) 70 25

1987. River Tourist Ships. Multicoloured.

5758. 5 k. Type **2314** 25 10
5759. 10 k. "Aleksandr Pushkin" 40 15
5760 30 k. "Sovetsky Soyuz" 1·00 45

1987. West European Art in Hermitage Museum, Leningrad. Multicoloured.

5761 4 k. Type **2315** 15 10
5762 5 k. "St. Sebastian" (Titian) 15 10
5763 10 k. "Justice" (drawing, Albrecht Durer) .. 30 15
5764 30 k. "Adoration of the Magi" (Pieter Breughel the younger) (horiz) .. 90 45
5765 50 k. "Statue of Ceres" (Peter Paul Rubens) 1·50 70

2316. Car Production Line and Lenin Hydro-electric Power Station.

2317. Pushkin (after T. Rait).

1987. 250th Anniv of Togliatti (formerly Stavropol).

5766 **2316** 5 k. multicoloured .. 25 10

1987. 150th Death Anniv. of Aleksandr S. Pushkin (poet).

5767. **2317.** 5 k. deep brown, yellow and brown 20 10

2318. Kovpak.

2319. Congress Emblem.

1987. Birth Centenary of Major-General Sidor Artemevich Kovpak.

5768. **2318.** 5 k. black 20 10

1987. World Women's Congress, Moscow.

5769. **2319.** 10 k. multicoloured 30 15

2320. Arms, Kremlin, Docks, Drama Theatre and Yermak Monument.

2321. Party Flag and Mozambican.

1987. 400th Anniv of Tobolsk, Siberia.
5770 **2320** 5 k. multicoloured . . 20 10

1987. 25th Anniv of Mozambique Liberation Front (FRELIMO) (5771) and 10th Anniv of U.S.S.R.–Mozambique Friendship and Co-operation Treaty (5772). Multicoloured.
5771 5 k. Type **2321** 20 10
5772 5 k. Mozambique and U.S.S.R. flags . . 20 10

2322. "Scolopendrium vulgare".

2323. Moscow Kremlin and Indian Coin.

1987. Ferns. Multicoloured.
5773. 4 k. Type **2322** 15 10
5774. 5 k. "Ceterach officinarum" . . 20 10
5775. 10 k. "Salvinia natans" (horiz.) 35 15
5776. 15 k. "Matteuccia struthiopteris" . . 55 25
5777. 50 k. "Adiantum pedatum" . . . . 1·50 70

1987. Indian Festival in U.S.S.R. (5778) and U.S.S.R. Festival in India (5779). Mult.
5778. 5 k. Type **2323** 20 15
5779. 5 k. Hammer, sickle, open book, satellite and Red Fort, Delhi . . 20 15

2324. Rossiya Hotel (venue), Globe and Film.

2325. Cosmonauts training.

1987. 15th International Film Festival, Moscow.
5780. **2324.** 10 k. multicoloured 35 15

1987. Soviet–Syrian Space Flight. Mult.
5781. 5 k. Type **2325** . . 20 10
5782. 10 k. Moscow–Damascus satellite link and cosmonauts watching television screen . . 35 15
5783. 15 k. Cosmonauts at Gagarin monument, Zvezdny 55 25

2326. Emblem and Vienna Headquarters.

1987. 30th Anniv. of International Atomic Energy Agency.
5785. **2326.** 20 k. multicoloured 60 30

2327. 14th–16th Century Messenger.

1987. Russian Postal History.
5786. **2327.** 4 k. black & brown 15 10
5787. – 5 k. black & brown 20 10
5788. – 10 k. black & brown 35 15
5789. – 30 k. black & brown 1·00 45
5790. – 35 k. black & brown 1·25 50

DESIGNS: 5 k. 17th–19th-century horse-drawn sledge and 17th-century postman. 10 k. 16th- and 18th-century sailing packets. 30 k. 19th-century railway mail vans. 35 k. 1905 post car and 1926 "AMO-F-15" van.

2328. "V. I. Lenin" (P. V. Vasilev).

1987. 70th Anniv. of October Revolution. Multicoloured.
5792 5 k. Type **2328** 20 15
5793 5 k. "V.I. Lenin proclaims Soviet Power" (V. A. Serov) 20 15
5794 5 k. "Long Live the Socialist Revolution!" (V. V. Kuznetsov) . . 20 15
5795 5 k. "Storming the Winter Palace" (V. A. Serov) (69 × 32 mm) 20 15
5796 5 k. "On the Eve of the Storm" (portraying Lenin, Sverdlov and Podvoisky) (V.V. Pimenov) (69 × 32 mm) 20 15

2330. Postyshev.

2331. Yuri Dolgoruky (founder) Monument.

1987. Birth Centenary of Pavel Petrovich Postyshev (revolutionary).
5799. **2330.** 5 k. blue 20 10

1987. 840th Anniv. of Moscow.
5800. **2331.** 5 k. brown, yellow and orange . . 20 10

2332. Ulugh Beg (astronomer and mathematician).

1987. Scientists.
5801. **2332.** 5 k. multicoloured 25 15
5802. – 5 k. black, green and blue 25 15
5803. – 5 k. deep brown, brown and blue . . 25 15

DESIGNS: No. 5801, Type **2332** (550th anniv. of "New Astronomical Tables"). 5802, Isaac Newton (300th anniv. of "Principia Mathematica"). 5803, Marie Curie (120th birth anniv.).

Всесоюзная
филателистическая выставка
„70 лет Великого Октября"
(**2334**.)

1987. "70th Anniv. of October Revolution" All-Union Stamp Exhibition. No. 5795 optd. with T **2334**.
5805. 5 k. multicoloured . . 25 20

2335. "There will be Cities in the Taiga" (A. A. Yakovlev).

2336. Reed.

1987. Soviet Paintings of the 1980s. Mult.
5806 4 k. Type **2335** 15 10
5807 5 k. "Mother" (V. V. Shcherbakov) 15 10
5808 10 k. "My Quiet Homeland" (V. M. Sidorov) (horiz) 30 15
5809 30 k. "In Yakutsk, Land of Pyotr Alekseev" (A. N. Osipov) (horiz) . . 90 45
5810 35 k. "Ivan's Return" (V. I. Yerofeev) (horiz) . . 1·25 55

1987. Birth Centenary of John Reed (American journalist and founder of U.S. Communist Party).
5812 **2336** 10 k. brn, yell & blk 35 15

2337. Marshak.

1987. Birth Centenary of Samuil Yakovlevich Marshak (poet).
5813. **2337.** 5 k. brown 20 10

2338. Chavchavadze.

1987. 150th Birth Anniv. of Ilya Grigoryevich Chavchavadze (writer).
5814. **2338.** 5 k. blue 20 10

2339. Indira Gandhi.

2340. Vadim N. Podbelsky (revolutionary).

1987. 70th Birth Anniv of Indira Gandhi (former Indian Prime Minister, 1966–77 and 1980–84).
5815 **2339** 5 k. brown and black 30 10

1987. Birth Centenaries.
5816 **2340** 5 k. black 20 10
5817 – 5 k. blue 20 10

DESIGN: No. 5817, Academician Nikolai Ivanovich Vavilov (geneticist).

2341. Tokamak Thermonuclear System.

2342. Bagramyan.

1987. Science.
5818. **2341.** 5 k. brown and grey 20 10
5819. – 10 k. green, blue and black . . 35 15
5820. – 20 k. black, stone and drab . . 60 30

DESIGNS: 10 k. Kola borehole. 20 k. "Ratan-600" radio telescope.

1987. 90th Birth Anniv of Marshal Ivan Khristoforovich Bagramyan.
5821 **2342** 5 k. brown 20 10

2343. Moscow Kremlin.

2344. Flags, Spassky Tower, Moscow, and Capitol, Washington.

1987. New Year.
5822. **2343.** 5 k. multicoloured 15 10

1987. Soviet–American Intermediate- and short-range Nuclear Weapons Treaty.
5823 **2344** 10 k. multicoloured . . 35 15

2345. Grigori Andreevich Spiridov and "Tri Svyatitelya".

1987. Russian Naval Commanders (1st series).
5824 **2345** 4 k. blue & deep blue 15 10
5825 – 5 k. purple and blue 20 10
5826 – 10 k. purple and blue 35 15
5827 – 25 k. blue & dp blue 85 35
5828 – 30 k. blue & dp blue 95 45

DESIGNS: 5 k. Fyodor Fyodorovich Ushakov and "Sv. Pavel". 10 k. Dmitri Nikolaevich Senyavin and Battle of Afon. 25 k. Mikhail Petrovich Lazarev and "Azov". 30 k. Pavel Stepanovich Nakhimov and "Imperatritsa Maria".

See also Nos. 6091/6.

2346. Torch.

2347. Biathlon.

1987. 30th Anniv. of Asia–Africa Solidarity Organization.
5829. **2346.** 10 k. multicoloured 30 15

1988. Winter Olympic Games, Calgary. Mult.
5830. 5 k. Type **2347** 20 10
5831. 10 k. Cross-country skiing 35 15
5832. 15 k. Slalom 45 25
5833. 20 k. Figure skating (pairs) 60 30
5834. 30 k. Ski jumping . . 95 45

2348. 1918 Stamps.

2349. Emblem.

1988. 70th Anniv. of First Soviet Postage Stamps.
5836. **2348.** 10 k. blue, brown and gold 35 15
5837. 10 k. brown, blue and gold 35 15

On No. 5836 the lower stamp depicted is the 35 k. in blue, on No. 5837 the lower stamp is the 70 k. in brown.

1988. 40th Anniv. of W.H.O.
5838. **2349.** 35 k. gold, blue and black . . . . 1·25 55

2350. Byron.

1988. Birth Bicentenary of Lord Byron (English poet).
5839. **2350.** 15 k. black, green and blue 45 25

2351. Exchange Activities and National Flags.

2352. Lomov-Oppokov.

1988. 30th Anniv. of Agreement on Cultural, Technical and Educational Exchanges with U.S.A.
5840. **2351.** 20 k. multicoloured 60 30

1988. Birth Centenary of Georgy Ippolitovich Lomov-Oppokov (Communist party official).
5841. **2352.** 5 k. black & brown 10 5

2353. "Little Humpbacked Horse" (dir. I. Ivanov-Vano, animated L. Milchin).

1988. Soviet Cartoon Films. Multicoloured.
5842 1 k. Type **2353** 10 10
5843 3 k. "Winnie the Pooh" (dir. F. Khitruk, animated V. Zuikov and E. Nazarov) . . 10 10
5844 4 k. "Gena the Crocodile" (dir. R. Kachanov, animated L. Sharts-mann) 15 10
5845 5 k. "Just You Wait!" (dir. V. Kotyonochkin, animated S. Rusakov) 20 10
5846 10 k. "Hedgehog in a Mist" (dir. Yu. Norshtein, animated F. Yarbusova) 30 15

2354. Bonch-Bruevich.

2355. Nurse and Emblems.

1988. Birth Centenary of Mikhail Alexandrovich Bonch-Bruevich (radio engineer).
5848. **2354.** 10 k. black & brown 30 15

1988. 125th Anniv. of International Red Cross and Red Crescent.
5849. **2355.** 15 k. black, blue and red 45 25

2356. Skater.

1988. World Speed Skating Championships, Alma-Ata.
5850. **2356.** 15 k. blue, violet & black 45 25

2357. Makarenko.

1988. Birth Centenary of Anton Semenovich Makarenko (educationist and writer).
5851 **2357** 10 k. green 30 15

2358. Skorina.

2359. Banners and Globe.

1988. 500th Birth Anniv of Frantsisk Skorina (printer).
5852 **2358** 5 k. black 20 10

1988. Labour Day.
5853 **2359** 5 k. multicoloured . . 20 10

2360. Kingisepp.

2361. Track and Athlete.

1988. Birth Centenary of Victor Eduardovich Kingisepp (revolutionary).
5854. **2360.** 5 k. green 20 10

1988. Centenary of Russian Athletics.
5855. **2361.** 15 k. multicoloured 45 25

2362 M. S. Shaginyan

1988. Birth Centenary of Marietta Sergeevna Shaginyan (writer).
5856 **2362** 10 k. brown 30 10

2363 Palace of Congresses, Moscow, Finlandia Hall, Helsinki, and National Flags

2364 "Mir"–"Soyuz TM" Space Complex and "Progress" Spacecraft

1988. 40th Anniv of U.S.S.R.–Finland Friendship Treaty.
5857 **2363** 15 k. multicoloured . . 45 25

1988. Cosmonautics Day.
5858 **2364** 15 k. multicoloured . . 45 25

2365 Sochi

1988. 150th Anniv of Sochi.
5859 **2365** 5 k. multicoloured . . 20 10

2366 "Victory" (P. A. Krivonogov)

1988. V. E. Day (8 May).
5860 **2366** 5 k. multicoloured . . 20 10

2367 Lenin Museum, Moscow

1988. 118th Birth Anniv of Lenin. Designs showing branches of Lenin Central Museum.
5861 **2367** 5 k. brown, deep brown and gold . . 20 10
5862 – 5 k. red, pur & gold 20 10
5863 – 5 k. ochre, brn & gold 20 10
5864 – 5 k. yell, grn & gold 20 10
DESIGNS: No. 5862, Kiev; 5863, Leningrad; 5864, Krasnoyarsk.
See also Nos. 5990/2 and 6131/3.

2368 Akulov

2369 Soviet Display Emblem

1988. Birth Centenary of Ivan Alekseevich Akulov (Communist Party official).
5865 **2368** 5 k. blue 20 10

1988. "Expo 88" World's Fair, Brisbane.
5866 **2369** 20 k. multicoloured 60 30

2370 Marx

2373 Shvernik

2371 Soldiers and Workers

1988. 170th Birth Anniv of Karl Marx.
5867 **2370** 5 k. brown 20 10

1988. Perestroika (Reformation).
5868 **2371** 5 k. multicoloured . . 20 10
5869 – 5 k. brn, red & orge 20 10
DESIGN: No. 5869, Banner, industrial scenes and worker.

1988. Birth Centenary of Nikolai Mikhailovich Shvernik (politician).
5871 **2373** 5 k. black 20 10

2374 Russian Borzoi

1988. Hunting Dogs. Multicoloured.
5872 5 k. Type **2374** 20 10
5873 10 k. Kirgiz borzoi . . 30 15
5874 15 k. Russian hound . . 45 25
5875 20 k. Russian spaniel . . 60 30
5876 35 k. East Siberian husky 1·00 50

2375 Flags, Spassky Tower and Handshake

2376 Kuibyshev

1988. Soviet–American Summit, Moscow.
5877 **2375** 5 k. multicoloured . . 20 10

1988. Birth Centenary of Valerian Vladimirovich Kuibyshev (politician).
5878 **2376** 5 k. brown 20 10

2377 Flags, "Mir" Space Station and "Soyuz TM" Spacecraft.

2378 Crowd and Peace Banners

1988. Soviet–Bulgarian Space Flight.
5879 **2377** 15 k. multicoloured . . 45 25

1988. "For a Nuclear-free World".
5880 **2378** 5 k. multicoloured . . 20 10

2379 Red Flag, Hammer and Sickle and Laurel Branch

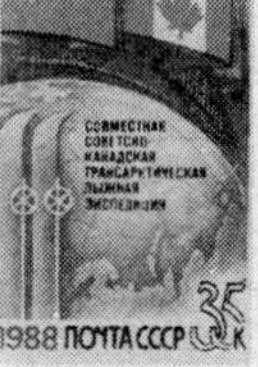

2380 Flags, Skis and Globe

1988. 19th Soviet Communist Party Conference, Moscow (1st issue). Mult.
5881 5 k. Type **2379** 20 10
5882 5 k. Lenin on red flag and interior of Palace of Congresses (35 × 23 mm) 20 10
See also Nos. 5960/2.

1988. Soviet–Canadian Transarctic Ski Expedition.
5884 **2380** 35 k. multicoloured . . 1·00 50

2381 Hurdling

2382 Giant Bellflower

1988. Olympic Games, Seoul. Multicoloured.
5885 5 k. Type **2381** 20 10
5886 10 k. Long jumping . . 30 15
5887 15 k. Basketball 45 25
5888 20 k. Gymnastics . . 60 30
5889 30 k. Swimming 90 45

1988. Deciduous Forest Flowers. Mult.
5891 5 k. Type **2382** 20 10
5892 10 k. Spring pea (horiz) .. 30 15
5893 15 k. Lungwort 45 25
5894 20 k. Turk's-cap lily .. 60 30
5895 35 k. "Ficaria verna" .. 1·00 50

2383 Phobos and "Phobos" Space Probe

2384 Komsomol Badge

1988. Phobos (Mars Moon) International Space Project.
5896 **2383** 10 k. multicoloured .. 30 15

1988. 70th Anniv of Leninist Young Communist League (Komsomol).
5897 **2384** 5 k. multicoloured .. 20 10

2385 Mandela

Филвыставка. Москва
(2387)

2386 "Obeyan Serebryanyi, Light Grey Arab Stallion" (N. E. Sverchkov)

1988. 70th Birthday of Nelson Mandela (African nationalist).
5898 **2385** 10 k. multicoloured .. 30 15

1988. Paintings in Moscow Horse Breeding Museum. Multicoloured.
5899 5 k. Type **2386** 20 10
5900 10 k. "Konvoets" (Kabardin breed) (M. A. Vrubel) (vert) 35 15
5901 15 k. "Horsewoman on Orlov-Rastopchin Horse" (N. E. Sverchkov) 45 25
5902 20 k. "Letuchy, Grey Stallion of Orlov Trotter Breed" (V. A. Serov) (vert) 60 30
5903 30 k. "Sardar, an Akhaltekin Stallion" (A. B. Villevalde) .. 95 45

1988. Stamp Exhibition, Moscow. No. 5897 optd with T **2387**.
5904 **2384** 5 k. multicoloured .. 20 10

2388 Voikov

2389 "Portrait of O. K. Lansere" (Z. E Serebryakova)

1988. Birth Centenary of Pyotr Lazarevich Voikov (diplomat).
5905 **2388** 5 k. black 20 10

1988. Soviet Culture Fund. Multicoloured.
5906 10 k.+5 k. Type **2389** .. 45 25
5907 15 k.+7 k. "Boyarynya (noblewoman) looking at Embroidery Design" (K. V. Lebedev) (horiz) 65 35
5908 30 k.+15 k. "Talent" (N. P. Bogdanov-Belsky) .. 1·40 70

2390 Envelopes and U.P.U. Emblem

2391 "Mir" Space Station and "Soyuz-TM" Spacecraft

1988. International Correspondence Week.
5910 **2390** 5 k. turq, blue & blk 20 10

1988. Soviet–Afghan Space Flight.
5911 **2391** 15 k. grn, red & blk 45 25

2392 Emblem and Open Book

2393 Kviring

1988. 30th Anniv of "Problems of Peace and Socialism" (magazine).
5912 **2392** 10 k. multicoloured .. 30 15

1988. Birth Centenary of Emmanuil Ionovich Kviring (politician).
5913 **2393** 5 k. black 20 10

2394 "Ilya Muromets' (Russia) (R. Smirnova)

2395 "Appeal of the Leader" (detail, I. M. Toidze)

1988. Epic Poems of Soviet Union (1st series). Illustrations by artists named. Mult.
5914 10 k. Type **2394** 30 15
5915 10 k. "Cossack Golota" (Ukraine) (M. Deregus) (horiz) 30 15
5916 10 k. "Musician-Magician" (Byelorussia) (N. Poplavskaya) 30 15
5917 10 k. "Koblandy Batyr" (Kazakhstan) (I. Isabaev) (horiz) .. 30 15
5918 10 k. "Alpamysh" (Uzbekistan) (R. Khalilov) 30 15
See also Nos. 6017/21 and 6139/43.

1988. 71st Anniv of October Revolution.
5919 **2395** 5 k. multicoloured .. 20 10

2396 Bolotov

2397 Tupolev

1988. 250th Birth Anniv of Andrei Timofeevich Bolotov (agriculturalist).
5920 **2396** 10 k. brown 30 15

1988. Birth Centenary of Academician Andrei Nikolaevich Tupolev (aircraft designer).
5921 **2397** 10 k. blue 30 15

2398 Bear

2399 "Sibir" (atomic ice-breaker)

1988. Zoo Relief Fund. Multicoloured.
5922 10 k.+5 k. Type **2398** .. 45 25
5923 10 k.+5 k. Wolf .. 45 25
5924 20 k.+10 k. Fox .. 95 45
5925 20 k.+10 k. Wild boar .. 95 45
5926 20 k.+10 k. Lynx .. 95 45

1988. Soviet Arctic Expedition.
5927 **2399** 20 k. multicoloured .. 60 30

2400 Ustinov

2401 National Initials

1988. 80th Birth Anniv of Marshal Dmitri Fyodorovich Ustinov.
5928 **2400** 5 k. brown 20 10

1988. 10th Anniv of U.S.S.R.–Vietnam Friendship Treaty.
5929 **2401** 10 k. multicoloured .. 30 15

2402 Building Facade

1988. 50th Anniv of State House of Broadcasting and Sound Recording.
5930 **2402** 10 k. multicoloured .. 30 15

2403 Emblem

1988. 40th Anniv of Declaration of Human Rights.
5931 **2403** 10 k. multicoloured .. 30 15

2404 Life Guard of Preobrazhensky Regt. with Peter I's New Year Decree

1988. New Year.
5932 **2404** 5 k. multicoloured .. 20 10

2405 Flags and Cosmonauts

1988. Soviet–French Space Flight.
5933 **2405** 15 k. multicoloured .. 45 25

2406 "Skating Rink" (Olya Krutova)

2407 Lacis

1988. Lenin Soviet Childrens' Fund. Children's Paintings. Multicoloured.
5934 5 k.+2 k. Type **2406** .. 25 15
5935 5 k.+2 k. "Cock" (Nasta Shcheglova) 25 15
5936 5 k.+2 k. "May is flying over the Meadows, May is flying over the Fields" (Larisa Gaidash) 25 15

1988. Birth Centenary of Martins Lacis (revolutionary).
5937 **2407** 5 k. green 20 10

★
КОСМИЧЕСКАЯ ПОЧТА
(2408)

2410 Post Messenger

1988. "Space Post". No. 4682 optd with T **2408**.
5938 1 r. blue .. .. .. 3·00 1·50

1988.
5940 **2410** 1 k. brown 10 10
6073 – 2 k. brown 10 10
5941 – 3 k. green 10 10
6075 – 4 k. blue 10 10
6076 – 5 k. red 15 10
6077 – 7 k. blue 15 10
6078 – 10 k. brown .. 25 15
6079 – 12 k. purple .. 30 20
6080 – 13 k. violet .. 30 20
6081 – 15 k. blue .. 35 20
6082 – 20 k. brown .. 45 25
6083 – 25 k. green .. 55 30
6084 – 30 k. blue .. 65 35
6085 – 35 k. brown .. 75 40
6086 – 50 k. blue .. 1·00 50
6087 – 1 r. blue .. .. 1·90 1·00

DESIGNS: 2 k. Old mail transport (sailing packet, steam train and mail coach); 3 k. "Aurora" (cruiser); 4 k. Spassky Tower and Lenin's Tomb, Red Square, Moscow; 5 k. State emblem and flag; 7 k. Modern mail transport (aircraft, liner, train and mail van); 10 k. "The Worker and the Collective Farmer" (statue, V. I. Mukhina); 12 k. Rocket on launch pad; 13 k. Satellite; 15 k. "Orbit" dish aerial; 20 k. Symbols of art and literature; 25 k. "The Discus-thrower" (5th-century Greek statue by Miron); 30 k. Map of Antarctica and penguins; 35 k. "Mercury" (statue, Giovanni da Bologna); 50 k. White cranes; 1 r. Universal Postal Union emblem.

2411 Great Cascade and Samson Fountain

2412 1st-cent B.C. Gold Coin of Tigran the Great

1988. Petrodvorets Fountains. Each green and grey.
5952 5 k. Type **2411** 20 10
5953 10 k. Adam fountain (D. Bonazza) 30 15
5954 15 k. Golden Mountain cascade (Niccolo Miketti and Mikhail Zemtsov) 45 25
5955 30 k. Roman fountains (Bartolomeo Rastrelli) 95 45
5956 50 k. Oaklet trick fountain (Rastrelli) .. 1·50 1·00

1988. Armenian Earthquake Relief. Armenian History. Multicoloured.

5957	20 k.+10 k. Type **2412** ..	95	45
5958	30 k.+15 k. Ripsime Church	1·25	65
5959	50 k.+25 k. "Madonna and Child" (18th-century fresco, Ovnat Ovnatanyan)	2·25	1·25

2413 Hammer and Sickle

1988. 19th All-Union Communist Party Conference, Moscow (2nd issue). Mult.

5960	5 k. Type **2413**	20	10
5961	5 k. Hammer and sickle and building girders ..	20	10
5962	5 k. Hammer and sickle and wheat	20	10

2415 "Vostok" Rocket, "Lunar 1", Earth and Moon

2416 Virtanen

1989. 30th Anniv of First Russian Moon Flight.

5964 **2415** 15 k. multicoloured .. 45 25

1989. Birth Cent of Jalmari Virtanen (poet).

5965 **2416** 5 k. brown and bistre 20 10

2417 Headquarters Building, Moscow

1989. 40th Anniv of Council for Mutual Economic Aid.

5966 **2417** 10 k. multicoloured .. 30 15

2418 Forest Protection

2419 18th-century Samovar

1989. Nature Conservation. Multicoloured.

5967	5 k. Type **2418**	30	20
5968	10 k. Arctic preservation	30	15
5969	15 k. Anti-desertification campaign	40	20

1989. Russian Samovars in State Museum, Leningrad. Multicoloured.

5970	5 k. Type **2419**	20	10
5971	10 k. 19th-century barrel samovar by Ivan Lisitsin of Tula ..	30	15
5972	20 k. 1830s Kabachok travelling samovar by Sokolov Brothers factory, Tula ..	55	30
5973	30 k. 1840s samovar by Nikolai Malikov factory, Tula	85	45

2420 Mussorgsky and Scene from "Boris Godunov"

2421 Dybenko

1989. 150th Birth Anniv of Modest Petrovich Mussorgsky (composer).

5974 **2420** 10 k. purple & brown 30 15

1989. Birth Centenary of Pavel Dybenko (military leader).

5975 **2421** 5 k. black 20 10

2422 Shevchenko

2423 "Lilium speciosum"

1989. 175th Birth Anniv of Taras Shevchenko (Ukrainian poet and painter).

5976 **2422** 5 k. brown, grn & blk 20 10

1989. Lilies. Multicoloured.

5977	5 k. Type **2423**	20	10
5978	10 k. "African Queen" ..	30	15
5979	15 k. "Eclat du Soir" ..	40	20
5980	30 k. "White Tiger" ..	85	45

2424 Marten

1989. Zoo Relief Fund. Multicoloured.

5981	10 k.+5 k. Type **2424** ..	40	20
5982	10 k.+5 k. Squirrel ..	40	20
5983	20 k.+10 k. Hare ..	85	45
5984	20 k.+10 k. Hedgehog ..	85	45
5985	20 k.+10 k. Badger ..	85	45

2426 "Victory Banner" (P. Loginov and V. Pamfilov)

1989. Victory Day.

5987 **2426** 5 k. multicoloured .. 20 10

2427 "Mir" Space Station

1989. Cosmonautics Day.

5988 **2427** 15 k. multicoloured .. 40 20

2428 Emblem and Flags

2430 Statue

1989. U.S.–Soviet Bering Bridge Expedition.

5989 **2428** 10 k. multicoloured .. 30 15

1989. 119th Birth Anniv of Lenin. As T **2367**. Branches of Lenin Central Museum.

5990	5 k. brown, ochre & gold	20	10
5991	5 k. dp brown, brn & gold	20	10
5992	5 k. multicoloured ..	20	10

DESIGNS: No. 5990, Frunze; 5991, Kazan; 5992, Kuibyshev

1989. 70th Anniv of First Hungarian Soviet Republic.

5994 **2430** 5 k. multicoloured .. 20 10

2431 "Motherland" Statue

2432 Drone

1989. 400th Anniv of Volgograd (formerly Tsaritsyn).

5995 **2431** 5 k. multicoloured .. 20 10

1989. Bees. Multicoloured.

5996	5 k. Type **2432**	20	10
5997	10 k. Bees, flowers and hive	30	15
5998	20 k. Bee on flower ..	55	30
5999	35 k. Feeding queen bee	90	45

2433 Negative and Positive Images

2434 Map above Dove as Galley

1989. 150th Anniv of Photography.

6000 **2433** 5 k. multicoloured .. 20 10

1989. "Europe—Our Common Home". Mult.

6001	5 k. Type **2434**	20	10
6002	10 k. Laying foundations of Peace	30	15
6003	15 k. Storks' nest ..	40	20

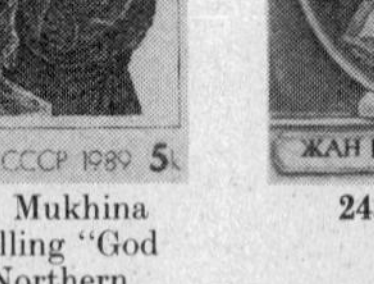

2435 Mukhina modelling "God of Northern Wind" (after M. Nesterov)

2436 Racine

1989. Birth Centenary of Vera I. Mukhina (sculptress).

6004 **2435** 5 k. blue 20 10

1989. 150th Birth Anniv of Jean Racine (dramatist).

6005 **2436** 15 k. multicoloured .. 40 20

2437 Rabbit

1989. Lenin Soviet Children's Fund. Children's Paintings. Multicoloured.

6006	5 k.+2 k. Type **2437** ..	25	10
6007	5 k.+2 k. Cat	25	10
6008	5 k.+2 k. Nurse ..	25	10

See also Nos. 6162/4.

2438 Kuratov

1989. 150th Birth Anniv of Ivan Kuratov (writer).

6009 **2438** 5 k. dp brown & brn 20 10

2439 Emblem

2440 Common Shelduck

1989. 13th World Youth and Students' Festival, Pyongyang.

6010 **2439** 10 k. multicoloured .. 30 15

1989. Ducks (1st series). Multicoloured.

6011	5 k. Type **2440**	20	10
6012	15 k. Green-winged teal ..	40	20
6013	20 k. Ruddy shelduck ..	55	30

See also Nos. 6159/61, 6264/6, 6368/70 and 6420/2.

2441 "Storming of Bastille" (Gelman after Monnet)

1989. Bicentenary of French Revolution.

6014	**2441** 5 k. multicoloured ..	20	10
6015	– 15 k. blue blk & red	40	20
6016	– 20 k. blue, blk & red	50	25

DESIGNS: 15 k. Jean-Paul Marat, Georges Danton and Maximilien Robespierre; 20 k. "Marseillaise" (relief by F. Rude from Arc de Triomphe).

1989. Epic Poems of Soviet Union (2nd series). Illustrations by named artists. As T **2394**. Multicoloured.

6017	10 k. "Amirani" (Georgia) (V. Oniani)	30	15
6018	10 k. "Koroglu" (Azerbaijan) (A. Gadzhiev) ..	30	15
6019	10 k. "Fir, Queen of Grass Snakes" (Lithuania) (A. Makunaite)	30	15
6020	10 k. "Mioritsa" (Moldavia) (I. Bogdesko) ..	30	15
6021	10 k. "Lachplesis" (Lettish) (G. Wilks) ..	30	15

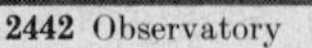

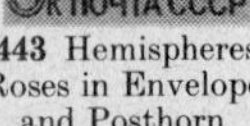

2442 Observatory

2443 Hemispheres, Roses in Envelope and Posthorn

1989. 150th Anniv of Pulkovo Observatory.

6022 **2442** 10 k. multicoloured .. 35 15

1989. International Letter Week.
6023 **2443** 5 k. multicoloured .. 20 10

2444 Lynx

2446 Buildings, Container Ship and Bicentenary Emblem

1989. 50th Anniv of Tallin Zoo.
6024 **2444** 10 k. multicoloured .. 30 15

1989 Bicentenary of Nikolaev.
6026 **2446** 5 k. multicoloured .. 20 10

2447 Nkrumah

2448 1921 40 r. Stamp

1989. 80th Birth Anniv of Kwame Nkrumah (first Prime Minister and President of Ghana).
6027 **2447** 10 k. multicoloured .. 30 15

1989. 6th All-Union Philatelic Society Congress, Moscow.
6028 **2448** 10 k. multicoloured .. 30 15

2449 Cooper

1989. Birth Bicentenary of James Fenimore Cooper (writer) (1st issue).
6029 **2449** 15 k. multicoloured .. 40 20
See also Nos. 6055/9.

2450 V. L. Durov (trainer) and Sealions

1989. 70th Anniv of Soviet Circus. Mult.
6030 1 k. Type **2450** 10 10
6031 3 k. M. N. Rumyantsev (clown "Karandash") with donkey 10 10
6032 4 k. V. I. Filatov (founder of Bear Circus) and bears on motor cycle) 15 10
6033 5 k. E. T. Kio (illusionist) and act 20 10
6034 10 k. V. E. Lazarenko (clown and acrobat) and act 30 15

2451 Emblem on Glove

2452 Li Dazhao

1989. International Amateur Boxing Association Championship, Moscow.
6036 **2451** 15 k. multicoloured .. 40 20

1989. Birth Centenary of Li Dazhao (co-founder of Chinese Communist Party).
6037 **2452** 5 k. brn, stone & blk 20 10

2453 Khetagurov

1989. 130th Birth Anniv of Kosta Khetagurov (Ossetian writer).
6038 **2453** 5 k. brown 20 10

2454 "October Guardsmen" (M. M. Chepik)

1989. 72nd Anniv of October Revolution.
6039 **2454** 5 k. multicoloured .. 20 10

2455 Russian Spoons, Psaltery, Balalaika, Zhaleika and Accordion

1989. Traditional Musical Instruments (1st series). Multicoloured.
6040 10 k. Type **2455** 30 15
6041 10 k. Ukrainian bandura, trembita, drymba, svyril (pipes) and dulcimer 30 15
6042 10 k. Byelorussian tambourine, bastlya (fiddle), lera and dudka (pipe) 30 15
6043 10 k. Uzbek nagors (drums), rubab, zang, karnai and gidzhak .. 30 15
See also Nos. 6183/6 and 6303/5.

2456 "Demonstration of First Radio Receiver, 1895" (N. A. Sysoev)

2457 National Flag and Provincial Arms

1989. 130th Birth Anniv of Aleksandr Stepanovich Popov (radio pioneer).
6044 **2456** 10 k. multicoloured .. 30 15

1989. 40th Anniv of German Democratic Republic.
6045 **2457** 5 k. multicoloured .. 20 10

2458 Polish National Colours forming "45"

2459 Kosior

1989. 45th Anniv of Liberation of Poland.
6046 **2458** 5 k. multicoloured .. 20 10

1989. Birth Centenary of Stanislav Vikentievich Kosior (vice-chairman of Council of People's Commissars).
6047 **2459** 5 k. black 20 10

2460 Nehru

2461 "Village Market" (A. V. Makovsky)

1989. Birth Centenary of Jawaharlal Nehru (Indian statesman).
6048 **2460** 15 k. brown 40 20

1989. Soviet Culture Fund. Multicoloured.
6049 4 k.+2. k. Type **2461** .. 20 10
6050 5 k.+2 k. "Lady in Hat" (E. L. Zelenin) .. 25 15
6051 10 k.+5 k. "Portrait of the Actress Bazhenova" (A. F. Sofronova) .. 40 20
6052 20 k.+10 k. "Two Women" (Hugo Shaiber) 75 40
6053 30 k.+15 k. 19th-century teapot and plates from Popov porcelain works 1·10 55

2462 Berzin

2463 "The Hunter"

1989. Birth Centenary of Yan Karlovich Berzin (head of Red Army Intelligence).
6054 **2462** 5 k. black 20 10

1989. Birth Bicentenary of James Fenimore Cooper (writer) (2nd issue). Illustrations of his novels. Multicoloured.
6055 20 k. Type **2463** 50 25
6056 20 k. "Last of the Mohicans" 50 25
6057 20 k. "The Pathfinder" .. 50 25
6058 20 k. "The Pioneers" .. 50 25
6059 20 k. "The Prairie" .. 50 25
Nos. 6055/9 were printed together, se-tenant, forming a composite design.

2464 St. Basil's Cathedral and Minin and Pozharsky Statue, Moscow

2465 Dymkovo Toy

1989. Historical Monuments (1st series). Multicoloured.
6060 15 k. Type **2464** 40 20
6061 15 k. Sts. Peter and Paul Cathedral and statue of Peter I, Leningrad .. 40 20
6062 15 k. St. Sophia's Cathedral and statue of Bogdan Chmielnitsky, Kiev 40 20
6063 15 k. Khodzha Ahmed Yasavi mausoleum, Turkestan 40 20
6064 15 k. Khazret Khyzr Mosque, Samarkand .. 40 20
See also Nos. 6165/72 and 6231/3.

1989. New Year.
6065 **2465** 5 k. multicoloured .. 20 10

2466 Soviet Lunar Vehicle

2468 Acid Rain destroying Rose

1989. "Expo 89" International Stamp Exhibition, Washington D.C. Mult.
6066 25 k. Type **2466** 65 35
6067 25 k. Astronaut and landing module on Moon 65 35
6068 25 k. Cosmonauts on Mars 65 35
6069 25 k. Flag and shield on Mars 65 35

1989. Russian Naval Commanders (2nd series). As T **2345**.
6091 5 k. blue and brown .. 10 15
6092 10 k. blue and brown .. 25 15
6093 15 k. blue and deep blue 35 20
6094 20 k. blue and deep blue 45 25
6095 30 k. blue and brown .. 65 35
6096 35 k. blue and brown .. 75 40
DESIGNS: 5 k. V. A. Kornilov and "Pervaz Bati". 10 k. V. I. Istomin and "Parizh". 15 k. G. I. Nevelskoi and "Baikal". 20 k. G. I. Butakov and iron-clad squadron. 30 k. A. A. Popov, "Pyotr Veliky" and "Vitze Admiral Popov". 35 k. S. O. Makarov, "Intibah" (Turkish warship) and "Veliky Khyaz Konstantin".

1990. Nature Conservation. Multicoloured.
6097 10 k. Type **2468** 25 15
6098 15 k. Oil-smeared bird perching on globe .. 35 20
6099 20 k. Blade sawing down tree 45 25

2469 Ladya Monument and Golden Gates, Kiev (Ukraine)

2470 Flag and Hanoi Monument

1990. Republic Capitals. Multicoloured.
6100 5 k. Lenin Palace of Culture, Government House and Academy of Sciences, Alma-Ata (Kazakhstan) 15 10
6101 5 k. Library, Mollanepes Theatre and War Heroes Monument, Ashkhabad (Turkmenistan) 15 10
6102 5 k. Maiden's Tower and Divan-Khane Palace, Baku (Azerbaijan) .. 15 10
6103 5 k. Sadriddin Aini Theatre and Avicenna Monument, Dushanbe (Tadzhikistan) .. 15 10
6104 4 k. Spendyarov Theatre and David Sasunsky Monument, Yerevan (Armenia) 15 10
6105 5 k. Satylganov Philharmonic Society building and Manas Memorial, Frunze (Kirgizia) .. 15 10
6106 5 k. Type **2469** .. 15 10
6107 5 k. Cathedral and Victory Arch, Kishinev (Moldavia) 15 10
6108 5 k. Government House and Liberation Monument, Minsk (Byelorussia) 15 10
6109 5 k. Konstantino-Yeleninsky Tower and Ivan the Great Bell Tower, Moscow (Russian Federation) .. 15 10
6110 5 k. Cathedral, "Three Brothers" building and Freedom Monument, Riga (Latvia) .. 15 10
6111 5 k. Herman the Long, Oliviste Church, Cathedral and Town Hall towers and wall turret, Tallin (Estonia) 15 10
6112 5 k. Kukeldash Medrese and University, Tashkent (Uzbekistan) .. 15 10

6113 5 k. Metekh Temple and Vakhtang Gorgasal Monument, Tbilisi (Georgia) 15 10
6114 5 k. Gediminas Tower and St. Anne's Church, Vilnius (Lithuania) .. 15 10

1990. 60th Anniv of Vietnamese Communist Party.
6115 **2470** 5 k. multicoloured .. 15 10

2471 Ho Chi Minh

2472 Snowy Owl

1990. Birth Centenary of Ho Chi Minh (Vietnamese leader).
6116 **2471** 10 k. brown and black 25 15

1990. Owls. Multicoloured.
6117 10 k. Type **2472** 25 15
6118 20 k. Eagle owl (vert) .. 45 20
6119 55 k. Long-eared owl .. 1·10 55

2473 Sailing Ship, Posthorn and Penny Black

1990. 150th Anniv of the Penny Black.
6120 **2473** 10 k. multicoloured 25 15
6121 – 20 k. black and gold 45 25
6122 – 20 k. black and gold 45 25
6123 – 35 k. multicoloured 75 40
6124 – 35 k. multicoloured 75 40
DESIGNS: No. 6121, Anniversary emblem and Penny Black (lettered "T P"); 6122, As No. 6121 but stamp lettered "T F"; 6123, "Stamp World London 90" International Stamp Exhibition emblem and Penny Black (lettered "V K"); 6124, As No. 6123 but stamp lettered "A H".

2474 Electric Cables

1990. 125th Anniversary of I.T.U.
6126 **2474** 20 k. multicoloured .. 45 25

2475 Flowers

1990. Labour Day.
6127 **2475** 5 k. multicoloured .. 15 10

2476 "Victory, 1945" (A. Lysenko)

1990. 45th Anniv of Victory in Second World War.
6128 **2476** 5 k. multicoloured .. 15 10

2477 "Mir" Space Complex and Cosmonaut

2478 Lenin

1990. Cosmonauts Day.
6129 **2477** 20 k. multicoloured .. 45 25

1990. "Leniniana '90" All-Union Stamp Exhibition.
6130 **2478** 5 k. brown 15 10

1990. 120th Birth Anniv of Lenin. Branches of Lenin Central Museum. As T **2367**.
6131 5 k. red, lake and gold .. 15 10
6132 5 k. pink, purple and gold 15 10
6133 5 k. multicoloured .. 15 10
DESIGNS: No. 6131, Ulyanovsk; 6132, Baku; 6133, Tashkent.

2479 Scene from "Iolanta" (opera) and Tchaikovsky

1990. 150th Birth Anniv of Pyotr Ilich Tchaikovsky (composer).
6134 **2479** 15 k. black 35 20

2480 Golden Eagle

1990. Zoo Relief Fund. Multicoloured.
6135 10 k.+5 k. Type **2480** .. 35 20
6136 20 k.+10 k. Saker falcon ("Falco cherrug") .. 65 35
6137 20 k.+10 k. Raven ("Corvus corax") .. 65 35

2481 Etching by G. A. Echeistov

2482 Goalkeeper and Players

1990. 550th Anniv of "Dzhangar" (Kalmuk folk epic).
6138 **2481** 10 k. ochre, brn & blk 25 15

1990. Epic Poems of Soviet Union (3rd series). Illustrations by named artists. As T **2394**. Multicoloured.
6139 10 k. "Manas" (Kirgizia) (T. Gertsen) (horiz) .. 25 15
6140 10 k. "Gurugli" (Tadzhikistan) (I. Martynov) (horiz) 25 15
6141 10 k. "David Sasunsky" (Armenia) (M. Abegyan) 25 15
6142 10 k. "Gerogly" (Turkmenistan) (I. Klychev) 25 15
6143 10 k. "Kalevipoeg" (Estonia) (O. Kallis) .. 25 15

1990. World Cup Football Championship, Italy. Multicoloured.
6144 5 k. Type **2482** 15 10
6145 10 k. Players 25 15
6146 15 k. Attempted tackle .. 35 20
6147 25 k. Referee and players 55 30
6148 35 k. Goalkeeper saving ball 75 40

2483 Globe and Finlandia Hall, Helsinki

2484 Competitors and Target

1990. 15th Anniv of European Security and Co-operation Conference, Helsinki.
6149 **2483** 15 k. multicoloured .. 35 20

1990. 45th World Shooting Championships, Moscow.
6150 **2484** 15 k. multicoloured .. 35 20

2485 Glaciology Research

1990. Soviet–Australian Scientific Co-operation in Antarctica. Multicoloured.
6151 5 k. Type **2485** 15 10
6152 50 k. Krill (marine biology research) .. .. 1·00 50

2486 Emblem and Sports Pictograms

1990. Goodwill Games, Seattle.
6154 **2486** 10 k. multicoloured .. 25 15

2488 Greylag Geese

1990. Poultry. Multicoloured.
6156 5 k. Type **2488** 15 10
6157 10 k. Adlers (chickens) .. 25 15
6158 15 k. Bronze North Caucasian turkeys .. 35 20

2489 Mallards

1990. Ducks (2nd series). Multicoloured.
6159 5 k. Type **2489** 15 10
6160 15 k. Goldeneyes .. 35 20
6161 20 k. Red-crested pochards 45 25

1990. Lenin Soviet Children's Fund. Children's Paintings. As T **2437**. Mult.
6162 5 k.+2 k. Clown .. 20 10
6163 5 k.+2 k. Ladies in crinolines 20 10
6164 5 k.+2 k. Children with banner 20 10

1990. Historical Monuments (2nd series). As T **2464**. Multicoloured.
6165 15 k. St. Nshan's Church, Akhpat (Armenia) .. 35 20
6166 15 k. Shirvanshah Palace, Baku (Azerbaijan) .. 35 20
6167 15 k. Soroki Fortress and statue of Stefan III, Kishinev (Moldavia) .. 35 20
6168 15 k. Spaso-Efrosinevsky Cathedral, Polotsk (Byelorussia) 35 20
6169 15 k. St. Peter's Church and 16th-century Riga (Latvia) 35 20
6170 15 k. St. Nicholas's Church and carving of city arms, Tallin (Estonia) 35 20

6171 15 k. Mtatsminda Pantheon and statue of Nikoloz Baratashvili, Tbilisi (Georgia) .. 35 20
6172 15 k. Cathedral and bell tower, Vilnius (Lithuania) 35 20

2490 Sordes

1990. Prehistoric Animals. Multicoloured.
6173 1 k. Type **2490** 10 10
6174 3 k. Chalicotherium (vert) 10 10
6175 5 k. Indricotherium (vert) 15 10
6176 10 k. Saurolophus (vert) 25 15
6177 20 k. Thyestes 45 25

2491 "St Basil's Cathedral and Kremlin, Moscow" (Sanjay Adhikari)

2492 Pigeon Post

1990. Indo–Soviet Friendship. Children's Paintings. Multicoloured.
6178 10 k. Type **2491** 25 10
6179 10 k. "Life in India" (Tanya Vorontsova) .. 25 10

1990. Letter Writing Week.
6180 **2492** 5 k. blue 15 10

2493 Traffic on Urban Roads

2495 Killer Whales

1990. Traffic Safety Week.
6181 **2493** 5 k. multicoloured .. 15 10

1990. Traditional Musical Instruments (2nd series). As T **2455**. Multicoloured.
6183 10 k. Azerbaijani balalian, shar and caz (stringed instruments), zurna and drum 25 15
6184 10 k. Georgian bagpipes, tambourine, flute, pipes and chonguri (stringed instrument) 25 15
6185 10 k. Kazakh flute, rattle, daubra and kobyz (stringed instruments) 25 15
6186 10 k. Lithuanian bagpipes, horns and kankles .. 25 15

1990. Marine Mammals.
6187 25 k. Type **2495** 55 30
6188 25 k. Northern sealions .. 55 30
6189 25 k. Sea otter 55 30
6190 25 k. Common dolphin .. 55 30

2496 "Lenin among Delegates to Second Congress of Soviets" (S. V. Gerasimov)

2497 Ivan Bunin (1933)

1990. 73rd Anniv of October Revolution.
6191 **2496** 5 k. multicoloured .. 15 10

1990. Nobel Prize Winners for Literature.
6192 **2497** 15 k. brown .. 35 20
6193 – 15 k. brown .. 35 20
6194 – 15 k. black 35 20
DESIGNS: No. 6193, Mikhail Sholokhov (1965); 6194, Boris Pasternak.

2498 "Sever-2"

1990. Research Submarines. Multicoloured.
6195 5 k. Type **2498** 15 10
6196 10 k. "Tinro-2" 25 15
6197 15 k. "Argus" 35 20
6198 25 k. "Paisis" 55 30
6199 35 k. "Mir" 75 40

2499 "Motherland" Statue (E. Kocher), Screen and Emblem

Филателистическая выставка „Армения-90" (**2500**)

Восстановление, милосердие, помощь (**2501**)

1990. "Armenia '90" Stamp Exhibition, Yerevan. (a) Type **2499**.
6200 **2499** 10 k. multicoloured 25 15

(b) Nos. 5957/9 optd with T **2500** or as T **2501**
6201 **2500** 20 k. + 10 k. mult .. 65 35
6202 **2501** 30 k. + 15 k. mult .. 95 50
6203 50 k. + 25 k. mult .. 1·50 75

2502 S. A. Vaupshasov

2503 Soviet and Japanese Flags above Earth

1990. Intelligence Agents.
6204 **2502** 5 k. deep green, green and black .. 15 10
6205 – 5 k. deep brown, brown and black 15 10
6206 – 5 k. deep blue, blue and black .. 15 10
6207 – 5 k. brn, buff & blk 15 10
6208 – 5 k. brown, bistre and black .. 15 10
DESIGNS: No. 6205, R. I. Abel; 6206, Kim Philby; 6207, I. D. Kudrya; 6208, K. T. Molodyi.

1990. Soviet–Japanese Space Flight.
6209 **2503** 20 k. multicoloured .. 45 25

2504 Grandfather Frost and Toys

1990. New Year.
6210 **2504** 5 k. multicoloured .. 15 10

MINIMUM PRICE

The minimum price quoted is 5p which represents a handling charge rather than a basis for valuing common stamps. For further notes about prices see introductory pages.

2505 "Unkrada"

1990. Soviet Culture Fund. Paintings by N. K. Rerikh. Multicoloured.
6211 10 k. + 5 k. Type **2505** .. 35 20
6212 20 k. + 10 k. "Pskovo-Pechorsky Monastery' 65 35

2507 Globe, Eiffel Tower and Flags

1990. "Charter for New Europe". Signing of European Conventional Arms Treaty, Paris.
6214 **2507** 30 k. multicoloured .. 65 35

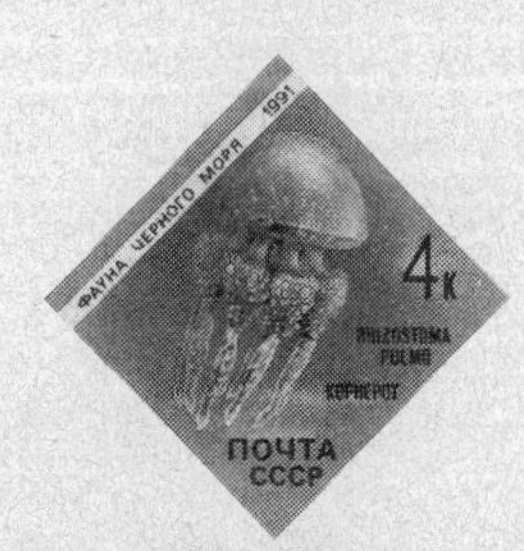

2508 Jellyfish

1991. Marine Animals. Multicoloured.
6215 4 k. Type **2508** 15 10
6216 5 k. Anemone 15 10
6217 10 k. Atlantic spiny dogfish 25 15
6218 15 k. European anchovy 30 20
6219 20 k. Bottle-nosed dolphin 45 25

2509 Keres

1991. 75th Birth Anniv of Paul Keres (chess player).
6220 **2509** 15 k. brown 35 20

2510 Radioactive Particles killing Vegetation

1991. 5th Anniv of Chernobyl Nuclear Power Station Disaster.
6221 **2510** 15 k. multicoloured .. 35 20

2511 "Sorrento Coast with View of Capri" (Shchedrin)

1991. Birth Bicentenary of Silvestr Shchedrin and 150th Birth Anniv of Arkhip Kuindzhi (painters). Multicoloured.
6222 10 k. Type **2511** 25 15
6223 10 k. "New Rome. View of St. Angelo's Castle" (Shchedrin) 25 15
6224 10 k. "Evening in the Ukraine" (Kuindzhi) .. 25 15
6225 10 k. "Birch Grove" (Kuindzhi) 25 15

2512 White Stork

1991. Zoo Relief Fund.
6226 **2512** 10 k. + 5 k. mult .. 35 20

2513 Fish and Bell Tower, Volga

1991. Environmental Protection. Mult.
6227 10 k. Type **2513** 25 15
6228 15 k. Sable and Lake Baikal 35 20
6229 20 k. Saiga and dried bed of Aral Sea 45 25

1991. Historical Monuments (3rd series). As T **2464**. Multicoloured.
6231 15 k. Minaret, Uzgen, Kirgizia 35 20
6232 15 k. Mohammed Bashar Mausoleum, Tadzhikistan 35 20
6233 15 k. Talkhatan-baba Mosque, Turkmenistan 35 20

2515 G. Shelikhov and Kodiak, 1784

1991. 500th Anniv of Discovery of America by Columbus. Russian Settlements.
6234 **2515** 20 k. blue and black 45 25
6235 – 30 k. bistre, brown and black .. 65 35
6236 – 50 k. orange, brown and black .. 1·00 50
DESIGNS: 30 k. Aleksandr Baranov and Sitka, 1804; 50 k. I. Kuskov and Fort Ross, California, 1812.

2516 Satellite and Liner

2517 Yuri Gagarin in Uniform

1991. 10th Anniv of United Nations Transport and Communications in Asia and the Pacific Programme.
6237 **2516** 10 k. multicoloured .. 20 10

1991. Cosmonautics Day. 30th Anniv of First Man in Space. Each brown.
6238 25 k. Type **2517** 50 25
6239 25 k. Gagarin wearing space suit 50 25
6240 25 k. Gagarin in uniform with cap 50 25
6241 25 k. Gagarin in civilian dress 50 25

2519 "May 1945" (A. and S. Tkachev)

1991. Victory Day.
6244 **2519** 5 k. multicoloured .. 10 10

2520 "Lenin working on Book 'Materialism and Empirical Criticism' in Geneva Library" (P. Belousov)

1991. 121st Birth Anniv of Lenin.
6245 **2520** 5 k. multicoloured .. 10 10

2521 Prokofiev

1991. Birth Centenary of Sergei Prokofiev (composer).
6246 **2521** 15 k. brown 30 15

2522 "Cypripedium calceolus"

2523 Ilya I. Mechnikov (medicine, 1908)

1991. Orchids. Multicoloured.
6247 3 k. Type **2522** 10 10
6248 5 k. "Orchis purpurea" .. 10 10
6249 10 k. "Ophrys apifera" .. 20 10
6250 20 k. "Calypso bulbosa" 40 20
6251 25 k. "Epipactis palustris" 50 25

1991. Nobel Prize Winners. Each black.
6252 15 k. Type **2523** 30 15
6253 15 k. Ivan P. Pavlov (medicine, 1904) .. 30 15
6254 15 k. A. D. Sakharov (physics, 1975) .. 30 15

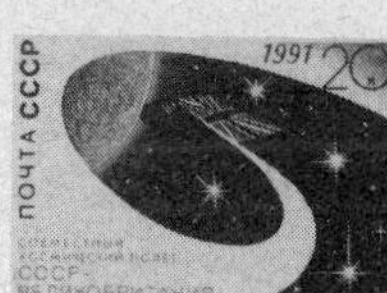

2524 Soviet and British Flags in Space

1991. Soviet–British Space Flight.
6255 **2524** 20 k. multicoloured .. 40 20

2525 Saroyan

1991. 10th Death Anniv of William Saroyan (writer).
6256 **2525** 1 r. multicoloured .. 2·00 2·00

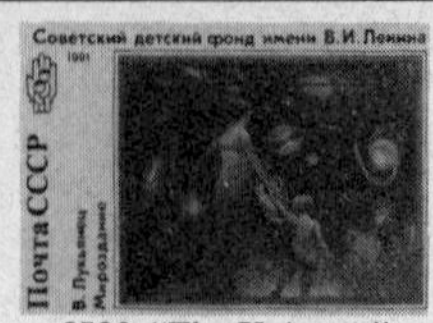
2526 "The Universe"

1991. Lenin Soviet Children's Fund. Paintings by V. Lukyanets. Multicoloured.
6257 10 k. Type **2526** 20 10
6258 10 k. "Another Planet" .. 20 10

2527 Miniature from "Ostromirov Gospel" (first book written in Cyrillic), 1056–57

1991. Culture of Medieval Russia. Mult.
6259 10 k. Type **2527** 20 10
6260 15 k. Page from "Russian Truth" (code of laws), 11th-13th century .. 30 15
6261 20 k. Portrait of Sergy Radonezhsky (embroidered book cover), 1424 40 20
6262 25 k. "The Trinity" (icon, Andrei Rublev), 1411 .. 50 25
6263 30 k. Illustration from "Book of the Apostles", 1564 .. .. .. 60 30

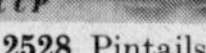
2528 Pintails **2529** Emblem

1991. Ducks (3rd series). Multicoloured.
6264 5 k. Type **2528** 10 10
6265 15 k. Greater scaups .. 30 15
6266 20 k. White-headed ducks 40 20

1991. European Conference on Security and Co-operation Session, Moscow.
6267 **2529** 10 k. multicoloured .. 20 10

2530 Patroness

2531 Woman in Traditional Costume

1991. Soviet Charity and Health Fund.
6268 **2530** 20 k.+10 k. mult .. 60 30

1991. 1st Anniv of Declaration of Ukrainian Sovereignty.
6269 **2531** 30 k. multicoloured .. 60 30

2532 "Albatros"

2534 Girl with Letter

2533 "Sv. Pyotr" and Route Map

1991. Airships. Multicoloured.
6270 1 k. Type **2532** 10 10
6271 3 k. GA-42 .. .. 15 10
6272 4 k. "Norge" (horiz) .. 15 10
6273 5 k. "Pobeda" (horiz) .. 15 10
6274 20 k. "Graf Zeppelin" (horiz) 55 20

1991. 250th Anniv of Bering's and Chirikov's Expedition. Multicoloured.
6275 30 k. Type **2533** 60 30
6276 30 k. Sighting land .. 60 30

1991. Letter Writing Week.
6277 **2534** 7 k. brown 15 10

2535 Bell and Bell Towers

2536 Kayak Race and "Santa Maria"

1991. Soviet Culture Fund.
6278 **2535** 20 k.+10 k. mult .. 60 30

1991. Olympic Games, Barcelona (1992) (1st issue). Multicoloured.
6279 10 k. Type **2536** 20 10
6280 20 k. Running and Barcelona Cathedral .. 40 20
6281 30 k. Football and stadium 60 30
See also Nos. 6358/61.

2537 Rainbow, Globe and Flags

2538 Ascension Day (Armenia)

1991. Soviet–Austrian Space Flight.
6282 **2537** 20 k. multicoloured .. 40 20

1991. Folk Festivals. Multicoloured.
6283 15 k. Type **2538** 30 15
6284 15 k. Women carrying dishes of wheat (Novruz holiday, Azerbaijan) .. 30 15
6285 15 k. Throwing garlands in water (Ivan Kupala summer holiday, Byelorussia) 30 15
6286 15 k. Stick wrestling and dancing round decorated tree (New Year, Estonia) (horiz) .. 30 15
6287 15 k. Masked dancers (Berikaoba spring holiday, Georgia) .. 30 15
6288 15 k. Riders with goat skin (Kazakhstan) (horiz) 30 15
6289 15 k. Couple on horses (Kirgizia) (horiz) .. 30 15
6290 15 k. Couple leaping over flames (Ligo (Ivan Kupala) holiday, Latvia) (horiz) .. 30 15
6291 15 k. Family on way to church (Palm Sunday, Lithuania) (horiz) .. 30 15
6292 15 k. Man in beribboned hat and musicians (Plugusorul (New Year) holiday, Moldova) .. 30 15
6293 15 k. Sledge ride (Shrovetide, Russia) .. 30 15
6294 15 k. Musicians on carpet and stilt-walkers (Novruz holiday, Tadzhikistan) 30 15
6295 15 k. Wrestlers (Harvest holiday, Turkmenistan) (horiz) 30 15
6296 15 k. Dancers and couple with lute and tambourine (Christmas, Ukraine) (horiz) .. 30 15
6297 15 k. Girls with tulips (Tulip holiday, Uzbekistan) 30 15

2539 Dimitry Komar **2540** Federation Government House and Flag

1991. Defeat of Attempted Coup. Mult.
6298 7 k. Type **2539** 15 10
6299 7 k. Ilya Krichevsky .. 15 10
6300 7 k. Vladimir Usov .. 15 10
Nos. 6298/6300 depict victims killed in opposing the attempted coup.

1991. Election of Boris Yeltsin as President of the Russian Federation.
6302 **2540** 7 k. blue, gold & red 15 10

1991. Traditional Musical Instruments (3rd series). As T **2455**. Multicoloured.
6303 10 k. Kirgiz flutes, komuzes and kyyak (string instruments) .. 20 10
6304 10 k. Latvian ganurags and stabule (wind), tambourine,duga and kokle (string instruments) .. 20 10
6305 10 k. Moldavian flute, bagpipes, nai (pipes), kobza and tsambal (string instruments) .. 20 10

2541 Decorations and Gifts

2542 Nikolai Mikhailovich Karamzin

1991. New Year.
6306 **2541** 7 k. multicoloured .. 15 10

1991. Historians' Birth Anniversaries. Mult.
6307 10 k. Type **2542** (225th anniv) 20 10
6308 10 k. V. O. Klyuchevsky (150th anniv) .. 20 10
6309 10 k. S. M. Solovev (171st anniv) 20 10
6310 10 k. V. N. Tatishchev (after A. Osipov) (305th anniv) 20 10

2543 Cross-country Skiing and Ski Jumping

2546 Golden Gate, Vladimir

1992. Winter Olympic Games, Albertville. Multicoloured.
6311 14 k. Type **2543** 30 15
6312 1 r. Acrobatic skiing .. 2·00 1·00
6313 2 r. Two and four-man bobsleighs .. .. 4·00 2·00

1992.
6317 **2546** 10 k. orange .. 10 10
6318 – 15 k. brown .. 10 10
6319 – 20 k. red .. 10 10
6320 – 25 k. red .. 10 10
6321 – 30 k. black .. 10 10
6322 – 50 k. black .. 10 10
6323 – 55 k. turquoise .. 10 10
6324 – 60 k. green .. 10 10
6324a – 80 k. purple .. 15 10
6325 – 1 r. brown .. 20 10
6326 – 1 r. 50 green .. 30 15
6327 – 2 r. blue 40 20
6328 – 3 r. red 65 35
6328a – 4 r. brown .. 40 20
6329 – 5 r. brown .. 1·10 55
6329a – 6 r. blue 60 30
6330 – 10 r. blue .. .. 2·10 1·10
6330a – 15 r. brown .. 30 15
6331 – 25 r. red .. 5·25 2·50
6332 – 45 r. blue 80 40
6341 – 50 r. violet .. 1·25 65
6333 – 75 r. brown .. 1·60 80
6334 – 100 r. green .. 21·00 11·00
6342 – 250 r. green .. 1·25 65
6347 – 500 r. red .. 2·50 1·25
DESIGNS: 15 k. Pskov Kremlin; 20, 50 k. St. George killing dragon; 25, 55 k. Victory Arch, Moscow; 30, 80 k. "Millenium of Russia" monument (M. Mikeshin), Novgorod; 60 k. Minin and Pozharsky Statue, Moscow; 1, 4 r. Church, Kizki; 1r. 50, 6 r. Statue of Peter I, St. Petersburg; 2 r. St. Basil's Cathedral, Moscow; 3 r. Tretyakov Gallery, Moscow; 5 r. Morosov House, Moscow; 10 r. St. Isaac's Cathedral, St. Petersburg; 15, 45 r. "The Horse Tamer", St. Petersburg; 25, 75 r. Yuri Dolgoruky Monument, Moscow; 50 r. Rostov Kremlin; 100 r. Moscow Kremlin; 250 r. Church, Bogulyubov; 500 r. Lomonosov University, Moscow.

2547 "Victory" (N. N. Baskakov)

2548 Wood Grouse, Oak and Pine

1992. 47th Anniv of Victory in Second World War.
6350 **2547** 5 k. multicoloured .. 10 10

1992. Prioksko-Terrasnyi Nature Reserve.
6351 **2548** 50 k. multicoloured .. 10 10

2549 "Mir" Space Station, Flags and Cosmonauts

2551 Pinocchio

1992. Russian–German Joint Space Flight.
6352 **2549** 5 r. multicoloured .. 1·10 55

1992. Characters from Children's Books (1st series). Multicoloured.
6354 25 k. Type **2551** 10 10
6355 30 k. Cipollino 10 10
6356 35 k. Dunno 10 10
6357 50 k. Karlson 10 10
See also Nos. 6391/5.

2552 Russian Cosmonaut and Space Shuttle

2553 Handball

1992. International Space Year. Mult.
6358 25 r. Type **2552** .. .. 5·25 2·75
6359 25 r. American astronaut and "Mir" space station 5·25 2·75
6360 25 r. "Apollo" and "Vostok" spacecraft and sputnik .. .. 5·25 2·75
6361 25 r. "Soyuz", "Mercury" and "Gemini" spacecraft .. .. .. 5·25 2·75
Nos. 6344/47 were issued together, se-tenant, forming a composite design.

1992. Olympic Games, Barcelona (2nd issue).

6362 2553 1 r. multicoloured .. 20 10
6363 – 2 r. red, blue & black 40 20
6364 – 3 r. red, green & blk 65 35

DESIGNS—HORIZ. 2 r. Fencing; 3 r. Judo.

2554 L. A. Zagoskin and Yukon River, Alaska, 1842–44

1992. Expeditions. Multicoloured.

6365 55 k. Type 2554 .. .. 10 10
6366 70 k. N. N. Miklukho-Maklai in New Guinea, 1871–74 .. .. 15 10
6367 1 r. G. I. Langsdorf and route map of expedition to Brazil, 1822–28 .. 20 10

2555 Garganeys

1992. Ducks (4th series). Multicoloured.

6368 1 r. Type 2555 .. .. 15 10
6369 2 r. European pochards .. 20 10
6370 3 r. Falcated teals .. 65 35

2556 "Taj Mahal Mausoleum in Agra"

1992. 150th Birth Anniv of Vasily Vasilevich Vereshchagin (painter).

6371 1 r. 50 Type 2556 .. 30 15
6372 1 r. 50 "Don't Touch, Let Me Approach!" .. 30 15

2557 "The Saviour" (icon, Andrei Rublev)

2558 Cathedral of the Assumption

1992.

6373 2557 1 r. multicoloured .. 20 10

1992. Moscow Kremlin Cathedrals. Mult.

6374 1 r. Type 2558 .. .. 20 10
6375 1 r. Cathedral of the Annunciation (15th century) 20 10
6376 1 r. Archangel Cathedral (16th century) 20 10

See also Nos. 6415/17 and 6440/2.

2559 Russian "Nutcracker" Puppets

2560 "Meeting of Joachim and Anne"

1992. Centenary of First Production of Tchaikovsky's "Nutcracker" Ballet. Mult.

6377 10 r. Type 2559 .. .. 2·10 1·10
6378 10 r. German "Nutcracker" puppets .. 2·10 1·10
6379 25 r. Pas de deux from ballet .. .. .. 5·25 2·75
6380 25 r. Dance of the toys .. 5·25 2·75

1992. Icons. Multicoloured.

6381 10 r. Type 2560 .. .. 2·10 1·10
6382 10 r. "Madonna and Child" .. .. 2·10 1·10
6383 10 r. "Archangel Gabriel" (head) .. .. 2·10 1·10
6384 10 r. "Saint Nicholas" (½-length portrait) .. 2·10 1·10

2561 Clockface and Festive Symbols

2562 "Discovery of America" Monument (Z. Tsereteli)

1992. New Year.

6385 2561 50 k. multicoloured .. 10 10

1992. 500th Anniv of Discovery of America by Columbus.

6386 2562 15 r. multicoloured .. 10 10

2563 Petipa and Scene from "Paquita"

2564 Scrub 'n' Rub

1993. 175th Birth Anniv of Marius Petipa (choreographer). Multicoloured.

6387 25 r. Type 2563 .. .. 20 10
6388 25 r. "Sleeping Beauty," 1890 .. .. .. 20 10
6389 25 r. "Swan Lake", 1895 20 10
6390 25 r. "Raimunda", 1898 .. 20 10

1993. Characters from Children's Books (2nd series). Illustrations by Kornei Chukovsky. Multicoloured.

6391 2 r. Type 2564 .. .. 10 10
6392 3 r. Big Cockroach .. 15 10
6393 10 r. The Buzzer Fly .. 20 10
6394 15 r. Doctor Doolittle .. 30 15
6395 25 r. Barmalei 55 30

Nos. 6391/5 were issued together, se-tenant, forming a composite design.

2565 Castle

2566 Part of Diorama in Belgorod Museum

1993. 700th Anniv of Vyborg.

6396 2565 10 r. multicoloured .. 35 25

1993. Victory Day. 50th Anniv of Battle of Kursk.

6397 2566 10 r. multicoloured .. 35 20

2567 African Violet

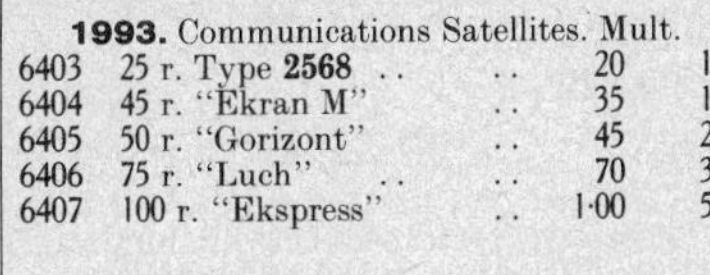

2568 "Molniya 3"

1993. Pot Plants. Multicoloured.

6398 10 r. Type 2567 .. .. 20 10
6399 15 r. "Hibiscus rosa-sinensis" 25 15
6400 25 r. "Cyclamen persicum" 55 30
6401 50 r. "Fuchsia hybrida" 1·10 55
6402 100 r. "Begonia semperflorens" .. 2·25 1·10

1993. Communications Satellites. Mult.

6403 25 r. Type 2568 .. .. 20 10
6404 45 r. "Ekran M" .. 35 15
6405 50 r. "Gorizont" .. 45 25
6406 75 r. "Luch" 70 35
6407 100 r. "Ekspress" .. 1·00 50

2569 Snuff Box (Dmitry Kolesnikov) and Tankard

2570 Map

1993. Silverware. Multicoloured.

6409 15 r. Type 2569 .. .. 10 10
6410 25 r. Teapot 10 10
6411 45 r. Vase 20 10
6412 75 r. Tray and candlestick 50 25
6413 100 r. Cream jug, coffee pot and sugar basin (Aleksandr Kordes) .. 80 40

1993. Novgorod Kremlin. As T 2558. Mult.

6415 25 r. Kukui and Knyazhaya Towers (14th–17th century) .. 20 10
6416 25 r. St. Sophia's Cathedral (11th century) 20 10
6417 25 r. St. Sophia belfry (15th–18th century) .. 20 10

1993. Inauguration of Denmark–Russia Submarine Cable and 500th Anniv of Friendship Treaty.

6419 2570 90 r. green & dp green 50 25

2571 Steller's Eider

1993. Ducks (5th series). Multicoloured.

6420 90 r. Type 2571 .. .. 55 25
6421 100 r. Eider 60 30
6422 250 r. King eider .. 1·75 90

2572 Ringed Seal

1993. Sea Animals. Multicoloured.

6423 50 r. Type 2572 .. .. 25 15
6424 60 r. "Paralithodes brevipes" (crab) .. 30 15
6425 90 r. "Todarodes pacificus" (squid) .. 55 25
6426 100 r. Salmon trout .. 60 30
6427 250 r. Fulmar .. .. 1·60 80

2573 Ceramic Candlestick, Skopino

2574 Banknotes and Coins

1993. Traditional Art. Multicoloured.

6428 50 r. Type 2573 .. .. 30 15
6429 50 r. Painted tray with picture "Summer Troika", Zhostovo (horiz) 30 15
6430 100 r. Painted box, lid and distaff, Gorodets .. 55 30
6431 100 r. Enamel icon of St. Dmitry of Solun, Rostov 55 30
6432 250 r. "The Resurrection" (lacquer miniature), Fedoskino .. .. 1·60 80

1993. 175th Anniv of Goznak (State printing works and mint).

6433 2574 100 r. multicoloured 70 35

2575 Peter I and "Goto Predestinatsiya"

1993. 300th Anniv of Russian Navy. Mult.

6434 100 r. Type 2575 .. 65 35
6435 100 r. K. A. Shilder and first all-metal submarine 65 35
6436 100 r. I. A. Amosov and "Arkhimed" (frigate) .. 65 35
6437 100 r. I. G. Bubnov and "Bars" (submarine) .. 65 35
6438 100 r. B. M. Malinin and "Dekabrist" (submarine) 65 35
6439 100 r. A. I. Maslov and "Kirov" (cruiser) .. 65 35

1993. Moscow Kremlin. As T 2558. Mult.

6440 100 r. Faceted Hall (15th century) 20 10
6441 100 r. Church of the Deposition of the Virgin's Robe (15th century) 20 10
6442 100 r. Grand Palace (17th century) 20 10

2576 Tiger

2577 Splash of Blood on Figure

1993. The Tiger. Multicoloured.

6443 50 r. Type 2576 .. .. 10 10
6444 100 r. Tiger in undergrowth 20 10
6445 250 r. Two tigers .. 45 25
6446 500 r. Tiger in snow .. 90 45

1993. Anti-AIDS Campaign.

6447 2577 90 r. multicoloured 20 10

EXPRESS STAMPS

E 171.

1932. Inscr. "EXPRES".

E 588. E 171. 5 k. sepia .. 4·00 2·25
E 589. – 10 k. purple .. 6·00 3·50
E 590. – 80 k. green .. 30·00 12·00

DESIGNS—HORIZ. 10 k. Express motor van. 80 k. Steam locomotive.

1932. Air. Airship Construction Fund. Imperf. or perf.

E 592. 166. 15 k. black .. .. 2·75 1·50

POSTAGE DUE STAMPS

Доплата 1 коп. ЗОЛОТОМ. (D 96.)

ДОПЛАТА 1 коп. (D 99)

1924. Surch. as Type D **96.**

No.	Type	Description	Unused	Used
~~D 401~~.	**45.**	1 k. on 35 k. blue ..	20	30
D 402.		3 k. on 35 k. blue ..	20	30
D 403.		5 k. on 35 k. blue ..	20	30
D 404.		8 k. on 35 k. blue ..	50	50
D 405.		10 k. on 35 k. blue ..	30	60
D 406.		12 k. on 70 k. brown	20	40
D 407.		14 k. on 35 k. blue ..	20	40
D 408.		32 k. on 35 k. blue ..	90	90
D 409.		40 k. on 35 k. blue ..	1·00	90

1924. Surch with Type D **99.**

No.	Type	Description	Unused	Used
D421	**48**	1 k. on 100 r. yellow ..	4·50	10·00

D 104.

1925.

No.	Type	Description	Unused	Used
D 464.	D **104.**	1 k. red	25	30
D 465.		2 k. violet ..	25	30
D 466.		3 k. blue	25	30
D 467.		7 k. yellow ..	35	30
D 468.		8 k. green ..	35	30
D 469.		10 k. blue ..	40	50
D 470.		14 k. brown ..	60	70

RUSSIAN POST OFFICES IN CHINA Pt. 17

Russian Post Offices were opened in various towns in Manchuria and China from 1870 onwards.

1899. 100 kopeks = 1 rouble.
1917. 100 cents = 1 dollar (Chinese).

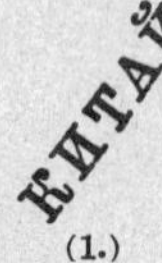

(1.)

1899. Arms types (with thunderbolts) of Russia optd. with T **1.**

No.	Type	Description	Unused	Used
1.	**9.**	1 k. orange	30	40
2.		2 k. green	40	40
3.		3 k. red	40	35
9.	**14.**	4 k. red	1·25	1·25
4.	**9.**	5 k. purple	50	50
5.		7 k. blue	50	50
6.	**14.**	10 k. blue	60	50
30.	**10.**	14 k. red and blue ..	75	1·25
31.		15 k. blue and brown ..	45	1·00
32.	**14.**	20 k. red and blue ..	40	1·25
33.	**10.**	25 k. violet and green ..	65	1·75
34.		35 k. green and purple ..	70	1·25
35.	**14.**	50 k. green and purple ..	85	1·25
36.	**10.**	70 k. orange and brown..	60	1·50
37.	**15.**	1 r. orange and brown ..	1·25	1·50
20.	**11.**	3 r. 50 grey and black ..	7·50	8·50
21.	**20.**	5 r. blue and grn. on grn.	4·50	5·50
22.	**11.**	7 r. yellow and black ..	8·00	9·00
23.	**20.**	10 r. grey and red on yell.	32·00	45·00

1910. Arms types of Russia optd. with T **1.**

No.	Type	Description	Unused	Used
24.	**22.**	1 k. orange	35	60
25.		2 k. green	40	60
26.		3 k. red	30	35
27.	**23.**	4 k. red	25	50
28.	**22.**	7 k. blue	35	65
29.	**23.**	10 k. blue	35	50

1917. Arms types of Russia surch. in "cents" and "dollars" diagonally in one line.

No.	Type	Description	Unused	Used
42.	**22.**	1 c. on 1 k. orange ..	40	1·50
43.		2 c. on 2 k. green.. ..	40	1·50
44.		3 c. on 3 k. red	50	1·50
45.	**23.**	4 c. on 4 k. red	40	1·50
46.	**22.**	5 c. on 5 k. lilac ..	75	2·25
47.	**23.**	10 c. on 10 k. blue ..	50	2·25
48.	**10.**	14 c. on 14 k. red & blue	1·00	3·75
49.		15 c. on 15 k. blue & pur.	1·00	3·00
50.	**14.**	20 c. on 20 k. red & blue	1·25	2·75
51.	**10.**	25 c. on 25 k. violet & grn.	1·25	3·00
52.		35 c. on 35 k. grn. & pur.	1·25	3·25
53	**.14.**	50 c. on 50 k. grn. & pur.	1·10	3·00
54.	**10.**	70 c. on 70 k. orge. & brn.	1·25	4·50
55.	**15.**	1 d .on 1 r. orge & brn. on brown ..	1·25	5·50
39.	**10.**	3 d. 50 on 3 r. 50 grey and black	7·00	12·00
40.	**20.**	5 d. on 5 r. blue and green	4·50	15·00
41.	**11.**	7 d. on 7 r. yellow & black	2·50	10·00
57.	**20.**	10 d. on 10 r. grey, red and yellow	20·00	45·00

1920. Arms types of Russia surch in "cents" in two lines. Perf or imperf.

No.	Type	Description	Unused	Used
65.	**22.**	1 c. on 1 k. orange ..	7·50	12·00
59.		2 c. on 2 k. green ..	2·50	10·00
60.		3 c. on 3 k. red	2·50	10·00
61.	**23.**	4 c. on 4 k. red	7·50	12·00
62.	**22.**	5 c. on 5 k. lilac.. ..	8·00	15·00
63.	**23.**	10 c. on 10 k. blue ..	30·00	45·00
64.	**22.**	10 c. on 10 k. on 7 k. blue	28·00	45·00

RUSSIAN POST OFFICES IN CRETE Pt. 3

(RETHYMNON PROVINCE)

The Russian Postal Service operated from 1 May to 29 July 1899.

4 metallik = 1 grosion (Turkish piastre).

These issues were optd with circular control marks as shown on T 3/4. Prices are for stamps with these marks, but unused examples without them are known.

1.

2.

1899. Imperf.

No.	Type	Description	Unused	Used
1.	**1.**	1 m. blue	38·00	14·00
2.	**2.**	1 m. green	10·00	7·50
3.		2 m. red	£275	£170
4.		2 m. green	10·00	7·50

3.

4.

1899. Without stars in oval.

No.	Type	Description	Unused	Used
5.	**3.**	1 m. pink	35·00	28·00
6.		2 m. pink	35·00	28·00
7.		1 g. pink	35·00	28·00
8.		1 m. blue	35·00	28·00
9.		2 m. blue	35·00	28·00
10.		1 g. blue	35·00	28·00
11.		1 m. green	35·00	28·00
12.		2 m. green	35·00	28·00
13.		1 g. green	35·00	28·00
14.		1 m. red	35·00	28·00
15.		2 m. red	35·00	28·00
16.		1 g. red	35·00	28·00
17.		1 m. orange	35·00	28·00
18.		2 m. orange	35·00	28·00
19.		1 g. orange	35·00	28·00
20.		1 m. yellow	35·00	28·00
21.		2 m. yellow	35·00	28·00
22.		1 g. yellow	35·00	28·00
23.		1 m. black	£550	£550
24.		2 m. black	£550	£550
25.		1 g. black	£475	£475

1899. Starred at each side.

No.	Type	Description	Unused	Used
26.	**4.**	1 m. pink	28·00	18·00
27.		2 m. pink	11·00	5·50
28.		1 g. pink	6·50	4·50
29.		1 m. blue	16·00	9·00
30.		2 m. blue	11·00	5·50
31.		1 g. blue	6·50	4·50
32.		1 m. green	16·00	9·00
33.		2 m. green	11·00	5·50
34.		1 g. green	6·50	4·50
35.		1 m. red	16·00	9·00
36.		2 m. red	11·00	5·50
37.		1 g. red	6·50	4·50

RUSSIAN POST OFFICES IN TURKEY Pt. 16

General issues for Russian P.Os in the Turkish Empire and stamps specially overprinted for use at particular offices.

1863. 100 kopeks = 1 rouble.
1900. 40 paras = 1 piastre.

1. Inscription = "Dispatch under Wrapper to the East".

1863. Imperf.

No.	Type	Description	Unused	Used
2a.	**1.**	6 k. blue	£190	£800

2.

3.

1865. Imperf.

No.	Type	Description	Unused	Used
4	**2**	(10 pa.) brown and blue ..	£600	£400
5	**3**	(2 pi.) blue and red ..	£800	£450

4.

5.

1865. Imperf.

No.	Type	Description	Unused	Used
6	**4**	(10 pa.) red and blue ..	20·00	35·00
7	**5**	(2 pi.) blue and red ..	35·00	42·00

The values of Nos. 4/7 were 10 pa. (or 2 k.) and 2 pi. (or 20 k.).

6. Inscription = " Eastern Correspondence ".

12.

1868. Perf.

No.	Type	Description	Unused	Used
14.	**6.**	1 k. brown	8·00	4·50
11.		3 k. green	22·00	13·00
16.		5 k. blue	5·50	3·25
17a.		10 k. red and green ..	4·00	3·25

See also Nos. 26/35.

1876. Surch. with large figures of value.

No.	Type	Description	Unused	Used
24.	**6.**	7 k. on 10 k. red & green	55·00	42·00
22.		8 k. on 10 k. red & green	60·00	55·00

1879.

No.	Type	Description	Unused	Used
26.	**6.**	1 k. black and yellow ..	2·25	1·25
32.		1 k. orange	50	35
27.		2 k. black and red ..	3·00	1·75
33.		2 k. green	50	35
34.		5 k. purple	1·25	1·00
28.		7 k. red and grey.. ..	4·50	1·10
35.		7 k. blue	85	35

1900. Arms types of Russia surch in "PARA" or "PIASTRES".

No.	Type	Description	Unused	Used
37	**9**	4 pa. on 1 k. orange ..	15	10
50	**22**	5 pa. on 1 k. orange ..	10	15
38	**9**	10 pa. on 2 k. green ..	40	25
51	**22**	10 pa. on 2 k. green ..	10	15
201		15 pa. on 3 k. red ..	20	5·00
41	**14**	20 pa. on 4 k. red ..	40	40
52	**23**	20 pa. on 4 k. red ..	10	15
42	**9**	20 pa. on 5 k. purple ..	40	40
181	**22**	20 pa. on 5 k. purple ..	10	15
43	**14**	1 pi. on 10 k. blue ..	20	20
53	**23**	1 pi. on 10 k. blue ..	10	15
182	**10**	1½ pi. on 15 k. bl & pur	15	20
183	**14**	2 pi. on 20 k. red & blue	15	20
184	**10**	2½ pi. on 25 k. vio & grn	15	20
185		3½ pi. on 35 k. grn & pur	20	30
54	**14**	5 pi. on 50 k. green & lil	50	75
55	**10**	7 pi. on 70 k. orge & brn	70	90
56	**15**	10 pi. on 1 r. orange and brown on brown ..	80	1·10
48	**11**	35 pi. on 3 r. 50 grey and black	6·00	6·00
202	**20**	50 pi. on 5 r. blue on grn	3·25	80·00
49	**11**	70 pi. on 7 r. yell & blk	9·00	9·00
203	**20**	100 pi. on 10 r. grey and red on yellow ..	14·00	£275

1909. As T **14**, **15** and **11** of Russia, but ship and date in centre as T **12**, and surch in "paras" or "piastres".

No.	Type	Description	Unused	Used
57	**14**	5 pa. on 1 k. orange ..	20	30
58		10 pa. on 2 k. green ..	30	40
59		20 pa. on 4 k. red ..	60	75
60		1 pi. on 10 k. blue ..	60	1·10
61		5 pi. on 50 k. grn & pur	1·25	2·50
62		7 pi. on 70 k. orge & brn	2·50	3·75
63	**15**	10 pi. on 1 r. orge & brn	3·75	6·50
64	**11**	35 pi. on 3 r. 50 green and purple	9·00	35·00
65		70 pi. on 7 r. pink & grn	22·00	55·00

The above stamps exist overprinted for Constantinople, Jaffa, Jerusalem, Kerassunde, Mount Athos, Salonika, Smyrna, Trebizonde, Beyrouth, Dardanelles, Mytilene and Rizeh. For full list see Part 10 (Russia) of the Stanley Gibbons Catalogue.

1913. Nos. 126/42 (Romanov types) of Russia surch.

No.	Description	Unused	Used
186	5 pa. on 1 k. orange ..	40	40
187	10 pa. on 3 k. green ..	40	40
188	15 pa. on 3 k. red ..	40	40
189	20 pa. on 4 k. red ..	40	40
190	1 pi. on 10 k. blue ..	40	40
191	1½ pi. on 15 k. brown ..	60	60
192	2 pi. on 20 k. green ..	70	70
193	2½ pi. on 25 k. purple ..	1·00	1·00
194	3½ pi. on 35 k. green & vio	2·00	2·00
195	5 pi. on 50 k. grey & brown	2·25	2·25
196	7 pi. on 70 k. brown & grn	7·00	17·00
197	10 pi. on 1 r. green ..	8·00	17·00
198	20 pi. on 2 r. brown ..	3·25	5·50
199	30 pi. on 3 r. violet ..	4·50	£170
200	50 pi. on 5 r. brown ..	90·00	£475

RWANDA Pt. 14

An independent republic established in July 1962, formerly part of Ruanda-Urundi.

100 centimes = 1 franc.

1. Pres. Kayibanda and Map.

1962. Independence.

No.	Type	Description	Unused	Used
1.	**1.**	10 c. sepia and green ..	10	10
2.	–	40 c. sepia and purple ..	10	10
3.	**1.**	1 f. sepia and blue ..	70	35
4.	–	1 f. 50 sepia and brown ..	10	10
5.	**1.**	3 f. 50 sepia and orange..	10	10
6.	–	6 f. 50 sepia and blue ..	15	10
7.	**1.**	10 f. sepia and olive ..	30	15
8.	–	20 f. sepia and red ..	60	30

DESIGN: Nos. 2, 4, 6, 8, are as Type **1** but with halo around Rwanda on map in place of " R ".

1963. Admission to U.N. No. 204 of Ruanda-Urundi with coloured frame obliterating old inscr. (colours below), and surch. **Admission a l'O.N.U. 18-9-1962 REPUBLIQUE RWANDAISE** and new value.

No.	Description	Unused	Used
9.	3 f. 50 on 3 f. grey ..	10	10
10.	6 f. 50 on 3 f. pink ..	1·10	90
11.	10 f. on 3 f. blue ..	25	25
12.	20 f. on 3 f. silver	40	40

1963. Flowers issue of Ruanda-Urundi (Nos. 178. etc.) optd. **REPUBLIQUE RWANDAISE** or surch. also in various coloured panels over old inscriptions and values. Flowers in natural colours.

No.	Description	Unused	Used
13.	25 c. orange and green ..	20	20
14.	40 c. salmon and green ..	20	20
15.	60 c. purple and green ..	20	20
16.	1 f. 25 blue and green ..	90	90
17.	1 f. 50 green and violet ..	65	65
18.	2 f. on 1 f. 50 green & violet	1·40	1·10
19.	4 f. on 1 f. 50 green & violet	1·40	1·10
20.	5 f. green and purple ..	1·40	1·10
21.	7 f. brown and green ..	1·40	1·10
22.	10 f. olive and purple ..	1·40	1·10

The coloured panels are in various shades of silver except No. 19 which is in blue.

4. Ears of Wheat and Native Implements.

1963. Freedom from Hunger.

No.	Type	Description	Unused	Used
23.	4.	2 f. brown and green ..	10	10
24.		4 f. mauve and blue ..	10	10
25.		7 f. red and grey	20	10
26.		10 f. green and yellow ..	75	55

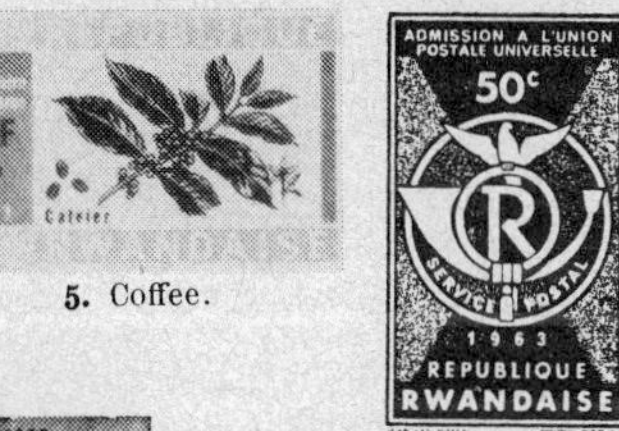

5. Coffee.

6. Postal Services Emblem.

8. Child Care. **7.** Emblems.

1963. 1st Anniv. of Independence.

No.	Type	Description	Unused	Used
27.	5.	10 c. brown and blue ..	10	10
28.	–	20 c. yellow and blue ..	10	10
29.	–	30 c. green and orange ..	10	10
30.	5.	40 c. brown and turquoise	10	10
31.	–	1 f. yellow and purple ..	10	10
32.	–	2 f. green and blue ..	80	45
33.	5.	4 f. brown and red ..	10	10
34.	–	7 f. yellow and green ..	20	15
35.	–	10 f. green and violet ..	35	30

DESIGNS: 20 c., 1 f., 7 f. Bananas. 30 c., 2 f. 10 f. Tea.

1963. African and Malagasian Postal and Telecommunications Union. As T **56** of Mauritania, but with "AERIENNE" omitted.

No.	Description	Unused	Used
36.	14 f. multicoloured	1·10	90

1963. Admission of Rwanda to U.P.U.

No.	Type	Description	Unused	Used
37.	6.	50 c. blue and pink ..	10	10
38.		1 f. 50 brown and blue ..	65	45
39.		3 f. purple and grey ..	10	10
40.		20 f. green and yellow ..	45	20

1963. 15th Anniv. of Declaration of Human Rights.

No.	Type	Description	Unused	Used
41.	7.	5 f. red	15	10
42.		6 f. violet	50	35
43.		10 f. blue	35	15

1963. Red Cross Centenary.

No.	Type	Description	Unused	Used
44.	8.	10 c. multicoloured ..	10	10
45.	–	20 c. multicoloured ..	10	10
46.	–	30 c. multicoloured ..	10	10
47.	–	40 c. brown, red and violet	10	10
48.	8.	2 f. multicoloured ..	80	60
49.	–	7 f. multicoloured ..	15	10
50.	–	10 f. brown, red & brown	20	15
51.	–	20 f. brown, red & orange	60	35

DESIGNS—HORIZ. 20 c., 7 f. Patient having blood test. 40 c., 20 f. Stretcher-party. VERT. 30 c., 10 f. Doctor examining child.

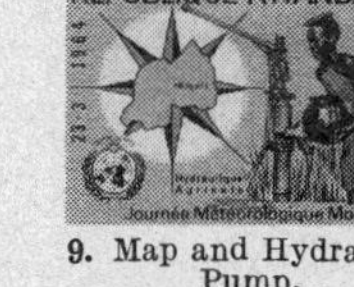

9. Map and Hydraulic Pump.

10. Boy with Crutch. **11.** Running.

1964. World Meteorological Day.

No.	Type	Description	Unused	Used
52.	9.	3 f. sepia, blue and green	10	10
53.		7 f. sepia, blue and red ..	35	20
54.		10 f. sepia, blue and orange	50	35

1964. Stamps of Ruanda-Urundi optd. **REPUBLIQUE RWANDAISE** or surch. also in black over coloured metallic panels obliterating old inscription or value.

No.	Description	Unused	Used
55.	10 c. on 20 c. (No. 204) ..	10	10
56.	20 c. (No. 204)	10	10
57.	30 c. on 1 f. 50 (No. 208) ..	10	10
58.	40 c. (No. 205)	10	10
59.	50 c. (No. 206)	10	10
60.	1 f. (No. 207)	10	10
61.	2 f. (No. 209)	10	10
62.	3 f. (No. 210)	10	10
63.	4 f. on 3 f. 50 on 3 f. (No. 228)	20	10
64.	5 f. (No. 211)	20	10
65.	7 f. 50 on 6 f. 50 (No. 212)	45	15
66.	8 f. (No. 213)	4·50	2·25
67.	10 f. (No. 214)	65	20
68.	20 f. (No. 229)	1·10	45
69.	50 f. (No. 230)	2·10	85

1964. Gatagara Re-education Centre.

No.	Type	Description	Unused	Used
70.	10.	10 c. sepia and violet ..	10	10
71.	–	40 c. sepia and blue ..	10	10
72.	–	4 f. sepia and brown ..	10	10
73.	10.	7 f. 50 sepia and green ..	35	15
74.	–	8 f. sepia and bistre ..	1·40	95
75.	–	10 f. sepia and purple ..	45	20

DESIGNS—HORIZ. 40 c., 8 f. Children operating sewing-machines. VERT. 4 f., 10 f. Crippled child on crutches.

1964. Olympic Games, Tokyo. Sportsmen in slate.

No.	Type	Description	Unused	Used
76.	11.	10 c. blue	10	10
77.	–	20 c. red	10	10
78.	–	30 c. turquoise	10	10
79.	–	40 c. brown	10	10
80.	11.	4 f. blue	10	10
81.	–	5 f. green	1·40	1·25
82.	–	20 f. purple	35	35
83.	–	50 f. grey	1·10	90

DESIGNS—VERT. 20 c., 5 f. Basketball. 40 c., 50 f. Football. HORIZ. 30 c., 20 f. High-jumping.

12. Faculties of "Letters" and "Sciences". **13.** Abraham Lincoln.

1965. National University. Multicoloured.

No.	Description	Unused	Used
84.	10 c. Type **12**	10	10
85.	20 c. Student with microscope and building ("Medicine")	10	10
86.	30 c. Scales of Justice, Hand of Law ("Social Sciences" and "Normal High School")	10	10
87.	40 c. University buildings ..	10	10
88.	5 f. Type **12**	10	10
89.	7 f. As 20 c.	15	10
90.	10 f. As 30 c.	1·00	85
91.	12 f. As 40 c.	30	15

The 20 c., 40 c., 7 f. and 12 f. are horiz.

1965. Death Cent. of Abraham Lincoln.

No.	Type	Description	Unused	Used
92.	13.	10 c. green and red ..	10	10
93.		20 c. brown and blue ..	10	10
94.		30 c. violet and red ..	10	10
95.		40 c. blue and brown ..	10	10
96.		9 f. brown and purple ..	20	15
97.		40 f. purple and green ..	1·90	70

14. Marabou Storks. **15.** "Telstar" Satellite.

1965. Kagera National Park. Multicoloured.

No.	Description	Unused	Used
98.	10 c. Type **14**	10	10
99.	20 c. Common zebras ..	10•	10
100.	30 c. Impalas	10	10
101.	40 c. Crowned cranes, hippopatami and Cattle egrets	10	10
102.	1 f. African buffaloes ..	10	10
103.	3 f. Hunting dogs	10	10
104.	5 f. Yellow baboons ..	4·25	1·10
105.	10 f. African elephant and map	20	15
106.	40 f. Reed cormorants and African darters	95	35
107.	100 f. Lions	2·25	50

SIZES: As Type **14**—VERT. 30 c., 1 f., 5 f. HORIZ. 20 c., 40 c., 3 f., 10 f. LARGER (45 × 25½ mm.): 40 f., 100 f.

1965. Cent. of I.T.U. Multicoloured.

No.	Description	Unused	Used
108.	10 c. Type **15**	10	10
109.	40 c. "Syncom" satellite ..	10	10
110.	4 f. 50 Type **15**	1·40	50
111.	50 f. "Syncom" satellite ..	90	35

16. "Colotis auriginеus". **17.** Cattle and I.C.Y. emblem.

1965. Rwanda Butterflies. Multicoloured.

No.	Description	Unused	Used
112.	10 c. "Papilio bromius" ..	10	10
113.	15 c. "Papilio hesperus" ..	10	10
114.	20 c. Type **16**	10	10
115.	30 c. "Amphicallia pactolicus"	10	10
116.	35 c. "Lobobunaea phaedusa"	10	10
117.	40 c. "Papilio jacksoni ruandana"	10	10
118.	1 f. 50 "Papilio dardanus dardanus"	10	10
119.	3 f. "Amaurina elliotti" ..	2·75	65
120.	4 f. "Colias electo pseudohecate"	1·75	55
121.	10 f. "Bunaea alcinoe" ..	35	15
122.	50 f. "Athletes gigas" ..	1·10	45
123.	100 f. "Charaxes ansorgei R."	2·25	65

The 10 c., 30 c., 35 c., 3 f., 4 f. and 100 f. are vert.

1965. Int. Co-operation Year.

No.	Type	Description	Unused	Used
124.	17.	10 c. green and yellow ..	10	10
125.	–	40 c. brown, blue & grn.	10	10
126.	–	4 f. 50 grn., brn. & yell.	1·10	50
127.	–	45 f. purple and brown	90	40

DESIGNS: 40 c. Crater lake and giant plants. 4 f. 50 Gazelle and candelabra tree. 45 f. Mt. Ruwenzori. Each with I.C.Y. emblem.

18. Pres. Kennedy, Globe and Satellites. **19.** Madonna and Child.

1965. 2nd Anniv. of Pres. Kennedy's Death.

No.	Type	Description	Unused	Used
128.	18.	10 c. brown and green ..	10	10
129.		40 c. brown and red ..	10	10
130.		50 c. brown and blue ..	10	10
131.		1 f. brown and olive ..	10	10
132.		8 f. brown and violet ..	1·75	1·10
133.		50 f. brown and grey ..	1·10	90

1965. Christmas.

No.	Type	Description	Unused	Used
134.	19.	10 c. green and gold ..	10	10
135.		40 c. brown and gold ..	10	10
136.		50 c. blue and gold ..	10	10
137.		4 f. black and gold ..	70	65
138.		6 f. violet and gold ..	15	10
139.		30 f. brown and gold ..	65	45

20. Father Damien.

1966. World Leprosy Day.

No.	Type	Description	Unused	Used
140.	20.	10 c. blue and brown ..	10	10
141.	–	40 c. red and blue ..	10	10
142.	20.	4 f. 50 slate and green	20	15
143.	–	45 f. brown and red ..	1·75	1·25

DESIGNS: 40 c., 45 f. Dr. Schweitzer.

21. Pope Paul, Rome and New York.

1966. Pope Paul's Visit to U.N. Organization.

No.	Type	Description	Unused	Used
144.	21.	10 c. blue and brown ..	10•	10
145.	–	40 c. indigo and blue ..	10	10
146.	21.	4 f. 50 blue and purple	1·60	1·00
147.	–	50 f. blue and green ..	1·00	55

DESIGNS: 40 c., 50 f. Pope Paul, Arms and U.N. emblem.

22. "Echinops amplexicaulis" and "E. bequaertii".

1966. Flowers. Multicoloured.

No.	Description	Unused	Used
148.	10 c. Type **22**	10	10
149.	20 c. "Haemanthus multiflorus"	10	10
150.	30 c. "Helichrysum ericirosenii"	10	10
151.	40 c. "Carissa edulis" ..	10	10
152.	1 f. "Spathodea campanulata"	10	10
153.	3 f. "Habenaria praestans"	10	10
154.	5 f. "Aloe lateritia" ..	3·50	1·90
155.	10 f. "Ammocharis tinneana"	30	20
156.	40 f. "Erythrina abyssinica"	85	50
157.	100 f. "Capparis tomentosa"	1·90	1·10

The 20 c., 40 c., 1 f., 3 f., 5 f. and 10 f. are vert.

23. W.H.O. Building.

1966. Inaug. of W.H.O. Headquarters, Geneva.

No.	Type	Description	Unused	Used
159.	23.	2 f. olive	10	10
160.		3 f. red	20	20
161.		5 f. blue	10	10

24. Football. **25.** Mother and Child within flames.

1966. "Youth and Sports".

No.	Type	Description	Unused	Used
162.	24.	10 c. blk., blue & green	10	10
163.	–	20 c. black, green & red	10	10
164.	–	30 c. black, purple & blue	10	10
165.	24.	40 c. blk. green & bistre	10	10
166.	–	9 f. black, purple & grey	20	10
167.	–	50 f. black, blue & pur.	1·10	1·00

DESIGNS: 20 c., 9 f. Basketball. 30 c., 50 f. Volleyball.

1966. Nuclear Disarmament.

No.	Type	Description	Unused	Used
168.	25.	20 c. brown, red & mve.	10	10
169.		30 c. brown, red & green	10	10
170.		50 c. brown, red & blue	10	10
171.		6 f. brown, red & yellow	10	10
172.		15 f. brown, red & turq.	65	30
173.		18 f. brown, red & lav.	65	40

26. Football.

27. Yellow-crested Helmet Shrike and Mikeno Volcano.

1966. World Cup Football Championships.

174. 26.	20 c. blue and orange..	10	10
175.	30 c. blue and violet ..	10	10
176.	50 c. blue and green ..	10	10
177.	6 f. blue and mauve ..	20	10
178.	12 f. blue and brown..	1·10	35
179.	25 f. indigo and blue..	2·25	60

1966. Rwanda Scenery.

180. 27.	10 c. green	10	10
181. –	40 c. lake	10	10
182. –	4 f. 50 blue	50	40
183. –	55 f. purple	60	45

DESIGNS—VERT. 40 c. Nyamiranga Falls (inscr "Nyamilanga"). 55 f. Rusumo Falls (inscr "Rusumu"). HORIZ. 4 f. 50 Gahinga and Mahubura Volcanoes, and giant plants.

28. U.N.E.S.C.O. and Cultural Emblems.

1966. 20th Anniv. of U.N.E.S.C.O.

184. 28.	20 c. mauve and blue..	10	10
185. –	30 c. turquoise & black	10	10
186. –	50 c. brown and black..	10	10
187. –	1 f. violet and black ..	10	10
188. 28.	5 f. green and brown ..	10	10
189. –	10 f. brown and black..	15	10
190. –	15 f. purple and blue ..	55	35
191. –	50 f. blue and black ..	65	50

DESIGNS: 30 c., 10 f. "Animal" primer. 50 c., 15 f. Atomic symbol and drill operator. 1 f., 50 f. Nubian monuments partly submerged in the Nile.

29. "Bitis gabonica".

1967. Snakes. Multicoloured.

192.	20 c. Head of Mamba ..	10	10
193.	30 c. Python	10	10
194.	50 c. Type 29	10	10
195.	1 f. "Naja melanoleuca"	10	10
196.	3 f. Head of python ..	10	10
197.	5 f. "Psammophis sibilans"	20	10
198.	20 f. "Dendroaspis jamesoni kaimosae"	55	35
199.	70 f. "Dasypeltis scabra"	65	45

The 30 c., 1 f., 5 f. and 70 f. are vert.

30. Girders and Tea Flower.

1967. Ntaruka Hydro-Electric Project.

200. 30.	20 c. blue and purple..	10	10
201. –	30 c. brown and black..	10	10
202. –	50 c. violet and brown..	10	10
203. 30.	4 f. purple and green ..	10	10
204. –	25 f. green and violet..	50	50
205. –	50 f. brown and blue ..	1·00	1·00

DESIGNS: 30 c., 25 f. Power conductors and pyrethrum flower. 50 c., 50 f. Barrage and coffee-beans.

33. "St. Martin" (Van Dyck).

1967. Paintings.

208. 33.	20 c. blk., gold & violet	10	10
209. –	40 c. black, gold & grn.	10	10
210. –	60 c. black, gold & red	10	10
211. –	80 c. black, gold & blue	10	10
212. 33.	9 f. black, gold & brown	90	50
213. –	15 f. black, gold & red	35	20
214. –	18 f. blk., gold & bronze	35	20
215. –	26 f. black, gold & lake	45	45

PAINTINGS—HORIZ. 40 c., 15 f. "Rebecca and Eliezer" (Murillo). 80 c., 26 f. "Job and his Friends" (attributed to Il Calabrese). VERT. 60 c., 18 f. "St. Christopher" (D. Bouts).

34. Rwanda "Round Table" Emblem and Common Zebra's Head.

1967. Rwanda "Round Table" Fund for Charitable Works. Each with "Round Table" Emblem. Multicoloured.

216.	20 c. Type 34	10	10
217.	40 c. African elephant's head	10	10
218.	60 c. African buffalo's head	10	10
219.	80 c. Impalas head ..	10	10
220.	18 f. Ear of wheat.. ..	35	15
221.	100 f. Palm..	1·60	90

35. "Africa Place" and Dancers.

1967. World Fair, Montreal.

222. 35.	20 c. blue and sepia ..	10	10
223. –	30 c. purple and sepia	10	10
224. –	50 c. orange and sepia	10	10
225. –	1 f. green and sepia ..	10	10
226. –	3 f. violet and sepia ..	10	10
227. 35.	15 f. green and sepia ..	15	15
228. –	34 f. red and sepia ..	50	40
229. –	40 f. turquoise and sepia	70	55

DESIGNS: "Africa Place" (two different views used alternately in order of value): 30 c., 3 f. Drum and handicrafts. 50 c., 40 f. Dancers leaping. 1 f., 34 f. Spears, shields and weapons.

1967. Air. 5th Anniv. of U.A.M.P.T. As T 101 of Mauritania.

230.	6 f. slate, brown and lake	20	10
231.	18 f. purple and brown ..	65	35
232.	30 f. red, green and blue..	1·10	65

36. Common Zebra's Head and Lion's Emblem.

37. Red Bishop.

1967. 50th Anniv. of Lions Int.

233. 36.	20 c. black, blue & violet	10	10
234.	80 c. black, blue & green	10	10
235.	1 f. black, blue and red	10	10
236.	8 f. black, blue & brown	20	10
237.	10 f. black, blue & ult.	30	20
238.	50 f. black, blue & green	1·10	70

1967. Birds of Rwanda. Multicoloured.

239.	20 c. Type 37	10	10
240.	40 c. Woodland Kingfisher	10	10
241.	60 c. Red-billed Quelea ..	10	10
242.	80 c. Double-toothed Barbet	10	10
243.	2 f. Pin-tailed Whydah ..	15	10
244.	3 f. Red-chested Cuckoo ..	20	10
245.	18 f. Green Wood Hoopoe	90	15
246.	25 f. Cinnamon-chested Bee Eater	1·25	25
247.	80 f. Regal Sunbird ..	3·00	80
248.	100 f. Fan-tailed Whydah	4·00	95

The 40 c., 80 c., 3 f., 25 f. and 100 f. are horiz.

39. Running, and Mexican Antiquities.

1968. Olympic Games, Mexico. (1st issue). Multicoloured.

250.	20 c. Type 39	10	10
251.	40 c. Hammer-throwing ..	10	10
252.	60 c. Hurdling	10	10
253.	80 c. Javelin-throwing ..	10	10
254.	8 f. Football (vert.) ..	20	10
255.	10 f. Mexican horseman and cacti (vert.)	20	10
256.	12 f. Hockey (vert.) ..	30	10
257.	18 f. Cathedral (vert.) ..	45	15
258.	20 f. Boxing (vert.) ..	65	30
259.	30 f. Mexico City (vert.) ..	80	35

The 20 c. to 80 c. include Mexican Antiquities in their designs.

41. "Diaphananthe fragrantissima".

1968. Flowers. Multicoloured.

261.	20 c. Type 41	10	10
262.	40 c. "Phaeomeria speciosa"	10	10
263.	60 c. "Ravenala madagascariensis"	10	10
264.	80 c. "Costus afer" ..	10	10
265.	2 f. Banana Flowers ..	10	10
266.	3 f. Flowers and young fruit of Papaw	10	10
267.	18 f. "Clerodendron sp."	35	15
268.	25 f. Sweet potato flowers	45	30
269.	80 f. Baobab flower ..	1·60	80
270.	100 f. Passion flower ..	1·90	90

42. Horse-jumping. 43. Tuareg (Algeria).

1968. Olympic Games, Mexico (2nd issue).

271. 42.	20 c. brown and orange	10	10
272. –	40 c. brown & turquoise	10	10
273. –	60 c. brown and purple	10	10
274. –	80 c. brown and blue..	10	10
275. –	38 f. brown and red	50	40
276. –	60 f. brown and green..	1·10	65

SPORTS: 40 c. Judo. 60 c. Fencing. 80 c. High-jumping. 38 f. High-diving. 60 f. Weightlifting. Each design also represents the location of previous Olympics as at left in Type 42.

1968. African National Costumes (1st series). Multicoloured.

277.	30 c. Type 43	10	10
278.	40 c. Upper Volta	10	10
279.	60 c. Senegal	10	10
280.	70 c. Rwanda	10	10
281.	8 f. Morocco	10	10
282.	20 f. Nigeria	35	20
283.	40 f. Zambia	80	35
284.	50 f. Kenya	1·10	55

See also Nos. 345/52.

1968. Air. "Philexafrique" Stamp Exn., Abidjan (Ivory Coast, 1969) (1st issue). As T 113a of Mauritania.

286.	100 f. "Alexandre Lenoir" (J. L. David)	3·25	1·60

45. Rwanda Scene and Stamp of Ruanda-Urundi (1953).

1969. Air. "Philexafrique" Stamp Exn. (2nd issue).

287. 45.	50 f. multicoloured ..	1·90	1·25

46. "The Musical Angels" (Van Eyck).

47. Tuareg Tribesmen.

1969. "Paintings and Music". Mult.

288.	20 c. Type 46 (postage) ..	10	10
289.	40 c. "The Angels' Concert" (M. Grunewald) ..	10	10
290.	60 c. "The Singing Boy" (Frans Hals)	10	10
291.	80 c. "The Lute-player" (G. Terborch)	10	10
292.	2 f. "The Fifer" (Manet) ..	10	10
293.	6 f. "Young Girls at the Piano" (Renoir) ..	15	10
294.	50 f. "The Music Lesson" (Fragonard) (air) ..	1·40	85
295.	100 f. "Angels Playing their Musical Instruments" (Memling)	2·75	1·60

The 100 f. is horiz.

1969. African Headdresses (1st series). Multicoloured.

297.	20 c. Type 47	10	10
298.	40 c. Young Ovambo woman	10	10
299.	60 c. Ancient Guinean and Middle Congo festival head-dresses	10	10
300.	80 c. Guinean "Dagger" dancer	10	10
301.	8 f. Nigerian Muslims ..	10	10
302.	20 f. Luba dancer, Kabondo (Congo)	40	20
303.	40 f. Senegalese and Gambian women	85	45
304.	80 f. Rwanda dancer ..	1·90	1·00

See also Nos. 408/15.

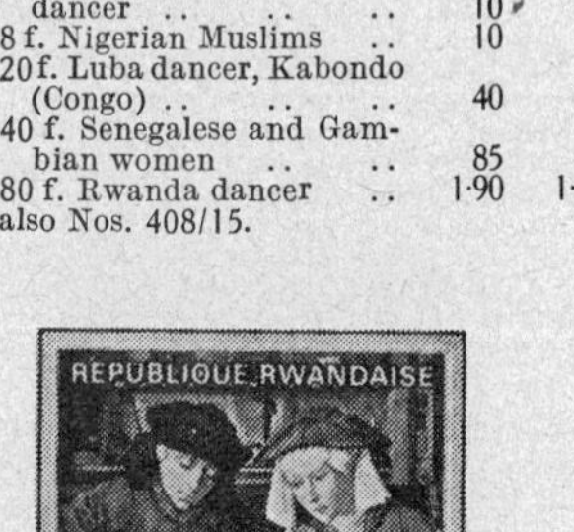

48. "The Moneylender and his Wife" (Quentin Metsys).

1969. 5th Anniv. of African Development Bank.

305. 48.	30 f. mult. on silver ..	55	50
306. –	70 f. mult. on gold ..	1·60	1·40

DESIGN: 70 f. "The Moneylender and his Wife" (Van Reymerswaele).

50. Pyrethrum.

51. Revolutionary.

1969. Medicinal Plants. Multicoloured.

308.	20 c. Type 50	10	10
309.	40 c. Aloes	10	10
310.	60 c. Cola	10	10
311.	80 c. Coca	10	10
312.	3 f. Hagenia	10	10
313.	75 f. Cassia	1·40	80
314.	80 f. Cinchona	1·90	90
315.	100 f. Tephrosia	2·25	1·10

1969. 10th Anniv. of Revolution.

316. **51.** 6 f. multicoloured .. 15 10
317. 18 f. multicoloured .. 50 45
318. 40 f. multicoloured .. 1·00 95

53. "Napoleon on Horseback" (David).

1969. Birth Bicent. of Napoleon Bonaparte. Multicoloured. Portraits of Napoleon. Artists name given.

320. 20 c. Type **53** 10 10
321. 40 c. Debret 10 10
322. 60 c. Gautherot 10 10
323. 80 c. Ingres 10 10
324. 8 f. Pajou 20 15
325. 20 f. Gros 55 40
326. 40 f. Gros .. .. .. 1·00 55
327. 80 f. David .. .. .. 2·25 1·25

54. "The Quarryman" (O. Bonnevalle).

1969. 50th Anniv. of I.L.O. Mult.

328. 20 c. Type **54** 10 10
329. 40 c. "Ploughing" (detail, Brueghel's "Descent of Icarus") 10 10
330. 60 c. "The Fisherman" (C. Meunier) 10 10
331. 80 c. "Ostend Slipway" (J. van Noten) 10 10
332. 8 f. "The Cook" (P. Aertsen) 20 10
333. 10 f. "Vulcan's Blacksmiths" (Velazquez) 35 15
334. 50 f. "Hiercheuse" (C. Meunier) .. .. 1·25 60
335. 70 f. "The Miner" (P. Paulus) .. .. 1·60 80

Nos. 330, 332 and 334/5 are vert.

55. "The Derby at Epsom" (Gericault).

1970. Paintings of Horses. Multicoloured.

336. 20 c. Type **55** 10 10
337. 40 c. "Horses leaving the sea" (Delacroix) .. 10 10
338. 60 c. "Charles V at Muhlberg" (Titian) 10 10
339. 80 c. "To the Races, Amateur Jockeys" (Degas) 10 10
340. 8 f. "Horsemen at Rest" (Wouwermans) 20 10
341. 20 f. "Officer of the Imperial Guard" (Gericault) 60 30
342. 40 f. "Horse and Dromedary" (Bonnevalle) .. .. 1·25 45
343. 80 f. "The Prodigal Child" (Rubens) .. .. 1·60 80

Nos. 338 and 341 are vert.

1970. African National Costumes (2nd series). As T **43**. Multicoloured.

345. 20 c. Tharaka Meru woman 10 10
346. 30 c. Niger flautist .. 10 10
347. 50 c. Tunisian water-carrier 10 10
348. 1 f. Kano ceremonial (Nigeria) 10 10
349. 3 f. Mali troubador .. 10 10
350. 5 f. Quipongo, Angola women 10 10
351. 50 f. Mauritanian at prayer 95 55
352. 90 f. Sinehatiali dancers, Ivory Coast .. .. 1·75 1·00

INDEX

Countries can be quickly located by referring to the index at the end of this volume.

58. Footballer attacking Goal.

1970. World Cup Football Championships, Mexico.

353. **58.** 20 c. multicoloured .. 10 10
354. – 30 c. multicoloured .. 10 10
355. – 50 c. multicoloured .. 10 10
356. – 1 f. multicoloured .. 10 10
357. – 6 f. multicoloured .. 10 10
358. – 18 f. multicoloured .. 45 30
359. – 30 f. multicoloured .. 60 45
360. – 90 f. multicoloured .. 1·75 95

Nos. 354/60 show footballers in various positions, similar to Type **58**.

59. Flowers and Green Peafowl.

1970. "EXPO 70", World Fair, Osaka, Japan. Multicoloured.

361. 20 c. Type **59** 10 10
362. 30 c. Torii gate and "Hibiscus" (Yashuda) 10 10
363. 50 c. Dancer and "Musician" (Katayama) 10 10
364. 1 f. Sun Tower and "Warrior" 10 10
365. 3 f. House and "Seated Buddha" 10 10
366. 5 f. Pagoda and "Head of Girl" (Yamakawa) 10 10
367. 20 f. Greeting and "Imperial Palace" .. 55 35
368. 70 f. Expo emblem and "Horseman" .. .. 1·60 90

60. Two Young Gorillas.

1970. Gorillas of the Mountains.

369. **60.** 20 c. black and green .. 10 10
370. – 40 c. black, brn. & pur. 10 10
371. – 60 c. black, blue & brn. 10 10
372. – 80 c. blk., orge. & brn. 10 10
373. – 1 f. black and mauve 10 10
374. – 2 f. multicoloured .. 10 10
375. – 15 f. black and sepia .. 45 20
376. – 100 f. black, brn. & blue 2·75 1·60

GORILLA—VERT. 40 c. Squatting. 80 c. Beating chest. 2 f. Eating banana. 100 f. With young. HORIZ. 60 c. Walking. 1 f. With family. 15 f. Heads.

61. Cinchona Bark. **62.** Rocket in Flight.

1970. 150th Anniv. of Discovery of Quinine. Multicoloured.

377. 20 c. Type **61** 10 10
378. 80 c. Pharmaceutical equipment 10 10
379. 1 f. Anopheles mosquito .. 10 10
380. 3 f. Malaria patient and nurse 10 10
381. 25 f. "Attack" on mosquito 55 35
382. 70 f. Pelletier and Caventou (discoverers of quinine) 1·50 80

1970. Moon Missions. Multicoloured.

383. 20 c. Type **62** 10 10
384. 30 c. Separation during orbit 10 10
385. 50 c. Spaceship above the moon 10 10
386. 1 f. Module and astronauts on moon 10 10
387. 3 f. Take-off from the moon 10 10
388. 5 f. Return journey to earth 15 10
389. 10 f. Final separation before landing 30 15
390. 80 f. Splashdown .. .. 1·75 1·40

63. F. D. Roosevelt and "Brasscattleya olympia alba". **65.** Pope Paul VI.

1970. 25th Death Anniv. of F. D. Roosevelt. Portraits and Orchids.

391. **63.** 20 c. brn., blue & black 10 10
392. – 30 c. brown, red & black 10 10
393. – 50 c. brn., orge. and blk. 10 10
394. – 1 f. brn., green & black 10 10
395. – 2 f. grn., brn. and blk. 10 10
396. – 6 f. grn., pur. and blk. 20 15
397. – 30 f. green, blue & black 90 40
398. – 60 f. green, red & black 1·60 70

ORCHIDS: 30 c. "Laeliocattleya callistoglossa". 50 c. "Chondrorrhyncha chestertoni". 1 f. "Paphiopedilum". 2 f. "Cymbidium hybride". 6 f. "Cattleya labiata". 30 f. "Dendrobium nobile". 60 f. "Laelia gouldiana".

1970. Cent. of 1st Vatican Council.

400. **65.** 10 c. brown and gold .. 10 10
401. – 20 c. green and gold .. 10 10
402. – 30 c. lake and gold .. 10 10
403. – 40 c. blue and gold .. 10 10
404. – 1 f. violet and gold .. 10 10
405. – 18 f. purple and gold .. 50 20
406. – 20 f. orange and gold .. 60 20
407. – 60 f. brown and gold .. 1·60 70

POPES: 20 c. John XXIII. 30 c. Pius XII. 40 c. Pius XI. 1 f. Benedict XV. 18 f. Pius X. 20 f. Leo XIII. 60 f. Pius IX.

1971. African Headdresses (2nd series). Multicoloured designs as T **47**.

408. 20 c. Rendille woman .. 10 10
409. 30 c. Chad woman 10 10
410. 50 c. Bororo man (Niger) .. 10 10
411. 1 f. Masai man (Kenya) .. 10 10
412. 5 f. Air girl (Niger) .. 10 10
413. 18 f. Rwanda woman .. 35 20
414. 25 f. Mauritania man .. 65 35
415. 50 f. Rwanda girls .. .. 1·25 65

68. "Beethoven" (C. Horneman). **72.** "Durer" (self-portrait).

69. Horse-jumping.

1971. Birth Cent. (1970) of Beethoven. Portraits and funeral scene by various artists. Multicoloured.

418. 20 c. Type **68** 10 10
419. 30 c. K. Stieler 10 10
420. 50 c. F. Schimon 10 10
421. 3 f. H. Best 10 10
422. 6 f. W. Fassbender .. 30 10
423. 90 f. "Beethoven's Burial" (Stober) .. .. 2·10 1·25

1971. Olympic Games, Munich (1972). (1st issue).

424. **69.** 20 c. gold and black .. 10 10
425. – 30 c. gold and purple .. 10 10
426. – 50 c. gold and violet .. 10 10
427. – 1 f. gold and green .. 10 10
428. – 8 f. gold and red .. 20 10
429. – 10 f. gold and violet .. 30 15
430. – 20 f. gold and brown .. 50 30
431. – 60 f. gold and green .. 1·40 65

DESIGNS: 30 c. Running (start). 50 c. Basketball. 1 f. High-jumping. 8 f. Boxing. 10 f. Pole-vaulting. 20 f. Wrestling. 60 f. Gymnastics.

See also Nos. 490/7.

1971. Air. 10th Anniv. of U.A.M.P.T. As T **139a** of Mauritania. Multicoloured.

432. 100 f. U.A.M.P.T. H.Q. and Rwandaise woman and child .. .. 2·75 1·60

HAVE YOU READ THE NOTES AT THE BEGINNING OF THIS CATALOGUE?

These often provide answers to the enquiries we receive.

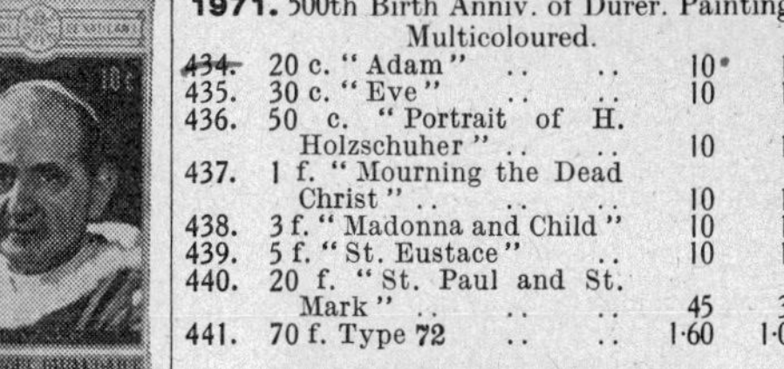

1971. 500th Birth Anniv. of Durer. Paintings. Multicoloured.

434. 20 c. "Adam" 10 10
435. 30 c. "Eve" 10 10
436. 50 c. "Portrait of H. Holzschuher" 10 10
437. 1 f. "Mourning the Dead Christ" 10 10
438. 3 f. "Madonna and Child" 10 10
439. 5 f. "St. Eustace" .. 10 10
440. 20 f. "St. Paul and St. Mark" 45 30
441. 70 f. Type **72** .. .. 1·60 1·00

73. Astronauts in Moon Rover.

1972. Moon Mission of "Apollo 15".

442. **73.** 600 f. gold .. .. 65·00

74. Participation in Sport.

1972. National Guard. Multicoloured.

443. 4 f. Type **74** 10 10
444. 6 f. Transport of emergency supplies 15 10
445. 15 f. Helicopter transport for the sick 40 20
446. 25 f. Participation in health service 65 35
447. 50 f. Guard, map and emblem (vert.) .. .. 1·25 1·10

75. Ice-hockey.

1972. Winter Olympic Games, Sapporo, Japan. Multicoloured.

448. 20 c. Type **75** 10 10
449. 30 c. Speed-skating .. 10 10
450. 50 c. Ski-jumping .. 10 10
451. 1 f. Figure-skating .. 10 10
452. 6 f. Cross-country skiing .. 10 10
453. 12 f. Slalom 15 15
454. 20 f. Tobogganing .. 45 20
455. 60 f. Downhill skiing .. 1·40 1·10

76. Savanna Monkey and Impala.

1972. Akagera National Park. Multicoloured.

456. 20 c. Type **76** 10 10
457. 30 c. African buffalo .. 10 10
458. 50 c. Common zebra .. 10 10
459. 1 f. White rhinoceros .. 10 10
460. 2 f. Warthogs 10 10
461. 6 f. Hippopotamus .. 15 10
462. 18 f. Spotted hyenas .. 30 20
463. 32 f. Helmet Guineafowl .. 2·00 60
464. 60 f. Waterbucks .. .. 1·60 1·10
465. 80 f. Lion and lioness .. 2·25 1·60

77. Family supporting Flag. **78.** Variable Sunbirds.

1972. 10th Anniv. of Referendum.

466. **77.** 6 f. multicoloured .. 10 10
467. 18 f. multicoloured .. 45 35
468. 60 f. multicoloured .. 1·25 1·10

1972. Rwanda Birds. Multicoloured.
469. 20 c. Common Waxbills .. 15 10
470. 30 c. Collared Sunbird .. 15 10
471. 50 c. Type **78** 15 10
472. 1 f. Greater Double-collared Sunbird 15 10
473. 4 f. Ruwenzori Puff-back Flycather 15 10
474. 6 f. Red-billed Fire Finch 20 15
475. 10 f. Scarlet-chested Sunbird 50 15
476. 18 f. Red-headed Quelea .. 85 30
477. 60 f. Common Gonolek .. 3·00 1·25
478. 100 f. African Golden Oriole .. .. .. 4·25 2·10

79. King Baudouin and Queen Fabiola with President and Mrs. Kayibanda in Rwanda.

1972. "Belgica 72" Stamp Exhib., Brussels.
479. – 18 f. multicoloured .. 45 45
480. – 22 f. multicoloured .. 65 55
481. **79.** 40 f. blue, blk. & gold .. 1·10 95
DESIGNS: 18 f. Rwanda village. 22 f. View of Bruges.
Nos. 479/80 are smaller, size 39 × 36 mm.

80. Announcement of Independence.

1972. 10th Anniv. of Independence.
482. **80.** 20 c. green and gold .. 10 10
483. – 30 c. purple and gold .. 10 10
484. – 50 c. sepia and gold .. 10 10
485. – 6 f. blue and gold .. 10 10
486. – 10 f. purple and gold .. 15 10
487. – 15 f. blue and gold .. 35 20
488. – 18 f. brown and gold .. 45 30
489. – 50 f. green and gold .. 1·10 70
DESIGNS—HORIZ. 30 c. Promotion ceremony, officers of the National Guard. 50 c. Pres. Kayibanda, wife and family. 6 f. Pres. Kayibanda casting vote in legislative elections. 10 f. Pres. and Mrs. Kayibanda at "Festival of Justice". 15 f. President and members of National Assembly. 18 f. Investiture of Pres. Kayibanda. VERT. 50 f. President Kayibanda.

81. Horse-jumping.

1972. Olympic Games, Munich. (2nd issue).
490. **81.** 20 c. green and gold .. 10 10
491. – 30 c. violet and gold .. 10 10
492. – 50 c. green and gold .. 10 10
493. – 1 f. purple and gold .. 10 10
494. – 6 f. black and gold .. 10 10
495. – 18 f. brown and gold .. 35 30
496. – 30 f. violet and gold .. 80 55
497. – 44 f. blue and gold .. 1·10 65
DESIGNS: 30 c. Hockey. 50 c. Football. 1 f. Long jumping. 6 f. Cycling. 18 f. Yachting. 30 f. Hurdling. 44 f. Gymnastics.

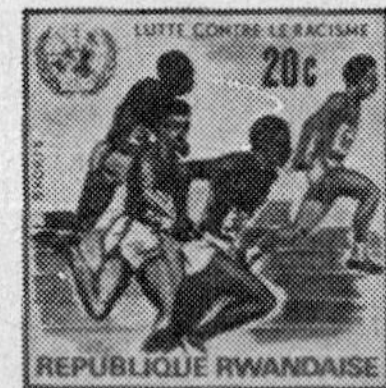

82. Runners.

1972. Racial Equality Year. "Working Together". Multicoloured.
498. 20 c. Type **82** 10 10
499. 30 c. Musicians 10 10
500. 50 c. Ballet dancers .. 10 10
501. 1 f. Medical team in operating theatre 10 10
502. 6 f. Weaver and painter .. 10 10
503. 18 f. Children in class .. 35 20
504. 24 f. Laboratory technicians 55 35
505. 50 f. U.N. emblem and hands of four races .. .. 1·00 65

84. "Phymateus brunneri".

1973. Rwanda Insects. Multicoloured.
507. 20 c. Type **84** 10 10
508. 30 c. "Diopsis fumipennis" (vert.) 10 10
509. 50 c. "Kitoko alberti" .. 10 10
510. 1 f. "Archibracon fasciatus" (vert.) 10 10
511. 2 f. "Ornithacris cyanea imperialis" 10 10
512. 6 f. "Clitodaca fenestralis" (vert.) 15 10
513. 18 f. "Senaspis oesacus" 40 20
514. 22 f. "Phonoctonus grandis" (vert.) 55 35
515. 70 f. "Loba leopardina" .. 1·90 1·25
516. 100 f. "Ceratocoris distortus" (vert.) .. .. 3·50 2·00

85. "Emile Zola" (Manet). **86.** Longombe.

1973. Int. Book Year. "Readers and Writers". Paintings and portraits. Mult.
518. 20 c. Type **85** 10 10
519. 30 c. "Rembrandt's Mother" (Rembrandt) .. 10 10
520. 50 c. "St. Jerome removing Thorn from Lion's paw" (Colantonio) 10 10
521. 1 f. "St. Peter and St. Paul" (El Greco) .. 10 10
522. 2 f. "Virgin and Child" (Van der Weyden) .. 10 10
523. 6 f. "St. Jerome in his Cell" (Antonella de Messina) 15 10
524. 40 f. St. Barbara" (Master of Flemalle) .. 1·00 60
525. 100 f. "Don Quixote" (O. Bonnevalle) .. 2·10 1·60

1973. Musical Instruments. Multicoloured.
527. 20 c. Type **86** 10 10
528. 30 c. Horn.. .. .. 10 10
529. 50 c. "Xylophone" .. 10 10
530. 1 f. "Harp" 10 10
531. 4 f. Alur horns 10 10
532. 6 f. Horn, bells and drum .. 10 10
533. 18 f. Drums 40 40
534. 90 f. Gourds .. .. 2·00 1·40

87. "Rubens and Isabelle Brandt" (Rubens). **88.** Map of Africa and Doves.

1973. "IBRA" Stamp Exhibition, Munich. Famous Paintings. Multicoloured.
535. 20 c. Type **87** 10 10
536. 30 c. "Portrait of a Lady" (Cranach the Younger) .. 10 10
537. 50 c. "Woman peeling Turnips" (Chardin) .. 10 10
538. 1 f. "Abduction of the Daughters of Leucippe" (Rubens) 10 10
539. 2 f. "Virgin and Child" (Lippi) 10 10
540. 6 f. "Boys eating Fruit" (Murillo) 20 10
541. 40 f. "The Sickness of Love" (Steen) 90 45
542. 100 f. "Jesus divested of His Garments" (El Greco) 2·25 1·40

1973. 10th Anniv. of O.A.U. Mult.
544. 6 f. Type **88** 20 10
545. 94 f. Map of Africa and hands .. .. .. 2·25 1·90

1973. Pan-African Drought Relief. Nos. 308/13 and 315 optd. **SECHERESSE SOLIDARITE AFRICAINE** and No. 315 additionally surch.
546. **50.** 20 c. multicoloured .. 10 10
547. – 40 c. multicoloured .. 10 10
548. – 60 c. multicoloured .. 10 10
549. – 80 c. multicoloured .. 10 10
550. – 3 f. multicoloured .. 10 10
551. – 75 f. multicoloured .. 1·60 1·40
552. – 100 f. + 50 f. mult. .. 4·50 4·00

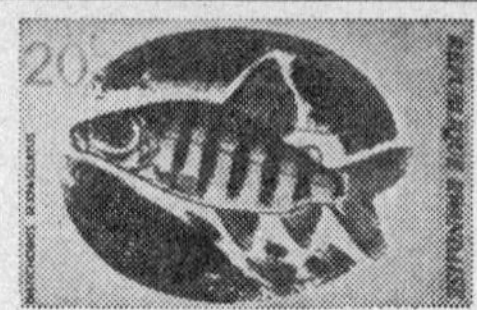

90. "Distichodus sexfasciatus".

1973. Fishes. Multicoloured.
553. 20 c. Type **90** 10 10
554. 30 c. "Hydrocyon forkalii" 10 10
555. 50 c. "Synodontis angelicus" 10 10
556. 1 f. "Tilapia nilotica" .. 10 10
557. 2 f. "Protopterus aethiopicus" 10 10
558. 6 f. "Pareutropius mandevillei" 20 10
559. 40 f. "Phenacogrammus interruptus" 90 65
560. 150 f. "Julidochromis ornatus" .. .. 3·50 2·50

1973. 12th Anniv. of U.A.M.P.T. As T **155a** of Mauritania.
562. 100 f. blue, brown, mauve 3·25 3·25

1973. African Fortnight, Brussels. Nos. 408/15 optd. **QUINZAINE AFRICAINE BRUXELLES 15/30 SEPT. 1973** and globe.
563. 20 c. multicoloured .. 10 10
564. 30 c. multicoloured .. 10 10
565. 50 c. multicoloured .. 10 10
566. 1 f. multicoloured .. 10 10
567. 5 f. multicoloured .. 10 10
568. 18 f. multicoloured .. 40 20
569. 25 f. multicoloured .. 50 45
570. 50 f. multicoloured .. 1·40 85

1973. Air. Congress of French-speaking Nations, Liege. No. 432 optd. **LIEGE ACCUEILLE LES PAYS DE LANGUE FRANCAISE 1973** (No. 562) or congress emblem (No. 563).
571. 100 f. multicoloured .. 4·00 2·75
572. 100 f. multicoloured .. 4·00 2·75

1973. 25th Anniv. of Declaration of Human Rights. Nos. 443/7 optd. with Human Rights emblem.
574. **74.** 4 f. multicoloured .. 10 10
575. – 6 f. multicoloured .. 10 10
576. – 15 f. multicoloured .. 30 15
577. – 25 f. multicoloured .. 60 40
578. – 50 f. multicoloured .. 1·10 70

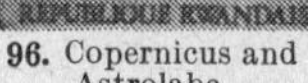

96. Copernicus and Astrolabe. **97.** Pres. Habyarimana.

1973. 500th Birth Anniv. of Copernicus. Mult.
580. 20 c. Type **96** 10 10
581. 30 c. Copernicus 10 10
582. 50 c. Copernicus and heliocentric system 10 10
583. 1 f. Type **96** 10 10
584. 18 f. As 30 c. 40 30
585. 80 f. As 50 c. .. .. 1·60 1·10

1974. "New Regime".
587. **97.** 1 f. brown, black & buff 10 10
588. 2 f. brown, black & blue 10 10
589. 5 f. brown, black & red 10 10
590. 6 f. brown, black & blue 10 10
591. 26 f. brown, black & lilac 55 45
592. 60 f. brown, black & green 1·25 1·00

99. Yugoslavia v Zaire. **101.** "Diane de Poitiers" (Fontainebleau School).

100. Marconi's Steam Yacht "Elettra".

1974. World Cup Football Championships, West Germany. Players represent specified teams. Multicoloured.
594. 20 c. Type **99** 10 10
595. 40 c. Netherlands v Sweden 10 10
596. 60 c. West Germany v Australia 10 10
597. 80 c. Haiti v Argentina .. 10 10
598. 2 f. Brazil v Scotland .. 10 10
599. 6 f. Bulgaria v Uruguay .. 10 10
600. 40 f. Italy v Poland .. 80 65
601. 50 f. Chile v East Germany 1·40 1·00

1974. Birth Centenary of Guglielmo Marconi (radio pioneer). Multicoloured.
602 20 c. Type **100** 20 10
603 30 c. Cruiser "Carlo Alberto" 20 10
604 50 c. Marconi's telegraph equipment 10 10
605 4 f. "Global Telecommunications" 10 10
606 35 f. Early radio receiver 85 45
607 60 f. Marconi and Poldhu radio station .. .. 1·50 1·10

1974. Int. Stamp Exhibitions "Stockholmia" and "Internaba". Paintings from Stockholm and Basle. Multicoloured.
609. 20 c. Type **101** 10 10
610. 30 c. "The Flute-player" (J. Leyster) 10 10
611. 50 c. "Virgin Mary and Child" (G. David) .. 10 10
612. 1 f. "The Triumph of Venus" (F. Boucher) 10 10
613. 10 f. "Harlequin Seated" (P. Picasso) 15 10
614. 18 f. "Virgin and Child" (15th-century) 35 15
615. 20 f. "The Beheading of St. John" (H. Fries) .. 45 35
616. 50 f. "The Daughter of Andersdotter" (J. Huckert) 1·40 1·00

102. Monastic Messenger. **105.** Head of Uganda Kob.

1974. Cent. of U.P.U. Mult.
619. 20 c. Type **102** 10 10
620. 30 c. Inca messenger .. 10 10
621. 50 c. Moroccan postman .. 10 10
622. 1 f. Indian postman .. 10 10
623. 18 f. Polynesian postman .. 55 40
624. 80 f. Early Rwanda messenger with horn and drum .. 1·75 1·40

1974. 15th Anniv. of Revolution. Nos. 316/18 optd. **1974 15e ANNIVERSAIRE.**
625. **51.** 6 f. multicoloured ..
626. 18 f. multicoloured ..
627. 40 f. multicoloured ..
Set of 3 .. .. .. 11·00 9·50

1974. 10th Anniv. of African Development Bank. Nos. 305/6 optd. **1974 10e ANNIVERSAIRE.**
629. **48.** 30 f. multicoloured .. 85 65
630. – 70 f. multicoloured .. 1·90 1·40

1975. Antelopes. Multicoloured.
631. 20 c. Type **105** 10 10
632. 30 c. Bongo with calf (horiz.) 10 10
633. 50 c. Roan antelope and Sable antelope heads .. 10 10
634. 1 f. Young sitatungas (horiz.) 10 10
635. 4 f. Great kudu 10 10
636. 10 f. Impala family (horiz.) 30 10
637. 34 f. Waterbuck head .. 90 45
638. 100 f. Giant eland (horiz.) 2·75 2·25

108. Pyrethrum Daisies. **111.** Globe and Emblem.

110. Eastern White Pelicans.

1975. Agricultural Labour Year. Mult.
642. 20 c. Type **108** 10 10
643. 30 c. Tea plant 10 10
644. 50 c. Coffee berries .. 10 10
645. 4 f. Bananas 10 10
646. 10 f. Maize 20 10
647. 12 f. Sorghum 35 15
648. 26 f. Rice 80 45
649. 47 f. Coffee cultivation .. 1·60 90

1975. Holy Year. Nos. 400/7 optd **1975 ANNEE SAINTE.**
652. **65.** 10 c. brown and gold .. 10 10
653. – 20 c. green and gold .. 10 10
654. – 30 c. lake and gold .. 10 10
655. – 40 c. blue and gold .. 10 10
656. – 1 f. violet and gold .. 10 10
657. – 18 f. purple and gold .. 40 20
658. – 20 f. orange and gold .. 45 20
659. – 60 f. brown and gold .. 1·90 1·25

1975. Aquatic Birds. Multicoloured.
660. 20 c. Type **110** 20 10
661. 30 c. Malachite Kingfisher 20 10
662. 50 c. Goliath Herons .. 20 10
663. 1 f. Saddle-bill Stork .. 20 10
664. 4 f. African Jacana .. 40 15
665. 10 f. African Darter .. 70 35
666. 34 f. Sacred Ibis .. .. 1·75 95
667. 80 f. Hartlaub's Duck (vert.) .. .. .. 4·75 2·50

1975. World Population Year (1974). Mult.
669. 20 f. Type **111** 45 30
670. 26 f. Population graph .. 65 35
671. 34 f. Symbolic doorway .. 95 50

112. "La Toilette" (M. Cassatt). **113.** "Arts".

1975. International Women's Year. Mult.
672. 20 c. Type **112** 10 10
673. 30 c. "Mother and Child" (G. Melchers) 10 10
674. 50 c. "The Milk Jug" (Vermeer) 10 10
675. 1 f. "The Water-carrier" (Goya) 10 10
676. 8 f. Coffee-picking .. 20 10
677. 12 f. Laboratory technician 35 20
678. 18 f. Rwandaise mother and child 55 20
679. 60 f. Woman carrying water-jug .. .. 1·50 1·25

1975. 10th Anniv. of National University. The Faculties. Multicoloured.
681. 20 c. Type **113** 10 10
682. 30 c. "Medicine" 10 10
683. 1 f. 50 "Jurisprudence" 10 10
684. 18 f. "Science" 40 20
685. 26 f. "Commerce" .. 45 30
686. 34 f. University Building, Kigali 85 55

114. Cattle at Pool, and "Impatiens stuhlmannii".

1975. Protection of Nature. Multicoloured.
688. 20 c. Type **114** 10 10
689. 30 c. Euphorbia "candelabra" and savannah bush 10 10
690. 50 c. Bush fire and "Tapinanthus prunifolius" .. 10 10
691. 5 f. Lake Bulera and "Nymphaea lotus" .. 10 10
692. 8 f. Soil erosion and "Protea madiensis" .. 15 10
693. 10 f. Protected marshland and "Melanthera brownei" 20 15
694. 26 f. Giant lobelias and groundsel 55 40
695. 100 f. Sabyinyo volcano and "Polystachya kermesina" .. .. 2·25 1·60

1975. Pan-African Drought Relief. Nos. 345/52 optd. or surch. **SECHERESSE SOLIDARITE 1975.** (both words share same capital letter).
696. 20 c. multicoloured .. 10 10
697. 30 c. multicoloured .. 10 10
698. 50 c. multicoloured .. 10 10
699. 1 f. multicoloured .. 10 10
700. 3 f. multicoloured .. 10 10
701. 5 f. multicoloured .. 15 10
702. 50 f.+25 f. multicoloured 1·60 1·25
703. 90 f.+25 f. multicoloured 2·40 2·00

116. Loading Aircraft. **117.** African Woman with Basket on Head.

1975. Year of Increased Production. Mult.
704. 20 c. Type **116** 10 10
705. 30 c. Coffee-picking plant 10 10
706. 50 c. Lathe-operator .. 10 10
707. 10 f. Farmer with hoe (vert.) 15 10
708. 35 f. Coffee-picking (vert.) 60 55
709. 54 f. Mechanical plough .. 1·10 95

1975. "Themabelga" Stamp Exhibition Brussels. African Costumes.
710. **117.** 20 c. multicoloured .. 10 10
711. – 30 c. multicoloured .. 10 10
712. – 50 c. multicoloured .. 10 10
713. – 1 f. multicoloured .. 10 10
714. – 5 f. multicoloured .. 10 10
715. – 7 f. multicoloured .. 15 10
716. – 35 f. multicoloured .. 70 60
717. – 51 f. multicoloured .. 1·40 95
DESIGNS: 30 c. to 51 f. Various Rwanda costumes.

118. Dr. Schweitzer, Organ Pipes and Music Score.

1976. World Leprosy Day.
719. – 20 c. lilac, brn. and blk. 10 10
720. – 30 c. lilac, grn. and blk. 10 10
721. **118.** 50 c. lilac, brn. and blk. 10 10
722. – 1 f. lilac, pur. and blk. 10 10
723. – 3 f. lilac, blue and black 10 10
724. – 5 f. lilac, brn. and black 10 10
725. **118.** 10 f. lilac, blue and blk. 30 10
726. – 80 f. lilac, red and black 1·90 1·40
DESIGNS: Dr. Schweitzer and: 20 c. Piano keyboard and music. 30 c. Lambarene Hospital. 1 f. Lambarene residence. 3 f. as 20 c. 5 f. As 30 c. 80 f. As 1 f.

119. "Surrender at Yorktown".

1976. Bicent. of American Revolution. Mult.
727. 20 c. Type **119** 10 10
728. 30 c. "The Sergeant-Instructor at Valley Forge" .. 10 10
729. 50 c. "Presentation of Captured Yorktown Flags to Congress" 10 10
730. 1 f. "Washington at Fort Lee" 10 10
731. 18 f. "Washington boarding a British warship" .. 45 30
732. 26 f. "Washington studies Battle-plans" 55 40
733. 34 f. "Washington firing a Cannon" 90 55
734. 40 f. "Crossing the Delaware" .. .. .. 1·00 85

120. Sister Yohana. **121.** Yachting.

1976. 75th Anniv. of Catholic Church in Rwanda. Multicoloured.
736. 20 c. Type **120** 10 10
737. 30 c. Abdon Sabakati .. 10 10
738. 50 c. Father Alphonse Brard 10 10
739. 4 f. Abbe Balthazar Gafuku 10 10
740. 10 f. Monseigneur Bigirumwami 20 10
741. 25 f. Save Catholic Church (horiz.) 60 45
742. 60 f. Kabgayi Catholic Cathedral (horiz.) .. 1·25 80

1976. Olympic Games, Montreal (1st issue).
743. **121.** 20 c. brown and green .. 10 10
744. – 30 c. blue and green .. 10 10
745. – 50 c. black and green .. 10 10
746. – 1 f. violet and green .. 10 10
747. – 10 f. blue and green .. 20 10
748. – 18 f. brown and green .. 35 30
749. – 29 f. purple and green .. 80 60
750. – 51 f. deep green & green 1·00 80
DESIGNS: 30 c. Horse-jumping. 50 c. Long-jumping. 1 f. Hockey. 10 f. Swimming. 18 f. Football. 29 f. Boxing. 51 f. Gymnastics.
See also Nos. 767/74.

122. Bell's Experimental Telephone and Manual Switchboard.

1976. Telephone Centenary.
751. **122.** 20 c. brown and blue .. 10 10
752. – 30 c. blue and violet .. 10 10
753. – 50 c. brown and blue .. 10 10
754. – 1 f. orange and blue .. 10 10
755. – 4 f. mauve and blue .. 10 10
756. – 8 f. green and blue .. 15 10
757. – 26 f. red and blue .. 70 55
758. – 60 f. lilac and blue .. 1·40 1·00
DESIGNS: 30 c. Early telephone and man making call. 50 c. Early telephone and woman making call. 1 f. Early telephone and exchange building. 4 f. Alexander Graham Bell and "candlestick" telephone. 8 f. Rwanda subscriber and dial telephone. 26 f. Dish aerial, satellite and modern hand set. 60 f. Rwanda, PTT building, operator and push-button telephone.

1976. Bicent. of Declaration of American Independence. Nos. 727/34 optd. **INDEPENDENCE DAY** and Bicentennial Emblem.
759. **119.** 20 c. multicoloured .. 10 10
760. – 30 c. multicoloured .. 10 10
761. – 50 c. multicoloured .. 10 10
762. – 1 f. multicoloured .. 10 10
763. – 18 f. multicoloured .. 35 20
764. – 26 f. multicoloured .. 65 45
765. – 34 f. multicoloured .. 80 55
766. – 40 f. multicoloured .. 1·10 80

124. Football. **125.** "Apollo" and "Soyuz" Launches and ASTP Badge.

1976. Olympic Games, Montreal (2nd issue). Multicoloured.
767. 20 c. Type **124** 10 10
768. 30 c. Rifle-shooting .. 10 10
769. 50 c. Canoeing 10 10
770. 1 f. Gymnastics 10 10
771. 10 f. Weightlifting .. 15 10
772. 12 f. Diving 30 20
773. 26 f. Horse-riding .. 55 40
774. 50 f. Throwing the hammer 1·40 90

1976. "Apollo – Soyuz" Test Project. Multicoloured.
776. 20 c. Type **125** 10 10
777. 30 c. "Soyuz" rocket .. 10 10
778. 50 c. "Apollo" rocket .. 10 10
779. 1 f. "Apollo" after separation 10 10
780. 2 f. Approach to link-up .. 10 10
781. 12 f. Spacecraft docked .. 35 15
782. 30 f. Sectional view of interiors 85 55
783. 54 f. "Apollo" splashdown 1·40 95

126. "Eulophia cucullata". **128.** Hands embracing. "Cultural Collaboration".

1976. Rwandaise Orchids. Multicoloured.
784. 20 c. Type **126** 10 10
785. 30 c. "Eulophia streptopetala" 10 10
786. 50 c. "Disa stairsii" .. 10 10
787. 1 f. "Aerangis kotschyana" 10 10
788. 10 f. "Eulophia abyssinica" 20 10
789. 12 f. "Bonatea steudneri" 35 15
790. 26 f. "Ansellia gigantea" 80 45
791. 50 f. "Eulophia angolensis" 1·60 90

1977. World Leprosy Day. Nos. 719/26 optd. with **JOURNEE MONDIALE 1977.**
793. – 20 c. lilac, brown & black 10 10
794. – 30 c. lilac, green & black 10 10
795. **118.** 50 c. lilac, brown & black 10 10
796. – 1 f. lilac, purple & black 10 10
797. – 3 f. lilac, blue and black 10 10
798. – 5 f. lilac, brown & black 20 10
799. **118.** 10 f. lilac, brown & black 35 20
800. – 80 f. lilac, red and black 1·60 1·60

1977. 10th OCAM Summit Meeting, Kigali. Multicoloured.
801. 10 f. Type **128** 30 10
802. 26 f. Hands embracing "Technical Collaboration" 70 40
803. 64 f. Hands embracing "Economic Collaboration" .. .. .. 1·25 90

1977. World Water Conference. Nos. 688/95 optd. **CONFERENCE MONDIALE DE L'EAU.**
805. **114.** 20 c. multicoloured .. 10 10
806. – 30 c. multicoloured .. 10 10
807. – 50 c. multicoloured .. 10 10
808. – 5 f. multicoloured .. 15 10
809. – 8 f. multicoloured .. 20 10
810. – 10 f. multicoloured .. 40 15
811. – 26 f. multicoloured .. 1·10 50
812. – 100 f. multicoloured .. 3·25 2·50

131. Roman Signal Post and African Tam-Tam. **132.** "The Ascent to Calvary" (detail).

1977. World Telecommunications Day. Multicoloured.
813. 20 c. Type **131** 10 10
814. 30 c. Chappe's semaphore and post-rider 10 10
815. 50 c. Morse code 10 10
816. 1 f. "Goliath" laying Channel cable 10 10
817. 4 f. Telephone, radio and television 10 10
818. 18 f. "Kingsport" and maritime communications satellite 65 40
819. 26 f. Telecommunications satellite and aerial .. 50 40
820. 50 f. "Mariner 2" satellite 1·40 90

1977. 400th Birth Anniv. of Peter Paul Rubens. Multicoloured.
823. 20 c. Type **132** 10 10
824. 30 c. "The Judgement of Paris" (horiz.) .. 10 10
825. 50 c. "Marie de Medici, Queen of France" .. 10 10
826. 1 f. "Heads of Negroes" (horiz.) 10 10
827. 4 f. "St. Idelfonse Triptych" (detail) 10 10
828. 8 f. "Helene Fourment with her Children" (horiz.) .. 15 10
829. 26 f. "St. Idelfonse Triptych" (detail different) 55 40
830. 60 f. "Helene Fourment" 1·50 1·00

1977. Air. 10th Anniv. of International French Language Council. As T **236a** of Mali.
831. 50 f. multicoloured .. 1·60 1·10

135. Long-crested Eagle. **138.** Scout playing Whistle.

1977. Birds of Prey. Multicoloured.
833. 20 c. Type **135** 10 10
834. 30 c. African harrier hawk 10 10
835. 50 c. African fish eagle .. 10 10
836. 1 f. Hooded vulture .. 10 10
837. 3 f. Augur buzzard .. 15 10
838. 5 f. Black kite 20 10
839. 20 f. Black-shouldered kite 90 55
840. 100 f. Bateleur .. .. 4·25 2·75

1977. Dr. Wernher von Braun Commemoration. Nos. 776/83 optd. with **memoriam WERNHER VON BRAUN 1912–1977.**
841. 20 c. Type **125** 10 10
842. 30 c. "Soyuz" rocket .. 10 10
843. 50 c. "Apollo" rocket .. 10 10
844. 1 f. "Apollo" after separation 10 10
845. 2 f. Approach to link-up .. 10 10
846. 12 f. Spacecraft docked .. 40 20
847. 30 f. Sectional view of interiors .. .. .. 1·00 50
848. 54 f. "Apollo" after splashdown .. .. .. 2·25 1·25

1978. 10th Anniv. of Rwanda Scout Association. Multicoloured.
851. 20 c. Type 138 .. .. 10 10
852. 30 c. Camp fire 10 10
853. 50 c. Scouts constructing a platform 10 10
854. 1 f. Two scouts 10 10
855. 10 f. Scouts on look-out .. 20 10
856. 18 f. Scouts in canoe .. 45 35
857. 26 f. Cooking at camp fire 55 35
858. 44 f. Lord Baden-Powell .. 1·10 70

139. Chimpanzees. **140.** " Euporus strangulatus ".

1978. Apes. Multicoloured.
859. 20 c. Type **139** 10 10
860. 30 c. Gorilla 10 10
861. 50 c. Eastern black-and-white colobus 10 10
862. 3 f. Eastern needle-clawed bushbaby 10 10
863. 10 f. Mona monkey .. 30 10
864. 26 f. Potto 65 40
865. 60 f. Savanna monkey .. 1·60 90
866. 150 f. Olive baboon .. 3·50 2·10

1978. Beetles. Multicoloured.
867. 20 c. Type **140** 10 10
868. 30 c. " Rhina afzelii " (vert.) 10 10
869. 50 c. " Pentalobus Palini " 10 10
870. 3 f. " Courynodes dejeani " (vert.) 10 10
871. 10 f. " Mecynorhina torquata " 20 10
872. 15 f. " Mecocerus rhombeus " (vert.) 30 10
873. 20 f. " Macrotoma serripes " 50 20
874. 25 f. " Neptunides stanleyi " (vert.) 65 40
875. 26 f. " Petrognatha gigas " 65 40
876. 100 f. " Eudicella gralli " (vert.) .. .. 2·75 1·90

141. Poling Boat across River of Poverty.

1978. National Revolutionary Development Movement. Multicoloured.
877. 4 f. Type **141** 10 10
878. 10 f. Poling boat to right .. 15 10
879. 26 f. Type **141** 60 40
880. 60 f. As 10 f. .. .. 1·10 85

142. Footballers, Cup and Flags of Netherlands and Peru.

1978. World Cup Football Championship, Argentina. Multicoloured.
881. 20 c. Type **142** 10 10
882. 30 c. Flags of FIFA, Sweden and Spain 10 10
883. 50 c. Mascot and flags of Scotland and Iran 10 10
884. 2 f. Emblem and flags of West Germany & Tunisia 10 10
885. 3 f. Cup and flags of Italy and Hungary 10 10
886. 10 f. Flags of FIFA, Brazil and Austria 20 10
887. 34 f. Mascot and flags of Poland and Mexico .. 60 45
888. 100 f. Emblem and flags of Argentina and France .. 2·25 1·40
No. 883 shows the Union Jack.

143. Wright Brothers and " Flyer ".

1978. Aviation History. Multicoloured.
889. 20 c. Type **143** 10 10
890. 30 c. Santos Dumont and " Canard 14 bis ", 1906 10 10
891. 50 c. Henry Farman and " Voisin No. 1 bis ", 1908 10 10
892. 1 f. Jan Olieslaegers and Bleriot, 1910 .. .. 10 10
893. 3 f. Marshal Balbo and Savoia " S–17 ", 1919 .. 10 10
894. 10 f. Charles Lindbergh and " Spirit of St. Louis ", 1927 .. .. .. 15 10
895. 55 f. Hugo Junkers and Junkers " JU 52/3m ", 1932 .. .. .. 1·10 55
896. 60 f. Igor Sikorsky and Sikorsky " VS 300 ", 1939 .. .. .. 1·60 85

1978. Air. "Philexafrique" Stamp Exhibition, Libreville, Gabon and Int. Stamp Fair, Essen, West Germany. As T **262** of Niger. Multicoloured.
898. 30 f. Great Spotted Woodpecker and Oldenburg 1852 $\frac{1}{3}$ sgr. stamp .. 1·75 95
899. 30 f. Greater Kudu and Rwanda 1967 20 c. stamp 1·75 95

1978. 15th Anniv. of Organization for African Unity. Nos. 544/5 optd. **1963 1978.**
901. **88.** 6 f. multicoloured .. 30 10
902. – 94 f. multicoloured .. 1·90 1·10

146. Spur-winged Goose and Mallard. **147.** " Papilio demodocus ".

1978. Stock Rearing Year. Multicoloured.
903. 20 c. Type **146** 10 10
904. 30 c. Goats (horiz.) .. 10 10
905. 50 c. Chickens 10 10
906. 4 f. Rabbits (horiz.) .. 15 10
907. 5 f. Pigs 15 10
908. 15 f. Common Turkey (horiz.) 80 45
909. 50 f. Sheep and cattle .. 1·25 50
910. 75 f. Bull (horiz.) .. 1·60 70

1979. Butterflies. Multicoloured.
911. 20 c. Type **147** 10 10
912. 30 c. " Precis octavia " .. 10 10
913. 50 c. " Charaxes smaragdalis caerulea " 10 10
914. 4 f. " Charaxes guderiana " 15 10
915. 15 f. " Colotis evippe " .. 20 10
916. 30 f. " Danais limniace petiverana " 55 30
917. 50 f. " Byblia acheloia " 1·25 55
918. 150 f. " Utetheisa pulchella " .. .. .. 3·50 1·40

148. " Euphorbia grantii " and Women weaving. **149.** " Polyscias fulva ".

1979. " Philexafrique " Exhibition, Libreville. Multicoloured.
919. 40 f. Type **148** .. .. 1·40 85
920. 60 f. Drummers and " Intelsat " satellite .. 2·25 1·10

1979. Trees. Multicoloured.
921. 20 c. Type **149** 10 10
922. 30 c. " Entandrophragma excelsum " (horiz.) .. 10 10
923. 50 c. " Ilex mitis " .. 10 10
924. 4 f. " Kigelia africana " (horiz.) 15 10
925. 15 f. " Ficus thonningi " 35 10
926. 20 f. " Acacia senegal " (horiz.) 50 20
927. 50 f. " Symphonia globulifera " .. .. 1·25 45
928. 110 f. " Acacia sieberana " (horiz.) .. .. 2·50 1·25

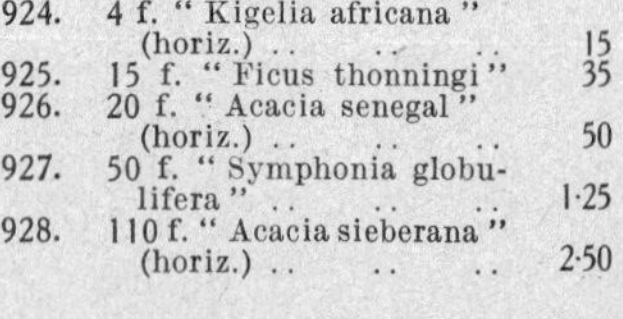

150. European Girl. **151.** Basket Weaving.

1979. International Year of the Child. Each brown, gold and stone.
929. 26 f. Type **150** 65 35
930. 26 f. Asian 65 35
931. 26 f. Eskimo 65 35
932. 26 f. Asian boy 65 35
933. 26 f. African 65 35
934. 26 f. South American Indian 65 35
935. 26 f. Polynesian 65 35
936. 26 f. European girl (different) 65 35
937. 42 f. European and African (horiz.) .. .. .. 1·40 65

1979. Handicrafts. Multicoloured.
939. 50 c. Type **151** 10 10
940. 1 f. 50 Wood carving (vert.) 10 10
941. 2 f. Metal working .. 10 10
942. 10 f. Basket work (vert.) .. 35 10
943. 20 f. Basket weaving (different) 50 20
944. 26 f. Mural painting (vert.) 65 30
945. 40 f. Pottery 95 40
946. 100 f. Smelting (vert.) .. 2·25 1·10

153. Rowland Hill and 40 c. Ruanda Stamp of 1916. **154.** Strange Weaver.

1979. Death Centenary of Sir Rowland Hill. Multicoloured.
948. 20 c. Type **153** 10 10
949. 30 c. 1916 Occupation stamp 10 10
950. 50 c. 1918 "A.O." overprint 10 10
951. 3 f. 1925 overprinted 60 c. stamp 10 10
952. 10 f. 1931 50 c. African buffalo stamp 30 10
953. 26 f. 1942 20 f Common zebra stamp 65 15
954. 60 f. 1953 25 f. Protea stamp .. .. 1·40 60
955. 100 f. 1960 Olympic stamp 2·75 1·10

1980. Birds. Multicoloured.
956. 20 c. Type **154** 15 10
957. 30 c. Regal Sunbird (vert.) 15 10
958. 50 c. White-spotted Crake 15 10
959. 3 f. Crowned Hornbill .. 20 10
960. 10 f. Barred Owlet (vert.) 45 25
961. 26 f. African Emerald Cuckoo .. .. 1·00 60
962. 60 f. Black-crowned Waxbill (vert.) .. .. .. 2·10 1·25
963. 100 f. Crowned Eagle (vert.) 3·75 2·25

155. Armstrong's first Step on Moon. **156.** Butare Rotary Club Banner, Globe and Chicago Club Emblem of 1905.

1980. 10th Anniv. of "Apollo 11" Moon Landing. Multicoloured.
964. 50 c. Type **155** 10 10
965. 1 f. 50 Aldrin descending to Moon's surface .. 10 10
966. 8 f. Planting the American flag 30 10
967. 30 f. Placing seismometer .. 65 35
968. 50 f. Taking samples .. 1·10 45
969. 60 f. Setting-up experiment 1·40 65

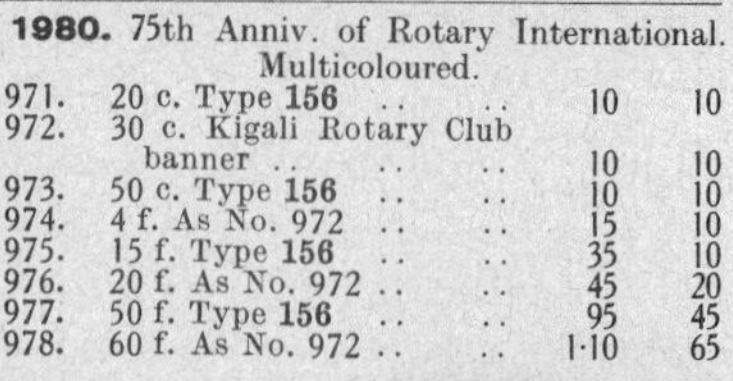

1980. 75th Anniv. of Rotary International. Multicoloured.
971. 20 c. Type **156** 10 10
972. 30 c. Kigali Rotary Club banner 10 10
973. 50 c. Type **156** 10 10
974. 4 f. As No. 972 .. .. 15 10
975. 15 f. Type **156** 35 10
976. 20 f. As No. 972 .. .. 45 20
977. 50 f. Type **156** 95 45
978. 60 f. As No. 972 .. .. 1·10 65

157. Gymnastics. **159.** " Geaster ".

1980. Olympic Games, Moscow.
979. **157.** 20 c. yellow and black 10 10
980. – 30 c. green and black .. 10 10
981. – 50 c. red and black .. 10 10
982. – 3 f. blue and black .. 15 10
983. – 20 f. orange and black 45 20
984. – 26 f. purple and black 50 25
985. – 50 f. turquoise & black 1·10 45
986. – 100 f. brown and black 2·50 1·10
DESIGNS: 30 c. Basketball. 50 c. Cycling. 3 f. Boxing. 20 f. Archery. 26 f. Weightlifting. 50 f. Javelin. 100 f. Fencing.

1980. Mushrooms. Multicoloured.
988. 20 c. Type **159** 10 10
989. 30 c. " Lentinus atrobrunneus " 10 10
990. 50 c. " Gomphus stereoides " 10 10
991. 4 f. " Cantharellus cibarius " 20 10
992. 10 f. "Stilbothamnium dybowskii " 45 20
993. 15 f. " Xeromphalina tenuipes " 65 20
994. 70 f. " Podoscypha elegans " 2·75 80
995. 100 f. " Mycena " .. 5·50 1·60

160. " At the Theatre " (Toulouse-Lautrec).

1980. Impressionist Paintings. Multicoloured.
996 20 c. "Still Life" (horiz) (Renoir) 10 10
997 30 c. Type **160** 10 10
998 50 c. "Seaside Garden" (Monet) (horiz) .. 10 10
999 4 f. "Mother and Child" (Mary Cassatt) .. 10 10
1000 5 f. "Starry Night" (Van Gogh) (horiz) .. 20 10
1001 10 f. "Three Dancers at their Toilette" (Degas) 35 10
1002 50 f. "The Card Players" (Cezanne) (horiz) .. 1·10 45
1003 70 f. "Tahitian Girls" (Gauguin) .. .. 1·75 65
1004 100 f. "La Grande Jatte" (Seurat) (horiz) .. 2·75 90

162. Revolutionary Scene.

1980. 150th Anniv. of Belgian Independence. Scenes of the Independence War from Contemporary Engravings.
1007. **162.** 20 c. green and brown 10 10
1008. – 30 c. buff and brown 10 10
1009. – 50 c. blue and brown 10 10
1010. – 9 f. orange and brown 20 10
1011. – 10 f. mauve & brown 30 10
1012. – 20 f. green and brown 45 20
1013. – 70 f. pink and brown 1·50 65
1014. – 90 f. yellow & brown 1·90 1·00

163. Draining the Marshes.

1980. Soil Protection and Conservation Year. Multicoloured.
1015 20 c. Type **163** 10 10
1016 30 c. Bullock in pen (mixed farming and land fertilization) .. 10 10
1017 1 f. 50 Land irrgation and rice 10 10
1018 8 f. Soil erosion and planting of trees 20 10
1019 10 f. Terrace 30 15
1020 40 f. Crop Fields .. 1·00 40
1021 90 f. Bean Crop .. 2·10 85
1022 100 f. Picking tea .. 2·25 1·10

164. " Pavetta rwandensis ".

1981. Flowers. Multicoloured.
1023. 20 c. Type **164** 10 10
1024. 30 c. " Cyrtorchis praetermissa " .. 10 10
1025. 50 c. " Pavonia urens " 10 10
1026. 4 f. " Cynorkis kassnerana " 10 10
1027. 5 f " Gardenia ternifolia " 15 10
1028. 10 f. " Leptactina platyphylla " 20 10
1029. 20 f. " Lobelia petiolata " 50 15
1030. 40 f. " Tapinanthus brunneus " 90 45
1031. 70 f. " Impatiens niamniamensis " .. 1·60 65
1032. 150 f. " Dissotis rwandensis " .. .. 4·00 1·60

165. Mother and Child. **166.** Carol Singers.

1981. SOS Children's Village. Multicoloured.
1033. 20 c. Type **165** 10 10
1034. 30 c. Child with pots .. 10 10
1035. 50 c. Children drawing .. 10 10
1036. 1 f. Girl sewing 10 10
1037. 8 f. Children playing .. 20 10
1038. 10 f. Girl knitting .. 20 10
1039. 70 f. Children making models .. .. 1·50 70
1040. 150 f. Mother and children 3·25 1·60

1981. Paintings by Norman Rockwell. Mult.
1041. 20 c. Type **166** 10 10
1042. 30 c. People of different races 10 10
1043. 50 c. Father Christmas .. 10 10
1044. 1 f. Coachman 10 10
1045. 8 f. Man at piano .. 15 10
1046. 20 f. " Springtime " .. 50 20
1047. 50 f. Man making donation to girl " nurse " .. 1·00 45
1048. 70 f. Clown .. .. 1·50 70

167. Serval.

1981. Carnivorous Animals. Multicoloured.
1049. 20 c. Type **167** 10 10
1050. 30 c. Black-backed jackal 10 10
1051. 2 f. Servaline genet .. 10 10
1052. 2 f. 50 Banded mongoose 10 10
1053. 10 f. Zorilla 20 10
1054. 15 f. Zaire clawless otter 35 10
1055. 70 f. African golden cat 1·50 70
1056. 200 f. Hunting dog (vert.) .. .. .. 5·25 2·25

168. Drummer.

1981. Telecommunications and Health. Multicoloured.
1057. 20 c. Type **168** 10 10
1058. 30 c. Telephone receiver and world map .. 10 10
1059. 2 f. Aeroplane and radar screen 10 10
1060. 2 f. 50 Satellite and computer tape .. 10 10
1061. 10 f. Satellite orbit and dish aerial 20 10
1062. 15 f. Tanker and radar equipment 35 25
1063. 70 f. Red Cross helicopter 1·90 70
1064. 200 f. Satellite .. .. 4·25 2·25

169. " St. Benedict leaving His Parents ". **170.** Disabled Child painting with Mouth.

1981. 1500th Birth Anniv. of St. Benedict. Multicoloured.
1065. 20 c. Type **169** 10 10
1066. 30 c. Portrait (10th century) (vert.) .. 10 10
1067. 50 c. Portrait (detail from " The Virgin of the Misericord " polyptich) (vert.) 10 10
1068. 4 f. " St. Benedict presenting the Rules of His Order " 10 10
1069. 5 f. " St. Benedict and His Monks at their Meal " 15 10
1070. 20 f. Portrait (13th century) (vert.) .. 45 15
1071. 70 f. St. Benedict at prayer (detail from " Our Lady in Glory with Sts. Gregory and Benedict ") (vert.) .. .. .. 1·50 85
1072. 100 f. " Priest bringing the Easter Meal to St. Benedict " (Jan van Coninxlo) .. .. 2·40 95

1981. International Year of Disabled Persons. Multicoloured.
1073. 20 c. Type **170** 10 10
1074. 30 c. Boys on crutches playing football .. 10 10
1075. 4 f. 50 Disabled girl knitting 10 10
1076. 5 f. Disabled child painting pot 15 10
1077. 10 f. Boy in wheelchair using saw 20 10
1078. 60 f. Child using sign language .. .. 1·25 60
1079. 70 f. Child in wheelchair playing with puzzle .. 1·60 70
1080. 100 f. Disabled child 2·25 1·10

172. Kob drinking at Pool.

1981. Rural Water Supplies. Multicoloured.
1082. 20 c. Type **172** 10 10
1083. 30 c. Women collecting water (vert.) 10 10
1084. 50 c. Constructing a pipeline 10 10
1085. 10 f. Woman collecting water from pipe (vert.) 20 10
1086. 10 f. Man drinking .. 45 20
1087. 70 f. Woman collecting water (vert.) .. .. 1·50 70
1088. 100 f. Floating pump (vert.) .. .. .. 2·50 1·10

173. Cattle.

1982. World Food Day. Multicoloured.
1089. 20 c. Type **173** 10 10
1090. 30 c. Bee keeping 10 10
1091. 50 c. Fish 10 10
1092. 1 f. Avocado 10 10
1093. 8 f. Boy eating banana .. 10 10
1094. 20 f. Sorghum 45 15
1095. 70 f. Vegetables .. .. 1·50 65
1096. 100 f. Three generations and balanced diet .. 2·50 1·10

174. " Hibiscus berberidifolius ".

1982. Flowers. Multicoloured.
1097. 20 c. Type **174** 10 10
1098. 30 c. " Hypericum lanceolatum " (vert.) 10 10
1099. 50 c. " Canarina eminii " 10 10
1100. 4 f. " Polygala ruwenzoriensis " 10 10
1101. 10 f. " Kniphofia grantii " (vert.) 15 10
1102. 35 f. " Euphorbia candelabrum " (vert.) 65 35
1103. 70 f. " Disa erubescens " (vert.) .. .. 1·50 55
1104. 80 f. " Gloriosa simplex " 1·90 80

175. Pres. Habyarimana and Flags.

1982. 20th Anniv. of Independence. Mult.
1105. 10 f. Type **175** 20 10
1106. 20 f. Hands releasing doves (Peace) .. 35 20
1107. 30 f. Clasped hands and flag (Unity) 65 35
1108. 50 f. Building (Development) .. .. .. 1·00 50

176. Football.

1982. World Cup Football Championship, Spain.
1109. **176.** 20 c. multicoloured .. 10 10
1110. – 30 c. multicoloured .. 10 10
1111. – 1 f. 50 multicoloured 10 10
1112. – 8 f. multicoloured .. 15 10
1113. – 10 f. multicoloured .. 20 10
1114. – 20 f. multicoloured .. 40 15
1115. – 70 f. multicoloured .. 1·60 65
1116. – 90 f. multicoloured .. 2·25 85
DESIGNS: 30 c. to 90 f. Designs show different players.

177. Microscope and Slide.

1982. Centenary of Discovery of Tubercle Bacillus. Multicoloured.
1117. 10 f. Type **177** 15 10
1118. 20 f. Hand with test tube and slide 40 15
1119. 70 f. Lungs and slide .. 1·60 65
1120. 100 f. Dr. Robert Koch .. 2·25 95

180. African Elephants.

1982. 10th Anniv. of United Nations Environment Programme. Multicoloured.
1123. 20 c. Type **180** 10 10
1124. 30 c. Lion hunting impala 10 10
1125. 50 c. Flower 10 10
1126. 4 f. African buffalo .. 10 10
1127. 5 f. Impala 10 10
1128. 10 f. Flower (different) .. 20 10
1129. 20 f. Common zebra .. 45 15
1130. 40 f. Crowned cranes .. 90 35
1131. 50 f. African fish eagle .. 1·25 55
1132. 70 f. Woman with basket of fruit .. .. 1·60 80

181. Scout tending Injured Kob.

1982. 75th Anniv. of Scout Movement. Mult.
1133. 20 c. Type **181** 10 10
1134. 30 c. Tents and northern doubled-collared sunbird 45 15
1135. 1 f. 50 Campfire 10 10
1136. 8 f. Scout 15 10
1137. 10 f. Knot 20 10
1138. 20 f. Tent and campfire 40 15
1139. 70 f. Scout cutting stake 1·60 80
1140. 90 f. Scout salute .. 2·25 1·00

182. Northern Doubled-collared Sunbird. **183.** Driving Cattle.

1983. Nectar-sucking Birds. Multicoloured.
1141. 20 c. Type **182** 10 10
1142. 30 c. Regal sunbird (horiz.) 10 10
1143. 50 c. Red-tufted malachite sunbird .. 10 10
1144. 4 f. Bronze sunbird (horiz.) 10 10
1145. 5 f. Collared sunbird .. 20 10
1146. 10 f. Blue-headed sunbird (horiz.) 45 20
1147. 20 f. Purple-breasted sunbird 90 45
1148. 40 f. Coppery sunbird (horiz.) .. .. 1·75 85
1149. 50 f. Olive-bellied sunbird .. .. 2·10 1·10
1150. 70 f. Red-chested sunbird (horiz.) .. .. 2·75 1·60

1983. Campaign Against Soil Erosion. Mult.
1151. 20 c. Type **183** 10 10
1152. 30 c. Pineapple plantation 10 10
1153. 50 c. Interrupted ditches 10 10
1154. 9 f. Hedged terraces .. 20 10
1155. 10 f. Re-afforestation .. 20 10
1156. 20 f. Anti-erosion barriers 40 15
1157. 30 f. Contour planting .. 65 30
1158. 50 f. Terraces .. .. 1·00 40
1159. 60 f. River bank protection 1·40 60
1160. 70 f. Alternate fallow and planted strips .. .. 1·60 80

184. Feeding Ducks. **185.** Young Gorillas.

1983. Birth Cent. of Cardinal Cardijan (founder of Young Catholic Workers Movement). Multicoloured.
1161. 20 c. Type **184** 10 10
1162. 30 c. Harvesting bananas 10 10
1163. 50 c. Carrying melons .. 10 10
1164. 10 f. Wood carving .. 20 10
1165. 19 f. Making shoes .. 35 15
1166. 20 f. Children in field of millet 45 15
1167. 70 f. Embroidering .. 1·40 60
1168. 80 f. Cardinal Cardijan .. 1·60 65

1983. Mountain Gorillas. Multicoloured.
1169. 20 c. Type **185** 10 10
1170. 30 c. Gorilla family .. 10 10
1171. 9 f. 50 Young and adult .. 20 10
1172. 10 f. Mother with young 20 10
1173. 20 f. Heads 40 15
1174. 30 f. Adult and head .. 65 20
1175. 60 f. Adult (vert.) .. 1·50 55
1176. 70 f. Close-up of adult (vert.) .. .. .. 1·75 60

187. "Hagenia abyssinica".

1984. Trees. Multicoloured.

1178.	20 c. Type **187**	10	10
1179.	30 c. "Dracaena steudneri"	10	10
1180.	50 c. "Phoenix reclinata"	10	10
1181.	10 f. "Podocarpus milanjianus"	15	10
1182.	19 f. "Entada abyssinica"	40	15
1183.	70 f. "Parinari excelsa"	1·60	65
1184.	100 f. "Newtonia buchananii"	2·00	95
1185.	200 f. "Acacia gerrardi" (vert.)	4·50	1·60

188. Diesel Train. **189.** "Le Martial", 1783.

1984. World Communications Year. Mult.

1186.	20 c. Type **188**	10	10
1187.	30 c. Liner and radar	15	10
1188.	4 f. 50 Radio and transmitter	15	10
1189.	10 f. Telephone dial and cable	20	10
1190.	15 f. Letters and newspaper	35	10
1191.	50 f. Aircraft and control tower	1·10	45
1192.	70 f. Television and antenna	1·60	65
1193.	100 f. Satellite and computer tape	2·50	90

1984. Bicent. of Manned Flight. Mult.

1194.	20 c. Type **189**	10	10
1195.	30 c. De Rozier and Marquis d'Arlandes flight, 1783	10	10
1196.	50 c. Charles and Robert (1783) and Blanchard (1784) flights	10	10
1197.	9 f. M. and Mme. Blanchard	20	10
1198.	10 f. Blanchard and Jeffries, 1785	20	10
1199.	50 f. Demuyter (1937) and and Piccard and Kipfer (1931) flights	1·10	40
1200.	80 f. Modern hot-air balloons	2·50	1·00
1201.	200 f. Trans-Atlantic flight, 1978	3·00	1·60

190. Equestrian.

1984. Olympic Games, Los Angeles. Multicoloured.

1202.	20 c. Type **190**	10	10
1203.	30 c. Windsurfing	15	10
1204.	50 c. Football	10	10
1205.	9 f. Swimming	20	10
1206.	10 f. Hockey	20	10
1207.	40 f. Fencing	90	35
1208.	80 f. Running	1·60	65
1209.	200 f. Boxing	4·50	1·75

191. Mare and Foal.

1984. Common Zebras and African Buffaloes. Multicoloured.

1210.	20 c. Type **191**	10	10
1211.	30 c. Buffalo and calf (vert.)	10	10
1212.	50 c. Pair of zebras (vert.)	10	10
1213.	9 f. Zebras fighting	20	10
1214.	10 f. Close-up of buffalo (vert.)	30	10
1215.	80 f. Herd of zebras	1·90	80
1216.	100 f. Close-up of zebras (vert.)	2·25	90
1217.	200 f. Buffalo charging	4·50	1·90

193. Gorillas at Water-hole.

1985. Gorillas. Multicoloured.

1219.	10 f. Type **193**	30	15
1220	15 f. Two gorillas in tree	45	15
1221.	25 f. Gorilla family	65	30
1222.	30 f. Three adults	85	50

194. Man feeding Fowl.

1985. Food Production Year. Multicoloured.

1224.	20 c. Type **194**	10	10
1225.	30 c. Men carrying pineapples	15	10
1226.	50 c. Farm animals	10	10
1227.	9 f. Men filling sacks with produce	20	10
1228.	10 f. Agricultural instruction	30	10
1229.	50 f. Sowing seeds	1·00	45
1230.	80 f. Storing produce	1·60	65
1231.	100 f. Working in banana plantation	2·10	80

195. Emblem.

1985. 10th Anniv. of National Revolutionary Redevelopment Movement.

1232.	**195.** 10 f. multicoloured	20	10
1233.	30 f. multicoloured	65	30
1234.	70 f. multicoloured	1·60	70

196. U.N. Emblem within "40".

1985. 40th Anniv. of U.N.O.

1235.	**196.** 50 f. multicoloured	1·10	55
1236.	100 f. multicoloured	2·25	1·10

197. Barn Owls.

1985. Birth Bicentenary of John J. Audubon (ornithologist). Multicoloured.

1237.	10 f. Type **197**	40	25
1238.	20 f. White-faced scops owls	85	50
1239.	40 f. Ruby-throated humming birds	1·60	1·00
1240.	80 f. Eastern meadowlarks	3·75	2·25

198. "Participation, Development and Peace".

1985. International Youth Year. Mult.

1241.	7 f. Type **198**	15	10
1242.	9 f. Cycling	30	10
1243.	44 f. Youths carrying articles on head (teamwork)	1·10	45
1244.	80 f. Education	1·75	80

1985. 75th Anniv. of Girl Guide movement. Nos. 1133/40 optd. **1910/1985** and guide emblem.

1245.	20 c. Type **181**	10	10
1246.	30 c. Tents	10	10
1247.	1 f. 50 Campfire	10	10
1248.	8 f. Scout	20	10
1249.	10 f. Knot	20	10
1250.	20 f. Tent and campfire	45	10
1251.	70 f. Scout cutting stake	1·60	65
1252.	90 f. Scout salute	2·25	90

201. Container Lorry (Transport).

1986. Transport and Communications. Multicoloured.

1254.	10 f. Type **201**	35	10
1255.	30 f. Handstamping cover (posts)	80	35
1256.	40 f. Kigali Earth Station (telecommunication)	1·10	45
1257.	80 f. Kigali airport (aviation) (48 × 31 mm.)	1·75	1·25

1986. Intensified Agriculture Year. Nos. 1152/60 optd. **ANNEE 1986 INTENSIFICATION AGRICOLE** or surch. also.

1258.	9 f. Hedged terraces	20	10
1259.	10 f. Re-afforestation	20	10
1260.	10 f. on 30 c. Pineapple plantation	20	10
1261.	10 f. on 50 c. Interrupted ditches	20	10
1262.	20 f. Anti-erosion barriers	45	20
1263.	30 f. Contour planning	65	35
1264.	50 f. Terraces	1·10	50
1265.	60 f. River bank protection	1·40	55
1266.	70 f. Alternate fallow and planted strips	1·60	70

203. Morocco v. England.

1986. World Cup Football Championship, Mexico. Multicoloured.

1267.	2 f. Type **203**	10	10
1268.	4 f. Paraguay v. Iraq	10	10
1269.	5 f. Brazil v. Spain	10	10
1270.	10 f. Italy v. Argentina	30	10
1271.	40 f. Mexico v. Belgium	1·00	40
1272.	45 f. France v. Russia	1·10	45

204. Roan Antelopes.

1986. Akagera National Park. Multicoloured.

1273.	4 f. Type **204**	10	10
1274.	7 f. Whale-headed storks	50	10
1275.	9 f. Cape eland	15	10
1276.	10 f. Giraffe	30	10
1277.	80 f. African elephant	1·90	85
1278.	90 f. Crocodile	2·25	1·00
1279.	100 f. Heuglin's masked weavers	4·50	3·00
1280.	100 f. Zebras and eastern white pelican	4·50	3·00

205. People of Different Races on Globe.

1986. Christmas. International Peace Year. Multicoloured.

1281.	10 f. Type **205**	35	15
1282.	15 f. Dove and globe	45	15
1283.	30 f. Type **205**	80	35
1284.	70 f. As No. 1282	1·75	1·00

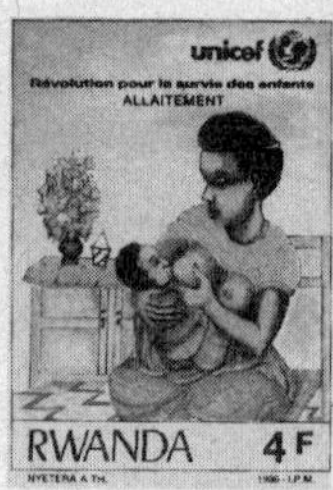

206. Mother breast-feeding Baby.

1987. U.N.I.C.E.F. Child Survival Campaign. Multicoloured.

1285.	4 f. Type **206**	15	15
1286.	6 f. Mother giving oral rehydration therapy to baby	20	15
1287.	10 f. Nurse immunising baby	35	25
1288.	70 f. Nurse weighing baby and graph	1·75	1·60

207. Couple packing Baskets with Food.

1987. Food Self-sufficiency Year. Mult.

1289.	5 f. Type **207**	10	10
1290.	7 f. Woman and baskets of food	15	10
1291.	40 f. Man with basket of fish and fruits	1·25	45
1292.	60 f. Fruits and vegetables	1·90	80

208. Pres. Habyarimana and Soldiers.

1987. 25th Anniv. of Independence. Mult.
1293. 10 f. Type **208** 20 10
1294. 40 f. President at meeting 90 45
1295. 70 f. President with Pope John Paul II .. .. 2·25 85
1296. 100 f. Pres. Habyarimana (vert.) .. .. .. 2·25 1·10

209. Bananas.

1987. Fruits. Multicoloured.
1297. 10 f. Type **209** 20 10
1298. 40 f. Pineapples (horiz.) 90 45
1299. 80 f. Papaya (horiz.) .. 2·25 90
1300. 90 f. Avocados (horiz.) .. 2·50 1·00
1301. 100 f. Strawberries .. 2·50 1·10

210. Mother carrying cub.

1987. The Leopard. Multicoloured.
1302. 50 f. Type **210** .. .. 1·40 55
1303. 50 f. Leopards fighting .. 1·40 55
1304. 50 f. Leopard with prey 1·40 55
1305. 50 f. Leopard with prey in tree .. .. .. 1·40 55
1306. 50 f. Leopard leaping from tree .. .. 1·40 55

211. Village activities.

1987. International Volunteers Day. Mult.
1307. 5 f. Type **211** 10 10
1308. 12 f. Pupils in schoolroom 35 10
1309. 20 f. View of village .. 55 30
1310. 60 f. Woman tending oxen .. .. .. 1·75 85

213 Carpenter's Shop

1988. Rural Incomes Protection Year. Mult.
1312 10 f. Type **213** 20 10
1313 40 f. Dairy farm 95 95
1314 60 f. Workers in field .. 1·50 30
1315 80 f. Selling baskets of eggs .. .. .. 2·10 95

214 Chimpanzees

1988. Primates of Nyungwe Forest. Mult.
1316 2 f. Type **214** 15 10
1317 3 f. Black and white colobus 15 10
1318 10 f. Lesser bushbabies .. 30 15
1319 90 f. Monkeys .. .. 2·40 95

215 Boxing

1988. Olympic Games, Seoul. Multicoloured.
1320 5 f. Type **215** 10 10
1321 7 f. Relay race 15 10
1322 8 f. Table tennis .. 20 10
1323 10 f. Running 35 15
1324 90 f. Hurdling .. .. 2·25 1·00

216 "25" on Map of Africa

219 "Plectranthus barbatus"

218 Newspaper Fragment and Refugees in Boat

1988. 25th Anniv of Organization of African Unity. Multicoloured.
1325 5 f. Type **216** 15 10
1326 7 f. Hands clasped across map 20 10
1327 8 f. Building on map .. 20 10
1328 90 f. Words forming map 2·40 1·00

1988. 125th Anniv of Red Cross Movement. Multicoloured.
1330 10 f. Type **218** 20 10
1331 30 f. Red Cross workers and patient 80 35
1332 40 f. Red Cross worker and elderly lady (vert) 95 40
1333 100 f. Red Cross worker and family (vert) .. 2·75 1·25

1989. Plants. Multicoloured.
1334 5 f. Type **219** 10 10
1335 10 f. "Tetradenia riparia" 30 10
1336 20 f. "Hygrophila auriculata" 60 20
1337 40 f. "Datura stramonium" .. .. .. 1·25 45
1338 50 f. "Pavetta ternifolia" 1·60 60

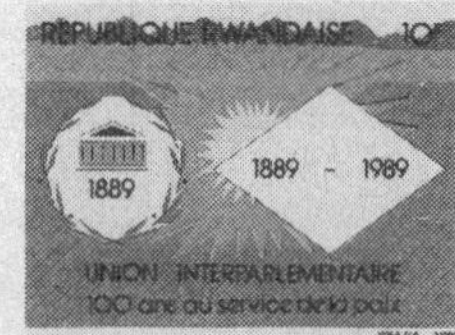

220 Emblem, Dates and Sunburst

1989. Centenary of Interparliamentary Union. Multicoloured.
1339 10 f. Type **220** 30 10
1340 30 f. Lake 85 35
1341 70 f. River .. .. 1·60 80
1342 90 f. Sun's rays .. .. 2·25 1·00

222 Throwing Clay and Finished Pots

1989. Rural Self-help Year. Multicoloured.
1344 10 f. Type **222** 30 10
1345 70 f. Carrying baskets of produce (vert) .. 1·60 80
1346 90 f. Firing clay pots .. 2·50 90
1347 200 f. Clearing roadway .. 5·00 1·60

223 "Triumph of Marat" (Boilly)

1990. Bicentenary of French Revolution. Multicoloured.
1348 10 f. Type **223** 30 10
1349 60 f. "Rouget de Lisle singing La Marseillaise" (Pils) .. .. .. 1·60 65
1350 70 f. "Oath of the Tennis Court" (Jacques Louis David) .. .. .. 1·75 90
1351 100 f. "Trial of Louis XVI" (Joseph Court) 2·75 1·10

224 Old and New Lifestyles

1990. 30th Anniv of Revolution. Mult.
1352 10 f. Type **224** 30 10
1353 60 f. Couple holding farming implements (vert) .. .. .. 1·60 55
1354 70 f. Modernisation .. 1·75 55
1355 100 f. Flag, map and warrior .. .. 2·50 90

225 Construction

1990. 25th Anniv (1989) of African Development Bank. Multicoloured.
1356 10 f. Type **225** 30 10
1357 20 f. Tea picking .. 55 35
1358 40 f. Road building .. 1·10 45
1359 90 f. Tea pickers and modern housing .. 2·50 80

1990. World Cup Football Championship, Italy. Nos. 1267/72 optd **ITALIA 90.**
1361 **203** 2 f. multicoloured .. 10 10
1362 – 4 f. multicoloured .. 10 10
1363 – 5 f. multicoloured .. 15 10
1364 – 10 f. multicoloured .. 30 20
1365 – 40 f. multicoloured .. 1·00 55
1366 – 45 f. multicoloured .. 1·10 85

228 Pope John Paul II

1990. Papal Visit. Multicoloured.
1367 10 f. Type **228** 30 10
1368 70 f. Pope giving blessing 2·25 1·00

229 Adults learning Alphabet at School

1991. International Literacy Year (1990). Multicoloured.
1370 10 f. Type **229** 15 10
1371 20 f. Children reading at school 35 20
1372 50 f. Lowland villagers learning alphabet in field 90 55
1373 90 f. Highland villagers learning alphabet outdoors .. .. 1·40 80

230 Tool-making

1991. Self-help Organizations. Multicoloured.
1374 10 f. Type **230** 15 10
1375 20 f. Rearing livestock .. 35 20
1376 50 f. Textile manufacture 90 55
1377 90 f. Construction .. 1·40 80

RYUKYU ISLANDS Pt. 18

Group of islands between Japan and Formosa formerly Japanese until occupied by U.S. forces in 1945. After a period of military rule they became semi-autonomous under U.S. administration. The Amami Oshima group reverted to Japan in December 1953. The remaining islands were returned to Japan on 15 May 1972. Japanese stamps are now in use.

1948. 100 sen = 1 yen.
1958. 100 cents = 1 dollar (U.S.).

1. Cycad Palm.

3. Junk.

1948.

1. **1.** 5 s. purple .. .. 2·75 1·75
2. – 10 s. green .. .. .. 3·00 2·25
3. **1.** 20 s. green .. .. .. 2·25 2·25
4. **3.** 30 s. red .. .. .. 3·25 2·00
5. – 40 s. purple .. .. 2·75 1·75
6. **3.** 50 s. blue .. .. .. 3·50 2·50
7. – 1 y. blue .. .. .. 3·50 2·50

DESIGNS: 10 s., 40 s. Easter lily. 1 y. Farmer with hoe.

6. Shi-Shi Roof Tiles.

12. Dove over Map of Ryukyus.

1950.

8. **6.** 50 s. red 25 25
10. – 1 y. blue .. .. .. 2·25 1·25
11. – 2 y. purple .. .. 8·50 3·00
12. – 3 y. red .. .. .. 18·00 8·00
13. – 4 y. slate .. .. .. 5·00 3·00
14. – 5 y. green .. .. 8·00 4·50

DESIGNS: 1 y. Shuri woman. 2 y. Former Okinawa Palace, Shuri. 3 y. Dragon's head. 4 y. Okinawa women. 5 y. Sea shells.

1950. Air.

15. **12.** 8 y. blue .. .. 45·00 16·00
16. 12 y. green .. .. 30·00 13·00
17. 16 y. red .. .. 15·00 12·00

14. University and Shuri Castle.

15. Pine Tree.

1951. Inauguration of Ryukyu University.

19 **14** 3 y. brown .. .. 35·00 18·00

1951. Afforestation Week.

20. **15.** 3 y. green .. .. 35·00 18·00

16. Flying Goddess.

改 訂
*
10圓

(17.)

1951. Air.

21. **16.** 13 y. blue .. .. .. 1·50 30
22. 18 y. green .. .. 2·00 3·00
23. 30 y. mauve .. .. 3·25 1·25
24. 40 y. purple .. .. 5·00 2·25
25. 50 y. orange .. .. 6·50 3·25

1952. Surch. as T **17.**

27. **6.** 10 y. on 50 s. red .. .. 7·00 5·50
29. – 100 y. on 2 y. pur. (No. 11) £1500 £750

18. Dove and Bean Seedling.

19. Madanbashi Bridge.

1952. Establishment of Ryukyuan Govt.

30. **18.** 3 y. lake .. .. .. 70·00 20·00

1952.

31. **19.** 1 y. red 25 35
32. – 2 y. green 30 25
33. – 3 y. blue 40 25
34. – 6 y. blue .. .. .. 3·25 3·00
35. – 10 y. red .. .. .. 1·25 50
36. – 30 y. olive .. .. .. 4·75 2·50
37. – 50 y. purple .. .. .. 5·25 2·00
38. – 100 y. red .. .. .. 11·00 1·25

DESIGNS: 2 y. Presence Chamber, Shuri Palace. 3 y. Shuri Gate. 6 y. Sogenji Temple Wall. 10 y. Bensaitendo Temple. 30 y. Sonohyamutake Gate. 50 y. Tamaudum Mausoleum, Shuri. 100 y. Hosho-chai Bridge.

27. Reception at Shuri Castle.

28. Perry and American Fleet at Naha Harbour.

29. Chofu Ota and Matrix.

1953. Centenary of Commodore Perry's Visit to Okinawa.

39 **27** 3 y. purple .. .. 7·50 3·25
40 **28** 6 y. blue .. .. 1·00 2·40

1953. 3rd Press Week.

41. **29.** 4 y. brown .. .. 8·50 5·00

30. Wine Flask to fit around Waist.

33. Shigo Toma and Pen-nib.

1954.

42. **30.** 4 y. brown 50 35
43. – 15 y. red .. .. 2·25 1·75
44. – 20 y. orange .. .. 3·25 2·25

DESIGNS: 15 y. Tung Dar Bon (lacquer bowl). 20 y. Kasuri (textile pattern).

1954. 4th Press Week.

45. **33.** 4 y. blue .. .. 5·50 3·25

34. Noguni Shrine and Sweet Potatoes.

35. Stylised Trees.

1955. 350th Anniv of Introduction of Sweet Potato Plant.

46 **34** 4 y. blue .. .. 9·00 4·00

1956. Afforestation Week.

47. **35.** 4 y. green. .. .. 5·50 3·00

38. Nidotekito Dance.

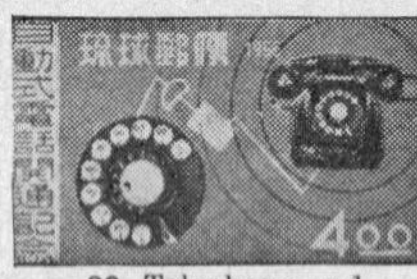

39. Telephone and Dial.

1956. National Dances.

48. – 5 y. purple .. .. 1·10 60
49. – 8 y. violet .. .. 1·40 1·25
50. **38.** 14 y. brown .. .. 2·25 2·25

DESIGNS: 5 y. Willow dance. 8 y. Straw-hat dance.

1956. Inauguration of Telephone Dialling System.

51 **39** 4 y. violet .. .. 8·00 7·00

40. Floral Garland.

41. Flying Goddess.

1956. New Year.

52. **40.** 2 y. multicoloured .. 1·40 1·40

1957. Air.

53 **41** 15 y. green .. .. 1·50 25
54 20 y. red .. .. 3·75 2·75
55 35 y. green .. .. 7·50 3·50
56 45 y. brown .. .. 12·00 5·00
57 60 y. grey .. .. 16·00 7·25

42. Rocket " Pencils".

43. Phoenix.

1957. 7th Press Week.

58. **42.** 4 y. blue 55 55

1957. New Year.

59. **43.** 2 y. multicoloured .. 20 20

44. Various Ryukyuan Postage Stamps.

45. Stylized Dollar sign over Yen Symbol.

1958. 10th Anniv. of First Postage Stamps of Ryukyu Is.

60. **44.** 4 y. multicoloured .. 60 40

1958. With or without gum (Nos. 68/69), no gum (others).

61. **45.** ½ c. yellow 25 20
62. 1 c. green 25 20
63. 2 c. blue 25 20
64. 3 c. red 20 15
65. 4 c. green 60 40
66. 5 c. brown .. .. 2·00 40
67. 10 c. turquoise .. .. 3·25 40
68. 25 c. lavender .. .. 3·25 60
69. 50 c. grey .. .. 6·50 75
70. $1 purple .. .. 8·00 1·00

46. Gateway of Courtesy.

1958. Restoration of Shuri Gateway.

71. **46.** 3 c. multicoloured .. 60 40

47. Lion Dance.

48. Trees.

1958. New Year.

72. **47.** 1½ c. multicoloured .. 20 25

1959. Afforestation Week.

73. **48.** 3 c. multicoloured .. 60 60

49. Atlas Moth.

50. Hibiscus.

1959. Japanese Biological Teachers' Conf., Okinawa.

74. **49.** 3 c. multicoloured .. 1·50 1·25

1959. Multicoloured.
(a) Inscr as in T**50**.

75 ½ c. Type **50** 30 20
76 3 c. Tropical fish .. .. 1·10 25
77 8 c. Sea shells .. .. 6·50 2·00
78 13 c. Leaf butterfly (value at left) .. .. 2·00 1·50
79 17 c. Jellyfish .. .. 17·00 5·50

(b) Inscr smaller and 13 c. with value at right.

87. ½ c. Type **50** 20 15
88. 3 c. As No. 76 .. .. 2·00 20
89. 8 c. As No. 77 .. .. 1·00 1·00
90. 13 c. As No. 78 .. .. 1·50 1·00
91. 17 c. As No. 79 .. .. 5·50 3·25

55. Yakazi (Ryukyuan Toy).

改訂 9¢

(56.)

1959. New Year.

80. **55.** 1½ c. multicoloured .. 50 40

1959 Air. Surch. as T **56.**

81. **41.** 9 c. on 15 y. turquoise .. 2·00 35
82. 14 c. on 20 y. lake .. 2·25 2·25
83. 19 c. on 35 y. green .. 4·00 2·50
84. 27 c. on 45 y. brown .. 8·00 5·50
85. 35 c. on 60 y. grey .. 10·00 7·00

57. University Badge.

60. " Manjuru ".

1960. 10th Anniv of University of the Ryukyus.

86 **57** 3 c. multicoloured .. 75 60

1960. Air. Surch.

92. **30.** 9 c. on 4 y. brown .. 4·00 60
93. – 14 c. on 5 y. pur. (No. 48) 2·00 2·00
94. – 19 c. on 15 y. red (No. 43) 3·25 2·75
95. **38.** 27 c. on 14 y. brown .. 5·00 4·25
96. – 35 c. on 20 y. orge. (No. 44) 5·50 5·25

1960. Ryukyun Dances. Multicoloured.
(a) Inscr. as in T **60.**

97. 1 c. Type **60** .. .. 1·25 75
98. 2½ c. " Inohabushi " .. 1·25 75
99. 5 c. " Hatomabushi " .. 70 75
100. 10 c. " Hanafu " 95 75

(b) As T **60** but additionally inscr. " RYUKYUS ".

107 1 c. Type **60** 15 15
108 2½ c. As No. 98 .. .. 25 15
109 4 c. As No. 98 .. .. 15 15
110 5 c. As No. 99 .. .. 20 25
111 10 c. As No. 100 .. .. 40 15
112 20 c. "Shudun" .. .. 1·00 35
113 25 c. "Haodori" .. .. 1·00 60
114 50 c. "Nobori Kuduchi" .. 1·50 60
115 $1 "Koteibushi" .. .. 2·00 70

65. Start of Race.

1960. 8th Kyushu Athletic Meeting.

101. – 3 c. red, green and blue 4·75 1·50
102. **65.** 8 c. green and orange .. 75 1·00

DESIGN: 3 c. Torch and coastal scene.

66. Little Egret and Rising Sun.

67. Bull Fight.

1960. National Census.

103. **66.** 3 c. brown .. .. 4·00 1·00

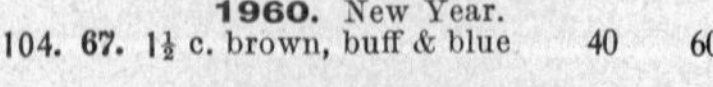

1960. New Year.

104. **67.** 1½ c. brown, buff & blue 40 60

68. Native Pine Tree.

1961. Afforestation Week.

105 **68** 3 c. dp green, red & grn 1·25 60

69. Naha, Junk, Liner and City Seal.

1961. 40th Anniv. of Naha City.

106. **69.** 3 c. turquoise .. .. 1·75 1·25

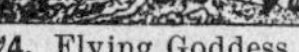

74. Flying Goddess.

79. White Silver Temple

1961. Air.
116. **74.** 9 c. multicoloured .. 40 15
117. – 14 c. multicoloured .. 60 60
118. – 19 c. multicoloured .. 1·10 75
119. – 27 c. multicoloured .. 1·25 75
120. – 35 c. multicoloured .. 1·60 75
DESIGNS: 14 c. Flying goddess playing flute. 19 c., 27 c. Wind gods. 35 c. Flying goddess over trees.

1961. Unification of Itoman District and Takamine, Kanegushiku and Miwa Villages.
121. **79.** 3 c. brown 75 50

80. Books and Bird.

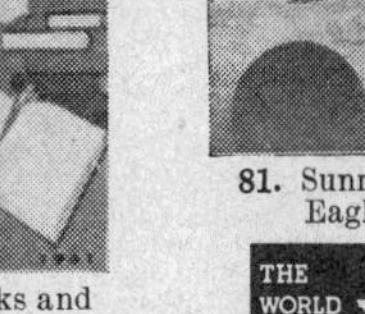

81. Sunrise and Eagles.

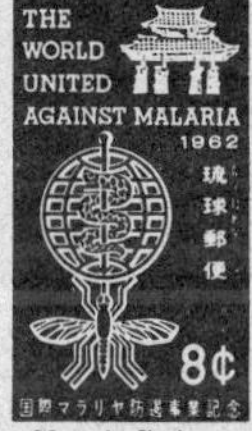

85. Shuri Gate and Campaign Emblem.

82. Govt. Building, Steps and Trees.

1961. 10th Anniv. of Ryukyu Book Week.
122. **80.** 3 c. multicoloured .. 1·00 75

1961. New Year.
123. **81.** 1½ c. red, black and gold 2·25 1·00

1962. 10th Anniv. of Ryukyu Government.
124. **82.** 1½ c. multicoloured .. 50 60
125. – 3 c. grey, green and red 75 75
DESIGN: 3 c. Government Building.

1962. Malaria Eradication. Multicoloured.
126 3 c. "Anopheles hyrcanus sinensis" (mosquito) .. 50 50
127 8 c. Type **85** .. .. 1·00 1·50

86. Windmill, Dolls and Horse.

87. "Hibiscus lilaceus".

1962. Children's Day.
128. **86.** 3 c. multicoloured .. 1·25 1·25

1962. Ryukyu Flowers. Multicoloured.
129. ½ c. Type **87** 15 15
142. 1½ c. "Etithyllum strictum" 30 20
130. 2 c. "Ixora chinensis" .. 15 25
131. 3 c. "Erythrina indica" 25 20
132. 3 c. "Caesalpinia pulcherrima" 20 20
133. 8 c. "Schima mertensiana" 45 25
134. 13 c. "Impatiens balsamina" 70 50
135. 15 c. "Hamaomoto" (herb) 85 55
136. 17 c. "Alpinia speciosa" .. 1·00 30
No. 142 is smaller, 18¾ × 22½ mm.

95. Akaeware Bowl.

1962. Philatelic Week.
137. **95.** 3 c. multicoloured .. 3·50 3·25

96. Kendo (Japanese Fencing).

1962. All-Japan Kendo Meeting.
138. **96.** 3 c. multicoloured .. 4·00 2·25

97. "Hare and Water" (textile design).

98. Reaching Maturity (clay relief).

1962. New Year.
139. **97.** 1½ c. multicoloured .. 1·00 1·00

1963. Adults' Day.
140. **98.** 3 c. gold, black and blue 55 40

99. Trees and Wooded Hills.

101. Okinawa Highway.

1963. Afforestation Week.
141. **99.** 3 c. multicoloured .. 55 40

1963. Opening of Okinawa Highway.
143. **101.** 3 c. multicoloured .. 65 60

102. Black Kites over Islands.

103. Shioya Bridge.

1963. Bird Week.
144. **102.** 3 c. multicoloured .. 1·25 75

1963. Opening of Shioya Bridge, Okinawa.
145. **103.** 3 c. multicoloured .. 75 60

104. Lacquerware Bowl.

105. Jetliner and Shuri Gate.

1963. Philatelic Week.
146. **104.** 3 c. multicoloured .. 2·50 1·50

1963. Air.
147. **105.** 5½ c. multicoloured .. 15 25
148. – 7 c. black, red and blue 25 25
DESIGN: 7 c. Jetliner over sea.

107. Map and Emblem.

108. Nakagusuku Castle Ruins.

1963. Meeting of Junior International Chamber, Naha.
149. **107.** 3 c. multicoloured .. 50 40

1963. Ancient Buildings Protection Week.
150. **108.** 3 c. multicoloured .. 60 50

109. Flame.

110. Bingata "dragon" (textile design).

1963. 15th Anniv. of Declaration of Human Rights.
151. **109.** 3 c. multicoloured .. 40 25

1963. New Year.
152. **110.** 1½ c. multicoloured .. 25 25

111. Carnation.

112. Pineapples and Sugar-cane.

1964. Mothers' Day.
153. **111.** 3 c. multicoloured .. 25 25

1964. Agricultural Census.
154. **112.** 3 c. multicoloured .. 35 25

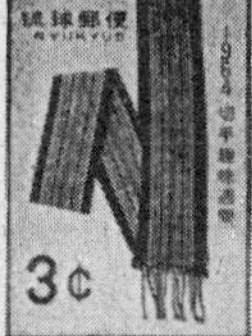

113. Hand-woven Sash.

114. Girl Scout and Emblem.

1964. Philatelic Week.
155 **113** 3 c. ochre, blue & pink 40 20

1964. 10th Anniv. of Ryukyu Girl Scouts.
156. **114.** 3 c. multicoloured .. 25 25

115. Transmitting Tower.

117. Shuri Gate and Olympic Torch.

1964. Inauguration of Ryukyu–Japan Microwave Link.
157. **115.** 3 c. green and black .. 60 75
158. – 8 c. blue and black .. 90 75
DESIGN: 8 c. "Bowl" receiving aerial. Both stamps have "1963" cancelled by bars and "1964" inserted in black.

1964. Passage of Olympic Torch through Okinawa.
159. **117.** 3 c. multicoloured .. 20 20

118. "Naihanchi" (Karate stance).

121. "Miyara Dunchi" (old Ryukyuan Residence).

1964. Karate ("self-defence"). Multicoloured.
160 3 c. Type **118** 55 40
161 3 c. "Makiwara" (Karate training) 45 50
162 3 c. "Kumite" exercise .. 45 50

1964. Ancient Buildings Protection Week.
163. **121.** 3 c. multicoloured .. 25 25

122. Bingata "snake" (textile design).

123. Boy Scouts, Badge and Shuri Gate.

1964. New Year.
164. **122.** 1½ c. multicoloured .. 25 25

1965. 10th Anniv of Ryukyuan Boy Scouts.
165 **123** 3 c. multicoloured .. 25 25

124. "Samisen" (musical instrument).

126. Kin Power Station.

127. I.C.Y. Emblem and "Globe".

125. Stadium.

1965. Philatelic Week.
166. **124.** 3 c. multicoloured .. 25 25

1965. Completion of Onoyama Sports Ground.
167. **125.** 3 c. multicoloured .. 25 25

1965. Completion of Kin Power Plant.
168. **126.** 3 c. multicoloured .. 20 20

1965. International Co-operation Year and 20th Anniv of United Nations.
169 **127** 3 c. multicoloured .. 15 25

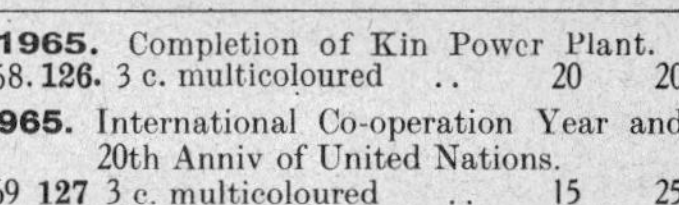

128. City Hall, Naha.

129. Semaruhakogame Turtle.

1965. Completion of Naha City Hall.
170. **128.** 3 c. multicoloured .. 20 25

1965. Ryukyuan Turtles. Multicoloured.
171 3 c. Type **129** 30 25
172 3 c. Taimai or hawksbill turtle 25 25
173 3 c. Yamagame or hill tortoise 25 25

132. Bingata "horse" (textile design).

133. Pryer's Woodpecker.

1965. New Year.
174. **132.** 1½ c. multicoloured .. 15 25

1966. "Natural Monument" (Wildlife). Multicoloured.
175. 3 c. Type **133** 25 25
176. 3 c. Sika deer 25 25
177. 3 c. Dugong 25 25

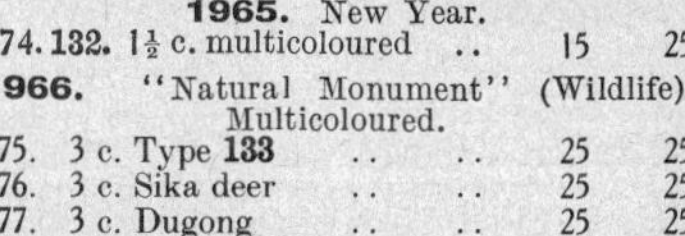

136. Pacific Swallow.

137. Lilies and Ruins.

1966. Bird Week.
178. **136.** 3 c. multicoloured .. 45 35

1966. Memorial Day (Battle of Okinawa).
179. **137.** 3 c. multicoloured .. 15 25

138. University of the Ryukyus.

139. Lacquer Box.

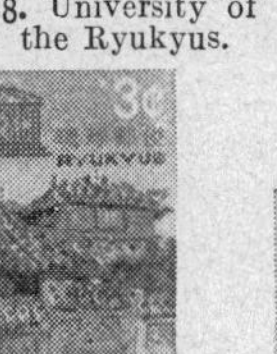

140. Ryukyuan Tiled House.

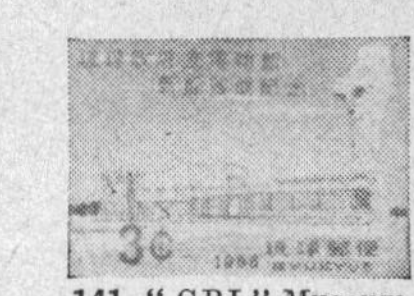

141. "GRI" Museum Shuri.

1966. Transfer of University of the Ryukyus to Government Administration.
180. **138.** 3 c. multicoloured .. 15 25

1966. Philatelic Week.
181. **139.** 3 c. multicoloured .. 20 25

1966. 20th Anniv. of U.N.E.S.C.O.
182. **140.** 3 c. multicoloured .. 15 25

1966. Completion of Government Museum, Shuri.
183. **141.** 3 c. multicoloured .. 15 25

142. Nakasone-Tuimya Tomb.

143. Bingata "ram" (textile design).

1966. Ancient Buildings Protection Week.
184. **142.** 3 c. multicoloured .. 15 25

1966. New Year.
185. **143.** 1½ c. multicoloured .. 15 25

144. Clown Fish. 149. Tsuboya Urn.

1966. Tropical Fish. Multicoloured.

186.	3 c. Type **144**	25	25
187.	3 c. Box fish	25	25
188.	3 c. Forceps Fish	25	25
189.	3 c. Spotted Triggerfish ..	25	25
190.	3 c. Saddleback Butterfly	25	25

1967. Philatelic Week.

191. **149.** 3 c. multicoloured .. 20 20

150. Episcopal Mitre. 155. Roof Tiles and Emblem.

1967. Sea Shells. Multicoloured.

192.	3 c. Type **150**	25	25
193.	3 c. Venus Comb Murex ..	25	25
194.	3 c. Chiragra Spider Conch	30	25
195.	3 c. Green Turban	30	25
196.	3 c. Bubble Conch ..	50	25

1967. Int. Tourist Year.

197. **155.** 3 c. multicoloured .. 20 25

156. Mobile Clinic. 157. Hojo Bridge, Enkaku.

1967. 15th Anniv of Anti-T.B. Association.

198 **156** 3 c. multicoloured .. 20 20

1967. Ancient Buildings Protection Week.

199. **157.** 3 c. multicoloured .. 15 25

158. Bingata "monkey" (textile design). 159. T.V. Tower and Map.

1967. New Year.

200. **158.** 1½ c. multicoloured .. 15 25

1967. Opening of T.V. Broadcasting Stations in Miyako and Yaeyama.

201. **159.** 3 c. multicoloured .. 15 25

160. Dr. Nakachi and Assistant. 161. Medicine Case (after Sokei Dana).

1968. 120th Anniv. of 1st Ryukyu Vaccination (by Dr. Kijin Nakachi).

202. **160.** 3 c. multicoloured .. 15 25

1968. Philatelic Week.

203. **161.** 3 c. multicoloured .. 25 25

162. Young Man, Book, Map and Library.

1968. Library Week.

204. **162.** 3 c. multicoloured .. 25 25

163. Postmen with Ryukyu Stamp of 1948.

1968. 20th Anniv. of 1st Ryukyu Islands Stamps.

205. **163.** 3 c. multicoloured .. 25 25

164. Temple Gate. 165. Old Man Dancing.

1968. Restoration of Enkaku Temple Gate.

206. **164.** 3 c. multicoloured .. 25 25

1968. Old People's Day.

207. **165.** 3 c. multicoloured .. 25 25

166. "Mictyris longicarpus".

1968. Crabs. Multicoloured.

208.	3 c. Type **166**	55	60
209.	3 c. "Uca dubia" ..	50	60
210.	3 c. "Baptozius vinosus"	50	60
211.	3 c. "Cardisoma carnifex"	60	60
212.	3 c. "Ocypode ceratophthalma"	60	60

171. Saraswati Pavilion. 172. Player.

1968. Ancient Buildings Protection Week.

213. **171.** 3 c. multicoloured .. 25 25

1968. 35th All-Japan East v. West Men's Softball Tennis Tournament, Onoyama.

214 **172** 3 c. multicoloured .. 25 25

173. Bingata "Cock" (textile design). 174. Boxer.

1968. New Year.

215. **173.** 1½ c. multicoloured .. 30 20

1969. 20th All-Japan Boxing Championships.

216. **174.** 3 c. multicoloured .. 25 25

175. Inkwell Screen. 176. U.H.F. Antennae and Map.

1969. Philatelic Week.

217. **175.** 3 c. multicoloured .. 30 25

1969. Inauguration of Okinawa-Sakishima U.H.F. Radio Service.

218. **176.** 3 c. multicoloured .. 20 25

177. "Gate of Courtesy". 178. "Tug of War" Festival.

1969. 22nd All-Japan Formative Education Study Conf., Naha.

219. **177.** 3 c. multicoloured .. 20 25

1969. Traditional Religious Ceremonies. Mult.

220.	3 c. Type **178**	50	40
221.	3 c. "Hari" canoe race ..	50	40
222.	3 c. "Izaiho" religious ceremony	50	40
223.	3 c. "Ushideiku" Dance	60	40
224.	3 c. "Sea God" Dance ..	60	40

1969. No. 131 surch.

225. ½ c. on 3 c. multicoloured .. 15 25

184. Nakamura-Ke.

1969. Ancient Buildings Protection Week.

226. **184.** 3 c. multicoloured .. 20 20

185. Kyuzo Toyama and Map. 186. Bingata "dog and flowers" (textile design).

1969. 70th Anniv. of Toyama's Ryukyu–Hawaii Emigration Project.

227. **185.** 3 c. multicoloured .. 35 35

No. 227 has "1970" cancelled by bars and "1969" inserted in black.

1969. New Year.

228. **186.** 1½ c. multicoloured .. 15 20

187. Sake Flask. 188. "Shushin-Kaneiri".

189/92.

1970. Philatelic Week.

229. **187.** 3 c. multicoloured .. 30 20

1970. "Kumi-Odori" Ryukyu Theatre. Multicoloured.

230.	3 c. Type **188**	70	55
231.	3 c. "Chu-nusudu" (**189**).	70	55
232.	3 c. "Mekarushi" (**190**) ..	70	55
233.	3 c. "Nidotichiuchi" (**191**)	70	55
234.	3 c. "Kokonomaki" (**192**)	70	55

193. Observatory.

194. Noboru Jahana (politician).

197. "Population". 198. "Great Cycad of Une".

1970. Completion of Underwater Observatory Busena-Misaki, Nago.

240. **193.** 3 c. multicoloured .. 20 25

1970. Famous Ryukyuans.

241.	**194.**	3 c. red	50	60
242.	–	3 c. green	70	60
243.	–	3 c. black	50	60

PORTRAITS: No. 242, Saion Gushichan Bunjaku (statesman). No. 243, Choho Giwan (Regent).

1970. Population Census.

244. **197.** 3 c. multicoloured .. 20 25

1970. Ancient Buildings Protection Week.

245. **198.** 3 c. multicoloured .. 30 25

199. Ryukyu Islands, Flag and Japanese Diet. 200. "Wild Boar" (Bingata textile design).

1970. Election of Ryukyu Representatives to the Japanese Diet.

246. **199.** 3 c. multicoloured .. 60 60

1970. New Year.

247. **200.** 1½ c. multicoloured .. 30 25

201. "Jibata" (hand-loom). 202. "Filature" (spinning-wheel).

203. Farm-worker wearing "Shurunnu" coat and "Kubagasa" Hat. 204. Woman using "Shiri-usni" (rice huller).

205. Fisherman's "Umi-Fujo" (box) and "Yuyui" (bailer).

1971. Ryukyu Handicrafts.

248.	**201.**	3 c. multicoloured ..	30	30
249.	**202.**	3 c. multicoloured ..	30	30
250.	**203.**	3 c. multicoloured ..	30	30
251.	**204.**	3 c. multicoloured ..	45	30
252.	**205.**	3 c. multicoloured ..	30	30

206. "Taku" (container). 208. Restored Battlefield, Okinawa.

207. Civic Emblem with Old and New City Views.

1971. Philatelic Week.

253. **206.** 3 c. multicoloured .. 25 25

1971. 50th Anniv. of Naha's City Status.

254. **207.** 3 c. multicoloured .. 30 25

1971. Government Parks. Multicoloured.

255.	3 c. Type **208**	30	30
256.	3 c. Haneji inland sea ..	30	30
257.	4 c. Yabuchi Island ..	30	30

211. Deva King Torinji Temple. 212. "Rat" (Bingata textile pattern).

1971. Ancient Buildings Protection Week.

258. **211.** 4 c. multicoloured .. 25 25

1971. New Year.

259. **212.** 2 c. multicoloured .. 30 20

213. Student Nurse and Candle. 214. Islands and Sunset.

1971. 25th Anniv. of Nurses' Training Scheme.

260. **213.** 4 c. multicoloured .. 25 25

1972. Maritime Scenery. Multicoloured.

261.	5 c. Type **214**	30	70
262.	5 c. Coral reef	30	70
263.	5 c. Islands and Short-tailed Albatross ..	80	70

217. Dove and Flags of Japan and U.S.A.　**218.** Yushbin (ceremonial sake (container).

1972. Ratification of Treaty for Return of Ryukyu Islands to Japan.

264.	217.	5 c. multicoloured	40	1·00

1972. Philatelic Week.

265.	218.	5 c. multicoloured	50	1·00

SPECIAL DELIVERY STAMP

F 13. Sea horse.

1951.

E 18.	E13.	5 y. blue	17·00	15·00

SAAR　Pt. 7

A German territory to the S.E. of Luxembourg. Occupied by France under League of Nations control from 1920 to 1935. Following a plebiscite, Saar returned to Germany in 1935 when German stamps were used until the French occupation in 1945 when Nos. F 1/13 of Germany replaced them followed by Nos. 203, etc. The territory was autonomous under French protection until it again returned to Germany at the end of 1956 following a national referendum. Issues from 1957 were authorised by the German Federal Republic pending the adoption of German currency on 6 July 1959, after which West German stamps were used.

1920–May 1921. 100 pfennig = 1 mark.
May 1921–March 1935. 100 centimes = 1 franc.
1935–47. 100 pfennig = 1 reichsmark.
1947. 100 pfennig = 1 saarmark.
November 1947–July 1959. 100 centimes = 1 franc.
From 1959. 100 pfennig = 1 Deutsche mark.

LEAGUE OF NATIONS COMMISSION

1920. German stamps inscr. "DEUTSCHES REICH" optd. **Sarre** and bar.

1.	24.	2 pf. grey	75	2·25
2.		2½ p. grey	1·75	3·50
3.	10.	3 pf. brown	60	1·50
4.		5 pf. green	15	25
5.	24.	7½ pf. orange	40	70
6.	10.	10 pf. red	15	25
7.	24.	15 pf. violet	15	25
8.	10.	20 pf. blue	15	25
9.		25 pf. blk. & red on yell.	6·00	12·00
10.		30 pf. blk. & or. on buff	10·00	20·00
11.	24.	35 pf. brown	25	45
12.	10.	40 pf. black and red	30	45
13.		50 pf. blk. & pur. on buff	25	45
14.		60 pf. purple	30	45
15.		75 pf. black and green	30	45
16.		80 pf. blk. & red on rose	£200	£225
17a.	12.	1 m. red	16·00	32·00

1920. Bavarian stamps optd. **Sarre** or **SARRE** and bars.

18.	15.	5 pf. green	50	1·00
19.		10 pf. red	50	1·25
20a.		15 pf. red	60	1·60
21.		20 pf. blue	50	1·25
22.		25 pf. grey	5·00	13·00
23.		30 pf. orange	4·50	8·50
24.		40 pf. olive	5·50	13·00
25.		50 pf. brown	65	1·25
26.		60 pf. green	95	3·00
27.	16.	1 m. brown	8·50	25·00
28.		2 m. violet	50·00	£110
29.		3 m. red	75·00	£850
30.	–	5 m. blue (No. 192)	£800	£200
31.	–	10 m. green (No. 193)	90·00	£200

1920. German stamps inscr. "DEUTSCHES REICH" optd. **SAARGEBIET.**

32.	10.	5 pf. green	20	25
33.		5 pf. brown	35	45
34.		10 pf. red	20	25
35.		10 pf. orange	25	25
36.	24.	15 pf. violet	20	25
37.	10.	20 pf. blue	20	25
38.		20 pf. green	30	45
39.		30 pf. blk. & orge. on buff	25	25
40.		30 pf. blue	40	65
41.		40 pf. black and red	25	25
42.		40 pf. red	55	60
43.		50 pf. blk. & pur. on buff	30	35
44.		60 pf. purple	30	35
45.		75 pf. black and green	30	35
46.	12.	1 m. 25 green	2·50	1·25
47.		1 m. 50 brown	2·50	1·25
48.	13.	2 m. 50 red	3·00	9·50
49.	10.	4 m. red and black	5·50	19·00

1920. Stamps of Germany optd. as above and surch.

50.	10.	20 on 75 pf. blk. & grn.	30	1·00
51.	24.	5 m. on 15 pf. purple	4·50	12·00
52.		10 m. on 15 pf. purple	5·50	15·00

9. Miner.　**11.** Colliery Shafthead.

12. Burbach Steelworks.

1921.

53.	–	5 pf. violet and olive	20	25
54.	9.	10 pf. orange and blue	20	20
55.	–	20 pf. blue and green	50	25
56.	–	25 pf. blue and brown	35	25
57.	–	30 pf. brown and green	30	40
58.	–	40 pf. red	30	35
59.	–	50 pf. black and grey	1·40	2·00
60.	–	60 pf. brown and red	1·00	2·25
61.	–	80 pf. blue	40	85
62.	–	1 m. black and red	50	75
63.	11.	1 m. 25 green and brown	60	1·25
64.	–	2 m. black and orange	2·25	3·25
65.	–	3 m. black and brown	2·50	8·00
66.	–	5 m. violet and yellow	5·00	17·00
67.	–	10 m. brown and green	7·50	21·00
68.	12.	25 m. blue, black and red	25·00	55·00

DESIGNS—As Type **11.** HORIZ. 5 pf. Mill above Mettlach. 20 pf. Pit-head at Reden. 25 pf. River traffic, Saarbrucken. 30 pf. River Saar at Mettlach. 40 pf. Slag-heap, Volklingen. 50 pf. Signal gantry, Saarbrucken. 80 pf. "Old Bridge", Saarbrucken. 1 m. Wire-rope Railway. 2 m. Town Hall, Saarbrucken. 3 m. Pottery, Mettlach. 5 m. St. Ludwig's Church. 10 m. Chief Magistrate's and Saar Commissioner's Offices. VERT. 60 pf. Gothic Chapel, Mettlach.

1921. Nos. 55/68 surch. in new currency.

70.	3 c. on 20 pf. blue & green	40	20
71.	5 c. on 25 pf. blue and brown	15	30
72.	10 c. on 30 pf. brown & green	25	30
73.	15 c. on 40 pf. red	35	25
74.	20 c. on 50 pf. black & grey	70	15
75.	25 c. on 60 pf. brown & red	35	25
76.	30 c. on 80 pf. blue	1·00	40
77.	40 c. on 1 m. black and red	1·75	40
78.	50 c. on 1 m. 25 green & brn.	2·75	60
79.	75 c. on 2 m. black & orange	2·75	90
80.	1 f. on 3 m. black and brown	2·75	1·50
81.	2 f. on 5 m. violet & yellow	8·50	5·00
82.	3 f. on 10 m. brown & green	10·00	19·00
83.	5 f. on 25 m. blue, blk. & red	16·00	26·00

1922. Larger designs (except 5 f.) and value in French currency.

84	3 c. green (as No. 62)	20	35
85	5 c. blk & orge (as No. 54)	20	10
86	10 c. green (as No. 61)	25	10
87	15 c. brown (as No. 62)	25	15
98	15 c. orange (as No. 62)	2·25	35
88	20 c. bl & yell (as No. 64)	1·25	15
100	25 c. red & yell (as No. 64)	1·50	20
90	30 c. red & yell (as No. 58)	25	40
91	40 c. brn & yell (as No. 65)	50	10
92	50 c. blue & yell (as No. 56)	75	10
101	75 c. grn & yell (as No. 65)	15·00	1·75
94	1 f. brown (as No. 66)	1·00	35
95	2 f. violet (as No. 63)	3·00	2·00
96	3 f. grn & orge (as No. 60)	2·50	2·00
97	5 f. brn & choc (as No. 68)	35·00	60·00

14. Madonna of Blieskastel.　**15.** Army Medical Service.

1925.

102.	14.	45 c. plum	2·25	2·25
103.		10 f. brn. (31×36 mm.)	10·00	24·00

1926. Welfare Fund.

104.	15.	20 c.+20 c. olive	6·00	13·00
105.	–	40 c.+40 c. brown	6·50	16·00
106.	–	50 c.+50 c. orange	6·50	12·00
107.	–	1 f. 50+1 f. 50 blue	14·00	40·00

DESIGN: 40 c. Hospital work (nurse and patient). 50 c. Child Welfare (children at a spring). 1 f. 50. Maternity Nursing Service.

18. Tholey Abbey.

1926.

108.	–	10 c. brown	50	15
109.	–	15 c. green	40	70
110.	–	20 c. brown	35	15
111.	18.	25 c. blue	40	35
112.	–	30 c. green	50	15
113.	–	40 c. sepia	50	15
114.	18.	50 c. red	50	15
114a.	–	60 c. orange	1·25	20
115.	–	75 c. purple	50	15
116.	–	80 c. orange	2·75	6·50
116a.	–	90 c. red	7·00	17·00
117.	–	1 f. violet	2·25	20
118.	–	1 f. 50 blue	6·00	20
119.	–	2 f. red	6·00	25
120.	–	3 f. olive	14·00	75
121.	–	5 f. brown	16·00	5·50

DESIGNS—VERT.: 10 c., 30 c. Fountain, St. Johann, Saarbrucken. HORIZ.: 15 c., 75 c. Saar Valley near Gudingen. 20 c., 40 c., 90 c. View from Saarlouis fortifications. 60 c., 80 c., 1 f. Colliery Shafthead. 1 f. 50 c., 2 f., 3 f., 5 f. Burbach Steelworks.

1927. Welfare Fund. Optd. **1927-28.**

122.	15.	20 c.+20 c. olive	26·00	16·00
123.		40 c.+40 c. brown	24·00	20·00
124.		50 c.+50 c. orange	20·00	16·00
125.		1 f. 50+1 f. 50 blue	29·00	42·00

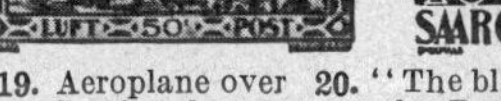

19. Aeroplane over Saarbrucken.　**20.** "The blind Beggar" by Dyckmanns.

1928. Air.

126.	19.	50 c. red	2·50	2·50
127.		1 f. violet	3·25	3·25

1928. Christmas Charity.

128	20	40 c. (+40 c.) brown	7·00	22·00
129		50 c. (+50 c.) red	7·00	22·00
130		1 f. (+1 f.) violet	7·00	22·00
131	–	1 f. 50 (+1 f. 50) blue	7·00	22·00
132	–	2 f. (+2 f.) red	8·00	24·00
133	–	3 f. (+3 f.) green	8·00	24·00
134	–	10 f. (+10 f.) brown	£400	£3000

DESIGNS: 1 f. 50, 2 f., 3 f. "Almsgiving" by Schiestl. 10 f. "Charity" by Raphael (picture in circle).

1929. Christmas Charity. Paintings. As T **20.**

135	40 c. (+15 c.) green	1·50	3·25
136	50 c. (+20 c.) red	3·50	5·50
137	1 f. (+50 c.) purple	3·50	7·00
138	1 f. 50 (+75 c.) blue	3·50	7·00
139	2 f. (+1 f.) red	3·50	7·00
140	3 f. (+2 f.) green	5·50	16·00
141	10 f. (+8 f.) brown	35·00	85·00

DESIGNS: 40 c. to 1 f. "Orphaned" by H. Kaulbach. 1 f. 50, 2 f., 3 f. "St. Ottilia" by M. Feuerstein. 10 f. "The Little Madonna" by Ferruzzio.

1930. Nos. 114 and 116 surch.

141a.	18.	40 c. on 50 c. red	85	1·10
142.	–	60 c. on 80 c. orange	85	1·90

1931. Christmas Charity (1930 issue). Paintings. As T **20.**

143	40 c. (+15 c.) brown	5·00	17·00
144	60 c. (+20 c.) orange	5·00	17·00
145	1 f. (+50 c.) red	6·50	32·00
146	1 f. 50 (+75 c.) blue	8·00	32·00
147	2 f. (+1 f.) brown	8·00	32·00
148	3 f. (+2 f.) green	11·00	32·00
149	10 f. (+10 f.) brown	65·00	£250

DESIGNS: 40 c., 60 c., 1 f. 50, "The Safetyman" (miner and lamp) by F. Zolnhofer. 1 f., 2 f., 3 f. "The Good Samaritan" by J. Heinemann. 10 f. "At the Window" by F. G. Waldmuller.

1931. Christmas Charity. Paintings. As T **20.**

150	40 c. (+15 c.) brown	10·00	25·00
151	60 c. (+20 c.) red	10·00	25·00
152	1 f. (+50 c.) purple	13·00	40·00
153	1 f. 50 (+75 c.) blue	15·00	40·00
154	2 f. (+1 f.) red	17·00	40·00
155	3 f. (+2 f.) green	23·00	75·00
156	5 f. (+5 f.) brown	55·00	£275

DESIGNS: 40 c. to 1 f. "St. Martin" by F. Boehle. 1 f. 50, 2 f., 3 f. "Charity" by Ridgeway-Knight. 5 f. "The Widow's Mite" by Dubufe.

MINIMUM PRICE

The minimum price quoted is 5p which represents a handling charge rather than a basis for valuing common stamps. For further notes about prices see introductory pages.

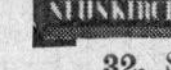

29. Saar Airport.　**30.** Kirkel Castle Ruins.　**33.** "Love".　**32.** Scene of the Disaster.

1932. Air.

157.	29.	60 c. red	5·00	2·50
158.		5 fr. brown	35·00	85·00

1932. Christmas Charity.

159	30	40 c. (+15 c.) brown	7·00	22·00
160	–	60 c. (+20 c.) red	7·00	22·00
161	–	1 f. (+50 c.) purple	10·00	35·00
162	–	1 f. 50 (+75 c.) blue	16·00	42·00
163	–	2 f. (+1 f.) red	16·00	42·00
164	–	3 f. (+2 f.) green	40·00	£140
165	–	5 f. (+5 f.) brown	65·00	£225

DESIGNS—VERT. 60 c. Blieskastel Church. 1 f. Ottweiler Church. 1 f. 50, St. Michael's Church, Saarbrucken. 2 f. Cathedral and fountain, St. Wendel. 3 f. St. John's Church, Saarbrucken. HORIZ. 5 f. Kerpen Castle, Illingen.

1933. Neunkirchen Explosion Disaster.

166.	32.	60 c.+60 c. orange	8·50	16·00
167.		3 f.+3 f. green	35·00	40·00
168.		5 f.+5 f. brown	35·00	60·00

1934. Christmas Charity.

169	33	40 c. (+15 c.) brown	4·25	13·00
170	–	60 c. (+20 c.) red	4·25	13·00
171	–	1 f. (+50 c.) mauve	6·00	16·00
172	–	1 f. 50 (+75 c.) blue	11·00	30·00
173	–	2 f. (+1 f.) red	10·00	27·00
174	–	3 f. (+2 f.) green	11·00	30·00
175	–	5 f. (+5 f.) brown	25·00	65·00

DESIGNS: 60 c. "Solicitude". 1 f. "Peace". 1 f. 50 "Consolation". 2 f. "Welfare". 3 f. "Truth". 5 f. Countess Elizabeth von Nassau.

Nos. 169/74 show statues by C. L. Pozzi in church of St. Louis, Saarbrucken.

1934. Saar Plebiscite. Optd. **VOLKSABSTIMMUNG 1935.**

(a) Postage. On Nos. 108/15, 116a/21 and 103.

176.	–	10 c. brown	40	55
177.	–	15 c. green	40	55
178.	–	20 c. orange	35	35
179.	18.	25 c. blue	55	1·25
180.	–	30 c. green	35	30
181.	–	40 c. sepia	35	40
182.	18.	50 c. lake	60	1·10
183.	–	60 c. orange	35	30
184.	–	75 c. purple	60	1·25
185.	–	90 c. red	60	1·25
186.	–	1 f. violet	70	1·25
187.	–	1 f. 50 c. blue	3·00	3·50
188.	–	2 f. red	4·50	4·75
189.	–	3 f. olive	7·50	6·50
190.	–	5 f. brown	32·00	32·00
191.	14.	10 f. brown	22·00	50·00

(b) Air. On Nos. 126/7 and 157/8.

192.	19.	50 c. red	3·50	8·00
193.	29.	60 c. red	2·00	2·50
194.	19.	1 f. violet	4·75	10·00
195.	29.	5 f. brown	7·50	13·00

(c) Charity. On Nos. 169/75.

196	33	40 c. (+15 c.) brown	3·00	9·50
197	–	60 c. (+20 c.) red	3·00	9·50
198	–	1 f. (+50 c.) mauve	7·50	22·00
199	–	1 f. 50 (+75 c.) blue	7·50	22·00
200	–	2 f. (+1 f.) red	9·50	28·00
201	–	3 f. (+2 f.) green	8·00	25·00
202	–	5 f. (+5 f.) brown	14·00	32·00

FRENCH OCCUPATION

36. Coal-miner.　**37.** Loop of the Saar.

1947. Inscr. "SAAR".

203.	36.	2 pf. grey	10	15
204.		3 pf. orange	10	50
205.		6 pf. green	10	20
206.		8 pf. red	10	20
207.		10 pf. mauve	10	15
208.		12 pf. green	10	10
209.	–	15 pf. brown	10	55
210.	–	16 pf. blue	10	15
211.	–	20 pf. red	10	15
212.	–	24 pf. brown	10	10
213.	–	25 pf. mauve	40	16·00
214.	–	30 pf. green	15	45
215.	–	40 pf. brown	15	45
216.	–	45 pf. red	45	12·00
217.	–	50 pf. violet	35	15·00
218.	–	60 pf. violet	35	15·00

219. – 75 pf. blue 10 30
220. – 80 pf. orange 10 30
221. – 84 pf. brown 10 30
222. **37.** 1 m. green 10 40

DESIGNS—SMALL SIZE: 15 pf. to 24 pf. Steel workers. 25 pf. to 50 pf. Sugar Beet harvesters. 60 pf. to 80 pf. Mettlach Abbey. As T **37**—VERT. 84 pf. Marshal Ney.

1947. As last surch. in French currency.
223. **36.** 10 c. on 2 pf. grey .. 10 50
224. 60 c. 3 pf. orange .. 10 50
225. 1 f. on 10 pf. mauve .. 10 50
226. 2 f. on 12 pf. green .. 10 65
227. – 3 f. on 15 pf. brown .. 10 50
228. – 4 f. on 16 pf. blue .. 15 5·00
229. – 5 pf. on 20 pf. red .. 10 80
230. – 6 f. on 24 pf. brown .. 10 50
231. – 9 f. on 30 pf. green .. 30 6·50
232. – 10 f. on 50 pf. violet .. 30 10·00
233. – 14 f. on 60 pf. violet .. 45 6·00
234. – 20 f. on 84 pf. brown .. 30 8·00
235. **37.** 50 pf. on 1 m. green .. 1·10 12·00

42. Clasped Hands.

43. Builders.

44. Saar Valley.

1948. Inscr. "SAARPOST".
236. **42.** 10 c. red (postage) .. 60 1·40
237. 60 c. blue .. .. 60 1·40
238. 1 f. black 25 15
239. – 2 f. red 25 10
240. – 3 f. brown 30 10
241. – 4 f. red 30 10
242. – 5 f. violet 30 15
243. – 6 f. red 65 15
244. – 9 f. blue .. .. 5·50 25
245. – 10 f. blue .. .. 2·50 20
246. – 14 f. purple .. .. 3·00 65
247. **43.** 20 f. red .. .. 6·50 65
248. – 50 f. blue .. .. 16·00 2·50

249. **44.** 25 f. red (air) .. .. 5·00 3·50
250. 50 f. blue .. .. 2·75 1·75
251. 200 f. red .. .. 24·00 28·00

DESIGNS—As Type **42**: 2 f., 3 f. Man's head. 4 f., 5 f. Woman's head. 6 f., 9 f. Miner's head. As Type **43**: 10 f. Blast-furnace chimney. 14 f. Foundry. 50 f. Facade of Mettlach Abbey.

46. Floods in St. Johann, Saarbrucken.

47. Map of Saarland.

1948. Flood Disaster Relief Fund. Flood scenes. Inscr. as in T **46**.
252 5 f.+5 f. green (postage) .. 3·50 18·00
253 6 f.+4 f. purple .. .. 3·50 18·00
254 12 f.+8 f. red .. .. 3·75 24·00
255 18 f.+12 f. blue .. .. 5·50 30·00

256 25 f.+25 f. brown (air) .. 23·00 £130

DESIGNS—VERT. 18 f. Flooded street, Saarbrucken. HORIZ. 5 f. Flooded industrial area. 12 f. Landtag building, Saarbrucken. 25 f. Floods at Ensdorf, Saarlouis.

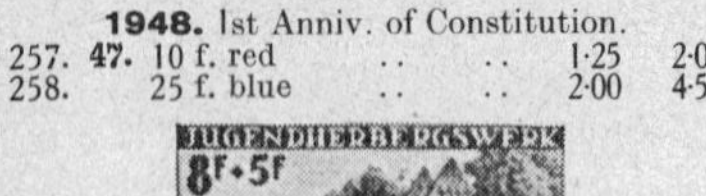

1948. 1st Anniv. of Constitution.
257. **47.** 10 f. red .. .. 1·25 2·00
258. 25 f. blue .. .. 2·00 4·50

48. Hikers and Ludweiler Hostel.

1949. Youth Hostels Fund.
259. **48.** 8 f.+5 f. brown .. 1·75 4·75
260. – 10 f.+7 f. green .. 2·00 3·50

DESIGN: 10 f. Hikers and Weisskirchen hostel.

49. Chemical Research.

50. Mare and Foal.

1949. Saar University.
261. **49.** 15 f. red .. .. 3·50 15

1949. Horse Day.
262. **50.** 15 f.+5 f. red .. .. 15·00 23·00
263. – 25 f.+15 f. blue .. 17·00 27·00

DESIGN: 25 f. Two horses in steeple-chase.

51. Symbolic of Typography.

52. Labourer and Foundry.

1949.
264. – 10 c. purple .. .. 20 1·40
265. – 60 c. black .. .. 30 1·40
266. – 1 f. red .. .. 1·40 10
267. – 3 f. brown .. .. 8·50 30
268. – 5 f. violet .. .. 2·00 10
269. – 6 f. green .. .. 13·00 60
270. – 8 f. olive 75 35
271. **51.** 10 f. orange .. .. 5·00 10
272. – 12 f. green .. .. 16·00 10
273. – 15 f. red .. .. 8·50 15
274. – 18 f. mauve .. .. 3·00 4·00
275. **52.** 20 f. grey .. .. 2·00 15
276. – 25 f. blue .. .. 22·00 15
277. – 30 f. red .. .. 16·00 45
278. – 45 f. purple .. .. 5·50 35
279. – 60 f. green .. .. 5·50 1·50
280. – 100 f. sepia .. .. 12·00 1·60

DESIGNS—As Type **51**: 10 c. Building trade. 60 c. Beethoven. 1 f. and 3 f. Heavy industries. 5 f. Slag heap. 6 f. and 15 f. Colliery. 8 f. Posthorn and telephone. 12 f. and 18 f. Pottery As Type **52**: VERT. 25 f. Blast furnace worker. 60 f. Landsweiler. 100 f. Wiebelskirchen. HORIZ. 30 f. St. Arnual. 45 f. "Giant's Boot", Rentrisch.

53. Detail from "Moses Striking the Rock" (Murillo).

54. A. Kolping.

55. P. Wust.

1949. National Relief Fund.
281. **53.** 8 f.+2 f. blue .. .. 7·50 23·00
282. – 12 f.+3 f. green .. 9·50 25·00
283. – 15 f. +5 f. red .. 13·00 45·00
284. – 25 f.+10 f. blue .. 18·00 80·00
285. – 50 f.+20 f. purple .. 32·00 £120

DESIGNS—VERT. 12 f. "Our Lord healing the Paralytic" (Murillo). 15 f. "The Sick Child" (Metsu). 25 f." St. Thomas of Villanueva" (Murillo). 50 f. "Madonna of Blieskastel".

1950. Honouring Adolf Kolping (miners' padre).
286. **54.** 15 f.+5 f. red .. .. 24·00 55·00

1950. 10th Death Anniv. of Peter Wust (philosopher).
287. **55.** 15 f. red .. .. 4·25 4·25

56. Mail Coach.

1950. Stamp Day.
288. **56.** 15 f.+5 f. brn. & red 55·00 80·00

57. "Food for the Hungry".

58. St. Peter.

59. Town Hall, Ottweiler.

1950. Red Cross Fund
289. **57.** 25 f.+10 f. lake & red 23·00 45·00

1950. Holy Year.
290. **58.** 12 f. green .. .. 3·00 6·00
291. 15 f. red .. .. 3·50 6·00
292. 25 f. blue .. .. 6·50 14·00

1950. 400th Anniv. of Ottweiler.
293. **59.** 10 f. brown .. .. 3·00 6·50

61.

1950. Saar's Admission to Council of Europe.
294. **61.** 25 f. blue (postage) .. 40·00 5·00

295. 200 f. red (air) £150 £225

62. St. Lutwinus Enters Monastery.

DESIGNS: 12 f. Lutwinus builds Mettlach Abbey. 15 f. Lutwinus as Abbot. 25 f. Bishop Lutwinus confirming children at Rheims. 50 f. Lutwinus helping needy.

1950. National Relief Fund. Inscr. "VOLKSHILFE".
296. **62.** 8 f.+2 f. brown .. 5·00 17·00
297. – 12 f.+3 f. green .. 5·00 17·00
298. – 15 f.+5 f. brown .. 5·50 28·00
299. – 25 f.+10 f. blue .. 8·50 40·00
300. – 50 f.+20 f. red .. 12·00 60·00

63. Orphans.

65. Allegory.

64. Mail-carriers, 1760.

1951. Red Cross Fund.
301. **63.** 25 f.+10 f. green & red 20·00 40·00

1951. Stamp Day.
302. **64.** 15 f. purple .. 6·00 14·00

1951. Trade Fair.
303. **65.** 15 f. green .. .. 2·00 3·75

66. Flowers and Building.

67. Calvin and Luther.

1951. Horticultural Show, Bexbach.
304. **66.** 15 f. green .. .. 2·50 85

1951. 375th Anniv. of Reformation in Saar.
305. **67.** 15 f.+5 f. brown .. 1·25 5·00

68. "The Good Mother" (Lepicie).

69. Mounted Postman.

1951. National Relief Fund. Inscr. "VOLKSHILFE 1951".
306. **68.** 12 f.+3 f. green .. 4·50 14·00
307. – 15 f.+5 f. violet .. 4·50 14·00
308. – 18 f.+7 f. lake .. 5·00 15·00
309. – 30 f.+10 f. blue .. 8·00 22·00
310. – 50 f.+20 f. brown .. 18·00 48·00

PAINTINGS—VERT. 18 f. "Outside the Theatre" (Kampf). 18 f. "Sisters of Charity" (Browne). 30 f. "The Good Samaritan" (Bassano). 50 f. "St. Martin and the Poor" (Van Dyck).

1952. Stamp Day.
311. **69.** 30 f.+10 f. blue .. 8·00 18·00

70. Athlete bearing Olympic Flame.

71. Globe and Emblem.

1952. 15th Olympic Games, Helsinki. Inscr. "OLYMPISCHE SPIELE 1952".
312. **70.** 15 f.+5 f. green .. 2·50 6·00
313. – 30 f.+5 f. blue .. 3·00 8·50

DESIGN: 30 f. Hand, laurels and globe.

1952. Saar Fair.
314 **71** 15 f. red .. .. 1·50 75

72. Red Cross and Refugees.

73. G.P.O., Saarbrucken.

1952. Red Cross Week.
315. **72.** 15 f. red .. .. 1·50 75

1952. (A) Without inscr in or below design. (B) With inscr.
316. – 1 f. green (B) 15 10
317. – 2 f. violet 15 10
318. – 3 f. red 15 10
319. **73.** 5 f. turquoise (A) .. 6·00 10
320. 5 f. turquoise (B) .. 20 10
321. – 6 f. purple 35 10
322. – 10 f. olive 40 10
323. **73.** 12 f. green (B) 40 10
324. – 15 f. sepia (A) .. .. 8·00 10
325. – 15 f. sepia (B) .. .. 5·00 10
326. – 15 f. red (B) 25 10
327. – 18 f. purple .. .. 2·75 3·25
329. – 30 f. blue 85 50
334. – 500 f. lake .. .. 17·00 50·00

DESIGNS—HORIZ. 1 f., 15 f. (3) Colliery shaft-head. 2 f., 10 f. Ludwigs High School, Saarbrucken. 3 f., 18 f. Gersweiler Bridge. 6 f. Mettlach Bridge. 30 f. University Library, Saarbrucken. VERT. 500 f. St. Ludwig's Church, Saarbrucken.

74. "Count Stroganov as a Boy" (Greuze).

75. Fair Symbol.

1952. National Relief Fund. Paintings inscr. "VOLKSHILFE 1952".
335. **74.** 15 f.+5 f. sepia .. 2·75 7·00
336. – 18 f.+7 f. lake .. 3·25 9·00
337. – 30 f.+10 f. blue .. 4·00 11·00

PAINTINGS: 18 f. "The Holy Shepherd" (Murillo). 30 f. Portrait of a Boy (Kraus).

1953. Saar Fair.
338. **75.** 15 f. blue .. .. 1·50 90

76. Postilions. 77. Henri Dunant.

1953. Stamp Day.
339. 76. 15 f. blue .. .. 2·50 9·00

1953. Red Cross Week and 125th Anniv. of Birth of Dunant (the founder).
340. 77. 15 f.+5 f. brown & red 1·50 4·25

78. "Painter's Young Son" (Rubens). 79. St. Benedict Blessing St. Maurus.

1953. National Relief Fund. Paintings inscr. "VOLKSHILFE 1953".
341. – 15 pf.+5 f. violet .. 1·25 3·75
342. – 18 f.+7 f. red .. .. 1·40 5·00
343. 78. 30 f.+10 f. green .. 2·75 7·50
DESIGNS—VERT. 15 f. "Clarice Strozzi" (Titian). HORIZ. 18 f. "Painter's Children" (Rubens).

1953. Tholey Abbey Fund.
344. 79. 30 f.+10 f. black .. 1·50 5·50

80. Saar Fair. 82. Red Cross and Child.

81. Postal Motor Coach.

1954. Saar Fair.
345. 80. 15 f. green .. .. 1·40 70

1954. Stamp Day.
346. 81. 15 f. red .. .. 2·50 9·00

1954. Red Cross Week.
347. 82. 15 f.+5 f. brown .. 1·75 5·00

83. Madonna and Child (Holbein).

1954. Marian Year.
348. 83. 5 f. red .. .. .. 70 1·50
349. – 10 f. green .. .. 90 2·25
350. – 15 f. blue .. .. 1·40 3·25
DESIGNS: 10 f. "Sistine Madonna" (Raphael). 15 f. "Madonna and Child with Pear" (Durer).

MORE DETAILED LISTS
are given in the Stanley Gibbons Catalogues referred to in the country headings.
For lists of current volumes see Introduction.

84. "Street Urchin with a Melon" (Murillo). 85. Cyclist and Flag. 86. Rotary Emblem and Industrial Plant.

1954. National Relief Fund. Paintings inscr. "VOLKSHILFE 1954".
351. 84. 5 f.+3 f. red 30 75
352. – 10 f.+5 f. green .. 35 95
353. – 15 f.+7 f. violet .. 40 1·10
DESIGNS: 10 f. "Maria de Medici" (A. Bronzino). 15 f. "Baron Emil von Maucler" (J. F. Dietrich).

1955. World Cross-Country Cycle Race.
354. 85. 15 f. blue, red and black 30 40

1955. 50th Anniv. of Rotary Int.
355. 86. 15 f. brown 25 40

87. Exhibitors' Flags. 88. Nurse and Baby.

1955. Saar Fair.
356. 87. 15 f. yell., bl. & grn. 20 50

1955. Red Cross Week.
357. 88. 15 f.+5 f. black & red 30 65

89. Postman. 91. "Mother" (Durer).

1955. Stamp Day.
358. 89. 15 f. purple .. .. 40 1·25

1955. Referendum. Optd. **VOLKSBEFRAGUNG 1955.**
359. 15 f. red (No. 326) .. 15 35
360. 18 f. purple (No. 327) .. 15 40
361. 30 f. blue (No. 329) .. 25 55

1955. National Relief Fund. Durer paintings inscr. as in T 91.
362. 91. 5 f.+3 f. green .. 35 55
363. – 10 f.+5 f. olive .. 60 1·40
364. – 15 f.+7 f. bistre .. 70 1·25
PAINTINGS: 10 f. "The Praying Hands". 15 f. "The Old Man from Antwerp".

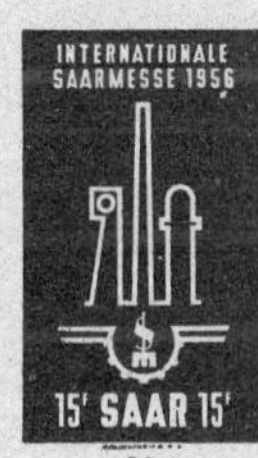

92. 93. Radio Tower.

1956. Saar Fair.
365. 92. 15 f. green and red .. 15 45

1956. Stamp Day.
366. 93. 15 f. green 15 45

94. Casualty Station. 95.

1956. Red Cross Week.
367. 94. 15 f.+5 f. brown .. 20 50

1956. Olympic Games.
368. 95. 12 f.+3 f. blue & green 15 35
369. 15 f.+5 f. sepia & purple 15 35

96. Winterberg Memorial. 97. "Portrait of Lucrezia Crivelli" (da Vinci).

1956. Winterberg Memorial Reconstruction Fund.
370. 96. 5 f.+2 f. green .. 10 20
371. 112 f.+3 f. purple .. 15 30
372. 15 f.+5 f. brown .. 15 30

1956. National Relief Fund. Inscr. as in T 97.
373. 97. 5 f.+3 f. blue 10 20
374. – 10 f.+5 f. red 15 25
375. – 15 f.+7 f. green .. 20 45
PAINTINGS—VERT. 10 f. "Saskia" (Rembrandt). 15 f. "Lady Playing Spinet" (Floris).

RETURN TO GERMANY

98. Arms of the Saar. 99. President Heuss.

1957. Return of the Saar to Germany.
376. 99. 15 f. blue and orange .. 10 25

1957. (a) Without "F" after figure of value.
377. 99. 1 f. green 10 15
378. 2 f. violet 10 15
379. 3 f. brown 10 15
380. 4 f. mauve 20 60
381. 5 f. olive 10 10
382. 6 f. red 15 40
383. 10 f. grey 10 30
384. 12 f. orange 10 10
385. 15 f. turquoise .. 20 10
386. 18 f. red .. .. 70 1·40
387. 25 f. mauve 30 55
388. 30 f. purple 35 55
389. 45 f. olive .. .. 1·25 2·50
390. 50 f. brown .. .. 1·25 1·00
391. 60 f. red .. .. 1·60 2·75
392. 70 f. salmon .. .. 3·00 4·50
393. 80 f. olive .. .. 1·10 2·50
394. 90 f. grey .. .. 2·75 4·50
395. 100 f. red (24 × 29½ mm.) 2·50 8·50
396. 200 f. lilac (24 × 29½ mm.) 5·50 21·00

(b) With "F" after figure of value.
406. 99. 1 f. grey 10 20
407. 3 f. blue 10 20
408. 5 f. olive 10 10
409. 6 f. brown 20 60
410. 10 f. violet 20 25
411. 12 f. brown 20 10
412. 15 f. green 35 10
413. 18 f. grey .. .. 2·00 5·00
414. 20 f. olive .. .. 1·25 2·25
415. 25 f. brown 55 45
416. 30 f. mauve .. .. 1·10 45
417. 35 f. brown .. .. 2·75 3·25
418. 45 f. turquoise .. 2·00 3·50
419. 50 f. brown .. .. 1·10 1·25
420. 70 f. green .. .. 4·50 5·50
421. 80 f. blue .. .. 2·75 4·50
422. 90 f. red .. .. 5·50 7·50
423. 100 f. yellow .. .. 4·50 5·50
424. 200 f. green .. .. 10·00 22·00
425. 300 f. blue .. .. 13·00 26·00
Nos. 423/5 are larger, 24¼ × 29½ mm.

100. Iron Foundry. 101. Arms of Merzig and St. Pierre Church.

1957. Saar Fair.
397. 100. 15 f. red and sepia .. 10 20

1957. Centenary of Merzig.
398. 101. 15 f. blue 10 20

101a. "Europa" Tree. 101b. Young Miner.

1957. Europa.
399. 101a. 20 f. orange & yell. 30 70
400. 35 f. violet and pink 50 80

1957. Humanitarian Relief Fund.
401. 101b. 6 f.+4 f. blk. & brn. 10 15
402. – 12 f.+6 f. blk. & grn. 10 15
403. – 15 f.+7 f. blk. & red 15 30
404. – 30 f.+10 f. blk. & bl. 45 70
DESIGNS: 12 f. Miner drilling at coalface. 15 f. Miner with coal-cutting machine. 30 f. Operator at mine lift-shaft.

101c. Carrier Pigeons. 101d. Max and Moritz (Cartoon characters).

1957. Int. Correspondence Week.
405. 101c. 15 f. black and red 10 20

1958. 150th Death Anniv. of Wilhelm Busch (writer and illustrator).
426. 101d. 12 f. olive and black 10 15
427. – 15 f. red and black 10 30
DESIGN: 15 f. Wilhelm Busch.

101e. "Prevent Forest Fires". 101g. "The Fox who stole the Goose".

101f. Diesel and 1st Oil Engine.

1958. Forest Fires Prevention Campaign.
428. 101e. 15 f. black and red 10 20

1958. Birth Centenary of Rudolf Diesel (engineer).
429. 101f. 12 f. turquoise .. 15 25

1958. Berlin Students' Fund.
430. 101g. 12 f.+6 f. brown, black and green 10 20
431. – 15 f.+7 f. brown, green and red .. 10 25
DESIGN: 15 f. "A Hunter from the Palatinate".

102. Saarbrucken Town Hall and Fair Emblem. 103. Homburg.

1958. Saar Fair.
432. 102. 15 f. red 10 20

1958. 400th Anniv. of Homburg.
433. 103. 15 f. green 10 20

103a. Emblem. 103b. Schulze-Dilitzsch.

1958. 150th Anniv. of German Gymnastics.
434. **103a.** 12 f. black, green and grey 10 20

1958. 150th Birth Anniv. of Schulze-Delitzsch (pioneer of German Co-operative Movement).
435. **103b.** 12 f. green 10 20

103c. "Europa".

103d. Friedrich Raiffeisen (philanthropist).

436. **103c.** 12 f. blue and green 40 70
437. – 30 f. red and blue 60 90

1958. Humanitarian Relief and Welfare Funds.
438. **103d.** 6 f.+4 f. brown 10 15
439. – 12 f.+6 f. red, yellow and green 10 20
440. – 15 f.+7 f. blue, green and red 20 35
441. – 30 f.+10 f. yellow, green and blue 25 45

DESIGNS: Inscr. "WOHLFAHRTSMARKE". 12 f. Dairymaid. 15 f. Vine dresser. 30 f. Farm labourer.

103e. Fugger.

104. Hands holding Crates.

1959. 500th Birth Anniv. of Jakib Fugger (merchant prince).
442. **103e.** 15 f. black and red 10 20

1959. Saar Fair.
443. **104.** 15 f. lake 10 20

105. Saarbrucken.

105a. Humboldt.

1959. 50th Anniv. of Greater Saarbrucken.
444. **105.** 15 f. blue 10 20

1959. Death Centenary of Alexander von Humboldt (naturalist).
445. **105a.** 15 f. blue 10 20

OFFICIAL STAMPS

1922. Nos. 84 to 94 optd. **DIENSTMARKE.**
O 98. 3 c. green 85 24·00
O 99. 5 c. black and orange 35 15
O 100. 10 c. green 35 15
O 101. 15 c. brown 35 15
O 109. 15 c. orange 2·25 30
O 102. 20 c. blue and yellow 35 15
O 111. 25 c. red and yellow 2·25 30
O 104. 30 c. red and yellow 35 15
O 105. 40 c. brown and yellow 65 15
O 106. 50 c. blue and yellow 70 15
O 112. 75 c. green and yellow 4·75 1·50
O 108a. 1 f. brown 8·00 1·75

1927. Nos. 108/15, 117 and 119 optd. **DIENSTMARKE.**
O128 10 c. brown 1·40 1·50
O129 15 c. green 1·75 6·50
O130 20 c. brown 1·40 1·10
O131 25 c. blue 1·75 4·50
O122 30 c. green 1·75 20
O133 40 c. brown 1·25 20
O134 50 c. red 1·25 20
O135 60 c. orange 90 20
O136 75 c. purple 1·25 55
O137 1 f. violet 1·75 30
O138 2 f. red 4·00 50

O 51. Arms.

1949.
O 264. O 51. 10 c. red 35 22·00
O 265. 30 c. black 25 22·00
O 266. 1 f. green 25 20
O 267. 2 f. red 1·40 1·25
O 268. 5 f. blue 45 20
O 269. 10 f. black 65 75
O 270. 12 f. mauve 5·50 7·00
O 271. 15 f. blue 65 20
O 272. 20 f. green 1·60 75
O 273. 30 f. mauve 2·00 4·00
O 274. 50 f. purple 2·00 3·25
O 275. 100 f. brown 90·00 £190

STE. MARIE DE MADAGASCAR Pt. 6

An island off the east coast of Madagascar. From 1898 used the stamps of Madagascar and Dependencies.

100 centimes = 1 franc.

1894. "Tablet" key-type inscr "STE MARIE DE MADAGASCAR" in red (1, 5, 15, 25, 75 c., 1 f.) or blue (others).
1 D 1 c. black on blue 65 65
2 2 c. brown on buff 90 80
3 4 c. brown on grey 2·75 2·25
4 5 c. green on green 5·50 5·00
5 10 c. black on lilac 7·75 4·75
6 15 c. blue 15·00 14·50
7 20 c. red on green 13·50 9·50
8 25 c. black on pink 7·50 6·75
9 30 c. brown on drab 6·75 6·25
10 40 c. red on yellow 8·25 6·00
11 50 c. red on pink 32·00 22·00
12 75 c. brown on orange 48·00 24·00
13 1 f. green 30·00 17·00

ST. PIERRE ET MIQUELON Pt. 6

A group of French islands off the S. coast of Newfoundland. The group became an Overseas Department of France on 1 July 1976. The stamps of France were used in the islands from 1 April 1978 until 3 February 1986. Separate issues for the group were reintroduced in 1986.

100 centimes = 1 franc.

1885. Stamps of French Colonies surch **S P M** and value in figures only.
1 J 5 on 2 c. brown on buff £4250 £1600
4 5 on 4 c. brown on grey £275 £200
8 05 on 20 c. red on green 17·00 21·00
9 H 05 on 35 c. black on yell 85·00 60·00
5 05 on 40 c. red on yellow 70·00 30·00
10 05 on 75 c. red £200 £150
11 05 on 1 f. green 17·00 15·00
6 10 on 40 c. red on yellow 18·00 15·00
7 15 on 40 c. red on yellow 17·00 15·00
3 25 on 1 f. green £1700 £1100

The surcharge on No. 1 is always inverted.

1891. French Colonies "Commerce" type surch **15 c. S P M.**
15 J 15 c. on 30 c. brn on drab 24·00 21·00
16 15 c. on 35 c. blk on orge £425 £300
17 15 c. on 40 c. red on yell 60·00 48·00

1891. Stamps of French Colonies, "Commerce" type, optd **ST-PIERRE M-on.**
23 J 1 c. black on blue 6·75 5·00
24 2 c. brown on buff 6·75 5·50
25 4 c. brown on grey 7·50 5·50
26 5 c. green on green 7·50 5·00
22 10 c. black on lilac 11·00 11·00
28 15 c. blue on blue 17·00 9·75
29 20 c. red on green 48·00 42·00
30 25 c. black on pink 18·00 12·00
31 30 c. brown on drab 70·00 60·00
32 35 c. black on orange £300 £225
33 40 c. red on yellow 48·00 42·00
34 75 c. red on pink 75·00 60·00
35 1 f. green 48·00 42·00

1891. Stamps of French Colonies, "Commerce" type, surch **ST-PIERRE M-on** and new value in figures and words (**cent.**) above and below opt.
36 J 1 c. on 5 c. green on green 5·00 4·25
37 1 c. on 10 c. black on lilac 6·75 5·50
38 1 c. on 25 c. black on pink 4·50 4·25
39 2 c. on 10 c. black on lilac 4·75 3·75
40 2 c. on 15 c. blue on blue 4·00 4·00
41 2 c. on 25 c. black on pink 4·00 4·00
42 4 c. on 20 c. red on green 4·00 3·75
43 4 c. on 25 c. black on pink 4·00 4·25
44 4 c. on 30 c. brn on drab 12·00 11·00
45 4 c. on 40 c. red on yellow 17·00 9·75

1892. Nos. 26 and 30 surch with figure only on top of opt.
49 J 1 on 5 c. green on green 6·50 3·75
46 1 on 25 c. black on pink 4·00 3·75
50 2 on 5 c. green on green 7·25 7·25
47 2 on 25 c. black on pink 4·00 3·75
51 4 on 5 c. green on green 7·25 6·50
48 4 on 25 c. black on pink 3·75 3·75

1892. Postage Due stamps of French Colonies optd **T ST-PIERRE M-on P.**
52. U. 10 c. black 21·00 21·00
53. 20 c. black 13·50 14·00
54. 30 c. black 15·00 15·00
55. 40 c. black 15·00 15·00
56. 60 c. black 70·00 70·00
57. 1 f. brown 95·00 95·00
58. 2 f. brown £160 £160
59. 5 f. brown £275 £275

1892. "Tablet" key-type inscr "ST. PIERRE ET MIQUELON".
60 D 1 c. black and red on blue 50 50
61 2 c. brown & blue on buff 45 55
62 4 c. brown & blue on grey 1·00 90
63 5 c. green and red 1·50 1·25
64 10 c. black & blue on lilac 3·50 2·50
74 10 c. red and blue 2·50 95
65 15 c. blue and red 4·75 1·90
75 15 c. grey and red 60·00 30·00
66 20 c. red & blue on green 15·00 11·00
67 25 c. black & red on pink 5·50 1·25
76 25 c. blue and red 8·75 6·25
68 30 c. brown & bl on drab 5·25 2·75
77 35 c. black & red on yell 3·75 3·50
69 40 c. red & blue on yellow 4·75 2·75
70 50 c. red and blue on pink 30·00 20·00
78 50 c. brown & red on blue 20·00 18·00
71 75 c. brown & red on orge 17·00 13·50
72 1 f. green and red 14·00 8·25

17. Fisherman.

18. Glaucous Gull.

19. Fishing Brigantine.

1909.
79 17 1 c. brown and red 20 25
80 2 c. blue and brown 20 25
81 4 c. brown and violet 20 30
82 5 c. olive and green 30 40
109 5 c. black and blue 20 30
83 10 c. red and pink 35 40
110 10 c. olive and green 30 40
111 10 c. mauve and bistre 30 40
84 15 c. red and purple 30 40
85 20 c. purple and brown 70 70
86 18 25 c. blue and deep blue 1·50 1·00
112 25 c. green and brown 45 50
87 30 c. brown and orange 75 70
113 30 c. red and carmine 45 45
114 30 c. blue and red 40 35
115 30 c. green and olive 40 45
88 35 c. brown and green 45 35
89 40 c. green and brown 1·75 1·10
90 45 c. green and violet 45 45
91 50 c. green and brown 75 70
116 50 c. light blue and blue 70 70
117 50 c. mauve and bistre 45 45
118 60 c. red and blue 45 45
119 65 c. brown and mauve 80 80
92 75 c. green and brown 70 70
120 90 c. red and scarlet 14·00 15·00
93 19 1 f. blue and green 2·00 1·40
121 1 f. 10 red and green 2·00 2·00
122 1 f. 50 blue & ultram 6·25 6·25
94 2 f. brown and violet 2·00 1·50
123 3 f. mauve on pink 6·00 6·25
95 5 f. green and brown 6·25 4·25

1912. "Tablet" issue surch in figures.
96 D 05 on 2 c. brown and blue on buff 1·40 1·40
97 05 on 4 c. brown and blue on grey 25 35
98 05 on 15 c. blue and red 35 35
99 05 on 20 c. red and blue on green 25 35
100 05 on 25 c. black and red on pink 30 35
101 05 on 30 c. brown and blue on drab 35 45
102 05 on 35 c. black and red on yellow 70 70
103 10 on 40 c. red and blue on yellow 30 30
104 10 on 50 c. red and blue 40 45
105 10 on 75 c. brown and red on orange 1·10 1·25
106 10 on 1 f. green and red 1·50 1·50

1915. Red Cross. Surch **5c** and red cross.
107 17 10 c.+5 c. red and pink 60 70
108 15 c.+5 c. red & purple 70 85

1924. Surch with new value.
124 17 25 c. on 15 c. red & pur 30 40
125 19 25 c. on 2 f. brown & vio 30 40
126 25 c. on 5 f. green & brn 30 40
127 18 65 on 45 c. green & vio 80 90
128 85 on 75 c. green & brn 80 90
129 90 c. on 75 c. red and scarlet 1·25 1·50
130 19 1 f. 25 on 1 f. ultramarine and blue 1·25 1·50
131 1 f. 50 on 1 f. blue and light blue 2·00 2·00
132 3 f. on 5 f. mauve & brn 1·60 1·75
133 10 f. on 5 f. green & red 10·00 10·50
134 20 f. on 5 f. red & violet 15·00 15·00

1931. International Colonial Exhibition, Paris, key-types inscr "ST. PIERRE ET MIQUELON".
135 E 40 c. green and black 1·75 1·75
136 F 50 c. mauve and black 1·75 1·60
137 G 90 c. red and black 1·75 1·75
138 H 1 f. 50 blue and black 1·75 1·75

27. Map of St. Pierre et Miquelon.

28. Galantry Lighthouse.

29. "Jacques Coeur" (trawler).

1932.
139 27 1 c. blue and purple 15 25
140 28 2 c. green and black 25 35
141 29 4 c. brown and red 25 40
142 5 c. brown and mauve 25 40
143 28 10 c. black and purple 35 45
144 15 c. mauve and blue 65 65
145 27 20 c. red and black 65 70
146 25 c. green and mauve 65 70
147 29 30 c. green and olive 70 70
148 40 c. brown and blue 70 70
149 28 45 c. green and red 70 65
150 50 c. green and brown 70 70
151 29 65 c. red and brown 95 1·00
152 27 75 c. red and green 95 95
153 90 c. scarlet and red 95 95
154 29 1 f. scarlet and red 70 70
155 27 1 f. 25 red and blue 95 95
156 1 f. 50 blue & deep blue 95 1·00
157 29 1 f. 75 brown and black 1·25 1·25
158 2 f. green and black 5·25 5·50
159 28 3 f. brown and green 7·00 7·00
160 5 f. brown and red 17·00 17·00
161 29 10 f. mauve and green 42·00 42·00
162 27 20 f. green and red 42·00 42·00

1934. 400th Anniv of Cartier's Discovery of Canada. Optd **JACQUES CARTIER 1534-1934.**
163 28 50 c. green and brown 1·60 1·75
164 27 75 c. red and green 2·00 2·00
165 1 f. 50 blue & deep blue 2·50 2·50
166 29 1 f. 75 brown and black 2·75 2·75
167 28 5 f. brown and red 19·00 19·00

32. Commerce.

39. Dog Team.

1937. International Exhibition, Paris.
168 32 20 c. violet 1·10 1·10
169 – 30 c. green 1·10 1·10
170 – 40 c. red 1·10 1·10
171 – 50 c. brown and blue 1·00 1·10
172 – 90 c. red 1·00 1·10
173 – 1 f. 50 blue 1·00 1·10

DESIGNS—VERT. 50 c. Agriculture. HORIZ. 30 c. Sailing ships. 40 c. Women of three races. 90 c. France extends Torch of Civilisation. 1 f. 50, Diane de Poitiers.

1938. International Anti-cancer Fund. As T 22 of Mauritania.
174 1 f. 75+50 c. blue 7·75 8·25

1938.

175. 39. 2 c. green 20 35
176. 3 c. brown 20 35
177. 4 c. purple 20 35
178. 5 c. red 20 30
179. 10 c. brown 25 30
180. 15 c. purple 25 35
181. 20 c. violet 25 35
182. 25 c. blue .. .. 1·00 1·25
183. – 30 c. purple 25 35
184. – 35 c. green 35 45
185. – 40 c. blue 25 35
186. – 45 c. green 30 35
187. – 50 c. red 25 35
188. – 55 c. blue .. .. 1·50 1·50
189. – 60 c. violet 25 35
190. – 65 c. brown .. .. 2·25 2·50
191. – 70 c. orange 35 35
192. – 80 c. violet 60 60
193. – 90 c. blue 35 35
194. – 1 f. red .. .. 5·75 6·00
195. – 1 f. olive 35 45
196. – 1 f. 25 red .. .. 1·10 1·10
197. – 1 f. 40 brown 45 50
198. – 1 f. 50 green 40 50
199. – 1 f. 60 purple 45 45
200. – 1 f. 75 blue 85 85
201. – 2 f. purple 30 40
202. – 2 f. 25 blue 55 55
203. – 2 f. 50 orange 85 80
204. – 3 f. brown 35 45
205. – 5 f. red 55 60
206. – 10 f. blue 85 85
207. – 20 f. olive .. .. 1·10 1·10

DESIGNS: 30 to 70 c. St. Pierre harbour. 80 c. to 1 f. 75 Pointe aux Canons lighthouse (wrongly inscr "PHARE DE LA TORTUE"). 2 to 20 f. Soldiers' Cove, Langlade.

1939. New York World's Fair. As T **28** of Mauritania.

208. 1 f. 25 red 80 85
209. 2 f. 25 blue 80 85

1939. 150th Anniv of French Revolution. As T **29** of Mauritania.

210 45 c.+25 c. green & black 5·50 5·50
211 70 c.+30 c. brown & black 5·50 5·50
212 90 c.+35 c. orange & black 5·50 5·50
213 1 f. 25+1 f. red and black 5·50 5·50
214 2 f. 25+2 f. blue and black 5·50 5·50

1941. Free French Plebiscite. Stamps of 1938 optd **Noel 1941 FRANCE LIBRE F. N. F. L.** or surch also.

215 39 10 c. brown .. .. 28·00 28·00
216 20 c. violet .. .. 28·00 28·00
217 25 c. blue .. .. 28·00 28·00
218 – 40 c. blue .. .. 28·00 28·00
219 – 45 c. green .. .. 28·00 28·00
220 – 65 c. brown .. .. 28·00 28·00
221 – 70 c. orange .. .. 28·00 28·00
222 – 80 c. violet .. .. 28·00 28·00
223 – 90 c. blue .. .. 28·00 28·00
224 – 1 f. green .. .. 28·00 28·00
225 – 1 f. 25 red .. .. 28·00 28·00
226 – 1 f. 40 brown .. .. 35·00 35·00
227 – 1 f. 60 purple .. .. 35·00 35·00
228 – 1 f. 75 blue .. .. 35·00 35·00
229 – 2 f. purple .. .. 35·00 35·00
230 – 2 f. 25 blue .. .. 35·00 35·00
231 – 2 f. 50 orange .. .. 35·00 35·00
232 – 3 f. brown .. .. 35·00 35·00
233 39 10 f. on 10 c. brown .. 60·00 60·00
234 – 20 f. on 90 c. blue .. 60·00 60·00

"F.N.F.L." = Forces Navales Francaises Libres (Free French Naval Forces).

1941. Various stamps optd **FRANCE LIBRE F. N. F. L.** or surch also.

(a) Nos. 111 and 114.

245. 17. 10 c. mauve and bistre .. £750 £750
246. 18. 30 c. blue and lake .. £750 £750

(b) On stamps of 1932.

247. 28. 2 c. green and black .. £160 £160
248. 29. 4 c. brown and red .. 35·00 35·00
249. 5 c. brown and mauve .. £600 £600
250. 40 c. brown and blue .. 10·50 10·50
251. 28. 45 c. green and red .. £120 £120
252. 50 c. green and brown .. 8·25 8·25
253. 29. 65 c. red and brown .. 24·00 24·00
254. 1 f. red and brown .. £250 £250
255. 1 f. 75 brown and black 8·25 8·25
256. 2 f. green and black .. 11·00 11·00
257. 28. 5 f. brown and red .. £225 £225
258. 29. 5 f. on 1 f. 75 brn. & blk. 9·75 9·75

(c) On stamps of 1938.

259. 39. 2 c. green £300 £300
260. 3 c. brown .. .. 90·00 90·00
261. 4 c. purple .. .. 70·00 70·00
262. 5 c. red £625 £625
263. 10 c. brown .. .. 9·00 9·00
264. 15 c. purple £1000 £1000
265. 20 c. violet £140 £140
266. 20 c. on 10 c. brown .. 7·00 7·00
267. 25 c. blue .. .. 9·00 9·00
268. 30 c. on 10 c. brown .. 4·75 4·75
269. – 35 c. green £525 £525
270. – 40 c. blue .. .. 11·00 11·00
271. – 45 c. green .. .. 11·00 11·00
272. – 55 c. blue £6000 £6000
273. – 60 c. violet £400 £400
274. – 60 c. on 90 c. blue .. 5·50 5·50
275. – 65 c. brown .. .. 14·00 14·00
276. – 70 c. orange .. .. 24·00 24·00
277. – 80 c. violet £300 £300
278. – 90 c. blue .. .. 12·50 12·50
279. – 1 f. green .. .. 14·00 14·00
280. – 1 f. 25 red .. .. 11·00 11·00
281. – 1 f. 40 brown .. .. 9·75 9·75
282. – 1 f. 50 green £550 £550
283. – 1 f. 50 on 90 c. blue .. 8·25 8·25
284. – 1 f. 60 purple .. .. 11·00 11·00
285. – 2 f. purple .. .. 42·00 42·00
286. – 2 f. 25 blue .. .. 11·00 11·00
287. – 2 f. 50 orange .. .. 14·00 14·00
288. 7. 2 f. 50 on 10 c. brown .. 11·00 11·00
289. – 3 f. brown £6500 £6500
290. – 5 f. red £1500 £1500
291. 7. 10 f. on 10 c. brown .. 38·00 38·00
292. – 20 f. olive £575 £575
293. – 20 f. on 90 c. blue .. 42·00 42·00

(d) On Nos. 208/9.

294. 1 f. 25 red .. .. 8·25 8·25
295. 2 f. 25 blue .. .. 7·75 8·25
296. 2 f. 50 on 1 f. 25 red .. 11·00 11·00
297. 3 f. on 2 f. 25 blue .. 11·00 11·00

1942. Stamps of 1932 optd **FRANCE LIBRE F. N. F. L.** or surch also.

304 27 20 c. red and black .. £250 £250
305 75 c. red and green .. 14·00 14·00
306 1 f. 25 red and blue .. 11·00 11·00
307 1 f. 50 blue & deep blue £300 £300
308 10 f. on 1 f. 25 red & bl 24·00 24·00
309 20 f. on 75 c. red & green 35·00 35·00

1942. Social Welfare Fund. Nos. 279 and 287 further surch. **OEUVRES SOCIALES,** cross and premium.

320. 1 f.+50 c. green .. .. 35·00 35·00
321. 2 f. 50+1 f. orange .. 35·00 35·00

54. Soldiers' Cove, Langlade.

55. Allegory of Fishing.

47. Fishing Schooner.

1942. (a) Postage.

322 47 5 c. blue 20 30
323 10 c. pink 15 25
324 25 c. green 15 25
325 30 c. black 15 25
326 40 c. blue 15 25
327 60 c. purple 15 25
328 1 f. violet 25 35
329 1 f. 50 red 60 70
330 2 f. brown 35 45
331 2 f. 50 blue 65 70
332 4 f. orange 35 45
333 5 f. purple 35 45
334 10 f. blue 60 70
335 20 f. green .. .. 1·00 1·10

(b) Air. As T **30** of New Caledonia.

336. 1 f. orange 25 35
337. 1 f. 50 red 25 35
338. 5 f. purple 35 45
339. 10 f. black 60 70
340. 25 f. blue 75 85
341. 50 f. green .. .. 85 1·00
342. 100 f. red .. .. 1·25 1·40

1944. Mutual Aid and Red Cross Funds. As T **31** of New Caledonia.

343. 5 f.+20 f. blue .. .. 80 1·00

1945. Eboue. As T **32** of New Caledonia.

344. 2 f. black 50 60
345. 25 f. green 75 85

1945. Surch.

346. 47. 50 c. on 5 c. blue .. 25 35
347. 70 c. on 5 c. blue .. 25 35
348. 80 c. on 5 c. blue .. 30 40
349. 1 f. 20 on 5 c. blue .. 30 40
350. 2 f. 40 on 25 c. green .. 30 40
351. 3 f. on 25 c. green .. 45 55
352. 4 f. 50 on 25 c. green .. 80 90
353. 15 f. on 2 f. 50 blue .. 1·00 1·10

1946. Air. Victory. As T **34** of New Caledonia.

354. 8 f. red .. .. 75 1·00

1946. Air. From Chad to the Rhine. As Nos. 300/305 of New Caledonia.

355. 5 f. red 80 85
356. 10 f. lilac 80 85
357. 15 f. black .. .. 90 1·00
358. 20 f. violet .. .. 90 1·00
359. 25 f. brown .. .. 1·60 1·75
360. 50 f. black .. .. 1·60 1·75

56. Aircraft and Wrecked Fishing Schooner.

1947.

361. 54. 10 c. brown (postage) .. 15 25
362. 30 c. violet 15 25
363. 40 c. purple 15 30
364. 50 c. blue 15 30
365. 55. 60 c. red 25 35
366. 80 c. blue 25 40
367. 1 f. green 25 35
368. – 1 f. 20 green 40 45
369. – 1 f. 50 black 40 45
370. – 2 f. red 40 35
371. – 3 f. violet 85 90
372. – 3 f. 60 red 80 85
373. – 4 f. purple 75 70
374. – 5 f. yellow 80 80
375. – 6 f. blue 80 80
376. – 8 f. sepia .. .. 1·25 1·00
377. – 10 f. green .. .. 1·10 95
378. – 15 f. green .. .. 1·25 1·25
379. – 17 f. blue .. .. 2·00 1·50
380. – 20 f. red .. .. 1·25 1·25
381. – 25 f. blue .. .. 1·50 1·50
382. – 50 f. green and red (air) 3·25 2·50
383. 56. 100 f. green .. .. 4·75 3·75
384. – 200 f. blue and red .. 8·75 4·75

DESIGNS—As Type **55**: 1 f. 20 to 2 f. Cross and fishermen. 3 f. to 4 f. Weighing fish. 5 f., 6 f., 10 f. Trawler "Colonel Pleven". 8 f., 17 f. Red fox. 15 f., 20 f., 25 f. Windswept mountain landscape. As Type **56**: 50 f. Aircraft and fishing village. 200 f. Aircraft and snow-bound fishing schooner.

1949. Air. 75th Anniv. of U.P.U. As T **38** of New Caledonia.

395. 25 f. multicoloured .. 7·50 8·50

1950. Colonial Welfare Fund. As T **39** of New Caledonia.

396 10 f.+2 f. red and brown 3·00 3·50

1952. Centenary of Military Medal. As T **40** of New Caledonia.

397 8 f. blue, yellow and green 3·50 4·25

1954. Air. 10th Anniv. of Liberation. As T **42** of New Caledonia.

398. 15 f. red and brown .. 4·50 4·75

62. Refrigeration Plant.

63. Codfish.

64. Dog and Coastal Scene.

1955.

399 62 30 c. blue & dp bl (post) 25 25
400 63 40 c. brown and blue .. 15 30
401 62 50 c. brown, grey & blk 20 35
402 63 1 f. brown and green .. 25 35
403 2 f. indigo and blue .. 25 35
404 62 3 f. purple 40 40
405 – 4 f. purple, red and lake 50 50
406 – 10 f. brown, blue & turq 75 70
407 – 20 f. multicoloured .. 2·00 1·50
408 – 25 f. brown, green & bl 2·75 2·25
409 62 40 f. multicoloured .. 1·60 1·60
410 64 50 f. multicoloured (air) 24·00 15·00
411 – 100 f. black and grey .. 8·50 6·50
412 – 500 f. indigo and blue 35·00 19·00

DESIGNS—As Type **62/3**: 4 f., 10 f. Pointe aux Canons Lighthouse and fishing dinghies. 20 f. Ice hockey players. 25 f. American minks. As Type **64**: 100 f. Sud Aviation Caravelle airliner over St. Pierre and Miquelon. 500 f. Douglas DC-3 over St. Pierre port.

65. Trawler "Galantry".

67. "Picea".

1956. Economic and Social Development Fund.

413. 65. 15 f. sepia and brown .. 1·25 90

1958. 10th Anniv. of Declaration of Human Rights. As T **48** of New Caledonia.

414. 20 f. brown and blue .. 1·50 1·25

1959.

415 67 5 f. multicoloured .. 1·25 90

68. Flaming Torches.

1959. Air. Adoption of Constitution.

416. 68. 200 f. grn., lake & violet 9·50 6·50

69. "Cypripedium acaule".

1962. Flowers.

417. 69. 25 f. purple, orange and green (postage) .. 3·50 3·25
418. – 50 f. red and green .. 5·50 3·50
419. – 100 f. orange, red and green (air) .. .. 8·50 3·50

DESIGNS—VERT. 50 f. "Calopogon pulchellus". HORIZ. (48×27 mm.): 100 f. "Sarracenia purpurea".

70. Submarine "Surcouf" and Map.

1962. Air. 20th Anniv. of Adherence to Free French Government.

420. 70. 500 f. black, blue & red £100 70·00

1962. Air. 1st Transatlantic TV Satellite Link. As T **50** of New Caledonia.

421 50 f. brown, green & sepia 5·50 3·50

72. Eiders.

73. Dr. A. Calmette.

1963. Birds.

422. 72. 50 c. bistre, blk. & bl. 1·00 65
423. – 1 f. brown, mauve & blue 1·25 80
424. – 2 f. brown, blk. & blue, 1·40 1·10
425. – 6 f. bistre, bl. & turq. 2·50 1·60

DESIGNS: 1 f. Rock ptarmigan. 2 f. Semi-palmated plovers. 6 f. Blue-winged teal.

1963. Birth Centenary of Dr. Albert Calmette (bacteriologist).

426. 73. 30 f. brown, and blue 6·00 3·50

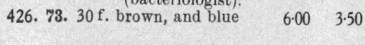

74. Landing of Governor from "Garonne".

1963. Air. Bicent. of Arrival of First Governor (Dangeac) in St. Pierre and Miquelon.

427. 74. 200 f. blue, grn. & brn. 15·00 8·00

1963. Red Cross Centenary. As T **53** of New Caledonia.

428 25 f. red, grey and blue .. 7·00 4·00

1963. 15th Anniv. of Declaration of Human Rights. As T **54** of New Caledonia.

429. 20 f. orange, purple & blue 4·00 2·25

1964. "PHILATEC 1964" Int. Stamp Exn., Paris. As T **54c** of New Caledonia.

430. 60 f. blue, green and purple 8·00 6·00

ANIMALS: 4 f. Red fox. 5 f. Roe deer. 34 f. Charolais bull.

78. Common Rabbits.

1964. Fauna.

431. 78. 3 f. choc., brown & green 1·40 1·10
432. – 4 f. sepia, blue and green 2·00 1·40
433. – 5 f. brown, sepia & blue 2·50 1·90
434. – 34 f. brown, green & blue 6·00 3·50

79. Airliner and Map.

1964. Air. 1st St. Pierre-New York Airmail Flight.

435. 79. 100 f. brown and blue .. 10·00 5·50

1965. Centenary of I.T.U. As T **56** of New Caledonia.

436 40 f. blue, brown & purple 17·00 6·50

1966. Air. Launching of 1st French Satellite. As Nos. 398/9 of New Caledonia.

437. 25 f. brown, blue and red .. 5·00 3·50
438. 30 f. brown, blue and red .. 5·00 3·50

1966. Air. Launching of Satellite "D1". As T **56e** of New Caledonia.

439. 48 f. blue, green and lake .. 6·50 4·50

83. "Revanche" and Settlers.

1966. Air. 150th Anniv. of Return of Islands to France.

440. 83. 100 f. multicoloured .. 10·00 4·50

84. "Journal Officiel" and Old and New Printing Presses.

86. Trawler and Harbour Plan.

85. Map and Fishing Dinghies.

1966. Air. Centenary of "Journal Officiel" Printing Works.

441. 84. 60 f. plum, lake and blue 9·00 4·00

1967. Air. Pres. De Gaulle's Visit.

442. 85. 25 f. brown, blue & red 20·00 11·00
443. – 100 f. blue, turq. & pur. 30·00 20·00

DESIGN: 100 f. Maps and cruiser "Richelieu".

1967. Opening of St. Pierre's New Harbour.

444. 86. 48 f. brown, blue & red 5·00 2·75

87. Map and Control Tower.

1967. Opening of St. Pierre Airport.

445. 87. 30 f. multicoloured .. 2·25 1·40

88. T.V. Receiver, Aerial and Map.

1967. Inaug. of Television Service.

446. 88. 40 f. red, green & olive 5·00 2·75

89. Speed Skating.

91. J. D. Cassini (discoverer of group), Compasses and Chart.

1968. Air. Winter Olympic Games, Grenoble. Multicoloured.

447. 50 f. Type **89** .. .. 6·00 3·50
448. 60 f. Ice-hockey goalkeeper 7·50 4·50

1968. 20th Anniv. of W.H.O. As T **68** of New Caledonia.

449. 10 f. red, yellow and blue 5·50 2·75

1968. Famous Visitors to St. Pierre and Miquelon (1st series).

450. 91. 4 f. brown, yellow & lake 2·75 2·25
451. – 6 f. multicoloured .. 3·50 2·50
452. – 15 f. multicoloured .. 4·50 3·00
453. – 25 f. multicoloured .. 7·00 4·50

CELEBRITIES: 6 f. Rene de Chateaubriand and warship. 15 f. Prince de Joinville, "Belle Poule" (sail frigate) and "Cassard" (survey ship). 25 f. Admiral Gauchet and flagship "Provence" (Ile aux Chiens expedition).

1968. Human Rights Year. As T **69** of New Caledonia.

454. 20 f. red, blue & yell. 7·00 4·00

93. War Memorial, St. Pierre.

1968. Air. 50th Anniv. of Armistice.

455. 93. 500 f. multicoloured .. 18·00 14·00

1969. Air. 1st Flight of "Concorde". As T **75** of New Caledonia.

456. 34 f. brown & olive .. 20·00 10·00

95. Mountain Stream, Langlade.

1969. Tourism.

457. 95. 5 f. brn., bl. & grn. (post. 3·50 2·25
458. – 15 f. brown, green & blue 4·00 3·00
459. – 50 f. purple, ol. & bl. (air) 10·00 5·50
460. – 100 f. brn., ind. & blue .. 18·00 11·00

DESIGNS: 15 f. River-bank, Debon, Langlade. 50 f. Wild Horses, Miquelon. 100 f. Gathering wood, Miquelon. The 50 f. and 100 f. are larger (48 × 27 mm.).

96. Treasury.

1969. Public Buildings and Monuments.

461. 96. 10 f. black, red and blue 2·75 1·60
462. – 25 f. red, ultram. & blue 4·50 2·75
463. – 30 f. brown, green & blue 5·00 3·50
464. – 60 f. black, red and blue 10·00 5·50

DESIGNS: 25 f. Maritime Fisheries Scientific and Technical Institute. 30 f. Unknown Sailor's Monument. 60 f. St. Christopher's College.

97. "L'Estoile" and Granville, 1690.

1969. Maritime Links with France.

465. 97. 34 f. lake, green and emerald (postage) .. 7·50 3·00
466. – 40 f. green, red & bistre 10·00 5·00
467. – 48 f. multicoloured .. 13·50 8·00
468. – 200 f. black, lake and green (air) .. 30·00 11·00

DESIGNS—As Type **97**: 40 f. "La Jolie" and St. Jean de Luz, 1750. 48 f. "La Juste" and La Rochelle, 1860. 48 × 27 mm: 200 f. "L'Esperance" and St. Malo, 1600.

98. Pierre Loti, Ship and Book Titles.

1969. Air. Pierre Loti (explorer and writer) Commemoration.

469 98 300 f. multicoloured .. 35·00 20·00

99. Ringed Seals.

1969. Marine Animals.

470. 99. 1 f. brn., purple & lake 4·00 2·25
471. – 3 f. blue, green and red 4·00 2·25
472. – 4 f. green, brown and red 4·00 2·25
473. – 6 f. violet, green and red 4·00 2·25

DESIGNS: 3 f. Sperm whales. 4 f. Long-finned pilot whale. 6 f. Common dolphins.

1969. 50th Anniv. of Int. Labour Organization. As T **79** of New Caledonia.

474. 20 f. brown, slate & salmon 6·50 2·75

1970. New U.P.U. Headquarters Building, Berne. As T **81** of New Caledonia.

475. 25 f. brown, blue & red 6·50 2·75
476. 34 f. slate, brown & purple 10·00 5·50

102. Rocket and Japanese Women.

104. "Rubus chamaemorus".

103. Rowing Fours.

1970. Air. World Fair "EXPO 70", Osaka, Japan.

477. 102. 34 f. brn., lake & blue 11·00 5·50
478. – 85 f. blue, red & orge. 20·00 11·00

DESIGN—HORIZ. 85 f. "Mountain Landscape" (Y. Taikan) and Expo "star".

1970. World Rowing Championships. St. Catherine, Canada.

479. 103. 20 f. brn., bl. & pale bl. 6·00 3·50

1970. Fruit Plants.

480. 104. 3 f. green, pur. & brn. 1·40 80
481. – 4 f. yell., red and green 1·60 1·00
482. – 5 f. red, green & violet 1·75 1·40
483. – 6 f. violet, green & purple 3·00 1·60

PLANTS: 4 f. "Fragaria vesca". 5 f. "Rubus idaeus". 6 f. "Vaccinium myrtillus".

105. Ewe and Lamb.

1970. Livestock Breeding.

484. 105. 15 f. brown, purple & grn. 4·50 2·75
485. – 30 f. brn., grey and green 5·50 2·75
486. – 34 f. brn., purple & gree 8·00 5·00
487. – 48 f. purple, brn. & bl. 8·50 4·00

DESIGNS: 30 f. Animal quarantine station. 34 f. Charolais bull. 48 f. Refrigeration plant and "Narrando" (trawler).

106. Etienne Francois, Duke of Choiseul, and Warships.

1970. Air. Celebrities of St. Pierre and Miquelon.

488. 106. 25 f. brown, blue & pur. 5·50 2·75
489. – 50 f. brown, purple & grn. 10·00 6·50
490. – 60 f. brown, green & pur. 12·50 6·00

DESIGNS 50 f. Jacques Cartier and "Grande Hermine". 60 f. Sebastien Le Gonard de Sourdeval and 17th-century French galleons.

107. "St. Francis of Assisi", 1900.

1971. Fisheries' Protection Vessels.

491. 107. 30 f. red, blue & turq... 21·00 8·50
492. – 35 f. brn., grn. & blue .. 23·00 9·50
493. – 40 f. brn., blue & green 23·00 9·50
494. – 80 f. blk., grn. & blue .. 27·00 18·00

DESIGNS: 35 f. "St. Jehanne", 1920. 40 f. "L'Aventure, 1950. 80 f. "Commandant Bourdais", 1970.

108. "Aconite".

1971. 30th Anniv of Allegiance to Free French Movement. British Corvettes on loan to Free French.

495 108 22 f. black, green & bl 11·00 8·00
496 – 25 f. brown, turq & bl 11·00 8·00
497 – 50 f. black, turq & blue 22·00 16·00

DESIGNS: 25 f. "Alyssum". 50 f. "Mimosa".

109. Ship's Bell.

111. Haddock.

1971. St. Pierre Museum. Multicoloured.

498. 20 f. Type **109** .. .. 6·50 3·50
499. 45 f. Navigational instruments and charts (horiz.) 10·00 4·50

1971. 1st Death Anniv. of De Gaulle. As Nos. 493/4 of New Caledonia.

500. 35 f. black and red .. 9·00 5·50
501. 45 f. black and red .. 13·50 7·75

1972. Ocean Fish.

502 111 2 f. indigo, red & blue 3·50 2·25
503 – 3 f. brown and green 3·50 2·25
504 – 5 f. red and blue .. 5·00 2·75
505 – 10 f. green and emerald 8·50 4·50

DESIGNS: 3 f. Dab. 5 f. Sea perch. 10 c. Cod.

112. De Gaulle and Servicemen.

1972. Air. General De Gaulle Commem.
506. **112.** 100 f. brn., grn. & pur. 20·00 10·00

113. Long-tailed Ducks. 116. Swimming Pool.

114. Montcalm and Warships.

1973. Currency Revaluation.
507 **113** 6 c. brown, purple and blue (postage) .. 1·10 90
508 – 10 c. black, red & blue 1·40 1·10
509 – 20 c. bis, ultram & bl 1·60 1·10
510 **113** 40 c. brown, grn & vio 2·50 1·60
511 – 70 c. black, red & green 3·50 1·90
512 – 90 c. bistre, blue & pur 9·00 6·00
513 **114** 1 f. 60 violet, indigo and blue (air) .. 5·00 2·75
514 – 2 f. purple, green & vio 6·50 3·50
515 – 4 f. green, mve & brn 11·00 5·50
DESIGNS—As Type **113**. 10 c., 70 c. Atlantic puffins. 20 c., 90 c. Snowy owls. As Type **114**. HORIZ. 4 f. La Salle, map and warships. VERT. 2 f. Frontenac and various scenes.

1973. Inaug. of St. Pierre Cultural Centre.
521. **116.** 60 c. brn., blue and red 4·50 2·50
522. – 1 f. purple, orge. and blue 5·50 2·75
DESIGN: 1 f. Centre building.

117. "Transall C-160" in flight.

1973. Air.
523. **117.** 10 f. multicoloured .. 35·00 20·00

118. Met. Balloon and Weather Ship. 120. Clasped Hands on Red Cross.

119. Northern Gannet with Letter.

1974. World Meteorological Day.
524. **118.** 1 f. 60 blue, green & red 9·50 5·00

1974. Cent of Universal Postal Union.
525 **119** 70 c. ultram, bl & red 4·50 2·25
526 90 c. blue, red and lake 6·00 3·50

1974. Campaign for Blood Donors.
527. **120.** 1 f. 50 multicoloured .. 9·00 4·50

121. Arms and Map of Islands.

1974. Air.
528. **121.** 2 f. multicoloured .. 10·00 4·50

122. Banknotes in "Fish" Money-box. 123. Copernicus and Famous Scientists.

1974. Cent. of St. Pierre Savings Bank.
529. **122.** 50 c. brown, blue & black 4·50 2·50

1974. Air. 500th Birth Anniv. (1973) of Nicholas Copernicus (astronomer).
530. **123.** 4 f. violet, red and blue 12·00 6·00

124. St. Pierre Church and Caspian Tern, Kittiwake and Great Auk.

1974. Island Churches.
531. **124.** 6 c. black, brn. & green 2·75 1·10
532. – 10 c. ind., blue & brown 2·75 1·10
533. – 20 c. multicoloured .. 4·00 2·25
DESIGNS: 10 c. Miquelon Church an fish. 20 c. Our Lady of the Seamen Church and fishermen.

125. Red Admiral. 126. Cod and St.-Pierre et Miquelon Stamp of 1909.

1986. Christmas.

1975. Butterflies. Multicoloured.
534 1 f. Type **125** .. .. 6·00 2·25
535 1 f. 20 Orange tiger .. 7·00 3·50

1975. Air. "Arphila 75" International Stamp Exhibition, Paris.
536. **126.** 4 f. red, indigo and blue 15·00 7·00

127. "Pottery" (Potter's Wheel and products). 128. Pointe–Plate Lighthouse and Brunnich's Gillemot and Double-crested Cormorant.

1975. Artisan Handicrafts.
537. **127.** 50 c. pur., brn. and grn. 4·00 2·25
538. – 60 c. blue and yellow .. 4·00 2·25
DESIGNS: 60 c. "Sculpture" (Wood-carving of Virgin and Child).

1975. Lighthouses.
539. **128.** 6 c. black violet & green 1·60 1·10
540. – 10 c. purple, green & slate 2·75 1·60
541. – 20 c brn., indigo & blue 4·00 2·75
DESIGNS: 10 c. Galantry Lighthouse, Atlantic puffin and pintail. 20 c. Cap Blanc Lighthouse and blue whale.

129. Judo.

1975. Air. "Pre-Olympic Year". Olympic Games, Montreal (1976).
542. **129.** 1 f. 90 blue, red & violet 6·50 3·50

130. "Concorde" in Flight.

1976. Air. "Concorde's" First Commercial Flight.
543. **130.** 10 f. indigo, blue & red 22·00 11·00

1976. President Pompidou Commemoration. As T **125** of New Caledonia.
544 1 f. 10 grey and purple .. 5·50 3·50

132. Alexander Graham Bell and Early Telephone. 134. Basketball.

133. Washington and Lafayette.

1976. Air. Telephone Centenary.
545. **132.** 5 f. blue, orange and red 7·50 4·00

1976. Bicent. of American Revolution.
546. **133.** 1 f. multicoloured .. 4·50 2·75

1976. Olympic Games, Montreal.
547 **134** 70 c. agate, blue & brn 3·50 2·75
548 – 2 f. 50 turq, grn & emer 10·00 5·00
DESIGN—HORIZ. 2 f. 50, Swimming.

135. Vigie Dam.

1976.
549. **135.** 2 f. 20 brn., blue & turq. 5·75 4·00

136. "Croix de Lorraine."

1976. Stern Trawlers. Multicoloured.
550 1 f. 20 Type **136** .. .. 5·50 3·50
551 1 f. 40 "Geolette" .. 10·00 5·50

1986. Nos. 2444 etc. of France optd. **ST-PIERRE ET MIQUELON.**
552. **916.** 5 c. green 30 30
553. 10 c. red 20 20
554. 20 c. green 20 20
555. 30 c. red 20 20
556. 40 c. brown 20 20
557. 50 c. mauve 20 20
558. 1 f. green 30 30
559. 1 f. 80 green 55 40
560. 2 f. green 65 45
561. 2 f. 20 red 80 45
562. 3 f. brown .. .. 1·10 90
563. 3 f. 20 blue .. .. 1·25 90
564. 4 f. red .. .. 1·40 1·00
565. 5 f. blue .. .. 1·75 1·50
566. 10 f. violet .. .. 3·50 2·25

138. Open Book.

1986. 450th Anniv of Discovery of Islands by Jacques Cartier and 1st Anniv of New Constitution.
567 **138** 2 f. 20 brown, deep brown and green .. 1·40 80

139. Statue and Harbour.

1986. Centenary of Statue of Liberty.
568. **139.** 2 f. 50 blue and red .. 1·50 90

141. Fish and Detection Equipment. 142. "Nativity". (stained glass window, L. Balmet).

1986. Fishing.
578 **141** 1 f. red 50 35
579 1 f. 10 orange .. 45 35
580 1 f. 30 red 55 35
581 1 f. 40 blue 70 45
582 1 f. 40 red 55 35
583 1 f. 50 blue 65 45
584 1 f. 60 green 80 45
585 1 f. 70 green 65 45

586. **142.** 2 f. 20 multicoloured .. 1·40 80

143. Buff Cap ("Hygrophorus pratensis").

1987.
587 **143** 2 f. 50 brown and ochre 1·50 90
See also Nos. 598, 609 and 645.

144. Dunan and Hospital.

1987. Dr. Francois Dunan Commemoration.
588. **144.** 2 f. 20 black, brown and blue .. .. 1·00 65

145. Ocean-racing Yachts.

1987. Transatlantic Yacht Race (Lorient–St. Pierre et Miquelon–Lorient.
589. **145.** 5 f. brown, deep blue and blue .. .. 2·25 1·10

146. Maps.

1987. Visit of President Francois Mitterand.
590. **146.** 2 f. 20 multicoloured 1·40 90

147. Schooner on Slipway and Share Certificate.

1987. Centenary of Marine Slipway.
591. **147.** 2 f. 50 brown and light brown .. .. 1·40 90

148. Hawker-Siddeley "HS. 748". (St. Pierre–Montreal first flight, 1987).

1987. Air. Airplanes named "Ville de St. Pierre".
592 **148** 5 f. blue, green & turq 2·25 1·10
593 – 10 f. dp blue, bl & orge 4·50 2·25
DESIGN: 10 f. Latecoere 522 flying boat (first flight, 1939).

149. "La Normande" (trawler).

1987.
594. **149.** 3 f. multicoloured .. 2·25 1·60

150. "St. Christopher carrying Christ Child" (stained glass window by L. Balmet) and Scout Emblem.

1987. Christmas. 50th Anniv. of Scouting.
595. **150.** 2 f. 20 multicoloured 1·25 80

151. Horses and Ducks.

1987. Natural Heritage. Le Grand Barachois. Each orange, green and brown.
596 3 f. Type **151** .. .. 1·60 1·00
597 3 f. Canada geese, gulls and seals .. .. 1·60 1·00
Nos. 596/7 were printed together, se-tenant, with intervening half stamp-size label, each strip forming a composite design.

1988. Fungi. As T **143.**
598 2 f. 50 black, orange & brn 1·00 65
DESIGN: "Russula paludosa".

152. Ice Hockey Goalkeeper.

1988. Winter Olympic Games, Calgary.
599. **152.** 5 f. blue and red .. 2·00 1·40

153 Thomas and Camera

1988. Birth Centenary of Dr. Louis Thomas (photographer).
600 **153** 2 f. 20 brown, deep brown and blue .. 90 55

154 Airship "Hindenburg"

1988. Air. Aircraft. Each black, blue and purple.
601 5 f. Type **154** .. .. 2·25 1·10
602 10 f. Douglas "DC 3" .. 4·50 2·25

1988. "Philexfrance 89" International Stamp Exhibition, Paris. No. 2821 of France optd. **ST-PIERRE ET MIQUELON.**
603 **1073** 2 f. 20 red, black & blue 1·50 80

156 "Nellie J. Banks" and Crates

1988. 50th Anniv of End of Prohibition and Last Liquor Smuggling Run from St.-Pierre to Canada.
604 **156** 2 f. 50 ultram, brn & bl 1·50 90

157 "Le Marmouset" (stern trawler)

1988.
605 **157** 3 f. multicoloured .. 1·40 90
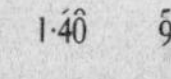

158 Ross Cove

1988. Natural Heritage. Each brown, deep blue and blue.
606 2 f. 20 Type **158** 80 55
607 13 f. 70 Cap Perce .. 4·50 3·25

159 Stained Glass Window

160 Judo

1988. Christmas.
608 **159** 2 f. 20 multicoloured .. 80 55

1989. Fungi. As T **143.**
609 2 f. 50 brown and red .. 80 45
DESIGN: 2 f. 50, "Tricholoma virgatum".

1989. 25th Anniv of Judo in St. Pierre.
610 **160** 5 f. black, green & orge 1·75 1·10

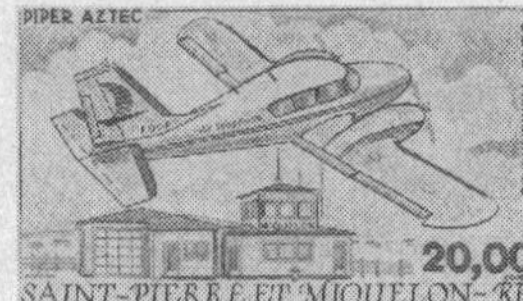

161 "Liberty" (Roger Druet)

1989. Bicentenary of French Revolution and Declaration of Rights of Man. Multicoloured.
611 2 f. 20 Type **161** 95 65
612 2 f. 20 "Equality" .. 95 65
613 2 f. 20 "Fraternity" .. 95 65

162 "Piper "Aztec"

1989. Air.
614 **162** 20 f. brown, light brown and blue .. 5·50 2·75

164 Fisherman in Boat

1989. Natural Heritage. Ile aux Marins. Each brown, blue and green.
616 2 f. 20 Type **164** 85 60
617 13 f. 70 Boy flying kite from boat .. 5·25 3·75

165 "Le Malabar" (ocean-going tug)

1989.
618 **165** 3 f. multicoloured .. 1·00 60

166 Georges Landry and Emblem

1989. Centenary of Islands' Bank.
619 **166** 2 f. 20 blue and brown 80 45

167 "Christmas" (Magali Olano)

1989. Christmas.
620 **167** 2 f. 20 multicoloured .. 65 45

1990. Stamps of France optd **ST-PIERRE ET MIQUELON.**

621	**1118**	10 c. brown	10	10
622		20 c. green	10	10
623		50 c. violet	10	10
624		1 f. orange	20	10
625		2 f. green	45	25
626		2 f. 10 green	45	25
627		2 f. 20 green	50	30
628		2 f. 30 red	50	30
629		2 f. 40 green	55	35
630		2 f. 50 red	55	35
631		3 f. 20 blue	70	40
632		3 f. 40 blue	75	45
633		3 f. 50 green	80	50
634		3 f. 80 mauve ..	85	50
635		4 f. mauve	90	55
636		4 f. 20 mauve ..	95	55
637		4 f. 40 blue	1·00	60
638		5 f. blue	1·10	65
639		10 f. violet	2·25	1·40

The 2 f. 50 exists both perforated (ordinary gum) and imperforate (self-adhesive).

1990. Fungi. As T **143.**
645 2 f. 50 brown, black & orge 90 55
DESIGN: 2 f. 50, Hedgehog fungus "Hydnum repandum".

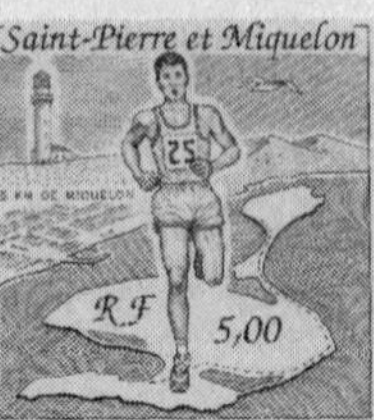

168 "Pou du Ciel" and Gull

1990. Air.
646 **168** 5 f. green, blue & brown 1·40 90

169 De Gaulle and Soldiers

1990. 50th Anniv of De Gaulle's Call to Resist.
647 **169** 2 f. 30 purple, red & bl 80 45
For design as T **169** but inscr "1890–1970", see No. 653.

170 Runner and Map

1990. Miquelon 25 Km. Race.
648 **170** 5 f. black, blue & brown 1·25 55

171 Moose, Micmac Canoe and Woman

1990.

649 171 2 f. 50 orange, brn & bl 80 45

172 "Saint-Denis" and "Saint-Pierre" at Moorings

1990. Trawlers.

650 172 3 f. multicoloured .. 90 60

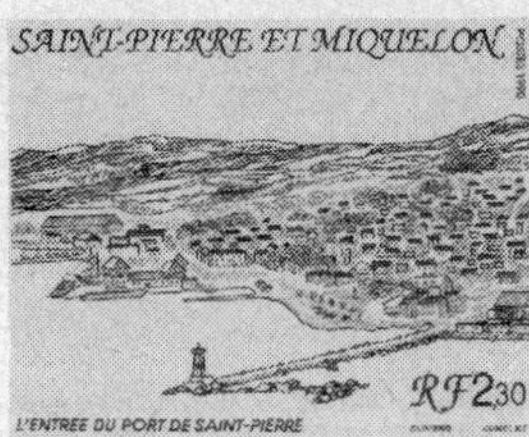

173 Entrance to Saint-Pierre Port

1990. St.-Pierre. Each brown, green and blue.

651 2 f. 30 Type **173** 75 45
652 14 f. 50 Interpeche fish factory .. .. .. 4·00 2·40

Nos. 651/2 were issued together, se-tenant, with intervening label, forming a composite design of part of St.-Pierre coastline.

1990. Birth Centenary of Charles de Gaulle (French statesman). As T **169** but inscribed "1890–1970". Each purple, red and blue.

653 1 f. 70 Type **169** 55 35
654 2 f. 30 De Gaulle and trawler 70 45

174 Christmas Scene (Cindy Lechevallier)

1990. Christmas.

655 174 2 f. 30 multicoloured .. 65 45

175 Short-tailed Swallowtail on "Heracleum maximum"

176 Sail-makers' Tools and Sails

1991.

656 175 2 f. 50 multicoloured .. 80 45

1991.

657 176 1 f. 40 green and yellow 45 20
658 1 f. 70 red and yellow 50 35

177 Ile aux Marins

1991. Old Views.

659 177 1 f. 70 blue 50 35
660 – 1 f. 70 blue 50 35
661 – 1 f. 70 blue 50 35
662 – 1 f. 70 blue 50 35
663 177 2 f. 50 red 70 45
664 – 2 f. 50 red 70 45
665 – 2 f. 50 red 70 45
666 – 2 f. 50 red 70 45

DESIGNS: Nos. 660, 664, Langlade; 661, 665, Miquelon; 662, 666, Saint-Pierre.

178 Piper "Tomahawk"

1991. Air.

667 178 10 f. blue, turq & brown 2·75 1·60

179 Musicians

1991. Centenary of Lyre Music Society.

668 179 2 f. 50 red, brn & orge 80 45

180 Oars

1991. St.-Pierre–Newfoundland Crossing by Rowing Boat.

669 180 2 f. 50 multicoloured .. 80 45

181 Pelota Players

1991. Basque Sports.

670 181 5 f. green and red .. 1·40 65

182 Fishermen

1991. Natural Heritage. Multicoloured.

671 2 f. 50 Type **182** 75 45
672 14 f. 50 Canada geese and shore .. .. .. 3·75 2·40

Nos. 671/2 were issued together, se-tenant, forming a composite design of Savoyard.

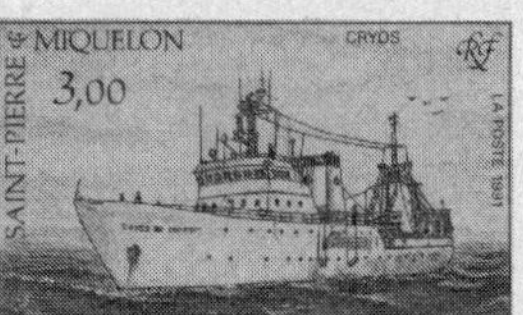

183 "Croys" (stern trawler)

1991.

673 183 3 f. multicoloured .. 90 60

184 Free French Central Bank 100 f. Note

1991. 50th Anniv of Central Economic Co-operation Bank.

674 184 2 f. 50 multicoloured .. 80 45

185 Naval Forces and Cross of Lorraine

1991. Christmas. 50th Anniv of Adherence to Free French Government.

675 185 2 f. 50 multicoloured .. 80 45

186 Muselier and Harbour

1992. 110th Birth Anniv of Admiral E. Muselier (commander of 1941 Free French landing force).

676 186 2 f. 50 multicoloured .. 65 35

187 Ice Skating

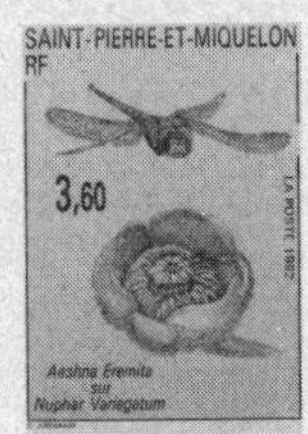

188 "Aeshna eremita" and "Nuphar variegatum"

1992. Winter Olympic Games, Albertville.

677 187 5 f. blue, ultram & mve 1·10 70

1992.

678 188 3 f. 60 multicoloured .. 80 50

189 Boat-building Tools and Stern of Ship

1992.

679 189 1 f. 50 brown and blue 45 30
680 1 f. 80 blue and azure 55 40

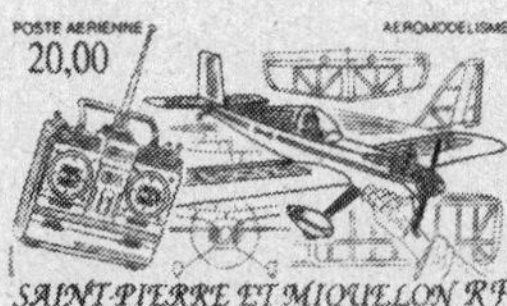

190 Model Aircraft and Remote Control

1992.

681 190 20 f. red, orange & brn 4·50 2·75

191 Ile aux Marins Lighthouse

1992. Lighthouses. Multicoloured.

682 2 f. 50 Type **191** 55 35
683 2 f. 50 Galantry 55 35
684 2 f. 50 Old Rouge Feu Lighthouse, St. Pierre .. 55 35
685 2 f. 50 Pointe-Plate .. 55 35

192 Cones and Woodpecker

1992. Natural Heritage. Dolisie Valley, Langlade. Multicoloured.

686 2 f. 50 Type **192** 55 35
687 15 f. 10 Valley and berries 3·25 2·00

193 Columbus and Map on Sails

1992. 500th Anniv of Discovery of America by Columbus.

688 193 5 f. 10 multicoloured .. 1·10 90

194 Baron de l'Esperance, Map and Settlers

1992. 230th Anniv (1993) of Resettlement by French of Miquelon.

689 194 2 f 50 brown, blue & red 55 35

195 Nativity

1992. Christmas.

690 195 2 f. 50 multicoloured .. 55 35

196 Birot and Free French Corvette

1993. 50th Death Anniv (1992) of Commander R. Birot.

691 196 2 f. 50 multiciloured .. 60 40

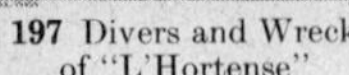

197 Divers and Wreck of "L'Hortense"

198 Longhorn Beetle on "Cichorium intybus"

1993. Deep Sea Diving.

692	**197**	5 f. multicoloured ..	1·25	75

1993.

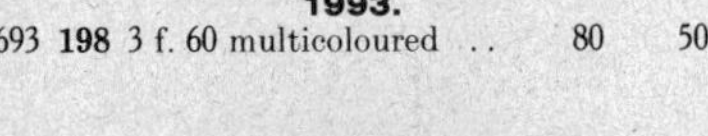

693	**198**	3 f. 60 multicoloured ..	80	50

199 Cutting-up Cod

1993.

694	**199**	1 f. 50 multicoloured ..	35	25
695		1 f. 80 multicoloured ..	40	25

200 Greater Puffin

1993. Air. Migratory Birds. Multicoloured.

696		5 f. Type **200**	1·10	70
697		10 f. Golden plover ..	2·25	1·40

201 Fleet of Ships

1993. Bicentenary of Settlement of Madeleine Islands.

698	**201**	5 f. 10 blue, green & brn	1·10	70

1993. No. 3121 of France optd **ST-PIERRE ET MIQUELON**.

699	**1118**	(–) red	60	40

202 Frogfish

1993. Fishes. Multicoloured.

700		2 f. 80 Type **202**	65	40
701		2 f. 80 Fishermen and capelin	65	40
702		2 f. 80 Skate ("Le Raie")	65	40
703		2 f. 80 Halibut ("Le Fletan")	65	40

203 Pine Cones, Otter and Left Bank

1993. Natural Heritage. Sylvain Hills. Mult.

704		2 f. 80 Type **203**	65	40
705		16 f. Otter on all fours, pine cones and right bank	3·75	2·25

Nos. 704/5 were issued together, se-tenant, with intervening ½ stamp-size label, forming a composite design of an otter pool.

204 Prefect's Residence

1993.

707	**204**	3 f. 70 blue, yell & brn	85	50

205 Father Christmas waving to Child

1993. Christmas.

708	**205**	2 f. 80 multicoloured ..	65	40

206 Blaison and "Surcouf" (Free French submarine)

1994. 50th Death Anniv (1992) of Commander Louis Blaison.

709	**206**	2 f. 80 multicoloured ..	65	40

PARCEL POST STAMPS

1901. Optd. **COLIS POSTAUX.**

P 79.	D.	10 c. black on lilac ..	55·00	55·00

1901. Optd. **Colis Postaux.**

P 80.	D.	10 c. red	9·00	9·00

1917. Nos. 83 and 85 optd **Colis Postaux**.

P109	**17**	10 c. red and pink ..	1·25	1·40
P110		20 c. purple & brown	1·25	1·10

1941. Free French Plebiscite. No. P 110 optd. **Noel 1941. FRANCE LIBRE F. N. F. L.**

P 303.	**17.**	20 c. purple and brown	£550	£550

POSTAGE DUE STAMPS

1892. Postage Due stamps of French Colonies optd. **ST-PIERRE M-on.**

D 60.	U	5 c. black	40·00	42·00
D 61.		10 c. black	10·00	10·00
D 62.		15 c. black	10·00	10·00
D 63.		20 c. black	10·00	10·00
D 64.		30 c. black	10·00	10·00
D 65.		40 c. black	9·25	10·50
D 66.		60 c. black	42·00	42·00
D 67.		1 f. brown	90·00	90·00
D 68.		2 f. brown	90·00	90·00

1925. Postage Due type of France optd **SAINT-PIERRE -ET- MIQUELON** or surch also **centimes a percevoir** and value in figures.

D 135.	D **11.**	5 c. blue	25	40
D 136.		10 c. brown	30	50
D 137.		20 c. olive	40	50
D 138.		25 c. red	40	50
D 139.		30 c. red	55	60
D 140.		45 c. green	55	60
D 141.		50 c. red	1·10	1·25
D 142.		60 c. on 50 c. brown	1·10	1·25
D 143.		1 f. red	1·25	1·50
D 144.		2 f. on 1 f. red ..	1·75	2·00
D 145.		3 f. mauve	5·50	5·50

D 30. Newfoundland Dog.

D 40. Codfish.

1932.

D 163.	D **30.**	5 c. black and blue	75	80
D 164.		10 c. black & green	85	80
D 165.		20 c. black and red	1·10	1·10
D 166.		25 c. black and purple	1·10	1·10
D 167.		30 c. black & orange	2·00	2·00
D 168.		45 c. black and blue	2·25	2·25
D 169.		50 c. black and green	4·00	4·25
D 170.		60 c. black and red	5·50	5·50
D 171.		1 f. black and brown	14·00	14·00
D 172.		2 f. black and purple	21·00	21·00
D 173.		3 f. black and brown	23·00	23·00

1938.

D 208.	D **40.**	5 c. black	25	35
D 209.		10 c. purple ..	15	30
D 210.		15 c. green	25	35
D 211.		20 c. blue	25	35
D 212.		30 c. red	25	35
D 213.		50 c. green	30	45
D 214.		60 c. blue	25	45
D 215.		1 f. red	40	45
D 216.		2 f. brown	1·40	1·60
D 217.		3 f. violet	2·50	1·60

1941. Free French Plebiscite. Nos. D208/17 optd **NOEL 1941 F. N. F. L.**

D 235.	D **40.**	5 c. black	15·00	15·00
D 236.		10 c. purple ..	15·00	15·00
D 237.		15 c. green	15·00	15·00
D 238.		20 c. blue	15·00	15·00
D 239.		30 c. red	15·00	15·00
D 240.		50 c. green	28·00	28·00
D 241.		60 c. blue	65·00	65·00
D 242.		1 f. red	75·00	75·00
D 243.		2 f. brown	80·00	80·00
D 244.		3 f. violet	90·00	90·00

1941. Postage Due stamps of 1932 optd **FRANCE LIBRE F. N. F. L.** or surch also.

D 298.	D **30.**	25 c. blk. & pur. ..	£190	£190
D 299.		30 c. blk. & orange	£190	£190
D 300.		50 c. blk. & green ..	£625	£625
D 301.		2 f. blk. & purple ..	28·00	28·00
D 302.		3 f. on 2 f. blk. & pur.	14·00	14·00

1941. Free French Plebiscite. Nos. D 208/17 optd. **FRANCE LIBRE F. N. F. L.**

D 310.	D **40.**	5 c. black	28·00	28·00
D 311.		10 c. purple ..	5·50	5·50
D 312.		15 c. green	5·50	5·50
D 313.		20 c. blue	5·50	5·50
D 314.		30 c. red	5·50	5·50
D 315.		50 c. green	5·50	5·50
D 316.		60 c. blue	6·75	7·00
D 317.		1 f. red	14·00	14·00
D 318.		2 f. brown	14·00	14·00
D 319.		3 f. violet	£350	£350

D 57. Arms and Galleon.

D 115. Newfoundland Dog and Shipwreck Scene.

1947.

D 385.	D **57.**	10 c. orange ..	15	25
D 386.		30 c. blue	15	30
D 387.		50 c. green	25	30
D 388.		1 f. red	25	35
D 389.		2 f. green	25	35
D 390.		3 f. violet	55	60
D 391.		4 f. brown	55	60
D 392.		5 f. green	55	60
D 393.		10 f. black	70	75
D 394.		20 f. red	80	90

1973.

D516	D **115**	2 c. black & brown	60	60
D517		10 c. black & violet	90	90
D518		20 c. black & blue	1·40	1·40
D519		30 c. black and red	2·25	2·25
D520		1 f. black and blue	5·50	5·50

1986. Nos. D2493/2502 of France optd **ST-PIERRE ET MIQUELON**.

D 569.	10 c. brown and black ..	20	20
D 570.	20 c. black	20	20
D 571.	30 c. red, brown & blk.	20	20
D 572.	40 c. blue, brown & blk.	20	20
D 573.	50 c. red and black ..	20	20
D 574.	1 f. black	30	30
D 575.	2 f. yellow and black ..	65	65
D 576.	3 f. black and red ..	1·00	1·00
D 577.	4 f. brown and black ..	1·40	1·40
D 578.	5 f. blue, red & blk.	1·75	1·75

ST. THOMAS AND PRINCE IS.

Pt. 9; Pt. 14

Two islands in the Gulf of Guinea off the West coast of Africa. A colony and then an Overseas Province of Portugal until 1975, when it became an independent republic.

1870. 1000 reis = 1 milreis.
1913. 100 centavos = 1 escudo.
1977. 100 cents = 1 dobra.

1870. "Crown" key-type inscr. "S. THOME E PRINCIPE".

17	P	5 r. black	70	65
18		10 r. orange	7·00	4·50
29		10 r. green	3·00	2·25
20		20 r. olive	1·50	1·00
30		20 r. red	1·40	1·25
21a		25 r. red	70	55
31		25 r. lilac	1·25	80
12		40 r. blue	2·25	1·90
32		40 r. yellow	2·00	1·75
25		50 r. green	6·00	5·00
33		50 r. blue	1·50	80
26		100 r. lilac	3·25	2·75
15		200 r. orange	3·50	2·50
16		300 r. brown	3·50	2·75

1887. "Embossed" key-type inscr. "S. THOME E PRINCIPE".

38	Q	5 r. black	1·75	1·50
42		10 r. green	2·25	1·25
43		20 r. red	2·25	1·75
44		25 r. mauve	2·25	90
45		40 r. brown	2·00	1·40
40		50 r. blue	2·25	1·25
47		100 r. brown	2·25	1·25
48		200 r. lilac	6·50	5·00
49		300 r. orange	6·50	5·00

1889. Stamps of 1887 surch. No gum.

50.	Q.	5 r. on 10 r. green ..	12·00	9·50
51.		5 r. on 20 r. red	12·00	9·50
52.		50 r. on 40 r. brown ..	38·00	30·00

1895. "Figures" key-type inscr. "S. THOME E PRINCIPE".

60.	R.	5 r. yellow	55	40
61.		10 r. mauve	70	60
53.		15 r. brown	90	60
54.		20 r. lilac	90	60
62.		25 r. green	90	35
63.		50 r. blue	90	35
55.		75 r. red	1·90	1·60
64.		80 r. green	5·00	4·00
56.		100 r. brown on buff ..	2·00	1·40
57.		150 r. red on rose ..	2·75	2·40
58.		200 r. blue on blue ..	3·25	2·75
59.		300 r. blue on brown ..	4·00	3·00

1898. "King Carlos" key-types inscr "S. THOME E PRINCIPE". Name and value in red (500 r.) or black (others).

66.	S.	2½ r. grey	15	15
67.		5 r. orange	15	15
68.		10 r. green	20	15
69.		15 r. brown	80	65
113.		15 r. green	50	35
70.		20 r. lilac	40	20
71.		25 r. green	30	20
114.		25 r. red	50	35
72.		50 r. blue	35	25
115.		50 r. brown	2·00	1·40
116.		65 r. blue	4·00	3·00
73.		75 r. red	5·00	2·50
117.		75 r. purple	1·00	70
74.		80 r. mauve	2·00	1·50
75.		100 r. blue on blue ..	1·25	90
118.		115 r. brown on pink ..	4·25	3·25
119.		130 r. brown on yellow ..	4·25	3·25
76.		150 r. brown on yellow ..	2·00	1·00
77.		200 r. purple on pink ..	2·50	80
78.		300 r. blue on pink ..	2·75	1·75
120.		400 r. blue on yellow ..	5·00	3·50
79.		500 r. black on blue ..	3·50	2·00
80.		700 r. mauve on yellow	6·00	4·25

1902. Surch with new value.

121	S	50 r. on 65 r. blue ..	1·50	1·00
85	R	65 r. on 5 r. yellow ..	1·50	1·25
86		65 r. on 10 r. mauve ..	1·50	1·25
87		65 r. on 15 r. brown ..	1·50	1·25
81	Q	65 r. on 20 r. red ..	3·00	2·00
88	R	65 r. on 20 r. lilac ..	1·50	1·25
83	Q	65 r. on 25 r. mauve ..	2·00	1·60
84		65 r. on 100 r. brown ..	2·00	1·75
90		115 r. on 10 r. green ..	2·00	1·75
92	R	115 r. on 25 r. green ..	1·50	1·25
89	P	115 r. on 50 r. green ..	4·50	1·50
93	R	115 r. on 150 r. red on rose	1·50	1·25
94		115 r. on 200 r. blue on bl	1·50	1·25
91	Q	115 r. on 300 r. orange ..	2·00	1·75
95		130 r. on 5 r. black ..	2·00	1·75
98	R	130 r. on 75 r. red ..	1·50	1·25
99		130 r. on 100 r. brown on buff	1·50	1·50
97	Q	130 r. on 200 r. lilac ..	2·50	1·75
100	R	130 r. on 300 r. blue on brown	1·50	1·00
108	V	400 r. on 2½ r. brown ..	50	50
101	P	400 r. on 10 r. orange ..	14·00	7·50
102	Q	400 r. on 40 r. brown ..	3·50	2·50
103		400 r. on 50 r. blue ..	4·00	3·50
105	R	400 r. on 50 r. blue ..	50	50
107		400 r. on 80 r. green ..	90	70

1903. Stamps of 1898 optd. **PROVISORIO.**

109.	S.	15 r. brown	90	40
110.		25 r. green	90	40
111.		50 r. blue	95	40
112.		75 r. red	2·00	1·50

1911. Stamps of 1898 optd. **REPUBLICA.**
122 S 2½ r. grey 15 15
123 5 r. orange 15 15
124 10 r. green 15 15
125 15 r. green 15 15
126 20 r. lilac 15 15
127 25 r. red 15 15
128 50 r. brown 15 15
129 75 r. purple 15 15
130 100 r. blue on blue .. 25 20
131 115 r. brown on pink .. 60 40
132 130 r. brown on yellow .. 60 45
267 200 r. purple on pink .. 80 50
134 400 r. blue on yellow .. 75 45
268 500 r. black on blue .. 60 50
136 700 r. mauve on yellow 70 45

1912. King Manoel" key-type inscr. "S. THOME E. PRINCIPE" and optd. **REPUBLICA.**
137. T. 2½ r. lilac 10 10
138. 5 r. black 10 10
139. 10 r. green 10 10
140. 20 r. red 60 40
141. 25 r. brown 30 20
142. 50 r. blue 30 20
143. 75 r. brown 30 20
144. 100 r. brown on green 50 30
145. 200 r. green on pink .. 80 75
146. 300 r. black on blue .. 80 75

1913. Nos. 109 and 111/2 optd. **REPUBLICA.**
159 S 15 r. brown 80 75
243 50 r. blue 25 20
272 75 r. red .. .. .. 3·50 2·50

1913. Stamps of 1902 optd. **REPUBLICA.**
244 S 50 r. on 65 r. blue .. 25 20
245 Q 115 r. on 10 r. green .. 1·00 75
246 R 115 r. on 25 r. green .. 20 15
164 P 115 r. on 50 r. green .. 38·00 35·00
247 R 115 r. on 150 r. red on rose 20 15
248 115 r. on 200 r. blue on blue 20 15
249 Q 115 r. on 300 r. orange .. 1·00 80
250 130 r. on 5 r. black .. 1·75 1·25
251 R 130 r. on 75 r. red .. 20 15
252 130 r. on 100 r. brown on buff 50 45
253 Q 130 r. on 200 r. lilac .. 65 50
254 R 130 r. on 300 r. blue on brown 50 30
197 V 400 r. on 2½ r. brown .. 1·00 90
168 Q 400 r. on 50 r. blue .. 22·00 20·00
200 R 400 r. on 50 r. blue .. 1·25 1·00
202 400 r. on 80 r. green .. 1·40 1·00

1913. Surch. **REPUBLICA S. TOME E PRINCIPE** and new value on "Vasco da Gama" stamps of

(a) **Portuguese Colonies.**
203. ½ c. on 2½ r. green .. 50 40
204. ½ c. on 5 r. red 50 40
205. 1 c. on 10 r. purple .. 50 40
206. 2½ c. on 25 r. green .. 50 40
207. 5 c. on 50 r. blue 50 40
208. 7½ c. on 75 r. brown .. 80 65
209. 10 c. on 100 r. brown .. 50 40
210. 15 c. on 150 r. bistre .. 50 40

(b) **Macao.**
211. ½ c. on ½ c. green 70 50
212. ½ c. on 1 a. red 70 50
213. 1 c. on 2 a. purple .. 45 35
214. 2½ c. on 4 a. green .. 45 35
215. 5 c. on 8 a. blue 80 60
216. 7½ c. on 12 a. brown .. 90 90
217. 10 c. on 16 a. brown .. 80 60
218. 15 c. on 24 a. bistre .. 60 50

(c) **Timor.**
219. ½ c. on ½ a. green .. 70 50
220. ½ c. on 1 a. red .. 70 50
221. 1 c. on 2 a. purple .. 40 30
222. 2½ c. on 4 a. green .. 40 30
223. 5 c. on 8 a. blue 90 70
224. 7½ c. on 12 a. brown .. 90 75
225. 10 c. on 16 a. brown .. 80 60
226. 15 c. on 24 a. bistre .. 50 45

1914. "Ceres" key-type inscr. "S. TOME E PRINCIPE".
276 U ¼ c. olive 10 10
281 ½ c. black 15 15
282 1 c. green 15 15
283 1½ c. brown 15 15
284 2 c. red 15 15
285 2 c. grey 15 15
286 2½ c. violet 15 10
287 3 c. orange 15 15
288 4 c. red 15 15
289 4½ c. grey 15 15
290 5 c. blue 15 15
291 6 c. mauve 15 15
292 7 c. blue 15 15
293 7½ c. brown 15 15
294 8 c. grey 15 15
295 10 c. brown 15 15
296 12 c. green 25 20
297 15 c. red 15 15
298 20 c. green 20 15
299 24 c. blue 45 35
300 25 c. brown 45 35
239 30 c. brown on green .. 75 75
301 30 c. green 30 20
240 40 c. brown on red .. 75 75
302 40 c. blue 30 20
241 50 c. orange on pink .. 2·00 1·50
303 50 c. mauve 30 20
304 60 c. blue 30 20
305 60 c. pink 80 35
306 80 c. red 90 35
242 1 e. green on blue .. 2·00 1·50
307 1 e. pink 90 65
308 1 e. blue 75 45
309 2 e. purple .. .. 1·00 60
310 5 e. brown .. .. 7·00 2·50
311 10 e. pink .. .. 12·00 5·00
312 20 e. green .. .. 26·00 16·00

1919. "King Carlos" key-type of St. Thomas and Prince Islands surch. **PROVISORIO** and **REPUBLICA** and new value.
255. S. 2½ r. on 15 r. brown .. 35 25

1919. "King Carlos" key-type of St. Thomas and Prince Islands surch. **REPUBLICA** and new value.
256. S. ½ c. on 2½ r. grey .. 1·10 1·40
257. 1 c. on 2½ r. grey .. 1·00 80
258. 2½ c. on 2½ r. grey .. 45 30

1919. "Ceres" key-types of St. Thomas and Prince Islands surch.
259. U. ½ c. on ½ c. olive .. 80 70
260. 2 c. on ½ c. olive .. 80 70
261. 2½ c. on ½ c. olive .. 2·75 2·50

1919. "Ceres" key-type of St. Thomas and Prince Islands surch. **$04 Centavos** and with old value blocked out.
262. U. 4 c. on 2½ c. violet .. 30 25

1923. Stamps of 1913 (optd REPUBLICA) surch **DEZ CENTAVOS** and bars.
313 R 10 c. on 115 r. on 25 r. green 25 20
314 10 c. on 115 r. on 150 r. red on rose 25 20
316 10 c. on 115 r. on 200 r. blue on blue 25 20
317 10 c. on 130 r. on 75 r. red 25 20
318 10 c. on 130 r. on 100 r. brown on buff .. 25 20
319 10 c. on 130 r. on 300 r. blue on brown .. 25 20

1925. Stamps of 1902 surch. **Republica 40 C.** and bars over original surcharge.
321. V. 40 c. on 400 r. on 2½ r. brn 30 20
322. R. 40 c. on 400 r. on 80 r. grn. 30 20

1931. Nos. 307 and 309 surch.
323. U. 70 c. on 1 e. pink .. 75 60
324. 1 e. 40 on 2 e. purple .. 1·25 80

1934. As T **24** of Portuguese Guinea (new "Ceres" type).
325. 1 c. brown 15 15
326. 5 c. sepia 15 15
327. 10 c. mauve 15 15
328. 15 c. black 15 15
329. 20 c. grey 15 15
330. 30 c. green 15 15
331. 40 c. red 15 15
332. 45 c. blue 20 25
333. 50 c. brown 15 10
334. 60 c. olive 25 20
335. 70 c. brown 25 20
336. 80 c. green 25 20
337. 85 c. red .. .. 1·00 85
338. 1 e. red 40 15
339. 1 e. 40 blue .. .. 1·25 70
340. 2 e. mauve .. .. 1·25 80
341. 5 e. green .. .. 2·75 1·75
342. 10 e. brown .. .. 7·00 4·00
343. 20 e. orange .. .. 24·00 14·00

1938. As T **54** and **56** of Macao, but inscr. "S. TOME".
344. **54.** 1 c. olive (postage) 10 10
345. 5 c. brown 10 10
346. 10 c. red 10 10
347. 15 c. purple 10 10
348. 20 c. slate 10 10
349. – 30 c. purple 15 10
350. – 35 c. green 20 15
351. – 40 c. brown 20 15
352. – 50 c. mauve 20 15
353. – 60 c. black 20 15
354. – 70 c. violet 20 15
355. – 80 c. orange 20 15
356. – 1 e. red 65 20
357. – 1 e. 75 blue 60 35
358. – 2 e. red .. .. 7·00 2·00
359. – 5 e. olive .. .. 6·00 2·00
360. – 10 e. blue .. .. 9·00 2·25
361. – 20 e. brown .. .. 15·00 3·00
362. **56.** 10 c. red (air) .. 25·00 18·00
363. 20 c. violet .. .. 10·00 8·00
364. 50 c. orange 65 50
365. 1 e. blue 90 75
366. 2 e. red .. .. 1·50 1·25
367. 3 e. green .. .. 2·50 1·90
368. 5 e. brown .. .. 3·50 3·00
369. 9 e. red .. .. 3·75 3·00
370. 10 e. mauve .. .. 3·75 3·00
Designs: 30 to 50 c. Mousinho de Albuquerque. 60 c. to 1 e. Dam. 1 e. 75 to 5 e. Prince Henry the Navigator. 10, 20 e. Afonso de Albuquerque.
See also Nos. 374/400.

37. Portuguese Colonial Column.

41. Cola Nuts.

1938. President's Colonial Tour.
371. **37.** 80 c. green 80 50
372. 1 e. 75 blue .. .. 3·00 1·75
373. 20 e. brown .. .. 15·00 7·00

1939. As Nos. 344/70 but inscr "S. TOME e PRINCIPE".
374. **54.** 1 c. olive (postage) 10 10
375. 5 c. brown 10 10
376. 10 c. red 10 10
377. 15 c. purple 10 10
378. 20 c. slate 20 10
379. – 30 c. purple 15 10
380. – 35 c. green 15 15
381. – 40 c. brown 20 15
382. – 50 c. mauve 20 15
383. – 60 c. black 25 15
384. – 70 c. violet 25 15
385. – 80 c. orange 25 15
386. – 1 e. red 35 20
387. – 1 e. 75 blue 60 30
388. – 2 e. red .. .. 1·00 55
389. – 5 e. olive .. .. 2·25 1·40
390. – 10 e. blue .. .. 6·00 1·75
391. – 20 e. brown .. .. 8·00 2·50
392. **56.** 10 c. red (air) 10 10
393. 20 c. violet 10 10
394. 50 c. orange 10 10
395. 1 e. blue 15 15
396. 2 e. red 40 35
397. 3 e. green 60 45
398. 5 e. brown .. .. 1·40 85
399. 9 e. red .. .. 2·00 1·25
400. 10 e. mauve .. .. 2·00 1·25

1948. Fruits.
401. **41.** 5 c. black and yellow .. 15 10
402. – 10 c. black and salmon .. 15 10
403. – 30 c. black and grey .. 1·00 50
404. – 50 c. brown and yellow .. 1·50 55
405. – 1 e. red .. .. .. 2·00 60
406. – 1 e. 75 blue and grey .. 3·50 2·00
407. – 2 e. black and green .. 3·00 60
408. – 5 e. brown and mauve .. 7·50 4·00
409. – 10 e. black and mauve .. 11·00 8·00
410. – 20 e. black and grey .. 25·00 13·00
Designs: 10 c. Bread-fruit. 30 c. Custard-apple. 50 c. Cocoa beans. 1 e. Coffee. 1 e. 75, Dendem. 2 e. Abacate. 5 e. Pineapple. 10 e. Mango. 20 e. Coconuts.

1948. Honouring the Statue of Our Lady of Fatima. As T **62** of Macao.
411. 50 c. violet .. .. 3·25 1·75

1949. 75th Anniv. of U.P.U. As T **34** of Portuguese Guinea.
412. 3 e. 50 black .. .. 3·00 2·25

1950. Holy Year. As Nos. 425/6 of Macao.
413. 2 e. 50 blue .. .. 1·00 75
414. 4 e. orange .. .. 2·25 1·75

1951. Termination of Holy Year. As T **69** of Macao.
415 4 e. indigo and blue .. 1·25 85

46. Doctor examining Patients.

48. J. de Santarem.

1952. 1st Tropical Medicine Congress, Lisbon.
416. **46.** 10 c. blue and brown 15 15

1952. Portuguese Navigators. Multicoloured.
417 10 c. Type **48** 10 10
418 30 c. P. Escobar 10 10
419 50 c. F. de Po 10 10
420 1 e. A. Esteves 45 10
421 2 e. L. Goncalves 30 15
422 3 e. 50 M. Fernandes .. 30 15

49. Cloisters of Monastery.

51. Route of President's Tour.

1953. Missionary Art Exhibition.
423. **49.** 10 c. sepia and green .. 10 10
424. 50 c. brown and orange .. 30 20
425. 3 e. indigo and blue .. 1·00 75

1953. Centenary of First Portuguese Postage Stamps. As T **75** of Macao.
426 50 c. multicoloured .. 30 25

1954. Presidential Visit.
427 **51** 15 c. multicoloured .. 15 10
428 5 e. multicoloured .. 50 40

1954. 4th Cent of Sao Paulo. As T **76** of Macao.
429 2 e. 50 multicoloured .. 30 20

1958. Brussels International Exhibition. As T **44** of Portuguese Guinea.
430 2 e. 50 multicoloured .. 35 25

1958. 6th Int. Congress of Tropical Medicines. As T **79** of Macao.
431. 5 e. multicoloured .. 1·25 80
Design: 5 e. "Cassia occidentalis" (plant).

55. Points of Compass.

56. "Religion"

1960. 500th Death Anniv. of Prince Henry the Navigator.
432. **55.** 10 e. multicoloured .. 45 35

1960. 10th Anniv. of African Technical Co-operation Commission.
433. **56.** 1 e. 50 multicoloured .. 25 15

1962. Sports. As T **82** of Macao. Mult.
434. 50 c. Fishing 10 10
435. 1 e. Gymnastics 30 10
436. 1 e. 50 Handball 35 15
437. 2 e. Yachting 40 20
438. 2 e. 50 Running 50 40
439. 20 e. Skin-diving .. .. 1·25 90

1962. Malaria Eradication. Mosquito design as T **83** of Macao. Multicoloured.
440 2 e. 50 "Anopheles gambiae" 35 30

1963. 10th Anniv. of T.A.P. Airline. As T **52** of Portuguese Guinea.
441. 1 e. 50 multicoloured .. 30 30

1964. Centenary of National Overseas Bank. As T **84** of Macao, but portrait of F. de Oliveira Chamico.
442 2 e. 50 multicoloured .. 35 25

1965. Cent. of I.T.U. As T **85** of Macao.
443. 2 e. 50 multicoloured .. 80 45

62. Infantry Officer 1788.

73. Pero Escobar and Joao de Santarem.

1965. Portuguese Military Uniforms. Mult.
444. 20 c. Type **62** 15 10
445. 35 c. Infantry sergeant, 1788 15 10
446. 40 c. Infantry corporal, 1788 10 10
447. 1 e. Infantryman, 1788 .. 70 40
448. 2 e. 50 Artillery officer, 1806 70 40
449. 5 e. Light Infantryman, 1811 1·10 80
450. 7 e. 50 Infantry sapper, 1833 1·75 1·10
451. 10 e. Lancers officer, 1834 2·00 1·50

1966. 40th Anniv of National Revolution. As T **86** of Macao, but showing different buildings. Multicoloured.
452 4 e. Arts and Crafts School and Anti-T.B. clinic .. 30 20

1967. Centenary of Military Naval Assn. As T **88** of Macao. Multicoloured.
453 1 e. 50 C. Rodrigues and corvette "Vasco da Gama" 45 35
454 2 e. 50 A. Kopke, microscope and "Glossina palpalis" (insect) .. 75 45

1967. 50th Anniv. of Fatima Apparitions. As T **89** of Macao.
455. 2 e. 50 multicoloured .. 15 10
Design: 2 e. 50, Apparition appearing to children and Valinhos Monument.

1968. 500th Birth Anniv. of Pedro Cabral (explorer). As T **90** of Macao. Multicoloured.
456 1 e. 50 Medal of the Jeronimos Monastery (vert) .. 30 20

1969. Birth Cent. of Admiral Gago Coutinho. As T **91** of Macao. Multicoloured.
457 2 e. Island route-map and monument 40 20

1969. 500th Birth Anniv. of Vasco da Gama (explorer). As T **92** of Macao. Mult.
458. 2 e. 50 Da Gama's fleet 15 15

1969. Centenary of Overseas Administrative Reforms. As T **93** of Macao.
459. 2 e. 50 multicoloured .. 10 10

1969. 500th Birth Anniv of King Manoel I. As T **95** of Macao. Multicoloured.
460 4 e. Manoel I Gate, Guarda See 25 15

1969. 500th Anniv. of Discovery of St. Thomas and Prince Islands.
461. **73.** 2 e. 50 multicoloured .. 15 10

74. President A. Tomas.

76. Stamps on Coffee Plant.

1970. Presidential Visit.
462. **74.** 2 e. 50 multicoloured .. 20 10

1970. Birth Cent. of Marshal Carmona. Multicoloured. As T **96** of Macao.
463. 5 e. Portrait in Marshal's uniform 20 15

1970. Stamp Centenary. Multicoloured.
464 1 e. Type **76** 10 10
465 1 e. 50 Head Post Office, St. Thomas (horiz) .. 15 10
466 2 e. 50 Se Cathedral, St. Thomas 25 15

77. "Descent from the Cross" and Caravel at St. Thomas.

78. Running and Throwing the Javelin.

1972. 400th Anniv of Camoens' "The Lusiads" (epic poem).
467 **77** 20 e. multicoloured .. 3·50 1·00

1972. Olympic Games, Munich.
468. **78.** 1 e. 50 multicoloured .. 10 10

79. Seaplane "Lusitania" and Cruiser "Gladiolus" off Rock of San Pedro.

1972. 50th Anniv. of 1st Flight, Lisbon-Rio de Janeiro.
469. **79.** 2 e. 50 multicoloured .. 30 15

1973. Centenary of World Meteorological Organization. As T **102** of Macao.
470. 5 e. multicoloured .. 30 25

81. Flags of Portugal and St. Thomas and Prince Islands.

1975. Independence.
471. **81.** 3 e. multicoloured .. 10 10
472. 10 e. multicoloured .. 55 20
473. 20 e. multicoloured .. 1·00 55
474. 50 e. multicoloured .. 2·50 1·60

82. National Flag.

1975. Independence Proclamation.
475. **82.** 1 e. 50 multicoloured .. 10 10
476. 4 e. multicoloured .. 20 15
477. 7 e. 50 multicoloured .. 45 35
478. 20 e. multicoloured .. 1·00 60
479. 50 e. multicoloured .. 2·75 1·60

83. Diagram and Hand.

1976. National Reconstruction Fund.
480. **83.** 1 e. multicoloured .. 10 10
481. 1 e. 50 multicoloured .. 10 10
482. 2 e. multicoloured .. 20 10

1976. Optd. **Rep. Democr. 12-7-75.**
483. **48.** 10 c. Joao de Santarem
484. **62.** 20 c. Infantry officer, 1788
485. – 30 c. Pedro Escobar (No. 418) .. ..
486. – 35 c. Infantry sergeant, 1788 .. ..
487. – 40 c. Infantry corporal, 1788 .. ..
488. – 50 c. Fernao de Po (No. 419) .. ..
489. – 1 e. Alvaro Esteves (No. 420) .. ..
490. – 2 e. 50 Rebello da Silva (No. 459) .. ..
491. **73.** 2 e. 50 Escobar and Santarem
492. – 3 e. 50 Martim Fernandes (No. 422) .. ..
493. – 4 e. Manoel Gate (No. 460)
494. – 5 e. W.M.O. emblem (No. 470) .. ..
495. – 7 e. 50 Infantry sapper, 1833 (No. 450) ..
496. – 10 e. Compass rose (No. 432).
Set of 14 .. .. 4·50 3·25

85. President Pinto da Costa and National Flag.

1976. 1st Anniv. of Independence.
497. 2 e. Type **85** 20 10
498. 3 e. 50 Proclamation of Independence, 12 July 1975 .. .. 20 10
499. 4 e. 50 As 3 e. 50 .. 45 20
500. 12 e. 50 Type **85** .. 90 45

1977. 2nd Anniv. of Independence. No. 439 optd. **Rep. Democr 12-7-77.**
501. 20 e. multicoloured .. 80 80

CHARITY TAX STAMPS

The notes under this heading in Portugal also apply here.

1925. Marquis de Pombal Commemoration. Stamps of Portugal, but inscr "S. TOME E PRINCIPE".
C323 C **73** 15 c. black & orange 20 20
C324 – 15 c. black & orange 20 20
C325 C **75** 15 c. black & orange 20 20

1946. Fiscal stamps as in Type C **1** of Portuguese Colonies surch **Assistencia** and new value.
C 401. 50 c. on 1 e. green .. 3·00
C 402. 50 c. on 4 e. red .. 5·50
C 403. 1 e. on 4 e. red .. .. 5·50
C 404. 1 e. on 5 e. red .. .. 4·00
C 405. 1 e. on 6 e. green .. 3·00
C 406. 1 e. on 7 e. green .. 3·00
C 409. 1 e. on 10 e. red .. 5·50
C 410. 1 e. 50 on 7 e. green .. 3·50
C 411. 1 e. 50 on 8 e. green .. 4·00
C 412. 2 e. 50 on 7 e. green .. 3·00
C 413. 2 e. 50 on 9 e. green .. 3·00
C 414. 2 e. 50 on 10 e. green .. 3·00

40. Arms.

1948. Value in black.
C 415. **40.** 50 c. green 30 25
C 416. 1 e. red 60 50
C 417. 1 e. green 15 15
C 418. 1 e. 50 brown .. 75 50

1965. (a) Surch. **"um escudo 1 $00"** and two heavy bars.
C 452. **40.** 1 e. on 5 e. yellow .. 4·00 3·00

(b) Surch. **"Um escudo".**
C 453. **40.** 1 e. on 1 e. green .. 40 40

(c) As No. C 417 but inscr. "UM ESCUDO" at foot, surch. **"1 $00".**
C454. **40.** 1 e. on 1 e. green .. 40 40

d) Inscr. "Cinco escudos 5 $00" further surch. **"Um escudo 1 $00'.**
C 455. **40.** 1 e. on 5 e. yellow .. 1·10 1·00

NEWSPAPER STAMPS

1982. Surch $2\frac{1}{2}$ **RS.** No gum.
N 53. Q. $2\frac{1}{2}$ r. on 5 r. black .. 18·00 13·00
N 54. $2\frac{1}{2}$ r. on 10 r. green .. 21·00 15·00
N 55. $2\frac{1}{2}$ r. on 20 r. red .. 22·00 15·00

1893. "Newspaper" key-type inscr. "S. THOME E PRINCIPE".
N 59. V. $2\frac{1}{2}$ r. brown 40 35

1899. No. N 59 optd. **PROVISORIO.**
N 81. V. $2\frac{1}{2}$ r. brown .. .. 10·00 4·50

POSTAGE DUE STAMPS

1904. "Due" key-type inscr "S. THOME E PRINCIPE". Name and value in black.
D 121. W. 5 r. green 20 20
D 122. 10 r. grey 25 25
D 123. 20 r. brown 25 25
D 124. 30 r. orange 25 25
D 125. 50 r. brown 45 35
D 126. 60 r. brown 80 50
D 127. 100 r. mauve .. 1·40 1·25
D 128. 130 r. blue .. .. 2·00 1·25
D 129. 200 r. red .. .. 2·00 1·40
D 130. 500 r. lilac .. .. 2·50 2·00

1911. As last optd. **REPUBLICA.**
D 137. W. 5 r. green 15 15
D 138. 10 r. grey 15 15
D 139. 20 r. brown 15 15
D 140. 30 r. orange 15 15
D 141. 50 r. brown 15 15
D 142. 60 r. brown 30 30
D 143. 100 r. mauve .. 30 30
D 144. 130 r. blue 30 30
D 145. 200 r. red 30 30
D 146. 500 r. lilac 50 50

1921. "Due" key-type inscr. "S. TOME E PRINCIPE" or "S. THOME E PRINCIPE". Currency changed.
D 313. W. $\frac{1}{2}$ c. green 15 15
D 314. 1 c. grey 15 15
D 315. 2 c. brown 15 15
D 316. 3 c. orange 15 15
D 317. 5 c. brown 15 15
D 318. 6 c. brown 15 15
D 319. 10 c. mauve 15 15
D 320. 13 c. blue 20 20
D 321. 20 c. red 20 20
D 322. 50 c. lilac 25 25

1925. As Nos. C323/5 optd **MULTA.**
D323 C **73** 30 c. black & orange 20 20
D324 – 30 c. black & orange 20 20
D325 C **75** 30 c. black & orange 20 20

1952. As Type D **70** of Macao, but inscr. "S. TOME E PRINCIPE". Numerals in red, name in black.
D 417. 10 c. brown and yellow 10 10
D 418. 30 c. brown and blue .. 10 10
D 419. 50 c. blue and pink .. 10 10
D 420. 1 e. blue and olive .. 10 10
D 421. 2 e. green and orange .. 15 15
D 422. 5 e. brown and lilac .. 20 20

APPENDIX

The following stamps have either been issued in excess of postal needs or have not been available to the public in reasonable quantities at face value. Such stamps may later be given full listing if there is evidence of regular post use.

1977.

400th Birth Anniv. of Rubens. 1, 5, 10, 15, 20, 50 e.

150th Death Anniv. of Beethoven. 20, 30, 50 e.

Centenary of U.P.U. Surch. on Navigators and Military Uniforms issues of Portuguese administration. 1 e. on 10 c., 3 e. on 30 c., 3 e. 50 on 3 e 50, 5 e. on 50 c., 10 e. on 10 c., 15 e. on 3 e. 50, 20 e. on 20 c., 30 e. on 30 c., 35 e. on 35 c., 40 e. on 40 c.

Christmas. 5, 10, 25, 50, 70 d.

60th Anniv. of Russian Revolution. 15, 30, 40, 50 d.

1st Death Anniv. of Mao Tse-tung. 50 d.

1978.

Nobel Peace Prizes to International Organizations. Surch. on Navigators and Military Uniforms issues of Portuguese administration 3 d. on 30 c., 5 d. on 50 c., 10 d. on 10 c., 15 d. on 3 e. 50, 20 d. on 20 c., 35 d. on 35 c.

3rd Anniv. of Independence. 5 d. ×3.

3rd Anniv. of Admission to United Nations. Surch. on Military Uniform issue. 40 d. on 40 c.

International Stamp Exhibition, Essen. 10 d. ×5.

Centenary of U.P.U. 5 d. ×4, 15 d. ×4.

New Currency. 1st Anniv. 5 d. ×5, 8 d. ×5.

World Cup Football Championship, Argentina. 3 d ×4, 25 d. ×3.

1979.

World Cup Winners. Optd. on 1978 World Cup issues. 3 d. ×4, 25 d. ×3.

Butterflies. 50 c., 10 d., 11 d. ×4.

Flowers. 1 d., 8 d. ×4, 25 d.

Telecommunications Day and 50th Anniv. of C.C.I.R. 1, 11, 14, 17 d.

International Year of the Child. 1, 7, 14, 17 d.

450th Death Anniv. of Durer. 50 c. ×2, 1, 7, 8, 25 d.

History of Aviation. 50 c., 1, 5, 7, 8, 17 d.

History of Navigation. 50 c., 1, 3, 5, 8, 25 d.

Birds. Postage 50 c. ×2, 1, 7, 8 d.; Air 100 d.

1980.

Fishes. Postage 50 c., 1, 5, 7, 8 d.; Air 50 d.

Balloons. 50 c., 1, 3, 7, 8, 25 d.

Airships. 50 c., 1, 3, 7, 8, 17 d.

Olympic Games. 50 c., 11 d. ×4.

Death Centenary of Sir Rowland Hill. 50 c., 1, 8, 20 d.

10th Anniv. of First Manned Moon Landing. 50 c., 1, 14, 17 d.

1981.

Olympic Games, Moscow. Optd. on 1977 Mao Tse-tung issue. 50 d.

SAMOA Pt. 7

Islands in the W. Pacific administered jointly from 1889–99 by Gt. Britain, Germany and the U.S.A. (Stamps issued between 1887 and 1899 are listed in volume 3). In 1899 the eastern islands were assigned to the U.S.A. and the western to Germany.

GERMAN COLONY.

100 pfennig = 1 mark.

1900. Stamps of Germany optd. **Samoa.**
G1. **8.** 3 pf. brown .. .. 7·00 10·00
G2. 5 pf. green .. .. 11·00 14·00
G3. **9.** 10 pf. red .. .. .. 7·00 14·00
G4. 20 pf. blue .. .. 16·00 23·00
G5. 25 pf. orange .. .. 40·00 85·00
G6. 50 pf. brown .. .. 40·00 65·00

1901. "Yacht" key-types inscr. "SAMOA".
G7. N. 3 pf. brown 70 75
G8. 5 pf. green 85 75
G9. 10 pf. red 85 75
G10. 20 pf. blue .. .. 60 1·50
G11. 25 pf. blk. & red on yellow 1·00 12·00
G12. 30 pf. blk. & orge. on buff 1·00 12·00
G13. 40 pf. black and red .. 1·00 13·00
G14. 50 pf. blk. & pur. on buff 1·10 13·00
G15. 80 pf. black & red on rose 2·50 32·00
G16. O. 1 m. red .. .. .. 2·75 55·00
G17. 2 m. blue .. .. 3·75 85·00
G18. 3 m. black .. .. 5·50 £140
G19 5 m. red and black .. £130 £475

The colony was occupied by British forces in 1914 and a League of Nations mandate given to New Zealand in 1920. For stamps issued by New Zealand administration, see volume 3.

SAN MARINO Pt. 8

An independent Republic lying near the E. coast of the Italian peninsula.

100 centesimi = 1 lira.

1.

2.

1877.
1 **1** 2 c. green .. .. 3·25 2·00
18 2 c. blue .. .. 3·00 2·50
32 2 c. purple .. .. 2·00 1·75
2 **2** 5 c. yellow .. .. 32·00 6·00
33 5 c. green .. .. 1·50 70
3 10 c. blue .. .. 45·00 5·50
20 10 c. green .. .. 2·50 1·25
34 10 c. red .. .. .. 1·50 80
21 15 c. red .. .. .. 75·00 16·00
4 20 c. red .. .. .. 6·50 2·00
35 20 c. lilac .. .. 2·25 2·00
5 25 c. purple .. .. 45·00 6·50
36 25 c. blue .. .. 1·75 1·25
6 30 c. brown .. .. £325 25·00
22 30 c. yellow .. .. 3·25 2·25
7 40 c. mauve .. .. £325 25·00
23 40 c. brown .. .. 2·00 2·00
24 45 c. green .. .. 2·00 2·00
25 65 c. brown .. .. 2·00 1·75
26 1 l. red and yellow .. £1200 £300
37 1 l. blue £1100 £275
27 2 l. brown and buff .. 30·00 24·00
28 5 l. red and blue .. 85·00 90·00

1892. Surch. **Cmi.** and figure of value.
10c. **2.** 5 c. on 10 c. blue .. .. 35·00 6·00
12. 5 c. on 30 c. brown .. £275 35·00
16. 10 c. on 20 c. red .. 17·00 1·50

1892. Surch. **10 10.**
17. **2.** 10 c. on 20 c. red .. £150 2·50

13. Government Palace. **14.**

15. Interior of Government Palace.

17. Statue of Liberty.

1894. Opening of new Government Palace and Installation of New Regent.
29 **13** 25 c. purple and blue .. 2·00 70
30 **14** 50 c. purple and red .. 10·00 2·00
31 **15** 1 l. purple and green .. 10·00 2·50

1899.
38. **17.** 2 c. brown 70 55
39. 5 c. orange .. .. 1·10 85
See also Nos. 86/91.

18. 19. Mt. Titano.

1903.

40 18 2 c. lilac .. .. 4·00 1·10
73 2 c. brown 10 10
74 19 5 c. green 10 10
111 5 c. purple 10 10
42 10 c. pink .. .. 1·50 55
75 10 c. orange 10 10
112 10 c. green 10 10
76 15 c. green 15 15
113 15 c. purple 15 15
43 20 c. orange .. .. 45·00 9·00
77 20 c. brown 15 15
114 20 c. green 15 15
44 25 c. blue .. .. 5·50 1·10
78 25 c. grey 15 15
115 25 c. violet 15 15
45 30 c. red .. .. 2·00 2·50
79 30 c. mauve 25 25
116 30 c. orange .. .. 3·75 35
46 40 c. red .. .. 3·50 3·00
80 40 c. pink 25 25
117 40 c. brown 15 15
47 45 c. yellow .. .. 3·50 3·25
81 50 c. purple 35 35
118 50 c. grey 15 15
119 60 c. red 20 20
48 65 c. brown .. .. 3·50 3·25
82 80 c. blue 55 55
83 90 c. brown 55 55
49 1 l. green .. .. 10·00 5·50
120 1 l. blue 25 25
50 2 l. violet £500 £130
85 2 l. red .. .. 7·50 7·50
121 2 l. green .. .. 1·60 1·60
122 5 l. blue .. .. 5·50 5·50

1905. Surch. **1905 15.**

52. **19.** 15 c. on 20 c. orange .. 2·25 1·75

22. 23. 26. Statue of Liberty.

1907.

53a. **22.** 1 c. brown 80 80
54. **23.** 15 c. grey .. .. 8·00 1·75

1917. For Combatants. Surch. **1917 Pro combattenti** and value.

55. **18.** 25 c. on 2 c. lilac .. 80 90
56. **19.** 50 c. on 2 l. violet .. 15·00 18·00

1918. Surch. **Cent. 20 1918.**

57. **23.** 20 c. on 15 c. grey .. 1·25 1·10

1918. War Casualties Fund. Inscr. as in T **26.**

58. **26.** 2 c. (+5 c.) blk. & lilac 15 20
59. 5 c. (+5 c.) black & grn. 15 20
60. 10 c. (+5 c.) blk. & red 15 20
61. 20 c. (+5 c.) blk. & orge. 15 20
62. 25 c. (+5 c.) blk. & blue 30 35
63. 45 c. (+5 c.) blk. & brn. 30 35
64. – 1 l. (+5 c.) blk. & green 4·00 4·50
65. – 2 l. (+5 c.) blk. & lilac 3·25 3·50
66. – 3 l. (+5 c.) blk. & red 3·25 3·50

DESIGN—HORIZ. 1 l., 2 l., 3 l. San Marino.

1918. Italian Victory over Austria and Premium for War Casualties Fund. Optd **3 Novembre 1918.**

67. **26.** 20 c. (+5 c.) blk. & orge. 55 70
68. 25 c. (+5 c.) blk. & bl. 55 70
69. 45 c. (+5 c.) blk. & brn. 55 70
70. – 1 l. (+5 c.) blk. & green 55 70
71. – 2 l. (+5 c.) blk. & lilac 3·25 3·50
72. – 3 l. (+5 c.) black & red 3·25 3·50

1922. Re-issue of T **17.**

86. **17.** 2 c. purple 10 10
87. 5 c. olive 10 10
88. 10 c. brown 10 10
89. 20 c. brown 15 15
90. 25 c. blue 20 20
91. 45 c. lake 60 60

30. Arbe (Rab). 31. St. Marinus.

1923. Delivery to San Marino of Italian Flag flown on Arbe, after the island returned to Yugoslavia.

92 **30** 50 c. green 20 20

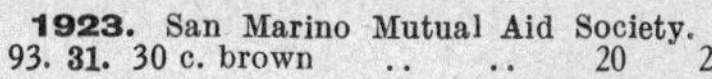

1923. San Marino Mutual Aid Society.

93. **31.** 30 c. brown 20 20

32. Mt. Titano. 33. "Liberty". 34.

1923. Red Cross.

94. **32.** 5 c. + 5 c. olive .. 15 15
95. 10 c. + 5 c. orange .. 15 15
96. 15 c. + 5 c. green .. 15 15
97. 25 c. + 5 c. lake .. 30 30
98. 40 c. + 5 c. purple .. 60 60
99. 50 c. + 5 c. grey .. 45 20
100. **33.** 1 l. + 5 c. blue and black 1·00 1·00

1923. San Marino Volunteers in the Great War.

101. **34.** 1 l. brown .. .. 4·00 4·00

35. Garibaldi. 36.

1924. 75th Anniv. of Garibaldi's Refuge in San Marino.

102. **35.** 30 c. purple 70 70
103. 50 c. brown 75 75
104 60 c. lake 90 90
105. **36.** 1 l. blue .. .. 1·60 1·60
106. 2 l. green .. .. 1·90 1·90

1924. Red Cross stamps of 1918 **surch.**

107. **26.** 30 c. on 45 c. blk. & brn. 30 35
108. – 60 c. on 1 l. blk. & grn. 3·00 3·00
109. – 1 l. on 2 l. black & lilac 5·50 5·50
110. – 2 l. on 3 l. black & red 4·50 4·50

1926. Surch.

123. **19.** 75 c. on 80 c. blue .. 40 40
124. 1 l. 20 on 90 c. brown .. 40 40
125. 1 l. 25 on 90 c. brown .. 1·00 1·00
126. 2 l. 50 on 80 c. blue .. 1·60 1·60

40. Onofri. 44. San Marino War. Memorial.

1926. Death Centenary of Antonio Onofri, "Father of the Country".

127. **40.** 10 c. black and blue .. 10 10
128. 20 c. black and olive .. 55 55
129. 45 c. black and violet .. 30 30
130. 65 c. black and green .. 30 30
131. 1 l. black and orange .. 1·25 1·25
132. 2 l. black and red .. 1·25 1·25

1926. No. E 92 surch. **Lire 1,85.**

133. **19.** 1 l. 85 on 60 c. violet .. 40 45

1927. Surch.

134. **40.** 1 l. 25 on 1 l. blk. & orge. 85 1·00
135. 2 l. 50 on 2 l. blk. & red 2·25 2·50
136. 5 l. on 2 l. black & red .. 19·00 20·00

1927. Unissued Express stamp (No. 115 surch **ESPRESSO 50**) ruled through and surch **L. 1,75.**

137 **19** 1 l. 75 on 50 c. on 25 c. violet 70 75

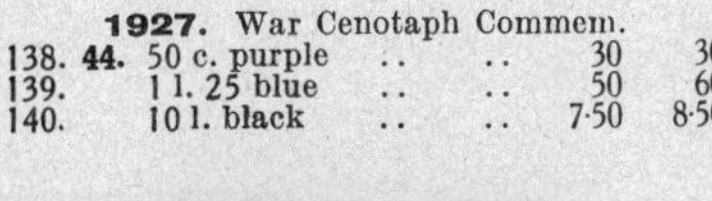

1927. War Cenotaph Commem.

138. **44.** 50 c. purple 30 30
139. 1 l. 25 blue 50 60
140. 10 l. black .. .. 7·50 8·50

45. Franciscan Convent and Capuchin Church.

1928. 700th Death Anniv. of St. Francis of Assisi.

141. **45.** 50 c. red .. .. 9·50 1·25
142. 1 l. 25 blue .. .. 1·60 1·60
143. – 2 l. 50 brown .. .. 1·60 1·60
144. – 5 l. violet .. .. 11·00 9·50

DESIGN: 2 l. 50, 5 l. Death of St. Francis.

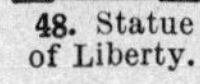
46. La Rocca Fortress. 47. Government Palace. 48. Statue of Liberty.

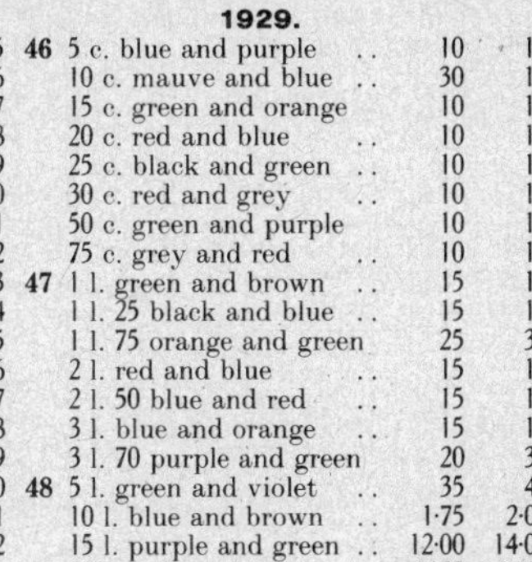

1929.

145 **46** 5 c. blue and purple .. 10 10
146 10 c. mauve and blue .. 30 10
147 15 c. green and orange .. 10 10
148 20 c. red and blue .. 10 10
149 25 c. black and green .. 10 10
150 30 c. red and grey .. 10 10
151 50 c. green and purple .. 10 10
152 75 c. grey and red .. 10 10
153 **47** 1 l. green and brown .. 15 10
154 1 l. 25 black and blue .. 15 10
155 1 l. 75 orange and green 25 35
156 2 l. red and blue .. 15 15
157 2 l. 50 blue and red .. 15 15
158 3 l. blue and orange .. 15 15
159 3 l. 70 purple and green 20 35
160 **48** 5 l. green and violet .. 35 40
161 10 l. blue and brown .. 1·75 2·00
162 15 l. purple and green .. 12·00 14·00
163 20 l. red and blue .. £150 £170

50. Mt. Titano. 51. G.P.O., San Marino.

1931. Air.

164. **50.** 50 c. green 50 50
165. 80 c. red 70 70
166. 1 l. brown 70 70
167. 2 l. purple 75 75
168. 2 l. 60 blue .. .. 9·00 11·00
169. 3 l. grey .. .. 9·00 11·00
170. 5 l. olive .. .. 2·00 2·00
171. 7 l. 70 sepia .. .. 2·50 2·50
172. 9 l. orange .. .. 2·75 2·75
173. 10 l. blue £120 £140

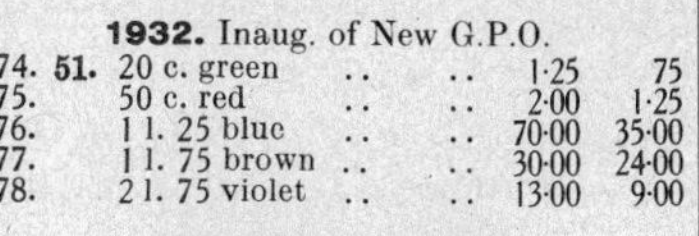

1932. Inaug. of New G.P.O.

174. **51.** 20 c. green .. .. 1·25 75
175. 50 c. red .. .. 2·00 1·25
176. 1 l. 25 blue .. .. 70·00 35·00
177. 1 l. 75 brown .. .. 30·00 24·00
178. 2 l. 75 violet .. .. 13·00 9·00

52. San Marino Railway Station.

1932. Opening of Electric Railway between San Marino and Rimini.

179. **52.** 20 c. green .. .. 1·25 1·25
180. 50 c. red .. .. 1·50 1·50
181. 1 l. 25 blue .. .. 2·25 2·25
182. 5 l. brown .. .. 30·00 30·00

53. Garibaldi.

DESIGN: 75 c. to 5 l. Garibaldi's arrival at San Marino.

1932. 50th Death Anniv. of Garibaldi.

183. **53.** 10 c. brown 45 45
184. 20 c. violet 25 25
185. 25 c. green 40 40
186. 50 c. brown .. .. 1·25 1·25
187. – 75 c. red .. .. 1·25 1·25
188. – 1 l. 25 blue .. .. 3·00 3·00
189. – 2 l. 75 orange .. .. 8·00 10·00
190. – 5 l. olive £110 £130

1933. Air. "Graf Zeppelin". Surch. **ZEPPELIN 1933** under airship and new value.

191. **50.** 3 l. on 50 c. orange .. 65 48·00
192. 5 l. on 80 c. olive .. 26·00 48·00
193. 10 l. on 1 l. blue .. 26·00 65·00
194. 12 l. on 2 l. brown .. 27·00 75·00
195. 15 l. on 2 l. 60 red .. 27·00 85·00
196. 20 l. on 3 l. green .. 27·00 £100

1933. 20th Italian Philatelic Congress. Surch **28 MAGGIO 1933 CONVEGNO FILATELICO** and new value.

197. **51.** 25 c. on 2 l. 75 violet 50 60
198. 50 c. on 1 l. 75 brown .. 2·00 2·00
199. 75 c. on 2 l. 75 violet .. 8·00 8·00
200. 1 l. 25 on 1 l. 75 brown £170 £190

1934. Philatelic Exn. Surch. **12-27 APRILE 1934 MOSTRA FILATELICA** and value with wheel.

201. **51.** 25 c. on 1 l. 25 blue .. 40 40
202. 50 c. on 1 l. 75 brown .. 75 75
203. 75 c. on 50 c. red .. 1·75 1·75
204. 1 l. 25 on 20 c. green .. 13·00 15·00

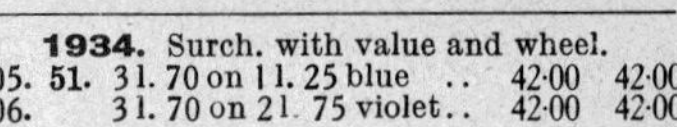

1934. Surch. with value and wheel.

205. **51.** 3 l. 70 on 1 l. 25 blue .. 42·00 42·00
206. 3 l. 70 on 2 l. 75 violet .. 42·00 42·00

58. Ascent to Mt. Titano. 59. Melchiorre Delfico.

1935. 12th Anniv. of San Marino Fascist Party.

207. **58.** 5 c. black and brown .. 10 15
208. 10 c. black and violet .. 10 15
209. 20 c. black and orange .. 10 15
210. 25 c. black and green .. 10 15
211. 50 c. black and bistre .. 20 35
212. 75 c. black and lake .. 80 90
213. 1 l. 25 black and blue .. 2·25 2·50

1935. Death Centenary of Delfico (historian of San Marino).

214. **59.** 5 c. black and red .. 10 15
215. $7\frac{1}{2}$ c. black and brown .. 10 15
216. 10 c. black and green .. 10 15
217. 15 c. black and red .. 3·25 80
218. 20 c. black and orange 10 20
219. 25 c. black and green .. 20 20
220. – 30 c. black and violet .. 20 20
221. – 50 c. black & green .. 80 80
222. – 75 c. black and red .. 3·00 3·00
223. – 1 l. 25 black and blue .. 80 80
224. – 1 l. 50 black and brown 11·00 12·00
225. – 1 l. 75 black and orange 14·00 15·00

DESIGN—(25 × 35 mm.): 30 c. to 1 l. 75, Statue of Delfico.

1936. Surch. (a) Postage.

226 **40** 80 c. on 45 c. black & vio 1·40 1·75
227 80 c. on 65 c. blk & grn 1·40 1·75
228 **45** 2 l. 05 on 1 l. 25 blue .. 3·75 3·75
229 – 2 l. 75 on 2 l. 50 brown (No. 143) .. .. 16·00 24·00

(b) Air.

230 **50** 75 c. on 50 c. green .. 1·40 1·75
231 75 c. on 80 c. red .. 5·50 6·00

1941. Surch **10.**

233 **19** 10 c. on 15 c. purple .. 10 10
234 10 c. on 30 c. orange .. 45 40

1942. Air. Surch. **Lire 10** and bars.

235. **50.** 10 l. on 2 l. 60 blue .. 70·00 85·00
236. 10 l. on 3 l. grey .. 16·00 19·00

67. Gajarda Tower, Arbe, and Flags of Italy and San Marino.

1942. Restoration of Italian Flag to Arbe.

237. **67.** 10 c. red & bistre (post.) 10 10
238. 15 c. red and brown .. 10 10
239. 20 c. grey and olive .. 10 10
240. 25 c. blue and green .. 10 10
241. 50 c. brown and red .. 10 10
242. 75 c. grey and red .. 10 10
243. – 1 l. 25 grey and blue .. 10 10
244. – 1 l. 75 grey and brown .. 10 10
245. – 2 l. 75 blue and bistre 25 30
246. – 5 l. brown and green .. 2·00 3·50
247. – 25 c. grey & brn. (air) .. 10 10
248. – 50 c. brown and green .. 10 10
249. – 75 c. brown and blue .. 10 10
250. – 1 l. brown and bistre .. 20 20
251. – 5 l. blue and bistre .. 3·00 3·50

DESIGNS—As Type **67**: HORIZ. Nos. 243/6 Galleon in Arbe Harbour. VERT. Nos. 247/51, Granda Belfry, Arbe.

1942. Italian Philatelic Congress. Surch. **GIORNATA FILATELICA RIMINI—SAN MARINO 3 AGOSTO 1942 (1641 d. F.R.)** and value in figures.

252. **67.** 30 c. on 10 c. red & bistre 10 10

1942. Surch.

253. **67.** 30 c. on 20 c. grey & olive 20 20
254. – 20 l. on 75 c. black and red (No. 222) .. 5·50 6·50

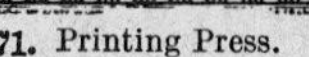

71. Printing Press. 72. Newspapers.

1943. Press Propaganda.
255. **71.** 10 c. green 10 10
256. 15 c. brown 10 10
257. 20 c. brown 10 10
258. 30 c. purple 10 10
259. 50 c. blue 10 10
260. 75 c. red 10 10
261. **72.** 1 l. 25 blue 10 10
262. 1 l. 75 violet 10 10
263. 5 l. blue 20 25
264. 10 l. brown .. .. 2·00 2·25

1943. Philatelic Exhibition. Optd **GIORNATA FILATELICA RIMINI – SAN MARINO 5 LUGLIO 1943 (1642 d. F.R.).**
265 71 30 c. purple 10 10
266 50 c. blue 10 10

74. Gateway. **75.** War Memorial.

1943. Fall of Fascism. Unissued series for 20th Anniv of Fascism optd **28 LVGLIO 1943 1642 d. F.R.** (the "d." is omitted on T 74) and bars cancelling commemorative inscription.
267. **74.** 5 c. brown (postage) .. 10 10
268. 10 c. orange 10 10
269. 20 c. blue 10 10
270. 25 c. green 10 10
271. 30 c. red 10 10
272. 50 c. violet 10 10
273. 75 c. red 10 10
274. **75.** 1 l. 25 blue 10 10
275. 1 l. 75 orange 10 10
276. 2 l. 75 brown 15 15
277. 5 l. green 35 45
278. 10 l. violet 55 70
279. 20 l. blue .. .. 1·40 1·60
280. – 25 c. brown (air) .. 10 10
281. – 50 c. red 10 10
282. – 75 c. brown 10 10
283. – 1 l. purple 10 10
284. – 2 l. blue 10 10
285. – 5 l. orange 35 35
286. – 10 l. green 50 55
287. – 20 l. black .. .. 2·00 2·25
DESIGN—Air: Nos. 280/7, Map of San Marino.

1943. Provisional Govt. Optd. **GOVERNO PROVVISORIO** over ornamentation.
288. **74.** 5 c. brown (postage) .. 10 10
289. 10 c. orange 10 10
290. 20 c. blue 10 10
291. 25 c. green 10 10
292. 30 c. red 10 10
293. 50 c. violet 10 10
294. 75 c. red 10 10
295. **75.** 1 l. 25 blue 10 10
296. 1 l. 75 orange 15 15
297. 5 l. green 35 40
298. 20 l. blue .. .. 1·00 1·25
299. – 25 c. brown (air) .. 10 10
300. – 50 c. red 10 10
301. – 75 c. brown 10 10
302. – 1 l. purple 10 10
303. – 5 l. orange 35 45
304. – 20 l. black .. .. 1·50 1·75

78. St. Marinus. **80.** Govt. Palace.

79. Mt. Titano. **81.** Govt. Palace.

1944.
305. **78.** 20 l. + 10 l. brn. (post.) 40 60
306. **79.** 20 l. + 10 l. olive (air) .. 40 60

1945. 50th Anniv. of Government Palace.
307. **80.** 25 l. purple (postage) .. 7·00 2·50
308. **81.** 25 l. brown (air) .. 7·00 2·50

82. Arms of Montegiardino.

83. Arms of San Marino.

1945. Arms types.
309. – 10 c. blue 10 10
310. **82.** 20 c. red 10 10
311. – 40 c. orange 10 10
312. **82.** 60 c. slate 10 10
313. – 80 c. green 10 10
314. – 1 l. red 10 10
315. – 1 l. 20 violet 10 10
316. – 2 l. brown 20 10
317. – 3 l. blue 20 10
317a. – 4 l. orange 20 10
318. – 5 l. brown 10 10
319. – 10 l. red and brown .. 2·50 85
318a. – 15 l. blue .. .. 1·75 85
320. – 20 l. red and blue .. 5·00 1·40
321. – 20 l. brown and blue .. 8·50 1·40
322. **82.** 25 l. blue and brown .. 7·00 1·50
323. **83.** 50 l. blue and olive .. 9·50 5·50
DESIGNS (Arms of San Marino and villages in the Republic):—10 c., 1 l., 1 l. 20, 15 l. Faetano. 40 c., 5 l. San Marino. 80 c., 2 l., 3 l., 4 l. Fiorentino. 10 l. Borgomaggiore. 20 l. (2) Serravalle.

84. U.N.R.R.A. Aid for San Marino.

1946. U.N.R.R.A.
324. **84.** 100 l. red, purple and orange .. 3·25 3·50

85. Airplane and Mt. Titano.

1946. Air.
325 – 25 c. grey 10 10
326 **85** 75 c. red 10 10
327 – 1 l. brown 10 10
328 **85** 2 l. green 10 10
329 3 l. violet 10 10
330 – 5 l. blue 10 10
331 – 10 l. red 15 15
334 – 20 l. purple .. .. 1·50 1·60
332 – 35 l. red .. .. 5·50 3·50
335 – 50 l. green .. .. 11·00 5·50
333 – 100 l. brown .. .. 2·25 1·10
DESIGNS—HORIZ. 25 c., 1, 10 l. Wings over Mt. Titano. 100 l. Airplane over Globe. VERT. 5, 20, 35, 50 l. Four airplanes over Mt. Titano.

1946. Stamp Day. Surch **L. 10.**
336 83 50 l. + 10 l. blue & green 12·00 6·50

1946. National Philatelic Convention. Nos. 329/31 but colours changed and without "POSTA AEREA" surch **CONVEGNO FILATELICO 30 NOVEMBRE 1946** and premium.
336a **86** 3 l. + 25 l. brown .. 1·00 55
336b – 5 l. + 25 l. orange .. 1·00 55
336c – 10 l. + 50 l. blue .. 11·00 5·50

87. Quotation from F.D.R. on Liberty.

88. Franklin D. Roosevelt.

1947. In Memory of President Franklin D. Roosevelt.
336d. **87.** 1 l. brn. & ochre (post.) 10 10
336e. **88.** 2 l. brown and blue .. 10 10
336f. – 5 l. multicoloured .. 10 10
336g. – 15 l. multicoloured .. 15 10
336h. **87.** 50 l. brown and red .. 60 40
336i. **88.** 100 l. brown and violet 1·00 65
DESIGN—HORIZ.: 5 l., 15 l. Roosevelt and flags of San Marino and U.S.A.
336j. – 1 l. brn. & blue (air) .. 10 10
336k. – 2 l. brown and red .. 10 10
336l. – 5 l. multicoloured .. 10 10
336m. – 20 l. brown and purple 20 10
336n. – 31 l. brn. & orange .. 65 35
336o. – 50 l. brown and red .. 1·25 65
336p. – 100 l. brown and blue 1·75 1·00
336q. – 200 l. multicoloured .. 18·00 19·00
DESIGNS—HORIZ. 1 l., 31 l., 50 l. Roosevelt and eagle. 2 l., 20 l., 100 l. Roosevelt and San Marino arms. VERT. 5 l., 200 l. Roosevelt and flags of San Marino and U.S.A.

1947. Surch. in figures.
336r. **87.** 3 on 1 l. brown and ochre (postage) .. 55 35
336s. **88.** 4 on 2 l. brown and bl. 55 35
336t. – 6 on 5 l. multicoloured (No. 336f) .. 55 35
336u. – 3 on 1 l. brown and blue (No. 336j) (air) 55 35
336v. – 4 on 2 l. brown and red (No. 336k) .. 55 35
336w. – 6 on 5 l. multicoloured (No. 336l) .. 55 35

1947. No. 317a surch.
337. 6 l. on 4 l. orange 20 10
338. 21 l. on 4 l. orange .. 80 65

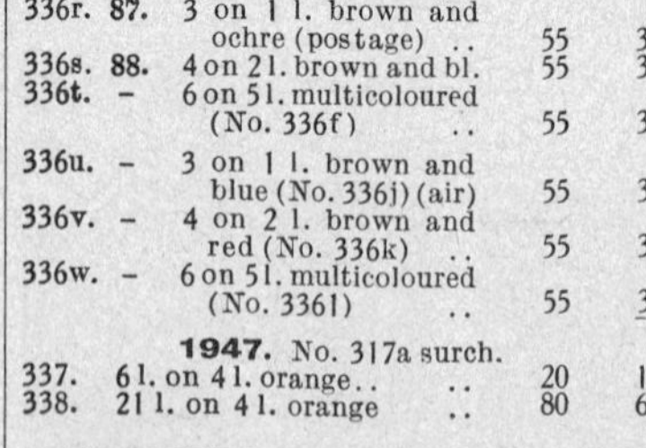

91. St. Marinus Founding Republic. **94.** Mt. Titano, Statue of Liberty and 1847 U.S.A. Stamp.

95. Mt. Titano and 1847 U.S.A. Stamp.

1947. Reconstruction.
339. **91.** 1 l. mve. & grn. (post.) 10 10
340. 2 l. olive and mauve .. 10 10
341. 4 l. green and brown .. 10 10
342. 10 l. blue and orange .. 10 10
343. 25 l. mauve and red .. 70 55
344. 50 l. brown and green .. 18·00 9·00
345. 25 l. blue & orge (air) .. 2·25 1·10
346. 50 l. blue and brown .. 4·50 2·25
Nos. 343/6 are larger (24½ × 32 mm) and have two rows of ornaments forming the frame.

1947. Air. Rimini Philatelic Exhibition. No. 333 optd **Giornata Filatelica Rimini–San Marino 18 Luglio 1947.**
347 100 l. brown .. .. 1·00 70

1947. Reconstruction. Surch + and value in figures.
348 **91** 1 l. + 1 mauve and green 10 10
349 1 l. + 2 mauve and green 10 10
350 1 l. + 3 mauve and green 10 10
351 1 l. + 4 mauve and green 10 10
352 1 l. + 5 mauve and green 10 10
353 2 l. + 1 green and mauve 10 10
354 2 l. + 2 green and mauve 10 10
355 2 l. + 3 green and mauve 10 10
356 2 l. + 4 green and mauve 10 10
357 2 l. + 5 green and mauve 10 10
358 4 l. + 1 green and brown 3·00 1·50
359 4 l. + 2 green and brown 3·00 1·50

1947. Cent. of 1st U.S.A. Postage Stamp
360. **94.** 2 l. brn. & pur. (post.) 10 10
361. – 3 l. grey, red and blue 10 10
362. **94.** 6 l. green and blue .. 10 10
363. – 15 l. violet, red and blue 30 20
364. – 35 l. brown, red and blue 1·00 70
365. – 50 l. green, red and blue 1·25 70
366. **95.** 100 l. brn. & vio. (air) 9·00 5·00
DESIGNS: 3 l., 35 l. U.S.A. stamps, 5 c. and 10 c., 1847 and 90 c., 1869 and flags of U.S.A. and San Marino. 15 l., 50 l. Similar but differently arranged.

96. Worker and San Marino Flag.

1948. Workers' Issue.
367. **96.** 5 l. brown 10 10
368. 8 l. green 10 10
369. 30 l. red 25 20
370. 50 l. brown and mauve 1·60 80
371. 100 l. blue and violet .. 32·00 15·00
See also Nos. 506/7.

1948. Surch **L.100** between circular ornaments.
372 59 100 l. on 15 c. blk & red 38·00 22·00

1948. Air. Surch. **POSTA AEREA 200.**
373. **91.** 200 l. on 25 l. mauve and red (No. 343) 17·00 17·00

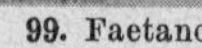

99. Faetano.

100. Mt. Titano.

1949.
374 – 1 l. blue and black .. 10 10
375 – 2 l. red and purple .. 10 10
376 **99** 3 l. blue and violet .. 10 10
377 – 4 l. violet and black 10 10
378 – 5 l. brown and purple 10 10
379 **99** 6 l. black and blue .. 55 20
380 **100** 8 l. brown & dp brn 40 20
381 – 10 l. blue and black 45 10
382 – 12 l. violet and red .. 1·00 40
383 – 15 l. red and violet .. 2·75 60
383a **99** 20 l. brown and blue 5·50 65
384 – 35 l. violet and green 5·00 1·50
385 – 50 l. brown and red .. 2·75 65
385a – 55 l. green and blue 30·00 12·00
386 **100** 100 l. green & brown 75·00 18·00
387 – 200 l. brown and blue 75·00 38·00
DESIGNS—HORIZ. 1, 5, 35 l. Guaita Tower and walls. 2, 12, 50 l. Serravalle and Mt Titano. 4, 15, 55 l. Franciscan Convent and Capuchin Church. VERT. 10, 200 l. Guaita Tower.
For similar stamps see Nos. 491/5, 522a/7a and 794/9.

1949. Stamp Day. Optd. **Gionata Filatelica San Marino - Riccione 28-6-1949.**
388. **91.** 1 l. mauve and green .. 15 10
389. 2 l. olive and mauve .. 15 10

104. Garibaldi.

105. Garibaldi in San Marino.

1949. Centenary of Garibaldi's Retreat from Rome. (a) Postage. Portraits as T **104**.
(i) Size 22 × 28 mm.
390 – 1 l. red and black .. 10 10
391 – 2 l. blue and brown .. 10 10
392 **104** 3 l. green and red .. 10 10
393 – 4 l. brown and blue .. 10 10
(ii) Size 27 × 37 mm.
394 – 5 l. brown and mauve 10 10
395 – 15 l. blue and red .. 1·00 55
396 – 20 l. red and violet .. 1·50 75
397 **104** 50 l. violet and purple 16·00 8·50
(b) Air. (i) Size 28 × 22 mm.
398 **105** 2 l. blue and purple .. 10 10
399 3 l. black and green .. 10 10
400 5 l. green and blue .. 15 15
(ii) Size 37 × 27 mm.
401 **105** 25 l. violet and green 3·50 1·75
402 65 l. black and green .. 11·00 5·50
PORTRAITS—VERT. 1, 20 l. Francesco Nullo. 2, 5 l. Anita Garibaldi. 4, 15 l. Ugo Bassi.
See also Nos. 538/44.

106. Mail Coach and Mt. Titano.

1949. 75th Anniv of U.P.U.
403 **106** 100 l. purple & bl (post) 8·00 5·00
404 200 l. blue (air) .. 1·50 1·25
405 300 l. brown, light brown and purple .. 10·00 10·00

107. Mt. Titano from Serravalle.

108. Second and Guaita Towers.

109. Guaita Tower.

1950. Air. Views.

406 107 2 l. green and violet .. 10 10
407 – 3 l. brown and blue .. 10 10
408 108 5 l. red and brown (22×28 mm) .. 10 10
409 – 10 l. blue and green .. 1·10 20
410 – 15 l. violet and black 1·60 25
411 – 55 l. green and blue .. 18·00 9·00
412 107 100 l. black and red (37×27 mm) .. 10·00 2·50
413 108 250 l. brown and violet 40·00 12·00
414 109 500 l. brown and green (37×27 mm) .. £110 70·00
415 500 l. purple, grn & bl 60·00 48·00

DESIGNS—As Type **107**: 3 l. Distant view of Domagnano. 10 l. Domagnano. 15 l. San Marino from St. Mustiola. As Type **108**: 55 l. Borgo Maggiore.

1950. Air. 28th Milan Fair. As Nos. 408, 410 and 411 but in different colours, optd. **XXVIII FIERA INTERNAZIONALE DI MILANO APRILE 1950.**

416. 5 l. green and blue .. 10 10
417. 15 l. black and red .. 80 60
418. 55 l. brown and violet .. 3·50 2·50

111. Government Palace. **113.** Flag, 'Plane and Mt. Titano.

1951. Red Cross.

419. 111. 25 l. pur., red & brown 6·50 3·00
420. – 75 l. sepia, red & brown 9·00 6·00
421. – 100 l. black, red & brown 9·50 5·00

DESIGNS—HORIZ. 75 l. Archway of Murata Nuova. VERT. 100 l. Guaita Tower.

1951. Air. Stamp Day. No. 415 surch **Giornata Filatelica San Marino–Riccione 20-8-1951** and new value.

422 109 300 l. on 500 l. purple, green and blue .. 35·00 28·00

1951. Air.

423 113 1000 l. blue and brown £300 £190

1951. Air. Italian Flood Relief. Surch. **Pro-alluvionati italiani 1951 L. 100** and bars.

424. 108. 100 l. on 250 l. brown and violet .. 5·50 3·50

115. "Columbus at the Council of Salamanca" (after Barabino).

1952. 500th Birth Anniv (1951) of Christopher Columbus.

425 115 1 l. orange & grn (post) 10 15
426 – 2 l. brown and violet 10 15
427 – 3 l. violet and brown 10 15
428 – 4 l. blue and brown .. 10 15
429 – 5 l. green and turquoise 20 20
430 – 10 l. brown and black 60 40
431 – 15 l. red and black .. 1·25 60
432 – 20 l. blue and green .. 1·75 70
433 – 25 l. purple and brown 7·00 2·50
434 115 60 l. brown and violet 9·00 4·50
435 – 80 l. grey and black .. 25·00 11·00
436 – 200 l. green and blue .. 45·00 22·00
437 – 200 l. blue & black (air) 35·00 16·00

DESIGNS—HORIZ. 2, 25 l. Columbus and fleet. 3, 10, 20 l. Landing in America. 4, 15, 80 l. Red Indians and American settlers. 5, 200 (No. 436) l. Columbus and Map of America. 200 l. (No. 437), Columbus, Statue of Liberty (New York) and skyscrapers.

1952. Trieste Fair. As Columbus issue of 1952, but colours changed, optd **FIERA DI TRIESTE 1952**.

438 1 l. violet and brown (post) 10 15
439 2 l. red and black .. 10 15
440 3 l. green and turquoise .. 10 15
441 4 l. brown and black .. 10 15
442 5 l. mauve and violet .. 30 30
443 10 l. blue and brown .. 1·75 75
444 15 l. red and blue .. 6·00 2·50
445 200 l. brown and black (air) 35·00 16·00

117. Rose.

118. Cyclamen, Rose San Marino and Riccione

1952. Air. Stamp Day and Philatelic Exn.

446. – 1 l. purple and violet .. 10* 10
447. – 2 l. green and blue .. 10 10
448. 117. 3 l. red and sepia .. 10 10
449. 118. 5 l. brown and purple .. 10 10
450. 25 l. green and violet .. 35 35
451. 200 l. multicoloured .. 35·00 18·00

DESIGNS—As Type **117**: 1 l. Cyclamen. 2 l. San Marino and Riccione.

DESIGN: 75 l. 'Plane over Mt. Titano.

119. Aeroplane over San Marino.

1952. Air. Aerial Survey of San Marino.

452. 119. 25 l. green .. .. 1·75 1·00
453. – 75 l. violet and brown .. 5·50 3·50

120. "The Discus Thrower".

121. Tennis.

1953. Sports.

454. 120. 1 l. blk. & brn. (postage) 10 10
455. 121. 2 l. brown and black .. 10 10
456. – 3 l. turquoise and black 10 10
457. – 4 l. blue and green .. 10 10
458. – 5 l. green and brown .. 10 10
459. – 10 l. red and blue .. 30 30
460. – 25 l. brown and black .. 2·00 90
461. – 100 l. grey and brown .. 7·00 3·00
462. – 200 l. turq. & grn. (air) 75·00 38·00

DESIGNS—As Type **120**: 3 l. Running. As Type **121**: HORIZ. 4 l. Cycling. 5 l. Football. 100 l. Roller skating. 200 l. Skiing. VERT. 10 l. Model glider flying. 25 l. Shooting.
See also No. 584.

1953. Stamp Day and Philatelic Exn. As No. 461 but colour changed, optd. **GIORNATA FILATELICA S. MARINO-RICCIONE 24 AGOSTO 1953.**

463. 100 l. green and blue .. 18·00 10·00

FLOWERS: 2 l. "Parrot" tulip. 3 l. Oleander. 4 l. Cornflower. 5 l. Carnation. 10 l. Iris. 25 l. Cyclamen. 80 l. Geranium. 100 l. Rose.

123. Narcissus.

1953. Flowers.

464. 123. 1 l. blue, green & yellow 10 10
465. – 2 l. blue, green & yellow 10 10
466. – 3 l. blue, green & yellow 10 10
467. – 4 l. blue, green & yellow 10 10
468. – 5 l. green and red .. 10 10
469. – 10 l. blue, green & yellow 20 20
470. – 25 l. blue, green and red 3·50 1·40
471. – 80 l. blue, green & red .. 17·00 9·00
472. – 100 l. blue, green & red 26·00 13·00

124. Mt. Titano and Arms.

1954. Air.

473. 124. 1000 l. sepia and blue 65·00 50·00

125. Walking. **126.** Statue of Liberty.

1954. Sports.

474. 125. 1 l. mauve and violet .. 10 10
475. – 2 l. violet and green .. 10 10
476. – 3 l. chestnut and brown 10 10
477. – 4 l. blue.. .. .. 10 10
478. – 5 l. sepia and green .. 10 10
479. – 8 l. lilac and mauve .. 20 10
480. – 12 l. red and black .. 20 10
481. – 25 l. green and blue .. 65 20
482. 125. 80 l. turquoise and blue 1·10 60
483. – 200 l. brown and lilac .. 5·00 2·50
484. – 250 l. multicoloured .. 55·00 29·00

DESIGNS—HORIZ. 2 l. Fencing. 3 l. Boxing. 5 l. Motor-cycle racing. 8 l. Throwing the javelin. 12 l. Car racing. VERT. 4 l., 200 l., 250 l. Gymnastics. 25 l. Wrestling.

1954.

485. 126. 20 l. blue & brn. (post.) 20 10
486. 60 l. green and red .. 70 35
487. 120 l. brown & blue (air) 1·25 60

127. Hurdling. **128.** Yacht.

1955. Air. 1st Int. Exn. of Olympic Stamps.

488. 127. 80 l. black and red .. 1·10 60
489. – 120 l. red and green .. 1·60 1·00

DESIGN—HORIZ. 120 l. Relay racing.

1955. 7th International Philatelic Exhibition.

490 128 100 l. black and blue .. 3·25 1·50
See also No. 518.

1955. As T **99**.

491 5 l. brown and blue .. 10 10
492 10 l. green and orange .. 10 10
493 15 l. red and green .. 10 10
494 25 l. violet and brown .. 10 10
495 35 l. red and lilac .. 30 15

DESIGNS—HORIZ. 5, 25 l. Archway of Murata Nuova. VERT. 10, 35 l. Guaita Tower. 15 l. Government Palace.
See also Nos. 519/21 and 797/9.

129. Ice Skating. **130.** Pointer.

1955. Winter Olympic Games, Cortina D'Ampezzo.

496. 129. 1 l. brown & yell. (post.) 10 10
497. – 2 l. blue and red .. 10 10
498. – 3 l. black and brown .. 10 10
499. – 4 l. brown and green .. 10 10
500. – 5 l. blue and red .. 10 10
501. – 10 l. blue and pink .. 20 15
502. – 25 l. black and red .. 1·00 55
503. – 50 l. brown and blue .. 2·50 1·25
504. – 100 l. black and green .. 7·50 3·00
505. – 200 l. blk. & orge. (air) .. 27·00 14·00

DESIGNS—HORIZ. 2, 25 l. Skiing. 3, 50 l. Bobsleighing. 5, 100 l. Ice hockey. 200 l. Ski jumping. VERT. 4 l. Slalom racing. 10 l. Figure skating.

1956. Winter Relief Fund. As T **96** but additionally inscr. "ASSISTENZA INVERNALE".

506. 50 l. green .. .. .. 5·00 4·50

1956. 50th Anniv. of "Arengo" (San Marino Parliament). As T **96** but additionally inscr. "50° ANNIVERSARIO ARENGO 25 MARZO 1906".

507. 50 l. blue .. .. .. 5·00 4·50

1956. Dogs. 25 l. to 100 l. have multicoloured centres.

508. 130. 1 l. brown and blue .. 10 10
509. – 2 l. grey and red .. 10 10
510. – 3 l. brown and blue .. 10 10
511. – 4 l. grey and turquoise 10 10
512. – 5 l. brown and red .. 10 10
513. – 10 l. brown and blue .. 10 10
514. – 25 l. blue 30 15
515. – 60 l. red .. .. 2·00 1·25
516. – 80 l. blue .. .. 3·50 1·75
517. – 100 l. red .. .. 6·00 3·25

DOGS: 2 l. Borzoi. 3 l. Sheepdog. 4 l. Greyhound. 5 l. Boxer. 10 l. Great dane. 25 l. Irish setter. 60 l. Alsatian. 80 l. Rough collie. 100 l. Foxhound.

1956. Philatelic Exn. As T **128** but inscr "1956".

518. 128. 100 l. sepia & turquoise 1·75 1·25

1956. International Philatelic Congress. Designs as Nos. 491/5 but larger and new values inscr "CONGRESSO INTERNAZ. PERITI FILATELICI SAN MARINO SALSOMAGGIORE 6–8 OTTOBRE 1956".

519 20 l. brown and blue .. 40 20
520 80 l. red and violet .. 4·00 2·50
521 100 l. green and orange .. 1·40 1·25

SIZES—26½×37 mm. 20 l. Guaita Tower. 100 l. Government Palace. 36½×27 mm. 80 l. Archway Murata Nuova.

1956. Air. No. 504 optd. with an aeroplane and **POSTA AEREA.**

522. 100 l. black and green .. 1·40 1·25

1957. As T **99**.

522a 1 l. green and deep green 10 10
523 2 l. red and green .. 10 10
524 3 l. brown and blue .. 10 10
524a 4 l. blue and brown .. 10 10
525 20 l. green and deep green 15 10
525a 30 l. violet and brown .. 55 30
526 60 l. violet and brown .. 85 60
526a 115 l. brown and blue .. 35 25
527 125 l. blue and black .. 45 30
527a 500 l. black and green .. 55·00 30·00

DESIGNS—VERT: 2 l. Borgo Maggiore Church. 3, 30 l. Town gate, San Marino. 4, 125 l. View of San Marino from southern wall. 20, 115 l. Borgo Maggiore market-place. HORIZ: 1, 60 l. View of San Marino from Hospital Avenue. 37½×28 mm: 500 l. Panorama of San Marino.
See also Nos. 794/6.

132. Marguerites. **134.** St. Marinus Statue and Fair Entrance.

1957. Flowers as T **132** in natural colours. Background colour blue (Nos. 528/32), rest multicoloured.

528. 1 l. Type **132** 10 10
529. 2 l. Polyanthuses 10 10
530. 3 l. Lilies 10 10
531. 4 l. Orchid 10 10
532. 5 l. Lilies of the Valley .. 10 10
533. 10 l. Poppies 10 10
534. 25 l. Pansies 10 10
535. 60 l. Gladiolus 45 30
536. 80 l. Wild Roses 90 50
537. 100 l. Anemones .. .. 1·50 85

1957. 150th Birth Anniv of Garibaldi. As T **104** but inscr "COMMEMORAZIONE 150° NASCITA G. GARIBALDI 1807 1957".

(a) Size 22×28 mm.

538 – 2 l. blue and violet (as No. 391) 10 10
539 – 3 l. green and red (as No. 390) 10 10
540 104 5 l. drab and brown .. 10 10

(b) Size 27×37 mm.

541 – 15 l. violet and blue (as No. 395) 10 10
542 – 25 l. black and green (as No. 396) .. 20 20
543 – 50 l. brown and violet (as No. 394) .. 1·40 1·00
544 104 100 l. violet and brown 1·40 1·00

1958. 36th Milan Fair.

545. 134. 15 l. yell. & blue (post.) 15 10
546. – 60 l. green and red .. 50 55
547. – 125 l. blue & brn. (air) 2·25 2·00

DESIGNS—HORIZ. 60 l. Italian pavilion and giant arch. VERT. 125 l. Helicopter and aeroplane over fair.

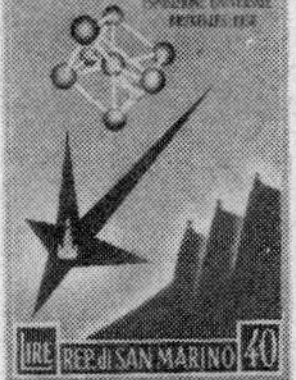

135. Exhibition Emblem, Atomium and Mt. Titano. **136.** View of San Marino.

1958. Brussels Int. Exn.

548. 135. 40 l. sepia and green .. 20 15
549. 60 l. lake and blue .. 25 30

1958. Air.

550. 136. 200 l. blue and brown .. 2·00 2·00
551. – 300 l. violet and red .. 2·00 2·00

DESIGN: 300 l. Mt. Titano.

137. Wheat. **138.** Naples 10 grana stamp of 1858, and Bay of Naples.

1958. Fruit and Agricultural Products.
552 **137** 1 l. yellow and blue .. 10 10
553 – 2 l. red and green .. 10 10
554 – 3 l. orange and blue .. 10 10
555 – 4 l. red and green .. 10 10
556 – 5 l. yellow, green & bl 10 10
557 **137** 15 l. yellow, brn & bl 10 10
558 – 25 l. multicoloured .. 10 10
559 – 40 l. multicoloured .. 35 20
560 – 80 l. multicoloured .. 75 40
561 – 125 l. multicoloured .. 3·25 1·50
Designs: 2, 125 l. Maize. 3, 80 l. Grapes. 4, 25 l. Peaches. 5, 40 l. Plums.

1958. Cent. of First Naples Postage Stamps.
562. **138.** 25 l. brn. & blue (post.) 30 20
563. 125 l. brown & bistre-brown (air) .. 2·00 1·40
The Naples stamp on No. 563 is the 50 gr.

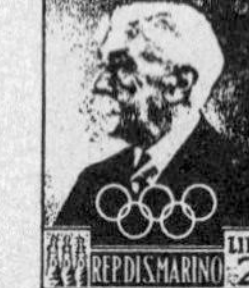

139. Mediterranean Gull. **140.** P. de Coubertin (founder).

1959. Air. Native Birds.
564 **139** 5 l. black and green .. 20 10
565 – 10 l. brown, black & bl 20 10
566 – 15 l. multicoloured .. 20 10
567 – 120 l. multicoloured .. 1·10 35
568 – 250 l. black, yell & grn 3·25 1·00
Birds: 10 l. Common kestrel. 15 l. Mallard. 120 l. Rock dove. 250 l. Barn swallow.

1959. Pre-Olympic Games Issue.
569. **140.** 2 l. blk., & brn. (post.) 10 10
570. – 3 l. sepia and mauve .. 10 10
571. – 5 l. green and blue .. 10 10
572. – 30 l. black and violet .. 10 10
573. – 60 l. sepia and green .. 10 10
574. – 80 l. green and lake .. 10 10
575. – 120 l. brown (air) .. 80 70
Portraits—As Type **140**: 3 l. A. Bonacossa. 5 l. A. Brundage. 30 l. C. Montu. 60 l. J. S. Edstrom. 80 l. De Baillet-Latour. Horiz. (36×21½ mm.): 120 l. De Coubertin and Olympic Flame. All, except the founder, De Coubertin, are executives of the Olympic Games Committee.

141. Vickers "Viscount" over Mt. Titano.

1959. Air "Alitalia" Inaugural Flight, Rimini-London.
576. **141.** 120 l. violet .. .. 1·50 1·00

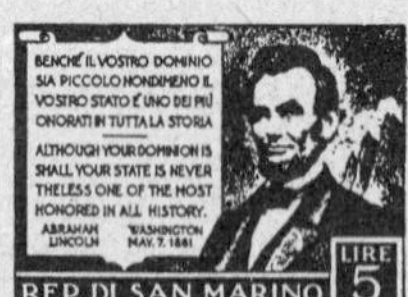

142. Abraham Lincoln and Scroll.

1959. Abraham Lincoln's 150th Birth Anniv. Inscr. "ABRAMO LINCOLN 1809–1959".
577. **142.** 5 l. brn. & sepia (post.) 10 10
578. – 10 l. green and blue .. 10 10
579. – 15 l. grey and green .. 10 10
580. – 70 l. violet 85 60
581. – 200 l. blue (air) .. 3·00 2·50
Designs—Portraits of Lincoln with: horiz. 10 l. Map of San Marino. 15 l. Govt. Palace, San Marino. 200 l. Mt. Titano. vert. 70 l. Mt. Titano.

143. 1859 Romagna ½ b. stamp and Arch of Augustus, Rimini. **144.** Portal of Messina Cathedral and ½ gr. Sicily stamp.

1959. Romagna Stamp Centenary Inscr. "1859–1959".
582. **143.** 30 l. brn., & sepia (post.) 20 15
583. – 120 l. grn. & blk. (air) 1·40 1·25
Design: 120 l. 1859 Romagna 3 b. stamp and view of Bologna.

1959. World University Games, Turin. Inscr "UNIVERSIADE TORINO 1959".
584 **120** 30 l. red 40 35

1959. Sicily Stamp Centenary.
585. **144.** 1 l. brn. & yell. (post.) .. 10 10
586. – 2 l. red and olive .. 10 10
587. – 3 l. slate and blue .. 10 10
588. – 4 l. brown and red .. 10 10
589. – 5 l. mauve and blue .. 10 10
590. – 25 l. multicoloured .. 10 10
591. – 60 l. multicoloured .. 10 10
592. – 200 l. multicoloured (air) 75 65
Designs—vert. 2 l. Selinunte Temple (1 gr.). 3 l. Erice Church (2 gr.). 4 l. "Concordia" Temple, Agrigento (5 gr.). 5 l. "Castor and Pollux" Temple, Agrigento (10 gr.). 25 l. "St. John of the Hermits" Church, Palermo (20 gr.). horiz. 60 l. Taormina (50 gr.). 200 l. Bay of Palermo (50 gr.).

145. Golden Oriole. **146.** Putting the Shot.

1960. Birds.
593. **145.** 1 l. yell., olive and blue 10 10
594. – 2 l. brown, red and green 10 10
595. – 3 l. red, brown and green 10 10
596. – 4 l. black, brown & grn. 10 10
597. – 5 l. red, brown and green 10 10
598. – 10 l. multicoloured .. 10 10
599. – 25 l. multicoloured .. 55 15
600. – 60 l. multicoloured .. 1·90 70
601. – 80 l. multicoloured .. 3·25 1·25
602. – 110 l. multicoloured .. 3·75 1·75
Designs—vert. 2 l. Nightingale. 4 l. Hoopoe. 10 l. Goldfinch. 25 l. Common kingfisher. 80 l. Green woodpecker. 110 l. Red-breasted flycatcher. horiz. 3 l. Woodcock. 5 l. Red-legged partridge. 60 l. Ring-necked pheasant.

1960. Olympic Games.
603 **146** 1 l. violet & red (post) 10 10
604 – 2 l. orange and black 10 10
605 – 3 l. violet and brown 10 10
606 – 4 l. brown and red .. 10 10
607 – 5 l. blue and brown .. 10 10
608 – 10 l. blue and brown .. 10 10
609 – 15 l. violet and green 10 10
610 – 25 l. orange and green 10 10
611 – 60 l. brown and green 10 10
612 – 110 l. red, black & grn 10 10
613 – 20 l. violet (air) .. 10 10
614 – 40 l. red and brown .. 10 10
615 – 80 l. yellow and blue .. 15 10
616 – 125 l. brown and red .. 25 20
Designs—vert. 2 l. Gymnastics. 3 l. Long-distance walking. 4 l. Boxing. 10 l. Cycling. 20 l. Handball. 40 l. Breasting the tape. 60 l. Football. horiz. 5 l. Fencing. 15 l. Hockey. 25 l. Rowing. 80 l. Diving. 110 l. Horse-jumping. 125 l. Rifle-shooting.

147. Melvin Jones (founder) and Lions International H.Q.

1960. Lions International Commem.
617. – 30 l. brn. & violet (post.) 10 10
618. **147.** 45 l. brown and violet .. 40 40
619. – 60 l. red and blue .. 10 10
620. – 115 l. green and black .. 40 40
621. – 150 l. brown and violet 1·60 1·40
622. – 200 l. blue & green (air) 3·25 3·25
Designs—vert. 30 l. Mt. Titano. 60 l. San Marino Government Palace. horiz. 115 l. Pres. Clarence Sturm. 150 l. Vice-Pres. Finis E. Davis. 200 l. Globe. All designs except Type **147** bear the Lions emblem.

148. Riccione. **149.** "Youth with Basket of Fruit".

1960. 12th Riccione-San Marino Stamp Day. Centres multicoloured.
623. **148.** 30 l. red (post.) .. 30 15
624. 125 l. blue (air) .. .. 1·40 1·25

1960. 350th Death Anniv. of Michelangelo Merisi da Caravaggio (painter).
625. **149.** 200 l. multicoloured .. 4·25 4·00

150. Hunting Roe Deer.

1961. Hunting (1st issue). Historical Scenes.
626 **150** 1 l. blue and mauve .. 10 10
627 – 2 l. red and brown .. 10 10
628 – 3 l. black and red .. 10 10
629 – 4 l. red and blue .. 10 10
630 – 5 l. brown and green .. 10 10
631 – 10 l. violet and orange 10 10
632 – 30 l. blue and yellow .. 10 10
633 – 60 l. brown, orge & blk 20 15
634 – 70 l. red, purple & grn 30 20
635 – 115 l. blue, pur & blk 60 40
Designs—vert. 2 l. 16th-cent. falconer. 10 l. 16th-cent. falconer (mounted). 60 l. 17th-cent. hunter with rifle and dog. horiz. 3 l. 16th-cent. wild boar-hunt. 4 l. Duck-shooting with crossbow (16th-cent.). 5 l. 16th-cent. stag-hunt with bow and arrow. 30 l. 17th-cent. huntsman with horn and dogs. 70 l. 18th-cent. hunter and beater. 115 l. Duck-shooting with bow and arrow (18th-cent.).
See also Nos. 679/88.

151. Agusta-Bell 47-J "Ranger" Helicopter near Mt. Titano.

1961. Air.
636. **151.** 1,000 l. red .. .. 30·00 24·00

152. Guaita Tower, Mt. Titano and 1858 Sardinian Stamp.

1961. Centenary of Italian Independence. Philatelic Exhibition, Turin.
637. **152.** 30 l. multicoloured .. 50 40
638. 70 l. multicoloured .. 70 55
639. 200 l. multicoloured .. 80 60

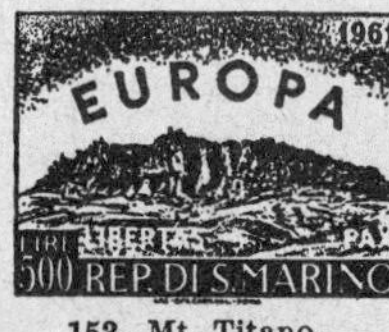

153. Mt. Titano. **155.** King Enzo's Palace, Bologna.

1961. Europa.
640. **153.** 500 l. green & brown 4·50 5·00

1961. Bologna Stamp Exhibition. Inscr. "BOLOGNA".
641. **155.** 30 l. black and blue .. 10 10
642. – 70 l. black and myrtle 15 10
643. – 100 l. black and brown 15 15
Designs: 70 l. Gateway of Merchant's Palace. 100 l. Towers of Garisenda and Asinelli, Bologna.

156. Duryea—U.S.A., 1892.

1962. Veteran Motor Cars.
644. 1 l. blue and brown .. 10 10
645. 2 l. orange and blue .. 10 10
646. 3 l. orange and black .. 10 10
647. 4 l. red and black .. 10 10
648. 5 l. orange and violet .. 10 10
649. 10 l. orange and black .. 10 10
650. 15 l. red and black .. 10 10
651. 20 l. blue and black .. 10 10
652. 25 l. orange and black .. 10 10
653. 30 l. buff and black .. 10 10
654. 50 l. mauve and black .. 10 10
655. 70 l. green and black .. 20 10
656. 100 l. red, yellow and black 25 15
657. 115 l. grn., orange & black 25 15
658. 150 l. yellow, orge. & blk. 50 30
Motor cars—horiz. 1 l. Type **156**. 2 l. Panhard and Levassor, 1895. 3 l. Peugeot "Vis-a-vis", 1895. 4 l. Daimler, 1899. 10 l. Decauville, 1900. 15 l. Wolseley, 1901. 20 l. Benz, 1902. 25 l. Napier, 1903. 50 l. Oldsmobile, 1904. 100 l. Isotta Fraschini, 1908. 115 l. Bianchi, 1910. 150 l. Alfa, 1910. vert. 5 l. F.I.A.T., 1899. 30 l. White, 1903. 70 l. Renault, 1904.

157. Wright "Flyer". **158.** Roping Down.

1962. "Vintage" Aircraft.
659. 1 l. black and yellow .. 10 10
660. 2 l. brown and green .. 10 10
661. 3 l. brown and green .. 10 10
662. 4 l. black and bistre .. 10 10
663. 5 l. red and blue 10 10
664. 10 l. brown and turquoise 10 10
665. 30 l. bistre and blue .. 10 10
666. 60 l. bistre and violet .. 15 15
667. 70 l. black and orange .. 20 15
668. 115 l. bistre, black & green 45 30
Designs—Aircraft constructed and flown by: 1 l. Type **157**. 2 l. Ernest Archdeacon. 3 l. Albert and Emile Bonnet-Labranche. 4 l. Glenn Curtiss. 5 l. Henri Farman. 10 l. Louis Bleriot. 30 l. Hubert Latham. 60 l. Alberto Santos-Dumont. 70 l. Alliott Verdon-Roe. 115 l. Faccioli.

1962. Mountaineering.
669. 1 l. bistre and black .. 10 10
670. 2 l. turquoise and black .. 10 10
671. 3 l. purple and black .. 10 10
672. 4 l. blue and black .. 10 10
673. 5 l. orange and black .. 10 10
674. 15 l. yellow and black .. 10 10
675. 30 l. red and black .. 10 10
676. 40 l. blue and black .. 10 10
677. 85 l. green and black .. 20 20
678. 115 l. blue and black .. 30 30
Designs: 1 l. Type **158**. 2 l. Sassolungo. 3 l. Mt. Titano. 4 l. Three Lavaredo peaks. 5 l. The Matterhorn. 15 l. Skier. 30 l. Climber negotiating overhang. 40 l. Step-cutting in ice. 85 l. Aiguille du Geant. 115 l. Citadel of Mt. Titano.

159. Hunter and Retriever.

1962. Hunting (2nd issue). Modern scenes.
679. 1 l. deep purple and green 10 10
680. 2 l. blue and orange .. 10 10
681. 3 l. black and blue .. 10 10
682. 4 l. sepia and brown .. 10 10
683. 5 l. brown and green .. 10 10
684. 15 l. black and brown .. 15 10
685. 50 l. sepia and green .. 15 10
686. 70 l. turquoise and red .. 20 15
687. 100 l. black and red .. 50 50
688. 150 l. green and lilac .. 50 50
Designs—horiz. 1 l. Type **159**. Hunting: 3 l. Marsh ducks (with decoys). 4 l. Roe deer. 5 l. Grey partridge. 15 l. Lapwing. 50 l. Partridge. 70 l. Marsh geese. 100 l. Wild boar. vert. 2 l. Huntsman and hounds. 150 l. Hunter shooting pheasant.

160. Arrows encircling "Europa".

1962. Europa.
689. **160.** 200 l. red and black .. 1·25 1·25

161. Egyptian Merchant Ship, 2000 B.C.

1963. Historical Ships.
690. 1 l. blue and orange .. 10 10
691. 2 l. sepia and purple .. 10 10
692. 3 l. sepia and mauve .. 10 10
693. 4 l. dull purple and grey .. 10 10
694. 5 l. sepia and yellow .. 10 10
695. 10 l. brown and green .. 10 10
696. 30 l. sepia and blue .. 65 35
697. 60 l. blue and green .. 50 40
698. 70 l. red and deep grey .. 70 70
699. 115 l. brown and blue .. 1·40 1·10

DESIGNS—HORIZ. 1 l. Type **161**. 2 l. Greek trier, 5th century, B.C. 3 l. Roman trireme, 1st century, B.C. 4 l. Viking longship, 10th century. 5 l. The "Santa Maria". 30 l. Galley circa 1600. 115 l. "Duncan Dunbar" (full-rigged merchantman), 1850. VERT. 10 l. Carrack circa 1550. 60 l. "Sovereign of the Seas" (English galleon), 1637. 70 l. Danish ship of the line, circa 1750.

162. "The Fornarina" (or "The Veiled Woman"). **163.** Saracen Game, Arezzo.

1963. Paintings by Raphael. Multicoloured.
700. 30 l. Type **162** 35 35
701. 70 l. Self-portrait 15 15
702. 100 l. Sistine Madonna (detail of woman praying) .. 20 20
703. 200 l. "Portrait of a Young Woman" (Maddalena Strozzi) 35 35
The 200 l. is larger (27 × 44 mm.)

1963. Ancient Tournaments.
704 **163** 1 l. mauve 10 10
705 – 2 l. black 10 10
706 – 3 l. black 10 10
707 – 4 l. violet 10 10
708 – 5 l. violet 10 10
709 – 10 l. green 10 10
710 – 30 l. red 10 10
711 – 60 l. blue 10 10
712 – 70 l. brown 10 10
713 – 115 l. black 20 20

TOURNAMENTS—HORIZ. 2 l. 14th-century, French cavaliers. 4 l. 15th-century, Presenting arms to an English cavalier. 30 l. Quintana game, Foligno. 70 l. 15th-century, Cavaliers (from castle mural, Malpaga). VERT. 3 l. Crossbow Championships, Gubbio. 5 l. 16th-century, Cavaliers, Florence. 10 l. Quintana game, Ascoli Piceno. 60 l. Palio (horse-race), Siena. 115 l. 13th-century, The Crusades: cavaliers' challenge.

164. Peacock. **165.** Corner of Government Palace, San Marino.

1963. Butterflies. Multicoloured.
714 25 l. Type **164** 15 10
715 30 l. "Nessaea obrinus" .. 20 10
716 60 l. Large tortoiseshell .. 30 15
717 70 l. Peacock (horiz) .. 35 20
718 115 l. "Papilio blumei" (horiz) 50 25

1963. San Marino–Riccione Stamp Fair.
719. **165.** 100 l. black and blue .. 15 15
720. – 100 l. blue and sepia .. 15 15
DESIGN: No. 720 Fountain, Riccione.

166. Pole Vaulting. **167.** "E" and Flag of San Marino.

1963. Olympic Games, Tokyo (1964) (1st issue).
721. – 1 l. purple and orange 10 10
722. **166.** 2 l. sepia and green .. 10 10
723. – 3 l. sepia and blue .. 10 10
724. – 4 l. sepia and blue .. 10 10
725. – 5 l. sepia and red .. 10 10
726. – 10 l. mauve and purple 10 10
727. – 30 l. purple and grey .. 10 10
728. – 60 l. sepia and yellow .. 10 10
729. – 70 l. sepia and blue .. 10 10
730. – 115 l. sepia and green 15 10

SPORTS—HORIZ. 1 l. Hurdling. 3 l. Relay-racing. 4 l. High jumping (men). 5 l. Football. 10 l. High jumping (women). 60 l. Throwing the javelin. 70 l. Water-polo. 115 l. Throwing the hammer. VERT. 30 l. Throwing the discus.
See also Nos. 743/52.

1963. Europa.
731. **167.** 200 l. blue and brown 30 30

168. Tupolev "TU-104A". **169.** Running.

1963. Air. Contemporary Aircraft.
732 **168** 5 l. purple, brown & bl 10 10
733 – 10 l. blue and red .. 10 10
734 – 15 l. red, mauve & vio 10 10
735 – 25 l. red, mauve & vio 10 10
736 – 50 l. red and blue .. 10 10
737 – 75 l. orange and green 10 10
738 – 120 l. red and blue .. 20 20
739 – 200 l. black and yellow 20 15
740 – 300 l. black and orange 20 20
741 – 500 l. multicoloured .. 3·25 2·75
742 – 1000 l. multicoloured .. 2·00 1·60

AIRCRAFT—HORIZ. 15 l. Douglas "DC-8". 25 l. Boeing "707". 50 l. Vickers "Viscount 837". 120 l. Vickers "VC-10". 200 l. D. H. "Comet 4 C". 300 l. Boeing "727". 1000 l. Boeing "707". VERT. 10 l. Boeing "707". 75 l. "Caravelle". 500 l. Rolls Royce "Dart" turbo-prop engine.

1964. Olympic Games, Tokyo (2nd issue).
743 **169** 1 l. brown and green .. 10 10
744 – 2 l. brown and sepia .. 10 10
745 – 3 l. brown and black .. 10 10
746 – 4 l. blue and red .. 10 10
747 – 5 l. brown and blue .. 10 10
748 – 15 l. purple and orange 10 10
749 – 30 l. blue and light blue 10 10
750 – 70 l. brown and green 15 15
751 – 120 l. brown and blue 15 15
752 – 150 l. purple and red .. 20 20

DESIGNS—VERT. 2 l. Gymnastics. 3 l. Basket-ball. 120 l. Cycling. 150 l. Fencing. HORIZ. 4 l. Pistol-shooting. 5 l. Rowing. 15 l. Long jumping. 30 l. Diving. 70 l. Sprinting.

1964. "Towards Tokyo" Sports Stamp Exn. Rimini. As Nos. 749/50, but inscr. "VERSO TOKIO" and colours changed.
753. 30 l. blue and violet .. 15 10
754. 70 l. brown and turquoise 15 10

170. Murray Blenkinsop Locomotive (1812).

1964. "Story of the Locomotive".
755. **170.** 1 l. black and buff .. 10 10
756. – 2 l. black and green .. 10 10
757. – 3 l. black and violet .. 10 10
758. – 4 l. black and yellow .. 10 10
759. – 5 l. black and salmon .. 10 10
760. – 15 l. black and green .. 10 10
761. – 20 l. black and pink .. 10 10
762. – 25 l. black & blue .. 10 10
763. – 90 l. black and orange 35 35
764. – 110 l. black and blue .. 75 75

LOCOMOTIVES: 2 l. "Puffing Billy" (1813). 3 l. "Locomotion No. 1" (1825). 4 l. "Rocket" (1829). 5 l. "Lion" (1838). 15 l. "Bayard" (1839). 20 l. Crampton type (1849). 50 l. "Little England" (1851). 90 l. "Spitfire" (c. 1860). 110 l. "Rogers" (c. 1865).

171. Baseball Players.

1964. 7th European Baseball Championships Milan.
765. **171.** 30 l. sepia and green .. 15 10
766. – 70 l. black and red .. 15 15
DESIGN: 70 l. Player pitching ball.

172. "E" and Part of Globe.

1964. Europa.
767. **172.** 200 l. red, blue & lt. bl. 30 30

173. Pres. Kennedy giving Inaugural Address. **174.** Cyclists at Government Palace.

1964. 1st Death Anniv of John F. Kennedy (President of U.S.A.). Multicoloured.
768 70 l. Type **173** 15 15
769 130 l. Pres. Kennedy and U.S. flag (vert) .. 15 15

1965. Cycle Tour of Italy.
770. **174.** 30 l. sepia 10 10
771. – 70 l. purple 10 10
772. – 200 l. red 15 10
DESIGNS:—Cyclists passing: 70 l. "The Rock". 200 l. Mt. Titano.

175. Brontosaurus. **176.** Rooks on Chessboard.

1965. Prehistoric Animals.
773. **175.** 1 l. purple and green .. 10 10
774. – 2 l. black and blue .. 10 10
775. – 3 l. yellow and green .. 10 10
776. – 4 l. brown and blue .. 10 10
777. – 5 l. purple and green .. 10 10
778. – 10 l. purple and green 10 10
779. – 75 l. blue and turquoise 35 15
780. – 100 l. purple and green 50 15
781. – 200 l. purple and green 80 25

ANIMALS—VERT. 2 l. Brachyosaurus. HORIZ. 3 l. Pteranodon. 4 l. Elasmosaurus. 5 l. Tyrannosaurus. 10 l. Stegosaurus. 75 l. Thamatosaurus Victor. 100 l. Iguanodon. 200 l. Triceratops.

1965. Europa.
782. **176.** 200 l. multicoloured .. 30 25

177. Dante.

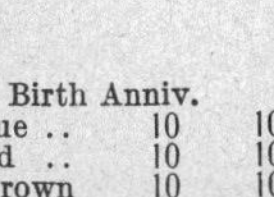
DESIGNS: 90 l. "Hell". 130 l. "Purgatory". 140 l. "Paradise".

1965. Dante's 700th Birth Anniv.
783. **177.** 40 l. sepia and blue .. 10 10
784. – 90 l. sepia and red .. 10 10
785. – 130 l. sepia and brown 10 10
786. – 140 l. sepia and blue .. 10 10

178. Mt. Titano and Flags.

1965. Visit of Pres. Saragat of Italy.
787. **178.** 115 l. multicoloured .. 10 10

179. Trotting.

1966. Equestrian Sports. Multicoloured.
788. 10 l. Type **179** 15 10
789. 20 l. Cross-country racing 15 10
790. 40 l. Horse-jumping .. 15 10
791. 70 l. Horse-racing .. 15 10
792. 90 l. Steeple-chasing .. 20 15
793. 170 l. Polo 25 15
The 20 l. and 170 l. are vert.

1966. New values in previous designs.
794 5 l. brown & blue (as 522a) 10 10
795 10 l. green & black (as 524) 10 10
796 15 l. violet & brn (as 524a) 10 10
797 40 l. red and lilac (as 491) 10 10
798 90 l. blue and black (as 492) 10 10
799 140 l. orange & vio (as 493) 10 10

180. "La Bella".

1966. Paintings by Titian. Multicoloured.
800. 40 l. Type **180** 10 10
801. 90 l. "The Three Graces" 15 15
802. 100 l. "The Three Graces" 15 15
803. 170 l. "Sacred and Profane Love" 20 20
The 90 l. and 100 l. show different details from the picture.

181. Stone Bass.

1966. Sea Animals. Multicoloured.
804. 1 l. Type **181** 10 10
805. 2 l. Cuckoo Wrasse .. 10 10
806. 3 l. Common Dolphin .. 10 10
807. 4 l. John Dory 10 10
808. 5 l. Octopus 10 10
809. 10 l. Orange Scorpionfish 10 10
810. 40 l. Electric Ray .. 10 10
811. 90 l. Medusa 15 10
812. 115 l. Seahorse 15 10
813. 130 l. Dentex 20 10
The 5, 40, 90 and 115 l. are vert.

182. Our Lady of Europe. **183.** Peony.

1966. Europa.
814. **182.** 200 l. multicoloured .. 30 30

1967. Flowers. Multicoloured.
815. 5 l. Type **183** 10 10
816. 10 l. Campanula 10 10
817. 15 l. Pyrenean poppy .. 10 10
818. 20 l. Purple deadnettle .. 10 10
819. 40 l. Hemerocallis .. 10 10
820. 140 l. Gentian 15 10
821. 170 l. Thistle 15 10
Each flower has a different background view of Mt. Titano.

184. St. Marinus. **185.** Map of Europe.

1967. Paintings by Francesco Barbieri (Guercino). Multicoloured.

No.	Type	Description	Unused	Used
822		40 l. Type **184**	10	10
823		170 l. "St. Francis"	15	15
824		190 l. "Return of the Prodigal Son" (45×37 mm)	15	15

1967. Europa.

No.	Type	Description	Unused	Used
825	185	200 l. green and orange	30	30

186. Caesar's Mushroom. **187.** Salisbury Cathedral.

1967. Fungi. Multicoloured.

No.	Type	Description	Unused	Used
826		5 l. Type **186**	15	10
827		15 l. The miller	15	10
828		20 l. Parasol mushroom	15	10
829		40 l. Cep	15	10
830		50 l. "Russula paludosa"	15	10
831		170 l. St. George's mushroom	20	20

1967. Gothic Cathedrals.

No.	Type	Description	Unused	Used
832.	–	20 l. violet on cream	10	10
833.	–	40 l. green on cream	10	10
834.	–	80 l. blue on cream	10	10
835.	**187.**	90 l. sepia on cream	10	10
836.	–	170 l. red on cream	15	15

DESIGNS: 20 l. Amiens. 40 l. Siena. 80 l. Toledo. 170 l. Cologne.

188. Cimabue Crucifix, Florence.

1967. Christmas.

No.	Type	Description	Unused	Used
837.	**188.**	300 l. brown and violet	30	30

189. Arms of San Marino. **190.** Europa "Key".

1968. Arms of San Marino Villages. Mult.

No.	Type	Description	Unused	Used
838.		2 l. Type **189**	10	10
839.		3 l. Penna Rossa	10	10
840.		5 l. Fiorentino	10	10
841.		10 l. Montecerreto	10	10
842.		25 l. Serravalle	10	10
843.		35 l. Montegiardino	10	10
844.		50 l. Faetano	10	10
845.		90 l. Borgo Maggiore	10	10
846.		180 l. Montelupo	15	10
847.		500 l. State crest	35	35

1968. Europa.

No.	Type	Description	Unused	Used
848.	**190.**	250 l. brown	30	30

HAVE YOU READ THE NOTES AT THE BEGINNING OF THIS CATALOGUE?
These often provide answers to the enquiries we receive.

191. "The Battle of San Romano" (detail, P. Uccello).

1968. 671st Birth Anniv of Paolo Uccello (painter).

No.	Type	Description	Unused	Used
849.	**191.**	50 l. black on lilac	10	10
850.	–	90 l. black on lilac	15	15
851.	–	130 l. black on lilac	15	15
852.	–	230 l. black on pink	25	25

All stamps show details of "The Battle of San Romano". The 90 l. is vert.

192. "The Nativity" (detail, Botticelli).

1968. Christmas.

No.	Type	Description	Unused	Used
853.	**192.**	50 l. deep blue	10	10
854.		90 l. deep red	10	10
855.		180 l. sepia	10	10

193. "Peace".

1969. "The Good Government" (frescoes) by Ambrogio Lorenzetti.

No.	Type	Description	Unused	Used
856.	**193.**	50 l. blue	10	10
857.	–	80 l. sepia	10	10
858.	–	90 l. violet	10	10
859.	–	180 l. red	15	15

DESIGNS—VERT. 80 l. "Justice". 90 l. "Temperance". HORIZ. 180 l. View of Siena.

194. "Young Soldier" (Bramante).

1969. 525th Birth Anniv. of Donato Bramante (architect and painter). Mult.

No.	Type	Description	Unused	Used
860.		50 l. Type **194**	15	15
861.		90 l. "Old Soldier" (Bramante)	15	15

195. Colonnade.

1969. Europa.

No.	Type	Description	Unused	Used
862.	**195.**	50 l. green	15	15
863.		180 l. purple	15	15

196. Benched Carriage ("Char-a-banc").

1969. Horses and Carriages. Multicoloured.

No.	Type	Description	Unused	Used
864.		5 l. Type **196**	10	10
865.		10 l. Barouche	10	10
866.		25 l. Private Drag	10	10
867.		40 l. Hansom Cab	10	10
868.		50 l. Curricle	10	10
869.		90 l. Wagonette	15	15
870.		180 l. Spider Phaeton	15	15

197. Mt. Titano. **198.** "Faith".

1969. Paintings by R. Viola. Multicoloured.

No.	Type	Description	Unused	Used
871		20 l. Type **197**	10	10
872		180 l. "Pier at Rimini"	15	15
873		200 l. "Pier at Riccione" (horiz)	15	15

1969. Christmas. "The Theological Virtues", by Raphael.

No.	Type	Description	Unused	Used
874.	**198.**	20 l. violet and orange	10	10
875.	–	180 l. violet and green	15	15
876.	–	200 l. violet and buff	15	15

DESIGNS: 180 l. "Hope". 200 l. "Charity".

199. "Aries".

1970. Signs of the Zodiac. Multicoloured.

No.	Type	Description	Unused	Used
877.		1 l. Type **199**	10	10
878.		2 l. "Taurus"	10	10
879.		3 l. "Gemini"	10	10
880.		4 l. "Cancer"	10	10
881.		5 l. "Leo"	10	10
882.		10 l. "Virgo"	10	10
883.		15 l. "Libra"	10	10
884.		20 l. "Scorpio"	10	10
885.		70 l. "Sagittarius"	10	10
886.		90 l. "Capricorn"	15	10
887.		100 l. "Aquarius"	20	10
888.		180 l. "Pisces"	70	30

200. "Flaming Sun". **202.** St. Francis' Gate.

201. "The Fleet in the Bay of Naples" (Pieter Brueghel, the elder).

1970. Europa.

No.	Type	Description	Unused	Used
889.	**200.**	90 l. red and green	15	15
890.		180 l. red and yellow	15	15

1970. 10th "Europa" Stamp Exn., Naples.

No.	Type	Description	Unused	Used
891.	**201.**	230 l. multicoloured	30	30

1970. 65th Anniv. of Rotary Int. and 10th Anniv. of San Marino Rotary Club. Mult.

No.	Type	Description	Unused	Used
892.		180 l. Type **202**	15	15
893.		220 l. "Rocco" Fort, Mt. Titano	15	15

MINIMUM PRICE
The minimum price quoted is 5p which represents a handling charge rather than a basis for valuing common stamps. For further notes about prices see introductory pages.

203. "Girl with Mandolin". **204.** Black Pete.

1970. Death Bicentenary of Giambattista Tiepolo (painter).

No.	Type	Description	Unused	Used
894.		50 l. Type **203**	10	10
895.		180 l. "Girl with Parrot"	25	15
896.		220 l. "Rinaldo and Armida Surprised"	15	15

SIZES: 180 l. As Type **203**. 220 l. 57×37 mm.

1970. 4th Death Anniv of Walt Disney (film producer). Cartoon Characters. Mult.

No.	Type	Description	Unused	Used
897		1 l. Type **204**	10	10
898		2 l. Gyro Gearloose	10	10
899		3 l. Pluto	10	10
900		4 l. Minnie Mouse	10	10
901		5 l. Donald Duck	10	10
902		10 l. Goofy	10	10
903		15 l. Scrooge McDuck	10	10
904		50 l. Hewey, Dewey and Louie	40	20
905		90 l. Mickey Mouse	65	30
906		220 l. Walt Disney and scene from "The Jungle Book" (horiz)	4·00	3·00

205. "Customs House, Venice".

1971. "Save Venice" Campaign. Paintings by Canaletto. Multicoloured.

No.	Type	Description	Unused	Used
907.		20 l. Type **205**	15	10
908.		180 l. "Grand Canal, Balbi Palace and Rialto Bridge, Venice"	30	30
909.		200 l. "St. Mark's and Doge's Palace"	35	35

206. Congress Building and San Marino flag.

1971. Italian Philatelic Press Union Congress, San Marino. Multicoloured.

No.	Type	Description	Unused	Used
910		20 l. Type **206**	10	10
911		90 l. Government Palace door and emblems (vert)	10	10
912		180 l. Type **206**	15	15

207. Europa Chain. **209.** Day Lily.

208. "Duck" Jug with "Lasa" Decoration.

1971. Europa.

No.	Type	Description	Unused	Used
913.	**207.**	50 l. blue and yellow	15	15
914.		90 l. orange and blue	15	15

1971. Etruscan Art (1st series).

No.	Type	Description	Unused	Used
915.	**208.**	50 l. black and orange	10	10
916.	–	80 l. black and green	10	10
917.	–	90 l. black and green	10	10
918.	–	180 l. black and orange	15	15

DESIGNS—VERT. 80 l. Head of Hermes (bust). 90 l. Man and Wife (relief on sarcophagus). HORIZ. 180 l. Chimera (bronze).

See also Nos. 1018/21.

1971. Flowers. Multicoloured.

919	1 l. Type **209**	10	10
920	2 l. "Phlox paniculata" ..	10	10
921	3 l. Wild pink	10	10
922	4 l. Globe flower	10	10
923	5 l. "Centaurea dealbata"	10	10
924	10 l. Peony	10	10
925	15 l. Christmas rose ..	10	10
926	50 l. Pasque flower ..	15	10
927	90 l. "Gaillardia aristata"	15	15
928	220 l. "Aster dumosus" ..	35	30

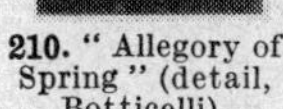

210. "Allegory of Spring" (detail, Botticelli). **211.** "Communications".

1972. "Allegory of Spring" by Sandro Botticelli. Multicoloured.

929	50 l. Type **210**	10	10
930	180 l. The Three Graces (27 × 37 mm)	20	20
931	220 l. Flora	25	25

1972. Europa.

932. **211.**	50 l. multicoloured ..	20	15
933.	90 l. multicoloured ..	20	15

212. "Taming the Bear".

1972. "Life of St. Marinus". 16th-century Paintings from former Government Palace.

934 **212**	25 l. black and buff ..	10	10
935 –	55 l. black and orange ..	10	10
936 –	100 l. black and blue ..	15	10
937 –	130 l. black and yellow ..	15	15

DESIGNS: 55 l. "The Conversion of Donna Felicissima". 100 l. "Hostile archers turned to stone". 130 l. "Mount Titano given to St. Marinus".

213. House Sparrow. **214.** "Healthy Man".

1972. Birds. Multicoloured.

938.	1 l. Type **213**	10	10
939.	2 l. Firecrest	10	10
940.	3 l. Blue tit	10	10
941.	4 l. Ortolan bunting ..	10	10
942.	5 l. Bluethroat	10	10
943.	10 l. Bullfinch	20	10
944.	25 l. Linnet	20	10
945.	50 l. Black-eared wheatear	35	15
946.	90 l. Sardinian warbler ..	45	20
947.	220 l. Greenfinch	1·00	35

1972. World Heart Month. Multicoloured.

948	50 l. Type **214**	15	15
949	90 l. "Sick Man" (horiz) ..	15	15

215. Veterans Emblem. **216.** Plane over Mt. Titano.

1972. "Veterans of Philately" Award of Italian Philatelic Federation.

950. **215.**	25 l. gold and blue ..	10	10

1972. Air.

951. **216.**	1000 l. multicoloured ..	1·25	80

217. Five-cent Coin of 1864.

1972. San Marino Coinage.

952. **217.**	5 l. bronze, blk. & grey	10	10
953. –	10 l. bronze, blk. & orge.	10	10
954. –	15 l. silver, blk. & red	10	10
955. –	20 l. silver, blk. & pur.	10	10
956. –	25 l. silver, blk. & blue	10	10
957. –	50 l. silver, blk. & blue	15	10
958. –	55 l. silver, blk. & ochre	15	15
959. –	220 l. gold, blk. & green	20	20

COINS (obverse and reverse on each stamp): 10 l. 10 c. of 1935. 15 l. 1 l. of 1906. 20 l. 5 l. of 1898. 25 l. 5 l. of 1937. 50 l. 10 l. of 1932. 55 l. 20 l. of 1938. 220 l. 20 l. of 1925.

218. New York, 1673.

1973. "Interpex" Stamp Exhibition and Important Cities of the World (1st series). New York.

960 **218**	200 l. multicoloured ..	35	35
961 –	300 l. purple, blue & black	40	40

DESIGN: 300 l. New York, 1973.

See also Nos. 1032/3, 1075/6, 1144/5, 1160/1, 1197/8, 1215/16, 1230/1, 1259/60, 1271/2, 1306/7, 1331/2 and 1358/9.

219. Printing Press. **220.** "Sportsmen".

1973. Tourist Press Congress.

962. **219.**	50 l. multicoloured ..	10	10

1973. Youth Games.

963. **220.**	100 l. multicoloured ..	10	10

221. Europa "Posthorn". **222.** Grapes.

1973. Europa.

964 **221**	20 l. green, blue and flesh	10	10
965	180 l. mauve, red and blue	70	70

1973. Fruits. Multicoloured.

966.	1 l. Type **222**	10	10
967.	2 l. Mandarines	10	10
968.	3 l. Apples	10	10
969.	4 l. Plums	10	10
970.	5 l. Strawberries	10	10
971.	10 l. Pears	10	10
972.	25 l. Cherries	10	10
973.	50 l. Pomegranate ..	20	10
974.	90 l. Apricots	25	20
975	200 l. Peaches	45	30

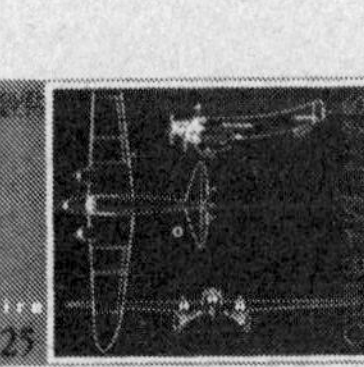

223. Couzinet "70" Arc-en-Ciel. **224.** Crossbowman, Serravalle Castle.

1973. "Story of the Aeroplane".

976 **223**	25 l. blue, yell & gold	10	10
977 –	55 l. blue, grey & gold	10	10
978 –	60 l. blue, pink & gold	10	10
979 –	90 l. blue, bistre & gold	15	10
980 –	220 l. blue, orge & gold	25	15

DESIGNS: 55 l. Macchi "MC-72/181" Castoldi. 60 l. Antonov "Ant-9". 90 l. Ryan "NX-211" "Spirit of St. Louis". 220 l. Handley Page "HP-42E".

1973. San Marino's Victory in Crossbow Tournaments, Masaa Marittima. Mult.

981	5 l. Type **224**	10	10
982	10 l. Crossbowman, Pennarossa	10	10
983	15 l. Drummer, Montegiardino Castle ..	10	10
984	20 l. Trumpeter, Fiorentino Castle	10	10
985	30 l. Crossbowman, Montecerreto Castle ..	10	10
986	40 l. Crossbowman, Borgo Maggiore Castle ..	15	10
987	50 l. Trumpeter, Guaita Castle	15	10
988	80 l. Crossbowman, Faetano Castle ..	20	15
989	200 l. Crossbowman, Montelupo Castle ..	45	20

225. "Adoration of the Magi" (detail). **226.** Combat Shield, (16th century).

1973. Christmas. 600th Birth Anniv of Gentile da Fabriano. Details of Gentile's altarpiece "Adoration of the Magi".

990. **225.**	5 l. multicoloured ..	10	10
991. –	30 l. multicoloured ..	10	10
992. –	115 l. multicoloured ..	10	10
993. –	250 l. multicoloured ..	20	20

1974. Ancient Weapons from "Cesta" Museum, San Marino.

994. **226.**	5 l. blk. brn. & grn...	10	10
995. –	10 l. blk., blue & brn.	10	10
996. –	15 l. blk., blue & light bl.	10	10
997. –	20 l. blk., bl. & brn...	10	10
998. –	30 l. blk., brn. & blue	10	10
999. –	50 l. blk.. blue & pink	10	10
1000. –	80 l. blk., blue & lilac	15	10
1001. –	250 l. blk. & yellow..	25	15

DESIGNS: 10 l. German armour (16th century). 15 l. Crested morion (16th century). 20 l. Horse head-armour (15th-16th century). 30 l. Italian morion with crest (16th-17th century). 50 l. Gauntlets and sword pommel (16th century). 80 l. Sallet helmet (16th century). 250 l. Sforza shield (16th century).

227. "The Joy of Living" (Emilio Greco).

1974. Europa. Sculpture.

1002. **227.**	100 l. black and brown	15	15
1003. –	200 l. black and green	15	15

DESIGN: 200 l. "The Joy of Living" (complete sculpture).

228. "Sea and Mountains". **229.** Arms of Sansepolcro.

1974. San-Marino-Riccione Stamp Fair.

1004. **228.**	50 l. multicoloured ..	5	5

1974. 9th Crossbow Tournament, San Marino. Arms. Multicoloured.

1005.	15 l. Type **229**	75	75
1006.	20 l. Massa Marittima ..	75	75
1007.	50 l. San Marino ..	75	75
1008.	115 l. Gubbio	75	75
1009.	300 l. Lucca	75	75

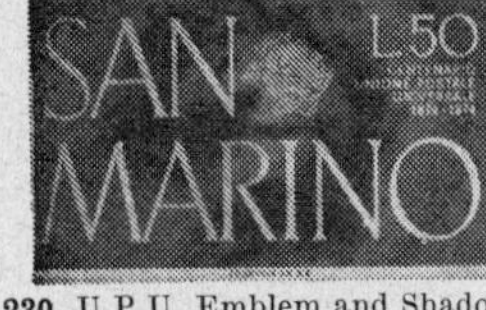

230. U.P.U. Emblem and Shadow.

1974. Cent. of Universal Postal Union.

1010. **230.**	50 l. multicoloured ..	15	15
1011.	90 l. multicoloured ..	15	15

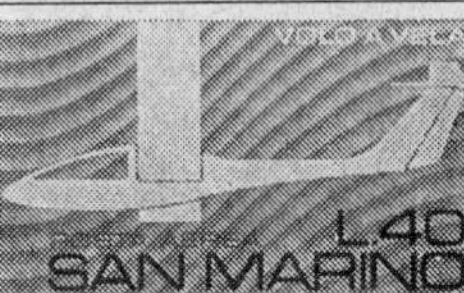

231. Glider.

1974. Air. 50th Anniv of Gliding in Italy.

1012 **231**	40 l. blue, green & brn	10	10
1013 –	120 l. blue, lt bl & vio	10	10
1014 –	500 l. vio, mve & red	30	35

DESIGNS: 120, 500 l. Gliders in "air currents" (both different).

232. Mt. Titano and Verses of Hymn. **233.** "Madonna and Child" (4th-century painting).

1974. Death Centenary of Nicolo Tommaseo (writer).

1015 **232**	50 l. black, grn & red	15	15
1016 –	150 l. black, yell & bl	15	15

DESIGN: 150 l. Portrait of Tommaseo.

1974. Christmas.

1017. **233.**	250 l. multicoloured	30	30

234. "Dancing Scene", Tomb of the Leopards, Tarquinia.

1975. Etruscan Art (2nd series). Tomb Paintings. Multicoloured.

1018.	20 l. Type **234**	10	10
1019.	30 l. "Chariot Race", Tomb of the Hill, Chiusi	10	10
1020.	180 l. "Achilles and Troilus", Tomb of the Bulls, Tarquinia ..	30	15
1021.	220 l. "Dancers", Tomb of the Triclinium, Tarquinia	40	25

235. "Escape Tunnel". **236.** "The Blessing".

1975. 30th Anniv of Escape of 100,000 Italian Wartime Refugees to San Marino.

1022 **235**	50 l. multicoloured ..	15	10

1975. Europa. Details from "St. Marinus" by Guercino. Mult.

1023.	100 l. Type **236**	15	15
1024.	200 l. "St. Marinus" ..	25	25

237. "The Virgin Mary". **238.** "Aphrodite" (sculpture).

1975. Holy Year. Details from Frescoes by Giotto from Scrovegni Chapel, Padua. Multicoloured.
1025. 10 l. Type **237** 10 10
1026. 40 l. " Virgin and Child " 10 10
1027. 50 l. " Heads of Angels ". 10 10
1028. 100 l. " Mary Magdalene " (horiz.) 10 10
1029. 500 l. " Heads of Saints " (horiz.) 35 35

1975. 15th Europa Stamp Exhibition, Naples.
1030 **238** 50 l. black, grey & vio 10 10

239. Congress Emblem.

1975. " Eurocophar " International Pharmaceutical Congress, San Marino.
1031. **239.** 100 l. multicoloured 15 10

240. Tokyo, 1835.

1975. Important Cities of the World (2nd series). Tokyo. Multicoloured.
1032 200 l. Type **240** 30 30
1033 300 l. Tokyo, 1975 .. 40 40

241. " Woman on Balcony ".

242. " Head of the Child " (detail).

1975. International Women's Year. Paintings by Gentilini. Multicoloured.
1034. 50 l. Type **241** 10 10
1035. 150 l. " Heads of Two Women " (horiz.) .. 20 15
1036. 230 l. " Profile of Girl " 35 25

1975. Christmas. 500th Birth Anniv of Michelangelo. Painting "Doni Madonna" and details. Multicoloured.
1037. 50 l. Type **242** 10 10
1038. 100 l. "Head of Virgin" (detail) 15 15
1039. 250 l. "Doni Madonna" 25 25

243. " Modesty ".

244. Capitol, Washington.

1976. "The Civil Virtues". Sketches by Emilio Greco.
1039a – 5 l. black and lilac .. 10 10
1040 **243** 10 l. black and stone 10 10
1041 – 20 l. black and lilac 10 10
1041a – 35 l. black and stone 10 10
1042 – 50 l. black and green 10 10
1043 – 70 l. black and pink 10 10
1044 – 90 l. black and pink 10 10
1045 – 100 l. black and pink 10 10
1046 – 120 l. black and blue 10 10
1047 – 150 l. black and lilac 10 10
1048 – 160 l. black & green 15 15
1049 – 170 l. black and flesh 15 15
1050 – 220 l. black and grey 20 15
1051 – 250 l. black & yellow 25 20
1052 – 300 l. black and grey 30 20
1053 – 320 l. black & mauve 30 20
1054 – 500 l. black & stone 40 30
1055. – 1000 l. black and blue 70 50
1055a. 2000 l. black & cream 1·75 1·75
DESIGNS: 5 l. " Wisdom ". 20 l., 160 l. " Temperance ". 35 l. " Love ". 50 l., 70 l. " Fortitude ". 90 l., 220 l. " Prudence ". 100 l., 120 l. " Altruism ". 150 l., 170 l. " Hope ". 250 l. " Justice ". 300 l., 320 l. " Faith ". 500 l. " Honesty ". 1000 l. " Industry ". 2000 l. " Faithfulness ".

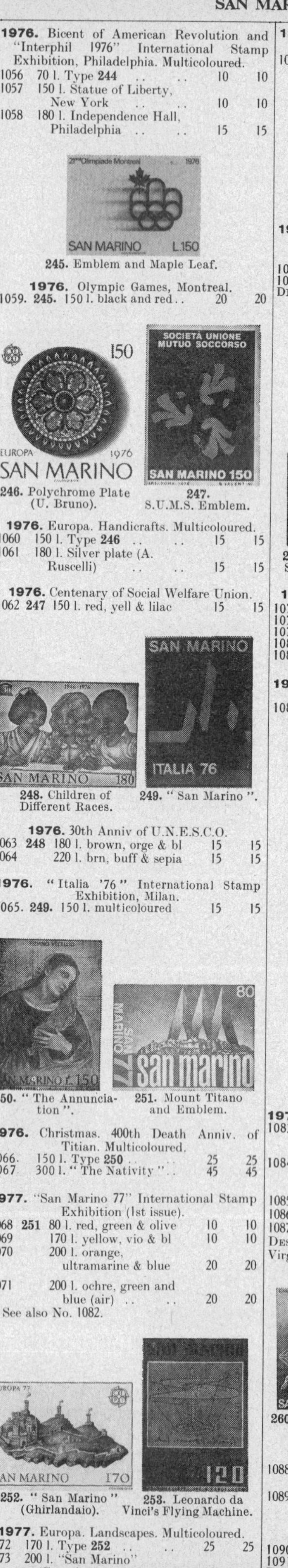

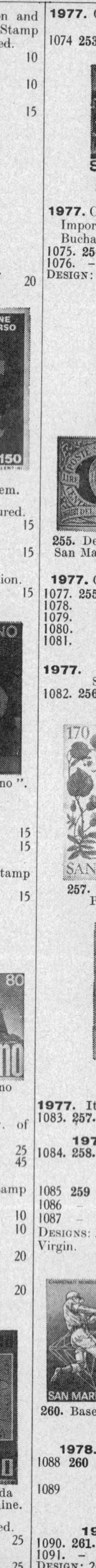

1976. Bicent of American Revolution and "Interphil 1976" International Stamp Exhibition, Philadelphia. Multicoloured.
1056 70 l. Type **244** 10 10
1057 150 l. Statue of Liberty, New York 10 10
1058 180 l. Independence Hall, Philadelphia 15 15

245. Emblem and Maple Leaf.

1976. Olympic Games, Montreal.
1059. **245.** 150 l. black and red .. 20 20

246. Polychrome Plate (U. Bruno).

247. S.U.M.S. Emblem.

1976. Europa. Handicrafts. Multicoloured.
1060 150 l. Type **246** 15 15
1061 180 l. Silver plate (A. Ruscelli) 15 15

1976. Centenary of Social Welfare Union.
1062 **247** 150 l. red, yell & lilac 15 15

248. Children of Different Races.

249. " San Marino ".

1976. 30th Anniv of U.N.E.S.C.O.
1063 **248** 180 l. brown, orge & bl 15 15
1064 220 l. brn, buff & sepia 15 15

1976. " Italia '76 " International Stamp Exhibition, Milan.
1065. **249.** 150 l. multicoloured 15 15

250. " The Annunciation ".

251. Mount Titano and Emblem.

1976. Christmas. 400th Death Anniv. of Titian. Multicoloured.
1066. 150 l. Type **250** 25 25
1067 300 l. " The Nativity " .. 45 45

1977. "San Marino 77" International Stamp Exhibition (1st issue).
1068 **251** 80 l. red, green & olive 10 10
1069 170 l. yellow, vio & bl 10 10
1070 200 l. orange, ultramarine & blue 20 20
1071 200 l. ochre, green and blue (air) .. 20 20
See also No. 1082.

252. " San Marino " (Ghirlandaio).

253. Leonardo da Vinci's Flying Machine.

1977. Europa. Landscapes. Multicoloured.
1072 170 l. Type **252** 25 25
1073 200 l. "San Marino" (Guercino) 25 25

1977. Centenary of Enrico Forlanini's First Vertical Flight Experiment.
1074 **253** 120 l. multicoloured .. 15 10

254. University Square, 1877.

1977. Centenary of Rumanian Independence. Important Cities of the World (3rd series). Bucharest.
1075. **254.** 200 l. green and blue 25 25
1076. – 400 l. brown and stone 35 35
DESIGN: 400 l. City centre, 1977.

255. Design of First San Marino Stamp.

256. " St. Marinus Blessing " (Retrosi).

1977. Cent. of San Marino Postage Stamps.
1077. **255.** 40 l. green 10 10
1078. 70 l. blue 10 10
1079. 170 l. red 15 15
1080. 500 l. brown 40 45
1081. 1000 l. lilac 70 80

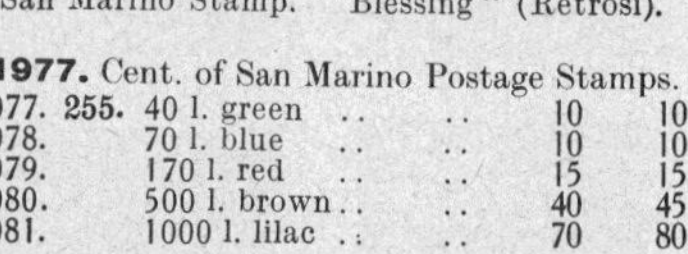

1977. " San Marino 1977 " International Stamp Exhibition (2nd issue).
1082. **256.** 1000 l. multicoloured 1·40 1·60

257. Medicinal Plants.

259. Angel.

258. Woman gripped by Octopus.

1977. Italian Pharmacists Union Congress.
1083. **257.** 170 l. multicoloured 30 20

1977. World Rheumatism Year.
1084. **258.** 200 l. multicoloured 30 25

1977. Christmas.
1085 **259** 170 l. black, grey & sil 25 25
1086 – 230 l. black, grey & sil 25 25
1087 – 300 l. black, grey & sil 35 35
DESIGNS: 230 l. Palm tree and olive. 300 l. The Virgin.

260. Baseball Player.

261. San Francesco Gate.

1978. World Baseball Championships.
1088 **260** 90 l. black, blue and ultramarine .. 15 15
1089 120 l. black, light green and green .. 15 15

1978. Europa. Architecture.
1090. **261.** 170 l. blue & pale blue 20 20
1091. – 200 l. brown & stone 25 25
DESIGN: 200 l. Ripa Gate.

262. Feather.

263. Mt. Titano and Antenna.

1978. World Hypertension Month.
1092. **262.** 320 l. black, red & blue 40 35

1978. San Marino's Admission to the I.T.U.
1093. **263.** 10 l. yellow and red .. 10 10
1094. 200 l. blue and violet 20 20

264. Hawk and Slender-billed Gull.

1978. 30th San Marino–Riccione Stamp Fair.
1095. **264.** 120 l. multicoloured 40 15
1096. 170 l. multicoloured 60 25

265. Wright Brothers' Aircraft " Flyer ".

266. Allegory of Human Rights.

1978. Air. 75th Anniv. of First Powered Flight.
1097. **265.** 10 l. multicoloured .. 10 10
1098. 50 l. multicoloured .. 10 10
1099. 200 l. multicoloured 15 15

1978. 30th Anniv. of Declaration of Human Rights.
1100. **266.** 200 l. multicoloured 30 25

267. Holly.

1978. Christmas. Multicoloured.
1101. 10 l. Type **267** 10 10
1102. 120 l. Star 15 10
1103. 170 l. Snowflakes .. 15 15

268. Albert Einstein.

1979. Birth Cent. of Albert Einstein (physicist).
1104. **268.** 120 l. brown, sepia and light grey .. 20 15

269. Motor-coach, 1915.

1979. Europa. Multicoloured.
1105. 170 l. Type **269** 30 25
1106. 220 l. Horse-drawn stage coach 35 30

270. San Marino Crossbowmen Federation Emblem.

271. Maigret (G. Simenon).

1979. 14th Crossbow Tournament.
1107. **270.** 120 l. multicoloured 20 15

1979. Fictional Detectives. Multicoloured
1108. 10 l. Type 271 .. .. 10 10
1109. 80 l. Perry Mason (S. Gardner) 15 10
1110. 150 l. Nero Wolfe (R. Stout) 25 15
1111. 170 l. Ellery Queen (F. Dannay and M. B. Lee) 30 15
1112. 220 l. Sherlock Holmes (A. Conan Doyle) 50 25

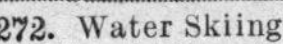

272. Water Skiing. **273.** St. Apollonia.

1979. Water Skiing Championships, Castelgandolfo.
1113. **272.** 150 l. grn., bl. & blk. 20 15

1979. 13th International Stomatology Congress.
1114. **273.** 170 l. multicoloured 30 20

274. " Knowledge ". **275.** Horse Chestnut and Red Deer.

1979. International Year of the Child. Multicoloured.
1115. 20 l. Type 274 .. .. 10 10
1116. 120 l. " Friendship " .. 15 15
1117. 170 l. " Equality " .. 15 15
1118. 220 l. " Love " .. 20 20
1119. 350 l. " Existence " .. 30 30

1979. Environment Protection. Trees and Animals. Multicoloured.
1120 5 l. Type 275 .. .. 10 10
1121 10 l. Cedar of Lebanon and golden eagle .. 40 10
1122 35 l. Flowering dogwood and common racoon .. 25 10
1123 50 l. Banyan and tiger .. 25 10
1124 70 l. Stone pine and hoopoe 85 20
1125 90 l. Larch and yellow-throated marten .. 20 15
1126 100 l. Tasmanian blue gum and koala 20 15
1127 120 l. Date palm and dromedary 20 15
1128 150 l. Silver maple and American beaver .. 20 20
1129 170 l. Baobab and African elephant 45 25

276. " Disturbing Muses ". **277.** St. Joseph.

1979. 1st Death Anniv of Giorgio de Chirico (painter). Multicoloured.
1130 40 l. Type 276 .. .. 10 10
1131 150 l. "Ancient Horses" .. 15 10
1132 170 l. "Self-portrait" .. 20 10

1979. Christmas. "The Holy Family" (fresco) by Antonio Alberti or details from it.
1133 80 l. Type 277 .. .. 10 10
1134 170 l. Infant Jesus .. 20 20
1135 220 l. Magus .. 25 25
1136 320 l. "The Holy Family" 30 30

278. St. Benedict of Nursia. **279.** Cigarette Ends.

1980. 1500th Birth Anniv. of Saint Benedict of Nursia (founder of Benedictine Order).
1137. **278.** 170 l. multicoloured 30 25

1980. Anti-Smoking Campaign. Mult.
1138 120 l. Type 279 .. .. 15 10
1139 220 l. Face hidden by cigarettes 30 30
1140 520 l. Face wreathed in smoke 70 50

280. Naples. **281.** Giovanbattista Belluzzi (military architect).

1980. "Europa" Stamp Exhibition, Naples.
1141. **280.** 170 l. multicoloured 30 20

1980. Europa. Multicoloured.
1142. 170 l. Type 281 .. .. 20 20
1143. 220 l. Antonio Orafo (silver and goldsmith) .. 30 30

282. London, 1850.

1980. "London 1980" International Stamp Exhibition and Important Cities of the World (4th series). London.
1144. **282.** 200 l. brown & green 30 30
1145. – 400 l. blue and lilac .. 40 40
DESIGN: 400 l. London, 1980.

283. Cycling. **284.** Stolz and Score of " Philatelic Waltz ".

1980. Olympic Games, Moscow.
1146 283 70 l. black, emerald and green 10 10
1147 – 90 l. black, orge & brn 10 10
1148 – 170 l. blk, red & mve 15 15
1149 – 350 l. black, bl & dp bl 20 20
1150 – 450 l. black, vio & bl 30 30
DESIGNS: 90 l. Basketball. 170 l. Running. 350 l. Gymnastics. 450 l. High jumping.

1980. Birth Centenary of Robert Stolz (composer).
1151. **284.** 120 l. blue and black 30 15

285. Weightlifting. **286.** City Fortifications.

1980. European Junior Weightlifting Championship.
1152. **285.** 170 l. red, blk. & grn. 30 25

1980. World Tourism Conference, Manila.
1153. **286.** 220 l. multicoloured 30 20

287. " The Annunciation " (detail). **288.** St. Joseph's Eve Bonfire.

1980. Christmas. Details of Paintings by Andrea del Sarto. Multicoloured.
1154. 180 l. " Madonna of the Harpies " (detail) .. 20 20
1155. 250 l. " Annunciation " (Mary) 35 35
1156. 500 l. Type 287 .. .. 55 55

1981. Europa. Multicoloured.
1157. 200 l. Type 288 .. .. 25 25
1158. 300 l. National Day fireworks 30 30

289. Hands holding Broken Branch.

1981. International Year of Disabled Persons.
1159. **289.** 300 l. brown, green & light green .. 30 30

290. "St. Charles' Square, 1817" (Jakob Alt).

1981. "WIPA 1981" International Stamp Exhibition and Important Cities of the World (5th series). Vienna. Multicoloured.
1160. 200 l. Type 290 .. .. 30 30
1161. 300 l. St. Charles' Square, 1981 .. .. .. 60 60

291. Motor Cyclist. **292.** Girl playing Pipes.

1981. San Marino Motor Cycle Grand Prix.
1162 291 200 l. multicoloured .. 30 25

1981. Birth Bimillenary of Virgil (poet).
1163. **292.** 300 l. grey and silver 35 40
1164. – 550 l. grey and silver 55 65
1165. – 1500 l. grey and silver 1·25 1·50
DESIGNS: 550 l. Soldier. 1500 l. Shepherd.

293. House. **294.** Judo.

1981. Urban Development Scheme. Mult.
1167 20 l. Type 293 .. .. 10 10
1168 80 l. Tree (provision of green belts) 15 10
1169 400 l. Gas flame (power plants) 35 35

1981. European Junior Judo Championships, San Marino.
1170. **294.** 300. l multicoloured 45 35

295. "Girl with Dove" (Picasso). **296.** Bread.

1981. Birth Centenary of Pablo Picasso (artist). Multicoloured.
1171 150 l. Type 295 .. .. 20 20
1172 200 l. "Homage to Picasso" (detail, Renato Guttuso) .. 30 30

1981. World Food Day.
1173. **296.** 300 l. multicoloured .. 40 35

297. King Presenting Gift. **298.** Cancellation and " San Marino 82 " Emblem.

1981. Christmas. 500th Birth Anniv of Benvenuto Tisi da Garofalo (artist). Details from "Adoration of the Magi and St. Bartholomew". Multicoloured.
1174 200 l. Type 297 .. .. 20 20
1175 300 l. Kneeling king .. 35 35
1176 600 l. Virgin and Child .. 65 65

1982. Centenary of Postal Stationery.
1177 298 200 l. multicoloured .. 30 20

299. " The Cicada and the Ant " (Aesop fable).

1982. Cent. of Savings Bank.
1178. **299.** 300 l. multicoloured 40 35

300. Assembly of Heads of Families, 1906. **301.** Archimedes.

1982. Europa. Multicoloured.
1179. 300 l. Type 300 .. .. 40 40
1180. 450 l. Napoleon at the border of San Marino, 1797 .. .. .. 50 50

1982. Pioneers of Science.
1181. **301.** 20 l. red and black .. 10 10
1182. – 30 l. blue and black .. 10 10
1183. – 40 l. brown and black 10 10
1184. – 50 l. green and black 10 10
1185. – 60 l. red and black .. 10 10
1186. – 100 l. brown & black 15 10
1187. – 150 l. brown & black 15 15
1188. – 200 l. brown & black 20 15
1189. – 250 l. red and black .. 25 25
1190. – 300 l. green and black 30 25
1191. – 350 l. green and black 40 35
1192. – 400 l. red and black .. 45 45
1193. – 450 l. red and black .. 45 45
1194. – 1000 l. red & black .. 1·00 1·00
1195. – 1400 l. red and black 1·50 1·50
1196. – 5000 l. black and blue 5·00 5·00
DESIGNS: 30 l. Copernicus. 40 l. Isaac Newton. 50 l. Antoine Lavoisier. 60 l. Marie Curie. 100 l. Robert Koch. 150 l. Alexander Fleming. 200 l. Thomas Edison. 250 l. Alessnbdro Volta. 300 l. Guglielmo Marconi. 350 l. Evangelista Torricelli. 400 l. Carl Linnaeus. 450 l. Hippocrates. 1000 l. Pythagoras. 1400 l. Leonardo da Vinci. 5000 l. Galileo.

302. "Notre Dame", 1806 (J. Hill).

1982. "Philexfrance 82" International Stamp Exhibition and Important Cities of the World (6th series). Paris.

1197 300 l. buff and black .. 30 30
1198 450 l. multicoloured .. 40 40

DESIGNS: 450 l. Notre Dame and Ile de Cite, 1982.

303. Hands and Birds.

304. Pope John Paul II.

1982. 800th Birth Anniv. of St. Francis of Assisi.

1199. **303.** 200 l. multicoloured 30 25

1982. Visit of Pope John Paul II to San Marino.

1200 **304** 900 l. purple, deep green and green .. 1·25 1·00

305. Globe encircled by Flag Stamps.

306. Face besplattered with Blood.

1982. 5th Anniv. of International Association of Stamp Catalogue Editors.

1201. **305.** 300 l. multicoloured 35 35

1982. 15th International Congress of Amnesty International, Rimini.

1202 **306** 700 l. red and black .. 70 70

307. "Accipe Lampadam Ardentem" (detail).

308. Refugee.

1982. Christmas. Paintings by Gregorio Sciltian. Multicoloured.

1203 200 l. Type **307** 25 25
1204 300 l. "Madonna della Citta" (detail) .. 40 40
1205 450 l. Angel (detail, "Accipe Sal Sapientiae") 55 55

1982. "For Refugees".

1206. **308.** 300 l. + 100 l. mult. .. 35 35

309. Begni Building and Quill.

310. Formula One Racing Cars.

1983. Cent. of Secondary School.

1207. **309.** 300 l. multicoloured 30 30

1983. San Marino Formula One Grand Prix.

1208. **310.** 50 l. multicoloured .. 15 10
1209. 350 l. multicoloured 50 40

311. Auguste Piccard and Aerostat.

312. Amateur Radio Operator.

1983. Europa. Multicoloured.

1210. 400 l. Type **311** 75 75
1211. 500 l. Piccard and bathyscaphe, 1948 .. .. 1·00 1·00

1983. World Communications Year.

1212. **312.** 400 l. blk., blue & red 35 35
1213. 500 l. blk., brn. and red 50 50

DESIGN: 500 l. Postman on bicycle.

313. Montgolfier Balloon.

1983. Bicent. of Manned Flight.

1214. **313.** 500 l. multicoloured 50 50

314. "Rio de Janeiro, 1845" (Richard Bate).

1983. "Brasiliana 83" International Stamp Exhibition and Important Cities of the World (7th series). Rio de Janeiro. Mult.

1215. 400 l. Type **314** 35 35
1216. 1400 l. Rio de Janeiro, 1983 1·50 1·50

315. Feeding Colt.

1983. World Food Programme.

1217. **315.** 500 l. multicoloured 60 60

316. "Madonna of the Grand Duke".

317. Demetrius Vikelas.

1983. Christmas. 500th Birth Anniv. of Raphael. Multicoloured.

1218. 300 l. Type **316** 40 40
1219. 400 l. "Madonna of the Goldfinch" (detail) .. 45 45
1220. 500 l. "Madonna of the Chair" (detail) .. 60 60

1984. 90th Anniv of International Olympic Committee. I.O.C. Presidents.

1221 **317** 300 l. black and green 25 25
1222 – 400 l. purple and blue 35 35
1223 – 550 l. lilac and green 50 50

DESIGNS: 400 l. Lord Killanin. 550 l. Juan Samaranch.

318. Bridge.

1984. Europa. 25th Anniv of C.E.P.T.

1224 **318** 400 l. yell, vio & blk 80 80
1225 550 l. yell, red & blk 95 95

319. Flag Waver.

321. Motocross.

1984. Flag Wavers. Multicoloured.

1226. 300 l. Type **319.** 30 30
1227. 400 l. Waver with two flags 40 40

1984. World Motocross Championship.

1229. **321.** 450 l. multicoloured 55 45

322. Collins Street, 1839.

1984. "Ausipex 84" International Stamp Exhibition, Melbourne, and Important Cities of the World (8th series). Multicoloured.

1230. 1500 l. Type **322** .. .. 1·60 1·60
1231. 2000 l. Collins Street, 1984 2·75 2·75

323. Pres. Pertini and San Marino City.

1984. Visit of President Sandro Pertini of Italy.

1232. 323. 1950 l. multicoloured 2·10 2·10

324. "Universe".

325. Angel with Book.

1984. Youth Philately. Multicoloured.

1233. 50 l. Type **324** 10 10
1234. 100 l. Caveman and modern man framed by television ("The Evolution of Life") .. 10 10
1235. 150 l. Pipe smoker driving car ("The World in which we live") .. 20 15
1236. 200 l. Man with fig leaf and snake with apple ("Mankind") 25 20
1237. 450 l. Scientist with H-bomb ("Science") .. 45 45
1238. 550 l. Man in barrel with books and candle ("Philosophy") .. 55 55

1984. Christmas. Designs showing details of "Madonna of San Girolano" by Correggio. Multicoloured.

1239. 400 l. Type **325** 45 45
1240. 450 l. Virgin and child .. 55 55
1241. 550 l. Attendant .. 65 65

326. Johann Sebastian Bach and Score.

327. State Flags, Stadium and Swimming Pictogram.

1985. Europa.

1242. **326.** 450 l. black & brown 80 80
1243. – 600 l. black and green 1·25 1·25

DESIGN: 600 l. Vincenzo Bellini and score.

1985. First Small States Games. Mult.

1244. 50 l. Type **327** 10 10
1245. 350 l. Flags, stadium and running pictogram .. 35 35
1246. 400 l. Flags, stadium and shooting pictogram .. 40 40
1247. 450 l. Flags, stadium and cycling pictogram .. 45 45
1248. 600 l. Flags, stadium and handball pictogram .. 65 65

328. Sunset and Birds.

329. Face and Hand holding Dove.

1985. Emigration.

1249. **328.** 600 l. multicoloured 60 60

1985. International Youth Year.

1250. **329.** 400 l. yellow, blue and gold 40 40
1251. – 600 l. gold, blue and yellow 60 60

DESIGN: 600 l. Girl's face, dove and horse's head.

330. Camera and San Marino Palace.

331. Sun breaking through Clouds and Sapling.

1985. 18th International Federation of Photographic Art Congress.

1252. **330.** 450 l. multicoloured 60 60

1985. Tenth Anniv. of Helsinki European Security and Co-operation Conference.

1253. **331.** 600 l. multicoloured 60 60

332. Don Abbondio and Don Rodrigo's Henchman.

1985. Birth Bicent of Alessandro Manzoni (writer). Scenes from "I Promessi Sposi".

1254. **332.** 400 l. green 35 35
1255. – 450 l. brown 40 40
1256. – 600 l. blue 55 55

DESIGNS: 450 l. Forcing curate to bless wedding. 600 l. Plague in Milan.

333. Fish caught on Hook.

1985. World Angling Championships, River Arno, Florence.

1257. **333.** 600 l. multicoloured 55 55

334. Cat (after Pompeian mosaic).

1985. International Feline Federation Congress.

1258. **334.** 600 l. multicoloured 70 55

335. Colosseum, 85 A.D.

1985. "Italia 85" International Stamp Exhibition, Rome, and Important Cities of the World (9th series). Multicoloured.

1259. 1000 l. Type **335** 90 90
1260. 1500 l. Colosseum, 1985 .. 1·60 1·60

336. Flying Angel.

1985. Christmas. Multicoloured.

1261. 400 l. Type **336** 55 55
1262. 450 l. Madonna and child 60 60
1263. 600 l. Angel resting .. 75 75

337. Aerial View of Cailungo Hospital. **338.** "Giotto" Space Probe.

1986. 30th Anniv. of Social Security Institute (450 l.), and World Health Day (650 l.). Multicoloured.

1264. 450 l. Type **337** 60 60
1265. 650 l. Front view of Cailungo hospital .. 65 65

1986. Appearance of Halley's Comet. Multicoloured.

1266. 550 l. Type **338** 70 70
1267. 1000 l. "Adoration of the Magi" (Giotto) .. 1·10 1·10

339. Player and Emblem. **340.** Deer.

1986. World Table Tennis Championships, Rimini.

1268 **339** 450 l. bl, ultram & red 60 60

1986. Europa. Multicoloured.

1269. 550 l. Type **340** .. .. 1·75 1·75
1270. 650 l. Common kestrel .. 2·00 2·00

341. Water Tower, 1870 (lithograph, Charles Shober).

1986. "Ameripex" International Stamp Exhibition, Chicago, and Important Cities of the World (10th series). Multicoloured.

1271. 2000 l. Type **341** .. .. 2·50 2·50
1272. 3000 l. Water tower, 1986 3·50 3·50

342. Swallows.

344. "Apollo Dancing with the Muses" (detail, Giulio Romano).

1986. International Peace Year.

1273. **342.** 550 l. multicoloured 75 65

1986. 25th Anniv. of San Marino Choral Society.

1275. **344.** 450 l. multicoloured 60 60

345. Boules Player. **346.** Boy.

1986. European Boules Championships, San Marino.

1276 **345** 550 l. multicoloured .. 70 70

1986. 40th Anniv. of U.N.I.C.E.F. Child Survival Campaign.

1277. **346.** 650 l. multicoloured 80 80

347. "St. John the Baptist".

1986. Christmas. Triptych by Hans Memling. Multicoloured.

1278 450 l. Type **347** 75 75
1279 550 l. "Madonna and Child" 85 85
1280 650 l. "St. John the Evangelist" 90 90

348. Motor Car and Route Map (Paris–Peking Rally, 1907).

1987. Motor Rallies. Multicoloured.

1281 500 l. Type **348** 80 80
1282 600 l. Peugeot "205" (15th San Marino Rally) .. 85 85
1283 700 l. Motor car and crowds (60th anniv of Mille Miglia) 95 95

349. Sketch of Church. **350.** Modern Sculpture (Reffi Busignani).

1987. Europa. Architecture. Our Lady of Consolation Church, Borgomaggiore (Giovanni Michelucci).

1284. **349.** 600 l. black and red 1·25 1·25
1285. – 700 l. black & yellow. 1·50 1·50

DESIGN: 700 l. Church interior.

1987. Modern Sculptures in San Marino. Designs showing works by artists named. Multicoloured.

1286. 50 l. Type **350** 10 10
1287. 100 l. Bini 10 10
1288. 200 l. Guguianu 20 20
1289. 300 l. Berti 30 30
1290. 400 l. Crocetti 40 40
1291. 500 l. Berti 45 45
1292. 600 l. Messina 55 55
1293. 1000 l. Minguzzi 90 90
1294. 2200 l. Greco .. .. 2·00 2·00
1295. 10000 l. Sassu .. .. 9·00 9·00

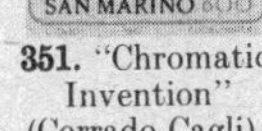

351. "Chromatic Invention" (Corrado Cagli). **352.** Micro-light Aircraft, San Marino Air Club.

1987. Art Biennale.

1300. – 500 l. bl., blk. & red 60 60
1301. **351.** 600 l. multicoloured 80 80

DESIGN: 500 l. "From My Brazilian Diary—Virgin Forest" (Emilio Vedova).

1987.

1302. **352.** 600 l. multicoloured 80 80

353. Bust of Mahatma Gandhi in Gandhi Square, San Marino. **354.** Olympic Rings and Hurdler in "Stamp".

1987. "A Society based on Non-violence".

1303. **353.** 500 l. multicoloured 75 65

1987. "Olymphilex" Olympic Stamps Exhibition and World Light Athletics Championships, Rome.

1304 **354** 600 l. multicoloured .. 70 70

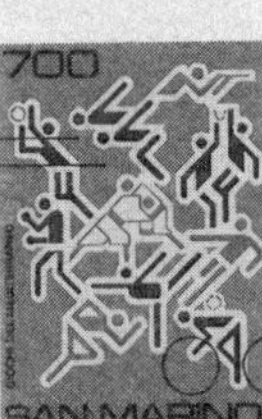

355. Sports Pictograms. **357.** "The Annunciation" (detail).

356. "View from Round Tower, 1836" (anon).

1987. Mediterranean Games, Syria.

1305 **355** 700 l. red, blue & black 80 80

1987. "Hafnia 87" International Stamp Exhibition, Copenhagen, and Important Cities of the World (11th series). Mult.

1306. 1200 l. Type **356** .. .. 1·50 1·75
1307. 2200 l. View from Round Tower, 1987 .. .. 2·00 2·25

1987. Christmas. 600th Birth Anniv of Fra Giovanni of Florence (Beato Angelico). Multicoloured.

1308 600 l. Type **357** 75 75
1309 600 l. Madonna and Child (detail, Triptych of Cortona) 75 75
1310 600 l. Saint (detail, "The Annunciation") .. 75 75

358. 1923 30 c., 1944 20 l. + 10 l. and 1975 200 l. Stamps of St. Marinus. **359.** Maglev Monorail "Bullet" Train and Globe.

1988. Thematic Collecting. Multicoloured.

1311 50 l. Type **358** 10 10
1312 150 l. Aerogramme and 1933 3 l. "Graf Zeppelin" stamp (transport) 20 20
1313 300 l. 1954 5 l. and 1981 200 l. motor cycle racing stamps and 1986 meter mark showing motor cycle (sport) 40 40
1314 350 l. 1978 200 l. human rights stamp on cover and 1982 200 l. St. Francis of Assisi stamp (art) 45 45
1315 1000 l. 1949 50 l. Garibaldi stamp, 1985 450 l. Europa stamp and 1952 1 l. Columbus stamp (famous people) .. 1·25 1·25

See also Nos. 1340/4 and 1393/7.

1988. Europa. Transport and Communications. Multicoloured.

1316 600 l. Type **359** .. .. 1·00 1·00
1317 700 l. Optical fibres and globe .. .. .. 1·50 1·50

360 Carlo Malagola and Palazzo della Mercanzia **361** "La Strada"

1988. 900th Anniv of Bologna University. Multicoloured.

1318 550 l. Type **360** 60 60
1319 650 l. Pietro Ellero and Palazzo del Podesta .. 75 75
1320 1300 l. Giosue Carducci and Pala dei Mercanti 1·25 1·25
1321 1700 l. Giovanni Pascoli and Atheneum .. 1·50 1·50

1988. Award of Celebrities of Showbusiness Prize to Federico Fellini (film director). Film posters. Multicoloured.

1322 300 l. Type **361** 35 35
1323 900 l. "La Dolce Vita" .. 1·10 1·10
1324 1200 l. "Amarcord" .. 1·40 1·40

362 Mt. Titano from Beach

1988. 40th Riccione Stamp Fair.

1325 **362** 750 l. blue, grn & mve 80 80

363 Healthy Tree with Diseased Roots

1988. Present Day Problems. International AIDS Congress, San Marino.

1326 **363** 250 l. multicoloured .. 35 35
1327 – 350 l. red and black .. 45 45
1328 – 650 l. multicoloured .. 85 85
1329 – 1000 l. multicoloured 1·00 1·00

DESIGNS: 350 l. "AIDS" crumbling; 650 l. Knotted cord and emblem of virus; 1000 l. Printed information.

365 "Kurhaus, Scheveningen, 1885" (anon)

1988. "Filacept" International Stamp Exhibition, The Hague, and Important Cities of the World (12th series). Mult.
1331 1600 l. Type **365** .. .. 1·50 1·50
1332 3000 l. Kurhaus, Scheveningen, 1988 .. 3·00 3·00

366 "Angel with Violin"

367 Bird in Tree (Federica Sparagna)

1988. Christmas. 550th Birth Anniv of Melozzo da Forli. Multicoloured.
1333 650 l. Type **366** 75 75
1334 650 l. "Angel of the Annunciation" (20 × 37 mm) 75 75
1335 650 l. "Angel with Mandolin" 75 75

1989. "Nature is Beautiful. Nature is Useful. Nature is...". Multicoloured.
1336 200 l. Type **367** 25 25
1337 500 l. Birds beneath tree (Giovanni Monteduro) 70 70
1338 650 l. Landscape (Rosa Mannarino) 85 85
Nos. 1336/8 depict the first three winning entries in a children's drawing competition.

1989. Postal History. As T **358**. Mult.
1340 100 l. "San Marino 1977" Exhibition 1000 l. stamp on cover (postal tariffs) 15 15
1341 200 l. 350 l. stamp on cover (cancellations) .. 25 25
1342 400 l. Parcel receipt (parcel post) 45 45
1343 500 l. Essay by Martin Riester, 1865 .. .. 60 60
1344 1000 l. 1862 handstamp on cover (pre-stamp period) .. .. 1·25 1·25

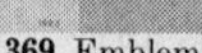

369 Emblem

370 Oath of the Tennis Court

1989. Sport. Multicoloured.
1345 650 l. Type **369** (30th anniv of San Marino Olympic Committee) .. 85 85
1346 750 l. Emblems (admission of San Marino Football Federation to UEFA and FIFA) 95 95
1347 850 l. Tennis racquet and ball (San Marino championships) .. 1·00 1·00
1348 1300 l. Formula I racing car (San Marino Grand Prix, Imola) .. .. 1·40 1·40

1989. Bicent of French Revolution. Mult.
1349 700 l. Type **370** .. .. 1·00 1·00
1350 1000 l. Arrest of Louis XVI .. .. .. 1·50 1·50
1351 1800 l. Napoleon's army 2·25 2·25

371 "Marguerite and Armand"

372 "Angel of the Annunciation"

1989. Award of Celebrities of Show Business Prize to Rudolph Nureyev (ballet dancer). Multicoloured.
1352 1200 l. Type **371** .. .. 1·40 1·40
1353 1500 l. "Apollo Musagete" 1·75 1·75
1354 1700 l. Ken Russell's film "Valentino" .. .. 2·25 2·25

1989. Christmas. Details of the polyptych in Church of Servants of Mary. Mult.
1355 650 l. Type **372** .. .. 1·00 1·00
1356 650 l. "Nativity" (50 × 40 mm) .. .. .. 1·00 1·00
1357 650 l. Mary ("Annunciation") .. .. .. 1·00 1·00

373 Capitol, 1850

1989. "World Stamp Expo '89" International Stamp Exhibition, Washington D.C. and Important Cities of the World (13th series). Multicoloured.
1358 2000 l. Type **373** .. .. 2·25 2·25
1359 2500 l. Capitol, 1989 .. 3·00 3·00

374 Old Post Office

375 "Martyrdom of St. Agatha" (Tiepolo) and Cardinal Alberoni leaving City

1990. Europa. Post Office Buildings. Mult.
1360 700 l. Type **374** .. .. 1·00 1·00
1361 800 l. Dogana Post Office 1·25 1·25

1990. 250th Anniv of End of Cardinal Alberoni's Occupation of San Marino.
1362 **375** 3500 l. multicoloured 4·00 4·00

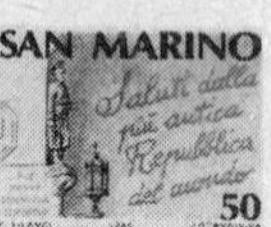

376 Map pinpointing San Marino

377 Statue, Government Palace

1990. European Tourism Year. Multicoloured.
1366 50 l. Type **377** 10 10
1367 50 l. Liberty Statue and English inscription .. 10 10
1368 50 l. Government Palace and German inscription 10 10
1369 50 l. Man with flag and French inscription .. 10 10
1363 600 l. Type **376** 80 80
1364 600 l. Aerial view showing villages 80 80
1365 600 l. First Tower .. 80 80
See also Nos. 1424/7.

379 Olivier in "Hamlet"

380 Mt. Titano and State Flags

1990. Award of Celebrities of Show Business Prize to Laurence Olivier (actor). Mult.
1374 600 l. Type **379** 90 90
1375 700 l. "Richard III" .. 1·10 1·10
1376 1500 l. "The Runner" .. 2·50 2·50
Nos. 1374/6 are wrongly inscribed "Lawrence".

1990. Visit of President Francesco Cossiga of Italy.
1377 **380** 600 l. multicoloured .. 75 75

381 Pinocchio

1990. Death Centenary of Carlo Collodi (writer). Characters from "Pinocchio". Multicoloured.
1378 250 l. Type **381** 30 30
1379 400 l. Geppetto 50 50
1380 450 l. Blue fairy 55 55
1381 600 l. Cat and wolf .. 75 75

382 Pre-Columbian Civilizations

1990. 500th Anniv (1992) of Discovery of America by Columbus (1st issue). Mult.
1382 1500 l. Type **382** .. .. 2·25 2·25
1383 2000 l. Produce of the New World .. .. 2·50 2·50
See also Nos. 1401/2 and 1417/18.

383 Mary and Two Kings

384 Swallowtail on "Ephedra major"

1990. Christmas. Details of Cuciniello Crib. Multicoloured.
1384 750 l. Type **383** .. .. 1·00 1·00
1385 750 l. Baby Jesus in manger and third King 1·00 1·00
Nos. 1384/5 were issued together, se-tenant, forming a composite design.

1990. Flora and Fauna. Multicoloured.
1386 200 l. Type **384** 25 25
1387 300 l. "Apoderus coryli" (weevil) and hazelnut 35 35
1388 500 l. Garden dormouse and acorns of holm oak 60 60
1389 1000 l. Green lizard and "Ophrys bertolonii" (orchid) .. .. 1·50 1·50
1390 2000 l. Firecrest on black pine .. .. 3·25 3·25

INDEX
Countries can be quickly located by referring to the index at the end of this volume.

385 Launch of "Ariane-4"

1991. Europa. Europe in Space. Mult.
1391 750 l. Type **385** .. .. 3·00 3·00
1392 800 l. "E.R.S.-1" survey satellite .. .. 3·00 3·00

1991. World of Stamps. As T **358**. Mult.
1393 100 l. Stamp shop .. 15 15
1394 150 l. Stamp club .. 20 20
1395 200 l. Exhibition .. 25 25
1396 450 l. Stamp album and catalogues 50 50
1397 1500 l. Philatelic publications (25th anniv of Italian Philatelic Press Union) .. .. 1·75 1·75

386 Torch Bearer leaving Athens

387 Cat

1991. Olympic Games, Barcelona (1992). Mult.
1398 400 l. Type **386** 50 50
1399 600 l. Torch bearer passing through San Marino 70 70
1400 2000 l. Torch bearer arriving in Barcelona .. 2·50 2·50

1991. 500th Anniv (1992) of Discovery of America by Columbus (2nd issue). As T **382**. Multicoloured.
1401 750 l. Navigational dividers, quadrant, hour-glass, compass and route map .. .. 1·25 1·25
1402 3000 l. "Santa Maria", "Nina" and "Pinta" .. 4·50 4·50

1991. Pets. Multicoloured.
1403 500 l. Type **387** 70 70
1404 550 l. Hamster on wheel 75 75
1405 750 l. Great Dane and pomeranian .. .. 1·10 1·10
1406 1000 l. Aquarium fishes .. 1·40 1·40
1407 1200 l. Canaries in cage .. 1·75 1·75

388 Players, Balls and Baskets

391 Keep

389 James Clerk-Maxwell (physicist)

1991. Centenary of Basketball. Multicoloured.
1408 650 l. Type **388** .. .. 1·25 1·25
1409 750 l. James Naismith (inventor) and players 1·50 1·50

1991. 100 Years of Radio (1st issue).
1410 **389** 750 l. multicoloured .. 1·00 1·00
Clerk-Maxwell formulated the theory of electromagnetic radiation.
See also Nos. 1431 and 1452.

1991. Christmas. La Rocca fortress. Mult.
1412 600 l. Type **391** (postage) 75 75
1413 750 l. Inland view of fortress 90 90
1414 1200 l. Fortress on crag (air) .. .. .. 1·60 1·60

392 "Bianca and Falliero" (Pesaro production)

1992. Birth Bicentenary of Gioachino Rossini (composer). Scenes from productions of his operas. Multicoloured.
1415 750 l. Type **392** 80 80
1416 1200 l. "The Barber of Seville" (La Scala Theatre, Milan) .. 1·25 1·25

1992. 500th Anniv of Discovery of America by Columbus (3rd issue). As T **382**. Mult.
1417 1500 l. Amerindians watching fleet .. 1·50 1·50
1418 2000 l. Route map of the four voyages .. .. 2·00 2·00

SAN MARINO

393 Roses

394 Courting Couple

1992. Plants. Multicoloured.
1419 50 l. Type **393** 10 10
1420 200 l. Ficus as house plant 20 20
1421 300 l. Orchid in conservatory 30 30
1422 450 l. Cacti in pots .. 45 45
1423 5000 l. Pelargoniums in trough .. .. 5·00 5·00

1992. Tourism. Multicoloured.
(a) As T **377**
1424 50 l. Man with crossbow and Italian inscription 10 10
1425 50 l. Tennis player and English inscription .. 10 10
1426 50 l. Motor cycle rider and French inscription .. 10 10
1427 50 l. Ferrari racing car and German inscription 10 10
(b) As T **394**
1428 600 l. Type **394** 65 65
1429 600 l. Man in restaurant 65 65
1430 600 l. Woman reading on veranda 65 65

1992. 100 Years (1995) of Radio (2nd issue). As T **389**. Multicoloured.
1431 750 l. Heinrich Rudolf Hertz (physicist) .. 80 80
Hertz proved Clerk-Maxwell's theory.

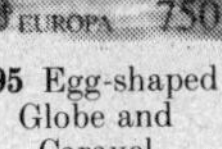

395 Egg-shaped Globe and Caravel

397 Inedible Mushrooms

1992. Europa. 500th Anniv of Discovery of America. Multicoloured.
1432 750 l. Type **395** 80 80
1433 850 l. Caravel and island inside broken egg .. 90 90

1992. 3rd Titano Mycological Exhibition, Borgo Maggiore. Multicoloured.
1435 250 l. Type **397** 25 25
1436 250 l. Inedible mushrooms (different) 25 25
1437 350 l. Edible mushrooms in bowl 35 35
1438 350 l. Edible mushrooms on cloth 35 35
Stamps of the same value were issued together, se-tenant, each pair forming a composite design.

398 View and Arms of San Marino

399 "La Sacra Conversazione"

1992. Admission of San Marino to United Nations Organization. Multicoloured.
1439 1000 l. Type **398** .. .. 1·00 1·00
1440 1000 l. View of San Marino (different) and United Nations emblem .. 1·00 1·00

1992. Christmas. 500th Death Anniv of Piero della Francesca (artist). Multicoloured.
1441 750 l. Type **399** 75 75
1442 750 l. Close-up of Madonna 75 75
1443 750 l. Close-up of shell decoration 75 75

400 Tennis Player

401 Stars

1993. Sporting Events. Multicoloured.
1444 300 l. Type **400** (Italian and San Marino Youth Games) 30 30
1445 400 l. Cross-country skiers (European Youth Olympic Days (winter), Aosta, Italy) 40 40
1446 550 l. Runners (European Youth Olympic Days (summer), Eindhoven, Netherlands) 50 50
1447 600 l. Fisherman (Freshwater Angling Clubs World Championship, Ostellato, Italy) .. 60 60
1448 700 l. Runners breasting tape (Small States Games, Malta) .. 70 70
1449 1300 l. Sprinters (Mediterranean Games, Rousillon, France) .. 1·25 1·25

1993. Europa. Contemporary Art.
1450 **401** 750 l. multicoloured .. 65 65
1451 – 850 l. blue and orange 70 70
DESIGN: 850 l. Silhouette.

1993. 100 Years (1995) of Radio (3rd issue). As T **389**. Multicoloured.
1452 750 l. Edouard Branly (physicist) and his "radioconductor" .. 65 65
Branly developed a method of revealing Hertzian waves.

404 Mourning Cloak ("Nymphalis antiopa")

406 Carlo Goldoni

1993. Butterflies. Multicoloured.
1454 250 l. Type **404** 20 20
1455 250 l. Glanvill's fritillary ("Melitaea cinxia") .. 20 20
1456 250 l. Clouded yellow ("Colias crocea") .. 20 20
1457 250 l. Scare swallowtail ("Iphiclides podalirius") 20 20

1993. Anniversaries. Multicoloured.
1459 550 l. Type **406** (dramatist, death bicentenary) 45 45
1460 650 l. Horace (Quintus Horatius Flaccus) (poet) (2000th death anniv) 55 55
1461 850 l. Scene from opera "Orpheus" by Claudio Monteverdi (composer, 350th death anniv) (horiz) 70 70
1462 1850 l. Guy de Maupassant (writer, death centenary) (horiz) 1·50 1·50

407 San Marino

1993. Christmas. Multicoloured.
1463 600 l. Type **407** 50 50
1464 750 l. "Adoration of the Child" (Gerrit van Honthorst) (horiz) .. 65 65
1465 850 l. "Adoration of the Shepherds" (Van Honthorst) 70 70

EXPRESS LETTER STAMPS

E **22.** Mt. Titano and "Liberty".

1907.
E 53. E **22.** 25 c. red .. .. 5·50 3·50

1923. Optd. **ESPRESSO.**
E 92. **19.** 60 c. violet 30 30

1923. Surch. **Cent. 60.**
E 93. E **22.** 60 c. on 25 c. red .. 30 30

E **34.**

1923. Red Cross.
E 101. E **34.** 60 c. + 5 c. red .. 70 80

1926. No. E 92 surch. **Lire 1,25.**
E 134. **19.** 1 l. 25 on 60 c. violet 55 55

1927. No. E 93 surch. **L. 1,25** and bars over old surch.
E 138. E **22.** 1 l. 25 on 60 c. on 25 c. red 45 45

E **50.** Statue of Liberty and View of San Marino.

1929. As Type E **50**, without "UNION POSTALE UNIVERSELLE" and inscr. "ESPRESSO".
E 164. E **50.** 1 l. 25 green .. 15 15

1929. Optd **UNION POSTALE UNIVERSELLE** as in Type E **50**.
E165 E **50** 2 l. 50 blue 55 55

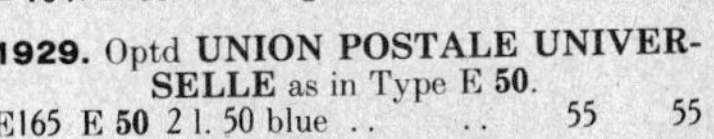

E **78.**

1943.
E 305. E **78.** 1 l. 25 green .. 10 10
E 306. 2 l. 50 orange .. 10 10

E **79.** Mt. Titano.

1945.
E 307. E **79** 2 l. 50 green .. 10 10
E 308. 5 l. orange .. 10 10
E 309. 5 l. red 65 65
E 310. 10 l. blue .. .. 1·90 1·40
E 419. 60 l. red .. .. 7·00 4·50

E **87.** Pegasus and Mt. Titano.

1946.
E 337. E **87.** 30 l. blue .. .. 6·00 4·00
E 420. 80 l. blue .. .. 7·00 5·00

1947. Surch.
E 339. E **79.** 15 l. on 5 l. red .. 30 25
E 340. 15 l. on 10 l. blue .. 30 25
E 374. E **87.** 35 l. on 30 l. blue .. 45·00 22·00
E 341. 60 l. on 30 l. blue .. 4·25 4·25
E 545. E **79.** 75 l. on 60 l. red .. 2·00 1·75
E 375. E **87.** 80 l. on 30 l. blue .. 27·00 15·00
E 546. 100 l. on 80 l. blue 2·00 1·75
E 783. E**180.** 120 l. on 75 l. black and yellow .. 20 15
E 784. 135 l. on 100 l. black and orange .. 20 15

E 180. Crossbow and Three " Castles ".

1966.

E 800. E 180. 75 l. blk. and yell. 10 10
E 801. 80 l. blk. and pur. 10 10
E 802. 100 l. blk. and orge. 10 10

No. E 800 has crossbow in white without " shadows ".

PARCEL POST STAMPS

Unused and used prices are for complete stamps.

P 46.

1928.

P 145. P 46 5 c. purple and blue .. 10 10
P 146. 10 c. blue 10 10
P 147. 20 c. black and blue .. 10 10
P 148. 25 c. red and blue .. 10 10
P 149. 30 c. blue 10 10
P 150. 50 c. orange and blue 10 10
P 151. 60 c. red and blue .. 10 10
P 152. 1 l. violet and red .. 15 15
P 153. 2 l. green and red .. 20 20
P 154. 3 l. bistre and red .. 25 25
P 155. 4 l. grey and red .. 30 30
P 156. 10 l. mauve and red .. 1·25 1·25
P 157. 12 l. lake and red .. 3·50 3·50
P 158. 15 l. olive and red .. 6·00 6·00
P 159. 20 l. purple and red .. 7·50 7·50

1945.

P309 P 46 5 c. purple and red 10 10
P310 10 c. brown & black 10 10
P311 20 c. red and green 10 10
P312 25 c. yellow & black 10 10
P313 30 c. mauve and red 10 10
P314 50 c. violet and black 10 10
P315 60 c. red and black 10 10
P316 1 l. brown and blue 10 10
P317 2 l. brown and blue 10 10
P318 3 l. grey and brown 10 10
P319 4 l. green and brown 10 10
P320 10 l. grey and violet 10 10
P770 10 l. green and red 10 10
P321 12 l. green and blue 2·25 1·25
P322 15 l. green and violet 2·00 1·25
P323 20 l. violet & brown 1·60 1·25
P324 25 l. red and blue 35·00 20·00
P771 50 l. yellow and red 10 10
P455 300 l. violet and red £150 £100
P773 300 l. violet & brown 40 40
P526 500 l. brown and red 2·75 2·25
P775 1000 l. green & brown 1·00 1·00

1948. Nos. P324 and P771 surch in figures and wavy lines on each half of design.

P524 P 46 100 l. on 50 l. .. 70 60
P375 200 l. on 25 l. .. £160 70·00

POSTAGE DUE STAMPS

D 18.

D 82.

1897.

D 38. D 18. 5 c. brown and green 10 10
D 39. 10 c. brown and green 10 10
D 40. 30 c. brown and green 40 35
D 41. 50 c. brown and green 1·00 70
D 42. 60 c. brown and green 2·50 2·00
D 43. 1 l. brown and red .. 1·50 1·10
D 44. 3 l. brown and red .. 6·50 7·50
D 45. 5 l. brown and red .. 26·00 15·00
D 46. 10 l. brown and red .. 8·50 15·00

1924.

D 102. D18 5 c. brown and red .. 10 10
D 103. 10 c. brown and red .. 10 10
D 104. 30 c. brown and red .. 15 15
D 105. 50 c. brown and red .. 30 30
D 106. 60 c. brown and red .. 1·75 1·75
D 107. 1 l. brown and green 2·00 2·00
D 108. 3 l. brown and green 8·00 8·00
D 109. 5 l. brown and green 8·00 8·00
D 110. 10 l. brown and green £110 £120

1925.

D 111. D18 5 c. brown and blue 10 10
D 113. 10 c. brown and blue 10 10
D 114. 15 c. brown and blue 10 10
D 115. 20 c. brown and blue 20 20
D 116 25 c. brown and blue 35 35
D 117. 30 c. brown and blue 15 15
D 118. 40 c. brown and blue 1·60 1·40
D 119. 50 c. brown and blue 25 25
D 120. 60 c. brown and blue 55 55
D 121. 1 l. brown and orange 1·40 45
D 122. 2 l. brown and orange 80 90
D 123. 3 l. brown and orange 24·00 15·00
D 124. 5 l. brown and orange 8·00 2·25
D 125. 10 l. brown & orange 12·00 3·75
D 126. 15 l. brown & orange 60 60
D 127. 25 l. brown & orange 18·00 12·00
D 128. 30 l. brown & orange 3·75 5·50
D 129. 50 l. brown & orange 4·75 6·00

1931. As Type D 18, but with centre obliterated in black and new values superimposed in silver.

D 164. D18. 15 c. on 5 c. blue .. 10 10
D 165. 15 c. on 10 c. blue .. 10 10
D 166. 15 c. on 30 c. blue .. 10 10
D 167. 20 c. on 5 c. blue .. 10 10
D 168. 20 c. on 10 c. blue .. 10 10
D 169. 20 c. on 30 c. blue .. 10 10
D 170. 25 c. on 5 c. blue .. 55 25
D 171. 25 c. on 10 c. blue .. 55 25
D 172. 25 c. on 30 c. blue .. 4·00 2·50
D 173. 40 c. on 5 c. blue .. 30 10
D 174. 40 c. on 10 c. blue .. 30 10
D 175. 40 c. on 30 c. blue .. 30 10
D 176. 2 l. on 5 c. blue .. 25·00 16·00
D 177. 2 l. on 10 c. blue .. 42·00 26·00
D 178. 2 l. on 30 c. blue .. 32·00 20·00

1936. Surch. in figures and words and bars. D 233/8 and D 242 are brown and blue; the rest brown and orange.

D 233. D18. 10 c. on 5 c. .. 25 25
D 234. 25 c. on 30 c. .. 5·50 5·00
D 236. 50 c. on 5 c. .. 1·60 70
D 237. 1 l. on 30 c. .. 17·00 3·25
D 238. 1 l. on 40 c. .. 5·50 3·25
D 239. 1 l. on 3 l. .. 15·00 1·00
D 240. 1 l. on 25 l. .. 40·00 6·50
D 241. 2 l. on 15 l. .. 17·00 9·00
D 242. 3 l. on 20 c. .. 20·00 14·00
D 243. 25 l. on 50 l. .. 1·25 1·75

1945.

D 309. D82. 5 c. green 10 10
D 310. 10 c. brown 10 10
D 311. 15 c. red 10 10
D 312. 20 c. blue 10 10
D 313. 25 c. violet 10 10
D 314. 30 c. mauve 10 10
D 315. 40 c. yellow 10 10
D 316. 50 c. slate 10 10
D 317. 60 c. brown 10 10
D 318. 1 l. orange 10 10
D 319. 2 l. red 15 15
D 320. 5 l. violet 20 20
D 321. 10 l. blue 25 25
D 322. 20 l. green .. .. 8·50 5·00
D 323. 25 l. brown .. .. 8·50 5·00
D 324. 50 l. brown .. .. 8·50 5·00

SANTANDER Pt. 20

One of the states of the Granadine Confederation.

A department of Colombia from 1886, now uses Colombian stamps.

100 centavos = 1 peso.

1.

2.

1884. Imperf.

1. 1. 1 c. blue 15 15
2. 5 c. red 30 25
3. 10 c. violet 50 50

1886. Imperf.

4. 2. 1 c. blue 40 40
5. 5 c. red 12 12
6. 10 c. lilac 20 20

1887. T 1 but inscr. "REPUBLICA DE COLOMBIA". Imperf.

7. 1 c. blue 12 12
8. 5 c. red 45 45
9. 10 c. violet .. .. 1·50 1·50

3.

4.

5.

6. 7.

1890. Perf.

10. 3. 1 c. blue 12 12
11. 4. 5 c. red 60 60
12. 5. 10 c. violet 25 25

1895.

14. 6. 5 c. red on buff 35 30

1895.

15. 7. 5 c. brown 60 60
16. 5 c. green 60 60

8.

9.

10.

1899.

17. 8. 1 c. black on green .. 20 20
18. 9. 5 c. black on red 20 20
19. 10. 10 c. blue 35 35

F 11.

1903. Fiscal stamp as Type F 11 optd. **Provisional Correos de Santander.** Imperf.

21. F 11. 50 c. red 20 20

SARDINIA Pt. 8

A former Italian kingdom, including the island of Sardinia, a large part of the mainland and parts of what is now S.E. France. The Kingdom of Italy was formed by the adhesion of other Italian states to Sardinia, whose king became the first ruler of united Italy.

100 centesimi = 1 lira.

1. Victor Emmanuel II. 2.

1851. Imperf.

1. 1. 5 c. black £2750 £1600
3. 20 c. blue .. .. .. £3000 80·00
7. 40 c. red £3000 £3000

1853. Embossed on coloured paper. Imperf.

9 1 5 c. on green £5000 £900
10 20 c. on blue .. .. £5000 80·00
11 40 c. on red £3250 £850

1854. Embossed on white paper. Imperf.

13 1 5 c. green £24000 £425
15 20 c. blue .. .. £7500 70·00
18 40 c. red £65000 £2250

1855. Head embossed. Imperf.

28 2 5 c. green .. .. 3·00 9·50
40 10 c. bistre .. .. 3·00 5·00
39 10 c. brown .. .. 28·00 11·00
35 10 c. grey .. .. 70·00 55·00
48 20 c. blue .. .. 42·00 5·00
55 40 c. red .. .. 8·00 16·00
60 80 c. yellow .. .. 11·00 £130
61 3 l. bronze £250 £2500

For Type 2 perf, see Italy Nos. 1/4.

NEWSPAPER STAMPS

N 3.

1861. Numerals embossed. Imperf.

N62 N 3 1 c. black .. .. 75 2·25
N63 2 c. black .. .. 48·00 48·00

For 2 c. stamps of similar types in yellow see Italy No. N5.

SASENO Pt. 3

An island off the W. coast of Albania, temporarily occupied by Italy.

100 centesimi = 1 lira.

1923. Stamps of Italy optd. SASENO.

1. 38. 10 c. red .. .. 1·00 3·75
2. 15 c. grey .. .. 1·00 3·75
3. 41. 20 c. orange .. .. 1·00 3·75
4. 39. 25 c. blue .. .. 1·00 3·75
5. 30 c. brown .. .. 1·00 3·75
6. 50 c. mauve .. .. 1·00 3·75
7. 60 c. red .. .. 2·00 4·25
8. 34. 1 l. brown and green .. 2·00 4·25

SAUDI ARABIA Pt. 19

Formerly under Turkish rule, the Hejaz became an independent kingdom in 1916, but was conquered by the Sultan of Nejd in 1926 who became King of Hejaz and Nejd when combined issues of stamps were used. In 1932 the name of the state was changed to the Saudi Arabian Kingdom.

1916. 40 paras = 1 piastre.
1929. 110 guerche = 10 riyal = 1 gold sovereign.
1952. 440 guerche = 40 riyal = 1 gold sovereign.
1960. 100 halalah = 20 guerche = 1 riyal. 1 piastre = 1 guerche.
1976. 100 halalas = 1 rial.

A. HEJAZ

5. From Stucco Work over Entrance to Cairo Railway Station.

1916. As T 5 (various Arabic designs). Perf. or roul.

11. 1 pa. purple .. .. 2·00 50
12. ⅛ pi. yellow .. .. 2·75 80
13. ¼ pi. green .. .. 2·75 80
14. ½ pi. red .. .. 3·00 1·10
15. 1 pi. blue .. .. 3·00 1·10
16. 2 pi. red .. .. 15·00 4·00

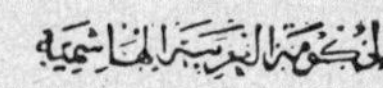

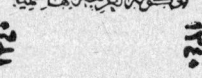

(7. "1340 Hashemite Kingdom 1340").

1921. Optd with T 7.

21 1 pa. purple .. .. 20·00 10·00
22 ⅛ pi. yellow .. .. 30·00 15·00
23 ¼ pi. green .. .. 8·00 5·00
24 ½ pi. red .. .. 12·00 6·00
26 1 pi. blue .. .. 10·00 5·00
28 2 pi. red .. .. 15·00 8·00

نصف قرش
(8.) (½ pi.).

قرش واحد
(9.) (1 pi.).

1921. No. 21 surch with T 8 or 9.

29 ½ pi. on 1 pa. purple .. £180 60·00
30 1 pi. on 1 pa. purple .. £180 60·00

(10. " 1340 Hashemite Kingdom 1340 ").

1922. Nos. 11 to 16 optd with T 10.

31. 1 pa. purple .. .. 3·00 1·00
32. ⅛ pi. yellow .. .. 12·00 4·00
33. ¼ pi. green .. .. 2·50 1·00
34. ½ pi. red .. .. 2·50 75
35. 1 pi. blue .. .. 4·00 75
36. 2 pi. red .. .. 7·50 4·00

1922. No. 31 surch with T 8 or 9.

37. ½ pi. on 1 pa. purple .. 15·00 5·00
38. 1 pi. on 1 pa. purple .. 4·00 25

11. Meccan Sherifian Arms.

1922.

39. 11. ⅛ pi. brown .. .. 1·00 30
57. ¼ pi. green .. .. 5·00 4·00
41. ½ pi. red 50 20
42. 1 pi. blue .. .. 1·00 20
43. 1½ pi. violet .. .. 1·00 30
44. 2 pi. orange .. .. 1·50 40
45. 3 pi. brown .. .. 2·00 50
46. 5 pi. olive .. .. 4·00 1·00
58. 10 pi. brown and mauve .. 6·00 5·00

ربع قرش
(12.) (¼ pi.).

عشرة قروش
(13.) (10 pi.).

تذكار الخلافة
شعبان
١٣٤٢
(14.)

1923. Surch. with T 12 (¼ pi.) or T 13 (10 pi.).

47. 11. ¼ pi. on ⅛ pi. brown .. 20·00 10·00
49. 10 pi. on 5 pi. olive .. 25·00 20·00

1924. Proclamation of King Hussein as Caliph. Optd. with T 14.

50. 11. ⅛ pi. brown .. .. 3·00 2·00
51. ½ pi. red .. .. 2·00 1·00
52. 1 pi. blue .. .. 3·00 2·00
53. 1½ pi. violet .. .. 3·00 2·00
54. 2 pi. orange .. .. 3·00 2·00
55. 3 pi. brown .. .. 4·00 3·00
56. 5 pi. olive .. .. 4·00 3·00

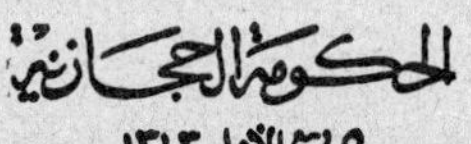
(15. "Hejaz Government. 4th October, 1924").

1924. Optd with T **15**.

66 1 pa. purple (No. 11) .. 15·00 6·00
77 1 pa. purple (No. 31) .. £100 50·00
59 ⅛ pi. yellow (No. 12) .. 20·00 6·00
78 ⅛ pi. yellow (No. 32) .. £1500
68 ¼ pi. green (No. 13) .. 20·00 9·00
79 ¼ pi. green (No. 33) .. 50·00 30·00
71 ½ pi. red (No. 14) .. 45·00 20·00
76 ½ pi. red (No. 24) £1650
80 ½ pi. red (No. 34) .. 60·00 40·00
86 ½ pi. red (No. 41) £950
84 ½ pi. on 1 pa. purple (No. 37) £120 50·00
73 1 pi. blue (No. 15) .. 30·00 12·00
81 1 pi. blue (No. 35) .. £100 50·00
85 1 pi. on 1 pa. purple (No. 38) £100 45·00
74 2 pi. red (No. 16) .. .. 40·00 15·00
83 2 pi. red (No. 36) .. .. £100 50·00
87 10 pi. purple and mauve (No. 58) £700

(16. "Hejaz Government, 4th October, 1924").

1924. Nos. 13 and 39/58 optd with T **16**.

105 ⅛ pi. brown .. .. 15·00 1·75
90 – ¼ pi. green (No. 13) .. 45·00 12·00
96 **11** ¼ pi. green .. .. 18·00 5·50
116 ½ pi. red .. .. 4·00 2·00
98 1 pi. blue .. .. 12·00 3·25
99 1½ pi. violet .. .. 5·00 1·75
119 2 pi. orange .. .. 4·00 2·00
120 3 pi. brown .. .. 5·00 2·10
103 5 pi. olive .. .. 5·00 1·75
104 10 pi. brown & mauve 15·00 6·00
The overprint on No. 90 is smaller.

1925. Nos. 50/6 optd. with T **16**.

136 **11.** ⅛ pi. brown .. .. 50·00 6·00
137 ½ pi. red .. .. .. 70·00 6·50
138 1 pi. blue .. .. 75·00 6·00
139 1½ pi. violet .. .. 50·00 6·50
140 2 pi. orange .. .. 75·00 10·00
141 3 pi. brown .. .. 70·00 17·00
142 5 pi. olive .. .. 70·00 6·50

(17.) (18.)

1925. Stamps of 1922 surch. as Type **17**.

148. **11.** ¼ pi. on ⅛ pi. brown .. 60·00
149. ¼ pi. on ½ pi. red .. 60·00
150. 1 pi. on 2 pi. orange .. 80·00
151. 1 pi. on 3 pi. brown .. 80·00
153. 10 pi. on 5 pi. olive .. £100

1925. Nos. 148/53 further surch. with values in larger type as Type **18**.

154. **11.** ¼ pi. on ¼ pi. on ⅛ pi. brown 20·00 6·00
155. ¼ pi. on ¼ pi. on ½ pi. red 20·00 6·00
157. 1 pi. on 1 pi. on 2 pi. orge. 20·00 9·00
158. 1 pi. on 1 pi. on 3 pi. brn. 20·00 9·00
160. 10 pi. on 10 pi. on 5 pi. olive 10·00 6·00

(19.)

1925. Stamps of 1922 surch. as T **19**.

172 **11.** ⅛ pi. on ½ pi. red .. .. 5·00 3·00
173 ¼ pi. on ½ pi. red .. .. 5·00 3·00
173b 1 pi. on ½ pi. red .. .. 5·00 3·00
173c 1 pi. on 1½ pi. violet .. 5·00 3·00
174 1 pi. on 2 pi. orange .. 5·00 3·00
175 1 pi. on 3 pi. brown .. 5·00 3·00
176 10 pi. on 5 pi. olive .. 5·00 3·00

20.

(24.)

1925. As T **20** (various Arabic designs) optd. with T **24**.

177. ⅛ pi. brown .. .. 1·00 1·00
178. ¼ pi. blue .. .. 1·00 1·00
179. ½ pi. red .. .. 1·50 1·50
180. 1 pi. green .. .. 1·50 1·50
181. 1½ pi. orange .. .. 1·50 1·50
182. 2 pi. blue .. .. 1·50 1·50
183. 3 pi. olive .. .. 2·00 2·00
184. 5 pi. brown .. .. 2·00 2·00
185. 10 pi. green and red .. 3·00 3·00

B. NEJD

(25.) "Nejd Sultanate Post 1343". (29.) "1343 Commemoration of First Pilgrimage under Sultan of Nejd".

1925. Various stamps optd. with T **25**.
(a) Stamps of Turkey.

190. **30.** 5 pa. orange (No. 583) 15·00 10·00
191. 10 pa. green (No. 503) 15·00 11·00

26. 27.

(b) Hejaz Fiscal stamps.
(i) Notarial stamps.

192. **26.** 1 pi. violet .. .. 10·00 10·00
193. 2 pi. blue .. .. 10·00 10·00

(ii) Bill stamp.

194. **27.** 1 pi. violet .. .. 10·00 10·00

28.

(iii) Railway Tax Stamps.

195. **28.** 1 pi. blue .. .. 12·00 12·00
196. 2 pi. orange .. .. 16·00 16·00
197. 3 pi. lilac .. .. 18·00 18·00

(c) Hejaz Postage stamps (1922 issues).

198a. **11.** ⅛ pi. brown .. .. 12·00 10·00
198c. ⅛ pi. red .. .. 15·00 15·00
199a. ½ pi. red .. .. 7·50 7·50
200. 1½ pi. lilac .. .. 15·00 15·00
201. 2 pi. orange .. .. 25·00 25·00
202. 3 pi. red .. .. 15·00 15·00

(29). "1343 Commemoration of First Pilgrimage under Sultan of Nejd".

(30). "Wednesday". (31).

1925. Pilgrimage Commemoration. Various stamps optd. with T **29** and **30** and surch as T **31**.
(a) 1914 pictorial stamps of Turkey.

210. 1 pi. on 10 pa. green (503) 75·00 30·00
211. 5 pi. on 1 pi. blue (518) .. 75·00 30·00

(b) 1916 stamps of Hejaz.

212. 2 pi. on 1 pa purple .. £125 50·00
213. 4 pi. on ⅛ pi yellow .. £300 £125

(c) Railway Tax stamp.

214. **28.** 3 pi. lilac .. .. £175 60·00

(32). "Nejd Sultanate Post".

1925. Various stamps optd. with T **32**.
(a) Stamps of Turkey.

215. **30.** 5 pa. orange .. .. 10·00 7·50
216. – 10 pa. green (No. 503) 12·00 10·00

(b) Hejaz Fiscal stamps.
(i) Notarial stamp.

217. **26.** 2 pi. blue .. .. 8·00 7·50

(ii) Railway Tax Stamps.

218b. **28.** 1 pi. blue .. .. 10·00 6·00
219. 2 pi. orange .. .. 15·00 6·00
220. 3 pi. lilac .. .. 20·00 10·00
221. 5 pi. green .. .. 20·00 7·00

(c) Hejaz Postage stamps.
(i) Nos. 35/6.

222. 1 pi. blue .. .. .. 60·00 60·00
223. 2 pi. red .. .. .. 60·00 60·00

(ii) Stamps of 1922.

224. **11.** ⅛ pi. brown £2500
225. ½ pi. red .. .. 5·00 2·00
226. 1 pi. violet .. .. 12·00 10·00
227. 1½ pi. red .. .. 12·00 10·00
228. 2 pi. orange .. .. 35·00 20·00
229. 2 pi. purple .. .. 25·00 20·00
230. 3 pi. red .. .. 15·00 12·00
231. 5 bi. red .. .. 20·00 18·00

(33). (1 pi.). (34). (1½ pi.). (35). (2 pi.).

1925. Stamps optd. with T **32** further surch. with T **33/5**.

239. **11.** 1 pi. on ½ pi. red (225) 4·00 1·50
241. 1½ pi. on ½ pi. red .. 5·00 1·50
243. 2 pi. on 3 pi. red (230) 10·00 2·00

(36). "Postage of Nejd, 1344, Commemoration of Medina". (37). "Commemoration of Jeddah, Postage of Nejd".

1925. Capture of Medina. Railway Tax stamps of Hejaz optd. with T **36**.

244. **28.** 1 pi. on 10 pi. mauve and violet .. .. 55·00 35·00
245. 2 pi. on 50 pi. red and blue .. .. .. 55·00 35·00
246. 3 pi. on 100 pi. brown 55·00 35·00
247. 4 pi. on 500 pi. red .. 55·00 35·00
248. 5 pi. on 1000 pi. violet and red .. .. 55·00 35·00

1925. Capture of Jeddah. Optd. with T **37**.

249. **28.** 1 pi. on 10 pi. mauve and violet .. .. 55·00 35·00
250. 2 pi. on 50 pi. red and blue .. .. .. 55·00 35·00
251. 3 pi. on 100 pi. brown 55·00 35·00
252. 4 pi. on 500 pi. red .. 55·00 35·00
253. 5 pi. on 1000 pi. violet and red .. .. 55·00 35·00

C. HEJAZ-NEJD

38. 39.

1926.

254 **38** ¼ pi. violet .. .. 7·00 2·00
261 ¼ pi. orange .. .. 5·00 60
255 ½ pi. grey .. .. 7·00 2·00
262 ½ pi. green .. .. 3·00 30
256 1 pi. blue .. .. 8·00 2·50
263 1 pi. red .. .. 2·50 30
257 **39** 2 pi. green .. .. 7·00 2·00
264 2 pi. purple .. .. 2·50 30
259 3 pi. red .. .. 10·00 2·50
265 3 pi. blue .. .. 2·50 30
260 5 pi. red .. .. 8·00 2·00
266 5 pi. brown .. .. 5·00 60

(40.). "Islamic Congress, 1 June, 1926".

1926. Pan-Islamic Congress, Cairo. Optd. With T **40**.

275. **38.** ⅛ pi. orange .. .. 7·00 2·00
276. ½ pi. green .. .. 7·00 2·00
277. 1 pi. red .. .. 7·00 2·00
278. **39.** 2 pi. purple .. .. 7·00 2·00
279. 3 pi. blue .. .. 7·00 2·00
280. 5 pi. brown .. .. 7·00 2·00

41. Tougra of Ibn Saud. (42. "25th Rajab 1345").

1926.

284. **41.** ⅛ pi. brown .. .. 10·00 50
285. ¼ pi. green .. .. 10·00 50
286. ½ pi. red .. .. 10·00 20
287. 1 pi. purple .. .. 10·00 50
288. 1½ pi. blue .. .. 10·00 50
289. 3 pi. olive .. .. 16·00 1·75
290. 5 pi. brown .. .. 20·00 2·50
291. 10 pi. brown .. .. 60·00 5·00

1927. Establishment of Kingdom. Optd. with T **42**.

294. **41.** ⅛ pi. brown .. .. 10·00 5·00
295. ¼ pi. green .. .. 10·00 5·00
296. ½ pi. red .. .. 10·00 5·00
297. 1 pi. purple .. .. 10·00 5·00
298. 1½ pi. blue .. .. 10·00 5·00
299. 3 pi. olive .. .. 10·00 5·00
300. 5 pi. brown .. .. 10·00 5·00
301. 10 pi. brown .. .. 12·00 6·00

43. 44.

1929.

302. **43.** 1¾ g. blue .. .. 10·00 70
303. 20 g. violet .. .. 35·00 6·00
304. 30 g. green .. .. 50·00 8·00

1930 4th Anniv of King Ibn Saud's Accession.

305. **44.** ½ g. red .. .. .. 10·00 2·00
306. 1½ g. violet .. .. 10·00 1·50
307. 1¾ g. blue .. .. 15·00 2·00
308. 3½ g. green .. .. 15·00 2·25
309. 5 g. purple .. .. 25·00 3·00

45. 46.

1931.

310. **45.** ⅛ g. yellow .. .. 8·00 1·25
311. ¼ g. green .. .. 8·00 70
312. 1¾ g. blue .. .. 25·00 80

1932.

313. **46.** ¼ g. green .. .. 12·00 1·00
314. ½ g. red .. .. .. 30·00 1·25
315. 2¼ g. blue .. .. 50·00 1·50

D. SAUDI ARABIA

47.

1932. Proclamation of Emir Saud as Heir Apparent.

316. **47.** ¼ g. green .. .. 6·00
317. ½ g. red .. .. .. 6·00 2·00
318. 1½ g. blue .. .. 12·00
319. 3 g. green .. .. 15·00
320. 3½ g. blue .. .. 18·00 3·00
321. 5 g. yellow .. .. 50·00 15·00
322. 10 g. orange .. .. 80·00
323. 20 g. violet £110
324. 30 g. violet £200
325. ¼ s. red £150
326. ½ s. brown £400
327. 1 s. purple £800

48. 49.

1934. Charity Tax. Fund for Wounded in War with Yemen.

328. **48.** ⅛ g. red .. .. £150 4·00

1934.

329 49. $\frac{1}{8}$ g. yellow .. .. 2·50 20
330 $\frac{1}{4}$ g. green .. .. 3·25 20
331a $\frac{1}{2}$ g. red .. .. 1·00 10
332 $\frac{7}{8}$ g. blue .. .. 3·00 4·00
333a 1 g. green .. .. 1·00 10
334 2 g. olive .. .. 6·00 50
335 $2\frac{7}{8}$ g. violet .. .. 4·00 25
336b 3 g. blue .. .. 3·00 20
337 $3\frac{1}{2}$ g. blue .. .. 20·00 1·75
338a 5 g. brown .. .. 3·00 20
339b 10 g. violet .. .. 8·00 1·50
340a 20 g. purple .. .. 10·00 50
341 100 g. violet .. .. £100 8·00
342a 200 g. brown .. .. 80·00 12·00

50. General Hospital, Mecca.

1936. Charity. Medical Aid. Perf. or roul.

(a) Three palm trees.

345. 50. $\frac{1}{8}$ g. red (37 × 20 mm.) .. £375 7·50
346. $\frac{1}{8}$ g. red ($30\frac{1}{2}$ × 18 mm.) 50·00 50

(b) One palm tree.

350. 50. $\frac{1}{8}$ g. red ($30\frac{1}{2}$ × 18 mm.) 1·50 10
351. $\frac{1}{4}$ g. red ($30\frac{1}{2}$ × 18 mm.) 1·00 10

53. Egyptian Royal Yacht "Fakhr el Bihar", Radhwa.
54. Map of Saudi Arabia, Flags and Emblem.

1945. Meeting of King Ibn Saud and King Farouk of Egypt at Radhwa.

352. 53. $\frac{1}{2}$ g. red .. .. .. 4·00 2·00
353. 3 g. blue .. .. .. 8·00 5·00
354. 5 g. violet .. .. 18·00 10·00
355. 10 g. purple .. .. 40·00 20·00

1946. Obligatory Tax. Return of King Ibn Saud from Egypt.

356a 54 $\frac{1}{2}$ g. mauve .. .. 12·00 50

55. Airspeed "Ambassador".
56. Arms of Saudi Arabia and Afghanistan.

1949. Air.

357. 55. 1 g. green .. .. 2·50 10
358. 3 g. blue .. .. 3·00 10
359. 4 g. orange .. .. 3·00 10
360. 10 g. violet .. .. 12·00 20
361. 20 g. brown .. .. 30·00 30
362. 100 g. purple .. .. 90·00 7·00

1950. Visit of King Mohamed Zahir Shah of Afghanistan.

363. 56. $\frac{1}{2}$ g. red .. .. 7·00 1·75
364. 3 g. blue .. .. 9·00 2·50

57. Al-Murabba Palace, Riyadh.
58. Arms of Saudi Arabia and Jordan.

1950. 50th Anniv of Capture of Riyadh by King Abdulaziz Ibn Saud. Centres in purple.

365. 57. $\frac{1}{2}$ g. purple .. .. 4·00 1·00
366. 1 g. blue .. .. 6·00 1·50
367. 3 g. violet .. .. 10·00 2·50
368. 5 g. orange .. .. 20·00 4·00
369. 10 g. green .. .. 35·00 9·00

1951. Visit of King Talal of Jordan.

370. 58. $\frac{1}{2}$ g. red .. .. 7·00 2·00
371. 3 g. blue .. .. 14·00 4·00

59. Arabs and Train.
60. Arms of Saudi Arabia and Lebanon.

1952. Inaug. of Dammam-Riyadh Railway.

372. 59. $\frac{1}{2}$ g. brown .. .. 7·50 2·00
373. 1 g. green .. .. 10·00 2·25
374. 3 g. mauve .. .. 15·00 2·00
375. 10 g. red .. .. 30·00 8·50
376. 20 g. blue .. .. 65·00 20·00

1953. Visit of President Chamoun of Lebanon.

377. 60. $\frac{1}{2}$ g. red .. .. .. 7·50 1·75
378. 3 g. blue .. .. .. 12·50 3·75

61.
62. Arms of Saudi Arabia and Jordan.

1953. Visit of Governor-General of Pakistan.

379. 61. $\frac{1}{2}$ g. red .. .. .. 7·50 1·75
380. 3 g. blue .. .. .. 12·50 2·75

1953. Visit of King Hussein of Jordan.

381. 62. $\frac{1}{2}$ g. red .. .. .. 8·00 1·75
382. 3 g. blue .. .. .. 14·00 3·75

1955. Arab Postal Union. As T **96a** of Syria but smaller, 20 × 34 mm. Inscr. "ROYAUME DE L'ARABIE SOUDITE" at top.

383. $\frac{1}{2}$ g. green .. .. 3·00 1·00
384. 3 g. violet .. .. .. 8·00 2·50
385. 4 g. orange .. .. 13·00 4·50

1960. Inaug. of Arab League Centre, Cairo. As T **154a** of Syria but inscr. "S.A.K.".

386. 2 p. black and green .. 1·50 60

63. Congress Building.

1960. Arab Postal Union Congress, Riyadh.

387. 63. 2 p. blue 60 20
388. 5 p. purple .. .. 1·75 50
389. 10 p. green .. .. 4·00 1·50

64. Radio Mast and Globe.
65. Refugee Camp.

1960. Inaug. of Direct Wireless Service.

390. 64. 2 p. red and black .. 1·25 50
391. 5 p. purple and red .. 2·00 75
392. 10 p. deep blue and blue 4·00 1·50

1960. World Refugee Year.

393. 65. 2 p. blue 30 20
394. 8 p. violet .. .. 1·00 50
395. 10 p. green .. .. 1·25 70

66. Gas Oil Plant.
67. Wadi Hanifa Dam, near Riyadh.

68. Convair 440. (I). (II).

1960. Cartouche of King Saud as Type I. Size $27\frac{1}{2}$ × 22 mm. (a) Postage (i) Type **66**.

396. $\frac{1}{2}$ p. orange and red .. 1·00 50
397. 1 p. red and blue .. .. 1·25 15
398. 2 p. blue and red .. .. 1·25 15
399. 3 p. green and violet .. 1·00 20
400. 4 p. purple and green .. 1·50 15
401. 5 p. lake and purple .. 1·50 10
402. 6 p. lilac and brown .. 1·50 15
403. 7 p. myrtle and violet .. 1·50 10
404. 8 p. black and green .. 2·00 10
405. 9 p. brown and blue .. 2·25 30
406. 10 p. red and blue .. 2·00 2·00
407. 20 p. black and brown .. 5·00 20
408. 50 p. green and brown .. 20·00 1·50
409. 75 p. purple and red .. 40·00 10·00
410. 100 p. brown and blue .. 40·00 4·50
411. 200 p. bronze and black .. 75·00 4·50

(ii) Type **67**.

412. $\frac{1}{2}$ p. orange and brown .. 50 50
413. 1 p. purple and olive .. 90 15
414. 2 p. sepia and blue .. 50 15
415. 3 p. blue and sepia .. 50 25
416. 4 p. chestnut and brown .. 50 15
417. 5 p. purple and sepia .. 50 10
418. 6 p. red and black .. 2·25 10
419. 7 p. olive and red .. 80 10
420. 8 p. purple and blue .. 2·00 15
421. 9 p. red and brown .. 2·25 45
422. 10 p. lake and green .. 2·25 10
423. 20 p. green and brown .. 3·50 1·00
424. 50 p. brown and black .. 20·00 1·25
425. 75 p. grey and brown .. 40·00 12·00
426. 100 p. turquoise and blue 35·00 2·50
427. 200 p. green and purple .. 65·00 3·00

(b) Air. Type **68**.

428. 1 p. green and lilac .. 50 35
429. 2 p. purple and green .. 50 15
430. 3 p. blue and mauve .. 60 15
431. 4 p. purple and blue .. 70 15
432. 5 p. red and green .. 70 10
433. 6 p. grey and brown .. 1·25 45
434. 8 p. olive and red .. 1·40 15
435. 9 p. brown and violet .. 2·00 40
436. 10 p. brown and purple .. 3·50 50
437. 15 p. brown and blue .. 3·50 50
438. 20 p. green and brown .. 4·00 40
439. 30 p. turquoise and bistre 15·00 25
440. 50 p. blue and green .. 20·00 50
441. 100 p. brown and grey .. 42·00 4·00
442. 200 p. black and purple .. 65·00 11·00

See also Nos. 487/92, 529/610 and 660/744.

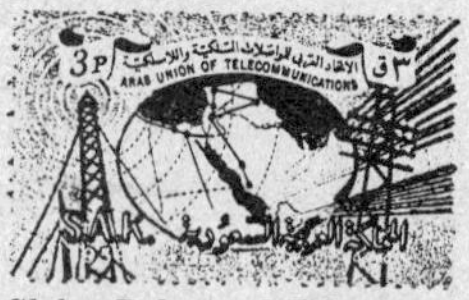

69. Globe, Pylon and Telegraph Pole.

1960. 6th Anniv (1959) of Arab Telecommunications Union.

443. 69. 3 p. purple .. .. 1·25 30
444. 6 p. black .. .. 3·00 30
445. 8 p. brown .. .. 3·50 25

71. Dammam Port.
72. Campaign Emblem.

1961. Opening of Dammam Port Extension.

446. 71. 3 p. violet .. .. 1·25 20
447. 6 p. blue .. .. 2·00 80
448. 8 p. green .. .. 3·00 20

1962. Arab League Week. As T **76** of Libya but larger, 25 × 41 mm. Inscr. "S.A.K.".

449. 3 p. green 90 45
450. 6 p. red .. .. .. 1·75 40
451. 8 p. green .. .. .. 3·00 15

1962. Malaria Eradication.

452. 72. 3 p. red and blue .. 30 20
453. 6 p. green and blue .. 60 30
454. 8 p. black and purple .. 1·00 50

73. Koran.

1963. 1st Anniv. of Islamic Institute, Medina.

456. 73. $2\frac{1}{2}$ p. purple and salmon 1·00 50
457. $7\frac{1}{2}$ p. blue and green .. 2·50 15
458. $9\frac{1}{2}$ p. green and black .. 3·50 2·50

74. Emblem within Hands.
75. Boeing "707" over Airport.

1963. Freedom From Hunger.

459. 74. $2\frac{1}{2}$ p. mauve and salmon 60 50
460. $7\frac{1}{2}$ p. purple and pink .. 2·00 20
461. 9 p. brown and blue .. 2·50 2·50

1963. Opening of Dhahran Airport and Inauguration of Jet Service.

462. 75. 1 p. violet and brown .. 1·25 65
463. $3\frac{1}{2}$ p. blue and green .. 3·75 1·25
464. 6 p. green and red .. 4·75 1·50
465. $7\frac{1}{2}$ p. mauve and blue .. 4·75 1·75
466. $9\frac{1}{2}$ p. red and violet .. 7·50 2·50

1963. As T **66/8** but redrawn in larger format (29 × 23 mm.) Cartouche of King Saud as Type I.

(a) Postage. (i) T **66**.

487. $\frac{1}{2}$ p. orange and red .. 15·00 2·50
488. 1 p. orange and blue .. 10·00 1·50

(ii) T **67**.

489. $\frac{1}{2}$ p. orange and bistre .. 15·00 50

(b) Air. T **68**.

490. 3 p. blue and red .. .. 7·00 1·00
491. 10 p. brown and black .. 10·00 40
492. 20 p. green and brown .. 18·00 10

Nos. 487/92 are widely spaced in the sheets, thus producing wide margins.

76. "Flame of Freedom".
77. Arms and King Faisal.

1964. 15th Anniv. of Declaration of Human Rights.

493. 76. 3 p. blue, violet & salmon 3·00 50
494. 6 p. bl., grn. & pale blue 4·00 1·75
495. 9 p. blue, brown & flesh 7·00 60

1964. Installation of King Faisal.

496. 77. 4 p. blue and green .. 4·00 30

80. Boeing 720–B.
81. Kaaba, Mecca.

1964. As T **66/7** but completely redrawn (Arabic inscr. closer to top frame) and T **80**. Smaller size, $26\frac{3}{4}$ × $21\frac{3}{4}$ mm. Cartouche of King Saud as Type I.

(a) Postage. (i) Type **66**.

529. 1 p. red and blue .. .. 8·50 50
530. 2 p. blue and red .. .. 8·50 50
531. 3 p. green and violet .. 7·00 20
532. 4 p. purple and green .. 7·50 25
533. 5 p. lake and purple .. 25·00 15
534. 6 p. chocolate and brown 65·00 2·00
535. 7 p. green and lilac .. 25·00 30
536. 8 p. black and green .. 10·00 10
537. 9 p. brown and blue .. 16·00 60
538. 10 p. red and blue .. £500 5·00
539. 11 p. orange and green .. 8·00 3·25
540. 12 p. green and ochre .. 8·00 1·25
541. 13 p. blue and red .. 8·00 1·00
542. 14 p. brown and lilac .. 9·00 1·00
543. 15 p. brown and red .. 9·00 35
544. 16 p. red and green .. 9·00 1·00
545. 17 p. brown and cerise .. 9·00 2·00
546. 18 p. blue and black .. 10·00 1·40
547. 19 p. yellow and brown .. 10·00 35
548. 20 p. black and brown .. 35·00 1·00
549. 23 p. red and orange .. 11·00 1·25
550. 24 p. yellow and green .. 12·00 2·00
551. 26 p. brown and purple .. 13·00 1·60
552. 27 p. black and red .. 13·00 1·60
553. 31 p. red and turquoise .. 25·00 2·25
554. 33 p. black and brown .. 25·00 2·75
555. 50 p. green and brown .. £200 6·00
555a. 100 p. chocolate and deep blue .. .. ..
556. 200 p. green and slate .. £250 12·00

(ii) Type **67**.

557. 1 p. purple and olive .. 20·00 30
558. 2 p. sepia and blue .. 7·00 30
559. 3 p. blue and sepia .. 7·50 10
560. 4 p. chestnut and brown .. 7·00 10
561. 5 p. purple and black .. 7·00 10
562. 6 p. red and black .. 7·00 30
563. 7 p. black and brown .. 7·00 40
564. 8 p. agate and blue .. 60·00 10
565. 9 p. red and brown .. 60·00 2·50
566. 10 p. brown and green .. 40·00 1·25
567. 11 p. green and red .. 8·00 2·50
568. 12 p. blue and orange .. 8·00 1·00
569. 13 p. red and olive .. 8·00 1·25
570. 14 p. green and brown .. 8·00 1·25
571. 15 p. green and sepia .. 9·00 1·00
572. 16 p. red and lilac .. 9·50 1·00
573. 17 p. blue and purple .. 9·50 1·60
574. 18 p. blue and green .. 9·50 1·60
575. 19 p. ochre and black .. 11·00 1·60
576. 20 p. green and brown .. 17·00 1·00
577. 23 p. purple and brown .. 13·00 1·40
578. 24 p. blue and red .. 13·00 1·60
579. 26 p. yellow and olive .. 13·00 2·00
580. 27 p. purple and blue .. 13·00 2·00
581. 31 p. blue and black .. 15·00 2·00
582. 33 p. purple and green .. 15·00 2·10
582a. 50 p. brown and black .. .. ..
583. 100 p. turquoise and blue £350 12·00
584. 200 p. green and purple .. £200 15·00

(b) Air. Type **80**.

585. 1 p. green and purple .. £100 6·00
586. 2 p. purple and green .. £525 22·00
587. 3 p. blue and red .. .. 9·00 40
588. 4 p. purple and blue .. 7·00 10
589. 5 p. red and green .. £750 35·00
590. 6 p. slate and brown .. 75·00 4·00
591. 7 p. green and mauve .. 7·50 60
592. 8 p. olive and red .. £100 1·00
593. 9 p. brown and violet .. 7·50 4·00
594. 10 p. purple and black .. 75·00 4·00
595. 11 p. buff and green .. £150 4·00
596. 12 p. grey and orange .. 7·50 1·00
597. 13 p. green and myrtle .. 7·50 1·00
598. 14 p. orange and blue .. 7·50 1·00
599. 15 p. brown and blue .. 75·00 2·50
600. 16 p. blue and black .. 10·00 1·25
601. 17 p. brown and ochre .. 10·00 1·25
602. 18 p. green and blue .. 10·00 1·40
603. 19 p. orange and mauve .. 10·00 1·40
604. 20 p. green and brown .. 85·00 6·00
605. 23 p. ochre and green .. 45·00 8·00
606. 24 p. sepia and blue .. 13·00 1·60
607. 26 p. green and red .. 13·00 1·60
608. 27 p. green and sepia .. 13·00 1·60
609. 31 p. red and mauve .. 15·00 2·00
610. 33 p. purple and red .. 18·00 2·75
610a. 50 p. indigo and bright green .. .. ..
610b. 100 p. black-brown and grey .. .. ..
610c. 200 p. olive-brown and brown-purple .. ..

1965. Moslem League Conf., Mecca.

611. 81. 4 p. black and brown .. 1·25 60
612. 6 p. black and mauve .. 5·50 1·40
613. 10 p. black and green .. 13·00 60

82. Arms of Saudi Arabia and Tunisia.

1965. Visit of President Bourguiba of Tunisia.

614.	**82.**	4 p. silver and mauve ..	1·25	75
615.		8 p. silver and violet ..	4·75	50
616.		10 p. silver and blue ..	6·50	50

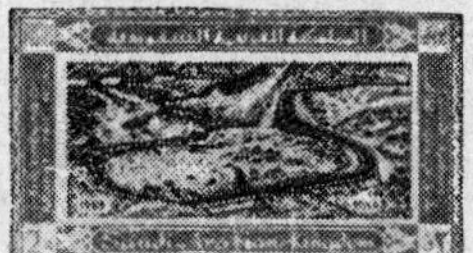

83. Highway.

1965. Opening of Arafat–Taif Highway.

617.	**83.**	2 p. black and red ..	2·00	25
618.		4 p. black and blue ..	2·50	50
619.		6 p. black and violet ..	3·50	1·00
620.		8 p. black and green ..	5·50	75

84. I.C.Y. Emblem.

1965. Int. Co-operation Year.

621.	**84.**	1 p. brown and yellow ..	50	60
622.		2 p. green and salmon ..	80	70
623.		3 p. olive and blue ..	1·00	75
624.		4 p. black and olive ..	1·50	90
625.		10 p. purple and orange	3·00	1·25

85. I.T.U. Symbol and Emblems.

1965. Cent. of I.T.U.

626.	**85.**	3 p. black and blue ..	50	40
627.		4 p. green and violet ..	90	60
628.		8 p. brown and green ..	1·50	40
629.		10 p. green and orange	2·50	75

86. Lamp and Burning Library.

1966. Burning of Algiers Library in 1962.

630.	**86.**	1 p. red	2·00	1·75
631.		2 p. red	2·00	1·75
632.		3 p. purple	5·00	2·50
633.		4 p. violet	8·00	4·00
634.		5 p. mauve	10·00	5·50
635.		6 p. red	15·00	7·50

87. A.P.U. Emblem.

89. Scout Badges.

90. W.H.O. Building.

88. Dagger on Deir Yassin, Palestine.

1966. 10th Anniv. (1964) of Arab Postal Union.

636.	**87.**	3 p. olive and plum ..	1·40	90
637.		4 p. olive and blue ..	2·00	1·10
638.		6 p. olive and purple ..	2·75	20
639.		7 p. olive and green ..	3·25	2·25

1966. Deir Yassin Massacre.

640.	**88.**	2 p. black and green ..	2·50	85
641.		4 p. black and brown ..	3·75	1·00
642.		6 p. black and blue ..	6·00	1·40
643.		8 p. black and orange ..	10·00	1·75

1966. Arab Scout Jamboree.

644.	**89.**	4 p. multicoloured ..	5·50	2·00
645.		8 p. multicoloured ..	5·50	1·25
646.		10 p. multicoloured ..	7·00	1·25

1966. W.H.O. Headquarters, Geneva. Inaug.

647.	**90.**	4 p. multicoloured ..	1·50	75
648.		6 p. multicoloured ..	2·00	1·00
649.		10 p. multicoloured ..	3·50	75

91. U.N.E.S.C.O. Emblem.

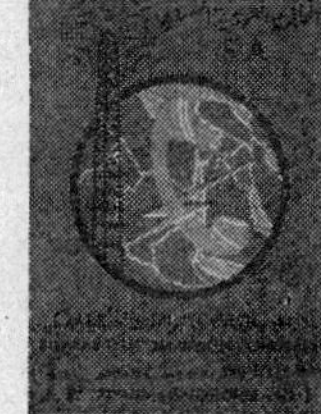

92. Radio Mast, Telephone and Map.

1966. 20th Anniv. of U.N.E.S.C.O.

650.	**91.**	1 p. multicoloured ..	75	40
651.		2 p. multicoloured ..	1·00	40
652.		3 p. multicoloured ..	1·00	40
653.		4 p. multicoloured ..	2·00	90
654.		10 p. multicoloured ..	3·00	75

1966. 8th Arab Telecommunications Union Congress, Riyadh.

655.	**92.**	1 p. multicoloured ..	75	50
656.		2 p. multicoloured ..	1·25	70
657.		4 p. multicoloured ..	1·75	85
658.		6 p. multicoloured ..	4·00	1·25
659.		7 p. multicoloured ..	5·50	1·50

1966. As 1964 issue, but with cartouche of King Faisal as Type II (see above No. 396).

(a) Postage. (i) Type **66.**

755.	1 p. red and blue	5·00	1·00
661.	2 p. blue and red	5·50	25
662.	3 p. green and violet ..	7·50	10
663.	4 p. purple and green ..	10·00	20
664.	5 p. brown and purple ..	15·00	10
760.	6 p. chocolate and brown	15·00	50
666.	7 p. green and lilac ..	23·00	90
667.	8 p. green and turquoise ..	7·00	10
668.	9 p. brown and blue ..	7·00	10
669.	10 p. red and blue ..	7·50	60
765.	11 p. orange and green ..	22·00	80
671.	12 p. green and brown ..	8·50	1·00
672.	13 p. blue and red ..	10·00	1·25
673.	14 p. brown and lilac ..	10·00	1·25
674.	15 p. brown and red ..	9·00	70
675.	16 p. red and green ..	9·00	1·40
676.	17 p. brown and red ..	9·00	1·00
677.	18 p. blue and black ..	9·00	1·25
678.	19 p. yellow and brown ..	9·00	1·00
679.	20 p. brown and bistre ..	11·00	1·25
680.	23 p. red and orange ..	18·00	2·00
681.	24 p. yellow and green ..	14·00	1·40
681a.	26 p. brown and purple ..	£125	20·00
682.	27 p. black and red ..	15·00	1·75
683.	31 p. red and green ..	15·00	1·75
684.	33 p. black and brown ..	15·00	1·75
685.	50 p. green and lake-brown	£120	
686.	100 p. black and blue ..	£100	25·00
687.	200 p. green and black ..	£325	50·00

(ii) Type **67.**

688.	1 p. purple and green ..	£150	8·00
689.	2 p. brown and blue ..	6·00	50
690.	3 p. blue and brown ..	10·00	20
691.	4 p. orange and brown ..	6·00	20
782.	5 p. purple and black ..	22·00	1·25
783.	6 p. red and black ..	17·00	15
694.	7 p. black and brown ..	10·00	40
695.	8 p. brown and blue ..	10·00	10
696.	9 p. red and brown ..	10·00	60
697.	10 p. brown and green ..	10·00	30
698.	11 p. green and red ..	10·00	80
699.	12 p. purple and orange ..	10·00	1·00
700.	13 p. red and green ..	12·00	1·25
701.	14 p. green and brown ..	12·00	80
702.	15 p. green and brown ..	14·00	25
703.	16 p. lilac and red ..	14·00	1·25
704.	17 p. blue and purple ..	12·00	1·00
705.	18 p. blue and green ..	14·00	1·25
706.	19 p. brown and black ..	10·00	1·00
707.	20 p. green and brown ..	40·00	2·00
708.	23 p. purple and brown ..	£125	20·00
708a.	24 p. blue and red ..	55·00	10·00
709.	26 p. brown and green ..	14·00	1·60
711.	27 p. purple and blue ..	12·00	1·60
712.	33 p. purple and green ..	14·00	1·60
713.	50 p. brown and black ..	28·00	5·00
714.	100 p. blue and deep blue	£150	12·00
715.	200 p. green and purple ..	£150	12·00

(b) Air. Type **80.**

716.	1 p. green and purple ..	6·00	20
717.	2 p. purple and green ..	6·00	20
718.	3 p. blue and red	7·00	20
719.	4 p. purple and blue ..	7·00	20
720.	5 p. red and green ..	£500	60·00
721.	6 p. grey and brown ..	£100	8·00
812.	7 p. green and mauve ..	15·00	1·25
813.	8 p. green and red ..	30·00	10
724.	9 p. brown and violet ..	8·00	50
725.	10 p. brown and black ..	10·00	50
726.	11 p. brown and green ..	9·00	50
727.	12 p. dull grey and orange	10·00	50
728.	13 p. green and myrtle ..	11·00	1·00
729.	14 p. orange and blue ..	10·00	1·25
730.	15 p. brown and blue ..	12·00	1·25
731.	16 p. blue and black ..	14·00	50
732.	17 p. brown and yellow ..	14·00	1·25
733.	18 p. green and blue ..	14·00	1·25
734.	19 p. orange and mauve ..	17·00	4·00
735.	20 p. green and brown ..	£100	4·00
736.	23 p. brown and green ..	11·00	1·40
737.	24 p. brown and blue ..	17·00	1·40
741.	33 p. purple and red ..	12·00	2·40
742.	50 p. indigo and green ..	£750	
743.	100 p. brown and grey ..	£750	
744.	200 p. black and purple ..	£750	30·00

93. Moot Emblem.

94. Meteorological Apparatus.

1967. 2nd Rover Moot, Mecca.

745.	**93.**	1 p. multicoloured ..	2·25	85
746.		2 p. multicoloured ..	2·75	85
747.		3 p. multicoloured ..	2·75	85
748.		4 p. multicoloured ..	3·75	85
749.		10 p. multicoloured ..	9·00	2·25

1967. World Meteorological Day.

750.	**94.**	1 p. mauve	1·50	85
751.		2 p. violet	1·50	85
752.		3 p. olive	2·50	1·00
753.		4 p. green	4·00	1·00
754.		10 p. blue	7·50	2·50

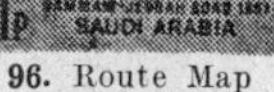

96. Route Map and Dates.

97. The Prophet's Mosque, Medina.

98. Prophet's Mosque Extension.

99. Ancient Wall Tomb, Madayin Saleh.

100. Colonnade, Sacred Mosque, Mecca.

101. Camels and Oil Derrick.

102. Arab Stallion.

103. Holy Ka'aba, Mecca.

1968. Inauguration of Dammam–Jeddah Highway.

834.	**96.**	1 p. multicoloured ..	1·25	50
835.		2 p. multicoloured ..	1·50	50
836.		3 p. multicoloured ..	1·50	50
837.		4 p. multicoloured ..	11·00	2·00
838.		10 p. multicoloured ..	15·00	3·25

1968.

(a) Type **97.**

839	**97**	1 p. green and orange ..	3·00	20
840		2 p. green and brown ..	3·00	20
841		3 p. green and violet ..	3·00	30
858		4 p. green and ochre ..	3·00	35
843		5 p. green and purple ..	5·00	30
860		6 p. green and black ..	6·00	2·00
861		10 p. green and brown	5·00	1·25
949		20 p. green and brown	10·00	1·60
864		50 p. green and purple	15·00	3·00
865		100 p. green and blue ..	10·00	5·00
866		200 p. green and red ..	8·00	8·00

(b) Type **98.**

952.	**98.**	1 p. green and orange ..	2·00	20
953.		2 p. green and brown ..	2·00	30
867.		3 p. green and black ..	3·00	20
868.		4 p. green and red ..	2·00	35
851.		5 p. green and red ..	3·50	50
852.		6 p. green and blue ..	5·00	80
870a.		8 p. green and red ..	4·75	25
853.		10 p. green and brown	6·00	1·25
940.		20 p. green and violet ..	7·00	50

(c) Type **99.**

876.	**99.**	2 p. brown and blue ..	20·00	2·50
878.		4 p. light brn. and brn.	5·00	30
880.		7 p. brown and orange ..	40·00	5·00
881.		10 p. brown and green ..	12·00	2·00
883.		20 p. brown and purple	10·00	1·25

(d) Type **100.**

887.	**100.**	3 p. grey and red ..	£450	40·00
888.		4 p. grey and green ..	3·00	30
891.		10 p. grey and purple ..	7·00	2·00

(e) Type **101.**

898.	**101.**	4 p. red and lilac ..	15·00	1·25
901.		10 p. red and blue ..	12·00	2·00

(f) Type **102.**

908.	**102.**	4 p. brown and purple	5·50	30
911.		10 p. brown and black	10·00	1·60
912.		14 p. brown and blue ..	40·00	2·50
913.		20 p. brown and green	10·00	1·25

(g) Type **103.**

1016	**103.**	4 p. black and green ..	1·50	30
923		6 p. black and purple	4·00	30
924		8 p. black and red ..	4·00	15
1018		10 p. black and red ..	3·25	80

104. Saker Falcon.

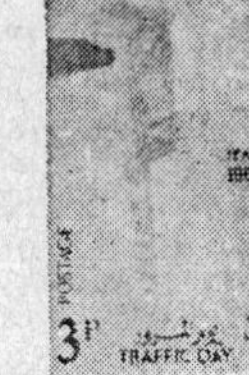

105. Traffic Signals.

1968. Air.

1022.	**104.**	1 p. brown and green	2·25	20
1023.		4 p. orange and red ..	80·00	7·50
1024.		10 p. brown and blue	20·00	2·00
1025.		20 p. brown and green	40·00	2·50

1969. Traffic Day.

1026.	**105.**	3 p. red, green and blue	1·00	25
1027.		4 p. red, green & brown	2·50	25
1028.		10 p. red, green & purple	6·00	1·25

106. Scout Emblem, Camp and Flag.

1969. 3rd Arab Rover Moot, Mecca.

1029.	**106.**	1 p. multicoloured ..	1·75	90
1030.		4 p. multicoloured ..	5·50	1·50
1031.		10 p. multicoloured ..	18·00	7·00

107. W.H.O. Emblem.

1969. 20th Anniv. (1968) of W.H.O.

1032.	**107.**	4 p. multicoloured ..	6·00	50

108. Conference Emblem.

109. Satellite, Dish Aerial and Open Book.

1970. Islamic Foreign Ministers' Conf., Jeddah.

1033.	**108.**	4 p. black and blue ..	1·00	25
1034.		10 p. black and ochre	2·00	30

1970. World Telecommunications Day.

1035.	**109.**	4 p. blue, mauve and ultramarine ..	3·50	40
1036.		10 p. blue, mauve & grn.	7·50	1·75

MINIMUM PRICE

The minimum price quoted is 5p which represents a handling charge rather than a basis for valuing common stamps. For further notes about prices see introductory pages.

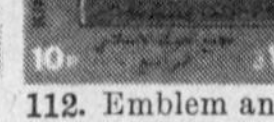

110. Steel Rolling-mill. 112. Emblem and Arab Archway.

1970. Inauguration (1967) of First Arabian Steel Rolling-mill.
1037. 110. 3 p. multicoloured .. 2·25 20
1038. 4 p. multicoloured .. 3·25 25
1039. 10 p. multicoloured .. 6·00 1·25

1971. 4th Arab Rover Moot, Mecca.
1049. 112. 10 p. multicoloured .. 6·00 1·25

113. Global Emblem.

1971. World Telecommunications Day.
1050. 113. 4 p. black & blue .. 1·00 25
1051. 10 p. black and lilac .. 2·50 75

114. University "Tower" Emblem. 115. I.E.Y. Emblem.

1971. 4th Anniv. of Inauguration of King Abdulaziz National University.
1052. 114. 3 p. black and green 1·00 25
1053. 4 p. black and brown 1·50 40
1054. 10 p. black and blue 4·00 1·25

1971. Int. Education Year (1970).
1055. 115. 4 p. brown and green 3·25 10

116. Arab League Emblem. 117. O.P.E.C. Emblem.

1971. Arab Propaganda Week.
1056. 116. 10 p. multicoloured .. 3·75 1·50

1971. 10th Anniv. of O.P.E.C.
1057. 117. 4 p. blue .. .. 6·50 45
O.P.E.C.=Organisation of Petroleum Exporting Countries.

118. Globe. 120. Writing in Book.

119. Telephone within Dial.

1972. World Telecommunications Day.
1058. 118. 4 p. multicoloured .. 4·00 45

1972. Inauguration of Automatic Telephone System (1969).
1059. 119. 1 p. black, green & red 1·00 40
1060. 4 p. black, turq. & grn. 2·25 40
1061. 5 p. blk., grn. & mauve 2·75 65
1062. 10 p. blk., grn. & brn. 7·50 1·75

1973. World Literacy Day (1972).
1063. 120. 10 p. multicoloured .. 3·00 70

121. Mosque, Mecca, and Moot Emblem.

1973. Fifth Arab Rover Moot, Mecca. Mult.
1064. 4 p. Type 121 .. .. 3·50 80
1065. 6 p. Holy Ka'aba, Mecca 7·00 1·50
1066. 10 p. Rover encampment 10·00 3·50

122. Globe and Map of Palestine. 123. Leaf and Emblem.

1973. Universal Palestine Week.
1067. 122. 4 p. red, yellow & grey 2·00 30
1068. 10 p. red, yellow and blue 4·50 1·25

1973. Int. Hydrological Decade.
1069. 123. 4 p. multicoloured .. 4·00 45

124. A.P.U. Emblem.

1973. 25th Anniv. of Founding of Arab Postal Union at Sofar Conference.
1070. 124. 4 p. multicoloured .. 3·25 40
1071. 10 p. multicoloured .. 5·25 1·75

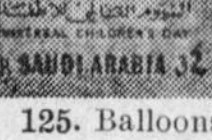

125. Balloons. 126. U.P.U. Monument and Postal Emblems.

1973. Universal Children's Day (1971).
1072. 125. 4 p. multicoloured .. 3·25 40

1974. Centenary of U.P.U.
1073. 126. 3 p. multicoloured .. 15·00 3·50
1074. 4 p. multicoloured .. 30·00 6·50
1075. 10 p. multicoloured .. 45·00 7·50

127. Handclasp and U.N.E.S.C.O. Emblem.

1974. International Book Year (1972).
1076. 127. 4 p. multicoloured .. 7·00 40
1077. 10 p. multicoloured .. 10·00 3·00

128. Desalination Works.

1974. Inauguration of Sea-water Desalination Plant, Jeddah (1971).
1078. 128. 4 p. blue and orange .. 2·50 40
1079. 6 p. lilac and green .. 3·75 85
1080. 10 p. black and red .. 8·00 1·75

129. Interpol Emblem. 130. Tower, Emblem and Hand with Letter.

1974. 50th Anniv. (1973) of International Criminal Police Organization (Interpol.
1081. 129. 4 p. blue and red .. 7·00 50
1082. 10 p. blue and green 13·00 2·25

1974. Third Session of Arab Postal Studies Consultative Council, Riyadh.
1083. 130. 4 p. multicoloured .. 4·00 40

131. New Headquarters Building.

1974. Inauguration (1970) of New U.P.U. Headquarters, Berne.
1084. 131. 3 p. multicoloured .. 5·00 65
1085. 4 p. multicoloured .. 10·00 1·00
1086. 10 p. multicoloured .. 25·00 3·75

132. Armed Forces and Flame.

1974. King Faisal Military Cantonment (1971).
1087. 132. 3 p. multicoloured .. 2·25 40
1088. 4 p. multicoloured .. 3·75 45
1089. 10 p. multicoloured .. 11·00 2·50

133. Red Crescent "Flower". 134. Scout Emblem and Minarets.

1974. Saudi Arabian Red Crescent Society. 10th Anniv. (1973).
1090. 133. 4 p. multicoloured .. 1·75 1·25
1091. 6 p. multicoloured .. 3·25 2·50
1092. 10 p. multicoloured .. 9·50 2·00

1974. 6th Arab Rover Moot, Mecca.
1093. 134. 4 p. multicoloured .. 4·00 50
1094. 6 p. multicoloured .. 5·50 90
1095. 10 p. multicoloured .. 8·50 2·50

INDEX

Countries can be quickly located by referring to the index at the end of this volume.

135. Reading Braille.

1975. Day of the Blind.
1096. 135. 4 p. multicoloured .. 2·75 45
1097. 10 p. multicoloured .. 5·25 75

136. Anemometer and U.N. Emblem as Weather Balloon.

1975. Centenary (1973) of World Meteorological Organization.
1098. 136. 4 p. multicoloured .. 4·00 45

137. King Faisal. 138. Conference Emblem.

1975. King Faisal Memorial Issue.
1099. 137. 4 p. purple and green 2·50 25
1100. 16 p. green and violet 7·50 10
1101. 23 p. violet and green 10·00 1·75

1975. Sixth Islamic Conference of Foreign Ministers, Jeddah.
1103. 138. 10 p. black and brown 2·00 2·00

139. Wheat and Sun.

1975. 29th Anniv. of Charity Society.
1104. 139. 4 p. multicoloured .. 3·00 30
1105. 10 p. multicoloured .. 4·00 80

140. Kaaba, Handclasp and Globe.

1975. Moslem Organizations Conf., Mecca.
1106. 140. 4 p. multicoloured .. 1·50 15
1107. 10 p. multicoloured .. 3·00 75

141. "Tristar".

1975. 30th Anniv. of National Airline "Saudia".

1108.	141.	4 p. multicoloured ..	2·50	45
1109.		10 p. multicoloured ..	5·00	1·25

142. Mecca and Riyadh.

1975. Conference Locations.

1110.	142.	10 p. multicoloured ..	3·00	60

143. Friday Mosque, Medina and Juwatha Mosque, Al-Hasa.

1975. Islamic Holy Places.

1111.	143.	4 p. multicoloured ..	2·00	25
1112.		10 p. multicoloured ..	4·50	75

144. F.A.O. Emblem.

1975. 10th Anniv. (1973) of World Food Programme.

1113.	144.	4 p. multicoloured ..	1·00	20
1114.		10 p. multicoloured ..	2·50	75

145. Conference Emblem.

1976. Islamic Solidarity Conf. of Science and Technology, Mecca.

1115.	145.	4 p. multicoloured ..	12·00	45

146. Map and T.V. Screen.

1976. 10th Anniv (1975) of Saudi Arabian Television Service.

1116	146	4 p. multicoloured ..	8·00	45

147. Ear of Wheat, Atomic Symbol and Graph.

1976. 2nd Five-year Plan.

1117.	147.	20 h. multicoloured ..	1·50	35
1118.		50 h. multicoloured ..	3·00	75

148. Quba Mosque, Medina.

149. Holy Kaaba, Mecca.

150. Oil Rig Al-Khafji.

1976. Size 36×26 mm. (a) Type **148.**

1122b.	20 h. black and orange ..	85	15
1128a.	50 h. violet and green ..	2·75	40

(b) Type **149.**

1137.	5 h. black and lilac ..	10	10
1138.	10 h. black and lavender	20	10
1139.	15 h. black and pink ..	50	10
1140.	20 h. black and blue ..	50	10
1141.	25 h. black and yellow ..	50	10
1142.	30 h. black and green ..	60	15
1143.	35 h. black and cinnamon	40	10
1144.	40 h. black and green ..	1·50	25
1145.	45 h. black and claret ..	50	10
1146.	50 h. black and red ..	50	15
1149.	65 h. black and blue ..	70	20
1151.	1 r. black and yellow ..	1·00	25
1152.	2 r. black and green ..	2·00	50

(c) Type **150.**

1167	5 h. blue and orange ..	25	10
1168	10 h. green and orange ..	15	10
1169a	15 h. brown and orange	25	10
1170	20 h. green and orange ..	30	10
1171	25 h. purple and orange ..	30	10
1172a	30 h. blue and orange ..	50	10
1173	35 h. brown and orange ..	50	10
1174	40 h. red and orange ..	60	10
1175	45 h. mauve and orange	70	10
1176b	50 h. pink and orange ..	60	15
1177	55 h. green and orange ..	25·00	2·50
1187	65 h. brown and orange ..	1·00	20
1188	1 r. slate and orange ..	1·00	35
1181	2 r. purple and red ..	2·25	50

For Types **149/50** in smaller size, see Nos. 1283/1325 and 1435/7.

151. Globe and Telephones.

1976. Telephone Centenary.

1191.	151.	50 h. multicoloured ..	3·00	60

152. Emblem and Heads of State.

153. Kaaba and Spinning Wheel.

1976. Arab League Summit Conference.

1192.	152.	20 h. green and blue	2·75	45

1976. 50th Anniv of Manufacture of Ka'aba Covering.

1193.	153.	20 h. multicoloured	2·50	30

154. Eye and W.H.O. Emblem.

1976. Prevention of Blindness.

1194.	154.	20 h. multicoloured ..	3·50	25

155. Emblem.

1976. Islamic Jurisprudence Conference.

1195.	155.	20 h. orge., blue & brn.	2·00	25

156. Emblem.

157. King Khaled.

1977. 25th Anniv. of Sharia Law College, Mecca.

1196.	156.	4 p. green and red ..	3·00	25

1977. 2nd Anniv. of Installation of King Khaled.

(a) With incorrect dates at foot.

1197.	157.	20 h. brown and green	20·00	30·00
1198.		80 h. black and green	20·00	25·00

(b) With corrected dates.

1199.	157.	20 h. brown and green	1·00	25
1200.		80 h. black and green	3·00	60

On Nos. 1197/8 the two Arabic dates end with the same characters. On the correct version of the design, they do not.

158. Diesel Train and Map.

1977. 25th Anniv. (1976) of Damman/Riyadh Railway.

1201.	158.	20 h. multicoloured ..	10·00	1·50

159/62. "The Four Imams". (Illustration reduced. Actual size 58×58 mm.)

1977.

1202.	159.	20 h. yellow and grey	4·50	1·50
1203.	160.	20 h. yellow and grey	4·50	1·50
1204.	161.	20 h. yellow and grey	4·50	1·50
1205.	162.	20 h. yellow and grey	4·50	1·50

Nos. 1202/5 were issued se-tenant as a composite design.

163. Moenjodaro Ruins, Pakistan.

164. Map by al-Idrisi.

1977. "Save Moenjodaro", Campaign.

1206.	163.	50 h. multicoloured ..	3·00	30

1977. First International Arab History Symposium.

1207.	164.	20 h. multicoloured ..	1·25	25
1208.		50 h. multicoloured ..	2·25	35

165. King Faisal Hospital, Riyadh.

1977. Opening of King Faisal Hospital.

1209.	165.	20 h. multicoloured ..	1·75	30
1210.		50 h. multicoloured ..	3·50	45

166. A.P.U. Emblem.

167. Kaaba, Book and Lighthouse.

1977. 25th Anniv. of Arab Postal Union.

1211.	166.	20 h. multicoloured ..	75	25
1212.		80 h. multicoloured ..	3·00	50

1977. First World Conference on Muslim Education.

1213.	167.	20 h. blue and yellow	1·50	25

168. Taiz–Abha–Jizan Road and Route Map.

1978. Opening of Taiz–Abha–Jizan Road.

1214.	168.	20 h. multicoloured ..	75	20
1215.		80 h. multicoloured ..	2·00	45

169. Mount Arafat, Pilgrims and Kaaba.

1978. Pilgrimage to Mecca.

1216.	169.	20 h. multicoloured ..	75	20
1217.		80 h. multicoloured ..	2·00	45

170. Posthorn Dhow.

171. 5 g. Stamp of 1930.

1979. 2nd Gulf Postal Organization Conference, Dubai.

1218.	170.	20 h. multicoloured ..	40	20
1219.		50 h. multicoloured ..	1·00	35

1979. 50th Anniv. of First Commemorative Stamp Issue.

1220.	171.	20 h. multicoloured ..	60	25
1221.		50 h. multicoloured ..	1·50	35
1222.		115 h. multicoloured	3·25	1·25

172. Crown Prince Fahd.

1979. Crown Prince Fahd's Birthday.

1224.	172.	20 h. multicoloured ..	1·25	20
1225.		50 h. multicoloured ..	2·50	40

173. Dome of the Rock, Jerusalem.

174. Golden Door of Kaaba, Mecca.

1979. Solidarity with Palestinians.
1226. **173.** 20 h. multicoloured .. 90 35

1979. New Gold Doors installed on Kaaba.
1227. **174.** 20 h. multicoloured 50 20
1228. 80 h. multicoloured .. 1·75 45

175. The Kaaba, Mecca.

1979. Pilgrimage to Mecca.
1229. **175.** 20 h. multicoloured .. 40 20
1230. 50 h. multicoloured .. 1·25 40

176. " Birds in a Forest ".

1980. International Year of the Child. Children's Paintings. Multicoloured.
1231. 20 h. Type **176** .. .. 4·00 40
1232. 50 h. " Paper Lanterns " 11·00 2·00

177. King Abdulaziz Ibn Saud.

1980. 80th Anniv. of Saudi Armed Forces.
1233. **177.** 20 h. multicoloured 1·00 15
1234. 80 h. multicoloured 4·00 60

178. Emblem.

179. Globe and Books.

1980. 35th Anniv. of Arab League.
1235. **178.** 20 h. grn., blk. & bl. 45 10

1980. 50th Anniv. of International Bureau of Education.
1236. **179.** 50 h. multicoloured 90 20

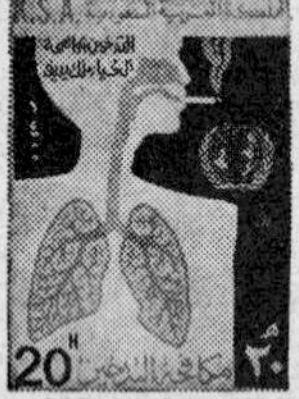
180. Polluted Air Passages and W.H.O. Emblem.

181. O.P.E.C. Emblem and Globe.

1980. Anti-Smoking Campaign.
1237. **180.** 20 h. multicoloured 75 15
1238. – 50 h. multicoloured 2·50 30
DESIGN: 50 h. Cigarette crossed through and W.H.O. emblem.

1980. 20th Anniv. of Organization of Petroleum Exporting Countries. Mult.
1239. 20 h. Type **181** 75 15
1240. 50 h. Figures supporting O.P.E.C. emblem 2·50 30

182. Pilgrims leaving Airplane.

1980. Pilgrimage to Mecca.
1241. **182.** 20 h. multicoloured 50 15
1242. 50 h. multicoloured 1·50 30

183. Kaaba Mecca.

184. Thour Cave, Mecca, and Quba Mosque, Medina on Map.

1981. 3rd Islamic Summit Conference, Mecca. Multicoloured.
1243. 20 h. Type **183** 50 20
1244. 20 h. Prophet's Mosque, Medina 50 20
1245. 20 h. Dome of the Rock, Jerusalem 50 20
1246. 20 h. Conference emblem (36 × 36 mm.) .. 50 20

1981. 1400th Anniv. of Hegira.
1247. **184.** 20 h. multicoloured .. 50 20
1248. 50 h. multicoloured .. 1·50 35
1249. 80 h. multicoloured .. 2·50 50

185. Royal Corporation of Jubeil and Yanbou Emblem.

1981. Industry Week.
1250. **185.** 20 h. brn. orge. & silver 40 15
1251. 80 h. brn., orge. & gold 1·50 35

186. Satellite Earth Station.

187. Emblem of Arab Towns Organization.

1981. Communications Achievements.
1252. – 20 h. gold, blk. & blue 50 20
1253. – 80 h. multicoloured .. 1·75 30
1254. **186.** 115 h. multicoloured 2·50 75
DESIGNS—HORIZ.—SQUARE. 20 h. Modern Telephone and graph. 80 h. Microwave antenna on map of Saudi Arabia.

1981. Arab Towns Day.
1255. **187.** 20 h. multicoloured .. 40 10
1256. 65 h. multicoloured .. 90 20
1257. 80 h. multicoloured .. 1·25 35
1258. 115 h. multicoloured 1·75 40

188. Aircraft over Terminal Buildings.

189. Flags of participating Countries and Saudi Team Emblem.

1981. Inauguration of King Abdulaziz International Airport, Jeddah. Multicoloured.
1259. 20 h. Type **188** 50 20
1260. 80 h. Waiting halls .. 2·25 45

1981. World Cup Football Championship Preliminary Round.
1261. **189.** 20 h. multicoloured .. 50 20
1262. 80 h. multicoloured .. 2·00 35

190. Blind Person reading Braille.

191. Wheat and Cogwheel on Graph.

1981. International Year of Disabled Persons. Multicoloured.
1263. 20 h. Type **190** 75 20
1264. 50 h. Disabled person weaving from wheelchair 2·50 40

1981. Third Five Year Plan.
1265. **191.** 20 h. multicoloured .. 15 10

192. King Abdulaziz Ibn Saud and Map of Saudi Arabia.

1981. 50th Anniv. of Unification of Saudi Arabia.
1266. **192.** 5 h. multicoloured .. 10 10
1267. 10 h. multicoloured .. 10 10
1268. 15 h. multicoloured .. 15 10
1269. 20 h. multicoloured .. 15 10
1270. 50 h. multicoloured .. 35 20
1271. 65 h. multicoloured .. 45 25
1272. 80 h. multicoloured .. 65 30
1273. 115 h. multicoloured 1·00 45

193. Pilgrims passing through Almasa'a Arcade.

1981. Pilgrimage to Mecca.
1275. **193.** 20 h. multicoloured .. 25 15
1276. 65 h. multicoloured .. 75 40

194. Tractor.

1981. World Food Day.
1277. **194.** 20 h. multicoloured .. 25 10

195. Conference Emblem.

1981. Second Session of Gulf Co-operative Council Summit Conference, Riyadh.
1278. **195.** 20 h. multicoloured .. 15 10
1279. 80 h. multicoloured .. 55 30

196. University Emblem.

1982. 25th Anniv. of King Saud University.
1280. **196.** 20 h. multicoloured .. 15 10
1281. 50 h. multicoloured .. 35 20

1982. As T **149/150**, but in smaller size, 25 × 20 mm.

(a) Type **149.**
1283d 10 h. black and lilac .. 15 10
1284 15 h. black and pink .. 12 10
1285c 20 h. black and blue .. 15 10
1291c 50 h. black and red .. 35 20
1294c 65 h. black and blue .. 45 25
1301c 1 r. black and green .. 75 40

(b) Type **150**.
1306a 5 h. blue and orange .. 35 20
1307c 10 h. green and orange .. 25 15
1308c 15 h. brown and orange 20 10
1309c 20 h. green and orange .. 20 15
1310 25 h. purple and orange 45 10
1315c 50 h. pink and orange .. 35 20
1318c 65 h. brown and orange 45 25
1325c 1 r. green and orange .. 75 40

197. Riyadh Postal Building.

198. Riyadh Television Centre.

1982. New Postal Buildings. Multicoloured.
1330. 20 h. Type **197** 15 10
1331. 65 h. Jeddah 45 25
1332. 80 h. Dammam 55 30
1333. 115 h. Postal mechanised sorting 85 45

1982. Riyadh Television Centre.
1335. **198.** 20 h. multicoloured .. 25 10

199. Football and King's Cup.

200. A.P.U. Emblem and Map.

1982. 25th Anniv. of King's Cup Football Championship.
1336. **199.** 20 h. multicoloured .. 15 10
1337. 65 h. multicoloured .. 45 25

1982. 30th Anniv. of Arab Postal Union. Multicoloured.
1338. 20 h. A.P.U. Emblem and Arabic " 30 " 15 10
1339. 65 h. Type **200** 45 25

201. Pilgrims at Muzdalefa looking for stones to stone the Devil.

1982. Pilgrimage to Mecca.
1340. **201.** 20 h. multicoloured .. 20 10
1341. 50 h. multicoloured .. 45 20

202. Saudi Arabian and World Standards Organizations Emblems.

1982. World Standards Day.
1342. **202.** 20 h. multicoloured .. 20 10

203. Tractor.

1982. World Food Day.
1343. **203.** 20 h. multicoloured 15 10

204. King Fahd.

1983. Installation of King Fahd.
1344. **204.** 20 h. multicoloured . . 25 15
1345. 50 h. multicoloured . . 50 30
1346. 65 h. multicoloured . . 65 35
1347. 80 h. multicoloured . . 80 50
1348. 115 h. multicoloured 1·25 70

205. Crown Prince Abdullah.

1983. Installation of Crown Prince.
1349. **205.** 20 h. multicoloured . . 25 15
1350. 50 h. multicoloured . . 50 30
1351. 65 h. multicoloured . . 65 35
1352. 80 h. multicoloured . . 80 50
1353. 115 h. multicoloured 1·25 70

206. Dome of the Rock, Jerusalem.

1983. Solidarity with Palestinians.
1354. **206.** 20 h. multicoloured . . 45 15

207. Container Ship "Bar'zan".

1983. 6th Anniv. of United Arab Shipping Company. Multicoloured.
1355. 20 h. Type **207** 40 25
1356. 65 h. "Al Drieya" . . 1·25 60

208. Stoning the Devil. **209.** Saudi Arabia Post and U.P.U. Emblems.

1983. Pilgrimage to Mecca.
1357. **208.** 20 h. multicoloured 25 15
1358. 65 h. multicoloured 65 40

1983. World Communications Year. Mult.
1359. 20 h. Type **209** 20 15
1360. 80 h. Saudi Arabia telephone and I.T.U. emblems 70 35

210. Terminal Building.

1983. Opening of King Khaled International Airport, Riyadh. Multicoloured.
1361. 20 h. Type **210** 35 20
1362. 65 h. Embarkation wing of terminal . . . . 1·25 70

211. Wheat and F.A.O. Emblem. **212.** Al Aqsa Mosque, Jerusalem.

1983. World Food Day.
1363. **211.** 20 h. multicoloured . . 30 10

1983. Solidarity with Palestinians.
1364. **212.** 20 h. brn., bl. & grn. 40 15

213. Riyadh.

214. Shobra Palace, Taif.

215. Jeddah.

1984. Saudi Cities.
(a) Riyadh
1365 **213** 20 h. multicoloured 15 10
1366 50 h. multicoloured 1·00 20
1370a 75 h. multicoloured 25 15
1371 150 h. multicoloured 95 30
(b) Taif
1367 **214** 20 h. multicoloured . . 15 10
1373 50 h. multicoloured . . 35 15
1374 75 h. multicoloured . . 20 10
1375 150 h. multicoloured 95 30
(c) Jeddah
1377 **215** 50 h. multicoloured . . 35 15
1378 75 h. multicoloured . . 25 10
1379 150 h. multicoloured 95 30

223. Family and House.

1984. 10th Anniv. of Estate Development Fund.
1385. **223.** 20 h. multicoloured 25 15

224. Solar Panels and Symbols

1984. Al-Eyenah Solar Village. Mult.
1386. 20 h Type **224** 30 20
1387. 80 h. Sun and solar panels . . . . . . 1·10 50

225. Al-Kheef Mosque, Mina.

1984. Pilgrimage to Mecca. Multicoloured.
1389. 20 h. Type **225** 30 15
1390. 65 h. Al-Kheef Mosque, Mina (different) . . 1·10 50

226. Olympic and Saudi Football Federation Emblems. **227.** Wheat and F.A.O. Emblem.

1984. Qualification of Saudi Football Team for Olympic Games.
1391. **226.** 20 h. multicoloured 30 15
1392. 115 h. multicoloured 1·50 1·00
Nos. 1391/2 have the incorrect spellings "Gamos" and "Olympied".

1984. World Food Day.
1393. **227.** 20 h. green, buff and black 30 15

228. Olympic Rings and "90".

1984. 90th Anniv. of International Olympic Committee.
1394. **228.** 20 h. multicoloured 40 15
1395. 50 h. multicoloured 1·10 40

229. "Arabsat" and Globe.

1985. Launch of "Arabsat" Satellite.
1396. **229.** 20 h. multicoloured 30 15

230. Emblem and Koran.

1985. International Koran Reading Competition.
1397. **230.** 20 h. multicoloured 40 20
1398. 65 h. multicoloured 1·40 60

231. King Fahd and Jubail Industrial Complex.

1985. Five year Plan. Multicoloured.
1399. 20 h. Type **231** 50 40
1400. 50 h. King Fahd, T.V. tower, dish aerial and microwave tower . . 85 60
1401. 65 h. King Fahd and agricultural landscape 1·10 80
1402. 80 h. King Fahd and Yanbu industrial complex . . . . 1·40 1·10

232. I.Y.Y. Emblem.

1985. International Youth Year.
1403. **232.** 20 h multicoloured . . 35 20
1404. 80 h. multicoloured 1·25 60

233. Map and Wheat. **235.** "Arabsat 2" Satellite and Launch of "Discovery" (space shuttle).

234. Loading Berth, Yanbu.

1985. "Self Sufficiency in Wheat Production".
1405. **233.** 20 h. multicoloured 30 15

1985. Abqaiq-Yanbu Oil Pipeline. Mult.
1406. 20 h. Type **234** 30 20
1407. 65 h. Pipeline and map 1·25 65

1985. First Arab Astronaut, Prince Sultan Ibn Salman Al-Saud. Multicoloured.
1408. 20 h. Type **235** 30 15
1409. 115 h. Space shuttle and mission emblem (51 × 26 mm.) . . . . 1·75 85

236. "40" and U.N. Emblem.

1985. 40th Anniv. of U.N.O.
1410. **236.** 20 h. light blue, blue and green 25 10

237. Highway and Map of Route.

1985. Mecca–Medina Highway.
1411. **237.** 20 h. multicoloured 25 15
1412. 65 h. multicoloured 75 45

238. Coded Envelope and Post Emblem.

1985. Post Code Publicity.
1413. **238.** 20 h. multicoloured 25 10

239. Trophy and Football.

1985. Victory in 8th (1984) Asian Football Cup Championship.
1414. **239.** 20 h. multicoloured 25 15
1415. 65 h. multicoloured 70 40
1416. 115 h. multicoloured 1·40 85

240. Pilgrims around Kaaba.

1985. Pilgrimage to Mecca.
1417. **240.** 10 h. multicoloured 15 10
1418. 15 h. multicoloured 20 15
1419. 20 h. multicoloured 30 15
1420. 65 h. multicoloured 85 50

241. Olympic Rings and Council Emblem.

1985. First Arabian Gulf Co-operative Council Olympic Day.
1421. **241.** 20 h. multicoloured 30 15
1422. 115 h. multicoloured 1·50 80

242. Irrigation System.

1985. World Food Day.
1423. **242.** 20 h. multicoloured 30 15
1424. 65 h. multicoloured 1·10 45

243. King Abdulaziz and Horsemen.

1985. International Conference on King Abdulaziz.
1425. **243.** 15 h. multicoloured 20 15
1426. 20 h. multicoloured 25 15
1427. 65 h. multicoloured 75 50
1428. 80 h. multicoloured 1·10 70

244. Building within Roll of Printed Paper.

1985. King Fahd Holy Koran Press Compound, Medina. Multicoloured.
1430. 20 h. Type **244** 25 15
1431. 65 h. Open book sculpture within roll of printed paper 75 50

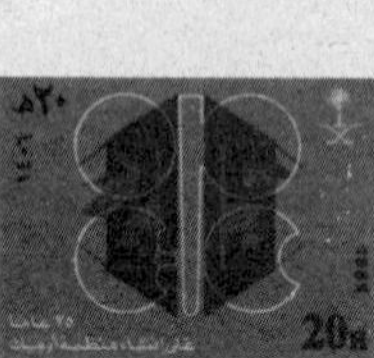

245. O.P.E.C. Emblem and "25"'.

246 Doves and I.P.Y. Emblem.

1985. 25th Anniv. of Organization of Petroleum Exporting Countries.
1432. **245.** 20 h. deep brown, brown and black . . 25 15
1433. 65 h. multicoloured 75 50

1986. International Peace Year.
1434. **246.** 20 h. multicoloured 75 25

1986. As T **149** but size 29 × 19 mm.
1435. 10 h. black and violet . .
1436. 20 h. black and blue . .
1437. 50 h. black and red . .

247. Riyadh.

248. Child in Droplet.

1986. 50th Anniv of Riyadh Municipality.
1438a **247** 20 h. multicoloured 25 15
1439 65 h. multicoloured 85 60

1986. World Health Day.
1440. **248.** 20 h. multicoloured 30 20
1441. 50 h. multicoloured 1·10 75

249. Electricity Pylon and Flashes.

1986. 10th Anniv. of General Electricity Corporation.
1442. **249.** 20 h. multicoloured 20 15
1443. 65 h. multicoloured 60 40

250. Route Map of Cable.

1986. Inauguration of Singapore–Marseilles Communications Cable.
1444. **250.** 20 h. multicoloured 25 15
1445. 50 h. multicoloured 65 40

251. Houses and Soldier. **252.** Holy Kaaba.

1986. National Guards Housing Project, Riyadh.
1446. **251.** 20 h. multicoloured 25 20
1447. 65 h. multicoloured 75 55

1986.
1448 **252** 30 h. black and green 35 15
1449 40 h. black and mauve 45 15
1450 50 h. black and green 15 10
1452 75 h. black and blue 20 10
1456 150 h. black & mauve 40 20

253. Mount Arafat, Pilgrims and Kaaba.

1986. Pilgrimage to Mecca. Multicoloured.
1460. 20 h. Type **253** 65 50
1461. 20 h. Pilgrims leaving airplane 80 60
1462. 20 h. Stoning the Devil 65 50
1463. 20 h. Pilgrims at Muzdalefa looking for stones to stone the Devil 65 50
1464. 20 h. Pilgrims passing through Almasa'a Arcade 65 50
1465. 20 h. Kaaba, Mecca . . 65 50
1466. 20 h. Pilgrims around Kaaba 65 50
1467. 20 h. Al-Kheef Mosque, Mina 65 50

254. Refinery.

255. Palm Tree and Wheat in Globe.

1986. 50th Anniv. of Discovery of Oil in Saudi Arabia. Multicoloured.
1468. 20 h. Type **254** 25 15
1469. 65 h. Oil derrick on map 85 60

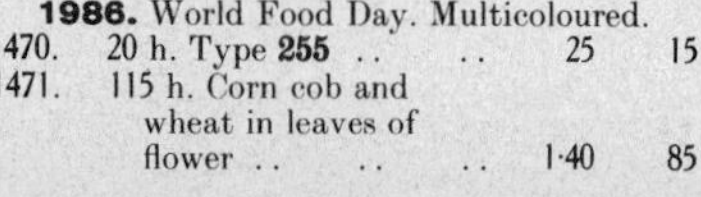

1986. World Food Day. Multicoloured.
1470. 20 h. Type **255** 25 15
1471. 115 h. Corn cob and wheat in leaves of flower . . . . . . 1·40 85

256. Scroll behind Dagger and Pool of Blood.

1986. 4th Anniv. of Massacre of Palestinian Refugees at Sabra and Shatila Camps, Lebanon.
1472. **256.** 80 h. multicoloured 1·00 30
1473. 115 h. multicoloured 1·40 95

257.

258.

259.

260.

261.

262.

263.

1986. University Crests.

(a) Imam Mohammed ibn Saud Islamic University, Riyadh.
1474 **257** 15 h. black and green 20 10
1475 20 h. black and blue 20 10
1476 50 h. black and blue 30 15
1477 65 h. black and blue 40 20
1477a 75 h. black and blue 25 20
1478 100 h. black and red 80 25
1479 150 h. black and red 90 40

(b) Umm al-Qura University, Mecca
1481 **258** 50 h. black and blue 30 15
1482 65 h. black and blue 40 20
1482a 75 h. black and blue 20 10
1483 100 h. black and pink 80 25
1484 150 h. black and red 90 40

(c) King Saud University, Riyadh
1487 **259** 50 h. black and blue 30 15
1488 75 h. black and blue 25 20
1489 100 h. black and red 80 25
1490 150 h. black and red 90 40

(d) King Abulaziz University, Jeddah
1493 **260** 50 h. black and blue 30 10
1494 75 h. black and blue 25 20
1496 150 h. black and red 90 40

(e) King Faisal University, Al-Hasa
1499 **261** 50 h. black and blue 30 15
1500 75 h. black and blue 25 20
1502 150 h. black and red 90 40

(f) King Fahd University of Petroleum and Minerals, Dhahran
1505 **262** 50 h. black and blue 30 15
1506 75 h. black and blue 25 20
1508 150 h. black and red 90 40

(g) Islamic University, Medina
1511 **263** 50 h. black and blue 30 15
1512 75 h. black and blue 25 20
1514 150 h. black and red 90 40

264. Road Bridge and Aerial View of Causeway (left).

1986. Saudi Arabia–Bahrain Causeway. Mult.
1515. 20 h. Type **264** 75 60
1516. 20 h. Road bridge and aerial view of causeway (right) . . 75 60

265. Olympic Torch and Rings.

1986. 90th Anniv. of Modern Olympic Games.
1517. **265.** 20 h. multicoloured 35 15
1518. 100 h. multicoloured 1·75 1·00

266. Oil Derrick and Refinery.

1987. 25th Anniv. of General Petroleum and Mineral Organization.
1519. **266.** 50 h. multicoloured 75 30
1520. 100 h. multicoloured 1·50 95

267. Mosque and Model of Extension.

1987. Restoration and Extension of Quba Mosque, Medina.
1521. **267.** 50 h. multicoloured 75 30
1522. 75 h. multicoloured 1·10 70

268. Drill-Press Operator.

1987. Technical and Vocational Training. Multicoloured.
1523 50 h. Type **268** 60 50
1524 50 h. Lathe operator . . 60 50
1525 50 h. Laboratory technician 60 50
1526 50 h. Welder 60 50

Nos. 1523/6 were printed together se-tenant, each block forming an overall design of a cog wheel.

269. Pyramid, Riyadh T.V. Transmitter, King Khaled International Airport and Fort.

270. Dish Aerials and Satellite.

1987. "Saudi Arabia—Yesterday and Today" Exhibition, Cairo.
1527. **269.** 50 h. multicoloured 80 40
1528. 75 h. multicoloured 1·25 85

1987. King Fahd Space Communications City, Umm al Salam, Jeddah. Mult.
1529. 50 h. Type **270** 55 30
1530. 75 h. Dish aerials and buildings (51 × 26 mm.) 85 70

271. Map and Rifleman.

273. Emblems.

272. Mosque and Pilgrims.

1987. Afghan Resistance to Occupation.
1531. **271.** 50 h. multicoloured 60 30
1532. 100 h. multicoloured 1·00 70

1987. Pilgrimage to Mecca.
1533. **272.** 50 h. multicoloured 60 30
1534. 75 h. multicoloured 80 50
1535. 100 h. multicoloured 1·00 70

1987. 1st Anniv. of Disabled Children's Care Home.
1536. **273.** 50 h. multicoloured 65 30
1537. 75 h. multicoloured 95 70

274. Emblems and Hands writing on Airmail Envelope.

1987. World Post Day.
1538. **274.** 50 h. multicoloured 50 30
1539. 150 h. multicoloured 1·60 95

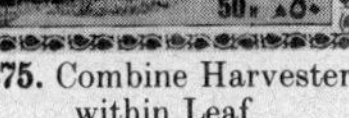
275. Combine Harvester within Leaf.

276. Woman and Children in Hand.

1987. World Food Day.
1540. **275.** 50 h. multicoloured 50 30
1541. 75 h. multicoloured 80 60

1987. 25th Anniv. of First Social Welfare Society.
1542. **276.** 50 h. multicoloured 50 30
1543. 100 h. multicoloured 90 70

277. Dome of the Rock, Jerusalem.

1987.
1544. **277.** 75 h. multicoloured 80 35
1545. 150 h. multicoloured 1·60 90

278. Mosque.

1987. Expansion of Prophet's Mosque, Medina.
1546. **278.** 50 h. multicoloured 60 25
1547. 75 h. multicoloured 80 40
1548. 150 h. multicoloured 1·60 80

279. Dome of the Rock, Horseman and Battle Scene.

280. Emblem.

1987. 800th Anniv of Battle of Hattin.
1550. **279.** 75 h. multicoloured 80 45
1551. 150 h. multicoloured 1·60 95

1987. 8th Supreme Council Session of Gulf Co-operation Council, Riyadh.
1552. **280.** 50 h. multicoloured 55 25
1553. 75 h. multicoloured 85 30

281. Road as "3" and Ship.

282. Aerial View of Stadium and Sports Pictograms.

1988. 3rd International Roads Federation (Middle East Region) Meeting, Riyadh.
1554. **281.** 50 h. multicoloured 55 25
1555. 75 h. multicoloured 85 50

1988. Inauguration of International King Fahd Stadium, Riyadh. Multicoloured.
1556. 50 h. Type **282** 55 20
1557. 150 h. Side view of stadium and sports pictograms (51 × 26 mm.) .. .. 1·60 1·10

283. Anniversary Emblem and W.H.O. Building.

1988. World Health Day. 40th Anniv. of W.H.O.
1558. **283.** 50 h. multicoloured 55 25
1559. 75 h. multicoloured 85 50

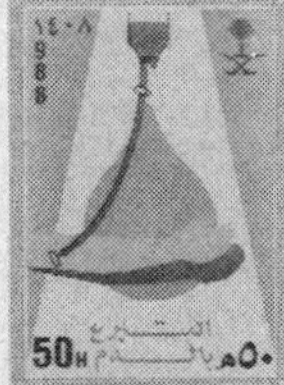
284 Bottle, Arm and Blood Drop

1988. Blood Donation.
1560 **284** 50 h. multicoloured .. 55 30
1561 75h. multicoloured .. 85 55

285 Mosque, Holy Kaaba and King Fahd

1988. Appointment of King Fahd as Custodian of Two Holy Mosques.
1562 **285** 50 h. multicoloured .. 40 25
1563 75 h. multicoloured .. 60 40
1564 150 h. multicoloured 1·00 70

286 Clean Air, Land and Sea

287 Palestinian Flag, Hand holding Stone and Crowd

1988. Environmental Protection.
1566 **286** 50 h. multicoloured .. 55 25
1567 75 h. multicoloured .. 85 50

1988. Palestinian "Intifida" Movement.
1568 **287** 75 h. multicoloured .. 85 40
1569 150 h. multicoloured 1·75 85

288 Pilgrims at al-Sail al-Kabir Migat

1988. Pilgrimage to Mecca.
1570 **288** 50 h. multicoloured .. 55 25
1571 75 h. multicoloured .. 85 50

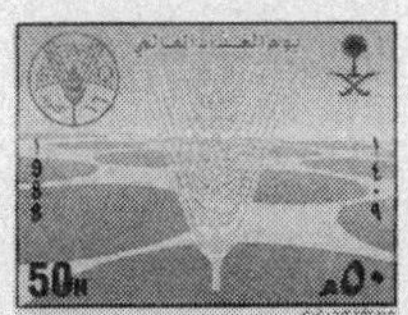
289 Ear of Wheat

1988. World Food Day.
1572 **289** 50 h. multicoloured .. 45 25
1573 75 h. multicoloured .. 75 45

290 Mosque

1988. Expansion of Qiblatayn Mosque, Medina.
1574 **290** 50 h. multicoloured 45 25
1575 75 h. multicoloured 75 45

291 Footballer and Trophy on Globe

1989. World Youth Football Cup, Saudi Arabia.
1576 **291** 75 h. multicoloured 65 40
1577 150 h. multicoloured 1·10 50

292 W.H.O. Emblem and Means of Communication

294 Palestinian Flag and Dome of the Rock, Jerusalem

293 Shuaibah Desalination Plant, Red Sea

1989. World Health Day.
1578 **292** 50 h. multicoloured .. 35 15
1579 75 h. multicoloured .. 65 40

1989. 1st Anniv of Sea Water Desalination and Electricity Power Station.
1580 **293** 50 h. multicoloured .. 30 15
1581 75 h. multicoloured .. 55 35

1989. "Freedom of Palestine".
1582 **294** 50 h. multicoloured .. 30 15
1583 75 h. multicoloured .. 45 25

295 Attan'eem Migat, Mecca

1989. Pilgrimage to Mecca.
1584 **295** 50 h. multicoloured .. 30 15
1585 75 h. multicoloured .. 45 25

296 Ears of Wheat encircling Globe

297 Hands holding Trophy aloft

1989. World Food Day.
1586 **296** 75 h. multicoloured .. 45 25
1587 150 h. multicoloured 90 40

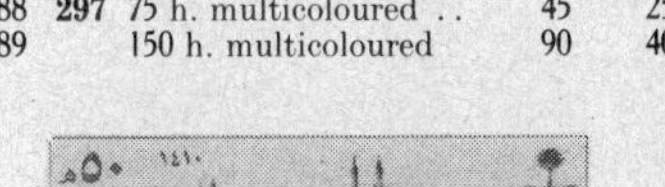
1989. 3rd World Under-16 JVC Cup Soccer Championship, Scotland.
1588 **297** 75 h. multicoloured .. 45 25
1589 150 h. multicoloured 90 40

298 Mosque after Expansion

1989. Expansion of Holy Mosque, Mecca.
1590 **298** 50 h. multicoloured .. 30 15
1591 75 h. multicoloured .. 45 25
1592 150 h. multicoloured 90 40

299 Emblem and Arabic Letters

1990. International Literacy Year.
1595 **299** 50 h. multicoloured .. 30 15
1596 75 h. multicoloured .. 45 25

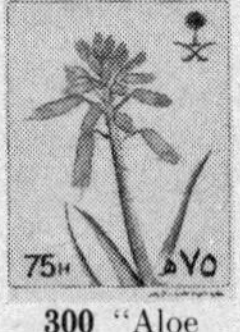
300 "Aloe sheilaa"

301 "Blopharis ciliaris"

302 'Pergularia tormentosa"

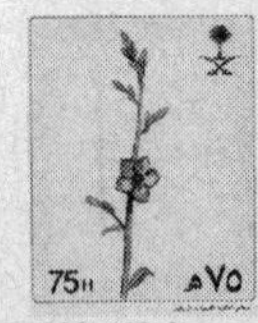
303 "Talinam cuneifolium"

304 "Echium horridum"

305 "Cleome arabica"

306 "Iris sisyrinchium"

307 "Senecio desfontaini"

308 "Cistanche phelypaea"

309 "Plumbago zeylanica"

310 "Cappario cartilaginea"

311 "Peganum harmala"

312 Acacia

313 "Cagea reticulata"

314 "Diplotakis harra"

315 "Anvillea garcini"

316 "Striga asiatica"

317 "Rhanterium eppaposum"

318 "Oenostachys abyssinica"

319 "Roemeria dodecandra"

320 Poppy

1990. Flowers.

1597	**300**	50 h. multicoloured ..	30	15
1598	**301**	50 h. multicoloured ..	30	15
1599	**302**	50 h. multicoloured ..	30	15
1600	**303**	50 h. multicoloured ..	30	15
1601	**304**	50 h. multicoloured ..	30	15
1602	**305**	50 h. multicoloured ..	30	15
1603	**306**	50 h. multicoloured ..	30	15
1604	**307**	50 h. multicoloured ..	30	15
1605	**308**	50 h. multicoloured ..	30	15
1606	**309**	50 h. multicoloured ..	30	15
1607	**310**	50 h. multicoloured ..	30	15
1608	**311**	50 h. multicoloured ..	30	15
1609	**312**	50 h. multicoloured ..	30	15
1610	**313**	50 h. multicoloured ..	30	15
1611	**314**	50 h. multicoloured ..	30	15
1612	**315**	50 h. multicoloured ..	30	15
1613	**316**	50 h. multicoloured ..	30	15
1614	**317**	50 h. multicoloured ..	20	15
1615	**318**	50 h. multicoloured ..	30	15
1616	**319**	50 h. multicoloured ..	30	15
1617	**320**	50 h. multicoloured ..	30	15
1618	**300**	75 h. multicoloured ..	45	25
1619	**301**	75 h. multicoloured ..	45	25
1620	**302**	75 h. multicoloured ..	45	25
1621	**303**	75 h. multicoloured ..	45	25
1622	**304**	75 h. multicoloured ..	45	25
1623	**305**	75 h. multicoloured ..	45	25
1624	**306**	75 h. multicoloured ..	45	25
1625	**307**	75 h. multicoloured ..	45	25
1626	**308**	75 h. multicoloured ..	45	25
1627	**309**	75 h. multicoloured ..	45	25
1628	**310**	75 h. multicoloured ..	45	25
1629	**311**	75 h. multicoloured ..	45	25
1630	**312**	75 h. multicoloured ..	45	25
1631	**313**	75 h. multicoloured ..	45	25
1632	**314**	75 h. multicoloured ..	45	25
1633	**315**	75 h. multicoloured ..	45	25
1634	**316**	75 h. multicoloured ..	45	25
1635	**317**	75 h. multicoloured ..	45	25
1636	**318**	75 h. multicoloured ..	45	25
1637	**319**	75 h. multicoloured ..	45	25
1638	**320**	75 h. multicoloured ..	45	25
1639	**300**	150 h. multicoloured	90	40
1640	**301**	150 h. multicoloured	90	40
1641	**302**	150 h. multicoloured	90	40
1642	**303**	150 h. multicoloured	90	40
1643	**304**	150 h. multicoloured	90	40
1644	**305**	150 h. multicoloured	90	40
1645	**306**	150 h. multicoloured	90	40
1646	**307**	150 h. multicoloured	90	40
1647	**308**	150 h. multicoloured	90	40
1648	**309**	150 h. multicoloured	90	40
1649	**310**	150 h. multicoloured	90	40
1650	**311**	150 h. multicoloured	90	40
1651	**312**	150 h. multicoloured	90	40
1652	**313**	150 h. multicoloured	90	40
1653	**314**	150 h. multicoloured	90	40
1654	**315**	150 h. multicoloured	90	40
1655	**316**	150 h. multicoloured	90	40
1656	**317**	150 h. multicoloured	90	40
1657	**318**	150 h. multicoloured	90	40
1658	**319**	150 h. multicoloured	90	40
1659	**320**	150 h. multicoloured	90	40

321 "20" within Crescent and Circle

1990. 20th Anniv of Islamic Conference Organization.

1660	**321**	75 h. multicoloured ..	45	25
1661		150 h. multicoloured	90	40

322 Globe and W.H.O. Emblem

1990. World Health Day.

1662	**322**	75 h. multicoloured ..	20	10
1663		150 h. multicoloured	40	20

323 White Horse

1990. 25th Anniv of Horsemanship Club. Mult.

(a) Size 38 × 29 mm

1664	50 h. Type **323**	15	10
1665	50 h. Brown horse ..	15	10
1666	50 h. White horse with dark muzzle	15	10
1667	50 h. Chestnut horse ..	15	10

(b) Size 36 × 27 mm

1668	50 h. As No. 1667 ..	15	10
1669	75 h. As No. 1665 ..	20	10
1670	100 h. Type **323**	30	15
1671	150 h. As No. 1666 ..	40	20

324 El Johfah Migat, Rabegh

1990. Pilgrimage to Mecca.

1672	**324**	75 h. multicoloured ..	20	10
1673		150 h. multicoloured	40	20

325 T.V. Tower and Centre

1990. 25th Anniv of Saudi Television.

1674	**325**	75 h. multicoloured ..	20	10
1675		150 h. multicoloured	40	20

326 Ornament

1990. Islamic Heritage Year. Multicoloured.

1676	75 h. Type **326**	20	10
1677	75 h. Mosque	20	10
1678	75 h. Arabic script ..	20	10
1679	75 h. Decoration with stylized minarets ..	20	10

327 Boeing "747" and International Flights Route Map

1990. 45th Anniv of Saudi Airlines. Mult.

1680	75 h. Type **327**	25	10
1681	75 h. Airplane and domestic flights route map	25	10
1682	150 h. Type **327**	45	25
1683	150 h. As No. 1681 ..	45	25

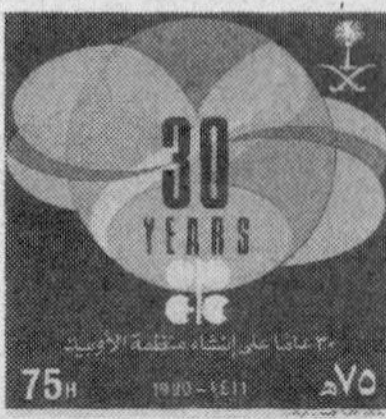
328 Anniversary Emblem

1990. 30th Anniv of O.P.E.C.

1684	**328**	75 h. multicoloured ..	20	10
1685		150 h. multicoloured	40	20

329 World Map

1990. World Food Day.

1686	**329**	75 h. multicoloured ..	20	10
1687		150 h. multicoloured	40	20

330 Industrial Site, Irrigation System and Oil Refinery

1990. 5th Five Year Plan. Multicoloured.

1688	75 h. Type **330**	20	10
1689	75 h. Radio tower, road and mine	20	10
1690	75 h. Monument, sports stadium and vocational training	20	10
1691	75 h. Television tower, environmental protection and modern building	20	10

331 Arabic Script and Decoration

332 Tidal Wave, Erupting Volcano and Earthquake-damaged House

1991. Battle of Badr, 624 A.D.

1692	**331**	75 h. green and orange	25	15
1693		150 h. dp bl, bl & grn	45	25

1991. World Health Day. Natural Disasters Relief.

1694	**332**	75 h. multicoloured ..	25	15
1695		150 h. multicoloured	45	25

333 Mountain Gazelle

334 Ibex

335 Arabian Oryx

336 Sand Fox

337 Bat

338 Striped Hyena

339 Sand Cat

340 Dugong

341 Arabian Leopard

1991. Animals.

1696	**333**	25 h. multicoloured ..	10	10
1697	**334**	25 h. multicoloured ..	10	10
1698	**335**	25 h. multicoloured ..	10	10
1699	**336**	25 h. multicoloured ..	10	10
1700	**337**	25 h. multicoloured ..	10	10
1701	**338**	25 h. multicoloured ..	10	10
1702	**339**	25 h. multicoloured ..	10	10
1703	**340**	25 h. multicoloured ..	10	10
1704	**341**	25 h. multicoloured ..	10	10
1705	**333**	50 h. multicoloured ..	15	10
1706	**334**	50 h. multicoloured ..	15	10
1707	**335**	50 h. multicoloured ..	15	10
1708	**336**	50 h. multicoloured ..	15	10
1709	**337**	50 h. multicoloured ..	15	10
1710	**338**	50 h. multicoloured ..	15	10
1711	**339**	50 h. multicoloured ..	15	10
1712	**340**	50 h. multicoloured ..	15	10
1713	**341**	50 h. multicoloured ..	15	10
1714	**333**	75 h. multicoloured ..	25	15
1715	**334**	75 h. multicoloured ..	25	15
1716	**335**	75 h. multicoloured ..	25	15
1717	**336**	75 h. multicoloured ..	25	15
1718	**337**	75 h. multicoloured ..	25	15
1719	**338**	75 h. multicoloured ..	25	15
1720	**339**	75 h. multicoloured ..	25	15
1721	**340**	75 h. multicoloured ..	25	15
1722	**341**	75 h. multicoloured ..	25	15
1723	**333**	100 h. multicoloured	30	15
1724	**334**	100 h. multicoloured	30	15
1725	**335**	100 h. multicoloured	30	15
1726	**336**	100 h. multicoloured	30	15
1727	**337**	100 h. multicoloured	30	15
1728	**338**	100 h. multicoloured	30	15
1729	**339**	100 h. multicoloured	30	15
1730	**340**	100 h. multicoloured	30	15
1731	**341**	100 h. multicoloured	30	15
1732	**333**	150 h. multicoloured	45	25
1733	**334**	150 h. multicoloured	45	25
1734	**335**	150 h. multicoloured	45	25
1735	**336**	150 h. multicoloured	45	25
1736	**337**	150 h. multicoloured	45	25
1737	**338**	150 h. multicoloured	45	25
1738	**339**	150 h. multicoloured	45	25
1739	**340**	150 h. multicoloured	45	25
1740	**341**	150 h. multicoloured	45	25

342 Flag and Map of Kuwait

343 Rainbow and Arrows

1991. Liberation of Kuwait.

1741	**342**	75 h. multicoloured ..	25	15
1742		150 h. multicoloured	45	25

1991. World Telecommunications Day.

1743	**343**	75 h. multicoloured ..	25	15
1744		150 h. multicoloured	45	25

344 Thee el Halifa Migat, Medina

1991. Pilgrimmage to Mecca.

1745	**344**	75 h. multicoloured ..	25	15
1746		150 h. multicoloured	45	25

345 Blackboard and I.L.Y. Emblem

346 Olive Branch and F.A.O. Emblem

1991. International Literacy Year.

1747	**345**	75 h. multicoloured ..	25	15
1748		150 h. multicoloured	45	25

1991. World Food Day.

1749	**346**	75 h. multicoloured ..	25	15
1750		150 h. multicoloured	45	25

347 Child's Profile and Emblem

1991. World Children's Day.

1751	**347**	75 h. multicoloured ..	25	15
1752		150 h. multicoloured	45	25

348 Woodpecker

349 Arabian Bustard

350 Lark

351 Turtle Dove

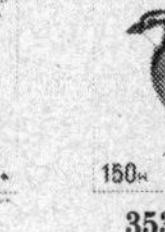

352 Heron

353 Partridge

354 Hoopoe

355 Falcon

356 Houbara Bustard

1992. Birds.

1771	**348**	75 h. multicoloured ..	25	15
1772	**349**	75 h. multicoloured ..	25	15
1773	**350**	75 h. multicoloured ..	25	15
1774	**351**	75 h. multicoloured ..	25	15
1775	**352**	75 h. multicoloured ..	25	15
1776	**353**	75 h. multicoloured ..	25	15
1777	**354**	75 h. multicoloured ..	25	15
1778	**355**	75 h. multicoloured ..	25	15
1779	**356**	75 h. multicoloured ..	25	15
1780	**348**	100 h. multicoloured	35	20
1781	**349**	100 h. multicoloured	35	20
1782	**350**	100 h. multicoloured	35	20
1783	**351**	100 h. multicoloured	35	20
1784	**352**	100 h. multicoloured	35	20
1785	**353**	100 h. multicoloured	35	20
1786	**354**	100 h. multicoloured	35	20
1787	**355**	100 h. multicoloured	35	20
1788	**356**	100 h. multicoloured	35	20
1789	**348**	150 h. multicoloured	55	30
1790	**349**	150 h. multicoloured	55	30
1791	**350**	150 h. multicoloured	55	30
1792	**351**	150 h. multicoloured	55	30
1793	**352**	150 h. multicoloured	55	30
1794	**353**	150 h. multicoloured	55	30
1795	**354**	150 h. multicoloured	55	30
1796	**355**	150 h. multicoloured	55	30
1797	**356**	150 h. multicoloured	55	30

MORE DETAILED LISTS
are given in the Stanley Gibbons Catalogues referred to in the country headings.
For lists of current volumes see Introduction.

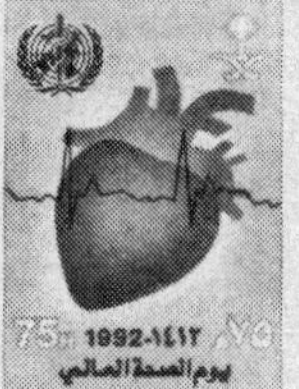

357 Heart and Cardiograph

358 Arabic Script

1992. World Health Day.

1798	**357**	75 h. multicoloured ..	25	15
1799		150 h. multicoloured	55	30

1992. Battle of Mt. Uhod (between Mecca and Medina, 625 A.D.) Commemoration.

1800	**358**	75 h. green and orange	25	15
1801		150 h. dp bl, bl & grn	55	30

359 Mosque, Yalamlam Miqat

1992. Pilgrimage to Mecca.

1802	**359**	75 h. multicoloured ..	25	15
1803		150 h. multicoloured	55	30

360 Human Pyramid inside House

1992. Population and Housing Census.

1804	**360**	75 h. multicoloured ..	25	15
1805		150 h. multicoloured	55	30

361 Vegetables

1992. World Food Day. Multicoloured.

1806	75 h. Type **361**	25	15
1807	150 h. Fruits	55	30

362 Regions System

363 Consultative Council System

364 Essential Governing System

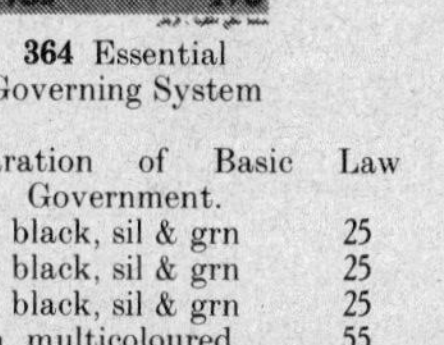

1992. Declaration of Basic Law of Government.

1808	**362**	75 h. black, sil & grn	25	15
1809	**363**	75 h. black, sil & grn	25	15
1810	**364**	75 h. black, sil & grn	25	15
1811	**362**	150 h. multicoloured	55	30
1812	**363**	150 h. multicoloured	55	30
1813	**364**	150 h. multicoloured	55	30

365 Flags, Globe and King Fahd Stadium

366 Blood Spot and W.H.O. Emblem

1993. Continental Cup Football Championship, Saudi Arabia.

1815	**365**	75 h. multicoloured ..	25	15
1816		150 h. multicoloured	55	30

1993. World Health Day.

1817	**366**	75 h. multicoloured ..	25	15
1818		150 h. multicoloured	55	30

367 Arabic Script

368 I.T.U. Emblem

1993. Battle of Khandaq (between Mecca and Medina, 627 A.D.) Commemoration.

1819	**367**	75 h. green and orange	25	15
1820		150 h. dp bl, bl & grn	55	30

1993. 25th Anniv of World Telecommunications Day.

1821	**368**	75 h. multicoloured ..	25	15
1822		150 h. multicoloured	55	30

369 That Irq Migat

1993. Pilgrimage to Mecca.

1823	**369**	75 h. multicoloured ..	25	15
1824		150 h. multicoloured	55	30

370 Desert, Oasis, Mountains and Sea Environments

1993. World Food Day.

1825	**370**	75 h. multicoloured ..	25	15
1826		150 h. multicoloured	55	30

NEWSPAPER STAMPS.
NEJD.

(N 29).

1925. Nos. 198a and 199a optd. with Type N 29.

No.	Type	Description	Unused	Used
N208.	11.	⅛ pi. brown	£1750	
N209.		½ pi. red	£5750	

OFFICIAL STAMPS
SAUDI ARABIA

O 52. O 72.

1939.

No.	Type	Description	Unused	Used
O 347.	O 52.	3 g. blue	4·00	1·50
O 348.		5 g. mauve	5·00	1·60
O 349.		20 g. brown	7·00	4·00
O 350.		50 g. turquoise	18·00	10·00
O 351.		100 g. olive	70·00	40·00
O 352.		200 g. purple	60·00	80·00

1961. Size 18½ × 22½ mm.

No.	Type	Description	Unused	Used
O 449.	O 72.	1 p. black	1·00	50
O 450.		2 p. green	1·50	60
O 451.		3 p. bistre	2·00	90
O 452.		4 p. blue	2·50	1·25
O 453.		5 p. red	3·00	1·50
O 454.		10 p. purple	5·00	2·75
O 455.		20 p. violet	10·00	4·50
O 456.		50 p. brown	25·00	15·00
O 457.		100 p. bronze	55·00	30·00

1964. Size 21 × 26 mm.

No.	Type	Description	Unused	Used
O 497.	O 72.	1 p. black	2·00	60
O 498.		2 p. green	4·00	1·25
O 504.		3 p. ochre	5·00	2·00
O 505.		4 p. blue	5·00	2·00
O 506.		5 p. red	3·00	3·00
O 507.		6 p. purple	5·00	3·00
O 508.		7 p. green	8·00	3·00
O 509.		8 p. red	8·00	3·00
O 510.		9 p. red	40·00	
O 511.		10 p. brown	8·00	3·00
O 512.		11 p. turquoise	50·00	
O 513.		12 p. violet	50·00	
O 514.		13 p. turquoise	9·00	4·00
O 515.		14 p. violet	9·00	4·00
O 516.		15 p. orange	65·00	7·50
O 517.		16 p. black	65·00	7·50
O 518.		17 p. green	65·00	
O 519.		18 p. yellow	65·00	
O 520.		19 p. purple	65·00	
O 521.		23 p. blue	80·00	
O 522.		24 p. green	65·00	
O 523.		26 p. bistre	65·00	
O 524.		27 p. lilac	65·00	
O 525.		31 p. brown	£110	
O 526.		33 p. light green	£110	
O 527.		50 p. olive	£650	
O 528.		100 p. olive	£550	

O 111.

1970.

No.	Type	Description	Unused	Used
O 1040.	O 111.	1 p. brown	5·00	25
O 1041.		2 p. green	5·00	25
O 1042.		3 p. mauve	7·00	40
O 1043.		4 p. blue	10·00	50
O 1044.		5 p. red	10·00	60
O 1045.		6 p. orange	10·00	75
O 1046.		7 p. red		
O 1047.		8 p. violet		
O 1048.		9 p. blue		
O 1049.		10 p. blue	7·50	1·25
O 1050.		11 p. green		
O 1050a.		12 p. brown		
O 1051.		20 p. blue	12·00	2·00
O 1051b.		23 p. brown		
O 1052.		31 p. purple	14·50	3·00
O 1053.		50 p. brown		
O 1054.		100 p. green		

POSTAGE DUE STAMPS
A. HEJAZ

D 7. From Old Door at El Ashra Barsbai, Shari El Ashrafuga, Cairo.

(D 11.)

1917. Arabic designs as Type D 7.

No.	Type	Description	Unused	Used
D 17.		20 pa. red	5·00	1·00
D 18.		1 pi. blue	5·00	1·00
D 19.		2 pi. red	5·00	1·00

1921. Nos. D 17/19 optd with T 7.

No.	Type	Description	Unused	Used
D 31a		20 pa. red	20·00	
D 33		1 pi. blue	10·00	2·50
D 34		2 pi. red	10·00	3·00

1922. Nos. D 17/9 optd with T 10.

No.	Type	Description	Unused	Used
D 39		20 pa. red	25·00	12·00
D 40		1 pi. blue	3·00	60
D 41		2 pi. red	5·00	70

1923. Optd. with Type D 11.

No.	Type	Description	Unused	Used
D 47.	11.	½ pi. red	7·00	2·00
D 48.		1 pi. blue	9·00	5·00
D 49.		2 pi. orange	5·00	3·00

1924. Nos. D 47/9 optd with T 14.

No.	Type	Description	Unused	Used
D 57	11	½ pi. red	£2500	
D 58		1 pi. blue	£2500	
D 59		2 pi. orange	£2500	

1925. Nos. D 17/9 optd. with T 15.

No.	Type	Description	Unused	Used
D 88		20 pa. red	£400	£350
D 90		1 pi. blue	20·00	12·00
D 92		2 pi. red	15·00	10·00

1925. Nos. D 17/9 optd. with T 16.

No.	Type	Description	Unused	Used
D 93.		20 pa. red	£750	
D 94.		1 pi. blue	20·00	
D 96.		2 pi. red	15·00	

(D 17.)

(D 18.)

D 25.

1925. Stamps of 1924 (optd T 16) optd with Type D 17.

No.	Type	Description	Unused	Used
D 149.	11.	½ pi. red	70·00	
D 150.		1½ pi. violet	70·00	
D 151.		2 pi. orange	70·00	
D 152.		3 pi. brown	70·00	
D 153.		5 pi. olive	70·00	

1925. Stamps of 1922 optd. with Type D18.

No.	Type	Description	Unused	Used
D 154.	11.	⅛ pi. brown	30·00	
D 155.		½ pi. red	30·00	
D 156.		1 pi. blue	30·00	
D 157.		1½ pi. lilac	30·00	
D 158.		2 pi. orange	30·00	
D 160.		3 pi. brown	30·00	
D 161.		5 pi. olive	40·00	
D 162.		10 pi. brown and mauve	40·00	

1925. Nos. D 154/62 optd. with Type D17.

No.	Type	Description	Unused	Used
D 163.	11.	⅛ pi. brown	15·00	4·50
D 164.		½ pi. red	15·00	4·50
D 165.		1 pi. blue	20·00	6·00
D 166.		1½ pi. lilac	15·00	4·50
D 167.		2 pi. orange	15·00	4·50
D 169.		3 pi. brown	15·00	4·50
D 170.		5 pi. olive	15·00	4·50
D 171.		10 pi. brown and mauve	20·00	9·00

1925. Optd. with T 24.

No.	Type	Description	Unused	Used
D 186.	D 25.	½ pi. blue	2·00	
D 187.		1 pi. orange	2·00	
D 188.		2 pi. brown	2·00	
D 189.		3 pi. red	2·00	

These stamps without overprint were not officially issued

B. NEJD.

1925. Nos. D47/9 of Hejaz optd. with T 25.

No.	Type	Description	Unused	Used
D203.	11.	½ pi. red	20·00	
D204c.		1 pi. blue	35·00	
D205c.		2 pi. orange	35·00	

(D 29).

(D 33).

1925. Hejaz Postage Stamps of 1922 optd. with Type D 29.

No.	Type	Description	Unused	Used
D206.	11.	½ pi. red	28·00	
D207.		3 pi. red	28·00	

1925. Postage stamps optd with T 32 futher optd with Type 33.

No.	Type	Description	Unused	Used
D232.	28.	1 pi. blue	15·00	
D233.		2 pi. orange	15·00	
D234.	11.	3 pi. red	12·00	
D236.	28.	5 pi. green	25·00	

1925. No. D 40 of Hejaz optd. with T 32.

No.	Type	Description	Unused	Used
D238.	D 7.	1 pi. blue	55·00	

C. HEJAZ-NEJD.

D 40.

D 42. Tougra of Ibn Saud.

1926.

No.	Type	Description	Unused	Used
D 267	D 40	½ pi. red	2·50	1·00
D 270		2 pi. orange	2·50	
D 272		6 pi. brown	2·50	

1926. Pan-Islamic Congress, Cairo. Optd. with T 40.

No.	Type	Description	Unused	Used
D 281.	D 40.	½ pi. red	6·00	2·00
D 282.		2 pi. orange	6·00	2·00
D 283.		6 pi. brown	6·00	2·00

1927.

No.	Type	Description	Unused	Used
D 292.	D 42.	1 pi. grey	15·00	2·00
D 293.		2 pi. violet	17·00	2·00

D. SAUDI ARABIA.

1935. No. 331a optd **T** in a circle.

No.	Type	Description	Unused	Used
D 343	49	½ g. red	£200	

D 52.

D 72.

1937.

No.	Type	Description	Unused	Used
D 347.	D 52.	½ g. brown	7·00	4·40
D 348.		1 g. blue	8·00	4·50
D 349.		2 g purple	14·00	10·00

1961.

No.	Type	Description	Unused	Used
D 449.	D 72.	1 p. violet	5·00	7·00
D 450.		2 p. green	7·00	9·00
D 451.		4 p. red	12·00	15·00

SAXONY Pt. 7

A former kingdom in S. Germany. Stamps superseded in 1868 by those of the North German Federation.

10 pfennige = 1 neugroschen.
30 neugroschen = 1 thaler.

1. 2. 3. Friedrich August II.

1850. Imperf.

No.	Type	Description	Unused	Used
1.	1.	3 pf. red	£4500	£4250

1851. Imperf.

No.	Type	Description	Unused	Used
7.	2.	3 pf. green	90·00	65·00

1851. Imperf.

No.	Type	Description	Unused	Used
10.	3.	½ ngr. black on grey	48·00	7·50
12.		1 ngr. black on red	48·00	7·00
13.		2 ngr. black on blue	£200	42·00
14.		3 ngr. black on yellow	£130	16·00

4. King Johann I. 5. 6.

1855. Imperf.

No.	Type	Description	Unused	Used
16	4	½ ngr. black on grey	8·00	2·25
18		1 ngr. black on red	8·00	1·50
20		2 ngr. black on blue	25·00	5·50
23		3 ngr. black on yellow	16·00	3·25
24		5 ngr. red	65·00	32·00
28		10 ngr. blue	£200	£225

1863. Perf.

No.	Type	Description	Unused	Used
31	5	3 pf. green	75	15·00
36		½ ngr. orange	60	2·25
39	6	1 ngr. red	60	85
40		2 ngr. blue	1·00	3·25
42		3 ngr. brown	1·25	6·50
45		5 ngr. blue	6·50	32·00
46		5 ngr. purple	13·00	35·00
49		5 ngr. grey	6·50	£100

SCHLESWIG (SLESVIG) Pt. 7

Stamps issued during the plebiscite of 1920.

100 pfennig = 1 German mark.
100 ore = 1 Danish krone.

1. Arms. 3. View of Schleswig.

1920.

No.	Type	Description	Unused	Used
1.	1.	2½ pf. grey	10	10
2.		5 pf. green	10	10
3.		7½ pf. brown	10	10
4.		10 pf. red	10	10
5.		15 pf. red	10	10
6.		20 pf. blue	10	15
7.		25 pf. orange	25	25
8.		35 pf. brown	45	45
9.		40 pf. violet	25	20
10.		75 pf. green	40	1·00
11.	3.	1 m. brown	35	65
12.		2 m. blue	70	1·75
13.		5 m. green	1·00	3·00
14.		10 m. red	2·00	5·00

1920. Values in Danish currency and optd. **1. ZONE.**

No.	Type	Description	Unused	Used
29.	1.	1 ore grey	10	60
30.		5 ore green	10	30
31.		7 ore brown	10	45
32.		10 ore red	15	60
33.		15 ore red	15	60
34.		20 ore blue	15	75
35.		25 ore orange	30	2·75
36.		35 ore brown	90	6·00
37.		40 ore violet	40	2·00
38.		75 ore green	40	4·00
39.	3.	1 k. brown	60	4·50
40.		2 k. blue	5·50	27·00
41.		5 k. green	3·50	27·00
42.		10 k. red	8·50	50·0

OFFICIAL STAMPS

1920. Nos. 1/14 optd **C.I.S.** (="Comission Interallieé Slesvig").

No.	Type	Description	Unused	Used
O15	1	2½ pf. grey	45·00	70·00
O16		5 pf. green	45·00	80·00
O17		7½ pf. brown	45·00	70·00
O18		10 pf. red	45·00	80·00
O19		15 pf. red	32·00	40·00
O20		20 pf. blue	40·00	45·00
O21		25 pf. orange	85·00	£120
O22		35 pf. brown	85·00	£130
O23		40 pf. violet	70·00	75·00
O24		75 pf. green	75·00	£190
O25	3	1 m. brown	80·00	£190
O26		2 m. blue	£130	£200
O27		5 m. green	£170	£350
O28		10 m. red	£350	£475

SCHLESWIG-HOLSTEIN Pt. 7

Two former grand-duchies to the S. of Denmark, annexed to Prussia in 1866. Part of Schleswig reverted to Denmark as a result of the plebiscite of 1920. The remainder is part of West Germany.

16 schilling = 1 mark.

1.

2.

1850. Imperf.

No.	Type	Description	Unused	Used
2.	1.	1 s. blue	£250	£4500
4.		2 s. red	£450	£6000

1865. Inscr. "SCHLESWIG-HOLSTEIN". Roul.

No.	Type	Description	Unused	Used
6.	2.	½ s. red	25·00	42·00
7.		1¼ s. green	11·00	18·00
8.		1⅓ s. mauve	38·00	£120
9.		2 s. blue	40·00	£225
10.		4 s. bistre	48·00	£1100

1864. Inscr. "HERZOGTH. SCHLESWIG". Roul.

No.	Type	Description	Unused	Used
24.	2.	½ s. green	26·00	48·00
21.		1¼ s. green	38·00	13·00
25.		1¼ s. lilac	55·00	14·00
27.		1⅓ s. red	26·00	60·00
28.		2 s. blue	22·00	48·00
22.		4 s. red	95·00	£400
29.		4 s. bistre	26·00	80·00

6.

9.

10.

1864. Imperf. or roul.

No.	Type	Description	Unused	Used
51	6	1¼ s. blue	35·00	45·00
59	9	1¼ s. blue	32·00	14·00

1865. Roul.

No.	Type	Description	Unused	Used
61.	10.	½ s. green	55·00	90·00
62.		1½ s. mauve	32·00	15·00
63.		1⅓ s. red	55·00	38·00
64.		2 s. blue	40·00	42·00
65.		4 s. bistre	45·00	70·00

On the 1⅓ s. and 4 s. the word "SCHILLING" is inside the central oval.

1868. Inscr. "HERZOGTH. HOLSTEIN". Roul.

No.	Type	Description	Unused	Used
66.	2.	1¼ s. purple	60·00	15·00
67.		2 s. blue	£120	£130

SENEGAL Pt. 6; Pt. 14

A French colony incorporated in French West Africa in 1944. In 1958 Senegal became an autonomous State within the French Community and in 1959 joined the Sudan to form the Mali Federation. In 1960 the Federation broke up with Mali and Senegal becoming independent republics.

100 centimes = 1 franc.

1887. Stamps of French Colonies, "Commerce" type, surch in figures.

No.	Type	Description	Unused	Used
1	J	5 on 20 c. red on green	£120	£120
2		5 on 30 c. brown on drab	£190	£190
3		10 on 4 c. brown on grey	50·00	50·00
4a		10 on 20 c. red on green	£375	£375
5		15 on 20 c. red on green	40·00	40·00

1892. Stamps of French Colonies, "Commerce" type, surch **Senegal** and new value.
6 J 75 on 15 c. blue on blue .. £350 £120
7 1 f. on 5 c. green on green £350 £140

1892. "Tablet" key-type inscr "SENEGAL ET DEPENDANCES".
8 D 1 c. black and red on blue 50 40
9 2 c. brown & blue on buff 1·40 1·00
10 4 c. red and blue on grey 90 90
21 5 c. green and red .. 85 40
12 10 c. black & blue on lilac 4·75 3·00
22 10 c. red and blue .. 2·25 40
13 15 c. blue and red .. 4·25 75
23 15 c. grey and red .. 2·25 80
14 20 c. red & blue on green 4·00 4·00
15 25 c. black & red on pink 6·00 2·25
24 25 c. blue and red .. 14·00 20·00
16 30 c. brown & bl on drab 6·75 5·00
17 40 c. red & blue on yellow 13·00 12·00
18 50 c. red and blue on pink 16·00 16·00
25 50 c. brown & red on blue 27·00 27·00
19 75 c. brown & red on orge 8·50 10·00
20 1 f. green and red .. 10·50 10·00

1903. Surch.
26 D 5 on 40 c. red & bl on yell 8·25 8·50
27 10 on 50 c. red and blue on pink .. .. 11·50 11·50
28 10 on 75 c. brown and red on orange .. .. 11·50 11·50
29 10 on 1 f. green and red 50·00 45·00

1906. "Faidherbe", "Palms" and "Balay" key-types inscr "SENEGAL".
33 I 1 c. grey and red .. 70 30
34 2 c. brown and red .. 70 40
34a 2 c. brown and blue .. 2·00 2·00
35 4 c. brown & red on blue 80 25
36 5 c. green and red .. 1·50 35
37 10 c. pink and blue .. 4·75 35
38 15 c. violet and red .. 4·00 1·75
39 J 20 c. black & red on blue 3·00 1·75
40 25 c. blue and red .. 1·10 75
41 30 c. brn & red on pink 3·50 3·50
42 35 c. black & red on yell 12·00 85
43 40 c. red & blue on blue 5·25 5·00
44 45 c. brown & red on grn 11·00 8·75
45 50 c. violet and red .. 5·00 4·25
46 75 c. green & red on orge 3·75 2·75
47 K 1 f. black & red on blue 14·50 12·50
48 2 f. blue and red on pink 22·00 17·00
49 5 f. red & blue on yellow 40·00 35·00

1912. Surch.
58 D 05 on 15 c. grey and red 25 40
59 05 on 20 c. red and blue on green 45 70
60 05 on 30 c. brown and blue on drab 45 70
61 10 on 40 c. red and blue on yellow 50 70
62 10 on 50 c. red and blue 1·75 2·00
63 10 on 75 c. brown and red on orange .. .. 3·00 3·75

33. Market.

1914.
64 33 1 c. violet and brown .. 10 10
65 2 c. blue and black .. 10 10
66 4 c. brown and grey .. 10 10
67 5 c. green & light green 10 10
91 5 c. red and black .. 15 10
68 10 c. pink and red .. 20 10
92 10 c. green & light green 25 20
113 10 c. blue and purple .. 10 10
69 15 c. purple and brown 10 10
70 20 c. grey and brown .. 10 15
114 20 c. green 10 25
115 20 c. blue and grey .. 20 30
71 25 c. blue & ultramarine 20 15
93 25 c. black and red .. 10 10
72 30 c. pink and black .. 10 10
94 30 c. carmine and red .. 30 45
116 30 c. blue and grey .. 20 30
117 30 c. green and olive .. 35 35
73 35 c. violet and orange 10 10
74 40 c. green and violet .. 45 10
75 45 c. brown and blue .. 70 80
95 45 c. blue and red .. 15 35
118 45 c. red and carmine .. 20 20
119 45 c. red and brown .. 1·90 2·00
76 50 c. blue and purple .. 45 60
96 50 c. blue & ultramarine 65 95
120 50 c. green and red .. 15 10
121 60 c. violet on pink .. 15 30
122 65 c. green and red .. 80 1·00
77 75 c. pink and grey .. 35 65
123 75 c. light blue and blue 35 50
124 75 c. blue and pink .. 75 75
125 90 c. carmine and red .. 70 65
78 1 f. black and violet .. 35 65
126 1 f. blue 60 50
127 1 f. blue and black .. 60 20
128 1 f. 10 black and green 2·00 2·00
129 1 f. 25 red and green .. 60 60
130 1 f. 50 light blue & blue 1·25 75
131 1 f. 75 green and brown 4·75 50
79 2 f. blue and pink .. 1·60 1·50
97 2 f. brown and blue .. 1·40 45
132 3 f. mauve on pink .. 2·50 75
80 5 f. violet and green .. 2·00 70

1915. Surch **5c** and red cross.
89 33 10 c.+5 c. pink and red 60 85
90 15 c.+5 c. purple & brn 50 90

1922. Surch.
102 33 0,01 on 15 c. pur & brn 15 40
103 0,02 on 15 c. pur & brn 15 40
104 0,04 on 15 c. pur & brn 15 35
105 0,05 on 15 c. pur & brn 15 35
106 25 c. on 5 f. violet & grn 20 45
98 60 on 75 c. violet on pink 50 30
99 65 on 15 c. purple & brn 50 30
100 85 on 15 c. purple & brn 60 80
101 85 on 75 c. pink and grey 65 80
107 90 c. on 75 c. pink & red 35 60
108 1 f. 25 on 1 f. blue .. 30 40
109 1 f. 50 on 1 f. lt bl & bl 55 45
110 3 f. on 5 f. brown & pur 75 50
111 10 f. on 5 f. red and blue 3·75 2·00
112 20 f. on 5 f. brn & mve 4·75 4·00

1931. "Colonial Exhibition" key types.
135 E 40 c. green and black .. 1·40 1·40
136 F 50 c. mauve and black 1·40 1·40
137 G 90 c. red and black .. 1·25 1·25
138 H 1 f. 50 blue and black .. 1·40 1·40

38. Faidherbe Bridge, Dakar. 39. Senegalese Girl.

1935.
139. 38. 1 c. blue (postage) .. 10 30
140. 2 c. brown 10 25
141. 3 c. violet 10 25
142. 4 c. blue 10 30
143. 5 c. orange 10 15
144. 10 c. purple 10 20
145. 15 c. black 10 15
146. 20 c. red 10 20
147. 25 c. brown 25 15
148. 30 c. green 15 30
149. 39. 35 c. green 45 50
150. 38. 40 c. red 15 20
151. 45 c. green 15 30
152. A. 50 c. orange 10 20
153. 39. 55 c. brown 40 40
154. A. 60 c. violet 20 25
155. 65 c. violet 15 30
156. 70 c. brown 45 50
157. 75 c. brown 70 40
158. 39. 80 c. violet 65 50
159. A. 90 c. red 85 95
160. 39. 90 c. violet 40 40
161. A. 1 f. violet .. .. 6·00 1·25
162. 39. 1 f. red .. .. .. 1·25 60
163. 1 f. brown 15 15
164. A. 1 f. 25 brown 30 55
165. 1 f. 25 red 30 55
166. 1 f. 40 green 30 40
167. 1 f. 50 blue 20 30
168. 1 f. 60 blue 30 40
169. 1 f. 75 green 35 20
170. 39. 1 f. 75 blue 55 60
171. A. 2 f. blue 45 20
172. 39. 2 f. 25 blue 40 50
173. 2 f. 50 black 65 85
174. A. 3 f. green 30 20
175. 5 f. brown 20 30
176. 10 f. red 80 50
177. 20 f. grey 65 50
178. B. 25 c. brown (air) .. 20 40
179. 50 c. red 40 60
180. 1 f. purple 30 30
181. 1 f. 25 green 20 35
182. 1 f. 90 blue 40 50
183. 2 f. blue 25 15
184. 2 f. 90 red 35 40
185. 3 f. green 30 25
186. C. 3 f. 50 violet 30 20
187. B. 4 f. 50 green 35 45
188. C. 4 f. 75 orange 40 55
189. B. 4 f. 90 brown 40 55
190. C. 6 f. 50 blue 65 65
191. B. 6 f. 90 orange 45 45
192. C. 8 f. black .. .. 1·00 75
193. 15 f. red 70 65

DESIGNS—HORIZ. A, Djourbel Mosque. B, African landscape. C, Airplane over camel caravan.

1937. International Exhibition, Paris. As Nos. 168/73 of St.-Pierre et Miquelon.
194. 20 c. violet 40 60
195. 30 c. green 40 55
196. 40 c. red 35 55
197. 50 c. brown 35 70
198. 90 c. red 35 70
199. 1 f. 50 blue .. .. 50 1·40

1938. International Anti-cancer Fund. As T 22 of Mauritania.
201 1 f. 75+50 c. blue .. 3·50 6·00

1939. Death Centenary of Rene Caillie (explorer). As T 27 of Mauritania.
202. 90 c. orange 25 35
203. 2 f. violet 35 50
204. 2 f. 25 blue 35 50

1939. New York World's Fair. As T 28 of Mauritania.
205 1 f. 25 red 40 50
206 2 f. 25 blue 40 55

1939. 150th Anniv of French Revolution. As T 29 of Mauritania.
207 45 c.+25 c. green and black (postage) .. 4·00 4·75
208 70 c.+30 c. brown & black 4·00 4·75
209 90 c.+35 c. orange & black 4·00 4·75
210 1 f. 25+1 f. red and black 4·25 4·75
211 2 f. 25 f.+2 f. blue & black 4·25 4·75
212 4 f. 75+4 f. blk & orge (air) 6·75 6·75

1941. National Defence Fund. Surch. **SECOURS NATIONAL** and value.
213 +1 f. on 50 c. (No. 152) 2·00 2·00
214 +2 f. on 80 c. (No. 158) .. 2·00 2·00
215 +2 f. on 1 f. 50 (No. 167) 3·00 3·00
216 +3 f. on 2 f. (No. 171) .. 2·75 2·75

1942. Air. Colonial Child Welfare Fund. As Nos. 98g/i of Niger.
216a 1 f. 50+3 f. 50 green .. 15
216b 2 f.+6 f. brown 15
216c 3 f.+9f. red 15

1942. Air. "Imperial Fortnight". As No. 98j of Niger.
216d 1 f. 20+1 f. 80 blue & red 15

1942. Air. As T 32 of Mauritania but inscr "SENEGAL" and similar design.
217 50 f. green and yellow .. 1·00 1·25
218 100 f. blue and red .. 1·50 1·50
DESIGN—48×26 mm: 100 f. Twin-engined airliner landing.

1944. Stamps of 1935 surch.
219 38 1 f. 50 on 15 c. black .. 40 30
220 A 1 f. 50 on 65 c. violet .. 30 40
221 38 4 f. 50 on 15 c. black .. 40 40
222 5 f. 50 on 2 c. brown .. 85 80
223 A 5 f. 50 on 65 c. violet .. 40 50
224 38 10 f. on 15 c. black .. 1·10 1·00
225 A 50 f. on 65 c. violet .. 1·25 1·25

1944. No. 202 surch.
226 20 f. on 90 c. orange 65 75
227 50 f. on 90 c. orange 1·90 2·00

42. African Buffalo.

44. Mother and Child. 43. African Fish Eagle

1960. Niokolo-Koba National Park.
228. – 5 f. purple, black & green 15 10
229. 42. 10 f. purple, black & green 35 15
230. – 15 f. purple, brown & sepia 40 30
231. – 20 f. brn., green & chest. 50 30
232. – 25 f. brn., choc. & grn. 60 30
233. – 85 f. multicoloured .. 1·90 1·00
ANIMALS—VERT. 5 f. Roan antelope. 15 f. Warthog. 20 f. Giant eland. 85 f. Waterbuck. HORIZ. 25 f. Bushbuck.

1960. Air.
234. – 50 f. multicoloured .. 3·25 1·25
235. – 100 f. multicoloured .. 5·50 1·75
236. – 200 f. multicoloured .. 11·00 5·50
237. – 250 f. multicoloured .. 14·00 6·75
238. 43. 500 f. multicoloured .. 28·00 9·25
BIRDS—VERT. 50 f. Carmine Bee Eater. 200 f. Violet Turaco. 250 f. Red Bishop. HORIZ. 100 f. Abyssinian Roller.

1961. Independence Commem.
239. 44. 25 f. brown, blue & green 25 20

45. Pirogue Race.

DESIGNS: 50 c. African wrestling. 2 f. Horse race. 30 f. African dancers. 45 f. Lion game.

1961. Sports.
240. – 50 c. brown, blue & sepia 5 5
241. 45. 1 f. purple, turq. & green 5 5
242. – 2 f. sepia, bistre and blue 8 5
243. – 30 f. purple and red .. 70 25
244. – 45 f. black, blue & brown 95 35

46. Senegal Flag, U.N. Emblem and H.Q. Building.

1962. 1st Anniv. of Admission of Senegal to U.N.O.
245. 46. 10 f. red, ochre and green 15 15
246. 30 f. green, ochre and red 30 25
247. 85 f. multicoloured .. 1·10 55

47. I.T.U. Emblems, African Map and Telephonist. 48. Boxing.

1962. 1st I.T.U. African Plan Sub-Committee Meeting, Dakar.
248. 47. 25 f. multicoloured .. 25 20

1962. Air. "Air Afrique" Airline. As T 42 of Mauritania.
249. 25 f. purple, brown & myrtle 35 20

1962. Malaria Eradication. As T 43 of Mauritania.
250. 25 f.+5 f. turquoise .. 40 40

1962. 1st Anniv. of Union of African and Malagasy states. As T 45 of Mauritania.
251. 72. 30 f. turquoise 40 35

1963. Freedom from Hunger. As T 51 of Mauritania.
252. 25 f.+5 f. olive, brn. & vio. 35 35

1963. Dakar Games. Inscr. as in T 48. Centres brown; inscr. and frame colours given.
253. 48. 10 f. red and green .. 15 8
254. – 15 f. ochre and blue .. 20 12
255. – 20 f. red and blue .. 25 15
256. – 25 f. green and blue .. 30 20
257. – 30 f. red and green .. 70 25
258. – 85 f. blue .. .. 1·60 1·00
DESIGNS—HORIZ. 15 f. Diving. 20 f. High-jumping. VERT. 25 f. Football. 30 f. Basket-ball. 85 f. Running.

49. Main Motif of U.P.U. Monument, Berne.

51. G. Berger, Owl and "Prospective" (book). 50. "Charaxes varanes".

1963. 2nd Anniv. of Admission to U.P.U..
259. 49. 10 f. red and green .. 20 12
260. 15 f. brown and blue .. 20 20
261. 30 f. blue and brown .. 45 25

1963. Butterflies. Butterflies in natural colours; inscr. in black; background colours given.
262. 50. 30 f. blue 90 40
263. – 45 f. orange .. .. 1·40 60
264. – 50 f. yellow .. .. 1·50 85
265. – 85 f. red .. .. 3·75 1·40
266. – 100 f. blue .. .. 4·50 2·10
267. – 500 f. green .. .. 15·00 6·75
BUTTERFLIES: 45 f. "Papilio nireus". 10 f. "Colotis danae". 85 f. "Epiphora bauhiniae". 100 f. "Junonia hierta". 500 f. "Danaus chrysippus".

1963. Air. 2nd Anniv. of African and Malagasian Posts and Telecommunications Union. As T 56 of Mauritania.
268. 85 f. multicoloured .. 1·10 55

1963. 3rd Death Anniv. of Prof. Gaston Berger (educationalist).
269. 51. 25 f. multicoloured .. 30 20

1963. Air. 1st Anniv. of "Air Afrique" and "DC-8" Service Inaug. As T 59 of Mauritania.
270. 50 f. multicoloured .. 1·25 55

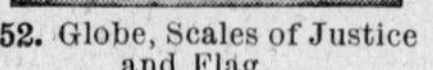

52. Globe, Scales of Justice and Flag. 53. Mother and Child.

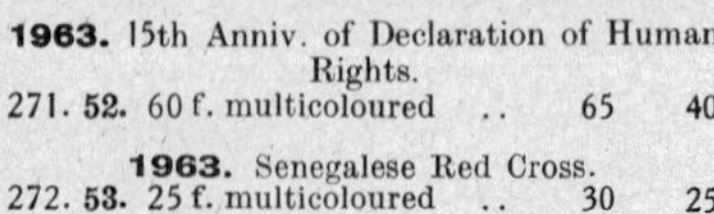

1963. 15th Anniv. of Declaration of Human Rights.
271. **52.** 60 f. multicoloured .. 65 40

1963. Senegalese Red Cross.
272. **53.** 25 f. multicoloured .. 30 25

54. Temple Gods, Abu Simbel.

1964. Air. Nubian Monuments Preservation Fund.
273. **54.** 25 f.+5 f. brown, green and turquoise .. 1·10 70

55. Independence Monument. 57. Titanium Sand Dredger.

56. Allegorical Figures of Twin Towns.

1964. Air.
274. **55.** 300 f. multicoloured 3·50 1·75

1964. Air. World Twin Towns Federation Congress, Dakar.
275. **56.** 150 f. brn., blk. & turq. 2·75 1·40

1964. Senegal Industries.
276. **57.** 5 f. brn., turq. & lake .. 15 15
277. – 10 f. blue, brown & grn. 15 10
278. – 15 f. brn., green & blue 20 10
279. – 20 f. pur., bistre & blue 25 10
280. – 25 f. black, ochre & blue 30 10
281. – 85 f. brown, blue and red 1·60 1·10
DESIGNS: 10 f. Titanium sorting works. 15 f. Rufisque cement works. 20 f. Loading phosphate at Pallo. 25 f. Working phosphate at Taiba. 85 f. Mineral wharf, Dakar.

58. "Supporting the Globe".

1964. Air. "Europafrique".
282. **58.** 50 f. multicoloured .. 1·25 55

59. Basketball. 60. "Syncom 2" Satellite and Rocket.

1964. Air. Olympic Games, Tokyo.
283. **59.** 85 f. brown and blue .. 1·75 70
284. – 100 f. purple and green 2·00 90
DESIGN: 100 f. Pole-vaulting.

1964. Air. Space Telecommunications.
285. **60.** 150 f. blue, brn. & grn. 2·00 1·25

1964. French, African and Malagasy Co-operation. As T **68** of Mauritania.
286. 100 f. brown, red and green 1·40 90

61. Church of Ste. Therese, Dakar.

63. Child and Microscope. 62. Pres. Kennedy.

1964. Religious Buildings.
287. **61.** 5 f. lake, green and blue 8 5
288. – 10 f. brown, black & blue 12 8
289. – 15 f. slate, brown & blue 20 15
DESIGNS—HORIZ. 10 f. Touba Mosque. VERT. 15 f. Dakar Mosque.

1964. Air. Pres. Kennedy Commem.
290. **62.** 100 f. brn., yell. & grn. 1·75 1·00

1965. Anti-Leprosy Campaign.
292. **63.** 20 f. blk., grn. and brn. 25 20
293. – 65 f. multicoloured .. 90 45
DESIGN: 65 f. Peycouk Village.

64. Haute Casamance.

1965. Senegal Landscapes.
294. **64.** 25 f. green, brown and blue (postage) .. 25 15
295. – 30 f. blue, green & brn. 30 15
296. – 45 f. green and brown .. 75 30
297. – 100 f. black, green and bistre (air) .. 1·50 70
DESIGNS: 30 f. Sangalkam. 45 f. Senegal River forest region. 100 f. Banks of Gambia River, East Senegal (48 × 27 mm.).

65. A. Seck (Director of Posts, 1873-1931). 66. Berthon-Ader Telephone.

1965. Postal Services Commem.
298. **65.** 10 f. black and brown .. 15 12
299. – 15 f. brown and green .. 20 12
DESIGN—HORIZ. 15 f. P.T.T. Headquarters, Dakar.

1965. I.T.U. Cent.
300. **66.** 50 f. brn., bistre & grn. 50 30
301. – 60 f. red, green and blue 80 50
302. – 85 f. purple, red & blue 80 50
DESIGNS: 60 f. Cable-ship "Alsace". 85 f. Picard's submarine telegraph cable relay apparatus.

67. Ploughing with Oxen.

68. Goree Pirogue under Sail. 69. Woman holding Child and U.N. Emblems.

1965. Rural Development.
303. **67.** 25 f. brn., vio. & bronze 35 25
304. – 60 f. multicoloured .. 90 45
305. – 85 f. black, red & green 1·25 55
DESIGNS—VERT. 50 f. Millet cultivation. HORIZ. 85 f. Rice cultivation, Casamance.

1965. Senegal Pirogues. Multicoloured.
306. 10 f. Type **68** 20 15
307. 20 f. Large pirogue at Soumbedioune 25 15
308. 30 f. One-man pirogue at Fadiouth Island .. 65 20
309. 45 f. One-man pirogue on Senegal River 95 65

1965. Air. Int. Co-operation Year.
310. **69.** 50 f. brown, grn. & blue 55 30

70. "Fruit of Cashew Tree". 71. "The Gentleman of Fashion". 72. Tom-tom Player.

1965. Fruits. Multicoloured.
311. 10 f. Type **70** 15 10
312. 15 f. Papaw 20 15
313. 20 f. Mango 25 10
314. 30 f. Groundnuts 30 15

1966. Goree Puppets.
315. **71.** 1 f. blue, brown and red 5 5
316. – 2 f. orange, brown & blue 5 5
317. – 3 f. blue, brown and red 5 5
318. – 4 f. green, brown & violet 10 8
PUPPETS: 2 f. "The Lady of Fashion". 3 f. "The Pedlar". 4 f. "The Pounder".

1966. World Festival of Negro Arts, Dakar ("Announcement").
319. **72.** 30 f. brown, red & green 30 15
See also Nos. 327/30.

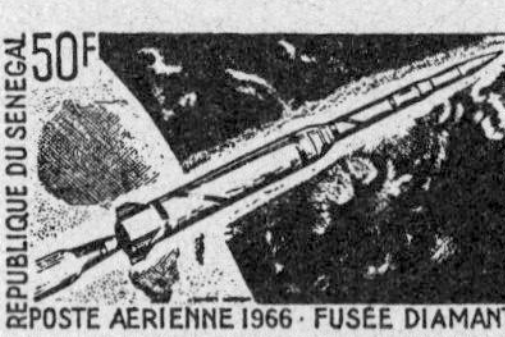

73. Rocket "Diamant".

1966. Air. French Satellites.
320. **73.** 50 f. red, blue and brown 70 40
321. – 50 f. black, brown & grn. 70 40
322. – 90 f. blue, brown & slate 1·40 75
DESIGNS: No. 321, Satellite "A 1". No. 322, Rocket "Scout" and satellite "FR 1".

74. Mackerel Tuna. 76. Arms of Senegal.

75. Satellite "D1".

1966. Senegal Fishes. Multicoloured.
323. 20 f. Type **74** 25 15
324. 30 f. Grouper 40 20
325. 50 f. Wrasse 90 35
326. 100 f. Parrot fish .. .. 1·75 65

1966. World Festival of Negro Arts, Dakar. As T **72**.
327. 15 f. lake, orange and blue 15 15
328. 30 f. lake, yellow and blue 35 20
329. 75 f. black, lake and blue 1·25 55
330. 90 f. lake, black and orange 1·40 65
DESIGNS: 15 f. Statuette ("Sculpture"). 30 f. Musical instrument ("Music"). 75 f. Carving ("Dance"). 90 f. Ideogram.

1966. Air. Launching of Satellite "D 1".
332. **75.** 100 f. blue, lake & violet 1·50 65

1966.
333. **76.** 30 f. multicoloured .. 25 12

1966. Air. Inaug. of "DC-8F" Air Services. As T **87** of Mauritania.
334. 30 f. yellow, black & brown 30 20

77. "Argemone Mexicana". 79. Port of Ile de Goree.

78. Couzinet "Arc-en-Ciel" (aircraft).

1966. Flowers. Multicoloured.
335. 45 f. Type **77** 45 20
336. 55 f. "Dichrostachys glomerata" 50 25
337. 60 f. "Haemanthus multiflorus" 60 35
338. 90 f. "Adansonia digitata" 1·50 50

1966. Air. 30th Anniv. of Disappearance of Jean Mermoz (aviator).
339. **78.** 20 f. slate, purple & blue 30 20
340. – 35 f. slate, brown & green 70 20
341. – 100 f. lake, emer. & grn. 1·25 45
342. – 150 f. lake, black & blue 2·50 1·00
DESIGNS—HORIZ. 35 f. Latecoere 300 flying-boat, "Croix du Sud". 100 f. Map of Mermoz's last flight across Atlantic Ocean. VERT. 150 f. Jean Mermoz.

1966. Tourism.
343. **79.** 20 f. lake, blue & black 20 12
344. – 25 f. sepia, green & red 1·00 20
345. – 30 f. blue, red and green 30 10
346. – 50 f. blue, green & red 50 20
347. – 90 f. black, green and blue 1·10 45
DESIGNS: 25 f. Liner "France" at Dakar. 30 f. N'Gor Hotel and tourist cabins. 50 f. N'Gor Bay and Hotel. 90 f. Town Hall, Dakar.

80. Laying Water Mains.

1967. Int. Hydrological Decade.
348. **80.** 10 f. blue, green & brown 15 12
349. – 20 f. brn., green & blue 30 20
350. – 30 f. blue, orge. & black 35 20
351. – 50 f. lake, flesh and blue 75 20
DESIGNS—HORIZ. 20 f. Cattle at trough. VERT. 30 f. Decade emblem. 50 f. Obtaining water from primitive well.

81. Terminal Building, Dakar-Yoff Airport.

1967. Air.
352. **81.** 200 f. indigo, blue & brn. 2·50 1·00

82. Lions Emblem.

1967. 50th Anniv. of Lions Int.
353. **82.** 30 f. multicoloured .. 35 20

83. Blaise Diagne.

1967. 95th Birth Anniv. of Blaise Diagne (statesman).
354. **83.** 30 f. brn., grn. and pur. 30 20

84. Spiny Mimosa.

1967. Air. Flowers. Multicoloured.
355. 100 f. Type **84** .. .. 2·00 75
356. 150 f. Barbary fig.. .. 3·00 1·75

85. " Les Demoiselles d'Avignon " (Picasso). 86. Carved Eagle and Kudu's Head.

1967. Air.
357. **85.** 100 f. multicoloured .. 2·25 1·10

1967. "EXPO 67" World Fair, Montreal.
358. **86.** 90 f. black and red .. 1·25 50
359 – 150 f. multicoloured .. 1·75 75
DESIGN: 150 f. Maple Leaf and flags.

1967. Air. 5th Anniv. of U.A.M.P.T. As T **101** of Mauritania.
360. 100 f. red, green and violet 90 50

87. I.T.Y. Emblem. 88. Currency Tokens.

1967. Int. Tourist Year.
361. **87.** 50 f. black and blue .. 80 35
362. – 100 f. black, grn. & orge. 2·50 1·00
DESIGN: 100 f. Tourist photographing hippopotamus.

1967. 5th Anniv. of West African Monetary Union.
363. **88.** 30 f. violet, purple & grey 25 15

89. " Lyre " Stone, Kaffrine. 90. Nurse feeding baby.

1967. 6th Pan-American Prehistory Congress, Dakar.
364. **89.** 30 f. red, blue and green 25 12
365. – 70 f. red, brown & blue 65 30
DESIGN: 70 f. Ancient bowl, Bandiala.

1967. Senegalese Red Cross.
366. **90.** 50 f. lake, red and green 50 25

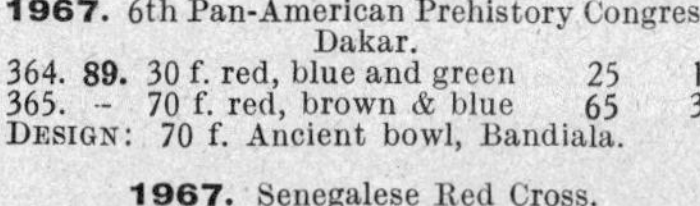

91. Human Rights Emblem. 92. Chancellor Adenauer.

1968. Human Rights Year.
367. **91.** 30 f. gold and green .. 35 20

1968. Air. Adenauer Commem.
368. **92.** 100 f. sepia, red & green 1·40 55

93. Weather Balloon, Flourishing Plants and W.M.O. Emblem. 94. Parliament Building, Dakar.

1968. Air. World Meteorological Day.
370. **93.** 50 f. green, blue & black 65 40

1968. Inter-Parliamentary Union Meeting, Dakar.
371. **94.** 30 f. red 30 15

95. Spiny Lobster. 96. Lesser Pied Kingfisher.

1968. Marine Crustacea. Multicoloured.
372. 10 f. Type **95** 15 8
373. 20 f. Sea crawfish 25 15
374. 35 f. Prawn 75 20
375. 100 f. Gooseneck barnacle 2·10 65

1968. Birds. Multicoloured.
376. 5 f. Type **96** (postage) .. 50 15
377. 15 f. African Jacana .. 75 25
378. 70 f. African Darter .. 2·50 1·50
379. 250 f. Village Weaver (air) 6·50 2·50
380. 300 f. Comb Duck .. 9·75 3·50
381. 500 f. Bateleur .. .. 16·00 6·50
Nos. 380/81 are 45½ × 26 mm.

97. Ox and Syringe. 98. Hurdling.

1968. Campaign for Prevention of Cattle Plague.
382. **97.** 30 f. red, green and blue 55 20

1968. Air. Olympic Games, Mexico.
383. **98.** 20 f. brn., green & blue 20 12
384. – 30 f. brn., ochre & pur. 25 15
385. – 50 f. lake, brown & blue 75 35
386. – 75 f. bistre, brn. & grn. 1·25 60
DESIGNS: 30 f. Throwing the javelin. 50 f. Judo. 75 f. Basketball.

1968. Air. "Philexafrique" Stamp Exn., Abidjan (1st issue) (1969). As T **113a** of Mauritania. Multicoloured.
387. 100 f. "Young Girl Reading a letter" (J. Baoux) .. 2·25 2·00

99. Senegalese Boy. 101. Faculty Building.

1968. 20th Anniv. of W.H.O.
388. **99.** 30 f. black, red & green 25 25
389. 45 f. black, green & brn. 60 20

1969. Faculty of Medicine and Pharmaceutics, and Sixth "Medical Days", Dakar.
391. **101.** 30 f. blue and green .. 30 20
392. – 50 f. green, red & brown 35 25
DESIGN—VERT. 50 f. Emblem of "Medical Days".

1969. Air. "Philexafrique" Stamp Exn., Abidjan, Ivory Coast (2nd issue). As T **114a** of Mauritania.
393. 50 f. violet, slate and green 1·25 1·25
DESIGN: 50 f. Modern Dakar and Senegal stamp of 1935.

102. Panet, Camels and Route-map.

1969. 150th Birth Anniv. of Leopold Panet, 1st Explorer of the Mauritanian Sahara.
394. **102.** 75 f. brown and blue 1·50 75

103. A.I.T.Y. Emblem.

1969. Air. African Int. Tourist Year.
395. **103.** 100 f. red, green and blue 75 45

104. I.L.O. Emblem. 105. Pres. Lamine Gueye.

1969. 50th Anniv. of I.L.O.
396. **104.** 30 f. black and turquoise 25 15
397. 45 f. black and red .. 40 20

1969. Air. President Gueye Memorial.
398. **105.** 30 f. black, buff & brown 25 15
399. – 45 f. black, blue & brown 35 20
DESIGN: 45 f. Pres. Lamine Gueye (different).

106. Arms of Casamance.

1969. Senegal Arms. Multicoloured.
401. 15 f. Type **106** 15 10
402. 20 f. Arms of Ile de Goree 20 12

1969. 5th Anniv. of African Development Bank. As T **122a** of Mauritania.
403. 30 f. brown, green & slate 25 15
404. 45 f. brown and green .. 35 20

108. Mahatma Gandhi. 109. "Transmission of Thought" (O. Faye).

1969. Birth Cent. of Mahatma Gandhi.
405. **108.** 50 f. multicoloured .. 45 25

1969. Air. Tapestries. Multicoloured.
407. 25 f. Type **109** 60 20
408. 30 f. "The Blue Cock" (Mamadou Niang) .. 35 20
409. 45 f. "The Fairy" (Papa Sidi Diop) 85 50
410. 50 f. "Fari" (A. N'Diaye) 1·25 75
411. 75 f. "Lunaris" (J. Lurcat) 1·25 70
SIZES—VERT. 30 f., 45 f. 37 × 49 mm. HORIZ. 50 f. 49 × 37 mm.

110. Baila Bridge.

1969. Air. Europafrique.
412. **110.** 100 f. multicoloured .. 1·25 45

111. Rotary Emblem and " Sailing Ship ".

1969. 30th Anniv. of Dakar Rotary Club.
413. **111.** 30 f. yellow, blk. & blue 35 20

1969. 10th Anniv. of A.S.E.C.N.A. As T **94a** of Niger.
414. 100 f. slate.. .. .. 90 35

113. Cape Skiring, Casamance. 115. Bottle-nosed Dolphins.

114. Lecrivain, Aircraft and Route.

1969. Tourism.
415. **113.** 20 f. green, lake & blue 20 12
416. – 30 f. lake, brown & blue 25 12
417. – 35 f. black, brown & blue 1·10 30
418. – 45 f. lake and blue .. 75 20
DESIGNS: 30 f. Tourist camp, Niokolo-Koba. 35 f. Herd of African elephants, Niokolo-Koba Park. 45 f. Millet granaries on stilts, Fadiouth Island.

1970. Air. 40th Anniv. of Disappearance of Emile Lecrivain (aviator).
419. **114.** 50 f. lake, slate & green 1·00 40

1970.
420. **115.** 50 f. multicoloured .. 1·40 60

116. R. Maran (Martinique).

1970. Air. Negro Celebrities (1st series).
421. 116. 30 f. brown, green & lake 25 15
422. – 45 f. brown, blue & pink 40 25
423. – 50 f. brn., green & yell. 45 35
PORTRAITS: 45 f. M. Garvey (Jamaica). 50 f. Dr. P. Mars (Haiti).
See also Nos. 457/60.

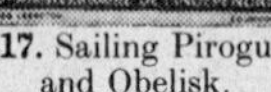

117. Sailing Pirogue and Obelisk. 118. Lenin.

1970. Air. 10th Anniv. of Independence.
424. 117. 500 f. multicoloured .. 5·00 2·75

1970. Birth Centenary of Lenin.
426 118 30 f. brown, stone & red 25 15

119. Bay of Naples, and Post Office, Dakar.

1970. Air. 10th "Europa" Stamp Exn., Naples.
428. 119. 100 f. multicoloured .. 1·25 55

1970. New U.P.U. Headquarters Building, Berne. As T 81 of New Caledonia.
429. 30 f. plum, blue and lake .. 25 15
430. 45 f. brown, lake and green 45 20

121. Nagakawa and Mt. Fuji.

1970. Air. World Fair "EXPO 70", Osaka, Japan.
431. – 25 f. red, green & lake 20 15
432. 121. 75 f. red, blue & green 55 30
433. – 150 f. red, brown & blue 1·60 70
DESIGNS—VERT. 25 f. "Woman playing guitar" (Hokusai), and Sun tower. 150 f. "Nanboku beauty" (Shuncho).

122. Harbour Quayside, Dakar.

1970. Air. Industrial and Urban Development.
434. 122. 30 f. blue, black and red 25 15
435. – 100 f. brn., grn. & slate 1·40 45
DESIGN: 100 f. Aerial view of city centre, Dakar.

123. Beethoven, Napoleon and Evocation of Eroica Symphony.

1970. Air. Birth Bicent. of Beethoven.
436. 123. 50 f. brn., orge. & green 45 35
437. – 100 f. red and blue .. 1·40 75
DESIGN: 100 f. Beethoven with quillpen and scroll.

124. Heads of Four Races.

1970. Air. 25th Anniv. of U.N.O.
438. 124. 100 f. multicoloured .. 1·25 55

125. Looms and Textile Works, Thies.

1970. "Industrialisation".
439. 125. 30 f. red, blue and green 30 15
440. – 45 f. blue, brown and red 40 20
DESIGN: 45 f. Fertiliser plant, Dakar.

126 Scouts in Camp. 127. Three Heads and Sun.

1970. 1st African Scouting Conference, Dakar. Multicoloured.
441 30 f. Type 26 .. .. 30 20
442 100 f. Scout badge, Lord Baden-Powell and map 1·40 45

1970. Int. Education Year.
443. 127. 25 f. brown, blue & orge. 25 12
444. – 40 f. multicoloured .. 45 20
DESIGN: 40 f. Map of Africa on Globe, and two heads.

128. Arms of Senegal. 129. De Gaulle, Map, Ears of Wheat and Cogwheel.

1970.
445. 128. 30 f. multicoloured .. 35 15
446. 35 f. multicoloured .. 35 15
446a. 50 f. multicoloured .. 35 15
446b. 65 f. multicoloured .. 35 15
803. 95 f. multicoloured .. 35 30

1970. Air. "De Gaulle the De-coloniser". Multicoloured.
447. 50 f. Type 129 .. .. 1·25 60
448. 100 f. De Gaulle, and map within "sun" .. 2·50 1·50

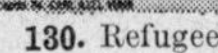

130. Refugees. 131. "Mbayang" Horse.

1971. 20th Anniv. of U.N. High Commissioner for Refugees. Multicoloured.
449. 40 f. Type 130 (postage) .. 35 20
450. 100 f. Building house (air) 80 55
No. 450 is 46 × 27 mm.

1971. Horse-breeding Improvement Campaign. Multicoloured.
451. 25 f. "Madjiguene" .. 25 15
452. 40 f. Type 131 .. .. 65 20
453. 100 f. "Pass" .. .. 1·40 85
454. 125 f. "Pepe" .. .. 2·00 1·10

INDEX
Countries can be quickly located by referring to the index at the end of this volume.

132. European Girl and African Boy. 133. Phillis Wheatley.

1971. Racial Equality Year. Multicoloured.
455. 30 f. Type 132 .. .. 25 15
456. 50 f. People of four races (horiz.) (37 × 30 mm.) .. 40 25

1971. Air. Negro Celebrities (2nd series). Multicoloured.
457. 25 f. Type 133 .. .. 20 15
458. 40 f. J. E. K. Aggrey .. 35 20
459. 60 f. A. Le Roy Locke .. 55 25
460. 100 f. Booker T. Washington 1·10 45

134. "Telephones". 135. "Napoleon as First Consul" (Ingres).

1971. World Telecommunications Day.
461. 134. 30 f. brn., grn. & purple 25 15
462. – 40 f. brown, red & blue 35 20
DESIGN 40 f. "Telecommunications" theme.

1971. Air. 150th Death Anniv. of Napoleon. Multicoloured.
463. 15 f. Type 135 .. .. 30 25
464. 25 f. "Napoleon in 1809" (Lefevre) 70 30
465. 35 f. "Napoleon on his Death-bed" (Rouget) .. 1·00 45
466. 50 f. "The Awakening to Immortality" (bronze by Rude) .. .. 1·75 80

136. Pres. Nasser. 138. A. Nobel.

137. Hayashida (drummer).

1971. Air. Nasser Commemoration.
467. 136. 50 f. multicoloured .. 45 25

1971. 13th World Scout Jamboree, Asagiri, Japan. Multicoloured.
468. 35 f. Type 137 .. .. 25 12
469. 50 f. Japonica 40 20
470. 65 f. Judo 50 25
471. 75 f. Mt. Fuji 60 30

1971. Air. 75th Anniv of Alfred Nobel (scientist and philanthropist).
472 138 100 f. multicoloured .. 1·25 60

139. Persian Flag and Senegal Arms.

1971. Air. 2500th Anniv. of Persian Empire.
473. 139. 200 f. multicoloured .. 2·00 1·00

140. Map and Emblem.

1971. 25th Anniv. of U.N.I.C.E.F. Mult.
474. 35 f. Type 140 .. .. 35 20
475. 100 f. Nurse, children and U.N.I.C.E.F. emblem .. 1·25 55

1971. Air. 10th Anniv. of U.A.M.P.T. As T 139a of Mauritania. Multicoloured.
476. 100 f. U.A.M.P.T. H.Q., Brazzaville and arms of Senegal 80 40

142. Louis Armstrong. 143. Trying for Goal.

1971. Air. Louis Armstrong Commem.
477. 142. 150 f. brown and gold 2·50 1·25

1971. 6th African Basketball Championships, Dakar. Multicoloured.
478. 35 f. Type 143 .. .. 30 15
479. 40 f. Players reaching for ball 35 25
480. 75 f. Championships emblem 1·00 60

144. Ice-skating.

1971. Air. Winter Olympic Games, Sapporo, Japan. Multicoloured.
481. 5 f. Type 144 .. .. 12 5
482. 10 f. Bob-sleighing .. 12 5
483. 125 f. Cross-country skiing 1·40 60

145. "Il Fonteghetto della Farina" (detail, Canaletto).

1972. Air. U.N.E.S.C.O. "Save Venice" Campaign. Multicoloured.
484. 50 f. Type 145 .. .. 50 30
485. 100 f. "Giudecca e S. Giorgio Maggiore" (detail –Guardi) (vert.) .. 1·25 70

146. "Albouri and Queen Seb Fall" (scene from "The Exile of Albouri").

1972. Int. Theatre Day. Multicoloured.
486. 35 f. Type 146 (postage) 35 20
487. 40 f. Scene from "The Merchant of Venice" .. 65 25
488. 150 f. Daniel Sorano as "Shylock" ("The Merchant of Venice") (vert.) (air) .. .. .. 2·75 1·50

147. Human Heart.

1972. World Heart Month.
489. 147. 35 f. brown and blue .. 25 15
490. – 40 f. pur., grn. & emer. 30 20
DESIGN: 40 f. Doctor and patient.

148. Vegetation in Desert.

1972. U.N. Environmental Conservation Conf., Stockholm. Multicoloured.
491. 35 f. Type **148** (postage) .. 35 20
492. 100 f. Oil slick on shore (air) 1·25 60

149. Tartarin of Tarascon shooting Lion.

1972. 75th Death Anniv. of Alphonse Daudet (writer).
493. **149.** 40 f. red, grn. & brown 45 30
494. – 100 f. brn., light bl. & bl. 1·25 50
DESIGN: 100 f. Daudet and scene from "Tartarin de Tarascon".

151. Wrestling. **152.** Emperor Haile Selassie and Flags.

1972. Olympic Games, Munich. Mult.
496. 15 f. Type **151** 20 12
497. 20 f. Running (100 metres) 20 15
498. 100 f. Basketball .. 1·10 45
499. 125 f. Judo .. .. 1·40 55

1972. Air. Emperor Haile Selassie 80th Birthday.
501. **152.** 100 f. multicoloured 95 55

153. Children reading Book. **154.** "Senegalese Elegance".

1972. Int. Book Year.
502. **153.** 50 f. multicoloured .. 45 20

1972.

502a	154	5 f. blue	10	10
502b		10 f. red ..	15	10
502c		15 f. orange ..	15	10
502d		20 f. purple	15	10
503		25 f. black	20	10
503a		30 f. brown	15	10
504		40 f. blue	30	10
504a		45 f. orange	10	10
504b		50 f. red	10	10
504c		60 f. green	35	10
504d		75 f. purple	55	35
504e		90 f. red	65	35
504f		125 f. blue	30	20
504g		145 f. orange ..	35	25

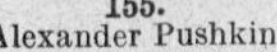
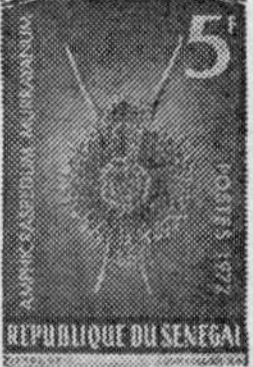

155. Alexander Pushkin. **157.** "Amphicraspedum murrayanum".

1972. Pushkin (writer). Commem.
505. **155.** 100 f. purple & pink .. 1·25 50

1972. 10th Anniv. of West African Monetary Union. As T **149** of Mauritania.
506. 40 f. brn., grey and blue .. 50 15

1972. Protozoa and Large Fishes. Mult.
507. 5 f. Type **157** (postage) .. 8 5
508. 10 f. "Pterocanium tricolpum" 15 8
509. 15 f. "Ceratospyris polygona" 15 10
510. 20 f. "Cortiniscus typicus" 15 10
511. 30 f. "Theopera cortina" .. 15 10
512. 50 f. Swordfish (air) .. 1·00 50
513. 65 f. Killer whale .. .. 1·00 65
514. 75 f. Whale shark .. .. 1·50 80
515. 125 f. Fin whale .. .. 2·25 1·25
Nos. 512/15 are size 45 × 27 mm.

1972. No. 353 surch. **1872-1972** and value.
516. **83.** 100 f. on 30 f. brown, green and chestnut .. 1·40 60

159. Melchior. **160.** "Sharing the Load".

1972. Christmas. Nativity Scene and Three Kings. Multicoloured.
517. 10 f. Type **159** 15 12
518. 15 f. Gaspard 20 12
519. 40 f. Balthazar 40 20
520. 60 f. Joseph 80 40
521. 100 f. Mary and Baby Jesus (African representation) 1·50 65

1973. Europafrique.
522. **160.** 65 f. black and green 55 30

161. Palace of the Republic.

1973. Air.
523. **161.** 100 f. multicoloured .. 1·10 60

162. Station and Aerial.

1973. Inauguration of Satellite Earth Station, Gandoul.
524. **162.** 40 f. multicoloured .. 35 20

163. Hotel Teranga.

1973. Air. Opening of Hotel Teranga, Dakar.
525. **163.** 100 f. multicoloured .. 1·10 60

164. "Lions" African Emblem.

1973. Air. 15th Lions Int. District 403 Congress, Dakar.
526. **164.** 150 f. multicoloured .. 1·50 85

165. Stages of Eclipse.

1973. Eclipse of the Sun. Multicoloured.
527. 35 f. Type **165** 30 15
528. 65 f. Eclipse in diagramatic form 50 25
529. 150 f. Eclipse and "Skylab 1" 1·60 75

166. Symbolic Torch.

1973. 10th Anniv. of Organization of African Unity.
530. **166.** 75 f. multicoloured .. 55 40

1973. "Drought Relief". African Solidarity. No. 451 surch. **SECHERESSE SOLIDARITE AFRICAINE** and value.
531. 100 f. on 25 f. multicoloured 1·50 75

168. "Couple with Mimosa" (Chagall).

1973. Air.
532. **168.** 200 f. multicoloured .. 3·75 2·25

169. "Riccione 1973". **171.** W.M.O. Emblem and Child.

1973. Air. Int. Stamp Exhibition, Riccione (Italy).
533. **169.** 100 f. violet, green & red 1·25 55

1973. U.A.M.P.T. As T **155a** of Mauritania.
534. 100 f. violet, green and red 70 35

1973. Centenary of World Meteorological Organization.
535. **171.** 50 f. multicoloured .. 35 15

172. Interpol H.Q., Paris. **174.** Flame Emblem and People.

1973. 50th Anniv. of Int. Criminal Police Organization (Interpol).
536. **172.** 75 f. brn., blue & green 1·00 40

1973. Air. 25th Anniv. of Declaration of Human Rights. Multicoloured.
538. 35 f. Type **174** 30 15
539. 65 f. Emblem and drummer 70 25

175. R. Follereau (rehabilitation pioneer) and Map.

1973. Air. Centenary of Discovery of Leprosy Bacillus.
540. **175.** 40 f. brn., grn. & violet 35 15
541. – 100 f. purple, red & grn. 1·25 50
DESIGN: 100 f. Dr. G. Hansen (discoverer of leprosy bacillus) and laboratory equipment.

176. "Key" Emblem. **177.** Amilcar Cabral and Weapons.

1973. Air. World Twinned Towns Congress, Dakar. Multicoloured.
542. 50 f. Type **176** 45 20
543. 125 f. Arms of Dakar and meeting of citizens (horiz.) 1·25 50

1974. Amilcar Cabral (Guinea Bissau guerilla leader). Commemoration.
544. **177.** 75 f. multicoloured .. 55 40

178. Peters's Finfoot.

1974. Air. Birds of Djoudj Park. Mult.
545. 1 f. Type **178** 10 10
546. 2 f. White Spoonbills .. 10 10
547. 3 f. Crowned Cranes .. 10 10
548. 4 f. Little Egret 20 10
549. 250 f. Greater Flamingoes (gold value) .. .. 7·00 2·00
550. 250 f. Greater Flamingoes (blk. value) .. .. 7·00 2·00

179. "Tiger attacking Wild Horse".

1974. Air. Paintings by Delacroix. Mult.
551. 150 f. Type **179** .. .. 2·00 80
552. 200 f. "Tiger-hunting" .. 2·40 1·25

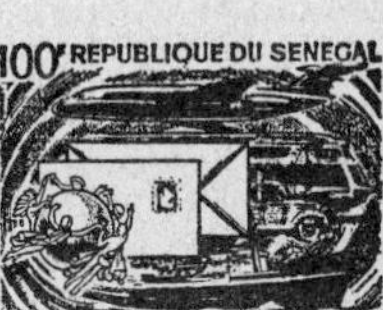

180. Athletes on Podium. **182.** U.P.U. Emblem, Letters and Transport.

181. World Cup, Footballers and "Munich".

1974. National Youth Week. Multicoloured.
553. 35 f. Type **180** 30 15
554. 40 f. Dancer with mask .. 35 20

1974. World Cup Football Championships. Footballers and locations.
555. 25 f. Type **181** 15 10
556. 40 f. "Hamburg" 30 15
557. 65 f. "Hanover" 45 20
558. 70 f. "Stuttgart" 45 25

1974. Cent. of U.P.U.
559. **182.** 100 f. green, blue and lilac 1·25 60

183. Archway, and Africans at Work.

184. Dakar, "Gateway to Africa".

1974. First Dakar International Fair.
560. **183.** 100 f. brown, orange & blue (postage) .. 1·00 35
561. **184.** 350 f. silver (air) .. 4·00
562. 1500 f. gold .. .. 19·00
Nos. 561/2 are embossed on foil.

1975. West Germany's Victory in World Cup Football Championships, Munich. No. 566 surch. **ALLEMAGNE RFA-HOLLANDE 2-1** and value.
563. 200 f. on 40 f. mult. .. 2·00 1·25

186. Pres. Senghor and King Baudouin.

1975. Visit of King Baudouin of the Belgians.
564. **186.** 65 f. blue and purple.. 50 25
565. 100 f. green and orange 1·25 45

187. I.L.O. Emblem.

1975. Labour Day.
566. **187.** 125 f multicoloured .. 1·10 45

188. "Apollo" and "Soyuz" Spacecraft.

1975. Air. "Apollo-Soyuz" Space Co-operation Project.
567. **188.** 125 f. green, blue & red 1·25 60

189. Spanish "Stamp" Globe and Letters.

1975. "Espana 75" (Madrid) and "Arphila 75" (Paris) International Stamp Exhibitions.
568. **189.** 55 f. red, blue & green 60 30
569. – 95 f. light brn. and brn. 1·75 70
DESIGN: 95 f. Head of Apollo and "Arphila" Emblem.

190. Classroom and Tractor.

1975. Technical Education.
570. **190.** 85 f. brown, blue & blk. 75 30

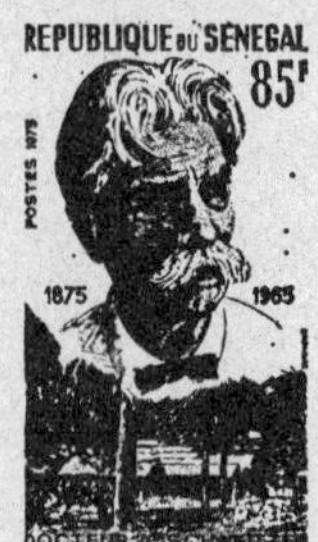

191. Dr. Schweitzer

1975. Birth Cent. of Dr. Albert Schweitzer.
571. **191.** 85 f. lilac and green .. 90 55

192. Soldier, Flag and Map of Sinai Desert 1973–74.

1975. Senegalese Battalion with U.N.
572. **192.** 100 f. multicoloured .. 90 40

193. Stamps and Map of Italy. 194. Woman pounding Maize.

1975. Air. Riccione Stamp Exhibition.
573. **193.** 125 f. brown, red & lilac 1·25 75

1975. International Women's Year. Mult.
574. 55 f. Type **194** 35 20
575. 75 f. Mother and child with woman doctor (horiz.).. 90 25

1975. Air. "Apollo-Soyuz" Space Link. Optd. **JONCTION 17 Juil. 1975.**
576. **188.** 125 f. green, blue & red 1·10 60

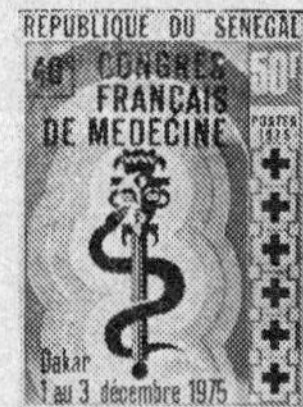

196. Stylised Caduceus.

1975. French Medical Congress, Dakar.
577. **196.** 50 f. multicoloured .. 25 12

197. "Massacre of Boston" (A. Chappel).

1975. Air. Bicentenary of American Revolution. (1st issue).
578. **197.** 250 f. brn., red & blue 2·50 1·00
579. – 500 f. red and blue .. 5·00 2·50
DESIGN: 500 f. Siege of Yorktown.
See also No. 593.

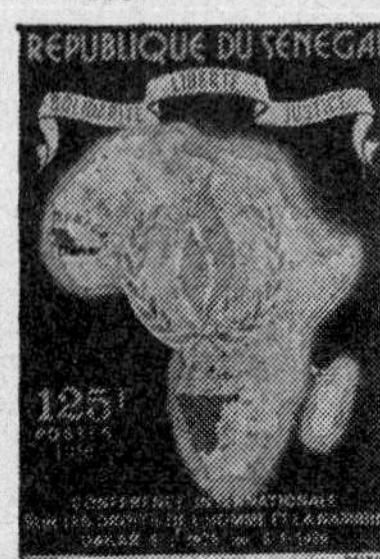

198. Emblem on Map of Africa.

1976. Int. "Rights of Man" and Namibia Conferences, Dakar.
580. **198.** 125 f. multicoloured.. 60 30

199. "Concorde" and Flight Locations.

1976. Air. "Concorde's" 1st Commercial Flight.
581. **199.** 300 f. multicoloured .. 4·50 2·25
See also No. 641.

200. Deep-sea Fishing.

1976. "Expo", Okinawa. Multicoloured.
582. 140 f. Type **200** .. .. 1·50 1·00
583. 200 f. Yacht-racing .. 2·00 1·25

201. Serval.

1976. Basse Casamance Nat. Park. Fauna. Multicoloured.
584. 2 f. Type **201** 10 10
585. 3 f. Bar-tailed godwit (marsh bird) 70 30
586. 4 f. Bush pig 10 10
587. 5 f. African fish eagle .. 90 45
588. 250 f. Sitatunga (males) .. 2·75 1·50
589. 250 f. Sitatunga (females) 2·75 1·50

202. Alexander Graham Bell.

1976. Telephone Centenary.
590. **202.** 175 f. multicoloured .. 1·40 85

203. Map of Africa.

1976. GADEF Scientific and Cultural Days
591. **203.** 60 f. multicoloured .. 35 20

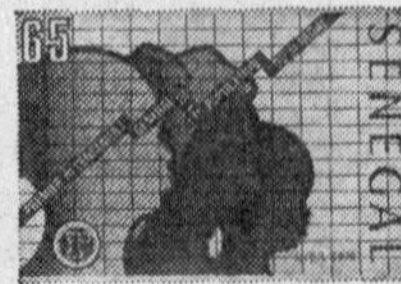

204. Heads on Graphs.

1976. First Population Census.
592. **204.** 65 f. multicoloured .. 35 25

205. Jefferson reading Independence Declaration.

1976. Bicent. of American Revolution (2nd issue).
593. **205.** 50 f. blk., red and blue 35 20

206. Plant Cultivation.

1976. Operation "Sahel Vert".
594. **206.** 60 f. multicoloured .. 35 20

207. Scouts around Camp-fire.

1976. First All-African Scouts Jamboree, Jos, Nigeria. Multicoloured.
595. 80 f. Type **207** 45 35
596. 100 f. Emblem and map (vert.) 90 45

208. Swimming. 210. Emblem and Map.

1976. Olympic Games, Montreal. Mult.
597. 5 f. Type **208** (postage).. 8 8
598. 10 f. Weightlifting .. 10 10
599. 15 f. Hurdling (horiz.) .. 12 8
600. 20 f. Horse-jumping (horiz.) 12 8
601. 25 f. Steeplechasing (horiz.) 12 8
602. 50 f. Wrestling (horiz.) .. 25 15
603. 60 f. Hockey 30 20
604. 65 f. Running 35 20
605. 70 f. Gymnastics.. .. 40 25
606. 100 f. Cycling (horiz.) 50 30
607. 400 f. Boxing (horiz.) (air) 3·00 40
607a. 500 f. Judo.. .. .. 3·50 1·10
608. 1000 f. Basketball (41 × 41 mm.) .. .. .. 6·50 3·50
608a. 1500 f. Running (41 × 41 mm.) .. .. .. 10·00 5·00

1976. President Senghor's 70th Birthday. Multicoloured.
610. 40 f. Type **210** 25 20
611. 60 f. Star over world map 35 25
612. 70 f. Technicians and symbol 45 30
613. 200 f. President Senghor and extended hands .. 1·60 75

211. Harvesting Tomatoes.

1976. Tomato Production.
614. **211.** 180 f. multicoloured.. 1·75 1·00

212. "Concorde" and Route Plan.

1976. Air. Dakar International Fair.
615. **212.** 500 f. silver .. .. 4·50
616. 1,500 f. gold .. .. 18·00

213. Black Peoples' "Charter". 214. Mohammed Ali and Joe Frazier.

1977. Black Peoples' Day.
617. **213.** 60 f. multicoloured .. 35 25

1977. World Boxing Championship.

618. **214.** 60 f. black and blue .. 35 15
619. – 150 f. black and green 1·40 50

DESIGN—HORIZ. 150 f. Mohammed Ali landing punch.

215. Dancer and Musicians.

1977. 2nd World Black and African Festival of Arts and Culture, Lagos (Nigeria). Multicoloured.

620. 50 f. Type **215** 25 20
621. 75 f. Statuette and masks 70 25
622. 100 f. Statuette and dancers 90 45

216. Cog Wheels.

1977. 1st Anniv. of Dakar Industrial Zone.

623. **216.** 70 f. brown and green 40 20

217. Hauling in Net. **218.** Burnt Tree in "Flame".

1977. Fishing. Multicoloured.

624. 25 f. Type **217** (Postage)
625. 5 f. Fishing by trawl-line (air) .. .. ..
626. 10 f. Harpooning ..
627. 15 f. Pirogue breasting wave
628. 20 f. Displaying prize catch

1977. Fight Against Forest Fires. Mult.

629. 40 f. Type **218** 20 15
630. 60 f. Firefighting vehicle (horiz.) 40 25

219. Industrial and Pre-Industrial Communication.

1977. World Telecommunications Day. Multicoloured.

631. 80 f. Type **219** 45 35
632. 100 f. Printed circuit (vert.) 70 45

220. Arms of Senegal. **221.** Woman rowing on River.

1977. 10th Anniv. of International French Language Council. Multicoloured.

633. 65 f. Type **220** 35 20
634. 250 f. As T **236a** of Mali .. 1·75 1·00

1977. "Amphilex 1977" International Stamp Exhibition, Amsterdam. Multicoloured.

635. 50 f. Type **221** 30 25
636. 125 f. Senegalese woman .. 70 45

222. "Viking" and Control Centre. **223.** Class in Front of Blackboard.

1977. Air. "Viking" Space Mission to Mars.

637. **222.** 300 f. multicoloured .. 2·00 1·25

1977. Literacy Week. Multicoloured.

638. 60 f. Type **223** 35 25
639. 65 f. Man with alphabet table 35 25

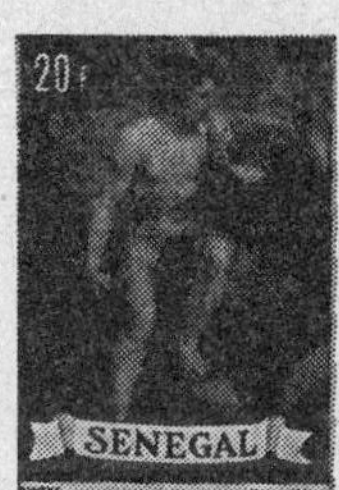

224. "Mercury and Argus" (Rubens). **226.** "Adoration of the Kings".

1977. Paintings. Multicoloured.

640. 20 f. Type **224** 10 8
641. 25 f. "Daniel and the Lions" (Rubens) 12 10
642. 40 f. "The Empress" .. (Titian) 20 15
643. 60 f. "Flora" (Titian) .. 30 20
644. 65 f. "Jo la belle Irlandaise" (Courbet) .. 35 20
645. 100 f. "The Painter's Studio" (Courbet) .. 1·00 55

1977. Air. First Paris–New York Commercial Flight of "Concorde". Optd. **PARIS—NEW YORK 22.11.77.**

646. **199.** 300 f. multicoloured .. 4·25 2·25

1977. Christmas. Multicoloured.

647. 20 f. Type **226** 10 8
648. 25 f. Fanal (celebration) .. 12 10
649. 40 f. Family Christmas tree 20 15
650. 100 f. "Three Wise Men" (horiz.) .. .. .. 1·00 40

227. Wrestler. **228.** Dakar Cathedral and Parthenon, Athens.

1978. Tourism. Multicoloured.

651. 10 f. Type **227** 10 10
652. 30 f. Soumbedioun Regatta (canoes) 20 15
653. 65 f. Soumbedioun Regatta (race) (horiz.) 45 25
654. 100 f. Dancers (horiz.) .. 95 50

1978. U.N.E.S.C.O. Campaign for Protection of Monuments.

655. **228.** 75 f. multicoloured .. 35 25

229. Solar Pump.

1978. Sources of Energy. Multicoloured.

656. 50 f. Type **229** 25 15
657. 95 f. Electricity power station 75 30

230. Caspian and Royal Terns.

1978. Saloum Delta National Park. Multicoloured.

658. 5 f. Type **230** 10 10
659. 10 f. Pink-backed Pelicans 15 10
660. 15 f. Grey Heron and Warthog 25 20
661. 20 f. Greater Flamingoes 25 20
662. 150 f. Grey Heron and Royal Terns .. .. 1·90 80
663. 150 f. Abyssinian Ground Hornbill and Warthog .. 1·90 80

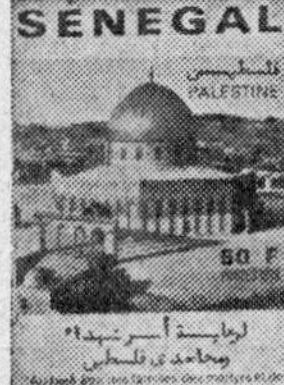

231. Dome of the Rock. **232.** Mahatma Gandhi.

1978. Palestine Freedom-Fighters.

664. **231.** 60 f. multicoloured .. 30 20

1978. Apostles of Non-Violence. Mult.

665. 125 f. Type **232** 85 50
666. 150 f. Martin Luther King 90 60

233. Jenner and Vaccination of Children. **234.** Players, and Flags of Group 1 Countries.

1978. Global Eradication of Smallpox.

668. **233.** 60 f. multicoloured .. 30 20

1978. World Cup Football Championship Argentina. Multicoloured.

669. 25 f. Type **234** 12 10
670. 40 f. Players and flags of Group 2 countries .. 20 12
671. 65 f. Players and flags of Group 3 countries .. 30 20
672. 100 f. Players and flags of Group 4 countries .. 70 30

235. Symbols of Technology, Equipment, Industrialisation.

1978. Third International Fair, Dakar.

674. **235.** 110 f. multicoloured .. 75 30

236. Wright Brothers and "Flyer".

1978. Conquest of Space. Multicoloured.

675. 75 f. Type **236** (75th anniv of first powered flight) .. 40 20
676. 100 f. Yuri Gagarin (10th death anniv. of first cosmonaut) 55 30
677. 200 f. "Apollo 8" (10th anniv. of first-manned moon orbit .. .. 1·25 60

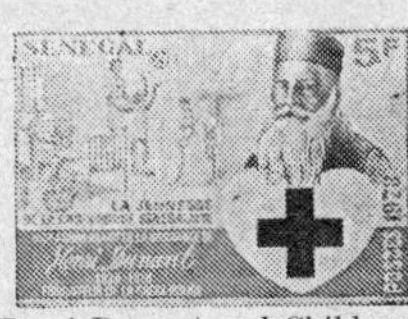

237. Henri Dunant and Children's Ward.

1978. 150th Birth Anniv. of Henri Dunant (founder of the Red Cross).

679. **237.** 5 f. blue, black and red 5 5
680. – 20 f. multicoloured .. 12 10

DESIGN: 20 f. Henri Dunant and scenes of Red Cross aid.

1978. Air. "Philexafrique", Stamp Exhibition, Libreville, Gabon and International Stamp Fair, Essen, West Germany. As T **262** of Niger.

681. 100 f. Capercaillie and Schleswig-Holstein 1850 1 s. stamp .. 1·50 1·25
682. 100 f. Lion and Senegal 1960 200 f. Violet Turaco 1·50 1·25

238. Telecommunications.

1978. Post Office Achievements. Multicoloured.

683. 50 f. Type **238** 25 12
684. 60 f. Social welfare .. 30 20
685. 65 f. Travelling Post Office 30 20

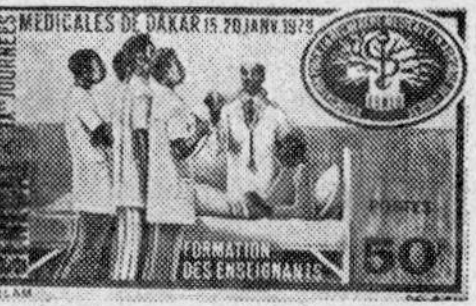

239. Doctor with Students.

1979. 9th Medical Days, Dakar. Multicoloured.

686. 50 f. Type **239** 25 15
687. 100 f. Problems of pollution 70 45

240. Agriculture.

1979. Professional Conscience. Multicoloured.

688. 30 f. Type **240** 15 10
689. 150 f. Symbols of progress 1·00 45

241. Open Air Class.

1979. S.O.S. Children's Village. Multicoloured.

690. 40 f. Type **241** 20 12
691. 60 f. View of Village .. 30 20

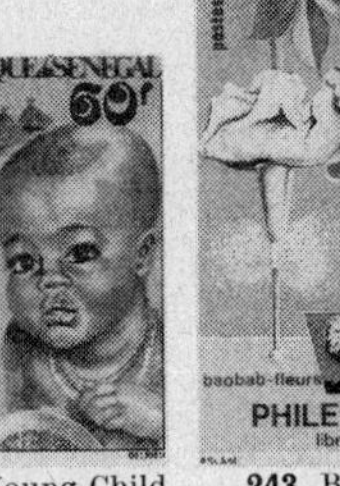

242. Young Child. **243.** Baobab Flower and Tree and Independence Monument.

1979. International Year of the Child. Multicoloured.

692. 60 f. Type **242** 30 20
693. 65 f. Children with book .. 30 20

1979. "Philexafrique 2" Stamp Exhibition, Libreville, Gabon. Multicoloured.

694. 60 f. Type **243** 70 60
695. 150 f. Drum, early telegraph apparatus and dish aerial (square, 36 × 36 mm.) 1·75 1·25

244. Children ushered into Open Book.

1979. 50th Anniv. of International Bureau of Education.

696. **244.** 250 f. multicoloured .. 1·40 80

245. Hill and Senegal 100 f. Stamp of 1960.

1979. Death Cent. of Sir Rowland Hill.

697. **245.** 500 f. multicoloured .. 3·50 2·00

246. " Black Trees ".

247. Start of Race.

1979. Paintings by Friedensreich Hundertwasser. Multicoloured.

698. 60 f. Type **246** 75 25
699. 100 f. " Head " .. .. 1·00 75
700. 200 f. " Rainbow Windows " .. .. 2·00 1·25

1980. First African Athletic Championships. Multicoloured.

702. 20 f. Type **247** 12 8
703. 25 f. Javelin 12 8
704. 50 f. Passing the relay baton 25 12
705. 100 f. Discus 45 30

248. Musicians.

1980. Mudra African Arts Festival.

706. 50 f. Type **248** 25 12
707. 100 f. Dancers 70 25
708. 200 f. Dancers & drummer 1·25 70

249. Lions Emblem.

1980. 22nd Congress of Lions' Club District 403, Dakar.

709. **249.** 100 f. multicoloured .. 45 25

250. Chimpanzees.

1980. Niokolo-Koba National Park. Multicoloured.

710. 40 f. Type **250** 25 10
711. 60 f. African elephants .. 35 20
712. 65 f. Giant elands 60 20
713. 100 f. Spotted hyenas .. 85 30
714. 200 f. Wildlife on the savannah .. .. 1·75 70
715. 200 f. Simenti Hotel .. 1·75 70

Nos. 714/15 were issued together, se-tenant, forming a composite design.

251. Watering Sapling.

252. Women with Bowls of Rice Flour and Electric Mill.

1980. Tree Planting Year.

717. **251.** 60 f. multicoloured .. 30 20
718. 65 f. multicoloured .. 60 20

1980. Rural Women. Multicoloured.

719. 50 f. Street market (horiz.) 25 12
720. 100 f. Type **252** 45 30
721. 200 f. Drawing water (horiz.) 1·25 70

INDEX

Countries can be quickly located by referring to the index at the end of this volume.

253. Wrestling.

1980. Olympic Games, Moscow. Mult.

722. 60 f. Type **253** 30 20
723. 65 f. Running 30 20
724. 70 f. Games emblems .. 35 25
725. 100 f. Judo 45 30
726. 200 f. Basketball .. 1·25 70

254. Dabry, Gimie, Mermoz and Aircraft.

1980. Air. 50th Anniv. of First South Atlantic Airmail Flight.

728. **254.** 300 f. multicoloured 2·00 1·00

255. Caspian Tern, Eastern White Pelicans and Grey-headed Gulls (Pointe Kalissaye Bird Sanctuary).

1981. National Parks. Multicoloured.

729. 50 f. Type **255** 60 20
730. 70 f. Slender-billed gulls and gull-billed tern (Langue de Barbarie) .. 65 30
731. 85 f. Turtle and crab (Madeline Islands) .. 40 25
732. 150 f. White-breasted cormorant and red-billed tropic bird (Madeline Islands) .. .. .. 1·75 70

256. Healthy Activities.

257. Fair Visitors beneath Tree.

1981. Anti-Smoking Campaign. Mult.

734. 75 f. Type **256** 30 30
735. 80 f. Cancerous mouth with pipe 35 35

1981. Fourth International Fair, Dakar.

736. **257.** 80 f. multicoloured .. 35 35

258. Lat Dior Damel Teigne.

259. " Nymphaea lotus ".

1982. National Heroes. Lat Dior. Mult.

737. 80 f. Type **258** 35 25
738. 500 f. Lat Dior on horseback .. .. .. 3·00 1·25

1982. Flowers. Multicoloured.

739. 50 f. Type **259** 20 20
740. 75 f. " Strophanthus sarmentosus " 30 30
741. 200 f. " Crinum moorei " 1·25 75
742. 225 f. " Cochlospermum tinctorium " .. .. 1·50 1·00

260. " Euryphrene senegalensis " (male and female).

1982. Butterflies. Multicoloured.

743. 45 f. Type **260** 60 35
744. 55 f. " Hypolimnas salmacis, Precis octavia " and " Salamis cytora " .. 75 45
745. 75 f. " Cymothoe caenis " and " Cyrestis camillus " 90 55
746. 80 f. " Precis cebrene, Junonia terea " and " Salamis parhassus " .. 1·10 70

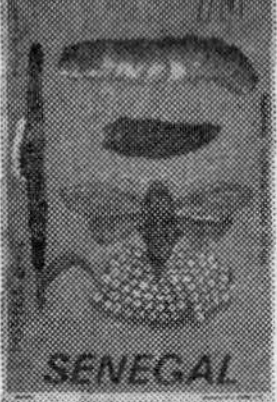

261. "Rhaguva albipunctella"

262. Flags and Three-dimensional Map of Senegambia.

1982. Harmful Insects. Multicoloured.

748. 75 f. Type **261** 50 45
749. 80 f. " Amsacta moloneyi, Tolyposporium penicillariae " and " Sclerospore graminicola " (horiz.) .. 1·00 50
750. 100 f. " Amsacta moloneyi " 70 60

1982. Senegambia Confederation. Mult.

751. 225 f. Type **262** .. .. 1·25 60
752. 350 f. Arms of Senegal and Gambia .. .. 2·00 90

1982. Birds. Multicoloured.

753. 45 f. Type **263** 40 30
754. 75 f. Saddle-bill stork .. 85 35
755. 80 f. White-throated francolin .. .. .. 1·00 40
756. 500 f. Tawny eagle .. 5·00 2·75

264. Footballer and Emblem.

265. Flag " Stamp " and Ribbon.

1982. World Cup Football championship Spain. Multicoloured.

757. 30 f. Type **264** 12 12
758. 50 f. Footballer 20 20
759. 75 f. Football 30 30
760. 80 f. World Cup and emblem 35 35

1982. " Philexfrance 82 " International Stamp Exhibition, Paris. Multicoloured.

762. 100 f. Type **265** 40 25
763. 500 f. Arms " stamp " between circling arrows 3·00 1·50

266. Exhibition Poster.

1983. Stamp Exhibition, Dakar. Multicoloured.

764. 60 f. Type **266** 25 20
765. 70 f. Butterfly stamps .. 25 20
766. 90 f. Stamps and magnifying glass 30 25
767. 95 f. Exhibition hall and Dakar arms on stamp .. 75 30

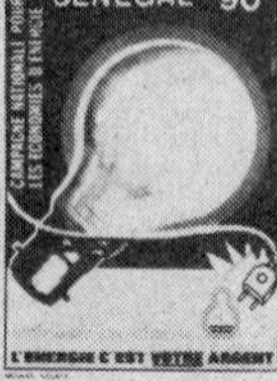

267. Light Bulb.

268. Torch on Map of Africa.

1983. Energy Conservation. Multicoloured.

768. 90 f. Type **267** .. 55 30
769. 95 f. Cars queueing for petrol 60 30
770. 260 f. Woman cooking .. 1·60 85

1983. " For Namibian Independence ". Multicoloured.

771. 90 f. Type **268** 55 30
772. 95 f. Clenched fist and broken chain on map of Africa 60 30
773. 260 f. Woman with torch on map of Africa .. 1·90 85

263. Black-tailed Godwit.

269. Agency Building, Ziguinchor.

270. Dakar Rotary Banner.

1983. 20th Anniv. of West African Monetary Union. Multicoloured.

774. 60 f. Type **269** 25 20
775. 65 f. Headquarters building, Dakar (vert.) .. 25 25

1983. 1st Anniv. of Dakar Alizes Rotary Club.

776. **270.** 70 f. multicoloured .. 50 25
777. 500 f. multicoloured .. 3·25 1·75

271. Customs Council Headquarters.

272. Anniversary Emblem.

1983. 30th Anniv. of Customs Co-operation Council.

778. **271.** 90 f. multicoloured .. 30 30
779. 300 f. multicoloured .. 2·00 1·00

1984. 25th Anniv. of Economic Commission for Africa.

780. **272.** 90 f. multicoloured .. 30 30
781. 95 f. multicoloured .. 60 30

273. Village.

1984. S.O.S. Children's Village. Multicoloured.

782. 90 f. Type **273** 30 30
783. 95 f. Foster-mother and child (vert.) 65 30
784. 115 f. Foster-family .. 80 40
785. 260 f. House (vert.) .. 1·75 85

274. Scout Salute.

275. Javelin-throwing

1984. 75th Anniv. of Boy Scout Movement. Multicoloured.

786. 60 f. Type **274** 20 15
787. 70 f. Scout badge .. 25 20
788. 90 f. Scouts of different nations 35 30
789. 95 f. Lord Baden-Powell (founder) 40 35

1984. Olympic Games, Los Angeles. Mult.

790. 90 f. Type **275** 35 30
791. 95 f. Hurdling 40 35
792. 165 f. Football .. .. 1·10 70

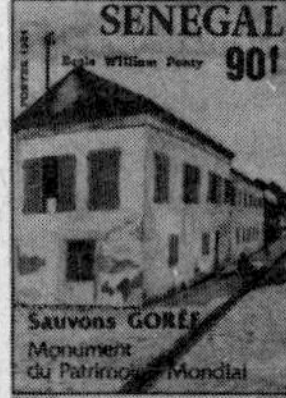

276. Basket of Food, Fishing and Farming.

278. William Ponty School.

1984. World Food Day. Multicoloured. Inscr **"16 OCTOBRE 1983".**

794. 65 f. Type **276** 25 20
795. 70 f. Woman cooking and child (vert.) 50 20
796. 225 f. Group and food .. 1·60 85

1984. Drought Aid. No. 785 optd. **Aide au Sahel 84.**

797. 260 f. multicoloured .. 1·75 1·25

1984. World Heritage. Goree Island.

798. **278.** 90 f. multicoloured .. 35 30
799. – 95 f. black and blue .. 40 35
800. – 250 f. multicoloured .. 1·75 85
801. – 500 f. multicoloured .. 3·50 2·00

DESIGNS—HORIZ. 95 f. Map of Goree. 500 f. Slaves' House. VERT. 250 f. Goree Historical Museum.

279. Pump and Sprinkler.

280. Globe, Envelopes and Map.

1985. Irrigation Project. Multicoloured.

810. 40 f. Type **279** 15 12
811. 50 f. Tap and dam .. 15 12
812. 90 f. Storage tanks and cattle 60 25
813. 250 f. Women at water pump .. .. .. 1·75 85

1985. World Communications Year (1984).

814. **280.** 90 f. multicoloured .. 30 25
815. – 95 f. bl., grn. & brn. 35 30
816. – 350 f. multicoloured .. 2·25 1·10

DESIGNS: 95 f. Maps of Africa and Senegal and aerial. 350 f. Globe, dove and map of Senegal.

281. Stringed Instrument and Flute.

1985. Musical Instruments. Multicoloured.

817. 50 f. Type **281** 15 12
818. 85 f. Drums and stringed instrument 30 25
819. 125 f. Musician, stringed instruments, xylophone and drums 85 40
820. 250 f. Stringed instruments 1·60 85

282. Sea-Plane and Map.

1985. Air. 55th Anniv. of First Airmail Flight across South Atlantic.

821. **282.** 250 f. multicoloured .. 2·25 1·10

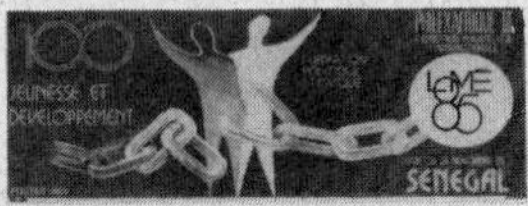

283. People and Broken Chain.

1985. "Philexafrique" International Stamp Exhibition, Lome, Togo. "Youth and Development". Multicoloured.

822. 100 f. Type **283** (political and civic education) .. 45 40
823. 125 f. Carpenter and draughtsman (professional education) .. 75 45
824. 150 f. Couple looking at planets (general education) 90 60
825. 175 f. Farm workers (food self-sufficiency) .. .. 1·00 80

284. Laboratory and Farm Workers.

1985. International Youth Year. Mult.

826. 40 f. Type **284** 20 15
827. 50 f. Young people, forms of communication and globe 20 15
828. 90 f. Youth building "Peace" monument .. 40 35
829. 125 f. Youth, football and globe 90 45

285. Man, Woman and Boy.

1985. National Costumes. Multicoloured.

830. 40 f. Type **285** 20 15
831. 95 f. Man in straw hat and striped gown (vert.) .. 40 35
832. 100 f. Seated woman (vert.) 45 40
833. 150 f. Man and woman (vert.) 90 60

286. Men bringing Boat Ashore.

1986. Fishing at Kayar. Multicoloured.

834. 40 f. Type **286** 20 15
835. 50 f. Women waiting on shore 20 15
836. 100 f. Man with large fish (vert.) 70 40
837. 125 f. Sorting the catch (vert.) 95 45
838. 150 f. View of beach .. 1·00 60

287. Perruque and Ceeli.

288. Flags and Football.

1986. Hairstyles. Multicoloured.

839. 90 f. Type **287** 40 30
840. 125 f. Ndungu, Kearly and Rasta 50 40
841. 250 f. Jamono Kura and Kooraa .. .. .. 1·50 60
842. 300 f. Mbaram and Jeere .. 1·75 70

1986. African Football Cup, Cairo. Mult.

843. 115 f. Type **288** 70 35
844. 125 f. Footballer and map 75 45
845. 135 f. Lion rampant with torch ascending pyramid (horiz.) 80 50
846. 165 f. Lions rampant beneath flag (horiz.) .. 1·00 65

1986. 5th Convention of District 403 of Lions International. No. 818 surch. **Ve CONVENTION MULTI-DISTRICT 8–10 MAI 1986.**

847. 165 f. on 85 f. Drums and stringed instrument .. 1·00 65

290. Doe and Calf.

1986. Ndama Gazelle. Multicoloured.

848. 15 f. Type **290** 8 5
849. 45 f. Group of gazelle resting 20 15
850. 85 f. Gazelle among dead trees 35 30
851. 125 f. Gazelle running .. 1·00 45

291. Immunising Child.

294. Ostriches.

292. Trophy, Footballers and Terracotta Offertory Vessel.

1986. U.N.I.C.E.F. Child Survival Campaign. Multicoloured.

852. 50 f. Type **291** 20 15
853. 85 f. Child drinking from bowl 40 35

1986. World Cup Football Championship, Mexico. Multicoloured.

(a) As T **292.**

854. 125 f. Type **292** 50 45
855. 135 f. Trophy, footballers and stucco Maya head from Palenque 80 50
856. 165 f. Gold breastplate, footballers and trophy .. 1·00 65
857. 340 f. Teotihuacan porcelain mask, footballers and trophy .. 2·00 90

(b) Nos. 854/7 optd. **ARGENTINA 3 R.F.A. 2.**

858. 125 f. Type **292** 50 45
859. 135 f. Trophy, footballers and stucco Maya head of Palenque 80 50
860. 165 f. Gold breastplate, footballers and trophy .. 1·00 65
861. 340 f. Teotihuacan porcelain mask, footballers and trophy .. 2·00 90

1986. Guembeul Nature Reserve. Mult.

862. 50 f. Type **294** .. .. 1·00 30
863. 65 f. Gazelles 25 20
864. 85 f. Giraffes 60 30
865. 100 f. Ostrich, buffalo, gazelle and giraffe .. 1·75 80
866. 150 f. Buffalo .. .. 1·10 60

295. Man with Puppet (Xuusmaanapaa).

296. Statue of Liberty.

1986. Christmas. Customs. Multicoloured.

867. 70 f. Type **295** 25 20
868. 85 f. Setting up fanal (Fente) (horiz.) 30 25
869. 150 f. Decorating fanal (Jebele) 90 55
870. 250 f. Boy praying before candle and Nativity scene (horiz.) .. .. 1·50 75

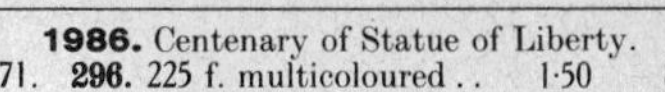

1986. Centenary of Statue of Liberty.

871. **296.** 225 f. multicoloured .. 1·50 80

297. Jellyfish and Coral.

1987. Marine Fauna. Multicoloured.

872. 50 f. Type **297** 20 15
873. 85 f. Sea urchin and starfish 30 25
874. 100 f. Norway lobster .. 70 35
875. 150 f. Common dolphin .. 1·00 55
876. 200 f. Octopus .. .. 1·40 75

298. Motor Cyclist and Lorry.

299. Hands over Antelope.

1987. Paris–Dakar Rally. Multicoloured.

877. 115 f. Type **298** 80 40
878. 125 f. Thierry Sabine, helicopter, motor cyclist, lorry and car (horiz.) .. 1·50 60
879. 135 f. Sabine and motor car (horiz.) .. .. .. 1·00 45
880. 340 f. Eiffel Tower, car and huts .. .. .. 2·40 1·10

1987. Endangered Fauna in Ferlo National Park. Multicoloured.

881. 55 f. Type **299** 20 15
882. 70 f. Ostriches 75 30
883. 85 f. Warthog 60 25
884. 90 f. Elephant 60 30

300. Spacecraft above Earth.

1987. 10th Anniv. of "Gemini 8"-Agena Flight.

885. **300.** 320 f. multicoloured .. 2·00 1·10

301. International Express Mail Emblem.

1987. Centenary of First Senegal Stamp. Multicoloured.

887. 100 f. Type **301** 40 35
888. 130 f. 1892 4 c. Senegal and Dependencies stamp .. 75 45
889. 140 f. 1961 Senegal independence stamp 80 50
890. 145 f. 1935 30 c. and 1 f. 25 Senegal stamps 85 50
891. 320 f. Senegal 1887 15 c. on 20 c. stamp and cancellation .. .. 2·00 1·10

302. Hand gripping Bloodied Claw above Map of South Africa.

1987. Anti-Apartheid Campaign. Mult.

892. 130 f. Type **302** 80 45
893. 140 f. Broken and bloodied chain in fist (vert.) .. 85 50
894. 145 f. Skeleton with scythe, dove and globe 85 50

303. Emblem.

1987. 20th Anniv. of Intelsat. Multicoloured.

895.	50 f. Type **303**	20	15
896.	125 f. Satellite and emblem	50	45
897.	150 f. Emblem and globe	60	55
898.	200 f. Globe and satellite	1·25	75

304. Emblem and Crowd. **305.** Yacht and Sun.

1987. West African Cities Organization. Multicoloured.

899.	40 f. Type **304**	15	12
900.	125 f. Emblem and clasped hands	75	45

1987. 45th Anniv. of Dakar Rotary Club.

901.	**305.** 500 f. multicoloured	3·25	1·50

306. U.N. Building, New York. **307.** Fr. Daniel Brottier (founder) and Angel.

1987. 40th Anniv. (1985) of U.N.O. Multicoloured.

902.	85 f. Type **306**	60	25
903.	95 f. Emblem	65	35
904.	150 f. Hands of different races and emblem	90	55

1987. 50th Anniv. of Cathedral of African Remembrance. Multicoloured.

905.	130 f. Type **307**	85	45
906.	140 f. Cathedral in 1936 and 1986	85	50

308. Hand pouring Grain into Globe.

1987. World Food Day. Multicoloured.

907.	130 f. Type **308**	80	45
908.	140 f. Ear of wheat and F.A.O. emblem rising as sun (horiz.)	85	50
909.	145 f. Emblem	85	50

309. Servals.

1987. Basse Casamance National Park. Mult.

910	115 f. Type **309**	70	40
911	135 f. Demidoff's galagos	90	45
912	150 f. Bush pig	1·00	55
913	250 f. Leopards	1·60	90
914	300 f. Little egrets	5·50	2·75
915	300 f. Carmine bee eaters	5·50	2·75

310. Wrestlers.

1987. Senegalese Wrestling. Multicoloured.

916.	115 f. Type **310**	70	40
917.	125 f. Wrestlers and musicians	70	45
918.	135 f. Wrestlers (vert.)	80	45
919.	165 f. Referee wrestlers and crowd (vert.)	1·00	55

311. African Open-bill Stork. **312.** Boy dreaming of Father Christmas's Visit.

1987. Djoudj National Park. Multicoloured.

920	115 f. Type **311**	95	55
921	125 f. Greater flamingoes (horiz)	1·10	65
922	135 f. Pink-backed pelican and greater flamingoes (horiz)	1·40	65
923	300 f. Pink-backed pelicans	2·75	1·25
924	350 f. As No. 921	3·00	1·75
925	350 f. As No. 922	3·00	1·75

1987. Christmas. Multicoloured.

926.	145 f. Type **312**	85	50
927.	150 f. Star behind Virgin gazing at Child	90	55
928.	180 f. Nativity scene above people praying in church	1·25	65
929.	200 f. Nativity scene in candle glow	1·25	75

313 Battle of Dekhele

1988. Death Centenary of Lat-Dior. Mult.

930	130 f. Type **313**	1·00	45
931	160 f. Lat-Dior on his horse "Maalaw"	1·00	60

314 10th Anniv Emblem and Map

1988. Dakar International Fair.

932 **314**	125 f. multicoloured	75	45

315 Catfish

1988. Fishes. Multicoloured.

933	5 f. Type **315**	5	5
934	100 f. Angel fish	40	35
935	145 f. Common barb	90	50
936	180 f. Carp	1·40	90

316 W.M.O. Emblem and Means of Conveying Information

1988. World Meteorology Day.

937 **316**	145 f. multicoloured	90	30

317 Motor Cyclist

1988. 10th Anniv of Paris–Dakar Rally. Mult.

938	145 f. Type **317**	90	50
939	180 f. Rally car and emblem	1·00	65
940	200 f. Rally cars and man	1·25	70
941	410 f. Thierry Sabine and motor cyclist	2·75	1·50

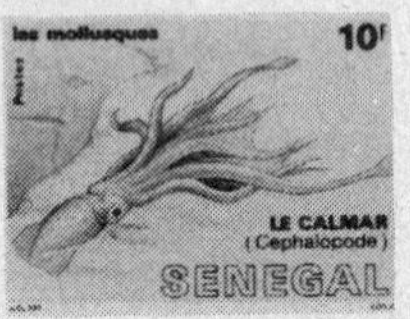

318 Squid

1988. Molluscs. Multicoloured.

942	10 f. Type **318**	5	5
943	20 f. "Donax trunculus" (bivalve)	8	5
944	145 f. "Achatina fulica" (snail) (vert)	90	50
945	165 f. "Helix nemoralis" (snail)	1·10	60

319 Football, Cup and Map

1988. Africa Cup Football Championship, Rabat. Multicoloured.

946	80 f. Type **319**	30	25
947	100 f. Player's leg and ball (vert)	40	35
948	145 f. Match scene and map of Africa (vert)	90	50
949	180 f. Emblem and cup (vert)	1·25	65

320 Corps Member and Children **321** "Dictyota atomaria"

1988. 25th Anniv of American Peace Corps in Senegal.

950 **320**	190 f. multicoloured	1·25	65

1988. Marine Flora. Multicoloured.

951	10 f. Type **321**	5	5
952	65 f. "Agarum gmelini"	25	20
953	145 f. "Saccorrhiza bulbosa"	90	55
954	180 f. "Rhodymenia palmetta"	1·25	65

1988. Riccione Stamp Fair. No. 891 optd **RICCIONE 88 27-29-08-89.**

955	320 f. multicoloured	1·75	1·25

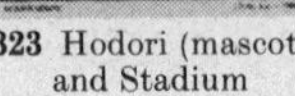

323 Hodori (mascot) and Stadium **325** Thies Phosphate Mine

324 Thierno Saidou Nourou Tall Centre

1988. Olympic Games, Seoul. Multicoloured.

956	5 f. Type **323**	5	5
957	75 f. Athletics, swimming and football	30	25
958	300 f. Hodori, flame and sports pictograms	1·75	1·00
959	410 f. Emblem and athletics pictogram	2·40	1·40

1988.

960 **324**	125 f. multicoloured	70	60

1988. Senegal Industries. Multicoloured.

961	5 f. Type **325**	5	5
962	20 f. Chemical industry	8	5
963	145 f. Diourbel factory	85	50
964	410 f. Mbao refinery	2·40	1·40

326 Children and Government Palace

1988. Postcards of 1900. Multicoloured.

965	20 f. Type **326**	8	5
966	145 f. Wrestlers and St. Louis Grand Mosque	85	50
967	180 f. Old Dakar railway station and young woman	1·10	65
968	200 f. Goree Governor's residence and young woman	1·25	70

327 "Packia biglobosa" **328** Mask, Rally Car and Eiffel Tower

1988. Flowers. Multicoloured.

969	20 f. Type **327**	8	5
970	60 f. "Euphorbia pulcherrima"	20	15
971	65 f. "Cyrtosperma senegalense"	25	20
972	410 f. "Bombax costatum"	2·60	1·40

1989. 11th Paris–Dakar Rally. Multicoloured.

973	10 f. Type **328**	5	5
974	145 f. Crash helmet and sand dunes	60	55
975	180 f. Turban and motor cyclist	1·10	70
976	220 f. Motor cyclist and Thierry Sabine	1·40	85

329 Teranga Hotel

330 Senegal Tourism Emblem

1989. Tourism (1st series). Multicoloured.
977 10 f. Type **329** 5 5
978 80 f. Thatched hut and shades on beach .. 30 25
979 100 f. Saly hotel 40 35
980 350 f. Dior hotel .. .. 2·50 1·25

1989. Tourism (2nd series). Multicoloured.
981 130 f. Type **330** 75 45
982 140 f. Rural tourism (horiz) 85 50
983 145 f. Fishing (horiz) .. 1·00 55
984 180 f. Water sports (horiz) 1·00 70

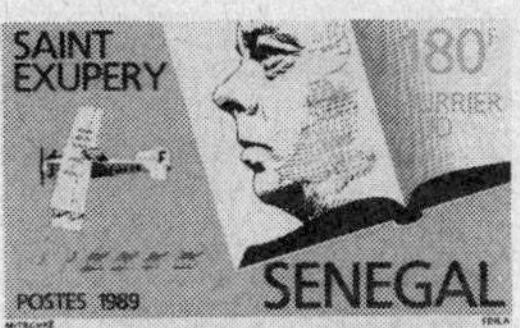

331 Saint-Exupery and Scene from "Courrier Sud"

1989. 45th Anniv of Disappearance of Antoine de Saint-Exupery (pilot and writer).
985 **331** 180 f. black, orange and grey .. .. 1·40 50
986 – 220 f. black, bl & grey 1·75 75
987 – 410 f. multicoloured .. 3·50 1·25
DESIGNS: 220 f. Scene from "Vol de Nuit"; 410 f. Scene from "Pilote de Guerre".

332 Presentation of Lists of Grievances by People of St. Louis

1989. Bicentenary of French Revolution. Multicoloured.
988 180 f. Type **332** .. .. 1·25 1·00
989 220 f. Declaration of Rights of Man, quill pen in hand and phrygian cap (vert) .. .. .. 1·25 1·10
990 300 f. Revolutionaries and flag .. .. .. 2·00 1·50

333 Arts and Culture

335 Stamps

1989. 3rd Francophone Summit. Mult.
991 5 f. Type **333** 5 5
992 30 f. Education (horiz) .. 12 10
993 100 f. Communication (horiz) 40 35
994 200 f. Development (horiz) 1·25 75

1989. No. 960 surch.
995 555 f. on 125 f. mult .. 2·75 1·00

1989. "Philexfrance 89" International Stamp Exhibition, Paris. Multicoloured.
996 10 f. Type **335** 5 5
997 25 f. Stamp on map of France (vert) 10 8
998 75 f. Couple viewing stamp on easel (vert) .. 30 25
999 145 f. Sticking stamp on envelope (vert) .. 60 55

336 "30", Dish Aerial and Envelope

337 Record Stacks and 1922 Postcard

1989. 30th Anniversary Meeting of West African Post and Telecommunications Administrations Conference, Dakar. Mult.
1000 25 f. Type **336** 10 8
1001 30 f. Telephone handset, punched tape and map on stamp 12 10
1002 180 f. Map of Africa, stamp and telephone earpiece .. .. 1·10 70
1003 220 f. Stamp, satellite, globe and map of Africa 1·25 85

1989. 75th Anniv (1988) of Senegal Archives. Multicoloured.
1004 15 f. Type **337** 5 5
1005 40 f. 1825 document .. 15 10
1006 145 f. 1825 document and archive building .. 85 55
1007 180 f. Bound volume .. 1·00 70

338 Jar with Lid

339 Nehru

1989. Pottery. Multicoloured.
1008 15 f. Type **338** 5 5
1009 30 f. Potter at work .. 12 10
1010 75 f. Stacked pots .. 30 25
1011 145 f. Woman carrying pots 85 55

1989. Birth Centenary of Jawaharlal Nehru (Indian statesman).
1012 **339** 220 f. multicoloured .. 1·25 85
1013 – 410 f. black, red & yell 2·50 1·40
DESIGN—HORIZ. 410 f. Nehru (different).

340 Swimming Crab

1989. Marine Life. Multicoloured.
1014 10 f. Type **340** 5 5
1015 60 f. Seahorse (vert) .. 25 20
1016 145 f. Barnacles .. 85 55
1017 220 f. Sand-hopper .. 1·25 85

341 Clasped Hand and People of Different Races

342 Pilgrims

1989. World Aids Day. Multicoloured.
1018 5 f. Type **341** 5 5
1019 100 f. People under umbrella 40 35
1020 145 f. Fist smashing Aids virus 85 55
1021 180 f. Hammer smashing Aids virus .. .. 1·10 70

1989. Centenary of Pilgrimage to Our Lady of Popenguine. Multicoloured.
1022 145 f. Type **342** 60 55
1023 180 f. Our Lady of Popenguine Church .. 1·10 70

343 White-breasted Cormorant and African Darter, Djoudj

344 Boy looking at Christmas Tree

1989. National Parks. Multicoloured.
1024 10 f. Type **343** 10 10
1025 45 f. Grey-headed gulls, Langue de Barbarie .. 30 20
1026 100 f. Blue-cheeked bee eater and crested eagle, Basse Casamance .. 55 45
1027 180 f. Western reef herons, Saloum .. .. 1·75 85

1989. Christmas. Multicoloured.
1028 10 f. Type **344** 5 5
1029 25 f. Teddy bear and bauble hanging from tree 10 8
1030 30 f. Animals around Baby Jesus 12 10
1031 200 f. Madonna and Child 1·25 75

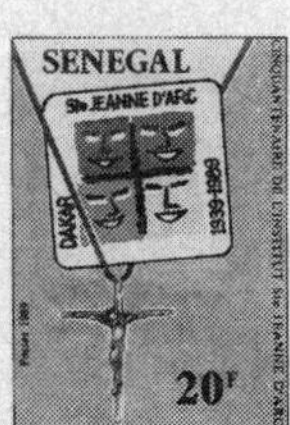

345 Crucifix and Anniversary Emblem

1989. 50th Anniv of St. Joan of Arc Institute, Dakar. Multicoloured.
1032 20 f. Type **345** 8 5
1033 500 f. Emblem and Institute building .. 2·75 1·40

346 Seaplane

1989. 79th Anniv of First Flight of Henri Fabre's Seaplane. Multicoloured.
1034 125 f. Type **346** 60 55
1035 130 f. Fabre working on seaplane 60 55
1036 475 f. Diagrams and Fabre (vert) .. .. 3·25 1·00

347 Basketball

1990. Olympic Games, Barcelona (1992). Mult.
1038 10 f. Type **347** 5 5
1039 130 f. High jumping .. 50 45
1040 180 f. Throwing the discus 75 70
1041 190 f. Running .. 80 75
1042 315 f. Lawn tennis .. 1·25 1·00
1043 475 f. Show jumping .. 1·90 1·75

348 Rally Car

1990. 12th Paris–Dakar Rally. Multicoloured.
1045 20 f. Type **348** 8 5
1046 25 f. Motor cycle and sidecar 10 8
1047 180 f. Crowd cheering winning driver .. 1·10 70
1048 200 f. Thierry Sabine and car .. .. .. 1·10 75

349 Piazza della Signoria, Florence, and Footballer

1990. World Cup Football Championship, Italy. Multicoloured.
1049 45 f. Type **349** 20 15
1050 140 f. Piazza Navona, Rome 55 25
1051 180 f. "Virgin with St. Anne and Infant Jesus" (Leonardo da Vinci) .. 75 30
1052 220 f. "Giuseppe Garibaldi" (oil painting) 1·10 30
1053 300 f. "Sistine Madonna" (Raphael) .. .. 1·50 40
1054 415 f. "Virgin and Child" (Danielle da Volterra) 2·10 70

350 Footballer

351 Facsimile Telegraphy

1990. African Nations Cup Football Championship, Algeria. Multicoloured.
1056 20 f. Type **350** 8 5
1057 60 f. Goalkeeper 25 20
1058 100 f. Clasped hands and pennants 40 35
1059 500 f. Trophy .. .. 3·00 1·75

1990. Postal Services. Multicoloured.
1060 5 f. Type **351** 5 5
1061 15 f. Express Mail Service 5 5
1062 100 f. Postal cheques .. 40 35
1063 180 f. Savings 75 40

352 Hands and Umbrella protecting Children

353 Envelopes on Map

1990. Louga S.O.S. Children's Village. Mult.
1064 5 f. Type **352** 5 5
1065 500 f. Children under umbrella .. .. 2·50 1·25

1990. 20th Anniv of Multinational Postal Training School, Abidjan. Multicoloured.
1066 145 f. Type **353** 60 55
1067 180 f. Man carrying wreath containing envelope 75 70

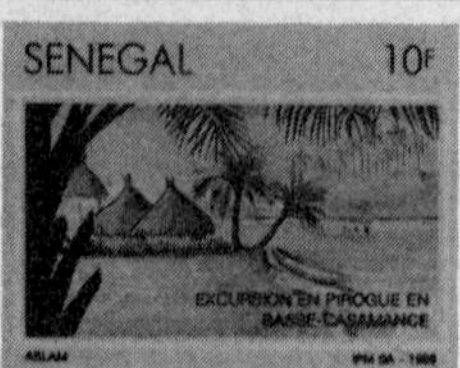

354 Excursion by Pirogue, Basse-Casamance

1990. Tourism. Multicoloured.

1068	10 f. Type **354**	10	10
1069	25 f. Hotel and beach, Goree	10	10
1070	30 f. Houses on stilts, Fadiouth	15	10
1071	40 f. Rose Lake and salt drying	15	10

355 Camp

1990. Scouting. Multicoloured.

1072	30 f. Type **355**	12	10
1073	100 f. Scouts trekking alongside lake ..	40	35
1074	145 f. Scouts trekking through hilly landscape	60	55
1075	200 f. Scout and emblem (vert)	80	75

356 "Cassia tora" **357** Angels and Tree

1990. Medicinal Plants. Multicoloured.

1076	95 f. Type **356**	40	35
1077	105 f. "Tamarind" ..	45	40
1078	125 f. "Cassia occidentalis"	50	45
1079	175 f. "Leptadenia hastata"	70	65

1990. Christmas.

1080	**357**	25 f. multicoloured ..	10	8
1081	–	145 f. multicoloured ..	60	55
1082	–	180 f. orge, red & blk	75	70
1083	–	200 f. multicoloured ..	80	75

DESIGNS: 145 f. Angel trumpeting stars; 180 f. Adoration of Three Kings; 200 f. Donkey and cow gazing at Child.

358 Anniversary Emblem **359** Rally Car

1991. 125th Anniv (1988) of Int. Red Cross and 25th Anniv of Senegal Red Cross.

1084	**358**	180 f. multicoloured ..	70	45

1991. 13th Paris–Dakar Rally. Multicoloured.

1085	15 f. Type **359**	5	5
1086	125 f. Car and motor cycle at night	50	35
1087	180 f. Rally car (different)	70	45
1088	220 f. Motor cycles ..	90	60

360 African Python

1991. Reptiles. Multicoloured.

1089	15 f. Type **360**	5	5
1090	60 f. Common green turtle	25	15
1091	100 f. Nile crocodile ..	40	25
1092	180 f. Senegal chameleon	70	45

361 Sphinx, House of Slaves, Frescoes, Kirdi Houses and Mohammed's Tomb **362** Nobel

1991. "Fespaco", 12th Pan-African Cinema and Television Festival. Multicoloured.

1093	30 f. Type **361**	10	5
1094	60 f. Dogon mask, B. Dioulasso Mosque, drawing of Osiris, and camel rider	25	15
1095	100 f. Rabat, "Seated Scribe" (Egyptian statue), drum and camels	40	25
1096	180 f. Pyramids of Egypt, Djenne Mosque, Guinean mask, Moroccan architecture and Moorish door decorations	70	45

1991. 95th Death Anniv of Alfred Nobel (founder of Nobel prizes). Multicoloured. Self-adhesive.

1097	145 f. Type **362**	60	40
1098	180 f. Nobel and prize presentation (horiz) ..	70	45

363 Oribi

1991. National Parks. Multicoloured.

1099	5 f. Type **363**	5	5
1100	10 f. Dorcas gazelle ..	5	5
1101	180 f. Kob	70	45
1102	555 f. Hartebeest ..	2·25	1·50

364 Cashew

1991. Trees and their Fruit. Multicoloured.

1103	90 f. Type **364**	35	25
1104	100 f. Mango	45	25
1105	125 f. Sugar-palm (vert)	50	35
1106	145 f. Oil palm (vert) ..	60	45

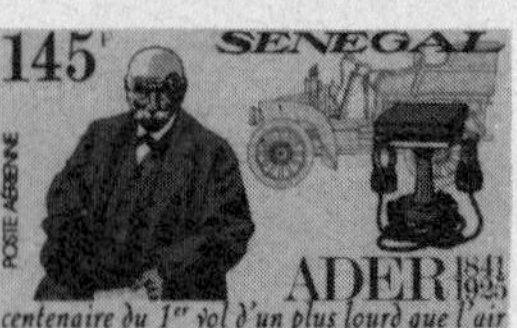

365 Ader, Motor Car and Telephone

1991. Air. Centenary (1990) of First Heavier-than-air Powered Flight. Multicoloured.

1107	145 f. Type **365**	60	40
1108	180 f. Clement Ader and his aircraft "L'Eole" ..	90	55
1109	615 f. "L'Eole" and Ader (vert)	3·00	2·00

366 Columbus and Haitians

1991. 500th Anniv (1992) of Discovery of America by Columbus. Multicoloured.

1111	100 f. Type **366**	40	25
1112	145 f. Arms of Castile and Leon (vert)	60	40
1113	180 f. "Santa Maria" and Columbus	70	45
1114	200 f. Vicente Yanez Pinzon and "Nina" ..	80	55
1115	220 f. Martin Alonzo Pinzon and "Pinta" ..	90	60
1116	500 f. Details of charts ..	2·00	1·25
1117	625 f. Compass rose and Columbus with charts	2·50	1·75

367 Armstrong

1991. 20th Death Anniv of Louis Armstrong (musician). Multicoloured.

1118	10 f. Type **367**	5	5
1119	145 f. Armstrong singing	60	40
1120	180 f. Armstrong and trumpets	70	45
1121	220 f. Armstrong playing trumpet	90	65

368 Yuri Gagarin and "Vostok 1"

1991. 30th Anniv of First Man in Space. Mult.

1125	15 f. Type **368**	5	5
1126	145 f. "Vostok 1" and Gagarin in spacesuit ..	60	40
1127	180 f. Gagarin in spacesuit and "Vostok 1" (different)	70	45
1128	220 f. Globe, "Vostok 1" and Gagarin in flying kit	90	60

369 Flags and Water dripping into Bowl **370** Star and Crescents

1991. "Water, Source of Life". Senegal–Saudi Arabia Rural Water Supply Co-operation. Multicoloured.

1129	30 f. Type **369**	10	5
1130	145 f. Tap and village ..	60	40
1131	180 f. Tap dripping and flags	70	45
1132	220 f. Water tower and village	90	60

1991. 6th Summit Meeting of Islamic Conference Organization, Dakar. Mult.

1133	15 f. Type **370**	5	5
1134	145 f. Hands	60	40
1135	180 f. Conference centre and accommodation ..	70	45
1136	220 f. Grand Mosque, Dakar	90	60

MORE DETAILED LISTS
are given in the Stanley Gibbons Catalogues referred to in the country headings.
For lists of current volumes see Introduction.

371 Player shooting at Basket **372** Giving Blessing

1991. Centenary of Basketball. Mult.

1137	125 f. Type **371**	50	35
1138	145 f. Player approaching basket	60	40
1139	180 f. King and Queen of the Basket	70	45
1140	220 f. Lion, trophies and ball	90	60

1991. Christmas. Multicoloured.

1141	5 f. Type **372**	5	5
1142	145 f. Madonna and Child	60	40
1143	160 f. Angels and star ..	65	45
1144	220 f. Animals and Baby Jesus	90	60

373 Bust of Mozart and Score **374** Flags on Player's Sock

1991. Death Bicentenary of Wolfgang Amadeus Mozart (composer). Mult.

1145	5 f. Type **373**	5	5
1146	150 f. Mozart conducting	60	40
1147	180 f. Mozart at keyboard	70	45
1148	220 f. Mozart and score ..	90	60

1992. 18th African Nations Cup Football Championship. Multicoloured.

1149	10 f. Type **374**	5	5
1150	145 f. Footballs forming "92"	70	45
1151	200 f. Cup and mascot ..	95	65
1152	220 f. Players	1·10	75

1992. Papal Visit. No. 1143 surch **VISITE DU PAPE JEAN PAUL II AU SENEGAL 19 - 23 / 02 / 92 180F.**

1153	180 f. on 160 f. mult ..	85	55

376 Saloum Delta

1992. National Parks. Multicoloured.

1154	10 f. Type **376**	5	5
1155	125 f. Djoudj	60	40
1156	145 f. Niokolo-Koba ..	70	45
1157	220 f. Basse Casamance ..	1·10	75

377 Oil Wells, Flag and Bombs **378** Frozen Fish

1992. Participation of Senegal Contingent in Gulf War. Multicoloured.

1158	30 f. Type **377**	15	10
1159	145 f. Senegalese officer ..	70	45
1160	180 f. Kaaba and Senegalese guard ..	85	55
1161	220 f. Map, dove and flag	1·10	75

1992. Fish Products. Multicoloured.

1162	5 f. Type **378**	5	5
1163	60 f. Sandwich seller and platters of fish ..	30	20
1164	100 f. Woman filleting fish	40	25
1165	150 f. Women packing prawns	70	45

379 Niokolo Complex

1992. Tourist Sites. Multicoloured.
1166 5 f. Type **379** 5 5
1167 10 f. Basse Casamance .. 5 5
1168 150 f. Dakar 70 45
1169 200 f. Saint-Louis .. 95 65

380 Teacher and Pupils carrying Saplings

1992. Reforestation by Schoolchildren. Mult.
1170 145 f. Type **380** 70 45
1171 180 f. Planting sapling .. 85 55
1172 200 f. Planting saplings (different) 95 65
1173 220 f. Watering-in sapling (vert) .. .. .. 1·10 75

381 People with Cleaning Materials

1992. Manpower Services Operation, Setal. Multicoloured.
1174 25 f. Type **381** 10 5
1175 145 f. Clearing road .. 70 45
1176 180 f. Sweeping streets (vert) 85 55
1177 220 f. Painting kerbstones (vert) .. .. .. 1·10 75

382 Education

1992. Rights of the Child. Multicoloured.
1178 20 f. Type **382** 10 5
1179 45 f. Vocational training 20 15
1180 165 f. Instruction .. 80 55
1181 180 f. Health 85 55

383 Customs Post (Free Trade)

1992. African Integration. Multicoloured.
1182 10 f. Type **383** 5 5
1183 30 f. Silhouettes (youth activities) 15 10
1184 145 f. Communications equipment 70 45
1185 220 f. Women's movements .. .. .. 1·10 75

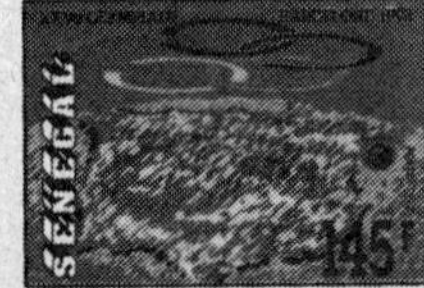

384 Rings and Map of Spain

1992. Olympic Games, Barcelona. Mult.
1186 145 f. Type **384** 70 45
1187 180 f. Runner (vert) .. 85 55
1188 200 f. Sprinter .. 95 65
1189 300 f. Athlete carrying torch (vert) .. .. 1·40 95

385 Passenger Carriages

1992. "The Blue Train". Multicoloured.
1190 70 f. Type **385** 35 25
1191 145 f. Locomotives and carriages 70 45
1192 200 f. Train and track on map 95 65
1193 220 f. Railway station .. 1·10 75

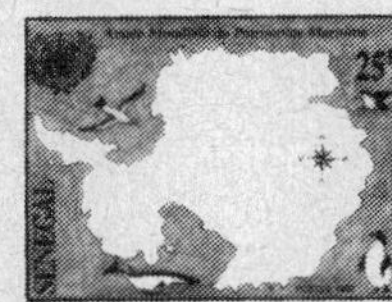

386 Sealife around Map of Antarctic

1992. International Maritime Heritage Year.
1194 **386** 25 f. black, blue & yell 10 5
1195 – 100 f. multicoloured .. 40 25
1196 – 180 f. multicoloured .. 85 55
1197 – 220 f. multicoloured .. 1·10 75
DESIGNS—VERT. 100 f. Marine life caught in sun ray; 180 f. United Nations seminar; 220 f. Fish, ship, flags and hands holding globe.

387 Coral

1992. Corals.
1198 **387** 50 f. multicoloured .. 25 15
1199 – 100 f. multicoloured .. 40 25
1200 – 145 f. mult (vert) .. 70 45
1201 – 220 f. multicoloured .. 1·10 75
DESIGNS: 100 f. to 220 f. Different corals.

388 Adenauer

389 Crab

1992. 25th Death Anniv of Konrad Adenauer (German statesman). Multicoloured.
1202 5 f. Type **388** 5 5
1203 145 f. Schaumburg Palace and flags (horiz) .. 70 45
1204 180 f. German flag and handshake (horiz) .. 85 55
1205 220 f. Map, flag and emblem of Germany (horiz) .. .. 1·10 75

1992. Crustaceans. Multicoloured.
1206 20 f. Type **389** 10 5
1207 30 f. Sea spider 15 10
1208 180 f. Crayfish 85 55
1209 200 f. King prawn .. 95 65

390 "Parkia biglobosa"

1992. Flowers and their Fruits. Mult.
1210 10 f. Type **390** 5 5
1211 50 f. Desert date .. 25 15
1212 200 f. "Parinari macrphylla" 95 65
1213 220 f. Cactus .. .. 1·10 75

391 Rocket and Earth

1992. 30th Anniv of First American Manned Orbit of the Earth. Multicoloured.
1214 15 f. Type **391** 5 5
1215 145 f. American flag and John Glenn 35 25
1216 180 f. Rocket launch and globe 45 30
1217 200 f. Astronaut and rocket on launch-pad (vert) 45 30

392 Bakari II and Map from 14th-century Catalan Atlas

1992. Bakari II. Multicoloured.
1218 100 f. Type **392** 40 25
1219 145 f. Giant Mexican carved head and map from 15th-century atlas 75 45

393 Picture Frame and Obelisk

394 Children dancing round Decorated Globe

1992. Dakar Biennale. Multicoloured.
1220 20 f. Type **393** 5 5
1221 50 f. Mask hanging from window frame .. 10 10
1222 145 f. Open book .. 35 25
1223 220 f. Traditional string instrument 50 35

1992. Christmas. Multicoloured.
1224 15 f. Type **394** 5 5
1225 145 f. People around tree (vert) 35 25
1226 180 f. Jesus (vert) .. 45 30
1227 200 f. Father Christmas (vert) 45 30

1993. 15th Paris–Dakar Rally. Nos. 941 and 975 surch **Dakar le 17-01-93** and new value.
1228 145 f. on 180 f. mult .. 35 25
1229 220 f. on 410 f. mult .. 50 35

396 First Aid Post

1993. Accident Prevention Campaign. Mult.
1230 20 f. Type **396** (prevention, security and first aid) 5 5
1231 25 f. The Sonacos incident (reinforcement of preventative measures) (36 × 28 mm) 10 5
1232 145 f. Chemical accident (need for vigilance and security) (36 × 28 mm) 35 25
1233 200 f. Helicopter rescue (rapid and efficient intervention at air disasters) 45 30

397 Seck

398 Spotted Hyena

1993. 120th Birth Anniv of Abdoulaye Seck (Director of Posts and Telecommunications).
1234 **397** 220 f. multicoloured .. 50 35

1993. Wild Animals. Multicoloured.
1235 30 f. Type **398** 5 5
1236 50 f. Lioness 10 5
1237 70 f. Leopard 15 10
1238 150 f. Giraffe (vert) .. 35 25
1239 180 f. Stag 45 30

OFFICIAL STAMPS

O **45.** Arms of Dakar.

O **78.** Baobab Tree.

1961. Figures of value in black.
O 240. O **45.** 1 f. black and blue .. 5 5
O 241. 2 f. blue and yellow 5 5
O 242. 5 f. lake and green .. 8 8
O 243. 10 f. red and blue .. 10 8
O 244. 25 f. blue and red .. 20 12
O 245. 50 f. red and grey .. 75 30
O 246. 85 f. purple & orange 1·40 45
O 247. 100 f. red and green 2·00 1·10

1966.
O 339 O **78** 1 f. black & yell 5 5
O 340 5 f. black & orge 5 5
O 341 10 f. black & red 8 5
O 342 20 f. black & pur 12 5
O 342a 25 f. blk & mave 12 5
O 343 30 f. black & blue 15 8
O 344 35 f. black & blue 20 10
O 344a 40 f. black & blue 20 10
O1122 50 f. black & red 20 15
O 345 55 f. black & grn 35 20
O 345a 60 f. black & grn 45 20
O 346 90 f. black & grn 50 35
O 347 100 f. black & brn 60 40
O1123 145 f. black & grn 55 35
O1124 180 f. blk & orge 70 45

1969. No. O 345 surch.
O 390. O **78.** 60 f. on 55 f. black and green .. 85 10

POSTAGE DUE STAMPS

1903. Postage Due stamps of French Colonies surch.
D30 U 10 on 50 c. purple .. 50·00 50·00
D31 10 on 60 c. brn on buff 50·00 50·00
D32 10 on 1 f. pink on buff £250 £250

1906. "Natives" key-type.
D50 L 5 c. green and red .. 3·00 3·00
D51 10 c. purple and blue .. 4·00 3·50
D52 15 c. blue & red on blue 4·50 4·25
D53 20 c. black & red on yell 5·25 3·75
D54 30 c. red & bl on cream 6·00 5·25
D55 50 c. violet and red .. 6·00 5·50
D56 60 c. blk & red on buff 7·50 7·25
D57 1 f. black & red on pink 12·00 13·00

1915. "Figure" key-type.
D 81. M. 5 c. green 15 30
D 82. 10 c. red 25 20
D 83. 15 c. grey 25 25
D 84. 20 c. brown 50 40
D 85. 30 c. blue 75 70
D 86. 50 c. black .. .. 1·00 90
D 87. 60 c. orange .. 1·25 1·25
D 88. 1 f. violet .. .. 1·40 1·50

1927. Surch. in figures.
D 133. M. 2 f. on 1 f. purple .. 2·75 2·75
D 134. 3 f. on 1 f. brown .. 2·75 2·75

D **40.**

1935.
D 194. D **40.** 5 c. green 10 25
D 195. 10 c. orange .. 10 25
D 196. 15 c. violet 10 25
D 197. 20 c. olive 10 25
D 198. 30 c. brown .. 10 25
D 199. 50 c. purple .. 40 65
D 200. 60 c. yellow .. 75 80
D 201. 1 f. black 50 50
D 202. 2 f. blue 55 65
D 203. 3 f. red 75 95

D 43.

D 77. Lion's Head.

1961.

D 239. D 43. 1 f. orange and red 5 5
D 240. 2 f. blue and red .. 5 5
D 241. 5 f. brown and red 10 10
D 242. 20 f. green and red 25 25
D 243. 25 f. purple and red 5·50 5·50

1966. Head in gold and black; value in black.

D 339. D 77. 1 f. red 12 12
D 340. 2 f. brown .. 12 12
D 341. 5 f. violet 20 20
D 342. 10 f. blue 40 40
D 343. 20 f. green.. .. 50 50
D 344. 30 f. grey 65 65
D 345. 60 f. blue 65 65
D 346. 90 f. purple .. 75 75

SENEGAMBIA AND NIGER Pt. 6

A French colony later re-named Upper Senegal and Niger, and later French Sudan.

100 centimes = 1 franc

1903. "Tablet" key-type inscr "SENEGAMBIE ET NIGER" in red (1, 5, 15, 25, 75 c., 1 f.) or blue (others).

22 D 1 c. black on blue .. 50 1·10
23 2 c. brown on buff .. 1·00 1·25
24 4 c. brown on grey .. 1·40 2·25
25 5 c. green .. .. 3·75 2·00
26 10 c. red .. .. 3·75 2·00
27 15 c. grey .. .. 6·75 5·75
28 20 c. red on green .. 6·50 6·75
29 25 c. blue .. .. 9·50 9·50
30 30 c. brown on drab .. 8·75 9·50
31 40 c. red on yellow .. 14·00 14·00
32 50 c. brown on blue .. 25·00 28·00
33 75 c. brown on orange .. 30·00 32·00
34 1 f. green .. .. 38·00 40·00

SERBIA Pt. 3

A kingdom in the Balkans, S.E. Europe. Part of Yugoslavia since 1918. except during the Second World War when stamps were issued by a German-sponsored Government.

100 paras = 1 dinar.

2. Prince Michael (Obrenovich III).

3. Prince Milan (Obrenovich IV).

5. King Milan I.

1866. Perf.

12. 2. 10 p. orange .. .. 70·00 90·00
15. 20 p. red .. .. .. 12·50 18·00
14. 40 p. blue .. .. .. 42·00 32·00

1869. Perf.

42. 3. 10 p. brown .. .. 4·75 4·00
45. 10 p. orange .. .. 1·25 3·00
31. 15 p. orange .. .. 45·00 23·00
43. 20 p. blue .. .. .. 1·10 1·25
39. 25 p. red .. .. .. 1·90 4·75
34. 35 p. green .. .. 3·50 3·50
47. 40 p. mauve .. .. 1·90 1·50
36. 50 p. green .. .. 6·00 4·75

1880. Perf.

54a. 5. 5 p. green 25 10
55. 10 p. red 50 10
56. 20 p. orange 35 20
57a. 25 p. blue .. .. 1·25 15
58. 50 p. brown .. .. 1·00 2·10
59. 1 d. violet .. .. 6·75 7·50

6.

7.

10.

King Alexander (Obrenovich V.).

1890.

60. 6. 5 p. green 25 10
61. 10 p. red 50 10
62. 15 p. mauve 50 10
63. 20 p. orange 45 10
64. 25 p. blue 60 20
65. 50 p. brown .. .. 2·40 2·40
66. 1 d. lilac .. .. .. 8·75 7·75

1894.

75. 7. 1 p. red 5 5
76. 5 p. green 75 5
68. 10 p. red .. .. .. 2·00 5
69. 15 p. mauve .. .. 4·00 5
79. 20 p. orange .. .. 4·50 10
80. 25 p. blue .. .. 4·50 15
81a. 50 p. brown .. .. 9·00 80
73. 1 d. green .. .. 1·25 1·60
74. 1 d. red on blue .. 7·50 2·50

1900. Surch.

82. 7. 10 p. on 20 p. red .. 1·00 5
84. 15 p. on 1 d. red on blue .. 3·75 75

1901.

85a. 10. 5 p. green 10 5
86. 10 p. red 10 5
87. 15 p. mauve 10 5
88. 20 p. orange 10 5
89. 25 p. blue 15 5
90. 50 p. yellow 20 12
91. – 1 d. brown .. .. 60 1·40
92a. – 3 d. pink .. .. 6·25 8·75
93a. – 5 d. violet .. .. 6·25 9·50

The 1 d. to 5 d. are larger.

12. King Alexander I (Obrenovich V).

14. Karageorge and Peter I.

1903. Optd. with shield.

94. 12. 1 p. black and red .. 30 60
95. 5 p. black and green .. 25 5
96. 10 p. black and red .. 10 5
97. 15 p. black and grey .. 10 5
98. 20 p. black and orange 15 10
99. 25 p. black and blue .. 20 10
100. 50 p. black and grey .. 3·00 55
101. 1 d. black and green .. 9·50 3·00
102. 3 d. black and lilac .. 1·90 2·25
103. 5 d. black and brown .. 1·90 2·50

1903. Surch. **1 NAPA 1.**

104. 12. 1 p. on 5 d. black & brown 95 2·50

1904. Coronation. Cent. of Karageorgevich Dynasty. Dated "1804 1904".

108. 14. 5 p. green 10 5
109. 10 p. red 10 5
110. 15 p. purple 10 10
111. 25 p. blue 15 15
112. 50 p. brown 25 25
113. – 1 d. bistre 60 75
114. – 3 d. green .. .. 1·50 3·00
115. – 5 d. violet .. .. 1·90 3·75

DESIGN: 1 d., 3 d., 5 d. Karageorge and insurgents, 1804.

16. Peter I.

17. Peter I.

1905.

116. 16. 1 p. black and grey .. 12 5
117. 5 p. black and green .. 20 5
118. 10 p. black and red .. 1·90 5
119. 15 p. black and mauve 2·10 5
120. 20 p. black and yellow 3·75 5
121. 25 p. black and blue .. 5·25 5
122. 30 p. black and green .. 2·75 10
123. 50 p. black and brown 3·75 10
135. 1 d. black and bistre .. 80 12
136. 3 d. black and green .. 80 80
137. 5 d. black and violet .. 3·00 2·25

1911.

146. 17. 1 p. black 5 5
147. 2 p. violet 5 5
169. 5 p. green 5 5
170. 10 p. red 5 5
150. 15 p. purple 70 5
171. 15 p. black 5 5
151. 20 p. yellow 70 10
172. 20 p. brown 35 20
173. 25 p. blue 5 5
153. 30 p. green 20 15
173a. 30 p. bronze 5 20
154. 50 p. brown 30 20
174. 50 p. red 5 20
155. 1 d. orange .. .. 18·00 32·00
175. 1 d. green .. .. 1·00 1·75
156. 3 d. lake .. .. .. 24·00 70·00
176. 3 d. yellow .. .. 95·00 £375
177. 5 d. violet .. .. 2·10 17·00

19. Peter I on the Battlefield.

20. Peter I and Prince Alexander.

1915.

178. 19. 5 p. green .. .. 12 1·00
179. 10 p. red .. .. 12 1·25
179a. 15 p. grey .. .. 3·00
179b. 20 p. brown 40
179c. 25 p. blue .. .. 6·25
179d. 30 p. green .. .. 3·00
179e. 50 p. brown .. .. 24·00

1918.

194. 20. 1 p. black 8 5
195. 2 p. olive 8 5
196. 5 p. green 8 5
197. 10 p. red 8 5
198. 15 p. sepia 8 5
199. 20 p. brown 8 5
208. 20 p. mauve .. .. 1·40 75
200. 25 p. blue 8 5
201. 30 p. olive 8 5
202. 50 p. mauve 8 5
220. 1 d. brown 8 5
204. 3 d. slate 90 75
205. 5 d. brown .. .. 1·50 90

NEWSPAPER STAMPS

1.

4. King Milan.

1866. Imperf.

N 7. 1. 1 p. green on red .. 45·00
N 4. 2 p. brown on lilac .. 60·00

1867. Perf.

N 17. 2. 1 p. olive .. .. 9·25 £550
N 18. 2 p. brown .. .. 15·00 £500

1868. Imperf.

N 19. 2. 1 p. green .. .. 15·00
N 20. 2 p. brown .. .. 24·00

1869. Perf.

N 49. 3. 1 p. yellow .. .. 1·25 £275

1872. Imperf.

N 51. 3. 1 p. yellow .. .. 5·50 11·00
N 52. 4. 2 p. black .. .. 1·90 9·25

POSTAGE DUE STAMPS

D 8.

D 21.

1895.

D 87. D 8. 5 p. mauve 40 25
D 83. 10 p. blue .. .. 2·50 20
D 91. 20 p. brown 15 45
D 85. 30 p. green 12 35
D 86. 50 p. red 15 45

1918.

D 227. D 21. 5 p. red 15 15
D 232. 5 p. brown 20 25
D 228. 10 p. green 15 15
D 229. 20 p. brown 15 15
D 230. 30 p. blue 15 15
D 233. 30 p. grey 30 35
D 231. 50 p. brown 75 35

GERMAN OCCUPATION

1941. Stamps of Yugoslavia on paper with coloured network optd. **SERBIEN** reading downwards.

G 1. 99. 25 p. black 8 75
G 2. 50 p. orange 5 20
G 3. 1 d. green 8 20
G 4. 1 d. 50 red 8 20
G 5. 2 d. red 8 20
G 6. 3 d. brown .. .. 75 4·25
G 7. 4 d. blue 12 55
G 8. 5 d. blue .. .. 40 1·75
G 9. 5 d. 50 violet .. .. 40 1·75
G 10. 6 d. blue .. .. 40 1·75
G 11. 8 d. brown .. .. 55 2·75
G 12. 12 d. violet .. .. 55 2·75
G 13. 16 d. purple .. .. 90 7·00
G 14. 20 d. blue .. .. 90 8·50
G 15. 30 d. pink .. .. 4·50 55·00

1941. Air. Stamps of Yugoslavia on paper with coloured network, optd. **SERBIEN.**

G 16. 80. 50 p. brown .. .. 3·50 19·00
G 17. – 1 d. green (No. 361) .. 3·50 19·00
G 18. – 2 d. blue (No. 362) .. 3·50 19·00
G 19. – 2 d. 50 red (No. 363) .. 3·50 19·00
G 20. 80. 5 d. violet .. .. 3·50 19·00
G 21. – 10 d. red (No. 365) .. 3·50 19·00
G 22. – 20 d. green (No. 366) 3·50 19·00
G 23. – 30 d. blue (No. 367) .. 4·75 21·00
G 24. – 40 d. green (No. 443) 8·00 £100
G 25. – 50 d. blue (No. 444) .. 40·00 80·00

1941. Air. As last, but without network surch. **SERBIEN** and value.

G 26. – 1 d. on 10 d. red (No. 365) .. .. .. 2·00 13·50
G 27. – 3 d. on 20 d. grn. (No. 366) .. .. .. 2·00 13·50
G 28. – 6 d. on 30 d. blue (No. 367) .. .. .. 2·00 13·50
G 29. – 8 d. on 40 d. grn. (No. 443) .. .. .. 2·50 38·00
G 30. – 12 d. on 50 d. bl. (No. 444) .. .. .. 4·75 65·00

1941. As Nos. G1/15, but with **SERBIEN** reading upwards.

G 31. 99. 25 p. black .. .. 10 3·00
G 32. 50 p. orange 10 55
G 33. 1 d. green 12 35
G 34. 1 d. 50 red 12 60
G 35. 2 d. red 12 35
G 36. 3 d. brown .. .. 25 4·00
G 37. 4 d. blue 20 35
G 38. 5 d. blue .. .. 20 1·00
G 39. 5 d. 50 violet .. .. 40 3·00
G 40. 6 d. blue .. .. 50 3·00
G 41. 8 d. brown .. .. 70 3·00
G 42. 12 d. violet .. .. 90 3·00
G 43. 16 d. purple .. .. 90 8·50
G 44. 20 d. blue .. .. 90 14·00
G 45. 30 d. pink .. .. 5·50 48·00

4. Smederovo Fortress.

6. Christ and the Virgin Mary.

1941. Smederevo Explosion Relief Fund.

G 46. 4. 50 p.+1 d. brown .. 15 70
G 47. – 1 d.+2 d. green .. 15 75
G 48. – 1 d. 50+3 d. purple .. 30 1·25
G 49. 4. 2 d.+4 d. blue .. 40 2·00

DESIGN: 1 d., 1 d. 50, Refugees.

1941. Prisoners of War Fund.

G 50. 6. 50 p.+1 d. 50 brown 20 3·00
G 51. 1 d.+3 d. green .. 20 3·00
G 52. 2 d.+6 d. red .. 20 3·00
G 53. 4 d.+12 d. blue .. 20 3·00

This set also exists with an optd. network, both plain and incorporating a large "E", this letter being either normal or reversed.

7. 8.

1942. Anti-Masonic Exn. Dated "22.X.1941".

G 54. 7. 50 p.+50 p. brown .. 12 35
G 55. – 1 d.+1 d. green .. 12 35
G 56. 8. 2 d.+2 d. red .. 25 75
G 57. – 4 d.+4 d. blue .. 25 75

DESIGNS—HORIZ. 1 d. Hand grasping snake. VERT. 4 d. Peasant demolishing masonic symbols.

9. Kalenic. 11. Mother and Children.

1942. Monasteries.

G 58. – 50 p. violet 5 12
G 59. 9. 1 d. red 5 10
G 60. – 1 d. 50 brown .. 70 2·50
G 61. – 1 d. 50 green 5 12
G 62. – 2 d. purple 5 12
G 63. – 3 d. blue .. .. 70 2·50
G 64. 3 d. pink 5 12
G 65. – 4 d. blue 5 15
G 66. – 7 d. green 5 15
G 67. – 12 d. red .. .. 15 1·00
G 68. – 16 d. black .. .. 45 1·50

DESIGNS—VERT. 50 p. Lazarica. 1 d. 50, Ravanica. 12 d. Gornjak. 16 d. Studenica. HORIZ. 2 d. Manasija. 3 d. Ljubostinja. 4 d. Sopocani. 7 d. Zica.

1942. As Nos. G50/53, colours changed.

G 68a. 6. 0·50 d.+1·50 d. brn. 50 1·40
G 68b. 1 d.+3 d. green .. 50 1·40
G 68c. 2 d.+6 d. red .. 50 1·40
G 68d. 4 d.+12 d. blue .. 50 1·40

1942. Air. 1939 issue of Yugoslavia optd. with aeroplane and surch. new value.

G 69. 99. 2 on 2 d. mauve .. 10 1·25
G 70. 4 on 4 d. blue .. 10 1·25
G 71. 10 on 12 d. violet .. 15 2·00
G 72. 14 on 20 d. blue .. 15 2·00
G 73. 20 on 30 d. pink .. 50 9·00

1942. War Orphans Fund.

G 74. 11. 2 d.+6 d. violet .. 1·00 2·50
G 75. 4 d.+8 d. blue .. 1·00 2·50
G 76. 7 d.+13 d. green .. 1·00 2·50
G 77. 20 d.+40 d. red .. 1·00 2·50

12. Broken Sword. 13. Post Rider.

1943. War Invalids' Relief Fund.

G 78. 12. 1 d. 50+1 d. 50 brn. 40 90
G 79. – 2 d.+3 d. green .. 40 90
G 80. – 3 d.+5 d. mauve .. 60 1·60
G 81. – 4 d.+10 d. blue .. 90 2·50

DESIGNS—HORIZ. 2 d. Fallen standard bearer. 3 d. Wounded soldier (seated). VERT. 4 d. Nurse tending soldier.

1943. Postal Centenary. Inscr. "15.X.1843–15.X.1943".

G 82. 13. 3 d. red and lilac .. 30 1·10
G 83. – 8 d. mauve and grey 30 1·10
G 84. – 9 d. green and brown 75 1·00
G 85. – 30 d. brown and green 30 1·10
G 86. – 50 d. blue and red .. 30 1·10

DESIGNS—HORIZ. 8 d. Horse wagon. 9 d. Railway van. 30 d. Postal motor van. 50 d. Mail 'plane.

1943. Bombing of Nish Relief Fund. Monasteries issue of 1942 on paper with network, surch. ...**20-X-1943** and value in figures.

G 87. 50 p.+2 d. violet .. .. 8 2·00
G 88. 1 d.+3 d. red .. .. 8 2·00
G 89. 1 d. 50+4 d. green .. 8 2·00
G 90. 2 d.+5 d. purple .. .. 12 2·00
G 91. 3 d.+7 d. pink .. .. 12 2·00
G 92. 4 d.+9 d. blue .. .. 12 2·00
G 93. 7 d.+15 d. green .. .. 40 2·50
G 94. 12 d.+25 d. red .. .. 40 8·00
G 95. 16 d.+33 d. black .. .. 65 13·00

OFFICIAL STAMP

O 12.

1943.

GO 78. O 12. 3 d. red .. .. 30 1·00

POSTAGE DUE STAMPS

D 2. D 3. D 13.

1941. Unissued Postage Due stamps optd. **SERBIEN.**

GD 16. D 2. 50 p. violet .. 35 2·75
GD 17. 1 d. red .. .. 35 2·75
GD 18. 2 d. blue .. .. 35 2·75
GD 19. 3 d. red .. .. 45 3·50
GD 20. D 3. 4 d. blue .. .. 75 7·50
GD 21. 5 d. orange .. 75 7·50
GD 22. 10 d. violet .. 2·00 17·00
GD 23. 20 d. green .. 6·00 70·00

1942. Types D 2 and D 3 without opt. Bottom inscription on white background.

GD 69. D 2. 1 d. red and green 12 1·50
GD 70. 2 d. blue and red .. 12 1·50
GD 71. 3 d. red and blue .. 20 2·50
GD 72. D 3. 4 d. blue and red .. 20 2·50
GD 73. 5 d. orange & bl. 30 2·75
GD 74. 10 d. violet and red 35 6·50
GD 75. 20 d. green and red 95 16·00

1943.

GD 82. D 13. 50 p. black .. 15 1·00
GD 83. 3 d. violet .. 15 1·00
GD 84. 4 d. blue .. 15 1·00
GD 85. 5 d. green .. 15 1·00
GD 86. 6 d. orange .. 25 2·75
GD 87. 10 d. red .. 40 6·00
GD 88. 20 d. blue .. 1·00 13·00

SERBIAN OCCUPATION OF HUNGARY Pt. 2

BARANYA

100 filler = 1 korona.

1919. Stamps of Hungary optd. **1919 Baranya** or surch. also.

(a) "Turul" Type.

1. 7. 6 f. drab 15 15
2. 50 f. lake on blue .. 5 5
3. 60 f. green on red .. 25 25
4. 70 f. brown on green .. 5 5
5. 80 f. violet .. .. 1·75 1·75

(b) War Charity stamp of 1915.

6. 7. 50+2 f. lake on blue .. 3·75 3·75

(c) War Charity stamps of 1916.

8. 20. 10 f. (+2 f.) red .. 5 5
9. – 15 f. (+2 f.) violet .. 5 5

(d) Harvesters and Parliament Types.

10. 18. 2 f. brown 10 10
11. 3 f. red 10 10
12. 5 f. green 10 10
13. 6 f. blue 25 25
14. 15 f. violet 10 10
15. 20 f. brown .. 10·00 10·00
16. 25 f. blue 95 95
17. 35 f. brown .. 2·50 2·50
18. 40 f. olive .. 10·00 10·00
19. 45 on 2 f. brown .. 20 20
20. 45 on 5 f. green .. 5 5
21. 45 on 15 f. violet .. 5 5
22. 19. 50 f. purple 35 35
23. 75 f. blue 12 12
24. 80 f. green 15 15
25. 1 k. lake 15 15
26. 2 k. brown 15 15
27. 3 k. grey and violet .. 15 15
28. 5 k. brown 40 40
29. 60 k. lilac and brown .. 3·00 3·00

(e) Karl and Zita stamps.

30. 27. 10 f. red 5 5
31. 20 f. brown 5 5
32. 25 f. blue 55 55
33. 28. 40 f. olive .. .. 6·00 6·00

The following (Nos. 34/6) are also optd. **KOZTARSASAG.**

(f) Harvesters Types.

34. 18. 2 f. brown .. .. 1·50 1·50
35. 45 on 2 f. brown .. 20 20

(g) Zita stamp.

36. 28. 40 f. olive .. .. 8·00 8·00

1919. Stamps of Hungary surch. **BARANYA** and value.

(h) Harvesters and Parliament Types.

42. 18. 20 on 2 f. brown .. 4·00 4·00
43. 50 on 5 f. green .. .. 2·25 2·25
44. 150 on 15 f. violet .. 80 80
45. 19. 200 on 75 f. blue .. 60 60

(k) Harvester Type inscr. "MAGYAR POSTA".

46. 18. 20 on 2 f. brown .. 10 10
47. 30 on 6 f. blue 20 20
48. 50 on 5 f. green .. 10 10
49. 100 on 25 f. blue .. 10 10
50. 100 on 40 f. olive .. 10 10
51. 100 on 45 f. orange .. 30 30
52. 150 on 20 f. brown .. 25 25

(m) Karl stamp optd. **KOZTARSASAG.**

53. 27. 150 on 15 f. violet .. 75 75

EXPRESS LETTER STAMP

1919. No. E 245 optd. **1919 Baranya.**

E 37. E 18. 105 on 2 f. olive and red 55 55

1919. No. E 245 surch. **BARANYA** and value

E 55. E 18. 10 on 2 f. olive and red 15 15

NEWSPAPER STAMP

1919. No. N 136 surch. **BARANYA** and value.

N 54. N 9. 10 on 2 (f.) orange .. 20 20

POSTAGE DUE STAMPS

1919. Nos. D 191 etc. optd. **BARANYA** or surch. also.

D 38. D 9. 2 f. red .. .. 2·50 2·50
D 39. 10 f. red and green .. 45 45
D 40. 20 f. red and green .. 45 45
D 41. 40 on 2 f. red and green 45 45

SAVINGS BANK STAMP

1919. No. B 199 surch. **BARANYA** and value.

B 56. B 17. 10 on 10 f. purple .. 10 10

TEMESVAR

Temesvar was later occupied by Rumania which issued stamps for this area. It was then incorporated in Rumania and renamed Timosoara.

100 filler = 1 korona.

1919. Stamps of Hungary surch.

(a) War Charity stamp of 1916.

1. 20. 45 f. on 10 f. (+2 f.) red .. 10 10

(b) Harvesters Type.

2. 18. 10 f. on 2 f. brown .. 10 10
3. 30 f. on 2 f. brown .. 10 10
4. 1 k. 50 on 15 f. violet .. 12 12

(c) Karl stamp.

5. 27. 50 f. on 20 f. brown .. 10 10

POSTAGE DUE STAMPS

1919. No. D 191 surch.

D 6. D 9. 40 f. on 2 f. red & green 10 10
D 7. 60 f. on 2 f. red & green 10 10
D 8. 100 f. on 2 f. red & green 10 10

SHANGHAI Pt. 17

A seaport on the E coast of China, which for a time had a separate postal system.

1865. 10 cash = 1 candareen.
100 candareens = 1 tael.
1890. 100 cents = 1 dollar (Chinese).

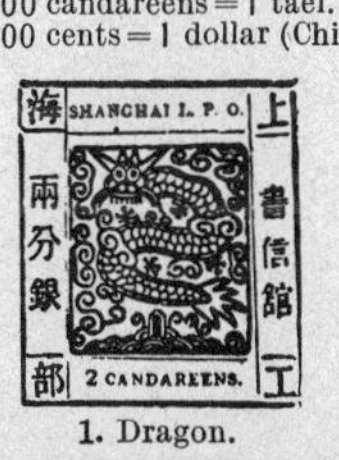

1. Dragon.

1865. Value in candareens. Imperf.

(a) "CANDAREEN" in singular.

28 1 1 ca. blue .. .. 32·00 £300
12 2 ca. black .. .. 85·00 £375
29 3 ca. brown .. .. 28·00
13 4 ca. yellow .. .. 85·00 £375
14 8 ca. green .. .. 60·00
15 16 ca. red .. .. 85·00

(b) "CANDAREENS" in plural

30 1 2 ca. black .. .. 28·00
31 3 ca. brown .. .. 25·00 £325
3 4 ca. yellow .. .. 85·00 £350
18 6 ca. brown .. .. 42·00
20 6 ca. red .. .. 60·00
4 8 ca. green .. .. 90·00 £550
21 12 ca. brown .. .. 40·00
22 16 ca. red .. .. 40·00

2.

6.

1866. Value in cents. Perf.

32. 2. 2 c. red .. .. .. 5·50 17·00
33. 4 c. lilac .. .. .. 9·00 28·00
34. 8 c. blue .. .. .. 12·00 32·00
35. 16 c. green .. .. 18·00 38·00

1867. Value in candareens.

37 6 1 ca. brown .. .. 3·75 6·00
62 1 ca. yellow .. .. 4·50 8·00
73 1 ca. red £350 £650
38 3 ca. yellow .. .. 10·00 22·00
60 3 ca. red .. .. 8·50 10·00
39 6 ca. grey .. .. 10·00 45·00
64 6 ca. green .. .. 35·00
65 9 ca. grey .. .. 42·00
40 12 ca. brown .. .. 18·00 45·00

1873. Surch. with value in English and Chinese.

41. 2. 1 ca. on 2 c. red .. .. 14·00 22·00
44a. 1 ca. on 4 c. lilac .. 8·50 9·00
46. 1 ca. on 8 c. blue .. 11·00 12·00
48. 1 ca. on 16 c. green .. £650 £500
50. 3 ca. on 2 c. red .. .. 42·00 42·00
52. 3 ca. on 16 c. green .. £800 £800

1873. Surch. with value in English and Chinese.

67 6 1 ca. on 3 ca. red .. 25·00 22·00
53 1 ca. on 3 ca. yellow .. £2000 £1800
54 1 ca. on 6 ca. grey .. £150 £120
69 1 ca. on 6 ca. green .. 40·00 35·00
70 1 ca. on 9 ca. grey .. 85·00 85·00
56 1 ca. on 12 ca. brown .. £120 £110
58 3 ca. on 12 ca. brown .. £900 £750

1877. Value in cash.

75 6 20 cash mauve .. .. 2·00 2·75
93 20 cash green .. .. 1·75 2·25
114 20 cash grey .. .. 1·10 1·00
81 40 cash red .. .. 3·50 4·00
94 40 cash brown .. .. 2·00 3·25
107 40 cash black .. .. 1·90 2·75
82 60 cash green .. .. 3·50 3·50
95 60 cash violet .. .. 3·25 4·00
108 60 cash red .. .. 3·25 4·50
83 80 cash blue .. .. 4·00 6·50
96 80 cash brown .. .. 2·75 3·25
109 80 cash green .. .. 2·75 2·75
84 100 cash brown .. .. 4·00 6·00
97 100 cash yellow .. .. 3·75 3·75
110 100 cash blue .. .. 4·00 4·75

1879. Surch. in English and Chinese.

89 6. 20 cash on 40 cash red .. 5·75 6·50
103 20 cash on 40 cash brown 8·00 10·00
105 20 cash on 80 cash brown 3·50 3·00
111 20 cash on 80 cash green 3·25 3·25
112 20 cash on 100 cash blue 3·25 3·25
100 40 cash on 80 cash brown 2·00 3·25
101 40 cash on 100 cash yell 2·75 2·75
90 60 cash on 80 cash blue 12·00 16·00
88 60 cash on 100 cash brn 11·00 18·00
102 60 cash on 100 cash yell 3·50 4·00

1886. Surch. **20 CASH** in English and Chinese in double-lined frame.

104. 6. 20 cash on 40 cash brown 10·00 7·50

1889. Surch. **100 CASH** over **20 CASH** in English and Chinese in double-lined frame.

113. 6. 100 cash on 20 cash on 100 cash yellow .. 30·00 38·00

16. 25.

26.

1890. Value in cents.

119. 16. 2 c. brown .. .. 1·00 1·00
142. 2 c. green 75 75
143. 5 c. red .. .. 2·25 2·25
122. 10 c. black .. .. 3·25 3·75
144. 10 c. orange .. .. 7·00 7·00
121. 15 c. blue .. .. 6·50 7·00
145. 15 c. mauve .. .. 3·50 3·75
124. 20 c. mauve .. .. 3·50 3·75
146. 20 c. brown .. .. 4·00 3·75

1892. Surch. **2 Cts.** and in Chinese.

141. 16. 2 c. on 5 c. red .. .. 32·00 14·00

1893. Surch. in words in English and Chinese.

147. 16. ½ c. on 15 c. mauve .. 3·25 3·00
148. 1 c. on 20 c. brown .. 3·25 3·00

1893. Surch. **½ Ct.** or **1 Ct.**

152. 16. ½ c. on half of 5 c. red .. 2·75 2·75
155. 1 c. on half of 2 c. brown 70 70
156. 1 c. on half of 2 c. green 3·75 3·75

1893. Inscriptions in outer frame in black.

165. 25. ½ c. orange 20 20
166. 1 c. brown 20 20
187. 2 c. red 25 50
188. 4 c. orange on yellow .. 1·25 1·75
161. 5 c. blue 35 50
189. 6 c. red on rose .. .. 1·90 2·10
167. 10 c. green 45 65
163. 15 c. yellow .. .. 70 1·00
168. 20 c. mauve .. .. 75 1·10

1893. Jubilee of First Settlement.
176. **26.** 2 c. red and black .. 50 65

1893. Optd. **1843. Jubilee 1893.** Inscriptions in outer frame in black.
177. **25.** ½ c. orange 20 20
178. 1 c. brown 25 25
179. 2 c. red 30 35
180. 5 c. blue .. .. 1·25 1·50
181. 10 c. green .. .. 1·75 2·10
182. 15 c. yellow .. .. 2·75 3·00
183. 20 c. mauve .. .. 2·75 3·00

1896. Surch. in English and Chinese.
184. **25.** 4 c. on 15 c. yellow .. 3·75 3·75
185. 6 c. on 20 c. mauve .. 3·25 3·25

POSTAGE DUE STAMPS

1892. T **16** optd. **Postage Due.**
D 134. 2 c. brown 60 50
D 135. 5 c. red .. .. 1·90 2·25
D 130. 10 c. black .. .. 8·50 8·50
D 138. 10 c. orange .. .. 3·25 4·00
D 131. 15 c. blue .. .. 6·00 7·00
D 139. 15 c. mauve .. .. 6·00 9·00
D 132. 20 c. mauve .. .. 4·50 4·75
D 140. 20 c. brown .. .. 6·00 7·00

D **26.**

1893. Inscriptions in outer frame in black.
D 169. D **1.** ½ c. orange .. 15 25
D 170. 1 c. brown .. 15 15
D 171. 2 c. red .. 15 40
D 172. 5 c. blue .. 30 45
D 173. 10 c. green .. 35 65
D 174. 15 c. yellow .. 40 1·00
D 175. 20 c. mauve .. 50 90

SHARJAH Pt. 19

Part of the Trucial States on the Persian Gulf. Embodies the principalities of Diba, Khor Fakkan and Kalba.

On 2nd December, 1971, Sharjah, together with six other Gulf Shaikdoms, formed the United Arab Emirates.

1963. 100 naye paise = 1 rupee.
1966. 100 dirhams = 1 riyal.

IMPERF STAMPS. Some sets exist also imperf. in limited quantities.

1. Shaikh Saqr bin Sultan al Qasimi, Flag and Map.

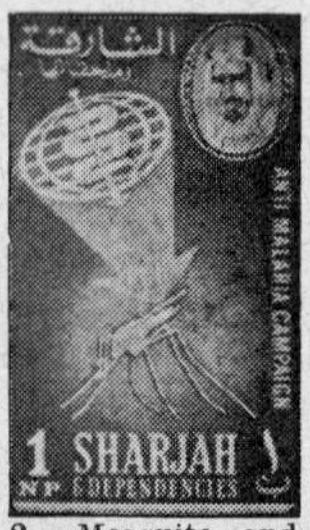

2. Mosquito and W.H.O. Emblem.

1963. Multicoloured.
1. **1.** 1 n.p. (postage) 10 10
2. 2 n.p. 10 10
3. 3 n.p. 10 10
4. 4 n.p. 10 10
5. 5 n.p. 10 10
6. 6 n.p. 10 10
7. 8 n.p. 10 10
8. 10 n.p. 10 10
9. 16 n.p. 15 10
10. 20 n.p. 20 10
11. 30 n.p. 25 10
12. 40 n.p. 30 15
13. 50 n.p. 40 20
14. 75 n.p. .. .. 1·00 45
15. 100 n.p. .. .. 1·50 70
16. 1 r. (air) 75 30
17. 2 r. .. .. 1·40 65
18. 3 r. .. .. 1·75 95
19. 4 r. .. .. 2·50 2·25
20. 5 r. .. .. 2·25 2·00
21. 10 r. .. .. 6·00 3·50

The air stamps are as T1 but additionally inscr. "AIR MAIL" in English and Arabic, and with a hawk in flight.

1963. Malaria Eradication.
22. **2.** 1 n.p. turquoise .. 10 10
23. 2 n.p. blue .. 10 10
24. 3 n.p. violet .. 10 10
25. 4 n.p. green .. 10 10
26. 90 n.p. brown .. 1·60 1·10

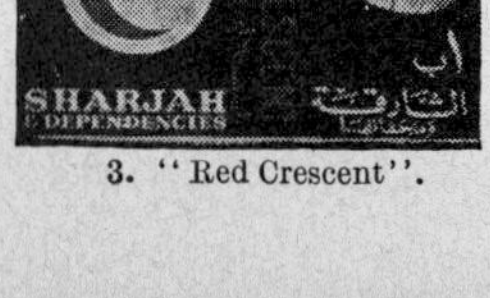

3. "Red Crescent".

1963. Red Cross Centenary.
27. **3.** 1 n.p. red and purple .. 10 10
28. 2 n.p. red and turquoise .. 10 10
29. 3 n.p. red and blue .. 10 10
30. 4 n.p. red and deep green 10 10
31. 5 n.p. red and sepia .. 10 10
32. 85 n.p. red and green .. 1·40 55

4. Campaign Emblem between Hands.

1963. Freedom from Hunger.
33. **4.** 1 n.p. green 10 10
34. 2 n.p. brown 10 10
35. 3 n.p. olive 10 10
36. 4 n.p. blue 10 10
37. 90 n.p. red .. .. 1·50 55

1963. Surch.
38. **4.** 10 n.p. on 1 n.p. green .. 15 15
39. 20 n.p. on 2 n.p. brown .. 25 20
40. 30 n.p. on 3 n.p. olive .. 40 30
41. 40 n.p. on 4 n.p. blue .. 50 40
42. 75 n.p. on 90 n.p. red .. 1·25 85
43. 80 n.p. on 90 n.p. red .. 1·25 85
44. **2.** 1 r. on 90 n.p. brown .. 1·50 1·25

1964. Air. Pres. Kennedy Memorial Issue (1st issue). Nos. 16/21 optd. **In Memoriam John F. Kennedy 1917-1963** in English and Arabic, and emblems.
45. **1.** 1 r. multicoloured .. 1·10 1·10
46. 2 r. multicoloured .. 2·25 2·25
47. 3 r. multicoloured .. 4·50 4·50
48. 4 r. multicoloured .. 5·50 5·00
49. 5 r. multicoloured .. 8·00 7·00
50. 10 r. multicoloured .. 12·00 11·00

See also Nos. 98/100.

7. Orbiting Astronomical Observatory.

1964. Scientific Space Research.
51. 1 n.p. blue (Type **7**) .. 10 10
52. 2 n.p. green and brown .. 10 10
53. 3 n.p. turquoise and black .. 10 10
54. 4 n.p. black and bistre .. 10 10
55. 5 n.p. bistre and violet .. 10 10
56. 35 n.p. violet and turquoise 70 55
57. 50 n.p. brown and green .. 1·10 70

DESIGNS: 2 n.p. "Nimbus" weather satellite. 3 n.p. "Pioneer V" space probe. 4 n.p. "Explorer XIII" satellite. 5 n.p. "Explorer XII" satellite. 35 n.p. Project "Relay" satellite. 50 n.p. Orbiting solar observatory.

8. Running.

1964. Olympic Games, Tokyo (1st issue).
58. 1 n.p. blue, turquoise and yellow (Type **8**) 10 10
59. 2 n.p. red and turquoise .. 10 10
60. 3 n.p. brown and green .. 10 10
61. 4 n.p. turquoise and light brown 10 10
62. 20 n.p. blue and brown .. 25 15
63. 30 n.p. bistre and pink .. 25 15
64. 40 n.p. violet and yellow .. 50 30
65. 1 r. brown and blue .. 1·25 80

DESIGNS: 2 n.p. Throwing the discus. 3 n.p. Hurdling. 4 n.p. Putting the shot. 20 n.p. High jumping. 30 n.p. Weightlifting. 40 n.p. Throwing the javelin. 1 r. High diving.

See also Nos. 90/7.

9. Flame and World Map.

1964. Air. Human Rights Day.
66. **9.** 50 n.p. brown 35 20
67. 1 r. violet 70 40
68. 150 n.p. green .. .. 1·00 60

10. Girl Scouts Marching.

1964. Sharjah Girl Scouts.
69. **10.** 1 n.p. green 10 10
70. 2 n.p. green 10 10
71. 3 n.p. blue 10 10
72. 4 n.p. violet 10 10
73. 5 n.p. red 10 10
74. 2 r. brown .. .. 2·50 1·50

11. Khor Fakkan.

1964. Air. Multicoloured.
75. 10 n.p. Type **11** 15 15
76. 20 n.p. Bedouin camp, Beni Qatab 20 15
77. 30 n.p. Dhaid oasis .. 25 15
78. 40 n.p. Kalba Castle .. 35 20
79. 75 n.p. Street and Wind tower, Sharjah .. 80 40
80. 100 n.p. Fortress .. 1·40 60

12. "Mr. Gus" (oil rig).

13. Scout at Attention.

1964. Air. New York World's Fair. Multicoloured.
81. 20 n.p. Type **12** .. 30 15
82. 40 n.p. Unisphere .. 20 15
83. 1 r. New York skyline (85½ × 44½ mm.) .. 55 40

1964. Sharjah Boy Scouts.
84. **13.** 1 n.p. olive 10 10
85. – 2 n.p. green 10 10
86. – 3 n.p. blue 10 10
87. **13.** 4 n.p. violet 10 10
88. – 5 n.p. mauve 10 10
89. – 2 r. brown .. .. 2·50 1·25

DESIGNS—HORIZ. 2 n.p., 5 n.p. Scouts marching. VERT. 3 n.p., 2 r. Boy Scout.

14. Olympic Torch.

1964. Olympic Games, Tokyo (2nd issue).
90. **14.** 1 n.p. olive 10 10
91. 2 n.p. blue 10 10
92. 3 n.p. brown 10 10
93. 4 n.p. turquoise 10 10
94. 5 n.p. violet 10 10
95. 40 n.p. blue 40 25
96. 50 n.p. brown 55 35
97. 2 r. ochre .. .. 1·75 1·25

15. Pres. Kennedy and Statue of Liberty.

1964. Air. Pres. Kennedy Commem. (2nd issue). Inscr. in gold.
98. **15.** 40 n.p. blue, brn. & grn. 65 55
99. 60 n.p. brn., grn. & blue 95 80
100. 100 n.p. grn., blue & brn. 1·60 1·10

16. Rock Dove.

1965. Air. Birds. Multicoloured.
101. 30 n.p. Type **16** 50 15
102. 40 n.p. Red junglefowl .. 60 25
103. 75 n.p. Hoopoe .. .. 1·75 50
104. 150 n.p. Type **16** .. 2·40 90
105. 2 r. Red junglefowl .. 3·00 1·25
106. 3 r. Hoopoe .. .. 5·50 2·75

17. Early Telephone.

1965. "Science, Transport and Communications".
107. **17.** 1 n.p. black and red .. 10 10
108. **A.** 1 n.p. black and red .. 10 10
109. **B.** 2 n.p. blue and orange 10 10
110. **C.** 2 n.p. blue and orange 10 10
111. **D.** 3 n.p. sepia and green .. 10 10
112. **E.** 3 n.p. sepia and green .. 10 10
113. **F.** 4 n.p. violet and green 10 10
114. **G.** 4 n.p. violet and green 10 10
115. **H.** 5 n.p. brown and green 10 10
116. **I.** 5 n.p. brown and green 10 10
117. **J.** 30 n.p. indigo and blue 50 25
118. **K.** 30 n.p. indigo and blue 50 25
119. **L.** 40 n.p. blue and yellow 50 25
120. **M.** 40 n.p. blue and yellow 50 25
121. **N.** 50 n.p. brown and blue 60 40
122. **O.** 50 n.p. brown and blue 60 40
123. **P.** 75 n.p. sepia and green 75 45
124. **Q.** 75 n.p. sepia and green 75 45
125. **R.** 1 r. blue and yellow 1·75 80
126. **S.** 1 r. blue and yellow .. 1·75 80

DESIGNS: A, Modern teleprinter. B, 1895 Car. C, 1964 American car. D, Early X-ray apparatus. E, T.V. X-ray machine. F, Early mailcoach. G. "Telstar" satellite. H, Medieval ship. I, Nuclear-powered freighter "Savannah". J, Early astronomers. K, Jodrel Bank radio-telescope. L, Greek messengers. M, "Relay" satellite. N, "Man's early flight" (Lilienthal's glider). O, Caravelle jetliner. P, Persian waterwheel. Q, Hydro-electric dam. R, Old steam locomotive. S, Modern diesel train.

1965. Air. Churchill Commem. (1st issue). Optd. **In Memoriam Sir Winston Churchill 1874-1965** in English and Arabic.
127. **15.** 40 n.p. blue, brn. & grn. 45 20
128. 60 n.p. brn., grn. & blue 70 25
129. 100 n.p. grn., blue & brn. 90 30

See also Nos. 201/4.

1965. 10th Anniv. (1964) of Arab Postal Union's Permanent Office. Similar design to T **43** of of Kuwait.
130. 5 n.p. blue and yellow .. 10 10
131. 30 n.p. blue and red .. 20 15
132. 65 n.p. green and orange .. 55 35

1965. Various issues of Shakh Saqr with portrait obliterated with three or four horizontal bars.

(a) Postage. Nos. 5, 8/13.
150. **1.** 5 n.p. multicoloured .. 10 15
151. 10 n.p. multicoloured .. 10 15
152. 16 n.p. multicoloured .. 20 15
153. 20 n.p. multicoloured .. 20 15
154. 30 n.p. multicoloured .. 25 20
155. 40 n.p. multicoloured .. 30 15
156. 50 n.p. multicoloured .. 35 25

(b) Air. (i) Nos. 16, 18/21.
157. **1.** 1 r. multicoloured .. 60 30
158. 3 r. multicoloured .. 1·75 1·25
159. 4 r. multicoloured .. 2·00 1·50
160. 5 r. multicoloured .. 2·75 2·25
161. 10 r. multicoloured .. 5·50 4·75

(ii) Nos. 75/80.

144.	11.	10 n.p. multicoloured ..	15	15
145.	–	20 n.p. multicoloured ..	20	15
146.	–	30 n.p. multicoloured ..	25	15
147.	–	40 n.p. multicoloured ..	35	15
148.	–	75 n.p. multicoloured ..	70	40
149.	–	100 n.p. multicoloured ..	80	45

22. Rameses II in his War Chariot.

23. Cable-laying Ship "Monarch IV" and COMPAC Cable Route Map.

1965. Nubian Monuments Preservation.

162.	22.	5 n.p. blue and yellow ..	10	10
163.		10 n.p. green and brown	15	10
164.		30 n.p. blue and orange	35	20
165.		55 n.p. violet and blue ..	60	30

1965. I.T.U. Cent. Country name in gold.

166.	23.	1 n.p. brown and blue ..	10	10
167.	–	2 n.p. brown and blue ..	10	10
168.	–	3 n.p. violet and green ..	10	10
169.	–	4 n.p. brown and blue ..	10	10
170.	23.	5 n.p. ochre and violet ..	10	10
171.	–	50 n.p. purple and black	75	20
172.	–	1 r. green and ochre ..	1·40	45
173.	–	120 n.p. red and green ..	2·00	65

DESIGNS: 2 n.p., 120 n.p. "Relay I" satellite and tracking station, Goonhilly Down. 3 n.p., 50 n.p. "Telstar" satellite and Atlas-Agena Rocket on launching pad. 4 n.p., 1 r. "Syncom" satellite, Post Office Tower (London) and horn paraboloid reflector aerial.

24. Running.

1965. Pan-American Games, Cairo.

174.	24.	50 n.p. turquoise & lilac	50	20
175.	–	50 n.p. green and brown	50	20
176.	–	50 n.p. lilac and sepia ..	50	20
177.	–	50 n.p. sepia and green	50	20
178.	–	50 n.p. brown and turq.	50	20

SPORTS: No. 175, Pole-vaulting. No. 176, Boxing. No. 177, High-jumping. No. 178, Long-jumping.

25. Flags (reverse of 5 r. coin).

1966. Arabian Gulf Area Monetary Conf. Circular designs on silver foil, backed with paper inscr. "Walsall Security Paper" in English and Arabic. Imperf.

(a) Diameter $1\frac{5}{8}$ in.

179.	25.	50 n.p. black	60	50
180.	–	75 n.p. violet	60	50

(b) Diameter $2\frac{1}{16}$ in.

181.	25.	1 r. purple	75	65
182.	–	3 r. blue	2·00	1·75

(c) Diameter $2\frac{1}{2}$ in.

183.	25.	4 r. green	2·75	2·75
184.	–	5 r. orange	3·00	3·00

COINS: 75 n.p., 3 r. and 5 r. show the obverse (Pres. Kennedy).

1966. "Rendezvous in Space". Nos. 33/6 optd. **15-12-1965 Rendezvous in SPACE**, two space capsules and four bars obliterating portrait or surch. also in English and Arabic.

185.	4.	1 n.p. green	10	10
186.		2 n.p. brown	10	10
187.		3 n.p. olive	10	10
188.		4 n.p. blue	10	10
189.		15 n.p. on 1 n.p. green ..	25	15
190.		30 n.p. on 2 n.p. brown ..	30	20
191.		50 n.p. on 3 n.p. olive ..	70	50
192.		1 r. on 4 n.p. blue ..	80	60

27. I.C.Y. Emblem and Prime Minister Harold Wilson.

1966. Int. Co-operation Year.

193.	27.	80 n.p. sepia and violet	70	20
194.	–	80 n.p. brown and green	70	20
195.	–	80 n.p. olive and red ..	70	20
196.	–	80 n.p. purple and blue	70	20
197.	–	80 n.p. blue and red ..	70	20
198.	–	80 n.p. plum and olive ..	70	20
199.	–	80 n.p. blue and grey ..	70	20
200.	–	80 n.p. purple and ochre	70	20

DESIGNS—I.C.Y. emblem and "World Leaders": No. 194, Chancellor Erhard. No. 195, Pres. Nasser. No. 196, Pres. Johnson. No. 197, Pope Paul VI. No. 198, Pres. De Gaulle. No. 199, Shaikh Isa bin Sulman al-Khalifa (Bahrain). No. 200, King Faisal (Saudi Arabia).

28. Sir Winston Churchill, Pen and Ink, and Books.

1966. Churchill Commem. (2nd issue). Multicoloured, printed on gold foil, backed with paper.

201.		2 r. Type **28**.	1·00	60
202.		3 r. Churchill and Houses of Parliament, pen and ink	1·50	1·10
203.		4 r. Churchill and St. Paul's Cathedral	2·25	1·50
204.		5 r. Churchill and "Big Ben" (clock tower, Houses of Parliament) and Tower Bridge	2·75	2·00

29. Banded Butterfly-fish.

1966. Fishes. Multicoloured.

206.		1 n.p. Type **29**	10	10
207.		2 n.p. Striped surgeon-fish	10	10
208.		3 n.p. Young imperial angel-fish	10	10
209.		4 n.p. False mouthbreeder	10	10
210.		5 n.p. Undulate trigger-fish	10	10
211.		15 n.p. Moonfish	25	10
212.		20 n.p. Clown butterfly-fish	35	10
213.		30 n.p. Moorish goddess ..	40	10
214.		40 n.p. Zebra-striped angel-fish	50	10
215.		50 n.p. False mouth breeder	55	10
216.		75 n.p. Undulate trigger-fish	70	20
217.		1 r. Zebra-striped angel-fish	80	25
218.		2 r. Moorish goddess ..	1·75	45
219.		3 r. Clown butterfly-fish ..	2·50	80
220.		4 r. Moonfish	2·75	95
221.		5 r. Young imperial angel-fish	3·25	1·25
222.		10 r. Type **29**	5·50	2·25

30. Arms of Munich and "Souvenir Sheet".

34. Pres. Kennedy.

33. Greek 6th-cent. Ball-player.

1966. International Philatelic Federation and International Philatelic Journalists Association Congresses, Munich. Mult.

223.		80 n.p. Type **30**	35	15
224.		120 n.p. Frauenkirche, Munich	45	20
225.		2 r. Statue and Hall of Fame, Munich (horiz. 81 × 41 mm.)	75	35

NEW CURRENCY SURCHARGES. During the latter half of 1966 various issues appeared surcharged in dirhams and riyals. The 1966 definitives with this surcharge are listed below as there is evidence of their postal use. Nos. 102, 107/126, 135, 145, 150/61 and 174/84 also exist with these surcharges.

Earlier in 1966 Nos. 98/100, 171/3, 193/4, 196, 198, 200/5 appeared surcharged in piastres and rials. As Sharjah did not adopt this currency their status is uncertain.

1966. Nos. 206/22 with currency names changed by overprinting in English and Arabic.

226.	29.	1 d. multicoloured ..	10	10
227.	–	2 d. multicoloured ..	10	10
228.	–	3 d. multicoloured ..	10	10
229.	–	4 d. multicoloured ..	10	10
230.	–	5 d. multicoloured ..	10	10
231.	–	15 d. multicoloured ..	25	10
232.	–	20 d. multicoloured ..	35	10
233.	–	30 d. multicoloured ..	40	10
234.	–	40 d. multicoloured ..	50	10
235.	–	50 d. multicoloured ..	55	20
236.	–	75 d. multicoloured ..	75	30
237.	–	1 r. multicoloured ..	85	35
238.	–	2 r. multicoloured ..	1·40	75
239.	–	3 r. multicoloured ..	2·00	1·50
240.	–	4 r. multicoloured ..	2·50	1·75
241.	–	5 r. multicoloured ..	3·25	2·00
242.	29.	10 r. multicoloured ..	5·50	3·75

1966. World Cup Football Championships. Designs printed on coloured metal foil-surfaced paper. Multicoloured.

243.		½ r. Type **33**	35	15
244.		½ r. Tsu-chu "Kick-ball" game, China, circa 175 B.C.	35	15
245.		½ r. 14th-cent. ball game ..	35	15
246.		½ r. Blowing up ball-bladder (17th-cent.)	35	15
247.		½ r. Football game, Barnet, England, circa 1750 ..	35	15
248.		½ r. England v. Scotland game, Kennington Oval (London), 1879	35	15
249.		½ r. Victorious England team, Wembley, 1966 (56 × 35½ mm.)	35	15

1966. 3rd Death Anniv. of Pres. Kennedy and Inaug. of Arlington Memorial.

251.		50 d. Type **34**	25	15
252.		2 r. Sharjah 50 n.p. Kennedy stamp of 1964	1·00	50
253.		2 r. 50 Pres. Kennedy's grave (horiz. 55 × 42 mm.)	1·25	65

35. Shaikh Khalid bin Mohammed al Qasimi and Arms.

1968. Multicoloured.

255.		5 d. Type **35** (postage) ..	15	15
256.		10 d. Flag	15	15
257.		15 d. Flag and arms (vert.)	20	15
258.		20 d. Decorative pattern (vert.)	20	15
259.		35 d. Type **35** (air)	40	20
260.		40 d. As 10 d.	40	15
261.		60 d. As 15 d.	55	20
262.		75 d. As 20 d.	70	30
363.		1 r. Type **35**	85	30
264.		2 r. As 10d.	1·75	75
265.		3 r. As 15 d.	2·50	1·25
266.		4 r. As 20 d.	3·25	1·75
267.		5 r. Type **35**	4·00	1·75
268.		10 r. As 10 d.	7·50	4·50

OFFICIAL STAMPS

1966. Optd. **ON STATE SERVICE** in English and Arabic.

O 101.	1.	8 n.p.	15	15
O 102.		10 n.p.	15	15
O 103.		16 n.p.	30	15
O 104.		20 n.p.	30	15
O 105.		30 n.p.	40	20
O 106.		40 n.p.	60	30
O 107.		50 n.p.	1·00	55
O 108.		75 n.p.	1·75	1·25
O 109.		100 n.p.	2·25	1·40

For later issues see **UNITED ARAB EMIRATES.**

APPENDIX

The following stamps have either been issued in excess of postal needs or have not been available to the public in reasonable quantities at face value. Such stamps may later be given full listing if there is evidence of regular postal use.

1967.

Post Day. Japanese Paintings. 1 r. × 3.

United Nations. 22nd Anniv. 10, 30, 60 d.

Olympics Preparation, Mexico 1968. Postage 1, 2, 3, 10 d.; Air 30, 60 d., 2 r.

Flowers and Butterflies. Postage 1, 2, 3, 4, 5, 10, 20 d.; Air 30, 60 d., 1, 2 r.

Famous Paintings. Postage 1, 2, 3, 4, 5, 30, 40, 60, 75 d.; Air 1, 2, 3, 4, 5 r.

1968.

Winter Olympic Games, Grenoble. Postage 1, 2, 3, 4, 5 d.; Air 1, 2, 3 r.

12th World Jamboree. Postage 1, 2, 3, 4, 5 10 d.; Air 30, 50, 60 d., 1 r. 50.

Grenoble Olympic Medal Winners. Optd. on Winter Olympics, Grenoble issue. Postage 1, 2, 3, 4, 5 d.; Air 1, 2, 3 r.

Mothers' Day. Paintings. Postage 10, 20, 30, 40 d.; Air 1, 2, 3. 4 r.

American Paintings. Postage 20, 30, 40, 50, 60 d.; Air 1, 4, 5 r.

Egyptian Art. 15, 25, 35, 45, 55, 65, 75, 95 d.

Martyrs of Liberty. Air 35 d. × 4, 60 d. × 4, 1 r. × 4.

Olympic Games Mexico. 10, 20, 30 d., 2 r., 2 r. 40, 5 r.

Previous Olympic Games. Air 25, 50, 75 d., 1 r. 50, 3, 4 r.

Sportsmen and women. Postage 20, 30, 40, 60 d., 1 r. 50, 2 r. 50; Air 25, 50 d., 1, 2 r., 3 r. 25, 4, 4 r.

Robert Kennedy Memorial. Optd. on American Paintings issue. Air 4 r.

Olympic Medal Winners, Mexico. 35, 50, 60 d · 1, 2, 4 r.

1969.

Famous Men and Women. Postage 10, 20, 25, 35, 50, 60 d.; Air 1, 2, 3, 4, 5, 6 r.

"Apollo 8" Moon Mission. Postage 5 d. × 6; Air 10, 15, 20 d., 2, 3, 4 r.

"Apollo 11" Moon Mission (1st series). Postage 5 d. × 8; Air 75 d. × 8, 1 r. × 8.

Post Day. Famous Ships. Postage 5 d. × 8; Air 90 d. × 8.

"Apollo 12" Moon Mission. Optd on Famous Ships issue. 5 d. × 8.

1970.

U.N.I.C.E.F. Paintings of Children. Postage 5 d. × 9; Air 20, 25, 35, 40, 50, 60, 75 d., 1, 3 r.

Animals. Postage 3 d. × 14, 10, 10, 15, 15 d.; Air 20, 20, 35, 35 d., 1, 1, 2, 2 r.

"Expo 70" World Fair, Osaka, Japan (1st series). Japanese Paintings. Postage 3 d. × 4; Air 1 r. × 4.

"Expo 70" World Fair, Osaka, Japan (2nd series). Pavilions. Postage 2, 2, 3, 3 d.; Air 40 d. × 4.

Paintings of Napoleon. Postage 3 d. × 5; Air 20, 30, 40, 60 d., 2 r.

De Gaulle Commemoration. Postage 3 d. × 5; Air 20, 30, 40, 60 d., 2 r.

5th Anniv. of Ruler's Accession. Postage 5 d. × 5; Air 20 d., 35 d. × 5, 40 d. × 5, 60 d. × 5; the 5 40 d. values also exist each surch. 5 d.

"Mercury" and "Vostok" Moon Missions. Postage 1, 2, 3, 4, 5 d.; Air 25, 40, 85 d., 1, 2 r.

"Gemini" Space Programme. Postage 1, 2, 3, 4, 5 d.; Air 25, 40, 85 d., 1, 2 r.

"Apollo", "Voskhod" and "Soyuz" Projects. Postage 1, 2, 3, 4, 5 d.; Air 25, 40, 85 d., 1, 2 r.

Events of 1970. Postage 1 d. × 5, 5 d.; Air 75 d., 1, 2, 3 r.

200th Birth Anniv. of Beethoven. Postage 3 d. × 5; Air 35, 40, 60 d., 1, 2 r.

Mozart. Postage 3 d. × 5; Air 35, 40, 60 d., 1, 2 r.

The Life of Christ (1st series). Postage 1, 2, 3, 4, 5 d.; Air 25, 40, 60 d., 1, 2 r.

1971.

"Apollo 14" Moon Mission. Optd. on 1969 "Apollo 11" issue. Postage 5 d. × 4; Air 75 d. × 4.

Post Day 1970. Cars. Postage 1, 2, 3, 4, 5 d.; Air 25, 50, 60 d., 2, 3 r.

Post Day (1st series). American Cars. Postage 1, 2, 3, 4, 5 d.; Air 35, 50 d., 1, 2, 3 r.

Post Day (2nd series). Trains. Postage 1, 2, 3, 4, 5 d.; Air 25, 50, 60 d., 1, 2 r.

Pres. Nasser Commemoration. Postage 5 d. × 5; Air 20, 35, 40, 60 d., 2 r.

Safe return of "Apollo 13". Optd. on 1969 "Apollo 8" issue. Air 10, 15, 20 d., 2, 3, 4 r.

De Gaulle Memorial. Postage 3, 4, 5, 6, 7 d.; Air 40, 60, 75 d., 1, 2 r.

Olympics Preparation, Munich 1972. Postage 2, 3, 4, 5, 6 d.; Air 35, 40, 60 d., 1, 2 r.

Miracles of Christ. Postage 1, 2, 3, 4, 5 d.; Air 25, 40, 60 d., 1, 2 r.

6th Anniv. of Ruler's Accession. Postage 5 d. × 3; Air 75 d. × 4, 1 r. × 3, 2 r., 3 r. × 4, 5 r.

Proclamation of the United Arab Emirates. Air 25, 35, 65, 75 d., 1, 2 r.

Various surcharges. Postage 35 d. on 5 d. (No. 255) 35 d. on 5 d. (Winter Olympics, listed above, 1968); Air 60 d. on 75 d. (No. 262) 65 d. on 75 d. (Proclamation of UAE, listed above), 65 d. on 1 r. (Proclamation of UAE, listed above) 65 d. on 2 r. (Proclamation of UAE, listed above).

1972.

Sport. Postage 2, 3, 4, 5, 6 d.; Air 35, 40, 60 d., 1, 2 r.

The Life of Christ (2nd series). Postage 1, 2, 3, 4, 5 d.; Air 25, 40, 60 d., 1, 2 r.

Winter Olympics Preparation, Sapporo, Postage 2, 3, 4, 5, 6 d.; Air 35, 40, 60 d., 1, 2 r.

Safe return of "Apollo 14". Optd. on 1969 "Apollo 11" issue. Postage 5 d. × 4; Air 1 r. × 4.

Previous World Cup Winners. Postage 5, 10, 15, 20, 25 d.; Air 35, 75 d., 1, 2, 3 r.

Sapporo Olympic Medal Winners. Paintings, Postage 5, 10, 15, 20, 25 d.; Air 35, 75 d., 1, 2, 3 r.

Famous people, Churchill, De Gaulle and John Kennedy. Postage 5 d. × 4, 10 d. × 4, 35 d. × 4; Air 75 d. × 4, 1 r. × 4, 3 r. × 4.

Olympic Games, Munich. Postage 5, 10, 15, 20, 25 d.; Air 35, 75 d., 1, 2, 3 r.

Cats. Postage 20, 25 d.; Air 75 d., 1, 2 r.

Birds (1st series). Postage 20, 25, 75 d., Air 1, 2 r.

"Apollo 11" Moon Mission (2nd series). Air 1 r. × 5.

"Apollo 16" Moon Mission. Air 1 r. × 5.

Dogs. Postage 20, 25 d.; Air 75 d., 1, 2 r.

"Apollo 17" Moon Mission. Postage 1, 1 r.; Air 1 r. × 3.

Munich Olympic Medal Winners. Air 5 r. × 20.

Horses. Postage 20, 25 d.; Air 75 d., 1, 2 r.

"Apollo 17" Astronauts. Postage 1, 1 r.; Air 1 r. × 3.

Butterflies. Postage 20, 25 d.; Air 75 d., 1, 2 r.

"Luna 9" Soviet Space Programme. Postage 1, 1 r.; Air 1 r. × 3.

Monkeys. Postage 20, 25 d.; Air 75 d., 1, 2 r.

Birds (2nd series). Air 25, 25, 35, 35, 50, 50, 65, 65 d., 1 r. × 6, 3, 3 r.

Fish. Air 25, 35, 50, 65 d., 1 r. × 5, 3 r.

Insects. Air 25, 35, 50, 65 d., 1, 3 r.

Flowers. Postage 25, 35, 50, 65 d., 1, 3 r.; Air 1 r. × 4.

Fruit. Air 1 r. × 4.

Children. Air 1 4 r. × 4.

Eastern Antiquities. Air 25, 35, 40, 65, 75 d., 3 r., 1 r. × 4.

Planetary Exploration. Postage 1 r. × 3; Air 1, 1 r.

13th World Jamboree. Postage 2 d. × 3, 3 d. × 3, 4 d. × 3, 5 d. × 3, 6 d. × 3; Air 35 d. × 3, 75 d. × 3, 1 r. × 3, 2 r. × 3, 3 r. × 3.

A number of issues on gold or silver foil also exist, but it is understood that these were mainly for presentation purposes, although valid for postage.

In common with the other states of the United Arab Emirates the Sharjah stamp contract was terminated on 1 August 1972, and further new issues released after that date were unauthorised.

SIBERIA — Pt. 10

Various Anti-Bolshevist governments existed in this area, culminating in Kolchak's assumption of power as "Supreme Ruler". The Kolchak Government fell in January 1920; provincial issues followed until the area was incorporated into the Soviet Union in 1922.

100 kopeks = 1 rouble.

1919. Admiral Kolchak Govt. Arms types of Russia surch. in figures, or in figures and words (rouble values). Imperf. or perf.

5.	**22.**	35 on 2 k. green	25	1·25
6.		50 on 3 k. red	25	1·40
3.		70 on 1 k. orange	30	3·25
8.	**23.**	1 r. on 4 k. red	40	1·40
9.	**22.**	3 r. on 7 k. blue	70	3·50
10.	**10.**	5 r. on 14 k. red and blue	1·25	8·00

1920. Transbaikal Province. Ataman Semyonov regime. Arms types of Russia surch. thus: **p. 1 p.** Perf.

11.	**23.**	1 r. on 4 k. red	17·00	26·00
12.	**14.**	2 r. 50 on 20 k. red & blue	17·00	24·00
13.	**22.**	5 r. on 5 k. red	10·00	17·00
14.	**10.**	10 r. on 70 k. orge. & brn.	17·00	27·00

6.

1920. Amur Province. Imperf.

15.	**6.**	2 r. red	1·60	4·50
16.		3 r. green	1·60	4·50
17.		5 r. blue	1·60	4·50
18.		15 r. brown	1·60	4·50
19.		30 r. mauve	1·60	4·50

FAR EASTERN REPUBLIC

1920. Vladivostock issue. Optd. **D B P** in fancy letters or surch. also. Imperf. or perf. (a) On Arms types of Russia.

32	**22**	1 k. orange	3·75	6·50
33		2 k. green	1·90	2·50
21		3 k. red	2·40	3·25
39	**10**	3 k. on 35 k. grn. & purple	4·00	5·00
22	**23**	4 k. red	2·00	4·75
40	**10**	4 k. on 70 k. orge. & brn.	2·50	3·50
41		7 k. on 15 k. blue & purple	1·25	1·75
23	**23**	10 k. blue	38·00	45·00
44	**11**	10 k. on 3 r. 50 green and brown	5·00	7·00
24	**10**	14 k. red and blue	6·50	15·00
25		15 k. blue and purple	4·25	6·00
25	**14**	20 k. red and blue	32·00	45·00
27	**10**	20 k. on 14 k. red & blue	3·00	4·75
28		25 k. mauve and green	4·00	8·00
29		35 k. green and purple	16·00	26·00
30	**14**	50 k. green and purple	3·25	6·50
35	**15**	1 r. orange and brown	8·00	17·00

(b) On Nos. 5 and 3 of Siberia.

37.	**22.**	35 k. on 2 k. green	2·75	4·00
38.		70 k. on 1 k. orange	2·25	4·00

(c) on Postal Savings Bank stamps of Russia

45		1 k. on 5 k. green on buff	5·00	7·00
46		2 k. on 10 k. brn on buff	7·00	10·00

10. 11. 13.

1921. Chita issue. Imperf.

47	**10**	1 k. orange	50	1·10
48		3 k. red	50	60
49	**11**	4 k. brown and red	20	50
50	**10**	5 k. brown	40	70
51b		7 k. blue	40	1·00
52	**11**	10 k. red and blue	30	70
53	**10**	15 k. red	40	1·00
54	**11**	20 k. red and blue	40	1·00
55		30 k. red and green	45	1·25
56		50 k. red and black	1·00	2·00

1922. Vladivostok issue. 5th Anniv of Russian October Revolution. Optd **1917 7-XI 1922.** Imperf.

57.	**13.**	2 k. green	8·00	10·00
58.		4 k. red	8·00	10·00
59.		5 k. brown	9·00	16·00
60.		10 k. blue	9·00	16·00

PRIAMUR AND MARITIME PROVINCES

Anti-Bolshevist Government.

1921. Vladivostok issue. Imperf.

61.	**13.**	2 k. green	40	65
62.		4 k. red	40	65
63.		5 k. purple	50	95
64.		10 k. blue	95	1·60

(15.) (16. Trans. "Priamur Territory".) (18.)

1922. Anniv. of Priamur Provisional Govt. Optd. with T **15.**

89.	**13.**	2 k. green	13·00	17·00
90.		4 k. red	13·00	17·00
91.		5 k. purple	13·00	17·00
92.		10 k. blue	13·00	17·00

1922. Optd. or surch. as T **16.**

93.	**13.**	1 k. on 2 k. green	1·40	3·50
94.		2 k. green	1·40	3·50
95.		3 k. on 4 k. red	1·40	3·50
96.		4 k. red	1·40	3·50
97.		5 k. purple	1·40	3·50
98.		10 k. blue	1·40	3·50

1922. Optd. as T **16.** Imperf. or perf.

(a) On Arms types of Russia.

114.	**22.**	1 k. orange	1·75	5·00
115.		2 k. green	2·50	7·50
116		3 k. red	4·25	13·00
102	**23.**	4 k. red	1·25	3·50
118	**22.**	5 k. red	7·00	20·00
104		7 k. blue	13·00	28·00
105	**23.**	10 k. blue	13·00	28·00
106	**10.**	14 k. red and blue	30·00	60·00
107.		15 k. blue and purple	2·50	6·00
108.	**14.**	20 k. red and blue	4·00	10·00
109.	**10.**	20 k. on 14 k. red & blue	38·00	80·00
110.		25 k. mauve and green	11·00	24·00
111.		35 k. green and purple	1·75	5·00
112.	**14.**	50 k. green and purple	2·25	6·00
113.	**10.**	70 k. orange and brown	7·00	18·00
121.	**15.**	1 r. orange and brown	6·00	17·00

(b) On Nos. 5 and 3 of Siberia.

122.	**22.**	35 k. on 2 k. green	22·00	38·00
123.		70 k. on 1 k. orange	30·00	55·00

1922. Nos. 37 and 38 optd **ПЗК** and three bars. Imperf. or perf.

125.	**22.**	35 k. on 2 k. green	2·00	4·00
126.		70 k. on 1 k. orange	3·25	7·00

SOVIET UNION ISSUE FOR THE FAR EAST.

1923. Stamps of Russia surch. as T **18.** Imperf. or perf.

131.	**79.**	1 k. on 100 r. red	35	60
128.		2 k. on 70 r. purple	25	35
129.	**78.**	5 k. on 10 r. blue	25	50
130.	**79.**	10 k. on 50 r. brown	35	50

SICILY — Pt. 8

An island to the S. of Italy, which, with Naples, formed the Kingdom of the Two Sicilies, until incorporated in the Kingdom of Italy.

100 grano = 1 ducato.

1. King "Bomba".

1859. Imperf.

1	**1**	½ g. yellow	£250	£650
2b		1 g. olive	£100	85·00
3		2 g. blue	70·00	55·00
4		5 g. red	£425	£300
5		10 g. blue	£425	£200
6		20 g. grey	£450	£375
7		50 g. brown	£450	£3750

SLOVAKIA — Pt. 5

Formerly part of Hungary, Slovakia joined with Bohemia and Moravia in 1918 to form Czechoslovakia. From 1939 to 1945 they were separate states.

In 1993 the federation of Czechoslovakia was dissolved and Slovakia became an independent republic.

100 haleru = 1 koruna.

1939. Stamps of Czechoslovakia optd. **Slovensky stat 1939.**

2.	**34.**	5 h. blue	65	90
3.		10 h. brown	15	15
4.		20 h. red	10	10
5.		25 h. green	1·60	1·60
6.		30 h. purple	10	10
7.	**59.**	40 h. blue	15	15
8.	**60a.**	50 h. green	10	10
9.	**66.**	50 h. green	10	10
10.	**60a.**	60 h. violet	10	10
11.		60 h. blue	9·25	8·25
12.	**61.**	1 k. red	10	10
13.	–	1 k. 20 purple (No. 354)	25	30
14.	**64.**	1 k. 50 red	25	30
15.	–	1 k. 60 olive (No. 355a)	2·50	2·50
16.	–	2 k. green (No. 356)	2·50	2·50
17.	–	2 k. 50 blue (No. 357)	40	50
18.	–	3 k. brown (No. 358)	50	65
19.	–	3 k. 50 violet (No. 359)	27·00	25·00
20.	**65.**	4 k. violet	13·50	11·50
21.	–	5 k. green (No. 361)	15·00	13·50
22.	–	10 k. blue (No. 362)	£100	95·00

4. Father Hlinka. 7. Krivan. 8. Chamois.

9. Mgr. Tiso. 10. Weaving. 11. Sawyer.

12. Presidential Palace, Bratislava. 13. Rev. J. Murgas and Wireless Masts.

1939. As T **4** but inscr. "CESKO-SLOVENSKO SLOVENSKA POSTA", optd. **SLOVENSKY STAT.**

23.	**4.**	50 h. green	2·00	65
24.		1 k. red	1·60	65

1939. Perf or imperf.

25.	**4.**	5 h. blue	40	40
26.		10 h. olive	65	55
27a.		20 h. red	85	65
28.		30 h. violet	65	55
29.		50 h. green	65	55
33.		1 k. red	65	45
34a.		2 k. 50 blue	1·00	35
35a.		3 k. sepia	2·00	65

1939.

40.	–	5 h. olive	15	25
41.	**7.**	10 h. brown	10	15
125.		10 h. red	15	25
42.	–	20 h. grey	10	15
126.	–	20 h. blue	15	25
43.	**8.**	25 h. brown	40	20
127.		25 h. purple	15	25
44.	–	30 h. brown	20	20
128.	–	30 h. purple	15	25
45.	**9.**	50 h. olive	40	30
129.	–	50 h. green	15	25
46.	**9.**	70 h. brown	60	20
47.	**10.**	2 k. green	6·00	45
48.	**11.**	4 k. brown	1·40	70
49.	–	5 k. red	90	30
50.	**12.**	10 k. blue	75	70

DESIGNS—As Type **7**: 5 h., 50 h. (No. 129), Zelene Pleso. 20 h. Kvety Satier (Edelweiss), 30 h. Javorina. As Type **11**: 5 k. Woman filling ewer at spring. Nos. 125, 126, 127, 128, and 129 are 18½ × 22½ mm. and Nos. 40/1, 42, 43 and 44 are 17½ × 21 mm.

1939. 10th Death Anniv. of Rev. J. Murgas.

53	**13**	60 h. violet	20	20
52		1 k. 20 grey	50	20

1939. Child Welfare. As No. 45 but larger (24 × 30 mm) and inscr "+2.50 DETOM".

54		2 k. 50 + 2 k. 50 blue	3·25	3·00

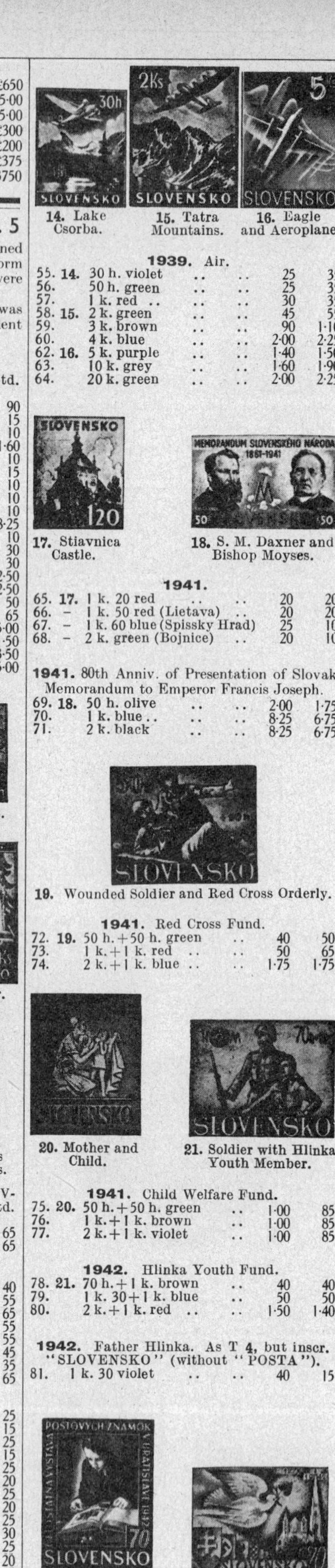

14. Lake Csorba. 15. Tatra Mountains. 16. Eagle and Aeroplane.

1939. Air.

55.	**14.**	30 h. violet	25	35
56.		50 h. green	25	35
57.		1 k. red	30	35
58.	**15.**	2 k. green	45	55
59.		3 k. brown	90	1·10
60.		4 k. blue	2·00	2·25
62.	**16.**	5 k. purple	1·40	1·50
63.		10 k. grey	1·60	1·90
64.		20 k. green	2·00	2·25

17. Stiavnica Castle. 18. S. M. Daxner and Bishop Moyses.

1941.

65.	**17.**	1 k. 20 red	20	20
66.	–	1 k. 50 red (Lietava)	20	20
67.	–	1 k. 60 blue (Spissky Hrad)	25	10
68.	–	2 k. green (Bojnice)	20	10

1941. 80th Anniv. of Presentation of Slovak Memorandum to Emperor Francis Joseph.

69.	**18.**	50 h. olive	2·00	1·75
70.		1 k. blue	8·25	6·75
71.		2 k. black	8·25	6·75

19. Wounded Soldier and Red Cross Orderly.

1941. Red Cross Fund.

72.	**19.**	50 h. + 50 h. green	40	50
73.		1 k. + 1 k. red	50	65
74.		2 k. + 1 k. blue	1·75	1·75

20. Mother and Child. 21. Soldier with Hlinka Youth Member.

1941. Child Welfare Fund.

75.	**20.**	50 h. + 50 h. green	1·00	85
76.		1 k. + 1 k. brown	1·00	85
77.		2 k. + 1 k. violet	1·00	85

1942. Hlinka Youth Fund.

78.	**21.**	70 h. + 1 k. brown	40	40
79.		1 k. 30 + 1 k. blue	50	50
80.		2 k. + 1 k. red	1·50	1·40

1942. Father Hlinka. As T **4**, but inscr. "SLOVENSKO" (without "POSTA").

81.		1 k. 30 violet	40	15

22. Boy Stamp Collector.

23. Dove and St. Stephens.

1942. Philatelic Exn., Bratislava. Inscr. as in T **22.**

82.	–	30 h. green	90	1·00
83.	**22.**	70 h. red	90	1·00
84.	–	80 h. violet	90	1·00
85.	–	1 k. 30 brown	90	1·00

DESIGNS: 30 h., 1 k. 30, Posthorn round various arms about Bratislava. 80 h. Postmaster-General examining stamps.

1942. European Postal Congress.

86.	**23.**	70 h. green	1·00	1·00
87.		1 k. 30 olive	1·00	1·00
88.		2 k. blue	2·00	2·75

24. Inaugural Ceremony. **25.** L. Stur.

1942. 15th Anniv of Foundation of National Literacy Society.

89.	**24.**	70 h. black	15	15
90.		1 k. red	25	25
91.		1 k. 30 blue	15	20
92.		2 k. brown	25	25
93.		3 k. green	40	40
94.		4 k. violet	40	40

1943.

95.	**25.**	80 h. green	15	10
96.	–	1 k. red	20	20
97.	–	1 k. 30 blue	15	10

PORTRAITS: 1 k. M. Razus. 1 k. 30, Father Hlinka.

27. National Costumes. **30.** Railway Tunnel.

29. Infantry.

1943. Winter Relief Fund.

98.	**27.**	50 h.+50 h. green	35	25
99.	–	70 h.+1 k. red	35	25
100.	–	80 h.+2 k. blue	35	30

DESIGNS: 70 h. Mother and child. 80 h. Mother and two children.

1943. Fighting Forces.

106.	**29.**	70 h.+2 k. lake	60	75
107.	–	1 k. 30+2 k. blue	75	85
108.	–	2 k.+2 k. olive	80	95

DESIGNS—HORIZ. 2 k. Artillery. VERT. 1 k. 30, Air Force.

1943. Opening of the Strazke-Presov Railway. Inscr. "5 IX 1943".

109.	–	70 h. purple	80	1·00
110.	–	80 h. blue	1·00	1·25
111.	**30.**	1 k. 30 black	1·00	1·40
112.	–	2 k. brown	1·25	2·00

DESIGNS—HORIZ. 70 h. Presov Church. 2 k. Railway viaduct. VERT. 80 h. Railway locomotive.

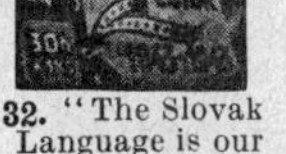

32. "The Slovak Language is our Life". **33.** National Museum.

1943. Culture Fund.

113.	**32.**	30 h.+1 k. brown	40	30
114.	**33.**	70 h.+1 k. green	50	50
115.	–	80 h.+2 k. blue	40	30
116.	–	1 k. 30+2 k. brown	40	30

DESIGNS—HORIZ. 80 h. Matica Slovenska College. VERT. 1 k. 30, Agricultural Student.

34. Prince Pribina Okolo. **35.** Footballer.

1944. 5th Anniv. of Declaration of Independence.

117.	**34.**	50 h. green	10	10
118.	–	70 h. mauve	10	10
119.	–	80 h. brown	10	10
120.	–	1 k. 30 blue	15	10
121.	–	2 k. blue	15	20
122.	–	3 k. brown	35	35
123.	–	5 k. violet	65	65
124.	–	10 k. black	2·40	2·00

DESIGNS: 70 h. Prince Mojmir. 80 h. Prince Ratislav. 1 k. 30, King Svatopluk. 2 k. Prince Kocel. 3 k. Prince Mojmir II. 5 k. Prince Svatopluk II. 10 k. Prince Braslav.

1944. Sports.

130.	**35.**	70 h.+70 h. olive	85	85
131.	–	1 k.+1 k. violet	85	1·00
132.	–	1 k. 30+1 k. 30 green	85	1·00
133.	–	2 k.+2 k. brown	1·00	1·40

DESIGNS—VERT. 1 k. Skiing. 1 k. 30, Diving. HORIZ. 2 k. Running.

36. Symbolic of "Protection".

1944. Protection Series.

134.	**36.**	70 h.+4 k. blue	1·10	1·50
135.		1 k. 30+4 k. brown	1·10	1·50
136.		2 k. green	70	30
137.		3 k. 80 purple	70	50

37. Children Playing. **38.** Mgr. Tiso.

1944. Child Welfare.

138.	**37.**	2 k.+4 k. blue	4·00	4·00

1945.

139.	**38.**	1 k. orange	1·00	75
140.		1 k. 50 brown	20	20
141.		2 k. green	25	20
142.		4 k. red	1·00	75
143.		5 k. blue	1·00	75
144.		10 k. purple	50	30

INDEPENDENT STATE

39 Arms 40 Ruzomberok

1993.

145	39	3 k. multicoloured	10	10
146		8 k. mult (26 × 40 mm)	35	10

1993. Churches.

147	40	5 k. blue and red	20	10
148	–	10 k. lilac and orange	40	10

DESIGN—VERT. 10 k. Kosice.

41 Pres. Michal Kovac 42 St. John and Charles Bridge, Prague

1993.

149	41	2 k. black	10	10
150	–	3 k. brown and mauve	10	10

DESIGN: 3 k. Pres. Kovac.

1993. 600th Death Anniv of St. John of Nepomuk (patron saint of Bohemia).

151	42	8 k. multicoloured	35	10

43 Pedunculate Oak 44 Jan Levoslav Bella (composer)

1993. Trees. Multicoloured.

152	3 k. Type **43**	10	10
153	4 k. Hornbeam	15	10
154	10 k. Scots pine	40	10

1993. Anniversaries.

155	44	5 k. cream, brown & bl	20	10
156	–	8 k. brown, sepia & red	35	10
157	–	20 k. buff, blue & orange	85	25

DESIGNS: 5 k. Type **44** (150th birth anniv); 8 k. Alexander Dubcek (statesman) (1st death anniv); 20 k. Jan Kollar (poet and scholar) (birth bicentenary).

45 "Woman with Jug" (Marian Cunderlik)

1993. Europa. Contemporary Art.

158	45	14 k. multicoloured	60	20

46 Sun 47 Arms of Dubnica nad Vahom

1993. Anniversaries. Multicoloured.

159	2 k. Type **46** (150th anniv of Slovakian written language)	10	10
160	8 k. Sts. Cyril and Methodius (1130th anniv of arrival in Moravia)	35	10

1993.

161	47	1 k. silver, black & blue	10	10

48 "The Big Pets" (Lane Smith) 49 Zvolen Castle

1993. 14th Biennial Exhibition of Book Illustrations for Children.

162	48	5 k. multicoloured	20	10

1993.

163	49	30 k. black, blue and red	1·25	40

NEWSPAPER STAMPS

1939. Nos. N 364/72 of Czechoslovakia optd. **1939. SLOVENSKY STAT.**

N 25.	2 h. brown	30	35
N 26.	5 h. blue	30	35
N 27.	7 h. orange	30	35
N 28.	9 h. green	30	35
N 29.	10 h. lake	30	35
N 30.	12 h. blue	30	35
N 31.	20 h. green	65	80
N 32.	50 h. brown	2·75	2·25
N 33.	1 k. olive	9·25	8·25

N 7. N 29. Printer's Type.

1939. Imperf.

N 40	N 7	2 h. brown	20	15
N 65		5 h. blue	20	20
N 42		7 h. orange	20	20
N 43		9 h. green	20	20
N 66		10 h. red	20	15
N 45		12 h. blue	20	25
N 67		15 h. purple	20	15
N 68		20 h. green	40	45
N 69		25 h. blue	30	45
N 70		40 h. red	40	45
N 71		50 h. brown	65	50
N 72		1 k. green	65	50
N 73		2 k. green	1·60	90

1943. Imperf.

N 101.	**N 29.**	10 h. green	15	15
N 102.		15 h. brown	15	15
N 103.		20 h. blue	15	15
N 104.		50 h. red	20	25
N 105.		1 k. green	40	40
N 106.		2 k. blue	65	85

PERSONAL DELIVERY STAMPS

P 17.

1940. Imperf.

P 65.	**P 17.**	50 h. blue	1·00	1·60
P 66.		50 h. red	1·00	1·60

POSTAGE DUE STAMPS

D 13. D 24.

1939.

D 51.	**D 13.**	5 h. blue	25	40
D 52.		10 h. blue	25	25
D 53.		20 h. blue	40	25
D 54.		30 h. blue	1·50	1·10
D 55.		40 h. blue	50	50
D 56.		50 h. blue	1·00	1·00
D 57.		60 h. blue	1·00	1·00
D 58.		1 k. red	1·25	1·25
D 59.		2 k. red	10·00	8·25
D 60.		5 k. red	2·50	2·50
D 61.		10 k. red	3·25	3·00
D 62.		20 k. red	16·00	9·00

1942.

D 89.	**D 24.**	10 h. brown	20	30
D 90.		20 h. brown	20	30
D 91.		40 h. brown	20	30
D 92.		50 h. brown	1·10	60
D 93.		60 h. brown	15	20
D 94.		80 h. brown	20	20
D 95.		1 k. red	25	20
D 96.		1 k. 10 red	50	70
D 97.		1 k. 30 red	30	20
D 98.		1 k. 60 red	40	20
D 99.		2 k. red	50	20
D 100.		2 k. 60 red	1·40	1·00
D 101.		3 k. 50 red	8·25	6·75
D 102.		5 k. red	3·00	2·25
D 103.		10 k. red	3·25	2·75

SLOVENIA Pt. 3

Formerly part of Austria, in 1918 Slovenia was combined with other areas to form Yugoslavia. Separate stamps were issued during the Second World War whilst under Italian and German Occupation.

In 1991 Slovenia seceded and became an independent state.

1941. 100 paras = 1 dinar.
1991. Tolar.

ITALIAN OCCUPATION, 1941

Co. Ci.
(1).

1941. Nos. 330/1 and 414/26 of Yugoslavia optd. with Type **1**.

1. **99.** 25 p. black 5 12
2. 50 p. orange 5 20
3. 1 d. green 5 12
4. 1 d. 50 red 5 20
5. 2 d. red 5 12
6. 3 d. brown 5 20
7. 4 d. blue 5 20
8. 5 d. blue 5 20
9. 5 d. 50 violet 5 20
10. 6 d. blue 10 30
11. 8 d. brown 10 40
12. **70.** 10 d. violet 15 35
13. **99.** 12 d. violet 20 30
14. **70.** 15 d. olive .. .. 60·00 70·00
15. **99.** 16 d. purple 20 40
16. 20 d. blue .. .. 1·60 2·25
17. 30 d. pink .. .. 9·00 13·50

1941. Nos. 330 and 414/26 of Yugoslavia optd. **R. Commissariato Civile Territori Sloveni occupati LUBIANA**, with four lines of dots at foot.

23. **99.** 25 p. black 5 20
24. 50 p. orange 8 20
25. 1 d. green 5 20
26. 1 d. 50 red 5 12
27. 2 d. red 5 12
28. 3 d. brown 10 30
29. 4 d. blue 5 12
30. 5 d. blue 25 75
31. 5 d. 50 violet 12 25
32. 6 d. blue 12 25
33. 8 d. brown 12 25
34. **70.** 10 d. violet 45 90
35. **99.** 12 d. violet 20 45
36. 16 d. purple 70 90
37. 20 d. blue .. .. 1·60 2·50
38. 30 d. pink .. .. 15·00 22·00

1941. Nos. 446/9 of Yugoslavia optd. as Nos. 23/38 but with only three lines of dots at foot.

45. 50 p.+50 p. on 5 d. violet 2·25 4·25
46. 1 d.+1 d. on 10 d. lake .. 2·25 4·25
47. 1 d.50+1 d. 50on 20d. grn. 2·25 4·25
48. 2 d.+2 d. on 30 d. .. 2·25 4·25

1941. Nos. 360/7 and 443/4 of Yugoslavia optd. as Nos. 23/38, with three or four (No. 57) lines of dots at foot.

49. 50 p. brown .. .. .. 70 1·25
50. 1 d. green .. .. .. 70 1·25
51. 2 d. blue .. .. .. 85 1·25
52. 2 d. 50 red .. .. .. 85 1·25
53. 5 d. violet .. .. .. 1·90 2·50
54. 10 d. lake .. .. .. 1·90 2·50
55. 20 d. green .. .. .. 10·00 15·00
56. 30 d. blue .. .. .. 26·00 27·00
57. 40 d. green .. .. .. 55·00 70·00
58. 50 d. blue .. .. .. 45·00 60·00

1941. Nos. 26 and 29 surch.

59. **99.** 0 d. 50 on 1 d. 50 red .. 5 8
60. 0 d. 50 on 1 d. 50 red .. £130 £225
61. 1 d. on 4 d. blue.. .. 5 15

POSTAGE DUE STAMPS

1941. Postage Due stamps of Yugoslavia, Nos. D 89/93 optd. with Type **1**.

D 18. D **56.** 50 p. violet.. .. 12 30
D 19. 1 d. mauve.. .. 12 30
D 20. 2 d. blue 15 30
D 21. 5 d. orange.. .. 1·50 2·00
D 22. 10 d. brown .. .. 1·50 2·00

Optd. as Nos. 18/33, but with four lines of dots at top.

D 40. D **56.** 50 p. violet.. .. 5 15
D 41. 1 d. mauve.. .. 5 15
D 42. 2 d. blue 20 55
D 43. 5 d. orange.. .. 9·25 12·50
D 44. 10 d. brown .. .. 2·25 3·00

Optd. as Nos. D 6/10, but with narrower lettering.

D 62. D **56.** 50 p. violet.. .. 30 70
D 63. 1 d. mauve.. .. 40 80
D 64. 2 d. blue .. .. 7·00 11·00

GERMAN OCCUPATION, 1943–45

PROVINZ LJUBLJANIKA POKRAJINA LAIBACH (3.)

LJUBLJANIKA PROVINZ LAIBACH POKRAJINA (4.)

1944. Stamps of Italy optd. with Types **3** or **4**. (a) On Postage stamps of 1929. Nos. 239, etc.

65. **4.** 5 c. brown 8 90
66. **3.** 10 c. brown 8 90
67. **4.** 15 c. green 10 75
68. **3.** 20 c. red 8 90
69. **4.** 25 c. green 8 90
70. **3.** 30 c. brown 8 90
71. **4.** 35 c. blue 10 70
72. **3.** 50 c. violet .. .. 10 1·10
73. **4.** 75 c. red .. .. 10 2·10
74. **3.** 1 l. violet .. .. 20 2·10
75. **4.** 1 l. 25 blue .. .. 12 1·25
76. **3.** 1 l. 75 orange .. .. 75 8·50
77. **4.** 2 l. red .. .. 15 1·90
78. **3.** 10 l. violet .. .. 3·75 24·00

Surch. with new value.

79. – 2 l. 55 on 5 c. brown .. 25 4·50
80. **4.** 5 l. on 25 c. green .. 30 6·00
81. 20 l. on 20 c. red .. 3·00 30·00
82. **3.** 25 l. on 2 l. red .. 3·75 60·00
83. **4.** 50 l. on 1 l. 75 orange .. 6·75 £100

In No. 79 the overprint inscriptions are at each side of the eagle.

(b) On Air stamps, Nos. 270, etc.

84. **4.** 25 c. green .. .. 1·00 1·50
85. **3.** 50 c. brown .. .. 4·25 30·00
86. **4.** 75 c. brown .. .. 1·50 9·00
87. **3.** 1 l. violet .. .. 5·00 22·50
88. **4.** 2 l. blue .. .. 2·50 13·00
89. **3.** 5 l. green .. .. 2·50 19·00
90. **4.** 10 l. red .. .. 2·25 15·00

(c) On Air Express stamp.

E 91. **3.** 2 l. black (No. E 370) 7·50 48·00

(d) On Express Letter stamp.

E 92. **3.** 1 l. 25 green (No. E 350) 1·40 7·50

1944. Red Cross. Express Letter stamps of Italy surch. as Types **3** or **4** with a red cross and new value alongside.

102.E **132.** 1 l. 25+50 l. green .. 24·00 £300
103. 2 l. 50+50 l. orange.. 24·00 £300

1944. Homeless Relief Fund. Express Letter stamps of Italy surch. as Types **3** and **4**, but in circular frame, and **BREZDOMCEM DEN OBDACHLOSEN** alongside with new value between.

104. E **132.** 1 l. 25+50 l. green.. 24·00 £300
105. 2 l. 50+50 l. orge... 24·00 £300

1944. Air. Orphans' Fund. Air stamps of Italy Nos. 270, etc., surch as Types **3** and **4**, but in circular frame between **DEN WAISEN SIROTAM** and new value.

106. – 25 c.+10 l. green .. 10·00 £180
107. **110.** 50 c.+10 l. brown .. 10·00 £180
108. – 75 c.+20 l. brown .. 10·00 £180
109. – 1 l.+20 l. violet .. 10·00 £180
110. **113.** 2 l.+20 l. blue .. 10·00 £180
111. **110.** 5 l.+20 l. green .. 10·00 £180

1944. Air. Winter Relief Fund. Air stamps of Italy Nos. 270, etc., surch. as Types **3** and **4**. but between **ZIMSKA POMOC WINTERHILFE** and new value.

112. – 25 c.+10 l. green .. 10·00 £180
113. **110.** 50 c.+10 l. brown .. 10·00 £180
114. – 75 c.+20 l. brown .. 10·00 £180
115. – 1 l.+20 l. violet .. 10·00 £180
116. **113.** 2 l.+20 l. blue .. 10·00 £180
117. **110.** 5 l.+20 l. green .. 10·00 £180

9. Railway Viaduct, Borovnice.

10. Church in Novo Mesto.

1945. Inscr. "PROVINZ LAIBACH".

118. – 5 c. brown .. .. 20 1·50
119. – 10 c. orange .. .. 20 1·50
120. **9.** 20 c. brown .. .. 50 1·50
121. – 25 c. green .. .. 20 1·50
122. **10.** 50 c. violet .. .. 20 1·50
123. – 75 c. red .. .. 20 1·50
124. – 1 l. green .. .. 20 1·75
125. – 1 l. 25 blue .. .. 20 3·25
126. – 1 l. 50 green .. .. 35 3·25
127. – 2 l. blue .. .. 30 5·25
128. – 2 l. 50 brown .. .. 30 5·25
129. – 3 l. mauve .. .. 60 9·25
130. – 5 l. brown .. .. 85 9·25
131. – 10 l. green .. .. 2·10 45·00
132. – 20 l. blue .. .. 12·50 £140
133. – 30 l. red .. .. 70·00 £600

DESIGNS—VERT. 5 c. Stalagmites, Krizna Jama. 1 l. 25, Kocevje. 1 l. 50, Borovnice Falls. 3 l. Castle Zuzemberg. 30 l. View and Tabor Church. HORIZ. 10 c. Zirknitz Lake. 25 c. Farm near Ljubljana. 75 c. View from Ribnica. 1 l. Old Castle, Ljubljana. 2 l. Castle, Kostanjevica. 2 l. 50, Castle, Turjak. 5 l. View on River Krka. 10 l. Castle, Otocec. 20 l. Farm at Dolenjskom.

POSTAGE DUE STAMPS

(D 5.)

PROVINZ 30 LAIBACH (D 6.)

1944. Postage Due stamps of Italy, Nos. D 395, etc., optd. as Type D **5**.

D 93. D **141.** 5 c. brown .. 1·10 8·50
D 94. 10 c. blue .. 1·10 8·50
D 95. 20 c. red 15 35
D 96. 25 c. green .. 15 35
D 97. 50 c. violet .. 15 35
D 98. D **142.** 1 l. orange .. 60 6·25
D 99. 2 l. green .. .. 60 6·25

Surch. as Type D **6**.

D 100. D **141.** 30 c. on 50 c. violet 15 35
D 101. 40 c. on 5 c. brown 15 35

INDEPENDENT STATE

11 Parliament Building

12 Arms

1991. Declaration of Independence.

134 **11** 5 d. multicoloured .. 25 20

1991.

135 **12** 1 t. multicoloured .. 5 5
136 4 t. multicoloured .. 15 15
137 5 t. multicoloured .. 15 15
138 11 t. multicoloured .. 25 25

13 Ski Jumping

1992. Winter Olympic Games, Albertville. Multicoloured.

139 30 t. Type **13** 85 85
140 50 t. Slalom .. .. 1·40 1·40

14 Arms

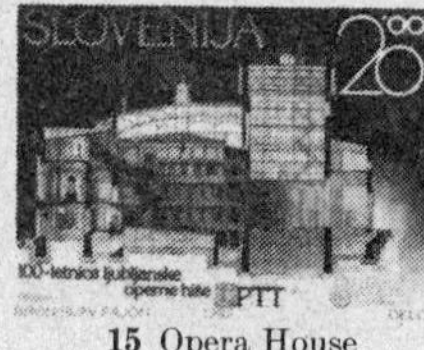

15 Opera House

1992. Multicoloured, background colours given.

141 **14** 1 t. brown 5 5
142 2 t. purple 5 5
143 4 t. green 15 15
144 5 t. red 15 15
145 6 t. yellow 20 20
146 11 t. orange 25 25
147 15 t. blue 30 30
148 20 t. violet 50 50
149 50 t. green 85 85
150 100 t. grey .. .. 1·60 1·60

1992. Centenary of Ljubljana Opera House.

155 **15** 20 t. multicoloured .. 25 25

16 Tartini and Violins

1992. 300th Birth Anniv of Giuseppe Tartini (violinist and composer).

156 **16** 27 t. multicoloured .. 35 35

17 Map and Marko Anton Kappus preaching to Amerindians

18

1992. 500th Anniv of Discovery of America by Columbus. Multicoloured.

157 27 t. Type **17** 35 35
158 47 t. Map and "Santa Maria" 60 60

1992. Obligatory Tax. Red Cross.

159 **18** 3 t. black, red and blue 5 5

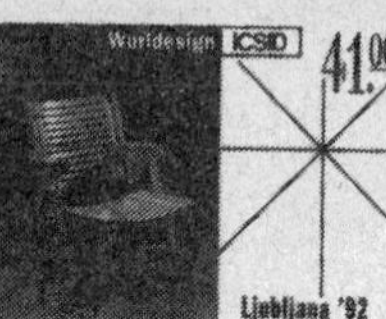

19 Collapsible Chair by Niko Kralj and Map

20 Slomsek

1992. World Industrial Design Congress, Ljubljana.

160 **19** 41 t. multicoloured .. 55 55

1992. 130th Death Anniv of Anton Slomsek, Bishop of Maribor.

161 **20** 41 t. multicoloured .. 55 55

21 Wreckage

22 Rescuing Mountaineer

1992. Obligatory Tax. Solidarity Week. Perf and Imperf.

162 **21** 3 t. brown, black & red 5 5

1992. 80th Anniv of Alpine Rescue Service.

164 **22** 41 t. multicoloured .. 55 55

23 River Jousting

24 Linden Leaf and Flowers

1992. 900th Anniv of River Jousting in Ljubljana.

165 **23** 6 t. multicoloured .. 10 10

1992. 1st Anniv of Independence.

166 **24** 41 t. multicoloured .. 55 55

25 Leon Stukelj and Medals

1992. Olympic Games, Barcelona. Mult.

167 40 t. Type **25** 50 50
168 46 t. Head of Apoxymenos repeated in three Slovene colours .. 60 60

26 Sheepdog

1992. "Psov '92" World Dog-training Championships, Ljubljana.

169 **26** 40 t. multicoloured .. 50 50

MINIMUM PRICE

The minimum price quoted is 5p which represents a handling charge rather than a basis for valuing common stamps. For further notes about prices see introductory pages.

27 Hand crushing Cigarettes

28 Kogoj and scene from "Black Masks" (opera)

1992. Obligatory Tax. Red Cross. Anti-smoking Week.
170 **27** 3 t. multicoloured .. 5 5

1992. Birth Centenary of Marij Kogoj (composer).
171 **28** 40 t. multicoloured .. 50 50

29 Langus (self-portrait)

1992. Birth Bicentenary of Matevz Langus (painter).
172 **29** 40 t. multicoloured .. 50 50

30 Nativity

1992. Christmas. Multicoloured.
173 6 t. Type **30** 10 10
174 7 t. Type **30** 10 10
175 41 t. "Madonna and Child" (stained-glass window by V. Sorli-Puc in St. Mary's Church, Bovec) (vert) 55 55

31 View of Earth from Space and Satellite

1992. Birth Centenary of Herman Potocnik (space flight pioneer).
176 **31** 46 t. multicoloured .. 60 60

32 Illustration from "Solzice"

1993. Birth Centenary of Prezihov Voranc (writer).
177 **32** 7 t. multicoloured .. 10 10

33 "Underneath the Birches"

1993. 50th Death Anniv of Rihard Jakopic (painter).
178 **33** 44 t. multicoloured .. 45 45

34 Bust of Stefan (J. Savinsek)

35 Honey-cake from Skofja Loka

1993. Death Centenary of Jozef Stefan (physicist).
179 **34** 51 t. multicoloured .. . 50 50

1993. Slovene Culture.
180 **35** 1 t. brown, cinnamon and deep brown .. 10 10
181 – 2 t. green and lt green 10 10
184 – 5 t. grey and mauve .. 10 10
185 – 6 t. lt green, grn & yell 10 10
186 – 7 t. red, crimson & grey 10 10
187 – 8 t. grn, dp grn & olive 10 10
188 – 9 t. red, brown and grey 10 10
189 – 10 t. brown and lt brown 10 10
191 – 20 t. green and grey .. 20 20
195 – 44 t. lt blue, black & bl 45 45
196 – 50 t. purple and mauve 50 50
198 – 100 t. deep brown, light brown and brown .. 1·00 1·00

DESINS: 2 t. Musical pipes; 5 t. Storage barn; 6 t. Shepherd's hut, Velika; 7 t. Zither; 8 t. Mill on the Mur; 9 t. Sledge; 10 t. Drum; 20 t. House, Prekmurju; 44 t. House, Karst. 50 t. Wind-propelled pump; 100 t. Cake.

36 Mountains and Founder Members

1993. Centenary of Alpine Association.
199 **36** 7 t. multicoloured .. 10 10

37 Cop's Route up Triglav

38 Chainbreaker

1993. Birth Centenary of Joza Cop (climber and mountain rescuer).
200 **37** 44 t. multicoloured .. 45 45

1993. 75th Anniv of Slovenian Postal Service.
201 **38** 7 t. multicoloured .. 10 10

39 "St. Nicholas" (altar painting, Tintoretto)

40 "Table in Pompeii" (Marij Pregelj)

1993. 500th Anniv of College Chapter of Novo Mesto. Multicoloured.
202 7 t. Type **39** 10 10
203 44 t. Arms 45 45

1993. Europa. Contemporary Art. Mult.
204 44 t. Type **40** 45 45
205 159 t. "Girl with Toy" (Gabrijel Stupica) .. 1·60 1·60

41 "Schwagerina carniolica"

42

1993. Fossils.
206 **41** 44 t. multicoloured .. 45 45

1993. Obligatory Tax. Red Cross.
207 **42** 3 t. 50 black, red & blue 10 10

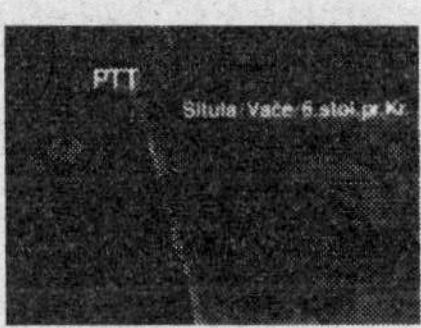

43 6th-century B.C. Vase

44 Red Cross Rescue Workers

1993. 1st Anniv of Admission to United Nations Organization.
208 **43** 62 t. multicoloured .. 65 65

1993. Obligatory Tax. Solidarity Week.
209 **44** 3 t. 50 multicoloured .. 10 10

45 Basketball, Hurdling and Swimming

1993. Mediterranean Games, Roussillon (Languedoc).
210 **45** 36 t. multicoloured .. 35 35

46 "Battle of Sisak" (Janez Valvasor)

1993. 400th Anniv of Battle of Sisak.
211 **46** 49 t. multicoloured .. 50 50

47 "Monolistra spinosissima"

1993. Cave Fauna. Multicoloured.
212 7 t. Type **47** 10 10
213 40 t. "Aphaenopidius kamnikensis" (insect) .. 40 40
214 55 t. "Proteus anguinus" 55 55
215 65 t. "Zospeum spelaeum" (mollusc) 65 65

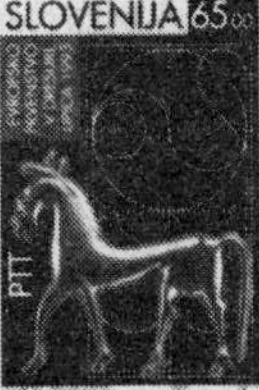

48 Horse and Diagram of Movements

49 Boy smoking and Emblem

1993. European Dressage Championships, Lipica.
216 **48** 65 t. multicoloured .. 65 65

1993. Obligatory Tax. Red Cross. Anti-smoking Week.
217 **49** 4 t. 50 multicoloured .. 10 10

50 Arms (death anniv of Johnann Valvasor (historian))

1993. 300th Anniversaries.
218 **50** 9 t. black, lilac and gold 10 10
219 – 65 t. black, stone & gold 65 65

DESIGN: 65 t. Arms of Academia Operosorum.

51 Christmas Crib

1993. Christmas. Multicoloured.
220 9 t. Type **51** 10 10
221 65 t. Dr. Joze Pogacnik (archbishop) 65 65

SOMALIA Pt. 8; Pt. 14

A former Italian colony in East Africa on the Gulf of Aden, including Benadir (S. Somaliland), and Jubaland. Under British Administration 1943–50 (for stamps issued during this period see volume 3). Then under United Nations control with Italian Administration. Became independent on 1st July, 1960. Following a revolution in Oct. 1969, the country was designated "Somali Democratic Republic". See also Middle East Forces.

1903. 16 annas = 1 rupia.
1905. 100 centesimi = 1 lira.
1922. 100 besa = 1 rupia.
1926. 100 centesimi = 1 lira.
1950. 100 centesimi = 1 somalo.
1961. 100 cents = 1 Somali shilling.

ITALIAN COLONY

1. African Elephant.

2. Somali Lion.

1903.
1. 1. 1 b. brown 19·00 2·75
2. 2 b. green 2·25 1·00
3. 2. 1 a. red 2·50 1·90
4. 2 a. orange 5·00 8·50
5. 2½ a. blue 2·25 3·00
6. 5 a. yellow 5·00 10·00
7. 10 a. lilac 5·00 10·00

1905. Surch. with new value without bars at top.
10. 1. 2 c. on 1 b. brown 4·50 12·00
11. 5 c. on 2 b. green 4·50 8·00
12. 10 c. on 1 a. red 4·50 7·00
13. 15 c. on 2 a. orange 4·50 7·00
8. 15 c. on 5 a. yellow £1400 £225
13a. 20 c. on 2 a. orange 7·00 3·00
14. 25 c. on 2½ a. blue 7·00 7·00
9. 40 c. on 10 a. lilac £325 £100
15. 50 c. on 5 a. yellow 9·50 14·00
16. 1 l. on 10 a. lilac 9·50 16·00
For stamps with bars at top, see Nos. 68, etc.

Nos. 19 to 160 are all, except where stated, Italian stamps, sometimes in new colours, optd. **SOMALIA ITALIANA** or **SOMALIA.**

1916. Nos. 15 and 16 re-surcharged and with bars cancelling original surcharge.
17. 2. 5 c. on 50 c. on 5 a. yellow 14·00 20·00
18. 20 c. on 1 l. on 10 a. lilac 4·00 10·00

1916. Red Cross stamps optd. or surch. **20** also.
19. 53. 10 c.+5 c. red 1·50 3·75
20. 54. 15 c.+5 c. grey 5·00 15·00
21. 20 c.+5 c. orange 5·00 15·00
22. 20 on 15 c.+5 c. grey 1·50 5·00

1922. Nos. 12, etc., again surch. at top.
23. 1. 3 b. on 5 c. on 2 b. green 5·50 13·00
24. 2. 6 b. on 10 c. on 1 a. red 7·00 10·00
25. 9 b. on 15 c. on 2 a. orange 7·00 10·00
26. 15 b. on 25 c. on 2½ a. blue 8·50 10·00
27. 30 b. on 50 c. on 5 a. yell. 9·50 24·00
28. 60 b. on 1 l. on 10 a. lilac 9·50 32·00

1922. Victory stamps surch.
29. 62. 3 b. on 5 c. green 40 2·00
30. 6 b. on 10 c. red 40 2·00
31. 9 b. on 15 c. grey 40 3·25
32. 15 b. on 25 c. blue 40 3·25

1923. Nos. 11 to 16 re-surcharged with new values and bars. (No. 33 is optd. with bars only at bottom.)
33. 1. 2 c. on 1 b. brown 4·25 13·00
34. 2 on 2 c. on 1 b. brown 4·25 13·00
35. 3 on 2 c. on 1 b. brown 4·25 13·00
36. 2. 5 b. on 50 c. on 5 a. yellow 4·25 10·00
37. 1. 6 on 5 c. on 2 b. green 5·50 7·50
38. 2. 18 b. on 10 c. on 1 a. red 5·50 7·50
39. 20 b. on 15 c. on 2 a. orge. 7·00 10·00
40. 25 b. on 15 c. on 2 a. orge. 8·00 10·00
41. 30 b. on 25 c. on 2½ a. blue 9·50 12·00
42. 60 b. on 1 l. on 10 a. lilac 10·00 27·00
43. 1 r. on 1 l. on 10 a. lilac 12·00 32·00

1923. Propaganda of Faith stamps surch.
44. 66. 6 b. on 20 c. orge & grn. 1·10 5·50
45. 13 b. on 30 c. orge. & red 1·10 5·50
46. 20 b. on 50 c. orge. & vio. 75 4·75
47. 30 b. on 1 l. orge. & blue 75 4·75

1923. Fascisti stamps surch.
48. 73. 3 b. on 10 c. green 1·75 6·00
49. 13 b. on 30 c. violet 1·75 6·00
50. 20 b. on 50 c. red 1·75 6·00
51. 74. 30 b. on 1 l. blue 1·75 6·00
52. 1 r. on 2 l. brown 1·75 6·00
53. 75. 3 l. on 5 f. black and blue 1·75 7·50

1924. Manzoni stamps surch.
54. 77. 6 b. on 10 c. black & red 60 12·00
55. 9 b. on 15 c. black & grn. 60 12·00
56. 13 b. on 30 c. black 60 12·00
57. 20 b. on 50 c. blk. & brn. 60 12·00
58. 30 b. on 1 l. black & blue 15·00 90·00
59. 3 r. on 5 l. black & purple £200 £950

1925. Holy Year stamps surch.
60. – 6 b.+3 b. on 20 c.+10 c. brown and green 75 4·25
61. 81. 13 b.+6 b. on 30 c.+15 c. brown and chocolate 75 4·25
62. – 15 b.+8 b. on 50 c.+25 c. brown & violet 75 4·25
63. – 18 b.+9 b. on 60 c.+30 c. brown and red 75 4·25
64. – 30 b.+15 b. on 1 l.+50 c purple and blue 75 4·25
65. – 1 r.+50 b. on 5 l.+2l. 50 c. purple and red 75 4·25

1925. Royal Jubilee Stamp optd.
66. 82. 60 c. red 15 2·75
67. 1 l. blue 2·25 19·00
67a. 1 l. 25 c. blue 35 8·50

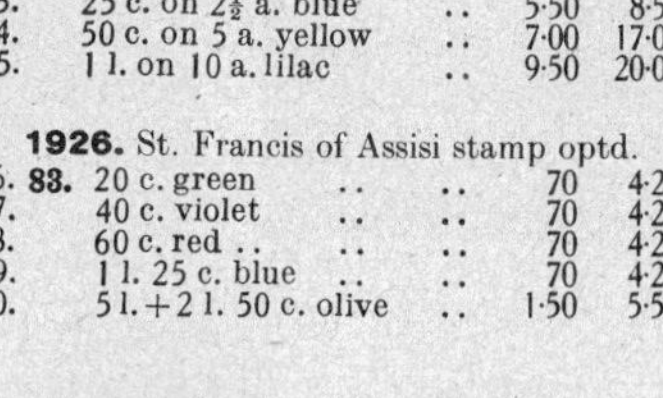

1926. Nos. 10/13, and 13a/16 optd. with bars at top.
68. 1. 2 c. on 1 b. brown 9·50 25·00
69. 5 c. on 2 b. green 7·00 20·00
70. 2. 10 c. on 1 a. red 4·25 4·75
71. 15 c. on 2 a. orange 4·25 5·50
72. 20 c. on 2 a. orange 5·50 7·50
73. 25 c. on 2½ a. blue 5·50 8·50
74. 50 c. on 5 a. yellow 7·00 17·00
75. 1 l. on 10 a. lilac 9·50 20·00

1926. St. Francis of Assisi stamp optd.
76. 83. 20 c. green 70 4·25
77. 40 c. violet 70 4·25
78. 60 c. red 70 4·25
79. 1 l. 25 c. blue 70 4·25
80. 5 l.+2 l. 50 c. olive 1·50 5·50

21.

25.

1926. Italian Colonial Institute.
81. 21. 5 c.+5 c. brown 20 2·25
82. 10 c.+5 c. olive 20 2·25
83. 20 c.+5 c. green 20 2·25
84. 40 c.+5 c. red 20 2·25
85. 60 c.+5 c. orange 20 2·25
86. 1 l.+5 c. blue 20 2·25

1926. Italian stamps optd.
87. 31. 2 c. brown 1·00 2·25
88. 33. 5 c. green 1·40 2·25
89. 92. 7½ c. brown 4·75 17·00
90. 37. 10 c. red 85 40
91. 39. 20 c. purple 90 70
92. 34. 25 c. green 35 30
92a 39. 30 c. black 4·00 6·00
93. 91. 50 c. grey and brown 4·00 4·25
94. 92. 50 c. mauve 11·00 22·00
95. 39. 60 c. orange 1·10 1·25
96. 34. 75 c. red 35·00 5·00
97. 1 l. brown and green 1·10 60
98. 1 l. 25 c. blue 3·50 1·00
99. 91. 1 l. 75 brown 18·00 7·00
100. 34. 2 l. green and orange 6·00 2·50
101. 2 l. 50 c. green & orange 7·50 3·00
102. 5 l. blue and red 17·00 12·00
103. 10 l. red and olive 17·00 15·00

1927. First National Defence issue optd.
104. 89. 40 c.+20 c. black & brn. 80 4·25
105. – 60 c.+30 c. brown & red 80 4·25
106. – 1 l. 25+60 c. blk. & blue 80 4·25
107. – 5 l.+2 l. 50 blk. & grn. 1·25 6·50

1927. Centenary of Volta.
108. 90. 20 c. violet 3·00 10·00
109. 50 c. orange 3·00 7·00
110. 1 l. 25 blue 4·00 11·00

1928. 45th Anniv. of Italian-African Society.
111. 25. 20 c.+5 c. green 60 3·50
112. 30 c.+5 c. red 60 3·50
113. 50 c.+10 c. violet 60 3·50
114. 1 l. 25+20 c. blue 60 3·50

1929. Second National Defence issue.
115. 89. 30 c.+10 c. black & red 1·00 4·75
116. – 50 c.+20 c. black & lilac 1·00 4·75
117. – 1 l. 25+50 c. blue & brn. 1·40 6·00
118. – 5 l.+2 l. black and olive 1·40 6·00

1929. Montecassino Abbey.
119. 104. 20 c. green 1·75 4·25
120. – 25 c. orange 1·75 4·25
121. – 50 c.+10 c. red 1·75 8·50
122. – 75 c.+15 c. brown 1·75 8·50
123. 104. 1 l. 25+25 c. purple 3·25 8·50
124. – 5 l.+1 l. blue 3·25 8·50
125. – 10 l.+2 l. brown 3·25 10·00

1930. Royal Wedding.
126. 109. 20 c. green 40 1·90
127. 50 c.+10 c. orange 35 2·50
128. 1 l. 25+25 c. red 35 2·75

1930. Ferrucci.
129. 114. 20 c. violet 50 1·60
130. – 25 c. green (No. 283) 50 1·60
131. – 50 c. black (as No. 284) 50 1·60
132. – 1 l. 25 blue (No. 285) 50 1·60
133. – 5 l.+2 l. red (as No. 286) 1·75 2·75

1930. Third National Defence issue.
134. 89. 30 c.+10 c. grn. & olive 4·00 15·00
135. – 50 c.+10 c. violet & olive 4·00 15·00
136. – 1 l. 25+30 c. brown 4·00 15·00
137. – 5 l.+1 l. 50 grn. & blue 12·00 42·00

29. Irrigation Canal.

1930. 25th Anniv. (1929) of Colonial Agricultural Institute.
138. 29. 50 c.+20 c. brown 75 5·00
139. 1 l. 25+20 c. blue 75 5·00
140. 1 l. 75+20 c. green 75 5·00
141. 2 l. 55+50 c. violet 1·50 5·00
142. 5 l.+1 l. red 1·50 5·00

1930. Bimillenary of Virgil.
143. 15 c. violet 25 1·40
144. 20 c. brown 25 1·40
145. 25 c. green 25 1·40
146. 30 c. brown 25 1·40
147. 50 c. purple 25 1·10
148. 75 c. red 25 1·40
149. 1 l. 25 blue 25 1·40
150. 5 l.+1 l. 50 purple 1·75 7·00
151. 10 l.+2 l. 50 brown 1·75 7·00

1931. Portraits.
152. – 25 c. green 2·25 4·25
153. 103. 50 c. violet 5·50 1·00

1931. St. Anthony of Padua.
154. 121. 20 c. brown 55 2·50
155. – 25 c. green 55 2·50
156. – 30 c. brown 55 2·50
157. – 50 c. purple 55 1·40
158. – 75 c. grey 55 2·50
159. – 1 l. 25 blue 55 2·50
160. – 5 l.+2 l. 50 brown 2·00 11·00

32. Tower at Mnara-Ciromo.

33. Hippopotamus.

1932.
161a. – 5 c. brown 15 10
162a. – 7½ c. violet 15 1·10
163a. – 10 c. black 15 10
164a. – 15 c. olive 15 30
165a. 32. 20 c. red 15 10
166a. 25 c. green 15 10
167a. 30 c. brown 20 20
168a. – 35 c. blue 65 1·50
169a. – 50 c. violet 2·75 10
170. – 75 c. red 85 40
171. – 1 l. 25 blue 1·75 25
172. – 1 l. 75 orange 1·25 25
173. – 2 l. red 70 35
174. – 2 l. 55 slate 12·00 20·00
175a. – 5 l. red 4·50 1·25
176. 33. 10 l. violet 7·50 4·50
177. – 20 l. green 18·00 20·00
178. – 25 l. blue 30·00 30·00
Designs—Horiz. 5 c., 7½ c., 10 c., 15 c. Francesco Crispi Lighthouse, Cape Guardafui, 35 c., 50 c., 75 c. Governor's Residence, Mogadishu. 25 l. Lioness. Vert. 1 l. 25, 1 l. 75, 2 l. Ant-hill. 2 l. 55, 5 l. Ostrich. 20 l. Lesser kudu.

1934. Abruzzi issue. Optd. **ONORANZE AL DUCA DEGLI ABRUZZI.**
179. 10 c. brown 2·50 8·00
180. 25 c. green 2·50 8·00
181. 50 c. mauve 1·90 8·00
182. 1 l. 25 blue 1·90 8·00
183. 5 l. black 3·00 8·00
184. 10 l. red 2·50 8·00
185. 20 l. green 2·50 8·00
186. 25 l. blue 2·50 8·00
Designs as Nos. 163a to 178.

35. Woman and Child.

37. King Victor Emmanuel III.

36.

1934. 2nd Int. Colonial Exn., Naples.
187. 35. 5 c. green & brown (post.) 1·50 6·00
188. 10 c. brown and black 1·50 6·00
189. 20 c. red and slate 1·50 6·00
190. 50 c. violet and brown 1·50 6·00
191. 60 c. brown and slate 1·50 6·00
192. 1 l. 25 blue and green 1·50 6·00
193. – 25 c. blue & orange (air) 1·50 6·00
194. – 50 c. green and slate 1·50 6·00
195. – 75 c. brown and orange 1·50 6·00
196. – 80 c. brown and green 1·50 6·00
197. – 1 l. red and green 1·50 6·00
198. – 2 l. blue and brown 1·50 6·00
Designs: 25 c. to 75 c. Aeroplane over River Juba. 80 c. to 2 l. Cheetahs watching aeroplane.

1934. Air. Rome-Mogadishu Flight.
199. 36. 25 c.+10 c. green 1·75 5·00
200. 50 c.+10 c. brown 1·75 5·00
201. 75 c.+15 c. red 1·75 5·00
202. 80 c.+15 c. black 1·75 5·00
203. 1 l.+20 c. red 1·75 5·00
204. 2 l.+20 c. blue 1·75 5·00
205. 3 l.+25 c. violet 14·00 40·00
206. 5 l.+25 c. orange 14·00 40·00
207. 10 l.+30 c. purple 14·00 40·00
208. 25 l.+2 l. green 14·00 40·00

1934. King of Italy's Visit to Italian Somaliland.
209. 37. 5 c.+5 c. black 65 3·00
210. 7½ c.+7½ c. purple 65 3·00
211. 15 c.+10 c. green 65 3·00
212. 20 c.+10 c. red 65 3·00
213. 25 c.+10 c. green 65 3·00
214. 30 c.+10 c. brown 65 3·00
215. 50 c.+10 c. violet 65 3·00
216. 75 c.+15 c. red 65 3·00
217. 1 l. 25+15 c. blue 65 3·00
218. 1 l. 75+25 c. orange 65 3·00
219. 2 l. 75+25 c. slate 7·50 29·00
220. 5 l.+1 l. red 7·50 29·00
221. 10 l.+1 l. 80 red 7·50 29·00
222. – 25 l.+2 l. 75 brn. & red 55·00 95·00
Design (36×44 mm.): 25 l. King Victor Emmanuel III on horseback.

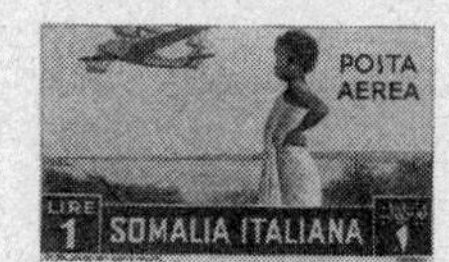

38a. Native Girl and Aeroplane.

1936. Air.
223. – 25 c. green 85 2·00
224. – 50 c. brown 20 15
225. – 60 c. orange 1·10 4·25
226. – 75 c. brown 70 90
227. 38a. 1 l. blue 15 10
228. – 1 l. 50 violet 70 35
229. – 2 l. blue 1·60 85
230. 38a. 3 l. red 5·00 2·25
231. – 5 l. green 5·00 2·75
232. – 10 l. red 6·00 9·00
Designs: 25 c., 1 l. 50, Banana trees. 50 c., 2 l. Native woman in cotton plantation. 60 c., 5 l. Orchard. 75 c., 10 l. Native women harvesting.

ITALIAN TRUST TERRITORY

40. Tower at Mnara-Ciromo.

41. Ostrich.

42. Governor's Residence, Mogadishu.

43. River Scene.

1950.
233. 40. 1 c. black (postage) 10 10
234. 41. 5 c. red 75 25
235. 42. 6 c. violet 15 10
236. 40. 8 c. green 15 10
237. 42. 10 c. green 10 10
238. 41. 20 c. turquoise 1·25 20
239. 40. 35 c. red 35 20
240. 42. 55 c. blue 45 35
241. 41. 60 c. violet 1·75 35
242. 40. 65 c. brown 70 15
243. 42. 1 s. orange 85 15
244. 43. 30 c. brown (air) 30 30
245. 45 c. red 30 30
246. 65 c. slate 30 30
247. 70 c. blue 30 30
248. 90 c. brown 30 30
249. 1 s. purple 45 30
250. 1 s. 35 violet 70 70
251. 1 s. 50 turquoise 85 50
252. 3 s. blue 7·00 2·25
253. 5 s. brown 8·00 3·00
254. 10 s. orange 9·50 2·25

44. Councillors. **45.** Symbol of Fair.

1951. 1st Territorial Council.
255. **44.** 20 c. brn. & grn. (post.) 2·00 20
256. 55 c. violet and sepia .. 3·75 3·50
257. – 1 s. blue and violet (air) 2·25 70
258. – 1 s. 50 brown and green 3·75 2·75
DESIGN—Inscr. as Type **44**: 1 s. and 1 s. 50, Flags and aeroplane over Mogadiscio.

1952. 1st Somali Fair, Mogadiscio.
259. **45.** 25 c. brn. & red (postage) 1·75 1·75
260. 55 c. brown and blue .. 1·75 1·75
261. – 1 s. 20 blue & bistre (air) 2·00 2·00
DESIGN: 1 s. 20, Palm tree, aeroplane and minaret.

46. Mother and Baby. **47.** Somali and Entrance to Fair.

1953. Anti-Tuberculosis Campaign.
262. **46.** 5 c. brn. & vio. (postage) 10 10
263. 25 c. brown and red .. 15 10
264. 50 c. brown and blue .. 70 70
265. 1 s. 20 brn. & grn. (air) 85 85

1953. 2nd Somali Fair, Mogadiscio.
266. **47.** 25 c. green (postage) .. 20 20
267. 60 c. blue 40 40
268. – 1 s. 20 lake (air) .. 40 40
269. – 1 s. 50 brown 40 40
DESIGN: 1 s. 20, 1 s. 50, Palm, aeroplane and entrance.

48. Stamps of 1903 and Map.

1953. 50th Anniv. of First Stamps of Italian Somaliland.
(a) Postage.
270. **48.** 25 c. brown, red & lake 25 25
271. 35 c. brown, red & green 25 25
272. 60 c. brown, red & orge. 25 25
(b) Air. Aeroplane on Map.
273. **48.** 60 c. brown, red & chest. 45 45
274. 1 s. brown, red & black 45 45

49. Aeroplane and Constellations.

1953. Air. 75th Anniv. of U.P.U.
275. **49.** 1 s. 20 red and buff .. 35 35
276. 1 s. 50 brown and buff .. 40 40
277. 2 s. green and blue .. 45 40

50. Somali Bush Country. **51.** Alexander Is. and R. Juba.

1954. Leprosy Convention.
278. **50.** 25 c. green & blue (post.) 30 30
279. 60 c. sepia and brown .. 30 30
280. **51.** 1 s. 20 brn. and grn. (air) 40 40
281. 2 s. violet and red .. 55 65

52. Somali Flag. **52a.** " Adenium Somalense ".

1954. Institution of Somali Flag.
282. **52.** 25 c. multicoloured (post.) 25 25
283. 1 s. 20 multicoloured (air) 25 25

1955. Floral Designs.
290a. **52a.** 1 c. red, black and blue 10 10
285. – 5 c. mauve, grn. & blue 10 10
290c. – 10 c. yell., grn. & lilac 10 10
290d. – 15 c. yellow, grn. & red 20 20
290e. – 25 c. yell., grn. & brn. 15 10
290f. – 50 c. multicoloured .. 30 30
288. – 60 c. red, grn. & black 10 15
289. – 1 s. yell., grn. & purple 15 20
290. – 1 s. 20 yell., grn. & sep. 20 20
FLOWERS—VERT. 5 c. " Haemanthus multiflorus martyn ". 10 c. " Grinum scabrum ". 15 c. " Adansonia digitata ". 25 c. " Poinciana elata ". 50 c. " Gloriosa virescens ". 60 c. " Calatropis procera ". 1 s. " Pancratium trainthum her ". 1 s. 20, " Sesamothamnus bussernus ".

54. Oribi. **54a.** Lesser Kudu.

1955. Air. Antelopes. (a) As T **54**. Heads in black and orange.
291. **54.** 35 c. green 30 20
292. – 45 c. violet .. .. 1·25 35
293. – 50 c. violet 30 20
294. – 75 c. red 65 25
295. – 1 s. 20 turquoise .. 65 25
296. – 1 s. 50 blue 75 45
ANTELOPES: 45 c. Salt's dik-dik. 50 c. Speke's gazelle. 75 c. Gerenuk 1 s. 20, Soemmering's gazelle. 1 s. 50, Waterbuck.

(b) As T **54a**.
296a. **54a.** 3 s. purple and brown 1·00 85
296b. – 5 s. yellow and black 1·00 85
DESIGN: 5 s. Hunter's hartebeest.

55. Native Weaver. **56.** Voters and Map.

1955. 3rd Somali Fair.
297. **55.** 25 c. brown (postage) .. 25 25
298. – 30 c. green 25 25
299. – 45 c. brown & orge. (air) 25 25
300. – 1 s. 20 blue and pink .. 35 35
DESIGNS: 30 c. Cattle fording river. 45 c. Camels around well. 1 s. 20, Native women at well.

1956. 1st Legislative Assembly.
301. **56.** 5 c. brn. & grey (post) .. 10 10
302. 10 c. brown and olive .. 10 10
303. 25 c. brown and red .. 10 10
304. 60 c. brown & blue (air) 15 15
305. 1 s. 20 brown & orange 20 20

57. Somali Arms. **58.** Falcheiro Barrage.

1957. Inauguration of National Emblem. Arms in blue and ochre.
306. **57.** 5 c. brown (postage) .. 10 10
307. 25 c. red 15 15
308. 60 c. violet 15 15
309. 45 c. blue (air) .. 20 20
310. 1 s. 20 green 25 25

1957. 4th Somali Fair.
311. **58.** 5 c. lilac & brown (post.) 10 10
312. – 10 c. green and bistre .. 10 10
313. – 25 c. blue and red .. 15 15
314. – 60 c. sepia and blue (air) 25 25
315. – 1 s. 20 black and red .. 25 25
DESIGNS—HORIZ. 10 c. Juba River bridge. 25 c. Silos at Margherita. 60 c. Irrigation canal VERT. 1 s. 20, Oil well.

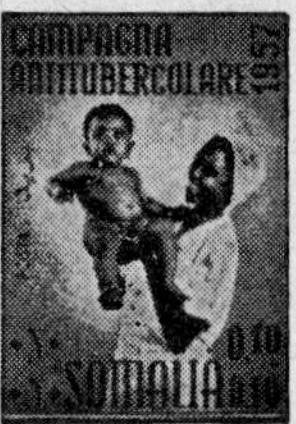

59. Somali nurse with baby. **60.** Track running.

1957. Tuberculosis Relief Campaign.
316. **59.** 10 c.+10 c. sepia & red (postage) 15 15
317. 25 c.+10 c. sepia & green 15 15
318. 55 c.+20 c. sepia and blue (air) 20 20
319. 1 s. 20 c.+20 c. sepia and violet 30 30

1958. Sports.
320. **60.** 2 c. lilac (postage) .. 10 10
321. – 4 c. green (Football) .. 10 10
322. – 5 c. red (Discus) .. 10 10
323. – 6 c. grey (Motor-cycling) 10 10
324. – 8 c. blue (Fencing) .. 10 10
325. – 10 c. orange (Archery) .. 10 10
326. – 25 c. green (Boxing) .. 10 10
327. – 60 c. brn. (air) (Running) 10 10
328. – 1 s. 20 blue (Cycling) 15 15
329. – 1 s. 50 red (Basketball) 20 15
The 4, 6, 10 and 25 c. are horiz. designs and the remainder vert.

61. The Constitution, and Assembly Building, Mogadishu. **62.** White Stork.

1959. Opening of Constituent Assembly. Insor. " ASSEMBLEA COSTITUENTE ".
330. **61.** 5 c. blue & green (post.) 10 10
331. 25 c. blue and bistre .. 10 10
332. – 1 s. 20 blue and bistre (air) 25 25
333. – 1 s. 50 blue and green 25 25
DESIGN—HORIZ. 1 s. 20, 1 s. 50, Police bugler.

1959. Somali Water Birds.
334. **62.** 5 c. black, red & yellow (postage) .. 20 10
335. – 10 c. red, yell. & brown 20 10
336. – 15 c. black and orange 20 10
337. – 25 c. black, orange & red 20 10
338. – 1 s. 20, black, red and violet (air) .. 1·10 50
339. – 2 s. red and blue .. 1·10 50
BIRDS—VERT. 10 c. Saddle-bill Stork. 15 c. Sacred ibis. 25 c. Pink-backed Pelicans. HORIZ. 1 s. 20, Marabou Stork. 2 s. Great Egret.

63. Incense Tree. **64.** Institute Badge.

1959. 5th Somali Fair.
340. **63.** 20 c. blk. & orge. (post.) 10 10
341. – 60 c. black, red & orange 20 20
342. – 1 s. 20 black & red (air) 25 25
343. – 2 s. blk., orge. & brown 40 40
DESIGNS—VERT. 60 c. Somali child with incense-burner. HORIZ. 1 s. 20, 15th-century B.C. incense shipment. 2 s. Incense-burner and Mogadishu Harbour.

1960. Opening of University Institute of Somalia, Mogadishu. Inscr. as in T **64**.
344. **34.** 5 c. red & brown (post.) 10 10
345. – 50 c. brown and blue .. 10 10
346. – 80 c. black and red .. 20 20
347. – 45 c. brown, black and green (air) 20 20
348. – 1s. 20 ultram., blk. & bl. 35 35
DESIGNS—HORIZ. 45 c., 1 s. 20, Institute buildings. 50 c. Map of Africa. VERT. 80 c. Institute emblem.

65. " The Horn of Africa ".

1960. World Refugee Year.
349. **65.** 10 c. green, black and brown (postage) .. 10 10
350. – 60 c. brn., ochre & blk. 10 10
351. – 80 c. green, blk. & pink 10 10
352. – 1 s. 50 red, blue and green (air) .. .. 1·00 40
DESIGNS—HORIZ. 60 c. Similar to Type **35**. VERT. 80 c. Palm. 1 s. 50, White Stork.

REPUBLIC.

1960. Optd. **Somaliland Independence 26. June 1960.**
353. 10 c. yellow, green & lilac (No. 290c) (postage) .. 12·00 12·00
354. 50 c. blk., orge. and violet (No. 293) (air) .. 22·00 17·00
355. 1 s. 20 blk., orge. & turq. (No. 295) .. .. 19·00 17·00
Nos. 353/5 were only issued in the former British protectorate, which united with Somalia when the latter became independent on 1st July, 1960.

67. Gazelle and Map of Africa. **68.** Olympic Flame and Somali Flag.

1960. Proclamation of Independence.
356. **67.** 5 c. brn., bl. & lilac (post.) 20 20
357. – 25 c. blue 35 35
358. – 1 s. brown, red & green (air) 40 20
359. – 1 s. 80 blue and orange 1·10 90
DESIGNS—VERT. 25 c. U.N. Flag and Headquarters Building. HORIZ. 1 s. Chamber of Deputies, Montecitorio Palace, Rome. 1 s. 80, Somali Flag.

1960. Olympic Games. Inscr. " 1960 ".
360. **68.** 5 c. blue & grn. (post) .. 15 10
361. – 10 c. blue and yellow .. 15 10
362. – 45 c. blue and lilac (air) 10 15
363. – 1 s. 80 blue and red .. 1·10 95
DESIGNS: 10 c. Relay race. 45 c. Runner breasting tape. 1 s. 80, Runner.

69. Child drawing Giraffe. **70.** Girl harvesting Papaws.

1960. Child Welfare. Inscr. " PRO INFANZIA ".
364. **69.** 10 c. black, brown and green (postage) .. 10 10
365. – 15 c. blk., light grn. & red 15 15
366. – 25 c. brn., blk. & yell. .. 30 30
367. – 3 s. orange, black, blue and green (air) .. 1·60 1·10
ANIMALS: 15 c. Common zebra. 25 c. Black rhinoceros. 3 s. Leopard.

1961. Multicoloured. Designs each show a girl harvesting. 75 c. and 80 c. are horiz.
368. 5 c. Type **70** 10 10
369. 10 c. Girl harvesting durra 10 10
370. 20 c. Cotton 15 15
371. 25 c. Sesame 15 15
372. 40 c. Sugar cane 20 20
373. 50 c. Bananas 35 35
374. 75 c. Groundnuts 55 55
375. 80 c. Grapefruit .. .. 1·10 1·10

71. "Amauris hyalites".

72. Shield, Bow and Arrow, Quiver and Dagger.

73. Girl embroidering. 74. Mosquito.

1961. Air. Butterflies. Multicoloured.

376 60 c. Type 71 .. .. 25 15
377 90 c. "Euryphura chalcis" 30 20
378 1 s. "Papilio lormieri" .. 3·25 25
379 1 s. 80 "Druryia antimachus" 75 45
380 3 s. "Danaus formosa" .. 90 60
381 5 s. "Papilio phorcas" .. 3·25 90
382 10 s. "Charaxes cynthia" 6·75 2·40

1961. 6th Somali Trade Fair.

383. **72.** 25 c. yellow, black and red (postage) .. 10 10
384. – 45 c. yell., blk. & green 20 20
385. – 1s. yell., blk. & bl. (air) 55 45
386. – 1s. 80 brn., blk. & yellow 1·10 65

DESIGNS (Handicrafts)—VERT. 45 c. "Tungi" wooden vase and pottery. HORIZ. 1s. National head-dress, support and comb. 1s. 80, Statuettes of camel and man, and balancing novelty.

1962. Child Welfare. Tropical Fishes. Inscr. "PRO INFANZIA". Multicoloured.

387. 15 c. Type 73 (postage) .. 15 15
388. 25 c. Blue Angelfish .. 15 15
389. 40 c. Wrasse .. 80 80
390. 2 s. 70 Red Snapper (air) 2·25 1·10

1962. Malaria Eradication. Inscr. "MONDO UNITO CONTRO LA MALARIA".

391. **74.** 10 c. green & red (post) 15 15
392. – 25 c. brown and mauve 30 30
393. – 1s. brown and black (air) 55 20
394. – 1 s. 80 green and black .. 1·10 90

DESIGNS—VERT. 25 c. Insecticide sprayer. 1s., 1s. 80, Campaign emblem and mosquitoes.

75. Auxiliaries tending Casualty. 76. Wooden Spoon and Fork.

1963. Women's Auxiliary Forces Formation. Multicoloured.

395. 5 c. Policewoman (post.) 10 10
396. 10 c. Army auxiliary .. 20 20
397. 25 c. Policewomen with Patrol car 35 35
398. 75 c. Type 75 .. .. 45 45
399. 1 s. Policewomen marching with flag (air) 55 35
400. 1 s. 80 Army auxiliaries at attention with flag .. 1·40 80

The 5 c., 10 c. and 25 c. are horiz.

1963. Freedom from Hunger.

401. **76.** 75 c. brn. & grn. (post.) 45 45
402. – 1s. multicoloured (air) .. 1·10 65

DESIGN: 1s. Sower.

77. Pres. Osman and Arms. 78. Open-air Theatre.

1963. 3rd Anniv. of Independence. Arms in blue and yellow.

403. **77.** 25 c. sepia & blue (post.) 30 15
404. 1s. sepia and red (air) .. 65 35
405. 1s. 80 sepia and green .. 1·00 55

1963. 7th Somali Fair.

406. **78.** 25 c. green (postage) .. 20 20
407. – 55 c. red 65 45
408. – 1s. 80 blue (air) .. .. 1·40 90

DESIGNS: 55 c. African Trade Building. 1s. 80, Government Pavilion.

79. Credit Bank, Mogadishu. 80. Running.

1964. 10th Anniv. of Somali Credit Bank. Multicoloured.

409. 60 c. Type 79 (postage) .. 45 20
410. 1 s. Map of Somalia and Globe (air) 90 45
411. 1 s. 80 Bank Emblem .. 1·40 90

1964. Olympic Games, Tokyo. Colours: sepia, brown and blue.

412. 10 c. Type 80 (postage) .. 15 15
413. 25 c. High-jumping .. 20 20
414. 90 c. Diving (air) 55 45
415. 1 s. 80 Footballer .. 1·10 65

81. Douglas "DC-3" Airliner.

1964. Inaug. of Somali Airlines.

416. **81.** 5 c. blue and red (post.) 20 35
417. – 20 c. blue and orange 65 35
418. – 1 s. ochre & green (air) 1·10 55
419. – 1 s. 80 blue and black 2·25 1·60

DESIGNS: 20 c. Passengers disembarking from "DC-3". "DC-3" in flight over: 1 s. African elephants. 1 s. 80, Mogadishu.

82. Refugees. 83. I.T.U. Emblem on Map of Africa.

1964. Somali Refugees Fund.

420. **82.** 25 c.+10 c. red and blue (postage) 55 20
421. – 75 c.+20 c. purple, black and red (air) .. 45 45
422. – 1 s. 80+50 c. green, black and bistre .. 1·50 1·25

DESIGNS—HORIZ. 75 c. Ruined houses. VERT. 1 s. 80, Soldier with child refugees.

1965. I.T.U. Cent.

423. **83.** 25 c. blue & orge. (post.) 45 10
424. 1 s. black and green (air) 85 55
425. 1 s. 80 brown and mauve 1·60 1·10

84. Tanning.

1965. Somali Industries.

426. **84.** 10 c. sepia and buff (post.) 15 15
427. – 25 c. sepia and pink .. 20 15
428. – 35 c. sepia and blue .. 35 15
429. – 1 s. 50 sepia & grn. (air) 1·10 55
430. – 2 s. sepia and mauve .. 2·25 1·10

DESIGNS: 25 c. Meat processing and canning. 35 c. Fish processing and canning. 1 s. 50, Sugar—cutting cane and refining. 2 s. Dairying—milking and bottling.

85. Hottentot Fig and Gazelle.

1965. Somali Flora and Fauna. Mult.

431. 20 c. Type 85 .. .. 10 10
432. 60 c. African tulips and giraffes 20 10
433. 1 s. White lotus and Greater Flamingoes .. 45 20
434. 1 s. 30 Pervincia and Ostriches 90 45
435. 1 s. 80 Bignonia and common zebras .. .. 2·25 80

86. Narina Trogon.

1966. Somali Birds. Multicoloured.

436. 25 c. Type 86 .. .. 40 10
437. 35 c. Bateleur (vert.) .. 50 10
438. 50 c. Ruppell's griffon .. 65 25
439. 1 s. 30 Common roller .. 1·25 35
440. 2 s. Vulturine guineafowl (vert.) .. .. .. 1·50 55

87. Globe and U.N. Emblem.

1966. 21st Anniv. of U.N.O. Multicoloured.

441. 35 c. Type 87 .. .. 35 15
442. 1 s. Map of Africa and U.N. emblem 45 20
443. 1 s. 50 Map of Somalia and U.N. emblem 90 45

88. Woman sitting on Crocodile.

1966. Somali Art. Showing Paintings from Garesa Museum, Mogadishu. Multicoloured.

444. 25 c. Type 88 .. .. 10 10
445. 1 s. Woman and warrior .. 20 10
446. 1 s. 50 Boy leading camel 45 20
447. 2 s. Women pounding grain 90 55

89. U.N.E.S.C.O. Emblem and Palm. 90. Oribi.

1966. 20th Anniv. of U.N.E.S.C.O.

448. **89.** 35 c. black, red and grey 10 10
449. 1 s. black, green & yell. 15 10
450. 1 s. 80 black, blue & red 85 45

1967. Antelopes.

451. **90.** 35 c. ochre, blk. & blue 10 10
452. – 60 c. brown, black & orge. 15 15
453. – 1 s. bistre, black & red 30 20
454. – 1 s. 80 ochre, blk. & grn. 1·10 60

ANTELOPES: 60 c. Kirk's dik-dik. 1 s. Gerenuk gazelle. 1 s. 80, Soemmering's gazelle.

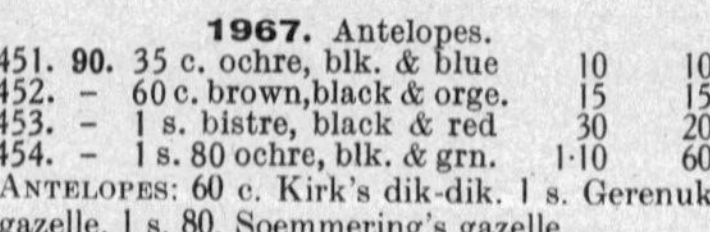

91. Somali Dancers. 92. Badge and Scout Saluting.

1967. "Popular Dances". Designs showing dancers.

455. **91.** 25 c. multicoloured .. 10 10
456. 50 c. multicoloured .. 10 10
457. 1 s. 30 multicoloured .. 35 30
458. 2 s. multicoloured .. 1·10 60

1967. World Scout Jamboree. Multicoloured.

459. 35 c. Type 92 .. .. 10 10
460. 50 c. Scouts and flags .. 15 10
461. 1 s. Camp scene 40 20
462. 1 s. 80 Jamboree emblem .. 1·00 65

93. Pres. Schermarche and King Faisal.

1967. Visit of King Faisal of Saudi Arabia.

463. **93.** 50 c. black & blue (post.) 20 10
464. – 1 s. multicoloured .. 45 35
465. – 1 s. 80 multicoloured (air) 90 55

DESIGNS: 1 s. Somali and Saudi Arabian flags 1 s. 80, Kaaba, Mecca and portraits as Type 93.

94. Sweetlips.

1967. Fishes. Multicoloured.

466. 35 c. Type 94 .. .. 10 10
467. 50 c. Butterfly fish .. 20 10
468. 1 s. Lunar-tailed bullseye 45 35
469. 1 s. 80 Speckled grouper .. 90 55

95. Inoculation. 96. Somali Girl with Lemons.

1968. 20th Anniv. of W.H.O.

470. **95.** 35 c. multicoloured .. 10 10
471. – 1 s. black, brown & green 20 20
472. – 1 s. 80 blk., brn. & orge. 90 55

DESIGNS: 1 s. Chest examination. 1 s. 80, Heart examination.

1968. Agricultural Produce. Multicoloured.

473. 5 c. Type 96 .. .. 10 10
474. 10 c. Oranges 10 10
475. 25 c. Coconuts 10 10
476. 35 c. Papaws 15 10
477. 40 c. Mangoes 15 10
478. 50 c. Grapefruit 15 10
479. 1 s. Bananas 55 20
480. 1 s. 30 Cotton bolls .. 85 45

Each design includes a Somali girl.

97. Waterbuck. 98. Throwing the Javelin.

1968. Somali Antelopes. Multicoloured.

481. 1 s 50 Type 97 .. .. 35 20
482. 1 s. 80 Speke's gazelle .. 45 35
483. 2 s. Lesser kudu 60 35
484. 5 s. Hunter's hartebeest .. 1·40 80
485. 10 s. Dibatag gazelle .. 4·50 1·60

1968. Olympic Games, Mexico.

486. **98.** 35 c. black, brn. & lemon 10 10
487. – 50 c. black, brn. & red 10 10
488. – 80 c. blk., brn. & purple 20 20
489. – 1 s. 50 blk., brn. & grn. 1·40 65

DESIGNS: 50 c. Running. 80 c. Pole-vaulting. 1s. 50, Basketball.

99. Great Egret. 100. "Pounding Meal".

1968. Air. Birds. Multicoloured.

491. 35 c. Type 99 .. .. 30 20
492. 1 s. Carmine Bee Eater .. 50 20
493. 1 s. 30 Yellow-bellied Green Pigeon 80 45
494. 1 s. 80 Paradise Whydah 2·25 80

1968. Somali Art.
495. **100.** 25 c. brn., black & lilac 15 10
496. – 35 c. brown, black & red 15 10
497. – 2 s. 80 brn., blk. & grn. 20 20
DESIGNS: (wood-carvings) 35 c. "Preparing food". 2 s. 80, "Rug-making".

101. Cornflower. **102.** Workers at Anvil.

1969. Flowers. Multicoloured.
498. 40 c. Type **101** 10 10
499. 80 c. Sunflower 20 15
500. 1 s. Oleander 55 30
501. 1 s. 80 Chrysanthemum .. 1·40 85

1969. 50th Anniv. of I.L.O. Mult.
502. 25 c. Type **102** 10 10
503. 1 s. Ploughing with oxen 20 20
504. 1 s. 80 Drawing water for irrigation 80 45

103. Gandhi, and Hands releasing Dove.

1969. Birth Cent. of Mahatma Gandhi.
505. – 35 c. purple 10 10
506. **103.** 1 s. 50 orange 45 30
507. – 1 s. 80 brown .. .. 1·10 70
DESIGNS—VERT. (Size 25½ × 36 mm.): 35 c. Mahatma Gandhi. 1 s. 80, Gandhi seated.

SOMALI DEMOCRATIC REPUBLIC.

An issue for the "Apollo 11" Moon Landing was prepared in 1970, but not issued.

104. "Charaxes varanes". **105.** Lenin with Children.

1970. Butterflies. Multicoloured.
508 25 c. Type **104** 15 10
509 50 c. "Cethosia lamarcki" 40 10
510 1 s. 50 "Troides aeacus" .. 55 45
511 2 s. "Chrysiridia ripheus" 1·40 55

1970. Birth Cent. of Lenin.
512. **105.** 25 c. multicoloured .. 10 10
513. – 1 s. multicoloured .. 20 15
514. – 1 s. 80 black, orange and brown 80 55
DESIGNS—VERT. 1 s. Lenin making speech. HORIZ. 1 s. 80, Lenin at desk.

106. Dove feeding Young.

1970. 10th Anniv. of Independence.
515. 25 c. Type **106** 10 10
516. 35 c. Dagahtur Memorial .. 10 10
517. 1 s. Somali arms (vert.) .. 35 20
518. 2 s. 80 Camel and star (vert.) .. .. .. 1·10 90

107. Tractor and Produce.

1970. 1st Anniv. of 21st October Revolution.
519. **107.** 35 c. multicoloured .. 10 10
520. – 40 c. black and blue .. 10 10
521. – 1 s. black and brown .. 35 20
522. – 1 s. 80 multicoloured .. 80 45
DESIGNS: 40 c. Soldier and flag. 1 s. Hand on open book. 1 s. 80, Emblems of Peace, Justice and Prosperity.

108. African within Snake's Coils.

1971. Racial Equality Year.
523. **108.** 1 s. 30 multicoloured .. 45 20
524. – 1 s. 80 blk., red & brn. 65 45
DESIGN: 1 s. 80, Human figures, chain and barbed wire.

109. I.T.U. Emblem.

1971. World Telecommunications Day.
525 **109.** 25 c. blk., ultram. & blue 10 10
526. – 2 s. 80 blk., bl. & green 1·10 65
DESIGN: 2 s. 80, Global emblem.

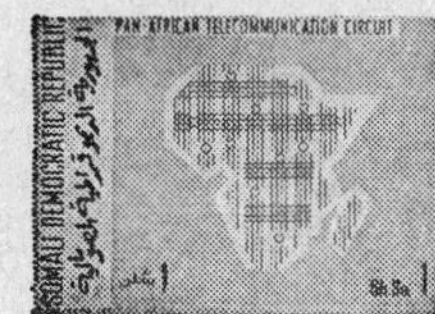

110. Telecommunications Map.

1971. Pan-African Telecommunications Network.
527. **110.** 1 s. grn., blk. and blue 35 20
528. – 1 s. 50 blk., grn. & yell. 80 35
DESIGN: 1 s. 50 similar to Type **110** but with different network pattern.

111. White Rhinoceros.

1971. Wild Animals.
529. **111.** 35 c. multicoloured .. 20 20
530. – 1 s. multicoloured .. 35 35
531. – 1 s. 30 black, yellow and violet 90 90
532. – 1 s. 80 multicoloured .. 1·40 1·40
DESIGNS: 1 s. Cheetahs. 1 s. 30, Common zebras. 1 s. 80, Lion attacking dromedary.

112. Ancient Desert City.

1971. East and Central African Summit Conference, Mogadishu.
533. **112.** 1 s. 30 brn., blk. & red 55 55
534. – 1 s. 50 multicoloured .. 95 95
DESIGN: 1 s. 50, Headquarters building, Mogadishu.

113. Memorial.

1971. 2nd Anniv. of Revolution.
535. **113.** 10 c. black, cobalt & bl. 10 10
536. – 1 s. multicoloured .. 30 30
537. – 1 s. 35 multicoloured .. 1·00 1·00
DESIGNS: 1 s. Agricultural workers. 1 s. 35, Building workers.

114. Inoculating Cattle.

1971. Rinderpest Control Programme. Multicoloured.
538. 40 c. Type **114** 55 35
539. 1 s. 80 Herdsmen with cattle 1·10 80

115. A.P.U. Emblem and Back of Airmail Envelope.

1972. 10th Anniv. of African Postal Union.
540. 1 s. 50 A.P.U. emblem and dove with letter (post) .. 80 55
541. 1 s. 30 Type **115** (air) .. 90 65

116. Mother and Child. **117.** Dromedary.

1972. 25th Anniv. of U.N.I.C.E.F.
542. **116.** 50 c. black, brown and light brown 20 10
543. – 2 s. 80 multicoloured .. 1·40 1·00
DESIGN—HORIZ. 2 s. 80, U.N.I.C.E.F. emblem and schoolchildren.

1972. Domestic Animals.
544. **117.** 5 c. multicoloured .. 10 10
545. – 10 c. multicoloured .. 10 10
546. – 20 c. multicoloured .. 10 10
547. – 40 c. black, brown & red 20 20
548. – 1 s. 70 black, green & black 1·60 1·60
DESIGNS: 10 c. Cattle on quayside. 20 c. Bull. 40 c. Black-headed sheep. 1 s. 70, Goat

118. Child within Cupped Hands.

1972. 3rd Anniv. of 21st October Revolution. Multicoloured.
549. 70 c. Type **118.** 20 10
550. 1 s. Parade of standards .. 30 15
551. 1 s. 50 Youth Camps emblem 90 55

119. Folk Dancers.

1973. Folk Dances. Multicoloured.
552. 5 c. Type **119.** 10 10
553. 40 c. Pair of dancers (vert.) 10 10
554. 1 s. Team of dancers (vert.) 45 20
555. 2 s. Three dancers .. 1·00 55

120. Old Alphabet in Flames. **121.** Soldiers and Chains within O.A.U. Emblem.

1973. Introduction of New Somali Script.
556. **120.** 40 c. multicoloured .. 10 10
557. – 1 s. multicoloured .. 20 15
558. – 2 s. black, stone & yellow 80 55
DESIGNS—HORIZ. 1 s. Alphabet in sun's rays. 2 s. Writing new script.

1974. 10th Anniv. (1973) of Organization of African Unity. Multicoloured.
559. 40 c. Type **121** 20 10
560. 2 s. Spiral on map of Africa 90 65

122. Hurdling. **123.** Somali Youth and Girl.

1974. Sports.
561. **122.** 50 c. black, red & orange 15 10
562. – 1 s. black, grey & green 35 20
563. – 2 s. 40 blk., grey & olive 90 55
DESIGNS—HORIZ. 1 s. Running. VERT. 1 s. 40, Basketball.

1974. Guulwade Youth Movement. Mult.
564. 40 c. Type **123** 10 10
565. 2 s. Guulwade members helping old woman .. 1·00 65

124. Map of League Members.

1974. 30th Anniv. (1975) of Arab League. Multicoloured.
566. 1 s. 50 Type **124** .. 55 35
567. 1 s. 70 Flags of Arab League countries 85 55

125. Desert Landscape.

1974. 5th Anniv. of 21 October Revolution. Multicoloured.
568. 40 c. Type **125** 20 15
569. 2 s. Somali villagers reading books (vert.) 90 65

126. Doves. **128.**

1975. Cent. of U.P.U. Multicoloured.
570. 50 c. Type **126** 30 10
571. 3 s. Mounted postman .. 2·00 1·00

1975. African Postal Union. As T **126.** Multicoloured.
572. 1 s. Maps of Africa (repetitive motif) 35 20
573. 1 s. 50 Dove with letter .. 1·00 65

1975. Traditional Costumes.
574. **128.** 10 c. multicoloured .. 10 10
575. – 40 c. multicoloured .. 10 10
576. – 50 c. multicoloured .. 15 10
577. – 1 s. multicoloured .. 35 20
578. – 5 s. multicoloured .. 2·10 85
579. – 10 s. multicoloured .. 4·50 2·50
DESIGNS: 40 c. to 10 s. Various costumes.

129. Independence Square, Mogadishu. **130.** Hassan Statue.

1976. Int. Women's Year. Multicoloured.
580. 50 c. Type **129** 30 10
581. 2 s. 30 I.W.Y. emblem (horiz.) .. .. .. 1·40 1·00

1976. Sayed M. A. Hassan Commemoration. Multicoloured.
582. 50 c. Type **130** 15 10
583. 60 c. Hassan directing warriors (vert.) 20 10
584. 1 s. 50 Hassan inspiring warriors (vert.) 55 35
585. 2 s. 30 Hassan leading attack .. .. .. 1·60 55

131. Nurse and Child. **132.** "Cypraea gracilis".

1976. Famine Relief. Multicoloured.
586. 75 c. + 25 c. Type **131** .. 45 45
587. 80 c. + 20 c. Devastated land (horiz.) 45 45
588. 2 s. 40 + 10 c. Somali family with produce 80 80
589. 2 s. 90 + 10 c. Relief emblem and medical officer (horiz.) 1·60 1·60

1976. Somali Seashells. Multicoloured.
590. 50 c. Type **132** 20 15
591. 75 c. " Charonia bardayi " 20 15
592. 1 s. " Chlamys townsendi " 35 20
593. 2 s. " Cymatium ranzanii " 90 55
594. 2 s. 75 " Conus argillaceus " 1·10 85
595. 2 s. 90 " Strombus oldi " 1·60 85

133. Benin Head and Hunters.

1977. Second World Black and African Festival of Arts and Cultures, Lagos, Nigeria. Multicoloured.
597. 50 c. Type **133** 20 15
598. 75 c. Handicrafts 35 30
599. 2 s. Dancers 85 65
600. 2 s. 90 Musicians .. .. 1·60 1·10
The Benin Head appears on all designs.

134. Somali Flags. **135.** Hunting Dog.

1977. 1st Anniv. of Somali Socialist Revolutionary Party. Multicoloured.
601. 75 c. Type **134** 20 10
602. 1 s. Somali Arms (horiz.) .. 35 20
603. 1 s. 50 Pres. Barre and globe (horiz.) 55 35
604. 2 s. Arms over rising sun 85 45

1977. Protected Animals. Multicoloured.
605. 50 c. Type **135** 15 10
606. 75 c. Lesser bushbaby .. 20 10
607. 1 s. African ass 45 20
608. 1 s. 50 Aardwolf 55 35
609. 2 s. Greater kudu .. .. 1·10 55
610. 3 s. Giraffe .. .. .. 2·00 90

136. Da Vinci's Helicopter. **137.** Dome of the Rock.

1977. 30th Anniv. of I.C.A.O. Multicoloured.
612. 1 s. Type **136** 35 25
613. 1 s. 50 Montgolfier Brothers' balloon 45 35
614. 2 s. Wright Brothers' " Flyer " 65 45
615. 2 s. 90 Boeing " 720B " of Somali Airlines .. .. 1·40 65

1978. Palestine Freedom-Fighters.
617. **137.** 75 c. black, green & pink 20 10
618. 2 s. black, red and blue 90 55

138. Stadium and Footballer.

1978. World Cup Football Championship, Argentina. Multicoloured.
619. 1 s. 50 Type **138** 45 35
620. 4 s. 90 Stadium and goal-keeper .. .. .. 1·50 1·00
621. 5 s. 50 Stadium and footballer (different) .. 2·00 1·40

139. " Acacia tortilis ".

1978. Trees. Multicoloured.
623. 40 c. Type **139** 15 10
624. 50 c. " Ficus sycomorus " (vert.) 30 20
625. 75 c. " Terminalia catapa " (vert.) 45 35
626. 2 s. 90 " Adansonia digitata " .. .. 1·40 65

140. " Hibiscus rosa-sinensis ". **142.** " Child going to School " (Ahmed Dahir Mohamed).

141. Fishing from Punt and "Siganus rivulatus".

1978. Flowers. Multicoloured.
627. 50 c. Type **140** 20 10
628. 1 s. " Cassia baccarinii " 45 20
629. 1 s. 50 " Kigelia somalensis " 80 45
630. 2 s. 30 " Dichrostachys glomerata " .. .. 1·40 65

1979. Fishing. Multicoloured.
632. 75 c. Type **141** 20 10
633. 80 c. Fishing from felucca and "Gaterin gaterinus" 20 15
634. 2 s. 30 Fishing fleet and "Hypacanthus amia" .. 1·00 55
635. 2 s. 50 Trawler and "Scomberomorus commersoni" 1·40 85

1979. International Year of the Child. Children's Paintings. Multicoloured.
636. 50 c. Type **142** 15 10
637. 75 c. " Sailboat " (M. A. Mohamed) 20 15
638. 1 s. 50 " House in the Country " (A. M. Ali) .. 45 30
639. 3 s. " Bird on Blossoming Branch " (A. A. Siyad) 1·10 65

143. University Students and Open-air Class.

1979. 10th Anniv. of Revolution. Mult.
641. 20 c. Type **143** 10 10
642. 50 c. Housing construction 10 10
643. 75 c. Children at play .. 20 10
644. 1 s. Health and agriculture 35 20
645. 2 s. 40 Hydro-electric power 80 45
646. 3 s. Telecommunications .. 1·25 65

144. " Barbopsis devecchii ".

1979. Fish. Multicoloured.
647. 50 c. Type **144** 20 10
648. 90 c. " Phreatichthys andruzzi " 50 20
649. 1 s. " Uegitglanis zammaranoi " 65 35
650. 2 s. 50 " Pardiglanis tarabinii " .. .. .. 1·10 65

145. Taleh Fortress.

1980. First International Congress of Somali Studies.
652. **145.** 2 s. 25 multicoloured .. 85 45
653. 3 s. 50 multicoloured .. 1·10 65

146. Marka.

1980. Landscapes (1st series). Multicoloured.
654. 75 c. Type **146** 20 10
655. 1 s. Gandershe 35 20
656. 2 s. 30 Afgooye 85 35
657. 3 s. 50 Mogadishu .. 1·10 65
See also Nos. 673/6.

147. Pygmy Puff-back Flycatcher. **148.** Parabolic Antenna and Shepherd.

1980. Birds. Multicoloured.
658. 1 s. Type **147** 40 20
659. 2 s. 25 Golden-winged Grosbeak .. .. 1·00 35
660. 5 s. Red-crowned Bush Shrike .. .. .. 1·60 1·10

1981. World Telecommunications Day.
662. **148.** 1 s. multicoloured .. 40 20
663. – 3 s. blue, black and red 1·00 55
664. – 4 s. 60 multicoloured .. 1·40 90
DESIGNS: 3 s., 4 s. 60, Ribbons forming caduceus, I.T.U. and W.H.O. emblems.

149. F.A.O. Emblem and Stylised Wheat. **150.** Refugee Family.

1981. World Food Day. Multicoloured.
665. 75 c. Type **149** 20 15
666. 3 s. 25 F.A.O. emblem on stylized field (horiz.) .. 1·10 55
667. 5 s. 50 Type **149** .. .. 2·00 95

1981. Refugee Aid.
668. **150.** 2 s. + 50 c. multicoloured 70 45
669. 6 s. 80 + 50 c. multicoloured .. .. 2·50 1·25

151. Mosques, Mecca and Medina. **153.** Footballer.

1981. 1500th Anniv. of Hejira.
671. **151.** 1 s. 50 multicoloured .. 45 35
672. 3 s. 80 multicoloured .. 1·50 80

1982. Landscapes (2nd series). As T **146.** Multicoloured.
673. 2 s. 25 Balcad 80 45
674. 4 s. Jowhar .. .. 1·40 90
675. 5 s. 50 Golaleey .. .. 1·60 1·10
676. 8 s. 30 Muqdisho .. .. 2·75 2·00

1982. World Cup Football Championship, Spain. Multicoloured.
677. 1 s. Type **153** 35 20
678. 1 s. 50 Footballer running to right 80 45
679. 3 s. 25 Footballer running to left .. .. .. 1·60 1·00

154. I.T.U. Emblem.

1982. I.T.U. Delegates' Conference, Nairobi.
681. **154.** 75 c. multicoloured .. 20 15
682. 3 s. 25 multicoloured 1·10 65
683. 5 s. 50 multicoloured .. 2·00 1·10

155. " Bitis arietans somalica ".

1982. Snakes. Multicoloured.
684. 2 s. 80 Type **155** .. .. 1·10 45
685. 3 s. 20 " Psammophis punctulatus trivirgatus " 1·60 65
686. 4 s. 60 " Rhamphiophis oxyrhynchis rostratus " 2·25 1·10

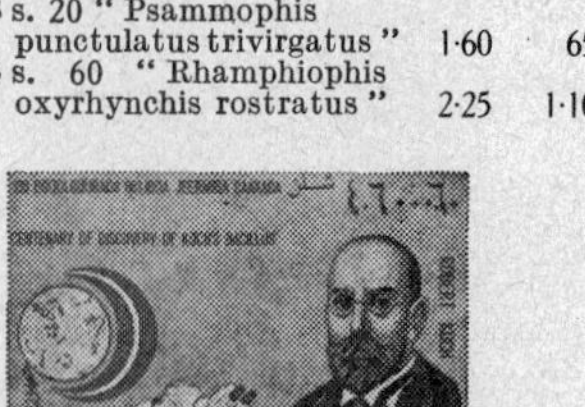

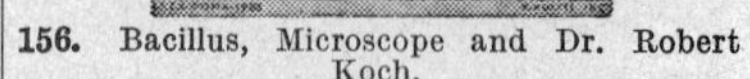

156. Bacillus, Microscope and Dr. Robert Koch.

1982. Cent. of Discovery of Tubercle Bacillus.
688. **156.** 4 s. 60 + 60 c. mult. .. 1·10 1·10
689. 5 s. 80 + 60 c. mult. .. 1·40 1·40

157. Somali Woman. **158.** W.C.Y. Emblem.

1982.
690. **157.** 1 s. multicoloured .. 15 10
691. 5 s. 20 multicoloured .. 80 35
692. 5 s. 80 multicoloured .. 1·00 45
693. 6 s. 40 multicoloured .. 1·10 60
694. 9 s. 40 multicoloured .. 1·60 1·00
695. 25 s. multicoloured .. 4·25 1·60

1983. World Communications Year.
696. **158.** 5 s. 20 multicoloured .. 45 35
697. 6 s. 40 multicoloured .. 85 40

159. View of Hamburg.

1983. Second International Congress of Somali Studies, Hamburg. Multicoloured.
698. 5 s. 20 Type **159** 85 65
699. 6 s. 40 View of Hamburg (different) .. .. 1·25 1·00

160. Air Force Uniform.

1983. Military Uniforms. Multicoloured.
700. 3 s. 20 Type **160** 85 55
701. 3 s. 20 Women's Auxiliary Corps 85 55
702. 3 s. 20 Border Police .. 85 55
703. 3 s. 20 People's Militia .. 85 55
704. 3 s. 20 Infantry 85 55
705. 3 s. 20 Custodial Corps .. 85 55
706. 3 s. 20 Police Force .. 85 55
707. 3 s. 20 Navy 85 55

161. Barawe.

1983. Landscapes. Multicoloured.
708. 2 s. 80 Type **161** 55 35
709. 3 s. 20 Bur Hakaba .. 65 45
710. 5 s. 50 Baydhabo .. .. 1·00 60
711. 8 s. 60 Dooy Nuunaay .. 1·60 1·10

162. "Volutocorbis rosavittoriae".

1984. Shells. Multicoloured.

712. 2 s. 80 Type **162** 55 35
713. 3 s. 20 "Phalium bituberculosum" 80 45
714. 5 s. 50 "Conus milne-edwardsi" .. .. 2·00 90

163. Running.

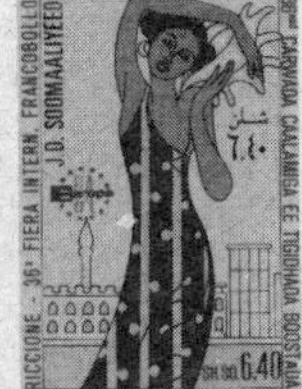

165. Girl holding Shell to Ear.

164. North African Crested Porcupine.

1984. Olympic Games, Los Angeles. Multicoloured.

716. 1 s. 50 Type **163** 35 20
717. 3 s. Throwing the discus .. 80 45
718. 8 s. High jumping.. .. 2·25 1·00

1984. Mammals. Multicoloured.

720. 1 s. Type **164** 20 20
721. 1 s. 50 White-tailed mongoose 35 20
722. 2 s. Banded mongoose .. 55 35
723. 4 s. Ratel .. .. .. 1·10 65

1984. 36th International Fair, Riccione.

725. **165.** 5 s. 20 multicoloured 1·60 65
726. 6 s. 40 multicoloured 2·25 1·00

166. Emblem within Winged Horse.

1985. 40th Anniv. of International Civil Aviation Organization.

727. **166.** 3 s. multicoloured .. 65 35
728. 6 s. 40 multicoloured 1·10 80

167. Aquila.

169. Woman and Posthorn.

168. Ras Kiambone.

1985. Constellations. Illustrations from "The Book of Stars" by Abd al-Rahman al-Sufi. Multicoloured.

730. 4 s. 30 Type **167** 55 20
731. 11 s. Taurus .. .. 1·40 65
732. 12 s. 50 Aries .. .. 1·60 80
733. 13 s. Orion .. .. .. 2·00 1·10

1985. Architecture (1st series). Multicoloured.

734. 2 s. Type **168** 20 20
735. 6 s. 60 Hannassa 90 35
736. 10 s. Mnarani .. .. 1·10 65
737. 18 s. 60 Ras Kiambone (different) .. .. 2·25 1·25

See also Nos. 758/61.

1985. "Italia '85" Stamp Exhibition, Rome.

738. **169.** 2 s. multicoloured .. 55 35
739. 20 s. multicoloured .. 2·75 1·40

170. Persian Leaf-nosed Bat.

1985. Bats. Multicoloured.

741. 2 s. 50 Type **170** 55 35
742. 4 s. 50 Heart-nosed false vampire bat 85 55
743. 16 s. Wrinkle-lipped bat .. 2·25 1·40
744. 18 s. Mozambique sheath-tailed bat .. .. 2·50 1·60

171. Kenyan and Somali Presidents, Solar System and Industry.

1986. Trade Agreement with Kenya.

746. **171.** 9 s. multicoloured .. 65 45
747. 14 s. 50 multicoloured 1·60 65

172. Flower Arrangement.

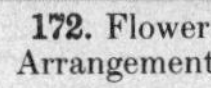

173. Seated Man holding Pottery Flask.

1986. "Euroflora" International Flower Exhibition, Genoa. Multicoloured.

748. 10 s. Type **172** 65 55
749. 15 s. Flower arrangement (different) .. .. 1·60 1·10

1986. 3rd International Somali Studies Conference, Rome.

751. **173.** 11 s. 35 multicoloured 65 45
752. 20 s. multicoloured .. 1·60 90

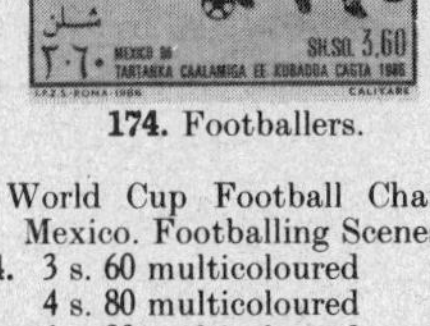

174. Footballers.

1986. World Cup Football Championship, Mexico. Footballing Scenes.

753. **174.** 3 s. 60 multicoloured 35 20
754. – 4 s. 80 multicoloured 45 20
755. – 6 s. 80 multicoloured 90 45
756. – 22 s. 60 multicoloured 1·50 1·10

1986. Architecture (2nd series). As T **168**. Multicoloured.

758. 10 s. Bulaxaar ruins .. 55 30
759. 15 s. Saylac mosque .. 85 45
760. 20 s. Saylac mosque (different) .. .. 1·40 65
761. 31 s. Jasiiradaha Jawaay tomb .. .. .. 2·25 1·10

175. Rehabilitation Centre, Mogadishu.

176. Runner.

1987. Norwegian Red Cross in Somalia.

762. **175.** 56 s. multicoloured .. 2·75 2·25

1987. "Olymphilex '87" Olympic Stamps Exhibition, Rome. Multicoloured.

764. 20 s. Type **176** 85 55
765. 48 s. Javelin thrower .. 2·00 1·10

177. Modern and Shanty Towns.

178. Western Indian Ocean 160,000,000 Years Ago.

1987. International Year of Shelter for the Homeless.

767. **177.** 53 s. multicoloured .. 1·40 65
768. 72 s. multicoloured .. 2·00 1·10

1987. "Geosom 87" Geological Evolution of Western Indian Ocean Symposium. Mult.

769. 10 s. Type **178** 20 10
770. 20 s. 60,000,000 years ago .. 55 20
771. 40 s. 15,000,000 years ago .. 90 45
772. 50 s. Today .. .. 1·60 90

179 Baby receiving Oral Vaccination (Italian inscr)

180 Somali Hare

1988. 40th Anniv of W.H.O.

774 **179** 50 s. multicoloured .. 45 20
775 168 s. multicoloured (English inscr) .. 1·75 90

1989. Animals. Multicoloured.

776 75 s. Type **180** 45 20
777 198 s. African buffalo .. 1·10 35
778 200 s. Hamadryas baboon (horiz) .. .. .. 1·25 45
779 216 s. Hippopotamus (horiz) .. .. .. 1·60 65

181 Water Lily and Boys playing Football

1989. 20th Anniv of 21 October Revolution. Multicoloured.

781 70 s. Type **181** 35 20
782 100 s. Boys playing on swing 45 20
783 150 s. Girls on see-saw .. 90 35
784 300 s. Girl skipping and boy rolling hoop .. 1·60 65

182 Dove and Broken Chain

183 Sun, Building and Scaffolding

1991. Liberation.

(a) Type **182** (without opt)

785 **182** 150 s. multicoloured .. 85 35
786 300 s. multicoloured .. 1·60 80

(b) No. 785 additionally optd **"FREEDOM"**

787 **182** 150 s. multicoloured .. 3·00 2·75

1991. Reconstruction.

788 **183** 70 s. multicoloured .. 35 20
789 100 s. multicoloured .. 55 35
790 150 s. multicoloured .. 80 45
791 300 s. multicoloured .. 1·60 65

AIR EXPRESS STAMP

E 61. Young Gazelles.

1958.

E 330. E **61.** 1 s. 70 c. red and black 85 85

EXPRESS LETTER STAMPS

1923. Express Letter stamps of Italy surch. **Somalia Italiana** and value.

E 44. E **12.** 30 b. on 60 c. red .. 11·00 12·00
E 45. E **13.** 60 b. on 1 l. 20 red & bl. 16·00 17·00

E 17.

1924.

E 60. E **17.** 30 b. brown & red 5·00 6·00
E 61. 60 b. red and blue 7·00 8·50

No. E 61 is inscr. "EXPRES".

1926. Nos. E 60/1 surch.

E 104. 70 c. on 30 b. brn. & red 5·50 6·00
E 106. 1 l. 25 on 30 b. brn. & red 7·00 8·50
E 105. 2 l. 50 on 60 b. red & blue 5·00 7·50

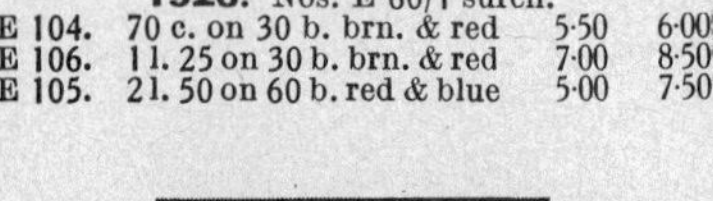

E 44. Grant's Gazelle.

1950.

E 255. E **44.** 40 c. turquoise .. 1·25 60
E 256. 80 c. violet .. .. 1·75 1·75

E **54.** "Gardenia Lutea Fresen".

1955.

E 291. E **54.** 50 c. yell., grn. & lilac 30 30
E 292. – 1 s. red, green & blue 55 55

FLOWER: 1 s. "Eryhrina Melanocantha Taub".

PARCEL POST STAMPS

Parcel Post stamps of Italy optd. or surch. on each half of stamp.

1920 Optd. **SOMALIA ITALIANA.**

P 23. P **53.** 5 c. brown .. .. 1·40 30
P 24. 10 c. blue .. .. 1·75 30
P 25. 20 c. black .. .. 48·00 6·00
P 26. 25c. red .. .. 4·50 50
P 27. 50 c. orange .. .. 38·00 4·50
P 28. 1 l. violet .. .. 16·00 75
P 29. 2 l. green .. .. 19·00 1·25
P 30. 3 l. yellow .. .. 21·00 2·25
P 31. 4 l. grey .. .. 23·00 6·00
P 89. 10 l. purple .. .. 10·00 4·50
P 90. 12 l. brown .. .. 10·00 4·50
P 91. 15 l. olive .. .. 10·00 4·50
P 92. 20 l. purple .. .. 10·00 4·50

1922. Optd. **SOMALIA.**

P 32. P **53.** 25 c. red .. .. 19·00 5·00
P 33. 50 c. orange .. 24·00 1·50
P 34. 1 l. violet .. .. 24·00 1·50
P 35. 2 l. green .. .. 28·00 2·00
P 36. 3 l. yellow .. .. 35·00 5·00
P 37. 4 l. grey .. .. 35·00 5·00

1923. Surch. **SOMALIA ITALIANA** and value.

P 44. P **53.** 3 b. on 5 c. brown .. 1·75 40
P 45. 5 b. on 5 c. brown .. 1·75 40
P 46. 10 b. on 10 c. blue 1·75 40
P 47. 25 b. on 25 c. red .. 7·00 60
P 48. 50 b. on 50 c. orange 12·00 1·10
P 49. 1 r. on 1 l. violet .. 17·00 1·50
P 50. 2 r. on 2 l. green .. 21·00 2·50
P 51. 3 r. on 3 l. yellow .. 24·00 4·50
P 52. 4 r. on 4 l. grey .. 26·00 7·00

1928. Optd. **SOMALIA ITALIANA.**

P 111. P **92.** 5 c. brown 60 80
P 112. 10 c. blue 80 80
P 126. 25 c. red .. .. 45·00 6·00
P 114. 30 c. blue 20 40
P 116. 60 c. red 20 40
P 127. 1 l. violet .. .. 19·00 2·00
P 128. 2 l. green .. .. 21·00 2·00
P 119. 3 l. yellow 70 80
P 120. 4 l. black .. .. 70 1·00
P 121. 10 l. mauve .. £200 12·00
P 122. 20 l. purple .. .. £200 12·00

P **44.**

1950.

P 255. P **44.** 1 c. red 45 45
P 256. 3 c. slate 45 45
P 257. 5 c. purple 45 45
P 258. 10 c. orange .. 45 45
P 259. 20 c. brown .. 45 45
P 260. 50 c. turquoise .. 70 70
P 261. 1 s. violet .. .. 3·50 3·50
P 262. 2 s. brown .. .. 4·75 4·75
P 263. 3 s. blue .. .. 5·00 5·00

Unused prices are for complete stamps, used prices are for half stamps except in the case of Nos. P 255/63.

POSTAGE DUE STAMPS

Postage Due stamps of Italy optd. or surch.

1906. Optd. **Somalia Italiana Meridionale.**

D 17. D **12.** 5 c. purple and orange 3·00 16·00
D 18. 10 c. purple & orange 22·00 19·00
D 19. 20 c. purple & orange 14·00 19·00
D 20. 30 c. purple & orange 11·00 19·00
D 21. 40 c. purple & orange 48·00 24·00
D 22. 50 c. purple & orange 24·00 24·00
D 23. 60 c. purple & orange 19·00 24·00
D 24. 1 l. purple and blue .. £300 80·00
D 25. 2 l. purple and blue .. £275 90·00
D 26. 5 l. purple and blue .. £275 90·00
D 27. 10 l. purple and blue 65·00 £130

1909. Optd. **Somalia Italiana.**

D 28. D **12.** 5 c. purple and orange 2·00 4·50
D 29. 10 c. purple & orange 2·00 4·50
D 30. 20 c. purple & orange 3·25 9·00
D 31. 30 c. purple & orange 9·00 15·00
D 32. 40 c. purple & orange 9·00 15·00
D 33. 50 c. purple & orange 9·00 15·00
D 34. 60 c. purple & orange 14·00 24·00
D 35. 1 l. purple and blue .. 32·00 18·00
D 36. 2 l. purple and blue .. 38·00 55·00
D 37. 5 l. purple and blue .. 48·00 70·00
D 38. 10 l. purple and blue 8·00 28·00

1923. Stamps without figures of value, surch. **Somalia Italiana** and value in "besa" or "rupia" in figures and words.

D 49. D **12.** 1 b. black and orange 75 1·75
D 50. 2 b. black and orange 75 1·75
D 51. 3 b. black and orange 75 1·75
D 52. 5 b. black and orange 85 1·75
D 53. 10 b. black & orange 85 1·75
D 54. 20 b. black & orange 85 1·75
D 55. 40 b. black & orange 85 1·75
D 56. 1 r. black and blue .. 1·25 2·50

1926. Optd. **Somalia Italiana** and surch. with figures only.

D 76. 5 c. black and orange 9·00 4·50
D 77. 10 c. black and orange 7·50 4·50
D 78. 20 c. black and orange 9·00 4·50
D 79. 30 c. black and orange 9·00 4·50
D 80. 40 c. black and orange 9·00 4·50
D 81. 50 c. black and orange 12·00 4·50
D 82. 60 c. black and orange 12·00 4·50
D 83. 1 l. black and blue .. 17·00 5·50
D 84. 2 l. black and blue .. 20·00 5·50
D 85. 5 l. black and blue .. 20·00 5·50
D 86. 10 l. black and blue 20·00 5·50

1934. Optd. **SOMALIA ITALIANA.**

D 187. D **141.** 5 c. brown .. 40 1·60
D 188. 10 c. blue .. 40 1·60
D 189. 20 c. red .. .. 2·50 2·50
D 190. 25 c. green .. 2·50 2·50
D 191. 30 c. orange .. 5·00 5·50
D 192. 40 c. brown .. 5·00 6·00
D 193. 50 c. violet .. 6·50 1·40
D 194. 60 c. blue .. 10·00 12·00
D 195. D **142.** 1 l. orange .. 13·00 3·75
D 196. 2 l. green .. .. 20·00 17·00
D 197. 5 l. violet .. 21·00 26·00
D 198. 10 l. blue .. .. 21·00 32·00
D 199. 20 l. red .. .. 24·00 38·00

D **44.**

1950.

D 255. D **44.** 1 c. slate 20 20
D 256. 2 c. blue 20 20
D 257. 5 c. turquoise .. 20 20
D 258. 10 c. purple .. 20 20
D 259. 40 c. violet .. .. 1·10 1·10
D 260. 1 s. brown .. .. 2·00 2·00

SOUTH AFRICA BC

The Union of S. Africa consists of the provinces of the Cape of Good Hope, Natal, the Orange Free State and the Transvaal. Became an independent republic outside the Commonwealth on 31 May, 1961 (for previous issues see volume 3).

100 cents = 1 rand.

110. African Pygmy Kingfisher.

115. Burchell's Gonolek.

1961. Republic issue.

238 **110** $\frac{1}{2}$ c. blue, red and brown 10 10
199 – 1 c. red and grey .. 10 10
200 – $1\frac{1}{2}$ c. lake and purple .. 10 10
229 – 2 c. blue and yellow .. 15 15
230 – $2\frac{1}{2}$ c. violet and green .. 10 10
243 **115** 3 c. red and blue .. 30 10
243b – 4 c. violet and green .. 75 30
204 – 5 c. yellow & turquoise 30 10
290 – 6 c. brown and green .. 1·00 30
205 – $7\frac{1}{2}$ c. brown and green .. 60 10
292 – 9 c. red, yell. & green 1·50 30
233 – 10 c. sepia and green .. 40 10
247 – $12\frac{1}{2}$ c. red, yell. & myrtle 1·75 40
248 – 15 c. black, olive & orge. 1·75 25
234 – 20 c. turq., red & salmon 1·50 70
250 – 50 c. black and blue .. 4·00 40
251 – 1 r. orge., green & blue 4·00 1·00

DESIGNS—As Type **110**—VERT. 1 c. Kafferboom flower. HORIZ. $1\frac{1}{2}$ c. Afrikander bull. As Type **115**—HORIZ. 2 c. Pouring gold. 50 c. Cape Town Harbour. 1 r. Strelitzia (flower). VERT. $2\frac{1}{2}$, 4 c. Groot Constantia. 5 c. Baobab tree. 6, $7\frac{1}{2}$ c. Maize. 9, $12\frac{1}{2}$ c. Protea (flower). 10 c. Cape Town Castle Entrance. 15 c. Industry. 20 c. Secretary bird.

Most values exist in two forms showing differences in the size of the inscriptions and figures of value.

See also Nos. 276/7.

123. Bleriot Monoplane and Boeing 707 Airliner over Table Mountain.

124. Folk-dancers.

1962. 50th Anniv. of First South African Aerial Post.

220. **123.** 3 c. blue and red .. 20 10

1962. 50th Anniv. of Volkspele (Folk-dancing) in South Africa.

221. **124.** $2\frac{1}{2}$ c. red and brown .. 15 10

125. Emigrant Ship "The Chapman".

126. Red Disa (orchid), Castle Rock and Gardens.

128. Centenary Emblem and Nurse.

1962. Unveiling of Precinct Stone, British Settlers Mounment, Grahamstown.

222 **125** $2\frac{1}{2}$ c. green and purple 40 10
223 $12\frac{1}{2}$ c. blue and brown 3·00 1·75

1963 50th Anniv of Kirstenbosch Botanic Gardens, Cape Town.

224. **126.** $2\frac{1}{2}$ c. multicoloured .. 20 10

1963. Cent of Red Cross. Inscr. "1863–1963".

225. **128.** $2\frac{1}{2}$ c. red, blk. & purple 20 10
226. – $12\frac{1}{2}$ c. red and blue .. 4·00 1·00

DESIGN—HORIZ. $12\frac{1}{2}$ c. Centenary emblem and globe.

130. Assembly Building, Umtata.

145. "Springbok" Badge of Rugby Board.

1963. 1st Meeting of Transkei Legislative Assembly.

237. **130.** $2\frac{1}{2}$ c. sepia and green .. 10 10

1964. 75th Anniv. of South African Rugby Board.

252. **145.** $2\frac{1}{2}$ c. brown and green .. 15 10
253. – $12\frac{1}{2}$ c. black and green .. 5·50 4·25

DESIGN—HORIZ. $12\frac{1}{2}$ c. Rugby footballer.

147. Calvin.

148. Nurse's Lamp.

1964. 400th Death Anniv. of Calvin (Protestant Reformer).

254. **147.** $2\frac{1}{2}$ c. cerise, violet & brn. 10 10

1964. 50th Anniv. South African Nursing Association.

255. **148.** $2\frac{1}{2}$ c. blue and gold .. 10 10
257. – $12\frac{1}{2}$ c. blue and gold .. 3·25 2·00

DESIGN—HORIZ. $12\frac{1}{2}$ c. Nurse holding lamp.

150. I.T.U. Emblem and Satellites.

152. Pulpit in Groote Kerk, Cape Town.

1965. Centenary of I.T.U.

258. **150.** $2\frac{1}{2}$ c. orange and blue .. 25 10
259. – $12\frac{1}{2}$ c. purple and green 3·00 1·75

DESIGN: $12\frac{1}{2}$ c. I.T.U. Emblem and symbols.

1965. Tercentenary of Nederduites Gereformeerde Kerk (Dutch Reformed Church) in South Africa.

260. **152.** $2\frac{1}{2}$ c. brown and yellow 15 10
261. – $12\frac{1}{2}$ c. black, orge. & blue 1·75 1·25

DESIGN—HORIZ. $12\frac{1}{2}$ c. Church emblem.

155. Bird in Flight.

1965. 5th Anniv. of Republic. Bilingual pairs.

262. – 1 c. blk., grn. & yellow 45 45
263. **155.** $2\frac{1}{2}$ c. blue, indigo & grn. 1·25 1·25
264. – 3 c. red, yellow & brown 4·75 4·75
265. – $7\frac{1}{2}$ c. blue, ultram & yell. 5·50 6·00

DESIGNS—VERT. 1 c. Diamond. 3 c. Maize plants. HORIZ. $7\frac{1}{2}$ c. Mountain landscape.

158. Verwoerd and Union Buildings, Pretoria.

161. "Martin Luther" (Cranach the Elder).

1966. Verwoerd Commem.

266. **158.** $2\frac{1}{2}$ c. brown and turquoise 10 10
267. – 3 c. brown and green .. 10 10
268. – $12\frac{1}{2}$ c. brown and blue .. 70 60

DESIGNS: 3 c. "Dr. H. F. Verwoerd." (I. Henkel). $12\frac{1}{2}$ c. Verwoerd and map of South Africa.

1967. 450th Anniv. of Reformation.

269. **161.** $2\frac{1}{2}$ c. black and red .. 10 10
270. – $12\frac{1}{2}$ c. black and orange 1·75 2·25

DESIGN: $12\frac{1}{2}$ c. Wittenberg Church door.

163. " Profile of Pres. Fouche." (I. Henkel). 165. Hertzog in 1902.

1968. Inauguration of President Fouche.
271. 163. 2½ c. brown 10 10
272. – 12½ c. blue .. .. 80 1·25
DESIGN: 12½ c. Portrait of Pres. Fouche.

1968. Inauguration of General Hertzog Monument, Bloemfontein.
273. 165. 2½ c. blk., brn. and yell. 10 10
274. – 3 c. multicoloured .. 15 10
275. – 12½ c. blk., red & orge. (vert.) .. .. .. 2·00 1·25
DESIGNS: 3 c. Hertzog in 1924. 12½ c. Hertzog Monument.

168. Natal Kingfisher. 170. Springbok and Olympic Torch.

1969.
276. 168. ½ c. blue, red and ochre 10 30
277. – 1 c. red and brown .. 10 10
DESIGN—VERT. 1 c. Kafferboom Flower.

1969. South African Games, Bloemfontein.
278 170 2½ c. black, red & green 15 10
279 12½ c. black, red & brn 1·25 1·50

171. Professor Barnard and Groote Schuur Hospital.

1969. World's 1st Heart Transplant and 47th South African Medical Assn. Congress.
280. 171. 2½ c. purple and red .. 15 10
281. – 12½ c. red and blue .. 1·75 2·25
DESIGN: 12½ c. Hands holding heart.

173. Mail Coach.

1969. Centenary of 1st Stamps of the South African Republic (Transvaal).
297. 173. 2½ c. yell., blue & brown 15 10
298. – 12½ c. grn., gold and brn. 3·25 3·25
DESIGN—VERT. 12½ c. Transvaal stamp of 1869.

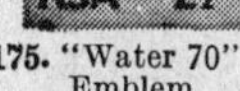

175. "Water 70" Emblem. 177. "The Sower".

1970. Water 70 Campaign.
299. 175. 2½ c. grn., blue & brown 30 10
300. – 3 c. blue and buff (horiz.) 30 20
DESIGN: 3 c. Symbolic Waves.

1970 150th Anniv. of Bible Society of South Africa.
301 177 2½ c. multicoloured .. 15 10
302 – 12½ c. gold, black & bl 2·50 2·50
DESIGN—HORIZ. 12½ c. "Biblia" and open book.

178. J. G. Strijdom and Strijdom Tower. 179. Map and Antarctic Landscape.

1971. "Interstex" Stamp Exhibition, Cape Town.
303 178 5 c. blue, black & yell 20 10

1971. 10th Anniv. of Antarctic Treaty.
304. 179. 12½ c. black, blue & red 5·00 5·50

180. " Landing of British Settlers, 1820 " (T. Baines).

1971. 10th Anniv. of Republic of South Africa.
305 180 2 c. flesh and red .. 15 10
306 – 4 c. green and black .. 15 10
DESIGN—VERT. 4 c. Presidents Steyn and Kruger and Treaty of Vereeniging Monument.

181. View of Dam.

1972. Opening of Hendrik Verwoerd Dam. Multicoloured.
307 4 c. Type 181 .. .. 20 10
308 5 c. Aerial view of dam .. 25 10
309 10 c. Dam and surrounding country (58 × 21 mm) .. 1·50 2·25

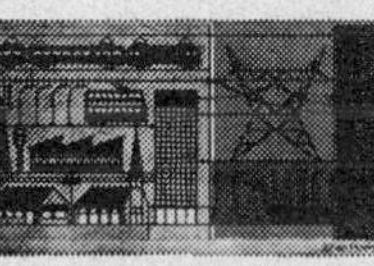

182. Sheep. 183. Black and Siamese Cats.

1972. Sheep and Wool Industry.
310 182 4 c. multicoloured .. 30 10
311 – 15 c. stone, dp bl & bl 3·25 20
DESIGN: 15 c. Lamb.

1972. Centenary of Societies for the Prevention of Cruelty to Animals.
312. 183. 5 c. multicoloured .. 1·75 10

184. Transport and Industry. 185. University Coat of Arms.

1973. 50th Anniv. of ESCOM (Electricity Supply Commission). Multicoloured.
326 4 c. Type 184 .. .. 20 10
327 5 c. Pylon (21 × 28 mm) .. 30 10
328 15 c. Cooling towers (21 × 28 mm) .. .. 3·00 3·50

1973. Cent of University of South Africa.
329. 185. 4 c. multicoloured .. 20 10
330. – 5 c. multicoloured .. 30 15
331. – 15 c. black and gold .. 3·00 3·25
DESIGNS—HORIZ. (38 × 21 mm.). 5 c. University Complex, Pretoria. VERT. (As Type 185). 15 c. Old University building, Cape Town.

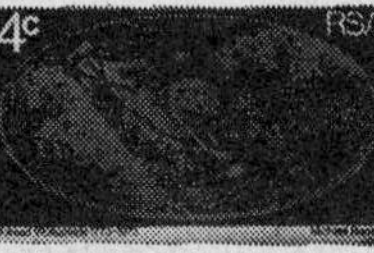

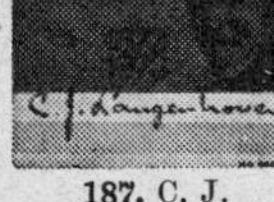

186. Rescuing Sailors. 187. C. J. Langenhoven.

1973. Bicentenary of Rescue by Wolraad Woltemade.
332. 186. 4 c. brn., grn. & black 20 10
333. – 5 c. olive, grn. & black 40 10
334. – 15 c. brn., green & blk. 5·00 6·00
DESIGNS: 5 c. "De Jonge Thomas" foundering. 15 c. "De Jonge Thomas" breaking up and sailors drowning.

1973. Birth Cent. of C. J. Langenhoven (politician and composer of national anthem).
335. 187. 4 c. multicoloured .. 25 10
336. – 5 c. multicoloured .. 35 10
337. – 15 c. multicoloured .. 5·50 5·50
Nos. 336/7 are as Type 187 but with motifs re-arranged. The 5 c. is vert., 21 × 38 mm., and the 15 c. is horiz., 38 × 21 mm.

188. Communications Map.

1973. World Communications Day.
338. 188. 15 c. multicoloured .. 80 1·40

189. Restored Buildings. 190. Burgerspond (obverse & reverse).

1974. Restoration of Tulbagh. Multicoloured.
340 4 c. Type 189 .. .. 15 10
341 5 c. Restored Church Street (58 × 21 mm) .. 40 60

1974. Centenary of Burgerspond (coin).
342. 190. 9 c. brn., red and olive 60 95

191. Dr. Malan. 192. Congress Emblem.

1974. Birth Centenary of Dr. D. F. Malan (Prime Minister).
343. 191. 4 c. blue and light blue 15 10

1974. 15th World Sugar Congress, Durban.
344. 192. 15 c. blue and silver .. 1·00 1·50

193. "50" and Radio Waves.

1974. 50th Anniv. of Broadcasting in South Africa.
345. 193. 4 c. red and black .. 10 10

194. Monument Building.

1974. Inauguration of British Settlers' Monument, Grahamstown.
346. 194. 5 c. red and black .. 10 10

195. Stamps of the South African Provinces.

1974. Centenary of Universal Postal Union.
347. 195. 15 c. multicoloured .. 80 80

196. Iris. 197. Bokmakierie Shrikes.

1974. Multicoloured.
(a) As Type 196.
348. 1 c. Type 196 .. .. 10 10
349a. 2 c. Wild Heath 10 10
350a. 3 c. Geranium 10 10
351a. 4 c. Arum Lily 10 10
352. 5 c. Cape Gannet (horiz.) 20 10
353. 6 c. Galjoen (fish) (horiz.) 25 10
354. 7 c. Zebra Fish (horiz.) .. 25 10
355. 9 c. Angel Fish (horiz.) .. 30 10
356. 10 c. Moorish Idol (horiz.) 30 10
357. 14 c. Roman (fish) (horiz.) 30 10
358. 15 c. Greater Double-collared Sunbird (horiz.) .. 30 10
359. 20 c. Yellow-billed Hornbill (horiz.) 45 10
360. 25 c. Barberton Daisy .. 45 10
(b) As Type 197.
361. 30 c. Type 197 .. .. 8·00 70
362. 50 c. Stanley Cranes .. 2·50 35
363. 1 r. Bateleur .. .. 8·50 3·00

1974. Coil Stamps. As Nos. 348/9a, 352 and 356. Colours changed.
370a 196 1 c. violet and pink .. 55 50
371 – 2 c. green and yellow .. 80 50
372 – 5 c. black and blue .. 2·00 80
373a – 10 c. violet and blue .. 4·00 4·00

198. Voortrekker Monument and Encampment.

1974. 25th Anniv. of Voortrekker Monument, Pretoria.
374. 198. 4 c. multicoloured .. 20 30

199. SASOL Complex.

1975. 25th Anniv. of South African Coal, Oil and Gas Corporation Ltd. (SASOL).
375. 199. 15 c. multicoloured .. 1·25 1·75

200. President Diederichs. 201. Jan Smuts.

1975. Inauguration of State President.
376. 200. 4 c. brown and gold .. 10 10
377. 15 c. blue and gold .. 70 1·25

1975. Smuts Commemoration.
378. 201. 4 c. black and grey .. 10 10

202. " Dutch East Indiaman, Table Bay ".

1975. Death Centenary of Thomas Baines (painter). Multicoloured.
379. 5 c. Type 202 .. .. 20 10
380. 9 c. " Cradock, 1848 " .. 30 20
381. 15 c. " Thirsty Flat, 1848 " 50 50
382. 30 c. " Pretoria, 1874 " .. 1·00 1·75

203. Gideon Malherbe's House, Paarl.

1975. Cent. of Genootskap van Regte Afrikaners (Afrikaner Language Movement).
384. 203. 4 c. multicoloured .. 10 10

204. " Automatic Sorting ".

205. Title Page of " Die Afrikaanse Patriot ".

1975. Postal Mechanisation.
385. **204.** 4 c. multicoloured .. 10 10

1975. Inaug. of Language Monument, Paarl.
386. **205.** 4 c. blk., brn. and orge. 10 10
387. – 5 c. multicoloured .. 10 10
DESIGN: 5 c. " Africkaanse Taalmonument ".

206. Table Mountain.

1975. Tourism. Multicoloured.
388. 15 c. Type **206** .. .. 4·50 5·00
389. 15 c. Johannesburg .. 4·50 5·00
390. 15 c. Cape Vineyards .. 4·50 5·00
391. 15 c. Lions in Kruger National Park .. .. 4·50 5·00

207. Globe and Satellites.

1975. Satellite Communication.
392. **207.** 15 c. multicoloured .. 40 40

208. Bowls.

210. " Picnic under a Baobab Tree ".

1976. Sporting Commems.
393. **208.** 15 c. black and green .. 30 70
394. – 15 c. black and green .. 75 1·40
395. – 15 c. black and green .. 40 60
396. – 15 c. black and green .. 45 55
DESIGNS AND EVENTS: No. 393, Type **208** (World Bowls Championships, Johannesburg). No. 394, Batsman (Organised Cricket in South Africa, Cent.), No. 395, Polo player. No. 396, Gary Player (golfer).

1976. South Africa's World Bowls Championship Victory. No. 393 optd. **WERELD-KAMPIOENE WORLD CHAMPIONS.**
398. **208.** 15 c. black and green .. 30 70

1976. Birth Centenary of Erich Mayer (painter). Multicoloured.
399 4 c. Type **210** 15 10
400 10 c. "Foot of the Blaawberg" 35 25
401 15 c. "Harteespoort Dam" 60 1·00
402 20 c. "Street scene, Doornfontein" .. .. 80 1·50

211. Cheetah.

1976. World Environment Day. Mult.
404. 3 c. Type **211** 15 10
405. 10 c. Black Rhinoceros .. 70 35
406. 15 c. Blesbok .. 85 1·10
407. 20 c. Mountain Zebra .. 1·25 1·75

212. " Emily Hobhouse." (H. Naude).

214. Family with Globe.

213. Steam Packet, 1876.

1976. 50th Death Anniv. of Emily Hobhouse (welfare worker).
408. **212.** 4 c. multicoloured .. 10 10

1976. Centenary of Ocean Mail Service.
409. **213.** 10 c. multicoloured .. 60 85

1976. Family Planning and Child Welfare.
410 **214** 4 c. brown and orange 10 10

215. Glasses of Wine.

216. Dr. Jacob Du Toit.

1977. International Wine Symposium, Cape Town.
411. **215.** 15 c. multicoloured .. 40 85

1977. Birth Centenary of J. D. Du Toit (theologian and poet).
412. **216.** 4 c. multicoloured .. 10 10

217. Palace of Justice.

1977. Centenary of Transvaal Supreme Court.
413. **217.** 4 c. brown .. 10 10

218. " Protea repens ".

219. Gymnast.

1977. Multicoloured.
414 1 c. Type **218** 10 10
415 2 c. " P. punctata " .. 15 30
416 3 c. " P. neriifolia " .. 10 10
417 4 c. " P. longifolia " .. 10 10
418 5 c. " P. cynaroides " .. 10 10
419b 6 c. " P. canaliculata " .. 30 40
420b 7 c. " P. lorea " .. 20 30
421a 8 c. " P. mundii " .. 15 10
422 9 c. " P. roupelliae " .. 20 40
423a 10 c. " P. aristata " .. 30 10
424 15 c. " P. eximia " .. 25 10
425 20 c. " P. magnifica " .. 30 10
426c 25 c. " P. grandiceps " .. 40 40
427 30 c. " P. amplexicaulis " 45 10
428a 50 c. " Leucospermum cordifolium " .. 45 15
429a 1 r. " Paranomus reflexus " 80 75
430a 2 r. " Orothamnus zeyheri " 1·50 1·00

1977. Coil Stamps. As T **218.** Mult.
431. 1 c. " Leucadendron argenteum " 35 60
432. 2 c. " Mimetes cucullatus " 35 60
433. 5 c. " Serruria florida " .. 35 60
434. 10 c. " Leucadendron sessile " 35 70

1977. 8th Congress of Int. Assn. of Physical Education and Sports for Girls and Women.
435. **219.** 15 c. blk., red and yell. 30 30

220. Metrication Symbol on Globe.

1977. Metrication.
436. **220.** 15 c. multicoloured .. 30 30

INDEX

Countries can be quickly located by referring to the index at the end of this volume.

221. Atomic Diagram.

1977. Uranium Development.
437. **221.** 15 c. multicoloured .. 30 30

222. National Flag.

224. Dr. Andrew Murray.

223. Walvis Bay, 1878.

1977. 50th Anniv. of National Flag.
438. **222.** 5 c. multicoloured .. 10 10

1977. Centenary of Annexation of Walvis Bay.
439. **223.** 15 c. multicoloured .. 60 40

1978. 150th Birth Anniv. of Dr. Andrew Murray (church statesman).
440. **224.** 4 c. multicoloured .. 10 10

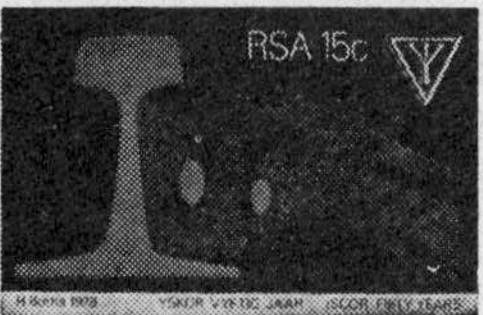

225. Steel Rail.

1978. 50th Anniv. of ISCOR (South African Iron and Steel Industrial Corporation).
441. **225.** 15 c. multicoloured .. 40 30

226. Richards Bay.

1978. Harbours. Multicoloured.
442. 15 c. Type **226** .. .. 80 1·25
443. 15 c. Saldanhabaai .. 80 1·25

227. "Shepherd's Lonely Dwelling, Riversdale",

1978. 125th Birth Anniv. of J. E. A. Volschenk (painter). Multicoloured.
444 10 c. Type **146** 20 20
445 15 c. "Clouds and Sunshine, Loneberg Range, Riversdale" .. 50 35
446 20 c. "At the Foot of the Mountain" .. .. 70 1·00
447 25 c. "Evening on the Veldt" .. .. .. 80 1·75

228. Pres. B. J. Vorster.

1978. Inauguration of President Vorster.
449a.**228.** 4 c. brown and gold .. 10 15
450. 15 c. violet and gold .. 25 60

229. Golden Gate.

1978. Tourism. Multicoloured.
451. 10 c. Type **229** 25 15
452. 15 c. Blyde River Canyon 55 50
453. 20 c. Amphitheatre, Drakensberg .. .. .. 75 1·25
454. 25 c. Cango Caves .. 90 1·75

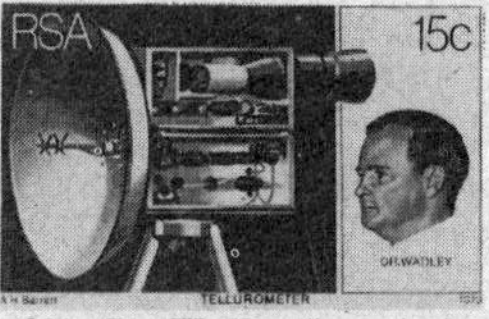

230. Dr. Wadley (inventor) and Tellurometer.

1979. 25th Anniv. of Tellurometer (radio distance measurer).
455. **230.** 15 c. multicoloured .. 20 20

231. 1929 4d. Airmail Stamp.

1979. 50th Anniv. of Stamp Production in South Africa.
456. **231.** 15 c. green, cream and grey 20 20

232. " Save Fuel ".

1979. Fuel Conservation.
457. **232.** 4 c. black and red .. 25 50
458. – 4 c. black and red .. 25 50
No. 458 is as Type **232** but with face value and country initials in bottom left-hand corner, and Afrikaans inscription above English.

233. Isandlwana.

1979. Centenary of Zulu War.
459. **233.** 4 c. black and red .. 15 10
460. – 15 c. black and red .. 45 45
461. – 20 c. black and red .. 60 75
DESIGNS: 15 c. Ulundi. 20 c. Rorke's Drift.

234. " Health Care ".

235. Children looking at Candle.

1979. Health Year.
463. **234.** 4 c. multicoloured .. 10 10

1979. 50th Anniv. of Christmas Stamp Fund.
464. **235.** 4 c. multicoloured .. 10 10

236. University of Cape Town.

237. " Gary Player ".

1979. 50th Anniv. of University of Cape Town.
465a. **236.** 4 c. multicoloured .. 15 15

1979. "Rosafari 1979" World Rose Convention, Pretoria. Multicoloured.

466. 4 c. Type **237** 15 10
467. 15 c. "Prof. Chris Barnard" 50 40
468. 20 c. "Southern Sun" .. 60 50
469. 25 c. "Soaring Wings" .. 70 65

238. University of Stellenbosch.

1979. 300th Anniv. of Stellenbosch (oldest town in South Africa). Multicoloured.

471. 4 c. Type **238** 10 10
472. 15 c. Rhenish Church on the Braak 20 40

239. F.A.K. Emblem. **240.** "Still-life with Sweet Peas".

1979. 50th Anniv. of F.A.K. (Federation of Afrikaans Cultural Societies).

473. **239.** 4 c. multicoloured .. 10 15

1980. Paintings by Pieter Wenning. Mult.

474 5 c. Type **240** 10 10
475 25 c. "House in the Suburbs, Cape Town" (44½ × 37 mm) 30 60

241. "Cullinan II". **242.** C. L. Leipoldt.

1980. World Diamond Congresses, Johannesburg. Multicoloured.

477. 15 c. Type **241** 60 60
478. 20 c. "Cullinan I (Great Star of Africa)" .. 65 65

1980. Birth Cent. of C. L. Leipoldt (poet).

479. **242.** 5 c. multicoloured .. 10 10

243. University of Pretoria. **244.** "Marine with Shipping" (Willem van de Velde).

1980. 50th Anniv. of University of Pretoria.

480. **243.** 5 c. multicoloured .. 10 10

1980. Paintings from South African National Gallery, Cape Town. Multicoloured.

481. 5 c. Type **244** 10 10
482. 10 c. "Firetail and his Trainer" (George Stubbs) 15 20
483. 15 c. "Lavinia" (Thomas Gainsborough) (vert.) .. 20 45
484. 20 c. "Classical Landscape" (Pieter Post) .. 25 65

245. Joubert, Kruger and M. Pretorius (Triumvirate Government). **246.** Boers advancing up Amajuba Mountain.

1980. Cent. of Paardekraal Monument (cairn commemorating formation of Boer Triumvirate Government). Multicoloured.

486. 5 c. Type **245** 10 10
487. 10 c. Paardekraal Monument (vert.) 20 40

1981. Centenary of Battle of Amajuba. Mult.

488. 5 c. Type **246** 25 10
489. 15 c. British troops defending hill (horiz.) .. 55 50

247. Ballet "Raka".

1981. Opening of State Theatre, Pretoria. Multicoloured.

490. 20 c. Type **247** 25 30
491. 25 c. Opera "Aida" .. 30 35

248. Former Presidents C. R. Swart, J. J. Fouche, N. Diederichs and B. J. Vorster.

1981. 20th Anniversary of Republic.

493. **248.** 5 c. black, grn. and brn. 15 10
494. – 15 c. multicoloured .. 30 30

DESIGN—28 × 22 mm. 15 c. President Marais Viljoen.

249. Girl with Hearing Aid. **250.** Microscope.

1981. Centenary of Institutes for Deaf and Blind, Worcester. Mult.

495. 5 c. Type **249** 10 10
496. 15 c. Boy reading braille 20 25

1981. 50th Anniv. of National Cancer Association.

497. **250.** 5 c. multicoloured .. 10 10

251. "Calanthe natalensis". **252.** Voortrekkers in Uniform.

1981. 10th World Orchid Conference, Durban. Multicoloured.

498. 5 c. Type **251** 15 10
499. 15 c. "Eulophia speciosa" 30 35
500. 20 c. "Disperis fanniniae" 40 65
501. 25 c. "Disa uniflora" .. 50 90

1981. 50th Anniv. of Voortrekker Movement (Afrikaans cultural youth organization).

503. **252.** 5 c. multicoloured .. 10 10

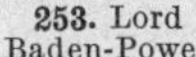

253. Lord Baden-Powell **254.** Dr. Robert Koch.

1982. 75th Anniv. Boy Scout Movement.

504. **253.** 15 c. multicoloured .. 15 15

1981. Cent. of Discovery of Tubercle Bacillus.

505. **254.** 20 c. multicoloured .. 15 30

255. "Maria van Riejbeck" submarine.

1982. 25th Anniv. of Simonstown, South African Naval Base. Multicoloured.

506. 8 c. Type **255** 10 10
507. 15 c. Missile patrol vessel 15 30
508. 20 c. Miiesweeper 25 50
509. 25 c. Harbour patrol boats 30 70

256. Old Provost, Grahamstown. **257.** Bradysaurus.

1982. South African Architecture.

511 **256** 1 c. brown 15 20
512b – 2 c. green 10 20
513 – 3 c. violet 30 40
514 – 4 c. green 20 15
515 – 5 c. red 30 30
515a – 5 c. purple 10 10
516 – 6 c. green 45 30
517 – 7 c. green 20 20
518a – 8 c. blue 20 10
519 – 9 c. mauve 30 20
520 – 10 c. red 40 30
520a – 10 c. brown 35 10
520b – 11 c. red 40 15
520c – 12 c. blue 60 10
520d – 14 c. brown 75 10
521 – 15 c. blue 30 15
521a – 16 c. red 80 40
522b – 20 c. red 65 30
522 – 20 c. black 80 10
523 – 25 c. brown 40 30
524 – 30 c. brown 65 30
525b – 50 c. blue .. .. 1·50 15
526 – 1 r. violet .. .. 1·00 15
527. – 2 r. red .. .. 2·00 30

DESIGNS—(28 × 20mm). 2 c. Tuynhuys, Cape Town. 3 c. Applehof, Bloemfontein 4 c. Raadsaal, Pretoria. 5 c. Cape Town Castle. 6 c. Goewermentsgebou, Bloemfontein. 7 c. Drostdy, Graaff-Reinet. 8 c. Leeuwenhof, Cape Town. 9 c. Libertas, Pretoria. 10 c. City Hall, Pietermaritzberg. 11 c. City Hall, Kimberley. 12 c. City Hall, Port Elizabeth. 14 c. City Hall, Johannesburg. 15 c. Matjesfontein. 16 c. City Hall, Durban. 20 c. Post Office, Durban. 25 c. Melrose House, Pretoria. (45 × 28mm). 30 c. Old Legislative Assembly Building, Pietermaritzburg. 50 c. Raadsaal, Bloemfontein. 1 r. Houses of Parliament, Cape Town. 2 r. Uniegebou, Pretoria.

1982. Coil Stamps. As T **256**.

528. 1 c. brown 30 50
529. 2 c. green 30 55
530. 5 c. brown 30 55
531. 10 c. brown 30 60

DESIGNS: 1 c. Drostdy, Swellendam. 2 c. City Hall, East London. 5 c. Head Post Office, Johannesburg. 10 c. Morgenster, Somerset West.

1982. Karoo Fossils. Multicoloured.

532. 8 c. Type **257** 40 10
533. 15 c. Lystrosaurus .. 55 60
534. 20 c. Euparkeria 70 75
535. 25 c. Thinaxodon 80 85

258. Gough Island Base.

1983. Weather Stations. Multicoloured.

537. 8 c. Type **258** 20 10
538. 20 c. Marion Island base .. 45 45
539. 25 c. Taking meteorological readings .. 45 50
540. 40 c. Launching weather ballon, Sanae .. 70 90

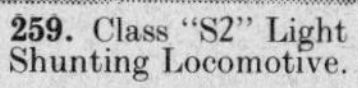

259. Class "S2" Light Shunting Locomotive. **260.** Rugby.

1983. Steam Railway Locomotives. Mult.

541 10 c. Type **259** 35 10
542 20 c. Class "16E" express locomotive 70 65
543 25 c. Class "6H" locomotive 80 90
544. 40 c. Class "15F" main-line locomotive .. .. 1·25 1·40

1983. Sport in South Africa. Mult.

545. 10 c. Type **260** 15 10
546. 20 c. Soccer (horiz.) .. 35 35
547. 25 c. Yachting 45 45
548. 40 c. Horse-racing (horiz.) 75 75

261. Plettenberg Bay.

1983. Tourism. Beaches. Multicoloured.

549. 10 c. Type **261** 10 10
550. 20 c. Durban 25 30
551. 25 c. West coast 30 35
552. 40 c. Clifton 50 65

262. Thomas Pringle. **263.** Manganese.

1984. South African English Authors.

554. **262.** 10 c. brn., lt. brn. & grey 10 10
555. – 20 c. brn., grn. & grey 25 40
556. – 25 c. brn., pink & grey 30 50
557. – 40 c. brn., lt. brn. & grey 50 85

DESIGNS: 20 c. Pauline Smith. 25 c. Olive Schreiner. 40 c. Sir Percy Fitzpatrick.

1984. Strategic Minerals. Multicoloured.

558. 11 c. Type **263** 40 10
559. 20 c. Chromium 75 65
560. 25 c. Vanadium 90 90
561. 30 c. Titanium .. .. 1·00 1·25

264. Bloukrans River Bridge.

1984. South African Bridges. Multicoloured.

562. 11 c. Type **264** 40 10
563. 25 c. Durban four level interchange 80 70
564. 30 c. Mfolozi rail bridge .. 85 75
565. 45 c. Gouritz River bridge 1·10 1·50

265. Preamble to the Constitution in Afrikaans. **266.** Pres. P.W. Botha.

1984. New Constitution.

566 – 11 c. stone, black & bis 90 1·00
567 **265** 11 c. stone, black & bis 90 1·00
568 – 25 c. stone, pur & bis 60 65
569 – 30 c. multicoloured .. 60 65

DESIGNS: No. 566, Preamble to the Constitution in English. 568. Last two lines of National Anthem. 569, South African coat of arms.

1984. Inauguration of President Botha.

570. **266.** 11 c. multicoloured .. 30 10
571. 25 c. multicoloured .. 55 40

267. Pro Patria Medal

268. "Reflections" (Frans Oerder).

1984. Military Decorations. Multicoloured.

572. 11 c. Type **267** 25 10
573. 25 c. De Wet Decoration .. 55 45
574. 30 c. John Chard Decoration 60 65
575. 45 c. Honoris Crux (Diamond) Decoration .. 85 1·10

1985. Paintings by Frans Oerder. Multicoloured.

577. 11 c. Type **268**. .. 30 15
578. 25 c. "Ladies in a Garden" 45 35
579. 30 c. "Still-life with Lobster" 50 45
580. 50 c. "Still-life with Marigolds" 80 70

269. Cape Parliament Building.

270. Freesia.

1985. Centenary of Cape Parliament Building. Multicoloured.

582. 12 c. Type **269** 30 10
583. 25 c. Speaker's Chair .. 45 45
584. 30 c. "National Convention 1908–9" (Edward Roworth) 60 70
585. 50 c. Republic Parliamentary emblem .. .. 95 1·10

1985. Floral Emigrants. Multicoloured.

586. 12 c. Type **270** 30 10
587. 25 c. Nerine 55 55
588. 30 c. Ixia 65 70
589. 50 c. Gladiolus .. .. 90 1·10

271. Sugar Bowl.

1985. Cape Silverware. Multicoloured.

590. 12 c. Type **271** 30 10
591. 25 c. Teapot 60 50
592. 30 c. Loving cup (vert.) .. 65 65
593. 50 c. Coffee pot (vert.) .. 95 1·25

272. Blood Donor Session.

1986. Blood Donor Campaign. Multicoloured.

594. 12 c. Type **272** 45 10
595. 20 c. Baby receiving blood transfusion 75 60
596. 25 c. Operation in progress 80 75
597. 30 c. Ambulanceman and accident victim .. .. 95 1·10

273. National Flag.

1986. 25th Anniv. of Republic of South Africa.

598. 14 c. Type **273** .. .. 75 1·00
599. 14 c. As Type **273**, but inscr "UNITY IS STRENGTH" .. .. 75 1·00

274. Drostdyhof, Graaff-Reinet.

1986. Restoration of Historic Buildings. Multicoloured.

600. 14 c. Type **274** 40 10
601. 20 c. Pilgrim's Rest mining village 70 50
602. 25 c. Strapp's Store, Bethlehem 75 70
603. 30 c. Palmdene, Pietermaritzburg .. .. 90 1·00

275. Von Brandis Square, Johannesburg, c 1900.

1986. Centenary of Johannesburg. Mult.

604. 14 c. Type **275** 35 10
605. 20 c. Gold mine (26 × 20 mm.) 90 80
606. 25 c. Johannesburg skyline, 1986 .. .. .. 95 90
607. 30 c. Gold bars (26 × 20 mm.) .. .. 1·25 1·50

276. Gordon's Rock, Paarlberg,

277. "Chaetodera regalis".

1986. Rock Formations. Multicoloured.

608. 14 c. Type **276** 50 10
609. 20 c. The Column, Drakensberg 75 80
610. 25 c. Maltese Cross, Sederberge .. .. 85 1·00
611. 30 c. Bourke's Luck Potholes, Blyde River Gorge 1·10 1·40

1987. South African Beetles. Multicoloured.

612. 14 c. Type **277** 50 10
613. 20 c. "Trichostetha fascicularis" 70 75
614. 25 c. "Julodis viridipes" .. 85 1·00
615. 30 c. "Ceroplesis militaris" 1·10 1·50

278. Eland, Sebaaieni Cave.

1987. Rock Paintings. Multicoloured.

616. 16 c. Type **278** 50 10
617. 20 c. Leaping lion, Clocolan 75 75
618. 25 c. Black Wildebeest, uMhlwazini Valley .. 90 1·00
619. 30 c. Bushman dance, Floukraal .. .. 1·10 1·50

279. Oude Pastorie, Paarl.

1987. 300th Anniv. of Paarl. Multicoloured.

620. 16 c. Type **279** 40 10
621. 20 c. Grapevines 65 70
622. 25 c. Wagon-building .. 70 85
623. 30 c. KWV Cathedral Wine Cellar .. .. .. 95 1·25

1987. Natal Flood Relief Fund (1st issue). No. 521a surch.

624. 16 c. + 10 c. rosine (surch **VLOEDRAMP NATAL +10 c.**) 45 65
625. 16 c. + 10 c. (surch. **NATAL FLOOD DISASTER +10 c.**) 45 65

See also Nos. 629/30 and 635/6.

281. "Belshazzar's Feast (Rembrandt).

1987. The Bible Society of South Africa. Multicoloured.

626. 16 c. "The Bible" in 75 languages (54 × 34 mm.) 40 10
627. 30 c. Type **281** 70 60
628. 50 c. "St. Matthew and the Angel" (Rembrandt) (vert.) 90 90

1987. Natal Flood Relief Fund (2nd issue). No. 626 surch.

629. 16 c. + 10 c. multicoloured (surch as No. 625) .. 45 65
630. 16 c. + 10 c. multicoloured (surch as No. 624) .. 45 65

282. Bartolomeu Dias and Cape of Good Hope.

1988. 500th Anniv. of Discovery of Cape of Good Hope by Bartolomeu Dias. Multicoloured.

631. 16 c. Type **282** 55 10
632. 30 c. Kwaaihoek Monument 80 75
633. 40 c. Caravels .. .. 90 1·00
634. 50 c. Martellus map, c. 1489 1·25 1·60

1988. Natal Flood Relief Fund (3rd issue). No. 631 surch.

635. 16 c. + 10 c. multicoloured (surch as No. 624) .. 45 65
636 16 c. + 10 c. multicoloured (surch. as No. 625) .. 45 65

283. Huguenot Monument, Franschhoek.

1988. 300th Anniv. of Arrival of First French Huguenots at the Cape. Multicoloured.

637. 16 c. Type **283** 30 10
638. 30 c. Map of France showing Huguenot areas .. 70 70
639. 40 c. Title page of French/Dutch New Testament of 1672 .. .. 80 80
640. 50 c. St. Bartholomew's Day Massacre, Paris, 1572 .. .. .. 1·00 1·25

1988. Flood Relief Fund Nos. 637/40 surch in English (**National Flood Disaster**) (E) or in Afrikaans (**Nasionale Vloedramp**) (A).

641 16 c. + 10 c. mult (E) .. 40 40
642 16 c. + 10 c. mult (A) .. 40 40
643 30 c. + 10 c. mult (A) .. 55 55
644 30 c. + 10 c. mult (E) .. 55 55
645 40 c. + 10 c. mult (A) .. 70 70
646 40 c. + 10 c. mult (E) .. 70 70
647 50 c. + 10 c. mult (E) .. 90 90
648 50 c. + 10 c. mult (A) .. 90 90

285 Pelican Point Lighthouse, Walvis Bay

1988. Lighthouses. Multicoloured.

649 16 c. Type **285** 50 10
650 30 c. Green Point, Cape Town 70 55
651 40 c. Cape Agulhas .. 90 85
652 50 c. Umhlanga Rocks, Durban .. .. 1·25 1·10

286 "Huernia zebrina"

287 Map of Great Trek Routes

1988. Succulents. Multicoloured.

654 1 c. Type **286** 10 10
655 2 c. "Euphorbia symmetrica" 10 10
656 5 c. "Lithops dorotheae" 10 10
657 7 c. "Gibbaeum nebrawnii" 10 10
658 10 c. "Didymaotus lapidiformis" 10 10
659 16 c. "Vanheerdea divergens" 15 10
659a 18 c. "Faucaria tigrina" 30 10
660 20 c. "Conophytum mundum" 20 10
660a 21 c. "Gasteria armstrongii" 20 10
661 25 c. "Cheiridopsis peculiaris" 20 15
662 30 c. "Tavaresia barklyi" 30 10
663 35 c. "Dinteranthus wilmotianus" 30 20
664 40 c. "Frithia pulchra" .. 35 25
665 50 c. "Lapidaria margaretae" 35 25
666 90 c. "Dioscorea elephantipes" 60 45
667 1 r. "Trichocaulon cactiforme" 60 50
668 2 r. "Crassula columnaris" 1·25 90
668a 5 r. "Anacampseros albissima" .. .. 3·00 2·40

See also No. 778.

1988. Coil stamps. As T **286**. Multicoloured.

669 1 c. "Adromischus marianiae" 75 90
670 2 c. "Titanopsis calcarea" 30 30
671 5 c. "Dactylopsis digitata" 30 30
672 10 c. "Pleiospilos bolusii" 35 35

1988. 150th Anniv of Great Trek. Mult.

673 16 c. Type **287** 50 10
674 30 c. "Exodus" (tapestry by W. Coetzer) (56 × 20 mm) 80 80
675 40 c. "Crossing the Drakensberg" (tapestry by W. Coetzer) (77 × 20 mm) 95 95
676 50 c. "After the Service, Church of the Vow" (J. H. Pierneef) (horiz) .. 1·25 1·60

288 Coelacanth

1989. 50th Anniv of Discovery of Coelacanth. Multicoloured.

677 16 c. Type **288** 55 15
678 30 c. Prof. J. L. B. Smith and Dr. M. Courtenay-Latimer examining Coelacanth 85 65
679 40 c. J. L. B. Smith Institute of Ichthyology, Grahamstown .. .. 1·00 1·00
680 50 c. Coelacanth and "GEO" midget submarine .. .. 1·25 1·50

289 Man-made Desert

1989. National Grazing Strategy. Mult.
681 18 c. Type **289** 40 15
682 30 c. Formation of erosion gully 75 75
683 40 c. Concrete barrage in gully 80 90
684 50 c. Reclaimed veldt .. 90 1·25

290 South Africa v France Match, 1980

1989. Centenary of South African Rugby Board. Multicoloured.
685 18 c. Type **290** 35 15
686 30 c. South Africa v Australia, 1963 .. .. 60 60
687 40 c. South Africa v New Zealand, 1937 .. .. 75 80
688 50 c. South Africa v British Isles, 1896 .. .. 85 95

291 "Composition in Blue"

292 Pres. F. W. de Klerk

1989. Paintings by Jacob Hendrik Pierneef. Multicoloured.
689 18 c. Type **291** 30 15
690 30 c. "Zanzibar" 50 50
691 40 c. "The Bushveld" .. 65 70
692 50 c. "Cape Homestead" .. 75 85

1989. Inauguration of President F. W. de Klerk. Multicoloured.
694 18 c. Type **292** 40 10
695 45 c. F. W. de Klerk (different) 70 90

293 Gas-drilling Rig, Mossel Bay

1989. Energy Sources. Multicoloured.
696 18 c. Type **293** 40 10
697 30 c. Coal to oil conversion plant 60 50
698 40 c. Nuclear power station 70 65
699 50 c. Thermal electric power station 80 90

294 Electric Goods Train and Map of Railway Routes

1990. Co-operation in Southern Africa. Mult.
700 18 c. Cahora Bassa Hydro-electric Scheme, Mozambique, and map of transmission lines (68 × 26 mm) 50 50
701 30 c. Type **294** 70 50
702 40 c. Projected dam on upper Orange River, Lesotho, and map of Highlands Water Project (68 × 26 mm) 85 65
703 50 c. Cow, syringe and outline map of Africa .. 95 85

295 Great Britain 1840 Penny Black

296 Knysna Turaco

1990. National Stamp Day. Multicoloured.
705 21 c. Type **295** 40 40
706 21 c. Cape of Good Hope 1853 4d. triangular pair 40 40
707 21 c. Natal 1857 1s. .. 40 40
708 21 c. Orange Free State 1868 1s. 40 40
709 21 c. Transvaal 1869 1s. .. 40 40

1990. Birds. Multicoloured.
710 21 c. Type **296** 30 10
711 35 c. Red-capped robin chat 40 40
712 40 c. Rufous-naped bush lark 40 50
713 50 c. Bokmakierie shrike .. 55 75

297 Karoo Landscape near Britstown

298 Woltemade Cross for Bravery

1990. Tourism. Multicoloured.
714 50 c. Type **297** 65 75
715 50 c. Camps Bay, Cape of Good Hope 65 75
716 50 c. Giraffes in Kruger National Park .. 65 75
717 50 c. Boschendal Vineyard, Drakenstein Mts .. 65 65

1990. National Orders. Multicoloured.
718 21 c. Type **298** 25 25
719 21 c. Order of the Southern Cross 25 25
720 21 c. Order of the Star of South Africa .. 25 25
721 21 c. Order for Meritorious Service 25 25
722 21 c. Order of Good Hope 25 25

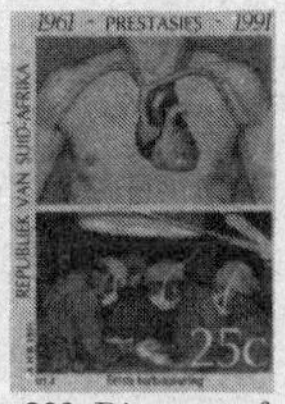

299 Boer Horses

300 Diagram of Human Heart and Transplant Operation

1991. Animal Breeding in South Africa. Mult.
724 21 c. Type **299** .. 30 30
725 21 c. Bonsmara bull .. 30 30
726 21 c. Dorper sheep .. 30 30
727 21 c. Ridgeback dogs .. 30 30
728 21 c. Putterie racing pigeons 30 30

1991. 30th Anniv of Republic. Scientific and Technological Achievements. Mult.
729 25 c. Type **300** 20 10
730 40 c. Matimba Power Station (horiz) 35 35
731 50 c. Dolos design break-water (horiz) 45 45
732 60 c. Western Deep Levels gold mine 60 60

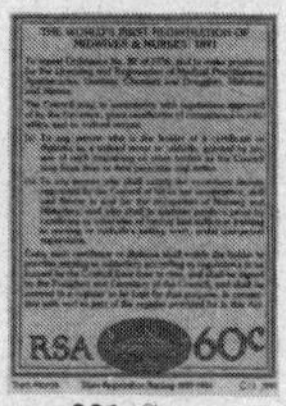

301 State Registration of Nurses Act, 1891

302 South Africa Post Office Ltd Emblem

1991. Centenary of State Registration for Nurses and Midwives.
733 **301** 60 c. multicoloured .. 60 60

1991. Establishment of Post Office Ltd and Telekom Ltd.Multicoloured.
734 27 c. Type **302** 25 25
735 27 c. Telekom SA Ltd emblem 25 25

303 Sir Arnold Theiler (veterinarian)

1991. South African Scientists. Multicoloured.
736 27 c. Type **303** 20 15
737 45 c. Sir Basil Schonland (physicist) 40 40
738 65 c. Dr. Robert Broom (palaeontologist) .. 50 50
739 85 c. Dr. Alex du Toit (geologist) 65 65

304 "Agulhas" (Antarctic research ship)

1991. 30th Anniv of Antarctic Treaty. Mult.
740 27 c. Type **304** 30 10
741 65 c. Chart showing South African National Antarctic Expedition base 80 70

305 Soil Conservation

306 Dutch Fleet approaching Table Bay

1992. Environmental Conservation. Mult.
742 27 c. Type **305** 20 10
743 65 c. Water pollution .. 55 55
744 85 c. Air pollution .. 75 75

1992. National Stamp Day. Cape of Good Hope Postal Stones. Multicoloured.
745 35 c. Type **306** 25 25
746 35 c. Landing for water and provisions 25 25
747 35 c. Discovering a postal stone 25 25
748 35 c. Leaving letters under a stone 25 25
749 35 c. Reading letters .. 25 25

307 Queen Anne Settee, c 1750

1992. Antique Cape Furniture. Multicoloured.
750 35 c. Type **307** 25 25
751 35 c. Stinkwood settee, c 1800 .. .. .. 25 25
752 35 c. Canopy bed, c 1800 (vert) 25 25
753 35 c. 19th-century rocking cradle 25 25
754 35 c. Waterbutt, c 1800 (vert) 25 25
755 35 c. Flemish style cabinet, c 1700 (vert) 25 25
756 35 c. Armoire, c 1780 (vert) 25 25
757 35 c. Late 17th-century church chair (vert) .. 25 25
758 35 c. Tub chair, c 1770 (vert) 25 25
759 35 c. Bible desk, c 1750 (vert) 25 25

308 Grand Prix Motor Racing

309 "Women's Monument" (Van Wouw)

1992. Sports. Multicoloured.
760 35 c. Type **308** 25 25
761 35 c. Football 25 25
762 55 c. Total Paris–Cape Motor Rally 35 35
763 70 c. Athletics 50 50
764 90 c. Rugby 65 65
765 1 r. 05 Cricket .. .. 1·00 1·00

1992. 130th Birth Anniv of Anton van Wouw (sculptor). Multicoloured.
767 35 c. Type **309** 30 20
768 70 c. "Sekupu Player" .. 60 60
769 90 c. "The Hunter" .. 80 80
770 1 r. 05 "Postman Lehman" 85 1·00

310 Walvis Bay Harbour

311 Bristol Boxkite, 1907

1993. South African Harbours. Mutlicoloured.
772 35 c. Type **310** 25 20
773 55 c. East London .. 35 35
774 70 c. Port Elizabeth .. 50 50
775 90 c. Cape Town 70 75
776 1 r. 05 Durban 80 95

1993. Succulents. As T **286**, but inscr "Standardised mail" in English and Afrikaans.
778 (-) "Stapelia grandiflora" 20 25
No. 778 was sold at 45 c.

1993. Aviation in South Africa. Mult.
779 45 c. Type **311** 30 30
780 45 c. Voisin, 1909 .. 30 30
781 45 c. Bleriot XI, 1911 .. 30 30
782 45 c. Paterson No. 2 Biplane, 1913 .. .. 30 30
783 45 c. Henri Farman F 27, 1915 .. .. .. 30 30
784 45 c. BE 2e, 1918 .. .. 30 30
785 45 c. Vickers Vimy "Silver Queen", 1920 .. .. 30 30
786 45 c. SE-5a, 1921 .. .. 30 30
787 45 c. Avro 504k, 1921 .. 30 30
788 45 c. Armstrong-Whitworth Atalanta, 1930 .. .. .. 30 30
789 45 c. DH66 Hercules, 1931 30 30
790 45 c. Westland Wapiti, 1931 .. .. .. 30 30
791 45 c. Junkers F 13, 1932 .. 30 30
792 45 c. Handley Page HP-42, 1933 .. .. .. 30 30
793 45 c. Junkers Ju52/3m, 1934 30 30
794 45 c. Junkers Ju86, 1936 .. 30 30
795 45 c. Hawker Hartbees, 1936 .. .. .. 30 30
796 45 c. Short Empire flying boat "Canopus", 1937 .. 30 30
797 45 c. Miles Master II and Airspeed AS-10 Oxford, 1940 .. .. .. 30 30
798 45 c. Harvard Mk IIa, 1942 30 30
799 45 c. Short Sunderland flying boat, 1945 .. 30 30
800 45 c. Avro York, 1946 .. 30 30
801 45 c. Douglas DC-7B, 1955 30 30
802 45 c. Sikorsky S-55c helicopter, 1956 .. 30 30
803 45 c. Boeing 707-344, 1959 30 30

312 Table Mountain Ghost (frog)

313 Dragoons carrying Mail between Cape Town and False Bay, 1803

1993. Endangered Fauna. Multicoloured.
(a) Face values as T **312**.
804 1 c. Type **312** 10 10
805 2 c. Smith's dwarf chameleon 10 10
806 5 c. Giant girdle-tailed lizard 10 10
807 10 c. Geometric tortoise .. 10 10
808 20 c. African hedgehog .. 10 10
809 40 c. Riverine rabbit .. 15 20
810 50 c. Samango monkey .. 20 25
811 55 c. Aardwolf 20 25
812 60 c. Cape hunting dog .. 25 30
813 70 c. Roan antelope .. 30 35
814 75 c. African striped weasel 30 35
815 80 c. Kori bustard .. 35 40
816 90 c. Jackass penguin .. 35 40
817 1 r. Wattled crane .. 40 45
818 2 r. Blue swallow .. 80 85
819 5 r. Martial eagle .. 2·00 2·10
820 10 r. Bateleur .. .. 4·00 4·00

(b) Inscr "Standardised mail" in Afrikaans and English

821 (-) Black rhinoceros .. 20 25

No. 821 was initially sold at 45 c., but it is intended that this will be increased to reflect future postage rates.

1993. National Stamp Day. Early 19th-century Postal Services. Multicoloured.

822 45 c. Type **313** 30 25
823 65 c. Ox wagon carrying Stellenbosch to Cape Town mail, 1803 .. 45 50
824 85 c. Khoi-Khoin mail runners from Stellenbosch, 1803 .. 65 70
825 1 r. 05 Mounted postmen, 1804 .. .. .. 80 90

314 Flowers from Namaqualand

1993. Tourism. Multicoloured.

826 85 c. Type **314** (Afrikaans inscr) 55 55
827 85 c. North Beach, Durban (English inscr) 55 55
828 85 c. Lion (German inscr) 55 55
829 85 c. Apple Express excursion train (Dutch inscr) 55 55
830 85 c. Gemsbok (antelope) (French inscr) 55 55

315 Grapes and Packing Bench

1994. Export Fruits. Multicoloured.

831 85 c. Type **315** 35 40
832 90 c. Apple and picker .. 35 40
833 1 r. 05 Plum and fork-lift truck 40 45
834 1 r. 25 Orange and tractor with trailer 50 55
835 1 r. 40 Avocado and loading freighter .. 55 60

POSTAGE DUE STAMPS

D 6.

D 8.

1961. (A) Inscr. as in Type D **6**; (B) English at top and left, Afrikans at bottom and right.

D59 D **6** 1 c. black and red (A) 20 55
D60 1 c. black and red (B) 20 30
D61 2 c. blk. & vio. (A) 30 85
D53 2 c. black & violet (B) 40 55
D54 4 c. myrtle & grn. (A) .. .. 3·00 2·00
D54a 4 c. myrtle & grn. (B) 8·00 11·00
D63 4 c. blk. & grn. (A) 17·00 20·00
D64 4 c. blk. & grn. (B) 17·00 20·00
D55 5 c. indigo & blue (B) 2·25 3·00
D65 5 c. blk. & bl. (A) .. 50 50
D66 5 c. black & blue (B) 50 50
D67 6 c. grn. & salmon (A) .. .. 3·50 7·00
D68 6 c. grn. & salmon (B) 3·50 7·00
D58 10 c. sepia and purple-brown (B) 3·50 2·25
D69 10 c. black and purple-brown (A) 1·00 2·75
D70 10 c. black & purple-brown (B) .. 1·00 2·75

1972.

D 75. D **8.** 1 c. green .. .. 50 1·75
D 76. 2 c. orange .. .. 70 2·00
D 77. 4 c. plum .. .. 1·50 2·50
D 78. 6 c. yellow .. .. 1·75 3·50
D 79. 8 c. blue .. .. 2·00 4·50
D 80. 10 c. red .. .. 4·00 6·00

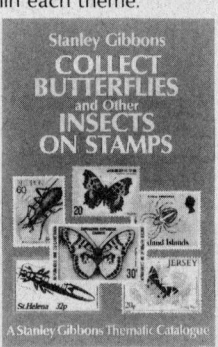

SOUTH KASAI Pt. 14

100 centimes = 1 franc.

Region of Zaire around the town of Bakwanga. The area was declared autonomous in 1960, during the upheaval following independence, but returned to the control of the central government in Oct. 1962.

Various stamps of Belgian Congo were overprinted "ETAT AUTONOME DU SUD-KASAI" and some surcharged in addition with new values. These were put on sale at the Philatelic Bureau in Brussels and were also valid for use in South Kasai but no supplies were sent out.

1. Leopard's Head and "V". 2. A. D. Kalonji.

1961.
1. 1. 1 f. multicoloured 8 8
2. 1 f. 50 multicoloured .. 10 10
3. 3 f. 50 multicoloured .. 15 15
4. 8 f. multicoloured 25 25
5. 10 f. multicoloured 30 30

1961.
6. 2. 6 f. 50 brown, blue & black 20 20
7. 9 f. light brn., brn. & blk. 25 25
8. 14 f. 50 brown, grn. & blk. 40 40
9. 20 f. multicoloured .. 45 1·45

SOUTH RUSSIA Pt. 10

Stamps of various anti-Bolshevist forces and temporary governments in S. Russia after the revolution.

100 kopeks = 1 rouble.

A. KUBAN TERRITORY: COSSACK GOVERNMENT.

1918. Arms type of Russia surch Imperf or perf.
8 22 25 k. on 1 k. orange .. 25 45
2 50 k. on 2 k. green .. 15 25
23 70 k. on 1 k. orange .. 30 55
10 70 k. on 5 k. red .. 35 60
11 1 r. on 3 k. red .. 20 50
13 23 3 r. on 4 k. red .. 7·50 11·00
14 10 r. on 4 k. red .. 4·00 5·00
15 10 10 r. on 15 k. blue & pur 70 1·10
16 22 25 r. on 3 k. red .. 4·00 3·00
17 25 r. on 7 k. blue .. 30·00 60·00
18 10 25 r. on 14 k. red & blue 70·00 £100
19 25 r. on 25 k. mve & grn 35·00 65·00

1919. Postal Savings Bank stamps of Russia surch.
20. 10 r. on 1 k. red on buff .. 30·00 70·00
21. 10 r. on 5 k. green on buff .. 32·00 70·00
22. 10 r. on 10 k. brown on buff 75·00 £225

B. DON TERRITORY: COSSACK GOVERNMENT.

1919. Arms type of Russia surch. in figures only. Imperf. or perf.
25. 22. 25 k. on 1 k. orange .. 20 45
29. 25 k. on 2 k. green .. 20 40
30. 25 k. on 3 k. red .. 25 60
31. 23. 25 k. on 4 k. red .. 20 45
32. 22. 50 k. on 7 k. blue .. 1·75 2·75

10. T. Ermak (16th century Cossack Ataman). 13.

1919. Currency stamp with arms and seven-line imprint on back used for postage.
33. 10. 20 k. green .. .. 16·00 £100

C. CRIMEA: REGIONAL GOVERNMENT.

1919. Arms type of Russia surch. **35 Kon.** Imperf.
34. 22. 35 k. on 1 k. orange .. 15 40

1919. Currency and postage stamp. Arms and inscription on back. Imperf.
35. 13. 50 k. brown on buff .. 13·00 16·00

D. SOUTH RUSSIA: GOVERNMENT OF GENERAL DENIKIN.

1919. Nos. G6 and G10 of Ukraine surch. in figs.
36. G 1. 35 k. on 10 s. brown .. 3·75 14·00
37. G 5. 70 k. on 50 s. red .. 13·00 40·00

15. 16.

1919. Imperf. or perf.
38. 15. 5 k. yellow 10 15
39. 10 k. green 10 15
40. 15 k. red 10 15
41. 35 k. blue 10 15
42. 70 k. blue 10 15
43. 16. 1 r. red and brown .. 15 35
44. 2 r. yellow and lilac .. 35 55
45. 3 r. green and brown .. 35 60
46. 5 r. violet and blue .. 1·00 1·50
47. 7 r. pink and green .. 80 1·75
48. 10 r. grey and red .. 1·50 2·00
Higher values similar to Type 16 are bogus

E. SOUTH RUSSIA: GOVERNMENT OF GENERAL WRANGEL.

5 пять рублей. (17.)

ЮГЪ РОССIИ. 100 рублей. (18.)

1920. Crimea issue. Surch. with T 17.
(a) On Arms types of Russia. Imperf. or perf.
52. 22. 5 r. on 5 k. red .. 1·00 3·75
54. 14. 5 r. on 20 k. red and blue 1·75 3·75
(b) On No. 41 of South Russia.
55. 15. 5 r. on 35 k. blue .. 4·50 12·00

1920. Arms type of Russia surch. with T 18. Imperf. or perf.
56. 22. 100 r. on 1 k. orange .. 1·75

SOUTHERN YEMEN Pt. 19

PEOPLE'S REPUBLIC

Independent Republic comprising the areas formerly known as Aden, the Aden States and the South Arabian Federation.

From 30 November, 1970, the country was renamed The Peoples Democratic Republic of Yemen.

1968. 1000 fils = 1 dinar.

1968. Stamps of South Arabian Federation optd. **PEOPLE'S REPUBLIC OF SOUTHERN YEMEN** in English and Arabic, in four lines (Nos. 1/10) or three lines (Nos. 11/14) and bold bar.
1. 2. 5 f. blue 10 10
2. 10 f. lavender 10 10
3. 15 f. green 10 10
4. 20 f. green 15 10
5. 25 f. brown 15 10
6. 30 f. bistre 20 10
7. 35 f. brown 25 20
8. 50 f. red 30 25
9. 65 f. green 35 30
10. 75 f. red 45 35
11. 3. 100 f. multicoloured .. 60 40
12. 250 f. multicoloured .. 1·40 90
13. 500 f. multicoloured .. 2·50 1·90
14. 1 d. multicoloured .. 6·50 4·00

3. National Flag across Globe.

1968. Independence. Multicoloured.
15. 10 f. Type 3 .. .. 10 10
16. 15 f. Revolutionary (vert.) 10 10
17. 50 f. Aden harbour .. 30 30
18. 100f. Cotton-picking .. 70 60

4. Girl Guides.

1968. Aden Girl Guides' Movement.
19 – 10 f. brown and blue .. 20 10
20 – 25 f. blue and brown .. 35 15
21 4 50 f. blue, brown & yellow 70 40
DESIGNS—HORIZ. 10 f. Guides around campfire. VERT. 25 f. Brownies.

5. Revolutionary Soldier.

1968. Revolution Day.
22. 5. 20 f. brown and blue .. 20 15
23. – 30 f. brown and green .. 25 20
24. – 100 f. red and yellow .. 75 60
DESIGNS—HORIZ. 30 f. Radfan Mountains ("where first martyr fell"). VERT. 100 f. Open book and torch ("Freedom, Socialism and Unity").

6. Sculptured Plaque ("Assyrian influence").

1968. Antiquities.
25 – 5 f. yellow and green .. 10 10
26 – 35 f. blue and purple .. 30 20
27 6 50 f. buff and blue .. 50 30
28 – 65 f. green and purple .. 60 45
DESIGNS—VERT. 5 f. King Yusdqil Far'am of Ausan (statue). 35 f. Sculptured figure ("African-inspired"). HORIZ. 65 f. Bull's head ("Moon God").

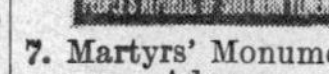

7. Martyrs' Monument, Aden. 8. Albert Thomas Memorial, Geneva.

1969. Martyrs' Day.
29. 7. 15 f. multicoloured .. 10 10
30. 35 f. multicoloured .. 25 20
31. 100 f. multicoloured .. 60 45

1969. 50th Anniv. of I.L.O.
32. 8. 10 f. sepia, black and green 10 10
33. 25 f. sepia, black & mauve 25 20

9. Teacher and Class.

1969. Int. Literacy Day.
34. 9. 35 f. multicoloured .. 30 25
35. 100 f. multicoloured .. 65 50

10. Mahatma Gandhi. 11. Yemeni Family.

1969. Birth Cent. of Mahatma Gandhi.
36. 10. 35 f. purple and blue .. 1·00 35

1969. Family Day.
37. 11. 25 f. multicoloured .. 25 15
38. 75 f. multicoloured .. 60 45

12. U.N. Headquarters, New York.

1969. United Nations Day.
39. 12. 20 f. multicoloured .. 15 10
40. 65 f. multicoloured .. 50 35

13. Map and Flag.

1969. 2nd Anniv. of Independence. Mult.
41. 15 f. Type 13 .. .. 12 10
42. 35 f. Type 13 .. .. 25 20
43. 40 f. Bulldozers 30 25
44. 50 f. As No. 43 .. .. 35 30

14. Arab League Flag, Emblem and Map.

1970. 25th Anniv of Arab League.
45. 14. 35 f. multicoloured .. 25 25

15. Lenin. 16. Palestinian Guerrilla.

1970. Birth Cent. of Lenin.
46. 15. 75 f. multicoloured .. 70 50

1970. Palestine Day. Multicoloured.
47 15 f. Type 16 .. .. 25 10
48 35 f. Guerrilla and attack on aircraft 90 30
49 50 f. Guerrillas and Palestinian flag (horiz) .. 85 40

17. New Headquarters Building, Berne.

1970. Inauguration of New U.P.U. Headquarters Building, Berne.
50. 17. 15 f. green and orange .. 15 10
51. 65 f. red and buff .. 40 30

18. Girl with Pitcher.

1970. National Costumes. Multicoloured.
52. 10 f. Type 18 .. .. 25 10
53. 15 f. Woman in veil .. 35 15
54. 20 f. Girl in burnous .. 45 15
55. 50 f. Three Yemeni men .. 75 30

19. Dromedary and Calf.

1970. Fauna. Multicoloured.
56. 15 f. Type 19 .. .. 25 20
57. 25 f. Goats 40 30
58. 35 f. Arabian oryx and kid 75 60
59. 65 f. Socotran dwarf cows .. 1·00 85

20. Torch and Flags.

1970. 7th Revolution Day. Multicoloured.
60. 25 f. Type 20 .. .. 20 15
61. 35 f. National Front H.Q. (57×27 mm). .. 40 30
62. 50 f. Farmer and soldier (42×25 mm.) .. 50 40

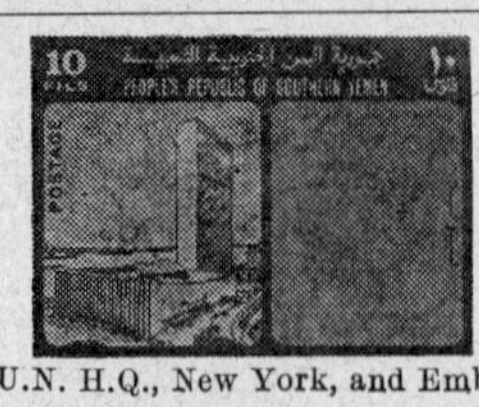

21. U.N. H.Q., New York, and Emblem.

1970. 25th Anniv. of United Nations.

63.	**21.**	10 f. orange and blue ..	10	10
64.		65 f. red and blue ..	50	40

For later issues see **YEMEN PEOPLE'S DEMOCRATIC REPUBLIC.**

SPAIN — Pt. 9

A kingdom in S.W. Europe; a republic between 1873 and 1874, and from 1931 until 1939.

1850. 8½ (later 8) cuartos = 1 real.
1866. 80 cuartos = 100 centimos de escudo = 1 escudo.
1867. 1000 milesimas = 100 centimos de escudo = 80 cuartos = 1 escudo.
1872. 100 centimos = 1 peseta.

1. 2. 3. Queen Isabella II.

1850. Imperf.

2.	**1.**	6 c. black ..	£225	15·00
3.		12 c. lilac ..	£1500	£180
4.	**2.**	5 r. red ..	£1200	£180
5.		6 r. blue ..	£2000	£550
6.		10 r. green ..	£2750	£1300

1851. Imperf.

9.	**3.**	6 c. black ..	£150	2·50
10.		12 c. lilac ..	£2000	£130
11.		2 r. red ..	£9000	£5000
12.		5 r. red ..	£1500	£160
13.		6 r. blue ..	£2250	£650
14.		10 r. green ..	£1800	£350

4. 5. 7. Arms of Castile and Leon.

1852. Imperf.

16.	**4.**	6 c. red ..	£200	9·00
17.		12 c. purple ..	£1200	£100
18.		2 r. red ..	£8000	£3000
19.		5 r. green ..	£1200	95·00
20.		6 r. blue ..	£2250	£350

1853. Imperf.

22.	**5.**	6 c. red ..	£225	1·50
23.		12 c. purple ..	£1100	85·00
24.		2 r. orange ..	£7500	£2500
25.		5 r. green ..	£1000	85·00
26.		6 r. blue ..	£1800	£300

1854. Imperf.

32.	**7.**	2 c. green ..	£1200	£300
33.		4 c. red ..	£180	1·50
34.		6 c. red ..	£180	1·40
35.		1 r. blue ..	£1600	£200
36.		2 r. orange ..	£750	80·00
37.		5 r. green ..	£800	80·00
38.		6 r. blue ..	£1200	£200

9. 12. 13.

1855. Imperf.

58.	**9.**	2 c. green ..	£250	25·00
55a.		4 c. red ..	3·50	30
56.		1 r. blue ..	14·00	9·00
62.		2 r. purple ..	42·00	15·00

1860. Imperf.

63.	**12.**	2 c. green on green ..	£200	14·00
64.		4 c. orange on green ..	25·00	60
65.		12 c. red on buff ..	£200	10·00
66.		19 c. brown on brown ..	£1500	£850
67.		1 r. blue on green ..	£110	7·00
68.		2 r. lilac on lilac ..	£180	6·50

1862. Imperf.

69.	**13.**	2 c. blue on yellow ..	24·00	9·00
70.		4 c. brown on brown ..	1·50	45
71.		12 c. blue on red ..	30·00	8·00
72.		19 c. red on lilac ..	£110	£130
73a.		1 r. brown on yellow ..	35·00	16·00
74.		2 r. green on red ..	23·00	10·00

14. 15. 16.

1864. Imperf.

75.	**14.**	2 c. blue on lilac ..	30·00	12·00
76.		4 c. red on red ..	1·75	60
77.		12 c. green on red ..	30·00	10·00
78.		19 c. lilac on lilac ..	£120	£140
79.		1 r. brown on green ..	£110	60·00
80.		2 r. blue on red ..	30·00	9·00

1865. Imperf.

81	15	2 c. red ..	£160	19·00
82		12 c. red and blue ..	£250	17·00
83		19 c. red and brown ..	£900	£425
84		1 r. green ..	£225	45·00
85		2 r. mauve ..	£220	28·00
85b		2 r. red ..	£275	50·00
85e		2 r. yellow ..	£250	40·00

1865. Perf.

86	15	2 c. red ..	£275	65·00
87		4 c. blue ..	30·00	75
88		12 c. red and blue ..	£350	40·00
89		19 c. red and brown ..	£2250	£1400
90		1 r. green ..	£1000	£275
91		2 r. purple ..	£650	£150
91b		2 r. orange ..	£650	£175

1866. Perf.

92	16	2 c. red ..	£140	15·00
93		4 c. blue ..	25·00	70
94a		12 c. orange ..	£130	10·00
95		19 c. brown ..	£550	£250
96a		10 c. de esc. green ..	£175	16·00
97		20 c. de esc. lilac ..	£130	14·00

1866. As T 14, but dated 1866, and perf.

98		20 c. de esc. lilac ..	£550	40·00

19. 25. 26.

1867. Inscr "CORREOS DE ESPANA". Various frames.

99a	19	2 c. brown ..	£225	24·00
100		4 c. blue ..	20·00	70
101a		12 c. orange ..	£130	5·00
102		19 c. red ..	£750	£250
150		19 c. brown ..	£1300	£400
103		10 c. de esc. green ..	£140	15·00
104		20 c. de esc. lilac ..	65·00	6·00

1867. Various frames.

105.	**25.**	5 m. green ..	26·00	9·00
106.		10 m. brown ..	26·00	7·50
107.	**26.**	25 m. red and blue ..	£140	15·00
145.		25 m. blue ..	£190	12·00
108.		50 m. brown ..	14·00	60
146a.		50 m. purple ..	17·00	50
147.		100 m. brown ..	£300	45·00
148.		200 m. green ..	£120	9·00

1868. Various stamps optd **HABILITADO POR LA NACION**.

109	25	5 m. green ..	16·00	5·00
118		10 m. browm ..	12·00	5·50
111	26	25 m. red and blue ..	35·00	12·00
151		25 m. blue ..	26·00	9·00
112		50 m. brown ..	6·50	4·50
152		50 m. purple ..	7·00	3·50
153		100 m. brown ..	75·00	25·00
154		200 m. green ..	24·00	8·00
113	19	10 c. de esc. green ..	24·00	10·00
114		20 c. de esc. lilac ..	27·00	7·50
125		12 c. orange ..	32·00	10·00
116		19 c. red ..	£350	£150
156		19 c. brown ..	£650	£170

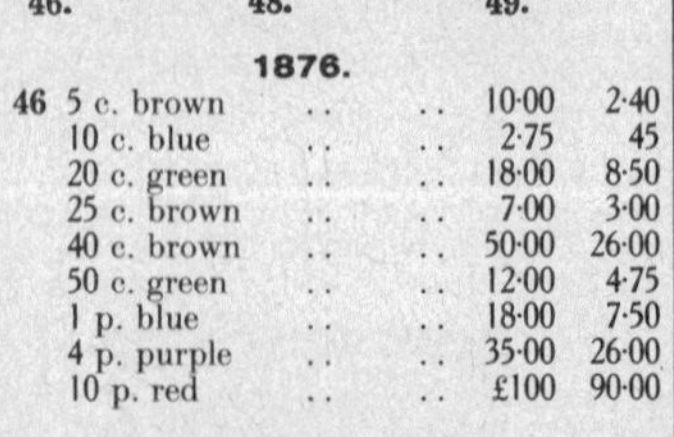

36. 38a. 38.

1870.

172	36	1 m. brown on buff ..	7·00	6·00
173		2 m. black on buff ..	8·00	7·50
174		4 m. brown ..	15·00	12·00
175		10 m. red ..	18·00	5·50
176		25 m. mauve ..	40·00	7·00
177		50 m. blue ..	11·00	45
178		100 m. brown ..	27·00	6·00
179		200 m. brown ..	27·00	6·00
180		400 m. green ..	£180	22·00
181		12 c. red ..	£180	6·50
182		19 c. green ..	£275	£160
183		1 esc. 600 m. lilac ..	£800	£400
184		2 esc. blue ..	£650	£225

1872.

185	38a	¼ c. blue ..	2·00	2·00
186	38	¼ c. green ..	1·10	1·10
187	38a	¼ c. green ..	15	10

1872. As T 25, but currency in centavos de peseta.

192.	**25.**	2 c. lilac ..	20·00	8·50
193.		5 c. green ..	£110	45·00

40. King Amadeo. 41. 42. Allegorical Figure of Peace.

1872.

194.	**40.**	5 c. red ..	20·00	6·00
195b.		6 c. blue ..	£100	18·00
196.		10 c. lilac ..	£225	90·00
197.		10 c. blue ..	6·50	45
199.		12 c. lilac ..	14·00	1·75
200.		20 c. lilac ..	85·00	30·00
201.		25 c. brown ..	35·00	7·00
202.		40 c. brown ..	60·00	7·00
203a.		50 c. green ..	85·00	7·00
204.	**41.**	1 p. lilac ..	80·00	25·00
205.		4 p. brown ..	£400	£275
206.		10 p. green ..	£1200	£950

1873.

207.	**42.**	2 c. orange ..	13·00	6·00
208.		5 c. red ..	32·00	6·00
209.		10 c. green ..	8·00	45
210.		20 c. black ..	75·00	20·00
211.		25 c. brown ..	28·00	7·00
212.		40 c. purple ..	32·00	7·50
213.		50 c. blue ..	12·00	7·50
214.		1 p. lilac ..	42·00	17·00
215.		4 p. brown ..	£450	£275
216.		10 p. purple ..	£1300	£1000

43. Allegorical Figure of Justice. 44. 45. King Alfonso XII.

1874.

217.	**43.**	2 c. yellow ..	23·00	8·00
218a.		5 c. mauve ..	32·00	6·50
219.		10 c. blue ..	10·00	40
220.		20 c. green ..	£120	35·00
221.		25 c. brown ..	35·00	7·50
222a.		40 c. mauve ..	£275	9·00
223.		50 c. orange ..	80·00	9·00
224.		1 p. green ..	65·00	18·00
225.		4 p. red ..	£400	£250
226.		10 p. black ..	£1800	£1100

1874.

227.	**44.**	10 c. brown ..	18·00	90

1875.

228.	**45.**	2 c. brown ..	18·00	6·50
229.		5 c. lilac ..	45·00	8·50
230.		10 c. blue ..	8·00	45
231.		20 c. orange ..	£200	60·00
232.		25 c. red ..	40·00	6·50
233.		40 c. brown ..	80·00	30·00
234.		50 c. mauve ..	£110	21·00
235.		1 p. black ..	£140	40·00
236.		4 p. green ..	£275	£190
237.		10 p. blue ..	£900	£750

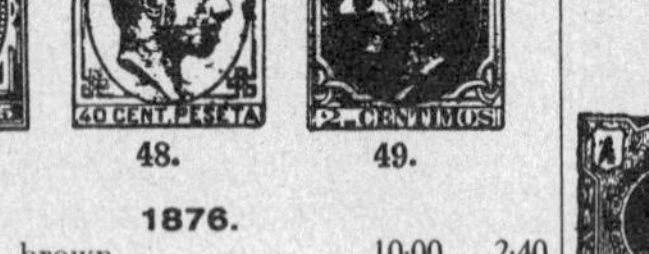

46. 48. 49.

1876.

238	46	5 c. brown ..	10·00	2·40
239		10 c. blue ..	2·75	45
240		20 c. green ..	18·00	8·50
241		25 c. brown ..	7·00	3·00
242		40 c. brown ..	50·00	26·00
243		50 c. green ..	12·00	4·75
244		1 p. blue ..	18·00	7·50
245		4 p. purple ..	35·00	26·00
246		10 p. red ..	£100	90·00

1878.

253.	**48.**	2 c. mauve ..	20·00	7·50
254.		5 c. yellow ..	32·00	7·50
255.		10 c. brown ..	7·00	40
256.		20 c. black ..	£100	70·00
257.		25 c. olive ..	20·00	1·75
258.		40 c. brown ..	£120	80·00
259.		50 c. green ..	70·00	7·50
260.		1 p. grey ..	60·00	18·00
261.		4 p. violet ..	£120	70·00
262.		10 p. blue ..	£225	£200

1879.

263	49	2 c. black ..	5·00	50
264		5 c. green ..	10·00	95
265		10 c. pink ..	9·50	40
266		20 c. brown ..	85·00	12·00
267		25 c. lilac ..	11·00	40
268		40 c. brown ..	23·00	4·25
269		50 c. yellow ..	75·00	4·25
270		1 p. red ..	75·00	1·90
271		4 p. grey ..	£325	23·00
272		10 p. bistre ..	£1000	£180

50. 51. King Alfonso XIII. 52.

1882.

273.	**50.**	15 c. pink ..	7·50	30
273b.		15 c. yellow ..	22·00	70
274.		30 c. mauve ..	£180	5·50
275.		75 c. violet ..	£180	5·50

1889.

276.	**51.**	2 c. green ..	4·25	30
289.		2 c. black ..	20·00	3·50
277.		5 c. blue ..	7·00	15
290.		5 c. green ..	60·00	1·00
278.		10 c. brown ..	10·00	15
291.		10 c. red ..	£140	3·25
279.		15 c. brown ..	3·00	15
280.		20 c. green ..	27·00	3·00
281.		25 c. blue ..	9·00	15
282.		30 c. grey ..	45·00	2·00
283.		40 c. brown ..	42·00	1·90
284.		50 c. red ..	42·00	1·00
285.		75 c. orange ..	95·00	2·10
286.		1 p. purple ..	32·00	30
287.		4 p. red ..	£375	21·00
288.		10 p. red ..	£550	50·00

For 15 c. yellow see No. O 289.

1900.

292a	52	2 c. brown ..	2·40	15
293		5 c. green ..	5·00	15
294		10 c. red ..	7·00	15
295		15 c. black ..	13·00	15
296		15 c. mauve ..	10·00	15
297		15 c. violet ..	4·75	15
298		20 c. black ..	24·00	85
299		25 c. blue ..	4·50	15
300		30 c. green ..	26·00	30
301		40 c. bistre ..	80·00	3·00
302		40 c. pink ..	£170	1·50
303		50 c. blue ..	27·00	30
304		1 p. purple ..	25·00	30
305		4 p. purple ..	£170	11·00
306		10 p. orange ..	£160	45·00

54. Quixote setting out.

1905. Tercentenary of Publication of Cervantes' "Don Quixote".

307.	**54.**	5 c. green ..	1·00	70
308.	–	10 c. red ..	2·00	1·00
309.	–	15 c. violet ..	2·00	1·00
310.	–	25 c. blue ..	5·00	1·25
311.	–	30 c. green ..	30·00	5·50
312.	–	40 c. red ..	65·00	15·00
313.	–	50 c. grey ..	14·00	4·00
314.	–	1 p. red ..	£200	55·00
315.	–	4 p. violet ..	80·00	55·00
316.	–	10 p. orange ..	£130	85·00

DESIGNS: 10 c. Quixote attacking windmill. 15 c. Meeting country girls. 25 c. Sancho Panza tossed in a blanket. 30 c. Don Quixote knighted by innkeeper. 40 c. Tilting at the flock of sheep. 50 c. On the wooden horse. 1 p. Adventure with lions. 4 p. In the bullock-cart. 10 p. The enchanted lady.

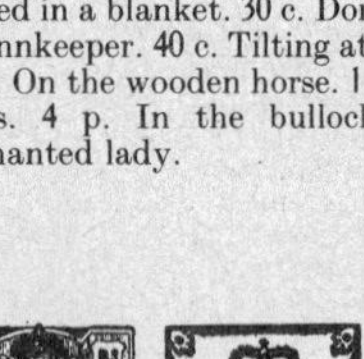

64. 66. 67. G.P.O., Madrid.

1909.

329	64	2 c. brown ..	40	10
330		5 c. green ..	1·10	10
331		10 c. red ..	1·40	10
332		15 c. violet ..	7·00	10
343		15 c. yellow ..	3·50	10
321		20 c. green ..	27·00	7·00
335		20 c. violet ..	27·00	10
336		25 c. blue ..	2·75	10
337		30 c. green ..	7·00	10
338		40 c. pink ..	11·00	20
339		50 c. blue ..	9·00	15
340		1 p. red ..	24·00	20
341		4 p. purple ..	65·00	6·00
342		10 p. orange ..	75·00	12·00

1920. Air. Optd. **CORREO AEREO.**

353.	**64.**	5 c. green ..	1·00	50
354.		10 c. red ..	1·50	70
355.		25 c. blue ..	2·00	90
356.		50 c. blue ..	10·00	3·50
357.		1 p. red ..	30·00	14·00

1920. Imperf.

358.	**66.**	1 c. green ..	20	10

1920. U.P.U. Congress, Madrid.
361. 67. 1 c. black and blue 20 10
362. 2 c. black and brown 20 10
363. 5 c. black and green 80 70
364. 10 c. black and red 80 60
365. 15 c. black and yellow 1·25 90
366. 20 c. black and violet 1·75 90
367. 25 c. black and blue 1·90 1·90
368. 30 c. black and green 5·00 3·00
369. 40 c. black and red 20·00 4·50
370. 50 c. black and blue 23·00 15·00
371. 1 p. black and red 25·00 12·00
372. 4 p. black and brown 75·00 50·00
373. 10 p. black and orange £150 £100

68. 69.

1922.
374 68 2 c. green 35 10
375 5 c. purple 3·25 10
376 5 c. red 1·50 10
377 10 c. red 1·50 60
378a 10 c. green 1·50 10
380 15 c. blue 6·00 10
382 20 c. violet 3·00 10
383a 25 c. red 3·00 10
387 30 c. brown 9·00 15
388 40 c. blue 3·50 10
389 50 c. orange 14·00 10
391 69 1 p. grey 13·00 10
392 4 p. red 55·00 3·00
393 10 p. brown 25·00 9·00

70. Princesses Maria Cristina and Beatriz. 71. King Alfonso XIII.

1926. Red Cross.
394. 70. 1 c. black 1·50 1·00
395. – 2 c. blue 1·50 1·00
396. – 5 c. purple 3·00 2·00
397. – 10 c. green 3·00 2·00
398. 70. 15 c. blue 1·00 85
399. – 20 c. violet 1·00 85
400. 71. 25 c. red 25 20
401. 70. 30 c. green 24·00 22·00
402. – 40 c. blue 15·00 12·00
403. – 50 c. orange 5·00 12·00
404. – 1 p. grey 1·00 50
405. – 4 p. red 50 50
406. 71. 10 p. brown 75 75
DESIGNS—VERT. 2 c., 50 c. Queen Victoria Eugenie as nurse. 5 c., 40 c., 4 p. Queen Victoria Eugenie. 10 c., 20 c., 1 p. Prince of Asturias.

75. Dornier WAL Flying-boat.

76. Route Map and Breguet 19 A2 Aircraft.

1926. Air. Red Cross and Trans-Atlantic and Madrid–Manila Flights.
407. 75. 5 c. violet and black 1·50 1·75
408. 10 c. black and blue 1·50 1·75
409. 76. 15 c. blue and orange 20 15
410. 20 c. red and green 20 15
411. 75. 25 c. black and red 20 15
412. 76. 30 c. brown and blue 20 15
413. 40 c. green and brown 20 15
414. 75. 50 c. black and red 20 15
415. 1 p. green and black 2·25 1·75
416. 76. 4 p. red and yellow 60·00 50·00

1927. 25th Anniv. of Coronation. Red Cross stamps of 1926 optd. either **17-V 1902 17-V 1927 A XIII**, or same dates and **ALFONSO XIII** and laurel wreath.
417. 70. 1 c. black 3·50 3·00
418. – 2 c. blue 6·00 4·75
419. – 5 c. purple 1·50 1·50
420. – 10 c. green 40·00 38·00
421. 70. 15 c. blue 1·25 1·00
422. – 20 c. violet 2·25 1·90
423. 71. 25 c. red 35 30
424. 70. 30 c. green 70 60
425. – 40 c. blue 70 55
426. – 50 c. orange 70 55
427. – 1 p. grey 1·10 1·00
428. – 4 p. red 6·00 5·00
429. 71. 10 p. brown 25·00 25·00

1927. Red Cross stamps of 1926 optd. **17-V-1902 17-V-1927 ALFONSO XIII** and surch. also.
430. – 3 c. on 2 c. blue 7·00 6·50
431. – 4 c. on 2 c. blue 7·00 6·50
432. 71. 10 c. on 25 c. red 35 15
433. 25 c. on 25 c. red 35 15
434. – 55 c. on 2 c. blue 70 60
435. – 55 c. on 10 c. green 45·00 42·00
436. – 55 c. on 20 c. violet 45·00 42·00
437. 70. 75 c. on 15 c. blue 25 25
438. 75 c. on 30 c. green £130 £125
439. – 80 c. on 5 c. purple 40·00 32·00
440. – 2 p. on 40 c. blue 55 45
441. – 2 p. on 1 p. grey 55 45
442. – 5 p. on 50 c. orange 1·40 1·00
443. – 5 p. on 4 p. red 2·25 1·50
444. 71. 10 p. on 10 p. brown 20·00 20·00

1927. Red Cross Air stamps of 1926 optd. either **17-V-1902 17-V-1927 A XIII**, or **17 MAYO 17 1902 1927 ALFONSO XIII.**
445. 75. 5 c. violet and black 1·50 1·50
446. 10 c. black and blue 1·50 1·50
447. 76. 15 c. blue and orange 40 40
448. 20 c. red and green 40 40
449. 75. 25 c. black and red 40 40
450. 76. 30 c. brown and blue 40 40
451. 40 c. green and brown 40 40
452. 75. 50 c. black and red 40 40
453. 1 p. green and black 2·00 2·25
454. 76. 4 p. red and yellow 80·00 70·00

1927. Red Cross Air stamps optd. as last and surch. **75 CTS. 75.**
455. 75. 75 c. on 5 c. vio. & blk. 3·50 2·50
456. 75 c. on 10 c. blk. & bl. 15·00 11·00
457. 75 c. on 25 c. blk. & red 30·00 25·00
458. 75 c. on 50 c. blk. & red 13·00 11·00

1927. Red Cross stamps of Spanish Morocco and Nos. 24/5 of Spanish P.Os. in Tangier optd as above or surch also.
462 – 55 c. on 4 p. brown (122) 10·00 10·00
463 71 80 c. on 10 p. lilac (123) 10·00 10·00
460 1 p. on 10 p. lilac (25) 35·00 38·00
461 – 4 p. brown (No. 24) 15·00 12·00

1927. Red Cross stamps of Cape Juby surch. and optd. as above.
464. – 5 p. on 4 p. brown (34) 28·00 30·00
465. 71. 10 p. on 10 p. lilac (35) 18·00 18·00

1927. Red Cross stamps of Spanish Guinea surch. and optd. as above.
466. 71. 1 p. on 10 p. lilac (232) 9·00 9·00
467. – 2 p. on 4 p. brown (231) 9·00 9·00

1927. Red Cross stamps of Spanish Sahara surch. and optd. as above.
468. 71. 80 c. on 10 p. lilac (24) 14·00 14·00
469. – 2 p. on 4 p. brown (23) 10·00 9·00

82. Pope Pius XI and King Alfonso XIII.

1928. Rome Catacombs Restoration Fund.
470 82 2 c. black and violet 20 20
471 2 c. black and purple 35 30
486 2 c. red and black 25 20
487 2 c. red and blue 35 30
472 3 c. violet and black 20 20
473 3 c. violet and blue 35 30
488 3 c. blue and bistre 20 20
489 3 c. blue and green 35 30
474 5 c. violet and green 70 35
490 5 c. red and purple 70 35
475 10 c. black and green 1·10 85
491 10 c. blue and green 1·10 85
476 15 c. violet and green 4·00 3·50
492 15 c. red and blue 4·00 3·50
477 25 c. violet and red 4·00 3·50
493 25 c. blue and brown 4·00 3·50
478 40 c. black and blue 15 15
494 40 c. red and blue 15 15
479 55 c. violet and brown 15 15
495 55 c. blue and brown 15 15
480 80 c. black and red 15 15
496 80 c. red and black 15 15
481 1 p. violet and grey 15 15
497 1 p. red and yellow 15 15
482 2 p. black and brown 4·50 4·50
498 2 p. blue and grey 4·50 4·50
483 3 p. violet and pink 4·50 4·50
499 3 p. red and violet 4·50 4·50
484 4 p. black and purple 4·50 4·50
500 4 p. red and purple 4·50 4·50
485 5 p. violet and black 4·50 4·50
501 5 p. blue and yellow 4·50 4·50

83. A Spanish Caravel, Seville in background. 84. Miniature of Exhibition Poster.

1929. Seville and Barcelona Exhibitions. Inscr. "EXPOSICION GENERAL (or GRAL.) ESPANOLA".
502. 83. 1 c. blue 20 20
503. 84. 2 c. green 20 20
504. – 5 c. red 35 30
505. – 10 c. green 40 35
506. 83. 15 c. blue 30 25
507. 84. 20 c. violet 40 35
508. 83. 25 c. red 40 35
509. – 30 c. brown 3·00 3·00
510. – 40 c. blue 3·75 3·00
511. 84. 50 c. orange 3·00 3·00
512. – 1 p. grey 5·50 5·00
513. – 4 p. red 16·00 15·00
514. – 10 p. brown 35·00 35·00
DESIGNS—VERT. 5, 30 c., 1 p. View of exhibition. HORIZ. 10, 40 c., 4, 10 p. Alfonso XIII and Barcelona.

87. "Spirit of St. Louis" over Coast.

1929. Air. Seville and Barcelona Exns.
515. 87. 5 c. brown 5·00 4·25
516. 10 c. red 5·00 4·25
517. 25 c. blue 5·00 4·75
518. 50 c. violet 6·00 6·25
519. 1 p. green 28·00 26·00
520. 4 p. black 22·00 21·00

1929. Meeting of Council of League of Nations at Madrid. Optd. **Sociedad de las Naciones LV reunion del Consejo Madrid.**
521 66 1 c. green 40 35
522 68 2 c. green 40 35
523 5 c. red 40 35
524 10 c. green 40 35
525 15 c. blue 40 35
526 20 c. violet 40 35
527 25 c. red 30 25
528 30 c. brown 1·90 1·25
529 40 c. blue 1·90 1·25
530 50 c. orange 1·90 1·25
531 69 1 p. grey 8·50 7·00
532 4 p. red 8·50 7·00
533 10 p. brown 30·00 27·00

89. Steam Locomotive. 90.

1930. 11th Int. Railway Congress, Madrid.
534. 89. 1 c. turquoise (postage) 40 40
535. 2 c. green 40 40
536. 5 c. red 40 40
537. 10 c. green 40 40
538. 15 c. blue 40 40
539. 20 c. violet 40 40
540. 25 c. red 40 40
541. 30 c. brown 1·75 1·75
542. 40 c. blue 1·75 1·75
543. 50 c. orange 4·00 4·00
544. – 1 p. grey 5·50 5·50
545. – 4 p. red 60·00 60·00
546. – 10 p. brown £300 £300
DESIGN—VERT. 1 p. to 10 p. Steam locomotive at points.

547. 90. 5 c. brown (air) 5·50 5·50
548. 10 c. red 5·50 5·50
549. 25 c. blue 5·50 5·50
550. 50 c. violet 14·00 14·00
551. 1 p. green 27·00 27·00
552. 4 p. black 27·00 27·00

91. Francisco Goya (after Lopez). 92.

93. "The Naked Maja".

1930. Death Cent. of Goya (painter). (a) Postage.
553. 91. 1 c. yellow 10 10
554. 2 c. brown 10 10
555. 92. 2 c. olive 10 10
556. 91. 5 c. mauve 10 10
557. 92. 5 c. violet 10 10
558. 91. 10 c. green 20 15
559. 15 c. blue 15 10
560. 20 c. red 15 10
561. 25 c. red 15 10
562. 92. 25 c. red 35 35
563. 91. 30 c. brown 4·50 3·75
564. 40 c. blue 4·50 3·75
565. 50 c. orange 4·50 3·75
566. 1 p. black 6·00 4·50
567. 93. 1 p. purple 85 70
568. 4 p. black 60 50
569. 10 p. brown 12·00 10·00

94. "Flight". 97. King Alfonso XIII.

(b) Air. Designs show works by Goya, all with curious flying figures.
570. 94. 5 c. yellow and red 10 10
571. – 5 c. blue and olive 10 10
572. – 10 c. green and blue 15 10
573. – 15 c. orange and black 15 10
574. – 20 c. red and blue 15 10
575. 94. 25 c. red and deep red 20 10
576. – 30 c. violet and brown 40 30
577. – 40 c. blue and violet 40 30
578. – 50 c. green and red 40 30
579. – 1 p. purple and plum 40 30
580. – 4 p. black and red 2·50 2·00
581. – 4 p. grey and black 2·50 2·00
582. – 10 p. brn. and deep brn. 10·00 10·00
The 5 c. (No. 571), 10 c., 20 c., 40 c., 1 p., 4 p. (No. 581) and 10 p. are vert. and the 30 c., 50 c. and 4 p. (No. 580) are horiz.

1930.
583. 97. 2 c. brown 10 10
584. 5 c. grey 50 10
585. 10 c. green 2·75 10
586. 15 c. turquoise 9·00 10
587. 20 c. violet 5·00 40
588. 25 c. red 50 10
589. 30 c. red 11·00 90
590. 40 c. blue 15·00 60
592. 50 c. orange 15·00 1·25

98. The "Santa Maria". 99.

100. "Santa Maria", "Pinta" and "Nina".

101. The Departure from Palos.

1930. Columbus issue.
593. 98. 1 c. brown 15 10
594. 2 c. olive 15 10
595. 99. 2 c. olive 15 10
596. 98. 5 c. red 15 10
597. 99. 5 c. red 15 10
598. 10 c. green 1·00 75
599. 98. 15 c. blue 1·00 75
600. 99. 20 c. violet 1·00 1·00
601. 100. 25 c. red 1·00 1·00
602. 101. 30 c. brown and blue 5·00 5·00
603. 100. 40 c. blue 4·75 4·00
604. 101. 50 c. violet, blue & pur. 5·50 5·00
605. 100. 1 p. black 5·50 5·00
606. – 4 p. black and blue 5·00 5·50
607. – 10 p. brown and purple 25·00 27·00
DESIGNS—As Type 101: 4, 10 p. Arrival in America.

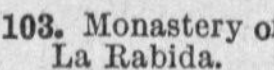

103. Monastery of La Rabida. **104.** Martin Pinzon.

106. Columbus.

1930. "Columbus" Air stamps (for Europe and Africa).

608.	103.	5 c. red ..	10	10
609.		5 c. brown	10	10
610.		10 c. green	20	15
611.		15 c. violet	20	15
612.		20 c. blue	20	15
613.	104.	25 c. red	20	15
614.	–	30 c. brown	1·50	1·50
615.	104.	40 c. blue	1·50	1·50
616.	–	50 c. orange	1·50	1·50
617.	104.	1 p. violet	1·50	1·50
618.	106.	4 p. olive	1·50	1·50
619.		10 p. brown	8·50	9·00

DESIGN—As Type 104: 30 c., 50 c. Vincent Pinzon.

107. Monastery of La Rabida.

108. Columbus. **109.** Columbus and the brothers Pinzon.

1930. "Columbus" Air stamps (for America and Philippines).

620.	107.	5 c. red ..	10	10
621.		10 c. green	15	10
622.	108.	25 c. red	15	10
623.		50 c. grey	1·75	1·75
624.		1 p. brown	1·75	1·75
625.	109.	4 p. blue	1·75	1·75
626.		10 p. purple	7·50	8·50

110. Arms of Bolivia and Paraguay.

113. Sidar (Mexico). **114.** King, Queen and Columbus.

1930. Spanish-American Exhibition. Views of pavilions of various countries.

627	110	1 c. green (postage)	10	10
628	–	2 c. brown (C. America)	10	10
629	–	5 c. brown (Venezuela)	10	10
630	–	10 c. sepia (Colombia)	25	20
631	–	15 c. blue (Dominican Republic)	25	20
632	–	20 c. violet (Uruguay)	25	20
633	–	25 c. red (Argentina)	25	20
634	–	25 c. red (Chile)	25	20
635	–	30 c. purple (Brazil)	1·00	1·10
636	–	40 c. blue (Mexico)	55	50
637	–	40 c. blue (Cuba)	55	50
638	–	50 c. orange (Peru)	1·25	1·50
639	–	1 p. blue (U.S.A.)	1·75	2·25
640	–	4 p. purple (Portugal)	12·00	15·00
641	–	10 p. brown	1·00	1·50

The 10 p. shows King Alfonso and Queen Victoria, maps of S. America and Spain, and the Giralda, Seville. The 2, 5 c., 4, 10 p. are vert.

643	–	5 c. black (air)	30	15
644	–	10 c. green	30	15
645	–	25 c. blue	30	15
646	–	50 c. blue	60	75
647	113	50 c. black	60	75
648	–	1 p. red	1·25	1·50
649	–	1 p. purple	35·00	32·00
650	–	1 p. green	1·25	1·50
651	114	4 p. blue	2·25	3·00

DESIGNS: Portraits of aviators and views as Types 113/14—HORIZ. 5 c. Santos Dumont (Brazil). 10 c. Teodoro Fels (Argentina). 25 c. Dagoberto Godoy (Chile). 50 c. Cabral and Coutinho (Portugal) (No. 646). 1 p. Charles Lindbergh (United States) (No. 650). VERT. 1 p. Jimenez and Iglesias (Spain) (Nos. 648/9).

115. **121.** The Fountain of the Lions.

1930.

652.	115.	5 c. black	5·00	10

1931. Optd. REPUBLICA.

(a) Postage.

660	66	1 c. green (Imperf)	10	10
673	97	2 c. brown	10	10
662		5 c. brown	15	15
671	115	5 c. black	2·10	2·10
675	97	10 c. green	25	25
664		15 c. green	80	80
677		20 c. violet	50	35
678		25 c. red	50	35
667		30 c. red	5·50	5·50
668		40 c. blue	1·50	1·25
669		50 c. orange	1·50	1·25
670	69	1 p. grey	10·00	8·00

(b) Air. On Nos. 353/6.

683.	64.	5 c. green	9·00	8·50
684.		10 c. red	9·00	8·50
685.		25 c. blue	13·00	12·00
686.		50 c. blue	24·00	20·00

1931. Optd. **Republica Espanola** in two lines continuously.

687.	97.	2 c. brown	10	10
688.		5 c. grey	25	10
689.		10 c. green	25	10
690.		15 c. turquoise	2·25	10
691.		20 c. violet	1·10	60
692.		25 c. red	35	10
693.		30 c. red	3·00	60
694.		40 c. blue	3·00	60
695.		50 c. orange	6·50	40
696.	69.	1 p. grey	42·00	60

1931. 3rd Pan-American Postal Union Congress. (a) Postage.

697.	121.	5c. purple	10	10
698.	–	10 c. green	35	35
699.	–	15 c. violet	35	35
700.	–	25 c. red	35	35
701.	–	30 c. olive	35	35
702.	121.	40 c. blue	75	55
703.	–	50 c. red	75	55
704.	–	1 p. black	1·40	1·10
705.	–	4 p. purple	7·00	6·50
706.	–	10 p. brown	22·00	22·00

DESIGNS—VERT. 10 c., 25 c., 50 c. Cordoba Cathedral. HORIZ. 15 c., 1 p. Alcantara Bridge, Toledo. 30 c. Dr. F. Garcia y Santos. 4 p., 10 p. Revolutionaries hoisting Republican flag, 14 April, 1931.

123. Royal Palace and San Francisco el Grande.

(b) Air.

707.	123.	5 c. red ..	10	10
708.		10 c. green	10	10
709.		25 c. red	10	10
710.	–	50 c. blue	40	35
711.	–	1 p. violet	60	50
712.	–	4 p. black	8·00	8·50

DESIGNS—HORIZ. 50 c., 1 p. G.P.O. and Cibeles Fountain. 4 p. The Calle de Alcala.

125a. Montserrat Arms. **125b.** Plane above Montserrat.

1931. 900th Anniv. of Montserrat Monastery.

713.	125a.	1 c. green (postage)	1·50	1·50
714.		2 c. brown	1·00	1·00
715.		5 c. brown	1·00	1·00
716.		10 c. green	1·00	1·00
717.	–	15 c. green	1·50	1·50
718.	–	20 c. purple	3·00	3·00
719.	–	25 c. red	4·50	4·50
720.	–	30 c. red	35·00	35·00
721.	–	40 c. blue	25·00	25·00
722.	–	50 c. orange	50·00	50·00
723.	–	1 p. blue	50·00	50·00
724.	–	4 p. mauve	£400	£400
725.	–	10 p. brown	£300	£300

DESIGNS: 15 c., 50 c. Monks planning Monastery. 20 c., 30 c. "Black Virgin" (full length). 25 c., 1 p., 10 p. "Black Virgin" (profile). 40 c., 4 p. Monastery.

726.	125b.	5 c. brown (air)	50	50
727.		10 c. green	2·50	2·50
728.		25 c. red	10·00	10·00
729.		50 c. orange	30·00	30·00
730.		1 p. blue	20·00	20·00

143. **144.** **126.** Blasco Ibanez.

127. Pi y Margall. **128.** Joaquin Costa. **129.** Mariana Pineda.

130. Nicolas Salmeron. **131.** Concepcion Arenal. **132.** Ruiz Zorrilla.

133. Pablo Iglesias. **134.** Ramon y Cajal. **135.** Azcarate.

136. Jovellanos. **137.** Pablo Iglesias. **138.** Emilio Castelar.

139. Pablo Iglesias. **140.** Velazquez. **141.** F. Salvoechea.

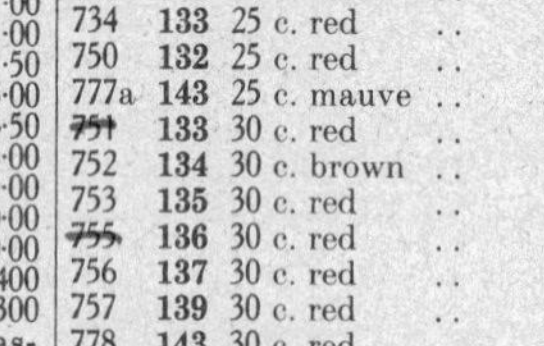

142. Cuenca.

1931.

770	143	1 c. green (imperf)	10	10
738	126	2 c. brown	10	10
771	143	2 c. brown	25	10
772	144	2 c. brown	10	10
731	127	5 c. brown	2·40	20
740	126	5 c. brown	10	10
773	143	5 c. brown	10	10
741	128	10 c. green	4·00	10
742	129	10 c. green	10	10
774	143	10 c. green	10	10
744	130	15 c. green	60	10
745	131	15 c. green	55	10
747		15 c. black	20	10
775	143	15 c. green	10	10
748	127	20 c. violet	30	10
776a	143	20 c. violet	10	10
734	133	25 c. red	19·00	40
750	132	25 c. red	45	10
777a	143	25 c. mauve	10	10
751	133	30 c. red	1·60	10
752	134	30 c. brown	12·00	50
753	135	30 c. red	7·50	20
755	136	30 c. red	10	10
756	137	30 c. red	10	10
757	139	30 c. red	1·10	35
778	143	30 c. red	10	10
758	138	40 c. blue	20	10
759		40 c. red	1·10	35
760	139	45 c. red	10	10
761	130	50 c. orange	21·00	35
762		50 c. blue	1·00	35
763	140	50 c. blue	10	10
764	138	60 c. green	15	15
765	141	60 c. blue	75	70
766		60 c. orange	5·00	4·00
767c	142	1 p. black	15	10
768c	–	4 p. mauve	50	30
769c	–	10 p. brown	1·00	50

DESIGNS—As Type 142: 4 p. Castle of Segovia. 10 p. Sun Gate, Toledo.

145. Cierva Autogyro C.30 over Seville.

1935.

780.	145.	2 p. blue	65	20

146. Lope De Vega's Book-plate. **148.** Scene from "Peribanez".

1935. 300th Death Anniv of Lope de Vega (author).

781.	146.	15 c. green	6·00	25
782.	–	30 c. red	2·40	20
783.	–	50 c. blue	12·00	1·90
784.	148.	1 p. black	20·00	1·25

DESIGN—As Type 146: 30 c., 50 c. Lope de Vega (after Tristan).

149. Old-time Map of the Amazon.

1935. Iglesias' Amazon Expedition.

785.	149.	30 c. red	2·25	70

150. M. Moya. **151.** House of Nazareth and Rotary Press.

152. Pyrenean Eagle and Newspapers.

153. Aeroplane over Press Association Building.

1936. 40th Anniv. of Madrid Press Association.

786. **150.** 1 c. red (postage) 10 10
787. – 2 c. brown 10 10
788. – 5 c. sepia 10 10
789. – 10 c. green 10 10
790. **150.** 15 c. green 15 10
791. – 20 c. violet 15 10
792. – 25 c. mauve 15 10
793. – 30 c. red 10 10
794. **150.** 40 c. orange 45 10
795. – 50 c. blue 30 10
796. – 60 c. olive 50 15
797. – 1 p. black 50 15
798. **151.** 2 p. blue .. .. 6·50 2·25
799. – 4 p. red .. .. 6·50 4·25
800. – 10 p. lake .. .. 16·00 10·00

PORTRAITS: 2 c., 20 c., 50 c. T. L. de Tena. 5 c., 25 c., 60 c. J. F. Rodriguez. 10 c., 30 c., 1 p. A. Lerroux. SIZES: 1 c. to 10 c. 22 × 27 mm.; 15 c. to 30 c. 24 × 30 mm.; 40 c. to 1 p. 26 × 31½ mm.

801. **152.** 1 c. red (air) 10 10
802. **153.** 2 c. brown 15 15
803. **152.** 5 c. sepia 10 10
804. **153.** 10 c. green 15 15
805. – 15 c. blue 15 10
806. **152.** 20 c. violet 15 10
807. **153.** 25 c. mauve 15 15
808. – 30 c. red 10 10
809. **152.** 40 c. orange 45 70
810. – 50 c. blue 30 70
811. **153.** 60 c. olive 50 70
812. – 1 p. black 60 70
813. – 2 p. blue .. .. 4·00 3·00
814. – 4 p. red .. .. 4·50 4·50
815. – 10 p. lake .. .. 12·00 8·00

DESIGNS—VERT. 15, 30, 50 c., 1 p. Cierva Autogyro C. 30 over House of Nazareth. HORIZ. 2, 4, 10 p. Don Quixote on wooden horse.

155. Gregorio Fernandez.

156.

1936. 300th Birth Anniv of Gregorio Fernandez (sculptor).

816 155 30 c. red .. .. 1·50 70

1939. First National Philatelic Exhibition, Madrid.

(a) Postage.

817. **156.** 10 c. brown .. .. 40·00 45·00
818. 15 c. green .. .. 40·00 45·00

(b) Air. Optd. **CORREO AEREO.**

819. **156.** 10 c. red £130 £130
820. 15 c. blue £130 £130

1936. Manila–Madrid Flight of Arnaiz and Calvo. Optd. **VUELO MANILA MADRID 1936 ARNAIZ CALVO.**

821. **137.** 30 c. red .. .. 5·00 3·25

159.

160a. Republican Symbol.

1937. Fiscal stamp of Asturias and Leon surch.

822. **159.** 25 c. on 5 c. red .. 16·00 5·50
823. 45 c. on 5 c. red .. 6·00 3·00
824. 60 c. on 5 c. red .. 40 35
825. 1 p. on 5 c. red .. 35 30

1938. Surch. **45 centimos.**

826. **143.** 45 c. on 1 c. green (imperf.) .. 5·00 5·00
827. 45 c. on 1 c. grn. (perf.) 30 25
830. 45 c. on 2 c. brown .. 12·00 9·50
831. **144.** 45 c. on 2 c. brown .. 10 10
832. **126.** 45 c. on 2 c. brown .. 24·00 20·00

1938.

833. **160a.** 40 c. red 10 10
834. 45 c. red 10 10
835. 50 c. blue 10 10
836. 60 c. blue 40 30

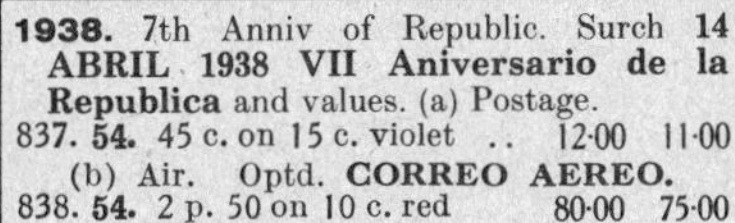

1938. 7th Anniv of Republic. Surch **14 ABRIL 1938 VII Aniversario de la Republica** and values. (a) Postage.

837. **54.** 45 c. on 15 c. violet .. 12·00 11·00

(b) Air. Optd. **CORREO AEREO.**

838. **54.** 2 p. 50 on 10 c. red 80·00 75·00

163. Defence of Madrid.

1938. Defence of Madrid Relief Fund.

(a) Postage.

839. **163.** 45 c.+2 p. bl. & light bl. 50 40

(b) Air. Surch. **AEREO+5 Pts.**

841. **163.** 45 c.+2 p.+5 p. blue and light blue .. £200 £190

1938. Labour Day. Surch. **FIESTA DEL TRABAJO 1 MAYO 1938** and values.

843. **54.** 45 c. on 15 c. violet .. 2·75 2·75
844. 1 p. on 15 c. violet .. 5·00 4·25

167. Statue of Liberty and Flags.

1938. 150th Anniv. of U.S. Constitution.

(a) Postage.

845. **167.** 1 p. multicoloured .. 12·00 12·00

(b) Air. Surch. **AEREO+5 Pts.**

847. **167.** 1 p.+5 p. multicoloured £180 £160

169.

172. Steelworks.

1938. Red Cross (a) Postage.

849. **169.** 45 c.+5 p. red .. 55 50

(b) Air. Surcharged **Aereo** and new value.

850 **169.** 45 c.+5 p.+3 p. red .. 8·00 8·00

1938. Air. No. 719 surch. with two aeroplanes and **CORREO AEREO** repeated twice and value.

851. 50 c. on 25 c. red .. .. 23·00 23·00
852. 1 p. on 25 c. red .. .. 1·50 1·00
853. 1 p. 25 on 25 c. red .. 1·50 1·00
854. 1 p. 50 on 25 c. red .. 1·50 1·00
855. 2 p. on 25 c. red .. .. 26·00 24·00

1938. Workers of Sagunto.

856. **172.** 45 c. black 15 15
857. – 1 p. 25 blue 15 15

DESIGN: 1 p. 25, Blast furnace and air raid victims.

173. "Isaac Peral".

1938. Submarine Service.

857a. **173.** 1 p. blue .. .. 5·50 5·50
857b. – 2 p. brown .. .. 10·00 10·00
857c. – 4 p. orange .. .. 10·00 10·00
857d. – 6 p. blue .. .. 15·00 18·00
857e. – 10 p. red .. .. 35·00 42·00
857f. – 15 p. green £375 £400

DESIGNS: 2 p., 6 p. "Narcisco Monturiol". 4 p. 10 p., "B-2".

174. Troops on the alert.

176a. Man and Woman in Firing Position.

1938. In honour of 43rd Division. Perf. or imperf.

858. **174.** 25 c. green .. .. 8·00 7·00
859. – 45 c. brown .. .. 8·00 7·00

DESIGN—VERT. 45 c. Two soldiers on guard.

1938. 2nd Anniv of Defence of Madrid. Optd **SECUNDO ANIVERSARIO DE LA HEROICA DEFENSA DE MADRID 7 NOV. 1938.**

860. **163.** 45 c.+2 p. blue .. 2·50 2·00

1938. No. 719 surch. **2'50 PTAS** and bars and ornaments.

861. 2 p. 50 on 25 c. red .. 15 15

1938. In honour of the Militia.

861b. **176a.** 5 c. brown .. .. 2·75 2·40
861c. 10 c. purple .. .. 2·75 2·40
861d. 25 c. green .. .. 2·75 2·40
861e. – 45 c. red .. .. 2·75 2·40
861f. – 60 c. blue .. .. 4·75 4·00
861g. – 1 p. 20 black .. £100 95·00
861h. – 2 p. orange .. .. 30·00 30·00
861i. – 5 p. brown £170 £140
861j. – 10 p. green .. .. 35·00 30·00

DESIGNS—HORIZ. 45 c., 60 c., 1 p. 20 Militia with machine gun. VERT. 2 p., 5 p., 10 p. Grenade-thrower.

NATIONAL STATE

The Civil War began on July 17, 1936. Until it ended on April 1, 1939, the stamps listed below were current only in areas held by the forces of General Franco.

179.

177. Seville Cathedral.

178. Xavier Castle, Navarre.

180. Cordoba Cathedral.

1936.

868. **179.** 1 c. green (imperf.) .. 4·75 5·00
869. 2 c. brown 55 35
862. – 5 c. brown 60 50
870. – 10 c. green 55 35
863. – 15 c. green 60 35
864. **177.** 25 c. red 60 35
865. **178.** 30 c. red 60 35
871. – 50 c. blue .. .. 13·00 10·00
872. **180.** 60 c. green 85 70
867. – 1 p. black .. .. 5·50 2·40
873. – 4 p. lilac, red & yellow 45·00 25·00
874. – 10 p. brown .. .. 48·00 25·00

DESIGNS—VERT. 5 c. Burgos Cathedral. 4 p. National Flag of Malaga. HORIZ. As Type **178**: 15 c. Zaragoza Cathedral. 1 p. Alcantara Bridge and Alcazar, Toledo. As Type **180**: 10 c. Salamanca University. 50 c. Court of Lions, Granada. 10 p. Troops disembarking at Algeciras.

181.

182.

183. "El Cid".

184. Isabella the Catholic.

1937.

875 **181** 1 c. green (imperf) .. 10 10
876 **182** 2 c. brown 10 10
902 **183** 5 c. brown 10 10
879 10 c. green 10 10
903 10 c. red 10 10
896 15 c. green 40 10
880 **184** 15 c. black 20 10
881 20 c. violet 30 10
882 25 c. red 25 10
883 30 c. red 40 10
885 40 c. orange .. .. 1·75 10
886 50 c. blue .. .. 1·75 10
887 60 c. yellow 30 10
897 70 c. blue 60 10
888 1 p. blue .. .. 14·00 35
889 4 p. mauve .. .. 18·00 4·25
891 **183** 10 p. blue .. .. 25·00 11·00

186. Santiago Cathedral.

189.

1937. Holy Year of Compostela.

905. – 15 c. brown .. .. 1·00 70
906. **186.** 30 c. red .. .. 3·75 35
908. – 1 p. orange and blue 10·00 3·50

DESIGNS—VERT. 15c. St. James of Compostela. HORIZ. 1 p. Portico de la Gloria.

1937. Anti-Tuberculosis Fund. Cross in red.

913. **189.** 10 c. blue and black .. 4·00 1·00

190. Ferdinand the Catholic.

192.

1938.

917. **190.** 15 c. green .. .. 1·25 10
918. 20 c. violet .. .. 10·00 1·50
919. 25 c. red 60 10
921. 30 c. red .. .. 4·50 10

1938. Air. Optd. **correo aereo.**

922. **190.** 50 c. blue 85 45
923. 1 p. blue .. .. 2·75 55

1938. 2nd Anniv. of National Uprising.

926. **192.** 15 c. green .. .. 4·50 4·00
927. 25 c. red .. .. 4·50 4·00
928. 30 c. blue .. .. 2·50 2·50
929. 1 p. brown and yellow 75·00 65·00

193. Isabella the Catholic.

194.

1938.

930. **193.** 20 c. violet 75 15
931. 25 c. red .. .. 7·50 40
932. 30 c. red 40 15
933. 40 c. mauve 50 10
934. 50 c. blue .. .. 25·00 1·75
935. 1 p. blue .. .. 8·00 70

1938. Anti-Tuberculosis Fund. Cross in red.

940. **194.** 10 c. blue and black .. 4·00 1·40

195. Juan de la Cierva and Autogyro "C.30".

196. General Franco.

1939. Air.

1010 **195** 20 c. orange 15 10
1011 25 c. red 15 10
943 35 c. mauve 50 30
1013 50 c. brown 35 10
945 1 p. blue 55 20
1015 2 p. green .. .. 2·10 10
947 4 p. blue .. .. 4·50 2·00
1017 10 p. violet .. .. 5·00 50

1939.

960 **196** 5 c. brown 35 10
961 10 c. red .. .. 1·75 45
962 15 c. green 40 10
1114 20 c. violet 20 10
1115 25 c. purple .. 20 10
950 30 c. red 25 10
1116 30 c. blue 25 10
1117 35 c. blue 35 10
951 40 c. green 30 10
1118 40 c. grey 35 10
952 45 c. red .. .. 2·00 1·90
1119 45 c. blue 10 10
1120 50 c. grey 25 10
1121 60 c. orange .. 20 10
955 70 c. blue 50 10
956 1 Pts. black .. 12·00 10
974 1 PTA. black .. 5·50 10

975 1 PTS. grey .. 60·00 50
957 2 Pts. brown .. 18·00 1·00
1124 2 PTAS. brown .. 7·00 10
958 4 Pts. purple .. 95·00 12·00
977a 4 PTAS. red .. 10·00 10
959 10 Pts. brown .. 48·00 29·00
978 10 PTS. brown .. £140 2·75
1126 10 PTAS. brown .. 3·00 30
For 10 c. brown imperf., see No. 981.

197. "Spain" and Wreath of Peace.

1939. Homage to the Army.
980. 197. 10 c. blue 15 10

1939. Anti-Tuberculosis Fund. Imperf.
981. 196. 10 c. brown 15 10

198. Ruins of Belchite.

1940. Zaragoza Cathedral Restoration Fund and 19th Cent. of Apparition of Virgin of El Pilar at Zaragoza.
(a) Postage.
982. 198. 10 c.+5 c. brn. & blue 10 10
983. – 15 c.+10 c. olive & lilac 15 10
984. – 20 c.+10 c. bl. & violet 15 10
985. – 25 c.+10 c. brown & red 15 10
986. – 40 c.+10 c. pur. & grn. 10 10
987. – 45 c.+15 c. red & blue 30 20
988. 198. 70 c.+20 c. blk. & brn. 30 20
989. – 80 c.+20 c. violet & red 35 25
990. – 1 p.+30 c. pur. & blk. 35 25
991. – 1 p. 40+40 c. blk. & pur. 30·00 25·00
992. – 1 p. 50+50 c. pur. & bl. 40 35
993. – 2 p. 50+50 c. bl. & pur. 40 35
994. – 4 p.+1 p. slate & lilac 10·00 8·00
995. – 10 p.+4 p. brn. & blue £140 £140
DESIGNS—HORIZ. 15 c., 80 c. Procession of the Rosary. 20 c., 1 p. 50, El Pilar. 25 c., 1 p. Mother Rafols praying. 40 c., 2 p. 50, Sanctuary of the Virgin. 45 c., 1 p. 40, Oath of the besieged. 4 p. Miracle of Calanda. 10 p. Virgin appearing to St. James.
(b) Air.
996. 25 c.+5 c. slate & purple 25 20
997. 50 c.+5 c. violet and red 25 20
998. 65 c.+15 c. blue & violet 25 20
999. 70 c.+15 c. violet & slate 25 20
1000. 90 c.+20 c. red & brown 25 20
1001. 1 p. 20+30 c. pur. & vio. 25 20
1002. 1 p. 40+40 c. brn. & bl. 25 30
1003. 2 p.+50 c. vio. & purple 35 30
1004. 4 p.+1 p. purple & green 8·50 6·00
1005. 10 p.+4 p. blue & brown £190 £170
DESIGNS—VERT. 25 c., 70 c. Prayer during bombardment. 50 c., 1 p. 40, Caravel and Image of the Virgin. 65 c., 90 c. The Assumption. 1 p. 20, 2 p. Coronation of the Virgin. 4 p. "The Cave", after Goya. 10 p. Bombing of Zaragoza Cathedral.

199. Gen. Franco.

200. Knight and Cross of Lorraine.

1940. Anti-Tuberculosis Fund.
1006. 199. 10 c. violet & red (post.) 10 10
1007. 20 c.+5 c. grn. & red 40 45
1008. 40 c.+10 c. blue & red 55 20
1009. 10 c. pink & red (air) 50 40

1941. Anti-Tuberculosis Fund.
1018. 200. 10 c. blk. & red (post.) 15 10
1019. 20 c.+5 c. violet & red 50 30
1020. 40 c.+10 c. slate & red 50 30
1021. 10 c. blue & red (air) 25 20

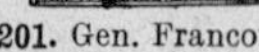
201. Gen. Franco.

202. St. John of the Cross.

1942.
1022. 201. 40 c. brown 50 15
1023. 75 c. blue .. .. 4·50 35
1024a. 90 c. green 40 10
1025b. 1 p. 35 violet 35 10

1942. 400th Birth Anniv. of St. John of the Cross.
1026. 202. 20 c. violet 70 10
1027. 40 c. orange .. .. 1·40 30
1028. 75 c. blue .. .. 1·60 1·60

203. Doves and Lorraine Cross.

DESIGN—HORIZ. No. 1032, Lorraine Cross and two doves in flight.

1942. Anti-T.B. Fund. Inscr. "1942-43".
1029. 203. 10 c. pink & red (post.) 15 10
1030. 20 c.+5 c. brn. & red 1·10 1·10
1031. 40 c.+10 c. grn. & red 85 20
1032. – 10 c. pink & red (air) 75 30

204.

St. James of Compostela. 205.

1943. Holy Year. Inscr. "ANO SANTO 1943".
1033. 204. 20 c. blue 20 15
1034. – 20 c. red 20 15
1035. – 20 c. lilac 20 15
1036. – 40 c. brown 60 20
1037. 205. 40 c. green 50 20
1038. – 40 c. brown 75 20
1039. – 75 c. blue .. .. 2·25 2·25
1040. – 75 c. blue .. .. 2·75 2·50
1041. – 75 c. blue .. .. 30·00 25·00
DESIGNS—VERT. Nos. 1034 and 1040. Details of pillars in Santiago Cathedral. No. 1036, St. James enthroned. No. 1038, Portal of Santiago Cathedral. No. 1039, Censer. No. 1041, Santiago Cathedral. HORIZ. No. 1035, Tomb of St. James.

206.

207. 10th-cent. Tower.

208. Arms of Soria.

1943. Anti-Tuberculosis Fund. Inscr. "1943-1944".
1042. 206. 10 c. vio. & red (post.) 30 25
1043. 20 c.+5 c. green & red 3·00 1·40
1044. 40 c.+10 c. blue & red 2·00 1·00
1045. – 10 c. violet and red (air) 55 55
DESIGN: No. 1045. Lorraine Cross and outline of bird.

1944. Millenary of Castile. Arms designs as T 208 inscr. "Milenario de Castilla".
1046. 207. 20 c. lilac 20 20
1047. 208. 20 c. lilac 20 15
1048. – 20 c. lilac 20 20
1049. – 40 c. brown .. .. 3·00 45
1050. – 40 c. brown .. .. 3·00 45
1051. – 40 c. brown .. .. 2·75 50
1052. – 75 c. blue .. .. 3·00 2·50
1053. – 75 c. blue .. .. 2·75 2·50
1054. – 75 c. blue .. .. 2·25 2·50
DESIGNS: No. 1048, Avila (Shield at left). No. 1049, Castile (Arms in centre). No. 1050, Segovia (Shield at left). No. 1051, Burgos (Shield at right). No. 1052, Avila (Shield at left). No. 1053, Fernan Gonzalez, founder of Castile (Helmet, bow and arrows at left). No. 1054, Santander (Shield at right).

209. "Dr. Thebussem" (M. P. Figuera author and postal historian).

1944. Air. Stamp Day
1055. 146. 5 p. blue .. .. 19·00 16·00

210.

211. Quevedo.

1944. Anti-Tuberculosis Fund. Inscr. "1944 1945". (a) Postage.
1056. 210. 10 c. orange & red .. 15 10
1057. 20 c.+5 c. blk. & red 30 25
1058. 40 c.+10 c. violet & red 50 20
1059. 80 c.+10 c. bl. & red 8·00 7·50
(b) Air. Inscr. "CORRESPONDENCIA AEREA".
1060. – 25 c. orange and red .. 3·50 3·50
DESIGN—HORIZ. No. 1060, Hospital.

1945. 300th Death Anniv. of Francisco de Quevedo (author).
1061. 211. 40 c. brown 70 45

212. Conde de San Luis, Mail Vehicle of 1850, and Aeroplane.

1945. Air. Stamp Day.
1062. 212. 10 p. green .. .. 27·00 18·00

213. Carlos de Haya Gonzalez.

214. J. Garcia Morato.

1945. Air. Civil War Air Aces.
1063. 213. 4 p. red .. .. 15·00 6·00
1064. 214. 10 p. purple .. .. 35·00 8·00

215. St. George and Dragon.

216. Lorraine Cross and Eagle.

1945. Anti-T.B. Fund.
1065. 215. 10 c. orge. & red (post.) 22 10
1066. 20 c.+5 c. green & red 30 20
1067. 40 c.+10 c. vio. & red 40 20
1068. 80 c.+10 c. bl. & red 12·00 8·00
1069. 216. 25 c. red (air) .. 1·75 1·25

217. E. A. de Nebrija (compiler of first Spanish Grammar).

219. Statue of Fray Bartolome de las Casas and native Indian.

1946. Stamp Day and Day of the Race.
1070. 217. 50 c. red (postage) .. 50 30
1071. – 75 c. blue 60 35
1072. 219. 5 p. 50 green (air) .. 3·25 2·25
DESIGN—As Type 217: 75 c. Salamanca University and signature of F. F. de Vitoria (founder of International Law).

220. Self-portrait of Goya.
221. Woman and Child.
222. B. J. Feijoo y Montenegro.

1946. Birth Bicentenary of Goya (painter).
1073. 220. 25 c. red 10 10
1074. 50 c. green 15 10
1075. 75 c. blue 75 60

1946. Anti-Tuberculosis Fund. Dated. "1946 1947".
1076. 221. 5 c. violet and red (postage) .. 10 10
1077. 10 c. grn. and red .. 10 10
1078. – 25 c. orge. & red (air) 30 20
DESIGN—HORIZ. 25 c. Eagle.

1947.
1079. 222. 50 c. green 70 40

223. Don Quixote in Library.

224. Don Quixote.

1947. Stamp Day and 400th Birth Anniv. of Cervantes.
1080. 223. 50 c. brown (postage) 30 20
1081. 224. 75 c. blue 60 35
1082. – 5 p. 50 violet (air) .. 6·00 4·00
DESIGN—HORIZ. 5 p. 50, Quixote on Wooden Horse (after Gustav Dore).

226. Manuel de Falla (composer).

228. Lorraine Cross.

229. General Franco.

1947. Air.
1083. 226. 25 p. purple .. .. 45·00 15·00
1084. – 50 p. red .. .. £160 25·00
PORTRAIT: 50 p. Ignacio Zuloaga (painter).

1947. Anti-Tuberculosis Fund. Dated. "1947 1948".
1085. 228. 5 c. brn. & red (post.) 10 10
1086. – 10 c. blue and red .. 10 10
1087. – 25 c. mve. & red (air) 30 20
DESIGNS—VERT. 10 c. Deckchair in garden. Horiz. 25 c. Sanatorium.

1948.
1088. 229. 5 c. brown 10 10
1088a. 5 c. olive 45 10
1089. 15 c. green 30 10
1090. 50 c. brown 30 10
1091. 80 c. lake .. .. 5·00 10

230. Hernando Cortes.

232. Gen. Franco and Castillo de la Mota.
233. Ferdinand III of Castile.

1948.
1092. 230. 35 c. black 20 15
1093. – 70 c. purple .. .. 2·50 2·00
PORTRAIT: 70 c. M. Aleman (writer).

1948.
1094. 232. 25 c. orange .. 10 10
1095. 30 c. myrtle .. 10 10
1096. 35 c. green .. 10 10
1097. 40 c. brown .. 90 10
1098. 45 c. pink .. 45 10
1099. 45 c. red .. 1·50 10
1100. 50 c. purple .. 1·75 10
1101. 70 c. violet .. 2·50 15
1102. 75 c. blue .. 2·25 20
1103. 1 p. pink .. 7·50 10

1948. 700th Anniv. of Institution of Castilian Navy.
1104. 233. 25 c. violet 30 10
1105. – 30 c. red (Admiral R. de Bonifaz) .. 20 10

235. Marquis of Salamanca.

236. Diesel Train.

1948. Stamp Day and Spanish Railway Cent. Inscr. "F.F.C.C. ESPAÑOLES 1848 1948".
1106. 235. 50 c. brown (postage) 75 10
1107. – 5 p. green .. .. 2·25 10
1108. 236. 2 p. red (air) .. 3·25 1·40
DESIGN—HORIZ. 5 p. Garganta de Pancorbo Viaduct.

238. Aesculapius.

240. Globe and Buildings.

1948. Anti-Tuberculosis Fund. Dated "1948 1949".

No.	Type	Description	Unused	Used
1109.	238.	5 c. brn. & red (post.)	10	10
1110.		10 c. green and red ..	10	10
1111.		50 c.+10 c. brn. & red	1·00	75
1112.	–	25 c. bl. & red (air) ..	40	30

DESIGN: 25 c. Aeroplane over sanatorium.

1949. Relief of War Victims. As T 183, but larger and inscr. "AUXILIO A LAS VICTIMAS DE LA GUERRA 1946".

No.	Type	Description	Unused	Used
1113.		5 c. violet	25	10

1949. 75th Anniv. of U.P.U.

No.	Type	Description	Unused	Used
1127.	240.	50 c. brown (postage)	85	15
1128.		75 c. blue	60	35
1129.		4 p. olive (air) ..	50	30

241. Galleon. 242. San Juan de Dios and a Leper.

1949. Anti-Tuberculosis Fund. Inscr. "1949 1950".

No.	Type	Description	Unused	Used
1130.	241.	5 c. vio. & red (post.)	10	10
1131.		10 c. green and red ..	10	10
1132.		50 c.+10 c. bis. & red	40	30
1133.	–	25 c. deep red and red (air)	25	15

DESIGN: 25 c. Bell.

1950. 400th Death Anniv. of San Juan de Dios.

No.	Type	Description	Unused	Used
1134.	242.	1 p. violet	18·00	4·50

243. Calderon de la Barca (dramatist).

244. Isabella II.

1950. Portraits.

No.	Type	Description	Unused	Used
1135.	243.	5 c. brown	20	10
1136.	–	10 c. lake	20	10
1137.	–	15 c. green	70	10
1138.	–	20 c. violet	50	10
1139.	–	2 p. blue	35·00	15
1140.	–	4 p. 50 purple	70	50

PORTRAITS—VERT. 10 c. Lope de Vega (author). 15 c. T. de Molina (poet). 20 c. Ruiz de Alarcon (author). 2 p. Dr. Ramon y Cajal (physician). 4 p. 50, Dr. Ferran y Clua (bacteriologist).

1950. Stamp Cent. Imperf.

(a) Postage. Reproduction of T 1.

No.	Type	Description	Unused	Used
1141.	244.	50 c. violet ..	13·00	7·50
1142.		75 c. blue ..	13·00	7·50
1143.		10 p. black	£150	£110
1144.		15 p. red	£150	£110

(b) Air. Reproduction of T 2.

No.	Type	Description	Unused	Used
1145.	–	1 p. purple	13·00	7·50
1146.	–	2 p. 50 brown ..	13·00	7·50
1147.	–	20 p. blue	£150	£110
1148.	–	25 p. green	£150	£110

1950. Gen. Franco's Canary Is. Visit. Nos. 1100 and 1103 surch. **VISITA DEL CAUDILLO A CANARIAS OCTUBRE 1950 SOBRETASA DIEZ CTS** and No. 1083 with **Correspondencia por avion** also.

No.	Type	Description	Unused	Used
1149.	232.	10 c. on 50 c. purple (postage)	45·00	35·00
1150.		10 c. on 1 p. pink ..	45·00	35·00
1151.	226.	10 c. on 25 p. pur. (air)	£450	£225

246. Candle and Conifer.

247. Map.

1950. Anti-T.B. Fund. Cross in red. Inscr. "1950 1951".

No.	Type	Description	Unused	Used
1152.	246.	5 c. violet (postage)	10	10
1153.		10 c. green	10	10
1154.		50 c.+10 c. brown ..	3·75	1·40
1155.	–	25 c. blue (air) ..	80	70

DESIGN: 25 c. Dove and flowers.

1951. Air. 6th Conference of Spanish-American Postal Union.

No.	Type	Description	Unused	Used
1156	247	1 p. blue	7·50	2·00

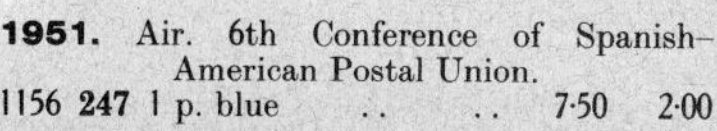

248. Isabella the Catholic.

248a. St. Antonio Claret.

1951. 5th Cent. of Birth of Isabella.

No.	Type	Description	Unused	Used
1157.	248.	50 c. brown	1·00	45
1158.		75 c. blue	1·50	45
1159.		90 c. purple	1·00	30
1160.		1 p. 50 orange ..	17·00	8·00
1161.		2 p. 80 olive	35·00	25·00

1951. Stamp Day.

No.	Type	Description	Unused	Used
1162.	248a.	50 c. blue	7·00	2·50

249. Children on Beach.

250. Isabella the Catholic.

1951. Anti-Tuberculosis Fund. Cross in red.

No.	Type	Description	Unused	Used
1163.	249.	5 c. red (post.) ..	15	10
1164.		10 c. green ..	60	10
1165.	–	25 c. brown (air) ..	1·00	15

DESIGN: 25 c. Nurse and child.

1951. Air. Stamp Day and 500th Birth Anniv. of Isabella the Catholic.

No.	Type	Description	Unused	Used
1166.	250.	60 c. green	11·00	50
1167.		90 c. yellow	1·50	70
1168.		1 p. 30 red	10·00	5·50
1169.		1 p. 90 sepia	7·50	7·50
1170.		2 p. 30 blue	5·00	3·00

251. Ferdinand the Catholic.

252. St. Maria Micaela.

1952. 500th Birth Anniv. of Ferdinand the Catholic.

No.	Type	Description	Unused	Used
1171.	251.	50 c. green	1·00	35
1172.		75 c. blue	6·50	1·75
1173.		90 c. purple	1·00	35
1174.		1 p. 50 orange ..	17·00	8·00
1175.		2 p. 80 brown ..	25·00	17·00

1952. 35th International Eucharistic Congress, Barcelona.

No.	Type	Description	Unused	Used
1176	252	60 c. red (postage)	20	10
1177	–	1 p. green (air) ..	6·00	40

DESIGN: 1 p. "The Eucharist" (Tiepolo).

252a. St. Francis Xavier.

254. Nurse and Baby.

1952. Air. 400th Death Anniv. of St. Francis Xavier.

No.	Type	Description	Unused	Used
1178.	252a.	2 p. blue	60·00	20·00

1952. Air. Stamp Day and 500th Anniv. of Birth of Ferdinand the Catholic. As T 250 but interior scene and portrait of Ferdinand the Catholic.

No.	Type	Description	Unused	Used
1179.		60 c. green	45	20
1180.		90 c. orange	45	20
1181.		1 p. 30 red	85	20
1182.		1 p. 90 brown ..	5·50	2·75
1183.		2 p. 30 blue	15·00	11·00

1953. Anti-Tuberculosis Fund. Cross in red.

No.	Type	Description	Unused	Used
1184.	254.	5 c. lake (postage) ..	70	10
1185.		10 c. green	1·60	10
1186.	–	25 c. brown (air) ..	7·00	3·00

DESIGN: 25 c. Girl and angel.

255. J. Sorolla (painter).

256. Bas-relief.

257. Fray Luis de Leon.

1953. Air.

No.	Type	Description	Unused	Used
1229	–	25 p. black	30·00	70·00
1187	255	50 p. violet	£550	18·00
1230	–	50 p. violet	10·00	1·25

PORTRAITS: No. 1229, Fortuny (painter). 1230, T. Quevedo (engineer and inventor).

1953. Stamp Day and 700th Anniv. of Salamanca University. Inscr. "UNIVDAD DE SALAMANCA".

No.	Type	Description	Unused	Used
1188.	256.	50 c. red	60	10
1189.	257.	90 c. green	3·00	2·40
1190.	–	2 p. brown	23·00	3·00

DESIGN—As Type 185—HORIZ. 2 p. Salamanca University.

258. M. L. de Legazpi (founder of Manila).

259. "St. Mary Magdalene". 260. St. James of Compostela.

1953. Air. Signing of Filipino-Spanish Postal Convention.

No.	Type	Description	Unused	Used
1191.	258.	25 p. black	£140	30·00

1954. Death Tercent. of Ribera (painter).

No.	Type	Description	Unused	Used
1192.	259.	1 p. 25 lake	15	10

1954. Holy Year.

No.	Type	Description	Unused	Used
1193.	260.	50 c. brown	20	10
1194.	–	3 p. blue	50·00	2·50

DESIGN: 3 p. Santiago Cathedral.

261. "Purity" (after Cano).

262. M. Menendez Pelayo (Historian).

1954. Marian Year.

No.	Type	Description	Unused	Used
1195	261	10 c. red	10	10
1196	–	15 c. green	10	10
1197	–	25 c. violet	15	10
1198	–	30 c. brown	20	10
1199	–	50 c. green	90	10
1200	–	60 c. black	20	10
1201	–	80 c. green	5·00	10
1202	–	1 p. violet	5·00	10
1203	–	2 p. brown	1·25	10
1204	–	3 p. blue	1·25	90

DESIGNS: 15 c. Virgin of Begona, Bilbao. 25 c. Virgin of the Abandoned, Valencia Cathedral. 30 c. The "Black Virgin" of Montserrat. 50 c. El Pilar Virgin, Zaragoza. 60 c. Covadonga Virgin. 80 c. Virgin of the Kings, Seville Cathedral. 1 p. Almudena Virgin, Madrid. 2 p. Virgin of Africa. 3 p. Guadalupe Virgin.

1954. Stamp Day.

No.	Type	Description	Unused	Used
1205.	262.	80 c. green	10·00	20

263. Gen. Franco.

265. St. Ignatius of Loyola.

1955.

No.	Type	Description	Unused	Used
1206.	263.	10 c. lake	10	10
1207.		15 c. ochre	10	10
1208.		20 c. myrtle	10	10
1209.		25 c. violet	10	10
1210.		30 c. brown	10	10
1211.		40 c. purple	10	10
1212.		50 c. brown	10	10
1213.		60 c. purple	20	10
1214.		70 c. myrtle	25	10
1215.		80 c. turquoise	15	10
1216.		1 p. orange	10	10
1217.		1 p. 40 mauve	30	10
1218.		1 p. 50 turquoise	10	10
1219.		1 p. 80 green	35	10
1220.		2 p. red	35·00	90
1221.		2 p. mauve	15	10
1222.		3 p. blue	15	10
1222a.		4 p. red	30	10
1223.		5 p. brown	25	10
1224.		6 p. black	30	10
1224a.		7 p. blue	20	10
1225.		8 p. violet	25	10
1226.		10 p. sage	35	10
1226a.		12 p. green	15	10
1226b.		20 p. red	45	10

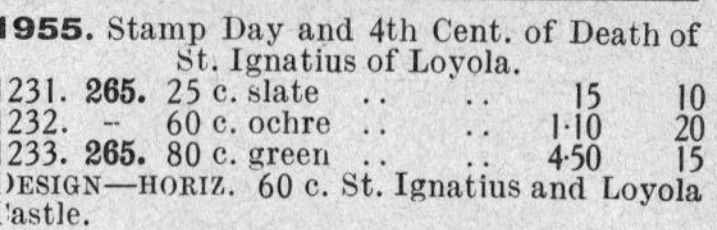

1955. Stamp Day and 4th Cent. of Death of St. Ignatius of Loyola.

No.	Type	Description	Unused	Used
1231.	265.	25 c. slate	15	10
1232.	–	60 c. ochre	1·10	20
1233.	265.	80 c. green	4·50	15

DESIGN—HORIZ. 60 c. St. Ignatius and Loyola Castle.

266. Aeroplane and Caravel.

1955. Air.

No.	Type	Description	Unused	Used
1234.	266.	20 c. myrtle	10	10
1235.		25 c. slate	10	10
1236.		50 c. brown	15	10
1237.		1 p. red	15	10
1238.		1 p. 10 green ..	20	10
1239.		1 p. 40 mauve ..	25	10
1240.		3 p. blue	25	10
1241.		4 p. 80 yellow ..	25	10
1242.		5 p. brown	2·25	10
1243.		7 p. mauve	75	20
1244.		10 p. green	1·10	25

267. "Telecommunications".

269. "The Holy Family" (after El Greco).

270.

1955. Cent. of Telegraphs in Spain.

No.	Type	Description	Unused	Used
1245.	267.	15 c. brown	55	15
1246.		80 c. green	12·00	25
1247.		3 p. blue	23·00	1·00

1955. 500th Anniv. of Canonization of St. Vincent Ferrer. As T 259 but portrait of the Saint (after C. Vilar).

No.	Type	Description	Unused	Used
1248.		15 c. ochre	70	20

1955. Christmas.

No.	Type	Description	Unused	Used
1249.	269.	80 c. myrtle	5·00	45

1956. 20th Anniv. of Civil War.

No.	Type	Description	Unused	Used
1250.	270.	15 c. brown and bistre	15	10
1251.		50 c. olive and green	1·00	40
1252.		80 c. grey and mauve	9·00	20
1253.		3 p. blue and ultram.	10·00	1·75

271. "Ciudad de Toledo".

272. The "Black Virgin".

1956. First Floating Exhibition of National Products.

No.	Type	Description	Unused	Used
1254.	271.	3 p. blue	6·00	1·75

1956. 75th Anniv of "Black Virgin" of Montserrat.

No.	Type	Description	Unused	Used
1255.	272.	15 c. brown	10	10
1256.	–	60 c. purple	55	30
1257.	272.	80 c. green	75	35

DESIGN—VERT. 60 c. Montserrat Monastery.

273. Archangel Gabriel.

274. "Statistics".

275. Hermitage and Monument.

276. Refugee Children.

1956. Stamp Day.

No.	Type	Description	Unused	Used
1258.	273.	80 c. green	95	50

1956. Centenary of Statistics in Spain.
1259. **274.** 15 c. ochre 40 25
1260. 80 c. green .. .. 5·00 50
1261. 1 p. red .. .. 5·00 50

1956. 20th Anniv. of Gen. Franco's Assumption of Office as Head of State.
1262. **275.** 80 c. green .. .. 4·50 30

1956. Hungarian Children's Relief.
1263. **276.** 10 c. lake 10 10
1264. 15 c. brown 15 10
1265. 50 c. sepia 40 20
1266. 80 c. green .. .. 4·00 15
1267. 1 p. red .. .. 4·00 15
1268. 3 p. blue .. .. 12·00 1·75

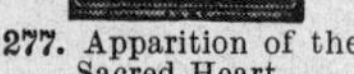

277. Apparition of the Sacred Heart.

278. "The Great Captain".

1957. Stamp Day and Centenary Feast of the Sacred Heart.
1269. **277.** 15 c. olive 10 10
1270. 60 c. purple 50 10
1271. 80 c. green 50 10

1958. 5th Birth Cent. of Gonzalves de Cordoba.
1272. **278.** 1 p. 80 green .. 15 10

279. Francisco Goya after Lopez.

280. Exhibition Emblem.

1958. Stamp Day and Goya (painter) Commem. Frames in gold.
1273. – 15 c. ochre 10 10
1274. – 40 c. purple 10 10
1275. – 50 c. olive 10 10
1276. – 60 c. purple 15 10
1277. – 70 c. green 15 10
1278. **279.** 80 c. myrtle 20 10
1279. – 1 p. red 20 10
1280. – 1 p. 80 green .. 25 10
1281. – 2 p. mauve 55 30
1282. – 3 p. blue .. .. 1·00 50

Paintings—Horiz. 15 c. "The Sunshade". 3 p. "The Drinker". Vert. 40 c. "The Bookseller's Wife". 50 c. "The Count of Fernan-Nunez". 60 c. "The Crockery Vendor". 70 c. "Dona Isabel Cobos de Porcel". 1 p. "The Carnival Doll". 1 p. 80, "Marianito Goya". 2 p. "The Vintage".

For similar designs see Nos. 1301/10, 1333/42, 1391/1400, 1479/88, 1495/8, 1559/68, 1627/36, 1718/27 1770/9 1837/46 1912/21, 1968/77, 2021/30, 2077/84, 2135/42 and 2204/11.

1958. Brussels Int. Exn.
1283 **280** 80 c. brown, red and deep brown 50 10
1284 3 p. blue, red & blk .. 2·00 80

281. Emperor Charles V (after Strigell).

1958. 4th Death Cent. of Emperor Charles V.
1287. **281.** 15 c. brown and ochre 10 10
1288. – 50 c. olive and green 15 10
1289. – 70 c. green and drab 30 20
1290. – 80 c. green and brown 20 10
1291. **281.** 1 p. red and buff .. 40 10
1292. – 1 p. 80 emer. & green 30 20
1293. – 2 p. purple and grey 95 60
1294. – 3 p. blue and brown 2·25 1·25

Portraits of Charles V: 50 c., 1 p. 80, At Battle of Muhlberg (after Titian). 70 c., 2 p. (after Leoni). 80 c., 3 p. (after Titian).

282. Talgo Express and Escorial.

Designs—vert. 60 c., 2 p. Diesel train on viaduct, Despenaperros Gorge. horiz. 80 c., 3 p. Steam locomotive and Castillo de La Mota.

1958. 17th Int. Railway Congress, Madrid. Inscr. "XVII CONGRESO", etc.
1295. **282.** 15 c. ochre 15 50
1296. – 60 c. plum 20 10
1297. – 80 c. green 35 10
1298. **282.** 1 p. orange .. .. 1·00 10
1299. – 2 p. purple .. .. 1·00 10
1300. – 3 p. blue .. .. 3·00 90

1959. Stamp Day and Velazquez Commem. Designs as T **279**. Frames in gold.
1301. 15 c. sepia 10 10
1302. 40 c. purple 10 10
1303. 50 c. olive 10 10
1304. 60 c. sepia 10 10
1305. 70 c. green 10 10
1306. 80 c. myrtle 10 10
1307. 1 p. brown 15 10
1308. 1 p. 80 green 10 10
1309. 2 p. purple 25 20
1310. 3 p. blue 45 45

Paintings—Horiz. 15 c. "The Drunkards". Vert. 40 c. "The Spinners" (detail). 50 c. "The Surrender of Breda". 60 c. "Las Meninas". 70 c. "Balthasar Don Carlos". 80 c. Self-portrait. 1 p. "The Coronation of the Virgin". 1 p. 80, "Aesop". 2 p. "The Forge of Vulcan". 3 p. "Menippus".

284. The Holy Cross of the Valley of the Fallen.

1959. Completion of Holy Cross Monastery.
1311. **284.** 80 c. green and sepia 20 10

285. Mazarin and Luis de Haro (after tapestry by Lebrun).

286. Monastery from Courtyard.

1959. 300th Anniv of Treaty of the Pyrenees.
1312 **285** 1 p. brown and gold .. 20 10

1959. 50th Anniv. of Entry of Franciscan Community into Guadeloupe Monastery.
1313. **286.** 15 c. brown 10 10
1314. – 80 c. myrtle 20 10
1315. – 1 p. red 25 10

Designs: 80 c. Exterior view of monastery. 1 p. Entrance doors of church.

287. "The Holy Family" (after Goya).

288. Pass with Muleta.

1959. Christmas.
1316. **287.** 1 p. brown 30 10

1960. Bullfighting.
1317. – 15 c. brown & ochre (postage) .. 10 10
1318. – 20 c. violet and blue 10 10
1319. – 25 c. black 10 10
1320. – 30 c. sepia and bistre 10 10
1321. – 50 c. violet and sepia 25 10
1322. – 70 c. turq. and brown 25 10
1323. **288.** 80 c. green and turq. 10 10
1324. – 1 p. brown and red .. 55 10
1325. – 1 p. 40 red and brown 10 10
1326. – 1 p. 50 green and blue 10 10
1327. – 1 p. 80 blue and green 10 10
1328. – 5 p. lake and brown .. 1·10 60
1329. – 25 c. pur. & mve. (air) 15 10
1330. – 50 c. blue & turquoise 20 10
1331. – 1 p. red and deep red 45 10
1332. – 5 p. violet and purple 1·10 50

Designs—Horiz. No. 1317, Fighting bull. No. 1318, Rounding-up bull. No. 1327, Placing darts from horseback. No. 1330, Pass with cape. No. 1332, Bull-ring. vert. No. 1319, Corralling bulls at Pamplona. No. 1320, Bull entering ring. No. 1321, As No. 1330 (different pass). No. 1322, Banderillero placing darts. No. 1323/6, As Type **288** (different passes with muleta). No. 1328, Old-time bull-fighter. No. 1329, Village bull-ring. No. 1331, Dedicating the bull.

1960. Stamp Day and Murillo Commem. (painter). Designs as T **279**. Frames in gold.
1333. 25 c. violet 10 10
1334. 40 c. purple 15 10
1335. 50 c. deep olive 20 10
1336. 70 c. green 20 10
1337. 80 c. turquoise 20 10
1338. 1 p. brown 20 10
1339. 1 p. 50 turquoise .. 20 10
1340. 2 p. 50 red 30 10
1341. 3 p. blue .. .. 1·40 65
1342. 5 p. brown 50 25

Paintings—vert. 25 c. "The Good Shepherd". 40 c. "Rebecca and Elizer". 50 c. "The Virgin of the Rosary". 70 c. "The Immaculate Conception". 80 c. "Children with Shells". 1 p. Self-portrait. 2 p. 50, "The Dice Game". 3 p. "Children Eating". 5 p. "Children with Coins". horiz. 1 p. 50, "The Holy Family with Bird".

289. "Christ of Lepanto".

290. Pelota Player.

1960. Int. Philatelic Congress and Exn. Barcelona. Inscr. "CIF".
1343. **289.** 70 c. lake & grn. (post.) 2·00 1·50
1344. – 80 c. black and sage .. 2·00 1·50
1345. **289.** 1 p. purple and red .. 2·00 1·50
1346. – 2 p. 50 slate and violet 2·00 1·50
1347. **289.** 5 p. sepia and bistre .. 2·00 1·50
1348. – 10 p. sepia and ochre 2·00 1·50
1349. **290.** 1 p. black & red (air) 4·50 3·25
1350. 5 p. red and brown .. 4·50 3·25
1351. 6 p. red and purple .. 4·50 3·25
1352. 10 p. red and green .. 4·50 3·25

Design—vert. Nos. 1344, 1346, 1348, Church of the Holy Family, Barcelona.

291. St. John of Ribera. **292.** St. Vincent de Paul. **293.** Menendez de Aviles.

1960. Canonization of St. John of Ribera.
1353. **291.** 1 p. brown 40 10
1354. 2 p. 50 mauve 10 10

1960. Europa. 1st Anniv of European Postal and Telecommunications Conference. As T **129a** of Luxembourg but size $38\frac{1}{2} \times 22$ mm.
1355. 1 p. drab and myrtle 2·25 20
1356. 5 p. red and brown .. 2·25 35

1960. 300th Death Anniv of St. Vincent de Paul.
1357 **292** 25 c. violet 10 10
1358 1 p. brown 30 10

1960. 400th Anniv. of Discovery and Colonization of Florida.
1359. **293.** 25 c. violet and blue 10 10
1360. – 70 c. myrtle & salmon 10 10
1361. – 80 c. green and stone 10 10
1362. – 1 p. brown and yellow 15 10
1363. **293.** 2 p. red and pink .. 30 10
1364. – 2 p. 50 mauve & olive 50 10
1365. – 3 p. blue and green .. 2·25 40
1366. – 5 p. sepia and bistre 1·75 75

Portraits: 70 c., 2 p. 50, Hernando de Soto. 80 c., 3 p. Ponce de Leon. 1 p., 5 p. Cabeza de Vaca.

INDEX

Countries can be quickly located by referring to the index at the end of this volume.

294. Running.

295. Albeniz.

296. Cloisters.

297. "The Nativity" (Velazquez).

1960. Sports.
1367. **294.** 25 c. brown and violet-blue (postage) .. 10 10
1368. – 40 c. orange and violet 10 10
1369. – 70 c. red and green .. 30 10
1370. – 80 c. red and green .. 20 10
1371. – 1 p. green and red .. 60 10
1372. **294.** 1 p. 50 sepia & turq. 30 10
1373. – 2 p. green and purple 80 10
1374. – 2 p. 50 green & mauve 30 10
1375. – 3 p. red and blue .. 45 15
1376. – 5 p. blue and brown .. 80 30
1377. – 1 p. 25 red & brn. (air) 35 10
1378. – 1 p. 50 brown & violet 35 10
1379. – 6 p. red and violet .. 80 45
1380. – 10 p. red and olive .. 95 55

Designs—horiz. 40 c., 2 p. Cycling. 70 c., 2 p. 50, Football. 1 p., 5 p. Hockey. 1 p. 25, 6 p. Horse-jumping. vert. 80 c., 3 p. Gymnastics. 1 p. 50 (air), 10 p. Pelota.

1960. Birth Cent. of Isaac Albeniz (composer).
1381. **295.** 25 c. violet 10 10
1382. 1 p. brown 30 10

1960. Samos Monastery.
1383. **296.** 80 c. turq. and green 10 10
1384. – 1 p. lake and brown 1·50 10
1385. – 5 p. sepia and bistre 90 50

Designs—vert. 1 p. Fountain. 5 p. Portico and facade.

1960. Christmas.
1386. **297.** 1 p. brown 20 10

298. "The Flight to Egypt" (after Bayeu).

299. L. F. Moratin (after Goya).

1961. World Refugee Year.
1387. **298.** 1 p. brown 45 10
1388. 5 p. brown 80 10

1961. Birth Bicentenary of Moratin (poet and dramatist).
1389 **299** 1 p. red 20 10
1390 1 p. 50 turquoise .. 10 10

1961. Stamp Day and El Greco Commem. (painter). Designs as T **279**. Frames in gold.
1391. 25 c. purple 25 10
1392. 40 c. purple 20 10
1393. 70 c. green 25 20
1394. 80 c. turquoise 25 10
1395. 1 p. purple .. .. 2·00 10
1396. 1 p. 50 turquoise .. 35 10
1397. 2 p. 50 lake 35 10
1398. 3 p. blue .. .. 1·00 70
1399. 5 p. sepia .. .. 2·50 1·75
1400. 10 p. violet 50 40

Paintings: 25 c. "St. Peter". 40 c. Part of "The Holy Family". 70 c. Part of "The Agony in the Garden". 80 c. "Man with Hand on Breast". 1 p. Self-portrait. 1 p. 50, "The Baptism of Christ". 2 p. 50, "The Holy Trinity". 3 p. "Burial of the Count of Orgaz". 5 p. "The Spoliation". 10 p. "The Martyrdom of St. Maurice".

301. Velazquez (Prado Memorial).

302. "Stamp" and "Postmark".

1961. 300th Death Anniv of Velazquez.
1401. **301.** 80 c. green and blue 1·40 20
1402. – 1 p. brown and red .. 2·75 20
1403. – 2 p. 50 violet and blue 85 30
1404. – 10 p. grn. & light grn. 2·25 80
PAINTINGS—VERT. 1 p. "The Duke of Olivares". 2 p. 50, "Princess Margarita. HORIZ. Part of "The Spinners".

1961. World Stamp Day.
1409. **302.** 25 c. black and red .. 15 10
1410. 1 p. red and black .. 1·60 10
1411. 10 p. green and purple 1·60 50

303. Vazquez de Mella. **304.** Gen. Franco.

1961. Birth Centenary of Juan Vazquez de Mella (politician and writer).
1412 **303** 1 p. red 50 10
1413 2 p. 30 purple .. 15 15

1961. 25th Anniv. of National Uprising. Multicoloured.
1414 70 c. Angel and flag .. 20 10
1415 80 c. Straits of Gibraltar 20 10
1416 1 p. Knight and Alcazar, Toledo 35 10
1417 1 p. 50 Victory Arch .. 25 10
1418 2 p. Knight crossing River Ebro 25 10
1419 2 p. 30 Soldier, flag and troops 25 10
1420 2 p. 50 Shipbuilding 30 30
1421 3 p. Steelworks .. 40 30
1422 5 p. Map of Spain showing electric power stations 2·75 1·25
1423 6 p. Irrigation (woman beside dam) .. 1·50 1·00
1424 8 p. Mine .. .. 1·00 55
1425 10 p. Type **304** .. 75 55
The 5 p. is horiz and the rest vert.

305. " Portico de la Gloria " (Cathedral of Santiago de Compostela). **306.** L. de Gongora (after Velazquez).

1961. Council of Europe's Romanesque Art Exhibition. Inscr. as in T **305.**
1426. **305.** 25 c. violet and gold 45 10
1427. – 1 p. brown and gold 45 10
1428. – 2 p. purple and gold 60 10
1429. – 3 p. multicoloured .. 1·00 15
DESIGNS: 1 p. Courtyard of Dominican Monastery, Santo Domingo de Silos. 2 p. Madonna of Irache. 3 p. " Christos Pantocrator " (from Tahull Church fresco).

1961. 400th Birth Anniv. of De Gongora (poet).
1430. **306.** 25 c. violet .. 10 10
1431. 1 p. brown .. 20 10

307. Doves and C.E.P.T. Emblem. **308.** Burgos Cathedral.

1961. Europa.
1432. **307.** 1 p. red 15 10
1433. 5 p. brown 40 30

1961. 25th Anniv. of Gen. Franco as Head of State.
1434. **308.** 1 p. green and gold .. 20 10

309. S. de Belalcazar.

310. Courtyard.

1961. Explorers and Colonizers of America (1st series).
1435. **309.** 25 c. violet and green 10 10
1436. – 70 c. green and buff .. 15 10
1437. – 80 c. green and pink .. 15 10
1438. – 1 p. blue and flesh .. 55 10
1439. **309.** 2 p. red and blue .. 3·50 10
1440. – 2 p. 50 purple & mve. 80 35
1441. – 3 p. blue and grey .. 1·75 60
1442. – 5 p. brown & yellow 1·90 75
PORTRAITS: 70 c., 2 p. 50, B de Lezo. 80 c., 3 p. R. de Bastidas. 1 p., 5 p. N. de Chaves.
See also Nos. 1515/22, 1587/94, 1683/90, 1738/45, 1810/17, 1877/84, 1947/51, 1997/2001 and 2054/8.

1961. Escorial.
1443. – 70 c. green and turq. 20 10
1444. **310.** 80 c. slate and green 20 10
1445. – 1 p. red and brown .. 65 10
1446. – 2 p. 50 purple & violet 50 10
1447. – 5 p. sepia and ochre .. 1·75 55
1448. – 6 p. purple and blue 2·00 1·40
DESIGNS—VERT. 70 c. Patio of the Kings. 2 p. 50, Grand Staircase. 6 p. High Altar. HORIZ. 1 p. Monk's Garden. 5 p. View of Escorial.

311. King Alfonso XII Monument. **312.** Santa Maria del Naranco Church.

1961. 400th Anniv of Madrid as Capital of Spain.
1449. **311.** 25 c. purple and green 25 10
1450. – 1 p. brown and bistre 45 10
1451. – 2 p. purple and grey 45 10
1452. – 2 p. 50 violet and red 40 10
1453. – 3 p. black and blue .. 90 40
1454. – 5 p. blue and brown 2·00 55
DESIGNS—VERT. 1 p. King Philip II (after Pantoja.) 5 p. Plaza, Madrid. HORIZ. 2 p. Town Hall, Madrid. 2 p. 50, Fountain of Cybele. 3 p. Portals of Alcala Palace.

1961. 1200th Anniv of Oviedo.
1455. **312.** 25 c. violet and green 10 10
1456. – 1 p. brown and bistre 35 10
1457. – 2 p. sepia and purple 75 10
1458. – 2 p. 50 violet & purple 20 10
1459. – 3 p. black and blue .. 75 40
1460. – 5 p. brown and green 1·10 55
DESIGNS: 1 p. Fruela (portrait). 2 p. Cross of the Angels. 2 p. 50, Alfonso II. 3 p. Alfonso III. 5 p. Apostles of the Holy Hall, Oviedo Cathedral.

313. " The Nativity " (after Gines). **314.** Cierva Autogyro.

1961. Christmas.
1461. **313.** 1 p. plum 30 10

1961. 50th Anniv. of Spanish Aviation.
1462. **314.** 1 p. violet and blue .. 20 10
1463. – 2 p. green and lilac .. 40 15
1464. – 3 p. black and green .. 2·25 40
1465. – 5 p. purple and slate 4·25 1·40
1466. – 10 p. brown and blue 1·90 50
DESIGNS—HORIZ. 2 p. " Plus Ultra " flying-boat (Dornier WAL). 3 p. Madrid–Manila flight plane " Jesus del Gran Poder " (Breguet 19 GR). VERT. 5 p. Avro " 504 K " 'plane hunting Great Bustard. 10 p. Madonna of Loreto (patron saint).

315. Arms of Alava. **316.** " Ecstasy of St. Teresa " (Bernini).

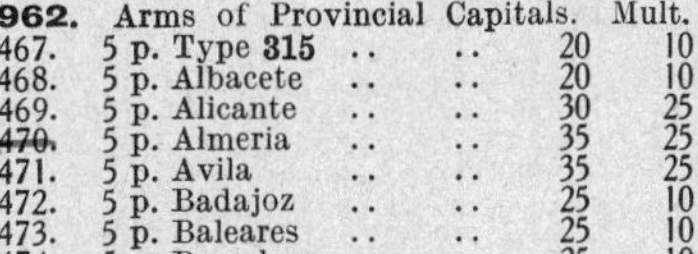

1962. Arms of Provincial Capitals. Mult.
1467. 5 p. Type **315** 20 10
1468. 5 p. Albacete 20 10
1469. 5 p. Alicante 30 25
1470. 5 p. Almeria 35 25
1471. 5 p. Avila 35 25
1472. 5 p. Badajoz 25 10
1473. 5 p. Baleares 25 10
1474. 5 p. Barcelona 25 10
1475. 5 p. Burgos .. .. 1·10 30
1476. 5 p. Caceres 75 20
1477. 5 p. Cadiz 90 25
1478. 5 p. Castellon de la Plana 6·00 1·75
See also Nos. 1542/53, 1612/23, 1692/1703 and 1756/64.

1962. Stamp Day and Zurbaran Commem. (painter). Designs as T **279.** Frames in gold.
1479. 25 c. olive 10 10
1480. 40 c. purple 10 10
1481. 70 c. green 15 10
1482. 80 c. turquoise 15 10
1483. 1 p. sepia .. .. 2·75 10
1484. 1 p. 50 turquoise .. 40 10
1485. 2 p. 50 lake 40 10
1486. 3 p. blue 40 35
1487. 5 p. brown .. .. 1·10 80
1488. 10 p. olive .. .. 1·10 85
PAINTINGS—HORIZ. 25 c. " Martyr ". VERT. 40 c. " Burial of St. Catalina ". 70 c. " St. Casilda ". 80 c. " Jesus crowning St. Joseph ". 1 p. Self-portrait. 1 p. 50, " St. Hieronymus ". 2 p. 50, " Madonna of the Grace ". 3 p. Detail from " Apotheosis of St. Thomas Aquinas ". 5 p. " Madonna as a Child ". 10 p. " The Immaculate Madonna ".

1962. 4th Cent. of Teresian Reformation.
1489. – 25 c. violet 10 10
1490. **316.** 1 p. brown 20 10
1491. – 3 p. blue .. .. 1·40 20
DESIGNS—As Type **316**: 25 c. St. Joseph's Monastery, Avila. ($22 \times 38\frac{1}{2}$ mm): 3 p. "St. Teresa of Avila" (Velazquez).

317. Mercury. **318.** St. Benedict. **319.** El Cid (R. Diaz de Vivar), after statue by J. Cristobal.

1962. World Stamp Day.
1492. **317.** 25 c. pink, pur. & vio. 10 10
1493. 1 p. yellow, brown and bistre 20 10
1494. 10 p. green & turq... 1·75 55

1962. Rubens Paintings. Designs as T **279.** Frames in gold.
1495. 25 c. violet 40 15
1496. 1 p. brown .. .. 2·00 10
1497. 3 p. turquoise .. .. 2·00 1·00
1498. 10 p. green .. .. 2·00 1·25
PAINTINGS—As Type **279**: 25 c. Ferdinand of Austria. 1 p. Self-portrait. 3 p. Philip II. (26×39 mm): 10 p. Duke Lerma.

1962. 400th Death Anniv. of Alonso Berruguete (sculptor). Sculptures by Berruguete.
1499. **318.** 25 c. mauve and blue 10 10
1500. – 80 c. green and brown 25 10
1501. – 1 p. red and stone .. 50 10
1502. – 2 p. mauve and stone 3·00 10
1503. – 3 p. blue and mauve 1·25 75
1504. – 10 p. brown and pink 1·25 50
SCULPTURES: 80 c. " The Apostle ". 1 p. " St. Peter ". 2 p. " St. Christopher and Child Jesus ". 3 p. " Ecce Homo ". 10 p. " St. Sebastian ".

1962. El Cid Campeador Commem. Inscr. " EL CID ".
1505. **319.** 1 p. drab and green .. 15 10
1506. – 2 p. violet and sepia .. 1·25 10
1507. – 3 p. green and blue .. 3·50 1·10
1508. – 10 p. green and yellow 1·75 75
DESIGNS—VERT. 2 p. El Cid (equestrian statue by A. Huntington). HORIZ. 3 p. El Cid's treasure chest. 10 p. Oath-taking ceremony of Santa Gadea.

320. Bee and Honeycomb. **321.** Throwing the Discus.

1962. Europa.
1509. **320.** 1 p. red 40 10
1510. 5 p. green .. 1·50 30

1962. 2nd Spanish-American Athletic Games, Madrid.
1511. **321.** 25 c. violet & pale pink 10 10
1512. – 80 c. green and yellow 40 10
1513. – 1 p. sepia and salmon 20 10
1514. – 3 p. blue and pale blue 20 15
DESIGNS: 80 c. Running. 1 p. Hurdling. 3 p. Start of sprint.

1962. Explorers and Colonizers of America (2nd series). As T **309.**
1515. 25 c. purple and grey .. 10 10
1516. 70 c. green and pale pink 70 10
1517. 80 c. green and yellow .. 55 10
1518. 1 p. brown and green .. 95 10
1519. 2 p. lake and pale blue .. 2·50 10
1520. 2 p. 50 violet & pale brn. 55 20
1521. 3 p. blue and pink .. 6·00 75
1522. 5 p. brown & pale yellow 2·75 1·00
PORTRAITS: 25 c., 2 p. A. de Mendoza. 70 c., 2 p. 50, J. de Quesada. 80 c., 3 p. J. de Garay 1 p., 5 p. P. de la Gasca.

322. U.P.A.E. Emblem. **323.** " The Annunciation " (after Murillo).

1962. 50th Anniv of Postal Union of the Americas and Spain.
1523 **322** 1 p. brn, grn & dp grn 20 10

1962. Mysteries of the Rosary.
1524. **323.** 25 c. brn. & vio. (post.) 10 10
1525. – 70 c. turq. and green 10 10
1526. – 80 c. turq. and olive 10 10
1527. – 1 p. sepia and green 2·25 60
1528. – 1 p. 50 blue and green 10 5
1529. – 2 p. sepia and violet .. 70 40
1530. – 2 p. 50 red and purple 20 15
1531. – 3 p. black and violet 20 15
1532. – 5 p. lake and brown .. 35 35
1533. – 8 p. black and purple 35 30
1534. – 10 p. green and myrtle 50 30
1535. – 25 c. violet and slate (air) 10 5
1536. – 1 p. olive and purple 20 15
1537. – 5 p. lake and purple .. 35 25
1538. – 10 p. yell.-grn. & grey 85 55
PAINTINGS—" Joyful Mysteries ": No. 1525, " Visit of Elizabeth " (Correa). No. 1526, " The Birth of Christ " (Murillo). No. 1527, " Christ shown to the Elders " (Campana). No. 1528, " Jesus lost and found in the Temple " (unknown artist). " Sorrowful Mysteries ": No. 1529, " Prayer on the Mount of Olives " (Giaquinto). No. 1530, " Scourging " (Cano). No. 1531, " The Crown of Thorns " (Tiepolo). No. 1532, " Carrying the cross " (El Greco). No. 1533, " The Crucifixion " (Murillo). " Glorious Mysteries ": No. 1534, " The Resurrection " (Murillo). No. 1535, " The Ascension " (Bayeu). No. 1536, " The Sending-forth of the Holy Ghost " (El Greco). No. 1537 " The Assumption of the Virgin " (Cerezo). No. 1538, " The Coronation of the Virgin " (El Greco).

324. " The Nativity " (after Pedro de Mena). **325.** Campaign Emblem and Swamp.

1962. Christmas.
1539. **324.** 1 p. olive 50 10

1962. Malaria Eradication.
1540. **325.** 1 p. blk., yell. & grn. 30 10

326. Pope John and Dome of St. Peter's. **327.** "St. Paul" (after El Greco)

1962. Ecumenical Council. Vatican City (1st issue).
1541. **326.** 1 p. slate and purple 30 10
See also Nos. 1601 and 1755.

1963. Arms of Provincial Capitals. As T **315.** Multicoloured.
1542. 5 p. Ciudad Real .. 75 25
1543. 5 p. Cordoba .. .. 6·00 1·50
1544. 5 p. Coruna 75 30
1545. 5 p. Cuenca 75 30
1546. 5 p. Fernando Poo .. 1·50 90
1547. 5 p. Gerona 15 10
1548. 5 p. Gran Canaria .. 15 10
1549. 5 p. Granada 30 20
1550. 5 p. Guadalajara .. 75 25
1551. 5 p. Guipuzcoa 15 10
1552. 5 p. Huelva 15 10
1553. 5 p. Huesca 15 10

1963. 1900th Anniv. of Arrival of St. Paul in Spain.
1554. **327.** 1 p. sepia, olive & brn. 50 10

328. Poblet Monastery. **329.** Mail Coach.

1963. Poblet Monastery.
1555. **328.** 25 c. pur., sepia & grn. 10 10
1556. – 1 p. orange and red .. 50 10
1557. – 3 p. blue and violet .. 1·00 20
1558. – 5 p. ochre and brown 1·75 1·00
DESIGNS—VERT. 1 p. Tomb. 5 p. Arch. HORIZ. 3 p. Aerial view of monastery.

1963. Stamp Day and Ribera Commem. (painter). As T **279.** Frames in gold.
1559. 25 c. violet 10 10
1560. 40 c. purple 10 10
1561. 70 c. green 25 10
1562. 80 c. turquoise 25 10
1563. 1 p. brown 25 10
1564. 1 p. 50 turquoise .. 25 10
1565. 2 p. 50 red .. .. 1·10 15
1566. 3 p. blue .. .. .. 1·10 30
1567. 5 p. brown .. .. 4·50 1·40
1568. 10 p. brown-purple .. 1·10 70
PAINTINGS: 25 c. "Archimedes". 40 c. "Jacob's Flock". 70 c. "Triumph of Bacchus". 80 c. "St. Christopher". 1 p. Self-portrait. 1 p. 50, "St. Andrew". 2 p. 50, "St. John the Baptist". 3 p. "St. Onofrius". 5 p. "St. Peter". 10 p. "The Madonna".

1963. Cent of Paris Postal Conference.
1569 **329** 1 p. multicoloured .. 10 10

330. Globe.

1963. World Stamp Day.
1570. **330.** 25 c. multicoloured .. 15 10
1571. 1 p. multicoloured .. 25 10
1572. 10 p. multicoloured .. 1·75 30

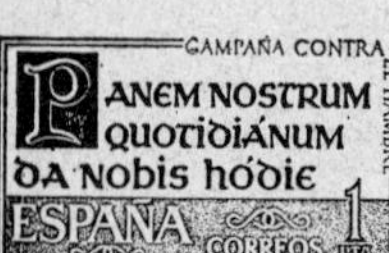

331. "Give us this day our daily bread". **332.** Pillars and Globes.

1963. Freedom from Hunger.
1573. **331.** 1 p. multicoloured .. 20 10

1963. Spanish Cultural Institutions Congress. Multicoloured.
1574. 25 c. Type **332** 15 10
1575. 80 c. "Santa Maria", "Pinta" and "Nina" 30 10
1576. 1 p. Columbus 30 10

333. Civic Seals. **334.** "St. Maria of Europe".

1963. 150th Anniv. of San Sebastian.
1577. **333.** 25 c. blue and green .. 10 10
1578. – 80 c. red and purple 20 10
1579. – 1 p. green and bistre 20 10
DESIGNS: 80 c. City aflame. 1 p. View of San Sebastian, 1836.

1963. Europa.
1580. **334.** 1 p. brown and bistre 30 10
1581. 5 p. sepia and green .. 80 30

335. Arms of the Order of Mercy. **336.** Scenes from parable of the Good Samaritan.

1963. 75th Anniv of the Order of Mercy.
1582. **335.** 25 c. red, gold & blk. 10 10
1583. – 80 c. sepia and green 10 10
1584. – 1 p. purple and blue 15 15
1585. – 1 p. 50 brown & blue 15 10
1586. – 3 p. black and violet 25 15
DESIGNS: 80 c. King Jaime I. 1 p. Our Lady of Mercy. 1 p. 50, St. Pedro Nolasco. 3 p. St. Raimundo de Penafort.

1963. Explorers and Colonizers of America (3rd series). As T **309.**
1587. 25 c. deep blue and blue 25 10
1588. 70 c. green and salmon .. 25 10
1589. 80 c. green and cream .. 50 10
1590. 1 p. blue and salmon .. 50 10
1591. 2 p. red and blue .. 2·00 10
1592. 2 p. 50 violet and flesh .. 1·25 10
1593. 3 p. deep blue and pink 2·25 10
1594. 5 p. brown and cream .. 2·50 1·40
PORTRAITS: 25 c., 2 p. Brother J. Serra. 70 c., 2 p. 50, Vasco Nunez de Balboa. 80 c., 3 p. J. de Galvez. 1 p., 5 p. D. Garcia de Paredes.

1963. Red Cross Cent.
1595. **336.** 1 p. violet, red & gold 15 10

337. "The Nativity" (after sculpture by Berruguete). **338.** Fr. Raimundo Lulio.

1963. Christmas.
1596. **337.** 1 p. green 15 10

1963. Famous Spaniards (1st series).
1597. **338.** 1 p. blk. & vio. (post.) 25 10
1598. – 1 p. 50 violet & sepia 25 10
1599. – 25 p. purple and red (air) .. .. 1·25 25
1600. – 50 p. black and green 1·25 40
PORTRAITS: 1 p. 50, Cardinal Belluga. 25 p. King Recaredo. 50 p. Cardinal Cisneros.
See also Nos. 1714/17.

339. Pope Paul and Dome of St. Peter's.

1963. Ecumenical Council, Vatican City (2nd issue).
1601. **339.** 1 p. black & turquoise 20 10

340. Alcazar de Segovia. **341.** Santa Maria Monastery.

1964. Tourist Series.
1602. – 40 c. brn., blue & grn. 15 10
1603. – 50 c. sepia and blue .. 15 10
1604. – 70 c. blue and green .. 15 10
1605. – 70 c. brown and lilac 15 10
1606. – 80 c. black and blue .. 25 10
1607. **340.** 1 p. lilac and violet .. 15 10
1608. – 1 p. red and purple .. 15 10
1609. – 1 p. black and green .. 15 10
1610. – 1 p. red and purple .. 15 10
1611. – 1 p. 50 brown, green and blue 15 10
DESIGNS—HORIZ. No. 1602, Potes. No. 1604, Crypt of St. Isidore (Leon). No. 1608, Lion Court of the Alhambra (Granada). No. 1611, Gerona. VERT. No. 1603, Leon Cathedral. No. 1605, Costa Brava. No. 1606, "Christ of the Lanterns" (Cordoba). No. 1609, Drach Caves (Majorca). No. 1610, Mosque (Cordoba).
See also Nos. 1704/13, 1786/95, 1798/1805, 1860/6, 1867/74, 1933/42, 1985/9, 1993/6, 2035/9, 2040/5, 2311/6, 2379/84, 2466/7, 2575/8, 2696/2700, 2744/8, 2858/9, 2870/1, and 2915/18.

1964. Arms of Provincial Capitals. As T **315.** Multicoloured.
1612. 5 p. Ifni 25 10
1613. 5 p. Jaen 25 10
1614. 5 p. Leon 25 10
1615. 5 p. Lerida 25 10
1616. 5 p. Logrono 25 10
1617. 5 p. Lugo 25 10
1618. 5 p. Madrid 25 10
1619. 5 p. Malaga 25 10
1620. 5 p. Murcia 25 10
1621. 5 p. Navarra 25 10
1622. 5 p. Orense 25 10
1623. 5 p. Oviedo 25 10

1964. Monastery of Santa Maria, Huerta.
1624. – 1 p. bronze and green 10 10
1625. – 2 p. sepia, blk. & turq. 10 10
1626. **341.** 5 p. slate and violet .. 1·50 40
DESIGNS—VERT. 1 p. Great Hall. 2 p. Cloisters.

1964. Stamp Day and Sorolla Commem. (painter). As T **279.** Frames in gold.
1627. 25 c. violet 10 10
1628. 40 c. purple 10 10
1629. 70 c. green 10 10
1630. 80 c. turquoise 10 10
1631. 1 p. brown 10 10
1632. 1 p. 50 turquoise .. 10 10
1633. 2 p. 50 mauve 15 10
1634. 3 p. blue 40 20
1635. 5 p. brown .. .. 1·00 75
1636. 10 p. green 60 20
PAINTINGS—VERT. 25 c. "The Earthen Jar". 70 c. "La Mancha Types". 80 c. "Valencian Fisherwoman". 1 p. Self-portrait. 5 p. "Pulling the Boat". 10 p. "Valencian Couple on Horse". HORIZ. 40 c. "Castilian Oxherd". 1 p. 50, "The Cattlepen". 2 p. 50, "And people say fish is dear" (fish market). 3 p. "Children on the Beach".

342. "25 Years of Peace".

1964. 25th Anniv. of End of Spanish Civil War.
1637. **342.** 25 c. gold, grn. & blk. 10 10
1638. – 30 c. salmon, blue and green 10 10
1639. – 40 c. black and gold .. 10 10
1640. – 50 c. multicoloured .. 10 10
1641. – 70 c. multicoloured .. 10 10
1642. – 80 c. multicoloured .. 10 10
1643. – 1 p. multicoloured .. 35 10
1644. – 1 p. 50 olive, red & blue 25 10
1645. – 2 p. multicoloured .. 25 10
1646. – 2 p. 50 multicoloured 25 10
1647. – 3 p. multicoloured .. 1·25 50
1648. – 5 p. red, green & gold 50 25
1649. – 6 p. multicoloured .. 80 40
1650. – 10 p. multicoloured .. 80 40
DESIGNS—VERT. 30 c. Athletes ("Sport"). 50 c. Apartment-houses ("National Housing Plan"). 1 p. Graph and symbols ("Economic Development"). 1 p. 50, Rocks and tower ("Construction"). 2 p. 50, Wheatear and dam ("Irrigation"). 5 p. "Tree of Learning" ("Scientific Research"). 10 p. Gen. Franco. HORIZ. 40 c. T.V. screen and symbols ("Radio and T.V."). 70 c. Wheatears, tractor and landscape ("Agriculture"). 80 c. Tree and forests ("Reafforestation"). 2 p. Forms of transport ("Transport and Communications"). 3 p. Pylon and part of dial ("Electrification"). 6 p. Ancient buildings ("Tourism").

343. Spanish Pavilion at Fair. **344.** 6 c. Stamp of 1850 and Globe.

1964. New York World's Fair.
1651. **343.** 1 p. green & turquoise 35 10
1652. – 1 p. 50 brown & red 10 10
1653. – 2 p. 50 green and blue 15 10
1654. – 5 p. red 45 45
1655. – 50 p. blue and grey .. 1·50 40
DESIGNS—VERT. 1 p. 50, Bullfighting. 2 p. 50, Castillo de la Mota. 5 p. Spanish dancing. 50 p. Pelota.

1964. World Stamp Day.
1656. **344.** 25 c. red and purple .. 10 10
1657. 1 p. green and blue .. 25 10
1658. 10 p. orange and red 65 30

345. Macarena Virgin. **346.** Medieval Ship.

1964. Canonical Coronation of Macarena Virgin.
1659. **345.** 1 p. green and yellow 15 10

1964. Spanish Navy Commem.
1660. **346.** 15 c. slate and purple 10 10
1661. – 25 c. green and orange 10 10
1662. – 40 c. grey and blue .. 10 10
1663. – 50 c. green and slate 10 10
1664. – 70 c. violet and blue 10 10
1665. – 80 c. blue and green 10 10
1666. – 1 p. purple and brown 10 10
1667. – 1 p. 50 sepia and red 10 10
1668. – 2 p. black and green 1·00 10
1669. – 2 p. 50 red and violet 25 10
1670. – 3 p. blue and brown 25 10
1671. – 5 p. blue and green .. 1·10 55
1672. – 6 p. violet & turquoise 70 50
1673. – 10 p. red and orange 70 30
SHIPS—VERT. 25 c. Carrack. 1 p. Ship of the line "Santissima Trinidad". 1 p. 50, Corvette "Atrevida". HORIZ. 40 c. "Santa Maria". 50 c. Galley. 70 c. Galleon. 80 c. Xebec. 2 p. Steam frigate "Isabel II". 2 p. 50, Frigate "Numancia". 3 p. Destroyer "Destructor". 5 p. Isaac Peral's submarine. 6 p. Cruiser "Baleares". 10 p. Cadet schooner "Juan Sebastian de Elcano".

347. Europa "Flower". **348.** "The Virgin of the Castle".

1964. Europa.
1674. **347.** 1 p. ochre, red & green 50 10
1675. 5 p. blue, purple & grn. 1·50 35

1964. 700th Anniv. of Reconquest of Jerez.
1676. **348.** 25 c. brown and buff 15 10
1677. 1 p. blue and grey .. 15 10

349. Putting the Shot. **350.** "Adoration of the Shepherds" (after Zurbaran).

1965. Olympic Games, Tokyo and Innsbruck. Olympic rings in gold.
1678. **349.** 25 c. blue and orange 10 10
1679. – 80 c. blue and green 10 10
1680. – 1 p. blue & light blue 10 10
1681. – 3 p. blue and buff .. 15 15
1682. – 5 p. blue and violet .. 15 15
DESIGNS: 80 c. Long jumping. 1 p. Skiing (slalom). 3 p. Judo. 5 p. Throwing the discus.

1964. Explorers and Colonizers of America (4th series). As T **309.** Inscr. "1964" at foot.
1683. 25 c. violet and pale blue 10 10
1684. 70 c. olive and pink .. 10 10
1685. 80 c. green and buff .. 30 20
1686. 1 p. violet and buff .. 30 10
1687. 2 p. olive and blue .. 30 10
1688. 2 p. 50 purple and turq. 20 15
1689. 3 p. blue and grey .. 2·00 55
1690. 5 p. brown and cream .. 1·40 70
PORTRAITS: 25 c., 2 p. D. de Almagro. 70 c., 2 p. 50, F. de Toledo. 80 c., 3 p. T. de Mogrovejo. 1 p., 5 p. F. Pizarro.

1964. Christmas.
1691. **350.** 1 p. brown 10 10

1965. Arms of Provincial Capitals. As T **315.** Multicoloured.
1692. 5 p. Palencia 25 10
1693. 5 p. Pontevedra 25 10
1694. 5 p. Rio Muni 25 10
1695. 5 p. Sahara 25 10
1696. 5 p. Salamanca 25 10
1697. 5 p. Santander 25 10
1698. 5 p. Segovia 25 10
1699. 5 p. Seville 25 10
1700. 5 p. Soria 25 10
1701. 5 p. Tarragona 25 10
1702. 5 p. Tenerife 25 10
1703. 5 p. Teruel 25 10

1965. Tourist Series. As T **340.**
1704. 25 c. black and blue .. 20 10
1705. 30 c. brown and turquoise 20 10
1706. 50 c. purple and red .. 20 10
1707. 70 c. indigo and blue .. 20 10
1708. 80 c. purple and mauve 20 10
1709. 1 p. mauve, red and sepia 20 10
1710. 2 p. 50 purple and brown 20 10
1711. 2 p. 50 olive and blue .. 20 10
1712. 3 p. purple and purple .. 20 10
1713. 6 p. violet and slate .. 20 10
DESIGNS—VERT. 25 c. Columbus Monument, Barcelona. 30 c. Santa Maria Church, Burgos. 50 c. Synagogue, Toledo. 80 c. Seville Cathedral. 1 p. Cudillero Port. 2 p. 50 (No. 1710), Burgos Cathedral (interior). 3 p. Bridge at Cambados (Pontevedra). 6 p. Ceiling, Lonja (Valencia). HORIZ. 70 c. Zamora. 2 p. 50 (No. 1711), Mogrovejo (Santander).

1965. Famous Spaniards (2nd series). As T **338.**
1714. 25 c. sepia and turquoise 10 10
1715. 70 c. deep blue and blue 20 10
1716. 2 p. 50 sepia and bronze 20 10
1717. 5 p. bronze and green .. 40 10
PORTRAITS: 25 c. Donoso Cortes. 70 c. King Alfonso X (the Saint). 2 p. 50, G. M. de Jovellanos. 5 p. St. Dominic de Guzman.

1965. Stamp Day and J. Romero de Torres Commem. Designs as T **279**. Frames in gold.
1718. 25 c. purple 10 10
1719. 40 c. purple 10 10
1720. 70 c. green 10 10
1721. 80 c. turquoise 10 10
1722. 1 p. brown 10 10
1723. 1 p. 50 turquoise 10 10
1724. 2 p. 50 mauve 10 10
1725. 3 p. blue 15 10
1726. 5 p. brown 25 10
1727. 10 p. green 30 15
PAINTINGS (by J. Romero de Torres): 25 c. "Girl with Jar". 40 c. "The Song". 70 c. "The Virgin of the Lanterns". 80 c. "Girl with Guitar". 1 p. Self-portrait. 1 p. 50, "Poem of Cordoba". 2 p. 50, "Marta and Maria". 3 p. "Poem of Cordoba" (different). 5 p. "A Little Charcoal-maker". 10 p. "Long Live the Hair!".

351. Bulls and Stamps. **352.** I.T.U. Emblem and Symbols.

1965. World Stamp Day.
1728. **351.** 25 c. multicoloured 10 10
1729. 1 p. multicoloured 20 10
1730. 10 p. multicoloured 80 30

1965. Centenary of I.T.U.
1731 **352** 1 p. red, black & pink 10 10

353. Pilgrim. **354.** Spanish Knight and Banners.

1965. Holy Year of Santiago de Compostela. Multicoloured.
1732. 1 p. Type **353** 10 10
1733. 2 p. Pilgrim (profile) 15 10

1965. 400th Anniv. of Florida Settlement.
1734. **354.** 3 p. black, red & yell. 15 10

355. St. Benedict (after sculpture by Pereira). **356.** Sports Palace, Madrid.

1965. Europa.
1735. **355.** 1 p. green & emerald 35 10
1736. 5 p. violet and purple 1·10 10

1965. Int. Olympic Committee Meeting, Madrid.
1737. **356.** 1 p. brown, gold & grey 10 10

1965. Explorers and Colonisers of America (5th series). As T **309**. Inscr. "1965" at foot.
1738. 25 c. violet and green 10 10
1739. 70 c. brown and pink 10 10
1740. 80 c. green and cream 10 10
1741. 1 p. violet and buff 10 10
1742. 2 p. brown and blue 15 10
1743. 2 p. 50 purple & turquoise 15 10
1744. 3 p. blue and grey 75 15
1745. 5 p. brown and yellow 75 20
PORTRAITS: 25 c., 2 p. Don Fadrique de Toledo. 70 c., 2 p. 50, Padre Jose de Anchieta. 80 c., 3 p. Francisco de Orellana. 1 p., 5 p. St. Luis Beltran.

357. Cloisters. **358.** Spanish 1 r. Stamp of 1865.

1965. Yuste Monastery.
1746. **357.** 1 p. blue and sepia 10 10
1747. – 2 p. sepia and brown 20 10
1748. – 5 p. green and blue 25 10
DESIGNS—VERT. 2 p. Charles V room. HORIZ. 5 p. Courtyard.

1965. Cent. of Spanish Perforated Stamps.
1749. **358.** 80 c. green and bronze 15 10
1750. – 1 p. brown and purple 15 10
1751. – 5 p. brown and sepia 20 10
DESIGNS: 1 p. 1865 19 c. stamp. 5 p. 1865 2 r. stamp.

359. "The Nativity" (after Mayno).

1965. Christmas.
1752. **359.** 1 p. green and blue 10 10

360. Madonna of Antipolo. **361.** Globe. **362.** Admiral Alvaro de Bazan.

1965. 400th Anniv. of Christianity in the Philippines.
1753. **360.** 1 p. brown, blk. & buff 25 10
1754. – 3 p. blue and grey 30 10
DESIGN: 3 p. Father Urdaneta.

1965. 21st Ecumenical Council, Vatican City (3rd issue).
1755. **361.** 1 p. multicoloured 20 10

1966. Arms of Provincial Capitals. As T **315**. Multicoloured.
1756. 5 p. Toledo 25 10
1757. 5 p. Valencia 25 10
1758. 5 p. Valladolid 25 10
1759. 5 p. Vizcaya 25 10
1760. 5 p. Zamora 25 10
1761. 5 p. Zaragoza 25 10
1762. 5 p. Ceuta 25 10
1763. 5 p. Melilla 25 10
1764. 10 p. Spain (26×38½ mm.) 25 10

1966. Celebrities (1st series).
1765. **362.** 25 c. black and blue (postage) 10 10
1766. – 2 p. violet and purple 15 10
1767. – 25 p. bronze & green (air) 1·50 20
1768. – 50 p. grey-blue & blue 2·25 30
PORTRAITS: 2 p. Benito Daza de Valdes (doctor). 25 p. Seneca. 50 p. St. Damaso.
See also Nos. 1849/52.

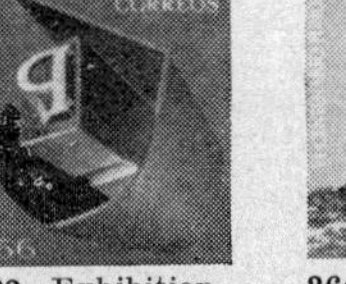

363. Exhibition Emblem. **364.** Luno Church.

1966. Graphic Arts Exn., "Graphispack", Barcelona.
1769. **363.** 1 p. green, blue & red 15 10

1966. Stamp Day and J. M. Sert Commem. Designs as T **279**. Frames in gold.
1770. 25 c. violet 10 10
1771. 40 c. purple 10 10
1772. 70 c. green 10 10
1773. 80 c. bronze 10 10
1774. 1 p. brown 10 10
1775. 1 p. 50 blue 10 10
1776. 2 p. 50 red 10 10
1777. 3 p. blue 15 10
1778. 5 p. sepia 15 10
1779. 10 p. green 20 10
PAINTINGS (by J. M. Sert)—VERT. 25 c. "The Magic Ball". 70 c. "Christ Addressing the Disciples". 80 c. "The Balloonists". 1 p. Self-portrait. 1 p. 50, "Audacity". 2 p. 50, "Justice". 3 p. "Jacob's Struggle with the Angel". 5 p. "The Five Parts of the World". 10 p. "St. Peter and St. Paul". HORIZ. 40 c. "Memories of Toledo".

1966. 600th Anniv of Guernica. Multicoloured.
1780. 80 c. Type **364** 10 10
1781. 1 p. Arms of Guernica 10 10
1782. 3 p. "Tree of Guernica" 10 10

365. Postmarked 6 cuartos Stamp of 1850.

1966. World Stamp Day.
1783. **365.** 25 c. multicoloured 10 10
1784. – 1 p. multicoloured 10 10
1785. – 10 p. multicoloured 40 15
DESIGNS—POSTMARKED STAMPS: 1 p. 5 r. of 1850. 10 p. 10 r. of 1850.

1966. Tourist Series. As T **340**.
1786. 10 c. emerald and green 10 10
1787. 15 c. bistre and green 10 10
1788. 40 c. brown and chestnut 10 10
1789. 50 c. purple and red 10 10
1790. 80 c. purple and mauve 10 10
1791. 1 p. turquoise and blue 10 10
1792. 1 p. 50 black and blue 10 10
1793. 2 p. brown and blue 10 10
1794. 3 p. brown and blue 10 10
1795. 10 p. blue and turquoise 20 10
DESIGNS—VERT. 10 c. Bohi waterfalls (Lerida). 40 c. Sigena monastery (Huesca). 50 c. Santo Domingo Church (Soria). 80 c. Golden Tower (Seville). 1 p. El Teide (Canaries). 10 p. Church of St. Gregory (Valladolid). HORIZ. 15 c. Torla (Huesca). 1 p. 50, Cathedral Guadalupe. 2 p. University, Alcala de Henares. 3 p. La Seo Cathedral (Lerida).

366. Tree and Globe. **367.** Crown and Anchor.

1966. World Forestry Congress.
1796. **366.** 1 p. green, brown and deep brown 15 10

1966. Naval Week, Barcelona.
1797. **367.** 1 p. blue and grey 15 10

368. Butron Castle (Vizcaya). **370.** "Europa and the Bull".

369. Don Quixote, Dulcinea and Aldonza Lorenzo. **371.** Horseman in the Sky.

1966. Spanish Castles (1st series).
1798. – 10 c. sepia and blue 10 10
1799. – 25 c. purple and violet 10 10
1800. – 40 c. green & turquoise 10 10
1801. – 50 c. blue and indigo 15 10
1802. – 70 c. blue & ultram. 15 10
1803. **368.** 80 c. green and violet 20 20
1804. – 1 p. olive and brown 20 10
1805. – 3 p. purple and red 25 10
CASTLES—HORIZ. 10 c. Guadamur (Toledo). 25 c. Alcazar (Segovia). 40 c. La Mota (Medina del Campo). 50 c. Olite (Navarra). 70 c. Monteagudo (Murcia). 1 p. Manzanares (Madrid). VERT. 3 p. Almansa (Albacete).

1966. 4th World Psychiatric Congress, Madrid.
1806. **369.** 1 p. 50 multicoloured 10 10

1966. Europa.
1807. **370.** 1 p. multicoloured 35 10
1808. 5 p. multicoloured 75 10

1966. 17th Int. Astronautics Federation Congress, Madrid.
1809. **371.** 1 p. 50 red, blk. & blue 10 10

1966. Explorers and Colonisers of America (6th series). As T **309**. Inscr. "1966" at foot.
1810. 30 c. bistre and brown 10 10
1811. 50 c. red and green 10 10
1812. 1 p. violet and blue 10 10
1813. 1 p. 20 slate and grey 10 10
1814. 1 p. 50 myrtle and green 15 10
1815. 3 p. blue 15 10
1816. 3 p. 50 violet and lilac 15 10
1817. 6 p. brown and buff 20 10
DESIGNS: 30 c. A. de Mendoza. 50 c. Title page of Dominican Fathers' "Christian Doctrine". 1 p. J. A. Manso de Velasco. 1 p. 20, Coins of Lima Mint (1699). 1 p. 50, M. de Castro y Padilla. 3 p. Oruro Convent. 3 p. 50, M. de Amat. 6 p. Inca postal runner.

372. R. del Valle Inclan. **373.** Monastery Facade.

1966. Spanish Writers.
1818. **372.** 1 p. 50 green & black 10 10
1819. – 3 p. violet and black 10 10
1820. – 6 p. blue and black 15 10
WRITERS: 3 p. Carlos Arniches. 6 p. J. Benavente y Martinez.
See also Nos. 1888/91.

1966. St. Mary's Carthusian Monastery, Jerez.
1821. **373.** 1 p. indigo and blue 10 10
1822. – 2 p. light grn. and grn. 10 10
1823. – 5 p. plum and purple 20 10
DESIGNS—HORIZ. 2 p. Cloisters. 5 p. Gateway.

374. "The Nativity" (after P. Duque Cornejo). **375.** Alava Costume.

1966. Christmas.
1824. **374.** 1 p. 50 multicoloured 10 10

1967. Provincial Costumes. Multicoloured.
1825. 6 p. Type **375** 15 10
1826. 6 p. Albacete 15 10
1827. 6 p. Alicante 15 10
1828. 6 p. Almeria 15 10
1829. 6 p. Avila 15 10
1830. 6 p. Badajoz 15 10
1831. 6 p. Baleares 15 10
1832. 6 p. Barcelona 15 10
1833. 6 p. Burgos 15 10
1834. 6 p. Caceres 15 10
1835. 6 p. Cadiz 15 10
1836. 6 p. Castellon de la Plana 15 10
See also Nos. 1897/1908, 1956/67, 2007/18 and 2072/6.

376. Archers.

1967. Stamp Day. Cave Paintings. Mult.
1837. 40 c. Type **376** 10 10
1838. 50 c. Boar-hunting 10 10
1839. 1 p. Trees (vert.) 10 10
1840. 1 p. 20 Bison 10 10
1841. 1 p. 50 Hands 10 10
1842. 2 p. Hunter (vert.) 10 10
1843. 2 p. 50 Deer (vert.) 10 10
1844. 3 p. 50 Hunters 10 10
1845. 4 p. Chamois-hunters (vt.) 10 10
1846. 6 p. Deer-hunter (vert.) 15 10

377. Cathedral, Palma de Mallorca, and Union Emblem.

1967. Interparliamentary Union Congress, Palma de Mallorca.
1847 **377** 1 p. 50 green 10 10

378. Wilhelm Rontgen (physicist).

1967. Radiology Congress, Barcelona.
1848. **378.** 1 p. 50 green 40 10

1967. Celebrities (2nd series). As T **362**.
1849. 1 p. 20 violet and purple 15 10
1850. 3 p. 50 purple 15 10
1851. 4 p. sepia and brown 75 10
1852. 25 p. grey and blue 35 10
PORTRAITS: 1 p. 20, Averroes (physician and philosopher). 3 p. 50, Acosta (poet). 4 p. Maimonides (physician and philosopher). 25 p. Andres Laguna (physician).

379. Cogwheels.

381. Spanish 5 r. Stamp of 1850 with Numeral Postmark.

380. Fair Building.

1967. Europa.
1853. **379.** 1 p. 50 grn., brn. & red 35 10
1854. 6 p. violet, blue & pur. 30 10

1967. 50th Anniv. of Valencia Int. Samples Fair.
1855. **380.** 1 p. 50 green 10 10

1967. World Stamp Day.
1856. **381.** 40 c. brn., blue & blk. 10 10
1857. – 1 p. 50 lake, black and green 10 10
1858. – 6 p. blue, red & black 10 10
DESIGNS: 1 p. 50, Spanish 12 c. stamp of 1850 with crowned "M" (Madrid) postmark. 6 p. Spanish 6 r. stamp of 1850 with "I.R." postmark.
See also Nos. 1927/8, 1980/1, 2032, 2091, 2150 and 2185.

382. Sleeping Vagrant and "Guardian Angel".

383. I.T.Y. Emblem.

1967. National Day for Caritas Welfare Organization.
1859. **382.** 1 p. 50 multicoloured 10 10

1967. Tourist Series and Int. Tourist Year.
1860. – 10 c. black and blue 10 10
1861. – 1 p. black and blue .. 10 10
1862. – 1 p. 50 black & brown 10 10
1863. – 2 p. 50 blue and turq. 10 10
1864. **383.** 3 p. 50 blue & purple 10 10
1865. – 5 p. bronze and green 10 10
1866. – 6 p. purple & mauve 20 10
DESIGNS: 10 c. Betanzos Church (Corunna). 1 p. St. Miguel's Tower (Palencia). 1 p. 50, Castellers (acrobats). 2 p. 50, Columbus Monument (Huelva). 5 p. "Enchanted City" (Cuenca). 6 p. Church of our Lady, Sanlucar (Cadiz).

1967. Spanish Castles (2nd series). As T **368.**
1867. 50 c. brown and grey .. 15 10
1868. 1 p. violet and grey .. 25 10
1869. 1 p. 50 green and blue .. 25 10
1870. 2 p. brown and red .. 25 10
1871. 2 p. 50 brown and green 25 10
1872. 5 p. blue and purple .. 30 10
1873. 6 p. sepia and brown .. 30 10
1874. 10 p. green and blue .. 35 10
CASTLES—HORIZ. 50 c. Balsareny (Barcelona). 1 p. Jarandilla (Caceres). 1 p. 50. Almodovar (Cordoba). 2 p. 50, Peniscola (Castellon). 5 p. Coca (Segovia). 6 p. Loarre (Huesca). 10 p. Belmonte (Cuenca). VERT. 2 p. Ponferrada (Leon).

384. Globe and Snow Crystal.

385. Map of the Americas, Spain and the Philippines.

1967. 12th Int. Refrigeration Congress, Madrid.
1875. **384.** 1 p. 50 blue 10 10

1967. 4th Spanish Portuguese, American and Philippine Municipalities Congress, Barcelona.
1876. **385.** 1 p. 50 violet.. .. 15 10

1967. Explorers and Colonisers of America (7th series). As T **309.** Inscr. "1967" at foot.
1877. 40 c. olive and orange .. 15 10
1878. 50 c. agate and grey .. 15 10
1879. 1 p. mauve and blue .. 15 10
1880. 1 p. 20 green and cream.. 15 10
1881. 1 p. 50 green and flesh .. 15 10
1882. 3 p. violet and buff .. 15 10
1883. 3 p. 50 blue and pink .. 15 10
1884. 6 p. brown 20 10
DESIGNS—VERT. 40 c. J. Francisco de la Bodega y Quadra. 50 c. Map of Nutka coast. 1 p. F. A. Mourelle. 1 f. 50, E. J. Martinez. 3 p. 50, Cayetano Valdes y Florez. HORIZ. 1 p. 20, View of Nutka. 3 p. Map of Californian coast. 6 p. San Elias, Alaska.

387. Ploughing with Oxen.

388. Main Portal, Veruela Monastery.

1967. 2000th Anniv. of Caceres. Mult.
1885. 1 p. 50 Statue and archway 10 10
1886. 3 p. 50 Type **387** .. 10 10
1887. 6 p. Roman coins .. 15 10
Nos. 1885 and 1887 are vert.

1967. Anniversaries. Portraits as T **372.**
1888. 1 p. 20 brown and black 10 10
1889. 1 p. 50 green and black.. 10 10
1890. 3 p. 50 violet and black 10 10
1891. 6 p. blue and black .. 10 10
DESIGNS: 1 p. 20, P. de S. Jose Bethencourt (founder of Bethlehemite Order, 300th death anniv.). 1 p. 50, Enrique Granados (composer, birth centenary). 3 p. 50, Ruben Dario (poet, birth centenary). 6 p. San Ildefonso, Archbishop of Toledo (after El Greco) (1900th death anniv).

1967. Veruela Monastery.
1892. **388.** 1 p. 50 blue & ultram. 10 10
1893. – 3 p. 50 grey and green 10 10
1894. – 6 p. purple and brown 30 10
DESIGNS—HORIZ. 3 p. 50, Aerial view of Monastery. 6 p. Cloisters.

389. "The Canonization of San Jose de Calasanz" (from painting by Goya).

390. "The Nativity" (Salzillo).

1967. Bicentenary of Canonization of San Jose de Calasanz.
1895. **389.** 1 p. 50 multicoloured 15 10

1967. Christmas.
1896. **390.** 1 p. 50 multicoloured 10 10

1968. Provincial Costumes. As T **375.** Multicoloured.
1897. 6 p. Ciudad Real .. 15 10
1898. 6 p. Cordoba 15 10
1899. 6 p. Coruna 15 10
1900. 6 p. Cuenca 15 10
1901. 6 p. Fernando Poo .. 15 10
1902. 6 p. Gerona 15 10
1903. 6 p. Las Palmas (Gran Canaria) 15 10
1904. 6 p. Granada 15 10
1905. 6 p. Guadalajara .. 15 10
1906. 6 p. Guipuzcoa 15 10
1907. 6 p. Huelva 15 10
1908. 6 p. Huesca 15 10

391. Slalom.

1968. Winter Olympic Games, Grenoble. Multicoloured.
1909 1 p. 50 Type **391** .. 10 10
1910 3 p. 50 Bobsleighing (vert) 20 10
1911 6 p. Ice hockey 20 10

1968. Stamp Day and Fortuny Commem. As T **279.** Frames in gold.
1912. 40 c. purple 10 10
1913. 50 c. green 10 10
1914. 1 p. brown 10 10
1915. 1 p. 20 violet 10 10
1916. 1 p. 50 green 10 10
1917. 2 p. brown 10 10
1918. 2 p. 50 red 10 10
1919. 3 p. 50 brown 30 10
1920. 4 p. olive 10 10
1921. 6 p. blue 20 10
Fortuny Paintings—HORIZ. 40 c. "The Vicarage". 1 p. 20, "The Print Collector". 6 p. "Queen Christina". VERT. 50 c. "Fantasia". 1 p. "Idyll". 1 p. 50, Self-portrait. 2 p. "Old Man Naked to the Sun". 2 p. 50, "Typical Calabrian". 3 p. 50, "Portrait of Lady". 4 p. "Battle of Tetuan".

392. Beatriz Galindo.

1968. Famous Spanish Women. With background scenes.
1922. **392.** 1 p. 20 brown and bistre 10 10
1923. – 1 p. 50 blue & turquoise 10 10
1924. – 3 p. 50 violet .. 15 10
1925. – 6 p. black and blue.. 20 10
WOMEN: 1 p. 50. Agustina de Aragon. 3 p. 50, Maria Pacheco. 6 p. Rosalia de Castro.

393. Europa "Key".

1968. Europa.
1926. **393.** 3 p. 50 gold, brn. & blue 30 10

1968. World Stamp Day. As T **381,** but stamps and postmarks changed. Inscr. "1968".
1927. 1 p. 50 black, brown & blue 10 10
1928. 3 p. 50 blue, black & grn. 20 10
DESIGNS: 1 p. 50, Spanish 6 c. stamp of 1850 with Puebla (Galicia) postmark. 3 p. 50, Spanish 6 r. stamp of 1850 with Serena postmark.

394. Emperor Galba's Coin.

395. Human Rights Emblem.

1968. 1900th Anniv of Foundation of Leon by VIIth Roman Legion
1929. 1 p. brown and purple 10 10
1930. – 1 p. 50 brown & yellow 10 10
1931. **394.** 3 p. 50 green & ochre 30 10
DESIGNS—VERT. 1 p. Inscribed tile and town map of Leon (26 × 47 mm.). 1 p. 50, Legionary with standard (statue).

1968. Human Rights Year.
1932. **395.** 3 p. 50 red, grn. & blue 15 10

1968. Tourist Series. As T **340.**
1933. 50 c. brown 10 10
1934. 1 p. 20 green 10 10
1935. 1 p. 50 blue and green .. 10 10
1936. 2 p. purple 20 10
1937. 3 p. 50 purple 10 10
DESIGNS—VERT. 50 c. Count Benavente's Palace, Baeza. 1 p. 50, Sepulchre, St. Vincent's Church, Avila. 3 p. 50, Main portal, Church of Santa Maria, Sanguesa (Navarra). HORIZ. 1 p. 20, View of Salamanca. 2 p. "The King's Page" (statue), Siguenza Cathedral.

1968. Spanish Castles (3rd series). As T **368.**
1938. 40 c. sepia and blue .. 15 10
1939. 1 p. 20 purple 10 10
1940. 1 p. 50 black and bistre 10 10
1941. 2 p. 50 bronze & green .. 35 10
1942. 6 p. turquoise and blue .. 50 10
DESIGNS—HORIZ. 40 c. Escalona. 1 p. 20, Fuensaldana. 1 p. 50, Penafiel. 2 p. 50, Villasobroso. VERT. 6 p. Frias.

396. Rifle-shooting.

1968. Olympic Games, Mexico. Multicoloured.
1943 1 p. Type **396** 15 10
1944 1 p. 50 Horse-jumping .. 15 10
1945 3 p. 50 Cycling 25 10
1946 6 p. Yachting (vert) .. 20 10

1968. Explorers and Colonisers of America (8th series). As T **309** but inscr. "1968" at foot.
1947 40 c. blue and light blue 10 10
1948 1 p. purple and blue .. 10 10
1949 1 p. 50 green and flesh .. 10 10
1950 3 p. 50 blue and mauve .. 25 10
1951 6 p. brown and yellow .. 30 20
DESIGNS—VERT. 40 c. Map of Orinoco missions. 1 p. Diego de Losada (founder of Caracas). 1 p. 50, Arms of the Losadas. 3 p. 50, Diego de Henares (builder of Caracas). HORIZ. 6 p. Old plan of Santiago de Leon de Caracas.

397. Monastery Building.

398. "The Nativity" (Barocci).

1968. Santa Maria del Parral Monastery.
1952. **397.** 1 p. 50 lilac and blue 10 10
1953. – 3 p. 50 brown & choc. 35 10
1954. – 6 p. brown and red .. 40 10
DESIGNS—VERT. 3 p. 50, Cloisters. 6 p. "Santa Maria del Parral".

1968. Christmas.
1955. **398.** 1 p. 50 multicoloured 15 10

1969. Provincial Costumes. As T **375.** Multicoloured.
1956. 6 p. Ifni 15 10
1957. 6 p. Jaen 15 10
1958. 6 p. Leon 15 10
1959. 6 p. Lerida 15 10
1960. 6 p. Logrono 15 10
1961. 6 p. Lugo 15 10
1962. 6 p. Madrid 15 10
1963. 6 p. Malaga 15 10
1964. 6 p. Murcia 15 10
1965. 6 p. Navarra 15 10
1966. 6 p. Orense 15 10
1967. 6 p. Oviedo 15 10

1969. Stamp Day and Alonso Cano Commem. Various paintings as T **279.** Frames gold: centre colours below.
1968. 40 c. red 10 10
1969. 50 c. green 10 10
1970. 1 p. sepia 10 10
1971. 1 p. 50 green 10 10
1972. 2 p. brown 20 10
1973. 2 p. 50 mauve 15 10
1974. 3 p. blue 15 10
1975. 3 p. 50 purple 15 10
1976. 4 p. purple 15 10
1977. 6 p. blue 25 10
Alonso Cano paintings—VERT. 40 c. "St. Agnes". 50 c. "St. Joseph". 1 p. "Christ supported by an Angel". 1 p. 50, "Alonso Cano" (Velazquez). 2 p. "The Holy Family". 2 p. 50, "The Circumcision". 3 p. "Jesus and the Samaritan". 3 p. 50, "Madonna and Child". 6 p. "The Vision of St. John the Baptist". HORIZ. 4 p. "St. John Capistrano and St. Bernardin".

399. Molecules and Diagram.

1969. 6th European Biochemical Congress.
1978. **399.** 1 p. 50 multicoloured 10 10

400. Colonnade.

1969. Europa.
1979. **400.** 3 p. 50 multicoloured 35 10

1969. World Stamp Day. As T **381.**
1980. 1 p. 50 black, red & green 10 10
1981. 3 p. 50 green, red & blue 15 10
DESIGNS: 1 p. 50, Spanish 6 c. stamp of 1851 with "A 3 1851" postmark. 3 p. 50, Spanish 10 r. stamp of 1851 with "CORVERA" postmark.

401. Spectrum.

1969. 15th Int. Spectroscopical Conf., Madrid.
1982. **401.** 1 p. 50 multicoloured 10 10

402. Red Cross Symbols and Globe.

403. Capital, Lugo Cathedral.

1969. 50th Anniv. of League of Red Cross Societies.
1983. **402.** 1 p. 50 multicoloured 25 10

1969. 300th Anniv. of Dedication of Galicia to Jesus Christ.
1984. **403.** 1 p. 50 brn., blk. & grn. 10 10

1969. Spanish Castles (4th series). As T **368**.
1985. 1 p. purple and green .. 15 10
1986. 1 p. 50 blue and violet .. 25 10
1987. 2 p. 50 lilac and blue .. 20 10
1988. 3 p. 50 brown and green 30 10
1989. 6 p. drab and green .. 30 10
CASTLES—HORIZ. 1 p. Turegano. 1 p. 50, Villalonso. 2 p. 50, Velez Blanco. 3 p. 50, Castilnovo. 6 p. Torrelobaton.

404. Franciscan Friar and Child. **405.** Rock of Gibraltar.

1969. Bicent. of San Diego (California).
1990. **404.** 1 p. 50 multicoloured 10 10

1969. Aid for Spanish "ex-Gibraltar" Workers.
1991. **405.** 1 p. 50 blue 35 10
1992. – 2 p. purple 45 10
DESIGN: 2 p. Aerial view of Rock.

1969. Tourist Series. As T **340**.
1993. 1 p. 50 green and turquoise 20 10
1994. 3 p. turquoise and green 25 10
1995. 3 p. 50 blue and green .. 25 10
1996. 6 p. violet and green .. 25 10
DESIGNS—HORIZ. 1 p. 50, Alcaniz (Teruel). VERT. 3 p. Murcia Cathedral. 3 p. 50, "The Lady of Elche" (sculpture). 6 p. Church of Our Lady of the Redonda, Logrono.

1969. Explorers and Colonisers of America (9th series). Chile. As T **309**. Inscr. "1969" at foot.
1997. 40 c. brown on blue .. 10 10
1998. 1 p. 50 violet on flesh .. 10 10
1999. 2 p. green on mauve .. 25 10
2000. 3 p. 50 green on cream .. 30 10
2001. 6 p. brown on cream .. 40 10
DESIGNS—VERT. 40 c. Convent of Santo Domingo, Santiago de Chile. 2 p. Ambrosio O'Higgins. 3 p. 50, Pedro de Valdivia (founder of Santiago de Chile). HORIZ. 1 p. 50, Chilean Mint. 6 p. Cal y Canto Bridge.

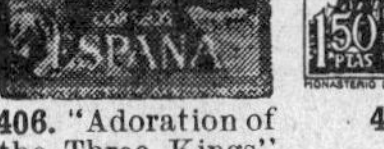
406. "Adoration of the Three Kings" (Maino). **407.** Las Huelgas Monastery.

1969. Christmas. Multicoloured.
2002. 1 p. 50 Type **406** .. 10 10
2003. 2 p. "The Nativity" (Gerona Cathedral) .. 15 10

1969. Las Huelgas Monastery, Burgos.
2004. **407.** 1 p. 50 slate and green 35 10
2005. – 3 p. 50 blue 30 10
2006. – 6 p. olive and green 45 10
DESIGNS—HORIZ. 3 p. 50, Tombs. VERT. 6 p. Cloisters.

1970. Provincial Costumes. As T **375**. Multicoloured.
2007. 6 p. Palencia 15 10
2008. 6 p. Pontevedra 15 10
2009. 6 p. Sahara 15 10
2010. 6 p. Salamanca 15 10
2011. 6 p. Santa Cruz de Tenerife 15 10
2012. 6 p. Santander 15 10
2013. 6 p. Segovia 15 10
2014. 6 p. Seville 15 10
2015. 6 p. Soria 15 10
2016. 6 p. Tarragona 15 10
2017. 6 p. Teruel 15 10
2018. 6 p. Toledo 15 10

408. Blessed Juan of Avila (after El Greco). **409.** "St. Stephen".

1970. Spanish Celebrities.
2019. **408.** 25 p. blue and lilac .. 3·25 10
2020. – 50 p. brown and orge. 2·50 30
DESIGN: 25 p. Type **408** (400th Death Anniv.). 50 p. Cardinal Rodrigo Ximenes de Rada (after J. de Borgena) (800th Birth Anniv.).
See also Nos. 2129/31.

1970. Stamp Day and Luis de Morales Commem. Various paintings. Multicoloured.
2021. 50 c. Type **409** 10 10
2022. 1 p. "The Annunciation" 10 10
2023. 1 p. 50 "Virgin and Child with St. John" .. 20 10
2024. 2 p. "Virgin and Child" 20 10
2025. 3 p. "The Presentation of the Infant Christ" .. 10 10
2026. 3 p. 50 "St. Jerome" .. 10 10
2027. 4 p. "St. John of Ribera" 20 10
2028. 5 p. "Ecce Homo" .. 20 10
2029. 6 p. "Pieta" 20 15
2030. 10 p. "St. Francis of Assisi" 30 20
See also Nos. 2077/84, 2135/42, 2204/11, 2261/8, 2420/7, 2478/85, 2529/36 and 2585/90.

410. "Flaming Sun".

1970. Europa.
2031. **410.** 3 p. 50 gold & ultram. 30 10

1970. World Stamp Day. As T **381** but stamp and postmark changed.
2032. 2 p. red, black and green 35 10
DESIGN: 2 p. Spanish 12 c. stamp of 1860 with railway cachet.

411. Fair Building. **412.** Gen. Primo de Rivera.

1970. 50th Anniv. of Barcelona Fair.
2033. **411.** 15 p. multicoloured 45 10

1970. Birth Cent. of General Primo de Rivera.
2034. **412.** 2 p. grn., brn. & buff 15 10

1970. Spanish Castles (5th series). As T **368**.
2035. 1 p. black and blue .. 75 10
2036. 1 p. 20 blue and turquoise 50 10
2037. 3 p. 50 brown and green 75 10
2038. 6 p. violet and brown .. 75 10
2039. 10 p. brown & chestnut 1·25 10
CASTLES—HORIZ. 1 p. Valencia de Don Juan. 1 p. 20, Monterrey. 3 p. 50, Mombeltran. 6 p. Sadaba. 10 p. Bellver.

1970. Tourist series. As T **340**.
2040. 50 c. lilac and blue .. 10 10
2041. 1 p. brown and ochre .. 25 10
2042. 1 p. 50 green and blue .. 20 10
2043. 2 p. blue and deep blue .. 80 10
2044. 3 p. 50 blue and violet .. 40 10
2045. 5 p. brown and blue .. 1·25 10
DESIGNS—HORIZ. 50 c. Alcazaba, Almeria. 1 p. Malaga Cathedral. 2 p. St. Francis' Convent, Orense. VERT. 1 p. 50, Our Lady of the Assumption, Lequeitio. 3 p. 50, The Lonja, Zaragoza. 5 p. The Portalon, Vitoria.

413. 17th-century Tailor.

1970. Int. Tailoring Congress.
2046. **413.** 2 p. violet, red & brn. 10 10

414. Diver on Map.

1970. 12th European Swimming, Diving and Water-polo Championships, Barcelona.
2047. **414.** 2 p. brn., blue and grn. 10 10

415. Concha Espina. **416.** Survey Map of Southern Spain and North Africa.

1970. Spanish Writers.
2048. **415.** 50 c. blue, brn. & buff 10 10
2049. – 1 p. violet, grn. & drab 10 10
2050. – 1 p. 50 grn., blue & drab 15 10
2051. – 2 p. olive, grn. & buff 25 10
2052. – 2 p. 50 pur., vio. & ochre 20 10
2053. – 3 p. 50 red, brn. & lilac 20 10
WRITERS: 1 p. Guillen de Castro. 1 p. 50, J. R. Jimenez. 2 p. G. A. Becquer. 2 p. 50, Miguel de Unamuno. 3 p. 50, J. M. Gabriel y Galan.

1970. Explorers and Colonisers of America (10th series). Mexico. Designs as T **309**.
2054. 40 c. green on pale green 10 10
2055. 1 p. 50 brown on blue .. 25 10
2056. 2 p. violet on cream .. 60 10
2057. 3 p. 50 grn. on light grn. 35 10
2058. 6 p. blue on pink .. 50 10
DESIGNS—VERT. 40 c. House of Queretaro. 2 p. Vasco de Quiroga. 3 p. 50, F. Juan de Zumarraga. 6 p. Morelia Cathedral. HORIZ. 1 p. 50, Cathedral, Mexico City.

1970. Centenary of Spanish Geographical and Survey Institute.
2059. **416.** 2 p. multicoloured .. 30 10

417. "The Adoration of the Shepherds" (El Greco). **418.** U.N. Emblem and New York Headquarters.

1970. Christmas. Multicoloured.
2060. 1 p. 50 Type **417** 15 10
2061. 2 p. "The Adoration of the Shepherds" (Murillo) 15 10

1970. 25th Anniv. of United Nations.
2062. **418.** 8 p. multicoloured .. 20 10

419. Ripoll Monastery. **420.** Pilgrims' Route Map.

1970. Ripoll Monastery.
2063. – 2 p. purple & violet 90 10
2064. **419.** 3 p. 50 purple & orge. 45 10
2065. – 5 p. green and slate 1·50 10
DESIGNS: 2 p. Entrance. 5 p. Cloisters.

1971. Holy Year of Compostela (1st issue). "St. James in Europe".
2066. **420.** 50 c. brown & blue .. 10 10
2067. – 1 p. black & brown .. 20 10
2068. – 1 p. 50 purple & green 35 10
2069. – 2 p. brown & purple .. 30 10
2070. – 3 p. dp. blue and blue 40 10
2071. – 4 p. olive 60 10
DESIGNS—VERT. 1 p. Statue of St. Brigid, Vadstena (Sweden). 1 p. 50, St. Jacques Church tower, Paris. 2 p. "St. James" (carving from altar, Pistoia, Italy). HORIZ. 3 p. St. David's Cathedral, Wales. 4 p. Carving from Ark of Charlemagne (Aachen, West Germany).
See also Nos. 2105/11 and 2121/8.

1971. Provincial Costumes. As T **375**. Mult.
2072. 6 p. Valencia 25 10
2073. 8 p. Valladolid 30 10
2074. 8 p. Vizcaya 30 10
2075. 8 p. Zamora 30 10
2076. 8 p. Zaragoza 30 10

1971. Stamp Day and Ignacio Zuloaga Commem. Paintings as T **409**. Mult.
2077. 50 c. "My Uncle Daniel" 15 10
2078. 1 p. "Segovia" (horiz.) 15 10
2079. 1 p. 50 "The Duchess of Alba" 15 10
2080. 2 p. "Ignacio Zuloaga" (self-portrait) 35 10
2081. 3 p. "Juan Belmonte" 40 10
2082. 4 p. "The Countess of Noailles" 25 10
2083. 5 p. "Pablo Uranga" .. 35 10
2084. 8 p. "Boatmen's Houses, Lerma" (horiz.) .. 45 15

421. Amadeo Vives (composer).

1971. Spanish Celebrities. Multicoloured.
2085. 1 p. Type **421** 40 10
2086. 2 p. St. Teresa of Avila (mystic) 45 10
2087. 8 p. B. Perez Galdos (writer) 45 10
2088. 15 p. R. Menendez Pidal (writer) 45 10

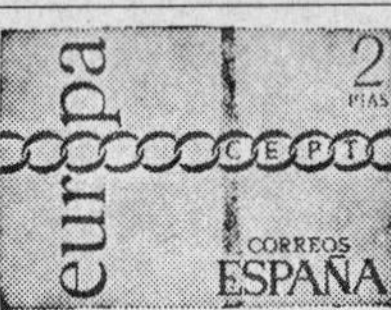

422. Europa Chain.

1971. Europa.
2089. **422.** 2 p. brn., violet & blue 1·50 10
2090. 8 p. brown, light green and green 60 15

1971. World Stamp Day. As T **381** but with different stamp and postmark.
2091. 2 p. black, blue & green 25 10
DESIGN: 2 p. Spanish 6 c. stamp of 1850 with "A.s" postmark.

423. Gymnast on Vaulting-horse.

1971. 9th European Male Gymnastics Cup Championships, Madrid. Multicoloured.
1092 1 p. Type **423** 25 10
2093 2 p. Gymnast on bar .. 25 10

424. Great Bustard.

1971. Spanish Fauna (1st series). Mult.
2094. 1 p. Type **424** .. .. 1·00 10
2095. 2 p. Lynx 95 10
2096. 3 p. Brown Bear 95 10
2097. 5 p. Red-legged Partridge (vert.) .. .. 2·25 20
2098. 8 p. Spanish Ibex (vert.) 1·25 25
See also Nos. 2160/4, 2192/6, 2250/4, 2317/21, 2452/6 and 2579/83.

426. Legionaires in Battle.

1971. 50th Anniv. of Spanish Foreign Legion. Multicoloured.
2101. 1 p. Type **426** 10 10
2102. 2 p. Ceremonial Parade .. 75 10
2103. 5 p. Memorial Service .. 75 10
2104. 8 p. Officer and mobile column 60 20

1971. Holy Year of Compostela (2nd issue). "En Route to Santiago". As T **420**.
2105. 50 c. purple and blue .. 10 10
2106. 6 p. blue 30 10
2107. 7 p. purple & dull purple 40 10
2108. 7 p. 50 red and purple .. 30 20
2109. 8 p. purple and green .. 30 10
2110. 9 p. violet and green .. 30 20
2111. 10 p. brown and green .. 55 10
DESIGNS—HORIZ. 50 c. Pilgrims' route map of northern Spain. 7 p. 50, Cloisters, Najera Monastery. 9 p. Eunate Monastery. VERT. 6 p. "Pilgrims" (sculpture, Royal Hospital, Burgos). 7 p. Gateway, St. Domingo de la Calzada Monastery. 8 p. Statue of Christ, Puente de la Reina. 10 p. Cross of Roncesvalles.

427. "Children of the World". **428.** "Battle of Lepanto" (after L. Valdes).

1971. 25th Anniv. of U.N.I.C.E.F.
2112. **427.** 8 p. multicoloured .. 20 10

1971. 400th Anniv. of Battle of Lepanto.
2113. – 2 p. grn. & brn. (vert.) 1·40 10
2114. 428. 5 p. chocolate & brn. 1·50 10
2115. – 8 p. blue & red (vert.) 1·75 25
DESIGNS: 2 p. "Don John of Austria" (S. Coello). 8 p. Standard of the Holy League.

429. Hockey Players. 431. "The Nativity" (detail from altar, Avia).

430. De Havilland "DH-9" Biplane over Seville.

1971. World Hockey Cup Championships, Barcelona.
2116. 429. 5 p. multicoloured .. 1·25 10

1971. 50th Anniv. of Spanish Airmail Services. Multicoloured.
2117. 2 p. Type 430 .. .. 60 10
2118. 15 p. Boeing "747" "Jumbo-jet" over Madrid 65 10

1971. Christmas. Multicoloured.
2119. 2 p. Type 431 .. .. 20 10
2120. 8 p. "The Birth" (detail from altar, Sagar) .. 20 10

1971. Holy Year of Compostela (3rd issue). As T 420.
2121. 1 p. black and green .. 30 10
2122. 1 p. 50 violet and purple 20 10
2123. 2 p. blue and green .. 1·00 10
2124. 2 p. 50 violet and red .. 30 10
2125. 3 p. purple and red .. 45 10
2126. 3 p. 50 green and pink .. 35 10
2127. 4 p. brown and blue .. 35 10
2128. 5 p. black and green .. 70 10
DESIGNS—VERT. 1 p. Santiago Cathedral. 2 p. Lugo Cathedral. 3 p. Astorga Cathedral. 4 p. San Tirso, Sahagun. HORIZ. 1 p. 50, Pilgrim approaching Santiago de Compostela. 2 p. 50, Villafranca del Bierzo. 3 p. 50, San Marcos, Leon. 5 p. San Martin, Fromista.

1972. Spanish Celebrities. As T 408.
2129. 15 p. green and brown .. 30 10
2130. 25 p. black and green .. 30 10
2131. 50 p. brown and red .. 50 20
CELEBRITIES: 15 p. Emilia Pardo Bazan (novelist). 25 p. Jose de Espronceda (poet). 50 p. Fernan Gonzalez (first king of Castile).

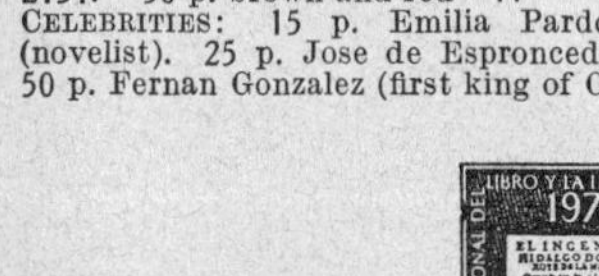

432. Ski Jumping. 433. Title-page of "Don Quixote" (1605).

1972. Winter Olympic Games, Sapporo, Japan. Multicoloured.
2132 2 p. Type 432 .. .. 55 10
2133 15 p. Figure skating (vert) 40 20

1972. International Book Year.
2134 433 2 p. red and brown .. 30 10

1972. Stamp Day and Solana Commem. Paintings by Solana. As T 409. Mult.
2135 1 p. "Clowns" (horiz) .. 35 10
2136 2 p. "Solana and Family" (self-portrait) 80 10
2137 3 p. "Blind Musician" .. 80 10
2138 4 p. "Return of the Fisherman" 70 10
2139 5 p. "Decorating Masks" 1·75 10
2140 7 p. "The Bibliophile" .. 60 10
2141 10 p. "Merchant Navy Captain" 80 10
2142 15 p. "Pombo Reunion" (vert) 80 10

HAVE YOU READ THE NOTES AT THE BEGINNING OF THIS CATALOGUE?
These often provide answers to the enquiries we receive.

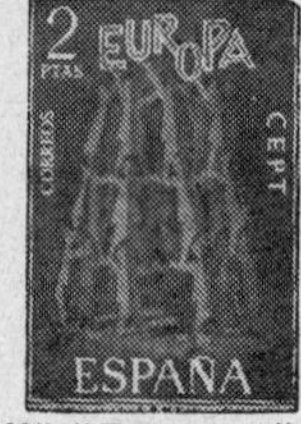

434. "Abies pinsapo". 435. "Europeans".

1972. Flora (1st series). Multicoloured.
2143 1 p. Type 434 .. .. 50 10
2144 2 p. Strawberry tree .. 70 10
2145 3 p. Maritime pine .. 75 10
2146 5 p. Holm oak .. 80 10
2147 8 p. "Juniperus thurifera" 90 10
See also Nos. 2178/82, 2278/82 and 2299/303.

1972. Europa. Multicoloured.
2148. 2 p. Type 435 .. .. 3·25 10
2149. 8 p. "Communications" .. 2·00 10

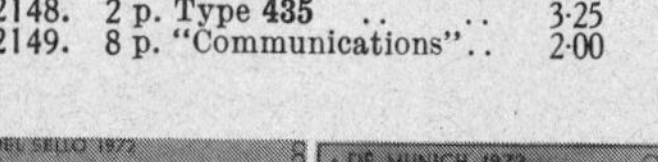

436. Cordoba Pre-stamp Postmark. 437. Fencing.

1972. World Stamp Day.
2150. 436. 2 p. red, blk. & brown 10 10

1972. Spanish Castles (6th series). As T 368.
2151. 1 p. brown and green .. 1·00 10
2152. 2 p. brown and green .. 1·40 10
2153. 3 p. brown and red .. 1·40 10
2154. 5 p. green and blue .. 1·50 15
2155. 10 p. violet and blue .. 3·25 15
CASTLES—VERT. 1 p. Sajazarra. HORIZ. 2 p. Santa Catalina. 3 p. Biar. 5 p. San Servando. 10 p. Pedraza.

1972. Olympic Games, Munich. Multicoloured.
2156 1 p. Type 437 .. .. 20 10
2157 2 p. Weightlifting (vert) 35 10
2158 5 p. Rowing (vert) .. 35 10
2159 8 p. Pole vaulting (vert) 35 15

438. Chamois. 439. Brigadier M. A. de Ustariz.

1972. Spanish Fauna (2nd series). Mult.
2160 1 p. Pyrenean desman .. 25 10
2161 2 p. Type 438 .. .. 60 10
2162 3 p. Wolf 80 10
2163 5 p. Egyptian mongoose (horiz) .. .. 1·25 10
2164 7 p. Small-spotted genet (horiz) .. .. 1·00 10

1972. "Spain in the New World" (1st series). 450th Anniv of Puerto Rico. Multicoloured.
2165. 1 p. Type 439 .. .. 30 10
2166. 2 p. View of San Juan, 1870 (horiz.) .. 45 10
2167. 5 p. View of San Juan, 1625 (horiz.) .. 50 10
2168. 8 p. Map of Plaza de Bahia, 1792 (horiz.) .. 70 20
See also Nos. 2212/5, 2271/4, 2338/41 and 2430/3.

440. Facade of Monastery. 441. Grand Lyceum Theatre.

1972. Monastery of St. Thomas, Avila.
2169. 440. 2 p. green and blue .. 1·25 10
2170. – 8 p. purple & brown 85 10
2171. – 15 p. blue and purple 1·40 15
DESIGNS—VERT. 8 p. Interior of Monastery. HORIZ. 15 p. Cloisters.

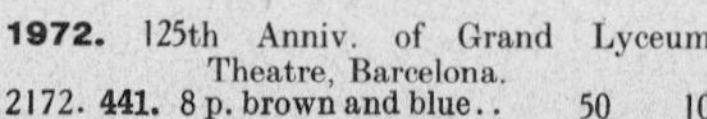

1972. 125th Anniv. of Grand Lyceum Theatre, Barcelona.
2172. 441. 8 p. brown and blue .. 50 10

442. "The Nativity".

1972. Christmas. Murals in Royal Collegiate Basilica of San Isidoro, Leon. Mult.
2173. 2 p. Type 442 .. .. 20 10
2174. 8 p. "The Annunciation" 20 10

443. J. de Herrera and Escorial.

1973. Spanish Architects (1st series).
2175. 443. 8 p. green and sepia .. 1·00 10
2176. – 10 p. blue and brown 2·00 15
2177. – 15 p. blue and green .. 75 10
DESIGNS: 10 p. J. de Villanueva and Prado. 15 p. V. Rodriguez and Apollo Fountain, Madrid.
See also Nos. 2295/7.

444. "Apollonias canariensis".

1973. Spanish Flora (2nd series). Canary Islands. Multicoloured.
2178. 1 p. Type 444 .. .. 30 10
2179. 2 p. "Myrica faya" .. 85 10
2180. 4 p. "Phoenix canariensis" 30 10
2181. 5 p. "Ilex canariensis" .. 85 10
2182. 15 p. "Dracaena draco" 40 10
Nos. 2179/82 are vert.

445. Roman Mosaic. 446. Iznajar Dam.

1973. Europa.
2183. 445. 2 p. multicoloured .. 1·50 10
2184. – 8 p. blue, red & black 1·00 10
DESIGN—HORIZ. (37×26 mm.) 8 p. Europa "Posthorn".

1973. World Stamp Day. As T 381, but with different stamp and postmark.
2185. 2 p. red, blue and black .. 10 10
DESIGN: 2 p. Spanish 6 r. stamp of 1853 with Madrid postmark.

1973. 11th Congress of Int. High Dams Commission, Madrid.
2186. 446. 8 p. multicoloured .. 30 10

1973. Tourist Series. As T 340.
2187. 1 p. brown and green .. 30 10
2188. 2 p. green and dark green 80 10
2189. 3 p. brown & light brown 70 10
2190. 5 p. violet and blue .. 1·50 10
2191. 8 p. red and green .. 1·25 20
DESIGNS—HORIZ. 1 p. Gateway, Onate University, Guipuzcoa. 2 p. Town Square, Lugo. 5 p. Columbus' House, Las Palmas. 8 p. Windmills, La Mancha. VERT. 3 p. Llerena Square, Badajoz.

447. Black-bellied Sandgrouse. 448. Hermandad Standard-bearer, Castile, 1488.

1973. Spanish Fauna (3rd series). Birds. Mult.
2192. 1 p. Type 447 .. .. 60 15
2193. 2 p. Black Stork .. 1·25 15
2194. 5 p. Azure-winged Magpie (vert.) .. .. 1·75 15
2195. 7 p. Imperial Eagle .. 2·00 15
2196. 15 p. Red-crested Pochard (vert.) .. .. .. 1·25 40

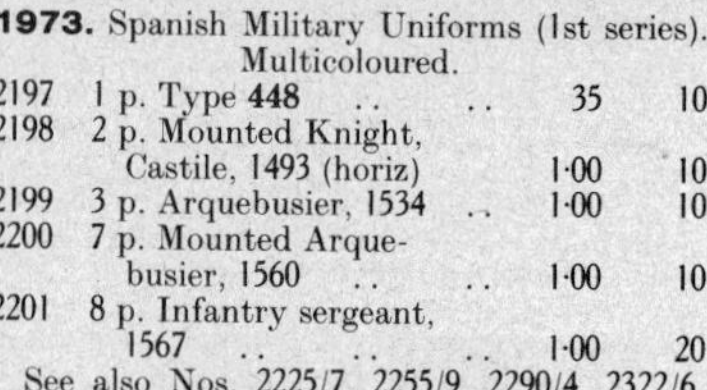

1973. Spanish Military Uniforms (1st series). Multicoloured.
2197 1 p. Type 448 .. .. 35 10
2198 2 p. Mounted Knight, Castile, 1493 (horiz) 1·00 10
2199 3 p. Arquebusier, 1534 .. 1·00 10
2200 7 p. Mounted Arquebusier, 1560 .. .. 1·00 10
2201 8 p. Infantry sergeant, 1567 .. .. .. 1·00 20
See also Nos. 2225/7, 2255/9, 2290/4, 2322/6, 2410/14, 2441/5, 2472/6 and 2499/503.

449. Fishes in Net.

1973. World Fishing Fair and Congress, Vigo.
2202. 449. 2 p. multicoloured .. 10 10

450. Conference Building.

1973. I.T.U. Conf., Torremolinos.
2203. 450. 8 p. multicoloured .. 15 10

1973. Stamp Day and Vicente Lopez Commemoration. Paintings. As T 409. Mult.
2204. 1 p. "Ferdinand VII" .. 10 10
2205. 2 p. Self-portrait 30 10
2206. 3 p. "La Senora de Carvallo" 30 10
2207. 4 p. "M. de Castelldosrrius" 20 10
2208. 5 p. "Isabella II" .. 20 10
2209. 7 p. "Goya" .. 20 10
2210. 10 p. "Maria Amalia of Saxony" .. 20 10
2211. 15 p. "The Organist, Felix Lopez" 30 15

451. Leon Cathedral, Nicaragua. 452. Pope Gregory XI receiving St. Jerome's Petition.

1973. "Spain in the New World" (2nd series). Nicaragua. Multicoloured.
2212. 1 p. Type 451 .. .. 10 10
2213. 2 p. Subtiava Church .. 35 10
2214. 5 p. Colonial-style house (vert.) 45 10
2215. 8 p. Rio San Juan Castle 35 10

1973. 600th Anniv. of Order of St. Jerome.
2216. 452. 2 p. multicoloured .. 25 10

453. Courtyard. 454. "The Nativity", (pillar capital, Silos).

1973. Monastery of Santo Domingo de Silos, Burgos.
2217 453 2 p. purple and brown 60 10
2218 – 8 p. purple and blue 60 10
2219 – 15 p. blue and green 60 10
DESIGNS—HORIZ. 8 p. Cloisters. VERT. 15 p. "Three Saints" (statue).

1973. Christmas. Multicoloured.
2220. 2 p. Type 454 .. .. 20 10
2221. 8 p. "Adoration of the Kings" (bas-relief, Butrera) (horiz.) 15 10

455. Map of Spain and the Americas.

1973. 500th Anniv. of Spanish Printing.
2222. 455. 1 p. blue and green .. 60 10
2223. – 7 p. violet and blue .. 70 10
2224. – 15 p. green and purple 75 15
DESIGNS—VERT. 7 p. "Teacher and pupils" (ancient woodcut). 15 p. "Los Siondales" (manuscript).

1974. Spanish Military Uniforms (2nd series). As T 448. Multicoloured.
2225. 1 p. Mounted arquebusier, 1603 .. .. .. 35 10
2226. 2 p. Arquebusier, 1632 .. 1·00 10
2227. 3 p. Mounted cuirassier, 1635 .. .. .. 1·25 10
2228. 5 p. Mounted drummer, 1677 .. .. .. 1·50 20
2229. 9 p. "Viejos Morados" Regiment, Musketeers, 1694 .. .. .. 1·10 20

456. 14th-century Nautical Chart. 457. M. Biada (construction engineer) and Early Locomotive.

1974. 50th Anniv. of Spanish Higher Geographical Council.
2230. 456. 2 p. multicoloured .. 25 10

1974. 125th Anniv of Barcelona–Mataro Railway.
2231 457 2 p. multicoloured .. 50 10

458. Stamp Collector, Album and Magnifier. 459. "Woman with Offering".

1974. "ESPANA 75" Int. Stamp Exhibition, Madrid.
2232. 458. 2 p. multicoloured .. 10 10
2233. – 5 p. blue, blk. & brn. 45 10
2234. – 8 p. multicoloured .. 30 15
DESIGNS—DIAMOND (43×43 mm.). 5 p. Exhibition emblem. 8 p. Globe and arrows.

1974. Europa. Stone Sculptures. Mult.
2235. 2 p. Type 459 .. .. 2·25 10
2236. 8 p. "Woman from Baza" 1·00 15

460. 2 r. Stamp of 1854 with Seville Postmark.

1974. World Stamp Day.
2237. 460. 2 p. multicoloured .. 40 10

461. Jaime Balmes (philosopher) and Monastery. 462. Bramante's "Little Temple", Rome.

1974. Spanish Celebrities.
2238. 461. 8 p. brown and blue .. 55 10
2239. – 10 p. brown and red 1·50 10
2240. – 15 p. blue and brown 75 10
DESIGNS: 10 p. Pedro Poveda (educationalist) and mountain village. 15 p. Jorge Juan (cosmographer and mariner) and shipyard.

1974. Centenary of Spanish Fine Arts Academy, Rome.
2241. 462. 5 p. multicoloured .. 35 10

463. Roman Aqueduct, Segovia.

1974. Spain as a Province of the Roman Empire.
2242. 463. 1 p. black and brown 10 10
2243. – 2 p. brown and green 50 10
2244. – 3 p. brn. & light brn. 15 10
2245. – 4 p. blue and green .. 15 10
2246. – 5 p. purple and blue 20 10
2247. – 7 p. purple and green 20 10
2248. – 8 p. green and red .. 20 10
2249. – 9 p. brown and purple 20 15
DESIGNS—HORIZ. 2 p. Roman Bridge, Alcantara. 3 p. Martial (poet) giving public reading. 5 p. Theatre, Merida. 7 p. Ossio, 1st Bishop of Cordoba, addressing the Synod. VERT. 4 p. Triumphal Arch, Bara. 8 p. Ruins of Curia, Talavera la Vieja. 9 p. Statue of Emperor Trajan.

464. Tortoise.

1974. Fauna (4th series). Reptiles. Mult.
2250. 1 p. Type 464 .. .. 25 10
2251. 2 p. Chameleon 75 10
2252. 5 p. Gecko .. .. 1·25 10
2253. 7 p. Green Lizard .. 1·10 15
2254. 15 p. Adder .. .. 1·00 15

1974. Spanish Military Uniforms (3rd series). As T 448. Multicoloured.
2255. 1 p. Dismounted trooper, Hussars de la Muerte, 1705 .. .. .. 15 10
2256. 2 p. Officer, Royal Regiment of Artillery, 1710 60 10
2257. 3 p. Drummer and fifer, Granada Regiment, 1734 90 10
2258. 7 p. Guidon-bearer, Numancia Dragoons, 1737 60 10
2259. 8 p. Ensign with standard, Zamora Regiment, 1739 75 15

465. Swimmer making Rescue.

1974. 18th World Life-saving Championships. Barcelona.
2260. 465. 2 p. multicoloured .. 30 10

1974. Stamp Day and Eduardo Rosales. Commemoration. Various Paintings as T 409. Multicoloured.
2261. 1 p. "Tobias and the Angel" 15 10
2262. 2 p. Self-portrait .. 15 10
2263. 3 p. "Testament of Isabella the Catholic" (horiz.) .. 25 10
2264. 4 p. "Nena" 25 10
2265. 5 p. "Presentation of Don Juan of Austria" (horiz.) 30 10
2266. 7 p. "The First Steps" (horiz.) 25 10
2267. 10 p. "St. John the Evangelist" 40 10
2268. 15 p. "St. Matthew the Evangelist" 40 20

466. Figure with Letter and Posthorns. 467. Sobremonte's House, Cordoba.

1974. Centenary of U.P.U. Multicoloured.
2269. 2 p. Type 466 .. .. 30 10
2270. 8 p. U.P.U. Monument, Berne 25 10

1974. "Spain in the New World" (3rd series). Argentina. Mult.
2271. 1 p. Type 467 .. .. 20 10
2272. 2 p. Town Hall, Buenos Aires (1929) .. 40 10
2273. 5 p. Ruins of St. Ignacio de Mini (vert.) .. 40 10
2274. 10 p. "The Gaucho" (M. Fierro) (vert.) .. 30 10

468. "Nativity" (detail, Valdavia Church). 469. "Teucrium lanigerum".

1974. Christmas. Church Fonts. Mult.
2275 2 p. Type 468 .. .. 15 10
2276 3 p. "Adoration of the Kings", Valcobero Church (vert) 20 10
2277 8 p. As No. 2276 .. .. 20 10

1974. Flora (3rd series). Multicoloured.
2278. 1 p. Type 469 .. .. 15 10
2279. 2 p. "Hypericum ericoides" 35 10
2280. 4 p. "Thymus longiflorus" 20 10
2281. 5 p. "Anthyllis onobrychioides" .. 40 10
2282. 8 p. "Helianthemum paniculatum" .. 40 10
The 1 p. and 8 p. are wrongly inscribed "Teucriun" and "Helianthemun" respectively

470. Leyre Monastery. 471. Spanish 6 c. and 5 p. Stamps of 1850 and 1975.

1974. Leyre Monastery.
2283 470 2 p. grey and green .. 75 10
2284 – 8 p. red and brown .. 25 10
2285 – 15 p. dp green & green 40 10
DESIGNS—VERT. 8 p. Pillars and bas-relief. HORIZ. 15 p. Crypt.

1975. 125th Anniv of Spanish Postage Stamps.
2286. 471. 2 p. blue 35 10
2287. – 3 p. brown & green .. 65 10
2288. – 8 p. mauve & violet .. 1·10 10
2289. – 10 p. green & purple 75 15
DESIGNS—HORIZ. 3 p. Mail coach, 1850. 8 p. Sail packet of West Indian service. VERT. 10 p. St. Mark's Chapel.

1975. Spanish Military Uniforms (4th series). As T 448. Multicoloured.
2290. 1 p. Toledo Regiment, 1750 .. .. .. 50 10
2291. 2 p. Royal Corps of Artillery, 1762 .. .. 1·00 10
2292. 3 p. Queen's Regt. of the Line, 1763 .. .. 2·00 10
2293. 5 p. Vitoria Regt. of Fusiliers, 1766 .. .. 1·00 10
2294. 10 p. Dragoon of Sagunto Regt., 1775 .. .. 2·00 10

1975. Spanish Architects (2nd series). As T 443.
2295. 8 p. olive and green .. 50 10
2296. 10 p. brown and red .. 50 10
2297. 15 p. black and brown .. 75 10
ARCHITECTS: 8 p. Antonio Gaudi and apartment building. 10 p. Antonio Palacios and palace. 15 p. Secundino Zuazo and block of flats.

473. Almonds.

1975. Flora (4th series). Multicoloured.
2299. 1 p. Type 473 .. .. 15 10
2300. 2 p. Pomegranates (vert.) 60 10
2301. 3 p. Oranges (vert.) .. 60 10
2302. 4 p. Chestnuts (vert.) .. 35 10
2303. 5 p. Apples (vert.) .. 35 10

474. Woman and pitcher, La Aranya. 475. Early Leon Postmark.

1975. Europa. Primitive Cave Paintings.
2304 474 3 p. red, brn & stone 95 10
2305 – 12 p. mve, blk & brn 1·10 10
DESIGN—HORIZ. 12 p. Horse, Tito Bustillo.

1975. World Stamp Day.
2306. 475. 3 p. multicoloured .. 30 10

476. Emblem and Inscription. 477. Farm Scene.

1975. First General Assembly of World Tourism Organisation, Madrid.
2307. 476. 3 p. blue 25 10

1975. 25th Anniv. of "Feria del Campo".
2308. 477. 3 p. multicoloured .. 25 10

478. Heads of Different Races.

1975. International Women's Year.
2309. 478. 3 p. multicoloured .. 30 10

479. Virgin of Cabeza Sanctuary and Forces Emblems.

1975. Defence of Virgin of Cabeza Sanctuary during Civil War.
2310. 479. 3 p. multicoloured .. 25 10

1975. Tourist Series. As T 340.
2311. 1 p. black and purple .. 10 10
2312. 2 p. brown and lake .. 20 10
2313. 3 p. black and blue .. 20 10
2314. 4 p. mauve and red .. 10 10
2315. 5 p. blue and green .. 30 10
2316. 7 p. dp. blue and blue .. 60 10
DESIGNS—HORIZ. 1 p. Cervantes' cell, Argamasilla de Alba. 2 p. St. Martin's Bridge, Toledo. 3 p. St. Peter's Church, Tarrasa. VERT. 4 p. Alhambra archway, Granada. 5 p., Mijas village, Malaga. 7 p. St. Mary's Chapel, Tarrasa.

480. Salamander Lizard.

1975. Spanish Fauna (5th series). Reptiles and Amphibians. Multicoloured.
2317. 1 p. Type 480 .. .. 35 10
2318. 2 p. Triton lizard .. 75 10
2319. 3 p. Tree-frog 75 10
2320. 6 p. Toad 55 10
2321. 7 p. Frog 60 10

1975. Spanish Military Uniforms (5th series). As T 448. Multicoloured.
2322. 1 p. Montesa Regt. 1788 30 10
2323. 2 p. Asturias Regt. of Fusiliers, 1789 .. .. 80 10
2324. 3 p. Infantry of the Line, 1802 .. .. .. 50 10
2325. 4 p. Royal Corps of Artillery, 1803 .. .. 50 10
2326. 7 p. Royal Engineers Regt., 1809 .. .. .. 60 10

481. Child.

1975. Child Welfare.
2327. 481. 3 p. multicoloured .. 25 10

482. Scroll.

1975. Latin Notaries Congress, Barcelona.
2328. **482.** 3 p. multicoloured .. 25 10

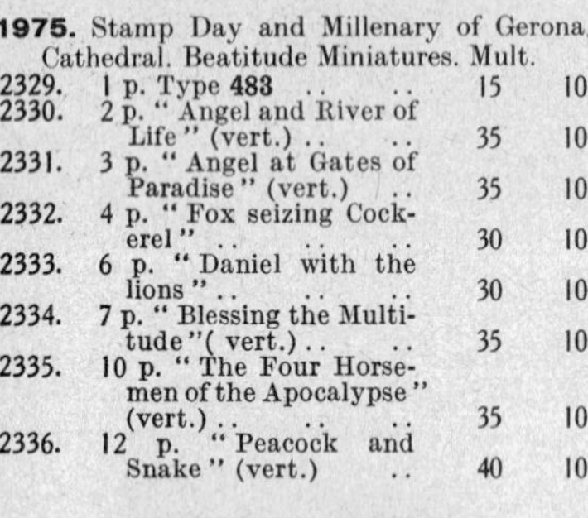

483. " Blessing the Birds ".

1975. Stamp Day and Millenary of Gerona Cathedral. Beatitude Miniatures. Mult.
2329. 1 p. Type **483** 15 10
2330. 2 p. " Angel and River of Life " (vert.) 35 10
2331. 3 p. " Angel at Gates of Paradise " (vert.) .. 35 10
2332. 4 p. " Fox seizing Cockerel " 30 10
2333. 6 p. " Daniel with the lions " 30 10
2334. 7 p. " Blessing the Multitude " (vert.) 35 10
2335. 10 p. " The Four Horsemen of the Apocalypse " (vert.) 35 10
2336. 12 p. " Peacock and Snake " (vert.) .. 40 10

484. Industry Emblems.

1975. Spanish Industry.
2337. **484.** 3 p. violet and purple 15 10

485. El Cabildo, Montevideo.

1975. "Spain in the New World" (4th series). 150th Anniv of Uruguayan Independence. Multicoloured.
2338. 1 p. Type **485** 15 10
2339. 2 p. Ox wagon 35 10
2340. 3 p. Fortress, St. Teresa 35 10
2341. 8 p. Cathedral, Montevideo (vert.) 35 10

486. San Juan de la Pena Monastery.

487. " Virgin and Child ".

1975. San Juan de la Pena Monastery Commemoration.
2342. **486.** 3 p. brown and green 30 10
2343. – 8 p. violet and mauve 15 10
2344. – 10 p. red and mauve 45 10
DESIGNS—HORIZ. 8 p. Cloisters. VERT. 10 p. Pillars.

1975. Christmas. Navarra Art. Multicoloured.
2345. 3 p. Type **487** 40 10
2346. 12 p. " The Flight into Egypt " (horiz.) .. 40 10

488. King Juan Carlos I.

489. Virgin of Pontevedra.

1975. Proclamation of King Juan Carlos I. Multicoloured.
2347. 3 p. Type **488** 30 10
2348. 3 p. Queen Sophia .. 30 10
2349. 3 p. King Juan Carlos and Queen Sophia (33 × 33 mm.) 30 10
2350. 12 p. As No. 2349 .. 50 10

1975. Holy Year of Compostela.
2351. **489.** 3 p. brown and orange 35 10

490. Mountain Scene and Emblem.

491. Cosme Damian Churruca.

1976. Cent. of Catalunya Excursion Centre.
2352. **490.** 6 p. multicoloured .. 15 10

1976. Spanish Navigators.
2353 **491** 7 p. black and brown 1·40 10
2354 – 12 p. violet 75 10
2355 – 50 p. brown and green 1·00 15
NAVIGATORS—VERT. 12 p. Luis de Requesens. HORIZ. 50 p. Juan Sebastian del Cano "Victoria".

492. Alexander Graham Bell and Telephone Equipment.

1976. Telephone Centenary.
2356. **492.** 3 p. multicoloured .. 40 10

493. Crossing the Road.

1976. Road Safety. Multicoloured.
2357 1 p. Type **493** 30 10
2358 3 p. Dangerous driving (vert) 85 10
2359 5 p. Wearing of seat-belts 75 10

494. St. George on Horseback.

1976. 700th Anniv. of St. George's Guardianship of Alcoy.
2360. **494.** 3 p. multicoloured .. 30 10

495. Talavera Pottery. **496.** Spanish 1851 6 r. Stamp with Coruna Postmark.

1976. Europa. Multicoloured.
2361. 3 p. Type **495** .. .. 1·40 10
2362. 12 p. Camarinas Lace-making .. .. 1·90 10

1976. World Stamp Day.
2363 **496** 3 p. red, blue & black 30 10

497. Coins.

1976. Bimillenary of Zaragoza. Roman Antiquities.
2364 **497** 3 p. brown and black 2·75 10
2365 – 7 p. blue and black .. 1·50 10
2366 – 25 p. brown and black 1·50 10
DESIGNS—HORIZ. 7 p. Plan of site and coin. VERT. 25 p. Mosaic.

498. Rifle, 1757.

1976. Bicent. of American Revolution.
2367. **498.** 1 p. blue and brown .. 50 10
2368. – 3 p. brown and green 1·75 10
2369. – 5 p. green and brown 80 10
2370. – 12 p. brown and green 1·00 10
DESIGNS: 3 p. Bernado de Galvez and emblem. 5 p. Richmond $1 banknote of 1861. 12 p. Battle of Pensacola.

499. Customs-house, Cadiz.

1976. Spanish Customs Buildings.
2371. **499.** 1 p. brown and black 30 10
2372. – 3 p. brown and green 90 10
2373. – 7 p. purple and brown 1·75 10
BUILDINGS: 3 p. Madrid. 7 p. Barcelona.

500. Savings Jar and " Industry ".

501. King Juan Carlos I, Queen Sophia and Map of the Americas.

1976. Spanish Post Office. Multicoloured.
2374 1 p. Type **500** 30 10
2375 3 p. Railway mail-sorting van 75 10
2376 6 p. Mounted postman (horiz) 30 10
2377 10 p. Automatic letter sorting equipment (horiz) 90 10

1976. Royal Visit to America (1st issue).
2378 **501** 12 p. multicoloured .. 40 10
See also No. 2434.

1976. Tourist Series. As T **340.**
2379. 1 p. brown and grey .. 25 10
2380. 2 p. blue and green .. 75 10
2381. 3 p. brown and red .. 60 10
2382. 4 p. blue and brown .. 30 10
2383. 7 p. brown and blue .. 80 10
2384. 12 p. purple and mauve .. 1·00 10
DESIGNS—HORIZ. 1 p. Cloisters, San Marcos, Leon. 2 p. Las Canadas, Tenerife. 4 p. Cruz de Tejeda, Las Palmas. 7 p. Gredos, Avila. 12 p. La Arruzafa, Cordoba. VERT. 3 p. Hospice of the Catholic Kings, Santiago de Compostela.

502. Rowing.

1976. Olympic Games, Montreal. Mult.
2385. 1 p. Type **502** 15 10
2386. 2 p. Boxing 35 10
2387. 3 p. Wrestling (vert.) .. 50 10
2388. 12 p. Basketball (vert.) .. 50 10

503. King Juan Carlos I.

504. " Giving Blood ".

1976.
2389. **503.** 10 c. orange .. 10 10
2390. 25 c. yellow .. 10 10
2391. 30 c. blue .. 10 10
2392. 50 c. purple .. 10 10
2393. 1 p. green 10 10
2394. 1 p. 50 red 10 10
2395. 2 p. blue 10 10
2396. 3 p. green 10 10
2397. 4 p. turquoise .. 10 10
2398. 5 p. red 10 10
2399. 6 p. turquoise .. 15 10
2400. 7 p. olive 10 10
2401. 8 p. blue 15 10
2402. 10 p. red 15 10
2403. 12 p. brown .. 15 10
2403a. 13 p. brown .. 25 10
2403b. 14 p. orange .. 15 10
2404. 15 p. violet 30 10
2405. 16 p. brown .. 30 10
2405a. 17 p. blue 30 10
2406. 19 p. orange .. 30 10
2407. 20 p. red 30 10
2408. 30 p. green 35 10
2409. 50 p. red 55 10
2409a. **503.** 60 p. blue 70 10
2409b. 75 p. green 85 10
2409c. 85 p. grey 95 10
2409d. – 100 p. brown .. 1·10 10
2409e. – 200 p. green .. .. 2·25 20
2409f. – 500 p. blue .. .. 5·00 40
Nos. 2409 d/f are as Type **503**, but larger, 25 × 30 mm.

1976. Spanish Military Uniforms (6th series). As T **448**. Multicoloured.
2410. 1 p. Alcantara Regiment, 1815 .. .. .. 25 10
2411. 2 p. Regiment of the line, 1821 .. .. .. 1·25 10
2412. 3 p. Gala Engineers, 1825 55 10
2413. 7 p. Artillery Regiment, 1828 .. .. .. 35 10
2414. 25 p. Light Infantry Regiment, 1830 .. 65 15

1976. Blood Donors Publicity.
2415 **504** 3 p. red and black .. 15 10

505. Batitales Mosaic.

506. Parliament House, Madrid.

1976. Bimillenary of Lugo.
2416. **505.** 1 p. purple and black 35 10
2417. – 3 p. brown and black 75 10
2418. – 7 p. red and green .. 75 10
DESIGNS: 3 p. Old City Wall. 7 p. Roman coins.

1976. 63rd Inter-Parliamentary Union Congress, Madrid.
2419. **506.** 12 p. brown and green 35 10

1976. Stamp Day and Luis Menendez Commemoration. Paintings as T **409**. Mult.
2420 1 p. "Jug, Cherries, Plums and Cheese" 15 10
2421 2 p. "Jar, Melon, Oranges and Savouries" .. 15 10
2422 3 p. "Barrel, Pears and Melon" 35 10
2423 4 p. "Pigeons, Basket and Bowl" 20 10
2424 6 p. "Fish and Oranges" (horiz) 25 10
2425 7 p. "Melon and Bread" (horiz) 25 10
2426 10 p. "Jug, Plums and Bread" (horiz) .. 35 10
2427 12 p. "Pomegranates, Apples and Grapes" (horiz) 35 10

507. " The Nativity ".

508. Nicoya Church.

1976. Christmas. Multicoloured.
2428. 3 p. Type **507** .. 85 10
2429. 12 p. St. Christopher carrying Holy Child (vert.) 1·75 10

1976. " Spain in the New World " (5th series). Costa Rica. Multicoloured.
2430. 1 p. Type **508** 15 10
2431. 2 p. Juan Vazquez de Coronado 30 10
2432. 3 p. Orosi Mission (horiz.) 35 10
2433. 12 p. Tomas de Acosta .. 35 10

1976. Royal Visit to America (2nd issue). As T **501**. Multicoloured.
2434 12 p. "Santa Maria" and South America .. 50 10

510. San Pedro de Alcantara Monastery.

1976. Monastery of San Pedro de Alcantara.
2435. **510.** 3 p. brown and purple 35 10
2436. – 7 p. purple and blue .. 40 10
2437. – 20 p. choc. and brown 55 10
DESIGNS—VERT. 7 p. High Altar. 20 p. San Pedro de Alcantara.

511. Hand releasing Doves.

1976. Civil War Invalids' Association.
2438. **511.** 3 p. multicoloured .. 30 10

512. Pablo Casals and Cello.

1976. Birth Centenaries.
2439. **512.** 3 p. black and blue .. 40 10
2440. – 5 p. green and red .. 40 10
DESIGN: 5 p. Manuel de Falla and "Fire Dance".

1977. Spanish Military Uniforms (7th series). Vert. designs as T **448**. Multicoloured.
2441. 1 p. Outrider, Calatrava Lancers, 1844 .. .. 20 10
2442. 2 p. Sapper, Engineers' Regt., 1850 .. .. 40 10
2443. 3 p. Corporal, Light Infantry, 1861 .. 40 10
2444. 4 p. Drum Major, Infantry of the Line, 1861 .. 25 10
2445. 20 p. Captain, Horse Artillery, 1862 .. 75 10

513. King James I and Arms of Aragon.

1977. 700th Death Anniv of King James I.
2446 **513** 4 p. brown and violet 25 10

514. Jacinto Verdaguer (poet). **516.** Salmon.

515. King Charles III.

1977. Spanish Celebrities.
2447. **514.** 5 p. red and violet .. 40 10
2448. – 7 p. green and brown 40 10
2449. – 12 p. turquoise & blue 45 10
2450. – 50 p. brown & green 75 10
DESIGNS: 7 p. Miguel Servet (theologian and physician). 12 p. Pablo Sarasate (violinist). 50 p. Francisco Tarrega (guitarist).

1977. Bicentenary of Economic Society of the Friends of the Land.
2451 **515** 4 p. brown and green 30 10

1977. Spanish Fauna (6th series). Freshwater Fishes. Multicoloured.
2452. 1 p. Type **516** 20 10
2453. 2 p. Brown trout (horiz.) 40 10
2454. 3 p. Eel (horiz.) 35 10
2455. 4 p. Carp (horiz.) .. 30 10
2456. 6 p. Barbel (horiz.) .. 40 10

517. Skiing.

1977. World Ski Championships, Granada.
2457. **517.** 5 p. multicoloured .. 30 10

518. La Cuadra, 1902.

1977. Vintage Cars. Multicoloured.
2458. 2 p. Type **518** 20 10
2459. 4 p. Hispano Suiza, 1916 25 10
2460. 5 p. Elizade, 1915 .. 35 10
2461. 7 p. Abadal, 1914 .. 45 10

519. Donana.

1977. Europa. Landscapes, National Parks. Multicoloured.
2462. 3 p. Type **519** 35 10
2463. 12 p. Ordesa 75 10

520. Plaza Mayor, Madrid and Stamps.

1977. 50th Anniv. of Philatelic Bourse on Plaza Mayor, Madrid.
2464. **520.** 3 p. grn., red and vio. 25 10

521. Enrique de Osso (founder).

1977. Centenary of Society of St. Theresa of Jesus.
2465. **521.** 8 p. multicoloured .. 25 10

1977. Tourist Series. As T **340.**
2466. 1 p. brown and orange .. 20 10
2467. 2 p. grey and brown .. 20 10
2468. 3 p. purple and blue .. 20 10
2469. 4 p. green and blue .. 20 10
2470. 7 p. grey and brown .. 20 10
2471. 12 p. brown and violet .. 25 10
DESIGNS—HORIZ. 1 p. Toledo Gate, Ciudad Real. 2 p. Roman Aqueduct, Almunecar. 7 p. Ampudia Castle, Palencia. 12 p. Bisagra Gate, Toledo. VERT. 3 p. Jaen Cathedral. 4 p. Bridge and Gate, Ronda Gorge, Malaga.

1977. Spanish Military Uniforms (8th series). As T **448**. Multicoloured.
2472. 1 p. Administration officer, 1875 .. .. 10 10
2473. 2 p. Lancer, 1883 .. 25 10
2474. 3 p. General Staff commander, 1884 .. 25 10
2475. 7 p. Trumpeter, Divisional Artillery, 1887 .. 20 10
2476. 25 p. Medical Corps officer, 1895 .. .. 40 10

522. San Marino de la Cogalla (carving) and Early Castilian Manuscript.

1977. Millenary of Castilian Language.
2477. **522.** 5 p. brn., grn. & pur. 30 10

1977. Stamp Day and F. Madrazo (painter) Commemoration. Portraits. As T **409.** Multicoloured.
2478. 1 p. "The Youth of Florez" 15 10
2479. 2 p. "Duke of San Miguel" 20 10
2480. 3 p. "C. Coronado" .. 20 10
2481. 4 p. "Campoamor" .. 15 10
2482. 6 p. "Marquesa de Montelo" 15 10
2483. 7 p. "Rivadeneyra" .. 15 10
2484. 10 p. "Countess of Vilches" 25 10
2485. 15 p. "Gomez de Avellaneda" 35 10

523. Sailing Ship and Map of Mail Routes to America.

1977. Bicentenary of Mail to the Indies, and "Espamer 77" Stamp Exhibition, Barcelona.
2486 **523** 15 p. green and brown 70 50

524. St. Francis's Church.

1977. Spanish–Guatemalan Relations. Guatemala City Buildings. Multicoloured.
2487. 1 p. Type **524** 15 10
2488. 3 p. High-rise flats .. 15 10
2489. 7 p. Government Palace 25 10
2490. 12 p. Monument, Columbus Square 30 10

525. Monastery Building.

1977. St. Peter's Monastery, Cardena, Commemoration.
2491. **525.** 3 p. grey and blue .. 15 10
2492. – 7 p. red and brown .. 10 10
2493. – 20 p. grey and green 25 10
DESIGNS: 7 p. Cloisters. 20 p. El Cid (effigy).

526. Adoration of the Kings.

1977. Christmas. Miniatures from Manuscript "Romanico de Huesca". Multicoloured.
2494. 5 p. Type **526** 15 10
2495. 12 p. Flight into Egypt (vert.) 20 10

527. Rohrbach "RO-VIII" 1927, and "DC10" Airliner.

1977. 50th Anniv of IBERIA (State airline).
2496 **527** 12 p. multicoloured .. 60 10

528. Crown Prince Felipe. **529.** Judo.

1977. Felipe de Borbon, Prince of Asturias.
2497 **528** 5 p. multicoloured .. 30 10

1977. 10th World Judo Championships.
2498. **529.** 3 p. blk., red and brn. 40 10

1977. Spanish Military Uniforms (9th series). Multicoloured. Vert. designs as T **448.**
2499. 1 p. Ensign, Colour Detachment, Royal Infantry Regiment, 1908 .. 15 10
2500. 2 p. Pavia Hussars' Colonel, 1909 .. .. .. 15 10
2501. 3 p. Horse Artillery Ensign, 1912 .. .. 20 10
2502. 5 p. Engineers' Captain, 1921 .. .. .. 20 10
2503. 12 p. Captain-General of the Armed Forces, 1925 20 10

530. Hilarion Eslava (composer). **531.** "The Deposition of Christ" (detail Juan de Juni).

1977. Spanish Celebrities.
2504 **530** 5 p. black and purple 15 10
2505 – 8 p. black and green 15 10
2506 – 25 p. black and green 35 10
2507 – 50 p. purple & brown 60 10
DESIGNS: 8 p. Jose Clara (sculptor). 25 p. Pio Baroja (writer). 50 p. Antonio Machado (writer).

1978. Anniversaries of Artists.
2508 **531** 3 p. multicoloured .. 10 10
2509 – 3 p. multicoloured .. 10 10
2510 – 3 p. mauve and violet 10 10
2511 – 5 p. multicoloured .. 15 10
2512 – 5 p. multicoloured .. 15 10
2513 – 5 p. brown and black 15 10
2514 – 8 p. multicoloured .. 15 10
2515 – 8 p. multicoloured .. 15 10
2516 – 8 p. pink and green .. 15 10
DESIGNS—As T **531**. No. 2510, Portrait of Juan de Juni (sculptor, 400th death anniv). 2511, Detail of "Rape of the Sabines" (Rubens). 2513, Artist's palette and Rubens's signature. 2514, Detail of "Bacchanal" (Titian). 2516, Artist's palette and Titian's initial. 46 × 25 mm: 2509, Different detail of "Deposition of Christ" and sculptor's tools. 2512, Different detail of "Rape of the Sabines" and portrait of Rubens (400th birth anniv). 2515, Different detail of "Bacchanal" and portrait of Titian (500th birth anniv).

532. Edelweiss in the Pyrenees.

1978. Protection of the Environment. Mult.
2517 3 p. Type **532** 15 10
2518 5 p. Fish and red-breasted merganser 35 10
2519 7 p. Forest (fire prevention) 25 10
2520 12 p. Tanker, oil rig and industrial complex (protection of the sea) 25 10
2521 20 p. Audouin's gull and Mediterranean monk seal (vert) 55 25

533. Palace of Charles V, Granada.

1978. Europa.
2522. **533.** 5 p. green & light green 25 10
2523. – 12 p. red and green .. 30 10
DESIGN: 12 p. Exchange building, Seville.

534. Council Emblem and Map of Spain.

1978. Membership of the Council of Europe
2524. **534.** 12 p. multicoloured .. 20 10

535. Columbus Hermitage.

1978. 500th Anniv of Las Palmas. Gran Canaria. Multicoloured.

2525. 3 p. 16th cent. plan of city (horiz.) 10 10
2526. 5 p. Type **535** 10 10
2527. 12 p. Las Palmas (16th century) (horiz.) .. 15 10

536. Post Box, Stamp, U.P.U. Emblem and Postal Transport.

1978. World Stamp Day.

2528 **536** 5 p. green & dp green 30 10

1978. Stamp Day and Picasso Commemoration. As T **409**. Multicoloured.

2529 3 p. "Portrait of Senora Canals" 15 10
2530 5 p. Self-portrait .. 15 10
2531 8 p. "Portrait of Jaime Sabartes" 15 10
2532 10 p. "The End of the Number" 20 10
2533 12 p. "Science and Charity" (horiz) .. 20 10
2534 15 p. "Las Meninas" (horiz) 25 10
2535 20 p. "The Pigeons" .. 25 10
2536 25 p. "The Painter and Model" (horiz) .. 30 10

537. Jose de San Martin.

1978. Latin-American Heroes.

2537. **537.** 7 p. brown and red .. 10 10
2538. – 12 p. violet and red .. 20 20

DESIGNS: 12 p. Simon Bolivar.

538. Flight into Egypt.

1978. Christmas. Capitals from Santa Maria de Nieva. Multicoloured.

2539 5 p. Type **538** 10 10
2540 12 p. The Annunciation .. 15 10

539. Aztec Calendar. 540. Philip V.

1978. Royal Visits to Mexico, Peru and Argentina. Multicoloured.

2541. 5 p. Type **539** 10 10
2542. 5 p. Macchu Piccu, Peru 10 10
2543. 5 p. Pre-Columbian pots, Argentina .. 10 10

1978. Spanish Kings and Queens of the House of Bourbon.

2544. **540.** 5 p. red and blue .. 10 10
2545. – 5 p. deep green and light green .. 10 10
2546. – 8 p. lake and blue .. 20 10
2547. – 10 p. black and green 20 10
2548. – 12 p. lake and brown 25 10
2549. – 15 p. blue and green .. 25 10
2550. – 20 p. blue and olive .. 30 10
2551. – 25 p. violet and blue 35 10
2552. – 50 p. brown and red .. 60 15
2553. – 100 p. violet and blue 1·25 40

DESIGNS: 5 p. (2545), Luis I. 8 p. Ferdinand VI. 10 p. Charles III. 12 p. Charles IV. 15 p. Ferdinand VII. 20 p. Isabel II. 25 p. Alfonso XII. 50 p. Alfonso XIII. 100 p. Juan Carlos I.

541. Miniatures from Bible.

1978. Millenary of Consecration of Third Basilica of Santa Maria, Ripoll.

2554. **541.** 5 p. multicoloured .. 15 10

542. Flag, First Lines of Constitution and Cortes Building.

1978. New Constitution.

2555. **542.** 5 p. multicoloured .. 15 10

543. Car and Oil Drop. 544. St. Jean Baptiste de la Salle (founder).

1979. Energy Conservation. Multicoloured.

2556. 5 p. Type **543** 10 10
2557. 8 p. Insulated house and thermometer 10 10
2558. 10 p. Hand removing electric plug .. 15 10

1979. Centenary of Brothers of the Christian Schools in Spain.

2559. **544.** 5 p. brn., blue & mve. 10 10

545. Jorge Manrique (poet). 546. Running and Jumping.

1979. Spanish Celebrities.

2560. **545.** 5 p. brown and green 10 10
2561. – 8 p. blue and red .. 10 10
2562. – 10 p. violet & brown 10 10
2563. – 20 p. green & bistre .. 30 10

DESIGNS: 8 p. Fernan Caballero (novelist). 10 p. Francisco Villaespesa (poet). 20 p. Gregorio Maranon (writer).

1979. Sport for All.

2564. **546.** 5 p. red, grn. & black 10 10
2565. – 8 p. bl., ochre & black 10 10
2566. – 10 p. brn., blue & blk. 10 10

DESIGNS: 8 p. Football, running, skipping and cycling. 10 p. Running.

547. School Library (child's drawing). 548. Cabinet Messenger and Postilion, 1761.

1979. International Year of the Child.

2567. **547.** 5 p. multicoloured .. 15 10

1979. Europa.

2568. **548.** 5 p. deep brown and brown on yellow .. 20 10
2569. – 12 p. green and brown on yellow .. 25 10

DESIGN—HORIZ. 12 p. Manuel de Ysasi (postal reformer).

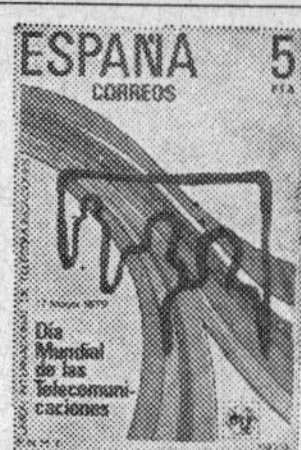

549. Wave Pattern and Television Screen.

1979. World Telecommunications Day. Multicoloured.

2570. 5 p. Type **549** 10 10
2571. 8 p. Satellite and receiving aerial (horiz.) .. 20 10

550. First Bulgarian Stamp and Exhibition Hall.

1979. "Philaserdica 79" Stamp Exhibition, Sofia.

2572. **550.** 12 p. multicoloured .. 15 10

551. Tank, Destroyer "Roger de Lauria" and Jet Fighter.

1979. Armed Forces Day.

2573. **551.** 5 p. multicoloured .. 60 10

552. King receiving Messenger.

1979. Stamp Day.

2574. **552.** 5 p. multicoloured .. 25 10

1979. Tourist Series. As T **340**.

2575. 5 p. lilac and blue .. 10 10
2576. 8 p. brown and blue .. 10 10
2577. 10 p. green and myrtle .. 10 10
2578. 20 p. sepia and brown .. 15 10

DESIGNS—VERT. 5 p. Daroca Gate, Zaragoza. 8 p. Gerona Cathedral. 10 p. Interior of Carthusian Monastery Church, Granada. 20 p. Portal of Marques de Dos Aguas Palace, Valencia.

553. Turkey Sponge.

1979. Spanish Fauna (7th series). Invertebrates. Multicoloured.

2579 5 p. Type **553** 10 10
2580 7 p. Crayfish 10 10
2581 8 p. "Buthus europaeus" .. 10 10
2582 20 p. Starfish 20 10
2583 25 p. Sea anenome 30 10

554. Antonio Gutierrez. 555. Cathedral and Statue of Virgin and Child, Zaragoza.

1979. Defence of Tenerife, 1797.

2584. **554.** 5 p. multicoloured .. 30 10

1979. Stamp Day and J. de Juanes (painter) Commemoration. Religious Paintings as T **409**. Multicoloured.

2585. 8 p. "Immaculate Conception" 15 10
2586. 10 p. "Holy Family" .. 15 10
2587. 15 p. "Ecce Homo" .. 25 10
2588. 20 p. "St. Stephen in the Synagogue" .. 25 10
2589. 25 p. "The Last Supper" (horiz.) 30 10
2590. 50 p. "Adoration of the Mystic Lamb" (horiz.) 50 20

1979. 8th Mariological Congress, Zaragoza.

2591. **555.** 5 p. multicoloured .. 30 10

556. St. Bartholomew's College, Bogota.

1979. Latin-American Architecture.

2592. **556.** 7 p. green, blue & brn. 10 10
2593. – 12 p. indigo, pur. & brn. 15 10

DESIGN: 12 p. University of San Marcos, Lima.

557. Hands and Governor's Palace, Barcelona. 558. Autonomy Statute.

1979. Catalonian Autonomy.

2594 **557** 8 p. multicoloured .. 25 10

1979. Basque Autonomy.

2595 **558** 8 p. multicoloured .. 30 10

559. Prince of Asturias and Hospital.

1979. Centenary of Hospital of the Child Jesus, Madrid.

2596. **559.** 5 p. multicoloured .. 30 10

560. Barcelona Tax Stamp, 1929.

1979. 50th Anniv of Barcelona Exhibition. Tax Stamps.

2597 **560** 5 p. multicoloured .. 25 10

561. The Nativity.

1979. Christmas. Capitals from San Pedro el Viejo, Huesca. Multicoloured.

2598. 8 p. Type **561** 10 10
2599. 19 p. Flight into Egypt .. 20 10

562. Charles I.

1979. Spanish Kings of the House of Hapsburg.

2600. **562.** 15 p. green and blue .. 30 10
2601. – 20 p. blue and mauve 35 10
2602. – 25 p. violet and brown 45 10
2603. – 50 p. brown and green 75 20
2604. – 100 p. mauve & brown 1·25 35

DESIGNS: 20 p. Philip II. 25 p. Philip III. 50 p. Philip IV. 100 p. Charles II.

563. Olive Plantation and Harvester.

1979. International Olive Oil Year.
2605 563 8 p. multicoloured .. 30 10

564. Electric Train.

1980. Public Transport.
2606. 564. 3 p. lake and brown.. 10 10
2607. – 4 p. blue and brown.. 10 10
2608. – 5 p. green and brown 15 10
DESIGNS: 4 p. Motorbus. 5 p. Underground train.

565. Steel Products.

1980. Spanish Exports (1st series). Mult.
2609 5 p. Type 565 .. .. 10 10
2610 8 p. Tankers 10 10
2611 13 p. Footwear 15 10
2612 19 p. Industrial machines 20 10
2613 25 p. Factory buildings, bridge and symbols of technology 30 10
See also Nos. 2653/5.

566. Federico Garcia Lorca.

1980. Europa. Writers.
2614. 566. 8 p. violet and green 15 10
2615. – 19 p. brown and green 30 10
DESIGN: 19 p. J. Ortega y Gasset.

567. Footballers.

1980. World Cup Football Championship, Spain (1982) (1st issue). Multicoloured
2616. 8 p. Type 567 .. .. 15 10
2617. 19 p. Football and flags.. 35 10
See also Nos. 2640/1, 2668/9 and 2683/4.

568. Armed Forces.

1980. Armed Forces Day.
2618. 568. 8 p. multicoloured .. 50 10

569. Bourbon Arms, Ministry of Finance, Madrid.

1980. Public Finances under the Bourbons.
2619. 569. 8 p. deep brn. & brn. 15 10

570. Helen Keller.

1980. Birth Cent. of Helen Keller.
2620. 570. 19 p. red and green.. 30 10

571. Postal Courier (14th cent.).

1980. Stamp Day.
2621. 571. 8 p. brn., stone & red 20 10

572. King Alfonso XIII and Count of Maceda at Exhibition.

573. Altar of the Virgin, La Palma Cathedral.

1980. 50th Anniv. of First National Stamp Exhibition.
2622. 572. 8 p. multicoloured .. 30 10

1980. 300th Anniv. of Appearance of the Holy Virgin at La Palma.
2623. 573. 8 p. brown and black 25 10

574. Ramon Perez de Ayala.

1980. Birth Centenary of Ramon Perez de Ayala (writer).
2624. 574. 100 p. green & brown 95 20

576. Juan de Garay and Founding of Buenos Aires (after Moreno Carbonero).

1980. 400th Anniv. of Buenos Aires.
2626. 576. 19 p. bl., grn. & red.. 20 10

578. Palace of Congresses, Madrid.

579. " Nativity " (mural from Church of Santa Mariade, Cines, Oza de los Rios).

1980. European Security and Co-operation Conference, Madrid.
2628. 578. 22 p. multicoloured.. 25 10

1980. Christmas. Multicoloured.
2629. 10 p. Type 579 .. .. 10 10
2630. 22 p. " Adoration of the Kings " (doorway of Church of St. Nicholas of Cines, Oza de los Rios) (horiz.) 25 10

580. Pedro Vives and Airplane.

1980. Aviation Pioneers. Multicoloured.
2631. 5 p. Type 580 .. .. 15 10
2632. 10 p. Benito Loygorri .. 15 10
2633. 15 p. Alfonso de Orleans 30 10
2634. 22 p. Alfredo Kindelan 40 10

581. Games Emblem and Skier.

1981. Winter University Games.
2635. 581. 30 p. multicoloured .. 30 10

582. " Homage to Picasso " (Joan Miro).

1981. Birth Cent. of Pablo Picasso (artist).
2636. 582. 100 p. multicoloured 1·25 20

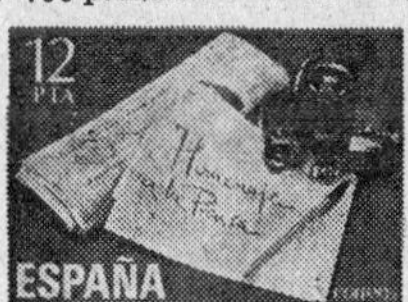

583. Newspaper, Camera and Notepaper and Pen.

1981. The Press.
2637. 583. 12 p. multicoloured .. 20 10

584. Map of Galicia, Arms and National Anthem.

1981. Galician Autonomy.
2638. 584. 12 p. multicoloured.. 25 10

585. Mosaic forming Human Figure.

586. Heading Ball.

1981. International Year of Disabled Persons.
2639 585 30 p. multicoloured .. 40 10

1981. World Cup Football Championship (1982) (2nd issue). Multicoloured.
2640. 12 p. Type 586 .. .. 35 10
2641. 30 p. Kicking ball (horiz.) 55 10

587. La Jota (folk dance).

588. King Juan Carlos reviewing Army.

1981. Europa.
2642. 587. 12 p. blk. and brown 20 10
2643. – 30 p. dp. lilac & lilac 40 10
DESIGN: 30 p. Procession of the Virgin of Rocio

1981. Armed Forces Day.
2644. 588. 12 p. multicoloured .. 15 10

589. Gabriel Miro (writer).

590. Messenger (14th century woodcut).

1981. Spanish Celebrities.
2645. 589. 6 p. violet and green 15 10
2646. – 12 p. brown and violet 20 10
2647. – 30 p. green and brown 35 10
DESIGNS: 12 p. Francisco de Quevedo (writer). 30 p. St. Benedict.

1981. Stamp Day.
2648. 590. 12 p. pink, brn. & grn. 30 10

591. Map of the Balearics (from Atlas of Diego Homem, 1563).

1981. Spanish Islands. Multicoloured.
2649. 7 p. Type 591 .. .. 15 10
2650. 12 p. Map of the Canary Islands (from map of Mateo Prunes, 1563).. 20 10

592. Alfonso XII, Juan Carlos and Arms.

1981. Cent. of Public Prosecutors Office.
2651. 592. 50 p. brn., grn. and blue 85 10

593. King Sancho VI of Navarre with Foundation Charter.

1981. 800th Anniv. of Vitoria.
2652. 593. 12 p. multicoloured .. 15 10

594. Citrus Fruit.

1981. Spanish Exports (2nd series). Mult.
2653. 6 p. Type 594 .. .. 10 10
2654. 12 p. Wine 15 10
2655. 30 p. Aircraft, car and lorry 45 10

595. Foodstuffs.

1981. World Food Day.
2656. 595. 30 p. multicoloured .. 30 10

597. Congress Palace, Buenos Aires.

598. "Adoration of the Kings" (from Cervera de Pisuerg).

1981. "Espamer 81" International Stamp Exhibition, Buenos Aires.

2658. **597.** 12 p. red and blue .. 15 10

1981. Christmas. Multicoloured.

2659 12 p. Type **598** 15 10

2660 30 p. "Nativity" (from Paredes de Nava) .. 30 10

599. Plaza de Espana, Seville.

1981. Air.

2661. **599.** 13 p. green and blue 25 10

2662. – 20 p. blue and brown 35 10

DESIGN: 20 p. Rande Bridge, Ria de Vigo.

600. Telegraph Operator.

1981. Postal and Telecommunications Museum, Madrid.

2663. **600.** 7 p. green and brown 10 10

2664. – 12 p. brown and violet 15 10

DESIGN: 12 p. Post wagon.

601. Royal Mint, Seville.

602. Iparraguirre.

1981. Financial Administration by the Bourbons in Spain and Indies.

2666. **601.** 12 p. brown and grey 15 10

1981. Death Centenary of Jose Maria Iparraguirre.

2667. **602.** 12 p. blue and black 15 10

603. Publicity Poster by Juan Miro.

604. Andres Bello (author and philosopher) (Birth bicent.)

1982. World Cup Football Championship, Spain (3rd issue). Multicoloured.

2668. 14 p. Type **603** 30 10

2669. 33 p. World Cup trophy and championship emblem 50 15

1982. Anniversaries (1981).

2670. **604.** 30 p. deep green and green 35 10

2671. – 30 p. green and blue 35 10

2672. – 50 p. violet and black 55 15

DESIGNS: No. 2671, J. R. Jimenez (author, birth centenary). No. 2672, P. Calderon (playwright, 300th death anniv.).

605. St. James of Compostela (Codex illustration).

606. Manuel Fernandez Caballero.

1982. Holy Year of Compostela.

2673. **605.** 14 p. multicoloured .. 15 10

1982. Masters of Operetta (1st series). As T **606** (2674, 2676, 2678) or T **625** (others). Multicoloured.

2674 3 p. Type **606** 10 10

2675 3 p. Scene from "Gigantes y Cabezudos" (horiz) .. 10 10

2676 6 p. Amadeo Vives Roig 10 10

2677 6 p. Scene from "Maruxa" (horiz) 10 10

2678 8 p. Tomas Breton y Hernandez 15 10

2679 8 p. Scene from "La Verbena de la Paloma" (horiz) 15 10

See also Nos. 2713/18 and 2772/7.

607. Arms, Seals and Signatures (Unification of Spain, 1479).

1982. Europa. Multicoloured.

2680 14 p. Type **607** 15 10

2681 33 p. Symbolic ship, Columbus map of "La Spanola" and signature (Discovery of America) 40 10

608. Swords, Arms and Flag.

609. Tackling.

1982. Armed Forces Day and Centenary of General Military Academy.

2682. **608.** 14 p. multicoloured .. 15 10

1982. World Cup Football Championship, Spain (4th issue). Multicoloured.

2683. 14 p. Type **609** 25 10

2884. 33 p. Goal 55 10

610. "St. Andrew and St. Francis".

612. "Transplants".

611. Map of Tenerife and Letter.

1982. Air. Paintings by El Greco. Mult.

2686. 13 p. Type **610** 20 10

2687. 20 p. "St. Thomas" .. 30 10

1982. Stamp Day.

2688. **611.** 14 p. multicoloured .. 30 10

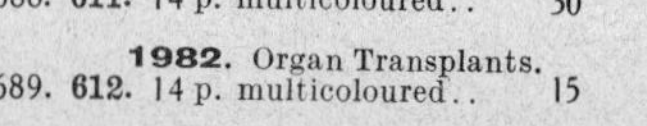

1982. Organ Transplants.

2689. **612.** 14 p. multicoloured .. 15 10

613. Storks and Modern Locomotive.

1982. 23rd International Railway Congress, Malaga. Multicoloured.

2690 9 p. Type **613** 15 10

2691 14 p. Locomotive "Antigua" (37 × 26 mm) .. 50 10

2692 33 p. Locomotive "Montana" (wrongly inscr "Santa Fe") (37 × 26 mm) 60 10

614. La Fortaleza, San Juan.

1982. "Espamer' 82" Stamp Exhibition, San Juan, Puerto Rico.

2693. **614.** 33 p. blue and lilac .. 35 10

615. St. Theresa of Avila (sculpture by Gregorio Hernandez).

1982. 400th Death Anniv. of St. Theresa of Avila.

2694. **615.** 33 p. brown, blue and green 35 15

616. Pope John Paul II.

1982. Papal Visit.

2695. **616.** 14 p. blue and brown 25 10

1982. Tourist Series. As Type **340**.

2696. 4 p. blue and grey .. 10 10

2697. 6 p. grey and blue .. 10 10

2698. 9 p. lilac and blue .. 10 10

2699. 14 p. lilac and blue .. 15 10

2700. 33 p. brown and red .. 35 10

DESIGNS—VERT. 4 p. Arab water-wheel, Alcantarilla. 9 p. Dying Christ, Seville. 14 p. St. Martin's Tower, Teruel. 33 p. St. Andrew's Gate, Villalpando. HORIZ. 6 p. Bank of Spain, Madrid.

617. "Adoration of The Kings" (sculpture, Covarrubias Collegiate Church).

618. "The Prophet".

1982. Christmas. Multicoloured.

2701. 14 p. Type **617** 15 10

2702. 33 p. "The Flight into Egypt" (painting) .. 35 10

1982. Birth Centenary of Pablo Gargallo (sculptor).

2703. **618.** 14 p. green and blue 15 10

619. St. John Bosco (founder) and Children.

1982. Cent. of Salesian Schools in Spain.

2704. **619.** 14 p. multicoloured .. 15 10

620. Arms of Spain.

1983.

2705. **620.** 14 p. multicoloured .. 15 10

621. Sunrise over Andalusia.

1983. Andalusian Autonomy.

2706. **621.** 14 p. multicoloured .. 15 10

622. Arms of Cantabria, Mountains and Monuments.

1983. Cantabrian Autonomy.

2707. **622.** 14 p. multicoloured .. 15 10

623. National Police.

624. Cycling.

1983. State Security Forces. Multicoloured.

2708. 9 p. Type **623** 10 10

2709. 14 p. Civil Guard .. 15 10

2710. 33 p. Superior Police Corps 35 10

1983. Air. Sports. Multicoloured.

2711. 13 p. Type **624** 15 10

2712. 20 p. Bowling (horiz.) .. 20 10

625. Scene from "La Parranda".

1983. Masters of Operetta (2nd series). As T **625** (2714, 2716, 2718) or T **606** (others). Multicoloured.

2713. 4 p. Francisco Alonso (vert.) 10 10

2714. 4 p. Type **625** .. 10 10

2715. 6 p. Jacinto Guerrero (vert.) 15 10

2716. 6 p. Scene from "La Rosa del Azafran" .. 15 10

2717. 9 p. Jesus de Guridi (vert.) 30 10

2718. 9 p. Scene from "El Caserio" 30 10

626. Cervantes and Scene from " Don Quixote ".

1983. Europa.
2719. **626.** 16 p. red and green .. 20 10
2720. – 38 p. sepia and brown 40 10
DESIGN: 38 p. Torres Quevedo and Niagara cable-car.

627. Francisco Salzillo (artist). **628.** W.C.Y. Emblem.

1983. Spanish Celebrities.
2721. **627.** 16 p. purple and green 40 10
2722. – 38 p. blue and brown 50 10
2723. – 50 p. blue and brown 70 15
2724. – 100 p. brown & violet 1·25 20
DESIGNS: 38 p. Antonio Soler (composer). 50 p. Joaquin Turina (composer). 100 p. St. Isidro Labrador (patron saint of Madrid).

1983. World Communications Year.
2725. **628.** 38 p. multicoloured .. 40 10

629. Leaves.

1983. Riojan Autonomy.
2726. **629.** 16 p. multicoloured .. 20 10

630. Army Monument, Burgos.

1983. Armed Forces Day.
2727. **630.** 16 p. multicoloured .. 20 10

631. Burgos Setter.

1983. Spanish Dogs.
2728. **631.** 10 p. blue, brn. & red 15 10
2729. – 16 p. multicoloured .. 25 10
2730. – 26 p. multicoloured .. 30 10
2731. – 38 p. multicoloured .. 40 10
DESIGNS: 16 p. Spanish mastiff. 26 p. Ibiza spaniel. 38 p. Navarrese basset.

632. Juan-Jose and Fausto Elhuyar y de Suvisa.

1983. Anniversaries. Multicoloured.
2732. 16 p. Type **632** (Bicentenary of discovery of Wolfram) 20 10
2733. 38 p. Scout camp (75th anniv. of Boy Scout Movement) 40 10
2734. 50 p. University of Zaragoza (400th anniv.) .. 50 15

633. Arms of Murcia.

1983. Murcian Autonomy.
2735. **633.** 16 p. multicoloured .. 30 10

634. Covadonga Basilica and Victory Cross.

1983. Autonomy of Asturias.
2736. **634.** 14 p. multicoloured .. 30 10

635. National Statistical Institute, Madrid.

1983. 44th International Institute Statistics Congress.
2737. **635.** 38 p. multicoloured .. 40 10

636. Roman Horse-drawn Mail Cart.

1983. Stamp Day.
2738. **636.** 16 p. pink and brown 20 10

637. Palace and Arms of Valencia.

1983. Valencia Autonomy.
2739. **637.** 16 p. multicoloured .. 30 10

638. Seville (illustration from " Floods of Guadalquivir " by Francisco Palomo).

1983. America–Spain.
2740. **638.** 38 p. violet and blue 40 10

639. " Biblical King " (Leon Cathedral).

1983. Stained Glass Windows. Multicoloured.
2741. 10 p. Type **639**. 20 10
2742. 16 p. "Epiphany" and Gerona Cathedral .. 35 10
2743. 38 p. "St. James" and Santiago de Compostela Hospital 55 10

1983. Tourist Series. As T **340**.
2744. 3 p. blue and green .. 10 10
2745. 6 p. indigo 10 10
2746. 16 p. violet and red .. 20 10
2747. 38 p. red and brown .. 40 10
2748. 50 p. red and brown .. 50 15
DESIGNS: 3 p. Church and tower, Llivia, Gerona. 6 p. Santa Maria del Mar, Barcelona. 16 p. Ceuta Cathedral. 38 p. Bridge gateway, Melilla. 50 p. Charity Hospital, Seville.

640. " Nativity " (altarpiece, Tortosa). **641.** Indalecio Prieto.

1983. Christmas. Multicoloured.
2749. 16 p. Type **640** 20 10
2750. 38 p. " Adoration of the Kings " (altarpiece, Vich) 40 10

1983. Birth Centenary of Indalecio Prieto (politician).
2751. **641.** 16 p. brown and black 20 10

642. Worker falling from Scaffolding.

1984. Safety at Work. Multicoloured.
2752 7 p. Type **642** 10 10
2753 10 p. Burning factory and extinguisher 10 10
2754 16 p. Electric plug and wiring, cutters, gloved hands and warning sign 20 10

643. Tree.

1984. Estremaduran Autonomy.
2755. **643.** 16 p. multicoloured .. 20 10

644. Burgos Cathedral and Coat of Arms.

1984. 1500th Anniv. of Burgos City.
2756. **644.** 16 p. brown and blue 20 10

645. Carnival Dancer, Santa Cruz, Tenerife.

1984. Festivals. Multicoloured.
2757. 16 p. Type **645** 20 10
2758. 16 p. Carnival figure and fireworks, Valencia .. 20 10

646. "Man" (Leonardo da Vinci).

1984. Man and Biosphere.
2759. **646.** 38 p. multicoloured 40 10

647. Map and Flag of Aragon and "Justice".

1984. Aragon Autonomy.
2760. **647.** 16 p. multicoloured 20 10

649. F.I.P. Emblem.

1984. 53rd International Philatelic Federation Congress, Madrid.
2762. **649.** 38 p. red and violet 40 10

650. Bridge.

1984. Europa.
2763 **650** 16 p. red 30 10
2764 38 p. blue 50 10

651. Monument to the Alcantara Cazadores Regiment, Valladolid (Mariano Benlliure). **652.** Arms of Canary Islands.

1984. Armed Forces Day.
2765. **651.** 17 p. multicoloured 40 10

1984. Autonomy of Canary Islands.
2766. **652.** 16 p. multicoloured 35 10

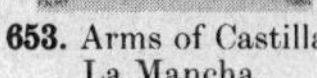

653. Arms of Castilla-La Mancha. **655.** "James III confirming Grants".

654. King Alfonso X, the Wise, of Castile and Leon (700th death anniv).

1984. Autonomy of Castilla-La Mancha.
2767. **653.** 17 p. multicoloured 30 10

1984. Anniversaries.
2768 **654** 16 p. red, blue & black 20 10
2769 – 38 p. blue, red & black 40 10
DESIGN: 38 p. Ignacio Barraquer (ophthalmologist, birth centenary).

1984. Autonomy of Balearic Islands.
2770 **655** 17 p. multicoloured .. 30 10

656. Running before Bulls.

1984. Pamplona Festival, San Fermin.

2771 **656** 17 p. multicoloured .. 35 10

1984. Masters of Operetta (3rd series). Horiz. designs as T **625** (2772, 2775/6) or vert. designs as T **606** (others). Multicoloured.

2772.	6 p. Scene from "El Nino Judio"	10	10
2773.	6 p. Pablo Luna ..	10	10
2774.	7 p. Ruperto Chapi ..	15	10
2775.	7 p. Scene from "La Revoltosa"	15	10
2776.	10 p. Scene from "La Reina Mora"	20	10
2777.	10 p. Jose Serrano ..	20	10

657. Bronze of Swimmer ready to Dive.

1984. Olympic Games, Los Angeles. Mult.

2778	1 p. Roman quadriga (horiz)	10	10
2779	2 p. Type **657**	10	10
2780	5 p. Bronze of two wrestlers (horiz) ..	10	10
2781	8 p. "The Discus-thrower" (statue, Miron) ..	15	10

658. Arms and Map of Navarra.

1984. Autonomy of Navarra.

2782 **658** 17 p. multicoloured .. 30 10

659. Cyclist. **660.** Arms (Levante Building Salamanca University).

1984. International Cycling Championship, Barcelona.

2783 **659** 17 p. multicoloured .. 30 10

1984. Autonomy of Castilla y Leon.

2784 **660** 17 p. multicoloured .. 30 10

661. Women gathering Grapes.

1984. Vintage Festival, Jerez.

2785. **661.** 17 p. multicoloured 45 10

662. Egeria on Donkey and Map of Middle East.

1984. 1600th Anniv. of Nun Egeria's Visit to Middle East.

2786. **662.** 40 p. multicoloured 45 10

663. Arab Courier.

1984. Stamp Day.

2787. **663.** 17 p. multicoloured 40 10

664. Father Junipero Serra. **665.** "Adoration of the Kings" (Miguel Moguer) (Campos altarpiece).

1984. Death Bicentenary of Father Junipero Serra (missionary).

2788 **664** 40 p. red and blue .. 45 10

1984. Christmas. Multicoloured.

2789	17 p. "Nativity" (15th-century retable) (horiz)	25	10
2790	40 p. Type **665**	45	10

668. Arms, Buildings and Trees.

1984. Autonomy of Madrid.

2791. **666.** 17 p. multicoloured 45 10

667. Flags and Andean Condor.

1985. 15th Anniv (1984) of Andes Pact.

2792 **667** 17 p. multicoloured .. 30 10

668. "Virgin of Louvain" (attr. Jan Gossaert). **669.** College Porch and Tympanum.

1985. "Europalia 85 Espana" Festival.

2793 **668** 40 p. multicoloured .. 55 10

1985. 500th Anniv of Santa Cruz College, Valladolid University.

2794 **669** 17 p. yellow, brn & red 35 10

670. Flames and "Olymphilex '85".

1985. "Olymphilex 85" International Olympic Stamps Exhibition, Lausanne.

2795 **670** 40 p. red, yellow & blk 50 10

671. Havana Cathedral.

1985. "Espamer '85" International Stamp Exhibition, Havana, Cuba.

2796 **671** 40 p. blue and purple 50 10

672. Couple in Traditional Dress on Horseback.

1985. April Fair, Seville.

2797. **672.** 17 p. multicoloured 45 10

673. Heads as Holder for Flames.

1985. International Youth Year.

2798. **673.** 17 p. green, black and red 30 10

674. Moors and Christians fighting.

1985. Festival of Moors and Christians, Alcoy.

2799. **674.** 17 p. multicoloured 40 10

675. Don Antonio de Cabezon (organist).

1985. Europa.

2800	**675**	18 p. red, black and blue on yellow ..	50	10
2801	–	45 p. red, black and green on yellow ..	75	10

Design: 45 p. Musicians of National Youth Orchestra.

676. Capitania General Headquarters, La Coruna.

1985. Armed Forces Day.

2802. **676.** 18 p. multicoloured 50 10

677. Carlos III's Arms, 1785 Decree and "Santissima Trinidad".

1985. Bicent. of National Flag. Mult.

2803.	18 p. Type **677**	25	10
2804.	18 p. State arms, 1978 constitution and lion (detail from House of Deputies)	25	10

678. Sunflower and Bird.

1985. World Environment Day.

2805. **678.** 17 p. multicoloured 65 10

679. Monstrance in decorated Street. **680.** King Juan Carlos I.

1985. Corpus Christi Festival, Toledo.

2806. **679.** 18 p. multicoloured 45 10

1985.

2807	**680**	10 c. blue	10	10
2808		50 c. green	10	10
2809		1 p. blue	10	10
2810		2 p. green	10	10
2811		3 p. brown	10	10
2812		4 p. bistre	10	10
2813		5 p. purple	10	10
2814		6 p. brown	10	10
2815		7 p. violet	10	10
2816		7 p. green	10	10
2817		8 p. grey	10	10
2818		10 p. red	10	10
2819		12 p. red	10	10
2820		13 p. blue	15	10
2821		15 p. green	15	10
2822		17 p. orange ..	15	10
2823		18 p. green	15	10
2824		19 p. brown ..	15	10
2825		20 p. mauve ..	15	10
2825a		25 p. green	30	10
2825b		27 p. mauve ..	30	10
2826		30 p. blue	25	10
2827		45 p. green	30	10
2828		50 p. blue	50	10
2828a		55 p. brown ..	60	15
2829		60 p. red	60	15
2830		75 p. mauve ..	75	25

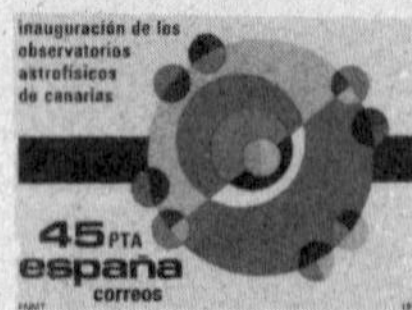

681. Planetary System.

1985. Inauguration of Astrophysical Observatories, Canary Islands.

2831. **681.** 45 p. multicoloured 50 10

682. Ataulfo Argenta (conductor).

1985. European Music Year. Multicoloured.

2832.	12 p. Type **682**	35	10
2833.	17 p. Tomas Luis de Victoria (composer) ..	45	10
2834.	45 p. Fernando Sor (guitarist and composer)	65	10

683. Bernal Diaz del Castillo (conquistador).

1985. Celebrities.

2835. **683.** 7 p. red, black and green on yellow .. 15 10
2836. – 12 p. red, black and blue on yellow .. 20 10
2837. – 17 p. green, red and black on yellow .. 25 10
2838. – 45 p. green, black and brown on yellow 40 10

DESIGNS: 12 p. Esteban Terradas (mathematician). 17 p. Vicente Aleixandre (poet). 45 p. Leon Felipe Camino (poet).

684. Canoeist.

1985. "Descent down the Sella" Canoe Festival, Asturias.

2839 **684** 17 p. multicoloured .. 40 10

685. Monk returning with Rotulet to Savigni Abbey, 1122.

686. Ribbon Exercise.

1985. Stamp Day.

2840. **685.** 17 p. multicoloured 40 10

1985. 12th World Rhythmic Gymnastics Championship, Valladolid. Multicoloured.

2841. 17 p. Type **686** 35 10
2842. 45 p. Hoop exercise .. 55 10

688. "Virgin and Child" (Escalas Chapel, Seville Cathedral).

690. Subalpine Warbler.

689. "Nativity" (detail of altarpiece by Ramon de Mur).

1985. Stained Glass Windows. Multicoloured.

2844 7 p. Type **688** 15 10
2845 12 p. Monk (Toledo Cathedral) 35 10
2846 17 p. King Enrique II of Castile and Leon (Alcazar of Segovia) .. 40 10

1985. Christmas. Multicoloured.

2847. 17 p. Type **689** 35 10
2848. 45 p. "Adoration of the Magi" (embroidered frontal, after Jaume Huguet) 65 10

1985. Birds Multicoloured.

2849. 6 p. Type **690** 25 10
2850. 7 p. Rock thrush .. 45 10
2851. 12 p. Spotless starling .. 55 10
2852. 17 p. Bearded reedling .. 60 10

691. Count of Penaflorida.

1985. Death Bicentenary of Count of Penaflorida (founder of Economic Society of Friends of the Land).

2853 **691** 17 p. blue 40 10

692. Royal Palace, Madrid.

1986. Admission of Spain and Portugal to European Economic Community. Mult.

2854 7 p. Type **692** 15 10
2855 17 p. Map and flags of member countries .. 25 10
2856 30 p. Hall of columns, Royal Palace 50 10
2857 45 p. Flags of Portugal and Spain uniting with flags of other members 60 10

1986. Tourist Series. As T **340**.

2858. 12 p. black and red .. 30 10
2859. 35 p. brown and blue .. 55 10

DESIGNS: 12 p. Lupiana Monastery, Guadalajara. 35 p. Balcony of Europe, Nerja.

693. Merino.

1986. Second World Conference on Merinos.

2860. **693.** 45 p. multicoloured 85 10

694. "Revellers" (detail, F. Hohenleiter).

1986. Cadiz Carnival.

2861. **694.** 17 p. multicoloured 40 10

695. Helmets and Flower.

1986. International Peace Year.

2862. **695.** 45 p. multicoloured 55 10

696. Organ Pipes.

1986. Religious Music Week, Cuenca.

2863. **696.** 17 p. multicoloured 40 10

INDEX

Countries can be quickly located by referring to the index at the end of this volume.

697. "Swearing in of Regent, Queen Maria Cristina" (detail, Joaquin Sorolla y Bastida).

1986. Centenary of Chambers of Commerce, Industry and Navigation.

2864 **697** 17 p. black and green 35 10

698. Man with Suitcase.

1986. Emigration.

2865. **698.** 45 p. multicoloured 60 10

699. Boy and Birds.

1986. Europa. Multicoloured.

2866. 17 p. Type **699** 50 10
2867. 45 p. Woman watering young tree 75 10

700. Our Lady of the Dew.

1986. Our Lady of the Dew Festival, Rocio, near Almonte.

2868. **700.** 17 p. multicoloured 40 10

701. Capitania General Building, Tenerife.

1986. Armed Forces Day.

2869. **701.** 17 p. multicoloured 40 10

1986. Tourist Series. As T **340**. Mult.

2870. 12 p. black and blue .. 30 10
2871. 35 p. brown and blue .. 65 10

DESIGNS: 12 p. Ciudad Rodrigo Cathedral, Salamanca. 35 p. Calella lighthouse, Barcelona.

702. Hands and Ball.

1986. 10th World Basketball Championship.

2872 **702** 45 p. multicoloured .. 65 10

703. Francisco Loscos (botanist).

704. Apostles awaiting Angels carrying Virgin's Soul.

1986. Celebrities.

2873. **703.** 7 p. green and black 10 10
2874. – 11 p. red and black 20 10
2875. – 17 p. brown & black 25 10
2876. – 45 p. purple, orange, and black 55 10

DESIGNS: 11 p. Salvador Espriu (writer); 17 p. Azorin Jose Martinez Ruiz (writer); 45 p. Juan Gris (artist).

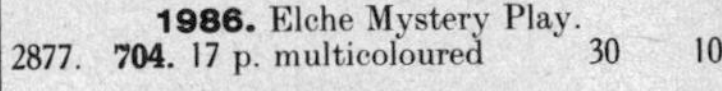

1986. Elche Mystery Play.

2877. **704.** 17 p. multicoloured 30 10

705. Swimmer.

1986. 5th World Swimming, Water Polo, Leap and Synchronous Swimming Championships.

2878 **705** 45 p. multicoloured .. 65 10

706. Pelota Player.

1986. 10th World Pelota Championship.

2879 **706** 17 p. multicoloured .. 40 10

707. King's Messenger with Letter summoning Nobleman to Court.

1986. Stamp Day.

2880. **707.** 17 p. multicoloured 30 10

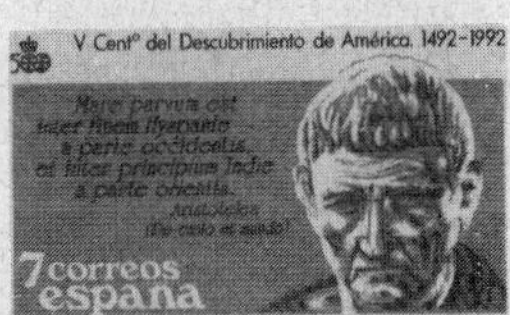

709. Aristotle.

1986. 500th Anniv. (1992) of Discovery of America by Columbus. (1st issue). Designs showing historic figures and prophecies of discovery of New World.

2882. **709.** 7 p. black and mauve 10 10
2883. – 12 p. black and lilac 15 10
2884. – 17 p. black & yellow 25 10
2885. – 30 p. black & mauve 40 10
2886. – 35 p. black and green 50 10
2887. – 45 p. black & orange 65 10

DESIGNS: 12 p. Seneca and quote from "Medea"; 17 p. St. Isidoro of Seville and quote from "Etymologies"; 30 p. Cardinal Pierre d'Ailly and quote from "Imago Mundi"; 35 p. Mayan and quote from "Chilam Balam" books; 45 p. Conquistador and quote from "Chilam Balam" books.

See also Nos. 2932/7, 2983/8, 3035/40, 3079/82 and 3126/9.

710. Gaspar de Portola.

711. "Holy Family" (detail, Diego de Siloe).

1986. Death Bicentenary of Gaspar de Portola (first Governor of California).

2888 **710** 22 p. blue, red & black .. 55 10

1986. Christmas. Wood Carvings. Mult.

2889 19 p. Type **711** 30 10
2890 48 p. "Nativity" (detail, Toledo Cathedral altarpiece, Felipe de Borgona) (horiz) .. 65 10

712. Abd-er Rahman II and Cordoba Mosque.

1986. Hispanic Islamic Culture.

2891. **712.** 7 p. brown and red .. 15 10
2892. – 12 p. brown and red 25 10
2893. – 17 p. blue and black 35 10
2894. – 45 p. green and black 80 10

DESIGNS: 12 p. Ibn Hazm (writer) and burning book; 17 p. Al-Zarqali (astronomer) and azophea (astrolabe); 45 p. King Alfonso VII of Castile and Leon and scholars of Toledo School of Translators.

713. "The Good Curate".

1986. Birth Centenary of Alfonso Castelao (artist and writer).

2895 **713** 32 p. multicoloured .. 45 10

714. Chateau de la Muette (headquarters).

1987. 25th Anniv. of Organization for Economic Co-operation and Development.

2896. **714.** 48 p. multicoloured 90 10

715. Abstract Shapes.

1987 "Expo 92" World's Fair, Seville (1st issue). Multicoloured.

2897. 19 p. Type **715** 20 10
2898. 48 p. Moon surface, Earth and symbol .. 50 10

See also Nos. 2941/2, 2951/2, 3004/7, 3052/5, 3094/7, 3143 and 3148/71.

716. Francisco de Vitoria.

1987. 500th Birth Anniv. of Francisco de Vitoria (jurist).

2899. **716.** 48 p. brown 70 10

717. 18th-century Warship and Standard Bearer.

718. University.

1987. 450th Anniv. of Marine Corps.

2900. **717.** 19 p. multicoloured 40 10

1987. Centenary of Deusto University.

2901. **718.** 19 p. red, green and black 30 10

719. Breastfeeding Baby.

1987. U.N.I.C.E.F. Child Survival Campaign.

2902. **719.** 19 p. brown and deep brown 40 10

720. Crowd.

721. 15th-century Pharmacy Jar, Manises.

1987. 175th Anniv. of Constitution of Cadiz. Multicoloured.

2903 25 p. Type **720** 30 10
2904 25 p. Crowd and herald on steps 30 10
2905 25 p. Dignitaries on dais 30 10
2906 25 p. Crown and Constitution 30 10

Nos. 2903/6 were printed together, se-tenant, the first three stamps forming a composite design showing "The Promulgation of the Constitution of 1812" by Salvador Viniegra.

1987. Ceramics. Multicoloured.

2907 7 p. Type **721** 25 10
2908 14 p. 20th-century glazed figure, Sargadelos .. 25 10
2909 19 p. 18th-century vase, Buen Retiro 30 10
2910 32 p. 20th-century pot, Salvatierra de los Barros 35 10
2911 40 p. 18th-century jar, Talavera 45 10
2912 48 p. 18-19th century jug, Granada 55 10

722. "Procession at Dawn, Zamora" (Gallego Marquina).

723. Bilbao Bank, Madrid (Saenz de Oiza).

1987. Holy Week Festivals. Multicoloured.

2913 19 p. Type **722** 35 10
2914 48 p. Gate of Pardon, Seville Cathedral and "Passion" (statue by Martinez Montanes) .. 50 10

1987. Tourist Series. As T **340**.

2915 14 p. green and blue .. 20 10
2916 19 p. deep green and green 30 10
2917 40 p. brown 50 10
2918 48 p. black 55 10

DESIGNS—HORIZ. 14 p. Ifach Rock, Calpe, Alicante; 19 p. Ruins of Church of Santa Maria d'Ozo, Pontevedra; 40 p. Palace of Sonanes, Villacarriedo, Santander. VERT. 48 p. 11th-century monastery of Sant Joan de les Abadesses, Gerona.

1987. Europa. Architecture.

2919 **723** 19p. multicoloured .. 25 10
2920 – 48 p. brn, bistre & grn 45 10

DESIGN—HORIZ. 14 p. National Museum of Roman Art, Merida (Rafael Moneo).

724. Horse's Head and Harnessed Pair.

1987. Jerez Horse Fair.

2921 **724** 19 p. multicoloured .. 35 10

725. Carande.

1987. Birth Centenary of Ramon Carande (historian and Honorary Postman).

2922 **725** 40 p. black and brown 50 10

726. Numbers on Pen Nib.

1987. Postal Coding.

2923 **726** 19 p. multicoloured .. 30 10

727. Arms and School.

1987. 75th Anniv. of Eibar Armoury School.

2924. **727.** 20 p. multicoloured 30 10

728. Batllo House Chimneys (Antonio Gaudi).

1987. Nomination of Barcelona as 1992 Olympic Games Host City. Multicoloured.

2925. 32 p. Type **728** 35 10
2926. 65 p. Athletes 85 10

729. Festival Poster (Fabri).

1987. 25th Pyrenees Folklore Festival, Jaca.

2927. **729.** 50 p. multicoloured 65 10

730. Monturiol (after Marti Alsina) and Diagrams of Submarine "Ictineo".

1987. Death Centenary of Narcis Monturiol (scientist).

2928 **730** 20 p. black and brown 30 10

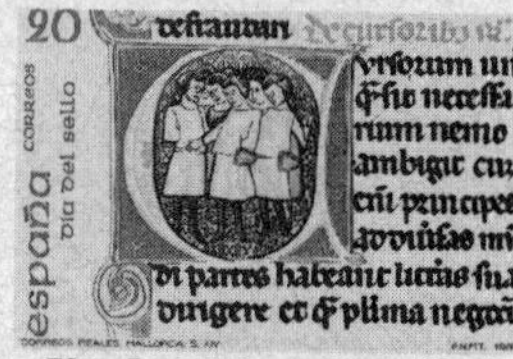

731. Detail from Jaime II of Majorca's Law appointing Couriers.

1987. Stamp Day.

2929. **731.** 20 p. multicoloured 30 10

734. Amerigo Vespucci.

1987. 500th Anniv (1992) of Discovery of America by Columbus (2nd issue). Explorers. Multicoloured.

2932 14 p. Type **734** 20 10
2933 20 p. King Ferdinand and Queen Isabella the Catholic and arms on ships 25 10
2934 32 p. Juan Perez and departing ships .. 35 10
2935 40 p. Juan de la Cosa and ships 55 10
2936 50 p. Map, ship and Christopher Columbus 75 10
2937 65p. Native on shore, aproaching ships and Martin Alonzo and Vincente Yanez Pinzon 90 10

735. Star and Baubles.

736. Macho (self-sculpture).

1987. Christmas. Multicoloured.

2938 20 p. Type **735** 35 10
2939 50 p. Zambomba and tambourine 50 10

1987. Birth Centenary of Victorio Macho (sculptor).

2940 **736** 50 p. brown and black 60 10

1987. "Expo '92" World's Fair, Seville (2nd issue). As Nos. 2897/8 but values changed. Multicoloured.

2941. 20 p. Type **715** 35 10
2942. 50 p. As No. 2898 .. 75 10

737. Queen Sofia.

739. Speed Skating.

738. Campoamor.

1988. 50th Birthdays of King Juan Carlos I and Queen Sofia. Each brown, yellow and violet.
2943 20 p. Type **737** 25 10
2944 20 p. King Juan Carlos I 25 10

1988. Birth Centenary of Clara Campoamor (politician and women's suffrage campaigner).
2945. **738.** 20 p. multicoloured 30 10

1988. Winter Olympic Games, Calgary.
2946. **739.** 45 p. multicoloured 55 10

740 "Christ tied to the Pillar" (statue) and Valladolid Cathedral

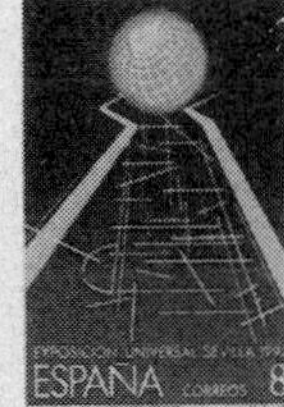
742 Globe and Stylized Roads

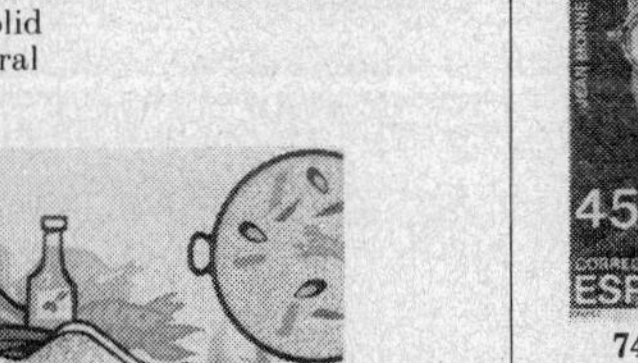
741 Ingredients for and Dish of Paella

1988. Holy Week Festivals. Multicoloured.
2947 20 p. Type **740** 25 10
2948 50 p. Float depicting Christ carrying the Cross, Malaga 60 10

1988. Tourist Series. Multicoloured.
2949 18 p. Type **741** 25 20
2950 45 p. Covadonga National Park (70th anniv of National Parks) . . 60 10

1988. "Expo '92" World's Fair, Seville (3rd issue).
2951 8 p. Type **742** 10 10
2952 45 p. Compass rose and globe (horiz) 55 10

743 18th-Century Valencian Chalice

744 Francis of Taxis (organiser of European postal service, 1505)

1988. Glassware. Multicoloured.
2953 20 p. Type **743** 25 10
2954 20 p. 18th-century pitcher, Cadalso de los Vidrios, Madrid 25 10
2955 20 p. 18th-century crystal sweet jar, La Granja de San Ildefonso 25 10
2956 20 p. 18th-century Andalusian two-handled jug, Castril . . 25 10
2957 20 p. 17th-century Catalan four-spouted jug . . 25 10
2958 20 p. 20th-century bottle, Balearic Islands . . 25 10

1988. Stamp Day.
2959 **744** 20 p. violet and brown 25 10

745 Pablo Iglesias (first President)

1988. Centenary of General Workers' Union.
2960 **745** 20 p. multicoloured . . 25 10

746 "La Junta" (1st Cuban railway locomotive), 1837.

1988. Europa. Transport and Communications.
2961 **746** 20 p. red and black . . 25 10
2962 – 50 p. green and black 60 10
DESIGN: 50 p. Light telegraph, Philippines, 1818.

747 Monnet

749 Couple in Granada

748 Emblem

1988. Birth Cent of Jean Monnet (statesman).
2963 **747** 45 p. blue 55 10

1988. Centenary of 1888 Universal Exhibition, Barcelona.
2964 **748** 50 p. multicoloured . . 60 10

1988. International Festival of Music and Dance, Granada.
2965 **749** 50 p. multicoloured . . 60 10

750 Bull

1988. "Expo 88" World's Fair, Brisbane.
2966 **750** 50 p. multicoloured . . 60 10

751 "Virgin of Hope"

1988. Coronation of "Virgin of Hope", Malaga.
2967 **751** 20 p. multicoloured . . 25 10

753 Orreo (agricultural store), Cantabria

1988. Tourist Series.
2969 **753** 18 p. green, brn & bl 25 10
2970 – 45 p. blk, brn & ochre 55 10
DESIGN: 45 p. Dulzaina (wind instrument), Castilla y Leon.

754 Players

1988. 28th World Roller Skate Hockey Championship, La Coruna.
2971 **754** 20 p. multicoloured . . 25 10

755 Congress Emblem

756 "Olympic" Class Yacht

1988. 1st Spanish Regional Homes and Centres World Congress, Madrid.
2972 **755** 20 p. multicoloured . . 25 10

1988. Olympic Games, Seoul.
2973 **756** 50 p. multicoloured . . 60 10

757 Borrell II, Count of Barcelona

1988. Millenary of Catalonia.
2974 **757** 20 p. multicoloured . . 25 10

758 King Alfonso IX of Leon (detail of Codex of Toxos Outos)

1988. 800th Anniv of 1st Leon Parliament.
2975 **758** 20 p. multicoloured . . 25 10

759 Emblem on Band around Peace Year Stamps

1988. 25th Anniv of Spanish Philatelic Associations Federation.
2976 **759** 20 p. multicoloured . . 25 10

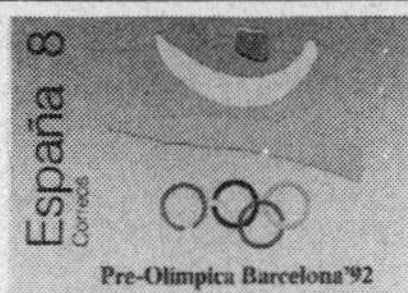
760 Games Emblem

1988. Olympic Games, Barcelona (1992) (1st issue). Designs showing stylized representations of sports. Multicoloured.
2977 8 p. Type **760** 10 10
2978 20 p.+5 p. Athletics . . 30 20
2979 45 p.+5 p. Badminton . . 60 40
2980 50 p.+5 p. Basketball . . 65 45
See also Nos. 3008/11, 3031/3, 3056/8, 3076/8, 3098/3100, 3123/5, 3144/6, 3180/2 and 3183/5.

761 Palace of the Generality, Valencia, and Seal of Jaime I

762 Manuel Alonso Martinez (statesman)

1988. 750th Anniv of Re-conquest of Valencia by King Jaime I of Aragon.
2981 **761** 20 p. multicoloured . . 25 10

1988. Centenary of Civil Code.
2982 **762** 20 p. multicoloured . . 25 10

763 Hernan Cortes and Quetzalcoatl Serpent

1988. 500th Anniv (1992) of Discovery of America by Columbus (3rd issue). Each red, blue and orange.
2983 10 p. Type **763** 10 10
2984 10 p. Vasco Nunez de Balboa and waves . . 10 10
2985 20 p. Francisco Pizarro and guanaco 25 10
2986 20 p. Ferdinand Magellan, Juan Sebastian del Cano and globe . . 25 10
2987 50 p. Alvăr Nunez Cabeza de Vaca and river . . 60 10
2988 50 p. Andres de Urdaneta and maritime currents 60 10

764 Enrique III of Castile and Leon (first Prince of Asturias)

1988. 600th Anniv of Title of Prince of Asturias.
2989 **764** 20 p. multicoloured . . 25 10

765 Snowflakes

1988. Christmas. Multicoloured.
2990 20 p. Type **765** 25 10
2991 50 p. Shepherd carrying sheep (vert) 60 10

766 Cordoba Mosque

1988. U.N.E.S.C.O. World Heritage Sites.
2992 **766** 18 p. brown 20 10
2993 – 20 p. blue 25 10
2994 – 45 p. brown 55 10
2995 – 50 p. green 60 10
DESIGNS—VERT. 20 p. Burgos Cathedral. HORIZ. 45 p. San Lorenzo Monastery, El Escorial; 50 p. Alhambra, Granada.

767 Representation of Political Parties

1988. 10th Anniv of Constitution.
2996 **767** 20 p. multicoloured . . 25 10

769 Blind Person

1988. 50th Anniv of National Organization for the Blind.
2998 **769** 20 p. multicoloured . . 25 10

770 Luis de Granada

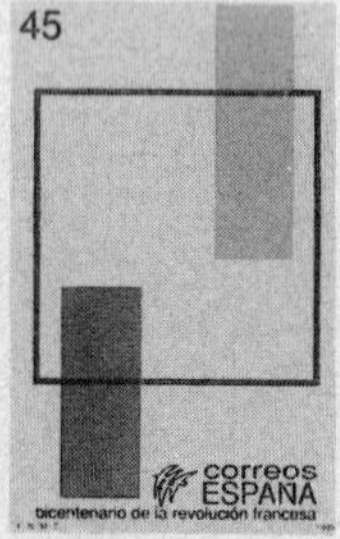
772 Abstract

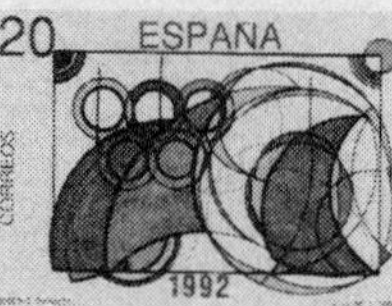
771 Olympic Rings and Sails (Natalia Barrio Fernandez)

1988. 400th Death Anniv of Brother Luis de Granada (mystic).
2999 **770** 20 p. multicoloured . . 25 10

1989. Children's Stamp Designs. Mult.
3000 20 p. Type **771** . . 25 10
3001 20 p. Magnifying glass on stamp (Jose Luis Villegas Lopez) (vert) 25 10

1989. Bicentenary of French Revolution.
3002 **772** 45 p. red, blue & black 55 10

MINIMUM PRICE
The minimum price quoted is 5p which represents a handling charge rather than a basis for valuing common stamps. For further notes about prices see introductory pages.

773 Maria de Maeztu

774 London, 1851

1989. 107th Birth Anniv of Maria de Maeztu (educationist).
3003 **773** 20 p. multicoloured . . 20 10

1989. "Expo '92" World's Fair, Seville (4th issue). Great Exhibitions. Multicoloured.
3004 8 p.+5 p. Type **774** . . 15 10
3005 8 p.+5 p. Paris, 1889 . . 15 10
3006 20 p.+5 p. Brussels, 1958 30 20
3007 20 p.+5 p. Osaka, 1970 . . 30 20

1989. Olympic Games, Barcelona (1992) (2nd issue). As T **760**. Multicoloured.
3008 8 p.+5 p. Handball . . 15 10
3009 18 p.+5 p. Boxing . . 25 15
3010 20 p.+5 p. Cycling . . 30 20
3011 45 p.+5 p. Show jumping 60 40

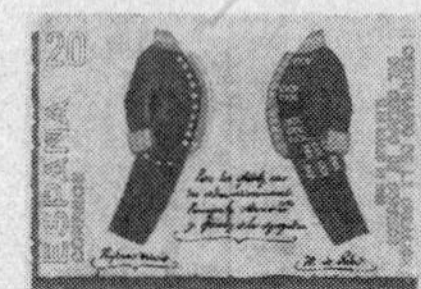
775 Uniforms, 1889

1989. Centenary of Post Office
3012 **775** 20 p. multicoloured . . 20 10

776 International Postal Service Treaty, 1601

777 Entrance Door

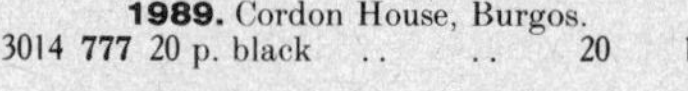

1989. Stamp Day.
3013 **776** 20 p. black 20 10

1989. Cordon House, Burgos.
3014 **777** 20 p. black 20 10

778 Skittles

781 Manuscript and Portrait

779 European Flag

1989. Europa. Children's Toys. Multicoloured.
3015 40 p. Type **778** 50 10
3016 50 p. Spinning top . . 60 10

1989. Spanish Presidency of European Economic Community.
3017 **779** 45 p. multicoloured 55 10

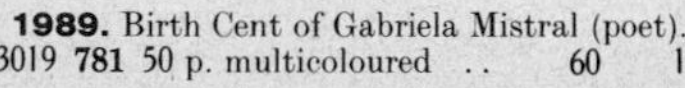

1989. Birth Cent of Gabriela Mistral (poet).
3019 **781** 50 p. multicoloured . . 60 10

782 Flags forming Ballot Box

1989. European Parliament Elections.
3020 **782** 45 p. multicoloured . . 55 10

783 Catalonia

1989. Lace. Typical designs from named region.
3021 **783** 20 p. blue and brown 20 10
3022 – 20 p. blue and brown 20 10
3023 – 20 p. blue 20 10
3024 – 20 p. blue 20 10
3025 – 20 p. blue and brown 20 10
3026 – 20 p. blue and brown 20 10
DESIGNS: No. 3022, Andalucia; 3023, Extremadura; 3024, Canary Islands; 3025, Castilla–La Mancha; 3026, Galicia.

784 Pope John Paul II and Youths

1989. 3rd Papal Visit.
3027 **784** 50 p. green, brn & blk 55 10

785 Foot leaving Starting Block

1989. World Cup Athletics Championships, Barcelona.
3028 **785** 50 p. multicoloured . . 55 10

786 Chaplin

787 1 p. Stamp

1989. Birth Centenary of Charlie Chaplin (actor).
3029 **786** 50 p. multicoloured . . 55 10

1989. Centenary of First King Alfonso XIII Stamps.
3030 **787** 50 p. brn, grey & red 55 10

1989. Olympic Games, Barcelona (1992) (3rd issue). As T **760**.
3031 18 p.+5 p. Fencing . . 25 20
3032 20 p.+5 p. Football . . 25 20
3033 45 p.+5 p. Gymnastics . . 55 40

788 Fr. Andres Manjon (founder)

1989. Centenary of Ave Maria Schools.
3034 **788** 20 p. multicoloured . . 20 10

789 Maize

1989. 500th Anniv (1992) of Discovery of America by Columbus (4th issue). Mult.
3035 8 p.+5 p. Type **789** . . 15 10
3036 8 p.+5 p. Cacao nut . . 15 10
3037 20 p.+5 p. Tomato . . 25 20
3038 20 p.+5 p. Horse . . 25 20
3039 50 p.+5 p. Potato . . 60 45
3040 50 p.+5 p. Turkey . . 60 45

790 Inca irrigating Corn (from "New Chronicle" by Waman Puma)

791 "Navidad 89"

1989. America. Pre-Columbian Life.
3041 **790** 50 p. multicoloured . . 55 10

1989. Christmas. Multicoloured.
3042 20 p. Type **791** 20 10
3043 45 p. Girl with Christmas present (horiz) . . 50 10

792 Altamira Caves

1989. World Heritage Sites. Multicoloured.
3044 20 p. Type **792** 20 10
3045 20 p. Segovia Aqueduct . . 20 10
3046 20 p. Santiago de Compostela 20 10
3047 20 p. Guell Park and Palace and Mila House 20 10

794 Olympic Rings, Compass Rose, Church of Holy Family, Barcelona, and Seville

795 Getxo City Hall and Competitor

1990. Children's Stamp Design.
3049 **794** 20 p. multicoloured . . 20 10

1990. World Cyclo-cross Championship, Getxo.
3050 **795** 20 p. multicoloured . . 20 10

796 Victoria Kent

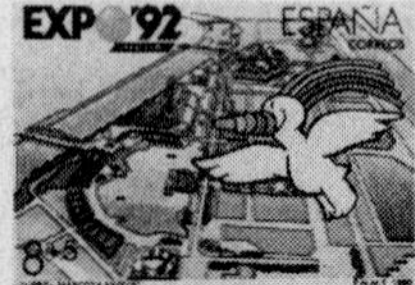
797 Curro (mascot) flying over Path of Discoveries

1990. 3rd Death Anniv of Victoria Kent (prison reformer).
3051 **796** 20 p. lilac 20 10

1990. "Expo '92" World's Fair, Seville (5th issue). Multicoloured.
3052 8 p.+5 p. Type **797** .. 15 10
3053 20 p.+5 p. Curro and Exhibtion building .. 25 20
3054 45 p.+5 p. Curro and view of Project Cartuja '93 .. .. .. 55 40
3055 50 p.+5 p. Curro crossing bridge in Project Cartuja '93 .. .. 60 45

1990. Olympic Games, Barcelona (1992) (4th issue). As T **760**. Multicoloured.
3056 18 p.+5 p. Weightlifting 25 20
3057 20 p.+5 p. Hockey .. 25 20
3058 45 p.+5 p. Judo .. 55 40

798 Rafael Alvarez Sereix (Honorary Postman)

1990. Stamp Day.
3059 **798** 20 p. flesh, brn & grn 20 10

799 Vitoria Post Office

1990. Europa. Post Office Buildings.
3060 20 p. Type **799** 20 10
3061 50 p. Malaga Post Office (vert) 55 10

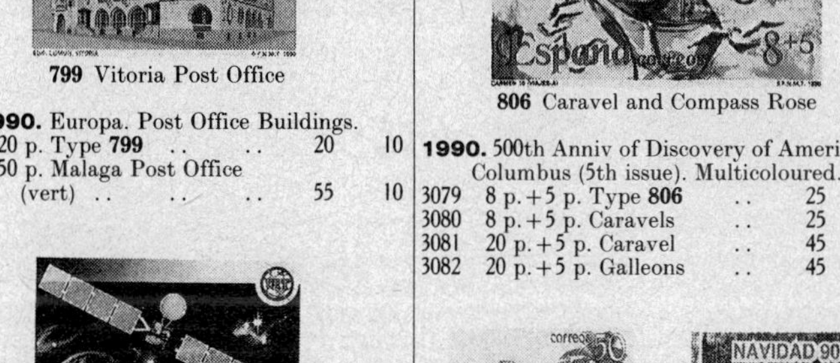

800 "Hispasat" Communications Satellite

1990. 125th Anniv of I.T.U.
3062 **800** 8 p. multicoloured .. 10 10

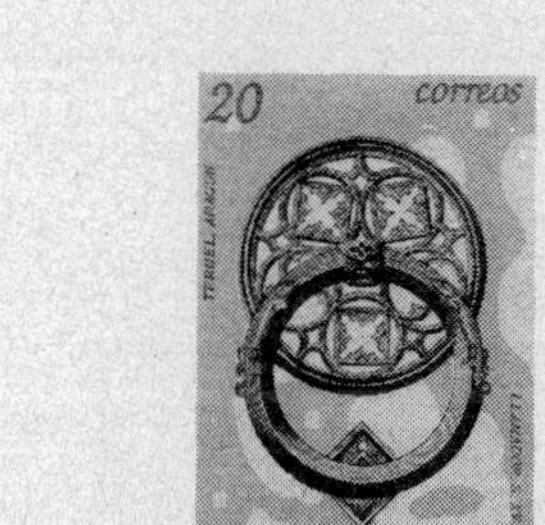

801 Door Knocker, Aragon

1990. Wrought Ironwork. Each black, brown and red.
3063 20 p. Type **801** 20 10
3064 20 p. Door knocker, Andalucia 20 10
3065 20 p. Pistol, Catalonia .. 20 10
3066 20 p. Door knocker, Castilla-La Mancha .. 20 10
3067 20 p. Mirror with lock, Galicia 20 10
3068 20 p. Basque fireback .. 20 10

MORE DETAILED LISTS
are given in the Stanley Gibbons Catalogues referred to in the country headings.
For lists of current volumes see Introduction.

803 "Charity" (Lopez Alonso)

805 Poster

1990. Anniversaries.
3070 **803** 8 p. multicoloured .. 10 10
3071 – 20 p. multicoloured .. 20 10
3072 – 45 p. orange & brown 50 10
3073 – 50 p. red and blue .. 55 10
DESIGNS—VERT. 8 p. Type **803** (bicent of arrival in Spain of Daughters of Charity); 50 p. Page of book (500th anniv of publication of "Tirant lo Blanch". HORIZ. 20 p. Music score and Jose Padilla (composer, birth centenary (1989)); 45 p. Palace of Kings of Navarre (900th anniv of Estella).

1990. 17th International Historical Sciences Congress, Madrid.
3075 **805** 50 p. multicoloured .. 55 10

1990. Olympic Games, Barcelona (1992) (5th issue). As T **760**. Multicoloured.
3076 8 p.+5 p. Wrestling .. 15 10
3077 18 p.+5 p. Swimming .. 25 20
3078 20 p.+5 p. Baseball .. 25 20

806 Caravel and Compass Rose

1990. 500th Anniv of Discovery of America by Columbus (5th issue). Multicoloured.
3079 8 p.+5 p. Type **806** .. 25 15
3080 8 p.+5 p. Caravels .. 25 15
3081 20 p.+5 p. Caravel .. 45 25
3082 20 p.+5 p. Galleons .. 45 25

807 Puerto Rican Todys

808 Sun

1990. America. The Natural World.
3083 **807** 50 p. multicoloured .. 55 10

1990. Christmas. Details of "Cosmic Poem" by Jose Antonio Sistiaga. Multicoloured.
3084 25 p. Type **808** 25 10
3085 45 p. Moon (horiz) .. 50 10

810 Tourism Logo (Joan Miro)

811 Church of St. Miguel de Lillo, Oviedo

1990. European Tourism Year.
3087 **810** 45 p. multicoloured .. 50 10

1990. World Heritage Sites. Multicoloured.
3088 20 p. Type **811** 20 10
3089 20 p. St. Peter's Tower, Teruel 20 10
3090 20 p. Bujaco Tower, Caceres (horiz) .. 20 10
3091 20 p. St. Vincent's Church, Avila (horiz) .. 20 10

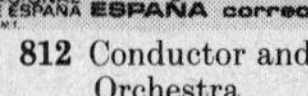

812 Conductor and Orchestra

813 Maria Moliner

1990. Spanish National Orchestra.
3092 **812** 25 p. grn, turq & blk 25 10

1991. 10th Death Anniv of Maria Moliner (philologist).
3093 **813** 25 p. multicoloured .. 25 10

814 La Cartuja (Santa Maria de las Cuevas Monastery)

1991. "Expo 92" World's Fair, Seville (6th issue). Views of Seville. Multicoloured.
3094 15 p.+5 p. Type **814** .. 20 15
3095 25 p.+5 p. The Auditorium 30 25
3096 45 p.+5 p. La Cartuja bridge 55 45
3097 55 p.+5 p. La Barqueta bridge 65 50

1991. Olympic Games, Barcelona (1992) (6th series). As T **760**.
3098 15 p.+5 p. grey, black and red 20 15
3099 25 p.+5 p. multicoloured 30 25
3100 45 p.+5 p. multicoloured 55 45
DESIGNS: 15 p. Modern pentathlon; 25 p. Canoeing; 45 p. Rowing.

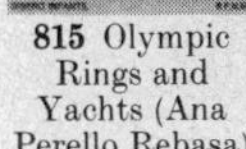

815 Olympic Rings and Yachts (Ana Perello Rebasa)

817 Juan de Tassis y Peralta (Chief Courier to Kings Philip III and IV)

1991. Children's Stamp Design.
3101 **815** 25 p. multicoloured .. 30 10

1991. Stamp Day.
3103 **817** 25 p. black 30 10

819 Dish Aerials, INTA-NASA Earth Station, Robledo de Chavela

1991. Europa. Europe in Space. Mult.
3105 25 p. Type **819** 30 10
3106 45 p. "Olympus I" telecommunications satellite 50 10

820 Table and Chair (400th death anniv of St. John of the Cross)

1991. Anniversaries.
3107 **820** 15 p. multicoloured .. 15 10
3108 – 15 p. orge, red & blk 15 10
3109 – 25 p. multicoloured .. 30 10
3110 – 25 p. multicoloured .. 30 10
DESIGNS—VERT. No. 3108, Brother Luis Ponce de Leon (translator and poet, 400th death anniv); 3109, Banner and cap (500th birth anniv of St. Ignatius de Loyola (founder of Society of Jesus)); 3110, Abd-er Rahman III, Emir of Cordoba (1100th birth anniv).

821 Apollo Fountain

1991. Madrid. European City of Culture (1st issue). Multicoloured.
3111 15 p.+5 p. Type **821** .. 20 15
3112 25 p.+5 p. "Don Alvaro de Bazan" (statue, Mariano Benlliure) 30 25
3113 45 p.+5 p. Bank of Spain 55 45
3114 55 p.+5 p. Cloisters, St. Isidro Institute .. 65 50
See also Nos. 3195/8.

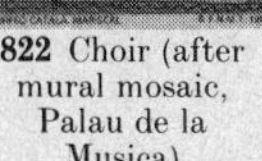

822 Choir (after mural mosaic, Palau de la Musica)

823 Basque Drug Cupboard

1991. Centenary of Orfeo Catala (Barcelona choral group).
3115 **822** 25 p. multicoloured .. 30 10

1991. Furniture. Multicoloured.
3116 25 p. Type **823** 30 10
3117 25 p. Kitchen dresser, Castilla y Leon .. 30 10
3118 25 p. Chair, Murcia .. 30 10
3119 25 p. Cradle, Andalucia .. 30 10
3120 25 p. Travelling chest, Castilla-La Mancha .. 30 10
3121 25 p. Bridal chest, Catalonia .. 30 10

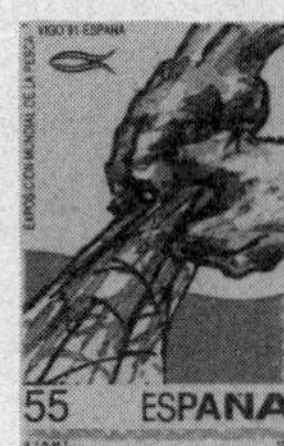

824 Hands holding Net

1991. World Fishing Exhibition, Vigo.
3122 **824** 55 p. multicoloured .. 60 10

1991. Olympic Games, Barcelona (1992) (7th series). As T **760**. Multicoloured.
3123 15 p.+5 p. Tennis .. 20 15
3124 25 p.+5 p. Table tennis 30 25
3125 55 p.+5 p. Shooting .. 65 50

825 Garcilaso de la Vega (Spanish-Inca poet)

1991. 500th Anniv of Discovery of America by Columbus (6th issue). Multicoloured.
3126 15 p.+5 p. Type **825** .. 20 15
3127 25 p.+5 p. Pope Alexander VI 30 25
3128 45 p.+5 p. Luis de Santangel (banker) .. 55 45
3129 55 p.+5 p. Brother Toribio Motolinia (missionary) 65 50

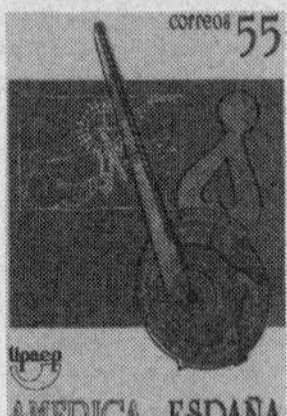

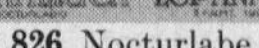

826 Nocturlabe

827 "Nativity" (from "New Chronicle" by Guaman Poma de Ayala)

1991. America. Voyages of Discovery.
3130 **826** 55 p. brown and purple 60 10

1991. Christmas. Icons.
3131 **827** 25 p. buff and brown 30 10
3132 – 45 p. multicoloured .. 50 10
DESIGN: 45 p. "Nativity" (16th-century icon).

829 Alcantara Gate, Toledo

830 Gen. Carlos Ibanez de Ibero (cartographer)

1991. World Heritage Sites.
3134 **829** 25 p. agate and brown 30 10
3135 – 25 p. black and brown 30 10
3136 – 25 p. brown and blue 30 10
3137 – 25 p. violet and green 30 10
DESIGNS—VERT. No. 3135, Casa de las Conchas, Salamanca. HORIZ. No. 3136, Seville Cathedral; 3137, Aeonio (flower) and Garajonay National Park, Gomera.

1991. Anniversaries and Events. Mult.
3138 25 p. Type **830** (death centenary 30 10
3139 55 p. "Las Palmas" (Antarctic survey ship) (meeting of Antarctic Treaty members, Madrid) 95 15

831 Margarita Xirgu

1992. 23rd Death Anniv of Margarita Xirgu (actress).
3140 **831** 25 p. brown and red .. 30 10

832 "Expo 92, Seville"

1992. Children's Stamp Design.
3141 **832** 25 p. multicoloured .. 30 10

833 Pedro Rodriguez, Count of Campomanes (administrator and postal consultant)

1992. Stamp Day.
3142 **833** 27 p. multicoloured .. 30 10

834 Spanish Pavilion

1992. "Expo '92" World's Fair, Seville (7th issue).
3143 **834** 27 p. grey, black & brn 30 10

1992. Olympic Games, Barcelona (8th issue). As T **760**. Multicoloured.
3144 15 p.+5 p. Archery .. 20 15
3145 25 p.+5 p. Sailing .. 35 30
3146 55 p.+5 p. Volleyball .. 70 55

836 Cable-cars

1992. "Expo '92" World's Fair, Seville (8th issue). Multicoloured.
3148 17 p. Exhibition World Trade Centre 20 10
3149 17 p. Type **836** 20 10
3150 17 p. Fourth Avenue .. 20 10
3151 17 p. Barqueta entrance 20 10
3152 17 p. Nature pavilion .. 20 10
3153 17 p. Bioclimatic sphere 20 10
3154 17 p. Alamillo bridge .. 20 10
3155 17 p. Press centre .. 20 10
3156 17 p. Pavilion of the 15th Century 20 10
3157 17 p. Expo harbour .. 20 10
3158 17 p. Tourist train .. 20 10
3159 17 p. One-day entrance ticket showing bridge 20 10
3160 27 p. Santa Maria de las Cuevas Carthusian monastery 30 10
3161 27 p. Palisade 30 10
3162 27 p. Monorail 30 10
3163 27 p. Avenue of Europe .. 30 10
3164 27 p. Pavilion of Discovery 30 10
3165 27 p. Auditorium .. 30 10
3166 27 p. First Avenue .. 30 10
3167 27 p. Square of the Future 30 10
3168 27 p. Italica entrance .. 30 10
3169 27 p. Last avenue .. 30 10
3170 27 p. Theatre 30 10
3171 27 p. Curro (official mascot) 30 10

837 Wheelchair Sports

1992. Paralympic (Physically Handicapped) Games, Barcelona.
3173 **837** 27 p. multicoloured .. 30 10

839 "Preparation before leaving Palos" (R. Espejo)

841 "Water and the Environment"

1992. Europa. 500th Anniv of Discovery of America by Columbus.
3175 **839** 17 p. multicoloured .. 20 10
3176 – 45 p. grey and brown 50 10
DESIGN: 45 p. Map of the Americas, Columbus's fleet and Monastery of Santa Maria de La Rabida.

1992. World Environment Day.
3178 **841** 27 p. blue and yellow 30 10

842 "Albertville", Olympic Rings and "Barcelona"

1992. Winter Olympic Games, Albertville, and Summer Games, Barcelona.
3179 **842** 45 p. multicoloured .. 50 10

843 Victorious Athlete

1992. Olympic Games, Barcelona (9th issue). Multicoloured.
3180 17 p.+5 p. Type **843** .. 25 20
3181 17 p.+5 p. Cobi (official mascot) 25 20
3182 17 p.+5 p. Olympic torch (horiz) 25 20

844 Olympic Stadium

845 Cobi holding Magnifying Glass and Stamp Album

1992. Olympic Games, Barcelona (10th issue). Multicoloured.
3183 27 p.+5 p. Type **844** .. 35 30
3184 27 p.+5 p. San Jordi sports arena .. 35 30
3185 27 p.+5 p. I.N.E.F. sports university 35 30

1992. "Olymphilex 92" International Stamp Exhibition, Barcelona. Multicoloured.
3186 17 p.+5 p. Type **845** .. 25 20
3187 17 p.+5 p. Church of the Holy Family, Barcelona, and exhibition emblem .. 25 20

846 Athletes

1992. Paralympic (Mentally Handicapped) Games, Madrid.
3188 **846** 27 p. blue and red .. 30 10

848 Quarterdeck of "Santa Maria"

1992. America. 500th Anniv of Discovery of America by Columbus.
3190 **848** 60 p. brown, cinnamon & ochre 70 10

849 Luis Vives (philosopher)

850 Helmet of Mercury and European Community Emblem

1992. Anniversaries. Multicoloured.
3191 17 p. Type **849** (500th birth anniv) 20 10
3192 27 p. Pamplona Choir (centenary) (horiz) .. 30 10

1992. European Single Market.
3193 **850** 45 p. blue and yellow 55 10

851 "Nativity" (Obdulia Acevedo)

852 Municipal Museum

1992. Christmas.
3194 **851** 27 p. multicoloured .. 30 10

1992. Madrid, European City of Culture (2nd issue). Multicoloured.
3195 17 p.+5 p. Type **852** .. 25 20
3196 17 p.+5 p. Queen Sofia Art Museum 25 20
3197 17 p.+5 p. Prado Museum 25 20
3198 17 p.+5 p. Royal Theatre 25 20

854 Bird, Sun, Leaves and Silhouettes

855 Maria Zambrano

1993. Public Services. Protection of the Environment.
3200 **854** 28 p. blue and green .. 30 10

1993. 2nd Death Anniv of Maria Zambrano (writer).
3201 **855** 45 p. multicoloured .. 50 10

856 Figures and Blue Cross

857 Segovia

1993. Public Services. Health and Sanitation.
3202 **856** 65 p. blue and green .. 75 10

1993. Birth Centenary of Andres Segovia (guitarist).
3203 **857** 65 p. black and brown 75 10

858 Post-box, Cadiz, 1908

1993. Stamp Day.
3204 **858** 28 p. multicoloured .. 30 10

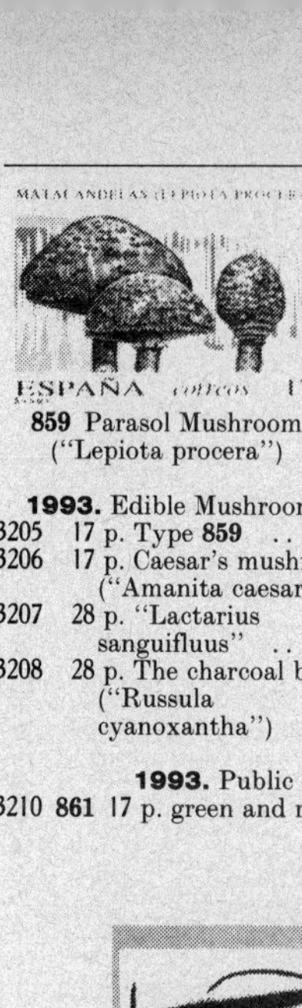

859 Parasol Mushroom ("Lepiota procera")

861 Road Safety

1993. Edible Mushrooms. Multicoloured.

3205	17 p. Type **859**	15	10
3206	17 p. Caesar's mushroom ("Amanita caesarea")	15	10
3207	28 p. "Lactarius sanguifluus"	30	10
3208	28 p. The charcoal burner ("Russula cyanoxantha")	30	10

1993. Public Services.

3210 **861**	17 p. green and red	15	10

863 "Fusees"

1993. Europa. Contemporary Art. Paintings by Joan Miro.

3212 **863**	45 p. black and blue	45	10
3213 –	65 p. multicoloured	65	10

DESIGN—VERT. 65 p. "La Bague d'Aurore".

864 "Translation of Body from Palestine to Galicia" (detail of altarpiece, Santiago de Compostela Cathedral)

1993. St. James's Holy Year (1st issue). Multicoloured.

3214	17 p. Type **864**	15	10
3215	28 p. "Discovery of St. James's tomb by Bishop Teodomiro" (miniature from "Tumbo A" (codex)) ..	30	10
3216	45 p. "St. James" (illuminated initial letter from Bull issued by Pope Alexander III declaring Holy Years of St. James)	45	10

See also No. 3218.

865 Letters, Map and Satellite

1993. World Telecommunications Day.

3217 **865**	28 p. multicoloured ..	30	10

866 Bagpipe Player (Isaac Diaz Pardo)

867 King Juan Carlos I

1993. St. James's Holy Year (2nd issue).

3218 **866**	28 p. multicoloured ..	30	10

1993.

3220 **867**	17 p. orange and gold	15	10
3225	28 p. brown and gold	30	10
3227	45 p. green and gold	45	10
3229	65 p. orange and gold	65	10

868 "Water and the Environment"

869 Count of Barcelona

1993. World Environment Day.

3240 **868**	28 p. multicoloured ..	30	10

1993. Juan de Borbon, Count of Barcelona (King Juan Carlos's father) Commem.

3241 **869**	28 p. multicoloured ..	30	10

870 Locomotive

1993. Centenary of Igualada–Martorell Railway.

3242 **870**	45 p. green and black	45	10

871 "The Mint" (lithograph, Pic de Leopold, 1866)

1993. Cent of National Coin and Stamp Mint.

3243 **871**	65 p. blue	65	10

872 Alejandro Malaspina (navigator)

873 "Road to Santiago" (Alejandro Mayor Gamo)

1993. Explorers. Multicoloured.

3244	45 p. Type **872**	45	10
3245	65 p. Jose Celestino Mutis (naturalist) (vert) ..	65	10

1993. Children's Stamp Design.

3246 **873**	45 p. multicoloured ..	45	10

874 Black Stork

1993. America. Endangered Animals.

3247 **874**	65 p. black and orange	65	10
3248 –	65 p. black and red ..	65	10

DESIGN: No. 3248, Lammergeier.

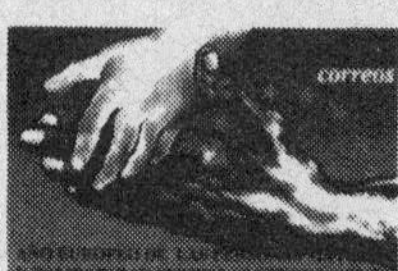

875 Old and Young Hands

1993. European Year of Senior Citizens and Solidarity between Generations.

3249 **875**	45 p. multicoloured ..	45	10

876 Star and Three Wise Men

877 Guillen

1993. Christmas. Multicoloured.

3250	17 p. Type **876**	15	10
3251	28 p. Holy Family (vert)	30	10

1993. Birth Centenary of Jorge Guillen (poet).

3252 **877**	28 p. green	30	10

878 Santa Maria de Poblet Monastery, Tarragona

1993. World Heritage Sites.

3253 **878**	50 p. brown, bl & grn	50	10

879 Luis Bunuel and Camera

1994. Spanish Cinema. Multicoloured.

3254	29 p. Type **879**	30	25
3255	55 p. Segundo de Chomon and scene from "Goblin House"	55	45

EXPRESS LETTER STAMPS

E 53. Pegasus and Arms.

1905.

E 308.	E **53**.	20 c. red	30·00	30

E 77. Spanish Royal Family.

1926. Red Cross.

E 417.	E **77**.	20 c. purple ..	5·00	5·00

1927. No. E 417 optd. **17-V-1902 17-V-1927 ALFONSO XIII.**

E 459.	E **77**.	20 c. purple ..	4·50	4·50

E 88. Gazelle.

E 89.

1929. Seville and Barcelona Exhibitions.

E 521.	E **88**.	20 c. red	12·00	10·00

1929.

E 522	E **89**.	20 c. red	13·00	70

1929. Optd. **Sociedad de las Naciones LV reunion del Consejo Madrid.**

E 534.	E **89**.	20 c. red ..	9·50	9·00

1930. Optd. **URGENCIA.**

E 535	E **89**.	20 c. red	11·00	50

E 91.

1930. 11th Int. Railway Congress.

E 553.	E **91**.	20 c. red	75·00	85·00

1930. "Goya" type optd. **URGENTE.**

E 570.	**91**.	20 c. mauve ..	30	25

1930. Air. "Goya" type optd. **URGENTE.**

E 583.	–	20 c. brown and grey	30	25

1930. "Columbus" type optd. **URGENTE.**

E 608.	**99**.	20 c. purple ..	2·00	2·00

E 113. Seville Exhibition.

1930. Spanish-American Exn.

E 643.	E **113**.	20 c. orange ..	25	20

1931. Optd. **REPUBLICA.**

E 660.	E **89**.	20 c. red (No. E 535)	5·50	6·50
E 672.		20 c. red (No. E 522)	5·50	5·50

1931. Optd. **Republica Espanola** in two lines continuously.

E697	E **89**	29 c. red (No. E522)	5·50	55

E 126.

E 145.

1931. 900th Anniv. of Montserrat Monastery.

E 731.	E **126**.	20 c. red.. ..	20·00	20·00

1934.

E 779.	E **145**.	20 c. red	10	10

E 152. Newspaper Boy. E 185. Pegasus.

1936. 40th Anniv. of Madrid Press Assoc.
E 801. E 152. 20 c. red 30 25

1937.
E 906. E 185. 20 c. brown .. 1·00 15

E 198. Pegasus. E 199.

1939.
E 1022. E 198. 25 c. red .. 20 10

1940. 19th Centenary of Apparition of Virgin of El Pilar at Zaragoza.
E 1006. E 199. 25 c.+5 c. red & buff 30 25

E 270. "Speed". E 271. Centaur.

1956.
E 1250. E 270. 2 p. red .. 10 10
E 1251. 3 p. red .. 10 10
E 1252. E 271. 4 p. mauve & black 15 10
E 1253. E 270. 5 p. red 25 10
E 1254. E 271. 6 p. 50 red & violet 20 10

E 425. Roman Chariot.

1971.
E 2099. E 425. 10 p. grn., blk. & red 10 10
E 2100. – 15 p. blue, blk. & red 20 10
DESIGN—VERT. 15 p. Letter encircling Globe.

E 862 Arrows (communications)

1993. Public Services.
E3211 E 862 180 p. red & yellow 1·75 10

OFFICIAL STAMPS

O 9. O 52.

1854.
O 46. O 9. ½ onza black on orge. 2·10 1·00
O 47. 1 onza black on red .. 3·25 1·40
O 48. 4 onza black on green 7·50 2·10
O 49. 1 libra black on blue 40·00 25·00

1855 Similar to Type O 9, but Arms in oval frame, inscr. “ CORREO OFICIAL ”.
O 50. ½ onza black on yellow 1·75 1·00
O 51. 1 onza black on red .. 1·75 1·00
O 52. 4 onza black on green 3·25 1·90
O 53. 1 libra black on lilac 14·00 7·75

1895.
O 289. 51. 15 c. yellow .. 6·50 65
O 290. O 52. (No value) Red 6·00 1·10
O 291. (No value) Blue .. 15·00 4·00

O 66. National Library.

O 67. Cervantes. O 68.

1916. Death Tercent. of Cervantes. (a) For use by Members of the Chamber of Deputies.
O 353. – Black and violet .. 80 80
O 354. O 66. Black and green .. 80 80
O 355. O 67. Black and violet .. 80 80
O 356. O 68. Black and red .. 80 80

(b) For use by Members of the Senate.
O 357. – Black and green .. 80 80
O 358. O 66. Black and red .. 80 80
O 359. O 67. Black and brown .. 80 80
O 360. O 68. Black and brown .. 80 80
DESIGN—As Type O 66: Chamber of Deputies.

1931. 3rd Pan-American Postal Union Congress. T 121, etc. Optd. **Oficial.**
O 707. 5 c. brown 20 15
O 708. 10 c. green 20 15
O 709. 15 c. violet 20 15
O 710. 25 c. red 20 15
O 711. 30 c. olive 20 15
O 712. 40 c. blue 35 35
O 713. 50 c. orange 35 35
O 714. 1 p. grey 35 35
O 715. 4 p. mauve .. .. 5·50 5·50
O 716. 10 p. brown .. .. 14·00 16·00

Air. T 123, etc., optd. **OFICIAL.**
O 717. 5 c. brown 10 10
O 718. 10 c. green 10 10
O 719. 25 c. red 10 10
O 720. 50 c. blue 10 10
O 721. 1 p. lilac 10 10
O 722. 4 p. grey .. .. 3·75 4·50

WAR TAX STAMPS

W 42. W 48. W 49.

1874. The 5 c. perf. or imperf.
W 217. W 42. 5 c. de p. black .. 7·50 75
W 218. 10 c. de p. blue .. 12·00 2·10

1875. As Type W 42, but large figures in bottom corners.
W 228. 5 c. de p. green .. 6·00 80
W 229. 10 c. de p. mauve .. 13·00 3·00

1876.
W 253. W 48. 5 c. de p. green .. 2·40 65
W 254. 10 c. de p. blue .. 2·40 65
W 258. W 49. 15 c. de p. red .. 10·00 50
W 255. W 48. 25 c. de p. black.. 25·00 7·00
W 259. W 49. 50 c. de p. yellow £350 50·00
W 256. W 48. 1 p. lilac .. £225 45·00
W 257. 5 p. red .. £300 £120

W 52. W 53. W 163.

1897. Inscr “1897–1898”.
W 289. W 52. 5 c. green .. .. 3·00 50
W 290. 10 c. green .. .. 3·00 50
W 291. 15 c. green £325 £120
W 292. 20 c. green .. .. 6·50 1·25

1898. Inscr “1898–99”.
W 293. W 52. 5 c. black .. .. 1·75 60
W 294. 10 c. black .. .. 1·75 60
W 295. 15 c. black .. .. 38·00 8·00
W 296. 20 c. black .. .. 3·00 1·25

1898.
W 297. W 53. 5 c. black .. .. 6·00 25

1938.
W 839. W 163. 10 c. red .. 30 30
W 840. 20 c. blue .. 30 30
W 841. 60 c. red .. 80 80
W 842. 1 p. blue .. 85 85
W 843. 2 p. green .. 90 90
W 844. 10 p. blue .. 95 95
Nos. W 842/3 have coloured figures of value on white backgrounds.

SPANISH GUINEA Pt. 9

A Spanish colony consisting of the islands of Fernando Poo, Annobon and the Corisco Islands off the west coast of Africa and Rio Muni on the mainland. In 1959 it was divided into the two Spanish Overseas Provinces of Fernando Poo and Rio Muni.

100 centimos = 1 peseta.

1902. “ Curly Head ” key-type inscr. “ GUINEA ESPANOLA 1902 ”.
1. Z. 5 c. green .. .. .. 10·00 1·00
2. 10 c. grey .. .. .. 10·00 1·00
3. 25 c. red .. .. .. 50·00 8·50
4. 50 c. brown .. .. .. 50·00 7·50
5. 75 c. lilac .. .. .. 50·00 7·50
6. 1 p. red .. .. .. 80·00 7·50
7. 2 p. green .. .. .. 90·00 11·00
8. 5 p. orange .. .. .. £150 45·00

1903. Fiscal stamps inscr “POSESIONES ESPANOLAS DE AFRICA OCCIDENTAL”, surch **HABILITADO PARA CORREOS 10 cen de peseta.**
9 10 c. on 25 c. black .. £300 £120
10 10 c. on 50 c. orange .. 85·00 20·00
11 10 c. on 1 p. 25 pink .. £450 £200
12 10 c. on 2 p. red .. £500 £300
13a 10 c. on 2 p. 50 brown .. £850 £375
14a 10 c. on 5 p. black .. £800 £275
15 10 c. on 10 p. brown .. £650 £275
16 10 c. on 5 p. lilac .. £500 £275
17 10 c. on 25 p. blue .. £550 £275
18 10 c. on 50 p. brown .. £600 £400
19 10 c. on 75 p. violet .. £800 £400
20 10 c. on 100 p. green .. £1100 £450

1903. “ Curly Head ” key-type inscr. “ GUINEA CONTIAL-ESPANOLA PARA 1903 ”.
21. Z. ¼ c. black 70 20
22. ½ c. green 70 20
23. 1 c. red 70 15
24. 2 c. olive 70 15
25. 3 c. brown 70 15
26. 4 c. red 70 15
27. 5 c. brown 70 15
28. 10 c. brown .. .. .. 1·00 20
29. 15 c. blue .. .. .. 3·75 1·50
30. 25 c. orange .. .. .. 3·75 2·25
31. 50 c. red .. .. .. 7·50 2·50
32. 75 c. lilac .. .. .. 10·00 2·50
33. 1 p. green .. .. .. 17·00 3·75
34. 2 p. green .. .. .. 17·00 3·75
35. 3 p. red .. .. .. 40·00 4·75
36. 4 p. blue .. .. .. 55·00 8·00
37. 5 p. purple .. .. .. 85·00 15·00
38. 10 p. red .. .. .. 1·40 15·00

1905. “ Curly-Head ” key-type inscr. as above but dated “ 1905 ”.
39. Z. 1 c. black 15 10
40. 2 c. green 15 10
41. 3 c. red 15 10
42. 4 c. green 15 10
43. 5 c. brown 15 10
44. 10 c. red 70 35
45. 15 c. brown .. .. .. 2·50 1·00
46. 25 c. brown .. .. .. 2·50 1·00
47. 50 c. blue .. .. .. 5·50 3·25
48. 75 c. orange .. .. .. 6·00 3·25
49. 1 p. red .. .. .. 6·00 3·25
50. 2 p. lilac .. .. .. 12·00 5·50
51. 3 p. green .. .. .. 29·00 12·00
52. 4 p. green .. .. .. 29·00 15·00
53. 5 p. red .. .. .. 50·00 15·00
54. 10 p. blue .. .. .. 85·00 42·00

1905. No. 19/34 of Elobey optd **CONTINENTAL GUINEA CORREOS ASSOBLA.**
55 Z 1 c. pink .. .. .. 5·00 1·40
56 2 c. purple .. .. .. 5·00 1·40
57 3 c. black .. .. .. 5·00 1·40
58 4 c. red .. .. .. 5·00 1·40
59 5 c. green .. .. .. 5·00 1·40
60 10 c. green .. .. .. 8·50 4·25
61 15 c. lilac .. .. .. 15·00 6·50
62 25 c. red .. .. .. 15·00 7·00
63 50 c. orange .. .. .. 20·00 10·00
64 75 c. blue .. .. .. 25·00 12·00
65 1 p. brown .. .. .. 42·00 20·00
66 2 p. brown .. .. .. 55·00 15·00
67 3 p. red .. .. .. 85·00 30·00
68 4 p. brown £300 £110
69 5 p. green £300 £100
70 10 p. red £1300 £600

1907. As T 3 of Rio de Oro, but inscr “GUINEA CONTIAL ESPANOLA”.
71. 1 c. green 40 10
72. 2 c. blue 40 10
73. 3 c. lilac 40 10
74. 4 c. green 40 10
75. 5 c. red 40 10
76. 10 c. orange .. .. .. 2·25 45
77. 15 c. brown .. .. .. 1·50 30
78. 25 c. blue .. .. .. 1·50 30
79. 50 c. brown .. .. .. 1·50 30
80. 75 c. blue .. .. .. 1·50 30
81. 1 p. orange .. .. .. 2·75 50
82. 2 p. brown .. .. .. 6·00 2·00
83. 3 p. black .. .. .. 6·00 2·00
84. 4 p. red .. .. .. 7·00 2·00
85. 5 p. green .. .. .. 7·50 3·00
86. 10 p. purple .. .. .. 11·00 4·00

1908. Surch. **HABILITADO PARA** and value in figures and **CTMS.**
87. 3. 05 c. on 1 c. green .. 2·75 2·00
88. 05 c. on 2 c. blue.. .. 2·75 2·00
89. 05 c. on 3 c. lilac .. 2·75 2·00
90. 05 c. on 4 c. green .. 2·75 2·00
91. 05 c. on 10 c. orange .. 2·75 2·00
92. 15 c. on 10 c. orange .. 13·00 9·00

1909. Fiscal stamps inscr “TERRITORIOS ESPANOLES DEL AFRICA OCCIDENTAL”, surch **HABILITADO PARA CORREOS 10 cen de peseta.**
93 10 c. on 50 c. green .. 50·00 35·00
94 10 c. on 1 p. 25 .. £140 45·00
95 10 c. on 2 p. brown .. £375 £225
96 10 c. on 5 p. mauve .. £375 £225
97 10 c. on 25 p. brown .. £475 £325
98 10 c. on 50 p. red .. £1600 £850
99 10 c. on 75 p. pink .. £1600 £850
100 10 c. on 100 p. orange .. £1600 £850

1909. As T 7 of Rio de Oro but inscr. “ TERRITORIOS ESPANOLES DEL GOLFO DE GUINEA ”.
101. 1 c. brown 10 10
102. 2 c. red 10 10
103. 5 c. green 85 10
104. 10 c. red 30 10
105. 15 c. brown 30 10
106. 20 c. mauve 45 20
107. 25 c. blue 50 20
108. 30 c. brown 50 25
109. 40 c. red 35 20
110. 50 c. lilac 35 20
111. 1 p. green .. .. 11·00 3·50
112. 4 p. orange .. .. 3·50 2·75
113. 10 p. red .. .. 4·00 2·75
This set was also issued optd. **GUINEA 1911** in an oval.

1911. Nos. 101/13 optd **GUINEA 1911.**
114 1 c. brown 20 15
115 2 c. red 20 15
116 5 c. green 70 15
117 10 c. red 55 20
118 15 c. brown 70 35
119 20 c. mauve .. .. 1·00 50
120 25 c. blue .. .. 1·25 85
121 30 c. brown .. .. 1·50 1·00
122 40 c. red .. .. 1·75 1·75
123 50 c. lilac .. .. 2·50 2·50
124 1 p. green .. .. 25·00 6·50
125 4 p. orange .. .. 14·00 7·00
126 10 p. orange .. .. 17·00 9·00

1912. As T 11 of Rio de Oro, but inscr. “ TERRS. ESPANOLES DEL GOLFO DE GUINEA ”.
127. 1 c. black 10 10
128. 2 c. brown 10 10
129. 5 c. green 10 10
130. 10 c. red 20 10
131. 15 c. red 20 10
132. 20 c. red 30 10
133. 25 c. blue 20 10
134. 30 c. red .. .. 1·75 80
135. 40 c. red .. .. 1·25 50
136. 50 c. orange 90 20
137. 1 p. lilac .. .. 1·50 90
138. 4 p. mauve .. .. 3·50 2·00
139. 10 p. green .. .. 7·50 4·50
This set was also issued optd. **1917.**

1914. As T 12 of Rio de Oro but inscr. as 1912 issue.
140. 1 c. violet 20 10
141. 2 c. red 20 15
142. 5 c. green 20 10
143. 10 c. red 20 15
144. 15 c. purple 20 15
145. 20 c. brown 50 20
146. 25 c. blue 25 20
147. 30 c. brown 90 35
148. 40 c. green 90 35
149. 50 c. red 40 20
150. 1 p. orange .. .. 1·10 85
151. 4 p. red .. .. 4·25 2·50
152. 10 p. brown .. .. 5·50 3·50

1917. Nos. 127/39 optd **1917.**
153 1 c. black .. .. 55·00 22·00
154 2 c. brown .. .. 55·00 22·00
155 5 c. green 35 20
156 10 c. red 35 20
157 15 c. purple 35 20
158 20 c. red 35 15
159 25 c. blue 15 15
160 30 c. red 35 20
161 40 c. pink 50 30
162 50 c. orange 30 20
163 1 p. lilac 50 30
164 4 p. mauve .. .. 6·00 2·75
165 10 p. green .. .. 6·00 2·75

1918. Stamps of 1912 surch. **HTADO-1917.** and value in figures and words.
166. 11. 5 c. on 40 c. red .. 25·00 8·50
167. 10 c. on 4 p. mauve .. 25·00 8·50
168. 15 c. on 20 c. red .. 50·00 15·00
169. 25 c. on 10 p. green .. 50·00 15·00

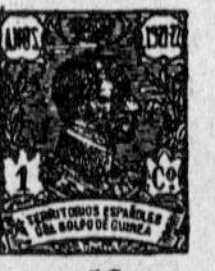

12. 13. 14. Nipa House.

1919.
170. 12. 1 c. violet 70 20
171. 2 c. red 70 20
172. 5 c. red 70 20
173. 10 c. purple .. .. 1·00 20
174. 15 c. brown .. .. 1·00 35
175. 20 c. blue .. .. 1·00 20
176. 25 c. green .. .. 1·00 35
177. 30 c. orange .. .. 1·00 35
178. 40 c. orange .. .. 3·25 35
179. 50 c. red .. .. 3·50 35
180. 1 p. green .. .. 3·75 1·25
181. 4 p. red .. .. 8·50 3·75
182. 10 p. brown .. .. 14·00 5·50

1920. As T 15 of Rio de Oro, but inscr as T 12.

183. 1 c. brown 15 10
184. 2 c. red 15 10
185. 5 c. green 20 15
186. 10 c. red 20 10
187. 15 c. orange 20 15
188. 20 c. yellow 20 15
189. 25 c. blue 40 15
190. 30 c. green .. .. 25·00 7·50
191. 40 c. brown 35 25
192. 50 c. purple .. .. 1·25 25
193. 1 p. brown .. .. 1·50 35
194. 4 p. red .. .. .. 3·75 2·25
195. 10 p. violet .. .. 5·50 4·00

1922.

196. **13.** 1 c. brown 35 10
197. 2 c. red 35 10
198. 5 c. green 35 10
199. 10 c. red .. .. 2·25 35
200. 15 c. orange 35 10
201. 20 c. mauve .. .. 1·40 30
202. 25 c. blue .. .. 2·40 35
203. 30 c. violet .. .. 2·25 40
204. 40 c. blue .. .. 2·00 20
205. 50 c. red .. .. 2·00 20
206. 1 p. green .. .. 2·00 40
207. 4 p. brown .. .. 7·50 4·75
208. 10 p. yellow .. .. 15·00 7·50

1925.

209. **14.** 5 c. blue and brown .. 20 10
210. 10 c. blue and green .. 20 10
211. 15 c. black and red .. 20 20
212. 20 c. black and violet .. 20 10
213. 25 c. black and red .. 45 30
214. 30 c. black and orange .. 45 20
215. 40 c. black and blue .. 45 20
216. 50 c. black and red .. 45 20
217. 60 c. black and brown .. 50 20
218. 1 p. black and violet .. 1·75 20
219. 4 p. black and blue .. 4·50 1·75
220. 10 p. black and green .. 9·00 4·50

1926. Red Cross stamps of Spain optd **GUINEA ESPAÑOLA**.

221 – 5 c. brown .. .. 4·00 2·50
222 – 10 c. green .. .. 4·00 2·50
223 **70** 15 c. violet .. .. 1·00 80
224 – 20 c. purple .. .. 1·00 80
225 **71** 25 c. red .. .. 1·00 80
226 **70** 30 c. green .. .. 1·00 80
227 – 40 c. blue 20 20
228 – 50 c. red 20 20
229 **71** 60 c. green 20 20
230 – 1 p. red 20 20
231 – 4 p. bistre 75 75
232 **71** 10 p. violet .. .. 2·75 2·00

1929. Seville and Barcelona Exhibition stamps of Spain (1929) optd. **GUINEA.**

233. 5 c. red 10 10
234. 10 c. green 10 10
235. 15 c. blue 10 10
236. 20 c. violet 10 10
237. 25 c. red 10 10
238. 30 c. brown 10 10
239. 40 c. blue 20 20
240. 50 c. orange 20 20
241. 1 p. grey .. .. .. 1·75 1·50
242. 4 p. red .. .. .. 3·50 3·00
243. 10 p. brown .. .. 7·00 5·50

17. Porter. **24.** **26.** Gen. Franco.

1931.

244 **17** 1 c. green 10 10
245 2 c. brown 10 10
246 5 c. black 10 10
318 5 c. grey .. .. 1·50 10
247 10 c. green 10 10
248 15 c. black 20 10
290 15 c. green .. .. 2·25 10
249 20 c. violet 20 10
250 – 25 c. red 20 10
251 – 30 c. red 20 10
252 – 40 c. blue 65 45
320 – 40 c. green 65 10
253 – 50 c. orange .. .. 1·50 90
292 – 50 c. blue .. .. 6·00 50
254 – 80 c. blue .. .. 2·50 1·50
255 – 1 p. black .. .. 3·75 2·75
256 – 4 p. mauve .. .. 29·00 12·00
257 – 5 p. brown .. .. 12·00 9·00

DESIGNS: 25 c. to 50 c. Native drummers. 80 c. to 5 p. King Alfonso XIII and Queen Victoria.

1931. Optd. **REPUBLICA ESPAÑOLA** horiz.

258. **17.** 1 c. green 10 10
259. 2 c. brown 10 10
260. 5 c. grey 15 10
261. 10 c. green 15 10
262. 15 c. blue 15 10
263. 20 c. violet 15 10
264. – 25 c. red 15 10
265. – 30 c. red 35 20
266. – 40 c. blue .. .. 1·00 35
267. – 50 c. orange .. .. 7·50 4·00
268. – 80 c. blue .. .. 2·50 1·25
269. – 1 p. black .. .. 8·50 2·50
270. – 4 p. red .. .. .. 13·00 7·50
271. – 5 p. brown .. .. 13·00 7·50

1933. Optd **Republica Espanola**.

272. **17.** 1 c. green 10 10
273. 2 c. brown 10 10
274. 5 c. grey 15 10
275. 10 c. green 15 10
276. 15 c. blue 15 10
277. 20 c. violet 35 10
278. – 25 c. red 30 20
279. – 30 c. red 30 20
280. – 40 c. blue .. .. 2·00 50
281. – 50 c. orange .. .. 8·00 3·00
282. – 80 c. blue .. .. 3·75 2·50
283. – 1 p. black .. .. 8·50 2·75
284. – 4 p. red .. .. .. 27·00 12·00
285. – 5 p. brown .. .. 29·00 12·00

1937. Surch. **HABILITADO 30 Cts.**

293. – 30 c. on 40 c. (No. 252) .. 2·75 1·75
294. – 30 c. on 40 c. (No. 266) .. 11·00 2·50
295. – 30 c. on 40 c. (No. 280) .. 40·00 12·00

1939. Stamps of Spain, 1937, optd. **Territorios Espanoles del Golfo de Guinea** in script type.

296. **183.** 10 c. green .. .. 1·50 35
297. **184.** 15 c. black .. .. 1·50 35
298. 20 c. violet .. .. 3·25 1·10
299. 25 c. red .. .. 3·25 1·10

1939. Surch. **Habilitado 40 cts.**

300. – 40 c. on 80 c. (No. 268) .. 8·50 4·50
301. – 40 c. on 80 c. (No. 282) .. 8·50 3·00

1940. Fiscal stamps as T 24 inscr "ESPECIAL MOVIL", "TIMBRE MOVIL" or "IMPUESTO SOBRE CONTRATOS" and surch or optd **Habilitado Correos.**

302. 5 c. red .. .. .. 8·50 2·25
304. 5 c. on 35 c. green .. 8·00 2·40
307. 10 c. on 75 c. brown .. 12·00 3·50
308. 15 c. on 1 p. 50 violet .. 10·00 3·00
305. 25 c. on 60 c. brown .. 8·50 2·75
306. 50 c. on 75 c. sepia .. 11·00 3·25
310. 1 p. bistre .. .. .. £120 40·00
303. 1 p. on 15 c. olive .. 7·00 5·50
316. 1 p. on 17 p. red .. .. 65·00 20·00
315. 1 p. on 40 p. green .. 17·00 5·50

1940.

311. **26.** 5 c. brown .. .. 2·50 45
312. 40 c. blue .. .. 3·25 45
314. 50 c. green .. .. 3·75 45

1941. Air. Fiscal stamp as T 24 inscr. "IMPUESTO SOBRE CONTRATOS" surch. **Habilitado para Correo Aereo Intercolonial Una Peseta** and bar.

317a. 1 p. on 17 p. red .. 45·00 12·00

1942. No. 249 surch **Habilitado 3 Pesetas**.

321 **17** 3 p. on 20 c. violet .. 9·50 1·50

1942. Stamps of Spain, 1939, optd. **Golfo de Guinea.**

322 **196** 1 PTA. black 45 20
323 4 PTAS. pink .. 6·00 50

1942. Air. Air stamp of Spain optd. **Golfo de Guinea.**

324. **195.** 1 p. blue .. .. 1·75 20

1943. Stamp of Spain, 1939, optd. **Territorios espanoles del Golfo de Guinea.**

325. **196.** 2 PTAS. brown .. 1·00 20

1948. Air. Ministerial Visit. No. 323 optd **CORREO AEREO Viaje Ministerial 10-19 Enero 1948.**

326 **196** 4 PTAS. pink .. .. 7·50 2·75

1949. Nos. 322 and 325 surch **Habilitado para** and value in words.

327. **196.** 5 c. on 1 PTA. black .. 20 10
328. 15 c. on 2 PTAS. brown 20 10

33. Native in Pirogue.

1949. 75th Anniv. of U.P.U.

329. **33.** 4 p. violet .. .. 1·75 50

34. Count Argalejo and San Carlos Bay.

35. San Carlos Bay. **36.** Manuel Iradier y Bulfy.

1949. Air. Colonial Stamp Day.

330. **34.** 5 p. green .. .. 1·75 50

1949.

331. **35.** 2 c. brown 20 10
332. – 5 c. violet 20 10
333. – 10 c. blue 20 10
334. – 15 c. black 20 10
335. **35.** 25 c. purple 20 10
336. – 30 c. yellow 20 10
337. – 40 c. olive 20 10
338. – 45 c. red 20 10
339. **35.** 50 c. orange 20 10
340. – 75 c. blue 20 10
341. – 90 c. green 20 10
342. – 1 p. slate .. .. 1·50 20
343. **35.** 1 p. 35 violet .. .. 5·00 85
344. – 2 p. grey .. .. 13·00 2·00
345. – 5 p. mauve .. .. 18·00 6·00
346. **35.** 10 p. brown .. .. 70·00 20·00

DESIGNS: 5 c., 30 c., 75 c., 2 p. Benito River rapids. 10 c., 40 c., 90 c., 5 p. Coast scene and Clarence Peak, Fernando Poo. 15 c., 45 c., 1 p. Niepan Benito River.

1950. Air. Colonial Stamp Day.

347. **36.** 5 p. brown .. .. 2·50 55

37. Hands and Natives. **38.** Mt. Mioco.

1951. Native Welfare.

348. **37.** 50 c.+10 c. blue .. 30 20
349. 1 p.+25 c. green .. 13·00 3·75
350. 6 p. 50+1 p. 65 orange 3·50 1·75

1951. Air.

351. – 25 c. yellow 10 10
352. **38.** 50 c. mauve 10 10
353. – 1 p. green 15 10
354. – 2 p. blue 35 10
355. **38.** 3 p. 25 violet 95 10
356. – 5 p. sepia .. .. 6·50 2·00
357. – 10 p. red .. .. 25·00 5·50

DESIGNS: 25 c., 2 p., 10 p. Benito Rapids. 1 p., 5 p. Santa Isabel Bay.

1951. Air. 500th Birth Anniv. of Isabella the Catholic. As T 9a of Spanish Sahara.

358. 5 p. blue .. .. .. 22·00 3·25

40. Native and map.

39. Leopard. **41.** Native man.

1951. Colonial Stamp Day.

359. **39.** 5 c.+5 c. brown .. 15 10
360. 10 c.+5 c. orange .. 15 10
361. 60 c.+15 c. olive .. 30 20

1951. Int. W. African Conf.

362. **40.** 50 c. orange 30 10
363. 5 p. blue .. .. 8·50 1·25

1952.

364. **41.** 5 c. brown 10 10
365. 50 c. olive 10 10
366. 5 p. violet .. .. 2·50 10

42. "Crinum Giganteum". **43.** Ferdinand the Catholic. **44.** Brown-cheeked Hornbills.

1952. Native Welfare Fund

367. **42.** 5 c.+5 c. brown .. 15 10
368. 50 c.+10 c. black .. 20 10
369. 2 p.+30 c. blue .. 1·50 70

1952. Air. 500th Birth Anniv. of Ferdinand the Catholic.

370. **43.** 5 p. brown .. .. 30·00 4·75

1952. Colonial Stamp Day.

371. **44.** 5 c.+5 c. brown .. 35 10
372. 10 c.+5 c. purple .. 55 30
373. 60 c.+15 c. green .. 85 50

45. Native Musician. **46.** Native Woman and Dove.

1953. Native Welfare Fund. Inscr. "PRO INDIGENAS 1953".

374. **45.** 5 c.+5 c. lake 15 10
375. – 10 c.+5 c. purple .. 15 10
376. **45.** 15 c. olive 15 10
377. – 60 c. brown 15 10

DESIGN: 10 c., 60 c. Musician facing right.

1953.

378. **46.** 5 c. orange 10 10
379. 10 c. purple 10 10
380. 60 c. brown 10 10
381. – 1 p. lilac .. .. 1·00 10
382. – 1 p. 90 green .. 2·50 30

DESIGN: 1 p., 1 p. 90, Native drummer.

47. "Tragocephala nobilis". **48.** Hunting with Bow and Arrow.

1953. Colonial Stamp Day. Inscr. "DIA DEL SELLO COLONIAL 1953".

383. **47.** 5 c.+5 c. blue 10 10
384. – 10 c.+5 c. purple .. 30 10
385. **47.** 15 c. green 25 20
386. – 60 c. brown 50 20

DESIGN: 10, 60 c. "Druryia antimachus" (butter- fly).

1954. Native Welfare Fund. Inscr. "PRO-INDIGENAS 1954".

387. **48.** 5 c.+5 c. lake 10 10
388. – 10 c.+5 c. lilac .. 10 10
389. **48.** 15 c. green 10 10
390. – 60 c. brown 30 10

DESIGN: 10, 60 c. Native hunting elephant with spear.

49. Turtle.

50. M. Iradier y Bulfy. **51.** Native Priest

1954. Colonial Stamp Day. Inscr. "DIA DEL SELLO COLONIAL 1954".

391. **49.** 5 c.+5 c. red 10 10
392. – 10 c.+5 c. purple .. 10 10
393. **49.** 15 c. green 10 10
394. – 60 c. brown 30 15

DESIGN: 10 c., 60 c. "Leptocharias smithi" (Fish).

1955. Birth Cent. of Iradier (explorer).

395. **50.** 60 c. brown 20 10
396. 1 p. violet .. .. 3·50 30

1955. Centenary of Apostolic Prefecture in Fernando Poo.

397. **51.** 10 c.+5 c. purple .. 10 10
398. – 25 c.+10 c. violet .. 10 10
399. **51.** 50 c. olive 15 10

DESIGN: 25 c. "Baptism".

52. Footballers. **53.** El Pardo Palace, Madrid.

1955. Air.

400. **52.** 25 c. grey 10 10
401. 50 c. olive 10 10
402. 1 p. 50 brown .. .. 1·25 10
403. 4 p. red .. .. 3·50 20
404. 10 p. green .. .. 2·50 20

1955. Treaty of Pardo, 1778.

405. **53.** 5 c. brown 10 10
406. 15 c. red 10 10
407. 80 c. green 10 10

54. Moustached Monkeys. **55.** "Orquidea".

1955. Colonial Stamp Day. Inscr. "DIA DEL SELLO COLONIAL 1955".

408. **54.** 5 c.+5 c. lake & brown 20 15
409. – 15 c.+5 c. sepia & lake 20 15
410. **54.** 70 c. blue and slate .. 25 20

DESIGN—HORIZ. 15 c. Talapoin and young.

1956. Native Welfare Fund. Inscr. "PRO INDIGENAS 1956".

411. **55.** 5 c. + 5 c. olive .. 10 10
412. – 15 c.+5 c. ochre .. 10 10
413. **55.** 20 c. turquoise.. .. 20 10
414. – 50 c. brown 25 10

DESIGN: 15 c., 50 c. "Strophantus kombe".

56. Arms of Santa Isabel. **57.** Grey Parrot. **58.** "Flight".

1956. Colonial Stamp Day. Inscr. "DIA DEL SELLO 1956".

415. **56.** 5 c.+5 c. brown .. 10 10
416. – 15 c.+5 c. violet .. 10 10
417. **56.** 70 c. green 10 10

DESIGN—HORIZ. 15 c. Arms of Bata and natives.

1957. Native Welfare Fund. Inscr. "PRO INDIGENAS 1957".

418. **57.** 5 c.+5 c. purple .. 15 10
419. – 15 c.+5 c. ochre .. 15 10
420. **57.** 70 c. green 35 15

DESIGN—HORIZ. 15 c. Parrot in flight.

1957. Air. 30th Anniv. of Spain-Fernando Poo Flight by "Atlantida" Seaplane Squadron.

421. **58.** 25 p. sepia and bistre 8·00 85

DESIGN—VERT. 15 c., 70 c. African elephant trumpeting.

59. African Elephant and Calf.

1957. Colonial Stamp Day.

422. **59.** 10 c.+5 c. mauve .. 10 10
423. – 15 c.+5 c. brown .. 15 10
424. **59.** 20 c. turquoise.. .. 15 10
425. – 70 c. green 25 10

60. Doves and Arms of Valencia and Santa Isabel.

61. Boxing. **62.** Missionary holding Cross.

1958. "Aid for Valencia".

426. **60.** 10 c.+5 c. brown .. 10 10
427. 15 c.+10 c. ochre .. 10 10
428. 50 c.+10 c. brown .. 10 10

1958. Sports.

429. **61.** 5 c. brown 10 10
430. – 10 c. brown 10 10
431. – 15 c. bistre 10 10
432. – 80 c. green 10 10
433. **61.** 1 p. salmon 10 10
434. – 2 p. purple 20 10
435. – 2 p. 30 violet 35 10
436. – 3 p. blue 35 10

DESIGNS—VERT. 10 c., 2 p. Basketball. 80 c., 3 p. Running. HORIZ. 15 c., 2 p. 30, Long jumping.

1958. Native Welfare Fund. Inscr. "1883 PRO-INDIGENAS 1958".

437. **62.** 10 c.+5 c. brown .. 10 10
438. – 15 c.+5 c. ochre .. 10 10
439. **62.** 20 c. turquoise.. .. 10 10
440. – 70 c. green 10 10

DESIGN: 15 c., 70 c. The Crucifixion.

63. "Danaus chrysippus". **64.** Digitalis. **65.** Boy on "Penny-farthing" Cycle.

1958. Colonial Stamp Day. Inscr. "1958".

441. **63.** 10 c.+5 c. red.. .. 15 10
442. – 25 c.+10 c. violet .. 25 10
443. – 50 c.+10 c. olive .. 30 10

DESIGNS: 25 c., 50 c. Different views of butterflies on plants.

1959. Child Welfare Fund. Floral designs as T **64.** Inscr. "PRO-INFANCIA 1959".

444. **64.** 10 c.+5 c. lake.. .. 10 10
445. – 15 c.+5 c. ochre .. 15 10
446. – 20 c. myrtle 15 10
447. **64.** 70 c. green 15 10

DESIGN: 15 c., 20 c. Castor bean.

1959. Colonial Stamp Day. Inscr. "1959".

448. **65.** 10 c.+5 c. lake .. 20 10
449. – 20 c.+5 c. myrtle .. 20 10
450. – 50 c.+20 c. olive .. 20 10

DESIGNS: 20 c. Racing cyclists. 50 c. Winning cyclist.

EXPRESS LETTER STAMP

E **38.** Fernando Poo.

1951.

E 358. E **38.** 25 c. red 20 15

SPANISH MOROCCO Pt. 9

100 centimos = 1 peseta.

I. SPANISH POST OFFICES IN MOROCCO.

Nos. 2/150, except Nos. 93/8 and 124/37 are all stamps of Spain overprinted.

1903. Optd. **CORREO ESPANOL MARRUECOS:**

2. **38a.** ¼ c. green 30 10

1903. Optd. **CORREO ESPANOL MARRUECOS.**

3 **52** 2 c. brown 75 30
4 5 c. green 85 20
5 10 c. red .. .. 1·00 10
6 15 c. violet .. .. 1·25 20
7 20 c. black .. .. 4·75 90
8 25 c. blue 50 20
9 30 c. green .. .. 2·75 95
10 40 c. pink .. .. 5·50 1·75
11 50 c. blue .. .. 2·75 1·10
12 1 p. purple .. .. 6·50 2·25
13 4 p. purple .. .. 15·00 3·00
14 10 p. orange .. .. 15·00 8·00

1908. Stamps of Spain handstamped **TETUAN.**

15 **38a** ¼ c. green .. .. 7·00 3·00
16 **52** 2 c. brown .. .. 32·00 12·00
17 5 c. green .. .. 45·00 32·00
18 10 c. red .. .. 42·00 22·00
19 15 c. violet .. .. 45·00 24·00
20 20 c. black £130 £110
21 25 c. blue .. .. 65·00 35·00
22 30 c. green .. .. £150 55·00
23 40 c. bistre £200 £110

1908. Nos. 2/5 and 7/8 handstamped **TETUAN.**

24. **38a.** ¼ c. green .. .. 11·00 10·00
25. **52.** 2 c. brown .. .. £120 55·00
26. 5 c. green .. .. 95·00 30·00
27. 10 c. red .. .. £100 30·00
28. 20 c. grey £250 £120
29. 25 c. blue .. .. 85·00 35·00

1909. Optd **CORREO ESPANOL MARRUECOS.**

30. **64.** 2 c. brown 30 10
31. 5 c. green .. .. 1·50 10
32. 10 c. red .. .. 1·75 10
33. 15 c. violet .. .. 4·25 15
34. 20 c. green .. .. 10·00 25·00
35. 25 c. blue .. .. 70·00
36. 30 c. green .. .. 3·25 15
37. 40 c. pink .. .. 3·25 15
38. 50 c. blue .. .. 6·00 3·00
39. 1 p. lake .. .. 12·00 6·00
40. 4 p. purple .. .. 70·00
41. 10 p. orange .. .. 70·00

After the appearance of Nos. 42/54 for the Spanish Protectorate in 1914, the use of Nos. 30/41 was restricted to Tangier.

II. SPANISH PROTECTORATE (excluding Tangier).

1914. Optd. **MARRUECOS.**

42. **38a.** ¼ c. green 10 10
43. **64.** 2 c. brown 10 10
44. 5 c. green.. .. .. 20 15
45. 10 c. red 20 15
46. 15 c. violet 60 45
47. 20 c. green .. .. 1·50 85
48. 25 c. blue .. .. 1·50 50
49. 30 c. green .. .. 2·75 1·10
50. 40 c. pink .. .. 6·00 2·00
51. 50 c. blue .. .. 3·00 1·10
52. 1 p. red .. .. 3·00 1·50
53. 4 p. purple .. .. 14·00 9·50
54. 10 p. orange .. .. 20·00 11·00

1915. Optd. **PROTECTORADO ESPANOL EN MARRUECOS.**

55. **38a.** ¼ c. green.. .. .. 15 10
56. **64.** 2 c. brown 10 10
57. 5 c. green 30 10
58. 10 c. red 25 10
59. 15 c. violet 30 10
60. 20 c. green 85 15
61. 25 c. blue 70 15
62. 30 c. green 95 20
63. 40 c. pink .. .. 1·50 20
64. 50 c. blue.. .. .. 2·50 15
65. 1 p. red .. .. 2·50 20
66. 4 p. purple .. .. 15·00 9·00
67. 10 p. orange .. .. 25·00 10·00

1916. Optd. **ZONA DE PROTECTORADO ESPANOL EN MARRUECOS.**

68. **38a.** ¼ c. green.. .. .. 30 10
69. **66.** 1 c. green.. .. .. 1·10 10
70. **64.** 2 c. brown 80 10
71. 5 c. green.. .. .. 2·75 10
72. 10 c. red .. .. 3·50 10
73. 15 c. orange .. .. 4·00 10
74. 20 c. violet .. .. 7·50 10
75. 25 c. blue .. .. 12·00 1·10
76. 30 c. green .. .. 15·00 8·00
77. 40 c. red .. .. 18·00 30
78. 50 c. blue .. .. 9·00 15
79. 1 p. red .. .. 22·00 1·00
80. 4 p. purple .. .. 30·00 13·00
81. 10 p. orange .. .. 70·00 25·00

1920. Optd. **PROTECTORADO ESPANOL EN MARRUECOS** perf. through centre and each half **surch.** in figures and words.

82. **64.** 10 c.+10 c. on 20 c. green 5·00 1·75
83. 15 c.+15 c. on 30 c. green 10·00 7·00

1920. No. E 68 perf through centre, and each half surch **10 centimos.**

84 E **53** 10 c.+10 c. on 20 c. red 11·00 7·50

1920. Fiscal stamps showing figure of Justice, bisected and surch. **CORREOS** and value.

93. 5 c. on 5 p. blue.. .. 9·00 1·75
94. 5 c. on 10 p. green .. 40 10
95. 10 c. on 25 p. green .. 40 10
96. 10 c. on 50 p. grey .. 45 10
97. 15 c. on 100 p. red .. 45 10
98. 15 c. on 500 p. red .. 12·00 5·00

1923. Optd **ZONA DE PROTECTORADO ESPANOL EN MARRUECOS.**

101 **68** 2 c. green 45 10
102 5 c. purple 45 10
103 10 c. green .. .. 1·50 10
105 15 c. blue .. .. 1·50 10
106 20 c. violet .. .. 3·50 10
107 25 c. red .. .. 7·00 55
108 40 c. blue .. .. 7·50 2·00
109 50 c. orange .. .. 18·00 2·75
110 **69** 1 p. grey .. .. 28·00 2·00

1926. Red Cross stamps optd. **ZONA PROTECTORADO ESPANOL.**

111 **70** 1 c. orange .. .. 3·25 2·25
112 – 2 c. red .. .. 3·25 2·25
113 – 5 c. brown .. .. 1·50 1·00
114 – 10 c. green .. .. 1·50 1·00
115 **70** 15 c. violet 60 50
116 – 20 c. purple 60 50
117 **71** 25 c. red 60 50
118 **70** 30 c. green 60 50
119 – 40 c. blue 20 25
120 – 50 c. red 20 25
121 – 1 p. red 35 35
122 – 4 p. bistre 35 35
123 **71** 10 p. violet .. .. 1·75 1·25

11. Mosque of Alcazarquivir. **12.** Moorish Gateway, Larache.

1928.

124. **11.** 1 c. red 10 10
126. 2 c. violet 25 20
127. 3 c. blue 10 10
128. 10 c. green 10 10
129. 15 c. brown 30 10
130. **12.** 20 c. olive 30 10
131. 25 c. red 30 10
132. 30 c. brown 80 10
133. 40 c. blue .. .. 1·25 10
134. 50 c. purple .. .. 2·25 10
135. – 1 p. green .. .. 3·50 20
136. – 2 p. 50 purple .. .. 12·00 3·75
137. – 4 p. blue .. .. .. 8·00 1·50

DESIGNS—HORIZ. 1 p. Well at Alhucemas. 2 p. 50 Xauen. 4 p. Tetuan.

1929. Seville–Barcelona Exhibition stamps, Nos. 502/14 optd. **PROTECTORADO MARRUECOS.**

138. 1 c. blue 15 10
139. 2 c. green 10 10
140. 5 c. red 10 10
141. 10 c. green 10 10
142. 15 c. blue 10 10
143. 20 c. violet 10 10
144. 25 c. red 10 10
145. 30 c. brown 25 25
146. 40 c. blue 30 30
147. 50 c. orange 30 30
148. 1 p. grey .. .. .. 2·25 1·25
149. 4 p. red .. .. .. 4·50 4·00
150. 10 p. brown .. .. 8·50 6·50

14. Xauen. **15.** Market-place, Larache.

1933.

151. **14.** 1 c. red 10 10
152. – 2 c. green 10 10
153. – 5 c. mauve 10 10
154. – 10 c. green 20 10
155. – 15 c. yellow 90 10
156. **14.** 20 c. green 35 10
157. – 25 c. red .. .. .. 10·00 20
165. – 25 c. violet 60 10
158. – 30 c. lake .. .. 2·50 10
166. – 30 c. red .. .. .. 8·00 10
159. **15.** 40 c. blue .. .. 5·50 10
167. – 40 c. red .. .. .. 4·50 15
160. – 50 c. red .. .. 17·00 2·50
168. – 50 c. blue .. .. 4·50 15
169. – 60 c. green .. .. 4·25 15
161. – 1 p. grey .. .. 6·50 10
170. – 2 p. lake .. .. 22·00 3·00
162. – 2 p. 50 c. brown .. 12·00 2·50
163. – 4 p. green .. .. 12·00 2·50
164. – 5 p. black .. .. 15·00 2·50

DESIGNS—HORIZ. 2 c., 1 p. Xauen. 5 c., 2 p. 50 c. Arcila. 25 c. (No. 157), 5 p. Sultan and bodyguard. 30 c. (No. 166), 50 c. (No. 168), 2 p. Forest at Ketama. VERT. 10 c., 30 c. (No. 158), Tetuan. 15 c., 4 p. Alcazarquivir. 25 c. (No. 165), 40 c. (No. 167), Wayside scene at Arcila.

See also Nos. 177/83 and 213/6.

1936. Air. No. 157 surch with new value and **18-7-36.**

171 25 c.+2 p. on 25 c. red .. 12·00 4·00

1936. Surch.

172. – 1 c. on 4 p. blue (137) 25 10
173. – 2 c. on 2 p. 50 pur. (136) 25 10
174. **12.** 5 c. on 25 c. red (131).. 15 10
175. – 10 c. on 1 p. green (135) 4·25 2·25
176. E **12.** 15 c. on 20 c. black 3·75 1·10

1937. Pictorials as T **14/15.**

177. 1 c. green 10 10
178. 2 c. mauve 10 10
179. 5 c. orange 15 10
180. 15 c. violet 15 10
181. 30 c. red 35 10
182. 1 p. blue .. .. 3·50 35
183. 10 p. brown .. .. 30·00 9·00

DESIGNS—VERT. 1 c., 15 c. Caliph and Viziers. 30 c. Tetuan. 1 p. Arcila. 10 p. Caliph on horseback. HORIZ. 2 c. Bokoia. 5 c. Alcazarquivir.

18. Legionaries.

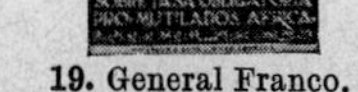

19. General Franco.

1937. 1st Anniv. of Civil War.
184. – 1 c. blue 10 10
185. 18. 2 c. brown 10 10
186. – 5 c. mauve 10 10
187. – 10 c. green 10 10
188. – 15 c. blue 10 10
189. – 20 c. purple 10 10
190. – 25 c. mauve 10 10
191. – 30 c. red 10 10
192. – 40 c. orange 10 10
193. – 50 c. blue 10 10
194. – 60 c. green 10 10
195. – 1 p. violet 10 10
196. – 2 p. blue .. .. .. 4·50 3·00
197. – 2 p. 50 black .. .. 4·50 3·25
198. – 4 p. brown .. .. 4·50 3·25
199. – 10 p. black .. .. 4·75 3·50
DESIGNS—VERT. 1 c. Sentry. 5 c. Trooper. 10 c. Volunteers. 15 c. Colour bearer. 20 c. Desert halt. 25 c. Ifni mounted riflemen. 30 c. Trumpeters. 40 c. Cape Juby Camel Corps. 50 c. Infantryman 60 c., 1, 2, 4 p. Sherifian Guards. 2 p. 50, Cavalryman. HORIZ. 10 p. "Road to Victory".

1937. Obligatory Tax. Disabled Soldiers in N. Africa.
200 19 10 c. brown 40 10
202 10 c. blue 40 10

20. Yellow-billed Stork over Mosque.

22. Soldier on Horseback.

1938. Air.
203. – 5 c. brown 10 10
204. 20. 10 c. green 45 10
205. – 25 c. red 10 10
206. – 40 c. blue .. .. 2·00 70
207. 50 c. mauve 10 10
208. – 75 c. blue 10 10
209. – 1 p. brown 10 10
210. – 1 p. 50 violet .. .. 2·50 30
211. – 2 p. red 40 10
212. – 3 p. black .. .. 1·50 20
DESIGNS—VERT. 5 c. Mosque de Baja, Tetuan. 25 c. Straits of Gibraltar. 40 c. Desert natives. 1 p. Mounted postman. 1 p. 50 Farmers. 2 p. Sunset. 3 p. Shadow of airplane over city. HORIZ. 50 c. Airplane over Tetuan. 75 c. Airplane over Larache.

1939. Pictorials as T 14.
213. 5 c. orange 25 10
214. 10 c. green 25 10
215. 15 c. brown 45 10
216. 20 c. blue 45 10
DESIGNS: 5 c. "Carta de Marruecos". 10 c "Carta de Espana". 15 c. Larache. 20 c. Tetuan.

1940. Pictorials as T 14, inscr. "ZONA" on back.
217. 1 c. brown 10 10
218. 2 c. olive 10 10
219. 5 c. blue 20 10
220. 10 c. lilac 15 10
221. 15 c. green 15 10
222. 20 c. violet 15 10
223. 25 c. sepia 15 10
224. 30 c. green 15 10
225. 40 c. green 15 10
226. 45 c. orange .. .. 1·25 10
227. 50 c. brown 50 10
228. 70 c. blue 50 10
229. 1 p. brown and blue .. 1·50 10
230. 2 p. 50 green and brown 7·50 2·25
231. 5 p. sepia and purple .. 1·50 20
232. 10 p. brown and olive .. 14·00 4·25
DESIGNS—VERT. 1 c. Postman. 2 c. Pillar-box. 5 c. Winter landscape. 10 c. Alcazar street. 15 c. Castle wall, Xauen. 20 c. Palace sentry, Tetuan. 25 c. Caliph on horseback. 30 c. Market-place, Larache. 40 c. Gateway, Tetuan. 45 c. Gateway, Xauen. 50 c. Street, Alcazarquivir. 70 c. Post Office. 1 p. Spanish War veterans. 2 p. 50, Flag bearers. 5 p. and 10 p. Cavalry.

1940. 4th Anniv. of Civil War. Nos. 184/99 optd. **17-VII-940 4o. ANIVERSARIO.**
233. 1 c. blue 50 50
234. 2 c. brown 50 50
235. 5 c. mauve 50 50
236. 10 c. green 50 50
237. 15 c. blue 50 50
238. 20 c. purple 50 50
239. 25 c. mauve 50 50
240. 30 c. red 50 50
241. 40 c. orange .. .. 1·25 1·25
242. 50 c. blue .. .. 1·25 1·25
243. 60 c. green .. .. 1·25 1·25
244. 1 p. violet .. .. 1·25 1·25
245. 2 p. blue .. .. 28·00 28·00
246. 2 p. 50 black .. .. 28·00 28·00
247. 4 p. brown .. .. 28·00 28·00
248. 10 p. black .. .. 28·00 28·00

1941. Obligatory Tax for Disabled Soldiers.
249. 22. 10 c. green .. .. 2·00 10
250. 10 c. pink .. .. 2·00 10
251. 10 c. red .. .. 2·00 10
252. 10 c. blue .. .. 2·00 10

25. General Franco.

23. Larache.

26. Homeward Bound.

1941.
253. 23. 5 c. brown & deep brown 10 10
263. – 5 c. blue 15 10
254. – 10 c. deep red and red .. 15 10
255. – 15 c. yellow and green .. 15 10
256. – 20 c. blue and deep blue 35 10
264. – 40 c. brown .. .. 15·00 20
257. – 40 c. red and purple .. 95 10
DESIGNS: 5 c. blue, 10 c. Alcazarquivir. 15 c., 40 c. brown, Larache market. 20 c. Moorish house. 40 c. purple, Gateway, Tangier.

1942. Air. New designs as T 14, optd. Z.
258. 5 c. blue 10 10
259. 10 c. brown 10 10
260. 15 c. green 10 10
261. 90 c. red 10 10
262. 5 p. black 95 50
DESIGNS—VERT. 5 c. Atlas mountains. 10 c. Mosque at Tangier. 15 c. Velez fortress. 90 c. Sanjurjo harbour. 5 p. Straits of Gibraltar.

1943. Obligatory Tax for Disabled Soldiers.
265. 25. 10 c. grey .. .. 3·75 10
266. 10 c. blue .. .. 3·75 10
267. 10 c. brown .. .. 3·75 10
268. 10 c. violet .. .. 3·75 10
283. 10 c. brown and mauve 3·50 10
284. 10 c. green and orange .. 3·50 10
295. 10 c. brown and blue .. 3·50 10
296. 10 c. lilac and grey .. 3·50 10

1944. Agricultural scenes.
269. – 1 c. blue and brown .. 25 10
270. – 2 c. green 10 10
271. 26. 5 c. black and brown .. 10 10
272. – 10 c. orange and blue .. 10 10
273. – 15 c. green 10 10
274. – 20 c. black and red .. 10 10
275. – 25 c. brown and blue .. 15 10
276. – 30 c. blue and green .. 1·00 25
277. – 40 c. purple and brown 10 10
278. 26. 50 c. brown and blue .. 30 10
279. – 75 c. blue and green .. 35 10
280. – 1 p. brown and blue .. 35 10
281. – 2 p. 50 blue and black .. 4·00 1·75
282. – 10 p. black and orange 7·00 3·50
DESIGNS—HORIZ. 1 c., 30 c. Ploughing. 2 c., 40 c. Harvesting. 10 c., 75 c. Threshing. 15 c. 1 p. Vegetable garden. 20 c., 2 p. 50, Gathering oranges. 25 c., 10 p. Shepherd and flock.

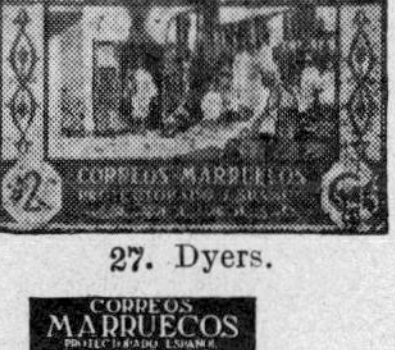
27. Dyers.

28. Sanatorium.

29. Sanatorium.

30. Steam Goods Train.

1946. Craftsmen.
285. – 1 c. brown and purple .. 10 10
286. 27. 2 c. violet and green .. 10 10
287. – 10 c. blue and orange .. 10 10
288. 27. 15 c. green and blue .. 10 10
289. – 25 c. blue and green .. 10 10
290. – 40 c. brown and blue .. 10 10
291. 27. 45 c. red and black .. 40 10
292. – 1 p. blue and green .. 50 10
293. – 2 p. 50 green & orange 1·60 50
294. – 10 p. grey and blue .. 2·75 1·40
DESIGNS: 1 c., 10 c., 25 c. Potters. 40 c. Blacksmiths. 1 p. Cobblers. 2 p. 50, Weavers. 10 p. Metal workers.

1946. Anti-T.B. Fund.
297. – 10 c. green and red .. 10 10
298. 28. 25 c. brown and red .. 10 10
299. – 25 c.+5 c. vio. & red .. 10 10
300. – 50 c.+10 c. blue & red 35 25
301. – 90 c.+10 c. brn. & red 65 35
DESIGNS: 10 c. Emblem and arabesque ornamentation. 25 c.+5 c. Mountain roadway. 40 c.+10 c. Fountain. 90 c.+10 c. Wayfarers.

1947. Anti-T.B. Fund.
302. – 10 c. blue and red .. 10 10
303. 29. 25 c. brn. and red .. 10 10
304. – 25 c.+5 c. lilac & red .. 10 10
305. – 50 c.+10 c. blue & red 35 20
306. – 90 c.+10 c. brn. & red 60 40
DESIGNS: 10 c. Emblem, mosque and palm tree. 25 c.+5 c. Hospital ward. 50 c.+10 c. Nurse and children. 90 c.+10 c. Arab swordsman.

1948. Transport and Commerce.
307. 30. 2 c. brown and violet .. 20 10
308. – 5 c. violet and red .. 10 10
309. – 15 c. green and blue .. 10 10
310. – 25 c. green and black .. 10 10
311. – 35 c. black and blue .. 10 10
312. – 50 c. violet and orange 10 10
313. – 70 c. blue and green .. 10 10
314. – 90 c. green and red .. 15 10
315. – 1 p. violet and blue .. 40 10
316. 30. 2 p. 50 green and purple 7·50 7·50
317. – 10 p. blue and black .. 1·75 1·10
DESIGNS: 5, 35 c. Road transport, 15, 70 c. Urban market. 25, 90 c. Rural market. 50 c., 1 p. Camel caravan. 10 p. "Arango" (freighter) at quay.

31. Emblem.

32. Herald.

1948. Anti-T.B. Fund.
318. 31. 10 c. green and red .. 10 10
319. – 25 c. green and red .. 1·25 60
320. 32. 50 c.+10 c. pur. & red 20 10
321. – 90 c.+10 c. blk. & red 80 35
322. – 2 p. 50+50 c. sep. & red 7·00 2·75
323. – 5 p.+1 p. vio. & red .. 10·00 4·00
DESIGNS: 25 c. Aeroplane over sanatorium. 90 c. Arab swordsman. 2 p. 50, Natives sitting in the sun. 5 p. Aeroplane over Ben Karrich.

33. Market Day.

34. Caliph on Horseback.

1949. Air.
324. – 5 c. green and purple .. 10 10
325. 33. 10 c. mauve and black 10 10
326. – 30 c. grey and blue .. 10 10
327. – 1 p. 75 blue and black .. 10 10
328. 33. 3 p. black and blue .. 20 10
329. – 4 p. red and black .. 40 25
330. – 6 p. 50 brown and green 1·10 25
331. – 8 p. blue and mauve .. 2·00 45
DESIGNS—VERT. 5 c., 1 p. 75, Straits of Gibraltar. 30 c., 4 p. Kebira Fortress. 6 p. 50. Arrival of mail 'plane. 8p. Galloping horseman.

1949. Caliph's Wedding Celebrations.
332. 34. 50 c.+10 c. red (postage) 20 20
333. – 1 p.+10 c. black (air) .. 70 30
DESIGN: 1 p. Wedding crowds in palace grounds.

35. Emblem.

36. Postman. 1890.

37. Morabito.

1949. Anti-T.B. Fund.
334. 35. 5 c. green and red .. 10 10
335. – 10 c. blue and red .. 10 10
336. – 25 c. black and red .. 50 20
337. – 50 c.+10 c. brn. & red 30 10
338. – 90 c.+10 c. grn. & red 85 20
DESIGNS: 10 c. Road to recovery. 25 c. Palm tree and tower. 50 c. Flag and followers. 90 c. Moorish horseman.

1950. 75th Anniv. of U.P.U.
339. 36. 5 c. blue and brown .. 10 10
340. – 10 c. black and blue .. 10 10
341. – 15 c. green and black .. 10 10
342. – 35 c. black and violet .. 10 10
343. – 45 c. mauve and red .. 15 15
344. 36. 50 c. black and green .. 10 10
345. – 75 c. blue and deep blue 10 10
346. 36. 90 c. red and black .. 10 10
347. – 1 p. green and purple .. 10 10
348. – 1 p. 50 blue and red .. 25 10
349. – 5 p. purple and black .. 50 15
350. – 10 p. blue and violet .. 14·00 12·00
DESIGNS: 10, 45 c., 1 p. Mounted postman. 15 c., 1 p. 50, Mail coach. 35, 75 c., 5 p. Mail van. 10 p. Steam mail train.

1950. Anti-T.B. Fund.
351. – 5 c. black and red .. 10 10
352. – 10 c. green and red .. 10 10
353. – 25 c. blue and red .. 55 30
354. – 50 c.+10 c. brn. & red 25 10
355. 37. 90 c.+10 c. grn. & red 1·25 50
DESIGNS: 5 c. Arab horseman. 10 c. Fort. 25 c. Sanatorium. 50 c. Crowd at Fountain of Life.

38. Hunting.

40. Mounted Riflemen.

39. Emblem.

1950.
356. 38. 5 c. mauve and brown 10 10
357. – 10 c. grey and red .. 10 10
358. 38. 50 c. sepia and green .. 10 10
359. – 1 p. red and violet .. 40 10
360. – 5 p. violet and red .. 70 10
361. – 10 p. red and green .. 2·00 50
DESIGNS: 10 c., 1 p. Hunters and hounds. 5 p. Fishermen. 10 p. Carabo (fishing boat).

1951. Anti-T.B. Fund.
362. 39. 5 c. green and red .. 10 10
363. – 10 c. blue and red .. 10 10
364. – 25 c. black and red .. 60 35
365. – 50 c.+10 c. brown & red 10 10
366. – 90 c.+10 c. blue & red 30 15
367. – 1 p.+5 p. blue and red 8·00 3·50
368. – 1 p. 10+25 c. sepia & red 2·75 1·75
DESIGNS: 10 c. Natives and children. 25 c. Airplane over Nubes. 50 c. Moorish horsemen. 90 c. Riverside fortress. 1 p. Brig "Hernan Cortes". 1 p. 10, Airplane over caravan.

1952.
369. 40. 5 c. brown and blue .. 10 10
370. – 10 c. mauve and sepia .. 10 10
371. – 15 c. green and black .. 10 10
372. – 20 c. purple and green .. 10 10
373. – 25 c. blue and red .. 10 10
374. – 35 c. orange and olive .. 10 10
375. – 45 c. red 10 10
376. – 50 c. green and red .. 10 10
377. – 75 c. blue and purple .. 10 10
378. – 90 c. purple and blue .. 10 10
379. – 1 p. brown and blue .. 10 10
380. – 5 p. blue and red .. 1·60 35
381. – 10 p. black and green .. 2·40 50
DESIGNS—HORIZ. 10 c. Grooms leading horses. 15 c. Parade of horsemen. 20 c. Peasants. 25 c. Monastic procession. 35 c. Native band. 45 c. Tribesmen. 50 c. Natives overlooking roof tops. 75 c. Inside a tea house. 90 c. Wedding procession. 1 p. Pilgrims on horseback. 5 p. Storyteller and audience. 10 p. Natives talking.

41. Road to Tetuan.

42. Natives at Prayer.

1952. Air. Tetuan Postal Museum Fund.
382 41 2 p. blue and black .. 10 10
383 – 4 p. red and black .. 30 10
384 – 8 p. green and black .. 40 25
385 – 16 p. brown and black .. 2·00 80
DESIGNS: 4 p. Moors watching airplane. 8 p. Horseman and airplane. 16 p. Shadow of airplane over Tetuan.

1952. Anti-T.B. Fund. Frame in red.
386 42 5 c. green 10 10
387 – 10 c. brown 10 10
388 – 25 c. blue 30 20
389 – 50 c.+10 c. black .. 10 10
390 – 60 c.+25 c. green .. 60 35
391 – 90 c.+10 c. purple .. 60 35
392 – 1 p. 10+25 c. violet .. 1·50 75
393 – 5 p.+2 p. black .. 3·75 2·00
DESIGNS: 10 c. Beggars outside doorway. 25 c. Airplane over cactus. 50 c. Natives on horseback. 60 c. Airplane over palms. 90 c. Hilltop fortress. 1 p. 10, Airplane over agaves. 5 p. Mounted warrior.

43. Sidi Saidi.

46.

47. Water-carrier.

1953. Air.
394. – 35 c. red and blue .. 15 10
395. 43. 60 c. green and lake .. 15 10
396. – 1 p. black and blue .. 25 10
397. – 4 p. 50 brn. and lake .. 85 20
DESIGNS: 35 c. Carabo (fishing boat). 1 p. 10, Le Yunta (ploughing). 4 p. 50, Fortress, Xauen.

1953. Air. No. 208 surch. **50.**
398. 50 c. on 75 c. blue 30 10

1953. Anti-T.B. Fund. As T **32** but inscr. "PRO TUBERCULOSOS 1953". Frame in red.
400 5 c. green 10 10
401 10 c. purple 10 10
402 25 c. green 55 35
403 50 c.+10 c. violet .. 10 10
404 60 c.+25 c. brown .. 1·25 10
405 90 c.+10 c. black .. 40 30
406 1 p. 10+25 c. brown .. 2·00 1·25
407 5 p.+2 p. blue .. .. 6·50 4·00
DESIGNS: 5 c. Herald. 10 c. Moorish horseman. 25 c. Aeroplane over Ben Karrich. 50 c. Mounted warrior. 60 c. Aeroplane over sanatorium. 90 c. Moorish horseman. 1 p. 10, Aeroplane over sea. 5 p. Arab swordsman.

1953.
408. **46.** 5 c. red 10 10
409. 10 c. green 10 10

1953. 25th Anniv. of 1st Pictorial Stamps of Spanish Morocco.
410. – 25 c. purple and green .. 10 10
411. **47.** 50 c. green and red .. 10 10
412. – 90 c. orange and blue .. 10 10
413. – 1 p. green and brown .. 10 10
414. – 1 p. 25 mauve and green 10 10
415. – 2 p. blue and purple .. 20 20
416. **47.** 2 p. 50 orange and grey 50 20
417. – 4 p. 50 green and mauve 2·25 30
418. – 10 p. black and green .. 2·50 85
DESIGNS—VERT. 35 c., 1 p. 25, Mountain women. 90 c., 2 p. Mountain tribesmen. 1 p. 4 p. 50, Veiled Moorish women. 10 p. Arab dignitary.

1954. Anti-T.B. Fund. As T **32**, but inscr. "PRO TUBERCULOSOS 1954". Frame in red.
419. 5 c turquoise 10 10
420. 5 c.+5 c. purple 50 25
421. 10 c. sepia 10 10
422. 25 c. blue 15 15
423. 50 c.+10 c. green 50 40
424. 5 p.+2 p. black .. .. 4·75 3·50
DESIGNS: 5 c. Convent. 5 c.+ 5 c. White Stork on a tower. 10 c. Moroccan family. 25 c. Aeroplane over Spanish coast. 50 c. Father and child. 5 p. Chapel.

48. Saida Gate. **49.** Celebrations.

1955. Frames in black.
425. – 15 c. green 10 10
426. **48.** 25 c. purple 10 10
427. – 80 c. blue 10 10
428. **48.** 1 p. mauve 20 10
429. – 15 p. turquoise .. .. 2·40 85
DESIGNS: 15 c., 80 c. Queen's Gate. 15 p. Ceuta Gate.

1955. 30th Anniv. of Caliph's Accession.
430. **49.** 15 c. olive and brown .. 10 10
431. – 25 c. lake and purple .. 10 10
432. – 30 c. green and sepia .. 10 10
433. **49.** 70 c. green and myrtle .. 10 10
434. – 80 c. brown and olive .. 10 10
435. – 1 p. brown and blue .. 10 10
436. **49.** 1 p. 80 violet and black 20 10
437. – 3 p. grey and blue .. 20 10
438. – 5 p. brown and myrtle .. 1·25 40
439. – 15 p. green and brown .. 2·40 1·40
DESIGNS: 25 c. 80 c., 3 p. Caliph's portrait. 30 c., 1 p., 5 p. Procession. 15 p. Coat of Arms.

EXPRESS LETTER STAMPS
Express Letter Stamps of Spain overprinted.

1914. Optd. **MARRUECOS.**
E 55. E **53.** 20 c. red .. .. 2·50 1·00

1915. Optd. **PROTECTORADO ESPANOL EN MARRUECOS.**
E 68. E **53.** 20 c. red .. .. 1·75 80

1923. Optd. **ZONA DE PROTECTORADO ESPANOL EN MARRUECOS.**
E 111. E **53.** 20 c. red .. .. 6·00 3·25

1926. Red Cross. Optd. **ZONA PROTECTORADO ESPANOL.**
E 124. E **77.** 20 c. black and blue 1·50 1·25

E **12.** Moorish Courier.

1928.
E 138. E **12.** 20 c. black .. 2·00 1·50

E **16.** E **19.** Moorish Courier. E **21.**

1935.
E 171. E **16.** 20 c. red 85 10

1937. 1st Anniv. of Civil War.
E 200. E **19.** 20 c. red 10 10

1940.
E 233. E **21.** 25 c. red 30 20

1940. No. E 200 optd. as Nos. 233/48 and surch. also.
E 249. E **19.** 25 c. on 20 c. red .. 9·00 9·00

E **37.** Air Mail 1935. E **41.** Moorish Courier.

1950. 75th Anniv. of U.P.U.
E 351. E **37.** 25 c. black and red .. 10·00 10·00

1952.
E 382. E **41.** 25 c. red 10 10

E **48.** Moorish Courier. E **49.** Tangier Gate.

1953. 25th Anniv. of First Pictorial Stamps of Spanish Morocco.
E 419. E **48.** 25 c. mauve & blue 20 25

1955.
E 430. E **49.** 2 p. violet and black 15 10

For later issues see **MOROCCO.**

SPANISH POST OFFICES IN TANGIER Pt. 9

See note below No. 41 of Spanish P.O.s in Morocco, concerning the exclusive use of Nos. 30/41 in Tangier after 1914.

Postage stamps of Spain overprinted.

1921. Optd. **CORREO ESPANOL MARRUECOS.**
1. **66.** 1 c. green 20 10
2. **64.** 2 c. brown £225
3. 15 c. yellow .. .. 1·50 10
4. 20 c. violet .. .. 2·25 10

1939. Optd as 1921.
5 **68** 2 c. green .. .. 2·25 10
6 5 c. purple .. .. 2·25 10
7 5 c. red .. .. 2·25 10
8a 10 c. green .. .. 2·25 20
10 20 c. violet .. .. 4·50 10
11 50 c. orange .. .. 20·00 2·25
12 **69** 10 p. brown .. .. 2·50 2·50

1926. Red Cross stamps optd. **CORREO ESPANOL TANGER.**
13. **70.** 1 c. orange .. .. 2·75 2·50
14. – 2 c. red .. .. 2·75 2·50
15. – 5 c. grey .. .. 1·50 1·00
16. – 10 c. green .. .. 1·50 1·00
17. **70.** 15 c. violet 70 50
18. – 20 c. purple 70 50
19. **71.** 25 c. red 70 50
20. **70.** 30 c. olive 75 50
21. – 40 c. blue 25 25
22. – 50 c. brown 25 25
23. – 1 p. red 35 30
24. – 4 p. brown 45 40
25. **71.** 10 p. lilac .. .. 1·75 1·25

1929. Seville-Barcelona Exhibition stamps, Nos. 504/14 optd. **TANGER.**
27. 5 c. red 10 10
28. 10 c. green 10 10
29. 15 c. blue 25 10
30. 20 c. violet 10 10
31. 25 c. red 25 10
32. 30 c. brown 15 10
33. 40 c. blue 25 25
34. 50 c. orange 25 25
35. 1 p. grey .. .. 2·50 2·50
36. 4 p. red .. .. 5·75 4·50
37. 10 p. brown .. .. 8·50 6·50

1930. Optd. as 1921.
38. **97.** 10 c. green .. .. 3·50 20
39. 15 c. turquoise .. .. 80·00 50
40. 20 c. violet .. .. 2·50 25
41. 30 c. red .. .. 2·75 45
42. 40 c. blue .. .. 10·00 2·75

1933. Optd. **MARRUECOS.**
43. **143.** 1 c. green (imperf.) .. 15 10
44. 2 c. brown 15 10
45. **127.** 5 c. brown 15 10
46. **128.** 10 c. green 15 10
47. **130.** 15 c. blue 15 10
48. **127.** 20 c. violet 15 10
49. **132.** 25 c. red 15 10
50. **133.** 30 c. red .. .. 32·00 2·50
51. **138.** 40 c. blue 30 10
52. **130.** 50 c. orange 70 10
53. **138.** 60 c. green 70 10
54. **142.** 1 p. black 70 10
55. – 4 p. mauve .. .. 2·00 1·25
56. – 10 p. brown .. .. 2·75 2·75

1937. Optd. **TANGER.**
58. **143.** 1 c. green (imperf.) .. 25 10
59. 2 c. brown 35 10
60. **127.** 5 c. brown 35 10
61. **128.** 10 c. green 35 10
62. **130.** 15 c. blue 40 35
63. **127.** 20 c. violet 40 35
64. **132.** 25 c. red 40 10
65. **136.** 30 c. red 40 35
66. **138.** 40 c. blue .. .. 1·10 35
67. **130.** 50 c. orange .. .. 2·75 35
68. **142.** 1 p. black .. .. 4·75 2·00
69. – 4 p. mauve (No. 768c) .. £140
70. – 10 p. brown (No. 769c) .. £190

1938. Optd. **Correo Espanol Tanger.**
71. **143.** 5 c. brown .. .. 1·00 50
72. 10 c. green .. .. 1·25 50
73. 15 c. green .. .. 1·10 50
74. 20 c. violet .. .. 1·10 35
75. 25 c. mauve .. .. 1·25 35
76. 30 c. red .. .. 4·40 1·75
77. **160a.** 40 c. red .. .. 2·25 75
78. 45 c. red .. .. 1·10 20
79. 50 c. blue .. .. 1·25 20
80. 60 c. blue .. .. 2·75 75
81. **145.** 2 p. blue .. .. 20·00 6·00
82. – 4 p. mauve (No. 768c) 18·00 7·50

1938. Air. Optd. **Correo Aereo TANGER.**
83. **143.** 25 c. mauve 75 25
84. **160a.** 50 c. blue 75 25

1938. Air. Optd. **CORREO AEREO TANGER.**
86. **142.** 1 p. black 85 25
85. **145.** 2 p. blue .. .. 6·50 1·40
87. – 4 p. mauve (No. 768c) .. 5·50 1·75
88. – 10 p. brown (No. 769c) .. 32·00 22·00

1939. Optd. **Tanger.**
89. **143.** 5 c. brown 30 20
90. 10 c. green 30 20
91. 15 c. green 30 20
92. 20 c. violet 30 20
93. 25 c. mauve 30 20
94. 30 c. red 30 20
95. **160a.** 40 c. red 30 20
96. 45 c. red 30 20
97. 50 c. blue 90 55
98. 60 c. blue 40 20
99. **142.** 1 p. black 65 30
100. **145.** 2 p. blue .. .. 17·00 9·00
101. – 4 p. mauve (No. 768c) 16·00 8·50
102. – 10 p. brown (No. 769c) 17·00 11·00

1939. Air. Optd. **Via Aerea Tanger.**
103. **143.** 5 c. brown 45 40
104. 10 c. green 45 40
105. 15 c. green 40 35
106. 20 c. violet 40 35
107. 25 c. mauve 40 35
108. 30 c. red 80 50
109. **160a.** 40 c. red .. .. 28·00
110. 45 c. red 20 20
111. 50 c. blue .. .. 55·00
112. 60 c. blue .. .. 55·00 12·00
113. **142.** 1 p. black .. .. 20·00
114. – 4 p. mauve (No. 768c) 25·00 17·00
115. – 10 p. brown (No. 769c) 80·00

1939. Air. Express Letter stamp optd. **Via Aerea Tanger.**
116. E **145.** 20 c. red .. .. 1·75 1·00

1939. Various fiscal types inscr. "DERECHOS CONSULARES ESPANOLES" optd. **Correo Tanger.**
117. 50 c. pink .. .. 12·00 10·00
118. 1 p. pink .. .. 2·75 2·25
119. 2 p. pink .. .. 2·50 2·25
120. 5 p. red and green .. 3·50 2·75
121. 10 p. red and violet .. 16·00 13·00

1939. Air. Various fiscal types inscr. "DERECHOS CONSULARES ESPANOLES" optd. **Correo Aereo Tanger.**
122. 1 p. blue .. .. 32·00 30·00
123. 2 p. blue .. .. 30·00 30·00
124. 5 p. blue .. .. 4·50 4·50
125. 10 p. blue .. .. 4·75 4·50

15. Moroccan Woman. **16.** Twin-engined Aeroplane.

1948.
126. – 1 c. green 10 10
127. – 2 c. orange 10 10
128. – 5 c. purple 10 10
129. – 10 c. blue 10 10
130. – 20 c. sepia 15 10
131. – 25 c. green 15 10
132. – 30 c. grey 45 10
133. – 45 c. red 45 10
134. **15.** 50 c. red 40 10
135. – 75 c. blue 75 10
136. – 90 c. green 55 10
137. – 1 p. 35 red .. .. 1·90 30
138. **15.** 2 p. violet .. .. 3·25 35
139. – 10 p. green .. .. 3·75 55
DESIGNS: 1 c., 2 c. Woman's head facing right. 5 c., 25 c. Palm tree. 10 c., 20 c. Woman's head facing left. 30 c., 1 p. 35, Old map of Tangier. 45 c., 10 p. Street scene. 75 c., 90 c. Head of Moor.

1949. Air.
140. – 20 c. brown 45 10
141. **16.** 25 c. red 45 10
142. – 35 c. green 50 10
143. – 1 p. violet .. .. 1·25 10
144. **16.** 2 p. green .. .. 2·50 30
145. – 10 p. purple .. .. 3·25 1·10
DESIGNS: 20 c., 1 p. Aeroplane and map. 35 c., 10 p. Aeroplane in clouds.

EXPRESS LETTER STAMPS
Express Letter Stamps of Spain overprinted.

1926. Red Cross. Optd. **CORREO ESPANOL TANGER.**
E 26. E **77.** 20 c. black and blue 1·50 1·10

1933. No. E 17 optd. **MARRUECOS.**
E 57. E **145.** 20 c. red .. .. 1·25 20

E **17.** Courier

1949
E 146. E **17.** 25 c. red 60 20

SPANISH SAHARA Pt. 9

Former Spanish territory on the north-west coast of Africa, previously called Rio de Oro. Later divided between Morocco and Mauritania.

100 centimos = 1 peseta.

1. Tuareg and Camel.

1924.
1. **1.** 5 c. green .. .. 1·40 30
2. 10 c. green .. .. 1·40 30
3. 15 c. blue .. .. 1·40 30
4. 20 c. violet .. .. 1·40 35
5. 25 c. red .. .. 1·40 35
6. 30 c. brown .. .. 1·40 35
7. 40 c. blue .. .. 1·40 35
8. 50 c. orange .. .. 1·40 35
9. 60 c. purple .. .. 1·40 35
10. 1 p. red .. .. 6·50 1·75
11. 4 p. brown .. .. 32·00 10·00
12. 10 p. purple .. .. 65·00 28·00

1926. Red Cross stamps of Spain optd. **SAHARA ESPANOL.**
13. – 5 c. grey .. .. 3·75 3·25
14. – 10 c. green .. .. 3·75 3·25
15. **70.** 15 c. violet .. .. 1·40 1·00
16. – 20 c. purple .. .. 1·40 1·00
17. **71.** 25 c. red .. .. 1·40 1·00
18. **70.** 30 c. olive .. .. 1·40 1·00
19. – 40 c. blue 15 20
20. – 50 c. brown 15 20
21. **71.** 60 c. green 15 20
22. – 1 p. red 15 20
23. – 4 p. brown .. .. 1·10 75
24. **71.** 10 p. lilac .. .. 3·25 2·50

1929. Seville and Barcelona Exn. stamps of Spain. Nos. 504/14, optd. **SAHARA.**
25. 5 c. red 10 15
26. 10 c. green 10 15
27. 15 c. blue 10 15
28. 20 c. violet 10 15
29. 25 c. red 10 15
30. 30 c. brown 10 15
31. 40 c. blue 25 25
32. 50 c. orange 25 25
33. 1 p. grey .. .. 1·00 1·00
34. 4 p. red .. .. 6·50 4·50
35. 10 p. brown .. .. 12·00 9·00

1931. Optd. **Republica Espanola.**
36. **1.** 5 c. green 40 35
37. 10 c. green 40 35
38. 15 c. blue 45 35
39. 20 c. violet 45 35
40. 25 c. red 45 35
41. 30 c. brown 45 35
42. 40 c. blue .. .. 2·75 45
43. 50 c. orange .. .. 3·00 1·25
44. 60 c. purple .. .. 3·25 1·10
45. 1 p. red .. .. 3·00 1·00
46. 4 p. brown .. .. 25·00 10·00
47. 10 p. purple .. .. 45·00 15·00

1941. Stamps of Spain optd. SAHARA ESPAÑOL.
47a. 181. 1 c. green .. .. 1·40 1·40
47b. 182. 2 c. brown .. .. 1·40 1·40
48. 183. 5 c. brown 35 35
49. 10 c. red .. .. 1·40 1·40
50. 15 c. green 35 35
51. 196. 20 c. violet 35 35
52. 25 c. red 85 70
53. 30 c. blue 85 80
54. 40 c. green 35 35
55. 50 c. blue .. .. 4·00 85
56. 70 c. blue .. .. 3·00 1·40
57. 1 PTA. black .. 13·00 2·00
58. 2 PTAS. brown .. 70·00 40·00
59. 4 PTAS. red .. .. £140 90·00
60. 10 PTS. brown .. £350 £120

6. Dorcas Gazelles. 7. Ostriches.

1943.
61. 6. 1 c. mauve & brown (post.) 10 10
62. – 2 c. blue and green .. 10 10
63. – 5 c. blue and red .. 10 10
64. 6. 15 c. green and myrtle .. 15 15
65. – 20 c. brown and mauve .. 15 15
66. 6. 40 c. mauve and purple .. 15 15
67. – 45 red and purple .. 25 25
68. – 75 c. blue and indigo .. 35 35
69. 6. 1 p. brown and red .. 1·10 1·10
70. – 3 p. green and violet .. 2·25 2·00
71. – 10 p. black and sepia .. 24·00 20·00
DESIGNS—VERT. 2 c., 20 c., 45 c., 3 p. Camel caravan. 5 c., 75 c., 10 p. Camel troops.
72. 7. 5 c. brown and red (air) .. 75 30
73. – 25 c. olive and green .. 20 15
74. 7. 50 c. turquoise and blue .. 1·50 40
75. – 1 p. blue and mauve .. 50 25
76. 7. 1 p. 40 blue and green .. 2·00 45
77. – 2 p. brown and purple .. 85 85
78. 7. 5 p. mauve and brown .. 4·75 2·50
79. – 6 p. green and blue .. 18·00 16·00
DESIGN: 25 c., 1 p., 2 p., 6 p. Aeroplane and camels.

8. Boy Carrying Lamb. 9. Diego de Herrera.

1950. Child Welfare.
80. 8. 50 c.+10 c. brown .. 25 20
81. 1 p.+25 c. red .. 11·00 4·75
82. 6 p. 50+1 p. 65 green .. 6·00 1·60

1950. Air. Colonial Stamp Day.
83. 9. 5 p. violet .. .. .. 2·75 1·00

9a. Woman and Dove. 9b. General Franco.

1951. Air. 500th Birth Anniv. of Isabella the Catholic.
84. 9a. 5 p. green .. .. 25·00 5·50

1951. Visit of Gen. Franco.
85. 9b. 50 c. orange 10 10
86. 1 p. brown 35 35
87. 5 p. turquoise .. .. 38·00 12·00

10. Dromedary and Calf. 11. Native Woman. 12. Morion, Sword and Banner.

1951. Colonial Stamp Day.
88. 10. 5 c.+5 c. brown 10 10
89. 10 c.+5 c. orange 10 10
90. 60 c.+15 c. olive 30 10

1952. Child Welfare Fund.
91. 11. 5 c.+5 c. brown 10 10
92. 50 c.+10 c. black 10 10
93. 2 p.+30 c. blue .. .. 1·75 90

1952. Air. 500th Birth Anniv. of Ferdinand the Catholic.
94. 12. 5 p. brown .. .. 30·00 6·00

13. Head of Ostrich. 14. "Geography". 15. Woman Musician.

1952. Colonial Stamp Day.
95. 13. 5 c.+5 c. brown 15 10
96. 10 c.+5 c. red 25 10
97. 60 c.+15 c. green 50 20

1953. 75th Anniv. of Royal Geographical Society.
98. 14. 5 c. red 10 10
99. 35 c. green 10 10
100. 60 c. brown 20 10

1953. Child Welfare Fund. Inscr. "PRO INFANCIA 1953".
101. 15. 5 c.+5 c. brown .. 10 10
102. – 10 c.+5 c. purple .. 10 10
103. 15. 15 c. olive 10 10
104. – 60 c. brown 15 10
DESIGN: 10 c., 60 c. Native man musician.

16.
DESIGN—HORIZ. 10 c., 60 c. Two fishes.

1953. Colonial Stamp Day. Inscr. "DIA DEL SELLO COLONIAL 1953".
105. 16. 5 c.+5 c. violet .. 10 10
106. – 10 c.+5 c. green .. 15 10
107. 16. 15 c. olive 15 10
108. – 60 c. orange 15 10

17. Hurdlers.

1954. Child Welfare Fund. Inscr. "PRO INFANCIA 1954".
109. 17. 5 c.+5 c. brown .. 10 10
110. – 10 c.+5 c. violet .. 10 10
111. 17. 15 c. green 10 10
112. – 60 c. brown 10 10
DESIGN—VERT. 10, 60 c. Native runner.

18. Flying Fish.

1954. Colonial Stamp Day. Inscr. "DIA DEL SELLO COLONIAL 1954".
113. 18. 5 c.+5 c. red 10 10
114. – 10 c.+5 c. purple .. 15 10
115. 18. 15 c. green 15 10
116. – 60 c. brown 20 10
DESIGN—HORIZ. 10, 60 c. "Sparus auratus" (fish).

19. E. Bonelli.
DESIGN: 25 c. Bonelli and Felucca.

1955. Birth Cent. of Bonelli (explorer).
117. 19. 10 c.+5 c. purple .. 10 10
118. – 25 c.+10 c. violet .. 10 10
119. 19. 50 c. olive 10 10

20. Scimitar Oryx. 21. "Antirrhinum Ramosissimum".

1955. Colonial Stamp Day. Inscr. "DIA DEL SELLO COLONIAL 1955".
120. 20. 5 c.+5 c. brown .. 10 10
121. – 15 c.+5 c. bistre .. 15 10
122. 20. 70 c. green 25 10
DESIGN: 15 c. Scimitar oryx's head.

1956. Child Welfare Fund. Inscr. "PRO-INFANCIA 1956".
123. 21. 5 c.+5 c. olive 10 10
124. – 15 c.+5 c. ochre .. 10 10
125. 21. 20 c. turquoise 15 10
126. – 50 c. brown 20 10
DESIGN: 15 c., 50 c. "Sesuvium portulacastrum" (wrongly inscr. "Sesivium").

22. Arms of Aaiun and Native on Camel. 23. Dromedaries.

1956. Colonial Stamp Day. Inscr. "DIA DEL SELLO 1956".
127. 22. 5 c.+5 c. blk. & violet .. 10 10
128. – 15 c.+5 c. green & ochre 15 10
129. 22. 70 c. brown and green .. 15 10
DESIGN—VERT. 15 c. Arms of Villa Cisneros and native chief.

1957. Animals.
130. 23. 5 c. violet 10 10
131. – 15 c. ochre 50 10
132. – 50 c. brown 10 10
133. 23. 70 c. green .. .. 1·25 20
134. – 80 c. turquoise .. .. 2·50 20
135. – 1 p. 80 mauve .. .. 1·25 20
DESIGNS: 15 c., 80 c. Ostrich. 50 c., 1 p. 80, Dorcas gazelle.

24. Golden Eagle. 25. Head of Striped Hyena.

1957. Child Welfare Fund. Inscr. "PRO-INFANCIA 1957".
136. 24. 5 c.+5 c. brown .. 15 10
137. – 15 c.+5 c. bistre .. 20 15
138. 24. 70 c. green 40 30
DESIGN: 15 c. Tawny Eagle in flight.

1957. Colonial Stamp Day. Inscr. DIA DEL SELLO 1957".
139. 25. 10 c.+5 c. purple .. 10 10
140. – 15 c.+5 c. ochre .. 10 10
141. 25. 20 c. green 10 10
142. – 70 c. myrtle 15 10
DESIGN: 15 c., 70 c. Striped hyena.

26. White Stork and Arms of Valencia and Aaiun. 27. Cervantes.

1958. Aid for Valencia.
143. 26. 10 c.+5 c. brown .. 20 10
144. 15 c.+10 c. ochre .. 20 10
145. 50 c.+10 c. brown .. 25 10

1958. Child Welfare Fund. Inscr. "1958".
146. 27. 10 c.+5 c. brn. & chest. 10 10
147. – 15 c.+5 c. myrtle & orge. 10 10
148. – 20 c. green & brown .. 10 10
149. 27. 50 c. green & yellow .. 10 10
DESIGNS—VERT. 15 c. Don Quixote and Sancho Panza on horseback. HORIZ. 20 c. Don Quixote and the lion.

28. Hoopoe Lark. 29. Lope de Vega (author). 30. Grey Heron.

1958. Colonial Stamp Day. Inscr. "1958".
150. 28. 10 c.+5 c. red 25 15
151. – 25 c.+10 c. violet .. 25 15
152. – 50 c.+10 c. olive .. 25 15
DESIGNS—HORIZ. 25 c. Hoopoe lark feeding young. VERT. 50 c. Fulvous babbler.

1959. Child Welfare Fund. Inscr. "PRO INFANCIA 1959".
153. 29. 10 c.+5 c. olive & brn. 10 10
154. – 15 c.+5 c. brn. & bistre 10 10
155. – 20 c. sepia and green .. 10 10
156. 29. 70 c. myrtle and green .. 10 10
DESIGNS—Characters from the comedy "The Star of Seville": 15 c. Spanish lady. 20 c. Caballero.

1959. Birds.
157. 30. 25 c. violet 15 10
158. – 50 c. green 15 10
159. – 75 c. sepia 15 10
160. 30. 1 p. red 15 10
161. – 1 p. 50 green 15 10
162. – 2 p. purple .. .. 1·75 10
163. 30. 3 p. blue .. .. 1·75 15
164. – 5 p. brown .. .. 3·25 35
165. – 10 p. olive .. .. 10·00 5·75
DESIGNS: 50 c., 1 p. 50, 5 p. European Sparrowhawk. 75 c., 2 p., 10 p. Herring gull.

31. Saharan Postman. 32. F. de Quevedo (writer).

1959. Colonial Stamp Day. Inscr. "1959".
166. 31. 10 c.+5 c. brn. & red .. 10 10
167. – 20 c.+5 c. brn. & grn. 10 10
168. – 50 c.+20 c. slate & olive 10 10
DESIGNS: 20 c. Postman tendering letters. 50 c. Camel postman.

1960. Child Welfare Fund. Inscr. "PRO-INFANCIA 1960".
169. 32. 10 c.+5 c. purple .. 10 10
170. – 15 c.+5 c. bistre .. 10 10
171. – 35 c. green 10 10
172. 32. 80 c. turquoise 10 10
DESIGNS — VERT. (representing Quevedo's works): 15 c. Winged wheel and hour-glass. 25 c. Man in plumed hat wearing cloak and sword.

33. Leopard. 34. Houbara Bustard. 35. Cameleer and Plane.

1960. Stamp Day. Inscr. "1960".
173. 33. 10 c.+5 c. mauve .. 10 10
174. – 20 c.+5 c.myrtle .. 10 10
175. – 30 c.+10 c. brown .. 35 15
176. – 50 c.+20 c. brown .. 20 10
DESIGNS: 20 c. Fennec fox. 30 c. Golden eagle defying leopard. 50 c. Red fox.

1961.
177. 34. 25 c. violet 15 10
178. – 50 c. brown 15 10
179. 34. 75 c. dull purple .. 15 10
180. – 1 p. red 15 10
181. 34. 1 p. 50 green 15 15
182. – 2 p. mauve .. .. 1·40 15
183. 34. 3 p. blue .. .. 2·25 15
184. – 5 p. brown .. .. 2·50 50
185. 34. 10 p. olive .. .. 4·75 1·50
DESIGN: 50 c., 1 p., 2 p., 5 p. Rock doves.

1961. Air.
186. 35. 25 p. sepia .. .. 3·25 85

36. Dorcas Gazelle. 37.

1961. Child Welfare. Inscr. "PRO-INFANCIA 1961".
187. 36. 10 c.+5 c. red 10 10
188. – 25 c.+10 c. violet .. 15 10
189. 36. 80 c.+20 c. green .. 15 10
DESIGN: 25 c. One dorcas gazelle.

1961. 25th Anniv. of Gen. Franco as Head of State.
190. – 25 c. grey 10 10
191. **37.** 50 c. olive 10 10
192. – 70 c. green 10 10
193. **37.** 1 p. orange 10 10
DESIGNS—VERT. 25 c. Map. 7 c. Aaiun Chapel.

38. A. Fernandez de Lugo. **39.** "Neurada procumbres linn". **40.** Two Barred Fishes.

1961. Stamp Day. Inscr. "DIA DEL SELLO 1961".
194. **38.** 10 c.+5 c. salmon .. 10 10
195. – 25 c.+10 c. plum .. 10 10
196. **38.** 30 c.+10 c. brown .. 10 10
197. – 1 p.+10 c. orange .. 15 10
PORTRAIT: 25 c., 1 p. D. de Herrera.

1962. Flowers.
198. **39.** 25 c. violet 10 10
199. – 50 c. sepia 10 10
200. – 70 c. green 10 10
201. **39.** 1 p. orange 10 10
202. – 1 p. 50 turquoise .. 50 10
203. – 2 p. purple .. .. 1·75 10
204. **39.** 3 p. blue .. .. 2·50 30
205. – 10 p. olive .. .. 5·00 1·40
FLOWERS: 50 c., 1 p. 50, 10 p. "Anabasis articulata moq". 70 c., 2 p. "Euphorbia resinifera".

1962. Child Welfare.
206. **40.** 25 c. violet 10 10
207. – 50 c. green 15 10
208. **40.** 1 p. brown 15 10
DESIGN—HORIZ. 50 c. Two fishes.

41. Goats. **42.** Seville Cathedral.

1962. Stamp Day.
209. **41.** 15 c. green 10 10
210. – 35 c. purple 10 10
211. **41.** 1 p. brown 15 10
DESIGN: 35 c. Sheep.

1963. Seville Flood Relief
212. **42.** 50 c. olive 15 10
213. 1 p. brown 10 10

43. Cameleer and Camel. **44.** Dove in Hands.

1963. Child Welfare. Inscr. "PRO-INFANCIA 1963".
214. – 25 c. violet 10 10
215. **43.** 50 c. grey 10 10
216. – 1 p. red 15 10
DESIGN: 25 c., 1 p. Three camels.

1963. "For Barcelona".
217. **44.** 50 c. turquoise 10 10
218. 1 p. brown 10 10

45. Fish ("Zeus faber"). **46.** "Hyles lineata". **47.** Mounted Dromedary and Microphone.

1964. Stamp Day. Inscr. "DIA DEL SELLO 1963".
219. **45.** 25 c. violet 15 10
220. – 50 c. olive 20 10
221. **45.** 1 p. brown 30 10
FISH—VERT. 50 c. "Cossus pulchra".

1964. Child Welfare.
222. **46.** 25 c. violet 15 10
223. – 50 c. olive 25 10
224. **46.** 1 p. red 25 10
DESIGN—VERT. 50 c. Carpenter moths.

1964.
225. **47.** 25 c. purple 10 10
226. – 50 c. olive 10 10
227. – 70 c. green 10 10
228. **47.** 1 p. purple 10 10
229. – 1 p. 50 turquoise .. 10 10
230. – 2 p. turquoise 25 15
231. – 3 p. blue 35 15
232. – 10 p. lake .. .. 2·00 85
DESIGNS: 50 c., 1 p. 50, 3 p. Flute-player. 70 c., 2 p., 10 p. Women drummer.

48. Barbary Ground Squirrel.

1964. Stamp Day.
233. – 50 c. olive 10 10
234. **48.** 1 p. lake 15 10
235. – 1 p. 50 green 15 10
DESIGN—VERT. 50 c., 1 p. 50, Eurasian red squirrel eating.

49. Doctor tending Patient, and Hospital.

1965. 25th Anniv. of End of Spanish Civil War.
236. – 50 c. olive 10 10
237. **49.** 1 p. red 15 10
238. – 1 p. 50 blue 15 10
DESIGNS—VERT. 50 c. Saharan Woman. 1 p. 50, Desert Installation and Cameleer.

50. "Anthia sexmaculata". **51.** Handball.

1965. Child Welfare. Insects.
239. **50.** 50 c. blue 10 10
240. – 1 p. green 10 10
241. **50.** 1 p. 50 brown 15 10
242. – 3 p. blue .. .. 1·25 60
INSECTS—VERT. 1 p., 3 p. "Blepharopsis mendica".

1965. Stamp Day.
243. **51.** 50 c. red 10 10
244. – 1 p. purple 15 10
245. **51.** 1 p. 50 blue 20 10
DESIGN: 1 p. Arms of Spanish Sahara.

52. Bows of "Rio de Oro".

1966. Child Welfare.
246. **52.** 50 c. olive 10 10
247. 1 p. brown 10 10
248. – 1 p. 50 green 15 10
DESIGN: 1 p. 50, Freighter "Fuerta Ventura".

53. "Parathunnus obesus" (fish). **54.** Fig.

1966. Stamp Day.
249. **53.** 10 c. blue and yellow .. 10 10
250. – 40 c. grey and salmon .. 15 10
251. **53.** 1 p. 50 brown and green 25 10
252. – 4 p. purple and green .. 30 10
DESIGN—VERT. 40 c., 4 p. "Mola mola" (fish).

1967. Child Welfare.
253. **54.** 10 c. yellow and blue .. 10 10
254. – 40 c. purple and green .. 10 10
255. **54.** 1 p. 50 yellow and green 20 10
256. – 4 p. orange and blue .. 35 10
DESIGN: 40 c., 4 p. Lupin.

55. Quay, Aaiun.

1967. Inaug. of Sahara Ports.
257. **55.** 1 p. 50 brown and blue 10 10
258. – 4 p. ochre and blue .. 20 10
DESIGN: 4 p. Port of Villa Cisneros.

56. Ruddy Shelduck. **56a.** Scorpio (scorpion).

1968. Stamp Day.
259. **56.** 1 p. brown and green .. 25 10
260. – 1 p. 50 mauve and black 35 15
261. – 3 p. 50 lake and brown 45 30
DESIGNS—VERT. 1 p. 50, Greater flamingo. HORIZ. 3 p. 50, Rufous bushchat.

1968. Child Welfare. Signs of the Zodiac.
262. **56a.** 1 p. mauve on yellow 20 10
263. – 1 p. 50 brown on pink 25 10
264. – 2 p. 50 violet on yell. 35 15
DESIGNS: 1 p. 50, Capricorn (goat). 2 p. 50, Virgo (virgin).

57. Dove, and Stamp within Posthorn. **58.** Head of Dorcas Gazelle.

1968. Stamp Day.
265. **57.** 1 p. blue and purple .. 10 10
266. – 1 p. 50 grn. & light grn. 10 10
267. – 2 p. 50 blue and orange 20 10
DESIGNS: 1 p. 50, Postal handstamp, stamps and letter. 2 p. 50, Saharan postman.

1969. Child Welfare.
268. **58.** 1 p. brown and black .. 15 10
269. – 1 p. 50 brown and black 25 10
270. – 2 p. 50 brown and black 25 10
271. – 6 p. brown and black .. 40 20
DESIGNS: 1 p. 50, Dorcas gazelle tending young. 2 p. 50, Dorcas gazelle and camel. 6 p. Dorcas gazelle leaping.

59. Woman beating Drum. **61.** Dorcas Gazelle and Arms of El Aaiun.

60. "Grammodes boisdeffrei".

1960. Stamp Day.
272. **59.** 50 c. brown and bistre .. 15 10
273. – 1 p. 50 turquoise & green 15 10
274. – 2 p. blue and brown .. 15 30
275. – 25 p. brown and green .. 1·50 30
DESIGNS—VERT. 1 p. 50, Man playing flute. HORIZ. 2 p. Drum and mounted cameleer. 25 p. Flute.

1970. Child Welfare. As T **58.**
276. 50 c. ochre and blue .. 20 10
277. 2 p. brown and blue .. 25 10
278. 2 p. 50 ochre and blue .. 35 10
279. 6 p. ochre and blue .. 45 20
DESIGNS: 50 c. Fennec fox. 2 p. Fennec fox walking. 2 p. 50, Head of Fennec fox. 6 p. Fennec fox family.

1970. Stamp Day. Butterflies. Mult.
280. 50 c. Type **60** 20 10
281. 1 p. Type **60** 30 10
282. 2 p. "Danaus chrysippus" .. 30 10
283. 5 p. As 2 p. .. 45 10
284. 8 p. "Celerio euphorbiae" 65 20

1971. Child Welfare.
285. **61.** 1 p. multicoloured .. 10 10
286. – 2 p. green and olive .. 10 10
287. – 5 p. blue, brown & grey 15 10
288. – 25 p. green, grey & blue 90 20
DESIGNS—VERT. 25 p. Smara Mosque. HORIZ. 2 p. Tourist Inn, Aaiun. 5 p. Assembly House, Aaiun.

63. Trumpeter Finch.

1971. Stamp Day. Multicoloured.
290. 1 p. 50 Type **63** 40 15
291. 2 p. Type **63** 60 15
292. 5 p. Cream-coloured Courser 80 20
293. 24 p. Lanner Falcon .. 2·50 45

64. Seated Woman. **65.** Tuareg Woman.

1972. Saharan Nomads.
294. **64.** 1 p. blk., pink & blue .. 10 10
295. – 1 p. 50 slate, lilac & brn. 10 10
296. – 2 p. blk., flesh & green .. 10 10
297. **64.** 5 p. purple, ol. & grn. 10 10
298. – 8 p. violet, green & blk. 25 10
299. – 10 p. grn., grey & blk. .. 40 10
300. – 12 p. multicoloured .. 45 20
301. – 15 p. multicoloured .. 55 30
302. – 24 p. multicoloured .. 1·10 40
DESIGNS: 1 p. 50, 2 p. Squatting nomad. 8 p. 10 p. Head of Nomad. 12 p. Woman with bangles. 15 p. Nomad with rifle. 24 p. Woman displaying trinkets.

1972. Child Welfare. Multicoloured.
303. 8 p. Type **65** 30 10
304. 12 p. Tuareg elder .. 40 20

66. Mother and Child. **67.** Sahara Desert.

1972. Stamp Day. Multicoloured.
305. 4 p. Type **66** 20 10
306. 15 p. Nomad 50 20

1973. Child Welfare. Multicoloured.
307. 2 p. Type **67** 15 10
308. 7 p. City Gate, El Aaiun .. 20 10

68. Villa Cisneros.

1973. Stamp Day. Multicoloured.
309. 2 p. Type **68** 10 10
310. 7 p. Tuareg (vert.) .. 20 10

69. U.P.U. Monument, Berne.
70. Archway, Smara Mosque.

1974. Cent. of Universal Postal Union.
311. 69. 15 p. multicoloured .. 45 15

1974. Child Welfare. Multicoloured.
312. 1 p. Type 70 .. .. 10 10
313. 2 p. Villa Cisneros Mosque 15 10

71. Eagle Owl.

1974. Stamp Day. Multicoloured.
314. 2 p. Type 71 .. .. 65 10
315. 5 p. Lappet-faced Vulture 1·10 15

72. "Espana" Emblem and Spanish Sahara Stamp.
74. Tuareg Elder.

73. Desert Conference.

1975. "Espana 75" International Stamp Exhibition, Madrid.
316. 72. 8 p. yellow, blue & blk. 30 10

1975. Child Welfare. Multicoloured.
317. 1 p. 50 Type 73 .. .. 15 10
318. 3 p. Desert oasis 15 10

1975.
319. 74. 3 p. pur., grn and blk... 15 10

EXPRESS LETTER STAMP

1943. Design as No. 63 inscr. "URGENTE".
E 80. 25 c. red and myrtle .. 70 70

E 62. Despatch-rider.

1971.
E 289. E 62. 10 p. brown and red 65 30

MORE DETAILED LISTS

are given in the Stanley Gibbons Catalogues referred to in the country headings.
For lists of current volumes see Introduction.

SPANISH WEST AFRICA Pt. 9

100 centimos = 1 peseta.
Issues for use in Ifni and Spanish Sahara.

1. Native.
2. Isabella the Catholic.

1949. 75th Anniv of U.P.U.
1 1 4 p. green .. .. .. 2·25 1·00

1949. Air. Colonial Stamp Day.
2. 2. 5 p. brown .. .. .. 1·75 80

3. Tents.

1950.
3. 3. 2 c. brown 10 10
4. – 5 c. violet 10 10
5. – 10 c. blue 10 10
6. – 15 c. black 25 10
7. 3. 25 c. brown 25 10
8. – 30 c. yellow 20 10
9. – 40 c. olive 20 10
10. – 45 c. red 20 10
11. 3. 50 c. orange 20 10
12. – 75 c. blue 20 15
13. – 90 c. green 20 10
14. – 1 p. grey 20 10
15. 3. 1 p. 35 violet 85 40
16. – 2 p. sepia .. .. .. 1·50 1·00
17. – 5 p. mauve .. .. 12·00 2·25
18. 3. 10 p. brown .. .. 22·00 12·00

Designs: 5, 30, 75 c., 2 p. Palm trees, Lake Tinzgarrentz. 10, 40, 90 c., 5 p. Camels and irrigation. 15, 45 c., 1 p. Camel transport.

8. Camel Train.

Designs: 25 c. 2 p., 10 p. Desert Camp. 1 p., 5 p. Four Camels.

1951. Air.
19. – 25 c. yellow 30 10
20. 8. 50 c. mauve 15 10
21. – 1 p. green 35 10
22. – 2 p. blue 65 10
23. 8. 3 p. 25 violet .. .. 1·25 45
24. – 5 p. sepia .. .. .. 11·00 1·50
25. – 10 p. red .. .. .. 22·00 9·00

EXPRESS LETTER STAMP

E 10. Port Tilimenzo.

1951.
E 26. E 10. 25 c. red .. .. 1·00 35

SUDAN Pt. 14

A territory in Africa, extending S. from Egypt towards the equator, jointly administered by Gt. Britain and Egypt until 1954 when the territory was granted a large measure of self-government. Became independent 1 Jan. 1956 (for issues before this date see volume 3).

1000 milliemes = 100 piastres = £1 Sudanese.

52. "Independent Sudan".

1956. Independence Commemoration.
143. 52. 15 m. orange & purple 15 10
144. 3 p. orange and blue 35 15
145. 5 p. orange and green .. 50 35

53. Globe on Rhinoceros (Badge of Sudan).
54. Sudanese Soldier and Farmer.

1958. Arab Postal Congress, Khartoum.
146. 53. 15 m. orange and purple 20 10
147. 3 p. orange and blue .. 35 15
148. 5 p. orange and green .. 50 35

1959. 1st Anniv. of Army Revolution.
149. 54. 15 m. yell., blue & brn. 15 10
150. 3 p. multicoloured .. 50 20
151. 55 m. multicoloured .. 65 40

1960. Inaug. of Arab League Centre, Cairo. As T 154a of Syria.
152. 15 m. black and green .. 15 10

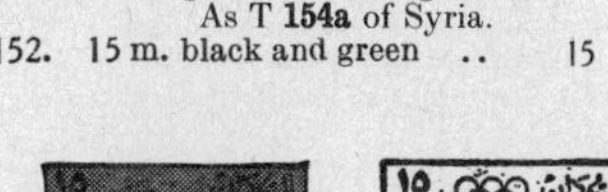

55. Refugees.
56. Football.

1960. World Refugee Year.
153. 55. 15 m. blue, black & brn. 15 15
154. 55 m. red, black & sepia 55 45

1960. Olympic Games, Rome.
155. 56. 15 m. multicoloured .. 20 10
156. 3 p. multicoloured .. 45 25
157. 55 m. multicoloured .. 65 35

57. Forest.
58. King Ta'rhaqa.

1960. 5th World Forestry Congress, Seattle.
158. 57. 15 m. grn., brn. and red 15 10
159. 3 p. green, brown and deep green .. 35 20
160. 55 m. multicoloured .. 60 35

1961. Sudanese Nubian Monuments Preservation Campaign.
161. 58. 15 m. brown and green 20 10
162. 3 p. violet and orange .. 35 20
163. 55 m. brown and blue .. 60 35

59. Girl with Book.
60. "The World United against Malaria".

1961. "50 Years of Girls' Education in the Sudan".
164. 59. 15 m. mve., pur. & blue 15 10
165. 3 p. blue, orge. & black 40 20
166. 55 m. brn., green & blk. 55 40

1962. Malaria Eradication.
167. 60. 15 m. violet, blue & blk. 15 10
168. 55 m. green, emer. & blk. 50 35

1962. Arab League Week. As T 76 of Libya but larger, 24 × 41 mm.
169. 15 m. orange 15 10
170. 55 m. turquoise 45 35

62. Republican Palace.
63. Nile Felucca.

64. Camel Postman.
65. Campaign Emblem and "Millet" Cobs.

1962.
185 62 5 m. blue 10 10
186 – 10 m. purple and blue 10 10
187 – 15 m. purple, orge & bis 10 10
188 62 2 p. purple 10 10
189 – 3 p. brown & green .. 20 10
190 – 35 m. brn, dp brn & grn 55 10
191 – 4 p. mauve, red & blue 55 10
192 – 55 m. black and green 55 20
193 – 6 p. brown and blue .. 65 20
194 – 8 p. green 65 20
195 63 10 p. brown, bistre & bl 80 35
196 – 20 p. green and bronze 1·40 55
194a – 25 p. brown and green 10 10
197 – 50 p. green, blue & blk 3·50 1·25
469 64 £S1 brown and green .. 7·25 4·25
198 – £S5 green and brown .. 45 25
199 63 £S10 orange and green 90 40

Designs: As Type 62—horiz. 15 m. "Tabbaque" (food cover). 55 m., 6, 25 p. Cattle. 8 p. Date palms. vert. 10 m., 3 p. Cotton picking. 35 m., 4 p. Wild game. As Type 63—horiz. 20 p., $S5 Bohein Temple. 50 p. Sennar Dam.

1963. Freedom from Hunger.
226. 65. 15 m. green and brown 15 15
227. 55 m. violet, lilac & blue 55 35

66. Centenary Emblem and Medallions.
67. "Knight".

1963. Centenary of Red Cross.
228. 66. 15 m. multicoloured .. 35 15
229. 55 m. multicoloured .. 65 35

1964. Nubian Monuments Preservation. Frescoes from Faras Church, Nubia. Multicoloured.
230. 15 m. Type 67 .. .. 20 15
231. 30 m. "Saint" (horiz.) .. 35 20
232. 55 m. "Angel" 85 55

68. Sudan Map.
69. Chainbreakers and Mrs. E. Roosevelt.

1964. New York World's Fair. Mult.
233. 15 m. Khashm el Girba Dam 10 10
234. 3 p. Sudan Pavilion .. 20 15
235. 55 m. Type 68 .. .. 50 30
Nos. 233/4 are horiz.

1964. 80th Birth Anniv. of Mrs. Eleanor Roosevelt (Human Rights pioneer).
236. 69. 15 m. blue and black .. 10 10
237. 3 p. violet and black .. 30 15
238. 55 m. brown and black 45 30

70. Postal Union Emblem.
71. I.T.U. Symbol and Emblems.

1964. 10th Anniv. of Arab Postal Union's Permanent Bureau.
239. 70. 15 m. black, gold & red 10 10
240. 3 p. black, gold & green 30 15
241. 55 m. blk., gold & violet 45 30

1965. Centenary of I.T.U.
242. 71. 15 m. brown and gold .. 10 10
243. 3 p. black and gold .. 30 15
244. 55 m. green and gold .. 45 30

72. Gurashi (martyr) and Demonstrators.

1965. 1st Anniv. of 21 October Revolution.
245. **72.** 15 m. black and brown 10 10
246. 3 p. black and red .. 20 15
247. 55 m. black and grey .. 45 30

73. I.C.Y. Emblem. **74.** El Siddig El Mahdi.

1965. Int. Co-operation Year.
248. **73.** 15 m. lilac and black .. 10 10
249. 3 p. green and black .. 20 15
250. 55 m. red and black .. 45 30

1966. 5th Death Anniv. of Imam El Siddig El Mahdi.
251. **74.** 15 m. violet and blue .. 35 15
252. 3 p. brown and orange 50 35
253. 55 m. brown and grey 1·10 60

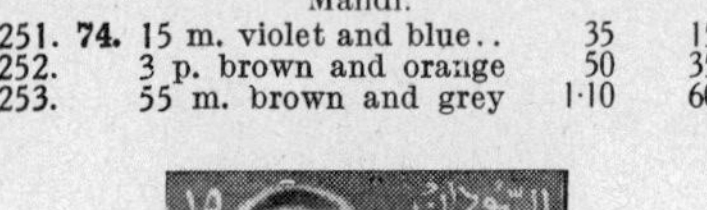

75. M. Zaroug (politician).

1966. Mubarak Zaroug Commem.
254. **75.** 15 m. olive and pink .. 35 15
255. 3 p. green & light green 50 35
256. 55 m. brown & chestnut 1·10 55

76. W.H.O. Building. **77.** Crests of Upper Nile, Blue Nile and Kassala Provinces.

1966. Inaug. of W.H.O. Headquarters, Geneva.
257. **76.** 15 m. blue 10 10
258. 3 p. purple 20 15
259. 55 m. brown 45 30

1967. "The Month of the South".
260. **77.** 15 m. multicoloured .. 10 10
261. – 3 p. multicoloured .. 20 10
262. – 55 m. multicoloured .. 80 40
DESIGNS (Crests of): 3 p. Equatoria, Kordofan and Khartoum Provinces. 55 m. Bahr El Gazal, Darfur and Northern Provinces.

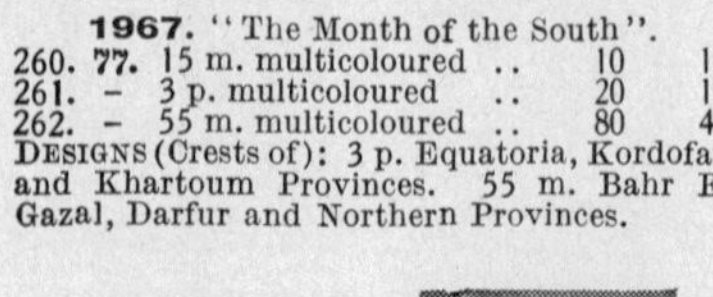

78. Giraffe and Tourist Emblem. **79.** Handclasp Emblem.

1967. Int. Tourist Year.
263. **78.** 15 m. multicoloured .. 20 10
264. 3 p. multicoloured .. 45 25
265. 55 m. multicoloured .. 70 25

1967. Arab Summit Conf., Khartoum.
266. **79.** 15 m. multicoloured .. 10 10
267. 3 p. green and orange .. 20 10
268. 55 m. violet and yellow 45 20

80. P.L.O. Shoulder Flash.

1967. Palestine Liberation Organization.
269. **80.** 15 m. multicoloured .. 10 10
270. 3 p. multicoloured .. 20 10
271. 55 m. multicoloured .. 45 20

81. Mohamed Nur El Din.

1968. Nur El Din (politician) Commem.
272. **81.** 15 m. green and blue .. 35 15
273. 3 p. bistre and blue .. 50 30
274. 55 m. ultramarine & blue 1·10 50

82. Abdullahi El Fadil El Mahdi.

1968. Abdullahi El Fadil El Mahdi (Ansar leader) Commem.
275. **82.** 15 m. violet and blue .. 35 15
276. 3 p. green and blue .. 50 30
277. 55 m. green and orange 1·10 50

83. Ahmed Yousif Hashim.

1968. 10th Death Anniv. of Ahmed Yousif Hashim (journalist).
278. **83.** 15 m. brown and green 35 10
279. 3 p. brown and blue .. 50 10
280. 55 m. violet and blue .. 1·10 30

84. Mohamed Ahmed El Mardi.

1968. Mohamed Ahmed El Mardi (politician) Commem.
281. **84.** 15 m. ultramarine & blue 35 15
282. 3 p. orange, blue & pink 50 35
283. 55 m. brown and blue .. 1·10 55

85. Douglas DC-3 Airliner.

1968. 20th Anniv. of Sudan Airways. Mult.
284. 15 m. Type **85** 10 10
285. 2 p. De Havilland "Dove" 20 10
286. 3 p. Fokker "Friendship" 40 20
287. 55 m. Comet 4-C 65 45

87. Anniversary and Bank Emblems.

1969. 5th Anniv. of African Development Bank.
288. **87.** 2 p. black and gold .. 15 10
289. 4 p. red and gold .. 30 15
290. 65 m. green and gold .. 45 20

88. I.L.O. Emblem.

1969. 50th Anniv. of Int. Labour Organization.
291. **88.** 2 p. black, red and blue 15 10
292. 4 p. black, blue & yellow 30 15
293. 65 m. black, mve. & grn. 45 20

89. "Solidarity of the People".

1970. 1st Anniv. of May 25th Revolution. (1st issue).
294. **89.** 2 p. multicoloured
295. 4 p. multicoloured
296. 65 m. multicoloured Set of 3 25·00
Nos. 294/6 were withdrawn on day of issue (25 May) as being unsatisfactory. They were later replaced by Nos. 297/9 and the 1st issue may be easily distinguished by the figures of value which appear on the extreme left of the design.

90. "Solidarity of the People".

1970. 1st Anniv. of May 25th Revolution. (2nd issue).
297. **90.** 2 p. brown, green & red 15 10
298. 4 p. blue, green and red 35 15
299. 65 m. green, blue & red 50 25

91. Map of Egypt, Libya and Sudan. **92.** I.E.Y. Emblem.

1971. 1st Anniv. of Tripoli Charter.
300. **91.** 2 p. green, black & red 20 10

1971. Int. Education Year.
301. **92.** 2 p. multicoloured .. 15 10
302. 4 p. multicoloured .. 30 10
303. 65 m. multicoloured .. 45 20

93. Laurel and Bayonets on Star. **94.** Emblems of Arab League and Sudan Republic.

1971. 2nd Anniv. of 25th May Revolution.
304. **93.** 2 p. blk., green & yell. 15 10
305. 4 p. black, green & blue 35 15
306. 10½ p. blk., green & grey 60 35

1972. 25th Anniv. of Arab League.
307. **94.** 2 p. black, yell. & green 15 10
308. 4 p. multicoloured .. 35 15
309. 10½ p. multicoloured .. 70 35

95. U.N. Emblem and Text. **96.** Cogwheel Emblem.

1972. 25th Anniv. of United Nations.
310. **95.** 2 p. green, orge. & red .. 15 10
311. 4 p. blue, orge. & red .. 35 15
312. 10½ p. blk., orge. & red 70 40

1972. World Standards Day (14.10.71).
313. **96.** 2 p. multicoloured .. 15 10
314. 4 p. multicoloured .. 40 20
315. 10½ p. multicoloured .. 85 55

97. Sudanese Arms and Pres. Nemery.

1972. Presidential Elections.
316. **97.** 2 p. multicoloured .. 15 10
317. 4 p. multicoloured .. 35 15
318. 10½ p. multicoloured .. 70 40

98. Arms and Emblem.

1972. Socialist Union's Founding Congress (January, 1972).
319. **98.** 2 p. black, yellow & blue 10 10
320. 4 p. mauve, yellow & blk. 20 15
321. 10½ p. black, yell. & grn. 65 25

99. Airmail Envelope and A.P.U. Emblem.

1972. 10th Anniv. of African Postal Union. (1971).
322. **99.** 2 p. multicoloured .. 10 10
323. 4 p. multicoloured .. 20 15
324. 10½ p. multicoloured .. 80 30

100. Provincial Emblems. **101.** Emperor Haile Selassie of Ethiopia.

1973. National Unity.
325. **100.** 2 p. multicoloured .. 10 10
326. – 4 p. brown and black .. 20 10
327. – 10½ p. grn., orge. & silver 80 35
DESIGNS—HORIZ. 4 p. Revolutionary Council. VERT. 10½ p. Entwined trees.

1973. 80th Birthday of Emperor Haile Selassie.
328. **101.** 2 p. multicoloured .. 20 15
329. 4 p. multicoloured .. 50 20
330. 10½ p. multicoloured .. 1·10 45

102. President Nasser **104.** Scout Emblem.

103. Ancient Gateway.

1973. 3rd Death Anniv. of Pres. Nasser.
331. **102.** 2 p. black 10 10
332. 4 p. black and green .. 20 10
333. 10½ p. black and violet 65 35

1973. 10th Anniv. of World Food Programme.
334. **103.** 2 p. multicoloured .. 10 10
335. 4 p. multicoloured .. 20 10
336. 10½ p. multicoloured .. 80 45

1973. World Scout Conference, Nairobi and Addis Ababa.
337. **104.** 2 p. multicoloured .. 30 10
338. 4 p. multicoloured .. 45 20
339. 10½ p. multicoloured .. 95 55

105. Interpol Emblem.

1974. 50th Anniv. of Int. Criminal Police Organization (Interpol).
340. **105.** 2 p. multicoloured .. 10 10
341. 4 p. multicoloured .. 30 15
342. 10½ p. multicoloured .. 70 35

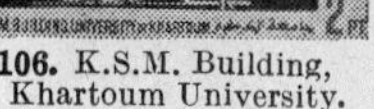

106. K.S.M. Building, Khartoum University. **107.** African Postal Union Emblem.

1974. 50th Anniv. of Faculty of Medicine, Khartoum University.

343. **106.** 2 p. multicoloured .. 15 10
344. 4 p. green, brn. & red .. 35 10
345. 10½ p. red, brn. & grn. 70 45

1974. Centenary of Universal Postal Union. Multicoloured.

346. 2 p. Type **107** 10 10
347. 4 p. Arab Postal Union emblem 20 15
348. 10½ p. Universal Postal Union emblem 80 35

108. A. A. Latif and A. F. Elmaz (revolution leaders).

1975. 50th Anniv. of 1924 Revolution.

349. **108.** 2½ p. green and blue .. 10 10
350. 4 p. red and blue .. 20 10
351. 10½ p. brown and blue .. 80 35

109. Bank and Commemorative Emblems.

1975. 10th Anniv. of African Development Bank.

352. **109.** 2½ p. multicoloured .. 10 10
353. 4 p. multicoloured .. 20 10
354. 10½ p. multicoloured .. 80 35

110. Earth Station and Camel Postman. **111.** Woman, Flag and IWY Emblem.

1976. Inauguration of Satellite Earth Station.

355. **110.** 2½ p. multicoloured .. 15 10
356. 4 p. multicoloured .. 30 15
357. 10½ p. multicoloured .. 65 35

1976. International Women's Year.

358. **111.** 2½ p. multicoloured .. 10 10
359. 4 p. multicoloured .. 30 15
360. 10½ p. multicoloured .. 70 35

112. Arms of Sudan and " Gold Medal ". **113.** " Unity ".

1976. Olympic Games, Montreal.

361. **112.** 2½ p. multicoloured .. 40 10
362. 4 p. multicoloured .. 45 20
363. 10½ p. multicoloured .. 1·10 55

1977. 5th Anniv. of National Unity.

364. **113.** 2½ p. red, black and blue 10 10
365. 4 p. red, black and green 20 15
366. 10½ p. red, black & brn. 65 30

114. Archbishop Capucci.

1977. Archbishop Capucci's Imprisonment. Commemoration.

367. **114.** 2½ p. black 45 10
368. 4 p. black and green .. 65 20
369. 10½ p. black and red .. 1·10 45

115. Fair Emblem and Flags.

1978. International Fair, Khartoum.

370. **115.** 3 p. multicoloured .. 20 10
371. 4 p. multicoloured .. 35 15
372. 10½p. multicoloured .. 55 25

117. Commemorative and A.P.U. Emblems.

1978. Silver Jubilee of Arab Postal Union.

373. **117.** 3 p. blk., silver & red .. 15 10
374. 4 p. blk., silver & green 30 10
375. 10½ p. black, silver & blue 65 35

118. Jinnah and Sudanese Flag.

1978. Birth Cent. of Mohammed Ali Jinnah (first Governor-General of Pakistan).

376. **118.** 3 p. multicoloured .. 20 10
377. 4 p. multicoloured .. 35 15
378. 10½ p. multicoloured .. 55 25

119. Desert Scene.

1978. U.N. Conference on Desertification.

379. **119.** 3 p. black, yell. & green 20 10
380. 4 p. blac! , pink & green 35 15
381. 10½ p. blk., brn. & grn. 85 45

120. Lion God Apedemek and O.A.U. Emblem. **121.** Sudanese Flag.

1978. 15th African Summit Conference, Khartoum.

382. **120.** 3 p. black, yell. & purple 15 10
383. 4 p. black, yell. & blue 30 15
384. 10½ p. black, yell. & grn. 55 30

1979. 10th Anniv of May Revolution.

385 121 3½ p. multicoloured .. 15 10
386 6 p. multicoloured .. 35 15
387 13 p. multicoloured .. 60 30

122. I.B.E. and U.N.E.S.C.O. Emblems. **123.** I.Y.C. Emblem and Hands carrying Child.

1980. 50th Anniv. of International Bureau of Education. (1979).

388. **122.** 4½ p. black and orange 20 15
389. 8 p. black and green .. 45 25
390. 15½ p. black and blue .. 90 40

1980. International Year of the Child (1979).

391. **123.** 4½ p. multicoloured .. 20 15
392. 8 p. multicoloured .. 40 25
393. 15½ p. multicoloured .. 70 40

124. National Flag, Arms and Sudanese Warrior.

1982. 25th Anniv. of Independence.

396. **124.** 60 m. multicoloured .. 20 10
397. 120 m. multicoloured .. 45 20
398. 250 m. multicoloured .. 90 45

125. Hands reaching for F.A.O. Emblem on Map of Sudan.

1983. World Food Day.

399. **125.** 60 m. blue, grn. & blk. 20 10
400. – 120 m. grn., blk. & red 45 20
401. – 250 m. grn., blk. & red 90 45

Designs: 120 m. F.A.O. emblem, crops and cattle. 250 m. Emblem, crops and cattle on map of Sudan.

126. Commission Emblem. **127.** Warrior on Horseback.

1984. 25th Anniv. of Economic Commission for Africa.

402. **126.** 10 p. lilac and silver .. 20 15
403. 25 p. blue and silver .. 55 35
404. 40 p. green and silver 1·00 60

1984. Centenary of Shaykan Battle, Kordofan.

405. **127.** 10 p. multicoloured .. 20 15
406. 25 p. multicoloured .. 55 35
407. 40 p. multicoloured .. 90 50

128. Sudan Olympic Committee Emblem. **129.** Emblem and Flags.

1984. First Olympic Week.

408. **128.** 10 p. multicoloured .. 20 15
409. 25 p. multicoloured .. 60 30
410. 40 p. multicoloured .. 1·10 55

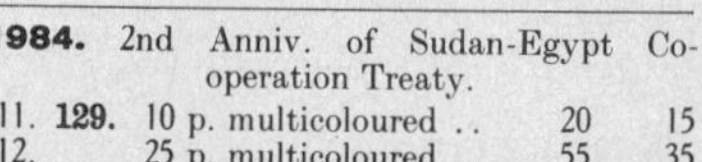
1984. 2nd Anniv. of Sudan-Egypt Co-operation Treaty.

411. **129.** 10 p. multicoloured .. 20 15
412. 25 p. multicoloured .. 55 35
413. 40 p. multicoloured .. 90 50

130. Institute Emblem. **131.** Map and Broken Chain.

1985. 50th Anniv. of Bakht Erruda Teacher Training Institute, Edddueim Town.

414. **130.** 10 p. multicoloured .. 20 15
415. 25 p. multicoloured .. 55 35
416. 40 p. multicoloured .. 90 50

1986. 1st Anniv. of 6th April Rising.

417. **131.** 5 p. blk., grn. & brn. 10 10
418. 25 p. blk., grn. & bl. 55 30
419. 40 p. blk., grn. & brn. 90 45

132. Fishermen hauling in Nets.

1988. World Food Day (1986).

420. **132.** 25 p. black, silver and brown 30 15
421. – 30 p. green and black 35 15
422. – 50 p. multicoloured .. 55 35
423. – 75 p. black deep blue and blue 80 45
424. – 300 p. blue, black and silver .. .. 3·00 1·40

Designs—vert. 30 p. Two fishes. horiz. 50 p. Plant and globe. 75 p. Outline of fish and waves. 300 p. Shoal of fish.

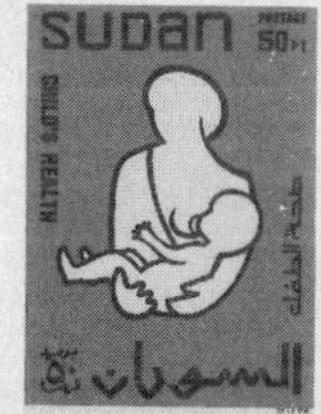

133. Mother breastfeeding Baby. **134.** Emblem.

1988. Child Health Campaign.

426. **133.** 50 p. black and mauve 55 20
427. – 75 p. multicoloured .. 85 35
428. – 100 p. multicoloured 1·10 45
429. – 150 p. multicoloured 1·60 65

Designs—horiz. No. 427, Mother spoon-feeding child. 428, Child being given oral vaccination. 429, Children on scales.

1988. 30th Anniv of Sudan Red Crescent.

431 **134** 40 p. black, yell & red 40 30
432 – 100 p. black, red & grn 90 60
433 – 150 p. black, red & bl 1·25 80

DESIGNS: 100 p. Candle; 150 p. Figure with crescent on head.

135 Anniversary Emblem

1988. 75th Anniv of Bank of Khartoum. Mult.

434 40 p. Type **135** 40 20
435 100 p. Bubbles and medal 90 45
436 150 p. Inscription and emblem .. .. 1·25 65

136 Plough

137 Emblem

1988. World Food Day. The Small Farmer. Multicoloured.

437 40 p. Type **136** 40 20
438 100 p. Farmer ploughing .. 90 45
439 150 p. Farmer drawing water from river .. 1·25 65

1989. "Freedom of Palestine".

440 **137** 100 p. multicoloured .. 50 20
441 150 p. multicoloured .. 80 35
442 200 p. multicoloured .. 95 55

138 Crowd of Youths

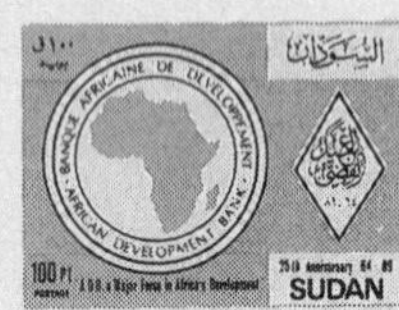

139 Emblem

1989. Palestinian "Intifada" Movement.

443 **138** 100 p. multicoloured .. 50 20
444 150 p. multicoloured .. 80 35
445 200 p. multicoloured .. 95 55

1989. 25th Anniv of African Development Bank.

446 **139** 100 p. grn, blk & silver 50 20
447 150 p. blue, blk & silver 80 35
448 200 p. pur, blk & silver 95 55

140 Map

141 Leopard

1990. 34th Anniv of Independence.

449 **140** 50 p. blue and yellow 20 10
450 100 p. brown & yellow 50 20
451 150 p. mauve & yellow 80 35
452 200 p. mauve & yellow 1·00 55

1990. Mammals. Multicoloured.

453 25 p. Type **141** 15 10
454 50 p. African elephant .. 35 20
455 75 p. Giraffe (vert) .. 45 35
456 100 p. White rhinoceros .. 60 45
457 125 p. Addax (vert) .. 65 55

142 Zande Hornbill

146 Flag

143 Mardoum Dance

1990. Birds. Multicoloured.

458 25 p. Type **142** 15 10
459 50 p. Marabou stork .. 35 20
460 75 p. Buff-crested bustard 50 35
461 100 p. Saddle-bill stork .. 65 45
462 150 p. Bald ibis 85 55

1990. Traditional Dances. Multicoloured.

463 25 p. Type **143** 15 10
464 50 p. Zandi dance (vert) .. 35 20
465 75 p. Kambala dance (vert) 45 35
466 100 p. Nubian dance (vert) 60 45
467 125 p. Sword dance .. 65 55

1990. No. 195 surch with new value in Arabic.

468 **63** £S1 on 10 p. brn, bis & bl 10 10

1991. 1st Anniv of "National Salvation Revolution".

470 **146** 150 p. multicoloured .. 10 5
471 200 p. multicoloured .. 15 5
472 250 p. multicoloured .. 20 10
473 £S5 multicoloured .. 40 25
474 £S10 multicoloured .. 75 65

147 Shoebill

148 Camel Postman

1991. (a) As T **147**. Multicoloured.

475 25 p. Type **147** 5 5
476 50 p. Sunflower 5 5
477 75 p. Collecting gum arabic 5 5
478 100 p. Cotton 10 5
479 125 p. Crowned crane .. 10 5
480 150 p. Kenana Sugar Co Ltd (29½ × 25 mm) .. 10 5
481 175 p. Secretary bird (24 × 30½ mm) .. 15 5
482 £S2 Atbara Cement Factory (29½ × 25 mm) .. 15 5
483 250 p. King Taharka (statue) (26 × 37 mm) .. 20 10
484 £S3 Republican Palace (26 × 37 mm) .. 25 15
485 £S4 Hug (scent container) (24 × 30½ mm) .. 30 20
486 £S5 Gabanah (coffee pot) (24 × 30½ mm) .. 40 30

(b) As T **148**. Multicoloured.

487 £S8 Devil Firefish (horiz) 60 50
488 £S10 Goat, ox and camel (horiz) 75 65
489 £S15 Nubian ibex .. 1·25 1·00
490 £S20 Type **148** .. .. 1·50 1·10

150 Campaign Emblem

1991. Pan-African Campaign against Rinderpest.

507 **150** £S1 black and green .. 10 5
508 £S2 violet and green .. 15 5
509 £S5 orange and green 40 30

OFFICIAL STAMPS.

ح.س.
(O 65. "S.G.")

1962. Nos. 171/84 optd with Type O **65** (larger on 10 p. to £S10).

O185 **62** 5 m. blue 10 10
O186 – 10 m. purple and blue 10 10
O187 – 15 m. pur, orge & bis 10 10
O188 **62** 2 p. violet 10 10
O189 – 3 p. brown & green 45 10
O190 – 35 m. brown, deep brown and green .. 55 20
O191 – 4 p. purple, red & bl 65 20
O192 – 55 m. brown & green 90 20
O193 – 6 p. brown and blue 90 35
O194 – 8 p. green .. .. 1·10 55
O222 **63** 10 p. brown, blk & bl 1·10 55
O223 – 20 p. green and olive 2·75 90
O223a – 25 p. brown & green 10 10
O224 – 50 p. green, bl & blk 4·50 2·00
O198 **64** £S1 brown and green 9·00 4·50
O226 – £S5 green and brown 65 40
O227 **63** £S10 orange and blue 1·40 85

1991. Nos. 475/90 optd similarly to Type O **65**.

O491 25 p. multicoloured .. 5 5
O492 50 p. multicoloured .. 5 5
O493 75 p. multicoloured .. 10 5
O494 100 p. multicoloured .. 15 10
O495 125 p. multicoloured .. 15 10
O496 150 p. multicoloured .. 20 10
O497 175 p. multicoloured .. 25 15
O498 £S2 multicoloured .. 25 15
O499 250 p. multicoloured .. 35 20
O500 £S3 multicoloured .. 40 25
O501 £S4 multicoloured .. 55 35
O502 £S5 multicoloured .. 65 40
O503 £S8 multicoloured .. 1·10 65
O504 £S10 multicoloured .. 1·40 85
O505 £S15 multicoloured .. 2·00 1·25
O506 £S20 multicoloured .. 2·75 1·75

SURINAM Pt. 4; Pt. 20

A Netherlands colony on the north-east coast of South America. In December 1954 Surinam became an autonomous state within the Kingdom of the Netherlands.

Became an independent state in November 1975.

100 cents = 1 gulden.

1. King William III.

3.

1873. No gum.

32. **1.** 1 c. grey .. .. .. 1·25 1·40
33. 2 c. yellow 60 55
14. 2½ c. red 65 35
15. 3 c. green .. .. .. 15·00 11·00
16. 5 c. lilac .. .. .. 17·00 4·25
17. 10 c. bistre .. .. 2·25 1·75
34. 12½ c. blue .. .. 14·00 4·25
18. 15 c. grey .. .. 17·00 4·50
19. 20 c. green .. .. 35·00 24·00
20. 25 c. blue .. .. .. 85·00 7·50
22. 30 c. brown .. .. 29·00 25·00
23. 40 c. brown .. .. 24·00 22·00
12. 50 c. brown .. .. 28·00 16·00
35. 1 g. grey and brown .. 45·00 50·00
13. 2½ g. brown and green .. 60·00 55·00

The gulden values are larger.

1890.

44. **3.** 1 c. grey 45 65
45. 2 c. brown .. .. 1·10 90
46. 2½ c. red .. .. .. 1·75 80
47. 3 c. green .. .. .. 4·25 2·75
48. 5 c. blue .. .. .. 24·00 1·40

1892. Surch. **2½ CENT.**

53. **1.** 2½ c. on 50 c. brown .. £275 9·00

5.

6. Queen Wilhelmina.

1892. No gum.

56 **5** 2½ c. black and yellow .. 85 50

1892.

63. **6.** 10 c. bistre .. .. 35·00 1·75
64. 12½ c. mauve .. .. 45·00 4·25
65. 15 c. grey .. .. .. 1·50 1·00
66. 20 c. green .. .. 2·25 1·25
67. 25 c. blue .. .. .. 9·00 3·25
68. 30 c. brown .. .. 2·25 1·40

1898. Surch. **10 CENT.**

69. **1.** 10 c. on 12½ c. blue .. 25·00 2·75
70. 10 c. on 15 c. grey .. 60·00 50·00
71. 10 c. on 20 c. green .. 3·00 2·75
72. 10 c. on 25 c. blue .. 7·00 4·25
74. 10 c. on 30 c. brown .. 3·00 3·00

1900. Stamps of Netherlands surch **SURINAME** and value.

77 **13** 50 c. on 50 c. red & green 24·00 6·00
78 **11** 1 g. on 1 g. green .. 18·00 12·00
79 2½ g. on 2½ g. lilac .. 13·00 9·50

1900. Surch.

83 **1** 25 c. on 40 c. brown .. 1·75 2·25
84 25 c. on 50 c. brown .. 1·50 1·25
86 50 c. on 1 g. grey & brown 28·00 28·00
82 50 c. on 2½ g. brown & grn £130 £180

11. (Shaded background).

12.

13.

1902.

87. **11.** ½ c. lilac 55 45
88. 1 c. green .. .. 1·40 15
89. 2 c. brown .. .. 8·50 2·50
90. 2½ c. green .. .. 3·00 3·00
91. 3 c. yellow .. .. 4·50 2·50
92. 5 c. red .. .. .. 5·50 15
93. 7½ c. grey .. .. 14·00 6·00
94. **12.** 10 c. slate .. .. 10·00 70
95. 12½ c. blue .. .. 1·40 15
96. 15 c. brown .. .. 24·00 8·00
97. 20 c. green .. .. 26·00 3·75
98. 22½ c. green and brown 17·00 9·00
99. 25 c. violet .. .. 18·00 1·00
100. 30 c. brown .. .. 42·00 12·00
101. 50 c. brown .. .. 25·00 5·50

1907.

102 **13** 1 g. purple .. .. 50·00 8·50
103 2½ g. slate .. .. 48·00 65·00

14.

17.

1909. Roul or perf. No gum.

No.	Type	Description	Unused	Used
104	**14**	5 c. red ..	8·50	8·00

1911. Surch with crown and value.

No.	Type	Description	Unused	Used
106	**3**	½ c. on 1 c. grey	70	70
107		½ c. on 2 c. brown	6·00	8·00
108	**6**	15 c. on 25 c. blue	65·00	60·00
109		20 c. on 30 c. brown	7·50	7·00
110	–	30 c. on 2½ g. on 2½ g. purple (No. 79)	£130	£120

1912. No gum.

No.	Type	Description	Unused	Used
113.	**17.**	½ c. lilac	60	60
114.		2½ c. green	65	60
115.		5 c. red..	6·50	6·00
116.		12½ c. blue	9·50	8·50

18. (unshaded background).

19.

20.

21.

1913. With or without gum.

No.	Type	Description	Unused	Used
117	**18**	½ c. lilac	20	25
118		1 c. green	20	15
119		1½ c. blue	20	15
120		2 c. brown	80	1·10
121		2½ c. green	45	10
122		3 c. yellow	50	40
123		3 c. green	2·25	2·25
125		4 c. blue	6·50	3·75
126		5 c. pink	1·00	10
127		5 c. green	1·00	75
128		5 c. violet	1·00	10
129		6 c. buff	2·25	2·25
130		6 c. red	2·00	30
131		7½ c. brown	75	15
132		7½ c. red	1·00	30
133		7½ c. yellow	7·50	7·50
134		10 c. lilac	3·25	2·75
135		10 c. red	2·75	30
136	**19**	10 c. red	1·25	45
137		12½ c. blue	1·50	40
138		12½ c. red	1·50	1·75
139		15 c. green	45	45
140		15 c. blue	6·00	3·75
142		20 c. blue	2·25	1·25
143		20 c. green	2·50	1·75
144		22½ c. orange ..	1·75	2·25
145		25 c. mauve	3·00	30
146		30 c. grey	3·75	90
147		32½ c. violet and orange	13·00	17·00
148		35 c. blue and orange	4·00	3·75
149	**20**	50 c. green	2·75	40
150		1 g. brown	3·75	30
151		1½ g. purple	30·00	30·00
152a		2½ g. pink	22·00	22·00

1923. Queen's Silver Jubilee.

No.	Type	Description	Unused	Used
169a.	**21.**	5 c. green	50	55
170.		10 c. red	85	1·25
171.		20 c. blue	2·00	2·40
172a.		50 c. orange	11·00	19·00
173.		1 g. purple	20·00	12·00
174.		2 g. 50 grey	60·00	£2·00
175.		5 g. brown	75·00	£225

1925. Surch.

No.	Type	Description	Unused	Used
176	**18**	3 c on 5 c. green	70	80
177	**19**	10 c. on 12½ c. red	1·60	1·50
180		12½ c. on 22½ c. orange	21·00	24·00
178		15 c. on 12½ c. blue	1·25	1·10
179		15 c. on 20 c. blue	1·10	1·00

1926. Postage Due stamps surch **Frankeerzegel 12½ CENT SURINAME.**

(a) In three lines with bars.

No.	Type	Description	Unused	Used
181	**D 6**	12½ c. on 40 c. mauve and black ..	1·75	1·75

(b) In four lines without bars

No.	Type	Description	Unused	Used
182	**D 6**	12½ c. on 40 c. lilac ..	25·00	25·00

28.

29.

32. Indigenous Disease.

1927.

No.	Type	Description	Unused	Used
183.	**28.**	10 c. red	70	30
184.		12½ c. orange	1·40	1·50
185.		15 c. blue	1·60	45
186.		20 c. blue	1·60	40
187.		21 c. brown	13·00	14·00
188.		22½ c. brown	7·50	9·50
189.		25 c. purple	2·50	55
190.		30 c. green	2·50	90
191.		35 c. sepia	2·75	3·00

1927. Green Cross Fund. Various designs incorporating green cross.

No.	Type	Description	Unused	Used
192.	**29.**	2 c.+2 c. green & slate	1·00	1·00
193.	–	5 c.+3 c. green & purple	1·00	1·00
194.	–	10 c.+ 3 c. green & red	1·50	1·50

1927. Unissued Marine Insurance stamps (as Type M **22** of Netherlands but inscr "SURINAME") surch **FRANKEER ZEGEL** and value.

No.	Description	Unused	Used
195	3 c. on 15 c. green	15	20
196	10 c. on 60 c. red ..	20	25
197	12½ c. on 75 c. brown	25	15
198	15 c. on 1 g. 50 blue	1·90	1·90
199	25 c. on 2 g. 25 brown	4·25	4·00
200	30 c. on 4½ g. black	10·00	8·50
201	50 c. on 7½ g. red ..	4·25	4·00

1928. Governor Van Heemstrastichting Medical Foundation Fund.

No.	Type	Description	Unused	Used
202.	**32.**	1½ c.+1½ c. blue	4·25	4·25
203.		2 c.+ 2 c. green	4·25	4·25
204.		5 c.+3 c. violet	4·25	4·25
205.		7½ c.+2½ c. red	4·25	4·25

33. The Good Samaritan.

35. Mercury and Posthorn.

1929. Green Cross Fund.

No.	Type	Description	Unused	Used
206.	**33.**	1½ c.+1½ c. green	6·00	6·00
207.		2 c.+2 c. red ..	6·00	6·00
208.		5 c.+3 c. blue	6·00	6·00
209.		6 c.+4 c. black	6·00	6·00

1930. No. 132 surch **6**.

No.	Type	Description	Unused	Used
210	**18**	6 c. on 7½ c. red	1·60	70

1930. Air.

No.	Type	Description	Unused	Used
276	**35**	10 c. red	1·40	25
212		15 c. blue	3·25	55
213		20 c. green	10	20
214		40 c. red	20	30
215		60 c. purple	40	35
216		1 g. black	1·25	1·40
217		1½ g. brown	1·40	1·50
281		2½ g. yellow	8·50	11·00
282		5 g. green	£180	£275
283		10 g. bistre	22·00	56·00

1931. Air. "Dornier 10" Flight. Optd **Vlucht Do. X. 1931**.

No.	Type	Description	Unused	Used
218	**35**	10 c. red	18·00	15·00
219		15 c. blue	18·00	15·00
220		20 c. green	18·00	15·00
221		40 c. red	27·00	22·00
222		60 c. purple	60·00	50·00
223		1 g. black	70·00	60·00
224		1½ g. brown	70·00	65·00

37. Mother and Child.

37a. William I (after Key).

1931. Child Welfare.

No.	Type	Description	Unused	Used
225.	**37.**	1½ c.+1½ c. black	4·25	4·25
226.		2 c.+2 c. red ..	4·25	4·25
227.		5 c.+3 c. blue ..	4·25	4·25
228.		6 c.+4 c. green	4·25	4·25

1933. 400th Birth Anniv of William I of Orange.

No.	Type	Description	Unused	Used
229	**37a**	6 c. red	4·50	1·40

38. "Supplication".

1935. Bicent of Moravian Mission in Surinam.

No.	Type	Description	Unused	Used
230.	**38.**	1 c.+½ c. brown	2·75	1·75
231.		2 c.+1 c. blue	2·40	1·75
232.	–	3 c.+1½ c. green	2·75	2·75
233.	–	4 c.+2 c. orange	2·75	2·75
234.	–	5 c.+2½ c. black	2·75	3·00
235.	**38.**	10 c.+5 c. red	2·75	3·00

DESIGN: 3 c., 4 c., 5 c. Cross and clasped hands.

39. "Johannes van Walbeeck" (galleon).

40. Queen Wilhelmina.

1936.

No.	Type	Description	Unused	Used
236.	**39.**	½ c. brown	20	25
237.		1 c. green	30	10
238.		1½ c. blue	45	35
239.		2 c. brown	55	25
240.		2½ c. green	10	15
241.		3 c. blue	50	35
242.		4 c. orange	55	65
243.		5 c. grey	55	20
244.		6 c. red	2·25	1·60
245.		7½ c. purple	10	10
246.	**40.**	10 c. red	65	10
247.		12½ c. green	3·00	1·00
248.		15 c. blue	1·00	5·00
249.		20 c. orange	1·75	50
250.		21 c. black	2·50	2·75
251.		25 c. red	2·00	85
252.		30 c. purple	3·00	70
253.		35 c. bistre	3·50	3·25
254.		50 c. green	3·50	1·40
255.		1 g. blue	6·50	1·50
256.		1 g. 50 brown ..	18·00	14·00
257.		2 g. 50 red	11·00	7·00

Nos. 254/7 are larger (22 × 33 mm.).

41. "Infant Support".

42. "Emancipation".

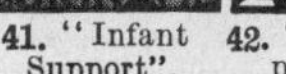

42a. Surinam Girl.

1936. Child Welfare.

No.	Type	Description	Unused	Used
258.	**41.**	2 c.+1 c. green	2·50	2·50
259.		3 c.+1½ c. blue	2·50	2·50
260.		5 c.+2½ c. black	3·00	3·00
261.		10 c.+5 c. red	3·00	3·00

1938. 75th Anniv of Liberation of Slaves in Surinam and Paramaribo Girls' School Funds.

No.	Type	Description	Unused	Used
262.	**42.**	2½ c.+2 c. green	1·60	1·40
263.	**42a.**	3 c.+2 c. black..	1·60	1·40
264.		5 c.+3 c. brown	1·75	1·60
265.		7½ c.+5 c. blue	1·75	1·60

1938. 40th Anniv. of Coronation. As T **87** of Netherlands.

No.	Description	Unused	Used
266.	2 c. violet	35	25
267.	7½ c. red..	80	75
268.	15 c. blue	2·25	2·00

44. Creole.

44d. Dutch Royal Family.

1940. Social Welfare Fund.

No.	Type	Description	Unused	Used
269.	**44.**	2½ c.+2 c. green	1·60	1·75
270.	–	3 c.+2 c. red..	1·60	1·75
271.	–	5 c.+3 c. blue	1·60	1·75
272.	–	7½ c.+5 c. red	1·60	1·75

DESIGNS: 3 c. Javanese woman. 5 c. Hindu woman. 7½ c. Indian woman.

1941. Prince Bernhard and "Spitfire" Funds. As T **69** of Netherlands Indies.

No.	Description	Unused	Used
273.	7½ c.+7½ c. blue & orange	2·00	2·75
274.	15 c.+15 c. blue and red	2·10	2·75
275.	1 g.+1 g. blue and grey ..	15·00	20·00

1941. As T **94** of Netherlands.

No.	Description	Unused	Used
342.	12½ c. blue	25	20
284.	15 c. blue	11·00	6·00

1942. Red Cross. Surch. with red cross and new values.

No.	Type	Description	Unused	Used
289.	**39.**	2 c.+2 c. brown (post.)	1·00	1·75
291.		2½ c.+2 c. green	1·00	1·75
292.		7½ c.+5 c. purple	1·00	1·75
293.	**35.**	10 c.+5 c. red (air) ..	2·75	4·25

1943. Birth of Princess Margriet.

No.	Type	Description	Unused	Used
294.	**44d.**	2½ c. orange ..	20	40
295.		7½ c. red	20	15
296.		15 c. black	1·40	1·50
297.		40 c. blue	1·75	1·75

1945. Surch.

No.	Type	Description	Unused	Used
298.	**39.**	½ c. on 1 c. green	10	20
299.		1½ c. on 7½ c. purple	10	20
300.		2½ c. on 7½ c. purple	1·75	2·25
301.	**40.**	2½ c. on 10 c. red	85	20
302.		5 c. on 10 c. red	60	45
303.		7½ c. on 10 c. red	65	45

1945. Air. Surch.

No.	Type	Description	Unused	Used
304.	**35.**	22½ c. on 60 c. purple ..	35	60
305.		1 g. on 2½ g. yellow	13·00	13·00
306.		5 g. on 10 g. bistre	17·00	18·00

1945. National Welfare Fund. Surch. **CENT/ VOOR HET/ NATIONAAL/ STEUNFONDS** and premium.

No.	Type	Description	Unused	Used
307.	**49.**	7½ c.+5 c. orange	7·00	8·00
308.	**50.**	15 c.+10 c. brown	2·00	1·75
309.		20 c.+15 c. green	2·00	1·75
310.		22½ c.+20 c. grey	2·00	1·75
311.		40 c.+35 c. red	2·00	1·75
312.		60 c.+50 c. violet	2·00	1·75

49. Sugar-cane Train.

50. Queen Wilhelmina. 51.

53. Star.

1945.

No.	Type	Description	Unused	Used
313.	–	1 c. red ..	50	50
314.	–	1½ c. red	1·00	1·00
315.	–	2 c. violet	45	35
316.	–	2½ c. brown	45	35
317.	–	3 c. green	1·00	50
318.	–	4 c. brown	95	55
319.	–	5 c. blue	1·75	45
320.	–	6 c. olive	1·60	1·25
321.	**49.**	7½ c. orange	2·75	75
322.	**50.**	10 c. blue	1·25	10
323.		15 c. brown	1·50	20
324.		20 c. green	2·50	15
325.		22½ c. grey	3·00	70
326.		25 c. red	8·00	3·25
327.		30 c. olive	7·50	40
328.		35 c. blue	13·00	6·00
329.		40 c. red	7·50	25
330.		50 c. red	7·50	20
331.		60 c. violet	7·50	65
332.	**51.**	1 g. brown	10·00	25
333.		1 g. 50 lilac	90	60
334.		2 g. 50 brown ..	16·00	70
335.		5 g. red ..	35·00	9·50
336.		10 g. orange	60·00	15·00

DESIGNS—As Type **49**: 1 c. Bauxite mine, Moengo. 1½ c. Natives in canoes. 2 c. Native and stream. 2½ c. Road in Coronie. 3 c. River Surinam near Berg en Dal. 4 c. Government Square, Paramaribo. 5 c. Mining gold. 6 c. Street in Paramaribo.

1946. Air. Anti-tuberculosis Fund. Surch **LUCHT POST** and premium.

No.	Type	Description	Unused	Used
340	**50**	10 c.+40 c. blue	1·00	1·00
341		15 c.+60 c. brown	1·00	1·00

1947. Anti-Leprosy Fund.

No.	Type	Description	Unused	Used
343.	**53.**	7½ c.+12½ c. orge. (post.)	2·50	2·25
344.		12½ c.+37½ c. blue ..	2·50	2·25
345.		22½ c.+27½ c. grey (air)	2·50	2·25
346.		27½ c.+47½ c. green ..	2·50	2·25

1948. Types of Netherlands inscr. "SURINAME".

(a) Numeral type as **T 118.**

No.	Description	Unused	Used
347.	1 c. red	10	10
348.	1½ c. purple	10	20
349.	2 c. violet	25	10
350.	2½ c. green	1·25	15
351.	3 c. green	15	10
352.	4 c. brown	20	15
353.	5 c. blue	1·25	10
354.	7½ c. orange	2·75	1·10

(b) Portrait of Queen Wilhelmina as T **119**.

No.	Description	Unused	Used
355.	5 c. blue	35	15
356.	6 c. green	90	65
357.	7½ c. red	35	20
358.	10 c. blue	55	10
359.	12½ c. blue	1·00	90
360.	15 c. brown	1·40	30
361.	17½ c. purple	1·60	1·25
362.	20 c. green	1·25	15
363.	22½ c. blue	1·25	65
364.	25 c. red	1·25	25
365.	27½ c. red	1·25	20
366.	30 c. green	1·60	15
367.	37½ c. brown	2·50	2·00
368.	40 c. purple	1·75	25
369.	50 c. orange	1·90	25
370.	60 c. violet	2·00	35
371.	70 c. black	2·25	50

1948. Queen Wilhelmina's Golden Jubilee. As T **125** of Netherlands.

372. 7½ c. orange 65 60
373. 12½ c. blue 65 60

1948. Accession of Queen Juliana. As T **126** of Netherlands.

374 7½ c. orange .. .. 2·00 2·25
375 12½ c. blue .. .. 2·00 2·25

55. Women of Netherlands and Surinam. **56.** Marie Curie.

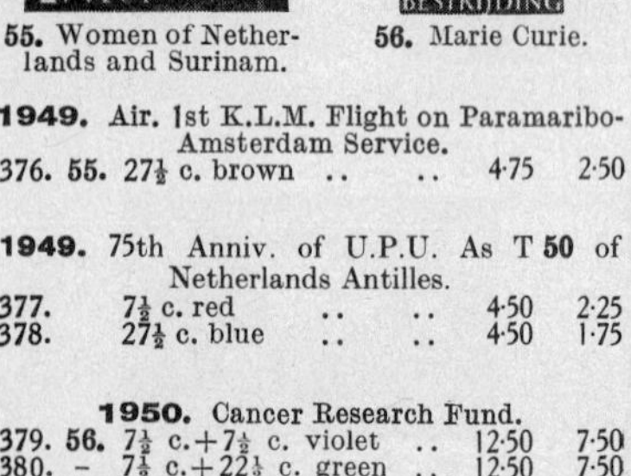

1949. Air. 1st K.L.M. Flight on Paramaribo-Amsterdam Service.

376. **55.** 27½ c. brown .. .. 4·75 2·50

1949. 75th Anniv. of U.P.U. As T **50** of Netherlands Antilles.

377. 7½ c. red .. .. 4·50 2·25
378. 27½ c. blue .. .. 4·50 1·75

1950. Cancer Research Fund.

379. **56.** 7½ c.+7½ c. violet .. 12·50 7·50
380. – 7½ c.+22½ c. green .. 12·50 7·50
381. – 27½ c.+12½ c. blue .. 12·50 7·50
382. **56.** 27½ c.+97½ c. brown .. 12·50 7·50
PORTRAIT—Nos. 380/1, Wilhelm Rontgen.

1950. Surch. **1 Cent** and bars.

383. **49.** 1 c. on 7½ c. orange .. 1·00 1·60

1951. Portrait of Queen Juliana as T **129/30** of Netherlands.

395. **129.** 10 c. blue 35 10
396. 15 c. brown 95 25
397. 20 c. turquoise .. 2·25 10
398. 25 c. red .. .. 1·50 35
399. 27½ c. lake .. .. 1·40 15
400. 30 c. green .. .. 1·40 30
401. 35 c. olive .. .. 1·60 1·00
402. 40 c. mauve .. .. 1·75 35
403. 50 c. orange .. .. 2·25 35
404. **130.** 1 g. brown .. .. 24·00 30

1953. Netherlands Flood Relief Fund. Nos. 374/5 surch. **STORMRAMP NEDERLAND 1953** and premium.

405. 12½ c.+7½ c. on 7½ c. orange 2·25 2·25
406. 20 c.+10 c. on 12½ c. blue 2·25 2·25

60. Fisherman. **61.** Surinam Stadium.

1953.

407 – 2 c. brown 10 10
408 **60** 2½ c. green 25 20
409 – 5 c. grey 25 10
410 – 6 c. blue .. .. 1·50 1·10
411 – 7½ c. violet 15 10
412 – 10 c. red 20 10
413 – 12½ c. blue .. .. 1·60 1·25
414 – 15 c. red .. .. 1·75 30
415 – 17½ c. brown .. .. 3·00 1·75
416 – 20 c. green 45 10
417 – 25 c. green .. .. 2·25 70
DESIGNS—HORIZ. 2 c. Native shooting fish. 10 c. Woman gathering fruit. VERT. 5 c. Bauxite mine. 6 c. Log raft. 7½ c. Ploughing with buffalo. 12½ c. "Kwie Kwie" fish. 15 c. Blue and yellow macaw. 17½ c. Nine-banded armadillo. 20 c. Poling pirogue. 25 c. Iguana.

1953. Sports Week.

419. **61.** 10 c.+5 c. red .. .. 8·50 7·00
420. 15 c.+7½ c. brown .. 8·50 7·00
421. 30 c.+15 c. green .. 8·50 7·00

62. Posthorn and Globe. **63.** Native Children and Youth Centre.

1954. Air. 25th Anniv. of Surinam Airlines.

422. **62.** 15 c. blue .. .. 1·10 1·00

1954. Child Welfare Fund.

423. **63.** 7½ c.+3 c. purple .. 5·50 4·50
424. 10 c.+5 c. green .. 5·50 4·50
425. 15 c.+7½ c. brown .. 5·50 4·50
426. 30 c.+15 c. blue .. 5·50 4·50

1954. Ratification of Statute for the Kingdom. As T **158** of Netherlands.

427. 7½ c. purple 50 60

64. Doves of Peace. **65.** Gathering Bananas.

1955. 10th Anniv. of Liberation of Netherlands and War Victims Relief Fund.

428. **64.** 7½ c.+3½ c. red .. 2·50 2·50
429. 15 c.+8 c. blue .. 2·50 2·50

1955. 4th Caribbean Tourist Assn. Meeting.

430. **65.** 2 c. green .. .. 1·40 1·10
431. – 7½ c. yellow .. .. 2·00 1·75
432. – 10 c. brown .. .. 2·00 1·75
433. – 15 c. blue .. .. 2·00 1·75
DESIGNS: 7½ c. Pounding rice. 10 c. Preparing cassava. 15 c. Fishing.

66. Caduceus and Globe. **67.** Queen Juliana and Prince Bernhard.

1955. Surinam Fair.

434. **66.** 5 c. blue 35 25

1955. Royal Visit.

435. **67.** 7½ c.+2½ c. olive .. 50 50

68. Flags and Caribbean Map. **69.** Façade of 19th-century Theatre.

1956. 10th Anniv. of Caribbean Commission.

447. **68.** 10 c. blue and red .. 25 25

1958. 120th Anniv. of "Thalia" Amateur Dramatic Society.

448. **69.** 7½ c.+3 c. blue & black 40 45
449. – 10 c.+5 c. purple & blk. 40 45
450. – 15 c.+7½ c. grn. & blk. 40 45
451. – 20 c.+10 c. orge. & blk. 40 45
DESIGNS: 10 c. Early 20th-century theatre. 15 c. Modern theatre. 20 c. Performance on stage.

1959. No. 399 surch **8 C.**

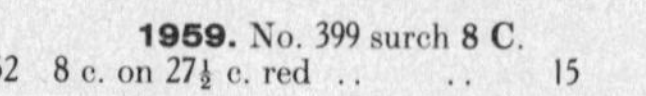

452 8 c. on 27½ c. red 15 15

71. Queen Juliana. **72.** Symbolic Plants.

1959.

453. **71.** 1 g. purple .. .. 1·40 10
454. 1 g. 50 brown .. .. 2·25 45
455. 2 g. 50 red .. .. 3·00 25
456. 5 g. blue .. .. 6·00 25

1959. 5th Anniv. of Ratification of Statute for the Kingdom.

457. **72.** 20 c. multicoloured .. 2·00 1·25

73. Wooden Utensils. **74.** Boeing "707" Airliner.

1960. Surinam Handicrafts.

458. **73.** 8 c.+4 c. multicoloured 80 80
459. – 10 c.+5 c. red, blue and brown 80 80
460. – 15 c.+7 c. grn., brn. & red 80 80
461. – 20 c.+10 c. multicoloured 80 80
DESIGNS: 10 c. Indian chief's headgear. 15 c. Clay pottery. 20 c. Wooden stool.

1960. Opening of Zanderij Airport Building.

462. – 8 c. blue .. .. 1·25 1·25
463. – 10 c. green .. .. 1·75 1·50
464. – 15 c. red .. .. 1·75 1·50
465. – 20 c. lilac .. .. 1·90 1·75
466. **74.** 40 c. brown .. .. 2·75 2·75
DESIGNS: 8 c. Charles Lindbergh's seaplane (1929). 10 c. Fokker 'plane "Snip" (1934). 15 c. Cessna 170-B 'plane (1954). 20 c. "Super-Constellation" (1957).

75. "Uprooted Tree". **76.** Surinam Flag.

1960. World Refugee Year.

467. **75.** 8 c.+4 c. grn. & brown 15 20
468. 10 c.+5 c. green & blue 15 20

1960. Freedom Day. Multicoloured.

469 10 c. Type **76** 40 40
470 15 c. Coat-of-arms (30×26 mm) 40 40

77. Putting the Shot. **78.** Bananas.

1960. Olympic Games, Rome.

471. **77.** 8 c.+4 c. brown, black and grey 60 60
472. – 10 c.+5 c. brown, black and orange 75 75
473. – 15 c.+7 c. brown, black and violet 80 80
474. – 20 c.+10 c. brown, black and blue 80 80
475. – 40 c.+20 c. brown, black and green 80 80
DESIGNS: 10 c. Basketball. 15 c. Running. 20 c. Swimming. 40 c. Football.

1961. Local Produce.

476. **78.** 1 c. yell., black & green 10 10
477. – 2 c. green, black & yell. 10 10
478. – 3 c. brown, blk. & choc. 10 10
479. – 4 c. yellow, black & blue 10 10
480. – 5 c. red, black & brown 10 10
481. – 6 c. yellow, blk. & grn. 10 10
482. – 8 c. yellow, black & blue 10 10
DESIGNS: 2 c. Citrus fruit. 3 c. Cocoa. 4 c. Sugar-cane. 5 c. Coffee. 6 c. Coconuts. 8 c. Rice.

79. Treasury. **80.** Commander Shepard, Rocket and Globe.

1961. Surinam Buildings. Multicoloured.

483. 10 c. Type **79** 15 10
484. 15 c. Court of Justice .. 20 10
485. 20 c. Concordia Masonic Lodge 25 15
486. 25 c. Neve Shalom Synagogue 65 30
487. 30 c. Lock Gate, Nieuw Amsterdam .. .. 1·40 1·25
488. 35 c. Government Building 1·40 1·40
489. 40 c. Governor's House .. 65 50
490. 50 c. Legislative Assembly 70 25
491. 60 c. Old Dutch Reform Church 80 75
492. 70 c. Fort Zeelandia (1790) 1·00 1·00
The 10, 15, 20 and 30 c. are vert and the rest horiz.

1961. Air. "Man in Space". Multicoloured.

493 15 c. Globe and astronaut in capsule 70 75
494 20 c. Type **80** 70 75

81. Girl Scout saluting. **82.** Dag Hammarskjold.

1961. Caribbean Girl Scout Jamborette. Mult.

495 8 c.+2 c. Semaphoring (horiz) 45 35
496 10 c+3 c. Type **81** .. 45 35
497 15 c.+4 c. Brownies around a "toadstool" (horiz) 45 35
498 20 c.+5 c. Campfire sing-song 45 45
499 25 c.+6 c. Lighting fire (horiz) 45 45

1962. Dag Hammarskjold Memorial Issue.

500. **82.** 10 c. black and blue .. 10 12
501. 20 c. black and violet 15 20

1962. Royal Silver Wedding. As T **187** of Netherlands.

502. 20 c. green 30 25

83. "Hibiscus rosa sinensis". **84.** Campaign Emblem.

1962. Red Cross Fund. Flowers in natural colours. Background colours given.

503. **83.** 8 c.+4 c. olive.. .. 30 30
504. – 10 c.+5 c. blue .. 30 30
505. – 15 c.+6 c. brown .. 30 30
506. – 20 c.+10 c. violet .. 30 30
507. – 25 c.+12 c. turquoise.. 30 30
FLOWERS: 10 c. "Caesalpinia pulcherrima". 15 c. "Heliconia psittacorum". 20 c. "Lochnera rosea". 25 c. "Ixora macrothyrsa".

1962. Malaria Eradication.

508. **84.** 8 c. red 15 15
509. 10 c. blue 15 20

85. Stoelmans Guesthouse.

1962. Opening of New Hotels. Mult.

510. 10 c. Type **85** 30 30
511. 15 c. Torarica Hotel .. 30 30

86. Sisters' Residence. **87.** Wildfowl.

1962. Nunnery and Hospital of the Deaconesses. Multicoloured.

512. 10 c. Type **86** 30 30
513. 20 c. Hospital building .. 30 30

1962. Animal Protection Fund.
514. 87. 2 c.+1 c. red and blue .. 10 10
515. – 8 c.+2 c. red and black 20 20
516. – 10 c.+3 c. black & green 20 20
517. – 15 c.+4 c. black and red 25 25
ANIMALS: 8 c. Dog. 10 c. Donkey. 15 c. Horse.

88. Emblem in Hands. 89. "Freedom".

1963. Freedom from Hunger.
518. 88. 10 c. red 15 15
519. – 20 c. blue 15 15
DESIGN—VERT. 20 c. Tilling the land.

1963. Centenary of Abolition of Slavery in Dutch West Indies.
520. 89. 10 c. black and red .. 15 15
521. 20 c. black and green .. 15 15

90. Indian Girl. 91. U.S. "X-15" Aircraft.

1963. Child Welfare Fund.
522. 90. 8 c.+3 c. green .. 10 10
523. – 10 c.+4 c. brown .. 10 10
524. – 15 c.+10 c. blue .. 25 25
525. – 20 c.+10 c. red .. 25 25
526. – 40 c.+20 c. purple .. 35 35
PORTRAIT OF CHILDREN: 10 c. Bush negro. 15 c. Hindustani. 20 c. Indonesian. 40 c. Chinese.

1963. 150th Anniv. of Kingdom of the Netherlands. As T 199 of Netherlands but smaller, size 26×26 mm.
528. 199. 10 c. blk., bistre & blue 10 10

1964. Aeronautical and Astronomical Foundation, Surinam.
529. 3 c.+2 c. sepia and lake .. 15 15
530. 8 c.+4 c. sep., indigo & blue 20 20
531. 10 c.+5 c. sepia and green 20 20
532. 15 c.+7 c. sepia and brown 20 20
533. 20 c.+10 c. sepia & violet 25 25
DESIGNS: 3 c., 15 c. Type 91. 8 c. Foundation Flag. 10 c., 20 c. Agena B-Ranger rocket.

92. "Camp Fire". 93. Skipping.

1964. Scout Jamborette, Paramaribo, and 40th Anniv of Surinam Boy Scouts Assn.
534 92 3 c.+1 c. light yellow, yellow and bistre .. 15 15
535 8 c.+4 c. brown, blue and deep blue .. 15 15
536 10 c.+5 c. brown, red and deep red .. 15 15
537 20 c.+10 c. brown, green and blue .. 20 20

1964. Child Welfare.
538. 93. 8 c.+3 c. blue 10 10
539. – 10 c.+4 c. red 10 10
540. – 15 c.+9 c. green .. 10 10
541. – 20 c.+10 c. purple .. 15 15
DESIGNS: 10 c. Children swinging. 15 c. Child on scooter. 20 c. Child with hoop.

94. Crown and Wreath. 95. Expectant Mother ("Prenatal Care").

1964. 10th Anniv. of Statute of the Kingdom.
543. 94. 25 c. multicoloured .. 20 20

1965. 50th Anniv. of "Het Groene Kruis" (The Green Cross).
544. 95. 4 c.+2 c. green .. 15 15
545. – 10 c.+5 c. brown & grn. 15 15
546. – 15 c.+7 c. blue & green 15 15
547. – 25 c.+12 c. violet & grn. 20 20
DESIGNS: 10 c. Mother and baby ("Infant care"). 15 c. Young girl ("Child care"). 25 c. Old man ("Care in old age").

96. Abraham Lincoln. 97. I.C.Y. Emblem.

1965. Death Cent. of Abraham Lincoln.
548. 96. 25 c. purple and bistre .. 10 10

1965. Int. Co-operation Year.
549. 97. 10 c. orange and blue .. 10 10
550. 15 c. red and blue .. 10 10

98. Surinam Waterworks. 99. Bauxite Mine, Moengo.

1965. Air. Size 25×18 mm.
551. 98. 10 c. green 10 10
552. – 15 c. ochre 15 10
553. – 20 c. green 20 10
554. – 25 c. indigo 25 10
555. – 30 c. turquoise 25 15
556. – 35 c. red 35 20
557. – 40 c. orange 35 15
558. – 45 c. red 40 45
559. – 50 c. red 45 15
560. 98. 55 c. green 45 25
561. – 65 c. yellow 50 35
562. – 75 c. blue 55 35
DESIGNS: 15 c., 65 c. Brewery. 20 c. River scene. 25 c., 75 c. Timber yard. 30 c. Bauxite mine. 35 c., 50 c. Poelepantje Bridge. 40 c. Shipping. 45 c. Jetty.

For same designs but size 22×18 mm, see Nos. 843a/h.

1965. Opening of Brokopondo Power Station.
563. 99. 10 c. ochre 25 25
564. – 15 c. green 10 10
565. – 20 c. blue 10 10
566. – 25 c. red 15 15
DESIGNS: 15 c. Alum-earth works, Paranam. 20 c. Power station and dam, Afobaka. 25 c. Aluminium smeltery, Paranam.

100. Girl with Leopard. 101. Red-breasted Blackbird.

1965. Child Welfare.
567 100 4 c.+4 c. black, turquoise and green 15 15
568 – 10 c.+5 c. black, brown & light brown 15 15
569 – 15 c.+7 c. black, orange and red 15 15
570 – 25 c.+10 c. black, blue and cobalt 15 15
DESIGNS: 10 c. Boy with monkey. 15 c. Girl with tortoise. 25 c. Boy with rabbit.

1966. Intergovernmental Committee for European Migration (I.C.E.M.) Fund. As T 215 of Netherlands.
572. 10 c.+5 c. green & black .. 10 10
573. 25 c.+10 c. red and black 15 15

1966. Birds. Multicoloured.
575. 1 c. Type 101 .. .. 35 15
576. 2 c. Great kiskadee .. 35 15
577. 3 c. Silver-beaked tanager 35 15
578. 4 c. Ruddy ground dove .. 35 15
579. 5 c. Blue-grey tanager .. 35 15
580. 6 c. Straight-billed hermit 35 15
581. 8 c. Turquoise tanager .. 35 15
582. 10 c. Pale-breasted thrush 35 15

102. Hospital Building. 103. Father P. Donders.

1966. Opening of Central Hospital, Paramaribo. Multicoloured.
583. 10 c. Type 102 .. .. 10 10
584. 15 c. Different view .. 10 10

1966. Cent. of Redemptorists Mission.
585. 103. 4 c. black and brown .. 10 10
586. – 10 c. black, brown & red 10 10
587. – 15 c. black and ochre .. 10 10
588. – 25 c. black and lilac .. 15 15
DESIGNS: 10 c. Batavia Church, Coppename. 15 c. Mgr. J. B. Swinkels. 25 c. Paramaribo Cathedral.

104. Mary Magdalene and Disciples. 105. "Century Tree".

1966. Easter Charity.
589. 104. 10 c.+5 c. black, red and gold 15 15
590. 15 c.+8 c. black, violet and blue 15 15
591. 20 c.+10 c. black, yellow and blue 15 15
592. 25 c.+12 c. black, green and gold 20 20
593. 30 c.+15 c. black, blue and gold 20 20

On Nos. 590/3 the emblems at bottom left differ for each value. These represent various welfare organizations.

1966. Centenary of Surinam Parliament.
594 105 25 c. black, green & red 10 10
595 30 c. black, red & green 10 10

106. TV Mast, Eye and Globe. 107. Boys with Bamboo Gun.

1966. Inaug. of Surinam Television Service.
596. 106. 25 c. red and blue .. 10 10
597. 30 c. red and brown .. 10 10

1966. Child Welfare. Multicoloured.
598. 10 c.+5 c. Type 107 .. 10 10
599. 15 c.+8 c. Boy pouring liquid on another .. 15 15
600. 20 c.+10 c. Children re-
601. joicing 10 10
25 c.+12 c. Children on merry-go-round .. 15 15
602. 30 c.+15 c. Children decorating room .. 20 20

The designs symbolise New Year's Eve, the End of Lent, Liberation Day, Queen's Birthday and Christmas respectively.

108. Mining Bauxite, 1916. 109. "The Good Samaritan".

1966. 50th Anniv. of Surinam Bauxite Industry.
604. 108. 20 c. black, orge. & yell. 25 10
605. – 25 c. black, orge. & blue 25 10
DESIGN: 25 c. Modern bauxite plant.

1967. Easter Charity. Printed in black, background colours given.
606. 109. 10 c.+5 c. yellow .. 10 10
607. – 15 c.+8 c. blue .. 15 15
608. – 20 c.+10 c. ochre .. 15 15
609. – 25 c.+12 c. pink .. 20 20
610. – 30 c.+15 c. green .. 20 20
DESIGNS—15 to 30 c. Various episodes illustrating the parable of "The Good Samaritan".

110. Central Bank.

1967. 10th Anniv. of Surinam Central Bank.
611. 110. 10 c. black and yellow .. 10 10
612. – 25 c. black and lilac .. 10 10
DESIGN: 25 c. Aerial view of Central Bank.

111. Amelia Earhart and Aircraft in Flight. 112. Siva Nataraja and Ballerina's Foot.

1967. 30th Anniv. of Visit of Amelia Earhart to Surinam.
613. 111. 20 c. red and yellow .. 15 10
614. 25 c. green and yellow 15 10

1967. 20th Anniv. of Surinam Cultural Centre. Multicoloured.
615. 10 c. Type 112 .. .. 10 10
616. 25 c. "Bashi-Lele" mask and violin scroll .. 10 10

113. Fort Zeelandia, Paramaribo (c. 1670). 114. Stilt-walking.

1967. 300th Anniv. of Treaty of Breda. Multicoloured.
617. 10 c. Type 113 .. .. 15 15
618. 20 c. Nieuw Amsterdam (c. 1660) 20 20
619. 25 c. Breda Castle (c. 1667) 20 20

1967. Child Welfare. Multicoloured.
620. 10 c.+5 c. Type 114 .. 10 10
621. 15 c.+8 c. Playing marbles 20 20
622. 20 c.+10 c. Playing dibs 20 20
623. 25 c.+12 c. Kite-flying .. 20 20
624. 30 c.+15 c. "Cooking" game 25 25

115. "Cross of Ashes". 116. W.H.O. Emblem.

1968. Easter Charity.
626. 10 c.+5 c. grey and violet 10 10
627. 15 c.+8 c. green and red .. 15 15
628. 20 c.+10 c. green & yellow 20 20
629. 25 c.+12 c. black and grey 20 20
630. 30 c.+15 c. brown & yellow 20 20
DESIGNS: 10 c. Type 115 (Ash Wednesday); 15 c. Palm branches (Palm Sunday); 20 c. Cup and wafer (Maundy Thursday); 25 c. Cross (Good Friday); 30 c. Symbol of Christ (Easter).

1968. 20th Anniv. of W.H.O.
631. 116. 10 c. blue and purple .. 10 10
632. 25 c. violet and blue .. 20 20

117. Chandelier, Reformed Church. 119. Map of Joden Savanne.

118. Missionary Shop, 1768.

1968. 300th Anniv. of Reformed Church, Paramaribo.
633. 117. 10 c. blue 10 10
634. – 25 c. green 15 15
DESIGN: 25 c. No. 633 reversed; chandelier on left.

1968. Bicentenary of Evangelist Brothers' Missionary Store, G. Kersten and Co.
635. 118. 10 c. black and yellow .. 10 10
636. – 25 c. black and blue .. 15 15
637. – 30 c. black and mauve 15 15
DESIGNS: 25 c. Paramaribo Church and Kersten's store, 1868; 30 c. Kersten's modern store, Paramaribo.

1968. Restoration of Joden Savanne Synagogue. Multicoloured.
638. 20 c. Type **119** 40 40
639. 25 c. Synagogue, 1685 .. 40 40
640. 30 c. Gravestone at Joden Savanne, dated 1733 .. 50 50

120. Playing Hopscotch. **121.** Western Hemisphere illuminated by Full Moon.

1968. Child Welfare.
641. **120.** 10 c.+5 c. black & brn. 10 10
642. – 15 c.+8 c. black & blue 15 15
643. – 20 c.+10 c. black & pink 15 15
644. – 25 c.+12 c. black & grn. 25 25
645. – 30 c.+15 c. blk. & lilac 30 30
DESIGNS: 15 c. Forming "pyramids"; 20 c. Playing ball; 25 c. Handicrafts; 30 c. Tug-of-war.

1969. Easter Charity.
647. **121.** 10 c.+5 c. blue & pale blue 25 25
648. 15 c.+8 c. grey & yellow 25 25
649. 20 c.+10 c. turq. & green 30 30
650. 25 c.+12 c. brown & buff 30 30
651. 30 c.+15 c. violet & grey 30 30

122. Cayman. **123.** Mahatma Gandhi.

1969. Opening of Surinam Zoo, Paramaribo. Multicoloured.
652. 10 c. Type **122** 45 35
653. 20 c. Common squirrel-monkey (vert.) 45 35
654. 25 c. Nine-banded armadillo 45 35

1969. Birth Cent. of Mahatma Gandhi.
655. **123.** 25 c. black and red .. 40 25

124. I.L.O. Emblem. **125.** Pillow Fight.

1969. 50th Anniv. of Int. Labour Organization.
656. **124.** 10 c. green and black .. 15 15
657. 25 c. red and black .. 20 20

1969. Child Welfare.
658. 10 c.+5 c. purple and blue 10 10
659. 15 c.+8 c. brown & yellow 25 25
660. 20 c.+10 c. blue and grey 20 20
661. 25 c.+12 c. blue and pink 25 25
662. 30 c.+15 c. brown & green 25 25
DESIGNS: 10 c. Type **125**. 15 c. Eating contest. 20 c. Pole-climbing. 25 c. Sack-race. 30 c. Obstacle-race.

1969. 15th Anniv of Statute for the Kingdom. As T **240** of Netherlands.
664 25 c. multicoloured .. 25 25

127. "Flower". **128.** "1950–1970".

1970. Easter Charity. "Wonderful Nature". Multicoloured.
665. 10 c.+5 c. Type **127** .. 55 55
666. 15 c.+8 c. "Butterfly" .. 55 55
667. 20 c.+10 c. "Bird" .. 55 55
668. 25 c.+12 c. "Sun" .. 55 55
669. 30 c.+15 c. "Star" .. 55 55

1970. 20th Anniv. of Secondary Education in Surinam.
670. **128.** 10 c. yellow, green & brn. 10 10
671. 25 c. yellow, blue & grn. 15 15

129. New U.P.U. Headquarters Building. **130.** U.N. "Diamond".

1970. New U.P.U. Headquarters Building.
672. **129.** 10 c. vio., blue & turq. 15 15
673. – 25 c. black and red .. 20 20
DESIGN: 25 c. Aerial view of H.Q. Building.

1970. 25th Anniv. of United Nations.
674. **130.** 10 c. multicoloured .. 15 15
675. 25 c. multicoloured .. 20 20

131. Aircraft over Paramaribo Town Plan. **132.** Football Pitch (ball in centre).

1970. " 40 years of Inland Airmail Flights ".
676. **131.** 10 c. grey, ultram. & bl. 25 25
677. – 20 c. grey, red & yell. 25 25
678. – 25 c. grey, red and pink 25 25
DESIGNS: As Type **131**, but showing different background maps—20 c. Totness. 25 c. Nieuw-Nickerie.

1970. 50th Anniv. of Surinam Football Association.
679. **132.** 4 c. brn., yell. & black 10 10
680. – 10 c. brn., olive & black 20 20
681. – 15 c. brn., grn. & black 20 20
682. – 25 c. brn., grn. & black 30 30
DESIGNS: As Type **132**, but with ball 10 c. in " corner "; 15 c. at side (" throw-in "); 25 c. at top (" goal ").

133. Beethoven (1786). **134.** Cocoi Heron.

1970. Child Welfare. Birth Bicentenary of Beethoven (composer).
683. **133.** 10 c.+5 c. yellow, drab and green .. 75 60
684. – 15 c.+8 c. yellow, drab and red .. 80 65
685. – 20 c.+10 c. yellow, drab and blue .. 80 65
686. – 25 c.+12 c. yellow, drab and orange .. 85 60
687. – 30 c.+15 c. yellow, drab and violet .. 85 60
DESIGNS: Beethoven 15 c. 1804; 20 c. 1812; 25 c. 1814; 30 c. 1827.

1971. 25th Anniv. of Netherlands–Surinam–Netherlands Antilles Air Service. Multicoloured.
689. 15 c. Type **134** .. 65 50
690. 20 c. Greater flamingo .. 85 55
691. 25 c. Scarlet macaw .. 95 55

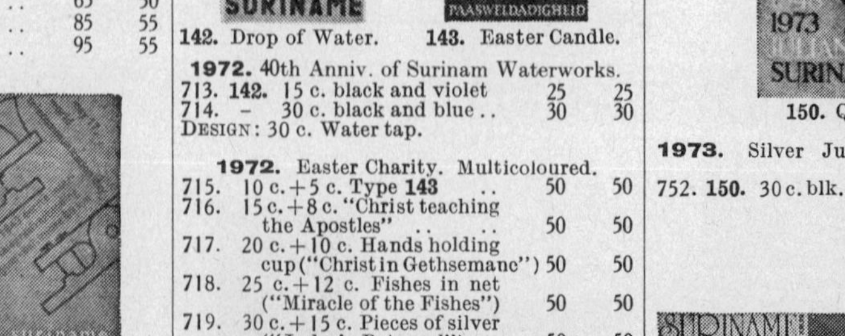

135. Donkey and Palm. **136.** Morse Key.

1971. Easter. The Bible Story. Multicoloured.
692. 10 c.+5 c. Type **135** .. 55 55
693. 15 c.+8 c. Cockerel .. 60 60
694. 20 c.+10 c. Lamb 60 60
695. 25 c.+12 c. Crown of Thorns 60 60
696. 30 c.+15 c. Sun ("The Resurrection") 60 60

1971. World Telecommunications Day. Mult.
697. 15 c. Type **136** 45 45
698. 20 c. Telephones 50 50
699. 25 c. Lunar module and telescope 60 60
EVENTS: 15 c. First National telegraph, Washington—Baltimore, 1843. 20 c. First international telephone communication, England—Sweden, 1926. 25 c. First interplanetary television communication, Earth—Moon, 1969.

137. Prince Bernhard. **138.** Population Map.

1971. Prince Bernhard's 60th Birthday.
700 **137** 25 c. multicoloured .. 30 25

1971. 50th Anniv of First Census and Introduction of Civil Registration.
701 **138** 15 c. blue, black & red 15 15
702 30 c. red, black & blue 25 25
DESIGN: 30 c. "Individual" representing civil registration.

139. William Mogge's Map of Surinam.

1971. 300th Anniv. of First Surinam Map.
703. **139.** 30 c. brown on yellow 65 45

140. Leap-frog. **141.** Plan of Albina.

1971. Child Welfare. Details from Brueghel's "Children's Games". Multicoloured.
704. 10 c. + 5 c. Type **140** .. 65 65
705 15 c. + 8 c. Strewing flowers 65 65
706. 20 c. + 10 c. Rolling hoop 65 65
707. 25 c. + 12 c. Playing ball 70 70
708. 30 c. + 15 c. Stilt-walking 70 70

1971. 125th Anniv. of Albina Settlement.
710. **141.** 15 c. black on blue .. 30 30
711. – 20 c. black on green .. 30 30
712. – 25 c. black on yellow 30 30
DESIGNS—HORIZ. 20 c. Albina and River Marowijne. VERT. 25 c. August Kappler (naturalist and founder).

142. Drop of Water. **143.** Easter Candle.

1972. 40th Anniv. of Surinam Waterworks.
713. **142.** 15 c. black and violet 25 25
714. – 30 c. black and blue .. 30 30
DESIGN: 30 c. Water tap.

1972. Easter Charity. Multicoloured.
715. 10 c.+5 c. Type **143** .. 50 50
716. 15 c.+8 c. "Christ teaching the Apostles" 50 50
717. 20 c.+10 c. Hands holding cup ("Christ in Gethsemane") 50 50
718. 25 c.+12 c. Fishes in net ("Miracle of the Fishes") 50 50
719. 30 c.+15 c. Pieces of silver ("Judas's Betrayal") .. 50 50

144. "Eucyane bicolor". **145.** Air-letter Motif.

1972. Moths and Butterflies. Multicoloured.
720 15 c. Type **144** 30 15
721 20 c. Gold drop 30 15
722 25 c. Orange swallowtail .. 40 20
723 30 c. White tailed page .. 40 10
724 35 c. "Stalachtis calliope" 60 35
725 40 c. "Stalachtis phlegia" 60 25
726 45 c. Malachite 60 10
727 50 c. Spear-winged cattle heart 75 10
728 55 c. Red anartia .. 90 50
729 60 c. Five continent butterfly .. .. 1·00 80
730 65 c. Doris .. .. 1·00 50
731 70 c. "Nessaea obrinus" .. 1·10 75
732 75 c. Cracker .. .. 1·00 45

1972. 50th Anniv. of 1st Airmail in Surinam.
733. **145.** 15 c. red and blue .. 20 20
734. 30 c. blue and red .. 25 25

146. Doll and Toys (kindergarten). **147.** Giant Tree.

1972. Child Welfare. Multicoloured.
735. 10 c.+5 c. Type **146** .. 50 45
736. 15 c.+8 c. Clock and abacus (primary education) .. 50 45
737. 20 c.+10 c. Blocks (primary education) 50 45
738. 25 c.+12 c. Molecule complex (secondary education) 55 50
739. 30 c.+15 c. Wrench and blue-print (technical education) 55 50

1972. 25th Anniv. of Surinam Forestry Commission.
741. **147.** 15 c. brown & yellow 25 25
742. – 20 c. brn., black & blue 30 30
743. – 30 c. choc., brn. & grn. 40 40
DESIGNS: 20 c. Aerial transport of logs. 30 c. Planting tree.

148. " The Storm on the Lake ". **149.** Hindu Peasant Woman.

1973. Easter Charity. Jesus's Life and Death. Multicoloured.
744. 10 c.+5 c. Type **148** .. 50 50
745. 15 c.+8 c. "Washing the Disciples' Feet" .. 50 50
746. 20 c.+10 c. "Jesus taken to Execution" 50 50
747. 25 c.+12 c. The Cross .. 50 50
748. 30 c.+15 c. "The Men of Emmaus" 50 50

1973. Centenary of Arrival of Indian Immigrants in Surinam.
749 **149** 15 c. violet and yellow 25 20
750 – 25 c. red and grey .. 25 20
751 – 30 c. orange and blue 35 30
DESIGNS: 25 c. J. F. A. Cateau van Rosevelt, Head of Department of Immigration, holding map. 30 c. Symbols of immigration.

150. Queen Juliana.

1973. Silver Jubilee of Queen Juliana's Reign.
752. **150.** 30 c. blk., orge. & silver 50 50

151. Florence Nightingale and Red Cross. **152.** Interpol Emblem.

1973. 30th Anniv. of Surinam Red Cross.
753. **151.** 30 c.+10 c. multicoloured 70 70

1973. 50th Anniv. of International Criminal Police Organization (Interpol). Multicoloured.

754. 15 c. Type **152** 40 25

755. 30 c. Emblem within passport stamp 40 30

153. Flower. 154. Carrier-pigeons.

1973. Child Welfare.

756. **153.** 10 c.+5 c. multicoloured 30 30

757. – 15 c.+8 c. green, brn. and emerald 45 45

758. – 20 c.+10 c. violet, blue and green 35 35

759. – 25 c.+12 c. multicoloured 55 55

760. – 30 c.+15 c. multicoloured 55 55

DESIGNS: 15 c. Tree. 20 c. Dog. 25 c. House. 30 c. Doll.

1973. Stamp Centenary.

762. **154.** 15 c. green and blue 15 15

763. – 25 c. multicoloured 25 25

764. – 30 c. multicoloured 60 60

DESIGNS: 25 c. Postman. 30 c. Map and postal routes.

155. "Quassia amara". 156. Nurse and Blood Transfusion Equipment.

1974. Easter Charity Flowers. Multicoloured.

765. 10 c.+5 c. Type **155** 45 45

766. 15 c.+8 c. "Passiflora quadrangularis" 45 45

767. 20 c.+10 c. "Combretum rotundifolium" 45 45

768. 25 c.+12 c. "Cassia alata" 50 50

769. 30 c.+15 c. "Asclepias curassavica" 60 50

1974. 75th Anniv. of Surinam Medical School. Multicoloured.

770. 15 c. Type **156** 20 15

771. 30 c. Microscope slide and oscilloscope scanner 30 20

157. Aerial Crop-spraying. 158. Commemorative Text superimposed on Early Newspaper.

1974. 25th Anniv. of Mechanised Agriculture. Multicoloured.

772. 15 c. Type **157** 20 15

773. 30 c. Fertiliser plant 25 20

1974. Bicentenary of Surinam's "Weekly Wednesday" Newspaper.

774. **158.** 15 c. multicoloured 20 15

775. 30 c. multicoloured 25 20

159. Scout and Tent. 160. G.P.O., Paramaribo.

1974. "50 Years of Scouting in Surinam". Multicoloured.

776. 10 c.+5 c. Type **159** 35 35

777. 15 c.+8 c. Jamboree emblem 35 35

778. 20 c.+10 c. Scouts and badge 40 40

1974. Cent. of Universal Postal Union.

779. **160.** 15 c. black and brown 20 20

780. – 30 c. black and blue 25 25

DESIGN: 30 c. G.P.O., Paramaribo (different view).

161. Girl with Fruit.

1974. Child Welfare.

781. **161.** 10 c.+5 c. green, emerald and pink 25 25

782. – 15 c.+8 c. brown, mve. and green 35 35

783. – 20 c.+10 c. yellow, orange and mauve 35 35

784. – 25 c.+12 c. brown, lilac and yellow 55 55

785. – 30 c.+15 c. cobalt, blue and lilac 65 65

DESIGNS: 15 c. Birds and nest. 20 c. Mother and Child with flower. 25 c. Young boy in cornfield. 30 c. Children at play.

162. Panning for Gold. 163. "I am the Good Shepherd".

1975. Cent. of Prospecting Concession Policy.

787. **162.** 15 c. brown and bistre 25 20

788. – 30 c. purple and red 30 25

DESIGN: 30 c. Claws of modern excavator.

1975. Easter Charity.

789. **163.** 15 c.+5 c. yellow and green 45 40

790. – 20 c.+10 c. yellow and blue 60 60

791. – 30 c.+15 c. yellow and red 70 65

792. – 35 c.+20 c. blue and violet 70 65

DESIGNS—Quotations from the New Testament. 20 c. "I do not know the man". 30 c. "He is not here; He has been raised again". 35 c. "Because you have seen Me you have found faith. Happy are they who never saw Me and yet have found faith".

164. "Looking to Equality, Education and Peace". 165. "Weights and Measures".

1975. International Women's Year.

793. **164.** 15 c.+5 c. blue & green 60 55

794. 30 c.+15 c. vio. & mauve 60 55

1975. Centenary of Metre Convention.

795. **165.** 15 c. multicoloured 30 30

796. 25 c. multicoloured 30 30

796a. 30 c. multicoloured 40 30

166. Caribbean Water Jug. 167. "Labour and Technology".

1975. Child Welfare. Multicoloured.

797. 15 c.+5 c. Type **166** 55 55

798. 20 c.+10 c. Indian arrow-head 85 75

799. 30 c.+15 c. "Maluana" (protection against evil spirits) 85 85

800. 35 c.+20 c. Indian arrow-head (different) 2·40 2·25

1975. Independence. "Nation in Development". Multicoloured.

802. 25 c. Type **167** 20 20

803. 50 c. Open book ("Education and Art") 50 50

804. 75 c. Hands with ball ("Physical Training) 70 70

168. Central Bank, Paramaribo. 169. "Oncidium lanceanum".

1975.

805. **168.** 1 g. blk., mve. and pur. 90 25

806. 1½ g. blk., orge. & brn. 1·50 25

807. 2½ g. blk., red and brn. 2·75 35

808. 5 g. blk., emer. & grn. 5·50 55

808a. 10 g. blk., bl. & dp. bl. 11·00 1·10

1976. Surinam Orchids. Multicoloured.

809. 1 c. Type **169** 5 5

810. 2 c. "Epidendrum stenopetalum" 5 5

811. 3 c. "Brassia lanceana" 5 5

812. 4 c. "Epidendrum ibaguense" 5 5

813. 5 c. "Epidendrum fragans" 5 5

170. Surinam Flag. 171. "Feeding the Hungry".

1976. Multicoloured.

814. 25 c. Type **170** 30 30

815. 35 c. Surinam arms 35 35

1976. Easter. Paintings in Alkmaar Church. Multicoloured.

816. 20 c.+10 c. Type **171** 30 30

817. 25 c.+15 c. "Visiting the Sick" 35 35

818. 30 c.+15 c. "Clothing the Naked" 40 40

819. 35 c.+15 c. "Burying the Dead" 45 55

820. 50 c.+25 c. "Refreshing the Thirsty" 70 80

172. "Pomacanthus semicirculatus".

1976. Fishes. Multicoloured.

822. 1 c. Type **172** (postage) 5 5

823. 2 c. "Adioryx diadema" 5 5

824. 3 c. "Pogonoculius zebra" 5 5

825. 4 c. "Balistes vetula" 5 5

826. 5 c. "Myripristis jacobus" 5 5

827. 35 c. "Chaetodon unimaculatus" (air) 40 35

828. 60 c. "Centropyge loriculus" 70 60

829. 95 c. "Chaetodon collare" 1·00 90

173. Early Telephone and Switchboard.

1976. Telephone Centenary.

830. 20 c. Type **173** 25 20

831. 35 c. Globe, satellite and modern telephone 40 35

174. "Anansi Tori" (A. Baag).

1976. Paintings by Surinam Artists. Mult.

832. 20 c. Type **174** 25 20

833. 30 c. "Surinam Now" (R. Chang). 35 30

834. 35 c. "Lamentation" (N. Hatterman) (vert.) 45 40

835. 50 c. "Chess-players" (Q. Jan Telting) 60 55

175. "Join or Die" (Franklin's "Divided Snake" poster of 1754).

1976. Bicentenary of American Revolution.

836. **175.** 20 c. blk., grn. & cream 25 20

837. 60 c. black, red and cream 75 75

176. Pekinese. 177. "Ionopsis utricularioides".

1976. Child Welfare. Pet Dogs.

838. 20 c.+10 c. Type **176** 40 40

839. 25 c.+10 c. Alsatian 45 45

840. 30 c.+10 c. Dachshund 55 55

841. 35 c.+15 c. Surinam breed 60 60

842. 50 c.+25 c. Mongrel 85 85

1976. As Nos. 551/7 and new values but size 22×18 mm.

843a – 5 c. brown 10 10

843b **98** 10 c. green 15 10

843c – 20 c. green 25 15

843d – 25 c. blue 25 15

843e – 30 c. green 30 15

843f – 35 c. red 35 20

843g – 40 c. orange 50 25

843h – 60 c. red 75 35

NEW VALUES: 5 c. Brewery. 60 c. Jetty.

1977. Surinam Orchids. Multicoloured.

844. 20 c. Type **177** 30 25

845. 30 c. "Rodiguezia secunda" 45 40

846. 35 c. "Oncidium pusillum" 50 45

847. 55 c. "Sobralia sessulis" 75 65

848. 60 c. "Octomeria surinamensis" 80 70

178. Javanese Costume. 179. Triptych, left panel (Jan Mostaert).

1977. Surinam Costumes (1st series). Mult.

849. 10 c. Type **178** 12 10

850. 15 c. Forest Negro 20 15

851. 35 c. Chinese 40 35

852. 60 c. Creole 75 65

853. 75 c. Aborigine Indian 95 85

854. 1 g. Hindustani 1·25 1·25

DESIGNS: 15 c. to 1 g. Various women's festival costumes.

See also Nos. 906/11.

1977. Easter. Multicoloured.

855. 20 c.+10 c. Type **179** 25 30

856. 25 c.+15 c. Right panel 35 40

857. 30 c.+15 c. Right panel 40 45

858. 35 c.+15 c. Centre panel (30×38 mm.) 50 55

859. 50 c.+25 c. Left panel 70 80

20 c. and 25 c. show the triptych closed, the 30 c. and 50 c. show designs on the reverse of the doors, and the 35 c. shows the centre panel.

180. Green Honeycreeper.

1977. Air. Birds. Multicoloured.

860. 20 c. Red-breasted Blackbird 60 35

861. 25 c. Type **180** 70 40

862. 30 c. Paradise Tanager 75 45

863. 40 c. Spot-tailed Nightjar 90 55

864. 45 c. Yellow-backed Tanager 95 60

865. 50 c. White-tailed Golden-throat 1·00 70

866. 55 c. Grey-breasted Sabre-wing 1·10 75

867. 60 c. Caica Parrot (vert.) 1·10 80

868. 65 c. Cuvier's Toucan (vert.) 1·25 90

869. 70 c. Crimson-hooded Manakin (vert.) 1·40 95

870. 75 c. Hawk-headed Parrot (vert.) 1·50 1·00

871. 80 c. Spangled Cotinga (vert.) 1·75 1·10

872. 85 c. Black-tailed Trogon (vert.) 1·90 1·25

872a 90 c. Orange-winged Amazon (vert.) 1·75 1·10

873. 95 c. Black-banded Owl (vert.) 2·00 1·40

181. " Liopropoma carmabi ".

1977. Fishes. Multicoloured.
875. 1 c. Type **181** (postage) .. 5 5
876. 2 c. " Holacanthus ciliaris " 5 5
877. 3 c. " Opistognathus aurifrons " 5 5
878. 4 c. " Anisotremus virginicus " 5 5
879. 5 c. " Gramma loreto " .. 5 5
880. 60 c. " Chaetodon striatus " (air) 75 65
881. 90 c. " Bodianus pulchellus " 1·10 95
882. 120 c. " Centropyge argi " 1·50 1·40

182. Edison's Phonograph, 1877.

1977. Cent. of Sound Reproduction. Mult.
883. 20 c. Type **182** 25 20
883a. 60 c. Modern gramophone turntable 75 75

183. Paddle Steamer " Curacao ".

185. Dog.

1977. 150th Anniv. of Regular Passenger Steam Service with Netherlands.
884. **183.** 5 c. blue and pale blue 15 10
885. – 15 c. red and orange .. 30 15
886. – 30 c. black and ochre .. 40 35
887. – 35 c. black and olive .. 50 40
888. – 60 c. black and lilac .. 80 70
889. – 95 c. green & pale green 1·50 1·50
DESIGNS: 15 c. Hellevoetsluis port. 30 c. Chart of steamer route from Hellevoetsluis to Paramaribo. 35 c. Log of " Curacao ". 60 c. Chart of Paramaribo and 1852 postmark. 95 c. Passenger liner " Stuyvesant ".

1977. Surch.
890. – 1 c. on 25 c. multicoloured (No. 722) .. 10 5
891. **144.** 4 c. on 15 c. mult. .. 10 5
892. – 4 c. on 30 c. multicoloured (No. 723) .. 10 5
893. – 5 c. on 40 c. multicoloured (No. 725) .. 10 5
894. – 10 c. on 75 c. multicoloured (No. 732) .. 15 15
The word " LUCHTPOST " (" AIR-MAIL "). on the original stamp is obliterated by bars.

1977. Child Welfare. Multicoloured.
895. 20 c.+10 c. Type **185** .. 30 35
896. 25 c.+15 c. Monkey .. 40 45
897. 30 c.+15 c. Rabbit .. 45 50
898. 35 c.+15 c. Cat 50 55
899. 50 c.+25 c. Parrot .. 75 80

186. " Passiflora quadrangularis ".

187. Javanese Costume.

1978. Flowers. Multicoloured.
901. 20 c. Type **186** 25 20
902. 30 c. " Centropogon surinamensis " 35 30
903. 55 c. " Gloxinia perennis " 65 55
904. 60 c. " Hydrocleys nymphoides " 70 60
905. 75 c. " Clusia grandiflora " 85 75

1978. Surinam Costumes (2nd series). Mult.
906. 10 c. Type **187** 12 10
907. 20 c. Forest Negro .. 25 20
908. 35 c. Chinese 40 35
909. 60 c. Creole 75 60
910. 75 c. Aborigine Indian .. 85 75
911. 1 g. Hindustani .. .. 1·25 1·25

188. Cross and Halo.

189. Municipal Church, 1783.

1978. Easter Charity.
912. **188.** 20 c.+10 c. mult. .. 30 35
913. – 25 c.+15 c., brn., yell. and red 45 50
914. – 30 c.+15 c. brown, red and yellow 50 55
915. – 35 c.+15 c. brown, violet and red .. 55 60
916. – 60 c.+30 c. brown, yellow and green .. 1·00 1·10
DESIGNS: 25 c. Serpent and Cross. 30 c. Blood and lamb. 35 c. Passover dish and chalice. 60 c. Eclipse and crucifix.

1978. Bicentenary of Church of Evangelistic Brothers Community.
917. **189.** 10 c. brn., blk. & blue 10 10
918. – 20 c. black and grey .. 20 20
919. – 55 c. black and purple 55 55
920. – 60 c. black and orange 70 70
DESIGNS: 20 c. Brother Johannes King, 1830–1899. 55 c. Modern Municipal Church. 60 c. Brother Johannes Raillard, 1939–1954.

190. " Nannacara anomala ".

192. Coconuts.

1978. Tropical Fish. Multicoloured.
921. 1 c. Type **190** (postage) .. 5 5
922. 2 c. " Leporinus fasciatus " 5 5
923. 3 c. " Pristella riddlei " .. 5 5
924. 4 c. " Nannostomus beckfordi " 5 5
925. 5 c. " Rivulus agilae " .. 5 5
926. 60 c. " Astyanax species " (air) 75 65
927. 90 c. " Corydoras wotroi " 1·25 1·10
928. 120 c. " Gasteropelecus sternicla " .. .. 1·50 1·40

1978. Fruits. Multicoloured.
930 5 c. Type **192** 5 5
931 10 c. Citrus 10 10
932 15 c. Papaya 15 15
933a 20 c. Bananas 15 15
934 25 c. Sour-sop 25 25
934b 30 c. Cacao 25 25
935 35 c. Water melons .. 35 35

193. Children's Heads and Kittens.

194. Daedalus and Icarus.

1978. Child Welfare.
936. **193.** 20 c.+10 c. mult. .. 25 30
937. – 25 c.+15 c. mult. .. 35 40
938. – 30 c.+15 c. mult. .. 40 45
939. – 35 c.+15 c. mult. .. 40 45
940. – 60 c.+30 c. mult. .. 80 90
DESIGNS: 25 c. to 60 c. Different designs showing kittens at play.

1978. 75th Anniv. of First Powered Flight. Multicoloured.
942. 20 c. Type **194** 25 20
943. 60 c. " Flyer I " (horiz.) .. 60 50
944. 95 c. Douglas " DC–8 " (horiz.) 85 70
945. 125 c. " Concorde " (horiz.) 1·25 1·25

195. Black Curassow.

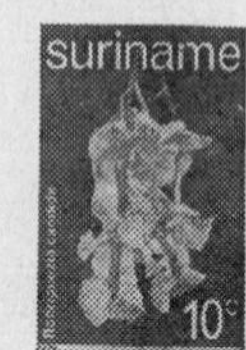

196. " Rodriguezia candida ".

1979. Air.
946. **195.** 5 g. purple .. .. 7·50 6·00

1979. Orchids. Multicoloured.
947. 10 c. Type **196** 12 10
948. 20 c. " Stanhopea grandiflora " 25 20
949. 35 c. " Scuticaria steelei " 40 35
950. 60 c. " Bollea violacea " .. 65 60

197. Javanese Dance.

198. Church, Chalice and Cross.

1979. Dancing Costumes. Multicoloured.
951. 5 c. Type **197** 5 5
952. 10 c. Forest Negro .. 10 10
953. 15 c. Chinese 20 15
954. 20 c. Creole 20 20
955. 25 c. Aborigine Indian .. 25 20
956. 25 c. Hindustani 35 35

1979. Easter Charity.
957. **198.** 20 c.+10 c. multicoloured 25 30
958. – 30 c.+15 c. multicoloured 35 40
959. – 35 c.+15 c. multicoloured 40 45
960. – 40 c.+20 c. multicoloured 45 50
961. – 60 c.+30 c. multicoloured 70 80
DESIGNS: 30 c. to 60 c. Different Churches.

199. " Equetus pulchellus ".

1979. Fishes. Multicoloured.
962. 1 c. Type **199** (postage) .. 5 5
963. 2 c. " Apogon binotatus " 5 5
964. 3 c. " Anisotremus virginicus " 5 5
965. 5 c. " Bodianus rufus " .. 5 5
966. 35 c. " Microspathodon chrysurus " 35 35
967. 60 c. " Cantherinus macrocerus " (air) 65 65
968. 90 c. " Holocentrus rufus " 95 95
969. 120 c. " Holacanthus tricolor " .. .. 1·25 1·25

200. Javanese Wooden Head.

1979. Art Objects. Multicoloured.
970. 20 c. Type **200** 20 20
971. 35 c. American Indian hair ornament 30 30
972. 60 c. Javanese horse's head 55 55

201. S.O.S. Children's Village and Emblem.

202. Sir Rowland Hill.

1979. International Year of the Child. Multicoloured.
973. 20 c. Type **201** 20 15
974. 60 c. Different view of Village, and emblem .. 55 55

1979. Death Centenary of Sir Rowland Hill.
975 **202** 1 g. green and yellow .. 1·00 1·00

203. Bird, Running Youth and Blood Transfusion Bottle.

204. Javanese.

1979. Child Welfare.
976. **203.** 20 c.+10 c. blk., vio. & red 25 30
977. 30 c.+15 c. blk., red & violet 40 45
978. 35 c.+15 c. mult. .. 45 50
979. 40 c.+20 c. mult. .. 50 55
980. 60 c.+30 c. mult. .. 70 80

1980. Children's Costumes. Multicoloured.
982. 10 c. Type **204** 10 8
983. 15 c. Forest negro .. 15 12
984. 25 c. Chinese 25 20
985. 60 c. Creole 55 55
986. 90 c. Indian 80 80
987. 1 g. Hindustani 85 85

205. Handshake and Rotary Emblem.

206. Church Interior.

1980. 75th Anniv. of Rotary International. Each blue and yellow.
988. 20 c. Type **205** 20 20
989. 60 c. Globe and rotary emblem 50 50

1980. Easter Charity. Various Easter symbols.
990. **206.** 20 c.+10 c. mult. .. 25 30
991. – 30 c.+15 c. mult. .. 40 45
992. – 40 c.+20 c. mult. .. 50 55
993. – 50 c.+25 c. mult. .. 60 70
994. – 60 c.+30 c. mult. .. 70 80

207. Mail Coach.

208. Weightlifting.

1980. " London 1980 " International Stamp Exhibition.
995. **207.** 50 c. yellow, blk. & bl. 40 40
996. – 1 g. yellow, blk. & pur. 80 80
997. – 2 g. pink, blk. & turq. 1·60 1·60
DESIGNS: 1 g. Sir Rowland Hill. 2 g. People posting letters.

1980. Olympic Games, Moscow.
999. **208.** 20 c. multicoloured .. 20 20
1000. – 30 c. multicoloured .. 25 25
1001. – 50 c. green, yellow & red 40 40
1002. – 75 c. multicoloured .. 60 60
1003. – 150 c. multicoloured 1·25 1·25
DESIGNS: 30 c. Diving. 50 c. Gymnastics. 75 c. Basketball. 150 c. Running.

209. " Osteoglossum bicirrhosum ".

210. Anansi disguised as Spider.

1980. Tropical Fishes. Multicoloured.
1005 10 c. Type **209** (postage) 10 8
1006 15 c. "Colossoma species" 15 12
1007 25 c "Hemigrammus pulcher" 25 20
1008 30 c. "Petitella georgiae" 30 25
1009 45 c. "Copeina guttata" 45 40
1010 60 c. "Symhysodon discus" (air) 60 55
1011 75 c. "Aequidens curviceps" 70 65
1012 90 c. "Catoprion mento" 80 75

1980. Child Welfare. " The Story of Anansi and his Creditors ".
1013. **210.** 20 c.+10 c. bistre and yellow 30 35
1014. – 25 c.+15 c. yellow, brown and orange 35 40
1015. – 30 c.+15 c. brown, red and orange .. 40 45
1016. – 35 c.+15 c. green, bright grn. & yell. 45 50
1017. – 60 c.+30 c. mult. .. 80 90
DESIGNS: (Anansi in various disguises) 25 c. Bear. 30 c. Cockerel. 35 c. Hunter. 60 c. Beetle.

212. Old Woman Reading.

213. " Passiflora laurifolia ".

1980. Welfare of the Aged. Multicoloured.
1020. 25 c.+10 c. Type **212** .. 30 35
1021. 50 c.+15 c. Old man tending flowers .. 50 60
1022. 75 c.+20 c. Grandfather and grandchildren .. 80 90

1981. Flower Drawings by Maria Sibylle Merian. Multicoloured.
1023. 20 c. Type **213** 20 20
1024. 30 c. "Aphelandra pectinata" 30 25
1025. 60 c. "Caesalpinia pulcherrima" 55 55
1026. 75 c. "Hibiscus mutabilis" 70 70
1027. 1 g. 25 "Hippeastrum puniceum" .. .. 1·25 1·25

214. Justice and Text "Renewal of the Governmental and Political Order". **215.** Christ with Jug.

1981. The Four Renewals.
1028 – 30 c. yellow, brown and deep yellow .. 25 25
1029 – 60 c. orge, brn & red 50 50
1030 – 75 c. green, deep green and olive .. 60 60
1031 214 1 g. deep yellow, green and yellow .. 80 80
DESIGNS: 30 c. "Renewal of the Economic Order". 60 c. "Renewal of the Educational Order". 75 c. "Renewal of the Social Order".

1981. Easter Charity. Multicoloured.
1033. 20 c.+10 c. Type **215** .. 25 30
1034. 30 c.+15 c. Christ and pointing hand .. 40 45
1035. 50 c.+25 c. Christ and Roman soldier .. 60 65
1036. 60 c.+30 c. Christ wearing crown of thorns .. 70 80
1037. 75 c.+35 c. Christ and Mary 80 90

218. "Phyllomedusa hypochondrialis".

1981. Frogs. Multicoloured.
1040. 40 c. Type **218** (postage) 40 35
1041. 50 c. "Leptodactylus pentadactylus" .. 45 40
1042. 60 c. "Hyla boans" .. 55 50
1043. 75 c. "Phyllomedusa burmeisteri" (vert.) (air) 70 65
1044. 1 g. "Dendrobates tinctorius" (vert.) .. 90 85
1045. 1 g. 25 "Bufo guttatus" (vert.) .. .. .. 1·25 1·25

219. Deaf Child.

1981. International Year of Disabled Persons.
1046. **219.** 50 c. yellow and green 40 40
1047. – 100 c. yell. and green 80 80
1048. – 150 c. yellow and red 1·25 1·25
DESIGNS: 100 c. Child reading braille. 150 c. Woman in wheelchair.

220. Planter's House on the Parakreek River. **221.** Indian Girl.

1981. Illustrations to "Journey to Surinam" by P. I. Benoit. Multicoloured.
1049. 20 c. Type **220** 20 20
1050. 30 c. Sarameca Street, Paramaribo 25 25
1051. 75 c. Negro hamlet, Paramaribo 60 60
1052. 1 g. Fish market, Paramaribo 80 80
1053. 1 g. 25 Blaauwe Berg Cascade .. .. 1·00 1·00

1981. Child Welfare. Multicoloured.
1055. 20 c.+10 c. Type **221** .. 25 30
1056. 30 c.+15 c. Negro girl .. 40 45
1057. 50 c.+25 c. Hindustani girl 60 70
1058. 60 c.+30 c. Javanese girl 70 80
1059. 75 c.+35 c. Chinese girl 80 90

222. Satellites orbiting Earth.

1982. Peaceful Uses of Outer Space. Mult.
1061. 35 c. Type **222** 35 30
1062. 65 c. Space Shuttle .. 60 55
1063. 1 g. U.S.–Russian space link 85 85

223. "Caretta caretta". **224.** Pattern from Stained Glass Window.

1982. Turtles. Multicoloured.
1064. 5 c. Type **223** (postage) .. 5 5
1065. 10 c. "Chelonia mydas" 10 8
1066. 20 c. "Dermochelys coriacea" 20 20
1067. 25 c. "Eretmochelys imbricata" .. 25 25
1068. 35 c. "Lepidochelys olivacea" 30 30
1069. 65 c. "Platemys platycephala" (air) 60 60
1070. 75 c. "Phrynops gibba" 75 75
1071. 125 c. "Rihnoclemys punctularia" .. .. 1·10 1·10

1982. Easter. Stained-glass windows, Church of Saints Peter and Paul, Paramaribo.
1072. **224.** 20 c.+10 c. mult .. 25 30
1073. – 35 c.+15 c. mult. .. 40 45
1074. – 50 c.+25 c. mult. .. 60 70
1075. – 65 c.+30 c. mult. .. 75 85
1076. – 75 c.+35 c. mult. .. 80 90
DESIGNS: 35 c. to 75 c. Different patterns.

225. Lions Emblem. **226.** Father Donders with the Sick.

1982. 25th Anniv. of Surinam Lions Club.
1077. **225.** 35 c. multicoloured .. 30 30
1078. 70 c. multicoloured .. 60 60

1982. Beatification of Father Peter Donders.
1079. **226.** 35 c. multicoloured .. 30 30
1080. – 65 c. silver, black and red 50 50
DESIGN: 65 c. Portrait, birthplace, Tilburg, and map of South America.

227. Stamp Designer. **228.** Dr. Robert Koch.

1982. "Philexfrance 82" International Stamp Exhibition, Paris. Multicoloured.
1082. 50 c. Type **227** 40 40
1083. 100 c. Stamp printing .. 80 80
1084. 150 c. Stamp collector .. 1·25 1·25

1982. Cent of Discovery of Tubercle Bacillus.
1086. **228.** 35 c. yellow and green 35 30
1087. – 65 c. orange and brown 60 55
1088. – 150 c. light blue, blue and red .. .. 1·50 1·50
DESIGNS: 65 c. Dr. Koch and microscope. 150 c. Dr. Koch and Bacillus.

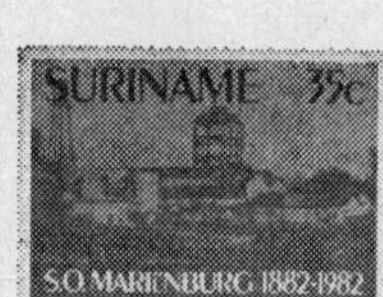

229. Sugar Mill. **230.** Cleaning Tools and Flag.

1982. Cent. of Marienburg Sugar Company.
1089. **229.** 35 c. yellow, green and black 30 30
1090. – 65 c. orange and brn. 50 50
1091. – 100 c. light blue, blue and black .. .. 1·10 1·10
1092. – 150 c. lilac and purple 1·25 1·25
DESIGNS: 65 c. Workers in cane fields. 100 c. Sugar cane railway. 150 c. Mill machinery.

1982. Child Welfare. "Keep Surinam Tidy" (children's paintings). Multicoloured.
1093. 20 c.+10 c. Type **230** .. 25 30
1094. 35 c.+15 c. Man with barrow 40 45
1095. 50 c.+25 c. Litter bin and cleaning tools 60 70
1096. 65 c.+30 c. Spraying weeds 75 85
1097. 75 c.+35 c. Litter bin .. 85 95

231. Municipal Church, Paramaribo.

1982. 250th Anniv. of Moravian Church Mission in the Caribbean.
1099. **231.** 35 c. multicoloured .. 30 30
1100. – 65 c. light blue, black and blue 50 50
1101. – 150 c. multicoloured 1·25 1·25
DESIGNS—HORIZ. 65 c. Aerial view of St. Thomas Monastery. VERT. 150 c. Johann Leonhardt Dober (missionary).

232. "Erythrina fusca".

1983. Flower Paintings by Maria Sibylle Merian. Multicoloured.
1102. 1 c. Type **232** 5 5
1103. 2 c. "Ipomoea acuminata" 5 5
1104. 3 c. "Heliconia psittacorum" 5 5
1105. 5 c. "Ipomoea" 5 5
1106. 10 c. "Herba non denominata" 10 8
1107. 15 c. "Anacardium occidentale" 15 12
1108. 20 c. "Inga edulis" (vert.) 20 15
1109. 25 c. "Abelmoschus moschatus" (vert.) .. 25 20
1110. 30 c. "Argemone mexicana" (vert.) 30 25
1111. 35 c. "Costus arabicus" (vert.) 35 30
1112. 45 c. "Muellera frutescens (vert.) 45 45
1113. 65 c. "Punica granatum" (vert.) 60 60

233. Scout Anniversary Emblem. **234.** Dove of Peace.

1983. Year of the Scout.
1114. **233.** 40 c. mve., vio. & grn. 45 40
1115. – 65 c. pale grey, bl. & grey 70 60
1116. – 70 c. multicoloured .. 80 70
1117. – 80 c. bl., lt. grn. & grn. 85 80
DESIGNS: 65 c. Lord Baden-Powell. 70 c. Tent and campfire. 80 c. Axe in tree trunk.

1983. Easter. Multicoloured.
1118. 10 c.+5 c. Type **234** .. 12 15
1119. 15 c.+5 c. Bread .. 20 25
1120. 25 c.+10 c. Fish .. 30 35
1121. 50 c.+25 c. Eye .. 60 70
1122. 65 c.+30 c. Chalice .. 75 85

235. Drawing by Raphael.

1983. 500th Birth Anniv. of Raphael.
1123. **235.** 5 c. multicoloured .. 5 5
1124. – 10 c. multicoloured .. 8 8
1125. – 40 c. multicoloured .. 35 35
1126. – 65 c. multicoloured .. 60 60
1127. – 70 c. multicoloured .. 65 65
1128. – 80 c. multicoloured .. 70 70
DESIGNS: Drawings by Raphael.

236. 1 c. Coin. **237.** "25" on Map of Surinam.

1983. Coins and Banknotes. Multicoloured.
1129. 5 c. Type **236** 5 5
1130. 10 c. 5 c. coin 10 8
1131. 40 c. 10 c. coin 45 40
1132. 65 c. 25 c. coin 65 65
1133. 70 c. 1 g. note 70 70
1134. 80 c. 2½ g. note .. .. 1·50 90

1983. 25th Anniv. of Department of Construction. Multicoloured.
1135. 25 c. Type **237** 25 25
1136. 50 c. Construction vehicles on map 45 45

238. "Papilio anchisiades". **239.** Montgolfier Balloon, September 1783.

1983. Butterfly paintings by Maria Sibylle Merian. Multicoloured.
1137 1 c. Type **238** 10 10
1138 2 c. "Urania leilus" .. 10 10
1139 3 c. "Morpho deidamia" 10 10
1140 5 c. "Thysania agrippina" 10 10
1141 10 c. "Morpho sp." .. 20 10
1142 15 c. "Philaethria dido" 30 20
1143 20 c. "Morpho menelaus" (horiz) 40 25
1144 25 c. "Protoparce rustica" (horiz) 50 30
1145 30 c. "Rothschildia aurota" (horiz) .. 60 40
1146 35 c. "Phoebis sennae" (horiz) 80 50
1147 45 c. "Papilio androgeos" (horiz) 90 70
1148 65 c. "Dupo vitis" (horiz) .. 1·40 1·00

1983. Bicent. of Manned Flight. Mult.
1149. 5 c. Type **239** 5 5
1150. 10 c. Montgolfier balloon (First manned flight by D'Arlandes and Pilatre de Rozier, November 1783) 10 10
1151. 40 c. Robert Brothers' balloon (Flight by J. A. C. Charles, December 1783) 40 40
1152. 65 c. Gambetta's Balloon, 1870 .. .. 65 65
1153. 70 c. "Double Eagle II" (Transatlantic flight, 1978) 70 70
1154. 80 c. Balloons at International Balloon Festival, Albuquerque, U.S.A. 75 75

240. Calabash Pitcher. **241.** Martin Luther.

1983. Child Welfare. Caribbean Artifacts. Multicoloured.
1155 10 c.+5 c. Type **240** .. 12 15
1156 15 c.+5 c. Umari (head-dress) 15 20
1157 25 c.+10 c. Maraka (medicine man's rattle) .. 20 35
1158 50 c.+25 c. Manari (sieve) 60 70
1159 65 c.+30 c. Pasuwa/pakara (basket) .. 70 80

1983. 500th Birth Anniv of Martin Luther (Protestant reformer).
1161 **241** 25 c. yellow, brown and black .. 20 20
1162 – 50 c. pink, pur & blk 40 40
DESIGN: 50 c. Selling of indulgences.

242. " Catasetum discolor ".
243. " Arca zebra ".

1983. Orchids. Multicoloured.
1163. 5 c. Type **242** 5 5
1164. 10 c. " Menadenium labiosum " 10 8
1165. 40 c. " Comparettia falcata " 45 40
1166. 50 c. " Rodriguezia decora " 70 60
1167. 70 c. " Oncidium papilio " 80 70
1168. 75 c. " Epidendrum porpax " 85 75

1984. Sea Shells. Multicoloured.
1169. 40 c. Type **243** 40 40
1170. 65 c. " Trachycardium egmontianum " 70 70
1171. 70 c. " Tellina radiata " 70 70
1172. 80 c. " Vermicularia knorrii " 80 80

244. Cross and Flower
245. Flying Boat landing.

1984. Easter. Multicoloured.
1173 10 c.+5 c. Type **244** .. 12 15
1174 15 c.+5 c. Cross & gate of cemetery 15 20
1175 25 c.+10 c Candle flames 30 35
1176 50 c.+25 c. Cross and crown of thorns .. 60 70
1177 65 c.+30 c. Lamp .. 70 80

1984. 40th Anniv. of I.C.A.O. Multicoloured.
1178 35 c. Type **245** 40 40
1179 65 c. Surinam Airways twinhopper 85 85

246. Running.
247. Emblem of 8th Caribbean Scout Jamboree.

1984. Olympic Games, Los Angeles. Multicoloured.
1180. 2 c. Type **246** 5 5
1181. 3 c. Javelin, discus and long jump 5 5
1182. 5 c. Massage 5 5
1183. 10 c. Rubbing with ointment 8 8
1184. 15 c. Wrestling 12 12
1185. 20 c. Boxing 20 20
1186. 30 c. Horse-racing .. 30 30
1187. 35 c. Chariot-racing .. 35 35
1188. 45 c. Temple of Olympia 40 40
1189. 50 c. Entrance to Stadium, Olympia 45 45
1190. 65 c. Stadium, Olympia 60 60
1191. 75 c. Zeus 70 70

1984. 60th Anniv. of Scouting in Surinam. Multicoloured.
1193. 30 c.+10 c. Type **247** .. 40 40
1194. 35 c.+10 c. Scout saluting 50 50
1195. 50 c.+10 c. Scout camp 65 65
1196. 90 c.+10 c. Campfire and map 95 95

248. Ball entering Basket.
249. Red Square, Moscow.

1984. International Military Sports Council Basketball Championship. Multicoloured.
1197. 50 c. Type **248** 50 45
1198. 90 c. Ball leaving basket 85 75

1984. World Chess Championship, Moscow.
1199 **249** 10 c. brown 10 10
1200 – 15 c. green & lt green 15 15
1201 – 30 c. lt brown & brn 30 30
1202 – 50 c. brown & purple 50 50
1203 – 75 c. brown & lt brn 80 80
1204 – 90 c. green and blue 90 90
DESIGNS: 15 c. Knight, king and pawn on board. 30 c. Gary Kasparov. 50 c. Start of game and clock. 75 c. Anatoly Karpov. 90 c. Position during Andersen-Kizeritski game.

250. Children collecting Milk from Cow.
251. Kite.

1984. World Food Day. Multicoloured.
1206. 50 c. Type **250** 50 45
1207. 90 c. Platter of food .. 85 75

1984. Child Welfare. Multicoloured.
1208. 5 c.+5 c. Type **251** .. 10 10
1209 10 c.+5 c. Kites .. 15 15
1210. 30 c.+10 c. Pingi-pingi-kasi (game) 40 40
1211. 50 c.+25 c. Cricket .. 85 85
1212. 90 c.+30 c. Peroen, peroen (game) .. .. .. 1·10 1·10

252. Leaf Cactus.

1985. Cacti. Multicoloured.
1215. 5 c. Type **252** 5 5
1216. 10 c. Melocactus .. 10 10
1217. 30 c. Pillar cactus .. 25 25
1218. 50 c. Fig cactus .. 45 45
1219. 75 c. Night queen .. 70 70
1220. 90 c. Segment cactus .. 80 80

253. "Peace" and Star.
254. Crosses.

1985. 5th Anniv. of Revolution. Mult.
1221 5 c. Type **253** 5 5
1222 30 c. "Unity in labour" and manual workers .. 20 20
1223 50 c. "5 years of Steadfastness" and flower .. 40 40
1224 75 c. "Progress" and wheat as flower .. 60 60
1225 90 c. "Unity", flower and dove 70 70

1985. Easter. Multicoloured.
1227 5 c.+5 c. Type **254** .. 8 8
1228 10 c.+5 c. Crosses (different) 10 10
1229 30 c.+15 c. Sun's rays illuminating crosses .. 30 30
1230 50 c.+25 c. Crosses (different) 55 65
1231 90 c.+30 c. Crosses and leaves (Resurrection) .. 75 85

255. Emblem.
256. U.N. Emblem and State Arms.

1985. 75th Anniv of Chamber of Commerce and Industry.
1232. **255.** 50 c. yell., grn. & red 40 40
1233. – 90 c. grn., bl. & yell. 70 70
DESIGN: 90 c. Chamber of Commerce building.

1985. 40th Anniv. of U.N.O.
1234. **256.** 50 c. multicoloured .. 40 40
1235. 90 c. multicoloured .. 70 70

257. Sugar-cane Train (detail of 1945 stamp).

1985. Railway Locomotives.
1236. **257.** 5 c. orange and blue 10 5
1237. – 5 c. grn., red & bl. 10 5
1238. – 10 c. multicoloured .. 15 10
1239. – 10 c. multicoloured .. 15 10
1240. – 20 c. multicoloured .. 30 20
1241. – 20 c. multicoloured .. 30 20
1242. – 30 c. multicoloured .. 55 30
1243. – 30 c. multicoloured .. 55 30
1244. – 50 c. multicoloured .. 95 55
1245. – 50 c. multicoloured .. 95 55
1246. – 75 c. multicoloured .. 1·25 80
1247. – 75 c. multicoloured .. 1·25 80
DESIGNS: No. 1237, Monaco 3 f. Postage Due train stamp. 1238, Steam Locomotive "Dam". 1239, Modern electric locomotive and carriage unit. 1240, Steam locomotive "3737". 1241, Electric locomotive "NS–IC III". 1242, Stephenson's "Rocket". 1243, French "TGV" (high speed) locomotive. 1244, Stephenson's "Der Adler". 1245, French double-decker "UB2N". 1246, American locomotive "The General". 1247, Japanese "Shinkansen" train.

258. Purple Gallinule.
259. German Letterbox, 1900.

1985. Birds. Multicoloured.
1248. 1 g. Type **258** .. .. 1·10 1·00
1249. 1 g. 50 Rufescent tiger heron .. .. .. 1·50 1·40
1250. 2 g. 50 Scarlet ibis .. 2·75 2·50
1251. 5 g. Guianan cock of the rock .. .. .. 3·50 3·00
1252. 10 g. Harpy eagle .. 7·50 7·00

1985. Old Letterboxes. Multicoloured.
1254. 15 c. Type **259** 12 12
1255. 30 c. French letterbox, 1900 .. .. .. 20 20
1256. 50 c. English pillar box, 1932 .. .. .. 35 35
1257. 90 c. Dutch letterbox, 1850 .. .. .. 55 55

260. Emblem on Map.
261. Studying.

1985. 25th Anniv. of Evangelical Brotherhood in Surinam.
1258. **260.** 30 c.+10 c. mult. .. 30 30
1259. – 50 c.+10 c. red, yellow and brown 45 45
1260. – 90 c.+20 c. yellow, brown and red .. 75 75
DESIGNS: 50 c. Different population groups around cross and clasped hands emblem. 90 c. List of work undertaken by Brotherhood.

1985. Child Welfare. Multicoloured.
1261 5 c.+5 c. Type **261** .. 8 8
1262 10 c.+5 c. Writing alphabet on board 12 12
1263 30 c.+10 c. Writing .. 30 30
1264 50 c.+25 c. Reading .. 55 55
1265 90 c.+30 c. Thinking .. 80 80

1985. Victory of Kasparov in World Chess Championship. No. 1201 optd **KACTTAPOB Wereldkampioen 9 nov. 1985.**
1267 30 c. light brown & brown 30 20

263. Agriculture.
264. "Epidendrum ciliare".

1985. 10th Anniv of Independence.
1268 **263** 50 c. yellow and green 40 40
1269 – 90 c. orange & brown 70 70
DESIGN: 90 c. Industry.

1986. Orchids, Multicoloured.
1271. 5 c. Type **264** 5 5
1272. 15 c. "Cycnoches chlorochilon" 12 12
1273. 30 c. "Epidendrum anceps" 25 25
1274. 50 c. "Epidendrum vespa" 45 45

265. Bayeux Tapestry (detail).
266. Couple and Palm Leaves.

1986. Appearance of Halley's Comet. Multicoloured.
1275. 50 c. Type **265** 35 35
1276. 110 c. Comet 75 75

1986. Easter.
1277. **266.** 5 c.+5 c. mult. .. 8 8
1278. 10 c.+5 c. mult. .. 12 12
1279. 30 c.+15 c. mult. .. 30 30
1280. 50 c.+25 c. mult. .. 55 55
1281. 90 c.+30 c. mult. .. 80 80

1986. Nos. 1244/5 surch.
1282. 15 c. on 50 c. mult. .. 45 15
1283. 15 c. on 50 c. mult. .. 45 20

268. Cathedral.

270. National Forestry Emblem.

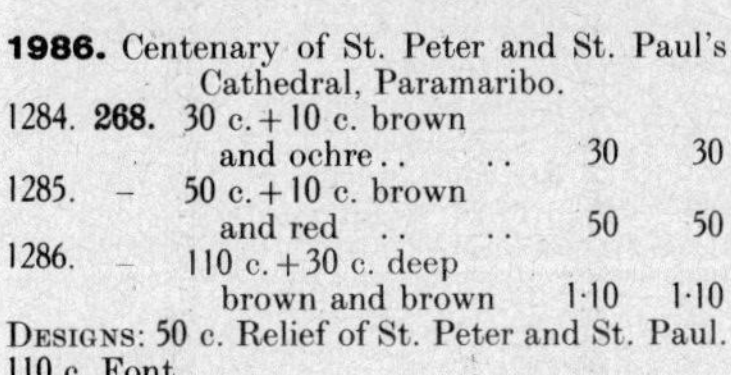

1986. Centenary of St. Peter and St. Paul's Cathedral, Paramaribo.
1284. **268.** 30 c. + 10 c. brown and ochre 30 30
1285. – 50 c. + 10 c. brown and red 50 50
1286. – 110 c. + 30 c. deep brown and brown 1·10 1·10
DESIGNS: 50 c. Relief of St. Peter and St. Paul. 110 c. Font.

1986. 150th Anniv of Finance Building. No. 1133 surch **30 c 150 jaar FINANCIËNGE BOUW**.
1287. 30 c. on 70 c. mult. 30 30

1986. Centenary of Foresters' Court Charity. Multicoloured.
1288. 50 c. + 20 c. Type **270** . . 60 60
1289. 110 c. + 30 c. First Court building . . . . 1·25 1·25

271. Emblem.

273. Children playing Hopscotch.

1986. 50th Anniv. of Surinam Shipping Line. Multicoloured.
1290. 50 c. Type **271** 40 40
1291. 110 c. Container ship "Saramacca" . . . . 2·00 1·10

1986. No. 862 surch **15ct.**
1292 5 c. on 30 c. multicoloured 60 25

1986. Child Welfare. Multicoloured.
1293. 5 c. + 5 c. Type **273** . . 8 8
1294. 10 c. + 5 c. Ballet class . . 12 12
1295. 30 c. + 10 c. Children boarding library bus . . 35 35
1296. 50 c. + 25 c. Boys at display of craftwork . . 65 65
1297. 110 c. + 30 c. Children in class . . . . . . 1·10 1·10

274. Red Howler.

275. Emblem.

1987. Monkeys. Multicoloured.
1299. 35 c. Type **274** 30 30
1300. 60 c. Night monkey . . 55 55
1301. 110 c. Common squirrel-monkey 85 85
1302. 120 c. Red uakari . . 90 90

1987. Centenary of Esperanto (invented language). Multicoloured.
1303. 60 c. Type **275** 55 55
1304. 110 c. Dove holding "Esperanto" banner across world map . . 85 85
1305. 120 c. L. L. Zamenhof (inventor) 90 90

1987. Various stamps surch.
1306. – 10 c. on 85 c. mult. (No. 872) 50 20
1307. – 10 c. on 95 c. mult. (No. 873) 50 20
1308. **168.** 50 c. on $1\frac{1}{2}$ g. black, orange and brown 45 45
1309. 60 c. on $2\frac{1}{2}$ g. black, red and brown . . 55 55

277. "Crucifixion".

278. Mushroom (Brownie emblem).

1987. Easter. Etchings by Rembrandt. Each light mauve, mauve and black.
1310. 5 c. + 5 c. Type **277** . . 8 8
1311. 10 c. + 5 c. "Christ on the Cross" 12 12
1312. 35 c. + 15 c. "Descent from the Cross" . . 35 35
1313. 60 c. + 30 c. "Christ carried to His Tomb" 65 65
1314. 110 c. + 50 c. "Entombment of Christ" . . 1·10 1·10

1987. 40th Anniv. of Surinam Girl Guides.
1315. **278.** 15 c. + 10 c. mult. . . 20 20
1316. – 60 c. + 10 c. mult. . . 50 50
1317. – 110 c. + 10 c. mult. . . 80 80
1318. – 120 c. + 10 c. green, black and yellow 90 90
DESIGNS: 60 c. Cloverleaf and star (Guide emblem). 110 c. Campfire (Rangers emblem) on Guide trefoil. 120 c. Ivy leaves (Captain's emblem).

279. Football.

280. Commission Emblem.

1987. 10th Pan-American Games, Indianapolis.
1319. **279.** 90 c. blue, green and brown 80 80
1320. – 110 c. blue, light blue and brown . . 90 90
1321. – 150 c. blue, mauve and brown . . 1·25 1·25
DESIGNS: 110 c. Swimming. 150 c. Basketball.

1987. 40th Anniv. of Forestry Commission. Multicoloured.
1322 90 c. Type **280** 80 80
1323 120 c. Loading tree trunks for export 95 95
1324 150 c. Parrot in forest . . 1·75 1·25

282. Boy and Tents.

283. Banana.

1987. International Year of Shelter for the Homeless (90, 120 c.) and Centenary of Salvation Army in the Caribbean Territory (150 c.). Multicoloured.
1331 90 c. Type **282** 70 70
1332 120 c. Shanty Town and man 85 85
1333 150 c. William and Catherine Booth and emblem . . . . 1·10 1·10

1987. Fruits. Multicoloured.
1334. 10 c. Type **283** 8 8
1335. 15 c. Cacao bean 12 12
1336. 20 c. Pineapple 15 15
1337. 25 c. Papaya 20 20
1338. 35 c. China orange 30 30

284. Degen, 1808.

1987. Aircraft. Multicoloured.
1339 25 c. Type **284** 20 20
1340 25 c. Ultra light 20 20
1341 35 c. J. C. H. Ellehammer's airplane, 1906 30 30
1342 35 c. "Concorde" . . 30 30
1343 60 c. Fokker "F7", 1924 . . 50 50
1344 60 c. Fokker "F28" . . 50 50
1345 90 c. Spin Fokker, 1910 . . 75 75
1346 90 c. Douglas "DC 10" . . 75 75
1347 110 c. "Orion", 1932 . . 80 80
1348 110 c. Boeing "747" . . 80 80
1349 120 c. 1967 Amelia Earhart 25 c. stamp 95 95
1350 120 c. 1978 "DC 8" 95 c. stamp 95 95

285. Herring-bone Design.

287. Ganges Gavial.

1987. Child Welfare. Indian Weaving.
1351 **285** 50 c. + 25 c. grn & blk 65 65
1352 – 60 c. + 30 c. orange and black . . 70 70
1353 – 110 c. + 50 c. red & blk 1·25 1·25
DESIGNS: 60 c. Tortoise-back design. 110 c. Concentric diamonds design.

1987. Nos. 869 and 805 surch.
1356. – 25 c. on 70 c. mult. . . 60 40
1357. **168.** 35 c on 1 g. black, mauve and purple 60 60

1988. Reptiles. Multicoloured.
1358. 50 c. Type **287** 40 40
1359. 60 c. Nile crocodile . . 50 50
1360. 90 c. Black cayman . . 70 70
1361. 110 c. Mississippi alligator 80 80

288. Javanese Costumes.

290. Cross and Chalice.

1988. Wedding Costumes. Multicoloured.
1362 35 c. Type **288** 30 30
1363 60 c. Bushman 50 50
1364 80 c. Chinese 65 65
1365 110 c. Creole 80 80
1366 120 c. Amerindian . . 85 85
1367 130 c. Hindustan . . 90 90

1988. Various stamps surch.
1369 – 60 c. on 75 c. mult (No. 1246) . . 1·40 1·00
1369 – 60 c. on 75 c. mult (No. 1247) . . 1·40 1·00
1370 **168** 125 c. on 10 g. black, blue & deep blue . . 1·75 1·75

1988. Easter.
1371 **290** 50 c. + 25 c. mult . . 65 65
1372 60 c. + 30 c. mult . . 75 75
1373 110 c. + 50 c. mult . . 1·40 1·40

291. Relay.

292 Abaisa Monument

1988. Olympic Games, Seoul. Multicoloured.
1374 90 c. Type **291** 80 80
1375 110 c. Football 90 90
1376 120 c. Pole vaulting . . 1·00 1·00
1377 250 c. Tennis . . . . 2·00 2·00

1988. 125th Anniv of Abolition of Slavery. Multicoloured.
1379 50 c. Type **292** 50 50
1380 110 c. Kwakoe monument 90 90
1381 120 c. Anton de Kom's house . . . . 1·10 1·10

293 Combine Harvester

294 Egypt 1906 4 m. Stamp

1988. 10th Anniv of International Agricultural Development Fund. "For a World without Hunger". Multicoloured.
1382 105 c. Type **293** 90 90
1383 110 c. Fishing 95 95
1384 125 c. Cultivation . . 1·25 1·25

1988. "Filacept" International Stamp Exhibition, The Hague.
1385 **294** 120 c. red, blk & orge 1·00 1·00
1386 – 150 c. grn, blk & bl 1·25 1·25
1387 – 250 c. red, black & deep red . . . . 2·25 2·25
DESIGNS: No. 1386, Netherlands 1952 10 c. Stamp Centenary stamp; 1387, Surinam 1949 $7\frac{1}{2}$ c. U.P.U stamp.

295 Anniversary Emblem

296 Symbolic Representation of Butterfly Stroke

1988. 125th Anniv of Red Cross. Mult.
1389 60 c. + 30 c. Type **295** . . 85 85
1390 120 c. + 60 c. Anniversary emblem and red cross in blood drop . . . . 1·60 1·60

1988. Anthony Nesty, Seoul Olympic Gold Medal Winner for 100 m. Butterfly.
1391 **296** 110 c. multicoloured . . 95 95

297 "Man and Animal"

1988. 25th Anniv of Child Welfare Stamps. Multicoloured.
1392 50 c. + 25 c. Type **297** . . 70 70
1393 60 c. + 30 c. "The Child in Nature" 85 85
1394 110 c. + 50 c. Children helping each other ("Stop Drugs") . . 1·50 1·50

1988. Nos. 1238/9 and 1244/5 surch.
1396 2 c. on 10 c. multicoloured (No. 1238) 5 5
1397 2 c. on 10 c. multicoloured (No. 1239) 5 5
1398 3 c. on 50 c. multicoloured (No. 1244) 5 5
1399 3 c. on 50 c. multicolured (No. 1245) 5 5

299 Otter on Rock

300 "The Passion" (left wing)

1989. Otters. Multicoloured.
1400 10 c. Type **299** 10 10
1401 20 c. Two otters 20 10
1402 25 c. Two otters (different) 25 25
1403 30 c. Otter with fish . . 30 30
1404 185 c. Two otters (vert) (air) . . . . . . 1·60 1·60

1989. Easter. Altarpiece by Tamas of Koloszvar. Multicoloured.
1405 60 c. + 30 c. Type **300** . . 85 85
1406 105 c. + 50 c. "Crucifixion" (centre panel) (28 × 36 mm) . . . . . . 1·50 1·50
1407 110 c. + 55 c. "Resurrection" (right wing) . . 1·50 1·50

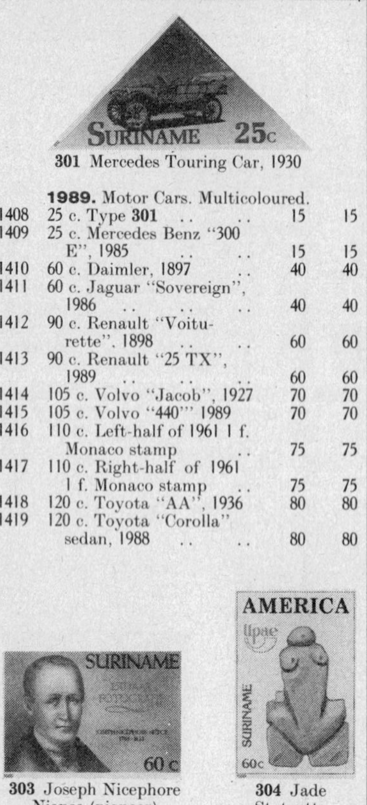

301 Mercedes Touring Car, 1930

1989. Motor Cars. Multicoloured.

1408 25 c. Type **301** 15 15
1409 25 c. Mercedes Benz "300 E", 1985 . . . . 15 15
1410 60 c. Daimler, 1897 . . 40 40
1411 60 c. Jaguar "Sovereign", 1986 . . . . . . 40 40
1412 90 c. Renault "Voiturette", 1898 . . . . 60 60
1413 90 c. Renault "25 TX", 1989 . . . . . . 60 60
1414 105 c. Volvo "Jacob", 1927 70 70
1415 105 c. Volvo "440" 1989 70 70
1416 110 c. Left-half of 1961 1 f. Monaco stamp . . 75 75
1417 110 c. Right-half of 1961 1 f. Monaco stamp . . 75 75
1418 120 c. Toyota "AA", 1936 80 80
1419 120 c. Toyota "Corolla" sedan, 1988 . . . . 80 80

303 Joseph Nicephore Niepce (pioneer)

304 Jade Statuette

1989. 150th Anniv of Photography. Mult.

1421 60 c. Type **303** 40 40
1422 110 c. First camera using daguerreotype process 75 75
1423 120 c. Louis Jacques Mande Daguerre (inventor of daguerreotype process) 80 80

1989. America. Pre-Columbian Artefacts. Multicoloured.

1424 60 c. Type **304** 40 40
1425 110 c. Statuette of pregnant woman . . 75 75

305 1976 25 c. Surinam Stamp

306 "Children Helping Each Other" (Gianna Karg)

1989. "World Stamp Expo '89" International Stamp Exhibition, Washington, D.C. Mult.

1426 110 c. Type **305** 75 75
1427 150 c. 1950 3 c. U.S.A. White House stamp . . 1·00 1·00
1428 250 c. 1976 60 c. Surinam "Divided Snake" stamp 1·75 1·75

1989. Child Welfare. Children's Paintings. Multicoloured.

1430 60 c. + 30 c. Type **306** . . 60 60
1431 105 c. + 50 c. "Child and Nature" (Tamara Busropan) . . . . 1·00 1·00
1432 110 c. + 55 c. "In the School Bus" (Cindy Kross) . . . . 1·10 1·10

307 Local Emblem

308 Temple

1990. International Literacy Year. Mult.

1434 60 c. Type **307** 40 40
1435 110 c. I.L.Y. emblem . . 75 75
1436 120 c. Emblems and boy reading 80 80

1990. 60th Anniv of Arya Dewaker Temple.

1437 **308** 60 c. brown, red & blk 40 40
1438 110 c. violet and black 75 75
1439 200 c. green and black 1·40 1·40

309 Mary and Baby Jesus

310 Surinam 1930 10 c. Air Stamp

1990. Easter. Multicoloured.

1440 60 c. + 30 c. Type **309** . . 55 55
1441 105 c. + 50 c. Jesus teaching 90 90
1442 110 c. + 55 c. Jesus's body taken from cross . . 1·00 1·00

1990. "Stamp World London 90" International Stamp Exhibition, London, and 150th Anniv of the Penny Black. Mult.

1443 110 c. Type **310** 65 65
1444 200 c. Penny Black . . 1·25 1·25
1445 250 c. G.B. 1929 2½d. Postal Union Congress stamp 1·50 1·50

311 Couple carrying Goods

313 Swamp

312 Pomegranate

1990. Centenary of Javanese Immigration. Multicoloured.

1447 60 c. Type **311** 35 35
1448 110 c. Woman 65 65
1449 120 c. Man 70 70

1990. Flowers. Paintings by Maria Sibylle Merian. Multicoloured.

1450 25 c. Type **312** 15 15
1451 25 c. Passion flower . . 15 15
1452 35 c. "Hippeastrum puniceum" 20 20
1453 35 c. Sweet potato . . 20 20
1454 60 c. Rose of Sharon . . 35 35
1455 60 c. Jasmine 35 35
1456 105 c. Blushing hibiscus . . 60 60
1457 105 c. "Musa serapionis" 60 60
1458 110 c. Frangipani . . 65 65
1459 110 c. "Hibiscus diversifolius" 65 65
1460 120 c. Annatt ("Bixa orellana") 70 70
1461 120 c. Dawrf poinciana ("Caesalpinia pulcherima") 70 70

1990. America. Natural World.

1462 **313** 60 c. multicoloured . . 35 35
1463 110 c. multicoloured . . 65 65

314 Anniversary Emblem

315 Fish and Flag as Map

1990. Centenary of Organization of American States.

1464 **314** 100 c. multicoloured . . 65 65

1990. 15th Anniv of Independence. Mult.

1465 10 c. Type **315** 5 5
1466 60 c. Passion flower and flag as map . . 35 35
1467 110 c. Dove and flag as map 65 65

316 Painting by Janneke Fleskens

1990. Child Welfare. The Child in Nature. Paintings by children named. Mult.

1468 60 c. + 30 c. Type **316** . . 55 55
1469 105 c. + 50 c. Tahlita Zuiverloon 90 90
1470 110 c. + 55 c. Samuel Jensen . . . . 1·00 1·00

317 Toucan

1991. Birds. Multicoloured.

1472 10 c. Type **317** 5 5
1473 15 g. Parrot . . . . 9·75 9·75

318 Christ carrying Cross

319 Shipping Company Store

1991. Easter. Multicoloured.

1474 60 c. + 30 c. Type **318** . . 60 60
1475 105 c. + 50 c. Christ wearing crown of thorns 1·00 1·00
1476 110 c. + 55 c. Woman cradling Christ's body 1·10 1·10

1991. Buildings.

1478 **319** 35 c. black, bl & lt bl 20 20
1479 – 60 c. black, green and emerald 40 40
1480 – 75 c. blk, yell & lemon 50 50
1481 – 105 c. black, orange and light orange . . 70 70
1482 – 110 c. blk, pink & red 70 70
1483 – 200 c. black, deep mauve and mauve 1·25 1·25

DESIGNS: 60 c. Upper class house; 75 c. House converted into Labour Inspection offices; 105 c. Plantation supervisor's house; 110 c. Ministry of Labour building; 200 c. Houses.

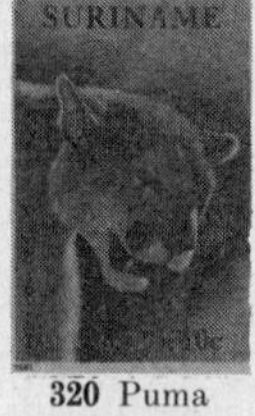

320 Puma

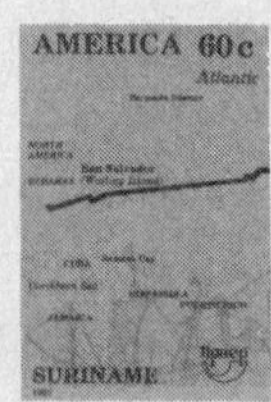

321 Route Map to Bahamas via San Salvador

1991. The Puma. Multicoloured.

1484 10 c. Type **320** (postage) 5 5
1485 20 c. Stalking 15 15
1486 25 c. Stretching 15 15
1487 30 c. Licking nose . . 20 20
1488 125 c. Lying down (horiz) (air) 80 80
1489 500 c. Leaping (horiz) . . 3·25 3·25

1991. America. Voyages of Discovery. Each red, blue and black.

1490 60 c. Type **321** 65 65
1491 110 c. Route map from Canary Islands . . 1·00 1·00

Nos. 1490/1 were printed together, se-tenant, forming a composite design.

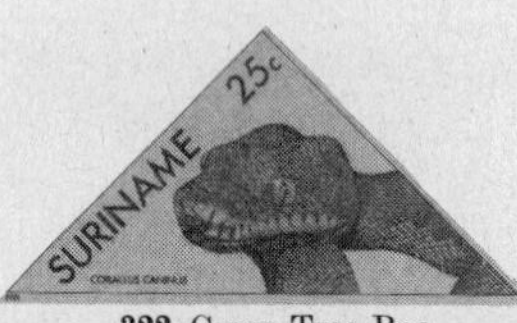

322 Green Tree Boa ("Corallus caninus")

1991. Snakes. Multicoloured.

1492 25 c. Type **322** 15 15
1493 25 c. Garden tree boa ("Corallus enydris") . . 15 15
1494 35 c. Boa constrictor . . 20 20
1495 35 c. Bushmaster ("Lachesis muta") . . 20 20
1496 60 c. South American rattlesnake ("Crotalus durissus") 40 40
1497 60 c. Surinam coral snake ("Micrurus surinamensis") 40 40
1498 75 c. Mussurana ("Clelia cloelia") 50 50
1499 75 c. Anaconda ("Eunectes murinus") 50 50
1500 110 c. Rainbow boa ("Epicrutes cenchris") 70 70
1501 110 c. Sipo ("Chrironius carinatus") 70 70
1502 200 c. Black and yellow rat snake ("Spilotes pullatus") . . . . 1·25 1·25
1503 200 c. Vine snake ("Oxybelis argenteus") 1·25 1·25

323 Child in Wheelchair

324 "Cycnoches haagii"

1991. Child Welfare. Multicoloured.

1504 60 c. + 30 c. Type **323** . . 60 60
1505 105 c. + 50 c. Trees and girl . . . . . . 1·10 1·00
1506 110 c. + 55 c. Girls playing in yard . . . . 1·10 1·10

1992. Orchids. Multicoloured.

1508 50 c. Type **324** 30 30
1509 60 c. "Lycaste cristata" 40 40
1510 75 c. "Galeandra dives" (horiz) 50 50
1511 125 c. "Vanilla mexicana" 80 80
1512 150 c. "Cyrtopodium glutiniferum" . . 1·00 1·00
1513 250 c. "Gongora quinquenervis" . . 1·60 1·60

325 Crucifixion

327 Basketball

1992. Easter. Multicoloured.

1514 60 c. + 30 c. Type **325** . . 70 70
1515 105 c. + 50 c. Women taking away Christ's body . . . . 1·10 1·10
1516 110 c. + 55 c. The Resurrection . . 1·25 1·25

1992. Olympic Games, Barcelona. Mult.

1518 35 c. Type **327** 25 25
1519 60 c. Volleyball 45 45
1520 75 c. Sprinting 55 55
1521 125 c. Football 95 95
1522 150 c. Cycling . . . . 1·10 1·10
1523 250 c. Swimming . . 1·90 1·90

328 Emblems

1992. 50th Anniv of Young Women's Christian Association.

1525 **328** 60 c. multicoloured . . 45 45
1526 250 c. multicoloured 1·90 1·90

1992. Nos. 1236/7 surch **1 c.**

1527 1 c. on 5 c. orange & blue 5 5
1528 1 c. on 5 c. green, red & bl 5 5

330 Nau

331 Matzeliger and Shoe-lasting Machine

1992. 500th Anniv of Expulsion of Jews from Spain.

1529	**330**	250 c. multicoloured ..	2·25	2·25

1992. 140th Birth Anniv of Jan E. Matzeliger (inventor).

1530	**331**	60 c. multicoloured ..	45	45
1531		250 c. multicoloured	1·90	1·90

332 Amerindian Ornament

333 Tree with Child's Face

1992. America. 500th Anniv of Discovery of America by Columbus.

1532	**332**	60 c. multicoloured ..	45	45
1533		250 c. multicoloured	1·90	1·90

1992. Child Welfare. Multicoloured.

1534	60 c.+30 c. Type **333** ..	70	70
1535	105 c.+50 c. Tree with child's face beside flower	1·10	1·10
1536	110 c.+55 c. Children hanging from tree ..	1·25	1·25

334 Star and Holly

336 "Costus arabicus"

1992. Christmas. Multicoloured.

1538	10 c. Type **334**	10	10
1539	60 c. Candle	45	45
1540	250 c. Parcels	1·90	1·90
1541	400 c. Crown	3·00	3·00

1993. Birds.

(a) Postage. As T **258**. Multicoloured.

1542	25 g. Owl	19·00	19·00

(b) Air. No. 865 surch **35 ct**

1543	35 c. on 50 c. mult ..	25	25

1993. Medicinal Plants. Multicoloured.

1544	50 c. Type **336**	40	40
1545	75 c. "Quassia amara" ..	55	55
1546	125 c. "Combretum rotundifolium" (horiz)	95	95
1547	500 c. "Bixa orellana" (horiz)	3·75	3·75

337 Christ and Cross

339 90 r. "Bull's Eye" Stamp

338 Long-horned Beetle ("Macrodontia cervicornis")

1993. Easter. Multicoloured.

1548	60 c.+30 c. Type **337** ..	70	70
1549	110 c.+50 c. Crucifixion	1·25	1·25
1550	125 c.+60 c. Resurrection	1·40	1·40

1993. Insects. Multicoloured.

1551	25 c. Type **338**	20	20
1552	25 c. Locust	20	20
1553	35 c. Weevil ("Curculionidae") ..	25	25
1554	35 c. Grasshopper ("Acrididae")	25	25
1555	50 c. Goliath beetle ('Euchroma gigantea")	40	40
1556	50 c. Bush cricket ("Tettigonidae") ..	40	40
1557	100 c. "Tettigonidae" ..	75	75
1558	100 c. Scarab beetle ("Phanaeus festivus")	75	75
1559	175 c. Cricket ("Grylllidae") ..	1·25	1·25
1560	175 c. Dung beetle ("Phanaeus lancifer")	1·25	1·25
1561	220 c. "Tettigonidae" (different)	1·60	1·60
1562	220 c. Longhorm beetle ("Batus barbicornis")	1·60	1·60

1993. 150th Anniv of First Brazilian Stamps and "Brasiliana 93" International Stamp Exhibition, Rio de Janeiro.

1563	**339**	50 c. black and violet	40	40
1564	–	250 c. black and blue	1·90	1·90
1565	–	500 c. black and green	3·75	3·75

DESIGNS: 250 c. 60 r. "Bull's eye" stamp; 500 c. 30 r. "Bull's eye" stamp.

340 Dwarf Cayman

341 Afro-Caribbean Angel

1993. America. Endangered Animals.

1567	**340**	50 c. multicoloured ..	40	40
1568		100 c. multicoloured	75	75

1993. Christmas. Multicoloured.

1569	25 c. Type **341**	20	20
1570	45 c. Asian angel ..	35	35
1571	50 c. Oriental angel ..	40	40
1572	150 c. Amerindian angel	1·10	1·10

342 Hopscotch

1993. Child Welfare. Children's Games.

1573	**342**	25 g.+10 g. brn & grn	25	25
1574	–	35 g.+10 g. brn & bl	35	35
1575	–	50 g.+25 g. brn & grn	55	55
1576	–	75 g.+25 g. brn & bl	75	75

DESIGNS: 35 g. Hopscotch (different); 50 g. Djoel (variant of hopscotch); 75 g. Djoel (different).

POSTAGE DUE STAMPS

D 2.

D 6.

1885.

D 36.	D **2.**	$2\frac{1}{2}$ c. mauve & black	2·00	2·00
D 37.		5 c. mauve and black	6·00	6·00
D 38.		10 c. mauve & black	£100	70·00
D 39.		20 c. mauve & black	6·00	6·00
D 40.		25 c. mauve & black	9·00	9·00
D 41.		30 c. mauve & black	2·50	2·50
D 42.		40 c. mauve & black	4·00	4·00
D 43.		50 c. mauve & black	2·25	2·25

1892.

D 57.	D **6.**	$2\frac{1}{2}$ c. mauve & black	20	20
D 58.		5 c. mauve and black	80	65
D 59.		10 c. mauve & black	15·00	11·00
D 60.		20 c. mauve & black	1·75	1·10
D 61.		25 c. mauve & black	6·50	5·50
D 62.		40 c. mauve & black	2·00	2·40

1911.

D 111.	D **3.**	10 c. on 30 c. mauve and black ..	65·00	65·00
D 112.		10 c. on 50 c. mauve and black ..	95·00	95·00

1913.

D 153.	D **6.**	$\frac{1}{2}$ c. lilac	10	10
D 154.		1 c. lilac	10	15
D 155.		2 c. lilac	15	20
D 156.		$2\frac{1}{2}$ c. lilac	15	10
D 157.		5 c. lilac	10	10
D 158.		10 c. lilac	15	10
D 159.		12 c. lilac	20	20
D 160.		$12\frac{1}{2}$ c. lilac	20	10
D 161.		15 c. lilac	25	25
D 162.		20 c. lilac	60	25
D 163.		25 c. lilac	25	10
D 164.		30 c. lilac	20	35
D 165.		40 c. lilac	9·00	9·50
D 166.		50 c. lilac	75	65
D 167.		75 c. lilac	90	90
D 168.		1 g. lilac	1·10	90

D 52.

D 68.

1945.

D 337.	D **52.**	1 c. purple	30	35
D 338.		5 c. purple	3·25	1·40
D 339.		25 c. purple ..	8·50	20

1950. As Type D **121** of Netherlands.

D 384.	1 c. purple	1·60	1·75
D 385.	2 c. purple	2·25	2·00
D 386.	$2\frac{1}{2}$ c. purple ..	2·50	1·50
D 387.	5 c. purple	3·50	30
D 388.	10 c. purple ..	2·25	30
D 389.	15 c. purple ..	6·50	2·50
D 390.	20 c. purple ..	1·50	3·25
D 391.	25 c. purple ..	21·00	20
D 392.	50 c. purple ..	24·00	1·40
D 393.	75 c. purple ..	35·00	27·00
D 394.	1 g. purple	26·00	6·00

1956.

D 436.	D **68.**	1 c. purple	10	10
D 437.		2 c. purple	35	20
D 438.		$2\frac{1}{2}$ c. purple ..	35	30
D 439.		5 c. purple	25	25
D 440.		10 c. purple ..	35	30
D 441.		15 c. purple ..	60	45
D 442.		20 c. purple ..	60	50
D 443.		25 c. purple ..	65	20
D 444.		50 c. purple ..	1·60	35
D 445.		75 c. purple ..	2·25	1·00
D 446.		1 g. purple	3·00	10

1987. Various stamps optd. **TE BETALEN.**

D 1325.	65 c. mult. (No. 868) ..	1·00	50
D 1326.	65 c. mult. (No. 1132)	50	50
D 1327.	80 c. mult. (No. 1134)	1·00	60
D 1328.	90 c. mult. (No. 872a)	1·10	70
D 1329.	95 c. mult. (No. 873) ..	1·25	75
D 1330.	1 g. mult. (No. 1248) ..	1·25	75

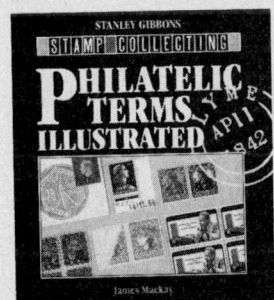

SWEDEN Pt. 11

A kingdom of N. Europe, united to Norway till 1905.

1855. 48 skilling banco = 1 riksdaler.
1858. 100 ore = 1 riksdaler.
1875. 100 ore = 1 krona.

1. 2. 3.

1855.
1. 1. 3 s. b. green £4500 £2250
2. 4 s. b. blue .. .. £850 55·00
3. 6 s. b. grey £5000 £600
3b. 6 s. b. brown £4500 £650
4. 8 s. b. orange £3000 £350
5. 24 s. b. red £4500 £1600

1858.
6b. 1. 5 ore green .. .. £130 13·00
7a. 9 ore lilac £275 £140
8a. 12 ore blue .. .. £120 2·00
9. 24 ore orange .. .. £250 18·00
10a. 30 ore brown .. .. £250 18·00
11b. 50 ore red .. .. £300 55·00

1862.
12c. 2. 3 ore brown .. .. 45·00 13·00

1866.
13. 3. 17 ore purple £350 £110
14. 17 ore grey £550 £550
15b. 20 ore red .. .. £130 14·00

4. 6. King Oscar II. 5.

1872.
29. 4. 2 ore orange .. .. 2·00 2·25
16a. 3 ore brown .. .. 22·00 2·50
31. 4 ore grey .. .. 16·00 50
32. 5 ore green .. .. 35·00 30
33a. 6 ore purple .. .. 18·00 18·00
20. 6 ore olive .. .. £450 35·00
34. 6. 10 ore red .. .. 70·00 5
21. 4. 12 ore blue .. .. 12·50 20
35. 20 ore red .. .. 70·00 30
23a. 24 ore yellow .. .. 29·00 10·00
36. 30 ore brown £100 55
37a. 50 ore red .. .. £140 3·50
26. 5. 1 r. blue and brown .. £400 48·00
38. 1 k. blue and brown .. 55·00 1·50

On No. 26 the value is expressed as one riksdaler; on No. 38 the value is one krona.

1889. Surch. with new value and Arms.
39. 4. 10 ore on 12 ore blue .. 2·00 3·00
40. 10 ore on 24 ore yellow .. 12·00 27·00

9. 10. Oscar II. 11.

1891.
41. 9. 1 ore blue and brown .. 1·00 15
42a. 2 ore yellow and blue .. 3·50 5
43. 3 ore orange and brown .. 75 80
44. 4 ore blue and red .. 6·25 5
45c. 10. 5 ore green .. .. 1·90 5
46. 8 ore purple .. .. 3·50 50
47. 10 ore red .. .. 4·00 5
48. 15 ore brown .. .. 16·00 10
49. 20 ore blue .. .. 16·00 5
50. 25 ore orange .. .. 22·00 10
51a. 30 ore brown .. .. 35·00 10
53. 50 ore grey .. .. 45·00 15
54. 11. 1 k. grey and red .. 80·00 1·25

13. G.P.O., Stockholm. 14. 15. Gustav V.

1903. Opening of new Post Office.
57. 13. 5 k. blue .. .. .. £180 19·00

1910.
65. 14. 1 ore black 10 10
66. 2 ore orange 10 5
67. 3 ore brown 10 10
68. 4 ore mauve 10 5
69. 15. 5 ore green .. .. 1·10 5
70. 7 ore green 10 5
71. 8 ore purple 10 20
72. 10 ore red .. .. 1·75 5
73. 12 ore red 15 5
74. 15 ore brown .. .. 4·00 5
75. 20 ore blue .. .. 4·25 5
76. 25 ore orange 20 8
77. 27 ore blue 40 70
78. 30 ore brown .. .. 11·00 5
79. 35 ore violet .. .. 12·50 5
80. 40 ore green .. .. 22·00 5
81. 50 ore grey .. .. 35·00 5
82. 55 ore blue £900 £2250
83. 65 ore green .. .. 80 1·50
84. 80 ore black £900 £2250
85. 90 ore green 85 30
86. 1 k. black on yellow .. 65·00 20
64. 5 k. purple on yellow .. 1·90 2·00

1916. Clothing Fund for Mobilized Reservists ("Landstorm"). Surch. **FRIMARKE LANDSTORMEN** and value in figures and words round Arms.
86a. 4. 5+5 on 2 ore orange .. 3·75 4·50
86b. 5+5 on 3 ore brown .. 3·75 4·50
86c. 5+5 on 4 ore grey .. 3·75 4·50
86d. 5+5 on 5 ore green .. 3·75 4·50
86e. 5+5 on 6 ore mauve .. 3·75 4·50
86f. 10+10 on 12 ore blue .. 3·75 4·50
86g. 10+10 on 20 ore red .. 3·75 4·50
86h. 10+10 on 24 ore yellow 3·75 4·50
86i. 10+10 on 30 ore brown 3·75 4·50
86j. 10+10 on 50 ore red .. 3·75 4·50

1916. Clothing Fund for Mobilized Reservists. Surch. **LANDSTORMEN** and **FRIMARKE SVERIGE** in frame round Arms and value in figures and words.
86k. D 6. 5+5 on 1 ore black .. 8·00 4·00
86l. 5+5 on 3 ore red .. 2·50 2·50
86m. 5+5 on 5 ore brown .. 2·25 2·50
86n. 5+10 on 6 ore orange 3·50 3·50
86o. 5+15 on 12 ore red .. 20·00 14·00
86p. 10+20 on 20 ore blue 8·50 10·50
86q. 10+40 on 24 ore mauve 30·00 65·00
86r. 10+20 on 30 ore green 2·75 4·50
86s. 10+40 on 50 ore brn... 14·00 21·00
86t. 10+90 on 1 k. black and brown .. 90·00 £200
86u. 13. 10 ore + 4 k, 90 ore on 5 k. blue .. .. 90·00 £200

1917. Surch. in figures only.
87. 15. 7 on 10 ore red 20 20
88. 12 on 25 ore orange .. 1·60 25
89. 12 on 65 ore green .. 1·25 60
90. 27 on 55 ore blue .. 70 1·00
91. 27 on 65 ore green .. 1·75 2·00
92. 27 on 80 ore black .. 90 1·25
93. 1.98 k. on 5 k. pur. on yell. 2·00 2·75
94. 2.12 k. on 5 k. pur. on yell. 2·00 2·75

1918. Landstorm Fund. Charity stamps of 1916 surch.
94a. 4. 7+3 on 5 ore on 2 ore .. 5·50 7·00
94b. 7+3 on 5 ore on 3 ore .. 1·75 1·40
94c. 7+3 on 5 ore on 4 ore .. 1·75 1·40
94d. 7+3 on 5 ore on 5 ore .. 1·75 1·40
94e. 7+3 on 5 ore on 6 ore .. 1·75 1·40
94f. 12+8 on 10 ore on 12 ore 1·75 1·40
94g. 12+8 on 10 ore on 20 ore 1·75 1·40
94h. 12+8 on 10 ore on 24 ore 1·75 1·40
94i 12+8 on 10 ore on 30 ore 1·75 1·40
94j. 12+8 on 10 ore on 50 ore 1·75 1·40

PERFORATIONS. From 1920 onwards except where otherwise stated all stamps are imperf. × perf. from coils but the lower values also come perf. all round or perf. on two or three adjacent sides from booklets apart from a few values issued in the early part of the period which also come perf. all round from sheets.

19. Arms. 20. Lion (after sculpture by B. Foucquet).

21. Gustav V. 22. Emblem of Swedish Post.

1920.
95. 19. 3 ore brown 55 5
96. 20. 5 ore green .. .. 2·25 20
97a. 5 ore brown .. .. 60 1·40
98. 10 ore green .. .. 1·25 20
99. 10 ore violet .. .. 2·50 5
102a. 21. 10 ore red .. .. 6·25 2·50
103. 15 ore red 15 20
104a. 20 ore blue .. .. 12·50 3·00
100. 20. 25 ore orange .. .. 12·50 25
101. 30 ore brown 20 15
105. 22. 35 ore yellow .. .. 26·00 20
106. 40 ore olive .. .. 22·00 30
107. 45 ore brown 70 40
108. 60 ore purple .. .. 11·00 10
109. 70 ore brown 45 85
110. 80 ore green 30 15
111. 85 ore green .. .. 2·00 40
112. 90 ore blue .. .. 32·00 20
113. 1 k. orange .. .. 4·50 10
114. 110 ore blue 40 15
115. 115 ore brown .. .. 4·50 30
116. 120 ore black .. .. 35·00 45
117. 120 ore mauve .. .. 3·50 8
118. 140 ore black 65 15
119. 145 ore green .. .. 4·25 70

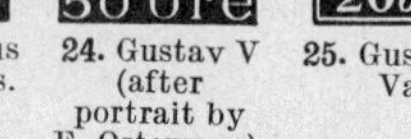
23. Gustavus II Adolphus. 24. Gustav V (after portrait by E. Osterman). 25. Gustavus Vasa.

1920. Tercentenary of Swedish Post between Stockholm and Hamburg.
120. 23. 20 ore blue .. .. 1·25 12

1920. Air. Official stamps surch. **LUFTPOST** and value.
120a. O 17. 10 on 3 ore brown .. 3·00 4·25
120b. 20 on 2 ore yellow .. 5·50 7·00
120c. 50 on 4 ore lilac .. 17·00 19·00

1921.
121. 24. 15 ore violet .. .. 10·00 5
122. 15 ore red .. .. 10·00 15
123. 15 ore brown .. .. 3·25 5
124. 20 ore violet 20 5
125. 20 ore red .. .. 12·00 20
126. 20 ore orange 20 15
128. 25 ore red 40 60
129. 25 ore blue .. .. 10·00 5
131. 25 ore orange .. .. 22·00 10
133. 30 ore brown .. .. 25·00 5
134. 30 ore blue .. .. 3·75 5
135. 35 ore mauve .. .. 9·00 5
136. 40 ore blue 30 35
137. 40 ore olive .. .. 20·00 30
138. 45 ore brown .. .. 2·25 30
139a. 50 ore black .. .. 1·00 10
140. 85 ore green .. .. 9·00 1·25
141. 115 ore brown .. .. 9·00 1·25
142. 145 ore green .. .. 7·00 1·25

1921. 400th Anniv. of Liberation of Sweden.
143. 25. 20 ore violet .. .. 6·75 9·75
144. 110 ore blue .. .. 35·00 3·50
145. 140 ore black .. .. 17·00 3·50

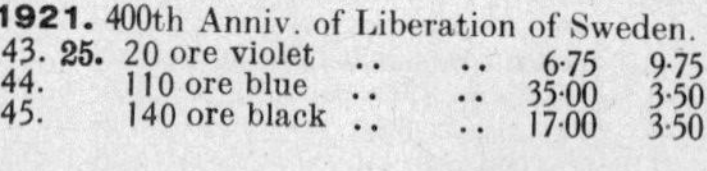

26. Old City, Stockholm. 27. Gustav V.

1924. 8th Congress of U.P.U. Perf.
146. 26. 5 ore brown .. .. 1·40 2·00
147. 10 ore green .. .. 1·40 2·00
148. 15 ore violet .. .. 1·25 1·40
149. 20 ore red .. .. 8·50 8·75
150. 25 ore orange .. .. 12·50 12·50
151. 30 ore blue .. .. 10·50 10·50
152. 35 ore black .. .. 14·00 14·00
153. 40 ore green .. .. 20·00 20·00
154. 45 ore brown .. .. 22·00 22·00
155. 50 ore grey .. .. 22·00 22·00
156. 60 ore red .. .. 40·00 40·00
157. 80 ore green .. .. 25·00 25·00
158. 27. 1 k. green .. .. 55·00 60·00
159. 2 k. red £140 £180
160. 5 k. blue £325 £325

28. Post-rider and Seaplane. 29. Carrier-pigeon.

1924. 50th Anniv. of U.P.U. Perf.
161. 28. 5 ore brown .. .. 1·75 2·25
162. 10 ore green .. .. 1·75 2·00
163. 15 ore violet .. .. 1·75 1·50
164. 20 ore red .. .. 13·00 20·00
165. 25 ore orange .. .. 15·00 21·00
166. 30 ore blue .. .. 15·00 12·00
167. 35 ore black .. .. 19·00 26·00
168. 40 ore green .. .. 20·00 22·00
169. 45 ore brown .. .. 25·00 24·00
170. 50 ore grey .. .. 32·00 26·00
171. 60 ore red .. .. 35·00 45·00
172. 80 ore green .. .. 30·00 23·00
173. 29. 1 k. green .. .. 60·00 75·00
174. 2 k. red .. .. £175 65·00
175. 5 k. blue £250 £175

29a. King Gustav V. 29c. Night flight over Stockholm (Junkers "F 13").

1928. 70th Birthday of King Gustav V and Cancer Research Fund. Perf.
175a. 29a. 5+5 ore green .. 3·00 5·25
175b. 10+5 ore violet .. 3·00 5·25
175c. 15+5 ore red .. 3·00 5·25
175d. 20+5 ore orange .. 4·25 3·00
175e. 25+5 ore blue .. 4·25 3·00

1930. Air.
175f. 29c. 10 ore blue 15 40
175g. 50 ore violet .. .. 40 1·00

30. Royal Palace, Stockholm. 31. Death of Gustavus Adolphus at Lutzen.

1931. Perf.
176. 30. 5 k. green .. .. 80·00 6·25

1932. Death Tercent. of Gustavus Adolphus.
177a. 31. 10 ore violet .. .. 1·75 10
178. 15 ore red .. .. 1·75 10
179. 25 ore blue .. .. 5·50 55
180. 90 ore green .. .. 18·00 1·50

32. Allegory of Thrift. 33. Stockholm Cathedral.

1933. 50th Anniv. of Swedish Postal Savings Bank.
181. 32. 5 ore green .. .. 1·25 30

1935. 500th Anniv. of First Swedish Parliament. Stockholm Buildings.
182. – 5 ore green .. .. 1·00 10
183. – 10 ore violet .. .. 3·75 10
184. 33. 15 ore red .. .. 1·40 10
185. – 25 ore blue .. .. 7·00 45
186. – 35 ore red .. .. 10·50 1·40
187. – 60 ore red .. .. 13·00 1·40

DESIGNS: 5 ore Old City Hall. 10 ore Exchange. 25 ore House of the Nobility. 35 ore Houses of Parliament. 60 ore Arms of Engelbrekt.

35. A. Oxenstierna (after D. Dumonstier). 38. Mail-plane (Junkers "JU 34") over Scandinavia.

1936. Tercentenary of Swedish Post.
188. 35. 5 ore green .. .. 1·25 10
189. – 10 ore violet .. .. 1·25 10
190. – 15 ore red .. .. 1·75 10
191. – 20 ore blue .. .. 8·00 2·50
192. – 25 ore blue .. .. 6·00 40
193. – 30 ore brown .. .. 13·00 1·75
194. – 35 ore purple .. .. 4·25 85
195. – 40 ore green .. .. 7·50 2·00
196. – 45 ore green .. .. 5·50 2·25
197. – 50 ore grey .. .. 18·00 1·75
198. – 60 ore purple .. .. 28·00 50
199. – 1 k. blue .. .. 8·00 5·00

DESIGNS: 10 ore, Early courier. 15 ore, Post rider. 20 ore, Sailing packet "Hiorten". 25 ore, Paddle-steamer "Constitutionen". 30 ore, Mail coach. 35 ore, Arms. 40 ore, Steam train. 45 ore, A.W. Roos (Postmaster General 1867–89). 50 ore, Motor bus and trailer. 60 ore, Liner "Gripsholm". 1 k. Junkers Ju 52/3m seaplane.

For similar designs, but dated "1972" at foot, see Nos. 700/4.

1936. Inauguration of Bromma Aerodrome.
200. 38. 50 ore blue .. .. 5·50 6·50

39. E. Swedenborg (after P. Krafft). 40. Governor Printz and Red Indian.

1938. 250th Birth Anniv. of Swedenborg.
201. **39.** 10 ore violet 70 5
202. 100 ore green .. .. 5·00 90

1938. 300th Anniv. of Founding of New Sweden, U.S.A.
203. **40.** 5 ore green 40 10
204. – 15 ore brown 75 10
205. – 20 ore red .. .. 1·25 50
206. – 30 ore blue .. .. 3·50 65
207. – 60 ore purple .. .. 4·50 20
DESIGNS: 15 ore Emigrant ships "Calmare Nyckel" and "Fagel Grip". 20 ore Swedish landing in America. 30 ore First Swedish church, Wilmington. 60 ore Queen Christina (after S. Bourdon).

41. King Gustav V. 42. 43. Small Arms of Sweden.

1938. 80th Birthday of King Gustav V.
208. **41.** 5 ore green 55 5
209. 15 ore brown 55 5
210. 30 ore blue .. .. 14·00 55

1939.
234b. **42.** 5 ore green 10 5
299. 5 ore orange 15 5
235b. 10 ore violet 10 5
300. 10 ore green 15 5
236b. 15 ore brown 10 5
237. 20 ore red 10 5
238. 25 ore orange 95 5
301. 25 ore violet .. .. 1·25 5
239. 30 ore blue 30 5
240. 35 ore purple 90 5
241. 40 ore olive 90 5
242. 45 ore brown 90 5
243. 50 ore grey .. .. 1·75 5
301a. **43.** 50 ore grey .. .. 5·25 5
302. 55 ore brown .. .. 2·50 20
221. 60 ore red .. .. 1·40 5
302a. 65 ore green 70 5
302b. 70 ore blue .. .. 3·50 1·10
302c. 75 ore brown .. .. 4·50 75
303. 80 ore olive 85 5
222. 85 ore green 70 20
303a. 85 ore brown .. .. 8·00 1·10
223. 90 ore blue .. .. 1·75 5
224. 1 k. orange 50 5
303b. 1 k. 5 blue .. .. 2·00 40
304. 1 k. 10 ore violet .. .. 7·00 5
225. 1 k. 15 ore brown 70 10
226. 1 k. 20 ore purple .. .. 2·00 10
304a. 1 k. 20 blue .. .. 5·25 2·00
305. 1 k. 40 ore green .. .. 1·00 5
227. 1 k. 45 ore green .. .. 3·25 50
305a. 1 k. 50 ore purple .. .. 1·60 1·10
305b. 1 k. 50 brown .. .. 1·40 35
305c. 1 k. 70 ore red .. .. 2·00 5
306. 1 k. 75 ore blue .. .. 26·00 6·00
306a. 1 k. 80 blue .. .. 2·25 40
306b. 1 k. 85 blue .. .. 7·00 45
306c. 2 k. purple .. .. 1·00 5
306ca. 2 k. cerise 65 5
306d. 2 k. 10 ore blue .. .. 10·50 10
306e. 2 k. 15 olive .. .. 8·75 40
306f. 2 k. 30 purple .. .. 18·00 20
306g. 2 k. 50 green 80 5
306h. 2 k. 55 red .. .. 5·25 1·40
306i. 2 k. 80 red .. .. 4·50 20
306j. 2 k. 85 orange .. .. 4·50 3·00
306k. 3 k. blue .. .. 1·60 5

44. P. H. Ling (after J. G. Sandberg). 45. Carl von Linne (Linnaeus) (after A. Roslin). 47. Carl Michael Bellman.

1939. Death Centenary of P. H. Ling (creator of "Swedish Drill").
228. **44.** 5 ore green 10 5
229. 25 ore brown 75 15

1939. Bicent. of Swedish Academy of Sciences.
230a. – 10 ore violet .. .. 1·75 40
231. **45.** 15 ore brown 20 5
232. – 30 ore blue .. .. 10·50 25
233. **45.** 50 ore grey .. .. 9·75 55
PORTRAIT: 10 ore, 30 ore J. J. Berzelius (after O. J. Sodermark).

1940. Birth Bicent. of C. M. Bellman (poet).
244. **47.** 5 ore green 10 5
245. 35 ore red 55 15

48. Johan Tobias Sergel (self-portrait bust). 49. Reformers presenting Bible to Gustavus Vasa.

1940. Birth Bicent. of Sergel (sculptor).
246. **48.** 15 ore brown .. .. 1·75 5
247. 50 ore grey .. .. 12·50 60

1941. 400th Anniv. of First Authorised Version of Bible in Swedish.
248. **49.** 15 ore brown 20 5
249. 90 ore blue .. .. 14·00 55

50. Hasjo Belfry. 50a. Royal Palace, Stockholm.

1941. 50th Anniv. of Foundation of Skansen open-air Museum.
250. **50.** 10 ore violet .. .. 1·00 10
251. 60 ore red .. .. 8·50 30

1941. Perf.
252b. **50a.** 5 k. blue .. .. 1·40 30

51. A. Hazelius. 52. St. Bridget (from altar painting, Vasteras Cathedral). 53. Mute Swans.

1941. Artur Hazelius (founder of Skansen Museum).
253. **51.** 5 ore green 10 5
254. 1 k. orange .. .. 6·25 1·75

1941. 550th Anniv. of Canonization of St. Bridget (Foundress of Brigittine Order of Our Saviour).
255. **52.** 15 ore brown 10 5
256. 120 ore purple .. .. 30·00 9·00

1942. Perf.
257a **53.** 20 k. blue .. .. 3·50 40

54. King Gustavus III (after A. Roslin). 55. Count Rudenschold and Nils Mansson.

1942. 150th Anniv. of National Museum, Stockholm.
258. **54.** 20 ore red 30 5
259. – 40 ore olive .. .. 18·00 75
PORTRAIT: 40 ore Carl Gustaf Tessin (architect and chancery president) (after Gustav Lundberg).

1942. Centenary of Institution of National Elementary Education.
260. **55.** 10 ore red 20 30
261. 90 ore blue .. .. 2·75 5·00

56. Carl. Wilhelm Scheele. 57. King Gustav V. 58. Rifle Assn. Badge.

1942. Birth Bicent. of C. W. Scheele (chemist).
262. **56.** 5 ore green 10 5
263. 60 ore red .. .. 6·25 25

1943. 85th Birthday of King Gustav V.
264. **57.** 20 ore red 50 15
265. 30 ore blue .. .. 1·00 1·75
266. 60 ore purple .. .. 1·50 2·25

1943. 50th Anniv. of National Voluntary Rifle Association.
267. **58.** 10 ore purple 10 5
268. 90 ore blue .. .. 3·50 25

59. O. Montelius (after E. Stenberg). 60. First Swedish Navigators' Chart. 61. "Smalands Lejon".

1943. Birth Centenary of Oscar Montelius (archaeologist).
269. **59.** 5 ore green 10 5
270. 120 ore purple .. .. 6·25 1·75

1944. Tercent. of 1st Swedish Marine Chart.
271. **60.** 5 ore green 12 5
272. 60 ore red .. .. 5·50 25

1944. Swedish Fleet (Tercentenary of Battle of Femern).
273. **61.** 10 ore violet 20 10
274. – 20 ore red 40 10
275. – 30 ore blue 55 50
276. – 40 ore olive 70 40
277. – 90 ore grey .. .. 9·00 1·25
DESIGNS—27 × 22½ mm: 30 ore, "Kung Karl" (ship of the line). 40 ore, Stern of "Amphion" (royal yacht). 90 ore, "Gustav V" (cruiser). 18½ × 20½ mm: 20 ore, Admiral C. Fleming (after L. Pasch).
See also Nos. 517/22.

62. Red Cross. 63. Press Symbols.

1945. 80th Anniv. of Swedish Red Cross and Birthday of Prince Carl.
278. **62.** 20 ore red 40 5

1945. Tercentenary of Swedish Press.
279. **63.** 5 ore green 10 10
280. 60 ore red .. .. 7·00 20

64. Viktor Rydberg (after A. Edelfelt). 65. Oak tree, Savings Banks' Symbol.

1945. 50th Death Anniv. of Viktor Rydberg (author).
281. **64.** 20 ore red 20 5
282. 90 ore blue .. .. 7·75 25

1945. 125th Anniv. of Swedish Savings Banks.
283. **65.** 10 ore violet 10 10
284. 40 ore olive .. .. 1·10 65

66. Cathedral Model. 67. Lund Cathedral.

1946. 800th Anniv. of Lund Cathedral.
285. **66.** 15 ore brown 60 20
286. **67.** 20 ore red 20 5
287. **66.** 90 ore blue .. .. 8·50 60

68. Mare and Foal. 69. E. Tegner (after J. N. Bystrom). 70. A. Nobel.

1946. Cent. of Swedish Agricultural Show.
288. **68.** 5 ore green 15 5
289. 60 ore red .. .. 5·25 20

1946. Death Cent. of Esaias Tegner (poet).
290. **69.** 10 ore violet 10 5
291. 40 ore olive .. .. 1·00 25

1946. 50th Death Anniv. of Alfred Nobel (scientist and creator of Nobel Foundation).
292. **70.** 20 ore red 65 5
293. 30 ore blue .. .. 1·75 45

71. E. G. Geijer (after J. G. Sandberg). 72. King Gustav V. 73. Ploughman and Skyscraper.

1947. Death Cent. of Erik Gustav Geijer (historian, philospher, poet and composer).
294. **71.** 5 ore green 10 5
295. 90 ore blue .. .. 4·25 20

1947. Forty Years Reign of King Gustav V.
296. **72.** 10 ore violet 10 5
297. 20 ore red 20 15
298. 60 ore purple .. .. 1·25 1·25

1948. Centenary of Swedish Pioneers' in U.S.A.
307. **73.** 15 ore brown 15 5
308. 30 ore blue 60 25
309. 1 k. orange .. .. 2·00 60

73a. King Gustav V. 74. J. A. Strindberg (after R. Bergh). 75. Gymnastics.

1948. King Gustav V's 90th Birthday, and Youth Fund.
309a. **73a.** 10 ore + 10 ore green .. 30 55
309ba. 20 ore + 10 ore red .. 40 60
309c. 30 ore + 10 ore blue .. 30 40

1949. Birth Cent. of Strindberg (dramatist).
310. **74.** 20 ore red 20 10
311. 30 ore blue 70 70
312. 80 ore olive .. .. 2·50 35

1949. 2nd Lingiad, Stockholm.
313. **75.** 5 ore blue 8 10
314. 15 ore brown 8 5

76. Globe and Hand Writing. 77.

1949. 75th Anniv. of U.P.U.
315. **76.** 10 ore green 10 5
316. 20 ore red 10 5
317. **77.** 30 ore blue 25 25

78. King Gustav VI Adolf. 79. Christopher Polhem (after G. E. Schroder). 80.

1951. (a) Coloured lettering and figures.
318. **78.** 10 ore green 15 5
318b. 10 ore brown 10 5
319. 15 ore brown 25 5
388. 15 ore red 15 5
320. 20 ore red 30 5
391. 20 ore black 20 5
322a. 25 ore black 45 5
323a. 25 ore red 40 15
324a. 25 ore blue 15 5
392. 25 ore sepia 20 5
393. 30 ore blue 30 5
326. 30 ore sepia 40 20
326a. 30 ore red .. .. 19·00 5
327. 40 ore blue 80 5
394. 40 ore green 70 5

(b) White lettering and figures.
429. **78.** 15 ore red 10 5
430. 20 ore black 25 5
431a. 25 ore brown 10 5
432a. 30 ore blue 45 5
433a. 30 ore violet 30 20
433b. 30 ore red 50 60
434. 35 ore violet 50 5
435a. 35 ore blue 20 5
436. 35 ore black 50 5
437. 40 ore green 70 5
438a. 40 ore blue 20 5
439a. 45 ore orange 30 5
439c. 45 ore blue 30 5
440. 50 ore olive 70 5
440a. 50 ore green 40 5
440c. 55 ore red 40 5
441. 60 ore red 70 30
441a. 65 ore blue 65 5
441c. 70 ore mauve 50 5
441d. 85 ore purple .. .. 1·00 20

1951. Death Bicent. of Polhem (engineer).
329a. **79.** 25 ore black 85 20
330. 45 ore brown 35 30

1951.
385. **80.** 5 ore red 5 5
386. 10 ore blue 5 5
387a. 10 ore brown 5 5
389. 15 ore green 5 5
390a. 15 ore brown 30 30

81. Olavus Petri Preaching. 81a. King Gustav VI Adolf.

1952. 400th Death Anniv. of Petri (reformer).
332. **81.** 25 ore black 20 10
333. 1 k. 40 ore brown .. .. 3·00 60

1952. 70th Birthday of King Gustav VI Adolf and Culture Fund.
333a. **81a.** 10 ore + 10 ore green .. 20 20
333b. 25 ore + 10 ore red .. 30 30
333c. 40 ore + 10 ore blue .. 25 25

82. Ski Jumping. 83. Stockholm, 1650.

1953. 50th Anniv of Swedish Athletic Assn.
334 **82** 10 ore green 30 20
335 – 15 ore brown 70 70
336 – 40 ore blue .. .. 1·00 85
337 – 1 k. 40 mauve .. .. 3·50 90
DESIGNS—HORIZ. 1 k. 40, Wrestling. VERT. 15 ore Ice hockey. 40 ore Slingball.

1953. 700th Anniv. of Stockholm.
338. **83.** 25 ore blue 20 10
339. – 1 k. 70 red .. .. 3·00 55
DESIGN: 1 k. 70, Seal of Stockholm 1296 (obverse and reverse).

84. "Radio".

85. Skier.

1953. Cent. of Telecommunications in Sweden.
340. – 25 ore blue ("Telephones") 20 10
341. 84. 40 ore green 85 80
342. – 60 ore red ("Telegraphs") .. .. 1·75 1·40

1954. World Skiing Championships.
343. 85. 20 ore grey 30 30
344. – 1 k. blue (Women skier) 9·50 80

86. Anna Maria Lenngren (after medallion, J. T. Sergel).

87. Rock-carvings.

88.

1954. Birth Bicentenary of Anna Maria Lenngren (poetess).
345. 86. 20 ore grey 20 20
346. 65 ore brown .. .. 7·75 1·10

1954.
347. 87. 50 ore grey 30 5
348. 55 ore red 85 20
349. 60 ore red 40 5
350. 65 ore green .. .. 1·50 20
351. 70 ore orange 50 15
352. 75 ore brown .. .. 2·40 15
353. 80 ore green 50 5
355. 90 ore blue 75 5
356. 95 ore violet .. .. 5·25 5·25

1955. Cent. of 1st Swedish Postage Stamps.
362. 88. 25 ore blue 8 5
363. 40 ore green 80 25

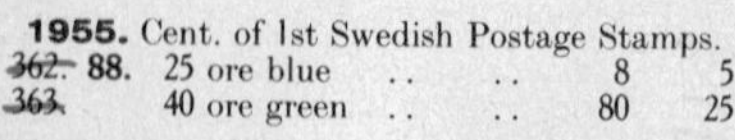

89. Swedish Flag.

91. P. D. A. Atterbom (after Fogelberg).

1955. National Flag Day. Perf.
364. 89. 10 ore yellow, bl. & grn. 10 10
365. 15 ore yellow, bl. & red 15 10

1955. Cent. of 1st Swedish Postage Stamps and "Stockholmia" Philatelic Exn. As T 1 but with two rules through bottom panel. Perf.
366. 1. 3 ore green .. .. 2·50 4·25
367. 4 ore blue .. .. 2·50 4·25
368. 6 ore grey .. .. 2·50 4·25
369. 8 ore yellow .. .. 2·50 4·25
370. 24 ore red .. .. 2·50 4·25
Nos. 366/70 were sold only at the Exhibition in single sets, at 2 k. 45 ore (45 ore face + 2 k. entrance fee).

1955. Death Cent. of Atterbom (poet).
371. 91. 20 ore blue 20 5
372. 1 k. 40 brown .. .. 3·25 55

92. Greek Horseman, (from Parthenon Frieze).

93. Railway Construction.

1956. 16th Olympic Games Equestrian Competitions, Stockholm.
373. 92. 20 ore red 10 10
374. 25 ore blue 25 5
375. 40 ore green .. .. 1·25 1·00

1956. Northern Countries' Day. As T 101a of Norway.
376. 25 ore red 70 10
377. 40 ore blue .. .. 2·75 50

1956. Centenary of Swedish Railways.
378. 93. 10 ore green 55 15
379. – 25 ore blue 40 15
380. – 40 ore orange .. .. 3·00 2·75
DESIGNS: 25 ore First Swedish steam locomotive, "Fryckstad". 40 ore Arsta Bridge, Stockholm.

94. Trawler in Distress and Lifeboat.

1957. 50th Anniv. of Swedish Life Saving Service.
381a. 94. 30 ore blue .. .. 3·00 1·10
382. 1 k. 40 red .. .. 4·00 90

95. Galleon and "Gripsholm II".

96. Postal Helicopter.

1958. Postal Services Commem.
395. 95. 15 ore red 20 10
396. 96. 30 ore blue 15 10
397. 95. 40 ore green .. .. 4·25 2·10
398. 96. 1 k. 40 brown .. .. 4·50 75

97. Footballer.

98. Bessemer Tilting-furnace.

1958. World Football Championships.
399. 97. 15 ore red 10 10
400. 20 ore green 20 10
401. 1 k. 20 blue .. .. 1·10 65

1958. Cent. of Swedish Steel Industry.
402. 98. 30 ore blue 20 10
403. 170 ore brown .. .. 3·50 65

99. Selma Lagerlof (after bust by G. Malmquist).

100. Overhead Power Lines.

101. Henri Dunant (founder).

1958. Birth Cent. of Selma Lagerlof (writer).
404. 99. 20 ore red 10 10
405. 30 ore blue 15 5
406. 80 ore green 50 60

1959. 50th Anniv. of Swedish State Power Board.
407. 100. 30 ore blue 25 10
408. – 90 ore red .. .. 3·50 1·75
DESIGN—HORIZ. 90 ore Dam sluice-gates.

1959. Red Cross Centenary.
409. 101. 30 ore + 10 ore red .. 40 50

102. V. von Heidenstam.

103. Forest Trees.

104. S. Arrhenius.

1959. Birth Centenary of Verner von Heidenstam (poet).
410. 102. 15 ore red 60 10
411. 1 k. black .. .. 4·75 60

1959. Centenary of Crown Lands and Forests Administration.
412a. 103. 30 ore green .. .. 1·00 10
413. – 1 k. 40 brown .. .. 4·25 50
DESIGN: 1 k. 40, Forester felling tree.

1959. Birth Cent. of Arrhenius (chemist).
414. 104. 15 ore brown 20 5
415. 1 k. 70 blue .. .. 3·75 35

105. Anders Zorn (self-portrait).

106. "Uprooted Tree".

1960. Birth Cent. of Zorn (painter and etcher).
416. 105. 30 ore grey 20 5
417. 80 ore brown .. .. 2·75 1·00

1960. World Refugee Year.
418. 106. 20 ore brown 10 10
419. – 40 ore violet 20 20
DESIGN—VERT. 40 ore Refugees.

107. Target-shooting.

108. G. Froding.

1960. Centenary of Voluntary Shooting Organization.
420. 107. 15 ore red 20 10
421. – 90 ore turquoise .. 2·10 90
DESIGN: 90 ore Organization members marching, 1860.

1960. Birth Cent. of Gustav Froding (poet).
422. 108. 30 ore brown 20 10
423. 1 k. 40 green .. .. 3·00 25

1960. Europa. As T. 113a of Norway.
424. 40 ore blue 10 10
425. 1 k. red 25 25

109. H. Branting.

111. "Coronation of Gustav III" (after Pilo).

1960. Birth Centenary of Hjalmar Branting (statesman).
426. 109. 15 ore red 10 5
427. 1 k. 70 blue .. .. 3·50 30

1961. 10th Anniv. of Scandinavian Airlines System (SAS). As T 113b of Norway.
428. 40 ore blue 20 10

1961. 250th Birth Anniv. of Carl Gustav Pilo. (painter).
442. 111. 30 ore brown 20 10
443. 1 k. 40 blue .. .. 3·50 65

112. J. Alstromer (after bust by P. H. l'Archeveque).

113. Printing Works and Library.

1961. Death Bicentenary of Jonas Alstromer (industrial reformer).
444. 112. 15 ore purple 15 5
445. 90 ore blue 90 65

1961. Tercent. of Royal Library Regulation.
446. 113. 20 ore red 10 10
447. 1 k. blue .. .. 8·75 55

114. Motif on Runic Stone at Oland.

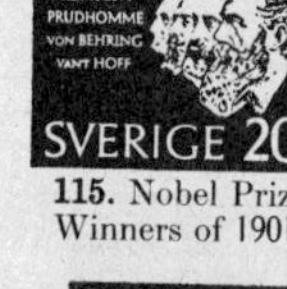
115. Nobel Prize Winners of 1901.

116. Postman's Footprints.

117. Code, Voting Instrument and Mallet.

1961.
448. 114. 10 k. purple .. .. 10·50 40

1961. Nobel Prize Winners.
449. 115. 20 ore red 15 10
450. 40 ore blue 25 10
451. 50 ore green 25 10
See also Nos. 458/9, 471a/2, 477/8, 488/9, 523/4, 546/7 and 573/4.

1962. Centenary of Swedish Local Mail Delivery Service.
452. 116. 30 ore violet 10 10
453. 1 k. 70 red .. .. 3·50 20

1962. Centenary of Municipal Laws.
454. 117. 30 ore blue 20 10
455. 2 k. red .. .. 3·50 30

118. St. George and Dragon, Storkyrkan ("Great Church"), Stockholm.

119. Ice-hockey Player.

118a. King Gustav VI Adolf and Cultural Themes.

1962. Swedish Monuments (1st series).
456. 118. 20 ore red 15 10
457. – 50 ore green 40 10
DESIGN—HORIZ. 50 ore Skokloster Castle.
See also Nos. 469/70 and 479/80.

1962. King Gustav's 80th Birthday and Swedish Culture Fund.
457b. 118a. 20 ore + 10 ore brown 10 20
457c. 35 ore + 10 ore blue .. 10 20

1962. Nobel Prize Winners. As T 115 but inscr. "NOBELPRIS 1902".
458. 25 ore red 25 20
459. 50 ore blue 35 10
PORTRAITS: Nobel Prize Winners of 1902. 25 ore, Theodore Mommsen (literature) and Sir Ronald Ross (medicine). 50 ore, Emily Herman Fischer (chemistry) and Pieter Zeeman and Hendrik Lorentz (physics).

1963. World Ice Hockey Championships.
460. 119. 25 ore 10 10
461. 1 k. 70 blue .. .. 2·25 30

120. Hands reaching for Wheat.

121. Engineering and Industrial Symbols.

1963. Freedom from Hunger.
462. 120. 35 ore mauve 10 5
463. 50 ore violet 20 15

1963. "Engineering and Industry".
464. 121. 50 ore black 20 10
465. 1 k. 05 orange .. .. 2·50 1·75

122. Dr. G. F. Du Rietz (after D. K. Ehrenstrahl).

123. Linne's Hammarby (country house).

1963. 300th Anniv. of Swedish Board of Health.
466. 122. 25 ore brown 20 10
467. 35 ore blue 20 5
468. 2 k. red .. .. 3·75 45

1963. Swedish Monuments (2nd series).
469. 123. 20 ore red 12 5
470. 50 ore green 20 10

1963. Nobel Prize Winners. As T 115 but inscr. "NOBELPRIS 1903".
471. 25 ore green 50 25
472. 50 ore brown 60 15
PORTRAITS: Nobel Prize winners of 1903. 25 ore, S. Vante Arrhenius (chemistry), Niels Ryberg Finsen (medicine) and Bjornstjerne Bjornson (literature). 50 ore, Antoine Henri Becquerel and Pierre and Marie Curie (physics).

124. Motif from poem "Elie Himmelsfard".

125. Seal of Archbishop Stefan.

1964. Birth Cent. of E. A. Karlfeldt (poet).
473. 124. 35 ore blue 50 5
474. 1 k. 05 red .. .. 4·25 2·10

1964. 800th Anniv. of Archbishopric of Uppsala.
475. 125. 40 ore green 10 10
476a. 60 ore brown 20 20

1964. Nobel Prize Winners. As T **115** but inscr. "NOBELPRIS 1904".
477. 30 ore blue 30 25
478. 40 ore red 30 5
PORTRAITS: Nobel Prize winners of 1904. 30 ore, Jose Echegaray y Eizaguirre and Frederic Mistral (literature) and J. W. Strutt (Lord Rayleigh) (physics). 40 ore, Sir William Ramsay (chemistry) and Ivan Petrovich Pavlov (medicine).

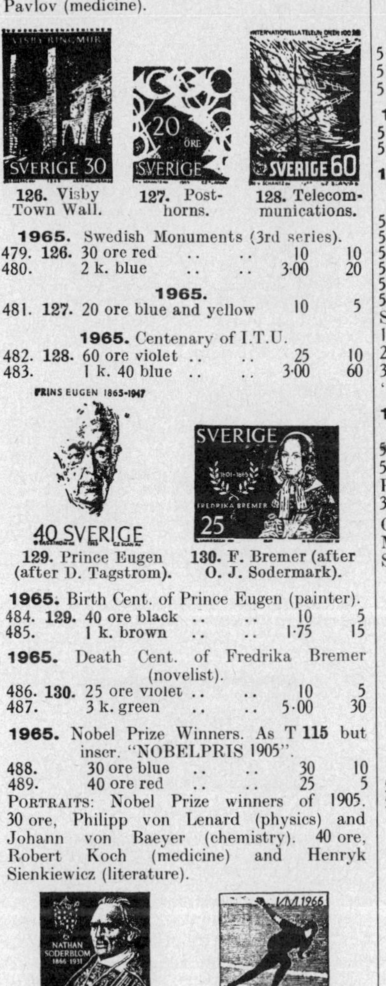

126. Visby Town Wall. **127.** Post-horns. **128.** Telecommunications.

1965. Swedish Monuments (3rd series).
479. **126.** 30 ore red 10 10
480. 2 k. blue .. .. 3·00 20

1965.
481. **127.** 20 ore blue and yellow 10 5

1965. Centenary of I.T.U.
482. **128.** 60 ore violet 25 10
483. 1 k. 40 blue .. .. 3·00 60

129. Prince Eugen (after D. Tagstrom). **130.** F. Bremer (after O. J. Sodermark).

1965. Birth Cent. of Prince Eugen (painter).
484. **129.** 40 ore black 10 5
485. 1 k. brown .. .. 1·75 15

1965. Death Cent. of Fredrika Bremer (novelist).
486. **130.** 25 ore violet 10 5
487. 3 k. green .. .. 5·00 30

1965. Nobel Prize Winners. As T **115** but inscr. "NOBELPRIS 1905".
488. 30 ore blue 30 10
489. 40 ore red 25 5
PORTRAITS: Nobel Prize winners of 1905. 30 ore, Philipp von Lenard (physics) and Johann von Baeyer (chemistry). 40 ore, Robert Koch (medicine) and Henryk Sienkiewicz (literature).

131. N. Soderblom. **132.** Skating.

1966. Birth Centenary of Nathan Soderblom, Archbishop of Uppsala.
490. **131.** 60 ore brown 20 12
491. 80 ore green 50 8

1966. World Men's Speed Skating Championships, Gothenburg.
492. **132.** 5 ore red 10 10
493. 25 ore green 15 15
494. 40 ore blue 20 30

134. Ale's Stones, Ship Grave, Kaseberga.

133. Entrance Hall, National Museum. **135.** Louis de Geer (advocate of reform).

1966. Centenary of Opening of National Museum Building.
495. **133.** 30 ore violet 10 10
496. 2 k. 30 green 60 70

1966.
498. – 35 ore brown and blue 10 5
499. **134.** 3 k. 50 grey .. .. 1·10 10
500. – 3 k. 70 violet .. .. 1·75 10
501. – 4 k. 50 red .. .. 2·00 10
502. – 7 k. red and blue .. 2·75 30
DESIGNS—HORIZ. 35 ore, Fjeld (mountains). 7 k. Gripsholm Castle. VERT. 3 k. 70, Lion Fortress, Gothenburg. 4 k. 50, Uppsala Cathedral (interior).

1966. Cent. of Representative Assembly Reform.
510. **135.** 40 ore blue 30 10
511. 3 k. red .. .. 4·25 40

136. Theatre Stage. **137.** C. J. Almqvist (after C. P. Mazer).

1966. Bicent. of Drottningholm Theatre.
512. **136.** 5 ore red on red .. 10 10
513. 25 ore brown on red .. 10 10
514. 40 ore purple on red 25 40

1966. Death Cent. of Carl Almqvist (writer).
515. **137.** 25 ore mauve 20 10
516. 1 k. green .. .. 2·10 20

1966. National Cancer Fund. Swedish Ships. Designs as T **61**, but with imprint "1966" at foot.
517. 10 ore red 10 20
518. 15 ore red 10 20
519. 20 ore green 10 20
520. 25 ore blue 10 12
521. 30 ore red 10 20
522. 40 ore red 10 20
SHIPS—HORIZ. 10 ore, "Smalands Lejon". 15 ore, "Calmare Nyckel" and "Fagel Grip". 20 ore, "Hiorten". 25 ore, "Constitutionen". 30 ore, "Kung Karl". 40 ore, Stern of "Amphion".

1966. Nobel Prize Winners. As T **115** but inscr. "NOBELPRIS 1906".
523. 30 ore red 30 20
524. 40 ore green 20 10
PORTRAITS: Nobel Prize winners of 1906. 30 ore. Sir Joseph John Thomson (physics) and Giosue Carducci (literature). 40 ore, Henri Moissan (chemistry) and Camillo Golgi and Santiago Romon y Cajal (medicine).

138. Handball. **139.** "E.F.T.A.".

1967. World Handball Championships.
525. **138.** 45 ore blue 10 10
526. 2 k. 70 mauve .. 2·50 80

1967. European Free Trade Assn. ("E.F.T.A.").
527. **139.** 70 ore orange 30 15

140. Table Tennis Player. **141.** Axeman and Beast.

1967. World Table Tennis Championships, Stockholm.
528. **140.** 35 ore mauve 10 8
529. 90 ore blue 70 30

1967. Iron Age Helmet Decorations, Oland.
530. **141.** 10 ore blue and brown 5 5
531. – 15 ore brown and blue 20 10
532. – 30 ore mauve & brown 20 12
533. – 35 ore brown & mauve 20 12
DESIGNS: 15 ore Man between two bears. 30 ore "Lion man" putting enemy to flight. 35 ore, Two warriors.

142. "Solidarity". **144.** 18th-Century Post-rider.

143. "Keep to the Right".

1967. Finnish Settlers in Sweden.
534. **142.** 10 ore multicoloured .. 5 5
535. 35 ore multicoloured .. 10 8

1967 Adoption of Changed Rule of the Road.
536. **143.** 35 ore black, orge. & bl. 10 5
537. 45 ore blk., orge. & grn. 10 5

1967.
538. **144.** 5 ore black and red .. 10 10
539. – 10 ore black and blue 15 10
539b. – 20 ore black on flesh .. 10 10
540. – 30 ore red and blue .. 10 10
541. – 40 ore blue, grn. & blk. 20 10
541b. – 45 ore black and blue 10 10
542. – 90 ore brown and blue 20 10
543. – 1 k. olive 30 10

DESIGNS—As T **144**: VERT. 10 ore, "Svert Skepp" (warship). 20 ore, "St. Stephen" (ceiling painting, Dadesjo Church, Smaland). 30 ore, Angelica plant on coast. HORIZ. 40 ore, Haverud Aqueduct, Dalsland Canal. $27\frac{1}{2} \times 22\frac{1}{2}$ mm: 45 ore, Floating logs. 90 ore, Elk. 1 k. Dancing cranes.

145. King Gustav VI Adolf. **146.** Berwald, Violin and Music.

1967. 85th Birthday of King Gustav VI Adolf.
544. **145.** 45 ore blue 10 5
545. 70 ore green 15 12

1967. Nobel Prize Winners. As T **115**, but inscr. "NOBELPRIS 1907".
546. 35 ore red 40 25
547. 45 ore blue 20 5
PORTRAITS: Nobel Prize winners of 1907. 35 ore, Eduard Buchner (chemistry) and Albert Abraham Michelson (physics). 45 ore, Charles Louis Alphonse Laveran (medicine) and Rudyard Kipling (literature).

1968. Death Centenary of Franz Berwald (composer).
548. **146.** 35 ore black and red .. 20 5
549. 2 k. black, blue & yell. 2·50 45

147. Bank Seal. **148.** Butterfly Orchids.

1968. 300th Anniv. of Bank of Sweden.
550. **147.** 45 ore blue 10 5
551. 70 ore black on salmon 15 10

1968. Wild Flowers.
552. **148.** 45 ore green 50 30
553. – 45 ore green 50 30
554. – 45 ore red and green .. 50 30
555. – 45 ore green 50 30
556. – 45 ore green 50 30
DESIGNS: No. 553, Wood anemone. No. 554, Wild rose. No. 555, Wild cherry. No. 556, Lily of the Valley.

149. University Seal.

1968. 300th Anniv. of Lund University. Perf.
557. **149.** 10 ore blue 5 5
558. 35 ore red 20 20

150. Ecumenical Emblem. **151.** "The Universe".

1968. 4th General Assembly of World Council of Churches, Uppsala.
559. **150.** 70 ore purple 20 20
560. 90 ore blue 60 10

1968. Centenary of the People's College.
561. **151.** 45 ore red 10 5
562. 2 k. blue .. .. 2·25 20

152. "Orienteer" crossing Forest. **153.** "The Tug of War" (wood-carving by Axel Petersson).

1968. World "Orienteering" Championships, Linkoping.
563. **152.** 40 ore red and violet 20 10
564. 2 k. 80 violet & green 2·50 2·25

1968. Birth Centenary of Axel Petersson ("Doderhultarn").
565. **153.** 5 ore green 5 5
566. 25 ore brown 65 85
567. 45 ore brown and sepia 10 10

154. Red Fox. **155.** "The Worker" (A. Amelin).

1968. Bruno Liljefors' Fauna Sketches. Perf.
568. – 30 ore blue 50 40
569. – 30 ore black 50 40
570. **154.** 30 ore brown 50 40
571. – 30 ore brown 50 40
572. – 30 ore blue 50 40
DESIGNS: No. 568, Arctic hare. No. 569, Great Black-backed gull. No. 571, Golden eagle and Carrion crows. No. 572, Stoat.

1968. Nobel Prize Winners. As T **115**, but inscr. "NOBELPRIS 1908".
573. 35 ore lake 20 12
574. 45 ore green 20 10
PORTRAITS: Nobel Prize winners of 1908. 35 ore, Ilya Mechnikov and Paul Ehrlich (medicine) and Lord Rutherford (chemistry). 45 ore, Gabriel Lippman (physics) and Rudoy Eucken (literature).

1969. 50th Anniv. of Northern Countries Union. As T **161a** of Norway.
575. 45 ore brown 20 10
576. 70 ore blue 35 40

1969. 50th Anniv. of Int. Labour Organization.
577. **155.** 55 ore red 10 5
578. 70 ore blue 50 25

156. Colonnade. **157.** A. Engstrom with Eagle Owl (self-portrait).

1969. Europa.
579. **156.** 70 ore multicoloured .. 35 10
580. 1 k. multicoloured .. 40 12

1969. Birth Centenary of Albert Engstrom (painter and writer).
581. **157.** 35 ore black 15 10
582. 55 ore blue 20 10

159. Tjorn Bridges. **160.** Helmeted Figure (Carving).

1969. Tjorn Bridges.
584. **159.** 15 ore blue on blue .. 1·50 20
585. – 30 ore green and black on blue .. .. 1·50 30
586. – 55 ore black and blue on blue .. .. 2·10 40
DESIGNS: 30 ore Tjorn Bridges (different). LARGER (41 × 19 mm.): 55 ore Tjorn Bridges (different).

1969. Warship "Wasa" Commem.
587. **160.** 55 ore red 20 15
588. – 55 ore brown 20 15
589. – 55 ore blue 40 30
590. – 55 ore brown 20 15
591. – 55 ore red 20 15
592. – 55 ore blue 40 30
DESIGNS—VERT. No. 588, Crowned Lion's Head (Carving). No. 590, Lion's Head (Carving). No. 591, Carved support. HORIZ. (46 × 28 mm.): No. 589, Ship's Coat-of-Arms. No. 592, Ship of the line "Wasa", 1628.

161. H. Soderberg (writer). **163.** "The Adventures of Nils" by S. Lagerlof (illus. by J. Bauer).

162. Lighthouses and Lightship "Cyklop".

1969. Birth Centenaries of Hjalmar Soderberg and Bo Bergman.
593. **161.** 45 ore brown on cream 20 10
594. – 55 ore olive on green.. 20 10
DESIGN—HORIZ. 55 ore, Bo Bergman (poet).

1969. 300th Anniv. of Swedish Lighthouse Service.
595. **162.** 30 ore black, red and grey 40 15
596. 55 ore blk., orge. & blue 40 10

1969. Swedish Fairy Tales. Perf.
597. – 35 ore brn., red & orge. 1·00 85
598. **163.** 35 ore brown .. .. 1·00 85
599. – 35 ore brn., red & orge. 1·00 85
600. – 35 ore brown .. .. 1·00 85
601. – 35 ore red and orange 1·00 85
DESIGNS: No. 597, "Pelle's New Suit" written and illus. by Elsa Beskow. No. 599, "Pippi Longstocking" (by A. Lindgren, illus. by I. Vang Nyman). No. 600, "Vill-Vallareman, the Shepherd" (from "With Pucks and Elves" illus. by J. Bauer). No. 601, "The Cat's Journey" written and illus. by I. Arosenius.

164. Emil Kocher (medicine) and Wilhelm Ostwald (chemistry).

165. Weathervane, Soderala Church.

1969. Nobel Prize Winners.
602. **164.** 45 ore green 30 30
603. – 55 ore black on flesh .. 30 8
604. – 70 ore black 50 40
DESIGNS: Prize winners of 1909. 56 ore Selma Lagerlof (literature). 70 ore Guglielmo Marconi and Ferdinand Braun (physics).

1970. Swedish Forgings.
605. **165.** 5 ore green and brown 25 15
606. – 10 ore green & brown 25 15
607. – 30 ore black and green 25 15
608. – 55 ore brown & green 30 15
DESIGNS—HORIZ. 10 ore, As Type **165**, but design and country name/figures of value in reverse order. 30 ore, Memorial Cross, Ekshărad Churchyard. VERT. 55 ore (larger, 24 × 44 mm.). 14th-century door, Bjorksta Church.

166. Seal of King Magnus Ladulas.

167. River Ljungan.

1970.
609. **166.** 2 k. 55 blue .. .. 1·00 35
610a. – 3 k. blue .. .. 1·00 5
611a. – 5 k. turquoise .. 1·10 5
DESIGNS: 3 k. Seal of Duke Erik Magnusson. 5 k. Great Seal of Erik IX.

1970. Nature Conservation Year.
612. **167.** 55 ore multicoloured .. 30 8
613. 70 ore multicoloured.. 40 35

168. View of Kiruna.

1970. Sweden within the Arctic Circle.
614. **168.** 45 ore brown 30 40
615. – 45 ore blue 30 40
616. – 45 ore green 30 40
617. – 45 ore brown 30 40
618. – 45 ore blue 30 40
DESIGNS: No. 615, Winter landscape and skiers. No. 616, Lake and Lapp hut, Stora National Park. No. 617, Reindeer herd. No. 618, Rocket-launching.

170. Chinese Palace, Drottningholm.

171. Lumber Trucks.

1970. Historic Buildings.
619. – 55 ore green 20 8
620. **170.** 2 k. multicoloured .. 1·25 20
DESIGN—VERT. (21 × 27½ mm.). 55 ore, Glimmingehus (15th-century Castle)

1970. Swedish Trade and Industry. Perf. (Nos. 621/6).
621. **171.** 70 ore brown and blue 4·25 3·75
622. – 70 ore blue, brn. & pur. 4·25 3·75
623. – 70 ore pur. and blue.. 4·25 3·75
624. – 70 ore blue & purple.. 4·25 3·75
625. – 70 ore blue & purple.. 4·25 3·75
626. – 70 ore brown & purple 4·25 3·75
627a. – 1 k. black on cream .. 30 10
DESIGNS—Size as Type **171**: No. 623, Ship's propeller. No. 624, Dam and electric locomotive. No. 626, Technician and machinery. (44 × 20 mm.): No. 622, Loading freighter at quayside. No. 625, Mine and ore train. (26 × 20 mm.): No. 627a, Miners at coal face.

173. Three Hearts.

1970. 25th Anniv. of United Nations.
628. **173.** 55 ore red, yell. & blk. 15 10
629. – 70 ore grn., yell. & blk. 25 20
DESIGN: 70 ore, Three four-leaved clovers.

174. Blackbird.

175. Paul Heyse. (literature).

1970. Christmas. Birds. Multicoloured.
630. 30 ore Type **174** 80 60
631. 30 ore Great tit 80 60
632. 30 ore Bullfinch 80 60
633. 30 ore Greenfinch 80 60
634. 30 ore Blue Tit 80 60

1970. Nobel Prize Winners.
635. **175.** 45 ore violet 40 20
636. – 55 ore blue 30 10
637. – 70 ore black 60 50
PORTRAITS: 55 ore Otto Wallach (chemistry) and Johannes van der Waals (physics). 70 ore Albrecht Kossel (medicine).

176. Ferry "Storskar" and Royal Palace, Stockholm.

178. Kerstin Hesselgren (Suffragette).

1971.
638. **176.** 80 ore black & blue 30 10
639. – 4 k. black 90 10
639a. – 6 k. blue 90 10
DESIGN: 4 k. 16th-century "Blood Money" Coins. 6 k. Gustav Vasa's Dollar.

1971. 50th Anniv. of Swedish Women's Suffrage.
640. **178.** 45 ore violet on green 30 10
641. 1 k. brown on yellow.. 45 10

179. Arctic Terns.

180. "The Prodigal Son" (painting, Sodra Rada Church).

1971. Nordic Help for Refugees Campaign.
642. **179.** 40 ore red 40 20
643. 55 ore blue 70 5

1971.
644. **180.** 15 ore olive on green.. 8 8
645. – 25 ore blue and ochre 8 8
646. – 25 ore blue and ochre 8 8
DESIGNS—HORIZ. (Panels from Grodinge Tapestry, Swedish Natural History Museum): No. 645, Griffin. No. 646, Lion.

182. Container Port, Gothenburg.

1971.
647. **182.** 55 ore violet and blue 25 30
648. – 60 ore brown on cream 15 10
649. – 75 ore deep green on pale green 25 10
DESIGNS: (28 × 23 mm.)—60 ore Timber-sledge. 75 ore Windmills, Oland.

184. Musical Score.

186. "The Three Wise Men".

185. "The Mail Coach" (after E. Schwab).

1971. Bicentenary of Swedish Royal Academy of Music.
650. **184.** 55 ore purple .. 20 10
651. 85 ore green 30 20

1971.
652. **185.** 1 k. 20 multicoloured 35 5

1971. Gotland Stone-masons Art.
653. **186.** 5 ore violet & brown 50 20
654. – 10 ore violet & green 50 20
655. – 55 ore green & brown 60 20
656. – 65 ore brown & violet 30 10
DESIGNS—VERT. 10 ore "Adam and Eve". HORIZ. (40 × 21 mm.)—55 ore "Winged Knight" and "Samson and the Lion". 65 ore "The Flight to Egypt".

187. Child beside Lorry Wheel.

188. State Sword of Gustavus Vasa, ca. 1500.

1971. Road Safety.
657. **187.** 35 ore black and red 20 20
658. 65 ore blue and red .. 25 10

1971. Swedish Crown Regalia. Mult.
659. 65 ore Type **188** 40 40
660. 65 ore Erik XIV's sceptre, 1561 .. .. .. 40 40
661. 65 ore Erik XIV's crown, 1561 .. .. .. 40 40
662. 65 ore Erik XIV's orb, 1561 40 40
663. 65 ore Karl IX's anointing horn, 1606 .. .. 40 40

189. Santa Claus and Gifts.

190. "Nils Holgersson on Goose" (from "The Wonderful Adventures of Nils" by Selma Lagerlof).

1971. Christmas. Traditional Prints.
664. **189.** 35 ore red 90 70
665. – 35 ore blue 90 70
666. – 35 ore purple 90 70
667. – 35 ore blue 90 70
668. – 35 ore green 90 70
DESIGNS: No. 665, Market scene. No. 666, Musical evening. No. 667, Skating. No. 668, Arriving for Christmas service.

1971.
669. **190.** 65 ore blue 20 5

191. Maurice Maeterlinck (literature).

192. Fencing.

1971. Nobel Prize Winners.
670. **191.** 55 ore orange 40 12
671. – 65 ore green 40 8
672. – 85 ore red 60 60
Prize winners of 1911. 65 ore Allvar Gullstrand (medicine) and Wilhelm Wien (physics). 85 ore Marie Curie (chemistry).

1972. Sportswomen. Perf.
673. **192.** 55 ore purple 60 60
674. – 55 ore blue 60 60
675. – 55 ore green 60 60
676. – 55 ore purple 60 60
677. – 55 ore blue 60 60
DESIGNS: No. 674, Diving. No. 675, Gymnastics. No. 676, Tennis. No. 677, Figure-skating.

193. L. J. Hierta (newspaper editor, statue by C. Eriksson).

195. Roe Deer.

1972. Anniversaries of Swedish Cultural Celebrities.
678. **193.** 35 ore multicoloured.. 12 8
679. – 50 ore violet 20 10
680. – 65 ore blue 30 10
681. – 85 ore multicoloured.. 30 10
DESIGNS AND ANNIVERSARIES—VERT. 35 ore (death cent.). 85 ore G. Stiernhielm (poet—300th death anniv.). HORIZ. 50 ore F. M. Franzen (poet and hymn-writer—birth bicent.). 65 ore Hugo Alfven (composer—birth cent.).

1972.
682. **195.** 95 ore brown on cream 20 10

196. Glass-blowing.

1972. Swedish Glass Industry.
683. **196.** 65 ore black 85 40
684. – 65 ore blue 85 40
685. – 65 ore red 85 40
686. – 65 ore black 85 40
687. – 65 ore blue 85 40
DESIGNS: No. 684, Glass-blowing (close-up). No. 685, Shaping glass. No. 686, Handling glass vase. No. 687, Bevelling glass vase.

197. Horses, Borgholm Castle (after N. Kreuger).

1972. Tourism in South-east Sweden.
688. **197.** 55 ore brown on cream 45 45
689. – 55 ore blue on cream.. 45 45
690. – 55 ore brown on cream 45 45
691. – 55 ore green on cream 45 45
692. – 55 ore blue on cream.. 45 45
DESIGNS: No. 689, Oland Bridge and sailing barque "Meta". 690, Kalmar Castle. 691, Salmon-fishing, Morrumsan. 692, Cadet schooner "Falken", Karlskrona Naval Base.

198. Conference Emblem and Motto, "Only One Earth".

1972. U.N. Environment Conservation Conference, Stockholm.
693. **198.** 65 ore blue and red on cream 20 10
694. – 85 ore mult. on cream 50 30
DESIGN—VERT. (28 × 45 mm.) 85 ore "Spring" (wooden relief by B. Hjorth).

199. Junkers "F-13".

201. Early Courier.

200. Reindeer and Sledge (woodcut from "Lapponia").

1972. Swedish Mailplanes.
695. **199.** 5 ore lilac 10 10
696. – 15 ore blue 40 10
697. – 25 ore blue 40 10
698. – 75 ore green 30 10
DESIGNS—HORIZ. (45 × 19 mm.) 15 ore Junkers "Ju-52". 25 ore Friedrichshafen "FF-49". 75 ore Douglas "DC-3".

1972. Centenary of "Lapponia" (book by J. Schefferus).
699. **200.** 1 k. 40 red on blue .. 35 5

1972. "Stockholmia 74" Exn. (1st issue) and Birth Centenary of Olle Hjortzberg (stamp designer). Perf.
700. **201.** 10 ore red 30 40
701. – 15 ore green 30 40
702. – 40 ore blue 60 60
703. – 50 ore brown 30 40
704. – 60 ore blue 40 40
DESIGNS: 15 ore Post-rider. 40 ore Steam mail train. 50 ore Motor bus and trailer. 60 ore Liner "Gripsholm".
See also Nos. 779/82.

202. Figurehead of "Amphion" (Per Ljung).

203. Christmas Candles (J. Wikstrom).

1972. Swedish 18th-cent. Art.
705. – 75 ore green 25 20
706. – 75 ore brown 25 20
707. **202.** 75 ore red 25 20
708. – 75 ore red 25 20
709. – 75 ore blk., brn. & red 25 20
710. – 75 ore blk., blue & brn. 25 20
DESIGNS—HORIZ. (59 × 24 mm.) No. 705, "Stockholm" (F. Martin). No. 706, "The Forge" (P. Hillestrom). As T **187**: No. 708, "Quadriga" (Sergel). VERT. (28 × 37 mm.) No. 709, "Lady with a Veil" (A. Roslin). No. 710, "Sophia Magdalena" (C. G. Pilo).

1972. Christmas. Multicoloured.
711 45 ore Type **203** 25 10
712 45 ore Father Christmas (E. Flygh) 25 10
713 75 ore Carol singers (S. Hagg) (40 × 23 mm) 40 5

204. King Gustav VI Adolf.

205. King Gustav with Book.

1972.
714. **204.** 75 ore blue 20 5
715. 1 k. red 35 5

1972. King Gustav VI Adolf's 90th Birthday.
716 **205** 75 ore blue .. .. 2·50 2·50
717 – 75 ore green .. .. 2·50 2·50
718 – 75 ore red .. .. 2·50 2·50
719 – 75 ore blue .. .. 2·50 2·50
720 – 75 ore green .. .. 2·50 2·50
DESIGNS: No. 717, Chinese objets d'art. No. 718, Opening Parliament. No. 719, Greek objets d'art. No. 720, King Gustav tending flowers.

1972. Nobel Prize winners. As T **191** but inscr. "Nobelpris 1912".
721. 60 ore brown 40 30
722. 65 ore blue 50 30
723. 75 ore violet 60 8
724. 1 k. brown 70 15
DESIGNS—HORIZ. 60 ore Paul Sabatier and Victor Grignard (chemistry). VERT. 65 ore Alexis Carrel (medicine). 75 ore Nils Gustav Dalen (physics). 1 k. Gerhart Hauptmann (literature).

207. "Tintomara" Stage Set (B–R. Hedwall).

208. Modern Mail Coach, Vietas.

1973. Bicentenary of Swedish Royal Theatre.
725. **207.** 75 ore green 30 5
726. – 1 k. purple 30 15
DESIGN—HORIZ. (41 × 23 mm.) 1 k. "Orpheus" (P. Hillestrom).

1973.
727. – 60 ore black on yellow 20 20
728. **208.** 70 ore orge., blue & grn. 25 5
DESIGN: 60 ore, Mail bus, 1923.

209. Vasa Ski Race.

210. Horse (bas relief).

1973. Tourism in Dalecarlia.
729. **209.** 65 ore green 30 25
730. – 65 ore green 30 25
731. – 65 ore black 30 25
732. – 65 ore green 30 25
733. – 65 ore lake 30 25
DESIGNS: No. 730, "Going to the Church in Mora" (A. Zorn). No. 731, Church stables in Rattvik. No. 732, "The Great Pit". No. 733, "Mid-summer Dance" (B. Nordenberg).

1973. Gottland's Picture Stones.
734. **210.** 5 ore purple 10 10
735. – 10 ore blue 10 10
DESIGN: 10 ore Viking ship (bas relief).

211. "Row of Willows" (P. Persson).

1973. Swedish Landscapes.
736. **211.** 40 ore brown 10 10
737. – 50 ore black and brown 10 5
738. – 55 ore green 20 5
DESIGNS—VERT. (20 × 28 mm.) 50 ore, "View of Trosa" (R. Ljunggren). HORIZ. (27 × 23 mm.) 55 ore, "Spring Birches" (O. Bergman).

212. Lumberman.

213. Observer reading Thermometer.

1973. 75th Anniv. of Swedish Confederation of Trade Unions.
739. **212.** 75 ore red 20 5
740. 1 k. 40 blue 40 10

1973. Centenary of I.M.O./W.M.O. and Swedish Meteorological Organizations.
741. **213.** 65 ore green .. .. 1·00 30
742. – 65 ore blue and black 1·00 30
DESIGN: No. 742, U.S. satellite weather picture.

214. Nordic House, Reykjavik.

1973. Nordic Countries' Postal Co-operation.
743. **214.** 75 ore multicoloured .. 30 5
744. 1 k. multicoloured .. 40 5

215. C. P. Thunberg, Japanese Flora and Scene.

1973. Swedish Explorers.
745. **215.** 1 k. brn., grn. and blue 90 1·00
746. – 1 k. multicoloured .. 90 1·00
747. – 1 k. brn., grn. and blue 90 1·00
748. – 1 k. multicoloured .. 90 1·00
749. – 1 k. multicoloured .. 90 1·00
DESIGNS: No. 746, A. Sparrman and Tahiti. No. 747, A. E. Nordenskiold and the "Vega". No. 748, S. A. Andree and wrecked balloon. No. 749, Sven Hedin and yaks.

216. Team of Oxen.

217. Grey Seal.

1973. Centenary of Nordic Museum.
750. **216.** 75 ore black .. .. 1·60 30
751. – 75 ore brown .. .. 1·60 30
752. – 75 ore black .. .. 1·60 30
753. – 75 ore purple .. .. 1·60 30
754. – 75 ore brown .. .. 1·60 30
DESIGNS: No. 751, Braking flax. No. 752, Potato-planting. No. 753, Baking bread, No. 754, Spring sowing.

1973. "Save Our Animals". Perf.
755. **217.** 10 ore green 10 10
756. – 20 ore violet 40 10
757. – 25 ore turquoise .. 10 10
758. – 55 ore turquoise .. 15 10
759. – 65 ore violet 25 10
760. – 75 ore green 60 15
DESIGNS: 20 ore Peregrine falcon. 25 ore Lynx. 55 ore European otter. 65 ore Wolf. 75 ore White-tailed sea-eagle.

218. King Gustav VI Adolf.

220. "Goosegirl" (E. Josephson).

219. "Country Dance" (J. Nilsson).

1973. King Gustav VI Adolf Memorial Issue.
761. **218.** 75 ore blue 20 5
762. 1 k. purple 30 10

1973. Christmas. Peasant Paintings. Mult.
763. 45 ore Type **219** 40 8
764. 45 ore "The Three Wise Men" (A. Clemetson) .. 40 8
765. 75 ore "Gourd Plant" (B. A. Hansson) (vert.) 1·40 8
766. 75 ore "The Rider" (K. E. Jonsson) (vert.) .. 1·40 8
Nos. 765/6 are size 23 × 28 mm.

1973. Ernst Josephson Commemoration.
767. **220.** 10 k. multicoloured .. 2·50 20

221. A. Werner (chemistry) and H. Kamerlingh-Onnes (physics).

1973. Nobel Prize-winners. Inscr. "NOBELPRIS 1913".
768. **221.** 75 ore violet 30 5
769. – 1 k. brown 35 10
770. – 1 k. 40 green 45 5
Prize winners of 1913: VERT. 1 k. Charles Robert Richet (medicine). 1 k. 40 Rabindranath Tagore (literature).

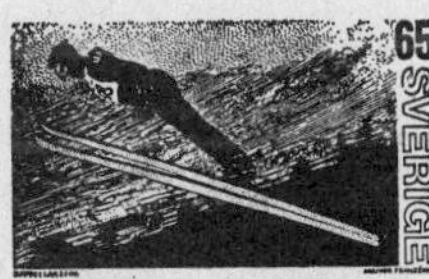

222. Ski Jumping.

1974. "Winter Sports on Skis".
771. **222.** 65 ore green 40 40
772. – 65 ore blue 40 40
773. – 65 ore green 40 40
774. – 65 ore red 40 40
775. – 65 ore blue 40 40
DESIGNS: No. 772, Cross-country (man). No. 773, Relay-racing. No. 774, Downhill-racing. No. 775, Cross-country (woman).

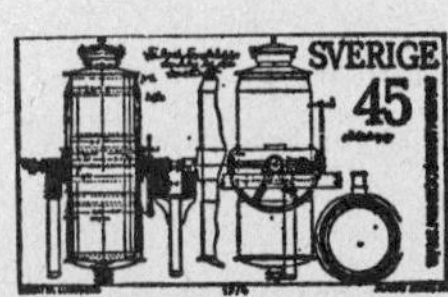

223. Ekman's Sulphite Pulping Machine.

1974. Swedish Anniversaries.
776. **223.** 45 ore brown on grey .. 15 5
777. – 60 ore green 20 10
778. – 75 ore red 25 5
DESIGNS AND EVENTS: 45 ore, Type **223** (centenary of 1st sulphite pulp plant, Bergvik). 60 ore, Hans Jarta and part of Government Act (birth bicent). 75 ore, Samuel Owen and engineers (birth bicent.).

224. U.P.U. Congress Stamp of 1924.

1974. "Stockholmia '74" Stamp Exn. (2nd issue).
779. **224.** 20 ore green 12 20
780. 25 ore blue 12 20
781. 30 ore brown 12 20
782. 35 ore red 12 20

225. Great Falls.

226. "Figure in a Storm". (B. Marklund).

1974.
784. **225.** 35 ore black and blue .. 12 5
785. – 75 ore brown 20 8
DESIGN—HORIZ. 75 ore Ystad (town).

1974. Europa. Sculptures.
786. **226.** 75 ore purple 30 5
787. – 1 k. green 40 5
DESIGN: 1 k. Picasso statue, Kristinehamn.

227. King Carl XVI Gustav.

228. Central Post Office, Stockholm.

1974.
788. **227.** 75 ore green 30 5
789. 90 ore blue 40 5
790. 1 k. purple 30 5
791. 1 k. 10 red 20 5
792. 1 k. 30 green 20 5
793. 1 k. 40 blue 30 15
794. 1 k. 50 mauve 30 5
795. 1 k. 70 orange 40 10
796. 2 k. brown 40 10

1974. Cent. of Universal Postal Union.
800. **228.** 75 ore purple .. .. 1·00 20
801. – 75 ore purple .. .. 1·00 20
802. – 1 k. green 35 10
DESIGNS—As Type **228**. No. 801, Interior of Central Post Office, Stockholm. 40 × 24 mm. No. 802, Rural postman.

229. Regatta.

1974. Tourism on Sweden's West Coast.
803. **229.** 65 ore red 30 30
804. – 65 ore blue 30 30
805. – 65 ore green 30 30
806. – 65 ore green 50 30
807. – 65 ore purple 30 30
DESIGNS: No. 804, Vinga Lighthouse. No. 805, Varberg Fortress. No. 806, Seine fishing. No. 807, Mollosund.

230. "Mr. Simmons" (A. Fridell).

231. Thread and Spool.

1974. Cent. of Publicists' Club (Swedish press, radio and television association).
808. **230.** 45 ore black 15 15
809. 1 k. 40 purple 35 5

1974. Swedish Textile and Clothing Industry.
810. **231.** 85 ore violet 25 25
811. – 85 ore black and orange 25 25
DESIGN: No. 811, Stylised sewing-machine.

232. Deer. **233.** Tanker "Bill".

1974. Christmas. Mosaic Embroideries of Mythical Creatures. Each turquoise, red and green (45 ore) or multicoloured (75 ore). Perf. (Nos. 812/21).

812. 45 ore Type **232** 70 70
813. 45 ore Griffin 70 70
814. 45 ore Lion 70 70
815. 45 ore Griffin 70 70
816. 45 ore Unicorn 70 70
817. 45 ore Horse 70 70
818. 45 ore Lion 70 70
819. 45 ore Griffin 70 70
820. 45 ore Lion 70 70
821. 45 ore Lion-like creature .. 70 70
822. 75 ore Deer-like creature .. 20 5

No. 813 is facing right and has inscr. at top, No. 815 faces left with similar inscr. and No. 819 has inscr. at bottom.

No. 814 has the inscr. at top, No. 818 has it at the foot of the design, the lion having blue claws, No. 820 has similar inscr., but white claws.

1974. Swedish Shipping. Each blue.

823. 1 k. Type **233** 60 60
824. 1 k. M.S. "Snow Storm" (liner) 60 60
825. 1 k. "Tor" and "Atle" (ice-breakers) 60 60
826. 1 k. "Skanes" (train ferry) 60 60
827. 1 k. Tugs "Bill", "Bull" and "Starkodder" .. 60 60

234. Max von Laue (physics). **235.** Sven Jerring (first announcer), Children and Microphone.

1974. Nobel Prize-winners.

828. **234.** 65 ore red 25 20
829. – 70 ore green 25 20
830. – 1 k. blue 35 15

Designs: —70 ore Theodore William Richards (chemistry). Richard Barany (medicine).

1974. 50th Anniv. of Swedish Broadcasting Corporation.

831. **235.** 75 ore blue and brown 70 20
832. – 75 ore blue and brown 70 20

Design: No. 832, Television camera at Parliamentary debate.

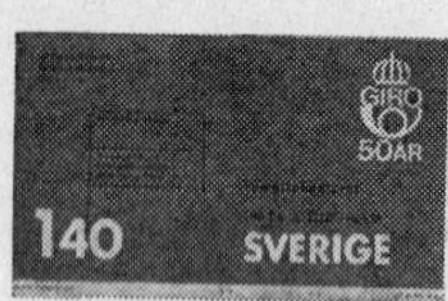

236. Giro Envelope.

1975. 50th Anniv. of Swedish Postal Giro Office.

833. **236.** 1 k. 40 black & brown 30 10

237. Male and Female Engineers. **238.** Bronze Helmet Decoration, Vendel.

1975. International Women's Year.

834. **237.** 75 ore green 20 5
835. – 1 k. purple 35 10

Design—vert. 1 k. Jenny Lind (singer) (portrait by O. J. Sodermark).

1975. Archaeological Discoveries.

836. **238.** 10 ore red 5 5
837. – 15 ore green 5 5
838. – 20 ore violet 5 5
839. – 25 ore yellow 5 5
840. – 55 ore brown 5 5

Designs: 15 ore Iron sword hilt and chapel, Vendel. 20 ore Iron shield buckle, Vendel. 25 ore Embossed gold plates (Gold Men), Eketorp Fortress, Oland. 55 ore Iron helmet, Vendel.

239. "New Year's Eve at Skansen" (Eric Hallstrom).

1975. Europa. Multicoloured.

841. 90 ore Type **239** 20 5
842. 1 k. 10 "Inferno" (August Strindberg) (vert.) .. 20 8

240. Metric tape-measure (centenary of Metre Convention). **241.** Western European hedgehog.

1975. Anniversaries.

843. **240.** 55 ore blue 20 10
844. – 70 ore sepia and brown 20 10
845. – 75 ore violet 20 10

Designs and events—horiz. (44 × 27 mm.) 70 ore Peter Hernqvist (founder) and title-page of his book "Comprehensive Thesis on Glanders in Horses" (bicent. of Swedish Veterinary Service). vert. (24 × 31 mm.) 75 ore "Folke Filbyter" (birth centenary of Carl Milles (sculptor)).

1975.

846. **241.** 55 ore black 20 5
847. – 75 ore red 20 5
848. – 1 k. 70 blue 40 10
849. – 2 k. purple 40 5
850. – 7 k. green .. .. 1·75 5

Designs—horiz. 75 ore Key-fiddler. 1 k. 70, Capercaillie ("cock of the woods"). vert. 2 k. Rok stone (ancient inscribed rock), Ostergotland. 7 k. Ballet dancers (from "Romeo and Juliet").

242. Village Buildings, Skelleftea.

1975. European Architectural Heritage Year.

851. **242.** 75 ore black 20 20
852. – 75 ore red 20 20
853. – 75 ore black 20 20
854. – 75 ore red 20 20
855. – 75 ore blue 20 20

Designs: No. 852, Iron-works, Engelsberg. No. 853, Gunpowder Tower, Visby, Gotland. No. 854, Iron-mine, Falun. No. 855, Rommehed military barracks, Dalecarlia.

243. Fire Brigade. **244.** "Fryckstad".

1975. "Watch, Guard and Help". Public Services.

856. **243.** 90 ore red 55 20
857. – 90 ore blue 55 20
858. – 90 ore red 55 20
859. – 90 ore blue 55 20
860. – 90 ore green 55 20

Designs: No. 857, Customs service. No. 858, Police service. No. 859, Ambulance and hospital service. No. 860, Shipwreck of "Merkur" (Sea rescue service).

1975. Swedish Steam Locomotives.

861. **244.** 5 ore green 10 10
862. – 5 ore blue 10 10
863. – 90 ore green 65 15

Designs—As Type **244**. No. 862, "Gotland". (49 × 22 mm.) 90 ore "Prince August".

245. Canoeing. **246.** "Madonna" (sculpture), Viklan church, Gotland.

1975. Scouting. Multicoloured.

864. 90 ore Type **245** 80 20
865. 90 ore Camping 80 20

1975. Christmas. Religious Art.

866. **246.** 55 ore multicoloured .. 20 5
867. – 55 ore multicoloured .. 20 5
868. – 55 ore multicoloured .. 20 5
869. – 90 ore brown 30 5
870. – 90 ore red 60 20
871. – 90 ore blue 60 20

Designs—vert. No. 867, "Birth of Christ" (embossed copper), Broddetorp church, Vastergotland. No. 868, "The Sun" (embossed copper), Broddetorp church, Vastergotland. No. 869, "Mourning Mary" (sculpture), Oja church, Gotland. horiz. Nos. 870, 871, "Jesse at Foot of Christ's genealogical tree" (retable), Lofta church, Smaland.

247. W. H. and W. L. Bragg (physics). **248.** Bronze Coiled Snake Brooch, Vendel.

1975. Nobel Prize Winners of 1915.

872. **247.** 75 ore purple 20 20
873. – 90 ore blue 30 10
874. – 1 k. 10 green 40 20

Designs: 90 ore Richard Willstatter (chemistry) 1 k. 10 Romain Rolland (literature).

1976.

875. **248.** 15 ore brown 10 5
876. – 20 ore green 10 5
877. – 30 ore purple 10 5
878. – 85 ore blue 30 10
879. – 90 ore blue 30 5
880. – 1 k. purple 20 5
881. – 1 k. 90 green 40 5
882. – 9 k. green .. .. 1·40 15

Designs—horiz. (21 × 19 mm.) 20 ore Pilgrim Badge. (28 × 21 mm.) 30 ore Drinking horn. 85 ore Common Guillemot and Razorbills. (28 × 23 mm.) 1 k. 90, "Cave of the Winds" (sculpture) (Eric Grate). vert. (21 × 28 mm.) 90 ore Chimney Sweep. 1 k. Bobbin lace-making. 9 k. "Girl's Head" (wood-carving) (Bror Hjorth).

249. Early and Modern Telephones. **250.** Wheat and Cornflower Seed.

1976. Telephone Centenary.

883. **249.** 1 k. 30 violet 30 15
884. 3 k. 40 red 80 15

1976. Swedish Seed-testing Centenary.

885. **250.** 65 ore brown 20 20
886. – 65 ore green and brown 20 20

Design: No. 886, Viable and non-viable plants.

251. Lapp Spoon. **253.** Ship's Wheel and Cross.

252. "View from Ringkallen" (H. Osslund).

1976. Europa. Handicrafts.

887. **251.** 1 k. black, pink & blue 35 5
888. – 1 k. 30 multicoloured .. 35 10

Design: 1 k. 30 Tile stove.

1976. Tourism. Angermanland.

889. **252.** 85 ore green 20 20
890. – 85 ore blue 20 20
891. – 85 ore brown 20 20
892. – 85 ore blue 20 20
893. – 85 ore brown 20 20

Designs: No. 890, Tug towing timber. No. 891, Hay-drying racks. No. 892, Granvagsnipan. No. 893, Seine-net fishing.

1976. Cent. of Swedish Seamen's Church.

894. **253.** 85 ore blue 25 10

254. Torgny Segerstedt and "Goteborg Handels-och Sjofartstidning".

1976. Birth Centenary of Torgny Segerstedt (newspaper editor).

895. **254.** 1 k. 90 black & brown 40 10

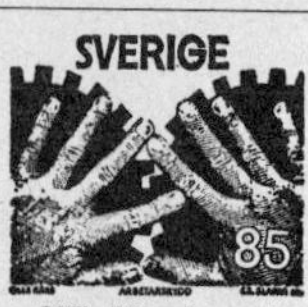

255. King Carl XVI Gustav and Queen Silvia. **257.** Hands and Cogwheels.

256. John Ericsson (marine propeller).

1976. Royal Wedding.

896. **255.** 1 k. red 20 5
897. 1 k. 30 green 30 12

1976. Swedish Technological Pioneers. Mult.

898. 1 k. 30 Type **256** 50 45
899. 1 k. 30 Helge Palmcrantz (hay maker) 50 45
900. 1 k. 30 Lars Magnus Ericsson (telephone improvements) 50 45
901. 1 k. 30 Sven Wingquist (ball bearing) 50 45
902. 1 k. 30 Gustaf de Laval (milk separator and reaction turbine) .. 50 45

1976. Industrial Safety.

903. **257.** 85 ore orange and violet 25 10
904. 1 k. green and brown .. 25 5

258. Verner von Heidenstam. **259.** "Archangel Michael Destroying Lucifer" (Flemish prayer book).

1976. Literature Nobel Prize Winner of 1916.

905. **258.** 1 k. green 30 10
906. 1 k. 30 blue 40 20

1976. Christmas. Mediaeval Book Illustrations. Multicoloured.

907. 65 ore Type **259** 20 5
908. 65 ore "St. Nicholas awakening Children from Dead" (Flemish prayer book) 20 12
909. 1 k. "Mary visiting Elizabeth" (Austrian prayer book) 30 5
910. 1 k. "Prayer to the Virgin" (Austrian prayer book) 30 12

Nos. 909/10 are vertical, 26 × 44 mm.

1977. Nordic Countries Co-operation in Nature Conservation and Environment Protection. As T **222** of Norway.

911. 1 k. multicoloured .. 30 10
912. 1 k. 30 multicoloured .. 20 20

261. Tawny Owl. **262.** "Politeness".

1977.

913. **261.** 45 ore green 30 20
914. – 70 ore blue 20 10
915. – 1 k. 40 brown 30 12
916. – 2 k. 10 brown 35 5

Designs—vert. (23 × 29 mm.) 70 ore Norwegian cast-iron stove decoration. horiz. (41 × 21 mm.) 1 k. 40 Gotland ponies. (28 × 22 mm.) 2 k. 10 Tailor.

1977. Birth Centenary of Oskar Andersson (cartoonist).

917. **262.** 75 ore black 15 10
918. 3 k. 80 red 70 20

263. Skating.

1977. Keep-fit Activities.

919. **263.** 95 ore blue 20 20
920. – 95 ore green 20 20
921. – 95 ore red 20 20
922. – 95 ore green 20 20
923. – 95 ore blue 20 20

Designs: No. 920, Swimming. No. 921, Cycling. No. 922, Jogging. No. 923, Badminton.

264. Gustavianum Building.

1977. 500th Anniv. of Uppsala University.
924. **264.** 1 k. 10 blk., yell. & blue 30 5

265. Winter Forest Scene.

1977. Europa. Landscapes. Multicoloured.
925. 1 k. 10 Type **265** 25 5
926. 1 k. 40 Rapadal valley, Sarek 35 5

266. Calle Schewen at Breakfast. **267.** Blackberries.

1977. Tourism.
927. **266.** 95 ore green 20 20
928. – 95 ore violet 50 20
929. – 95 ore black and red .. 20 20
930. – 95 ore blue 20 20
931. – 95 ore red 20 20
DESIGNS: No. 928, Black-headed Gull. No. 929, Calle Schewen dancing. No. 930, Fishing. No. 931, Sunset.

1977. Wild Berries. Multicoloured. Perf.
932. 75 ore Type **267** 20 20
933. 75 ore Cowberries .. 20 20
934. 75 ore Cloudberries .. 20 20
935. 75 ore Bilberries 20 20
936. 75 ore Strawberries .. 20 20

268. Horse-drawn Tram.

1977. Public Transport.
937. **268.** 1 k. 10 green 50 40
938. – 1 k. 10 blue 50 40
939. – 1 k. 10 blue 50 40
940. – 1 k. 10 blue 50 40
941. – 1 k. 10 green 50 40
DESIGN: No. 938, Electric tram. No. 939, Ferry "Djurgarden 6". No. 940, Articulated bus. No. 941, Underground train.

269. H. Pontoppidan and K. A. Gjellerup (literature). **270.** Erecting Sheaf for Birds.

1977. Nobel Prize Winners of 1917.
942. **269.** 1 k. 10 brown.. .. 30 10
943. – 1 k. 40 green 40 20
DESIGN: 1 k. 40, Charles Glover Barkla (physics).

1977. Christmas. Seasonal Customs.
944. **270.** 75 ore violet 20 10
945. – 75 ore orange 20 10
946. – 75 ore green 20 10
947. – 1 k. 10 green 30 10
948. – 1 k. 10 red 30 10
949. – 1 k. 10 blue 30 10
DESIGNS: No. 945, Making gingersnaps. No. 946, Bringing in the Christmas tree. No. 947, Preparing the traditional fish dish. No. 948, Making straw goats for the pantomime. No. 949, Candle-making.

271. Brown Bear. **272.** Orebro Castle.

1978.
950. **271.** 1 k. 15 brown.. .. 30 5
951. – 2 k. 50 blue 40 5
DESIGN: 2 k. 50, "Space without Affiliation" (sculpture by Arne Jones).

1978. Europa.
952. **272.** 1 k. 30 green 30 5
953. – 1 k. 70 brown.. .. 40 20
DESIGN—VERT. 1 k. 70, Doorway, Orebro Castle.

273. Pentecostal Meeting.

1978. Independent Christian Associations Perf.
954. **273.** 90 ore purple 30 30
955. – 90 ore black 30 30
956. – 90 ore violet 30 30
957. – 90 ore green 30 30
958. – 90 ore purple 30 30
DESIGNS: No. 955, Minister with children (Swedish Missionary Society). No. 956, Communion Service, Ethiopia (Evangelical National Missionary Society). No. 957, Baptism (Baptist Society). No. 958, Salvation Army Band.

274. Brosarp Hills.

1978. Travels of Carl Linne (botanist).
959. **274.** 1 k. 30 black 40 30
960. – 1 k. 30 blue .. .. 1·25 30
961. – 1 k. 30 purple.. .. 40 30
962. – 1 k. 30 red 40 30
963. – 1 k. 30 blue 40 30
964. – 1 k. 30 purple.. .. 40 30
DESIGNS—HORIZ. (58×23 mm.). No. 960, Avocets. (27×23 mm.). No. 961, Grindstone production. No. 962, "Linnaea borealis". VERT. (27×36 mm.). No. 963, Red limestone cliff. No. 964, Linnaeus wearing Lapp dress and Dutch doctor's hat, and carrying Lapp drum.

275. Glider over Alleberg Plateau.

1978. Tourism. Vastergotland.
965. **275.** 1 k. 15 green 40 30
966. – 1 k. 15 brown.. .. 40 30
967. – 1 k. 15 blue 40 30
968. – 1 k. 15 slate 40 30
969. – 1 k. 15 black & purple 40 30
DESIGNS: No. 966. Common Cranes. No. 967, Fortress on Lacko Island Skara. No. 968, Rock tomb, Luttra. No. 969. "Traders of South Vastergotland" (sculpture) (N. Sjogren).

276. Diploma and Laurel Wreath. **277.** "The Homecoming" (Carl Kylberg).

1978. Cent. of Stockholm University.
970. **276.** 2 k. 50 green on stone 45 10

1978. Paintings by Swedish Artists. Mult.
971. 90 ore Type **277** 30 10
972. 1 k. 15 "Standing Model seen from Behind" (Karl Isakson) 30 10
973. 4 k. 50 "Self-portrait with a Floral Wreath" (Ivar Arosenius) .. .. 1·10 20

278. Northern Arrow. **280.** "Russula decolorans".

279. Coronation Carriage, 1699.

1978.
974. **278.** 10 k. mauve .. .. 1·75 15

1978.
975. **279.** 1 k. 70 red on cream.. 40 30

1978. Edible Mushrooms. Multicoloured. Perf.
976. 1 k. 15 Type **280** 50 40
977. 1 k. 15 "Lycoperdon perlatum" 50 40
978. 1 k. 15 "Macrolepiota procera" 50 40
979. 1 k. 15 "Cantharellus cibarius" 50 40
980. 1 k. 15 "Boletus edulis" 50 40
981. 1 k. 15 "Ramaria botrytis" 50 40

281. Dalecarlian Horse. **282.** Fritz Haber (chemistry).

1978. Christmas. Old Toys.
982. **281.** 90 ore multicoloured .. 30 10
983. – 90 ore multicoloured .. 30 10
984. – 90 ore green and red .. 30 10
985. – 1 k. 30 multicoloured .. 30 10
986. – 1 k. 30 multicoloured .. 30 10
987. – 1 k. 30, blue 30 10
DESIGNS—VERT. No. 983, Swedish Court Doll. No. 984, Meccano. No. 987, Teddy bear. HORIZ. No. 985, Tops. No. 986, Equipage with water barrel (metal toy).

1978. Nobel Prize Winners of 1918.
988. **282.** 1 k. 30 brown.. .. 30 10
989. – 1 k. 70 blue 40 20
DESIGN: 1 k. 70, Max Planck (physics).

283. Bandy Players fighting for Ball.

1979. Bandy.
990. **283.** 1 k. 05 blue 20 5
991. 2 k. 50 orange 50 10

284. Child in Gas-mask. **285.** Wall Hanging.

1979. International Year of the Child.
992. **284.** 1 k. 70 blue 30 20

1979.
993. **285.** 4 k. blue and red .. 80 5

286. Carrier Pigeon and Hand with Quill. **287.** Sledge-boat.

288. Felling Tree.

1979. Rebate Stamp.
994. **286.** (1 k.) yell., blk. & blue 30 5
No. 994 was only issued in booklets of 20 sold at 20 k. or supplied in exchange for tokens distributed to all households in Sweden. Valid for inland postage only, they represented a rebate of 30 ore on the normal rate of 1 k. 30.

1979. Europa.
995. **287.** 1 k. 30 black and turq. 40 10
996. – 1 k. 70 black & brown 45 30
DESIGN: 1 k. 70 Hand using telegraph key.

1979. Farming.
997. **288.** 1 k. 30 blk., red & grn. 25 15
998. – 1 k. 30 green & black 25 15
999. – 1 k. 30 green & black 25 15
1000. – 1 k. 30 brown & green 25 15
1001. – 1 k. 30 red, blk. & grn. 25 15
DESIGNS: No. 998, Sowing. No. 999, Cows. No. 1000, Harvesting. No. 1001, Ploughing.

289. Tourist Launch "Juno".

1979. Tourism. Gota Canal.
1002. **289.** 1 k. 15 violet .. 45 45
1003. – 1 k. 15 green .. 45 45
1004. – 1 k. 15 purple .. 45 45
1005. – 1 k. 15 red 45 45
1006. – 1 k. 15 violet .. 45 45
1007. – 1 k. 15 green .. 45 45
DESIGNS—As T **289**: No. 1003, Borenshult lock. 27×23½ mm: No. 1004, Hajstorp roller bridge. 1005, Opening lock gates. 27×36½ mm: No. 1006, Motor barge "Wilhelm Tham" in lock. 1007, Kayak in lock.

290. "Aeshna cyanea". **291.** Workers leaving Sawmills.

1979. Wildlife.
1008. **290.** 60 ore violet.. .. 20 10
1009. – 65 ore olive 20 10
1010. – 80 ore green 25 10
DESIGNS: (41×21 mm.) 65 ore Pike. (27×22 mm.) 80 ore Green spotted toad.

1979. Centenary of Sundsvall Strike.
1011. **291.** 90 ore brown and red 20 10

292. Banner. **293.** J. J. Berzelius.

1979. Centenary of Swedish Temperance Movement.
1012. **292.** 1 k. 30 multicoloured 30 5

1979. Birth Bicentenaries of J. J. Berzelius (chemist) and J. O. Wallin (poet and hymn-writer).
1013. **293.** 1 k. 70 brown & green 40 20
1014. – 4 k. 50 blue .. 1·10 20
DESIGN: 4 k. 50, J. O. Wallin and hymn numbers.

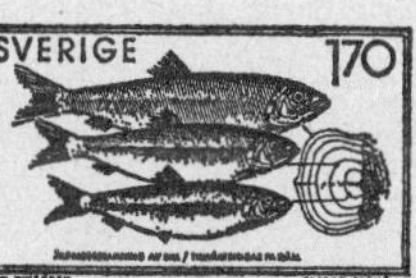

295. Herrings and Growth Marks. **296.** Ljusdal Costume.

1979. Marine Research.
1016. **295.** 1 k. 70 green and blue 35 40
1017. – 1 k. 70 brown .. 35 40
1018. – 1 k. 70 green and blue 35 40
1019. – 1 k. 70 brown .. 35 40
1020. – 1 k. 70 green and blue 35 40
DESIGNS: No. 1017, Acoustic survey of sea-bed. 1018, Plankton bloom. 1019, Echo-sounding chart of Baltic Sea, October 1978. 1020, Fishery research ship "Argos".

1979. Peasant Costumes and Jewellery.
1021. **296.** 90 ore multicoloured 20 20
1022. – 90 ore multicoloured 20 20
1023. – 90 ore blue 20 5
1024. – 1 k. 30 multicoloured 30 20
1025. – 1 k. 30 multicoloured 30 20
1026. – 1 k. 30 red 30 5
DESIGNS. (22×27 mm.) No. 1022, Osteraker costume. (21×27 mm.) No. 1023, Brooch from Jamtland. No. 1026, Brooch from Smaland. (23×40 mm.) No. 1024, Goinge church dress. No. 1025, Mora church dress.

297. Jules Bordet (chemistry).

298. Wind Power.

1979. Nobel Prize Winners of 1919.

1027. **297.** 1 k. 30 mauve 30 10
1028. – 1 k. 70 blue 40 40
1029. – 2 k. 50 green .. 70 20

DESIGNS: 1 k. 70, Johannes Stark (physics). 2 k. 50, Carl Spitteler (literature).

1980. Renewable Energy Sources.

1030. **298.** 1 k. 15 blue 30 30
1031. – 1 k. 15 ochre and green 30 30
1032. – 1 k. 15 orange .. 30 30
1033. – 1 k. 15 green .. 30 30
1034. – 1 k. 15 green and blue 30 30

DESIGNS: No. 1031, Biological energy. No. 1032, Solar energy. No. 1033, Geothermal energy. No. 1034, Wave energy.

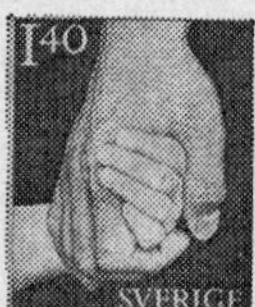

299. King Carl XVI Gustav and Princess Victoria. **300.** Child's Hand in Adult's.

1980. New Order of Succession to Throne.

1035. **299.** 1 k. 30 blue 20 10
1036. 1 k. 70 red 30 20

1980. Care.

1037. **300.** 1 k. 40 brown .. 25 5
1038. – 1 k. 60 green 25 20

DESIGN: 1 k. 60, Aged hand clasping stick.

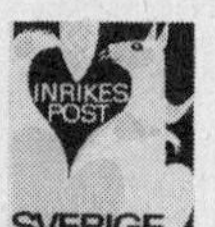

301. Squirrel. **302.** Elise Ottensen-Jensen (pioneer of birth control).

1980. Rebate Stamp.

1039. **301.** (1 k.) yellow, blue & blk. 30 10

No. 1039 was only issued in booklets of 20 sold at 20 k. or supplied in exchange for tokens distributed to all households in Sweden.

1980. Europa.

1040. **302.** 1 k. 30 green 30 5
1041. – 1 k. 70 red 30 25

DESIGN: 1 k. 70, Joe Hill (member of workers' movement).

303. Tybling Farm, Tyby.

1980. Tourism. Halsingland.

1042. **303.** 1 k. 15 red 30 30
1043. – 1 k. 15 blue & purple 30 30
1044. – 1 k. 15 green .. 30 30
1045. – 1 k. 15 purple .. 30 30
1046. – 1 k. 15 blue 30 30

DESIGNS: No. 1043, Old iron works, Iggesund. No. 1044, Bloxas ridge, Forsa. No. 1045, Banga farm, Alfta. No. 1046, Sunds Canal, Hudiksvall.

304. Chair from Scania (1831). **305.** Motif from film "Diagonal Symphony".

1980. Nordic Countries Co-operation.

1047. **304.** 1 k. 50 green .. 30 10
1048. – 2 k. brown 40 15

DESIGN: 2 k. Cradle from North Bothnia (19th cent.).

1980. Birth Bicentenary of Viking Eggeling (film-maker).

1049. **305.** 3 k. blue 60 10

307. Bamse.

308. " Necken " (Ernst Josephson).

1980. Christmas. Swedish Comic Strips.

1051. **307.** 1 k. 15 blue and red .. 20 10
1052. – 1 k. 15 multicoloured 20 10
1053. – 1 k. 50 black .. 30 10
1054. – 1 k. 50 multicoloured 30 10

DESIGNS—VERT. No. 1052, Karlsson. No. 1053, Adamson. HORIZ. No. 1054, Kronblom.

1980.

1055. **308.** 8 k. brn., blk. & grey 1·25 25

309. Knut Hamsun (literature).

310. Angel blowing Horn.

1980. Nobel Prize Winners of 1920.

1056. **309.** 1 k. 40 blue 30 20
1057. – 1 k. 40 red 30 20
1058. – 2 k. green 40 25
1059. – 2 k. brown 40 25

DESIGNS: No. 1057, August Krogh (medicine). No. 1058, Charles-Edouard Guillaume (physics). No. 1059, Walther Nernst (chemistry).

1980. Christmas.

1060. **310.** 1 k. 25 brown & blue 30 10

311. Ernst Wigforss.

312. Thor catching Midgard Serpent.

1981. Birth Centenary of Ernst Wigforss (politician).

1061. **311.** 5 k. red 90 20

1981. Norse Mythology.

1062. **312.** 10 ore black .. 5 5
1063. – 15 ore red 5 5
1064. – 50 ore red 10 10
1065. – 75 ore green .. 20 10
1066. – 1 k. black 20 10

DESIGNS: 15 ore Heimdall blowing horn. 50 ore Frey riding boar. 75 ore Frey in carriage drawn by cats. 1 k. Odin on eight-footed steed.

313. Gyrfalcon.

314. Troll.

1981.

1067. **313.** 50 k. brown and blue 7·50 2·75

1981. Europa.

1068. **314.** 1 k. 50 blue and brown 30 10
1069. – 2 k. red and green .. 40 15

DESIGN: 2 k. The Lady of the Woods.

315. Blind Boy feeling Globe.

316. Arms of Ostergotland.

1981. International Year of Disabled Persons.

1070. **315.** 1 k. 50 green .. 30 10
1071. 3 k. 50 violet .. 70 15

1981. Rebate stamps. Arms of Swedish Provinces (1st series). Multicoloured.

1072. 1 k. 40 Type **316** .. 30 10
1073. 1 k. 40 Jamtland .. 30 10
1074. 1 k. 40 Dalarna .. 30 10
1075. 1 k. 40 Bohuslan .. 30 10

See also Nos. 1112/15, 1153/6, 1186/9, 1246/9 and 1302/5.

317. King Carl XVI Gustav.

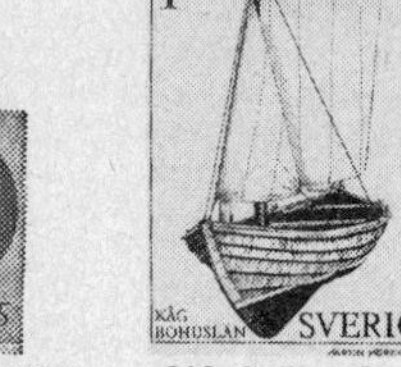

318. Sailing Boat from Bohuslan.

1981.

1076. **317.** 1 k. 65 green .. 30 5
1077. – 1 k. 75 blue 40 10
1077a. **317.** 1 k. 80 blue 30 5
1077b. 1 k. 90 brown .. 30 5
1078. 2 k. 40 purple .. 50 10
1078a. – 2 k. 40 green .. 50 10
1078b. **317.** 2 k. 70 purple .. 50 10
1078c. – 3 k. 20 red 60 15

DESIGN: 1 k. 75, 2 k. 40 (1078a), 3 k. 20, Queen Silvia.

1981. Provincial Sailing Boats.

1079. **318.** 1 k. 65 blue 40 20
1080. – 1 k. 65 blue 40 20
1081. – 1 k. 65 blue 40 20
1082. – 1 k. 65 blue 40 20
1083. – 1 k. 65 blue 40 20
1084. – 1 k. 65 blue 40 20

DESIGNS: No. 1080, Boat from Blekinge. No. 1081, Boat from Norrbotten. No. 1082, Boat from Halsingland. No. 1083, Boat from Gotland. No. 1084, Boat from Skane.

319. " Night and Day ".

320. Par Lagerkvist riding on Railway Trolley with Father (illustration from " Guest of Reality ").

1981.

1085. **319.** 1 k. 65 violet .. 30 5

1981.

1086. **320.** 1 k. 50 green .. 30 10

321. Electric Locomotive.

1981. " Sweden in the World ".

1087. **321.** 2 k. 40 red 50 40
1088. – 2 k. 40 red 50 40
1089. – 2 k. 40 purple .. 50 40
1090. – 2 k. 40 violet .. 50 40
1091. – 2 k. 40 blue 50 40
1092. – 2 k. 40 blue 50 40

DESIGNS:—HORIZ. No. 1088, Scania trucks with rock drilling equipment. No. 1089, Birgit Nilsson (opera singer) and Sixten Ehrling (conductor). No. 1090, North Sea gas pumping station. VERT. No. 1091, Bjorn Borg (tennis player). No. 1092, Ingemar Stenmark (skier).

322. Baker's Sign.

324. Wooden Bird.

1981. Business Mail.

1093. **322.** 2 k. 30 brown .. 50 10
1094. – 2 k. 30 brown .. 50 10

DESIGN: No. 1094, Pewterer's sign.

1981. Christmas.

1096. **324.** 1 k. 40 red 45 10
1097. – 1 k. 40 green .. 45 10

DESIGN: No. 1097, Wooden bird (different).

325. Albert Einstein (physics).

1981. Nobel Prize Winners of 1921.

1098. **325.** 1 k. 35 red 30 10
1099. – 1 k. 65 green .. 30 10
1100. – 2 k. 70 blue 60 20

DESIGNS: 1 k. 65, Anatole France (literature). 2 k. 70, Frederick Soddy (chemistry).

326. Knight on Horseback.

327. Impossible Triangle.

1982. Birth Centenary of John Bauer (illustrator of fairy tales).

1101. **326.** 1 k. 65 blue, yellow and lilac 30 30
1102. – 1 k. 65 multicoloured 30 30
1103. – 1 k. 65 orge. & yell. 30 30
1104. – 1 k. 65 yellow & lilac 30 30

DESIGNS: No. 1102, "What a wretched pale creature, said the Troll Woman". No. 1103, "The Princess beside the Forest Lake". No. 1104, "Now it is already twilight Night".

1982.

1105. **327.** 25 ore brown .. 5 5
1106. – 50 ore green 10 10
1107. – 75 ore blue 20 10
1108. – 1 k. 35 blue 25 10
1109. – 5 k. maroon .. 1·25 10

DESIGNS: 50 ore, 75 ore, Impossible Figures (different). 1 k. 35, Newspaper distributor. 5 k. "Graziella wonders if she could be a Model" (etching, Carl Larsson).

328. Villages before and after Land Reform.

1982. Europa.

1110. **328.** 1 k. 65 green and blk. 50 10
1111. – 2 k. 40 green .. 75 40

DESIGN: (26 × 22 mm.). 2 k. 40, Anders Celsius.

1982. Rebate Stamps. Arms of Swedish Provinces (2nd series). As T **316**. Mult.

1112. 1 k. 40 Dalsland .. 35 10
1113. 1 k. 40 Oland 35 10
1114. 1 k. 40 Vastmanland .. 35 10
1115. 1 k. 40 Halsingland .. 35 10

329. Elin Wagner. **330.** Burgher House.

1982. Birth Cent. of Elin Wagner (novelist).

1116. **329.** 1 k. 35 brown .. 30 10

1982. Centenary of Museum of Cultural History, Lund.

1117. **330.** 1 k. 65 brown .. 25 5
1118. – 2 k. 70 ochre .. 45 20

DESIGN: 2 k. 70, Embroidered lace.

331. Lateral Mark.

1982. New International Buoyage System.

1119. **331.** 1 k. 65 blue and green 50 20
1120. – 1 k. 65 green and blue 50 20
1121. – 1 k. 65 blue and deep blue 50 20
1122. – 1 k. 65 blue and green 50 20
1123. – 1 k. 65 blue and deep blue 50 20

DESIGNS: No. 1120, Cardinal mark and Sweden–Finland passenger ferry "Sally". No. 1121, Racing yachts and special mark. No. 1122, Safe-water mark. No. 1123, Pilot boat, isolated danger mark and lighthouse.

332. Scene from "The Emigrants" (film).

1982. Living Together.

1124. **332.** 1 k. 65 green 40 20
1125. – 1 k. 65 purple .. 40 20
1126. – 1 k. 65 blue 40 20
1127. – 1 k. 65 red 40 20

DESIGNS: No. 1125, Vietnamese boat people in factory. No. 1126, Immigrants examining local election literature. No. 1127, Three girls arm-in-arm.

334. Angel.

1982. Christmas. Medieval Glass Paintings from Lye Church. Multicoloured.

1129 1 k. 40 Type **334** 30 10
1130 1 k. 40 "The Child in the Temple" 30 10
1131 1 k. 40 "Adoration of the Magi" 30 30
1132 1 k. 40 "Tidings to the Shepherds" 30 30
1133 1 k. 40 "The Birth of Christ" 30 30

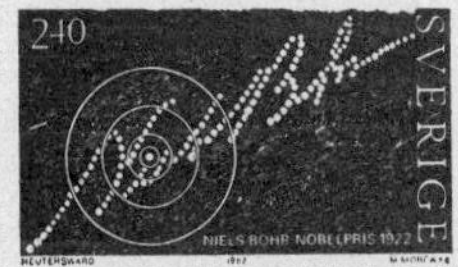

335. Quantum Mechanics (Niels Bohr, 1922).

1982. Nobel Prize Winners for Physics.

1134. **335.** 2 k. 40 blue 60 40
1135. – 2 k. 40 red 60 40
1136. – 2 k. 40 green .. 60 40
1137. – 2 k. 40 lilac .. 60 40
1138. – 2 k. 40 red 60 40

Designs: No. 1135, Fuse distribution (Erwin Schrodinger, 1933). No. 1136, Wave pattern (Louis de Broglie, 1929). No. 1137, Electrons (Paul Dirac, 1933). No. 1138, Atomic model (Werner Heisenberg, 1932).

336. Horse Chestnut.

337. Ferlin (statue by K. Bejemark).

1983. Fruits.

1139. **336.** 5 ore brown 10 5
1140. – 10 ore green .. 10 5
1141. – 15 ore red 10 5
1142. – 20 ore blue 10 10

Designs: 10 ore Norway maple. 15 ore Dog rose. 20 ore Blackthorn.

1983. 85th Birth Anniv. of Nils Ferlin (poet).

1143. **337.** 6 k. green .. .. 1·25 20

338. Peace March.

340. Family cycling in Countryside.

339. Lead Type.

1983. Cent. of Swedish Peace Movement.

1144. **338.** 1 k. 35 blue .. 25 25

1983. 500th Anniv. of Printing in Sweden.

1145. **339.** 1 k. 65 black and brown on stone .. 40 15
1146. – 1 k. 65 black, green and red on stone .. 40 15
1147. – 1 k. 65 brown and black on stone .. 40 15
1148. – 1 k. 65 black and brown on stone .. 40 15
1149. – 1 k. 65 brown, green and black on stone 40 15

Designs: No. 1146, Ox plough (illustration from "Dialogus creaturarum" by Johan Snell, 1483). No. 1147, Title page of Karl XII's Bible, 1703. No. 1148, 18th century alphabet books. No. 1149, Laser photocomposition.

1983. Nordic Countries' Postal Co-operation. "Visit the North".

1150. **340.** 1 k. 65 green .. 40 10
1151. – 2 k. 40 blue & brown 60 25

Design: 2 k. 40 Yachts at Stockholm.

341. Benjamin Franklin and Great Seal of Sweden.

1983. Bicentenary of Sweden-U.S.A. Treaty of Amity and Commerce.

1152. **341.** 2 k. 70 blue, brn. & blk. 50 30

1983. Rebate Stamps. Arms of Swedish Provinces (3rd series). As T **316.** Mult.

1153. 1 k. 60 Vastergotland .. 30 10
1154. 1 k. 60 Medelpad .. 30 10
1155. 1 k. 60 Gotland 30 10
1156. 1 k. 60 Gastrikland .. 30 10

342. Costume Sketch by Fernand Leger for "Creation du Monde".

343. Essay for Unissued Stamp, 1885.

1983. Europa.

1157. 1 k. 65 dp. brown & brown 30 5
1158. 2 k. 70 blue 50 25

Designs: 1 k. 65, Type **342** (Swedish Ballet). 2 k. 70 J. P. Johansson's adjustable spanner.

1983. "Stockholmia 86" International Exhibition (1st issue). Oscar II stamp designs by Max Mirowsky.

1159. **343.** 1 k. blue 25 25
1160. – 2 k. red 45 45
1161. – 3 k. blue 55 55
1162. – 4 k. green 75 75

Designs: 2 k. Issued stamp of 1885. 3 k. Essay for unissued stamp, 1891. 4 k. Issued stamp of 1891.

See also Nos. 1199/1202, 1252/5, 1285/8 and 1310/3.

344. Greater Karlso.

345. Fresh-water Snail.

1983.

1163. **344.** 1 k. 60 blue 30 5
1164. **345.** 1 k. 80 green 35 5
1165. – 2 k. 10 green 40 5

Design: (22 × 27 mm.)—2 k. 10 Arctic fox.

346. Bergman.

347. Helgeandsholmen, 1580 (after Franc Hogenberg) and Riksdag.

1983. Birth Centenary of Hjalmar Bergman (novelist and dramatist).

1166. **346.** 1 k. 80 blue 35 10
1167. – 1 k. 80 multicoloured 35 10

Design: No. 1167, Jac the Clown (novel character).

1983. Return of Riksdag (Parliament) to Helgeandsholmen Island Stockholm.

1168. **347.** 2 k. 70 maroon & bl. 45 35

348. Red Cross.

350. Dancing round the Christmas Tree.

1983. Swedish Red Cross.

1169. **348.** 1 k. 50 red 25 5

1983. Christmas. Early Christmas Cards. Multicoloured.

1171. 1 k. 60 Type **350** .. 30 15
1172. 1 k. 60 Straw goats .. 30 15
1173. 1 k. 60 The Christmas table 30 15
1174. 1 k. 60 Carrying Christmas presents on pole 30 15

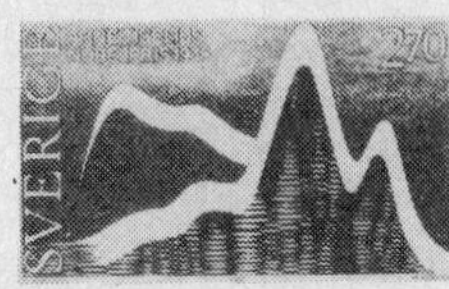

351. Electrophoresis (Arne Tiselius, 1948).

1983. Nobel Prize Winners for Chemistry.

1175. **351.** 2 k. 70 black .. 60 50
1176. – 2 k. 70 violet .. 60 50
1177. – 2 k. 70 mauve .. 60 50
1178. – 2 k. 70 violet .. 60 50
1179. – 2 k. 70 black .. 60 50

Designs: No. 1176, Radioactive isotopes (George de Hevesy, 1943). 1177, Electrolytic dissociation (Svante Arrhenius, 1903). 1178, Colloids (Theodor Svedberg, 1926). 1179, Fermentation of sugar (Hans von Euler-Chelpin, 1929).

352. Three Crowns (detail from Postal Savings Receipt).

1984. Centenary of Postal Savings.

1180. **352.** 100 ore orange .. 20 15
1181. – 1 k. 60 violet .. 30 15
1182. – 1 k. 80 purple .. 40 10

Designs: 1 k. 60, 1 k. 80 Postal Savings badge.

353. Bridge.

1984. Europa. 25th Anniv. of European Post and Telecommunications Conference.

1183. **353.** 1 k. 80 red 50 5
1184. 2 k. 70 blue 75 40

354. Norway Lemmings.

355. Paraffin Stove (F. W. Lindqvist).

1984. Swedish Mountain World.

1185. **354.** 1 k. 90 brown .. 40 10
1186. – 1 k. 90 blue 40 10
1187. – 2 k. green 45 10
1188. – 2 k. 25 black .. 55 25

Designs: No. 1186, Musk ox. 1187, Garden angelica. 1188, Tolpagorni mountain.

1984. Rebate Stamps. Arms of Swedish Provinces (4th series). As T **316.** Multicoloured.

1189. 1 k. 60 Sodermanland .. 30 10
1190. 1 k. 60 Blekinge 30 10
1191. 1 k. 60 Vasterbotten .. 30 10
1192. 1 k. 60 Skane 30 10

1984. "Made in Sweden". Centenary of Patent Office. Patented Swedish Inventions.

1193. **355.** 2 k. 70 red 90 50
1194. – 2 k. 70 lilac 90 50
1195. – 2 k. 70 green .. 90 50
1196. – 2 k. 70 green .. 90 50
1197. – 2 k. 70 lilac 90 50
1198. – 2 k. 70 blue 90 50

Designs: No. 1194, "ASEA IRB 6" industrial robot for arc welding. 1195, Vacuum cleaner (Axel Wennergren). 1196. "AQ 200" inboard/outboard engine. 1197, Integrated circuit. 1198, Tetrahedron container.

356. King Erik IV (after S. van der Meulen) and Letter to Queen Elizabeth I of England.

358. Genetic Symbols forming "100".

357. Jonkoping.

1984. "Stockholmia 86" International Stamp Exhibition (2nd issue).

1199. **356.** 1 k. brown, blue and deep blue .. 25 25
1200. – 2 k. multicoloured .. 45 45
1201. – 3 k. multicoloured .. 55 55
1202. – 4 k. multicoloured .. 75 75

Designs: 2 k. Erik Dahlbergh (architect) (after J. H. Stromer) and letter to Sten Bielke (Paymaster General), 1674. 3 k. Feather letter, 1843. 4 k. Harriet Bosse and letter from her husband, August Strindberg, 1905.

1984. Old Towns. 17th-century views by M. Karl (1207) or Erik Dahlbergh (others).

1203. **357.** 1 k. 90 blue 40 30
1204. – 1 k. 90 brown .. 40 30
1205. – 1 k. 90 blue 50 30
1206. – 1 k. 90 brown .. 40 30
1207. – 1 k. 90 blue 40 30
1208. – 1 k. 90 brown .. 40 30

Designs: No. 1204, Karlstad. 1205, Gavle. 1206, Sigtuna. 1207, Norrkoping. 1208. Vadstena.

1984. Cent. of Fredrika Bremer Association (for promotion of male/female equal rights).

1209. **358.** 1 k. 50 purple .. 30 5
1210. 6 k. 50 red .. .. 1·40 25

359. "Viking" in Orbit.

361. Hawfinch.

1984. Launch of Swedish "Viking" Satellite.

1211. **359.** 1 k. 90 ultramarine, blue and deep blue 35 5
1212. – 3 k. 20 green, yellow and black 55 25

Design: 3 k. 20 Dish aerial and rocket pad at Esrange space station.

1984. Christmas. Birds. Multicoloured.

1214. 1 k. 60 Type **361** .. 65 40
1215. 1 k. 60 Bohemian waxwing 65 40
1216. 1 k. 60 Great-spotted woodpecker 65 40
1217. 1 k. 60 European nuthatch 65 40

362. Inner Ear (Georg von Bekesy, 1961).

1984. Nobel Prize Winners for Medicine.

1218. **362.** 2 k. 70 blue, black and red 60 50
1219. – 2 k. 70 bl. and blk. .. 60 50
1220. – 2 k. 70 red, black and blue 60 50
1221. – 2 k. 70 bl. and blk. .. 60 50
1222. – 2 k. 70 red, black and blue 60 50

Designs: No. 1219, Nerve cell activation (John Eccles, Alan Hodgkin and Andrew Huxley, 1963). 1220, Nerve cell signals (Bernard Katz, Ulf von Euler and Julius Axelrod, 1970). 1221, Functions of the brain (Roger Sperry, 1981). 1222, Eye (David Hubel and Torsten Wiesel, 1981).

363. Post Office Emblem.

364. King Carl XVI Gustav.

1985.

1223. 363. 1 k. 60 blue .. 25 5
1224. 1 k. 70 violet .. 25 5
1326. 1 k. 80 mauve .. 35 5
1225. 2 k. 50 yellow .. 45 5
1226. 2 k. 80 green .. 45 5
1327. 3 k. 20 brown .. 50 5
1227. 4 k. red .. .. 1·00 35
1328. 6 k. turquoise .. 1·40 70

1985.

1228 364 2 k. black 35 5
1229 2 k. 10 blue .. 35 5
1230 2 k. 20 blue .. 35 5
1230a 2 k. 30 green .. 45 10
1230b 2 k. 50 purple .. 45 10
1231 2 k. 70 brown .. 45 10
1232 2 k. 90 green .. 55 10
1233 3 k. 10 brown .. 55 10
1234 – 3 k. 20 blue .. 55 10
1234a 364 3 k. 30 purple .. 60 10
1235 – 3 k. 40 red 60 10
1236 – 3 k. 60 green .. 60 10
1237 – 3 k. 90 blue .. 70 15
1238 – 4 k. 60 orange .. 85 75
DESIGNS: 3k. 20 and 3 k. 40 to 4 k. 60, Queen Silvia.

365. Hazel Dormouse.

366. Jan-Ove Waldner.

1985. Nature.

1240. 365. 2 k. brown and black 45 15
1241. – 2 k. orange and black 45 15
1242. – 2 k. 20 red 40 20
1243. – 3 k. 50 red and green 70 20
DESIGNS: No. 1241, Char. 1242, Black vanilla orchid. 1243, White water-lily.

1985. World Table Tennis Championships, Gothenburg.

1244. 366. 2 k. 70 blue 55 25
1245. – 3 k. 20 mauve .. 70 25
DESIGN: 3 k. 20 Cai Zhenhua (Chinese player).

1985. Rebate Stamps. Arms of Swedish Provinces (5th series). As T **316**. Multicoloured.

1246. 1 k. 80 Narke .. 40 10
1247. 1 k. 80 Angermanland .. 40 10
1248. 1 k. 80 Varmland .. 40 10
1249. 1 k. 80 Smaland 40 10

367. Clavichord.

1985. Europa. Music Year.

1250. 367. 2 k. purple on buff .. 70 5
1251. – 2 k. 70 brown on buff 90 40
DESIGN: 2 k. 70 Keyed fiddle.

368. "View of Slussen" (Sigrid Hjerten).

369. Syl Hostel, 1920.

1985. "Stockholmia '86" International Stamp Exhibition (3rd issue). Multicoloured.

1252. 2 k. Type **368** 40 40
1253. 2 k. "Skeppsholmen, Winter" (Gosta Adrian-Nilsson) .. 40 40
1254. 3 k. "A Summer's Night by Riddarholmen Canal" (Hilding Linnqvist) 55 55
1255. 4 k. "Klara Church Tower" (Otte Skold) .. 70 70

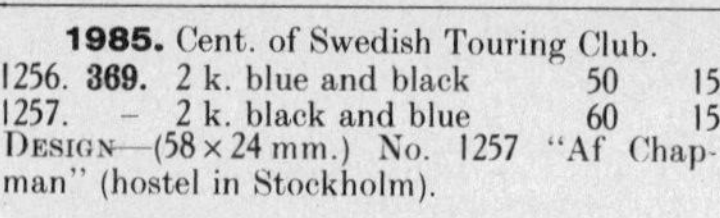

1985. Cent. of Swedish Touring Club.

1256. 369. 2 k. blue and black 50 15
1257. – 2 k. black and blue 60 15
DESIGN—(58×24 mm.) No. 1257 "Af Chapman" (hostel in Stockholm).

370. Canute and Helsingborg.

371. Nilsson's Music Shop Sign.

1985. 900th Anniv. of Saint Canute's Deed of Gift to Lund.

1258. – 2 k. blue and black 40 10
1259. 370. 2 k. red and black .. 40 10
DESIGN: No. 1258, Canute and Lund Cathedral.

1985. Trade Signs.

1260. 371. 10 ore blue 10 10
1261. – 20 ore brown .. 10 10
1262. – 20 ore brown .. 10 10
1263. – 50 ore blue 10 10
1264. – 2 k. green 35 10
DESIGNS: No. 1261, Erik Johansson's furrier's sign. 1262, O. L. Sjowals's coppersmith's sign. 1263, Bodecker's hatter's sign. 1264, Berggren's shoemaker's sign.

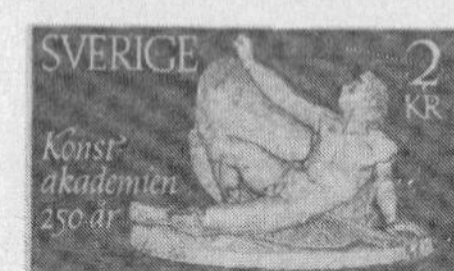

372. "Otryades" (Johan Tobias Sergel).

1985. 250th Anniv. of Royal Academy of Fine Arts.

1265. 372. 2 k. blue 35 5
1266. – 7 k. brown .. .. 1·75 30
DESIGN—(20×28 mm.). 7 k. "Baron Carl Fredrik Adelcrantz" (former Academy president) (Alexander Roslin).

373. Fox and Geese.

374. Burger Sjoberg (writer).

1985. Board Games.

1267. 373. 50 ore blue 10 10
1268. – 60 ore green 10 10
1269. – 70 ore yellow .. 10 10
1270. – 80 ore red 20 10
1271. – 90 ore mauve .. 20 10
1272. – 3 k. purple 70 20
DESIGNS—As T **373**. 60 ore Dominoes. 70 ore Ludo. 80 ore Chinese checkers. 90 ore Backgammon. (23×28 mm). 3 k. Chess.

1985. Birth Centenaries.

1273. – 1 k. 60 red and black 25 10
1274. 374. 4 k. green 85 25
DESIGN—(40×24 mm). 1 k. 60, Per Albin Hansson (politician).

376. "Annunciation".

377. American Deep South Scene (William Faulkner, 1949).

1985. Christmas. Medieval Church Frescoes by Albertus Pictor.

1276. 376. 1 k. 80 blue, brown and red 35 20
1277. – 1 k. 80 brown, blue and red .. 35 20
1278. – 1 k. 80 brown, blue and red 35 20
1279. – 1 k. 80 blue, brown and red 35 20
DESIGNS: No. 1277, "Birth of Christ". 1278, "Adoration of the Magi". 1279, "Mary as the Apocalyptic Virgin".

1985. Nobel Prize Winners for Literature.

1280. 377. 2 k. 70 green .. 55 40
1281. – 2 k. 70 brown, blue and green 55 40
1282. – 2 k. 70 green & brn. 55 40
1283. – 2 k. 70 green & blue 1·25 45
1284. – 2 k. 70 brown & bl. 55 40
DESIGNS: No. 1281, Icelandic scene (Halldor Kiljan Laxness, 1955). 1282, Guatemalan scene (Miguel Angel Asturias, 1967). 1283, Japanese scene (Yasunari Kawabata, 1968). 1284, Australian scene (Patrick White, 1973).

378. 1879 "20 TRETIO" Error.

379. Eiders.

1986. "Stockholmia 86" International Stamp Exhibition (4th issue).

1285. 378. 2 k. orge., pur. & grn. 35 35
1286. – 2 k. multicoloured .. 35 35
1287. – 3 k. purple, blue and green 50 50
1288. – 4 k. multicoloured .. 70 70
DESIGNS: No. 1286, Sven Ewert (engraver). 1287, Magnifying glass and United States 1938 Scandinavian Settlement 3 c. stamp. 1288, Boy soaking stamps.

1986. Water Birds.

1289. 379. 2 k. 10 blue and brn. 1·10 55
1290. – 2 k. 10 brown .. 1·10 55
1291. – 2 k. 30 blue .. .. 1·25 65
DESIGNS: No. 1290, Whimbrel. 1292, Black-throated diver.

380. Swedish Academy Emblem.

381. Jubilee Emblem.

1986. Bicentenaries of Swedish Academy and Royal Swedish Academy of Letters, History and Antiquities.

1292. 380. 1 k. 70 green and red on grey 25 10
1293. – 1 k. 70 blue and purple on grey .. 25 10
DESIGN: No. 1293, Royal Swedish Academy Emblem.

1986. 350th Anniv of Post Office.

1294 381 2 k. 10 blue and yellow 35 5

382. Palme.

383. Carl Gustaf Birdwatching.

1986. Olof Palme (Prime Minister) Commemoration.

1295. 382. 2 k. 10 purple .. 90 55
1296. 2 k. 90 black .. 1·00 80

1986. 40th Birthday of King Carl XVI Gustaf.

1297. 383. 2 k. 10 black & green 35 10
1298. – 2 k. 10 gold, mauve and blue 35 10
1299. – 2 k. 10 dp. bl. & bl. 35 10
1300. – 2 k. 10 gold, blue and deep blue 35 10
1301. – 2 k. 10 black & mve. 35 10
DESIGNS. No. 1298, 1300, Crowned cypher. 1299. King presenting Nobel Prize for Literature to Czeslaw Milosz. 1301, King and family during summer holiday at Solliden Palace.

1986. Rebate Stamps. Arms of Swedish Provinces (6th series). As T **316**. Mult.

1302. 1 k. 90 Harjedalen .. 45 10
1303. 1 k. 90 Uppland 45 10
1304. 1 k. 90 Halland .. 45 10
1305. 1 k. 90 Lappland .. 45 10

384. Uppsala.

385. Forest and Car Fumes.

1986. Nordic Countries' Postal Co-operation. Twinned Towns.

1306 384 2 k. 10 green, light brown and brown .. 35 10
1307 – 2 k. 90 grn, red & brn 55 25
DESIGN: 2 k. 90, Eskilstuna.

1986. Europa. Each black, green and red.

1308. 2 k. 10 Type **385** .. 35 5
1309. 2 k. 90 Forest and industrial pollution .. 55 30

386. Tomteboda Sorting Office (20th-century).

388. Olive Branch sweeping away Weapons.

1986. "Stockholmia 86" International Stamp Exhibition (5th issue). Multicoloured.

1310. 2 k. 10 19th-century mail carriage .. .. 6·00 6·00
1311. 2 k. 10 Type **386** .. 6·00 6·00
1312. 2 k. 90 17th-century farm-hand postal messenger 6·00 6·00
1313. 2 k. 90 18th-century Post-Office .. .. .. 6·00 6·00

1986. International Peace Year (1315) and 25th Anniv. of Amnesty International (1316).

1315. 388. 3 k. 40 green & blk. 65 20
1316. – 3 k. 40 red and black 65 20
DESIGN: No. 1316, Emblem above broken manacles.

389. Bertha von Suttner (founder of Austrian Society of Peace Lovers, 1905).

1986. Nobel Prize Winners for Peace.

1317. 389. 2 k. 90 blk., red & bl. 60 35
1318. – 2 k. 90 black and red 60 35
1319. – 2 k. 90 black, brown and blue 60 35
1320. – 2 k. 90 brown & blk. 60 35
1321. – 2 k. 90 red, black & blue 60 35
DESIGNS: No. 1318, Carl von Ossietzky (anti-Nazi fighter and concentration camp victim, 1935). 1319, Albert Luthuli (South African anti-apartheid leader, 1960). 1320, Martin Luther King (American civil rights leader, 1964). 1321, Mother Teresa (worker amongst poor of Calcutta, 1979).

390. Mail Van.

391. "Parnassius mnemosyne".

1986. Christmas. Designs showing village at Christmas. Multicoloured.

1322. 1 k. 90 Type **390** .. 35 15
1323. 1 k. 90 Postman on cycle delivering mail .. 35 15
1324. 1 k. 90 Children and sledge loaded with parcels 35 15
1325. 1 k. 90 Christmas tree, man carrying parcel and child posting letter 35 15

Nos. 1322/5 were printed together, se-tenant, forming a composite design.

1987. Threatened Species of Meadows and Pastures.

1331. **391.** 2 k. 10 black, green and purple .. 40 10
1332. – 2 k. 10 black, green and purple .. 40 10
1333. – 2 k. 50 brown .. 50 20
1334. – 4 k. 20 green and yellow 75 20

Designs: 2 k. 10, (1332), Field gentian. 2 k. 50, "Osmoderma eremita" (beetle). 4 k. 20, Arnica.

392. Saab "SF 340".

393. Boys flying over Rooftops ("Karlsson").

1987. Swedish Aircraft.

1335. **392.** 25 k. purple .. .. 4·00 25

1987. Rebate Stamps. Characters from Children's Books by Astrid Lindgren. Multicoloured.

1336. 1 k. 90 Type **393** .. 35 15
1337. 1 k. 90 Girl holding doll ("Bullerby Children") 35 15
1338. 1 k. 90 Girls dancing ("Madicken") 35 15
1339. 1 k. 90 Boys on horse ("Mio, Min Mio") .. 35 15
1340. 1 k. Boy doing hand-stand ("Nils Karlsson-Pyssling") 35 15
1341. 1 k. 90 Emil picking cherries ("Emil") .. 35 15
1342. 1 k. 90 "Ronja the Robber's Daughter" .. 35 15
1343. 1 k. 90 "Pippi Long-stocking" 35 15
1344. 1 k. 90 Dragon ("Brothers Lionheart") 35 15
1345. 1 k. 90 "Lotta" 35 15

394. Hans Brask, Bishop of Linkoping (sculpture, Karl-Olav Bjork).

395. Stockholm City Library (Gunnar Asplund).

1987. Town Anniversaries. Each brown, blue and black.

1346. 2 k. 10 Type **394** (700th anniv.) 35 15
1347. 2 k. 10 Nykoping Castle (800th anniv.) .. 35 15

1987. Europa. Architecture.

1348. **395.** 2 k. 10 brown & bl. 35 5
1349. – 3 k. 10 brown & grn. 50 30
1350. – 3 k. 10 purple & grn. 50 30

Design: No. 1350, Marcus Church (Sigurd Lewerentz).

396. "King Gustavus Vasa" (anon).

398. Clowns.

397. Raoul Wallenberg (rescuer of Hungarian Jews) and Prisoners.

1987. 450th Anniv. of Gripsholm Castle.

1351. **396.** 2 k. 10 multicoloured 35 15
1352. – 2 k. 10 multicoloured 35 15
1353. – 2 k. 10 multicoloured 35 15
1354. – 2 k. 10 brown, black and blue 35 15

Designs: No. 1352, "Blue Tiger" (David Klocker Ehrenstrahl). 1353, "Hedvig Charlotta Nordenflycht" (after Johan Henrik Scheffel). 1354, "Gripsholm Castle" (lithograph, Carl Johan Billmark).

1987. "In the Service of Humanity".

1355. **397.** 3 k. 10 blue 50 15
1356. – 3 k. 10 green .. 50 15
1357. – 3 k. 10 brown .. 50 15

Designs: No. 1356, Dag Hammarskjold (U.N. Secretary-General, 1953–1961). 1357, Folke Bernadotte (leader of "white bus" relief action to rescue prisoners, 1945).

1987. Stamp Day. Bicentenary of Circus in Sweden. Multicoloured.

1358. 2 k. 10 Type **398** .. 75 75
1359. 2 k. 10 Reino riding one-wheel cycle on wire .. 75 75
1360. 2 k. 10 Acrobat on horse-back 75 75

399. "Victoria cruziana" at Bergian Garden, Stockholm University.

400. Porridge left for the Grey Christmas Elf.

1987. Bicentenary of Swedish Botanical Gardens.

1361. **399.** 2 k. 10 green, deep green and blue .. 35 15
1362. – 2 k. 10 green & brn. 35 15
1363. – 2 k. 10 deep green, green and blue .. 35 15
1364. – 2 k. 10 yellow, brown and green 35 15

Designs: No. 1362, Uppsala University Baroque Garden plan and Carl Harleman (architect). 1363, Rock garden, Gothenburg Botanical Garden. 1364, "Liriodendron tulipifera", Lund Botanical Garden.

1987. Christmas. Folk Customs. Mult.

1365 2 k. Type **400** 35 15
1366 2 k. Staffan ride (watering horses in North-running spring on Boxing Day) 35 15
1367 2 k. Christmas Day sledge race home from church 35 15
1368 2 k. Bullfinches on corn sheaf 35 15

401. Pulsars (Antony Hewish, 1974).

1987. Nobel Prize Winners for Physics.

1369. **401.** 2 k. 90 blue 80 55
1370. – 2 k. 90 black .. 80 55
1371. – 2 k. 90 blue 80 55
1372. – 2 k. 90 blue 80 55
1373. – 2 k. 90 black .. 80 55

Designs: No. 1370, Formula of maximum white dwarf star mass (S. Chandrasekhar, 1983). 1371, Heavy atom nuclei construction (William Fowler, 1983). 1372, Temperature of cosmic background radiation (A. Penzias and R. Wilson, 1978). 1373, Radio telescopes receiving radio waves from galaxy (Martin Ryle, 1974).

402. Lake Hjalmaren Skiff.

404. White-tailed Sea Eagle.

403. Bishop Hill and Erik Jansson (founder).

1988. Inland Boats. Each purple on buff.

1374 3 k. 10 Type **402** .. 60 30
1375 3 k. 10 Lake Vattern market boat 60 30
1376 3 k. 10 River Byske logging boat 60 30
1377 3 k. 10 Lake Asen rowing boat 60 30
1378 3 k. 10 Lake Vanern ice boat 60 30
1379 3 k. 10 Lake Lockne church longboat .. 60 30

1988. 350th Anniv. of New Sweden (settlement in America).

1380. – 3 k. 60 multicoloured 85 70
1381. **403.** 3 k. 60 multicoloured 85 70
1382. – 3 k. 60 brown .. 85 70
1383. – 3 k. 60 blue & brown 85 70
1384. – 3 k. 60 blue, yellow and red 85 70
1385. – 3 k. 60 black, blue and red 85 70

Designs: As T **403**—No. 1380, Map, Settlers, Indians, "Calmare Nyckel" and "Fagel Grip". 27 × 23 mm—No. 1382, Carl Sandburg (American poet) and Jenny Lind (Swedish soprano). 1383, Charles Lindbergh (aviator) and "Spirit of St. Louis". 27 × 37 mm—No. 1384, Alan Bean (astronaut) on Moon with Hasselblad camera; 1385, Ice hockey.

1988. Coastal Wildlife.

1386. **404.** 2 k. 20 brown and red 40 15
1387. – 2 k. 20 brown & blue 40 15
1388. – 4 k. black, brown and green 80 40

Designs: No. 1387, Grey seal. 1388, Eel.

405 Daisies and Bluebells

406 Detail of "Creation" Stained Glass Window (Bo Beskow), Skara Cathedral

1988. Rebate stamps. Midsummer Festival. Multicoloured.

1389 2 k. Type **405** 40 15
1390 2 k. Garlanded longboat 40 15
1391 2 k. Children making garlands 40 15
1392 2 k. Raising the maypole 40 15
1393 2 k. Fiddlers 40 15
1394 2 k. "Norrskar" (tourist launch) 40 15
1395 2 k. Couples dancing .. 40 15
1396 2 k. Accordianist .. 40 15
1397 2 k. Archipelago with decorated landing stage 40 15
1398 2 k. Bouquet of seven wild flowers 40 15

1988. Anniversaries.

1399 **406** 2 k. 20 multicoloured 40 15
1400 – 4 k. 40 red on brown 1·10 40
1401 – 8 k. red, green & blk 1·60 1·10

DESIGNS: 2 k. 20, Type **406** (millenary of Skara). 23 × 41 mm: 4 k. 40, "Falun Copper Mine" (Pehr Hillestrom) (700th anniv of Stora Kopparberg (mining company)); 8 k. Scene from play "The Queen's Diamond Ornament" (bicentenary of Royal Dramatic Theatre, Stockholm).

407 "Self-Portrait" (Nils Dardel)

408 "X2" High-speed Train

1988. Swedish Artists in Paris. Multicoloured.

1402 2 k. 20 Type **407** .. 40 15
1403 2 k. 20 "Autumn, Gubbhuset" (Vera Nilsson) (40 × 43 mm) 40 15
1404 2 k. 20 "Self-Portrait" (Isaac Grunewald) .. 40 15
1405 2 k. 20 "Visit to an Eccentric Lady" (Nils Dardel) 40 15
1406 2 k. 20 "Soap Bubbles" (Vera Nilsson) (40 × 43 mm) 40 15
1407 2 k. 20 "The Singing Tree" (Isaac Grunewald) 40 15

1988. Europa. Transport and Communications.

1408 **408** 2 k. 20 blue, orange and brown .. 35 15
1409 3 k. 10 blue, black and purple .. 55 30
1410 – 3 k. 10 black & purple 55 30

DESIGN: No. 1410, Narrow-gauge steam locomotive.

409 Common Swift

410 Andersson

1988.

1411 **409** 20 k. purple & mauve 3·75 1·60

1988. Birth Centenary of Dan Andersson (poet). Each violet, green and blue.

1412 2 k. 20 Type **410** .. 40 15
1413 2 k. 20 Lake, Finnmarken (58 × 24 mm) 40 15

411 Players

412 Angel and Shepherds

1988. Swedish Football. Multicoloured.

1414 2 k. 20 Type **411** .. 75 75
1415 2 k. 20 Three players .. 75 75
1416 2 k. 20 Women players 75 75

1988. Christmas. Multicoloured.

1417 2 k. Type **412** 40 15
1418 2 k. Horse and angel .. 40 15
1419 2 k. Birds singing in trees 40 15
1420 2 k. Three kings 40 15
1421 2 k. Holy Family .. 40 15
1422 2 k. Shepherds and sheep 40 15

Nos. 1418/22 were printed together, se-tenant, forming a composite design.

413 Archaeologist, Carbon 14 Dating Graph and Tutankhamen

414 Nidingen 1946 Concrete and 1832 Twin Lighthouses

1988. Nobel Prize Winners for Chemistry. Multicoloured.

1423 3 k. 10 Type **413** (Willard Frank Libby, 1960) .. 60 30
1424 3 k. 10 Plastics molecules (Karl Ziegler and Giulio Natta, 1963) 60 30
1425 3 k. 10 Electron microscope (Aaron Klug, 1982) 60 30
1426 3 k. 10 Landscape and symbols (Ilya Prigogine, 1977) .. 60 30

1989. Lighthouses.

1427 414 1 k. 90 green, brown and black 40 15
1428 – 2 k. 70 blue, red and deep blue 50 25
1429 – 3 k. 80 brown, deep blue and blue .. 80 25
1430 – 3 k. 90 blk, red & brn 1·10 35

DESIGNS: 2 k. 70, Soderarm stone lighthouse; 3 k. 80, Sydostbrotten caisson lighthouse; 3 k. 90, Sandhammaren iron lghthouse.

415 Wolverine

1989. Animals in Threatened Habitats.

1431 415 2 k. 30 brown, orange and green .. 45 20
1432 – 2 k. 30 brown, green and orange .. 45 20
1433 – 2 k. 40 dp brown, brown and red .. 45 20
1434 – 2 k. 60 dp brown, brown and orange 50 25
1435 – 3 k. 30 deep green, green and brown 60 30
1436 – 4 k. 60 black, green and orange .. 85 50

DESIGNS: 2 k. 30 (1432), Ural owl; 2 k. 40, Lesser spotted woodpecker; 2 k. 60, Dunlin; 3 k. 30, Common tree frog; 4 k. 60, Red-breasted flycatcher.

416 Globe

1989. Opening of Globe Arena, Stockholm. Multicoloured.

1437 2 k. 30 Type 416 .. 45 20
1438 2 k. 30 Ice hockey .. 45 20
1439 2 k. 30 Gymnastics .. 45 20
1440 2 k. 30 Pop concert .. 45 20

417 Woman's Woollen Bib Front

418 Sailing

1989. Nordic Countries' Postal Co-operation. Traditional Lapp Costumes.

1441 2 k. 30 Type 417 .. 45 20
1442 3 k. 30 Man's belt pouch 90 30

1989. Rebate stamps. Summer Activities. Multicoloured.

1443 2 k. 10 Type 418 .. 50 15
1444 2 k. 10 Beach ball .. 50 15
1445 2 k. 10 Cycling .. 50 15
1446 2 k. 10 Canoeing .. 50 15
1447 2 k. 10 Fishing .. 50 15
1448 2 k. 10 Camping .. 50 15
1449 2 k. 10 Croquet .. 50 15
1450 2 k. 10 Badminton .. 50 15
1451 2 k. 10 Gardening .. 50 15
1452 2 k. 10 Sand castle, bucket and spade 50 15

419 "Protest March" (Nils Kreuger)

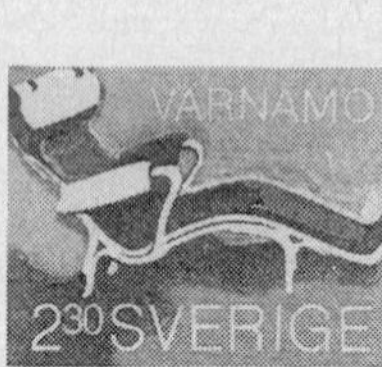

420 Playing with Boats

1989. Cent of Swedish Labour Movement.

1453 419 2 k. 30 black and red 45 20

1989. Europa. Children's Games and Toys.

1454 420 2 k. 30 brown .. 45 20
1455 3 k. 30 mauve .. 90 30
1456 – 3 k. 30 green .. 90 30

DESIGN: No. 1456, Girl riding kick-sled.

421 Lounger (Varnamo)

422 Researcher in Greenland and Temperature Curve

1989. Industries of Smaland Towns. Each mauve, orange and red.

1457 2 k. 30 Type 421 .. 45 20
1458 2 k. 30 Tools for self-assembly furniture (Almhult) 45 20
1459 2 k. 30 Sewing machine and embroidery (Husk-varna) 45 20
1460 2 k. 30 Blowing glass (Afors) 45 20
1461 2 k. 30 Coathanger hook and clothes-peg spring (Gnosjo) 45 20
1462 2 k. 30 Match (Jonkoping) 45 20

1989. 250th Anniv of Swedish Academy of Sciences. Polar Research. Multicoloured.

1463 3 k. 30 Type 422 .. 75 75
1464 3 k. 30 Abisko Natural Science Station, Lapland (40 × 43 mm) 75 75
1465 3 k. 30 "Oden" (ice research ship) and researchers 75 75
1466 3 k. 30 Otto Nordenskiold 1901–03 expedition's "Antarctic" and Emperor penguin with chick 75 75
1467 3 k. 30 1988 Antarctic expedition's vehicles and Hughes Model 500 helicopter (40 × 43 mm) 75 75
1468 3 k. 30 Geodimeter and McCormick's skua .. 75 75

423 Eagle Owl

1989.

1469 423 30 k. brn, blk & mve 5·75 4·25

424 Lapp Rhododendron

425 Jamthund

1989. National Parks. (1st series).

1470 424 2 k. 40 mve, grn & bl 45 20
1471 – 2 k. 40 mauve & green 45 20
1472 – 4 k. 30 red, black & bl 80 40

DESIGNS: No. 1471, Fairy slipper; 1472, Bla Jungfrun.

See also Nos. 1486/90.

1989. Cent of Swedish Kennel Club. Mult.

1473 2 k. 40 Type 425 .. 75 75
1474 2 k. 40 Hamilton fox-hound 75 75
1475 2 k. 40 Vastgota sheep dog 75 75

426 Decorated Tree

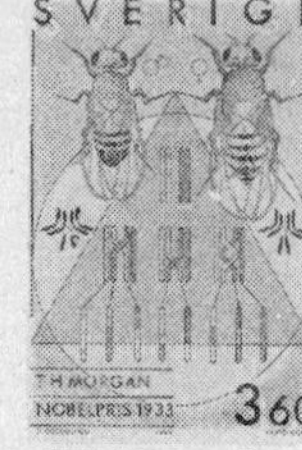

427 "Drosophila melanogaster" (T. H. Morgan, 1933)

1989. Christmas. Multicoloured.

1476 2 k. 10 Type 426 .. 40 15
1477 2 k. 10 Candelabra and food 40 15
1478 2 k. 10 Star, poinsettia and bowl of porridge .. 40 15
1479 2 k. 10 Decorated tree and straw donkey 40 15
1480 2 k. 10 Girl watching tele-vision 40 15
1481 2 k. 10 Family with present 40 15

Nos. 1476/81 were printed together se-tenant, forming a composite design.

1989. Nobel Prize Winners for Medicine.

1482 427 3 k. 60 brn, yell & bl 75 30
1483 – 3 k. 60 yell, bl & red 65 30
1484 – 3 k. 60 multicoloured 65 30
1485 – 3 k. 60 multicoloured 65 30

DESIGNS: No. 1483, X-ray diffractogram and D.N.A. molecule (F.H.C. Crick, J.D. Watson and M.H.F. Wilkins, 1962); 1484, D.N.A. molcule cut by restriction enzyme (W. Arber, D. Nathans and H.O. Smith, 1978); 1485, Maize kernels (Barbara McClintock, 1983).

428 Angso

1990. National Parks (2nd series).

1486 428 2 k. 50 blue, grn & red 60 20
1487 – 2 k. 50 red, green & bl 45 15
1488 – 3 k. 70 bl, brn & grn 70 35
1489 – 4 k. 10 bl, grn & brn 70 45
1490 – 4 k. 80 green, brn & bl 85 50

DESIGNS: No. 1487, Pieljekaise; 1488, Muddus; 1489, Padjelanta; 1490, Sanfjallet.

429 Lumberjacks

1990. Cent of Industrial Safety Inspectorate.

1491 429 2 k. 50 blue and brown 45 20

430 Postal Museum, Stockholm

431 Carved Bone Head Head and Cast Dragon

1990. Europa. Post Office Buildings.

1492 430 2 k. 50 brn, orge & bl 45 20
1493 – 3 k. 80 multicoloured 70 35
1494 – 3 k. 80 multicoloured 70 35

DESIGNS: No. 1493, Sollebrunn Post Office; 1494, Vasteras Post Office.

1990. Vikings. Multicoloured.

1495 2 k. 50 Type 431 .. 45 25
1496 2 k. 50 Returning Viking longships (34 × 29 mm) 60 25
1497 2 k. 50 Wooden houses (34 × 29 mm) 45 25
1498 2 k. 50 Bronze figurine of God of Fertility and silver cross 45 25
1499 2 k. 50 Crosier and gold embroidered deer .. 60 25
1500 2 k. 50 Vikings in round-ship (34 × 29 mm) .. 60 25
1501 2 k. 50 Vikings disem-barking (34 × 29 mm) .. 45 25
1502 2 k. 50 Vikings swords .. 45 25

Nos. 1496/7 and 1500/1 form a composite design.

432 Worker collecting Pollen

433 Bow of "Wasa" and Museum

1990. Rebate stamps. Honey Bees. Mult.

1503 2 k. 30 Type 432 .. 40 20
1504 2 k. 30 Worker on bilberry 40 20
1505 2 k. 30 Worker flying back to hive 40 20
1506 2 k. 30 Beehive 40 20
1507 2 k. 30 Bees building honeycombs 40 20
1508 2 k. 30 Drone 40 20
1509 2 k. 30 Queen 40 20
1510 2 k. 30 Swarm on branch 40 20
1511 2 k. 30 Beekeeper collect-ing frame 40 20
1512 2 k. 30 Pot of honey .. 40 20

1990. Opening of New "Wasa" (17th-century ship of the line) Museum.

1513 433 2 k. 50 black and red 55 20
1514 – 4 k. 60 blue and red .. 95 50

DESIGNS: 4 k. 60, Stern of "Wasa" and museum.

434 Endurance Event

1990. World Equestrian Games, Stockholm. Multicoloured.

1515 3 k. 80 Type 434 .. 70 35
1516 3 k. 80 Mark Todd on Carisma jumping wall (3-day event) .. 70 35
1517 3 k. 80 John Whitaker on Next Milton jumping fence (Show jumping) 70 35
1518 3 k. 80 Louise Nathorst (Dressage) 70 35
1519 3 k. 80 Team vaulting .. 70 35
1520 3 k. 80 Pahlsson brothers driving four-in-hand .. 70 35

435 Papermaking, 1600

436 "Dearest Brothers, Sisters and Friends"

1990. Centenary of Swedish Pulp and Paper Industry. Multicoloured.

1521 2 k. 50 Type 435 .. 45 20
1522 2 k. 50 Crown watermark 45 20
1523 2 k. 50 Foreign news-papers using Swedish newsprint 45 20
1524 2 k. 50 Rolls of paper .. 45 20

1990. 250th Birth Anniv of Carl Michael Bellman (poet) (1525/7) and Birth Centenary of Evert Taube (poet) (1528/30). Designs showing illustrations to various poems.

1525 436 2 k. 50 brown & black 45 25
1526 – 2 k. 50 multicoloured 45 25
1527 – 2 k. 50 black, bl & red 45 25
1528 – 2 k. 50 multicoloured 45 25
1529 – 2 k. 50 multicoloured 60 25
1530 – 2 k. 50 multicoloured 45 25

DESIGNS—As Type 436: No. 1527, "Fredman in the Gutter"; 1528, "Happy Baker of San Remo"; 1530, "Violava". 40 × 43 mm: 1526, "Proud City"; 1529, "At Sea".

437 Oved Castle

1990.

1531 437 40 k. brown, blk & red 7·50 3·75

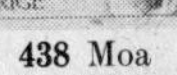

438 Moa Martinson **439** Box Camera with Bellows

1990. Birth Centenary of Moa Martinson (novelist).

1532 **438** 2 k. 50 black and red 45 20
1533 – 2 k. 50 black & violet 45 20

DESIGN: No. 1533, Fredrika and Sofi bathing (from "Women and Apple Trees").

1990. 150 Years of Photography. Mult.

1534 2 k. 50 Type **439** 45 20
1535 2 k. 50 August Strindberg (self-photograph) .. 45 20
1536 2 k. 50 Modern 35 mm camera 45 20

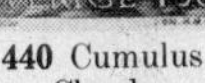

440 Cumulus Clouds **441** Christmas Cactus

1990. Clouds.

1537 **440** 4 k. 50 multicoloured 75 20
1538 – 4 k. 70 black and blue 1·00 50
1539 – 4 k. 90 blue, grn & brn 85 50
1540 – 5 k. 20 blue & ultram 90 50

DESIGNS: 4 k. 70, Cumulonimbus; 4 k. 90, Cirus uncinus; 5 k. 20, Altocumulus lenticularis.

1990. Christmas. Flowers. Multicoloured.

1541 2 k. 30 Type **441** .. 40 20
1542 2 k. 30 Christmas rose .. 40 20
1543 2 k. 30 Azalea 40 20
1544 2 k. 30 Amaryllis .. 40 20
1545 2 k. 30 Hyacinth .. 40 20
1546 2 k. 30 Poinsettia .. 40 20

442 Par Lagerkvist (1951)

1990. Nobel Prize Winners for Literature.

1547 **442** 3 k. 80 blue 70 35
1548 – 3 k. 80 red 70 35
1549 – 3 k. 80 green .. 70 35
1550 – 3 k. 80 violet .. 70 35

DESIGNS: No. 1548, Ernest Hemingway (1954); 1549, Albert Camus (1957); 1550, Boris Pasternak (1958).

443 European Catfish **444** Carta Marina, 1572 (Olaus Magnus)

1991. Fresh-water Fishes.

1551 **443** 2 k. 50 blk, grn & brn 45 20
1552 – 2 k. 50 blk, grn & brn 45 20
1553 – 5 k. black, blue & brn 90 45
1554 – 5 k. 40 blk, vio & red 1·00 50
1555 – 5 k. 50 black & green 1·00 50
1556 – 5 k. 60 blk, bl & orge 1·10 55

DESIGNS: No. 1552, European catfish (different); 1553, Siberian spiny loach; 1554, Gudgeon; 1555, Bearded stone loach; 1556, Verkhovka.

Nos. 1551/2 form a composite design of two catfish.

1991. Maps. Multicoloured.

1557 5 k. Type **444** 90 45
1558 5 k. Sweden, Denmark and Norway, 1662 (A. Bureus and J. Blaeu) (40 × 43 mm) 90 45
1559 5 k. Star globe, 1759 (Anders Akerman) .. 90 45
1560 5 k. Relief map of Areskutan, 1938 .. 90 45
1561 5 k. Stockholm old town, 1989 (40 × 43 mm) .. 90 45
1562 5 k. Bed-rock map of Areskutan, 1984 .. 90 45

445 Queen Silvia **447** Seglora Church

446 Drottningholm Palace (after Erik Dahlbergh)

1991.

1564 – 2 k. 80 blue 55 30
1565 – 2 k. 90 green .. 50 25
1566 – 3 k. 20 violet .. 55 25
1568 **445** 5 k. purple 90 45
1569 6 k. red .. .. 1·10 55
1570 6 k. 50 violet .. 1·10 55

DESIGN: 2 k. 80 to 3 k. 20, King Carl XVI Gustav.

1991. 10th Anniv of Royal Residence at Drottningholm Palace.

1576 **446** 25 k. ochre, blk & grn 4·50 2·25

1991. Rebate stamps. Centenary of Skansen Park, Stockholm. Multicoloured.

1577 2 k. 40 Type **447** .. 45 20
1578 2 k. 40 Celebration of Swedish Flag and National Days at Skansen 45 20
1579 2 k. 40 Wedding at Skansen 45 20
1580 2 k. 40 Animals, Skansen Zoo 45 20

448 Park Entrance **449** Polar Bears

1991. Centenary of Public Amusement Parks. Each blue. Imperf

1581 2 k. 50 Type **448** .. 50 25
1582 2 k. 50 Dancers and violinist 50 25

1991. Nordic Countries' Postal Co-operation. Tourism. Animals in Kolmarden Zoo.

1583 **449** 2 k. 50 blk, brn & bl 50 25
1584 – 4 k. red and purple .. 75 35

DESIGN: 4 k. Dolphins and trainer.

450 "Hermes" Rocket **451** Magda Julin (figure skating, Antwerp, 1920)

1991. Europa. Europe in Space. Mult.

1585 4 k. Type **450** .. 75 35
1586 4 k. "Freja" Northern Lights research satellite 75 35
1587 4 k. "Tele-X" television satellite 75 35

1991. Olympic Games Gold Medallists (1st issue). Multicoloured.

1588 2 k. 50 Type **451** 50 25
1589 2 k. 50 Toini Gustafsson (cross-country skiing, Grenoble, 1968) .. 50 25
1590 2 k. 50 Agneta Andersson and Anna Olsson (canoeing, Los Angeles, 1984) 50 25
1591 2 k. 50 Ulrika Knape (high diving, Munich, 1972) 50 25

See also Nos. 1619/22 and 1635/8.

452 Spetal Mine, Norberg (after Carl David af Uhr)

1991. Bergslagen Iron Industry. Mult.

1592 2 k. 50 Type **452** 50 25
1593 2 k. 50 Walloon smithy, Forsmark Mill (after J. Wilhem Wallender) .. 50 25
1594 2 k. 50 Forge (27 × 24 mm) 50 25
1595 2 k. 50 Foundry (after Johann Ahlback) (27 × 24 mm) 50 25
1596 2 k. 50 Dannemora Mine (after Elias Martin) (27 × 37 mm) 50 25
1597 2 k. 50 Pershyttan Mill (27 × 37 mm) 50 25

453 Stromsholm Castle

1991.

1598 **453** 10 k. green and black 1·90 95

454 Lena Philipsson **455** Close-up of Gustav III

1991. Rock and Pop Music. Multicoloured.

1599 2 k. 50 Type **454** .. 50 25
1600 2 k. 50 Roxette (duo) .. 50 25
1601 2 k. 50 Jerry Williams .. 50 25

1991. 70th Birthday of Czeslaw Slania (engraver). Designs showing "Coronation of King Gustav III" by Carl Gustav Pilo.

1602 **455** 10 k. blue .. .. 1·90 95
1603 – 10 k. violet .. .. 1·90 95
1604 – 10 k. black .. .. 1·90 95

DESIGNS: As T **455**—No. 1603, Close-up of lowering of crown onto King's head. 76 × 44 mm—1604, Complete picture.

456 Mans and Mari from "Spring to Winter" (Kaj Beckman) **457** Henri Dunant (founder of Red Cross), 1901

1991. Christmas. Illustrations from children's books. Multicoloured.

1605 2 k. 30 Type **456** .. 45 20
1606 2 k. 30 Family dancing round Christmas tree ("Peter and Lottas's Christmas", Elsa Beskow) 45 20
1607 2 k. 30 Dressed cat by Christmas tree ("Pettersson gets a Christmas Visit", Sven Nordqvist) 45 20
1608 2 k. 30 Girl by bed ("Little Anna's Christmas Present", Lasse Sandberg) .. 45 20

1991. Nobel Prize Winners for Peace.

1609 **457** 4 k. red 75 35
1610 – 4 k. green 75 35
1611 – 4 k. blue 75 35
1612 – 4 k. lilac 75 35

DESIGNS: No. 1610, Albert Schweitzer (medical missionary), 1953; 1611, Alva Myrdal (disarmament negotiator), 1982; 1612, Andrei Sakharov (human rights activist), 1975.

458 Mulle, the Forest Elf, with Children **459** Roe Buck

1992. Centenary of Outdoor Life Association.

1613 **458** 2 k. 30 blk, red & grn 45 20

1992. Wildlife.

1614 **459** 2 k. 80 brn, blk & grn 55 25
1615 – 2 k. 80 blk, brn & grn 55 25
1617 – 6 k. brown and black 1·10 55
1618 – 7 k. black and green 1·25 60

DESIGNS—As T **459**: No. 1615, Roe deer with fawn. 20 × 28 mm: 1617, Eurasian red squirrel; 1618, Elk.

1992. Olympic Games Gold Medallists (2nd issue). As T **451**. Multicoloured.

1619 2 k. 80 Gunde Svan (cross-country skiing, Sarajevo, 1984, and Calgary, 1988) .. 55 25
1620 2 k. 80 Thomas Wassberg (cross-country skiing, Lake Placid, 1980, and Sarajevo, 1984) .. 55 25
1621 2 k. 80 Tomas Gustafson (speed skating, Sarajevo, 1984, and Calgary, 1988) .. 55 25
1622 2 k. 80 Ingemar Stenmark (slalom, Lake Placid, 1980) 55 25

460 Gunnar Nordahl (Sweden)

1992. European Football Championships, Sweden. Each blue and green.

1623 2 k. 80 Type **460** .. 50 25
1624 2 k. 80 Lothar Matthaus (Germany) and Tomas Brolin (Sweden) .. 50 25

461 1855 3 s. Green

1992. Stamp Year.

1625 **461** 2 k. 80 grn, yell & blk 50 25
1626 4 k. 50 grn, yell & blk 80 40
1627 – 5 k. 50 yell, grey & blk 95 45

DESIGN: 5 k. 50, 1857 3 s. yellow error.

462 "Sprengtporten" (frigate), 1785 **463** Rabbit (Emma Westerberg)

1992. Europa. 500th Anniv of Discovery of America by Columbus. Multicoloured.

1628 4 k. 50 Type **462** .. 90 45
1629 4 k. 50 "Superb" (brig), 1855 .. .. 90 45
1630 4 k. 50 "Big T" (yacht) (competitor in Discovery Race) .. 90 45

1992. Rebate stamps. Centenary of "Kamratposten" (children's magazine). Multicoloured.

1631 2 k. 50 Type **463** .. 45 20
1632 2 k. 50 Horses (Helena Johansson) 45 20
1633 2 k. 50 Kitten (Sabina Ostermark) 45 20
1634 2 k. 50 Elephant (Hanna Bengtsson) 45 20

1992. Olympic Games Gold Medallists (3rd series). As T **451**. Multicoloured.

1635 5 k. 50 Gunnar Larsson (swimming, Munich, 1972) 95 45
1636 5 k. 50 Bernt Johansson (cycling, Montreal, 1976) 95 45
1637 5 k. 50 Anders Garderud (steeplechase, Montreal, 1976) 95 45
1638 5 k. 50 Gert Fredriksson (canoeing, London, 1948) 95 45

464 Karlberg Castle

1992.

1639 **464** 20 k. black, green & bl 3·50 1·75

465 Hand holding Flower

466 Gustaf Dalen's Sun Valve and First Automated Lighthouse, Gasfeten

1992. Greetings stamps. Multicoloured.

1640 2 k. 80 Type **465** .. 50 25
1641 2 k. 80 Wedge of cheese ("Lyckans ost") .. 50 25
1642 2 k. 80 New-born baby ("Lev val!") 50 25
1643 2 k. 80 Writing with feather ("Gratulerar") 50 25

1992. Centenary of Patent and Registration Office.

1644 **466** 2 k. 80 black and blue 50 25

467 Riksdag (Parliament), Helgeandsholmen Island

1992. 88th Interparliamentary Union Conference, Stockholm.

1645 **467** 2 k. 80 violet on buff 50 25

468 "Kitchen Maid" (Rembrandt)

469 Plateosaurus

1992. Bicentenary of National Museum of Fine Arts. Multicoloured.

1646 5 k. 50 Type **468** .. 95 45
1647 5 k. 50 "Triumph of Venus" (Francois Boucher) (40 × 43 mm) 95 45
1648 5 k. 50 "Portrait of a Girl" (Albrecht Durer) 95 45
1649 5 k. 50 Rorstrand vase decorated by Erik Wahlberg 95 45
1650 5 k. 50 "Seine Motif" (Carl Fredrik Hill) (40 × 43 mm) 95 45
1651 5 k. 50 "Sergel in his Studio" (Carl Larsson) 95 45

1992. Stamp Day. Prehistoric Animals. Mult.

1652 2 k. 80 Type **469** .. 50 25
1653 2 k. 80 Crocodile ("Thoracosaurus scanicus") .. 50 25
1654 2 k. 80 Woolly-haired rhino ("Coelodonta antiquitatis") 50 25
1655 2 k. 80 Mammoth ("Mammuthus primigenius") 50 25

470 Volvo "PV831", 1950

471 Osprey ("Pandion haliaetus")

1992. Swedish Cars.

1656 **470** 4 k. blue 70 35
1657 – 4 k. green and blue .. 70 35

DESIGN: No. 1657, Saab "92", 1950.

1992. Birds of the Baltic.

1658 **471** 4 k. 50 black and blue 80 40
1659 – 4 k. 50 brn, blk & bl 80 40
1660 – 4 k. 50 deep brown, brown and blue .. 80 40
1661 – 4 k. 50 blk, brn & bl 80 40

DESIGNS: No. 1659, Black-tailed godwit ("Limosa limosa"); 1660, Goosander ("Mergus merganser"); 1661, Common shelducks ("Tadorna tadorna").

472 "Meeting of Joachim and Anna"

473 Walcott

1992. Christmas. Icons. Multicoloured.

1662 2 k. 30 Type **472** .. 40 20
1663 2 k. 30 "Madonna and Child" 40 20
1664 2 k. 30 "Archangel Gabriel" (head) .. 40 20
1665 2 k. 30 "Saint Nicholas" (½-length portrait) .. 40 20

1992. Award of Nobel Literature Prize to Derek Walcott.

1666 **473** 5 k. 50 pur, bl & brn 95 45
1667 – 5 k. 50 pur, brn & bl 95 45

DESIGN: No. 1667, Palm trees, ocean and text.

474 Brown Bear Cubs

1993. Wildlife.

1668 **474** 2 k. 90 brown & black 50 25
1669 – 2 k. 90 brown & black 50 25
1671 – 3 k. multicoloured .. 50 25
1672 – 5 k. 80 blk, grey & brn 1·00 50
1673 – 12 k. brown, bl & red 2·10 1·00

DESIGNS—As T **474**: No. 1669 Brown bear. 27 × 21 mm. No. 1671, Polecat; 1672, Wolf. 21 × 27 mm. No. 1673, Lynx.

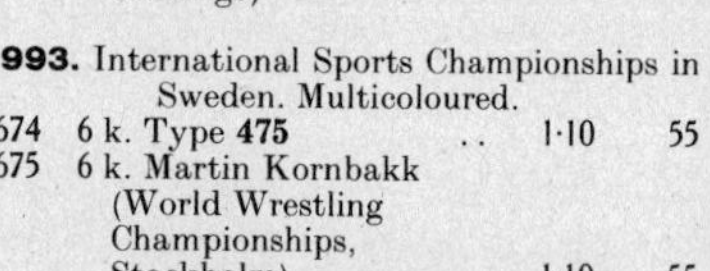

475 Big-bird Glider (World Gliding Championships, Borlange)

476 Gooseberries

1993. International Sports Championships in Sweden. Multicoloured.

1674 6 k. Type **475** .. 1·10 55
1675 6 k. Martin Kornbakk (World Wrestling Championships, Stockholm) .. .. 1·10 55
1676 6 k. Jorgen Persson (World Table Tennis Championships, Gothenburg) .. 1·10 55
1677 6 k. Lars Erik Andersson (European Bowling Championships, Malmo) 1·10 55
1678 6 k. Per Carlen (World Handball Championships, Gothenburg) .. 1·10 55
1679 6 k. Marie Helene Westin (World Cross-country Skiing Championships, Falun) .. .. 1·10 55

Nos. 1675/9 show Swedish competitors.

1993. Fruits.

1680 **476** 2 k. 40 green .. 40 15
1681 – 2 k. 40 green .. 40 15
1682 – 2 k. 40 red .. 40 15

DESIGNS: No. 1681, Pears; 1682, Cherries.

477 The Creation (relief, Uppsala Cathedral)

478 "Poseidon" (Carl Milles)

1993. 400th Anniv of Uppsala Convocation.

1683 **477** 2 k. 90 violet and buff 50 15
1684 – 2 k. 90 red and buff .. 50 15

DESIGN: No. 1684, Uppsala Cathedral before fire of 1702.

1993. Nordic Countries' Postal Co-operation. Tourism. Tourist attractions in Gothenburg.

1685 **478** 3 k. 50 green, yell & bl 60 35
1686 – 3 k. 50 indigo, yellow and blue 60 35

DESIGN: No. 1686, Liseberg Loop (fairground ride).

479 Ox-eye Daisies

480 "Oguasark" (Olle Baertling)

1993. Rebate stamps. Flowers. Mult.

1687 2 k. 60 Type **479** .. 45 15
1688 2 k. 60 Poppies .. 45 15
1689 2 k. 60 Buttercups .. 45 15
1690 2 k. 60 Bluebells .. 45 15

1993. Europa. Contemporary Art. Mult.

1691 5 k. Type **480** 85 50
1692 5 k. "Ade-Ledic-Nander II" (Oyvind Fahlstrom) (horiz) .. 85 50
1693 5 k. "The Cubist Chair" (Otto Carlsund) .. 85 50

481 Swallowtail ("Papilio machaon")

1993. Butterflies. Multicoloured.

1694 6 k. Type **481** .. .. 1·00 70
1695 6 k. Camberwell beauty ("Nymphalis antiopa") 1·00 70
1696 6 k. Moorland clouded yellow ("Colias palaeno") .. 1·00 70
1697 6 k. Scarce fritillary ("Euphydryas maturna") .. .. 1·00 70

482 Fireworks ("Hurray")

483 Red-breasted Merganser ("Mergus serrator")

1993. Greetings Stamps. Multicoloured.

1698 2 k. 90 Type **482** .. 50 15
1699 2 k. 90 "Hor av Dig" ("Get in touch") .. 50 15
1700 2 k. 90 "Tycker om Dig" ("I like you") .. 50 15
1701 2 k. 90 "Lycka Till" ("Good luck") .. 50 15

1993. Sea Birds. Multicoloured.

1702 5 k. Type **483** 85 50
1703 5 k. Velvet scoter ("Melanitta fusca") .. 85 50
1704 5 k. Tufted duck ("Aythya fuligula") .. 85 50
1705 5 k. Eider ("Somateria mollissima") .. 85 50

484 Surveyor, 1643 (cover of Johan Mansson's nautical book)

485 King Carl Gustav

1993. 350th Anniv of Hydrographic Service.

1706 **484** 2 k. 90 brn, bl & blk 50 15
1707 – 2 k. 90 brn, bl & blk 50 15

DESIGN: No. 1707, Survey ship "Nils Stromcrona", 1993.

1993. 20th Anniv of Accession of King Carl XVI Gustav and Queen Silvia's 50th Birthday. Multicoloured.

1708 8 k. Type **485** .. 1·40 80
1709 10 k. King Carl Gustav wearing medals .. 1·75 1·00
1710 10 k. Queen Silvia .. 1·75 1·00
1711 12 k. Family group and Stockholm and Drottningholm Palaces (75 × 44 mm) .. .. 2·10 1·25

486 Plaited Heart

487 Stockholm City Hall

1993. Christmas.

1712 **486** 2 k. 40 green .. 40 10
1713 – 2 k. 40 red 40 10

DESIGN: No. 1713, Straw goat.

1993. Award of Nobel Literature Prize to Toni Morrison.

1714 **487** 6 k. red and blue .. 1·00 60
1715 – 6 k. brown and red .. 1·00 60

DESIGN: No. 1715, Toni Morrison.

488 Victoria Plums

489 North Sweden Horse's Head

1994. Fruits.

1716	488	2 k. 80 multicoloured	50	15
1717	–	2 k. 80 multicoloured	50	15
1718	–	2 k. 80 lt green & grn	50	15

DESIGNS: No. 1717, Opal plums; 1718, "James Grieve" apples.

1994. Domestic Animals.

1719	489	3 k. 20 brown, agate and red	55	15
1720	–	3 k. 20 brown, agate and red	55	15
1721	–	3 k. 20 blk, brn & bl	55	15
1722	–	6 k. 40 black & green	1·10	65

DESIGNS—VERT. 1720, North Sweden horses in harness. HORIZ. 1721, Gotland sheep; 1722, Mountain cow.

490 Mother Svea and European Union Emblem

1994. Single European Market.

1723	490	5 k. blue	85	50

OFFICIAL STAMPS

O 6. O 17.

1874.

O 27.	O 6.	2 ore orange	1·40	1·75
O 28.		3 ore brown	1·75	1·75
O 29b		4 ore grey	1·25	25
O 30b.		5 ore green	1·25	10
O 31.		6 ore lilac	12·00	19·00
O 32.		6 ore grey	£250	85·00
O 33b.		10 ore red	1·50	10
O 34.		12 ore blue	19·00	10·50
O 35.		20 ore red	70·00	90
O 36.		20 ore blue	1·40	20
O 37.		24 ore yellow	17·00	8·75
O 38b.		30 ore brown	8·75	40
O 39.		50 ore red	85·00	10·50
O 40.		50 ore grey	7·00	1·00
O 41c.		1 k. blue and brown	7·00	1·25

1889. Surch. with value in ornamental scroll between two crowns.

O 42.	O 6.	10 ore on 12 ore blue	8·75	8·75
O 43.		10 ore on 24 ore yell.	12·00	16·00

1910.

O 87.	O 17.	1 ore black	15	20
O 101.		2 ore yellow	20	5
O 102.		3 ore brown	25	45
O 103.		4 ore lilac	20	20
O 104.		5 ore green	20	5
O 105.		7 ore green	40	50
O 91.		8 ore red	55	70
O 107.		10 ore red	20	5
O 108.		12 ore red	20	10
O 109.		15 ore brown	20	5
O 110.		20 ore blue	20	5
O 111.		25 ore orange	80	30
O 112.		30 ore brown	35	25
O 113.		35 ore violet	70	30
O 114.		50 ore grey	1·50	90
O 98.		1 k. black on yellow	7·00	5·50
O 99.		5 k. purple on yellow	8·75	4·50

POSTAGE DUE STAMPS

D 6.

1874.

D 27.	D 6.	1 ore black	2·10	2·10
D 28a.		3 ore red	3·50	3·50
D 29a.		5 ore brown	2·00	2·25
D 30a.		6 ore yellow	2·25	2·25
D 31a.		12 ore red	7·00	7·00
D 32.		20 ore blue	2·50	2·50
D 33.		24 ore lilac	12·00	12·00
D 34.		24 ore grey	50·00	48·00
D 35.		30 ore green	2·50	2·50
D 36.		50 ore brown	4·25	4·25
D 37.		1 k. blue and brown	22·00	22·00

SWITZERLAND Pt. 8

A federal republic of C. Europe between France, Germany and Italy.

100 rappen = 1 franken.
100 centimes = 1 franc.
100 centesimi = 1 franco.

These are expressions of the same currency in three languages.

For the issues under the Cantonal Administrations of Basel, Geneva and Zurich, see Stanley Gibbons' Part 8 (Italy and Switzerland) Catalogue.

1.

6.

1850. Inscr. "ORTS-POST". Imperf.

1.	1.	2½ r. black and red	£1500	£1000

1850. As T 1, but inscr. "POSTE LOCALE". Imperf.

3.	1.	2½ r. black and red	£1200	£900

1850. As T 1 but inscr "RAYON I, II, or III". Imperf.

6	1	5 r. red, black & blue (I)	£1000	£300
13		5 r. red and blue (I)	£350	90·00
10		10 r. red, black & yell (II)	£600	80·00
23		15 rp. red (III)	£1400	80·00
21		15 cts. red (III)	£8000	£700

1854. Imperf.

46	6	2 r. grey	£150	£300
47a		5 r. brown	£100	5·00
48		10 r. blue	£100	4·75
49a		15 r. rose	£190	25·00
50		20 r. orange	£225	35·00
51		40 r. green	£225	30·00
38		1 f. lilac	£700	£450

7.

9.

10.

1862. Perf.

52	7	2 c. grey	45·00	1·60
61		2 c. brown	1·00	25
61a		2 c. bistre	1·50	75
53		3 c. black	6·00	65·00
54		5 c. brown	1·60	10
55		10 c. blue	£180	10
62		10 c. pink	1·60	10
63		15 c. yellow	2·00	15·00
56a		20 c. orange	1·00	1·00
64		25 c. green	1·00	75
57		30 c. red	£700	15·00
65a		30 c. blue	£250	2·25
58		40 c. green	£700	35·00
66		40 c. grey	1·00	45·00
67		50 c. purple	35·00	10·00
59		60 c. bronze	£400	85·00
60a		1 f. gold	12·00	30·00

1882.

126B	9	2 c. brown	80	15
127cB		3 c. brown	1·50	1·50
128d		5 c. purple	11·00	10
196		5 c. green	3·00	10
130e		10 c. red	1·75	10
131e		12 c. blue	3·50	10
132		15 c. yellow	£110	10·00
133b		15 c. violet	25·00	70
214	10	20 c. orange	2·00	1·50
146cB		25 c. green	7·50	25
207		25 c. blue	5·00	50
202		30 c. brown	5·50	1·25
209		40 c. grey	28·00	5·50
150B		50 c. blue	38·00	2·50
218		50 c. green	5·00	2·50
138a		1 f. purple	£200	1·50
161		1 f. red	4·50	12·00
139		3 f. brown	£150	5·00

11.

1900. 25th Anniv. of U.P.U.

191.	11.	5 c. green	3·00	50
189.		10 c. red	10·00	40
190.		25 c. blue	15·00	7·50

14. Tell's Son. 15. 17.

1907.

241	14	2 c. yellow	20	20
242		3 c. brown	25	5·75
243		5 c. green	2·50	10
244	15	10 c. red	2·00	10
245		12 c. brown	30	2·00
246		15 c. mauve	3·50	5·00
248	17	20 c. yellow and red	1·60	20
249		25 c. blue and deep blue	1·60	10
250		30 c. green and brown	1·50	10
251		35 c. yellow and green	1·50	15
252		40 c. yellow and purple	13·00	20
253a		50 c. green & dp green	6·50	30
254		70 c. yellow and brown	55·00	2·50
255		1 f. green and purple	6·50	15
256		3 f. yellow and bistre	£175	65

For further stamps in Type 17 see Nos. 314, 1910 issue.

18. Cord in front of shaft.

19.

1908.

257.	18.	2 c. bistre	25	50
258.		3 c. violet	15	5·50
259.		5 c. green	2·00	10
260.	19.	10 c. red	60	10
261.		12 c. brown	75	10
262.		15 c. mauve	23·00	45

20a. Cord behind shaft.

21. William Tell.

1910.

266	20a	2 c. bistre	10	10
292		2½ c. purple	10	60
325b		2½ c. olive on buff	40	1·00
264		3 c. violet	10	10
293		3 c. brown	10	10
325c		3 c. blue on buff	2·00	4·50
267		5 c. green	55	10
309		5 c. orange on buff	10	10
326		5 c. lilac on buff	10	10
326b		5 c. purple on buff	10	10
326c		5 c. green on buff	25	10
294		7½ c. grey	1·00	10
326e		7½ c. green on buff	30	1·75
281	21	10 c. red on buff	45	10
310		10 c. green on buff	10	10
326g		10 c. violet on buff	1·00	10
282		12 c. brown on buff	35	3·25
295		13 c. green on buff	1·40	20
285		15 c. violet on buff	2·50	10
326i		15 c. red on buff	3·25	1·75
311		20 c. violet on buff	2·00	10
328		20 c. red on buff	35	10
313		25 c. red on buff	1·00	35
328c		25 c. brown on buff	3·25	75
329		30 c. blue on buff	8·00	10
315	17	40 c. blue	1·75	10
330		40 c. green & mauve	22·00	10
296		60 c. brown	8·50	10
331		70 c. buff and violet	15·00	60
297		80 c. buff and grey	9·50	20

22. The Mythen.

1914. Mountain views.

284.	22.	3 f. green	£800	3·00
298.		3 f. red	90·00	35·00
285.	–	5 f. blue	30·00	1·25
286.	–	10 f. purple	£120	1·25
331b.	–	10 f. green	£225	20·00

DESIGNS: 5 f. The Rutli. 10 f. The Jungfrau.

1915. Surch.

287.	20a.	1 c. on 2 c. bistre	10	15
303.		2½ c. on 3 c. brown	10	15
304.		3 c. on 2½ c. olive on buff	10	1·00
304a.		5 c. on 2 c. bistre	10	1·00
305.		5 c. on 7½ c. grey	10	10
305c.		5 c. on 7½ c. grn. on buff	15	4·75
306.	21.	10 c. on 13 c. olive on buff	15	1·40
288.	19.	13 c. on 12 c. brown	10	4·75
289.	21.	13 c. on 12 c. brn. on buff	20	70
307a.		20 c. on 15 c. vio. on buff	60	1·25
308.	17.	20 c. on 25 c. blue	15	25
290.		80 c. on 70 c. yell. & brn.	30·00	6·50

1919. Air. Optd with wings and propeller.

298a	17	30 c. green and brown	£120	£1100
299		50 c. green & dp green	40·00	85·00

30.

31.

32.

1919. Peace Celebrations

300.	30.	7½ c. olive and grey	65	1·10
301.	31.	10 c. yellow and red	1·00	3·25
302.	32.	15 c. yellow and violet	2·00	90

34.

35.

36.

37.

1923. Air.

317	34	15 c. green and red	2·75	4·25
317ab		20 c. green & dp grn	30	15
318		25 c. grey and blue	7·00	11·00
319	35	35 c. cinnamon & brn	14·00	35·00
320		40 c. lilac and violet	13·00	32·00
321	36	45 c. red and blue	1·50	4·50
322a		50 c. grey and red	1·25	75
323a	37	65 c. blue and lt blue	2·00	5·00
324		75 c. orange & purple	16·00	55·00
325a		1 f. violet and purple	3·00	1·75

38.

40. Seat of first U.P.U. Congress.

1924.

332	38	90 c. red & green on grn	14·00	20
333		1 f. 20 red and lake on pink	6·00	45
334		1 f. 50 red & blue on bl	22·00	60
335a		2 f. red & black on grey	45·00	2·25

1924. 50th Anniv. of U.P.U.

336.	–	20 c. red	40	40
337.	40.	30 c. blue	1·00	3·50

DESIGN: 20 c. As T 40 but with different frame.

INDEX

Countries can be quickly located by referring to the index at the end of this volume.

41.

Design: 2 f. Bird with letter in beak.

1929. Air.
339a 41 35 c. bistre and ochre 6·50 35·00
340a 40 c. blue and green .. 35·00 30·00
341a – 2 f. chocolate and brown on cinnamon 10·00 5·50

43. The Mythen.

1931.
342. 43. 3 f. brown .. .. 60·00 1·60

44. A Symbol of Peace.

45. "After the Darkness, Light".

46. Peace and the Air Post.

1932. International Disarmament Conference.
343 44 5 c. green (postage) .. 10 10
344 10 c. orange 20 10
~~345~~ 20 c. red 30 10
346 30 c. blue .. .. 3·00 30
347 60 c. brown .. .. 17·00 1·50
348 45 1 f. grey and blue .. 22·00 3·50
349 46 15 c. light green and green (air) .. .. 30 1·25
350 20 c. flesh and red .. 65 2·00
351 90 c. light blue and blue 8·00 22·00

47. Louis Favre (engineer).

48. Staubbach Falls.

1932. 50th Anniv of St. Gotthard Tunnel.
352 47 10 c. brown 10 10
353 – 20 c. red 25 20
354 – 30 c. blue .. .. 40 1·25
Designs: 20 c. Alfred Escher (President of Railway). 30 c. Emil Welti (founder).

1934. Landscapes.
355. 48. 3 c. olive .. .. 25 1·50
~~356.~~ – 5 c. green 25 10
~~357.~~ – 10 c. violet 50 10
358. – 15 c. orange 55 80
~~359.~~ – 20 c. red 80 10
360. – 25 c. brown .. .. 10·00 4·00
~~361.~~ – 30 c. blue .. .. 30·00 40
Designs: 5 c. Mt. Pilatus. 10 c. Chillon Castle and Dents du Midi. 15 c. Grimsel Pass. 20 c. Landwasser Viaduct, Filisur (St. Gotthard Railway). 25 c. Viamala Gorge. 30 c. Rhine Falls near Schaffhausen.

1935. Air. Surch.
362 34 10 on 15 c. green and red 5·00 30·00
363 46 10 on 15 c. light green and green 40 40
364 10 on 20 c. flesh and red 50 1·60
381 37 10 on 65 c. blue & lt blue 20 30
365 46 30 on 90 c. lt blue & blue 3·50 12·00
366 40 on 20 c. flesh and red 4·00 11·00
367 40 on 90 c. lt blue & blue 4·00 10·00

51. Freiburg Cowherd.

52. Staubbach Falls.

1936. National Defence Fund.
368. 51. 10 c.+5 c. purple .. 35 40
369. 20 c.+10 c. red .. .. 70 2·75
370. 30 c.+10 c. blue .. 3·50 12·00

1936. As T 48 but redrawn with figure of value lower down. Various landscapes.
371 52 3 c. olive 10 10
~~372~~ – 5 c. green 10 10
489 – 5 c. brown 20 10
~~373b~~ – 10 c. purple 35 10
~~373d~~ – 10 c. brown 10 10
~~490~~ – 10 c. green 30 10
374 – 15 c. orange 40 15
~~375b~~ – 20 c. red (Railway) .. 7·00 10
~~375d~~ – 20 c. red (Lake) .. 15 10
491 – 20 c. brown 60 10
376 – 25 c. brown 60 30
492 – 25 c. red .. .. 1·50 1·00
~~377~~ – 30 c. blue .. .. 1·00 10
378 – 35 c. green .. .. 1·00 50
~~379~~ – 40 c. grey .. .. 7·00 10
~~494~~ – 40 c. blue .. .. 21·00 20
Designs: 3 c. to 20 c. (No. 375b) As Nos. 355/9. 20 c. (Nos. 375d, 491) Lake Lugano and Mt. San Salvatore. 25 c. (No. 376) Viamala Gorge. 25 c. (No. 492) National Park. 30 c. Rhine Falls. 35 c. Mt. Neufalkenstein and Klus. 40 c. Mt. Santis and Lake Seealp.

53. Mobile P.O.

1937. For Mobile P.O. Mail.
380. 53. 10 c. yellow and black 30 10

55. International Labour Office.

Designs: 30 c., 60 c. Palace of League of Nations (different views). 1 f. International Labour Office.

1938.
382 55 20 c. red and buff .. 20 10
383 – 30 c. blue and light blue 30 10
384 – 60 c. brown and buff .. 1·75 85
385 – 1 f. black and buff .. 8·50 8·00

1938. Air. Special Flights. Surch. **1938 "PRO AERO" 75 75** and bars.
386. 36. 75 c. on 50 c. grn. & red † 4·50

60. William Tell's Chapel.

1938. National Fete. Fund for Swiss subjects abroad.
387 60 10 c.+10 c. violet & yell 40 25

61. First Act of Federal Parliament.

1938.
388A 61 3 f. brown on blue .. 15·00 1·50
388c 3 f. brown on buff .. 6·00 10
389A – 5 f. blue on blue .. 15·00 1·50
389c – 5 f. blue on buff .. 6·00 10
390A – 10 f. green on blue .. 65·00 20·00
390c – 10 f. green on buff .. 8·00 35
Designs: 5 f. "The Assembly at Stans". 10 f. Polling booth.

62. Symbolical of Swiss Culture.

64. Crossbow and Floral Branch.

1939. National Exhibition, Zurich. Inscr in French (F.), German (G.), or Italian (I.).

			F.		G.		I.	
~~391.~~	–	10 c. vio.	25	10	20	10	25	10
392.	62.	20 c. red	75	10	60	10	1·40	10
393.	–	30 c. blue & buff	3·60	2·00	2·75	50	3·00	4·50

Designs: 10 c. Group symbolic of Swiss Industry and Agriculture. 30 c. Piz Rosegg and Tschirva Glacier.

1939. National Exn., Zurich. Inscr. in French (F.), German (G.) or Italian (I.).

			F.		G.		I.	
394a	64	5 c. green	70	1·50	70	1·25	70	1·50
395a/b		10 c. brn	75	1·25	55	80	85	1·50
396a		20 c. red	1·50	1·25	1·25	1·00	1·40	2·25
397		30 c. blue	3·50	6·00	3·00	5·50	3·00	6·50

65. Laupen Castle.

1939. National Fete. Fund for Destitute Mothers.
398 65 10 c.+10 c. brown, grey and red 30 25

66. Geneva.

1939. 75th Anniv of Geneva (Red Cross) Convention.
399 66 20 c. red and buff .. 30 10
400 30 c. blue, grey and red 45 90

67. "Les Rangiers".

68. "William Tell" (Ferdinand Hodler).

1940. National Fete and Red Cross Fund. Memorial designs inscr. "FETE NATIONALE 1940" in German (5 c., 20 c.), Italian (10 c.) and French 30 c.).
401. – 5 c.+5 c. blk. & green 30 90
402. – 10 c.+5 c. black & orge. 30 25
403. – 20 c.+5 c. blk. & red .. 2·00 75
404. 67. 30 c.+10 c. blk. & blue 1·60 5·00
Designs—Battle Memorials: 5 c. Sempach. 10 c. Giornico. 20 c. Calven.

1941. Historical designs.
405 – 50 c. blue on green .. 5·00 10
~~406~~ 68 60 c. brn on cinnamon 6·00 10
407 – 70 c. purple on mauve 3·75 30
408 – 80 c. black on grey .. 1·10 10
408a – 80 c. black on mauve .. 1·50 20
~~409~~ – 90 c. red on pink .. 1·10 10
409a – 90 c. red on buff .. 2·00 30
~~410~~ – 1 f. green on green .. 1·25 10
411 – 1 f. 20 purple on grey 1·25 10
411a – 1 f. 20 purple on lilac 2·00 25
412 – 1 f. 50 blue on buff .. 1·50 10
~~413~~ – 2 f. red on pink .. 2·00 10
413a – 2 f. red on cream .. 3·50 25
Designs—(Works of Art): 50 c. "Oath of Union". (James Vibert). 70 c. "Kneeling Warrior" (Ferdinand Hodler). 80 c. "Dying Ensign" (Hodler). 90 c. "Standard Bearer" (Niklaus Deutsch). Portraits: 1 f. Col. Louis Pfyffer. 1 f. 20, George Jenatsch. 1 f. 50, Lt.-Gen. Francois de Reynold. 2 f. Col. Joachim Forrer.

69. Ploughing.

1941. Agricultural Development Plan.
~~414.~~ 69. 10 c. brown and buff .. 15 10

70. The Jungfrau.

71. Chemin Creux near Kussnacht.

1941. Air. Landscapes.
415 70 30 c. blue on orange .. 1·00 10
415a – 30 c. grey on orange .. 7·50 10·00
416 – 40 c. grey on orange .. 1·00 10
416a – 40 c. blue on orange .. 42·00 1·75
417 – 50 c. green on orange 1·25 10
418 – 60 c. brown on orange 1·75 10
419 – 70 c. violet on orange 1·25 30
420 – 1 f. green on orange .. 2·50 35
421 – 2 f. red on orange 6·50 1·50
422 – 5 f. blue on orange 25·00 7·50
Designs: 40 c. Valais. 50 c. Lake Leman. 60 c. Alpstein. 70 c. Ticino. 1 f. Lake Lucerne. 2 f. Engadine. 5 f. Churfirsten.

1941. Air. Special (Buochs-Payerne) Flights. No. 420, with **PRO AERO 28.V. 1941** added.
423. – 1 f. green on buff .. 5·50 20·00

1941. National Fete and 650th Anniv of Swiss Confederation.
424 – 10 c.+10 c. bl, red & yell 25 45
425 71 20 c.+10 c. scarlet, red and buff 25 40
Design: 10 c. Relief Map of Lake Lucerne with Arms of Uri, Schwyz and Unterwalden.

72. Arms of Berne, Masons laying Corner-stone and Knight.

1941. 750th Anniv. of Berne.
426. 72. 10 c. multicoloured .. 10 10

73. "To survive collect salvage".

1942. Salvage Campaign. Inscr. in French (F.), German (G.) or Italian (I.).

			F.		G.		I.	
427.	73.	10 c. brn.	50	15	10	10	7·00	2·00

Inscriptions: (G.) "Zum Durchhalten/Alstoffe sammeln"; (I.) "PER RESISTERE/RACCOGLIETE/LA ROBA VECCHIA".

74. View of Old Geneva.

75. Soldiers' Memorial at Forch, near Zurich.

1942. National Fete, National Relief Fund and Bimillenary of Geneva.
428 74 10 c.+10 c. black, yellow and red 30 40
429 75 20 c.+10 c. red & yellow 30 45

76.

1943. Cent. of Swiss Cantonal Postage Stamp.
430. 76. 10 c. (4+6) black .. 10 10

77. Intragna (Ticino).

78. Apollo of Olympia.

1943. National Fete and Youths' Vocational Training Fund.
431 77 10 c.+10 c. black, buff and red 30 45
432 – 20 c.+10 c. red and buff 35 65
DESIGN: 20 c. Federal Palace, Berne.

1943. Air. Special Flights. 30th Anniv of First Flight across Alps by Oscar Bider. No. 432 optd **PRO AERO 13 VII 1943** and value.
433 – 1 f. red and buff .. 2·00 9·00

1944. Olympic Games Jubilee.
434. 78. 10 c. black and orange 15 50
435. 20 c. black and red 35 50
436. 30 c. black and blue 70 7·50

79. Heiden.

DESIGNS: 10 c. St. Jacques on the R. Birs. 20 c. Castle Ruins, Mesocco. 30 c. Basel.

1944. National Fete and Red Cross Fund.
437 79 5 c.+5 c. grn, buff & red 35 1·50
438 – 10 c.+10 c. grey, buff and red 35 35
439 – 20 c.+10 c. red and buff 35 55
440 – 30 c.+10 c. blue, buff and red .. .. 3·00 12·50

80. D.H.3 Haefeli.

81. Symbolical of Faith, Hope and Charity.

1944. Air. 25th Anniv of National Air Post.
441 80 10 c. brown and olive .. 15 10
442 – 20 c. red amd buff .. 20 10
443 – 30 c. ultramarine & blue 40 45
444 – 1 f. 50 violet, pur & red 6·50 16·00
DESIGNS: 20 c. Fokker. 30 c. Lockheed-Orion. 1 f. 50, Douglas D.C.3.

1945. War Relief Fund.
445. 81. 10 c.+10 c. olive, black and grey .. 50 40
446. 20 c.+60 c. red, black and grey .. 1·75 4·50

82. Trans. "Peace to men of good will".

83. Olive Branch.

1945. Peace stamps. Inscr "PAX".
447 82 5 c. green and grey .. 10 15
448 10 c. brown and grey .. 25 10
449 20 c. red and grey .. 40 10
450 30 c. blue and grey .. 1·00 2·00
451 40 c. orange and grey .. 3·00 9·50
452 83 50 c. red and buff .. 3·50 15·00
453 – 60 c. grey and light grey 3·50 5·00
454 – 80 c. green and buff .. 8·00 60·00
455 – 1 f. blue and buff .. 11·00 65·00
456 – 2 f. brown and buff .. 38·00 £110
457 – 3 f. green on buff .. 50·00 38·00
458 – 5 f. brown on buff .. £150 £225
459 – 10 f. violet on buff .. £190 £100
DESIGNS—As Type **83**: 60 c. Keys. 80 c. Horn of plenty. 1 f. Dove. 2 f. Spade and flowers in ploughed field. 38×21 mm: 3 f. Crocuses. 5 f. Clasped hands. 10 f. Aged couple.

1945. Red Cross. As T **82**, but red cross and "5+10" in centre of stamp.
460. 5 c.+10 c. green .. 45 50

85. Silk Weaving.

1945. National Fete.
461 85 5 c.+5 c. green and red 75 1·50
462 – 10 c.+10 c. brown, grey and red 60 40
463 – 20 c.+10 c. red and buff 75 40
464 – 30 c.+10 c. blue, grey and red .. .. 9·00 24·00
DESIGNS: 10, 20 c. Jura and Emmental farm-houses. 30 c. Timbered house.

86. J. H. Pestalozzi.

87. Instructional Glider.

1946. Birth Bicentenary of J. H. Pestalozzi (educational reformer).
465. 86. 10 c. purple 10 10

1946. Air. Special (Lausanne, Lucerne, Locarno) Flights.
466. 87. 1 f. 50 red and grey 20·00 25·00

88. Cheese-Making.

89. Chalet in Appenzell.

DESIGNS: 10 c. Chalet in Vaud. 30 c. Chalet in Engadine.

1946. National Fete and Fund for Swiss Citizens Abroad.
467 88 5 c.+5 c. green and red 70 1·75
468 – 10 c.+10 c. brown, buff and red 50 50
469 89 20 c.+10 c. red and buff 60 50
470 – 30 c.+10 c. blue, grey and red .. .. 6·00 7·50

90. Douglas DC4 Aircraft, Statue of Liberty and St. Peter's Cathedral, Geneva.

1947. Air. 1st Geneva–New York "Swissair" Flight.
472 90 2 f. 50 dp blue, bl & red 11·50 16·00

92. Rorschach Station.

DESIGNS: 5 c. Platelayers. 20 c. Luen-Castiel station. 30 c. Fluelen station.

1947. Charity. National Fete, and Professional Education of Invalids and Anti-Cancer Funds. Inscr. "I VIII 1947". Arms in red.
473. – 5 c.+5 c. green .. 60 1·75
474. 92. 10 c.+10 c. blk. & buff 70 60
475. – 20 c.+10 c. red & buff 70 60
476. – 30 c.+10 c. blue & grey 5·00 8·00

93. "Limmat" First Swiss Steam Locomotive.

DESIGNS: 10c. Steam freight locomotive. 20 c. Electric train crossing Melide causeway. 30 c. Railway bridge.

1947. Centenary of Swiss Federal Railways.
477 93 5 c. green, yellow & blk 20 35
478 – 10 c. black and brown .. 30 10
479 – 20 c. red, buff and lake 40 10
480 – 30 c. blue, grey & lt bl 1·40 1·75

95. Sun of St. Moritz.

96. Ice Hockey

1948. Charity. 5th Winter Olympic Games.
481 95 5 c.+5 c. brn, yell & grn 50 1·25
482 – 10 c.+10 c. blue, light blue and brown .. 65 1·25
483 96 20 c.+10 c. yellow, black and purple .. .. 75 1·50
484 – 30 c.+10 c. black, light blue and blue .. 2·25 5·50
DESIGN: 10 c. Snow crystals. 30 c. Ski-runner.

97. Johann Rudolf Wettstein.

DESIGNS: 10 c. Neuchatel Castle. 20 c. Symbol of Helvetia. 30 c. Symbol of Federal State.

1948. Tercentenary of Treaty of Westphalia and Centenaries of the Neuchatel Revolution and Swiss Federation.
485 97 5 c. green and dp green 10 20
486 – 10 c. black and grey .. 15 10
487 – 20 c. red and pink .. 20 10
488 – 30 c. blue, grey & brown 60 75

99. Frontier Guard.

1948. National Fete and Anti-Tuberculosis Fund. Coat of arms in red.
495 99 5 c.+5 c. green .. 50 75
496 – 10 c.+10 c. slate & grey 50 50
497 – 20 c.+10 c. red and buff 50 60
498 – 30 c.+10 c. blue & grey 3·50 5·75
DESIGNS: 10c., 20 c., 30 c. Typical houses in Fribourg, Valais and Ticino respectively.

101. Glider.

1949. Air. Special (La Chaux-de-Fonds–St. Gallen–Lugano) Flights.
499. 101. 1 f. 50 purple & yellow 27·00 32·00

102. Posthorn.

1949. Centenary of Federal Post.
500 102 5 c. yell, pink & grey 10 20
501 – 20 c. yellow, vio & grey 30 10
502 – 30 c. yell, brn & grey 60 5·50
DESIGNS: 20 c. Mail coach drawn by five horses. 30 c. Postal motor coach and trailer.

103. Main Motif of U.P.U. Monument, Berne.

1949. 75th Anniv of U.P.U.
503 103 10 c. green 15 10
504 – 25 c. purple .. .. 70 7·00
505 – 40 c. blue .. .. 90 1·50
DESIGNS: 25 c. Globe and ribbon. 40 c. Globe and pigeons.

104. Postman.

1949. National Fete and Youth Fund. T **104** and designs as T **89**, but dated "I. VIII 1949". Arms in red.
506 104 5 c.+5 c. purple .. 40 1·00
507 – 10 c.+10 c. grn & buff 40 50
508 – 20 c.+10 c. brn & buff 50 50
509 – 40 c.+10 c. blue & lt bl 4·50 8·00
DESIGNS—Typical houses in: 10 c. Basel. 20 c. Lucerne. 40 c. Prattigaus.

106. High-tension Pylons.

107. Sitter Viaducts near St. Gall.

1949. Landscapes.
510. 106. 3 c. black .. .. 3·50 3·50
511. 107. 5 c. orange 30 10
512. – 10 c. green 25 10
513. – 15 c. turquoise .. 30 10
514a. – 20 c. purple 40 10
515. – 25 c. red 50 10
516. – 30 c. olive 60 10
517. – 35 c. brown 75 30
518. – 40 c. blue .. .. 3·00 10
519. – 50 c. grey .. .. 3·00 10
520. – 60 c. green .. .. 6·00 10
521. – 70 c. violet .. .. 2·25 25
DESIGNS: 10 c. Mountain cog railway, Rochers de Naye. 15 c. Rotary snowplough. 20 c. Grimsel Reservoir. 25 c. Lake Lugano and Melide railway causeway. 30 c. Verbois hydro-electric power station. 35 c. Alpine road (Val d'Anniviers). 40 c. Rhine harbour, Basel. 50 c. Suspension railway, Santis. 60 c. Railway viaduct, Landwasser. 70 c. Survey mark, Finsteraarhorn.

110. First Federal Postage Stamps.

111. Putting the Weight.

1950. National Fete, Red Cross Fund and Cent. of First Federal Postage Stamps. T **110** and designs, as T **111**, inscr. "I. VIII. 1950". Coat of arms in red.
522 110 5 c.+5 c. black .. 40 55
523 111 10 c.+10 c. grn & grey 1·10 50
524 – 20 c.+10 c. grn & grey 1·25 65
525 – 30 c.+10 c. mve & grey 6·50 15·00
526 – 40 c.+10 c. blue & grey 7·00 8·50
DESIGNS: 20 c. Wrestling. 30 c. Sprinting. 40 c. Rifle shooting.

112. Arms of Zurich.

113. Valaisan Polka.

1951. National Fete, Mother's Fund and 600th Anniv of Zurich. Coat of arms in red.
527 112 5 c.+5 c. black .. 50 50
528 113 10c.+10 c. grn & grey 1·25 50
529 – 20 c.+10 c. grn & grey 1·25 45
530 – 30 c.+10 c. mve & grey 7·00 12·00
531 – 40 c.+10 c. blue & grey 6·50 9·00
DESIGNS—As Type **113**: 20 c. Flag-swinging. 30 c. "Hornussen" (game). 40 c. Blowing alphorn.

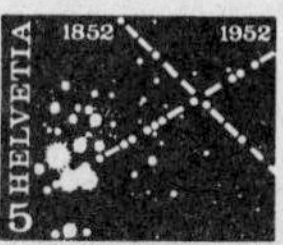

114. "Telegraph".

1952. Cent of Swiss Telecommunications.

532	114	5 c. orange and yellow	40	25
533	–	10 c. green and pink ..	50	10
534	–	20 c. mauve and lilac	65	10
535	–	40 c. blue and lt blue	3·00	2·75

DESIGNS: 10 c. "Telephone". 20 c. "Radio". 40 c. "Television".

115. Arms of Glarus and Zug. **116.** River Doubs.

1952. Pro Patria. Culture Funds and 600th Anniv of Glarus and Zug joining Confederation.

536	115	5 c.+5 c. red and black	50	60
537	116	10 c.+10 c. green and cream	60	40
538	–	20 c.+10 c. pur & pink	60	40
539	–	30 c.+10 c. brn & buff	4·25	6·00
540	–	40 c.+10 c. blue and light blue	4·50	5·75

DESIGNS—As T **116**. 20 c. St. Gotthard Lake. 30 c. River Moesa. 40 c. Marjelen Lake.

1953. Pro Patria. Emigrants' Fund and 600th Anniv of Berne joining Confederation.

541	5 c.+5 c. red and black ..	60	70
542	10 c.+10 c. green & cream	60	40
543	20 c.+10 c. purple & pink	60	40
544	30 c.+10 c. brown and buff	4·25	7·00
545	40 c. +10 c. blue & lt blue	4·25	6·00

DESIGNS—As T **115**: 5 c. Arms of Berne (inscr "BERN 1353"). As T **116** (inscr "PRO PATRIA 1953"): 10 c. Rapids, R. Reuss. 20 c. Lake Sihl. 30 c. Aqueduct, Bisse. 40 c. Lake Leman.

119. Zurich Airport.

1953. Inaug. of Zurich Airport.

546.	119.	40 c. blue, grey & red	4·75	7·00

DESIGN: 20 c. Alpine postal coach and Summer landscape.

120. Alpine Postal Coach and Winter Landscape.

1953. For Mobile P.O. Mail.

547.	120.	10 c. yell., grey & green	15	10
548.	–	20 c. yellow, lake & red	25	10

121. Ear of Wheat and Flower. **122.** Rhine Map and Steering Wheel.

1954. Publicity Issue.

549.	121.	10 c. yell., red & green	40	10
550.	–	20 c. multicoloured ..	80	10
551.	122.	25 c. green, blue & red	2·00	2·50
552.	–	40 c. blue yell. & black	2·40	1·50

Designs—HORIZ: 10 c. Type **121** (Agricultural Exhibition, Lucerne). 20 c. Winged spoon (Cooking Exhibition, Berne). 40 c. Football and world map (World Football Championship). VERT: 25 c. Type **122** (50th anniv of navigation of River Rhine).

123. Opening Bars of "Swiss Hymn".

1954. Pro Patria. Youth Fund and Death Centenary of Father Zwyssig (composer of "Swiss Hymn").

553	123	5 c.+5 c. green ..	40	75
554	–	10 c.+10 c. grn & turq	60	40
555	–	20 c.+10 c. purple and cream	60	40
556	–	30 c.+10 c. brn & buff	3·75	7·00
557	–	40 c.+10 c. deep blue and blue	3·75	5·50

DESIGNS: 10 c. Lake of Neuchatel. 20 c. Maggia River. 30 c. Taubenloch Gorge Waterfall, Schuss River. 40 c. Lake of Sils.

124. Lausanne Cathedral. **125.** Alphorn Blower.

1955. Publicity issue. Inscr. "1955".

558.	124.	5 c. multicoloured ..	40	10
559.	-	10 c. multicoloured ..	40	10
560.	125.	20 c. sepia and red ..	1·00	10
561.	–	40 c. red, black & blue	3·00	1·25

DESIGNS—HORIZ: 5 c. Type **124** (National Philatelic Exhibition, Lausanne). 10 c. Vaud girl's hat (Vevey Winegrower's Festival). 40 c. Car steering-wheel (25th International Motor Show, Geneva). VERT. 20 c. Type **125** (Alpine Herdsmen and Costume Festival, Interlaken).

126. Federal Institute of Technology, Zurich.

1955. Pro Patria. Mountain Population Fund and Centenary of Federal Institute of Technology.

562	126	5 c.+5 c. grey ..	60	60
563	–	10 c.+10 c. green and cream	60	40
564	–	20 c.+10 c. red & pink	60	40
565	–	30 c.+10 c. brn & buff	3·75	6·00
566	–	40 c.+10 c. deep blue and blue	3·75	5·50

DESIGNS: 10 c. Groundfey railway viaduct, River Saane. 20 c. Lake Aegeri. 30 c. Lake Grappelen. 40 c. Lake Bienne.

127. "Road Safety". **128.** "Swissair" planes.

1956. Publicity Issue. Inscr "1956".

567	–	5 c. yellow, black & grn	40	25
568	–	10 c. black, green & red	40	10
569	127	20 c. multicoloured ..	80	10
570	128	40 c. blue and red ..	2·50	80

DESIGNS: 5 c. First postal motor coach (50th anniv of postal motor coach service). 10 c. Electric train emerging from Simplon Tunnel and Stockalper Palace (50th anniv of opening of Simplon Tunnel).

The 40 c. commemorates 25th anniv of Swissair.

129. Rose, Scissors and Tape-measure. **130.** Printing Machine's Inking Rollers.

1956. Pro Patria. Swiss Women's Fund. T **129** and design as T **116** but inscr "PRO PATRIA 1956".

571	129	5 c.+5 c. green ..	60	75
572	–	10 c.+10 c. emerald and green	60	40
573	–	20 c.+10 c. pur & pink	60	50
574	–	30 c.+10 c. deep brown and brown	3·50	6·00
575	–	40 c.+10 c. deep blue and blue	3·50	5·00

DESIGNS: 10 c. R. Rhone at St. Maurice. 20 c. Katzensee. 30 c. R. Rhine at Trin. 40 c. Walensee.

1957. Publicity Issue. Inscr. "1957".

576.	130.	5 c. multicoloured ..	15	10
577.	–	10 c. brn., grn. & turq.	1·75	10
578.	–	20 c. grey and red ..	50	10
579.	–	40 c. multicoloured ..	2·00	80

DESIGNS: 10 c. Electric train crossing bridge (75th anniv of St. Gotthard Railway). 20 c. Civil Defence shield and coat of arms ("Civil Defence"). 40 c. Munatius Plancus, Basel and Rhine (2000th anniv of Basel).

The 5 c. commemorates "Graphic 57" International Exhibition, Lausanne.

131. Shields of Switzerland and the Red Cross. **132.** "Charity".

1957. Pro Patria. Swiss Red Cross and National Cancer League Funds. Cross in red.

580	131	5 c.+5 c. red and grey	40	60
581	132	10 c.+10 c. pur & grn	55	20
582		20 c.+10 c. grey & red	50	20
583		30 c.+10 c. blue & brn	4·00	5·00
584		40 c.+10 c. ochre & bl	4·00	3·75

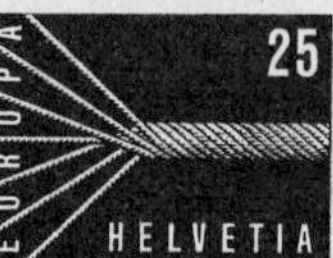

133. Symbol of Unity. **134.** Nyon Castle (2000th anniv of Nyon).

1957. Europa.

585.	133.	25 c. red	80	10
586.		40 c. blue	2·75	10

1958. Publicity Issue. Inscr. "1958".

587.	134.	5 c. violet, buff & olive	20	10
588.	–	10 c. myrtle, red & grn.	20	10
589.	–	20 c. red, lilac and deep red	40	10
590.	–	40 c. deep blue, red and blue	1·50	75

DESIGNS: 10 c. Woman's head with ribbons (Saffa Exhibition, Zurich). 20 c. Crossbow (25th anniv as symbol of Swiss manufacture). 40 c. Salvation Army bonnet (75th anniv of Salvation Army in Switzerland).

135. "Needy Mother". **136.** Fluorite.

1958. Pro Patria. For Needy Mothers, T **135** and designs showing minerals, rocks and fossils as T **136**. Inscr. "PRO PATRIA 1958".

591	5 c.+5 c. purple	30	50
592	10 c.+10 c. yell, grn & blk	40	30
593	20 c.+10 c. bis, red & blk	40	30
594	30 c.+10 c. pur, brn & blk	3·00	4·50
595	40 c.+10 c. turq, bl & blk	3·00	3·50

DESIGNS: 20 c. Ammonite. 30 c. Garnet. 40 c. Rock crystal.

137. Atomic Symbol.

1958. 2nd U.N. Atomic Conf., Geneva.

596.	137.	40 c. red, bl. & cream	40	35

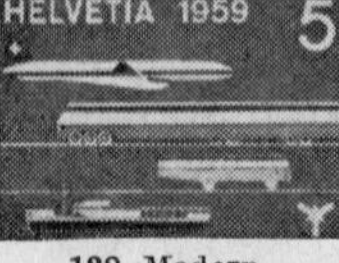
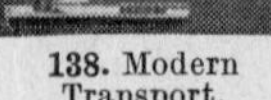

138. Modern Transport. **139.** "Swiss Citizens Abroad".

1959. Publicity Issue. Inscr. "1959".

597.	5 c. multicoloured ..	25	10
598.	10 c. yellow, grey & green	25	10
599.	20 c. multicoloured ..	55	10
600.	50 c. blue, violet & lt. blue	90	75

DESIGNS: 5 c. Type **138** (opening of "The Swiss House of Transport and Communications"). 10 c. Lictor's fasces of the Coat of Arms of St. Gall and posthorn (NABAG—National Philatelic Exhibition, St. Gall). 20 c. Owl, hare and fish (Protection of Animals). 50 c. J. Calvin, Th. de Beze and University building (4th cent of University of Geneva).

1959. Pro Patria. For Swiss Citizens Abroad. T **139** and other designs showing minerals, rocks and fossils as T **136**, and inscr "PRO PATRIA 1959".

601	5 c.+5 c. red and grey ..	30	50
602	10 c.+10 c. multicoloured	40	35
603	20 c.+10 c. multicoloured	40	35
604	30 c.+10 c. vio, brn & blk	2·25	2·75
605	40 c.+10 c. blue, turquoise and black ..	2·25	2·25

DESIGNS: 10 c. Agate. 20 c. Tourmaline. 30 c. Amethyst. 40 c. Fossilized giant salamander.

140. "Europa". **142.** "Campaign against Cancer".

1959. Europa.

606.	140.	30 c. red	40	10
607.		50 c. blue	40	10

1959. European P.T.T. Conf., Montreux. Optd. **REUNION DES PTT D'EUROPE 1959.**

608.	140.	30 c. red	8·50	7·00
609.		50 c. blue	8·50	7·00

1960. Publicity Issue. Inscr "1460–1960" (20 c.) or "1960" (50 c., 75 c.).

610	10 c. red, lt green & green	45	10
611	20 c. multicoloured ..	60	10
612	50 c. yellow, ultram & blue	75	90
613	75 c. red, black and blue	2·50	2·75

DESIGNS: 10 c. Type **142** (50th anniv of Swiss League for Cancer Control). 20 c. Charter and sceptre (500th anniv of Basel University). 50 c. "Uprooted tree" (World Refugee Year). 75 c. Douglas "DC-8" jet airliner ("Swissair enters the jet age").

143. 15th-century Schwyz Cantonal Messenger. **143a.** Lausanne Cathedral.

1960. Postal History and "Architectural Monuments" (1st series).

614	–	5 c. blue	10	10
615	143	10 c. green	10	10
616	–	15 c. red	15	10
617	–	20 c. mauve	20	10
618	143a	25 c. green	25	10
619p	–	30 c. red	25	10
620	–	35 c. red	50	45
621p	–	40 c. purple ..	35	10
622	–	50 c. blue	50	10
623	–	60 c. red	60	10
624	–	70 c. orange ..	70	40
625	–	75 c. blue	1·00	25
626p	–	80 c. purple ..	80	15
627p	–	90 c. green	80	10
628	–	1 f. orange	1·00	10
629	–	1 f. 20 red	1·10	10
632	–	1 f. 30 brown on lilac	1·25	10
630	–	1 f. 50 green ..	1·40	25
633	–	1 f. 70 purple on lilac	1·50	15
631	–	2 f. blue	6·00	65
634	–	2 f. 20 green on grn	2·00	40
635	–	2 f. 80 orge on orge	2·75	25

DESIGNS—HORIZ. 5 c. 17th-century Fribourg Cantonal messenger. 15 c. 17th-century mule-driver. 20 c. 19th-century mounted postman. 1 f. Fribourg Town Hall. 1 f. 20, Basel Gate, Solothurn. 1 f. 50, Ital Reding's house, Schwyz. 1 f. 70, 2 f., 2 f. 20 Abbey Church, Einsiedeln. VERT. 30 c. Grossmunster, Zurich. 35 c., 1 f. 30, Woodcutters Guildhall, Bienne. 40 c. St. Peter's Cathedral, Geneva. 50 c. Spalentor (gate), Basel. 60 c. Clock Tower, Berne. 70 c. Collegiate Church of St. Peter and St. Stephen, Bellinzona. 75 c. Kapellbrucke (bridge) and Water Tower, Lucerne. 80 c. St. Gall Cathedral. 90 c. Munot Fort, Schaffhausen. 2 f. 80, as 70 c. but redrawn without bell-tower.

See also Nos. 698/713.

144. Symbols of Occupational Trades. 145. "Aid for Development".

1960. Pro Patria. For Swiss Youth. T **144** and other designs showing minerals, rocks and fossils as T **136** and inscr. "PRO PATRIA 1960".

636 – 5 c.+5 c. multicoloured 60 75
637 – 10 c.+10 c. pink, green and black 60 25
638 – 20 c.+10 c. yellow, purple and black .. 60 25
639 – 30 c.+10 c. blue, brown and black .. .. 3·75 3·75
640 **144** 50 c.+10 c. gold & blue 3·75 3·25

Designs: 5 c. Smoky quartz. 10 c. Orthoclase (feldspar). 20 c. Gryphaea (fossilized shellfish). 30 c. Azurite. 50 c. Type **144** ("50 Years of National Day Collection").

1960. Europa. As T **129a** of Luxembourg, but size 33 × 23 mm.

642. 30 c. red 40 10
643. 50 c. blue 40 10

1961. Publicity Issue.

644 5 c. red, blue and grey .. 25 10
645 10 c. yellow and blue .. 25 10
646 20 c. multicoloured .. 70 10
647 50 c. red, green and blue 1·10 90

Designs: 5 c. Type **145** ("Aid to countries in process of development"). 10 c. Circular emblem ("Hyspa" Exhibition of 20th-century Hygiene, Gymnastics and Sport, Berne). 20 c. Hockey stick (World and European Ice Hockey Championships, Geneva and Lausanne). 50 c. Map of Switzerland with telephone centres as wiring diagram (inauguration of Swiss fully automatic telephone service).

146. "Cultural Works of Eternity". 147. Doves.

1961. Pro Patria. For Swiss Cultural Works, T **146** and other designs showing minerals, rocks and fossils as T **136** and inscr. "PROPATRIA 1961".

648. 5 c.+5 c. blue 20 40
649. 10 c.+10 c. purple, green and black 50 30
650. 20 c.+10 c. red, blue and black 60 30
651. 30 c.+10 c. turquoise, orange and black .. 1·75 3·00
652. 50 c.+10 c. bistre, blue and black .. .. 2·00 3·00

Designs: 10 c. Fluorite. 20 c. Petrified fish. 30 c. Lazulite. 50 c. Fossilised fern.

1961. Europa.

653. **147.** 30 c. red 40 10
654. 50 c. blue 50 10

148. St. Matthew. 149. W.H.O. Emblem and Mosquito.

1961. Wood Carvings from St. Oswald's Church, Zug.

655 **148** 3 f. mauve .. .. 3·00 10
656 – 5 f. blue .. .. 5·00 10
657 – 10 f. brown .. .. 9·00 15
658 – 20 f. red .. .. 18·00 1·75

Designs: 5 f. St. Mark. 10 f. St. Luke. 20 f. St. John.

1962. Publicity Issue.

659 5 c. multicoloured .. 60 10
660 10 c. bistre, purple & green 50 10
661 20 c. multicoloured .. 65 10
662 50 c. green, mauve & blue 90 80

Designs: 5 c. Electric Train (Introduction of TEE Trains). 10 c. Oarsman (World Rowing Championship, Lucerne). 20 c. Jungfraujoch and Monch (50th Anniv. of Jungfraujoch Railway Station). 50 c. Type **149** (Malaria Eradication).

150. Rousseau. 151. Obwalden Silver Half-taler.

1962. Pro Patria. For Swiss Old People's Homes and Cultural Works.

663 **150** 5 c.+5 c. blue .. 20 15
664 **151** 10 c.+10 c. blue, black and green 40 20
665 – 20 c.+10 c. yellow, black and red .. 40 20
666 – 30 c.+10 c. green, blue and red .. .. 1·10 1·60
667 – 50 c.+10 c. violet, black and blue .. 1·10 1·60

Coins—As Type **151**: 20 c. Schwyz gold ducat. 30 c. Uri batzen. 50 c. Nidwalden batzen.

152. Europa "Tree".

1962. Europa.

668. **152.** 30 c. orange, yell. & brn. 40 25
669. 50 c. blue, turq. & brn. 90 40

153. Campaign Emblem (Freedom from Hunger).

1963. Publicity Issue.

670. – 5 c. brown, red & blue 80 25
671. – 10 c. red, grey & green 40 10
672. – 20 c. lake, red and grey 1·50 10
673. **153.** 30 c. yell., ochre & grn. 1·50 1·50
674. – 50 c. red, silver & blue 75 60
675. – 50 c. multicoloured .. 75 60

Designs: No. 670, Boy scout (50th Anniv. of Swiss Boy Scout League). No. 671, Badge (Swiss Alpine Club Cent.). No. 672, Luegelkinn Viaduct (50th Anniv. of Lotschberg Railway). No. 674, Jubilee Emblem (Red Cross Cent.). No. 675, Hotel des Postes, Paris, 1863 (Paris Postal Conference).

154. Dr. Anna Heer (nursing pioneer). 155. Roll of Bandage.

1963. Pro Patria. For Swiss Medical and Refugee Aid. T **154** and other designs as T **155** showing Red Cross activities. Inscr. "PRO PATRIA 1963".

676. 5 c.+5 c. blue 20 25
677. 10 c.+10 c. red, grey and green 20 20
678. 20 c.+10 c. multicoloured 35 20
679. 30 c.+10 c. multicoloured 1·25 1·40
680. 50 c.+10 c. red, indigo & bl. 1·50 1·25

Designs: 20 c. Gift parcel. 30 c. Blood plasma. 50 c. Red Cross brassard.

156. Glider and Jet Aircraft. 157. "Co-operation".

1963. Air 25th Anniv. of Swiss "Pro Aero" Foundation. Berne–Locarno or Langenbruck–Berne (helicopter feeder) Special Flights.

681. **156.** 2 f. multicoloured .. 5·50 4·00

1963. Europa.

682. **157.** 50 c. ochre and blue .. 60 25

158. Exhibition Emblem. 159. Great St. Bernard Tunnel.

1963. Swiss National Exhibition, Lausanne.

683. **158.** 10 c. green and sepia .. 20 10
684. 20 c. red and sepia .. 30 10
685. – 50 c. blue and red .. 40 35
686. – 75 c. violet and red .. 60 50

Designs: 50 c. "Outlook" (emblem on globe and smaller globe). 75 c. "Insight" (emblem on large globe).

1964. Publicity Issue.

687. 5 c. blue, red and olive .. 20 10
688. 10 c. turquoise and blue .. 25 10
689. 20 c. multicoloured .. 40 10
690. 50 c. multicoloured .. 80 70

Designs: 5 c. Type **159** (Opening of Great St. Bernard Road Tunnel). 10 c. Ancient "god of the waters" (Protection of water supplies). 20 c. Swiss soldiers of 1864 and 1964 (Centenary of Swiss Association of Non-commissioned Officers). 50 c. Standards of Geneva and Swiss Confederation (150th anniv of arrival of Swiss in Geneva).

160. J. G. Bodmer (inventor). 161. Europa "Flower".

1964. Pro Patria. For Swiss Mountain Aid and Cultural Funds. T **160** and vert. designs of Swiss coins as T **151**. Inscr. "PRO PATRIA 1964".

691. 5 c.+5 c. blue 10 10
692. 10 c.+10 c. drab, blk. & grn. 20 15
693. 20 c.+10 c. blue, blk. & mve. 25 20
694. 30 c.+10 c. blue, blk. & orge. 75 80
695. 50 c.+10 c. olive, brn. & blue 80 80

Coins: 10 c. Zurich copper. 20 c. Basel "doppeldicken". 30 c. Geneva silver thaler. 50 c. Berne half gold florin.

1964. Europa.

696. **161.** 20 c. red 35 10
697. 50 c. blue 65 15

1964. "Architectural Monuments" (2nd series). As T **143a**.

698 5 c. mauve 10 10
699 10 c. blue 10 10
700 15 c. brown 15 10
701 20 c. green 15 10
702 30 c. red 25 10
703 50 c. blue 40 10
704 70 c. brown 60 10
705 1 f. green 85 10
706 1 f. 20 red .. .. 1·00 10
707 1 f. 30 blue .. .. 1·50 50
708 1 f. 50 green .. .. 1·25 10
709 1 f. 70 red .. .. 1·50 75
710 2 f. orange .. .. 1·75 15
711 2 f. 20 green .. .. 2·75 50
712 2 f. 50 green .. .. 2·25 25
713 3 f. 50 purple .. .. 3·00 25

Designs—horiz. 5 c. Lenzburg Castle. 10 c. Freuler Manrion, Nafels. 15 c. Mauritius Church, Appenzell. 20 c. Planta House, Samedan. 30 c. Town Square, Gais. 50 c. Neuchatel Castle and Collegiate Church. vert. 70 c. Lussy "Hochhus", Wolfenschiessen. 1 f. Riva San Vitale Church. 1 f. 20, Payerne Abbey Church. 1 f. 30, St. Pierre-de Clages Church. 1 f. 50, Gateway, Porrentruy. 1 f. 70, Frauenfeld Castle. 2 f. Castle Seedorf (Uri). 2 f. 20, Thomas Tower and Arch, Liestal. 2 f. 50, St. Oswald's Church, Zug. 3 f. 50, Benedictine Abbey, Engelberg.

162. Swiss 5 r. Stamp of 1854 with "Lozenge" Cancellation.

1965. Publicity Issue.

714. – 5 c. black, red and blue 10 10
715. **162.** 10 c. brown, blue & grn. 10 10
716. – 20 c. multicoloured .. 20 10
717. – 50 c. red, black & blue 40 35

Designs, etc: 5 c. Nurse and patient ("Nursing"). 10 c. Type **162** "NABRA 1965" National Stamp Exhibition, Berne). 20 c. WAC Officer (25th anniv of Women's Army Corps). 50 c. World telecommunications map (centenary of I.T.U.).

163. Father T. Florentini. 164. Fish-tailed Goose ("Evil").

1965. Pro Patria. For Swiss Abroad and Art Research. Inscr. "PRO PATRIA 1965".

719. **163.** 5 c.+5 c. blue .. 10 10
720. **164.** 10 c.+10 c. mult. .. 10 10
721. – 20 c.+10 c. mult. .. 15 10
722. – 30 c.+10 c. brn. & blue 30 35
723. – 50 c.+10 c. blue & brn. 50 40

Designs—As Type **164**: Ceiling paintings in St. Martin's Church, Zillis (Grisons). 20 c. One of the Magi journeying to Herod. 30 c. Fishermen. 50 c. The Temptation of Christ.

165. Swiss Emblem and Arms of Cantons.

1965. 150th Anniv. of Entry of Valais, Neuchatel and Geneva into Confederation.

724. **165.** 20 c. multicoloured .. 20 10

166. Matterhorn. 167. Europa "Sprig".

1965. Mobile P.O. Issue.

725. **166.** 10 c. multicoloured .. 20 10
726. 30 c. multicoloured .. 50 50

The 30 c. is inscr. "CERVIN".

1965. Europa.

727. **167.** 50 c. green and blue .. 40 20

168. I.T.U. Emblem and Satellites. 169. Figure Skating.

1965. I.T.U. Cent. Congress, Montreux. Multicoloured.

728. 10 c. Type **168** .. 10 10
729. 30 c. Symbols of world telecommunications .. 35 25

1965. World Figure Skating Championships, Davos.

730 **169** 5 c. multicoloured .. 10 10

170. Common Kingfisher. 171. H. Federer (author).

1966. Publicity Issue. Multicoloured.

731 10 c. Type **170** 15 10
732 20 c. Mercury's helmet and laurel twig 15 10
733 50 c. Phase in nuclear fission and flags .. 40 35

Publicity events: 10 c. Preservation of natural beauty. 20 c. 50th Swiss Industrial Fair, Bale (MUBA). 50 c. Int. Institute for Nuclear Research (CERN).

1966. Pro Patria. For Aid to Mothers. Inscr. "PRO PATRIA 1966".

734. **171.** 5 c.+5 c. blue .. 10 10
735. – 10 c.+10 c. mult. .. 10 10
736. – 20 c.+10 c. mult. .. 20 10
737. – 30 c.+10 c. mult. .. 30 30
738. – 50 c.+10 c. mult. .. 50 45

Designs—As Type **164**: "The Flight to Egypt". Ceiling paintings in St. Martin's Church, Zillis (Grisons): 10 c. Joseph's dream. 20 c. Joseph on his way. 30 c. Virgin and Child. 50 c. Angel pointing the way.

172. Society Emblem. 173. Europa "Ship".

1966. 50th Anniv. of New Helvetic Society for Swiss Abroad.

739. **172.** 20 c. red and blue .. 15 10

1966. Europa.

740. **173.** 20 c. red 20 10
741. 50 c. blue 45 15

174. Finsteraarhorn.

1966. "Swiss Alps".
742. 174. 10 c. multicoloured .. 10 10

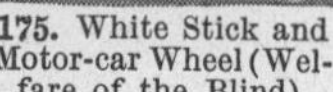

175. White Stick and Motor-car Wheel (Welfare of the Blind). 176. C.E.P.T. Emblem and Cogwheels.

1967. Publicity Issue.
743. 175. 10 c. multicoloured .. 10 10
744. – 20 c. multicoloured .. 15 10
DESIGN: 20 c. Flags of E.F.T.A. countries (Abolition of E.F.T.A. tariffs).

1967. Europa.
745. 176. 30 c. blue 25 10

177. Theodor Kocher (surgeon). 178. Cogwheel and Swiss Emblem.

1967. Pro Patria. For National Day Collection. Inscr. "PRO PATRIA 1967".
746. 177. 5 c.+5 c. blue .. 10 10
747. – 10 c.+10 c. mult. .. 10 10
748. – 20 c.+10 c. mult. .. 20 10
749. – 30 c.+10 c. mult. .. 30 30
750. – 50 c.+10 c. mult. .. 50 50
DESIGNS—As Type 164: Ceiling paintings in St. Martin's Church, Zillis (Grisons). 10 c. Annunciation to the Shepherds. 20 c. Christ and the woman of Samaria. 30 c. Adoration of the Magi. 50 c. Joseph seated on throne.

1967. Publicity Issue. Multicoloured.
751. 10 c. Type 178 .. .. 10 10
752. 20 c. Hour-glass and Sun 15 10
753. 30 c. San Bernadino tunnel 25 10
754. 50 c. "OCTI" emblem .. 40 35
PUBLICITY EVENTS: 10 c. 50th anniv. of Swiss Week. 20 c. 50th anniv. of Aged People Foundation. 30 c. Opening of San Bernardino road tunnel. 50 c. 75th anniv. of Central Office for International Railway Transport (OCTI).

179. "Mountains" and Swiss Emblem.

1968. Publicity Issue.
755. 10 c. multicoloured .. 10 10
756. 20 c. yellow, brown & blue 20 10
757. 30 c. blue, ochre and brown 35 10
758. 50 c. red, turquoise & blue 45 35
DESIGNS AND EVENTS: 10 c. T 179 (50th anniv of Swiss Women's Alpine Club). 20 c. Europa "Key" (Europa). 30 c. Staunton rook and chessboard (18th Chess Olympiad, Lugano). 50 c. Dispatch "satellites" and aircraft tail-fin (inauguration of new Geneva Air Terminal).

180. "Maius". 181. Protective Helmet.

1968. Pro Patria. For Nat. Day Collection. Inscr. "PRO PATRIA 1968".
759. 180. 10 c.+10 c. mult. .. 10 10
760. – 20 c.+10 c. mult. .. 20 10
761. – 30 c.+10 c. mult. .. 30 15
762. – 50 c.+20 c. mult. .. 50 50
DESIGNS: Stained-glass panels in the rose window, Lausanne Cathedral. 20 c. "Leo". 30 c. "Libra". 50 c. "Pisces" (symbols of the months and signs of the zodiac).

1968. Publicity Issue. Multicoloured.
763. 10 c. Type 181 .. .. 10 10
764. 20 c. Geneva and Zurich stamps of 1843 .. .. 20 10
765. 30 c. Part of Swiss map .. 25 10
766. 50 c. "Six Stars" (countries) and anchor .. 45 35
PUBLICITY EVENTS: 10 c. 50th Anniv. of Swiss Accident Insurance Company. 20 c. 125th Anniv. of Swiss stamps. 30 c. 25th Anniv. of Swiss Territorial Planning Society. 50 c. Cent. of Rhine Navigation Act.

182. Guide Camp and Emblem.

1969. Publicity Issue. Multicoloured.
767. 10 c. Type 182 .. .. 25 10
768. 20 c. Pegasus constellation 25 10
769. 30 c. Emblem of Comptoir Suisse 25 10
770. 50 c. Emblem of Gymnaestrade 40 40
771. 2 f. DH-3 "Haefeli" and DC-8 aircraft .. 1·75 1·40
EVENTS: 10 c. 50th anniv of Swiss Girl Guides' Federation. 20 c. Opening of first Swiss Planetarium, Lucerne. 30 c. 50th anniv of Comptoir Suisse, Lausanne. 50 c. 5th Gymnaestrada, Basel. 2 f. 50th anniv of Swiss Airmail Services.

183. Colonnade. 184. "St. Francis of Assisi preaching to the Birds" (Abbey-church, Konigsfelden).

1969. Europa.
772. 183. 30 c. multicoloured .. 25 10
773. 50 c. multicoloured .. 45 35

1969. Pro Patria. For National Day Collection. Stained-glass Windows. Multicoloured.
774. 10 c.+10 c. Type 184 .. 10 15
775. 20 c.+10 c. "The People of Israel drinking . . ." (Berne Cathedral) .. 20 15
776. 30 c.+10 c. "St. Christopher" (Laufelfingen Church, Basle) 30 20
777. 50 c.+20 c. "Madonna and Child" (St. Jacob's Chapel, Grapplang, Flums) 50 50

185. Kreuzberge. 186. Huldrych Zwingli (Protestant reformer).

1969. Publicity and "Swiss Alps" Issues. Multicoloured.
778. 20 c. Type 185 .. .. 25 10
779. 30 c. Children crossing road 25 10
780. 50 c. Hammersmith .. 45 35
EVENTS: 30 c. Road Safety campaign for children. 50 c. 50th anniv of I.L.O.

1969. Swiss Celebrities.
781. 186. 10 c. violet 10 10
782. – 20 c. green 20 10
783. – 30 c. red 25 10
784. – 50 c. blue 50 50
785. – 80 c. brown 65 60
CELEBRITIES: 20 c. General Henri Guisan. 30 c. Francesco Borromini (architect). 50 c. Othmar Schoeck (composer). 80 c. Germaine de Stael (writer).

187. Telex Tape. 188. "Flaming Sun".

1970. Publicity Issue. Multicoloured.
786. 20 c. Type 187 .. .. 20 10
787. 30 c. Fireman saving child 40 10
788. 30 c. "Chained wing" emblem 25 10
789. 50 c. U.N. emblem .. 30 45
790. 80 c. New U.P.U. Headquarters 80 70
EVENTS: 20 c. 75th anniv of Swiss Telegraphic Agency. 30 c. (No. 787), Centenary of Swiss Fireman's Assn. 30 c. (No. 788), 50th anniv of "Pro Infirmis" Foundation. 50 c. 25th anniv of U.N. Organization. 80 c. Inauguration of new U.P.U. headquarters, Berne.

1970. Europa.
791. 188. 30 c. red 30 10
792. 50 c. blue 50 30

1970. Pro Patria. For National Day Collection. Glass paintings by contemporary artists. As T 184 but inscr. "1970". Mult.
793. 10 c.+10 c. "Sailor" (G. Casty) 15 15
794. 20 c.+10 c. Architectonic composition (Celestino Piatti) 20 20
795. 30 c.+10 c. "Bull" symbol of Marduk, from "The Four Elements" (Hans Stocker) 30 15
796. 50 c.+20 c. "Man and Woman" (Max Hunziker and Karl Ganz) 50 55

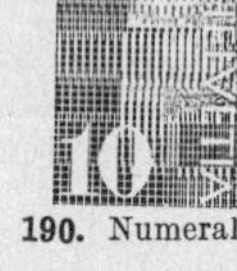

189. Footballer (75th Anniv. of Swiss Football Association). 190. Numeral.

1970. Publicity and "Swiss Alps" (30 c.) Issue. Multicoloured.
797. 10 c. Type 189 .. .. 30 10
798. 20 c. Census form and pencil (Federal Census) .. 20 10
799. 30 c. Piz Palu, Grisons .. 30 10
800. 50 c. Conservation Year Emblem (Nature Conservation Year) 45 40

1970. Coil Stamps.
801. 190. 10 c. red 10 10
802. 20 c. green 20 10
803. 50 c. blue 40 25

191. Female Gymnasts. ("Youth and Sport"). 193. Europa Chain.

1971. Publicity Issue.
804. 191. 10 c. multicoloured .. 20 20
805. – 10 c. multicoloured .. 20 20
806. – 20 c. multicoloured .. 20 10
807. – 30 c. multicoloured .. 25 10
808. – 50 c. brown and blue 45 35
809. – 80 c. multicoloured .. 75 60
DESIGNS AND EVENTS: 10 c. (No. 805), Male athletes ("Youth and Sport" Constitutional Amendment). 20 c. Stylized rose (Child Welfare). 30 c. "Rayon II" stamp of 1850 and basilisk ("NABA" Philatelic Exhib., Basel). 50 c. "Co-operation" symbol (Aid for technical development). 80 c. "Intelstat 4" (I.T.U. Space Conference).

1971. Europa.
811. 193. 30 c. yellow and mauve 30 10
812. 50 c. yellow and blue .. 50 25

1971. Pro Patria. For National Day Collection. Contemporary Glass Paintings. As T 184. Multicoloured.
813. 10 c.+10 c. "Religious Abstract", (J. F. Comment) 15 15
814. 20 c.+10 c. "Cockerel", (J. Prahin) 20 20
815. 30 c.+10 c. "Fox", (K. Volk) 30 20
816. 50 c.+20 c. "Christ's Passion" (B. Schorderet) .. 50 55

194. "Telecommunications Services". (50th anniv of Radio-Suisse). 195. Alexandre Yersin (bacteriologist).

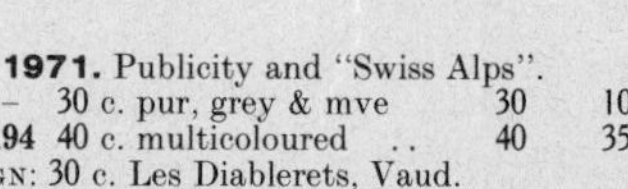

1971. Publicity and "Swiss Alps".
817 – 30 c. pur, grey & mve 30 10
818 194 40 c. multicoloured .. 40 35
DESIGN: 30 c. Les Diablerets, Vaud.

1971. Famous Physicians.
819 195 10 c. green 10 10
820 – 20 c. green 20 10
821 – 30 c. red 30 10
822 – 40 c. blue 60 60
823 – 80 c. purple 80 70
PHYSICIANS: 20 c. Auguste Forel (psychiatrist). 30 c. Jules Gonin (ophthalmologist). 40 c. Robert Koch (German bacteriologist). 80 c. Frederick Banting (Canadian physiologist).

196. Warning Triangle and Wrench (75th Annivs. of Motoring Organisations.)

1972. Publicity Issue.
824. 196. 10 c. multicoloured .. 10 10
825. – 20 c. multicoloured .. 25 10
826. – 30 c. orge., red & carmine 25 10
827. – 40 c. violet, grn. & blue 40 35
DESIGNS AND EVENTS: 20 c. Signal-box switch-table (125th Anniv. of Swiss Railways). 30 c. Stylized radio waves and girl's face (50th anniv. of Swiss Broadcasting). 40 c. Symbolic tree (50th "Swiss Citizens Abroad" Congress).

197. "Swissair" Boeing "747" "Jumbo Jet". 198. "Communications".

1972. Air. Pro Aero Foundation and 50th Annivs. of North Atlantic and Int. Airmail Services.
828. 197. 2 f.+1 f. multicoloured 2·25 2·25

1972. Europa.
829. 198. 30 c. multicoloured .. 25 10
830. 40 c. multicoloured .. 40 20

199. Late Stone Age Harpoon Heads. 200. Civil Defence Emblem.

1972. Pro Patria. For National Day Collection. Archaeological Discoveries (1st series). Multicoloured.
831. 10 c.+10 c. Type 199 .. 30 15
832. 20 c.+10 c. Bronze water-vessel, c. 570 B.C. .. 30 10
833. 30 c.+10 c. Gold Bust of Marcus Aurelius, 2nd-cent. A.D. 30 20
834. 40 c.+20 c. Alemannic disc, 7th-cent. A.D. .. 80 75
See also Nos. 869/72, 887/90 and 901/4.

1972. Publicity and "Swiss Alps" issue. Multicoloured.
835. 10 c. Type 200 .. .. 10 10
836. 20 c. Spannorter 30 10
837. 30 c. Rescue helicopter .. 35 10
838. 40 c. The "Four Elements" (53×31 mm.) 50 40
SUBJECTS: 10 c. Swiss Civil Defence. 20 c. Tourism. 30 c. Swiss Air Rescue Service. 40 c. Protection of the environment.

201. Alberto Giacometti (painter). 202. Dish Aerial.

1972. Swiss Celebrities.
839. 201. 10 c. black and brown 10 10
840. – 20 c. black and bistre 15 10
841. – 30 c. black and pink .. 25 10
842. – 40 c. black and blue .. 50 45
843. – 80 c. black and purple 75 75
PORTRAITS: 20 c. Charles Ramuz (novelist). 30 c. Le Corbusier (architect). 40 c. Albert Einstein (physicist). 80 c. Arthur Honegger (composer).

1973. Publicity Issue. Multicoloured.

844.	15 c. Type **202**	25	15
845.	30 c. Quill pen	25	10
846.	40 c. Interpol emblem	45	35

EVENTS: 15 c. Construction of Satellite Earth Station, Leuk-Brentjong. 30 c. Centenary of Swiss Association of Commercial Employees. 40 c. 50th Anniv. of International Criminal Police Organisation (Interpol).

203. Sottoceneri.

204. Toggenburg Inn Sign.

1973.

847	**203**	5 c. blue and yellow	10	10
848	–	10 c. green and purple	10	10
849	–	15 c. blue and orange	15	10
850	–	25 c. violet and green	20	10
851	–	30 c. violet and red	25	10
852	–	35 c. violet & orange	35	20
853	–	40 c. grey and blue	35	10
854	–	50 c. green and orange	45	10
855	–	60 c. brown and grey	55	10
856	–	70 c. green and purple	60	10
857	–	80 c. red and green	75	10
858	–	1 f. purple	85	10
859	–	1 f. 10 blue	95	10
860	–	1 f. 20 red	1·00	90
861	**204**	1 f. 30 orange	2·00	20
862	–	1 f. 50 green	1·25	10
863	–	1 f. 70 grey	1·50	25
864	–	1 f. 80 red	1·50	15
865	–	2 f. blue	1·75	10
866	–	2 f. 50 brown	2·00	25
866a	–	3 f. red	2·50	30
866b	–	3 f. 50 green	2·50	55

DESIGNS—As Type **203**: 10 c. Grisons. 15 c. Central Switzerland. 25 c. Jura. 30 c. Simmental. 35 c. Houses, Central Switzerland. 40 c. Vaud. 50 c. Valais. 60 c. Engadine. 70 c. Sopraceneri. 80 c. Eastern Switzerland. As Type **204**: 1 f. Rose window, Lausanne Cathedral. 1 f. 10, Gallus portal, Basel Cathedral. 1 f. 20, Romanesque capital, St.-Jean-Baptiste Church, Grandson. 1 f. 50, Medallion, St Georgen Monestry, Stein am Rhein. 1 f. 70, Roman Capital, St.-Jean-Baptiste Church, Grandson. 1 f. 80, Gargoyle, Berne Cathedral. 2 f. Oriel, Schaffhausen. 2 f. 50, Weathercock, St. Ursues Cathedral, Solothurn. 3 f. Font, St. Maurice Church, Saanen. 3 f. 50, Astronomical clock, Berne.

205. Europa " Posthorn ".

1973. Europa.

867	**205**	25 c. yellow and red	25	20
868		40 c. yellow and blue	40	25

1973. Pro Patria. For National Day Collection. Archaeological Discoveries. (2nd series). As T **199**, but horiz. Mult.

869.	15 c.+5 c. Rauraric jar	20	20
870.	30 c.+10 c. Head of a Gaul (bronze)	35	20
871.	40 c.+20 c. Almannic "Fish" brooches	70	65
872.	60 c.+20 c. Gold bowl	90	95

206. Horological Emblem.

1973. Publicity Issue. Multicoloured.

873.	15 c. Type **206**	15	10
874.	30 c. Skiing emblem	25	10
875.	40 c. Face of child	40	30

SUBJECTS: 15 c. Inaug. (1974) of Int. Horological Museum, Neuchatel. 30 c. World Alpine Skiing Championships, St. Moritz (1974). 40 c. "Terre des Hommes" (Child-care organisation).

207. Global Hostels.

209. "Continuity" (Max Bill).

1974. Publicity Issue. Multicoloured.

876.	15 c. Type **207**	15	10
877.	30 c. Gymnast and hurdlers	30	10
878.	40 c. Pistol and target	40	40

SUBJECTS: 15 c. "50 Years of Swiss Youth Hostels". 30 c. Centenary of Swiss Workmen's Gymnastics and Sports Assn. (S.A.T.U.S.). 40 c. World Shooting Championships, 1974.

1974. Europa. Swiss Sculptures.

880	**209**	30 c. black and red	25	10
881	–	40 c. brown, blue & blk	40	35

DESIGN: 40 c. "Amazone" (Carl Burckhardt).

210. Eugene Borel (first director of International Bureau, U.P.U.).

211. View of Berne.

1974. Centenary of U.P.U.

882.	**210.**	30 c. black and pink	25	10
883.	–	40 c. black and grey	40	35
884.	–	80 c. black and green	75	70

DESIGNS: 40 c. Heinrich von Stephan (founder of U.P.U.). 80 c. Montgomery Blair (U.S. Postmaster-General and initiator of 1863 Paris Postal Conference).

1974. 17th U.P.U. Congress, Lausanne. Multicoloured.

885.	30 c. Type **211**	30	25
886.	30 c. View of Lausanne	30	25

1974. Pro Patria. For National Day Collection. Archaeological Discoveries (3rd series). As T **199** but horiz. Multicoloured.

887.	15 c.+5 c. Glass bowl	25	20
888.	30 c.+10 c. Bull's head (bronze)	35	15
889.	40 c.+20 c. Gold brooch	65	65
890.	60 c.+20 c. "Bird" vessel (clay)	80	95

212. "Oath of Allegiance" (sculpture) (W. Witschi).

1974. Publicity Issue.

891	**212**	15 c. deep green, green and lilac	15	10
892	–	30 c. multicoloured	25	10
893	–	30 c. multicoloured	25	10

EVENTS AND COMMEMORATIONS: No. 891, Centenary of Federal Constitution. No. 892, Foundation emblem (Aid for Swiss Sport Foundation). No. 893, Posthorn and "postal transit" arrow (125th anniv of Federal Posts).

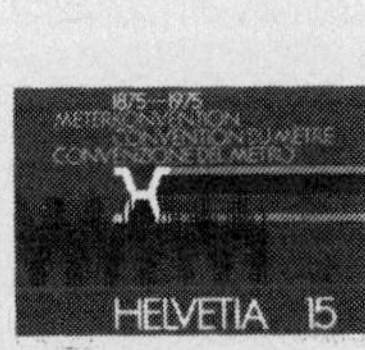

213. " Metre " and Krypton Line.

214. " The Monch " (F. Hodler).

1975. Publicity Issue.

894	**213**	15 c. orange, bl & grn	15	10
895	–	30 c. brown, pur & yell	25	10
896	–	60 c. red, black & blue	50	45
897	–	90 c. multicoloured	85	70

DESIGNS AND EVENTS: 15 c. Centenary of International Metre Convention. 30 c. Women talking (International Women's Year). 60 c. Red Cross Flag and barbed-wire (Conference on Humanitarian International Law, Geneva). 90 c. Airship "Ville de Lucerne", 1910. ("Aviation and Space Travel" Exhibition, Transport and Communications Museum, Lucerne).

1975. Europa. Paintings. Multicoloured.

898.	30 c. Type **214**	30	10
899.	50 c. " Still Life with Guitar " (R. Auberjonois)	50	40
900.	60 c. " L'effeuilleuse " (M. Barraud)	60	50

1975. Pro Patria. Archaeological Discoveries. (4th series). As T **199**. Multicoloured.

901.	15 c.+10 c. Gold brooch, Oron-le-Chatel	25	25
902.	30 c.+20 c. Bronze head of Bacchus, Avenches	40	30
903.	50 c.+20 c. Bronze daggers, Bois-de-Vaux, Lausanne	75	75
904.	60 c.+25 c. Glass decanter, Maralto	80	80

215. " Eliminate Obstacles! " Disabled Person in Wheelchair being dragged up steps.

1975. Publicity Issue.

905	**215**	15 c. black, grn & lilac	15	10
906	–	30 c. black, pink & red	25	10
907	–	50 c. brown and bistre	50	45
908	–	60 c. multicoloured	60	45

DESIGNS: 30 c. Organization emblem (Interconfessional Pastoral Care by Telephone Organization). 50 c. European Architectural Heritage Year emblem. 60 c. Beat Fischer von Reichenbach (founder) (300th anniv of Fischer postal service).

216. Forest Scene (Federal Forest Laws Cent.).

217. Floral Embroidery.

1976. Publicity Issue.

909	**216**	20 c. multicoloured	15	10
910	–	40 c. multicoloured	30	10
911	–	40 c. black, orge & pur	30	10
912	–	80 c. black and blue	75	60

DESIGNS: No. 910, Fruit and vegetables (campaign to promote nutriments as opposed to alcohol). 911, African child (fight against leprosy). 912, Early and modern telephones (telephone centenary).

1976. Europa. Handicrafts.

913	**217**	40 c. yell, brn & pink	35	10
914	–	80 c. blue, red & orchre	70	55

DESIGN: 80 c. Decorated pocket watch.

218. Kyburg Castle, Zurich.

219. Roe Deer, Barn Swallow and Frog (World Fed. for Protection of Animals).

1976. Pro Patria. Swiss Castles (1st series). Multicoloured.

915.	20 c.+10 c. Type **218**	30	25
916.	40 c.+20 c. Grandson, Vaud	60	25
917.	40 c.+20 c. Murten, Fribourg	60	25
918.	80 c.+40 c. Bellinzona, Ticino	1·25	1·25

See also Nos. 932/5, 955/8 and 977/80.

1976. Publicity Issue.

919	**219**	20 c. black, brn & grn	25	10
920	–	40 c. black, yell & red	30	10
921	–	40 c. multicoloured	40	10
922	–	80 c. red, violet & blue	75	70

DESIGNS: No. 920, "Sun" and inscription ("Save Energy" campaign). 921, St. Gotthard mountains (Swiss Alps). 922, Skater (World Speed Skating Championships, Davos).

220. Oskar Bider.

221. Blue Cross (society for care of alcoholics—Cent.).

1977. Aviation Pioneers.

923.	**220.**	40 c. blk., mauve & red	35	10
924.	–	80 c. blk., pur. and blue	90	80
925.	–	100 c. blk., grn. & bistre	90	70
926.	–	150 c. blk., brn. & turq.	1·50	1·00

DESIGNS: 80 c. Eduard Spelterini. 100 c. Armand Dufaux. 150 c. Walter Mittelholzer.

1977. Publicity Issues.

927.	**221.**	20 c. blue and brown	15	10
928.	–	40 c. multicoloured	35	10
929.	–	80 c. multicoloured	80	75

DESIGNS: 40 c. Festival emblem (Vevey vintage festival). 80 c. Balloons carrying letters (" Juphilex 1977 " youth stamp exhibition, Berne).

222. St. Ursanne.

223. Factory Worker.

1977. Europa. Landscapes. Multicoloured.

930.	40 c. Type **222**	35	10
931.	80 c. Sils-Baselgia	65	55

1977. Pro Patria. Swiss Castles (2nd series). As T **218**. Multicoloured.

932.	20 c.+10 c. Aigle, Vaud	25	25
933.	40 c.+20 c. Pratteln, Basel-Landschaft	40	15
934.	70 c.+30 c. Sargans, St. Gallen	1·00	1·25
935.	80 c.+40 c. Hallwil, Aargau	1·10	1·25

1977. Publicity Issue. Multicoloured.

936.	20 c. Type **223**	15	10
937.	40 c. Ionic capital	35	10
938.	80 c. Association emblem and butterfly	75	75

EVENTS. 20 c. Centenary of Federal Factories Act. 40 c. Protection of cultural monuments. 80 c. Swiss Footpaths Association.

224. Sternsingen, Bergun.

225. Mailcoach Route Plate, Vaud Canton.

1977. Regional Folk Customs.

939.	**224.**	5 c. green	10	10
940.	–	10 c. red	10	10
941.	–	20 c. orange	15	10
941b.	–	25 c. brown	40	15
941c.	–	30 c. green	35	10
942.	–	35 c. green	35	10
943.	–	40 c. red	35	10
943c.	–	45 c. blue	50	35
944.	–	50 c. red	45	10
944b.	–	60 c. brown	70	40
945.	–	70 c. lilac	65	10
946.	–	80 c. blue	75	20
947.	–	90 c. brown	85	25

DESIGNS: 10 c. Sechselauten, Zurich. 20 c. Silvesterklause, Herisau. 25 c. Chesstete, Solothurn. 30 c. Rollelibutzen, Alstatten. 35 c. Gansabhauet, Sursee. 40 c. Escalade, Geneva. 45 c. Klausjagen, Kussnacht. 50 c. Archetringele, Laupen. 60 c. Schnabelgeissen, Ottenbach. 70 c. Processioni storiche, Mendrisio. 80 c. Vogel Gryff, Basel. 90 c. Roitschaggata, Lotschental.

1978. Publicity Issue. Multicoloured.

948.	20 c. Type **225**	15	10
949.	40 c. View of Lucerne	35	10
950.	70 c. Title page of book " Melusine "	60	50
951.	80 c. Stylised camera and lens	70	70

EVENTS: 20 c. "Lemanex'78" National Stamp Exhibition. 40 c. 800th Anniv. of Lucerne. 70 c. 500th Anniv. of Printing at Geneva. 80 c. 2nd International Triennial Exhibition of Photography, Fribourg.

227. Stockalper Palace, Brig.

228. Abbe Joseph Bovet (composer).

1978. Europa.

953	**227**	40 c. multicoloured	35	10
954	–	80 c. blue, brown & blk	70	59

DESIGN: 80 c. Old Diet Hall, Berne.

1978. Pro Patria. Swiss Castles (3rd series). As T **218**.
955. 20 c.+10 c. Hagenwil, Thurgau 25 25
956. 40 c.+20 c. Burgdorf, Berne 40 20
957. 70 c.+30 c. Tarasp, Graubunden .. .. 1·00 1·25
958. 80 c.+40 c. Chillon, Vaud 1·10 1·25

1978. Celebrities.
959. **228.** 20 c. green 15 10
960. – 40 c. purple 35 10
961. – 70 c. grey .. .. 1·10 1·25
962. – 80 c. blue .. .. 2·50 2·75
DESIGNS: 40 c. Henri Dunant (founder of Red Cross). 70 c. Carl Gustav Jung (psychiatrist). 80 c. Auguste Piccard (physicist).

229. Worker wearing Goggles.

1978. Safety at Work. Multicoloured.
963. 40 c. Type **229** 40 15
964. 40 c. Worker wearing respirator 40 15
965. 40 c. Worker wearing safety helmet 40 15

230. Arms of Switzerland and Jura.

1978. Creation of Canton of Jura.
966 **230** 40 c. red, black & ochre 35 10

231. Rainer Maria Rilke (writer).

232. Othmar H. Ammann and Verrazano Narrows Bridge.

1979. Celebrities.
967. **231.** 20 c. green 15 10
968. – 40 c. red 35 10
969. – 70 c. brown 60 50
970. – 80 c. blue 70 50
DESIGNS: 40 c. Paul Klee (artist). 70 c. Hermann Hesse (novelist and poet). 80 c. Thomas Mann (novelist).

1979. Publicity Issue. Multicoloured.
971. 20 c. Type **232** 15 10
972. 40 c. Target and marker .. 30 10
973. 70 c. Hot-air balloon .. 70 55
974. 80 c. Aircraft tail fins .. 80 60
SUBJECTS: 20 c. Birth Centenary of O. H. Ammann (engineer). 40 c. 50th Federal Riflemen's Festival, Lucerne. 70 c. World Esperanto Congress, Lucerne. 80 c. Basel-Mulhouse Airport.

233. Old Letter Box, Basel.

234. Gold Stater.

1979. Europa.
975 **233** 40 c. multicoloured .. 35 10
976 – 80 c. blue, lt bl & ochre 75 70
DESIGN: 80 c. Alpine relay station on the Jungfraujoch.

1979. Pro Patria. Swiss Castles (4th series). As T **218**. Multicoloured.
977. 20 c.+10 c. Oron, Vaud .. 25 25
978. 40 c.+20 c. Spiez, Berne .. 40 15
979. 70 c.+30 c. Porrentruy, Jura 90 90
980. 80 c.+40 c. Rapperswil, St. Gallen .. .. .. 1·10 1·10

1979. Publicity Issue. Multicoloured.
981. 20 c. Type **234** 15 10
982. 40 c. Child on dove (horiz.) 35 10
983. 70 c. Morse key and satellite (horiz.) 60 50
984. 80 c. "Ariane" rocket .. 70 50
EVENTS: 20 c. Centenary of Swiss Numismatic Society. 40 c. International Year of the Child. 70 c. 50th Anniv. of Swiss Radio Amateurs. 80 c. European Space Agency programme.

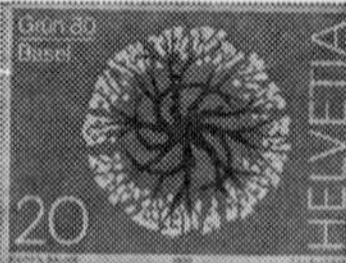

235. Tree in Blossom.

236. Johann Konrad Kern (politician).

1980. Publicity Issue. Multicoloured.
985. 20 c. Type **235** 15 10
986. 40 c. Milk vessel 35 10
987. 70 c. Winterthur Town Hall 60 50
988. 80 c. "Pic-Pic" motor car 80 65
SUBJECTS: 20 c. "Grun 80" Horticultural and Landscape Gardening Exhibition, Basel. 40 c. 50th anniv of Swiss Arts and Crafts Centre. 70 c. Centenary of Society for Swiss Art History. 80 c. 50th International Motor Show, Geneva.

1980. Europa.
989. **236.** 40 c. flesh, black & pink 35 10
990. – 80 c. flesh, blk. & blue 70 60
DESIGN: 80 c. Gustav Adolf Hasler (communications pioneer).

237. Mason and Carpenter.

238. Girocheque and Letter Box.

1980. Pro Patria. Trade and Craft Signs. Mult.
991. 20 c.+10 c. Type **237** .. 25 25
992. 40 c.+20 c. Barber .. 45 15
993. 70 c.+30 c. Hatter .. 90 1·00
994. 80 c.+40 c. Baker .. 1·10 1·10

1980. Swiss PTT Services.
995. **238.** 20 c. multicoloured .. 15 10
996. – 40 c. multicoloured .. 40 10
997. – 70 c. brn., blk. & lilac 65 50
998. – 80 c. multicoloured .. 80 55
DESIGNS: 40 c. Postbus. 70 c. Transfer roller (50th anniv of PTT postage stamp printing office). 80 c. Flowers and telephone (centenary of telephone in Switzerland).

239. Weather Chart.

1980. Publicity. Multicoloured.
999. 20 c. Type **239** 15 10
1000. 40 c. Figures and cross .. 35 10
1001. 80 c. Motorway sign .. 90 90
SUBJECTS: 20 c. Centenary of Swiss Meteorological Office. 40 c. Centenary of Swiss Trades Union Federation. 80 c. Opening of St. Gotthard road tunnel.

240. Granary from Kiesen.

1981. Publicity Issue. Multicoloured.
1002. 20 c. Type **240** 15 10
1003. 40 c. Disabled figures .. 35 10
1004. 70 c. "The Parish Clerk" (Albert Anker) (vert.) 70 70
1005. 80 c. Theodolite 75 55
1006. 110 c. Tail of DC9-81 .. 1·00 85
SUBJECTS: 20 c. Ballenberg Open-air Museum. 40 c. International Year of Disabled Persons. 70 c. 150th birth anniv of Albert Anker (artist). 80 c. 16th International Federation of Surveyors Congress, Montreux. 110 c. 50th anniv of Swissair.

241. Figure leaping from Earth.

242. Dancing Couple.

1981. 50th Anniv. of Swissair.
1007. **241.** 2 f.+1 f. lilac, violet and yellow .. 2·00 2·00

1981. Europa. Multicoloured.
1008. 40 c. Type **242** 35 10
1009. 80 c. Stone putter .. 80 70

243 Aarburg Post Office Sign, 1685.

244. Seal of Fribourg.

1981. Pro Patria. Postal Signs. Multicoloured.
1010 20 c.+10 c. Type **243** .. 30 30
1011 40 c.+20 c. Mail coach sign of Fribourg Cantonal office .. 50 20
1012 70 c.+30 c. Gordola post office sign (Ticino Cantonal Post) .. 90 95
1013 80 c.+40 c. Splugen post office sign .. .. 1·10 1·10

1981. 500th Anniv of Covenant of Stans.
1014 **244** 40 c. red, black & brn 35 15
1015 – 40 c. green, blk & red 35 15
1016 – 80 c. brown, blk & bl 70 60
DESIGNS: 40 c. (No. 1015) Seal of Solothurn. 80 c. Old Town Hall, Stans.

245. Voltage Regulator from Jungfrau Railway's Power Station.

1981. Publicity Issue. Multicoloured.
1017. 20 c. Type **245** 20 10
1018. 40 c. Crossbow quality seal 40 10
1019. 70 c. Group of youths .. 70 60
1020. 1 f. 10 Mosaic .. .. 1·00 85
SUBJECTS: 20 c. Opening of Technorama of Switzerland, Winterthur (museum of science and technology). 40 c. 50th anniv of Organization for Promotion of Swiss Products and Services. 70 c. 50th anniv of Swiss Association of Youth Organizations. 1 f. 10, Restoration of St. Peter's Cathedral, Geneva.

246. "C 4/5" Class Steam Locomotive.

1982. Centenary of St. Gotthard Railway.
1021 **246** 40 c. black and purple 35 20
1022 – 40 c. multicoloured .. 35 20
DESIGN: No. 1022, "Re 6/6" class electric locomotive.

247. Hoteliers Association Emblem.

1982. Publicity Issue. Multicoloured.
1023. 20 c. Type **247** 15 10
1024. 40 c. Flag formed by four 'Fs' 35 10
1025. 70 c. Gas flame encircling emblem 60 50
1026. 80 c. Lynx and scientific instruments 70 50
1027. 110 c. Retort .. .. 1·00 75
SUBJECTS: 20 c. Centenary of Swiss Hoteliers Association. 40 c. 150th Anniv. of Swiss Gymnastics Association. 70 c. 50th Anniv. of International Gas Union. 80 c. 150th Anniv. of Natural History Museum, Berne. 110 c. Centenary of Swiss Society of Chemical Industries.

248. "Swearing Oath of Eternal Fealty, Rutli Meadow" (detail of mural, Heinrich Danioth).

1982. Europa. Multicoloured.
1028. 40 c. Type **248** 50 10
1029. 80 c. Treaty of 1291 founding Swiss Confederation 85 65

249. "The Sun", Willisau.

250. "Aquarius" and Old Berne.

1982. Pro Patria. Inn Signs (1st series). Multicoloured.
1030 20 c.+10 c. Type **249** .. 30 30
1031 40 c.+20 c. "On the Wave", St. Saphorin .. 55 20
1032 70 c.+30 c. "The Three Kings", Rheinfelden .. 90 1·00
1033 80 c.+40 c. "The Crown", Winterhur .. .. 1·00 1·00
See also Nos. 1056/9.

1982. Signs of the Zodiac and Landscapes.
1034 **250** 1 f. multicoloured .. 80 10
1035 – 1 f. 10 brn, bl & vio 90 10
1036 – 1 f. 20 grn, bl & brn 1·00 10
1036a – 1 f. 40 multicoloured 1·10 75
1037 – 1 f. 50 deep blue, blue and orange .. 1·25 15
1038 – 1 f. 60 multicoloured 1·60 75
1039 – 1 f. 70 blue, brown and turquoise .. 1·40 10
1040 – 1 f. 80 brown, green and deep green .. 1·50 35
1041 – 2 f. blue, brn & dp bl 2·25 1·25
1042 – 2 f. blue, brn & dp bl 1·60 20
1042a – 2 f. 50, red, green and deep green .. 2·00 35
1043 – 3 f. red, green & blk 2·40 15
1044 – 4 f. green, vio & pur 3·25 40
1045 – 4 f. 50 ochre, blue and brown .. 3·75 60
DESIGNS 1 f. 10, "Pisces" and Nax near Sion. 1 f. 20, "Aries" and the Graustock, Obwalden. 1 f. 40, "Gemini" and Bischofszell. 1 f. 50, "Taurus" and Basel Cathedral. 1 f. 60, "Gemini" and Schonengrund. 1 f. 70, "Cancer" and Wetterhorn. 1 f. 80, "Leo" and Areuse Gorge. 2 f. (1041), "Virgo" and Aletsch Glacier. 2 f. (1042), "Virgo" and Schwarzsee above Zermatt. 2 f. 50, "Libra" and Fechy. 3 f. "Scorpio" and Corippo. 4 f. "Sagittarius" and Glarus. 4 f. 50, "Capricorn" and Schuls.

251. Articulated Tram.

1982. Publicity Issue. Multicoloured.
1046. 20 c. Type **251** 20 15
1047. 40 c. Salvation Army singer and guitarist .. 40 10
1048. 70 c. Dressage rider .. 75 55
1049. 80 c. Emblem 80 50
SUBJECTS: 20 c. Centenary of Zurich trams. 40 c. Centenary of Salvation Army in Switzerland. 70 c. World Dressage Championship, Lausanne. 80 c. 14th International Water Supply Association Congress, Zurich.

252. Perch.

253. Jost Burgi's Celestial Globe, 1594.

1983. **Publicity Issue. Multicoloured.**

1050. 20 c. Type **252** 20 10
1051. 40 c. University of Zurich 40 10
1052. 70 c Teleprinter tape forming "JP" .. 70 50
1053. 80 c. Micrometer and cycloidal computer drawing 80 50

EVENTS: 20 c. Centenary of Swiss Fishing and Pisciculture Federation. 40 c. 150th anniv. of University of Zurich. 70 c. Centenary of Swiss Journalists' Federation. 80 c. Centenary of Swiss Machine Manufacturers' Association.

1983. Europa.

1054. **253.** 40 c. orange, pink and brown 35 10
1055. – 80 c. grn., blue & blk. 70 60

DESIGN: 80 c. Niklaus Riggenbach's rack and pinion railway, 1871.

1983. Pro Patria. Inn Sings (2nd series). As T **249**. Multicoloured.

1056. 20 c.+10 c. "The Lion", Heimiswil 30 30
1057. 40 c.+20 c. "The Cross", Sachseln 60 20
1058. 70 c.+30 c. "The Jug", Lenzburg Castle .. 95 95
1059. 80 c.+40 c. "The Cavalier", St. George .. 1·10 1·00

254. Seal, 1832–48.

255. Gallo-Roman Capital, Martigny.

1983. 150th Anniv. of Basel-Land Canton.

1060. **254.** 40 c. multicoloured .. 35 10

1983. **Publicity Issue.**

1061. **255.** **20 c. orange and black** 25 10
1062. – **40 c. multicoloured** .. 45 10
1063. – **70 c. multicoloured** .. 75 60
1064. – **80 c. multicoloured** .. 75 60

DESIGNS: 20 c. Type **255** (Bimillenary of Octodurus/Martigny). 40 c. Bernese shepherd-dog and Schwyz hunting dog (Centenary of Swiss Kennel Club). 70 c. Cyclists (Centenary of Swiss Cyclists and Motor Cyclists Federation. 80 c. Carrier pigeon and world map (World Communications Year).

256. Pre-stamp Cover, 1839.

257. Bridge.

1984. Publicity Issue. Multicoloured.

1065. 25 c. Type **256** 25 15
1066. 50 c. Collegiate Church clock and buildings .. 50 10
1067. 80 c. Olympic rings and Lausanne 80 50

SUBJECTS: 25 c. National Stamp Exhibition, Zurich. 50 c. 1100th anniv. of Saint-Imier. 80 c. Permanent headquarters of International Olympic Committee at Lausanne.

1984. Europa. 25th Anniv. of European Posts and Telecommunications Conference.

1068 **257** 50 c. purple, red and crimson 40 10
1069 80 c. ultramarine, blue and deep blue .. 75 55

258. Hexagonal Stove from Rosenburg Mansion, Stans.

260. Burning Match.

1984. Pro Patria. Tiled Stoves. Mult.

1070. 35 c.+15 c. Type **258** .. 50 30
1071. 50 c.+20 c. Winterthur stove (by Hans Heinrich Pfau) Freuler Palace, Nafels 70 20
1072. 70 c.+30 c. Box-stove (by Rudolf Stern) from Plaisance, Riaz .. 90 1·00
1073. 80 c.+40 c. Frame-modelled stove (by Leonard Racle) .. 1·25 1·10

1984. Fire Prevention.

1075. **260.** 50 c. multicoloured .. 40 10

261. Railway Conductor's Equipment.

262. Ernest Ansermet (orchestral conductor).

1985. Publicity Issue. Multicoloured.

1076 35 c. Type **261** (cent of Train Staff Association) 40 15
1077 50 c. Stone with Latin inscription (200 years of Rhaeto-Romanic culture) 50 10
1078 70 c. Rescue of man (cent of International Lake Geneva Resue Society) 70 60
1079 80 c. Grande Dixence dam (International Large Dams Congress, Lausanne) 80 60

1985. Europa. Music Year. Multicoloured.

1080. 50 c. Type **262** 50 10
1081. 80 c. Frank Martin (composer) 85 60

263. Music Box, 1895.

1985. Pro Patria. Musical Instruments. Multicoloured.

1082. 25 c.+10 c. Type **263** .. 35 35
1083. 35 c.+15 c. 18th-century box rattle 50 50
1084. 50 c.+20 c. Emmental necked zither (by Peter Zaugg), 1828 .. 65 20
1085. 70 c.+30 c. Drum, 1571 1·00 1·00
1086. 80 c.+40 c. 20th-century diatonic accordion .. 1·25 1·00

264. Baker.

1985. Publicity Issue. Multicoloured.

1087. 50 c. Type **264** (centenary of Swiss Master Bakers' and Confectioners' Federation) 50 10
1088. 70 c. Cross on abstract background (50th anniv of Swiss Radio International) .. 70 60
1089. 80 c. Geometric pattern and emblem (Postal, Telegraph and Telephone International World Congress, Interlaken) 80 70

265. Intertwined Ropes.

1986. Publicity Issue.

1090. **265.** 35 c. multicoloured .. 35 15
1091. – 50 c. deep brown, brown and red .. 15 10
1092. – 80 c. orange, green and black .. 80 60
1093. – 90 c. multicoloured .. 90 60
1094. – 1 f. 10 multicoloured 1·10 95

DESIGNS: 35 c. Type **265** (50th anniv of Swiss Workers' Relief Organization). 50 c. Battle site on 1698 map (600th anniv of Battle of Sempach). 80 c. Statuette of Mercury (2000th anniv of Roman Chur). 90 c. Gallic head (2000th anniv of Vindonissa). 1 f. 10 Roman coin of Augustus (2000th anniv of Zurich).

266. Sportsmen.

267. Woman's Head.

1986. Pro Sport.

1095. **266.** 50 c.+20 c. mult. .. 70 50

1986. Europa. Multicoloured.

1096. 50 c. Type **267** 50 10
1097. 90 c. Man's head .. 90 60

268. "Bridge in the Sun" (Giovanni Gaicometti).

269. Franz Mail Van.

1986. Pro Patria. Paintings. Multicoloured.

1098. 35 c.+15 c. Type **268** .. 50 30
1099. 50 c.+20 c. "The Violet Hat" (Cuno Amiet) .. 70 20
1100. 80 c.+40 c. "After the Funeral" (Max Buri) 1·10 1·10
1101. 90 c.+40 c. "Still Life" (Felix Vallotton) .. 1·25 1·10

1986. The Post Past and Present.

1102 **269** 5 c. yellow, pur & red 10 10
1103 – 10 c. deep green, green and orange .. 10 10
1104 – 20 c. orange, brn & bl 20 15
1105 – 25 c. deep blue, blue and yellow .. 25 10
1106 – 30 c. grey, blk & yell 25 15
1107 – 35 c. lake, red and yell 30 15
1108 – 45 c. blue, black & brn 40 20
1109 – 50 c. violet, grn & pur 45 10
1110 – 60 c. orge, yell & brn 55 20
1111 – 75 c. grn, dp grn & red 70 45
1112 – 80 c. indigo, bl & brn 75 25
1113 – 90 c. deep green, brown and green .. 80 25

DESIGNS: 10 c. Mechanized parcel sorting; 20 c. Mule post; 25 c. Letter cancelling machine; 30 c. Stagecoach; 35 c. Post Office counter clerk; 45 c. Paddle-steamer "Stadt Luzern", 1830s; 50 c. Postman; 60 c. Loading mail bags onto airplane; 75 c. 17th-century mounted courier; 80 c. Town postman, 1900s; 90 c. Interior of railway mail sorting carriage.

270. Stylized Doves (International Peace Year).

1986. Publicity Issue. Multicoloured.

1115 35 c. Type **270** 35 20
1116 50 c. Sun behind snow-covered tree (50th anniv of Swiss Winter Relief Fund) 45 10
1117 80 c. Symbols of literature and art (cent of Berne Convention for protection of literary and artistic copyright) .. 85 70
1118 90 c. Red Cross, Red Crescent and symbols of aggression (25th Int Red Cross Conference meeting, Geneva) .. 95 70

271. Mobile Post Office.

1987. Publicity Issue. Multicoloured.

1119 35 c. Type **271** (50th anniv of mobile post offices) 40 20
1120 50 c. Lecturers of the seven faculties (450th anniv of Lausanne University) 45 10
1121 80 c. Profile, maple leaf and logarithmic spiral (150th anniv of Swiss Engineers' and Architects' Association) 90 80
1122 90 c. Airplane and electric train (Geneva Airport rail link) .. .. 1·00 80
1123 1 f. 10 Symbolic figure and water (2000th anniv of Baden thermal springs) .. .. 1·25 1·25

272. "Scarabaeus" (Bernhard Luginbuhl).

1987. Europa. Sculpture. Multicoloured.

1124 50 c. Type **272** 50 10
1125 90 c. "Carnival Fountain", Basel (Jean Tinguely) 90 85

273. Wall Cabinet, 1764.

1987. Pro Patria. Rustic Furniture. Mult.

1126. 35 c.+15 c. Type **273** .. 70 50
1127. 50 c.+20 c. 16th-century chest 85 70
1128. 80 c.+40 c. Cradle, 1782 1·25 1·40
1129. 90 c.+40 c. Wardrobe, 1698 .. .. .. 1·25 1·50

274. Butcher cutting Chops.

275. Zug Clock Tower.

1987. Publicity Issue. Multicoloured.

1130. 35 c. Type **274** (centenary of Swiss Master Butchers' Federation) 40 25
1131. 50 c. Profiles on stamps (50th anniv. of Stamp Day) 50 10
1132. 90 c. Cheesemaker breaking up curds (centenary of Swiss Dairying Association) 90 90

1987. Bicentenary of Tourism. Multicoloured.

1133. 50 c. Type **275** 55 10
1134. 80 c. St. Charles's church, Negrentino, Prugiasco/Blenio valley 85 80
1135. 90 c. Witches Tower, Sion 95 80
1136. 1 f. 40 Jorgenberg Castle, Waltensburg/Vuorz, Surselva .. .. 1·50 1·40

1987. Flood Victims Relief Fund. No. 1109 surch **7.9.87+50** and clasped hands.

1138 50 c.+50 c. vio, grn & pur 1·25 90

277. Society Emblem.

1988. Publicity Issue. Multicoloured.

1139 25 c. Type **277** (cent of Swiss Women's Benevolent Society) .. 35 20
1140 35 c. Brushing woman's hair (centenary of Swiss Master Hairdresser's Association) 40 25

1141 50 c. St. Fridolin banner and detail of Aegidius Tschudy's manuscript (600th anniv of Battle of Naefels) 50 10
1142 80 c. Map and farming country seen from Beromunster radio tower (European Campaign for Rural Areas) 80 80
1143 90 c. Girl playing shawm (50th anniv of Lucerne Int Music Festival) .. 1·00 90

278. "Auntie Ju" flying past Matterhorn.

279. Rudolf von Neuenburg.

1988. 50th Anniv. of Pro Aero Foundation.
1144. **278.** 140 c.+60 c. mult. .. 2·75 2·75

1988. Pro Patria. Minnesingers. Mult.
1145 35 c.+15 c. Type **279** .. 65 50
1146 50 c.+20 c. Rudolf von Rotenburg 85 25
1147 80 c.+40 c. Johannes Hadlaub .. .. 1·40 1·40
1148 90 c.+40 c. Hardegger .. 1·60 1·40

280 Arrows on Map of Europe

281 Snap Link

1988. Europa. Transport and Communications.
1149 **280** 50 c. bistre, emerald and green 50 10
1150 – 90 c. lilac, green & vio 1·00 80
DESIGN: 90 c. Computer circuit on map of Europe.

1988. Publicity Issue. Multicoloured.
1151 35 c. Type **281** (50th anniv of Swiss Accident Prevention Office) .. 40 25
1152 50 c. Drilling letters (cent of Swiss Metalworkers' and Watchmakers' Association) 50 10
1153 80 c. Triangulation pyramid, theodolite and map (150th anniv of Swiss Federal Office of Topography) 90 80
1154 90 c. International Red Cross Museum, Geneva (inauguration) .. 1·00 90

282 "Meta" (Jean Tinguely)

1988. Modern Art.
1155 **282** 90 c. multicoloured .. 4·00 4·00

283 Army Postman

1989. Publicity Issue. Multicoloured.
1156 25 c. Type **283** (centenary of Swiss Army postal service) 30 20
1157 35 c. Fontaine du Sauvage and Porte au Loup, Delemont (700th anniv of granting of town charter) 35 30
1158 50 c. Eye and composite wheel (cent of Public Transport Association) 50 10
1159 80 c. Diesel train on viaduct (centenary of Rhaetian railway) .. 90 80
1160 90 c. St. Bernard dog and hospice (2000th anniv of Great St. Bernard Pass) 1·00 80

284 King Friedrich II presenting Berne Town Charter (Bendicht Tschachtlan Chronicle)

285 Hopscotch

1989. Pro Patria. Medieval Chronicles. Multicoloured.
1161 35 c.+15 c. Type **284** .. 60 50
1162 50 c.+20 c. Adrian von Bubenberg watching troops entering Murten (Diebold Schilling's Berne Chronicle) .. 80 20
1163 80 c.+40 c. Messenger presenting missive to Council of Zurich (Gerold Edlibach Chronicle) .. .. 1·40 1·40
1164 90 c.+40 c. Schilling presenting Chronicle to Council of Lucerne (Diebold Schilling's Lucerne Chronicle) .. 1·50 1·40

1989. Europa. Children's Games. Mult.
1165 50 c. Type **285** 50 15
1166 90 c. Blind-man's buff .. 90 85

286 Bricklayer

287 Testing Device

1989. Occupations.
1168 **286** 2 f. 75 pur, blk & yell 2·50 50
1169 – 2 f. 80 yell, brn & bl 2·50 50
1171 – 3 f. 60 orge, brn & pur 3·25 70
1173 – 3 f. 75 deep green, green & light green 1·40 75
1174 – 5 f. ultram, stone & bl 4·75 1·40
1175 – 5 f. 50 grey, red and mauve .. 5·00 1·00
DESIGNS: 2 f. 80, Cook; 3 f. 60, Pharmacist; 3 f. 75 Fisherman; 5 f. Cheesemaker; 5 f. 50, Dressmaker.

1989. Publicity Issue. Multicoloured.
1181 35 c. Type **287** (cent of Swiss Electrotechnical Association) 40 20
1182 50 c. Family on butterfly (50th anniv of Swiss Travel Fund) 55 10
1183 80 c. "Wisdom" and "Science" (bronze statues) (centenary of Fribourg University) .. 90 75
1184 90 c. Audio tape (1st anniv of National Sound Archives) .. 1·00 85
1185 1 f. 40 Bands of colour forming bridge (centenary of Inter-parliamentary Union) 1·60 1·50

288 Exercises

1989. Pro Sport.
1186 **288** 50 c.+20 c. mult .. 85 75

289 1882 5 c. and 50 c. Stamps and Emblem

290 Cats

1990. Publicity Issue. Multicoloured.
1187 25 c. Type **289** (centenary of Union of Swiss Philatelic Societies) .. 30 20
1188 35 c. Locomotive and control car (inauguration of Zurich Rapid Transit System) .. 40 30
1189 50 c. Mountain farmer (50th anniv of Assistance for Mountain Communities) .. 55 10
1190 90 c. Ice hockey players (A-series World Ice Hockey Championships, Berne and Fribourg) .. 95 90

1990. Animals. Multicoloured.
1192 10 c. Cow 10 10
1197 50 c. Type **290** 45 10
1199 70 c. Rabbit 65 25
1200 80 c. Barn owl 85 45
1201 100 c. Horse and foal .. 95 85
1202 120 c. Dog .. .. 1·10 1·00
1203 160 c. Turkey .. .. 1·50 50

291 Flyswats and Starch Sprinklers Seller

292 Lucerne Post Office

1990 Pro Patria. Street Criers. Engravings by David Herrliberger. Multicoloured.
1205 35 c.+15 c. Type **291** .. 65 50
1206 50 c.+20 c. Clock seller .. 80 20
1207 80 c.+40 c. Knife grinder 1·25 1·40
1208 90 c.+40 c. Couple selling pinewood sticks .. 1·40 1·50

1990. Europa. Post Office Buildings. Mult.
1209 50 c. Type **292** 50 15
1210 90 c. Geneva Post Office 85 75

293 Conrad Ferdinand Meyer (writer)

294 Anniversary Emblem and Crosses

1990. Celebrities.
1211 **293** 35 c. black and green 40 25
1212 – 50 c. black and blue 50 15
1213 – 80 c. black and yellow 80 75
1214 – 90 c. black and pink 80 80
DESIGNS: 50 c. Angelika Kauffmann (painter); 80 c. Blaise Cendrars (writer); 90 c. Frank Buchser (painter).

1990. 700th Anniv (1991) of Swiss Confederation (1st issue).
1215 50 c. Type **294** 50 15
1216 90 c. Emblem and crosses (different) 85 85
See also Nos. 1219/22 and 1224.

296 Figures on Jigsaw Pieces

1990. Population Census.
1218 **296** 50 c. multicoloured .. 50 15

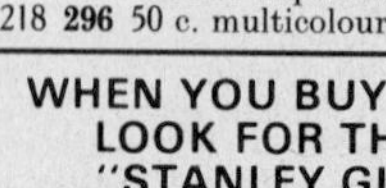

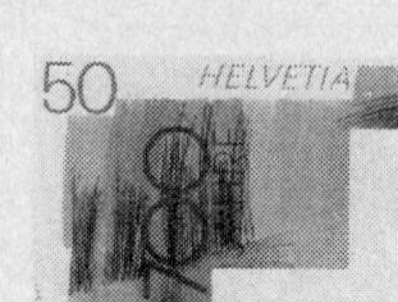

297 "700 JAHRE"

298 Alps and City Skyline

1991. 700th Anniv of Swiss Confederation (2nd issue). Multicoloured.
1219 50 c. Type **297** 45 15
1220 50 c. "700 ONNS" .. 45 15
1221 50 c. "700 ANS" .. 45 15
1222 50 c. "700 ANNI" .. 45 15
Nos. 1219/22 were printed together, se-tenant, forming a composite design of the Swiss cross in the centre.

1991. 800th Anniv of Berne.
1223 **298** 80 c. multicoloured .. 75 40

299 Federal Palace, Berne, and Capitol, Washington

1991. 700th Anniv of Swiss Confederation (3rd issue). Swiss Emigration to U.S.A.
1224 **299** 160 c. multicoloured 1·50 80

300 Jettison of "Ariane" Rocket Friction Protection Jacket

301 Abstract

1991. Europa. Europe in Space. Mult.
1225 50 c. Type **300** 50 15
1226 90 c. Orbit of Halley's Comet, "Giotto" space probe and its trajectory 85 75

1991. Pro Patria. Modern Art. Multicoloured.
1227 50 c.+20 c. Type **301** .. 75 20
1228 70 c.+30 c. Artist's monogram .. .. 1·00 1·00
1229 80 c.+40 c. "Labyrinth" 1·25 1·25
1230 90 c.+40 c. "Man and Beast" .. .. 1·40 1·50

302 Stone Bridge, Lavertezzo

1991. Bridges. Multicoloured.
1231 50 c. Type **302** 50 15
1232 70 c. Wooden Neubrugg, Bremgarten 65 75
1233 80 c. Koblenz-Felsenau iron truss railway bridge 75 75
1234 90 c. Ganter concrete bridge, Simplon Pass .. 85 80

303 P.T.T. Employees

304 Lake Moesola

1991. Centenary of Swiss Postal, Telephone and Telegraph Officials' Union.
1235 **303** 80 c. multicoloured .. 75 40

1991. Mountain Lakes.
1236 **304** 50 c. multicoloured .. 45 15
1237 – 80 c. brown, red & pur 75 15
DESIGN: 80 c. Fishing boat moored at jetty on Melchsee.

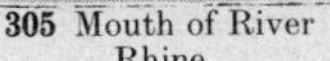

305 Mouth of River Rhine

306 Map of Americas and "Santa Maria"

1992. Publicity Issue. Multicoloured.

1238 50 c. Type **305** (centenary of Treaty for International Regulation of the Rhine) 45 25
1239 80 c. Family (50th anniv of Pro Familia) .. 75 40
1240 90 c. Chemical formula and model of difluorobutane molecule (cent of International Chemical Nomenclature Conference, Geneva) .. 80 70

1992. Europa. 500th Anniv of Discovery of America by Columbus. Multicoloured.

1241 50 c. Type **306** 45 15
1242 90 c. Route map of first voyage and sketch for statue of Columbus (Vincenzo Vela) .. 80 70

307 Skier

308 1780s Earthenware Plate, Heimberg

1992. Sierre International Comics Festival. Multicoloured.

1243 50 c. Type **307** 45 15
1244 80 c. Mouse-artist drawing strip 75 40
1245 90 c. Love-struck man holding bunch of stamp-flowers behind back 80 70

1992. Pro Patria. Folk Art. Multicoloured.

1246 50 c. +20 c. Type **308** .. 65 20
1247 70 c. +30 c. Paper cut-out by Johann Jakob Hauswirth 90 90
1248 80 c. +40 c. Maplewood cream spoon, Gruyeres 1·10 1·10
1249 90 c. +40 c. Carnation from 1780 embroidered saddle cloth, Grisons 1·25 1·25

309 Flags and Alps

310 Clowns on Trapeze

1992. Alpine Protection Convention.

1250 **309** 90 c. multicoloured .. 80 70

1992. The Circus. Multicoloured.

1251 50 c. Type **310** 45 15
1252 70 c. Sealion with Auguste the clown 65 60
1253 80 c. Chalky the clown and elephant 75 40
1254 90 c. Harlequin and horse 80 70

311 Sport Pictograms

1992. Pro Sport.

1255 **311** 50 c. +20 c. black & bl 65 65

312 Train and Map

313 "A" (first class) Mail

1992. Centenary (1993) of Central Office for International Rail Carriage.

1256 **312** 90 c. multicoloured .. 80 70

1993.

1257 **313** 60 c. dp blue, yell & bl 55 15
1258 – 80 c. red, orange and scarlet 75 40

DESIGN: 60 c. Lake Tanay.

314 Zurich and Geneva 1843 Stamps

315 Paracelsus (500th birth anniv) (after Augustin Hirschvogel)

1993. 150th Anniv of Swiss Postage Stamps. Multicoloured.

1259 60 c. Type **314** 55 15
1260 80 c. Postal cancellation (stamps for postage) .. 75 40
1261 100 c. Magnifying glass (stamp collecting) .. 95 85

1993. Publicity Issue.

1262 **315** 60 c. brn, grey & bl 55 15
1263 – 80 c. multicoloured 75 40
1264 – 180 c. mult 1·75 1·60

DESIGNS—VERT. 80 c. Discus thrower (from Greek vase) (inauguration of Olympic Museum, Lausanne). HORIZ. 180 c. Worker's head (centenary of International Metalworkers' Federation).

316 "Hohentwiel" (lake steamer) and Flags

317 Interior of Media House, Villeurbanne, France

1993. Lake Constance European Region.

1265 **316** 60 c. multicoloured .. 55 15

1993. Europa. Contemporary Architecture.

1266 **317** 60 c. bl, blk & grn 55 15
1267 – 80 c. red, black and grey 75 40

DESIGN: 80 c. House, Breganzona, Ticino.

318 Appenzell Dairyman's Earring

1993. Pro Patria. Folk Art. Multicoloured.

1268 60 c. +30 c. Type **318** .. 85 25
1269 60 c. +30 c. Fluhli enamelled glass bottle, 1738 .. .. .. 85 25
1270 80 c. +40 c. Driving cows to summer pasture (detail of mural, Sylvestre Pidoux) .. 1·10 1·10
1271 100 c. +40 c. Straw hat ornaments .. .. 1·25 1·25

319 "Work No. 095" (Emma Kunz)

320 Kapell Bridge and Water Tower, Lucerne

1993. Paintings by Swiss Women Artists. Multicoloured.

1272 60 c. Type **319** 55 15
1273 80 c. "Great Singer Lilas Goergens" (Aloise) (33 × 33 mm) 75 40
1274 100 c. "Under the Rain Cloud" (Meret Oppenheim) (33 × 33 mm) 95 85
1275 120 c. "Four Spaces with Horizontal Bands" (Sophi Taeuber-Arp) (33 × 33 mm) .. .. 1·10 1·00

1993. Kapell Bridge Restoration Fund.

1276 **320** 80 c. +20 c. carm & red 95 95

FRANK STAMPS

Issued to charity hospitals for free transmission of their mails.

F 21

F 49 Deaconess

1911. With control figures at top.

F268	F 21	2 c. red and green	10	15
F269		3 c. red and green	2·00	25
F270		5 c. red and green	60	10
F271		10 c. red and green	80	10
F272		15 c. red and green	15·00	2·00
F273		20 c. red and green	2·75	40

1935. With or without control figures.

F362B	F 49	5 c. green ..	1·25	2·25
F363B	–	10 c. violet ..	1·00	2·00
F364B	–	20 c. red	1·25	2·25

DESIGNS: 10 c. Sister of the Ingenbohl Order. 20 c. Henri Dunant (founder of Red Cross).

OFFICIAL STAMPS

1918. Optd **Industrielle Kriegs-wirtschaft.**

O308	20a	3 c. brown	4·25	15·00
O300		5 c. green	10·00	25·00
O310		7½ c. grey	5·50	14·00
O303	21	10 c. red on buff ..	13·00	30·00
O304		15 c. violet on buff	13·00	32·00
O313	17	20 c. yellow and red	9·00	30·00
O314		25 c. blue & dp blue	9·00	30·00
O315		30 c. green & brown	15·00	50·00

1938. Optd with Geneva Cross.

O381	52	3 c. olive	15	20
O382	–	5 c. green (No. 372) ..	15	20
O383	–	10 c. purple (No. 373b)	1·00	40
O384	–	15 c. orange (No. 374)	35	1·25
O385	–	20 c. red (No. 375d) ..	50	30
O386	–	25 c. brown (No. 376)	55	1·00
O387	–	30 c. blue (No. 377) ..	75	75
O388	–	35 c. green (No. 378) ..	70	1·00
O389	–	40 c. grey (No. 379) ..	70	50
O390	17	50 c. green & dp green	80	1·00
O391		60 c. brown	1·25	1·50
O392		70 c. buff and violet ..	75	3·00
O393		80 c. buff and grey ..	1·25	2·00
O395	38	90 c. red & grn on grn	1·60	2·50
O394	17	1 f. green and purple	1·50	2·25
O396	38	1 f. 20 red and lake on pink	1·75	3·00
O397		1 f. 50 red & blue on bl	2·25	4·50
O398	–	2 r. red & blk on grey	2·40	5·00

1942. Optd. **Officiel.**

(a) Landscape designs of 1936.

O 427.	3 c. olive	30	1·25
O 428.	5 c. green	30	15
O 430.	10 c. brown	25	30
O 431.	15 c. orange	60	1·25
O 432.	20 c. red (Lake) ..	60	20
O 433.	25 c. brown	65	1·75
O 434.	30 c. blue	1·75	60
O 435.	35 c. green	1·75	2·00
O 436.	40 c. grey	1·10	45

(b) Historical designs of 1941.

O437	–	50 c. blue on green ..	4·50	3·25
O438	68	60 c. brn on cinnamon	4·75	7·25
O439	–	70 c. purple on mauve	5·00	6·00
O440	–	80 c. black on grey ..	1·25	1·10
O441	–	90 c. red on pink ..	1·50	1·00
O442	–	1 f. green on green ..	1·75	1·50
O443	–	1 f. 20 purple on grey	1·90	1·75
O444	–	1 f. 50 blue on buff ..	2·25	2·75
O445	–	2 f. red on pink ..	3·00	3·00

1950. Landscape designs of 1949 optd. **Officiel.**

O 522.	107.	5 c. orange	70	60
O 523.	–	10 c. green	1·25	60
O 524.	–	15 c. turquoise ..	11·00	11·00
O 525.	–	20 c. purple	2·00	35
O 526.	–	25 c. red	5·00	6·00
O 527.	–	30 c. olive	3·00	2·00
O 528.	–	35 c. brown	5·00	9·00
O 529.	–	40 c. blue	5·00	2·50
O 530.	–	50 c. grey	6·00	6·00
O 531.	–	60 c. green	8·50	4·00
O 532.	–	70 c. violet	22·00	16·00

For Swiss stamps overprinted for the use of officials of the League of Nations, International Labour Office and other special U.N. Agencies having their headquarters at Geneva, see under UNITED NATIONS—GENEVA HEADQUARTERS.

POSTAGE DUE STAMPS

D 10.

D 21.

D 38.

1878.

D105 D 10 1 c. blue .. 1·25 75
D106 2 c. blue .. 1·25 75
D107B 3 c. blue .. 9·00 6·00
D108A 5 c. blue .. 12·00 5·00
D109B 10 c. blue .. £130 5·00
D110B 20 c. blue .. £150 3·00
D111B 50 c. blue .. £300 9·50
D112A 100 c. blue .. £400 10·00
D113A 500 c. blue .. £350 15·00

The 1 c. has a rayed background behind the figure of value.

1883. Numerals in red.

D 188F D 10 1 c. green .. 30 30
D 189D 3 c. green .. 2·75 2·75
D 190F 5 c. green .. 1·25 20
D 191F 10 c. green .. 2·75 25
D 192F 20 c. green .. 7·00 50
D 193F 50 c. green .. 11·00 1·90
D 194F 100 c. green .. 12·00 1·50
D 195D 500 c. green .. 95·00 11·00

The above were issued in a wide range of shades from pale turquoise to olive between 1883 and 1910. A detailed list of these appears in the Stanley Gibbons Part 8 (Italy and Switzerland) Catalogue.

1910.

D 274. D 21. 1 c. green and red 10 10
D 275. 3 c. green and red 10 10
D 276. 5 c. green and red .. 10 10
D 277. 10 c. green and red 60 10
D 278. 15 c. green and red 35 55
D 279. 20 c. green and red 11·00 10
D 280. 25 c. green and red 80 30
D 281. 30 c. green and red 65 25
D 282. 50 c. green and red 90 45

1916. Surch.

D299 D 21 5 c. on 3 c. red and green .. 10 20
D300 10 c. on 1 c. red and green .. .. 20 4·50
D301 10 c. on 3 c. red and green .. .. 20 1·00
D302 20 c. on 50 c. red and green .. 80 1·00

1924.

D332 D 38 5 c. red and olive .. 50 10
D333 10 c. red and olive 1·75 10
D334 15 c. red and olive 1·50 40
D335a 20 c. red and olive 3·00 80
D336 25 c. red and olive 1·75 35
D337 30 c. red and olive 1·75 40
D338 40 c. red and olive 2·40 40
D339 50 c. red and olive 2·40 50

1937. Surch.

D 380. D 38. 5 on 15 c. red & olive 75 3·25
D 381. 10 on 30 c. red & olive 75 1·00
D 382. 20 on 50 c. red & olive 1·50 4·00
D 383. 40 on 50 c. red & olive 2·50 10·00

D 54.

1938.

D 384. D 54. 5 c. red 35 10
D 385. 10 c. red 65 10
D 386. 15 c. red .. .. 75 1·60
D 387. 20 c. red 85 10
D 388. 25 c. red .. .. 1·00 1·50
D 389. 30 c. red .. .. 1·25 75
D 390. 40 c. red .. .. 1·50 20
D 391. 50 c. red .. .. 2·00 1·75

"PRO JUVENTUTE" CHARITY STAMPS

PREMIUMS. All "Pro Juventute" stamps are sold at an additional premium which goes to Benevolent Societies. Until 1937 these premiums were not shown on the stamps, but were as follows:

2 c. for all 3 c. franking values; 5 c. for all 5 c., 7½ c., 10 c., 15 c. and 20 c. values and 10 c. for all 30 c. and 40 c. values.

From 1937, when the premium first appeared on the designs, we show it in the catalogue listing.

C 1. Helvetia and Matterhorn.

C 2. Appenzell.

1913. Children's Fund.

J 1. C 1. 5 c. green .. .. 3·00 3·75

1915. Children's Fund.

J 1a. C 2. 5 c. green on buff .. 4·00 4·75
J 2. – 10 c. red on buff .. 95·00 60·00

DESIGN: 10 c. Girl of Lucerne.

C 4. Berne.

C 6. Valais.

C 9. Uri.

1916. Children's Fund.

J 3. – 3 c. violet on buff .. 6·00 23·00
J 4. C 4. 5 c. green on buff .. 11·00 4·50
J 5. – 10 c. red on buff .. 35·00 40·00

DESIGNS: 3 c., 10 c. Girls of Freiburg and Vaud.

1917. Children's Fund.

J 6. C 6. 3 c. violet on buff .. 5·50 27·00
J 7. – 5 c. green on buff .. 7·50 3·50
J 8. – 10 c. red on buff .. 24·00 16·00

DESIGNS: 5 c. Man of Unterwalden. 10 c. Girl of Ticino.

1918. Children's Fund. Dated "1918".

J 9. C 9. 10 c. red, yellow and black on buff .. 8·50 8·00
J 10. – 15 c. multicoloured on buff .. .. 10·00 5·00

ARMS: Geneva (15 c.).

1919. Children's Fund. As Type C 9 but dated "1919". Cream paper.

J 11. 7½ c. red, grey and black .. 3·00 8·00
J 12. 10 c. green, red and black 3·00 8·00
J 13. 15 c. red, violet and black 4·00 4·00

ARMS: 7½ c. Nidwalden. 10 c. Vaud. 15 c. Obwalden.

1920. Children's Fund. As Type C 9 but dated "1920". Cream paper.

J 14. 7½ c. red, grey and black .. 3·50 8·00
J 15. 10 c. blue, red and black .. 4·25 7·50
J 16. 15 c. red, blue, violet & blk. 3·00 2·75

ARMS: 7½ c. Schwyz. 10 c. Zurich. 15 c. Ticino.

1921. Children's Fund. As Type C 9 but dated "1921". Cream paper.

J 17. 10 c. red, green and black 75 1·75
J 18. 20 c. multicoloured .. 2·00 1·75
J 19. 40 c. red, blue and black 8·00 25·00

ARMS: 10 c. Valais. 20 c. Berne. 40 c. Switzerland.

1922. Children's Fund. As Type C 9 but dated "1922". Cream paper.

J 20. 5 c. orange, blue and black 75 3·75
J 21. 10 c. green and black .. 75 1·25
J 22. 20 c. violet, blue and black 75 1·25
J 23. 40 c. blue, red and black .. 8·50 32·00

ARMS: 5 c. Zug. 10 c. Friburg. 20 c. Lucerne. 40 c. Switzerland.

1923. Children's Fund. As Type C 9 but dated "1923". Cream paper.

J24 5 c. orange and black .. 35 1·75
J25 10 c. multicoloured .. 35 1·00
J26 20 c. multicoloured .. 35 1·00
J27 40 c. blue, red and black 7·50 25·00

ARMS: 5 c. Basel. 10 c. Glarus. 20 c. Neuchatel. 40 c. Switzerland.

1924. Children's Fund. As Type C 9 but dated "1924".

J 28. 5 c. black and lilac .. 20 80
J 29. 10 c. red, green and black on cream 20 70
J 30. 20 c. black, yellow and red on cream 30 70
J 31. 30 c. red, blue and black on cream .. .. 1·40 6·00

ARMS: 5 c. Appenzell. 10 c. Solothurn. 20 c. Schaffhausen. 30 c. Switzerland.

1925. Children's Fund. As Type C 9 but dated "1925". Cream paper.

J 32. 5 c. green, black & violet .. 20 65
J 33. 10 c. black and green .. 20 50
J 34. 20 c. multicoloured .. 30 55
J 35. 30 c. red, blue and black .. 1·10 5·50

ARMS: 5 c. St. Gall. 10 c. Appenzell-Ausser-Rhoden. 20 c. Graubunden. 30 c. Switzerland.

1926. Children's Fund. As Type C 9 but dated "1926". Cream paper.

J 36. 5 c. multicoloured .. 20 65
J 37. 10 c. green, black and red 20 55
J 38. 20 c. red, black and blue .. 30 55
J 39. 30 c. blue, red and black .. 1·10 5·50

ARMS: 5 c. Thurgau. 10 c. Basel. 20 c. Aargau. 30 c. Switzerland and Lion of Lucerne.

C 40. Forsaken Child.

C 42. J. H. Pestalozzi.

C 43. J. H. Pestalozzi.

1927. Children's Fund. Dated "1927"

J 40. C 40. 5 c. pur. & yell. on grey 15 60
J 41. – 10 c. grn. & red on grn. 15 20
J 42. C 42. 20 c. red 20 20
J 43. C 43. 30 c. blue and black .. 1·00 3·25

DESIGN—As Type C 40: 40 c. Orphan at Pestalozzi School.

C 44. Lausanne.

C 47. J. H. Dunant.

1928. Children's Fund. Dated "1928".

J 44. C 44. 5 c. red, purple and black on buff .. 15 65
J 45. – 10 c. red, green and black on buff .. 15 45
J 46. – 20 c. black, yellow and red on buff .. 15 30
J 47. C 47. 30 c. blue and red .. 1·40 3·00

DESIGNS—As Type C 44: 10 c. Arms of Winterhur. 20 c. Arms of St. Gall.

C 48. Mt. San Salvatore, Lake Lugano.

DESIGNS: 10 c. Mt. Titlis, Lake Engstlen. 20 c. Mt. Lyskamm from Riffelberg. 30 c. Nicholas de Flue.

1929. Children's Fund. Dated "1929".

J 48. C 48. 5 c. red and violet .. 15 60
J 49. – 10 c. blue and brown 15 25
J 50. – 20 c. blue and red .. 20 25
J 51. – 30 c. blue .. .. 1·60 6·00

C 50. Freiburg.

C 51. A. Bitzius—"Jeremias Gotthelf".

1930. Children's Fund. Dated "1930".

J 52. C 50. 5 c. blue, black and green on buff .. 15 70
J 53. – 10 c. multicoloured on buff 15 40
J 54. – 20 c. multicoloured on buff 20 40
J 55. C 51. 30 c. blue .. 1·50 3·75

ARMS—As Type C 51: 10 c. Altdorf. 20 c. Schaffhausen.

C 52. St. Moritz and Silvaplana Lakes.

DESIGNS: 10 c. The Wetterhorn. 20 c. Lac Leman. 30 c. Alexandre Vinet.

1931. Children's Fund. Dated "1931".

J 56. C 52. 5 c. green 40 90
J 57. – 10 c. violet 35 35
J 58. – 20 c. lake 50 40
J 59. – 30 c. blue .. .. 5·00 9·00

C 54. Flag swinging.

C 56. Vaud.

C 59. A. von Haller.

1932. Children's Fund. Dated "1932".

J 60. C 54. 5 c. red and green .. 55 1·00
J 61. – 10 c. orange .. .. 75 1·00
J 62. – 20 c. red .. .. 75 1·00
J 63. – 30 c. blue .. .. 2·40 4·75

DESIGNS: 10 c. Putting the weight. 20 c. Wrestlers. 30 c. Eugen Huber.

1933. Children's Fund. dated "1933".

J 64. C 56. 5 c. green and buff .. 40 80
J 65. – 10 c. violet and buff .. 40 40
J 66. – 20 c. scarlet and buff .. 55 40
J 67. – 30 c. blue .. .. 2·50 4·75

SWISS GIRL DESIGNS: Berne (10 c.), Ticino (20 c.). 30 c. Father Gregoire Girard.

1934. Children's Fund. Dated "1934".

J 68. – 5 c. green and buff .. 40 90
J 69. – 10 c. violet and buff .. 50 35
J 70. – 20 c. red and buff .. 50 35
J 71. C 59. 30 c. blue .. .. 2·40 5·00

SWISS GIRL DESIGNS—As Type C 56: 5 c. Appenzell. 10 c. Valais. 20 c. Graubunden.

C 61. Stefano Franscini.

C 62. H. G. Nageli.

1935. Children's Fund. Dated "1935".

J 72. – 5 c. green and buff .. 35 1·00
J 73. – 10 c. violet and buff .. 45 40
J 74. – 20 c. red and buff .. 45 60
J 75. C 61. 30 c. blue .. .. 2·50 5·50

DESIGNS—As Type C 56: Costumes of Basel (5 c.), Lucerne (10 c.) and Geneva (20 c.).

1936. Children's Fund.

J 76. C 62. 5 c. green 30 25
J 77. – 10 c. purple and buff 30 35
J 78. – 20 c. red and buff .. 35 50
J 79. – 30 c. blue and buff .. 3·75 10·00

DESIGNS—As Type C 56: Costumes of Neuchatel (10 c.), Schwyz (20 c.) and Zurich (30 c.).

C 64. Gen. Henri Dufour.

C 66. "Youth".

1937. Children's Fund.

J 80. C 64. 5 c.+5 c. green .. 10 15
J 81. – 10 c.+5 c. purple .. 10 15
J 82. C 66. 20 c.+5 c. red, buff and silver 40 30
J 83. – 30 c.+10 c. blue, buff and silver .. .. 1·50 3·00

DESIGNS: 10 c. Nicholas de Flue. 30 c. as Type C 66, but girl's head facing other way.

C 67. Salomon Gessner.

C 69. Gen. Herzog.

1938. Children's Fund. Dated "1938".

J 84. C 67. 5 c.+5 c. green .. 15 20
J 85. – 10 c.+5 c. vio. & buff 15 20
J 86. – 20 c.+5 c. red & buff 25 20
J 87. – 30 c.+10 c. blue & buff 1·60 3·00

SWISS GIRL DESIGNS as Type C 56: 10 c. St. Gall. 20 c. Uri. 30 c. Aargau.

1939. Children's Fund.

J 88. C 69. 5 c.+5 c. green .. 15 20
J 89. – 10 c.+5 c. vio. and buff 20 20
J 90. – 20 c.+5 c. red & buff 35 30
J 91. – 30 c.+10 c. blue & buff 1·75 4·25

SWISS GIRL DESIGNS—As Type C 56: 10 c. Freibourg. 20 c. Nidwalden. 30 c. Basel.

C 71. Gottfried Keller.

C 73. Johann Kaspar Lavater.

1940. Children's Fund. Dated "1940".

J 92. C 71. 5 c.+5 c. green .. 10 20
J 93. – 10 c.+5 c. brn. & buff 20 15
J 94. – 20 c.+5 c. red and buff 30 20
J 95. – 30 c.+10 c. blue & buff 1·50 6·00

SWISS GIRL DESIGNS—As Type C 56: 10 c. Thurgau. 20 c. Solothurn. 30 c. Zug.

1941. Children's Fund. Bicent. of Birth of Lavater (philosopher) and of Death of Richard (clockmaker). Dated "1941".

J 96. C 73. 5 c.+5 c. green .. 15 15
J 97. – 10 c.+5 c. brn. & buff 25 20
J 98. – 20 c.+5 c. red & buff 30 25
J 99. – 30 c.+10 c. blue .. 1·25 4·00

DESIGNS—Type C 56: 10 c., 20 c. Girls in costumes of Schaffhausen and Obwalden. As Type 73: 30 c. Daniel Jean Richard.

C 74. Niklaus Riggenbach (rack railway pioneer).

C 75. Emanuel von Fellenberg.

C 76. Silver Thistle.

1942. Children's Fund. Dated "1942".

J 100. C74. 5 c.+5 c. green .. 20 30
J 101. – 10 c.+5 c. brn. & buff 25 25
J 102. – 20 c.+5 c. red & buff 30 25
J 103. – 30 c.+10 c. blue .. 1·50 4·00

DESIGNS: 10 c. and 20 c. Girls and in costumes of Appenzell-Ausser-Rhoden and Glarus. 30 c. Conrad Escher von der Linth (statesman).

1943. Death Centenary of Philip Emanuel von Fellenberg (economist).

J104 C 75 5 c.+5 c. green .. 15 20
J105 C 76 10 c.+5 c. green, buff and grey .. 25 15
J106 – 20 c.+5 c. red, yellow and pink .. 30 15
J107 – 30 c.+10 c. blue, light blue & black 1·40 7·00

FLOWERS—As Type C 76: 20 c. Ladies slipper. 30 c. Gentain.

C 77. Numa Droz. C 78. Ludwig Forrer.

1944. Birth Centenary of Droz (statesman).

J 108. C 77. 5 c.+5 c. green .. 20 15
J 109. – 10 c.+5 c. olive, yellow and green 20 15
J 110. – 20 c.+5 c. red, yellow and grey .. 40 15
J 111. – 30 c.+10 c. blue, grey and blue .. .. 1·50 6·50

DESIGNS: 10 c. Edelweiss. 20 c. Martagon lily. 30 c. "Aquilegia alpina".

1945. Children's Fund. Cent. of Births of Ludwig Forrer (statesman) and Susanna Orelli (social reformer). Dated "1945".

J 112. C 78. 5 c.+5 c. green .. 30 25
J 113. – 10 c.+10 c. brown 30 15
J 114. – 20 c.+10 c. red, pink and yellow 60 15
J 115. – 30 c.+10 c. blue, mauve and grey .. 2·50 6·50

DESIGNS: 10 c. Susanna Orelli. 20 c. Alpine Dog Rose. 30 c. Spring Crocus.

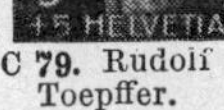

C 79. Rudolf Toepffer. C 80. Jacob Burckhardt (historian).

1946. Death Centenary of Rudolf Toepffer (author and painter). Type C 79 and floral designs inscr. "PRO JUVENTUTE 1946".

J 116. C 79. 5 c.+5 c. green .. 25 15
J 117. – 10 c.+10 c. green, grey and orange .. 30 15
J 118. – 20 c.+10 c. red, grey and yellow .. 40 15
J 119. – 30 c.+10 c. blue, grey and mauve .. 2·75 6·00

DESIGNS: 10 c. Narcissus. 20 c. Houseleek. 30 c. Blue Thistle.

1947. Children's Fund. Type C 80 and floral designs inscr. "PRO JUVENTUTE 1947".

J 120. C 80. 5 c.+5 c. green .. 15 15
J 121. – 10 c.+10 c. black, yellow and grey .. 25 15
J 122. – 20 c.+10 c. brown, orange and grey .. 35 15
J 123. – 30 c.+10 c. blue pink and grey .. 2·00 4·75

DESIGNS: 10 c. Alpine Primrose. 20 c. Orange Lily. 30 c. Cyclamen.

C 81. Gen. U. Wille. C 82. Nicholas Wengi.

1948. Children's Fund. Type C 81 and floral designs as Type C 76. Dated "1948".

J 124. C 81. 5 c.+5 c. purple .. 25 10
J 125. – 10 c.+10 c. green yellow and grey .. 40 15
J 126. – 20 c.+10 c. brown, red and buff .. 50 15
J 127. – 40 c.+10 c. blue yellow and grey .. 2·50 4·75

FLOWERS: 10 c. Yellow Foxglove. 20 c. Rust-leaved Alpine rose. 40 c. Lily of Paradise.

1949. Children's Fund. Type C 82 and floral designs inscr "PRO JUVENTUTRE 1949".

J128 C 82 5 c.+5 c. red .. 20 10
J129 – 10 c.+10 c. green, grey and yellow .. 30 15
J130 – 20 c.+10 c. brown, blue and buff .. 35 15
J131 – 40 c. blue, mauve and yellow .. 2·75 5·00

DESIGNS: 10 c. "Pulsatilla alpina". 20 c. Alpine clematis. 40 c. Superb pink.

C 83. General Theophil Sprecher von Bernegg. C 84. Red Admiral.

1950. Children's Fund. Inscr "PRO JUVENTUTE 1950".

J132 C 83 5 c.+5 c. brown .. 20 15
J133 C 84 10 c.+10 c. mult .. 50 20
J134 – 20 c.+10 c. black, blue and orange 55 20
J135 – 30 c.+10 c. brown, grey and mauve 5·00 12·00
J136 – 40 c.+10 c. yellow, brown and blue .. 4·25 9·50

DESIGNS: 20 c. Clifden's nonpareil (moth). 30 c. Honey bee. 40 c. Moorland clouded yellow (butterfly).

C 85. Johanna Spyri (authoress). C 86. "Portrait of a Boy" (Anker).

1951. Children's Fund. Type C 85 and various insects as Type C 84. Inscr "PRO JUVENTUTE 1951".

J137 C 85 5 c.+5 c. purple .. 20 10
J138 – 10 c.+10 c. bl & grn 40 20
J139 – 20 c.+10 c. black, cream and mauve 50 20
J140 – 30 c.+10 c. black, orange and green 4·00 8·00
F141 – 40 c.+10 c. brown, red and blue .. 4·00 7·50

INSECTS: 10 c. Banded agrion (dragonfly). 20 c. Scarce swallowtail (butterfly). 30 c. Orange-tip (butterfly). 40 c. Viennese emperor moth.

1952. Children's Fund. Type C 86 and insects as Type C 84. Inscr. "PRO JUVENTUTE 1952".

J 142. C 86. 5 c.+5 c. lake .. 20 15
J 143. – 10 c.+10 c. red, black and green 35 15
J 144. – 20 c.+10 c. cream, black and mauve 45 15
J 145. – 30 c.+10 c. blue, black and brown 3·50 6·50
J 146. – 40 c.+10 c. buff, brown and blue.. 3·50 6·50

INSECTS: 10 c. Seven-spotted ladybird. 20 c. Marbled white (butterfly). 30 c. Chalk-hill blue (butterfly). 40 c. Oak eggar moth.

1953. Children's Fund. Portraits as Type C 88 and insects as Type C 84. Inscr "PRO JUVENTUTE 1953".

J147 5 c.+5 c. red 20 10
J148 10 c.+10 c. pink, brown and green 35 15
J149 20 c.+10 c. black, buff and mauve 45 15
J150 30 c.+10 c. blk, red & grn 3·50 7·50
J151 40 c.+10 c. blue .. 4·25 5·50

DESIGNS: 5 c. "Portrait of a girl" (Anker). 10 c. Black arches moth. 20 c. Camberwell beauty (butterfly). 30 c. "Purpureus kaehleri" (long-horn beetle). 40 c. F. Hodler (self-portrait).

1954. Children's Fund. Portrait as Type C 85 and insects as Type C 84. Inscr. "PRO JUVENTUTE 1954".

J 152. 5 c.+5 c. brown .. 20 10
J 153. 10 c.+10 c. multicoloured 40 15
J 154. 20 c.+10 c. multicoloured 55 35
J 155. 30 c.+10 c. multicoloured 4·00 6·00
J 156. 40 c.+10 c. multicoloured 4·00 6·50

DESIGNS: 5 c. Jeremias Gotthelf (novelist, after A. Bitzius). 10 c. Garden tiger moth. 20 c. Buff-tailed bumble bee. 30 c. "Ascalaphus libelluloides" (owl-fly). 40 c. Swallowtail (butterfly).

1955. Children's Fund. Portrait as Type C 85 and insects as Type C 84. Inscr. "PRO JUVENTUTE 1955".

J 157. 5 c.+5 c. lake 20 15
J 158. 10 c.+10 c. multicoloured 40 20
J 159. 20 c.+10 c. multicoloured 45 20
J 160. 30 c.+10 c. multicoloured 4·00 4·50
J 161. 40 c.+10 c blk. red & bl. 4·00 4·50

DESIGNS: 5 c. C. Pictet-de-Rochemont. 10 c. Peacock (butterfly). 20 c. Great horntail. 30 c. Yellow tiger moth. 40 c. Apollo (butterfly).

1956. Children's Fund. Portrait as Type C 85 and insects as Type C 84. Inscr "PRO JUVENTUTE 1956".

J162 5 c.+5 c. purple .. 20 10
J163 10 c.+10 c. deep green, red and green .. 40 15
J164 20 c.+10 c. multicoloured 50 20
J165 30 c.+10 c. blue, indigo and yellow .. .. 2·40 4·25
J166 40 c.+10 c. yell, brn & bl 2·50 4·50

DESIGNS: 5 c. Carlo Maderno (architect). 10 c. Common burnet (moth) 20 c. Lesser purple emperor (butterfly). 30 c. Blue ground beetle. 40 c. Large white (butterfly).

1957. Children's Fund. Portrait as Type C 85 and insects as Type C 84. Inscr "PRO JUVENTUTE 1957".

J167 5 c.+5 c. purple .. 30 10
J168 10 c.+10 c. multicoloured 40 15
J169 20 c.+10 c. yellow, brown and mauve 45 15
J170 30 c.+10 c. emerald, green and purple .. 2·40 4·00
J171 40 c.+10 c. multicoloured 2·50 3·00

DESIGNS—VERT. 5 c. L. Euler (mathematician). 10 c. Clouded yellow (butterfly). 20 c. Magpie moth. 30 c. Rose chafer (beetle). 40 c. Rosy underwing (moth).

C 92. Albrecht von Haller (naturalist). C 93. Pansy.

1958. Children's Fund. Type C 92 and flowers as Type C 93. Inscr. "PRO JUVENTUTE 1958".

J 172. C 92. 5 c.+5 c. red .. 15 10
J 173. C 93. 10 c.+10 c. yellow, brown and green 40 10
J 174. – 20 c.+10 c. mult... 50 20
J 175. – 30 c.+10 c. mult... 2·00 2·75
J 176. – 40 c.+10 c. mult... 2·00 2·50

FLOWERS: 20 c. Chinese aster. 30 c. Morning glory. 40 c. Christmas rose.

1959. Children's Fund. Portrait as Type C 92 and flowers as Type C 93. Inscr. "PRO JUVENTUTE 1959".

J 177. 5 c.+5 c. red .. 15 10
J 178. 10 c.+10 c. mult. .. 30 15
J 179. 20 c.+10 c. red, green and purple .. 40 15
J 180. 30 c.+10 c. mult. .. 2·00 3·00
J 181. 50 c.+10 c. mult. .. 2·00 2·75

DESIGNS: 5 c. Karl Hilty (lawyer). 10 c. Marsh marigold. 20 c. Poppy. 30 c. Nasturtium. 50 c. Sweet pea.

1960. Children's Fund. Portrait as Type C 92 and flowers as Type C 93. Inscr. "PRO JUVENTUTE 1960".

J182 5 c.+5 c. blue .. 20 10
J183 10 c.+10 c. yellow, drab and green .. 30 15
J184 20 c.+10 c. green, brown and mauve .. 40 20
J185 30 c.+10 c. green, blue and brown .. 3·00 3·50
J186 50 c.+10 c. yell, grn & bl 3·00 3·00

DESIGNS: 5 c. Alexandre Calame (painter). 10 c. Dandelion. 20 c. Phlox. 30 c. Larkspur. 50 c. Thorn apple.

1961. Children's Fund. Portrait as Type C 92 and flowers as Type C 93. Inscr "PRO JUVENTUTE 1961".

J 187. 5 c.+5 c. blue 15 10
J 188. 10 c.+10 c. yellow, red and green .. 20 10
J 189. 20 c.+10 c. multicoloured 25 15
J 190. 30 c.+10 c. multicoloured 1·50 2·25
J 191. 50 c.+10 c. yellow, green, brown and blue .. 1·75 2·25

DESIGNS: 5 c. J. Furrer (First President of Swiss Confederation). 10 c. Sunflower. 20 c. Lily-of-the-Valley. 30 c. Iris. 50 c. Silverweed.

C 97. "Child's World". C 98. Mother and Child.

1962. Children's Fund. 50th Anniv. of Pro Juventute Foundation. Type C 97 and similar designs inscr. "1912–62" and Type C 98.

J 192. – 5 c.+5 c. mult. .. 15 10
J 193. C 97. 10 c.+10 c. red & green 25 10
J 194. C 98. 20 c.+10 c. mult... 50 20
J 195. – 30 c.+10 c. red, mauve & yellow 1·25 2·25
J 196. – 50 c.+10 c. yellow, brown and blue 1·50 2·25

DESIGNS—As Type C 97: 5 c. Apple blossom. 30 c. "Child's World" (child in meadow). 50 c. Forsythia.

1963. Children's Fund. Portrait as Type C 86 and flowers as Type C 93. Inscr "PRO JUVENTUTE 1963".

J197 5 c.+5 c. blue 10 35
J198 10 c.+10 c. mult .. 30 2·25
J199a 20 c.+10 c. orange, green and red 90 50
J200 30 c.+10 c. mult .. 1·50 1·50
J201 50 c.+10 c. purple, green and blue .. .. 1·50 1·50

DESIGNS: 5 c. "Portrait of a Boy" (Anker). 10 c. Oxeye daisy. 20 c. Geranium. 30 c. Cornflower. 50 c. Carnation.

1964. Children's Fund. Portrait as Type C 86 and flowers as Type C 93. Inscr "PRO JUVENTUTE 1964".

J 202. 5 c.+5 c. blue .. 10 10
J 203. 10 c.+10 c. orange, yellow and green 15 10
J 204. 20 c.+10 c. rose, green and red 20 10
J 205. 30 c.+10 c. purple, green and brown 50 50
J 206. 50 c.+10 c. multicoloured 65 60

DESIGNS: 5 c. "Portrait of a Girl" (Anker). 10 c. Daffodil. 20 c. Rose. 30 c. Red clover. 50 c. White water lily.

C 101. Western European Hedgehogs. C 102. Roe Deer.

1965. Children's Fund. Animals. Inscr. "PRO JUVENTUTE 1965".

J 207. C 101. 5 c.+5 c. ochre brown and red .. 10 10
J 208. – 10 c.+10 c. ochre brown, black & blue 10 10
J 209. – 20 c.+10 c. blue, brown and chestnut 30 10
J 210. – 30 c.+10 c. blue, black and yellow .. 35 40
J 211. – 50 c.+10 c. black brown and blue .. 50 50

ANIMALS: 10 c. Alpine marmots. 20 c. Red deer. 30 c. Eurasian Badgers. 50 c. Arctic hares.

1966. Children's Fund. Animals. As Type C 101 but inscr. "PRO JUVENTUTE 1966". Multicoloured.

J 212. 5 c.+5 c. Stoat 10 10
J 213. 10 c.+10 c. Eurasian red squirrel 10 10
J 214. 20 c.+10 c. Red fox .. 30 10
J 215. 30 c.+10 c. Brown hare 35 40
J 216. 50 c.+10 c. Chamois .. 50 50

1967. Children's Fund. Animals. Inscr "PRO JUVENTUTE 1967". Multicoloured.

J127 10 c.+10 c. Type C 102 .. 15 10
J128 20 c.+10 c. Pine marten 20 10
J129 30 c.+10 c. Ibex .. 30 10
J220 50 c.+20 c. European otter 50 50

1968. Children's Fund. Birds. As Type C 102 but inscr "1968". Multicoloured.

J221 10 c.+10 c. Capercaillie 25 10
J222 20 c.+10 c. Bullfinch .. 35 10
J223 30 c.+10 c. Woodchat shrike 50 15
J224 50 c.+20 c. Firecrest .. 85 60

1969. Children's Fund. Birds. As Type C **102**. Inscr "1969". Multicoloured.

J 225.	10 c.+10 c. Goldfinch ..	20	10
J 226.	20 c.+10 c. Golden Oriole	30	15
J 227.	30 c.+10 c. Wallcreeper	40	15
J 228.	50 c.+20 c. Jay	65	70

1970. Children's Fund. Birds. As Type C **102**. Inscr "1970". Multicoloured.

J 229.	10 c.+10 c. Blue Tits ..	15	15
J 230.	20 c.+10 c. Hoopoe ..	25	10
J 231.	30 c.+10 c. Great Spotted Woodpecker ..	35	15
J 232.	50 c.+20 c. Great Crested Grebes	80	95

1971. Children's Fund. Birds. As Type C 102. Inscr "1971". Multicoloured.

J 233.	10 c.+10 c. Redstarts ..	25	20
J 234.	20 c.+10 c. Bluethroats ..	45	10
J 235.	30 c.+10 c. Peregrine falcon	60	20
J 236.	40 c.+20 c. Mallards ..	1·40	1·10

C **104.** "McGredy's Sunset" Rose.

C **105.** Chestnut.

1972. Children's Fund. Roses. Mult.

J 237.	10 c.+10 c. Type C **104**	25	15
J 238.	20 c.+10 c. "Miracle"	35	15
J 239.	30 c.+10 c. "Papa Meilland"	60	15
J 240.	40 c.+20 c. "Madame Dimitriu"	1·00	1·00

See also Nos. J 258/61 and J 279/82.

1973. Children's Fund. "Fruits of the Forest". Multicoloured.

J 241.	15 c.+5 c. Type C **105** ..	15	10
J 242.	30 c.+10 c. Cherries ..	30	10
J 243.	40 c.+20 c. Blackberries	70	65
J 244.	60 c.+20 c. Bilberries ..	90	95

See also Nos. J 245/8, J 249/53 and J 254/7.

1974. Children's Fund. "Fruits of the Forest". Poisonous Plants. As Type C **105**. Inscr. "1974". Multicoloured.

J 245.	15 c.+10 c. Daphne ..	20	10
J 246.	30 c.+20 c. Belladonna	40	10
J 247.	50 c.+20 c. Laburnum	75	75
J 248.	60 c.+25 c. Mistletoe ..	90	75

1975. Children's Fund. As Type C **105**. Inscr "1975". Multicoloured.

J 249.	10 c.+5 c. "Post Brent" (postman's hamper) ..	10	10
J 250.	15 c.+10 c. Hepatica ..	20	15
J 251.	30 c.+20 c. Rowan ..	35	10
J 252.	50 c.+20 c. Yellow dead-nettle	75	75
J 253.	60 c.+25 c. Sycamore ..	80	75

1976. Children's Fund. "Fruits of the Forest". As Type C **105**. Inscr "1976". Muticoloured.

J 254.	20 c.+10 c. Barberry ..	25	15
J 255.	40 c.+20 c. Black elder	40	15
J 256.	40 c.+20 c. Lime ..	40	15
J 257.	80 c.+40 c. Lungwort ..	1·25	1·10

1977. Children's Fund. Roses. As Type C **104**. Inscr "1977". Multicoloured.

J258	20 c.+10 c. "Rosa foetida bicolor"	25	10
J259	40 c.+20 c. "Parfum de l'Hay"	45	10
J260	70 c.+30 c. "R. foetida persiana"	1·00	1·00
J261	80 c.+40 c. "R. centifolia muscosa"	1·10	1·10

C **106.** Arms of Aarburg.

C **107.** Letter Balance.

1978. Children's Fund. Communal Arms (1st series). Multicoloured.

J 262.	20 c.+10 c. Type C **106**	25	10
J 263.	40 c.+20 c. Gruyeres ..	45	10
J 264.	70 c.+30 c. Castasegna	1·00	1·00
J 265.	80 c.+40 c. Wangen ..	1·00	1·10

See also Nos. J 266/9, J 270/3 and J 274/7.

1979. Children's Fund. Communal Arms (2nd series). As Type C **106**. Multicoloured.

J 266.	20 c.+10 c. Cadro ..	20	15
J 267.	40 c.+20 c. Rute ..	40	10
J 268.	70 c.+30 c. Schwamendingen	90	95
J 269.	80 c.+40 c. Perroy ..	1·00	95

1980. Children's Fund. Arms of the Communes. As Type C **106**. Multicoloured.

J 270.	20 c.+10 c. Cortaillod ..	25	20
J 271.	40 c.+20 c. Sierre ..	50	10
J 272.	70 c.+30 c. Scuol ..	85	1·00
J 273.	80 c.+40 c. Wolfenschiessen	1·00	1·00

1981. Children's Fund. Arms of the Communes. As Type C **106**. Multicoloured.

J 274.	20 c.+10 c. Uffikon ..	30	20
J 275.	40 c.+20 c. Torre ..	50	10
J 276.	70 c.+30 c. Benken ..	85	1·00
J 277.	80 c.+40 c. Preverenges	1·00	1·00

1982. Children's Fund. Type C 107 and Roses as Type C 104. Multicoloured.

J 278.	10 c.+10 c. Type C **107**	20	20
J 279.	20 c.+10 c. "La Belle Portugaise" ..	25	15
J 280.	40 c.+20 c. "Hugh Dickson" ..	50	15
J 281.	70 c.+30 c. "Mermaid"	90	90
J 282.	80 c.+40 c. "Madame Caroline"	1·00	90

C **108.** Kitchen Stove, c. 1850.

C **109.** Heidi and Goat (Johanna Spyri).

1983. Children's Fund. Toys. Multicoloured.

J283	20 c.+10 c. Type C **108**	30	20
J284	40 c.+20 c. Rocking-horse, 1826 ..	55	15
J285	70 c.+30 c. Doll, c. 1870	1·00	95
J286	80 c.+40 c. Steam locomotive, c. 1900 ..	1·25	1·00

1984. Children's Fund. Characters from Children's Books. Multicoloured.

J 287.	35 c.+15 c. Type C **109**	50	35
J 288.	50 c.+20 c. Pinocchio and kite (Carlo Collodi)	75	10
J 289.	70 c.+30 c. Pippi Longstocking (Astrid Lindgren)	1·00	1·00
J 290.	80 c.+40 c. Max and Moritz on roof (Wilhelm Busch) ..	1·25	1·25

1985. Children's Fund. Characters from Children's Books. As Type C **109**. Mult.

J 291.	35 c.+15 c. Hansel, Gretel and Witch ..	50	35
J 292.	50 c.+20 c. Snow White and the Seven Dwarfs	75	15
J 293.	80 c.+40 c. Red Riding Hood and wolf ..	1·00	1·00
J 294.	90 c.+40 c. Cinderella and Prince Charming	1·25	1·25

C **110.** Teddy Bear.

C **111.** Girl carrying Pine Branch and Candle.

1986. Children's Fund. Toys. Multicoloured.

J 295.	35 c.+15 c. Type C **110**	50	45
J 296.	50 c.+20 c. Spinning top	65	70
J 297.	80 c.+40 c. Steamroller	1·50	1·40
J 298.	90 c.+40 c. Doll ..	1·60	1·50

1987. Children's Fund. Child Development. Pre-school Age. Multicoloured.

J 299.	25 c.+10 c. Type C **111**	40	30
J 300.	35 c.+15 c. Mother breast-feeding baby ..	60	55
J 301.	50 c.+20 c. Toddler playing with bricks ..	90	15
J 302.	80 c.+40 c. Children playing in sand ..	1·50	1·40
J 303.	90 c.+40 c. Father with child on his shoulders	1·50	1·50

C **112** Learning to Read

C **113** Community Work

1988. Children's Fund. Child Development. School Age. Multicoloured.

J304	35 c.+15 c. Type C **112** ..	60	50
J305	50 c.+20 c. Playing triangle	80	15
J306	80 c.+40 c. Learning arithmetic	1·40	1·40
J307	90 c.+40 c. Drawing ..	1·50	1·40

1989. Children's Fund. Child Development. Adolescence. Multicoloured.

J 308	35 c.+15 c. Type C **113**	60	50
J 309	50 c.+20 c. Young couple (friendship)	80	15
J 310	80 c.+40 c. Boy at computer screen (vocational training)	1·40	1·40
J 311	90 c.+40 c. Girl in laboratory (higher education and research)	1·50	1·50

C **114** Building Model Ship (hobbies)

C **115** Ramsons

1990. Child Development. Leisure Activities. Multicoloured.

J 312	35 c.+15 c. Type C **114**	60	50
J 313	50 c.+20 c. Youth group	80	15
J 314	80 c.+40 c. Sport ..	1·40	1·40
J 315	90 c.+40 c. Music ..	1·50	1·50

1991. Woodland Flowers. Multicoloured.

J316	50 c.+25 c. Type C **115** ..	75	15
J317	70 c.+30 c. Wood cranes-bill	1·00	1·00
J318	80 c.+40 c. Nettle-leaved bellflower	1·25	1·25
J319	90 c.+40 c. Few-leaved hawkweed	1·50	1·50

C **116** Melchior (wood puppet)

1992. Christmas (J320) and Trees (others). Multicoloured.

J320	50 c.+25 c. Type C **116** ..	70	15
J321	50 c.+25 c. Beech ..	70	15
J322	70 c.+30 c. Norway maple	90	90
J323	80 c.+40 c. Pedunculate oak	1·10	1·10
J324	90 c.+40 c. Norway spruce ..	1·25	1·25

Nos. J321/4 show silhouette of tree and close-up of its leaves and fruit.

C **117** Christmas Wreath

1993. Christmas (J325) and Woodland Plants (others). Multicoloured.

J325	60 c.+30 c. Type C **117** ..	85	25
J326	60 c.+30 c. Male fern ..	85	25
J327	80 c.+40 c. Guelder rose	1·10	1·10
J328	100 c.+50 c. "Mnium punctatum"	1·40	1·40

INTERNATIONAL ORGANIZATIONS SITUATED IN SWITZERLAND

The stamps listed under this heading were issued by the Swiss Post Office primarily for the use of officials of the Organizations named, situated in Geneva.

These stamps could not be legitimately obtained unused before February 1944.

A. LEAGUE OF NATIONS.

1922. Optd **SOCIETE DES NATIONS**.

LN 1	**20a**	2½ c. green on buff	—	20
LN 2		3 c. blue on buff ..	—	5·00
LN 3		5 c. orange on buff	—	3·00
LN 4		5 c. lilac on buff ..	—	1·90
LN 5		5 c. purple on buff	—	1·25
LN 5a		5 c. green on buff	—	5·00
LN 6		7½ c. green on buff	—	25
LN 7	**21**	10 c. green on buff	—	30
LN 8		10 c. violet on buff	—	85
LN 9		15 c. red on buff ..	—	80
LN10		20 c. violet on buff	—	4·00
LN11		20 c. red on buff ..	—	1·00
LN13		25 c. red on buff ..	—	60
LN14		25 c. brown on buff	—	7·00
LN15	**17**	30 c. green & brn	—	8·00
LN16	**21**	30 c. blue on buff	—	3·50
LN17	**17**	35 c. yellow & grn	—	4·00
LN18		40 c. blue ..	—	1·00
LN19		40 c. green & mve	—	4·00
LN20		50 c. grn & dp grn	—	4·00
LN21		60 c. brown ..	20·00	90
LN22a		70 c. buff & violet	1·00	2·00
LN23a		80 c. buff and grey	2·50	1·50
LN24a	**38**	90 c. red and green on green ..	—	3·00
LN25	**17**	1 f. green & purple	—	4·00
LN26b	**38**	1 f. 20 red and lake on pink ..	2·00	3·00
LN27a		1 f. 50 red and blue on blue ..	2·00	2·50
LN28a		2 f. red and black on grey ..	2·50	3·50
LN29	**22**	3 f. red	—	20·00
LN29a	**43**	3 f. brown ..	—	£140
LN30	–	5 f. blue (No. 285)	—	40·00
LN32	–	10 f. pur (No. 286)	—	£100
LN33	–	10 f. grn (No. 331b)	—	£110

1932. International Disarmament Conference. Optd **SOCIETE DES NATIONS**.

LN34	**44**	5 c. green	—	14·00
LN35		10 c. orange	—	1·00
LN36		20 c. red	—	1·00
LN37		30 c. blue	—	35·00
LN38		60 c. brown	—	10·00
LN39	**45**	1 f. grey and blue ..	—	10·00

1934. Landscape designs of 1934 optd **SOCIETE DES NATIONS**.

LN40	**48**	3 c. green	—	20
LN41	–	5 c. green	—	25
LN43	–	15 c. orange	—	75
LN45	–	25 c. brown	—	12·00
LN46	–	30 c. blue	—	1·10

1937. Landscape designs of 1936 optd **SOCIETE DES NATIONS**.

LN47	**52**	3 c. green	10	10
LN48	–	5 c. green	20	15
LN49aa	–	10 c. purple ..	—	80
LN49b	–	10 c. brown ..	55	60
LN50	–	15 c. orange ..	40	30
LN51	–	20 c. red (Railway)	—	1·25
LN51a	–	20 c. red (Lake) ..	60	1·00
LN52	–	25 c. brown ..	60	75
LN53	–	30 c. blue	60	70
LN54	–	35 c. green ..	60	75
LN55	–	40 c. grey ..	75	90

1938. Nos. 382/5 optd **SOCIETE DES NATIONS**.

LN56	**55**	20 c. red and buff ..	—	2·00
LN57	–	30 c. blue and lt blue	—	3·00
LN58	–	60 c. brown and buff	—	5·00
LN59	–	1 f. black and buff ..	—	6·00

1938. Nos. 382/5 optd **SERVICE DE LA SOCIETE DES NATIONS** in circle.

LN60	**55**	20 c. red and buff ..	—	2·00
LN61	–	30 c. blue and lt blue	—	3·50
LN62	–	60 c. brown and buff	—	6·00
LN63	–	1 f. black and buff	—	10·00

1939. Nos. 388c/90c optd **SOCIETE DES NATIONS**.

LN64	**61**	3 f. brown on buff ..	3·00	7·00
LN65	–	5 f. blue on buff ..	4·50	10·00
LN66	–	10 f. green on buff	9·50	24·00

1944. Optd. **COURRIER DE LA SOCIETE DES NATIONS.**

(a) Landscape designs of 1936.

LN 67.	**52.**	3 c. olive ..	15	20
LN 68.	–	5 c. green ..	15	20
LN 69.	–	10 c. brown	30	40
LN 70.	–	15 c. orange	25	30
LN 71.	–	20 c. red (lake)	40	45
LN 72.	–	25 c. brown	60	60
LN 73.	–	30 c. blue ..	70	70
LN 74.	–	35 c. green	75	75
LN 75.	–	40 c. grey ..	75	90

(b) Historical designs of 1941.

LN76	–	50 c. blue on green	1·00	1·50
LN77	68	60 c. brn on cinnamon	1·40	1·75
LN78	–	70 c. purple on mauve	1·40	2·00
LN79	–	80 c. black on grey	1·25	1·60
LN80	–	90 c. scarlet on pink	1·25	1·60
LN81	–	1 f. green on green	1·50	2·00
LN82	–	1 f. 20 purple on grey	1·60	2·40
LN83	–	1 f. 50 blue on buff	2·00	2·75
LN84	–	2 f. red on pink	3·00	3·25

(c) Parliament designs of 1938.

LN 85.	61.	3 f. brown on buff	5·00	7·00
LN 86.	–	5 f. blue on buff	6·50	10·00
LN 87.	–	10 f. green on buff	12·00	22·00

B. INTERNATIONAL LABOUR OFFICE

Optd **S.d.N. Bureau International du Travail** (Nos. LB1/47).

1923.

LB 1	20a	2½ c. green on buff	—	20
LB 2		3 c. blue on buff	—	85
LB 3		5 c. orange on buff	—	30
LB 4		5 c. purple on buff	—	20
LB 5		7½ c. green on buff	—	25
LB 6	21	10 c. green on buff	—	20
LB 8.		15 c. red on buff	—	90
LB 9		20 c. violet on buff	—	9·00
LB10		20 c. red on buff	—	4·00
LB11		25 c. red on buff	—	80
LB12		25 c. brown on buff	—	2·25
LB13	17	30 c. green & brn	—	40·00
LB14	21	30 c. blue on buff	—	1·50
LB15	17	35 c. yellow & grn	—	8·00
LB16		40 c. blue	—	90
LB17		40 c. green & mve	—	11·00
LB18a		50 c. grn & dp grn	1·50	1·50
LB19		60 c. brown	1·25	1·75
LB20a		70 c. buff & violet	1·50	2·50
LB21		80 c. buff and grey	8·50	1·50
LB22	38	90 c. red and green on green	—	3·25
LB23	17	1 f. green & purple	—	2·00
LB24b	38	1 f. 20 red and lake on pink	10·00	3·00
LB25a		1 f. 50 red and blue on blue	2·25	2·50
LB26a		2 f. red and black on grey	2·75	4·50
LB27	22	3 f. red	—	23·00
LB27a	43	3 f. brown	—	£160
LB28	–	5 f. blue (No. 285)	—	30·00
LB30	–	10 f. pur (No. 286)	—	£140
LB31	–	10 f. grn (No. 331a)	£120	

1932. Int. Disarmament Conference.

LB 32.	44.	5 c. green	—	90
LB 33.		10 c. orange	—	60
LB 34.		20 c. red	—	1·10
LB 35.		30 c. blue	—	7·00
LB 36.		60 c. sepia	—	7·50
LB 37.	45.	1 f. grey and blue	—	7·50

1937. Landscape design of 1934.

LB 38.	48.	3 c. olive	—	3·50

1937. Landscape designs of 1936.

LB39	52	3 c. green	20	15
LB40	–	5 c. green	20	15
LB41	–	10 c. purple	—	90
LB41b	–	10 c. brown	45	60
LB42	–	15 c. orange	40	30
LB43	–	20 c. red (Mountain)	—	70
LB43a	–	20 c. red (Lake)	45	1·00
LB44	–	25 c. brown	50	60
LB45	–	30 c. blue	55	70
LB46	–	35 c. green	55	1·00
LB47	–	40 c. grey	80	1·10

1938. Nos. 382/5 optd **S.d.N. Bureau International du Travail**.

LB48	55	20 c. red and buff	—	1·50
LB49	–	30 c. blue and lt blue	—	2·75
LB50	–	60 c. brown and buff	—	6·00
LB51	–	1 f. black and buff	—	6·50

1938. Nos. 382/5 optd **SERVICE DU BUREAU INTERNATIONAL DU TRAVAIL** in circle.

LB52	55	20 c. red and buff	—	4·50
LB53	–	30 c. blue and lt blue	—	3·50
LB54	–	60 c. brown and buff	—	6·50
LB55	–	1 f. black and buff	—	6·50

1939. Nos. 388c/90c optd **S.d.N. Bureau International du Travail**.

LB56	61	3 f. brown on buff	4·50	8·00
LB57	–	5 f. blue on buff	5·50	11·00
LB58	–	10 f. green on buff	9·50	24·00

1944. Optd. **COURRIER DU BUREAU INTERNATIONAL DU TRAVAIL.**

(a) Landscape designs of 1936.

LB 59.	52.	3 c. olive	20	20
LB 60.	–	5 c. green	20	20
LB 61	–	10 c. brown	30	30
LB 62.	–	15 c. orange	45	45
LB 63.	–	20 c. red (Lake)	70	70
LB 64.	–	25 c. brown	80	80
LB 65.	–	30 c. blue	1·10	1·10
LB 66.	–	35 c. green	1·25	1·25
LB 67.	–	40 c. grey	1·50	1·50

(b) Historical designs of 1941.

LB68	–	50 c. blue on green	2·50	4·50
LB69	68	60 c. brn on cinnamon	2·50	4·50
LB70	–	70 c. purple on mauve	2·50	4·00
LB71	–	80 c. black on grey	80	1·25
LB72	–	90 c. red on pink	80	1·25
LB73	–	1 f. green on green	90	1·25
LB74	–	1 f. 20 purple on grey	1·25	1·40
LB75	–	1 f. 50 blue on buff	1·40	1·50
LB76	–	2 f. red on pink	2·25	2·25

(c) Parliament designs of 1938.

LB77	61	3 f. brown on buff	5·00	6·00
LB78	–	5 f. blue on buff	6·50	8·00
LB79	–	10 f. green on buff	12·50	14·00

1950. Landscape designs of 1949 optd **BUREAU INTERNATIONAL DU TRAVAIL.**

LB80	107	5 c. orange	4·75	4·00
LB81	–	10 c. green	4·75	5·00
LB82	–	15 c. turquoise	6·50	5·00
LB83	–	20 c. purple	6·50	5·00
LB84	–	25 c. red	7·00	6·00
LB85	–	30 c. green	7·00	7·00
LB86	–	35 c. brown	7·00	7·00
LB87	–	40 c. blue	7·00	5·50
LB88	–	50 c. grey	9·50	7·50
LB89	–	60 c. green	10·00	8·50
LB90	–	70 c. violet	14·50	14·00

LB 4. Miners (bas-relief).

1952. Inscr as in Type LB 4.

LB91	LB 4	5 c. purple	10	10
LB92		10 c. green	10	10
LB94	–	20 c. red	15	15
LB95	–	30 c. orange	20	20
LB96	LB 4	40 c. blue	1·75	1·75
LB97		50 c. blue	30	30
LB98	–	60 c. brown	40	35
LB99	–	2 f. purple	1·25	75

DESIGN—HORIZ. 20, 30, 60 c., 2 f. Globe, flywheel and factory chimney.

1969. Pope Paul's Visit to Geneva. No. LB 95 optd **Visite du Pape Paul VI Geneve 10 juin 1969**.

LB100	LB 4	30 c. orange	15	15

LB 6. New Headquarters Building.

1974. Inauguration of New I.L.O. Headquarters, Geneva.

LB 101.	LB 6.	80 c. mult.	60	60

LB 7. Man at Lathe.

1975.

LB102	LB 7	30 c. brown	30	30
LB103	–	60 c. blue	45	45
LB104	–	90 c. brown, red and green	80	80
LB105	–	100 c. green	80	80
LB106	–	120 c. ochre & brn	1·00	1·00

DESIGNS: 60 c. Woman at drilling machine. 90 c. Welder and laboratory assistant. 100 c. Surveyor with theodolite. 120 c. Apprentice and instructor with slide rule.

C. INTERNATIONAL EDUCATION OFFICE

1944. Optd. **COURRIER DU BUREAU INTERNATIONAL D'EDUCATION.**

(a) Landscape designs of 1936.

LE 1.	52.	3 c. olive	20	50
LE 2.	–	5 c. green	50	1·40
LE 3.	–	10 c. brown	55	1·40
LE 4.	–	15 c. orange	50	1·40
LE 5.	–	20 c. red (Lake)	50	1·40
LE 6.	–	25 c. brown	50	1·40
LE 7.	–	30 c. blue	1·75	2·50
LE 8.	–	35 c. green	75	2·00
LE 9.	–	40 c. grey	90	2·25

(b) Historical designs of 1941.

LE10	–	50 c. blue on green	4·50	9·00
LE11	68	60 c. brn on cinnamon	4·50	9·00
LE12	–	70 c. purple on mauve	4·50	9·00
LE13	–	80 c. black on grey	60	1·40
LE14	–	90 c. red on pink	70	1·75
LE15	–	1 f. green on green	80	2·00
LE16	–	1 f. 20 purple on grey	1·10	2·50
LE17	–	1 f. 50 blue on buff	1·40	3·00
LE18		2 f. red on pink	1·75	4·00

(c) Parliament designs of 1938.

LE19	61	3 f. brown on buff	7·00	15·00
LE20	–	5 f. blue on buff	9·50	25·00
LE21	–	10 f. green on buff	14·00	35·00

1946. Optd **BIE**.

LE22	86	10 c. purple	15	15

Optd **BUREAU INTERNATIONAL D'EDUCATION** (Nos. LE 23/39).

1948. Landscape designs of 1936.

LE23		5 c. brown	2·50	2·75
LE24		10 c. green	2·50	2·75
LE25		20 c. brown	2·50	2·75
LE26		25 c. red	2·50	2·75
LE27		30 c. blue	2·50	2·75
LE28		40 c. blue	2·50	2·75

1950. Landscape designs of 1949.

LE29	107	5 c. orange	60	60
LE30	–	10 c. green	80	80
LE31	–	15 c. turquoise	90	90
LE32	–	20 c. purple	3·50	3·50
LE33	–	25 c. red	9·00	8·00
LE34	–	30 c. green	9·00	8·00
LE35	–	35 c. brown	5·50	7·00
LE36	–	40 c. blue	5·50	7·00
LE37	–	50 c. grey	6·00	7·50
LE38	–	60 c. green	7·50	8·50
LE39	–	70 c. violet	9·00	10·00

LE 3. Globe on Books.

1958. Inscr as in Type LE 3.

LE40	LE 3	5 c. purple	10	10
LE41		10 c. green	10	10
LE43	–	20 c. red	15	15
LE44	–	30 c. orange	25	25
LE45	LE 3	40 c. blue	2·25	2·25
LE46		50 c. blue	35	35
LE47	–	60 c. brown	50	50
LE48	–	2 f. purple	1·25	1·25

DESIGN—VERT. 20, 30, 60 c., 2 f. Pestalozzi Monument, Yverdon.

D. WORLD HEALTH ORGANIZATION

1948. Optd **ORGANISATION MONDIALE DE LA SANTE.**

(a) Landscape designs of 1936.

LH 1		5 c. brown (No. 489)	3·50	2·00
LH 2		10 c. green (No. 490)	3·50	4·00
LH 3		20 c. brown (No. 491)	3·50	4·50
LH 4		25 c. red (No. 492)	3·50	5·50
LH 5		40 c. blue (No. 494)	3·50	4·00

(b) Landscape designs of 1949.

LH 6	107	5 c. orange	45	30
LH 7	–	10 c. green	90	90
LH 8	–	15 c. turquoise	1·25	1·50
LH 9	–	20 c. purple	4·00	3·25
LH10	–	25 c. red	4·50	3·75
LH11	–	30 c. green	2·00	2·00
LH12	–	35 c. brown	2·75	4·00
LH13	–	40 c. blue	2·75	1·50
LH14	–	50 c. grey	3·00	3·75
LH15	–	60 c. green	3·75	3·50
LH16	–	70 c. violet	4·50	3·75

(c) Historical designs of 1941. Nos. 408/13.

LH17		80 c. black on grey	3·50	3·00
LH18		90 c. red on pink	7·00	5·50
LH19		1 f. green on green	3·50	3·00
LH20		1 f. 20 purple on grey	8·00	9·00
LH21		1 f. 50 blue on buff	18·00	10·00
LH22		2 f. red on pink	6·00	4·00

(d) Parliament designs of 1938.

LH23	61	3 f. brown on buff	38·00	32·00
LH24	–	5 f. blue on buff	15·00	8·00
LH25	–	10 f. green on buff	75·00	80·00

LH 2. Staff of Aesculapius.

1957.

LH26	LH 2	5 c. purple	10	10
LH27		10 c. green	10	10
LH29		20 c. red	15	15
LH30		30 c. orange	25	25
LH31		40 c. blue	2·25	2·25
LH32		50 c. blue	35	30
LH33		60 c. brown	45	45
LH34		2 f. purple	1·25	1·10

1962. Malaria Eradication. Optd. **ERADICATION DU PALUDISME.**

LH 35.	LH 2.	50 c. blue	25	35

LH 4. Staff of Aesculapius.

1975.

LH36	LH 4	30 c. green, purple and pink	25	30
LH37		60 c. yellow, blue and light blue	45	45
LH38		90 c. yellow, violet and light violet	75	60
LH39		100 c. blue, brown and orange	85	75
LH40		140 c. green, turquoise & red	1·25	1·25

E. INTERNATIONAL REFUGEES ORGANIZATION

Optd. **ORGANISATION INTERNATIONALE POUR LES REFUGIES.**

1950. (a) Landscape designs of 1949.

LR1	107	5 c. orange	16·00	10·00
LR2	–	10 c. green	16·00	10·00
LR3	–	20 c. purple	16·00	10·00
LR4	–	25 c. red	16·00	10·00
LR5	–	40 c. blue	16·00	10·00

(b) Historical designs of 1941. (Nos. 408/13).

LR6		80 c. black on grey	16·00	10·00
LR7		1 f. green on green	16·00	10·00
LR8		2 f. red on pink	16·00	10·00

F. WORLD METEOROLOGICAL ORGANIZATION

LM 1. "The Elements". LM 2. W.M.O. Emblem.

1956. Inscr, as in Type M 1.

LM1	LM 1	5 c. purple	10	10
LM2		10 c. green	10	10
LM4	–	20 c. red	20	20
LM5	–	30 c. orange	25	25
LM6	LM 1	40 c. blue	2·00	2·00
LM7		50 c. blue	35	30
LM8	–	60 c. brown	45	45
LM9	–	2 f. purple	1·25	1·25

DESIGN—HORIZ. 20, 30, 60 c., 2 f. Weathervane.

1973.

LM 10.	LM 2.	30 c. red	25	25
LM 11.		40 c. blue	30	30
LM 13.		1 f. brown	80	80

LM 3. W.M.O. Emblem.

1973. Centenary of I.M.O./W.M.O.

LM12	LM 3	80 c. violet & gold	60	60

G. UNIVERSAL POSTAL UNION

LP 1. U.P.U. Monument Berne. LP 2. "Letter Post".

1957. Inscr as in Type LP 1.

LP1	LP 1	5 c. purple	10	10
LP2	–	10 c. green	10	10
LP4	–	20 c. red	20	20
LP5	–	30 c. orange	25	25
LP6	LP 1	40 c. blue	2·00	2·00
LP7		50 c. blue	35	35
LP8	–	60 c. brown	45	45
LP9	LP 1	2 f. purple	1·25	1·25

Design—horiz. 10, 20, 30, 60 c. Pegasus (sculpture).

1976.

LP10	LP 2	40 c. purple, blue and claret	35	35
LP11	–	80 c. multicoloured	70	70
LP12	–	90 c. multicoloured	80	80
LP13	–	100 c. multicoloured	85	85
LP14	–	120 c. multicoloured	1·00	1·00
LP15	–	140 c. grey, blue and red	1·25	1·25

DESIGNS: 80 c. "Parcel Post"; 90 c. "Financial Services"; 100 c. Technical co-operation; 120 c. Carrier pigeon, international reply coupon and postal money order; 140 c. Express Mail Service.

H. UNITED NATIONS

Optd. **NATIONS UNIES OFFICE EUROPEEN.**

1950. (a) Landscape designs of 1949.

LU 1	107	5 c. orange	45	90
LU 2	–	10 c. green	45	90
LU 3	–	15 c. turquoise	90	1·40
LU 4	–	20 c. purple	1·40	1·75
LU 5	–	25 c. red	2·75	4·00
LU 6	–	30 c. green	2·75	4·00
LU 7	–	35 c. brown	2·75	8·00
LU 8	–	40 c. blue	4·00	3·75
LU 9	–	50 c. grey	4·75	6·50
LU10	–	60 c. green	5·00	8·50
LU11	–	70 c. violet	6·00	8·00

(b) Historical designs of 1941 (Nos. 408/13).

LU12	80 c. black on grey	10·00	10·00
LU13	90 c. red on pink	10·00	10·00
LU14	1 f. green on green	10·00	10·00
LU15	1 f. 20 purple on grey	12·50	12·50
LU16	1 f. 50 blue on buff	12·50	14·00
LU17	2 f. red on pink	12·50	11·00

(c) Parliament designs of 1938.

LU18	61	3 f. brown on buff	£120	£120
LU19	–	5 f. blue on buff	£120	£120
LU20	–	10 f. green on buff	£150	£150

LU 2.

LU 4.

1955. 10th Anniv. of U.N.O.

LU 21.	LU 2.	40 c. blue & yellow	3·25	4·50

1955. Nos. LU 22/3 and LU 27/8 are as Type LU 2 but without dates.

LU22	–	5 c. purple	10	10
LU23	–	10 c. green	10	10
LU25	LU 4	20 c. red	20	20
LU26		30 c. orange	25	25
LU27	–	40 c. blue	4·50	4·00
LU28	–	50 c. blue	35	35
LU29	LU 4	60 c. brown	35	35
LU30		2 f. purple	1·25	1·00

1960. World Refugee Year. Nos. LU 25 and LU 28 optd. **ANNEE MONDIALE DU REFUGIE 1959 1960.**

LU 31.	20 c. red	15	15
LU 32.	50 c. blue	25	25

LU 6. Palace of Nations, Geneva.

1960. 15th Anniv. of U.N.O.

LU 33.	LU 6.	5 f. blue	3·50	3·50

LU 7.

LU 8. UNCSAT Emblem.

1962. Opening of U.N. Philatelic Museum, Geneva.

LU34	LU 7	10 c. green and red	10	10
LU35	–	30 c. red and blue	20	25
LU36	LU 7	50 c. blue and red	30	30
LU37	–	60 c. brown & grn	35	40

Design—horiz. 30, 60 c. As Type LU 4 but inscr "ONU MUSEE PHILATELIQUE".

1963. U.N. Scientific and Technological Conference, Geneva.

LU 38.	LU 8.	50 c. red and blue	30	30
LU 39.	–	2 f. green & purple	80	1·00

Design—horiz. 2 f. As Type LU 4, but with emblem.

From 1969 stamps for the Geneva Headquarters were issued by the United Nations (q.v.).

I. INTERNATIONAL TELECOMMUNICATION UNION

LT 1. Transmitting Aerial.

LT 2 New H.Q. Building

1958. Inscr as in Type LT 1.

LT1	LT 1	5 c. purple	10	10
LT2		10 c. green	10	10
LT4	–	20 c. red	20	20
LT5	–	30 c. orange	25	25
LT6	LT 1	40 c. blue	1·75	2·00
LT7		50 c. blue	35	35
LT8	–	60 c. brown	45	45
LT9	–	2 f. purple	1·25	1·25

Design—vert. 20, 30, 60 c., 2 f. Receiving aerials.

1973. Inauguration of New I.T.U. Headquarters, Geneva.

LT10	LT 2	80 c. black and blue	55	55

LT 3 Airliner and Ocean Liner

1976. World Telecommunications Network.

LT11	–	40 c. blue and red	35	35
LT12	LT 3	90 c. vio, bl & yell	75	75
LT13	–	1 f. red, grn & yell	80	80

Designs: 40 c. "Sound waves". 1 f. Face and microphone in television screen.

LT 4 Optical Fibre Cables

1988.

LT14	LT 4	1 f. 40 mult	1·75	1·75

J. WORLD INTELLECTUAL PROPERTY ORGANIZATION.

LV 1. WIPO Seal.

1989. Multicoloured.

LV1	40 c. Type LV 1	35	35
LV2	50 c. Face and symbolic representation of intellect	45	45
LV3	80 c. WIPO building, Geneva	70	70
LV4	100 c. Hand pressing buttons, retort and cogwheel (industrial property)	1·00	1·00
LV5	120 c. Head, ballet dancer, cello and book (Copyright)	1·25	1·25

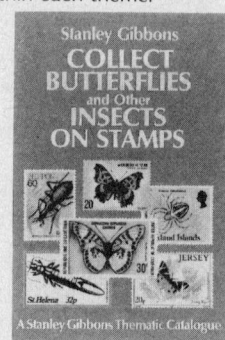

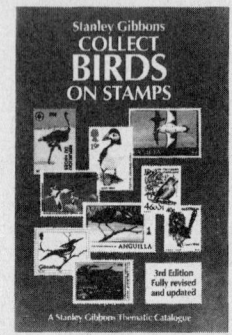

SYRIA Pt. 19

A country at the E. end of the Mediterranean Sea, formerly Turkish territory. Occupied by the Allies in 1918 and administered under French Military Occupation. An Arab kingdom was set up in the Aleppo and Damascus area during 1919, but the Emir Faisal came into conflict with the French and was defeated in July 1920. In April 1920, the Mandate was offered to France, becoming effective in September 1923. Separate governments were established for the Territories of Damascus, Aleppo, the Alaouites (including Latakia), Great Lebanon and the Jebel Druze. Syria became a republic in 1934, and the Mandate ended with full Independence in 1942. In 1958 the United Arab Republic was formed which comprised Egypt and Syria. Separate stamps were issued for each territory as they employed different currencies. In 1961 Syria left the U.A.R. and the Syrian Arab Republic was established.

1919. 40 paras = 10 milliemes = 1 piastre.
1920. 100 centimes (or centiemes) = 1 piastre.

A. FRENCH MILITARY OCCUPATION.

1919. Stamps of France surch. **T.E.O.** and value in "Milliemes" or "Piastres".

1. 11. 1 m. on 1 c. grey .. £110 £110
2. 2 m. on 2 c. red .. £325 £325
3. 3 m. on 3 c. orange .. £120 £120
4. 15. 4 m. on 15 c. green .. 20·00 20·00
5. 18. 5 m. on 5 c. green .. 10·00 10·00
6. 1 p. on 10 c. red .. 15·00 15·00
7. 2 p. on 25 c. blue .. 9·00 8·00
8. 13. 5 p. on 40 c. red and blue 11·00 11·00
9. 9 p. on 50 c. brown & lav. 25·00 25·00
10. 10 p. on 1 f. red & yellow 40·00 40·00

1919. "Blanc", "Mouchon" and "Merson" key-types of French Levant surch. **T.E.O.** and value in "Milliemes" or "Piastres".

11. A. 1 m. on 1 c. grey .. 20 20
12. 2 m. on 2 c. red .. 20 20
13. 3 m. on 3 c. orange .. 50 40
14. B. 4 m. on 15 c. red .. 25 25
15. A. 5 m. on 5 c. green .. 25 15
16. B. 1 p. on 25 c. blue .. 25 15
17. C. 2 p. on 50 c. brn. & lav... 40 40
18. 4 p. on 1 f. red and yellow 75 50
19. 8 p. on 2 f. lilac & yellow 2·50 2·25
20. 20 p. on 5 f. blue & yellow £160 £110

1920. Stamps of France surch. **O.M.F. Syrie** and value in "Milliemes" or "Piastres".

25. 11. 1 m. on 1 c. grey .. 20 20
26. 2 m. on 2 c. red .. 40 40
27. 18. 3 m. on 5 c. green .. 30 30
28. 5 m. on 10 c. red .. 20 20
29. 13. 20 p. on 5 f. blue & yellow 40·00 40·00

1920. Stamps of France surch. **O.M.F. Syrie** and value in two lines. (a) Value in "Centimes" or "Piastres".

31. 11. 25 c. on 1 c. grey .. 30 30
32. 50 c. on 2 c. red.. .. 30 30
33. 75 c. on 3 c. orange .. 30 30
35. 18. 1 p. on 5 c. green .. 15 15
36. 2 p. on 10 c. red .. 20 20
37. 2 p. on 25 c. blue .. 20 20
38. 3 p. on 25 c. blue .. 20 30
39. 15. 5 p. on 15 c. green .. 30 30
40. 13. 10 p. on 40 c. red & blue 40 40
41. 25 p. on 50 c. brn. & lav. 75 75
42. 50 p. on 1 f. red & yellow 12·00 12·00
44. 100 p. on 5 f. blue & yell. 23·00 23·00

(b) Value in "Centiemes".

45. 11. 25 c. on 1 c. grey .. 20 15
46. 50 c. on 2 c. red.. .. 15 15
47. 75 c. on 3 c. orange .. 30 30

1920. Air. Nos. 35, 39/40 optd. **POSTE PAR AVION** in frame.

57. 18. 1 p. on 5 c. green .. 90·00 25·00
58. 15. 5 p. on 15 c. green .. £170 25·00
59. 13. 10 p. on 40 c. red & blue £250 50·00

1921. Issued at Damascus. Nos. K 88/95 of Arab Kingdom surch **O.M.F. Syrie** and value in two lines in "Centiemes" or "Piastres".

60 K 3 25 c. on 1 m. .. 30 30
61 50 c. on 2/10 p. green .. 30 30
62 1 p. on 3/10 p. yellow .. 40 30
63 K 4 1 p. on 5 m. red .. 50 40
64a 2 p. on 5 m. red .. 60 40
65 K 3 3 p. on 1 p. blue .. 80 60
66 5 p. on 2 p. green .. 2·25 2·00
67 10 p. on 5 p. purple .. 4·00 2·75
68 25 p. on 10 p. grey .. 5·50 3·00

1921. Stamps of France surch. **O.M.F. Syrie** and value in two lines in "Centiemes" or "Piastres".

69 18 25 c. on 5 c. green .. 15 15
70 50 c. on 10 c. red .. 15 15
71 15 75 c. on 15 c. green .. 20 20
72 18 1 p. on 20 c. brown .. 10 10
73 13 2 p. on 40 c. red and blue 30 20
74 3 p. on 60 c. violet & blue 40 30
75 5 p. on 1 f. red & yellow 80 60
76 10 p. on 2 f. orange & grn 1·50 1·40
77 25 p. on 5 f. blue & yell 60·00 60·00

1921. Air. Nos. 72, 75/6 optd. **POSTE PAR AVION** in frame.

78. 18. 1 p. on 20 c. brown .. 45·00 23·00
79. 13. 5 p. on 1 f. red & yellow £250 90·00
80. 10 p. on 2 f. orge. & grn. 25·00 90·00

1921. Stamps of France surch. **O.M.F. Syrie** and value in "Piastres" in one line.

81. 13. 2 p. on 40 c. red and blue 20 10
82. 3 p. on 60 c. violet & blue 40 20
83. 5 p. on 1 f. red and yellow 2·50 2·25
84. 10 p. on 2 f. orge. & grn. 6·00 5·50
85. 25 p. on 5 f. blue & yellow 5·50 5·00

1921. Air. Nos. 72, 75/6 optd. **AVION.**

86. 18. 1 p. on 20 c. brown .. 35·00 9·00
87. 13. 5 p. on 1 f. red & yellow 85·00 18·00
88. 10 p. on 2 f. orge. & grn. £110 28·00

1922. Air. Nos. 81/4 optd **Poste par Avion.**

89. 13. 2 p. on 40 c. red and blue 10·00 10·00
90. 3 p. on 60 c. violet & blue 10·00 10·00
91. 5 p. on 1 f. red & yellow.. 10·00 10·00
92. 10 p. on 2 f. orge. & grn. 10·00 10·00

1922. Stamps of France surch **O.M.F. Syrie** and value in two lines in "Centiemes" or "Piastres".

93. 11. 10 c. on 2 c. red .. 20 20
94. 18. 10 c. on 5 c. orange .. 20 20
95. 25 c. on 5 c. orange .. 20 20
96. 50 c. on 10 c. green .. 30 20
96a. 1,25 p. on 25 c. blue .. 40 40
96b. 1,50 on 30 c. orange 25 20
96c. 13. 2 p. 50 on 50 c. brn. & lav. 30 30
96d. 15. 2,50 p. on 50 c. blue .. 40 30

B. ARAB KINGDOM.

Prior to the issues listed below, the Kingdom used stamps of Turkey variously overprinted. These are listed in Part 19 (Middle East) of the Stanley Gibbons Catalogue.

K 3. K 4.

1920. As Type K 3 (various sizes) and Type K 4.

K 88. K 3. 1 m. brown 10 10
K 89. 1/10 p. green 35 35
K 90. 3/10 p. yellow 15 15
K 91. K 4. 5 m. red 15 10
K 92. K 3. 1 p. blue 15 10
K 93. 2 p. green .. .. 1·50 50
K 94. 5 p. purple .. .. 10·00 2·00
K 95. 10 p. grey .. .. 10·00 3·00

For 1 p. black as Type K 3, see No. KD 96.

1920. Independence Commem. Optd. with Arabic inscription.

K 98. K 4. 5 m. red £130 £130

C. FRENCH MANDATED TERRITORY.

Nos 97/174 are all stamps of France surch.

Issues for Lebanon and Syria.

1923. Surch. **Syrie Grand Liban** in two lines and value in "Centiemes" or "Piastres".

97. 11. 10 c. on 2 c. red .. 10 10
98. 18. 25 c. on 5 c. orange .. 10 10
99. 50 c. on 10 c. green .. 20 20
100. 15. 75 c. on 15 c. green .. 20 20
101. 18. 1 p. on 20 c. brown .. 15 15
102. 1 p. 25 on 25 c. blue .. 20 20
103. 1 p. 50 on 30 c. orange 20 20
104. 1 p. 50 on 30 c. red .. 10 10
105. 15. 2 p. 50 on 50 c. blue .. 15 15

1923. Surch. **Syrie-Grand Liban** in one line and value in "Piastres".

106. 13. 2 p. on 40 c. red and blue 15 15
107. 3 p. on 60 c. violet & blue 30 30
108. 5 p. on 1 f. red & yellow 60 60
109. 10 p. on 2 f. orge. & grn. 3·25 3·25
110. 25 p. on 5 f. blue & yell . 11·00 11·00

1923. "Pasteur" issue surch. **Syrie Grand Liban** in two lines and value in "Centiemes" or "Piastres".

111. 30. 50 c. on 10 c. green .. 35 35
112. 1 p. 50 on 30 c. red .. 35 35
113. 2 p. 50 on 50 c. blue .. 35 35

1923. Air. Surch **Poste par Avion Syrie-Grand Liban** and value in "PIASTRES".

114. 13. 2 p. on 40 c. red & blue 16·00 16·00
115. 3 p. on 60 c. vio. & bl... 16·00 16·00
116. 5 p. on 1 f. red & yell... 16·00 16·00
117. 10 p. on 2 f. orange and green .. .. 16·00 16·00

Issues for Syria only.

1924. Surch. **SYRIE** and value in two lines.

118. 11. 10 c. on 2 c. red .. 10 10
119. 18. 25 c. on 5 c. orange .. 10 10
120. 50 c. on 10 c. green .. 15 15
121. 15. 75 c. on 15 c. green .. 15 15
122. 18. 1 p. on 20 c. brown .. 10 10
123. 1 p. 25 on 25 c. blue .. 30 30
124. 1 p. 50 on 30 c. orange 30 30
125. 1 p. 50 on 30 c. red .. 30 30
126. 15. 2 p. 50 on 50 c. blue .. 30 30

1924. Surch. **SYRIE** and value in one line.

127. 13. 2 p. on 40 c. red and blue 20 15
128. 3 p. on 60 c. violet & blue 35 30
129. 5 p. on 1 f. red & yellow 1·10 1·10
130. 10 p. on 2 f. orge. & grn. 1·10 1·10
131. 25 p. on 5 f. blue & yell. 2·00 2·00

1924. "Pasteur" issue surch. **SYRIE** and value in two lines.

132. 30. 50 c. on 10 c. green .. 10 10
133. 1 p. 50 on 30 c. red .. 30 25
134. 2 p. 50 on 50 c. blue .. 10 10

1924. Air. Surch **Poste par Avion Syrie** and value.

135. 13. 2 p. on 40 c. red & blue 1·10 1·10
136. 3 p. on 60 c. vio. & blue 1·10 1·10
137. 5 p. on 1 f. red & yellow 1·10 1·10
138. 10 p. on 2 f. orge. & grn. 1·10 1·10

1924. Olympic Games issue (Nos. 401/4) surch. **SYRIE** and value in two lines.

139. 31. 50 c. on 10 c. green .. 25·00 25·00
140. – 1 p. 25 on 25 c. red .. 25·00 25·00
141. – 1 p. 50 on 30 c. red & blk 25·00 25·00
142. – 2 p. 50 on 50 c. blue .. 25·00 25·00

1924. Surch. **Syrie** and value and **Arabic inscription.**

143. 11. 0 p. 10 on 2 c. red .. 10 10
144. 18. 0 p. 25 on 5 c. orange .. 10 10
145. 0 p. 50 on 10 c. green .. 15 15
146. 15. 0 p. 75 on 15 c. green .. 15 15
147. 18. 1 p. on 20 c. brown .. 10 10
148. 1 p. 25 on 25 c. blue .. 15 15
149. 1 p. 50 on 30 c. red .. 20 20
150. 1 p. 50 on 30 c. orange 13·00 13·00
151. 2 p. on 35 c. violet .. 15 15
152. 13. 2 p. on 40 c. red and blue 15 15
153. 2 p. on 45 c. grn. & blue 1·60 1·60
154. 3 p. on 60 c. violet & blue 30 30
155. 15. 3 p. on 60 c. violet .. 30 30
156. 4 p. on 85 c. red .. 15 15
157. 13. 5 p. on 1 f. red & yellow 40 40
158. 10 p. on 2 f. orge. & grn. 70 70
159. 25 p. on 5 f. blue & yell. 70 70

1924. "Pasteur" issue surch. **Syrie** and value and Arabic inscription.

160. 30. 0 p. 50 on 10 c. green .. 20 20
161. 0 p. 75 on 15 c. green .. 40 40
162. 1 p. 50 on 30 c. red .. 30 30
163. 2 p. on 45 c. red .. 20 20
164. 2 p. 50 on 50 c. blue .. 40 40
165. 4 p. on 75 c. blue .. 50 50

1924. Olympic Games issue (Nos. 401/4) surch. **Syrie** and value and Arabic inscription.

166. 31. 0 p. 50 on 10 c. green .. 25·00 25·00
167. – 1 p. 25 on 25 c. red .. 25·00 25·00
168. – 1 p. 50 on 30 c. red & blk 25·00 25·00
169. – 2 p. 50 on 50 c. blue .. 25·00 25·00

1924. Ronsard stamp surch. **Syrie** and value and Arabic inscription.

170. 35. 4 p. on 75 c. blue .. 30 30

1924. Air Surch **Syrie Avion**, new value and Arabic inscription.

171. 13. 2 p. on 40 c. red & blue 2·00 2·00
172. 3 p. on 60 c. vio. & blue 2·00 2·00
173. 5 p. on 1 f. red & yell... 2·00 2·00
174. 10 p. on 2 f. orge. & grn. 2·00 2·00

16. Hama.

17. Merkab. 18. Damascus.

1925. Views.

175. 16. 0 p. 10 violet 10 10
176. 17. 0 p. 25 black 35 25
177. – 0 p. 50 green 25 15
178. – 0 p. 75 red 20 10
179. 18. 1 p. red 20 5
180. – 1 p. 25 green 70 50
181. – 1 p. 50 red 15 10
182. – 2 p. sepia 35 10
183. – 2 p. 50 blue 45 35
184. – 3 p. brown 20 10
185. – 5 p. violet 55 10
186. – 10 p. plum 85 10
187. – 25 p. blue .. .. 1·25 70

DESIGNS—As Type 17: 50 c. Alexandretta. 75 c. Hama. 1 p. 25, Latakia. 1 p. 50, Damascus. 2 p., 25 p. Palmyra (different views). 2 p. 50, Kalat Yamoun. 3 p. Bridge of Daphne. 5 p., 10 p. Aleppo (different views).

1925. Air. Nos. 182 etc. optd. **AVION** and Arabic inscription.

188. 2 p. sepia 85 85
189. 3 p. brown 85 85
190. 5 p. violet 85 85
191. 10 p. plum 85 85

1926. Air. Nos. 182 etc. optd. with aeroplane.

192. 2 p. sepia 40 40
193. 3 p. brown 50 50
194. 5 p. violet 60 60
195. 10 p. plum 60 60

1926. War Refugees Fund. Nos. 176 and Nos. 192/5 etc. surch. **Secours aux Refugies Afft,** value and Arabic inscr.

196. 17. 0 p. 25 on 0 p. 25 black (postage) .. .. 1·00 1·00
197. – 0 p. 25 on 0 p. 50 green .. 1·00 1·00
198. – 0 p. 25 on 0 p. 75 red .. 1·00 1·00
199. 18. 0 p. 50 on 1 p. red .. 1·00 1·00
200. – 0 p. 50 on 1 p. 25 green 1·00 1·00
201. – 0 p. 50 on 1 p. 50 red .. 1·00 1·00
202. – 0 p. 75 on 2 p. sepia .. 1·00 1·00
203. – 0 p. 75 on 2 p. 50 blue .. 1·00 1·00
204. – 1 p. on 3 p. brown .. 1·00 1·00
205. – 1 p. on 5 p. violet .. 1·00 1·00
206. – 2 p. on 10 p. plum .. 1·00 1·00
207. – 5 p. on 25 p. blue .. 1·00 1·00
208. – 1 p. on 2 p. sepia (air) .. 1·00 1·00
209. – 2 p. on 3 p. brown .. 1·00 1·00
210. – 3 p. on 5 p. violet .. 1·00 1·00
211. – 5 p. on 10 p. plum .. 1·00 1·00

1926. No. 176, etc., surch. with new value in English and Arabic figures and bars.

222 1 p. on 3 p. brown .. 35 20
223 2 p. on 1 p. 25 green .. 25 10
212 3 p. 50 on 75 c. red .. 20 10
214 4 p. on 25 c. black .. 20 10
215 4 p. 50 on 75 c. red .. 20 10
216 6 p. on 2 p. 50 blue .. 20 10
217 7 p. 50 on 2 p. 50 blue .. 20 10
218 12 p. on 1 p. 25 green .. 20 10
219 15 p. on 25 p. blue .. 20 15
220 20 p. on 1 p. 25 green .. 30 15

1928. No. 175 surch. in English and Arabic figures and single bar.

221. 05 on 0 p. 10 violet .. 10 10

1929. Air. Nos. 177, etc., optd. with aeroplane or surch. also in English and Arabic figures and bars.

225. 0 p. 50 green 30 20
226. 1 p. red 40 40
227. 2 p. on 1 p. 25 green .. 70 70
228. 15 p. on 25 p. blue .. 1·00 1·00
229. 25 p. blue .. .. 1·75 2·00

1929. Damascus Industrial Exn. Nos. 177 etc and various air stamps optd. **EXPOSITION INDUSTRIELLE DAMAS 1929** and Arabic inscr.

230 0 p. 50 green (postage) .. 1·40 1·40
231 1 p. red .. .. 1·40 1·40
232 1 p. 50 red .. .. 1·40 1·40
233 3 p. brown .. .. 1·40 1·40
234 5 p. violet .. .. 1·40 1·40
235 10 p. plum .. .. 1·40 1·40
236 25 p. blue .. .. 1·40 1·40

237 0 p. 50 green (No. 225) (air) 1·00 1·00
238 1 p. red (No. 226) .. 1·00 1·00
239 2 p. sepia (No. 192) .. 1·00 1·00
240 3 p. brown (No. 193) .. 1·00 1·00
241 5 p. violet (No. 194) .. 1·00 1·00
242 10 p. plum (No. 195) .. 1·00 1·00
243 25 p. (No. 229) .. .. 1·00 1·00

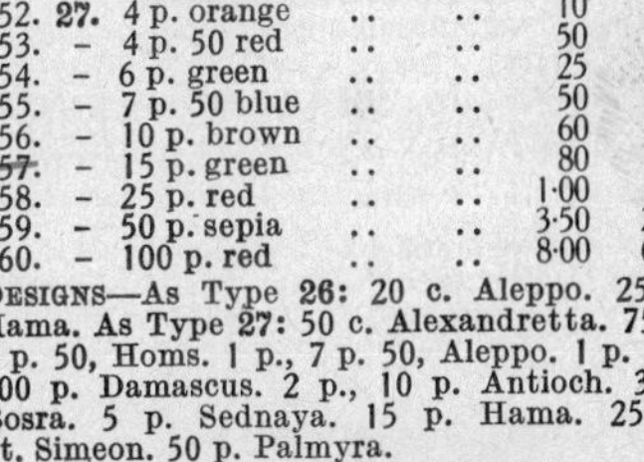

26. Hama. 27. Damascus.

1930. Views.

244. 26. 0 p. 10 purple 10 10
245. – 0 p. 20 blue 10 10
245a. – 0 p. 20 red 10 10
246. – 0 p. 25 green 10 10
246a. – 0 p. 25 violet 10 10
247. – 0 p. 50 violet 10 10
247a. – 0 p. 75 red 10 10
248. – 1 p. green 10 10
248a. – 1 p. brown 10 10
249. – 1 p. 50 brown .. .. 2·50 1·75
249a. – 1 p. 50 green 25 20
250. – 2 p. violet 10 10
251. – 3 p. green 50 30
252. 27. 4 p. orange 10 10
253. – 4 p. 50 red 50 25
254. – 6 p. green 25 15
255. – 7 p. 50 blue 50 25
256. – 10 p. brown 60 10
257. – 15 p. green 80 40
258. – 25 p. red .. .. 1·00 55
259. – 50 p. sepia .. .. 3·50 2·25
260. – 100 p. red .. .. 8·00 6·00

DESIGNS—As Type 26: 20 c. Aleppo. 25 c. Hama. As Type 27: 50 c. Alexandretta. 75 c, 4 p. 50, Homs. 1 p., 7 p. 50, Aleppo. 1 p. 50., 100 p. Damascus. 2 p., 10 p. Antioch. 3 p. Bosra. 5 p. Sednaya. 15 p. Hama. 25 p. St. Simeon. 50 p. Palmyra.

28. River Euphrates.

1931. Air. Views with aeroplane.

261 – 0 p. 50 yellow (Homs) 35 15
261a – 0 p. 50 brown (Homs) 40 20
262 – 1 p. brown (Damascus) 40 20
263 28 2 p. blue .. .. 1·25 60
264 – 3 p. green (Palmyra) .. 40 20
265 – 5 p. purple (Deir-el-Zor) 40 20
266 – 10 p. blue (Damascus) 40 20
267 – 15 p. red (Aleppo citadel) 80 60
268 – 25 p. orange (Hama) .. 1·00 60
269 – 50 p. black (Zebdani) 1·25 80
270 – 100 p. mauve (Telebisse) .. 1·40 90

D. REPUBLIC UNDER FRENCH MANDATE.

29. Parliament House, Damascus.

30. Aboulula el Maari.

31. Aeroplane over Bloudan.

1934. Establishment of Republic.

271. **29.** 0 p. 10 olive (postage) .. 60 60
272. 0 p. 20 black 60 60
273. 0 p. 25 red 60 60
274. 0 p. 50 blue 60 60
275. 0 p. 75 purple 60 60
276. **30.** 1 p. red .. .. 1·50 1·50
277. 1 p. 50 green .. .. 2·50 2·50
278. 2 p. red .. .. 2·50 2·50
279. 3 p. blue .. .. 2·50 2·50
280. 4 p. violet .. .. 2·50 2·50
281. 4 p. 50 red .. .. 2·50 2·50
282. 5 p. blue .. .. 2·50 2·50
283. 6 p. brown .. .. 2·50 2·50
284. 7 p. 50 blue .. .. 2·50 2·50
285. – 10 p. brown .. .. 4·00 4·00
286. – 15 p. blue .. .. 5·50 5·50
287. – 25 p. red .. .. 8·50 8·50
288. – 50 p. brown .. .. 15·00 15·00
289. – 100 p. red .. .. 23·00 23·00

DESIGNS—As Type **30**: Nos. 285/7, President Mohammed Ali Bey el Abed. Nos. 288/9, Sultan Saladin.

290. **31.** 0 p. 50 brown (air) .. 1·00 1·00
291. 1 p. green .. .. 1·00 1·00
292. 2 p. blue .. .. 1·00 1·00
293. 3 p. red .. .. 1·00 1·00
294. 5 p. purple .. .. 1·25 1·25
295. 10 p. violet .. .. 12·00 12·00
296. 15 p. brown .. .. 13·00 13·00
297. 25 p. blue .. .. 15·00 15·00
298. 50 p. black .. .. 26·00 26·00
299. 100 p. red .. .. 50·00 50·00

1936. Damascus Fair. Optd. **FOIRE DE DAMAS 1936** in Arabic and French.

(a) Postage stamps of 1930.

300. – 0 p. 50 violet .. .. 1·00 1·00
301. – 1 p. brown .. .. 1·00 1·00
302. – 2 p. violet .. .. 1·00 1·00
303. – 3 p. green .. .. 1·00 1·00
304. **27.** 4 p. orange .. .. 1·00 1·00
305. – 4 p. 50 red .. .. 1·00 1·00
306. – 6 p. green .. .. 1·00 1·00
307. – 7 p. 50 blue .. .. 1·25 1·25
308. – 10 p. brown .. .. 1·75 1·75

(b) Air stamps of 1931.

309. – 0 p. 50 sepia .. .. 2·00 2·00
310. – 1 p. brown .. .. 2·00 2·00
311. **28.** 2 p. blue .. .. 2·00 2·00
312. – 3 p. green .. .. 2·00 2·00
313. – 5 p. purple .. .. 2·00 2·00

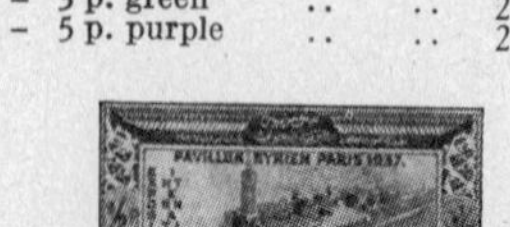

33. Exhibition Pavilion.

1937. Air. Paris International Exn.

314. **33.** ½ p. green .. .. 1·00 1·00
315. 1 p. green .. .. 1·00 1·00
316. 2 p. brown .. .. 1·00 1·00
317. 3 p. red .. .. 1·00 1·00
318. 5 p. orange .. .. 1·00 1·00
319. 10 p. green .. .. 1·75 1·75
320. 15 p. blue .. .. 2·00 2·00
321. 25 p. violet .. .. 2·00 2·00

34. Aleppo.

DESIGN: 1, 3, 10, 25 p. Aeroplane over Damascus.

1937. Air.

322. **34.** ½ p. violet 30 30
323. – 1 p. black 30 30
324. **34.** 2 p. green 30 30
325. – 3 p. blue 30 30
326. **34.** 5 p. mauve 80 80
327. – 10 p. brown 60 60
328. **34.** 15 p. brown .. .. 2·25 2·25
329. – 25 p. blue .. .. 2·50 2·50

1938. Stamps of 1930 surch. in English and Arabic figures and bars.

330. 0 p. 25 on 0 p 75 red .. 10 10
331. 0 p. 50 on 1 p. 50 green .. 10 10
332. 2 p. on 7 p. 50 blue .. 15 10
333. 2 p. 50 on 4 p. orange .. 20 15
334. 5 p. on 7 p. 50 blue .. 25 20
335. 10 p. on 50 p. sepia .. 55 55
336. 10 p. on 100 p. red .. 60 60

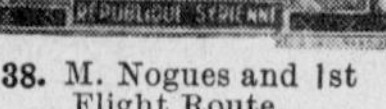

38. M. Nogues and 1st Flight Route.

39. President Atasi.

1938. Air. 10th Anniv. of 1st Air Service Flight between France and Syria.

337. **38.** 10 p. green .. .. 1·50 1·50

1938. Unissued stamp surch. **12.50** and in Arabic figures.

338. **39.** 12 p. 50 on 10 p. blue 40 30

1938.

338a. **39.** 10 p. blue 30 20
339. 20 p. sepia 45 30

41. Palmyra.

1940.

340. **41.** 5 p. pink 20 15

42. Damascus Museum. 45. Deir-el-Zor Bridge.

341. **42.** 0 p. 10 red (postage) .. 10 10
342. 0 p. 20 blue 10 10
343. 0 p. 25 brown 10 10
344. 0 p. 50 blue 10 10
345. – 1 p. blue 10 10
346. – 1 p. 50 brown 10 10
347. – 2 p. 50 green 10 10
348. – 5 p. violet 20 10
349. – 7 p. 50 red 40 30
350. – 50 p. purple 90 70

DESIGNS—As Type **45**: 1 p., 1 p. 50, 2 p. 50, Hotel de Bloudan. 5 p., 7 p. 50, 50 p. Kasr-el-Heir Fortress.

351. **45.** 0 p. 25 black (air) .. 10 10
352. 0 p. 50 blue 10 10
353. 1 p. blue 15 10
354. 2 p. brown 15 15
355. 5 p. green 40 40
356. 10 p. red 60 60
357. 50 p. violet .. .. 1·75 1·75

E. SYRIAN REPUBLIC.

46. President Sheikh Taj Addin-el-Husni. 47

1942. National Independence. Inscr. "PROCLAMATION/DE L'INDEPENDANCE/27 Septembre 1941".

358. **46.** 0 p. 50 green (postage) 2·50 2·50
359. 1 p. 50 sepia .. .. 2·50 2·50
360. 6 p. red .. .. 2·50 2·50
361. 15 p. blue .. .. 2·50 2·50
362. – 10 p. blue (air) .. .. 2·00 2·00
363. – 50 p. purple .. .. 2·00 2·00

DESIGN: 10 p., 50 p. As Type **46**, but President bareheaded and aeroplane inset.

1942. (a) Postage. Portrait in oval frame.

364. **47.** 6 p. red and pink .. 1·50 1·50
365. 15 p. blue .. .. 1·50 1·50

(b) Air. Portrait in rectangular frame.

366. 10 p. green .. .. 2·75 2·75

48. Syria and late President's portrait. 49. Shukri Bey al-Quwatli.

1943. Union of Latakia and Jebel Druze with Syria. (a) President bare-headed.

367. **48.** 1 p. green (postage) .. 1·25 1·25
368. 4 p. brown .. .. 1·25 1·25
369. 8 p. violet .. .. 1·25 1·25
370. 10 p. orange .. .. 1·25 1·25
371. 20 p. blue .. .. 1·25 1·25

(b) President wearing turban.

372. 2 p. brown (air) .. 1·25 1·25
373. 10 p. purple .. .. 1·25 1·25
374. 20 p. blue .. .. 1·25 1·25
375. 50 p. pink .. .. 1·25 1·25

1943. Death of President Sheikh Taj Addin-el-Husni. Nos. 367/375 optd. with narrow black border.

376. **48.** 1 p. green (postage) .. 1·25 1·25
377. 4 p. brown .. .. 1·25 1·25
378. 8 p. violet .. .. 1·25 1·25
379. 10 p. orange .. .. 1·25 1·25
380. 20 p. blue .. .. 1·25 1·25
381. – 2 p. brown (air) .. 1·25 1·25
382. – 10 p. purple .. .. 1·25 1·25
383. – 20 p. blue .. .. 1·25 1·25
384. – 50 p. pink .. .. 1·25 1·25

1944. Air.

385. **49.** 200 p. purple .. .. 5·50 5·50
386. 500 p. blue .. .. 9·00 9·00

(**50.** Trans. "First Congress of Arab Lawyers, Damascus".) (**51.** Trans. "Aboulula-el-Maari. Commemorative of Millenary, 363–1363".)

1944. Air. 1st Arab Lawyers' Congress. Optd. with T **50**.

387 – 10 p. brown (No. 327) .. 1·50 1·50
388 – 15 p. red (No. 267) .. 1·50 1·50
389 – 25 p. orge (No. 268) .. 1·50 1·50
390 – 100 p. mauve (No. 270) 4·50 4·50
391 **49** 200 p. purple .. .. 6·00 6·00

1945. Millenary of Aboulula-el-Maari (Arab poet and philosopher). Optd. with T **51**.

392. – 2 p. 50 green (No. 347) (postage) .. .. 2·00 2·00
393 – 7 p. 50 red (No. 349) .. 2·00 2·00
394. – 15 p. red (No. 267) (air) 1·50 1·50
395. – 25 p. orge. (No. 268) .. 1·50 1·50
396. **49.** 500 p. blue .. .. 12·00 12·00

52. Pres. Shukri Bey al-Quwatli.

53. Pres. Shukri Bey al-Quwatli.

1945. Resumption of Constitutional Govt.

397. **52.** 4 p. violet (postage) .. 25 25
398. 6 p. blue 25 25
399. 10 p. red 25 25
400. 15 p. brown 40 40
401. 20 p. green 45 45
402. 40 p. orange 85 75
403. **53.** 5 p. green (air) 25 30
404. 10 p. red 25 30
405. 15 p. orange 25 30
406. 25 p. blue 60 30
407. 50 p. violet .. .. 1·00 30
408. 100 p. brown .. .. 2·00 60
409. 200 p. brown .. .. 5·00 2·25

POSTES SYRIE (**54.**)

12P½ POSTES SYRIE (**55.**)

1945. Fiscal stamps inscr. "TIMBRE FISCAL", optd. with T **54**.

410. 25 p. brown .. .. 2·50 2·50
411. 50 p. on 75 p. brown .. 3·00 3·00
412. 75 p. brown .. .. 4·50 4·50
413. 100 p. green .. .. 5·00 5·00

1945. Fiscal stamps surch. as T **55** or optd. with T **54** and additional Arabic inscription.

414. 12½ p. on 15 p. green .. 1·40 1·40
415. 25 p. on 25 s. purple .. 1·60 1·60
416. 50 p. on 75 p. brown .. 1·10 1·10
417. 50 p. mauve .. .. 3·00 3·00
418. 100 p. green .. .. 2·00 2·00

(**56.**)

57. Ear of Wheat.

58. President Shukri Bey al-Quwatli.

60. Arab Horse.

1946. Fiscal stamp optd. with T **56**.

419. 200 p. blue .. .. 15·00 8·50

1946.

420 **57.** 0 p. 50 orange (postage) 15 10
421 1 p. violet 40 10
422 2 p. 50 grey 45 15
423 5 p. green 60 20
424 **58.** 7 p. 50 brown 20 10
425 10 p. blue 20 10
426 12 p. 50 violet 75 15
427 – 15 p. red 30 15
428 – 20 p. violet 45 25
429 – 25 p. blue 75 25
430 **60.** 50 p. brown .. .. 3·75 60
431 100 p. green .. .. 8·00 1·40
432a 200 p. purple .. .. 45·00 3·75

DESIGN—As Type **58**: 15 p., 20 p., 25 p. Pres. Shukri Bey al-Quwatli bareheaded.

433. – 3 p. brown (air) .. 40 10
434. – 5 p. green 40 10
435. – 6 p. orange 40 10
436. – 10 p. grey 30 10
437. – 15 p. red 30 10
438. – 25 p. blue 45 15
439. – 50 p. violet 60 15
440. – 100 p. green .. .. 1·50 35
441. – 200 p. brown .. .. 3·75 90
442. – 300 p. brown .. .. 12·00 1·50
443. – 500 p. olive .. .. 13·00 3·00

DESIGNS—HORIZ. 3 p., 5 p., 6 p. Flock of sheep. 10 p., 15 p., 25 p. Kattineh dam. 50 p., 100 p., 200 p. Temple ruins, Kanaouat. 300 p., 500 p. Sultan Ibrahim Mosque.

(**65.**)

1946. Withdrawal of Allied Forces. Optd. with T **65**. (a) Postage.

444. **58.** 10 p. blue 40 40
445. 12 p. 50 violet 55 55
446. **60.** 50 p. brown .. .. 1·50 1·50

(b) Air.

447. – 25 p. blue (No. 438) .. 1·25 80

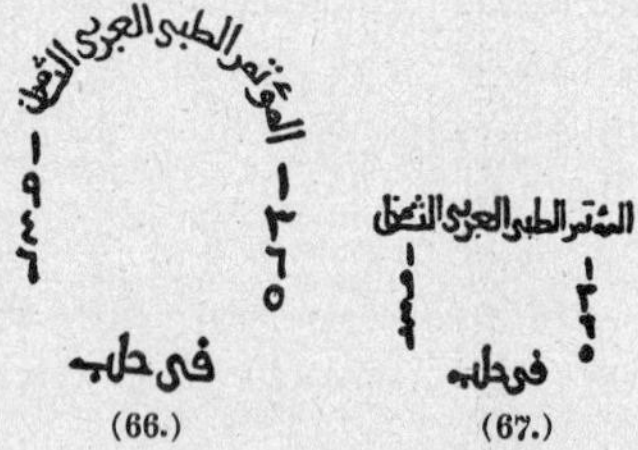

(**66.**) (**67.**)

1946. 8th Arab Medical Congress, Aleppo.

(a) Postage. Optd. with T **66**.

448. 25 p. blue (No. 429) .. 1·00 75

(b) Air. Optd. with T **67**.

449. 25 p. blue (No. 438) .. 1·10 70
450. 50 p. violet (No. 439) .. 1·90 1·10
451. 100 p. green (No. 440) .. 3·50 2·00

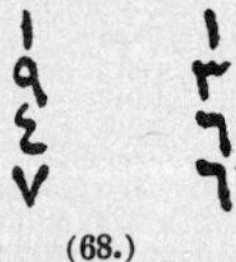

(**68.**)

1947. 1st Anniv. of Evacuation of Allied Forces. Nos. 444/447 optd. as T **68** ("1947").

452. **58.** 10 p. blue (postage) .. 40 10
453. 12 p. 50 violet 55 15
454. **60.** 50 p. brown .. .. 1·50 45
455. – 25 p. blue (air) .. .. 1·25 70

69. Hercules and Lion.

70. Mosaic of the Mosque of the Omayades.

71. Courtyard of Azem Palace.

72. Congress Symbol.

1947. 1st Arab Archaeological Congress, Damascus. Inscr. "1er CONGRES ARCHEOLOGIQUE ARABE–1947".

456. **69.** 12 p. 50 green (postage) 50 40
457. **70.** 25 p. blue .. .. 1·10 60
458. – 12 p. 50 violet (air) .. 75 30
459. – 50 p. brown .. .. 2·50 1·25

DESIGNS—HORIZ. 12 p. 50, Window at Kasr El-Heir El-Gharbi. 50 p. King Hazekil's throne.

1947. 3rd Arab Engineers Congress Damascus. Inscr. "3e CONGRES DES INGENIEURS ARABES 1947".

460. **71.** 12 p. 50 purple (post.) 40 35
461. – 25 p. blue 80 45

462. – 12 p. 50 olive (air) .. 55 30
463. **72.** 50 p. violet .. .. 1·90 1·25

DESIGNS—HORIZ. No. 461, Telephone Exchange Building. No. 462, Fortress at Kasr El-Heir El-Charqui.

73. Parliament Building.

74. Pres. Shukri Bey al-Quwatli.

1948. Re-election of Pres. Shukri Bey al-Quwatli.

464. **73.** 12 p. 50 brown & grey (postage) 40 20
465. **74.** 25 p. mauve 60 40

466. **73.** 12 p. 50 blue and violet (air) 35 20
467. **74.** 50 p. purple and green .. 1·60 70

75. Syrian Arms.

76. Soldier and Flag.

1948. Compulsory Military Service.

468. **75.** 12 p. 50 brown and grey (postage) 40 25
469. **76.** 25 p. multicoloured .. 65 35

470. **75.** 12 p. 50 blue (air) .. 55 25
471. **76.** 50 p. grn., red and blk. 1·90 60

1948. Surch. (a) Postage.

472. – 50 c. on 75 c. red (No. 247a) 20 10
472ab. **60.** 2 p. 50 on 200 p. purple 35 10
472b. 10 p. on 100 p. green .. 45 20
473. 25 p. on 200 p. purple .. 30·00 30

(b) Air.

474. – 2 p. 50 on 3 p. (No. 433) 10 10
475. – 2 p. 50 on 6 p. (No. 435) 10 10
475a. – 2 p. 50 on 100 p. (No. 440) 10 10
476. – 25 p. on 200 p. (No. 441) 75 20
477. – 50 p. on 300 p. (No. 442) 15·00 75
478. – 50 p. on 500 p. (No. 443) 15·00 75

78. Palmyra.

79. President Husni el Zaim and Aeroplane over Damascus.

1949. 75th Anniv. of U.P.U.

479. – 12 p. 50 violet (postage) 1·50 1·50
480. **78.** 25 p. blue .. .. 2·00 2·00

481. – 12 p. 50 purple (air) .. 4·50 4·50
482. **79.** 50 p. slate .. .. 13·00 9·00

DESIGNS—HORIZ. No. 479, Ain-el-Arous. No. 481, Globe and mountains.

80. President Husni el-Zaim.

81. Pres. Husni el-Zaim and Map.

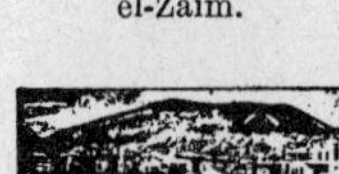

83. Damascus.

82. Tel-Chehab.

1949. Revolution of 30 March, 1949.

483. **80.** 25 p. blue (postage) .. 60 35
484. 50 p. brown (air) .. 2·25 1·75

1949. Presidential Election.

485. **81.** 25 p. brn. & blue (post.) 2·00 1·25
486. 50 p. blue and red (air) 2·25 1·75

1949.

487. **82.** 5 p. grey 35 10
488. 7 p. 50 brown 50 10
524. 7 p. 50 green .. .. 2·50 15
489. **83.** 12 p. 50 purple .. 60 15
490. 25 p. blue .. .. 1·25 35

84.

85. G.P.O. Damascus.

86. Port of Latakia.

1950.

491. **84.** 0 p. 50 brown 15 10
492. 2 p. 50 pink 20 10
493. – 10 p. violet .. .. 7·50 25
494. – 12 p. 50 green 70 40
495. **85.** 25 p. blue .. .. 1·25 25
496. 50 p. black .. .. 3·50 50

DESIGN—HORIZ. 10 p., 12 p. 50, Road to Damascus.

1950. Air.

497 **86** 2 p. 50 violet 60 10
498 10 p. turquoise .. 1·00 10
526 10 p. blue 60 10
499 15 p. brown .. .. 2·00 20
500 25 p. blue .. .. 4·50 25

87. Parliament Building.

88. Book and Torch.

1951. New Constitution, 1950.

501. **87.** 12 p. 50 black (postage) 25 20
502. 25 p. blue 40 30

503. **88.** 12 p. 50 red (air) .. 25 15
504. 50 p. purple 80 70

89. Hama.

1952.

505. **89.** 0 p. 50 sepia (postage) .. 15 10
506. 2 p. 50 slate 25 10
507. 5 p. green 30 10
508. 10 p. red 45 10
509. – 12 p. 50 black 85 10
510. – 15 p. red .. .. 2·00 25
511. – 25 p. blue .. .. 6·50 35
512. – 100 p. bistre .. .. 30·00 1·75

513. – 2 p. 50 red (air) .. 20 10
514. – 5 p. green 40 10
515. – 15 p. violet 55 15
516. – 25 p. blue 75 25
517. – 100 p. purple .. .. 6·00 75

DESIGNS—Postage: 12 p. 50 to 100 p. Palace of Justice, Damascus. Air: 2 p. 50 to 15 p. Palmyra. 25 p., 100 p. Citadel, Aleppo.

1952. Air. United Nations Social Welfare Seminar, Damascus. Optd. **U.N.S.W.S. Damascus 8-20 Dec. 1952** and curved line of Arabic.

518 **86** 10 p. turquoise .. 1·25 1·00
519 15 p. violet (No. 515) 1·25 1·00
520 25 p. blue (No. 516) 2·00 1·50
521 50 p. violet (No. 439) .. 5·50 2·00

91. Qalaat el Hasn Fortress.

92. "Labour".

93. "Family".

94. "Communications".

1953. (a) Postage. View as T **59**.

522. **91.** 0 p. 50 red 10 10
523. 2 p. 50 brown 25 10
525. 12 p. 50 blue .. .. 7·00 15
527. – 50 p. brown .. .. 1·50 25

DESIGN: 50 p. G.P.O., Aleppo.

1954.

528. **92.** 1 p. olive (postage) .. 10 10
529. 2½ p. lake 10 10
530. 5 p. blue 10 10
531. **93.** 7½ p. lake 20 10
532. 10 p. black 30 10
533. 12½ p. violet 45 10
534. – 20 p. red 70 20
535. – 25 p. violet .. .. 1·50 30
536. – 50 p. green .. .. 5·00 65

537. **94.** 5 p. violet (air) .. 20 10
538. 10 p. brown 30 10
539. 15 p. green 30 10
540. – 30 p. brown 70 20
541. – 35 p. blue .. .. 1·00 20
542. – 40 p. orange .. .. 3·25 35
543. – 50 p. purple .. .. 1·50 45
544. – 70 p. violet .. .. 4·00 55

DESIGNS—HORIZ. (As Type **93**): Postage 20 p. to 50 p. "Industry". Air. 30 p. to 70 p. Syrian University.

95.

96a.

1954. Air. Damascus Fair. Inscr. as in T **95**.

545. **95.** 40 p. magenta 65 35
546. – 50 p. green 80 40

DESIGN—VERT. 50 p. Mosque and Syrian flag.

1954. Cotton Festival, Aleppo. Optd. **FESTIVAL du COTON, Alep. oct. 1954** and Arab inscription.

547. **93.** 10 p. black (postage) .. 60 25
548. – 25 p. violet (No. 535) .. 70 35

549. – 50 p. brown (No. 527) (air) 65 50
550. – 100 p. pur. (No. 517) .. 1·25 90

1955. Arab Postal Union.

551. **96a.** 12½ p. green (postage) .. 40 15
552. 25 p. violet 55 25

553. 5 p. brown (air) .. 25 10

97.

98.

1955. Air. Middle East Rotary Congress.

554. **97.** 35 p. red 55 35
555. 65 p. green .. .. 1·00 65

1955. Air. 50th Anniv. of Rotary International.

556. **98.** 25 p. violet 40 25
557. 75 p. turquoise .. .. 1·25 80

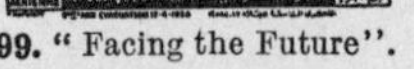
99. "Facing the Future".

100. Mother and Child.

1955. Air. 9th Anniv. of Evacuation of Allied Forces.

558. **99.** 40 p. mauve 40 35
559. – 60 p. blue .. .. 2·00 40

DESIGN: 60 p. Tank and infantry attack. See also Nos. 847/9.

1955. Mothers' Day.

560. **100.** 25 p. red (postage) .. 40 25

561. 35 p. violet (air) .. 60 40
562. 40 p. black 90 45

101. Aeroplane, Flag and Crowd.

102. Syrian Pavilion.

1955. Air. Emigrants' Congress.

563. **101.** 5 p. mauve 35 15
564. – 15 p. blue 40 25

DESIGN: 15 p. Aeroplane over globe.

1955. Air. Int. Fair, Damascus.

565. **102.** 25 p.+5 p. black .. 40 40
566. – 35 p.+5 p. blue .. 45 45
567. – 40 p.+10 p. mauve .. 55 55
568. – 70 p.+10 p. green .. 1·10 1·10

DESIGNS: 35 p., 40 p. "Industry and Agriculture". 70 p. Exhibition pavilions and flags.

103. Mother and Baby.

104. U.N. Emblem and Torch.

1955. Air. Int. Children's Day.

569. **103.** 25 p. blue 50 30
570. 50 p. purple 90 45

1955. 10th Anniv. of U.N.O.

571. **104.** 7½ p. red (postage) .. 35 25
572. 12½ p. slate 55 30

573. – 15 p. blue (air) .. 50 25
574. – 35 p. sepia 90 45

DESIGN: 15, 35 p. Globe, dove and Scales of Justice.

105. Saracen Gate, Aleppo Citadel.

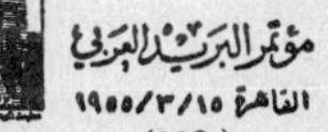

(106.)

1955. Installation of Aleppo Water Supply from R. Euphrates.

575. **105.** 7 p. 50 violet (postage) 20 10
576. 12 p. 50 red 25 15

577. 30 p. blue (air) .. 1·50 70

1955. 2nd Arab Postal Union Congress, Cairo. Nos. 551/553 optd. with T **106**.

578. 12½ p. green (postage) .. 20 15
579. 25 p. violet 60 30

580. 5 p. brown (air) .. 30 15

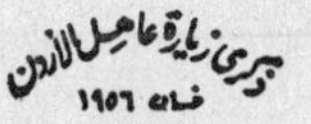

(107.)

108. Monument.

1956. Visit of King Hussein of Jordan. Nos. 551/553 optd. with T **107**.

581. 12½ p. green (postage) .. 35 25
582. 25 p. violet 55 55

583. 5 p. brown (air) .. 35 20

1956. Air. 10th Anniv. of Evacuation of Allied Forces.

584. **108.** 35 p. sepia .. .. 1·10 60
585. – 65 p. red .. .. 2·00 1·10
586. – 75 p. grey .. .. 2·50 1·25

DESIGNS: 65 p. Winged female figure. 75 p. Pres. Shukri Bey al-Quwatli.

109. Pres. Shukri Bey-al-Quwatli. 110. Cotton. 111. Gate of Kasr-al-Heir, Palmyra.

1956. Air.

587. 109. 100 p. black .. .. 1·50 85
588. 200 p. violet .. .. 3·00 1·25
589. 300 p. red .. .. 25·00 2·25
590. 500 p. green .. .. 7·50 4·00

1956. Aleppo Cotton Festival.

591. 110. 2½ p. green 30 15

1956. Air. Nos. 565/8 with premiums obliterated by bars.

592. 102. 25 p. black .. .. 1·50 15
593. – 35 p. blue .. .. 1·75 20
594. – 40 p. mauve .. .. 2·75 35
595. – 70 p. green .. .. 4·00 80

1956. Air. 3rd Int. Fair, Damascus.

596. 111. 15 p. sepia 25 25
597. – 20 p. blue 35 35
598. – 30 p. green 45 45
599. – 35 p. blue 55 55
600. – 50 p. red 70 70

DESIGNS: 20 p. Cotton mill. 30 p. Tractor. 35 p. Phoenician galley and cog-wheels. 50 p. Textiles, carpets and pottery.

112. Clay Alphabetical Tablet.

DESIGNS—VERT. 30 p. Syrian legionary's helmet. HORIZ. 50 p. Lintel of Belshamine Temple, Palmyra.

1956. Air. Int. Campaign for Museums.

601. 112. 20 p. black 55 30
602. – 30 p. red 80 35
603. – 50 p. sepia .. .. 1·40 85

1956. 11th Anniv. of U.N.O. Nos. 571/574 optd. **11 eme ANNIVERSAIRE de L'ONU** in French and Arabic.

604. 104. 7½ p. red (postage) .. 40 25
605. 12½ p. slate .. 45 35
606. – 15 p. blue (air).. 85 35
607. – 35 p. sepia .. .. 1·50 80

114. Oaks and Mosque.

1956. Air. Afforestation Day.

608. 114. 10 p. brown 30 15
609. 40 p. grey 65 45

115. Azem Palace, Damascus.

1957.

610. 115. 12½ p. purple .. 25 10
611. 15 p. black 45 10

116. "Resistance".

1957. Syrian Defence Force.

612. 116. 5 p. mauve 25 10
613. 20 p. slate 45 15

1957. Evacuation of Port Said. Optd. **22.12.56 EVACUATION PORT SAID** in French and Arabic.

614. 116. 5 p. mauve 20 10
615. 20 p. slate 35 25

118. Mother and Child. 119. "Sword of Liberty".

1957. Air. Mothers' Day.

616. – 40 p. blue 50 35
617. 118. 60 p. red 80 50

DESIGN: 40 p. Mother fondling child.

1957. Air. 11th Anniv. of Evacuation of Allied Forces.

618. 119 10 p. brown 15 10
619. – 15 p. green 25 10
620. – 25 p. violet 30 15
621. – 35 p. mauve 45 35
622. 119 40 p. grey 75 45

DESIGNS: 15 p., 35 p. Woman holding torch and map. 25 p. Pres. Shukri Bey al-Quwatli.

120. Freighter "Latakia" and Fair Emblem. 121. "Cotton".

1957. Air. 4th Damascus Fair.

623. 120. 25 p. purple 25 15
624. – 30 p. brown 30 25
625. – 35 p. blue 50 35
626. – 40 p. green 65 40
627. 120. 70 p. olive 90 50

DESIGNS—VERT. 30 p., 40 p. Girls harvesting and cotton picking. HORIZ. 35 p. Interior of processing plant.

1957. Aleppo Cotton Festival.

628. 121. 12½ p. blk. & grn. (post.) 35 20
629. 17½ p. black & orge. (air) 40 25
630. 40 p. black and blue .. 65 35

122. Children at Work and Play. 123. Letter and Post-box.

1957. Int. Children's Day.

631. 122. 12½ p. olive (postage).. 45 25
632. 17½ p. blue (air) .. 80 30
633. 20 p. brown .. 80 30

1957. Int. Correspondence Week.

634. 123. 5 p. mauve (postage) .. 40 20
635. – 5 p. green (air).. .. 35 15

DESIGN: No. 635, Family writing letters.

اسبوع التحصين
١٩٥٧-٧-١ تشرين الثاني

(124.)

126. Sailplane. 125. Scales of Justice, Map and Damascus Silhouette.

1957. National Defence Week. Optd with Type 124.

636. 116. 5 p. mauve 15 10
637. 20 p. slate 30 25

1957. 3rd Arab Lawyers Union Congress, Damascus.

638. 125. 12½ p. green (postage) 20 15
639. 17½ p. red (air).. .. 35 25
640. 40 p. sepia 50 35

1957. Air. Gliding Festival.

641. 126. 25 p. brown .. .. 1·00 25
642. 35 p. green .. .. 1·40 35
643. 40 p. blue .. .. 2·25 50

127. Torch and Map. 128. Khaled Ibn el Walid Mosque, Homs.

1957. Afro-Asian Jurists Congress, Damascus.

644. 127. 20 p. drab (postage) .. 35 15
645. 30 p. green (air) .. 40 25
646. 50 p. violet 45 35

1957.

647. 128. 2½ p. brown 15 10

UNITED ARAB REPUBLIC

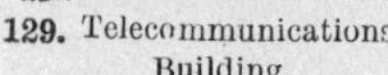

129. Telecommunications Building. 129a. Union of Egypt and Syria.

1958. Five Year Plan.

648. 129. 25 p. blue (postage) 25 20
649. 10 p. green (air) .. 20 10
650. – 15 p. brown 25 15

DESIGN—VERT. 15 p. Telephone, radio tower and telegraph pole.

1958. Birth of United Arab Republic.

651. 129a. 12½ p. green & yellow (post.) .. 20 10
652. 17½ p. brown & blue (air) 35 20

130. "Eternal Flame".

DESIGN: 35 p., 45 p. Broken chain, dove and olive branch.

1958. 12th Anniv. of Evacuation of Allied Forces.

653. 130. 5 p. vio. & lemon (post.) 40 20
654. 15 p. red and green .. 55 35
655. – 35 p. black and red (air) 75 35
656. – 45 p. brown and blue .. 1·40 45

131. Scout fixing Tent-peg.

1958. Air. 3rd Pan-Arab Scout Jamboree.

657. 131. 35 p. sepia .. .. 3·00 1·50
658. 40 p. blue .. .. 3·50 2·25

132. Mosque, Chimneys and Cogwheel. 133. Bronze Rattle.

1958. Air. 5th Int. Fair, Damascus. Inscr. "1.9.58".

659. – 25 p. red 50 35
660. – 30 p. green 75 50
661. 132. 45 p. violet 90 55

DESIGNS—HORIZ. 25 p. View of Fair. VERT. 30 p. Minaret, vase and emblem.

1958. Ancient Syrian Art.

662. 133. 10 p. olive 10 10
663. – 15 p. brown 15 10
664. – 20 p. purple 15 15
665. – 30 p. sepia 20 12
666. – 40 p. grey 35 20
667. – 60 p. green 60 25
668. – 75 p. blue 90 35
669. – 100 p. red .. .. 1·25 50
670. – 150 p. purple .. .. 2·50 70

DESIGNS: 15 p. Goddess of Spring. 20 p. "Lamgi Mari" (statue). 30 p. Mithras fighting bull. 40 p. Aspasia. 60 p. Minerva. 75 p. Ancient gourd. 100 p. Enamelled vase. 150 p. Mosaic from Omayyad Mosque, Damascus.

1958. Int. Children's Day. Optd. **R A U** and Arabic inscription.

670a. 122. 12½ p. olive (postage) 35·00 30·00
670b. 17½ p. blue (air) .. 22·00 22·00
670c. 20 p. brown .. .. 22·00 22·00

134. Cotton and Textiles. 134a. Hand holding Torch, and Iraqi Flag.

1958. Air. Aleppo Cotton Festival.

671. 134. 25 p. yellow and sepia 50 40
672. 35 p. red and sepia .. 75 55

1958. Republic of Iraq Commem.

673. 134a. 12½ p. red 25 10

135. Children and Gliders. 137. U.N. Emblem and Charter.

136. Damascus.

1958. Air. Gliding Festival.

674. 135. 7½ p. green 80 30
675. 12½ p. olive .. .. 2·25 1·25

1958. 4th N.E. Regional Conf., Damascus.

676. 136. 12½ p. green (postage) 30 10
677. 17½ p. violet (air) .. 30 15

1958. Air. 10th Anniv. of Declaration of Human Rights.

678. 137. 25 p. purple 20 20
679. 35 p. grey 35 25
680. 40 p. brown 45 30

137a. U.A.R. Postal Emblem. 137b.

1959. Post Day and Postal Employees' Social Fund.

681. 137a. 20 p. + 10 p. red, black and green 45 45

1959. 1st Anniv of United Arab Republic.

682. 137b. 12½ p. red, black and green .. 20 10

138. Secondary School, Damascus.

1959.

683. 138. 12½ p. green 15 10

138a. "Telecommunications".

1959. Air. Arab Telecommunications Union Commemoration.
684. **138a.** 40 p. black and green 60 25

1959. No 684 optd **2nd CONFERANCE DAMASCUS 1.3.1959** in English and Arabic.
685. **138a.** 40 p. black & green 35 20

139a. U.A.R. and Yemeni Flags.

1959. 1st Anniv. of Proclamation of United Arab States (U.A.R. and Yemen).
686. **139a.** 12½ p. red and green 25 10

140. Mother with Children. **142.**

1959. Arab Mothers' Day.
687. **140.** 15 p. pink 25 10
688. 25 p. green 30 20

1959. Surch **U . A . R 2½ p** and also in Arabic.
689 **92** 2½ p. on 1 p. olive .. 10 10

1959. Air. 13th Anniv of Evacuation of Allied Forces.
690. **142.** 15 p. green and yellow 25 10
691. – 35 p. red and grey .. 40 25
DESIGN: 35 p. Broken chain and flame.

143.  **144.** " Emigration ".

1959. Patterns as T **143.**
692. **143.** 2½ p. violet 10 10
693. – 5 p. olive 10 10
694. – 7½ p. blue 15 10
695. – 10 p. green 15 10
DESIGNS show different styles of ornamental scrollwork.

1959. Air. Emigrants' Congress.
696. **144.** 80 p. black, red & green 80 45

الجمهورية العربية المتحدة
U.A.R
(145.)

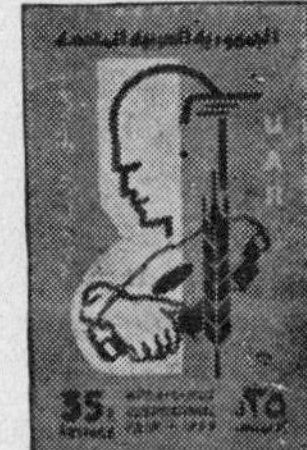
147.

146. Oil Refinery.

1959. Optd as T **145.**
697 **115.** 15 p. black (postage) 35 15
698 – 50 p. green (No. 536) .. 1·00 50
699 – 5 p. grn. (No. 635) (air) 15 10
700 – 50 p. purple (No. 543).. 80 25
701 – 70 p. violet (No. 544).. 1·50 35

1959. Air. Inaug of Oil Refinery.
702 **146** 50 p. red, black & blue 1·75 40

1959. 6th Damascus Fair.
703. **147.** 35 p. grn., vio. & grey 40 25

148.  **149.** Child and Factory.

1959. Air. Aleppo Cotton Festival.
704. **148.** 45 p. slate 50 20
705. 50 p. red 50 30

1959. Air. Children's Day.
706. **149.** 25 p. red, blue & lilac 30 15

150. Boys' College, Damascus. **150a.** "Shield against Aggression".

1959.
707. **150.** 25 p. blue 50 15
708. – 35 p. brown 60 20
DESIGN: 35 p. Girls' College, Damascus.

1959. Army Day.
709. **150a.** 50 p. sepia 75 35

151. Ears of Corn, Cotton, Cogwheel and Factories. **152.** Mosque and Oaks.

1959. Industrial and Agricultural Production Fair, Aleppo.
710. **151.** 35 p. brn., blue & grey 45 25

1959. Tree Day.
711. **152.** 12½ p. brown and green 30 10

153. A. R. Kawakbi.  **153a.**

1960. 50th Death Anniv. of A. R. Kawakbi (writer).
712. **153.** 15 p. deep green .. 25 10

1960. 2nd Anniv. of U.A.R.
713. **153a.** 12½ p. green and red 20 10

154. Diesel Train.

1960. Latakia-Aleppo Railway Project.
714. **154.** 12½ p. brn., blk. & blue 1·50 65

154a. Arab League Centre, Cairo.

1960. Inaug. of Arab League Centre, Cairo.
715. **154a.** 12½ p. black & green 20 10

1960. Mothers' Day. Optd. **ARAB MOTHERS DAY 1960** in English and Arabic.
716. **140.** 15 p. pink 25 10
717. 25 p. green 30 20

155a. Refugee Children.

1960. World Refugee Year.
718. **155a.** 12½ p. red 15 10
719. 50 p. green 30 30

156. Government Building and Inscription.

1960. 14th Anniv. of Evacuation of Allied Forces.
720. **156.** 12½ p. multicoloured.. 35 10

157. Hittin School.

1960.
721. **157.** 17½ p. lilac 30 10

1960. Industrial and Agricultural Production Fair, Aleppo. Optd. **1960** and in Arabic.
722 **151** 35 p. brown, bl & grey 30 20

159. Mobile Crane and Compasses.

١٩٦٠
(160.)

1960. Air. 7th Int. Damascus Fair.
723. **159.** 50 p. blk., bistre & red 50 35

1960. Air. Aleppo Cotton Festival. Optd with T **160.**
724. **148.** 45 p. slate 45 20
725. 50 p. red 50 30

161. **162.** Basketball.

1960. Children's Day.
726. **161.** 35 p. brown and green 55 25

1960. Air. Olympic Games.
727. **162.** 15 p. brn., blk. & blue 25 10
728. – 20 p. brn., blk. & blue 40 15
729. – 25 p. vio., blk. and yell. 40 15
730. – 40 p. vio., red and blk. 70 35
DESIGNS: 20 p. Swimming. 25 p. Fencing (Arab-style). 40 p. Horse-jumping.

١٩٦٠
1960
(163.)

164. 'UN' and Globe.

1960. Tree Day. Optd. with T **163.**
731. **152.** 12½ p. brown and green 30 15

1960. Air. 15th Anniv. of U.N.O.
732. **164.** 35 p. red, grn. & blue 25 20
733. 50 p. bl., ochre & red 35 25

165. Hanano. **165a.**

1961. Air. 25th Death Anniv (1960) of Ibrahim Hanano (patriot)
734. **165.** 50 p. grn. and drab.. 45 30

1961. 3rd Anniv. of U.A.R.
735. **165a.** 12½ p. violet .. 20 10

166. St. Simeon's Monastery. **167.** Raising the Flag.

1961.
736. **166.** 12½ p. blue (postage).. 20 10
746. – 200 p. blue (air) .. 2·75 60
DESIGN—VERT. 200 p. Entrance to St. Simeon's Monastery.

1961. Air. 15th Anniv. of Evacuation of Allied Forces.
737. **167.** 40 p. green 50 25

168. Eye and Hand "reading" Braille. **169.** Palestinian and Map.

1961. Air. U.N. Campaign for Welfare of Blind.
738. **168.** 40 p.+10 p. black and green 45 55

1961. Air. Palestine Day.
739. **169.** 50 p. blue and black.. 1·25 30

170. Cogwheel and Corn. **171.** Abou Tammam (796–846)

1961. Industrial and Agricultural Production Fair, Aleppo.
740. **170.** 12½ p. multicoloured.. 25 20

1961. Air. Abou Tammam (writer) Commem.
741. **171.** 50 p. brown .. . 55 25

MINIMUM PRICE

The minimum price quoted is 5p which represents a handling charge rather than a basis for valuing common stamps. For further notes about prices see introductory pages.

172. Damascus University. Discus-thrower and Lyre. **173.** Open Window on World.

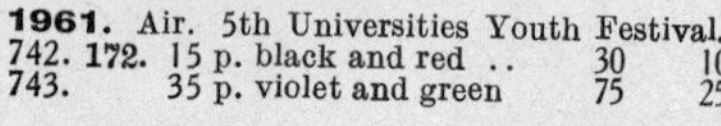
1961. Air. 5th Universities Youth Festival.
742. **172.** 15 p. black and red .. 30 10
743. 35 p. violet and green 75 25

1961. Air. 8th Int. Damascus Fair.
744. **173.** 17½ p. violet and green 20 10
745. – 50 p. violet and black 45 25
DESIGN: 50 p. U.A.R. Pavilion.

SYRIAN ARAB REPUBLIC

175. Assembly Chamber. **176.** The Noria, Hama.

177. Arch of Triumph, Latakia. **178.** Arab League Emblem and Headquarters, Cairo.

1961. Establishment of Syrian Arab Republic.
747. **175.** 15 p. purple .. 20 10
748. 35 p. olive 50 25

1961.
749 **176** 2½ p. red (postage) .. 10 10
750 5 p. blue 20 10
751 A 7½ p. green 40 10
752 10 p. orange .. 60 10
753 **177** 12½ p. drab .. .. 1·00 10
754 B 12½ p. green 75 10
755 15 p. blue 75 10
756 17½ p. brown .. 85 10
757 22½ p. turquoise .. 9·00 10
758 **177** 25 p. brown .. .. 1·00 10
759 B 45 p. yellow (air) .. 75 25
760 50 p. red .. .. 1·00 35
761 C 85 p. purple .. .. 1·50 40
762 100 p. purple .. 1·75 45
763 D 200 p. green .. .. 3·50 80
764 300 p. blue .. .. 3·75 90
764a 500 p. purple .. 6·00 2·00
764b 1000 p. black .. 12·00 3·50
DESIGNS: A. Khaled Iin-el-walid Mosque, Homs. B, "The Beauty of Palmyra" (statue). C, Archway and columns, Palmyra. D, King Zahir Biyar's tomb.
See also Nos. 799/800.

1962. Air. Arab League Week.
765. **178.** 17½ p. turq. and green 15 10
766. 22½ p. violet and blue 25 20
767. 50 p. sepia and salmon 50 25

179. Campaign Emblem. **180.** Prancing Horse.

1962. Air. Malaria Eradication.
768 **179** 12½ p. violet, sep & bl 15 10
769 50 p. grn, brn & yell 35 30

1962. Air. 16th Anniv of Evacuation of Allied Forces.
770. **180.** 45 p. orange and violet 50 25
771. – 55 p. violet and blue .. 65 30
DESIGN: 55 p. Military commander.

181. Qalb Lozah Church. **182.** Martyrs' Memorial, Swaida.

1962.
772. **181.** 17½ p. olive 40 10
773. 35 p. turquoise .. 55 25

1962. Syrian Revolution Commem.
774. **182.** 12½ p. brown and drab 15 10
775. 35 p. turq. & light green 35 20

183. Jupiter Temple Gate. **184.** Globe, Monument and Handclasp.

1962.
776. **183.** 2½ p. turquoise .. 15 10
777. 5 p. brown 30 10
778. 7½ p. sepia 70 10
779. 10 p. purple 25 10

1962. Air. 9th Int. Fair, Damascus.
780. **184.** 17½ p. brown & purple 15 10
781. 22½ p. mauve and red 20 15
782. – 40 p. dull purple and pale brown 30 20
783. – 45 p. turquoise & green 45 25
DESIGN: 40 p., 45 p. Fair entrance.

185. Festival Emblem. **186.** Pres. Kudsi.

1962. Air. Aleppo Cotton Festival.
784. **185.** 12½ p. multicoloured .. 25 15
785. 50 p. multicoloured .. 40 35
See also Nos. 820/1.

1962. Presidential Elections.
786. **186.** 12½ p. brown and blue (postage) .. 20 10
787. 50 p. blue and buff (air) 40 25

187. Zenobia. **188.** Saadallah el-Jabiri.

1962. Air.
788. **187.** 45 p. violet .. .. 1·00 15
789. 50 p. red .. .. 1·00 20
790. 85 p. turquoise .. 95 30
791. 100 p. purple .. .. 1·25 50
See also Nos. 801/4.

1962. Air. 15th Death Anniv of Saadallah el-Jabiri (revolutionary).
792. **188.** 50 p. blue 40 25

189. Moharde Woman. **190.** Ears of Wheat, Hand and Globe.

1962. Air. Women in Regional Costumes. Multicoloured.
793. 40 p. Marje Sultan 40 15
794. 45 p. Kalamoun 50 20
795. 50 p. Type **189** 60 20
796. 55 p. Jabal al-Arab .. 70 30
797. 60 p. Afrine 75 30
798. 65 p. Hauran 90 35

1963. As Nos. 754/7 (Type B) and T **187** but smaller (20 × 26 mm).
799. B. 2½ p. violet 20 10
800. 5 p. purple 20 10
801. **187.** 7½ p. slate 75 10
802. 10 p. drab .. .. 1·00 10
803. 12½ p. blue .. .. 1·50 10
804 15 p. brown .. .. 2·00 15

1963. Freedom from Hunger.
805. **190.** 12½ p. blk. & bl. (post.) 20 10
806. – 50 p. black & red (air) 60 25
DESIGN: 50 p. Bird feeding young in nest.

191. Feris el-Khouri (politician). **192.** S.A.R. Emblem.

1963. Air. 17th Anniv. of Evacuation of Allied Forces.
807. **191.** 17½ p. sepia 25 15
808. **192.** 22½ p. turq. and black 25 15

193. Eagle. **194.** Ala el-Ma'ari (bust).

1963. Air. Baathist Revolution Commem.
809. **193.** 12½ p. green 10 10
810. 50 p. mauve 40 30

1963. Air. 990th Birth Anniv of Ala el-Ma'ari (poet).
811. **194.** 50 p. violet 45 25

195. Copper Water Jug. **196.** Central Bank.

1963. Air. 10th Int. Fair, Damascus. Hookah in yellow, red and black.
812. **195.** 37½ p. blue 40 20
813. 50 p. blue 50 25

1963. Damascus Buildings.
814. – 17½ p. violet .. .. 1·00 10
815. – 22½ p. violet .. .. 1·50 10
816. **196.** 25 p. brown 60 20
817. – 35 p. mauve .. .. 2·00 20
BUILDINGS: 17½ p. Hejaz Railway Station. 22½ p. Mouassat Hospital. 35 p. Post Office, Al-Jalaa.

197. "Red Crescent" and Centenary Emblem. **198.** Child with Ball.

1963. Air. Red Cross Centenary. Crescent in red.
818. **197.** 15 p. black and blue .. 35 20
819. – 50 p. black and green .. 65 35
DESIGN: 50 p. "Red Crescent", globe and centenary emblem.

1963. Aleppo Cotton Festival. As T **185** but inscr. "POSTAGE" and "1963" in place of "AIRMAIL" and "1962".
820. **185.** 17½ p. multicoloured .. 20 10
821. 22½ p. multicoloured .. 35 15

1963. Children's Day.
822. **198.** 12½ p. light and deep green 15 10
823. 22½ p. green and red .. 30 10

199. Firas el-Hamadani. **200.** Flame on Head.

1963. Air. Death Millenary of Abou Firas el-Hamadani (poet).
824. **199.** 50 p. sepia and bistre 45 30

1963. Air. 15th Anniv. of Declaration of Human Rights. Flame in red.
825. **200.** 17½ p. black and grey 15 10
826. 22½ p. black and green 20 15
827. 50 p. black and violet 35 25

201. Emblem and Flag.

1964. Air. 1st Anniv. of 8th March Baathist Revolution. Emblem and flag in red, black and green; inscr. in black.
828. **201.** 15 p. green 10 10
829. 17½ p. pink 15 10
830. 22½ p. grey 25 15

202. Ugharit Princess. **203.** Chahba, Thalassa, Mosaic.

1964.
831. **202.** 2½ p. grey (postage) .. 10 10
832. 5 p. brown 10 10
833. 7½ p. purple 15 10
834. 10 p. green 20 10
835. 12½ p. violet 25 10
836. 17½ p. blue 40 10
837. 20 p. red .. .. 1·50 10
838. 25 p. orange .. .. 2·00 15
839. **203.** 27½ p. red (air) .. 45 10
840. 45 p. brown 70 15
841. 50 p. green 75 15
842. 55 p. bronze 80 25
843. 60 p. blue .. .. 1·25 30

204. Kaaba, Mecca, and Mosque, Damascus **205.** Abou al Zahrawi.

1964. Air. 1st Arab Moslem Wakf Ministers' Conference.
844. **204.** 12½ p. black and blue 10 10
845. 22½ p. blk. & mauve .. 20 15
846. 50 p. black and green 40 25

1964. Air. 18th Anniv. of Evacuation of Allied Forces. As T **99** but larger (38½ × 26 mm.) inscr. "1964".
847. **99.** 20 p. blue 15 10
848. 25 p. mauve 20 15
849. 60 p. green 35 25

1964. Air. 4th Arab Dental and Oral Surgery Congress, Damascus.
850. **205.** 60 p. brown 70 30

206. Bronze Chimes.

207. Cotton Plant and Symbols.

(208.)

209. Aero Club Emblem.

1964. Air. 11th Int. Fair, Damascus.
851. 206. 20 p. multicoloured .. 25 10
852. – 25 p. multicoloured .. 25 15
DESIGN: 25 p. Fair emblem.

1964. Air. Aleppo Cotton Festival. No. 854 is optd. with T 208.
853. 207. 25 p. multicoloured .. 25 10
854. 25 p. multicoloured .. 25 10

1964. Air. 10th Anniv. of Syrian Aero Club.
855. 209. 12½ p. black and green 20 10
856. 17½ p. black and red .. 25 15
857. 20 p. black and blue .. 45 15

210. A.P.U. Emblem.

211. Book within Hands.

1964. Air. 10th Anniv. of Arab Postal Union.
858. 210. 12½ p. black and orange 10 10
859. 20 p. black and green 15 10
860. 25 p. black and mauve 20 15

1964. Air. Burning of Algiers Library.
861. 211. 12½ p. black and green 10 10
862. 17½ p. black and red .. 15 10
863. 20 p. black and blue .. 20 15

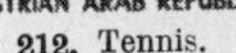

212. Tennis.

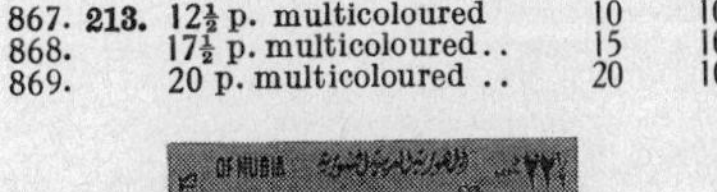

213. Flag, Map and Revolutionaries.

1965. Air. Olympic Games, Tokyo. Mult.
864. 12½ p. Type 212 .. .. 15 10
865. 17½ p. Wrestling 25 10
866. 20 p. Weightlifting .. 30 15

1965. 2nd Anniv of Baathist Revolution of March 8th 1963.
867. 213. 12½ p. multicoloured 10 10
868. 17½ p. multicoloured .. 15 10
869. 20 p. multicoloured .. 20 10

214. Rameses II in War Chariot, Abu Simbel.

1965. Air. Nubian Monuments Preservation.
870. 214. 22½ p. blk., bl. & grn. 40 10
871. – 50 p. blk., grn. & bl... 60 25
DESIGN: 50 p. Heads of Rameses II.

215. Weather Instruments and Map.

1965. World Meteorological Day.
872. 215. 12½ p. black and purple 10 10
873. 27½ p. black and blue .. 20 15

216. Al-Radi.

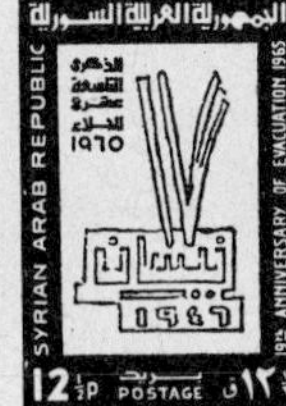

217. Evacuation Symbol.

1965. Air. 950th Death Anniv of Al-Sharif al-Radi (writer).
874. 216. 50 p. black 40 25

1965. 19th Anniv. of Evacuation of Allied Forces.
875. 217. 12½ p. green and blue 10 10
876. 27½ p. lilac and red .. 25 15

218. Hippocrates and Avicenna.

1965. Air. "Medical Days of the Near and Middle East".
877. 218. 60 p. black and green 75 45

219. Dagger on Deir Yassin, Palestine.

220. I.T.U. Emblem and Symbols.

1965. Air. Deir Yassin Massacre on 9 April 1948.
878. 219. 12½ p. multicoloured .. 40 10
879. 60 p. multicoloured .. 1·00 30

1965. Air. I.T.U. Cent.
880. 220. 12½ p. multicoloured .. 25 10
881. 27½ p. multicoloured .. 40 15
882. 60 p. multicoloured .. 70 45

221. Arab Family, Flags and Map.

222. Hands holding Hoe and Pick.

1965. Palestine Week.
883. 221. 12½ p.+5 p. mult. .. 40 25
884. 25 p.+5 p. mult. .. 50 40

1965. Peasants' Union.
885. 222. 2½ p. green 10 10
886. 12½ p. violet 10 10
887. 15 p. purple 10 10
The above stamps are inscr. "RERUBLIC" for "REPUBLIC".

223. Welcoming Emigrant.

224. Fair Entrance.

1965. Air. "Welcome Arab Emigrants".
888. 223. 25 p. multicoloured .. 25 10
889. 100 p. multicoloured .. 65 30

1965. Air. 12th Int. Fair, Damascus. Multicoloured.
890. 12½ p. Type 224 .. .. 10 10
891. 27½ p. Globe and compasses 20 10
892. 60 p. Syrian brassware .. 35 25

226. Cotton Boll and Shuttles.

227. I.C.Y. Emblem and View of Damascus.

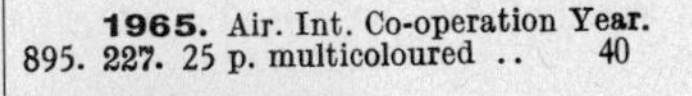

1965. Air. Aleppo Industrial and Agricultural Production Fair. Optd. **INDUSTRIAL & AGRICULTURAL PRODUCTION FAIR—ALEPPO 1965** in English and Arabic.
893 226 25 p. multicoloured .. 20 10

1965. Air. Aleppo Cotton Festival.
894 226 25 p. multicoloured .. 20 10

1965. Air. Int. Co-operation Year.
895. 227. 25 p. multicoloured .. 40 15

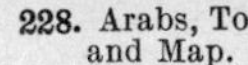

228. Arabs, Torch and Map.

229. Industrial Workers.

1965. National Revolution Council.
896. 228. 12½ p. multicoloured .. 10 10
897. 25 p. multicoloured .. 20 10

1966. Labour Unions.
898. 229. 12½ p. blue 10 10
899. 15 p. red 10 10
900. 20 p. lilac 20 10
901. 25 p. drab 30 15

230. Radio Aerial, Globe and Flag.

231. Dove-shaped Hand holding Flower.

1966. Air. Arab Information Ministers' Conf. Damascus.
902. 230. 25 p. multicoloured .. 20 10
903. 60 p. multicoloured .. 40 25

1966. Air. 3rd Anniv. of March 8th Revolution. Multicoloured.
904. 12½ p. Type 231 .. .. 10 10
905. 17½ p. Revolutionaries (horiz.) 10 10
906. 50 p. Type 231 .. .. 60 25

232. Colossi, Abu Simbel.

233. Roman Lamp.

1966. Air. Nubian Monuments Preservation Week.
907. 232. 25 p. blue 35 10
908. 60 p. grey 75 25

1966.
909. 233. 2½ p. green 10 10
910. 5 p. purple 30 10
911. – 7½ p. brown 15 10
912. – 10 p. violet 25 10
DESIGN: 7½ p., 10 p. 12th-cent. Islamic vessel.

234. U.N. Emblem and Headquarters.

1966. Air. 20th Anniv. of U.N.
913. 234. 25 p. black and grey .. 15 10
914. 50 p. black and green .. 30 20

236. "Evacuation" (abstract).

237. Workers marching across Globe.

1966. 20th Anniv of Evacuation of Allied Forces.
916. 236. 12½ p. multicoloured .. 10 10
917. 27½ p. multicoloured .. 20 15

1966. Air. Labour Day.
918. 237. 60 p. multicoloured .. 35 25

238. W.H.O. Building.

239. Traffic Signals and Map on Hand.

1966. Air. Inauguration of W.H.O. Headquarters, Geneva.
919. 238. 60 p. black, blue & yell. 60 25

1966. Air. Traffic Day.
920. 239. 25 p. multicoloured .. 50 10

240. Astarte and Tyche (wrongly inscr. "ASTRATE").

241. Fair Emblem.

1966. Air.
921. 240. 50 p. brown .. .. 1·00 20
922. 60 p. grey .. .. 1·25 25

1966. Air. 13th Int. Fair, Damascus.
923. 241. 12½ p. multicoloured .. 10 10
924. 60 p. multicoloured .. 35 30

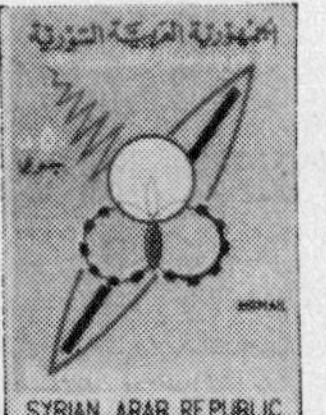

242. Shuttle (stylised).

243. Decade Emblem.

1966. Air. Aleppo Cotton Festival.
925. 242. 50 p. blk., red & grey .. 35 25

1966. Air. Int. Hydrological Decade.
926. 243. 12½ p. blk., orge & grn. 15 10
927. 60 p. blk., orge. & blue 50 30

244. Emir Abd-el-Kader.

245. U.N.R.W.A. Emblem.

1966. Air. Return of Emir Abd-el-Kader's Remains to Algiers.
928. 244. 12½ p. black & green .. 20 10
929. 50 p. brown & green .. 35 25

1966. Air. 21st Anniv. of U.N. Day and Refugee Week.
930. 245. 12½ p.+2½ p. black and blue 10 10
931. 50 p.+5 p. black and green 25 35

246. Handclasp and Map. 247. Doves and Oil Pipelines.

1967. Air. Solidarity Congress, Damascus.
932. 246. 20 p. multicoloured .. 15 10
933. 25 p. multicoloured .. 20 15

1967. Air. 4th Anniv of Baathist Revolution of 8 March 1963.
934. 247. 17½ p. multicoloured.. 20 10
935. 25 p. multicoloured .. 25 15
936. 27½ p. multicoloured.. 30 15

248. Soldier and Citizens with Banner. 249. Workers' Monument, Damascus.

1967. Air. 21st Anniv. of Evacuation.
937. 248. 17½ p. green 20 10
938. 25 p. purple 25 15
939. 27½ p. blue 30 15

1967. Air. Labour Day.
940. 249. 12½ p. turquoise .. 10 10
941. 50 p. mauve 35 25

250. Core Bust. 251. "African woman" (vase).

252. Head of a Young Man from Amrith. 253. Flags and Fair Entrance.

1967.
942. 250. 2½ p. green (postage).. 10 10
943. 5 p. red 10 10
944. 10 p. blue 15 10
945. 12½ p. brown 20 10
946. 251. 15 p. purple 20 10
947. 20 p. blue 30 10
948. 25 p. green 40 10
949. 27½ p. blue 60 10
950. 252. 45 p. red (air).. .. 70 20
951. 50 p. red 80 20
952. 60 p. turquoise .. 1·25 35
953. – 100 p. green .. .. 1·40 45
954. – 500 p. red .. .. 6·00 2·25
DESIGN—VERT. 100 p., 500 p. Bust of Princess (2nd-century bronze).

1967. Air. 14th International Damascus Fair.
955. 253. 12½ p. multicoloured.. 10 10
956. 60 p. multicoloured .. 35 25

254. Statue of Ur-Nina and Tourist Emblem. 255. Cotton Boll and Cogwheel.

1967. Air. International Tourist Year
957. 254. 12½ p. purple, blk. & bl. 10 10
958. 25 p. red, black & blue 15 10
959. 27½ p. bl., blk. & lt. bl. 25 15

1967. Air. Aleppo Cotton Festival.
961. 255. 12½ p. black, brown and yellow 10 10
962. 60 p. black, brown and yellow 30 25

1967. Air. Industrial and Agricultural Production Fair, Aleppo. Optd **INDUSTRIAL AND AGRICULTURAL PRODUCTION FAIR ALEPPO 1967** in English and Arabic.
963. 255. 12½ p. blk., brn. & yell. 10 10
964. 60 p. blk., brn. & yell. 30 25

257. Ibn el-Naphis (scientist). 258. Acclaiming Human Rights.

1967. Air. Sciences Week.
965. 257. 12½ p. red and green.. 10 10
966. 27½ p. mauve and blue 15 10

1968. Air. Human Rights Year.
967. 258. 12½ p. black, turquoise and blue 10 10
968. 60 p. black, red & pink 30 25

259. Learning to Read. 260. "The Arab Revolutionary" (Damascus statue).

1968. Air. Literacy Campaign.
970. 259. 12½ p. multicoloured.. 10 10
971. – 17½ p. multicoloured.. 10 10
972. 259. 25 p. multicoloured .. 20 10
973. – 45 p. multicoloured .. 25 20
DESIGN: 17½p., 45 p. Flaming torch and open book.

1968. 5th Anniv. of March 8th Baathist Revolution.
974. 260. 12½ p. brn., yell. & blk. 10 10
975. 25 p. mve., pink & blk. 20 10
976. 27½ p. green, light green and black 20 15

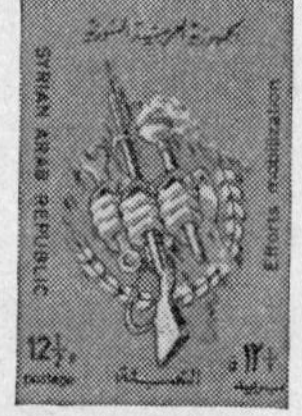

261. Map of North Africa and Arabia. 263. Hands holding Spanner, Rifle & Torch.

262. Euphrates Dam.

1968. 21st Anniv of Baath Arab Socialist Party.
977. 261. 12½ p. multicoloured.. 10 10
978. 60 p. multicoloured .. 35 25

1968. Air. Euphrates Dam Project.
979. 262. 12½ p. multicoloured.. 20 10
980. 17½ p. multicoloured.. 25 15
981. 25 p. multicoloured .. 50 20

1968. "Mobilisation Efforts".
982. 263. 12½ p. multicoloured.. 10 10
983. 17½ p. multicoloured.. 15 10
984. 25 p. multicoloured .. 25 10

264. Railway Track and Sun. 266. Torch, Map and Laurel.

265. Oil Pipeline Map.

1968. 22nd Anniv. of Evacuation of Allied Forces.
985. 264. 12½ p. multicoloured.. 75 60
986. 27½ p. multicoloured.. 1·75 1·40

1968. Syrian Oil Exploration.
987. 265. 12½ p. blue, green and yellow 25 10
988. 17½ p. blue, brn. & pink 50 20

1968. Palestine Day.
989. 266. 12½ p. multicoloured.. 20 10
990. 25 p. multicoloured .. 40 15
991. 27½ p. multicoloured.. 65 20

267. Refugee Family.

1968. Red Crescent Refugees Fund.
992. 267. 12½ p.+2½ p. black, purple and blue .. 20 25
993. 27½ p.+7½ p. black, red and violet 20 25

268. Avenzoar (physician) and W.H.O. Emblem. 269. Ear of Corn, Cogwheel and Saracen Gate, Aleppo Citadel.

1968. Air. 20th Anniv. of W.H.O.
994. 268. 12½ p. multicoloured.. 15 10
995. – 25 p. multicoloured .. 25 10
996. – 60 p. multicoloured .. 45 25
DESIGNS—As Type 268, but with different portraits of Arab physicians: 25 p. Razi. 60 p. Jabir.

1968. Industrial and Agricultural Production Fair, Aleppo.
997. 269. 12½ p. multicoloured.. 10 10
998. 27½ p. multicoloured.. 15 10

270. Emblems of Fair, Agriculture and Industry. 271. Gathering Cotton.

1968. 15th Int. Damascus Fair.
999. 270. 12½ p. blk., grn. & brn. 10 10
1000. – 27½ p. multicoloured 20 10
1001. 270. 60 p. blk., orge. & blue 30 25
DESIGN—HORIZ. 27½ p. Flag, hand with torch and emblems.

1968. Aleppo Cotton Festival.
1002. 271. 12½ p. multicoloured 10 10
1003. 27½ p. multicoloured 15 10

272. Monastery of St. Simeon the Stylite. 273. Oil Derrick.

1968. Air. Ancient Monuments (1st series).
1004. 272. 15 p. green and brown 15 10
1005. – 17½ p. purple, brown and chocolate .. 20 10
1006. – 22½ p. multicoloured 25 15
1007. – 45 p. multicoloured.. 40 20
1008. – 50 p. brown, sepia and blue 45 25
DESIGNS—VERT. 17½ p. El Tekkieh Mosque, Damascus. 22½ p. Temple columns, Palmyra. HORIZ. 45 p. Chapel of St. Paul Bab Kisan. 50 p. Amphitheatre, Bosra.
See also Nos. 1026/30.

1968.
1009. 273. 2½ p. green and blue 15 10
1010. 5 p. blue and green.. 15 10
1011. 7½ p. blue and green 20 10
1012. 10 p. green and yellow 20 10
1013. 12½ p. red and yellow 30 10
1014. 15 p. brown and bistre 35 10
1015. 27½ p. brown & orge. 55 15

274. Al-Jahez (scientist). 275. Throwing the Hammer.

1968. 9th Science Week.
1016. 274. 12½ p. black and olive 10 10
1017. 27½ p. black and grey 15 15

1968. Air. Olympic Games, Mexico.
1018. 275. 12½ p. black, mauve and green 10 10
1019. – 25 p. blk., red & grn. 15 10
1020. – 27½ p. black, grey and green 20 15
1021. – 60 p. multicoloured.. 30 25
DESIGNS—VERT. 25 p. Throwing the discus. 27½ p. Running. 60 p. Basketball. HORIZ. (53×36 mm.). 50 p. Polo.

276. Aerial View of Airport.

1969. Air. Construction of Damascus Int. Airport.
1023. 276. 12½ p. grn., bl. & yell. 25 10
1024. 17½ p. violet, red and green 30 10
1025. 60 p. black, mauve and yellow .. 85 30

277. Baal-Shamin Temple, Palmyra.

1969. Air. Ancient Monuments (2nd series). Multicoloured.
1026 25 p. Type 277 .. .. 25 10
1027 45 p. Omayyad Mosque, Damascus (vert) .. 35 15
1028 50 p. Amphitheatre, Palmyra 40 20
1029 60 p. Khaled ibn el-Walid Mosque, Homs (vert) .. 45 20
1030 100 p. St Simeon's Column, Jebel Samaan 70 35

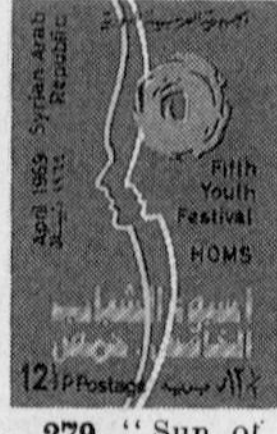

278. "Sun", and Clenched Fists in Broken Handcuffs. 279. "Sun of Freedom".

1969. 6th Anniv. of March 8th Baathist Revolution.
1031. 278. 12½ p. multicoloured 10 10
1032. 25 p. multicoloured.. 20 10
1033. 27½ p. multicoloured 20 10

1969. 5th Youth Week.
1034. 279. 12½ p. red, yellow and blue 10 10
1035. 25 p. red, yellow and green 15 10

280. Symbols of Progress.

281. "Workers", Cogwheel and I.L.O. Emblem.

1969. 23rd Anniv. of Evacuation of Allied Forces.

1036. **280.** 12½ p. multicoloured 10 10
1037. 27½ p. multicoloured 15 10

1969. Air. 50th Anniv. of I.L.O.

1038. **281.** 12½ p. multicoloured 10 10
1039. 27½ p. multicoloured 20 10

282. Russian Dancers.

283. " Fortune " (statue).

1969. Air. 16th Int. Damascus Fair. Mult.

1041. 12½ p. Type **282** 25 20
1042. 27½ p. Ballet dancers .. 40 25
1043. 45 p. Lebanese dancers .. 40 35
1044. 55 p. Egyptian dancers .. 50 35
1045. 60 p. Bulgarian dancers 55 35

1969. Air. 9th Int. Archaeological Congress, Damascus. Multicoloured.

1046. 17½ p. Type **283** 20 10
1047. 25 p. "Lady from Palmyra" (statue) 25 15
1048. 60 p. "Motherhood" (statue) 55 25

284. Children dancing.

285. Mahatma Gandhi.

1969. Air. Children's Day.

1049. **284.** 12½ p. green, blue and turquoise 15 10
1050. 25 p. violet, bl. & red 20 10
1051. 27½ p. grey and blue 25 15

1969. Birth Cent. of Mahatma Gandhi.

1052. **285.** 12½ p. brown and buff 25 15
1053. 27½ p. green and yellow 65 25

286. Cotton.

287. " Arab World" (6th Arab Science Congress).

1969. Aleppo Cotton Festival.

1054. **286.** 12½ p. multicoloured 10 10
1055. 17½ p. multicoloured 10 10
1056. 25 p. multicoloured 15 10

1969. 10th Science Week.

1057. **287.** 12½ p. blue and green 10 10
1058. – 25 p. violet and pink 20 15
1059. – 27½ p. ochre and green 25 15

DESIGNS: 25 p. Arab Academy (50th Anniv.). 27½ p. Damascus University (50th Anniv. of Faculty of Medicine.).

288. Cockerel.

1969. Air. Damascus Agricultural Museum. Multicoloured.

1060. 12½ p. Type **288** 20 15
1061. 17½ p. Cow 20 15
1062. 20 p. Maize 25 20
1063. 50 p. Olives 30 25

289. Rising Sun, Hand and Book.

1970. 7th Anniv. of March 8th Baathist Revolution.

1064. **289.** 17½ p. blk., brn. & blue 10 10
1065. 25 p. blk., blue & red 15 10
1066. 27½ p. blk., brn. & grn. 20 15

290. Map of Arab World, League Emblem and Flag.

1970. Silver Jubilee of Arab League.

1067. **290.** 12½p. multicoloured .. 10 10
1068. 25 p. multicoloured .. 15 10
1069. 27½ p. multicoloured .. 20 15

291. Dish Aerial and Hand on Book.

292. Lenin.

1970. Air. World Meteorological Day.

1070. **291.** 25 p. blk., yell & grn. 40 15
1071. 60 p. blk., yell. & blue 60 30

1970. Air. Birth Cent. of Lenin.

1072. **292.** 15 p. brown and red 15 10
1073. 60 p. green and red .. 45 30

293. Battle of Hattin.

1970. 24th Anniv. of Evacuation of Allied Forces.

1074. **293.** 15 p. brown & cream 25 15
1075. 35 p. violet and cream 40 25

294. Emblem of Workers' Syndicate.

970. Air. Labour Day.

1076. **294.** 15 p. brown & green 10 10
1077. 60 p. brown & orange 35 30

295. Young Syrians and Map.

1970. Revolution's Youth Union. 1st Youth Week.

1078. **295.** 15 p. green and ochre 15 10
1079. 25 p. brown and ochre 20 15

This issue is inscr. " YOUTH'S FIRST WEAK " in error.

296. Refugee Family.

1970. World Arab Refugee Week.

1080. **296.** 15 p. multicoloured .. 10 10
1081. 25 p. multicoloured .. 15 10
1082. 35 p. multicoloured .. 20 15

297. Dish Aerial and Open Book.

1970. Air. World Telecommunications Day.

1083 **297** 15 p. black and lilac 15 10
1084 60 p. black and blue 55 30

298. New U.P.U. Headquarters Building.

1970. New U.P.U. Headquarters Building.

1085. **298.** 15 p. multicoloured .. 10 10
1086. 60 p. multicoloured .. 40 30

299. " Industry " and Graph.

300. Khaled ibn el-Walid.

1970.

1087. **299.** 2½ p. red and brown (postage) 15 10
1088. 5 p. blue and orange 40 10
1089. 7½ p. black and purple 20 10
1090. 10 p. bistre and brown 20 10
1091. 12½ p. red and blue .. 20 10
1092. 15 p. purple and green 30 10
1093. 20 p. red and blue .. 45 10
1094. 22½ p. black & brown 50 10
1095. 25 p. blue and grey .. 50 10
1096. 27½ p. brown & green 75 10
1097. 35 p. green and red .. 80 15
1098. **300.** 45 p. mauve (air) .. 80 15
1099. 50 p. green 85 20
1100. 60 p. purple 90 30
1101. 100 p. blue .. .. 1·00 25
1102. 200 p. green .. .. 3·00 75
1103. 300 p. violet .. .. 4·00 1·50
1104. 500 p. black .. .. 5·50 2·75

301. Medieval Warriors.

1970. Air. Folk Tales and Legends.

1105. **301.** 5 p. multicoloured .. 20 20
1106. – 10 p. multicoloured .. 20 20
1107. – 15 p. multicoloured .. 20 20
1108. – 20 p. multicoloured .. 25 25
1109. – 60 p. multicoloured .. 45 45

Nos. 1106/9 show horsemen similar to Type **301**.

302. Cotton.

1970. Aleppo Agricultural and Industrial Fair. Multicoloured.

1110. 5 p. Type **302** 15 15
1111. 10 p. Tomatoes 15 15
1112. 15 p. Tobacco 15 15
1113. 20 p. Sugar beet 20 20
1114. 35 p. Wheat 30 30

303. Mosque in Flames.

1970. Air. 1st Anniv. of Burning of Al Aqsa Mosque, Jerusalem.

1115. **303.** 15 p. multicoloured .. 40 15
1116. 60 p. multicoloured .. 1·00 40

304. Wood-Carving.

1970. Air. 17th Damascus Int. Fair. Mult.

1117. 15 p. Type **304** 20 20
1118. 20 p. Jewellery 20 20
1119. 25 p. Glass-making .. 25 25
1120. 30 p. Copper-engraving .. 35 35
1121. 60 p. Shell-work 40 40

305. Scout, Encampment and Badge.

1970. 9th Pan-Arab Scout Jamboree, Damascus.

1122. **305.** 15 p. grey-green .. 50 15

306. Olive Tree and Emblem.

307. I.E.Y. Emblem.

1970. World Year of Olive-oil Production.

1123. **306.** 15 p. multicoloured .. 20 10
1124. 25 p. multicoloured .. 30 15

1970. Air. International Education Year.

1125. **307.** 15 p. brn., grn. & blk. 10 10
1126. 60 p. brn., bl. & blk. 40 30

308. U.N. Emblems.

1970. Air. 25th Anniv. of U.N.O.

1127. **308.** 15 p. multicoloured .. 10 10
1128. 60 p. multicoloured .. 35 30

309. Protective Shield.

310. Girl holding Garland.

1971. 8th Anniv. of March 8th Baathist Revolution.

1129 **309** 15 p. blue, yell & grn 10 10
1130 22½ p. grn, yell & brn 15 10
1131 27½ p. brn, yell & bl 20 15

1971. Air. 25th Anniv of Evacuation of Allied Forces.

1132. **310.** 15 p. multicoloured.. 15 10
1133. 60 p. multicoloured .. 50 30

311. Globe and World Races.

1971. Air. Racial Equality Year.

1134. **311.** 15 p. multicoloured .. 10 10
1135. 60 p. multicoloured .. 35 25

312. Soldier, Worker and Labour Emblems.

1971. Labour Day.

1136 312 15 p. purple, bl & yell 10 10
1137 25 p. deep blue, blue and yellow .. 20 15

313. Hailing Traffic.

1971. World Traffic Day.

1138. **313.** 15 p. red, blue & black 40 10
1139. – 25 p. multicoloured.. 60 15
1140. **313.** 45 p. red, yell. & blk. 1·00 40

DESIGN—VERT. 25 p. Traffic signs and signal lights.

314. Cotton, Cogwheel and Factories.

1971. Aleppo Agricultural and Industrial Fair.

1141. **314.** 15 p. blk., blue & grn. 15 10
1142. 30 p. blk., red & pink 25 15

315. A.P.U. Emblem.

317. Flag and Federation Map.

316. Peppers and Fertilizer Plant.

1971. 25th Anniv. of Sofar Conference and founding of Arab Postal Union.

1143. **315.** 15 p. multicoloured.. 12 10
1144. 20 p. multicoloured.. 20 10

1971. 18th Damascus Int. Fair. Industries. Multicoloured.

1145. 5 p. Type **316** 10 10
1146. 15 p. TV set and telephone ("Electronics") .. 15 10
1147. 35 p. Oil lamp and dish ("Glassware") .. 45 15
1148. 50 p. Part of carpet ("Carpets") 65 30

1971. Arab Federation Referendum.

1149. **317.** 15 p. black, red & grn. 15 10

318. Pres. Hafez al-Assad and People's Council Chamber.

1971. Air. People's Council and Presidential Election.

1150. **318.** 15 p. multicoloured.. 15 10
1151. 65 p. multicoloured.. 45 25

319. Pres. Nasser.

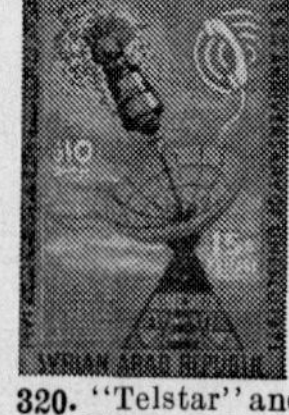

320. "Telstar" and Dish Aerial.

1971. Air. 1st Death Anniv of Pres. Nasser of Egypt.

1152. **319.** 15 p. brown & green 20 10
1153. 20 p. brown and grey 30 10

1971. 25th Anniv. of U.N.E.S.C.O.

1154. **320.** 15 p. multicoloured.. 20 10
1155. 50 p. multicoloured.. 60 25

321. Flaming Torch.

322. Quill-pen and Open Book.

1971. "Movement of 16 November 1970".

1156. **321.** 15 p. multicoloured.. 10 10
1157. 20 p. multicoloured.. 20 15

1971. 8th Writers' Congress.

1158. **322.** 15 p. brn., orge. and turquoise 15 10

323. Children with Ball.

324. Book Year Emblem.

1971. 25th Anniv. of U.N.I.C.E.F.

1159 323 15 p. red, blue and deep blue 15 10
1160 25 p. ochre, grn & bl 25 15

1972. Int. Book Year.

1161. **324.** 15 p. lilac, blue & brn. 15 10
1162. 20 p. green, light green & brown 25 15

325. Emblems of Reconstruction.

326. Baath Party Emblem.

1972. 9th Anniv. of March 8th Baathist Revolution.

1163. **325.** 15 p. vio. & green .. 15 10
1164. 20 p. lake and brown 20 10

1972. 25th Anniv. of Baath Party.

1165. **326.** 15 p. multicoloured.. 15 10
1166. 20 p. multicoloured.. 20 10

327. Eagle, Factory Chimneys and Rifles.

328. Flowers and Broken Chain.

1972. 1st Anniv. of Arab Republics Federation.

1167. **327.** 15 p. gold, blk. & red 15 10

1972. 26th Anniv. of Evacuation of Allied Forces.

1168. **328.** 15 p. grey and red .. 20 10
1169. 50 p. grey & green .. 60 35

329. Hand with Spanner.

331. Environment Emblem.

330. Telecommunications Emblem.

1972. Labour Day.

1170. **329.** 15 p. multicoloured.. 15 10
1171. 50 p. multicoloured.. 40 30

1972. Air. World Telecommunications Day.

1172. **330.** 15 p. multicoloured.. 25 10
1173. 50 p. multicoloured.. 75 30

1972. U.N. Environmental Conservation Conf., Stockholm.

1174. **331.** 15 p. bl., azure & pink 25 10
1175. 50 p. pur., orge. & yell. 75 35

332. Discus, Football and Swimming.

1972. Olympic Games, Munich.

1176. **332.** 15 p. vio., black & brn. 15 10
1177. – 60 p. orge., blk. & bl. 55 40

DESIGN: 60 p. Running, gymnastics and fencing.

334. Dove and Factory.

335. President Hafez al-Assad.

1972. Aleppo Agricultural and Industrial Fair.

1179. **334.** 15 p. multicoloured.. 20 10
1180. 20 p. multicoloured.. 25 10

1972. Air.

1181. **335.** 100 p. green .. 1·50 40
1182. 500 p. brown .. 5·00 1·60

336. Women's Dance.

1972. 19th Damascus Int. Fair. Mult.

1183. 15 p. Type **336** .. 25 10
1184. 20 p. Tambourine dance 35 15
1185. 50 p. Men's drum dance 80 45

337. Airline Emblem.

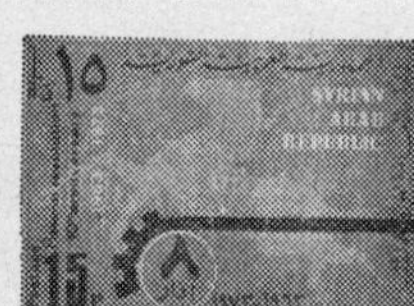

338. Emblem of Revolution.

1972. Air. 25th Anniv. of "Syrianair" Airline.

1186 337 15 p. blue, light blue and black .. 30 10
1187 50p. blue, grey & blk 95 25

1973. 10th Anniv. of March 8th Baathist Revolution.

1188. **338.** 15 p. green, red & blk. 10 10
1189. 20 p. orge., red & blk. 15 10
1190. 25 p. blue, red & blk. 20 10

339. Human Heart.

340. Emblems of Agriculture and Industry.

1973. 25th Anniv. of W.H.O.

1191 339 15 p. blue, pur & grey 30 10
1192 20 p. blue, pur & brn 80 25

1973. 27th Anniv. of Evacuation of Allied Forces.

1193. **340.** 15 p. multicoloured.. 15 10
1194. 20 p. multicoloured.. 15 10

341. Globe and Workers.

1973. Labour Day.

1195. **341.** 15 p. blk., pink & yell. 10 10
1196. 50 p. blk., blue & buff 40 25

342. Family and Emblems.

343. Three Heads.

1973. 10th Anniv. of World Food Programme.

1197. **342.** 15 p. brown and green 20 10
1198. 50 p. blue and purple 55 20

1973. Childrens Day

1199 343 $2\frac{1}{2}$ p. green 10 10
1200 5 p. orange 10 10
1201 – $7\frac{1}{2}$ p. brown 15 10
1202 – 10 p. red 15 10
1203 343 15 p. blue 25 10
1204 – 25 p. blue 30 10
1205 – 35 p. blue 45 10
1206 – 55 p. green 75 15
1207 – 70 p. purple .. .. 1·25 20

DESIGNS—HORIZ. $7\frac{1}{2}$ p., 10 p., 55 p. As Type **343**, but with one head above the other two. VERT. 25 p., 35 p., 70 p. Similar to Type **343**, but with heads in vertical arrangement.

344. Stock.

1973. Int. Flower Show, Damascus. Mult.

1208. 5 p. Type **344** 25 25
1209. 10 p. Gardenia 25 25
1210. 15 p. Jasmine 30 30
1211. 20 p. Rose 35 35
1212. 25 p. Narcissus 40 40

345. Cogs and Flowers.

1973. Aleppo Agricultural and Industrial Fair.

1213. **345.** 15 p. multicoloured.. 15 10

346. Euphrates Dam.

1973. Euphrates Dam Project. Diversion of the River.

1214. **346.** 15 p. multicoloured.. 50 20
1215. 50 p. multicoloured.. 1·25 45

347. Deir Ezzor Costume.

348. Anniversary Emblem.

1973. 20th Damascus International Fair. Costumes. Multicoloured.

1216. 5 p. Type **347** 25 25
1217. 10 p. Hassake 30 30
1218. 20 p. As Sahel 40 40
1219. 25 p. Zakie 40 40
1220. 50 p. Sarakeb 45 45

1973. 25th Anniv. of Declaration of Human Rights.
1221. **348.** 15 p. blk., red & grn. 10 10
1222. 50 p. blk., red & blue 30 15

349. Citadel of Ja'abar.

1973. "Save the Euphrates Monuments" Campaign. Multicoloured.
1223. 10 p. Type **349** .. 15 10
1224. 15 p. Meskeneh Minaret (vert.) 25 10
1225. 25 p. Psyche, Anab al-Safinah (vert.) 45 20

350. W.M.O. Emblem.

1973. Cent. of W.M.O.
1226. **350.** 70 p. multicoloured .. 60 25

351. Ancient City of Maalula.

1973. Arab Emigrants' Congress, Buenos Aires.
1227. **351.** 15 p. black and blue 15 10
1228. – 50 p. black and brown 45 20
DESIGN: 50 p. Ruins of Afamia.

352. Soldier and Workers. **353.** Copernicus.

1973. 3rd Anniv. of November 16th Revolution.
1229. **352.** 15 p. blue & brown .. 10 10
1230. 25 p. violet and red .. 20 10

1973. 14th Science Week
1231 **353** 15 p. black and gold 25 10
1232 – 25 p. black and gold 40 15
DESIGN: 25 p. Al-Biruni.

354. National Symbols. **355.** U.P.U. Monument, Berne.

1974. 11th Anniv. of March 8th Baathist Revolution.
1233. **354.** 20 p. blue and green 10 10
1234. 25 p. blue and green 10 10

1974. Centenary of U.P.U. Mult.
1235. 15 p. Type **355** 10 10
1236. 20 p. Emblem on airmail letter (horiz.) 15 10
1237. 70 p. Type **355** 40 35

356. Postal Institute.

1974. Inauguration of Higher Arab Postal Institute, Damascus.
1238. **356.** 15 p. multicoloured .. 15 10

357. Sun and Monument. **358.** Machine Fitter.

1974. 28th Anniv. of Evacuation of Allied Forces.
1239. **357.** 15 p. multicoloured .. 10 10
1240. 20 p. multicoloured .. 15 10

1974. Labour Day.
1241. **358.** 15 p. multicoloured .. 10 10
1242. 50 p. multicoloured .. 30 20

359. Abul Fida (historian). **360.** Diamond and Part of Cogwheel.

1974. Famous Arabs.
1243. **359.** 100 p. green .. .. 1·00 35
1244. – 200 p. brown .. 2·00 70
DESIGN: 200 p. Al-Farabi (philosopher and encyclopedist.)

1974. 21st Damascus International Fair. Multicoloured.
1245. 15 p. Type **360** .. 10 10
1246. 25 p. "Sun" within cogwheel 15 10

361. Figs. **362.** Flowers within Drop of Blood.

1974. Aleppo Agricultural and Industrial Fair. Fruits. Multicoloured.
1247. 5 p. Type **361** 25 25
1248. 15 p. Grapes 25 25
1249. 20 p. Pomegranates .. 30 30
1250. 25 p. Cherries 30 30
1251. 35 p. Rose-hips 35 35

1974. 1st Anniv. of October Liberation War. Multicoloured.
1252. 15 p. Type **362** 20 10
1253. 20 p. Flower and stars .. 30 10

363. Knight and Rook. **364.** Symbolic Figure, Globe and Emblem.

1974. 50th Anniv of International Chess Federation.
1254. **363.** 15 p. bl., lt. bl. & blk. 60 15
1255. – 50 p. multicoloured .. 2·25 1·25
DESIGN: 50 p. Knight on chessboard.

1974. World Population Year.
1256. **364.** 50 p. multicoloured .. 35 20

365. Ishtup-ilum. **366.** Oil Rig and Crowd.

1974. Statuettes.
1257. **365.** 20 p. green 20 10
1258. – 55 p. brown 35 15
1259. – 70 p. blue 55 20
DESIGNS: 55 p. Woman with vase. 70 p. Ur-nina.

1975. 12th Anniv. of Baathist Revolution of 8 March 1963.
1260. **366.** 15 p. multicoloured .. 20 10

367. Savings Emblem and Family ("Savings Certificates"). **368.** Dove Emblem.

1975. Savings Campaign.
1261. **367.** 15 p. blk., orge. & grn. 10 10
1262. – 20 p. brn., blk. & pink 20 10
DESIGN: 20 p. Family with savings box and letter ("Postal Savings Bank").

1975. 29th Anniv. of Evacuation of Allied Forces.
1263. **368.** 15 p. multicoloured .. 10 10
1264. 25 p. multicoloured .. 15 10

369. Worker supporting Cog. **370.** Camomile.

1975. Labour Day.
1265. **369.** 15 p. multicoloured .. 10 10
1266. 25 p. multicoloured .. 15 10

1975. International Flower Show, Damascus. Multicoloured.
1267. 5 p. Type **370** .. 20 20
1268. 10 p. Chincherinchi .. 25 25
1269. 15 p. Carnations .. 25 25
1270. 20 p. Poppy 30 30
1271. 25 p. Honeysuckle .. 30 30

371. "Destruction and Reconstruction".

1975. Reoccupation of Qneitra.
1272. **371.** 50 p. multicoloured .. 45 20

372. Apples. **373.** Arabesque Pattern.

1975. Aleppo Agricultural and Industrial Fair. Fruits. Multicoloured.
1273. 5 p. Type **372** 20 20
1274. 10 p. Quinces 25 25
1275. 15 p. Apricots 25 25
1276. 20 p. Grapes 30 30
1277. 25 p. Figs 30 30

1975. 22nd International Damascus Fair.
1278. **373.** 15 p. multicoloured .. 10 10
1279. 35 p. multicoloured .. 30 15

374. Pres. Hafez al-Assad.

1975. 5th Anniv. of "Movement of 16 November 1970".
1280. **374.** 15 p. multicoloured .. 10 10
1281. 50 p. multicoloured .. 30 20

375. Symbolic Woman. **376.** Bronze "Horse" Lamp.

1976. Int. Women's Year. Multicoloured.
1282. 10 p. Type **375** 10 10
1283. 15 p. "Motherhood" .. 10 10
1284. 25 p. "Education" .. 15 15
1285. 50 p. "Science" .. 35 20

1976.
1286 – 5 p. green 10 10
1287 **376** 10 p. green 15 10
1288 – 10 p. blue 15 10
1289 – 15 p. brown 15 10
1290 **376** 20 p. red 20 10
1291 25 p. blue 20 10
1292 – 30 p. brown 25 10
1293 – 35 p. green 25 10
1294 – 40 p. orange .. 25 10
1295 – 50 p. blue 60 10
1296 – 55 p. mauve .. 35 10
1297 – 60 p. violet .. 1·75 15
1298 – 70 p. red 45 10
1299 – 75 p. orange .. 75 25
1300 – 80 p. green .. 1·50 15
1301 – 100 p. mauve .. 70 25
1302 – 200 p. blue .. 1·25 45
1303 – 300 p. mauve .. 2·00 55
1304 – 500 p. grey .. .. 6·50 1·75
1305 – 1000 p. green .. 8·00 2·50
DESIGNS—VERT. 5 p. Wall-painting showing figure of a man. 10 p. (No. 1288) Flying goddess with wreath. 30, 35, 40 p. Man's head inkstand. 50, 55, 60 p. Nike. 70, 75, 80 p. Hera. 100 p. Imdugub-Mari (bird goddess). 200 p. Arab astrolabe. 500 p. Palmyrean coin of Valabathus. 1000 p. Abraxas stone. HORIZ. 15 p. Wall-painting showing figures. 300 p. Herodian coin from Palmyra.

377. National Theatre, Damascus.

1976. 13th Anniv. of March 8th Baathist Revolution.
1306. **377.** 25 p. grn., blk. & silver 15 10
1307. 35 p. olive, blk. & silver 20 15

378. Nurse and Emblem. **380.** Eagle and Stars.

379. Syrian 5 m. Stamp of 1920.

1976. 8th Arab Red Crescent and Red Cross Societies' Conf., Damascus.
1308. **378.** 25 p. blue, blk. & red 20 10
1309. 100 p. vio., blk. & red 75 50

1976. Post Day.
1310. **379.** 25 p. multicoloured .. 20 10
1311. 35 p. multicoloured .. 30 15

1976. 30th Anniv. of Allied Forces Evacuation.
1312. **380.** 25 p. multicoloured .. 15 10
1313. 35 p. multicoloured .. 20 15

381. Hand gripping Spanner. **382.** Cotton Boll.

1976. Labour Day.
1314. **381.** 25 p. blue and black .. 15 10
1315. – 60 p. multicoloured .. 45 25
DESIGN: 60 p. Hand supporting globe.

1976. Aleppo Agricultural and Industrial Fair.
1316. **382.** 25 p. multicoloured .. 15 10
1317. 35 p. multicoloured .. 30 15

383. Tulips.

1976. International Flower Show, Damascus. Multicoloured.
1318. 5 p. Type **383** 20 20
1319. 15 p. Yellow daisies .. 25 25
1320. 20 p. Turk's-cap lilies .. 25 25
1321. 25 p. Irises .. 30 30
1322. 35 p. Honeysuckle .. 35 35

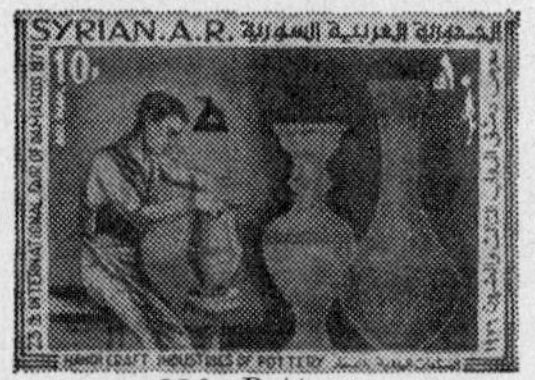

384. Pottery.

1976. Air. 23rd International Damascus Fair. Handicraft Industries. Multicoloured.
1323. 10 Type **384** 25 25
1324. 25 p. Rug-making .. 35 35
1325. 30 p. Metalware 35 35
1326. 35 p. Wickerware .. 35 35
1327. 100 p. Wood-carving .. 55 55

385. People supporting Olive Branch.

1976. Non-aligned Countries Summit Conference, Colombo. Multicoloured.
1328 40 p. Type **385** 25 20
1329 60 p. Symbolic arrow penetrating "grey curtain" 35 25

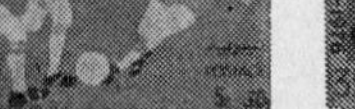

386. Football. **387.** Construction Emblems.

1976. Fifth Pan-Arab Games. Multicoloured.
1330. 5 p. Type **386** 25 25
1331. 10 p. Swimming 30 30
1332. 25 p. Running 35 35
1333. 35 p. Basketball .. 40 40
1334. 50 p. Throwing the javelin 45 45

1976. 6th Anniv. of Movement of 16 November.
1336. **387.** 35 p. multicoloured .. 20 10

388. "The Fox and the Crow". **389.** Muhammad Kurd-Ali (philosopher).

1976. Fairy Tales. Multicoloured.
1337. 10 p. Type **388** 25 25
1338. 15 p. "The Hare and the Tortoise" (horiz.) .. 25 25
1339. 20 p. "Little Red Riding Hood" 30 30
1340. 25 p. "The Wolf and the Goats" (horiz.) .. 30 30
1341. 35 p. "The Wolf and the Lamb" 35 35

1976. Birth Cent of Muhammad Kurd-Ali.
1342. **389.** 25 p. multicoloured .. 20 10

390. Boeing 747.

1977. Civil Aviation Day.
1343. **390.** 35 p. multicoloured .. 75 20

391. Woman hoisting Flag. **392.** A.P.U. Emblem.

1977. 14th Anniv of 8th March Baathist Revolution.
1344. **391.** 35 p. multicoloured .. 25 15

1977. 25th Anniv. of Arab Postal Union.
1345. **392.** 35 p. multicoloured .. 25 10

393. Mounted Horseman.

1977. 31st Anniv. of Evacuation of Foreign Troops from Syria.
1346. **393.** 100 p. multicoloured 75 50

394. Industrial Scene and Tools.

1977. Labour Day.
1347. **394.** 60 p. multicoloured .. 35 20

395. I.C.A.O. Emblem, Plane and Globe.

1977. 30th Anniv. of I.C.A.O.
1348. **395.** 100 p. multicoloured 1·00 75

396. Lemon. **397.** Mallows.

1977. International Agricultural Fair, Aleppo. Multicoloured.
1349. 10 p. Type **396** 25 25
1350. 20 p. Lime 30 30
1351. 25 p. Grapefruit 30 30
1352. 35 p. Oranges 35 35
1353. 60 p. Tangerines 40 40

1977. International Flower Show. Mult.
1354. 10 p. Type **397** 20 20
1355. 20 p. Cockscomb 25 25
1356. 25 p. Convolvulus .. 25 25
1357. 35 p. Balsam 30 30
1358. 60 p. Lilac 40 40

398. Young Pioneers and Emblem.

1977. Al Baath Pioneers Organization.
1359. **398.** 35 p. multicoloured .. 25 15

399. Arabesque Pattern and Coffee Pot. **400.** Globe and Measures.

1977. 24th International Damascus Fair.
1360. **399.** 25 p. red, blue & blk. 15 10
1361. 60 p. brn., grn. & blk. 35 25

1977. World Standards Day.
1362. **400.** 15 p. multicoloured .. 10 10

401. Microscope, Book and Lyre.

1977. 30th Anniv. of U.N.E.S.C.O.
1363. **401.** 25 p. multicoloured .. 15 10

402. Shield, Surgeon and Crab. **403.** Archbishop Capucci and Map of Palestine.

1977. Fighting Cancer Week.
1364. **402.** 100 p. multicoloured 70 35

1977. 3rd Anniv. of Archbishop Capucci's Arrest.
1365. **403.** 60 p. multicoloured .. 65 20

404. Blind Man, Eye and Globe. **405.** Dome of the Rock, Jerusalem.

1977. World Blind Week.
1366. **404.** 55 p. multicoloured .. 40 20
1367. 70 p. multicoloured .. 60 25

1977. Palestinian Welfare.
1368. **405.** 5 p. multicoloured .. 40 15
1369. 10 p. multicoloured .. 60 15

406. Pres. Hafez al-Assad and Government Palace, Damascus. **408.** Arrow and Blood Circulation.

407. Goldfinch.

1977. 7th Anniv. of Movement of 16 November.
1370. **406.** 50 p. multicoloured 20 10

1978. Birds. Multicoloured.
1371. 10 p. Type **407** .. .. 1·50 90
1372. 20 p. Peregrine falcon .. 1·75 1·25
1373. 25 p. Rock dove .. 1·75 1·25
1374. 35 p. Hoopoe .. .. 3·25 1·50
1375. 60 p. Chukar partridge .. 4·00 2·00

1978. World Health Day "Fighting Blood Pressure".
1376. **408.** 100 p. multicoloured 70 30

409. Factory, Moon and Stars. **410.** Geometric Design.

1978. 32nd Anniv. of Evacuation of Foreign Troops.
1377. **409.** 35 p. grn., orge. & blk. 20 10

1978. 14th Arab Engineering Conference, Damascus.
1378. **410.** 25 p. green and black 20 10

411. Map of Arab Countries, Flag, Eye and Police. **412.** Trout.

1978. Sixth Arab Conference of Police Commanders.
1379. **411.** 35 p. multicoloured .. 45 15

1978. Fishes. Multicoloured
1380 10 p. Type **412** 25 25
1381 20 p. Sea-bream 30 30
1382 25 p. Grouper 30 30
1383 35 p. Goatfish 35 35
1384 60 p. Catfish 45 45

413. President Assad.

1978. Air. Re-election of President Hafez al-Assad.
1385. **413.** 25 p. multicoloured .. 15 10
1386. 35 p. multicoloured .. 20 15
1387. 60 p. multicoloured .. 30 15

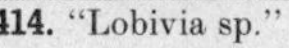

414. "Lobivia sp."

415. President Hafez al-Assad.

1978. International Flower Show, Damascus. Multicoloured.

1389. 25 p. Type **414** 25 25
1390. 30 p. "Mamillaria sp." .. 30 30
1391. 35 p. "Opuntia sp." .. 30 30
1392. 50 p. "Chamaecereus sp." 35 35
1393. 60 p. "Mamillaria sp." (different) 35 35

1978. 8th Anniv. of November 16th Revolution.

1394. **415.** 60 p. multicoloured .. 25 15

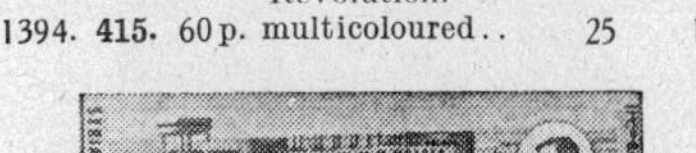

416. Euphrates Dam.

1978. Inauguration of Euphrates Dam.

1395. **416.** 60 p. multicoloured .. 55 25

417. Fair Emblem.

418. Averroes (philosopher).

1979. 25th Int. Damascus Fair.

1396. **417.** 25 p. multicoloured .. 15 10
1397. 35 p. multicoloured .. 20 10

1979. Averroes Commemoration.

1399. **418.** 100 p. multicoloured 70 50

419. Standing Figures within Globe.

420. Pyramid and Flower.

1979. International Year to Combat Racism.

1400. **419.** 35 p. multicoloured .. 20 10

1979. 16th Anniv. of Baathist 8th March Revolution.

1401. **420.** 100 p. multicoloured 60 25

421. Hands Supporting Globe.

422. Helmet of Homs.

1979. 30th Anniv. of Declaration of Human Rights.

1402. **421.** 60 p. multicoloured .. 30 10

1979. Exhibits from National Museum, Damascus.

1403. – 5p. red 10 10
1404. – 10p. green 10 10
1405. – 15p. mauve 10 10
1406. **422.** 20 p. green 10 10
1407. – 25 p. red 10 10
1408. – 35 p. brown 10 10
1409. – 75 p. blue 35 20
1410. – 160 p. green 70 40
1411. – 500 p. brown .. 4·00 1·10

DESIGNS—VERT. 5 p., 160 p. Umayyad window. 10 p. Figurine. 15 p. Rakka horseman (Abbeid ceramic). 25 p. Head of Clipeata (Cleopatra). 35 p. Seated statue of Ishtar (Astarte). HORIZ. 75 p. Abdul Mali gold coin. 500 p. Umar B. Abdul Aziz gold coin.

423. Geometric Design and Flame.

424. Ibn Assaker.

1979. 33rd Anniv. of Evacuation of Foreign Troops from Syria.

1416. **423.** 35 p. multicoloured .. 20 10

1979. 900th Anniv. of Ibn Assaker (historian and biographer).

1417. **424.** 75 p. brn., bl. & grn. 35 20

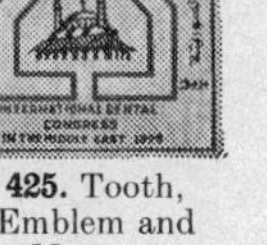

425. Tooth, Emblem and Mosque.

426. Welder working on Power Pylon.

1979. International Middle East Dental Congress.

1418. **425.** 35 p. multicoloured 30 10

1979. Labour Day.

1419. **426.** 50 p. multicoloured 25 15
1420. 75 p. multicoloured 30 20

427. Girl holding Emblem with Flowers.

428. Wright Brothers' "Flyer".

1979. International Year of the Child. Multicoloured.

1421. 10 p. Type **427** 10 10
1422. 15 p. Boy and globe .. 20 10

1979. 75th Anniv. of First Powered Flight. Multicoloured.

1423. 50 p. Type **428**. 35 20
1424. 75 p. Bleriot's plane crossing English Channel .. 50 25
1425. 100 p. Lindbergh's "Spirit of St. Louis" 75 40

429. Power Station.

430. Flags and Pavilion.

1979.

1426. **429.** 5 p. blue 10 10
1427. 10 p. mauve 10 10
1428. 15 p. green 15 10

1979. 26th International Damascus Fair. Multicoloured.

1429. 60 p. Type **430** 25 15
1430. 75 p. Lamp post and flags 30 20

431. Running.

1979. Eighth Mediterranean Games, Split. Multicoloured.

1431. 25 p. Type **431** 15 10
1432. 35 p. Swimmer on starting-block 20 10
1433. 50 p. Football 25 15

432. President Assad with Symbols of Agriculture and Industry.

1979. 9th Anniv. of Movement of 16 November 1970.

1434. **432.** 100 p. multicoloured 1·25 20

433. "Papilio machaon".

434. Astrolabe.

1979. Butterflies. Multicoloured.

1435 20 p. Type **433** 40 20
1436 25 p. "Inachis io" .. 45 20
1437 30 p. "Limenitis camilla" 55 20
1438 35 p. "Morpho cypris" .. 60 20
1439 50 p. "Parnassius apollo" 75 30

1979. International Flower Show, Damascus. Designs similar to T **414** showing various roses.

1440. 5 p. multicoloured .. 10 10
1441. 10 p. multicoloured .. 15 10
1442. 15 p. multicoloured .. 20 10
1443. 50 p. multicoloured .. 40 20
1444. 75 p. multicoloured .. 65 30
1445. 100 p. multicoloured .. 90 45

1980. Second International History of Arabic Sciences Symposium.

1446. **434.** 50 p. violet 25 10
1447. 100 p. brown .. 50 25
1448. 1000 p. green .. 4·00 2·50

435. "8" over Buildings.

436. Smoker.

1980. 17th Anniv. of Baathist Revolution of 8 March 1963.

1449. **435.** 40 p. multicoloured 20 10

1980. World Health Day. Anti-smoking Campaign.

1450. **436.** 60 p. brn., grn. & blk. 60 25
1451. – 100 p. multicoloured 90 40

DESIGN: 100 p. Skull and cigarette.

437. Monument.

1980. 34th Anniv. of Evacuation of Foreign Troops from Syria.

1452 **437** 40 p. multicoloured .. 25 10
1453 60 p. multicoloured .. 30 15

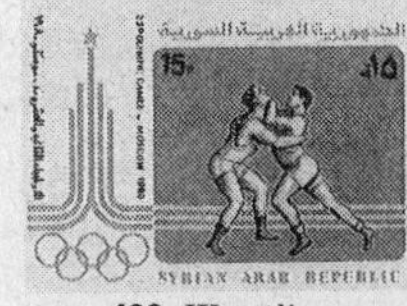

438. Wrestling.

1980. Olympic Games, Moscow. Mult.

1454. 15 p. Type **438** 10 10
1455. 25 p. Fencing 15 10
1456. 35 p. Weightlifting .. 20 10
1457. 50 p. Judo 25 10
1458. 75 p. Boxing 35 20

439. "Savings".

1980. Savings Certificates.

1460. **439.** 25 p. vio., red & bl. 15 10

440. "Aladdin and the Magic Lamp".

1980. Popular Stories. Multicoloured.

1461. 15 p. "Sinbad the Sailor" 20 20
1462. 20 p. "Shahrazad and Shahrayar" 30 30
1463. 35 p. "Ali Baba and the Forty Thieves" .. 35 35
1464. 50 p. "Hassan the Clever" 40 40
1465. 100 p. Type **440** 55 55

441. Kaaba and Mosque, Mecca.

1980. 1400th Anniv. of Hegira.

1466. **441.** 35 p. multicoloured 25 15

442. Daffodils.

443. "Industry".

1980. International Flower Show, Damascus. Multicoloured.

1467. 20 p. Type **442** 25 25
1468. 30 p. Dahlias 30 30
1469. 40 p. Bergamot 35 35
1470. 60 p. Globe Flowers .. 40 40
1471. 100 p. Cornflowers .. 55 55

1980. 10th Anniv. of Movement of 16 November 1970.

1472. **443.** 100 p. multicoloured 55 25

444. Construction Worker.

445. Children encircling Globe.

1980. Labour Day.

1473. **444.** 35 p. multicoloured 20 15

1980. International Children's Day.

1474. **445.** 25 p. grn., black & yellow 20 10

446. Steam-powered Passenger Wagon, 1830.

447. Mother's Arms around Child.

1980. Cars. Multicoloured.

1475. 25 p. Type **446** 30 30
1476. 35 p. Benz, 1899 .. 35 35
1477. 40 p. Rolls-Royce, 1903 35 35
1478. 50 p. Mercedes, 1906 .. 40 40
1479. 60 p. Austin, 1915 .. 50 50

1980. Mother's Day. Multicoloured.
1480. 40 p. Type **447** 25 10
1481. 100 p. Faces of mother and child 45 25

448. Fair Emblem.

1980. 27th International Damascus Fair. Mult.
1482 50 p. Type **448** 30 15
1483 100 p. As T **448** but with different motif on right 60 30

449. Armed Forces.

1980. Army Day.
1484. **449.** 50 p. multicoloured .. 1·00 30

450. Arabesque Pattern. **451.** Geometric Design, Laurel and Hand holding Torch.

1981. 18th Anniv. of Baathist Revolution of 8 March 1963.
1485. **450.** 50 p. multicoloured .. 35 15

1981. 35th Anniv. of Evacuation of Foreign Troops from Syria.
1486. **451.** 50 p. multicoloured .. 35 15

452. Mosque and Script.

1981. History of Arab-Islamic Civilization World Conference, Damascus.
1487. **452.** 100 p. pale green, green and black .. 80 50

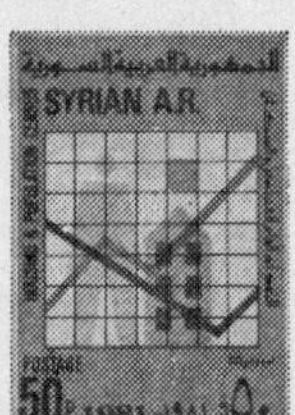
453. Marching Workers and Emblem. **454.** Human Figure and House on Graph.

1981. May Day.
1488. **453.** 100 p. multicoloured 60 35

1981. Housing and Population Census.
1489. **454.** 50 p. multicoloured .. 35 15

455. Family and Savings Emblem. **456.** Dove and Map on Globe.

1981. Savings Certificates.
1490. **455.** 50 p. black and brown 35 15

1981. International Syrian and Palestinian Solidarity Conference, Damascus.
1491. **456.** 160 p. multicoloured 1·75 85

457. Avicenna. **459.** Festival Emblem.

458. Glass Lamp.

1981. Birth Millenary of Avicenna (philosopher and physician).
1492. **457.** 100 p. multicoloured 80 50

1981. Damascus Museum Exhibits.
1493. **458.** 50 p. red 50 20
1494. – 180 p. multicoloured 1·50 80
1495. – 180 p. multicoloured 1·50 80
DESIGNS: No. 1494, "Grand Mosque, Damascus" (painting). No. 1495, Hunting scene (tapestry).

1981. Youth Festival.
1496. **459.** 60 p. multicoloured .. 45 20

460. Decorative Pattern. **461.** Palestinians and Dome of the Rock.

1981. 28th International Damascus Fair.
1497. **460.** 50 p. mve., blue & grn. 40 15
1498. – 160 p. brn., yell. & lilac 1·00 50
DESIGN: 160 p. Globe encircled by wheat and cogwheel.

1981. Palestinian Solidarity.
1499. **461.** 100 p. multicoloured 1·25 55

462. F.A.O. Emblem. **463.** Tobacco Flowers.

1981. World Food Day.
1500. **462.** 180 p. blue, green & black .. .. 1·50 80

1981. International Flower Show, Damascus. Multicoloured.
1501. 25 p. Type **463** 45 45
1502. 40 p. Mimosa 60 60
1503. 50 p. Ixias 70 70
1504. 60 p. Passion flower .. 70 70
1505. 100 p. Dendrobium .. 95 95

464. Hands releasing Dove and Horseman.

1981. 1300th Anniv. of Bulgarian State.
1506. **464.** 380 p. multicoloured 2·50 1·75

465. Classroom.

1981. International Children's Day.
1507. **465.** 180 p. black, red & green .. .. 1·50 80

467. President Assad and Diesel Train. **468.** Symbols of Development.

1981. 11th Anniv. of Movement of 16 November 1970.
1509. **467.** 60 p. blue, black and brown .. .. 1·50 35

1982. 19th Anniv. of Baathist Revolution of 8 March 1963.
1510. **468.** 50 p. grey, red and black 45 15

469. Robert Koch and Microscope. **470.** Pattern and Hand holding Rifle

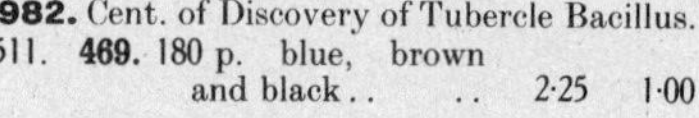

1982. Cent. of Discovery of Tubercle Bacillus.
1511. **469.** 180 p. blue, brown and black .. .. 2·25 1·00

1982. 36th Anniv. of Evacuation of Foreign Troops from Syria.
1512. **470.** 70 p. red and blue .. 65 35

471. Disabled People and Emblem. **472.** A.P.U. Emblem.

1982. International Year of Disabled Persons (1981).
1513. **471.** 90 p. black, blue and yellow .. .. 1·25 55

1982. 30th Anniv. of Arab Postal Union.
1514. **472.** 60 p. red, green and yellow 60 30

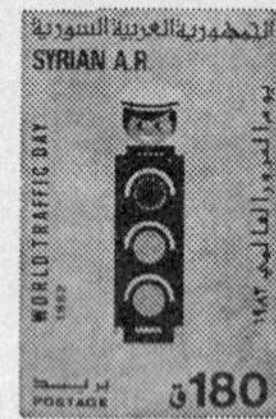
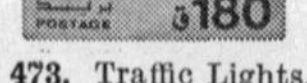

473. Traffic Lights. **475.** Oil Rig, Factory Chimneys and Hand holding Torch.

474. Geometric Pattern.

1982. World Traffic Day.
1515. **473.** 180 p. black, red and blue .. .. 2·75 1·50

1982. World Telecommunications Day.
1516. **474.** 180 p. pale yellow, brown and yellow 1·75 1·25

1982. Labour Day.
1517. **475.** 180 p. red, blue and light blue .. .. 1·75 1·25

476. Mother and Children. **477.** Olives.

1982. Mothers' Day.
1518. **476.** 40 p. green 30 15
1519. – 75 p. brown 50 35

1982.
1520 **477.** 50 p. green 40 15
1521. 60 p. grey 25 15
1522. – 100 p. mauve .. 1·00 25
1523. – 150 p. blue .. 1·50 30
1524. – 180 p. red 75 45
DESIGNS: 100 p., 180 p. Harbour. 150 p. President Assad.

479. Footballer.

1982. World Cup Football Championship, Spain. Multicoloured.
1525. 40 p. Type **479** 40 20
1526. 60 p. Two footballers .. 55 30
1527. 100 p. Two footballers (different) 90 70

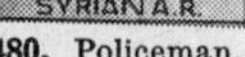

480. Policeman. **481.** Government Building.

1982. Police Day.
1529. **480.** 50 p. black, red and green .. .. 1·25 40

1982.
1530. **481.** 30 p. brown 25 10
1531. – 70 p. green 35 20
1532. – 200 p. red .. .. 2·50 85
DESIGNS—HORIZ. 200 p. Ruins. VERT. 70 p. Arched wall.

482. Communications Emblem and Map.

1982. Arab Telecommunications Day.
1533. **482.** 50 p. light blue, blue and red 75 30

483. Scout pitching Tent.

1982. 75th Anniv. of Boy Scout Movement.
1534. **483.** 160 p. green .. .. 2·50 1·25

484. Dish Aerial and World Map.

1982. I.T.U. Delegates' Conference, Nairobi.
1535. **484.** 180 p. light blue, blue and red .. .. 2·25 1·25

485. President Assad.

1982. 12th Anniv. of Movement of 16 November.

1536. **485.** 50 p. blue and grey 70 30

486. Water-wheel, Hama.

487. Dragonfly.

1982.

1537. **486.** 5 p. brown 10 10
1538. 10 p. violet 10 10
1539. 20 p. red 20 10
1540. 50 p. blue 50 20

1982. Insects. Multicoloured.

1541 5 p. Type **487** 30 30
1542 10 p. "Lucanus cervus" .. 30 30
1543 20 p. "Coccinella septem-punctata" 45 45
1544 40 p. "Schistocerca gregaria" 90 90
1545 50 p. "Apis mellifera" .. 1·10 1·10

488. Honeysuckle.

489. Satellites within Dove.

1982. International Flower Show. Damascus. Multicoloured.

1546. 50 p. Type **488** 85 40
1547. 60 p. Geranium .. .. 1·00 60

1982. U.N. Conference on Exploration and Peaceful Uses of Outer Space, Vienna.

1548. **489.** 50 p. multicoloured 90 30

490. Dove on Gun.

1982. International Palestine Day.

1549. **490.** 50 p. multicoloured 1·25 40

491. Damascus Airport.

1983. 20th Anniv. of Baathist Revolution of 8 March.

1550. **491.** 60 p. multicoloured 1·25 50

492. I.T.U., U.P.U. and W.C.Y. Emblems.

1983. World Communications Year.

1551. **492.** 180 p. multicoloured 2·25 1·50

493. Figurine.

1983.

1552. **493.** 380 p. brown & green 3·00 1·40

494. Pharmacist.

1983. Arab Pharmacists' Day.

1553. **494.** 100 p. multicoloured 1·75 75

495. Liberation Monument, Qneitra.

496. Wave within Ship's Wheel.

1983. 9th Anniv. of Liberation of Qneitra.

1554. **495.** 50 p. green 70 30
1555. – 100 p. brown .. 1·25 70

DESIGN: 100 p. Ruined buildings.

1983. 25th Anniv. of I.M.O.

1556. **496.** 180 p. multicoloured 2·25 1·25

497. Flame on Map.

1983. Namibia Day.

1557. **497.** 180 p. blue, mauve and black .. .. 2·25 1·25

498. I.S.O. Emblem. and Factory.

499. Gateway, Bosra.

1983. World Standards Day.

1558. **498.** 50 p. multicoloured 65 30
1559. – 100 p. vio., green & black .. 1·40 70

DESIGN: 100 p. I.S.O. emblem and measuring equipment.

1983. 10th Anniv. of World Heritage Agreement.

1560. **499.** 60 p. brown 80 40

500. Flowers.

501. Farmland.

1983. International Flower Show, Damascus. Multicoloured.

1561. 50 p. Type **500** 80 35
1562. 60 p. Hibiscus 95 45

1983. World Food Day.

1563. **501.** 180 p. green, cream and deep green .. 2·25 1·25

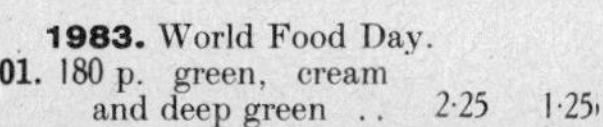

502. Factory.

503. Statuette.

1983.

1564. **502.** 50 p. green 40 20

1984. International Deir Ez-Zor History and Archaeology Symposium.

1565. **503.** 225 p. brown .. 2·25 1·25

504. Aleppo.

505. Alassad Library.

1984. International Symposium for the Conservation of Aleppo.

1566. **504.** 245 p. multicoloured 2·25 1·25

1984. 21st Anniv. of Baathist Revolution of 8 March.

1567. **505.** 60 p. multicoloured 70 40

506. Bodies and Mourning Women with Child.

1984. Sabra and Shatila (refugee camps in Lebanon) Massacres.

1568. **506.** 225 p. multicoloured 2·00 1·10

507. Mother and Child.

509. Swimming.

508. Dam, Emblem and Pioneers.

1984. Mothers' Day.

1569. **507.** 245 p. brn. & grn. .. 2·00 1·25

1984. 9th Regional Festival of Al Baath Pioneers. Multicoloured.

1570. 50 p. Type **508** 60 35
1571. 60 p. Pioneers, ruins and emblems 80 50

1984. Olympic Games, Los Angeles. Multicoloured.

1572. 30 p. Type **509** 30 30
1573. 50 p. Wrestling 45 45
1574. 60 p. Running 50 50
1575. 70 p. Boxing 60 60
1576. 90 p. Football 75 75

510. Flowers.

511. Pres. Assad and Text.

1984. International Flower Show, Damascus. Multicoloured.

1578. 245 p. Type **510** .. .. 2·00 1·25
1579. 285 p. Flowers (different) 2·25 1·75

1984. 4th Revolutionary Youth Union Congress.

1580. **511.** 50 p. brown, deep brown and green 60 30
1581. – 60 p. multicoloured 80 50

DESIGN: 37 × 25 mm. 60 p. Pres. Assad and saluting youth.

512. Emblem and Administration Building, Damascus.

1984. Arab Postal Union Day.

1582. **512.** 60 p. multicoloured 75 40

513. Globe, Dish Aerial and Telephone.

514. Arabesque Pattern.

1984. World Telecommunications Day.

1583. **513.** 245 p. multicoloured 2·25 1·40

1984. 31st International Damascus Fair. Multicoloured.

1584. 45 p. Type **514** 55 30
1585. 100 p. Ornate gold decoration .. .. 1·00 60

515. Stylized Airplanes and Emblem.

1984. 40th Anniv. of I.C.A.O.

1586. **515.** 45 p. lt. bl. & bl. .. 60 30
1587. – 245 p. light blue, blue and deep blue .. 2·25 1·25

DESIGN: 245 p. Emblem and stylized building.

516. Text, Flag and Pres. Assad.

1984. 14th Anniv. of Movement of 16 Nov 1970.

1588. **516.** 65 p. orange, black and brown .. 65 35

517. Palmyra Roman Arch and Colonnades.

1984. International Tourism Day.

1589. **517.** 100 p. brown, black and blue .. .. 1·00 45

INDEX

Countries can be quickly located by referring to the index at the end of this volume.

518. Wooded Landscape.

1985. Woodland Conservation.
1590. 518. 45 p. multicoloured 70 35

519. University and Students.

1985. 26th Anniv. (1984) of Aleppo University.
1591. 519. 45 p. black, blue and brown 60 35

520. Oil Lamp.

1985. 26th Anniv. (1984) of Supreme Council of Science.
1592. 520. 65 p. green, red and black 90 45

521. Soldier holding Flag.

1985. Army Day.
1593. 521. 65 p. deep brown and brown .. .. 1·00 45

522. Pres. Assad.

1985. Re-election of President Assad.
1594. 522. 200 p. multicoloured 1·25 75
1595. 300 p. multicoloured 2·00 1·25
1596. 500 p. multicoloured 3·50 1·90

523. Flag and Party Emblem.

524. Torch and "22".

1985. 8th Baath Arab Socialist Party Congress.
1598. 523. 50 p. multicoloured 65 35

1985. 22nd Anniv. of Baathist Revolution of 8 March 1963.
1599. 524. 60 p. multicoloured 70 35

525. Tractor and Cow.

1985. Aleppo Industrial and Agricultural Fair (1984). Multicoloured.
1600 65 p. Type 525 .. .. 70 45
1601 150 p. Fort and carrots (vert) .. .. .. 1·60 1·25

526. Liberation Monument, Qneitra.

1985. 10th Anniv. (1984) of Liberation of Qneitra.
1602. 526. 70 p. multicoloured 75 40

527. Parliament Building.

1985. 10th Anniv. of Arab Parliamentary Union.
1603. 527. 245 p. multicoloured 2·25 1·50

528. U.P.U. Emblem and Pigeon with Letter.

529. A.P.U. Emblem.

1985. World Post Day.
1604. 528. 285 p. multicoloured 2·25 1·50

1985. 12th Arab Postal Union Conference, Damascus.
1605. 529. 60 p. multicoloured 70 35

530. Medal.

1985. Labour Day.
1606. 530. 60 p. multicoloured 70 35

531. Old and New Locomotives.

1985. 2nd Scientific Symposium.
1607. 531. 60 p. blue .. .. 1·25 45

532. Emblem and Child with empty Bowl.

1985. U.N. Child Survival Campaign.
1608. 532. 60 p. black, green & pink 75 35

533. Pres. Assad and Road.

1985. 15th Anniv. of Movement of 16 Nov 1970.
1609. 533. 60 p. multicoloured 70 35

534. Emblem and "40".

535. Lily-flowered Tulip.

1985. 40th Anniv. of U.N.O.
1610. 534. 245 p. multicoloured 2·00 1·40

1986. International Flower Show, Damascus (1985). Multicoloured.
1611. 30 p. Type 535 .. .. 50 25
1612. 60 p. Tulip 90 65

536. Flask.

1986. 32nd International Damascus Fair (1985).
1613 536 60 p. multicoloured .. 75 35

537. Abd-er-Rahman I.

538. Pres. Hafez al-Assad.

1986. 1200th Anniv of Abd-er-Rahman I ad Dakhel, Emir of Cordoba.
1614. 537. 60 p. brown, pink and brown .. 75 35

1988.

1615	538	10 p. red	..	10	10
1616		30 p. blue	..	20	10
1616a		50 p lilac	..	10	10
1617		100 p. blue	..	65	20
1618		150 p. brown	..	90	25
1619		175 p. violet	..	1·10	30
1620		200 p. brown	..	1·25	35
1621		300 p. mauve	..	1·90	50
1622		500 p. orange	..	3·00	90
1623		550 p. red	..	3·50	1·25
1624		600 p. green	..	4·00	1·50
1625		1000 p. mauve	..	5·50	2·00
1626		2000 p. green	..	10·00	4·75

539. Tooth and Map.

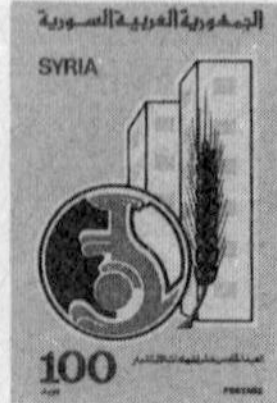
540. Tower Blocks, Ear of Wheat and Kangaroo.

1986. 19th Arab Dentists' Union Congress, Damascus.
1627 539 110 p. multicoloured .. 2·00 1·25

1986. 15th Anniv. of Syrian Investment Certificates.
1628 540 100 p. multicoloured .. 1·40 70

541. Traffic Policewoman, Globe and Traffic Lights.

542. Policeman and Building in Laurel Wreath.

1986. World Traffic Day.
1629 541 330 p. multicoloured .. 3·25 2·00

1986. Police Day.
1630 542 110 p. multicoloured .. 2·25 1·40

543. Industrial Symbols and Hand Holding Spanner.

544. Building.

1986. Labour Day.
1631 543 330 p. red, black & bl 2·50 1·90

1986. 12th Anniv. of Liberation of Qneitra.
1632 544 110 p. multicoloured .. 2·00 1·40

545. Pictogram and Ball.

546. Mother and Children.

1986. World Cup Football Championship, Mexico.
1633 545 330 p. multicoloured 2·50 1·50
1634 370 p. multicoloured 2·50 1·75

1986. Mothers' Day.
1636 546 100 p. multicoloured .. 1·50 75

547. Pres. Assad and Train.

1986. 23rd Anniv of Baathist Revolution of 8 March 1963.
1637 547 110 p. multicoloured 1·50 80

548. A.P.U. Emblem, Post Office and Box.

549. Fists, Map and Globe.

1986. Arab Post Day.
1638 548 110 p. multicoloured 1·75 85

1986. International Palestine Day.
1639 549 110 p. multicoloured .. 2·50 1·40

550. Tulips.

1986. International Flower Show, Damascus. Multicoloured.

1640	10 p. Type **550**	25	25
1641	50 p. Mauve flowers ..	60	60
1642	100 p. Yellow flowers ..	1·00	1·00
1643	110 p. Pink flowers ..	1·00	1·00
1644	330 p. Yellow flowers (different)	2·50	2·50

551. Pres. Assad and Tishreen Palace.

1986. 16th Anniv. of Movement of 16 Nov 1970.

1645 **551**	110 p. multicoloured ..	1·60	80

552. Rocket and Flags.

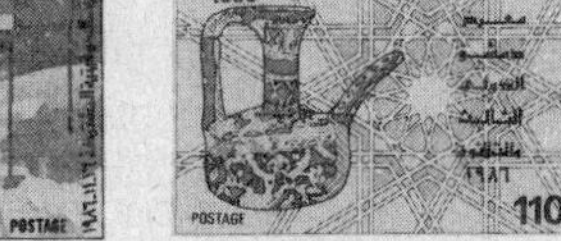

553. Jug and Star.

1986. 1st Anniv. of Announcement of Syrian–Soviet Space Flight.

1646 **552**	330 p. multicoloured ..	2·75	1·75

1986. 33rd International Damascus Fair.

1647 **553.**	110 p. multicoloured	1·25	80
1648 –	330 p. black, green and brown ..	3·00	1·75

DESIGN: 330 p. Coffee pot.

554 Girls and National Flag

1987. International Children's Art Exhibition.

1649 **554**	330 p. multicoloured ..	2·75	1·50

555 U.P.U. Emblem and Airmail Envelope

556 Children in Balloon over Town

1987. World Post Day.

1650 **555**	330 p. multicoloured ..	2·25	1·25

1987. International Children's Day.

1651 **556**	330 p. multicoloured ..	2·50	1·25

557 Citadel, Aleppo

1987. International Tourism Day.

~~1652~~	330 p. Type **557**	2·50	1·25
1653	370 p. Water-wheel, Hama	2·75	1·50

558 Industrial Symbols

1987. 24th Anniv of Baathist Revolution of 8 March 1963.

1654 **558**	100 p. multicoloured ..	1·00	60

559 Doves flying from Globe

560 Party Emblem

1987. International Peace Year.

1655 **559**	370 p. multicoloured ..	2·50	1·40

1987. 40th Anniv of Baath Arab Socialist Party.

1656 **560**	100 p. multicoloured ..	1·00	55

561 Stars

1987. 41st Anniv of Evacuation of Foreign Troops from Syria.

1657 **561**	100 p. multicoloured ..	1·00	55

562 Draughtsman

1987. 6th Arab Ministers of Culture Conference.

1658 **562**	330 p. blue, grn & blk	2·50	1·40

563 Map of Arab Postal Union Members.

564 Couple within Cogwheel

1987. Arab Post Day.

1659 **563**	110 p. multicoloured ..	1·25	65

1987. Labour Day.

1660 **564**	330 p. multicoloured ..	2·50	1·40

565 Statue

566 Pres. Assad with Children and Nurse

1987. 13th Anniv of Liberation of Qneitra.

1661 **565**	100 p. multicoloured ..	1·00	55

1987. Child Vaccination Campaign.

1662 **566**	100 p. multicoloured	1·00	60
1663	330 p. multicoloured	2·75	1·50

567 Dome of the Rock, Battle Scene and Saladin

1987. 800th Anniv of Battle of Hattin.

1664 **567**	110 p. multicoloured ..	1·25	65

568 Rocket Launch and National Flags

1987. Syrian–Soviet Space Flight. Mult.

1665	330 p. Type **568**	2·50	1·75
1666	330 p. Spacecraft docking with "Mir" space station (37 × 25 mm) ..	2·50	1·75
1667	330 p. Space capsule re-entering Earth's atmosphere and group of cosmonauts (25 × 37 mm)	2·50	1·75

569 Flags, Cosmonauts and Pres. Assad

1987. President's Space Conversation with Lt-Col. Mohammed Faris (Syrian cosmonaut).

1669 **569**	500 p. multicoloured ..	3·75	2·75

570 Stylized Flowers

571 Sports Pictograms

1987. 34th International Damascus Fair.

1670 **570**	330 p. multicoloured ..	2·00	1·40

1987. 10th Mediterranean Games, Latakia.

1671 **571**	100 p. purple & black	65	35
1672 –	110 p. multicoloured	70	55
1673 –	330 p. multicoloured	2·00	1·50
1674 –	370 p. multicoloured	2·25	1·75

DESIGNS: As Type **571**. HORIZ— 110 p. Swimming bird and emblem. 52 × 23 mm— 330 p. Phoenician galley (Games emblem); 370 p. Flags forming "SYRIA".

572 Soldier, Airplane, Ship and Tank

573 Trees, Sun and Birds

1987. Army Day.

1676 **572**	100 p. multicoloured ..	1·00	40

1987. Tree Day.

1677 **573**	330 p. multicoloured ..	2·00	1·40

574 Poppies

576 Barbed Wire around Map of Israel

575 Pres. Assad acknowledging Applause

1987. International Flower Show, Damascus.

1678	330 p. Type **574**	2·00	1·40
1679	370 p. Mauve flower ..	2·25	1·75

1987. 17th Anniv of Corrective Movement of 16 November 1970.

1680 **575**	150 p. multicoloured ..	1·00	70

1987. International Palestine Day.

1681 **576**	500 p. multicoloured ..	2·75	1·90

577 U.P.U. and U.N. Emblems

1988. World Post Day.

1682 **577**	500 p. multicoloured ..	2·75	1·90

578 Bosra Amphitheatre

1988. International Tourism Day. Mult.

1683	500 p. Type **578**	2·50	1·60
1684	500 p. Palmyra ruins ..	2·50	1·60

579 Children as Astronauts

1988. International Children's Day.

1685 **579**	500 p. multicoloured ..	2·50	1·60

580 Hand holding Torch

581 Woman cradling Baby, Children and Adults

1988. 25th Anniv of Baathist Revolution of 8 March 1963.

1686 **580**	150 p. multicoloured ..	90	60

1988. Mothers' Day.

1688 **581**	500 p. multicoloured ..	2·50	1·60

582 Arms, Cogwheel, Laurel Branch and Book

583 Dove, Airmail Envelope and Map

1988. 42nd Anniv of Evacuation of Foreign Troops from Syria.
1689 **582** 150 p. multicoloured .. 75 55

1988. Arab Post Day.
1690 **583** 150 p. multicoloured .. 75 55

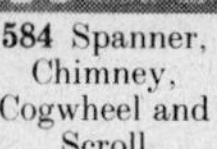

584 Spanner, Chimney, Cogwheel and Scroll

585 Modern Buildings

1988. Labour Day.
1691 **584** 550 p. multicoloured .. 2·25 1·50

1988. Arab Engineers' Union.
1692 **585** 150 p. multicoloured .. 75 55

586 Lily

1988. International Flower Show, Damascus. Multicoloured.
1693 550 p. Type **586** .. .. 2·25 1·50
1694 600 p. Carnations .. 2·25 1·50

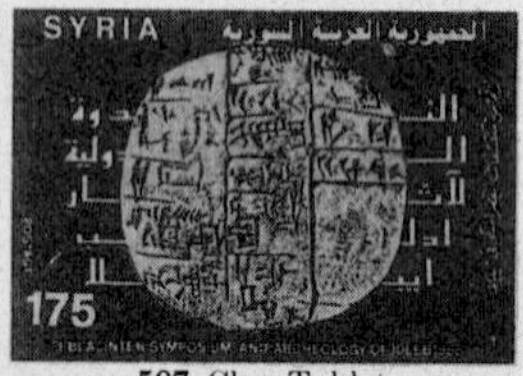

587 Clay Tablet

1988. International Symposium on Archaeology of Ebla.
1695 **587** 175 p. black & brown 55 40
1696 – 550 p. brown, bl & blk 1·40 90
1697 – 600 p. multicoloured 1·50 1·00
DESIGNS: 550 p. King making offering (carving from stone votive basin); 600 p. Golden statue of goddess Ishtar.

588 Old City

589 Emblem

1988. Preservation of Sana'a, Yemen.
1698 **588** 550 p. multicoloured .. 1·40 90

1988. Children's Day.
1699 **589** 600 p. black, yell & grn 1·50 1·00

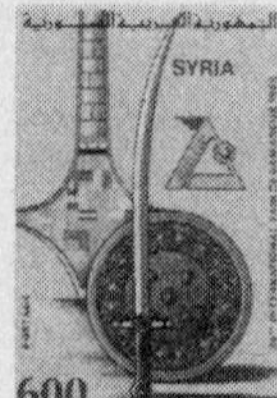

590 Sword, Shield and Emblems

591 Emblem and People

1988. 35th International Damascus Fair.
1700 **590** 600 p. multicoloured .. 1·50 1·00

1988. 40th Anniv of W.H.O.
1701 **591** 600 p. multicoloured .. 1·50 1·00

592 Emblems and Map

1988. 50th Anniv of Arab Scout Movement.
1702 **592** 150 p. multicoloured .. 50 35

593 Cycling

1988. Olympic Games, Seoul. Multicoloured.
1703 550 p. Type **593** .. .. 1·40 90
1704 600 p. Football .. .. 1·50 1·00

594 Old Houses and Modern Flats

1988. Housing. Multicoloured.
1706 150 p. Type **594** (Arab Housing Day) .. 50 35
1707 175 p. House and makeshift shelter (International Year of Shelter for the Homeless (1987)) 55 40
1708 550 p. Types of housing (World Housing Day) 1·40 90
1709 600 p. As No. 177 but inscr for International Day for Housing the Homeless .. .. 1·50 1·00

595 Euphrates Bridge, Deir el Zor

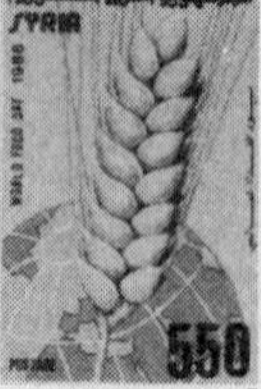

596 Ear of Wheat and Globe

1988. International Tourism Day. Mult.
1710 550 p. Type **595** .. .. 1·40 90
1711 600 p. Tetrapylon of Latakia .. .. 1·50 1·00

1988. World Food Day.
1712 **596** 550 p. multicoloured .. 1·40 90

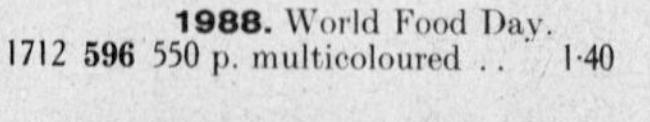

597 Al-Assad University Hospital.

1988. 18th Anniv of Corrective Movement of 16 November 1970.
1713 **597** 150 p. multicoloured .. 50 35

598 Tree and Flowers

599 Dove with Envelope over Globe

1988. Tree Day.
1714 **598** 600 p. multicoloured .. 1·50 1·00

1988. World Post Day.
1715 **599** 600 p. multicoloured .. 1·50 1·00

600 Emblem and Doctor within Stethoscope

602 Pres. Assad and Women

601 Symbols of Agriculture and Industry

1989. 10th Anniv of Arab Board for Medical Specializations.
1716 **600** 175 p. multicoloured .. 35 25

1989. 26th Anniv of Baathist Revolution of 8 March 1963.
1717 **601** 150 p. multicoloured .. 30 20

1989. 5th General Congress of Union Women.
1718 **602** 150 p. multicoloured .. 30 20

603 Candle and Books

1989. Arab Teachers' Day.
1719 **603** 175 p. multicoloured .. 35 25

604 Nehru

605 Mother and Children

1989. Birth Centenary of Jarwaharlal Nehru (Indian statesman).
1720 **604** 550 p. brown & lt brn 80 55

1989. Mothers' Day.
1721 **605** 550 p. multicoloured .. 80 55

606 Goldfinch

1989. Birds. Multicoloured.
1722 600 p. Type **606** .. .. 1·00 75
1723 600 p. European bee eater 1·00 75
1724 600 p. Turtle dove .. 1·00 75

607 State Arms on Map

608 Workers

1989. 43rd Anniv of Evacuation of Foreign Troops from Syria.
1725 **607** 150 p. multicoloured .. 30 20

1989. Labour Day.
1726 **608** 850 p. green and black 1·25 85

609 Snapdragons

610 Girl and Envelope

1989 . International Flower Show, Damascus. Multicoloured.
1727 150 p. Type **609** 30 20
1728 150 p. Canaria 30 20
1729 450 p. Cornflowers .. 70 50
1730 850 p. "Clematis sackmani" .. .. .. 1·25 85
1731 900 p. "Gesneriaceae" .. 1·25 85

1989. Arab Post Day.
1732 **610** 175 p. multicoloured .. 35 25

611 Emblem and Map

612 "Cynthia cardui"

1989. 13th Arab Teachers' Union General Congress.
1733 **611** 175 p. multicoloured .. 35 25

1989. Butterflies. Multicoloured.
1734 550 p. Type **612** .. .. 1·25 85
1735 550 p. "Colias crocea" .. 1·25 85
1736 550 p. "Pieris brassicae" 1·25 85

613 Symbols of International Co-operation

1989. World Telecommunications Day.
1737 **613** 550 p. multicoloured .. 80 55

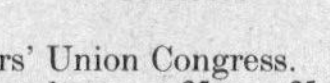

614 Emblem and Map

615 Monument and Al-Baath Pioneers

1989. 17th Arab Lawyers' Union Congress.
1738 **614** 175 p. multicoloured . . 35 25

1989. 15th Anniv of Liberation of Qneitra.
1739 **615** 450 p. multicoloured . . 70 50

616 Globe and Envelopes

1989. World Post Day.
1740 **616** 550 p. multicoloured . . 80 55

617 Parliament Building

1989. Cent of Interparliamentary Union.
1741 **617** 900 p. multicoloured . . 1·25 85

618 Emblem and Monument

619 Jaabar Castle, Raqqa

1989. 36th International Damascus Fair.
1742 **618** 450 p. multicoloured . . 20 15

1989. International Tourism Day. Mult.
1743 550 p. Type **619** 30 20
1744 600 p. Baal-Shamin Temple, Palmyra . . 30 20

620 Child's View of Intifida

621 Carp

1989. Palestinian "Intifida" Movement.
1745 **620** 550 p. multicoloured . . 30 20

1989. Fishes. Multicoloured.
1746 550 p. Type **621** 30 20
1747 600 p. Trout 30 20

622 Omayyad Palace, Pres. Assad and Ebla Hotel

1989. 19th Anniv of Corrective Movement of 16 November 1970.
1748 **622** 150p. multicoloured . . 10 10

623 Children of Different Races taking Food from Large Bowl

624 Dove, Globe and Children of Different Races

1990. World Food Day (1989).
1749 **623** 850 p. multicoloured . . 40 30

1990. International Children's Day.
1750 **624** 850 p. multicoloured . . 40 30

625 Flag, Emblem and Ear of Wheat

626 Tree-lined Road

1990. 5th Revolutionary Youth Union Congress.
1751 **625** 150 p. multicoloured . . 10 10

1990. 27th Anniv of Baathist Revolution of 8 March 1963.
1752 **626** 600 p. multicoloured . . 30 20

627 Flag and Arab Fighters

628 Woman carrying Child

1990. 44th Anniv of Evacuation of Foreign Troops from Syria.
1753 **627** 175 p. multicoloured . . 10 10

1990. Mothers' Day.
1754 **628** 550 p. multicoloured . . 30 20

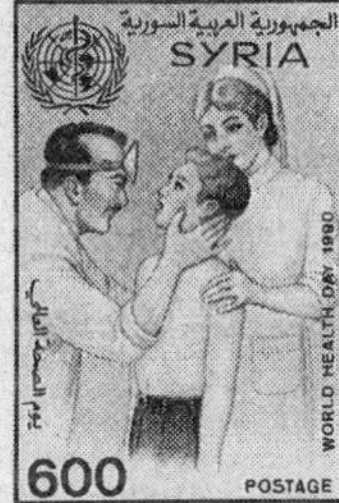

629 Globe and Couple

630 Doctor examining Boy

1990. Labour Day.
1755 **629** 550 p. multicoloured . . 30 20

1990. World Health Day.
1756 **630** 600 p. multicoloured . . 30 20

631 Lilies

633 Flag, Tree and City

632 Goalkeeper saving Goal

1990. International Flower Show, Damascus. Multicoloured.
1757 600 p. Type **631** 30 20
1758 600 p. Cyclamen 30 20
1759 600 p. Marigolds 30 20
1760 600 p. "Viburnum opulus" 30 20
1761 600 p. Swan river daisies 30 20

1990. World Cup Football Championship, Italy. Multicoloured.
1762 550 p. Type **632** 30 20
1763 550 p. Players marking opponent 30 20
1764 600 p. Map of Italy and ball (vert) 30 20

1990. 16th Anniv of Liberation of Qneitra.
1766 **633** 550 p. multicoloured . . 30 20

634 Man and Book

635 Weather Map

1990. International Literacy Year.
1767 **634** 550 p. multicoloured . . 30 20

1990. World Meterology Day.
1768 **635** 450 p. multicoloured . . 20 15

636 Emblem

637 Old and Modern Methods of Ploughing

1990. 37th International Damascus Fair.
1769 **636** 550 p. multicoloured . . 30 20

1990. United Nations Conference on Least Developed Countries.
1770 **637** 600 p. multicoloured . . 30 20

638 Boy watering Young Tree

639 Children with Bread and Water in Wheat Field

1990. Tree Day.
1771 **638** 550 p. multicoloured . . 30 20

1990. World Food Day.
1772 **639** 850 p. multicoloured . . 40 30

640 Al-Maqdisi and Map

641 Pres. Hafez al-Assad

1990. Death Millenary of Al-Maqdisi (geographer).
1773 **640** 550 p. multicoloured . . 30 20

1990.
(a) As T **538** but with full-face portrait.
1774 50 p. lilac 10 10
1775 70 p. grey 10 10
1776 100 p. blue 10 10
1777 150 p. brown 10 10
1778 300 p. mauve 20 15
1779 350 p. grey 20 15
1779a 400 p. red 25 20

(b) Type **641**.
1780 175 p. multicoloured . . 10 10
1781 300 p. multicoloured . . 15 10
1782 550 p. multicoloured . . 30 20
1783 600 p. multicoloured . . 30 20

(c) Horiz design with portrait as T **641** within decorative frame.
1786 1000 p. multicoloured . . 50 35
1787 1500 p. multicoloured . . 75 50
1788 2000 p. multicoloured . . 1·00 70
1789 2500 p. multicoloured . . 1·25 85

643 Control Tower, Airplane and Emblem

1990. Arab Civil Aviation Day.
1796 **643** 175 p. multicoloured . . 10 10

644 Emblem, Open Book, Cogwheel and Ear of Wheat

645 U.P.U. Emblem and Girl posting Letter

1990. 40th Anniv of United Nations Development Programme.
1797 **644** 550 p. multicoloured . . 30 20

1990. World Post Day.
1798 **645** 550 p. multicoloured . . 30 20

646 Leapfrog

647 Emblem, Flames and Open Book

1990. World Children's Day.
1799 **646** 550 p. multicoloured . . 30 20

1990. Arab–Spanish Cultural Symposium.
1800 **647** 550 p. multicoloured . . 30 20

648 Paths to and away from Aids

649 Modern Roads and Buildings

1990. World AIDS Day.
1801 **648** 550 p. multicoloured . . 30 20

1991. 28th Anniv of Baathist Revolution of 8 March 1963.
1802 **649** 150 p. multicoloured . . 10 10

650 Changefull Great Mars

651 Golden Orioles

1991. Butterflies. Multicoloured.
1803 550 p. Type **650** 30 20
1804 550 p. Small tortoiseshell 30 20
1805 550 p. "Machaon sp." .. 30 20

1991. Birds. Multicoloured.
1806 600 p. Type **651** 55 45
1807 600 p. House sparrows .. 55 45
1808 600 p. European roller .. 55 45

652 Three Generations

653 Statue

1991. Mothers' Day.
1809 **652** 550 p. multicoloured .. 30 20

1991. 45th Anniv of Evacuation of Foreign Troops from Syria.
1810 **653** 150 p. multicoloured .. 10 10

654 Dividers and Spanner

655 Daffodils

1991. Labour Day.
1811 **654** 550 p. multicoloured .. 30 20

1991. Int. Flower Show, Damascus. Mult.
1812 550 p. Type **655** 30 20
1813 600 p. Bee balm 30 20

656 City and Ruins

1991. 17th Anniv of Liberation of Qneitra.
1814 **656** 550 p. multicoloured .. 30 20

657 Running

658 Hall

1991. 11th Mediterranean Games, Athens. Multicoloured.
1815 550 p. Type **657** 30 20
1816 550 p. Football 30 20
1817 600 p. Show jumping .. 30 20

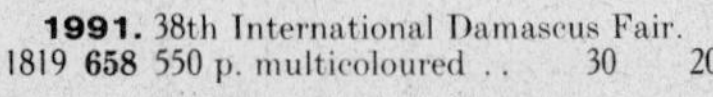

1991. 38th International Damascus Fair.
1819 **658** 550 p. multicoloured .. 30 20

659 Courtyard, Azem Palace, Damascus

660 People encircling Block of Flats

1991. International Tourism Day. Mult.
1820 450 p. Type **659** 25 20
1821 550 p. Castle, Arwad Island 30 20

1991. Housing Day.
1822 **660** 175 p. multicoloured .. 10 10

661 Roller Skating

662 Rhazes treating Patient

1991. International Children's Day.
1823 **661** 600 p. multicoloured .. 30 20

1991. Science Week.
1824 **662** 550 p. multicoloured .. 35 25

663 Envelopes and Globe

1991. World Post Day.
1825 **663** 550 p. multicoloured .. 35 25

664 Globe, Produce and Livestock

1991. World Food Day.
1826 **664** 550 p. multicoloured .. 35 25

665 Tomb of Unknown Soldier, Damascus

1991.
1827 **665** 600 p. multicoloured .. 40 30

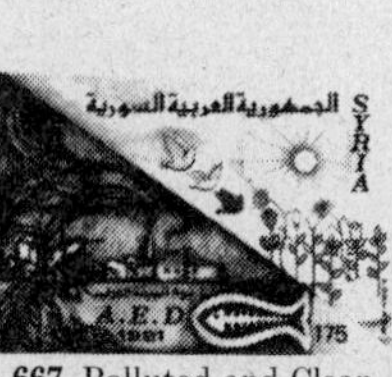

667 Polluted and Clean Environments

668 Transmission Mast, Globe and Satellite

1991. Environmental Protection.
1830 **667** 175 p. multicoloured .. 10 10

1991. International Telecommunications Fair.
1831 **668** 600 p. multicoloured .. 40 30

669 Leaf and Port

1992. 29th Anniv of Baathist Revolution of 8 March.
1832 **669** 600 p. multicoloured .. 40 30

671 Chimneys, Gun-barrel, Ear of Wheat, Dove and Flag

1992. 45th Anniv of Baath Arab Socialist Party.
1834 **671** 850 p. multicoloured .. 55 40

672 Crane and Mason building Wall

673 Girls at Pedestrian Crossing

1992. Labour Day.
1835 **672** 900 p. black, bl & mve 60 40

1992. Road Safety Campaign.
1836 **673** 850 p. multicoloured .. 55 40

674 Girl listening to Mother's Stomach

675 Memorial

1992. Mother's Day.
1837 **674** 900 p. multicoloured .. 60 40

1992. 46th Anniv of Evacuation of Foreign Troops from Syria.
1838 **675** 900 p. multicoloured .. 60 40

676 "Linum mucronatum"

677 Football

1992. International Flower Show, Damascus. Multicoloured.
1839 300 p. Type **676** 20 15
1840 800 p. "Yucca filamentosa" (vert) .. 50 35
1841 900 p. "Zinnia elegans" (vert) 60 40

1992. Olympic Games, Barcelona. Mult.
1842 150 p. Type **677** 10 10
1843 150 p. Running 10 10
1844 450 p. Swimming .. 30 20
1845 750 p. Wrestling .. 50 35

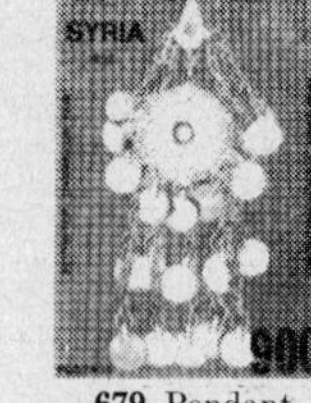

678 Smoker standing in Ashtray

679 Pendant

1992. Anti-smoking Campaign.
1847 **678** 750 p. multicoloured .. 50 35

1992. 39th International Damascus Fair.
1848 **679** 900 p. multicoloured .. 60 40

680 Football

1992. 7th Pan-Arab Games, Damascus. Mult.
1849 750 p. Type **680** 50 35
1850 850 p. Gymnastics .. 55 40
1851 900 p. Pole vaulting .. 60 40

681 Envelopes, Dove and Globe

682 Boy blowing Dandelion Clock

1992. World Post Day.
1852 **681** 600 p. multicoloured .. 40 30

1992. International Children's Day.
1853 **682** 850 p. multicoloured .. 55 40

683 Sebtt el-Mardini

684 Table Tennis

1992.
1854 **683** 850 p. multicoloured .. 55 40

1992. Paralympic Games for Mentally Handicapped, Madrid.
1855 **684** 850 p. multicoloured .. 55 40

685 Fountain

686 Tree

1992. 22nd Anniv of Corrective Movement of 16 November 1970.
1856 **685** 450 p. multicoloured .. 30 20

1992. Tree Day.
1857 **686** 600 p. multicoloured .. 40 30

687 Statue of Pres. Assad, Damascus

1993. 30th Anniv of Baathist Revolution of 8th March 1963.

1858	**687**	1100 p. multicoloured	70	50

688 Common Blue 689 Family

1993. Butterflies. Multicoloured.

1859	1000 p. Type **688** ..	65	45
1860	1500 p. Silver washed fritillary	1·00	70
1861	2500 p. Blue argus ..	1·60	1·10

1993. Mother's Day.

1862	**689**	1100 p. multicoloured	70	50

690 Saladin Monument, Damascus

1993. 47th Anniv of Evacuation of Foreign Troops from Syria.

1863	**690**	1100 p. multicoloured	70	50

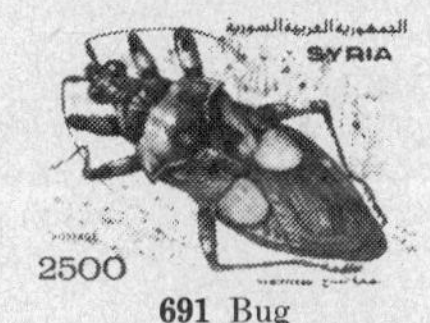

691 Bug

1993.

1864	**691**	2500 p. multicoloured	1·60	1·10

692 Tractor in Field of Crops

1993. 25th Anniv of Arab Agrarian Union.

1865	**692**	1150 p. multicoloured	75	50

693 Oil Workers

1993. Labour Day.

1866	**693**	1100 p. multicoloured	70	50

694 Eye and Eye-chart

1993. 2nd Pan-Arab Ophthalmology International Council Congress.

1867	**694**	1100 p. multicoloured	70	50

695 Landscapes and Eye 696 "Alcea setosa"

1993. 25th Anniv of National Ophthalmological Association.

1868	**695**	1150 p. multicoloured	75	50

1993. 21st International Flower Show, Damascus. Multicoloured.

1869	1000 p. Type **696** ..	65	45
1870	1100 p. Primulas ..	70	50
1871	1150 p. Gesnerias ..	75	50

697 Prism Tomb

1993. International Tourism Day.

1872	**697**	1000 p. multicoloured	65	45

698 Hand posting Letter and Globe

1993. World Post Day.

1873	**698**	1000 p. multicoloured	65	45

699 Boys playing Football 700 Ibn al-Bittar (chemist)

1993. International Children's Day.

1874	**699**	1150 p. multicoloured	70	50

1993. Science Week.

1875	**700**	1150 p. multicoloured	70	50

OBLIGATORY TAX STAMPS

T 57 T 58

T 59 T 60

T 61

1945. Syrian Army Fund. Revenue Stamps surch or optd.

T 419	T **57**	5 p. on 25 p. on 40 p. pink	60·00	2·00
T 420	–	5 p. on 25 p. on 40 p. pink	60·00	5·00
T 421	T **58**	5 p. on 25 p. on 40 p. pink	60·00	1·00
T 422	T **59**	5 p. blue	85·00	60
T 423	T **60**	5 p. blue	60·00	75
T 424	–	5 p. blue	70·00	20
T 425	T **61**	5 p. blue	70·00	70
T 426	–	5 p. blue	60·00	1·25

No. T 420 is as Type T **57** but with additional overprint as top line of Type T **61**.

No. T 424 has top line of overprint as Type T **59** and other lines as Type T **60**.

No. T 426 has top line overprinted as Type T **61** and other lines as Type T **60**.

POSTAGE DUE STAMPS

A. FRENCH MILITARY OCCUPATION

1920. "Mouchon" and "Merson" key-types of French Levant surch. **O.M.F. Syrie Ch taxe** and value.

D 48.	B.	1 p. on 10 c. red ..	90·00	90·00
D 49.		2 p. on 20 c. red ..	90·00	90·00
D 50.		3 p. on 30 c. mauve ..	90·00	90·00
D 51.	C.	4 p. on 40 c. red & blue	90·00	90·00

1920. Postage Due stamps of France surch. **O.M.F. Syrie** and value.

D 60.	D **11.**	50 c. on 10 c. brown ..	30	30
D 52.		1 p. on 10 c. brown ..	70	70
D 61.		1 p. on 20 c. olive ..	30	30
D 53.		2 p. on 20 c. olive ..	70	70
D 62.		2 p. on 30 c. red ..	1·00	1·00
D 54.		3 p. on 30 c. red ..	70	70
D 63.		3 p. on 50 c. purple ..	1·25	1·50
D 55.		4 p. on 50 c. red ..	2·50	3·00
D 64.		5 p. on 1 f. red on yellow	2·50	3·00

1921. Issued at Damascus. No. KD 96 of Arab Kingdom surch **O.M.F.Syrie Chiffre Taxe** and value.

D 69	K **3**	50 c. on 1 p. black ..	1·40	1·40
D 70		1 p. on 1 p. black ..	1·00	1·00

1921. Issued at Damascus. No. 64a/5 of Syria optd **TAXE**.

D 89	K **4**	2 p. on 5 m. red ..	2·25	2·25
D 90	K **3**	3 p. on 1 p. blue ..	5·00	5·00

B. ARAB KINGDOM

1920. As Type K **3** but colour changed.

KD 96	K **3**	1 p. black	1·00	1·00

C. FRENCH MANDATED TERRITORY.

1923. Postage Due stamps of France surch. Syrie Grand Liban in two lines and value.

D 118.	D **11.**	50 c. on 10 c. brown	40	40
D 119.		1 p. on 20 c. olive ..	70	70
D 120.		2 p. on 30 c. red ..	55	55
D 121.		3 p. on 50 c. purple	60	60
D 122.		5 p. on 1 f. red on yellow	1·75	2·00

1924. Postage Due stamps of France surch. SYRIE and value.

D 139.	D **11.**	50 c. on 10 c. brown	30	30
D 140.		1 p. on 20 c. olive ..	35	35
D 141.		2 p. on 30 c. red ..	50	50
D 142.		3 p. on 50 c. purple	50	50
D 143.		5 p. on 1 f. red on yellow	65	65

1924. Postage Due stamps of France surch. Syrie and value and also in Arabic.

D 175.	D **11.**	0 p. 50 on 10 c. brown	25	25
D 176.		1 p. on 20 c. olive ..	30	30
D 177.		2 p. on 30 c. red ..	40	40
D 178.		3 p. on 50 c. purple	40	40
D 179.		5 p. on 1 f. red on yellow	80	80

D **20.** Hama.

DESIGNS—VERT. 1 p. Antioch. HORIZ. 2 p. Tarsus. 3 p. Banias. 5 p. Castle. 8 p. Ornamental design. 15 p. Lion.

1925.

D 192.	D **20.**	0 p. 50 brown on yell.	15	15
D 193.	–	1 p. black on red ..	15	15
D 194.	–	2 p. black on blue ..	20	20
D 195.	–	3 p. black on orange	45	45
D 196.	–	5 p. black on green	60	60
D 197.	–	8 p. black on blue ..	2·00	2·00
D 198.	–	15 p. black on red ..	3·50	3·50

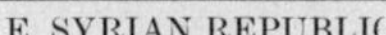

E. SYRIAN REPUBLIC

D **221.**

1965.

D 883.	D **221.**	2½ p. blue ..	25	15
D 884.		5 p. sepia ..	30	15
D 885.		10 p. green ..	35	15
D 886.		17½ p. red ..	75	80
D 887.		25 p. blue ..	1·00	1·10

TAHITI Pt. 6

The largest of the Society Islands in the S. Pacific Ocean. Later renamed Oceanic Settlements.

100 centimes = 1 franc.

1882. Stamps of French Colonies, "Peace and Commerce" type, surch. **25c.**

No.	Type	Description	Unused	Used
1.	H.	25 c. on 35 c. black on orange	£170	£160
3a.		25 c. on 40 c. red on yellow	£2500	£3000

1884. Stamps of French Colonies, "Commerce" (perf) and "Peace and Commerce" (imperf) types, surch **TAHITI** and value.

No.	Type	Description	Unused	Used
4	J	5 c. on 20 c. red on green	£120	£190
5		10 c. on 20 c. red on green	£160	£150
2	H	25 c. on 35 c. black on orge	£3000	£3000
6		25 c. on 1 f. green ..	£375	£300

1893. Stamps of French Colonies, "Commerce" type, optd **TAHITI.**

No.	Type	Description	Unused	Used
7	J	1 c. black on blue ..	£425	£375
8		2 c. brown on buff ..	£2000	£1500
9		4 c. brown on grey ..	£700	£550
10		5 c. green on green ..	20·00	20·00
11		10 c. black on lilac ..	20·00	20·00
12		15 c. blue	20·00	20·00
13		20 c. red on green ..	27·00	27·00
14		25 c. brown	£4250	£4250
15		25 c. black on pink ..	20·00	20·00
16		35 c. black on orange ..	£1400	£1200
17		75 c. red on pink	35·00	35·00
18		1 f. green	38·00	38·00

1893. Stamps of French Colonies, "Commerce" type, optd **1893 TAHITI.**

No.	Type	Description	Unused	Used
32	J	1 c. black on blue ..	£425	£400
33		2 c. brown on buff ..	£2250	£1700
34		4 c. brown on grey ..	£1000	£800
35		5 c. green on green ..	£575	£500
36		10 c. black on lilac ..	£190	£190
37		15 c. blue	20·00	20·00
38		20 c. red on green ..	20·00	20·00
39		25 c. brown	£17000	£15000
40		25 c. black on pink ..	20·00	20·00
41		35 c. black on orange ..	£1400	£1200
42		75 c. red on pink	20·00	20·00
43		1 f. green	20·00	20·00

1903. Stamps of Oceanic Settlements, "Tablet" key-type, surch **TAHITI 10 centimes.**

No.	Type	Description	Unused	Used
57	D	10 c. on 15 c. blue and red	4·00	4·00
58		10 c. on 25 c. black and red on pink	4·00	4·00
59		10 c. on 40 c. red and blue on yellow	4·75	4·75

1915. Stamps of Oceanic Settlements, "Tablet" key-type, optd **TAHITI** and red cross.

No.	Type	Description	Unused	Used
60	D	15 c. blue and red ..	£110	£110
61		15 c. grey and red ..	13·50	13·50

POSTAGE DUE STAMPS

1893. Postage Due stamps of French Colonies optd. **TAHITI.**

No.	Type	Description	Unused	Used
D 19.	U.	1 c. black	£250	£250
D 20.		2 c. black	£250	£250
D 21.		3 c. black	£300	£300
D 22.		4 c. black	£300	£300
D 23.		5 c. black	£300	£300
D 24.		10 c. black	£300	£300
D 25.		15 c. black	£300	£300
D 26.		20 c. black ..	£250	£250
D 27.		30 c. black	£300	£300
D 28.		40 c. black	£300	£300
D 29.		60 c. black	£300	£300
D 30.		1 f. brown	£575	£575
D 31.		2 f. brown	£575	£575

1893. Postage Due stamps of French Colonies optd. **1893 TAHITI.**

No.	Type	Description	Unused	Used
D 44.	U.	1 c. black	£1500	£1500
D 45.		2 c. black	£400	£400
D 46.		3 c. black	£400	£400
D 47.		4 c. black	£400	£400
D 48.		5 c. black	£400	£400
D 49.		10 c. black	£400	£400
D 50.		15 c. black	£400	£400
D 51.		20 c. black	£250	£250
D 52.		30 c. black	£400	£400
D 53.		40 c. black	£400	£400
D 54.		60 c. black	£400	£400
D 55.		1 f. brown	£400	£400
D 56.		2 f. brown	£400	£400

For later issues see **OCEANIC SETTLEMENTS.**

TAJIKISTAN Pt. 10

Formerly a constituent republic of the Soviet Union, Tajikistan became independent in 1991.

100 kopeks = 1 rouble

1 Hunter (gold relief)

2 Sheikh Muslihiddin Mosque

1992.

No.	Type	Description	Unused	Used
1	1	50 k. multicoloured ..	2·90	2·90

1992.

No.	Type	Description	Unused	Used
2	2	50 k. multicoloured ..	2·90	2·90

3 Traditional Musical Instruments

1992.

No.	Type	Description	Unused	Used
3	3	35 k. multicoloured ..	55	55

4 Argali

1992.

No.	Type	Description	Unused	Used
4	4	30 k. multicoloured ..	55	55

3.00

Тоҷикистон

5.00

1992

(5)

1992

Тадж.

(7)

1992. No. 2 surch as T **5.**

No.	Type	Description	Unused	Used
5	2	5 r. on 50 k. multicoloured	1·60	1·60
6		25 r. on 50 k. multicoloured	2·75	2·75

1992. No. 3 surch.

No.	Type	Description	Unused	Used
7	3	15 r. on 35 k. multicoloured	2·75	2·75
8		50 r. on 35 k. multicoloured	2·75	2·75

1993. No. 6072 of Russia surch as T **7.**

No.	Type	Description	Unused	Used
9	2410	3 r. on 1 k. brown ..	4·75	4·75
10		100 r. on 1 k. brown ..	4·75	4·75

60. 00

Тоҷикистон

10.00

(8)

(9)

1993. No. 6073 of Russia surch as T **8.**

No.	Type	Description	Unused	Used
11		10 r. on 2 k. brown ..	70	70
12		15 r. on 2 k. brown ..	70	70

On No. 12 the surcharge is in smaller letters.

1993. No. 1 surch with T **9.**

No.	Type	Description	Unused	Used
13	1	60 r. on 50 k. multicoloured	1·25	1·25

TCHONGKING (CHUNGKING) Pt. 17

An Indo-Chinese Post Office was opened at Chungking, in February 1902 and operated until it closed in December 1922.

1903. 100 centimes = 1 franc.
1919. 100 cents = 1 piastre.

Stamps of Indo-China surch.

1903. "Tablet" key-type surch. **TCHONGKING** and value in Chinese.

No.	Type	Description	Unused	Used
1.	D.	1 c. black on blue ..	80	80
2.		2 c. brown on buff ..	80	80
3.		4 c. brown on grey ..	80	80
4.		5 c. green	80	80
5.		10 c. red	80	80
6.		15 c. grey	90	80
7.		20 c. red on green ..	1·10	1·00
8.		25 c. blue	12·00	12·00
9.		25 c. black on red ..	1·50	1·40
10.		30 c. brown on drab ..	2·00	2·00
11.		40 c. red on yellow ..	12·00	12·00
12.		50 c. red on rose	70·00	65·00
13.		50 c. brown on blue ..	40·00	42·00
14.		75 c. brown on orange ..	12·00	12·00
15.		1 f. olive	13·00	13·00
16.		5 f. mauve on lilac ..	35·00	32·00

1906. Surch. **Tch'ong K'ing** and value in Chinese.

No.	Type	Description	Unused	Used
17	8	1 c. olive	45	45
18		2 c. red on yellow ..	45	45
19		4 c. purple on blue ..	45	45
20		5 c. green	45	45
21		10 c. red	45	45
22		15 c. brown on blue ..	2·25	2·00
23		20 c. red on green ..	60	60
24		25 c. blue	1·00	1·00
25		30 c. brown on cream ..	1·10	1·10
26		35 c. black on yellow ..	1·10	1·10
27		40 c. black on grey ..	1·75	1·90
28		50 c. brown on cream ..	1·50	1·50
29	D	75 c. brown on orange ..	10·00	10·00
30	8	1 f. green	6·00	5·75
31		2 f. brown on yellow ..	7·00	6·50
32	D	5 f. mauve on lilac ..	32·00	32·00
33	8	10 f. red on green ..	40·00	40·00

1908. Native types surch. **TCHONGKING** and value in Chinese.

No.	Type	Description	Unused	Used
34	10	1 c. black and brown ..	10	10
35		2 c. black and brown ..	12	12
36		4 c. black and blue ..	20	20
37		5 c. black and green ..	35	35
38		10 c. black and red ..	45	50
39		15 c. black and violet ..	60	65
40	11	20 c. black and violet ..	60	70
41		25 c. black and blue ..	60	65
42		30 c. black and brown ..	65	75
43		35 c. black and green ..	1·75	1·75
44		40 c. black and brown ..	3·25	3·25
45		50 c. black and red ..	2·25	2·25
46	12	75 c. black and orange ..	2·50	2·50
47	–	1 f. black and red	2·50	2·50
48	–	2 f. black and green ..	28·00	28·00
49	–	5 f. black and blue ..	9·00	9·00
50	–	10 f. black and violet ..	85·00	85·00

1919. As last surch. in addition in figures and words.

No.	Type	Description	Unused	Used
51	10	⅖ c. on 1 c. black & brown	15	15
52		⅘ c on 2 c. black & brown	20	20
53		1⅗ on 4 c. black and blue ..	30	25
54		2 c. on 5 c. black & green	20	15
55		4 c. on 10 c. black and red	15	15
56		6 c. on 15 c. black & violet	15	12
57	11	8 c. on 20 c. blk. and violet	15	12
58		10 c. on 25 c. black & blue	30	25
59		12 c. on 30 c. blk. & brown	35	25
60		14 c. on 35 c. black & green	35	15
61		16 c. on 40 c. black & brn.	45	35
62		20 c. on 50 c. black & red	2·25	2·00
63	12	30 c. on 75 c. black & orge.	45	30
64	–	40 c. on 1 f. black and red	80	45
65	–	80 c. on 2 f. black & green	2·25	2·25
66	–	2 p. on 5 f. black & blue	2·10	2·10
67	–	4 p. on 10 f. black & violet	2·50	2·50

TETE Pt. 9

Formerly using the stamps of Mozambique, this district of Mozambique was permitted to issue its own stamps from 1913 to 1920 when Mozambique stamps were again used.

100 centavos = 1 escudo.

1913. Surch. **REPUBLICA TETE** and new value on "Vasco da Gama" issues of

(a) **Portuguese Colonies.**

No.	Description	Unused	Used
1.	¼ c. on 2½ r. green ..	40	30
2.	½ c. on 5 r. red	40	30
3.	1 c. on 10 r. purple ..	40	30
4.	2½ c. on 25 r. green ..	40	30
5.	5 c. on 50 r. blue ..	40	30
6.	7½ c. on 75 r. brown ..	80	65
7.	10 c. on 100 r. brown ..	45	40
8.	15 c. on 150 r. bistre ..	45	40

(b) **Macao.**

No.	Description	Unused	Used
9.	¼ c. on ½ a. green ..	40	30
10.	½ c. on 1 a. red	40	30
11.	1 c. on 2 a. purple ..	40	30
12.	2½ c. on 4 a. green ..	40	30
13.	5 c. on 8 a. blue ..	40	30
14.	7½ c. on 12 a. brown ..	80	65
15.	10 c. on 16 a. brown ..	45	40
16.	15 c. on 24 a. yellow ..	45	40

(c) **Timor.**

No.	Description	Unused	Used
17.	¼ c. on ½ c. green ..	40	30
18.	½ c. on 1 a. red ..	40	30
19.	1 c. on 2 a purple ..	40	30
20.	2½ c. on 4 a. green ..	40	30
21.	5 c. on 8 a. blue ..	40	30
22.	7½ c. on 12 a. brown ..	80	65
23.	10 c. on 16 a. brown ..	45	40
24.	15 c. on 24 a. bistre ..	45	40

1914. "Ceres" key-type inscr. "TETE".

No.	Type	Description	Unused	Used
25.	U.	¼ c. olive	40	30
26.		½ c. black	40	30
27.		1 c. green	40	30
28.		1½ c. brown	40	30
29.		2 c. red	40	30
30.		2½ c. violet	40	30
31.		5 c. blue	40	30
32.		7½ c. brown	60	60
33.		8 c. grey	60	60
34.		10 c. brown	70	70
35.		15 c. red	90	70
36.		20 c. green	90	70
37.		30 c. brown on green ..	90	70
38.		40 c. brown on red ..	1·10	80
39.		50 c. orange on pink ..	1·10	1·00
40.		1 e. green on blue ..	1·40	1·25

THAILAND Pt. 21

An independent kingdom in S.E. Asia, previously known as Siam.

1883. 32 solot = 16 atts = 8 peinung (sio) = 4 songpy (sik) = 2 fuang = 1 salung. 4 salungs = 1 tical.
1909. 100 satangs = 1 tical.
1912. 100 satangs = 1 baht.

1. King Chulalongkorn. 2.

3. King Chulalongkorn. 9.

1883.

No.	Type	Description	Unused	Used
1.	1.	1 solot blue	2·40	3·00
2.		1 att red	3·25	4·50
3.		1 sio red	10·00	12·00
4.	2.	1 sik yellow	3·25	4·50
5.	3.	1 salung orange	15·00	16·00

1885. Surch. **1 Tical.**

No.	Type	Description	Unused	Used
7.	1.	1 t. on 1 solot blue ..	£120	£120

1887.

No.	Type	Description	Unused	Used
11.	9.	1 a. green	70	50
12.		2 a. green and red ..	90	65
13.		3 a. green and blue ..	3·00	1·75
14.		4 a. green and brown ..	2·50	1·25
15.		8 a. green and yellow ..	2·40	90
16.		12 a. purple and red ..	6·00	65
17.		24 a. purple and blue ..	7·00	1·00
18.		64 a. purple and brown ..	29·00	8·75

อัฐ (11.)

๑ อัฐ 1 (12.)

1889. Surch. with T **11.**

No.	Type	Description	Unused	Used
19.	1.	1 a. on 1 sio red ..	3·00	5·25

1889. Surch. as T **12.**

No.	Type	Description	Unused	Used
20.	9.	1 a. on 2 a. green and red	1·00	1·00
24.		1 a. on 3 a. green and blue	1·60	2·00
29.		2 a. on 3 a. green and blue	10·50	8·75

1 Att.

ราคา ๔ อัฐ (23.)

ราคา ๑ อัฐ (42.)

1892. Surch. with T **23.**

No.	Type	Description	Unused	Used
31.	9.	4 a. on 24 a. purple & blue	8·25	10·50

1892. Surch. as T **42.**

No.	Type	Description	Unused	Used
53.	9.	1 a. on 12 a. purple & red	2·50	3·00
45.		1 a. on 64 a. pur. & brown	40	40
48.		2 a. on 64 a. pur. & brown	50	60
58.		3 a. on 12 a. purple & red	1·40	1·25
60.		4 a. on 12 a. purple & red	2·40	45
33.		4 a. on 24 a. purple & blue	2·50	2·40
50.		10 a. on 24 a. purple & blue	1·25	65

49.

50.

53. Wat Cheng, "Temple of Light".

1899.

83. **49.** 1 a. green 30 15
68. 2 a. green 50 12
84. 2 a. red and blue 85 25
69. 3 a. red and blue .. .. 1·75 95
85. 3 a. green .. .. .. 5·25 4·75
70. 4 a. red 75 20
86. 4 a. brown and pink .. 2·40 95
87. 6 a. red .. .. .. 6·00 5·25
71. 8 a. green and orange .. 1·50 50
72. 10 a. blue .. .. .. 2·40 60
73. 12 a. purple and red .. 9·00 95
88. 14 a. blue .. .. .. 6·00 6·00
74. 24 a. purple and blue .. 42·00 5·75
89. 28 a. brown and blue .. 7·00 7·50
75. 64 a. purple and brown .. 16·00 2·40

1899.

76. **50.** 1 a. green .. .. 60·00 38·00
77. 2 a. green and red .. 75·00 45·00
78. 3 a. red and blue .. £150 £100
79. 4 a. black and green .. £225 £150
80. 10 a. red and green .. £350 £225

1905. Surch. in English and Siamese.

90. **49.** 1 a. on 14 a. blue .. 2·75 2·75
91. 2 a. on 28 a. brown & blue 3·00 3·00

1905.

92. **53.** 1 a. green and yellow 35 15
93. 2 a. grey and violet .. 50 15
105. 2 a. green .. .. 1·90 1·90
94. 3 a. green 50 35
106. 3 a. grey and violet .. 3·00 2·25
95. 4 a. red and sepia .. 1·60 45
107. 4 a. red .. .. 1·60 45
96. 5 a. red .. .. 1·75 1·25
97. 8 a. olive and black .. 1·60 45
108. 9 a. blue .. .. 5·25 3·50
98. 12 a. blue .. .. 4·00 1·40
109. 18 a. brown .. .. 14·50 7·25
99. 24 a. brown .. .. 7·00 2·40
100. 1 t. yellow and blue .. 12·00 70

1907. Tall Fiscal stamp with portrait and scales surch. **Siam postage** and new value.

101 10 t. green .. .. £150 50·00
102a 20 t. green £325 £130
103 40 t. green £600 £250

1907. Surch. **1 att** and thin line.

104. **9.** 1 a. on 24 s. pur. & blue 50 35

1908. Surch. in English and Siamese.

110. **9.** 2 a. on 24 a. pur. & blue 50 35
111. **53.** 4 on 5 a. red .. 3·00 1·75
112. **49.** 9 a. on 10 a. blue .. 3·50 1·75

1908. 40th Anniv. of Reign of King Chulalongkorn. Optd. **Jubilee 1868-1908** in English and Siamese.

113. **53.** 1 a. green and yellow .. 95 50
114. 3 a. green .. .. 1·40 85
115. 4 on 5 a. (No. 111) .. 2·75 1·40
116. 8 a. olive and black .. 7·25 8·25
117. 18 a. brown .. .. 10·50 8·00

61. Statue of King Chulalongkorn, Bangkok.

64. King Chulalongkorn.

1908.

118. **61.** 1 t. violet and green .. 7·00 1·25
119. 2 t. orange and purple 16·00 4·50
120. 3 t. blue and olive .. 19·00 6·00
121. 5 t. green and lilac .. 29·00 8·75
122. 10 t. red and olive .. £170 29·00
123. 20 t. brown and grey .. 60·00 27·00
124. 40 t. black and blue .. £100 60·00

1909. Surch. in satangs in English and Siamese.

125 **53** 2 s. on 1 a. green & yell. 35 15
126 2 s. on 2 a. green .. 35 20
164 2 s. on 2 a. grey & violet 85 65
129 3 s. on 3 a. green .. 35 15
130 3 s. on 3 a. grey & violet 35 20
131 6 s. on 4 a. red 35 25
133 6 s. on 4 a. red and sepia 18·00 23·00
134 6 s. on 5 a. red .. 50 35
138 **49** 6 s. on 6 a. red .. 1·00 90
135 **53** 12 s. on 8 a. olive & blk 1·25 40
136 14 s. on 9 a. blue .. 1·50 60
137 14 s. on 12 a. blue .. 9·00 9·00
139 **9** 14 s. on 12 a. pur. & red 29·00 35·00
140 **49** 14 s. on 14 a. blue .. 6·00 6·00

1910.

141. **64.** 2 s. green and orange .. 35 10
142. 3 s. green 35 12
143. 6 s. red 75 15
144. 12 s. brown and black .. 1·50 40
145. 14 s. blue .. .. 4·50 65
146. 28 s. brown .. .. 10·50 2·40

65. King Vijiravudh. **66.**

1912.

147. **65.** 2 s. brown 15 10
167. 3 s. green 50 15
168. 5 s. red 50 20
149. 6 s. red 50 12
169. 10 s. brown and black .. 65 20
150. 12 s. sepia and black .. 50 15
151. 14 s. blue .. .. 1·25 15
170. 15 s. blue 35 25
152. 28 s. brown .. .. 2·10 1·25
153. **66.** 1 b. sepia and blue .. 4·00 35
154. 2 b. sepia and red .. 5·00 65
155. 3 b. black and green .. 5·25 65
156. 5 b. black and violet .. 6·50 65
157. 10 b. purple and olive .. 27·00 11·00
176. 20 b. brown and green .. 45·00 9·50

1914. Surch. in English and Siamese.

165. **64.** 2 s. on 14 s. blue .. 50 35
159. **65.** 2 s. on 14 s. blue .. 35 15
160. 5 s. on 6 s. red 30 15
161. 10 s. on 12 s. sep. & blk. 65 15
162. 15 s. on 28 s. brown .. 60 15

1918. Optd. with small cross in circle.

177. **65.** 2 s. brown 30 30
178. 3 s. green 30 30
179. 5 s. red 65 75
180. 10 s. brown and black 90 1·25
181. 15 s. blue .. .. 85 1·25
182. **66.** 1 b. sepia and blue .. 4·50 6·00
183. 2 b. brown and red .. 7·25 8·75
184. 3 b. black and green .. 12·00 14·50
185. 5 b. black and violet .. 38·00 29·00
186. 10 b. purple and olive .. 90·00 75·00
187. 20 b. brown and green .. £300 £275

1918. Optd. **VICTORY** in English and Siamese.

188. **65.** 2 s. brown 50 15
189. 3 s. green 50 20
190. 5 s. red 20 30
191. 10 s brown and black .. 85 75
192. 15 s. blue 90 75
193. **66.** 1 b. sepia and blue .. 5·25 5·00
194. 2 b. brown and red .. 8·75 8·75
195. 3 b. black and green .. 10·50 10·50
196. 5 b. black and violet .. 29·00 29·00

1919. Surch. in English and Siamese figures.

197. **65.** 5 s. on 6 s. red 35 15
198. 10 s. on 12 s. sepia & blk. 65 15

(72a.) (72b.)

1920. Scouts' Fund. Various stamps handstamped.

(a) With Type **72a.**

199. **65.** 2 s. (+3 s.) brown .. 9·00 9·00
200. 3 s. (+2 s.) green .. 9·00 9·00
201. 5 s. on 6 s. (+20 s.) red (No. 160) .. .. 8·00 8·00
202. 10 s. on 12 s. (+5 s.) brn and black (No. 161) .. 9·00 9·00
203. 15 s. (+5 s.) blue .. 9·50 9·50
204. **53.** 1 t. (+25 s.) yell. & bl. 45·00 45·00

(b) With Type **72b.**

205. **65.** 2 s. (+3 s.) brown .. 9·00 9·00
206. 3 s. (+2 s.) green .. 9·00 9·00
207. **73.** 5 s. (+20 s.) red on pink 10·50 10·50
208. **65.** 10 s. on 12 s. (+5 s.) brn. & blk. (No. 161) 10·50 10·50
209. 15 s. (+5 s.) blue .. 21·00 21·00
210. **53.** 1 t. (+25 s.) yell. & bl. 45·00 45·00

These stamps were sold in aid of the "Wild Tiger" Scouts organisation at the premium stated.

73. (73a.)

1920.

211. **73.** 2 s. brown on yellow .. 35 12
212. 3 s. green on green .. 35 12
213. 3 s. brown 35 12
214. 5 s. red on pink .. 50 12
215. 5 s. green .. .. 1·60 40
216. 5 s. violet on mauve .. 75 12
217. 10 s. brown and black 60 12
218. 15 s. blue on blue .. 85 15
219. 15 s. red .. .. 3·25 50
220. 25 s. brown .. .. 3·00 25
221. 25 s. blue .. .. 1·25 20
222. 50 s. black and brown 3·25 40

1920. Scouts' Fund. Optd. with Type **73a.**

223. **73.** 2 s. brown on yellow .. 8·25 8·25
224. 3 s. green on green .. 8·25 8·25
225. 5 s. red on pink .. 8·25 8·25
226. 10 s. brown and black 8·25 8·25
227. 15 s. blue on blue .. 13·50 13·50
228. 25 s. brown .. .. 32·00 32·00
229. 50 s. black and brown 65·00 65·00

74. "Garuda" Bird. **75.** Coronation Stone.

1925. Air.

230. **74.** 2 s. purple on yellow .. 35 10
231. 3 s. brown 50 15
239. 5 s. green 25 10
240. 10 s. orange and black 1·00 10
241. 15 s. red .. .. 1·90 10
242. 25 s. blue 50 15
243. 50 s. black and brown .. 1·25 15
237. 1 b. sepia and blue .. 4·50 2·00

1926.

244. **75.** 1 t. green and lilac .. 2·25 40
245. 2 t. red .. .. .. 6·50 1·40
246. 3 t. blue and olive .. 13·00 7·75
247. 5 t. olive and violet .. 9·00 3·00
248. 10 t. brown and red .. 70·00 5·25
249. 20 t. brown and blue .. 65·00 18·00

1928. Surch. in English and Siamese.

250. **73.** 5 s. on 15 s. red .. 1·50 50
251. **65.** 10 s. on 28 s. brown .. 1·50 40

76. King Prajadhipok. **77.**

1928.

252. **76.** 2 s. brown 15 5
253. 3 s. green 15 8
254. 5 s. violet 15 8
255. 10 s. red 20 8
256. 15 s. blue 20 10
257. 25 s. orange and black .. 20 15
258. 50 s. black and orange .. 35 25
259. 80 s. black and blue .. 35 25
260. **77.** 1 b. black and blue .. 65 30
261. 2 b. brown and red .. 1·40 40
262. 3 b. black and green .. 2·25 65
263. 5 b. brown and violet .. 6·00 1·00
264. 10 b. purple and olive .. 8·25 1·00
265. 20 b. brown and green .. 13·00 2·40
266. 40 b. sepia and green .. 30·00 12·50

1930. Surch. in English and Siamese.

267. **64.** 10 s. on 12 s. brn. & blk. 25 25
268. 25 s. on 28 s. brown .. 45 35

79. Kings Prajadhipok and Chao Phya Chakri.

81. Chao Phya Chakri.

80. Kings Prajadhipok and Chao Phya Chakri.

1932. 150th Anniv. of Chakri Dynasty and of Bangkok as Capital and Opening of Memorial Bridge over Menam.

269. **79.** 2 s. red 35 10
270. 3 s. green 50 15
271. 5 s. violet 35 12
272. **80.** 10 s. black and red .. 65 15
273. 15 s. black and blue .. 1·50 35
274. 25 s. black and mauve .. 1·90 50
275. 50 s. black and red .. 3·50 90
276. **81.** 1 b. blue .. .. 10·50 2·25

(82.)

1939. Red Cross Fund. Membership of the International Red Cross. 75th Anniv. Surch. as T **82.**

277. **66.** 5+5 s. on 1 b. (193) .. 7·00 7·75
278. 10+5 s. on 2 b. (194) .. 9·00 10·50
279. 15+5 s. on 3 b. (195) .. 9·00 10·50

83. National Assembly Hall.

84. Chakri Palace and "Garuda" Bird.

1939. 7th Anniv. of Constitution and National Day (1st issue).

280. **83.** 2 s. lilac 50 15
281. 3 s. green 90 50
282. 5 s. mauve 90 12
283. 10 s. red .. .. 1·50 12
284. 15 s. blue .. .. 3·00 40

1940. National Day (2nd issue).

285. **84.** 2 s. lilac 50 25
286. 3 s. green 65 50
287. 5 s. mauve 90 10
288. 10 s. red .. .. 1·60 15
289. 15 s. blue .. .. 2·25 35

85. King Ananda Mahidol.

87. Ban Pa'im Palace, Ayuthia.

86. Ploughing Rice Field.

88. Monument of Democracy.

1941.

290. **85.** 2 s. brown 15 10
291. 3 s. green 15 12
292. 5 s. violet 15 10
293. 10 s. red 35 10
294. **86.** 15 s. grey and blue .. 25 12
295. 25 s. orange and slate .. 45 12
296. 50 s. grey and orange .. 50 12
297. **87.** 1 b. grey and blue .. 1·25 50
298. 2 b. grey and red .. 2·40 75
299. 3 b. grey and green .. 3·00 1·75
300. 5 b. red and black .. 7·75 4·50
301. 10 b. yellow and black 12·00 5·25

1942. Air.

302. **88.** 2 s. brown 50 30
303. 3 s. green .. .. 3·00 2·25
304. 5 s. purple 50 20
305. 10 s. red 30 25
306. 15 s. blue 50 25

89. King Ananda Mahidol.

91. Bangkaen Monument and Ears of Rice.

90. Indo-China War Monument, Bangkok.

1943.

307. **89.** 1 b. blue .. .. 2·00 50

1943.

311. **91.** 2 s. orange 35 20
309. **90.** 3 s. green 85 45
312. **91.** 10 s. red 65 20

92. King Bhumibol. **93.**

1947.

313. **92.** 5 s. violet 10 8
314. 10 s. red 12 8
315. 20 s. brown 10 8
316. 50 s. green 40 8
317. 1 b. blue and violet .. 1·90 10
318. 2 b. green and blue .. 3·25 30
319. 3 b. black and red .. 5·00 65
320. 5 b. red and green .. 10·00 1·50
321. 10 b. violet and sepia 16·00 75
322. 20 b. lilac and black .. 29·00 1·50

The baht values are larger, size $21\frac{1}{2} \times 27$ mm.

1947. Coming of Age of King Bhumibol.
323. **93.** 5 s. orange .. .. 1·60 35
324. 10 s. brown .. .. 1·50 55
325. 10 s. green 75 35
326. 20 s. blue 85 35
327. 50 s. green .. .. 2·25 1·40

94. King and Palace. **95.** King Bhumibol.

1950. King's Coronation.
328. **94.** 5 s. purple 10 8
329. 10 s. red 10 8
330. 15 s. violet 15 15
331. 20 s. brown 40 8
332. 80 s. green 85 65
333. 1 b. blue 65 10
334. 2 b. yellow .. .. 1·75 75
335. 3 b. grey .. .. 5·00 3·00

1951.
336. **95.** 5 s. purple 10 8
337. 10 s. green 10 8
338. 15 s. brown 12 10
339. 20 s. brown 12 8
340. 25 s. red 10 5
341. 50 s. olive 40 5
342. 1 b. blue 75 12
343. 1 b. 15 blue .. .. 1·60 10
344. 1 b. 25 lake .. .. 1·40 10
345. 2 b. green .. .. 1·40 10
346. 3 b. grey .. .. 2·50 12
347. 5 b. red and blue .. 4·50 12
348. 10 b. violet and sepia .. 16·00 25
349. 20 b. olive and black .. 29·00 3·25

96. U.N. Emblem. **97.** "Garuda" Bird.

1951. United Nations Day.
350. **96.** 25 s. blue 75 75

1952. Air.
351. **97.** 1 b. 50 purple .. 50 10
352. 2 b. blue 85 20
353. 3 b. grey 85 35

1952. United Nations Day. Optd. **1952.**
354. **96.** 25 s. blue 75 60

1952. 20th Anniv. of Constitution. Surch. with emblem and value.
355. **76.** 80 s.+20 s. black & blue 3·75 3·00

99. Dancer over Cross. **103.** Processional Elephant.

1953. 60th Anniv. of Thai Red Cross Society. Cross in red, figures in blue and red.
356. **99.** 25 s.+25 s. cream & grn. 1·00 1·00
357. 50 s.+50 s. cream & red 1·90 1·75
358. 1 b.+1 b. cream & blue 2·50 2·40

1953. United Nations Day. Optd. **1953.**
359. **96.** 25 s. blue 35 35

1954. United Nations Day. Optd. **1954** vert.
360. **96.** 25 s. blue 35 65

1955. Optd. **THAILAND** in English and Siamese.
361. **76.** 5 s. violet 75 55
362. 10 s. red 75 90

1955. Surch.
363. **92.** 5 s. on 20 s. brown .. 40 12
364. 10 s. on 20 s. brown 30 12

1955. 400th Birth Anniv. of King Naresuan.
365. **103.** 25 s. red 55 10
366. 80 s. purple .. .. 3·25 1·00
367. 1 b. 25 green .. .. 2·40 15
368. 2 b. blue .. .. 2·00 50
369. 3 b. lake .. .. 3·75 40

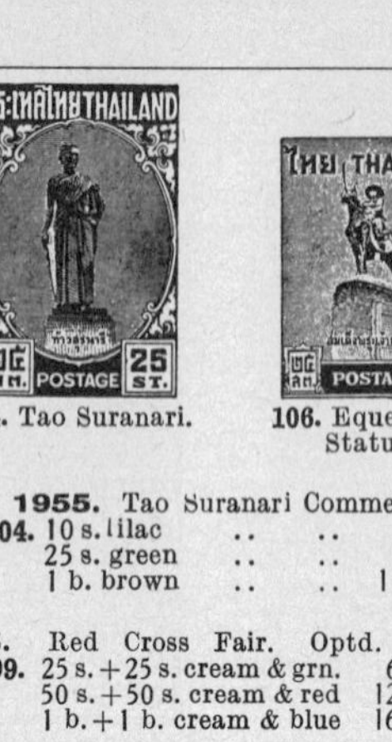

104. Tao Suranari. **106.** Equestrian Statue.

1955. Tao Suranari Commem.
370. **104.** 10 s. lilac 12 5
371. 25 s. green 30 8
372. 1 b. brown .. .. 1·75 35

1955. Red Cross Fair. Optd. **24 98.**
373. **99.** 25 s.+25 s. cream & grn. 6·25 3·00
374. 50 s.+50 s. cream & red 12·50 6·00
375. 1 b.+1 b. cream & blue 16·00 8·25

1955. King Taksin Commem.
376. **106.** 5 s. blue 10 5
377. 25 s. green 25 5
378. 1 b. 25 red .. .. 1·90 45

1955. U.N. Day. Optd. **1955** vert.
379. **96.** 25 s. blue 85 65

107. Don Chedi Pagoda. **108.** Dharmachakra and Sambar.

1956.
380. **107.** 10 s. green 15 12
381. 50 s. brown .. .. 1·40 25
382. 75 s. violet 50 40
383. 1 b. 50 brown 90 20

1956. U.N. Day. Optd. **1956** vert.
384. **96.** 25 s. blue 15 10

1957. 2500th Anniv. of Buddhist Era.
385. **108.** 5 s. sepia 10 10
386. 10 s. red 15 10
387. 15 s. green 20 20
388. – 20 s. orange 35 35
389. – 25 s. brown 12 5
390. – 50 s. mauve 35 10
391. – 1 b. bistre 45 15
392. – 1 b. 25 blue .. .. 1·90 55
393. – 2 b. purple .. .. 1·25 15
DESIGNS: 20 s. to 50 s. Hand of Peace and Dharmachakra. 1 b. to 2 b. Nakon Phatom pagoda.

110. U.N. Emblem and Laurel Sprays. **111.** Gateway to Grand Palace.

1957. United Nations Day.
394. **110.** 25 s. olive 20 10
395. 25 s. brown (1958) .. 15 10
400. 25 s. blue (1959) .. 15 10

1959. First South East Asia Peninsula Games (S.E.A.P.).
396. **111.** 10 s. orange 12 8
397. – 25 s. lake 10 8
398. – 1 b. 25 green 25 25
399. – 2 b. blue 45 15
DESIGNS: 25 s. Royal parasols. 1 b. 25, Bowman. 2 b. Wat Arun (temple) and prow of royal barge.

112. Pagoda. **113.** Wat Arun Temple. **114.** Indian Elephant.

1960. World Refugee Year.
401. **112.** 50 s. brown 15 12
402. 2 b. green 35 15

1960. Leprosy Relief Campaign.
403. **113.** 50 s. red 15 8
404. 2 b. blue 65 15

1960. 5th World Forestry Congress, Seattle.
405. **114.** 25 s. green 30 10

115. S.E.A.T.O. Emblem. **116.** Siamese Child.

1960. S.E.A.T.O. Day.
406. **115.** 50 s. brown 15 8

1960. Children's Day.
407. **116.** 50 s. mauve 15 8
408. 1 b. brown 25 15

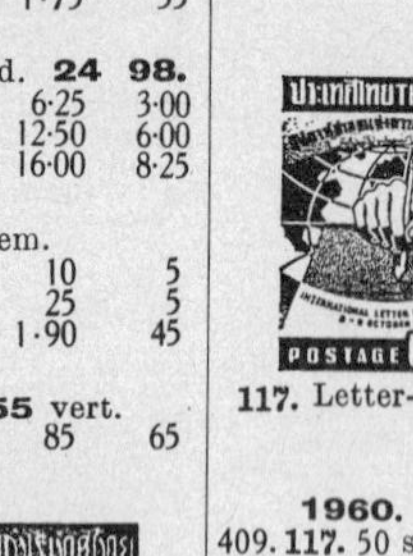

117. Letter-writing. **118.** U.N. Emblem and Globe.

1960. Int. Correspondence Week.
409. **117.** 50 s. mauve 15 8
410. 2 b. blue 60 15

1960. U.N. Day.
411. **118.** 50 s. violet 15 10
446. 50 s. lake (1961) .. 20 8
467. 50 s. red (1962) .. 15 8

119. King Bhumibol. **120.** Children in Garden.

1961.
422. **119.** 5 s. purple 12 5
423. 10 s. turquoise 8 5
424. 15 s. brown 8 5
425. 20 s. brown 10 5
426. 25 s. red 10 5
427. 50 s. olive 12 5
428. 80 s. orange 12 12
429. 1 b. brown and blue .. 15 8
430. 1 b. 25 olive and red .. 20 10
431. 1 b. 50 green and violet 20 8
432. 2 b. violet and red .. 40 12
433. 3 b. blue and brown .. 40 15
434. 4 b. black and bistre .. 60 50
435. 5 b. green and blue .. 1·50 10
436. 10 b. black and red .. 7·25 12
437. 20 b. blue and green .. 5·50 55
438. 25 b. blue and green .. 3·75 1·20
439. 40 b. black and yellow .. 6·25 1·90

1961. Children's Day.
440. **120.** 20 s. blue 12 8
441. 2 b. violet 40 20

121. Pen, Letters and Globe. **122.** Thai Scout Badge and Saluting Hand.

1961. Int. Correspondence Week.
442. – 25 s. myrtle 8 8
443. – 50 s. purple 10 10
444. **121.** 1 b. red 40 12
445. 2 b. blue 60 15
DESIGN: 25 s., 50 s. Pen, and world map on envelope.

1961. 50th Anniv. of Thai Scout Movement.
447. **122.** 50 s. mauve 10 10
448. – 1 b. green 15 12
449. – 2 b. blue 60 15
DESIGNS—VERT. 1 b. Scout camp and scout saluting flag. 2 b. King Vajiravudh in uniform, and scout, cub and guide marching.

123. Campaign Emblem and Temple. **124.** Bangkok.

1962. Malaria Eradication.
450. **123.** 5 s. brown 8 5
451. 10 s. brown 8 5
452. 20 s. blue 8 8
453. 50 s. red 12 5
454. – 1 b. green 15 8
455. – 1 b. 50 purple 35 15
456. – 2 b. blue 35 15
457. – 3 b. violet 75 25
DESIGN: 1 b. to 3 b. Thai fighting mosquitoes.

1962. "Century 21" Exhibition, Seattle.
458. **124.** 50 s. purple 15 10
459. 2 b. blue 40 15

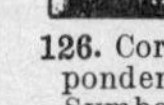

125. Thai Child with Doll. **126.** Correspondence Symbols. **127.** Exhibition Emblem.

1962. Children's Day.
460. **125.** 25 s. turquoise 10 5
461. 50 s. buff 15 10
462. 2 b. mauve 60 20

1962. Int. Correspondence Week.
463. **126.** 25 s. violet 8 5
464. 50 s. red 15 5
465. – 1 b. yellow 40 12
466. – 2 b. green 45 20
DESIGN: 1 b., 2 b. Quill pen.

1962. Students' Exn., Bangkok.
468. **127.** 50 s. bistre 15 8

128. Harvesting. **129.** "Temple Guardian".

1963. Freedom from Hunger.
469. **128.** 20 s. green 12 10
470. 50 s. brown 20 10

1963. 1st Anniv. of Asian-Oceanic Postal Union.
471. **129.** 50 s. green and brown .. 12 8

130. Centenary Emblem. **131.** G.P.O., Bangkok and (inset) old P.O.

1963. Red Cross Cent.
472. **130.** 50 s.+10 s. red & grey 20 12
473. – 50 s.+10 s. red & grey 20 12
DESIGNS: No. 473 As Type **130.** but with positions of emblem and inscr. reversed.

1963. 80th Anniv. of Post and Telegraph Department.
474. **131.** 50 s. green, orange and violet 15 8
475. 3 b. sepia, green and red 75 45

132. King Bhumibol. **133.** Children with Dolls.

1963.
476. **132.** 5 s. mauve 8 5
477. 10 s. green 8 5
478. 15 s. brown 8 5
479. 20 s. brown 8 5
480. 25 s. red 8 5
481. 50 s. drab 8 5
482. 75 s. lilac 15 5
483. 80 s. orange 10 8
484. 1 b. brown and blue .. 15 5
485. 1 b. 25 bistre and brown 20 8
486. 1 b. 50 green and violet 10 5
487. 2 b. violet and red .. 15 10
488. 3 b. blue and brown .. 30 10
489. 4 b. black and bistre .. 75 12
490. 5 b. green and blue .. 1·10 10
491. 10 b. black and red .. 2·10 12
492. 20 b. blue and green .. 11·50 50
493. 25 b. blue and bronze .. 4·50 75
494. 40 b. black and yellow .. 8·25 1·75

1963. Children's Day.
505. 133. 50 s. red 15 8
506. 2 b. blue 85 12

134. "Garuda" bird with Scroll in Beak.

1963. Int. Correspondence Week.
507. 134. 50 s. purple & turquoise 15 10
508. 1 b. purple and green .. 65 12
509. – 2 b. blue and bistre .. 1·25 45
510. – 3 b. green and brown .. 2·25 60
DESIGN: 2 b., 3 b. Thai women writing letters.

135. U.N. Emblem. 137. Mother and Child.

136. King Bhumibol.

1963. U.N. Day.
511. 135. 50 s. blue 15 5

1963. King Bhumibol's 36th Birthday.
512. 136. 1 b. 50 indigo, yell. & bl. 35 12
513. 5 b. blue, yell. & mauve 1·00 45

1964. 17th Anniv. of U.N.I.C.E.F.
514. 137. 50 s. blue 8 5
515. 2 b. olive 65 20

138. "Hand" of Flags, Pigeon and Globe.

1964. Int. Correspondence Week.
516. 138. 50 s. mauve and green .. 10 5
517. – 1 b. brown and green .. 25 10
518. – 2 b. violet and yellow .. 75 12
519. – 3 b. olive and blue .. 1·00 65
DESIGNS: 1 b. Thai girls and map. 2 b. Map, pen and pencil. 3 b. Hand with quill pen, and globe.

139. Globe and U.N. Emblem. 140. King Bhumibol and Queen Sirikit.

1964. United Nations Day.
520. 139. 50 s. grey 25 5

1965. 15th Royal Wedding Anniv.
521. 140. 2 b. multicoloured .. 65 10
522. 5 b. multicoloured .. 1·40 45

141. I.T.U. Emblem and Symbols.

1965. I.T.U. Cent.
523. 141. 1 b. green 50 12

INDEX
Countries can be quickly located by referring to the index at the end of this volume.

142. Goddess, Letters and Globes.

1965. Int. Correspondence Week. Mult.
524. 50 s. Type **142** 12 5
525. 1 b. Type **142** 20 8
526. 2 b. Handclasp, letters and world map .. .. 1·25 15
527. 3 b. As 2 b. .. .. 1·75 50

143. Grand Palace, Bangkok. 145. U.P.U. Monument Berne and map of Thailand.

1965. Int. Co-operation Year.
528. 143. 50 s. slate, yellow & blue 35 10

1965. 80th Anniv. of Thailand's Admission to the U.P.U.
529. 145. 20 s. blue and mauve .. 8 5
530. 50 s. black & turquoise 15 5
531. 1 b. orange and blue .. 50 10
532. 3 b. green and ochre .. 1·25 65

146. Child and Lotus.

1965. Children's Day.
533. 146. 50 s. brown and black .. 25 8
534. – 1 b. green and black .. 25 12
DESIGN: 1 b. Child mounting stairs.

147. Cycling.

1966. Publicity for 5th Asian Games, Bangkok.
535. 20 s. lake (Type **147**) .. 10 8
536. 25 s. violet (Tennis) .. 10 8
537. 50 s. red (Running) .. 12 5
538. 1 b. blue (Weightlifting) .. 50 10
539. 1 b. 25 black (Boxing) .. 50 25
540. 2 b. blue (Swimming) .. 1·10 12
541. 3 b. brown (Basketball) .. 1·75 65
542. 5 b. purple (Football) .. 3·25 2·10
See also Nos. 553/6.

148. Emblem and Fair Buildings. 149. "Reading and Writing".

1966. 1st. Int. Trade Fair, Bangkok.
543. 148. 50 s. purple 15 5
544. 1 b. brown 30 12

1966. Int. Correspondence Week.
545. – 50 s. red 10 5
546. – 1 b. brown 25 10
547. 149. 2 b. violet 65 5
548. 3 b. turquoise 95 55
DESIGN: 50 s., 1 b. "Map" envelope representing the five continents and pen.

150. U.N. Emblem.

152. Pra Buddha Bata (monastery).

151. "Goddess of Rice".

1966. United Nations Day.
549. 150. 50 s. blue 20 8

1966. Int. Rice Year.
550. 151. 50 s. blue and green .. 35 10
551. 3 b. red and purple .. 1·40 55

1966. 20th Anniv. of U.N.E.S.C.O.
552. 152. 50 s. olive and black .. 15 5

153. Thai Boxing. 154. "Channa triatus".

1966. 5th Asian Games Bangkok. Each black, red and brown.
553. 50 s. Type **153** 15 8
554. 1 b. Takraw (ball game) .. 95 75
555. 2 b. "Kite fighting" .. 2·10 1·00
556. 3 b. "Cudgel play" .. 3·25 2·25

1967. Fishes. Multicoloured.
557. 1 b. Type **154** 35 10
558. 2 b. "Rastrelliger brachysomus" .. .. 1·25 25
559. 3 b. "Puntius gonionotus" 1·75 30
560. 5 b. "Betta splendens" .. 3·00 45
DESIGNS—HORIZ. 2 b., 3 b., 45×26 mm.

155. Djarmachakra and Globe. 156. Great Indian Hornbill.

1967. Establishment of Buddhist World Fellowship Headquarters in Thailand.
561. 155. 2 b. black and yellow .. 50 12

1967. Birds. Multicoloured.
562. 20 s. Type **156** 30 10
563. 25 s. Hill myna 30 10
564. 50 s. White-rumped shama 35 10
565. 1 b. Siamese fireback pheasant .. .. 1·50 20
566. 1 b. 50 Spotted dove .. 1·25 35
567. 2 b. Sarus crane .. .. 5·75 50
568. 3 b. White-breasted kingfisher .. .. .. 4·25 1·90
569. 5 b. Asian open-bill stork 15·00 4·50

157. "Vandopsis parishii". 158. Thai House.

1967. Thai Orchids. Multicoloured.
570 20 s. Type **157** 10 8
571 50 s. "Ascocentrum curvifolium" 12 8
572 80 s. "Rhynchostylis retusa" 40 10
573 1 b. "Rhynchostylis gigantea" 25 12
574 1 b. 50 "Dendrobium alconeri" 60 8
575 2 b. "Paphiopedilum callosum" .. .. 1·90 10
576 3 b. "Dendrobium formosum" .. .. 1·40 15
577 5 b. "Dendrobium primulinum" .. .. 2·40 20

1967. Thai Architecture.
578. 158. 50 s. violet and blue .. 15 8
579. – 1 b. 50 chestnut & brown 50 15
580. – 2 b. blue and turquoise 1·00 25
581. – 3 b. sepia and yellow .. 1·90 95
BUILDINGS: 1 b. 50, Pagodas. 2 b. Temple bell-tower. 3 b. Temple.

159. Royal Barge "Sri Suphanahong" and Palace. 161. U.N. Emblem.

160. Dove, Globe, People and Letters.

1967. Int. Tourist Year.
582. 159. 2 b. sepia and blue .. 70 15

1967. Int. Correspondence Week.
583. 160. 50 s. multicoloured .. 10 8
584. 1 b. multicoloured .. 25 10
585. – 2 b. black and green .. 65 15
586. – 3 b. black and brown .. 1·00 85
DESIGN: 2 b., 3 b. Handclasp, Globe and Doves.

1967. U.N. Day.
587. 161. 50 s. multicoloured .. 15 8

162. National Flag.

1967. 50th Anniv. of Thai National Flag.
588. 162. 50 s. red, blue & turquoise 15 8
589. 2 b. red, blue and green 65 25

163. Elephant carrying Teak Log. 164. Satellite and Thai Tracking Station.

1968. Export Promotion.
590. 163. 2 b. brown and red .. 40 15
See also Nos. 630, 655 and 673.

1968. "Satellite Communications".
591. 164. 50 s. multicoloured .. 10 5
592. 3 b. multicoloured .. 55 25

165. "Goddess of the Earth".

1968. Int. Hydrological Decade.
593. 165. 50 s. multicoloured .. 15 8

166. Snakeskin Gourami.

1968. Thai Fishes (1st issue). Multicoloured.
594. 10 s. Type **166** 5 5
595. 20 s. Red-tailed Black Shark 10 8
596. 25 s. Barb 15 8
597. 50 s. Giant Catfish .. 15 8
598. 80 s. Thai Catfish .. 20 10
599. 1 b. 25 Goby 65 50
600. 1 b. 50 Thai Carp .. 1·90 1·40
601. 4 b. Knifefish .. .. 4·00 3·25
See also Nos. 955/8.

167. "Papilio arcturus".

1968. Thai Butterflies (1st issue). Mult.

No.	Type	Description	Unused	Used
602		50 s. Type **167**	20	8
603		1 b. "Papilio aecus" ..	65	10
604		3 b. "Papilio memnon" ..	1·90	1·00
605		4 b. "Papilio palinurus" ..	5·50	2·75

See also Nos. 967/70.

168. Queen Sirikit.

1968. Queen Sirikit's "Third Cycle" Anniversary. Stamps showing Queen Sirikit in different Thai costumes.

No.	Type	Description	Unused	Used
606.	**168.**	50 s. multicoloured ..	15	8
607.		2 b. multicoloured ..	50	25
608.		3 b. multicoloured ..	75	65
609.		5 b. multicoloured ..	2·50	65

169. W.H.O. Emblem and Medical Equipment.

1968. 20th Anniv. of W.H.O.

No.	Type	Description	Unused	Used
610.	**169.**	50 s. black and olive..	15	8

170. Globe, Letter and Pen.

1968. Int. Correspondence Week. Mult.

No.	Type	Description	Unused	Used
611.		50 s. Type **170**	10	5
612.		1 b. Globe on pen nib ..	20	10
613.		2 b. Type **170** ..	50	12
614.		3 b. Globe on pen nib ..	75	45

171. U.N. Emblem and Flags.

173. King Rama II.

172. Human Rights Emblem and Sculpture.

1968. United Nations Day.

No.	Type	Description	Unused	Used
615.	**171.**	50 s. multicoloured ..	12	8

1968. 20th Anniv. of Human Rights Year.

No.	Type	Description	Unused	Used
616.	**172.**	50 s. violet, red & green	15	8

1968. Bicent. of Birth of King Rama II.

No.	Type	Description	Unused	Used
617.	**173.**	50 s. yellow and brown	12	8

174. National Assembly Building.

1969. 1st Election Day under New Constitution.

No.	Type	Description	Unused	Used
618.	**174.**	50 s. multicoloured ..	10	8
619.		2 b. multicoloured ..	45	25

175. I.L.O. Emblem within Cogwheels.

1969. 50th Anniv. of I.L.O.

No.	Type	Description	Unused	Used
620.	**175.**	50 s. blue, blk. & violet	12	8

176. Ramwong Dance.

1969. Thai Classical Dances. Multicoloured.

No.	Type	Description	Unused	Used
621.		50 s. Type **176**	10	5
622.		1 b. Candle Dance ..	20	8
623.		2 b. Krathop Mai Dance ..	35	8
624.		3 b. Nohra Dance ..	75	25

177. "Letters by Post".

178. Globe in Hand.

1969. Int. Correspondence Week. Mult.

No.	Type	Description	Unused	Used
625.		50 s. Type **177**	10	5
626.		1 b. Type **177**	15	10
627.		2 b. Writing and posting a letter	30	15
628.		3 b. As 2 b.	60	35

1969. United Nations Day.

No.	Type	Description	Unused	Used
629.	**178.**	50 s. multicoloured ..	12	5

179. Tin Mine.

1969. Export Promotion and 2nd Technical Conference of the International Tin Council, Bangkok.

No.	Type	Description	Unused	Used
630.	**179.**	2 b. blue, purple and brown	20	8

180. Loy Krathong Festival.

1969. Thai Ceremonies and Festivals. Multicoloured.

No.	Type	Description	Unused	Used
631.		50 s. Type **180**	10	5
632.		1 b. Marriage ceremony ..	15	8
633.		2 b. Khwan ceremony ..	40	8
634.		5 b. Songkran festival ..	90	50

181. Breguet Mail-plane.

1969. 50th Anniv. of Thai Airmail Services.

No.	Type	Description	Unused	Used
635.	**181.**	1 b. brn., grn. and blue	30	10

182. "Phra Rama".

183. "Improvement of Productivity".

1969. Nang Yai Shadow Theatre. Mult.

No.	Type	Description	Unused	Used
636.		50 s. Type **182**	10	5
637.		2 b. "Ramasura"	20	15
638.		3 b. "Mekhala"	45	30
639.		5 b. "Ongkhot"	90	30

1969. Productivity Year.

No.	Type	Description	Unused	Used
640.	**183.**	50 s. multicoloured ..	12	5

184. Thai Temples within I.C.W. Emblem.

1970. 19th Triennial Conference of Int. Council of Women, Bangkok.

No.	Type	Description	Unused	Used
641.	**184.**	50 s. black and blue ..	12	5

185. Dish Aerials.

186. Households and Data.

1970. 3rd Anniv. of Thai Satellite Communications.

No.	Type	Description	Unused	Used
642.	**185.**	50 s. multicoloured ..	12	5

1970. 7th Population Census.

No.	Type	Description	Unused	Used
643.	**186.**	1 b. multicoloured ..	15	8

187. New Headquarters Building.

1970. Inauguration of New U.P.U. Headquarters Building, Berne.

No.	Type	Description	Unused	Used
644.	**187.**	50 s. blk., grn. and blue	12	5

188. Khun Ram Kamhang as Teacher.

1970. Int. Education Year.

No.	Type	Description	Unused	Used
645.	**188.**	50 s. multicoloured ..	12	5

189. Swimming Stadium.

1970. Sixth Asian Games, Bangkok.

No.	Type	Description	Unused	Used
646.	**189.**	50 s. lilac, red & yellow	10	5
647.	–	1 b. 50 grn., red & blue	10	8
648.	–	3 b. black, red & bronze	25	15
649.	–	5 b. blue, red and green	60	45

STADIUMS: 1 b. 50, Velodrome. 3 b. Suphajalasaya Stadium. 5 b. Kittikachorn Indoor Stadium.

See also No. 660.

190. Boy and Girl writing Letter.

1970. Int. Correspondence Week. Mult.

No.	Type	Description	Unused	Used
650.		50 s. Type **190**	10	8
651.		1 b. Woman writing letter	15	12
652.		2 b. Women reading letters	30	10
653.		3 b. Man reading letter ..	60	30

See also Nos. 683/6.

191. U.N. Emblem and Royal Palace, Bangkok.

194. King Bhumibol lighting Flame.

193. The Heroes of Bangrachan.

1970. 25th Anniv. of United Nations.

No.	Type	Description	Unused	Used
654.	**191.**	50 s. multicoloured ..	12	8

1970. Export Promotion.

No.	Type	Description	Unused	Used
655.		2 b. brn., red and green ..	25	8

DESIGN: 2 b. As Type **163**, but picturing rubber plantation.

1970. Heroes and Heroines of Thai History.

No.	Type	Description	Unused	Used
656.	**193.**	50 s. violet and red ..	8	5
657.	–	1 b. purple and violet	12	10
658.	–	2 b. brown and red ..	35	12
659.	–	3 b. green and blue ..	50	25

DESIGNS: 1 b. Heroines Thao Thepkrasatri and Thao Srisunthorn. 2 b. Queen Suriyothai riding an elephant. 3 b. Phraya Phichaidaphak.

1970. Inaug. of 6th Asian Games, Bangkok.

No.	Type	Description	Unused	Used
660.	**194.**	1 b. multicoloured ..	10	5

195. Woman playing So Sam Sai.

1970. Thai Musicians and Instruments. Multicoloured.

No.	Type	Description	Unused	Used
661.		50 s. Type **195**	8	5
662.		2 b. Khlui phiang-o (flute)	15	12
663.		3 b. Krachappi (guitar) ..	45	20
664.		5 b. Thon rammana (drums)	55	40

196. Chocolate-pointed Siamese.

1971. Siamese Cats. Multicoloured.

No.	Type	Description	Unused	Used
665.		50 s. Type **196**	8	5
666.		1 b. Blue-pointed cat ..	15	8
667.		2 b. Seal-pointed cat ..	35	15
668.		3 b. Pure White cat and kittens	75	60

197. Pagoda, Nakhon Si Thammarat.

1971. Buddhist Holy Places in Thailand. Pagodas.

669. **197.** 50 s. black, brn. & pink 10 5
670. – 1 b. brn., violet & grn. 15 8
671. – 3 b. sepia, orge. & brn. 50 10
672. – 4 b. brn., sepia & blue 85 65

DESIGNS: 1 b. Makhon Phanom. 3 b. Nakhon Pathom. 4 b. Chiang Mai.

1971. Export Promotion.

673. 2 b. multicoloured .. 45 8

DESIGN: 2 b. As Type **163**, but picturing corncob with cornfield.

199. Buddha's Birthplace, Lumbini, Nepal.

1971. 20th Anniv. of World Fellowship of Buddhists.

674. **199.** 50 s. black and blue .. 8 5
675. – 1 b. black and green .. 10 8
676. – 2 b. black and yellow 35 8
677. – 3 b. black and red .. 50 35

DESIGNS: 1 b. "Place of Enlightenment", Buddha Gaya, Bihar. 2 b. "Place of First Sermon", Sarnath, Banaras. 3 b. "Place of Final Passing Away", Kusinara.

200. King Bhumibol and Thai people. **201.** Floating Market, Wat Sai.

1971. 25th Anniv. of Coronation.

678. **200.** 50 s. multicoloured .. 40 8

1971. Visit ASEAN Year.

679. **201.** 4 b. multicoloured .. 90 15

ASEAN = Association of South East Asian Nations.

202. King and Queen in Scout Uniform.

1971. 60th Anniv. of Thai Boy Scout Movement.

680. **202.** 50 c. black, red & yell. 12 8

1971. "THAILANDAPEX 71" National Stamp Exhibition, Bangkok. Optd. **THAILANDAPEX '71** and **4-8 AUG. '71** in English and Thai, with map within "perforations", covering four stamps.

681. **119.** 80 s. orange (No. 428) 15 15
682. **132.** 80 s. orange (No. 483) 15 15

Prices are for blocks of four stamps showing the entire overprint. The overprint on No. 682 is smaller—size 23 × 26 mm.

1971. Int. Correspondence Week. As T **190**. Multicoloured.

683. 50 s. Two girls writing a letter 8 5
684. 1 b. Two girls reading letters 12 8
685. 2 b. Women with letter on veranda 20 8
686. 3 b. Man handing letter to woman 50 35

205. Marble Temple, Bangkok.

1971. United Nations Day.

687. **205.** 50 s. multicoloured .. 12 5

206. Raising Ducks.

1971. Rural Life. Multicoloured.

688. 50 s. Type **206** 8 5
689. 1 b. Growing tobacco seedlings 12 8
690. 2 b. Cooping fish 25 8
691. 3 b. Cleaning rice-seed .. 55 35

207. Mother and Child.

1971. 25th Anniv. of U.N.I.C.E.F.

692. **207.** 50 s. multicoloured .. 12 8

208. Costumes from Chaing Saen Period (17th-century).

1972. Historical Costumes. Multicoloured.

693. 50 s. Type **208** 10 8
694. 1 b. Sukhothai period (13th–14th centuries) 15 8
695. 1 b. 50 Ayudhya period (14th–17th centuries) 25 12
696. 2 b. Bangkok period (18th–19th centuries) .. 40 15

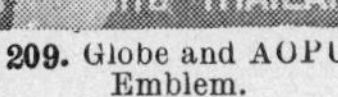

209. Globe and AOPU Emblem. **210.** King Bhumibol.

1972. 10th Anniv. of Asian-Oceanic Postal Union.

697. **209.** 75 s. blue 12 5

1972.

698. **210.** 10 s. green 5 5
699. 20 s. blue 10 5
700. 25 s. red 5 5
701. 50 s. olive 8 5
702. 75 s. lilac 10 5
703. 1 b. 25 pink, green and light green 15 10
704. 2 b. violet and red .. 15 10
705. 2 b. 75 green and red 12 5
706. 3 b. blue and sepia .. 15 8
707. 4 b. brown and blue .. 20 12
708. 5 b. brown and violet .. 40 8
709. 6 b. violet and green .. 25 15
710. 10 b. black and red .. 75 40
711. 20 b. green, orange and light orange .. 1·50 25
898d. 40 b. violet and brown 9·00 1·25
712a. 50 b. green and lilac .. 3·00 1·50
713 100 b. blue and orange 6·00 3·00

211. Two Women, Iko Tribe.

1972. Hill Tribes of Thailand. Multicoloured.

714. 50 s. Type **211** 8 5
715. 2 b. Musician and children, Musoe tribe 20 12
716. 4 b. Woman embroidering, Yao tribe 45 30
717. 5 b. Woman with chickens, Maeo tribe 55 25

212. Ruby.

1972. Precious Stones.

718. **212.** 75 s. multicoloured .. 10 5
719. – 2 b. multicoloured .. 25 10
720. – 4 b. black and green .. 50 25
721. – 6 b. brown, black and red 65 40

DESIGNS: 2 b. Yellow sapphire. 4 b. Zircon. 6 b. Star sapphire.

213. Prince Vajiralongkorn. **214.** Thai Ruan-ton Costume.

1972. Prince Vajiralongkorn's 20th Birthday.

722. **213.** 75 s. multicoloured .. 10 5

1972. Thai Women's National Costumes. Mult.

723. 75 s. Type **214** 10 5
724. 2 b. Thai Chitrlada .. 10 10
725. 4 b. Thai Chakri 40 30
726. 5 b. Thai Borompimarn .. 55 12

215. Rambutan.

1972. Thai Fruits. Multicoloured.

728. 75 s. Type **215** 10 5
729. 1 b. Mangosteen 15 10
730. 3 b. Durian 40 15
731. 5 b. Mango 85 40

216. Princess-Mother with Old People.

1972. Princess-Mother Sisangwan's 72nd Birthday.

732. **216.** 75 s. green and orange 12 8

217. Lod Cave, Phangnga.

1972. Int. Correspondence Week. Mult.

733. 75 s. Type **217** 10 5
734. 1 b. 25 Kang Kracharn Reservoir, Phetchaburi .. 15 10
735. 2 b. 75 Erawan Waterfall, Kanchanburi 35 8
736. 3 b. Nok-kaw Mountain, Loei 50 30

218. Globe on U.N. Emblem.

220. Crown Prince Vajiralongkorn.

219. Watphrajetubon Vimolmanklaram Rajvaramahaviharn (ancient university).

1972. 25th Anniv. of E.C.A.F.E.

737. **218.** 75 s. multicoloured .. 12 5

1972. International Book Year.

738. **219.** 75 s. multicoloured .. 15 5

1972. Investiture of Crown Prince.

739. **220.** 2 b. multicoloured .. 12 12

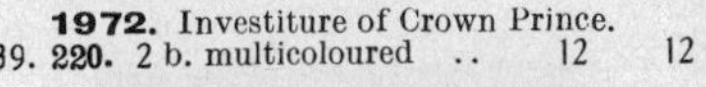

221. Servicemen and Flag.

1973. 25th Anniv. of Veterans' Day.

740. **221.** 75 s. multicoloured .. 12 8

1973. Red Cross Fair (1972). Nos. 472/3 surch.

741. **130.** 75 s. + 25 s. on 50 s. + 10 s. 30 30
742. – 75 s. + 25 s. on 50 s. + 10 s. 30 30

223. Emblem, Bank and Coin-box.

1973. 60th Anniv. of Government Savings Bank.

743. **223.** 75 s. multicoloured .. 12 8

224. "Celestial Being" and Emblem.

1973. 25th Anniv. of W.H.O.

744. **224.** 75 s. multicoloured .. 12 8

225. "Nymphaea pubescens".

1973. Lotus Flowers. Multicoloured.

745. 75 s. Type **225** 8 8
746. 1 b. 50 "Nymphaea pubescens" (different) .. 12 10
747. 2 b. "Nelumbo nucifera" .. 40 12
748. 4 b. "Nelumbo nucifera" (different) 60 30

227. King Bhumibol.

1973.

749. **227.** 5 s. purple 12 5
1031. 20 s. blue 5 5
1031a. 25 s. red 5 5
1032. 50 s. green 5 5
1032a. 75 s. violet 8 5
753. 5 b. brown and vio. 95 12
754. 6 b. violet and green 1·40 25
755. 10 b. brown and red 1·90 15
755a. 20 b. grn. and orge. 3·75 1·00

228. Silverware.

1973. Thai Handicrafts. Mult.

756. 75 s. Type **228** 10 8
757. 2 b. 75 Lacquerware .. 25 8
758. 4 b. Pottery 45 25
759. 5 b. Paper umbrellas .. 50 15

229. King Janaka's Procession.

1973. "Ramayana" Mural, Temple of Emerald Buddha, Bangkok.

760. **229.** 25 s. multicoloured .. 8 8
761. – 75 s. multicoloured .. 12 5
762. – 1 b. 50 multicoloured 12 10
763. – 2 b. multicoloured .. 65 35
764. – 2 b. 75 multicoloured 50 8
765. – 3 b. multicoloured .. 1·25 40
766. – 5 b. multicoloured .. 1·90 75
767. – 6 b. multicoloured .. 65 35

DESIGNS: Nos. 761/7, different details from the mural.

230. " Postal Services ".

1973. 90th Anniv. of Thai Post and Telegraph Department. Multicoloured.

768. 75 s. Type **230** 30 10
769. 2 b. "Telecommunication Services" 25 10

231. 1 Solot Stamp of 1883.

1973. "THAIPEX 73" Nat. Stamp Exn.

770. **231.** 75 s. blue and red .. 10 8
771. – 1 b. 25 red and blue .. 15 10
772. – 1 b. 50 violet and green 35 15
773. – 2 b. green and orange 35 25

DESIGNS: 1 b. 25, 6 s. stamp of 1912. 1 b. 50, 5 s. stamp of 1928. 2 b. 3 s. stamp of 1941.

232. Interpol Emblem.

1973. 50th Anniv. of International Criminal Police Organisation (Interpol).

775. **232.** 75 s. multicoloured .. 10 8

233. " Lilit Pralaw ".

1973. Int. Correspondence Week. Characters from Thai Literature. Multicoloured.

776. 75 s. Type **233** 8 8
777. 1 b. 50 "Khun Chang, Khun Phan" 15 12
778. 2 b. "Sang Thong" .. 25 15
779. 5 b. "Pha Apai Mance" .. 75 35

234. Wat Suan Dok Temple, Chiangmai.

1973. United Nations Day.

781. **234.** 75 s. multicoloured .. 10 5

235. Schomburgk's Deer.

1973. Protected Wild Animals. Mult.

782. 20 s. Type **235** 8 5
783. 25 s. Kouprey 8 5
784. 75 r. Common Gorals .. 12 8
785. 1 b. 25 Water buffaloes .. 25 15
786. 1 b. 50 Javan rhinoceros .. 25 12
787. 2 b. Thamin .. .. 1·50 85
788. 2 b. 75 Sumatran rhinoceros 25 12
789. 4 b. Mainland serows .. 85 85

236. Flame Emblem.

1973. 25th Anniv. of Declaration of Human Rights.

790. **236.** 75 s. multicoloured .. 10 5

238. Children within Flowers.

241. " Pha la Phiang Lai ".

240. Statue of Krom Luang Songkia Nakarin.

1973. Children's Day.

791. **238.** 75 s. multicoloured .. 10 5

1974. Red Cross Fair. Nos. 472/3 surch 75+25 and date

792. **130.** 75 s.+25 s. on 50 s.+10 s. 25 25
793. – 75 s.+25 s. on 50 s.+10 s. 25 25

1974. 84th Anniv. of Sirirai Hospital.

794. **240.** 75 s. multicoloured .. 10 8

1974. Thai Classical Dance. Multicoloured.

795. 75 s. Type **241** 10 5
796. 2 b. 75 "Phra Lak Phlaeng Rit" 15 8
797. 4 b. "Chin Sao Sai" .. 60 20
798. 5 b. "Charot Phra Sumen" 65 15

242. World's Largest Teak Amphur Nam-Pad

1974. Arbor Day.

799. **242.** 75 s. multicoloured .. 10 8

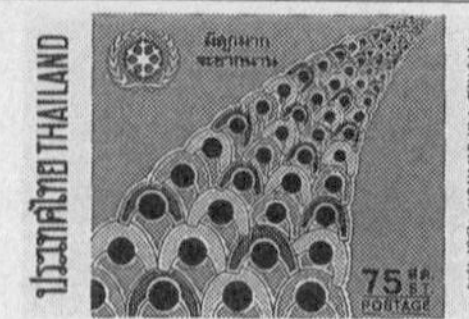

243. "Increasing Population".

1974. World Population Year.

800. **243.** 75 s. multicoloured .. 8 5

244. Royal Chariot.

1974. Cent. of National Museum. Mult.

801. 75 s. Type **244** 10 8
802. 2 b. Ban Chiang painted pottery vase 20 15
803. 2 b. 75 Avalokitesavara Bodhisattva statue .. 25 8
804. 3 b. King Mongkut Rama IV 45 25

245. "Cassia fistula".

1974. International Correspondence Week. Tropical Plants. Multicoloured.

805. 75 s. Type **245** 8 5
806. 2 b. 75 "Butea superba" .. 12 5
807. 3 b. "Jasminum sambac" 25 10
808. 4 b. "Lagerstroemia speciosa" 40 35

246. "UPU 100".

1974. Cent. of U.P.U.

810. **246.** 75 s. multicoloured .. 12 8

247. Wat Suthat Thepvararam.

1974. United Nations Day.

811. **247.** 75 s. multicoloured .. 12 8

248. Indian Elephant Round-up.

1974. Tourism.

812. **248.** 4 b. multicoloured .. 40 12

249. " Vanda coerulea ".

1974. Thai Orchids (1st series). Mult.

813. 75 s. Type **249** 10 5
814. 2 b. 75 " Dendrobium aggregatum " 20 8
815. 3 b. " Dendrobium scabrilingue " 25 12
816. 4 b. " Aerides falcata " var "houlletiana" 35 25

See also Nos. 847/50.

250. Boy riding Toy Horse.

1974. Children's Day.

818. **250.** 75 c. multicoloured .. 8 5

252. Democracy Monument.

1975. Democratic Institutions Campaign. Multicoloured.

819. 75 s. Type **252** 8 5
820. 2 b. " Rights and Liberties " 20 8
821. 2 b. 75 " Freedom to choose work " 35 8
822. 5 b. Top of Monument and text 45 35

1975. Red Cross Fair 1974. Nos. 472/3 surch. **1974** and new value in English and Thai.

823. **130.** 75 s.+25 s. on 50 s.+ 10 s. red and grey .. 25 25
824. – 75 s.+25 s. on 50 s.+ 10 s. red and grey .. 25 25

254. Marbled Cat.

1975. Protected Wild Animals (1st series). Multicoloured.

825. 20 s. Type **254** 10 10
826. 75 s. Gaur 12 5
827. 2 b. 75 Indian elephant .. 25 8
828. 3 b. Clouded leopard .. 40 30

See Nos. 913/16.

255. White-eyed River Martin.

1975. Thailand Birds. Multicoloured.

829. 75 s. Type **255** 65 20
830. 2 b. Asiatic paradise fly-catcher .. .. .. 1·10 40
831. 2 b. 75 Long-tailed broad-bill .. .. .. 1·60 65
832. 5 b. Sultan tit .. .. 2·75 1·40

256. King Bhumibol and Queen Sirikit.

1975. Silver Wedding of King Bhumibol and Queen Sirikit. Multicoloured.

833. 75 s. Type **256** 10 5
834. 3 b. As Type **256**, but different background .. 30 10

257. " Roundhouse Kick ".

1975. Thai Boxing. Multicoloured.

835. 75 s. Type **257** 10 5
836. 2 b. 75 " Reverse Elbow " 35 8
837. 3 b. " Flying Knee " .. 25 10
838. 5 b. " Ritual Homage " .. 60 40

258. Toskanth.

1975. Thai Culture. Masks. Multicoloured.
839. 75 s. Type **258** 12 8
840. 2 b. Kumbhakarn .. 20 10
841. 3 b. Rama. 60 10
842. 4 b. Hanuman .. .. 1·00 40

259. "Thaipex 75" Emblem.

1975. "Thaipex 75" National Stamp Exhibition, Bangkok. Multicoloured.
843. 75 s. Type **259** 12 5
844. 2 b. 75 Stamp designer .. 12 15
845. 4 b. Stamp printing works 35 25
846. 5 b. "Stamp collecting" 40 10

1975. Thai Orchids (2nd series). As T **249**. Multicoloured.
847. 75 s. "Dendrobium cruentum" 10 5
848. 2 b. "Dendrobium parishii" 15 10
849. 2 b. 75 "Vanda teres" .. 20 5
850. 5 b. "Vanda denisoniana" 40 25

260. "Mytillus smaragdinus".

1975. Seashells. Multicoloured.
852. 75 s. Type **260** .. 15 15
853. 1 b. "Turbo marmoratus" 10 5
854. 2 b. 75 "Oliva mustelina" 25 8
855. 5 b. "Cypraea moneta" .. 65 40

261. Yachting.

1975. 8th SEAP Games, Bangkok (1st issue).
856. **261.** 75 s. black and blue .. 10 8
857. – 1 b. 25 black and mauve .. 10 10
858. – 1 b. 50 black and red .. 8 12
859. – 2 b. black and green .. 40 25
DESIGNS: 1 b. 25, Badminton. 1 b. 50, Volley-ball. 2 b. Rifle and pistol shooting.
See also Nos. 878/81.

262. Pataya Beach.

1975. International Correspondence Week. Multicoloured.
861. 75 s. Type **262** 15 5
862. 2 b. Samila Beach .. 15 10
863. 3 b. Prachuap Bay .. 25 15
864. 5 b. Laem Singha Bay .. 60 35

263. Children within Letters "U N".

1975. United Nations Day.
865. **263.** 75 s. multicoloured .. 10 5

264. Early Telegraphs.

1975. Cent. of Telegraph Service. Mult.
866. 75 s. Type **264** 12 5
867. 2 b. 75 Teleprinter and dish aerial 20 8

265. "Sukhrip Khrong Muong".

1975. Thai Ceremonial Barges. Multicoloured.
868 75 s. Type **265** 15 10
869 1 b. Royal barge "Anekchat Phulbong" 20 10
870 2 b. Royal barge "Anantana Karot" .. 50 15
871 2 b. 75 "Krabi Ram Ron Rap" 50 10
872 3 b. "Asura Wayuphak" .. 95 25
873 4 b. "Asura Paksi" .. 65 40
874 5 b. Royal barge "Sri Suphanahong" .. 2·75 1·90
875 6 b. "Phail Rang Thamip" 2·10 85

266. King's Cipher and Thai Crown.

1976. King Bhumibol's 45th Birthday. Multicoloured.
876. 75 s. Type **266** 10 8
877. 5 b. King Bhumibol in uniform 40 12

267. Putting the Shot.

1976. 8th SEAP Games, Bangkok (2nd issue).
878. **267.** 1 b. black and orange 20 20
879. – 2 b. black and green .. 15 10
880. – 3 b. black and yellow .. 25 20
881. – 4 b. black and violet .. 35 20
DESIGNS: 2 b. Table-tennis. 3 b. Cycle-racing. 4 b. Relay-running.

268. I.W.Y. Emblem on Globe.

1976. International Women's Year.
883. **268.** 75 s. blue, orge. & blk. 12 5

269. Children writing.

1976. Children's Day.
884. **269.** 75 s. multicoloured .. 12 5

270. "Macrobrachium rosenbergii".

1976. Thai Lobsters and Shrimps. Mult.
885. 75 s. Type **270** 10 5
886. 2 b. "Penaeus merguiensis" 35 25
887. 2 b. 75 "Panulirus ornatus" 35 8
888. 5 b. "Penaeus monodon" 75 35

1976. Red Cross Fair 1975. Nos. 472/3 surch. **1975** and value.
889. **130.** 75 s.+25 s. on 50 s.+10 s. red and grey .. 8 10
890. – 75 s.+25 s. on 50 s.+10 s. red and grey .. 8 10

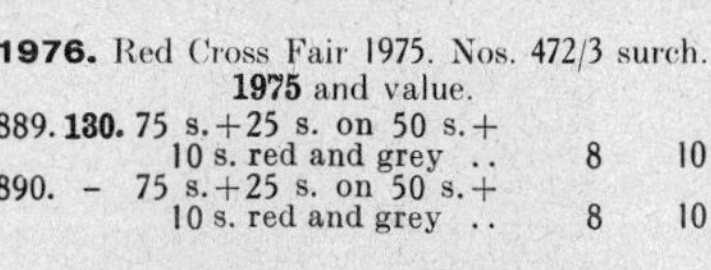

271. Golden-backed Three-toed Woodpecker. 272. Ban Chiang Pot.

1976. Thailand Birds (2nd series). Mult.
891. 1 b. Type **271** 70 35
892. 1 b. 50 Greater green-billed malcoha .. .. .. 1·25 40
893. 3 b. Long-billed scimitar babbler .. .. 1·90 70
894. 4 b. Green magpie .. 3·00 1·40

1976 Ban Chiang Pottery.
895. **272.** 1 b. multicoloured .. 10 8
896. – 2 b. multicoloured .. 40 10
897. – 3 b. multicoloured .. 60 8
898. – 4 b. multicoloured .. 75 50
DESIGNS. 2 b. to 4 b. Various items of pottery.

273. Postman of 1883. 275. "Drug Addictions".

274. Kinnari.

1976. Postmen's Uniforms. Multicoloured.
899. 1 b. Type **273** .. 10 10
900. 3 b. Postman of 1935 .. 25 10
901. 4 b. Postman of 1950 .. 60 25
902. 5 b. Postman of 1974 .. 50 15

1976. International Correspondence Week. Deities. Multicoloured.
903. 1 b. Type **274** 35 20
904. 2 b. Suphan-Mat-Cha .. 15 10
905. 4 b. Garuda 45 15
906. 5 b. Naga 40 10

1976. United Nations Day.
907. **275.** 1 b. multicoloured .. 10 8

276. Early and Modern Telephones.

1976. Telephone Centenary.
908. **276.** 1 b. multicoloured .. 12 10

277. Sivalaya.

1976. Thai Royal Halls. Multicoloured.
909. 1 b. Type **277** 10 8
910. 2 b. Cakri 25 20
911. 4 b. Mahisra 75 25
912. 5 b. Dusit 85 35

1976. Protected Wild Animals (2nd series). As T **254**. Multicoloured.
913. 1 b. Bangteng 10 15
914. 2 b. Malayan tapir .. 40 35
915. 4 b. Sambar 30 15
916. 5 b. Hog-deer 45 15

278. "From Child to Adult".

1977. Children's Day.
917. **278.** 1 b. multicoloured .. 10 8

279. Alsthom's Electric Locomotive.

1977. 80th Anniv. of Thai State Railway. Multicoloured.
918. 1 b. Type **279** 40 20
919. 2 b. Davenport's electric locomotive 65 30
920. 4 b. Pacific steam locomotive 1·90 95
921. 5 b. George Egestoff's steam locomotive .. .. 1·60 65

280. University Building.

1977. 60th Anniv. of Chulalongkorn University.
922. **280.** 1 b. multicoloured .. 10 8

281. Flags of A.O.P.U. Countries.

1977. 15th Anniv. of Asian-Oceanic Postal Union.
923. **281.** 1 b. multicoloured .. 10 8

282. Crippled Ex-Serviceman.

1977. Sai-Jai-Thai Foundation Day.
924. **282.** 5 b. multicoloured .. 70 15

1977. Red Cross Fair. Nos. 472/3 surch. **75+25 2520—1977.**
925. **130.** 75 s.+25 s. on 50 s.+10 s. red and grey .. 25 25
926. – 75 s.+25 s. on 50 s.+10 s. red and grey .. 25 25

284. "Phra Aphai Mani and Phisua Samut".

1977. Puppet Shows. Multicoloured.

927.	2 b. Type **284**	15	10
928.	3 b. " Rusi and Sutsakhon "	12	8
929.	4 b. " Nang Vali and Usren "	30	12
930.	5 b. " Phra Aphai Mani and Nang Laweng's portrait "	50	35

285. Drum Dance.

1977. Thai Folk Dances. Multicoloured.

931.	2 b. Type **285**	15	10
932.	3 b. Dance of Dip nets ..	12	8
933.	4 b. Harvesting dance ..	20	12
934.	5 b. Kan dance	25	10

286. 1 b. Stamp of 1972.

1977. "THAIPEX 77" National Stamp Exhibition.

935. **286.**	75 s. multicoloured ..	10	8

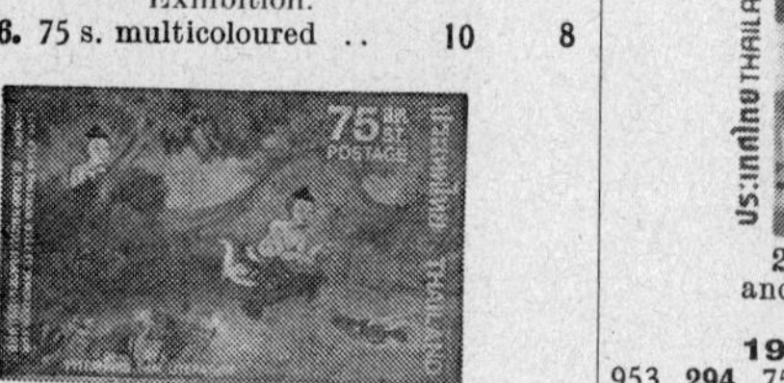

287. " Pla Bu Thong ".

1977. International Correspondence Week, Scenes from Thai Literature. Multicoloured.

936.	75 s. Type **287**	35	10
937.	2 b. " Krai Tnong " ..	15	10
938.	5 b. " Nang Kaew Na Ma "	30	8
939.	6 b. " Pra Rot Mali " ..	55	20

288. U.N. Building, Bangkok.

1977. United Nations Day.

940. **288.**	75 s. multicoloured ..	15	8

289. King Bhumibol in Scout Uniform, and Camp Fire.

1977. Ninth National Scout Jamboree.

941. **289.**	75 s. multicoloured ..	15	8

290. Map of A.S.E.A.N. Countries.

1977. 10th Anniv. of Association of South East Asian Nations.

942. **290.**	5 b. multicoloured ..	25	8

291. Elbow and Wrist Joints.

1977. World Rheumatism Year.

943. **291.**	75 s. multicoloured ..	12	5

292. Children with Thai Flag.

1978. Children's Day.

944. **292.**	75 s. multicoloured ..	12	5

293. " Dendrobium heterocarpum ".

1978. Ninth World Orchid Conference. Mult.

945.	75 s. Type **293**	15	10
946.	1 b. " Dendrobium pulchellum "	15	10
947.	1 b. 50 " Doritis pulcherrima—buyssoniana " ..	15	10
948.	2 b. " Dendrobium hercoglossum "	10	10
949.	2 b. 75 " Aerides odorata "	65	12
950.	3 b. " Trichoglottis fasciata "	25	8
951.	5 b. " Dendrobium wardianum "	25	12
952.	6 b. " Dendrobium senile "	1·00	25

294. Agricultural Scenes and Rice Production Graph.

1978. Agricultural Census.

953. **294.**	75 s. multicoloured ..	8	5

295. Blood Donation and Red Cross.

1978. Red Cross Fair.

954. **295.**	2 b. 75+25 s. multicoloured ..	15	15

296. " Anabas testudineus ".

1978. Fishes. Multicoloured.

955.	1 b. Type **296**	25	12
956.	2 b. " Datnioides microlepis "	10	8
957.	3 b. " Kryptopterus apogon "	12	8
958.	4 b. " Probarbus jullieni "	45	15

297. " Birth of Prince Siddhartha ".

1978. Mural Paintings. Multicoloured.

959.	2 b. Type **297** ..	25	8
960.	3 b. " Prince Siddhartha cuts his hair " ..	40	8
961.	5 b. " Buddha descends from Tavatimsa Heaven " ..	65	40
962.	6 b. " Buddha enters Nirvana "	50	35

298. Bhumibol Dam.

1978. Dams. Multicoloured.

963.	75 s. Type **298**	15	8
964.	2 b. Sirikit Dam	12	8
965.	2 b. 75 Vajiralongkorn Dam	20	10
966.	6 b. Ubolratana Dam ..	50	35

299. "Idea lynceus".

1978. Butterflies. Multicoloured.

967	2 b. Type **299**	20	10
968	3 b. "Sephisa chandra" ..	30	10
969	5 b. "Charaxes durnfordi"	1·40	60
970	6 b. "Cethosia penthesilea"	95	50

300. Phra Chedi Chai Mongkhon, Ayutthaya. **301.** Mother and Children.

1978. International Correspondence Week. Multicoloured.

971.	75 s. Type **300**	15	8
972.	2 b. Phra That Hariphunchai, Lamphun ..	20	8
973.	2 b. 75 Phra Borom That Chaiya, Surat Thani ..	30	10
974.	5 b. Phra That Choeng Chum, Sakon Nakhon ..	35	25

1978. United Nations Day.

975. **301.**	75 s. multicoloured ..	8	5

302. Basketball, Hockey and Boxing.

1978. 8th Asian Games. Bangkok. Mult.

976.	25 s. Silhouettes of boxers, footballer & pole-vaulter	12	5
977.	2 b. Javelin, weightlifting, running	15	8
978.	3 b. Yacht and sports equipment	20	12
979.	5 b. Type **302**	35	20

303. World Map and Different Races holding hands.

1978. International Anti-Apartheid Year.

980. **303.**	75 s. multicoloured ..	10	5

304. Children and S.O.S. Village, Tambol Bangpu.

1979. International Year of the Child. Mult.

981.	75 s. Children painting Thai flag (horiz.) ..	10	5
982.	75 s. Type **304**	10	5

305. " Matuta lunaris ".

1979. Crabs. Multicoloured.

983.	2 b. Type **305**	12	8
984.	2 b. 75 " Matuta planipes "	35	10
985.	3 b. " Portunus pelagicus "	20	12
986.	5 b. " Scylla serrata " ..	35	25

306. Eye and Blind People. **307.** Sugar Apples.

1979. Thai Red Cross Fair.

987. **306.**	75 s.+25 s. multicoloured	8	8

1979. Thai Fruits. Multicoloured.

988.	1 b. Type **307**	10	8
989.	2 b. Pineapple	10	5
990.	5 b. Bananas	45	15
991.	6 b. Longans	60	25

308. Planting Sapling.

1979. National Arbor Day.

992. **308.**	75 s. multicoloured ..	5	5

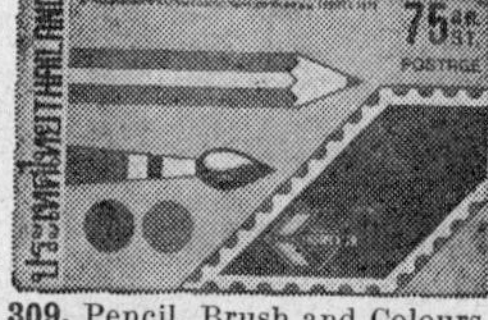

309. Pencil, Brush and Colours.

1979. " Thaipex '79 " 5th National Stamp Exhibition. Multicoloured.

993.	75 s. Type **309**	12	5
994.	2 b. Envelopes	15	5
995.	2 b. 75 Stamp stockbook	20	10
996.	5 b. Tweezers and magnifying glass	35	25

310. Baisi Pak Cham. **311.** U.N.O. Emblem, Farmer, Cattle and Wheat.

1979. International Correspondence Week. Multicoloured.

997.	75 s. Kruai Upatcha ..	12	8
998.	2 b. Type **310**	12	8
999.	2 b. 75 Krathong Dokmai	15	10
1000.	5 b. Phum Dokmai ..	25	15

1979. United Nations Day.

1001. **311.**	75 s. multicoloured ..	10	5

312. Frigate "Makutrajakumarn".

1979. Ships of the Royal Thai Navy. Mult.
1002. 2 b. Type **312** 30 15
1003. 3 b. Frigate "Tapi" .. 60 30
1004. 5 b. Missile craft "Prabparapak" .. 1·40 60
1005. 6 b. "T 91" patrol boat .. 1·00 60

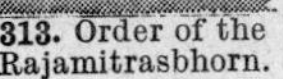
313. Order of the Rajamitrasbhorn. **314.** Transplanting Rice.

1979. Royal Orders and Decorations. Mult.
1006. 1 b. Type **313** 12 8
1007. 1 b. Rajamitrasbhorn ribbon 12 8
1008. 2 b. Order of the Royal House of Chakri .. 10 5
1009. 2 b. Royal House of Chakri ribbon 10 5
1010. 5 b. Order of the Nine Gems 25 15
1011. 5 b. Nine Gems ribbon .. 25 15
1012. 6 b. Knight Grand Cross of the Order of Chula Chom Klao 30 15
1013. 6 b. Chula Chom Klao ribbon 30 15

1980. Children's Day. Multicoloured.
1014. 75 s. Type **314** 10 5
1015. 75 s. Family in rice field 10 5

315. Family House and Map of Thailand. **316.** Golden-fronted Leafbird.

1980. Population and Housing Census.
1016. **315.** 75 s. multicoloured .. 8 5

1980. 9th Conference of International Commission for Bird Preservation, Asian Section. Multicoloured.
1017. 75 s. Type **316** 45 20
1018. 2 b. Chinese yellow tit .. 60 25
1019. 3 b. Chestnut-tailed minla .. .. 1·00 70
1020. 5 b. Scarlet minivet .. 1·50 80

317. Extracting Snake Venom.

1980. Red Cross Fair.
1021. **317.** 75 s. + 25 s. mult. .. 8 8

318. Smokers and diagram of Lungs.

1980. World Health Day. Anti-smoking Campaign.
1022. **318.** 75 s. multicoloured .. 8 5

319. Garuda and Rotary Emblem.

1980. 75th Anniv. of Rotary International.
1023. **319.** 5 b. multicoloured .. 25 15

320. Sai Yok Falls, Kanchanaburi.

1980. Waterfalls. Multicoloured.
1024 1 b. Type **320** 10 5
1025 2 b. Punyaban Falls, Ranong 15 8
1026 5 b. Heo Suwat Falls, Nakhan Ratchasima .. 40 20
1027 6 b. Siriphum Falls, Chiang Mai 35 20

321. Family and Reverse of F.A.O. Medal.

1980. Queen Sirikit's 48th Birthday. Mult.
1028. 75 s. Queen Sirikit (vert.) 8 5
1029. 5 b. Type **321** 25 15
1030. 5 b. Thai family and Ceres medal (obverse) .. 25 15

322. Khao Phanomrung Temple, Buri Ram.

1980. International Correspondence Week. Stone Temples. Multicoloured.
1033. 75 s. Type **322** 8 5
1034. 2 b. Prasat hin Prang Ku 10 5
1035. 2 b. 75 Prasat hin Pimai 15 10
1036. 5 b. Prasat hin Srikhoraphum 25 15

323. Princess Mother. **324.** Golden Mount Temple, Bangkok.

1980. The Princess Mother's 80th Birthday.
1037. **323.** 75 s. multicoloured .. 8 5

1980. United Nations Day.
1038. **324.** 75 s. multicoloured .. 8 5

325. King Bhumibol. **326.** King Rama VII signing Constitutional Document.

1980.
1039. **325.** 25 s. red 5 5
1039a. 50 s. green 5 5
1040. 75 s. violet 8 5
1041. 1 b. blue 8 5
1040a. 1 b. 25 green .. 8 5
1180a. 1 b. 50 orange .. 8 5
1041a. 2 b. purple and red 15 5
1180b. 2 b. brown 10 5
1042. 3 b. blue and brown 20 5
1042a. 4 b. brown and blue 25 5
1043. 5 b. brown and lilac 30 8
1044. 6 b. lilac and green 35 8
1044a. 6 b. 50 olive & grn. 35 10
1044b. 7 b. dp brn. & brn. 40 10
1044c. 7 b. 50 blue and red 45 15
1044d. 8 b. green and brn. 50 15
1045. 8 b. 50 brn. & grn. 55 15
1045a. 9 b. brown and blue 60 25
1046. 9 b. 50 grn. & olive 60 25
1047. 10 b. green and red 70 30
1047a. 20 b. green & orge. 1·40 60
1048. 50 b. green and lilac 3·00 1·50
1049. 100 b. bl. & orge. .. 6·50 3·00

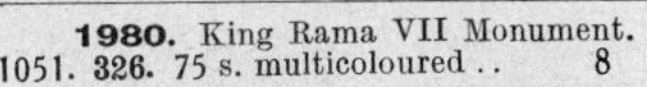
1980. King Rama VII Monument.
1051. **326.** 75 s. multicoloured .. 8 5

327. Bowl.

1980. Bencharong Ware. Multicoloured.
1052. 2 b. Type **327** 12 5
1053. 2 b. 75 Covered bowls .. 25 10
1054. 3 b. Jar 25 12
1055. 5 b. Stem plates .. 25 15

328. King Vajiravudh. **329.** "Youth in Electronics Age" (Veth Maichun).

1981. Birth Cent. of King Vajiravudh.
1056. **328.** 75 s. multicoloured .. 8 5

1981. Children's Day.
1057. **329.** 75 s. multicoloured .. 30 10

330. Mosque, Pattani Province.

1981. 1400th Anniv. of Hegira.
1058. **330** 5 b. multicoloured .. 25 15

331. Palm Leaf Fish Mobile

1981. International Handicraft Exhibition. Multicoloured.
1059. 75 s. Type **331** 8 5
1060. 75 s. Carved teakwood elephant 8 5
1061. 2 b. 75 Basketwork .. 15 8
1062. 2 b. 75 Thai folk dolls .. 15 8

332. Scout aiding Cripple. **334.** Ongkhot.

333. Red Cross Volunteer aiding Refugee.

1981. International Year of Disabled People. Multicoloured.
1063. 75 s. Type **332** 8 5
1064. 5 b. Disabled person cutting gem-stones 30 15

1981. Red Cross.
1065. **333.** 75 s. + 25 s. green and red 8 8

1981. Khon (Thai classical dance). Masks. Multicoloured.
1066. 75 s. Type **334** 10 8
1067. 2 b. Maiyarab 15 8
1068. 3 b. Sukrip 25 10
1069. 5 b. Indrajit 30 15

336. 8 a. Stamp. 1899.

1981. "Thaipex '81" National Stamp Exhibition. Multicoloured.
1070. 75 s. Type **336** 8 5
1071. 75 s. 28 s. stamp, 1910 .. 8 5
1072. 2 b. 75 50 s. stamp, 1919 15 8
1073. 2 b. 75 3 s. stamp, 1932 .. 15 8

337. Luang Praditphairo **338.** Mai Hok-Hian.

1981. Birth Centenary of Luang Praditphairo (musician).
1074. **337.** 1 b. 25 multicoloured 10 5

1981. International Correspondence Week. Dwarf Trees. Multicoloured.
1075. 75 s. Type **337** 8 5
1076. 2 b. Mai Kam-Ma-Lo .. 10 5
1077. 2 b. 75 Mai Khen .. 15 8
1078. 5 b. Mai Khabuan .. 25 15

339. Food Produce.

1981. World Food Day.
1079. **339.** 75 s. multicoloured .. 10 5

340. Samran Mukhamat Pavilion, Bangkok.

1981. United Nations Day.
1080. **340.** 1 b. 25 multicoloured 10 5

341. Expressway at Klongtoey.

1981. Inauguration of First Thai Expressway. Multicoloured.
1081. 1 b. Type **341** 8 5
1082. 5 b. Expressway interchange 25 10

342. King Cobra.

1981. Snakes. Multicoloured.
1083. 75 s. Type **342** 8 5
1084. 2 b. Banded krait .. 10 5
1085. 2 b. 75 Thai cobra .. 15 8
1086. 5 b. Malayan pit viper .. 25 12

343. Girl carrying Child.

344. Scouts reaching for Peace.

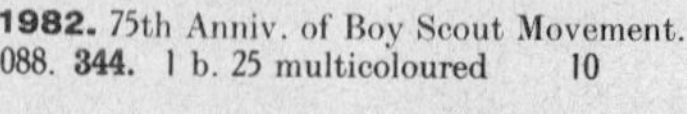

1982. Children's Day.

1087. **343.** 1 b. 25 multicoloured .. 10 5

1982. 75th Anniv. of Boy Scout Movement.

1088. **344.** 1 b. 25 multicoloured .. 10 5

345. King Buddha Yod-Fa (Rama I).

1982. Bicentenary of Chakri Dynasty and Bangkok. Multicoloured.

1089. 1 b. Type **345** 8 5
1090. 1 b. 25 Aerial view of Bangkok 10 5
1091. 2 b. King Buddha Lert La Naphalai (Rama II) 10 5
1092. 3 b. King Nang Klao (Rama III) 15 8
1093. 4 b. King Mongkut (Rama IV) 20 10
1094. 5 b. King Chulalongkorn (Rama V) 45 25
1095. 6 b. King Vajiravudh (Rama VI) 25 40
1096. 7 b. King Prajadhipok (Rama VII) 35 40
1097. 8 b. King Ananda Mahidol (Rama VIII) 60 45
1098. 9 b. King Bhumipol Adulyadej (Rama IX) 65 50

346. Dr. Robert Koch and Cross of Lorraine.

1982. Cent. of Discovery of Tubercle Bacillus.

1100. **346.** 1 b. 25 multicoloured 10 5

347. "Quisqualis indica".

1982. Flowers. Multicoloured.

1101. 1 b. 25 Type **347** 10 5
1102. 1 b. 50 " Murraya paniculata " 10 5
1103. 6 b. 50 " Mesua ferrea " 30 40
1104. 7 b. " Desmos chinensis " 35 45

348. Wat Bowon Sathan Sutthawat.

1982. " Bangkok 1983 " International Stamp Exhibition. (1st issue). Multicoloured.

1105. 1 b. 25 Type **348** 10 5
1106. 4 b. 25 Wat Phra Chetuphon Wimon Mangkalaram 20 10
1107. 6 b. 50 Wat Mahathat Yuwarat Rangsarit .. 30 15
1108. 7 b. Wat Phar Sri Rattana Satsadaram 35 40

See also Nos. 1133/4 and 1142/5.

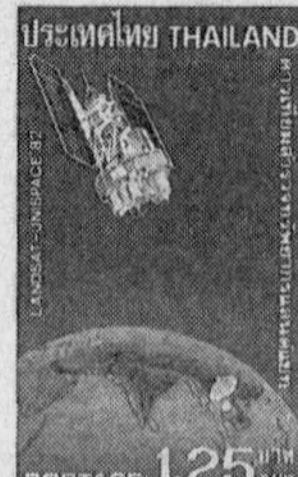

349. "Landsat" Satellite.

350. Prince Purachatra.

1982. Second U.N. Conference of the Exploration and Peaceful Uses of Outer Space, Vienna.

1110. **349.** 1 b. 25 multicoloured 10 5

1982. Birth Cent. of Prince Purachatra.

1111. **350.** 1 b. 25 multicoloured 10 5

351. Covered Jar.

1982. International Correspondence Week. Sangalok Pottery. Multicoloured.

1112. 1 b. 25 Type **351** .. 10 5
1113. 3 b. Small jar 15 8
1114. 4 b. 25 Celadon plate .. 20 10
1115. 7 b. Plate with fish design 60 15

352. Loha Prasat, Bangkok.

1982. United Nations Day.

1116. **352.** 1 b. 25 multicoloured 10 5

353. Chap and Ching.

1982. Thai Musical Instruments. Mult.

1117. 50 s. Type **353** 5 5
1118. 1 b. Pi nok and pi nai (pipes) 8 5
1119. 1 b. 25 Klong that and taphon (drums) .. 10 5
1120. 1 b. 50 Khong mong (gong) and krap (wooden sticks) .. 10 5
1121. 6 b. Khong wong yai (glockenspiel) 30 40
1122. 7 b. Khong wong lek (glockenspiel) 35 40
1123. 8 b. Ranat ek (xylophone) 40 50
1124. 9 b. Ranat thum (xylophone) 50 55

354. Pileated Gibbon

355. Emblem and Flag of Member Countries.

1982. National Wild Animal Preservation Day. Monkeys. Multicoloured.

1125. 1 b. 25 Type **354** .. 20 5
1126. 3 b. Pigtail macaque .. 35 8
1127. 5 b. Slow loris 65 10
1128. 7 b. Silvered leaf monkey 75 15

1982. 15th Anniv. of Association of South-East Asian Nations.

1129. **355.** 6 b. 50 multicoloured 35 15

356. Child sweeping.

1983. Children's Day.

1130. **356.** 1 b. 25 multicoloured 10 5

357. Postcodes

1983. 1st Anniv. of Postcodes. Mult.

1131. 1 b. 25 Type **357** .. 10 5
1132. 1 b. 25 Postcoded envelope 10 5

358. Old General Post Office.

1983. "Bangkok 1983" International Stamp Exhibition (2nd issue).

1133. **358.** 7 b. multicoloured .. 35 15
1134. 10 b. multicoloured 50 15

359. Junks.

1983. 25th Anniv. of International Maritime Organization.

1136. **359.** 1 b. 25 multicoloured 10 10

360. Civil Servant's Shoulder Strap.

1983. Civil Servants' Day.

1137. **360.** 1 b. 25 multicoloured 10 5

361. Giving and receiving Aid and Red Cross.

1983. Red Cross.

1138. **361.** 1 b. 25+25 s. mult. .. 10 10

362. Prince Sithiporn Kridakara.

364. Prince Bhanurangsi.

363. Satellite, Map and Dish Aerial.

1983. Birth Centenary of Prince Sithiporn Kridakara (agriculturalist).

1139. **362.** 1 b. 25 multicoloured 10 5

1983. Domestic Satellite Communications System.

1140. **363.** 2 b. multicoloured .. 15 8

1983. Prince Bhanurangsi (founder of Thai postal service) Commemoration.

1141. **364.** 1 b. 25 multicoloured 10 5

365. Post Box Clearance.

1983. " Bangkok 1983 " International Stamp Exhibition (3rd issue). Multicoloured.

1142. 1 b. 25 Type **365** 10 10
1143. 7 b. 50 Post office counter 45 40
1144. 8 b. 50 Mail transportation 1·00 65
1145. 9 b. 50 Mail delivery .. 65 60

366. Cable Map of A.S.E.A.N. Countries and Cable Ship.

1983. Inauguration of Malaysia–Singapore–Thailand Submarine Cable. Multicoloured.

1147. 1 b. 25 Type **366** .. 40 15
1148. 7 b. Map of new cable .. 40 15

367. Flower Coral ("Acropora asper").

1983. International Correspondence Week. Corals. Multicoloured.

1149. 2 b. Type **367** 15 8
1150. 3 b. Lesser valley coral 20 12
1151. 4 b. Mushroom coral .. 25 12
1152. 7 b. Common lettuce coral 40 40

368. Satellite and Submarine Cable Communications Equipment.

1983. World Communications Year. Mult.
1153. 2 b. Type **368** 15 8
1154. 3 b. Telegraph and telephone service equipment 20 12

369. Fishing for Skipjack.

1983. United Nations Day.
1155. **369.** 1 b. 25 multicoloured 10 5

370. Sangkhalok Pottery.

1983. 700th Anniv. of Thai Alphabet.
1156. **370.** 3 b. multicoloured .. 20 12
1157. – 7 b. black and brown 40 40
1158. – 8 b. multicoloured .. 50 45
1159. – 9 b. multicoloured .. 60 50

DESIGNS—HORIZ. 7 b. Thai characters. VERT. 8 b. Buddha (sculpture). 9 b. Mahathat Temple.

371. Prince Mahidol of Songkhla.

1983. Co-operation between Siriraj Hospital and Rockefeller Foundation.
1160. **371.** 9 b. 50 multicoloured 65 30

372. Lotus Blossoms within Heads.

1984. Children's Day.
1161. **372.** 1 b. 25 multicoloured 10 5

373. Running.

1984. 17th National Games, Phitsanulok Province. Multicoloured.
1162. 1 b. 25 Type **373** .. 8 5
1163. 3 b. Football 20 12

374. Skeletal Joints, Globe and Emblem.

1984. Fifth S.E.A.P.A.L. Rheumatology Congress.
1164. **374.** 1 b. 25 multicoloured 10 5

375. Statue of King Naresuan and Modern Armed Forces.

376. Royal Institute Emblem in Door Arch.

1984. Armed Forces Day.
1165. **375.** 1 b. 25 multicoloured 30 10

1984. 50th Anniv. of Royal Institute.
1166. **376.** 1 b. 25 multicoloured 10 5

1984. Red Cross. No. 954 surch.
1167. **295.** 3 b. 25+25 s. on 2 b. 75+25 s. mult. .. 25 12

378. King and Queen examining Development Project.

1984. Royal Initiated Projects. Multicoloured.
1168. 1 b. 25 Type **378** .. 10 10
1169. 1 b. 25 Improving barren area 10 10
1170. 1 b. 25 Dam, terrace farming and rain-making aircraft .. 25 10
1171. 1 b. 25 Crops, fish and farm animals 10 10
1172. 1 b. 25 King and Queen of Thailand 10 10

379. Dome Building and University Emblem.

1984. 50th Anniv. of Thammasat University.
1173. **379.** 1 b. 25 multicoloured 10 5

381. A.B.U. Emblem and Map.

1984. 20th Anniv. of Asia-Pacific Broadcasting Union.
1174. **381.** 4 b. multicoloured .. 25 12

382. Chiang Saen Style Buddha.

384. "Alocasia indica var. metallica".

1984. Thai Sculptures of Buddhas. Mult.
1175. 1 b. 25 Type **382** .. 10 5
1176. 7 b. Sukhothai style .. 40 15
1177. 8 b. 50 U Thong style .. 55 45
1178. 9 b. 50 Ayutthaya style 65 55

1984. International Correspondence Week. Medicinal Plants. Multicoloured.

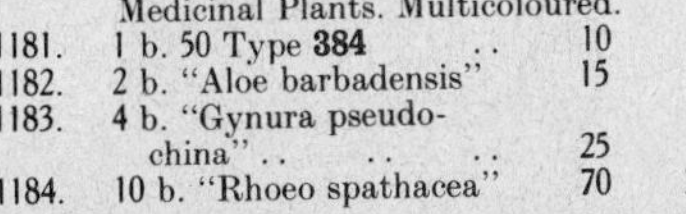

1181. 1 b. 50 Type **384** .. 10 5
1182. 2 b. "Aloe barbadensis" 15 8
1183. 4 b. "Gynura pseudo-china" 25 12
1184. 10 b. "Rhoeo spathacea" 70 35

385. Princess Mother.

386. Threshing Rice.

1984. 84th Birthday of Princess Mother.
1185. **385.** 1 b. 50 multicoloured 10 5

1984. United Nations Day.
1186. **386.** 1 b. 50 multicoloured 10 5

387. "Bhutanitis lidderdalei".

1984. Butterflies. Multicoloured.
1187 2 b. Type **387** 45 25
1188 3 b. "Stichophthalma louisa" 65 40
1189 5 b. "Parthenos sylvia" 90 50
1190 7 b. "Stichophthalma godfreyi" .. .. 1·25 50

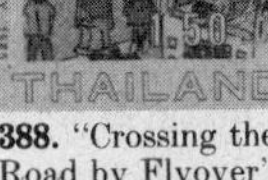

388. "Crossing the Road by Flyover" (U-Tai Raksorn).

390. Monument to Tao-Thep-Krasattri and Tao-Sri-Sundhorn.

389. Bangkok Mail Centre.

1985. Children's Day. Multicoloured.
1191. 1 b. 50 Type **388** .. 10 5
1192. 1 b. 50 "Crossing the Road by Flyover" (Sravudh Charoen-nawee) (horiz.) .. 10 5

1985. Inauguration of Bangkok Mail-sorting Centre.
1193. **389.** 1 b. 50 multicoloured 25 10

1985. Heroines of Phuket. Bicentennial Ceremony.
1194. **390.** 2 b. multicoloured .. 15 8

1985. Red Cross. No. 987 surch.
1195. **306.** 2 b. + 25 s. on 75 s. + 25 s. multicoloured 12 8

392. Bank Headquarters, Bangkok, and King Vajiravudh (Rama VI).

1985. 72nd Anniv. of Government Savings Bank.
1196. **392.** 1 b. 50 multicoloured 8 5

393. Satellite over Thai Buildings.

1985. 20th Anniv. of International Telecommunications Satellite Organization.
1197. **393.** 2 b. multicoloured .. 10 5

394. "DC-6" and Loi-Krathong Festival.

1985. 25th Anniv. of Thai Airways. Mult.
1198. 2 b. Type **394** 15 10
1199. 7 b. 50 "DC-10" and Thai classical dancing .. 1·00 55
1200. 8 b. 50 "Airbus A-300" and Thai buildings .. 1·10 80
1201. 9 b. 50 Boeing "747" and world landmarks .. 1·10 80

395. U.P.U. Emblem.

397. Aisvarya Pavillion.

396. Pigeon

1985. Centenary of Membership of U.P.U. and I.T.U. Multicoloured.
1202. 2 b. Type **395** 10 5
1203. 10 b. I.T.U. Embelm .. 55 55

1985. National Communications Day.
1204. **396.** 2 b. blue, red and deep blue 10 5

1985. "Thaipex '85" Stamp Exhibition. Multicoloured.
1205. 2 b. Type **397** 10 5
1206. 3 b. Varopas Piman Pavilion (horiz.) .. 15 8
1207. 7 b. Vehas Camrun Pavilion (horiz.) 35 40
1208. 10 b. Vitoon Tassana Tower 55 50

398. King Mongkut, Eclipsed Sun and Telescope.

1985. National Science Day.
1210. **398.** 2 b. multicoloured .. 10 5

399. Department Seals, 1885 and 1985.

1985. Centenary of Royal Thai Survey Department.
1211. **399.** 2 b. multicoloured .. 10 5

400. Boxing.

1985. 13th South-East Asia Games, Bangkok (1st issue). Multicoloured.

1212. 2 b. Type **400** 10 5
1213. 2 b. Putting the shot .. 10 5
1214. 2 b. Badminton 10 5
1215. 2 b. Javelin-throwing .. 10 5
1216. 2 b. Weightlifting .. 10 5

See also Nos. 1229/32.

401. "Allemanda cathartica".

402. Mothers and Children at Clinic.

1985. International Correspondence Week. Climbing Plants. Multicoloured.

1218. 2 b. Type **401.** 10 5
1219. 3 b. "Jasminum auriculatum" 15 8
1220. 7 b. Passion flower .. 35 15
1221. 10 b. "Antigonon leptopus" 55 20

1985. United Nations Day.

1222. **402.** 2 b. multicoloured .. 10 5

403. Prince Dhani Nivat.

404. Prince of Jainad.

1985. Birth Cent. of Prince Dhani Nivat.

1223. **403.** 2 b. multicoloured .. 10 5

1985. Birth Cent. of Rangsit, Prince of Jainad (Minister of Health).

1224. **404.** 1 b. 50 multicoloured 8 5

405. Emblem and Buildings.

1985. 5th Asian-Pacific Postal Union Congress.

1225. **405.** 2 b. multicoloured .. 10 5
1226. – 10 b. multicoloured 55 20

DESIGN: 10 b. As Type **405** but different buildings.

406. Emblem.

1985. International Youth Year.

1227. **406.** 2 b. multicoloured .. 10 5

INDEX

Countries can be quickly located by referring to the index at the end of this volume.

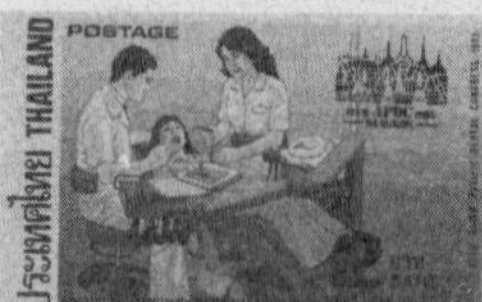

407. Dentist and Nurse tending Patient.

1985. 12th Asian-Pacific Dental Congress.

1228. **407.** 2 b. multicoloured .. 10 5

408. Volleyball.

409. Chevalier de Chaumont presenting Message from Louis XIV to King Narai the Great, 1685.

1985. 12th South-East Asia Games, Bangkok (2nd issue). Multicoloured.

1229. 1 b. Type **408** 5 5
1230. 2 b. Sepak-takraw .. 10 5
1231. 3 b. Gymnastics 15 8
1232. 4 b. Bowling 20 12

1985. 300th Anniv. of Franco-Thai Relations. Multicoloured.

1234. 2 b. Type **409** 10 5
1235. 8 b. 50 Siamese emissaries carrying reply from King Narai to Louis XIV 45 20

410. Emblem.

1986. 3rd Anniv. of International and Inauguration of Domestic Express Mail Services.

1236. **410.** 2 b. multicoloured .. 10 5

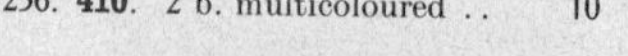

411. Green Turtle.

1986. Turtles. Multicoloured.

1237. 1 b. 50 Type **411** .. 8 5
1238. 3 b. Hawksbill turtle .. 15 8
1239. 5 b. Leatherback turtle 25 12
1240. 10 b. Olive turtle .. 55 20

412. Family picking Lotus.

414. Statue of Sunthon Phu.

1986. Children's Day.

1241. **412.** 2 b. multicoloured .. 10 5

1986. No. 1021 surch.

1242. **317.** 2 b. + 25 s. on 75 s. + 25 s. mult. 12 5

1986. Birth Bicentenary of Sunthon Phu (poet).

1243. **414.** 2 b. multicoloured .. 10 5

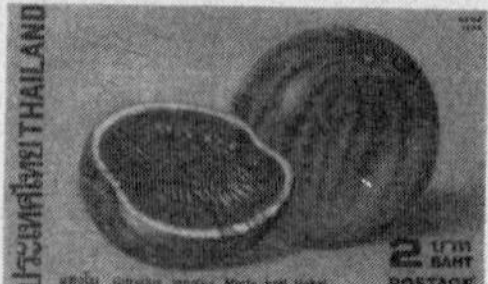

415. Watermelon.

1986. Fruit. Multicoloured.

1244. 2 b. Type **415** 10 5
1245. 2 b. Malay apple ("Eugenia malaccensis") 10 5
1246. 6 b. Pomelo ("Citrus maxima") 30 15
1247. 6 b. Papaya ("Carica papaya") 30 15

416. Trees on Grid and Water Line.

1986. National Tree Year.

1248. **416.** 2 b. multicoloured .. 10 5

417. Pigeon flying from Man's Head to Transmission Masts.

1986. National Communications Day.

1249. **417.** 2 b. multicoloured .. 10 5

418. Chalom.

1986. International Letter Writing Week. Baskets. Multicoloured.

1250. 2 b. Type **418** 10 5
1251. 2 b. Krabung 10 5
1252. 6 b. Kratib 30 15
1253. 6 b. Kaleb 30 15

419. Emblem and War Scenes.

1986. International Peace Year.

1254. **419.** 2 b. bl., dp. bl. & red 10 5

420. Industrial and Agricultural Scenes within Emblem.

1986. Productivity Year.

1255. **420.** 2 b. multicoloured .. 10 5

421. Scouts saluting and Scout helping Blind Man across Road.

1986. 75th Anniv. of Thai Scouting. Mult.

1256. 2 b. 50 Type **421** .. 15 8
1257. 2 b. 50 Scouting activities 15 8
1258. 2 b. 50 King and Queen making presentations to scouts 15 8
1259. 2 b. 50 15th Asia-Pacific Scout Conference, Thailand 15 8

422. "Vanda Varavuth".

1986. 6th ASEAN Orchid Congress, Thailand. Multicoloured.

1260. 2 b. Type **422** 10 5
1261. 3 b. "Ascocenda Emma" 15 8
1262. 4 b. "Dendrobium Sri-Siam" (horiz.) .. 20 12
1263. 5 b. "Dendrobium Ekapol Panda" (horiz.) 25 12

423. "Volvariella volvacea".

1986. Edible Mushrooms. Multicoloured.

1265. 2 b. Type **423** 25 10
1266. 2 b. White oyster mushroom ("Pleurotus ostreatus") 25 10
1267. 6 b. Ear mushroom ("Auricularia polytricha") 85 25
1268. 6 b. Abalone ("Pleurotus cystidiosus") 85 25

424. "Morulius chrysophekadion".

1986. 60th Anniv. of Fisheries Department. Multicoloured.

1269. 2 b. Type **424** 10 5
1270. 2 b. "Notopterus blanci" 10 5
1271. 7 b. "Scleropages formosus" 35 15
1272. 7 b. "Pangasianodon gigas" 35 15

1986. No. 1031 surch. **1 BAHT.**

1273. **227.** 1 b. on 20 s. blue .. 5 5

426. Children in Playground.

1987. National Children's Day. Mult.

1274. 2 b. Type **426** 8 5
1275. 2 b. Children in and around swimming pool 8 5

Nos. 1274/5 were printed together, se-tenant, forming a composite design showing "Our School" by Lawan Maneenetr.

427. "F16" and "F5" Airplanes and Pilot.

1987. 72nd Anniv. of Royal Thai Air Force.
1276. **427.** 2 b. multicoloured .. 25 10

428. King Rama III and Temples.

1987. Bicentenary of King Rama III.
1277. **428.** 2 b. multicoloured .. 8 5

429. Communications and Transport Systems.

1987. 75th Anniv. of Ministry of Communications.
1278. **429.** 2 b. multicoloured .. 25 10

1987. No. 1065 surch. **2+0.50 BAHT.**
1279. **333.** 2 b.+50 s. on 75 s.+ 25 s. green & red.. 10 5

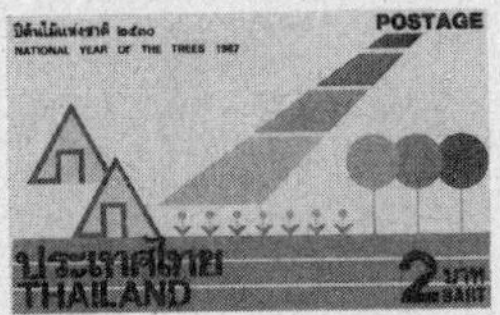

431. Tree-lined Street.

1987. National Tree Year.
1280. **431.** 2 b. multicoloured .. 8 5

432. Gold Peacock.

1987. "Thaipex '87" National Philatelic Exhibition. Handicrafts. Multicoloured.
1281. 2 b. Type **432** 8 5
1282. 2 b. Gold mirrors .. 8 5
1283. 6 b. Gold lustre water urn and finger bowls with trays 30 15
1284. 6 b. Gold swan vase .. 30 15

433. Flying Bird and Animal Horn (Somsak Junthavorn).

1987. National Communications Day.
1286. **433.** 2 b. multicoloured .. 8 5

434. King Rama IX at Presentation Ceremony, King Rama V and Emblem.

1987. Centenary of Chulachomklao Royal Military Academy, Khao Cha-Ngok.
1287. **434.** 2 b. multicoloured .. 8 5

435. Spiral Rope strands leading to Member Countries' Flags.

1987. 20th Anniv. of Association of South East Asian Nations.
1288. **435.** 2 b. multicoloured .. 8 5
1289. 3 b. multicoloured .. 15 5
1290. 4 b. multicoloured .. 20 12
1291. 5 b. multicoloured .. 25 12

436. People and Open Book.
437. Flower Offering Ceremony, Saraburi.

1987. International Literacy Day.
1292. **436.** 2 b. multicoloured .. 8 5

1987. Visit Thailand Year.
1293. 2 b. Type **437** 8 5
1294. 3 b. Duan Sib Festival, Nakhon Si Thammarat 15 8
1295. 5 b. Bang Fai Festival, Yasothon 25 12
1296. 7 b. Loi Krathong, Sukhothai 30 15

438. Ministry Building.

1987. 72nd Anniv. of Auditor General's Office.
1297. **438.** 2 b. multicoloured .. 8 5

439. Temple of Dawn, "Sri Suphanahong" (royal barge) and Mt. Fuji within "100".

1987. Centenary of Japan-Thailand Friendship Treaty.
1298. **439.** 2 b. multicoloured .. 15 10

440. Floral Tassel.

1987. International Letter Writing Week. Ceremonial Floral Garlands. Multicoloured.
1299. 2 b. Type **440** 8 5
1300. 3 b. Tasselled garland .. 15 8
1301. 5 b. Wrist garland .. 25 12
1302. 7 b. Double-ended garland 30 15

441. Thai Pavilion.

1987. Inauguration of Social Education and Cultural Centre.
1303. **441.** 2 b. multicoloured .. 8 5

442. King Bhumibol Adulyadej as a Boy.

1987. King Bhumibol Adulyadej's 60th Birthday. Multicoloured.
1304. 2 b. Type **442** 8 5
1305. 2 b. Wedding photograph of King Bhumibol Adulyadej and Queen Sirikit, 1950 8 5
1306. 2 b. King on throne during Accession ceremony at Paisan Hall, 1950 .. .. 8 5
1307. 2 b. King as monk on alms round 8 5
1308. 2 b. Elderly woman greeting King.. .. 8 5
1309. 2 b. King demonstrating to hill tribes how to take medicine .. 8 5
1310. 2 b. King and Queen visiting wounded servicemen 8 5
1311. 2 b. King examining new system for small farms 8 5
1313. 2 b. Princess Mother Somdej Phra Sri Nakarindra Boromrajjonnani .. 8 5
1314. 2 b. Crown Prince Maha Vajiralongkorn .. 8 5
1315. 2 b. Princess Maha Chakri Sirindhorn .. 8 5
1316. 2 b. Princess Chulabhorn 8 5
1317. 2 b. King Bhumibol Adulyadej and Queen Sirikit 8 5
1318. 2 b. King and family (48×33 mm.) 8 5
1319. 100 b. gold and deep bright blue (King Bhumibol Adulyadej) (48×33 mm.) .. .. 6·50 4·25

1987. No. 1180a surch. **2 BAHT.**
1320. **325.** 2 b. on 1 b. 50 orange 8 5

444. "Teacher's Day" (Nutchaliya Suddhiprasit).
445. Prince Kromamun Bridhyalongkorn (founder).

1988. National Children's Day.
1321. **444.** 2 b. multicoloured .. 8 5

1988. 72nd Anniv. of Thai Co-operatives.
1322. **445.** 2 b. multicoloured .. 8 5

446. Society Building.

1988. 84th Anniv. of Siam Society (for promotion of arts and sciences).
1323. **446.** 2 b. multicoloured .. 8 5

1988. No. 1040a surch. **1 BAHT.**
1324 **325** 1 b. on 1 b. 25 green .. 5 5

448 Phra Phai Luang Monastery

1988. Sukhothai Historical Park. Mult.
1325 2 b. Type **448** 10 5
1326 3 b. Traphang Thonglang Monastery 15 8
1327 4 b. Maha That Monastery 20 10
1328 6 b. Thewalai Maha Kaset 30 15

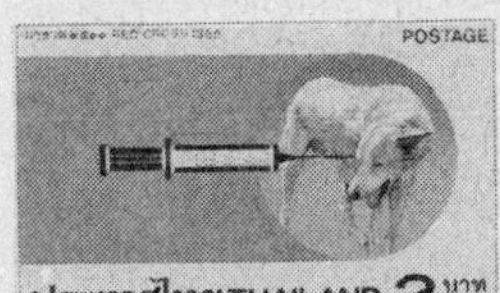

449 Syringe between Red Cross and Dog

1988. Red Cross Anti-hydrophobia Campaign.
1329 **449** 2 b. multicoloured .. 10 5

450 King Rama V (founder)
452 Hand holding Coloured Ribbons

451 Crested Fireback Pheasant

1988. Centenary of Siriraj Hospital.
1330 **450** 5 b. multicoloured .. 25 12

1988. Pheasants. Multicoloured.
1331 2 b. Type **451** 15 10
1332 3 b. Kalij pheasant .. 25 15
1333 6 b. Silver pheasant .. 45 25
1334 7 b. Mrs. Hume's pheasant 55 35

1988. Centenary of International Women's Council
1335 **452** 2 b. multicoloured .. 10 5

453 King Rama IX in King Rama V's Bodyguard's Uniform
454 King Rama IX in full Robes

1988.
1631 **453** 25 s. brown .. 5 5
1336 50 s. green 5 5
1336a 1 b. blue 5 5
1337 2 b. red 10 5
1338 3 b. blue and brown 15 8
1339 4 b. brown and blue 20 10
1340 5 b. brown and lilac 20 10
1341 6 b. purple and green 25 15
1341a 7 b. dp brown & brn 20 15
1342 8 b. green and red .. 35 20
1343 9 b. brown and blue 40 20
1344 10 b. green & brown 45 50
1345 20 b. green & orange 1·40 1·00
1346 25 b. blue and green 1·25 90
1347 50 b. green and lilac 3·25 2·40
1351 100 b. blue & orange 6·50 4·75

1988. 38th Anniv of Accession to Throne of King Rama IX. Multicoloured.
1356 2 b. Type **454** 10 5
1357 2 b. Great Crown of Victory 10 5
1358 2 b. Sword of Victory and scabbard (horiz) .. 10 5
1359 2 b. Sceptre (horiz) .. 10 5
1360 2 b. Royal Fan and Fly Whisk (horiz) 10 5
1361 2 b. Slippers (horiz) .. 10 5
1362 2 b. Atthathit Uthumphon Ratchaat throne (octagonal base) .. 10 5
1363 2 b. Phattrabit throne (rectangular base .. 10 5

1364 2 b. Phuttan Kanchanasinghat throne (gold throne on angular steps) 10 5
1365 2 b. Butsabokmala Mahachakkraphatphiman throne (ship shape) .. 10 5
1366 2 b. Throne inlaid with mother-of-pearl (blue throne on angular steps) 10 5
1367 2 b. Peony design niello throne (circular steps) 10 5

No. 1357 is 33×48mm and Nos. 1358/61 48×33mm in size.

455 Bridge, Bulding and Trees

1988. National Tree Year.
1369 **455** 2 b. multicoloured .. 10 5

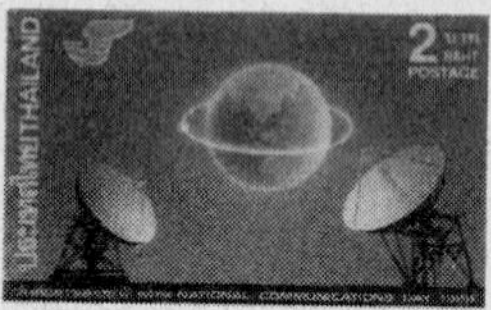

456 Globe and Dish Aerials

1988. National Communications Day.
1370 **456** 2 b. multicoloured .. 10 5

458 Grasshopper

1988. International Letter Writing Week. Woven Coconut-leaf Folk Toys. Mult.
1371 2 b. Type **458** 10 5
1372 2 b. Carp 10 5
1373 6 b. Bird 30 15
1374 6 b. Takro 30 15

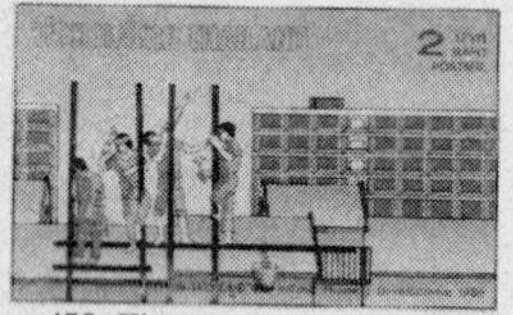

459 Flats and Construction Workers

1988. Housing Development.
1375 **459** 2 b. multicoloured .. 10 5

460 King Rama V in Full Uniform

461 Road Signs

1988. 120th Anniv of King's Own Bodyguard.
1376 **460** 2 b. multicoloured .. 10 5

1988. Road Safety Campaign.
1377 **461** 2 b. multicoloured .. 10 5

462 "Crotalaria sessiliflora"

464 Knight Grand Commander of Honourable Order of Rama

463 Buddha's Birthplace

1988. New Year. Multicoloured.
1378 1 b. Type **462** 5 5
1379 1 b. "Uvaria grandiflora" 5 5
1380 1 b. "Reinwardtia trigyna" 5 5
1381 1 b. "Impatiens griffithii" 5 5

1988. Buddha Monthon Celebrations. Mult.
1382 2 b. Type **463** 10 5
1383 3 b. Buddha's place of enlightenment .. 15 8
1384 4 b. Site of Buddha's first sermon 20 10
1385 5 b. Buddha's Place of Nirvana 25 15
1386 6 b. Buddha (vert) .. 30 15

1988. Insignia of Orders. Multicoloured.
1387 2 b. Type **464** 10 5
1388 2 b. Close-up of badge .. 10 5
1389 3 b. Knight Grand Cordon (Special Class) of Most Exalted Order of White Elephant 15 8
1390 3 b. Close-up of badge .. 15 8
1391 5 b. Knight Grand Cordon of Most Noble Order of Crown of Thailand .. 25 15
1392 5 b. Close-up of badge .. 25 15
1393 7 b. Close-up of Rarana Varabhorn Order of Merit 35 20
1394 7 b. Badge on chain of office 35 20

465 "Floating Market" (Thongbai Siyam)

1989. National Children's Day. Designs showing plasticine paintings by blind people. Multicoloured.
1395 2 b. Type **465** 20 10
1396 2 b. "Flying Birds" (Kwanchai Kerd-Daeng) 20 10
1397 2 b. "Little Mermaid" (Chalermpol Jiengmai) 20 10
1398 2 b. "Golden Fish" (Natetip Korsantirak) 20 10

466 Emblem and Symbols of Communication

1989. 12th Anniv of Thai Communications Authority.
1399 **466** 2 b. multicoloured .. 8 5

467 Statue of Kings Rama V and VI and Auditorium

1989. 72nd Anniv of Chulalongkorn University.
1400 **467** 2 b. multicoloured .. 8 5

468 Red Cross Worker

469 Phra Kaeo Monastery

1989. 96th Anniv of Thai Red Cross (1401) and 125th Anniv of International Red Cross (1402). Multicoloured.
1401 2 b. Type **468** 8 5
1402 10 b. Red Cross and pillar 45 50

1989. Phra Nakhon Khiri Historical Park. Multicoloured.
1403 2 b. Type **469** 8 5
1404 3 b. Chatchawan Wiangchai Observatory .. 15 8
1405 5 b. Phra That Chom Phet stupa 20 10
1406 6 b. Wetchayan Wichian Phrasat Throne Hall .. 25 15

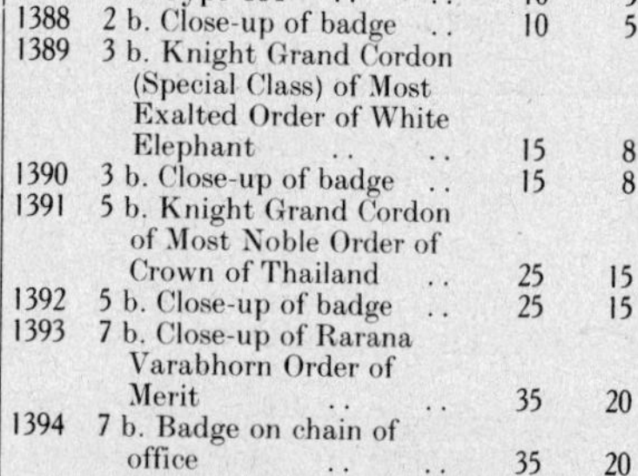

470 Lottery Office Building and Profit Recipients

1989. 50th Anniv of Government Lottery Office.
1407 **470** 2 b. multicoloured .. 8 5

471 Campaign Emblem and Figures

472 Gold Nielloware Figure

1989. International Anti-Drugs Day.
1408 **471** 2 b. multicoloured .. 8 5

1989. National Arts and Crafts Year. Mult.
1409 2 b. Type **472** 8 5
1410 2 b. Ceramics 8 5
1411 6 b. Ornament inlaid with gemstones (horiz) .. 25 15
1412 6 b. Rolls of cloth (horiz) 25 15

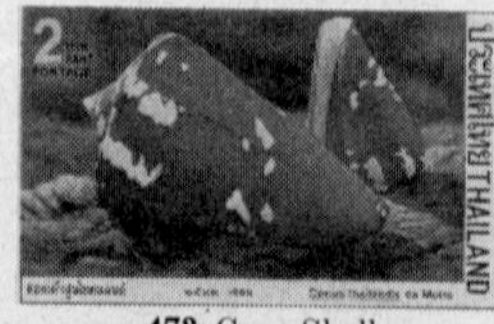

473 Cone Shell

1989. Shells. Multicoloured.
1413 2 b. Type **473** 8 5
1414 3 b. Thorny oyster .. 15 8
1415 6 b. Great spotted cowrie 25 15
1416 10 b. Emperor nautilus .. 45 25

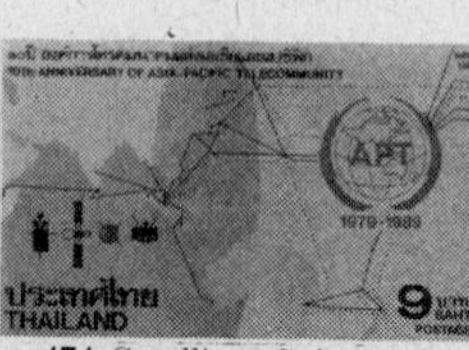

474 Satellites, Submarine Cable Network and Emblem

1989. 10th Anniv of Asia–Pacific Telecommunity.
1417 **474** 9 b. multicoloured .. 40 20

475 Phya Anuman Rajadhon

1989. Birth Centenary (1988) of Phya Anuman Rajadhon (writer).
1418 **475** 2 b. multicoloured .. 8 5

476 Emblem and School

1989. Centenary of Post and Telecommunications School.
1419 **476** 2 b. multicoloured .. 8 5

477 Communications Symbols

478 Post Box

1989. National Communications Day.
1420 **477** 2 b. multicoloured .. 20 10

1989. "Thaipex '89" National Stamp Exhibition. Post Boxes. Multicoloured.
1421 2 b. Type **478** 8 5
1422 3 b. Provincial box .. 15 8
1423 4 b. City box 20 10
1424 5 b. Imported English box 20 10
1425 6 b. West German box sent as gift on introduction of Thai Postal Service 25 15

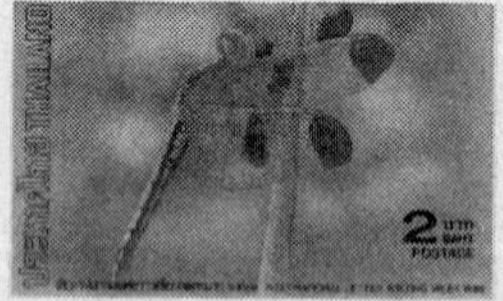

479 Dragonfly

1989. International Letter Writing Week. Multicoloured.
1426 2 b. Type **479** 10 10
1427 5 b. Dragonfly (different) 30 15
1428 6 b. Dragonfly (different) 35 20
1429 10 b. Damselfly .. 60 35

480 Means of Transport and Communications

1989. Asia–Pacific Transport and Communications Decade.
1431 **480** 2 b. multicoloured .. 20 10

481 Figure and "Thoughts"

482 "Hypericum uralum"

1989. Centenary of Mental Health Care.
1432 481 2 b. multicoloured .. 8 5

1989. New Year. Flowers. Multicoloured.
1433 1 b. Type 482 .. .. 5 5
1434 1 b. "Uraria rufescens" .. 5 5
1435 1 b. "Manglietia garrettii" 5 5
1436 1 b. "Aeschynanthus macranthus" 5 5

483 "Catacanthus incarnatus"

1989. Beetles. Multicoloured.
1438 2 b. Type 483 .. .. 10 10
1439 3 b. "Aristobia approximator" 25 10
1440 6 b. "Chrysochroa chinensis" 40 25
1441 10 b. "Enoplotrupes sharpi" 60 40

484 Medallists on Rostrum

1989. Sports Welfare Fund. Multicoloured.
1442 2 b.+1 b. Type 484 .. 15 15
1443 2 b.+1 b. Nurse attending fallen cyclist 15 15
1444 2 b.+1 b. Boxing .. 15 15
1445 2 b.+1 b. Football .. 15 15

485 Official, Family and Graph

1990. Population and Housing Census.
1446 485 2 b. multicoloured .. 8 5

486 Skipping (Phethai Setharangsi)

1990. National Children's Day. Multicoloured.
1447 2 b. Type 486 .. .. 8 5
1448 2 b. Various sports activities (Chalermpol Wongpim) (vert) .. 8 5

487 Skull splitting Heart

488 Tiap

1990. Red Cross. Anti-AIDS Campaign.
1449 487 2 b. blue, red & black 8 5

1990. Heritage Conservation Day. Mother-of-Pearl Inlaid Containers. Multicoloured.
1450 2 b. Type 488 .. .. 8 5
1451 2 b. Phan waenfa .. 8 5
1452 8 b. Lung (horiz) .. 30 15
1453 8 b. Chiat klom (horiz) .. 30 15

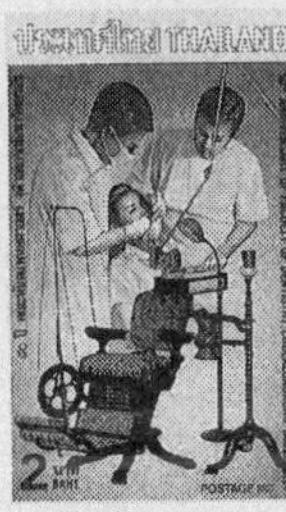

489 Dentistry Students and Old Chair

490 Tin

1990. 50th Anniv of Chulalongkorn University Dentistry Faculty.
1454 489 2 b. multicoloured .. 8 5

1990. Minerals. Multicoloured.
1455 2 b. Type 490 .. .. 8 5
1456 3 b. Zinc 10 5
1457 5 b. Lead 20 10
1458 6 b. Fluorite 25 15

491 Pigeon

1990. National Communications Day.
1465 491 2 b. blue, dp bl & pur 8 5

492 Pigeons and Evelopes

1990. 20th Anniv of Asian-Pacific Postal Training Centre, Bangkok.
1466 492 2 b. green, blue & blk 8 5
1467 8 b. blue, green & blk 30 15

493 Jaipur Foot Project

1990. 60th Anniv of Rotary International in Thailand. Multicoloured.
1468 2 b. Type 493 .. .. 8 5
1469 3 b. Child anti-polio vaccination campaign 10 5
1470 6 b. Literacy campaign .. 25 15
1471 8 b. King Chulalongkorn and his engraved cypher (Thai Museum, Nordkapp, Norway) .. 35 10

494 Account and Staff at Computer Terminals

1990. Centenary of Comptroller-General's Department.
1472 494 2 b. multicoloured .. 8 5

495 Flowers in Dish (Cho Muang)

1990. International Correspondence Week. Designs showing winning paintings in design competition. Multicoloured.
1473 2 b. Type 495 .. .. 8 5
1474 3 b. Flowers on tray (Cha Mongkut) 10 5
1475 5 b. Sweetmeats on tray with leaf design (Sane Chan) 20 10
1476 6 b. Fruit in bowl (Luk Chup) 25 15

496 Princess Mother with Flower

497 "Cyrtandromoea grandiflora"

1990. 90th Birthday of Princess Mother.
1478 496 2 b. multicoloured .. 8 5

1990. New Year. Flowers. Multicoloured.
1479 1 b. Type 497 .. 5 5
1480 1 b. "Rhododendron arboreum sp. delavayi" 5 5
1481 1 b. "Merremia vitifolia" 5 5
1482 1 b. "Afgekia mahidolae" 5 5

498 Wiman Mek Royal Hall

1990. Dusit Palace. Multicoloured.
1484 2 b. Type 498 .. .. 8 5
1485 3 b. Ratcharit Rungrot Royal House 10 5
1486 4 b. Aphisek Dusit Royal Hall 15 8
1487 5 b. Amphon Sathan Palace 20 10
1488 6 b. Udon Phak Royal Hall 25 15
1489 8 b. Anantasamakhom Throne Hall 30 15

499 Phrachetuphon Wimolmangkalaram Temple and Supreme Patriarch

1990. Birth Bicentenary of Supreme Patriarch Somdet Phra Maha Samanachao Kromphra Paramanuchitchinorot.
1490 499 2 b. multicoloured .. 8 5

500 Judo

1990. Sports Welfare Fund. Multicoloured.
1491 2 b.+1 b. Type 500 .. 10 10
1492 2 b.+1 b. Archery .. 10 10
1493 2 b.+1 b. High jumping 10 10
1494 2 b.+1 b. Windsurfing .. 20 15

501 Aspects of Petroleum Industry

1990. 12th Anniv of Thai Petroleum Authority.
1495 501 2 b. multicoloured .. 8 5

502 Mae Klong Railway Locomotive No. 6

1990. Steam Locomotives. Multicoloured.
1496 2 b. Type 502 .. .. 8 5
1497 3 b. "Sung Noen" locomotive No. 32 .. 10 5
1498 5 b. "C 56" locomotive No. 715 .. .. 20 10
1499 6 b. "Mikado" locomotive No. 953 .. .. 25 15

503 Luk Khang (tops)

1991. Children's Day. Games. Multicoloured.
1501 2 b. Type 503 .. .. 8 5
1502 3 b. Pid Ta Ti Mo (blindfolded child smashing vase) 10 5
1503 5 b. Doen Kala (walking on stones) 20 10
1504 6 b. Phong Phang (blind man's bluff) 25 15

504 Map, Surveyor and Cartographer

505 Princess (patron) wearing Red Cross Uniform

1991. Land Deeds Project.
1505 504 2 b. multicoloured .. 10 5

1991. Red Cross Fair. Princess Maha Chaki Sirindhorn's "Third Cycle" Birthday.
1506 505 2 b. multicoloured .. 10 5

506 "Indra's Heavenly Abode" **507** Goddess riding Goat

1991. Heritage Conservation Day. Floral Hanging Decorations. Multicoloured.
1508 2 b. Type **506** 10 5
1509 3 b. "Celestial Couch" .. 15 10
1510 4 b. "Crystal Ladder" .. 20 10
1511 5 b. "Crocodile" .. 20 10

1991. Songkran (New Year) Day. Year of the Goat.
1513 **507** 2 b. multicoloured .. 10 5

508 Prince Narisranuvattivongs

1991. 44th Death Anniv of Prince Narisranuvattivongs.
1515 **508** 2 b. brown, deep brown and yellow 10 5

509 Pink Lotus (Sutthiporn Wiset) **511** Yok

510 World Map, Communication Systems and Healthy Tree

1991. Runners-up in International Correspondence Week Competition. Mult.
1516 2 b. Type **509** 10 5
1517 3 b. Pink lotuses (Mathayom Suksa group, Khonkaen-vityayon School) .. 15 10
1518 5 b. White lotus (Rattanaporn Sukhasem) (horiz) .. 20 10
1519 6 b. Red lotuses (Phanupongs Saya-sombat and Kanokwan Cholaphum) (horiz) .. 30 15

1991. National Communications Day. "Communications and Preservation of the Environment".
1520 **510** 2 b. multicoloured .. 10 5

1991. "Thaipex '91" National Stamp Exhibition. Textile patterns. Mult.
1521 2 b. Type **511** 10 5
1522 4 b. Mudmee 20 10
1523 6 b. Khit 30 15
1524 8 b. Chok 35 20

512 Workers and Productivity Arrow

1991. International Productivity Congress.
1526 **512** 2 b. multicoloured .. 10 5

513 "Co-operation of Women around the World"

1991. 26th Int. Council of Women Triennial.
1527 **513** 2 b. multicoloured .. 10 5

514 Black

1991. International Correspondence Week. Japanese Bantams. Multicoloured.
1528 2 b. Type **514** 10 5
1529 3 b. Black-tailed buff .. 15 10
1530 6 b. Buff 30 15
1531 8 b. White 35 20

515 Silver Coin of King Rama IV and Wat Phra Sri Rattana Satsadaram

1991. World Bank and International Monetary Fund Annual Meetings. Mult.
1533 2 b. Type **515** 10 5
1534 4 b. Pod Duang money, Wat Mahathat Sukhothai and Wat Aroonrachawararam .. 20 10
1535 8 b. Chieng and Hoi money and Wat Phrathat Doi Suthep .. 35 20
1536 10 b. Funan, Dvaravati and Srivijaya money, Phra Pathom Chedi and Phra Borommathat Chaiya 45 25

516 1908 1 t. Stamp **518** "Dillenia obovata"

517 Adult and Calves

1991. "Bangkok 1993" International Stamp Exhibition (1st series). Stamps from the 1908 King Chulalongkorn issue. Multicoloured.
1538 2 b. Type **516** 10 5
1539 3 b. 2 t. stamp 15 10
1540 4 b. 3 t. stamp 20 10
1541 5 b. 5 t. stamp 20 10
1542 6 b. 10 t. stamp 30 15
1543 7 b. 20 t. stamp 30 15
1544 8 b. 40 t. stamp 35 20
See also Nos. 1626/9, 1666/9 and 1700/3.

1991. The Indian Elephant. Multicoloured.
1546 2 b. Type **517** 10 5
1547 4 b. Elephants pulling log 20 10
1548 6 b. Adult male resting .. 30 15
1549 8 b. Adults bathing .. 40 20

1991. New Year. Flowers. Multicoloured.
1551 1 b. Type **518** 5 5
1552 1 b. "Melastoma sanguineum" 5 5
1553 1 b. "Commelina diffusa" .. 5 5
1554 1 b. "Plumbago indica" .. 5 5

520 Jogging **522** Prince Mahidol

521 Large Indian Civet

1991. Sports Welfare Fund. Multicoloured.
1558 2 b.+1 b. Type **520** .. 15 10
1559 2 b.+1 b. Cycling .. 15 10
1560 2 b.+1 b. Skipping .. 15 10
1561 2 b.+1 b. Swimming .. 15 10

1991. Mammals. Multicoloured.
1562 2 b. Type **521** 10 5
1563 3 b. Banded linsang .. 15 10
1564 6 b. Asiatic golden cat .. 30 15
1565 8 b. Black giant squirrel 40 20

1992. Birth Centenary (1991) of Prince Mahidol of Songkla (pioneer of modern medicine in Thailand).
1567 **522** 2 b. brown, gold & yell 10 5

523 Archaeologists and Dinosaur Skeletons

1992. Centenary of Department of Mineral Resources. Multicoloured.
1568 2 b. Type **523** 10 10
1569 2 b. Mining excavation .. 10 10
1570 2 b. Extracting natural gas and oil 10 10
1571 2 b. Digging artesian wells 10 10

524 Drawing by Nachadong Bunprasoet

1992. Children's Day. "World under the Sea". Children's drawings. Multicoloured.
1572 2 b. Type **524** 10 5
1573 3 b. Fishes and seaweed (Varaporn Phadkhan) 15 10
1574 5 b. Mermaid (Phannipha Ngoenkon) (vert) .. 25 15

525 Battle Scene (mural, Chan Chittrakon)

1992. 400th Anniv of Duel between King Naresuan the Great of Thailand and Phra Maha Upparacha of Burma.
1575 **525** 2 b. multicoloured .. 10 5

526 "Paphiopedilum bellatulum"

1992. 4th Asia–Pacific Orchid Conference. Multicoloured.
1576 2 b. Type **526** 10 5
1577 2 b. "Paphiopedilum exul" 10 5
1578 3 b. "Paphiopedilum godefroyae" 15 10
1579 3 b. "Paphiopedilum concolor" 15 10
1580 6 b. "Paphiopedilum niveum" 30 15
1581 6 b. "Paphiopedilum villosum" 30 15
1582 10 b. "Paphiopedilum parishii" 50 25
1583 10 b. "Paphiopedilum sukhakulii" 50 25

527 "Innocent" (Kamolporn Tapsuang)

1992. Red Cross.
1585 **527** 2 b. multicoloured .. 10 5

528 Sugar Cane **529** Prince Rabi Badhanasakdi (founder of School of Law)

1992. 21st International Sugar Cane Technologists Society Congress.
1586 **528** 2 b. multicoloured .. 10 5

1992. Centenary of Ministry of Justice. Legal Reformers. Multicoloured.
1587 3 b. Type **529** 15 10
1588 5 b. King Rama V (reformer of Courts system) 25 15

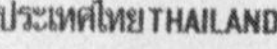

530 Container Ships and Lorry **531** Prince Damrong Rajanubharb (first Minister)

1992. 80th Anniv of Ministry of Transport and Communications. Multicoloured.
1589 2 b. Type **530** 10 10
1590 3 b. Train and bus .. 15 10
1591 5 b. Aircraft and control tower 25 15
1592 6 b. Lorry, satellites and aerials 30 15

1992. Centenary of Ministry of the Interior. Multicoloured.

1593 2 b. Type **531** 10 5
1594 2 b. Polling station .. 10 5
1595 2 b. Emergency services and army 10 5
1596 2 b. Child fetching water 10 5

532 Royal Ceremony of First Ploughing

1992. Centenary of Ministry of Agriculture Co-operatives.

1597 **532** 2 b. multicoloured .. 10 5
1598 3 b. multicoloured .. 15 10
1599 4 b. multicoloured .. 20 10
1600 5 b. multicoloured .. 25 15

533 Ministry

1992. Centenary of Ministry of Education.

1601 **533** 2 b. multicoloured .. 10 5

534 Western Region

1992. Thai Heritage Conservation Day. Traditional Carts. Multicoloured.

1602 2 b. Type **534** 10 5
1603 3 b. Northern region .. 15 10
1604 5 b. North-eastern region 25 15
1605 10 b. Eastern region .. 50 25

535 Demon riding Monkey

536 American Brahman and Livestock

1992. Songkran (New Year) Day. Year of the Monkey.

1607 **535** 2 b. multicoloured .. 10 5

1992. 50th Anniv of Department of Livestock Development.

1609 **536** 2 b. multicoloured .. 10 5

537 Birth of Buddha (mural, Wat Angkaeo, Bangkok)

538 Weather Balloon, Dish Aerial, Satellite and Map

1992. Wisakhabucha Day. Multicoloured.

1610 2 b. Type **537** 10 5
1611 3 b. "Enlightenment of Buddha" (illustation by Phraya Thewaphinimmit from biography) 15 10
1612 5 b. Death of Buddha (mural, Wsat Kanmatuyaram, Bangkok) .. 25 15

1992. 50th Anniv of Meteorological Department.

1613 **538** 2 b. multicoloured .. 10 5

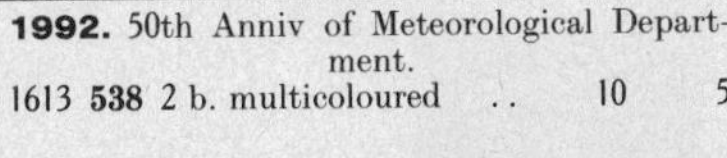

539 Bua Tong Field, Mae Hong Son Province

540 1887 64 a. stamp

1992. Association of South-East Asian Nations Tourism Year. Multicoloured.

1614 2 b. Type **539** 10 5
1615 3 b. Klong Larn Waterfall, Kamphaeng Phet Province 15 10
1616 4 b. Coral, Chumphon Province 20 10
1617 5 b. Khao Ta-Poo, Phangnga Province .. 25 15

1992. "Bangkok 1993" International Stamp Exhibition (2nd series). Multicoloured.

1618 2 b. Type **540** 10 5
1619 3 b. 1916 20 b. stamp .. 15 10
1620 5 b. 1928 40 b. stamp .. 25 15
1621 7 b. 1943 1 b. stamp .. 35 20
1622 8 b. 1947 20 b. stamp .. 40 20

541 Prince Chudadhuj Dharadilok

543 Culture and Sports

542 "Communications"

1992. Birth Centenary of Prince Chudadhuj Dharadilok of Bejraburna.

1624 **541** 2 b. multicoloured .. 10 5

1992. National Communications Day.

1625 **542** 2 b. multicoloured .. 10 5

1992. 25th Anniv of Association of South-East Asian Nations. Multicoloured.

1626 2 b. Type **543** 10 10
1627 3 b. Tourist sites .. 15 10
1628 5 b. Transport and communications .. 35 15
1629 7 b. Agriculture 35 20

544 Sirikit Medical Centre

1992. Inauguration of Sirikit Medical Centre.

1630 **544** 2 b. multicoloured .. 10 5

545 Wedding Ceremony

546 Queen Sirikit and Cipher

1992. 60th Birthday of Queen Sirikit.

(a) As T **545**. Multicoloured.

1635 2 b. Type **545** 10 5
1636 2 b. Royal couple seated at Coronation ceremony 10 5
1637 2 b. Anointment as Queen 10 5
1638 2 b. Seated on chair .. 10 5
1639 2 b. Visiting hospital patient 10 5
1640 2 b. Talking to subjects .. 10 5

(b) Royal Regalia. Enamelled gold objects. As T **546**. Multicoloured.

1642 2 b. Bowls on footed tray (betel and areca nut set) 10 5
1643 2 b. Kettle 10 5
1644 2 b. Water holder within bowl 10 5
1645 2 b. Box on footed tray (betel and areca nut set) 10 5
1646 2 b. Vase 10 5

(c) Type **546**

1647 **546** 100 b. blue and gold .. 5·25 2·75

547 Prince Wan Waithayakon

548 Bhirasri

1992. Birth Centenary (1991) of Prince Wan Waithayakon (diplomat).

1648 **547** 2 b. multicoloured .. 10 5

1992. Birth Centenary of Silpa Bhirasri (sculptor).

1649 **548** 2 b. multicoloured .. 10 5

549 "Catalaphyllia jardinei"

1992. International Correspondence Week. Corals. Multicoloured.

1650 2 b. Type **549** 10 5
1651 3 b. "Porites lutea" .. 15 10
1652 6 b. "Tubastraea coccinea" 30 15
1653 8 b. "Favia pallida" .. 40 20

550 "Rhododendron simsii"

551 Figures of Man and Woman

1992. New Year. Flowers. Multicoloured.

1655 1 b. Type **550** 5 5
1656 1 b. "Cynoglossum lanceolatum" 5 5
1657 1 b. "Tithonia diversifolia" 5 5
1658 1 b. "Agapetes parishii" 5 5

1992. 1st Asian Pacific Allergy and Immunology Congress, Bangkok.

1660 **551** 2 b. multicoloured .. 10 5

552 Anantasamakhom Throne Hall, National Assembly Building and King Prajadhipok's Monument

1992 60th Anniv of National Assembly.

1661 **552** 2 b. multicoloured .. 10 5

553 Bank's Emblem and Bang Khun Phrom Palace (old headquarters)

1992. 50th Anniv of Bank of Thailand.

1662 **553** 2 b. multicoloured .. 10 5

554 "River and Life" (Prathinthip Mensin)

1993. Children's Day. Children's drawings. Multicoloured.

1663 2 b. Type **554** 10 5
1664 2 b. "Lovely Wild Animals and Beautiful Forest" (Pratsani Thammaprasert) .. 10 5
1665 2 b. "Communications in the Next Decade" (Natchaliya Sutiprasit) 10 5

555 Kendi, Water Dropper and Bottle

1993. "Bangkok 1993" International Stamp Exhibition (3rd series). Traditional Pottery. Multicoloured.

1666 3 b. Type **555** 15 10
1667 6 b. Vase and bottles .. 30 15
1668 7 b. Bowls 35 20
1669 8 b. Jars 40 20

556 Anniversary Emblem

1993. Centenary of Thai Teacher Training Institute.

1671 **556** 2 b. multicoloured .. 10 5

557 Agricultural Produce

1993. 50th Anniv of Kasetsart University.

1672 **557** 2 b. multicoloured .. 10 5

558 Buddha preaching (mural, Kanmatuyaram Temple, Bangkok)

559 Queen Sri Bajarindra (first royal patron)

1993. Maghapuja Day.

1673	**558**	2 b. multicoloured ..	10	5

1993. Centenary of Thai Red Cross.

1674	**559**	2 b. multicoloured ..	10	5

560 Clock, Emblem and Attorney General

1993. Centenary of Attorney General's Office.

1675	**560**	2 b. multicoloured ..	10	5

561 Wat Chedi Chet Thaeo

1993. Thai Heritage Conservation Day. Si Satchanalai Historical Park, Sukhothai Province. Multicoloured.

1676	3 b. Type **561**	15	10
1677	4 b. Wat Chang Lom ..	20	10
1678	6 b. Wat Phra Si Rattanamahathat ..	30	15
1679	7 b. Wat Suan Kaeo Utthayan Noi ..	35	20

562 Demon riding Cock

1993. Songkran (New Year) Day. Year of the Cock.

1681	**562**	2 b. multicoloured ..	10	5

563 "Marasmius sp."

1993. Fungi. Multicoloured.

1683	2 b. Type **563**	10	5
1684	4 b. "Coprinus sp." ..	20	10
1685	6 b. "Mycena sp." ..	30	15
1686	8 b. "Cyathus sp." ..	45	25

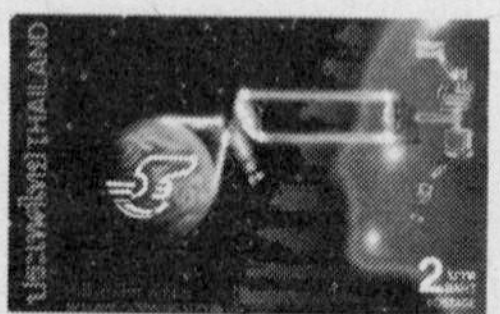

564 "Communications in the Next Decade"

1993. National Communications Day.

1688	**564**	2 b. multicoloured ..	10	5

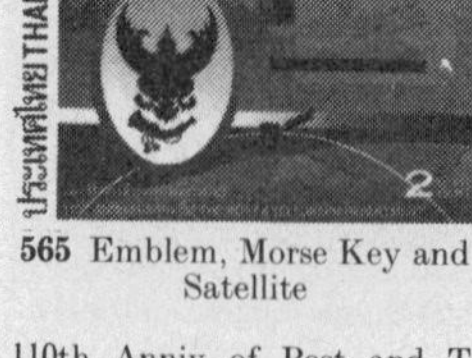

565 Emblem, Morse Key and Satellite

1993. 110th Anniv of Post and Telegraph Department.

1689	**565**	2 b. multicoloured ..	10	5

566 Monument, Park and Reservoir

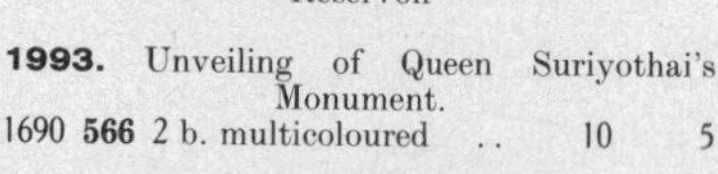

1993. Unveiling of Queen Suriyothai's Monument.

1690	**566**	2 b. multicoloured ..	10	5

567 Fawn Ridgeback

1993. International Correspondence Week. The Thai Ridgeback. Multicoloured.

1691	2 b. Type **567**	10	5
1692	3 b. Black	15	10
1693	5 b. Tan	25	15
1694	10 b. Grey	55	30

568 Tangerine

569 Bencharong Cosmetic Jar

1993. Fruits. Multicoloured.

1696	2 b. Type **568**	10	5
1697	3 b. Bananas	15	10
1698	6 b. Star gooseberry ..	30	15
1699	8 b. Marian plum ..	45	25

1993. "Bangkok 1993" International Stamp Exhibition (4th issue). Multicoloured.

1700	3 b. Type **569**	15	10
1701	5 b. Bencharong round cosmetic jar	25	15
1702	6 b. Lai Nam Thong tall cosmetic jar	30	15
1703	7 b. Lai Nam Thong cosmetic jar	35	20

570 Emblem and Oil Rigs

1993. 5th Association of South East Asian Nations Council on Petroleum Conference and Exhibition.

1705	**570**	2 b. multicoloured ..	10	5

571 King Prajadhipok

572 "Ipomea cairica"

1993. Birth Centenary of King Prajadhipok (Rama VII).

1706	**571**	2 b. brown and gold ..	10	5

1993. New Year. Flowers. Multicoloured.

1707	1 b. Type **572**	5	5
1708	1 b. "Decaschistia parviflora"	5	5
1709	1 b. "Hibiscus tiliaceus"	5	5
1710	1 b. "Passiflora foetida"	5	5

573 "THAICOM-1" Satellite, "Ariane 4" Rocket and Map of Thailand

1993. Launch of "THAICOM-1" (first Thai communications satellite).

1712	**573**	2 b. multicoloured ..	10	5

OFFICIAL STAMPS

O 133. (Trans. " For Government Service Statistical Research ".).

1963. No gum.

O 495.	O 133.	10 s. red and pink	8	5
O 496.		20 s. red and green	5	5
O 500.		20 s. green ..	5	5
O 497.		25 s. red and blue	5	5
O 501.		25 s. blue ..	5	5
O 502.		50 s. red ..	50	65
O 498.		1 b. red and silver	60	90
O 503.		1 b. silver ..	40	40
O 499.		2 b. red & bronze	1·10	95
O 504.		2 b. bistre ..	1·10	1·40

The above were used compulsorily by Government Departments between 1st Oct. 1963, and 31st Jan. 1964, to determine the amount of mail sent out by the different departments for the purpose of charging them in the future. They were postmarked in the usual way.

THESSALY Pt. 16

Special stamps issued during the Turkish occupation in the Graeco-Turkish War of 1898.
40 paras = 1 piastre.

20.

1898.
M 162. **20.** 10 pa. green .. .. 2·75 2·75
M 163. 20 pa. red .. .. 2·75 2·75
M 164. 1 pi. blue .. .. 2·75 2·75
M 165. 2 pi. orange .. .. 2·75 2·75
M 166. 5 pi. violet .. .. 2·75 2·75

THRACE Pt. 3

A portion of Greece to the N. of the Aegean Sea for which stamps were issued by the Allies in 1919 and by the Greek Government in 1920. Now uses Greek stamps.

1919. 100 stotinki = 1 leva.
1920. 100 lepta = 1 drachma.

1920. Stamps of Bulgaria optd. **THRACE INTERALLIEE** in two lines.
28. **49.** 1 s. black 10 15
29. 2 s. grey 10 15
30. **50.** 5 s. green 10 15
31. 10 s. red 10 15
32. 15 s. violet 15 15
33. – 25 s. black & blue (No. 165) 10 15
34. – 1 l. brown (No. 168) .. 65 1·00
35. – 2 l. brown (No. 19?) .. 1·25 1·50
36. – 3 l. red (No. 192) .. 1·75 2·50

1920. Stamps of Bulgaria optd. **THRACE INTERALLIEE** in one line.
40. **49.** 1 s. black 30 45
41. 2 s. grey 30 45
42. **50.** 5 s. green 20 15
43. – 10 s. red 20 15
44. 15 s. violet 35 35
45. – 25 s. black & blue (No. 165) 35 35

1920. Stamps of Bulgaria optd. **THRACE Interalliee** in two lines vertically.
46. **50.** 5 s. green 5 5
47. 10 s. red 5 5
48. 15 s. violet 5 5
49. 50 s. brown 25 25

1920. Stamps of Bulgaria optd. **THRACE OCCIDENTALE.**
50. **50.** 5 s. green 5 5
51. 10 s. red 5 5
52. 15 s. violet 5 5
53. 25 s. blue 5 5
54. 30 s. brown (imperf.) .. 15 15
55. 50 s. brown 10 10

Διοίκησις
Δυτικῆς
Θράκης
(8.)

1920. 1911 stamps of Greece optd. with T **8.**
69. **29.** 1 l. green 20 20
70. **30.** 2 l. red 20 20
71. **29.** 3 l. red 20 20
72. **31.** 5 l. green 20 20
73. **29.** 10 l. red 20 20
74. **30.** 15 l. blue 20 20
75. 25 l. blue 45 45
76. **31.** 30 l. red .. .. 14·00 14·00
77. **30.** 40 l. blue 90 90
78. **31.** 50 l. purple .. .. 1·00 1·00
79. **32.** 1 d. blue .. .. 5·50 5·50
80. 2 d. red .. .. .. 12·00 12·00
65. 3 d. red .. .. .. 32·00 32·00
66. 5 d. blue .. .. 11·00 11·00
67. 10 d. blue .. .. 7·00 7·00
68. – 25 d. blue (No. 212) .. 26·00 26·00
The opt. on the 25 d. is in **capital letters.**

1920. 1916 stamps of Greece with opt. Greece T **38,** optd. with T **8.**
81. **29.** 1 l. green (No. 269) .. 20 20
82. **30.** 2 l. red 20 20
83. **29.** 10 l. red 25 25
84. **30.** 20 l. purple 55 55
85. **31.** 30 l. red 70 70
86. **32.** 2 d. red .. .. .. 14·00 14·00
87. 3 d. red .. .. .. 4·50 4·50
88. 5 d. blue .. .. 17·00 17·00
89. 10 d. blue .. .. 12·00 12·00

Διοίκησις
Θράκης
(10.)

'Υπάτη Αρμοστεία
Θράκης
5 Λεπτά 5
(11.)

1920. Issue for E. Thrace. 1911 stamps of Greece optd. with T **10.**
93. **29.** 1 l. green 20 20
94. **30.** 2 l. red 20 20
95. **29.** 3 l. red 20 20
96. **31.** 5 l. green 20 20
97. **29.** 10 l. red 55 55
98. **30.** 20 l. lilac 55 55
99. 25 l. blue 80 80
100. 40 l. blue .. .. 1·50 1·50
101. **31.** 50 l. purple .. .. 1·75 1·75
102. **32.** 1 d. blue .. .. 5·50 5·50
103. 2 d. red .. .. 13·00 13·00
92. 25 d. blue (No. 212) .. 40·00 40·00

1920. 1916 stamps of Greece with opt. T **38** of Greece, optd. with T **10.**
104. **30.** 2 l. red (No. 270) .. 25 25
105. **31.** 5 l. green .. .. .. 1·40 1·40
106. **30.** 20 l. purple 50 50
107. **31.** 30 l. red 50 50
108. **32.** 3 d. red .. .. .. 5·00 5·00
109. 5 d. blue .. .. .. 9·50 9·50
110. 10 d. blue .. .. 19·00 19·00

1920. Occupation of Adrianople. Stamps of Turkey surch. as T **11.**
111. **72.** 1 l. on 5 pa. orange .. 45 60
112. – 5 l. on 3 pi. blue (No. 965) 45 55
113. – 20 l. on 1 pi. grn. (No. 964) 60 60
114. **69.** 25 l. on 5 pi. on 2 pa. blue 70 70
115. **78.** 50 l. on 5 pi. black & grn. 2·25 2·25
116. **74.** 1 d. on 20 pa. red .. 1·75 1·75
117. **30.** 2 d. on 10 pa. on 2 pa. olive 2·25 2·25
118. **85.** 3 d. on 1 pi. blue .. .. 6·00 6·00
119. **31.** 5 d. on 20 pa. red .. 7·50 7·50

POSTAGE DUE STAMPS

1919. Postage Due stamps of Bulgaria optd. **THRACE INTERALLIEE.** Perf.
D 37. D **37.** 5 s. green 15 15
D 38. 10 s. violet 25 25
D 39. 50 s. blue 40 50

1920. Postage Due stamps of Bulgaria optd. **THRACE OCCIDENTALE.** Imperf. or perf. (10 s.).
D 56. D **37.** 5 s. green 8 8
D 57. 10 s. violet 60 60
D 58. 20 s. orange 10 10
D 59. 50 s. blue 30 30

THURN AND TAXIS Pt. 7

The Counts of Thurn and Taxis had a postal monopoly in parts of Germany and issued special stamps.

N. District. 30 silbergroschen = 1 thaler.
S. District. 60 kreuzer = 1 gulden.

NORTHERN DISTRICT

1.

1852. Imperf.
1. **1.** ¼ s. black on brown .. £130 32·00
2. ⅓ s. black on pink .. 50·00 £250
3. ½ s. black on green .. £200 17·00
5. 1 s. black on blue .. £350 50·00
8. 2 s. black on rose .. £325 15·00
10. 3 s. black on yellow .. £300 9·00

1859. Imperf.
12. **1.** ¼ s. red .. .. .. 30·00 42·00
20. ¼ s. black .. .. .. 12·00 38·00
21. ⅓ s. green .. .. .. 15·00 £300
13. ½ s. green .. .. .. £150 55·00
23. ½ s. orange .. .. 48·00 26·00
14. 1 s. blue .. .. .. £150 17·00
25. 1 s. red .. .. .. 30·00 13·00
15. 2 s. red .. .. .. 80·00 42·00
27. 2 s. blue .. .. .. 22·00 60·00
17. 3 s. red .. .. .. 80·00 60·00
29. 3 s. brown .. .. 10·00 27·00
18. 5 s. mauve .. .. 1·00 £275
19. 10 s. orange .. .. 1·00 £550

1865. Rouletted.
31 1 ¼ s. black .. .. .. 8·50 £550
32 ⅓ s. green .. .. .. 10·00 £300
33 ½ s. yellow .. .. 20·00 32·00
34 1 s. red .. .. .. 22·00 16·00
35 2 s. blue .. .. .. 1·25 65·00
36 3 s. brown .. .. 1·75 28·00

SOUTHERN DISTRICT

3.

1852. Imperf.
51 3 1 k. black on green .. 85·00 9·50
53 3 k. black on blue .. £375 22·00
57 6 k. black on red .. £400 16·00
58 9 k. black on yellow .. £325 8·50

1859. Imperf.
60. **3.** 1 k. green .. .. .. 12·00 6·00
62. 3 k. blue .. .. .. £300 12·00
68. 3 k. red .. .. .. 27·00 10·00
63. 6 k. red .. .. .. £300 38·00
70. 6 k. blue .. .. .. 5·00 18·00
65. 9 k. yellow .. .. £300 50·00
73. 9 k. brown .. .. 5·00 18·00
66. 15 k. purple .. .. 1·00 £150
67. 30 k. orange .. .. 1·00 £425

1865. Roul.
74 3 1 k. green .. .. .. 11·00 12·00
81 3 k. red .. .. .. 1·00 17·00
76 6 k. blue .. .. .. 1·25 20·00
77 9 k. brown .. .. 1·25 23·00

TIBET Pt. 17

Former independent state in the Himalayas. now part of China.

A. CHINESE POST OFFICES

12 pies = 1 anna.
16 annas = 1 Indian rupee.

分 貳
One Anna
སྐར་གཉིས།
(C 1.)

1911. Stamps of China of 1898 surch. as Type C **1.**
C 1. **32.** 3 p. on 1 c. buff .. 2·25 5·00
C 2. ½ a. on 2 c. green .. 2·75 5·00
C 3. 1 a. on 4 c. red .. 3·00 6·00
C 4. 2 a. on 7 c. lake .. 3·25 7·00
C 5. 2½ a. on 10 c. blue .. 3·25 6·00
C 6. **33.** 3 a. on 16 c. olive .. 4·75 7·50
C 7. 4 a. on 20 c. red .. 6·50 10·00
C 8. 6 a. on 30 c. red .. 12·00 14·00
C 9. 12 a. on 50 c. green .. 20·00 20·00
C 10. **34.** 1 r. on $1 red & salmon £100 £120
C 11. 2 r. on $2 red & yell... £375 £450

These stamps were used in Post Offices set up by the Chinese army sent to Tibet in 1910. Following a revolt by the Tibetans these troops were withdrawn during 1912.

B. INDEPENDENT STATE

6⅔ trangka = 1 sang.

1. (⅙ t.) ⅓ t. ½ t. ⅔ t. 1 t. 1 s.

1912. Imperf.
1b **1.** ⅙ t. green .. .. .. 7·50 8·00
2 ⅓ t. blue .. .. .. 10·00 12·00
3 ½ t. purple .. .. 10·00 12·00
4 ⅔ t. red .. .. .. 15·00 17·00
5 1 t. red .. .. .. 18·00 25·00
6a 1 s. green .. .. .. 25·00 25·00

2. (4 t.).

1914. Imperf.
7b. **2.** 4 t. blue £200 £200
8b. 8 t. red £120 £120
In the 8 t. the rays from the circles in the corners of the stamp point outwards towards the corner.

3. (1 t.) Tibetan lion. ½ t. ⅔ t. 2 t. 4 t.

1933. Perf. or Imperf.
9a. **3.** ½ t. yellow to orange .. 7·50 8·00
10b. ⅔ t. blue .. .. .. 7·00 9·50
11a. 1 t. red .. .. .. 6·50 7·50
11b. 1 t. orange .. .. 6·50 8·00
12a. 2 t. red .. .. .. 6·50 7·50
12c. 2 t. orange .. .. 8·00 8·00
13d. 4 t. green .. .. 7·50 5·00

TIERRA DEL FUEGO Pt. 20

An island at the extreme S. of S. America. Stamp issued for use on correspondence to the mainland. Currency is expressed in centigrammes of gold dust.

1. Gold-digger's Pick and Hammer.

1891.
1. **1.** 10 c. red .. .. .. 12·00

TIMOR Pt. 9

The eastern part of Timor in the Malay Archipelago. Administered as part of Macao until 1896, then as a separate Portuguese Overseas Province until 1975.

Following a civil war and the intervention of Indonesian forces the territory was incorporated into Indonesia on 17th July, 1976.

1885. 1000 reis = 1 milreis.
1894. 100 avos = 1 pataca.
1960. 100 centavos = 1 escudo.

1885. "Crown" key-type inscr "MACAU" optd **TIMOR**.
1 P 5 r. black 80 70
2 10 r. green .. .. 1·75 1·50
3 20 r. red .. .. .. 3·00 1·75
4 25 r. lilac 60 40
5 40 r. yellow .. .. 1·75 1·25
6 50 r. blue 80 50
7 80 r. grey .. .. 1·75 1·25
8 100 r. purple 60 60
19 200 r. orange .. .. 1·25 1·10
20 300 r. brown .. .. 1·25 1·10

1887. "Embossed" key-type inscr. "CORREIO DE TIMOR".
21. Q. 5 r. black .. .. 1·25 80
22. 10 r. green .. .. 1·60 1·25
23. 20 r. red .. .. 1·60 1·25
24. 25 r. purple .. .. 2·50 1·50
25. 40 r. brown .. .. 3·25 1·75
26. 50 r. blue .. .. 3·25 1·75
27. 80 r. grey .. .. 4·00 1·90
28. 100 r. brown .. .. 3·75 2·10
29. 200 r. lilac .. .. 6·50 5·00
30. 300 r. orange .. .. 8·00 5·00

1892. "Embossed" key-type inscr "PROVINCIA DE MACAU" surch **TIMOR 30 30**. No gum.
32 Q 30 on 300 r. orange .. 1·90 1·25

1894. "Figures" key-type inscr. "TIMOR."
33. R. 5 r. orange 60 45
34. 10 r. mauve 75 60
35. 15 r. brown 80 60
36. 20 r. lilac 80 60
37. 25 r. green 80 60
38. 50 r. blue .. .. 1·90 1·50
39. 75 r. red .. .. .. 2·25 1·90
40. 80 r. green .. .. 2·25 1·90
41. 100 r. brown on buff .. 2·25 1·90
42. 150 r. red on rose .. 4·75 3·00
43. 200 r. blue on blue .. 4·75 3·75
44. 300 r. blue on brown .. 6·00 4·25

1894. "Embossed" key-type of Timor surch **PROVISORIO** and value in European and Chinese. No gum.
46. Q. 1 a. on 5 r. black .. 45 35
47. 2 a. on 10 r. green .. 60 50
48. 3 a. on 20 r red .. 80 60
49. 4 a. on 25 r. purple .. 80 50
50. 6 a. on 40 r. brown .. 1·75 1·00
51. 8 a. on 50 r. blue .. 2·00 1·25
52. 13 a. on 80 r. grey .. 2·50 3·00
53. 16 a. on 100 r. brown .. 3·50 3·00
54. 31 a. on 200 r. lilac .. 7·50 6·00
55. 47 a. on 300 r. orange .. 9·00 8·00

1895. No. 32 further surch **5 avos PROVISORIO** and Chinese characters with bars over the original surch.
56 Q 5 a. on 30 on 300 r. orange 2·00 1·75

1898. Vasco da Gama stamps of Portugal as T **40, 43** and **44,** but inscr. "TIMOR" and values in local currency.
58. ½ a. green 90 60
59. 1 a. red 90 60
60. 2 a. purple 70 40
61. 4 a. green 70 40
62. 8 a. blue .. .. 1·25 75
63. 12 a. brown .. .. 1·00 75
64. 16 a. brown .. .. 1·75 1·50
65. 24 a. brown .. .. 2·00 1·00

1898. "King Carlos" key-type inscr "TIMOR". Name and value in red (78 a.) or black (others). With or without gum.
68. S. ½ a. grey 25 25
69. 1 a. orange 25 25
70. 2 a. green 25 25
71. 2½ a. brown 70 60
72. 3 a. lilac 70 60
112. 3 a. green 90 75
73. 4 a. green 70 60
113. 5 a. red 90 75
114. 6 a. brown 90 75
74. 8 a. blue 70 60
115. 9 a. brown 90 75
75. 10 a. blue 70 60
116. 10 a. brown 90 75
76. 12 a. red .. .. 1·50 1·40
117. 12 a. blue .. .. 4·50 3·75
118. 13 a. purple .. .. 1·25 1·10
119. 15 a. lilac .. .. 2·10 1·50
78. 16 a. blue on blue .. 1·50 1·40
79. 20 a. brown on yellow .. 1·50 1·40
120. 22 a. brown on pink .. 2·10 1·90
80. 24 a. brown on buff .. 1·50 1·40
81. 31 a. purple on pink .. 1·50 1·40
121. 31 a. brown on yellow .. 2·10 1·75
82. 47 a. blue on pink .. 2·50 2·25
122. 47 a. purple on pink .. 2·40 1·75
83. 78 a. black on blue .. 3·25 2·25
123. 78 a. blue on yellow .. 4·50 3·00

1899. "King Carlos" key-type of Timor surch. **PROVISORIO** and value in figures and bars.
84. S. 10 on 16 a. blue on blue 1·25 1·00
85. 20 on 31 s. purple on pink 1·25 1·00

1902. Surch.
88 R 5 a. on 5 r. orange .. 60 50
86 Q 5 a. on 25 r. purple .. 80 70
89 R 5 a. on 25 r. green .. 60 50
90 5 a. on 50 r. blue .. 70 60
87 Q 5 a. on 200 r. lilac .. 1·25 90
95 V 6 a. on 2½ r. brown .. 40 30
92 Q 6 a. on 10 r. green .. 35·00 32·00
94 R 6 a. on 20 r. lilac .. 60 40
93 Q 6 a. on 300 r. orange .. 1·00 75
100 R 9 a. on 15 r. brown .. 70 55

98 Q 9 a. on 40 r. brown 1·00 80
101 R 9 a. on 75 r. red 70 55
99 Q 9 a. on 100 r. brown 1·00 80
124 S 10 a. on 12 a. blue 80 65
104 R 15 a. on 10 r. mauve 75 60
102 Q 15 a. on 20 r. red 1·50 1·00
103 15 a. on 50 r. blue 35·00 32·00
105 R 15 a. on 100 r. brown on buff 75 60
106 15 a. on 300 r. bl. on brn. 75 60
107 Q 22 a. on 80 r. grey 3·00 2·75
108 R 22 a. on 80 r. green 1·50 1·25
109 22 a. on 200 r. blue on bl. 1·50 1·25

1902. Nos. 72 and 76 optd **PROVISORIO**.
110. S. 3 a. lilac 80 60
111. 12 a. red 2·00 1·60

1911. Nos. 68, etc., optd. **REPUBLICA**
125. S. ½ a. grey 20 15
126. 1 a. orange 15 15
127. 2 a. green 20 15
128. 3 a. green 20 15
129. 5 a. red 30 20
130. 6 a. brown 30 20
131. 9 a. brown 30 20
132. 10 a. brown 30 20
133. 13 a. purple 30 20
134. 15 a. lilac 60 45
135. 22 a. brown on pink 65 45
136. 31 a. brown on yellow 65 50
163. 31 a. purple on pink 1·00 85
137. 47 a. purple on pink 1·25 90
165. 47 a. blue on pink 1·40 1·25
167. 78 a. blue on yellow 1·75 1·50
168. 78 a. black on blue 1·50 1·25

1911. No. 112 and provisional of 1902 optd **Republica**.
139 S 3 a. green 80 75
140 R 5 a. on 5 r. orange 40 40
141 5 a. on 25 r. green 40 40
142 5 a. on 50 r. blue 1·00 1·00
144 V 6 a. on 2½ r. brown 90 70
146 R 6 a. on 20 r. lilac 60 40
147 9 a. on 15 r. brown 60 40
148 S 10 a. on 12 r. blue 60 40
149 R 15 a. on 100 r. brown on buff 80 65
150 22 a. on 80 r. green 1·25 90
151 22 a. on 200 r. blue on bl 1·25 90

1913. Provisional stamps of 1902 optd **REPUBLICA**.
192 S 3 a. lilac (No. 110) 15 15
194 R 5 a. on 5 r. orange 15 15
195 5 a. on 25 r. green 15 15
196 5 a. on 50 r. blue 15 15
200 V 6 a. on 2½ r. brown 15 15
201 R 6 a. on 20 r. lilac 25 20
202 9 a. on 15 r. brown 25 20
203 9 a. on 75 r. red 30 20
193 S 10 a. on 12 a. blue 25 20
204 R 15 a. on 10 r. mauve 30 20
205 15 a. on 100 r. brown on buff 30 20
206 15 a. on 300 r. bl on brn 30 20
207 22 a. on 80 r. green 85 60
151 22 a. on 200 r. blue on bl 1·25 90

1913. Vasco da Gama stamps of Timor optd. **REPUBLICA** or surch. also.
169. ½ a. green 30 20
170. 1 a. red 30 20
171. 2 a. purple 30 20
172. 4 a. green 30 20
173. 8 a. blue 50 30
174. 10 a. on 12 a. brown 80 70
175. 16 a. brown 60 50
176. 24 a. bistre 90 70

1914. "Ceres" key-type inscr "TIMOR". Name and value in black.
177 U ¼ a. olive 20 20
178 1 a. black 20 20
213 1½ a. green 30 30
179 2 a. green 20 20
180 3 a. brown 35 30
181 4 a. red 35 30
182 6 a. violet 40 30
216 7 a. green 50 45
217 7½ a. blue 60 45
218 9 a. blue 80 50
183 10 a. blue 40 30
219 11 a. grey 90 85
184 12 a. brown 75 50
221 15 a. mauve 2·50 2·00
185 16 a. grey 75 50
222 18 a. blue 2·50 2·00
223 19 a. green 2·50 2·00
186 20 a. brown 5·50 2·00
224 36 a. blue 2·50 2·00
187 40 a. red 2·50 1·25
225 54 a. brown 2·50 2·00
188 58 a. brown on green 2·50 1·50
226 72 a. red 5·00 3·75
189 76 a. brown on red 2·75 2·25
190 1 p. orange on pink 5·00 3·75
191 3 p. green on blue 11·00 8·00
227 5 p. red 24·00 13·00

1920. No. 196 surch. **½ Avo P.P. nº. 68 19-3-1920** and bars.
229. R. ½ a. on 5 a. on 50 r. blue 2·00 1·90

1932. "Ceres" key-type of Timor surch. with new value and bars.
230. U. 6 a. on 72 a. red 35 30
231. 12 a. on 15 a. mauve 35 30

1935. As T **40** of Port. India ("Portugal" and San Gabriel), but inscr. "TIMOR".
232. **40.** ½ a. brown 15 15
233. 1 a. sepia 15 15
234. 2 a. green 15 15
235. 3 a. mauve 15 15
236. 4 a. black 20 15
237. 5 a. grey 20 20
238. 6 a. brown 20 20
239. 7 a. red 20 20
240. 8 a. blue 50 20
241. 10 a. red 30 20
242. 12 a. blue 30 20
243. 14 a. olive 40 20
244. 15 a. red 40 20
245. 20 a. orange 40 20
246. 30 a. green 40 20
247. 40 a. violet 1·60 80
248. 50 a. brown 1·60 80
249. 1 p. blue 3·25 2·25
250. 2 p. brown 8·50 3·75
251. 3 p. green 11·50 4·00
252. 5 p. mauve 19·00 8·00

1938. As T **54** and **56** of Macao. Name and value in black.
253 **54** 1 a. olive (postage) 15 15
254 2 a. brown 15 15
255 3 a. violet 15 15
256 4 a. green 15 15
257 – 5 a. red 15 15
258 – 6 a. slate 15 15
259 – 8 a. purple 15 15
260 – 10 a. mauve 15 15
261 – 12 a. red 20 15
262 – 15 a. orange 35 25
263 – 20 a. blue 35 25
264 – 40 a. black 60 35
265 – 50 a. brown 75 50
266 – 1 p. red 2·25 1·60
267 – 2 p. olive 5·00 1·60
268 – 3 p. blue 6·50 3·75
269 – 5 p. brown 17·00 7·00
270 **56** 1 a. red (air) 15 15
271 2 a. violet 15 15
272 3 a. orange 15 15
273 5 a. blue 15 15
274 10 a. red 40 30
275 20 a. green 80 60
276 50 a. brown 1·50 90
277 70 a. red 2·25 1·75
278 1 p. mauve 3·50 2·25
DESIGNS—POSTAGE: 5 a. to 8 a. Mousinho de Albuquerque. 10 a. to 15 a. Prince Henry the Navigator. 20 a. to 50 a. Dam. 1 p. to 5 p. Afonso de Albuquerque.

1946. Stamps as above but inscr "MOCAMBIQUE" surch **TIMOR** and new value.
279 **54** 1 a. on 15 c. purple (post.) 2·00 1·50
280 – 4 a. on 35 c. green 2·00 1·50
281 – 8 a. on 50 c. mauve 2·00 1·50
282 – 10 a. on 70 c. violet 2·00 1·50
283 – 12 a. on 1 e. red 2·00 1·50
284 – 20 a. on 1 e. 75 blue 2·00 1·50
285 **56** 8 a. on 50 c. orge. (air) 1·50 1·25
286 12 a. on 1 e. blue 1·50 1·25
287 40 a. on 3 e. green 1·50 1·25
288 50 a. on 5 e. brown 2·00 1·50
289 1 p. on 10 e. mauve 2·00 1·50

1947. Nos. 253/64 and 270/78 optd. **"LIBERTACAO"**.
290. **22.** 1 a. olive (postage) 6·00 3·75
291. 2 a. brown 10·00 6·00
292. 3 a. violet 4·00 2·25
293. 4 a. green 4·00 2·25
294. – 5 a. red 1·75 70
295. – 8 a. purple 40 30
296. – 10 a. mauve 2·00 85
297. – 12 a. red 2·00 85
298. – 15 a. orange 2·00 85
299. – 20 a. blue 18·00 12·00
300. – 40 a. black 4·25 3·00
301. **27.** 1 a. red (air) 5·50 2·50
302. 2 a. violet 5·50 2·50
303. 3 a. orange 5·50 2·50
304. 5 a. blue 5·50 2·50
305. 10 a. red 1·50 80
306. 20 a. green 1·50 80
307. 50 a. brown 1·50 80
308. 70 a. red 5·50 2·10
309. 1 p. mauve 2·75 80

30. Girl with Gong. **31.** Pottery-making.

1948. Natives.
310. – 1 a. brown and green 25 20
311. **30.** 3 a. brown and grey 80 40
312. – 4 a. green and pink 1·10 90
313. – 8 a. slate and red 60 20
314. – 10 a. green and orange 60 30
315. – 20 a. blue 60 30
316. – 1 p. blue and orange 9·00 1·75
317. – 3 p. brown and violet 12·00 4·00
DESIGNS: 1 a. Native woman. 4 a. Girl with baskets. 8 a. Chief of Aleixo de Ainaro. 10 a. Timor chief. 20 a. Warrior and horse. 1, 3 p. Tribal chieftains.

1948. Honouring the Statue of Our Lady of Fatima. As T **62** of Macao.
318. 8 a. grey 1·75 1·75

1949. 75th Anniv. of U.P.U. As T **64** of Macao.
319. 16 a. brown 3·00 2·25

1950.
320 **31** 20 a. blue 40 30
321 – 50 a. brown (Young girl) 80 40

1950. Holy Year. As Nos. 425/6 of Macao.
322. 40 a. green 50 50
323. 70 a. brown 90 90

32. "Belamcanda chinensis". **34.** Statue of The Virgin.

1950.
324. **32.** 1 a. red, green and grey 15 15
325. – 3 a. yell., green & brown 1·40 60
326. – 10 a. red, green and blue 1·50 40
327. – 16 a. multicoloured 3·25 90
328. – 20 a. yellow, grn. & grey 1·50 50
329. – 30 a. yell., green & blue 1·50 45
330. – 70 a. red, green & purple 2·00 90
331. – 1 p. red, yellow & green 3·50 1·25
332. – 2 p. green, yellow & red 5·50 3·50
333. – 5 p. pink, green and black 9·50 5·50
FLOWERS: 3 a. "Caesalphinia pulcherrima". 10 a. "Calotropis gigantea". 16 a. "Delonix regia". 20 a. "Plumeria rubra". 30 a. 'Allamanda cathartica". 70 a. "Haemanthus multiflorus". 1 p. "Bauhinia". 2 p. "Eurycles amboiniensis" 5 p. "Crinum longiflorum".

1951. Termination of Holy Year. As T **69** of Macao.
334 86 a. blue 85 85

1952. 1st Tropical Medicine Congress, Lisbon. As T **46** of St. Thomas and Prince Islands.
335. 10 a. brown and green 60 50
DESIGN: Nurse weighing baby.

1952. 400th Death Anniv of St. Francis Xavier. Designs as No. 452/4 of Macao.
336. 1 a. black and grey 10 10
337. 16 a. brown and buff 40 35
338. 1 p. red and slate 1·50 75

1953. Missionary Art Exhibition.
339. **34.** 3 a. brown and stone 10 10
340. 16 a. brown and bistre 35 30
341. 50 a. blue and stone 70 70

1954. Portuguese Stamp Cent. As T **75** of Macao.
342. 10 a. multicoloured 35 30

1954. 400th Anniv. of Sao Paulo. As T **76** of Macao.
343. 16 a. multicoloured 35 30

35. Map of Timor. **37.** Elephant Jar.

1956.
344. **35.** 1 a. multicoloured 10 10
345. 3 a. multicoloured 10 10
346. 8 a. multicoloured 15 10
347. 24 a. multicoloured 20 10
348. 32 a. multicoloured 30 15
349. 40 a. multicoloured 35 15
350. 1 p. multicoloured 1·25 35
351. 3 p. multicoloured 3·75 80

1958. 6th Int. Congress of Tropical Medicine. As T **79** of Macao.
352. 32 a. multicoloured 1·50 1·25
DESIGN: 32 a. "Calophyllum inophyllum" (plant).

1958. Brussels Int. Exn. As T **78** of Macao.
353. 40 a. multicoloured 30 20

1960. New currency. Nos. 344/51 surch thus: $05 and bars.
354 **35** 5 c. on 1 a. mult 10 10
355 10 c. on 3 a. mult 10 10
356 20 c. on 8 a. mult 10 10
357 30 c. on 24 a. mult 10 10
358 50 c. on 32 a. mult 10 10
359 1 e. on 40 c. mult 15 10
360 2 e. on 40 a. mult 20 10
361 5 e. on 1 p. mult 40 15
362 10 e. on 3 p. mult 1·50 50
363 15 e. on 3 p. mult 1·50 65

1960. 500th Death Anniv. of Prince Henry the Navigator. As T **55** of St. Thomas and Prince Islands.
364. 4 e. 50 multicoloured 25 20

1962. Timor Art. Multicoloured.
365 5 c. Type **37** 10 10
366 10 c. House on stilts 10 10
367 20 c. Idol 10 10
368 30 c. Rosary 20 15
369 50 c. Model of outrigger canoe (horiz) 15 15
370 1 e. Casket 45 15
371 2 e. 50 Archer 30 15
372 4 e. Elephant 30 15
373 5 e. Native climbing palm tree 45 15
374 10 e. Statuette of woman 75 15
375 20 e. Model of cockfight (horiz) 1·75 65
376 50 e. House, bird and cat 4·00 1·40

1962. Sports. As T **82** of Macao. Mult.
377. 50 c. Game shooting 10 10
378. 1 e. Horse-riding 30 15
379. 1 e. 50 Swimming 35 25
380. 2 e. Athletes 35 25
381. 2 e. 50 Football 40 30
382. 15 e. Big-game hunting 1·00 90

1962. Malaria Eradication. Mosquito design as T **83** of Macao. Multicoloured.
383 2 e. 50 "Anopheles sundaicus" 30 30

1964. Centenary of National Overseas Bank. As T **84** of Macao but portrait of M. P. Chagas.
384. 2 e. 50 multicoloured 30 30

1965. I.T.U. Cent. As T **85** of Macao.
385. 1 e. 50 multicoloured 60 40

1966. 40th Anniv of National Revolution. As T **86** of Macao but showing different buildings. Multicoloured.
386. 4 e. 50 Dr. V. Machado's College and Health Centre, Dili 50 35

1967. Centenary of Military Naval Assn. As T **88** of Macao. Multicoloured.
387 10 c. G. Coutinho and gunboat "Patria" 15 15
388 4 e. 50 S. Cabral and Fairey IIID seaplane "Lusitania" 95 65

39. Sepoy Officer, 1792. **40.** Pictorial Map of 1834, and Arms.

1967. Portuguese Military Uniforms. Mult.
389. 35 c. Type **39** 15 10
390. 1 c. Infantry officer, 1815 70 15
391. 1 e. 50 Infantryman 1879 15 10
392. 2 e. Infantryman, 1890 15 10
393. 2 e. 50 Infantry officer, 1903 20 10
394. 3 e. Sapper, 1918 35 20
395. 4 e. 50 Commando, 1964 75 20
396. 10 e. Parachutist, 1964 85 70

1967. 50th Anniv. of Fatima Apparitions. As T **89** of Macao.
397. 3 e. Virgin of the Pilgrims 15 10

1968. 500th Birth Anniv. of Pedro Cabral (explorer). As T **90** of Macao. Multicoloured.
398. 4 e. 50 Lopo Homem-Reineis' map, 1519 (horiz.) 40 25

1969. Birth Centenary of Admiral Gago Coutinho. As T **91** of Macao. Mult.
399 4 e. 50 Frigate "Almirante Gago Coutinho" (horiz) 1·75 70

1969. Bicentenary of Dili (capital of Timor).
400 **40** 1 e. multicoloured 15 15

1969. 500th Anniv. of Vasco da Gama (explorer). Multicoloured. As T **92** of Macao.
401. 5 e. Convent Medallion 20 15

1969. Centenary of Overseas Administrative Reforms. As T **93** of Macao.
402. 5 e. multicoloured 15 15

1969. 500th Birth Anniv. of King Manoel I. As T **95** of Macao. Multicoloured.
403. 4 e. Emblem of Manoel I in Jeronimos Monastery 25 15

41. Map, Sir Ross Smith, and Arms of Britain, Timor and Australia.

1969. 50th Anniv. of 1st England-Australia Flight.
404. **41.** 2 e. multicoloured 25 20

1970. Birth Centenary of Marshal Carmona. As T **96** of Macao.
414. 1 e. Portrait in civilian dress 10 10

1972. 400th Anniv of Camoens' "The Lusiads" (epic poem). As T **77** of St. Thomas and Prince Islands. Multicoloured.
415 1 e. Missionaries, natives and galleon 15 15

1972. Olympic Games, Munich. As T **78** of St. Thomas and Prince Islands. Mult.
416 4 e. 50 Football 20 20

1972. 50th Anniv of 1st Flight, Lisbon–Rio de Janeiro. As T **79** of St. Thomas and Prince Islands. Multicoloured.
417 1 e. Aviators G. Coutinho and S. Cabral in sea-plane 30 20

1973. W.M.O. Centenary. As T **102** of Macao.
418. 20 e. multicoloured .. 85 80

CHARITY TAX STAMPS

The notes under this heading in Portugal also apply here.

1919. "Ceres" key-type of Timor surch **2 AVOS TAXA DA GUERRA**. With or without gum.
C 228 U 2 a. on ½ a. olive .. 2·00 1·00

1919. No. 196 surch. **2 TAXA DE GUERRA and bars.**
C 230. R. 2 on 5 a. on 50 r. blue .. 28·00 16·00

1925. Marquis de Pombal Commem. Stamps of Portugal, but inscr. " TIMOR ".
C 231. C **4.** 2 a. red 20 20
C 232. – 2 a. red 20 20
C 233. C **5.** 2 a. red 20 20

1934. Educational Tax. Fiscal stamps with values in black optd **Instrucao D.L.n.º 7 de 3-2-1934** or surch also. With or without gum.
C 234. 2 a. green .. .. 1·00 90
C 235. 5 a. green .. .. 2·00 1·25
C 236. 7 a. on ½ a. red .. .. 2·00 1·40

1936. Fiscal stamps with value in black optd **Assistencia D.L.nº72**. With or without gum.
C253 10 a. red .. .. 1·40 1·10
C254 10 a. green .. .. 1·00 1·00

C 29. C 42. Woman and Star.

1948. No gum.
C310 10 a. blue .. .. 1·25 80
C311 20 a. green .. .. 1·50 1·00
The 20 a. has a different emblem.

1960. Similar design. New currency. No gum.
C366 70 c. blue 40 40
C367 1 e. 30 green 70 70

1969.
C 405. C **42.** 30 c. blue 10 10
C 406. 50 c. purple & orge. 10 10
C 407. 1 c. brown & yellow 15 15

1970. Nos. C366/7 surch **D. L. no.776** and value.
C 408. 30 c. on 70 c. blue .. 2·75 2·25
C 409. 30 c. on 1 e. 30 green .. 2·75 2·25
C 410. 50 c. on 70 c. blue .. 4·50 2·50
C 411. 50 c. on 1 e. 30 green .. 2·00 1·75
C 412. 1 e. on 70 c. blue .. 2·50 2·25
C 413. 1 e. on 1 e. 30 green .. 2·00 1·75

NEWSPAPER STAMPS

1892. "Embossed" key-type inscr "PROVINCIA DE MACAU" surch **JORNAES TIMOR 2½ 2½**. No gum.
N 31. Q. 2½ on 20 r. red 75 40
N 32. 2½ on 40 r. brown .. 75 40
N 33. 2½ on 80 r. grey 75 40

1893. " Newspaper " key-type inscr. " TIMOR ".
N 36. V. 2½ r. brown 30 25

1894. No. N36 surch ½ **avo PROVISORIO.**
N58 V ½ a. on 2½ r. brown .. 20 20

POSTAGE DUE STAMPS

1904. "Due" key-type inscr "TIMOR". Name and value in black with or without gum (1, 2 a.), no gum (others).
D 124. W. 1 a. green 20 20
D 125. 2 a. grey 20 20
D 126. 5 a. brown 45 40
D 127. 6 a. orange 45 40
D 128. 10 a. brown 50 45
D 129. 15 a. brown 90 85
D 130. 24 a. blue .. .. 2·25 1·50
D 131. 40 a. red .. .. 2·25 1·75
D 132. 50 a. orange .. .. 3·00 2·25
D 133. 1 p. lilac .. .. 5·00 4·00

1911. " Due " key-type of Timor optd. **REPUBLICA.**
D 139. W. 1 a. green 15 15
D 140. 2 a. grey 15 15
D 141. 5 a. brown 15 15
D 142. 6 a. orange 20 20
D 143. 10 a. brown 30 25
D 144. 15 a. brown 40 30
D 145. 24 a. blue 80 70
D 146. 40 a. red .. .. 1·00 90
D 147. 50 a. orange .. .. 1·25 90
D 148. 1 p. lilac .. .. 3·50 2·25

1925. Marquis de Pombal tax stamps, as Nos. C 231/3 of Timor, optd. **MULTA.**
D 231. C **73.** 4 a. red 20 20
D 232. – 4 a. red 20 20
D 233. C **75.** 4 a. red 20 20

1952. As Type D **70** of Macao, but inscr. " TIMOR PORTUGUES ". Numerals in red; name in black.
D 336. 1 a. sepia and brown .. 10 10
D 337. 3 a. brown and orange .. 10 10
D 338. 5 a. green and turquoise 10 10
D 339. 10 a. green and pale grn. 10 10
D 340. 30 a. violet & pale violet 20 15
D 341. 1 p. red & orange .. 40 30

TOGO Pt. 7; Pt. 6; Pt. 14

A territory in W. Africa, formerly a German Colony. Divided between France and Gt. Britain in 1919, the British portion being attached to the Gold Coast for administration and using the stamps of that country. In 1956 the French portion became an autonomous republic within the French Union. Full independence was achieved in April 1960.

GERMAN ISSUES

100 pfennig = 1 mark.

1897. Stamps of Germany optd. **TOGO.**
G 1a. **8.** 3 pf. brown .. .. 3·75 6·50
G 2. 5 pf. green .. .. 3·50 2·25
G 3. **9.** 10 pf. red .. .. 3·50 2·25
G 4. 20 pf. blue .. .. 4·50 12·00
G 5. 25 pf. orange .. .. 32·00 60·00
G 6. 50 pf. brown .. .. 32·00 60·00

1900. "Yacht" key-types inscr. "TOGO".
G 7 N. 3 pf. brown 65 75
G21 5 pf. green .. .. 1·00 1·60
G 9 10 pf. red .. .. 35·00 55
G10 20 pf. blue .. .. 85 1·25
G11 25 pf. blk. & red on buff 85 10·00
G12 30 pf. blk. & orge. on buff 1·25 10·00
G13 40 pf. black and red .. 85 10·00
G14 50 pf. black & purple on buff .. .. 1·25 8·50
G15 80 pf. black & red on rose 2·00 22·00
G16 O. 1 m. red .. .. 2·50 48·00
G17 2 m. blue .. .. 4·00 80·00
G18 3 m. black .. .. 6·00 £150
G19 5 m. red and black .. £100 £475

FRENCH OCCUPATION

1914. Stamps of German Colonies, "Yacht" key-type, optd **Togo Occupation franco-anglaise** or surch also.
1 N 05 on 3 pf. brown .. 35·00 35·00
9 5 pf. green £750 £325
2 10 on 5 pf. green .. 14·00 12·50
10 10 pf. red £875 £350
3 20 pf. blue .. .. 35·00 35·00
4 25 pf. black & red on yell 38·00 35·00
5 30 pf. blk & orge on orge 65·00 60·00
6 40 pf. black and red .. £450 £400
15 50 pf. black & pur on buff £7500 £6500
7 80 pf. black & red on pink £450 £400
16 O 1 m. red .. .. — £14000
17 2 m. blue .. .. — £14000
18 3 m. black .. .. — £14000
19 5 m. red and black .. .. —

1916. Stamps of Dahomey optd **TOGO Occupation franco-anglaise.**
20 **6** 1 c. black and violet .. 15 30
21 2 c. pink and brown .. 20 25
22 4 c. brown and black .. 20 25
23 5 c. green and light green 40 45
24 10 c. pink and orange .. 30 30
25 15 c. purple and red .. 60 60
26 20 c. brown and grey .. 45 45
27 25 c. blue and ultramarine 45 45
28 30 c. violet and brown .. 45 70
29 35 c. black and brown .. 60 90
30 40 c. orange and black .. 55 80
31 45 c. blue and grey .. 45 65
32 50 c. brown and chocolate 45 60
33 75 c. violet and blue .. 3·25 4·00
34 1 f. black and green .. 4·50 5·00
35 2 f. brown and yellow .. 6·00 6·75
36 5 f. blue and violet .. 7·25 5·50

FRENCH MANDATE

1921. Stamps of Dahomey optd **TOGO.**
37 **6** 1 c. green and grey .. 10 30
38 2 c. orange and blue .. 10 20
39 4 c. orange and green .. 20 30
40 5 c. black and red .. 20 30
41 10 c. green and turquoise 20 30
42 15 c. red and brown .. 40 60
43 20 c. orange and green .. 55 60
44 25 c. orange and grey .. 35 35
45 30 c. red and carmine .. 40 60
46 35 c. green and purple .. 55 75
47 40 c. grey and green .. 90 1·25
48 45 c. grey and purple .. 90 1·25
49 50 c. blue 45 50
50 75 c. blue and brown .. 95 1·25
51 1 f. blue and grey .. 1·10 1·25
52 2 f. red and green .. 3·25 3·50
53 5 f. black and yellow .. 4·75 4·75

1922. Stamps of 1921 (No. 57 colour changed) surch.
54 **6** 25 c. on 15 c. red & brown 20 25
55 25 c. on 2 f. red and green 25 40
56 25 c. on 5 f. black & orge 25 40
57 60 on 75 c. violet on pink 55 75
58 65 on 45 c. grey and purple 80 1·00
59 85 on 75 c. blue and brown 95 1·25

5. Coconut Palms.

1924.
60 **5** 1 c. black and yellow .. 10 15
61 2 c. black and red .. 10 20
62 4 c. black and blue .. 10 25
63 5 c. black and orange .. 10 10
64 10 c. black and mauve .. 10 10
65 – 15 c. black and green .. 10 10
66 20 c. black and grey .. 10 10
67 – 25 c. black & green on yell 10 10
68 – 30 c. black and green .. 30 30
69 – 30 c. green and olive .. 10 10
70 – 35 c. black and brown .. 20 25
71 – 35 c. green and turquoise 35 45
72 – 40 c. black and red .. 15 50
73 – 45 c. black and red .. 10 15
74 – 50 c. black & orange on bl 20 25
75 – 55 c. red and blue .. 10 10
76 – 60 c. black & pur on pink 30 55
77 – 60 c. red 10 30
78 – 65 c. brown and lilac .. 25 45
79 – 75 c. black and blue .. 20 35
80 – 80 c. lilac and black .. 35 35
81 – 85 c. brown and orange .. 60 75
82 – 90 c. pink and red .. 50 65
83 – 1 f. black & purple on blue 60 80
84 – 1 f. blue 45 60
85 – 1 f. green and lilac .. 1·40 1·40
86 – 1 f. orange and red .. 25 40
87 – 1 f. 10 brown and mauve 3·00 2·00
88 – 1 f. 25 red and mauve .. 65 70
89 – 1 f. 50 blue 25 35
90 – 1 f. 75 pink and brown .. 4·75 1·40
91 – 1 f. 75 blue & ultramarine 60 70
92 – 2 f. grey and black on blue 65 65
93 – 3 f. red and green .. 80 80
94 – 5 f. black & orange on bl 1·00 1·10
95 – 10 f. pink and brown .. 1·10 1·25
96 – 20 f. black & red on yellow 1·25 1·40
DESIGNS: 20 c. to 90 c. Cocoa trees. 1 f. to 20 f. palm trees.

1926. No. 84 surch.
98 1 f. 25 on 1 f. blue 25 25

1931. "Colonial Exhibition" key-types inscr "TOGO".
99 E 40 c. green and black .. 3·00 3·50
100 F 50 c. mauve and black 3·00 3·25
101 G 90 c. red and black .. 3·00 3·50
102 H 1 f. 50 blue and black .. 3·25 3·25

1937. International Exhibition, Paris. As Nos. 168/73 of St.-Pierre et Miquelon.
103. 20 c. violet .. .. 1·00 1·25
104. 30 c. green .. .. 1·00 1·40
105. 40 c. red .. .. 95 1·25
106. 50 c. brown .. .. 95 1·40
107. 90 c. red .. .. 95 1·25
108. 1 f. 50 blue .. .. 95 1·25

1938. International Anti-Cancer Fund. As T **22** of Mauritania.
109. 1 f. 75+50 c. blue .. 10·50 13·50

1939. Cent of Death of R. Caillie. As T **27** of Mauritania.
110. 90 c. orange 45 60
111. 2 f. violet 45 55
112. 2 f. 25 blue 45 50

1939. New York World's Fair. As T **28** of Mauritania.
113. 1 f. 25 red 45 60
114. 2 f. 25 blue 50 60

1939. 150th Anniv of French Revolution. As T **29** of Mauritania.
115 45 c.+25 c. green & black 4·00 4·75
116 70 c.+30 c. brown & black 4·00 4·75
117 90 c.+35 c. orange & black 4·00 4·75
118 1 f. 25+1 f. red and black 4·00 4·75
119 2 f. 25 + 2 f. blue & black 4·00 4·75

1940. Air. As T **30** of Mauritania.
120. 1 f. 90 blue 15 30
121. 2 f. 90 red 15 30
122. 4 f. 50 green 25 40
123. 4 f. 90 olive 35 50
124. 6 f. 90 orange 60 70

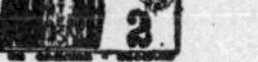

8. Pounding Meal.

9. Riverside Village.

10. Hunting.

11. Young Girl.

1940.
125. **8.** 2 c. violet 10 30
126. 3 c. green 10 30
127. 4 c. black 10 25
128. 5 c. red 10 25
129. 10 c. blue 10 25
130. 15 c. brown 10 30
131. **9.** 20 c. plum 10 25
132. 25 c. blue 10 20
133. 30 c. black 15 20
134. 40 c. red 20 30
135. 45 c. green 10 30
136. 50 c. brown 20 40
137. 60 c. violet 25 30
138. **10.** 70 c. black 40 55
139. 90 c. violet 65 85
140. 1 f. green 25 45
141. 1 f. 25 red 60 85
142. 1 f. 40 brown 30 55
143. 1 f. 60 orange 40 55
144. 2 f. blue 40 65
145. **11.** 2 f. 25 blue 70 90
146. 2 f. 50 red 65 75
147. 3 f. violet 50 75
148. 5 f. red 60 60
149. 10 f. violet 80 95
150. 20 f. black .. .. 1·50 10

1941. National Defence Fund. Surch. **SECOURS NATIONAL** and value.
151. +1 f. on 50 c. (No. 136) .. 2·00 2·00
152. +2 f. on 80 c. (No. 80) .. 2·75 3·00
153. +2 f. on 1 f. 50 (No. 89) 2·75 3·00
154. +3 f. on 2 f. (No. 144) .. 3·00 3·00

1942. Air. As T **32** of Mauritania.
154a 50 f. violet and yellow .. 70 80

1944. Nos. 75 and 82 surch **1 fr. 50.**
155 1 f. 50 on 55 c. red and blue 45 60
156 1 f. 50 on 90 c. pink & red 45 60

1944. No. 139 surch. in figures and ornament.
157. **10.** 3 f. 50 on 90 c. violet .. 45 60
158. 4 f. on 90 c. violet .. 45 60
159. 5 f. on 90 c. violet .. 70 90
160. 5 f. 50 on 90 c. violet .. 90 1·10
161. 10 f. on 90 c. violet .. 90 1·10
162. 20 f. on 90 c. violet .. 1·40 1·60

18. Oil Extraction Process.

19. Archer.

20. Postal Runner and Aeroplane.

1947.
163 **18** 10 c. red (postage) .. 15 25
164 30 c. blue 15 30
165 50 c. green 15 30
166 **19** 60 c. pink 15 30
167 1 f. brown 20 20
168 1 f. 20 green 20 40
169 – 1 f. 50 orange 35 60
170 – 2 f. bistre 35 35
171 – 2 f. 50 black .. .. 80 1·00
172 – 3 f. blue 40 65
173 – 3 f. 60 red 60 75
174 – 4 f. blue 40 45
175 – 5 f. brown .. .. 1·00 60
176 – 6 f. blue .. .. 1·00 1·25
177 – 10 f. red .. .. 1·25 40
178 – 15 f. green .. .. 1·40 50
179 – 20 f. green .. .. 1·25 70
180 – 25 f. pink .. .. 1·40 60

181 – 40 f. blue (air) .. .. 4·00 2·50
182 – 50 f. mauve and violet .. 1·90 1·10
183 – 100 f. brown and green .. 3·00 2·00
184 20 200 f. pink .. .. 5·00 4·00

DESIGNS—As Type 18: VERT. 1 f. 50 to 2 f. 50, Women hand-spinning cotton. HORIZ. 3 f. to 4 f. Drummer and village. 5 f. to 10 f. Red-fronted gazelles. 15 f. to 25 f. Trees and village. As Type 20: 40 f. African elephants and Sud-Ouest SO.95 Corse II. 50 f. Two-engined airplane. 100 f. Lockheed Constellation.

1949. Air. 75th Anniv of U.P.U. As T 38 of New Caledonia.
185 25 f. multicoloured .. 3·25 4·00

1950. Colonial Welfare Fund. As T 39 of New Caledonia.
186 10 f.+2 f. blue and indigo 2·00 2·25

1952. Centenary of Military Medal. As T 40 of New Caledonia.
187 15 f. brown, yellow & green 3·00 3·25

1954. Air. 10th Anniv of Liberation. As T 42 of New Caledonia.
188 15 f. violet and blue .. 2·50 2·75

22. Gathering Palm Nuts.

23. Roadway through Forest.

1954.
189. **22.** 8 f. purple, lake and violet (postage) .. 70 60
190. 15 f. brown, grey & blue 95 40
191. **23.** 500 f. blue & green (air) 35·00 28·00

AUTONOMOUS REPUBLIC

24. "Goliathus regius".

25. Rural School.

1955. Nature Protection.
192. **24.** 8 f. black and green .. 1·90 1·10

1956. Economic and Social Development Fund.
193. **25.** 15 f. brown & chestnut 3·00 1·40

26. Togolese Woman and Flag.

1957. New National Flag.
194. **26.** 15 f. brown, red & turq. 60 30

27. Togolese Woman and "Liberty" releasing Dove.

1957. Air. 1st Anniv. of Autonomous Republic.
195. **27.** 25 f. sepia, red and blue 55 45

28. Konkomba Helmet.

29. Kob.

30. Torch and Flags.

1957. Inscr "REPUBLIQUE AUTONOME DU TOGO".
196 **28** 30 c. lilac and red (post) 10 25
197 50 c. indigo and blue .. 10 25
198 1 f. lilac and purple .. 10 25
199 2 f. brown and green .. 10 25
200 3 f. black and green .. 15 25
201 **29** 4 f. black and blue .. 55 30
202 5 f. purple and grey .. 55 30
203 6 f. grey and red .. 70 35
204 8 f. violet and grey .. 70 35
205 10 f. brown and green .. 70 35
206 – 15 f. multicoloured .. 45 30
207 – 20 f. multicoloured .. 50 30
208 – 25 f. multicoloured .. 70 35
209 – 40 f. multicoloured .. 1·10 50
210 **30** 50 f. multicoloured (air) 1·10 50
211 100 f. multicoloured .. 2·00 1·10
212 200 f. multicoloured .. 3·75 1·90
213 – 500 f. indigo, green & bl 27·00 11·00

DESIGNS—HORIZ. 15 f. to 40 f. Teak forest. 48×27 mm. 500 f. Great egret.
See also Nos. 217/35.

31. "Human Rights".

32. "Bombax".

1958. 10th Anniv. of Human Rights Declaration.
214. **31.** 20 f. red and green .. 65 35

1959. Tropical Flora.
215. **32.** 5 f. multicoloured .. 40 30
216. – 20 f. yell., grn. & black 75 35
DESIGN—HORIZ. 20 f. "Tectona".

1959. As Nos. 196/213 but colours changed and inscr "REPUBLIQUE DU TOGO".
217 **28** 30 c. blue & black (post) 10 25
218 50 c. green and orange 20 25
219 1 f. purple and green .. 20 10
220 2 f. brown and green .. 20 10
221 3 f. violet and purple .. 20 25
222 **29** 4 f. violet and purple .. 45 30
223 5 f. brown and green .. 45 30
224 6 f. blue and ultramarine 45 40
225 8 f. bistre and green .. 45 35
226 10 f. brown and violet .. 45 30
227 – 15 f. multicoloured .. 50 30
228 – 20 f. multicoloured .. 60 50
229 – 25 f. multicoloured .. 80 45
230 – 40 f. multicoloured .. 1·00 45
231 – 25 f. brown, green and blue (air) .. 45 30
232 **30** 50 f. multicoloured .. 90 45
233 100 f. multicoloured .. 1·90 85
235 – 500 f. sepia, grn & pur 4·25 1·75

DESIGN—VERT. 25 f. (No. 231) Togo flag and shadow of airliner over Africa.

32a. Patient on Stretcher.

33. "The Five Continents".

1959. Red Cross Commem.
236. **32a.** 20 f.+5 f. red, orange and slate 80 80
237. – 30 f.+5 f. red, brown and blue 80 80
238. – 50 f.+10 f. red, brown and green 80 80

DESIGNS: 30 f. Mother feeding child. 50 f. Nurse superintending blood transfusion.

1959. United Nations Day.
239 **33** 15 f. blue and brown .. 30 30
240 20 f. blue and violet .. 35 30
241 25 f. blue and brown .. 45 35
242 40 f. blue and green .. 55 45
243 60 f. blue and red .. 75 50

INDEPENDENT REPUBLIC

34. Skiing.

35. "Uprooted Tree".

1960. Olympic Games, California and Rome.
244. **34.** 30 c. turq., red & green 15 25
245. – 50 c. pur., red & black 30 25
246. – 1 f. green, red & black .. 35 30
247. – 10 f. brn., blue & indigo 40 10
248. – 15 f. purple and green .. 45 40
249. – 20 f. choc., grn. & brn. 55 40
250. – 25 f. brn., red & orange 85 45

DESIGNS—HORIZ. 50 c. Ice hockey. 1 f. Tobogganing. 10 f. Cycling. 25 f. Running. VERT. 125 f. Throwing the discus. 20 f. Boxing.

1960. World Refugee Year.
251. **35.** 25 f.+5 f. green, brown and blue 55 75
252. – 45 f. + 5 f. olive, black and blue 75 75

DESIGN: 45 f. As Type **35** but "TOGO" at foot.

36. Prime Minister, S. Olympio and Flag.

37. Benin Hotel.

1960. Independence Commem. (a) Postage. Centres mult.; backgrounds cream; inscription and frame colours given.
253. **36.** 30 c. sepia 10 10
254. 50 c. brown 10 10
255. 1 f. purple 10 10
256. 10 f. blue 15 10
257. 20 f. red 40 15
258. 25 f. green 50 20

(b) Air.
259. **37.** 100 f. red, yell. & green 1·60 50
260. 200 f. multicoloured .. 2·75 90
261. – 500 f. brown and green 10·00 2·75

DESIGN—As Type **37**—VERT. 500 f. Palm-nut Vulture and map of Togo.

38. Union Jack and Flags.

1960. Four-Power "Summit" Conf., Paris. Flags and inscr. in red and blue.
262. **38.** 50 c. buff 10 10
263. – 1 f. turquoise 10 10
264. – 20 f. grey 35 20
265. – 25 f. blue 40 20

DESIGNS—As Type **38** but flags of: 1 f. Soviet Union. 20 f. France. 25 f. U.S.A. The Conference did not take place.

39. Togo Flag.

40. South African Crowned Cranes.

1961. Admission of Togo into U.N.O. Flag in red, yellow and green.
266. **39.** 30 c. red 10 10
267. 50 c. brown 10 10
268. 1 f. blue 10 10
269. 10 f. purple 20 10
270. 25 f. black 40 15
271. 30 f. violet 45 20

1961.
272. **40.** 1 f. multicoloured .. 50 10
273. 10 f. multicoloured .. 70 15
274. 25 f. multicoloured .. 1·10 40
275. 30 f. multicoloured .. 1·25 50

41. Augustino de Souza (statesman).

42. Daniel Beard (founder of American Boy Scout Movement) and Scout Badge.

1961. 1st Anniv. of Independence.
276. **41.** 50 c. black, red & yellow 10 10
277. 1 f. black, brown & grn. 10 10
278. 10 f. black, violet & blue 20 15
279. 25 f. black, grn. & sal. 40 10
280. 30 f. black, blue & mve. 50 20

1961. Boy Scout Movement Commem.
281. **42.** 50 c. lake, green and red 10 10
282. – 1 f. violet and red .. 10 10
283. – 10 f. black and brown .. 20 10
284. – 25 f. multicoloured .. 55 15
285. – 30 f. red, brown & grn. 65 20
286. – 100 f. mauve and blue .. 1·60 60

DESIGNS—HORIZ. 1 f. Lord Baden Powell. 10 f. Daniel Mensah ("Rover" Scout Chief). 100 f. Scout salute. VERT. 25 f. Chief Daniel Wilson (Togolese Scout). 30 f. Campfire on triangular emblem.

43. Plane and Motor Launch.

44. U.N.I.C.E.F. Emblem.

1961. U.N. Economic Commission on Africa. Multicoloured.
287. 20 f. Type **43** 30 15
288. 25 f. Electric train and gantry 70 15
289. 65 f. Excavator and pylons 65 30
290. 85 f. Microscope and atomic symbol .. .. 1·25 50

The designs are superimposed on a map of Africa spread over the four stamps when the 30 and 85 f. are mounted below the 20 and 25 f.

1961. 15th Anniv. of U.N.I.C.E.F.
291. **44.** 1 f. blue, green & black 10 10
292. – 10 f. multicoloured .. 15 10
293. – 20 f. multicoloured .. 20 10
294. – 25 f. multicoloured .. 45 20
295. – 30 f. multicoloured .. 80 20
296. – 85 f. multicoloured .. 1·25 60

DESIGNS: 10 f. to 85 f. Children dancing round the globe. The six stamps, arranged in the following order, form a composite picture: Upper row, 1, 25 and 20 f. Lower row, 10, 85 and 30 f.

45. Alan Shepard.

47. Togolese Girl.

1962. Space Flights Commem.
297. **45.** 50 c. green 10 10
298. – 1 f. mauve 15 10
299. **45.** 25 f. blue 35 20
300. – 30 f. violet 50 30

DESIGN: 1 f., 30 f. As Type **45** but portrait of Yuri Gagarin.

1962. Col. Glenn's Space Flight. Surch. **100 F COL. JOHN H. GLENN U S A VOL ORBITAL 20 FEVRIER 1962.**
301. **45.** 100 f. on 50 c. green .. 2·00 2·00

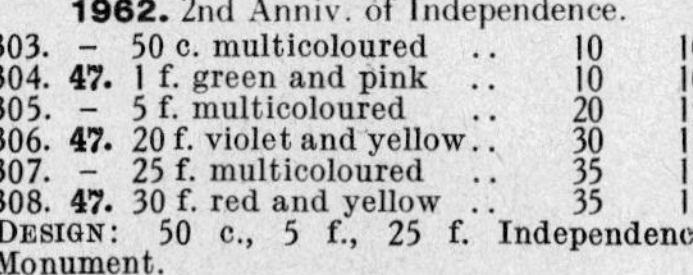

1962. 2nd Anniv. of Independence.
303. – 50 c. multicoloured .. 10 10
304. **47.** 1 f. green and pink .. 10 10
305. – 5 f. multicoloured .. 20 15
306. **47.** 20 f. violet and yellow .. 30 15
307. – 25 f. multicoloured .. 35 15
308. **47.** 30 f. red and yellow .. 35 15
DESIGN: 50 c., 5 f., 25 f. Independence Monument.

48. Arrows piercing mosquito.

1962. Malaria Eradication.
309. **48.** 10 f. multicoloured .. 30 10
310. 25 f. multicoloured .. 45 20
311. 30 f. multicoloured .. 50 35
312. 85 f. multicoloured .. 1·00 55

49. Presidents Kennedy and Olympio, and Capitol, Washington.

1962. Visit of President Olympio to U.S.A.
313. **49.** 50 c. slate and ochre .. 10 10
314. 1 f. slate and blue .. 10 10
315. 2 f. slate and red .. 10 10
316. 5 f. slate and mauve .. 10 10
317. 25 f. slate and lilac .. 40 15
318. 100 f. slate and green .. 1·60 70

50. Stamps of 1897 and Mail coach.

1963. 65th Anniv. of Togolese Postal Services.
319. **50.** 30 c. multicoloured (post.) 10 10
320. – 50 c. multicoloured .. 10 10
321. – 1 f. multicoloured .. 10 10
322. – 10 f. multicoloured .. 45 15
323. – 25 f. multicoloured .. 60 20
324. – 30 f. multicoloured .. 85 40
325. – 100 f. multicoloured (air) 2·25 80
DESIGNS (Togo stamps of): 50 c. 1900 and German imperial yacht "Hohenzollern". 1 f. 1915 and steam mail-train. 10 f. 1924 and motor-cycle mail carrier. 25 f. 1940 and mail-van. 30 f. 1947 and DC-3 aircraft. 100 f. 1960 and Boeing 707 aircraft.

51. Hands reaching for F.A.O. Emblem.

1963. Freedom from Hunger.
326. **51.** 50 c. multicoloured .. 10 10
327. 1 f. multicoloured .. 10 10
328. 25 f. multicoloured .. 60 20
329. 30 f. multicoloured .. 85 30

52. Lome Port and Togolese Flag. **53.** Centenary Emblem.

1963. 3rd Anniv. of Independence. Flag in red, yellow and green.
330. **52.** 50 c. black and brown .. 10 10
331. 1 f. black and red .. 15 10
332. 25 f. black and blue .. 35 20
333. 50 f. black and ochre .. 70 35

1963. Red Cross Cent. Flag red, yellow and green; cross red.
334. **53.** 25 f. blue and black .. 85 30
335. 30 f. green and black .. 1·10 40

54. Broken Shackles and Abraham Lincoln.

55. Flame and U.N. Emblem.

56. Hibiscus. **58.** Temple and Isis.

1963. Cent. of American Slaves' Emancipation. Centre in grey and green.
336. **54.** 50 c. blk. & brown (post) 10 10
337. 1 f. black and blue .. 10 10
338. 25 f. black and red .. 45 15
339. 100 f. black & orge. (air) 1·40 60

1963. 15th Anniv. of Declaration of Human Rights. Flame in red.
340. **55.** 50 c. blue & ultramarine 10 10
341. 1 f. green and black .. 15 10
342. 25 f. lilac and blue .. 40 15
343. 85 f. gold and blue .. 1·10 60

1964. Multicoloured.
344 50 c. "Odontoglossum grande" (orchid) (post) 10 10
345 1 f. Type **56** 10 10
346 2 f. "Papilio dardanus" (butterfly) 35 10
347 3 f. "Morpho aega" (butterfly) 55 10
348 4 f. "Pandinus imperator" (scorpion) 40 10
349 5 f. Tortoise 20 15
350 6 f. Strelitzia (flower) .. 55 15
351 8 f. Python 45 15
352 10 f. "Bunaea alcinde" (butterfly) 85 15
353 15 f. Chameleon .. .. 1·25 15
354 20 f. Octopus .. .. 1·25 20
355 25 f. "Zeus faber" (fish) .. 1·25 20
356 30 f. "Pomacanthus arcuatus" (fish) .. 1·50 35
357 40 f. Pygmy hippopotamus 2·00 35
358 45 f. African palm civet .. 3·25 60
359 60 f. Bohar reedbuck .. 4·50 90
360 85 f. Olive baboon .. 5·50 1·00
361 50 f. Black-bellied seed-cracker (air) .. .. 3·75 80
362 100 f. Black and white mannikin .. .. 6·00 1·25
363 200 f. Red-faced lovebird 14·00 3·00
364 250 f. Grey parrot .. 32·00 6·50
365 500 f. Yellow-breasted barbet .. .. .. 45·00 11·00

1964. President Kennedy Memorial Issue. Optd. **En Memoire de JOHN F. KENNEDY 1917-1963.** Centre in grey and green.
366. **54.** 50 c. blk. & brn. (post.) 15 10
367. 1 f. black and blue .. 15 10
368. 25 f. black and red .. 50 20
369. 100 f. blk. & orge. (air) 1·60 80

1964. Nubian Monuments Preservation.
370. **58.** 20 f. multicoloured .. 30 10
371. – 25 f. mauve and black .. 35 20
372. – 30 f. olive, black & yell. 50 30
DESIGNS: 25 f. Head of Rameses II, Abu Simbel. 30 f. Temple of Philae.

59. Phosphate Mine, Kpeme.

1964. 4th Anniv. of Independence.
373. **59.** 5 f. ochre, bistre & brn. 10 10
374. – 25 f. lake, brn. & violet 35 15
375. – 60 f. yell., olive & green 60 35
376. – 85 f. blue, slate & violet 1·25 50
DESIGNS: 25 f. Mine installations. 60 f. Phosphate train. 85 f. Loading phosphate onto "Panama Maru" bulk carrier.

HAVE YOU READ THE NOTES AT THE BEGINNING OF THIS CATALOGUE?
These often provide answers to the enquiries we receive.

60. Togolese Breaking Chain.

61. Pres. Grunitzky and "Papilio memnon".

1964. 1st Anniv. of African Heads of State Conf., Addis Ababa.
377. **60.** 5 f. sepia & orge. (post.) 15 10
378. 25 f. sepia and green .. 35 15
379. 85 f. sepia and red .. 95 45
380. 100 f. sepia & turq. (air) 1·25 65

1964. "National Union and Reconcilliation".
381. **61.** 1 f. violet and mauve .. 20 10
382. – 5 f. sepia and ochre .. 10 10
383. – 25 f. violet and blue .. 45 15
384. **61.** 45 f. purple and red .. 1·75 50
385. – 85 f. bronze and green .. 1·90 60
DESIGNS—President and : 5 f. Dove. 25 f., 85 f. Flowers.

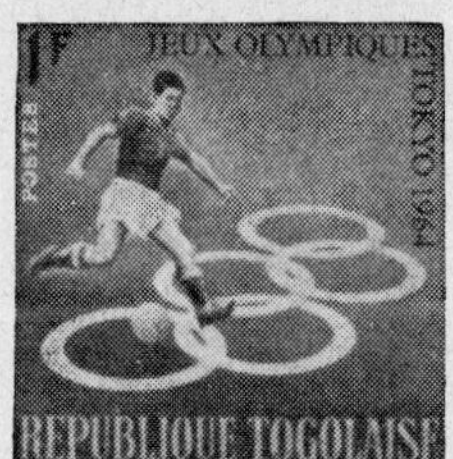

62. Football.

1964. Olympic Games, Tokyo.
386. **62.** 1 f. green (postage) .. 10 10
387. – 5 f. blue (Running) .. 15 15
388. – 25 f. red (Throwing the discus) 50 15
389. **62.** 45 f. turquoise 80 40
390. – 100 f. brown (Tennis) (air) .. .. .. 1·50 55

1964. French, African and Malagasy Co-operation. As T **68** of Mauritania.
391. 25 f. brn., bistre & purple 40 20

63. Early Balloons and Dirigible.

1984. Inaug. of "Air Togo" (National Airline).
392. **63.** 5 f. multicoloured (post.) 10 10
393. 10 f. blue, lake & green 30 10
394. – 25 f. ultram., orge. & bl. 50 15
395. – 45 f. mauve, grn. & blue 1·10 35
396. – 100 f. multicoloured (air) .. .. .. 1·90 80
DESIGNS: 25 f., 45 f. Early flying machines and Boeing jetliner. 100 f. Boeing jetliner and Togolese flag.

64. Sun, Globe and Satellites "Ogo" and "Mariner".

1964. Int. Quiet Sun Years. Sun yellow.
397. **64.** 10 f. blue and red .. 15 10
398. – 15 f. blue, brn. & mauve 20 10
399. – 20 f. green and violet .. 30 10
400. – 25 f. pur., green & blue 35 15
401. **64.** 45 f. blue and green .. 70 35
402. – 50 f. green and red .. 80 40
SATELLITES: 15 f., 25 f. "Tiros", "Telstar" and orbiting solar observatory. 20 f., 50 f. "Nimbus", "Syncom" and "Relay".

65. Pres. Grunitzky and the Mount of the Beatitudes Church.

1965. Israel–Togo Friendship. Inscr. "AMITIE ISRAEL–TOGO 1964".
403. – 5 f. purple 10 10
404. **65.** 20 f. blue and purple .. 20 10
405. – 25 f. turquoise and red 35 15
406. – 45 f. olive, bistre & pur. 70 35
407. – 85 f. turquoise & purple 1·10 50
DESIGNS—VERT. 5 f. Togolese stamps being printed on Israel press. HORIZ. 25 f., 85 f. Arms of Israel and Togo. 45 f. As Type **65** but showing old synagogue, Capernaum.

66. "Syncom 3", Dish Aerial and I.T.U. Emblem.

1965. I.T.U. Cent.
408. **66.** 10 f. turq. and green .. 15 10
409. 20 f. olive and black .. 35 15
410. 25 f. blue & ultramarine 40 15
411. 45 f. rose and red .. 70 35
412. 50 f. green and black .. 90 45

67. Abraham Lincoln. **68.** Throwing the Discus.

1965. Death Cent. of Lincoln.
413. **67.** 1 f. purple (postage) .. 10 10
414. 5 f. green 10 10
415. 20 f. brown 35 10
416. 25 f. blue 45 20
417. 100 f. olive (air) .. 1·60 70

1965. 1st African Games, Brazzaville. Flags in red, yellow and green.
418. **68.** 5 f. purple (postage) .. 10 10
419. – 10 f. blue 15 10
420. – 15 f. brown 35 10
421. – 25 f. purple 90 20
422. – 100 f. green (air) .. 1·50 65
SPORTS: 10 f. Throwing the javelin. 15 f. Handball. 25 f. Running. 100 f. Football.

69. Sir Winston Churchill.

DESIGNS—HORIZ. 10 f., 45 f. Stalin, Roosevelt and Churchill at Teheran Conference, 1943.

1965. Churchill Commem.
423. **69.** 5 f. green (postage) .. 10 10
424. – 10 f. violet and blue .. 15 10
425. **69.** 20 f. brown 40 15
426. – 45 f. blue 65 35
427. **69.** 85 f. red (air) .. .. 1·50 65

70. Unisphere.

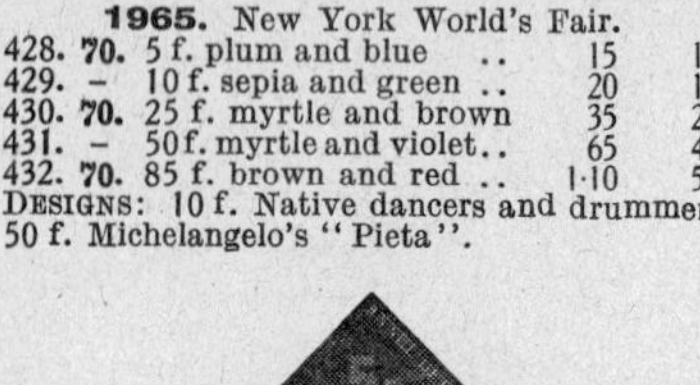

1965. New York World's Fair.

428. **70.** 5 f. plum and blue .. 15 10
429. – 10 f. sepia and green .. 20 10
430. **70.** 25 f. myrtle and brown 35 20
431. – 50 f. myrtle and violet.. 65 40
432. **70.** 85 f. brown and red .. 1·10 50

DESIGNS: 10 f. Native dancers and drummer. 50 f. Michelangelo's "Pieta".

71. " Laying bricks of peace ".

1965. Int. Co-operation Year.

433. **71.** 5 f. multicoloured .. 10 10
434. 15 f. multicoloured .. 15 15
435. – 25 f. multicoloured .. 30 15
436. – 40 f. multicoloured .. 60 30
437. – 85 f. multicoloured .. 1·00 50

DESIGNS: 25 f., 40 f. Hands supporting globe 85 f. I.C.Y. emblem.

72. Leonov with Camera.

1965. Astronauts in Space.

438. **72.** 25 f. mauve and blue.. 50 20
439. – 50 f. brown and green.. 90 40

DESIGN: 50 f. White with rocket-gun.

73. "ONU" and Doves.

1966. 20th Anniv. of U.N.O.

440. **73.** 5 f. brown, yellow and blue (postage) .. 10 10
441. – 10 f. blue, turquoise and orange 20 10
442. – 20 f. orange, green and light green 35 15
443. – 25 f. blue, turq. & yell. 45 20
444. – 100 f. ochre, blue and light blue (air) .. 1·60 55

DESIGNS: 10 f. U.N. Headquarters and emblem. 20 f. " ONU " and orchids. 25 f. U.N. Headquarters and Adlai Stevenson. 100 f. " ONU ", fruit and ears of wheat.

74. Pope Paul, Aircraft and U.N. Emblem.

1966. Pope Paul's Visit to U.N. Organization. Multicoloured.

445. 5 f. Type **74** (postage) .. 10 10
446. 15 f. Pope before microphones at U.N. (vert.) 20 10
447. 20 f. Pope and U.N. Headquarters 35 15
448. 30 f. As 15 f. 45 20
449. 45 f. Pope before microphones at U.N., and map (air) 80 30
450. 90 f. Type **74** .. .. 1·60 80

75. W.H.O. Building and Roses.

1966. Inaug. of W.H.O. Headquarters, Geneva. Multicoloured designs showing W.H.O. Building and flower as given.

451. 5 f. Type **75** (postage) .. 20 10
452. 10 f. Alstroemerias .. 35 10
453. 15 f. Asters 45 20
454. 20 f. Freesias 55 35
455. 30 f. Geraniums 65 35
456. 50 f. Asters (air) 95 35
457. 50 f. Type **75** .. .. 1·50 55

76. Surgical Operation.

1966. 7th Anniv. of Togolese Red Cross. Multicoloured.

459. 5 f. Type **76** (postage) .. 10 10
460. 10 f. Blood Transfusion .. 15 10
461. 15 f. Type **76** 30 15
462. 30 f. Blood transfusion .. 40 15
463. 45 f. African man & woman 70 45
464. 100 f. J. H. Dunant (air).. 1·75 90

1966. Space Achievements. Nos. 438/9 optd. as below or surch. also.

465. 50 f. **(ENVOLEE SURVEYOR 1)** 85 40
466. 50 f. **(ENVOLEE GEMINI 9)** 85 40
467. 100 f. on 25 f. **(ENVOLEE LUNA 9)** .. .. 1·60 70
468. 100 f. on 25 f. **(ENVOLEE VENUS 3)** .. .. 1·60 70

78. Wood-carving. 79. Togolese Man.

1966. Togolese Arts and Crafts.

469. **78.** 5 f. brn., yell. & bl. (post.) 10 10
470. – 10 f. brn., salmon & grn. 15 10
471. – 15 f. brown, yellow & red 30 15
472. – 30 f. brown, bistre & vio. 55 20
473. – 60 f. brown, salmon and blue (air) 85 45
474. **78.** 90 f. brn., yell. & red.. 1·40 60

DESIGNS: 10 f., 60 f. Basket-making. 15 f. Weaving. 30 f. Pottery.

1966. Air. "DC-8" Air Services Inaug. As T **87** of Mauritania.

475. 30 f. black, green & yellow 65 25

1966. Togolese Costumes and Dances. Multicoloured.

476. 5 f. Type **79** (postage) .. 10 10
477. 10 f. Togolese woman .. 10 10
478. 20 f. Female dancer .. 40 10
479. 25 f. Male Dancer.. .. 50 15
480. 30 f. Dancer in horned helmet 65 20
481. 45 f. Drummer .. .. 1·00 50
482. 50 f. Female dancer (air).. 85 45
483. 60 f. Dancer in horned helmet 1·40 60

80. Footballers and Jules Rimet Cup.

1966. World Cup Football Championships, England. Showing football scenes and Jules Rimet Cup.

484. **80.** 5 f. mult. (postage) .. 10 10
485. – 10 f. multicoloured .. 20 10
486. – 20 f. multicoloured .. 40 10
487. – 25 f. multicoloured .. 40 15
488. – 30 f. multicoloured .. 55 20
489. – 45 f. multicoloured .. 85 40
490. – 50 f. mult. (air).. .. 85 30
491. – 60 f. multicoloured .. 1·25 40

81. African Mouthbreeder.

1967. Fishes. Multicoloured designs showing fishes, with fishing craft in the background.

493. 5 f. Type **81** (postage) .. 20 10
494. 10 f. Golden Cavally .. 35 10
495. 15 f. Six Banded Distichodus 40 10
496. 25 f. Spotted Cichlid .. 60 20
497. 30 f. Type **81** 80 35
498. 45 f. As 10 f. (air).. .. 1·25 45
499. 90 f. As 15 f. .. .. 1·75 65

82. African Boy and Greyhound.

1967. 20th Anniv. (1966) of U.N.I.C.E.F.

500. **82.** 5 f. multicoloured (post.) 20 10
501. – 10 f. brn., grn., & lt. grn. 30 15
502. **82.** 15 f. blk., brn. & mauve 45 20
503. – 20 f. blk., ultram. & blue 60 30
504. **82.** 30 f. black, blue & olive 95 35
505. – 45 f. bronze, brown and yellow (air) .. .. 1·00 40
506. **82.** 90 f. blk., bronze & blue 1·50 55

DESIGNS: 10 f. Boy and Irish setter. 20 f. Girl and dobermann. 45 f. Girl and miniature poodle.

83. Launching "Diamant" Rocket.

1967. French Space Achievements. Mult.

508. 5 f. Type **83** (postage) .. 10 10
509. 10 f. Satellite " A–1 " (horiz.) 20 10
510. 15 f. Satellite " FR–1 " .. 30 10
511. 20 f. Satellite " D–1 " (horiz.) 40 15
512. 25 f. As 10 f. 50 30
513. 40 f. As 20 f. 70 35
514. 50 f. Type **83** (air) .. 95 40
515. 90 f. As 15 f. .. .. 1·50 55

84. Bach and Organ.

1967. 20th Anniv. (1966) of U.N.E.S.C.O.

517. **84.** 5 f. mult. (postage) .. 10 10
518. – 10 f. multicoloured .. 20 10
519. – 15 f. multicoloured .. 45 20
520. – 20 f. multicoloured .. 55 20
521. – 30 f. multicoloured .. 90 45
522. **84.** 45 f. multicoloured (air) 1·10 40
523. – 90 f. multicoloured .. 1·60 55

DESIGNS: 10 f., 90 f., Beethoven, violin and clarinet. 15 f., 30 f. Duke Ellington, saxophone, trumpet and drums. 20 f. Debussy, grand piano and harp.

85. British Pavilion and Lilies.

1967. World Fair, Montreal. Multicoloured.

525. 5 f. Type **85** (postage) .. 15 10
526. 10 f. French Pavilion and roses 20 10
527. 30 f. " Africa Place " and strelitzia 55 15
528. 45 f. As 10 f. (air) 85 35
529. 60 f. Type **85** 95 45
530. 90 f. As 30 f. .. .. 1·50 60
531. 105 f. U.S. pavilion and daisies .. .. .. 1·60 65

86. "Peace".

1967. Air. Disarmament. Designs showing sections of the "Peace" mural by J. Zanetti at the U.N. Headquarters Building Conf. Room.

533. **86.** 5 f. multicoloured .. 15 10
534. **A.** 15 f. multicoloured .. 20 10
535. **B.** 30 f. multicoloured .. 40 10
536. **86.** 45 f. multicoloured .. 70 35
537. **A.** 60 f. multicoloured .. 1·25 45
538. **B.** 90 f. multicoloured .. 1·60 55

87. Lions Emblem with Supporters.

1967. 50th Anniv. of Lions Int. Mult.

540. 10 f. Type **87** 20 10
541. 20 f. Flowers and Lions emblem 35 15
542. 30 f. Type **87** 45 20
543. 45 f. As 20 f. .. .. 1·25 45

88. Bohar Reedbuck.

1967. Wildlife.

544. **88.** 5 f. brown & pur. (post.) 10 10
545. – 10 f. blue, red & yellow 75 20
546. – 15 f. black, lilac & green 45 15
547. – 20 f. blue, sepia & yellow 1·25 30
548. – 25 f. brn., yellow & olive 85 35
549. – 30 f. blue, violet & yell. 1·75 55
550. – 45 f. brown & blue (air) 90 35
551. – 60 f. black, brown & grn. 1·25 50

DESIGNS: 10 f., 20 f., 30 f. Montagu's harriers (birds of prey). 15 f. Common zebra. 25 f. Leopard. 45 f. Lion. 60 f. African elephants.

1967. Air. 5th Anniv. of U.A.M.P.T. As T **101** of Mauritania.

552. 100 f. brown, blue & green 1·60 1·10

89. Stamp Auction and Togo Stamps—1 m. (German) of 1900 and 100 f. Conference of 1964.

1967. 70th Anniv. of 1st Togolese Stamps. Multicoloured.
553. 5 f. Type **89** (postage) .. 15 10
554. 10 f. Exhibition and 1d. (British) of 1915 and 50 f. I.T.U. of 1965 .. .. 15 10
555. 15 f. Stamp shop and 50 c. (French) of 1924 .. 40 10
556. 20 f. Stamp-packet vending machine and 5 f. U.N. of 1965 .. .. 40 10
557. 30 f. As 15 f. 60 30
558. 45 f. As 10 f. 85 40

559. 90 f. Type **89** (air) .. .. 1·50 60
560. 105 f. Father and son with album and 1 f. Kennedy of 1964 .. .. 1·75 80

1967. 5th Anniv. of West African Monetary Union. As T **103** of Mauritania.
562. 30 f. blue and green .. 55 30

90. Long-jumping.

1967. Olympic Games, Mexico and Grenoble (1968). Multicoloured.
563. 5 f. Type **90** (postage) .. 10 10
564. 15 f. Ski-jumping .. 20 10
565. 30 f. Relay Runners .. 55 20
566. 45 f. Bob-sleighing .. 90 35

567. 60 f. As 30 f. (air) .. 1·10 40
568. 90 f. Type **90** .. .. 1·00 55

1967. National Day (29 Sept.) Nos. 525/31 optd. **JOURNEE NATIONALE DU TOGO 29 SEPTEMBRE 1967.**
570. 5 f. multicoloured (postage) 35 20
571. 10 f. multicoloured .. 35 20
572. 30 f. multicoloured .. 1·00 40

573. 45 f. multicoloured (air) .. 40 20
574. 60 f. multicoloured .. 80 35
575. 90 f. multicoloured .. 1·25 45
576. 105 f. multicoloured .. 1·40 65

92. "The Gleaners" (Millet) and Benin Phosphate Mine.

1968. Paintings and Local Industries.
577. **92.** 10 f. multicoloured .. 10 10
578. A. 20 f. multicoloured .. 30 10
579. **92.** 30 f. multicoloured .. 45 15
580. A. 45 f. multicoloured .. 70 20
581. **92.** 60 f. multicoloured .. 95 45
582. A. 90 f. multicoloured .. 1·40 70
DESIGN: A, "The Weaver at the Loom" (Van Gogh) and textile plant, Dadia.

93. Brewing beer.

1968. Benin Brewery. Multicoloured.
583. 20 f. Type **93** 35 10
584. 30 f. "Drinking at a Bar" (detail from painting by Manet) 60 30
585. 45 f. Bottling-washing machine and bottle of Benin beer 70 40
The 30 f. is a vert. design.

94. Decade Emblem and Sunflowers.

96. Dr. Adenauer and Europa "Key".

95. Viking Longship and Portuguese Galleon.

1968. Int. Hydrological Decade.
586. **94.** 30 f. mult. (postage) .. 60 30
587. 60 f. multicoloured (air) 85 40

1988. Inaug. of Lome Port. Multicoloured.
588. 5 f. Type **95** (postage) .. 15 10
589. 10 f. Paddle-steamer "Clermont" and Liner "Athlone Castle" .. 20 10
590. 20 f. Quayside Lome Port 60 20
591. 30 f. Type **95** 85 35

592. 45 f. As 10 f. (air) .. 95 35
593. 90 f. Nuclear-powered freighter "Savannah" .. 1·60 55

1968. Adenauer (German statesman) Commem.
595. **96.** 90 f. multicoloured .. 1·60 80

97. "Dr. Turp's Anatomy Lesson" (Rembrandt).

1968. 20th Anniv. of World Health Organization. Paintings. Multicoloured.
596. 15 f. "Expulsion from the Garden of Eden" (Michelangelo) (postage) .. 30 10
597. 20 f. Type **97** 40 15
598. 30 f. "Johann Deyman's Anatomy Lesson" (Rembrandt) .. 55 20
599. 45 f. "Christ healing the sick" (Raphael) .. 85 35

600. 60 f. As 30 f. (air) .. 85 40
601. 90 f. As 45 f. .. 1·10 55

98. Wrestling.

1968. Olympic Games, Mexico. Mult.
603. 15 f. Type **98** (postage) .. 20 15
604. 20 f. Boxing 45 15
605. 30 f. Judo 50 20
606. 45 f. Running 80 35

607. 60 f. Type **98** (air) .. 90 40
608. 90 f. As 45 f. .. .. 1·25 55

99. "Try Your Luck".

100. Scout and Tent.

1968. 2nd Anniv. of National Lottery. Mult.
610. 30 f. Type **99** 55 25
611. 45 f. Lottery ticket, horse-shoe and cloverleaf .. 80 30

1968. Air. "Philexafrique" Stamp Exn., Abidjan (Ivory Coast 1969) (1st issue). As T **113a** of Mauritania. Multicoloured.
612. 100 f. "The Letter" (J. A. Franquelin) .. .. 2·75 1·90

1968. Togolese Scouts. Multicoloured.
613. 5 f. Type **100** (postage) .. 10 10
614. 10 f. Scoutmaster witn cubs 30 10
615. 20 f. Giving first aid .. 40 15
616. 30 f. Scout game 50 20
617. 45 f. As 10 f. 65 35

618. 60 f. As 20 f. (air) .. 90 45
619. 90 f. As 30 f. .. .. 1·25 65
The 10, 20, 45 and 60 f. are horiz.

101. "The Adoration of the Shepherds" (Giorgione).

1968. Christmas Paintings. Multicoloured.
621. 15 f. Type **101** (postage) 35 10
622. 20 f. "The Adoration of the Kings" (Brueghel) .. 45 10
623. 30 f. "The Adoration" (Botticelli) 55 15
624. 45 f. "The Adoration" (Durer) 90 35

625. 60 f. As 20 f. (air) .. 1·00 40
626. 90 f. As 45 f. .. .. 1·50 55

102. Martin Luther King.

104. Module landing on Moon.

103. Football.

1969. Human Rights Year.
628. **102.** 15 f. grn. & brn. (post.) 20 10
629. – 20 f. violet & turquoise 35 15
630. **102.** 30 f. blue and red .. 55 20
631. – 45 f. red and olive .. 1·10 45

632. – 60 f. blue & purple (air) 90 45
633. **102.** 90 f. brown and green .. 1·25 55
PORTRAITS: 20 f. Prof. Rene Cassin (Nobel Peace Prize-winner). 45 f. Pope John XXIII. 60 f. Robert F. Kennedy.

1969. Air. "Philexafrique" Stamp Exn. Abidjan, Ivory Coast (2nd issue). As T **114a** of Mauritania.
635. 50 f. red, brown and green 80 80
DESIGN: 50 f. Aledjo Rock and stamp of 1900.

1969. Inaug. of Sports Stadium, Lome.
636. **103.** 10 f. brown, red and green (post) .. 10 10
637. – 15 f. brown, blue and orange 30 10
638. – 20 f. brown, green and yellow 40 15
639. – 30 f. brown, blue and green 50 20
640. – 45 f. brown, violet and orange 65 30

641. – 60 f. brown, red and blue (air) .. 90 35
642. – 90 f. brown, mauve and blue .. .. 1·25 55
DESIGNS: 15 f. Handball. 20 f. Volleyball. 30 f. Basketball. 45 f. Tennis. 60 f. Boxing. 90 f. Cycling.

1969. 1st Man on the Moon. Multicoloured.
644. 1 f. Type **104** (postage) .. 10 10
645. 20 f. Astronaut and module on Moon 20 10
646. 30 f. As Type **104** .. 40 15
647. 45 f. As No. 645 .. .. 65 35

648. 60 f. Astronaut exploring lunar surface (air) .. 85 40
649. 100 f. Astronaut gathering Moon rock .. .. 1·40 70

105. "The Last Supper" (Tintoretto).

107. Bank in Hand and Emblem.

1969. Religious Paintings. Multicoloured.
651 5 f. Type **105** (postage) .. 15 10
652 10 f. "Christ's Vision at Emmaus" (Velazquez) 30 10
653 20 f. "Pentecost" (El Greco) 50 20
654 30 f. "The Annunciation" (Botticelli) 70 20
655 45 f. As 10 f. .. .. 1·10 45

656 90 f. As 20 f. (air) .. 1·90 65

1969. Eisenhower Commem. Nos. 628/33 optd. with Eisenhower's silhouette and **EN MEMOIRE DWIGHT D. EISENHOWER 1890-1968.**
658. **102.** 15 f. grn. & brn. (post.) 25 15
659. – 20 f. violet and turquoise 45 15
660. **102.** 30 f. blue and red .. 55 20
661. – 45 f. red and olive .. 95 30

662. – 60 f. blue & purple (air) 90 45
663. **102.** 90 f. brown and green .. 1·25 65

1969. 5th Anniv. of African Development Bank. Multicoloured.
665. 30 f. Type **107** (post) .. 85 20
666. 45 f. Diesel locomotive in hand, and emblem .. 1·10 35

667. 100 f. Farmer and cattle in hand, and emblem (air) 1·25 55

108. Dunant and Red Cross Workers.

1969. 50th Anniv. of League of Red Cross Societies. Multicoloured.
668. 15 f. Type **108** (postage) 35 10
669. 20 f. Pasteur and heip for flood victims .. 40 10
670. 30 f. Fleming and flood control 55 15
671. 45 f. Rontgen and Red Cross post 95 30

672. 60 f. As 45 f. (air) .. 90 45
673. 90 f. Type **108** .. 1·25 65

109. Weeding Corn.

1969. Young Pioneers Agricultural Organization. Multicoloured.
675. 1 f. Type **109** (postage) .. 10 10
676. 2 f. Glidji Agricultural Centre 10 10
677. 3 f. Founding meeting .. 10 10
678. 4 f. Glidji class 15 10
679. 5 f. Student "pyramid" 15 10
680. 7 f. Students threshing .. 15 10
681. 8 f. Gardening instruction 15 10
682. 10 f. Co-op village .. 15 10
683. 15 f. Students gardening .. 30 15
684. 20 f. Cattle-breeding .. 35 15
685. 25 f. Poultry-farming .. 45 15
686. 30 f. Independence parade 45 20
687. 40 f. Boys on high-wire .. 65 35
688. 45 f. Tractor and trailer .. 80 35
689. 50 f. Co-op village .. 85 35
690. 60 f. Tractor-driving tuition 90 45

691. 90 f. Harvesting manioc (air) .. .. 1·10 45
692. 100 f. Gardening instruction 1·40 55
693. 200 f. Thinning-out corn .. 2·25 1·10
694. 250 f. Drummers marching 4·25 1·50
695. 500 f. Young pioneers marching .. .. 9·50 3·00

111. Books and Map.

113. George Washington.

1969. 12th Anniv. of Int. African Library Development Assn.
700. **111.** 30 f. multicoloured .. 45 30

1969. Christmas. No. 644/5 and 647/9 optd. **JOYEUX NOEL.**

701. 1 f. Type **104** (postage) .. 35 20
702. 20 f. Astronaut and module on Moon .. .. 1·10 45
703. 45 f. As No. 645 .. .. 1·50 1·00
704. 60 f. Astronaut exploring lunar surface (air) .. 1·90 65
705. 100 f. Astronaut gathering Moon rock .. .. 3·00 1·00

1969. "Leaders of World Peace". Mult.

707. 15 f. Type **113** (postage) 30 10
708. 20 f. Albert Luthule .. 35 10
709. 30 f. Mahatma Gandhi .. 55 15
710. 45 f. Simon Bolivar .. 90 20
711. 60 f. Friedrich Ebert (air) 90 35
712. 90 f. As 30 f. .. .. 1·25 50

114. "Ploughing" (Klodt).

1970. 50th Anniv. of I.L.O. Paintings. Multicoloured.

713. 5 f. Type **114** (postage).. 10 10
714. 10 f. "Gardening" (Pissarro) 20 10
715. 20 f. "Harvesting Fruit" (Rivera) 35 10
716. 30 f. "Seeds of Spring" (Van Gogh) 80 35
717. 45 f. "Workers of the Fields" (Rivera) 80 35
718. 60 f. As 30 f. (air) .. 1·00 35
719. 90 f. As 45 f. .. .. 1·50 50

115. Model Coiffures.

1970. Togolese Hair styles. Multicoloured.

721. 5 f. Type **115** (postage) .. 15 10
722. 10 f. As T **115**, but different styles 35 10
723. 20 f. Fefe style .. 50 15
724. 30 f. Danmlongbedji style 1·25 20
725. 45 f. Blom style (air) .. 90 30
726. 90 f. Aklui and Danmlong-bedji styles .. .. 1·60 65

Nos. 723/5 are vert.

116. Togo Stamp and Independence Monument, Lome.

1970. 10th Anniv. of Independence. Mult.

727. 20 f. Type **116** (postage).. 45 15
728. 30 f. Pres. Eyadema and Palace 65 20
729. 50 f. Map, dove and monument (vert.) .. 1·10 35
730. 60 f. Togo stamp and monument (air) 80 30

117. New U.P.U. Headquarters Building.

1970. New U.P.U. Headquarters Building.

731. **117.** 30 f. violet and orange (postage) .. .. 1·00 35
732. 50 f. red and blue (air) 80 35

118. Italy and Uruguay.

1970. World Cup Football Championships, Mexico. Multicoloured.

733. 5 f. Type **118** (postage) .. 10 10
734. 10 f. England and Brazil.. 20 10
735. 15 f. Russia and Mexico.. 35 10
736. 20 f. Germany and Morocco 45 10
737. 30 f. Rumania and Czechoslovakia 85 20
738. 50 f. Sweden and Israel (air) 55 30
739. 60 f. Bulgaria and Peru .. 65 35
740. 90 f. Belgium and Salvador 1·25 50

119. Lenin.

1970. Birth Cent. of Lenin. Mult.

742. 30 f. Type **119** (postage).. 1·00 45
743. 50 f. "Peasant messengers with Lenin" (Serov) (air) 1·10 35

120. British Pavilion.

1970. "Expo 70", Osaka, Japan. Mult.

744. 2 f. Pennants, Sanyo. Pavilion (57×36 mm.).. 15 10
745. 20 f. Type **120** 20 10
746. 30 f. French Pavilion .. 45 15
747. 50 f. Soviet Pavilion .. 85 30
748. 60 f. Japanese Pavilion .. 1·10 45

121. Armstrong, Collins and Aldrin.

1970. "Apollo" Moon Flights. Mult.

750. 1 f. Type **121** (postage) .. 10 10
751. 2 f. U.S. flag and moon-rock 10 10
752. 20 f. Astronaut and module on Moon.. .. 35 10
753. 30 f. Conrad, Gordon and Bean 65 20
754. 50 f. As 2 f. .. .. 1·00 35
755. 200 f. Lovell, Haise and Swigert ("Apollo 13") (air) .. .. .. 2·50 1·40

1970. Safe Return of "Apollo 13". As Nos. 750/55 but additionally inscr. **FELICITATIONS BON RETOUR APOLLO XIII.**

757. **121.** 1 f. multicoloured (postage) 10 10
758. – 2 f. multicoloured .. 10 10
759. – 20 f. multicoloured .. 35 10
760. – 30 f. multicoloured .. 65 20
761. – 50 f. multicoloured .. 1·00 35
762. – 200 f. multicoloured (air) 2·50 1·60

123. "Euchloron megaera".

1970. Butterflies and Moths. Multicoloured.

764 1 f. Type **123** (postage) .. 15 10
765 2 f. "Cymothoe sangaris" 30 10
766 30 f. "Danaus chrysippus" 1·50 35
767 50 f. "Morpho sp." .. 2·75 65
768 60 f. Type **123** (air) .. 3·00 70
769 90 f. "Pseudacraea boisiduvali" .. .. 4·25 95

124. Painting by Velasquez (I.L.O.).

1970. 25th Anniv. of U.N.O. Mult.

770. 1 f. Type **124** (postage) .. 10 10
771. 15 f. Painting by Delacroix (F.A.O.).. .. 10 10
772. 20 f. Painting by Holbein (U.N.E.S.C.O.) .. 20 15
773. 30 f. Painting of U.N. H.Q., New York.. .. 60 15
774. 50 f. Painting by Renoir (U.N.I.C.E.F.) 90 35
775. 60 f. Painting by Van Gogh (U.P.U.) (air) .. 1·00 35
776. 90 f. Painting by Carpaccio (W.H.O./O.M.S.) .. 1·50 50

125. "The Nativity" (Botticelli).

1970. Christmas. "Nativity" Paintings by Old Masters. Multicoloured.

778. 15 f. Type **125** (postage).. 15 10
779. 20 f. Veronese 15 10
780. 30 f. El Greco 55 15
781. 50 f. Fra Angelico.. .. 90 30
782. 60 f. Botticelli (different) (air) .. .. .. 1·00 30
783. 90 f. Tiepolo .. .. 1·50 45

1971. De Gaulle Commemoration (1st issue). Nos. 708/9, 711/2 optd. **EN MEMOIRE Charles De Gaulle 1890–1970** or surch. in addition.

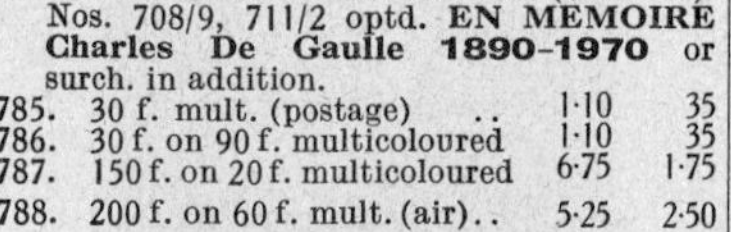

785. 30 f. mult. (postage) 1·10 35
786. 30 f. on 90 f. multicoloured 1·10 35
787. 150 f. on 20 f. multicoloured 6·75 1·75
788. 200 f. on 60 f. mult. (air).. 5·25 2·50

127. De Gaulle and Churchill.

1971. De Gaulle Commemoration. (2nd issue).

789. **127.** 20 f. bl. & blk. (postage) 55 15
790. – 30 f. red and black .. 65 20
791. – 40 f. green and black 1·00 40
792. – 50 f. brown and black 1·25 50
793. – 60 f. vio. & blk. (air) 2·25 55
794. – 90 f. blue and black .. 3·25 80

DESIGNS: 30 f. De Gaulle with Eisenhower. 40 f. With Pres. Kennedy. 50 f. With Adenauer. 60 f. With Pope Paul VI. 90 f. General De Gaulle.

128. Shepard and Moon Exploration.

1971. Moon Mission of "Apollo 14". Mult.

796. 1 f. Type **128** (postage) .. 10 10
797. 10 f. Mitchell and rock-gathering 15 10
798. 30 f. Roosa and module approaching Moon .. 50 15
799. 40 f. Launch from Moon.. 90 30
800. 50 f. "Apollo 14" emblem (air) 60 20
801. 100 f. As 40 f. .. .. 1·25 40
802. 200 f. As 50 f. .. .. 2·10 80

INDEX

Countries can be quickly located by referring to the index at the end of this volume.

129. "The Resurrection" (after Raphael).

1971. Easter. Paintings of "The Resurrection" by various artists. Multicoloured.

804. 1 f. Type **129** (postage) .. 15 10
805. 30 f. Master of Trebon .. 55 15
806. 40 f. Type **129** 95 30
807. 50 f. M. Grunewald (air) .. 80 30
808. 60 f. As 30 f. .. .. 1·00 40
809. 90 f. El Greco .. .. 1·50 55

130. Cocoa Tree and Pods.

1971. Int. Cocoa Day. Multicoloured.

811. 30 f. Type **130** (postage).. 55 15
812. 40 f. Sorting beans .. 85 20
813. 50 f. Drying beans.. .. 1·10 35
814. 60 f. Agricultural Ministry, Lome (air) 60 30
815. 90 f. Type **130** .. .. 1·10 50
816. 100 f. As 40 f. .. .. 1·25 60

131. Airliner over Control-tower. **132.** Napoleon.

1971. 10th Anniv. of A.S.E.C.N.A. (Aerial Navigation Security Agency).

817. **131.** 30 f. multicoloured (postage) 90 35
818. 100 f. multicoloured (air).. .. 1·50 65

1971. 150th Death Anniv. of Napoleon. Embossed on gold foil.

819. **132.** 1,000 f. gold .. .. 22·00

133. Great Market, Lome.

1971. Tourism. Multicoloured.

821. 20 f. Type **133** (postage) .. 35 10
822. 30 f. Wooden sculpture and protea 55 15
823. 40 f. Aledjo Gorge and olive baboon 80 20
824. 50 f. Vale Castle and red-fronted gazelle (air) .. 65 20
825. 60 f. Lake Togo and alligator 90 30
826. 100 f. Furnace, Tokpli, and hippopotamus .. .. 1·25 40

134. Gbatchoume Image.

1971. Togolese Religions. Multicoloured.

827. 20 f. Type **134** (postage) .. 35 15
828. 30 f. High priest, Temple of Atta Sakuma .. 50 20
829. 40 f. "Holy Stone" ceremony 85 30
830. 50 f. Moslem worshippers, Lome Mosque (air) .. 55 20
831. 60 f. Protestants 70 30
832. 90 f. Catholic ceremony, Djogbegan Monastery 95 40

1971. Memorial Issue for "Soyuz 11" Astronauts. Nos. 799/802 optd. **EN MEMOIRE DOBROVOLSKY - VOLKOV - PATSAYEV SOYUZ 11** or surch. also.

834. 40 f. multicoloured (postage) 1·00 35
835. 90 f. on 50 f. multicoloured (air) 90 35
836. 100 f. multicoloured .. 1·10 40
837. 200 f. multicoloured .. 2·00 65

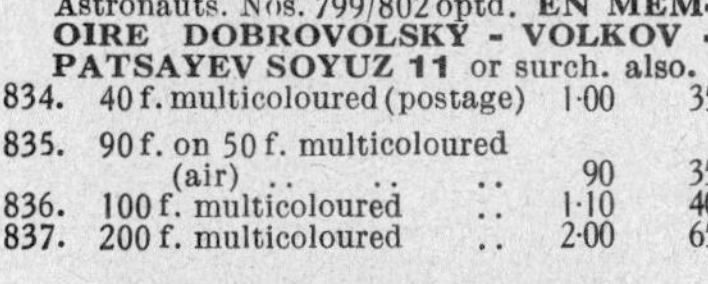

136. Ice-skating.

1971. Winter Games, Sapporo, Japan (1972). Multicoloured.

839. 1 f. Type **136** (postage) .. 10 10
840. 10 f. Slalom skiing 10 10
841. 20 f. Figure-skating .. 35 10
842. 30 f. Bob-sleighing .. 55 20
843. 50 f. Ice-hockey .. .. 1·10 35
844. 200 f. Ski-jumping (air) .. 2·25 95

1971. Air. 10th Anniv. of African and Malagasy Posts and Telecommunications Union. As T **139a** of Mauritania. Multicoloured.

846. 100 f. U.A.M.P.T. H.Q. and Adjogobo dancers .. 1·10 55

137. Togolese Child and Mask.

1971. Air. "Children of the World". Embossed on gold foil.

847. **137.** 1,500 f. gold .. .. 15·00

138. Wooden Crocodile.

1971. 25th Anniv. of U.N.I.C.E.F. Mult.

848. 20 f. Type **138** (postage) .. 20 10
849. 30 f. Toy "Bambi" and butterfly 45 15
850. 40 f. Toy monkey .. 80 30
851. 50 f. Wooden elephant on wheels .. .. .. 1·00 30
852. 60 f. Toy turtle (air) .. 55 20
853. 90 f. Toy parrot 85 35

139. "Virgin and Child" (Botticelli).

1971. Christmas. "Virgin and Child" Paintings by Old Masters. Multicoloured.

855. 10 f. Type **139** (postage) .. 10 10
856. 30 f. (Maitre de la Vie de Marie) 65 20
857. 40 f. (Durer) .. .. 1·10 35
858. 50 f. (Veronese) .. .. 1·40 45
859. 60 f. (Giorgione) (air) .. 1·00 35
860. 100 f. (Raphael) .. .. 1·75 55

140. St. Mark's Basilica, Venice.

1972. U.N.E.S.C.O. "Save Venice" Campaign. Multicoloured.

862. 30 f. Type **140** (postage) .. 90 30
863. 40 f. Rialto Bridge .. 1·25 40
864. 100 f. Doge's Palace (air) .. 1·40 65

141. "The Crucifixion" (unknown artist).

1972. Easter. Religious Paintings. Mult.

866. 25 f. Type **141** (postage) .. 45 15
867. 30 f. "The Deposition" (Botticelli) 70 15
868. 40 f. Type **141** 90 30
869. 50 f. "The Resurrection" (Thomas de Coloswar) (air) 85 20
870. 100 f. "The Ascension" (Mantegna) .. .. 1·60 40

142. Heart Emblem and Blacksmith.

145. Woman preparing Cassava.

143. Hotel de la Paix, Lome.

1972. World Heart Month. Multicoloured.

872. 30 f. Type **142** postage) .. 45 15
873. 40 f. Typist 55 20
874. 60 f. Javelin-thrower .. 85 35
875. 100 f. Type **142** (air) .. 1·25 45

1972. O.C.A.M. Summit Conf., Lome. Embossed on gold foil.

877. **143.** 1,000 f. gold, red & grn. 10·00

1972. Pres. Nixon's Visit to China. Nos. 823/4 optd. **VISITE DU PRESIDENT NIXON EN CHINE FEVRIER 1972.** and additionally surch. (No. 879).

878. 300 f. on 40 f. mult. (post.) 4·00 1·90
879. 50 f. multicoloured (air) .. 1·00 35

1972. Cassava Industries. Multicoloured.

880. 25 f. Collecting cassava (horiz.) (postage) .. 45 15
881. 40 f. Type **145** 65 20
882. 60 f. Cassava truck and factory (horiz.) (air) .. 90 20
883. 80 f. Mother with Benin tapioca cake .. .. 1·25 45

146. Video-telephone. **148.** Basketball.

1972. World Telecommunications Day. Multicoloured.

884. 40 f. Type **146** (postage) .. 1·00 35
885. 100 f. "Intelsat 4" and map of Africa (air) .. 1·50 45

1972. Air. Pres. Nixon's Visit to Russia. No. 743, surch. **VISITE DU PRESIDENT NIXON EN RUSSIE MAI 1972,** and value.

886. 300 f. on 50 f. multicoloured 5·00 2·75

1972. Olympic Games, Munich. Mult.

887. 30 f. Type **148** (postage) .. 50 15
888. 40 f. Running 65 20
889. 50 f. Throwing the discus .. 90 30
890. 90 f. Gymnastics (air) .. 65 35
891. 200 f. Type **148** .. .. 1·75 80

149. Pin-tailed Whydah. **150.** Paul Harris (founder).

1972. Exotic Birds. Multicoloured.

893. 25 f. Type **149** (postage) .. 55 40
894. 30 f. Broad-tailed paradise whydah 80 40
895. 40 f. Yellow-mantled whydah .. .. .. 1·10 55
896. 60 f. Long-tailed whydah 2·00 55
897. 90 f. Rose-ringed parakeet (air) .. .. .. 2·75 1·10

1972. Rotary International. Multicoloured.

899. 40 f. Type **150** (postage) .. 40 20
900. 50 f. Rotary and Togo flags 50 30
901. 60 f. Rotary emblem, map and laurel (air) .. 65 20
902. 90 f. As 50 f. 90 35
903. 100 f. Type **150** .. .. 1·25 45

151. "Mona Lisa" (L. da Vinci).

1972. Famous Paintings. Multicoloured.

905. 25 f. Type **151** (postage) .. 95 30
906. 40 f. "Virgin and Child" (Bellini) .. .. .. 1·10 30
907. 60 f. "Mystical Marriage of St. Catherine" (Master P.N.'s assistant) (air) .. 80 30
908. 80 f. "Self-portrait" (L. da Vinci) .. .. .. 1·10 35
909. 100 f. "St. Marie and Angels" (Botticelli) .. 1·40 50

1972. 10th Anniv. of West African Monetary Union. As T **149** of Mauritania.

911. 40 f. brn., grey and red .. 55 40

152. Party H.Q. of R.P.T., Pres. Pompidou and Eyadama.

1972. Visit of President Pompidou to Togo. Multicoloured.

912. 40 f. Type **152** (postage) .. 1·10 45
913. 100 f. Party H.Q. rear view and portraits as T **152** (air) 1·75 55

153. Goethe.

1972. Air. 140th Death Anniv. of Goethe (poet).

914. **153.** 100 f. multicoloured .. 1·50 65

154. "The Annunciation" (unknown artist).

1972. Christmas. Religious Paintings. Multicoloured.

915. 25 f. Type **154** (postage) .. 35 20
916. 30 f. "The Nativity" (Master Theodor of Prague) 55 20
917. 40 f. Type **154** 80 20
918. 60 f. As 30 f. (air) 80 20
919. 80 f. "The Adoration of the Magi" (unknown artist) .. .. .. 1·00 30
920. 100 f. "The Flight into Egypt" (Giotto) .. .. 1·25 45

155. R. Follerau and Allegory.

1973. "World Day of the Leper".

(a) Postage. 20th Anniv. of Follereau Foundation.

922. **155.** 40 f. violet and green .. 1·60 55

(b) Air. Cent. of Hansen's bacillus Discovery.

923. – 100 f. blue and red .. 2·50 85

DESIGN: 100 f. Dr. Hanson, microscope and bacillus slide.

156. W.H.O. Emblem. **157.** The Crucifixion.

1973. 25th Anniv. of W.H.O.

924. **156.** 30 f. multicoloured .. 45 15
925. 40 f. multicoloured .. 55 20

1973. Easter. Multicoloured.

926. 25 f. Type **157** (postage) .. 35 15
927. 30 f. The Deposition .. 55 20
928. 40 f. The Resurrection .. 80 20
929. 90 f. "Christ in Majesty" (air) .. .. .. 1·25 45

158. Astronauts Cernan, Evans and Schmitt.

1973. "Apollo 17" Moon Flight. Mult.

931. 30 f. Type **158** (postage) .. 80 15
932. 40 f. Moon rover .. .. 1·00 30
933. 100 f. Discovery of "orange" rock (air) .. 1·10 40
934. 200 f. Pres. Kennedy and lift-off .. .. .. 2·25 85

159. Erecting Tent.

160. Heliocentric System.

1973. Int., Scout Congress. Nairobi/Addis Ababa. Multicoloured.
936. 10 f. Type **159** (postage) .. 20 10
937. 20 f. Cooking meal (horiz.) 45 10
938. 30 f. Rope-climbing .. 65 15
939. 40 f. Type **159** 85 20
940. 100 f. Canoeing (horiz.) (air) 1·25 40
941. 200 f. As 20 f. .. .. 2·50 85

1973. 500th Birth Anniv. of Copernicus. Multicoloured.
943. 10 f. Type **160** (postage) .. 15 10
944. 20 f. Copernicus 30 10
945. 30 f. "Astronomy" and "Astronautics" .. 65 15
946. 40 f. Astrolabe 85 20
947. 90 f. Type **160** (air) .. 1·25 35
948. 100 f. As 20 f. .. .. 1·40 45

161. Ambulance Team.

1973. Togolese Red Cross. Multicoloured.
950. 40 f. Type **161** (postage) .. 90 35
951. 100 f. Dove of peace, sun and map (air) .. .. 1·90 65

1973. "Drought Relief". African Solidarity. No. 766 surch. **SECHERESSE SOLIDARITE AFRICAINE** and value.
952. 100 f. on 30 f. multicoloured 1·25 85

163. Classroom.

1973. Literacy Campaign. Multicoloured.
953. 30 f. Type **163** (postage) .. 35 15
954. 40 f. African reading book (vert.) 85 30
955. 90 f. Classroom (different) (air) 85 45

1973. African and Malagasy Posts and Telecommunications Union. As **T 155a** of Mauritania.
956. 100 f. red, yellow and pur. 1·10 65

164. Interpol Emblem and H.Q. Paris.

165. W.M.O. Emblem in Weather-vane.

1973. 50th Anniv. of Interpol.
957. **164.** 30 f. grn., brn. & yell. 45 15
958. 40 f. bl., mauve & grn. 65 20

1973. Centenary of W.M.O.
959. **165.** 40 f. grn., brn. & yell. (post.) 90 35
960. 200 f. brn., vio. & blue (air) 1·90 85

166. Togo Stamp and Diesel Locomotives.

1973. 75th Anniv. of Togolese Postal Services. Multicoloured.
961 25 f. Type **166** (postage) .. 50 15
962. 30 f. Togo stamp and mail coaches 60 20
963. 90 f. Togo stamps and mail-boats .. .. 1·60 45
964. 100 f. Togo stamps and mail-planes (air) .. .. 1·90 65

167. Kennedy and A. Schaerf.

168. Flame Emblem and "People".

1973. Pres. Kennedy's 10th Death Anniv.
966. **167.** 20 f. violet and black on blue (postage) .. 35 10
967. – 30 f. brown and black on brown 50 20
968. – 40 f. grn. & blk. on grn. 85 30
969. – 90 f. purple and black on mauve (air) .. 1·60 45
970. – 100 f. blue & blk. on bl. 1·60 45
971. – 200 f. brn. & blk. on brn. 2·75 80
DESIGNS: 30 f. Kennedy and Harold Macmillan. 40 f. Kennedy and Adenauer. 90 f. Kennedy and Charles de Gaulle. 100 f. Kennedy and Konrad Nikita Kruschev. 200 f. Kennedy and "Apollo" spacecraft.

1973. Air. 25th Anniv. of Declaration of Human Rights.
973. **168.** 250 f. multicoloured .. 2·75 1·40

169. "Virgin and Child" (anon.).

173. "Girl Before Mirror" (Picasso).

171. Footballers.

1973. Christmas. Multicoloured.
974. 25 f. Type **169** (postage) .. 50 15
975. 30 f. "Adoration of the Magi" (Vivarini) .. 60 20
976. 90 f. "Virgin and Child" (S. di Pietro) (air) .. 1·00 35
977. 100 f. "Adoration of the Magi" (anon.) .. .. 1·40 40

1974. Lome District Rotary International Convention. Nos. 899, 901 and 903 optd. **PREMIERE CONVENTION 210eme DISTRICT FEVRIER 1974 LOME.**
979. **150.** 40 f. mult. (postage) .. 55 35
980. – 60 f. mult. (air) .. 45 20
981. **150.** 100 f. multicoloured .. 90 35

1974. World Cup Football Championships, Munich.
982. **171.** 20 f. mult. (postage) .. 35 15
983. – 30 f. multicoloured .. 45 15
984. – 40 f. multicoloured .. 55 20
985. – 90 f. mult. (air) .. 90 35
986. – 100 f. multicoloured .. 1·00 40
987. – 200 f. multicoloured .. 2·00 70
DESIGNS: Nos. 983/7, similar designs to Type **171**, showing footballers in action.

1974. 10th Anniv. of World Food Programme. Nos. 880/1 optd. **10e ANNIVERSAIRE DU P. A. M.** or surch. also.
989. **145.** 40 f. multicoloured .. 55 35
990. – 100 f. on 25 f. mult. .. 1·25 80

1974. Picasso Commemoration. Mult.
991. 20 f. Type **173** (postage) .. 55 20
992. 30 f. "The Turkish Shawl" 80 35
993. 40 f. "Mandoline and Guitar" 1·10 35
994. 90 f. "The Muse" (air) .. 1·00 35
995. 100 f. "Les Demoiselles d'Avignon" .. .. 1·25 40
996. 200 f. "Sitting Nude" .. 2·50 85

174. Kpeme Village.

175. Togolese Postman.

1974. Coastal Scenes. Multicoloured.
998. 30 f. Type **174** (postage) 45 20
999. 40 f. Tropicana tourist village 65 40
1000. 90 f. Fisherman on Lake Togo (air) .. .. 1·00 35
1001. 100 f. Mouth of Aneche River .. .. .. 1·25 40

1974. Cent. of U.P.U. Mult.
1003. 30 f. Type **175** (postage) 40 20
1004. 40 f. Postman with cleft carrying-stick 50 30
1005. 50 f. Type **175** (air) .. 60 30
1006. 100 f. As 40 f. .. .. 1·25 45

1974. Council of Accord. 15th Anniv. As **T 158** of Dahomey.
1007. 40 f. multicoloured .. 50 30

177. Hauling-in Net.

178. Earth Station and Probe.

1974. Lagoon Fishing. Multicoloured.
1008. 30 f. Type **177** (postage) 45 20
1009. 40 f. Throwing net .. 65 30
1010. 90 f. Fishes in net (air) .. 1·00 30
1011. 100 f. Fishing with lines 1·25 35
1012. 200 f. Fishing with basket (vert.) .. .. .. 2·75 70

1974. U.S. "Jupiter" Space Mission. Mult.
1014. 30 f. Type **178** (postage) 35 15
1015. 40 f. Probe transmitting to Earth (horiz.) .. 45 20
1016. 100 f. Blast-off (air) .. 95 40
1017. 200 f. Jupiter probe (horiz.) 1·75 70

1974. "Internaba 1974" Stamp Exhibition Basel. Nos. 884/5 optd. **·INTERNABA 1974 · CENTENARIUM U P U** and emblem.
1019. **146.** 40 f. mult. (postage) 3·50 1·00
1020. – 100 f. mult. (air) .. 4·25 1·40

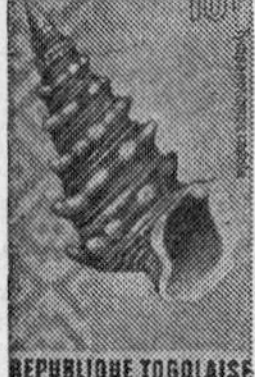
180. "Tympanotomus radula".

181. Groom with Horses.

1974. Seashells. Multicoloured.
1021. 10 f. Type **180** (postage) 20 15
1022. 20 f. "Tonna galea" .. 30 15
1023. 30 f. "Conus mercator" .. 45 15
1024. 40 f. "Cardium costatum" 70 15
1025. 90 f. "Alcithoe ponsonbyi" (air) .. .. .. 1·10 35
1026. 100 f. "Casmaria iredalei" 1·60 35

1974. Horse-racing. Multicoloured.
1028. 30 f. Type **181** (postage) 45 20
1029. 40 f. Exercising horses .. 65 30
1030. 90 f. Steeple-chaser taking fence (air) .. .. 1·00 35
1031. 100 f. Horses racing .. 1·50 45

1974. Air. West Germany's Victory in World Cup Football Championships, Munich. Nos. 890/1 optd. **COUPE DU MONDE DE FOOTBALL MUNICH 1974 VAINQUEURS REPUBLIQUE FEDERALE ALLEMAGNE.**
1033. – 90 f. multicoloured .. 90 35
1034. **148.** 200 f. multicoloured 1·75 80

183. Leopard.

1974. Wild Animals. Multicoloured.
1036. 20 f. Type **183** (postage) 35 15
1037. 30 f. Giraffes 45 20
1038. 40 f. Two African elephants 65 35
1039. 90 f. Lion and lioness (air) .. .. .. 1·00 45
1040. 100 f. Black rhinoceros and calf .. .. 1·50 45

184. Herd of Cows.

1974. Pastoral Economy. Multicoloured.
1042. 30 f. Type **184** (postage) 45 20
1043. 40 f. Milking 65 30
1044. 90 f. Cattle at water-hole (air) 85 45
1045. 100 f. Village cattle-pen .. 1·10 55

185. Churchill and Frigate H.M.S. "Loch Fada".

1974. Birth Cent. of Sir Winston Churchill. Multicoloured.
1047. 30 f. Type **185** (postage) 50 15
1048. 40 f. Churchill and fighter aircraft 60 20
1049. 100 f. Type **185** (air) .. 1·40 35
1050. 200 f. As 40 f. .. .. 2·25 80

1975. Opening of Hotel de la Paix, Lome. Optd. **Inauguration de la l'hotel Paix 9-1-75.**
1051a. **143.** 1000 f. gold, red and green .. .. 9·50

186. "Strelitzia reginae".

188. Radio Station, Kamina.

1975. Flowers of Togo. Multicoloured.
1052. 25 f. Type **186** (postage) 35 15
1053. 30 f. "Strophanthus sarmentosus" 45 15
1054. 40 f. "Chlamydocarya macrocarpa" (horiz.) .. 55 20
1055. 60 f. "Clerodendrum scandens" (horiz.) .. 90 35
1056. 100 f. "Clerodendrum thosonae" (horiz.) (air) 1·40 45
1057. 200 f. "Gloriosa superba" (horiz.) .. .. 2·50 65

1975. 70th Anniv. of Rotary International. Optd. **70e ANNIVERSAIRE 23 FEVRIER 1975.**
1059. **150.** 40 f. multicoloured (postage) 30 25
1060. – 90 f. multicoloured (No. 902) (air) .. 85 35
1061. **150.** 100 f. multicoloured 1·00 40

1975. Tourism. Multicoloured.
1062. 25 f. Type **188** 20 10
1063. 30 f. Benedictine Monastery, Zogbegan .. 35 20
1064. 40 f. Causeway, Atchinedji 45 30
1065. 60 f. Ayome Waterfalls .. 80 40

189. "Jesus Mocked" (El Greco).

190. Stilt-walking.

191. Hunting Bush Hare with Club.

1975. Easter. Multicoloured.
1066. 25 f. Type **189** (postage) 20 10
1067. 30 f. "The Crucifixion" (Master Janoslen) .. 35 10
1068. 40 f. "The Descent from the Cross" (Bellini) .. 55 20
1069. 90 f. "Pieta" (anon.) .. 95 40
1070. 100 f. "Christ Rising from the Grave" (Master MS) (air) .. .. .. 1·10 35
1071. 200 f. "The Holy Trinity" (detail) (Durer) .. 1·90 80

1975. 15th Anniv. of Independence. Mult.
1073. 25 f. Type **190** (postage) 30 10
1074. 30 f. Dancers 35 15
1075. 50 f. Independence parade (vert.) (air) .. 40 15
1076. 60 f. Dancer 60 35

1975. Hunting. Multicoloured.
1078. 30 f. Type **191** (postage) 45 20
1079. 40 f. Hunting Eurasian beavers with bow .. 55 35
1080. 90 f. Hunting red deer with snare (air) .. 1·25 45
1081. 100 f. Hunting wild boar with gun .. .. 1·40 55

192. Pounding Palm Nuts.

1975. Palm-oil Production. Multicoloured.
1082. 30 f. Type **192** (postage) 35 15
1083. 40 f. Extracting palm-oil (vert.) 40 20
1084. 85 f. Selling palm-oil (vert.) (air) 80 45
1085. 100 f. Oil-processing plant, Aloknegbe 90 55

193. "Apollo" and "Soyuz" in docking procedure.

1975. "Apollo-Soyuz" Space Link. Mult.
1087. 30 f. Type **193** (postage) 45 15
1088. 50 f. "Soyuz" spacecraft (vert.) (air) 40 15
1089. 60 f. Slaton Brand and Stafford ("Apollo" astronauts) 55 20
1090. 90 f. Leonov and Kubasov ("Soyuz" cosmonauts) 70 30
1091. 100 f. U.S., Soviet flags and "Apollo" and "Soyuz" linked .. 1·10 50
1092. 200 f. Emblem and Globe 2·25 65

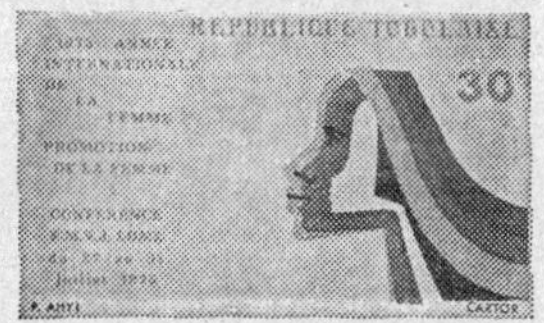

194. "African Women".

1975. International Women's Year.
1094. **194.** 30 f. multicoloured .. 40 15
1095. 40 f. multicoloured .. 45 20

195. Dr. Schweitzer, and Children drinking Milk.

1975. Birth Cent. of Dr. Albert Schweitzer. Multicoloured.
1096. 40 f. Type **195** (postage) 55 30
1097. 80 f. Schweitzer playing organ (vert.) (air) .. 90 30
1098. 90 f. Schweitzer feeding Eastern White Pelican (vert.) .. .. 1·10 35
1099. 100 f. Schweitzer and Lambarene Hospital .. 1·25 35

196. "Merchant writing Letter" (V. Carpaccio).
199. "Virgin and Child" (Mantegna).

1975. International Letter-writing Week. Multicoloured.
1101. 40 f. Type **196** (postage) 55 30
1102. 80 f. "Erasmus writing Letter" (Holbein) (air) 90 35

1975. 30th Anniv. of United Nations. Nos. 851/3 optd. **30eme Anniversaire des Nations-Unies.**
1103. 50 f. mult. (postage) 55 30
1104. 60 f. multicoloured (air) 50 20
1105. 90 f. multicoloured .. 60 30

1975. Air. World Scout Jamboree, Norway. Nos. 940/1 optd. **14eme JAMBOREE MONDIAL DES ECLAIREURS.**
1107. 100 f. multicoloured .. 95 45
1108. 200 f. multicoloured .. 1·75 80

1975. Christmas. "Virgin and Child" paintings by artists named. Multicoloured.
1110. 20 f. Type **199** (postage) 30 20
1111. 30 f. El Greco 40 20
1112. 40 f. Barend van Orley 45 20
1113. 90 f. Federigo Barocci (air) 80 30
1114. 100 f. Bellini 90 35
1115. 200 f. Correggio .. .. 1·60 55

200. Crashed Aircraft.

1975. Pres. Eyadema's Escape in Air Crash at Sarakawa.
1117. **200.** 50 f. multicoloured .. 7·25 5·00
1118. 60 f. multicoloured .. 7·25 5·00

200a. Pole Vault.

1976. Olympic Games. Montreal. Mult.
1118a. 1000 f. Type **200a** .. 10·00
1118b. 1000 f. Diving .. .. 10·00
1118c. 1000 f. Running .. 10·00
1118d. 1000 f. Show jumping .. 10·00
1118e 1000 f. Cycling .. .. 10·00

201. "Frigates forcing the Hudson Passage".

1976. Bicent. of American Revolution. Mult.
1119. 35 f. Type **201** (postage) 40 20
1120. 50 f. "George Washington" (G. Stuart) (vert.) .. 55 30
1121. 60 f. "Surrender of Burgoyne" (Trumbull) (air) 65 20
1122. 70 f. "Surrender at Trenton" (Trumbull) (vert.) 85 30
1123. 100 f. "Signing of Declaration of Independence" (Trumbull) 90 35
1124. 200 f. "Washington crossing the Delaware" (E. Leutze) .. .. 1·75 60

202. Cable-laying Ship.

203. Blind Man and Mosquito.

205. Exhibition Hall.
204. A.C.P. and C.E.E. Emblems.

1976. Telephone Centenary. Multicoloured.
1126. 25 f. Type **202** (postage) 20 15
1127. 30 f. Automatic telephone and tape-recording equipment 40 30
1128. 70 f. Edison and communications equipment (air) 55 30
1129. 105 f. Alexander Graham Bell, early and modern telephones 85 40

1976. World Health Day. Multicoloured.
1131. 50 f. Type **203** (postage) 65 30
1132. 60 f. Eye Examination (air) 55 20

1976. 1st Anniv. of A.C.P./C.E.E. Treaty (between Togo and European Common Market). Multicoloured.
1133. 10 f. Type **204** (postage) 15 10
1134. 50 f. Map of Africa, Europe and Asia 40 30
1135. 60 f. Type **204** (air) .. 45 20
1136. 70 f. As 50 f. 55 30

1976. Anniversaries. Multicoloured.
1136a. 5 f. Type **205** (postage) .. 10 10
1136b. 10 f. Electricity pylon and flags 15 10
1137. 50 f. Type **205** 50 30
1138. 60 f. As 10 f. (air) .. 50 30

The 5 f. and 50 f. commemorate the 10th Anniv. of the Marine Exhibition and the 10 f. and 60 f. the first Anniv. of the Ghana–Togo–Dahomey Electricity Link.

1976. Air. "Interphil '76" International Stamp Exhibition, Philadelphia. Nos. 1121/4 optd. **INTERPHIL MAI 29 - JUIN 6 1976.**
1139. 60 f. multicoloured .. 40 15
1140. 70 f. multicoloured .. 60 20
1141. 100 f. multicoloured .. 90 30
1142. 200 f. multicoloured .. 1·40 55

207. Running.

1976. Olympic Games, Montreal. Mult.
1144. 25 f. Type **207** (postage) 20 10
1145. 30 f. Canoeing 35 15
1146. 50 f. High-jumping .. 45 20
1147. 70 f. Sailing (air) .. 55 20
1148. 105 f. Motorcycling .. 85 35
1149. 200 f. Fencing .. .. 1·60 55

208. "Titan 3" and "Viking" Emblem.

1976. "Viking" Space Mission. Mult.
1151. 30 f. Type **208** (postage) 15 10
1152. 50 f. "Viking" en route between Earth and Mars 40 20
1153. 60 f. "Viking landing on Mars" (air) 55 20
1154. 70 f. Nodus Gordii, Mars 65 20
1155. 100 f. "Viking" over Mare Tyrrhenum 85 40
1156. 200 f. "Viking" landing on Mars (different) .. 1·50 55

209. "Young Routy".

1976. 75th Death Anniv. of Toulouse-Lautrec (painter). Multicoloured.
1158. 10 f. Type **209** (postage) 15 10
1159. 20 f. "Helene Vary" .. 40 15
1160. 35 f. "Louis Pascal" .. 65 15
1161. 60 f. "Carmen" (air) .. 80 20
1162. 70 f. "Maurice at the Somme" 90 30
1163. 200 f. "Messalina" .. 2·25 60

1976. International Children's Day. Nos. 905/1 optd. **Journee Internationale de l'Enfance.**
1165. 161. 40 f. multicoloured (postage) 45 15
1166. – 100 f. mult. (air) .. 80 45

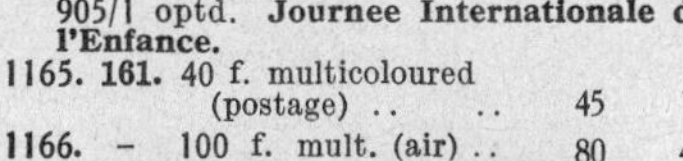

211. "Adoration of the Shepherds" (Pontormo).

1976. Christmas. Nativity scenes by artists named. Multicoloured.
1167. 25 f. Type **211** (postage) 35 15
1168. 30 f. Crivelli 45 15
1169. 50 f. Pontormo 80 20
1170. 70 f. Lotto (air) 65 20
1171. 105 f. Pontormo (different) 1·90 35
1172. 200 f. Lotto (different) .. 1·60 55

212. Quaid-i-Azam. **214.** Queen Elizabeth II.

1976. Birth Centenary of Mohammad Ali Jinnah, "Quaid-i-Azam".
1174. **212.** 50 f. multicoloured .. 55 30

1977. Gold Medal Winners, Montreal Olympic Games. Nos. 1146/47 and 1149 optd. **CHAMPIONS OLYMPIQUES** with events and countries.
1175. 50 f. mult. (postage) .. 50 20
1176. 70 f. multicoloured (air) 60 35
1177. 200 f. multicoloured .. 1·40 80

OPTD. 50 f. **SAUT EN HAUTEUR POLOGNE.** 70 f. **YACHTING - FLYING DUTCHMAN REPUBLIQUE FEDERALE ALLEMAGNE.** 200 f. **ESCRIME-FLEURET PAR EQUIPES REPUBLIQUE FEDERALE ALLEMAGNE.**

1977. Silver Jubilee of Queen Elizabeth II.
1179. **214.** 1000 f. multicoloured 7·75

215. Phosphate Complex, Kpeme.

1977. 10th Anniv. of Eyadema Regime. Multicoloured.
1181. 50 f. Type **215** (postage) 55 20
1182. 60 f. Parliament Building, Lome (air) .. 55 30
1183. 100 f. Crowd greeting Pres. Eyadema 80 40

216. Gongophone.

1977. Musical Instruments. Multicoloured.
1185. 5 f. Type **216** (postage) .. 15 10
1186. 10 f. Tamtam (vert.) .. 20 10
1187. 25 f. Dondon 55 15
1188. 60 f. Atopani (air) .. 65 20
1189. 80 f. One-string fiddle (vert.) .. .. 1·00 30
1190. 105 f. African flutes (vert.) 1·40 35

217. Victor Hugo and Guernsey Scene.

1977. 175th Birth Anniv. of Victor Hugo (writer). Multicoloured.
1192. 50 f. Victor Hugo as a young man, and residence (postage) .. 55 15
1193. 60 f. Type **217** (air) .. 60 30

218. Beethoven and Birthplace, Bonn.

1977. 150th Death Anniv. of Ludwig van Beethoven. Multicoloured.
1195. 30 f. Type **218** (postage) 55 15
1196. 50 f. Beethoven's bust and Heiligenstadt residence 65 20
1197. 100 f. Young Beethoven and grand piano (air) .. 1·10 35
1198. 200 f. Beethoven on deathbed and Trinity Church, Vienna .. .. .. 1·90 65

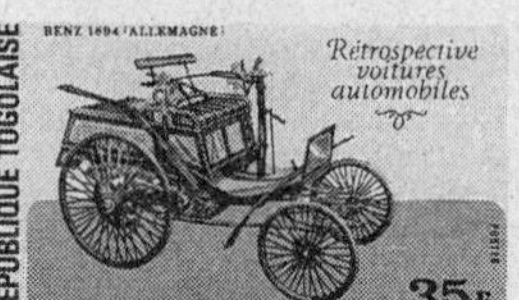

219. Benz 1894.

1977. Early Motor Cars. Multicoloured.
1200. 35 f. Type **219** (postage) 65 20
1201. 50 f. De Dion Bouton, 1903 .. .. .. 1·00 30
1202. 60 f. Cannstatt-Daimler, 1899 (air) 80 20
1203. 70 f. Sunbeam ,1904 .. 90 20
1204. 100 f. Renault, 1908 .. 1·10 35
1205. 200 f. Rolls-Royce, 1909 1·90 65

220. Lindbergh, Ground Crew and " Spirit of St. Louis ".

1977. 50th Anniv. of Lindbergh's Transatlantic Flight. Multicoloured.
1207. 25 f. Type **220** (postage) 35 15
1208. 50 f. Lindbergh before take-off 65 20
1209. 60 f. Lindbergh with son (air) 50 15
1210. 85 f. Lindbergh's home, Kent (England) .. 80 20
1211. 90 f. " Spirit of St. Louis " over Atlantic 80 30
1212. 100 f. " Concorde " over New York City .. 1·25 50

1977. 10th Anniv. of International French Language Council. Nos. 1192/3 optd. **10eme ANNIVERSAIRE DU CONSEIL INTERNATIONAL DE LA LANGUE FRANCAISE.**
1214. **217.** 50 f. multicoloured (postage) 60 40
1215. – 60 f. multicoloured (air) 55 35

222. Nile Crocodile.

1977. Endangered Wildlife. Multicoloured.
1216. 5 f. African crocodile (postage) 15 15
1217. 15 f. Type **222** 40 20
1218. 60 f. Western black-and-white colobus (air) .. 80 15
1219. 90 f. Chimpanzee (vert.) 90 20
1220. 100 f. Leopard .. .. 1·10 30
1221. 200 f. African manatee .. 1·90 55

223. Agricultural School, Tove.

1977. Agricultural Development. Mult.
1223. 50 f. Type **223** (postage) 50 20
1224. 60 f. Corn silo (air) .. 55 15
1225. 100 f. Hoeing and planting 70 30
1226. 200 f. Tractor .. .. 1·50 55

224. " Landscape at Sunset " (Rubens).

1977. 400th Birth Anniv. of Rubens. Mult.
1228. 15 f. Type **224** (postage) 35 10
1229. 35 f. " Exchange of the Princesses at Hendaye " 80 15
1230. 60 f. " Four Negro Heads " (air) 85 15
1231. 100 f. " Anne of Austria " 1·10 40

225. Shuttle after Landing.

1977. Space Shuttle. Multicoloured.
1233. 20 f. Type **225** (postage) 20 10
1234. 30 f. Launching 35 15
1235. 50 f. Ejecting propellant tanks 55 15
1236. 90 f. Retrieving a satellite (air) 70 20
1237. 100 f. Ejecting repaired satellite 85 30
1238. 200 f. Shuttle landing .. 1·50 60

226. Lafayette at 19 (after Le Mire).

227. Lenin and Cruiser " Aurora ".

1977. Bicentenary of Lafayette's Arrival in America.
1240. **226.** 25 f. brown, yellow and purple (postage) 30 10
1241. – 50 f. red, violet & pink 55 15
1242. – 60 f. turquoise, green and deep green (air) 50 15
1243. – 105 f. blue, light blue and purple .. 90 35
DESIGNS—HORIZ. 50 f. Lafayette at Montpelier. 60 f. Lafayette's arrival in New York. 105 f. Lafayette with Washington at Valley Forge.

1977. 60th Anniv. of Russian Revolution.
1245. **227.** 50 f. multicoloured .. 80 30

228. " Madonna and Child " (Lotto).

229. Edward Jenner.

1977. Christmas. " Madonna and Child " by artists named. Multicoloured.
1246. 20 f. Type **228** (postage) 20 15
1247. 30 f. Crivelli 35 15
1248. 50 f. C. Tura 55 15
1249. 90 f. Crivelli (different) (air) 65 30
1250. 100 f. Bellini 90 35
1251. 200 f. Crivelli (different) 1·50 55

1978. World Eradication of Smallpox.
1253. **229.** 5 f. ochre, blk. & lilac (postage) 10 10
1254. - 20 f. multicoloured .. 20 10
1255. **229.** 50 f. ochre, black and green (air).. .. 35 15
1256. – 60 f. multicoloured.. 40 15
DESIGN—HORIZ. 20 f., 60 f. Patients queueing for vaccination.

230. Wright Brothers.

1978. 75th Anniv. of 1st Flight by Wright Brothers. Multicoloured.
1258. 35 f. Type **230** (postage) 45 20
1259. 50 f. Wilbur Wright flying 'plane No. 3 .. .. 85 35
1260. 60 f. Orville Wright. Flight of 7 min. 31 sec. (air) .. .. .. 1·00 40
1261. 70 f. First flying accident 1·10 40
1262. 200 f. Wright brothers' cycle workshop, Dearborn, Michigan .. .. 1·40 55
1263. 300 f. First motorised flight .. .. .. 2·00 85

231. " Apollo 8 " (10th anniv. of first mission).

232. St. John.

1978. Anniversaries and Events. Mult.
1265. 1000 f. Type **231** .. 8·25
1266. 1000 f. High-jumping (Olympic Games, 1980) 8·25
1267. 1000 f. Westminster Abbey (25th anniv. of Queen Elizabeth II's Coronation) .. .. .. 8·25
1268. 1000 f. " Duke of Wellington " (150th death anniv. of Goya) .. 8·25
1269. 1000 f. Footballers and Cup (World Cup Football Championship) .. 8·25

1978. The Evangelists. Multicoloured.
1271. 5 f. Type **232** 10 10
1272. 10 f. St. Luke 10 10
1273. 25 f. St. Mark 20 10
1274. 30 f. St. Mathew .. 30 10

233. Fishing Harbour.

1978. Autonomous Port of Lome. Mult.
1276. 25 f. Type **233** (postage) 45 15
1277. 60 f. Industrial port (air) 55 20
1278. 100 f. Merchant port .. 80 30
1279. 200 f. General view .. 1·25 55

234. " Venera 1 " Probe.

235. Goalkeeper catching Ball.

1978. Space Mission–Venus. Multicoloured.
1281. 20 f. Type **234** (postage) 15 10
1282. 30 f. " Pioneer " (horiz.) 20 15
1283. 50 f. Soviet fuel base and antenna 40 15
1284. 90 f. " Venera " blast jets (horiz.) (air) 40 20
1285. 100 f. " Venera " antennae 55 30
1286. 200 f. " Pioneer " in orbit 1·00 55

1978. World Cup Football Championship, Argentina. Multicoloured.
1288. 30 f. Type **235** (postage) 30 10
1289. 50 f. Two players with ball 40 15
1290. 60 f. Heading the ball (air) 50 15
1291. 80 f. High kick 60 20
1292. 200 f. Chest stop .. 1·25 55
1293. 300 f. Player with ball .. 2·00 85

236. Thomas Edison (inventor).

237. " Celerifere ", 1818.

1978. Cent. of Invention of the Phonograph. Multicoloured.
1295. 30 f. Type **236** (postage) 20 10
1296. 50 f. Couple dancing to H.M.V. " Victor " phonograph 1905 .. 45 15
1297. 60 f. Edison's original phonograph (horiz.) (air) 40 15
1298. 80 f. Berliner's first phonograph, 1888 .. .. 50 20
1299. 200 f. Berliner's improved phonograph, 1894 (horiz.) 1·25 55
1300. 300 f. " His Master's Voice " phonograph, c. 1900 (horiz.) .. .. 2·00 85

1978. Early Bicycles. Multicoloured.
1302. 25 f. Type **237** (postage) 35 15
1303. 50 f. First bicycle side-car (vert.) 65 20
1304. 60 f. Bantam bicycle (vert.) (air) 55 15
1305. 85 f. Military folding bicycle 65 20
1306. 90 f. " La Draisienne " (vert.) 90 35
1307. 100 f. Penny-farthing (vert.) 95 40

238. Dunant's Birthplace, Geneva.

240. Eiffel Tower.

239. " Threshing " (Raoul Dufy).

1978. 150th Birth Anniv. of Henri Dunant (founder of Red Cross).
1309. **238.** 5 f. blue and red (post.) 10 10
1310. – 10 f. brown and red 15 10
1311. – 25 f. green and red.. 30 10
1312. – 60 f. purple and red (air) 55 20
DESIGNS: 10 f. Dunant at 35. 25 f. Tending battle casualties, 1864. 60 f. Red Cross pavilions, Paris Exhibition, 1867.

1978. Air. " Philexafrique " Stamp Exhibitions, Libreville (Gabon), and Int. Stamp Fair, Essen, West Germany. As T **262** of Niger. Multicoloured.
1314. 100 f. Jay and Thurn and Taxis ½ sgr. stamp of 1854 .. .. .. 1·90 1·40
1315. 100 f. Warthog and Togo 50 f. stamp, 1964 .. 1·90 1·40

1978. Artists' Anniversaries. Multicoloured.
1316. 25 f. Type **239** (25th death anniv.) (postage) 40 15
1317. 50 f. " Horsemen on the Seashore " (Gauguin—75th death anniv.) 70 15
1318. 60 f. " Langlois Bridge " (Van Gogh 125th Birth anniv.) (air) .. 50 15
1319. 70 f. " Sabbath of the Witches " (Goya—150th death anniv.) .. 60 20
1320. 90 f. " Christ Among the Doctors " (Durer—450th death anniv.) .. 80 30
1321. 200 f. " View of Arco " (Durer) .. .. .. 1·40 55

1978. Centenary of Paris U.P.U. Congress. Multicoloured.
1323 50 f. Type **240** (postage) 80 20
1324 60 f. Full-rigged ship "Slieve Roe" (air) 65 25
1325 105 f. Congress medallion 70 30
1326 200 f. 1870s locomotive .. 1·40 55

241. " Madonna and Child " (Antonello).

242. H.M.S. "Endeavour" and Route round New Zealand.

1978. Christmas. Paintings of the Virgin and Child by artists shown below. Mult.
1328. 20 f. Type **241** (postage) 20 15
1329. 30 f. Crivelli 35 15
1330. 50 f. Tura 55 15
1331. 90 f. Crivelli (different) (air) 65 30
1332. 100 f. Tura (different) .. 90 30
1333. 200 f. Crivelli (different) 1·50 55

1979. Death Bicentenary of Captain James Cook. Multicoloured.
1335. 25 f. Type **242** (postage) 50 15
1336. 50 f. Careening H.M.S. "Endeavour" (horiz.) 80 35
1337. 60 f. "Freelove" at Whitby (horiz.) (air) 75 35
1338. 70 f. Antarctic voyage of H.M.S. "Resolution" (horiz.) .. .. 1·25 45
1339. 90 f. Capt. Cook .. .. 1·25 45
1340. 200 f. Sail plan of H.M.S. "Endeavour" .. .. 2·50 1·10

243. Christ entering Jerusalem.

1979. Easter. Multicoloured.

1342. 30 f. Type **243** (postage) 20 10
1343. 40 f. The Last Supper (horiz.) 30 15
1344. 50 f. Descent from the Cross (horiz.) 40 15
1345. 60 f. Resurrection (air) .. 45 15
1346. 100 f. Ascension 65 30
1347. 200 f. Jesus appearing to Mary Magdalene .. 1·25 55

244. Statuette of Drummer.

1979. Air. " Philexafrique 2 " Stamp Exhibition, Libreville. Multicoloured.

1349. 60 f. Type **244** .. .. 1·10 55
1350. 100 f. Hands with letter 1·60 1·10

245. Einstein Observatory, Potsdam.

1979. Birth Centenary of Albert Einstein (physicist).

1351. **245.** 35 f. red, yellow and black (postage) .. 20 10
1352. – 50 f. grn., mve. & blk. 35 10
1353. – 60 f. multicoloured (air) 40 10
1354. – 85 f. lilac, brn. & blk. 60 15
1355. – 100 f. multicoloured 65 20
1356. – 200 f. grn., brn. & blk. 1·40 40

DESIGNS—HORIZ. 50 f. Einstein and J. R. Macdonald in Berlin, 1931. 60 f. Sight and actuality diagram. VERT. 85 f. Einstein playing violin. 100 f. Atomic symbol and relativity formula. 200 f. Albert Einstein.

246. Children with Flag.

247. Planting Sapling.

1979. International Year of the Child. Multicoloured.

1358. 5 f. Type **246** 10 10
1359. 10 f. Mother with children 10 10
1360. 15 f. Children's Village symbol on map of Africa (horiz.) 10 10
1361. 20 f. Woman taking children to Children's Village (horiz.) 15 10
1362. 25 f. Children sitting round Fan palm 30 10
1363. 30 f. Map of Togo showing Children's Villages .. 35 10

1979. Tree Day.

1365. **247.** 50 f. green and violet (postage) 50 15
1366. – 60 f. brn. and grn. (air) 55 20

DESIGN: 60 f. Watering sapling.

248. Sir Rowland Hill.

249. Stephenson's "Rocket", 1829.

1979. Death Centenary of Sir Rowland Hill. Multicoloured.

1367. 20 f. Type **248** (postage) 15 10
1368. 30 f. French mail sorting office in the reign of Louis XV (horiz.) .. 20 10
1369. 50 f. Parisian postbox, 1850 .. .. .. 40 15
1370. 90 f. Bellman collecting letters, 1820 (air) .. 60 20
1371. 100 f. " Centre-cycles ", used for mail delivery, 1880 (horiz.) 65 20
1372. 200 f. Post Office railway carriage, 1848 (horiz.) 1·25 40

1979. Railway Locomotives. Multicoloured.

1374. 35 f. Type **249** (postage) 35 10
1375. 50 f. William Norris' "Austria", 1843 .. 45 15
1376. 60 f. "The General", 1862 (air) 55 15
1377. 85 f. Stephenson locomotive, 1843 .. .. 75 35
1378. 100 f. De Witt Clinton train, 1831 .. .. 85 35
1379. 200 f. D. Joy's "Jenny Lind" .. .. .. 1·75 55

Nos. 1375/9 are horizontal.

250. Skiing.

251. Native Praying.

1979. Olympic Games, Lake Placid and Moscow. Multicoloured.

1381. 20 f. Type **250** (postage) 15 10
1382. 30 f. Yachting 20 15
1383. 50 f. Throwing the discus 40 10
1384. 90 f. Ski-jumping (air) .. 65 20
1385. 100 f. Canoeing 70 20
1386. 200 f. Gymnastics (ring exercise) .. .. 1·40 40

1979. Togo Religions.

1388. **251.** 30 f. brown, green and yellow (postage) .. 20 10
1389. – 50 f. blue, brn. & red 35 10
1390. – 60 f. purple, blue and buff (air) 45 15
1391. – 70 f. lilac, orge. & grn. 50 20

DESIGNS—HORIZ. 50 f. Catholic priests. 60 f. Muslims at prayer. 70 f. Protestant preachers.

252. Astronaut on Moon.

253. Dish Aerial.

1979. 10th Anniv. of First Moon Landing. Multicoloured.

1393. 35 f. Type **252** (postage) 30 10
1394. 50 f. Capsule orbiting Moon 40 10
1395. 60 f. Armstrong descending to Moon 45 10
1396. 70 f. Astronaut and flag (air) 50 15
1397. 200 f. Astronaut performing experiment .. 1·25 35
1398. 300 f. Module leaving Moon .. .. .. 2·00 50

1979. Third World Telecommunications Exposition, Geneva.

1400. – 50 f. light brown, brown and green (postage) 35 10
1401. **253.** 60 f. green, blue and deep blue (air) .. 50 20

DESIGN—HORIZ. 50 f. Television screen.

254. Pres. Eyadema.

1979. Air. 10th Anniv. of R.P.T. Mult.

1402. 1000 f. Pres. Eyadema and Party badge .. 6·75
1403. 1000 f. Type **254** .. .. 6·75

255. Holy Family.

256. Rotary Emblem.

1979. Christmas. Multicoloured.

1404. 20 f. Type **255** (postage) 15 10
1405. 30 f. Madonna and child and angels playing musical instruments .. 20 10
1406. 50 f. Adoration of the shepherds 40 10
1407. 90 f. Adoration of the Magi (air) 55 20
1408. 100 f. Mother presenting Child 70 20
1409. 200 f. The flight into Egypt 1·50 40

1980. 75th Anniv. of Rotary International. Multicoloured.

1411. 25 f. Type **256** (postage) 15 10
1412. 30 f. Anniversary emblem 30 10
1413. 40 f. Paul Harris (founder) 35 10
1414. 90 f. Figure exercising and sun (health) (air) .. 65 20
1415. 100 f. Fish and grain (food) 70 20
1416. 200 f. Family group (humanity) .. .. 1·40 40

257. Shooting (Biathlon).

1980. Winter Olympic Games, Lake Placid. Multicoloured.

1418. 50 f. Type **257** (postage) 50 10
1419. 60 f. Downhill skiing .. 40 10
1420. 100 f. Speed skating (air) 70 20
1421. 200 f. Cross-country skiing 1·40 40

258. Swimming.

1980. Olympic Games, Moscow. Multicoloured.

1423. 20 f. Type **258** (postage) 15 10
1424. 30 f. Gymnastics .. 20 10
1425. 50 f. Running 40 10
1426. 100 f. Fencing (air) .. 65 20
1427. 200 f. Pole vaulting .. 1·25 45
1428. 300 f. Hurdles .. .. 2·00 55

259. Truck going to Market.

1980. Market Scenes. Multicoloured.

1430 1 f. Grinding savo (post) 10 10
1431 2 f. Women preparing meat 10 10
1432 3 f. Type **259** 10 10
1433 4 f. Unloading produce .. 10 10
1434 5 f. Sugar-cane seller .. 10 10
1435 6 f. Barber doing child's hair 10 10
1436 7 f. Vegetable seller .. 10 10
1437 8 f. Mangoes (vert) .. 10 10
1438 9 f. Grain seller 10 10
1439 10 f. Fish seller 10 10
1440 15 f. Clay pot seller .. 10 10
1441 20 f. Straw baskets .. 15 10
1442 25 f. Lemon and onion seller (vert) 15 10
1443 30 f. Straw baskets (different) 20 10
1444 40 f. Shore market .. 30 15
1445 45 f. Selling cooked food 35 15
1446 50 f. Women carrying produce (vert) .. 35 15
1447 60 f. Selling oil 45 15
1448 90 f. Linen seller (air) .. 55 15
1449 100 f. Bananas 65 20
1450 200 f. Pottery .. .. 1·25 45
1451 250 f. Setting-up stalls .. 1·60 55
1452 500 f. Vegetable seller (different) .. .. 3·00 1·10
1453 1000 f. Drink seller .. 6·00 2·25

260. " Concorde " and Map of Africa.

1980. 20th Anniv. of African Air Safety Organization.

1458. **260.** 50 f. multicoloured (postage) 55 20
1459. 60 f. multicoloured (air) 55 25

261. " Christ with Angels " (Mantegna).

263. Radio Waves.

1980. Easter. Multicoloured.

1460. 30 f. Type **261** (postage) 30 15
1461. 40 f. " Christ with Disciples " (Crivelli) .. 40 15
1462. 50 f. " Christ borne by His Followers " (Pontormo) 45 15
1463. 60 f. " The Deposition " (Lotto) (air) 50 10
1464. 100 f. " The Crucifixion " (El Greco) 70 20
1465. 200 f. " Christ with Angels " (Crivelli) .. .. 1·40 45

1980. " London 1980 " International Stamp Exhibition. No. 1267 optd. **Londres 1980.**

1467. 1000 f. Westminster Abbey 7·25

1980. World Telecommunications Day.

1469. – 50 f. violet and green (postage) 45 10
1470. **263.** 60 f. pink, brown and blue (air) 50 15

DESIGN—HORIZ. 50 f. Satellite.

264. Red Cross and Globe.

265. Jules Verne.

1980. Togo Red Cross. Multicoloured.

1471. 50 f. Type **264** (postage) 55 10
1472. 60 f. Nurses and patient (air) 45 15

1980. 75th Death Anniv. of Jules Verne (writer). Multicoloured.

1473. 30 f. Type **265** (postage) 30 10
1474. 50 f. " 20,000 Leagues under the Sea " .. 40 10

1475. 60 f. "From the Earth to the Moon" (air) .. 40 15
1476. 80 f. "Around the World in Eighty Days" .. 55 20
1477. 100 f. "From the Earth to the Moon" (different) 1·40 60
1478. 200 f. "20,000 Leagues under the Sea" (different) .. .. .. 1·40 45

266. "Baroness James de Rothschild".

1980. Birth Bicent. of Jean Ingres (painter). Multicoloured.

1480. 25 f. Type **266** (postage) 35 10
1481. 30 f. "Napoleon I on the Imperial Throne" .. 55 10
1482. 40 f. "Don Pedro of Toledo putting down the Sword of Henry IV" .. 50 10
1483. 90 f. "Jupiter and Thetis" (air) 65 20
1484. 100 f. "The Countess of Hassonville" .. 85 20
1485. 200 f. "Tu Marcellus Eris" 1·50 35

267. Minnie holding Mirror for Leopard.

1980. Walt Disney Characters and Wildlife. Multicoloured.

1487. 1 f. Type **267** 10 10
1488. 2 f. Goofy cleaning hippo's teeth 10 10
1489. 3 f. Donald clinging to crocodile 10 10
1490. 4 f. Donald hanging over cliff edge from rhino's horn 10 10
1491. 5 f. Goofy riding a water buffalo 10 10
1492. 10 f. Monkey photographing Mickey 10 10
1493. 100 f. Doctor Mickey examining giraffe .. 80 20
1494. 300 f. Elephant showering Goofy .. .. .. 1·60 40

1980. 50th Anniv. of Pluto. Design as Type **267**.

1496. 200 f. Pluto in party mood 1·60 40

268. Wreath.

1980. Famous Men of the Decade.

1498. **268.** 25 f. orange and green (postage) .. 15 10
1499. – 40 f. deep grn. & grn. 65 20
1500. – 90 f. deep blue and blue (air) .. 60 20
1501. – 100 f. lilac and pink 1·10 20
1502. – 200 f. brown and ochre 1·25 35

DESIGNS: 40 f. Mao Tse Tung. 90 f. Pres. Allende. 100 f. Pope Paul VI. 200 f. Pres. Kenyatta.

269. Tourist Hotel Emblem.

270. Human Rights Emblem, and Map of Australia.

1980. World Tourism Conference, Manila. Multicoloured.

1504. 50 f. Type **269** 35 10
1505. 150 f. Conference emblem 1·00 35

1980. 30th Anniv. of Human Rights Convention.

1506. **270.** 30 f. violet, purple and black (postage) .. 30 10
1507. – 50 f. green, pale green and black 40 10
1508. – 60 f. deep blue, blue and black (air) .. 40 15
1509. – 150 f. brn. orge. & blk. 1·00 35

DESIGNS: 50 f. Map of Eurasia. 60 f. Map of the Americas. 150 f. Map of Africa.

271. Emblem.

1980. Air. General Conclave of French-speaking Countries of the American Order of Rosicrucians, Lome.

1511. **271.** 60 f. multicoloured .. 50 15

272. Church at Melk, Austria.

1980. Christmas. Multicoloured.

1512. 20 f. Type **272** (postage) 15 10
1513. 30 f. Tarragona Cathedral, Spain 20 10
1514. 50 f. Church of St. John the Baptist, Florence .. 35 10
1515. 100 f. Cologne Cathedral (air) 65 20
1516. 150 f. Notre-Dame, Paris 1·00 30
1517. 200 f. Canterbury Cathedral 1·40 35

1980. 5th Anniv. of African Posts and Telecommunications Union. As T **292** of Niger.

1519. 100 f. multicoloured .. 65 40

273. "February 2nd" Hotel.

1981. Inaug. of "February 2nd" Hotel.

1520. **273.** 50 f. multicoloured (postage) .. 45 15
1521. 60 f. multicoloured (air) 45 15

274. "Rembrandt's Father".

1981. Easter. Rembrandt Printings. Multicoloured.

1522. 30 f. Type **274** (postage) 30 10
1523. 40 f. "Self-Portrait" .. 35 10
1524. 50 f. "Rembrandt's Father as an Old Man" .. 40 10
1525. 60 f. "Rider on Horseback" 50 15
1526. 100 f. "Rembrandt's Mother" (air) .. 70 20
1527. 200 f. "Man in a Ruff" 1·50 45

275. Grey-necked Bald Crow.

1981. Birds. Multicoloured.

1529. 30 f. Type **275** (postage) 35 10
1530. 40 f. Splendid Sunbird .. 45 10
1531. 60 f. Violet Starling .. 55 15
1532. 90 f. Red-collard Whydah 90 20
1533. 50 f. Violet-backed Sunbird (air) 55 15
1534. 100 f. Red Bishop .. 1·00 30

276. Dish Aerial.

1981. 6th African Postal Union Council Meeting. Multicoloured.

1536. 70 f. Type **276** 50 15
1537. 90 f. Telecommunications control room 60 20
1538. 105 f. Map of Togo and Africa (vert.) 70 30

277. Blind Man with Guide Dog.

1981. International Year of Disabled People. Multicoloured.

1539. 70 f. Type **277** (postage) 85 30
1540. 90 f. One legged carpenter (air) 60 15
1541. 200 f. Wheelchair basketball .. .. .. 1·60 55

278. "Woman with Hat".

1981. Birth Centenary of Pablo Picasso. Multicoloured.

1543. 25 f. Type **278** (postage) 35 10
1544. 50 f. "She-goat" 45 10
1545. 60 f. "Violin" 55 15
1546. 90 f. "Violin and Bottle on Table" (air) .. 80 20
1547. 100 f. "Baboon with Young" 90 30
1548. 200 f. "Mandolin and Clarinet" .. .. 1·90 55

279. Aachen Cathedral, West Germany.

1981. World Heritage Convention. Multicoloured.

1550. 30 f. Type **279** (postage) 20 10
1551. 40 f. Yellowstone National Park, U.S.A. 30 10
1552. 50 f. Nahanni National Park, Canada .. 35 10
1553. 60 f. Cruciform rock churches, Lalibela, Ethiopia 40 15
1554. 100 f. Old city centre, Cracow, Poland (air) 65 20
1555. 200 f. Goree Island, Senegal 1·25 35

280. "Vostock I", (First Manned Space Flight. 20th Anniv.)

1981. Space Anniversaries. Multicoloured.

1557. 25 f. Type **280** (postage) 15 10
1558. 50 f. "Freedom 7". First American in space (20th anniv.) 35 10
1559. 60 f. "Lunar Orbiter I" (15th anniv.) 40 15
1560. 90 f. "Soyuz 10" (10th anniv.) (air) 60 15
1561. 100 f. Astronauts on Moon "(Apollo XIV". 100th Anniv.) 65 20

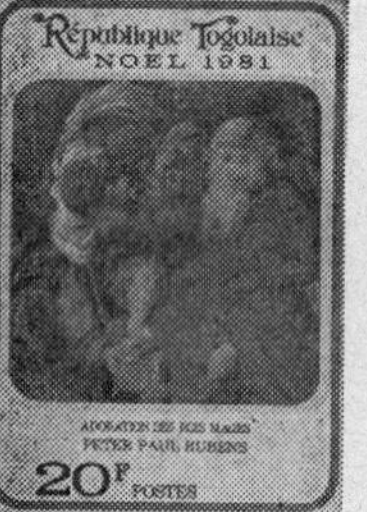

281. "Adoration of the Magi".

282. Association Emblem and Togo Flag.

1981. Christmas. Paintings by Rubens. Multicoloured.

1563. 20 f. Type **281** (postage) 15 10
1564. 30 f. "Adoration of the Shepherds" 20 10
1565. 50 f. "Coronation of St. Catherine" 40 10
1566. 100 f. "Adoration of the Magi" (different) (air) 60 20
1567. 200 f. "Madonna and Child" .. .. .. 1·40 45
1568. 300 f. "The Madonna giving the Robe to St. Idefonse" 2·25 65

1981. West African Rice Development Association.

1570. **282.** 70 f. multicoloured (postage) 60 20
1571. 105 f. multicoloured (air) 65 30

283. Peace Dove and National Flag.

1982. 15th Anniv. of National Liberation. Multicoloured.

1572. 70 f. Type **283** (postage) 55 20
1573. 90 f. Pres. Eyadema and citizens (vert.) .. 60 20
1574. 105 f. Pres. Eyadema and citizens holding hands (vert.) (air) .. 65 35
1575. 130 f. Hotel complex .. 90 45

284. Scouts.

1982. 75th Anniv. of Boy Scout Movement. Multicoloured.

1576. 70 f. Type **284** (postage) 50 15
1577. 90 f. Signalling (air) .. 65 20
1578. 120 f. Constructing a tower 85 30
1579. 130 f. Scouts with canoe 90 50
1580. 135 f. Scouts and tent .. 95 35

285. Moses and the Burning Bush. **286.** Togo and Italy Olympic Stamps.

1982. Easter. The Ten Commandments. Multicoloured.

1582. 10 f. Type **285** (postage) 10 10
1583. 25 f. Jephtha's daughter 15 10
1584. 30 f. St. Vincent Ferrer preaching in Verona .. 20 10
1585. 45 f. The denouncing of Noah 30 10
1586. 50 f. Cain and Abel .. 35 10
1587. 70 f. Potiphar's wife .. 50 20
1588. 90 f. Isaac blessing Jacob 60 35
1589. 105 f. Susannah and the elders (air) 65 30
1590. 120 f. Bathsheba .. 85 35

1982. Air. "Romolymphil" Stamp Exhibition.

1592. **286.** 105 f. multicoloured . 70 30

287. First Stamps of France and Togo.

1982. Air. "Philexfrance '82" International Stamp Exhibition.

1593. **287.** 90 f. multicoloured .. 65 40

288. Goalkeeper. **289.** "Papilio dardanus".

1982. World Cup Football Championship, Spain. Multicoloured.

1594. 25 f. Type **288** (postage) 15 10
1595. 45 f. Tackle 35 10
1596. 105 f. Heading ball (air) 65 20
1597. 200 f. Fighting for possession .. .. 1·25 45
1598. 300 f. Dribble .. .. 2·00 55

1982. Butterflies. Multicoloured.

1600 15 f. Type **289** (postage) 20 10
1601 20 f. "Belenois calypso" 35 10
1602 25 f. "Palla decius" .. 40 10
1603 90 f. "Euxanthe eurinome" (air) .. 1·40 90
1604 105 f. "Mylothris rhodope" .. .. 1·60 1·00

290. Infant Jesus.

1982. Christmas. Details of Raphael's "Madonna del Baldacchino". Multicoloured.

1606. 45 f. Type **290** 40 10
1607. 70 f. Madonna 55 15
1608. 105 f. Angel 70 20
1609. 130 f. Angel (different) .. 1·00 30
1610. 150 f. Putti .. .. 1·10 35

291. Building, Sokode.

1983. Visit of President Mitterrand of France. Multicoloured.

1612. 35 f. Type **291** (postage) 20 10
1613. 45 f. Children of different races and world map .. 35 15
1614. 70 f. French and Togolese soldiers (vert.) .. 55 20
1615. 90 f. President Mitterrand (air) (vert.) 70 30
1616. 105 f. Presidents Mitterrand and Eyadema shaking hands (vert.) .. 80 35
1617. 130 f. Presidents Mitterrand and Eyadema and crowds .. .. .. 1·00 40

1983. World Cup Football Championship Results. Nos. 1594/8 optd. **VAINQUER COUPE DU MONDE FOOTBALL 82 "ITALIE"**. Multicoloured.

1618. 25 f. Type **288** (postage) 15 10
1619. 45 f. Tackle 35 15
1620. 105 f. Heading ball (air) .. 65 35
1621. 200 f. Fighting for possession .. .. 1·25 55
1622. 300 f. Dribble .. .. 2·00 80

293. Map of Africa showing W.A.M.U. Members. **294.** Drummer.

1983. 20th Anniv. of West African Monetary Union. Multicoloured.

1624. 70 f. Type **293** 50 15
1625. 90 f. West African coin .. 60 20

1983. World Communications Year. Mult.

1626. 70 f. Type **294** (postage) 55 15
1627. 90 f. Modern post office and telecommunications system (air) 65 20

295. Boxing.

1983. Air. Pre-Olympic Year. Multicoloured.

1628. 70 f. Type **295** 50 15
1629. 90 f. Hurdles 60 20
1630. 105 f. Pole vault 65 20
1631. 130 f. Sprinting .. .. 1·00 30

296. Kondona Dance.

1983. Traditional Dances. Multicoloured.

1633. 70 f. Type **296** (postage) 60 20
1634. 90 f. Kondona dance (different) (air) .. 80 20
1635. 105 f. Toubole dance .. 90 20
1636. 130 f. Adjogbo dance .. 1·10 20

297. Painting by Bellini.

1983. Easter. Multicoloured.

1637. 35 f. Type **297** (postage) 30 10
1638. 70 f. Raphael (vert.) .. 50 15
1639. 90 f. Carracci (air) .. 65 20

298. Catholic Church, Kante.

1983. Christmas. Multicoloured.

1641. 70 f. Type **298** (postage) 50 15
1642. 90 f. Altar, Dapaong Cathedral (air) .. 60 20
1643. 105 f. Protestant church, Dapaong 70 20

299. Wrecked Aircraft.

1984. 10th Anniv. of Sarakawa Assassination Attempt. Multicoloured.

1645. 70 f. Type **299** (postage) 50 25
1646. 90 f. Wrecked aircraft (different) .. 60 30
1647. 120 f. Memorial Hall (air) 85 40
1648. 270 f. Statue of President Eyadema (vert.) .. 1·90 70

300. Picking Coffee Beans. **301.** Flags, Agriculture and Symbols of Unity and Growth.

1984. World Food Programme Day. Multicoloured.

1649. 35 f. Type **300** 20 10
1650. 70 f. Harvesting cocoa pods 50 15
1651. 90 f. Planting rice .. 65 20

1984. 25th Anniv. of Council of Unity.

1653. **301.** 70 f. multicoloured .. 50 15
1654. 90 f. multicoloured .. 60 20

1984. Air. 19th Universal Postal Union Congress, Hamburg. Nos. 1451/2 optd. **19E CONGRES UPU HAMBOURG 1984.**

1655. 250 f. multicoloured .. 1·60 85
1656. 500 f. multicoloured .. 3·25 1·60

303. Tim Thorpe (gold, pentathlon and decathlon, 1912). **304.** Thief on right-hand Cross.

1984. Air. Olympic Games Medal Winners (1st series). Multicoloured.

1657. 500 f. Type **303** .. .. 4·50 85
1658. 500 f. Mathias Behr (silver, fencing, 1984) 4·50 85
1659. 500 f. Fredy Schmidtke (gold, cycling, 1984) .. 4·50 85
1660. 500 f. Dietmar Mogenburg (gold, high jumping, 1984) .. 4·50 85
1661. 500 f. Sabine Everts (bronze, heptathlon, 1984) .. .. .. 4·50 85
1662. 500 f. Jesse Owens (gold, 200 metres, 1936 .. 4·50 85
1663. 500 f. Bob Beamon (gold, long jumping, 1968) .. 4·50 85
1664. 500 f. Muhammad Ali (gold, boxing, 1960) .. 22·00 85

See also Nos. 1825/32.

1984. Easter. Details from stained glass window in Norwich Cathedral. Multicoloured.

1665. 70 f. Roman guard (postage) 50 15
1666. 90 f. Mary Magdalene (air) 55 15
1667. 120 f. The Apostles comforting Mary 80 20
1668. 270 f. Type **304** .. 1·60 45
1669. 300 f. Thief on left-hand Cross .. .. 2·00 55

305. Baguida (site of Protectorate Treaty signature, 1884).

1984. Centenary of Proclamation of German Protectorate. Multicoloured.

1671 35 f. Type **305** 20 20
1672 35 f. Degbenou School, 1893 (horiz) 20 20
1673 35 f. Degbenou Catholic Mission, 1893 (horiz) .. 20 20
1674 35 f. Kara suspension bridge, 1911 (horiz) .. 20 20
1675 35 f. Adjido state school (horiz) 20 20
1676 35 f. Administration post, Sansane Mango, 1908 (horiz) 20 20
1677 35 f. Sokode cotton market, 1910 (horiz) .. 20 20
1678 45 f. Main street, Lome, 1895, and 5 m. "Yacht" stamp (horiz) 35 35
1679 45 f. Governor's Palace, Lome, 1905 (horiz) .. 35 35
1680 45 f. Drilling police squad, 1905 (horiz) 35 35
1681 45 f. Guillaume fountain, Atakpame, 1906 .. 35 35
1682 45 f. Constructing Lome–Atakpame railway (horiz) 35 35
1683 45 f. Rue de Commerce, Lome, and 10 pf. "Yacht" stamp (horiz) 35 35
1684 70 f. 20 pf. and 2 m. "Yacht" stamps, 1900 (horiz) 50 45
1685 70 f. Lome wharf, 1903 (horiz) 50 45
1686 90 f. Farming, Sansane Mango, 1908 (horiz) .. 60 55
1687 90 f. Chancellor Otto von Bismark 60 55
1688 90 f. Emperor Wilhelm II 60 55
1689 90 f. Commissoner J. von Puttkamer, 1891–93 .. 60 55
1690 90 f. Consul-General G. Nachtigal, 1884 .. 60 55
1691 90 f. Governor A. Koehler, 1895–1902 .. .. 60 55
1692 90 f. Governor W. Horn, 1902–1905 .. .. 60 55
1693 90 f. Governor J.G. von Zech, 1905–10 .. .. 60 55
1694 90 f. Governor E. Bruckner, 1911–12 .. .. 60 55
1695 90 f. Governor A. F. von Mecklenberg, 1912–14 .. 60 55
1696 90 f. Governor H. G. von Doering, 1914 .. .. 60 55
1697 120 f. Signing of Protectorate Treaty, 1885 (horiz) 90 85
1698 120 f. Postmen, 1885 .. 90 85
1699 150 f. Children dancing around maps and flags 1·10 95
1700 270 f. German gunboat "Mowe", 1884 (horiz) .. 2·00 1·75
1701 270 f. German sail corvette "Sophie", 1884 .. 2·00 1·75
1702 270 f. Steam train from Aneho railway, 1905 (horiz) .. .. 2·00 1·75
1703 270 f. "Mallet" train from Kpalime railway, 1907 (horiz) .. .. 2·00 1·75
1704 270 f. Flags and Presidents of Togo and Germany (horiz) .. 2·25 1·90

306. High Jumping.

1984. Air. Olympic Games, Los Angeles. Multicoloured.

1705.	70 f. Type **306**	45	25
1706.	90 f. Cycling	55	20
1707.	120 f. Football	80	30
1708.	250 f. Boxing (horiz.) ..	1·60	50
1709.	400 f. Running (horiz.) ..	2·75	80

307. Donald with Presents and Chip.

1984. 50th Anniv. of Donald Duck (cartoon character). Multicoloured.

1711.	1 f. Type **307** (postage) ..	10	10
1712.	2 f. Donald and Chip'n'Dale	10	10
1713.	3 f. Huey, Chip and Dale blowing up balloons ..	10	10
1714.	5 f. Donald and Chip holding birthday cake	10	10
1715.	10 f. Daisy kissing Donald	30	10
1716.	15 f. Goofy giving Donald his present ..	40	10
1717.	105 f. Huey, Dewey and Louie decorating cake (air)	85	15
1718.	500 f. Huey, Dewey, Louie and Donald with birthday cake ..	4·50	95
1719.	1000 f. Huey, Duey and Louie startling Donald	7·50	1·60

308. West African Manatee.

1984. Endangered Wildlife. Multicoloured.

1722.	45 f. Type **308** (postage)	85	15
1723.	70 f. Manatee (close up)	1·10	20
1724.	90 f. Manatees in water (air)	1·40	35
1725.	105 f. Manatee with cub	1·40	35

309. Flame and Eleanor Roosevelt.

1984. Birth Centenary of Eleanor Roosevelt. Multicoloured.

1727.	70 f. Type **309** (postage)	55	15
1728.	90 f. Eleanor Roosevelt and Statue of Liberty (air)	65	15

310. Lockheed "Constellation", 1944.

1984. 40th Anniv. of International Civil Aviation Organization. Multicoloured.

1729.	70 f. Type **310** (postage)	55	30
1730.	105 f. Boeing "707", 1954 (air)	60	40
1731.	200 f. Douglas "DC-8.61", 1966	1·25	80
1732.	500 f. "Concorde", 1966	3·25	1·75

311. Bristol "400"; 1947.

1984. Classic Cars. Multicoloured.

1734.	1 f. Type **311** (postage) ..	10	10
1735.	2 f. Frazer Nash "Standard", 1925 ..	10	10
1736.	3 f. Healey "Silverstone", 1950	10	10
1737.	4 f. Kissell "Gold Bug Speedstar", 1925 ..	10	10
1738.	50 f. La Salle 5 litre, 1927	80	15
1739.	90 f. Minerva 30 h.p., 1921 (air)	70	15
1740.	500 f. Morgan "Plus 4", 1950	4·25	95
1741.	1000 f. Napier "40/50 T75 Six", 1921	7·75	2·25

313. "Connestabile Madonna".

1984. Christmas. Paintings by Raphel. Multicoloured.

1744.	70 f. Type **313** (postage)	55	15
1745.	290 f. "The Cowper Madonna"	1·90	65
1746.	300 f. "The Alba Madonna"	2·00	65
1747.	500 f. "Madonna of the Curtain"	3·25	1·10

314. "Decapotable" Locomotive, Madeira.

1984. Railway Locomotives. Multicoloured.

1749.	1 f. Type **314** (postage) ..	10	10
1750.	2 f. British-made locomotive, Egyptian railway	10	10
1751.	3 f. "Garratt" locomotive, Algerian railway	10	10
1752.	4 f. Diesel train, Congo-Ocean railway ..	10	10
1753.	50 f. Italian-made locomotive, Libyan railway	65	15
1754.	90 f. No. "49" Northern railway locomotive (air)	55	15
1755.	105 f. "Mallet" locomotive, Togo railway	65	20
1756.	500 f. Steam locomotive, Rhodesian railway ..	3·75	70
1757.	1000 f. Beyer-Garratt steam locomotive, East African railway	7·25	2·25

315. Map of Americas and Flags.

316. St. Paul.

1984. Third E.E.C.-African States Convention, Lome. Multicoloured.

1759.	100 f. Type **315** ..	80	20
1760.	130 f. Map of Europe and Africa and flags ..	1·10	30
1761.	270 f. Map of Asia and Australasia and flags	2·00	60

Nos. 1759/61 were printed in se-tenant strips of three, forming a composite design showing map of the world.

1984. The Twelve Apostles. Multicoloured.

1763.	1 f. Type **316** (postage) ..	10	10
1764.	2 f. Saint Thomas ..	10	10
1765.	3 f. Saint Matthew ..	10	10
1766.	4 f. Saint James, the Less	10	10
1767.	5 f. Saint Simon, the Zealot	10	10
1768.	70 f. Saint Thaddeus ..	85	15
1769.	90 f. Saint Bartholomew (air)	55	15
1770.	105 f. Saint Philip ..	65	15
1771.	200 f. Saint John ..	1·25	35
1772.	270 f. Saint James, son of Zebedee	1·60	45
1773.	400 f. Saint Andrew ..	2·50	80
1774.	500 f. Saint Peter ..	3·25	90

317. Allez France.

1985. Racehorses. Multicoloured.

1776.	1 f. Type **317** (postage) ..	10	10
1777.	2 f. Arkle (vert.) ..	10	10
1778.	3 f. Jingle Creek (vert.)	10	10
1779.	4 f. Interco	10	10
1780.	50 f. Dawn Run	95	15
1781.	90 f. Seattle Slew (vert.) (air)	85	20
1782.	500 f. Nijinsky	4·75	90
1783.	1000 f. Politician ..	7·75	2·25

318. Map, Globe and Doves.

1985. Air. Peace and Human Rights. Multicoloured.

1785.	230 f. Type **318**	1·50	55
1786.	270 f. Palm tree by shore and emblem	1·75	55
1787.	500 f. Mining and emblem	3·25	1·10
1788.	1000 f. Human Rights monument	6·75	2·50

319. "Christ and the Fisherman".

1985. Easter. Paintings by Raphael. Mult.

1789.	70 f. "Christ and the Apostles" (postage) ..	55	15
1790.	90 f. Type **319** ..	60	20
1791.	135 f. "Christ making Benediction" (vert.) (air)	1·00	20
1792.	150 f. "The Entombment" (vert.) ..	1·10	30
1793.	250 f. "The Resurrection" (vert.)	1·75	50

320. Profiles and Emblem.

1985. 15th Anniv. of Cultural and Technical Co-operation Agency.

1835.	**320.** 70 f. multicoloured ..	50	20
1836.	90 f. multicoloured ..	60	30

321. Adifo Dance.

1985. Air. Traditional Dances. Multicoloured.

1797.	120 f. Type **321**	80	30
1798.	135 f. Whip dance ..	90	35
1799.	290 f. Idjombi dance ..	1·90	65
1800.	500 f. Moba dance ..	3·25	95

322. Kabye Man.

324. "Clavatula muricata".

323. Woman carrying Basket on Head and Workers on Map.

1985. Tribal Markings. Multicoloured.

1801.	25 f. Type **322** (postage)	15	10
1802.	70 f. Mollah woman ..	50	20
1803.	90 f. Moba man (air) ..	60	20
1804.	105 f. Kabye woman ..	80	20
1805.	270 f. Peda woman ..	1·90	65

1985. "Philexafrique" Stamp Exhibition, Lome. "Youth and Development". Mult.

1806.	200 f. Type **323**	1·60	90
1807.	200 f. Man ploughing field with oxen ..	1·60	90

1985. Sea Shells. Multicoloured.

1808.	70 f. Type **324** (postage)	70	15
1809.	90 f. "Marginella desjardini" (air) ..	80	20
1810.	120 f. "Clavatula nifat"	1·00	20
1811.	135 f. "Cypraea stercoraria"	1·10	20
1812.	270 f. "Conus genuanus"	2·25	45

1985. "Expo '85" World's Fair, Tsukuba, Japan. Nos. 1738 and 1741 optd. **EXPOSITION MONDIALE 1985 TSUKUBA, JAPON.**

1814.	50 f. La Salle 5 litre, 1927 (postage)	85	20
1815.	1000 f. Napier "40/50 T75 Six", 1921 (air) ..	9·50	2·75

326. Pope giving Blessing.

327. Brown Pelican.

1985. Air. Visit of Pope John Paul II. Multicoloured.

1817.	90 f. Pope and children	85	20
1818.	130 f. Type **326**	1·10	35
1819.	500 f. Pres. Eyadema greeting Pope ..	4·25	2·25

1985. Birth Bicentenary of John J. Audubon (ornithologist). Multicoloured.

1820.	120 f. Type **327** (postage)	1·40	85
1821.	270 f. Golden eagle ..	3·00	2·00
1822.	90 f. Bonaparte's gulls (air)	1·10	65
1823.	135 f. Great-tailed grackle	1·50	95
1824.	500 f. Red-headed woodpecker	6·25	4·00

1985. Air. Olympic Games Medal Winners (2nd series). Nos. 1657/64 optd.

1826. 500 f. **"ITALIE MEDAILLE D'OR"** .. 4·00 85
1827. 500 f. **"PHILIPPE BOISSE/FRANCE/ MEDAILLE D'OR"** .. 4·00 85
1828. 500 f. **"ROLF GOLZ/ R.F.A./MEDAILLE D'ARGENT"** .. .. 4·00 85
1829. 500 f. **"PATRIK SJOBERG/SUEDE/ MEDAILLE D'ARGENT"** .. .. 4·00 85
1830. 500 f. **"GLYNIS NUNN/ AUSTRALIE/ MEDAILLE D'OR"** .. 4·00 85
1831. 500 f. **"KIRK BAPTISTE/ETATS UNIS/MEDAILLE D'ARGENT"** .. .. 4·00 85
1832. 500 f. **"CARL LEWIS/ ETATS UNIS/ MEDAILLE D'OR"** .. 4·00 85
1833. 500 f. **"KEVIN BARRY/ NLE ZELANDE/ MEDAILLE D'ARGENT"** .. .. 4·00 85

330. Gongophone, Kante Horn and Drum.

1985. Air. "Philexafrique" Stamp Exhibition, Lome (2nd issue). Musical Instruments. Multicoloured.

1835. 100 f. Type **330** .. .. 1·40 65
1836. 100 f. Twin drums, Bassar horn and castanets .. .. 1·40 65

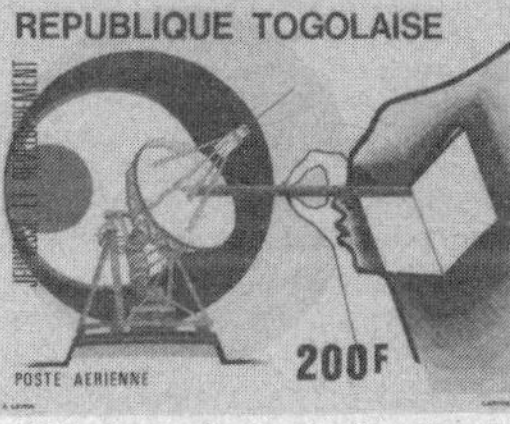

331. Open Book, Profile, Hand holding Pencil and Dish Aerial.

1985. Air. "Philexafrique" Stamp Exhibition, Lome (3rd issue). "Youth and Development". Multicoloured.

1837. 200 f. Type **331** .. .. 1·90 1·10
1838. 200 f. Profiles, factory, cogwheel and maize .. 1·90 1·10

332. Dove, Sun and U.N. Emblem.

1985. 40th Anniv. of U.N.O. Multicoloured.

1839. 90 f. Type **332** (postage) 60 20
1840. 115 f. Hands reaching up to Emblem 90 20
1841. 150 f. Building new bridge on river Kara (air) .. .. .. 1·10 35
1842. 250 f. Preparing experimental field of millet at Atalote, Keran .. 1·60 50
1843. 500 f. Pres. Eyadema, U.N. Secretary-General, U.N. and national flags .. .. 3·25 85

MINIMUM PRICE

The minimum price quoted is 5p which represents a handling charge rather than a basis for valuing common stamps. For further notes about prices see introductory pages.

333. "Madonna of the Rose Garden" (Sandro Botticelli).

1985. Christmas. Multicoloured.

1844. 90 f. Type **333** (postage) 65 20
1845. 115 f. "Madonna and Child" (11th-century Byzantine painting) (air) 90 20
1846. 150 f. "Rest during the flight into Egypt" (Gerard David) .. 1·00 30
1847. 160 f. "African Madonna" (16th-century statue) .. 1·10 30
1848. 250 f. "African Madonna" (statue, 1900) .. .. .. 2·00 45

1985. Various stamps optd.

(a) Nos. 1739/40 optd. **10e ANNIVERSAIRE DE APOLLO-SOYUZ.**

1850. 90 f. Minerva 30 h.p., 1921 .. .. .. 85 30
1851. 500 f. Morgan "Plus 4", 1950 .. .. .. 4·75 1·40

(b) Nos. 1752, 1755 and 1757 optd **80e ANNIVERSAIRE du/ROTARY INTERNATIONAL**

1853. 4 f. Train, Congo-Ocean railway 85 20
1854. 105 f. "Mallet" locomotive, Togo railways 65 30
1855. 1000 f. Beyer-Garratt steam locomotive, East African railway 8·25 2·75

(c) 150th Anniv. of German Railways. Nos. 1753/4 and 1756 optd. **"150e ANNIVERSAIRE/DE CHEMIN FER 'LUDWIG'".**

1857. 50 f. Italian-made locomotive, Libyan railway 85 20
1858. 90 f. No. "49" Northern railway locomotive .. 85 30
1859. 500 f. Locomotive, Rhodesian railway .. 4·75 1·40

(d) Nos. 1773/4 optd. **"75e ANNIVERSAIRE DE LA/MORT DE HENRI DUNANT/ FONDATEUR DE LA/CROIX ROUGE".**

1861. 400 f. Saint Andrew .. 3·25 1·10
1862. 500 f. Saint Peter .. 4·00 1·40

(e) Nos 1780 and 1783 optd. **"75e ANNIVERSAIRE/DU SCOUTISME FEMININ".**

1864. 50 f. Dawn Run 85 20
1865. 1000 f. Politician .. 8·25 2·25

335. "The Resurrection" (Andrea Mantegna).

336. "Suisei" Space Probe and Kohoutek's Comet.

1986. Easter. Multicoloured.

1867. 25 f. Type **335** (postage) 20 10
1868. 70 f. "Calvary" (Paul Veronese) .. 55 15
1869. 90 f. "The Last Supper" (Jacopo Robusti Tintoretto) (horiz.) (air) 65 30
1870. 200 f. "Christ in the Tomb" (Berruguette) (horiz.) .. .. 1·50 55

1986. Appearance of Halley's Comet (1st Issue). Multicoloured.

1872. 70 f. type **336** (postage) 55 15
1873. 90 f. "Vega I" space probe and people pointing at comet (air) 55 20
1874. 150 f. Comet and observation equipment .. 90 30
1875. 200 f. "Giotto" space probe and comet over town .. .. .. 1·25 40

See also Nos. 1917/20.

337. New York, Statue and Eiffel Tower.

338. Cashew Nut.

1986. Air. Centenary of Statue of Liberty. Multicoloured.

1877. 70 f. Type 337 .. .. 50 15
1878. 90 f. Statue, Arc de Triomphe and Brooklyn Bridge .. 60 20
1879. 500 f. Statue, Pantheon and Empire State Building .. .. 3·25 1·10

1986. Fruit. Multicoloured.

1880. 70 f. Type **338** (postage) 55 15
1881. 90 f. Pineapple 80 20
1882. 120 f. Avocado (air) .. 90 20
1883. 135 f. Papaw .. .. 1·10 20
1884. 290 f. Mango (vert.) .. 2·25 65

339. Footballers.

341. "Ramaria moelleriana".

1986. World Cup Football Championship, Mexico.

1885. **339.** 70 f. mult. (post.) .. 55 15
1886. – 90 f. mult. (air) .. 55 30
1887. – 130 f. multicoloured 85 35
1888. – 300 f. multicoloured 1·90 70

DESIGNS: 90 f. to 300 f. Various footballing scenes.

1986. Air. "Ameripex '86" International Stamp Exhibition, Chicago. Nos. 1718/19 optd. **AMERIPEX 86.**

1890. 500 f. Huey, Dewey, Louie and Donald with birthday cake .. 4·50 1·10
1891. 1000 f. Huey, Dewey and Louie startling Donald 8·25 2·25

1986. Fungi. Multicoloured.

1893. 70 f. Type **341** 50 30
1894. 90 f. "Hygrocybe firma" 60 40
1895. 150 f. "Kalchbrennera corallocephala" .. 1·10 75
1896. 200 f. "Cookeina tricholoma" .. .. 1·60 1·00

342. Hand framing Huts and Child.

1986. International Youth Year (1985). Multicoloured.

1897. 25 f. Type **342** 30 15
1898. 90 f. Children feeding birds .. .. .. 1·10 40

343. Wrestlers.

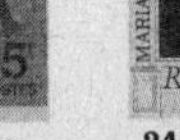

344. Miss Sarah Ferguson.

1986. Evala Wrestling Contest.

1899. **343.** 15 f. mult. (post.) .. 15 10
1900. – 20 f. multicoloured .. 30 10
1901. – 70 f. multicoloured .. 65 15
1902. – 90 f. mult. (air) .. 40 35

DESIGNS: 20 to 90 f. Wrestling scenes.

1986. Wedding of Prince Andrew. Mult.

1903. 10 f. Type **344** (postage) 55 10
1904. 1000 f. Prince Andrew (air) .. .. .. 6·75 2·25

1986. World Cup Winners. Nos. 1886/9 optd.

1906. 70 f. **DEMI-FINALE/ ARGENTINE 2/ BELGIQUE 0** (postage) 55 35
1907. 90 f. **DEMI-FINALE/ ALLEMAGNE/DE L'OUEST 2/FRANCE 0** (air) 55 20
1908. 130 f. **3 eme et 4 eme PLACE/FRANCE 4/ BELGIQUE 2** 85 35
1909. 300 f. **FINALE/ ARGENTINE 3/ALLEMAGNE/DE L'OUEST 2** .. .. .. 1·90 80

346. Fazao Hotel.

1986. Hotels. Multicoloured.

1910. 70 f. Type **346** (postage) 55 15
1911. 90 f. Sarakawa Hotel (air) 65 30
1912. 120 f. The Lake Hotel .. 90 40

347. Spur-winged Geese.

1986. Keran National Park. Multicoloured.

1913. 70 f. Type **347** (postage) 55 20
1914. 90 f. Antelope (air) .. 65 30
1915. 100 f. African elephant .. 80 35
1916. 130 f. Kob .. .. 1·00 45

1986. Appearance of Halley's Comet (2nd issue). Nos. 1872/5 optd. as T **213a** of Maldive Islands.

1917. **336.** 70 f. mult. (post.) .. 1·25 35
1918. – 90 f. mult. (air) .. 1·00 30
1919. – 150 f. multicoloured 1·50 40
1920. – 200 f. multicoloured 1·90 70

349. "The Annunciation".

350. Rainbow and Airplane.

1986. Christmas. Multicoloured.

1922. 45 f. Type **349** (postage) 45 15
1923. 120 f. "Nativity" (air) .. 90 35
1924. 130 f. "Adoration of the Magi" .. .. .. 1·10 45
1925. 200 f. "Flight into Egypt" .. .. 1·50 65

1986. Air. 25th Anniv. of Air Afrique.

1927. **350.** 90 f. multicoloured .. 75 45

351. Pres. Eyadema and Phosphate Mine.

1987. 20th Anniv. of National Liberation. Multicoloured.

1928.	35 f. Type **351** (postage)	20	10
1929.	50 f. Anie sugar refinery	35	15
1930.	70 f. Nangbeto dam ..	50	20
1931.	90 f. February 2 Hotel and Posts and Telecommunications building, Lome	60	20
1932.	100 f. Posts and Telecommunications building, Kara (air) ..	55	15
1933.	120 f. Peace monument	80	30
1934.	130 f. Baby being vaccinated	90	35

352. "The Last Supper".

1987. Easter. Paintings from Nadoba Church, Keran. Multicoloured.

1936.	90 f. Type **352** (postage)	65	30
1937.	130 f. "Christ on the Cross" (air)	90	30
1938.	300 f. "The Resurrection" ..	2·00	65

353. Adenauer speaking at the Bundestag.

1987. Air. 20th Death Anniv. of Konrad Adenauer (German Chancellor). Multicoloured.

1940.	120 f. Type **353**	85	30
1941.	500 f. Adenauer with John F. Kennedy ..	3·25	1·10

354. Player falling with Ball.

1987. World Rugby Football Cup. Mult.

1943.	70 f. Type **354** (postage)	80	30
1944.	130 f. Player running with ball (air).. ..	1·25	35
1945.	300 f. Scrum	2·75	1·25

355. "Adenium obesum".

1987. Flowers. Multicoloured.

1947.	70 f. Type **355** (postage)	60	20
1948.	90 f. "Amorphophallus abyssinicus" (vert.) (air)	65	30
1949.	100 f. "Ipomoea mauritiana"	80	30
1950.	120 f. "Salacia togoica" (vert.)	90	35

356. Wilhelm I Coin and Victory Statue.

1987. Air. 750th Anniv. of Berlin. Mult.

1951.	90 f. Type **356**	60	20
1952.	150 f. Friedrich III coin and Brandenburg Gate	1·00	35
1953.	300 f. Wilhelm II coin and Place de la Republique	2·00	65

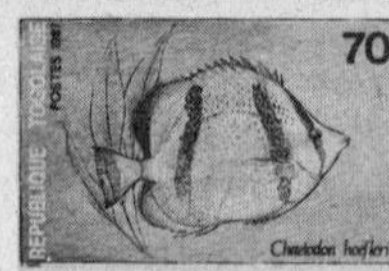
357. "Chaetodon hoefleri".

1987. Fishes. Multicoloured.

1955.	70 f. Type **357**	55	20
1956.	90 f. "Tetraodon lineatus"	65	25
1957.	120 f. "Chaetodipterus goreensis"	85	35
1958.	130 f. "Labeo parvus" ..	1·00	35

358. Long Jumping.

1987. Olympic Games, Seoul (1988). Mult.

1959.	70 f. Type **358** (postage)	60	20
1960.	90 f. Relay race (air) ..	60	20
1961.	200 f. Cycling	1·25	45
1962.	250 f. Javelin throwing..	1·60	55

1987. Endangered Wildlife. As Nos. 1722/5 but values changed and size 37 × 24 mm.

1964.	60 f. Type **308** (postage)	80	20
1965.	75 f. Manatee (close up)	90	35
1966.	80 f. Manatees in water	1·10	35
1967.	100 f. Manatee with cub (air)	1·40	40

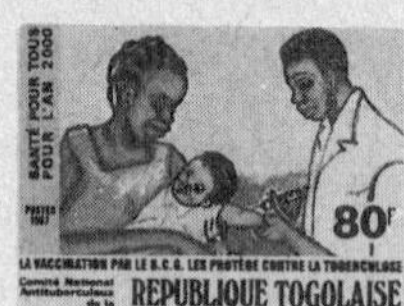
359. Doctor vaccinating Child.

1987. "Health for All by Year 2000". Anti-tuberculosis Campaign. Multicoloured.

1968.	80 f. Type **359** (postage)	55	30
1969.	90 f. Family under umbrella (vert.) (air)	60	30
1970.	115 f. Faculty of Medicine building, Lome University ..	80	35

360. "Spring or the Earthly Paradise".

1987. Christmas. Multicoloured.

1971.	40 f. Type **360** (postage)	35	10
1972.	45 f. "The Creation of Adam" (Michelangelo)	35	10
1973.	105 f. "Presentation in the Temple" (vert.) (air)	65	20
1974.	270 f. "The Original Sin" (vert.)	1·75	65

361 Men Ploughing and Women collecting Water

1988. 10th Anniv of Agricultural Development Fund.

1976	**361** 90 f. multicoloured ..	65	20

363 "The Dance"

1988. 15th Death Anniv of Pablo Picasso (painter). Multicoloured.

1978	45 f. Type **363** (postage)	45	10
1979	160 f. "Portrait of a Young Girl"	1·50	35
1980	300 f. "Gueridon" (air) ..	2·75	85

364 Cement

365 "Jesus and the Disciples at Emmaus"

1988. Industries. Multicoloured.

1982	125 f. Type **364**	85	30
1983	165 f. Brewery	1·10	40
1984	195 f. Phosphates ..	1·25	45
1985	200 f. Plastics	1·25	45
1986	300 f. Milling (vert) ..	2·10	65

1988. Easter. Stained Glass Windows. Mult.

1987	70 f. Type **365** (postage)	60	15
1988	90 f. "Mary at the Foot of the Cross"	80	20
1989	120 f. "Crucifixion" (air)	85	30
1990	200 f. "St. Thomas and Resurrected Jesus" ..	1·40	45

366 Paris Crowd welcoming Kennedy, 1961

367 Watchi Chief

1988. 25th Death Anniv of John F. Kennedy (U.S. President). Multicoloured.

1992	125 f. Type **366**	1·00	20
1993	155 f. Kennedy at Paris Town Hall (vert) ..	1·10	20
1994	165 f. Kennedy and De Gaulle at Elysee Palace (vert)	1·25	40
1995	180 f. John and Jacqueline Kennedy at Orly Airport	1·40	75

1988. Traditional Tribal Costumes. Mult.

1997	80 f. Type **367**	55	20
1998	125 f. Watchi woman ..	85	20
1999	165 f. Kotokoli man ..	1·10	35
2000	175 f. Ewe man	1·10	35

368 Basketball

369 People with Candles

1988. Olympic Games, Seoul. Multicoloured.

2002	70 f. Type **368** (postage)	50	15
2003	90 f. Tennis	60	20
2004	120 f. Archery (air) ..	85	30
2005	200 f. Throwing the discus	1·40	45

1988. 40th Anniv of W.H.O. Multicoloured.

2007	80 f. Type **369**	55	15
2008	125 f. Maps, emblem and "40"	85	20

370 Plaited Style

1988. Hairstyles. Multicoloured.

2009	80 f. Type **370**	55	20
2010	125 f. Knotted style ..	85	20
2011	170 f. Plaited style with bow	1·00	40
2012	180 f. Style with plaits all over head (vert) ..	1·25	40

371 Collecting Water (B. Gossner)

372 "Adoration of the Magi" (Pieter Brueghel the Elder)

1988. "Philtogo" National Stamp Exhibition. Designs depicting winning entries of a schools drawing competition. Multicoloured.

2014	10 f. Type **371**	10	10
2015	35 f. Villagers working on farm (K. Ekoue-Kouvahey)	20	10
2016	70 f. Family (A. Abbey)	65	15
2017	90 f. Village women preparing food (T. D. Lawson)	85	30
2018	120 f. Fishermen and boats on shore (A. Tazzar)	1·10	35

1988. Christmas. Multicoloured.

2019	80 f. Type **372** (postage)	55	20
2020	150 f. "The Virgin, The Infant Jesus, Saints Jerome and Dominic" (Fra. Filippo Lippi) (air)	1·00	20
2021	175 f. "The Madonna, The Infant Jesus, St. Joseph and the Infant St. John the Baptist" (Federico Barocci)	1·25	35
2022	195 f. "The Virgin and Child" (Gentile Bellini)	1·40	45

373 Aircraft Wreckage

1989. 15th Anniv of Sarakawa Assassination Attempt. Multicoloured.

2024	10 f. Type **373**	10	10
2025	80 f. Tail section (vert) ..	55	25
2026	125 f. Soldiers and wreckage	85	50

374 Anniversary Emblem

1989. 20th Anniv of Benin Electricity Community.

2027	**374** 80 f. multicoloured ..	60	20
2028	125 f. multicoloured ..	95	20

375 Boxing

1989. Prince Emanuel of Liechtenstein Foundation. Multicoloured.

2029 80 f. Type **375** 55 20
2030 125 f. Long jumping .. 55 30
2031 165 f. Running .. .. 1·10 40

376 Table Tennis

1989. Olympic Games, Barcelona (1992). Mult.

2032 80 f. Type **376** (postage) 65 20
2033 125 f. Running (horiz) .. 90 20
2034 165 f. Putting the shot .. 1·00 35
2035 175 f. Basketball .. 1·25 35
2036 380 f. High jumping (horiz) (air) .. .. 2·50 55
2037 425 f. Boxing (horiz) .. 3·00 55

377 Footballers and St. Janvier's Cathedral, Naples

1989. World Cup Football Championship, Italy. Multicoloured.

2039 80 f. Type **377** (postage) 55 20
2040 125 f. Milan Cathedral .. 85 20
2041 165 f. Bevilacqua Palace, Verona .. .. 1·10 35
2042 175 f. Baptistry, Florence 1·10 35
2043 380 f. Madama Palace, Turin (air) .. .. 2·75 55
2044 425 f. St. Laurent's Cathedral, Genoa .. 2·75 55

378 Bundestag

1989. 40th Anniv of Federal Republic of Germany. Multicoloured.

2046 90 f. Type **378** 65 20
2047 125 f. Konrad Adenauer (Chancellor, 1949–63) and Theodor Heuss (President, 1949–59) (vert) 95 30
2048 180 f. West German flag and emblem .. .. 1·25 40

379 Tractor, Map and Woman at Water-pump

1989. 30th Anniv of Council of Unity.

2049 **379** 75 f. multicoloured .. 55 20

380 Boys learning First Aid

1989. 125th Anniv of International Red Cross. Multicoloured.

2050 90 f. Type **380** 50 20
2051 125 f. Founding meeting 85 35

381 Storming the Bastille

383 People with Banners and Pres. Eyadema

382 Jacques Necker (statesman) and The Three Orders

1989. Bicentenary of French Revolution (1st issue). Multicoloured.

2052 90 f. Type **381** 65 20
2053 125 f. Oath of the Tennis Court (horiz) .. .. 1·00 35
2054 180 f. Abolition of privileges (horiz) .. 1·40 45

See also Nos. 2056/9.

1989. Bicentenary of French Revolution (2nd issue). Multicoloured.

2056 90 f. Type **382** (postage) 65 20
2057 190 f. Guy le Chapelier and abolition of seigneurial rights .. 1·50 45
2058 425 f. Talleyrand-Perigord (statesman) and La Fayette's oath .. 2·75 55
2059 480 f. Paul Barras (revolutionary) and overthrow of Robespierre .. .. 3·25 55

1989. 20th Anniv of Kpalime Appeal. Mult.

2061 90 f. Type **383** 60 20
2062 125 f. Pres. Eyadema addressing gathering .. 90 35

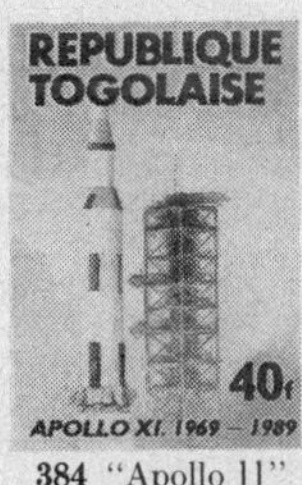

384 "Apollo 11" Launch

386 Emblem

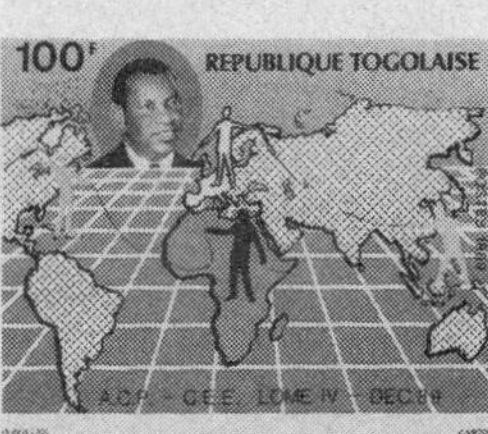

385 Figures on Map (dated "DEC.89")

1989. 20th Anniv of First Manned Landing on Moon. Multicoloured.

2063 40 f. Type **384** 30 10
2064 90 f. Space capsule in orbit 55 20
2065 150 f. Landing capsule .. 1·10 35
2066 250 f. Splashdown .. 1·60 45

1989. 4th Lome Convention (on relations between European Community and African, Caribbean and Pacific countries). Mult.

2068 100 f. Type **385** 80 30
2069 100 f. As T **385** but dated "15 DEC.89" 80 30

1990. 10th Anniv of Pan-African Postal Union.

2070 **386** 125 f. gold, blue & brn 90 30

387 Party Headquarters, Kara

1990. 20th Anniv (1989) of Rally of Togolese People Party. Multicoloured.

2071 45 f. Type **387** 35 15
2072 90 f. Pres. Eyadema and anniversary emblem .. 60 20

388 "Myrina silenus" and Scout

389 "Danaus chrysippus"

1990. Scouts, Butterflies and Fungi. Mult.

2073 80 f. Type **388** (postage) 65 15
2074 90 f. "Phlebobus silvaticus" (fungus) .. 65 15
2075 125 f. "Volvariella esculenta" (fungus) .. 90 20
2076 165 f. "Hypolycaena antifaunus" (butterfly) 1·10 35
2077 380 f. "Termitomyces striatus" (fungus) (air) 3·00 55
2078 425 f. "Axiocerces harpax" (butterfly) .. 3·00 55

1990. Butterflies. Multicoloured.

2080 5 f. Type **389** 10 10
2081 10 f. "Morpho aega" .. 10 10
2082 15 f. "Papilio demodocus" 10 10
2083 90 f. "Papilio dardanus" 60 35

390 Emblem

391 Nile Monitor

1990. 9th Convention of Lions Club Internationals District 403, Lome.

2085 **390** 90 f. multicoloured .. 60 35
2086 125 f. multicoloured .. 85 55
2087 165 f. multicoloured .. 1·10 80

1990. Reptiles. Multicoloured.

2088 1 f. Type **391** 10 10
2089 25 f. Puff adder 15 10
2090 60 f. Black-lipped cobra 45 15
2091 90 f. African rock python 65 20

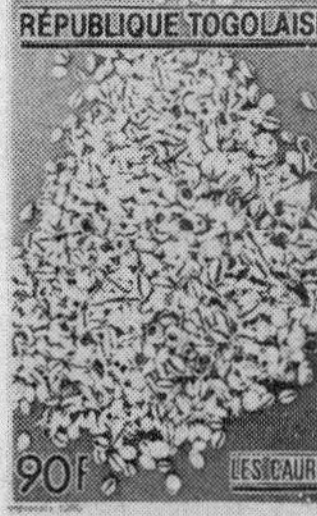

392 Pile of Cowrie Shells

393 Maps, Cogwheel and Arrows

1990. Cowrie Shells. Multicoloured.

2092 90 f. Type **392** 60 15
2093 125 f. Cowrie and bead ornament 95 20
2094 180 f. Headdress with cowries and animal horns .. .. .. 1·25 40

1990. United States–Togo Friendship. Mult.

2095 125 f. Type **393** 90 35
2096 180 f. Presidents Bush and Eyadema shaking hands (horiz) .. .. 1·25 35

394 Cinkasse Post Office

1990. Stamp Day.

2098 **394** 90 f. multicoloured .. 60 35

395 Addressing Crowd, Brazzaville, 1944

1990. 20th Death Anniv of Charles de Gaulle (statesman).

2099 **395** 125 f. multicoloured .. 85 45

396 Thatched Houses

1990. Traditional Housing. Multicoloured.

2100 90 f. Type **396** 60 35
2101 125 f. Village 85 45
2102 190 f. Tamberma house .. 1·25 65

397 Airport, Airplanes and Airline Emblems

1990. New Lome Airport.

2103 **397** 90 f. multicoloured .. 60 35

398 Woman carrying Basket on Head (Sikou Dapau)

1990.

2104 **398** 90 f. multicoloured .. 60 35

399 Chimpanzee, Missahoue Kloto

1991. Forests. Multicoloured.

No.	Type	Description		
2105		90 f. Type 399	60	35
2106		170 f. Parrot, Aledjo Florest	1·10	65
2107		185 f. Parrot, Chateau Vial Kloto Forest	1·25	65

400 Dancers

1992. Spirit Dances.

No.	Type	Description		
2108	400	90 f. multicoloured	60	35
2109	–	125 f. multicoloured	85	55
2110	–	190 f. multicoloured	1·25	80

DESIGNS: 125, 190 f. Various dances.

401 Royal Python hatching

1992. The Royal Python. Multicoloured.

No.	Type	Description		
2111		90 f. Type 401	60	35
2112		125 f. Hatchlings emerging from shells	85	35
2113		190 f. Hatchlings and empty shells	1·25	65
2114		300 f. Close-up of hatchling and empty shell	1·90	90

POSTAGE DUE STAMPS

1921. Postage Due stamps of Dahomey, "Figure" key-type, optd. **TOGO.**

No.	Type	Description		
D 54.	M.	5 c. green	40	70
D 55.		10 c. red	40	70
D 56.		15 c. grey	65	70
D 57.		20 c. brown	1·50	2·00
D 58.		30 c. blue	1·50	2·00
D 59.		50 c. black	1·10	1·40
D 60.		60 c. orange	1·40	1·60
D 61.		1 f. violet	2·75	3·25

D 8. Cotton Growing.

1925. Centres and inscr in black.

No.	Type	Description		
D 97	D 8	2 c. blue	10	30
D 98		4 c. red	10	30
D 99		5 c. green	10	30
D100		10 c. red	20	45
D101		15 c. yellow	20	45
D102		20 c. mauve	30	55
D103		25 c. grey	40	65
D104		30 c. yellow on blue	25	40
D105		50 c. brown	35	60
D106		60 c. green	45	70
D107		1 f. violet	50	80

1927. Surch.

No.	Type	Description		
D108	D 8	2 f. on 1 f. mauve and red	2·75	2·25
D109		3 f. on 1 f. blue and brown	2·50	3·25

D 12. Native Mask. D 21. D 31. Konkomba Helmet.

1940.

No.	Type	Description		
D 151.	D 12.	5 c. black	10	30
D 152.		10 c. green	15	25
D 153.		15 c. red	10	30
D 154.		20 c. blue	20	45
D 155.		30 c. brown	20	45
D 156.		50 c. olive	1·00	1·40
D 157.		60 c. violet	25	45
D 158.		1 f. blue	55	80
D 159.		2 f. red	30	60
D 160.		3 f. violet	60	85

1947.

No.	Type	Description		
D 185.	D 21.	10 c. blue	10	30
D 186.		30 c. red	10	30
D 187.		50 c. green	10	30
D 188.		1 f. brown	10	30
D 189.		2 f. red	20	40
D 190.		3 f. black	25	45
D 191.		4 f. blue	40	55
D 192.		5 f. brown	50	65
D 193.		10 f. orange	50	80
D 194.		20 f. blue	70	90

1957.

No.	Type	Description		
D214	D 31	1 f. violet	10	25
D215		2 f. orange	10	25
D216		3 f. grey	15	30
D217		4 f. red	15	30
D218		5 f. blue	15	30
D219		10 f. green	35	45
D220		20 f. purple	50	55

1959. As Nos. D 214/20 but colours changed and inscr. "REPUBLIQUE DU TOGO".

No.	Type	Description		
D 244.	D 31.	1 f. brown	10	25
D 245.		2 f. turquoise	10	25
D 246.		3 f. orange	10	25
D 247.		4 f. blue	15	30
D 248.		5 f. purple	15	30
D 249.		10 f. violet	25	45
D 250.		20 f. black	55	60

D 57. "Cardium costatum". D 110. Tomatoes.

1964. Seashells. Multicoloured.

D 366.	1 f. "Conus papilionaceus"	10	10
D 367.	2 f. "Marginella faba"	10	10
D 368.	3 f. "Cypraea stercoraria"	10	10
D 369.	4 f. "Strombus latus"	20	20
D 370.	5 f. Type D 57	45	45
D 371.	10 f. "Cancellaria cancellata"	55	55
D 372.	15 f. "Cymbium pepo"	1·60	1·60
D 373.	20 f. "Tympanotomus radula"	1·75	1·75

1969. Young Pioneers Agricultural Organization. Multicoloured.

D 696.	5 f. Type D 110	10	10
D 697.	10 f. Corn on the cob	30	30
D 698.	19 f. Red pepper	40	40
D 699.	20 f. Peanuts	55	55

1980. As T 259. Multicoloured.

D 1454.	5 f. Women examining produce (vert.)	10	10
D 1455.	10 f. Market stall	10	10
D 1456.	25 f. Poultry seller	15	10
D 1457.	50 f. Carvings and ornaments	35	15

APPENDIX

The following stamps have either been issued in excess of postal needs or have not been available to the public in reasonable quantities at face value. Such stamps may later be given full listing if there is evidence of regular postal use.

All embossed on gold foil

1989.

Prince Emanuel of Liechtenstein Foundation. Air. 1500 f. x 2

Bicentenary of French Revolution (2nd issue). Air. 1500 f.

Scouts, Butterflies and Fungi. Air. 1500 f.

TOLIMA — Pt. 20

One of the states of the Granadine Confederation.

A department of Colombia from 1886, now uses Colombian stamps.

100 centavos = 1 peso.

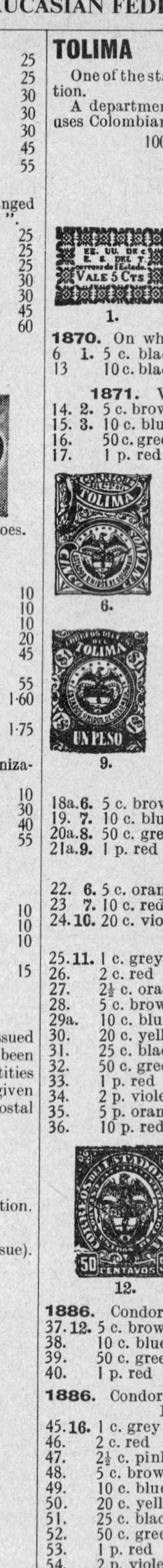

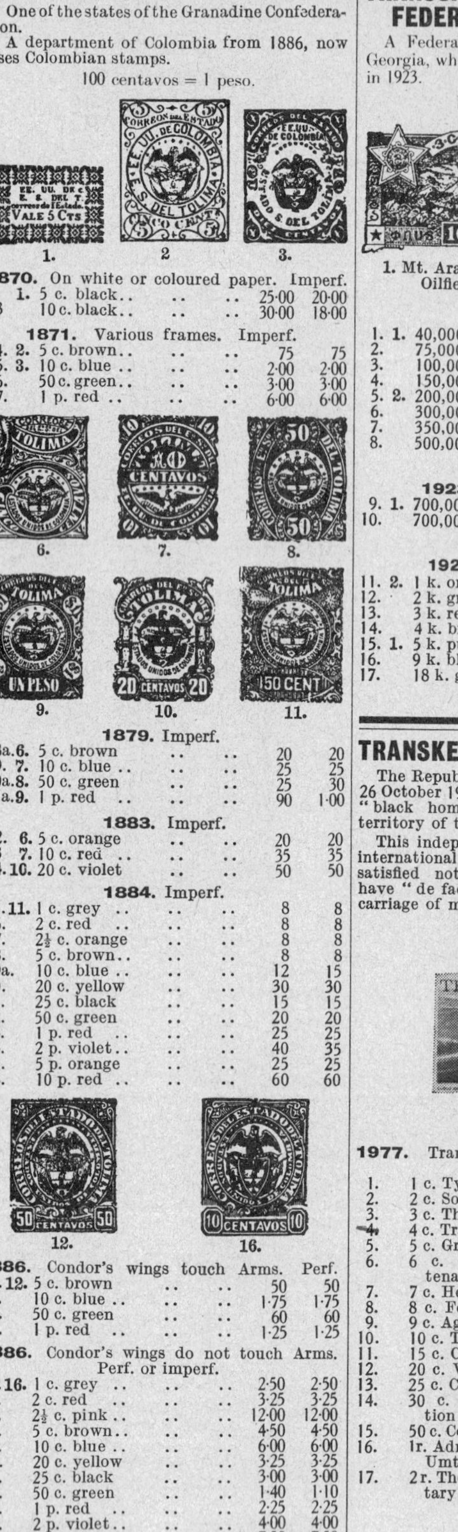

1. 2 3.

1870. On white or coloured paper. Imperf.

No.	Type	Description		
6	1.	5 c. black	25·00	20·00
13		10 c. black	30·00	18·00

1871. Various frames. Imperf.

No.	Type	Description		
14.	2.	5 c. brown	75	75
15.	3.	10 c. blue	2·00	2·00
16.		50 c. green	3·00	3·00
17.		1 p. red	6·00	6·00

6. 7. 8. 9. 10. 11.

1879. Imperf.

No.	Type	Description		
18a.	6.	5 c. brown	20	20
19.	7.	10 c. blue	25	25
20a.	8.	50 c. green	25	30
21a.	9.	1 p. red	90	1·00

1883. Imperf.

No.	Type	Description		
22.	6.	5 c. orange	20	20
23	7.	10 c. red	35	35
24.	10.	20 c. violet	50	50

1884. Imperf.

No.	Type	Description		
25.	11.	1 c. grey	8	8
26.		2 c. red	8	8
27.		2½ c. orange	8	8
28.		5 c. brown	8	8
29a.		10 c. blue	12	15
30.		20 c. yellow	30	30
31.		25 c. black	15	15
32.		50 c. green	20	20
33.		1 p. red	25	25
34.		2 p. violet	40	35
35.		5 p. orange	25	25
36.		10 p. red	60	60

12. 16.

1886. Condor's wings touch Arms. Perf.

No.	Type	Description		
37.	12.	5 c. brown	50	50
38.		10 c. blue	1·75	1·75
39.		50 c. green	60	60
40.		1 p. red	1·25	1·25

1886. Condor's wings do not touch Arms. Perf. or imperf.

No.	Type	Description		
45.	16.	1 c. grey	2·50	2·50
46.		2 c. red	3·25	3·25
47.		2½ c. pink	12·00	12·00
48.		5 c. brown	4·50	4·50
49.		10 c. blue	6·00	6·00
50.		20 c. yellow	3·25	3·25
51.		25 c. black	3·00	3·00
52.		50 c. green	1·40	1·10
53.		1 p. red	2·25	2·25
54.		2 p. violet	4·00	4·00
55.		5 p. orange	7·50	7·50
56.		10 p. red	3·50	3·50

20. 21.

1888. Perf.

No.	Type	Description		
67.	20.	1 c. blue on red	15	15
68.		2 c. green on green	15	15
69.		5 c. red	8	8
70.		10 c. green	20	25
71.		20 c. blue on yellow	30	30
65.		50 c. blue	45	45
72.		1 p. brown	75	75

1903. Imperf. or perf.

No.	Type	Description		
85.	21.	4 c. black on green	10	10
78.		10 c. blue	10	10
87.		20 c. orange	20	20
88.		50 c. black on red	12	12
81.		1 p. brown	5	5
82.		2 p. grey	5	5
91.		5 p. red	5	5
92.		10 p. black on blue	12	12
92a.		10 p. black on green	12	12

TRANSCAUCASIAN FEDERATION — Pt. 10

A Federation of Armenia, Azerbaijan and Georgia, which was absorbed into the U.S.S.R. in 1923.

100 kopeks = 1 rouble.

1. Mt. Ararat and Oilfield.

2. Mts. Ararat and Elbruz and Oil-derricks.

1923.

No.	Type	Description		
1.	1.	40,000 r. purple	1·50	3·00
2.		75,000 r. green	1·50	3·00
3.		100,000 r. grey	1·00	1·50
4.		150,000 r. red	70	90
5.	2.	200,000 r. green	1·00	50
6.		300,000 r. blue	70	1·40
7.		350,000 r. brown	70	1·40
8.		500,000 r. red	1·25	2·50

1923. Surch. **700000 RYb.**

No.	Type	Description		
9.	1.	700,000 r. on 40,000 r. pur.	1·50	3·00
10.		700,000 r. on 75,000 r. grn.	1·50	3·00

1923. Values in gold kopeks.

No.	Type	Description		
11.	2.	1 k. orange	70	1·25
12.		2 k. green	70	1·25
13.		3 k. red	70	1·25
14.		4 k. brown	70	1·00
15.	1.	5 k. purple	70	1·25
16.		9 k. blue	70	1·25
17.		18 k. grey	70	1·25

TRANSKEI — Pt. 14

The Republic of Transkei was established on 26 October 1976, as the first of the independent "black homelands" constructed from the territory of the Republic of South Africa.

This independence has so far not received international political recognition. We are satisfied notwithstanding that the stamps have "de facto" acceptance as valid for the carriage of mail outside Transkei.

100 cents = 1 rand.

1. Lubisi Dam.

1977. Transkei Scenes and Occupations. Multicoloured.

1.	1 c. Type 1	5	5
2.	2 c. Soil cultivation	5	5
3.	3 c. Threshing sorghum	5	5
4.	4 c. Transkei matron	8	8
5.	5 c. Grinding maize	8	8
6.	6 c. Cutting phormium tenax	8	8
7.	7 c. Herd-boy	10	10
8.	8 c. Felling timber	10	10
9.	9 c. Agricultural schooling	12	12
10.	10 c. Tea picking	12	12
11.	15 c. Carrying Wood	25	25
12.	20 c. Weaving industry	30	30
13.	25 c. Cattle	35	35
14.	30 c. Sledge transportation	85	40
15.	50 c. Coat of Arms and map	40	40
16.	1r. Administration building, Umtata	85	85
17.	2 r. The Bunga (Parliamentary building), Umtata	1·40	1·40

2. K. D. Matanzima.

4. "Artemisia afra".

3. Aeroplane.

1977. Independence. Multicoloured.

18.	4 c. Type 2	20	12
19.	10 c. Flag and mace	35	35
20.	15 c. K.D. Matanzima, Paramount Chief	1·00	1·00
21.	20 c. Coat of Arms	1·60	1·60

1977. Transkei Airways' Inaugural Flight. Multicoloured.

22. 4 c. Type 3 30 25
23. 15 c. Aeroplane landing at Matanzima Airport 1·25 1·25

1977. Medicinal Plants (1st series). Mult

24. 4 c. Type 4 15 10
25. 10 c. "Bulbine natalensis" 1·25 75
26. 15 c. "Melianthus major" 1·10 85
27. 20 c. "Cotyledon orbiculata" 3·00 1·75

See also Nos. 88/91.

5. Disc Jockey. 6. Blind Basket Weaver.

1977. 1st Anniv. of Transkei Radio. Mult.

28. 4 c. Type 5 15 10
29. 15 c. Announcer 75 75

1977. Aid for the Blind.

30. 6. 4 c. multicoloured 10 8
31. – 15 c. black, drab and gold 25 20
32. – 20 c. multicoloured 95 1·10

DESIGNS: 15 c. Hands reading braille. 20 c. Blind woman spinning.

7. Men's Carved Pipes.

1978. Transkei Pipes. Multicoloured.

33. 4 c. Type 7 10 8
34. 10 c. Two carved pipes 25 20
35. 15 c. Men's pipes 95 1·10
36. 20 c. Woman's and witch-doctor's pipes 1·10 1·10

8. Angora Goat. 9. "Carissa bispinosa".

1978. Weaving Industry. Multicoloured.

37. 4 c. Type 8 10 8
38. 10 c. Spinning mohair 25 20
39. 15 c. Dyeing mohair 60 60
40. 20 c. Weaving a mohair rug 80 80

1978. Edible Wild Fruits. Multicoloured.

41. 4 c. Type 9 10 8
42. 10 c. "Dovyalis caffra" 25 20
43. 15 c. "Harpephyllum caffrum" 35 30
44. 20 c. "Syzygium cordatum" 45 40

10. Calipers. 12. President Matanzima.

11. Chi Cha Youth.

1978. "Care for Cripples".

45. 10. 4 c. black and brown 10 8
46. – 10 c. black and grey 25 20
47. – 15 c. black and olive 35 30

DESIGNS: 10 c. Paraplegic child in wheel-chair. 15 c. Nurse examining child's leg.

1979. Initiation Ceremony of Xhosa Men (abakwetha). Multicoloured.

48. 4 c. Type 11 8 5
49. 10 c. Abakwetha in seclusion 25 20
50. 15 c. Umtshilo dance 35 30
51. 20 c. Leaving the sutu 45 40

1979. Second State President. Inaug.

52. 12. 4 c. red and gold 8 5
53. 15 c. green and gold 35 30

13. Windpump. 14. Magwa Falls.

1979. Water Resources. Multicoloured.

54. 4 c. Type 13 8 5
55. 10 c. Woman ladling water into jar 25 20
56. 15 c. Indwe River irrigation dam (horiz.) 35 30
57. 20 c. Ncora Dam (horiz.) 45 40

1979. Waterfalls. Multicoloured.

58. 4 c. Type 14 8 5
59. 10 c. Bawa Falls 25 20
60. 15 c. Waterfall Bluff (horiz.) 35 30
61. 20 c. Tsitsa Falls (horiz.) 45 40

15. Expectant Mother pouring Milk. 16. Black Gnat (dry fly).

1979. Child Health. Multicoloured.

62. 5 c. Type 15 8 5
63. 15 c. Mother breast-feeding baby 35 30
64. 20 c. Child being vaccinated 45 40

1980. Fishing Flies (1st series). Mult.

65. 5 c. Type 16 8 5
66. 5 c. Zug bug (nymph) 8 5
67. 5 c. March brown (wet fly) 8 5
68. 5 c. Durham Ranger (salmon fly) 8 5
69. 5 c. Colonel Bates (streamer) 8 5

See also Nos. 83/7, 99/103, 116/20 and 133/7.

17. Rotary Emblem. 18. "Encephalartos altensteinii".

1980. 75th Anniv. of Rotary International.

70. 17. 15 c. blue and gold 35 30

1980. Cycads. Multicoloured.

71. 5 c. Type 18 8 5
72. 10 c. "Encephalartos princeps" 25 20
73. 15 c. "Encephalartos villosus" 35 30
74. 20 c. "Encephalartos friderici-guilielmi" 45 40

19. Red-chested Cuckoo.

1980. Birds. Multicoloured.

75. 5 c. Type 19 15 5
76. 10 c. Cape Puff-back Flycatcher 40 20
77. 15 c. South African Crowned Crane 50 30
78. 20 c. Spectacled Weaver 60 40

20. "Hole in the Wall".

1980. Tourism. Multicoloured.

79. 5 c. Type 20 8 5
80. 10 c. Port St. Johns 25 20
81. 15 c. The Citadel 35 30
82. 20 c. The Archway 45 40

1981. Fishing Flies (2nd series). As T 16. Multicoloured.

83. 10 c. Kent's Lighting (streamer) 12 12
84. 10 c. Wickham's Fancy (dry fly) 12 12
85. 10 c. Jock Scott (wet fly) 12 12
86. 10 c. Green Highlander (salmon fly) 12 12
87. 10 c. Tan Nymph 12 12

1981. Medicinal Plants (2nd series). As T 4. Multicoloured.

88. 5 c. "Leonotis leonurus" 8 5
89. 15 c. "Euphorbia bupleurifolia" 25 25
90. 20 c. "Pelargonium reniforme" 30 30
91. 25 c. "Hibiscus trionum" 35 35

21. Eyamakhwenkwe.

1981. Xhosa Women's Headdresses. Mult.

92. 5 c. Type 21 5 5
93. 15 c. Eyabafana 12 12
94. 20 c. Umfazana 15 15
95. 25 c. Ixhegokazi 20 20

22. State House, Umtata.

1981. 5th Anniv. of Independence.

97. 22. 5 c. blk., brown and green 5 5
98. – 15 c. blk., brown and grn. 12 12

DESIGN: 15 c. University of Transkei.

1982. Fishing Flies (3rd series). As T 16. Multicoloured.

99. 10 c. Blue Charm 10 10
100. 10 c. Royal Coachman 10 10
101. 10 c. Light Spruce 10 10
102. 10 c. Montana nymph 10 10
103. 10 c. Butcher 10 10

23. Cub Scout. 24. Hippocrates.

1982. 75th Anniv. of Boy Scout Movement. Multicoloured.

104. 8 c. Type 23 8 8
105. 10 c. Scout planting tree 10 10
106. 20 c. Scout on raft 20 25
107. 25 c. Scout with dog 20 25

1982. Celebrities of Medicine (1st series). Multicoloured.

108. 15 c. Type 24 15 15
109. 20 c. Antonie van Leeuwenhoek 20 20
110. 25 c. William Harvey 25 25
111. 30 c. Joseph Lister 35 35

See also Nos. 125/8, 160/3, 176/9, 249/52, 273/6, 281/4 and 305/8.

25. City Hall.

1982. Umtata Centenary. Multicoloured.

112. 8 c. Type 25 8 8
113. 15 c. The Bunga 15 15
114. 20 c. Botha Sigcau Building 20 20
115. 25 c. Palace of Justice and K.D. Matanzima Building 25 25

1983. Fishing Flies (4th series). As T 16. Multicoloured.

116. 20 c. Alexandra 20 20
117. 20 c. Kent's Marbled Sedge 20 20
118. 20 c. White Marabou 20 20
119. 20 c. Mayfly Nymph 20 20
120. 20 c. Silver Wilkinson 20 20

26. Hotel Complex, Mzamba.

1983. Wildcoast Holiday Complex, Mzamba. Multicoloured.

121. 10 c. Type 26 10 12
122. 20 c. Beach scene 20 25
123. 25 c. Casino 25 30
124. 40 c. Carousel 40 45

1983. Celebrities of Medicine (2nd series). As T 24. Multicoloured.

125. 10 c. Edward Jenner 10 12
126. 20 c. Gregor Mendel 20 25
127. 25 c. Louis Pasteur 25 30
128. 40 c. Florence Nightingale 40 45

27. Lady Frere.

1983. Transkei Post Offices (1st series). Multicoloured.

129. 10 c. Type 27 10 12
130. 20 c. Idutywa 20 25
131. 25 c. Lusikisiki 25 30
132. 40 c. Cala 40 45

See also Nos. 156/9.

1984. Fishing Flies (5th series). As T 16. Multicoloured.

133. 20 c. Silver Grey 15 20
134. 20 c. Ginger Quill 15 20
135. 20 c. Hardy's Favourite 15 20
136. 20 c. March Brown 15 20
137. 20 c. Kent's Spectrum Mohawk 15 20

28. Amagqira.

1984. Xhosa Culture. Multicoloured.

138 1 c. Type 28 5 5
139 2 c. Horsemen 5 5
140 3 c. Mat making 5 5
141 4 c. Xhosa dancers 5 5
142 5 c. Shopping with donkeys 5 5
143 6 c. Young musicians 5 5
144 7 c. Fingo brides 5 5
145 8 c. Tasting the beer 8 10
146 9 c. Thinning the maize 10 12
147 10 c. Dancing demonstration 10 12
148 11 c. Water from the river 12 15
148a 12 c. Preparing a meal 12 15
148b 14 c. Weeding mealies 15 20
149 15 c. National sport: stick fighting 15 20
149a 16 c. Morning pasture 15 20
150 20 c. Abakhwetha dance 20 25
150a 21 c. Building of initiation hut 20 25
151 25 c. Tribesman singing 20 25
152 30 c. Jovial matrons 30 35
153 50 c. Pipe making 45 50
154 1 r. Intonjane 80 80
155 2 r. Abakhwetha 95 95

1984. Transkei Post Offices (2nd series). As T 27. Multicoloured.

156. 11 c. Umzimkulu 12 15
157. 20 c. Mount Fletcher 20 25
158. 25 c. Qumbu 20 25
159. 50 c. Umtata 45 50

1984. Celebrities of Medicine (3rd series). As T 24. Multicoloured.

160. 11 c. Nicholas of Cusa 12 15
161. 25 c. William Morton 20 25
162. 30 c. Wilhelm Rontgen 30 35
163. 45 c. Karl Landsteiner 40 50

29. Soil Erosion by Overgrazing.

1985. Soil Conservation. Multicoloured.

164.	11 c. Type **29**	12	15
165.	25 c. Removal of stock and construction of walls as sediment collectors	20	25
166.	30 c. Regeneration of vegetation	30	35
167.	50 c. Cattle grazing in lush landscape	45	50

30. Tsitsa Bridge.

1985. Bridges. Multicoloured.

168.	12 c. Type **30**	12	15
169.	25 c. White Kei bridge	15	20
170.	30 c. Mitchell bridge	25	30
171.	50 c. Umzimvubu bridge	40	45

31. Veneer-peeling Machine.

1985. Match Industry (Butterworth). Mult.

172.	12 c. Type **31**	8	10
173.	25 c. Cutting wood to size	15	20
174.	30 c. Dipping splints in chemical to form match heads	20	25
175.	50 c. Boxing matches	35	40

1985. Celebrities of Medicine (4th series). As T **24**. Multicoloured.

176.	12 c. Andreas Vesalius (anatomist)	8	10
177.	25 c. Marcello Malpighi (pioneer of microscopy)	15	20
178.	30 c. Francois Magendie (nutrionist)	20	25
179.	50 c. William Stewart Halsted (surgeon)	35	40

32. Early Street Scene.

1986. Historic Port St. Johns. Multicoloured.

180.	12 c. Type **32**	10	10
181.	20 c. Coaster "Umzimvubu" anchored at old jetty	30	15
182.	25 c. Wagons off-loading maize at jetty	15	20
183.	30 c. View of town at end of 19th century	20	25

33. "Aloe ferox". **34.** First Falls Station, Umtata River.

1986. Aloes. Multicoloured.

185.	14 c. Type **33**	10	12
186.	20 c. "Aloe arborescens"	12	15
187.	25 c. "Aloe maculata"	15	20
188.	30 c. "Aloe ecklonis"	20	25

1986. Hydro-electric Power Stations. Mult.

189.	14 c. Type **34**	10	12
190.	20 c. Second Falls, Umtata River	12	15
191.	25 c. Ncora, Qumanco River	20	25
192.	30 c. Collywobbles, Mbashe River	25	30

35. Prime Minister George Matanzima.

1986. 10th Anniv. of Independence. Mult.

193.	14 c. Type **35**	10	12
194.	20 c. Technical College, Umtata	12	15
195.	25 c. University of Transkei, Umtata	20	25
196.	30 c. Palace of Justice, Umtata	25	30

36. "Ulundi" flying through Clouds.

1987. 10th Anniv. of Transkei Airways Corporation. Multicoloured.

197.	14 c. Type **36**	10	12
198.	20 c. Tail fin of "Ulundi"	12	15
199.	25 c. Beechcraft "Kingair"	20	25
200.	30 c. Control tower, K. D. Matanzima Airport	25	30

37. Pondo Girl. **38.** "Latrodectus indistinctus".

1987. Transkei Beadwork. Multicoloured.

201.	16 c. Type **37**	8	8
202.	20 c. Bomvana woman	12	15
203.	25 c. Xessibe woman	15	20
204.	30 c. Xhosa man	15	20

1987. Spiders. Multicoloured.

205	16 c. Type **38**	10	10
206	20 c. "Naphila pilipes"	15	20
207	25 c. Wolf spider	25	25
208	30 c. "Argiope nigrovittata"	25	25

39. Common Black Pigs. **40.** "Plocamium corallorhiza".

1987. Domestic Animals. Multicoloured.

209.	16 c. Type **39**	8	8
210.	30 c. Goats	15	20
211.	40 c. Merino sheep	20	25
212.	50 c. Cattle	30	35

1988. Seaweed. Multicoloured.

213.	16 c. Type **40**	8	8
214.	30 c. "Gelidium amanzii"	15	20
215.	40 c. "Ecklonia biruncinata"	20	25
216.	50 c. "Halimeda cuneata"	30	35

41 Spinning

1988. Blanket Factory, Butterworth. Mult.

217	16 c. Type **41**	8	8
218	30 c. Warping	15	20
219	40 c. Weaving	20	25
220	50 c. Raising the nap	25	30

42 Map showing Wreck Site

1988. 206th Anniv of Shipwreck of "Grosvenor". Multicoloured.

221	16 c. Type **42**	20	10
222	30 c. "The Wreck of the Grosvenor" (R. Smirke)	15	20
223	40 c. Dirk hilt, dividers and coins from wreck	20	25
224	50 c. "African Hospitality" (G. Morland)	25	30

43 Small-spotted Cat

1988. Endangered Animals. Multicoloured.

225	16 c. Type **43**	8	8
226	30 c. Blue duiker	15	20
227	40 c. Oribi	20	25
228	50 c. Hunting dog	25	20

44 Class "14 CRB" Locomotives

1989. Trains. Multicoloured.

229	16 c. Type **44**	8	8
230	30 c. Class "14 CRB" locomotive and passenger train at Toleni Halt	15	20
231	40 c. Train on Great Kei River Bridge (vert)	20	25
232	50 c. Train in Kei Valley (vert)	25	30

45 Mat, Baskets and Jar

1989. Basketry. Multicoloured.

233	18 c. Type **45**	8	8
234	30 c. Basket and jar	15	20
235	40 c. Jars and bag	20	25
236	50 c. Dish and jars	25	30

46 Mackerel

1989. Seafood. Multicoloured.

237	18 c. Type **46**	8	8
238	30 c. Squid	15	20
239	40 c. Brown mussels	20	25
240	50 c. Rock lobster	25	30

47 Broom Cluster Fig

1989. Trees. Multicoloured.

241	18 c. Type **47**	8	8
242	30 c. Natal fig	15	20
243	40 c. Broad-leaved coral	20	25
244	50 c. Cabbage tree	25	30

48 "Ginkgo koningensis" **49** Aretacus (discoverer of diabetes)

1990. Plant Fossils. Multicoloured.

245	18 c. Type **48**	8	8
246	30 c. "Pseudoctenis spatulata"	15	20
247	40 c. "Rissikia media"	20	25
248	50 c. "Taeniopteris anavolans"	25	30

1990. Celebrities of Medicine (5th series). Diabetes Research. Multicoloured.

249	18 c. Type **49**	8	8
250	30 c. Claude Bernard (discovered sugar formation by liver)	15	20
251	40 c. Oscar Minkowski (discovered pancreas removal caused diabetes)	20	25
252	50 c. Frederick Banting (discoverer of insulin)	25	30

50 Diviner dancing to Drum **51** Soldier Lily

1990. Diviners. Multicoloured.

253	21 c. Type **50**	10	12
254	35 c. Lecturing Imichetywa (novitiates)	15	20
255	40 c. Neophyte initiation	15	20
256	50 c. Diviner's induction ceremony	20	25

1990. Flowers. Multicoloured.

257	21 c. Type **51**	10	12
258	35 c. "Disa crassicornis"	15	20
259	40 c. Christmas bells	15	20
260	50 c. Port St. John's creeper	20	25

52 Pink Ink Plant **53** Common Dolphin

1991. Parasitic Plants. Multicoloured.

261	21 c. Type **52**	10	12
262	35 c. White harveya	15	20
263	40 c. "Alectra sessiliflora"	15	20
264	50 c. "Hydnora africana"	20	25

1991. Dolphins. Multicoloured.

265	25 c. Type **53**	10	12
266	40 c. Bottle-nosed dolphin	15	20
267	50 c. Humpbacked dolphin	20	25
268	60 c. Risso's dolphin	25	30

54 South African Crowned Crane **55** Emil von Behring and Shibasaburo Kitasato (diphtheria)

1991. Endangered Birds. Multicoloured.

269	25 c. Type **54**	15	15
270	40 c. Cape vulture	25	25
271	50 c. Wattled crane	30	30
272	60 c. Egyptian vulture	40	40

1991. Celebrities of Medicine (6th series). Vaccine Development. Multicoloured.

273 25 c. Type **55** 10 10
274 40 c. Camille Guerin and Albert Calmette (tuberculosis) 15 20
275 50 c. Jonas Salk (poliomyelitis) 20 25
276 60 c. John Enders (measles) 25 30

56 "Eulophia speciosa"

57 Thomas Weller (researcher into infectious viruses)

1992. Orchids. Multicoloured.

277 27 c. Type **56** 10 15
278 45 c. "Satyrium sphaerocarpum" 20 25
279 65 c. "Disa scullyi" .. 25 30
280 85 c. "Disa tysonii" .. 35 40

1992. Celebrities of Medicine (7th series). Mult.

281 27 c. Type **57** 10 15
282 45 c. Ignaz Semmelweis (antiseptic pioneer) .. 20 25
283 65 c. Sir James Simpson (pioneer of chloroform as anaesthetic) .. 25 30
284 85 c. Rene Laennec (inventor of stethoscope) 35 40

58 Red-billed Pintail ("Anas erythrorhyncha")

59 "Pseudomelania sutherlandi" (gastropod)

1992. Waterfowl. Multicoloured.

285 35 c. Type **58** 15 15
286 35 c. Hottentot teal ("Anas hottentota") 15 15
287 70 c. Maccoa duck ("Oxyura punctata") .. 30 30
288 70 c. White-backed duck ("Thalassornis leuconotus") 30 30
289 90 c. African black duck ("Anas sparsa") .. 40 40
290 90 c. Egyptian goose ("Alopochen aegyptiacus") 40 40
291 1 r. 05 Cape shoveler ("Anas smithi") .. 45 45
292 1 r. 05 Cape teal ("Anas capensis") 45 45

1992. Marine Fossils. Multicoloured.

293 35 c. Type **59** 15 15
294 70 c. "Gaudryceras denseplicatum" (ammonite) 30 30
295 90 c. "Neithea quinquecostata" (bivalve) .. 40 40
296 1 r. 05 "Pugilina (Mayeria) acuticarinatus" (gastropod) 45 45

60 Papillon

1993. Dogs. Multicoloured.

297 35 c. Type **60** 15 15
298 70 c. Pekinese 30 30
299 90 c. Chihuahua 40 40
300 1 r. 05 Dachshund .. 45 45

61 Fabrosaurus

1993. Prehistoric Animals. Multicoloured.

301 45 c. Type **61** 15 15
302 65 c. Diictodon 25 25
303 85 c. Chasmatosaurus .. 30 30
304 1 r. 05 Rubidgea 40 40

62 Sir Alexander Fleming and Howard Florey (discoverer and refiner of penicillin)

63 Laughing Doves

1993. Celebrities of Medicine (8th series). Multicoloured.

305 45 c. Type **62** 15 15
306 65 c. Alexis Carrel (tissue transplantation pioneer) 25 25
307 85 c. James Lind (pioneer in prevention of scurvy) 30 30
308 1 r. 05 Santiago Ramon y Cajal (researcher into nervous system) .. 40 40

1993. Doves. Multicoloured.

309 45 c. Type **63** 15 15
310 65 c. Tambourine doves .. 25 25
311 85 c. Emerald-spotted wood doves 30 30
312 1 r. 05 Namaqua doves .. 40 40

64 "Clan Lindsay" (steamer) on rocks in Mazeppa Bay, 1898

1994. Shipwrecks. Multicoloured.

313 45 c. Type **64** 15 15
314 65 c. "Horizon" (freighter) on rocks near River Mngazi, 1967 .. .. 25 25
315 85 c. "Oceanos" (pleasure cruiser) sinking near Coffee Bay, 1991 .. 30 30
316 1 r. 05 "Forresbank" (freighter) on fire near River Mtakatye, 1958 .. 40 40

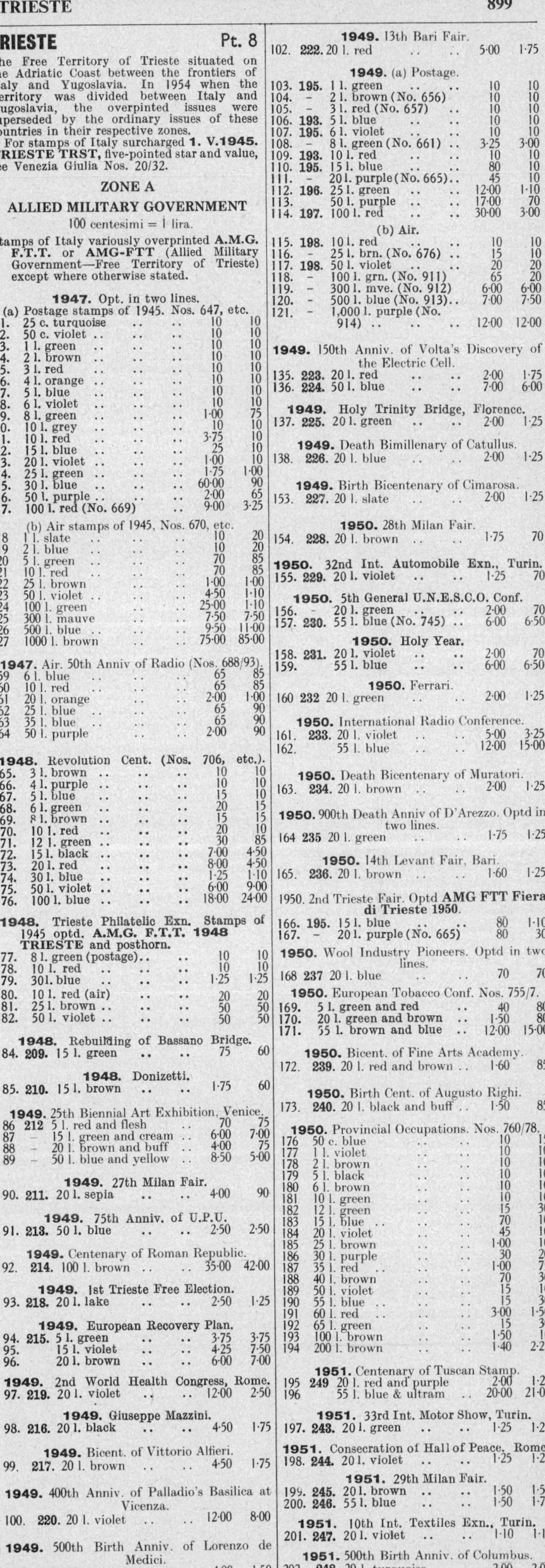

TRIESTE Pt. 8

The Free Territory of Trieste situated on the Adriatic Coast between the frontiers of Italy and Yugoslavia. In 1954 when the Territory was divided between Italy and Yugoslavia, the overpinted issues were superseded by the ordinary issues of these countries in their respective zones.

For stamps of Italy surcharged **1. V.1945. TRIESTE TRST,** five-pointed star and value, see Venezia Giulia Nos. 20/32.

ZONE A

ALLIED MILITARY GOVERNMENT

100 centesimi = 1 lira.

Stamps of Italy variously overprinted **A.M.G. F.T.T.** or **AMG-FTT** (Allied Military Government—Free Territory of Trieste) except where otherwise stated.

1947. Opt. in two lines.

(a) Postage stamps of 1945. Nos. 647, etc.

1. 25 c. turquoise 10 10
2. 50 c. violet 10 10
3. 1 l. green 10 10
4. 2 l. brown 10 10
5. 3 l. red 10 10
6. 4 l. orange 10 10
7. 5 l. blue 10 10
8. 6 l. violet 10 10
9. 8 l. green .. .. .. 1·00 75
10. 10 l. grey 10 10
11. 10 l. red .. .. .. 3·75 10
12. 15 l. blue 25 10
13. 20 l. violet .. .. .. 1·00 10
14. 25 l. green .. .. .. 1·75 1·00
15. 30 l. blue .. .. .. 60·00 90
16. 50 l. purple .. .. .. 2·00 65
17. 100 l. red (No. 669) .. 9·00 3·25

(b) Air stamps of 1945, Nos. 670, etc.

18 1 l. slate 10 20
19 2 l. blue 10 20
20 5 l. green 70 85
21 10 l. red 70 85
22 25 l. brown .. .. .. 1·00 1·00
23 50 l. violet .. .. .. 4·50 1·10
24 100 l. green .. .. .. 25·00 1·10
25 300 l. mauve .. .. 7·50 7·50
26 500 l. blue .. .. .. 9·50 11·00
27 1000 l. brown .. .. 75·00 85·00

1947. Air. 50th Anniv of Radio (Nos. 688/93).

59 6 l. blue 65 85
60 10 l. red 65 85
61 20 l. orange .. .. 2·00 1·00
62 25 l. blue 65 90
63 35 l. blue 65 90
64 50 l. purple .. .. 2·00 90

1948. Revolution Cent. (Nos. 706, etc.).

65. 3 l. brown 10 10
66. 4 l. purple 10 10
67. 5 l. blue 15 10
68. 6 l. green 20 15
69. 8 l. brown 15 15
70. 10 l. red 20 10
71. 12 l. green 30 85
72. 15 l. black .. .. .. 7·00 4·50
73. 20 l. red .. .. .. 8·00 4·50
74. 30 l. blue .. .. .. 1·25 1·10
75. 50 l. violet .. .. .. 6·00 9·00
76. 100 l. blue .. .. .. 18·00 24·00

1948. Trieste Philatelic Exn. Stamps of 1945 optd. **A.M.G. F.T.T. 1948 TRIESTE** and posthorn.

77. 8 l. green (postage) 10 10
78. 10 l. red 10 10
79. 30 l. blue .. .. .. 1·25 1·25
80. 10 l. red (air) 20 20
81. 25 l. brown 50 50
82. 50 l. violet 50 50

1948. Rebuilding of Bassano Bridge.

84. **209.** 15 l. green 75 60

1948. Donizetti.

85. **210.** 15 l. brown .. .. 1·75 60

1949. 25th Biennial Art Exhibition, Venice.

86 **212** 5 l. red and flesh .. 70 75
87 – 15 l. green and cream .. 6·00 7·00
88 – 20 l. brown and buff .. 4·00 75
89 – 50 l. blue and yellow .. 8·50 5·00

1949. 27th Milan Fair.

90. **211.** 20 l. sepia .. .. 4·00 90

1949. 75th Anniv. of U.P.U.

91. **213.** 50 l. blue .. .. 2·50 2·50

1949. Centenary of Roman Republic.

92. **214.** 100 l. brown .. .. 35·00 42·00

1949. 1st Trieste Free Election.

93. **218.** 20 l. lake .. .. 2·50 1·25

1949. European Recovery Plan.

94. **215.** 5 l. green .. .. 3·75 3·75
95. 15 l. violet .. .. 4·25 7·50
96. 20 l. brown .. .. 6·00 7·00

1949. 2nd World Health Congress, Rome.

97. **219.** 20 l. violet .. .. 12·00 2·50

1949. Giuseppe Mazzini.

98. **216.** 20 l. black .. .. 4·50 1·75

1949. Bicent. of Vittorio Alfieri.

99. **217.** 20 l. brown .. .. 4·50 1·75

1949. 400th Anniv. of Palladio's Basilica at Vicenza.

100. **220.** 20 l. violet .. .. 12·00 8·00

1949. 500th Birth Anniv. of Lorenzo de Medici.

101. **221.** 20 l. blue .. .. 4·00 1·50

1949. 13th Bari Fair.

102. **222.** 20 l. red .. .. 5·00 1·75

1949. (a) Postage.

103. **195.** 1 l. green 10 10
104. – 2 l. brown (No. 656) 10 10
105. – 3 l. red (No. 657) .. 10 10
106. **193.** 5 l. blue 10 10
107. **195.** 6 l. violet 10 10
108. – 8 l. green (No. 661) .. 3·25 3·00
109. **193.** 10 l. red 10 10
110. **195.** 15 l. blue 80 10
111. – 20 l. purple (No. 665) .. 45 10
112. **196.** 25 l. green .. .. 12·00 1·10
113. 50 l. purple .. .. 17·00 70
114. **197.** 100 l. red .. .. 30·00 3·00

(b) Air.

115. **198.** 10 l. red 10 10
116. – 25 l. brn. (No. 676) .. 15 10
117. **198.** 50 l. violet 20 20
118. – 100 l. grn. (No. 911) 65 20
119. – 300 l. mve. (No. 912) 6·00 6·00
120. – 500 l. blue (No. 913) .. 7·00 7·50
121. – 1,000 l. purple (No. 914) .. .. .. 12·00 12·00

1949. 150th Anniv. of Volta's Discovery of the Electric Cell.

135. **223.** 20 l. red .. .. 2·00 1·75
136. **224.** 50 l. blue .. .. 7·00 6·00

1949. Holy Trinity Bridge, Florence.

137. **225.** 20 l. green .. .. 2·00 1·25

1949. Death Bimillenary of Catullus.

138. **226.** 20 l. blue .. .. 2·00 1·25

1949. Birth Bicentenary of Cimarosa.

153. **227.** 20 l. slate .. .. 2·00 1·25

1950. 28th Milan Fair.

154. **228.** 20 l. brown .. .. 1·75 70

1950. 32nd Int. Automobile Exn., Turin.

155. **229.** 20 l. violet .. .. 1·25 70

1950. 5th General U.N.E.S.C.O. Conf.

156. – 20 l. green .. .. 2·00 70
157. **230.** 55 l. blue (No. 745) .. 6·00 6·50

1950. Holy Year.

158. **231.** 20 l. violet .. .. 2·00 70
159. 55 l. blue .. .. 6·00 6·50

1950. Ferrari.

160 **232** 20 l. green .. .. 2·00 1·25

1950. International Radio Conference.

161. **233.** 20 l. violet .. .. 5·00 3·25
162. 55 l. blue .. .. 12·00 15·00

1950. Death Bicentenary of Muratori.

163. **234.** 20 l. brown .. .. 2·00 1·25

1950. 900th Death Anniv of D'Arezzo. Optd in two lines.

164 **235** 20 l. green .. .. 1·75 1·25

1950. 14th Levant Fair, Bari.

165. **236.** 20 l. brown .. .. 1·60 1·25

1950. 2nd Trieste Fair. Optd **AMG FTT Fiera di Trieste 1950**.

166. **195.** 15 l. blue .. .. 80 1·10
167. – 20 l. purple (No. 665) 80 30

1950. Wool Industry Pioneers. Optd in two lines.

168 **237** 20 l. blue 70 70

1950. European Tobacco Conf. Nos. 755/7.

169. 5 l. green and red .. 40 80
170. 20 l. green and brown .. 1·50 80
171. 55 l. brown and blue .. 12·00 15·00

1950. Bicent. of Fine Arts Academy.

172. **239.** 20 l. red and brown .. 1·60 85

1950. Birth Cent. of Augusto Righi.

173. **240.** 20 l. black and buff .. 1·50 85

1950. Provincial Occupations. Nos. 760/78.

176 50 c. blue 10 15
177 1 l. violet 10 10
178 2 l. brown 10 10
179 5 l. black 10 10
180 6 l. brown 10 10
181 10 l. green 10 10
182 12 l. green 15 30
183 15 l. blue 70 10
184 20 l. violet 45 10
185 25 l. brown .. .. 1·00 10
186 30 l. purple 30 20
187 35 l. red .. .. 1·00 75
188 40 l. brown 70 30
189 50 l. violet 15 10
190 55 l. blue 15 30
191 60 l. red .. .. 3·00 1·50
192 65 l. green 15 30
193 100 l. brown .. .. 1·50 10
194 200 l. brown .. .. 1·40 2·25

1951. Centenary of Tuscan Stamp.

195 **249** 20 l. red and purple 2·00 1·25
196 55 l. blue & ultram .. 20·00 21·00

1951. 33rd Int. Motor Show, Turin.

197. **243.** 20 l. green .. .. 1·25 1·25

1951. Consecration of Hall of Peace, Rome.

198. **244.** 20 l. violet .. .. 1·25 1·25

1951. 29th Milan Fair.

199. **245.** 20 l. brown .. .. 1·50 1·50
200. **246.** 55 l. blue .. .. 1·50 1·75

1951. 10th Int. Textiles Exn., Turin.

201. **247.** 20 l. violet .. .. 1·10 1·10

1951. 500th Birth Anniv. of Columbus.

202. **248.** 20 l. turquoise .. 2·00 2·00

1951. Int. Gymnastic Festival, Florence.
203. **249.** 5 l. red and brown .. 3·25 5·50
204. 10 l. red and green .. 3·25 5·50
205. 15 l. red and blue .. 3·25 5·50

1951. Restoration of Montecassino Abbey.
206. **250.** 20 l. violet 60 50
207. – 55 l. blue (No. 791) .. 1·25 1·40

1951. 3rd Trieste Fair, Optd. **AMG-FTT FIERA di TRIESTE 1951.**
208. 6 l. brown (No. 764) .. 30 40
209. 20 l. violet (No. 768) .. 40 30
210. 55 l. blue (No. 774) .. 45 65

1951. 500th Birth Anniv of Perugino. Optd in two lines.
211 **251** 20 l. brown and sepia .. 55 50

1951. Triennial Art Exhibition, Milan.
212. **252.** 20 l. black and green.. 70 65
213. – 55 l. pink and blue (No. 794) .. 1·40 1·60

1951. World Cycling Championship.
214. **253.** 25 l. grey 85 50

1951. 15th Levant Fair, Bar.
215. **254.** 25 l. blue 70 55

1951. Birth Cent. of F. P. Michetti.
216. **255.** 25 l. brown 65 50

1951. Sardinian Stamp Centenary.
217. **256.** 10 l. black and sepia.. 35 50
218. – 25 l. green & red (799) 40 30
219. – 60 l. red and blue (800) 65 75

1951. 3rd Industrial and Commercial Census.
220 **257** 10 l. green 45 60

1951. 9th National Census.
221. **258.** 25 l. slate 45 35

1951. Forestry Festival.
222. **260.** 10 l. green and olive .. 50 75
223. – 25 l. green (No. 807).. 50 40

1951. Verdi.
224. – 10 l. green & pur. (803) 75 75
225. **259.** 25 l. sepia and brown.. 45 35
226. – 60 l. blue & green (805) 85 85

1952. Bellini.
227. **261.** 25 l. black 65 40

1952. Caserta Palace.
228. **262.** 25 l. brown and green 50 35

1952. 1st Int. Sports Stamps Exn., Rome.
229. **263.** 25 l. brown and black 35 25

1952. 30th Milan Fair.
230. **264.** 60 l. blue .. .. 1·00 1·40

1952. Leonardo da Vinci.
231. **265.** 25 l. orange 10 10
232. – 60 l. blue (813) .. 55 85
233. **265.** 80 l. red .. .. 1·25 35

1952. Overseas Fair, Naples.
234. **268.** 25 l. blue 35 30

1952. Modena and Parma Stamp Cent.
235. **267.** 25 l. black and brown 35 25
236. 60 l. indigo and blue.. 45 75

1952. 26th Biennial Art Exn., Venice.
237. **269.** 25 l. black and cream.. 35 25

1952. 30th Padua Fair.
238. **270.** 25 l. red and blue .. 35 25

1952. 4th Trieste Fair.
239. **271.** 25 l. grn., red & brown 35 25

1952. 16th Levant Fair, Bari.
240. **272.** 25 l. green 40 25

1952. Savonarola.
241. **273.** 25 l. violet 35 25

1952. 1st Private Aeronautics Conf., Rome.
242. **274.** 60 l. blue & deep blue 1·00 1·60

1952. Alpine Troops National Exn.
243. **275.** 25 l. grey 35 25

1952. Armed Forces Day.
244. **276.** 10 l. green 10 10
245. **277.** 25 l. sepia and brown.. 35 10
246. – 60 l. black & blue (827) 35 45

1952. Mission to Ethiopia.
247. **278.** 25 l. deep brown & brn. 45 30

1952. Birth Centenary of Gemito.
248. **279.** 25 l. brown 35 25

1952. Birth Centenary of Mancini.
249. **280.** 25 l. myrtle 35 25

1952. Martyrdom of Belfiore.
250. **281.** 25 l. blue and black .. 35 25

1953. Antonello Exhibition, Messina.
251. **282.** 25 l. red 35 25

1953. 20th "Mille Miglia" Car Race.
252. **283.** 25 l. violet 40 30

1953. Labour Orders of Merit.
253. **284.** 25 l. violet 35 25

1953. Birth Centenary of Corelli.
254. **285.** 25 l. brown 50 30

1953. Coin type.
255. **286.** 5 l. slate 10 10
256. 10 l. red 10 10
257. 12 l. green 10 10
258. 13 l. mauve 10 10
259. 20 l. brown 15 10
260. 25 l. violet 15 10
261. 35 l. red 35 35
262. 60 l. blue 35 35
263. 80 l. brown 40 40

1953. 7th Death Centenary of St. Clare.
264. **287.** 25 l. chestnut & brown 35 25

1953. 5th Trieste Fair. Optd. **V FIERA DI TRIESTE AMG FTT 1953.**
265. 10 l. green (No. 765) .. 20 35
266. 25 l. orange (No. 769) .. 25 20
267. 60 l. red (No. 775) .. 30 40

1953. Mountains Festival.
272. **288.** 25 l. green 45 25

1953. Int. Agricultural Exn., Rome.
273. **289.** 25 l. brown 25 20
274. 60 l. blue 35 40

1953. 4th Anniv. of Atlantic Pact.
275. **290.** 25 l. slate and yellow.. 45 35
276. 60 l. blue and mauve.. 1·60 1·75

1953. 5th Birth Centenary of Signorelli.
227. **291.** 25 l. green and brown 35 25

1953. 6th Int. Microbiological Congress, Rome.
278. **292.** 25 l. brown and slate 40 30

1953. Tourist Series. Nos. 855/60.
279 10 l. brown and sepia .. 15 15
280 12 l. black and blue .. 15 20
281 20 l. brown and orange .. 15 15
282 25 l. green and blue .. 15 10
283 35 l. brown and buff .. 25 30
284 60 l. blue and green .. 30 35

1954. 25th Anniv of Lateran Treaty.
285 **294** 25 l. sepia and brown 20 20
286 60 l. blue and light blue 30 40

1954. Television.
287. **295.** 25 l. violet 20 20
288. 60 l. turquoise .. 40 50

1954. Encouragement to Taxpayers.
289. **296.** 25 l. violet 40 25

1954. Milan–Turin Helicopter Mail Flight.
290. **297.** 25 l. green 35 25

1954. 10th Anniv. of Resistance Movement.
291. **298.** 25 l. black and brown 40 25

1954. 6th Trieste Fair. Nos. 858 and 860 of Italy optd **AMG-FTT FIERA DI TRIESTE 1954**.
292 – 25 l. green and blue .. 25 20
293 **293** 60 l. blue and green .. 35 40

1954. Birth Centenary of Catalani.
294. **299.** 25 l. green 45 25

1954. 7th Birth Centenary of Marco Polo.
295. **300.** 25 l. brown 20 20
296. 60 l. green 35 45

1954. 60th Anniv. of Italian Touring Club.
297. **301.** 25 l. green and red .. 50 55

1954. International Police Congress, Rome.
298. **302.** 25 l. red 20 15
299. 60 l. blue 25 30

CONCESSIONAL LETTER POST

1947. Optd **A.M.G. F.T.T.** in two lines.
CL44 – 1 l. brown (No. CL649) .. 10 10
CL45 CL **201** 8 l. red .. .. 1·50 30
CL46 CL **220** 15 l. violet .. 12·00 2·00

1949. Optd **AMG-FTT.**
CL122 CL **220** 15 l. violet .. 55 10
CL123 20 l. violet .. 85 10

CONCESSIONAL PARCEL POST

1953.
CP268 CP **288** 40 l. orange .. 1·50 15
CP269 50 l. blue .. 1·50 15
CP270 75 l. brown .. 1·50 15
CP271 110 l. pink .. 1·50 20

Unused prices are for the complete stamp, used prices for the left half of the stamp.

EXPRESS LETTER STAMPS

1947. Express Letter stamps optd. **A.M.G. F.T.T.** in two lines.
E 28. – 15 l. lake (No. E 681) 15 10
E 29. **200.** 25 l. orange .. .. 10·00 3·00
E 30. 30 l. violet 35 40
E 31. – 60 l. red (No. E 685).. 6·50 5·50

1948. Centenary of Revolution. Express Letter stamp optd **A.M.G.-F.T.T.**
E83 E **209** 35 l. violet .. 2·00 2·75

1950. Express Letter stamps optd **AMG-FTT** in one line.
E174 E **209** 50 l. purple .. 95 60
E175 – 60 l. red (No. E685) 95 60

PARCEL POST STAMPS
Prices are for complete stamps.

1947. Parcel Post stamps optd **A.M.G. F.T.T.** in two lines on each half of stamp.
P32 P **201** 1 l. brown 25 25
P33 2 l. blue 40 30
P34 3 l. orange 40 35
P35 4 l. grey 45 40
P36 5 l. purple .. .. 1·25 1·00
P37 10 l. violet .. .. 2·50 2·00
P38 20 l. purple .. .. 3·75 3·00
P39 50 l. red .. .. 5·00 4·75
P40 100 l. blue .. .. 6·50 6·50
P41 200 l. green £200 £225
P42 300 l. purple £100 £120
P43 500 l. brown .. .. 50·00 75·00

1949. Parcel Post stamps optd **AMG-FTT** in one line on each half of stamp.
P139 P **201** 1 l. brown 55 70
P140 2 l. blue 10 25
P141 3 l. orange 10 25
P142 4 l. grey 10 25
P143 5 l. purple 15 25
P144 10 l. violet 25 25
P145 20 l. purple 30 25
P146 30 l. purple 30 45
P147 50 l. red 70 25
P148 100 l. blue .. .. 1·40 1·40
P149 200 l. green .. .. 13·00 15·00
P150 300 l. purple .. .. 45·00 50·00
P151 500 l. brown .. .. 26·00 35·00
P152 P **928** 1,000 l. blue .. £130 £150

POSTAGE DUE STAMPS

1947. Postage Due stamps optd. **A.M.G. F.T.T.** in two lines.
D 44. D **192.** 1 l. orange .. 10 10
D 48. D **201.** 1 l. orange .. 10 30
D 49. 2 l. green 10 10
D 50. 3 l. red 40 65
D 51. 4 l. brown.. .. 3·25 4·25
D 45. D **192.** 5 l. violet .. .. 1·50 10
D 52. D **201.** 5 l. violet .. .. 30·00 6·00
D 53. 6 l. blue .. .. 10·00 10·00
D 54. 8 l. mauve .. .. 20·00 20·00
D 46. D **192.** 10 l. blue .. .. 2·00 35
D 55. D **201.** 10 l. blue .. .. 35·00 3·00
D 56. 12 l. brown .. .. 8·00 10·00
D 47. D **192.** 20 l. red .. .. 7·00 35
D 57. D **201.** 20 l. purple .. .. 7·00 1·50
D 58. 50 l. green.. .. 1·25 25

1949. Postage Due stamps optd. **AMG-FTT** in one line.
D 122. D **201.** 1 l. orange .. 10 10
D 123. 2 l. green.. .. 10 10
D 124. 3 l. red 10 10
D 125. 5 l. violet 30 10
D 126. 6 l. blue 10 10
D 127. 8 l. mauve 10 10
D 128. 10 l. blue.. .. 10 10
D 129. 12 l. brown 45 15
D 130. 20 l. purple .. .. 1·10 10
D 131. 25 l. red .. .. 1·00 1·25
D 132. 50 l. green .. .. 1·50 10
D 133. 100 l. orange .. 2·50 20
D 134. 500 l. pur. & blue 24·00 11·00

ZONE B

YUGOSLAV MILITARY GOVERNMENT

1948. 100 centesimi = 1 lira.
1949. 100 paras = 1 dinar.

Apart from the definitive issues illustrated below the following are stamps of Yugoslavia (sometimes in new colours), variously overprinted **STT VUJA** or **VUJA-STT** or (Nos. B 65 onwards) **STT VUJNA** unless otherwise stated.

B 1.

B 2.

1948. Labour Day.
B1 B **1** 100 l. red and stone (A) 1·50 1·25
B2 100 l. red and stone (B) 1·50 1·25
B3 100 l. red and stone (C) 1·50 1·25

Inscr in Slovene (A) "I.MAJ 1948 V STO"; Italian (B) "I. MAGGIO 1948 NEL TLT"; or Croat (C) "I. SVIBANJ 1948 U STT".

1948. Red Cross. No. 545 optd. and surch.
B 3a. **131.** 2 l. on 50 p. brn. & red 8·00 8·00

1948. Air. Economic Exn., Capodistria.
B 4. B **2.** 25 l. grey 75 55
B 5. 50 l. orange 75 55

B **3.** Clasped Hands, Hammer and Sickle.

B **4.** Fishermen and Flying-boat.

B **5.** Man with Donkey.

B **6.** Mediterranean Gull over Chimney.

1949. Labour Day.
B 6. B **3.** 10 l. black 30 15

1949. Air.
B 7. B **4.** 1 l. blue 15 15
B 8. B **5.** 2 l. brown 15 15
B 9. B **4.** 5 l. blue 15 15
B 10. B **5.** 10 l. violet 75 50
B 11. B **4.** 25 l. olive 90 90
B 12. B **5.** 50 l. green 90 90
B 13. B **6.** 100 l. purple.. .. 2·25 1·10

1949. Partisans issue.
B 14. **119.** 50 p. olive 10 10
B 15. 1 d. green 10 10
B 16. **120.** 2 d. red 10 10
B 17. – 3 d. red (No. 508) .. 10 10
B 18. **120.** 4 d. blue 10 10
B 19. – 5 d. blue (No. 511) .. 15 10
B 20. – 9 d. mauve (No. 514) 25 15
B 21. – 12 d. blue (No. 515) .. 1·50 90
B 22. **119.** 16 d. blue .. .. 1·10 80
B 23. – 20 d. red (No. 517) .. 2·00 1·25

1949. 75th Anniv. of U.P.U.
B 24. – 5 d. blue (No. 612) .. 9·00 9·00
B 25. **158.** 12 d. brown .. .. 9·00 9·00

1949. Air. Optd. **DIN** or surch. also.
B 26. B **4.** 1 d. blue 10 10
B 27. B **5.** 2 d. brown 10 10
B 28. B **4.** 5 d. blue 15 10
B 29. B **5.** 10 d. violet 30 25
B 30. B **4.** 15 d. on 25 l. olive .. 6·00 4·25
B 31. B **5.** 20 d. on 50 l. green 1·25 90
B 32. B **6.** 30 d. on 100 l. purple 2·00 90

1950. Centenary of Yugoslav Railways.
B 33. **116.** 2 d. green .. .. 1·50 1·00
B 34. – 3 d. red (No. 632) 2·25 1·40
B 35. – 5 d. blue (No. 633) .. 3·75 2·50
B 36. – 10 d. orange (No. 633a) 7·50 5·00

B **10.** Girl on Donkey.

B **11.** Workers.

1950.
B37 B **10** 50 p. slate .. 10 10
B38 – 1 d. red (Cockerel) 10 10
B38a – 1 d. brown (Cockerel) 15 10
B39 – 2 d. blue (Geese) .. 10 10
B40 – 3 d. brown (Bees) .. 20 10
B40a – 3 d. red (Bees) 20 10
B41 – 5 d. green (Oxen) .. 35 10
B42 – 10 c. brown (Turkey) 50 10
B43 – 15 d. violet (Kids) .. 3·50 3·00
B44 – 20 d. olive (Silkworms) 1·60 80

1950. May Day.
B 45. B **11.** 3 d. violet 50 40
B 46. 10 d. red 75 45

1950. Red Cross.
B 47. **160.** 50 p. brown and red 75 60

B **12.** Worker.

B **13.** P. P. Vergerio, Jr.

1951. May Day.
B 48. B **12.** 3 d. red 70 40
B 49. 10 d. olive 90 80

1951. Red Cross.
B 49a. **191.** 50 p. blue and red.. 7·50 6·00

1951. Festival of Italian Culture.
B 50. B **13.** 5 d. blue 75 60
B 51. 10 d. red 75 60
B 52. 20 d. brown 75 60

1951. Cultural Anniversaries.
B 53. **189.** 10 d. orange .. 80 45
B 54. – 12 d. blk. (As No. 699) 80 45

B **14a.** Koper Square.

B **15.** Cyclists.

1952. Air. 75th Anniv. of U.P.U.
B 54a. B **14a.** 5 d. brown .. 15·00 13·00
B 54b. – 15 d. blue .. 12·00 10·00
B 54c. – 25 d. green .. 7·50 5·50

DESIGNS—VERT. 15 d. Lighthouse, Piran. HORIZ. 25 d. Hotel, Portoroz.

1952. Physical Culture Propaganda.
B 55. B **15.** 5 d. brown 15 10
B 56. – 10 d. green 15 10
B 57. – 15 d. red 15 10
B 58. – 28 d. blue 45 25
B 59. – 50 d. lake 80 30
B 60. – 100 d. slate.. .. 4·00 3·00

DESIGNS: 10 d. Footballers. 15 d. Rowing four. 28 d. Yachts. 50 d. Netball players. 100 d. Diver.

1952. Marshall Tito's 60th Birthday. Stamps of Yugoslavia inscr. " STT VUJA ".
B 61. **196.** 15 d. brown .. 1·10 70
B 62. **197.** 28 d. lake .. 1·10 70
B 63. – 50 d. green (No. 729) 1·10 70

1952. Children's Week.
B 64. **198.** 15 d. red 75 30

1952. 15th Olympic Games, Helsinki. As Nos. 731/6.
B65 **199** 5 d. brown on flesh .. 30 10
B66 – 10 d. green on cream 30 10
B67 – 15 d. violet on mauve 30 10
B68 – 28 d. brown on buff .. 70 35
B69 – 50 d. brown on yellow 6·00 3·50
B70 – 100 d. blue on pink .. 20·00 15·00

1952. Navy Day. Nos. 737/9.
B 71. – 15 d. purple .. 1·50 1·50
B 72. **200.** 28 d. brown .. 1·50 1·50
B 73. – 50 d. black .. 2·00 1·50

1952. Red Cross.
B 74. **201.** 50 p. red, grey & blk. 30 30

1952. 6th Yugoslav Communist Party Congress.
B 75. **202.** 15 d. brown 60 50
B 76. 15 d. turquoise .. 60 50
B 77. 15 d. brown 60 50
B 78. 15 d. blue 60 50

B 17. Starfish.

1952. Philatelic Exhibition, Koper.
B78a **B 17** 15 d. lake .. .. 1·50 1·10

1953. Tesla.
B 79. **203.** 15 d. red 25 20
B 80. 30 d. blue .. .. 1·00 80

1953. Pictorials of 1950.
B 81 1 d. grey (705) .. .. 3·00 2·50
B 86 2 d. red (718) 10 10
B 82 3 d. red (655) 10 10
B 87 5 d. orange (719) .. 10 10
B106 10 d. green (721) .. 25 10
B 88 15 d. red (723) 20 10
B 84 30 d. blue (712) .. 40 15
B 85 50 d. green (714) .. 2·75 2·50

1953. United Nations. Nos. 747/9.
B 89. **204.** 15 d. green 10 10
B 90. – 30 d. blue 15 10
B 91. – 50 d. lake 55 35

1953. Adriatic Car Rally. As Nos. 750/3.
B 92. **205.** 15 d. brown & yellow 25 10
B 93. – 30 d. grn. & turquoise 25 10
B 94. – 50 d. lake and pink .. 25 10
B 95. – 70 d. indigo and blue 70 40

1953. Marshal Tito.
B96 **206** 50 d. green .. .. 1·50 90

1953. 38th Esperanto Congress, Zagreb.
B97 **207** 15 d. green and turquoise (postage) 1·25 1·25
B98 300 d. green and violet (air) £250 £275

1953. Liberation of Istria and Slovene Coast.
B 99. **208.** 15 d. blue .. .. 1·75 1·25

1953. Radicevic.
B 100. **210.** 15 d. black .. 1·10 75

1953. Red Cross.
B 101. **211.** 2 d. red and brown 40 40

1953. First Republican Legislative Assembly. As Nos. 762/4.
B 102. **212.** 15 d. slate 75 60
B 103. – 30 d. lake 75 60
B 104. – 50 d. green 75 60

1954. Air. As Nos. 675 etc.
B 108. 1 d. lilac 10 10
B 109. 2 d. green 10 10
B 110. 3 d. red 10 10
B 111. 5 d. brown 10 10
B 112. 10 d. turquoise 10 10
B 113. 20 d. brown 20 10
B 114. 30 d. blue 20 15
B 115. 50 d. olive 35 20
B 116. 100 d. red .. .. 1·25 90
B 117. 200 d. violet .. .. 3·00 1·40
B 118. 500 d. orange .. .. 12·00 12·50

1954. Animals. As Nos. 765/76.
B119 2 d. grey, buff and red .. 10 10
B120 5 d. slate, buff and grey 10 10
B121 10 d. brown and green .. 15 10
B122 15 d. brown and blue .. 20 10
B123 17 d. sepia and brown .. 20 10
B124 25 d. yellow, blue & ochre 40 10
B125 30 d. brown and violet .. 50 10
B126 35 d. black and purple .. 65 20
B127 50 d. brown and green .. 85 30
B128 65 d. black and brown .. 2·25 1·40
B129 70 d. brown and blue .. 4·00 1·50
B130 100 d. black and blue .. 7·00 8·00

1954. Serbian Insurrection. As Nos. 778/81.
B 131. – 15 d. multicoloured 60 30
B 132. **214.** 30 d. multicoloured 60 30
B 133. – 50 d. multicoloured 60 30
B 134. – 70 d. multicoloured 1·25 75

POSTAGE DUE STAMPS

1948. Red Cross. No. D 546 surch. **VUJA STT** and new value.
BD 4. **131.** 2 l. on 50 p. red & grn. £150 £150

1949. On 1946 issue.
BD 26. **D 126.** 50 p. orange .. 30 30
BD 27. 1 d. orange .. 30 30
BD 74. 1 d. brown .. 10 10
BD 28. 2 d. blue .. 45 30
BD 75. 2 d. green .. 10 10
BD 29. 3 d. green .. 30 20
BD 30. 5 d. violet .. 60 50
BD 76. 5 d. blue .. 15 10
BD 77. 10 d. red .. 10 10
BD 78. 20 d. violet .. 20 10
BD 79. 30 d. orange .. 20 15
BD 80. 50 d. blue .. 35 20
BD 81. 100 d. purple .. 4·00 4·00
Nos. BD 26/30 optd. **STT VUJA** and the rest **STT VUJNA.**

1950. Red Cross. No. D 617 optd. **VUJA STT.**
BD 48. **160.** 50 p. purple and red 1·25 90

BD **12.** Fish.

1950.
BD 49. – 0 d. 50 brown .. 15 15
BD 50. – 1 d. green .. 55 45
BD 51. **BD 12.** 2 d. blue .. 1·25 70
BD 52. 3 d. blue .. 1·25 70
BD 53. 5 d. purple .. 3·00 1·50
DESIGN: 0 d. 50, 1 d. Two fishes.

1951. Red Cross. No. D 703 optd. **STT VUJA.**
BD 54. **191.** 50 p. green and red £100 90·00

The following are optd. **STT VUJNA.**

1952. Red Cross. No. D 741.
BD 82. **D 202.** 50 p. red and grey 40 40

1953. Red Cross. As No. D762.
BD102 **211** 2 d. red and purple 50 50

TRIPOLITANIA Pt. 8

One of the provinces into which the Italian colony of Libya was divided.

100 centesimi = 1 lira.

Stamps optd. **Tripoli di Barberia** formerly listed here will be found under Italian P.O's in the Levant Nos. 171/81.

Nos. 1/138, except where otherwise described, are Italian stamps, sometimes in new colours, overprinted **TRIPOLITANIA.**

1923. Propagation of the Faith.
1. **66.** 20 c. orange and green .. 1·10 5·50
2. 30 c. orange and red .. 1·10 5·50
3. 50 c. orange and violet .. 75 4·75
4. 1 l. orange and blue .. 75 4·75

1923. Fascisti.
5. **73.** 10 c. green .. .. 1·40 6·00
6. 30 c. violet .. .. 1·40 6·00
7. 50 c. red .. .. 1·40 6·00
8. **74.** 1 l. blue .. .. 1·40 6·00
9. 2 l. brown .. .. 1·40 6·00
10. **75.** 5 l. black and blue .. 1·40 7·50

1924. Manzoni.
11 **77** 10 c. black and purple .. 60 12·00
12 – 15 c. black and green .. 60 12·00
13 – 30 c. black .. .. 60 12·00
14 – 50 c. black and brown .. 60 12·00
15 – 1 l. black and blue .. 15·00 90·00
16 – 5 l. black and purple .. £200 £950

1925. Holy Year.
17 – 20 c. + 10 c. brown & grn 75 4·25
18 **81** 30 c. + 15 c. brown & choc 75 4·25
19 – 50 c. + 25 c. brown & vio 75 4·25
20 – 60 c. + 30 c. brown & red 75 4·25
21 – 1 l. + 50 c. purple & blue 75 4·25
22 – 5 l. + 2 l. 50 purple & red 75 4·25

1925. Royal Jubilee.
23. **82.** 60 c. red .. .. 15 2·75
24. 1 l. blue .. .. 20 2·75
24c. 1 l. 25 blue .. .. 45 9·00

1926. St. Francis of Assisi.
25 **83** 20 c. green .. .. 70 4·25
26 – 40 c. violet .. .. 70 4·25
27 – 60 c. red .. .. 70 4·25
28 – 1 l. 25 blue .. .. 70 4·25
29 – 5 l. + 2 l. 50 olive .. 1·50 5·50

1926. As Colonial Propaganda stamps of Somalia, T **21**, but inscr. "TRIPOLITANIA".
30. 5 c. + 5 c. brown .. .. 20 2·25
31. 10 c. + 5 c. olive .. .. 20 2·25
32. 20 c. + 5 c. green .. .. 20 2·25
33. 40 c. + 5 c. red .. .. 20 2·25
34. 60 c. + 5 c. orange .. .. 20 2·25
35. 1 l. + 5 c. blue .. .. 20 2·25

6. Port of Tripoli.

9. Palm Tree.

1927. First Tripoli Trade Fair.
36. **6.** 20 c. + 05 c. black & pur. 1·50 2·50
37. 25 c. + 05 c. black & green 1·50 2·50
38. – 40 c. + 10 c. black & brn. 1·50 2·50
39. – 60 c. + 10 c. black & brown 1·50 2·50
40. – 75 c. + 20 c. black and red 1·50 2·50
41. – 1 l. 25 + 20 c. black & blue 5·50 8·50
DESIGNS: 40 c., 60 c. Arch of Marcus Aurelius, 75 c., 1 l. 25, View of Tripoli.

1927. 1st National Defence issue.
42. **88.** 40 + 20 c. black & brown 80 4·25
43. 60 + 30 c. brown and red 80 4·25
44. 1 l. 25 + 60 c. blk. & blue 80 4·25
45. 5 l. + 2 l. 50 blk. & green 1·25 6·50

1927. Death Centenary of Volta.
46. **91.** 20 c. violet .. .. 3·00 10·00
47. 50 c. orange .. .. 3·00 7·00
48. 1 l. 25 blue .. .. 4·00 10·00

1928. 2nd Tripoli Trade Fair.
49 – 30 c. + 20 c. brown & pur 1·40 4·25
50 **9** 50 c. + 20 c. brown & green 1·40 4·25
51 – 1 l. 25 + 20 c. brown & red 1·40 4·25
52 – 1 l. 75 + 20 c. brown & blue 1·40 4·25
53 – 2 l. 55 + 50 c. sepia & brn 2·00 6·00
54 – 5 l. + 1 l. brown and violet 2·75 9·00
DESIGNS—VERT. As T **9**: 30 c. Tripoli. 1 l. 25, Camel riders. 38 × 22½ mm: 1 l. 75, Arab citadel. 2 l. 55, Tripoli. 5 l. Desert outpost.

1928. 45th Anniv. of Italian-African Society. As T **25** of Somalia.
55. 20 c. + 5 c. green .. .. 60 3·50
56. 30 c. + 5 c. red .. .. 60 3·50
57. 50 c. + 10 c. violet .. .. 60 3·50
58. 1 l. 25 + 20 c. blue .. .. 60 3·50

1929. 2nd National Defence issue.
59 **89** 30 c. + 10 c. black and red 1·00 4·75
60 – 50 c. + 20 c. black & lilac 1·00 4·75
61 – 1 l. 25 + 50 c. blue & brn 1·40 6·00
62 – 5 l. + 2 l. black and olive 1·40 6·00

1929. 3rd Tripoli Trade Fair. Inscr "1929".
63. 30 c. + 20 c. black & red .. 4·50 12·00
64. 50 c. + 20 c. black and green 4·50 12·00
65. 1 l. 25 + 20 c. black and red 4·50 12·00
66. 1 l. 75 + 20 c. black and blue 4·50 12·00
67. 2 l. 55 + 50 c. black & brown 4·50 12·00
68. 5 l. + 1 l. black and violet 80·00 £170
DESIGNS—VERT As T **9**: 30 c., 1 l. 25, Different trees. 50 c. Dorcas gazelle. 38 × 22½ mm: 1 l. 75, Goats. 2 l. 55, Camel caravan. 5 l. Trees.

1929. Abbey of Montecassino.
69 **104** 20 c. green .. .. 1·75 4·25
70 – 25 c. orange .. .. 1·75 4·25
71 – 50 c. + 10 c. red .. 1·75 8·50
72 – 75 c. + 15 c. brown .. 1·75 8·50
73 **104** 1 l. 25 + 25 c. purple .. 3·25 8·50
74 – 5 l. + 1 l. blue .. .. 3·25 8·50
75 – 10 l. + 2 l. brown .. 3·25 10·00

1930. 4th Tripoli Trade Fair. Inscr "1930".
76. 30 c. brown .. .. 1·10 4·75
77. 50 c. violet .. .. 1·10 4·75
78. 1 l. 25 c. blue .. .. 1·10 4·75
79. 1 l. 75 c. + 20 c. red .. 1·10 7·00
80. 2 l. 55 c. + 45 c. green .. 7·00 12·00
81. 5 l. + 1 l. orange .. .. 7·00 15·00
82. 10 l. + 2 l. purple .. .. 7·00 17·00
DESIGNS—As T **9**: 30 c. Gathering bananas. 50 c. Tobacco plant. 1 l. 25, Venus of Cyrene. 38 × 22½ mm: 1 l. 75 Water-carriers. 2 l. 55, Blackbucks. 5 l. Motor and camel transport. 10 l. Rome pavilion.

1930. Marriage of Prince Humbolt and Princess Marie Jose.
83. **109.** 20 c. green .. .. 45 1·90
84. 50 c. + 10 c. orange .. 45 2·50
85. 1 l. 25 + 25 c. red .. 45 2·75

1930. Ferrucci.
86. **114.** 20 c. violet (postage) .. 50 1·60
87. – 25 c. green (No. 283) .. 50 1·60
88. – 50 c. black (as No. 284) 50 1·60
89. – 1 l. 25 blue (No. 285) .. 50 1·60
90. – 5 l. + 2 l. red (as No. 286) 1·75 2·75
91. **117.** 50 c. purple (air) .. 80 2·25
92. 1 l. blue .. .. 80 2·25
93. 5 l. + 2 l. red .. .. 4·50 10·00

1930. 3rd National Defence issue.
94 **89** 30 c. + 10 c. green & olive 4·00 15·00
95 – 50 c. + 10 c. violet & olive 4·00 15·00
96 – 1 l. 25 + 30 c. brown .. 4·00 15·00
97 – 5 l. + 1 l. 50 green & blue 12·00 42·00

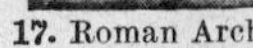
17. Roman Arch.

18. Columns of Leptis.

19.

1930. 25th Anniv. (1929) of Italian Colonial Agricultural Institute.
98. **17.** 50 c. + 20 c. brown .. 75 5·00
99. 1 l. 25 + 20 c. blue .. 75 5·00
100. 1 l. 75 + 20 c. green .. 75 5·00
101. 2 l. 55 + 50 c. violet .. 1·50 5·00
102. 5 l. + 1 l. red .. .. 1·50 5·00

1930. Virgil.
103 – 15 c. grey (postage) .. 25 1·40
104 – 20 c. brown .. .. 25 1·40
105 – 25 c. green .. .. 25 1·10
106 – 30 c. brown .. .. 25 1·40
107 – 50 c. purple .. .. 25 1·10
108 – 75 c. red .. .. 25 1·40
109 – 1 l. 25 blue .. .. 25 1·40
110 – 5 l. + 1 l. 50 purple .. 1·75 7·00
111 – 10 l. + 2 l. 50 brown .. 1·75 7·00
112 **119** 50 c. green (air) .. 70 2·25
113 1 l. red .. .. 70 2·25
114 7 l. 70 + 1 l. 30 brown .. 2·25 10·00
115 9 l. + 2 l. blue .. 2·25 10·00

1931. Air.
116. **18.** 50 c. red 20 10
117. 60 c. orange .. .. 1·60 6·00
117a. 75 c. blue .. .. 1·60 6·00
118. 80 c. purple .. .. 3·00 6·50
119. **19.** 1 l. blue 45 10
120. 1 l. 20 brown .. .. 6·50 10·00
121. 1 l. 50 orange .. .. 3·00 6·00
122. 5 l. green .. .. 7·00 7·00

20. Statue of Youth.

22.

1931. 5th Tripoli Trade Fair.
123 **20** 10 c. black (postage) .. 1·75 5·00
124 – 25 c. green .. .. 1·75 5·00
125 – 50 c. violet .. .. 1·75 5·00
126 – 1 l. 25 blue .. .. 1·75 5·00
127 – 1 l. 75 + 25 c. red .. 2·00 7·00
128 – 2 l. 75 + 45 c. orange .. 2·00 10·00
129 – 5 l. + 1 l. purple .. 7·00 17·00
130 – 10 l. + 2 l. brown .. 24·00 45·00
131 – 50 c. blue (air) .. .. 1·10 5·00
DESIGNS—As Type **20.** 25 c. Arab musician. 50 c. View of Zeughet. 1 l. 25, Snake charmer. 1 l. 75, House and windmill. 2 l. 75, Libyan "Zaptie". 5 l. Arab horseman. As Type **E 21.** 10 l. Exhibition Pavilion. 50 c. Air, Aeroplane over desert.

1931. St. Anthony of Padua.
132. **121.** 20 c. brown .. .. 55 2·50
133. – 25 c. green .. .. 55 2·50
134. – 30 c. brown .. .. 55 2·50
135. – 50 c. purple .. .. 55 1·40
136. – 75 c. grey .. .. 55 2·50
137. – 1 l. 25 blue .. .. 55 2·50
138. – 5 l. + 2 l. 50 brown .. 2·00 11·00

1931. Air. 25th Anniv. (1929) of Italian Colonial Agricultural Institute.
139. **22.** 50 c. blue .. .. 1·10 6·00
140. 80 c. violet .. .. 1·10 6·00
141. 1 l. black .. .. 1·10 6·00
142. 2 l. green .. .. 2·25 7·00
143. 5 l. + 2 l. red .. .. 3·50 15·00

23. Paw-paw Tree.

24. Arch of Marcus Aurelius.

1932. 6th Tripoli Trade Fair. Inscr. "1932".
144. **23.** 10 c. brown (postage) .. 2·75 6·00
145. – 20 c. red .. .. 2·75 6·00
146. – 25 c. green .. .. 2·75 6·00
147. – 30 c. black .. .. 2·75 6·00
148. – 50 c. violet .. .. 2·75 6·00
149. – 75 c. red .. .. 3·50 10·00
150. – 1 l. 25 c. blue .. .. 3·50 10·00
151. – 1. 75 c.+25 c. brown .. 15·00 32·00
152. – 5 l.+1 l. blue .. .. 16·00 45·00
153. – 10 l.+2 l. purple .. 42·00 90·00

154. – 50 c. blue (air) .. .. 4·50 12·00
155. – 1 l. brown .. .. 4·50 12·00
156. – 2 l.+1 l. black .. .. 14·00 45·00
157. – 5 l.+2 l. red .. .. 42·00 90·00
DESIGNS. POST.—VERT. 10 c. to 50 c. Various trees. 75 c. Roman mausoleum at Ghirza. 10 l. Dorcas gazelle. HORIZ. 1 l. 25 c. Mogadiscio aerodrome. 1 l. 75, Lioness. 5 l. Arab and camel. AIR—HORIZ. 50 c., 1 l. Seaplane over Bedouin camp. 2 l., 5 l. Seaplane over Tripoli.

1933. 7th Tripoli Trade Fair. Inscr. "1933"
158. – 10 c. purple (postage) .. 17·00 15·00
159. – 25 c. green .. .. 9·00 11·00
160. – 30 c. brown .. .. 9·00 15·00
161. **24.** 50 c. violet .. .. 9·00 9·00
162. – 1 l. 25 c. blue .. .. 19·00 38·00
163. – 5 l.+1 l. brown .. 29·00 85·00
164. – 10 l.+2 l. 50 c. red .. 29·00 85·00

165. – 50 c. green (air) .. .. 4·50 12·00
166. – 75 c. red .. .. 4·50 12·00
167. – 1 l. blue .. .. 4·50 12·00
168. – 2 l.+50 c. violet .. 9·00 24·00
169. – 5 l.+1 l. brown .. 12·00 32·00
170. – 10 l.+2 l. 50 black .. 12·00 32·00
DESIGNS. POST.—VERT. 10 c. Ostrich. 25 c. Incense plant. 1 l. 25 c. Golden eagle. 10 l. Tripoli and Fascist emblem. HORIZ. 30 c. Arab drummer. 5 l. Leopard. AIR—HORIZ. 50 c., 2 l. Seaplane over Tripoli. 75 c., 10 l. Aeroplane over Tagiura. 1 l., 5 l. Seaplane leaving Tripoli.

25. Mercury.

DESIGNS: 5 l., 15 l. Arch of Marcus Aurelius. 10 l., 20 l. "Dawn".

1933. "Graf Zeppelin" Air stamps. Inscr. "CROCIERA ZEPPELIN 1933".
171. **25.** 3 l. brown .. .. 4·00 35·00
172. – 5 l. violet .. .. 4·00 35·00
173. – 10 l. green .. .. 4·00 55·00
174. – 12 l. blue .. .. 4·00 85·00
175. – 15 l. red .. .. 4·00 70·00
176. – 20 l. black .. .. 4·00 95·00

26. "Flight".

1933. Air. Balbo Transatlantic Flight.
177. **26.** 19 l. 75 brown and black 9·50 £225
178. 44 l. 75 green and blue 9·50 £225

1934. Air. Rome-Buenos Aires Flight. Optd. with an aeroplane and **1934 XII PRIMO VOLO DIRETTO ROMA-BUENOS-AYRES**, etc., or surch. also in Italian and Arabic.
179. **19.** 2 l. on 5 l. brown .. 1·50 27·00
180. 3 l. on 5 l. green .. 1·50 27·00
181. 5 l. bistre .. .. 1·50 27·00
182. 10 l. on 5 l. red .. .. 1·50 27·00

27. Water Carriers.

1934. 8th Tripoli Trade Fair.
183. **27.** 10 c. brown (postage) .. 2·00 5·00
184. – 20 c. red .. .. 2·00 5·00
185. – 25 c. green .. .. 2·00 5·00
186. – 30 c. brown .. .. 2·00 5·00
187. – 50 c. violet .. .. 2·00 5·00
188. – 75 c. red .. .. 2·00 5·00
189. – 1 l. 25 blue .. .. 24·00 38·00
DESIGNS—VERT. 20 c. Arab. 25 c. Minaret. 50 c. Statue of Emperor Claudius. HORIZ. 30 c. 1 l. 25 Moslem Shrine. 75 c. Ruins of Ghadames.

190. 50 c. blue (air) .. .. 4·50 12·00
191. 75 c. orange .. .. 4·50 12·00
192. 5 l.+1 l. green .. .. 38·00 95·00
193. 10 l.+2 l. purple .. .. 38·00 95·00
194. 25 l.+3 l. brown .. .. 42·00 95·00
DESIGNS—HORIZ. 50 c., 5 l. Flying boat off Tripoli. 75 c., 10 l. Aeroplane over Mosque. VERT. 25 l. Aeroplane and Camel.
See also Nos. E 195/6.

1934. Air. Oasis Flight. As Nos. 190/4 optd. **CIRCUITO DELLE OASI TRIPOLI MAGGIO 1934—XII.**
197. 50 c. red .. .. .. 4·50 10·00
198. 75 c. yellow .. .. 4·50 10·00
199. 5 l.+1 l. brown .. .. 4·50 10·00
200. 10 l.+2 l. blue £140 £200
201. 25 l.+3 l. violet £140 £200
See also Nos. E 202/3.

29. Native Village.

DESIGNS: 25 c. to 75 c. Shadow of aeroplane over desert. 80 c. to 2 l. Arab camel corps and aeroplane.

1934. 2nd Int. Colonial Exn., Naples.
204. **29.** 5 c. brn. & green (post.) 1·25 5·50
205. 10 c. black and brown .. 1·25 5·50
206. 20 c. slate and red .. 1·25 5·50
207. 50 c. brown and violet .. 1·25 5·50
208. 60 c. slate and brown .. 1·25 5·50
209. 1 l. 25 green and blue .. 1·25 5·50

210. – 25 c. orange & blue (air) 1·25 5·50
211. – 50 c. slate and green .. 1·25 5·50
212. – 75 c. red and brown .. 1·25 5·50
213. – 80 c. green and brown .. 1·25 5·50
214. – 1 l. green and red .. 1·25 5·50
215. – 2 l. brown and blue .. 1·25 5·50

30.

1934. Air. Rome-Mogadiscio Flight.
216. **30.** 25 c.+10 c. green .. 1·75 5·00
217. 50 c.+10 c. brown .. 1·75 5·00
218. 75 c.+15 c. red .. 1·75 5·00
219. 80 c.+15 c. black .. 1·75 5·00
220. 1 l.+20 c. brown .. 1·75 5·00
221. 2 l.+20 c. blue .. 1·75 5·00
222. 3 l.+25 c. violet .. 14·00 40·00
223. 5 l.+25 c. orange .. 14·00 40·00
224. 10 l.+30 c. purple .. 14·00 40·00
225. 25 l.+2 l. green .. 14·00 40·00

32. Camel Transport.

1935. 9th Tripoli Exn.
226. – 10 c.+10 c. brown (post) 50 2·50
227. – 20 c.+10 c. red .. .. 50 2·50
228. – 50 c.+10 c. violet .. 50 2·50
229. – 75 c.+15 c. red .. .. 50 2·50
230. – 1 l. 25+25 c. blue .. 50 2·50
231. – 2 l.+50 c. green .. 50 2·50

232. – 25 c.+10 c. green (air) .. 70 3·00
233. **32.** 50 c.+10 c. slate .. 70 3·00
234. – 1 l.+25 c. blue .. 70 3·00
235. – 2 l.+30 c. red .. .. 70 3·00
236. – 3 l.+1 l. 50 brown .. 70 3·00
237. – 10 l.+5 l. purple .. 6·00 15·00
DESIGNS—VERT.—POSTAGE: 10 c., 20 c. Pomegranate tree. 50 c., 2 l. Arab flautist. 75 c., 1 l. 25, Arab in burnous. AIR: 25 c., 3 l. Watch-tower. HORIZ. 1 l., 10 l. Arab girl and aeroplane.
For issue inscr. "XII FIERA CAMPIONARIA TRIPOLI" and dated "1938", see Libya Nos. 88/95.

CONCESSIONAL LETTER POST

1931. Optd **TRIPOLITANIA.**
CL23 CL **109** 10 c. brown .. 3·50 4·50

EXPRESS LETTER STAMPS

Express stamps optd. **TRIPOLI DI BARBERIA** formerly listed here will be found under Italian P.O.s in the Levant. Nos. E 6/7.

1927. 1st Tripoli Exn. Inscr. "EXPRES"
E 42. 1 l. 25+30 c. blk. & vio. 5·00 7·00
E 43. 2 l. 50+1 l. blk. & orge. 5·00 7·00
DESIGN—HORIZ. As T 6. 1 l. 25, 2 l. 50, Camels and palm trees.

E 21. War Memorial.

1931. 5th Tripoli Exn. Inscr. "EXPRESSO".
E 132. E **21.** 1 l. 25+20 c. red .. 3·50 10·00

1934. Air. 8th Tripoli Trade Fair.
E 195. 2 l. 25 green .. .. 14·00 38·00
E 196. 4 l. 50+1 l. blue .. 14·00 38·00
DESIGN—As T **27.** Nos. E 195/6, Aeroplane over Bedouins.

1934. Air. Oasis Flight. As Nos. E 195/6 optd. **CIRCUITO DELLE OASI TRIPOLI MAGGIO 1934. XII.**
E 202. 2 l. 25 red .. .. 4·50 10·00
E 203. 4 l. 50+1 l. red .. 4·50 10·00

OFFICIAL STAMPS

1934. No. 225 (colour changed) optd **SERVIZIO DI STATO** amd Crown.
O226 **30** 25 l.+2 l. red £1300 £2750

From 1943 to 1951 Tripolitania was under British administration; stamps issued during this period are listed in Volume 3. From 1952 it was part of independent Libya.

TUNISIA Pt. 6; Pt. 14

Formerly a French Protectorate in N. Africa, Tunisia became an independent kingdom in 1956 and a republic in 1957.

1888. 100 centimes=1 franc.
1959. 1000 milliemes=1 dinar.

1.

2.

1888. Arms on plain background.
1 **1** 1 c. black on blue .. 1·75 1·10
2 2 c. brown on buff .. 1·40 1·10
3 5 c. green on green .. 12·50 7·00
4 15 c. blue on blue .. 32·00 9·00
5 25 c. black on pink .. 65·00 35·00
6 40 c. red on yellow .. 60·00 55·00
7 75 c. pink on pink .. 60·00 42·00
8 5 f. mauve on lilac .. £300 £200

1888. Arms on shaded background.
9 **2** 1 c. black on blue .. 50 20
10 2 c. brown on buff .. 60 30
22 5 c. green .. .. 4·00 25
12 10 c. black on lilac .. 5·00 30
23 10 c. red .. .. 3·25 25
13 15 c. blue .. .. 35·00 25
24 15 c. grey .. .. 3·25 25
15 20 c. red on green .. 5·50 25
16 25 c. black on pink .. 14·50 45
25 25 c. blue .. .. 8·00 40
26 35 c. brown .. .. 32·00 80
17 40 c. red on yellow .. 9·00 45
18 75 c. pink on pink .. £100 55·00
19 75 c. violet on yellow .. 14·50 2·75
20 1 f. green .. .. 19·00 3·00
27 2 f. lilac .. .. £120 95·00
21 5 f. mauve on lilac .. £120 55·00

1902. Surch. **25** and bars.
28. **2.** 25 on 15 c. blue .. .. 3·00 1·40

4. Mosque at Kairouan.

6. Ruins of Hadrian's Aqueduct.

5. Agriculture.

7. Carthaginian Galley.

1906.
30 **4** 1 c. black on yellow .. 10 10
31 2 c. brown 10 10
32 3 c. red 10 30
33 5 c. green on green .. 10 10
34 **5** 10 c. red 10 10
35 15 c. violet 40 15
36 20 c. brown 15 10
37 25 c. blue 65 10
38 **6** 35 c. brown and green .. 5·75 50
39 40 c. red and brown .. 3·00 25
40 75 c. red and purple .. 55 25
41 **7** 1 f. brown and red .. 65 35
42 2 f. green and brown .. 2·75 80
43 5 f. blue and violet .. 6·75 3·00
See also Nos. 72/8, 105 and 107/13.

1908. Surch.
44 **2** 10 on 15 c. grey 50 50
45 35 on 1 f. green .. .. 60 1·60
46 40 on 2 f. lilac .. .. 2·75 4·75
47 75 on 5 f. mauve on lilac 2·00 3·00

1911. Surch. in figures and bar.
48. **5.** 10 on 15 c. violet .. .. 1·25 20
60. 15 c. on 10 c. red 30 10
79. 20 c. on 15 c. violet .. 60 15

1915. Red Cross Fund. Optd. with red cross.
49. **5.** 15 c. violet 50 60

1916. Red Cross Fund. Optd with red cross and bars.
50 **4** 5 c. green on green .. 50 85

1916. Prisoners-of-War Fund. Surch. with red cross and **10 c.**
51. **5.** 10 c. on 15 c. brn. on blue 30 60
52. 10 c. on 20 c. brn. on yell. 30 60
53. 10 c. on 25 c. blue on green 1·25 2·25
54. **6.** 10 c. on 35 c. violet & grn. 2·25 4·00
55. 10 c. on 40 c. black & brn. 1·25 2·25
56. 10 c. on 75 c. grn. & red .. 2·75 5·00
57. **7.** 10 c. on 1 f. green and red 2·50 2·50
58. 10 c. on 2 f. blue & brown 60·00 60·00
59. 10 c. on 5 f. red and violet 70·00 65·00

1918. Prisoners-of-war Fund. Surch **15c** and red cross.
61. **5.** 15 c. on 20 c. blk. on grn. 40 95
62. 15 c. on 25 c. blue .. 50 95
63. **6.** 15 c. on 35 c. red & olive 1·00 1·50
64. 15 c. on 40 c. blue & brown 2·00 2·50
65. 15 c. on 75 c. blk. & red .. 3·50 4·50
66. **7.** 15 c. on 1 f. violet & red .. 11·50 13·50
67. 15 c. on 2 f. red & brown .. 45·00 50·00
68. 15 c. on 5 f. black & violet £100 £100

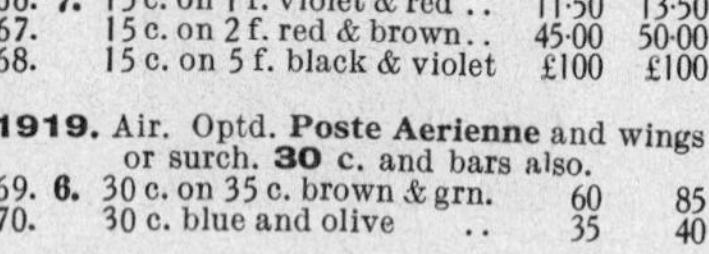

1919. Air. Optd. **Poste Aerienne** and wings or surch. **30 c.** and bars also.
69. **6.** 30 c. on 35 c. brown & grn. 60 85
70. 30 c. blue and olive .. 35 40

1920. New values and colours changed.
72 **4** 5 c. orange 10 20
73 **5** 10 c. green 25 30
74 25 c. violet 25 10
75 **6** 30 c. violet and purple .. 70 30
76 **5** 30 c. red 35 40
77 50 c. blue 30 25
78 **6** 60 c. violet and green .. 30 25

18. Ruin at Dougga.

1922.
80 **18** 10 c. green 10 20
81 30 c. red 60 90
82 50 c. blue 25 40
See also Nos. 104 and 106.

1923. War Wounded Fund. Surch **AFFt**, medal and new value.
83. **4.** 0 c. on 1 c. blue 30 45
84. 0 c. on 2 c. brown .. 30 45
85. 1 c. on 3 c. green .. 30 45
86. 2 c. on 5 c. mauve .. 30 45
87. **18.** 3 c. on 10 c. mve. on blue 30 45
88. **5.** 5 c. on 15 c. green .. 30 45
89. 5 c. on 20 c. blue on red 1·00 1·50
90. 5c. on 25 c. mauve on blue 1·00 1·50
91. **18.** 5 c. on 30 c. orange .. 1·00 1·50
92. **6.** 5 c. on 35 c. mve. & blue 1·00 1·50
93. 5 c. on 40 c. brn. & blue 1·10 1·50
94. **18.** 10 c. on 50 c. blk. on blue 1·25 1·60
95. **6.** 10 c. on 60 c. blue & brn. 1·25 1·40
96. 10 c. on 75 c. grn. & mve. 2·00 2·75
97. **7.** 25 c. on 1 f. mve. & lake 2·25 2·75
98. 25 c. on 2 f. red and blue 9·00 10·50
99. 25 c. on 5 f. brown & green 32·00 45·00

1923. Surch.
100 **4** 10 on 5 c. green on green 30 25
101 **5** 20 on 15 c. violet .. 60 55
102 30 on 20 c. brown .. 15 25
103 50 on 25 c. blue 60 10

1923. New values and colours.
104 **18** 10 c. pink 15 25
105 **5** 15 c. brown on orange .. 10 20
106 **18** 30 c. mauve 10 20
107 **5** 40 c. black on pink .. 40 45
108 40 c. green 10 15
109 **6** 60 c. carmine and red .. 30 30
110 75 c. scarlet and red .. 20 25
111 **7** 1 f. light blue and blue 25 25
112 2 f. red & green on pink 35 45
113 5 f. green and lilac .. 55 75

1925. Parcel Post stamps surch. **PROTECTION DE L'ENFANCE POSTES** and value in figures.
114. **P 8.** 1 c. on 5 c. red and brown on rose .. 10 40
115. 2 c. on 10 c. blue and brown on yellow .. 10 40
116. 3 c. on 20 c. red and purple on mauve .. 25 55
117. 5 c. on 25 c. red and green on green .. 50 70
118. 5 c. on 40 c. green and red on yellow .. 50 70
119. 10 c. on 50 c. green and violet on mauve .. 1·00 1·50
120. 10 c. on 75 c. brown and green on green .. 90 1·25
121. 25 c. on 1 f. green and blue on blue .. 90 1·40
122. 25 c. on 2 f. purple and red on rose .. 2·00 3·75
123. 25 c. on 5 f. brown and red on green .. 17·00 28·00

21. Arab Woman. 22. Grand Mosque, Tunis. 23. Mosque, Place Halfaouine, Tunis.

24. Amphitheatre El Djem.

1926.

124 21 1 c. red 10 15
125 2 c. green 10 15
126 3 c. blue 10 20
127 5 c. green 10 10
128 10 c. mauve 10 15
129 22 15 c. lilac 20 15
130 20 c. red 10 10
131 25 c. green 10 20
131a 25 c. mauve 15 15
132 30 c. mauve 15 15
133 30 c. green 15 20
134 40 c. brown 15 15
134a 45 c. green 50 60
135 23 50 c. black 10 10
135a 50 c. blue 45 10
135b 50 c. green 15 20
135c 60 c. red 15 30
135d 65 c. blue 35 20
135e 70 c. red 15 30
136 75 c. red 30 25
136a 75 c. mauve 30 10
137 80 c. blue 30 30
137a 80 c. brown 45 65
138 90 c. red 15 10
138a 90 c. blue .. .. 6·00 6·00
139 1 f. purple 25 10
139a 1 f. red 10 10
140 24 1 f. 05 pink and blue .. 25 25
141 1 f. 25 blue & light blue 50 65
141a 1 f. 25 red 55 65
141b 1 f. 30 violet and blue 55 65
141c 1 f. 40 purple 55 60
142 1 f. 50 blue & light blue 40 15
142a 1 f. 50 orange and red 50 65
143 2 f. brown and red .. 40 20
143a 2 f. red 50 15
143b 2 f. 25 blue 65 80
143c 2 f. 50 green 50 55
144 3 f. orange and blue .. 60 20
144a 3 f. violet 15 15
145 5 f. green & red on grn 75 45
145a 5 f. brown .. .. 1·00 1·40
146 10 f. grey & red on blue 3·25 1·50
146a 10 f. pink 65 75
146b 20 f. red & mve on pink 1·00 90

For similar designs see Nos. 172/91, 220/31 and 257/286.

1927. Surch **1f 50**.

147 24 1 f. 50 on 1 f. 25 blue and ultramarine 30 20

1927. Air. Optd **Poste Aerienne** and air-plane or surch in figures and bars also.

148 7 1 f. light blue and blue 40 50
152 24 1 f. 30 mauve & orange 1·50 1·90
169 1 f. 50 on 1 f. 30 mauve and orange .. .. 1·25 75
170 1 f. 50 on 1 f. 80 red and green .. .. 1·75 75
171 1 f. 50 on 2 f. 55 brown and mauve .. 4·00 1·50
149 6 1 f. 75 on 75 c. scarlet and red 40 70
150 7 1 f. 75 on 5 f. green and lilac .. .. 1·50 1·90
153 24 1 f. 80 red and green .. 2·00 2·00
151 7 2 f. red & green on pink 1·60 1·50
154 24 2 f. 55 brown and mauve 1·00 1·00

26. First Tunis–Chad Motor Service.

1928. Child Welfare.

155. 26. 40 c.+40 c. brown .. 60 80
156. 50 c.+50 c. purple .. 50 75
157. 75 c.+75 c. blue .. 50 80
158. 1 f.+1 f. red 50 85
159. 1 f. 50+1 f. 50 blue .. 50 80
160. 2 f.+2 f. green .. 60 1·10
161. 5 f.+5 f. brown .. 60 1·10

1928. Surch.

162 4 3 c. on 5 c. orange .. 10 30
163 5 10 c. on 15 c. brn on orge 15 20
164 18 25 c. on 30 c. mauve .. 15 20
165 23 40 c. on 80 c. blue .. 15 30
166 22 50 c. on 40 c. brown .. 3·00 25
167 23 50 c. on 75 c. red .. 25 40

1929. Precancelled **AFFRANCHts POSTES** and surch **10**.

168 22 10 on 30 c. mauve .. 60 90

28. 29. 30.

31.

1931.

172. 28. 1 c. blue 10 25
173. 2 c. brown 10 30
174. 3 c. black 15 40
175. 5 c. green 10 25
176. 10 c. red 10 30
177. 29. 15 c. purple 35 30
178. 20 c. brown 10 15
179. 25 c. red 10 15
180. 30 c. green 20 25
181. 40 c. orange 10 15
182. 30. 50 c. blue 20 10
183. 75 c. yellow 85 85
184. 90 c. red 30 45
185. 1 f. olive 20 20
186. 31. 1 f. 50 blue 30 25
187. 2 f. brown 40 30
188. 3 f. green .. .. 6·50 6·00
189. 5 f. red .. .. .. 15·00 13·50
190. 10 f. black .. .. 25·00 22·00
191. 20 f. brown .. .. 38·00 32·00

1937. Surch.

191a 23 25 c. on 65 c. blue .. 10 10
192 0.65 on 50 c. blue .. 25 10
193 65 on 50 c. blue .. 45 10
193b 1 FR. on 90 c. blue .. 45 15
193c 24 1 F. on 1 f. 25 red .. 20 30
193d 1 F. on 1 f.40 purple .. 20 30
193e 1 F. on 2 f. 25 blue .. 20 30
194 1 f. 75 on 1 f. 50 blue and light blue .. 2·00 1·00

1938. 50th Anniv. of Tunisian Postal Service. Surch. **1888 1938** and value.

196. 28. 1 c.+1 c. blue .. 80 1·25
197. 2 c.+2 c. brown .. 80 1·25
198. 3 c.+3 c. black .. 80 1·25
199. 5 c.+5 c. green .. 80 1·25
200. 10 c.+10 c. red .. 80 1·25
201. 29. 15 c.+15 c. purple .. 80 1·25
202. 20 c.+20 c. brown .. 80 1·25
203. 25 c.+25 c. red .. 80 1·25
204. 30 c.+30 c. green .. 80 1·25
205. 40 c.+40 c. orange .. 80 1·25
206. 30. 50 c.+50 c. blue .. 80 1·25
207. 75 c.+75 c. yellow .. 80 1·25
208. 90 c.+90 c. red .. 80 1·25
209. 1 f.+1 f. olive .. 80 1·25
210. 31. 1 f. 50+1 f. blue .. 80 1·25
211. 2 f.+1 f. 50 brown .. 1·50 2·00
212. 3 f.+2 f. green .. 1·50 2·25
213. 5 f.+3 f. red .. .. 7·00 11·50
214. 10 f.+5 f. black .. 17·00 28·00
215. 20 f.+10 f. brown .. 45·00 45·00

1941. National Relief. Surch. **SECOURS NATIONAL 1941** and value.

216. 22. 1 f. on 45 c. green .. 2·00 2·00
217. 24. 1 f. 30 on 1 f. 25 red .. 2·00 2·00
218. 1 f. 50 on 1 f. 40 purple 2·00 2·00
219. 2 f. on 2 f. 25 blue .. 2·00 2·00

1941. As stamps of 1926 but without monogram "RF".

220 22 30 c. red 55 65
221 23 1 f. 20 grey 15 30
222 1 f. 50 brown 25 20
223 24 2 f. 40 pink and red .. 30 45
224 2 f. 50 light blue & blue 30 40
225 3 f. violet 45 55
226 4 f. blue and black .. 25 25
227 4 f. 50 brown and green 30 45
228 5 f. black 30 25
229 10 f. violet and purple 30 25
230 15 f. red .. .. 2·50 2·25
231 20 f. red and lilac .. 1·40 85

41a. "Victory". 42. Allied Soldiers.

1943.

232. 41a. 1 f. 50 red 15 30

1943. Charity. Tunisian Liberation.

233. 42. 1 f. 50+8 f. 50 red .. 25 30

MORE DETAILED LISTS
are given in the Stanley Gibbons Catalogues referred to in the country headings.
For lists of current volumes see Introduction.

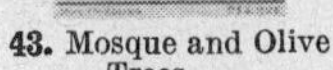

43. Mosque and Olive Trees. 44. Sidi Mahrez Mosque.

45. Ramparts of Sfax.

1944.

234. 43. 30 c. yellow 25 25
235. 40 c. brown 25 30
236. 60 c. orange 25 35
237. 70 c. red 25 35
238. 80 c. green 35 40
239. 90 c. violet 25 30
240. 1 f. red 25 30
241. 1 f. 50 blue 20 30
242. 2 f. 40 red 35 45
243. 2 f. 50 brown 25 35
244. 3 f. violet 25 25
245. 4 f. blue 30 25
246. 4 f. 50 green 40 35
247. 5 f. grey 35 25
248. 6 f. brown 40 25
249. 10 f. lake 45 35
250. 15 f. brown 50 40
251. 20 f. lilac 45 45

Nos. 234/41 are smaller (15½ × 19 mm.).

1944. Forces Welfare Fund. Surch **+48 frcs pour nos Combattants**.

252 43 2 f.+48 f. red (21¼ × 26½ mm) .. 60 80

1945. Forces Welfare Fund. Surch. **POUR NOS COMBATTANTS** and value.

253. 44. 1 f. 50+8 f. 50 brown 50 75
254. 45. 3 f.+12 f. green .. 60 80
255. – 4 f.+21 f. brown .. 50 75
256. – 10 f.+40 f. red .. 50 75

DESIGNS—HORIZ. 4 f. Camel patrol at Fort Saint. 10 f. Mosque at Sidi-bou-Said.

1945. New values and colours.

257. 23. 10 c. brown 10 25
258. 30 c. olive 10 25
259. 40 c. red 15 25
260. 50 c. turquoise 10 15
261. 60 c. blue 15 15
262. 80 c. green 15 15
263. 1 f. 20 brown 15 30
264. 1 f. 50 lilac 10 15
265. 2 f. green 10 15
267. 24. 2 f. 40 red 30 50
268. 23. 2 f. 50 brown 25 20
269. 24. 3 f. brown 10 10
270. 23. 3 f. red 15 15
271. 24. 4 f. blue 40 50
272. 23. 4 f. violet 40 25
273. 24. 4 f. violet 50 45
273a. 23. 4 f. orange 25 30
274. 4 f. 50 blue 25 20
275. 24. 5 f. green 20 20
275a. 23. 5 f. blue 35 40
275b. 5 f. green 30 10
276. 24. 6 f. blue 25 25
277. 6 f. red 50 50
278. 23. 6 f. red 15 15
279. 24. 10 f. orange 20 40
280. 10 f. blue 25 20
281. 15 f. mauve 20 20
281a. 23. 15 f. red 35 30
282. 24. 20 f. green 20 20
283. 25 f. violet 40 45
284. 25 f. orange 40 60
285. 50 f. red 50 50
286. 100 f. red 75 65

1945. Anti-Tuberculosis Fund. Type of France optd. **TUNISIE.**

287. 222. 2 f.+1 f. orange .. 30 35

1945. Postal Employees' War Victims' Fund. Type of France optd. **TUNISIE.**

288. 223. 4 f.+6 f. brown .. 30 45

1945. Stamp Day. Type of France (Louis XI) optd. **TUNISIE.**

289. 228. 2 f.+3 f. green .. 30 45

1945. War Veterans' Fund. Surch. **ANCIENS COMBATTANTS R F** and value.

290. 21. 4 f.+6 f. on 10 c. blue 30 45
291. 23. 10 f.+30 f. on 80 c. grn. 30 45

49. Legionary.

1946. Welfare Fund for French Troops in Indo-China.

292. 49. 20 f.+30 f. black, red and green .. .. 75 1·00

1946. Red Cross Fund. Surch. with cross **1946** and new values.

293. 23. 80 c.+50 c. green .. 45 60
294. 1 f. 50+1 f. 50 lilac .. 50 60
295. 2 f.+2 f. green .. 50 60
296. 24. 2 f. 40+2 f. red .. 60 75
297. 4 f.+4 f. blue .. 60 75

1946. Stamp Day. La Varane Type of France optd. **TUNISIE.**

298. 241. 3 f.+2 f. blue .. 60 65

1947. Stamp Day. Louvois Type of France optd. **TUNISIE.**

299. 253. 4 f. 50+5 f. 50 brown 55 70

1947. Naval Charities. Type of France surch. **TUNISIE** and new value.

300. 234. 10+15 on 2 f.+3 f. blue 60 70

1947. Welfare Fund. Surch. **SOLIDARITE 1947+40 F.**

301. 24. 10 f.+40 f. black .. 40 70

53. Arabesque Ornamentation from Great Mosque at Kairouan.

54. Neptune.

1947.

302 53 3 f. green and turquoise 50 60
303 4 f. red and purple .. 35 50
304 54 5 f. black and green .. 50 65
305 53 6 f. red and brown .. 10 10
306 54 10 f. black and brown 25 20
306a 53 10 f. violet 25 10
306b 12 f. brown 55 30
306c 12 f. orange and brown 40 20
306d 15 f. red and brown .. 65 50
307 54 18 f. blue and green .. 75 55
307a 25 f. turquoise and blue 95 40
307b 53 30 f. blue & deep blue 50 50

55. Feeding a Fledgling. 57. Triumphal Arch, Sbeitla.

1947. Infant Welfare Fund.

308. 55. 4 f. 50+5 f. 50 green .. 30 75
309. 6 f.+9 f. blue 30 75
310. 8 f.+17 f. red 30 75
311. 10 f.+40 f. violet .. 30 75

1948. Stamp Day. Type of France (Arago) optd. **TUNISIE.**

312. 253. 6 f.+4 f. red .. 50 90

1948. Anti-tuberculosis Fund. Surch **AIDEZ LES TUBERCULEUX +10f.**

313 53 4 f.+10 f. orange & green 40 65

1948. Army Welfare Fund.

315 57 10 f.+40 f. green & bis 70 85
316 18 f.+42 f. dp blue & bl 70 85

1949. Stamp Day. Type of France (Choiseul), optd. **TUNISIE.**

317. 278. 15 f.+5 f. black .. 90 1·25

58. Child in Cot.

1949. Child Welfare Fund.

318 58 25 f.+50 f. green .. 1·50 1·75

1957. Tunisian Army Fortnight. No. 417 optd. with T **87.**
452. 20 f. + 10 f. blue .. 55 55

1957. Proclamation of Republic.
453. **88.** 20 f. red .. .. 14·50 14·50
454. 25 f. violet .. .. 14·50 14·50
455. 30 f. brown .. .. 14·50 14·50

1957. 5th Int. Fair, Tunis. As No. 404 but additionally inscr. "5e FOIRE INTERNATIONALE" and Arabic inscriptions at sides, surch. + **10 F.**
456. 20 f. + 10 f. violet 45 45

90. Pres. Bourguiba on Ile de la Galite. **91.** Tunisian Emblems and Map.

1958. 6th Anniv. of Exile of Pres. Bourguiba.
457. **90.** 20 f. blue and brown .. 55 35
458. 25 f. blue and violet .. 55 35

1958. 2nd Anniv. of Independence.
459. **91.** 20 f. green and brown .. 35 15
460. – 25 f. brown and blue .. 35 15
461. – 30 f. brn., red-brn. & red 45 20
DESIGNS: 25 f. Mother and child. 30 f. Clenched fist holding Tunisian flag.
For 20 f. brown and blue see No. 464.

92. Andreas Vesalius (scientist) and A. ibn Khaldoun. **93.** Planting Olives.

1958. Brussels Int. Exn.
462. **92.** 30 f. green and bistre .. 45 20

1958. Labour Day.
463. **93.** 20 f. multicoloured .. 45 45

1958. 3rd Anniv. of Return of Pres. Bourguiba. As T **91** but with inscr. altered.
464. **91.** 20 f. brown and blue .. 40 20

94. **95.** Pres. Bourguiba.

1958. 1st Anniv. of Proclamation of Tunisian Republic.
465. **94.** 5 f. purple and bistre .. 45 20
466. 10 f. dp. grn. & light grn. 45 20
467. 15 f. brown and orange 45 20
468. 20 f. violet, olive & yell. 45 20
469. 25 f. purple 45 20

1958. Pres. Bourguiba's 55th Birthday.
470. **95.** 20 f. purple and violet .. 35 20

96. Fishermen with Catch. **97.** U.N.E.S.C.O. Headquarters, Paris.

1958. 6th Int. Fair.
471. **96.** 25 f. purple, red & green 55 35

1958. Inaug. of U.N.E.S.C.O. Building.
472. **97.** 25 f. myrtle 35 35

98. "Shedding the Veil". **99.** Hand holding plant.

1959. Emancipation of Tunisian Women.
473. **98.** 20 m. turquoise .. 45 30

1959. 25th Anniv of Neo-Destour (Nationalist Party) and Victory Congress.
474. **99.** 5 m. red, brown & purple 30 10
475. – 10 m. multicoloured .. 35 15
476. – 20 m. blue 40 20
477. – 30 m. blue, turq. & brn. 65 40
DESIGNS—VERT. 10 m. Tunisians with flaming torch and flag on shield. 20 m. Pres. Bourguiba in exile at Borj le Boeuf, 1954. HORIZ. 30 m. Pres. Bourguiba and Borj le Boeuf, 1934.

100. "Tunisia".

1959. 3rd Anniv. of Independence.
478. **100.** 50 m. multicoloured .. 65 35

101. Tunisian Horseman. **102.** "Freedom".

1959. Designs as T **101.**
479. ½ m. brn., green & emerald 15 10
480. 1 m. bistre and blue .. 10 10
481. 2 m. brown, yellow & blue 15 10
482. 3 m. myrtle 10 10
483. 4 m. brown 30 15
484. 5 m. myrtle 20 10
485. 6 m. violet 20 15
486. 8 m. purple 65 30
487. 10 m. red, green and bistre 20 10
487a. 12 m. violet and bistre .. 65 20
488. 15 m. blue 35 10
489. 16 m. green 30 20
490. 20 m. turquoise .. .. 1·00 30
491. 20 m. pur., olive & myrtle 1·90 20
492. 25 m. blue, brown & turq. 30 20
493. 30 m. brn., green & turq. 45 10
494. 40 m. green .. .. 1·60 20
495. 45 m. green 70 30
496. 50 m. multicoloured .. 90 20
497. 60 m. brown and green .. 90 35
498. 70 m. multicoloured .. 1·40 50
499. 75 m. brown .. .. 1·25 55
500. 90 m. brown, green & blue 1·25 55
501. 95 m. multicoloured .. 1·60 1·00
502. 100 m. multicoloured .. 1·75 90
503. 200 m. red, bistre and blue 4·50 2·25
504. ½ d. brown .. .. 12·00 6·00
505. 1 d. ochre and deep green 21·00 12·00
DESIGNS—VERT. ½ m. Ain Draham. 2 m. Camel-driver. 3 m. Saddler's shop. 5 m. Type **101.** 6 m. Weavers. 8 m. Gafsa. 10 m. Woman holding pomegranates. 12 m. Turner. 20 m. (No. 491), Gabes. 40 m. Kairouan. 70 m. Carpet weaver. 75 m. Nabeul vase. 95 m. Olive-gatherer. ½ d. Sbeitla. HORIZ. 1 m Kairouan environs. 4 m. Medenine. 15 m. Monastir. 16 m. Tunis. 20 m. (No. 490), Room in Arab house, Sidi-Bou-Said. 25 m. Sfax. 30 m. Aqueduct, Medjerda Valley. 45 m. Bizerta. 50 m. Djerba. 60 m. Le Jerid. 90 m. Le Kef. 100 m. Sidi-bou-Said highway. 200 m. Old port of Sfax. 1 d. Beja ploughman.

1959. Africa Freedom Day.
506. **102.** 40 m. brown and blue .. 50 35

103. Postman. **104.** Clenched Hands.

1959. Stamp Day.
507. **103.** 20 m. + 5 m. brn. & orge. 45 45

1959. U.N Day.
508. **104.** 80 m. brn., blue & pur. 65 45

105. **106.** Dancer and Coin.

1959. Red Crescent Day.
509. **105.** 10 m. + 5 m. mult. .. 35 35

1959. 1st Anniv. of Tunisian Central Bank.
510. **106.** 50 m. black and blue .. 50 50

107. "Uprooted Tree". **108.** Camel Rider Telephoning.

1960. World Refugee Year. Inscr. "ANNEE MONDIALE DES REFUGIES 1959–1960".
511. **107.** 20 m. blue 40 20
512. – 40 m. black and purple 50 35
DESIGN—HORIZ. 40 m. Doves.

1960. Stamp Day.
513. **108.** 60 m. + 5 m. orange, blue and olive 80 80

109. Pres. Bourguiba signing Promulgation. **110.** Fair Emblems.

1960. Promulgation of Constitution.
514. **109.** 20 m. red, brn. & green 40 35

1960. 5th Sousse National Fair.
515. **110.** 100 m. black and green 65 45

111. President Bourguiba. **112.** Jamboree Emblems.

1960.
516. **111.** 20 m. black 20 10
517. 30 m. black, red & blue 35 10
518. 40 m. black, red & green 45 20

1960. 4th Arab Scout Jamboree, Tunis.
519. **112.** 10 m. turquoise .. 35 35
520. – 25 m. pur., red & green 40 35
521. – 30 m. lake, vio. & grn. 60 35
522. – 40 m. blk., blue & red .. 65 40
523. – 60 m. vio., pur. & sepia 1·25 55
DESIGNS: 25 m. Saluting hand with scouts as fingers. 30 m. Camp bugler. 40 m. Scout peacock badge. 60 m. Scout by camp fire.

113. Cyclist in Stadium. **114.**

1960. Olympic Games.
524. **113.** 5 m. brown and olive .. 30 25
525. – 10 m. pur., grn. & blue 35 30
526. – 15 m. carmine and red .. 35 30
527. – 25 m. slate and blue .. 45 40
528. – 50 m. blue and green .. 85 65
DESIGNS: 10 m. Flowers composed of Olympic rings. 15 m. Girl with racquet. 25 m. Runner. 50 m. Handball player.

1960. 5th World Forestry Congress, Seattle.
529. **114.** 8 m. lake, green and blue 35 15
530. – 15 m. green 40 20
531. – 25 m. red, green & violet 65 30
532. – 50 m. turq., brn. & grn. 1·10 50
DESIGNS: 15 m. Removing bark from tree. 25 m. Tree within leaf. 50 m. Diamond pattern featuring palm.

115. U.N. Emblem and People's Arms. **116.** Dove of Peace. **117.** Tunisian Animals and Map of Africa.

1960. U.N. Day.
533. **115.** 40 m. blue, red & black 65 45

1961. 5th Anniv. of Independence.
534. **116.** 20 m. blue, bistre & pur. 30 20
535. 30 m. brn., violet & blue 35 20
536. 40 m. ultram., bl. & grn. 55 40
537. – 75 m. blue, mve. & olive 80 45
DESIGN: 75 m. Globe and Arms of Tunisia.

1961. Africa Day and 3rd Anniv. of Accra Conference. Inscr. "JOURNEE DE L'AFRIQUE 15.4.1961".
538. **117.** 40 m. green, brown and bistre 35 20
539. – 60 m. blk., brn. & turq. 40 30
540. – 100 m. violet, emerald and grey 70 45
541. – 200 m. brown & orange 1·40 1·00
DESIGNS (all showing outline of Africa): 50 m. Profiles of negress and Arab woman. 100 m. Masks and "Africa Day" in Arabic. 200 m. Clasped hands.

118. Stamps and Magnifier. **119.** "Celebration". **120.** Dag Hammarskjoeld.

1961. Stamp Day. Inscr. "JOURNEE DU TIMBRE 1961". Multicoloured.
542. 12 m. + 4 m. Kerkennah dancer and costume of stamps 45 45
543. 15 m. + 5 m. Mobile postal delivery 60 60
544. 20 m. + 6 m. Type **118** .. 65 65
545. 50 m. + 5 m. Postman in shirt depicting stamps 80 80
The 12 m. and 20 m. are vert. and the rest horiz.

1961. National Day.
546. **119.** 25 m. brn., red & violet 45 15
547. – 50 m. brn., choc. & grn. 45 20
548. – 95 m. mve., brn. & blue 65 40
DESIGNS: 50 m. Family celebrating in street. 95 m. Girl astride crescent moon.

1961. U.N. Day.
549. **120.** 40 m. blue 60 35

121. Arms of Tunisia. **122.** Mosquito in Web. **123.** African.

1962. 10th Anniv. of Independence Campaign. Arms in red, yellow, blue and black.
550. **121.** 1 m. yellow and black 10 10
551. 2 m. pink and black .. 15 15
552. 3 m. blue and black .. 15 15
553. 6 m. grey and black .. 20 20

1962. Malaria Eradication. Inscr. "LE MONDE UNI CONTRE LE PALUDISME".
554. 122. 20 m. brown 45 30
555. – 30 m. brn., grn. & choc. 45 30
556. – 40 m. red, grn. & brown 80 35
DESIGNS—VERT. 30 m. "Horseman" attacking mosquito. HORIZ. 40 m. Hands destroying mosquito.

1962. Africa Day. Inscr. "JOURNEE DE L'AFRIQUE 1962".
557. 123. 50 m. brown and buff .. 55 35
558. – 100 m. multicoloured .. 80 45
DESIGN: 100 m. Symbolic figure clasping "Africa".

124. Dancer.

125. Rejoicing Tunisians.

1962. May Day. Inscr. "FETE DU TRAVAIL 1962".
559. 124. 40 m. multicoloured .. 40 20
560. – 60 m. brown 45 30
DESIGN: 60 m. Worker with pneumatic drill.

1962. National Day.
561. 125. 20 m. black and salmon 50 35

126. Gabes Costume.

127. U.N. Emblem and Tunisian Flag.

1962. Republic Festival. Regional Costumes. Multicoloured.
562. 5 m. Type 126 .. .. 55 20
563. 10 m. Mahdia 65 35
564. 15 m. Kairouan 90 45
565. 20 m. Hammamet .. 1·10 55
566. 25 m. Djerba .. .. 1·25 55
567. 30 m. As 10 m. .. 1·25 65
568. 40 m. As 20 m. .. 1·40 65
569. 50 m. Type 126 .. 1·40 85
570. 55 m. Ksar Hellal .. 2·25 1·00
571. 60 m. Tunis .. .. 2·75 1·40

1962. U.N. Day.
572. 127. 20 m. red, black & grey 35 30
573. – 30 m. multicoloured .. 40 30
574. – 40 m. blue, black & brn. 65 35
DESIGNS—HORIZ. 30 m. "Plant" with three leaves and Globe. VERT: 40 m. Globe and dove.

128. A. Q. Chabbi (poet).

129. Pres. Bourguiba.

1962. Aboul Qasim Chabbi Commem.
575. 128. 15 m. violet 35 20

1962.
576. 129. 20 m. blue 15 15
577. 30 m. red 15 10
578. 40 m. green 20 15

130. Hached Telephone Exchange.

131. Runners.

1962. Modernisation of Telephone System.
579. 130. 5 m. multicoloured .. 30 20
580. – 10 m. multicoloured .. 35 20
581. – 15 m. multicoloured .. 50 35
582. – 50 m. flesh, brown & blk. 80 50
583. – 100 m. blue, pur. & blk. 1·75 90
584. – 200 m. multicoloured .. 2·40 1·40
DESIGNS: 10 m. Carthage Telephone Exchange. 15 m. Aerial equipment. 50 m. Telephone switchboard operators. 100 m. Telephone equipment as human figure. 200 m. Belvedere Telephone Exchange.

1963. 13th Int. Military Sports Council Cross-country Championships.
585. 131. 30 m. brn., grn. & blk. 60 45

132. Dove with Wheatear and Globe.

133. Centenary Emblem.

1963. Freedom from Hunger.
586. 132. 20 m. blue and brown 30 20
587. – 40 m. purple & brown 40 20
DESIGN: 40 m. Child taking nourishment.

1963. Red Cross Cent.
588. 133. 20 m. red, grey & brown 45 20

1963. U.N. Day. Nos. 542/5 optd. **1963 O.N.U.** in English and Arabic. Mult.
589. 12 m. + 4 m. 30 30
590. 15 m. + 5 m. 35 35
591. 20 m. + 6 m. 40 40
592. 50 m. + 5 m. 65 65

135. "Miss World".

136. "Out of Reach".

1963. 15th Anniv. of Declaration of Human Rights.
593. 135. 30 m. brown and green 45 30

1964. Nubian Monuments Preservation.
594. 136. 50 m. ochre, brn. & blue 45 30

137. "Unsettled Forecast".

138. Mohamed Ali (trade union leader).

1964. World Meteorological Day.
595. 137. 40 m. mauve, blue and brown 45 20

1964. 70th Birth Anniv. of Mohamed Ali.
596. 138. 50 m. purple 45 35

139. Africa within Flower.

140. Pres. Bourguiba.

1964. 1st Anniv. of Addis Ababa Conference of the Organization of African Unity.
597. 139. 60 m. multicoloured .. 50 30

1964. National Day.
598. 140. 20 m. blue 15 10
599. 30 m. brown 20 10

141. "Bizerte" ("ship").

142. Fulvous Babbler.

1964. Neo-Destour Congress, Bizerta.
600. 141. 50 m. green and black 40 30

1965. Air. Tunisian Birds. Multicoloured.
601. 25 m. Type 142 .. .. 1·75 50
602. 55 m. Great Grey Shrike 2·50 75
603. 55 m. Cream-coloured Courser .. .. 2·75 95
604. 100 m. Chaffinch .. 3·25 1·10
605. 150 m. Greater Flamingoes 5·75 2·40
606. 200 m. Barbary Partridge 8·75 2·75
607. 300 m. Common Roller .. 13·50 5·25
608. 500 m. Houbara Bustard 17·00 6·25
SIZES—As Type 142: 55 m. (both). Others, 23 × 32½ mm.

143. Early Telegraphist and Aerial Mast.

144. Carthaginian Coin.

1965. I.T.U. Cent.
609. 143. 55 m. blue and black 50 30

1965. Festival of Popular Arts, Carthage.
610. 144. 5 m. purple and green 15 10
611. 10 m. purple & yellow 30 20
612. 75 m. purple and blue 65 20

145. Girl reading Book.

146. Joined Hooks.

1965. Opening of Students' Home, Tunis.
613. 145. 25 m. blue, blk. & red 30 20
614. 40 m. blk., blue & red 40 20
615. 50 m. red, black & blue 45 30

1965. Int. Co-operation Year.
617. 146. 40 m. blue, pur. & blk. 45 25

147. Woman Bathing.

149. "Independence"

148. Pres. Bourguiba and Hands.

1966. Mineral Springs. Inscr. "EAUX MINERALES".
618. 147. 10 m. red, ochre & grey 30 20
619. – 20 m. multicoloured 40 30
620. – 30 m. red, blue & yellow 45 35
621. – 100 m. olive, yell. & bl. 1·10 55
DESIGNS: 20 m. Man pouring water. 30 m. Woman pouring water. 100 m. Mountain and fronds of tree.

1966. 10th Anniv. of Independence.
622. 148. 5 m. lilac and blue .. 15 10
623. 10 m. green and blue 20 15
624. 149. 25 m. multicoloured .. 20 15
625. – 40 m. multicoloured .. 55 20
626. – 60 m. multicoloured .. 80 35
DESIGNS—As Type 149—HORIZ. 40 m. "Development". VERT. 60 m. "Promotion of Culture" ("man" draped in books, palette, musical instruments, etc.).

150. Sectional Map of Africa.

152. "Athletics".

151. U.N.E.S.C.O. Emblem of the Muses.

1966. 2nd U.N. African Regional Cartographic Conf., Tunisia.
627. 150. 15 m. multicoloured .. 30 20
628. 35 m. multicoloured .. 35 20
629. 40 m. multicoloured .. 50 35

1966. 20th Anniv. of U.N.E.S.C.O.
631. 151. 100 m. brown and black 85 35

1967. Publicity for Mediterranean Games (September, 1967).
632. 152. 20 m. brown, blue & red 20 15
633. 30 m. black and blue 40 30

153. Gabes Costume and Fair Emblem.

154. Emblems of Civilisation.

1967. "Expo 67" World Fair, Montreal. T 154 and earlier designs redrawn as T 153.
634. – 50 m. mult. (As No. 566) 35 15
635. 153. 75 m. multicoloured .. 50 30
636. 154. 100 m. grn., blk. & turq. 80 30
637. 110 m. red, sep. & blue 95 40
638. – 155 m. mult. (As No. 605) 1·75 45

155. Tunisian Pavilion, Pres. Bourguiba and Map.

1967. "National Day at World Fair, Montreal".
639. 155. 65 m. purple and red .. 40 35
640. – 105 m. brn., red & blue 50 35
641. – 120 m. blue 60 40
642. – 200 m. blk., red & pur. 1·00 50
DESIGNS: 105 m. As Type 155, but with profile bust of Pres. Bourguiba. Tunisian pavilion (different view) with: 120 m. Silhouette and 200 m. Bust of Pres. Bourguiba.

156. "Tunisia" holding Clover.

158. Bas-relief from Statue of Apollo.

157. Tennis Club.

1967. 10th Anniv. of Republic. Mult.
643. 25 m. Type 156 .. .. 20 15
644. 40 m. Woman releasing doves (vert.) 35 15

1967. Mediterranean Games, Tunis.
645 **157** 5 m. red and green .. 20 20
646 – 10 m. multicoloured .. 20 15
647 – 15 m. black 35 20
648 – 35 m. turq, pur & blk 45 20
649 – 75 m. green, vio & red 80 40
DESIGNS—VERT. 10 m. " Spring Triumphs " (squared panel). HORIZ. 15 m. Olympic swimming pool. 35 m. Sports Palace. 75 m. Olympic stadium.

1967. Tunisian History Punic period.
650. **158.** 15 m. red, blk. & grn. 30 20
651. – 20 m. flesh, red & blue 35 20
652. – 25 m. brown and olive 45 20
653. – 30 m. red and grey .. 45 20
654. – 40 m. lemon, yell. & pur. 50 20
655. – 60 m. multicoloured .. 50 30
DESIGNS: 20 m. Sea horseman (Kerkouane medallion). 25 m. Hannibal (bronze bust). 30 m. " The Sacrifice " (votive stele). 40 m. Hamilcar (coin). 60 m. Glass funeral pendant mask.

159. "Human Rights". 160. "Electronic Man".

1968. Human Rights Year.
656. **159.** 25 m. red 40 35
657. 60 m. blue 45 20

1968. Electronics in Postal Service.
658. **160.** 25 m. blue, brn. & pur. 35 30
659. 40 m. black, brn. & grn. 35 30
660. 60 m. pur., slate & blue 45 35

161. " Doctor and Patient ". 162. Arabian Jasmine.

1968. 20th Anniv. of W.H.O.
661. **161.** 25 m. green & turquoise 40 35
662. 60 m. red and lake .. 45 35

1968. Tunisian Flowers. Multicoloured.
663. 5 m. Flax 20 15
664. 6 m. Indian shot 20 15
665. 10 m. Pomegranate .. 30 15
666. 12 m. Type **162** 30 15
667. 15 m. Raponticum .. 35 15
668. 20 m. Geranium 40 20
669. 25 m. Madonna lily .. 40 30
670. 40 m. Almond 60 30
671. 50 m. Capers 80 45
672. 60 m. Ariana rose .. .. 1·25 70
673. 100 m. Jasmine .. .. 1·60 1·10

163. Globe on " Sunflower ". 164. Flautist.

1968. Red Crescent Day.
674. **163.** 15 m. red, green & blue 35 30
675. – 25 m. red and purple .. 40 30
DESIGN: 25 m. Red crescent on wings of dove.

1968. Stamp Day.
676. **164.** 20 m. multicoloured .. 35 20
677. 50 m. multicoloured .. 40 35

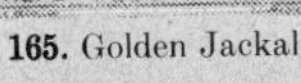

165. Golden Jackal.

166. Worker.

1968. Fauna. Multicoloured.
678. 5 m. Type **165** 20 15
679. 8 m. North African crested porcupine 30 20
680. 10 m. Dromedary 40 20
681. 15 m. Dorcas gazelle .. 50 20
682. 20 m. Fennec fox 80 45
683. 25 m. Algerian hedgehog .. 1·00 55
684. 40 m. Horse .. .. 1·40 80
685. 60 m. Wild boar .. .. 1·90 1·00

1969. 50th Anniv. of I.L.O. Mult.
686. 25 m. Type **166** 35 30
687. 60 m. Youth and girl holding "May 1" banner .. 50 35

167. Musicians and Veiled Dancers. 168. Tunisian Arms.

1969. Stamp Day.
688. **167.** 100 m. multicoloured .. 70 35

1969.
689. **168.** 15 m. multicoloured .. 20 20
690. 25 m. multicoloured .. 30 20
691. 40 m. multicoloured .. 35 20
692. 60 m. multicoloured .. 40 20

169. "Industrial Development". 170. Lute.

1969. 5th Anniv. of African Development Bank.
693. **169.** 60 m. multicoloured .. 40 30

1970. Musical Instruments. Multicoloured.
694. 25 m. Type **170** 45 35
695. 50 m. Zither 55 35
696. 70 m. Rehab 80 35
697. 90 m. Naghrat (drums) .. 1·00 35
Nos. 695 and 697 are horiz., size 33 × 22 mm

171. Nurse, Caduceus and Flags. 172. New U.P.U. Headquarters Building.

1970. Sixth North-African Maghreb Medical Seminar, Tunis.
698. **171.** 25 m. multicoloured .. 35 20

1970. New U.P.U. Headquarters Building, Berne.
699. **172.** 25 m. brown and red .. 40 20

173. Mounted Postman.

1970. Stamp Day. Multicoloured.
700. 25 m. Type **173** 20 20
701. 35 m. " Postmen of yesterday and today " (23 × 38 mm.) 35 20

174. U.N. Emblem, " N " and Dove forming " O.N.U. ".

175. " The Flower-seller ".

1970. 25th Anniv. of United Nations.
702. **174.** 40 m. multicoloured .. 40 20

1970. "Tunisian Life" (1st series). Mult.
703. 20 m. Type **175** 20 15
704. 25 m. "The husband's third day of marriage" 30 20
705. 35 m. "The Perfumer" .. 45 35
706. 40 m. "The Fish-seller" .. 50 35
707. 85 m. "The Coffee-house keeper" 80 35
See also Nos. 715/18, 757/62 and 819/23.

176. Lenin. 177. Dish Aerial and Flags.

1970. Birth Cent. of Lenin.
709. **176.** 60 m. lake 65 35

1971. Maghreban Posts and Telecommunications Co-ordination.
710. **177.** 25 m. multicoloured .. 40 35

178. U.N. Building and Symbol. 179. Globe and Satellites.

1971. Racial Equality Year.
711. **178.** 80 m. multicoloured .. 45 30

1971. World Telecommunications Day.
712. **179.** 70 m. multicoloured .. 40 20

180. Moon, Earth and Satellites.

1971. "Conquest of Space".
713. **180.** 15 m. black & blue .. 35 20
714. – 90 m. black & red .. 60 30
DESIGN: 90 m. Space allegory.

181. "The Pottery Dealer". 182. Pres. Bourguiba.

1971. " Tunisian Life " (2nd series). Mult.
715. 25 m. Type **181** 35 20
716. 30 m. "The Esparto dealer" 35 20
717. 40 m. "The Poulterer" .. 45 20
718. 50 m. "The Dyer" .. 55 30

1971. 8th P.S.D. Destourian Socialist Party Congress, Tunis. Multicoloured.
720. 25 m. Type **182** 20 20
721. 30 m. Bourguiba in bed, 1938 (horiz.) 20 20
722. 50 m. Bourguiba acclaimed 35 30
723. 80 m. Bourguiba—"Builder of the Nation" (horiz.) 45 30
SIZES: 30 m., 80 m. $13\frac{1}{2} \times 14$. 50 m. As Type **182**.

183. Shah Mohammed Riza Pahlavi and Achaemenidian Effigy. 184. Pimento.

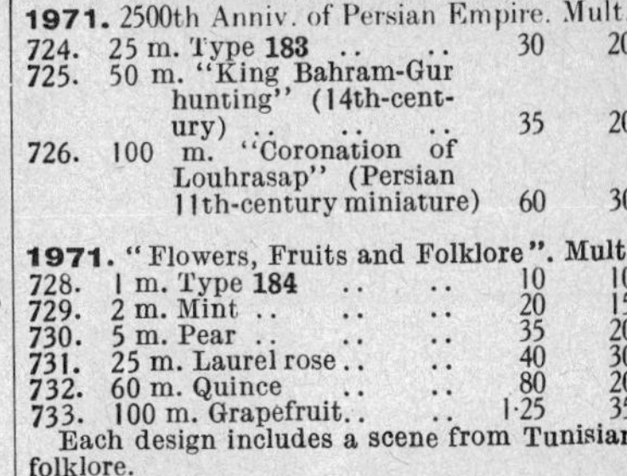

1971. 2500th Anniv. of Persian Empire. Mult.
724. 25 m. Type **183** 30 20
725. 50 m. "King Bahram-Gur hunting" (14th-century) 35 20
726. 100 m. "Coronation of Louhrasap" (Persian 11th-century miniature) 60 30

1971. " Flowers, Fruits and Folklore ". Mult.
728. 1 m. Type **184** 10 10
729. 2 m. Mint 20 15
730. 5 m. Pear 35 20
731. 25 m. Laurel rose 40 30
732. 60 m. Quince 80 20
733. 100 m. Grapefruit .. .. 1·25 35
Each design includes a scene from Tunisian folklore.

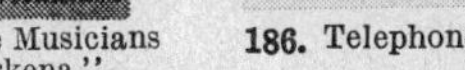

185. "The Musicians of Kerkena". 186. Telephone.

1971. Stamp Day.
735. **185.** 50 m. multicoloured .. 40 20

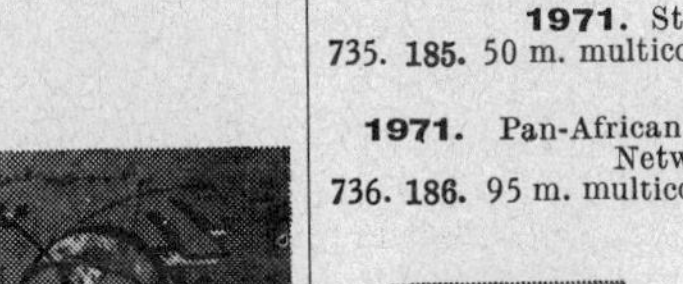

1971. Pan-African Telecommunications Network.
736. **186.** 95 m. multicoloured .. 50 45

187. U.N.I.C.E.F. Emblem. 189. Olive-tree Emblem.

188. Rialto Bridge, Venice.

1971. 25th Anniv. of U.N.I.C.E.F.
737. **187.** 110 m. multicoloured 50 35

1971. U.N.E.S.C.O. "Save Venice" Campaign. Multicoloured.
738. 25 m. Gondolier (vert.) .. 35 20
739. 30 m. De Medici and Palace (vert.) 40 20
740. 50 m. Prow of gondola (vert.) 45 35
741. 80 m. Type **188** 80 35

1972. World Olive-oil Year.
742. **189.** 60 m. multicoloured .. 40 20

190. Tunisian reading Book. 191. Heart Emblem.

1972. Int. Book Year.
743. **190.** 90 m. multicoloured .. 50 40

1972. World Health Day. Multicoloured.
744. 25 m. Type **191** 35 20
745. 60 m. Heart within " hour-glass " 55 35

192. " Old Age ".

193. " Only One Earth ".

1972. Tunisian Red Crescent.
746. **192.** 10 m.+10 m. vio. & red 35 30
747. – 75 m.+10 m. brn. & red 50 35
DESIGN: 75 m. Mother and Child ("Child Care").

1972. U.N. Environmental Conservation Conf., Stockholm.
748. **193.** 60 m. green and brown 50 20

194. Hurdling.

195. Chessboard.

1972. Olympic Games, Munich.
749. – 5 m. multicoloured .. 10 10
750. **194.** 15 m. multicoloured .. 15 10
751. – 20 m. blk., green & gold 15 10
752. – 25 m. multicoloured .. 15 15
753. – 60 m. multicoloured .. 35 20
754. – 80 m. multicoloured .. 45 30
DESIGNS—VERT. 5 m. Handball. 20 m. Athletes saluting. HORIZ. 25 m. Football. 60 m. Swimming. 80 m. Running.

1972. 20th Chess Olympiad, Skopje, Yugoslavia.
756. **195.** 60 m. multicoloured .. 90 55

196. "The Fisherman".

197. New P.T.T. H.Q., Tunis.

1972. "Tunisian Life" (3rd series). Mult.
757. 5 m. Type **196** 15 15
758. 10 m. "The Basket-maker" 20 15
759. 25 m. "The Musician" .. 30 15
760. 50 m. "The Berber Bride" 55 20
761. 60 m. "The Flower-seller" 80 20
762. 80 m. "The Mystic" .. 80 40

1972. Stamp Day.
764. **197.** 25 m. multicoloured .. 30 20

198. Dome of the Rock, Jerusalem.

199. Globe and Beribboned Pen.

1973. Dome of the Rock Commemoration.
765. **198.** 25 m. multicoloured .. 40 30

1973. 9th Arab Writers' Congress and 11th Poetry Festival. Multicoloured.
766. 25 m. Type **199** 20 20
767. 60 m. Lyre Emblem .. 35 20

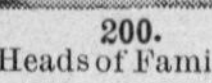
200. Heads of Family.

201. Figures "10" and Bird feeding Young.

1973. Family Planning. Multicoloured.
768. 20 m. Type **200** 20 20
769. 25 m. Family profiles and bird 35 30

1973. 10th Anniv. of World Food Programme. Multicoloured.
770. 25 m. Type **201** 30 20
771. 60 m. Symbolic "10" .. 30 20

202. Sculptured Roman Head.

203. Red Crescent Nurse.

1973. U.N.E.S.C.O. "Save Carthage" Campaign. Multicoloured.
772. 5 m. Type **202** 30 20
773. 25 m. Carthagian mosaics 45 35
774. 30 m. "Cycle of mosaics" 45 35
775. 40 m. "Goodwill" stele (vert.) 60 35
776. 60 m. Preacher's hand (from Korba statue) .. 70 35
777. 75 m. "Malga" (17th-century potsherd) (vert.) 85 40

1973. Tunisian Red Crescent.
779. **203.** 25 m.+10 m. mult. .. 45 35
780. – 60 m.+10 m. red & grey 65 35
DESIGN—HORIZ. 60 m. Arms of blood donors.

204. "World Telecommunications".

205. Smiling Youth.

1973. 5th World Telecommunications Day. Multicoloured.
781. 60 m. Type **204** 35 20
782. 75 m. "The Universe" .. 40 20

1973. 1st Pan-African Festival of Youth. Multicoloured.
783. 25 m. Festival Map .. 35 30
784. 40 m. Type **205** 40 30

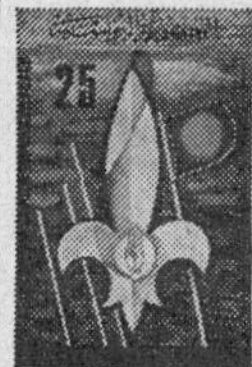

206. Scout Badge.

207. "Rover" in Car.

1973. International Scouting.
785. **206.** 25 m. multicoloured 35 30

1973. 2nd Pan-Arab Rover Rally.
786. **207.** 60 m. multicoloured .. 40 35

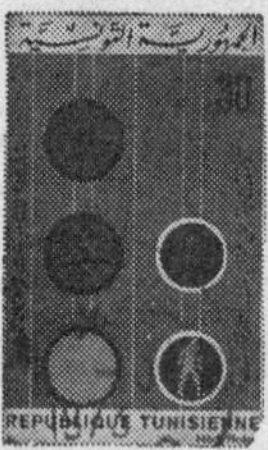
208. Traffic Lights.

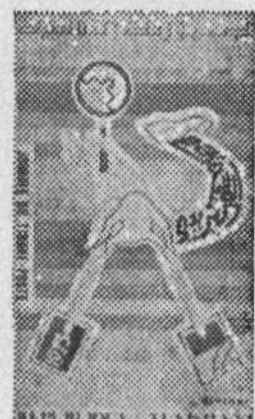
209. Winged Camel.

1973. Road Safety. Multicoloured.
787. 25 m. Motorway junction (horiz.) 35 30
788. 30 m. Type **208** 40 30

1973. Stamp Day. Multicoloured.
789. 10 m. Peacock ("collectors pride") (horiz.) .. 35 20
790. 65 m. Type **209** 40 35

210. Copernicus.

211. O.A.U. Emblems within Arms.

1973. 500th Birth Anniv. of Copernicus.
791. **210.** 60 m. multicoloured .. 55 35

1973. 10th Anniv. of Organization of African Unity.
792. **211.** 25 m. multicoloured .. 40 20

212. Interpol Emblem and Handclasp.

213. Flower Offering.

1973. 50th Anniv. of International Criminal Police Organization (Interpol).
793. **212.** 65 m. multicoloured .. 45 35

1973. 25th Anniv. of Declaration of Human Rights.
794. **213.** 60 m. multicoloured .. 55 35

214. W.M.O. H.Q., Geneva.

1973. W.M.O. Cent. Multicoloured.
795. 25 m. Type **214** 40 20
796. 60 m. Earth and emblems 45 30

215. President Bourguiba, 1934.

216. Scientist using Microscope.

1974. 40th Anniv. of Neo-Destour Party.
797. **215.** 15 m. purple, red & blk. 20 20
798. – 25 m. brn., orge. & blk. 20 20
799. – 60 m. bl., red & black .. 30 20
800. – 75 m. brn., mve. & blk. 35 20
801. – 100 m. grn., orge. & blk. 45 35
DESIGNS: Nos. 798/801, Various portraits of Pres. Bourguiba (founder), similar to Type **215**.

1974. 6th African Micro-Palaeontologica Conference, Tunis.
803. **216.** 60 m. multicoloured .. 85 45

217. "Blood Donation".

218. Telephonist holding Globe.

1974. Tunisian Red Crescent. Multicoloured.
804. 25 m.+10 m. Type **217** .. 35 35
805. 75 m.+10 m. "Blood Transfusion" 45 45

1974. Inauguration of International Automatic Telephone Service. Multicoloured.
806. 15 m. Type **218** 20 20
807. 60 m. Telephone dial .. 45 35

219. Population Emblems.

1974. World Population Year.
808. **219.** 110 m. multicoloured 55 35

220. Pres. Bourguiba and Emblem.

222. "Carrier-pigeons".

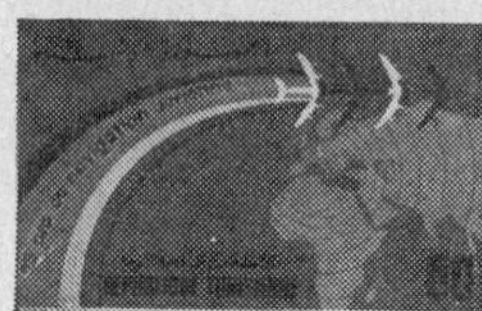

221. Aircraft crossing Globe.

1974. Destourian Socialist Party Congress.
809. **220.** 25 m. bl., turq. & blk. 20 20
810. – 60 m. red, yell. & black 30 25
811. – 200 m. pur., grn. & blk. 90 95
DESIGNS—HORIZ. 60 m. Pres. Bourguiba and sunflower. 200 m. Pres. Bourguiba and verbena.

1974. 25th Anniv. of Tunisian Aviation.
813. **221.** 60 m. multicoloured .. 45 35

1974. Cent. of U.P.U. Mult.
814. 25 m. Type **222** 35 25
815. 60 m. Handclasp 45 30

223. Bardo Palace as "Ballot Box".

224. Postman with Parcels on Head.

1974. Legislative and Presidential Elections.
816. **223.** 25 m. bl., grn. & blk.. 35 30
817. – 100 m. blk. & orange.. 50 35
DESIGN: 100 m. Pres. Bourguiba on poll card.

1974. Stamp Day.
818. **224.** 75 m. multicoloured .. 45 20

225. "The Water-carrier".

226. Stylised Bird.

1975. "Scenes from Tunisian Life". (4th series). Multicoloured.
819. 5 m. Type **225** 15 15
820. 15 m. "The Scent Sprinkler" 20 20
821. 25 m. "The Washer-women" 20 20
822. 60 m. "The Potter" .. 35 20
823. 110 m. "The Fruit-seller" 85 50

1975. 13th Arab Engineers' Union Conference, Tunis. Multicoloured.
825. 25 m. Skyscraper and scaffolding (vert.) 20 20
826. 65 m. Type **226** 40 30

227. Gold Coffee-pot and Tray.

1975. Handicrafts. Multicoloured.
827. 10 m. Type **227** 20 20
828. 15 m. Horseman and saddlery (embroidery) .. 20 20
829. 25 m. Still life (painting) 30 20
830. 30 m. Bird-cage (fine-crafts) (vert.) 35 20
831. 40 m. Silver head-dress (jewellery) (vert.) 35 20
832. 60 m. Textile patterns .. 55 30

228. Man and Scales. 229. " Telecommunications ".

1975. Tunisian Red Crescent Campaign against Malnutrition.
833. 228. 50 m. + 10 m. mult. .. 40 35

1975. 7th World Telecommunications Day.
834. 229. 50 m. multicoloured .. 30 20

230. Allegory of Victory. 231. Tunisian Woman.

1975. 20th Anniv. of "Victory" (Return of Bourguiba). Multicoloured.
835. 25 m. Type **230** 20 20
836. 65 m. Return of President Bourguiba (horiz.) .. 35 20

1975. International Women's Year.
837. 231. 110 m. multicoloured 55 30

232. Children on Road Crossing.

1975. Road Safety Campaign.
838. 232. 25 m. multicoloured .. 20 20

233. Jerba.

1975. " Tunisia, Yesterday and Today," (1st series). Multicoloured.
839. 10 m. Type **233** 20 20
840. 15 m. Tunis 20 20
841. 20 m. Monastir 20 20
842. 65 m. Sousse 45 30
843. 500 m. Tozeur .. .. 3·25 1·25
844. 1 d. Kairouan .. .. 5·50 2·25
See also Nos. 864/7.

234. Figures representing Sport. 235. Bouquet of flowers.

1975. 7th Mediterranean Games, Algiers. Multicoloured.
845. 25 m. Type **234** 20 20
846. 50 m. " Ship of sport " (horiz.) 35 20

1975. Stamp Day.
847. 235. 100 m. multicoloured 45 20

236. College Building.

1975. Centenary of Sadiki College.
848. 236. 25 m. multicoloured .. 30 20

237. " Duck ". 238. Early and Modern Telephones.

1976. Tunisian Mosaics. Multicoloured.
849. 5 m. Type **237** 30 20
850. 10 m. Fish 30 20
851. 25 m. Lioness (40 × 27 mm.) 55 45
852. 60 m. Gorgon (40 × 27 mm.) 60 45
853. 75 m. Circus Spectators (27 × 40 mm.) .. 65 45
854. 100 m. Virgil (27 × 40 mm.) 95 45

1976. Telephone Centenary.
856. 238. 150 m. multicoloured 55 30

239. Figures " 20 " and Banners. 240. Blind Man with Stick.

1976. 20th Anniv. of Independence. Mult.
857. 40 m. Type **239** 20 20
858. 100 m. Figures " 20 " and flag emblem 40 20
859. 150 m. Floral allegory of " Tunisia " 60 30

1976. World Health Day.
861. 240. 100 m. black and red .. 45 20

241. Blood Donation. 242. " Urban Development ".

1976. Tunisian Red Crescent.
862. 241. 40 m. + 10 m. mult. .. 40 30

1976. " Habitat " Human Settlements Conference, Vancouver.
863. 242. 40 m. multicoloured .. 30 20

243. Henna Tradition.

1976. "Tunisia, Yesterday and Today" (2nd series). Multicoloured.
864 40 m. Type **243** 20 20
865 50 m. Diving for sponges 35 20
866 65 m. Weaving 35 20
867 110 m. Pottery 50 35

244. " Spirit of 1776 " (Willard).

1976. Bicent. of American Revolution.
868. 244. 200 m. multicoloured 1·40 65

245. Running. 246. Girl reading Book.

1976. Olympic Games, Montreal. Mult.
870. 50 m. Type **245** 20 20
871. 75 m. Olympic flags and rings 35 20
872. 120 m. Olympic " dove " 55 30

1976. Literature for Children.
873. 246. 100 m. multicoloured 45 20

247. Bird and Faces Emblem. 248. Mausoleum, Tunis.

1976. 15th Anniv. of 1st Non-aligned Countries' Conference, Belgrade.
874. 247. 150 m. multicoloured 60 20

1976. Cultural Heritage. Multicoloured.
875. 85 m. Type **248** 35 20
876. 100 m. Great Mosque, Kairouan 40 20
877. 150 m. Ribat, Monastery 60 20
878. 200 m. Barber's Mosque, Kairouan 90 35

249. Emblem and Globe.

1976. 25th Anniv. of U.N. Postal Administration.
879. 249. 150 m. multicoloured 65 30

250. Red Crescent on Litter.

1977. Tunisian Red Crescent.
880. 250. 50 m. + 10 m. mult. .. 40 35

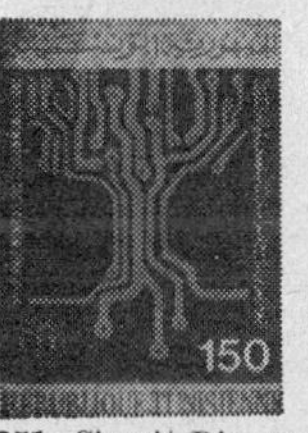

251. Circuit Diagram. 252. " Dialogue ".

1977. World Telecommunications Day.
881. 251. 150 m. multicoloured 65 40

1977. 10th Anniv. of International French Language Council.
882. 252. 100 m. multicoloured 80 35

253. Footballers. 254. Gold Coin.

1977. First World Junior Football Tournament.
883. 253. 150 m. multicoloured 90 45

1977. Cultural Patrimony. Multicoloured.
884. 10 m. Type **254** 10 10
885. 15 m. 13th-century stele .. 15 15
886. 20 m. 17th-century Illuminated manuscript .. 20 15
887. 30 m. Glass painting .. 35 20
888. 40 m. Ceramic pot decor .. 40 20
889. 50 m. Gate, Sidi-Bou-Said 45 20

255. " The Young Republic ". 257. Globe and Cogwheels.

256. A.P.U. Emblem within Postmark.

1977. 20th Anniv. of Republic. Mult.
890. 40 m. Type **255** 35 20
891. 100 m. " The Confident Republic " 40 20
892. 150 m. " The Determined Republic " 65 30

1977. 25th Anniv. of Arab Postal Union.
894. 256. 40 m. multicoloured .. 20 20

1977. World Rheumatism Year.
895. 257. 120 m. brn., red & blk. 65 35

258. Harvester and Rural Cameos.

1977. Rural Development.
896. 258. 40 m. multicoloured .. 35 20

259. Factory Workers. 260. Pres. Bourguiba and Flaming Torch within " 9 ".

1978. Employment Priority Plan. Mult.
897. 20 m. Forms of transport & driver (horiz.) 20 15
898. 40 m. Tractor driver and farm workers (horiz.) .. 20 20
899. 100 m. Type **259** 45 30

1978. 40th Anniv. of April 9th Revolution.
900. 260. 40 m. grn., brn. & olive 20 20
901. – 60 m. red, brn. & blk. 20 20
DESIGN: 60 m. President Bourguiba within figure " 9 ".

261. Policeman in Safety Helmet. 262. " Blood Donors ".

1978. Sixth Regional African Interpol Conference.
902. 261. 150 m. multicoloured 80 35

1978. Tunisian Red Crescent.
903. 262. 50 m. + 10 m. mult. .. 45 30

263. Goalkeeper catching World Cup Emblem. 264. Hammer and Chisel chipping away Apartheid.

1978. World Cup Football Championship, Argentina. Multicoloured.
904. 40 m. Type **263** 30 20
905. 150 m. Footballer, map and flags 85 35

1978. International Anti-Apartheid Year. Multicoloured.
906. 50 m. Type **264** 20 20
907. 100 m Black and white doves 45 30

265. Flora, Fauna, and Polluting Factory.
266. Crane removing Smallpox from Globe.

1978. Protection of Nature and the Environment. Multicoloured.
908. 10 m. Type **265** 15 15
909. 50 m. " Pollution of the oceans " 40 20
910. 120 m. " Making the deserts green 95 20

1978. Global Eradication of Smallpox.
911. **266.** 150 m. multicoloured 65 35

267. Zlass Horseman. **268.** Lenin Banner.

1978. Calligraphy, Art and Traditions. Multicoloured.
912. 5 m. Type **267** 10 10
913. 60 m. Jerba Wedding .. 30 15
914. 75 m. Women potters from the Mogods 40 15
915. 100 m. Dove over cupolas of Marabout Sidi Mahrez 45 20
916. 500 m. Opening of the ploughing season, Jenduba .. 3·00 1·00
917. 1 d. Man swinging between palm trees (Spring Festival, Tozeur) .. 4·75 1·90

1978. 60th Anniv. of Russian Revolution.
918. **268.** 150 m. multicoloured 85 45

269. Farhat Hached. **270.** Family Group.

1978. Farhat Hached (Trade Union leader). Commem.
919. **269.** 50 m. multicoloured .. 35 10

1978. 10th Anniv. of Tunisian Family Planning Association.
920. **270.** 50 m. multicoloured .. 40 20

271. " The Sun ". **273.** Hand holding Bird.

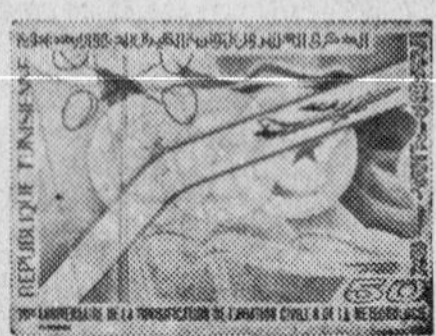

272. Aircraft and Flags.

1978. Solar Energy.
921. **271.** 100 m. multicoloured 60 20

1978. 20th Anniv. of Tunisian Civil Aeronautics and Meteorology.
922. **272.** 50 m. multicoloured .. 30 20

1979. Tunisian Red Crescent.
923. **273.** 50 m. + 10 m. mult. .. 40 30

274. Pres. Bourguiba. **275.** Sun, Yacht and Golfer.

1979. 20th Anniv. of Constitution.
924. **274.** 50 m. brn., yell. & blk. 20 20

1979. Inauguration of El Kantaoui Port.
925. **275.** 150 m. multicoloured 65 30

276. Korbous. **277.** Bow-net Making.

1979. Tunisian Landscapes. Multicoloured.
926. 50 m. Type **276** 15 10
927. 100 m. Mides 35 15

1979. Manual Labour. Multicoloured.
928. 10 m. Type **277** 15 10
929. 50 m. Bee-keeping .. 35 10

278. Pres. Bourguiba. **279.** Dish Aerial and Satellite.

1979. 10th Congress of Socialist Destourian Party.
930. **278.** 50 m. multicoloured .. 30 10

1979. 3rd World Telecommunications Exhibition, Geneva.
931. **279.** 150 m. multicoloured .. 65 35

280. World Map, Koran and Symbols of Arab Achievements. **281.** Children crossing Road.

1979. The Arabs.
932. **280.** 50 m. multicoloured .. 20 15

1979. International Year of the Child. Multicoloured.
933. 50 m. Type **281** 20 15
934. 100 m. Child, fruit and birds 50 20

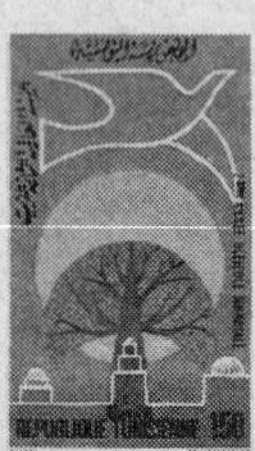

282. Dove and Olive Tree. **283.** Symbolic Figure.

1979. 2nd World Olive-oil Year.
935. **282.** 150 m. multicoloured 80 35

1979. 20th Anniv. of Central Bank of Tunisia.
936. **283.** 50 m. multicoloured .. 20 20

284. Children and Jujube Tree.

1979. Animals and Plants. Multicoloured.
937. 20 m. Type **284** 20 10
938. 30 m. Common Peafowl .. 35 15
939. 70 m. Goat 65 20
940. 85 m. Girl and date palm 70 20

285. Coded Letter.

1980. Introduction of Postal Coding.
941. **285.** 50 m. multicoloured .. 30 20

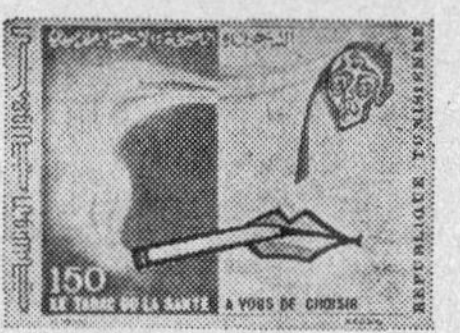

286. Smoker.

1980. World Health Day. Anti-smoking Campaign.
942. **286.** 150 m. multicoloured 65 30

287. Red Crescent and Globe forming an Eye. **288.** President Bourguiba, Flower and Open Book.

1980. Tunisian Red Crescent.
943. **287.** 20 m. + 10 m. mult. .. 40 30

1980. 25th Anniv. of Victory and Return of President Bourguiba. Multicoloured.
944. 50 m. Type **288** 20 20
945. 100 m. Pres. Bourguiba, dove and mosque .. 50 35

289. Gymnast as Butterfly. **290.** Tools.

1980. Turin Gymnastic Games.
946. **289.** 100 m. multicoloured 45 20

1980. Handicrafts. Multicoloured.
947. 30 m. Type **290** 30 20
948. 75 m. Woman embroidering 40 20

291. Ibn Khaldoun (philosopher). **292.** Avicenna.

1980. Ibn Khaldoun Commemoration.
949. **291.** 50 m. multicoloured .. 20 20

1980. Birth Milenary of Ibn Sina (philosopher).
950. **292.** 100 m. sepia and brown 65 35

293. Al-Biruni and Scientific Diagram.

1980. The Arabs.
951. **293.** 50 m. multicoloured .. 35 20

294. Yachts at Sidi Bou Said.

1980. Sidi Bou Said.
952. **294.** 100 m. multicoloured 65 35

295. " Tourists ".

1980. World Tourism Conference, Manila.
953. **295.** 150 m. multicoloured 55 20

296. " Wedding at Djerba ".

1980. Yahia (painter) Commemoration.
954. **296.** 50 m. multicoloured .. 40 30

297. Aircraft over Tozeur. **298.** " Eye ".

1980. Opening of Tozeur International Airport.
955. **297.** 85 m. multicoloured .. 35 20

1980. 7th Afro-Asiatic Congress on Ophthalmology.
956. **298.** 100 m. multicoloured 55 35

299. Spider's Web.

1980. 1400th Anniv. of Hegira. Mult.
957. 50 m. Type **299** 20 20
958. 80 m. Minarets 35 20

300. Face as Camera. **301.** "Ophrys scolopax scolopax".

1980. Carthage Cinematographic Days.
959. **300.** 100 m. multicoloured 45 30

1980. Flora and Fauna. Multicoloured.
960. 20 m. Type **301** 20 20
961. 25 m. "Cyclamen europaeum" 20 20
962. 50 m. Barbary sheep .. 20 20
963. 100 m. Golden eagle .. 45 30

302. Kairouan Mosque.

1980. Conservation of Kairouan.
964. **302.** 85 m. multicoloured .. 35 20

303. H. von Stephan. **304.** Hands holding Bottle containing Blood drop.

1981. 150th Birth Anniv. of Heinrich von Stephan (founder of U.P.U.).
965. **303.** 150 m. multicoloured 65 35

1981. 20th Anniv. of Tunisian Blood Donors Association.
966. **304.** 75 m. multicoloured .. 65 45

305. Flags and Pres. Bourguiba. **306.** Flower and Pres. Bourguiba.

1981. 25th Anniv. of Independence. Mult.
967. 50 m. Type **305** 20 20
968. 60 m. Bird and ribbons forming "25" 35 20
969. 85 m. Stylized birds .. 55 35
970. 120 m. Victory riding a winged horse 55 35

1981. Special Congress of Destourian Socialist Party. Multicoloured.
972. 50 m. Type **306** 20 15
973. 75 m. Arrows forming flower 35 20

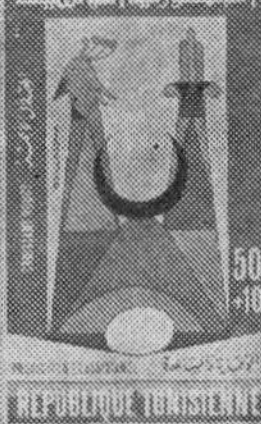

307. Mosque, Mahdia, and Galley. **308.** Stylized Peacock hatching Egg.

1981. Tourism. Multicoloured.
974. 50 m. Type **307** 20 20
975. 85 m. Djerid bride passing Great Mosque of Tozeur (vert.) 35 30
976. 100 m. Needle rocks, Tabarka 45 30

1981. Red Crescent.
977. **308.** 50 m.+10 m. multicoloured 35 35

309. I.T.U. and W.H.O. Emblems and Ribbons forming Caduceus. **310.** Flowers and Youths.

1981. World Telecommunications Day.
978. **309.** 150 m. multicoloured 60 30

1981. Youth Festival.
979. **310.** 100 m. multicoloured 45 20

311. Kemal Ataturk. **312.** Skifa Khala, Mahdia.

1981. Birth Cent. of Kemal Ataturk.
980. **311.** 150 m. multicoloured .. 65 35

1981. Tunisian Monuments.
981. **312.** 150 m. multicoloured 65 35

313. Cheikh Mohamed Tahar ben Achour and Minaret.

1981. Cheikh Mohamed Tahar ben Achour (scholar and teacher) Commemoration.
982. **313.** 200 m. multicoloured 1·00 45

314. Rejoicing Woman. **315.** Tree with Broken Branch.

1981. 25th Anniv. of Personal Status Code. Multicoloured.
983. 50 m. Type **314** 20 20
984. 100 m. Dove and head of woman 40 30

1981. International Year of Disabled People.
985. **315.** 250 m. multicoloured 1·00 65

316. Stylized Figure and Ka'aba, Mecca. **317.** Food Sources.

1981. Pilgrimage to Mecca.
986. **316.** 50 m. multicoloured 30 20

1981. World Food Day.
987. **317.** 200 m. multicoloured 90 50

318. Dome of the Rock.

1981. Palestinian Welfare.
988. **318.** 50 m.+5 m. mult. .. 35 20
989. 150 m.+5 m. mult. .. 60 35
990. 200 m.+5 m. mult. .. 90 50

319. Mnaguech (earring). **321.** Chemist (detail from 13th century manuscript).

320. Ship passing under Bridge.

1981. Jewellery. Multicoloured.
991. 150 m. Type **319** 60 30
992. 180 m. Mahfdha (pendant) (horiz.) 70 35
993. 200 m. Essalta (hairnet) .. 90 40

1981. Bizerta Drawbridge.
994. **320.** 230 m. multicoloured 80 40

1982. Arab Pharmacists' Union.
995. **321.** 80 m. multicoloured .. 55 35

322. Ring of People around Red Crescent.

1982. Red Crescent.
996. **322.** 80 m.+10 m. mult. .. 40 30

323. "Ocean Research". **324.** "Productive Family".

1982. International Symposium "Ocean Venture", Tunis.
997. **323.** 150 m. multicoloured 80 45

1982. The Productive Family.
998. **324.** 80 m. multicoloured .. 35 20

325. President Bourguiba and Woman's Head. **326.** Scout within "50".

1982. 25th Anniv. of Republic.
999. **325.** 80 m. blue and black 30 20
1000. – 100 m. multicoloured 40 30
1001. – 200 m. multicoloured 65 35

DESIGNS: 100 m. President and woman with "XXV" headband. 200 m. President and woman with "25" in hair.

1982. 75th Anniv. of Scout Movement and 50th Anniv. of Tunisian Scout Movement. Multicoloured.
1003. 80 m. Type **326** 35 20
1004. 200 m. Scout camp (vert.) 65 20

327. "Pseudophillipsia azzouzi". **328.** Tunisian Woman.

1982. Fossils. Multicoloured.
1005. 80 m. Type **327** 45 35
1006. 200 m. "Mediterraneotrigonia cherahilensis" 90 55
1007. 280 m. "Numidiopleura enigmatica" (horiz.) .. 1·10 80
1008. 300 m. "Micreschara tunisiensis" .. .. 1·40 90
1009. 500 m. "Mantelliceras pervinquieri" .. .. 2·75 1·40
1010. 1000 m. "Elephas africanavus" (horiz.) 5·50 2·75

1982. 30th Anniv. of Arab Postal Union.
1011. **328.** 80 m. multicoloured 40 20

329. I.T.U. Emblem. **330.** Tunisian Buildings and Congress Centre.

1982. I.T.U. Delegates' Conference, Nairobi.
1012. **329.** 200 m. multicoloured 65 45

1982. "Tunisia Land of Congresses".
1013. **330.** 200 m. multicoloured 65 30

331. "Feeding the World". **332.** Tahar Haddad.

1982. World Food Day.
1014. **331.** 200 m. multicoloured 65 30

1982. Tahar Haddad (social reformer) Commemoration.
1015. **332.** 200 m. brown .. 80 35

333. Microscope. **334.** Figure dancing in Rain.

1982. Cent. of Discovery of Tubercle Bacillus.
1016. **333.** 100 m. multicoloured 55 30

1982. Stories and Songs from Tunisia. Multicoloured.
1017. 20 m. Type **334** 15 15
1018. 30 m. Woman with broom 15 15
1019. 70 m. Boy and fisherman 20 15
1020. 80 m. Chicken (horiz.) .. 30 20
1021. 100 m. Woman admiring herself in mirror (horiz.) 40 20
1022. 120 m. Two girls .. 45 30

335. Clasped Hands and Palestine Flag.

1982. Palestinian Solidarity Day.
1023. **335.** 80 m. multicoloured 30 20

336. Farhat Hached. **337.** Bourguiba Sidi Saad Dam.

1982. 30th Death Anniv. of Farhat Hached.
1024. **336.** 80 m. red 35 20

1982. Inauguration of Bourguiba Sidi Saad Dam.
1025. **337.** 80 m. multicoloured 45 20

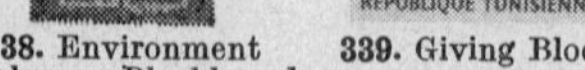

338. Environment Emblem on Blackboard.

339. Giving Blood.

1982. Opening of Environment Training Work School.

1026. **338.** 80 m. multicoloured 35 15

1983. Red Crescent.

1027. **339.** 80 m.+10 m. mult... 50 30

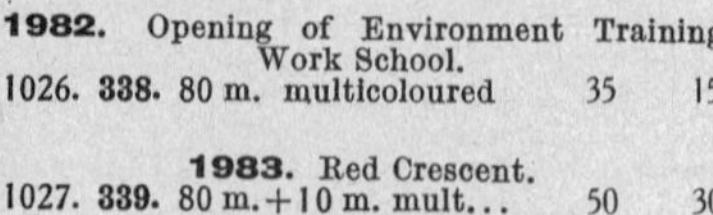

340. " Communications ".

1983. World Communications Year.

1028. **340.** 200 m. multicoloured 55 30

341. Dove and Map of Africa.

342. Customs Officer, Globes and Suitcases.

1983. 20th Anniv. of Organization of African Unity.

1029. **341.** 230 m. blue & dp. blue 65 40

1983. 20th Anniv. of Customs Co-operation Council.

1030. **342.** 100 m. multicoloured 35 20

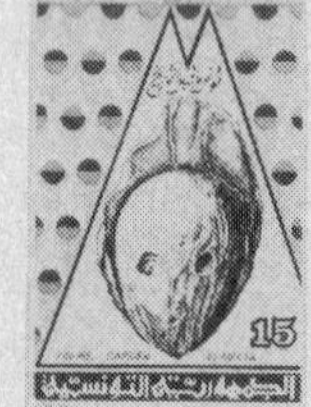

343. Aly Ben Ayed.

344. Carved Face, El Mekta.

1983. Aly Ben Ayed (actor) Commemoration.

1031. **343.** 80 m. red, black and deep red 30 30

1983. Pre-historic Artefacts. Mult.

1032. 15 m. Type **244** 20 20
1033. 20 m. Neolithic necklace, Kef el Agab (horiz.) .. 30 20
1034. 30 m. Neolithic grindstone, Redeyef (horiz.) .. 30 20
1035. 40 m. Animal petroglyph, Gafsa 35 20
1036. 80 m. Dolmen, Mactar (horiz.) 40 30
1037. 100 m. Bi-face flint, El Mekta 55 30

345. Dove, Barbed Wire and Dome of the Rock.

1983. Palestinian Welfare.

1038. **345.** 80 m.+5 m. mult. .. 40 40

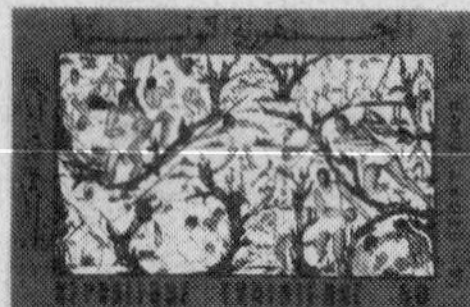

346. Sporting Activities.

1983. Sport for All.

1039. **346.** 40 m. multicoloured 15 10

347. Tunisian with Flag and French Freighter.

348. Fishing Boats and Fish.

1983. 20th Anniv. of Evacuation of Foreign Troops.

1040. **347.** 80 m. multicoloured 30 20

1983. World Fishing Day.

1041. **348.** 200 m. multicoloured 70 20

349. " The Weaver " (Hedi Khayachi).

1983. Hedi Khayachi (painter) Commem.

1042. **349.** 80 m. multicoloured 45 35

350. Saluting the Flag.

351. Air Hostess and Aircraft.

1983. Salute to the Flag.

1043. **350.** 100 m. multicoloured 35 20

1983. 25th Anniv. of Tunisian Civil Aviation and Meteorology.

1044. **351.** 150 m. multicoloured 55 20

352. Pres. Bourguiba and Archway.

353. Map of Africa.

1984. 50th Anniv. of Neo-Destour Party. Multicoloured.

1045. 40 m. Type **352** 15 10
1046. 70 m. Bourguiba & torch 20 10
1047. 80 m. Bourguiba and flag 30 15
1048. 150 m. Bourguiba & wall 50 30
1049. 200 m. Bourguiba & dove (horiz.) 60 35
1050. 230 m. Pres. Bourguiba (horiz.) 70 45

1984. Fourth School of Molecular Biology.

1052. **353.** 100 m. multicoloured 55 30

354. First Aid.

1984. Red Crescent.

1053. **354.** 80 m.+10 m. mult. 40 30

355. Ibn el Jazzar.

356. "Co-operation".

1984. Ibn el Jazzár (doctor). Commem.

1054. **355.** 80 m. multicoloured 40 30

1984. Economic Co-operation among Developing Countries.

1055. **356.** 230 m. multicoloured 80 35

357. Witch, Maiden and Coquette.

1984. Stories and Songs from Tunisia. Multicoloured.

1056. 20 m. Type **357** 10 10
1057. 80 m. Puppet, hands and mouse 30 20
1058. 100 m. Boy and horse (vert.) 35 15

358. Family facing the Future.

1984. 20th Anniv. of Tunisian Education and Family Organization.

1059. **358.** 80 m. multicoloured 30 20

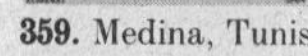

359. Medina, Tunis.

360. Aboul Qasim Chabbi.

1984. National Heritage Protection.

1060. **359.** 100 m. multicoloured 35 30

1984. 50th Death Anniv. of Aboul Qasim Chabbi (poet).

1061. **360.** 100 m. sepia, light brown and brown 35 20

361. Emblem, Stylised Bird and Airplane.

1984. 40th Anniv. of International Civil Aviation Organization.

1062. **361.** 200 m multicoloured 65 20

362. Band and Singers.

1984. Sahara Festival.

1063. **362.** 20 m. multicoloured 45 20

363. Telephonist, Satellite and Dish Aerial.

1984. 20th Anniv. of "Intelsat" Communication Satellite.

1064. **363.** 100 m. multicoloured 35 15

364. "Mediterranean Countryside".

1984. Jilani Abdulwahelb (artist). Commem.

1065. **364.** 100 m. multicoloured 55 35

365. Profile and Exterior of House.

366. Crescents and Stars within Circle.

1985. "Expo 85" World's Fair, Tsukuba.

1066. **365.** 200 m. multicoloured 65 35

1985. Red Crescent.

1067. **366.** 100 m+10 m. mult. 35 30

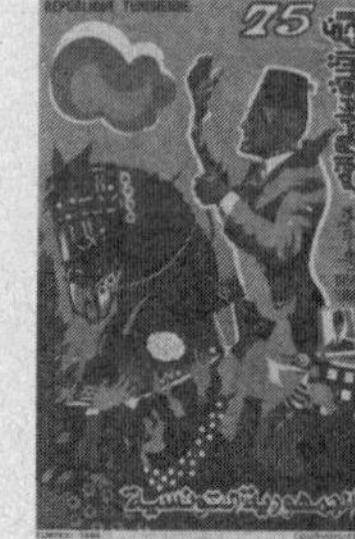

367. Hands reaching from Sea and Flames.

368. Pres. Bourguiba on Horseback.

1985. 3rd Civil Protection Week.

1068. **367.** 100 m. multicoloured 30 15

1985. 30th Anniv. of Independence. Mult.

1069. 75 m. Type **368** 20 10
1070. 100 m. Pres. Bourguiba in boat and crowd on quay (horiz.) 30 10
1071. 200 m. Pres. Bourguiba in sombrero 55 20
1072. 230 m. Pres. Bourguiba waving to crowd from balcony (horiz.) .. 60 20

369. Pres. Bourguiba and Ancient Sculpture.

1985. Tunisian Day at "Expo '85" World's Fair, Tsukuba.

1074. **369.** 250 m. multicoloured 80 30

MINIMUM PRICE

The minimum price quoted is 5p which represents a handling charge rather than a basis for valuing common stamps. For further notes about prices see introductory pages.

370. Images within Film.

372. Heart as Dove and I.Y.Y. Emblem.

371. Dark Clouds, Sun and Flowers.

1985. International Amateur Film Festival, Kelibia.

1075. **370.** 250 m. multicoloured 95 35

1985. Stories and Songs from Tunisia. Multicoloured.

1076. 25 m. Type **371** 10 10
1077. 50 m. Man's profile and hand holding women 15 10
1078. 100 m. Man and cooking pot over fire 35 15

1985. International Youth Year.

1079. **372.** 250 m. multicoloured 80 30

373. "The Perfumiers Hall".

1985. Painting by Hedi Larnaout.

1080. **373.** 100 m. multicoloured 45 20

374. Matmata Wedding Dress.

375. Stylised People and U.N. Emblem.

1985. Wedding Dresses (1st series). Mult.

1081. 20 m. Type **374** 10 10
1082. 50 m. Moknine dress . . 15 10
1083. 100 m. Tunis dress . . 35 15

See also Nos. 1099/1101.

1985. 40th Anniv. of U.N.O.

1084. **375.** 250 m. multicoloured 80 30

376. Harvest (Makthar stele).

1985. Food Self-sufficiency.

1085 **376** 100 m. multicoloured 35 20

377. Emblem illuminating Globe and Flags.

378. Aziza Othmana.

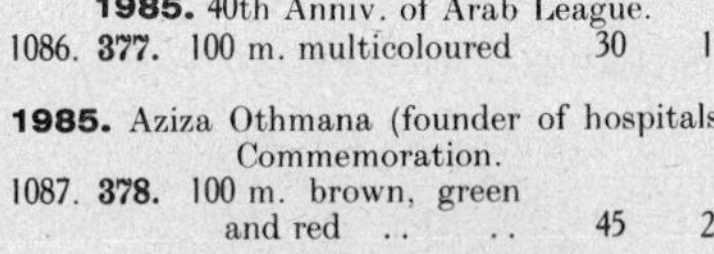

1985. 40th Anniv. of Arab League.

1086. **377.** 100 m. multicoloured 30 15

1985. Aziza Othmana (founder of hospitals) Commemoration.

1087. **378.** 100 m. brown, green and red 45 20

379. Surveying Instruments and Books forming Face.

380. Dove and Pres. Bourguiba.

1985. Centenary of Land Law.

1088. **379.** 100 m. multicoloured 30 10

1986. 30th Anniv. of Independence.

1089. **380.** 100 m. multicoloured 30 10
1090. – 120 m. black, blue and deep blue . . 35 15
1091. – 280 m. blue, violet and black 80 35
1092. – 300 m. multicoloured 85 40

DESIGNS—HORIZ. 120 m. Rocket. 280 m. Horse and rider. VERT. 300 m. Balloons.

381. Hulusi Behcet (dermatologist).

382. Map and Red Crescent.

1986. 3rd Mediterranean Rheumatology Days, Tunis, and Ninth International Society of Geographical Ophthalmology Congress, Monastir. Multicoloured.

1094. 300 m. Type **381** 1·25 35
1095. 380 m. Behcet and sun and eye emblems . . 1·60 45

1986. World Red Crescent and Red Cross Day.

1096. **382.** 120 m. + 10 m. mult. 40 30

383. Pres. Bourguiba, Symbols and "12".

1986. 12th Destourian Socialist Party Congress, Tunis. Multicoloured.

1097. 120 m. Type **383** . . 30 10
1098. 300 m. Flaming torch, Pres. Bourguiba and "12" 85 30

384. Homt Souk Dress.

385. Hassen Husni Abdulwaheb.

1986. Wedding Dresses (2nd series). Mult.

1099. 40 m. Type **384** 10 10
1100. 280 m. Mahdia dress . . 80 30
1101. 300 m. Nabeul dress . . 90 35

1986. Hassen Husni Abdulwaheb (historian) Commemoration.

1102. **385.** 160 m. red 55 20

386. Reconstructed View of Carthage.

1986. 2800th Anniv. of Foundation of Carthage.

1103. **386.** 2 d. purple . . . . 6·00 2·25

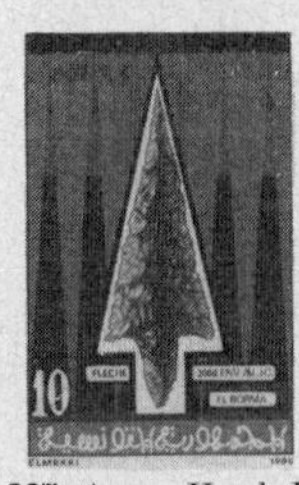

387. Arrow Head, El Borma, 3000 B.C.

388. "Bedouins".

1986. Prehistoric Artefacts. Multicoloured.

1104 10 m. Type **387** 20 20
1105 20 m. Tomb, Sejnane, 1000 B.C. 20 20
1106 50 m. Bas-relief, Zaghouan, 1000 B.C. (horiz) 35 20
1107 120 m. Neolithic vase, Kesra (horiz) 55 20
1108 160 m. Painting of Phoenician ship, Kef el Blida, 800 B.C. (horiz) 65 20
1109 250 m. 7th-century decorated pottery, Sejnane 1·40 40

1986. Painting by Ammar Farhat.

1110. **388.** 250 m. multicoloured 90 35

389. Doves and Globe.

1986. International Peace Year.

1111. **389.** 300 m. multicoloured 85 35

390. Emblem.

391. Computer Terminal.

1986. 40th Anniv. of F.A.O.

1112. **390.** 280 m. multicoloured 80 30

1986. Introduction of Computers into Education.

1113. **391.** 2 d. multicoloured . . 6·00 2·25

392. Mother and Child.

393. Mountain Gazelle (Chambi National Park).

1986. Child Survival.

1114. **392.** 120 m. multicoloured 35 10

1986. National Parks. Multicoloured.

1115. 60 m. Type **393** 15 10
1116. 120 m. Addax (Bou Hedma National Park) . . 30 10
1117. 350 m. Monk seal (Zembra and Zembretta National Park) . . 85 30
1118. 380 m. Greylag goose (Ichkeul National Park) 1·50 80

394. Pres. Bourgiba and Arms.

1987. Centenary of Monastir Municipality.

1119. **394.** 120 m. multicoloured 35 15

395. Radiation and Red Crescent Symbols in Face.

1987. Radiation Protection and Red Crescent.

1120. **395.** 150 m. + 10 m. mult. 55 45

396. Samuel Morse (inventor) and Morse Key.

1987. 150th Anniv. of Morse Telegraph.

1121. **396.** 500 m. multicoloured 1·40 55

397. Pres. Bourgiba and Woman's Head.

1987. 30th Anniv. of Republic. Designs each show Pres. Bourgiba and a different woman's head.

1122. **397.** 150 m. mauve, brown and yellow . . 35 25
1123. – 250 m. brown, red and yellow . . 55 25
1124. – 350 m. blue, brown and green 80 20
1125. – 500 m. multicoloured 1·10 35

398. Hand injecting Baby in Globe and Dove holding Syringe.

399. "The Road".

1987. Universal Vaccination for Everyone by 1990. 40th Anniv. of United Nations Children's Fund.

1127. **398.** 250 m. multicoloured 65 45

1987. 25th Death Anniv. of Azouz Ben Rais (painter).

1128. **399.** 250 m. multicoloured 90 45

400. Couple's Faces in House.

1987. Arab Housing Day.

1129. **400.** 150 m. multicoloured 40 30

INDEX

Countries can be quickly located by referring to the index at the end of this volume.

401. Dove carrying Parcel. **402.** Ibn Mandhour.

1987. 30th Anniv. of Consultative Postal Studies Council. Multicoloured.
1130. 150 m. Type **401** .. 35 10
1131. 350 m. Postman and electronically sorted letters 80 30

1987. 675th Death Anniv. of Ibn Mandhour (lexicographer).
1132. **402.** 250 m. purple .. 80 45

403. Bunches of Grapes. **404.** Player with Ball.

1987. International Vine Year.
1133. **403.** 250 m. multicoloured 80 35

1987. 6th African Nations Volleyball Championship, Tunis.
1134. **404.** 350 m. multicoloured 1·10 45

405. Players and Ball. **406.** Tunis Institute and Adrien Loir (first director).

1987. African Basketball Championships.
1135. **405.** 350 m. multicoloured 1·10 45

1987. Centenary of Pasteur Institute, Paris.
1136. **406.** 250 m. green, brown and black 80 35

407. Midoun. **408.** Narcissi.

1987. Costumes. Multicoloured.
1137. 20 m. Type **407** 10 10
1138. 30 m. Tozeur 10 10
1139. 150 m. Sfax 40 15

1987. Flowers. Multicoloured.
1140. 30 m. Type **408** 10 10
1141. 150 m. Gladioli 40 15
1142. 400 m. Iris .. .. 1·00 35
1143. 500 m. Tulips .. .. 1·25 55

409 Hand holding Scales of Justice

1988. Declaration of 7 November, 1987. Multicoloured.
1144 150 m. Type **409** (Justice for all) 35 20
1145 200 m. Girl with party badges as flowers in hair (Multi-party system) (vert) .. 45 20
1146 350 m. Girl in cornfield wearing coat of arms (International co-peration and friendship) 80 35
1147 370 m. Maghreb states emblem (vert) .. 90 35

410 Couple

1988. Youth and Change. Multicoloured.
1149 75 m. Type **410** 20 15
1150 150 m. Young people .. 35 15

411 Crowd with Banners

1988. 50th Anniv of Martyrs' Day.
1151 **411** 150 m. orange & brn 35 15
1152 – 500 m. multicoloured 1·10 40
DESIGN: 500 m. Martyrs monumemt.

412 Roses and Banners

1988. 125th Anniv of Red Cross.
1153 **412** 150 m.+10 m. mult .. 45 35

413 Hand saving drowning Country

1988. 1st Democratic Constitutional Assembly Congress.
1154 **413** 150 m. multicoloured 35 15

414 Sportsmen

1988. Olympic Games, Seoul. Multicoloured.
1155 150 m. Type **414** .. 40 20
1156 430 m. Sportsman (diff) .. 1·00 45

415 Beit Hussein Sari and Eye **416** "7" and Flowers

1988. Restoration of Sana'a, Yemen.
1157 **415** 200 m. multicoloured 45 20

1988. 1st Anniv of Presidency of Zine el Abidine.
1158 **416** 150 m. multicoloured 35 15

417 "Amilcar Beach, 1942"

1988. 70th Birth Anniv of Amara Debbeche (painter).
1159 **417** 100 m. multicoloured 35 20

418 Airplane and Globe forming "40" **419** Man Holding Book

1988. 40th Anniv of Tunis Air.
1160 **418** 500 m. multicoloured 1·50 70

1988. 40th Anniv of Declaration of Human Rights.
1161 **419** 370 m. black 85 45

420 Tweezers and Magnifying Glasses forming "100"

1988. Cent of First Tunisian Postage Stamps.
1162 **420** 150 m. multicoloured 55 30

421 18th-century Door, Rue du Tresor **422** Ali Douagi

1988. Tunis Doorways and Fountains. Mult.
1163 50 m. Type **421** 10 10
1164 70 m. 19th-century door, Rue el Mbazaa .. 15 10
1165 100 m. 15th-16th century door, Rue des Fabricants de Tamis .. 20 10
1166 150 m. 19th-century door, Rue Bach Hamba .. 30 15
1167 370 m. 16th-17th century door, Rue el Ariane .. 70 30
1168 400 m. Fountain, Manouba, 1793 .. 80 35

1989. 40th Death Anniv of Ali Douagi (writer).
1169 **422** 1 d. blue .. .. 2·25 65

423 Stretcher Bearers **424** Crippled Person and Healthy Girl

1989. Red Crescent.
1170 **423** 150 m.+10 m. mult .. 40 30

1989. National Day for Disabled People.
1171 **424** 150 m. multicoloured .. 45 20

425 Children using Computer and Microscope

1989. Knowledge Day.
1172 **425** 180 m. multicoloured 40 20

426 Clasped Hands

1989. 20th Anniv of Tunisian Family Planning Association.
1173 **426** 150 m. multicoloured 35 15

427 Family

1989. Family Welfare.
1174 **427** 150 m. multicoloured 35 15

428 Tortoise

1989. Endangered Animals. Multicoloured.
1175 250 m. Type **428** .. 65 35
1176 350 m. Oryx .. .. 1·00 45

429 Flags and Emblem **430** Beyram

1989. Tunis International Fair (1990). Mult.
1177 150 m. Type **429** .. 35 15
1178 370 m. Fair Pavilion .. 80 35

1989. Death Centenary of Mohamed Beyram (writer).
1179 **430** 150 m. purple & black 35 15

431 Actors wearing Comedy Masks **432** Monument, Tunis

1989. Carthage Theatre Festival.
1180 **431** 300 m. multicoloured 65 35

1989. 2nd Anniv of Declaration of 7 November 1987.
1181 **432** 150 m. multicoloured 35 20

433 Nehru
434 Members' Flags

1989. Birth Centenary of Jawaharlal Nehru (Indian statesman).
1182 **433** 300 m. brown 65 35

1990. Maghreb Union Presidential Summit.
1183 **434** 200 m. multicoloured 45 30

435 Museum and Sculptures

1990. Centenary of Bardo Museum.
1184 **435** 300 m. multicoloured 80 45

436 Ceramic Tiles, Vases and Crockery

1990. Arts and Crafts. Multicoloured.
1185 75 m. Type **436** 15 10
1186 100 m. Copper pots and grinder 20 15

437 Ram and Ewes

1990. Ram Museum. Multicoloured.
1187 400 m. Type **437** .. 90 35
1188 450 m. Ram's head .. 1·00 45

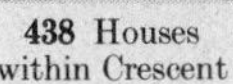

438 Houses within Crescent
440 Child's Drawing

439 Olympic Rings and Athlete

1990. Red Crescent.
1190 **438** 150 m. + 10 m. mult .. 35 20

1990. Tunisian Olympic Movement.
1191 **439** 150 m. multicoloured 35 15

1990. The Child and the Environment.
1192 **440** 150 m. multicoloured 35 15

441 Sbiba Horseman
442 Dougga

1990. Costumes. Multicoloured.
1193 150 m. Type **441** .. 45 35
1194 500 m. Bou Omrane man 1·40 65

1990. Tourism.
1195 **442** 300 m. multicoloured 65 35

443 Adults learning to Read and Write

1990. International Literacy Year.
1196 **443** 120 m. multicoloured 30 15

444 Figures, Tree and Fishes in Water
445 Fireworks and Date

1990. Water.
1197 **444** 150 m. multicoloured 45 30

1990. 3rd Anniv of Declaration of 7 November 1987. Multicoloured.
1198 150 m. Type **445** .. 35 15
1199 150 m. Clock tower .. 35 15

446 Kheireddine et Tounsi
447 Red Deer

1990. Death Centenary of Kheireddine et Tounsi (political reformer).
1200 **446** 150 m. green .. 45 20

1990 Flora and Fauna. Multicoloured.
1201 150 m. Type **447** .. 35 15
1202 200 m. Thistle 45 15
1203 300 m. Water buffalo .. 65 20
1204 600 m. Orchid .. .. 1·40 55

448 Members' Flags forming Star
449 Montazah Tabarka

1991. 2nd Anniv of Maghreb Union.
1205 **448** 180 m. multicoloured 45 20

1991. Tourism.
1206 **449** 450 m. multicoloured 1·00 45

450 Doves and Emblem
451 Sea Bream

1991. Red Crescent. Help for War Victims.
1207 **450** 180 m. + 10 m. mult .. 45 35

1991. Fishes. Multicoloured.
1208 180 m. Type **451** .. 45 20
1209 350 m. Red mullet .. 85 35
1210 450 m. Mackerel .. .. 1·10 45
1211 550 m. Gunner bream .. 1·40 65

452 Vase of Flowers (Taieb Khlif)

1991. Children's Rights.
1212 **452** 450 m. multicoloured 1·00 35

453 "Plein-Sud" (anon)

1991.
1213 **453** 400 m. multicoloured 90 35

454 Bracelets and Ring
455 Date and Profile of Woman

1991. Jewellery. Multicoloured.
1214 120 m. Type **454** .. 30 15
1215 180 m. Headdress and necklace (vert) .. 40 15
1216 220 m. Headdress, earrings and collar (vert) .. 45 20
1217 730 m. Key ring (vert) .. 1·60 80

1991. 4th Anniv of Declaration of 7 November 1987.
1218 **455** 180 m. multicoloured 45 20

456 Sorting Office

1991. Tunis-Carthage Sorting Office.
1219 **456** 80 m. blue, red & green 20 10

457 Dove and Globe
458 Bayram Ettounsi

1991. World Human Rights Day.
1220 **457** 450 m. blue .. .. 1·00 35

1991. 31st Death Anniv of Bayram Ettounsi.
1221 **458** 200 m. blue 45 15

459 Emblem on Microchip
460 G.P.O.

1992. "Expo '92" World's Fair, Seville.
1222 **459** 180 m. multicoloured 45 20

1992. Centenary of General Post Office, Tunis.
1223 **460** 180 m. brown .. 45 20
1224 – 450 m. brown .. 1·00 35
DESIGN—VERT. 450 m. Different view of G.P.O.

461 "When the Subconscious Awakes" (Moncef ben Amor)

1992.
1225 **461** 500 m. multicoloured 1·10 45

462 Running
463 European Bee Eater

1992. Olympic Games, Barcelona. Mult.
1226 180 m. Type **462** .. 65 30
1227 450 m. Judo (vert) .. 1·60 55

1992. Birds. Multicoloured.
1228 100 m. Type **463** .. 45 15
1229 180 m. Goldfinch .. 65 35
1230 200 m. Serin 85 35
1231 500 m. Greenfinch .. 1·60 85

464 President and Children
465 Women and Open Book

1992. United Nations Convention on Rights of the Child.
1233 **464** 180 m. multicoloured 45 30

1992. African Regional Human Rights Conference, Tunis.
1234 **465** 480 m. multicoloured 1·10 65

466 Ribbon forming "7"

467 "Acacia tortilis"

1992. 5th Anniv of Declaration of 7 November 1987. Multicoloured.

1235	180 m. Type **466** ..	45	20
1236	730 m. President with people and doves ..	1·75	90

1992. National Tree Day.

1237	**467**	180 m. multicoloured	45	30

468 Stylized Figure and Emblems

1992. International Nutrition Conference, Rome.

1238	**468**	450 m. multicoloured	1·10	55

469 Chemesse

470 "Billy Goat between Two Bushes" (El Jem)

1992. Traditional Costumes. Multicoloured.

1239	100 m. Type **469** ..	30	20
1240	350 m. Hanifites ..	85	45

1992. Mosaics. Multicoloured.

1241	100 m. Type **470** ..	30	15
1242	180 m. "Wild Duck" (El Jem)	50	35
1243	350 m. "Racehorse" (Sidi Abdallah)	90	45
1244	450 m. "Gazelle in the Grass" (El Jem) ..	1·10	70

471 Wolf

1993. Flora and Fauna. Multicoloured.

1245	20 m. Type **471**	10	10
1246	60 m. "Hoya carnosa" (plant) (vert)	10	10

472 Line Graph on World Map

1993. United Nations World Conference on Human Rights, Vienna.

1247	**472**	450 m. multicoloured	60	30

473 Publicity Poster inside Open Brief-case

474 "Relaxing on the Patio" (Ali Guermassi)

1993. Arab–African Fair, Tunis.

1248	**473**	450 m. multicoloured	60	30

1993.

1249	**474**	450 m. multicoloured	60	30

475 Conference Emblem

476 Blood Transfusion

1993. Constitutional Democratic Assembly Party Conference.

1250	**475**	180 m. red and black	25	15

1993. Red Crescent. "Dignity for All".

1251	**476**	120 m. + 30 m. mult ..	20	10

477 Louis Pasteur and Charles Nicolle (former director)

1993. Centenary of Pasteur Institute, Tunis.

1252	**477**	450 m. multicoloured	60	30

PARCEL POST STAMPS

P 8. Mail Carrier.

P 25. Date Gathering.

1906.

P 44.	P **8.**	5 c. purple and green	20	15
P 45.		10 c. pink and red ..	20	20
P 46.		20 c. red and brown ..	65	20
P 47.		25 c. brown and blue	1·00	20
P 48.		40 c. red and grey ..	1·00	25
P 49.		50 c. violet and brown	1·00	15
P 50.		75 c. blue and brown	2·00	20
P 51.		1 f. red and brown ..	1·40	10
P 52.		2 f. blue and red ..	3·75	25
P 53.		5 f. brown and violet	7·00	55

1926.

P147	P **25**	5 c. blue and brown	15	20
P148		10 c. mauve and red	20	20
P149		20 c. black and green	25	20
P150		25 c. black & brown	30	25
P151		40 c. green and red	65	70
P152		50 c. black & violet	65	75
P153		60 c. red and brown	65	70
P154		75 c. green and lilac	65	65
P155		80 c. brown and red	65	40
P156		1 f. pink and blue ..	60	35
P157		2 f. red and mauve	1·00	30
P158		4 f. black and red ..	1·25	25
P159		5 f. violet and brown	1·50	30
P160		10 f. green and red on green ..	1·75	50
P161		20 f. violet and green on pink	10·00	1·50

POSTAGE DUE STAMPS

D 3.

D 20. Carthaginian Statue.

D 36. Agricultural Produce.

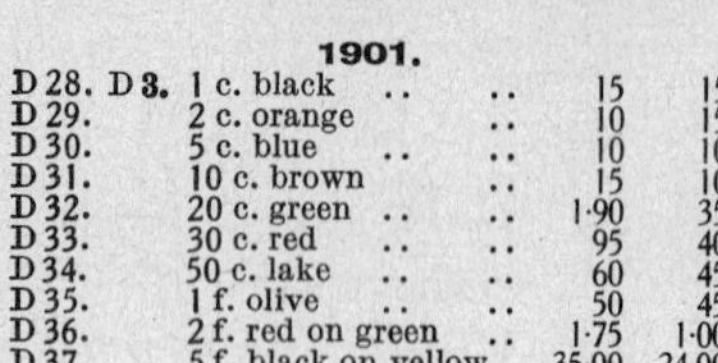

1901.

D 28.	D **3.**	1 c. black	15	15
D 29.		2 c. orange ..	10	15
D 30.		5 c. blue	10	10
D 31.		10 c. brown ..	15	10
D 32.		20 c. green	1·90	35
D 33.		30 c. red	95	40
D 34.		50 c. lake	60	45
D 35.		1 f. olive	50	45
D 36.		2 f. red on green ..	1·75	1·00
D 37.		5 f. black on yellow	35·00	24·00

1914. Surch. **2 FRANCS.**

D 49.	D **3.**	2 f. on 5 f. blk. on yell.	60	80

1923.

D100	D **20**	1 c. black	10	35
D101		2 c. black on yellow	10	40
D102		5 c. purple ..	10	40
D103		10 c. blue	20	25
D104		20 c. orange on yell	20	20
D105		30 c. brown ..	10	20
D106		50 c. red	40	30
D107		60 c. mauve ..	40	35
D108		80 c. brown ..	25	30
D109		90 c. red	40	40
D110		1 f. green	15	20
D111		2 f. green	20	25
D112		3 f. violet on pink	20	30
D113		5 f. violet	30	45

1945.

D287	D **20**	10 c. green ..	10	30
D288		50 c. violet ..	10	30
D289		2 f. pink	15	20
D290		4 f. blue	25	45
D291		10 f. mauve ..	25	45
D292		20 f. brown ..	60	55
D293		30 f. blue	80	70

No. D293 is inscribed "TIMBRE TAXE"

1957.

D 448.	D **86.**	1 f. green	20	20
D 449.		2 f. brown	20	20
D 450.		3 f. green	40	40
D 451.		4 f. blue	45	45
D 452.		5 f. mauve	45	45
D 453.		10 f. red	45	45
D 454.		20 f. sepia	1·40	1·40
D 455.		30 f. blue	1·60	1·60

1960. Inscr. " REPUBLIQUE TUNISIENNE " and new currency.

D 534.	D **86.**	1 m. green	10	10
D 535.		2 m. brown	10	10
D 536.		3 m. green	15	15
D 537.		4 m. blue	15	15
D 538.		5 m. violet	20	20
D 539.		10 m. red	40	40
D 540.		20 m. brown ..	60	60
D 541.		30 m. blue	70	70
D 542.		40 m. brown ..	15	15
D 543.		100 m. green ..	40	30

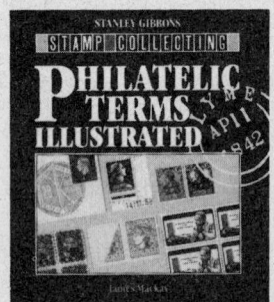

TURKEY Pt. 16

Formerly an empire, this country is now a republic, the greater part of its territory lying in Asia Minor.

1863. 40 paras = 1 piastre or grush.
1942. 100 paras = 1 kurus.
1947. 100 kurus = 1 lira.

For designs as Types **1, 2, 9, 15, 21, 23, 25, 28** and **30** but in black or brown, see Postage Due stamps.

1.

2.

1863. Imperf.
1. 1. 20 pa. black on yellow .. 60·00 25·00
2. 1 pi. black on purple .. 75·00 27·00
3. 2 pi. black on blue .. 85·00 38·00
4. 5 pi. black on red .. 95·00 55·00

1865. Perf.
11 2 10 pa. green .. .. 2·75 8·50
64 10 pa. mauve 15 40
35a 10 pa. brown .. .. 40·00 2·25
12 20 pa. yellow .. .. 90 1·50
65 20 pa. green 15 40
94 20 pa. grey 55 85
13 1 pi. lilac .. .. 1·75 2·00
66 1 pi. yellow 20 25
14 2 pi. blue .. .. 1·00 1·25
95 2 pi. red to brown .. 25 25
15 5 pi. red .. .. 50 2·25
46 5 pi. blue 20 95
39c 5 pi. grey .. .. 7·50 12·00
16 25 pi. orange .. .. 95·00 £130
48 25 pi. red .. .. 6·00 20·00

1876. Surch. with value in figures and **Pre.**
77. 2. ½ pre. on 10 pa. mauve .. 1·00 1·00
78. ½ pre. on 20 pa. green .. 2·25 2·25
79. 1½ pre. on 50 pa. red .. 20 2·50
80. 2 pre. on 2 pi. brown .. 8·00 2·25
81. 5 pre. on 5 pi. blue .. 1·00 10·00

9.

15.

1876.
89 9 5 pa. black and yellow 20 20
96 5 pa. lilac .. .. 35·00 38·00
109 5 pa. black 15 55
113 5 pa. green and yellow 15 15
82 10 pa. black and mauve 25 30
90 10 pa. black and green 20 20
97 10 pa. green 20 10
83 20 pa. purple and green 24·00 2·25
91 20 pa. black and pink .. 1·00 15
103 20 pa. pink 15 10
84 50 pa. blue and yellow 40 60
92 1 pi. black and grey (A) 1·50 15
93 1 pi. black and blue (B) 25·00 1·00
99 1 pi. blue 15 10
85 2 pi. black and flesh 20 35
126a 2 pi. yellow 20 20
110 2 pi. orange and blue .. 15 15
114 2 pi. mauve and grey .. 25 25
86 5 pi. pink and blue .. 75 1·50
115 5 pi. brown .. .. 75 2·50
111 5 pi. green .. .. 65 2·00
87 25 pi. purple and mauve 6·00 18·00
107 25 pi. black .. .. 65·00 £110
112 25 pi. brown .. .. 9·00 15·00
116 25 pi. red and yellow .. 9·00 22·00

1892. Various frames.
141 15 10 pa. green 15 10
142a 20 pa. red 25 10
143 1 pi. blue .. .. 4·50 10
144 2 pi. brown 40 15
145 5 pi. purple .. .. 1·50 2·00

1897. Surch **5 5 Cinq Paras.**
160 15 5 pa. on 10 pa. green .. 35 10

21.

22.

23.

1901. For Internal Mail.
167 21 5 pa. violet 15 10
168 10 pa. green 15 10
169 20 pa. red 15 10
170 1 pi. blue 15 10
171 2 pi. orange 40 10
203 5 pi. mauve .. .. 1·00 20
173 25 pi. brown .. .. 3·75 1·50
174 50 pi. brown .. .. 6·50 2·00

1901. For Foreign Mail.
175. 22. 5 pa. brown 25 15
176. 10 pa. green 15 10
177. 20 pa. mauve 15 10
178. 1 pi. blue 40 10
179. 2 pi. blue 60 20
180. 5 pi. brown .. .. 1·75 85
181. 25 pi. green .. .. 13·00 8·00
182. 50 pi. yellow .. .. 40·00 25·00

ب
(24.)

Type **24** is the Turkish letter "B" which stands for Behie = discount.

1905.
212 23 5 pa. brown 10 10
213 10 pa. green 10 10
214 20 pa. pink 10 10
215 1 pi. blue 15 10
216 2 pi. blue 25 10
217 2½ pi. purple 45 15
218 5 pi. brown 75 25
219 10 pi. orange .. .. 1·10 30
220 25 pi. green .. .. 2·75 1·75
221 50 pi. purple .. .. 12·00 4·75

1906. Optd with T **24**.
230 23 10 pa. green 20 10
231 20 pa. pink 20 10
232 1 pi. blue 40 10
233 2 pi. blue .. .. 3·00 2·50

25.

27.

28.

1908.
234 25 5 pa. brown 10 10
235 10 pa. green 20 10
236 20 pa. red .. .. 6·00 10
237 1 pi. blue .. .. 1·50 10
238 2 pi. black .. .. 1·75 15
239 2½ pi. brown 70 15
240 5 pi. purple .. .. 2·75 15
241 10 pi. red .. .. 8·00 1·75
242 25 pi. green .. .. 3·00 2·25
243 50 pi. brown .. .. 8·00 5·50

1908. Optd as T **24** but smaller.
252 25 10 pa. green 85 30
253 20 pa. red .. .. 1·25 40
254 1 pi. blue .. .. 1·90 70
255 2 pi. black .. .. 4·00 1·75

1908. Granting of Constitution.
256 27 5 pa. brown 20 15
257 10 pa. green 20 15
258 20 pa. red 45 25
259 1 pi. blue 50 25
260 2 pi. black .. .. 6·50 3·00

1909.
271 28 2 pa. green 10 10
261 5 pa. brown 10 10
262 10 pa. green 10 10
263 20 pa. red 15 10
264 1 pi. blue 25 10
265 2 pi. black 25 10
266 2½ pi. brown .. .. 8·50 6·00
267 5 pi. purple .. .. 1·75 20
268 10 pi. red .. .. 3·00 40
269 25 pi. green .. .. 55·00 25·00
270 50 pi. brown .. .. 22·00 22·00

1909. Optd as T **24** but smaller.
289 28 10 pa. green 35 10
290 20 pa. red 20 10
291 1 pi. blue 45 20
292 2 pi. black .. .. 6·00 3·25

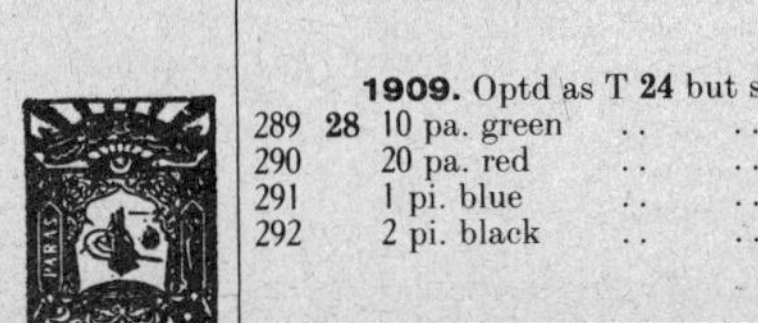

1910. No. 261 surch **2** and Turkish inscr.
296 28 2 pa. on 5 pa. brown .. 10 10

30. G.P.O. Constantinople.

31. Mosque of Selim.

1913.
333 30 2 pa. green 10 10
334 5 pa. bistre 10 10
335 10 pa. green 10 10
336 20 pa. pink 10 10
337 1 pi. blue 10 10
338 2 pi. grey 15 10
339 5 pi. purple 35 15
340 10 pi. red .. .. 1·25 55
341 25 pi. green .. .. 4·25 2·00
342 50 pi. brown .. .. 13·00 14·00

1913. Optd as T **24** but smaller.
343 30 10 pa. green 15 10
344 20 pa. pink 15 10
345 1 pi. blue 40 10
346 2 pi. grey .. .. 2·50 1·00

1913. Recapture of Adrianople.
353 31 10 pa. green 35 20
963 20 pa. red 15 10
355 40 pa. blue 85 55

For Type **31** surcharged, see Postage Due stamps.

32. Obelisk of Theodosius.

34. Leander's Tower.

1914.
499 32 2 pa. purple 10 20
500 – 4 pa. brown 10 25
501 34 5 pa. purple 10 10
961 5 pa. brown 10 15
502 – 6 pa. blue 15 30
503 – 10 pa. green 15 10
504 – 20 pa. red 40 10
518 – 1 pi. blue 30 10
964 – 1 pi. green .. .. 1·75 25
506 – 1½ pi. grey and red .. 40 35
507 – 1¾ pi. brown and grey .. 25 10
508 – 2 pi. black and green .. 1·00 30
509 – 2½ pi. green and orange 50 15
965 – 3 pi. blue 20 20
510 – 5 pi. lilac .. .. 2·75 40
966 – 5 pi. grey .. .. 6·50 50
511 – 10 pi. brown .. .. 3·75 50
967 – 10 pi. lilac .. .. 2·25 25
512 – 25 pi. green .. .. 24·00 2·75
968 – 25 pi. purple .. .. 60 1·25
513 – 50 pi. pink .. .. 3·50 2·25
969 – 50 pi. brown .. .. 75 2·50
514 – 100 pi. blue .. .. 22·00 18·00
515 – 200 pi. black and green £225 £150

DESIGNS—VERT. 4 pa. Column of Constantine. 6 pa. Seven Towers Castle, Yedikule. HORIZ. 10 pa. Lighthouse-Garden, Constantinople. 20 pa. Castle of Europe. 1 pi. Mosque of Sultan Ahmed. 1½ pi. Monument to Martyrs of Liberty. 1¾, 3 pi. Fountains of Suleiman. 2 pi. Cruiser "Hamidiye". 2½, 5 (966) pi. Candilli, Bosphorus. 5 pi. (510) Former Ministry of War. 10 pi. Sweet Waters of Europe. 25 pi. Suleiman Mosque. 50 pi. Bosphorus at Rumeli Hisar. 100 pi. Sultan Ahmed's Fountain. 200 pi. Sultan Mohammed V.

SIZES—As Type **32**: 4 pa., 6 pa.; 31½×20 mm. 10 pa. to 1 pi.; 26×21 mm. 1½ pi. to 2½ pi.; 38×24 mm. 5 pi. to 50 pi.; 40×25½ mm. 100 pi., 200 pi.

1914. Stamps of 1914 optd with small star.
516 10 pa. green 20 20
517 20 pa. red .. .. 2·25 40
518 1 pi. blue 45 15
519 1¾ pi. brown and grey .. 35 30
520 2 pi. black and green .. 12·00 1·00

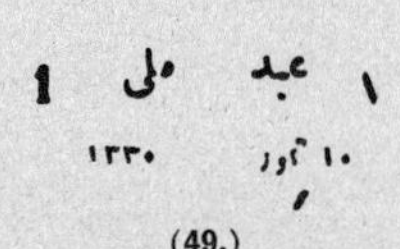
(49.)

1914. 7th Anniv. of Constitution No. 506 surch. with T **49.**
521. 1 pi. on 1½ pi. grey & red .. 75 75

(50.)

1914. Abrogation of the Capitulations Nos. 501/11 optd. with T **50.**
524. 5 pa. purple 25 25
526. 10 pa. green 35 30
527. 20 pa. red 75 35
528. 1 pi. blue .. .. 1·25 70
530. 2 pi. black and green .. 3·00 75
532. 5 pi. lilac .. .. 9·00 2·40
533. 10 pi. brown .. .. 20·00 14·00

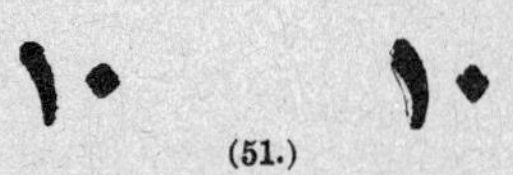
(51.)

1915. Nos. 514/5 surch. as T **51.**
534. 10 pi. on 100 pi. blue .. 18·00 7·50
535. 25 pi. on 200 pi. blk. & grn. 10·00 5·00

(53.) ("1331" = 1915)

1915. Various issues optd with T **53.**
I. On postage stamps.
(a) 1892 and 1897 issues
536 15 5 pa. on 10 pa. green .. 15 10
537 10 pa. green 15 10
538 2 pi. brown 20 10
539 5 pi. purple .. .. 1·50 25

(b) 1901 issues. (i) For Internal mail
540 21 5 pa. violet 10 10
541 10 pa. green 20 10
542 20 pa. red 20 10
543 1 pi. blue 40 10
544 2 pi. orange .. .. 1·50 20
545 5 pi. mauve 40 15
546 25 pi. brown .. .. 2·75 2·00

(ii) For foreign mail
547 22 5 pa. brown 10 10
548 1 pi. blue 40 15
549 2 pi. blue 40 10
550 5 pi. brown .. .. 2·50 60
551 25 pi. green .. .. 14·00 6·00

(c) 1905 and 1906 issues
552 23 5 pa. buff 10 10
553b 10 pa. green 25 10
561 10 pa. green (230) .. 20 10
554a 20 pa. pink 25 10
555a 1 pi. blue 60 10
556b 2 pi. grey 80 10
562 2 pi. grey (233) .. 75 20
557 2½ pi. purple 50 10
558a 5 pi. brown 75 10
559 10 pi. orange .. .. 3·00 60
560 25 pi. green .. .. 10·00 2·50

(d) 1908 issues
563 25 5 pa. brown .. .. 40·00 30·00
564 2 pi. black .. .. 35·00 15·00
569a 2 pi. black (255) .. 3·25 80
565 2½ pi. brown 60 20
566a 5 pi. purple .. .. 22·00 10·00
567 10 pi. red .. .. 3·25 1·50
568 25 pi. green .. .. 8·00 2·25

(e) 1909 issues
570 28 5 pa. brown 10 10
572 20 pa. red 20 10
579 20 pa. red (290) .. 15 10
573 1 pi. blue 40 10
581 1 pi. blue (291) .. 50 15
574 2 pi. black 40 10
582 2 pi. black (292) .. 45 15
575 2½ pi. brown .. .. 20·00 8·50
576 5 pi. purple 40 10
577 10 pi. red .. .. 2·25 20
578 25 pi. green £325 £300

(f) 1913 issues
583 30 5 pa. bistre 10 10
584 10 pa. green 10 10
591 10 pa. green (343) .. 25 15
585 20 pa. pink 10 10
592 20 pa. pink (344) .. 40 10
586 1 pi. blue 20 10
593 1 pi. blue (345) .. 50 15
587 2 pi. grey 75 25
594 2 pi. grey (346) .. 3·00 85
588 5 pi. purple .. .. 1·00 60
589 10 pi. red .. .. 3·25 60
590 25 pi. green .. .. 12·00 4·50

II. On printed matter stamps (for use as postage stamps).
(a) 1894 issue
595 15 10 pa. green 25 10
596 2 pi. brown .. .. 1·25 30

(b) 1901 issues
597 21 5 pa. violet 25 10
600 22 10 pa. green 20 10
598 21 20 pa. red 75 20
599 5 pi. mauve .. .. 6·00 1·10

(c) 1905 issue
601b 23 5 pa. buff 25 10
602 2 pi. grey 2·75 1·25
603 5 pi. brown 2·25 50

(d) 1908 issue
604 25 2 pi. black £250 £160
605a 5 pi. purple 3·75 40

(e) 1909 issue
606 28 5 pa. brown 20 10
608 5 pi. purple 30·00 10·00

(54.) (56.)

1915. Various issues optd with T **54** (star varies).

(I) On postage stamps.

(a) 1892 issue, also surch with T **56**
630 15 10 pa. on 20 pa. red 15 10

(b) 1901 issue
631 21 1 pi. blue 20 10
632a 5 pi. mauve 1·50 30

(c) 1905 and 1906 issues, Nos. 633 and 636 also surch with T **56**.
609a 23 10 pa. green 10 10
611b 10 pa. green (230) 4·75 1·75
633 10 pa. on 20 pa. pink 25 10
636 10 pa. on 20 pa. pink (231) 20 10
634 1 pi. blue 30 10
637 1 pi. blue (232) 25 10
610 10 pi. orange 2·25 40

(d) 1908 issues
612 25 10 pa. green 20 10
614a 10 pa. green (252) 35·00 22·00
638 20 pa. red
640a 20 pa. red (253) 25 15
641 1 pi. blue (254) 1·10 10
613 5 pi. purple 8·00 2·25
639 10 pi. red 60·00 40·00

(e) 1909 issues
616 28 10 pa. green 20 10
620 10 pa. green (289) 15 10
643 20 pa. red 15 10
647 20 pa. red (290) 10 10
645 1 pi. blue 15 10
649 1 pi. blue (291) 25 10
619 5 pi. purple 2·00 40
646 10 pi. red 22·00 20·00

(f) 1913 issues
623 30 10 pa. green 20 10
625 10 pa. green (343) 20 10
650 20 pa. pink 15 10
653 20 pa. pink (344) 15 10
624 1 pi. blue 25 10
652 10 pi. red 5·50 2·75

(g) 1916 Postal Jubilee issue
654 60 10 pa. red 15 10
655 20 pa. blue 20 10
656 1 pi. black and violet 15 10
657 5 pi. black and brown 60 15

II. On printed matter stamps (for use as postage stamps).

(a) 1894 issue, also surch with T **56**
658 15 10 pa. on 20 pa. red 15 10

(b) 1901 issue
659 22 5 pi. brown 2·00 60

(c) 1908 issue
626 25 10 pa. green 35·00 22·00
627 5 pi. purple 40·00 22·00

(d) 1909 issue
629 28 10 pa. green 15 10

(57.) (58.) (59.)
("1332" = 1916)

1916. Various issues optd with T **57**, some also surch in piastres as T **58**.

I. On postage stamps.

(a) 1892 and 1897 issues
660 15 5 pa. on 10 pa. grn (160) 15 10
661 10 pa. green 30 10
662 20 pa. red 15 10
663 1 pi. blue 12·00 12·00
664 2 pi. brown 1·25 65
665 5 pi. purple 12·00 12·00

(b) 1901 issues. (i) Internal mail
666 21 5 pa. violet 11·00 10·00
667 10 pa. green 50 35
668 20 pa. red 20 10
669 1 pi. blue 25 10
670 2 pi. orange 60 20
671a 10 pi. on 25 pi. brown 2·50 95
672 10 pi. on 50 pi. brown 3·25 1·25
673a 25 pi. brown 2·50 1·00
674 50 pi. brown 4·50 65

(ii) Foreign mail
675 22 5 pa. brown 10 10
676 10 pa. green 60 25
677 20 pa. mauve 15 10
678 1 pi. blue 30 10
679 2 pi. blue 1·75 95
680 5 pi. on 25 pi. green 15·00 14·00
681 10 pi. on 25 pi. green 15·00 14·00
682 25 pi. green 16·00 14·00

(c) 1905 and 1906 issues
683 23 5 pa. buff 15 15
692a 10 pa. green (230) 35 15
684 20 pa. pink 25 10
693 20 pa. pink (231) 35 15
685a 1 pi. blue 40 10
694a 1 pi. blue (232) 60 15
686a 2 pi. grey 1·25 40
687 2½ pi. purple 1·50 60
688 10 pi. on 25 pi. green 3·50 1·75
689 10 pi. on 50 pi. purple 3·75 1·50
690 25 pi. green 3·50 1·00
691 50 pi. purple 5·00 1·25

(d) 1908 issues
701 25 2 pi. black (255) 14·00 12·00
695 2½ pi. brown 12·00 11·00
696 10 pi. on 25 pi. green 5·50 3·25
697a 10 pi. on 50 pi. brown 14·00 14·00
698 25 pi. on 50 pi. brown 14·00 14·00
699 25 pi. green 3·50 3·25
700 50 pi. brown 15·00 15·00

(e) 1908 Constitution issue
702 27 5 pa. brown 15·00 15·00

(f) 1909 issues
703 28 5 pa. brown 15 10
704 10 pa. green 13·00 13·00
705 20 pa. red 14·00 13·00
707 1 pi. blue 85 15
711 1 pi. blue (291) 12·00 12·00
708 2 pi. black 1·10 45
712 2 pi. black (292) 12·00 12·00
709 2½ pi. brown 12·00 12·00
710 5 pi. purple 13·00 12·00

(g) 1913 issues
713 30 5 pa. bistre 15 10
714 20 pa. pink 45 20
715 1 pi. blue 45 10
720 1 pi. blue (345) 60 10
716 2 pi. grey 1·10 40
717 10 pi. on 50 pi. brown 4·00 1·90
718 25 pi. green 4·00 75
719 50 pi. brown 4·25 1·75

(h) 1913 Adrianople issue
721 31 10 pa. green 15 10
722 20 pa. red 60 20
723 40 pa. blue 75 40

(i) 1914 Constitution issue, with further surch
724 60 pa. on 1 pi. on 1½ pi. grey and red 1·00 25

(j) 1916 Postal Jubilee issue
725 60 5 pi. black and brown 50 10

(II) On printed matter stamps (for use as postage stamps).

(a) 1894 issue
726 15 5 pa. on 10 pa. green 15 10
727 10 pa. green 35 15
728 20 pa. red 20 15
729 5 pi. purple 15·00 15·00

(b) 1901 issues. (i) Internal mail
730 21 5 pa. violet 14·00 14·00
731 10 pa. green 14·00 14·00
732 20 pa. red 40 15
733 1 pi. blue 40 15
734 2 pi. orange 60 15

(ii) Foreign mail
735 22 5 pa. brown 15 10
736 10 pa. green 25 10
737 20 pa. mauve 20 10
738 1 pi. blue 35 15

(c) 1905 issue
739 23 5 pa. buff 15 10
740 10 pa. green 14·00 12·00
741 20 pa. pink 14·00 12·00
742a 1 pi. blue 60 15

(d) 1908 issue
743a 25 5 pa. brown 15·00 14·00

(e) 1909 issue
744 28 5 pa. brown 15·00 14·00

III. On 1913 Adrianople postage due issue (for use as postage stamps)
745 31 10 on 2 pa. on 10 pa. grn 18·00 12·00
746 20 on 5 pa. on 20 pa. red 18·00 12·00
747 40 on 10 pa. on 40 pa. bl 18·00 12·00

1916. Occupation of Sinai Peninsula. Optd. with T **59**.
749. 21. 5 pa. violet 45 25
750. 10 pa. green 60 25
751. 28. 20 pa. red 75 45
752. 1 pi. blue 1·00 45
753. 30. 5 pi. purple 10·00 3·75

60. Old G.P.O. Constantinople. (**61.**)

1916. Jubilee of Constantinople City Post.
754. 60. 5 pa. green 10 10
755. 10 pa. red 10 10
756. 20 pa. blue 20 10
757. 1 pi. black and violet 30 10
758. 5 pi. black and brown 7·00 85

1916. National Fete. Optd. with T **61**.
759. 15. 10 pa. green 85 1·00
760b. 23. 20 pa. red 90 55
761a. 1 pi. blue 1·25 60
762b. 2 pi. grey 2·50 55
763. 2½ pi. purple 3·25 55

62. Dolmabahce Palace.

63. Sentry. **64.** Sultan Mohamed V.

1916.
764 62 10 pi. violet 2·75 50
765 10 pi. green on grey 1·50 35
766 10 pi. brown 3·25 25
767 63 25 pi. red on buff 40 30
768 64 50 pi. red 1·75 70
769 50 pi. green on yellow 4·00 3·00
770 50 pi. blue 35 35

65. Off to the front. (**66.**)

1917. Charity.
771. 65. 10 pa. purple 10 10

1917. Various issues optd with T **66** or surch in addition.

A. On postage stamp issue of 1865.
782 2 10 pa. mauve 10·00 10·00
772a 20 pa. yellow 10·00 10·00
783 20 pa. green 10·00 10·00
785 20 pa. grey 10·00 10·00
773b 1 pi. lilac 10·00 10·00
784 1 pi. yellow 10·00 10·00
774 2 pi. blue 10·00 10·00
780 2 pi. red to brown 10·00 10·00
775 5 pi. red 10·00 10·00
778 5 pi. blue 10·00 10·00
779 25 pi. red 10·00 10·00

B. On surcharged postage stamp issue of 1876.
787 2 ¼ pre. on 10 pa. mauve 10·00 10·00
788 ½ pre. on 20 pa. green 10·00 10·00
789 1¼ pre. on 50 pa. red 10·00 10·00

C. On postage stamp issue of 1876.
790 9 5 pa. black and yellow 10·00 10·00
791 5 pa. black 40 50
792 10 pa. black and green 10·00 10·00
793 10 pa. green 10·00 10·00
794 50 pa. blue and yellow 10·00 10·00
795 2 pi. black and flesh 10·00 10·00
796 2 pi. ochre 10·00 10·00
797 2 pi. orange and blue 1·10 1·50
798 5 pi. brown 10·00 10·00
799 5 pi. green 10·00 10·00
801 25 pi. purple and mauve 10·00 10·00
802 25 pi. brown 10·00 10·00

D. On postage stamp issue of 1892.
803 15 20 pa. purple 50 50
804 2 pi. brown 1·25 1·25

E. On postage stamp issue of 1901.
805. 21. 5 pa. violet 10·00 10·00
806. 10 pa. green 1·00 1·00
807. 20 pa. red 25 20
808. 1 pi. blue 25 25
809. 2 pi. orange 75 75
810. 5 pi. mauve 10·00 10·00
811. 10 pi. on 50 pi. brown 10·00 10·00
812. 25 pi. brown 2·00 1·00

F. On postage stamp issue of 1901.
813. 22. 5 pa. brown 75 75
814. 20 pa. mauve 30 30
815. 1 pi. blue 1·00 1·00
816. 2 pi. blue 2·00 2·00
817. 5 pi. brown 10·00 10·00
818. 10 pi. on 50 pi. yellow 28·00 28·00
819. 25 pi. green 15·00 15·00

G. On postage stamp issues of 1905 and 1906.
820 23 5 pa. buff 10 10
821 10 pa. green 11·00 11·00
830 10 pa. green (No. 230) 15 15
822 20 pa. pink 15 10
831 20 pa. pink (No. 231) 25 15
823 1 pi. blue 10 10
832 1 pi. blue (No. 232) 60 25
824 2 pi. grey 1·00 50
833 2 pi. grey (No. 233) 10·00 10·00
825 2½ pi. purple 1·25 65
826 5 pi. brown 10·00 10·00
827 10 pi. orange 12·00 10·00
828 10 pi. on 50 pi. purple 10·00 10·00
829 25 pi. green 12·00 10·00

H. On postage stamp issues of 1908.
834a 25 5 pa. brown 1·00 1·00
835 10 pa. green 2·00 15
840 10 pa. green (No. 252) 10·00 10·00
841 1 pi. blue (No. 254) 10·00 10·00
836 2 pi. black 4·50 5·50
842 2 pi. black (No. 255) 4·00 3·25
837a 2½ pi. brown 6·50 6·50
838 10 pi. on 50 pi. brown 10·00 10·00
839 25 pi. green 10·00 10·00

I. On Constitution issue of 1908.
843 27 5 pa. brown 40 40

J. On postage stamp issues of 1909.
844 28 5 pa. brown 25 25
846 10 pa. green 20 20
854 10 pa. green (No. 289) 25·00 25·00
847 20 pa. red 25 25
849 1 pi. blue 25 25
856 1 pi. blue (No. 291) 50 50
850 2 pi. black 1·00 75
857 2 pi. black (No. 292) 5·50 5·50
851 2½ pi. brown 10·00 10·00
852a 5 pi. purple 10·00 10·00
853 10 pi. red 10·00 10·00

K. On postage stamp issues of 1913.
858 30 5 pa. bistre 30 30
859 10 pa. green 10·00 10·00
865 10 pa. green (No. 343) 40 40
860 20 pa. pink 30 30
861 1 pi. blue 30 30
866 1 pi. blue (No. 345) 1·00 1·00
862 2 pi. grey 75 75
867 2 pi. grey (No. 346) 10·00 10·00
863 5 pi. purple 10·00 10·00
864 10 pi. red 10·00 10·00

L. On Adrianople Commem. stamps of 1913.
868. 31. 10 pa. green 50 50
869. 40 pa. blue 65 65

M. On Constitution Commem. of 1914 with additional surch. in Turkish.
870. 60 pa. on 1 pi. on 1½ pi. grey and red (No. 521) 1·00 1·00

N. On postage stamp issue of 1916.
871 63 25 pi. red on buff 75 75
872 64 50 pi. red 6·50 3·25
873 50 pi. green on yellow 5·50 3·50
874 50 pi. blue 7·50 5·50

O. On stamps of Eastern Roumelia of 1881 (T **9** of Turkey but inscr. "ROUMELIE ORIENTALE" at left).
876. – 5 pa. lilac 11·00 11·00
877. – 10 pa. green 11·00 11·00
875. – 20 pa. black and red 11·00 11·00
878. – 20 pa. red 11·00 11·00

P. On printed matter stamps of 1893 optd. with Type **N 16**.
879. 15. 20 pa. red (No. N 156a) 1·00 1·00
880. 1 pi. blue (No. N 157) 20 20

Q. On printed matter stamps of 1901 optd. with Type **N 23**.
881. 21. 5 pa. violet (No. N 183) 50 50
882. 10 pa. green (No. N 184) 6·00 5·50
883. 20 pa. red (No. N 185) 50 25
884. 1 pi. blue (No. N 186) 60 50
885. 2 pi. orange (No. N 187) 60 50
886. 5 pi. mauve (No. N 188) 10·00 10·00

R. On printed matter stamps of 1901 optd. with Type **N 23**.
887. 22. 5 pa. brown (No. N 189) 75 75
888. 10 pa. green (No. N 190) 75 75
889. 20 pa. mauve (No. N 191) 75 75
890. 2 pi. blue (No. N 193) 10·00 10·00

S. On printed matter stamps of 1905 optd. with Type **N 23**.
891d 23 5 pa. brown (No. N222) 15 15
892 10 pa. green (No. N223) 60 60
893 20 pa. pink (No. N224) 15 10
894 1 pi. blue (No. N225) 25 15
895 2 pi. grey (No. N226) 10·00 10·00
896 5 pi. brown (No. N227) 10·00 10·00

T. On printed matter stamp of 1908 optd with Type N **27**.

897	**25**	5 pa. brown (No. N244)	10·00	10·00

U. On postage due stamps of 1865.

898	D 4	20 pa. brown	10·00	10·00
899		1 pi. brown	10·00	10·00
900		2 pi. brown	10·00	10·00
901		5 pi. brown	10·00	10·00
902		25 pi. brown	10·00	10·00

V. On postage due stamps of 1888.

904	**9**	1 pi. black (D118) ..	10·00	10·00
905		2 pi. black (D119) ..	10·00	10·00

W. On postage due stamps of 1892.

906.	**15.**	20 pa. black (D 146) ..	50	50
907.		1 pi. black (D148) ..	50	50
908.		2 pi. black (D 149) ..	50	25

X. On Adrianople commemoration issue of 1913 (postage due stamps surch in Arabic and again in Turkish).

909.	**31.**	10 on 2 pa. on 10 pa. green (D 356) ..	10	10
910.		20 on 5 pa. on 20 pa. red (D 357)	15	15
911.		40 on 10 pa. on 40 pa. blue (D 358) ..	30	30
912.		40 on 20 pa. on 40 pa. blue (D 359) ..	45	35

The overprints on printed matter and postage due stamps were used for ordinary postage.

67. In the Trenches.

69. Howitzer at Sedd el Bahr.

1917. Surch variously in Turkish.

913	**67**	5 pa. on 1 pi. red ..	10	10
915	**65**	10 pa. on 20 pa. red ..	20	10
914	**69**	5 pi. on 2 pa. blue ..	2·25	40

72. Mosque at Ortakoy.

73. Lighthouse, Achir Kapu.

74. Martyrs' Column.

77. Seraglio Point.

75. Map of Gallipoli. **76.**

1917.

916	**69**	2 pa. violet	10	20
917	**72**	5 pa. orange	10	15
918	**73**	10 pa. green	10	10
919	**74**	20 pa. red	10	10
920	**75**	1 pi. blue	25	10
921	**76**	50 pa. blue	10	45
921b	**77**	2 pi. blue and brown ..	45	15
922	–	5 pi. brown and blue ..	7·00	1·10

DESIGNS—As T **77**. 5 pi. Pyramids.

1918. Surch. **5 Piastres 5** and in Turkish.

923.	**69.**	5 pi. on 2 pa. blue ..	65	20

1918. No. 913 with additional surch.

924.	**67.**	2 pa. on 5 pa. on 1 pi. red	10	25

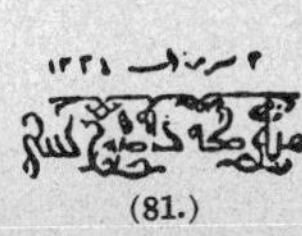

(**81.**)

84. Wells at Beersheba.

85. Sentry at Beersheba.

87. Turkish Column in Sinai.

1918. Armistice. Optd as T **81**.

925	**84**	20 pa. purple ..	15	40
926	**75**	1 pi. blue	1·75	2·75
927	**85**	1 pi. blue	50·00	50·00
937	D **51**	1 pi. blue (No. D518)	50·00	60·00
928	**76**	50 pa. blue	20	60
929	**77**	2 pi. blue and brown	20	75
930	–	2½ pi. green and orange (No. 509) ..	50·00	50·00
931	–	5 pi. brown and blue (No. 922)	20	85
932	**62**	10 pi. green on grey	2·25	4·50
933	**63**	25 pi. red on buff ..	2·25	4·50
934	**87**	25 pi. blue	50·00	50·00
935	–	50 pi. pink (No. 513)	50·00	50·00
936	**64**	50 pi. green on yellow	2·25	4·50

1918. Stamp of 1909 optd with Sultan's toughra and surch in Turkish.

938	**28**	5 pa. on 2 pa. green ..	10	40

86. Dome of the Rock, Jerusalem.

(**88.**)

1919. Optd with date as in T **88** and ornaments or inscription.

939	**84**	20 pa. purple	35	2·25
940	**85**	1 pi. blue	1·00	3·50
941	**86**	60 pa. on 10 pa. green ..	1·00	4·50
942	**87**	25 pi. blue	10·00	15·00

The illustrations Type **85** (optd with date and inscription at foot) and **86** (surch with T **88**) illustrate Nos. 940/1. Nos. 939 and 942 are overprinted with the date and the central motif only at bottom of Type **88**.

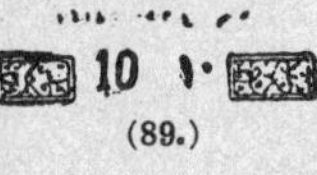

(**89.**)

(**91.**)

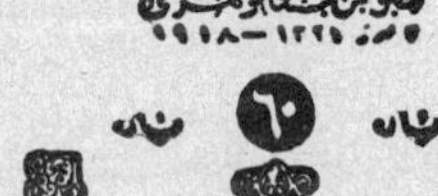

(**90.**)

1919. 1st Anniv of Sultan's Accession. Optd or surch as T **89, 90** or **91**.

943	**69**	2 pa. violet ..	40	75
944	**72**	5 pa. orange ..	10	45
945	**28**	5 pa. on 2 pa. green	10	25
946	**30**	10 pa. on 2 pa. grn	10	30
960a	D **49**	10 pa. on 5 pa. brn	7·50	8·50
947	**73**	10 pa. green ..	45	65
948	**74**	20 pa. red	15	45
960b	D **50**	20 pa. red	7·50	8·50
949	**75**	1 pi. blue	10	40
960c	D **51**	1 pi. blue	7·50	8·50
950	**76**	60 pa. on 50 pa. blue	75	1·50
951	**77**	60 pa. on 2 pi. blue and brown ..	15	1·00
952		2 pi. blue & brown	45	1·00
960d	D **52**	2 pi. blue ..	7·50	8·50
952a	–	2½ pi. green and orange (No. 509)	8·00	10·00
953	–	5 pi. brown and blue (No. 922) ..	15	1·00
954	**62**	10 pi. brown ..	1·00	2·25
955	**84**	10 pi. on 20 pa. pur	1·00	2·50
956	**63**	25 pi. red on buff ..	1·00	2·50
957	**85**	35 pi. on 1 pi. blue	2·50	3·50
958	**64**	50 pi. green on yell	4·50	7·00
958a		50 pi. red	8·50	10·00
959	**86**	100 pi. on 60 pa. on 10 pa. green ..	5·50	7·50
960	**87**	250 pi. on 25 pi. blue	7·50	8·50

Types **84** and **87** illustrate Nos. 955 and 960.

1921. Surch in figures and words and in Turkish characters.

970	**65**	30 pa. on 10 pa. purple	15	10
971	–	60 pa. on 10 pa. green (No. 503)	15	10
972	**67**	4½ pi. on 1 pi. red ..	1·00	75
973	–	7½ on 3 pi. blue (No. 965)	2·25	55

Numerous fiscal and other stamps were surcharged or overprinted by the Turkish Nationalist Government at Angora during 1921, but as they are not often met with by general collectors we omit them. A full listing will be found in Part 16 (Central Asia) of the Stanley Gibbons catalogue.

Nos. A79/90 and A119/24 were the only definitive issue of the Angora Government at this period.

A 24. National Pact.

A 25. Parliament House, Sivas.

1921.

A 79.	**A 24.**	10 pa. purple ..	20	10
A 80.	–	20 pa. green ..	25	10
A 81.	–	1 pi. blue	40	10
A 82.	–	2 pi. purple	85	10
A 83.	–	5 pi. blue	90	10
A 84.	–	10 pi. brown ..	3·00	10
A 85.	–	25 pi. red	4·25	10
A 86.	**A 25.**	50 pi. blue (A) ..	1·25	65
A 87.		50 pi. blue (B) ..	1·25	75
A 88.	–	100 pi. violet ..	30·00	1·00
A 89.	–	200 pi. violet ..	70·00	12·00
A 90.	–	500 pi. green ..	40·00	8·00

DESIGNS—HORIZ. 20 pa. Izmir Harbour. 1 pi. Mosque, Adrianople. 10 pi. Legendary grey wolf, Boz Kurt. 25 pi. Castle, Adana. 200 pi. Map of Anatoila. VERT. 2 pi. Mosque, Konya. 5 pi. Soldier taking oath. 100 pi. Mosque, Ourfa. 500 pi. Declaration of faith from Koran.

Type (B) of the 50 pi. is as illustrated. In Type (A) the inscription at the top is similar to that in Type A **30** and the figures in the value tablets are above instead of below the Turkish inscription.

A 30. First Parliament-house, Angora.

1922.

A 119.	**A 30.**	5 pa. mauve ..	20	10
A 120.		10 pa. green ..	25	10
A 121.		20 pa. red	35	20
A 122.		1 pi. orange ..	2·25	50
A 123.		2 pi. brown ..	9·50	1·25
A 124.		3 pi. red	1·00	90

(**94a.**)

1923. Izmir (Smyrna) Economic Congress. Nos. 918 and A80/4 optd with T **94a**.

973b	**73**	10 pa. green	1·75	1·25
973c	–	20 pa. green	1·75	1·25
973d	–	1 pi. blue	2·50	1·25
973e	–	2 pi. purple	3·75	3·25
973f	–	5 pi. blue	4·00	2·75
973g	–	10 pi. brown	7·50	6·00

95.

96. Kemal Ataturk and Sakarya Bridge.

1923.

974	**95**	10 pa. grey	25	10
975		20 pa. yellow ..	30	10
976		1 pi. mauve	30	10
977		1½ pi. green	35	10
978		2 pi. green	80	10
979		3 pi. brown	45	10
980		3¾ pi. brown ..	85	25
1001		4½ pi. red	50	10
1002		5 pi. violet	1·50	10
1003		7½ pi. blue	90	10
1004		10 pi. grey	3·25	25
1012a		10 pi. blue	28·00	15
986		11¼ pi. pink	1·10	35
1006		15 pi. brown ..	3·25	25
988		18¾ pi. green ..	1·75	60
989		22½ pi. orange ..	2·75	80
990		25 pi. brown ..	7·50	25
991		50 pi. grey	25·00	55
992		100 pi. purple ..	32·00	70
993		500 pi. green ..	£160	40·00

1924. Treaty of Lausanne.

1013.	**96.**	1½ pi. green	55	25
1014.		3 pi. violet	60	25
1015.		4½ pi. pink	1·00	95
1016.		5 pi. brown	1·50	25
1017.		7½ pi. blue	80	55
1018.		50 pi. orange	13·00	7·50
1019.		100 pi. purple ..	30·00	15·00
1020.		200 pi. olive	40·00	27·00

97. Legendary Blacksmith and Grey Wolf, Boz Kurt.

98. Gorge and R. Sakarya.

99. Fortress of Ankara.

100. Kemal Ataturk.

1926.

1021.	**97.**	10 pa. grey	10	10
1022.		20 pa. orange ..	15	10
1023.		1 gr. red	15	10
1024.	**98.**	2 gr. green	50	10
1025.		2½ gr. black	50	10
1026.		3 gr. red	60	10
1027.	**99.**	5 gr. violet	1·10	10
1028.		6 gr. red	60	10
1029.		10 gr. blue	1·60	10
1030.		15 gr. orange	2·00	10
1031.	**100.**	25 gr. black and green	4·50	10
1032.		50 gr. black and red ..	5·50	10
1033.		100 gr. black and olive	12·00	55
1034.		200 gr. black and brown	30·00	1·25

(**101.** "1927 Izmir Exhibition.")

(**102.** " Izmir, 9 Sept., 1928. ")

1927. Izmir (Smyrna) Exhibition. Optd with T **101**.

1035.	**97.**	1 gr. red	20	10
1036.	**98.**	2 gr. green	1·60	40
1037.		2½ gr. black	1·60	40
1038		3 gr. red	2·25	75
1039.	**99.**	5 gr. violet	85	35
1040.		6 gr. red	35	15
1041.		10 gr. blue	2·25	85
1042.		15 gr. orange	2·40	85
1043.	**100.**	25 gr. black and green	6·50	3·25
1044.		50 gr. black and red ..	11·00	6·00
1045.		100 gr. black and olive	25·00	25·00

1928. 2nd Izmir Exhibition. T **97/9** optd with T **102** and T **100** optd **928** and 2 lines of Turkish.

1053.	**97.**	10 pa. grey	15	10
1054.		20 pa. orange ..	15	10
1055.		1 gr. red	20	10
1056.	**98.**	2 gr. green	1·10	30
1057.		2½ gr. black	1·10	40
1058.		3 gr. red	1·10	75
1059.	**99.**	5 gr. violet	1·90	1·00
1060.		6 gr. red	65	10
1061.		10 gr. blue	1·90	65
1062.		15 gr. orange	2·10	50
1063.	**100.**	25 gr. black and green	6·00	2·25
1064.		50 gr. black and red ..	11·00	5·00
1065.		100 gr. black and olive	25·00	12·00
1066.		200 gr. black and brown	35·00	18·00

1929. Surch. with value in "Paradir" or "Kurustur".

No.	Type	Description	Unused	Used
1067.	97.	20 par. on 1 gr. red ..	40	10
1068.	99.	2½ kur. on 5 gr. violet	55	10
1069.		6 kur. on 10 gr. blue..	7·50	10

106. Bridge over Kizil-Irmak. 107. Gorge and R. Sakarya.

1929. T 106/7 and 1926 stamps but inscr "TURKIYE CUMHURIYETI".

No.	Type	Description	Unused	Used
1076	97	10 pa. green ..	10	10
1077	106	20 pa. violet ..	25	10
1078		1 k. green ..	50	10
1079	97	1½ k. green ..	15	10
1070	106	2 k. black ..	1·00	10
1080		2 k. violet ..	2·00	10
1081		2½ k. green ..	25	10
1072		3 k. purple ..	1·60	10
1082		3 k. red ..	2·75	10
1083	97	4 k. red ..	2·50	10
1084	99	5 k. purple ..	3·25	10
~~1085~~	97	6 k. blue ..	3·25	10
1086	107	7½ k. red ..	65	10
1088	99	12½ k. blue ..	45	10
1089		15 k. orange ..	55	10
1090	107	17½ k. black ..	65	50
1091	99	20 k. brown ..	20·00	25
1092	107	25 k. brown ..	1·75	15
1093	99	30 k. brown ..	1·75	15
1094	107	40 k. purple ..	2·00	15
1075	100	50 k. black and red ..	21·00	60

109. 112. 113.
Kemal Ataturk.

1930.

No.	Type	Description	Unused	Used
1095.	109.	50 k. black and red ..	1·90	10
1096.		100 k. black and olive	3·25	30
1097.		200 k. black and green	2·25	50
1098.		500 k. black and brown	12·00	2·25

1930. Opening of the Ankara–Sivas Railway. Surch **Sivas D.Y. 30 ag. 930** and value.

No.	Type	Description	Unused	Used
1099	97	10 pa. on 10 pa. green	10	10
1100	106	10 pa. on 20 pa. violet	15	10
1101		20 pa. on 1 k. green ..	15	10
1102	97	1 k. on 1½ k. green ..	20	15
1103	106	1½ k. on 2 k. violet ..	35	30
1104		2 k. on 2½ k. green ..	50	40
1105		2½ k. on 3 k. red ..	55	50
1106	97	3 k. on 4 k. red ..	70	40
1107	99	4 k. on 5 k. purple ..	1·40	1·25
1108	97	5 k. on 6 k. blue ..	1·90	1·75
1109	107	6 k. on 7½ k. red ..	70	65
1110	99	7½ k. on 12½ k. blue ..	95	85
1111		12½ k. on 15 k. orange	2·10	1·00
1112	107	15 k. on 17½ k. black	2·75	2·50
1113	99	17½ k. on 20 k. brown	2·75	2·00
1114	107	20 k. on 25 k. brown	2·75	2·50
1115	99	25 k. on 30 k. brown	2·75	2·50
1116	107	30 k. on 40 k. purple	3·75	3·00
1117	109	40 k. on 50 k. black and red ..	4·75	2·50
1118		50 k. on 100 k. black and green ..	27·00	8·00
1119		100 k. on 200 k. black and green ..	32·00	12·00
1120		250 k. on 500 k. black and brown ..	32·00	10·00

1931. Surch. **1 Kurus.**

No.	Type	Description	Unused	Used
1121.	97.	1 k. on 1½ k. green ..	1·25	10

1931.

No.	Type	Description	Unused	Used
1122	112	10 pa. green ..	10	10
1444		10 pa. brown ..	10	10
1444a		10 pa. red ..	10	10
1123		10 pa. orange ..	10	10
1445		20 pa. green ..	10	10
1453b		20 pa. yellow ..	10	10
1123a		30 pa. violet ..	10	10
~~1124~~	113	1 k. green ..	10	10
1453c		1 k. orange ..	10	10
1124a	112	1½ k. lilac ..	15	10
1125	113	2 k. violet ..	15	10
1125a		2 k. green ..	25	10
1447		2 k. mauve ..	25	10
1447a		2 k. yellow ..	60	10
1453d		2 k. pink ..	10	10
1126	112	2½ k. green ..	25	10
1126a	113	3 k. brown ..	20	10
1448		3 k. orange ..	45	10
1448a		3 k. blue ..	40	10
1127		4 k. black ..	1·75	10
1453f		4 k. green ..	20	10
1128		5 k. red ..	45	10
1128a		5 k. black ..	1·00	10
~~1453g~~		5 k. blue ..	20	10
1449a		5 k. purple ..	2·75	10
~~1129~~		6 k. blue ..	2·00	10
1129a		6 k. red ..	15	10
1130	112	7½ k. red ..	20	10
1130a	113	8 k. blue ..	40	10
1453h		8 k. violet ..	10	10
1131	112	10 k. black ..	2·25	10
1131a		10 k. blue ..	4·00	10
1450		10 k. brown ..	1·25	10
1453i		10 k. green ..	10	10
1132		12 k. brown ..	30	10
1453j		12 k. red ..	15	10
1133		12½ k. blue ..	35	10
1134		15 k. yellow ..	40	10
1451		15 k. violet ..	1·60	10
1453k		15 k. red ..	20	10
1135		20 k. green ..	40	10
1452		20 k. blue ..	10·00	10
1453la		20 k. purple ..	2·10	10
1136		25 k. blue ..	55	10
1137		30 k. purple ..	85	10
1453		30 k. pink ..	10·00	10
1453m		30 k. green ..	80	10
1138		100 k. brown ..	60	10
1139		200 k. violet ..	1·25	10
1453a		200 k. brown ..	4·50	45
1140		250 k. brown ..	4·50	10

114. Tree with Roots in Six Balkan Capitals. 115. "Rebirth of Turkey".

1931. 2nd Balkan Conf.

No.	Type	Description	Unused	Used
1141.	114.	2½ k. green ..	10	10
1142.		4 k. red ..	15	10
1143.		6 k. blue ..	15	10
1144.		7½ k. red ..	20	10
1145.		12 k. orange ..	20	10
1146.		12½ k. blue ..	35	10
1147.		30 k. violet ..	60	10
1148.		50 k. brown ..	1·00	10
1149.		100 k. purple ..	2·25	25

1933. 10th Anniv of Turkish Republic.

No.	Type	Description	Unused	Used
1150	115	1½ k. green ..	45	10
1151		2 k. bistre ..	45	10
1152	–	3 k. red ..	45	10
1153	–	6 k. blue ..	45	10
1154	115	12½ k. blue ..	1·10	75
1155		25 k. brown ..	2·75	2·75
1156	–	50 k. brown ..	4·50	2·75

DESIGN—HORIZ. 3, 6, 50 k. Wheat, cogwheels, factory, "X" and Kemal Ataturk.

1934. Air. Optd. **1934** and aeroplane or surch. also.

No.	Type	Description	Unused	Used
1157.	107.	7½ k. lake ..	40	25
1158.	99.	12½ k. on 15 k. orange	40	20
1159.	107.	20 k. on 25 k. brown	70	35
1160.		25 k. brown ..	90	55
1161.		40 k. purple ..	1·50	70

1934. Izmir International Fair. Optd **Izmir 9 Eylul 934 Sergisi** or surch also.

No.	Type	Description	Unused	Used
1162	97	10 pa. green ..	25	10
1163		1 k. on 1½ k. green ..	35	10
1164	107	2 k. on 25 k. brown ..	2·50	80
1165		5 k. on 7½ k. red ..	3·50	80
1166		6 k. on 17½ k. black ..	2·00	50
1167	99	12½ k. blue ..	4·50	1·00
1168		15 k. on 20 k. brown	42·00	20·00
1169	107	20 k. on 25 k. brown	32·00	32·00
1170	109	50 k. on 100 k. black and green ..	30·00	17·00

119. Alliance Badge. 120. Mrs. C. Chapman Catt.

1935. 12th Congress of the International Women's Alliance, Istanbul.

No.	Type	Description	Unused	Used
1171	119	20 pa. + 20 pa. bistre	35	25
1172	–	1 k. + 1 k. red ..	40	25
1173	–	2 k. + 2 k. blue ..	40	25
1174	–	2½ k. + 2½ k. green ..	40	30
1175	–	4 k. + 4 k. blue ..	65	55
1176	–	5 k. + 5 k. purple ..	90	75
1177	–	7½ k. + 7½ k. red ..	1·60	1·50
1178	120	10 k. + 10 k. orange ..	2·75	2·00
1179	–	12½ k. + 12½ k. blue ..	4·00	4·00
1180	–	15 k. + 15 k. violet ..	4·00	3·00
1181	–	20 k. + 20 k. red ..	8·00	6·00
1182	–	25 k. + 25 k. green ..	14·00	14·00
1183	–	30 k. + 30 k. blue ..	40·00	25·00
1184	–	50 k. + 50 k. green ..	85·00	65·00
1185	–	100 k. + 100 k. red ..	48·00	40·00

DESIGNS: 1 k. Woman teacher. 2 k. Woman farmer. 2½ k. Typist. 4 k. Woman pilot and policewoman. 5 k. Women voters. 7½ k. Yildiz Palace, Istanbul. 12½ k. Jane Addams. 15 k. Grazia Deledda. 20 k. Selma Lagerlof. 25 k. Bertha von Suttner. 30 k. Sigrid Undset. 50 k. Mme. Curie-Sklodowska. 100 k. Kemal Ataturk.

1936. Remilitarization of Dardanelles. Surch. **BOGAZLAR MUKAVELESININ IMZASI 20/7/1936** and value in figures.

No.	Type	Description	Unused	Used
1186.	107.	4 k. on 17½ k. black ..	1·25	65
1187.		5 k. on 25 k. brown ..	1·25	65
1188.	100.	6 k. on 50 k. black & red	75	20
1189.	109.	10 k. on 100 k. black and olive ..	1·00	20
1190.		20 k. on 200 k. black and green	2·25	25
1191.		50 k. on 500 k. black and brown ..	7·50	1·50

122. Stag. 124. Arms of Turkey, Greece, Rumania and Yugoslavia.

1937. 2nd Turkish Historical Congress.

No.	Type	Description	Unused	Used
1192.	122.	3 k. violet ..	60	25
1193.	–	6 k. blue ..	65	25
1194.	122.	7½ k. red ..	1·25	60
1195.	–	12½ k. blue ..	2·00	85

DESIGN: 6, 12½ k. Bust of Ataturk.

1937. Balkan Entente.

No.	Type	Description	Unused	Used
1196.	124.	8 k. red ..	4·50	1·25
1197.		12½ k. blue ..	9·50	1·75

1938. Air. Surch. **1937** with aeroplane above and value.

No.	Type	Description	Unused	Used
1198.	107.	4½ k. on 7½ k. lake ..	2·00	1·25
1199.	99.	9 k. on 15 k. orange ..	12·00	12·00
1200.	107.	35 k. on 40 k. purple..	3·25	9·75

127. Fig Tree. 129. Railway Bridge.

1938. Izmir International Fair.

No.	Type	Description	Unused	Used
1201	–	10 pa. brown ..	20	10
1202	–	30 pa. violet ..	20	10
1203	127	2½ k. green ..	30	15
1204	–	3 k. orange ..	20	10
1205	–	5 k. green ..	45	25
1206	–	6 k. brown ..	1·75	60
1207	–	7½ k. red ..	1·10	40
1208	–	8 k. red ..	75	45
1209	–	12 k. purple ..	65	45
1210	–	12½ k. blue ..	2·50	2·00

DESIGNS—HORIZ. 10 p. An Izmir boulevard. 30 p. Izmir Fair. 6 k. Woman gathering grapes. VERT. 3 k. Clock Tower, Hukunet Square. 5 k. Olive branch. 7½ k. Woman gathering grapes. 8 k. Izmir Harbour. 12 k. Equestrian statue of Ataturk. 12½ k. Ataturk.

1938. 15th Anniv. of Proclamation of Turkish Republic.

No.	Type	Description	Unused	Used
1211.	–	2½ k. green ..	15	10
1212.	–	3 k. red ..	15	10
1213.	–	6 k. bistre ..	25	25
1214.	129.	7½ k. red ..	2·25	60
1215.	–	8 k. purple ..	60	70
1216.	–	12½ k. blue ..	60	1·00

DESIGNS—HORIZ. 2½ k. Military display. 3 k. Aerial view of Kayseri. 8 k. Scout buglers. VERT. 6 k. Ataturk driving a tractor. 12½ k. Ataturk.

130. Kemal Ataturk teaching Alphabet.

1938. 10th Anniv. of Introduction of Latin Alphabet into Turkey.

No.	Type	Description	Unused	Used
1217.	130.	2½ k. green ..	25	15
1218.		3 k. orange ..	20	20
1219.		6 k. purple ..	25	20
1220.		7½ k. red ..	45	40
1221.		8 k. red ..	1·25	1·10
1222.		12½ k. blue ..	75	75

1938. Death of Kemal Ataturk. Mourning Issue. Optd **21-11-1938** and bar.

No.	Type	Description	Unused	Used
1223	113	3 k. brown ..	20	10
1224		5 k. red ..	20	10
1225		6 k. blue ..	35	30
1226	112	7½ k. red ..	25	10
1227	113	8 k. blue ..	50	40
1228	112	12½ k. blue ..	1·10	1·10

133. Presidents Inonu and Roosevelt and Map of North America.

1939. 150th Anniv of U.S. Constitution.

No.	Type	Description	Unused	Used
1229	–	2½ k. green, red & blue	15	15
1230	133	3 k. brown and blue	15	15
1231	–	6 k. violet, red & blue	15	15
1232	–	7½ k. red and blue ..	20	10
1233	133	8 k. purple and blue	35	35
1234	–	12½ k. ultram & blue	1·25	75

DESIGNS—VERT. 2½, 6 k. Turkish and U.S. flags. HORIZ. 7½, 12½ k. Ataturk and George Washington.

1939. Cession of Hatay to Turkey. Surch. **Hatayin Anavatana Kavusmasi 23/7/1939** and new values.

No.	Type	Description	Unused	Used
1235.	107.	3 k. on 25 k. brown	80	25
1236.	109.	6 k. on 200 k. black and green ..	10	20
1237.	107.	7½ k. on 25 k. brown..	2·00	30
1238.	109.	12 k. on 100 k. (1096)	25	25
1239.		12½ k. on 200 k. (1097)	40	40
1240.		17½ k. on 500 k. (1098)	45	60

135. Railway Bridge. 136. Kemal Ataturk.

1939. Opening of Ankara–Erzurum Railway.

No.	Type	Description	Unused	Used
1241.	135.	3 k. red ..	3·25	4·00
1242.	–	6 k. brown ..	6·00	8·50
1243.	–	7½ k. red ..	6·75	9·50
1244.	–	12½ k. blue ..	8·75	11·00

DESIGNS—VERT. 6 k. Locomotive. HORIZ. 7½ k. Railway and mountain gorge. 12½ k. Tunnel entrance at Atma-Bogazi.

1939. 1st Death Anniv of Kemal Ataturk.

No.	Type	Description	Unused	Used
1245.	–	2½ k. green ..	15	10
1246.	–	3 k. blue ..	20	15
1247.	–	5 k. brown ..	25	15
1248.	136.	6 k. brown ..	20	20
1249.	–	7½ k. red ..	35	40
1250.	–	8 k. olive ..	25	30
1251.	–	12½ k. blue ..	45	20
1252.	–	17½ k. red ..	1·25	95

DESIGNS: 2½ k. Ataturk's Residence. 3 k. to 17½k. Portraits of Kemal Ataturk as Type **136**.

1940. Balkan Entente. As T **103** of Yugoslavia, but with the torch and Arms of Turkey, Greece, Rumania and Yugoslavia rearranged.

No.	Type	Description	Unused	Used
1253.		8 k. light blue ..	1·25	40
1254.		10 k. deep blue ..	1·50	25

137. Namik Kemal. 139. Map and Census Figures.

1940. Birth Cent. of Namik Kemal (poet).

No.	Type	Description	Unused	Used
1255.	137.	6 k. brown ..	25	15
1256.		8 k. olive ..	45	45
1257.		12 k. red ..	60	45
1258.		12½ k. blue ..	1·50	1·00

1940. Izmir International Fair. Surch **IZMIR ENTERNASYONAL FUARI 1940** and value.

No.	Type	Description	Unused	Used
1259	109	6 k. on 200 k. black and green ..	30	25
1260		10 k. on 200 k. black and green ..	30	25
1261		12 k. on 500 k. black and brown	35	35

1940. National Census.

1262	139	10 pa. green	15	10
1263		3 k. orange	20	15
1264		6 k. red	35	30
1265		10 k. blue	90	60

140. Hurdling.

141. Postmen of 1840 and 1940.

1940. 11th Balkan Games.

1266.	–	3 k. olive	75	65
1267.	–	6 k. red	1·75	1·50
1268.	140.	8 k. brown	1·25	45
1269.	–	10 k. blue	1·75	2·00

Designs—vert. 3 k. Running. 6 k. Pole vaulting. 10 k. Throwing the discus.

1940. Cent. of 1st Adhesive Postage Stamps.

1270.	–	3 k. green	20	10
1271.	141.	6 k. red	40	30
1272.	–	10 k. blue	1·50	65
1273	–	12 k. brown	1·00	60

Designs—horiz. 3 k. Mail carriers on horseback. vert. 10 k. Early paddle-steamer and modern mail launch. 12 k. G.P.O., Istanbul.

142. Exhibition Building.

1941. Izmir International Fair.

1274	–	30 pa. green	20	10
1275	142	3 k. grey	10	10
1276	–	6 k. red	25	10
1277	–	10 k. blue	20	15
1278	–	12 k. purple	35	20
1279	–	17½ k. brown	65	50

Designs—horiz. 30 pa. Freighter "Etrusk" in Izmir harbour. 6, 17½ k. Exhibition pavilions. 12 k. Girl in field. vert. 10 k. Equestrian statue.

143. Barbarossa's Corsair Fleet. 144. Barbarossa.

1941. 400th Death Anniv of Barbarossa (Khair-ed-Din).

1280	–	20 pa. violet	10	10
1281	143	3 k. blue	20	10
1282		6 k. red	35	20
1283		10 k. blue	45	25
1284		12 k. brown	1·00	30
1285	144	17½ k. multicoloured	1·10	60

Design—(24×37 mm): 20 pa. Barbarossa's tomb.

1941. Air. Surch with airplane and new value.

1286.	107.	4½ k. on 25 k. brown	75	1·40
1287.	109.	9 k. on 200 k. blk. & grn.	6·00	5·00
1288.		35 k. on 500 k. black and brown	3·50	3·25

146. President Inonu. 147.

1942.

1289.	146.	0.25 k. bistre	10	10
1290.		0.50 k. green	10	10
1291.		1 k. grey	10	10
1292.		1½ k. mauve	10	10
1293.		2 k. green	10	10
1294.		4 k. brown	10	10
1295.		4½ k. black	10	10
1296.		5 k. blue	10	10
1297.		6 k. red	10	10
1298.		6¾ k. blue	45	10
1299.		9 k. violet	45	10
1300.		10 k. blue	15	10
1301.		13½ k. purple	15	10
1302.		16 k. green	20	10
1303.		17½ k. red	20	10
1304.		20 k. purple	35	10
1305.		27½ k. orange	25	10
1306.		37 k. brown	20	10
1307.		50 k. violet	40	10
1308.		100 k. brown	2·50	85
1309.	147.	200 k. brown	8·50	15

148. Ankara.

150. Pres. Inonu.

149. Tile-decorating.

1943. Inscr. "TURKIYE POSTALARI" between two crescents and stars.

1310.	148.	0.25 k. yellow	10	10
1311.	–	0.50 k. green	25	10
1312.	–	1 k. olive	10	10
1313.	–	1½ k. violet	10	10
1314.	–	2 k. green	20	10
1315.	–	4 k. red	85	15
1316.	–	4½ k. black	2·50	30
1317.	149.	5 k. blue	45	15
1318.	–	6 k. red	20	10
1319.	–	6¾ k. blue	15	10
1320.	–	10 k. blue	20	10
1321.	–	13½ k. mauve	25	10
1322.	–	16 k. green	1·10	15
1323.	–	17½ k. brown	45	10
1324.	–	20 k. brown	45	10
1325.	–	27½ k. orange	1·25	10
1326.	–	37 k. brown	40	10
1327.	–	50 k. purple	3·25	20
1328.	–	100 k. olive	4·50	20
1329.	150.	200 k. brown	6·50	15

Designs—vert. 0.50 k. Mohair goats. 2 k. Oranges. 4 k. Merino sheep. 4½ k. Steam train entering tunnel. 6 k. Statue of Kemal Ataturk, Ankara. 6¾, 10 k. Full-face portrait of Pres. Inonu. 17½ k. Republic Monument, Istanbul. 20 k. National Defence Monument, Ankara. 27½ k. P.O., Istanbul. 37 k. Monument at Afyon. 100 k. Ataturk and Inonu. horiz. 1 k. Antioch. 1½ k. Ankara Reservoir. 13½ k. National Assembly building. 16 k. View of Arnavutkoy. 50 k. People's House, Ankara.

152. Fair Entrance.

Designs—vert. 4½ k., 13½ k. Girl eating grapes. horiz. 6¾ k., 27½ k. Fair Pavilion.

1943. Izmir International Fair.

1330.	–	4½ k. grey	20	10
1331.	152.	6 k. red	20	10
1332.	–	6¾ k. blue	20	10
1333.	152.	10 k. blue	20	10
1334.	–	13½ k. brown	50	20
1335.	–	27½ k. grey	55	30

153. Marching Athletes.

154. Soldier guarding Flag.

1943. 20th Anniv. of Republic.

1336.	153.	4½ k. olive	40	25
1337.	154.	6 k. red	10	10
1338.	–	6¾ k. blue	60	60
1339.	–	10 k. blue	20	10
1340.	–	13½ k. olive	25	15
1341.	–	27½ k. brown	35	25

Designs—horiz. 6¾ k. Bridge. 10 k. Hospital. 13½ k. Ankara. vert. 27½ k. President Inonu.

155. Filling Census Form.

157. Pres. Inonu.

1945. National Census.

1342.	155.	4½ k. olive	45	20
1343.		9 k. violet	45	20
1344.		10 k. blue	45	20
1345.		18 k. red	95	40

1945. Surch. 4½ KURUS.

1346.		4½ k. on 6¾ k. blue (No. 1319)	20	10

1946.

1347.	157.	0.25 k. red	10	10
1348.		1 k. green	10	10
1349.		1½ k. purple	15	10
1350.		9 k. violet	35	10
1351.		10 k. blue	35	10
1352.		50 k. brown	3·25	15

158 U.S.S. "Missouri".

159. Sower.

1946. Visit of U.S. Battleship "Missouri" to Istanbul.

1353.	158.	9 k. violet	35	10
1354.		10 k. blue	50	15
1355.		27½ k. grey	1·10	35

1946. Agrarian Reform.

1356.	159.	9 k. violet	10	10
1357.		10 k. blue	10	10
1358.		18 k. olive	20	15
1359.		27½ k. orange	40	35

160. Dove of Peace.

161. Monument at Afyon.

1947. Izmir International Fair.

1360	160	15 k. purple & violet	10	10
1361		20 k. blue & deep blue	10	10
1362		30 k. brown and black	15	10
1363		1 l. olive and green	75	25

1947. 25th Anniv of Battle of Dumlupinar.

1364	161	10 k. brown & lt brn	10	10
1365	–	15 k. violet and grey	10	10
1366	–	20 k. blue and grey	15	10
1367	161	30 k. green and grey	20	10
1368	–	60 k. green and bistre	35	15
1369	–	1 l. green and grey	90	40

Designs: 15, 60 k. Ismet Inonu. 20 k., 1 l. Kemal Ataturk.

163. Istanbul, Grapes and Ribbon.

1947. Int. Vintners' Congress.

1370.	163.	15 k. purple	10	10
1371.		20 k. blue	10	10
1372.		60 k. brown	20	15

164. Steam Express Train.

165. Pres. Inonu.

1947. Int. Railway Congress, Istanbul.

1373.	164.	15 k. purple	80	40
1374.		20 k. blue	1·50	85
1375.		60 k. olive	1·60	1·75

1948.

1376.	165.	0.25 k. red	10	10
1377.		1 k. black	10	10
1378.		2 k. purple	10	10
1379.		3 k. orange	10	10
1380.		4 k. green	10	10
1381.		5 k. blue	10	10
1382.		10 k. brown	15	10
1383.		12 k. red	15	10
1384.		15 k. violet	15	10
1385.		20 k. blue	30	10
1386.		30 k. brown	70	15
1387.		60 k. black	1·00	15
1388.		1 l. olive	1·00	20
1389.		2 l. brown	15·00	45
1390.		5 l. purple	8·50	3·50

The lira values are larger.

167. Signing the Treaty.

168. Statue of Kemal Ataturk.

1948. 25th Anniv. of Treaty of Lausanne.

1391.	167.	15 k. purple	10	10
1392.	–	20 k. blue	15	20
1393.	–	40 k. green	30	20
1394.	167.	1 l. brown	1·00	40

Design: 20 k., 40 k. Lausanne Palace.

1948. 25th Anniv. of Proclamation of Republic.

1395.	168.	15 k. violet	10	10
1396.		20 k. blue	15	10
1397.		40 k. green	20	10
1398.		1 l. brown	1·00	55

170. Aeroplane over Izmir.

Designs: 20 k. Aeroplane over Ankara. 30 k. 1 l. Aeroplane over Istanbul.

1949. Air.

1399	170	5 k. violet and lilac	25	10
1400	–	20 k. brown and lilac	20	10
1401	–	30 k. green and grey	25	10
1402	170	40 k. blue & light blue	85	15
1403	–	50 k. brown & mauve	75	25
1404	–	1 l. green and blue	2·25	60

172. Wrestlers.

1949. 5th European Wrestling Championships. Designs depicting wrestling holds and inscr. as in T 172.

1405.	–	15 k. mauve (vert.)	1·75	60
1406.	–	20 k. blue (vert.)	2·75	1·25
1407.	172.	30 k. brown	2·25	25
1408.	–	60 k. green (horiz.)	4·00	2·25

173. Galley.

1949. Navy Day.

1409.	173.	5 k. violet	25	10
1410.	–	10 k. brown	60	10
1411.	–	15 k. red	65	10
1412.	–	20 k. blue	70	20
1413.	–	30 k. slate	1·25	40
1414.	–	40 k. olive	40	60

Designs—horiz. 15 k. Cruiser "Hamidiye". 20 k. Submarine "Sakarya". 30 k. Battle-cruiser "Yavuz". vert. 10 k. Ship of the line "Mahmudiye". 40 k. Statue of Barbarossa.

175. Exhibition Building.

1949. Istanbul Fair.

1415.	175.	15 k. brown	15	10
1416.		20 k. blue	15	10
1417.		30 k. olive	35	20

176. U.P.U. Monument, Berne.

1949. 75th Anniv. of U.P.U.

1418.	–	15 k. violet	10	10
1419.	–	20 k. blue	15	10
1420.	**176.**	30 k. red	15	10
1421.		40 k. green	40	15

DESIGN: 15 k., 20 k. as Type **176** but vert.

177. Aeroplane over Bogazia.

1950. Air.

1422.	**177.**	2 l. 50 green and blue	10·00	7·50

178. Youth, Istanbul and Ankara. 180. Voting.

1950. 2nd World Youth Union Meeting.

1423.	**178.**	15 k. violet	15	10
1424.		20 k. blue	25	15

1950. General Election.

1425.	**180.**	15 k. brown	10	10
1426.		20 k. blue	15	10
1427.	–	30 k. blue and green	25	10

DESIGN—HORIZ. 30 k. Kemal Ataturk and map of Turkey.

181. Hazel Nut. 182. Map and Statistics.

1950. Izmir Fair.

1428	**181**	8 k. green and yellow	20	10
1429	–	12 k. mauve	25	10
1430	–	15 k. brown	35	10
1431	–	20 k. blue & light blue	45	20
1432	–	30 k. brown	55	20

DESIGNS: 12 k. Acorns. 15 k. Cotton. 20 k. Fair symbol. 30 k. Tobacco.

1950. National Census.

1433.	**182.**	15 k. brown	20	10
1434.		20 k. blue	20	10

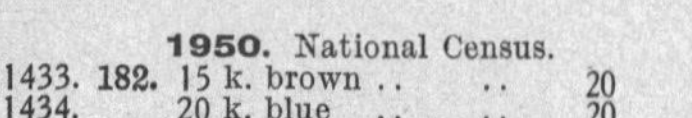

183. Bird-man and Tower. 184. Farabi (philosopher).

1950. Air. International Civil Aviation Congress, Istanbul.

1435	**183**	20 k. blue and green	50	10
1436	–	40 k. blue and brown	75	15
1437	–	60 k. blue and violet	1·75	75

DESIGNS—VERT. 40 k. Biplane over Taurus Mountains. HORIZ. 60 k. Modern airplane over Istanbul.

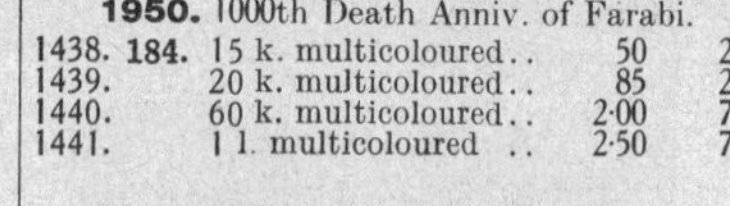

1950. 1000th Death Anniv. of Farabi.

1438.	**184.**	15 k. multicoloured	50	20
1439.		20 k. multicoloured	85	20
1440.		60 k. multicoloured	2·00	75
1441.		1 l. multicoloured	2·50	75

185. Mithat Pasha and Deposit Bank.

1950. 3rd Co-operative Congress, Istanbul.

1442.	**185.**	15 k. violet	30	10
1443.	–	20 k. blue	35	15

DESIGN: 20 k. Agricultural Bank.

1951. Air. Industrial Congress, Ankara. Nos. 1399, 1401 and 1403 optd. **SANAYI KONGRESI 9-NISAN-1951.**

1454	**170**	5 k. violet and lilac	50	80
1455	–	30 k. green and grey	50	20
1456	–	50 k. brown & mauve	1·25	30

187. "Iskendrun" (liner).

1951. 25th Anniv. of Coastal Trading Rights.

1457.	–	15 k. blue	55	15
1458.	**187.**	20 k. blue	85	15
1459.	–	30 k. grey	65	20
1460.	–	1 l. green	75	60

DESIGNS—HORIZ. 15 k. Tug "Hora" and liner "Providence". 30 k. Diver and launch. VERT. 1 l. Lighthouse.

188. Mosque of Sultan Ahmed. 189. Count Carton de Wiart.

1951. 40th Interparliamentary Conference, Istanbul.

1461.	**188.**	15 k. green	20	10
1462.	–	20 k. blue	20	10
1463.	**189.**	30 k. brown	40	10
1464.	–	60 k. purple	1·60	70

DESIGNS—As Type **188**: 20 k. Dolmabahce Palace. 60 k. Rumeli Tower.

190. F.A.O. Emblem and Silo. 191. A. H. Tarhan.

1952. U.N. Economic Conf., Ankara. Inscr. "Ankara 1951".

1465.	**190.**	15 k. green	30	20
1466.	–	20 k. violet	30	20
1467.	–	30 k. blue	40	20
1468.	–	60 k. red	75	40

DESIGNS: 20 k. Int. Bank emblem and hydro-electric station. 30 k. U.N. emblem and New York headquarters. 60 k. Ankara University.

1952. Birth Cent. of Tarhan (writer).

1469.	**191.**	15 k. purple	10	10
1470.		20 k. blue	10	10
1471.		30 k. brown	25	15
1472.		60 k. green	60	40

192. Bergama. 193. Kemal Ataturk.

1952. Views. Imperf or perf.

1473	**192**	1 k. orange	10	10
1474	–	2 k. green	10	10
1475	–	3 k. brown	10	10
1476	–	4 k. green	10	10
1477	–	5 k. brown	10	10
1478	**193**	10 k. brown	15	10
1479		12 k. red	20	10
1480		15 k. vio (medallion)	25	10
1481		20 k. blue (medallion)	75	10
1482	–	30 k. green	40	10
1483	–	40 k. blue	65	10
1484	–	50 k. green	65	10
1485	–	75 k. black	75	10
1486	–	1 l. violet	95	10
1487	–	2 l. blue	1·75	10
1488	–	5 l. brown	14·00	4·00

DESIGNS—VERT. 2 k. Ruins at Milas. 3 k. Karatay Gate, Konya. 4 k. Trees on Kozak Plateau. 5 k. Urgup. 30 k. Emirsultan Mosque, Bursa. 40 k. Yenicami (New Mosque), Istanbul. HORIZ. 50 k. Waterfall, Tarsus. 75 k. Rocks at Urgup. 1 l. Dolmabahce Palace, Istanbul. 2 l. Pavilion, Istanbul. 5 l. Interior of Istanbul Museum.

1952. Surch. **0.50 Kurus.**

1489.	**192.**	0.50 k. on 1 k. orange	20	10

196. Congress Building. 197. Turkish Sentry.

1952. 8th Int. Mechanics Congress, Istanbul.

1490.	**196.**	15 k. violet	35	15
1491.		20 k. blue	35	15
1492.		60 k. brown	75	25

1952. Turkish Participation in Korean War.

1493.	**197.**	15 k. slate	25	15
1494.	–	20 k. blue	20	15
1495.	–	30 k. brown	55	25
1496.	–	60 k. red and green	80	40

DESIGNS: 20 k. Turkish soldier and flag. 30 k. Soldier and Korean child reading paper. 60 k. Soldiers planting Turkish flag.

198. Doves, Hand and Red Crescent. 199. Bas-Relief on Monument. 200. Pigeon carrying Newspaper.

1952. 75th Anniv. of Red Crescent Society.

1497	**198.**	15 k. red and green	50	30
1498.	–	20 k. red and blue	1·00	50

DESIGN: 20 k. Red Crescent Flag.

1952. 75th Anniv. of Battle of Erzurum.

1499.	**199.**	15 k. violet	20	15
1500.	–	20 k. blue	20	15
1501.	–	40 k. grey	55	25

DESIGNS—HORIZ. 20 k. Azizye Monument, Erzurum. 40 k. View of Erzurum.

1952.

1502.	**200.**	0.50 k. green	10	10
1503.		0.50 k. violet	10	10
1503a.		0.50 k. orange	10	10
1503b.		0.50 k. brown	10	10

201. Rumeli Fort. 202. Sultan Mohammed II (after Gentile Bellini).

1953. 500th Anniv of Fall of Constantinople.

1504	**201**	5 k. blue & ultram	10	10
1505	–	8 k. grey	10	10
1506	–	10 k. blue	20	10
1507	–	12 k. purple	25	10
1508	–	15 k. brown	20	10
1509	–	20 k. red	30	15
1510	–	30 k. green	80	15
1511	–	40 k. violet	80	25
1512	–	60 k. brown	80	35
1513	–	1 l. green	1·75	60
1514	–	2 l. multicoloured	4·00	2·25
1515	**202**	2½ l. lt brn, yell & brn	5·00	3·25

DESIGNS—As Type **201**: HORIZ. 8 k. Turkish army at Edirne. 10 k. Horsemen and fleet. 12 k. Landing of Turkish army. 15 k. Topkapi ramparts. 40 k. Sultan Mohammed II and Patriarch Yenadios. 60 k. 15th-century map of Constantinople. 1 l. Mausoleum of Mohammed II. VERT. 20 k. Turkish army entering Constantinople. 30 k. Sultan Mohammed II Mosque. As Type **202**: 2 l. Sultan Mohammed II (after miniature by Sinan).

203. Odeon Theatre, Ephesus.

1953. Views of Ephesus. Inscr. "EFES". Multicoloured centres.

1516.	**203.**	12 k. green	15	10
1517.	–	15 k. violet	15	10
1518.	–	20 k. slate	25	10
1519.	–	40 k. turquoise	40	25
1520.	–	60 k. blue	30	25
1521.	–	1 l. red	1·25	60

DESIGNS: 15 k. St. John's Church and Acropolis. 20 k. Statue of Blessed Virgin, Panaya Kapulu. 40 k. Council Church ruins. 60 k. Grotto of the Seven Sleepers. 1 l. House of the Blessed Virgin, Panaya Kapulu.

DESIGN: 20 k. Pres. Bayar, Mithat Pasha and Ankara University.

204. Pres. Bayar, Mithat Pasha, Dr. Delitsch and Ankara Bank.

1953. 5th Int. Public Credit Congress.

1522.	**204.**	15 k. brown	15	10
1523.	–	20 k. turquoise	25	15

205. Berdan Barrage.

DESIGNS—HORIZ. 10 k. Combine-harvester. 20 k. Soldiers on parade. 30 k. Diesel-engined train. 35 k. Yesilkoy airport. VERT. 55 k. Kemal Ataturk.

1953. 30th Anniv. of Republic.

1524.	–	10 k. bistre	10	10
1525.	**205.**	15 k. slate	10	10
1526.	–	20 k. red	10	10
1527.	–	30 k. olive	3·50	1·75
1528.	–	35 k. blue	20	10
1529.	–	55 k. lilac	25	15

206. Kemal Ataturk and Mausoleum.

1953. Transfer of Ashes of Kemal Ataturk to Mausoleum.

1530.	**206.**	15 k. black	20	10
1531.		20 k. purple	55	15

207. Map of World and Compass.

DESIGNS: 20 k. Globe and stars. 40 k. Allegory of growth of N.A.T.O.

1954. 5th Anniv. of N.A.T.O.

1532.	**207.**	15 k. brown	25	25
1533.	–	20 k. blue	25	25
1534.	–	40 k. green	8·00	7·00

208. "Industry, Agriculture and Construction". 209. Flying Exercise.

1954. 5th Anniv. of Council of Europe.
1535 208. 10 k. brown .. .. 3·25 2·25
1536. – 15 k. green .. .. 2·25 2·00
1537. – 20 k. blue .. .. 2·25 2·00
1538. 208. 30 k. violet .. .. 12·00 7·50
DESIGN: 15 k., 20 k. Flag and figure of "Peace and Justice".

1954. 47th Conference of Int. Aeronautical Federation. Inscr. "20.IX.1954".
1539. 209. 20 k. black 20 10
1540. – 35 k. lilac 35 15
1541. – 45 k. blue 85 20
DESIGNS: 35 k. Baron de la Grange and glider. 45 k. Ataturk and formation of biplanes.

210. Z. Gokalp. 211. Yesilkoy Aerodrome.

1954. 30th Death Anniv. of Gokalp (sociologist).
1542. 210. 15 k. violet 10 10
1543. 20 k. green 20 10
1544. 30 k. red 35 15

1954. Air.
1545. 211. 5 k. blue and brown.. 15 10
1546. – 20 k. blue and brown 25 10
1547. – 35 k. blue and green.. 25 10
1548. 211. 40 k. blue and red .. 35 10
1549. – 45 k. blue and violet 55 20
1550. – 55 k. blue and black.. 1·25 25
DESIGNS: 20 k., 45 k. Frontal view of Yesilkoy Aerodrome. 35 k., 55 k. Ankara Aerodrome.

212. Kemal Ataturk. 213. Relief Map of the Dardanelles.

1955.
1551. 212. 15 k. red 10 10
1552. 20 k. blue 15 10
1553. 40 k. slate 20 10
1554. 50 k. green 30 10
1555. 75 k. brown 65 10

1955. 40th Anniv. of Battle of Canakkale (Dardanelles).
1556. 213. 15 k. green 10 10
1557. – 20 k. brown 15 10
1558. – 30 k. blue 50 20
1559. – 60 k. drab 60 35
DESIGNS—VERT. 20 k. Gunner Seyid loading gun. 60 k. Ataturk in uniform. HORIZ. 30 k. Minelayer "Nusret".

214. "Reconstruction". 215. Lilies.

1955. Town Planning Congress.
1560. 214. 15 k. grey 15 10
1561. 20 k. blue 20 10
1562. 50 k. brown 25 15
1563. 1 l. violet 60 25

1955. Spring Flower Festival. Inscr. "ISTANBUL 1955".
1564. – 10 k. red and green.. 30 10
1565. – 15 k. yellow and green 25 10
1566. – 20 k. red and green.. 35 10
1567. 215. 50 k. green and yellow 2·75 60
FLOWERS: 10 k. Carnations. 15 k. Tulips. 20 k. Roses.

216. First-aid Centre.

1955. 18th Congress of International Documentation Office of Military Medicine.
1568 216 20 k. red and grey .. 20 10
1569 – 30 k. green & lt green 45 15
DESIGN: 30 k. Gulhane Military Hospital, Ankara.

DESIGNS — VERT. 20 k. Footballers' badge. HORIZ. 1 l. Championship plaque.

217. Footballers.

1955. Int. Military Football Championships.
1570. 217. 15 k. blue 55 15
1571. – 20 k. red 30 10
1572. – 1 l. green .. .. 1·60 45

DESIGNS: 20 k. Dolmabahce Palace, Istanbul. 30 k. Police College, Ankara. 45 k. Police Martyrs' Monument, Istanbul.

218. Police Monument, Ankara.

1955. International Police Commission Meeting, Istanbul.
1573 218 15 k. green & turq .. 20 10
1574 – 20 k. violet and lilac 25 10
1575 – 30 k. black and grey 35 15
1576 – 45 k. brown & lt brn 85 25

219. Radio Mast. 220. Istanbul University.

1955. Cent. of Telecommunications in Turkey.
1577. – 15 k. olive 20 10
1578. 219. 20 k. red 20 10
1579. – 45 k. brown 25 10
1580. 219. 60 k. blue 35 15
DESIGN—HORIZ. 15 k., 45 k. Telegraph table and pole.

1955. 10th Meeting of Governors of Int. Reconstruction and Development Bank and Int. Monetary Fund.
1581. – 15 k. orange.. .. 20 10
1582. 220. 20 k. red 20 10
1583. – 60 k. purple.. .. 25 15
1584. – 1 l. blue 30 25
DESIGNS: 15 k. Faculty of Letters, Istanbul. 60 k. Hilton Hotel. 1 l. Kiz Kulesi.

221. Ruins, Istanbul. 222.

1955. 10th International Congress of Byzantine Research.
1585 221 15 k. green and blue 25 10
1586 – 20 k. red and orange 20 10
1587 – 30 k. brown and pink 30 10
1588 – 75 k. blue and lilac .. 70 25
DESIGNS—VERT. 20 k. Obelisk and Sultan Ahmed Mosque. 75 k. Map of Istanbul in 1422. HORIZ. 30 k. Church of St. Sophia.

1955. 10th Int. Road Planning Congress.
1589. – 20 k. mauve 20 10
1590. 222. 30 k. green 25 15
1591. – 55 k. blue .. .. 1·00 40
DESIGNS: 20 k. Congress emblem. 55 k. Bridges.

INDEX
Countries can be quickly located by referring to the index at the end of this volume.

223. Population Pictograph.

1955. National Census.
1592. 223. 15 k. grey and red .. 25 10
1593. 20 k. lilac and red .. 20 10
1594. 30 k. blue and red .. 20 10
1595. 60 k. green and red .. 40 10

224. Santa Claus Church, Demre. 225. Kemal Ataturk.

1955. Tourism.
1596 – 18 k. green and blue 25 10
1597 – 20 k. brown and blue 25 10
1598 – 30 k. brown and green 30 10
1599 – 45 k. green and brown 1·25 25
1600 – 50 k. brown and green 35 20
1601 224 65 k. black and red .. 65 15
DESIGNS—VERT. 18 k. Waterfall near Antalya. 45 k. Theatre doorway ruins, Side. 50 k. Countryside, Antalya. HORIZ. 20 k. Alanya. 30 k. Amphitheatre, Aspendos.

1955.
1602. 225. 0.50 k. pink 10 10
1603. 1 k. yellow 10 10
1604. 2 k. blue 10 10
1605. 3 k. red 10 10
1606. 5 k. brown 10 10
1606a. 6 k. green 25 10
1607. 10 k. green 10 10
1607a. 18 k. purple 25 10
1608. 20 k. blue 10 10
1609. 25 k. olive 25 10
1610. 30 k. violet 25 10
1611. 40 k. brown 25 10
1612. 75 k. slate .. .. 1·00 15

226. Mausoleum of Hudavent Hatum. 227. Zubeyde.

1956. 25th Anniv. of Turkish Historical Association.
1613 226 40 k. deep blue & blue 20 10

1956. Mothers' Day.
1614 227 20 k. brn & buff (perf) 10 10
1615 20 k. olive and green (imperf) 50 30

228. Shah of Iran and Queen Soraya. 229. Kemal Ataturk.

1956. Visit of Shah of Iran to Turkey.
1616 228 100 k. green and light green (perf) .. 60 10
1617 100 k. red and green (imperf) .. .. 5·00 5·00

1956.
1618. 229. ½ k. green 10 10
1619. 1 k. orange 10 10
1620. 3 k. green 10 10
1621. 5 k. violet 10 10
1622. 6 k. mauve 10 10
1623. 10 k. purple 10 10
1624. 12 k. brown 10 10
1625. 15 k. blue 10 10
1626. 18 k. pink 10 10
1627. 20 k. brown 10 10
1628. 25 k. green 15 10
1629. 30 k. slate 15 10
1630. 40 k. olive 15 10
1631. 50 k. orange 20 10
1632. 60 k. blue 25 10
1633. 70 k. turquoise 60 15
1634. 75 k. brown 50 10
See also Nos. 1659/78.

230. Erenkoy Sanatorium.

1956. Turkish Post Office Health Service.
1635. 230. 50 k. turquoise & pink 35 10

231. 232. Serpent in Bottle. 233. Medical Clinic, Kayseri.

1956. 25th Izmir Int. Fair.
1636. 231. 45 k. green (postage) 10 10
1637. 25 k. brown (air) .. 15 10

1956. Int. Anti-Alcoholism Congress.
1638. 232. 25 k. multicoloured.. 25 10

1956. 750th Anniv. of Medical Clinic Kayseri.
1639. 233. 60 k. violet & yellow 20 10

234. Sariyar Barrage. 235. Wrestling.

1956. Inaug. of Sariyar Dam.
1640. 234. 20 k. red 15 10
1641. 20 k. blue 15 10

1956. Olympic Games. Inscr. as in T 235.
1642. 235. 40 k. sepia on green.. 40 20
1643. – 65 k. red on grey .. 50 20
DESIGN: 65 k. Another wrestling match.

236. Mehmet Akif Ersoy. 237. Vase of Troy.

1956. 20th Death Anniv. of Ersoy (poet).
1644. 236. 20 k. brown & green 15 10
1645. 20 k. red and grey .. 15 10
1646. 20 k. violet and pink 15 10
Each stamp is inscribed with a different line of verse from the Turkish national anthem composed by Ersoy.

1956. Troy Commemoration. Inscr. "TRUVA (TROIA)".
1647. – 15 k. green 75 25
1648. 237. 20 k. purple 50 25
1649. – 30 k. brown 90 75
DESIGNS—HORIZ. 15 k. Troy Amphitheatre. 30 k. Trojan Horse.

238. Mobile X-ray Unit. 239. Pres. Heuss.

1957. T.B. Relief Campaign.
1650. 238. 25 k. red and drab.. 15 10

1957. Visit of President of West Germany.
1651 239 40 k. brown and yellow (postage) .. 25 10
1652 40 k. purple and pink (air) 20 10

240. View of Bergama.

1957. Bergama Fair.

1653.	240.	30 k. brown	15	10
1654.	–	40 k. green	10	10

DESIGN: 40 k. Folk-dancing.

241.

1957. Turkish-American Friendship.

1655.	241.	25 k. violet	20	10
1656.		40 k. blue	25	15

242. Osman Hamdi Bey (founder). 243. Kemal Ataturk.

1957. 75th Anniv. of Fine Arts Academy Istanbul.

1657.	242.	20 k. drab, buff & blk.	20	10
1658.	–	30 k. grey and green	25	10

DESIGN—HORIZ. 30 k. Hittite relic of Alacahoyuk. Inscr. "GUZEL SANATLAR AKADEMISI 75. YIL".

1957.

1659.	243.	½ k. brown	10	10
1660.		1 k. blue	10	10
1661.		2 k. violet	10	10
1662.		3 k. orange ..	10	10
1663.		5 k. green ..	10	10
1664.		6 k. green ..	10	10
1665.		10 k. violet ..	10	10
1666.		12 k. green ..	10	10
1667.		15 k. green ..	10	10
1668.		18 k. mauve ..	10	10
1669.		20 k. sepia ..	10	10
1670.		25 k. brown ..	10	10
1671.		30 k. blue ..	15	10
1672.		40 k. slate ..	15	10
1673.		50 k. yellow ..	20	10
1674.	243.	60 k. black ..	25	10
1675.		70 k. purple ..	25	10
1676.		75 k. olive ..	35	10
1677.	–	100 k. red ..	40	15
1678.	–	250 k. olive ..	1·00	40

Nos. 1677/8 are larger (21×29 mm.).

244. Mohamed Zahir Shah. 245. Amasya Medical Centre.

1957. Visit of Mohammed Zahir Shah of Afghanistan.

1679	244	45 k. red and orange (postage)	15	10
1680		25 k. deep green and green (air) ..	15	10

1957. 11th Congress of World Medical Association.

1681	245	25 k. red and yellow	10	10
1682	–	65 k. blue and yellow	30	15

DESIGN—HORIZ. 65 k. Sultan Mohammed School, 1557.

246. Sultan Mohammed II Mosque.

DESIGN—VERT. 1l. Mimar Koca Sinan (architect).

1957. 400th Anniv. of the Suleiman Mosque, Istanbul.

1683.	246.	20 k. green	10	10
1684.	–	1 l. brown	35	15

1957. 2nd Philatelic Exhibition, Istanbul. Surch. **50 Kurus ISTANBUL Filatelik II. Sergisi 1957.**

1685.		50 k. on 2 l. bl. (No. 1487)	25	10

248. Forestry Map of Turkey.

1957. Cent. of Forestry Teaching.

1686.	248.	20 k. green and brown	15	10
1687.	–	25 k. green and blue	20	10

DESIGN—VERT. 25 k. Planting fir-tree.

249. Fuzuli (poet).

250. Franklin.

1957. Fuzuli Year.

1688.	249.	50 k. multicoloured ..	25	10

1957. 250th Birth Anniv. of Benjamin Franklin.

1689.	250.	65 k. purple	25	10
1690.		65 k. blue	25	10

251. Mevlana's Tomb, Konya.

252. Adana.

1957. 750th Birth Anniv of Mevlana (poet).

1691	251	50 k. violet, bl & grn	20	15
1692	–	100 k. dp blue & blue	40	25

DESIGN—HORIZ. 100 k. Konya Museum.

1958. Turkish Towns. As T 252.

(a) 26×21 mm.

1693	5 k. brown (Adana) ..	10	10
1694	5 k. mauve (Adapazari) ..	10	10
1695	5 k. red (Adiyaman) ..	10	10
1696	5 k. brown (Afyon) ..	10	10
1697	5 k. green (Amasya) ..	10	10
1698	5 k. blue (Ankara) ..	10	10
1699	5 k. green (Antakya) ..	10	10
1700	5 k. green (Antalya) ..	10	10
1701	5 k. lilac (Artvin) ..	10	10
1702	5 k. orange (Aydin) ..	10	10
1703	5 k. violet (Balikesir) ..	10	10
1704	5 k. green (Bilecik) ..	10	10
1705	5 k. purple (Bingol) ..	10	10
1706	5 k. blue (Bitlis) ..	10	10
1707	5 k. purple (Bolu) ..	10	10
1708	5 k. brown (Burdur) ..	10	10
1709	5 k. green (Bursa) ..	10	10
1710	5 k. blue (Canakkale) ..	10	10
1711	5 k. violet (Cankiri) ..	10	10
1712	5 k. blue (Corum) ..	10	10
1713	5 k. blue (Denizli) ..	10	10
1714	5 k. orange (Diyarbakir)	10	10
1715	5 k. violet (Edirne) ..	10	10
1716	5 k. green (Elazig) ..	10	10
1717	5 k. blue (Erzincan) ..	10	10
1718	5 k. orange (Erzurum) ..	10	10
1719	5 k. green (Eskisehur) ..	10	10
1720	5 k. green (Gaziantep) ..	10	10
1721	5 k. blue (Giresun) ..	10	10
1722	5 k. blue (Gumusane) ..	10	10
1723	5 k. purple (Hakkari) ..	10	10
1724	5 k. mauve (Isparta) ..	10	10
1725	5 k. blue (Istanbul) ..	10	10
1726	5 k. blue (Izmir) ..	10	10
1727	5 k. blue (Izmit) ..	10	10
1728	5 k. violet (Karakose) ..	10	10
1729	5 k. green (Kars) ..	10	10
1730	5 k. mauve (Kastamonu)	10	10
1731	5 k. green (Kayseri) ..	10	10
1732	5 k. brown (Kirklareli) ..	10	10
1733	5 k. orange (Kirsehir) ..	10	10
1734	5 k. blue (Konya) ..	10	10
1735	5 k. violet (Kutahya) ..	10	10
1736	5 k. brown (Malatya) ..	10	10
1737	5 k. green (Manisa) ..	10	10
1738	5 k. purple (Maras) ..	10	10
1739	5 k. red (Mardin) ..	10	10
1740	5 k. green (Mersin) ..	10	10
1741	5 k. green (Mugla) ..	10	10
1742	5 k. green (Mus) ..	10	10
1743	5 k. green (Nevsehir) ..	10	10
1744	5 k. red (Nigde) ..	10	10
1745	5 k. blue (Ordu) ..	10	10
1746	5 k. violet (Rize) ..	10	10
1747	5 k. purple (Samsun) ..	10	10
1748	5 k. brown (Siirt) ..	10	10
1749	5 k. blue (Sinop) ..	10	10
1750	5 k. green (Sivas) ..	10	10
1751	5 k. blue (Tekirdag) ..	10	10
1752	5 k. red (Tokat) ..	10	10
1753	5 k. blue (Trabzon) ..	10	10
1754	5 k. orange (Tunceli) ..	10	10
1755	5 k. brown (Urfa) ..	10	10
1756	5 k. green (Usak) ..	10	10
1757	5 k. red (Van) ..	10	10
1758	5 k. mauve (Yozgat) ..	10	10
1759	5 k. blue (Zonguldak) ..	10	10

(b) 32½×22 mm.

1760	20 k. brown (Adana) ..	20	20
1761	20 k. mauve (Adapazari)	20	20
1762	20 k. red (Adiyaman) ..	20	20
1763	20 k. brown (Afyon) ..	20	20
1764	20 k. green (Amasya) ..	20	20
1765	20 k. blue (Ankara) ..	20	20
1766	20 k. blue (Antakya) ..	20	20
1767	20 k. green (Antalya) ..	20	20
1768	20 k. blue (Artvin) ..	20	20
1769	20 k. orange (Aydin) ..	20	20
1770	20 k. purple (Balikesir) ..	20	20
1771	20 k. green (Bilecik) ..	20	20
1772	20 k. grey (Bingol) ..	20	20
1773	20 k. violet (Bitlis) ..	20	20
1774	20 k. purple (Bolu) ..	20	20
1775	20 k. brown (Burdur) ..	20	20
1776	20 k. green (Bursa) ..	20	20
1777	20 k. blue (Canakkale) ..	20	20
1778	20 k. purple (Cankiri) ..	20	20
1779	20 k. grey (Corum) ..	20	20
1780	20 k. blue (Denizli) ..	20	20
1781	20 k. red (Diyarbakir) ..	20	20
1782	20 k. grey (Edirne) ..	20	20
1783	20 k. green (Elazig) ..	20	20
1784	20 k. blue (Erzincan) ..	20	20
1785	20 k. orange (Erzurum) ..	20	20
1786	20 k. green (Eskisehur) ..	20	20
1787	20 k. green (Gaziantep) ..	20	20
1788	20 k. blue (Giresun) ..	20	20
1789	20 k. blue (Gumusane) ..	20	20
1790	20 k. purple (Hakkari) ..	20	20
1791	20 k. mauve (Isparta) ..	20	20
1792	20 k. blue (Istanbul) ..	20	20
1793	20 k. blue (Izmir) ..	20	20
1794	20 k. green (Izmit) ..	20	20
1795	20 k. violet (Kayakose) ..	20	20
1796	20 k. green (Kars) ..	20	20
1797	20 k. mauve (Kastamonu)	20	20
1798	20 k. green (Kayseri) ..	20	20
1799	20 k. brown (Kirklareli) ..	20	20
1800	20 k. brown (Kirsehir) ..	20	20
1801	20 k. blue (Konya) ..	20	20
1802	20 k. violet (Kutahya) ..	20	20
1803	20 k. brown (Malatya) ..	20	20
1804	20 k. green (Manisa) ..	20	20
1805	20 k. purple (Maras) ..	20	20
1806	20 k. red (Mardin) ..	20	20
1807	20 k. green (Mersin) ..	20	20
1808	20 k. green (Mugla) ..	20	20
1809	20 k. green (Mus) ..	20	20
1810	20 k. green (Nevsehir) ..	20	20
1811	20 k. red (Nigde) ..	20	20
1812	20 k. blue (Ordu) ..	20	20
1813	20 k. violet (Rize) ..	20	20
1814	20 k. purple (Samsun) ..	20	20
1815	20 k. brown (Siirt) ..	20	20
1816	20 k. blue (Sinop) ..	20	20
1817	20 k. green (Sivas) ..	20	20
1818	20 k. blue (Tekirdag) ..	20	20
1819	20 k. red (Tokat) ..	20	20
1820	20 k. blue (Trabzon) ..	20	20
1821	20 k. red (Tunceli) ..	20	20
1822	20 k. brown (Urfa) ..	20	20
1823	20 k. grey (Usak) ..	20	20
1824	20 k. red (Van) ..	20	20
1825	20 k. red (Yozgat) ..	20	20
1826	20 k. blue (Zonguldak) ..	20	20

253.

254. Hierapolis at Pamukkale.

1958. 75th Anniv. of the Institute of Economics and Commerce, Ankara.

1827.	253.	20 k. orge., bl. & bistre	10	10
1828.		25 k. bl., orge. & bistre	10	10

1958. Pamukkale Tourist Publicity. Inscr. "PAMUKKALE".

1829.	254.	20 k. brown	10	10
1830.	–	25 k. blue	15	10

DESIGN—HORIZ. 25 k. Travertins (rocks) near Denizli.

HAVE YOU READ THE NOTES AT THE BEGINNING OF THIS CATALOGUE?
These often provide answers to the enquiries we receive.

255. Katib Celebi.

256. Letters.

1958. 300th Death Anniv. of Katib Celebi (author).

1831.	255.	50 k. + 10 k. black ..	20	15

1958. International Correspondence Week.

1832.	256.	20 k. orange and black	10	10

257. Symbol of Industry.

258. Symbol of "Europa".

1958. Industrial Fair, Istanbul.

1833.	257.	40 k. black and blue ..	15	10

1958. Europa.

1834.	258.	25 k. lilac and violet	20	10
1835.		40 k. blue and ultram.	30	10

259. Bulldozer.

260. Flame of Remembrance.

1958. 35th Anniv. of Republic.

1836.	259.	15 k. + 5 k. orange ..	10	10
1837.	–	20 k. + 5 k. brown ..	10	10
1838.	–	25 k. + 5 k. green ..	30	10

DESIGNS—VERT. 20 k. Portrait of Kemal Ataturk. HORIZ. 25 k. Army tanks and aircraft in flight.

1958. 20th Death Anniv. of Kemal Ataturk.

1839.	260.	25 k. red	10	10
1840.	–	75 k. green	20	15

DESIGN: 75 k. Sword, sprig and bust of Kemal Ataturk.

261.

262. Blackboard.

1959. 25th Anniv. of Faculty of Agriculture, Ankara University.

1841.	261.	25 k. yellow and violet	10	10

1959. 75th Anniv. of Boys' High School, Istanbul.

1842.	262.	75 k. black and yellow	25	15

263. Eagle.

BIRDS (in flight)—HORIZ. 40 k. Barn swallows. 65 k. Cranes. 85 k. Gulls. VERT. 125 k. House Martin. 155 k. Demoiselle Crane. 195 k. Gulls. 245 k. Turtle dove.

1959. Air. Birds.

1843.	–	40 k. purple & mauve	25	10
1844.	–	65 k. myrtle and turq.	30	15
1845.	–	85 k. blue and black ..	40	20
1846.	263.	105 k. bistre & yellow	40	20
1847.	–	125 k. lilac & violet ..	80	25
1848.	–	155 k. grn. & yell.-grn.	90	30
1849.	–	195 k. blue and black	80	45
1850.	–	245 k. brown & orge.	1·50	80

264. Theatre, Ankara.

1959. Centenary of Turkish Theatre.
1851 264 20 k. brown and green 10 10
1852 – 25 k. green and orange 10 10
DESIGN: 25 k. Portrait of Sinasi and masks.

265. "Karadeniz" (liner). 267. Northern Hemisphere and Stars.

1959.
1853 – 1 k. blue 10 10
1854 245 5 k. blue 20 10
1855 – 10 k. blue 10 10
1856 – 15 k. brown 20 10
1857 – 20 k. green 20 10
1858 – 25 k. lilac 15 10
1859 – 30 k. purple 20 10
1860 – 40 k. blue 20 10
1861 – 45 k. violet 20 10
1862 – 55 k. brown 25 10
1863 – 60 k. green 65 10
1864 – 75 k. olive .. .. 2·75 10
1865 – 90 k. blue .. .. 2·75 10
1866 – 100 k. grey .. .. 2·25 10
1867 – 120 k. purple .. 2·00 10
1868 – 150 k. orange .. 2·75 20
1869 – 200 k. green .. .. 2·75 25
1870 – 250 k. brown .. 2·75 45
1871 – 500 k. blue .. .. 6·00 60
DESIGNS—HORIZ. 1 k. Airliner. 10 k. Grain silo. 15 k. Steel works. 20 k. Euphrates Bridge. 25 k. Zonguldak Harbour. 30 k. Oil refinery. 40 k. Rumeli Hisari Fortress. 45 k. Sugar factory. 55 k. Coal mine. 150 k. Combine-harvester. VERT. 60 k. Telegraph pole. 75 k. Railway. 90 k. Crane loading ships. 100 k. Cement factory. 120 k. Coast road. 200 k. Electric transformer. 250 k., 500 k. Portrait of Ataturk.

1959. Postage Due stamps surch. **20=20** for ordinary postage.
1872. D 121. 20 k. on 20 pa. brn. 10 10
1873. 20 k. on 2 k. blue.. 10 10
1874. 20 k. on 3 k. violet 10 10
1875. 20 k. on 5 k. green 10 10
1876. 20 k. on 12 k. red.. 10 10

1959. 10th Anniv. of N.A.T.O.
1877. 267. 105 k. red 35 10
1878. 195 k. green 55 25

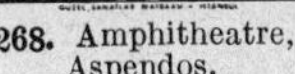
268. Amphitheatre, Aspendos. 270. Basketball Players.

1959. Aspendos Festival.
1879. 268. 20 k. violet and bistre 10 10
1880. 20 k. brown and green 10 10

1959. 10th Anniv of Council of Europe. Surch **X. YIL** in circle of stars, **105 AVRUPA KONSEYI**.
1881 259 105 k. on 15 k.+5 k. orange 40 15

1959. 11th European and Mediterranean Basketball Championships, Istanbul.
1882. 270. 25 k. red and blue .. 25 10

271. Marine Symbols. 272. Goreme.

1959. 50th Anniv. of Turkish Merchant Marine College.
1883. 271. 30 k. multicoloured .. 10 10
1884. – 40 k. multicoloured .. 15 10
DESIGN: 40 k. As 30 k. but sea-horse in place of anchor symbol.

1959. Tourist Publicity.
1885. 272. 105 k.+10 k. orange and violet .. 25 25

273. Mounted Warrior. 274. Istanbul.

1959. 888th Anniv. of Battle of Malazgirt.
1886. 273. 2½ l. purple and blue 50 15

1959. 15th Int. T.B. Conf., Istanbul.
1887. 274. 105 k.+10 k. blue and red 35 20

275. Ornamental Pattern. 276. Kemal Ataturk.

1959. 1st Int. Congress of Turkish Arts.
1888. 275. 30 k. red and black.. 10 10
1889. – 40 k. bl., blk. & ochre 15 10
1890. – 75 k. blue, yell. & red 30 10
DESIGNS—HORIZ. 40 k. Sultan Mohammed II Mosque in silhouette. VERT. 75 k. Circular ornament.

1959.
1891. 276. 500 k. blue .. .. 1·00 25

277. Faculty Building. 278. Crossed Sabres.

1959. Centenary of Turkish Political Science Faculty.
1892. 277. 40 k. brown & green 15 10
1893. 40 k. blue and brown 15 10
1894. – 1 l. ochre and violet.. 25 10
DESIGN—VERT. 1 l. "S.B.F." emblem of Faculty.

1960. 125th Anniv. of Territorial War College.
1895. 278. 30 k. red and yellow 10 10
1896. – 40 k. yell., brn. & lake 20 10
DESIGN: 40 k. Bayonet in bowl of fire.

DESIGN: 105 k. "Uprooted tree" and houses representing refugee camp.
279. "Uprooted Tree" and Globe.

1960. World Refugee Year.
1897. 279. 90 k. black & turq... 10 10
1898. – 105 k. black & yellow 10 10

280. Mental Home, Manisa. 281. Carnations.

1960. Manisa Fair. Inscr "MANISA MESIR BAYRAMI".
1899. 280. 40 k.+5 k. vio. & mve. 15 10
1900. 40 k.+5 k. grn. & blue 15 10
1901. – 90 k.+5 k. pur. & mve. 25 10
1902. – 105 k.+10 k. mult... 25 10
DESIGNS—VERT. 90 k. Sultan Mosque, Manisa. 30½ × 42½ mm: 105 k. Merkez Muslihittin Efendi (portrait).

1960. Spring Flowers Festival, Istanbul. Inscr. "1960". Flowers in natural colours. Colours of inscriptions and backgrounds given.
1903. 281. 30 k. red & yellow .. 20 15
1904. – 40 k. green and grey 25 20
1905. – 75 k. red and blue .. 50 25
1906. – 105 k. green and pink 70 25
FLOWERS: 40 k. Jasmine. 75 k. Rose. 105 k. Tulips.

282. Map of Cyprus.

1960. Proclamation of Cyprus Republic. Inscr. "KIBRIS CUMHURIYETI".
1907. 282. 40 k. mauve and blue 25 10
1908. – 105 k. yell., blue & grn. 45 20
DESIGN: 40 k. Town Centre, Nicosia.

283. Globe.

1960. 16th Women's Int. Council Meeting.
1909. 283. 30 k yellow and lilac 10 10
1910. – 75 k. drab and blue .. 25 10
DESIGN: 75 k. Women, "W.I.C." emblem and nest.

283a. Football. 285. "Population".

1960. Olympic Games.
1911 30 k. green (Type **283a**) .. 25 20
1912 30 k. black (Basketball) .. 25 20
1913 30 k. blue (Wrestling) .. 25 20
1914 30 k. purple (Hurdling) .. 25 20
1915 30 k. brown (Show jumping) 25 20

1960. Europa. As T **129a** of Luxembourg but size 32½ × 22½ mm.
1916. 75 k. turquoise and green 50 25
1917. 105 k. light and deep blue 75 25

1960. National Census.
1918. – 30 k.+5 k. red & blue 20 10
1919. 285. 50 k.+5 k. blue & turq 20 10
DESIGN—HORIZ. 30 k. Graph showing outlines of human faces.

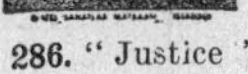

286. "Justice". 287. Agah Efendi and Front Page of Newspaper "Turcamani Ahval".

1960. Trial of Ex-Government Officials.
1920. – 40 k. bistre and violet 15 10
1921. – 105 k. red and green 15 10
1922. 286. 195 k. red and green 20 10
DESIGNS—HORIZ. 40 k, Badge of Turkish Army. 105 k. Trial scene.

1960. Turkish Press Cent.
1923. 287. 40 k. purple and blue 15 10
1924. 60 k. purple and ochre 20 10

288. U.N. Headquarters and Emblem. 289. Revolutionaries.

1960. 15th Anniv of U.N.O.
1925 – 90 k. ultramarine & bl 20 10
1926 288 105 k. brown & green 25 10
DESIGN—VERT. 90 k. U.N. emblem, "XV" and hand holding torch.

1960. Revolution of 27th May, 1960.
1927. 289. 10 k. grey and black 10 10
1928. – 30 k. violet .. 10 10
1929. – 40 k. red and black .. 10 10
1930. – 105 k. multicoloured 25 25
DESIGNS—HORIZ. 30 k. Kemal Ataturk and hand with torch. 105 k. Soldiers and wounded youth. VERT. 40 k. Prancing horse breaking chain.

290. Faculty Building.

1960. 25th Anniv of History and Geography Faculty.
1931. 290. 30 k. black and green 10 10
1932. – 40 k. black and buff.. 15 10
1933. – 60 k. olive, buff & grn. 20 10
DESIGNS—HORIZ. 40 k. Sun disc, cuneiform writing and map of Turkey. VERT. 60 k. Ataturk's statue.

291. "Communications and Transport". 292.

1961. 9th Central Treaty Organization Ministers' Meeting, Ankara.
1934. 291. 30 k. black and violet 30 15
1935. – 40 k. black and green 60 20
1936. – 75 k. black and blue 25 10
DESIGNS: 40 k. Road and rail construction, telephone and telegraph. 75 k. Parliament Building, Ankara.

1961. 1st Anniv of 27th May Revolution.
1937 292 30 k. multicoloured .. 10 10
1938 – 40 k. grn, cream & blk 15 10
1939 – 60 k. red, green and deep green .. 25 10
DESIGNS—HORIZ. 40 k. Boz Kurt and warriors. VERT. 60 k. "Progress".

293. Jet Plane and Rocket. 294. Old Observatory.

1961. 50th Anniv. of Turkish Air Force.
1940. – 38 k. orge., lake & blk. 20 10
1941. 293. 40 k. violet and red.. 20 10
1942. – 75 k. buff, grey & blk. 50 15
DESIGNS — HORIZ. 30 k. Rockets. VERT. 75 k. Ataturk, eagle and jet planes.

1961. 50th Anniv of Kandilli Observatory, Istanbul.
1943. 10 k.+5 k. turq. & green 10 10
1944. 30 k.+5 k. violet & black 20 10
1945. 40 k.+5 k. brown & sepia 20 10
1946. 75 k.+5 k. olive and green 40 15
DESIGNS—HORIZ. 30 k. Observatory emblem. 75 k. Observatory building. VERT. 40 k. F. Gokmen.

295. Kemal Ataturk. 295a.

1961.
1947. 295a. 1 k. brown 10 10
1948. 5 k. blue 20 10
1949. 295. 10 k. mauve .. 25 10
1950. 295a. 10 k. sepia 50 10
1951. 30 k. green .. 2·25 10
1952. 10 l. vio. (22 × 32 mm.) 5·50 15

296. Doves.

1961. Europa.
1960. 296. 30 k. blue 60 50
1961. 40 k. grey 60 50
1962. 75 k. red .. .. 1·00 50

297. Tulip and Cogwheel.

298. "The Constitution".

1961. Centenary of Professional and Technical Schools.
1963. 297. 30 k. pink, silver and slate.. .. .. 10 10
1964. – 75 k. red, blk. & blue 20 10
DESIGN—HORIZ. 75 k. Inscr. "100 Yili 1861–1961" and tulip-and-cogwheel emblem.

1961. Opening of Turkish Parliament.
1965. 298. 30 k. black, bis. & red 10 10
1966. 75 k. blk., grn. & blue 25 10

299. Insecticide-sprayers ("Malaria Eradication").

300. N.A.T.O. and Anniversary Emblems.

1961. 15th Anniv. of U.N.I.C.E.F.
1967. 299. 10 k.+5 k. turquoise 10 10
1968. – 30 k.+5 k. violet .. 20 10
1969. – 75 k.+5 k. brown .. 25 10
DESIGNS—HORIZ. 30 k. Mother and child ("Child Welfare"). VERT. 75 k. Mother giving pasteurized milk to children ("Education in Nourishment").

1962. 10th Anniv. of Turkish Admission to N.A.T.O.
1970. – 75 k., blk., silver & bl. 30 10
1971. 300. 105 k. blk., sil. & red 40 15
DESIGN—VERT. 75 k. Peace dove over N.A.T.O. and Anniv. emblems.

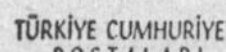

301. Mosquito on Map of Turkey.

302. "Strelitzia reginae".

1962. Malaria Eradication.
1972. 301. 30 k.+5 k. brown .. 15 10
1973. 75 k.+5 k. mve. & blk. 25 10

1962. Flowers. Multicoloured.
1974 30 k.+10 k. "Poinsettia pulcherrima" 35 15
1975 40 k.+10 k. Type 302 .. 40 20
1976 75 k.+10 k. "Nymphea alba" 75 25

303. Scouts in Camp.

304. Soldier (Victory Monument, Ankara).

1962. 50th Anniv. of Turkish Scout Movement.
1977. 303. 30 k. red, black & grn. 25 10
1978. – 60 k. red, blk. & lilac 35 10
1979. – 105 k. red, blk. & brn. 35 10
DESIGNS: 60 k. Two scouts with flag. 105 k. Wolf Cub and Brownie.

1962. 40th Anniv of Battle of Dumlupinar.
1980. 304. 30 k. green 15 10
1981. – 40 k. brown and black 20 10
1982. – 75 k. grey 35 10
DESIGNS—HORIZ. 40 k. Ox-cart carrying ammunition. (Victory Monument, Ankara). VERT. 75 k. Kemal Ataturk.

306. Shrine of the Virgin Mary.

305. Europa "Tree".

1962. Europa.
1983. 305. 75 k. sepia and green 30 20
1984. 105 k. sepia and red.. 35 30
1985. 195 k. sepia and blue 75 60

1962. Tourist Issue. Multicoloured.
1986. 30 k. Type 306 .. .. 20 10
1987. 40 k. Interior 25 15
1988. 75 k. Exterior 30 10
1989. 105 k. Statue of the Virgin 25 15
DESIGNS: The 40 and 75 k. show horiz. views of the Virgin Mary's house at Ephesus.

307. Turkish 20 pa. Stamp of 1863.

308. Julian's Column, Ankara.

1963. Stamp Centenary.
1990. 307. 10 k. blk., yell. & brn. 10 10
1991. – 30 k. blk., pink & vio. 20 10
1992. – 40 k. blk., blue & turq. 20 10
1993. – 75 k. blk., pink & brn. 35 15
DESIGNS—Turkish stamps of 1863: 30 k. (1 pi.). 40 k. (2 pi.). 75 k. (5 pi.).

1963.
1994. 308. 1 k. green and olive.. 10 10
1995. 1 k. violet 10 10
1996. – 5 k. sepia & light brn. 10 10
1997. – 10 k. mauve and green 15 10
1998. – 30 k. black and violet 75 10
1999. – 50 k. grn., blue & yell. 60 10
2000. – 60 k. grey .. .. 1·10 10
2001. – 100 k. brown .. 65 10
2002. – 150 k. green.. .. 4·25 25
DESIGNS—HORIZ. 5 k. Ethnographic Museum. 10 k. Citadel. 30 k. Educational Establishment, Gazi. 50 k. Ataturk's Mausoleum. 60 k. Presidential Palace, Ankara. 100 k. Ataturk's house. 150 k. National Museum, Ankara.

309. "Clinging to the World".

310. Wheat and Census Graph.

1963. Freedom from Hunger.
2010 309 30 k. deep blue & blue 10 10
2011 – 40 k. dp brown & brn 15 15
2012 – 75 k. dp green & green 25 20
DESIGNS: 40 k. Sowers. 75 k. Emblem and Globe with hands.

1963. Agricultural Census. Unissued stamps with "KASIM 1960" obliterated with bars. Inscr. "UMUMI ZIRAAT SAYIMI".
2013. 310. 40 k.+5 k. yellow, grn., blk. & lt. grn. 20 20
2014. – 60 k.+5 k. blk. & orge. 25 25
DESIGN—HORIZ. 60 k. Wheat and chart.

311. Atomic Symbol on Map.

312. Ucserefili Mosque.

1963. 1st Anniv. of Opening of Turkish Nuclear Research Centre.
2015 311 50 k. brown & dp brn 20 10
2016 – 60 k. multicoloured .. 25 15
2017 – 100 k. blue & ultram 60 25
DESIGNS: 60 k. Various symbols. 100 k. Emblem of Turkish Atomic Energy Commission.

1963. 600th Anniv of Conquest of Edirne.
2018 312 10 k. green, ultramarine and blue .. 10 10
2019 – 30 k. blue and red .. 15 10
2020 – 60 k. multicoloured .. 20 10
2021 – 100 k. multicoloured 55 20
DESIGNS—HORIZ. 30 k. Meric Bridge. 60 k. Kum Kasri (building). VERT. 100 k. Sultan Amurat I.

313. Soldier and Sun.

1963. 600th Anniv of Turkish Army.
2022 313 50 k. black, red & blue 20 10
2023 100 k. black, red & bis 35 25

314. Globe and Emblems.

315. Mithat Pasha (founder).

1963. Red Cross Cent. Multicoloured.
2024. 50 k.+10 k. Type 314 .. 25 25
2025. 60 k.+10 k. "Flowers" emblem (vert.) .. 35 30
2026. 100 k.+10 k. Three emblems on flags 45 40

1963. Centenary of Turkish Agricultural Bank.
2027. – 30 k. brown, green and yellow 10 10
2028. – 50 k. blue and lilac .. 20 10
2029. 315. 60 k. green and black 25 20
DESIGNS—HORIZ. 30 k. Ploughing and irrigation. 50 k. Agricultural Bank, Ankara.

316. Exhibition Hall, Istanbul, and 5 pi. stamp of 1863.

1963. "Istanbul 63" Int. Stamp Exn.
2030. 316. 10 k. salmon, black and yellow .. 10 10
2031. – 50 k. green, red and black 15 10
2032. – 60 k. sepia, blk. & blue 20 10
2033. – 100 k. violet & purple 40 30
2034. – 130 k. brn., orge. & yell. 60 40
DESIGNS: 50 k. Sultan Ahmed's Mosque, Obelisk and 3 pi. on 2 pa. Nationalist Government (Angora) stamps of 1920. 60 k. Istanbul skyline and 10 pi. (Angora) stamp of 1922. 100 k. Rumeli Fort and 6 k. stamp of 1929/30. 130 k. Ankara Fort and 12½ k. air stamp of 1934.

317. "Co-operation".

1963. Europa.
2035. 317. 50 k. orge., blk. & red 25 10
2036. 130 k. blue, blk. & grn. 45 25

318. Ataturk and Old Parliament House.

319. Kemal Ataturk.

1963. 40th Anniv. of Turkish Republic. Multicoloured.
2037. 30 k. Type 318 .. .. 20 10
2038. 50 k. Ataturk and flag .. 25 15
2039. 60 k. Ataturk and new Parliament House 35 20

1963. 25th Death Anniv. of Kemal Ataturk.
2040. 319. 50 k. multicoloured.. 20 15
2041. 60 k. multicoloured.. 30 20

320. R. S. Dag (painter).

321. N.A.T.O. Emblem and "XV".

1964. Cultural Celebrities.
2042. – 1 k. black and red .. 10 10
2043. – 5 k. black and green 10 10
2044. 320. 10 k. black and brown 10 10
2045. – 50 k. black and blue.. 45 10
2046. – 60 k. black and grey 95 15
2047. – 100 k. ultram. & blue 1·00 10
2048. – 130 k. black and green 2·75 20
PORTRAITS: 1 k. H. R. Gurpinar (romanticist, birth centenary). 5 k. J. H. Izmirli (savant, 20th birth anniv). 10 k. Type 320 (20th death anniv). 50 k. R. Z. M. Ekrem (writer, 50th death anniv). 60 k. A. M. Pasa (commander, 125th birth anniv). 100 k. A. Rasim (writer, birth centenary). 130 k. S. Zeki (mathematician, birth centenary).

1964. 15th Anniv. of N.A.T.O.
2049. 321. 50 k. red, vio. & turq. 25 10
2050. – 130 k. black and red 50 15
DESIGN: 130 k. N.A.T.O. emblem and laurel sprig.

322. "Europa" holding Torch.

1964. 15th Anniv of Council of Europe.
2051 332 50 k. blue, brn & yell 35 10
2052 – 130 k. orange, ultramarine and blue .. 50 25
DESIGN: 130 k. Torch and circlet of stars.

323. Haga Mosque, Istanbul.

324. Kars Castle.

1964. Tourist Issue.
2053 323 50 k. green and olive 25 15
2054 – 50 k. red and purple 25 15
2055 – 50 k. violet and blue 25 15
2056 – 60 k. green, blk & pur 35 20
2057 – 60 k. brown and sepia 35 20
DESIGNS—HORIZ. No. 2054, Temple of Zeus, Silifke. 2055, Amasra. VERT. No. 2056, Merzin. 2057, Augustus's Temple, Ankara.

1964. 900th Anniv. of Conquest of Kars.
2058. 324. 50 k. black and lilac 20 15
2059. – 130 k. multicoloured 45 25
DESIGN: 130 k. Alpaslan warrior.

325. Europa "Flower".

326. Grazing Cattle.

1964. Europa.
2060. 325. 50 k. bl., grey & orge. 50 20
2061. 130 k. purple, ol. & bl. 1·00 60

1964. Animal Protection Fund. Multicoloured.
2062. 10 k.+5 k. Type 326 .. 10 10
2063. 30 k.+5 k. Horned sheep 20 10
2064. 50 k.+5 k. Horses .. 30 10
2065. 60 k.+5 k. Three horned sheep 40 10
2066. 100 k.+5 k. Dairy cows.. 60 25
The 30 k. and 60 k. are vert.

327. Running.

328. Mustafa Resit.

1964. Olympic Games, Tokyo.
2067. **327.** 10 k.+5 k. black, red and brown .. 15 10
2068. – 50 k.+5 k. black, red and olive .. 25 10
2069. – 60 k.+5 k. black, red and blue .. 25 10
2070. – 100 k.+5 k. black, red and violet .. 50 25
DESIGNS—VERT. 50 k. Torch-bearer. 60 k. Wrestling. 100 k. Throwing the discus.

1964. 125th Anniv. of Reformation Decrees. Multicoloured.
2071. 50 k. Mustafa Resit and the pashas (horiz. 48×32 mm.) 25 10
2072. 60 k. Type **328** 25 10
2073. 100 k. As 50 k. 40 15

329. Kemal Ataturk. **330.** Glider.

1964.
2074. **329.** 1 k. green 10 10
2075. 5 k. blue 10 10
2076. 10 k. blue 20 10
2077. 25 k. green 50 10
2078. 30 k. purple 55 10
2079. 50 k. brown .. .. 1·40 10
2080. 150 k. orange .. 2·75 10

1965. 40th Anniv. of Turkish Civil Aviation League. Multicoloured.
2081. 60 k. Parachutist .. 25 10
2082. 90 k. Type **330** .. 35 10
2083. 130 k. Ataturk and squadron of aircraft .. 80 10
The 60 k. and 130 k. are vert.

331. CENTO Emblem. **332.** Monument and Soldiers.

1965. Completion of CENTO Telecommunications Projects. Multicoloured.
2084. 30 k. Type **331** 10 10
2085. 50 k. Aerial mast (vert.) 15 10
2086. 75 k. Hand pressing button (inaugural ceremony) 25 10

1965. 50th Anniv of Battle of the Dardanelles. Multicoloured.
2087. 50 k. + 10 k. Wreath & map 20 20
2088. 90 k. + 10 k. Type **332** .. 25 20
2089. 130 k. + 10 k. Dardanelles Monument and flag (vert.) 50 35

333. Beach at Ordu.

1965. Tourism. Multicoloured.
2090. 30 k. Type **333** 20 15
2091. 50 k. Manavgat Falls .. 25 10
2092. 60 k. Istanbul 25 10
2093. 100 k. Urfa 40 20
2094. 130 k. Alanya 70 25

334. I.T.U. Emblem and Symbols.

1965. I.T.U. Cent.
2095. **334.** 50 k. multicoloured .. 25 20
2096. 130 k. multicoloured 55 30

335. I.C.Y. Emblem.

1965. Int. Co-operation Year.
2097. **335.** 100 k. red, green and salmon 35 10
2098. 130 k. violet, green and grey 50 25

336. "Co-operation". **337.** R. N. Guntekin.

1965. 1st Anniv. of Regional Development Co-operation Pact. Multicoloured.
2099. 50 k. Type **336** 25 10
2100. 75 k. Globe and flags of Turkey, Iran and Pakistan 30 15

1965. Cultural Celebrities.
2101. **337.** 1 k. black and red .. 10 10
2102. – 5 k. black and blue .. 10 10
2103. – 10 k. black and ochre 15 10
2104. – 25 k. black and brown 30 10
2105. – 30 k. black and grey 30 10
2106. – 50 k. black & yellow 65 10
2107. – 60 k. black and purple 65 10
2108. – 150 k. black and green 1·10 10
2109. – 220 k. black & brown 90 35
PORTRAITS: 5 k. Dr. B. O. Akalin. 10 k. T. Fikret. 25 k. T. Cemil. 30 k. Ahmet Vefik Pasa. 50 k. O. Seyfettin. 60 k. K. Mimaroglu. 150 k. H. Z. Usakligil. 220 k. Y. K. Beyatli.

338. Kemal Ataturk and Signature. **339.** Tobacco Plant.

1965.
2110. **338.** 1 k. black and mauve 10 10
2111. 5 k. black and green .. 15 10
2112. 10 k. black and blue .. 15 10
2113. 50 k. black and gold .. 40 10
2114. 150 k. black & silver 85 10
See also Nos. 2170/4.

1965. 2nd Int. Tobacco Congress. Mult.
2115. 30 k.+5 k. Type **339** .. 25 20
2116. 50 k.+5 k. Leander's Tower and tobacco leaves (horiz.) 25 20
2117. 100 k.+5 k. Tobacco leaf 60 40

340. Europa "Sprig". **341.** Civilians Supporting Map.

1965. Europa.
2118. **340.** 50 k. green, bl. & grey 50 35
2119. 130 k. grn., blk. & ochre 1·25 1·00

1965. National Census. Inscr. "GENEL NUFUS SAYIMI".
2120. **341.** 10 k. multicoloured .. 10 10
2121. – 50 k. light green, green and black .. 20 10
2122. – 100 k. blk., bl. & orge. 25 15
DESIGNS—HORIZ. 50 k. Year "1965". VERT. 100 k. Human eye and figure.

342. Ankara Castle and Aircraft.

1965. "Ankara '65" National Stamp Exn. Inscr. "I. MILLI PUL SERGISI".
2123. **342.** 10 k. red, yell. & violet 10 10
2124. – 30 k. multicoloured .. 15 10
2125. – 50 k. blue, red & olive 20 10
2126. – 100 k. multicoloured 40 15
DESIGNS: 30 k. Archer. 50 k. Horseman. 100 k. Three thematic "stamps" and medal.

343. Training-ship "Savarona". **344.** Halide E. Adivar.

1965. Turkish Naval Society Congress.
2128. **343.** 50 k. brown and blue 35 20
2129. – 60 k. indigo and blue 45 20
2130. – 100 k. brown and blue 65 30
2131. – 130 k. purple and blue 1·10 60
2132. – 220 k. black and blue 1·90 90
DESIGNS: 60 k. Submarine "Piri Reis". 100 k. Destroyer "Alpaslan". 130 k. Destroyer "Gelibolu". 220 k. Destroyer "Gemlik".

1966. Cultural Celebrities.
2133. – 25 k. brown and grey 50 10
2134. – 30 k. brown & mauve 25 10
2135. **344.** 50 k. black and blue .. 25 10
2136. – 60 k. brown and green 60 10
2137. – 130 k. black and blue 1·50 15
PORTRAITS: 25 k. H. S. Arel. 30 k. K. Akdik. 60 k. Abdurrahman Seref. 130 k. Naima.

345. Roof Panel, Green Mausoleum, Burs. **346.** Volleyball.

1966. Turkish Faience. Multicoloured.
2138. 50 k. Type **345** 35 20
2139. 60 k. "Spring Flowers" Sultan Mausoleum, Istanbul .. .. 1·10 75
2140. 130 k. 16th-cent. tile, Iznik 75 40

1966. Int. Military Volleyball Championships.
2141. **346.** 50 k. multicoloured .. 35 20

347. Bodrum. **348.** Golden Pitcher.

1966. Tourism. Multicoloured.
2142. 10 k. Type **347** 10 10
2143. 30 k. Kusadasi 55 40
2144. 50 k. Anadoluhisari .. 15 10
2145. 90 k. Marmaris 30 20
2146. 100 k. Izmir 35 25
The 50 k. and 100 k. are horiz.

1966. Ancient Works of Art. Multicoloured.
2147. 30 k.+5 k. Ivory eagle and rabbit 35 20
2148. 50 k.+5 k. Deity in basalt 45 25
2149. 60 k.+5 k. Bronze bull .. 65 35
2150. 90 k.+5 k. Type **348** .. 80 40
The 30 k. is horiz.

349. View of Dam.

1966. Inaug. of Keban Dam. Mult.
2151. 50 k. Type **349** 15 10
2152. 60 k. Keban valley & bridge 45 10

350. King Faisal. **351.** "Stamp" and "Postmark".

1966. Visit of King of Saudi Arabia.
2153 **350** 100 k. deep red and red 55 30

1966. "Balkanfila" Stamp Exn., Istanbul. Multicoloured.
2154. 50 k. Type **351** 15 10
2155. 60 k. Stamp "flower" .. 20 15
2156. 75 k. "Stamps" in form of display frames .. 25 20

353. Sultan Suleiman on Horseback. **354.** Europa "Ship".

1966. 400th Death Anniv. of Sultan Suleiman. Multicoloured.
2158. 60 k. Type **353** 25 20
2159. 90 k. Mausoleum, Istanbul 55 25
2160. 130 k. Sultan Suleiman (profile) .. .. 1·25 65

1966. Europa.
2161. **354.** 50 k. ultram., bl. & blk. 75 25
2162. 130 k. pur., lilac & blk. 75 55

355. Grand Hotel Ephesus, Izmir.

1966. 33rd Int. Fairs Union Congress, Izmir. Multicoloured.
2163. 50 k.+5 k. Type **355** .. 20 10
2164. 60 k.+5 k. Konak Square, Izmir (vert.) 25 15
2165. 130 k.+5 k. Izmir Fair .. 35 20

356. "Education, Science and Culture".

1966. 20th Anniv. of U.N.E.S.C.O.
2166. **356.** 130 k. chestnut, yellow and brown .. 45 20

357. University of Technology. **358.** Ataturk (equestrian statue).

1966. 10th Anniv. of Middle East University of Technology. Multicoloured.
2167. 50 k. Type **357** 15 10
2168. 100 k. Atomic symbol .. 25 10
2169. 130 k. Symbols of the sciences 35 15

1966. As Nos. 2110/14.
2170. **338.** 25 k. black and green 15 10
2171. 30 k. black and pink 15 10
2172. 50 k. black and violet 50 10
2173. 90 k. black and brown 75 10
2174. 100 k. black and drab 80 10

1966. Greetings Card stamp.
2175 **358** 10 k. black and yellow 15 10
See also Nos. 2218/9, 2257/8, 2303 and 2418.

359. De Havilland "Dragon Rapide". **360.** A. Mithat (author).

1967. Air. Aircraft.
2176. **359.** 10 k. black and pink 25 10
2177. – 60 k. red, blk. & grn. 25 10
2178. – 130 k. red, blk. & blue 65 20
2179. – 220 k. red, sepia and ochre .. .. 1·10 35
2180. – 270 k. red, blue and salmon .. .. 1·75 50
DESIGNS: 60 k. Fokker F-27 "Friendship". 130 k. Douglas DC 9-30. 220 k. Douglas DC-3 "Dakota". 270 k. Vickers "Viscount".

1967. Cultural Celebrities.
2181. **360.** 1 k. black and green 10 10
2182. – 5 k. black and ochre.. 10 10
2183. – 50 k. black and violet 85 10
2184. – 100 k. black & yellow 1·50 10
2185. – 150 k. black & yellow 2·75 10
PORTRAITS: 5 k. T. Reis (naval commander). 50 k. S. Mehmet (statesman). 100 k. Nedim (philosopher). 150 k. O. Hamdi (painter).

361. Karogoz and Hacivat (puppets).

1967. Int. Tourist Year. Multicoloured.
2186. 50 k. Type **361** 40 10
2187. 60 k. Sword and shield game 50 15
2188. 90 k. Military band .. 80 40
2189. 100 k. Karagoz (puppet) (vert.) 95 45

362. "Vaccination".

363. Fallow Deer.

1967. 250th Anniv. of 1st Smallpox Vaccination, Edirne.
2190. **362.** 100 k. multicoloured 40 15

1967. Game Animals. Multicoloured.
2191. 50 k. Type **363** 45 10
2192. 60 k. Wild goat 50 20
2193. 100 k. Brown bear .. 75 25
2194. 130 k. Wild boar .. 1·00 35

364. Emblem and Footballers.

365. Cogwheels.

1967. 20th Int. Junior Football Tournament. Multicoloured.
2195. 50 k. Type **364** 75 15
2196. 130 k. Footballers and emblem 95 35

1967. Europa.
2197. **365.** 100 k.+10 k. mult... 40 15
2198. 130 k.+10 k. mult... 65 25

366. Kemal Ataturk.

367. Road Junction on Map.

1967.
2199. **366.** 10 k. black and green 1·00 10
2200. 50 k. black and pink 1·00 10

1967. Opening of "E 5" Motorway. Mult.
2201. 60 k.+5 k. Type **367** .. 20 10
2202. 130 k.+5 k. Motorway map and emblem (vert.) 40 15

368. Sivas Hospital.

1967. 750th Anniv. of Sivas Hospital.
2203. **368.** 50 k. multicoloured.. 25 10

369. Selim Tarcan and Olympic Rings.

1967. First Turkish Olympic Competitions, Istanbul. Multicoloured.
2204. 50 k. Type **369** 35 25
2205. 60 k. Pierre de Coubertin and Olympic rings .. 35 25

370. St. John's Church, Ephesus.

371. Common Kestrel.

1967. Pope Paul VI's Visit to Virgin Mary's House, Ephesus. Multicoloured.
2206. 130 k. Interior of Virgin Mary's House, Ephesus 35 15
2207. 220 k. Type **370** 60 20

1967. Air. Birds.
2208. **371.** 10 k. brown & salmon 85 15
2209. – 60 k. brown & yellow 55 15
2210. – 130 k. purple & blue 1·10 30
2211. – 220 k. sepia & green.. 1·40 45
2212. – 270 k. brown and lilac 1·75 55
DESIGNS: 60 k. Imperial eagle. 130 k. Pallid harrier. 220 k. European sparrow hawk. 270 k. Common buzzard.

372. Exhibition Emblem.

1967. Int. Ceramics Exn., Istanbul.
2213. **372.** 50 k. multicoloured.. 30 15

373. Emblem and Istanbul Skyline.

374. "Stamps" and Map.

1967. Congress of Int. Large Dams Commission, Istanbul.
2214. **373.** 130 k. blue and drab 30 20

1967. "Izmir 67" Stamp Exn. Mult.
2215. 50 k. Type **374** 20 12
2216. 60 k. "Stamps" and grapes 25 20

1967. Greetings Card Stamps. As T **358.**
2218. 10 k. black and green .. 25 10
2219. 10 k. black and red .. 25 10
DESIGNS: Equestrian statues of Ataturk at: No. 2218, Samsun. No. 2219, Izmir.

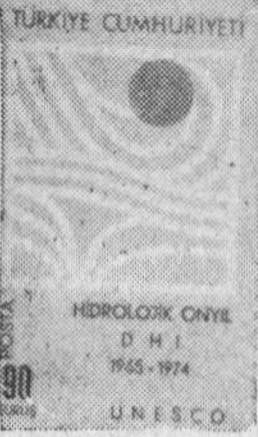
375. Decade Emblem.

376. Girl with Angora Cat.

1967. Int. Hydrological Decade.
2220. **375.** 90 k. yell., blk. & grn. 25 10
2221. 130 k. yell., blk. & lilac 25 15

1967. 125th Anniv. of Turkish Veterinary Medical Service. Multicoloured.
2222. 50 k. Type **376** 50 10
2223. 60 k. Horse 60 10

377. Human Rights Emblem.

378. Kemal Ataturk.

1968. Human Rights Year.
2224 **377** 50 k. multicoloured .. 10 10
2225 130 k. multicoloured 15 10

1968.
2226. **378.** 1 k. blue & pale blue 10 10
2227. 5 k. green & pale grn. 25 10
2228. 50 k. brown & yellow 1·25 10
2229. 200 k. brown & pink 2·50 15

379. "The Investiture".

1968. Turkish Book Miniatures. Mult.
2230 50 k. Type **379** 25 20
2231 60 k. "Suleiman the Magnificent receiving an ambassador" (vert) 35 20
2232 90 k. "The Sultan's Archery Practice" .. 45 30
2233 100 k. "The Musicians" .. 65 35

380. Scales of Justice.

1968. Turkish Courts Cent. Multicoloured.
(a) Supreme Court.
2234. 50 k. Type **380** 20 15
2235. 60 k. Ahmet Cevdet Pasha (president) and scroll .. 25 20
(b) Court of Appeal.
2236. 50 k. Book 20 15
2237. 60 k. Mithat Pasha (first president) and scroll .. 25 20

381. W.H.O. Emblem.

382. Europa "Key".

1968. 20th Anniv. of W.H.O.
2238. **381.** 130 k.+10 k. yellow, black and blue .. 55 30

1968. Europa.
2239. **382.** 100 k. yellow, red & bl. 75 25
2240. 130 k. yell., red & grn. 1·50 85

383. Etem Pasha and Dr. Marko.

1968. Turkish Red Crescent Fund. Mult.
2241. 50 k.+10 k. Type **383** .. 35 20
2242. 60 k.+10 k. Omer Pasha and Dr. Adbullah .. 40 35
2243. 100 k.+10 k. Kemal Ataturk and Dr. Refik Saydam in front of Red Crescent Headquarters (vert.) .. 50 40

384. "Kismet".

385. "Protection against Usury" (after Koseoglu).

1968. Sadun Boro's World Voyage in Ketch "Kismet".
2244 **384** 50 k. multicoloured .. 45 15

1968. Cent. of Pawnbroking Office, Istanbul.
2245. **385.** 50 k. multicoloured.. 30 20

386. Battle of Sakarya and Obverse of Medal.

1968. Independence Medal. Multicoloured.
2246. 50 k. Type **386** 20 20
2247. 130 k. National Anthem and reverse of medal.. 45 30

387. Old and New Emblems within "100".

1968. Centenary of Galatasaray High School. Multicoloured.
2248. 50 k. Type **387** .. 20 20
2249. 60 k. Gulbaba offering flowers to Bayazet II.. 30 20
2250. 100 k. Kemal Ataturk and School Building .. 45 35

388. President De Gaulle.

389. Kemal Ataturk.

1968. President De Gaulle's Visit to Turkey.
2251. **388.** 130 k. multicoloured 75 25

1968. 30th Death Anniv. of Kemal Ataturk.
2252. **389.** 30 k. blk. and yellow 15 10
2253. – 50 k. black and green 15 10
2254. – 60 k. black and turq. 50 20
2255. – 100 k. black, green & bistre 40 20
2256. – 250 k. multicoloured 1·25 40
DESIGNS: 50 k. Ataturk's Cenotaph. 60 k. Ataturk at carriage window. (32½×43 mm.). 100 k. Ataturk's portrait and "address to youth". 250 k. Ataturk in military uniform.

1968. Greetings Card Stamps. As T **358** but dated "1968".
2257. 10 k. black and mauve .. 10 10
2258. 10 k. black and blue .. 10 10
DESIGNS: Equestrian statues of Ataturk at: No. 2257, Antakya. No. 2258, Zonguldak.

390. Ince Minara Mosque, Konya.

391. Dove and N.A.T.O. Emblem.

1968. Historic Buildings.
2259 **390** 1 k. sepia and brown 10 10
2260 – 10 k. maroon & purple 15 10
2261 – 50 k. green and grey 60 10
2262 – 100 k. green & lt green 1·75 10
2263 – 200 k. blue & pale blue 1·25 10
DESIGNS: 10 k. Doner Kumbet (tomb), Kayseri. 50 k. Karatay University, Konya. 100 k. Ortakoy Mosque, Istanbul. 200 k. Ulu Mosque, Divrigi.

1969. 20th Anniv of N.A.T.O.
2264 **391** 50 k.+10 k. black, blue and green .. 35 15
2265 – 130 k.+10 k. gold, blue and deep blue 45 40
DESIGN: 130 k. Stars around globe, and N.A.T.O. Emblem.

392. "Education".

393. I.L.O. Emblem.

1969. Turkish Economy.

2266.	392.	1 k. black and red ..	10	10
2267.		1 k. black and green..	10	10
2268.		1 k. black and violet	10	10
2269.		1 k. black and brown	10	10
2270.		1 k. black and grey..	10	10
2271.	–	50 k. brown and ochre	40	10
2272.	–	90 k. black and olive	75	10
2273.	–	100 k. red and black..	65	10
2274.	–	180 k. violet & orange	1·75	10

DESIGNS: 50 k. Farm workers and tractor ("Agriculture"). 90 k. Ladle, factory and cogwheel ("Industry"). 100 k. Road sign and graph ("Highways"). 180 k. Derricks ("Oil Industry").

1969. 50th Anniv. of I.L.O.

2275. **393.** 130 k. red and black 25 10

394. "Hafsa Sultan" (unknown artist). **395.** Colonnade.

1969. Hafsa Sultan (medical pioneer) Commemoration.

2276 **394** 60 k. multicoloured .. 30 10

1969. Europa.

2277.	395.	100 k. multicoloured	40	25
2278.		130 k. multicoloured	75	40

396. Kemal Ataturk in 1919. **397.** Symbolic Map of Istanbul.

1969. 50th Anniv. of Kemal Ataturk's Landing at Samsun. Multicoloured.

2279	50 k. Type **396**	20	15
2280	60 k. Cargo liner "Bandirma" (horiz)	50	15

1969. 22nd Int. Chambers of Commerce Congress, Istanbul.

2281. **397.** 130 k. multicoloured 20 10

398. "Suleiman the Great holding Audience" (16th-cent. Turkish miniature). **399.** Kemal Ataturk in Civilian Dress.

1969. 5th Anniv. of Regional Co-operation for Development. Multicoloured.

2282.	50 k. Type **398**	30	15
2283.	80 k. "Kneeling Servant" (17th-cent. Persian) ..	45	20
2284.	130 k. "Lady on Balcony" (18th-cent. Mogul-Pakistan)	65	40

1969. 50th Anniv. of Erzurum Congress.

2285.	399.	50 k. black and violet	20	15
2286.	–	60 k. black and green	20	15

DESIGN—HORIZ. 60 k. Ataturk's statue, Erzurum.

401. Red Cross Societies' Emblems.

1969. 21st Int. Red. Cross Conf., Istanbul.

2291.	401.	100 k. + 10 k. red, blue and ultramarine ..	35	20
2292.	–	130 k. + 10 k. mult. ..	40	20

DESIGN: No. 2292, Conference emblem and silhouette of Istanbul.

402. Congress Hall

1969. 50th Anniv. of Sivas Congress.

2293.	402.	50 k. pur., blk. & red	20	15
2294.	–	60 k. olive, blk. & yell.	25	15

DESIGN: 60 k. Congress delegates.

403. Halay Scarf Dance.

1969. Turkish Folk-dances. Multicoloured.

2295.	30 k. Bar Dancers ..	15	15
2296.	50 k. Caydacira "candle" dance	30	20
2297.	60 k. Type **403** ..	35	25
2298.	100 k. Kilic-Kalkan sword dance	60	25
2299.	130 k. Zeybek Dance (vert.)	1·25	50

404. Bleriot Airplane "Prince Celaleddin".

1969. 55th Anniv of 1st Turkish Airmail Service.

2300	404	60 k. deep blue & blue	40	10
2301	–	75 k. black and bistre	25	15

DESIGN: 75 k. 1914 First Flight cover.

405. "Kutadgu Bilig".

1969. 900th Anniv. of "Kutadgu Bilig" (political manual) Completion.

2302. **405.** 130 k. brown, gold and bistre 25 10

1969. Greetings Card Stamp. As T **358.**

2303. 10 k. brown and green .. 10 10

DESIGN: 10 k. Equestrian statue of Ataturk at Bursa.

406. "Ataturk's Arrival" (S. Tuna).

1969. 50th Anniv. of Kemal Ataturk's Arrival in Ankara. Multicoloured.

2304.	50 k. Type **406**	30	10
2305.	60 k. Ataturk's motorcade	30	15

407. "Erosion Control".

1970. Nature Conservation Year. Mult.

2306.	50 k. + 10 k. Type **407** ..	25	20
2307.	60 k. + 10 k. "Protection of Flora" ..	40	25
2308.	130 k. + 10 k. "Protection of Wildlife" ..	90	75

408. Bosphorus Bridge (model). (Reduced size illus., actual size 79 × 30½ mm.)

1970. Commencement of work on Bosphorus Bridge. Multicoloured.

2309.	60 k. Type **408**	50	15
2310.	130 k. Symbolic bridge linking Europe & Asia	75	50

409. Ataturk and Signature. **410.** Education Year Emblem.

1970.

2311.	409.	1 k. brown and red..	10	10
2312.		50 k. green and olive	25	10

1970. Int. Education Year.

2313. **410.** 130 k. blue, pur. & mve. 25 10

411. Turkish Pavilion Emblem. **412.** Kemal Ataturk.

1970. World Fair "Expo 70", Osaka, Japan. Multicoloured.

2314.	50 k. Type **411**	15	10
2315.	100 k. Turkish pavilion and Expo emblem	30	10

1970.

2316	412	5 k. black and silver	10	10
2317		30 k. black and bistre	25	10
2318		50 k. black and pink	35	10
2319		75 k. black and lilac	85	10
2320		100 k. black and blue	60	10

413. Opening Ceremony.

1970. 50th Anniv. of Turkish National Assembly. Multicoloured.

2321.	50 k. Type **413**	15	10
2322.	60 k. First Assembly in session..	20	10

414. Emblem of Cartography Directorate.

1970. "75 Years of Turkish Cartography". Multicoloured.

2323.	50 k. Type **414**	10	10
2324.	60 k. Aircraft and contour map	35	10
2325.	100 k. Survey equipment	20	10
2326.	130 k. Lt.-Gen. Mehmet Sevki Pasha and relief map of Turkey ..	25	10

Nos. 2324 and 2326 are larger, size 48 × 33 mm.

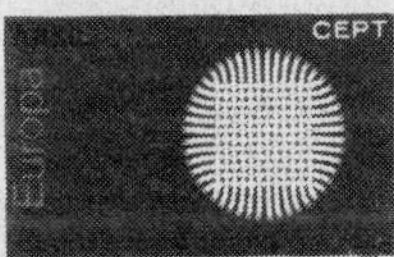

415. "Flaming Sun".

1970. Europa.

2327.	415.	100 k. red, orge. & blk.	45	10
2328.		130 k. grn., orge. & blk.	75	25

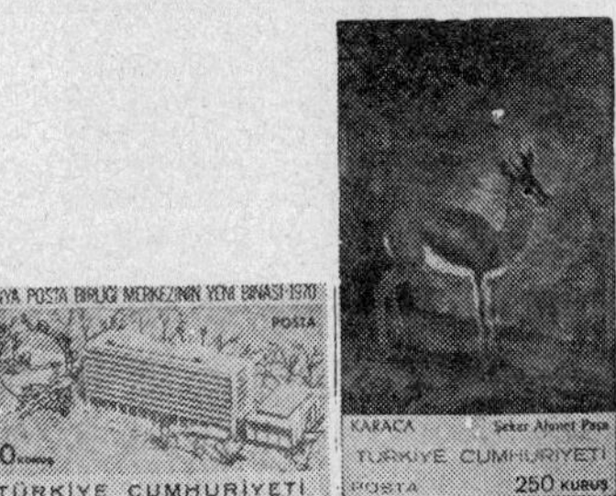

416. New U.P.U. Headquarters Building. **417.** "Roe-Deer" (Seker Ahmet Pasha).

1970. New U.P.U. Headquarters Building, Berne.

2329	416	60 k. black, bl & lt bl	15	10
2330		130 k. black, green and light green ..	25	10

1970. Turkish Paintings. Multicoloured.

2331.	250 k. Type **417**	80	50
2332.	250 k. "Lady with Mimosa" (Osman Hamdi)	80	50

See also Nos. 2349/50, 2364/5, 2396/7, 2416/17 and 2443/4.

418. "Turkish Folklore". **419.** Fethiye (Turkey).

1970. "Ankara 70" National Stamp Exhib. Multicoloured.

2333.	10 k. "Tree" of stamps and open album (vert.)	10	10
2334.	50 k. Type **418**	25	10
2335.	60 k. Ataturk statue and "stamps"	30	15

1970. 6th Anniv. of Regional Co-operation for Development. Multicoloured.

2337.	60 k. Type **419**	20	10
2338.	80 k. Seeyo-Se-Pol Bridge, Isfahan (Persia) ..	25	10
2339.	130 k. Saiful Malook Lake (Pakistan)	35	10

No. 2338 is larger, (41 × 26 mm.).

420. Tomb of Haci Bektas Veli. **421.** Symbolic "Fencer" and Globe.

1970. 700th Death Anniv. of Haci Bektas Veli (mystic). Multicoloured.

2340.	30 k. Type **420**	10	10
2341.	100 k. Sultan Balim's tomb (vert.)	35	10
2342.	180 k. Haci Bektas Veli (vert.)	40	15

No. 2342 is larger, size 32 × 49 mm.

1970. World Fencing Championships.

2343.	421.	90 k. + 10 k. black, blue and light blue	25	10
2344.	–	130 k. + 10 k. orange, green, black and blue	30	10

DESIGN: 130 k. Modern fencer, folk-dancer and globe.

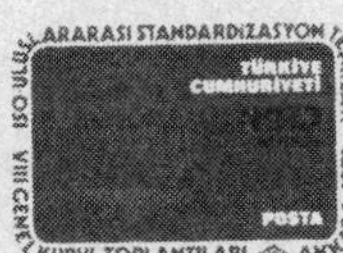

422. I.S.O. Emblem. **423.** U.N. Emblem within Windmill.

1970. 8th Int. Standardisation Organization General Assembly, Ankara.

2345.	422.	110 k. red, gold & blk.	25	10
2346.		150 k. blue, gold & blk.	30	15

1970. 25th Anniv. of United Nations. Mult.

2347.	100 k. Type **423**	30	10
2348.	220 k. "World's People supporting U.N. (vert.)	40	15

1970. Turkish Paintings. As T **417**. Mult.

2349	250 k. "Fevzi Cakmak" (Avni Lifij) (vert) ..	60	25
2350	250 k. "Fishing-boats" (Nazmi Ziya) (75 × 33 mm)	70	25

424. Turkish Troops Advancing.

1971. 50th Anniv. of 1st Battle of Inonu.

2351. **424.** 100 k. multicoloured 30 20

See also No. 2368.

425. Kemal Ataturk.

429. Hands enclosing "Four Races".

428. "Turkish Village" (A. Sekur).

1971.

2352 425 5 k. blue and grey .. 15 10
2353 25 k. red and grey .. 40 10
2354 – 25 k. brown and pink 15 10
2355 425 100 k. violet and grey 75 10
2356 – 100 k. green and flesh 60 10
2357 – 250 k. blue and drab 1·25 10
2358 425 400 k. green and bistre 1·50 10

DESIGNS: Nos. 2354, 2356 and 2357, Portraits similar to Type **425** but larger, 21 × 26 mm, and with face value at bottom right.

1971. Turkish Paintings. Multicoloured.

2364 250 k. Type **428** 65 25
2365 250 k. "Yildiz Palace Garden" (A.R. Bicakcilar) 65 25

See also Nos. 2396/7, 2416/17 and 2443/4.

1971. Racial Equality Year.

2366. **429.** 100 k. multicoloured 20 10
2367. 250 k. multicoloured 25 10

1971. 50th Anniv of Second Battle of Inonu. Design similar to T **424**. Multicoloured.

2368 100 k. Turkish machine-gunners 40 10

430. Europa Chain. 431. Pres. C. Gursel.

1971. Europa.

2369. **430.** 100 k. vio., yell & blue 55 25
2370. 150 k. grn., red & orge. 85 40

1971. 11th Anniv. of May 27th 1960 Revolution.

2371. **431.** 100 k. multicoloured 30 10

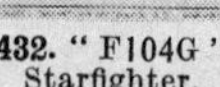
432. "F104G" Starfighter.

433. "Care of Children".

1971. Air. "60 Years of Turkish Aviation". Multicoloured.

2372. 110 k. Type **432** 60 10
2373. 200 k. Victory Monument, Afyon and aircraft .. 85 10
2374. 250 k. Air Force emblem and aircraft (horiz.) .. 95 10
2375. 325 k. Starfighters and pilot .. .. 1·50 10
2376. 400 k. Bleriot "XIb" aircraft of 1911 (horiz.) .. 1·25 10
2377. 475 k. Hezarfen Celebi's "bird" flight from Galata Tower (horiz.) .. 2·00 15

1971. 50th Anniv of Children's Protection Society.

2378. **433.** 50 k. + 10 k. red, pur. and black 20 10
2379. – 100 k. + 15 k. mult. 25 15
2380. – 110 k. + 15 k. mult. 35 15

DESIGNS—VERT. 100 k. Child standing on protective hand. HORIZ. 110 k. Mother and child.

434. Selimiye Mosque, Edirne.

1971. 7th Anniv. of Regional Co-operation for Development Pact. Mosques. Mult.

2381. 100 k. Type **434** 20 15
2382. 150 k. Chaharbagh Mosque School (Iran) 25 15
2383. 200 k. Badshahi Mosque (Pakistan) (horiz.) .. 50 25

435. Alpaslan (Seljuk leader) and Cavalry.

1971. 900th Anniv. of Battle of Malazgirt.

2384. **435.** 100 k. multicoloured 25 15
2385. – 250 k. red, yell. & blk. 55 25

DESIGN: 250 k. Seljuk mounted archer.

436. Officer and Troop Column.

1971. 50th Anniv of Battle of Sakarya.

2386 **436** 100 k. multicoloured .. 40 10

437. Diesel Train and Map. (Turkey–Iran route).

1971. Int. Rail Links.

2387. – 100 k. multicoloured 1·75 20
2388. – 110 k. violet and blue 1·60 20
2389. **437.** 250 k. multicoloured 75 45

DESIGNS: 100 k. Diesel train crossing bridge (Turkey–Bulgaria route). 110 k. Train ferry "Orhan Atliman", Lake Van (Turkey–Iran route).

438. Football.

1971. Mediterranean Games, Izmir.

2390. **438.** 100 k. blk., vio. & bl. 25 10
2391. – 200 k. multicoloured 30 15

DESIGN—VERT. 200 k. "Athlete and stadium".

439. Tomb of Cyrus the Great.

1971. 2500th Anniv of Persian Empire.

2393 **439** 25 k. multicoloured .. 15 10
2394 – 100 k. multicoloured 30 15
2395 – 150 k. brown and drab 50 15

1971. Turkish Paintings. As Type **428**. Mult.

2396 250 k. "Sultan Mohammed I and Entourage" .. 75 25
2397 250 k. "Cinilli Kosk Palace" 75 25

441. U.N.I.C.E.F. Emblem. 442. Yunus Emre.

1971. 25th Anniv. of U.N.I.C.E.F.

2404. **441.** 100 k. + 10 k. mult... 30 15
2405. 250 k. + 15 k. mult... 30 25

1971. 650th Death Anniv. of Yunus Emre (folk-poet).

2406. **442.** 100 k. multicoloured 30 20

443. First Turkish Map of the World (1072) and Book Year Emblem.

1972. Int. Book Year.

2407. **443.** 100 k. multicoloured 30 15

444. Doves and N.A.T.O. Emblem.

445. Human Heart.

1972. 20th Anniv. of Turkey's Membership of N.A.T.O.

2408. **444.** 100 k. blk., grey & grn. 65 20
2409. 250 k. blk., grey & bl. 1·10 45

1972. World Health Day.

2410. **445.** 250 k. + 25 k. red, blk. and grey 35 15

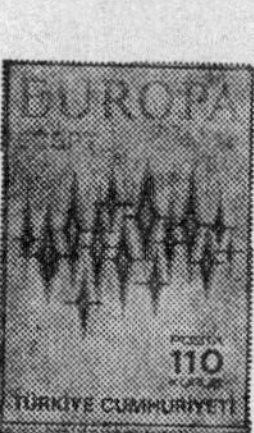
447. "Communications".

448. "Fisherman" (G. Dareli).

1972. Europa.

2414. **447.** 110 k. multicoloured 90 55
2415. 250 k. multicoloured 1·90 1·10

1972. Turkish Paintings. As T **428**. Mult.

2416. 250 k. "Gebze" (Osman Hamdi) 75 25
2417. 250 k. "Forest" (S. A. Pasa) 75 25

1972. As T 358.

2418 25 k. black and brown .. 10 10

DESIGN: 25 k. Equestrian statue of Ataturk at Ankara.

1972. Regional Co-operation for Development. Multicoloured.

2419 100 k. Type **448** 40 20
2420 125 k. "Will and Power" (Chughtai) 40 20
2421 150 k. "Iranian Woman" (Behzad) 65 35

INDEX

Countries can be quickly located by referring to the index at the end of this volume.

449. Olympic Rings.

1972. Olympic Games, Munich.

2422. **449.** 100 k. + 15 k. mult. .. 30 20
2423. – 110 k. + 25 k. mult. .. 35 20
2424. – 250 k. + 25 k. mult. .. 55 40

DESIGNS: 110 k. "Athletes". 250 k. "Stadium".

450. Ataturk at Observation Post.

1972. 50th Anniv of Turkish War of Liberation. Multicoloured.

(a) "Grand Offensive".

2425. 100 k. Type **450** 30 15
2426. 110 k. Artillery 40 20

(b) "Commander-in-Chief's Offensive".

2427. 100 k. Hand-to-hand fighting 30 15

(c) "Entry into Izmir".

2428. 100 k. Commanders in open car 30 15

451. "Diagnosis and Cure".

452. Kemal Ataturk.

1972. Fight Against Cancer.

2429. **451.** 100 k. red, blk & bl. 25 10

1972. Various sizes.

2430. **452.** 5 k. pale blue on blue 10 10
2430a. 25 k. orange on orange 10 10
2431. 100 k. lake on buff .. 60 10
2431a. 100 k. pale grey on grey 10 10
2431b. 100 k. olive on green 20 10
2432. 110 k. blue on blue .. 80 10
2432a. 125 k. green on grey 65 10
2433. 150 k. brown on buff 60 10
2433a. 150 k. green on green 10 10
2434. 175 k. pur. on yellow 80 10
2434a. 200 k. red on buff .. 60 10
2434b. 200 k. brown on buff 20 10
2435. 250 k. lilac on pink .. 75 10
3435a. 400 k. turquoise on blue 25 10
2436. 500 k. violet on pink 1·60 10
2437. 500 k. blue on blue .. 40 10
2438. 10 l. mauve on pink 1·25 10

453. U.I.C. Emblem.

454. University Emblem.

1972. 50th Anniv of International Railways Union.

2439 **453** 100 k. brn, buff & grn 60 15

1973. Bicent. of Technical University, Istanbul.

2440. **454.** 100 k. + 25 k. mult. 30 15

455. Europa "Posthorn".

456. Helmet and Sword.

1973. Europa.

2441. **455.** 110 k. multicoloured 65 20
2442. 250 k. multicoloured 1·00 35

1973. Turkish Painters. As T **428**. Mult.
2443 250 k. "Old Almshouse, Istanbul" (Ahmet Ziya Akbulut) (horiz) .. 65 30
2444 250 k. "Flowers in Vase" (Suleyman Seyyit) (vert) 65 30

1973. Land Forces Day.
2445. **456.** 90 k. grn., brn. & grey 15 10
2446. – 100 k. grn., brn. and light green .. 20 15
DESIGN: 100 k. As Type **456**, but wreath enclosing design.

457. Carved Head, Tomb of Antiochus I (Turkey).
458. Peace Dove and " 50 ".

1973. Regional Co-operation for Development. Multicoloured.
2447 100 k. Type **457** 20 10
2448 150 k. Statue, Lut excavations (Iran) .. 30 15
2449 200 k. Street in Moenjodaro (Pakistan) 40 20

1973. 50th Anniv. of Lausanne Peace Treaty.
2450. **458.** 100 k.+25 k. mult. 25 10

459. Minelayer "Nusret II".
460. " Al-Biruni" (from 16th-century miniature).

1973. Bicentenary of Turkish Navy. Mult.
2451 5 k. Type **459** 10 10
2452 25 k. Destroyer "Istanbul" 15 10
2453 100 k. Motor torpedo-boat "Simsek" 30 25
2454 250 k. Cadet brig "Nurud-i-Futuh" (48 × 32 mm) 2·25 45

1973. Millenary of Abu Reihan al-Biruni.
2455. **460.** 250 k. multicoloured 30 10

461. " Equal Opportunity ".
463. " Balkanfila" Emblem.

1973. Cent. of Darussafaka High School.
2456. **461.** 100 k. multicoloured 25 10

1973. " Balkanfila IV " Stamp Exhibition, Izmir (1st issue).
2458. **463.** 100 k. multicoloured 25 10
See also Nos. 2462/3.

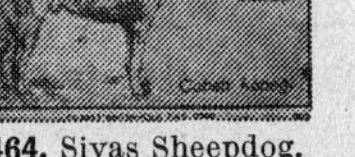

464. Sivas Sheepdog.
465. Kemal Ataturk.

1973. Animals.
2459 **464** 25 k. blue, yell & blk 10 10
2460 – 100 k. yellow, blk & bl 60 10
DESIGN: 100 k. Angora cat.

1973. 35th Death Anniv. of Kemal Ataturk.
2461. **465.** 100 k. brown and drab 25 10

466. Bosphorus and " Stamps ".
467. " Flower " Emblem.

1973. " Balkanfila IV " Stamp Exhibition (2nd issue). Multicoloured.
2462. 110 k. Type **466** .. 20 10
2463. 250 k. " Balkanfila " in decorative script .. 35 15

1973. 50th Anniv of Republic.
2464 **467** 100 k. red, violet & bl 15 10
2465 – 250 k. multicoloured 25 10
2466 – 475 k. yellow and blue 35 15
DESIGNS: 250 k. "Hands" supporting "50". 475 k. Cogwheels and ears of corn.

468. Bosphorus Bridge.
469. Bosphorus Bridge and U.N.I.C.E.F. Emblem.

1973. Opening of Bosphorus Bridge, Istanbul. Multicoloured.
2468. 100 k. Type **468** 25 10
2469. 150 k. View of Bosphorus and bridge 35 15

1973. U.N.I.C.E.F. Ceremony. Children of Europe and Asia linked by Bosphorus Bridge.
2470. **469.** 200 k. multicoloured 40 10

470. Mevlana Celaleddin.
471. Cotton.

1973. 700th Death Anniv of Mevlana Celaleddin (poet and mystic).
2471 – 100 k. green, bl & blk 20 10
2472 **470** 250 k. multicoloured 35 10
DESIGN: 100 k. Tomb and dancing dervishes.

1973. Export Products.
2473 **471** 75 k. grey, blue & blk 10 10
2474 – 90 k. bistre, bl & blk 15 10
2475 – 100 k. black, bl & grn 20 10
2476 – 250 k. multicoloured 1·25 15
2477 – 325 k. yellow, bl & blk 95 10
2478 – 475 k. black, bl & brn 60 10
DESIGNS: 90 k. Grapes. 100 k. Figs. 250 k. Citrus fruits. 325 k. Tobacco. 475 k. Hazelnuts.

472. Fokker " Fellowship " F-28.
473. President Inonu.

1973. Air. Multicoloured.
2479. 110 k. Type **472** 55 10
2480. 250 k. Douglas DC-10/10 85 10

1973. President Inonu's Death.
2481. **473.** 100 k. brown & buff.. 20 10

474. " Statue of a King " (Hittite era).
475. Doctor and Patient.

1974. Europa. Sculptures. Multicoloured.
2482. 110 k. Type **474** .. .. 1·25 30
2483. 250 k. " Statuette of a Child " (c. 2000 B.C.).. 2·25 55

1974. 75th Anniv. of Sisli Paediatrics Hospital.
2484. **475.** 110 k. blk., grey & bl. 20 10

476. Silver and Gold Idol.
477. Population Year Emblem.

1974. Archaeological Treasures. Multicoloured.
2485. 125 k. Type **476** 20 10
2486. 175 k. Painted jar (horiz.) 20 10
2487. 200 k. Bulls (statuettes) (horiz.) 35 10
2488. 250 k. Jug 45 25

1974. World Population Year.
2489. **477.** 250 k.+25 k. mult... 40 15

479. Turkish Carpet.
480. Dove and Map of Cyprus.

1974. Regional Co-operation for Development. Multicoloured.
2496. 100 k. Type **479** 40 10
2497. 150 k. Iranian carpet .. 95 15
2498. 200 k. Pakistani carpet 1·25 10

1974. Turkish Intervention in Cyprus.
2499. **480.** 250 k. multicoloured 50 10

481. " Getting to Grips ".
482. Dove with Letter.

1974. World Free-style Wrestling Championships, Ankara. Multicoloured.
2500. 90 k. Type **481** 25 10
2501. 100 k. " Throw " (vert.).. 30 10
2502. 250 k. " Lock " 40 20

1974. Centenary of Universal Postal Union.
2503 **482** 110 k. gold, dp bl & bl 20 10
2504 – 200 k. brown & green 35 15
2505 – 250 k. multicoloured 40 15
DESIGNS: 200 k. Dove. 250 k. Arrows encircling globe.

483. Open Book (Laws Reform).

1974. Works and Reforms of Ataturk (1st series).
2506 **453** 50 k. black and blue 10 10
2507 – 150 k. multicoloured 20 10
2508 – 400 k. multicoloured 50 10
DESIGNS—VERT. 150 k. " Tree " (" National Economy "). 400 k. Students facing Sun (" Reform of Education ").
See also Nos. 2543/5, 2566/8, 2597/9, 2639/41 and 2670/2.

HAVE YOU READ THE NOTES AT THE BEGINNING OF THIS CATALOGUE?
These often provide answers to the enquiries we receive.

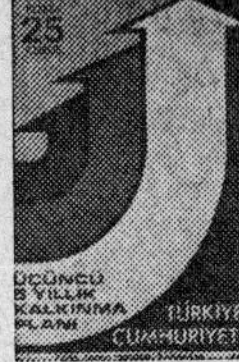

484. Marconi.
485. Arrows (3rd Five Year Development Programme).

1974. Birth Cent. of Marconi (radio pioneer).
2509. **484.** 250 k.+25 k. black, brown and red .. 40 30

1974. " Turkish Development ".
2510. **485.** 25 k. black and brown 15 10
2511. – 100 k. grey and brown 35 10
DESIGN—HORIZ. 100 k. Map of Turkey within cogwheel (industrialization).

486. Volleyball.
487. Dr. Albert Schweitzer.

1974. Ball Games.
2512. **486.** 125 k. black and blue 25 10
2513. – 175 k. black & orange 30 10
2514. – 250 k. black & green 40 10
DESIGNS: 175 k. Basketball. 250 k. Football.

1975. Birth Cent. of Dr. Albert Schweitzer.
2515. **487.** 250 k.+50 k. mult... 50 25

488. Automatic Telex Network.

1975. Posts and Telecommunications.
2516. **488.** 5 k. black and yellow 10 10
2517. – 50 k. green and orange 15 10
2518. – 100 k. black and blue 20 10
DESIGNS: 50 k. Postal cheques. 100 k. Radio-link.

489. "Going to the Classroom" (I. Sivga).
490. Karacaoglan Monument (H. Gezer), Mut.

1975. Children's Drawings. Multicoloured.
2519 25 k. Type **489** 10 10
2520 50 k. "View From a Village" (H. Dogru) .. 10 10
2521 100 k. "Folklore" (B. Aktan) .. 20 10

1975. Karacaoglan (musician) Commem.
2522 **490** 110 k. mve, grn & brn 40 10

491. "Orange gathering in Hatay " (C. Tollu).

1975. Europa. Paintings. Multicoloured.
2523 110 k. Type **491** 55 10
2524 250 k. "The Yoruks" (T. Zaim) 90 40

492. Turkish Porcelain Vase.

493. Namibia located on Map of Africa.

1975. Regional Co-operation for Development. Traditional Crafts. Multicoloured.

2525 110 k. Type **492** 35 15
2526 200 k. Ceramic plate (Iran) (horiz) 55 25
2527 250 k. Camel-skin vase (Pakistan) 75 35

1975. Namibia Day.

2528. **493.** 250 k. + 50 k. mult. 35 15

494. Horon Folk-dancers.

1975. Turkish Folk Dances. Multicoloured.

2529 100 k. Type **494** 25 10
2530 125 k. Kasik 25 10
2531 175 k. Bengi 35 10
2532 250 k. Kasap 45 15
2533 325 k. Kafkas (vert) .. 65 15

495. " Oguz Khan Slaying Dragon ".

497. Turbot.

1975. Tales of Dede Korkut. Multicoloured.

2534. 90 k. Type **495** 20 10
2535. 175 k. Tale of Duha Koca Oglu Deli Dumrul Hikayesi (horiz.) .. 25 10
2536. 200 k. " Pillaging of Home of Salur Kazan " .. 30 10

1975. Fishes. Multicoloured.

2538. 75 k. Type **497** 25 10
2539. 90 k. Common carp .. 40 10
2540. 175 k. Trout 50 10
2541. 250 k. Red mullet .. 1·10 15
2542. 475 k. Red bream .. 1·25 15

498. Two Women and Symbol (Women's Participation in Public Life).

1975. Reforms of Ataturk (2nd series).

2543 **498** 100 k. red, blk & stone 15 10
2544 – 110 k. multicoloured 15 10
2545 – 250 k. multicoloured 25 10

DESIGNS—VERT. 110 k. Symbol and inscription (Nationalization of Insurance Companies). HORIZ: 250 k. Arrows (Orientation of the Fine Arts).

499. Z. Gokalp.

500. Ceramic Plate.

1976. Birth Cent. of Ziya Gokalp (philosopher).

2546. **499.** 200 k.+25 k. mult. 25 10

1976. Europa. Multicoloured.

2547. 200 k. Type **500** 55 25
2548. 400 k. Dessert jug .. 1·25 45

501. Silhouette of Istanbul.

1976. Seventh Islamic Conf., Istanbul.

2549. **501.** 500 k. multicoloured 45 10

502. "Lunch in Field" (S. Yucel).

1976. "Samsun '76" Youth Stamp Exn. Mult.

2550 50 k. Type **502** 10 10
2551 200 k. "Boats on the Bosphorus (E. Kosemen) (vert) .. 20 10
2552 400 k. "Winter View" (R. Cetinkaya) 35 10

503. Sultan Marshes.

1976. European Wetlands Conservation Year. Turkish Landscapes. Multicoloured.

2553 150 k. Type **503** .. .. 1·60 50
2554 200 k. Lake Manyas .. 40 10
2555 250 k. Lake Borabey .. 60 10
2556 400 k. Manavgat Waterfalls 60 15

504. " Hodja with Liver ".

505. Games Emblem and Flame.

1976. Nasreddin Hodja (humourist) Commem. " The Liver and the Kite ". Multicoloured.

2557. 150 k. Type **504** 20 10
2558. 250 k. " Friend offers recipe " .. 25 10
2559. 600 k. " Kite takes liver, leaving recipe " .. 55 15

1976. Olympic Games, Montreal.

2560 **505** 100 k. red and blue .. 25 10
2561 – 400k. multicoloured .. 35 10
2562 – 600 k. multicoloured 55 15

DESIGNS—HORIZ. 400 k. "Athlete" as "76". VERT. 600 k. Games emblem.

506. Kemal Ataturk (Turkey).

1976. Regional Co-operation for Development. Heads of State. Multicoloured.

2563. 100 k. Type **506** 25 10
2564. 200 k. Riza Shah Pahlavi (Iran) 25 10
2565. 250 k. Mohammad Ali Jinnah (Pakistan) .. 35 15

507. Peace Dove and Sword (Army Reform).

508. White Spoonbill.

1976. "Words and Reforms of Ataturk" (3rd series).

2566 100 k. black and red .. 10 10
2567 200 k. multicoloured .. 20 10
2568 400 k. multicoloured .. 40 25

DESIGNS: 200 k. Words, books and listeners (Ataturk's speeches). 400 k. Peace doves and globe ("Peace throughout the World").

1976. Turkish Birds. Multicoloured.

2569. 100 k.+25 k. Type **508** .. 35 20
2570. 150 k.+25 k. Common roller 45 30
2571. 200 k.+25 k. Greater flamingo 60 40
2572. 400 k.+25 k. Waldrapp (horiz.) .. .. 1·25 60

509. "Hora" (oil exploration ship).

510. Musical Symbols.

1977.

2573 **509** 400 k. multicoloured .. 85 25

1977. 150th Anniv. of Presidential Symphony Orchestra.

2574. **510.** 200 k. multicoloured 25 10

511. Kemal Ataturk in " 100 ".

1977. Centenary of Parliament.

2575. **511.** 200 k. black and red 15 10
2576. – 400 k. black & brown 25 10

DESIGN: 400 k. Hand placing ballot-paper in box.

512. Pamukkale.

1977. Europa. Landscapes. Multicoloured.

2577. 200 k. Type **512** 75 20
2578. 400 k. Zelve .. .. 1·50 40

513. Edict of Karamanoglu Mehmet Bey and " Ongun " Bird.

1977. 700th Anniv. of Official Turkish Language.

2579. **513.** 200 k.+25 k. black and green 20 10

514. Head-shaped vase, Turkey.

1977. Regional Co-operation for Development. Pottery. Multicoloured.

2580. 100 k. Type **514** 25 10
2581. 255 k. Earthenware pot, Iran 45 10
2582. 675 k. Model bullock cart, Pakistan .. .. 1·10 10

515. Stylized Sailing Yacht.

522. " Globe " and Emblem.

1977. European Finn Class Sailing Championships.

2584. **515.** 150 k. black, blue and pale blue 25 10
2585. – 200 k blue and deep blue 45 15
2586. – 250 k. black and blue 65 20

DESIGNS—HORIZ. 200 k. VERT. 250 k. both showing stylized sailing yachts.

1977. Surch **10 KURUS**.

2592 **409** 10 k. on 1 k. brn & red 15 10

1977. 10th World Energy Conference.

2593 **522** 100 k.+25 k. black, brown and pink .. 15 10
2594 – 600 k.+50 k. red, black and blue .. 30 25

DESIGN: 600 k. Similar design showing a "globe" and emblem.

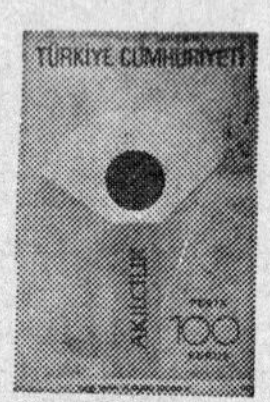

523. Kemal Ataturk.

524. " Head and Book " (Rationalism).

1977. Size $20\frac{1}{2} \times 22\frac{1}{2}$ mm.

2595. **523.** 200 k. blue on pale blue 25 10
2596. 250 k. turq. on pale blue 30 10

See also Nos. 2619/25.

1977. Works and Reforms of Ataturk (4th series). Multicoloured.

2597. 100 k. Type **524** 10 10
2598. 200 k. Words by Ataturk (National Sovereignty) 15 10
2599. 400 k. Symbol (Leadership for Liberation of Nations) 25 10

525. Allama Muhammad Iqbal.

526. Overturned Car.

1977. Birth Centenary of Allama Muhammad Iqbal (Pakistani poet).

2600. **525.** 400 k. multicoloured 25 10

1977. Road Safety.

2601 **526** 50 k. black, blue & red 10 10
2602 – 150 k. blk, grey & red 15 10
2603 – 250 k. blk, brn & red 20 10
2604 – 500 k. blk, grey & red 40 10
2605 – 800 k. deep green, green and red .. 65 10
2606 – 10 l. green, red & blk 75 10

DESIGNS—VERT. 150 k. Arrow crossing white lines and pool of blood. 500 k. "Children crossing" sign. 800 k. "No overtaking" sign. 10 l. Footprints in road and on pedestrian crossing. HORIZ. 250 k. Tractor pulling trailer loaded with people.

527. Lighted Match and Trees.

531. Riza Shah Pahlavi of Iran.

530. Ishakpasa Palace, Dogubeyazit.

1977. Forest Conservation.
2607. 527. 50 k. blk., red & grn. 15 10
2608. – 250 k. blk., grn. & grey 25 10
DESIGN: 250 k. "Tree germination".
See also No. 2699.

1978. Europa. Multicoloured.
2616. 2½ l. Type 530 .. .. 45 10
2617. 5 l. Anamur Castle 85 25

1978. Birth Centenary of Riza Shah Pahlavi of Iran.
2618. 531. 5 l. multicoloured .. 30 10

1978. As T 523 but larger, 19 × 25 mm.
2619. 10 k. brown 10 10
2620. 50 k. grey 10 10
2621. 1 l. red 10 10
2622. 2½ l. lilac 10 10
2623. 5 l. blue 20 10
2624. 25 l. blue and pale blue .. 85 10
2625. 50 l. orange & pale orange 2·00 10

532. Athletics.

1978. "Gymnasiade '78" World School Games.
2626 532 1 l. + 50 k. deep green and green .. 10 10
2627 – 2½ l. + 50 k. bl & orge 25 10
2628 – 5 l. + 50 k. blue & pink 30 15
2629 – 8 l. + 50 k. blue & grn 50 20
DESIGNS: 2½ l. Gymnastics. 5 l. Table tennis. 8 l. Swimming.

533. Salmon Rose

1978. Regional Co-operation for Development. Multicoloured.
2630 2½ l. Type 533 .. .. 40 10
2631 3½ l. Pink roses .. 60 10
2632 8 l. Red roses 70 10

534. Anti-Apartheid Year Emblem.
535. View of Ankara.

1978. International Anti-Apartheid Year.
2633. 534. 10 l. multicoloured .. 45 10

1978. Turkish–Libyan Friendship. Mult.
2634. 2½ l. Type 535 .. .. 25 10
2635. 5 l. View of Tripoli .. 35 10

536. Ribbon and Chain.
538. Independence Medal.

1978. 25th Anniv. of European Convention on Human Rights.
2636. 536. 2½ l. + 50 k. blue, green and black 35 20
2637. – 5 l. + 50 k. red, blue and black 65 30
DESIGN: 5 l. Ribbon and flower.

1978. Works and Reforms of Ataturk (5th series).
2639. 538. 2½ l. multicoloured .. 10 10
2640. – 3½ l. red and black .. 15 10
2641. – 5 l. multicoloured .. 30 10
DESIGNS—HORIZ. 3½ l. Talking heads (language reform). VERT. 5 l. "ABC" in Arabic and Roman scripts (adoption of Latin alphabet).

539. Bosphorus Waterside Residence of Koprulu Huseyin Pasa, Istanbul (1699).

1978. Traditional Turkish Houses. Mult.
2642. 1 l. Type 539 .. .. 10 10
2643. 2½ l. Residence of Saatci Ali Efendi, Izmit, 1774 20 10
2644. 3½ l. House of Bey, Kula (vert.) 30 10
2645. 5 l. House of Bahaeddin Aga, Milas (vert.) .. 35 10
2646. 8 l. House at Safranbolu 45 15

541. Children with Globe as Balloon.
542. Mail Transport.

1979. International Year of the Child.
2649. – 2½ l. + 50 k. black, gold and red .. 10 10
2650. 541. 5 l. + 50 k. multicoloured 30 15
2651. – 8 l. + 50 k. multicoloured 50 25
DESIGNS: 2½ l. Children embracing beneath hearts. 8 l. Adult and child balancing globe.

1979. Europa.
2652 542 2½ l. black, green & bl 35 10
2653 – 5 l. orange and black 15 10
2654 – 7½ l. black and blue .. 25 10
DESIGNS: 5 l. Telex keyboard, morse key and telegraph poles. 7½ l. Telephone dial and dish aerial.

543. Kemal Ataturk.
544. "Turkish Harvest" (Namik Ismail).

1979.
2655 543 50 k. green 10 10
2656 1 l. green & lt green 10 10
2657 2½ l. lilac 15 10
2657a 2½ l. blue 10 10
2748 2½ l. orange .. 15 10
2658 5 l. blue and lt blue 15 10
2659 7½ l. brown 40 10
2659a 7½ l. red 30 10
2660 10 l. mauve 50 10
2661a 10 l. mauve (22 × 22 mm) 40 10
2661 20 l. grey 40 10

1979. Regional Co-operation for Development. Paintings. Multicoloured.
2662 5 l. Type 544 .. .. 20 10
2663 7½ l. "Iranian Goldsmith" (Kamal el Molk) .. 25 10
2664 10 l. "Pakistan Village Scene" (Ustad Baksh) 35 20

545. Colemanite.
546. Highway forming Figure 8.

1979. 10th World Mining Congress. Mult.
2665. 5 l. Type 545 .. .. 40 10
2666. 7½ l. Chromite 50 10
2667. 10 l. Antimonite .. 60 10
2668. 15 l. Sulphur 75 10

1979. 8th European Communications Ministers' Symposium.
2669. 546. 5 l. multicoloured .. 60 25

547. "Confidence in Youth".
548. Poppy ("Papaver somniferum").

1979. Works and Reforms of Ataturk (6th series).
2670. 547. 2½ l. multicoloured .. 15 10
2671. – 3½ l. multicoloured .. 20 10
2672. – 5 l. black and orange 25 10
DESIGNS—HORIZ. 3½ l. "Secularism". VERT. 5 l. "National Oath".

1979. Flowers (1st series). Multicoloured.
2673. 5 l. Type 548 .. .. 25 10
2674. 7½ l. Oleander ("Nerium oleander") 30 10
2675. 10 l. Late Spider Orchid ("Ophrys holosericea") 1·00 20
2676. 15 l. Mandrake ("Mandragora autumnalis") 60 10
See also Nos. 2705/8.

549. Ibrahim Muteferrika (first printer) and Presses.

1979. 250th Anniv. of Turkish Printing.
2678. 549. 10 l. multicoloured .. 35 15

550. Black Partridge.
551. Olives, Leaves and Globe in Oil-drop.

1979. Wildlife Conservation. Multicoloured.
2679. 5 l. + 1 l. Type 550 .. 45 15
2680. 5 l. + 1 l. Great Bustard 45 15
2681. 5 l. + 1 l. Demoiselle Crane 45 15
2682. 5 l. + 1 l. Goitred gazelle 45 15
2683. 5 l. + 1 l. Mouflon .. 45 15
Nos. 2679/83 were issued together, se-tenant, forming a composite design.

1979. Second World Olive Oil Year.
2684 551 5 l. multicoloured 20 10
2685 – 10 l. yellow & green .. 35 10
DESIGN: 10 l. Globe in oil drop.

553. Uskudarli Hoca Ali Riza (artist).

1980. Europa. Multicoloured.
2692. 7½ l. Type 553 .. 20 10
2693. 10 l. Ali Sami Boyar (artist) 35 10
2694. 20 l. Dr. Hulusi Behcet (skin specialist) .. 60 20

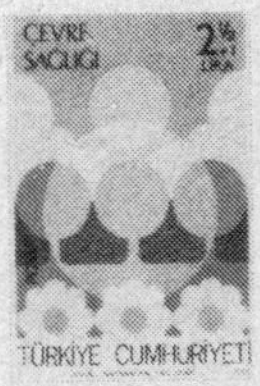

554. Flowers and Trees.
555. Lighted Match and Trees.

1980. Environmental Protection. Mult.
2695. 2½ l. + 1 l. Type 554 .. 10 10
2696. 7½ l. + 1 l. Sun and water 15 10
2697. 15 l. + 1 l. Factory polluting atmosphere 25 15
2698. 20 l. + 1 l. Flower surrounded by oil .. 35 25

1980. Forest Conservation.
2699. 555. 50 k. grn., red & brn. 10 10
See also No. 2607.

556. Seismological Graph.
557. Games Emblem and Pictograms.

1980. Seventh World Conference on Earthquake Engineering.
2700. – 7½ l. brn., blue & orge. 15 10
2701. 556. 20 l. blk., orge. & blue 40 20
DESIGN: 7½ l. Pictorial representation of earthquake within globe.

1980. First Islamic Games, Izmir. Mult.
2702. 7½ l. Type 557 .. .. 15 10
2703. 20 l. As No. 2702 but with different sports around emblem 40 20

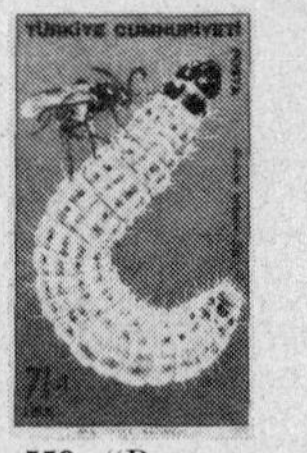

558. Ornamental Window.
559. "Bracon hebetor" and Larva of Dark Arches Moth.

1980. 1400th Anniv of Hejira.
2704 558 20 l. multicoloured .. 40 15

1980. Flowers (2nd series). As T 548. Mult.
2705. 2½ l. Manisa tulip ("Tulipa hayatii") 10 10
2706. 7½ l. Ephesian bellflower ("Campanula ephesia") 15 10
2707. 15 l. Crocus ("Crocus ancyrensis") 25 15
2708. 20 l. Anatolian orchid ("Orchis anatolica") .. 1·40 25

1980. Useful Insects (1st series). Mult.
2709 2½ l. + 1 l. "Rodolia cardinalis" (ladybird) and cottony cushion scale 25 15
2710 7½ + 1 l. Type 559 .. 25 20
2711 15 l. + 1 l. Caterpillar-hunter and larva of gypsy moth 35 25
2712 20 l. + 1 l. "Deraeocoris rutilus" (leaf bug) .. 40 30
See also Nos 2763/6.

560. Kemal Ataturk.
561. Ibn Sina Teaching.

1980.
2713 560 7½ l. brown and pink 20 10
2714 10 l. brown & lt brn 10 10
2719a 15 l. blue 20 10
2715 20 l. violet & mauve 25 10
2719b 20 l. orange .. 25 10
2716 30 l. grey and lt grey 75 10
2717 50 l. red and yellow 60 10
2719c 65 l. green 75 10
2718 75 l. green & lt green 1·10 10
2719d 90 l. mauve .. 1·25 10
2719 100 l. blue & lt blue 1·40 10

1980. Birth Millenary of Ibn Sina (Avicenna) (philosopher and physician). Multicoloured.
2720 7½ l. Type 561 .. .. 25 10
2721 20 l. Ibn Sina (vert) .. 45 15

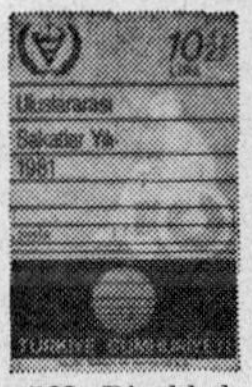

562. Ataturk and Figures "100".
563. Disabled Person in Wheelchair.

1981. "Balkanfila VIII" Stamp Exhibition, Ankara.
2722. 562. 10 l. red and black .. 25 10

1981. International Year of Disabled Persons.
2723. 563. 10 l. + 2½ l. multicoloured 25 20
2724. 20 l. + 2½ l. multicoloured 35 30

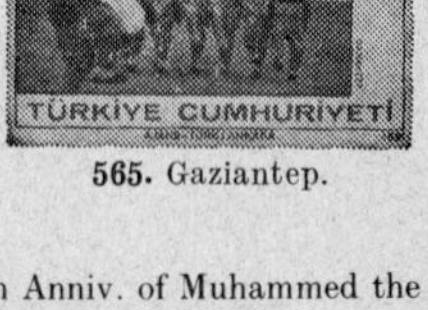

564. Sultan Mohammed the Conqueror.
565. Gaziantep.

1981. 500th Death Anniv. of Muhammed the Conqueror.
2725. 564. 10 l. multicoloured .. 20 10
2726. 20 l. multicoloured .. 35 20

1981. Folk Dances and Europa (35, 70 l.). Multicoloured.

2727. ½ l. Type **565** 15 10
2728. 10 l. Balikesir 15 10
2729. 15 l. Kahramanmaras .. 25 10
2730. 35 l. Antalya 60 30
2731. 70 l. Burdur .. .. 1·25 55

566. Ataturk in 1919. (S.G. 2279). **568.** Carpet.

1981. Birth Centenary of Kemal Ataturk. Previous stamps showing Ataturk. Mult.

2732 **566** 2½ l. multicoloured .. 10 10
2733 – 7½ l. black and brown 10 10
2734 – 10 l. multicoloured .. 15 10
2735 – 20 l. blue, red & black 25 15
2736 – 25 l. black, red & orge 30 20
2737 – 35 l. multicoloured .. 45 30

DESIGNS: 7½ l. Ataturk in civilian dress (S.G. No. 2285). 10 l. Ataturk and old Parliament House (S.G. No. 2037). 20 l. Ataturk teaching Latin alphabet (S.G. No. 1222). 25 l. Remilitarization of the Dardanelles surcharged stamp (S.G. No. 1188). 35 l. Ataturk in evening dress (from miniature sheet).

1981. Various stamps surch. **10 LIRA.**

2739. – 10 l. on 60 k. red, black and green (No. 2177) 25 10
2740. **452.** 10 l. on 110 k. blue on blue 25 10
2741. 10 l. on 400 k. turq. on blue 25 10
2742. – 10 l. on 800 k. green, turq. & red (No. 2605) 65 10

1981. 2nd International Congress of Turkish Folklore. Multicoloured.

2743. 7½ l. Type **568** 15 10
2744. 10 l. Embroidery .. 15 10
2745. 15 l. Drum and "zurna" 25 15
2746. 20 l. Embroidered napkin 40 15
2747. 30 l. Rug 50 20

570. Ataturk Centenary and E.P.S. Emblems.

1981. 5th European Physical Society General Congress.

2750. **570.** 10 l. multicoloured .. 30 10
2751. 30 l. multicoloured .. 45 20

571. F.A.O. Emblem.

1981. World Food Day.

2752. **571.** 10 l. multicoloured .. 20 10
2753. 30 l. multicoloured .. 50 20

572. Olive Branch and Constitution on Map of Turkey.

1981. Inauguration of Constituent Assembly.

2754. **572.** 10 l. multicoloured .. 25 10
2755. 30 l. multicoloured .. 45 30

574. Kemal Ataturk. **575** Green Tiger Beetle.

1981.

2762 **574** 2½ l. red on grey .. 15 10

1981. Useful Insects (2nd series). Mult.

2763 10 l. + 2½ l. Type **575** .. 30 20
2764 20 l. + 2½ l. "Syrphus vitripennis" (hover fly) 45 35
2765 30 l. + 2½ l. "Ascalaphus macaronius" (owl-fly) 60 45
2766 40 l. + 2½ l. "Empusa fasciata" 75 55

576. Students and Silhouette of Ataturk. **577.** Sun. **578.** Kemel Ataturk.

1981. Literacy Campaign.

2767 **576** 2½ l. orange and blue 15 10

1982. Energy Conservation.

2768 **577** 10 l. yellow, blue & grn 25 10

1982.

2769. **578.** 1 l. green 10 10
2770. – 2½ l. lilac 10 10
2771. – 5 l. blue 20 10
2772. – 10 l. red 30 10
2773. – 35 l. brown 65 10

DESIGNS: 2½ to 35 l. Different portraits of Ataturk.

579. "Magnolias". **580.** Dr. Tevfik Saglam.

1982. Birth Cent. of Ibrahim Calli (painter). Multicoloured

2774. 10 l. Type **579** 20 10
2775. 20 l. "Fishermen" (horiz.) 40 10
2776. 30 l. "Sewing Woman" 60 10

1982. Centenary of Discovery of Tubercle Bacillus. Multicoloured.

2777. 10 l. + 2½ l. Type **580** .. 30 15
2778. 30 l. + 2½ l. Dr. Robert Koch 60 35

582. Kul Tigin Monument. **584.** Demirkazik.

583. Tanker and Emblem.

1982. 1250th Anniv. of Kul Tigin Monument. Multicoloured.

2780. 10 l. Type **582** 15 10
2781. 30 l. Head of Kul Tilgin 35 15

1982. Inauguration of Pendik Shipyard.

2782. **583.** 30 l. multicoloured .. 35 15

1982. Anatolian Mountains. Multicoloured.

2783. 7½ l. Agri Dagi 15 10
2784. 10 l. Buzul Dagi (horiz.) 20 10
2785. 15 l. Type **584** 25 10
2786. 20 l. Erciyes (horiz.) .. 40 10
2787. 30 l. Kackar Dagi .. 55 10
2788. 35 l. Uludag (horiz.) .. 75 10

585. Colorado Potato Beetle.

1982. Insect Pests (1st series). Multicoloured.

2789 10 l. + 2½ l. "Eurydema spectabile" (shield-bug) 30 25
2790 15 l. + 2½ l. Olive fruit-fly 40 30
2791 20 l. + 2½ l. "Klapperichicen viridissima" (cicada) 45 40
2792 20 l. + 2½ l. Type **585** .. 60 50
2793 35 l. + 2½ l. "Rhynchites auratus" (weevil) .. 70 55

See also Nos. 2830/4.

586. Open Book and Figures. **587.** Drum.

1982. Cent. of Beyazit State Library.

2794. **586.** 30 l. multicoloured .. 35 10

1982. Musical Instruments. Multicoloured.

2796. 7½ l. Type **587** 20 10
2797. 10 l. Lute ("Baglama") 25 10
2798. 15 l. Horn ("Zurna") (horiz.) 30 10
2799. 20 l. Stringed instrument ("Kemence") (horiz.) 45 15
2800. 30 l. Flute ("Mey") .. 55 20

588. Temple of Artemis, Sart.

1982. Ancient Cities.

2801. **588.** 30 l. multicoloured .. 35 10

589. Family on Map.

1983. Family Planning and Mother and Child Health. Multicoloured.

2802. 10 l. Type **589** 20 10
2803. 35 l. Mother and child 25 10

590. Council Emblem.

1983. 30th Anniv. of Customs Co-operation Council.

2804. **590.** 45 l. multicoloured .. 65 15

591. People, Ballot Box and Constitution.

1983. 1982 Constitution. Multicoloured.

2805. 10 l. Type **591** 15 10
2806. 30 l. Constitution, scales and olive branch .. 30 10

592. Richard Wagner.

1983. Death Centenary of Richard Wagner (composer).

2807. **592.** 30 l. + 5 l. mult. .. 75 15

593. Hamdi Bey.

1983. 38th Death Anniv of Hamdi Bey (telegraphist).

2808 **593** 35 l. multicoloured .. 35 10

594. Piri Reis (geographer) and Map.

1983. Europa. Multicoloured.

2809 50 l. Type **594** 90 15
2810 100 l. Ulugh Bey (Central Asian ruler) and observatory .. .. 1·60 25

595. Olive Branch and Athletes.

1983. Youth Week.

2811. **595.** 15 l. multicoloured .. 20 10

596. Fokker "F-13" and Jet Airliner.

1983. 50th Anniv of Turkish State Airline. Multicoloured.

2812. 50 l. Type **596** .. .. 1·00 15
2813. 70 l. Airport at night .. 1·00 15

597. Hellenic Statue of Eros. **598.** Oludeniz.

1983. 18th Council of Europe Art Exhibition, Istanbul. Multicoloured.

2814 15 l. Type **597** 30 10
2815 35 l. Hittite carving of two-headed duck (horiz) 45 10
2816 50 l. Ottoman zinc flask and jug 75 15
2817 70 l. Busts of Marcus Aurelius and his wife Faustina (horiz) .. 85 15

1983. Coastal Protection. Multicoloured.

2818. 10 l. Type **598** 15 10
2819. 25 l. Olimpos 50 10
2820. 35 l. Kekova 65 15

1983. Nos. 2655 amd 2699 surch **5 LIRA.**

2821 **543** 5 l. on 50 k. green .. 25 10
2822 **555** 5 l. on 50 k. green, red and brown .. 25 10

600. Dove carrying Letter. **601.** Kemal Ataturk.

1983. World Communications Year. Mult.

2823 15 l. Type **600** 35 10
2824 50 l. Telephone pole and telephone wires (horiz) 45 10
2825 70 l. Telephone dial and letter within ornamental design .. 80 15

1983.

2826. **601.** 15 l. blue & light blue 15 10
2827. 50 l. blue and green .. 55 10
2828. 100 l. blue and orange 1·25 10

602. Topkapi Serail, Istanbul.

1983. Aga Khan Award for Architecture.
2829. **602.** 50 l. yell., blk. & grn. 65 10

1983. Insect Pests (2nd series). As Type **585.** Multicoloured.

2830	15 l. + 5 l. Sun pest ..	25	35
2831	25 l. + 5 l. "Phyllobius nigrofasciatus" (weevil)	45	45
2832	35 l. + 5 l. "Cercopis intermedia" (froghopper) ..	55	55
2833	50 l. + 10 l. Striped bug ..	80	80
2834	75 l. + 10 l. "Capnodis miliaris"	1·00	1·00

604. Map and Flag of Turkey.

1983. 60th Anniv. of Republic.
2836. **604.** 15 l. multicoloured .. 25 10
2837. 50 l. multicoloured .. 55 15

605. Temple of Aphrodite, Aphrodisias.

1983. Ancient Cities.
2838. **605.** 50 l. multicoloured .. 50 10

607. St. Sophia's from Sultan Ahmed Mosque, Istanbul.

1984. U.N.E.S.C.O. International Campaign for Istanbul and Goreme. Multicoloured.

2850	25 l. Type **607**	25	10
2851	35 l. Rock dwellings and chapels, Goreme ..	40	10
2852	50 l. Suleymaniye district, Istanbul	60	10

608. Police Badge and Ribbon protecting Citizens.

1984. Turkish Police Organization.
2853 **608** 15 l. multicoloured .. 20 10

609. Bridge. **610.** Kaftan (16th century).

1984. Europa. 25th Anniv of C.E.P.T.
2854 **609** 50 l. multicoloured .. 75 15
2855 100 l. multicoloured .. 1·50 25

1984. Topkapi Museum (1st series). Mult.

2856	20 l. + 5 l. Type **610** ..	40	15
2857	70 l. + 15 l. Ceremonial ewer	75	15
2858	90 l. + 20 l. Gold inlaid and jewelled swords ..	1·25	15
2859	100 l. + 25 l. Kaaba lock ..	1·50	20

See also Nos. 2892/5, 2925/8 and 2967/70.

611. Mete Khan and Flag of Great Hun Empire.

1984. Turkic States (1st series). Multicoloured.

2860	10 l. Type **611**	20	10
2861	20 l. Panu and flag of Western Hun Empire	40	10
2862	50 l. Attila and flag of European Hun Empire	75	15
2863	70 l. Aksunvar and flag of Ak Hun Empire ..	1·00	25

See also Nos. 2896/9, 2930/3 and 2971/4.

612. Peace Dove.

1984. 10th Anniv of Turkish Forces in Cyprus.
2864 **612** 70 l. multicoloured .. 60 10

613. Olympic Colours. **614.** Marsh Mallow.

1984. Olympic Games, Los Angeles. Mult.

2865	20 l. + 5 l. Type **613** ..	25	10
2866	70 l. + 15 l. Medallion of wrestler (vert) ..	80	15
2867	100 l. + 20 l. Stylised athlete	1·25	25

1984. Wild Flowers. Multicoloured.

2868	5 l. "Narcissus tazetta"	10	10
2868a	10 l. Type **614**	15	10
2869	20 l. Common poppy ..	15	10
2870	70 l. "Cyclamen pseudo-ibericum"	80	10
2870a	100 l. False chamomile	60	10
2871	200 l. Snowdrops ..	1·50	15
2872	300 l. "Tulipa sintenesii"	2·25	15

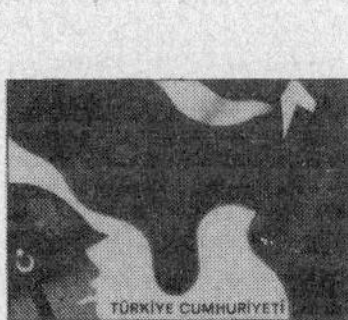

615. Soldier and Flag. **616.** Liquidamber.

1984. Armed Forces Day.

2873	**615**	20 l. multicoloured ..	15	10
2874	–	50 l. multicoloured ..	40	10
2875	–	70 l. red, blue & black	65	15
2876	–	90 l. multicoloured ..	75	15

Designs: 50 l. Olive branch as sword hilt. 70 l. Emblem, soldier and flag. 90 l. Soldier, olive branch and map.

1984. Forest Resources. Multicoloured.

2877.	10 l. Type **616**	25	10
2878.	20 l. Oriental Spruce ..	35	10
2879.	70 l. Oriental Beech ..	85	10
2880.	90 l. Cedar of Lebanon ..	1·00	15

617. Pres. Inonu. **618.** Detail of 13th-century Seljukian Carpet.

1984. Birth Centenary of Ismet Inonu (Prime Minister 1923–37 and 1962–65; President 1938–50).
2881 **617** 20 l. multicoloured .. 50 10

1984. First International Congress on Turkish Carpets.
2882. **618.** 70 l. multicoloured .. 30 10

619. Great Mosque and University, Harran.

1984. Ancient Cities.
2883. **619.** 70 l. multicoloured .. 60 10

620. Women and Ballot Box.

1984. 50th Anniv. of Turkish Women's Suffrage.
2884. **620.** 20 l. multicoloured .. 25 10

621. "Icarus" (Hans Herni).

1984. 40th Anniv. of I.C.A.O.
2885. **621.** 100 l. multicoloured 75 15

623. Glider and Parachutist.

1985. 60th Anniv. of Turkish Aviation League. Multicoloured.
2887. 10 l. Type **623** 45 15
2888. 20 l. Cameron "Viva-77" balloon (vert.) .. 55 15

624. Globe and Satellite. **625.** Score and Ulvi Cemal Erkin (composer).

1985. 20th Anniv. of International Telecommunications Satellite Organization.
2889. **624.** 100 l. multicoloured 65 15

1985. Europa. Music Year. Multicoloured.
2890 100 l. Type **625** .. .. 1·00 15
2891 200 l. Score and Mithat Fenmen (composer and pianist) .. .. 1·75 60

1985. Topkapi Museum (2nd series). As T **610.** Multicoloured.

2892.	10 l. + 5 l. Plate decorated with peacock ..	15	10
2893.	20 l. + 10 l. Jug and cup	25	15
2894.	100 l. + 15 l. Porcelain ewer and bowl ..	75	25
2895.	120 l. + 20 l. Chinese porcelain plate ..	90	30

1985. Turkic States (2nd series). As T **611.** Multicoloured.

2896.	10 l. Bilge Kagan and flag of Gokturk Empire	10	10
2897.	20 l. Bayan Kagan and flag of Avar Empire ..	20	10
2898.	70 l. Hazar Kagan and flag of Hazar Empire	50	15
2899.	100 l. Kutlug Kul Bilge Kagan and flag of Uygur Empire ..	75	15

626. Louis Pasteur working in Laboratory. **627.** I.Y.Y. Emblem within Globe and Profiles.

1985. Centenary of Discovery of Anti-rabies Vaccine.
2900. **626.** 100 l. + 15 l. mult. .. 75 15

1985. International Youth Year. Mult.
2901. 100 l. Type **627** 50 10
2902. 120 l. Globe and I.Y.Y. Emblem 85 10

628. Postman and Couple Dancing. **629.** Aynalikavak Palace.

1985. Introduction of Post Codes.

2903.	**628.**	10 l. blk., yell. & brn.	10	10
2904.		20 l. blk., yell. & red	15	10
2905.		20 l. blk., yell. & grn.	15	10
2906.		20 l. blk., yell. & bl.	15	10
2907.		70 l. bl., yell. & pur.	45	10
2908.		100 l. black, yellow & grey	65	10

1985. National Palaces Symposium. Multicoloured.
2909. 20 l. Type **629** 15 10
2910. 100 l. Beylerbeyi Palace 60 15

630. U.N. Emblem, Headquarters and Flags in "40".

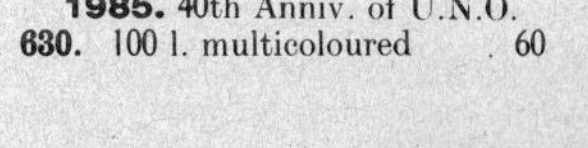

1985. 40th Anniv. of U.N.O.
2911. **630.** 100 l. multicoloured . 60 20

631. Alanya. **632.** Satellite and Infra-red Picture of Earth's Surface.

1985. Ancient Cities.
2912. **631.** 100 l. multicoloured 60 15

1985. 60th Anniv. of Meteorological Institute.
2913. **632.** 100 l. multicoloured 85 15

633. Emblem. **634.** Kemal Ataturk.

1985. Centenary of Isik Lyceum, Istanbul.
2914. **633.** 20 l. gold, bl. & red 25 10

1985.

2915	**634**	10 l. blue and cobalt	10	10
2916		20 l. brown and lilac	15	10
2917		100 l. purple and lilac	55	10

635. Girl and Flower.

1986. International 23rd April Children's Festival, Ankara. Multicoloured.

2918. 20 l. Type **635** 10 10
2919. 100 l. Family 35 10
2920. 120 l. Balloon seller .. 55 10

636. Boy drawing in Smoke from Chimney. **637.** Trophy.

1986. Europa. Multicoloured.

2921 100 l. Type **636** 55 10
2922 200 l. Plaster on dead half of leaf (vert) .. .. 1·25 50

1986. Ataturk International Peace Prize. Multicoloured.

2923. 20 l. Type **637** 10 10
2924. 100 l. Front view of trophy 35 10

1986. Topkapi Museum (3rd series). As T **610**. Multicoloured.

2925 20 l. + 5 l. Censer .. 15 10
2926 100 l. + 10 l. Jade and jewellered tankard .. 35 15
2927 120 l. + 15 l. Dagger and sheath 55 25
2928 200 l. + 30 l. Willow buckler 95 30

638. "Abdulhamit". **639.** Wrestlers oiling themselves.

1986. Centenary of Turkish Submarine Fleet.

2929. **638.** 20 l. multicoloured .. 15 10

1986. Turkic States (3rd series). As T **611**. Multicoloured.

2930 10 l. Bilge Kul Kadir Khan and flag of Kara Khanids Empire .. 15 10
2931 20 l. Alp Tekin and flag of Ghaznavids Empire .. 25 10
2932 100 l. Seljuk and flag of Great Seljuk Empire .. 60 10
2933 120 l. Muhammed Harezmsah and flag of Harezmsah State .. 85 10

1986. Kirkpinar Wrestling. Multicoloured.

2934. 10 l. Type **639** 10 10
2935. 20 l. Opening ceremony 15 10
2936. 100 l. Wrestlers 55 15

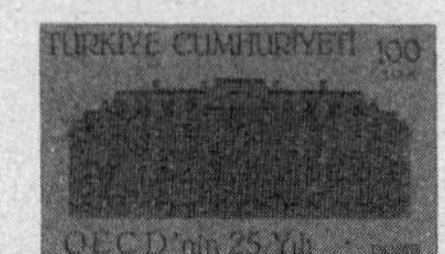
640. Chateau de la Muette, Paris (headquarters).

1986. 25th Anniv. of Organization for Economic Co-operation and Development.

2937. **640.** 100 l. multicoloured 55 10

641. Benz "Einspur" Tricar, 1886.

1986. Centenary of Motor Car. Multicoloured.

2938. 10 l. Type **641** 15 10
2939. 20 l. Rolls Royce "Silver Ghost", 1906 .. .. 35 10
2940. 100 l. Mercedes touring car, 1928 .. .. 60 15
2941. 200 l. Impression of speeding car .. .. 1·10 20

642. "Arrangement with Tulips" (Feyhaman Duran). **643.** Celal Bayar.

1986. Artists' Birth Centenaries. Mult.

2942 100 l. Type **642** 35 10
2943 120 l. "Landscape with Fountain" (Huseyin Avni Lifij) (horiz) .. 55 15

1986. Celal Bayar (Prime Minister 1937–39; President 1950–60) Commemoration.

2944. **643.** 20 l. brown, gold and mauve 10 10
2945. – 100 l. green, gold and mauve 45 10

DESIGN: 100 l. Profile of Celal Bayar.

645. Kubad-Abad.

1986. Ancient Cities.

2950. **645.** 100 l. multicoloured 45 10

646. N.A.T.O. Emblem and Dove with Olive Branch.

1986. 32nd N.A.T.O. Assembly, Istanbul.

2951. **646.** 100 l. + 20 l. mult. .. 55 15

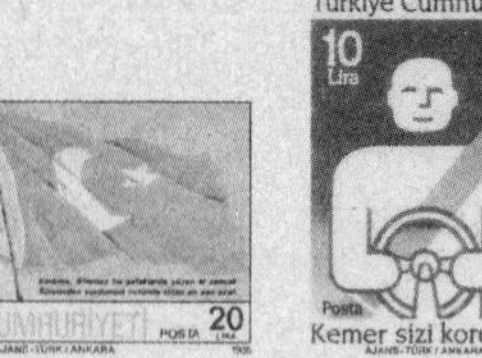
647. Ersoy and National Flag. **648.** Driver wearing Seat Belt.

1986. 50th Death Anniv. of Mehmet Akif Ersoy (composer of national anthem).

2952. **647.** 20 l. multicoloured .. 25 10

1987. Road Safety.

2953 **648** 10 l. violet, red & blue 15 10
2954 – 20 l. red, blue & brn 25 10
2955 – 150 l. brn, red & grn 85 10

DESIGNS: 20 l. Smashed drinking glass and road. 150 l. Broken speed limit sign and road.

649. Spurge Hawk Moth.

1987. Moths and Butterflies. Multicoloured.

2956 10 l. Type **649** .. 15 10
2957 20 l. Red admiral .. 20 15
2958 100 l. Jersey tiger moth .. 55 15
2959 120 l. Clouded yellow .. 65 20

650. Modern Housing and Emblem. **651.** Casting.

1987. International Year of Shelter for the Homeless.

2960. **650.** 200 l. multicoloured 75 10

1987. 50th Anniv. of Turkish Iron and Steel Works. Multicoloured.

2961 50 l. Type **651** 15 10
2962 200 l. Karabuk works .. 65 10

652. Map of Turkey and Grand National Assembly Building, Ankara.

1987. "Sovereignty belongs to the People".

2963 **652** 50 l. multicoloured .. 15 10

653. Turkish History Institution, Ankara (Turgut Cansever and Ertur Yener). **654.** Olympic Rings as Flames.

1987. Europa. Architecture. Multicoloured.

2964. 50 l. Type **653** 15 10
2965. 200 l. Social Insurance Institution, Zeyrek (Sedad Hakki Eldem) 75 10

1987. 92nd Session of International Olympic Committee, Istanbul.

2966. **654.** 200 l. multicoloured 75 10

1987. Topkapi Museum (4th series). As T **610**. Multicoloured.

2967 20 l. + 5 l. Crystal and jewelled ewer .. 20 10
2968 50 l. + 10 l. Emerald, gold and diamond ceiling pendant (horiz) .. 30 10
2969 200 l. + 15 l. Sherbet jug 85 15
2970 250 l. + 30 l. Crystal, gold and jewelled writing drawer (horiz) .. 1·10 20

1987. Turkic States (4th series). As T **611**. Multicoloured.

2971 10 l. Batu Khan and flag of Golden Horde State 15 10
2972 20 l. Timur (Tamerlane) and flag of Great Timur Empire 20 10
2973 50 l. I. Babur Shah and flag of Mughal Empire 25 10
2974 200 l. Osman Bey and flag of Ottoman Empire .. 65 10

655. Men.

1987. Paintings from Mehmet Siyah Kalem's "Album of the Conqueror". Multicoloured.

2975. 10 l. Type **655** 10 10
2976. 20 l. Donkey rider and attendants (horiz.) .. 10 10
2977. 50 l. Man whipping fallen horse (horiz.) 20 10
2978. 200 l. Demon 35 10

656. Cancer Cells and Pipette holding Drug.

1987. 15th International Chemotherapy Congress, Istanbul.

2979. **656.** 200 l. + 25 l. mult. 75 20

657. Ihlamur Pavilion.

1987. Royal Pavilions (1st series). Mult.

2980. 50 l. Type **657** 15 10
2981. 200 l. Kucuksu Pavilion 60 10

See also Nos. 3019/20.

658. Suleiman receiving Barbarossa (miniature).

1987. Suleiman the Magnificent. Mult.

2982 30 l. Suleiman 10 10
2983 50 l. Suleiman's tougra (horiz) 15 10
2984 200 l. Type **658** 35 10
2985 270 l. Sculpture of Suleiman from U.S. House of Representatives and inscribed scroll 40 10

660 Sinan and Selimiye Mosque, Edirne **661** Means of Transport

1988. 400th Death Anniv of Mimar Sinan (architect). Multicoloured.

2987 50 l. Type **660** 15 10
2988 200 l. Suleiman Mosque .. 55 10

1988. Europa. Transport and Communications. Multicoloured.

2989 200 l. Type **661** 30 10
2990 600 l. Electric impulses forming globe between telephone and computer terminal (horiz) .. 60 15

662 Syringes between Heathy and Sick Children

1988. Health. Multicoloured.

2991 50 l. Type **662** 10 10
2992 200 l. Capsules forming cross on bottle (vert) 20 10
2993 300 l. Heart in cogwheel and heart-shaped worker 35 10
2994 600 l. Organs for transplant on open hands (vert) .. 60 10

663 American Standard Steam Locomotive, 1850s

1988. Locomotives. Each agate, light brown and brown.
2995 50 l. Type **663** 15 10
2996 100 l. Steam locomotive, 1913 .. .. .. 35 10
2997 200 l. Henschel Krupp steam locomotive, 1926 50 20
2998 300 l. Toshiba "E 43001" electric locomotive, 1987 70 25
2999 600 l. MTE-Tulomsas diesel-electric locomotive, 1984 .. 1·10 25

664 Articulated Lorry

1988. 21st International Road Transport Union World Congress, Istanbul.
3000 **664** 200 l.+25 l. mult .. 25 15

665 Scales and Map

1988. 120th Anniv of Court of Cassation (appeal court).
3001 **665** 50 l. multicoloured .. 10 10

666 Faith Sultan Mohamed Bridge, Bosphorus

1988. Completion of Bridges. Multicoloured.
3002 200 l. Type **666** 25 10
3003 300 l. Seto Great road and rail bridge, Japan .. 35 10

667 Telephone Dial and Wires over Villages

1988. Completion of Telephone Network to Every Village.
3004 **667** 100 l. multicoloured .. 15 10

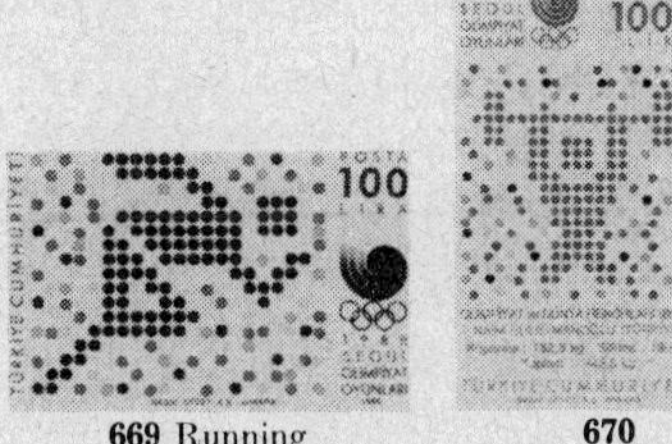

669 Running **670** Weightlifting

1988. Olympic Games, Seoul. Multicoloured.
3005 100 l. Type **669** 15 10
3006 200 l. Archery 20 10
3007 400 l. Weightlifting .. 30 10
3008 600 l. Football (vert) .. 55 15

1988. Naim Suleymanoglu, Olympic and World Record Holder for Weightlifting
3009 **670** 1000 l. multicoloured 85 15

671 Lush Scene in Hands surrounded by Barren Earth

672 Airplanes and Cogwheel

1988. European Campaign for Rural Areas. Multicoloured.
3010 100 l.+25 l. Type **671** .. 15 10
3011 400 l.+50 l. Rural scene in eye 60 15

1988. Turkish Aerospace Industries. Mult.
3012 50 l. Type **672** 10 10
3013 200 l. Birds forming airplane (horiz) .. 40 10

673 "Gonepteryx cleopatra"

1988. Butterflies. Multicoloured.
3014 100 l. Type **673** (wrongly inscr "G. rhamni") .. 10 10
3015 200 l. Hermit 25 15
3016 400 l. Eastern festoon .. 40 20
3017 600 l. Camberwell beauty 75 35

1988. Royal Pavilions (2nd series). As T **657**. Multicoloured.
3019 100 l. Kasr-i Humayun Imperial Lodge, Maslak 15 10
3020 400 l. Sale Pavilion, Yildiz 75 10

675 Large-leaved Lime

1988. Medicinal Plants. Multicoloured.
3022 150 l. Type **675** 20 10
3023 300 l. Common mallow .. 35 10
3024 600 l. Henbane 55 10
3025 900 l. Deadly nightshade 95 15

676 Seated Goddess with Child (clay Statuette)

1989. Archaeology (1st series). Multicoloured.
3026 150 l. Type **676** 10 10
3027 300 l. Lead figurine of god and goddess 25 10
3028 600 l. Clay human-shaped vase 55 10
3029 1000 l. Hittite ivory figurine of mountain god .. .. .. 1·00 15

See also Nos. 3062/5, 3104/7 and 3134/7.

1989. Nos. 2826, 2915 and 2916 surch.
3030 **601** 50 l. on 15 l. blue and light blue 10 10
3031 **634** 75 l. on 10 l. blue and cobalt 10 10
3032 – 150 l. on 20 l. brown and lilac 20 10

678 Dove and Emblem

1989. 40th Anniv of N.A.T.O.
3033 **678** 600 l. ultram, bl & red 35 10

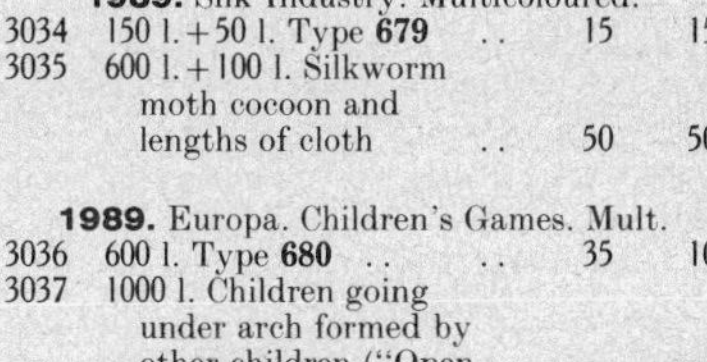

679 Silkworm Moth Larva on Leaf

680 Leap-frog

1989. Silk Industry. Multicoloured.
3034 150 l.+50 l. Type **679** .. 15 15
3035 600 l.+100 l. Silkworm moth cocoon and lengths of cloth .. 50 50

1989. Europa. Children's Games. Mult.
3036 600 l. Type **680** 35 10
3037 1000 l. Children going under arch formed by other children ("Open the Door, Head Bezirgan") 55 10

681 Arrow and Anniversary Emblem

1989. 40th Anniv of Council of Europe.
3038 **681** 600 l.+100 l. mult .. 50 20

683 Paddle-steamer "Sahilbent"

684 Birds

1989. Steamers. Multicoloured.
3045 150 l. Type **683** .. 40 15
3046 300 l. "Ragbet" (paddle-steamer) .. 50 15
3047 600 l. "Tari" (freighter) .. 75 20
3048 1000 l. "Guzelhisar" (ferry) .. .. 1·40 25

1989. Bicentenary of French Revolution.
3049 **684** 600 l. multicoloured .. 40 10

685 Kemal Ataturk

687 Camera

1989.
3050 **685** 2000 l. blue and grey 1·00 15
3051 5000 l. brown & grey 2·50 25

See also Nos. 3093/4, 3144 and 3199/3200.

1989. No. 2916 surch **LIRA 500**.
3052 **634** 500 l. on 20 l. brown and lilac 30 10

1989. 150th Anniv of Photography. Mult.
3053 175 l. Type **687** 10 10
3054 700 l. Coloured lens shutter 35 10

688 "Manzara" (Hikmet Onat)

689 Nehru

1989. State Exhibition of Paintings and Sculpture. Multicoloured.
3055 200 l. Type **688** 10 10
3056 700 l. "Sari Saz" (Bedri Rahmi Eyuboglu) .. 35 10
3057 1000 l. "Kadin" (sculpture, Zuhtu Muridoglu) 55 10

1989. Birth Centenary of Jawaharlal Nehru (Indian statesman).
3058 **689** 700 l. multicoloured .. 45 10

690 Loggerhead Turtle

691 Turkish Memorial

1989. Sea Turtles. Multicoloured.
3059 700 l. Type **690** 55 10
3060 1000 l. Common green turtle 75 20

1990. Archaeology (2nd series). As T **676**. Multicoloured.
3062 100 l. Ivory statuette of goddess (vert) .. 10 10
3063 200 l. Clay ram's head and antelope's head twin ceremonial vessel .. 10 10
3064 500 l. Gold goddess pendant (vert) .. 25 10
3065 700 l. Ivory statuette of lion 30 10

1990. 75th Anniv of Gallipoli Campaign.
3066 **691** 1000 l. multicoloured 55 10

692 Turkish Garden (left half)

1990. International Garden and Greenery Exposition, Osaka. Multicoloured.
3067 1000 l. Type **692** 55 10
3068 1000 l. Right half of garden 55 10

Nos. 3067/8 were issued together, se-tenant, forming a composite design.

1990. Various stanmps surch.
3069 – 50 l. on 5 l. mult (No. 2868) 10 10
3070 **648** 100 l. on 10 l. red, violet and blue .. 10 10
3071 150 l. on 10 l. red, violet and blue .. 10 10
3072 – 200 l. on 70 l. mult (No. 2870) 10 10
3073 – 300 l. on 20 l. red, blue & brown (No. 2954) 15 10
3074 – 300 l. on 70 l. mult (No. 2870) 15 10
3075 – 1500 l. on 20 l. mult (No. 2869) 15 10

694 "70" and Ataturk

695 Antalya

1990. 70th Anniv of Establishment of Nationalist Provisional Government.
3076 **694** 300 l. multicoloured .. 15 10

1990. European Tourism Year. Multicoloured.
3077 300 l.+50 l. Type **695** .. 15 10
3078 1000 l.+100 l. Istanbul .. 55 20

696 Ankara Post Office

697 Map and Dove as Open Book

1990. Europa. Post Office Buildings. Mult.
3079 700 l. Type **696** 30 10
3080 1000 l. Istanbul Post Office (horiz) 55 10

1990. European Supreme Courts' Conference, Ankara.
3081 **697** 1000 l. bl, dp bl & red 55 10

698 Fire Salamander

1990. World Environment Day. Mult.
3082 300 l. Type **698** 15 10
3083 500 l. Banded newt .. 25 10
3084 1000 l. Fire-bellied toads 55 10
3085 1500 l. Common tree frog (vert) 65 10

699 "Ertugrul" (frigate) and Turkish and Japanese Women

701 Smoker's Body shattering

1990. Centenary of First Turkish Envoy to Japan.
3086 **699** 1000 l. multicoloured 75 15

1990. Anti-addiction Campaign. Mult.
3087 300 l. on 50 l. Type **701** .. 15 10
3088 1000 l. on 100 l. Addict injecting drug into skeletal arm (horiz) .. 55 20

702 "Self-portrait"

703 Emblem, Pen, Open Book and Globe

1990. Death Centenary of Vincent van Gogh (painter). Multicoloured.
3089 300 l. Type **702** 15 10
3090 700 l. "Boats in Saintes Maries" (horiz) .. 30 10
3091 1000 l. "Sunflowers" .. 50 10
3092 1500 l. "Road with Cypress" 60 10

1990. As T **685** but inscription redrawn and dated "1990".
3093 **685** 500 l. green and grey 25 10
3094 1000 l. mauve & grey 50 10

1990. International Literacy Year.
3095 **703** 300 l. multicoloured .. 15 10

704 "Portrait" (Nurullah Berk)

705 Tatar Courier and Modern Postal Transport

1990. State Exhibition of Painting and Sculpture. Multicoloured.
3096 300 l. Type **704** 15 10
3097 700 l. "Derya Kuzulari" (Cevat Dereli) .. 30 10
3098 1000 l. "Artist's Mother" (bust) (Nijad Sirel) .. 50 10

1990. 150th Anniv of Ministry of Posts and Telecommunications. Multicoloured.
3099 200 l. Type **705** 10 10
3100 250 l. Computer terminal and Morse key .. 10 10
3101 400 l. Manual and digital telephone exchanges .. 20 10
3102 1500 l. Telegraph wires, dish aerial and satellite 60 10

1991. Archaeology (3rd series). As T **676**. Multicoloured.
3104 300 l. Clay figurine of woman (vert) 10 10
3105 500 l. Bronze sistrum (vert) 20 10
3106 1000 l. Clay kettle on stand (vert) 40 10
3107 1500 l. Clay ceremonial vessel (vert) 50 10

707 Lake Abant

708 Satellite and Map of Europe

1991. Lakes. Multicoloured.
3110 250 l. Type **707** 10 10
3111 500 l. Lake Egirdir .. 15 10
3112 1500 l. Lake Van .. 50 10

1991. Europa. Europe in Space. Mult.
3113 1000 l. Type **708** 40 10
3114 1500 l. Satellite and map of Europe (different) .. 50 10

709 Graph on Globe

1991. National Statistics Day.
3115 **709** 500 l. multicoloured .. 15 10

710 Cable Ship, Map, Cable and Telephone Handset

711 Emblem

1991. Eastern Mediterranean Fibre Optic Cable System (EMOS-1).
3116 **710** 500 l. multicoloured .. 20 10

1991. European Transport Ministers' Conference, Antalya.
3117 **711** 500 l. multicoloured .. 15 10

712 Emre

713 Harpsichord, Score and Mozart

1991. "Yunus Emre (13th-century poet) Year of Love". Multicoloured.
3118 500 l. + 100 l. Type **712** .. 15 10
3119 1500 l. + 100 l. Globe, and Emre as tree 45 20

1991. Death Bicentenary of Wolfgang Amadeus Mozart (composer).
3120 **713** 1500 l. + 100 l. mult .. 45 20

714 "Abdulcanbaz" (Turhan Selcuk)

1991. Caricature. Multicoloured.
3121 500 l. "Amcabey" (Cemal Nadir Guler) (horiz) .. 15 10
3122 Type **714** 30 10

715 13th-Century Seljukian Wall Plaque

716 Emblem

1991. Turkish Ceramics. Multicoloured.
3123 500 l. Type **715** 15 10
3124 1500 l. Late 16th-century Ottoman wall plaque .. 45 10

1991. Turkish Grand National Assembly and Protection of Human Rights International Symposium, Ankara.
3125 **716** 500 l. multicoloured .. 15 10

717 Dam, Water, and Sun

718 Keloglan and Genie with Tray of Food

1991. South-eastern Anatolia Project (hydro-electric power and irrigation development).
3126 **717** 500 l. multicoloured .. 15 10

1991. "Keloglan"(fairy tale). Multicoloured.
3127 500 l. Type **718** 10 10
3128 1000 l. Keloglan and dinner guests .. 25 10
3129 1500 l. Keloglan ploughing 35 10

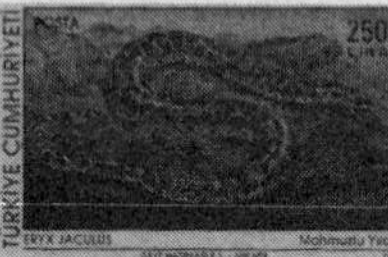
719 Sand Boa

1991. World Environment Day. Snakes. Mult.
3130 250 l. Type **719** .. 10 10
3131 500 l. Four-lined snake .. 10 10
3132 1000 l. Ottoman viper .. 25 10
3133 1500 l. Caucasus viper .. 35 10

1992. Archaeology (4th series). As T **676**. Multicoloured.
3134 300 l. Clay statuette of Mother Goddess (vert) 10 10
3135 500 l. Bronze statuette (vert) 10 10
3136 1000 l. Hittite clay vase (vert) 20 10
3137 1500 l. Urartian lion (vert) 25 10

721 Emblem and People

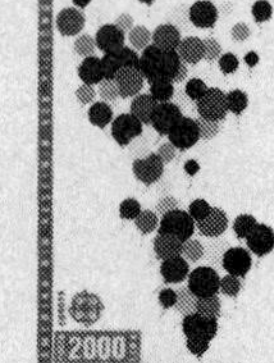
722 Balloons

1992. 30th Anniv of Supreme Court.
3140 **721** 500 l. + 100 l. mult .. 10 10

1992. Europa. 500th Anniv of Discovery of America by Columbus.
3141 – 1500 l. blue and red .. 20 10
3142 **722** 2000 l. multicoloured 30 10
DESIGN—HORIZ. 1500 l. Stylised caravel.

723 Immigrant Ship

724 Kemal Ataturk

1992. 500th Anniv of Jewish Immigration.
3143 **723** 1500 l. multicoloured 20 10

1992.
3144 – 250 l. orange, ochre and gold 10 10
3145 **724** 10000 l. bl, grey & gold 1·50 15
DESIGN: 250 l. Portrait of Ataturk as in Type **685**.

725 Court Emblem

726 Congress Emblem

1992. 130th Anniv of Court of Accounts.
3146 **725** 500 l. multicoloured .. 10 10

1992. 3rd Turkish Economy Congress, Izmir.
3147 **726** 1500 l. multicoloured 20 10

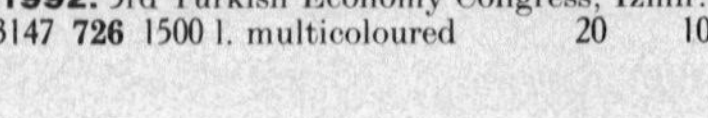

727 Lapwing

728 Ears of Grain, Cog-wheel and Hands

1992. World Environment Day. Birds. Mult.
3148 500 l. Type **727** 10 10
3149 1000 l. Golden oriole .. 15 10
3150 1500 l. Common shelduck 20 10
3151 2000 l. White-breasted kingfisher (vert) .. 30 10

1992. Black Sea Economic Co-operation Conference, Istanbul.
3152 **728** 1500 l. multicoloured 20 10

729 Doves forming Olympic Flame

730 Soldiers and Old Woman

1992. Olympic Games, Barcelona. Mult.

3153	500 l. Type **729**	10	10
3154	1000 l. Boxing	15	10
3155	1500 l. Weightlifting ..	20	10
3156	2000 l. Wrestling ..	30	10

1992. Legend of Anatolia. Multicoloured.

3157	500 l. Type **730**	10	10
3158	1000 l. Old woman filling trough with buttermilk	15	10
3159	1500 l. Soldiers drinking from trough	20	10

731 Bride and Mother-in-law Dolls from Merkez Kapikaya

732 Cherries

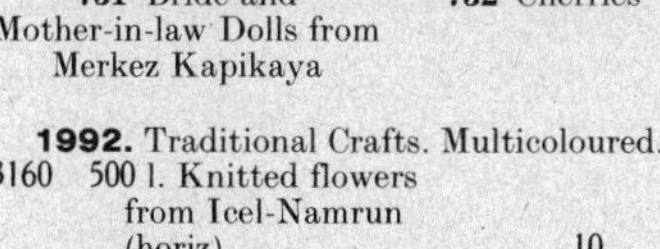

1992. Traditional Crafts. Multicoloured.

3160	500 l. Knitted flowers from Icel-Namrun (horiz)	10	10
3161	1000 l. Type **731**	15	10
3162	3000 l. Woven saddlebag from Hakkari (horiz)	40	10

1992. Fruit (1st series). Multicoloured.

3163	500 l. Type **732**	10	10
3164	1000 l. Apricots	15	10
3165	3000 l. Grapes	40	10
3166	5000 l. Apples	70	10

See also Nos. 3176/9.

734 Mountaineering

735 Sait Faik Abasiyanik

1992. 26th Anniv of Turkish Mountaineering Federation (3169) and 80th Anniv of Turkish Scout Movement (3170). Multicoloured.

3169	1000 l.+200 l. Type **734** ..	15	10
3170	3000 l.+200 l. Scouts watering sapling (horiz)	45	20

1992. Anniversaries. No value expressed.

3171	**735**	(T) blue, indigo & red	10	10
3172	–	(T) blue, orange & vio	10	10
3173	–	(M) blue, green & orge	15	10
3174	–	(M) blue, red & indigo	15	10
3175	–	(M) blue, red & green	15	10

DESIGNS: No. 3171, Type **935** (writer, 86th birth anniv); 3172, Fikret Mualla Saygi (painter, 25th death anniv); 3173, Muhsin Ertugrul (actor and producer, birth centenary); 3174, Cevat Sakir Kabaagacli (writer, 19th death anniv); 3175, Asik Veysel Satiroglu (poet, 98th birth anniv).

Nos. 3171/2 were intended for greeting cards and Nos. 3173/5 for inland letters.

1993. Fruit (2nd series). As T **732**. Mult.

3176	500 l. Bananas	10	10
3177	1000 l. Oranges	10	10
3178	3000 l. Pears	15	10
3179	5000 l. Pomegranates ..	20	10

736 Sculpture (Hadi Bara)

737 Terraces

1993. Europa. Contemporary Art. Mult.

3180	1000 l. Type **736**	10	10
3181	3000 l. Carved figure (Zuhtu Muridoglu) ..	15	10

1993. Campaign for Preservation of Pamukkale. Multicoloured.

3182	1000 l.+200 l. Type **737** ..	10	10
3183	3000 l.+500 l. Close-up of terrace	15	10

738 Buildings and Emblem

739 Rize

1993. Economic Co-operation Organization Conference, Istanbul.

3184	**738**	2500 l. ultramarine, blue and gold ..	10	10

1993. Traditional Houses. Multicoloured.

3185	1000 l. Type **739**	10	10
3186	2500 l. Rize (different) (horiz)	10	10
3187	3000 l. Trabzon	15	10
3188	5000 l. Black Sea houses (horiz)	20	10

740 Mausoleum

1993. 900th Birth Anniv of Hoca Ahmet Yesevi (philosopher).

3189	**740**	3000 l. gold, bl & lt bl	15	10

741 Haci Arif Bey

1993. Death Anniversaries. No value expressed. Each brown and red.

3190	(T) Type **741** (composer, 109th)	10	10
3191	(T) Neyzen Tevfik Kolayli (singer, 40th)	10	10
3192	(M) Orhan Veli Kanik (poet, 43rd)	10	10
3193	(M) Cahit Sitki Taranci (poet, 27th)	10	10
3194	(M) Munir Nurettin Seluk (composer, 12th) ..	10	10

Nos. 3190/1 were intended for greetings cards and Nos. 3192/4 for inland letters.

742 Emblem

1993. Istanbul's Bid to Host Summer Olympic Games in Year 2000.

3195	**742**	2500 l. multicoloured	10	10

1993. As T **685** but inscription redrawn and dated "1993".

3199	**685**	5000 l. violet and gold	20	10
3200		20000 l. mauve & gold	85	10

744 Amphora on Sea-bed

1993. Mediterranean Treaty. Multicoloured.

3201	1000 l. Type **744**	10	10
3202	3000 l. Dolphin	15	10

745 Emblem

1993. U.N. Natural Disaster Relief Day.

3203	**745**	3000 l.+500 l. mult ..	15	10

746 Prayer Mat

747 Laurel Wreath, Torch and Silhouette of Kemal Ataturk

1993. Handicrafts. Multicoloured.

3204	1000 l. Type **746**	10	10
3205	2500 l. Silver earrings ..	10	10
3206	5000 l. Crocheted purse ..	20	10

1993. 70th Anniv of Republic.

3207	**747**	1000 l. multicoloured	10	10

748 Man in Gas Mask and Fire

1993. Civil Defence.

3208	**748**	1000 l. multicoloured	10	10

OBLIGATORY TAX STAMPS

T **101.** Nurse bandaging Patient.

T **102.** Biplane.

1926. Red Crescent.

T 1035.	–	1 g. red, yell. & blk.	20	10
T 1036.	T **101**.	2½ g. multicoloured	25	10
T 1037.	–	5 g. multicoloured	35	15
T 1038.	–	10 g. multicoloured	70	45

DESIGNS—VERT. 1 g. Red Crescent and decorative archway. 5 g. Refugees. HORIZ. 10 g. Stretcher bearers.

1926. Aviation Fund.

T 1039.	T **102**.	20 pa. brn. & grn.	65	15
T 1040.		1 g. grn. & stone ..	65	15
T 1041.		5 g. vio. & green ..	1·50	25
T 1042.		5 g. red & green ..	19·00	2·10

The 5 g. stamps are 40×29 mm.

T **103.** Biplane over Ankara.

٢٠ پاره

(T **104**.)

1927. Aviation Fund.

T 1043	T **102**	20 pa. red & green	10	10
T 1044		1 g. green & ochre	10	10
T 1045	T **103**	2 g. brown & grn	50	40
T 1046		2½ g. red & green	2·50	2·00
T 1047		5 g. blue and buff	35	35
T 1048		10 g. green & pink	3·00	2·00
T 1049		15 g. green & yell	2·25	2·50
T 1050		20 g. brn & ochre	3·00	2·00
T 1051		50 g. blue & lt bl	5·50	4·00
T 1052		100 g. red & blue	35·00	23·00

The 20 pa. and 1 g. are 25×15 mm.

1927. Red Crescent No. T 1035 and charity labels surch. with Type T **104** or similar types.

T 1053.	20 pa. on 1 g. red, yellow and black ..	75	25
T 1054.	20 pa. on 1 g. brown ..	2·00	45
T 1055.	20 pa. on 2½ g. lilac ..	80	50

DESIGNS: 26×21 mm. No. T 1054, Hospital ship. No. T 1055, Nurse tending patient.

No. T1053 has an extra line of Turkish characters in the surcharge.

T **105.** Red Crescent on Map of Turkey.

T **106.** Cherubs holding Star.

1928. Red Crescent. Various frames. Crescent in red.

T 1067.	T **105**.	½ pi. brown ..	10	10
T 1068.		1 pi. purple ..	10	10
T 1069.		2½ pi. orange ..	10	10
T 1070.		5 pi. brown ..	10	10
T 1071.		10 pi. green ..	40	30
T 1072.		20 pi. blue ..	85	30
T 1073.		50 pi. purple ..	2·25	1·60

See also Nos. T 1171/4 and T 1198/1212.

1928. Child Welfare.

T 1074.	T **106**.	1 g. olive and red	10	10
T 1075.		2½ g. brown & red	20	10
T 1076.		5 g. green & red ..	25	20
T 1077.		25 g. black & red	2·00	1·10

See also Nos. T 1160/1 and T 1165/6.

1930. Aviation Fund. Nos. T1039, T1043, T1045 and T1049 surch.

T1099	T **102**	Bir (1) k. on 20 pa. brown & green	32·00	22·00
T1100		Bir (1) k. on 20 pa. red and green	10	10
T1101	T **103**	Yuz (100) pa. on 2 g. brn & grn	10	15
T1102	T **102**	5 k. on 20 pa. red and green ..	15	15
T1103		Bes (5) k. on 20 pa. red & grn	90	15
T1104	T **103**	On (10) k. on 2 g. brown & green	35	25
T1105		Elli (50) k. on 2 g. brown & green	3·25	1·25
T1106		Bir (1) l. on 2 g. brown & green	7·50	2·00
T1107		Bes (5) l. on 15 g. green & yellow	£180	£120

T 114. Biplane over Ankara. T 118. Biplane.

1931. Aviation Fund.
T 1141. T 114. 20 pa. black .. 30 10
See also Nos. T 1154/6.

1932. Child Welfare. No. T 1074 surch.
T1150 T 106. 20 pa. on 1 g. olive and red .. 30 10
T1153 3 k. on 1 g. olive and red .. 70 10

1932. Aviation Fund. As Type T 114 but larger, 22×30 mm. and with sky shaded.
T 1154. 1 k. purple 10 10
T 1155. 5 k. red 45 20
T 1156. 10 k. green 80 25

1932. Red Crescent. Nos. T 1067, T 1069 and T 1071 surch.
T 1157. T 105. 1 k. on 2½ pi. orge. 25 15
T 1158. 5 k. and ½ pi. brn. 50 20
T 1159. 5 k. on 10 pi. grn. 60 30

1933. Child Welfare. As Type T 106 but inscr. "IZMIR HIMAYEI ETFAL CEMIYETI".
T 1160. 1 k. violet and red .. 30 10
T 1161. 5 k. brown and red .. 75 35

1933. Aviation Fund.
T1162 T 118 On (10) pa. green 30 10
T1163 Bir (1) k. red .. 50 15
T1164 Bes (5) k. lilac .. 60 40

1934. Child Welfare. As Type T 106 but inscr. "Turkiye Himayeietfal Cemiyeti".
T 1165. 20 pa. purple and red 20 10
T 1166. 15 k. green and red .. 1·25 45

T 119. Red Crescent on Map of Turkey.

1934. Inscr "TURKIYE HILALIAHMER CEMIYETI" (different frame on 5 k.).
T 1171. T 119. ½ k. blue and red 10 10
T 1172. 1 k. brown & red 10 10
T 1173. 2½ k. brown & red 10 10
T 1174. 5 k. green & red .. 40 30
See also Nos. T 1198/1212.

1936. Child Welfare. Nos. T1074/5 and T1165 optd **P.Y.S** or surch also.
T 1186. T 106. 20 pa. pur. & red 75 25
T 1187. 1 g. olive and red 55 15
T 1188. 3 k. on 2½ g. brn. and red .. 75 35

1937. Red Crescent. As Types T 105 and T 119 but inscr "TURKIYE KIZILAY CEMIYETI". Various frames.
T1204 ½ k. blue and red .. 10 10
T1199 1 k. mauve and red .. 10 10
T1200 2½ k. orange and red .. 10 10
T1201 5 k. green and red .. 25 10
T1209 5 k. brown and red .. 60 15
T1202 10 k. green and red .. 75 25
T1203 20 k. black and red .. 1·25 60
T1211 50 k. purple and red .. 3·75 75
T1212 1 l. blue and red .. 12·00 2·25

1938. Child Welfare. No. T1075 surch.
(a) Value in figures and words above **P. Y. S.**
T1213 T 106 20 pa. on 2½ g. brown and red 45 20
T1214 1 k. on 2½ g. brown and red 45 20
(b) **P. Y. S.** above value in figures and words
T1215 T 106 20 pa. on 2½ g. brown and red 55 30
T1216 1 k. on 2½ g. brown and red 55 25
(c) **1 kurus**
T1217 T 106 1 k. on 2½ g. brown and red 65 20

T 138. Laughing Child. T 139. Nurse and Baby.

1940. Child Welfare. Star in red.
T 1259. T 138. 20 pa. green .. 10 10
T 1260. 1 k. lilac 10 10
T 1261. T 139. 1 k. blue 10 10
T 1262. 2½ k. mauve .. 10 10
T 1263. T 138. 3 k. black .. 10 10
T 1264. T 139. 5 k. lilac 15 10
T 1265. 10 k. green .. 60 20
T 1266. T 138. 15 k. blue .. 30 15
T 1267. T 139. 25 k. olive .. 1·25 40
T 1268. 50 k. olive .. 2·75 70

T 145. Soldier and Map of Turkey. T 151. Child Eating.

1941. National Defence.
T 1289. T 145. 1 k. violet .. 25 10
T 1290. 2 k. blue .. .. 1·50 10
T 1291. 3 k. brown .. 1·50 20
T 1292. 4 k. mauve .. 1·25 10
T 1293. 5 k. pink .. .. 5·50 40
T 1294. 10 k. blue .. 10·00 60

1943. Child Welfare. Inscr. "SEFKAT PULLARI 1943".
T 1330. T 151. 0·50 k. violet & red 10 10
T 1331. 0·50 k. green & red 10 10
T 1332. – 1 k. blue and red 10 10
T 1333. – 3 k. red & orange 25 10
T 1334. – 15 k. black, buff and red .. 40 20
T 1335. – 100 k. blue & red 1·25 60
DESIGNS—VERT. 1 k. Nurse with baby. 15 k. Baby and emblem. 100 k. President Inonu and child. HORIZ. 3 k. Nurse and child.

T 152. Child Welfare Emblem. T 155. Pres. Inonu and Victim.

1943. Child Welfare. Star in red.
T 1337. T 152. 20 pa. blue .. 10 10
T 1338. – 1 k. green .. 10 10
T 1339. – 3 k. brown .. 10 10
T 1340. – 5 k. orange .. 85 20
T 1341. – 5 k. brown .. 20 15
T 1342. – 10 k. red 25 15
T 1343. – 15 k. lilac .. 45 15
T 1344. – 25 k. violet .. 95 15
T 1345. – 50 k. blue .. 1·60 20
T 1346. – 100 k. green .. 3·00 40
DESIGNS—VERT. 1 k. Hospital. 3 k. Nurse and children. 5 k. Baby in cot. 10 k. Nurse bathing baby. 15 k. Nurse helping child to drink. 50 k. Child. HORIZ. 25 k. Baby with bottle. 100 k. Hospital.

1944. Red Crescent. Inscr. "TURKIYE KIZILAY CEMIYETI".
T1347 – 20 pa. brown, flesh, red and blue .. 15 10
T1348 T 155. 1 k. olive, yellow, deep olive & red 15 10
T1349 – 2½ k. blue and red 25 10
T1350 – 5 k. blue and red 70 10
T1351 – 10 k. blue, green and red .. 80 25
T1352 – 50 k. green, black and red .. 2·25 60
T1353 – 1 l. yellow, black and red .. 4·50 85
DESIGNS—VERT. 20 pa. Nurse tending dreaming patient. 5 k. Soldier and nurse. 10 k. Feeding victims. 50 k. Wounded soldiers on raft. 1 l. Nurse within red crescent. HORIZ. 2½ k. Stretcher bearers and hospital ship.

T 156. Nurse helping Child to Drink. T 159. Nurse tucking Baby in Cot.

1945. Child Welfare. Star in red.
T 1354. – 1 k. lilac 10 10
T 1355. – 2½ k. blue .. 20 15
T 1356. T 156. 5 k. green .. 20 15
T 1357. – 10 k. brown .. 75 25
T 1358. – 250 k. black .. 7·50 2·75
T 1359. – 500 k. violet .. 15·00 5·00
DESIGNS—VERT. 21×29 mm. 1 k. Nurse carrying baby. 2½ k. Nurse holding child. 10 k. Child sucking thumb. HORIZ. 28×22 mm. 250 k., 500 k. Emblem.

1946. 25th Anniv of Child Welfare Organization.
T 1360. T 159. 20 pa. brown & red 10 10
T 1361. – 1 k. blue and red 10 10
T 1362. – 2½ k. red 10 10
T 1363. – 5 k. brown and red 10 10
T 1364. – 15 k. purple & red 20 10
T 1365. – 25 k. green and red 50 30
T 1366. – 50 k. green and red 85 40
T 1367. – 150 k. brown & red 2·50 60
DESIGNS: 1 k. Mother and baby. 2½ k. Nurse holding child above head. 5 k. Doctor examining baby. 15 k. Nurse feeding baby. 25 k. Nurse bathing baby. 50 k. Nurse weighing baby. 150 k. Nurse, and child in cot.

T 160. Pres. Inonu and Victim. T 169. Nurse and Children playing.

1946. Red Crescent. As Nos. T1347/8, T1350 and T1353 and new design inscr "TURKIYE KIZILAY DERNEGI".
T1369 – 20 pa. yellow, grey blue and red .. 10 10
T1532 – 20 pa. brown, yellow, violet and red .. 10 10
T1370 T 155 1 k. multicoloured 1·00 10
T1371 T 160 1 k. brown, blue and red .. 20 10
T1533 – 1 k. grn, blk & red 10 10
T1372 – 5 k. blue and red 40 10
T1373 – 20 k. red, bl & pur 75 20
T1374 – 1 k. blk, yell & red 2·25 75
T1375 – 250 k. black, green and red .. 5·50 75
T1376 – 5 l. black, pink and red .. 7·50 75
T1377 – 10 l. blue and red 20·00 10·00
DESIGNS—VERT. 20 pa. As No. T1347. 1 k. (T1533), As No. T1352. 5 k. As No. T1350. 1 l. As No. T1353. 5 l. Nurse tending patient. 10 l. Soldier, red crescent and figure symbolising Victory. HORIZ. 20 k. Ankara Hospital. 250 k. Nurse helping injured soldier.

1948. Child Welfare. Star in red.
T 1399. T 169. 20 pa. blue .. 10 10
T 1400. – 20 pa. mauve .. 10 10
T 1401. – 1 k. green .. 10 10
T 1402. – 3 k. purple .. 25 25
T 1403. – 15 k. grey .. 1·40 50
T 1404. – 30 k. orange .. 2·25 1·25
T 1405. – 150 k. green .. 4·50 2·25
T 1406. – 300 k. red .. 5·50 4·00
DESIGNS—VERT. 20 pa. (No. 1400) Nurse and children walking. 1 k. Nurse feeding two children. 3 k. Nurse with three children. 15 k. Parents and two children. 150 k. Nurse holding baby. 300 k. Heads of nurse and child. HORIZ. 30 k. Father handing baby to nurse.

T 177. Ruins and Tent. T 179. "Grief".

1949. Red Crescent.
T 1422. T 177. 5 k. blk., red & pur. 25 10
T 1423. 10 k. purple, red and flesh .. 25 10

1950. Red Crescent. Crescent in red.
T 1425. T 179. ½ k. blue 55 25
T 1426. 1 k. blue 10 10
T 1427. 2 k. mauve .. 15 10
T 1428. 2½ k. orange .. 15 10
T 1429. 3 k. green .. 15 10
T 1430. 4 k. drab .. 25 20
T 1431. 5 k. blue 50 10
T 1432. 10 k. pink .. 90 15
T 1433. 25 k. brown .. 1·25 35
T 1434. – 50 k. blue .. 2·00 60
T 1435. – 100 k. green .. 3·50 75
DESIGN: 50 k., 100 k. Plant with broken stem.

1952.
(a) Red Crescent. Nos. T 1427 and T 1429/30 surch.
T1489 T 179 20 pa. on 2 k. mauve and red 25 10
T1490 20 pa. on 3 k. green and red 25 10
T1491 20 pa. on 4 k. drab and red .. 25 10
(b) Child Welfare. Nos. T 1355, T 1362 and T 1339 surch.
T 1492. – 1 k. on 2½ k. blue and red .. 20 10
T 1493. – 1 k. on 2½ k. red .. 20 10
T 1494. – 1 k. on 3 k. brown and red .. 20 10

T 208. Nurse and Baby. T 211. Globe and Flag.

1954. Child Welfare. Inscr. "SEFKAT PULLARI 1954".
T 1534. – 20 pa. yell. & orge. 10 10
T 1535. – 20 pa. green & red 10 10
T 1536. T 208. 1 k. blue and red 10 10
DESIGN: Nos. 1534/5, Nurse with two children
See also Nos. T 1569 and T 1573/4.

1954. Red Crescent.
T 1545. T 211. 1 k. multicoloured 10 10
T 1546. – 5 k. red, grey and green 10 10
T 1547. – 10 k. grey, green and red .. 15 10
DESIGNS: 5 k. Nurse with wings on cloud. 10 k. Arm and hand.
See also Nos. T1652, T1656/8, T1838 and T1840/3.

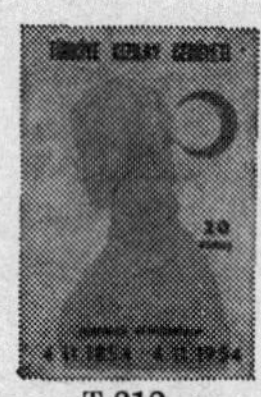

T 212. Florence Nightingale. T 215 Children kissing.

1954. Red Crescent. Centenary of Florence Nightingale's Arrival at Scutari.
T 1551. T 212. 20 k. green, brown and red .. 40 20
T 1552. – 30 k. brown, black and red .. 40 25
T 1553. – 50 k. stone, black and red .. 1·10 75
DESIGNS: 30 k. Florence Nightingale (three-quarter face). 50 k. Selimiye Barracks.

1955. Child Welfare. Inscr. "SEFKAT PULLARI 1955". Star in red.
T 1564. T 215. 20 pa. blue .. 10 10
T 1565. 20 pa. brown .. 10 10
T 1566. 1 k. purple .. 10 10
T 1567. 3 k. bistre .. 10 10
T 1568. 5 k. orange .. 10 10
T 1569. T 208. 10 k. green .. 1·10 60
T 1570. – 15 k. blue .. 10 10
T 1571. – 25 k. lake .. 75 25
T 1572. – 50 k. green .. 1·25 75
T 1573. T 208. 2½ l. brown .. 40·00 25·00
T 1574. 10 l. violet .. 95·00 50·00
DESIGN: 15 to 50 k. Nurse carrying baby.

1955. Red Crescent. Nos. T1373 and T1435 surch.
T1575 20 pa. on 20 k. red, blue and purple .. 10 10
T1576 20 pa. on 100 k. green and red 20 10

T 219. Nurse. T 227. Woman and Children.

1955. Red Crescent. Congress of International Council of Nurses.
T 1578. T 219. 10 k. brown, red and black .. 75 25
T 1579. – 15 k. green, red & black .. 75 25
T 1580. – 100 k. blue and red 1·75 1·00
DESIGNS—HORIZ. 15 k. Nurses marching. VERT. 100 k. Emblem, Red Cross and Red Crescent flags and nurses.

1956. Child Welfare. Star in red.
T 1614. T 227. 20 pa. salmon .. 10 10
T 1615. 20 pa. olive .. 10 10
T 1616. 1 k. blue 15 10
T 1617. 1 k. violet .. 15 10
T 1618. 3 k. brown .. 30 10
T 1619. – 10 k. red .. .. 1·50 10
T 1620. – 25 k. green .. 3·25 1·25
T 1621. – 50 k. blue .. 4·50 1·50
T 1622. – 2½ l. lilac .. 8·00 4·00
T 1623. – 5 l. brown .. 12·00 5·00
T 1624. – 10 l. green .. 22·00 10·00
DESIGNS: 10 k. to 50 k. Flag and building. 2½ l. to 10 l. Mother and baby.

1956. Red Crescent. No. T 1545 surch.
T 1625. T 211. 20 pa. on 1 k. mult. 15 10
T 1626. 2·5 k. on 1 k. mult. 10 10

1956. Child Welfare. Nos. 1399/1406 optd. **IV. DUNYA Cocuk Gunu 1 Ekim 1956.** Nos. 1644/6 surch. also.

T 1639.	T **169.**	20 pa. blue and red	3·75	3·75
T 1640.	–	20 pa. mauve & red	3·75	3·75
T 1641.	–	1 k. green and red	3·75	3·75
T 1642.	–	3 k. purple and red	3·75	3·75
T 1643.	–	15 k. grey and red	4·75	4·75
T 1644.	–	25 k. on 30 k. orge. and red ..	4·75	4·75
T 1645.	–	100 k. on 150 k. green and red ..	5·75	5·75
T 1646.	–	250 k. on 300 k. deep red and red	7·50	7·50

1957. Red Crescent. As No. T1373 but inscr "TURKIYE KIZILAY CEMIYETI", new design and as Nos. T1545/6. Crescent in red.

T1651	–	½ k. drab & brown	10	10
T1652	T **211**	1 k. blk, bis & grn	10	10
T1653	–	2½ k. grn & dp grn	10	10
T1655	–	20 k. red, brown and blue ..	25	15
T1656	T **211**	25 k. grey, black and green ..	55	45
T1657		50 k. blue & green	65	50
T1658		100 k. violet, black and green ..	1·50	75

Designs—vert. ½ k., 2½ k. Flower being watered. horiz. 20 k. Ankara Hospital.

T **239.** Two Babies. T **246.** Nurse and Child.

1957. Child Welfare.

T1659	T **239**	20 pa. green & red	10	10
T1660		20 pa. pink & red	10	10
T1661		1 k. blue and red	10	10
T1662		3 k. orange & red	40	15
T1683	T **246**	100 k. brn & red	75	25
T1684		150 k. green & red	75	25
T1685		250 k. violet & red	1·00	75

T **254.** Florence Nightingale. T **255.** Child's Head and Butterfly.

1958. Florence Nightingale Foundation. Crescent in red.

T 1829.	T **254.**	1 l. green	40	25
T 1830.		1½ l. grey ..	65	40
T 1831.		2½ l. blue	90	40

1958. Child Welfare. Butterflies. Mult.

T1832	20 k. Type **255** ..	25	15
T1833	25 k. Brimstone ..	25	15
T1834	50 k. Little tiger blue (horiz)	30	25
T1835	75 k. Green-veined white (horiz)	85	70
T1836	150 k. Peacock ..	2·00	1·50

1958. Red Crescent. As Nos. T1651/3, T1546 and T1656/8 but colours changed. Crescent in red.

T 1837.	–	½ k. lilac	15	10
T 1838.	T **211.**	1 k. black, brown and green ..	15	10
T 1839.	–	2½ k. grey and red	25	10
T 1840.	–	5 k. red, brown and green	35	10
T 1841.	T **211.**	25 k. black, green and brown ..	55	20
T 1842.		50 k. purple, black and green ..	1·75	25
T 1843.		100 k. drab, black and green ..	2·75	75

OFFICIAL STAMPS

O **160.** O **241.** O **284.** O **303.**

1947.

O 1360.	O **160.**	10 p. brown ..	10	10
O 1361.		1 k. green ..	10	10
O 1362.		2 k. purple ..	15	10
O 1363.		3 k. orange ..	15	10
O 1364.		5 k. turquoise ..	6·50	10
O 1365.		10 k. brown ..	1·50	10
O 1366.		15 k. violet ..	80	10
O 1367.		20 k. blue ..	85	10
O 1368.		30 k. olive ..	90	10
O 1369.		50 k. blue ..	90	10
O 1370.		1 l. green ..	1·00	10
O 1371.		2 l. red	1·25	10

1951. Postage stamps optd **RESMI** between bars with star and crescent above.

O1458	**165**	0.25 k. red ..	10	10
O1454		5 k. blue	20	10
O1461		10 k. brown ..	20	10
O1462		15 k. violet ..	40	10
O1456		20 k. blue	50	10
O1469		30 k. brown ..	35	10
O1470		60 k. black ..	1·00	10

1955. Postage stamps optd **RESMI** between wavy bars with star and crescent above or surch also.

O1568	**165**	0.25 k. red ..	10	10
O1587		½ k. on 1 k. black ..	10	10
O1569		1 k. black	10	10
O1570		2 k. purple ..	10	10
O1593		2 k. on 4 k. green ..	10	10
O1571		3 k. orange ..	10	10
O1594		3 k. on 4 k. green ..	10	10
O1572		4 k. green	10	10
O1573		5 k. on 15 k. violet	10	10
O1581		5 k. blue	35	10
O1595		10 k. on 12 k. red ..	10	10
O1574		10 k. on 15 k. violet	10	10
O1575		15 k. violet ..	10	10
O1576		20 k. blue	15	10
O1585		30 k. brown ..	60	10
O1577		40 k. on 1 l. olive ..	25	10
O1590		75 k. on 1 l. olive ..	60	10
O1578		75 k. on 2 l. brown	60	15
O1579		75 k. on 5 l. purple	6·00	2·75

1957.

O 1655.	O **241.**	5 k. blue ..	10	10
O 1843.		5 k. red	10	10
O 1656.		10 k. brown ..	10	10
O 1844.		10 k. olive ..	10	10
O 1657.		15 k. violet ..	10	10
O 1845.		15 k. red ..	10	10
O 1658.		20 k. red ..	10	10
O 1846.	O **241.**	20 k. violet ..	10	10
O 1659.		30 k. olive ..	10	10
O 1660.		40 k. purple ..	15	10
O 1847.		40 k. blue ..	10	10
O 1661.		50 k. grey ..	15	10
O 1662.		60 k. green ..	20	10
O 1848.		60 k. orange ..	30	10
O 1663.		75 k. orange ..	30	10
O 1849.		75 k. grey ..	30	10
O 1664.		100 k. green ..	35	10
O 1850.		100 k. violet ..	35	10
O 1665.		200 k. lake ..	70	25
O 1851.		200 k. brown ..	85	15

1960.

O1916	O **284**	1 k. orange ..	10	10
O1917		5 k. red	10	10
O1918		10 k. green ..	60	10
O1919		30 k. brown ..	10	10
O1920		60 k. green ..	20	10
O1921		1 l. purple ..	40	10
O1922		1½ l. blue ..	25	10
O1923		2½ l. violet ..	75	10
O1924		5 l. blue	4·50	20

1962.

O 1977.	O **303.**	1 k. brown ..	10	10
O 1978.		5 k. green ..	10	10
O 1979.		10 k. brown ..	10	10
O 1980.		15 k. blue ..	10	10
O 1981.		25 k. red ..	10	10
O 1982.		30 k. blue ..	15	10

1963. Surch.

O 2003.	O **303.**	50 k. on 30 k. blue	25	10
O 2004.	O **284.**	100 k. on 60 k. grn.	45	10

O **320.** O **329.** O **344.**

1963.

O2042	O **320**	1 k. green ..	10	10
O2043		5 k. brown ..	10	10
O2044		10 k. green ..	10	10
O2045		50 k. red ..	15	10
O2046		100 k. blue ..	30	10

1964.

O 2074.	O **329.**	1 k. grey ..	10	10
O 2075.		5 k. blue ..	15	10
O 2076.		10 k. yellow ..	15	10
O 2077.		30 k. red ..	40	10
O 2078.		50 k. green ..	40	10
O 2079.		60 k. brown ..	85	10
O 2080.		80 k. turquoise ..	2·25	10
O 2081.		130 k. blue ..	2·00	10
O 2082.		200 k. purple ..	3·25	10

1965.

O 2133.	O **344.**	1 k. green ..	10	10
O 2134.		10 k. blue ...	10	10
O 2135.		50 k. orange ..	20	10

O **358.** Usak Carpet. O **372.** Doves Emblem. O **383.**

1966. Turkish Carpets.

O 2175.	O **358.**	1 k. orange ..	10	10
O 2176.	–	50 k. green ..	10	10
O 2177.	–	100 k. red ..	30	10
O 2178.	–	150 k. blue ..	40	10
O 2179.	–	200 k. bistre ..	40	10
O 2180.	–	500 k. lilac ..	1·00	10

Designs (Carpets of): 50 k. Bergama. 100 k. Ladik. 150 k. Selcuk. 200 k. Nomad. 500 k. Anatolia.

1967.

O 2213.	O **372.**	1 k. blue & lt. bl.	10	10
O 2214.		50 k. blue & orge.	15	10
O 2215.		100 k. blue & mve.	25	10

1968.

O 2241.	O **383.**	50 k. brn. & grn.	10	10
O 2242.		150 k. blk. & orge.	25	10
O 2243.		500 k. brn. & blue	60	10

O **400.** O **427.** O **440.**

1969.

O 2287.	O **400.**	1 k. red & green	10	10
O 2288.		10 k. blue & grn.	10	10
O 2289.		50 k. brn. & grn.	10	10
O 2290.		100 k. mve. & grn.	35	10

1971.

O 2359.	O **427.**	5 k. blue & brown	10	10
O 2360.		10 k. red and blue	10	10
O 2361.		30 k. vio. & orge.	15	10
O 2362.		50 k. brn. & blue	20	10
O 2363.		75 k. grn. & buff	35	10

1971. Face-value and border colour given first.

O 2398.	O **440.**	5 k. blue & grey	10	10
O 2399.		25 k. grn. & brn.	10	10
O 2400.		100 k. brn. & grn.	25	10
O 2401.		200 k. brn. & ochre	20	10
O 2402.		250 k. pur. & vio.	25	10
O 2403.		500 k. blue & light blue	65	10

O **446.** O **462.** O **478.** Trellis Motif.

1972.

O 2411.	O **446.**	5 k. blue & brn.	10	10
O 2412.		100 k. grn. & brn.	25	10
O 2413.		200 k. red & brn.	40	20

1973.

O 2457.	O **462.**	100 k. bl. & cream	20	10

1974.

O 2490.	O **478.**	10 k. brn. on pink	10	10
O 2491.		25 k. pur. on blue	10	10
O 2492.		50 k. red on mve.	10	10
O 2493.		150 k. brn. on grn.	20	10
O 2494.		250 k. red on pink	30	10
O 2495.		500 k. brn. on yell.	65	10

O **496.** O **528.** O **529.**

1975.

O 2537.	O **496.**	100 k. red & blue	15	10

1977. Surch.

O2587	O **320**	5 k. on 1 k. green	10	10
O2588	O **329**	5 k. on 1 k. grey	10	10
O2589	O **344**	5 k. on 1 k. green	10	10
O2590	O **358**	5 k. on 1 k. orange	10	10
O2591	O **372**	5 k. on 1 k. blue and light blue	10	10

1977.

O2609	O **528**	250 k. green & blue	25	10

1978.

O2610	O **529**	50 k. pink and red	10	10
O2611		2½ l. buff & brown	10	10
O2612		4½ l. lilac & green	15	10
O2613		5 l. blue and violet	20	10
O2614		10 l. pale green and green ..	25	10
O2615		25 l. yellow & red	65	10

O **540.** O **552.** O **573.**

1979.

O2647	O **540**	50 k. deep orange and orange ..	10	10
O2648		2½ l. blue & lt blue	15	10

1979.

O2686	O **552**	50 k. violet & pink	10	10
O2687		1 l. red and green	10	10
O2688		2½ l. mauve and light mauve ..	10	10
O2689		5 l. purple & blue	15	10
O2690		7½ l. blue and lilac	20	10
O2691		10 l. blue and buff	60	10
O2692		35 l. pur & silver	45	10
O2693		50 l. blue and pink	65	10

1981.

O2756	O **573**	5 l. red and yellow	10	10
O2757		10 l. red and pink	15	10
O2758		35 l. mauve & grey	40	10
O2759		50 l. blue and pink	60	10
O2760		75 l. emerald and green	85	10
O2761		100 l. blue & lt bl	1·10	10

O **606.** O644. O **720.**

1983.

O2839	O **606**	5 l. blue & yellow	10	10
O2840		15 l. blue & yellow	15	10
O2841		20 l. blue and grey	15	10
O2842		50 l. blue & lt blue	40	10
O2843		65 l. blue & mauve	70	10
O2844		70 l. blue and pink	25	10
O2845		90 l. blue & brown	95	10
O2846		90 l. blue & lt blue	45	10
O2847		100 l. blue & green	60	10
O2848		125 l. blue & green	1·25	10
O2849		230 l. blue & orge	1·10	10

1986.

O 2946.	O **644.**	5 l. bl. & yell. ..	10	10
O 2947.		10 l. bl. & pink ..	10	10
O 2948.		20 l. bl. & grey ..	10	10
O 2949.		50 l. bl. & lt. bl.	15	10
O 2950.		100 l. bl. & grn.	40	10
O 2951.		300 l. bl. & lilac	65	10

1989. Various stamps surch.

O3039	O **644**	500 l. on 10 l. blue and pink ..	25	10
O3040	O **606**	500 l. on 15 l. blue and yellow ..	25	10
O3041	O **644**	500 l. on 20 l. blue and grey ..	25	10
O3042	O **606**	1000 l. on 70 l. blue and pink	50	10
O3043		1000 l. on 90 l. blue and brown	50	10
O3044		1250 l. on 230 l. blue and orange	50	10

1991. Nos. O2843 and O2846 surch.

O3108	O **606**	100 l. on 65 l. blue and mauve ..	10	10
O3109		250 l. on 90 l. blue and light blue	10	10

1992.

O3138	O **720**	3000 l. deep brown and brown ..	45	15
O3139		5000 l. grn & lt grn	75	25

O 733 O 743

1992.

O3167	O **733**	1000 l. blue & grn	15	10
O3168		10000 l. green & bl	1·40	45

1993.

O3196	O **743**	1000 l. green & brn	10	10
O3197		1500 l. green & brn	10	10
O3198		5000 l. brn & green	20	10

POSTAGE DUE STAMPS

D 2. D 4.

1863. Imperf.

D 7 D 2 20 pa. black on brown .. 55·00 22·00
D 8 1 pi. black on brown 66·00 24·00
D 9 2 pi. black on brown £225 65·00
D10 5 pi. black on brown £100 55·00

1865.

D18 D 4 20 pa. brown .. 15 1·10
D19 1 pi. brown 15 90
D74 2 pi. brown .. .. 30 1·00
D70 5 pi. brown .. .. 25 2·50
D76 25 pi. brown .. .. 5·00 12·00

1888. As T **9.**

D 117. **9.** 20 pa. black .. .. 25 1·10
D 118. 1 pi. black 25 75
D 119. 2 pi. black .. .. 25 1·00

1892. As T **15.**

D 146. **15.** 20 pa. black .. .. 1·50 45
D 147. 20 pa. black on red .. 20 50
D 148. 1 pi. black .. .. 2·75 95
D 149. 2 pi. black .. .. 1·25 60

1901. As T **21.**

D 195. **21.** 10 pa. black on red .. 55 30
D 196. 20 pa. black on red .. 60 50
D 197. 1 pi. black on red .. 50 45
D 198. 2 pi. black on red .. 75 45

1905. As T **23.**

D 228. **23.** 1 pi. black on red .. 85 75
D 229. 2 pi. black on red .. 1·75 1·75

1908. As T **25.**

D 250. **25.** 1 pi. black on red .. 15·00 1·50
D 251. 2 pi. black on red .. 2·00 4·75

1909. As T **28.**

D 288. **28.** 1 pi. black on red .. 2·50 7·50
D 287. 2 pi. black on red .. 18·00 20·00

1913. As T **30.**

D 347. **30.** 2 pa. black on red .. 10 40
D 348. 5 pa. black on red .. 10 40
D 349. 10 pa. black on red .. 10 40
D 350. 20 pa. black on red .. 10 40
D 351. 1 pi. black on red .. 85 75
D 352. 2 pi. black on red .. 1·75 3·25

1913. Adrianople issue surch.

D 356. **31.** 2 pa. on 10 pa. green 30 15
D 357. 5 pa. on 20 pa. red .. 40 30
D 358. 10 pa. on 40 pa. blue 1·25 60
D 359. 20 pa. on 40 pa. blue 3·50 1·75

D 49. D 50.

D 51. D 52.

1914.

D516 D 49 5 pa. brown .. 40 1·25
D517 D 50 20 pa. red .. .. 40 1·00
D518 D 51 1 pi. blue .. .. 75 1·25
D519 D 52 2 pi. blue .. .. 1·50 1·75

AD 26. D 101. Bridge over Kizil Irmak.

1921.

AD 91. AD 26. 20 pa. green .. 20 45
AD 92. 1 pi. green .. 30 50
AD 93. 2 pi. brown .. 1·10 1·10
AD 94. 3 pi. red .. 1·75 2·25
AD 95. 5 pi. blue .. 2·25 2·75

1926.

D 1035. D **101.** 20 pa. orange .. 35 20
D 1036. 1 gr. red .. 1·00 25
D 1037. 2 gr. green .. 1·10 45
D 1038. 3 gr. purple .. 1·60 50
D 1039. 5 gr. violet .. 3·75 1·45

D 121.

1936.

D 1186. D **121.** 20 pa. brown .. 10 10
D 1187. 2 k. blue .. 10 10
D 1188. 3 k. violet .. 10 10
D 1189. 5 k. green .. 10 10
D 1190. 12 k. red .. 10 10

PRINTED MATTER STAMPS

1879. Optd **IMPRIMES** in scroll.

N88 **9** 10 pa. black and mauve 65·00 45·00

(N 14.)

1891. Stamps of 1876 optd. with Type N **14.**

N 132. **9.** 10 pa. green .. .. 4·75 2·50
N 134. 20 pa. pink .. .. 6·50 2·00
N 136. 1 pi. blue .. .. 28·00 10·00
N 138. 2 pi. yellow .. .. £170 35·00
N 139. 5 pi. brown £225 £130

1892. Stamps of 1892 optd. with Type N **14.**

N 150. **15.** 10 pa. green .. .. 35·00 5·00
N 151. 20 pa. red .. .. 60·00 24·00
N 152. 1 pi. blue .. .. 15·00 8·00
N 153. 2 pi. brown .. .. 24·00 12·00
N 154. 5 pi. purple £350 £350

مطبوعه

(N 16.) (N 23.) (N 27.)

1894. Stamps of 1892 optd. with Type N **16.**

N 161. **15.** 5 pa. on 10 pa. grn. (160) 40 20
N 155. 10 pa. green 20 15
N 156a. 20 pa. red 20 15
N 157. 1 pi. blue 20 15
N 158. 2 pi. brown .. .. 4·50 1·50
N 159. 5 pi. purple .. .. 25·00 7·50

1901. Stamps of 1901 optd. with Type N **23.**

N 183. **21.** 5 pa. violet 25 15
N 184. 10 pa. green .. .. 2·75 50
N 185. 20 pa. red 15 10
N 186. 1 pi. blue .. .. 1·50 20
N 187. 2 pi. orange .. .. 7·50 1·10
N 188. 5 pi. mauve .. .. 15·00 6·50

1901. Stamps of 1901 optd. with Type N **23.**

N 189. **22.** 5 pa. brown 20 20
N 190. 10 pa. green 65 35
N 191. 20 pa. mauve .. .. 2·40 1·40
N 192. 1 pi. blue .. .. 3·75 1·90
N 193. 2 pi. blue .. .. 20·00 9·00
N 194. 5 pi. brown .. .. 30·00 16·00

1905. Stamps of 1905 optd with Type N **23.**

N222 **23** 5 pa. brown 20 10
N223 10 pa. green .. .. 2·75 80
N224 20 pa. pink 40 10
N225 1 pi. blue 40 10
N226 2 pi. blue .. .. 9·00 3·00
N227 5 pi. brown .. .. 15·00 5·00

1908. Stamps of 1908 optd with Type N **27.**

N244 **25** 5 pa. brown .. .. 2·00 15
N245 10 pa. green .. .. 2·00 15
N246 20 pa. red .. .. 2·10 55
N247 1 pi. blue .. .. 5·50 75
N248 2 pi. black .. .. 14·00 2·25
N249 5 pi. purple .. .. 22·00 4·00

1909. Stamps of 1909 optd with Type N **27.**

N276 **28** 5 pa. brown 45 15
N277 10 pa. green 70 15
N278 20 pa. red .. .. 5·50 75
N279 1 pi. blue .. .. 12·00 2·25
N280 2 pi. black .. .. 25·00 12·00
N281 5 pi. purple .. .. 28·00 12·00

1911. New value of 1909 issue.

N 332. **28.** 2 pa. olive 10 10

1920. No. 500 surch.

N 961. – 5 on 4 pa. brown .. 10 45

TUSCANY Pt. 8

Formerly an independent duchy in C. Italy, now part of Italy.

1851. 60 quattrini = 20 soldi = 12 crazie = 1 Tuscan lira.
1859. 1 Tuscan lira = 1 Italian lira.

1. Arms of Tuscany. 5. Arms of Savoy.

1851. Imperf.

24. **1.** 1 q. black £500 £650
5. 1 s. orange £5500 £1400
6. 2 s. red £22000 £4500
9. 1 c. red .. .. .. £2750 35·00
29. 2 c. blue .. .. .. £900 35·00
15. 4 c. green .. .. .. £2750 50·00
19. 6 c. blue .. .. .. £2750 55·00
21. 9 c. purple .. .. .. £7000 90·00
23. 60 c. red £48000 £15000

1860. Imperf.

36. **5.** 1 c. purple £800 £450
40. 5 c. green £4500 £110
43. 10 c. brown .. .. £650 13·00
45. 20 c. blue .. .. £3000 65·00
48. 40 c. red £4500 £120
50. 80 c. red £11000 £500
51. 3 l. yellow £110000 £48000

NEWSPAPER TAX STAMP

N 3

1854.

N1 N **3** 2 s. black .. .. 13·00

TUVA Pt. 10

A province lying between the Sajan and Tannu Ola range. Fromerly known as North Mongolia and Tannu Tuva was incorporated into the U.S.S.R. on 11th October 1944.

PRICES. The prices quoted in the used column are for stamps cancelled to order where these occur. Postally used copies are worth considerably more.

1926. 100 kopeks = 1 rouble.
1934. 100 kopeks = 1 tugrik.
1936. 100 kopeks = 1 aksha.

1. Wheel of Eternity.

1926.

1. **1.** 1 k. red .. .. .. 1·00 1·10
2. 2 k. blue .. .. .. 1·00 1·10
3. 5 k. orange .. .. .. 1·10 1·10
4. 8 k. green .. .. .. 1·25 1·25
5. 10 k. violet .. .. .. 1·25 1·25
6. 30 k. brown .. .. .. 1·50 1·25
7. 50 k. black .. .. .. 1·50 1·25
8. 1 r. turquoise .. .. 2·25 2·25
9. 3 r. red .. .. .. 4·00 4·50
10. 5 r. blue .. .. .. 7·00 6·00

The rouble values are larger $22\frac{1}{2} \times 30$ mm.

1927. Surch. **TOUVA POSTAGE** and value.

11 1 8 k. on 50 k. black .. 4·75 5·50
12 14 k. on 1 r. turquoise .. 5·00 5·50
13 18 k. on 3 r. red .. .. 7·50 9·00
14 28 k. on 5 r. blue .. .. 8·00 9·50

4. Tuvan Woman. 5. Map of Tuva.

6. Mongolian Sheep and Tents.

7. Fording a River.

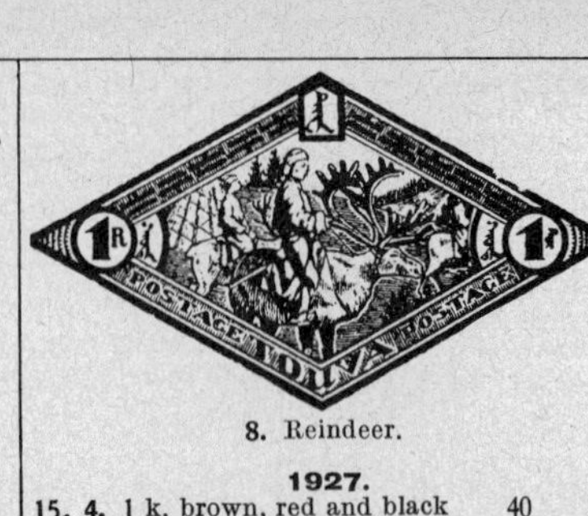

8. Reindeer.

1927.

15. **4.** 1 k. brown, red and black 40 35
16. – 2 k. brown, green & violet 80 45
17. – 3 k. green, yellow & black 1·25 50
18. – 4 k. brown and blue .. 45 35
19. – 5 k. blue, black and orange 45 35
20. **5.** 8 k. sepia, blue and red .. 55 55
21. – 10 k. red, black and green 3·50 75
22. – 14 k. orange and blue .. 6·50 3·25
23. **6.** 18 k. brown and blue .. 7·00 3·50
24. – 28 k. sepia and green .. 4·50 2·25
25. **7.** 40 k. green and red .. 3·25 2·00
26. – 50 k. brown, black & green 2·50 1·75
27. – 70 k. bistre and red .. 4·00 2·75
28. **8.** 1 r. violet and brown .. 7·50 5·50

DESIGNS—As Type 4: 2 k. Red deer. 3 k. Common goral. 4 k. Mongolian tent. 5 k. Tuvan man. As Type **5**: 10 k. Archers. 14 k. Camel caravan. As Type **6**: 28 k. Landscape. As Type **7**: 50 k. Girl carpet-weaver. 70 k. Horseman.

1932. Stamps of 1927 surch. **TbBA POSTA** and value (10 k. optd. only).

29. **7.** 1 k. on 40 k. green and red 4·75 6·50
30. – 2 k. on 50 k. brown, black and green .. .. 5·00 5·50
31. – 3 k. on 70 k. bistre and red 5·50 5·50
32. **5.** 5 k. on 8 k. sep., bl. & red 5·50 5·50
33. – 10 k. red, black and green 6·00 7·50
34. – 15 k. on 14 k. orge. & blue 6·50 7·00

1932. Stamps of 1927 surch.

35. **5.** 10 k. on 8 k. brown .. £120
36. – 15 k. on 14 k. orange & bl. £120
37. **6.** 35 k. on 18 k. brn. & blue 48·00 60·00
38. – 35 k. on 28 k. sepia & green 55·00 70·00

1933. Fiscal stamps (20 × 39 mm) surch **Posta** and value.

(a) Numerals $6\frac{3}{4}$ mm. tall.

39. 15 k. on 6 k. yellow .. 55·00 70·00
40. 35 k. on 15 k. brown .. £190 £275

(b) Numerals $5\frac{1}{4}$ mm. tall.

41. 15 k. on 6 k. yellow .. 70·00 90·00
42. 35 k. on 15 k. brown .. £225 £350

12. Mounted Hunter.

13. Interior of Tent.

14. Yak.

1934. Perf. or imperf.

43. **12.** 1 k. orange 75 40
44. – 2 k. green 90 75
45. **13.** 3 k. red 90 75
46. – 4 k. purple .. .. 1·50 1·50
47. **14.** 5 k. blue .. .. 1·50 1·50
48. – 10 k. brown .. .. 1·50 1·50
49. – 15 k. lake .. .. 1·50 1·50
50. – 20 k. black .. .. 2·25 2·00

DESIGNS—As Type **12**. 2 k. Hunter. As Type **13**. 4 k. Tractor. As Type **14**. 10 k. Camel caravan. 15 k. Lassoing reindeer. 20 k. Corsac fox-hunting.

15. Yaks.

16. Capercaillie.

1934. Air.

51	15	1 k. red	85	75
52	–	5 k. green	85	75
53	16	10 k. brown	2·75	2·25
54	–	15 k. red	1·60	75
55	–	25 k. purple	1·60	75
56	15	50 k. green	1·60	75
57	–	75 k. red	1·60	75
58	15	1 t. blue	1·60	1·25
59	–	2 t. blue (55 × 28 mm)	2·10	2·25

DESIGNS (embodying monoplane) As Type **15**. 5, 15 k. Camels. As Type **16**. 25 k. Argali. 75 k. Ox-cart. 2 t. Roe deer.

The 2 t. also come larger, 61 × 31 mm.

1935. No. 49 surch.

60.	20 k. on 15 k. lake	85·00	

18. Map of Tuva.

19. Rocky Outcrop.

1935. Landscapes.

61.	18.	1 k. orange	75	75
62.	–	3 k. green	75	75
63.	–	5 k. red	90	75
64.	–	10 k. violet	90	75
65.	19.	15 k. green	90	95
66.	–	25 k. blue	90	95
67.	–	50 k. sepia	90	1·00

DESIGNS—As Type **18**. 3 k., 5 k., 10 k. Views of River Yenisei. As Type **19**. 25 k. Bei-kem rapids. 50 k. Mounted hunter.

20. Eurasian Badger.

21. Corsac Fox.

22. Elk.

1935. Animals.

68.	20.	1 k. orange	90	85
69.	–	3 k. green	90	85
70.	–	5 k. mauve	90	90
71.	21.	10 k. red	90	90
72.	–	25 k. red	1·00	1·00
73.	–	50 k. blue	1·00	1·00
74.	22.	1 t. violet	1·00	1·00
75.	–	2 t. blue	1·00	1·00
76.	–	3 t. brown	1·10	1·10
77.	–	5 t. blue	1·25	1·25

DESIGNS—As Type **20**—VERT. 3 k. Eurasian red squirrel. HORIZ. 5 k. Sable. As Type **21**. 25 k. European otter. 50 k. Lynx. LARGER (61 × 31 mm), 2 t. Yak. 3 t. Bactrian camel. As Type **22**. 5 t. Brown bear.

See also No. 115.

23. Arms of Republic.

24. Wrestlers.

25. Herdsman.

26. Sports Meeting.

27. Partisans.

1936. 15th Anniv. of Independence. (a) Postage.

78.	23.	1 k. green	1·10	55
79.	–	2 k. sepia	1·10	55
80.	–	3 k. blue	1·25	60
81.	24.	4 k. red	1·50	60
82.	–	5 k. purple	2·50	50
83.	24.	6 k. green	2·50	50
84.	–	8 k. purple	2·25	55
85.	–	10 k. red	2·50	50
86.	–	12 k. agate	3·25	75
87.	–	15 k. green	3·50	55
88.	–	20 k. blue	3·50	75
89.	25.	25 k. red	3·00	55
90.	–	30 k. purple	6·00	1·00
91.	25.	35 k. red	2·50	55
92.	–	40 k. sepia	2·50	55
93.	–	50 k. blue	2·50	55
94.	26.	70 k. plum	3·50	1·10
95.	–	80 k. green	3·00	1·10
96.	27.	1 a. red	3·00	1·10
97.		2 a. red	3·00	1·10
98.	–	3 a. blue	3·25	1·10
99.	–	5 a. agate	3·25	1·40

DESIGNS—As Type **23**: 2 k. President Gyrmittazi. 3 k. Camel and driver. As Type **24**: 5, 8 k. Archers. 10, 15 k. Fisherman. 12, 20 k. Brown bear hunt. As Type **25**: 30 k. Bactrian camel and steam train. 40, 50 k. Horse-racing. As Type **26**: 80 k., 5 a. 1921 war scene. 3 a. Confiscation of cattle.

See also Nos. 116 and 118/19.

28. Yak Transport.

29. Horseman and Airship.

30. Seaplane over Waves.

(b) Air.

100.	28.	5 k. blue and flesh	2·25	75
101.	–	10 k. purple and brown	2·50	80
102.	28.	15 k. agate and grey	2·50	80
103.	29.	25 k. purple and cream	3·50	90
104.	–	50 k. red and cream	3·00	1·10
105.	29.	75 k. green and yellow	3·00	1·10
106.	30.	1 a. green and turquoise	3·00	1·25
107.		2 a. red and cream	3·50	1·25
108.		3 a. sepia and flesh	3·50	2·00

DESIGNS—As Type **28**. 10 k. Horse-drawn reaper. As Type **29**. 50 k. Feast of the Women.

See also No. 117.

1938. Various stamps surch wth large numerals and old values obliterated.

109.	5 k. on 2 a. red (No. 97)		
110.	5 k. on 2 a. red and cream (No. 107)		
111.	10 k. on 1 t. blue (No. 58)		
112.	20 k. on 50 k. sepia (No. 67)		
113.	30 k. on 2 a. red and cream (No. 107)		
114.	30 k. on 3 a. sepia & flesh (No. 108)		

See also Nos. 120/1.

1938. Previous types with designs modified and colours changed.

115.	5 k. green (No. 70)	85·00	
116.	10 k. blue (No. 85)	90·00	
117.	15 k. brown (No. 102)	85·00	
118.	20 k. red (No. 88)	£225	
119.	30 k. purple (As 95)	£100	

In Nos. 116/9 the dates have been removed and in No. 117 " AIR MAIL " also.

1939. Nos. 58 and 67 surch. with small thick numerals and old values obliterated.

120.	10 k. on 1 t. blue		
121.	20 k. on 50 k. sepia		

See also Nos. 122/3.

1940. Various stamps surch.

122.	10 k. on 1 t. blue (No. 58)		
123.	20 k. on 50 k. sep. (No. 67)		
124.	20 k. on 50 k. bl. (No. 73)		
125.	20 k. on 50 k. blue (No. 93)		
126.	20 k. on 50 k. red on cream (No. 104)		
127.	20 k. on 75 k. green and yellow (No. 105)		
128.	20 k. on 80 k. grn. (No. 95)		

1942. Nos. 98/9 surch.

129.	25 k. on 3 a. blue		
130.	25 k. on 5 a. agate		

34. Tuvan Woman.

1942. 21st Anniv. of Independence. Imperf.

131.	34.	25 k. blue	£225	
132.	–	25 k. blue	£225	
133.	–	25 k. blue	£225	

DESIGNS: No. 132, Agricultural Exhibition building. No. 133, Government building.

35. Coat of Arms.

36. Government Building.

1943. 22nd Anniv. of Independence. With or without gum.

134.	35.	25 k. blue	20·00	
135.		25 k. black	30·00	
136.		25 k. green	60·00	
137.	36.	50 k. green	60·00	

UBANGI-SHARI Pt. 6

Formerly part of the French Congo, Ubangi-Shari became a separate colony in 1904 (although stamps of French Congo continued to be used until 1915). From 1915 to 1922 it shared a postal administration with Chad.

From 1936 to 1958 Ubangi-Shari was part of French Equatorial Africa. In December 1958 it became the autonomous state of the Central African Republic.

100 centimes = 1 franc.

A. UBANGI-SHARI-CHAD.

1915. Stamps of Middle Congo optd OUBANGUI-CHARI-TCHAD.

1	1	1 c. green and brown	25	40
2		2 c. violet and brown	20	45
3		4 c. blue and brown	40	65
4		5 c. green and blue	30	50
19		5 c. yellow and blue	65	70
5		10 c. red and blue	70	80
20		10 c. green and turquoise	55	65
5a		15 c. purple and pink	1·40	1·40
6		20 c. brown and blue	2·25	2·50
7	2	25 c. blue and green	75	85
21		25 c. green and black	55	60
8		30 c. red and green	65	70
22		30 c. red	55	65
9		35 c. brown and blue	3·75	4·50
10		40 c. green and brown	3·75	5·50
11		45 c. violet and orange	3·50	5·50
12		50 c. green and orange	4·25	6·75
23		50 c. blue and green	55	70
13		75 c. brown and blue	9·00	11·00
14	3	1 f. green and violet	9·75	11·00
15		2 f. violet and green	10·00	11·00
16		5 f. blue and pink	35·00	38·00

1916. No. 5 surch **5c** and cross.

18	10 c. + 5 c. red and blue	55	80

B. UBANGI-SHARI.

1922. Stamps of Middle Congo, new colours, optd OUBANGUI-CHARI.

24	1	1 c. violet and green	35	55
25		2 c. green and pink	50	65
26		4 c. brown and purple	60	80
27		5 c. blue and pink	75	95
28		10 c. green and turquoise	1·40	1·40
29		15 c. pink and blue	1·50	1·90
30		20 c. brown and pink	4·00	5·75
31	2	25 c. violet and pink	3·00	5·00
32		30 c. red	2·00	3·00
33		35 c. violet and green	3·75	5·50
34		40 c. blue and mauve	3·25	5·00
35		45 c. brown and mauve	3·25	5·00
36		50 c. blue and light blue	2·00	3·00
37		60 on 75 c. violet on pink	2·50	3·25
38		75 c. brown and pink	3·50	5·75
39	3	1 f. green and blue	4·25	5·75
40		2 f. green and pink	5·25	8·00
41		5 f. green and brown	12·50	16·00

1924. Stamps of 1922 and similar stamps additionally overprinted AFRIQUE EQUATORIALE FRANCAISE.

42	1	1 c. violet and green	10	45
43		2 c. green and pink	10	45
44		4 c. brown & chocolate	10	45
44c		4 c. brown	1·10	1·10
45		5 c. blue and pink	15	45
46		10 c. green & turquoise	40	55
47		10 c. red and blue	30	45
48		15 c. pink and blue	45	75
49		20 c. brown and pink	40	65

No.	Type	Description	Unused	Used
50	2	25 c. violet and pink	45	30
51		30 c. red	35	45
52		30 c. brown and pink	45	45
53		30 c. olive and green	75	90
54		35 c. violet and green	20	45
55		40 c. blue and mauve	50	60
56		45 c. brown and mauve	55	70
57		50 c. blue and light blue	55	55
58		50 c. grey and blue	1·00	80
59		60 on 75 c. vio on pink	50	55
60		65 c. brown and blue	1·75	1·90
61		75 c. brown and pink	75	80
62		75 c. blue and light blue	50	60
63		75 c. purple and brown	1·60	1·90
64		90 c. pink and red	4·25	5·75
65a	3	1 f. green and blue	50	60
66		1 f. 10 brown and blue	2·00	2·25
67		1 f. 25 mauve and green	4·25	5·25
68		1 f. 50 ultramarine & bl	5·75	6·75
69		1 f. 75 brown and orange	7·50	7·50
70		2 f. green and pink	80	80
71		3 f. mauve on pink	5·25	5·50
72		5 f. green and brown	3·50	3·50

1925. As last but new colours and surch.

No.	Type	Description	Unused	Used
73	3	65 on 1 f. violet & brown	50	1·40
74		85 on 1 f. violet and brown	1·00	1·40
75	2	90 on 75 c. pink and red	95	1·40
76	3	1 f. 25 on 1 f. bl & ultram	70	80
77		1 f. 50 on 1 f. ultram & bl	1·00	85
78		3 f. on 5 f. brown and red	1·90	2·25
79		10 f. on 5 f. red and mauve	12·00	16·00
80		20 f. on 5 f. mauve & grey	20·00	23·00

1931. "International Colonial Exhibition" key-types inscr "OUBANGUI-CHARI".

No.	Type	Description	Unused	Used
103	E	40 c. green	3·00	4·50
104	F	50 c. mauve	3·00	3·75
105	G	90 c. red	3·00	4·50
106	H	1 f. 50 blue	3·50	3·75

POSTAGE DUE STAMPS

1928. Postage Due type of France optd **OUBANGUI- CHARI A. E. F.**

No.	Type	Description	Unused	Used
D 81.	D 11.	5 c. blue	85	1·90
D 82.		10 c. brown	1·00	1·90
D 83.		20 c. olive	1·40	1·90
D 84.		25 c. red	1·40	1·90
D 85.		30 c. red	1·40	1·90
D 86.		45 c. green	1·40	1·90
D 87.		50 c. purple	1·60	2·25
D 88.		60 c. brown on cream	1·90	2·75
D 89.		1 f. red on cream	2·25	3·50
D 90.		2 f. red	2·50	4·50
D 91.		3 f. violet	2·50	4·50

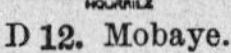
D 12. Mobaye.

D 13. E. Gentil.

1930.

No.	Type	Description	Unused	Used
D 92.	D 12.	5 c. olive and blue	40	80
D 93.		10 c. brown and red	50	1·10
D 94.		20 c. brown and green	80	1·40
D 95.		25 c. brown and blue	1·00	1·40
D 96.		30 c. green and brown	1·60	2·25
D 97.		45 c. olive and green	2·50	3·50
D 98.		50 c. brown and mauve	4·25	6·25
D 99.		60 c. black and violet	5·00	6·75
D 100.	D 13.	1 f. black and brown	1·75	2·50
D 101.		2 f. brown and mauve	2·00	4·00
D 102.		3 f. brown and red	2·50	6·00

UKRAINE — Pt. 10

A district of S.W. Russia, which issued stamps during its temporary independence after the Russian Revolution. In 1923 it became a constituent republic of the U.S.S.R.

In 1991 it became an independent republic.

1918. 100 kopeks = 1 rouble.
100 shagiv = 1 grivna (= ½ rouble).
1992 (Nov). Karovanets (coupon currency).

(6.)

(8.)

1918. Arms types of Russia optd. with Trident device in various types according to the district. Imperf. or perf.

No.	Type	Description	Unused	Used
L 51	22	1 k. orange	10	10
L 52		2 k. green	10	10
L 53		3 k. red	10	10
L 54	23	4 k. red	10	10
L 55	22	5 k. red	10	10
L138		7 k. blue	10	10
L 57	23	10 k. blue	10	10
L 58	22	10 k. on 7 k. blue	15	10
L159	9	14 k. red and blue	15	20
L 60		15 k. blue and purple	10	10
L 61	14	20 k. red and blue	10	10
L 62	9	20 k. on 14 k. red & blue	10	10
L145		25 k. mauve and green	10	25
L 64		35 k. green and purple	10	10
L 65	14	50 k. green and purple	10	10
L 66	9	70 k. orange and brown	10	10
L 47	15	1 r. orange and brown	15	15
L 72	11	3 r. 50 grey and black	10·00	16·00
L212		3 r. 50 green and brown	20	20
L 49	20	5 r. blue and green	40	60
L 73	11	7 r. yellow and black	7·00	10·00
L 14		7 r. pink and green	90	2·00
L 36	20	10 r. grey, red & yellow	5·50	6·50

1 Trident (from Arms of Grand Duke Vladimir the Great)

2 Peasant

3 Ceres

4 Trident

5

1918. Without inscription on back. Imperf.

No.	Type	Description	Unused	Used
1	1	10 s. brown on buff	20	50
2	2	20 s. brown	20	50
3	3	30 s. blue	20	50
4	4	40 s. green	20	50
5	5	50 s. red	20	50

1918. With trident and four lines of inscription on back.

No.	Type	Description	Unused	Used
6	1	10 s. brown	2·50	5·00
7	2	20 s. brown	2·50	5·00
8	3	30 s. blue	2·50	5·00
9	4	40 s. green	2·50	5·00
10	5	50 s. red	2·50	5·00

Trident.

Parliament Building.

Stamps of the above and similar designs were prepared for use but never used.

7 Spectre of famine

8 T. G. Shevchenko (Ukrainian poet)

1923. Charity.

No.	Type	Description	Unused	Used
12	7	10+10 k. blue & black	1·00	2·25
13	8	20+20 k. brn. & orge.	1·00	2·25
14	–	90+30 k. blk. & bistre	2·00	4·50
15	–	150+50 k. red & blk.	4·00	6·00

DESIGNS—VERT. 90 k. "Death" and peasant. 150 k. "Ukraine" (woman) distributing bread.

11 Cossack Chief with Musician and Standard Bearer

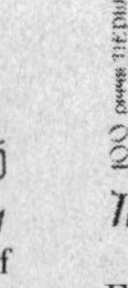
12 Ukrainian Emigrant Couple

1992. 500th Anniv (1990) of Ukraine Cossacks.
20 11 15 k. multicoloured .. 40 40

1992. Centenary (1991) of Ukrainian Emigration to Canada.
21 12 15 k. multicoloured .. 40 40

13 Mykola Lysenko and Score from "Taras Bulba"

1992. 150th Birth Anniv of Mykola Lysenko (composer).
22 13 1 r. brown, red & bistre 1·10 1·10

14 Mykola Kostomarov, Quill Pen and Scroll

15 Ceres

1992. 175th Birth Anniv of Mykola Kostamarov (historian).
23 14 20 k. brown & light brown 35 35

1992.

No.	Type	Description	Unused	Used
24	15	50 k. blue	10	10
25		70 k. brown	10	10
26		1 r. green	10	20
27		2 r. violet	15	15
28		5 r. blue	30	30
29		10 r. red	40	40
30		20 r. green	80	80
31		50 r. brown	2·00	2·00

16 Gymnastics

17 Ukraine Flag and Trident Symbol

1992. Olympic Games, Barcelona. Mult.

No.	Type	Description	Unused	Used
32		3 r. Type **16**	25	25
33		4 r. Pole vaulting	45	45
34		5 r. Type **16**	50	50

1992. 1st Anniv of Regained Independence.
35 17 2 r. multicoloured .. 35 35

18 Three Cranes on Globe

1992. World Congress of Ukranians, Kiev.
36 18 2 r. multicoloured .. 35 35

20 U.P.U. Symbol and Hand writing

1992. Correspondence Week.
38 20 5 r. multicoloured .. 50 50

21 Congress Emblem

1992. World Congress of Ukrainian Jurists, Kiev.
39 21 15 r. multicoloured .. 1·25 1·25

22 Embroidery

1992. Ukraine Folk Art.
40 22 0.50 k. black and orange 10 10

23 Arms of Austria and Ukraine with Traditional Costumes of Galicia and Bukovina

1992. Ukrainians in Austria.
41 23 5 k. multicoloured .. 1·25 1·25

24 Laying Foundation Stone, 1632

1992. 360th Anniv of Mogilyanska's Academy, Kiev.
42 24 1 k. 50 black, blue & brn 35 35

26 Lvov Arms

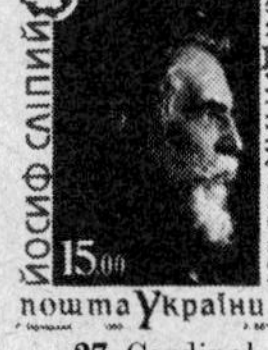
27 Cardinal Slipij

1993. Regional Arms.

No.	Type	Description	Unused	Used
44	26	3 k. blue, dp blue & gold	95	95
45	–	5 k. lake, gold and red	1·25	1·25

DESIGN: 5 k. Kiev.

1993. Birth Centenary (1992) of Cardinal Joseph Slipij.
68 27 15 k. multicoloured .. 1·75 1·75

28 Biplane

1993. 75th Anniv of First Vienna–Cracow–Lvov–Kiev Flight.

No.	Type	Description	Unused	Used
69	28	35 k. black, blue & mve	65	65
70	–	50 k. multicoloured	80	80

DESIGN: 50 k. Modern airplane.

29 Candles and Traditional Foods

1993. Easter.
71 29 15 k. multicoloured .. 1·25 1·25

30 "Country Wedding in Lower Austria" (Ferdinand Georg Waldmuller)

31 Cross and Figures

1993. 45th Anniv of Declaration of Human Rights.
72 30 5 k. multicoloured .. 1·25 1·25

1993. 60th Anniv of Famine Deaths.
73 31 75 k. brown 80 80

32 1918 10 sh. Stamp

1993. Stamp Day. 75th Anniv of First Ukrainian Postage Stamps.
74 32 100 k. blue and brown .. 1·00 1·00

33 Kiev

34 Mowing

1993. 50th Anniv of Liberation of Kiev.
75 33 75 k. multicoloured .. 90 90

1993. Agricultural Scenes.
76 34 50 k. green 10 10
77 – 100 k. blue 15 15
78 – 150 k. red 25 25
79 – 200 k. orange 30 30
80 – 300 k. purple 55 55
81 – 500 k. brown 85 85
DESIGNS: 100 k. Laden bullock carts; 150, 300 k. Shepherd and flock; 200, 500 k. Women cutting corn.

35 Madonna and Child

36 Agapit

1994. Ukranian Health Fund.
82 35 150 k. + 20 k. black, gold and red .. .. 1·40 1·40

1994. Agapit (medieval doctor).
83 36 200 k. black and red .. 1·75 1·75

37 Dog's-tooth Violet ("Erythronium dens-canis")

1994. Red Book of Ukraine. Multicoloured.
84 200 k. Type 37 .. .. 70 70
85 200 k. Lady's slipper ("Cypripedium calceolus") 70 70

UMM AL QIWAIN Pt. 19

One of the Trucial States in the Persian Gulf. In July 1971 formed the United Arab Emirates with five other Gulf Shaikdoms.

1964. 100 naye paise = 1 rupee.
1967. 100 dirhams = 1 riyal.

1. Shaikh Ahmed bin Rashid al Moalla and Mountain Gazelles.

1964. Multicoloured.

(a) Size as T 1.
1. 1 n.p. Type 1 .. .. 10 10
2. 2 n.p. Snake 10 10
3. 3 n.p. Striped hyena .. 10 10
4. 4 n.p. Fish 10 10
5. 5 n.p. Fish (different) .. 10 10
6. 10 n.p. Fish (different) .. 10 10
7. 15 n.p. Palace 10 10
8. 20 n.p. Town buildings .. 15 10
9. 30 n.p. Tower 20 10

(b) Size 42½ × 27 mm.
10. 40 n.p. Type 1 .. .. 40 10
11. 50 n.p. Snake 70 10
12. 70 n.p. Striped hyena .. 80 10
13. 1 r. Fish .. .. 1·00 10
14. 1 r. 50 Fish (different) .. 1·40 25
15. 2 r. Fish (different) .. 1·75 35

(c) Size 53½ × 33½ mm.
16. 3 r. Palace .. .. 2·25 55
17. 5 r. Town buildings .. 3·50 90
18. 10 r. Tower .. .. 5·00 1·50

2. Discus Thrower and Stadium.

1964. Olympic Games, Tokyo. Multicoloured.
19. 50 n.p. Type 2 .. .. 20 10
20. 1 r. Main stadium .. 45 15
21. 1 r. 50 Swimming pool .. 65 20
22. 2 r. Main stadium .. 90 30
23. 3 r. Komazawa gymnasium 1·25 40
24. 4 r. Stadium entrance .. 1·75 50
25. 5 r. Type 2 .. .. 2·00 70

3. Cortege leaving White House.

1965. Pres. Kennedy Commem. Each black and gold on coloured paper as given below.
26. 3. 10 n.p. pale blue 10 10
27. – 15 n.p. pale stone .. 10 10
28. – 50 n.p. pale stone .. 10 10
29. – 1 r. pale pink .. 20 10
30. – 2 r. pale stone .. 35 15
31. – 3 r. pale lavender .. 65 35
32. – 5 r. pale blue .. 95 45
33. – 7 r. 50 pale buff .. 2·25 75
DESIGNS (Funeral scenes): 15 n.p. Coffin-bearers. 50 n.p. Hearse. 1 r. Presidents Eisenhower and Truman. 2 r. Foreign dignitaries. (33 × 51 mm.). 3 r. Mrs. Kennedy and family at grave. 5 r. Last salute. 7 r. 50, Pres. Kennedy.

1965. Air. Designs similar to Nos. 1/9 but inscr. "AIR MAIL". Multicoloured.

(a) Size 43 × 26½ mm.
34. 15 n.p. type 1 .. .. 20 10
35. 25 n.p. Snake 25 10
36. 35 n.p. Striped hyena .. 35 10
37. 50 n.p. Fish 55 10
38. 75 n.p. Fish (different) .. 75 10
39. 1 r. Fish (different) .. 90 15

(b) Size 53 × 34 mm.
40. 2 r. Palace .. .. 1·25 30
41. 3 r. Town buildings .. 1·75 50
42. 5 r. Tower .. .. 2·50 90

4. Tribute to Ruler (reverse of 10 n.p. piece).

1965. Arabian Gulf Area Monetary Conf. Circular designs on silver foil, backed with paper inscr. overall "Walsall Security Paper" in English and Arabic. Imperf.

(a) Diameter $1\frac{11}{16}$ in.
43. 4. 10 n.p. purple and black .. 10 10
44. – 25 n.p. blue and green .. 15 15

(b) Diameter $2\frac{1}{16}$ in.
45. 4. 1 r. red and violet .. 45 45
46. – 2 r. green and orange .. 90 90

(c) Diameter 2½ in.
47. 4. 3 r. blue and mauve .. 1·25 1·25
48. – 5 r. purple and blue .. 1·90 1·90
SILVER PIECES: Nos. 44, 46, 48 each show the obverse side (Shaikh Ahmed).

5. "Penny Black" and Egyptian 5 p. stamp of 1866.

1966. Centenary Stamp Exn., Cairo.
49. 5. 3 n.p. multicoloured .. 10 10
50. – 5 n.p. multicoloured .. 10 10
51. – 7 n.p. multicoloured .. 10 10
52. – 10 n.p. multicoloured .. 10 10
53. – 15 n.p. multicoloured .. 10 10
54. – 25 n.p. multicoloured .. 10 10
55. – 50 n.p. multicoloured .. 25 10
56. – 75 n.p. multicoloured .. 35 10
57. – 1 r. multicoloured .. 45 15
58. – 2 r. multicoloured .. 90 35
DESIGNS: As Type 5, with Egyptian 5 p. stamp: 7 n.p. Brazil 30 r. "Bull's-eye" of 1843. 15 n.p. Mauritius "Post Office" One Penny of 1847. 50 n.p. Belgium 10 c. "Epaulettes" of 1849. 1 r. New South Wales One Penny and Victoria One Penny of 1850. As Type 5, but with Egyptian "Pyramid and Star" watermark of 1866: 5 n.p. Basle 2½ r. "Dove" of 1845, Geneva 5 c. + 5 c. "Double Eagle" and Zurich 4 r. "Numeral" of 1843. 10 n.p. U.S. St. Louis "Bears" 5 c., Baltimore 5 c. and New York 5 c. "Postmasters" stamps of 1845. 25 n.p. France 20 c. "Ceres" of 1849. 75 n.p. Bavaria 1 k. of 1850. 2 r. Spain 6 c. of 1850.

6. Sir Winston Churchill with Lord Alanbrooke and Field Marshal Montgomery.

1966. Churchill Commem. Multicoloured designs, each including Churchill.
59. 3 n.p. Type 6 .. .. 10 10
60. 4 n.p. With Roosevelt and Stalin at Yalta .. 10 10
61. 5 n.p. In garden at No. 10 Downing Street, London 10 10
62. 10 n.p. With Eisenhower .. 10 10
63. 15 n.p. With Lady Churchill in car 10 10
64. 50 n.p. Painting in Morocco 30 10
65. 75 n.p. Walking—on holiday 35 10
66. 1 r. Funeral cortege .. 50 15
67. 3 r. Lying-in-state, Westminster Hall .. .. 1·25 50
68. 5 r. Churchill giving "Victory" sign .. .. 2·25 75

7. Communications Satellite.

1966. Centenary of I.T.U. (in 1965). Designs showing communications satellites.
70. 7. 5 n.p. multicoloured .. 10 10
71. – 10 n.p. multicoloured .. 15 10
72. – 25 n.p. multicoloured .. 20 10
73. – 50 n.p. multicoloured .. 40 15
74. – 75 n.p. multicoloured .. 60 20
75. – 1 r. multicoloured .. 80 20
76. – 2 r. multicoloured .. 1·40 35
77. – 3 r. multicoloured .. 1·75 45
78. – 5 r. multicoloured .. 2·50 85

NEW CURRENCY SURCHARGES. In 1967 various issues appeared surcharged in dirhams and riyals. The 1964 definitives, 1965 air stamps and officials with this surcharge are listed as there is evidence of their postal use. Nos. 19/33 and 49/68 also exist with these surcharges.

1967. Various issues with currency names changed by overprinting.

(i) Nos. 1/18 (1964 Definitives).
80. 1 d. on 1 n.p. 10 10
81. 2 d. on 2 n.p. 10 10
82. 3 d. on 3 n.p. 10 10
83. 4 d. on 4 n.p. 10 10
84. 5 d. on 5 n.p. 10 10
85. 10 d. on 10 n.p. 10 10
86. 15 d. on 15 n.p. .. .. 2·50 1·00
87. 20 d. on 20 n.p. .. .. 2·50 1·00
88. 30 d. on 30 n.p. .. .. 2·50 1·00
89. 40 d. on 40 n.p. 40 20
90. 50 d. on 50 n.p. 50 30
91. 70 d. on 70 n.p. 60 35
92. 1 r. on 1 r. 75 40
93. 1 r. 50 on 1 r. 50 .. .. 1·25 70
94. 2 r. on 2 r. .. .. 1·50 85
95. 3 r. on 3 r. .. .. 6·50 2·50
96. 5 r. on 5 r. .. .. 8·50 3·75
97. 10 r. on 10 r. .. .. 13·00 6·00

(ii) Nos. 34/42 (Airmails).
98. 15 d. on 15 n.p. 15 10
99. 25 d. on 25 n.p. 20 10
100. 35 d. on 35 n.p. 25 20
101. 50 d. on 50 n.p. 45 25
102. 75 d. on 75 n.p. 55 30
103. 1 r. on 1 r. 70 40
104. 2 r. on 2 r. .. .. 2·50 90
105. 3 r. on 3 r. .. .. 2·50 1·25
106. 5 r. on 5 r. .. .. 3·50 2·50

9. Box Fish.

1967. Fish of the Arabian Gulf. Mult.

(a) Postage (i) Size 46 × 21 mm.
116. 1 d. Type 9 .. .. 10 10
117. 2 d. Parrot fish 10 10
118. 3 d. Sweet lips 10 10
119. 4 d. Butterfly fish 10 10
120. 5 d. Soldier fish 10 10
121. 10 d. Damsel fish 15 10
122. 15 d. Picasso triggerfish .. 15 10
123. 20 d. Striped triggerfish .. 25 10
124. 30 d. Israeli puffer 35 10

(ii) Size 56 × 26 mm.
125. 40 d. Type 9 .. .. 40 10
126. 50 d. As 2 d. 50 10
127. 70 d. As 3 d. 70 10
128. 1 r. As 4 d. 80 15
129. 1 r. 50 As 5 d. .. .. 1·25 25
130. 2 r. As 10 d. .. .. 1·40 35
131. 3 r. As 15 d. (No. 122) .. 2·00 45
132. 5 r. As 20 d. .. .. 3·25 75
133. 10 r. As 30 d. .. .. 5·00 1·50

(b) Air. Size 70 × 35 mm.
134. 15 d. Type 9 .. .. 15 10
135. 25 d. As 2 d. 25 10
136. 35 d. As 3 d. 35 10
137. 50 d. As 4 d. 50 10
138. 75 d. As 5 d. 70 10
139. 1 r. As 10 d. 80 15
140. 2 r. As 15 d. (No. 122) .. 1·40 35
141. 3 r. As 20 d. .. .. 2·00 45
142. 5 r. As 30 d. .. .. 3·25 75

OFFICIAL STAMPS

1965. Designs similar to Nos. 1/9, additionally inscr. "ON STATE'S SERVICE". Mult.

(a) Postage. Size 42½ × 26½ mm.
O 49. 25 n.p. Type 1 .. .. 15 10
O 50. 40 n.p. Snake 20 10
O 51. 50 n.p. Striped hyena .. 30 10
O 52. 75 n.p. Fish 40 15
O 53. 1 r. Fish (different) .. 55 20

(b) Air. (i) Size 42½ × 26½ mm.
O 54. 75 n.p. Fish (different) .. 40 15

(ii) Size 53 × 33½ mm.
O 55. 2 r. Palace 90 40
O 56. 3 r. Town buildings .. 1·25 60
O 57. 5 r. Tower .. .. 1·90 90

1967. Nos. O 1/9 with currency names changed by overprinting.
O 107. 25 d. on 25 n.p. (postage) 30 15
O 108. 40 d. on 40 n.p. 35 15
O 109. 50 d. on 50 n.p. 45 25
O 110. 75 d. on 75 n.p. 60 35
O 111. 1 r. on 1 r. 75 45
O 112. 75 d. on 75 n.p. (air) .. 60 35
O 113. 2 r. on 2 r. .. .. 1·75 90
O 114. 3 r. on 3 r. .. .. 2·25 1·25
O 115. 5 r. on 5 r. .. .. 3·25 1·90

For later issues see **UNITED ARAB EMIRATES.**

APPENDIX

The following stamps have either been issued in excess of postal needs or have not been available to the public in reasonable quantities at face value. Such stamps may later be given full listing if there is evidence of regular postal use.

1967.

Self-Portraits of Famous Painters. Postage 10, 15, 25, 50, 75 d., 1, 1 r. 50; Air 1 r. 25, 2, 2 r. 50, 3, 5 r.

Dogs. Postage 15, 25, 50, 75 d., 1 r.; Air 1 r. 25 2 r. 50, 4 r.

"Expo 67" World Fair, Montreal. Famous Paintings. 25, 50, 75 d., 1, 1 r. 50, 2, 3 r.

1968.

Falcons. Postage 15, 25, 50, 75 d., 1 r.; Air 1 r. 50, 3, 5 r.

Winter Olympic Games, Grenoble. Postage 10, 25, 75 d., 1 r.; Air 1 r. 50, 2, 3, 5 r.

Famous Paintings. Postage 25, 50, 75 d., 1, 1 r. 50, 2 r. 50; Air 1, 2, 3, 4, 5 r.

Olympic Games, Mexico (1st issue). Optd. on (a) 1964 Tokyo Olympic Games issue. Postage 1 r. 50, 2, 4, 5 r. (b) 1968 Winter Olympic Games issue. Air 1 r. 50, 2, 5 r.

Robert Kennedy Memorial. Optd. on 1965 Pres. Kennedy issue. Postage 3, 5, 7 r. 50.

Olympic Games, Mexico (2nd issue). Postage 10, 25, 50 d., 1, 2 r.; Air 2 r. 50, 3, 4, 5 r.

Still Life Paintings. Postage 25, 50 d., 1, 1 r. 50, 2 r.; Air 1 r. 25, 2 r. 50, 3. 3 r. 50, 5 r.

Mexico Olympic Medal Winners. Optd. on Olympic Games, Mexico issue. Postage 10, 25, 50 d., 1, 2 r.; Air 2 r. 50, 3, 4, 5 r.

Aviation History. Aircraft. Postage 25, 50 d., 1, 1 r. 50, 2 r.; Air 1 r. 25, 2 r. 50, 3, 5 r.

1969.

"Apollo 8" Moon Orbit. Optd. on 1968 Aviation History issue. Postage 25, 50 d., 1, 1 r. 50, 2 r.; Air 1 r. 25, 2 r. 50, 3, 5 r.

Horses (1st series). Postage 25, 50, 75 d., 1, 2 r.; Air 1 r. 50, 2 r. 50, 4, 5 r.

Olympic Games, Munich, 1972 (1st issue). Optd. on 1968 Olympic Games, Mexico issue, Postage 10. 25, 50 d., 1, 2 r.; Air 2 r. 50, 3. 4, 5 r.

Winter Olympic Games, Sapporo, 1972 (1st issue). Optd. on 1968 Winter Olympics, Grenoble issue. Postage 10, 25, 75 d., 1 r.; Air 1 r. 50, 2, 3, 5 r.

Veteran and Vintage Cars. Postage 15 d. × 8, 25 d. × 8, 50 d. × 8, 75 d. × 8; Air 1 r. × 8, 2 r. × 8.

Famous Films. Postage 10, 15, 25, 50, 75 d. 1 r.; Air 1 r. 25, 2. 2 r. 50, 3, 4, 5 r.

"Apollo 12" Moon Landing. 10, 20, 30, 50, 75 d., 1 r.

1970.

Apollo 13" Astronauts. 10, 30, 50 d.

"Expo 70" World Fair, Osaka Japan. 5, 10, 20, 40 d., 1, 1 r. 25.

150th Anniv. of British Landing on Trucial Coast. Uniforms. 10, 20, 30, 50, 75 d., 1 r.

1971.

Animals. Postage 10, 15. 20, 25 d.; Air 5 r.

Winter Olympic Games, Sapporo, 1972 (2nd issue). Postage 5, 10, 15, 20. 25 d.; Air 50, 75 d., 1, 3, 5 r.

Olympic Games, Munich, 1972 (2nd issue). Postage 5, 10, 15, 20, 25 d.; Air 50, 75 d., 1, 3, 5 r.

1972.

Durer's Religious Paintings. Postage 5, 10, 15, 20, 25 d.; Air 3 r.

Horses (2nd series). Postage 10, 15, 20, 25 d.; Air 50 d., 3 r.

Locomotives (plastic surfaced). Postage 5, 10, 20, 40, 50 d.; Air 6 r.

Winter Olympic Games, Sapporo, 1972 (3rd issue) (plastic surfaced). Postage 5, 10, 20, 40, 50 d.; Air 6 r.

Easter, Religious Paintings. Postage 5, 10, 20, 50 d.; Air 1, 3 r.

Kennedy brothers memorial. Postage 5, 10, 15, 20 d.; Air 1, 3 r.

Winston Churchill memorial. Postage 5, 10, 15, 20 d.; Air 3 r.

Arab rulers. Postage 5 d. × 6, 10 d. × 6, 15 d. × 6, 20 d. × 6; Air 3 r. × 6.

13th World Jamboree, 1971 (plastic surfaced). Postage 5, 10, 20, 40, 50 d.; Air 6 r.

Fish. Postage 5, 10, 20, 40, 50 d.; Air 6 r.

International Airlines. Postage 5, 10, 15, 20, 25 d.; Air 50 d.

"Apollo 15" Moon Mission. Postage 5, 10, 15, 20. 25 d.; Air 50, 75 d., 1, 3, 5 r.

Olympic Games, Munich, 1972 (3rd issue) (plastic surfaced). Postage 5, 10, 20, 40, 50 d.; Air 6 r.

2500th Anniv. Founding of Persian Empire. Postage 10, 20, 30, 40, 50, 60 d.; Air 1 r.

Portraits of Charles de Gaulle. 5, 10, 15, 20. 25 d.

Paintings of Napoleon. Postage 5, 10, 15, 20, 25 d.; Air 5 r.

Butterflies. Postage 5, 10, 15, 20, 25 d.; Air 3 r.

Penguins. Postage 5, 10, 15, 20 d.; Air 50 d., 4 r.

Cars. Postage 5. 10, 15, 20, 25 d.; Air 3 r.

Masks (1st series). Postage 5, 10, 15, 20, 25 d.; Air 50 d., 1, 3 r.

Dogs and Cats. Postage 5, 5, 10, 10, 15, 15, 20, 20, 25, 25 d.; Air 5, 5 r.

Roses. Postage 10, 15, 20, 25 d.; Air 50 d., 5 r.

Marine Fauna. Postage 5, 10, 15, 20, 25, 50 d.; Air 1, 3 r.

Masks (2nd series). Postage 5, 10, 15, 20, 25 d.; Air 50 d., 1, 3 r.

Navigators. Postage 5, 10, 15, 20, 25, 50 d.; Air 1, 3 r.

Exotic Birds (1st series). Horiz and vert designs. Air 1 r. × 16.

Exotic Birds (2nd series). Horiz designs. Air 1 r. × 16.

In common with the other states of the United Arab Emirates the Umm al Qiwain stamp contract was terminated on 1 August 1972 and any further new issues released after that date were unauthorised.

UNITED ARAB EMIRATES Pt. 19

Following the withdrawal of British forces from the Gulf and the ending of the Anglo-Trucial States treaties six of the states, Abu Dhabi, Ajman, Dubai, Fujeira, Sharjah and Umm al Qiwain, formed an independent Union on 2nd December 1971. The seventh state, Ras al Khaima, joined during February, 1972. Each emirate continued to use its own stamps, pending the introduction of a unified currency. A Union Postal administration came into being on 1st August 1972 and the first stamps appeared on 1st January 1973. (For Abu Dhabi stamps optd. U.A.E., etc., see under that heading.)

100 fils = 1 dirham.

1. U.A.E. Flag and Map of Gulf.

1973. Multicoloured.
(a) Size 42×25 mm.

1.	5 f. Type **1**	15	10
2.	10 f. Type **1**	20	10
3.	15 f. Eagle emblem	35	10
4.	35 f. As 15 f.	65	10

(b) Size 46×30 mm.

5.	65 f. Almaqta Bridge, Abu Dhabi	1·75	25
6.	75 f. Khor Fakkan, Sharjah	1·75	25
7.	1 d. Clock Tower, Dubai	1·75	25
8.	1¼ d. Buthnah Fort, Fujeira	1·75	55
9.	2 d. Alfalaj Fort, Umm al Qiwain	15·00	1·75
10.	3 d. Khor Khwair, Ras al Khaima	5·00	1·75
11.	5 d. Ruler's Palace, Ajman	6·00	3·00
12.	10 d. President Shaikh Zaid	9·50	7·50

2. Youth and Girl within Shield.

1973. National Youth Festival. Mult.

13.	10 f. Type **2**	1·50	15
14.	1 d. 25 Allegory of Youth	4·00	2·25

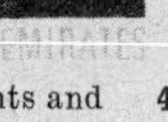
3. Traffic Lights and Road Sign.

4. " Three Races of the World ".

1973. Traffic Week. Multicoloured.

15.	35 f. Type **3**	1·25	20
16.	75 f. Pedestrian-crossing (horiz.)	2·25	90
17.	1 d. 25 Traffic Policeman	3·75	1·50

1973. 25th Anniv. of Declaration of Human Rights.

18.	**4.**	35 f. blk., yell. and blue	80	20
19.		65 f. black, yellow & red	1·25	65
20.		1¼ d. black, yellow & grn.	2·40	1·25

5. U.P.U. Emblem.

1974. Centenary of Universal Postal Union.

21.	**5.**	25 f. multicoloured	55	20
22.		60 f. multicoloured	1·25	75
23.		1¼ d. multicoloured	2·40	2·00

6. Medical Equipment. (Health Service).

1974. 3rd National Day.

24.	**6.**	10 f. red, brn. & lilac	45	15
25.	–	35 f. gold, grn. & blue	85	20
26.	–	65 f. brn., sepia and blue	1·40	70
27.	–	1¼ d. multicoloured	2·50	1·50

DESIGNS—HORIZ. (49 × 30 mm.). 35 f. Children reading (Education). 65 f. Tools and buildings (Construction). 1¼ d. U.A.E. flag with emblems of U.N. and Arab League.

7. Arab Couple with Candle and Book.

1974. International Literacy Day.

28.	**7.**	35 f. multicoloured	1·00	20
29.	–	65 f. blk., blue & brown	1·60	70
30.	–	1 d. 25 black, blue & brn.	2·00	1·25

DESIGN—VERT. 65 f., 1 d. 25 Arab couple with book.

8. Oil De-gassing Installation.

1975. 9th Arab Oil Conference. Multicoloured.

31	25 f. Type **8**	60	20
32	50 f. "Al Itticad" (offshore oil drilling platform)	1·40	35
33	100 f. Underwater storage tank	2·25	1·00
34	125 f. Marine oil production platform	3·00	1·75

9. Station and Dish Aerial.

1975. Opening of Jabal Ali Satellite Earth Station. Multicoloured.

36.	15 f. Type **9**	50	15
37.	35 f. Satellite beaming information to Earth	1·25	25
38.	65 f. As 35 f.	2·00	40
39.	2 d. Type **9**	4·75	2·50

10. "Snapshots" within Eagle Emblem.

11. Symbols of Learning.

1975. 4th National Day. Multicoloured

40	10 f. Type **10**	25	15
41	35 f. Shaikh Mohamed bin Hamad al Sharqi of Fujeira	85	35
42	60 f. Shaikh Rashid bin Humaid al Naimi of Ajman	1·25	40
43	80 f. Shaikh Ahmed bin Rashid al Moalla of Ummal Qiwain	1·75	80
44	90 f. Shaikh Sultan bin Mohammed al Qasimi of Sharjah	2·00	1·25
45	1 d. Shaikh Saqr bin Mohammed al Qasimi of Ras al Khaima	2·00	1·25
46	1 d. 40 Shaikh Rashid bin Said of Dubai	3·00	2·25
47	5 d. Shaikh Zaid bin Sultan al Nahayyan of Abu Dhabi, President of UAE	12·00	8·50

1976. Arabic Literacy Day. Multicoloured.

48.	15 f. Type **11**	35	10
49.	50 f. Arabs seeking enlightenment	1·25	35
50.	3 d. As 50 f.	5·00	3·00

1976. No. 6 surch in English and Arabic.

50a	50 f. on 75 f. multicoloured	20·00	15·00

12. Man and Road Signs.

13. Headphones.

1976. Traffic Week. Multicoloured.

51.	15 f. Type **12**	55	10
52.	80 f. Example of dangerous driving, and road signals (horiz.)	2·50	1·75
53.	140 f. Children on road crossing (horiz.)	4·75	3·25

1976. Int. Telecommunications Day.

54.	**13.**	50 f. multicoloured	55	25
55.		80 f. multicoloured	7·25	55
56.		2 d. multicoloured	3·50	2·00

14. U.A.E. Crest.

15. President Shaikh Zaid.

1976.

57	**14**	5 f. red	10	30
58		10 f. brown	15	20
59		15 f. pink	20	20
60		35 f. brown	35	10
61		50 f. violet	60	15
62		60 f. bistre	90	15
63		80 f. green	1·25	25
64		90 f. blue	1·50	10
65		1 d. blue	1·75	30
66		140 f. green	2·25	70
67		150 f. violet	2·75	95
68		2 d. grey	3·25	80
69		5 d. blue	7·00	3·50
70		10 d. mauve	12·00	8·00

1976. 5th National Day.

71.	**15.**	15 f. multicoloured	50	10
72.		140 f. multicoloured	1·40	1·10

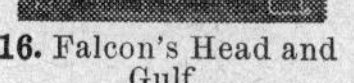

16. Falcon's Head and Gulf. **17.** Mohammed Ali Jinnah (Quaid-i-Azam).

1976. International Falconry Congress, Abu Dhabi.
73. **16.** 80 f. multicoloured .. 1·25 65
74. 2 d. multicoloured .. 2·75 1·75

1976. Birth Cent. of Mohammed Ali Jinnah.
75. **17.** 50 f. multicoloured .. 1·25 45
76. 80 f. multicoloured .. 2·00 1·40

19. A.P.U. Emblem. **20.** U.A.E. Crest.

1977. 25th Anniv. of Arab Postal Union.
78. **19.** 50 f. multicoloured .. 1·25 40
79. 80 f. multicoloured .. 2·00 1·25

1977.
80. **20.** 5 f. red and black .. 10 30
81. 10 f. brown and black .. 15 20
82. 15 f. pink and black .. 20 20
83. 35 f. brown and black .. 40 10
84. 50 f. mauve and black .. 65 15
85. 60 f. bistre and black .. 1·00 30
86. 80 f. green and black .. 1·00 20
87. 90 f. blue and black .. 1·00 10
88. 1 d. blue and black .. 1·40 25
89. 1 d. 40 green and black 2·00 60
90. 1 d. 50 violet and black 2·25 75
91. 2 d. grey and black .. 2·75 95
92. 5 d. turquoise and black 6·00 2·75
93. 10 d. mauve and black .. 10·00 5·50

21. Arab Scholar and Emblems.

1977. International Literacy Day.
94. **21.** 50 f. multicoloured .. 75 25
95. 3 d. multicoloured .. 2·75 1·75

22. Armoured Cars.

1977. Sixth National Day. Multicoloured.
96. 15 f. Type **22**
97. 50 f. Anti-aircraft missiles
98. 150 f. Soldiers marching
Set of 3 £250 —

Nos. 96/8 were withdrawn from sale on day of issue as the date in Arabic was wrongly inscribed backwards.

23. Posthorn Dhow. **24.** Koran on Map of World.

1979. 2nd Gulf Postal Organization Conf. Dubai.
99. **23.** 50 f. multicoloured .. 35 20
100. 5 d. multicoloured .. 3·00 2·50

1980. The Arabs.
101. **24.** 50 f. multicoloured .. 45 20
102. 1 d. 40 multicoloured .. 95 60
103. 3 d. multicoloured .. 2·00 1·50

25. Jet Fighters and Helicopter.

1980. 9th National Day.
104. **25.** 15 f. multicoloured .. 20 10
105. 50 f. multicoloured .. 65 20
106. 80 f. multicoloured .. 90 60
107. 150 f. multicoloured .. 1·60 1·25

26. Family on Graph. **27.** Mosque and Kaaba, Mecca.

1980. Population Census.
109. **26.** 15 f. blue and pink .. 20 10
110. – 80 f. brown and grey .. 80 35
111. – 90 f. brown and buff .. 1·00 50
112. **26.** 2 d. deep blue and blue 2·50 2·00

DESIGN: 80 f., 90 f. Figure standing in doorway.

1980. 1400th Anniv of Hejira.
113. **27.** 15 f. multicoloured .. 25 10
114. 80 f. multicoloured .. 80 35
115. 90 f. multicoloured .. 1·00 45
116. 140 f. multicoloured .. 2·25 1·50

28. Figures supporting O.P.E.C. Emblem. **29.** Policeman helping Child across Road.

1980. 20th Anniv. of Organization of Petroleum Exporting Countries. Mult.
118. 50 f. Type **28** 55 30
119. 80 f. Type **28** 90 45
120. 90 f. O.P.E.C. emblem and globe .. .. .. 1·10 50
121. 140 f. As No. 120 .. .. 2·00 1·50

1981. Traffic Week. Multicoloured.
123. 15 f. Type **29** 45 15
124. 50 f. Policeman and traffic signs (21 mm × 31 mm) .. 1·00 40
125. 80 f. Type **29** .. .. 1·50 70
126. 5 d. As No. 124 .. .. 4·75 4·25

30. Symbols of Industry.

1981. 10th National Day.
127. **30.** 25 f. blue and black .. 35 15
128. – 150 f. multicoloured .. 1·50 1·00
129. – 2 r. red, green and black 2·25 1·75

DESIGNS: 150 f. Soldiers. 2 r. Flag, U.N. and U.A.E. emblems.

31. Helping the Disabled (pictogram) and I.Y.D.P. Emblem. **32.** U.A.E. Crest

1981. International Year of Disabled Persons. Multicoloured.
130 25 f. Type **31** 40 15
131 45 f. Disabled person in wheelchair (pictogram) (vert) 70 30
132 150 f. As No. 131 .. .. 1·50 1·25
133 2 d. Type **31** .. .. 2·50 2·00

1982. Multicoloured. Background colour given.

(a) Size 17 × 21 mm.
134. **32.** 5 f. pink 10 10
135. 10 f. green 10 10
136. 15 f. violet 10 10
137. 25 f. brown 15 10
138. 35 f. brown 15 10
139. 50 f. blue 20 10
140. 75 f. yellow 35 25
141. 100 f. grey 45 35
142. 110 f. green 45 35
143. 125 f. mauve 55 40
144. 150 f. blue 70 50
145. 175 f. blue 80 60

(b) Size 23 × 27 mm.
146. **32.** 2 d. green 90 40
147. 250 f. pink .. .. 1·00 80
148. 3 d. blue .. .. 1·25 90
149. 5 d. yellow .. .. 1·60 1·10
150. 10 d. brown .. .. 3·25 2·00
151. 20 d. silver .. .. 6·00 4·00
151c. 50 d. red .. .. 18·00 13·00

33. Flags of Competing Countries and Emblem.

1982. Sixth Arab Gulf Football Championship. Multicoloured.
152 25 f. Type **33** 35 15
153 75 f. American bald eagle holding ball over stadium (vert) 80 45
154 125 f. Footballers (vert) .. 1·25 80
155 3 d. As No. 153 .. .. 2·75 2·50

34. Figure breaking Gun. **36.** Arab writing.

35. National Emblems.

1982. Second U.N. Disarmament Conference.
156. **34.** 25 f. multicoloured .. 40 15
157. 75 f. multicoloured .. 90 50
158. 125 f. multicoloured .. 1·50 1·00
159. 150 f. multicoloured .. 2·00 1·50

1982. 11th National Day. Multicoloured.
160 25 f. Type **35** 40 15
161 75 f. Dove and flag (vert) 90 50
162 125 f. As 75 f. .. .. 1·50 1·00
163 150 f. Type **35** .. .. 2·00 1·50

1983. Arab Literacy Day.
164 – 25 f. multicoloured .. 10·00
165 **36** 35 f. brown, violet & blk 40 20
166 – 75 f. yellow, black & pur 12·00
167 **36** 3 d. brown, yellow & blk 2·50 2·25

DESIGN: 25, 75 f. Koran and lamp.

37. W.C.Y. Emblem.

1983. World Communications Year.
168. **37.** 25 f. multicoloured .. 35 10
169. 150 f. multicoloured .. 1·50 1·00
170. 2 d. multicoloured .. 1·75 1·40
171. 3 d. multicoloured .. 2·50 2·25

38. Satellite Orbit within "20".

1984. 20th Anniv. of International Telecommunications Satellite Consortium.
172. **38.** 2 d. bl., pur. & dp bl. 2·25 1·75
173. 2½ d. blue, pur. & grn. 2·75 2·25

39 Shaikh Hamad bin Mohamed al Sharqi and Buthnah Fort, Fujeira.

1984. 13th National Day. Multicoloured.
174 1 d. Type **39** .. .. 1·10 95
175 1 d. Shaikh Rashid bin Ahmed al Moalla and Alfalaj Fort, Umm al Qiwain .. .. .. 1·10 95
176 1 d. Shaikh Humaid bin Rashid al Naimi and Palace, Ajman .. .. 1·10 95
177 1 d. Shaikh Saqr bin Mohamed al Qasimi and harbour, Ras al Khaima 1·10 95
178 1 d. Shaikh Zaid bin Sultan al Nahayyan and refinery, Abu Dhabi .. 1·10 95
179 1 d. Shaikh Sultan bin Mohamed al Qasimi, oil well and mosque, Sharjah .. .. 1·10 95
180 1 d. Shaikh Rashid bin Said and building, Dubai 1·10 95

40. Pictograms of Refuse Collection. **41.** Globe and Knights.

1985. Tidy Week.
181. **40.** 5 d. orange & black .. 5·50 4·25

1985. World Junior Chess Championship, Sharjah.
182. **41.** 2 d. multicoloured .. 2·75 1·75
183. 250 f. multicoloured .. 3·75 2·50

42. Map and Hand holding Flag. **43.** Stylised People and Map.

1985. 14th National Day.
184. **42.** 50 f. multicoloured .. 40 20
185. 3 d. multicoloured .. 2·75 1·50

1985. Population Census.
186. **43.** 50 f. multicoloured .. 40 20
187. 1 d. multicoloured .. 1·50 1·00
188. 3 d. multicoloured .. 1·75 1·25

MINIMUM PRICE

The minimum price quoted is 5p which represents a handling charge rather than a basis for valuing common stamps. For further notes about prices see introductory pages.

44. Profiles looking at Sapling. **45.** Emblem.

1985. International Youth Year. Mult.
189. 50 f. Type **44** 40 20
190. 175 f. Open book, flame and people between hemispheres (horiz.) .. 1·50 1·00
191. 2 d. Youth carrying globe on back .. .. .. 1·75 1·25

1986. Arabic Woman and Family Day.
192. **45.** 1 d. multicoloured .. 85 45
193. 3 d. multicoloured .. 2·25 1·50

46. Globe, Map and Posthorn. **47.** Sakar Falcon.

1986. 1st Anniv. of General Postal Authority. Multicoloured.
194 50 f. Type **46** 40 20
195 1 d. Banner around globe (vert) 85 50
196 2 d. As No. 195 .. .. 1·60 1·40
197 250 f. Type **46** .. .. 1·90 1·75

1986.
198. **47.** 50 f. gold, blue & grn. 35 35
199. 75 f. gold, blue & mve. 60 60
200. 125 f. gold, bl. & grey 90 90

48. Container Ship in Dock. **49.** Dawn, Satellite, Telephone Dial and Dish Aerials.

1986. 10th Anniv. of United Arab Shipping Company. Multicoloured.
201 2 d. Type **48** .. .. 1·75 1·25
202 3 d. Container ship at sea (vert) .. .. .. 2·25 1·50

1986. 10th Anniv. of Emirate Telecommunications Corporation.
203 250 f. Type **49** .. .. 2·00 1·50
204 3 d. As Type **49** but with sun behind emblem .. 2·25 1·75

50. Emblem, Airplane and Camel Rider. **51.** Emblem and Member States' Crests.

1986. 1st Anniv. of Emirates Airlines. Multicoloured.
205. 50 f. Type **50** 50 40
206. 175 f. Airplane, emblem and national colours .. 2·50 2·10

1986. 7th Supreme Council Session of Gulf Co-operation Council, Abu Dhabi.
207. 50 f. Type **51** 40 30
208. 1 d. 75 Emblem beneath tree .. .. .. 1·50 1·50
209. 3 d. As No. 208 .. .. 2·50 2·50

52. Dubai Trade Centre. **53.** Dhow, Oil Rig, Tower Block and Sun's Rays.

1986. 27th Chess Olympiad, Dubai. Mult
210 50 f. Type **52** 60 40
211 2 d. Chess players (miniature from King Alfonso X's "Book of Chess, Dice and Tablings") (horiz) .. 2·50 2·00
212 250 f. Chess players (miniature) (different) (horiz) .. .. .. 3·00 2·50

1986. 15th National Day. Multicoloured.
214 50 f. Type **53** 40 20
215 1 d. Type **53** 85 50
216 175 f. Flag and hands holding Arabic "15" (vert) .. .. .. 1·50 1·25
217 2 d. As No. 216 .. .. 1·90 1·75

54. Emblem.

1986. Arab Police Day.
218. **54.** 50 f. multicoloured .. 60 45
219. 1 d. multicoloured .. 1·25 1·00

55. Emblem on Landscape. **56.** Airplane and Map.

1987. Municipalities and Environment Week.
220. **55.** 50 f. multicoloured .. 40 35
221. 1 d. multicoloured .. 80 75

1987. 1st Anniv. of United Arab Emirates Flight Information Region.
222. **56.** 200 f. multicoloured .. 2·00 1·90
223. 250 f. multicoloured .. 2·25 2·10

57. Flower in Droplet. **58.** University Emblem.

1987. "Save Energy". Multicoloured.
224. 50 f. Type **57** 40 40
225. 2 d. Globe as sun over oil derrick .. .. .. 1·50 1·50

1987. 10th Anniv. of U.A.E. University.
226. **58.** 1 d. multicoloured .. 80 80
227. 3 d. multicoloured .. 2·25 2·25

59. Drilling Platform.

1987. 25th Anniv of first Crude Oil Shipment from Abu Dhabi.
228. **59.** 50 f. multicoloured .. 40 30
229. – 1 d. blue, black and light blue 80 70
230. – 175 f. grey, black and blue .. .. .. 1·40 1·40
231. – 2 d. multicoloured .. 1·90 1·90

DESIGNS—VERT. 1 d. Aerial view of drilling platform. 175 f. Rig workers with drill head. HORIZ. 2 d. Oil tanker at sea.

60. Trees and Dates in Arched Window. **61.** Graph and Woman holding Baby.

1987. Arab Palm Tree and Dates Day. Multicoloured.
232. 50 f. Type **60** 40 40
233. 1 d. Trees and fruit .. 80 80

1987. U.N.I.C.E.F. Child Survival Campaign.
234. **61.** 50 f. multicoloured .. 30 30
235. – 1 d. blue, black and flesh 60 60
236. – 175 f. black, green and deep green .. .. 1·00 1·00
237. – 2 d. multicoloured .. 1·40 1·40

DESIGNS—VERT. 1 d. Vaccinating baby. 175 f. Oral rehydration therapy. HORIZ. 2 d. Mother breastfeeding.

62. Emblem on Man's head and Globe. **63.** Salim bin Ali al-Owais.

1987. International Year of Shelter for the Homeless.
238. **62.** 2 d. multicoloured .. 1·50 1·50
239. 250 f. multicoloured .. 1·75 1·75

1987. Birth Centenary of Salim bin Ali al-Owais (poet).
240. **63.** 1 d. multicoloured .. 75 75
241. 2 d. multicoloured .. 1·50 1·50

64. Airplanes and Terminal Building.

1987. 6th Anniv. of Abu Dhabi International Airport. Multicoloured.
242. 50 f. Type **64** 55 50
243. 50 f. Reception area .. 55 50
244. 100 f. Airplane over air traffic control centre .. 1·10 1·00
245. 100 f. Airplanes at gangways .. .. .. 1·10 1·00

65 Writing in Sand, Oyster and Pearls

1988. National Arts Festival.
246 **65** 50 f. multicoloured .. 30 35
247 250 f. multicoloured .. 1·40 1·40

66 Fisherman on Shore (Layla Mohammed Khalfan)

1988. Children's Paintings. Multicoloured.
248 50 f. Type **66** 30 25
249 1 d. Woman and flowers (Zeinab Nasir Mohammed) (vert) .. 60 60
250 1 d. 75 Flowers with girls' faces (Fatma Ali Abdullah) (vert) .. 1·00 1·00
251 2 d. Teddy bear, cat and girls playing (Saaly Mohammed Jowda) .. 1·40 1·40

67. Masked Youth. **68.** Emblem and Urban and Desert Scenes.

1988. Palestinian "Intifida" Movement.
252 **67** 2 d. multicoloured .. 1·40 1·40
253 250 f. multicoloured .. 1·60 1·60

1988. National Banking Anniversaries. Mult.
254 50 f. Type **68** (20th anniv, National Bank of Abu Dhabi) 30 30
255 50 f. Emblem (25th anniv, National Bank of Dubai Ltd) 30 30

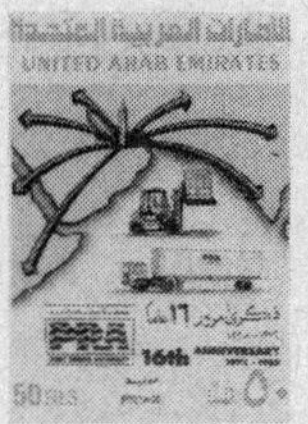

69 Map, Fork-lift Truck and Container Lorry **70** Swimming

1988. 16th Anniv of Port Rashid. Mult.
256 50 f. Type **69** 30 30
257 1 d. Container ship and view of port 60 60
258 175 f. Ro-ro ferry and small boats at anchorages .. .. .. 1·00 1·00
259 2 d. Container ship at dockside .. .. 1·40 1·40

1988. Olympic Games, Seoul. Multicoloured.
260 2 d. Type **70** .. .. 1·25 1·25
261 250 f. Cycling .. .. 1·40 1·40

71 Vase

1988. 1st Anniv of Ras al Khaimah National Museum. Multicoloured.
262 50 f. Type **71** 25 25
263 3 d. Gold ornament (horiz) 1·50 1·50

72 Emblem

1988. 18th Arab Scouts Conference, Abu Dhabi.
264 72 1 d. multicoloured .. 50 50

73 Dahlia

1989. 10th Tree Day. Multicoloured.
265 50 f. Ghaf tree 25 25
266 100 f. Palm tree 50 50
267 250 f. Type 73 .. .. 1·25 1·25

74 Airport

1989. 10th Anniv of Sharjah International Airport.
268 74 50 f. multicoloured .. 40 35
269 100 f. multicoloured .. 85 65

75 Sunderland Flying Boat

76 Newspaper

1989. 80th Anniv of Gulf Postal Services. Multicoloured.
270 50 f. Type 75 .. .. 35 25
271 3 d. "Bombala" (freighter) 1·25 1·25

1989. 20th Anniv of "Al-Ittihad" (newspaper). Multicoloured.
272 50 f. Type 76 .. .. 20 20
273 1 d. Newspaper offices .. 40 40

77 Emblem and Map

1989. 5th Anniv of Gulf Investment Corporation.
274 77 50 f. multicoloured .. 20 20
275 2 d. multicoloured .. 80 80

78 Offering Loaf to Child

1989. International Volunteer Day. U.A.E. Red Crescent Society. Multicoloured.
276 2 d. Type 78 .. .. 40 40
277 250 f. Crippled child in open hands (vert) .. 1·00 1·00

79 Bank Emblem and Buildings

80 Compass and Dhow

1989. 20th Anniv of Dubai Commercial Bank. Multicoloured.
278 50 f. Type 79 .. .. 20 20
279 1 d. Bank building .. 40 40

1989. Bin Majid (navigator) Commemoration. Multicoloured.
280 1 d. Type 80 .. .. 35 35
281 3 d. Dhow (vert) .. .. 1·40 1·40

81 Festival Sites

82 Saker Falcon

1990. 3rd Al Ain Festival
282 81 50 f. multicoloured .. 20 20
283 1 d. multicoloured .. 40 40

1990. Multicoloured, background colour given. (a) Size 17 × 22 mm.
284 82 5 f. blue 10 10
285 20 f. mauve 10 10
286 25 f. pink 10 10
287 50 f. brown 15 15
288 100 f. bistre 30 30
289 150 f. green 50 50
290 175 f. green 55 55

(b) Size 21 × 26 mm.
291 82 2 d. lilac 65 65
292 250 f. blue 80 80
293 3 d. pink 95 95
294 5 d. orange .. .. 1·60 1·60
295 10 d. yellow .. .. 3·25 3·25
296 20 d. green .. .. 6·25 6·25
297 50 d. green .. .. 16·00 16·00

83 Children and Leaves

84 Leaning Tower of Pisa, Flag and U.A.E. Mascot

1990. Children's Culture Festival.
301 83 50 f. multicoloured .. 15 15
302 250 f. multicoloured .. 80 80

1990. World Cup Football Championship, Italy. Multicoloured.
303 50 f. Type 84 .. .. 15 15
304 1 d. Desert, flag and mascot (vert) 30 30
305 2 d. Mascot on ball (vert) 60 60
306 250 f. Flags around mascot 80 80

85 Projects and Buildings

1990. 25th Anniv of Dubai Chamber of Commerce and Industry. Multicoloured.
308 85 50 f. multicoloured .. 25 25
309 1 d. multicoloured .. 45 45

86 Weeping Eyes and Child on Globe

87 "Catharanthus roseus"

1990. Child Survival Programme. Mult.
310 175 f. Type 86 .. .. 55 55
311 2 d. Emaciated child and newspapers 65 65

1990. Flowers. Multicoloured.
312 50 f. "Centavrea pseudo sinaica" 15 15
313 50 f. "Calotropis procera" 15 15
314 50 f. "Argyrolobeum roseum" 15 15
315 50 f. "Lamranthus roseus" 15 15
316 50 f. "Hibiscus rosa sinensis" 15 15
317 50 f. "Nerium oleander" .. 15 15
318 50 f. Type 87 .. .. 15 15
319 50 f. "Bougainvillaea glabra" 15 15

88 O.P.E.C. Emblem and Flame

89 Industrial Pollution and Dead Fish

1990. 30th Anniv of Organization of Petroleum Exporting Countries. Mult.
321 50 f. Emblem, flames, hands and oil rigs .. 20 15
322 1 d. Type 88 .. .. 30 30
323 175 f. Emblem and droplet 55 55

1990. "Our Planet Our Health". Mult.
324 50 f. Type 89 .. .. 15 15
325 3 d. Industrial and vehicle pollution covering globe 95 95

90 Grand Mosque, Abu Dhabi

91 U.A.E. Crest and Graph

1990. Mosques. Multicoloured.
326 1 d. Type 90 .. .. 30 30
327 2 d. Al-Jumeirah Mosque, Dubai (vert) 65 65

1990. 10th Anniv of Central Bank. Mult.
328 50 f. Type 91 .. .. 15 15
329 175 f. Banknotes and building (horiz) .. 55 55

92 Tree

93 Globes and Buildings

1990. International Conference on High Salinity Tolerant Plants, Al-Ain. Mult.
330 50 f. Type 92 .. .. 15 15
331 250 f. Trees along shoreline 80 80

1991. Abu Dhabi International Fair.
332 93 50 f. multicoloured .. 20 20
333 2 d. multicoloured .. 70 70

94 Emblem

1991. World Telecommunications Day. "Telecommunications and Safety of Human Life".
334 94 2 d. multicoloured .. 70 70
335 3 d. multicoloured .. 1·10 1·10

95 Shaikh Saqr Mosque, Ras al Khaimah

1991. Mosques. Multicoloured.
336 1 d. Type 95 .. .. 35 35
337 2 d. King Faisal Mosque, Sharjah 70 70
See also Nos. 371/2 and 411/12.

96 "Native Games" (Robba Mohamed Sofian)

1991. Children's Paintings. Multicoloured.
338 50 f. Type 96 .. .. 20 20
339 1 d. "National Day" (Yasmin Mohamed al-Rahim) 35 35
340 175 f. "Blind Man's Buff" (Amal Ibrahim Mohamed) 65 65
341 250 f. "Native Dance" (Amina Ali Hassan) .. 90 90

97 Yellow-marked Butterfly Fish

1991. Fishes. Multicoloured.
342 50 f. Type 97 .. .. 20 20
343 50 f. Red snapper .. 20 20
344 50 f. Golden trevally .. 20 20
345 50 f. Two-banded porgy .. 20 20
346 1 d. Black bream .. 35 35
347 1 d. Three-banded grunt .. 35 35
348 1 d. Greasy grouper .. 35 35
349 1 d. Rabbit fish 35 35

98 Shaikh Rashid and Airport

99 Fire Fighting

1991. 1st Death Anniv of Shaikh Rashid bin Said al-Maktoum (ruler of Dubai). Mult.
351 50 f. Type 98 .. .. 30 20
352 1 d. Shaikh Rashid and modern and old buildings (horiz) .. 35 35
353 175 f. Shaikh Rashid and seafront hotels .. 65 65
354 2 d. Jebel Ali container port, Shaikh Rashid and dish aerial (horiz) .. 70 70

1991. Civil Defence Day.
355 99 50 f. multicoloured .. 20 20
356 1 d. multicoloured .. 35 35

100 Airplane over Dubai Airport

101 Flags and Emblem

1991. International Aerospace Exhibition, Dubai. Multicoloured.
357 175 f. Type **100** 75 75
358 2 d. View of under-side of airplane over Dubai airport 85 85

1991. 10th Anniv of Gulf Co-operation Council.
359 **101** 50 f. multicoloured .. 20 20
360 3 d. multicoloured .. 1·10 1·10

102 Shaikh Zaid bin Sultan al Nahayyan of Abu Dhabi (President of U.A.E.)

1991. 20th National Day. Multicoloured.
361 75 f. Type **102** 25 25
362 75 f. Shaikh Humaid bin Rashid al Naimi of Ajman and fort (to right of stamp) with cannon 25 25
363 75 f. Shaikh Maktoum bin Rashid al-Maktoum of Dubai and fort (to left of stamp) with cannon .. 25 25
364 75 f. Shaikh Hamad bin Mohamed al Sharqi of Fujeira and fort on hillock 25 25
365 75 f. Shaikh Saqr bin Mohamed al-Qasimi of Ras al Khaima and fort (tower and tree in foreground) 25 25
366 75 f. Shaikh Sultan bin Mohamed al Qasimi of Sharjah and fort (to left of stamp with Arabs in doorway) 25 25
367 75 f. Shaikh Rashid bin Ahmed al Moalla of Umm al Qiwain and fort (to right of stamp with trees growing over walls) 25 25

103 Derrick

104 Fort Jahili, Al Ain

1992. 20th Anniv of Abu Dhabi National Oil Company.
369 **103** 175 f. multicoloured .. 65 65
370 250 f. multicoloured .. 90 90

1992. Mosques. As T **95**. Multicoloured.
371 50 f. Shaikh Rashid bin Humaid al Naimi Mosque, Ajman .. 20 20
372 1 d. Shaikh Ahmed bin Rashid al Moalla Mosque, Umm al Qiwain 35 35

1992. "Expo '92" World's Fair, Seville.
373 **104** 2 d. multicoloured .. 70 70
374 250 f. multicoloured .. 90 90

105 Emblem and Family

1992. Deaf Child Week. Multicoloured.
375 1 d. Type **105** 35 35
376 3 d. Hearing aid in ear .. 1·10 1·10

106 Aerial View of Port

1992. 20th Anniv of Zayed Sea Port, Abu Dhabi. Multicoloured.
377 50 f. Type **106** 20 20
378 1 d. Cranes on dockside .. 35 35
379 175 f. Loading container ship 65 65
380 2 d. Map showing routes from port 70 70

107 Yachting

108 Football Match (Najla Saif Mohamed Harib)

1992. Olympic Games, Barcelona. Mult.
381 50 f. Type **107** 20 20
382 1 d. Running 35 35
383 175 f. Swimming 65 65
384 250 f. Cycling 90 90

1992. Children's Paintings. Multicoloured.
386 50 f. Type **108** 20 20
387 1 d. Children in park (Anoud Adnan Ali Mohamed) 35 35
388 2 d. Family at playground (Ahlam Ibrahim Ahmed) 70 70
389 250 f. Children playing amongst trees (Dallal Ali Salih) 90 90

109 Bank Building

110 Tambourah

1992. 15th Anniv of Emirates Bank Int.
390 **109** 50 f. multicoloured .. 20 20
391 – 175 f. gold, brn & red 65 65
DESIGN—(33 × 40 mm) 175 f. Bank emblem.

1992. Musical Instruments. Multicoloured.
392 50 f. Type **110** 20 20
393 50 f. Oud (stringed instrument) 20 20
394 50 f. Rababah (stinged instrument with bow) .. 20 20
395 1 d. Mizmar (wind instrument) and shindo (drum) (horiz) 35 35
396 1 d. Marwas and duff (hand-held drums) (horiz) 35 35
397 1 d. Tabel (drum) and hibban (bagpipe) (horiz) 35 35

111 Emblem

1992. 13th Supreme Council Session of Gulf Co-operation Council, Abu Dhabi.
399 **111** 50 f. multicoloured .. 20 20
400 2 d. multicoloured .. 70 70

112 Camel Race

1992. The Dromedary. Multicoloured.
401 50 f. Type **112** 20 20
402 1 d. Camel riders and mother with young (vert) 35 35
403 175 f. Camels at well and mother with young .. 65 65
404 2 d. Camels (vert) .. 70 70

113 Golf

114 Club Building

1993. Tourism. Multicoloured.
405 50 f. Type **113** 20 20
406 1 d. Fishing (vert) .. 35 35
407 2 d. Sailing 70 70
408 250 f. Sight-seeing by car 90 90

1993. Dubai Creek Golf and Yacht Club. Mult.
409 2 d. Type **114** 70 70
410 250 f. Club building and sea shore 90 90

1993. Mosques. As T **95**. Multicoloured.
411 50 f. Thabit bin Khalid Mosque, Fujeira .. 20 20
412 1 d. Sharq al Morabbah Mosque, Al Ain .. 35 35

115 National Crest and Sports

1993. National Youth Festival. Mult.
413 50 f. Type **115** 20 20
414 3 d. National crest and sciences .. .. 1·10 1·10

116 "Conus textile"

1993. Sea Shells. Multicoloured.
415 25 f. Type **116** 10 10
416 50 f. "Pinctada radiata" .. 20 20
417 100 f. "Murex scolopax" .. 35 35
418 150 f. "Natica pulicaris" .. 55 55
419 175 f. "Lambis truncata sebae" 65 65
420 200 f. "Cardita bicolor" .. 75 75
421 250 f. "Cypraea grayana" 90 90
422 300 f. "Cymatium trilineatum" .. .. 1·10 1·10

117 Addict within Capsule

1993. Anti-drugs Campaign. Multicoloured.
423 50 f. Type **117** 20 20
424 1 d. Family on skull, globe and drugs (vert) .. 35 35

118 Commercial Buildings

119 Aerial View of Port

1993. 25th Anniv of Abu Dhabi National Bank. Multicoloured.
425 50 f. Type **118** 20 20
426 1 d. Bank emblem .. 35 35
427 175 f. Bank building and emblem 65 65
428 2 d. Commercial buildings within shield 75 75

1993. Dubai Ports Authority. Multicoloured.
429 50 f. Type **119** 20 20
430 1 d. Cranes loading containers 35 35
431 2 d. Aerial view of port (different) 75 75
432 250 f. Arrowed routes on globe 90 90

120 Soldiers on Parade (Mouza Musabah al-Mazroui)

1993. National Day. Children's Paintings. Multicoloured.
433 50 f. Type **120** 20 20
434 1 d. Woman and children (Shreen Naeem Hassan Radwan) (vert) .. 35 35
435 175 f. Flag and dhow (Samiha Mohamad Sultan) 65 65
436 2 d. Decorations and fireworks (Omer Abdulla Rabia Thani) 75 75

121 Hili Tomb

1993. Archaeological Finds from Al-Ain. Multicoloured.
437 50 f. Type **121** 20 20
438 1 d. Hili decorative tile .. 35 35
439 175 f. Qattarah figure .. 65 65
440 250 f. Hili bow 90 90

UNITED NATIONS Pt. 22; Pt. 8; Pt. 2

A. NEW YORK HEADQUARTERS

For use on mail posted at the Post Office at U.N. Headquarters, New York.

NOTE: Similar designs, but in different colours and with values in Swiss francs (F.S.) are issues of the Geneva Office. Those with face values in Austrian schilling are issues of the Vienna Office. These are listed after the New York issues.

100 cents = 1 dollar.

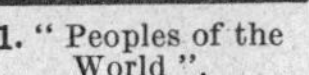

1. " Peoples of the World ". 3. U.N. Emblem.

1951.

1	1	1 c. mauve	10	10
2	–	1½ c. green	10	10
3	3	2 c. violet	10	10
4	–	3 c. blue and purple	10	10
5	–	5 c. blue	15	10
6	1	10 c. brown	15	10
7	–	15 c. blue and violet	20	15
8	–	20 c. brown	50	30
9	–	25 c. blue and black	45	30
10	–	50 c. blue	5·00	1·75
11	3	$1 red	2·00	85

DESIGNS—VERT. 1½, 50 c. U.N. Headquarters, New York. 5 c. Clasped hands. HORIZ. 3, 15, 25 c. U.N. flag. 20 c. Hemispheres amd U.N. emblem.

A 7. Sea-gull and Aeroplane.

1951. Air.

A12	A 3	6 c. red	15	15
A13		10 c. green	15	15
A14	–	15 c. blue	25	15
A15	–	25 c. black	90	40

DESIGN: 15, 25 c. Swallows and U.N. emblem.

7. Veteran's War Memorial Building, San Francisco.

1952. 7th Anniv of Signing of U.N. Charter.

12	7	5 c. blue	25	15

8. "Flame of Freedom". 9. Homeless Family.

1952. Human Rights Day.

13.	8.	3 c. green	15	15
14.		5 c. blue	40	15

1953. Protection for Refugees.

15.	9.	3 c. brown	15	15
16.		5 c. blue	70	30

10. " Universal Postal Union ".

1953. Universal Postal Union.

17.	10.	3 c. sepia	20	15
18.		5 c. blue	90	25

11. Gearwheels and U.N. Emblem. 12. " Flame of Freedom ".

1953. Technical Assistance for Under-developed Areas.

19.	11.	3 c. grey	15	15
20.		5 c. green	75	30

1953 Human Rights Day

21.	12.	3 c. blue	20	15
22.		5 c. red	1·40	25

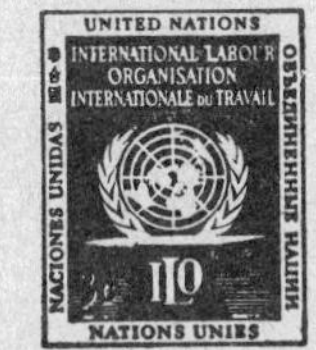

13. F.A.O. Symbol. 14. U.N. Emblem and Anvil.

1954. Food and Agriculture Organization.

23.	13.	3 c. yellow and green	40	15
24.		8 c. yellow and blue	85	40

NOTE. In the following issues the majority of the values unillustrated have the commemorative inscription or initials in another language.

1954. International Labour Organization.

25.	14.	3 c. brown	20	15
26.		8 c. mauve	1·50	40

15. U.N. European Office, Geneva. 16. Mother and Child.

1954. United Nations Day.

27.	15.	3 c. violet	2·75	60
28.		8 c. red	25	15

1954. Human Rights Day.

29.	16.	3 c. orange	6·50	1·25
30		8 c. green	25	15

17. " Flight ".

1955. Int. Civil Aviation Organization.

31.	17.	3 c. blue	2·50	40
32.		8 c. red	80	60

18. U.N.E.S.C.O. Symbol.

1955. U.N. Educational, Scientific and Cultural Organization.

33.	18.	3 c. mauve	40	15
34.		8 c. blue	15	15

19. U.N. Charter. 20. " Flame of Freedom ".

1955. 10th Anniv. of U.N.

35.	19.	3 c. red	2·50	35
36.		4 c. green	20	10
37.		8 c. black	20	15

1955. Human Rights Day.

39.	20.	3 c. blue	15	15
40.		8 c. green	50	20

21. "Telecommunication". 22. Staff of Aesculapius.

1956. Int. Telecommunication Union.

41.	21.	3 c. blue	40	15
42.		8 c. red	1·10	40

1956. World Health Organization.

43.	22.	3 c. blue	15	15
44.		8 c. brown	85	45

23. General Assembly.

1956. United Nations Day.

45.	23.	3 c. slate	10	10
46.		8 c. olive	15	15

24. "Flame of Freedom". 25. Weather Balloon.

1956. Human Rights Day.

47.	24.	3 c. purple	10	10
48.		8 c. blue	15	10

1957. World Meteorological Organization.

49.	25.	3 c. blue	10	10
50.		8 c. red	20	10

26. U.N.E.F. Badge. A 26. "Flight".

1957. United Nations Emergency Force.

51.	26.	3 c. blue	10	10
52.		8 c. red	15	10

1957. Air.

A51	A 26	4 c. brown	10	10
A52		5 c. red	10	10
A53	–	7 c. blue	20	15

DESIGN—HORIZ. 7 c U.N. flag and Douglas DC-8-60 Super Sixty airplane.

On the 5 c. value inscriptions are redrawn larger than those on Type A 26.

27. U.N. Emblem over Globe. 28. " Flames of Freedom ".

1957. U.N. Security Council.

55.	27.	3 c. brown	10	10
56.		8 c. green	15	10

1957. Human Rights Day.

57.	28.	3 c. brown	10	10
58.		8 c. black	10	10

29. Atomic Symbol. 30. Central Hall, Westminster (site of first General Assembly).

1958. Int. Atomic Energy Agency.

59.	29.	3 c. olive	10	10
60.		8 c. blue	15	10

1958. U.N. General Assembly Buildings.

61.	30.	3 c. blue	10	10
62.		8 c. purple	10	10

See also Nos. 69/70, 77/8 and 123/4.

31. U.N. Seal. 32. Cogwheels.

1958.

63	31	4 c. orange	10	10
64		8 c. blue	15	10

1958. Economic and Social Council.

65.	32.	4 c. turquoise	10	10
66		8 c. red	15	10

33. Hands holding Globe.

1958. Human Rights Day.

67.	33.	4 c. green	10	10
68.		8 c. brown	15	10

34. New York City Building, Flushing Meadows (1946–50). 35. Emblems of U.N., Industry and Agriculture.

1959. U.N. General Assembly Buildings.

69.	34.	4 c. mauve	10	10
70.		8 c. turquoise	15	10

1959. U.N. Economic Commission for Europe.

71.	35.	4 c. blue	10	10
72.		8 c. red	20	15

36. " The Age of Bronze " (Rodin). 37. " Protection for Refugees ".

1959. U.N. Trusteeship Council.

73.	36.	4 c. red	10	10
74.		8 c. green	15	10

1959. World Refugee Year.

75.	37.	4 c. red and bistre	10	10
76.		8 c. blue and bistre	10	10

38. Palais de Chaillot, Paris (1948, 1951). 39. Steel Girder and Map.

1960. U.N. General Assembly Buildings.

77.	38.	4 c. blue and purple	10	10
78.		8 c. brown and green	10	10

1960. U.N. Economic Commission for Asia and the Far East (" ECAFE ").

79.	39.	4 c. purple, buff and turq.	10	10
80		8 c green, pink and blue	15	15

40. Tree and Emblems. **41.** U.N. Headquarters and Emblem.

1960. 5th World Forestry Congress, Seattle.
81. **40.** 4 c. multicoloured .. 10 10
82. 8 c. multicoloured .. 20 15

1960. 15th Anniv. of U.N.
83. **41.** 4 c. blue 10 10
84. 8 c. black 20 10

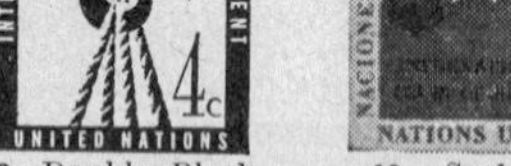

42. Double Block and Hook. **43.** Scales of Justice.

1960. Int. Bank for Reconstruction and Development ("World Bank").
86. **42.** 4 c. multicoloured .. 10 10
87. 8 c. multicoloured .. 20 10

1961. International Court of Justice.
88. **43.** 4 c. black, brown & yell. 10 10
89. 8 c. black, green & yell. 20 15

44. I.M.F. Emblem.

1961. Int. Monetary Fund.
90. **44.** 4 c. blue 10 10
91. 7 c. brown and yellow .. 20 15

45. "Peace". **53.** Globe and Weather Vane.

52. Flags.

1961.
92. **45.** 1 c. multicoloured .. 10 10
93. – 2 c. multicolured .. 10 10
94. – 3 c. multicoloured .. 10 10
95. – 5 c. red 15 10
96. – 7 c. brown, blk. & bl. 15 10
97. – 10 c. black, grn. & bl. 15 10
98. – 11 c. gold, light blue and blue 15 10
99. **52.** 30 c. multicoloured .. 35 15
100. **53.** 50 c. multicoloured .. 75 25

DESIGNS—HORIZ. (32×23 mm.) 2 c. Map of the World. 10 c. Three figures on globe ("Races United") ($30\frac{1}{2}\times23\frac{1}{2}$ mm.) 3 c. U.N. Flag. ($36\frac{1}{2}\times23\frac{1}{2}$ mm.) 5 c. Hands supporting "UN" and globe. ($37\frac{1}{2}\times22\frac{1}{2}$ mm.) 11 c. U.N. emblem across globe. VERT. (21×26 mm.) 7 c. U.N. emblem, as flowering plant.

For 1 c. in same design, but smaller, see No. 146, and for 5 c. multicoloured see No. 165.

54. Cogwheel and Map of S. America. **55.** Africa Hall, Addis Ababa.

1961. Economic Commission for Latin America.
101. **54.** 4 c. red, olive and blue 15 10
102. 11 c. purple, red & green 25 15

1961. Economic Commission for Africa.
103. **55.** 4 c. multicoloured .. 10 10
104. 11 c. multicoloured .. 20 15

56. Bird feeding Young. **57.** "Housing and Community Facilities".

1961. 15th Anniv. of U.N.I.C.E.F.
105. **56.** 3 c. multicoloured .. 10 10
106. 4 c. multicoloured .. 10 10
107. 13 c. multicoloured .. 20 15

1962. U.N. Housing and Related Community Facilities Programme.
108 **57** 4 c. multicoloured .. 10 10
109 7 c. multicoloured .. 15 10

58. Mosquito and W.H.O. Emblem. **59.** U.N. Flag at Half-Mast.

1962. Malaria Eradication.
110. **58.** 4 c. multicoloured .. 10 10
111. 11 c. multicoloured .. 15 10

1962. Dag Hammarskjold (U.N. Secretary-General, 1953–61) Memorial Issue.
112. **59.** 5 c. indigo, blue & black 10 10
113. 15 c. blue, grey & black 40 15

60. Congo on World Map. **61.** "Peace in Space".

1962. U.N. Congo Operation.
114. **60.** 4 c. multicoloured .. 15 10
115. 11 c. multicoloured .. 30 15

1962. U.N. Committee on Peaceful Uses of Outer Space.
116. **61.** 4 c. blue 10 10
117. 11 c. mauve 15 10

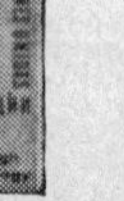

62. Conference Emblem. **63.** Wheat.

1963. Science and Technology Conf., Geneva.
118. **62.** 5 c multicoloured .. 10 10
119. 11 c multicoloured .. 20 15

1983. Freedom from Hunger.
120. **63.** 5 c. yell., grn. & orge. 15 10
121. 11 c. yell., red & orge. 20 15

A65. "Flight". **64.** "Bridge" over Map of West New Guinea.

1963. Air. Multicoloured.
A 122. 6 c. "Space" 10 10
A 123. 8 c. Type A65 .. .. 15 10
A 124. 13 c. "Bird" 20 15
A 125. 15 c. "Birds" in flight .. 25 15
A 126. 25 c. Aircraft and airmail envelope 50 20

SIZES—HORIZ. 6 c. As Type A **65**. 13 c., 25 c. $30\frac{1}{2}\times23$ mm. VERT. 15 c. $23\times30\frac{1}{2}$ mm.

1963. United Nations Temporary Executive Authority (UNTEA) in West New Guinea.
122. **64.** 25 c. green, blue & drab 40 15

65. General Assembly Building and Flags. **66.** "Flame of Freedom".

1963. U.N. General Assembly Buildings.
123. **65.** 5 c. multicoloured .. 10 10
124. 11 c. multicoloured .. 20 15

1963. 15th Anniv. of Declaration of Human Rights.
125. **66.** 5 c. multicoloured .. 10 10
126. 11 c. multicoloured .. 20 15

67. Ships at Sea.

1964. Inter-Governmental Maritime Consultative Organization (I.M.C.O.).
127. **67.** 5 c. multicoloured .. 15 10
128. 11 c. multicoloured .. 35 30

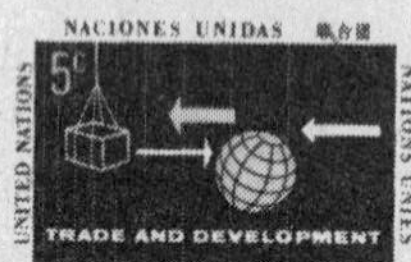

68. "Trade and Development".

1964. U.N. Trade and Development Conf., Geneva.
129. **68.** 5 c. yellow, black & red 10 10
130. 11 c. yellow, black & bis. 20 15

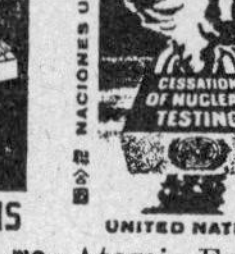

69. Opium Poppy and Reaching Hands. **70.** Atomic Explosion and Padlock.

1964. Narcotics Control.
131. **69.** 5 c. red and black .. 15 10
132. 11 c. green and black .. 40 20

1964. Cessation of Nuclear Testing.
133. **70.** 5 c. sepia and brown .. 10 10

71. "Teaching". **72.** Key, Globe and "Graph".

1964. "Education for Progress".
134. **71.** 4 c. multicoloured .. 10 10
135. 5 c. multicoloured .. 10 10
136. 11 c. multicoloured .. 15 15

1965. U.N. Special Fund.
137. **72.** 5 c. multicoloured .. 10 10
138. 11 c. multicoloured .. 20 15

INDEX

Countries can be quickly located by referring to the index at the end of this volume.

73. Cyprus "Leaves" and U.N. Emblem. **74.** "From Semaphore to Satellite".

1965. Peace-keeping Force in Cyprus.
139. **73.** 5 c. olive, blk. & orge. 10 10
140. 11 c. grn., blk. & lt. grn 20 15

1965. I.T.U. Cent.
141. **74.** 5 c. multicoloured .. 10 10
142. 11 c. multicoloured .. 25 20

75. I.C.Y. Emblem. **76.** "Peace".

1965. 20th Anniv of United Nations and International Co-operation Year.
143 **75** 5 c. blue 15 10
144 15 c. mauve 30 20

1965.
146 **76** 1 c. multicoloured .. 10 10
147 – 15 c. multicoloured .. 20 10
148 – 20 c. multicoloured .. 25 15
149 – 25 c. ultramarine & blue 40 15
150 – $1 blue and turquoise .. 1·25 60

DESIGNS—$24\frac{1}{2}\times30$ mm: 15 c. Opening words, U.N. Charter. 22×32 mm: 20 c. U.N. emblem and Headquarters. 24×24 mm: 25 c. U.N. emblem. 33×23 mm: $1 U.N. emblem encircled.

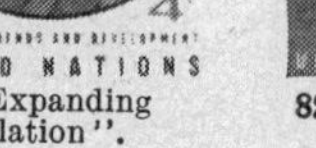

81. "Expanding Population". **82.** Globe and Flags.

1965. Population Trends and Development.
151. **81.** 4 c. multicoloured .. 10 10
152. 5 c. multicoloured .. 10 10
153. 11 c. multicoloured .. 20 15

1966. World Federation of United Nations Assns. (W.F.U.N.A.)
154. **82.** 5 c. multicoloured .. 10 10
155. 15 c. multicoloured .. 20 20

83. W.H.O. Building. **84.** Coffee.

1966. Inaug. of W.H.O. Headquarters, Geneva.
156. **83.** 5 c. multicoloured .. 10 10
157. 11 c. multicoloured .. 20 20

1966. Int. Coffee Agreement of 1962.
158. **84.** 5 c. multicoloured .. 10 10
159. 11 c. multicoloured .. 20 15

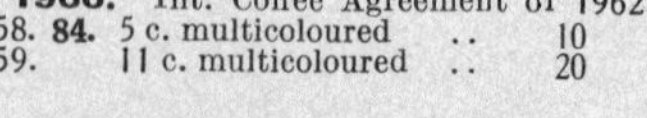

85. Military Observer. **86.** Children in Closed Rail Wagon.

1966. U.N. Military Observers.
160. **85.** 15 c. multicoloured .. 25 20

1966. 20th Anniv. of U.N.I.C.E.F. Mult.
161. 4 c. Type **86** 10 10
162. 5 c. Children in Locomotive and Tender .. 15 10
163. 11 c. Children in Open Rail Wagon 30 20

89. U.N. Headquarters and World Map.

91. "UN" and Emblem.

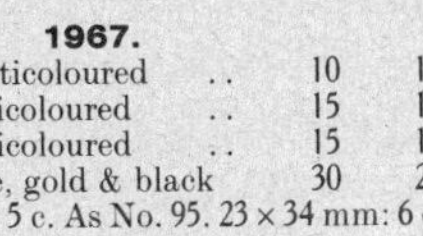

1967.

164 89 1½ c. multicoloured .. 10 10
165 – 5 c. multicoloured .. 15 10
166 – 6 c. multicoloured .. 15 10
167 91 13 c. blue, gold & black 30 20

DESIGNS—HORIZ: 5 c. As No. 95. 23 × 34 mm: 6 c. Aerial view of U.N. Headquarters.

92. "Progress through Development".

93. U.N. Emblem and Fireworks.

1967. U.N. Development Programme.

168. 92. 5 c. multicoloured .. 10 10
169. 11 c. multicoloured .. 20 15

1967. New Independent Nations Commem.

170. 93. 5 c. multicoloured .. 10 10
171. 11 c. multicoloured .. 20 15

94. "Peace".

99. Baggage Labels.

1967. "EXPO 67", World Fair Montreal.

172. 94. 4 c. brown and red .. 10 10
173. – 5 c. brown and blue .. 10 10
174. – 8 c. multicoloured .. 15 10
175. – 10 c. brown and green .. 20 15
176. – 15 c. chestnut & brown 30 30

DESIGNS—VERT. 5 c. "Justice". 10 c. "Fraternity". 15 c. "Truth." HORIZ. (32 × 23½ mm.). 8 c. Facade of U.N. Pavilion.

The above stamps are expressed in Canadian currency and were valid for postage only from the U.N. Pavilion at the World Fair.

1967. Int. Tourist Year.

177. 99. 5 c. multicoloured .. 15 10
178. 15 c. multicoloured .. 35 20

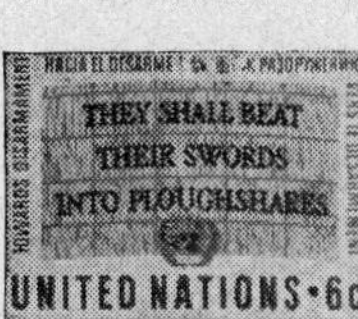

100. "Towards Disarmament".

101. "The Kiss of Peace" (part of Chagall's stained glass window).

1967. Disarmament Campaign.

179. 100. 6 c. multicoloured .. 10 10
180. 13 c. multicoloured .. 25 15

1967. United Nations Art (1st issue). Chagall's Memorial Window in U.N. Secretariat Building.

181. 101. 6 c. multicoloured .. 10 10

See also Nos. 185/6, 201/2, 203/4, 236/7 and 251/2.

MORE DETAILED LISTS
are given in the Stanley Gibbons Catalogues referred to in the country headings.
For lists of current volumes see Introduction.

103. Globe and Diagram of U.N. Organs.

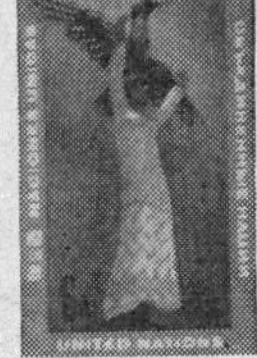

104. Starcke's Statue.

1968. U.N. Secretariat.

183. 103. 6 c. multicoloured .. 10 10
184. 13 c. multicoloured .. 20 15

1968. United Nations Art (2nd issue). Henrik Starcke's Statue in U.N. Trusteeship Council Chamber.

185. 104. 6 c. multicoloured .. 15 10
186. 75 c. multicoloured .. 1·00 70

105. Industrial Skyline.

1968. U.N. Industrial Development Organization (U.N.I.D.O.).

187. 105. 6 c. multicoloured .. 10 10
188. 13 c. multicoloured .. 20 15

A 106. "Winged Envelopes".

A 107. Aircraft and U.N. Emblem.

1968. Air.

A 189. A 106. 10 c. multicoloured 25 15
A 190. A 107. 20 c. multicoloured 30 25

106. Radar Scanner and Globes.

107. Human Rights Emblem.

1968. World Weather Watch.

189. 106. 6 c. multicoloured .. 15 10
190. 20 c. multicoloured .. 40 30

1968. Human Rights Year.

191. 107. 6 c. gold, ultram. & bl. 15 10
192. 13 c. gold, red & pink .. 20 15

108. Textbooks.

109. U.N. Building Santiago.

1969. United Nations Institute for Training and Research (U.N.I.T.A.R.).

193. 108. 6 c. multicoloured .. 10 10
194. 13 c. multicoloured .. 20 15

In the 13 c. the name and value panel is at foot of stamp.

1969. U.N. Building, Santiago, Chile.

195 109 6 c. blue, lt blue & grn 10 10
196 15 c. purple, red & buff 25 20

110. "Peace Through International Law".

111. "Labour and Development".

1969. 20th Anniv. of Session of U.N. Int. Law Commission.

197. 110. 6 c. multicoloured .. 10 10
198. 13 c. multicoloured .. 20 15

1969. 50th Anniv. of I.L.O.

199 111 6 c. multicoloured .. 10 10
200 – 20 c. multicoloured .. 30 20

112. "Ostrich".

114. Peace Bell.

1969. United Nations Art (3rd issue). 3rd-century A.D. Tunisian Mosaic, Delegates' North Lounge. Multicoloured.

201. 6 c. Type 112 .. .. 10 10
202. 13 c. "Ring-necked Pheasant" 20 15

1970. United Nations Art (4th issue). Japanese Peace Bell.

203. 114. 6 c. multicoloured .. 10 10
204. 25 c. multicoloured .. 35 30

115. River, Power Lines and Map.

116. "Fight Cancer".

1970. Lower Mekong Basin Development Project.

205. 115. 6 c. multicoloured .. 10 10
206. 13 c. multicoloured .. 20 15

1970. 10th Int. Cancer Congress, Houston, Texas.

207. 116. 6 c. black and blue .. 10 10
208. 13 c. black and olive .. 35 15

117. Laurel Branch.

120. Scales and Olive-branch.

1970. 25th Anniv of United Nations.

209 117 6 c. multicoloured .. 15 15
210 13 c. multicoloured .. 20 20
211 – 25 c. gold, lt blue & bl 40 40

DESIGN—VERT. 25 c. U.N. emblem.

On No. 210 the inscription is in French.

1970. "Peace, Justice and Progress" (Aims of the United Nations).

213. 120. 6 c. multicoloured .. 10 10
214. 13 c. multicoloured .. 20 15

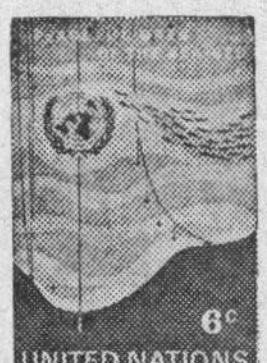

121. U.N. Emblem on Sea-bed.

122 "Refugees" (sculpture, Kaare Nygaard).

1971. Peaceful Uses of the Sea-bed.

215 121. 6 c. multicoloured .. 15 10

1971. U.N. Work with Refugees.

216. 122. 6 c. black, yellow & brn. 10 10
217. 13 c. black, turq. & blue 20 15

123. Wheatsheaf on Globe.

124. New U.P.U. H.Q. Building.

1971. World Food Programme.

218. 123. 13 c. multicoloured .. 30 20

1971. Opening of New U.P.U. Headquarters Building, Berne.

219. 124. 20 c. multicoloured .. 30 25

125. Four-leafed Clover.

127. U.N. H.Q., New York.

1971. Racial Equality Year. Multicoloured.

220. 8 c. Type 125 .. .. 15 10
221. 13 c. Linked globes (horiz.) 15 15

1971. Multicoloured.

222. 8 c. Type 127 .. .. 15 10
223. 60 c. U.N. emblem and flags 60 45
224. 95 c. "Letter Changing Hands" .. .. .. 1·00 45

130. "Maia" (Picasso).

131. "X" over Atomic Explosion.

1971. U.N. Int. Schools.

225. 130. 8 c. multicoloured .. 15 10
226. 21 c. multicoloured .. 35 30

1972. Non-proliferation of Nuclear Weapons.

227. 131. 8 c. blue, black & pink 30 15

132. "Proportions of Man" (Leonardo Da Vinci).

A 134. Birds in Flight.

1972. World Health Day.

228. 132. 15 c. multicoloured .. 30 15

1972. Air.

A229 – 9 c. multicoloured 15 10
A230 A 134 11 c. multicoloured 15 10
A231 – 17 c. orange, yellow and red .. 25 15
A232 – 21 c. multicoloured 30 20

DESIGNS—23 × 31 mm: 9 c. "Contemporary Flight". 38 × 23 mm: 17 c. Clouds. 33 × 23 mm: 21 c. "U.N." jetstream.

137. Environmental Emblem.

138. Europe "Flower".

1972. U.N. Environmental Conservation Conf., Stockholm.

233. 137. 8 c. multicoloured .. 15 10
234. 15 c. multicoloured .. 25 20

1972. Economic Commission for Europe (E.C.E.).
235. **138.** 21 c. multicoloured .. 35 30

139. " World United " (detail, Sert mural, Geneva).
140. Laurel and Broken Sword.

1972. United Nations Art (5th issue).
236 **139** 8 c. brn, gold & lt brn 15 10
237 15 c. brn, gold & grn 40 25

1973. Disarmament Decade.
238. **140.** 8 c. multicoloured .. 15 10
239. 15 c. multicoloured .. 25 20

141. Skull on Poppy.
142. Emblems within Honeycomb.

1973. "Stop Drug Abuse" Campaign.
240. **141.** 8 c. multicoloured .. 25 15
241 15 c. multicoloured .. 45 25

1973. U.N. Volunteers Programme.
242. **142.** 8 c. multicoloured .. 15 10
243. 21 c. multicoloured .. 35 30

143. Namibia on Map of Africa.

1973. U.N. Resolutions on Namibia (South West Africa).
244. **143.** 8 c. multicoloured .. 15 10
245. 15 c. multicoloured .. 35 30

144. Human Rights Flame.

1973. 25th Anniv. of Declaration of Human Rights.
246. **144.** 8 c. multicoloured .. 20 10
247. 21 c. multicoloured .. 35 30

145. H.Q., Building.

1973. Inauguration of New I.L.O. Headquarters Building, Geneva.
248. **145.** 10 c. multicoloured .. 20 10
249. 21 c. multicoloured .. 35 30

146. Globe within Posthorn.

1974. Cent. of U.P.U.
250. **146.** 10 c. multicoloured .. 15 10

147. "Children's Choir" (mural detail, C. Portinari).
148. Peace Dove.

1974. United Nations Art (6th issue). Brazilian Peace Mural, Delegates' Lobby.
251. **147.** 10 c. multicoloured .. 15 15
252. 18 c. multicoloured .. 25 25

1974.
253. **148.** 2 c. blue and ultram. 10 10
254. – 10 c. multicoloured .. 15 10
255. – 18 c. multicoloured .. 25 15
DESIGNS—VERT. 10 c. U.N. Headquarters, New York. 18 c. Globe over U.N. emblem and flags.

A 151. Globe and Jet Aircraft.
154. Young Children with Globe.

1974. Air. Multicoloured.
A 256. 13 c. Type **A 151.** .. 20 15
A 257. 18 c. " Channels of Communication " (38×23 mm.) .. 25 15
A 258. 26 c. Dove in Flight and U.N. Headquarters .. 35 30

1974. World Population Year.
259. **154.** 10 c. multicoloured .. 20 10
260. 18 c. multicoloured .. 35 30

155. Ship and Fish.
156. Satellite, Globe and Symbols.

1974. U.N. Conference on " Law of the Sea "
261. **155.** 10 c. multicoloured .. 25 15
262. 26 c. multicoloured .. 60 35

1975. Peaceful Uses of Outer Space.
263. **156.** 10 c. multicoloured .. 20 10
264. 26 c. multicoloured .. 45 40

157. " Sex Equality ".
158. " The Hope of Mankind ".

1975. International Women's Year.
265. **157.** 10 c. multicoloured .. 15 10
266. 18 c. multicoloured .. 30 25

1975. 30th Anniv of U.N.O.
267 **158** 10 c. multicoloured .. 15 10
268 26 c. multicoloured .. 35 30

160. Cupped Hand.
161. Wild Rose and Barbed Wire.

1975. "Namibia—United Nations Direct Responsibility".
270 **160** 10 c. multicoloured .. 20 10
271 18 c. multicoloured .. 25 25

1975. U.N. Peace-keeping Operations.
272. **161.** 13 c. blue 20 15
273. 26 c. mauve 40 35

162. " Bird of Peace ".
166. Linked Ribbons.

1976. Multicoloured.
274. 3 c. Type **162** 10 10
275. 4 c. " Gathering of Peoples " (39 × 23 mm.) .. 10 10
276. 30 c. U.N. flag (23 × 39 mm.) 50 30
277. 50 c. " Universal Peace " (dove and rainbow) (23 × 39 mm.) 95 50

1976. World Federation of U.N. Associations.
278. **166.** 13 c. multicoloured .. 15 10
279. 26 c. multicoloured .. 40 35

167. Globe and Crate.
168. Houses bordering Globe.

1976. U.N. Conf. on Trade and Development.
280. **167.** 13 c. multicoloured .. 25 15
281. 31 c. multicoloured .. 50 45

1976. U.N. Conf. on Human Settlements.
282. **168.** 13 c. multicoloured .. 25 15
283. 25 c. multicoloured .. 50 45

169. Magnifying Glass and Emblem.
170. Stylised Ear of Wheat.

1976. 25th Anniv. of U.N. Postal Administration.
284. **169.** 13 c. multicoloured .. 40 15
285. 31 c. multicoloured .. 2·75 1·10

1976. World Food Council.
286. **170.** 13 c. multicoloured .. 30 25

171. U.N. Emblem.
173. Rain Drops and Funnel.

172. W.I.P.O. Headquarters Building.

1976.
287. **171.** 9 c. multicoloured .. 20 10

1977. World Intellectual Property Organization Headquarters.
288. **172.** 13 c. multicoloured .. 25 15
289. 31 c. multicoloured .. 45 35

1977. United Nations Water Conference.
290. **173.** 13 c. multicoloured .. 25 15
291. 25 c. multicoloured .. 45 35

174. Severed Fuse.
175. Winged Airmail Letter.

1977. Security Council.
292. **174.** 13 c. multicoloured .. 15 15
293. 31 c. multicoloured .. 35 35

1977. Air. Multicoloured.
A294 25 c. Type **175** 35 30
A295 31 c. Globe and airplane (horiz) 40 40

177. " Combat Racism ".
178. Atomic Symbol and Produce.

1977. Campaign Against Racial Discrimination.
296. **177.** 13 c. black and yellow 25 15
297. 25 c. black and red .. 40 30

1977. Peaceful Uses of Atomic Energy.
298. **178.** 13 c. multicoloured .. 25 15
299. 18 c. multicoloured .. 35 25

179. U.N. Charter.

1978. Multicoloured.
300. 1 c. Type **179** 10 10
301. 25 c. Knotted flags .. 30 20
302. $1 Multi-racial group .. 1·40 80

182. Smallpox Bacilli.

1978. Global Eradication of Smallpox.
303. **182.** 13 c. black and red .. 30 15
304. 31 c. black and blue .. 65 45

183. Broken Manacle.
184. Clouds within Ribbon.

1978. "Namibia: Liberation, Justice, Co-operation".
305. **183.** 13 c. multicoloured .. 25 15
306. 18 c. multicoloured .. 35 30

1978. International Civil Aviation Organization—Safety in the Air.
307. **184.** 13 c. multicoloured .. 25 15
308. 25 c. multicoloured .. 40 35

185. General Assembly.

1978. General Assembly.
309. **185.** 13 c. multicoloured .. 20 15
310. 18 c. multicoloured .. 30 30

186. Hemispheres within Cogwheels.
187. Hand holding Olive Branch.

1978. Technical Co-operation among Developing Countries.
311. **186.** 13 c. multicoloured .. 25 15
312. 31 c. multicoloured .. 50 40

1979. Multicoloured.
313. 5 c. Type **187** 10 10
314. 14 c. Multiple "tree" .. 20 10
315. 15 c. Globe and peace dove 25 15
316. 20 c. Doves crossing globe 30 15

191. Fire and Flood.

1979. U.N. Disaster Relief Co-ordinator.
317. **191.** 15 c. multicoloured .. 25 20
318. 20 c. multicoloured .. 35 25

192. Child's Drawing. **193.** Olive Branch and Map of Namibia.

1979. International Year of the Child.
319. **192.** 15 c. multicoloured .. 30 15
320. 31 c. multicoloured .. 60 60

1979. "For a Free and Independent Namibia".
321. **193.** 15 c. multicoloured .. 20 15
322. 31 c. multicoloured .. 50 40

194. Sword and Scales of Justice. **195.** Graph.

1979. International Court of Justice.
323. **194.** 15 c. olive, grn. & blk. 20 15
324. 20 c. blue, pale blue and black 30 30

1980. New International Economic Order. Multicoloured.
325. 15 c. Type **195** 25 15
326. 31 c. Key 50 50

197. Doves. **198.** Helmet.

1980. U.N. Decade for Women.
327. **197.** 15 c. multicoloured .. 30 20
328. 20 c. multicoloured .. 35 30

1980. Peace-keeping Operations.
329. **198.** 15 c. blue and black .. 30 20
330. – 31 c. multicoloured .. 55 45
DESIGN: 31 c. "Peace-keeping".

200. "35" composed of Flags. **203.** Flag of Bangladesh.

1980. 35th Anniv. of United Nations. Mult.
331. 15 c. Type **200** 25 20
332. 31 c. Stylized flower .. 50 45

1980. Flags of Member Nations (1st series). Multicoloured.
334. 15 c. Type **203** 30 30
335. 15 c. Guinea 30 30
336. 15 c. Mali 30 30
337. 15 c. Surinam 30 30
338. 15 c. Cameroun 30 30
339. 15 c. Hungary 30 30
340. 15 c. Madagascar 30 30
341. 15 c. Rwanda 30 30
342. 15 c. El Salvador 30 30
343. 15 c. France 30 30
344. 15 c. Venezuela 30 30
345. 15 c. Yugoslavia 30 30
346. 15 c. Fiji 30 30
347. 15 c. Luxembourg 30 30
348. 15 c. Turkey 30 30
349. 15 c. Vietnam 30 30
See also Nos. 359/74, 383/98, 408/23, 434/9, 459/74, 486/501, 508/23, 537/52 and 563/78.

204. Various Emblems forming Bunch of Flowers.

1980. Economic and Social Council. Mult.
350. 15 c. Type **204** 30 20
351. 20 c. Economic and social emblems 40 30

206. Text and U.N. Emblem. **207.** Jigsaw.

1981. Inalienable Rights of the Palestinian People.
352. **206.** 15 c. multicoloured .. 30 20

1981. International Year of Disabled Persons.
353 **207** 20 c. multicoloured .. 35 30
354 – 35 c. black and orange 55 30
DESIGN: 35 c. Disabled person.

209. "Sebastrocrator Kaloyan and his wife Desislava" (13th-century Bulgarian fresco). **210.** Sun and Sea.

1981. Art.
355. **209.** 20 c. multicoloured .. 35 35
356. 31 c. multicoloured .. 55 60

1981. New and Renewable Sources of Energy.
357. **210.** 20 c. multicoloured .. 30 30
358. – 40 c. gold and blue .. 65 70
DESIGN: 40 c. U.N. Energy Conference emblem.

1981. Flags of Member Nations (2nd series). As T **203**. Multicoloured.
359. 20 c. Djibouti 30 30
360. 20 c. Sri Lanka 30 30
361. 20 c. Bolivia 30 30
362. 20 c. Equatorial Guinea .. 30 30
363. 20 c. Malta 30 30
364. 20 c. Czechoslovakia .. 30 30
365. 20 c. Thailand 30 30
366. 20 c. Trinidad and Tobago 30 30
367. 20 c. Ukranian S.S.R. .. 30 30
368. 20 c. Kuwait 30 30
369. 20 c. Sudan 30 30
370. 20 c. Egypt 30 30
371. 20 c. United States .. 30 30
372. 20 c. Singapore 30 30
373. 20 c. Panama 30 30
374. 20 c. Costa Rica 30 30

212. Grafted Plant. **214.** "Respect for Human Rights".

1981. 10th Anniv. of U.N. Volunteers Programme. Multicoloured.
375 18 c. Type **212** 30 25
376 28 c. "10" enclosing symbols of services .. 45 50

1982. Multicoloured.
377 17 c. Type **214** 25 10
378 28 c. "Granting of Independence to Colonial Countries and Peoples" 40 20
379 40 c. "Second Disarmament Decade" 60 30

217. Hand holding Seedling. **219.** Olive Branch and U.N. Emblem.

1982. Human Environment. Multicoloured.
380. 20 c. Type **217** 30 30
381. 40 c. Symbols of the Environment 65 70

1982. Second United Nations Conference on Exploration and Peaceful Uses of Outer Space.
382 **219** 20 c. ultramarine, blue and green 45 30

1982. Flags of Member Nations (3rd series). As T **203**. Multicoloured.
383. 20 c. Austria 30 30
384. 20 c. Malaysia 30 30
385. 20 c. Seychelles 30 30
386. 20 c. Ireland 30 30
387. 20 c. Mozambique 30 30
388. 20 c. Albania 30 30
389. 20 c. Dominica 30 30
390. 20 c. Solomon Islands .. 30 30
391. 20 c. Philippines 30 30
392. 20 c. Swaziland 30 30
393. 20 c. Nicaragua 30 30
394. 20 c. Burma 30 30
395. 20 c. Cape Verde 30 30
396. 20 c. Guyana 30 30
397. 20 c. Belgium 30 30
398. 20 c. Nigeria 30 30

220. Tree (flora). **222.** Interlocking Arrows.

1982. Conservation and Protection of Nature. Multicoloured.
399. 20 c. Type **220** 30 30
400. 28 c. Butterfly (insects) .. 50 60

1983. World Communications Year. Mult.
401. 20 c. Type **222** 50 35
402. 40 c. Cable network .. 90 75

224. Ship and Buoy. **226.** Giving Food.

1983. Safety at Sea: International Maritime Organization. Multicoloured.
403. 20 c. Type **224**. 60 35
404. 37 c. Stylized liner .. 1·00 90

1983. World Food Programme.
405 . **226.** 20 c. red 55 35

227. Coins and Cogwheels. **229.** "Window Right".

1983. Trade and Development. Mult.
406. 20 c. Type **227** 50 35
407. 28 c. Emblems of trade .. 75 55

1983. Flags of Member Nations (4th series). As T **203**. Multicoloured.
408. 20 c. United Kingdom .. 35 30
409. 20 c. Barbados 35 30
410. 20 c. Nepal 35 30
411. 20 c. Israel 35 30
412. 20 c. Malawi 35 30
413. 20 c. Byelorussian S.S.R. .. 35 30
414. 20 c. Jamaica 35 30
415. 20 c. Kenya 35 30
416. 20 c. China 35 30
417. 20 c. Peru 35 30
418. 20 c. Bulgaria 35 30
419. 20 c. Canada 35 30
420. 20 c. Somalia 35 30
421. 20 c. Senegal 35 30
422. 20 c. Brazil 35 30
423. 20 c. Sweden 35 30

1983. 35th Anniv. of Declaration of Human Rights. Multicoloured.
424. 20 c. Type **229** 40 25
425. 40 c. "Treaty with Nature" 1·00 70

231. World Population. **232.** Fertilizing Crops.

1984. International Conference on Population, Mexico
426. **231.** 20 c. multicoloured .. 50 20
427. 40 c. multicoloured .. 1·10 65

1984. World Food Day. Multicoloured.
428. 20 c. Type **232** 40 20
429. 40 c. Planting rice .. 85 45

234. Grand Canyon, U.S.A. **236.** Mother with Baby.

1984. World Heritage—U.N. Educational, Scientific and Cultural Organization. Mult.
430. 20 c. Type **234** 40 20
431. 50 c. Polonnaruwa, Sri Lanka .. .. .. 1·25 65

1984. Future for Refugees.
432. **236.** 20 c. brown and black 40 20
433. – 50 c. black and blue .. 1·00 70
DESIGN: 50 c. Mother with child.

1984. Flags of Member Nations (5th series). As T **203**. Multicoloured.
434. 20 c. Burundi 50 40
435. 20 c. Pakistan 50 40
436. 20 c. Benin 50 40
437. 20 c. Italy 50 40
438. 20 c. Poland 50 40
439. 20 c. Papua New Guinea .. 50 40
440. 20 c. Uruguay 50 40
441. 20 c. Chile 50 40
442. 20 c. Paraguay 50 40
443. 20 c. Bhutan 50 40
444. 20 c. Central African Republic 50 40
445. 20 c. Australia 50 40
446. 20 c. Tanzania 50 40
447. 20 c. United Arab Emirates 50 40
448. 20 c. Ecuador 50 40
449. 20 c. Bahamas 50 40

238. Emblem and Figures linking Arms. **239.** Turin Centre Emblem.

1984. International Youth Year.
450. **238.** 20 c. multicoloured .. 50 15
451. 35 c. multicoloured .. 90 40

1985. 20th Anniv. of Turin Centre of International Labour Organization.
452. **239.** 23 c. blue 60 35

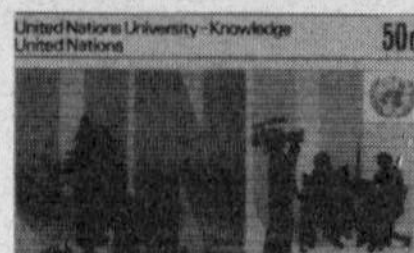

240. Farming and Mediums of Communication.

1985. 10th Anniv of United Nations University, Tokyo.
453. **240.** 50 c. multicoloured .. 1·25 75

241. People of Various Nations.

1985. Multicoloured.
454. 22 c. Type **241** 30 15
455. $3 Paintbrush and emblem 4·50 2·75

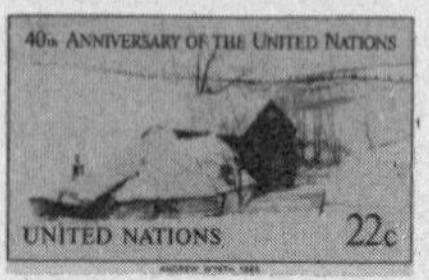

243. "Snow Scene" (Andrew Wyeth).

1985. 40th Anniv. of U.N.O. Multicoloured.
456. 22 c. Type **243** 45 20
457. 45 c. "Harvest Scene" (Andrew Wyeth) .. 95 65

1985. Flags of Member Nations (6th series). As T **203.** Multicoloured.
459. 22 c. Grenada 50 40
460. 22 c. Federal Republic of Germany 50 40
461. 22 c. Saudi Arabia 50 40
462. 22 c. Mexico 50 40
463. 22 c. Liberia 50 40
464. 22 c. Mauritius 50 40
465. 22 c. Chad 50 40
466. 22 c. Dominican Republic 50 40
467. 22 c. Oman 50 40
468. 22 c. Ghana 50 40
469. 22 c. Sierra Leone 50 40
470. 22 c. Finland 50 40
471. 22 c. Uganda 50 40
472. 22 c. Saint Thomas and Prince Islands 50 40
473. 22 c. U.S.S.R. 50 40
474. 22 c. India 50 40

246. Woman feeding Child. **248.** "Africa in Crisis".

1985. U.N.I.C.E.F. Child Survival Campaign. Multicoloured.
475. 22 c. Type **246** 45 25
476. 33 c. Mother breast-feeding child 85 55

1986. Africa in Crisis.
477. **248.** 22 c. multicoloured .. 45 25

249. Dam.

1986. Development Programme. Water Resources. Multicoloured.
478. 22 c. Type **249** .. .. 1·00 70
479. 22 c. Working in the fields 1·00 70
480. 22 c. Girls at waterhole .. 1·00 70
481. 22 c. Women at well .. 1·00 70
Nos. 478/81 were printed together, se-tenant, forming a composite design.

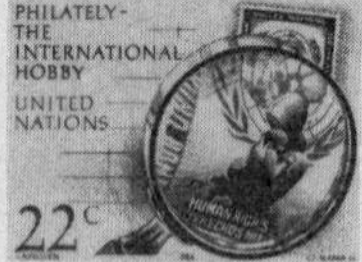

253. Magnifying Glass and Stamp. **255.** Peace Doves.

1986. Philately: the International Hobby.
482. **253.** 22 c. lilac and blue .. 50 20
483. – 44 c. brown and green 90 55
DESIGN: 44 c. Engraver.

1986. International Peace Year.
484. **255.** 22 c. multicoloured .. 60 20
485. – 33 c. multicoloured .. 80 50
DESIGN: 33 c. Words for "Peace" around U.N. Emblem.

1986. Flags of Member Nations (7th series). As T **203.** Multicoloured.
486 22 c. New Zealand .. 45 35
487 22 c. Laos 45 35
488 22 c. Burkina Faso .. 45 35
489 22 c. Gambia 45 35
490 22 c. Maldives 45 35
491 22 c. Ethiopia 45 35
492 22 c. Jordan 45 35
493 22 c. Zambia 45 35
494 22 c. Iceland 45 35
495 22 c. Antigua and Barbuda 45 35
496 22 c. Angola 45 35
497 22 c. Botswana 45 35
498 22 c. Rumania 45 35
499 22 c. Togo 45 35
500 22 c. Mauritania 45 35
501 22 c. Colombia 45 35

258. Trygve Lie (after Harald Dal). **259.** Men with Surveying Equipment and Blueprints.

1987. 9th Death Anniv. of Trygve Lie (first U.N. Secretary-General).
503. **258.** 22 c. multicoloured .. 45 20

1987. International Year of Shelter for the Homeless.
504 **259** 22 c. deep brown, brown and black .. 40 20
505 – 44 c. multicoloured .. 85 65
DESIGN: 44 c. Cutting bamboo.

261. Construction Workers.

1987. Anti-Drugs Campaign. Multicoloured.
506. 22 c. Type **261** 45 20
507. 33 c. University graduates 80 55

1987. Flags of Member Nations (8th series). As T **203.** Multicoloured.
508. 22 c. Comoros 40 30
509. 22 c. People's Democratic Republic of Yemen .. 40 30
510. 22 c. Mongolia 40 30
511. 22 c. Vanuatu 40 30
512. 22 c. Japan 40 30
513. 22 c. Gabon 40 30
514. 22 c. Zimbabwe 40 30
515. 22 c. Iraq 40 30
516. 22 c. Argentina 40 30
517. 22 c. Congo 40 30
518. 22 c. Niger 40 30
519. 22 c. St. Lucia 40 30
520. 22 c. Bahrain 40 30
521. 22 c. Haiti 40 30
522. 22 c. Afghanistan 40 30
523. 22 c. Greece 40 30

MINIMUM PRICE

The minimum price quoted is 5p which represents a handling charge rather than a basis for valuing common stamps. For further notes about prices see introductory pages.

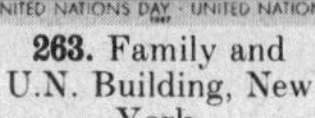

263. Family and U.N. Building, New York. **265.** Measles.

1987. United Nations Day. Mult.
524 22 c. Type **263** 35 15
525 39 c. Dancers 75 65

1987. "Immunize Every Child". Mult.
526. 22 c. Type **265** 40 15
527. 44 c. Tetanus 85 75

267. Wheat in Form of U.N. Emblem.

1988. "For a Better World".
528. **267.** 3 c. yellow, brown and black 15 10

268. Fisherman.

1988. International Fund for Agricultural Development "For a World Without Hunger" Campaign. Multicoloured.
529 2 c. Type **268** 40 15
530 33 c. Farmers ploughing with oxen 55 50

270. Tropical Rain Forest Canopy. **272.** Teacher at Blackboard.

1988. "Survival of the Forests". Mult.
531. 25 c. Type **270** .. .. 1·75 70
532. 44 c. Tropical rain forest floor .. .. 4·00 2·10
Nos. 531/2 were printed together, se-tenant, forming a composite design.

1988. International Volunteer Day. Mult.
533 25 c. Type **272** 30 15
534 50 c. Teaching basketry (horiz) 70 65

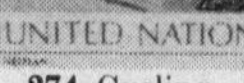

274 Cycling **276** Flame

1988. "Health in Sports". Multicoloured.
535 25 c. Type **274** 45 20
536 38 c. Marathon (horiz) .. 65 55

1988. Flags of Member Nations (9th series). As T **203.** Multicoloured.
537 25 c. Spain 40 30
538 25 c. St. Vincent and Grenadines 40 30
539 25 c. Ivory Coast 40 30
540 25 c. Lebanon 40 30
541 25 c. Yemen 40 30
542 25 c. Cuba 40 30
543 25 c. Denmark 40 30
544 25 c. Libya 40 30
545 25 c. Qatar 40 30
546 25 c. Zaire 40 30
547 25 c. Norway 40 30
548 25 c. German Democratic Republic 40 30
549 25 c. Iran 40 30
550 25 c. Tunisia 40 30
551 25 c. Samoa 40 30
552 25 c. Belize 40 30

1989. 40th Anniv of Declaration of Human Rights.
553 **276** 25 c. multicoloured .. 40 25

278 Electricity Production **280** "Blue Helmet" Soldier

1989. World Bank. Multicoloured.
555 25 c. Type **278** 40 15
556 45 c. Planting rice .. 70 50

1989. Award of Nobel Peace Prize to United Nations Peace-keeping Forces.
557 **280** 25 c. multicoloured .. 40 15

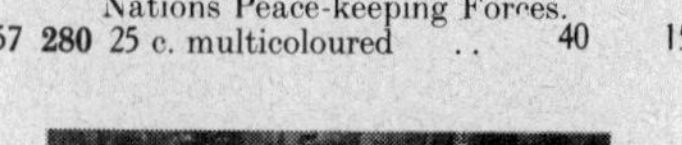

281 U.N. Headquarters, New York

1989.
558 **281** 45 c. multicoloured .. 70 40

282 Satellite Image of Storm over Chesapeake Bay Area **284** Band

1989. 25th Anniv of World Weather Watch. Multicoloured.
559 25 c. Type **282** 45 20
560 36 c. Typhoon Abby approaching China .. 65 40

1989. 10th Anniv of United Nations Vienna International Centre. Multicoloured.
561 25 c. Type **284** 45 15
562 90 c. Mountain and butterfly as tree .. .. 1·40 1·10

1989. Flags of Member Nations (10th series). As T **203.** Multicoloured.
563 25 c. Indonesia 35 30
564 25 c. Lesotho 35 30
565 25 c. Guatemala 35 30
566 25 c. Netherlands 35 30
567 25 c. Algeria 35 30
568 25 c. Brunei 35 30
569 25 c. St. Kitts and Nevis 35 30
570 25 c. United Nations .. 35 30
571 25 c. Honduras 35 30
572 25 c. Kampuchea 35 30
573 25 c. Guinea-Bissau .. 35 30
574 25 c. Cyprus 35 30
575 25 c. South Africa .. 35 30
576 25 c. Portugal 35 30
577 25 c. Morocco 35 30
578 25 c. Syria 35 30

286 "Table of Universal Brotherhood" (Jose Clemente Orozco) (Article 1) **288** Port Activities

1989. Declaration of Human Rights (1st series). Multicoloured.

579 25 c. Type **286** 40 15

580 45 c. "Composition II" (V. Kandinsky) (Article 2) 70 40

See also Nos. 592/3, 609/10, 626/7 and 637/8.

1990. International Trade Centre.

581 **288** 25 c. multicoloured .. 60 20

289 "AIDS"  **291** Madagascar Periwinkle

1990. Anti-AIDS Campaign. Multicoloured.

582 25 c. Type **289** 50 20

583 40 c. Group at risk .. 1·00 45

1990. Medicinal Plants. Multicoloured.

584 25 c. Type **291** 45 15

585 90 c. American ginseng .. 1·40 1·10

293 Ribbons forming "45"  **296** Youth waylaying Elderly Man

1990. 45th Anniv of U.N.O. Multicoloured.

586 25 c. Type **293** 50 20

587 45 c. "45" and U.N. emblem .. .. 1·40 80

1990. Crime Prevention. Multicoloured.

590 25 c. Type **296** 70 25

591 36 c. Burglars leaving burning building .. 1·40 80

1990. Universal Declaration of Human Rights (2nd series). As T **286**. Multicoloured.

592 25 c. Sarcophagus of Plotinus (detail) (Article 7) .. 35 20

593 45 c. "Combined Chambers of High Court of Appeal" (Charles Paul Renouard), from "The Dreyfus Case" (Article 8) 60 35

300/303 Alpine Lake and Wildlife

1991. Economic Commission for Europe. "For a Better Environment".

594 **300** 30 c. multicoloured .. 50 30

595 **301** 30 c. multicoloured .. 50 30

596 **302** 30 c. multicoloured .. 50 30

597 **303** 30 c. multicoloured .. 50 30

Nos. 594/7 were printed together, se-tenant, forming the composite design illustrated.

304 Desert  **306** U.N. Building

1991. 1st Anniv of Namibian Independence. Multicoloured.

598 30 c. Type **304** .. 45 20

599 50 c. Open grassland .. 75 45

1991.

600 **306** $2 blue .. .. 2·50 1·50

307 Children around Globe (Nicole Delia Legnani)

1991. 30th Anniv (1989) of U.N. Declaration on the Rights of the Child and 1990 World Summit on Children, New York. Children's Drawings. Multicoloured.

601 30 c. Type **307** 40 20

602 70 c. Dove, rainbow and houses (Alissa Duffy) .. 95 55

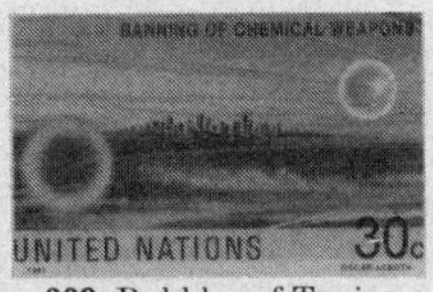

309 Bubbles of Toxin approaching City

1991. Banning of Chemical Weapons. Mult.

603 30 c. Type **309** 40 20

604 90 c. Hand pushing back barrels of toxins .. 95 55

311 U.N. Flag

1991. Muliticoloured.

605 30 c. Type **311** 40 15

606 50 c. "The Golden Rule" (mosaic, Norman Rockwell) (vert) .. 65 35

313 1951 1 c. Stamp

1991. 40th Anniv of United Nations Postal Administration.

607 **313** 30 c. red on cream .. 40 20

608 – 40 c. purple on cream 55 30

DESIGN: 40 c. 1951 2 c. stamp.

1991. Declaration of Human Rights (3rd series). As Type **286**. Multicoloured.

609 30 c. "The Last of England" (Ford Madox Brown) (Article 13) .. 40 20

610 50 c. "The Emigration to the East" (Tito Salas) (Article 14) 65 35

317 Uluru National Park, Australia  **319/20** Sea Life (½-size illustration)

1992. 20th Anniv of U.N.E.S.C.O. World Heritage Convention. Multicoloured.

611 30 c. Type **317** 40 20

612 50 c. Great Wall of China 65 25

1992. "Clean Oceans".

613 **319** 29 c. multicoloured .. 40 15

614 **320** 29 c. multicoloured .. 40 15

Nos. 613/14 were issued together, se-tenant, forming the composite design illustrated.

321/324 Planet Earth

1992. 2nd U.N. Conference on Environment and Development, Rio de Janeiro.

615 **321** 29 c. multicoloured .. 40 15

616 **322** 29 c. multicoloured .. 40 15

617 **323** 29 c. multicoloured .. 40 15

618 **324** 29 c. multicoloured .. 40 15

Nos. 615/18 were issued together, se-tenant, forming the composite design illustrated.

325/326 "Mission Planet Earth"

1992. International Space Year. Roul.

619 **325** 29 c. multicoloured .. 40 20

620 **326** 29 c. multicoloured .. 40 20

Nos. 619/20 were issued together, se-tenant, forming the composite design illustrated.

327 Winged Man with V.D.U.

1992. Commission on Science and Technology for Development. Multicoloured.

621 29 c. Type **327** 40 15

622 50 c. Man sitting in crocodile's mouth .. 65 35

329 Aerial View of Building

1992. United Nations University, Tokyo. Multicoloured.

623 4 c. Type **329** 10 10

624 40 c. Front elevation of building 55 30

331 U.N. Headquarters, New York  **334** Family Life

1992.

625 **331** 29 c. multicoloured .. 40 15

1992. Universal Declaration of Human Rights (4th series). As T **286**. Multicoloured.

626 29 c. "Lady writing a Letter with her Maid" (Johannes Vermeer) (Article 19) 40 15

627 50 c. "The Meeting" (Ester Almqvist) (Article 20) .. 65 35

1993. "Ageing: Dignity and Participation". 10th Anniv (1992) of International Plan of Action on Ageing. Multicoloured.

628 29 c. Type **334** 40 15

629 52 c. Health and nutrition 70 40

336 Queensland Hairy-nosed Wombat

1993. Endangered Species. Multicoloured.

630 29 c. Type **336** 40 15

631 29 c. Whooping crane .. 40 15

632 29 c. Giant clams .. 40 15

633 29 c. Sable antelope .. 40 15

340 "United Nations"

1993.

634 **340** 5 c. multicoloured .. 10 10

341 Personal Environment

1993. 45th Anniv of W.H.O. Multicoloured.

635 29 c. Type **341** 40 15

636 50 c. Family environment 65 35

1993. Declaration of Human Rights (5th series). As T **286**. Multicoloured.

637 29 c. "Shocking Corn" (Thomas Hart Benton) (Article 25) 40 15

638 35 c. "The Library" (Jacob Lawrence) (Article 26) .. 45 25

345/348 Peace

1993. International Peace Day. Roul.

639 **345** 29 c. multicoloured .. 40 15

640 **346** 29 c. multicoloured .. 40 15

641 **347** 29 c. multicoloured .. 40 15

642 **348** 29 c. multicoloured .. 40 15

Nos. 639/42 were issued together, se-tenant, forming the composite design illustrated.

349 Chameleon

1993. The Environment—Climate. Mult.

643 29 c. Type **349** 40 15

644 29 c. Storm 40 15

645 29 c. Antelopes fleeing from flood 40 15

646 29 c. Bird of paradise .. 40 15

Nos. 643/6 were issued together, se-tenant, forming a composite design.

B. GENEVA HEADQUARTERS

For use on mail posted at the United Nations Geneva headquarters. Before 1969 the Swiss PTT issued stamps for use at the Palais des Nations; these are listed at the end of Switzerland.

NOTE: References to numbers and types i. this section, other than to those with "G" prefix, are to the United Nations (New York Office) listing. Designs adapted for the Geneva issues are inscribed in French and have face values in francs.

G 4. Palais des Nations, Geneva.

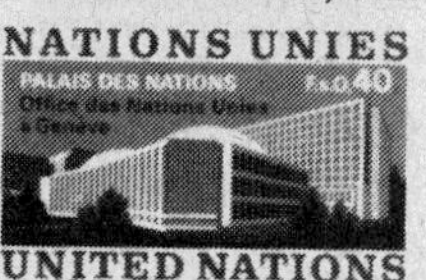

G 5. Palais des Nations, Geneva.

1969. Existing United Nations (New York) designs adapted with new colours and values in Swiss francs (F.S.). 30 and 40 c. new designs. Multicoloured unless otherwise stated.

G 1 – 5 c. (As No. 164) .. 10 10
G 2 – 10 c. (As No. 94) .. 10 10
G 3 – 20 c. (As No. 97) .. 15 15
G 4 **G 4** 30 c. multicoloured .. 25 20
G 5 **G 5** 40 c. multicoloured .. 30 30
G 6 – 50 c. (As No. 147, but scroll inscr in French) 40 40
G 7 – 60 c. gold, red and brown (As No. 98) 45 45
G 8 – 70 c. red, gold and black (As No. 167) 50 50
G 9 – 75 c. (As No. A 125) .. 55 55
G10 – 80 c. (As No. 148) .. 60 60
G11 **52** 90 c. (Inscr in French) 80 80
G12 – 1 f. deep green and green (As No. 149) 85 85
G13 **53** 2 f. multicoloured .. 1·50 1·50
G14 **104** 3 f. multicoloured .. 2·40 1·40
G15 **3** 10 f. blue .. .. 7·50 7·50

1971. Peaceful Uses of the Sea-bed.
G 16. **121.** 30 c. multicoloured .. 40 40

1971. United Nations Work with Refugees.
G 17. **122.** 50 c. blk., orge. & red 1·00 1·00

1971. World Food Programme.
G 18. **123.** 50 c. multicoloured .. 1·00 1·00

1971. Opening of new U.P.U. Headquarters Building, Berne.
G 19. **124.** 75 c. multicoloured .. 1·50 1·50

1971. Racial Equality Year. Designs as Nos. 220/1, with background colours changed.
G 20. 30 c. Type **125** 75 75
G 21. 50 c. Linked globes (horiz.) 75 75

1971. U.N. Int. Schools.
G 22. **130.** 1 f. 10 multicoloured 1·50 1·50

1972. Non-Proliferation of Nuclear Weapons.
G 23. **131.** 40 c. multicoloured .. 1·10 1·10

1972. World Health Day.
G 24. **132.** 80 c. multicoloured .. 1·00 1·00

1972. U.N. Environmental Conservation Conf., Stockholm.
G 25. **137.** 40 c. multicoloured .. 70 70
G 26. 80 c. multicoloured .. 1·10 1·10

1972. Economic Commission for Europe. (ECE).
G 27. **138.** 1 f. 10 multicoloured 1·90 1·90

1972. United Nations Art.
G 28. **139.** 40 c. multicoloured .. 75 75
G 29. 80 c. multicoloured .. 1·25 1·25

1973. Disarmament Decade.
G 30. **140.** 60 c. multicoloured .. 60 60
G 31. 1 f. 10 multicoloured 1·00 1·00

1973. "No Drugs" Campaign.
G 32. **141.** 60 c. multicoloured 1·25 1·25

1973. U.N. Volunteers Programme.
G 33. **142.** 80 c. multicoloured .. 85 85

1973. "Namibia" (South West Africa).
G 34. **143.** 60 c. multicoloured 85 85

1973. 25th Anniv. of Declaration of Human Rights.
G 35. **144.** 40 c. multicoloured .. 55 55
G 36. 80 c. multicoloured .. 1·10 1·10

1973. Inauguration of New I.L.O. Head quarters, Geneva.
G 37. **145.** 60 c. multicoloured .. 60 60
G 38. 80 c. multicoloured 1·00 1·00

1973. Centenary of Universal Postal Union.
G 39. **146.** 30 c. multicoloured .. 35 35
G 40. 60 c. multicoloured .. 55 55

1974. Brazilian Peace Mural.
G 41. **147.** 60 c. multicoloured .. 70 70
G 42. 1 f. multicoloured .. 1·10 1·10

1974. World Population Year.
G 43. **154.** 60 c. multicoloured .. 60 60
G 44. 80 c multicoloured .. 80 80

1974. U.N. Conf. on "Law of the Sea".
G 45. **155.** 1 f. 30 multicoloured 1·50 1·50

1975. Peaceful Uses of Outer Space.
G 46. **156.** 60 c multicoloured .. 70 70
G 47. 90 c. multicoloured .. 90 90

1975. International Women's Year.
G 48. **157.** 60 c. multicoloured .. 65 65
G 49. 90 c. multicoloured .. 85 85

1975. 30th Anniv of U.N.O.
G 50. **158.** 60 c. multicoloured .. 55 55
G 51. 90 c. multicoloured .. 70 70

1975. "Namibia-U.N. Direct Responsibility".
G 53. **160.** 50 c. multicoloured .. 55 55
G 54. 1 f. 30 multicoloured 1·25 1·25

1975. U.N. Peace-keeping Operations.
G 55. **161.** 60 c. turquoise .. 55 55
G 56. 70 c. violet 70 70

1976. World Federation of U.N. Associations.
G57 **166** 90 c. multicoloured .. 1·10 1·10

1976. U.N. Conf. on Trade and Development.
G 58. **167.** 1 f. 10 multicoloured 1·25 1·25

1976. U.N. Conf. on Human Settlements.
G 59. **168.** 40 c. multicoloured .. 30 30
G 60. 1 f. 50 multicoloured 1·25 1·25

G 46. U.N. Emblem within Posthorn. G 49. Rain Drop and Globe.

1976. 25th Anniv. of U.N. Postal Administration.
G 61. **G 46.** 80 c. multicoloured .. 3·00 3·00
G 62. 1 f. 10 multicoloured 3·00 3·00

1976. World Food Council Publicity.
G 63. **170.** 70 c. multicoloured .. 90 90

1977. World Intellectual Property Organization Publicity.
G 64. **172.** 80 c. multicoloured .. 90 90

1977. U.N. Water Conference.
G 65. **G 49.** 80 c. multicoloured .. 80 80
G 66. 1 f. 10 multicoloured 1·10 1·10

G 50. Protective Hands. G 51. "Intertwining of Races".

1977. Security Council Commemoration.
G 67. **G 50.** 80 c. multicoloured .. 60 60
G 68. 1 f. 10 multicoloured 90 90

1977. "Combat Racism".
G 69. **G 51.** 40 c. multicoloured .. 40 40
G 70. 1 f. 10 multicoloured 1·00 1·00

G 52. Atoms and Laurel Leaf. G 53. Tree and Birds.

1977. "Peaceful Uses for Atomic Energy".
G 71. **G 52.** 80 c. multicoloured .. 70 70
G 72. 1 f. 10 multicoloured 1·10 1·10

1978.
G 73. **G 53.** 35 c. multicoloured 30 30

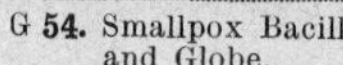

G 54. Smallpox Bacilli and Globe. G 56. Aircraft Flightpaths.

1978. Global Eradication of Smallpox.
G 74. **G 54.** 80 c. multicoloured .. 70 70
G 75. 1 f. 10 multicoloured 1·10 1·10

1978. "Namibia: Liberation, Justice, Co-operation".
G 76. **183.** 80 c. multicoloured .. 80 80

1978. International Civil Aviation Organization—Safety in the Air.
G 77. **G 56.** 70 c. multicoloured .. 60 60
G 78. 80 c. multicoloured .. 80 80

G 57. Globe, Flags and General Assembly Interior G 59. "Disaster".

1978. General Assembly.
G 79. **G 57.** 70 c. multicoloured 60 60
G 80. 1 f. 10 multicoloured 1·10 1·10

1978. Technical Co-operation among Developing Countries.
G 81. **186.** 80 c. multicoloured .. 70 70

1979. United Nations Disaster Relief Co-ordinator.
G 82. **G 59.** 80 c. multicoloured 65 65
G 83. 1 f. 50 multicoloured 1·40 1·40

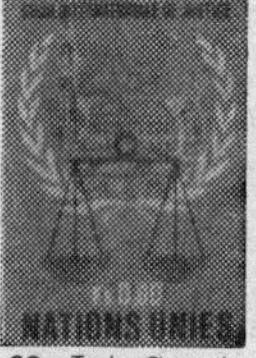
G 60. Children and Rainbow. G 62. Int. Court of Justice and Scales.

1979. International Year of the Child.
G 84. **G 60.** 80 c. multicoloured 2·00 2·00
G 85. 1 f. 10 multicoloured 2·00 2·00

1979. "For a Free and Independent Namibia".
G 86. **198.** 1 f. 10 multicoloured 1·00 1·00

1979. International Court of Justice.
G 87. **G 62.** 80 c. multicoloured 65 65
G 88. 1 f. 10 multicoloured 1·10 1·10

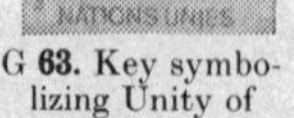

G 63. Key symbolizing Unity of Action. G 64. Emblem.

1980. New International Economic Order.
G 89. **G 63.** 80 c. multicoloured 70 70

1980. U.N. Decade for Women.
G 90. **G 64.** 40 c. multicoloured 45 45
G 91. 70 c. multicoloured 65 65

1980. Peace-keeping Operations.
G 92. **198.** 1 f. 10 blue and green 90 90

1980. 35th Anniv. of United Nations.
G 93. – 40 c. blk. and turquoise 40 40
G 94. **200.** 70 c. multicoloured 70 70
DESIGN: 40 c. Dove and "35".

1980. Economic and Social Council.
G 96. **204.** 40 c. multicoloured .. 35 35
G 97. – 70 c. blue, red and blk. 65 65
DESIGN: 70 c. Human figures ascending graph.

1981. Inalienable Rights of the Palestinian People.
G 98. **206.** 80 c. multicoloured .. 65 65

G 71. Disabled Person. G 77. "Anti Apartheid".

1981. International Year of Disabled Persons.
G 99. **G 71.** 40 c. black and blue 30 30
G 100. – 1 f. 50 black and red 1·25 1·25
DESIGN: 1f. 50, Knot pattern.

1981. Art.
G 101. **209.** 80 c. multicoloured 65 65

1981. New and Renewable Sources of Energy.
G 102. **210.** 1 f. 10 multicoloured 85 85

1981. 10th Anniv. of U.N. Volunteers Programme. Multicoloured.
G 103. 40 c. Type **212** 30 30
G 104. 70 c. Emblems of Science, Agriculture and Industry 55 55

1982. Multicoloured.
G 105. 30 c. Type **G 77** .. 20 20
G 106. 1 f. Flags 70 50

1982. Human Environment. Mult.
G 107. 40 c. Leaves 30 30
G 108. 1 f. 20 Type **217** .. 90 90

1982. Second United Nations Conference on Exploration and Peaceful Uses of Outer Space.
G 109 **219** 80 c. vio, pink & grn 60 60
G 110 – 1 f. multicoloured .. 75 75
DESIGN: 1 f. Satellite and emblems.

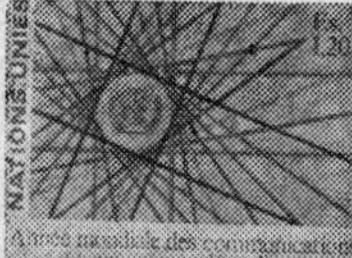
G 83. Bird. G 85. Cable Network.

1982. Conservation and Protection of Nature. Multicoloured.
G 111 40 c. Type **G 83** .. 30 30
G 112 1 f. 50 Snake (reptiles) 1·10 1·10

1983. World Communications Year.
G 113. **G 85.** 1 f. 20 multicoloured 90 90

1983. Safety at Sea: International Maritime Organization. Multicoloured
G 114. 40 c. Type **224** 35 35
G 115. 80 c. Radar Screen within Lifebelt 70 70

1983. World Food Programme.
G 116. **226.** 1 f. 50 blue .. .. 1·40 1·40

1983. Trade and Development. Mult.
G 117. 80 c. Type **227** 75 75
G 118. 1 f. 10 Exports .. .. 1·00 1·00

G 91. "Homo Humus Humanitas". G 93. World Housing.

1983. 35th Anniv of Universal Declaration of Human Rights. Multicoloured.
G 119. 40 c. Type **G 91** .. 30 30
G 120. 1 f. 20 "Droit de Creer" 90 90

1984. International Conference on Population, Mexico City.
G 121. **G 93.** 1 f. 20 mult. .. 1·25 1·25

G 94. Fishing.

1984. World Food Day. Multicoloured.
G 122. 50 c. Type **G 94** .. 40 40
G 123. 80 c. Planting saplings .. 65 65

G **96**. Fort St. Angelo, Malta (wrongly inscr "Valetta").

1984. World Heritage—U.N.E.S.C.O. Mult.
G 124. 50 c. Type G **96** .. 40 40
G 125. 70 c. Los Glaciares, Argentina 60 60

G **98**. Man and Woman. G **100**. Heads.

1984. Future for Refugees.
G 126. G **98**. 35 c. blk. & grn. 25 25
G 127. – 1 f. 50 blk. & brn. 1·10 1·10
DESIGN: 1 f. 50 Head of Woman.

1984. International Youth Year.
G 128. G **100**. 1 f. 20 mult. 90 90

1985. 20th Anniv. of Turin Centre of International Labour Organization.
G 129. **239**. 80 c. red .. 60 60
G 130. V **43**. 1 f. 20 green .. 90 90

G **103**. Ploughing and Group of People.

1985. 10th Anniv. of United Nations University, Tokyo. Multicoloured.
G 131. G **103**. 50 c. multicoloured 35 35
G 132. 80 c. multicoloured 55 55

G **104**. Postman. G **108**. Children.

1985.
G 133. G **104**. 20 c. mult. .. 10 10
G 134. – 1 f. 20 blue and black 80 80
DESIGN: 1 f. 20, Doves.

1985. 40th Anniv. of United Nations Organization. Multicoloured.
G 135. 50 c. Type **243** 40 40
G 136. 70 c. "Harvest Scene" (Andrew Wyeth) .. 60 60

1985. U.N.I.C.E.F. Child Survival Campaign. Multicoloured.
G 138. 50 c. Type G **108** .. 40 40
G 139. 1 f. 20 Child drinking .. 1·10 1·10

G **110**. Children raising Empty Bowls to weeping Mother. G **111**. Herring Gulls.

1986. Africa in Crisis.
G 140. G **110**. 1 f. 40 mult. .. 1·25 1·25

1986.
G 141. G. **111**. 5 c. mult. .. 10 10

G **112**. Tents in Clearing.

1986. Development Programme. Timber Production. Multicoloured.
G 142. 35 c. Type G **112** .. 85 85
G 143. 35 c. Felling tree .. 85 85
G 144. 35 c. Logs on lorries .. 85 85
G 145. 35 c. Girls with sapling .. 85 85
Nos. G 142/5 were printed together, se-tenant, forming a composite design.

1986. Philately: International Hobby.
G146 **253** 50 c. green and red .. 45 45
G147 – 80 c. black & orange 80 80
DESIGN: 80 c. United Nations stamps.

G **118**. Ribbon forming Dove.

1986. International Peace Year. Mult.
G 148. 45 c. Type G **118** .. 35 35
G 149. 1 f. 40 "Peace" and olive branch .. .. .. 1·25 1·25

1987. 9th Death Anniv. of Trygve Lie (first U.N. Secretary-General).
G 151. **258**. 1 f. 40 mult. .. 1·25 1·25

G **122**. Abstract. G **124**. Mixing Cement and Carrying Bricks.

1987. Multicoloured.
G 152. 90 c. Type G **122** .. 65 65
G 153. 1 f. 40 Armillary Sphere, Geneva Centre .. 95 95

1987. International Year of Shelter for the Homeless.
G 154. G **124**. 50 c. green and black 50 50
G 155. – 90 c. blue, turquoise and black 80 80
DESIGN: 90 c. Fitting windows and painting.

OUI À LA VIE · NON À LA DROGUE
Nations Unies F.s.0,80
G **126**. Mother and Baby.

1987. Anti-Drugs Campaign. Multicoloured.
G 156. 80 c. Type G **126** .. 75 75
G 157. 1 f. 20 Workers in paddy-field .. .. 1·25 1·25

G **128**. People in Boat and Palais des Nations, Geneva. G **130**. Whooping Cough.

1987. United Nations Day. Multicoloured.
G158 35 c. Type G **128** .. 35 35
G159 50 c. Dancers 50 50

1987. "Immunize Every Child". Mult.
G 160. 90 c. Type G **130** .. 85 85
G 161. 1 f. 70 Tuberculosis .. 1·75 1·75

G **132**. Goatherd. G **134**. People.

1988. International Fund for Agricultural Development "For a World Without Hunger" Campaign. Multicoloured.
G 162. 35 c. Type G **132** .. 30 30
G 163. 1 f. 40 Women and baskets of fruit .. 1·25 1·25

1988.
G 164. G **134**. 50 c. mult. .. 40 40

G **135**. Mountains and Pine Forest. G **137**. Instruction in Fruit Growing.

1988. "Survival of the Forests". Mult.
G 165. 50 c. Type G **135** .. 3·25 3·25
G 166. 1 f. 10 Pine forest and Lake Shore .. .. 3·25 3·25
Nos. G165/6 were printed together, se-tenant, forming a composite design.

1988. International Volunteer Day. Mult.
G167 80 c. Type G **137** .. 70 70
G168 90 c. Teaching animal husbandry 80 80

G **139** Football G **142** Communications

1988. "Health in Sports". Multicoloured.
G169 50 c. Type G **139** .. 45 45
G170 1 f. 40 Swimming .. 1·25 1·25

1988. 40th Anniv of Declaration of Human Rights.
G171 **276** 90 c. multicoloured 80 80

1989. World Bank.
G173 80 c. Type G **142** .. 70 70
G174 1 f. 40 Industry .. 1·25 1·25

1989. Award of Nobel Peace Prize to United Nations Peace-keeping Forces.
G175 **280** 90 c. multicoloured .. 80 80

G **145** Cold Arctic Air over Europe G **147** Tree and Birds

1989. 25th Anniv of World Weather Watch.
G176 90 c. Type G **145** .. 80 80
G177 1 f. 10 Surface temperatures of Kattegat 95 95

1989. 10th Anniv of United Nations Vienna International Centre.
G178 50 c. Type G **147** .. 45 45
G179 2 f. Woman and flower 1·75 1·75

G **149** "Young Mother Sewing" (Mary Cassatt) (Article 3)

1989. Universal Declaration of Human Rights (1st series). Multicoloured
G180 35 f. Type G **149** .. 25 25
G181 80 f. "Runaway Slave" (Albert Mangones) (Article 4) 60 60
See also Nos. G193/4, G209/10, G224/5 and G234/5.

1990. International Trade Centre.
G182 **287** 1 f. 50 multicoloured 1·25 1·25

G **152** Palais des Nations G **155** Frangipani

1990.
G183 G **152** 5 f. multicoloured 3·75 3·75

1990. Anti-AIDS Campaign. Multicoloured.
G184 50 c. Type **289** 45 45
G185 80 c. "Man" (Leonardo da Vinci) 70 70

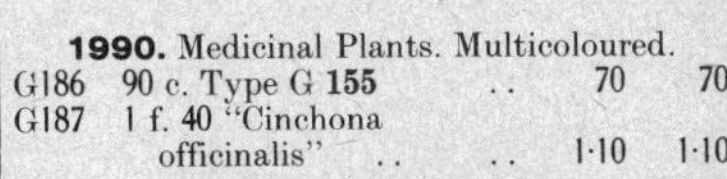

1990. Medicinal Plants. Multicoloured.
G186 90 c. Type G **155** .. 70 70
G187 1 f. 40 "Cinchona officinalis" .. .. 1·10 1·10

G **157** Projects forming "45"

1990. 45th Anniv of U.N.O. Multicoloured.
G188 90 c. Type G **157** .. 70 70
G189 1 f. 10 Dove and "45" 85 85

G **159** Men making Deal over Painting

1990. Crime Prevention. Multicoloured.
G191 50 c. Type G **159** .. 45 45
G192 2 f. Man spilling waste from cart .. .. 1·50 1·50

1990. Universal Declaration of Human Rights (2nd series). As Type G **149**.
G193 35 c. multicoloured .. 30 30
G194 90 c. black & flesh .. 75 75
DESIGNS: 35 c. "Prison Courtyard" (Vincent van Gogh) (Article 9); 90 c. "Katho's Son Redeems the Evil Doer from Execution" (Albrecht Durer) (Article 10).

G **163/166** Lake

1991. Economic Commission for Europe. "For a Better Environment".

G195 G **163** 90 c. multicoloured 80 80
G196 G **164** 90 c. multicoloured 80 80
G197 G **165** 90 c. multicoloured 80 80
G198 G **166** 90 c. multicoloured 80 80

Nos. G195/8 were issued together, se-tenant, forming the composite design illustrated.

G **167** Mountains

G **169** Papers and Ballot Box

1991. 1st Anniv of Namibian Independence. Multicoloured.

G199 70 c. Type G **167** .. 65 65
G200 90 c. Baobab 80 80

1991. Multicoloured.

G201 80 c. Type G **169** .. 75 75
G202 1 f. 50 U.N. emblem .. 1·40 1·40

G **171** Baby in Open Hands (Ryuta Nakajima)

1991. 30th Anniv (1989) of U.N. Declaration on the Rights of the Child and 1990 World Summit on Children, New York. Children's Drawings. Multicoloured.

G203 80 c. Type G **171** .. 75 75
G204 1 f. 10 Children playing amongst flowers (David Popper) .. 1·00 1·00

G **173** Bubble of Toxin, City and Drums

1991. Banning of Chemical Weapons. Mult.

G205 80 c. Type G **173** .. 75 75
G206 1 f. 40 Hand pushing back gas mask .. 1·25 1·25

G **175** U.N. (New York) 1951 15 c. Stamp

1991. 40th Anniv of United Nations Postal Administration.

G207 G **175** 50 c. blue and lilac on cream .. 45 45
G208 – 1 f. 60 bl on cream 1·50 1·50

DESIGN: 1 f. 60, U.N. (New York) 1951 50 c. stamp.

1991. Declaration of Human Rights (3rd series). As Type G **149**. Multicoloured.

G209 50 c. "Early Morning in Ro, 1925" (Paul Klee) (Article 15) .. 45 45
G210 90 c. "The Marriage of Arnolfini" (Jan van Eyck) (Article 16) .. 80 80

G **179** Sagarmatha National Park, Nepal

G **181** U.N. Headquarters, New York

1992. 20th Anniv of U.N.E.S.C.O. World Heritage Convention. Multicoloured.

G211 50 c. Type G **179** .. 45 45
G212 1 f. 10 Stonehenge, United Kingdom .. 1·00 1·00

1992.

G213 G **181** 3 f. multicoloured 2·75 2·75

G **182/3** Sea Life (½-size illustration)

1992. "Clean Oceans".

G214 G **182** 80 c. multicoloured 75 75
G215 G **183** 80 c. multicoloured 75 75

Nos. G214/15 were issued together, se-tenant, forming the composite design illustrated.

G **184/187** Planet Earth

1992. 2nd U.N. Conference on Environment and Development, Rio de Janeiro.

G216 G **184** 75 c. multicoloured 70 70
G217 G **185** 75 c. multicoloured 70 70
G218 G **186** 75 c. multicoloured 70 70
G219 G **187** 75 c. multicoloured 70 70

Nos. G216/19 were issued together, se-tenant, forming the composite design illustrated.

G **188/189** "Mission Planet Earth"

1992. International Space Year. Roul.

G220 G **188** 1 f. 10 mult .. 1·00 1·00
G221 G **189** 1 f. 10 mult .. 1·00 1·00

Nos. G220/1 were issued together, se-tenant, the composite design illustrated.

G **190** Women in Science and Technology

G **194** Voluntary Work

1992. Commission on Science and Technology for Development. Multicoloured.

G222 90 c. Type G **190** .. 80 80
G223 1 f. 60 Graduate using V.D.U. .. .. 1·50 1·50

1992. Universal Declaration of Human Rights (4th series). As Type G **149**. Multicoloured.

G224 50 c. "The Oath of the Tennis Court" (Jacques Louis David) (Article 21) 45 45
G225 90 c. "Rocking Chair I" (Henry Moore) (Article 22) 80 80

1993. "Ageing: Dignity and Participation". 10th Anniv (1992) of International Plan of Action on Ageing. Multicoloured.

G226 50 c. Type G **194** .. 45 45
G227 1 f. 60 Security of employment .. .. 1·50 1·50

G **196** Gorilla

1993. Endangered Species. Multicoloured.

G228 80 c. Type G **196** .. 70 70
G229 80 c. Peregrine falcon .. 70 70
G230 80 c. Amazon manatee .. 70 70
G231 80 c. Snow leopard .. 70 70

G **200** Neighbourhood and Community Environment

1993. 45th Anniv of W.H.O. Multicoloured.

G232 60 c. Type G **200** .. 55 55
G233 1 f. Urban environment 90 90

1993. Declaration of Human Rights (5th series). As Type G **149**. Multicoloured.

G234 50 c. "Three Musicians" (Pablo Picasso) (Article 27) 45 45
G235 90 c. "Voice of Space" (Rene Magritte) (Article 28) 80 80

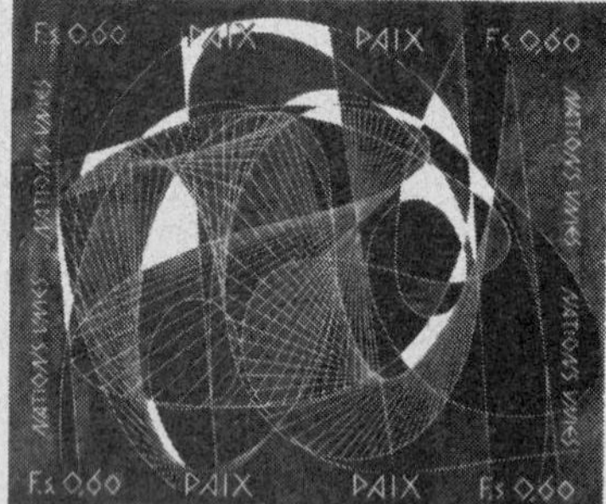

G **204/207** Peace

1993. International Peace Day. Roul.

G236 G **204** 60 c. multicoloured 55 55
G237 G **205** 60 c. multicoloured 55 55
G238 G **206** 60 c. multicoloured 55 55
G239 G **207** 60 c. multicoloured 55 55

Nos. G236/9 were issued together, se-tenant, forming the composite design illustrated.

G **208** Polar Bears

1993. The Environment—Climate. Mult.

G240 1 f. 10 Type G **208** .. 1·00 1·00
G241 1 f. 10 Whale in melting ice .. .. .. 1·00 1·00
G242 1 f. 10 Elephant seal .. 1·00 1·00
G243 1 f. 10 Penguins .. 1·00 1·00

Nos. G240/3 were issued together, se-tenant, forming a composite design.

C. VIENNA HEADQUARTERS.

For use on mail posted at the United Nations Vienna International Centre and by the International Atomic Energy Agency.

NOTE. Reference to numbers and types in this section, other than those with "V" prefix, are to the United Nations (New York or Geneva Headquarters) listing. Designs adapted for the Vienna issues are inscribed in Austrian and have face values in schillings.

V **4**. Donaupark Complex.

1979. Some designs adapted from issues of New York or Geneva Headquarters. Multicoloured.

V 1. 50 g. Type G **53** 10 10
V 2. 1 s. As No. 94 .. .. 10 10
V 3. 2 s. 50 Type **162** 30 30
V 3a. 3 s. "... for a better world" 35 35
V 4. 4 s. Type V **4** 45 45
V 5. 5 s. Type A **134** 55 55
V 6. 6 s. Aerial view of Donaupark (vert.) 65 65
V 7. 10 s. As Type **52**, but without frame .. .. 1·10 1·10

1980. New International Economic Order.

V 8. **195.** 4 s. multicoloured .. 1·00 90

V **9**. Dove and World Map.

1980. U.N. Decade for Women.

V 9. V **9**. 4 s. multicoloured .. 40 30
V 10. 6 s. multicoloured .. 85 65

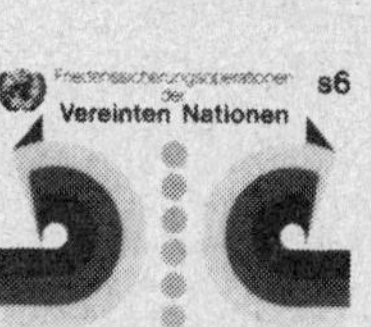

V **10**. "Peace-keeping".

V **13**. Economic and Social Emblems.

V **11**. Dove and "35".

1980. Peace-keeping Operations.

V 11. V **10**. 6 s. multicoloured .. 65 65

1980. 35th Anniv of U.N.O.

V 12 V **11** 4 s. black and red .. 35 30
V 13 – 6 s. multicoloured .. 75 70

DESIGNS: 6 s. Stylised flower.

1980. Economic and Social Council. Multicoloured.

V15 V **13** 4 s. multicoloured .. 45 40
V16 – 6 s. green, red & blk 65 55

DESIGN: 6 s. Figures ascending graph.

1981. Inalienable Rights of the Palestinian People.

V 17. **206.** 4 s. multicoloured .. 65 50

1981. International Year of Disabled Persons.

V 18. **207.** 4 s. multicoloured .. 45 35
V 19. – 6 s. orange and black 65 55

DESIGN: 6 s. Knot pattern.

1981. Art.

V 20. **209.** 6 s. multicoloured .. 60 60

V **19**. U.N. Energy Conference Emblem.

1981. New and Renewable Sources of Energy

V 21. V **19**. 7 s. 50 gold and mauve 70 70

V 20. Symbols of Services.

1981. 10th Anniv. of U.N. Volunteers Programme. Multicoloured.

V 22. 5 s. Type **V 20** 45 40
V 23. 7 s. Emblems of Science, Agriculture and Industry 65 60

V **22.** Symbols of the Environment. V **24.** Satellite amd Emblems.

1982. Human Environment. Multicoloured.

V 24. 5 s. Type V 22 .. .. 45 45
V 25. 7 s. Leaves 65 65

1982. Second United Nations Conference on Exploration and Peaceful Uses of Outer. Space.

V 26. V **24.** 5 s. multicoloured .. 70 60

V **25.** Fish. V **28.** Radar Screen within Lifebelt.

1982. Conservation and Protection of Nature. Multicoloured.

V 27. 5 s. Type **V 10** 60 60
V 28. 7 s. Elephant (mammals) 1·00 80

1983. World Communications Year.

V 29. **222.** 4 s. multicoloured .. 60 50

1983. Safety at Sea: International Maritime Organization. Multicoloured.

V 30. 4 s. Type **V 28** 50 50
V 31. 6 s. Stylized liner .. 75 75

1983. World Food Programme.

V 32. **226.** 5 s. green 60 50
V 33. 7 s. brown 65 60

V **31.** Exports. V **33.** " Die Zweite Haut ".

1983. Trade and Development. Multicoloured.

V 34. 4 s. Type **V 31** 50 40
V 35. 8 s. 50 Emblems of Trade 90 85

1983. 35th Anniv. of Declaration of Human Rights. Multicoloured.

V 36. 5 s. Type **V 33** 50 40
V 37. 7 s. " Recht auf Traume " 75 60

V **35.** World Agriculture. V **36.** Irrigation.

1984. International Conference on Population, Mexico City.

V 38. V **35.** 7 s. multicoloured .. 95 95

1984. World Food Day. Multicoloured.

V 39. 4 s. 50 Type **V 36** .. 45 45
V 40. 6 s. Combine harvesters .. 65 65

V **38.** Serengeti National Park, Tanzania. V **40.** Woman with Child

1984. World Heritage—U.N.E.S.C.O. Mult.

V41 3 s. 50 Type **V 38** .. 50 40
V42 15 s. Schibam, Yemen .. 1·50 1·75

1984. Future for Refugees.

V 43. V **40.** 4 s. 50 black and brown 55 45
V 44. – 8 s. 50 black and yellow 95 80

DESIGN: 8 s. 50 Woman.

V **42.** Stylized Figures. V **43.** U Thant Pavilion.

1984. International Youth Year.

V 45. V **42.** 3 s. 50 multicoloured 55 40
V 46. 6 s. 50 multicoloured 85 70

1985. 20th Anniv. of Turin Centre of International Labour Organization.

V 47. V **43.** 7 s. 50 violet .. 1·00 80

V **44.** Rural Scene and Researcher with Microscope.

1985. 10th Anniv of United Nations University, Tokyo.

V 48. V **44.** 8 s. 50 multicoloured 1·10 90

V **45.** "Boat". V **49.** Oral Immunization.

1985. Multicoloured.

V49 4 s. 50 Type **V 45** .. 50 50
V50 15 s. Sheltering under U.N. umbrella .. 1·50 1·75

1985. 40th Anniv. of United Nations Organization. Multicoloured.

V 51. 6 s. 50 Type **243** 80 65
V 52. 8 s. 50 "Harvest Scene" (Andrew Wyeth) .. 95 85

1985. U.N.I.C.E.F. Child Survival Campaign. Multicoloured.

V 54. 4 s. Type **V 49** 55 55
V 55. 6 s. Mother and baby .. 85 85

V **51.** "Africa in Crisis". V **52.** Growing Crops.

1986. Africa in Crisis.

V 56. V **51.** 8 s. multicoloured .. 1·00 90

1986. Development Programme. Village Scene. Multicoloured.

V 57. 4 s. 50 Type **V 52** .. 90 70
V 58. 4 s. 50 Villagers with livestock 90 70
V 59. 4 s. 50 Woodwork instructor 90 70
V 60. 4 s. 50 Nutrition instructor 90 70

Nos. V 57/60 were printed together, se-tenant, forming a composite design.

V **56.** United Nations Stamps. V **58.** Olive Branch and Rainbow.

1986. Philately: an International Hobby.

V 61 **V 56** 3 s. 50 blue & brown 50 40
V 62 – 6 s. 50 blue and red 75 70

DESIGN: 6 s. 50, Engraver.

1986. International Peace Year. Mult.

V 63. 5 s. Type **V 58** 65 55
V 64. 6 s. Doves on U.N. emblem 75 65

1986. 9th Death Anniv. of Trygve Lie (first U.N. Secretary-General).

V 66. **258.** 8 s. multicoloured 1·00 90

V **62.** Family looking at New Houses.

1987. International Year of Shelter for the Homeless.

V 67. V **62.** 4 s. orange, black and yellow .. 65 50
V 68. – 9 s. 50 orange and black .. 1·40 1·10

DESIGN: 9 s. 50 Family entering door of new house.

V **64.** Footballers.

1987. Anti-Drugs Campaign. Multicoloured.

V 69. 5 s. Type **V 64** 75 60
V 70. 8 s. Family .. .. 1·25 90

V **66.** U.N. Centre, Vienna.

1987. Multicoloured.

V 71. 2 s. Type **V 66** 25 25
V 72. 17 s. Wreath of olive leaves and doves around globe .. .. 1·90 1·90

V **68.** Dancers and Vienna Headquarters. V **70.** Poliomyelitis.

1987. United Nations Day. Multicoloured.

V73 5 s. Type **V 68** .. 70 60
V74 6 s. Dancers 80 70

1987. "Immunize Every Child". Mult.

V 75. 4 s. Type **V 70** 65 50
V 76. 9 s. 50 Diphtheria .. 1·25 1·10

V **72.** Woman planting.

1987. International Fund for Agricultural Development "For a World Without Hunger" Campaign. Multicoloured.

V 77. 4 s. Type **V 72** 55 55
V 78. 6 s. Women and food-stuffs 70 70

V **74.** Hills and Forest in Autumn. V **76.** Testing Blood Pressure.

1988. "Survival of the Forests". Mult.

V 79. 4 s. Type **V 74** .. .. 1·75 1·00
V 80. 5 s. Forest in autumn .. 2·25 1·00

Nos. V79/80 were printed together, se-tenant, forming a composite design.

1988. International Volunteer Day. Mult.

V81 6 s. Type **V 76** 80 70
V82 7 s. 50 Building houses (horiz) 95 80

V 78 Skiing V 81 Transport

1988. "Health in Sports". Multicoloured.

V83 6 s. Type **V 78** 75 70
V84 8 s. Tennis (horiz) 1·00 90

1988. 40th Anniv of Declaration of Human Rights.

V85 **276** 5 s. multicoloured .. 65 60

1989. World Bank. Multicoloured.

V87 5 s. 50 Type **V 81** .. 75 65
V88 8 s. Health and education 1·00 80

1989. Award of Nobel Peace Prize to United Nations Peace-keeping Forces.

V89 **280** 6 s. multicoloured .. 75 65

V 84 Depression over Italy V 86 Man in Winter Clothes

1989. 25th Anniv of World Weather Watch.

V90 4 s. Type **V 84** 60 40
V91 9 s. 50 Short-range rainfall forecast for Tokyo .. 1·25 90

1989. 10th Anniv of United Nations Vienna International Centre. Multicoloured.

V92 5 s. Type **V 86** 55 45
V93 7 s. 50 Abstract 85 70

HAVE YOU READ THE NOTES AT THE BEGINNING OF THIS CATALOGUE?

These often provide answers to the enquiries we receive.

V 88 "Prisoners" (Kathe Kollwitz) (Article 5)

V 91 "Earth" (painting by Kurt Regschek in IAEA building)

1989. Universal Declaration of Human Rights (1st series).
V94 V **88** 4 s. black 40 35
V95 – 6 s. multicoloured .. 70 65
DESIGN: 6 s. "Jurisprudence" (Rafael) (Article 6).
See also Nos. V107/8, V122/3, V138/9 and V149/50.

1990. International Trade Centre.
V96 **287** 12 s. multicoloured .. 1·75 1·75

1990.
V97 V **91** 1 s. 50 multicoloured 20 15

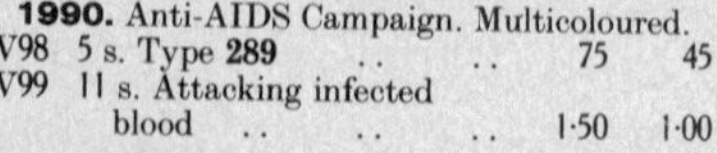

1990. Anti-AIDS Campaign. Multicoloured.
V98 5 s. Type **289** 75 45
V99 11 s. Attacking infected blood .. .. .. 1·50 1·00

V **94** Annatto

V **96** "45"

1990. Medicinal Plants. Multicoloured.
V100 4 s. 50 Type V **94** .. 60 40
V101 9 s. 50 Cundeamor .. 1·40 90

1990. 45th Anniv of U.N.O. Multicoloured.
V102 7 s. Type V **96** .. .. 1·00 80
V103 9 s. "45" (different) .. 1·40 1·10

V **98** Men Fighting

1990. Crime Prevention. Multicoloured.
V105 6 s. Type V **98** 85 70
V106 8 s. Masked man damaging painting .. 1·10 90

1990. Universal Declaration of Human Rights (2nd series). As Type V **88**. Multicoloured.
V107 4 s. 50 "Before the Judge" (Sandor Bihari) (Article 11) 60 50
V108 7 s. "Young Man Greeted by Woman writing Poem" (Suzuki Harunobu) (Article 12) 80 65

V102/5 Mediterranean Coastline and Wildlife

1991. Economic Commission for Europe. "For a Better Environment".
V109 V **102** 5 s. multicoloured 55 45
V110 V **103** 5 s. multicoloured 55 45
V111 V **104** 5 s. multicoloured 55 45
V112 V **105** 5 s. multicoloured 55 45
Nos. V109/12 were printed together, se-tenant, forming the composite design illustrated.

V **106** Scrubland

V **108** Different Races

1991. 1st Anniv of Namibian Independence. Multicoloured.
V113 6 s. Type V **106** .. 70 60
V114 9 s. 50 Sand dune .. 1·10 90

1991.
V115 V **108** 20 s. multicoloured 2·25 1·90

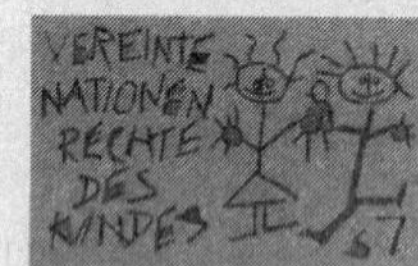

V **109** Boy and Girl (Anna Harmer)

1991. 30th Anniv (1989) of U.N. Declaration on the Rights of the Child and 1990 World Summit on Children, New York. Children's Drawings. Multicoloured.
V116 7 s. Type V **109** .. 85 65
V117 9 s. Child's world (Emiko Takegawa) .. .. 1·00 80

V **111** City, Bubbles of Toxin and Gas Mask

1991. Banning of Chemical Weapons. Mult.
V118 5 s. Type V **111** .. 55 45
V119 10 s. Hand pushing back cloud of toxin sprayed from airplane .. 1·10 90

V **113** U.N. (New York) 1951 20 c. Stamp

1991. 40th Anniv of United Nations Postal Administration.
V120 V **113** 5 s. brown on cream 55 45
V121 – 8 s. blue on cream 90 75
DESIGN: 8 s. U.N. (New York) 1951 5 c. stamp.

1991. Declaration of Human Rights (3rd series). As Type V **88**. Multicoloured.
V122 4 s. 50 Ancient Mexican pottery (Article 17) .. 50 40
V123 7 s. "Windows, 1912" (Robert Delaunay) (Article 18) 80 65

V **117** Iguacu National Park, Brazil

V **119/20** Sea Life (½-size illustration)

1992. 20th Anniv of U.N.E.S.C.O World Heritage Convention. Multicoloured.
V124 5 s. Type V **117** .. 55 45
V125 9 s. Abu Simbel, Egypt 1·00 80

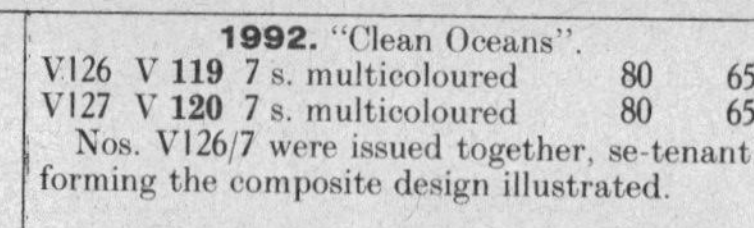

1992. "Clean Oceans".
V126 V **119** 7 s. multicoloured 80 65
V127 V **120** 7 s. multicoloured 80 65
Nos. V126/7 were issued together, se-tenant, forming the composite design illustrated.

V **121/124** Planet Earth

1992. 2nd U.N. Conference on Environment and Development, Rio de Janeiro.
V128 V **121** 5 s. 50 mult .. 60 50
V129 V **122** 5 s. 50 mult .. 60 50
V130 V **123** 5 s. 50 mult .. 60 50
V131 V **124** 5 s. 50 mult .. 60 50
Nos. V128/31 were issued together, se-tenant, forming the composite design illustrated.

V **125/126** "Mission Planet Earth"

1992. International Space Year. Roul.
V132 V **125** 10 s. multicoloured 1·10 90
V133 V **126** 10 s. multicoloured 1·10 90
Nos. V132/3 were issued together, se-tenant, forming the composite design illustrated.

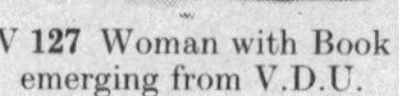

V **127** Woman with Book emerging from V.D.U.

V **129** Woman's Profile, Birds, Butterfly and Rose

1992. Commission on Science and Technology for Development. Multicoloured.
V134 5 s. 50 Type V **127** .. 60 50
V135 7 s. Flowers growing from thumb 80 65

1992. Multicoloured.
V136 5 s. 50 Type V **129** .. 60 50
V137 7 s. Vienna International Centre (horiz) 80 65

1992. Universal Declaration of Human Rights (4th series). As Type V **88**. Multicoloured.
V138 6 s. "The Builders" (Fernand Leger) (Article 23) 70 60
V139 10 s. "Sunday Afternoon on the Island of La Grande Jatte, 1884–86" (Article 24) .. .. 1·10 90

V **133** Housing and Environment

V **135** Grevy's Zebra

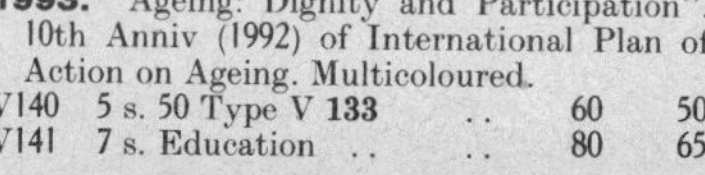

1993. "Ageing: Dignity and Participation". 10th Anniv (1992) of International Plan of Action on Ageing. Multicoloured.
V140 5 s. 50 Type V **133** .. 60 50
V141 7 s. Education 80 65

1993. Endangered Species. Multicoloured.
V142 7 s. Type V **135** .. 80 65
V143 7 s. Humboldt penguin 80 65
V144 7 s. Desert monitor .. 80 65
V145 7 s. Wolf 80 65

V **139** Globe, Doves and U.N. Emblem

V **140** Regional and National Environment

1993.
V146 V **139** 13 s. multicoloured 1·50 1·25

1993. 45th Anniv of W.H.O. Multicoloured.
V147 6 s. Type V **140** .. 70 60
V148 10 s. Continental and global environment .. 1·10 90

1993. Declaration of Human Rights (5th series). As Type V **88**. Multicoloured.
V149 5 s. "Lower Austrian Peasants' Wedding" (Ferdinand Waldmuller) (Article 29) .. 55 45
V150 6 s. "Outback" (Sally Morgan) (Article 30) .. 70 60

V **144/147** Peace

1993. International Peace Day. Roul.
V151 V **144** 5 s. 50 mult .. 60 50
V152 V **145** 5 s. 50 mult .. 60 50
V153 V **146** 5 s. 50 mult .. 60 50
V154 V **147** 5 s. 50 mult .. 60 50
Nos. V151/4 were issued together, se-tenant, forming the composite design illustrated.

V **148** Monkeys

1993. The Environment—Climate. Mult.
V155 7 s. Type V **148** .. 80 65
V156 7 s. Bluebird and factory chimneys 80 65
V157 7 s. Volcano, smokestacks and tree stumps .. 80 65
V158 7 s. Owl in desert .. 80 65
Nos. V155/8 were issued together, se-tenant, forming a composite design.

Sep '94
Nov '94

UNITED STATES OF AMERICA

Pt. 22

A Federal Republic in N. America, consisting of 50 states and one federal district.

100 cents = 1 dollar.

PRICES. On the issues before 1890 the gum is rarely complete and the unused prices quoted are for stamps with part original gum.

1. Franklin (after drawings by James B. Longacre).

2. Washington (after painting by Stuart).

1847. Imperf.

1.	1.	5 c. brown	£3750	£350
2.	2.	10 c. black	£14000	£1100

The 5 c. blue and 10 c. orange both **imperf.** come from miniature sheets issued in 1947 to commemorate the Centenary Philatelic Exhibition, New York.

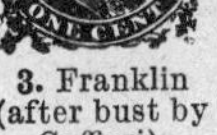

3. Franklin (after bust by Caffieri).

4. Washington (after bust by Houdon).

5. Jefferson (after painting by Stuart).

6. Washington. **7.** Washington **8.** Washington. (after paintings by Stuart).

9. Franklin (after bust by Caffieri).

10. Washington (after Trumbull painting).

1851. Imperf.

11.	3.	1 c. blue	£250	55·00
13a.	4.	3 c. red	90·00	4·25
14.	5.	5 c. brown	£6500	£650
16.	6.	10 c. green	£1300	£150
19.	7.	12 c. black	£1700	£170

1857. Perf.

26	3.	1 c. blue	75·00	14·00
28	4.	3 c. red	35·00	1·50
33	5.	5 c. brown	£325	£120
39	6.	10 c. green	£120	32·00
40c	7.	12 c. black	£180	60·00
41	8.	24 c. lilac	£375	£140
42	9.	30 c. orange	£550	£200
43	10.	90 c. blue	£850	£2750

11. Franklin.

12. Washington. **13.** Jefferson.

14. Washington. **15.** **16.** Washington.

17. Franklin. **18.** Washington.

19. Andrew Jackson (after miniature by J. W. Dodge).

20. Lincoln (from a photograph).

1861. Perf.

60b	11	1 c. blue	90·00	11·00
69	19	2 c. black	£110	16·00
62	12	3 c. red	45·00	60
63b	13	5 c. yellow	£3750	£275
72		5 c. brown	£250	38·00
64a	14	10 c. green	£190	18·00
65	15	12 c. black	£375	38·00
73	20	15 c. black	£375	50·00
66c	16	24 c. blue	£2750	£200
74		24 c. lilac	£200	32·00
74b		24 c. grey	£200	32·00
67	17	30 c. orange	£375	48·00
68a	18	90 c. blue	£1000	£170

21. Franklin (after Houdon bust). **22.** Post Rider. **23.** Steam Locomotive.

24. Washington (after Stuart).

25. Shield and Eagle.

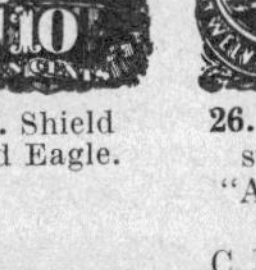

26. Paddle-steamer "Adriatic" (after C. Parsons).

27. Landing of Columbus (after Vanderlyn). **28.** Declaration of Independence (after Trumbull). **30.** Lincoln (from a photograph).

1869.

114	21	1 c. brown	£160	45·00
115	22	2 c. brown	£130	18·00
116	23	3 c. blue	£140	4·25
117	24	6 c. blue	£550	60·00
118	25	10 c. orange	£650	60·00
119	26	12 c. green	£550	65·00
121	27	15 c. blue and brown	£700	95·00
122	28	24 c. purple and green	£1700	£325
123	25	30 c. red and blue	£1800	£150
124	30	90 c. black and red	£5500	£900

31. Franklin.

32. Jackson. **33.** Washington.

34. Lincoln. **35.** Stanton. **36.** Jefferson.

37. Henry Clay. **38.** Daniel Webster. **39.** General Winfield Scott.

40. Alexander Hamilton. **41.** Commodore Perry.

42. General Zachary Taylor (from a daguerreotype).

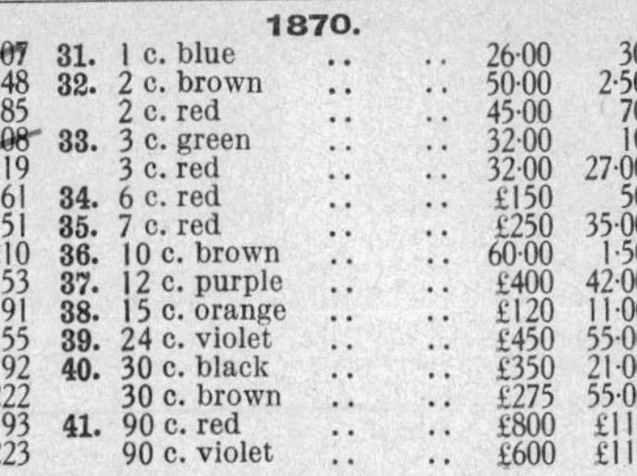

1870.

207	31.	1 c. blue	26·00	30
148	32.	2 c. brown	50·00	2·50
185		2 c. red	45·00	70
208	33.	3 c. green	32·00	10
219		3 c. red	32·00	27·00
161	34.	6 c. red	£150	50
151	35.	7 c. red	£250	35·00
210	36.	10 c. brown	60·00	1·50
153	37.	12 c. purple	£400	42·00
191	38.	15 c. orange	£120	11·00
155	39.	24 c. violet	£450	55·00
192	40.	30 c. black	£350	21·00
222		30 c. brown	£275	55·00
193	41.	90 c. red	£800	£110
223		90 c. violet	£600	£110

1875.

181.	42.	5 c. blue	£140	4·75

43. Garfield (from a photograph). **44.** Washington (after bust by Houdon). **45.** Jackson (after bust by Powers).

46. Franklin.

47. Franklin.

1882.

217.	46.	1 c. blue	45·00	40
213.	44.	2 c. brown	23·00	10
218.		2 c. green	17·00	10
214.	45.	4 c. green	£120	4·50
220.		4 c. red	£120	7·50
211.	43.	5 c. brown	90·00	2·50
221.		5 c. blue	£110	3·50

1890. No triangles in upper corners.

224.	47.	1 c. blue (Franklin)	14·00	10
225a.	–	2 c. red (Washington)	12·00	10
226.	–	3 c. violet (Jackson)	40·00	3·00
227.	–	4 c. sepia (Lincoln)	38·00	1·00
228.	–	5 c. brown (Grant)	40·00	1·00
229.	–	6 c. red (Garfield)	42·00	11·00
230.	–	8 c. purple (Sherman)	26·00	5·50
231.	–	10 c. green (Webster)	70·00	1·00
232.	–	15 c. blue (Clay)	£120	10·00
233.	–	30 c. black (Jefferson)	£180	14·00
234.	–	90 c. orange (Perry)	£300	70·00

58. Columbus in sight of land.

83. Jefferson.

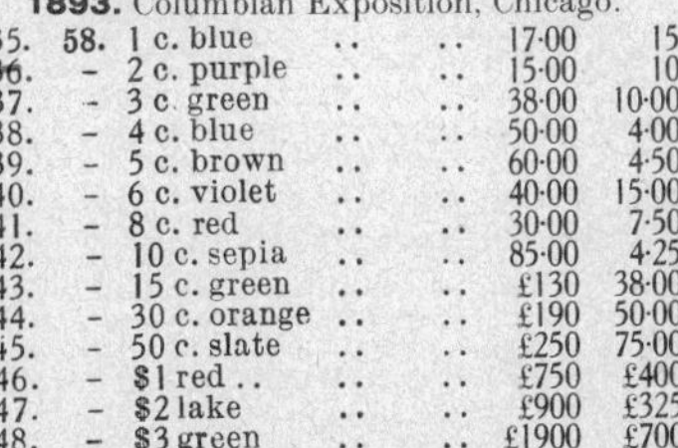

1893. Columbian Exposition, Chicago.

235.	58.	1 c. blue	17·00	15
236.	–	2 c. purple	15·00	10
237.	–	3 c. green	38·00	10·00
238.	–	4 c. blue	50·00	4·00
239.	–	5 c. brown	60·00	4·50
240.	–	6 c. violet	40·00	15·00
241.	–	8 c. red	30·00	7·50
242.	–	10 c. sepia	85·00	4·25
243.	–	15 c. green	£130	38·00
244.	–	30 c. orange	£190	50·00
245.	–	50 c. slate	£250	75·00
246.	–	$1 red	£750	£400
247.	–	$2 lake	£900	£325
248.	–	$3 green	£1900	£700
249a.	–	$4 red	£2750	£1000
250.	–	$5 black	£2750	£1100

DESIGNS: 2 c. Landing of Columbus. 3 c. "Santa Maria", Flagship of Columbus. 4 c. Fleet of Columbus. 5 c. Columbus soliciting aid of Isabella. 6 c. Columbus welcomed at Barcelona, Ferdinand (left) and Balboa (right). 8 c. Columbus restored to favour. 10 c. Columbus presenting natives. 15 c. Columbus announcing his discovery. 30 c. Columbus at La Rabida. 50 c. Recall of Columbus. $1, Isabella pledging her jewels. $2, Columbus in chains. $3, Columbus describing his third voyage. $4, Isabella and Columbus. $5, Columbus, America and Liberty.

1894. Triangles in upper corners as T 83. Same portraits as issue of 1890 except dollar values.

267	–	1 c. blue	3·50	10
283	–	1 c. green	6·00	10
270	–	2 c. red	2·75	10
271	–	3 c. violet	22·00	60
285	–	4 c. brown	20·00	40
273	–	5 c. brown	22·00	90
286	–	5 c. blue	22·00	30
274	–	6 c. brown	48·00	2·00
287a	–	6 c. purple	28·00	1·00
275	–	8 c. brown	25·00	60
276	–	10 c. green	35·00	60
289	–	10 c. brown	70·00	1·00
277	–	15 c. blue	£120	4·50
290	–	15 c. green	85·00	3·50
278	83	50 c. orange	£160	12·00
279	–	$1 black (Perry)	£350	40·00
281a	–	$2 blue (Madison)	£650	£190
282	–	$5 green (Marshall)	£1400	£300

88. Father Marquette on the Mississippi.

97 "City of Alpena" (Great Lakes steamer).

1898. Trans-Mississippi Exposition, Omaha.

291.	88.	1 c. green	18·00	2·75
292.	–	2 c. red	17·00	70
293.	–	4 c. orange	90·00	13·00
294.	–	5 c. blue	75·00	10·00
295.	–	8 c. purple	£120	21·00
296.	–	10 c. violet	£140	12·00
297.	–	50 c. green	£550	60·00
298.	–	$1 black	£1400	£375
299.	–	$2 brown	£2000	£700

DESIGNS: 2 c. Farming in West. 4 c. Indian hunting American bison. 5 c. Fremont on Rocky Mountains. 8 c. Troops guarding emigrant train. 10 c. Hardships of emigration. 50 c. Western mining prospector. $1, Western cattle in storm. $2, Bridge over Mississippi at St. Louis and paddle-steamer "Grey Eagle".

1901. Pan-American Exn., Buffalo. Inscr. "COMMEMORATIVE SERIES, 1901".

300.	97.	1 c. black and green	15·00	2·75
301.	–	2 c. black and red	15·00	75
302.	–	4 c. black and brown	65·00	10·00
303.	–	5 c. black and blue	85·00	13·00
304.	–	8 c. black and brown	£100	50·00
305.	–	10 c. black and brown	£160	20·00

DESIGNS: 2 c. "Empire State Express". 4 c. Automobile. 5 c. Railway bridge below Niagara Falls. 8 c. Canal locks at Sault Sainte Marie. 10 c. "Saint Paul" (liner).

103. Franklin. **104.** Washington. **105.** Jackson.

106. Grant. **107.** Lincoln. **108.** Garfield

109. Martha Washington. **110.** Webster. **111.** Harrison.

112. Clay. **113.** Jefferson. **114.** Farragut.

115. Madison.

116. Marshall.

1902. Inscr "SERIES 1902". 1, 4 and 5 c. perf or imperf.

306.	103.	1 c. green	6·00	10
307.	104.	2 c. red	7·00	10
308.	105.	3 c. violet	35·00	1·75
309.	106.	4 c. brown	35·00	70
310.	107.	5 c. blue	40·00	45
311.	108.	6 c. lake	42·00	1·40
312.	109.	8 c. violet	24·00	1·10
313.	110.	10 c. brown	50·00	70
314.	111.	13 c. purple	24·00	5·00
315.	112.	15 c. olive	95·00	3·25
316.	113.	50 c. orange	£250	14·00
317.	114.	$1 black	£550	32·00
485.	115.	$2 blue	£375	32·00
486.	116.	$5 green	£300	35·00

117. Washington (after Stuart).

118. Robert R. Livingston (after Stuart).

1903. Perf or imperf.

326	117	2 c. red	3·50	10

1904. Int. Exposition, St. Louis, and Louisiana Purchase. Inscr. "COMMEMORATIVE SERIES OF 1904".

330.	**118.**	1 c. green	20·00	2·75
331.	–	2 c. red	18·00	80
332.	–	3 c. violet	65·00	22·00
333.	–	5 c. blue	75·00	12·00
334.	–	10 c. brown	£130	18·00

DESIGNS: 2 c. Thomas Jefferson. 3 c. James Monroe (after Vanderlyn). 5 c. William McKinley. 10 c. Map of Louisiana Purchase.

123. Capt. John Smith, Pocahontas and Powhatan (after painting).

1907. Jamestown Exposition.

335.	**123.**	1 c. green	12·00	2·75
336.	–	2 c. red	15·00	1·75
337.	–	5 c. blue	65·00	17·00

DESIGNS: 2 c. Founding of Jamestown, 1607. 5 c. Princess Pocahontas.

126. Franklin. **127.** Washington **128.** (after Houdon bust).

1908. 1 to 5 c. perf or imperf.

338	126	1 c. green	4·00	10
505	128	1 c. green	25	10
339	127	2 c. red	3·75	10
506	128	2 c. red	20	10
537		3 c. violet	65	10
510		4 c. brown	10·00	10
503		5 c. blue	3·50	70
513		6 c. orange	11·00	15
514		7 c. black	22·00	85
344		8 c. green	23·00	1·75
345		10 c. yellow	45·00	1·00
346		13 c. green	25·00	16·00
347		15 c. blue	40·00	3·50
348		50 c. violet	£200	9·50
349		$1 black	£325	48·00

129. Lincoln (detail of statue by Saint Gaudens in Grant Park, Chicago).

1909. Birth Centenary of Abraham Lincoln. Perf or imperf.

374	129	2 c. red	3·75	1·50

130. Wm. H. Seward. **131.** "Clermont" and "Half Moon" on Hudson River.

1909. Alaska–Yukon–Pacific Exposition. Perf or imperf.

377	130	2 c. red	6·50	1·00

1909. Hudson-Fulton Celebration. Perf or imperf.

379	131	2 c. red	11·00	3·25

133. Franklin **138.** (after Caffieri bust).

1912.

515	133	8 c. olive	11·00	55
516		9 c. pink	13·00	1·50
517		10 c. yellow	15·00	10
518		11 c. green	8·00	2·50
519		12 c. brown	8·00	30
520		13 c. green	10·00	5·50
521		15 c. grey	3·00	70
522		20 c. blue	40·00	15
523		30 c. orange	30·00	55
524		50 c. lilac	70·00	40
525		$1 black	65·00	1·00
526	138	$2 black and orange	£650	£170
527		$2 black and red ..	£275	23·00
528		$5 black and green ..	£300	22·00

134. Balboa. **135.** Panama Canal (after model of Pedro Miguel Locks).

1913. Panama–Pacific Exposition. Inscr. "SAN FRANCISCO 1915".

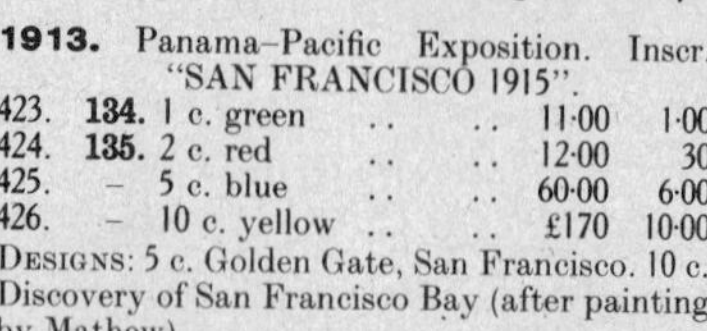

423.	**134.**	1 c. green	11·00	1·00
424.	**135.**	2 c. red	12·00	30
425.	–	5 c. blue	60·00	6·00
426.	–	10 c. yellow	£170	10·00

DESIGNS: 5 c. Golden Gate, San Francisco. 10 c. Discovery of San Francisco Bay (after painting by Mathew).

A **139.** Curtiss "Jenny". **139.** Liberty and Allies' Flags.

1918. Air.

A 546.	A **139**	6 c. orange	70·00	26·00
A 547.		16 c. green	£100	32·00
A 548.		24 c. blue and red ..	£100	35·00

1919. Victory.

546.	**139.**	3 c. violet	6·00	2·50

140. The "Mayflower".

1920. Tercent. of Landing of Pilgrim Fathers. Inscr. as in T **140.**

556.	**140.**	1 c. green	3·75	2·00
557.	–	2 c. red	6·50	1·25
558.	–	5 c. blue	32·00	10·00

DESIGNS: 2 c. Landing of the Pilgrims (after drawing by White). 5 c. Signing the Compact.

144. Franklin. **157.** Indian Chief. **158.** Statue of Liberty.

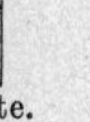

159. Golden Gate. **165.** America.

1922. ½ c. to 15 c. vert, 17 c. to $5 horiz. 1 to 2 c. perf or imperf.

559	–	½ c. brown (Hale) ..	15	10
632	144	1 c. green	15	10
605	–	1½ c. brown (Harding)	50	10
634	–	2 c. red (Washington)	15	10
636a	–	3 c. violet (Lincoln)	20	10
637	–	4 c. brown (Martha Washington) ..	2·75	10
608	–	5 c. bl (T. Roosevelt)	1·00	10
639	–	6 c. orange (Garfield)	2·25	10
640	–	7 c. black (McKinley)	2·25	10
641	–	8 c. green (Grant) ..	2·25	10
642	–	9 c. pink (Jefferson)	2·25	10
610	–	10 c. orange (Monroe)	3·00	10
571a	–	11 c. blue (Hayes) ..	1·50	15
571b	–	11 c. green (Hayes) ..	1·40	35
693	–	12 c. vio (Cleveland)	5·00	10
694	–	13 c. green (B. Harrison) ..	1·75	15
695	157	14 c. blue	3·00	40
696	158	15 c. grey	8·00	10
698	159	20 c. red	9·00	10
699	–	25 c. green (Niagara)	8·50	10
700	–	30 c. brown (American bison) ..	13·00	10
701	–	50 c. lilac (Arlington Amphitheatre and Unknown Soldier's Tomb)	38·00	10
579	–	$1 brown (Lincoln Memorial)	45·00	20
580	–	$2 blue (Capitol, Washington) ..	£100	5·50
581	165	$5 blue and red ..	£225	8·00

A **166.** Aeroplane Radiator and Propeller. A **168.** De Havilland Biplane.

1923. Air.

A 614.	A **166.**	8 c. green ..	30·00	14·00
A 615.	–	16 c. blue ..	95·00	32·00
A 616.	A **168.**	24 c. red	£110	28·00

DESIGN: 16 c. Air Mail Service insignia.

166. Harding. **167.** "Nieu Nederland" (emigrant ship).

1923. President Harding Memorial.

614.	**166.**	2 c. black	70	10

1924. Huguenot-Walloon Tercent.

618.	**167.**	1 c. green	3·25	3·00
619.	–	2 c. red	7·00	2·00
620.	–	5 c. blue	24·00	14·00

DESIGNS: 2 c. Landing at Fort Orange. 5 c. Ribault Memorial, Mayport, Florida.

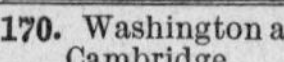

170. Washington at Cambridge. **173.** Sloop "Restaurationen".

1925. 150th Anniv. of Battle of Lexington and Concord.

621.	**170.**	1 c. green	3·00	3·00
622.	–	2 c. red	5·50	3·75
623.	–	5 c. blue	22·00	13·00

DESIGNS: 2 c. Battle of Lexington-Concord. 5 c. Statue of "Minute Man".

1925. Norse-American Centennial. Dated "1825 1925".

624.	**173.**	2 c. black and red ..	4·00	2·50
625.	–	5 c. black and blue ..	18·00	16·00

DESIGN: 5 c. "Raven" (replica Viking long-ship).

176. Wilson.

1925.

697	176	17 c. black	4·00	25

A **177.** Relief Map of U.S.A.

1926. Air.

A 628.	A **177.**	10 c. blue ..	3·00	20
A 629.		15 c. brown ..	3·25	2·00
A 630.		20 c. green ..	9·00	1·25

177. Liberty Bell.

1926. 150th Anniv. of Independence and Sesquicentennial Exhibition.

628.	**177.**	2 c. red	2·75	45

178. Ericsson Memorial (after statue by J. E. Fraser in Washington, D.C.). **179.** Alexander Hamilton's Battery (after painting by E. F. Ward).

1926. John Ericsson Commemoration.

629.	**178.**	5 c. violet	5·00	2·50

1926. 150th Anniv. of Battle of White Plains.

644	179	2 c. red	1·50	1·25

A **180.** The "Spirit of St. Louis".

1927. Air. Lindbergh's Transatlantic Flight.

A 646.	A **180.**	10 c. blue ..	8·50	1·25

181. Green Mountain Boy. **182.** Surrender of Gen. Burgoyne (after painting by Trumbull).

1927. 150th Anniv. of Independence of Vermont and Battle of Bennington.

646.	**181.**	2 c. red	1·25	80

1927. 150th Anniv. of Burgoyne Campaign.

647.	**182.**	2 c. red	3·00	2·00

183. Washington at Valley Forge (after engraving by J. C. McRae). A **184.** Air Beacon, Sherman Hill, Rocky Mountains.

1928. 150th Anniv. of Valley Forge.

648.	**183.**	2 c. red	70	35

1928. Air.

A 649.	A **184.**	5 c. blue and red	4·00	30

1928. 150th Anniv. of Discovery of Hawaii. Optd. **HAWAII 1778-1928.**

649	2 c. red (No. 634)	3·25	4·00
650	5 c. blue (No. 608) ..	12·00	15·00

1928. 150th Anniv. of Battle of Monmouth. Optd. **MOLLY PITCHER.**

651	2 c. red (No. 634)	1·00	1·00

DESIGN: 5 c. Globe and Aeroplane.

186. Wright Aeroplane.

1928. Civil Aeronautics Conference and 25th Anniv. of Wright Bros. First Flight.

652.	**186.**	2 c. red	1·25	90
653.	–	5 c. blue	6·00	2·75

188. George Rogers Clark at Vincennes (from painting by F. C. Yohn).

1929. 150th Anniv. of Surrender of Fort Sackville.

654.	**188.**	2 c. black and red ..	75	60

1929. Stamps of 1922 optd.

(a) **Kans.**

655.	**144.**	1 c. green	1·75	2·00
656.	**166.**	1½ c. brown	2·50	3·25
657.	–	2 c. red	3·00	65
658.	–	3 c. violet	13·00	12·00
659.	–	4 c. brown	15·00	7·00
660.	–	5 c. blue	11·00	8·50
661.	–	6 c. orange	24·00	17·00
662.	–	7 c. black	22·00	25·00
663.	–	8 c. olive	65·00	60·00
664.	–	9 c. red	11·00	10·00
665.	–	10 c. yellow	19·00	10·00

(b) **Nebr.**

666.	**144.**	1 c. green	2·00	1·75
667.	**166.**	1½ c. brown	2·25	2·75
668.	–	2 c. red	1·60	70
669.	–	3 c. violet	11·00	9·00
670.	–	4 c. brown	17·00	14·00
671.	–	5 c. blue	15·00	13·00
672.	–	6 c. orange	35·00	25·00
673.	–	7 c. black	19·00	16·00
674.	–	8 c. olive	25·00	22·00
675.	–	9 c. red	30·00	24·00
676.	–	10 c. yellow	90·00	16·00

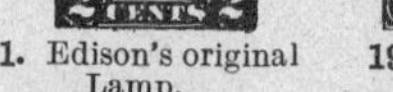

191. Edison's original Lamp. **192.** Maj.-Gen. Sullivan.

1929. 50th Anniv. of Edison's First Electric Lamp.

678.	**191.**	2 c. red	60	20

1929. 150th Anniv. of Maj.-Gen. Sullivan's Western Campaign.

680.	**192.**	2 c. red	55	50

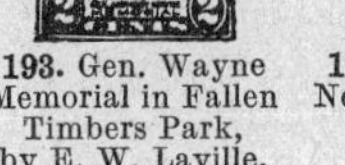

193. Gen. Wayne Memorial in Fallen Timbers Park, by E. W. Laville.
194. Ohio River Lock No. 5, Monongahela R.

1929. 135th Anniv. of Battle of Fallen Timbers.
681. 193. 2 c. red 75 75

1929. Completion of Ohio River Canalisation.
682. 194. 2 c. red 55 55

A195. Air Mail Pilot's Badge.
195. Seal of the Colony.

1930. Air.
A684 A 195 5 c violet .. .. 5·50 25
A685 6 c. orange .. 2·25 10
A686 8 c. green .. .. 2·25 15

1930. Massachusetts Bay Colony Tercent.
683. 195. 2 c. red 50 40

196. Governor and Indian.
A 197. Over the Atlantic.

1930. 250th Anniv of Original Settlement near Charleston.
684 196 2 c. red .. .. 1·00 1·10

1930. Air. "Graf Zeppelin" Europe-Pan-American Flight.
A 687. A 197. 65 c. green .. £300 £225
A 688. – $1.30 brown .. £650 £425
A 689. – $2.60 blue .. £1000 £650
DESIGNS: $1.30, Between continents. $2.60, Over the globe.

197. Harding.
199. George Washington (after statue by F. Vittor in Braddock, Pa.).

1930.
685 197 1½ c. brown 30 10
686 – 4 c. brown 80 10
DESIGN: 4 c. Taft.

1930. 175th Anniv. of Battle of Braddock's Field.
689. 199. 2 c. red 80 90

200. Gen. Wilhelm von Steuben (from medallion by Karl Dautert).
201. Gen. Casimir Pulaski (from etching by H. B. Hall).

1930. Birth Bicent. of Gen. von Steuben.
690. 200. 2 c. red 50 50

1931. 150th Anniv. of Gen. Pulaski's Death.
691. 201. 2 c. red 30 15

202. Red Cross Nurse (from poster "The World's Greatest Mother").
203. Rochambeau, Washington, De Grasse (Washington after painting by Trumbull, others from old engravings).

1931. 50th Anniv. of American Red Cross Society.
702. 202. 2 c. black and red .. 15 10

1931. 150th Anniv. of Surrender of Cornwallis at Yorktown.
703. 203. 2 c. black and red .. 30 25

204. George Washington. 205.

1932. Birth Bicent. of George Washington. Portraits dated "1732 1932".
704. 204. ½ c. sepia 10 10
705. 205. 1 c. green 10 10
706. – 1½ c. brown 50 10
707. – 2 c. red 10 10
708. – 3 c. violet 70 10
709. – 4 c. brown 40 10
710. – 5 c. blue .. .. 1·75 10
711. – 6 c. orange .. .. 3·25 10
712. – 7 c. black 50 15
713. – 8 c. olive .. .. 3·25 70
714. – 9 c. red .. .. 3·00 10
715. – 10 c. yellow .. .. 11·00 10
For 3 c. as No. 707, see No. 720.

216. Skiing. 217. Tree-planting.

1932. Winter Olympic Games, Lake Placid.
716. 216. 2 c. red 60 20

1932. 60th Anniv of Establishment of Arbor Day.
717. 217. 2 c. red 15 10

218. Sprinter. 219. Discus thrower. 221. Wm. Penn.

1932. Summer Olympic Games, Los Angeles.
718. 218. 3 c. violet .. 1·25 10
719. 219. 5 c. blue .. .. 2·25 30

1932. As No. 707, but without date.
720. 3 c. violet 20 10

1932. 250th Anniv. of Penn's Arrival in America.
723. 221. 3 c. violet 30 20

222. Webster. 223. Gen. Oglethorpe. 224. Washington's H.Q.

1932. 150th Birth Anniv. of Daniel Webster.
724. 222. 3 c. violet 35 30

1933. Bicent of Founding of Georgia.
725. 223. 3 c. violet 30 15

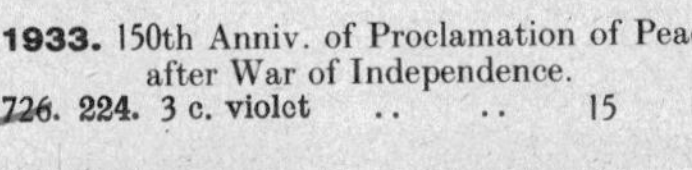

1933. 150th Anniv. of Proclamation of Peace after War of Independence.
726. 224. 3 c. violet 15 10

225. Fort Dearborn (after painting by Dwight Benton).
226. Federal Building.

1933. "Centenary of Progress" International Exhibition, Chicago.
727. 225. 1 c. green 15 10
728. 226. 3 c. violet 15 10

HAVE YOU READ THE NOTES AT THE BEGINNING OF THIS CATALOGUE?
These often provide answers to the enquiries we receive.

227. Agriculture, Commerce and Industry

1933. National Recovery Act.
729. 227. 3 c. violet 10 10

A 230. Chicago Federal Building, "Graf Zeppelin" and Friedrichshafen Hangar.

1933. Air. "Graf Zeppelin" Chicago Flight.
A 732. A 230. 50 c. green .. £100 75·00

230. Routes of various Admiral Byrd Flights.

1933. Byrd Antarctic Expedition.
752 230 3 c. blue 45 50

231. Gen. Kosciuszko (from statue in Lafayette Park, Washington).
233. The "Ark" and the "Dove" (from drawing by E. Tunis).

1933. 150th Anniv. of Naturalization of Kosciuszko.
733. 231. 5 c. blue 50 25

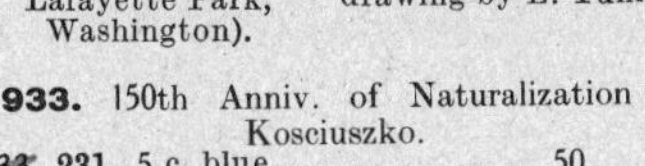

1934. Maryland Tercent.
735. 233. 3 c. red 20 15

234. "Portrait of my Mother" by Whistler.

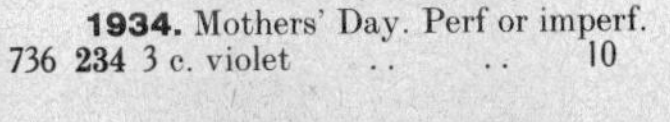

1934. Mothers' Day. Perf or imperf.
736 234 3 c. violet 10 10

235. Nicolet's Landing at Green Bay (after painting by E. W. Deming).

1934. Tercentenary of Wisconsin.
738. 235. 3 c. violet 15 10

236. "El Capitan", Yosemite.
237. Grand Canyon.

1934. National Parks. Perf. or imperf.
739 236 1 c. green 15 10
740 237 2 c. red 20 10
741 – 3 c. violet 25 10
742 – 4 c. brown 50 40
743 – 5 c. blue .. .. 1·00 70
744 – 6 c. blue .. .. 1·50 1·10
745 – 7 c. black 75 85
762 – 8 c. green .. .. 1·75 2·25
747 – 9 c. red .. .. 1·75 60
748 – 10 c. grey .. .. 3·50 90

DESIGNS—VERT. 5 c. "Old Faithful" geyser, Yellowstone. 8 c. Great White Throne, Zion. 10 c. Mount le Conte, Smoky Mountain. HORIZ. 3 c. Mirror Lake, Mt. Rainier. 4 c. Cliff dwellings, Mesa Verde. 6 c. Crater Lake and Wizard Is. 7 c. Great Head, Acadia. 9 c. Mt. Rockwell and Two Medicine Lake Glacier.

248. The Charter Oak.

1935. Connecticut Tercentenary.
771. 248. 3 c. purple 10 10

249. Exhibition Grounds, Point Loma and San Diego Bay.

1935. California Pacific Int. Exn., San Diego,
772. 249. 3 c. violet 10 10

250. Boulder Dam, Nevada.
251. Seal of Michigan.

1935. Dedication of Boulder Dam.
773. 250. 3 c. violet 15 10

1935. Michigan Centenary.
774. 251. 3 c. violet 10 10

A 253. "China Clipper".

1935. Air. Trans-Pacific Air Mail.
A 775. – 20 c. green .. 11·00 1·50
A 776. A 253. 25 c. blue .. 2·00 75
A 777. – 50 c. red .. .. 12·00 2·25
Nos. A 775 and A 777 are as Type **A 253** but without the date.

252. S. Houston, S. F. Austin, and the Alamo.
253. Roger Williams (from statue in Roger Williams Park, Providence, R.I.).

1936. Centenary of Declaration of Texan Independence.
775. 252. 3 c. violet 10 10

1936. Rhode Island Tercent.
776. 253. 3 c. violet 10 10

255. First Settlement, Old State House and Capitol.

1936. Centenary of Arkansas.
778. 255. 3 c. violet 10 10

256. Map of old Oregon Territory.

257. Susan B. Anthony (detail from statue by Adelaide Johnson in Capitol).

1936. Centenary of Oregon.

779.	**256.**	3 c. violet	15	10

1936. 16th Anniv. of Women's Suffrage.

780.	**257.**	3 c. purple	10	10

258. Washington and Greene, Mt. Vernon in background.

263. Jones, Barry and Battle of Flamborough Head.

1936. Army and Navy Heroes. (a) Army.

781.	**258.**	1 c. green	10	10
782.	–	2 c. red	10	10
783.	–	3 c. purple	20	10
784.	–	4 c. blue	40	15
785.	–	5 c. blue	70	15

DESIGNS: 2 c. Jackson, Scott and the Hermitage. 3 c. Sherman, Grant and Sheridan. 4 c. Lee, Jackson and Stratford Hall. 5 c. West Point Military Academy.

(b) Navy.

786.	**263.**	1 c. green	15	10
787.	–	2 c. red	15	10
788.	–	3 c. purple	25	10
789.	–	4 c. blue	40	15
790.	–	5 c. blue	70	15

DESIGNS: 2 c. Decatur, MacDonough and U.S.S. "United States". 3 c. Farragut, Porter and U.S.S. "Hartford". 4 c. Sampson, Dewey and Schley. 5 c. Seal of Naval Academy and cadets.

268. Cutler, Putnam and Map of N.W. Territory.

269. Virginia Dare.

1937. 150th Anniv of Enactment of North West Territory Ordinance.

791.	**268.**	3 c. violet	15	10

1937. 350th Birth Anniv. of Virginia Dare.

792.	**269.**	5 c. blue	15	15

271. Signing the Constitution (after painting by J. B. Stearns).

1937. 150th Anniv. of U.S. Constitution.

794.	**271.**	3 c. mauve	10	10

272. Statue to Kamehameha I, Honolulu.

273. Mt. McKinley, Alaska.

274. Fortaleza Castle, Puerto Rico.

275. Charlotte Amalie (St. Thomas), Virgin Is.

1937. Territorial Issue.

795.	**272.**	3 c. violet	10	10
796.	**273.**	3 c. violet	10	10
797.	**274.**	3 c. violet	10	10
798.	**275.**	3 c. mauve	10	10

276. Benjamin Franklin.

A 308. American Bald Eagle and Shield.

1938. Presidential Series.

799.	**276.**	½ c. orange	10	10
800.	–	1 c. green	10	10
801.	–	1½ c. brown	10	10
802.	–	2 c. red	10	10
803.	–	3 c. violet	10	10
804.	–	4 c. purple	50	10
805.	–	4½ c. grey	15	10
806.	–	5 c. blue	20	10
807.	–	6 c. red	30	10
808.	–	7 c. brown	35	10
809.	–	8 c. green	50	10
810.	–	9 c. pink	50	10
811.	–	10 c. red	35	10
812.	–	11 c. blue	60	10
813.	–	12 c. mauve	1·10	10
814.	–	13 c. green	1·50	10
815.	–	14 c. blue	80	10
816.	–	15 c. slate	55	10
817.	–	16 c. black	1·00	35
818.	–	17 c. red	1·00	15
819.	–	18 c. purple	1·60	10
820.	–	19 c. mauve	1·25	50
821.	–	20 c. green	70	10
822.	–	21 c. blue	1·75	15
823.	–	22 c. red	1·00	50
824.	–	24 c. black	3·00	15
825.	–	25 c. mauve	70	10
826.	–	30 c. blue	4·25	10
827.	–	50 c. lilac	6·50	10
828.	–	$1 black and purple ..	7·50	10
830.	–	$2 black and green ..	20·00	3·50
831.	–	$5 black and red ..	90·00	3·00

DESIGNS: 1 c. Washington. 1½ c. Martha Washington. 2 c. John Adams. 3 c. Jefferson. 4 c. Madison. 4½ c. White House. 5 c. James Monroe. 6 c. John Quincey Adams. 7 c. Jackson. 8 c. Martin Van Buren. 9 c. Wm. Henry Harrison. 10 c. John Tyler. 11 c. James K. Polk. 12 c. Zachary Taylor. 13 c. Millard Fillmore. 14 c. Franklin Pierce. 15 c. James Buchanan. 16 c. Lincoln. 17 c. Johnson. 18 c. Grant. 19 c. Rutherford B. Hayes. 20 c. James A. Garfield. 21 c. Chester A. Arthur. 22 c. Grover Cleveland. 24 c. Benjamin Harrison. 25 c. Wm. McKinley. 30 c. Theodore Roosevelt. 50 c. Taft. $1, Woodrow Wilson. $2, Harding. $5, Coolidge.

1938. Air.

A 845.	**A 308.**	6 c. red and blue	60	10

308. Colonial Court House.

309. Landing of the Swedes and Finns from "Calmare Nyckel" (after S. Arthurs).

1938. 150th Anniv. of Ratification of U.S. Constitution.

845.	**308.**	3 c. violet	15	10

1938. Tercentenary of Scandinavian Settlement in America.

846.	**309.**	3 c. mauve	15	10

310. Colonization of the West (from statue by G. Borglum at Marietta, Ohio).

311. Old Capitol Building, Iowa.

1938. Northwest Territory Sesquicent.

847.	**310.**	3 c. violet	15	10

1938. Iowa Territory Centennial.

848.	**311.**	3 c. violet	15	10

312. Tower of the Sun.

313. Trylon and Perisphere.

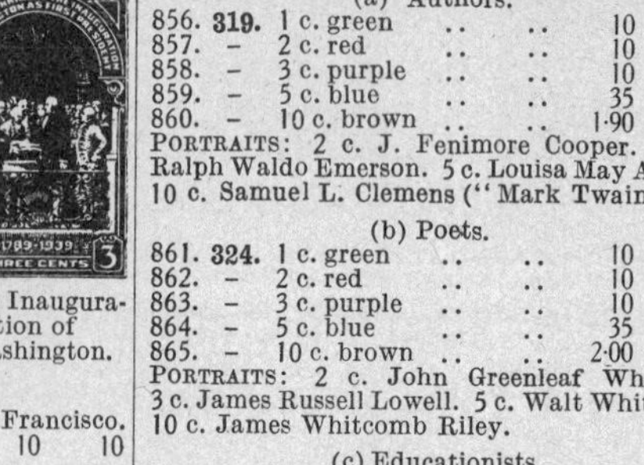

314. Inauguration of Washington.

1939. Golden Gate Int. Exn., San Francisco.

849	**312**	3 c. purple	10	10

1939. New York World's Fair.

850.	**313.**	3 c. violet	10	10

1939. 150th Anniv. of Election of Washington as First President.

851	**314**	3 c. purple	20	10

A 315. Winged Globe.

1939. Air.

A 852.	**A 315.**	30 c. blue ..	10·00	70

315. Baseball.

1939. Baseball Cent.

852.	**315.**	3 c. violet	45	10

316 T. Roosevelt, Goethals and "Andrea F. Luckenbach" in Gaillard Cut.

317. Stephen Daye Press (from sketch by G. F. Trenholm).

1939. 25th Anniv. of Opening of Panama Canal.

853	**316**	3 c. purple	25	10

1939. Tercent. of Printing in Colonial America.

854.	**317.**	3 c. violet	10	10

318. Washington, Montana, N. and S. Dakota.

319. Washington Irving.

324. Henry W. Longfellow.

329. Horace Mann.

334. John James Audubon.

339. Stephen Collins Foster. 344. Gilbert Charles Stuart. 349. Eli Whitney.

1939. 50th Anniv. of Statehood of Washington, Montana and N. and S. Dakota.

855.	**318.**	3 c. mauve	15	10

1940. Famous Americans.

(a) Authors.

856.	**319.**	1 c. green	10	10
857.	–	2 c. red	10	10
858.	–	3 c. purple	10	10
859.	–	5 c. blue	35	25
860.	–	10 c. brown	1·90	1·40

PORTRAITS: 2 c. J. Fenimore Cooper. 3 c. Ralph Waldo Emerson. 5 c. Louisa May Alcott. 10 c. Samuel L. Clemens ("Mark Twain").

(b) Poets.

861.	**324.**	1 c. green	10	10
862.	–	2 c. red	10	10
863.	–	3 c. purple	10	10
864.	–	5 c. blue	35	25
865.	–	10 c. brown	2·00	1·75

PORTRAITS: 2 c. John Greenleaf Whittier. 3 c. James Russell Lowell. 5 c. Walt Whitman. 10 c. James Whitcomb Riley.

(c) Educationists.

866.	**329.**	1 c. green	10	10
867.	–	2 c. red	10	10
868.	–	3 c. purple	20	10
869.	–	5 c. blue	45	25
870.	–	10 c. brown ..	1·75	1·40

PORTRAITS: 2 c. Mark Hopkins. 3 c. Charles W. Eliot. 5 c. Frances E. Willard. 10 c. Booker T. Washington.

(d) Scientists.

871.	**334.**	1 c. green	10	10
872.	–	2 c. red	10	10
873.	–	3 c. purple	10	10
874.	–	5 c. blue	30	25
875.	–	10 c. brown	1·10	1·00

PORTRAITS: 2 c. Dr. Crawford W. Long. 3 c. Luther Burbank. 5 c. Dr. Walter Reed. 10 c. Jane Addams.

(e) Composers.

876.	**339.**	1 c. green	10	10
877.	–	2 c. red	15	10
878.	–	3 c. purple	15	10
879.	–	5 c. blue	50	25
880.	–	10 c. brown	4·50	1·25

PORTRAITS: 2 c. John Philip Sousa. 3 c. Victor Herbert. 5 c. Edward A. MacDowell. 10 c. Ethelbert Nevin.

(f) Artists.

881.	**344.**	1 c. green	10	10
882.	–	2 c. red	10	10
883.	–	3 c. purple	10	10
884.	–	5 c. blue	50	25
885.	–	10 c. brown	1·75	1·40

PORTRAITS: 2 c. James A. McNeill Whistler. 3 c. Augustus Saint-Gaudens. 5 c. Daniel Chester French. 10 c. Frederic Remington.

(g) Inventors.

886.	**349.**	1 c. green	10	10
887.	–	2 c. red	10	10
888.	–	3 c. purple	15	10
889.	–	5 c. blue	85	30
890.	–	10 c. brown	11·00	2·00

PORTRAITS: 2 c. Samuel F. B. Morse. 3 c. Cyrus Hall McCormick. 5 c. Elias Howe. 10 c. Alexander Graham Bell.

354. "Pony Express".

355. "The Three Graces" (after Botticelli's "Spring").

1940. 80th Anniv of Inauguration of Pony Express.

891.	**354.**	3 c. red	30	10

1940. 50th Anniv. of Pan-American Union.

892.	**355.**	3 c. mauve	20	10

357. Wyoming State Seal.

356. State Capitol, Boise.

1940. 50th Anniv. of Idaho.

893.	**356.**	3 c. violet	20	10

1940. 50th Anniv. of Wyoming.

894.	**357.**	3 c purple	20	10

358. Coronado and His Captains (after painting by Gerald Cassidy).

360. Anti-aircraft Gun.

1940. 400th Anniv. of Coronado Expedition.

895.	**358.**	3 c. violet	20	10

1940. National Defence.

896. – 1 c. green 10 10
897. **360.** 2 c. red 10 10
898. – 3 c. violet 10 10

DESIGNS: 1 c. Statue of Liberty. 3 c. Hand holding torch.

362. Emancipation Monument (from statue by Thomas Ball, Lincoln Park, Washington).

363. State Capitol Building, Montpelier.

1940. 75th Anniv. of Abolition of Slavery.

899. **362.** 3 c. violet 20 10

1941. 150th Anniv. of Vermont.

900. **363.** 3 c. violet 20 10

A **364.** Mail Plane.

1941. Air.

A 901. A **364.** 6 c. red 15 10
A 902. 8 c. green 30 10
A 903. 10 c. violet .. .. 1·25 15
A 904. 15 c. red .. .. 3·00 10
A 905. 20 c. green .. .. 2·00 20
A 906. 30 c. blue .. .. 2·25 15
A 907. 50 c. orange .. 10·00 3·00

364. Daniel Boone and companions viewing Kentucky (from mural by Gilbert White in State Capitol, Frankfort).

365. Symbolical of Victory.

1942. 150th Anniv. of Kentucky.

901. **364.** 3 c. violet 15 10

1942. Independence Day.

902. **365.** 3 c. violet 10 10

366. Lincoln and Sun Yat-sen.

367. Allegory of Victory.

1942. Chinese War Effort.

903. **366.** 5 c. blue 30 20

1943. Allied Nations.

904. **367.** 2 c. red 10 10

368. Liberty holding Torch of Freedom and Enlightenment.

369. Flag of Poland.

1943. Four Freedoms.

905. **368.** 1 c. green 10 10

1943. Flags of Oppressed Nations. Frames in violet, flags in national colours.

906. 5 c. Type **369** .. 20 10
907. 5 c. Czechoslovakia .. 25 10
908. 5 c. Norway 15 10
909. 5 c. Luxembourg .. 15 10
910. 5 c. Netherlands .. 15 10
911. 5 c. Belgium 15 10
912. 5 c. France 20 10
913. 5 c. Greece 60 25
914. 5 c. Yugoslavia .. 45 15
915. 5 c. Albania 35 15
916. 5 c. Austria 30 15
917. 5 c. Denmark 40 15
918. 5 c. Korea 25 15

382. "Golden Spike Ceremony" (painting, John McQuarrie).

1944. 75th Anniv. of 1st Transcontinental Railway.

919. **382.** 3 c. violet 35 10

383. Paddle-steamer "Savannah".

1944. 125th Anniv of Transatlantic Crossing of "Savannah".

920 **383** 3 c. violet 10 10

384. "What Hath God Wrought".

1944. Centenary of 1st Telegraph Message.

921. **384.** 3 c. mauve 10 10

385. View of Corregidor.

1944. Defence of Corregidor.

922. **385.** 3 c. violet 15 10

386. Open-air Cinema.

1944. 50th Anniv. of Motion Pictures.

923. **386.** 3 c. violet 10 10

387. Gates of St. Augustine, State Seal and Capitol.

1945. Cent. of Statehood of Florida.

924. **387.** 3 c. purple 10 10

388. "Toward United Nations".

1945. San Francisco Conference.

925. **388.** 5 c. blue 10 10

389. Franklin D. Roosevelt and Hyde Park.

393. Raising U.S.A. Flag at Iwo Jima.

1945. Pres. Roosevelt Commem. Issue. Inscr. "1882 1945".

926. **389.** 1 c. green 10 10
927. – 2 c. red 10 10
928. – 3 c. violet 10 10
929. – 5 c. blue 15 10

DESIGNS: 2 c. "Little White House", Warm Springs, Georgia. 3 c. "White House" Washington. 5 c. Western Hemisphere and Four Freedoms.

1945. U.S. Marines.

930. **393.** 3 c. green 10 10

394. U.S. Troops Marching through Paris.

1945. U.S. Army.

931. **394.** 3 c. olive 10 10

395. U.S. Sailors.

1945. U.S. Navy.

932. **395.** 3 c. blue 10 10

396. "Authur Middleton" (supply ship) and Coastguard Landing Craft.

397. Alfred E. Smith.

1945. U.S. Coastguard.

933. **396.** 3 c. green 10 10

1945. Alfred E. Smith (Governor of New York) Commemoration.

934. **397.** 3 c. violet 10 10

398. Flags of U.S.A. and Texas.

1945. Cent. of Texas Statehood.

935. **398.** 3 c. blue 10 10

399. "Liberty" type Freighter unloading Cargo.

400. Honourable Discharge Emblem.

1946. U.S. Mercantile Marine.

936. **399.** 3 c. green 10 10

1946. Honouring Discharged Veterans of Second World War.

937. **400.** 3 c. violet 10 10

401. Andrew Jackson and John Sevier and Tennessee State Capitol.

1946. 150th Anniv. of Tennessee Statehood.

938. **401.** 3 c. violet 10 10

402. Iowa State Flag and Map.

1946. Cent. of Iowa Statehood.

939. **402.** 3 c. blue 10 10

403. Smithsonian Institution.

1946. Cent. of Smithsonian Institution.

940. **403.** 3 c. purple 10 10

A **404.** DC-4 "Skymaster".

1946. Air.

A 941. A **404.** 5 c. red 15 10

404. Entry into Santa Fe (after painting by Kenneth M. Chapman).

405. Thomas A. Edison.

1946. Centenary of Entry of Stephen Watts Kearny Expedition into Santa Fe.

941. **404.** 3 c. purple 10 10

1947. Birth Cent. of Thomas Edison (scientist).

942. **405.** 3 c. violet 10 10

A **406.** Douglas DC-4 Skymaster.

406. Joseph Pulitzer (from portrait by J. S. Sargent).

1947. Air.

A943 A **406** 5 c red 10 10
A944 6 c. red 15 10

1947. Birth Cent. of Joseph Pulitzer (journalist and newspaper publisher).

943. **406.** 3 c. violet 10 10

407. Washington, Franklin and Evolution of Postal Transport.

1947. U.S. Postage Stamp Centenary.

944. **407.** 3 c. blue 15 10

409. "The Doctor" (after painting by Sir Luke Fildes).

1947. Medical Profession.

946. **409.** 3 c. purple 10 10

410. Pioneer Caravan.

1947. Centenary of Utah.

947 **410** 3 c. violet 10 10

A **411.** Pan American Union Building, Washington.

1947. Air.

A948 A **411** 10 c. black .. 25 10
A949 – 15 c. green .. 30 10
A950 – 25 c. blue .. 75 10

DESIGNS: 15 c. Statue of Liberty and New York City. 25 c. San Francisco–Oakland Bay Suspension Bridge.

411 U.S.S. "Constitution".

412. Great Blue Heron and Map of Florida.

1947. 150th Anniv of Launching of Frigate U.S.S. "Constitution" ("Old Ironsides").

948 **411** 3 c. green 15 10

1947. Dedication of Everglades National Park Florida.

949. **412.** 3 c. green 30 10

413. George Washington Carver.

414. Sutter's Mill, Coloma.

1948. 5th Death Anniv. of George Washington Carver (scientist).

950. **413.** 3 c. violet 10 10

1948. Cent. of Discovery of Gold in California.

951. **414.** 3 c. violet 10 10

415. Gov. Winthrop Sargent, Map and Seal of Mississippi Territory (from portrait by Gilbert Stuart).

1948. 150th Anniv. of Mississippi Territory.
952. 415. 3 c. purple 10 10

416. Four Chaplains and Liner "Dorchester".

1948. 5th Death Anniv of George Fox, Clark Poling, John Washington and Alexander Goode (who gave up life-jackets).
953. 416. 3 c. black 10 10

417. Scroll and State Capitol, Madison.

1948. Centenary of Statehood of Wisconsin.
954 417 3 c. violet 10 10

418. Pioneer and Covered Wagon.

1948. Centenary of Swedish Pioneers in Middle West.
955. 418. 5 c. blue 15 10

419. Elizabeth Stanton, Carrie C. Catt, and Lucretia Mott.

A 420. Map of New York, Ring and Planes (from poster by G. A. Lorimer).

1948. Progress of American Women.
956. 419. 3 c. violet 10 10

1948. Air. Golden Anniv. of New York City Council.
A 957. 420. 5 c. red 15 10

420. William Allen White.

421. Niagara Railway Suspension Bridge (from print by H. Peters).

1948. Honouring W. A. White (editor and author).
957. 420. 3 c. purple 10 10

1948. Centenary of Friendship between United States and Canada.
958 421 3 c. blue 15 10

422. Francis Scott Key.

1948. Honouring F. S. Key (author of "Star Spangled Banner").
959. 422. 3 c. red 10 10

423. Boy and Girl Students.

1948. Salute to Youth.
960. 423. 3 c. blue 10 10

424. John McLoughlin, Jason Lee and Covered Wagon.

425. Harlan Fisk Stone.

1948. Oregon Territory Centennial.
961 424 3 c. red 10 10

1948. Honouring H. F. Stone (Chief Justice).
962. 425. 3 c. purple 10 10

426. Palomar Mountain Observatory.

427. Clara Barton and Cross.

1948. Dedication of Palomar Observatory.
963. 426. 3 c. blue 15 10

1948. Honouring Clara Barton (founder of American Red Cross).
964. 427. 3 c. red 10 10

428. Light Brahma Rooster.

1948. Cent of American Poultry Industry.
965. 428. 3 c. brown 10 10

429. Star and Palm Branch.

430. Fort Kearny and pioneers. (Pioneer group from sculpture on Nebraska State Capitol).

1948. Honouring Bereaved Mothers.
966. 429. 3 c. yellow 10 10

1948. Cent. of Fort Kearny, Nebraska.
967. 430. 3 c. violet 10 10

431. Peter Stuyvesant and Fire Engines (from painting in Library of Congress).

1948. Tercent. of Volunteer Firemen.
968. 431. 3 c. red 10 10

432. Indian Seals and Map of Oklahoma.

1948. Centenary of Five Civilised Indian Tribes of Oklahoma.
969. 432. 3 c. brown 10 10

433. Statue of Capt. William Owen " Bucky " O'Neill, Prescott, Arizona (S. H. Borglum).

1948. 50th Anniv. of Organization of Rough Riders.
970. 433. 3 c. purple 10 10

434. Juliette Gordon Low.

435. Will Rogers.

1948. Honouring Juliette Gordon Low (founder of U.S.A. Girl Scouts).
971. 434. 3 c. green 15 10

1948. Honouring Will Rogers (political commentator).
972. 435. 3 c. purple 10 10

436. Rocket Testing.

437. Moina Michael and Poppies.

1948. Centenary of Fort Bliss.
973. 436. 3 c. red 10 10

1948. Honouring Moina Michael (founder of memorial poppy).
974. 437. 3 c. red 10 10

438. Abraham Lincoln (from statue by D. C. French at Lincoln, Neb.).

439. Torch and Emblem.

1948. 85th Anniv of Gettysburg Address.
975 438 3 c. blue 10 10

1948. Cent. of American Turners' Society.
976. 439. 3 c. red 10 10

440. Joel Chandler Harris.

441. Pioneer and Red River Ox Cart.

1948. Birth Cent. of J. C. Harris (author).
977 440. 3 c. purple 10 10

1949. Cent. of Territorial Status of Minnesota.
978. 441. 3 c. green 10 10

442. Washington, Lee and University Building.

1949. Bicentenary of Washington and Lee University, Lexington, Virginia.
979. 442. 3 c. blue 10 10

443. Puerto Rican, Cogwheel and Ballot Box.

1949. First Gubernatorial Election in Puerto Rico.
980. 443. 3 c. green 10 10

A444. Wings, Seal, Carlyle House and Gadsby's Tavern.

1949. Air. Bicent. of Alexandria, Virginia.
A 981. A444. 6 c. red 15 10

444. Map, "Het Vergulde Vsanker" and Shield.

1949. Tercent. of Annapolis, Maryland.
981 444 3 c. green 10 10

445. Young and Old Soldiers.

446. Edgar Allan Poe.

1949. Final National Encampment of the Grand Army of the Republic.
982. 445. 3 c. red 10 10
For similar stamp see No. 995.

1949. Death Centenary of Edgar Allan Poe (poet and author).
983. 446. 3 c. purple 10 10

A447. U.P.U. Monument, Berne and P.O. Department, Washington.

DESIGNS: 15 c. Globe and birds. 25 c. Globe and aeroplane.

1949. Air. 75th Anniv. of U.P.U.
A 984. A 447. 10 c. violet .. 20 25
A 985. – 15 c. blue .. 30 35
A 986. – 25 c. red 40 45

A 450. Wright Brothers and Aeroplane.

1949. Air. 46th Anniv. of Wright Brothers' First Flight.
A 987. A450. 6 c. purple .. 20 10

447. Symbolic of Investments.

448. Samuel Gompers.

1950. 75th Anniv. of American Bankers' Assn.
984. 447. 3 c. green 10 10

1950. Birth Centenary of Samuel Gompers (labour leader).
985. 448. 3 c. purple 10 10

449. Statue of Freedom (by Crawford) on Capitol Dome.

450. The White House.

1950. National Capital Sesquicentennial.

986. **449.**	3 c. blue	10	10
987. **450.**	3 c. green	10	10
988. –	3 c. violet	10	10
989. –	3 c. purple	10	10

DESIGNS—HORIZ. No. 988, U.S. Supreme Court bldg. No. 989, Capitol, Washington.

453. "Casey" Jones and Railway Locomotives.

1950. Honouring Railway Engineers.
990. **453.** 3 c. purple 10 10

454. Kansas City in 1850 and 1950.

1950. Centenary of Kansas City.
991. **454.** 3 c. violet 10 10

455. Scouts and Badge.

1950. American Boy Scouts.
992. **455.** 3 c. brown 15 10

456. First Capitol and W. H. Harrison.

1950. Sesquicentennial of Indiana.
993. **456.** 3 c. blue 10 10

457. Pioneers.

1950. Centenary of California.
994. **457.** 3 c. yellow 10 10

1951. Final Reunion of United Confederate Veterans. As T 445, but initials at left and in hat badge changed to "UCV".
995. **445.** 3 c. grey 10 10

458. Log Cabin.

1951. Centenary of Nevada.
996. **458.** 3 c. olive 10 10

459. Cadillac Disembarking.

1951. 250th Anniv. of Landing of Cadillac at Detroit.
997. **459.** 3 c. blue 10 10

460. Mount of Holy Cross, State Seal and Capitol.

1951. 75th Anniv. of Colorado.
998. **460.** 3 c. violet 10 10

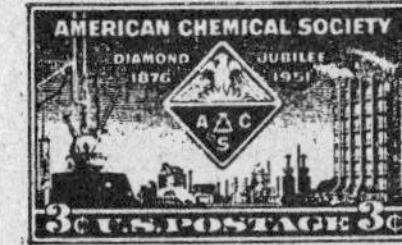

461. Emblem and Chemical Plant.

1951. 75th Anniv. of American Chemical Society.
999. **461.** 3 c. purple 10 10

462. Washington at Brooklyn.

1951. 175th Anniv. of Battle of Brooklyn.
1000. **462.** 3 c. violet 10 10

463. Betsy Ross and Flag.

1952. Birth Bicentenary of Betsy Ross (maker of first American flag).
1001. **463.** 3 c. red 10 10

464. Emblem and Young Club Members.

1952. 50th Anniv. of 4-H Clubs.
1002. **464.** 3 c. green 10 10

465. Rail Transport.

1952. 125th Anniv. of Baltimore and Ohio Railway.
1003. **465.** 3c. blue 15 10

466. Cars of 1902 and 1952.

467. "Torch of Freedom".

1952. 50th Anniv. of American Automobile Assn.
1004. **466.** 3 c. blue 10 10

1952. 3rd Anniv. of N.A.T.O.
1005. **467.** 3 c. violet 10 10

A 467. Diamond Head, Oahu, Honolulu.

1952. Air.
A1005 A **467** 80 c. purple .. 7·50 1·00

468. Grand Coulee Dam.

1952. 50th Anniv. of Columbia Basin Reclamation.
1006. **468.** 3 c. green 15 10

469. Lafayette and Flags.

1952. 175th Anniv. of Lafayette's Arrival in America.
1007. **469.** 3 c. blue 10 10

470. Mt. Rushmore National Memorial.

471. Bridges in 1852 and 1952.

1952. 25th Anniv. of Mt. Rushmore National Memorial.
1008. **470.** 3 c. green 15 10

1952. Centenary of American Society of Civil Engineers.
1009. **471.** 3 c. blue 15 10

472. Women in Uniform.

1952. Women's Services Commem.
1010. **472.** 3 c. blue 10 10

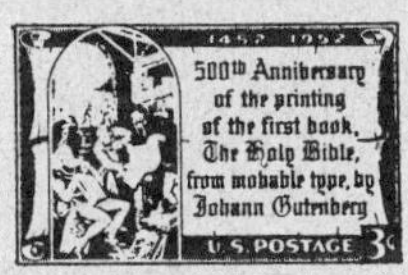

473. Gutenburg and Elector of Mainz (after Edward Laning).

1952. 500th Anniv. of Printing of First Book from Movable Type.
1011. **473.** 3 c. violet 10 10

474. Newspaperboy and Torch of Free Enterprise.

1952. Newspaperboys Commem.
1012. **474.** 3 c. violet 10 10

475. Red Cross and Globe.

1952. Int. Red Cross.
1013. **475.** 3 c. blue and red .. 10 10

476. Guardsman and amphibious Landing.

477. Map and Seal of Ohio.

1953. National Guard.
1014. **476.** 3 c. blue 10 10

1953. 150th Anniv. of Ohio.
1015. **477.** 3 c. sepia 10 10

478. Seal of Washington Territory and Settlers.

1953. Cent. of Washington Territory.
1016. **478.** 3 c. blue-green .. 10 10

479. Monroe, Livingston and Marbois signing Transfer (from sculpture plaque by Karl Bitter).

1953. 150th Anniv. of Louisiana Purchase.
1017. **479.** 3 c. purple 10 10

A 480. Early and Contemporary Aeroplanes.

1953. Air. 50th Anniv. of Aviation.
A 1018. A **480.** 6 c. red.. .. 15 15

480. Commodore Perry and U.S.S. "Susquehanna" and "Mississippi" in Tokyo Bay.

1953. Centenary of Opening of Japan to Foreign Trade.
1018. **480.** 5 c. turquoise .. 15 15

481. "Wisdom", "Justice and Divine Inspiration" and "Truth".

1953. 75th Anniv. of American Bar Assn.
1019. **481.** 3 c. violet 10 10

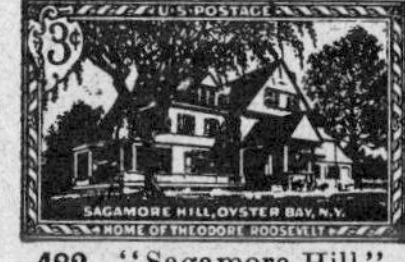

482. "Sagamore Hill".

1953. Opening of Theodore Roosevelt's Home.
1020. **482.** 3 c. green 10 10

483. Young Farmer and Landscape.

1953. 25th Anniv. of "Future Farmers of America".
1021. **483.** 3 c. blue 10 10

484. Truck and Distant City.

1953. 50th Anniv. of Trucking Industry.
1022. **484.** 3 c. violet 10 10

485. Gen. Patton and Tanks in Action.

1953. Gen. George Patton and U.S. Armoured Forces.
1023 **485** 3 c. violet 15 10

486. New York in 1653 and 1953.

1953. Tercent. of Foundation of New York City.
1024. **486.** 3 c. purple 10 10

487. Pioneer Family.

1953. Centenary of Gadsden Purchase.
1025. **487.** 3 c. chestnut .. 10 10

488. Low Memorial Library.

1954. Bicent. of Columbia University.
1026. **488.** 3 c. blue 10 10

490. Washington (after Stuart). 492. Mount Vernon. 501. Statue of Liberty.

1954. Liberty Issue.

1027.	–	½ c. red	10	10
1028.	**490.**	1 c. green	10	10
1029.	–	1¼ c. turquoise ..	10	10
1030.	**492.**	1½ c. lake	10	10
1031.	–	2 c. red	10	10
1032.	–	2½ c. blue	10	10
1033.	**501.**	3 c. violet	10	10
1034.	–	4 c. mauve	10	10
1035.	–	4½ c. green	20	10
1036.	–	5 c. blue	10	10
1037.	–	6 c. red	30	10
1038.	–	7 c. red	30	10
1039.	**501.**	8 c. red and blue ..	30	10
1040.	–	8 c. red and blue ..	30	10
1041.	–	8 c. brown	30	10
1042.	–	9 c. purple	40	10
1043.	–	10 c. red	20	10
1044.	–	11 c. blue and red ..	30	10
1045.	–	12 c. red	45	10
1046.	–	15 c. red	75	10
1047.	–	20 c. blue	50	10
1059.	–	25 c. turquoise ..	40	20
1049.	–	30 c. black	1·25	10
1050.	–	40 c. lake	1·75	10
1051.	–	50 c. violet	1·75	10
1052.	–	$1 violet	6·00	10
1053.	–	$5 black	70·00	3·50

DESIGNS—As Type **490:** ½ c. Benjamin Franklin. 2 c. Jefferson. 4 c. Lincoln. 5 c. Monroe. 6 c. Theodore Roosevelt. 7 c. Woodrow Wilson. 8 c. (No. 1040), As Type **501** but torch flame below "P". 8 c. (No. 1041), Gen. John J. Pershing. 11 c. As No. 1040. 12 c. Benjamin Harrison. 15 c. John Jay. 25 c. Paul Revere. 30 c. Robert E. Lee. 40 c. John Marshall. 50 c. Susan B. Anthony. $1, Patrick Henry. $5, Alexander Hamilton. As Type **492**—VERT. 2½ c. Bunker Hill Monument and Massachusetts flag. HORIZ. 1¼ c. Palace of the Governors, Santa Fe. 4½ c. The Hermitage. 9 c. The Alamo. 10 c. Independence Hall. 20 c. Monticello, Thomas Jefferson's home.

516. "The Sower" and Mitchell Pass (from statue on Capitol, Lincoln, Neb.).

1954. Centenary of Nebraska Territory.
1062. **516.** 3 c. violet 10 10

517. Pioneers and Cornfield. 518. George Eastman.

1954. Cent. of Kansas Territory.
1063. **517.** 3 c. salmon 10 10

1954. Cent. of Birth of Eastman (inventor).
1064. **518.** 3 c. purple 10 10

519. Landing on Riverbank, Missouri. A 520. American Bald Eagle in Flight.

1954. 150th Anniv. of Lewis and Clark Expedition.
1065. **519.** 3 c. purple 10 10

1954. Air.
A 1066. A **520.** 4 c. blue .. 15 10
A 1067. 5 c. red 15 10

520. "Peale in his Museum" (self-portrait). 521. Open Book and Symbols of Subjects Taught.

1955. 150th Anniv. of Pennsylvania Academy of Fine Arts.
1066. **520.** 3 c. purple 10 10

1955. Cent. of First Land-Grant Colleges.
1067. **521.** 3 c. green 10 10

522. Torch, Globe and Rotary Emblem.

1955. 50th Anniv. of Rotary International.
1068. **522.** 8 c. blue 15 10

523. Marine, Coastguard, Soldier, Sailor, Airman.

1955. Armed Forces Reserve.
1069. **523.** 3 c. purple 10 10

524. "The Old Man of the Mountains". 525. The Great Lakes and "Altadoc" (freighter).

1955. 150th Anniv of Discovery of "The Old Man of the Mountains" (New Hampshire landmark).
1070. **524.** 3 c. turquoise .. 15 10

1955. Soo Locks Cent.
1071. **525.** 3 c. blue 15 10

526.

1955. "Atoms for Peace".
1072. **526.** 3 c. blue 10 10

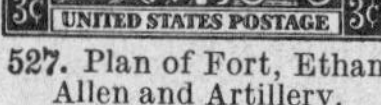

527. Plan of Fort, Ethan Allen and Artillery. 528. Mellon (after Edward Bailey).

1955. Bicent. of Fort Ticonderoga.
1073. **527.** 3 c. brown 10 10

1955. Birth Centenary of Andrew W. Mellon (philanthropist).
1074 **528** 3 c. red 10 10

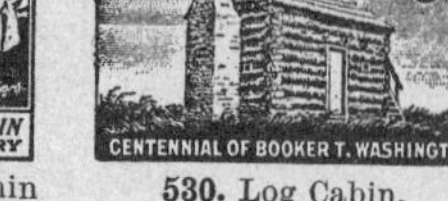

529. Benjamin Franklin (after painting by Benjamin West). 530. Log Cabin.

1956. 250th Birth Anniv. of Franklin.
1075. **529.** 3 c. red 10 10

1956. Birth Cent. of Booker T. Washington.
1076. **530.** 3 c. blue 10 10

532. New York Coliseum and Columbus Monument.

1956. 5th Int. Philatelic Exn., New York.
1078. **532.** 3 c. violet 10 10

533. Common Turkey. 536. H. W. Wiley.

1956. Wild Life Conservation.
1079. **533.** 3 c. purple 30 10
1080. – 3 c. sepia 25 10
1081. – 3 c. green 20 10
DESIGNS: No. 1080, Pronghorns. No. 1081, King Salmon.

1956. 50th Anniv. of Pure Food and Drug Laws.
1082. **536.** 3 c. green 10 10

537. Wheatland. 538. Mosaic by L. M. Winter, A.F.L.-C.I.O. Headquarters.

1956. Home of James Buchanan.
1083. **537.** 3 c. sepia 10 10

1956. Labour Day.
1084. **538.** 3 c. blue 10 10

539. Nassau Hall (contemporary engraving by Dawkins). 540. Devils Tower.

1956. Bicentenary of Nassau Hall.
1085. **539.** 3 c. black on orange .. 10 10

1956. 50th Anniv. of Devils Tower National Monument.
1086. **540.** 3 c. violet 10 10

541. "The Key to World Peace."

1956. Children's Friendship.
1087. **541.** 3 c. blue 10 10

542. Alexander Hamilton and Federal Hall, New York. 543. Woman, Children and Shield.

1957. Birth Bicent. of Alexander Hamilton.
1088. **542.** 3 c. red 10 10

1957. Infantile Paralysis Relief Campaign.
1089. **543.** 3 c. mauve 10 10

544. Survey Flag and Coastguard Vessels "Pathfinder", "Explorer" and "Surveyor".

1957. 150th Anniv. of Coast and Geodetic Survey.
1090. **544.** 3 c. blue 10 10

545. Ancient and Modern Capitals. 546. Eagle and Ladle.

1957. Cent. of American Institute of Architects.
1091. **545.** 3 c. mauve .. 10 10

1957. Cent. of American Steel Industry.
1092. **546.** 3 c. blue 10 10

547. Festival Emblem and Aircraft Carrier U.S.S. "Forrestal".

1957. Jamestown Festival and Int. Naval Review.
1093. **547.** 3 c. green 15 10

548. Arrow piercing Atomic Symbol.

1957. 50th Anniv. of Oklahoma Statehood.
1094. **548.** 3 c. blue 10 10

549. Teacher with Pupils.

1957. Teachers of America Commem.
1095. **549.** 3 c. red 10 10

550. U.S. Flag.

1957. Flag Issue.
1096. **550.** 4 c. red and blue .. 10 10

A 551. B 52 Stratofortress and Three F 104 Starfighters.

551. "Virginia of Sagadahock" and Arms of Maine.

1957. Air. 50th Anniv. of U.S. Air Force.
A 1097. A 551. 6 c. blue .. 15 10

1957. 350th Anniv. of American Shipbuilding.
1097. 551. 3 c. violet 10 10

552. Pres. Magsaysay of the Philippines (medallion).

553. Marquis de Lafayette (portrait by Court in Versailles Museum).

1958. Pres. Magsaysay Commemoration.
1098. 552. 8 c. ochre, blue & red 15 10

1957. Birth Bicent. of Marquis de Lafayette.
1099. 553. 3 c. red 10 10

554. Whooping Cranes.

555. "Religious Freedom".

1957. Wild Life Conservation.
1100 554 3 c. blue, orange & grn 30 10

1957. Tercent. of Flushing Remonstrance.
1101. 555. 3 c. black 10 10

556. "Abundance".

557. U.S. Pavilion.

1958. Gardening and Horticulture Commem.
1102. 556. 3 c. green 10 10

1958. Brussels Int. Exn.
1103. 557. 3 c. purple 10 10

558. James Monroe (portrait by Stuart).

559. Lake in Minnesota.

1958. Birth Bicent. of Pres. James Monroe.
1104. 558. 3 c. violet 10 10

1958. Cent. of Minnesota Statehood.
1105. 559. 3 c. green 10 10

560. Sun's Surface and Hands (after Michelangelo's "The Creation of Adam").

1958. I.G.Y.
1106. 560. 3 c. red and black .. 15 10

561. Gunston Hall (after drawing by Rene Clarke).

562. Mackinac Bridge.

1958. Bicentenary of Gunston Hall, Virginia (home of George Mason, patriot).
1107. 561. 3 c. green 10 10

1958. Mackinac Bridge Commem.
1108. 562. 3 c. turquoise .. 10 10

563. Simon Bolivar (after painting by Ricardo Arcevedo-Bernal).

A 564. Silhouette of Jet Airliner.

1958. Bolivar Commem.
1109. 563. 4 c. ochre 10 10
1110. 8 c. brown, blue & red 15 10
See also Nos. 1116/17, 1124/5, 1135/6, 1146/7, 1158/9, 1164/5, 1167/8 and 1173/4.

1958. Air.
A 1111. A 564. 7 c. blue .. 15 10
A 1112. 7 c. red 15 10

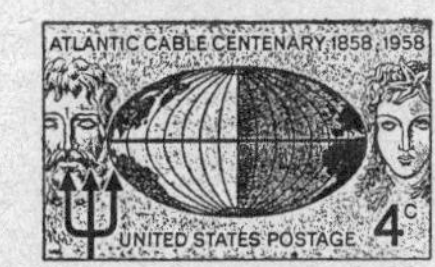

564. Globe, Neptune and Mermaid.

1958. Cent. of Inaug. of Atlantic Cable.
1111. 564. 4 c. purple 10 10

565. Abraham Lincoln (from painting by G. Healy).

570. Hand with Quill Pen and Printing Press.

1958. 150th Birth Anniv. of Lincoln.
1112. 565. 1 c. green 10 10
1113. – 3 c. red 15 10
1114. – 4 c. brown 15 10
1115. – 4 c. blue 15 10
DESIGNS: No. 1113, Bust of Lincoln. No. 1114, Addressing Electorate. No. 1115, Lincoln Statue, Washington.

1958. Kossuth Commem. Medallion portrait. As T 563.
1116. 4 c. green 10 10
1117. 8 c. brown, blue and red 15 10

1958. Freedom of the Press.
1118. 570. 4 c. black 10 10

571. Mail Coach under Attack.

572. Noah Webster (engraving by G. Paker after painting by James Herring).

1958. Overland Mail Cent.
1119. 571. 4 c. red 10 10

1958. Birth Bicentenary of Noah Webster (lexicographer).
1120. 572. 4 c. red 10 10

573. Forest Pines.

574. British Forces occupying Fort Duquesne (from etching by T. B. Smith).

1958. Forest Conservation.
1121. 573. 4 c. yellow, grn. & brn. 10 10

1958. Bicent. of Fort Duquesne.
1122. 574. 4 c. blue 10 10

A 575. Stars on Alaskan Map.

1959. Air. Alaska Statehood.
A 1123. A 575. 7 c. blue .. 25 10

575. Covered Wagon and Mt. Hood.

577. N.A.T.O. Emblem.

1959. Cent. of Oregon Statehood.
1123. 575. 4 c. green .. 10 10

1959. San Martin Commem. Medallion portrait as T 563.
1124. 4 c. blue 10 10
1125. 8 c. ochre, red and blue .. 15 10

1959. 10th Anniv. of N.A.T.O.
1126. 577. 4 c. blue 10 10

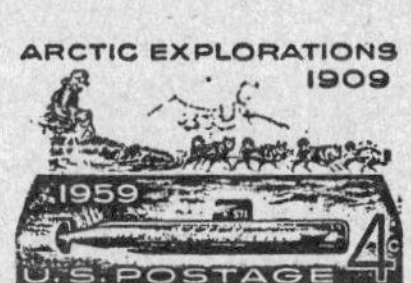

578. Peary with Dog-team and Submarine U.S.S. "Nautilus".

1959. Arctic Explorations by Robert Peary (50th anniv of reaching North Pole) and U.S.S. "Nautilus".
1127 578 4 c. blue 10 10

579.

1959. World Peace through World Trade.
1128. 579. 8 c. red 15 10

580. Discovery of Silver at Mt. Davidson, Nevada (from a print).

1959. Cent. of Discovery of Silver in Nevada.
1129. 580. 4 c. black 10 10

581. Maple Leaf linked with American Eagle.

1959. Opening of St. Lawrence Seaway.
1130. 581. 4 c. blue and red .. 10 10

582. New U.S. Flag (with 49 stars).

1959. Inaug. of New United States Flag.
1131. 582. 4 c. red, blue & orange 15 10

A 583. Balloon "Jupiter".

A 584. Hawaiian Warrior, Map and Star.

1959. Air. Cent. of Balloon "Jupiter's" Mail-carrying Flight.
A 1132. A 583. 7 c. red and blue 20 10

1959. Air. Hawaii Statehood.
A 1133. A 584. 7 c. red 20 10

583. "The Good Earth".

584. Oil Derrick.

1959. Soil Conservation.
1132. 583. 4 c. green, brown and blue .. 10 10

1959. Centenary of First Oil-well at Titusville, Pennsylvania.
1133. 584. 4 c. brown 10 10

A 585. Runner with Olympic Torch.

585. "Happy Children with Healthy Teeth".

1959. Air. 3rd Pan-American Games, Chicago.
A 1134. A 585. 10 c. red and blue 30 30

1959. Dental Health. Cent. of American Dental Assn.
1134. 585. 4 c. green 10 10

1959. Ernst Reuter Commem. Medallion portrait as T 563.
1135. 4 c grey 10 10
1136. 8 c. ochre, red and blue .. 20 10

A 588. Statue of Liberty.

587. Dr. E. McDowell (from painting).

1959. Air.
A 1137. – 10 c. blk. & grn. 1·75 70
A 1138. – 13 c. blk. & red .. 40 10
A 1139. A 588. 15 c. blk. & orge. (A) 35 10
A 1140. 15 c. blk. & orge. (B) 30 10
A 1141. – 25 c. blk. & brn. 50 10
DESIGNS: 10 c., 13 c. Liberty Bell. 15 c. Statue has double frame-line (A) or single frame-line (B). 25 c. Abraham Lincoln.

1959. 150th Anniv of First Recorded Successful Abdominal Operation.
1137. 587 4 c. purple 10 10

588.

1960. " American, Credo " series.
1138. **588.** 4 c. red and blue .. 15 10
1139. – 4 c. green and bistre 15 10
1140. – 4 c. red and grey .. 15 10
1141. – 4 c. blue and red .. 15 10
1142. – 4 c. green and purple 20 10
1143. – 4 c. brown and green 20 10
INSCRIPTIONS: No. 1139, " Fear to do ill, and you need fear Nought else " (Franklin). No. 1140, " I have sworn . . . Hostility against every form of TYRANNY over the mind of man" (Jefferson). No. 1141, " And this be our Motto in GOD is our TRUST " (Francis Scott Key). No. 1142, " Those who Deny freedom to others Deserve it not for Themselves " (Lincoln). No. 1143, " Give me LIBERTY or give me DEATH " (P. Henry).

594. Scout Saluting. **595.** Olympic Rings and Snow Crystal.

1960. 50th Anniv. of American Boy Scout Movement.
1144. **594.** 4 c. ochre, red & blue 10 10

1960. Winter Olympic Games.
1145. **595.** 4 c. blue 10 10

1960. Thomas Masaryk Commem. Medallion portrait as T **563.**
1146. 4 c. blue 10 10
1147. 8 c. ochre, red & blue 20 10

597. " Towards the Light ".

1960. World Refuge Year.
1148. **597.** 4 c. black 10 10

598. " Irrigation ".

599. S.E.A.T.O. Emblem.

1960. Water Conservation Campaign.
1149. **598.** 4 c. grn., brn. & blue 10 10

1960. S.E.A.T.O. Conf.
1150. **599.** 4 c. blue 10 10

600. Mother and Child.

601. New U.S. Flag (with 50 stars).

1960. American Womanhood Commem.
1151. **600.** 4 c. violet 10 10

1960. New United States Flag (50 Stars).
1152. **601** 4 c. red and blue .. 10 10

602. Pony Express.

603. Cripple operating Press.

1960. Centenary of Pony Express.
1153. **602** 4 c. brown 10 10

1960. Employment of the Handicapped Campaign.
1154. **603.** 4 c. blue 10 10

604. Congress Seal. **605.** Dolores Bell (Mexico). **606.** Washington Monument and Cherry Blossom.

1960. 5th World Forestry Congress, Seattle.
1155. **604.** 4 c. green 10 10

1960. 150th Anniv. of Mexican Independence.
1156. **605.** 4 c. red and green .. 10 10

1960. Cent. of U.S.–Japan Treaty.
1157. **606.** 4 c. red and turquoise 10 10

1960. Jan Paderewski Commem. Medallion portrait as T **563.**
1158. 4 c. blue 10 10
1159. 8 c. ochre, red and blue .. 20 10

608. Robert A. Taft.

609. Steering Wheel, Motor Transport and Globes.

1960. Robert A. Taft Memorial Issue.
1160 **608** 4 c. violet 10 10

1960. " Wheels of Freedom " (Motor Industry).
1161. **609.** 4 c. blue 10 10

610. Boy. **611.** New P.O. Building.

1960. Cent. of Boys' Clubs of America Movement.
1162. **610.** 4 c. red, blk. & indigo 10 10

1960. Inauguration of 1st U.S. Automated P.O., Providence, Rhode Island.
1163. **611.** 4 c. blue and red .. 15 10

1960. Marshal Mannerheim Commem. Medallion portrait as T **563.**
1164. 4 c. blue 10 10
1165. 8 c. ochre, red and blue .. 20 10

613. Camp Fire Girls Emblem. **615.** George.

1960. 50th Anniv. of Camp Fire Girls Movement.
1166. **613.** 4 c. red and blue .. 10 10

1960. Garibaldi Commem. Medallion portrait as T **563.**
1167. 4 c. green 10 10
1168. 8 c. ochre, red and blue .. 15 10

1960. Senator Walter F. George Memorial Issue.
1169 **615** 4 c. violet 10 10

616. Andrew Carnegie.

617. Dulles.

1960. Andrew Carnegie.
1170 **616** 4 c. red 10 10

1960. John Foster Dulles Memorial Issue.
1171 **617** 4 c. violet 10 10

618. " Echo I " Communications Satellite.

1960. " Communications for Peace ".
1172. **618.** 4 c. violet 20 10

1961. Mahatma Gandhi Commem. Medallion portrait as T **563.**
1173. 4 c. red on orange .. 20 10
1174. 8 c. ochre, red and blue .. 35 10

620. Trail Boss and Prairie.

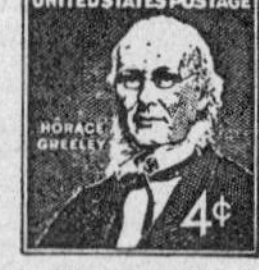

621. Horace Greeley (from steel engraving by A. H. Ritchie).

1961. Range Conservation.
1175 **620.** 4 c. blk., oran. & blue 15 10

1961. Horace Greeley (editor).
1176. **621.** 4 c. violet 10 10

622. Sea Coast Gun.

1961. Civil War Centennial. Battles.
1177. **622.** 4 c. green 20 10
1178. – 4 c. black on pink .. 20 10
1179. – 5 c. indigo and blue .. 20 10
1180. – 5 c. black and red .. 20 10
1181. – 5 c. black and blue .. 30 10
DESIGNS—HORIZ. No. 1178, Rifleman (Shiloh). 1179, Armed combat (Gettysburg). 1180, Artillery crew (Wilderness). VERT. No. 1181, Soldier and rifles (Appomattox).

627. Sunflower and Pioneers.

1961. Cent of Kansas Statehood.
1182 **627** 4 c. red, green and brown on yellow .. 10 10

628. Senator G. W. Norris

1961. Birth Cent. of George W. Norris.
1183. **628.** 4 c. green 10 10

629. Curtiss A–1 of 1911 (Navy's first Plane).

630. " Balanced Judgment ".

1961. 50th Anniv. of U.S. Naval Aviation.
1184. **629.** 4 c. blue 10 10

1961. 150th Anniv. of Workmen's Compensation Law.
1185. **630.** 4 c. blue 10 10

631. " The Smoke Signal " (after Remington). **632.** Dr. Sun Yat-sen. **633.** Basket-ball.

1961. Birth Centenary of Frederic Remington (painter).
1186. **631.** 4 c. multicoloured .. 10 10

1961. 50th Anniv. of Republic of China.
1187. **632.** 4 c. blue 10 10

1961. Birth Cent. of Dr. James A. Naismith (Inventor of basketball).
1188. **633.** 4 c. brown 15 10

634. Nurse lighting Candle of Dedication.

635. Ship Rock. New Mexico.

1961. Nursing.
1189. **634.** 4 c. multicoloured .. 10 10

1962. 50th Anniv. of Statehood of New Mexico.
1190. **635.** 4 c. lake, ochre & turq. 10 10

636. Saguaro Cactus and Flowers.

637. " U.S. Man in Space ".

1962. 50th Anniv of Arizona Statehood.
1191 **636** 4 c. blue, green & red 10 10

1962. Project Mercury. Colonel John Glenn's Space Flight.
1192 **637** 4 c. blue and yellow .. 10 10

638. U.S. and Campaign Emblems.

1962. Malaria Eradication.
1193. **638.** 4 c. ochre and blue .. 10 10

639. C. E. Hughes. **640.** Space Needle and Monorail.

1962. Birth Cent. of Chief Justice Hughes.
1194. **639.** 4 c. black on buff .. 10 10

1962. " Century 21 " Exn. (" World's Fair "), Seattle.
1195. **640.** 4 c. blue and red .. 10 10

641. Mississippi Sternwheel Steamer.

1962. 150th Anniv. of Lousiana Statehood.
1196. **641.** 4 c. myrtle, red & blue 10 10

642. Settler's Homestead.

1962. Centenary of Homestead Act.
1197. **642.** 4 c. grey 10 10

643. Girl Scout and Flag.

1962. 50th Anniv of U.S. Girl Scouts.
1198. **643.** 4 c. red 10 10

644. Senator McMahon and Atomic Symbol.

1962. Brien McMahon.
1199 **644** 4 c. violet 10 10

645. " Transfer of Skill". 646. Sam Rayburn.

1962. 25th Anniv. of National Apprenticeship Act.
1200. **645.** 4 c. black on olive .. 10 10

1962. Sam Rayburn (Speaker of House of Representatives) Commemoration.
1201. **646.** 4 c. brown and blue.. 10 10

647. Dag Hammarskjold and U.N. Headquarters.

648. Christmas Laurel Wreath.

1962. Hammarskjold.
1202. **647.** 4 c. brown, yell. & black 10 10
1203. 4 c. brn., yell. & black 10 10
No. 1203 has the yellow colour inverted and comes from a special printing made after a few examples had been discovered.

1962. Christmas.
1204. **648.** 4 c. green and red .. 10 10

649. " Lamp of Learning " and Map.

1962. Higher Education.
1205. **649.** 4 c. black and green.. 10 10

651. Washington (after Houdon).

A 652. Capitol, Washington and Airliner.

1962.
1206 – 1 c. green 10 10
1207 651 5 c. blue 10 10
Design: 1 c. Andrew Jackson.

1962. Air.
A1210 A 652 8 c. red 30 10

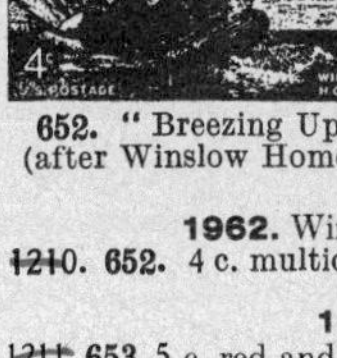

652. " Breezing Up " (after Winslow Homer).

653. U.S. Flag and White House.

1962. Winslow Homer.
1210. **652.** 4 c. multicoloured .. 10 10

1963.
1211 653 5 c. red and blue .. 15 10

654. Charter and Quill.

1963. 300th Anniv of Carolina Charter.
1212. **654.** 5 c. sepia and red .. 10 10

A 655. P.M.G. Montgomery Blair, Letters and Globe (after portrait by Thomas Sully).

655. " Food for Peace ".

1963. Air. Cent. of Paris Postal Conferences.
A 1213. A 655. 15 c. pur., bl. & red 60 40

1963. Freedom from Hunger.
1213. **655.** 5 c. brown, green & red 10 10

656. Map and State Capitol, Charleston.

A 657. American Bald Eagle.

1963. Cent. of West Virginia Statehood.
1214. **656.** 5 c. red, black & grn. 10 10

1963. Air.
A1215 A 657 6 c. red 30 10

657. Broken Link.

A 658. Amelia Earhart and Lockheed "Electra".

1963. Cent. of Emancipation Proclamation.
1215. **657.** 5 c. black, blue & red 20 10

1963. Air. Amelia Earhart Commem.
A 1216. A 658. 8 c. purple and red 25 10

658. Torch of Progress. 659. Cordell Hull.

1963. " Alliance for Progress ".
1216. **658.** 5 c. green and blue .. 10 10

1963. Cordell Hull Commem.
1217. **659.** 5 c. turquoise .. 10 10

660. Eleanor Roosevelt.

1963. Eleanor Roosevelt Commem.
1218. **660.** 5 c. violet 10 10

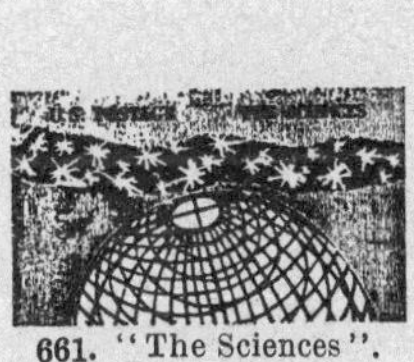

661. " The Sciences ". 662. City Mail Postman.

1963. Cent. of National Academy of Science.
1219. **661.** 5 c. black & turquoise 10 10

1963. Cent. of City Mail Delivery.
1220. **662.** 5 c. black, red & blue 10 10

663. Red Cross Flag and S.S. " Morning Light ".

664. Christmas Tree.

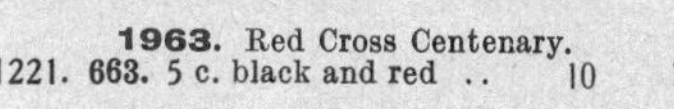

1963. Red Cross Centenary.
1221. **663.** 5 c. black and red .. 10 10

1963. Christmas.
1222. **664.** 5 c. black, blue & red 10 10

665. "Columbia Jays" (print) (Actually Collie's Magpie-jays).

666. Sam Houston (from lithograph by F. Davignon).

1963. John James Audubon Commem.
1223. **665.** 5 c. multicoloured .. 30 10
See also No. A 1304.

1964. Sam Houston Commem.
1224. **666.** 5 c. black 20 10

667. " Jerked Down ".

1964. Birth Cent. of C. M. Russell (artist).
1225. **667.** 5 c. multicoloured .. 20 10

668. Mall with Unisphere and "The Rocket Thrower" (after De Lue).

669. John Muir (naturalist), and Forest.

1964. New York World's Fair.
1226. **668.** 5 c. turquoise .. 10 10

1964. John Muir Commem.
1227. **669.** 5 c. brn., emer. & grn. 10 10

670. Pres. Kennedy and " Eternal Flame ".

671. Philip Carteret at Elizabethtown (1664) (after painting in Union County Courthouse).

1964. President Kennedy Memorial Issue.
1228. **670.** 5 c. blue on grey .. 15 10

1964. Tercent. of New Jersey.
1229. **671.** 5 c. blue 10 10

672. Virginia City in 19th Century.

673. U.S. Flag.

1964. Cent. of Nevada Statehood.
1230. **672.** 5 c. multicoloured .. 10 10

1964. " Register and Vote " Campaign.
1231. **673.** 5 c. red and blue .. 10 10

674. Shakespeare.

675. Drs. William and Charles Mayo (after J. E. Fraser).

1964. 400th Birth Anniv. of William Shakespeare.
1232. **674.** 5 c. sepia on buff .. 10 10

1964. Mayo Brothers (founders of Mayo Clinic). Commem.
1233. **675.** 5 c. green 10 10

A 676. R. H. Goddard, " Atlas " Rocket and Launching Tower.

1964. Air. Robert H. Goddard Commem.
A 1234. A 676. 8 c. bl., red & yell. 60 10

676. Lute, Horn and Music Score.

1964. American Music.
1234. **676.** 5 c. black, red and blue on pale blue .. 10 10

677. Sampler.

1964. " Homemakers " Commem.
1235. **677.** 5 c. multicoloured .. 10 10

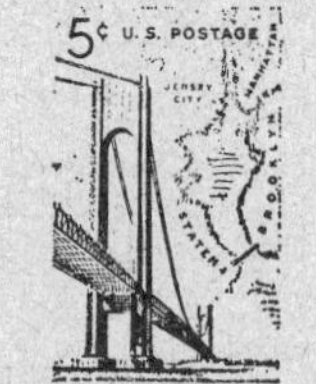

678. Holly. **682.** Verrazano-Narrows Bridge.

1964. Christmas. Each red, green and black.
1236. 5 c. Type **678** 30 10
1237. 5 c. Mistletoe 30 10
1238. 5 c. Poinsettia 30 10
1239. 5 c. Pine cone 30 10

1964. Opening of Verrazano-Narrows Bridge, New York.
1240. **682.** 5 c. green 10 10

683. " Abstract Art " (from lithograph by S. Davis).

1964. " To the Fine Arts ".
1241. **683.** 5 c. red, black & blue 15 10

684. Radio " Waves ". **685.** General Jackson leading Troops into Battle.

1964. Amateur Radio.
1242. **684.** 5 c. purple 10 10

1965. 150th Anniv. of Battle of New Orleans.
1243. **685.** 5 c. red, blue & black 15 10

686. Discus-thrower (Washington statue). **687.** Microscope and Stethoscope.

1965. Centenary of Sokol Physical Fitness Organization in the U.S.A.
1244. **686.** 5 c. blue and lake .. 10 10

1965. Crusade Against Cancer.
1245. **687.** 5 c. black, violet & red 10 10

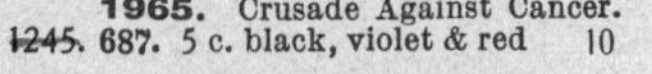

688. Sir Winston Churchill (from photo by Karsh).

1965. Churchill Commem.
1246. **688.** 5 c. black 10 10

689. Procession of Barons, and King John's Crown.

1965. 750th Anniv. of Magna Carta.
1247. **689.** 5 c. black, yell. & violet 10 10

690. I.C.Y. Emblem. **691.** " One hundred years of service ".

1965. Int. Co-operation Year.
1248. **690.** 5 c. black and blue .. 10 10

1965. Cent. of Salvation Army.
1249. **691.** 5 c. black, red & blue . 15 10

692. Dante. **693.** Herbert Hoover.

1965. 700th Anniv. of Dante's Birth.
1250. **692.** 5 c. red on flesh .. 10 10

1965. Hoover Commem.
1251. **693.** 5 c. red 10 10

694. Robert Fulton (after Houdon) and "Clermont". **695.** Spanish Knight and Banners.

1965. Birth Bicent. of Robert Fulton (inventor).
1252. **694.** 5 c. black and blue .. 10 10

1965. 400th Anniv. of Florida Settlement.
1253. **695.** 5 c. black, red & yellow 10 10

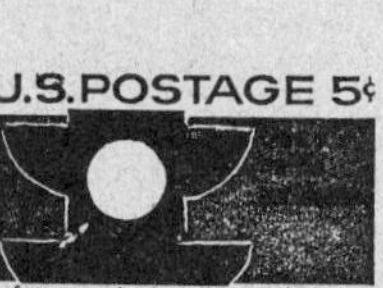

696. Traffic Signal. **697.** Elizabeth Clarke Copley (from " The Copley Family " by John S. Copley).

1965. Traffic Safety.
1254 **696** 5 c. red, black & green 10 10

1965. John Singleton Copley.
1255. **697.** 5 c. brown, drab & blk. 10 10

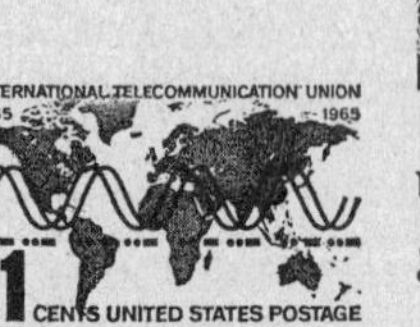

698. Radio " Waves " on World Map (based on Galt projection). **699.** Adlai Stevenson (from photo by P. Halsman).

1965. Centenary of I.T.U.
1256. 698 11 c. red, black & brn 35 15

1965. Stevenson Commem.
1257. **699.** 5 c. multicoloured .. 10 10

700. Archangel Gabriel (weathervane) (after painting by L. Chabot). **705.** Lincoln (after photo by M. Brady).

1965. Christmas.
1258. **700.** 5 c. green, ochre & red 10 10

1965. Prominent Americans (1st series).
1259 – 1 c. green 10 10
1260 – $1\frac{1}{4}$ c. green 10 15
1261 – 2 c. blue 10 10
1262 – 3 c. violet 10 10
1263 **705** 4 c. black 15 10
1265 – 5 c. blue 10 10
1266 – 6 c. brown 15 10
1282 – 6 c. brown 30 10
1267 – 8 c. violet 20 10
1268 – 10 c. purple 20 10
1269 – 12 c. black 20 10
1270 – 13 c. brown 20 10
1271 – 15 c. red 25 10
1272 – 20 c. green 30 10
1273 – 25 c. red 40 10
1274 – 30 c. purple 60 10
1275 – 40 c. blue 75 10
1276 – 50 c. purple .. .. 1·25 10
1283 – $1 purple .. .. 1·50 60
1278 – $5 black .. .. 8·50 1·25

DESIGNS—VERT. 1 c. Thomas Jefferson (after Rembrandt Peale). $1\frac{1}{4}$ c. Albert Gallatin. 2 c. Frank Lloyd Wright and Guggenheim Museum, New York. 5 c. Washington (after Rembrandt Peale). 6 c. (1282) Franklin D. Roosevelt. 8 c. Albert Einstein. 10 c. Andrew Jackson (after T. Sully). 13 c. John F. Kennedy. 15 c. Justice Wendell Holmes. 20 c. George C. Marshall. 25 c. Federick Douglass. 40 c. Tom Paine (after John W. Jarvis). 50 c. Lucy Stone. $1, Eugene O' Neill. $5, John Bassett Moore. HORIZ. 3 c. Francis Parkman. 6 c. (1266) Franklin D. Roosevelt. 12 c. Henry Ford and Model "T" Car. 30 c. John Dewey.

See also Nos. 1383/9.

719. " Migratory Birds ".

1966. 50th Anniv. of Migratory Bird Treaty.
1286. **719.** 5 c. red, blue and black 10 10

720. Dog. **721.** Seal, Emblem and Map.

1966. Humane Treatment of Animals.
1287. **720.** 5 c. black and brown 10 10

1966. 150th Anniv. of Indiana Statehood.
1288. **721.** 5 c. blue, brown & yell. 10 10

722. Lou Jacobs (clown). **723.** SIPEX " Letter ".

1966. The American Circus.
1289. **722.** 5 c. multicoloured .. 10 10

1966. 6th Int. Philatelic Exn., Washington. (SIPEX).
1290. **723.** 5 c. multicoloured .. 10 10

725. " Freedom " opposing " Tyranny ". **726.** Polish Eagle.

1966. 175th Anniv. of Bill of Rights.
1292. **725.** 5 c. red, indigo and blue 10 10

1966. Polish Millennium.
1293. **726.** 5 c. red 10 10

727. N.P.S. Emblem. **728.** Marines Past and Present.

1966. 50th Anniv. of National Park Service.
1294. **727.** 5 c. black, grn. & yell. 10 10

1966. 50th Anniv. of Marine Corps Reserve.
1295. **728.** 5 c. multicoloured .. 10 10

729. Women of 1891 and 1966. **730.** Johnny Appleseed and Apple.

1966. 75th Anniv. of General Federation of Women's Clubs.
1296. **729.** 5 c. black, pink & blue 10 10

1966. Johnny Appleseed.
1297. **730.** 5 c. black, red & green 10 10

731. Jefferson Memorial, Washington. **732.** Map of Great River Road.

1966. " Beautification of America " Campaign.
1298. **731.** 5 c. black, grn. & pink 10 10

1966. Opening of Great River Road.
1299. **732.** 5 c. red, yellow & blue 10 10

733. Statue of Liberty and U.S. Flag (after photo by B. Noble). **734.** " Madonna and Child " (after Memling).

1966. 25th Anniv. of U.S. Savings Bond Programme and Tribute to U.S. Servicemen.
1300. **733.** 5 c. multicoloured .. 10 10

1966. Christmas.
1301. **734.** 5 c. multicoloured .. 10 10

735. "The Boating Party" (after Mary Cassatt). **A736.** Tlingit Totem, Southern Alaska.

1966. Mary Cassatt.
1302. **735.** 5 c. multicoloured .. 10 10

1967. Air. Cent. of Alaska Purchase.
A 1303. A **736.** 8 c. brown .. 30 15

736. Recruiting Poster. **A 737.** "Columbia Jays" by Audubon.

1967. Centenary of National Grange (farmers' organization).
1303. **736.** 5 c. multicoloured .. 10 10

1967. Air.
A 1304. **A 737.** 20 c. multicoloured 1·60 10
See also No. 1223.

737. Canadian Landscape.

1967. Canadian Centennial.
1304. **737.** 5 c. multicoloured .. 10 10

738. Canal Barge.

1967. 150th Anniv. of Erie Canal.
1305. **738.** 5 c. multicoloured .. 10 10

739. Peace Dove Emblem.

1967. "Search for Peace" (Lions Int. essay theme).
1306. **739.** 5 c. black, red and blue 10 10

740. H. D. Thoreau. **742.** Radio Tower and "Waves".

NEBRASKA STATEHOOD
1867-1967
U.S. POSTAGE 5¢

741. Hereford Bull.

1967. 150th Birth Anniv. of Henry Thoreau (writer).
1307. **740.** 5 c. black, red & green 15 10

1967. Cent. of Nebraska Statehood.
1308. **741.** 5 c. multicoloured .. 10 10

1967. "Voice of America". 25th Anniv of Radio Branch of United States Information Agency.
1309. **742.** 5 c. black, red & blue 15 10

743. Davy Crockett and Pine.

1967. Davy Crockett Commem.
1310. **743.** 5 c. black, grn. & yell. 10 10

744. Astronaut in Space. **746.** "Planned City".

1967. U.S. Space Achievements. Mult.
1311. 5 c. Type **744** 40 15
1312. 5 c. "Gemini 4" over Earth 40 15
Nos. 1311/2 were issued together se-tenant, forming a composite design.

1967. Urban Planning.
1313. **746.** 5 c. ultram., blk. & bl. 10 10

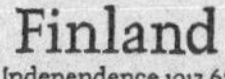

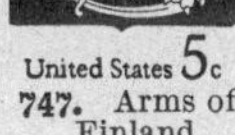

747. Arms of Finland. **748.** "The Biglin Brothers racing" (Eakins).

1967. 50th Anniv. of Finnish Independence.
1314. **747.** 5 c. blue 10 10

1967. Thomas Eakins.
1315. **748.** 5 c. multicoloured .. 15 10

749. "Madonna and Child with Angels" (Memling). **750.** Magnolia.

1967. Christmas.
1316. **749.** 5 c. multicoloured .. 10 10

1967. 150th Anniv. of Mississippi Statehood.
1317. **750.** 5 c. brown, green and turquoise 10 10

A 751. "Fifty Stars".  **751.** U.S. Flag and The White House.

1968. Air.
A 1318. **A 751.** 10 c. red .. 25 5

1968. Flag Issue.
1318 **751** 6 c. multicoloured .. 20 10
1320 8 c. multicoloured .. 25 10

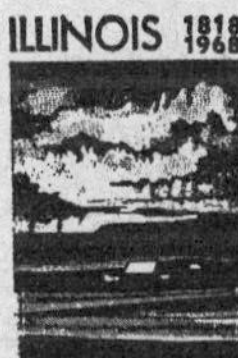

752. Homestead and Cornfield. **753.** Map of the Americas.

1968. 150th Anniv. of Illinois Statehood.
1323. **752.** 6 c. multicoloured .. 15 10

1968. "HemisFair '68" Exn, San Antonio.
1324 **753** 6 c. blue, pink & white 15 10

INDEX

Countries can be quickly located by referring to the index at the end of this volume.

754. Eagle with Pennant (after late 19th-century wood carving).

1968. "Airlift".
1325. **754.** $1 brown, blue & buff 2·75 1·25
No. 1325 was issued primarily for a special reduced-rate parcels service to forces personnel overseas and in Alaska, Hawaii and Puerto Rico.

755. Boys and Girls. **756.** Policeman with Small Boy.

A 756. Curtiss "Jenny".

1968. Youth Programme of Elks Benevolent Society.
1326. **755.** 6 c. blue and red .. 15 10

1968. Air. 50th Anniv of Scheduled Airmail Services.
A1327 **A 756** 10 c. blk, red & bl 30 10

1968. "Law and Order".
1328. **756.** 6 c. blue, red & black 15 10

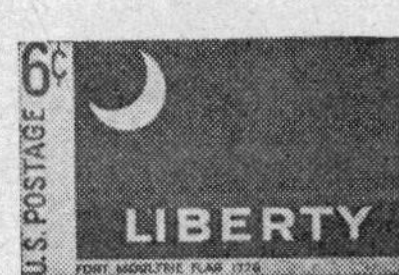

757. Eagle Weathervane. **758.** Fort Moultrie, 1776

1968. "Register and Vote".
1329 **757** 6 c. yellow, orge & blk 15 10

1968. Historic Flags.

1330.	**758.**	6 c. blue	45	20
1331.	–	6 c. red and blue ..	45	20
1332.	–	6 c. green and blue..	45	20
1333.	–	6 c. red and blue ..	45	20
1334.	–	6 c. blue, yell. & red..	45	20
1335.	–	6 c. red and blue ..	45	20
1336.	–	6 c. blue, red & green	45	20
1337.	–	6 c. red and blue ..	45	20
1338.	–	6 c. blue, red & yell..	45	20
1339.	–	6 c. red, yell. & blue..	45	20

FLAGS: No 1331, U. S. (Fort McHenry), 1795–1818. 1332, Washington's Cruisers, 1775. 1333, Bennington, 1777. 1334, Rhode Island, 1775. 1335, First Stars and Stripes, 1777. 1336, Bunker Hill, 1775. 1337, Grand Union, 1776. 1338, Philadelphia Light Horse, 1775. 1339, First Navy Jack, 1775.

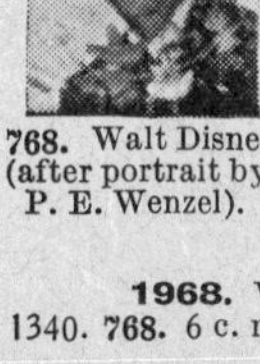

768. Walt Disney (after portrait by P. E. Wenzel). 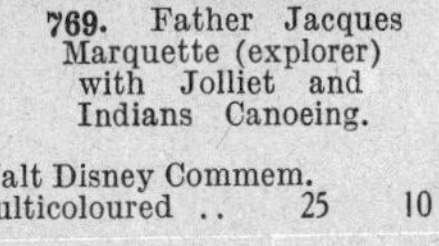 **769.** Father Jacques Marquette (explorer) with Jolliet and Indians Canoeing.

1968. Walt Disney Commem.
1340. **768.** 6 c. multicoloured .. 25 10

1968. Marquette Commem.
1341. **769.** 6 c. multicoloured .. 15 10

770. Rifle, Tomahawk, Powder-horn and Knife.

1968. Daniel Boone Commem.
1342. **770.** 6 c. multicoloured .. 15 10

771. Ship's Wheel and River Tanker.

1968. Arkansas River Navigation Project.
1343. **771.** 6 c. blk., bl. & light bl. 15 10

CHEROKEE STRIP

772. "Leif Erikson" (statue by Stirling Calder, Reykjavik, Iceland). **773.** Pioneers racing to Cherokee Strip.

1968. Leif Erikson Commem.
1344. **772.** 6 c. sepia and brown 15 10

1968. 75th Anniv. of Opening of Cherokee Strip to Settlers.
1345. **773.** 6 c. brown 15 10

774. "Battle of Bunker's Hill" (detail) (after John Trumbull). **775.** Wood Ducks.

1968. John Trumbull.
1346. **774.** 6 c. multicoloured .. 20 10

1968. Waterfowl Conservation.
1347. **775.** 6 c. multicoloured .. 30 10

776. "The Annunciation" (Jan van Eyck). **777.** "Chief Joseph" (after C. Hall).

1968. Christmas.
1348. **776.** 6 c. multicoloured .. 15 10

1968. "The American Indian".
1349. **777.** 6 c. multicoloured .. 30 10

A 778. "USA" and Jet Aircraft.

1968. Air.
A 1350. **A 778.** 20 c. red, bl. & blk. 60 10
A 1351. 21 c. bl., red & blk. 55 10

778. Capitol and Flowers ("Cities").

1969. " Beautification of America " Campaign.

1352. **778.** 6 c. multicoloured .. 40 10
1353. – 6 c. multicoloured .. 40 10
1354. – 6 c. multicoloured .. 40 10
1355. – 6 c. multicoloured .. 40 10

DESIGNS: No. 1353, Potomac River and Flowers (" Parks "). 1354, Motorway and Flowers (" Highways "). 1355, Road and Trees (" Streets ").

782. "Eagle" (U.S. Seal). **783.** "July Fourth".

1969. 50th Anniv. of American Legion.
1356. **782.** 6 c. black, blue & red 15 10

1969. Grandma Moses (Mrs. A. M. R. Moses).
1357. **783.** 6 c. multicoloured .. 15 10

784. Earth and Moon's Surface (from an astronaut's photograph). **785.** W. C. Handy (statue, Memphis).

1969 Moon Flight of " Apollo 8 ".
1358. **784.** 6 c. ochre, blue & blk. 20 10

1969. Handy (composer) Commem.
1359. **785.** 6 c. mauve, blue and violet 20 10

786. Belfry, Carmel Mission. **787.** Powell exploring Colorado River.

1969. Bicentenary of California.
1360. **786.** 6 c. multicoloured .. 15 10

1969. John Wesley Powell (geologist). Cent. of Colorado River Exploration.
1361. **787.** 6 c. multicoloured .. 15 10

788. Camellia and Common Flicker.

1969. 150th Anniv. of Alabama Statehood.
1362. **788.** 6 c. multicoloured .. 30 10

791. Ocotillo.

1969. 11th Int. Botanical Congress, Seattle. Multicoloured.

1363. 6 c. Douglas Fir .. 50 10
1364. 6 c. Lady's slipper .. 50 10
1365. 6 c. Type **791** 50 10
1366. 6 c. Franklinia 50 10

A **793.** Astronaut setting foot on Moon.

1969. Air. 1st Man on the Moon.
A1367. A **793.** 10 c. multicoloured 15 10

793. Daniel Webster and Dartmouth Hall. **794.** Striker.

1969. 150th Anniv. of Dartmouth College Legal Case.
1368. **793.** 6 c. green 15 10

1969. Cent. of Professional Baseball.
1369. **794.** 6 c. multicoloured .. 45 10

795. Footballer and Coach. **796.** Dwight D. Eisenhower (from photograph by B. Noble).

1969. Cent. of Intercollegiate Football.
1370. **795.** 6 c. green and red .. 25 10

1969. Eisenhower Commem.
1371. **796.** 6 c. black, blue & lake 20 10

797. " Winter Sunday in Norway, Maine " (unknown artist).

1969. Christmas.
1372. **797.** 6 c. multicoloured .. 15 10

798. Rehabilitated Child. **800.** " Old Models " (William Harnett).

1969. Rehabilitation of the Handicapped.
1373. **798.** 6 c. multicoloured .. 15 10

No. 1373 also commemorates the 50th anniv. of the National Society for Crippled Children and Adults.

1969. William M. Harnett.
1376. **800.** 6 c. multicoloured .. 10 10

804. Prehistoric Creatures (from mural by R. Zallinger in Yale's Peabody Museum).

1970. Natural History. Cent. of American Natural History Museum. Multicoloured.

1377 6 c. American bald eagle 30 10
1378 6 c. African elephant herd 30 10
1379 6 c. Haida ceremonial canoe 20 10
1380 6 c. Type **804** 20 10

805. "The Lighthouse at Two Lights" (painting by Edward Hopper in Metropolitan Museum of Art, New York).

1970. Maine Statehood Sesquicentennial.
1381. **805.** 6 c. multicoloured .. 30 10

806. American Bison.

1970. Wildlife Conservation.
1382. **806.** 6 c. black on brown .. 15 10

807. Dwight D. Eisenhower. **809.** Benjamin Franklin.

1970. Prominent Americans (2nd series).

1383 **807.** 6 c. blue 10 10
1384 **809.** 7 c. blue 10 10
1392 **807.** 8 c. maroon 30 10
1390 8 c. black, blue & red 10 10
1386 – 14 c. black 30 10
1387 – 16 c. brown 30 10
1388 – 18 c. violet 45 10
1389 – 21 c. green 50 10

DESIGNS—VERT. 14 c. F. H. La Guardia. 16 c. Ernest T. Pyle. 18 c. Dr. Elizabeth Blackwell. 21 c. Amadeo P. Giannini (after painting by J. Kozlowski).

822. Edgar Lee Masters. **823.** Suffragettes, 1920, and Woman operating Voting Machine.

1970. Edgar Lee Masters (poet) Commem.
1401 **822** 6 c. black and bistre .. 15 10

1970. 50th Anniv. of Women's Suffrage.
1402. **823.** 6 c. blue 15 10

824. Symbols of South Carolina.

1970. 300th Anniv of South Carolina.
1403. **824.** 6 c. multicoloured .. 15 10

825. Stone Mountain Memorial.

1970. Dedication of Stone Mountain Confederate Memorial.
1404 **825** 6 c. black 15 10

826. Fort Snelling and Keel Boat.

1970. 150th Anniv. of Fort Snelling, Minnesota.
1405. **826.** 6 c. multicoloured .. 15 10

828. City Park.

1970. Prevention of Pollution.

1406. 6 c. Wheat 45 10
1407. 6 c. Type **828** 45 10
1408. 6 c. Blue-gill 45 10
1409. 6 c. Western gull .. 60 10

832. Toy Locomotive (after drawing by C. Hemming).

1970. Christmas. Multicoloured.

1410. 6 c. " The Nativity " (L. Lotto) (vert.) .. 15 10
1411. 6 c. Type **832** .. 65 10
1412. 6 c. Toy horse on wheels 40 10
1413. 6 c. Mechanised tricycle 40 10
1414. 6 c. Doll's pram 40 10

Nos. 1412/14 are taken from "Golden Age of Toys" by Fondin and Remise.

836. " U.N. " and Emblem.

1970. 25th Anniv. of U.N.O.
1415. **836.** 6 c. red, blue and blk. 15 10

837. "Mayflower" and Pilgrims. **838.** Disabled American Veterans Emblems.

1970. 350th Anniv. of Landing of the Pilgrim Fathers in America.
1416. **837.** 6 c. multicoloured .. 20 10

1970. 50th Anniv. of Disabled American Veterans Organization, and Armed Forces Commemoration.
1417. **838.** 6 c. multicoloured .. 20 10
1418. – 6 c. black, blue & red 20 10

DESIGN: No. 1418, Inscriptions—"Prisoners of War", "Missing and Killed in Action".

840. Ewe and Lamb. **841.** General Douglas MacArthur.

1970. 450th Anniv. of Introduction of Sheep into North America.
1419. **840.** 6 c. multicoloured .. 15 10

1971. 91st Birth Anniv. of General Douglas MacArthur.
1420. **841.** 6 c. black, blue & red 15 10

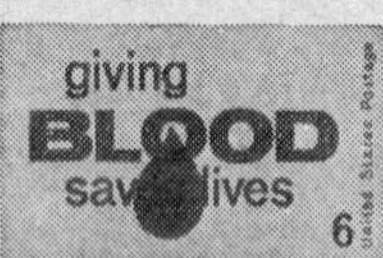

842. " Giving Blood Saves Lives ".

1971. Salute to Blood Donors.
1421. **842.** 6 c. deep blue, red & bl. 15 10

A **844.** Jet Aircraft. A **845.** Winged Letter.

1971. Air.

A1422. – 9 c. red 25 25
A1423. A **844.** 11 c. red .. 35 10
A1424. A **845.** 13 c. red .. 30 10

DESIGN—HORIZ. 9 c. Delta-wing plane.

846. " Settlers and Indians " (after mural " Independence and the Opening of the West " by Thomas H. Benton).

1971. 150th Anniv. of Missouri Statehood.
1427. **846.** 8 c. multicoloured .. 25 10

847. Trout.

1971. Wildlife Conservation. Multicoloured.

1428.	8 c. Type **847**	30	10
1429.	8 c. Alligator	30	10
1430.	8 c. Polar Bear and cubs	30	15
1431.	8 c. Californian Condor ..	30	10

851. Antarctic Map Emblem. 852. Postal Service Emblem.

1971. 10th Anniv of Antarctic Treaty.
1432 851 8 c. blue and red .. 20 10

1971. Reorganization of U.S. Post Office as U.S. Postal Service.
1433. 852. 8 c. multicoloured .. 15 10

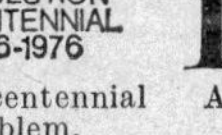

853. Bicentennial Emblem. A 854. Head of Statue of Liberty.

1971 American Revolution Bicentennial. Bicentennial Commission Emblem.
1434 853 8 c. multicoloured .. 25 10

1971. Air.
A 1435. A 854. 17 c. bl., red & grn. 55 10

855. "The Wake of the Ferry". (John Sloan).

1971. Birth Centenary of John Sloan (artist).
1436. 855. 8 c. multicoloured 15 10

856. Landing Module on Moon. 858. Emily Dickinson.

1971. Decade of U.S. Space Achievements. Multicoloured.

1437.	8 c. Type **856** ..	15	10
1438.	8 c. Astronauts in lunar rover	15	10

Nos. 1437/8 were issued together se-tenant, forming a composite design.

1971. 85th Death Anniv of Emily Dickinson (poet).
1439 858 8 c. mult on green 15 10

859. Watch-tower, El Morro, San Juan. 860. Drug Victim.

1971. 450th Anniv. of San Juan, Puerto Rico.
1440. 859. 8 c. multicoloured .. 15 10

1971. Drug Abuse Prevention Week.
1441. 860. 8 c. blk., new bl. & bl. 25 10

861. Hands reaching to "CARE". 866. "Adoration of the Shepherds" (Giorgione).

862. Decatur House, Washington D.C.

1971. 25th Anniv. of "CARE" (Co-operative for American Relief Everywhere).
1442. 861. 8 c. multicoloured .. 20 10

1971. Historic Preservation.

1443.	862.	8 c. blk & flesh on cream	20	10
1444.	–	8 c. blk. & flesh on cream	20	10
1445.	–	8 c. blk. & flesh on cream	25	10
1446.	–	8 c. blk. & flesh on cream	20	10

DESIGNS: No. 1444, Whaling ship, "Charles W. Morgan", Mystic, Conn. No. 1445, San Francisco cable-car. No. 1446, San Xavier del Bac Mission, Tucson, Arizona.

1971. Christmas. Multicoloured.

1447.	8 c. Type **866**	25	10
1448.	8 c. "Partridge in a Pear Tree"	30	10

868. Sidney Lanier. 869. Peace Corps Poster (D. Battle).

1972. 90th Death Anniv. (1971) of Sidney Lanier (poet).
1449. 868. 8 c. blk., brn. & blue 20 10

1972. Peace Corps.
1450. 869. 8 c. red, light bl. & bl. 15 10

870/873. Cape Hatteras National Seashore.

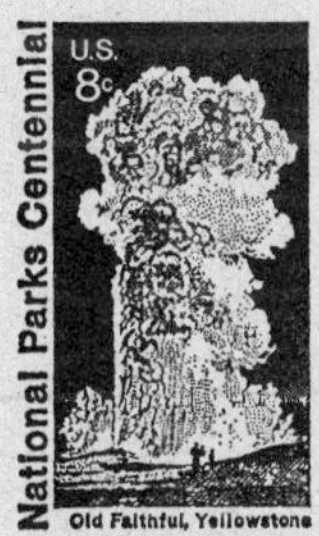

875. "Old Faithful", Yellowstone Park. A 877. Statue and Temple, City of Refuge, Hawaii.

1972. Cent. of National Parks.

1451.	870.	2 c. mult. (post.)	15	10
1452.	871.	2 c. mult.	15	10
1453.	872.	2 c. mult. ..	20	10
1454.	873.	2 c. mult. ..	20	10
1455.	–	6 c. mult. ..	20	10
1456.	875.	8 c. mult. ..	30	10
1457.	–	15 c. mult. ..	50	45
A 1458.	A 877.	11 c. mult. (air)	35	10

DESIGNS—HORIZ. (As Type A 877). 6 c. Theatre at Night, Wolf Trap Farm, Virginia. 15 c. Mt. McKinley, Alaska.

878. American Family. 879. Glassblower.

1972. Family Planning.
1459. 878. 8 c. multicoloured .. 20 10

1972. Bicent. of American Revolution. American Colonial Craftsmen.

1460.	879.	8 c. brown on yellow	20	10
1461.	–	8 c. brown on yellow	20	10
1462.	–	8 c. brown on yellow	20	10
1463.	–	8 c. brown on yellow	20	10

DESIGNS: No. 1461, Silversmith. No. 1462, Wigmaker. No. 1463, Hatter.

883. Cycling.

1972. Olympic Games, Munich and Sapporo, Japan. Multicoloured.

1464.	6 c. Type **883** (postage)	20	15
1465.	8 c. Bobsleighing ..	25	10
1466.	15 c. Running	40	40
A 1467.	11 c. Skiing (air) ..	35	15

887. Classroom Blackboard.

1972. 75th Anniv. of Parent Teacher Assn.
1468. 887. 8 c. black and yellow 15 10

888. Northern Fur Seals.

1972. Wildlife Conservation. Multicoloured.

1469.	8 c. Type **888**	20	10
1470	8 c. Common Cardinal (bird)	30	10
1471.	8 c. Brown Pelicans ..	30	10
1472.	8 c. American Bighorn ..	20	10

892. 19th-Century Country Post Office and Store.

1972. Centenary of Mail Order Business.
1473 892 8 c. multicoloured .. 15 10

893. "Quest for Health". 894. "Tom Sawyer" (N. Rockwell).

1972. 75th Anniv of American Osteopaths.
1474 893 8 c. multicoloured .. 15 10

1972. "The Adventures of Tom Sawyer" by Mark Twain.
1475. 894. 8 c. multicoloured .. 25 10

895. "Angels" (detail, "Mary, Queen of Heaven" by Master of the St. Lucy Legend). 897. Pharmaceutical Equipment.

1972. Christmas. Multicoloured.

1476.	8 c. Type **895**	20	10
1477.	8 c. Santa Claus	20	10

1972. 120th Anniv of American Pharmaceutical Association.
1478 897 8 c. multicoloured .. 25 10

898. Five Cent Stamp of 1847 under Magnifier.

1972. 125th Anniv. of 1st U.S. Stamp, and Stamp Collecting Promotion.
1479. 898. 8 c. brn., blk. and grn. 15 10

899. "LOVE".

1973. Greetings Stamp.
1480. 899. 8 c. red, green & blue 15 10

900. Pamphleteers with Press.

1973. American Revolution Bicentennial. Colonial Communications.

1481.	900.	8 c. grn., blue & red	25	10
1482.	–	8 c. black, red & blue	25	10
1483.	–	8 c. multicoloured ..	25	10
1484.	–	8 c. multicoloured ..	25	10

DESIGNS: No. 1482, Posting a Broadside. No. 1483, Post-rider. No. 1484, Drummer.

Copernicus 1473-1973 8¢US

904. George Gershwin (composer) and Scene from "Porgy and Bess". 908. Nicolas Copernicus (after 18th-cent. engraving).

1973. American Arts Commemoration. Mult.

1485.	8 c. Type **904**	25	10
1486.	8 c. Robinson Jeffers (poet) and People of Carmel ..	25	10
1487.	8 c. Henry Tanner (painter) and Palette ..	25	10
1488.	8 c. Willa Cather (novelist) and Pioneer Family ..	25	10

1973. 500th Birth Anniv. of Copernicus (astronomer).
1489. 908. 8 c. black and yellow 15 10

Harry S. Truman

U.S. Postage 8 cents

909. Counter Clerk.

919. Harry S. Truman.

1973. Postal Service Employees. Mult.

1490.	8 c. Type **909**	15	10
1491.	8 c. Collecting mail ..	15	10
1492.	8 c. Sorting on Conveyor Belt	15	10
1493.	8 c. Sorting parcels ..	15	10
1494.	8 c. Cancelling letters ..	15	10
1495.	8 c. Sorting letters by hand	15	10
1496.	8 c. Coding desks ..	15	10
1497.	8 c. Loading Mail-van ..	15	10
1498.	8 c. City Postman ..	15	10
1499.	8 c. Rural Postman ..	15	10

1973. Pres. Harry Truman. Commemoration.

1500. **919.**	8 c. black, red and blue.	15	10

920/923. Boston Tea Party. (Illustration reduced. Actual size 77 × 47 mm.).

1973. American Revolution Bicentennial. The Boston Tea Party.

1501. **920.**	8 c. multicoloured ..	15	10
1502. **921.**	8 c. multicoloured ..	15	10
1503. **922.**	8 c. multicoloured ..	15	10
1504. **923.**	8 c. multicoloured ..	15	10

924. Marconi's Spark Coil and Gap (1901).

1973. Progress in Electronics. Multicoloured.

1505.	6 c. Type **924** (postage) ..	20	15
1506.	8 c. Modern Transistor circuit	25	10
1507.	15 c. Early Microphone and Radio Speaker, Radio and T.V. Camera Tubes	45	40
A1508.	11 c. DeForest audions (1915) (air)	35	15

928. Lyndon B. Johnson (from painting by Elizabeth Shoumatoff).

929. Angus and Longhorn Cattle (painting by F. C. Murphy).

1973. Pres. Lyndon B. Johnson Commem.

1509 **928**	8 c. multicoloured ..	20	10

1973. "Rural America" Centenaries.

1510.	8 c. Type **929** ..	20	10
1511.	10 c. Institute Marquee	40	10
1512.	10 c. Steam train crossing Wheatfield ..	40	10

CENTENARIES: No. 1510, Introduction of Aberdeen Angus cattle into United States. No. 1511, Foundation of Chautauqua Institution (adult education organization). No. 1512, Introduction of hard winter wheat into Kansas.

MINIMUM PRICE

The minimum price quoted is 5p which represents a handling charge rather than a basis for valuing common stamps. For further notes about prices see introductory pages.

932. "Small Cowper Madonna" (Raphael).

933. Christmas Tree in Needlepoint.

1973. Christmas.

1513 **932**	8 c. multicoloured ..	20	10
1514 **933**	8 c. multicoloured ..	20	10

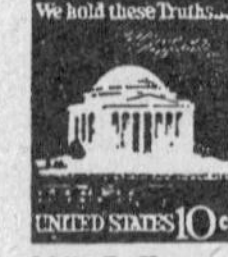

934. U.S. Flags of 1777 and 1973.

935. Jefferson Memorial.

936 "Mail Transport" (from poster by R. McDougall).

937. Liberty Bell.

1973.

1519. **937.**	6.3 c. red	20	20
1515. **934.**	10 c. red and blue ..	30	10
1516. **935.**	10 c. blue	30	10
1517. **936.**	10 c. multicoloured ..	20	10

A 938. Statue of Liberty.

1974. Air.

A 1521. **A 938.**	18 c. blk., red & bl.	70	40
A 1522. –	26 c. blk., bl. & red	80	10

DESIGN: 26 c. Mt. Rushmore National Memorial.

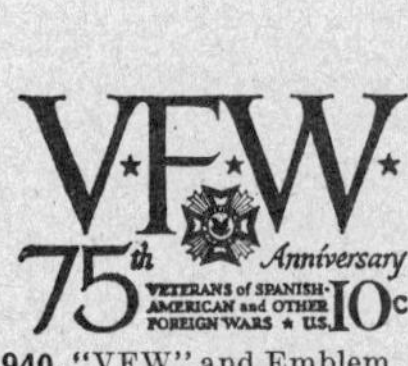

940. "VFW" and Emblem.

941. Robert Frost.

1974. 75th Anniv. of Veterans of Foreign Wars Organization.

1523. **940.**	10 c. red and blue ..	20	10

1974. Birth Cent. of Robert Frost (poet).

1524. **941.**	10 c. black	15	10

942. "Cosmic Jumper" and "Smiling Sage" ("Preserve the Environment" theme).

1974. " Expo 74 " World Fair, Spokane.

1525. **942.**	10 c. multicoloured ..	15	10

943. Horse-racing.

1974. Cent. of Kentucky Derby.

1526. **943.**	10 c. multicoloured ..	20	10

944. "Skylab" in Orbit.

1974. "Skylab" Space Project.

1527. **944.**	10 c. multicoloured ..	25	10

945. "Michelangelo" (detail from "School of Athens" by Raphael).

1974. Cent. of U.P.U. Mult.

1528.	10 c. Type **945**	15	10
1529.	10 c. "Five Feminine Virtues" (Hokusai) ..	15	10
1530.	10 c. "Old Scraps" (J. F. Peto)	15	10
1531.	10 c. "The Lovely Reader" (J. Liotard)	15	10
1532.	10 c. "Lady Writing Letter" (G. Terborch) ..	15	10
1533.	10 c. "Inkwell and Quill" (detail from "Young Boy with Top" by J. Chardin)	15	10
1534.	10 c. "Mrs. John Douglas" (T. Gainsborough) ..	15	10
1535.	10 c. "Don Antonio Noriega" (F. Goya) ..	15	10

955. Amethyst.

957. Covered Wagon at Fort Harrod.

1974. Mineral Heritage. Multicoloured.

1536.	10 c. Petrified Wood ..	25	10
1537.	10 c. Tourmaline ..	25	10
1538.	10 c. Type **955** ..	25	10
1539.	10 c. Rhodochrosite ..	25	10

1974. Bicentenary of Fort Harrod, First Settlement in Kentucky.

1540. **957.**	10 c. multicoloured ..	25	10

959. "We ask but for peace . . ." (First Continental Congress).

962. Slogan, Molecules and Petrol Drops.

1974. American Revolution Bicentennial. First Continental Congress.

1541. –	10 c. blue and red ..	25	10
1542. **959.**	10 c. grey, blue & red	25	10
1543. –	10 c. grey, red & blue	25	10
1544. –	10 c. red and blue ..	25	10

DESIGNS: No. 1541, Carpenters' Hall, Philadelphia. No. 1543, "Deriving their just powers . . ." (Declaration of Independence). No. 1544, Independence Hall, Philadelphia.

1974. Energy Conservation.

1545. **962.**	10 c. multicoloured ..	20	10

US 10c

Retarded Children Can Be Helped

963. " The Headless Horseman ".

964. Child clasping Hand.

1974. Washington Irving's "Legend of Sleepy Hollow".

1546. **963.**	10 c. multicoloured ..	20	10

1974. Help for Retarded Children.

1547. **964.**	10 c. lake and brown	25	10

966. " The Road—Winter " (from a Currier and Ives print, drawn by O. Knirsch).

1974. Christmas. Multicoloured.

1548.	10 c. "Angel" (detail, Perussis altarpiece) (vert.)	20	10
1549.	10 c. Type **966**	20	10
1550.	10 c. Dove Weathervane, Mount Vernon	20	10

No. 1550 has self-adhesive gum.

PIONEER ★ JUPITER

US 10c

968. "Benjamin West" (self-portrait).

969. "Pioneer" Spacecraft passing Jupiter.

1975. Benjamin West (painter) Commem.

1551. **968.**	10 c. multicoloured ..	15	10

1975. U.S. Unmanned Space Missions. Mult.

1552.	10 c. Type **969** ..	30	10
1553.	10 c. " Mariner 10 " Venus and Mercury	30	10

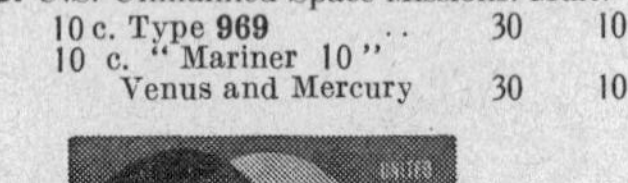

971. Overlapping Circles.

1975. Collective Bargaining in Labour Relations.

1554. **971.**	10 c. multicoloured ..	15	10

972. Sybil Ludington on Horseback.

1975. American Revolution Bicentennial. Contributors to the Cause.

1555. **972.**	8 c. multicoloured ..	20	20
1556. –	10 c. multicoloured ..	25	10
1557. –	10 c. multicoloured ..	25	10
1558. –	18 c. multicoloured ..	50	60

DESIGNS: No. 1556, Salem Poor loading Musket. No. 1557, Haym Salomon writing in ledger. No. 1558, Peter Francisco carrying cannon.

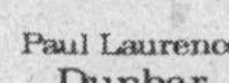

976. "Lexington" (from painting "Birth of Liberty" by H. Sandham).

977. Paul Laurence Dunbar (poet).

1975. American Revolution Bicentennial. Battles of Lexington and Concord.

1559. **976.**	10 c. multicoloured ..	25	10

1975. Dunbar Commemoration.

1560. **977.**	10 c. multicoloured ..	20	10

978. D. W. Griffith (film producer).

1975. Griffith Commemoration.

1561. **978.**	10 c. multicoloured ..	25	10

979. " Bunker Hill, 1775 ", (John Trumbull).

980. Marine with Musket.

1975. Bicent. of American Revolution. Battle of Bunker Hill.

1562. **979.** 10 c. multicoloured .. 25 10

1975. American Revolution Bicentennial. U.S. Military Services. Multicoloured.

1563. 10 c. Type **980** 25 10

1564. 10 c. Militiaman with Musket .. 25 10

1565. 10 c. Soldier with Flintlock 25 10

1566. 10 c. Sailor with Grappling-iron 25 10

984. Docking Manoeuvre.

1975. "Apollo-Soyuz" Space Test Project. Multicoloured.

1567. 10 c. Type **984** 20 10

1568. 10 c. Spacecraft Docked 20 10

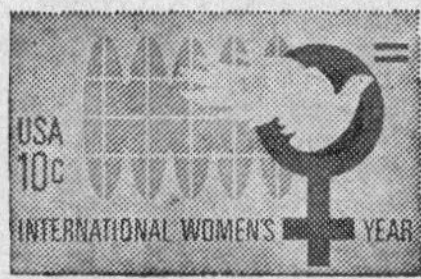

986. "Worldwide Equality".

1975. International Women's Year.

1569. **986.** 10 c. multicoloured .. 20 10

987. Stagecoach and Modern Lorry.

1975. Bicent. of Postal Services. Mult.

1571 10 c. Type **987** 20 10

1572 10 c. Early steam and modern diesel locomotives 20 10

1573 10 c. Early mailplane and jet airliner 20 10

1574 10 c. Telecommunications satellite 20 10

991. Law Book, Mallet and Globe.

1975. "World Peace through Law".

1575. **991.** 10 c. brown, blue & grn. 20 10

992. Coins and Engine-turned Motif.

1975. "Banking and Commerce".

1576. **992.** 10 c. multicoloured .. 20 10

1577. – 10 c. multicoloured .. 20 10

DESIGN: No. 1577, As Type **992**, but design reversed with different coins.

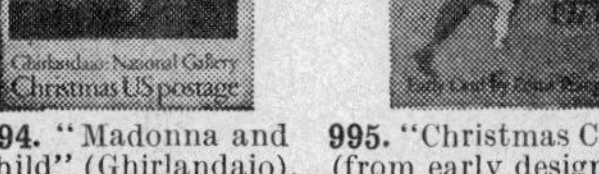

994. "Madonna and Child" (Ghirlandaio). **995.** "Christmas Card" (from early design by Louis Prang).

1975. Christmas.

1578. **994.** (10 c.) multicoloured 20 10

1579. **995.** (10 c.) multicoloured 20 10

Nos. 1578/9 were each sold at 10 c. Because of an imminent increase in the postage rates the two designs were issued without face values.

1002. Early Printing Press. **1020.** Flag over Independence Hall.

1975.

No.	Type	Description		
1580	–	1 c. deep bl. on grey	10	10
1581	–	2 c. red on cream ..	10	10
1582	–	3 c. olive on green ..	10	10
1597b	–	3.1 c. lake on yellow	15	10
1598	–	3.5 c. lilac on yellow	15	10
1582a	–	4 c. red on cream ..	10	10
1599	–	7.7 c. brn. on yellow	30	15
1600	–	7.9 c. red on yellow	30	15
1601	–	8.4 c. blue on yellow	30	15
1583	–	9 c. green on grey ..	25*	10
1584	–	9 c. green ..	30	10
1585	–	10 c. pur. on grey ..	15	10
1585a	**1002**	11 c. orge. on grey ..	20	10
1585b	–	12 c. brn. on grey ..	20	10
1586	–	13 c. brn. on cream	20	10
1595	–	13 c. multicoloured	40	10
1596	–	15 c. bl., red & blk.	45	10
1605	–	16 c. blue	50	15
1589	–	24 c. red on blue ..	70	10
1589a	–	28 c. brn. on blue ..	75	10
1590	–	29 c. bl. on light bl.	90	30
1591	–	30 c. grn. on turq...	55	10
1592	–	50 c. blk., red & brn.	70	10
1593	–	$1 multicoloured	1·50	10
1594	–	$2 multicoloured ..	3·00	20
1594a	–	$5 multicoloured ..	8·00	1·25

DESIGNS: 1 c. Inkwell and quill. 2 c. Speaker's stand. 3 c. Ballot box. 3.1 c. Guitar. 3.5 c. Weaver Violins. 4 c. Books, spectacles and bookmark. 7.7 c. Saxhorns. 7.9 c. Drum. 8.4 c. Grand Piano. 9 c. (both) Dome of Capitol. 10 c. "Contemplation of Justice" (statue, J. E. Fraser). 12 c. Statue of Liberty Torch. 13 c. (No. 1586) Liberty Bell. 13 c. (No. 1595) Eagle and shield. 15 c. Fort McHenry Flag. 16 c. Statue of Liberty. 24 c. Old North Church, Boston. 28 c. Fort Nisqually, Washington. 29 c. Sandy Hook Lighthouse, N.J. 30 c. Morris Township School. 50 c. Iron "Betty" lamp. $1, Rush lamp and candle holder. $2, Kerosene lamp. $5, Railway conductor's lantern.

1975.

1606 **1020** 13 c. red and blue .. 40 10

1606c – 13 c. red and blue .. 35 10

DESIGN: No. 1606c, Flag over Capitol, Washington.

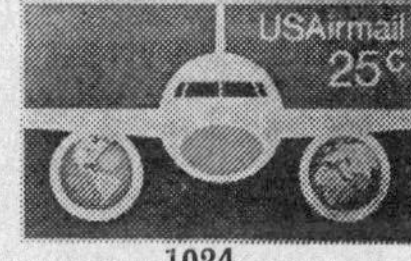

1021. Drummer Boy (after A. M. Willard). **1024.**

1976. American Revolution Bicentennial. "The Spirit of '76". Multicoloured.

1607 13 c. Type **1021** 20 10

1608 13 c. Old Drummer 20 10

1609 13 c. Fifer 20 10

Nos. 1607/9 were issued together, se-tenant, forming a composite design.

1976. Air.

A 1610. **1024.** 25 c. blk., bl., & red 50 10

A 1611. – 31 c. blk., bl. & red 55 10

DESIGN: 31 c. As 25 c., but with background of U.S. flag.

1026. "Interphil 76".

1976. "Interphil 76" International Stamp Exhibition, Philadelphia.

1612. **1026.** 13 c. red and blue .. 35 10

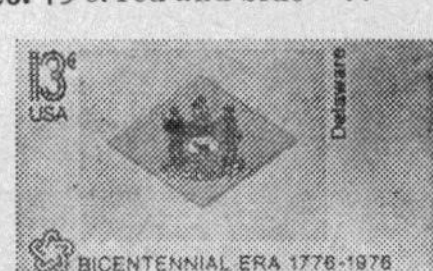

1027. Delaware Flag.

1976. Bicent. of American Revolution. State Flags. Multicoloured.

1613.	13 c. Type **1027** ..	30	20
1614.	13 c. Pennsylvania	30	20
1615.	13 c. New Jersey	30	20
1616.	13 c. Georgia ..	30	20
1617.	13 c. Connecticut	30	20
1618.	13 c. Massachusetts	30	20
1619.	13 c. Maryland ..	30	20
1620.	13 c. South Carolina	30	20
1621.	13 c. New Hampshire	30	20
1622.	13 c. Virginia ..	30	20
1623.	13 c. New York ..	30	20
1624.	13 c. North Carolina	30	20
1625.	13 c. Rhode Island	30	20
1626.	13 c. Vermont ..	30	20
1627.	13 c. Kentucky ..	30	20
1628.	13 c. Tennessee ..	30	20
1629.	13 c. Ohio ..	30	20
1630.	13 c. Louisiana ..	30	20
1631.	13 c. Indiana ..	30	20
1632.	13 c. Mississippi ..	30	20
1633.	13 c. Illinois ..	30	20
1634.	13 c. Alabama ..	30	20
1635.	13 c. Maine ..	30	20
1636.	13 c. Missouri ..	30	20
1637.	13 c. Arkansas ..	30	20
1638.	13 c. Michigan ..	30	20
1639.	13 c. Florida ..	30	20
1640.	13 c. Texas ..	30	20
1641.	13 c. Iowa ..	30	20
1642.	13 c. Wisconsin ..	30	20
1643.	13 c. California ..	30	20
1644.	13 c. Minnesota ..	30	20
1645.	13 c. Oregon ..	30	20
1646.	13 c. Kansas ..	30	20
1647.	13 c. West Virginia	30	20
1648.	13 c. Nevada ..	30	20
1649.	13 c. Nebraska ..	35	20
1650.	13 c. Colorado ..	30	20
1651.	13 c. North Dakota	30	20
1652.	13 c. South Dakota	30	20
1653.	13 c. Montana ..	30	20
1654.	13 c. Washington	30	20
1655.	13 c. Idaho ..	30	20
1656.	13 c. Wyoming ..	30	20
1657.	13 c. Utah ..	30	20
1658.	13 c. Oklahoma ..	30	20
1659.	13 c. New Mexico	30	20
1660.	13 c. Arizona ..	30	20
1661.	13 c. Alaska ..	30	20
1662.	13 c. Hawaii ..	30	20

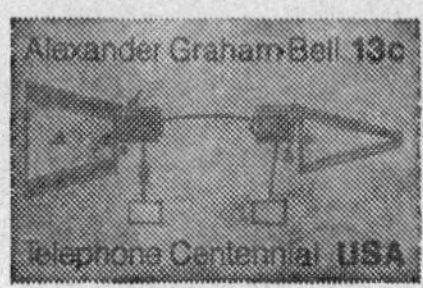

1028. Bell's Telephone.

1976. Telephone Centenary.

1663. **1028.** 13 c. violet, black and red on brown .. 25 10

1029. Ford-Pullman and Laird Swallow Aircraft.

1976. Commercial Aviation.

1664. **1029.** 13 c. multicoloured .. 20 10

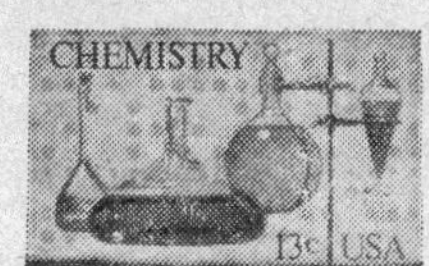

1030. Laboratory Equipment.

1976. Cent. of American Chemical Society.

1665. **1030.** 13 c. multicoloured .. 20 10

1035. Benjamin Franklin and 1776 Map of North America.

1976. American Revolution Bicentennial.

1667. **1035.** 13 c. multicoloured .. 20 10

1036. Part of Assembly. **1040.** Diving.

1976. American Revolution Bicentennial.

1668. **1036.** 13 c. multicoloured 30 10

1669. – 13 c. multicoloured 30 10

1670. – 13 c. multicoloured 30 10

1671. – 13 c. multicoloured 30 10

DESIGNS: Nos. 1668/71 as T **1036** form the complete painting "Signing of Declaration of Independence" (John Trumbull).

1976. Olympic Games, Innsbruck and Montreal. Multicoloured.

1672. 13 c. Type **1040** 25 10

1673. 13 c. Skiing 25 10

1674. 13 c. Running 25 10

1675. 13 c. Skating 25 10

1044. Clara Maass. **1045.** A. S. Ochs.

1976. Birth Centenary of Clara Maass (martyr to yellow fever).

1676. **1044.** 13 c. multicoloured .. 20 10

1976. Adolph S. Ochs (publisher of "New York Times") Commemoration.

1677 **1045** 13 c. black 20 10

1046. "Winter Pastime" (N. Currier). **1048.** "Washington at Princeton" (Peale).

1976. Christmas.

1678. 13 c. Type **1046** 20 10

1679. 13 c. "Nativity" (John S. Copley) 20 10

1977. American Revolution Bicentennial.

1680. **1048.** 13 c. multicoloured .. 20 10

1049. Early Gramophone.

1977. Centenary of Sound Recording.

1681. **1049.** 13 c. multicoloured .. 20 10

1050. Zia Pot.

1977. American Folk Art, Pueblo Art.

1682. 13 c. Type **1050** 20 10

1683. 13 c. San Ildefonso pot .. 20 10

1684. 13 c. Hopi pot 20 10

1685. 13 c. Acoma pot .. 20 10

1054. "Spirit of St. Louis".

1977. 50th Anniv. of Lindbergh's Transatlantic Flight.

1686. **1054.** 13 c. multicoloured .. 20 10

1055. Columbine and Rocky Mountains. **1056.** American Swallowtail.

1977. Cent (1976) of Colorado Statehood.

1687. **1055.** 13 c. multicoloured .. 20 10

1977. Butterflies. Multicoloured.

1688 13 c. Type **1056** 20 10

1689 13 c. Checkerspot .. 20 10

1690 13 c. Dogface 20 10

1691 13 c. Falcate orange-tip 20 10

1060. Marquis de Lafayette.

1977. American Revolution Bicentennial. Bicentenary of Lafayette's Landing on Coast of South Carolina.
1692. **1060.** 13 c. black, blue & red 20 10

1061. Seamstress.

1977. American Revolution Bicent. **"Skilled Hands for Independence". Multicoloured.**
1693. 13 c. Type **1061** 20 10
1694. 13 c. Blacksmith .. 20 10
1695. 13 c. Wheelwright .. 20 10
1696. 13 c. Leatherworker .. 20 10

1065. Peace Bridge and Dove.

1977. 50th Anniv of Opening of Peace Bridge.
1697. **1065.** 13 c. blue 20 10

1066. "Herkimer at Oriskany" (F. Yohn).

1977. American Revolution Bicentennial. Bicentenary of of Battle of Oriskany.
1698. **1066.** 13 c. multicoloured .. 20 10

1067. Farmhouses, El Pueblo.

1977. Bicentenary of First Civil Settlement in Alta California.
1699. **1067.** 13 c. multicoloured .. 20 10

1068. Members of the Continental Congress.

1977. Bicentenary of Drafting of the Articles of Constitution.
1700. **1068.** 13 c. brown and red .. 20 10

1069. "Vitaphone" Projector and Sound Equipment.

1977. 50th Anniv. of Talking Pictures.
1701. **1069.** 13 c. multicoloured .. 30 10

1070. "Surrender of Burgoyne at Saratoga" (J. Trumbull).

1977. American Revolution Bicentennial. Surrender of General Burgoyne.
1702. **1070.** 13 c. multicoloured .. 20 10

1071. "Conservation". **1073.** Washington at Valley Forge (after Leyendecker).

1977. Energy Conservation and Development.
1703. **1071.** 13 c. multicoloured .. 20 10
1704. – 13 c. multicoloured .. 20 10
DESIGN: No. 1704, "Development".

1977. Christmas.
1705. **1073.** 13 c. multicoloured .. 20 10
1706. – 13 c. multicoloured .. 20 10
DESIGN: No. 1706, Rural mailbox.

1075. Carl Sandburg. **1076.** Indian Head Penny.

1978. Birth Centenary of Carl Sandburg (poet and biographer).
1707. **1075.** 13 c. black and brown 20 10

1978.
1708. **1076.** 13 c. brn. & blue on buff 20 10

1077. Captain James Cook (after Nathaniel Dance). **1079.** Harriet Tubman and Slaves.

1978. Bicentenary of Capt. Cook's Visits to Hawaii and Alaska.
1709. **1077.** 13 c. blue 40 10
1710. – 13 c. green 40 10
DESIGN—HORIZ. No. 1710, H.M.S. "Resolution" and H.M.S. "Discovery" at Hawaii (after John Webber).

1978. Black Heritage. Harriet Tubman (organizer of slave "underground railway").
1711. **1079.** 13 c. multicoloured .. 20 10

1082. Quilt Design.

1978. American Folk Art. Quilts.
1712. – 13 c. brown and grey 20 10
1713. – 13 c. red and grey .. 20 10
1714. **1082.** 13 c. multicoloured 20 10
1715. – 13 c. multicoloured 20 10
DESIGNS: No. 1712, Chequered. No. 1713, Dotted. No. 1715, Striped.

1084. Ballet.

1978. American Dance.
1716. **1084.** 13 c. bl., mve. & blk. 20 10
1717. – 13 c. orge., red & blk. 20 10
1718. – 13 c. grn., yell. & blk. 20 10
1719. – 13 c. bl.,ultram.&blk. 20 10
DESIGNS: No. 1717, Theatre. No. 1718, Folk dance. No. 1719, Modern.

1088. "Louis XVI and Benjamin Franklin" (statuette, C. G. Sauvage). **1089.** Dr. Papanicolaou.

1978. Bicentenary of French Alliance.
1720 **1088** 13 c. black, bl & red 25 10

1978. Dr. George Papanicolaou (developer of Pap (cancer detection) test) Commemoration.
1721. **1089.** 13 c. brown .. 20 10

1090. American Eagle. **1091.** Jimmie Rodgers.

1978. No value expressed.
1722 **1090** (15 c.) orange .. 20 10
For "B" stamp see No. 1843, for "C" stamp Nos. 1909/10 and for "D" stamp Nos. 2137/8.

1978. Performing Arts and Artists. Jimmie Rodgers, "Father of Country Music".
1725. **1091.** 13 c. multicoloured 30 10

1093. Camera and Accessories. **1094.** George M. Cohan.

1978. Photography.
1727. **1093.** 15 c. multicoloured .. 20 10

1978. Performing Arts. Birth Centenary of George M. Cohan (actor and playwright).
1728. **1094.** 15 c. multicoloured 20 10

1095. "Red Masterpiece" and "Medallion" Roses. **1096.** "Viking 1" Lander scooping Soil from Mars.

1978. Roses.
1729 **1095** 15 c. red, orge & grn 50 10

1978. 2nd Anniv. of "Viking I" Landing on Mars.
1730. **1096.** 15 c. multicoloured 20 10

1097. Great Grey Owl. **1101.** Wright Brothers and "Flyer".

1978. Wildlife Conservation. American Owls. Multicoloured.
1731. 15 c. Type **1097** 40 10
1732. 15 c. Saw-whet Owl .. 40 10
1733. 15 c. Barred Owl .. 40 10
1734. 15 c. Great Horned Owl 40 10

1978. Air. 75th Anniv. of First Powered Flight. Multicoloured.
A 1735. 31 c. Type **1101** .. 75 10
A 1736. 31 c. "Flyer" and Wright Brothers (in bowler hats) .. 75 10

1103. White Pine. **1107.** "Madonna and Child with Cherubim" (Andrea della Robbia).

1978. American Trees. Multicoloured.
1737. 15 c. Type **1103** 30 10
1738. 15 c. Giant Sequoia .. 30 10
1739. 15 c. Grey Birch .. 30 10
1740. 15 c. White Oak .. 30 10

1978. Christmas. Multicoloured.
1741. 15 c. Type **1107** 20 10
1742. 15 c. Child on Rocking Horse 20 10

1109. Robert F. Kennedy. **1110.** Martin Luther King.

1979. Robert F. Kennedy Commemoration.
1743. **1109.** 15 c. blue 20 10

1979. Black Heritage. Martin Luther King (Civil Rights leader).
1744. **1110.** 15 c. multicoloured 20 10

1111. Children of Different Races. **1112.** John Steinbeck.

1979. Int. Year of the Child.
1745 **1111** 15 c. red 20 10

1979. Literary Arts. John Steinbeck (novelist).
1746. **1112.** 15 c. blue 20 10

1113. Einstein. **1114.** Chanute and Hang-glider.

1979. Birth Cent. of Albert Einstein (physicist).
1747. **1113.** 15 c. brown .. 20 10

1979. Air. Aviation Pioneers. Octave Chanute. Multicoloured.
A1748 21 c. Type **1114** 75 10
A1749 21 c. Chanute and hang-gliders 75 10

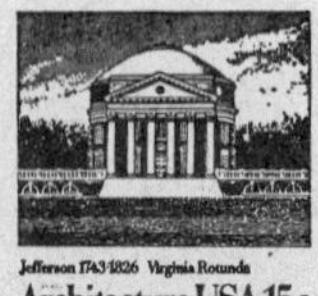

1116. Coffee Pot. **1120.** Virginia Rotunda (Thomas Jefferson).

1979. American Folk Art. Pennsylvania Toleware. Multicoloured.
1750 15 c. Type **1116** 20 10
1751 15 c. Tea caddy 20 10
1752 15 c. Suger bowl with lid 20 10
1753 15 c. Coffee pot with gooseneck spout .. 20 10

1979. American Architecture. Each black and red.
1754 15 c. Type **1120** .. 20 10
1755 15 c. Baltimore Cathedral (Benjamin Latrobe) .. 20 10
1756 15 c. Boston State House (Charles Bulfinch) .. 20 10
1757 15 c. Philadelphia Exchange (William Strickland) 20 10

1124. Persistent Trillium. 1128. Guide Dog.

1979. Endangered Flora. Multicoloured.

1758. 15 c. Type **1124** 20 10
1759. 15 c. Hawaiian Wild Broadbean 20 10
1760. 15 c. Contra Costa Wallflower 20 10
1761. 15 c. Antioch Dunes Evening Primrose 20 10

1979. 50th Anniv. of First U.S. Guide Dog Programme.

1762. **1128.** 15 c. multicoloured .. 30 10

1129. Child with Medal. **1130.** Throwing the Javelin (Decathlon).

1979. Special Olympic Games for the Handicapped.

1763. **1129.** 15 c. multicoloured .. 20 10

1979. Olympic Games, Moscow (1980). Multicoloured.

1764 10 c. Type **1130** (post) 15 10
1765 15 c. Running (horiz) 20 10
1766 15 c. Swimming (horiz) 20 10
1767 15 c. Rowing (horiz) .. 20 10
1768 15 c. Show jumping (horiz) 20 10
A1769 31 c. High jumping (horiz) (air) 50 55

1136. John Paul Jones (after Peale). **1137.** "Rest on the Flight to Egypt" (G. David).

1979. American Revolution Bicentennial. John Paul Jones (naval commander).

1770. **1136.** 15 c. multicoloured 20 10

1979. Christmas. Multicoloured

1771. 15 c. Type **1137** 20 10
1772. 15 c. Santa Claus tree ornament 20 10

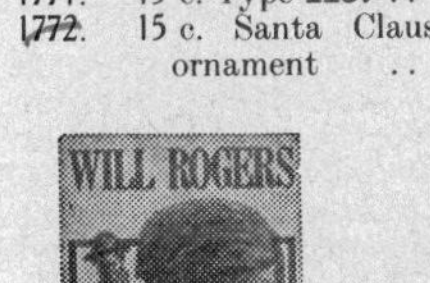

1139. Will Rogers. **1140.** Vietnam Service Medal Ribbon.

1979. Performing Arts and Artists. Will Rogers (cowboy philosopher).

1773. **1139.** 15 c. multicoloured 20 10

1979. Vietnam Veterans.

1774. **1140.** 15 c. multicoloured .. 20 10

1141. Wiley Post. **1143.** W. C. Fields.

1979. Air. Aviation Pioneers. Wiley Post. Multicoloured.

A 1775. 25 c. Type **1141** .. 1·50 40
A 1776. 25 c. Wiley Post and "Winnie Mae" aeroplane .. .. 1·50 40

1980. Performing Arts and Artists. W. C. Fields (comedian).

1777. **1143.** 15 c. multicoloured 20 10

1144. Speed Skating. **1148.** Robertson Windmill, Williamsburg, Va.

1980. Winter Olympic Games, Lake Placid Multicoloured.

1778. 15 c. Type **1144** 20 10
1779. 15 c. Downhill Skiing .. 20 10
1780. 15 c. Ski Jumping .. 20 10
1781. 15 c. Ice Hockey .. 20 10

1980. Windmills.

1782. **1148.** 15 c. brn. on yell. .. 45 10
1783. – 15 c. brn. on yell. .. 45 10
1784. – 15 c. brn. on yell. .. 45 10
1785. – 15 c. brn. on yell. .. 45 10
1786. – 15 c. brn. on yell. .. 45 10

DESIGNS: No. 1783, Replica of old windmill, Portsmouth, R.I. No. 1784, Cape Cod Windmill, Eastham, Mass. No. 1785, Dutch Mill, Fabyan Park Forest Preserve, Ill. No. 1786, Southwestern Windmill, Texas.

1153. Benjamin Banneker.

1980. Black Heritage. Benjamin Banneker (astronomer and mathematician).

1787. **1153.** 15 c. multicoloured 20 10

1154. Photograph and Envelope. 1157. "P.S. Write Soon".

1980. National Letter Writing Week.

1788. **1154.** 15 c. multicoloured 20 10
1789. **1157.** 15 c. multicoloured (purple background) 20 10
1790. – 15 c. multicoloured 20 10
1791. **1157.** 15 c. multicoloured (green background) 20 10
1792. – 15 c. multicoloured 20 10
1793. **1157.** 15 c. bl., blk. & red .. 20 10

DESIGNS—As T **1154**: No. 1790, Flowers and envelope. No. 1792, Capitol and envelope.

1158. Frances Perkins. **1159.** Dolley Madison (after Stuart).

1980. Frances Perkins (first woman Cabinet member) Commemoration.

1794. 1158. 15 c. blue 20 10

1980.

1795 **1159** 15 c. dp brown & brn 20 10

1160. Emily Bissell. **1161.** Helen Keller and Anne Sullivan.

1980. Emily Bissell (crusader against tuberculosis) Commemoration.

1796. **1160.** 15 c. black and red 25 10

1980. Birth Cent. of Helen Keller.

1797. **1161.** 15 c. multicoloured 20 10

1162. Veterans Administration Emblem. **1163.** Statue of Gen. Galvez, Mobile.

1980. 50th Anniv. of Veterans Administration.

1798. **1162.** 15 c. red & blue .. 20 10

1980. General Bernardo de Galvez (leader of Spanish forces in Louisiana during American Revolution) Commemoration.

1799. **1163.** 15 c. multicoloured 20 10

1164. Brain Corals. **1168.** American Bald Eagle.

1980. Coral Reefs. Multicoloured.

1800. 15 c. Type **1164** .. 20 10
1801. 15 c. Elkhorn Coral .. 20 10
1802. 15 c. Chalice Coral .. 20 10
1803. 15 c. Finger Coral .. 20 10

1980. Organized Labour.

1804. **1168.** 15 c. multicoloured 30 10

1169. Edith Wharton. **1170.** "Homage to the Square: Glow" (J. Albers).

1980. Literary Arts. Edith Wharton (novelist).

1805. **1169.** 15 c. violet 20 10

1980. American Education.

1806. **1170.** 15 c. multicoloured .. 20 10

1171. Heiltsuk, Bella Bella.

1980. American Folk Art. Indian Masks. Multicoloured.

1807. 15 c. Type **1171** 20 10
1808. 15 c. Chilkat Tlingit .. 20 10
1809. 15 c. Tlingit 20 10
1810. 15 c. Bella Coola .. 20 10

1175. Smithsonian Institution, Washington (James Renwick). **1179.** Philip Mazzei.

1980. American Architecture.

1811. **1175.** 15 c. black and red .. 20 10
1812. – 15 c. black and red .. 20 10
1813. – 15 c. black and red .. 20 10
1814. – 15 c. black and red .. 20 10

DESIGNS: No. 1812, Trinity Church, Boston (Henry Hobson Richardson). No. 1813, Penn Academy, Philadelphia (Frank Furness). No. 1814, Lyndhurst, Tarrytown, New York (Alexander Jackson Davis).

1980. Air. Philip Mazzei (patriot) Commem.

A 1815. **1179.** 40 c. multicoloured 50 15

1180. "Madonna and Child" (Epiphany Window, Washington Cathedral). **1181.** Antique Toys.

1980. Christmas.

1816. **1180.** 15 c. multicoloured .. 20 10
1817. **1181.** 15 c. multicoloured .. 20 10

1191. Sequoyah (Cherokee scholar) (after C. B. Wilson). **1203.** Blanche Stuart Scott.

1980. Great Americans. With "c" after face value.

1818 – 1 c. black 10 10
1819 – 2 c. black 10 10
1820 – 3 c. green 10 10
1821 – 4 c. violet 10 10
1822 – 5 c. red 10 10
1823 – 10 c. blue 25 10
1824 – 13 c. red 30 10
1825 – 17 c. green 30 10
1826 – 18 c. blue 40 10
1827 **1191** 19 c. brown .. 40 10
1828 – 20 c. purple .. 30 10
1829 – 20 c. green .. 45 10
1830 – 20 c. black .. 45 10
1831 – 30 c. green .. 40 10
1832 – 35 c. black .. 60 10
1833 – 37 c. blue .. 50 10
1834 – 40 c. green .. 70 10

DESIGNS: 1 c. Dorothea Dix (social pioneer). 2 c. Igor Stravinsky (composer). 3 c. Henry Clay (politician). 4 c. Carl Schurz (reformer). 5 c. Pearl Buck (author) (after F. Elliot). 10 c. Richard Russell (politician). 13 c. Crazy Horse (Sioux Chief) (after K. Ziolkowski). 17 c. Rachel Carson (scientist). 18 c. George Mason (patriot). 20 c. (1828), Ralph Bunche (U.N. Secretariat member). 20 c. (1829), Thomas H. Gallaudet (educator of the deaf). 20 c. (1830), Pres. Harry S. Truman. 30 c. Frank C. Laubach (literacy educator). 35 c. Charles R. Drew (surgeon). 37 c. Robert Millikan (physicist). 40 c. Lillian M. Gilbreth (engineer).

For similar designs without "c", see Nos. 2108/42.

1980. Air. Aviation Pioneers. Multicoloured.

A 1839. 28 c. Type **1203** .. 55 15
A 1840. 35 c. Glenn Curtiss .. 60 15

1205. Everett Dirksen. **1206.** Whitney Moore Young.

1981. Senator Everett Dirksen Commemoration.

1841 **1205** 15 c. grey 20 10

1981. Black Heritage. Whitney Moore Young (civil rights leader).

1842. **1206.** 15 c. multicoloured 20 10

1981. Non-denominational "B" stamp. As T **1090**.

1843. (18 c.) lilac 50 10

1207. Rose.

1981. Flowers. Multicoloured.

1846. 18 c. Type **1207** 25 10
1847. 18 c. Camellia 25 10
1848. 18 c. Dahlia 25 10
1849. 18 c. Lily 25 10

1211. "... for amber waves of grain".

1212. Stars.

1981.

1851 **1212** 6 c. blue and red .. 90 15
1850 **1211** 18 c. brown, red & bl 30 10
1852 – 18 c. lilac, red & blue 35 10
1853 – 18 c. brown, bl & red 55 10

DESIGNS—As T **1211**: No. 1852, "...for purple mountain majesties". No. 1853, "...from sea to shining sea".

1215. Nurse and Child.

1216. Money Box.

1981. Centenary of American Red Cross.
1854. **1215.** 18 c. multicoloured 25 10

1981. 150th Anniv. of First Savings and Loans Association.
1855. **1216.** 18 c. multicoloured 25 10

1217. American Bighorn.

1238. Detroit Electric Auto, 1917.

1981. Wildlife.

1856. **1217.** 18 c. brown .. 60 10
1857. – 18 c. brown .. 60 10
1858. – 18 c. brown .. 60 10
1859. – 18 c. brown .. 60 10
1860. – 18 c. brown .. 60 10
1861. – 18 c. brown .. 60 10
1862. – 18 c. brown .. 60 10
1863. – 18 c. brown .. 60 10
1864. – 18 c. brown .. 60 10
1865. – 18 c. brown .. 60 10

DESIGNS: No. 1857, Puma. No. 1858, Common Seal. No. 1859, American Bison. No. 1860, Brown Bear. No. 1861, Polar Bear. No. 1862, Red Deer. No. 1863, Elk. No. 1864, White-tailed Deer. No. 1865, Pronghorn.

1981. Transport. With "c" after face value.

1866 – 1 c. violet 10 10
1867 – 2 c. black 10 10
1868 – 3 c. green 10 10
1869 – 4 c. brown 10 10
1870 – 5 c. green 10 10
1871 – 5.2 c. red 15 10
1872 – 5.9 c. blue 10 10
1873 – 7.4 c. brown .. 25 10
1874 – 9.3 c. red 30 10
1875 – 10.9 c. mauve .. 50 10
1876a – 11 c. red 15 10
1877 **1238** 17 c. blue 20 10
1878 – 18 c. brown .. 40 10
1879 – 20 c. red 45 10

DESIGNS: 1 c. Omnibus, 1880s. 2 c. Locomotive, 1870s. 3 c. Handcar, 1880s. 4 c. Concord stage-coach, 1890s. 5 c. Pope motor cycle, 1913. 5.2 c. Sleigh, 1880s. 5.9 c. Bicycle, 1870s. 7.4 c. Baby buggy, 1880s. 9.3 c. Mail wagon, 1880s. 10.9 c. Hansom cab, 1890s. 11 c. Railway caboose, 1890s. 18 c. Surrey, 1890s. 20 c. Amoskeag fire pumper, 1860s.

For similar designs without "c", see Nos. 2150/74 and 2480/96.

1247. Exploring the Moon ("Apollo" mission).

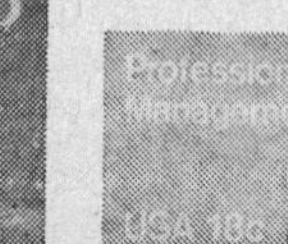

1255. Joseph Wharton (founder of Wharton School).

1981. Space Achievements.

1886. **1247.** 18 c. multicoloured 30 10
1887. – 18 c. multicoloured 30 10
1888. – 18 c. multicoloured 30 10
1889. – 18 c. multicoloured 30 10
1890. – 18 c. multicoloured 30 10
1891. – 18 c. multicoloured 30 10
1892. – 18 c. multicoloured 30 10
1893. – 18 c. multicoloured 30 10

DESIGNS: No. 1887, Space Shuttle loosing Boosters. No. 1888, Space Shuttle performing Experiment. No. 1889, Understanding the Sun ("Skylab"). No. 1890, Probing the Planets ("Pioneer II"). No. 1891, Space Shuttle Launch. No. 1892, Space Shuttle Landing. No. 1893, Comprehending the Universe (space telescope).

Nos. 1886/93 were issued together in se-tenant blocks of eight each block forming a composite design.

1981. Centenary of Professional Management Education.
1894. **1255.** 18 c. blue and black 25 10

1256. Great Blue Heron.

1260. Disabled Man Using Microscope.

1981. Wildlife Habitats.

1895. **1256.** 18 c. multicoloured 50 20
1896. – 18 c. multicoloured 50 20
1897. – 18 c. multicoloured 50 20
1898. – 18 c. multicoloured 50 20

DESIGNS: No. 1896, American Badger. No. 1897, Brown Bear. No. 1898, Ruffed Grouse.

1981. International Year of Disabled Persons.
1899. **1260.** 18 c. multicoloured 25 10

1261. Edna St. Vincent Millay.

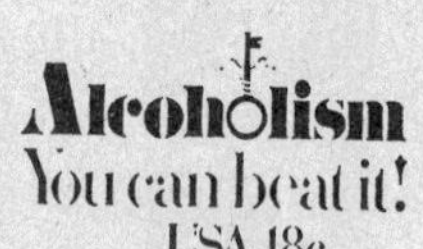

1262. "Alcoholism. You can beat it".

1981. Edna St. Vincent Millay (poet) Commemoration.
1900. **1261.** 18 c. multicoloured 25 10

1981. Anti-alcoholism Campaign.
1901. **1262.** 18 c. blue and black 25 10

1263. New York University Library (Stanford White).

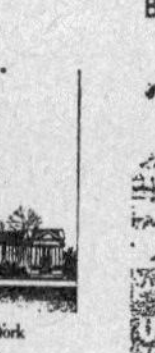

1267. Bobby Jones (golfer).

1981. American Architecture (3rd series).

1902. **1263.** 18 c. blk. & brn. .. 25 10
1903. – 18 c. blk. & brn. .. 25 10
1904. – 18 c. blk. & brn. .. 25 10
1905. – 18 c. blk. & brn. .. 25 10

DESIGNS: No. 1903, Biltmore House, Asheville, North Carolina (Richard Morris Hunt). 1904, Palace of Arts, San Francisco (Bernard Maybeck). 1905, Bank, Owatonna, Minnesota (Louis Sullivan).

1981. American Sports Personalities.

1906. **1267.** 18 c. green 50 10
1907. – 18 c. red 50 10

DESIGN: No. 1907, Babe Zaharias (golfer and athlete).

1269. "Coming through the Rye".

1981. Frederic Remington (sculptor) Commemoration.
1908. **1269.** 18 c. brown, green and pale brown .. 40 10

1981. Non-denominational "C" Stamp. As T **1090** but inscribed "Domestic Mail".

1909. (20 c.) brown (19 × 22 mm.) 40 10
1910. (20 c.) brown (15 × 18½ mm.) 45 10

1271. James Hoban and White House.

1981. 150th Death Anniv. of James Hoban (architect).

1912. **1271.** 18 c. multicoloured 40 20
1913. 20 c. multicoloured 40 10

1272. Map of Yorktown Peninsula.

1274. "Madonna and Child" (Botticelli).

1981. Bicentenary of Battles of Yorktown and Virginia Capes. Multicoloured.

1914. 18 c. Type **1272** .. 35 10
1915. 18 c. French ships blocking Chesapeake Bay .. 35 10

1981. Christmas. No value expressed. Mult.

1916. (20 c.) Type **1274** 25 10
1917. (20 c.) Teddy Bear on sleigh 25 10

1276. John Hanson.

1277. Barrel Cactus.

1981. John Hanson (American revolutionary leader) Commemoration.
1918. **1276.** 20 c. multicoloured 35 10

1981. Desert Plants. Multicoloured.

1919. 20 c. Type **1277** 50 10
1920. 20 c. Agave (horiz.) .. 50 10
1921. 20 c. Saguaro 50 10
1922. 20 c. Beavertail Cactus (horiz.) 50 10

1281. Flag over Supreme Court.

1282. American Bighorn.

1981.
1923. **1281.** 20 c. blk, red & blue 35 10

1982.
1926. **1282.** 20 c. blue 40 10

1283. Franklin D. Roosevelt.

1982. Birth Centenary of President Franklin D. Roosevelt.
1927. **1283.** 20 c. blue 30 10

INDEX

Countries can be quickly located by referring to the index at the end of this volume.

1284. Flowers spelling "Love".

1285. George Washington.

1982. Greetings Stamp.
1928. **1284.** 20 c. multicoloured 30 10

1982. 250th Birth Anniv. of George Washington.
1929. **1285.** 20 c. multicoloured 30 10

1286. Common Flicker (inscr "Yellowhammer") and Camellia (Alabama).

1287. Stripes in National Colours.

1982. State Birds and Flowers. Mult.

1930 20 c. Type **1286** 55 20
1931 20 c. Willow grouse (inscr "Ptarmigan") and forget-me-not (Alaska) 55 20
1932 20 c. Cactus wren and saguaro cactus blossom (Arizona) 55 20
1933 20 c. Northern mocking-bird and apple blossom (Arkansas) 55 20
1934 20 c. California quail and California poppy (California) 55 20
1935 20 c. Lark bunting and Rocky Mountain columbine (Colorado) .. 55 20
1936 20 c. American robin and mountain laurel (Connecticut) 55 20
1937 20 c. Blue hen chicken and peach blossom (Delaware) 55 20
1938 20 c. Northern mocking-bird and orange blossom (Florida) .. 55 20
1939 20 c. Brown thrasher and Cherokee rose (Georgia) 55 20
1940 20 c. Hawaiian goose and hibiscus (Hawaii) .. 55 20
1941 20 c. Mountain bluebird and syringa (Idaho) .. 55 20
1942 20 c. Common cardinal and violet (Illinois) .. 55 20
1943 20 c. Common cardinal and peony (Indiana) .. 55 20
1944 20 c. American (inscr "Eastern") goldfinch and wild rose (Iowa) .. 55 20
1945 20 c. Western meadow-lark and sunflower (Kansas) 55 20
1946 20 c. Common cardinal and goldenrod (Kentucky) 55 20
1947 20 c. Brown pelican and magnolia (Louisiana) .. 55 20
1948 20 c. Black-capped chickadee, white pine cone and tassel (Maine) 55 20
1949 20 c. Northern (inscr "Baltimore") oriole and black-eyed susan (Maryland) 55 20
1950 20 c. Black-capped chickadee and may-flower (Massachusetts) 55 20
1951 20 c. American robin and apple blossom (Michigan) 55 20
1952 20 c. Great northern diver (inscr "Common Loon") and showy lady slipper (Minnesota) 55 20
1953 20 c. Northern mocking-bird and magnolia (Mississippi) 55 20
1954 20 c. Eastern bluebird and red hawthorn (Missouri) 55 20
1955 20 c. Western meadow-lark and bitter-root (Montana) 55 20

1956 20 c. Western meadowlark and goldenrod (Nebraska) 55 20
1957 20 c. Mountain bluebird and sagebrush (Nevada) 55 20
1958 20 c. Purple finch and lilac (New Hampshire) 55 20
1959 20 c. American goldfinch and violet (New Jersey) 55 20
1960 20 c. Road-runner and yucca flower (New Mexico) 55 20
1961 20 c. Eastern bluebird and rose (New York) .. 55 20
1962 20 c. Common cardinal and flowering dogwood (North Carolina) .. 55 20
1963 20 c. Western meadowlark, and wild prairie rose (North Dakota) .. 55 20
1964 20 c. Common cardinal and red carnation (Ohio) 55 20
1965 20 c. Scissor-tailed flycatcher and mistletoe (Oklahoma) 55 20
1966 20 c. Western meadowlark and Oregon grape (Oregon) 55 20
1967 20 c. Ruffed grouse and mountain laurel (Pennsylvania) .. 55 20
1968 20 c. Rhode Island red and violet (Rhode Island) 55 20
1969 20 c. Carolina wren and Carolina jessamine (South Carolina) .. 55 20
1970 20 c. Ring-necked pheasant and pasque flower (South Dakota) 55 20
1971 20 c. Northern mockingbird and iris (Tennessee) 55 20
1972 20 c. Northern mockingbird and bluebonnet (Texas) 55 20
1973 20 c. California gull and sego lily (Utah) .. 55 20
1974 20 c. Hermit thrush and red clover (Vermont) .. 55 20
1975 20 c. Common cardinal and flowering dogwood (Virginia) 55 20
1976 20 c. American goldfinch and rhododendron (Washington) 55 20
1977 20 c. Common cardinal and "Rhododendron maximum" (West Virginia) 55 20
1978 20 c. American robin and wood violet (Wisconsin) 55 20
1979 20 c. Western meadowlark and Indian paintbrush (Wyoming) .. 55 20

1982. Bicentenary of U.S.A.–Netherlands Diplomatic Relations.
1980. **1287.** 20 c. red, bl. & blk. 30 10

1288. Library of Congress. **1289.** Garment Tag.

1982. Library of Congress.
1981. **1288.** 20 c. black and red 30 10

1982. Consumer Education
1982. **1289.** 20 c. blue 30 10

1290. Solar Energy. **1294.** Frontispiece from "Ragged Dick".

1982. Knoxville World's Fair.
1983. **1290.** 20 c. multicoloured 40 10
1984. – 20 c. multicoloured 40 10
1985. – 20 c. blue, light blue and black .. 40 10
1986. – 20 c. blue, black and brown .. 40 10
DESIGNS: No. 1984, Synthetic fuels. 1985, Breeder reactor. 1986, Fossil fuels.

1982. 150th Birth Anniv of Horatio Alger (novelist).
1987 **1294** 20 c. black and red on buff 30 10

1295. Family Group. **1296.** John, Ethel and Lionel Barrymore.

1982. Ageing Together.
1988. **1295.** 20 c. red 30 10

1982. Performing Arts and Artists. The Barrymores (theatrical family).
1989. **1296.** 20 c. multicoloured 30 10

1297. Dr. Mary Walker **1298.** Maple Leaf and Rose.

1982. Dr. Mary Walker (army surgeon) Commemoration.
1990. **1297.** 20 c. multicoloured 30 10

1982. 50th Anniv. of International Peace Garden (on U.S.A.–Canada border).
1991. **1298.** 20 c. multicoloured 30 10

1299. Typographic Design. **1300.** Jackie Robinson.

1982. America's Libraries.
1992. **1299.** 20 c. red and black 30 10

1982. Black Heritage. Jackie Robinson (baseball player).
1993. **1300.** 20 c. multicoloured 95 10

1301. Touro Synagogue.

1982. Touro Synagogue, Newport, Rhode Island.
1994. **1301.** 20 c. multicoloured 40 10

1302. Open Air Theatre.

1982. Wolf Trap Farm Park, Vienna, Virginia.
1995. **1302.** 20 c. multicoloured 35 10

HAVE YOU READ THE NOTES AT THE BEGINNING OF THIS CATALOGUE?
These often provide answers to the enquiries we receive.

1303. Fallingwater, Mill Run, Philadelphia (Frank Lloyd Wright).

1982. American Architecture.
1996. **1303.** 20 c. blk. & brn. .. 50 10
1997. – 20 c. blk. & brn. .. 50 10
1998. – 20 c. blk. & brn. .. 50 10
1999. – 20 c. blk. & brn. .. 50 10
DESIGNS: No. 1997, Illinois Institute of Technology, Chicago (Mies van der Rohe). 1998, Gropius House, Lincoln, Massachusetts (Walter Gropius). 1999, Dulles Airport, Washington D.C. (Eero Saarinen).

1307. St. Francis and Doves.

1982. 800th Birth Anniv. of St. Francis of Assisi.
2000. **1307.** 20 c. multicoloured 30 10

1308. Ponce de Leon and Map of Florida. **1309.** "Madonna and Child" (Tiepolo).

1982. Ponce de Leon (explorer). Commemoration.
2001. **1308.** 20 c. multicoloured 30 10

1982. Christmas. Multicoloured.
2002 20 c. Type **1309** 25 10
2003 20 c. Building a snowman (horiz) 35 10
2004 20 c. Sledging (horiz) .. 35 10
2005 20 c. Decorating a Christmas tree (horiz) 35 10
2006 20 c. Skating (horiz) .. 35 10

1314. Puppy and Kitten. **1316.** Industrial Complex.

1982.
2007. **1314.** 13 c. multicoloured 20 10

1983. Science and Industry.
2015. **1316.** 20 c. multicoloured 30 10

1317. Benjamin Franklin and Great Seal of Sweden.

1983. Bicentenary of Sweden–U.S.A. Treaty of Amity and Commerce.
2016. **1317.** 20 c. indigo, brown and black .. 30 10

1319/1320. Hot Air Ballooning.

1983. Bicentenary of Manned Flight. Mult.
2017 20 c. "Intrepid", 1861 (vert) 35 10
2018 20 c. Type **1319** 35 10
2019 20 c. Type **1320** 35 10
2020 20 c. "Explorer II", 1935 (vert) 35 10

1322. C.C.C. Workers repairing Trail.

1983. 50th Anniv. of Civilian Conservation Corps.
2021. **1322.** 20 c. multicoloured 30 10

1323. Shot Putting. **1327.** Joseph Priestley (after G. Stuart).

1983. Air. Olympic Games, Los Angeles (1984). (1st issue). Multicoloured
A 2022. 40 c. Type **1323** .. 60 25
A 2023. 40 c. Gymnastics .. 60 25
A 2024. 40 c. Swimming .. 60 25
A 2025. 40 c. Weightlifting .. 60 25
See also Nos A 2034/7, 2040/3, A 2058/61 and 2079/82.

1983. 250th Birth Anniv. of Joseph Priestley (discoverer of oxygen).
2026. **1327.** 20 c. multicoloured 30 10

1328. Reaching Hands.

1983. Voluntary Work.
2027. **1328.** 20 c. black & red .. 30 10

1329. "Concord".

1983. 300th Anniv. of First German Settlers in America.
2028. **1329.** 20 c. brown .. 40 10

1330. Joggers and Electrocardiograph Trace.

1983. Physical Fitness.
2029. **1330.** 20 c. multicoloured 30 10

1331. Brooklyn Bridge.

1983. Centenary of Brooklyn Bridge.
2030. **1331.** 20 c. blue 40 10

1332. Norris Hydro-electric Dam.

1983. 50th Anniv. of Tennessee Valley Authority.
2031. **1332.** 20 c. multicoloured 30 10

1333. Army, Air Force and Navy Medals of Honour. **1334.** Scott Joplin.

1983. Medal of Honour.
2032. **1333.** 20 c. multicoloured 30 10

1983. Black Heritage. Scott Joplin (ragtime composer).
2033. **1334.** 20 c. multicoloured 35 10

1335. Gymnastics. **1339.** Babe Ruth.

1983. Air. Olympic Games, Los Angeles (1984) (2nd issue). Multicoloured.
A 2034. 28 c. Type **1335** .. 60 15
A 2035. 28 c. Hurdling .. 60 15
A 2036. 28 c. Basketball .. 60 15
A 2037. 28 c. Football 60 15

1983. American Sports Personalities. Babe Ruth (baseball player).
2038. **1339.** 20 c. blue .. .. 1·00 10

1340. Hawthorne (after C. G. Thompson). **1341.** Discus.

1983. Literary Arts. Nathaniel Hawthorne (writer).
2039. **1340.** 20 c. multicoloured 30 10

1983. Olympic Games, Los Angeles (1984) (3rd issue). Multicoloured.
2040. 13 c. Type **1341** 25 10
2041. 13 c. High Jump .. 25 10
2042. 13 c. Archery 25 10
2043. 13 c. Boxing 25 10

1345. American Bald Eagle and Moon.

1983.
2044. **1345.** $9.35 multicoloured 17·00 7·00

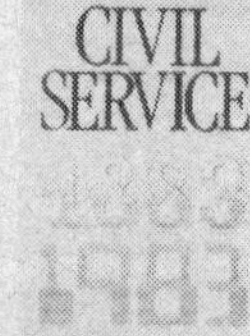

1346. Signing the Treaty of Paris (after Benjamin West). **1347.** Text in Early and Modern Type.

1983. Bicentenary of Treaty of Paris.
2045. **1346.** 20 c. multicoloured 35 10

1983. Centenary of Civil Service.
2046 **1347** 20 c. stone, red & blk 30 10

1348. Part of Proscenium and Modern Facade.

1983. Centenary of Metropolitan Opera, New York.
2047. **1348.** 20 c. yellow & pur. 40 10

1349. Charles Steinmetz and Graph.

1983. American Inventors.
2048. **1349.** 20 c. pink and black 35 10
2049. – 20 c. pink and black 35 10
2050. – 20 c. pink and black 35 10
2051. – 20 c. pink and black 35 10

DESIGNS: No. 2049, Edwin Armstrong and frequency modulator. 2050, Nikola Tesla and induction motor. 2051, Philo T. Farnsworth and television camera.

1353. "John Mason" Streetcar, New York, 1832.

1983. Streetcars. Multicoloured.
2052 20 c. Type **1353** 45 15
2053 20 c. Early electric streetcar, Montgomery, 1886 45 15
2054 20 c. "Bobtail" horsecar, Sulphur Rock, 1926 .. 45 15
2055 20 c. St. Charles Streetcar New Orleans, 1923 .. 45 15

1357. "Madonna and Child" (Raphael). **1358.** Santa Claus.

1983. Christmas.
2056. **1357.** 20 c. multicoloured 25 10
2057. **1358.** 20 c. multicoloured 25 10

1359. Fencing.

1983. Air. Olympic Games, Los Angeles (1984) (4th issue). Multicoloured.
A 2058. 35 c. Type **1359** .. 60 20
A 2059. 35 c. Cycling 60 20
A 2060. 35 c. Volleyball .. 60 20
A 2061. 35 c. Pole Vault .. 60 20

1363. Martin Luther.

1983. 500th Birth Anniv. of Martin Luther.
2062. **1363.** 20 c. multicoloured 30 10

1364. Reindeer and Pipeline. **1365.** Ice Dancing. **1369.** Column and "$" Sign.

1984. 25th Anniv. of Alaska Statehood.
2063. **1364.** 20 c. multicoloured 30 10

1984. Winter Olympic Games, Sarajevo. Multicoloured.
2064. 20 c. Type **1365** .. 50 10
2065. 20 c. Downhill skiing .. 50 10
2066. 20 c. Cross-country skiing 50 10
2067. 20 c. Ice hockey 50 10

1984. 50th Anniv of Federal Deposit Insurance Corporation.
2068. **1369.** 20 c. multicoloured 30 10

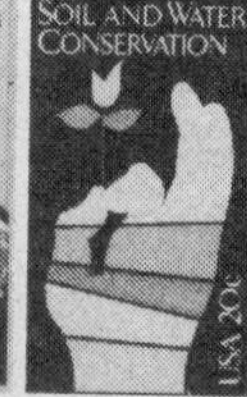

1370. "Love". **1371.** Carter G. Woodson. **1372.** Hand holding Plant.

1984. Greetings Stamp.
2069. **1370.** 20 c. multicoloured 30 10

1984. Black Heritage. Carter G. Woodson (historian).
2070. **1371.** 20 c. multicoloured 30 10

1984. 50th Anniv. of Soil and Water Conservation Movement.
2071. **1372.** 20 c. multicoloured 30 10

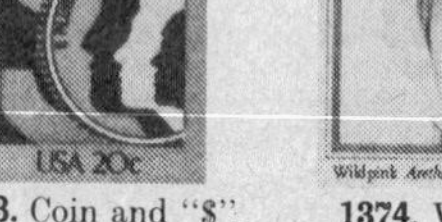

1373. Coin and "$" Sign. **1374.** Wild Pink.

1984. 50th Anniv of Credit Union Act.
2072. **1373.** 20 c. multicoloured 30 10

1984. Orchids. Multicoloured.
2073. 20 c. Type **1374** 50 10
2074. 20 c. Yellow Lady's-slipper 50 10
2075. 20 c. Spreading Pogonia 50 10
2076. 20 c. Pacific Calypso .. 50 10

1378. Eastern Polynesian Canoe and American Golden Plover.

1984. 25th Anniv. of Hawaii Statehood.
2077. **1378.** 20 c. multicoloured 50 10

1379. Silhouettes of Lincoln and Washington. **1380.** Diving.

1984. 50th Anniv. of National Archives.
2078. **1379.** 20 c. blk., ol. & red 30 10

1984. Olympic Games, Los Angeles (5th issue). Multicoloured.
2079. 20 c. Type **1380** 35 10
2080. 20 c. Long jump .. 35 10
2081. 20 c. Wrestling 35 10
2082. 20 c. Canoeing 35 10

1384. Bayou Wildlife.

1984. Louisiana World Exposition, New Orleans.
2083. **1384.** 20 c. multicoloured 40 10

1385. Laboratory Equipment.

1984. Health Research.
2084. **1385.** 20 c. multicoloured 30 10

1386. Fairbanks in Film Roles. **1387.** Jim Thorpe.

1984. Performing Arts and Artists. Douglas Fairbanks (film actor).
2085. **1386.** 20 c. multicoloured 40 10

1984. American Sports Personalities. Jim Thorpe (athlete, footballer and baseball player).
2086. **1387.** 20 c. brown 40 10

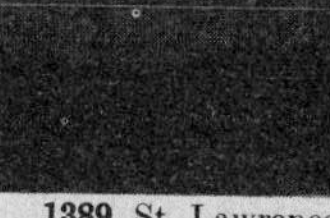

1388. John McCormack **1389.** St. Lawrence Seaway

1984. Performing Arts and Artists. John McCormack (singer).
2087. **1388.** 20 c. multicoloured 50 10

1984. 25th Anniv. of St. Lawrence Seaway.
2088. **1389.** 20 c. multicoloured 30 10

1390. "Mallards dropping In" (Jay Norwood Darling).

1984. 50th Anniv. of Migratory Bird Hunting and Conservation Stamp Act.
2089. **1390.** 20 c. blue 50 10

1391. "Elizabeth". **1392.** Melville (after J. O. Eaton).

1984. Explorers. 400th Anniversary of First Raleigh Expedition to Roanoke Island, North Carolina.
2090. **1391.** 20 c. multicoloured 40 10

1984. Literary Arts. Herman Melville (novelist).
2091. **1392.** 20 c. green 30 10

1393. Horace Moses. **1394.** Smokey Bear and American Black Bear Cub clinging to burnt Tree.

1984. Horace Moses (founder of Junior Achievement (training organization)) Commemoration.
2092. **1393.** 20 c. orange & blk. 30 10

1984. Smokey Bear (symbol of forest fire prevention campaign).
2093. **1394.** 20 c. multicoloured 30 10

1395. Clemente and Flag of Puerto Rico. **1396.** Beagle and Boston Terrier.

1984. American Sports Personalities. Roberto Clemente (baseball player).
2094. **1395.** 20 c. multicoloured 75 10

1984. Centenary of American Kennel Club. Multicoloured.

2095.	20 c. Type **1396**	50	10
2096.	20 c. Chesapeake Bay Retriever and Cocker Spaniel	50	10
2097.	20 c. Alaskan Malamute and Collie	50	10
2098.	20 c. Black and Tan Coonhound and American Foxhound ..	50	10

1400. McGruff (campaign character). **1401.** "Family Unity".

1984. National Crime Prevention Month.
2099. **1400** 20 c. multicoloured 30 10

1984. National Stamp Collecting Month.
2100. **1401.** 20 c. black, red and blue 30 10

1402. Eleanor Roosevelt. **1403.** Abraham Lincoln reading to his Son, Tad.

1984. Eleanor Roosevelt Commemoration.
2101. **1402.** 20 c. blue 30 10

1984. "Nation of Readers".
2102. **1403.** 20 c. brown and red 30 10

1404. "Madonna and Child" (Fra Filippo Lippi). **1406.** Uniformed Group and Flag.

1984. Christmas.
2103. 20 c. Type **1404** 25 10
2104. 20 c. Santa Claus .. 25 10

1984. Hispanic Americans.
2105. **1406.** 20 c. multicoloured 30 10

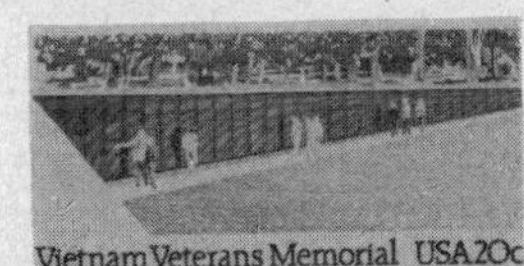

1407. Memorial (Maya Ying Lin).

1984. Vietnam Veterans Memorial, Washington, D.C.
2106. **1407.** 20 c. black, green and deep green .. 30 10

1408. Kern. **1409.** Margaret Mitchell (writer).

1985. Performing Arts and Artists. Birth Centenary of Jerome Kern (composer).
2107. **1408.** 22 c. multicoloured 30 10

1985. Great Americans. Without "c" after face value.

2108	**1409**	1 c. brown ..	10	10
2109	–	2 c. blue ..	10	10
2110	–	3 c. blue ..	10	10
2111	–	4 c. blue ..	10	10
2112	–	5 c. green ..	10	10
2113	–	6 c. red	10	10
2114	–	7 c. red	10	10
2115	–	8 c. brown ..	10	10
2116	–	9 c. green ..	10	10
2117	–	10 c. red ..	15	10
2118	–	11 c. blue ..	15	10
2119	–	14 c. green ..	20	10
2120	–	14 c. red ..	20	10
2121	–	15 c. purple ..	25	10
2122	–	17 c. green ..	25	10
2123	–	21 c. purple ..	30	10
2124	–	22 c. blue ..	30	10
2125	–	23 c. violet ..	30	10
2126	–	25 c. blue ..	30	10
2127	–	28 c. green ..	40	10
2128	–	39 c. mauve ..	45	10
2129	–	45 c. blue ..	70	10
2130ab	–	50 c. brown ..	65	10
2131	–	56 c. red ..	80	10
2132	–	65 c. blue ..	85	10
2133	–	$1 green ..	1·40	10
2134	–	$1 blue ..	1·25	10
2135	–	$2 violet ..	2·50	10
2136	–	$5 brown ..	7·25	1·50

Designs: 2 c. Mary Lyon (educator). 3 c. Paul Dudley White (cardiologist). 4 c. Father Flanagan (founder of Boys Town). 5 c. Hugo L. Black (Supreme Court Justice). 6 c. Walter Lippmann (journalist). 7 c. Abraham Baldwin (politician). 8 c. General Henry Knox. 9 c. Sylvanus Thayer (military educator) (after R. Weir). 10 c. Red Cloud (Oglala Sioux chief). 11 c. Alden Partridge (educationist). 14 c. (2119) Sinclair Lewis (writer) (after S. Melik). 14 c. (2120) Julia Ward Howe (author of "Battle Hymn of the Republic") (after J. Elliott). 15 c. Buffalo Bill Cody (showman). 17 c. Belva Ann Lockwood (women's rights campaigner). 21 c. Chester Carlson (inventor of photocopying). 22 c. J. J. Audubon (ornithologist). 23 c. Mary Cassatt (artist). 25 c. Jack London (writer). 28 c. Sitting Bull (Hunkpapa Sioux chief). 39 c. Grenville Clark (peace activist). 45 c. Dr. Harvey Cushing (neurosurgeon). 50 c. Admiral Chester W. Nimitz. 56 c. John Harvard (philanthropist) (after D. C. French). 65 c. Gen. Henry Harley "Hap" Arnold. $1 (2133) Bernard Revel (scholar). $1 (2134) Johns Hopkins (medical pioneer). $2 William Jennings Bryan (politician). $5 Bret Harte (writer).

1985. Non-denominational "D" Stamp. As T **1090** but inscribed "Domestic Mail".
2137. (22 c.) grn. (18 × 21 mm.) 30 10
2138. (22 c.) grn. (15 × 18 mm.) 60 10

1438. Alfred V. Verville.

1985. Air. Aviation Pioneers.
A2142 33 c. Type **1438** .. 45 15
A2143 39 c. Lawrence and Elmer Sperry .. 50 15

1440. Loading Mail into "China Clipper". **1441.** Mary McLeod Bethune.

1985. Air. 50th Anniv of First Transpacific Airmail Flight of "China Clipper".
A2144 **1440** 44 c. multicoloured 55 15

1985. Black Heritage. Mary McLeod Bethune (social activist).
2145 **1441** 22 c. multicoloured .. 40 10

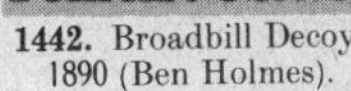

1442. Broadbill Decoy, 1890 (Ben Holmes). **1446.** Omnibus, 1880s.

1985. American Folk Art. Duck Decoys. Multicoloured.

2146	22 c. Type **1442**	45	10
2147	22 c. Mallard Decoy, 1900 (Percy Grant)	45	10
2148	22 c. Canvasback decoy, 1929 (Bob McGraw) ..	45	10
2149	22 c. Redhead decoy, 1925 (Keyes Chadwick)	45	10

1985. Transport. Without "c" after face value.

2150	**1446**	1 c. violet	10	10
2151	–	2 c. black	10	10
2152	–	3 c. purple ..	10	10
2153	–	3.4 c. green ..	10	10
2154	–	4.9 c. black ..	10	10
2155	–	5 c. black	10	10
2156	–	5.3 c. black ..	10	10
2157	–	5.5 c. red	10	10
2158	–	6 c. brown ..	10	10
2159	–	7.1 c. red ..	10	10
2160	–	7.6 c. brown ..	10	10
2161	–	8.3 c. green ..	10	10
2162	–	8.4 c. purple ..	10	10
2163	–	8.5 c. green ..	10	10
2163a	–	10 c. blue	15	10
2164	–	10.1 c. grey ..	20	10
2165	–	11 c. black ..	15	10
2166	–	12 c. blue	15	10
2167	–	12.5 c. green ..	15	10
2167b	–	13 c. black ..	15	10
2168	–	13.2 c. green ..	20	10
2169	–	14 c. blue	20	10
2170	–	15 c. violet ..	25	10
2170b	–	16.7 c. red ..	25	10
2171	–	17 c. blue	25	10
2172	–	17.5 c. violet ..	25	10
2172b	–	20 c. purple ..	25	10
2172c	–	20.5 c. red ..	25	10
2172d	–	21 c. green ..	25	10
2173	–	24.1 c. blue ..	35	10
2174	–	25 c. brown ..	35	10

Designs: 2 c. Locomotive, 1870s. 3 c. Conestoga wagon, 1800s. 3.4 c. School bus, 1920s. 4.9 c. Buckboard, 1880s. 5 c. Milk wagon, 1900s. 5.3 c. Lift, 1900s. 5.5 c. Star Route truck, 1910s. 6 c. Tricycle, 1880s. 7.1 c. Tractor, 1920s. 7.6 c. Carreta, 1770s. 8.3 c. "McKean" ambulance, 1860s. 8.4 c. Wheelchair, 1920s. 8.5 c. Tow truck, 1920s. 10 c. Canal barge, 1880s. 10.1 c. Oil Wagon, 1890s. 11 c. Stutz "Bearcat", 1933. 12 c. Stanley "Steamer", 1909. 12.5 c. Pushcart, 1880s. 13 c. Police patrol wagon, 1880s. 13.2. Coal wagon, 1870s. 14 c. Iceboat, 1880s. 15 c. Tug, 1900s. 16.7 c. Popcorn wagon, 1902. 17 c. Dog sledge, 1920s. 17.5 c. Marmon "Wasp", 1911. 20 c. Cable car, 1880s. 20.5 c. Ahrens-Fox fire engine, 1900s. 21 c. Railway mail van, 1920s. 24.1 c. Pope tandem, 1890s. 25 c. Bread wagon, 1880s.

The 5.3, 7.6, 8.4, 13, 13.2, 16.7, 21 and 24.1 c. were only issued with precancelled inscription of the type of service in red and the 20.5 c. in black. Prices in the unused column are for stamps with full gum.

1471. Ice Skating, Skiing and Emblem. **1472.** Flag over Capitol, Washington.

1985. Winter Special Olympic Games, Park City, Utah.
2175. **1471.** 22 c. multicoloured 40 10

1985.
2176. **1472.** 22 c. black, red and blue 30 10
2178. – 22 c. black, red and blue 40 10

Designs—40 × 22 mm. No. 2178, Flag over Capitol, Washington, and inscription "Of the People By the People For the People".

1474. Frilled Dogwinkle. **1479.** Coloured Lines and "Love".

1985. Sea Shells.

2179.	**1474.**	22 c. red and black	55	10
2180.	–	22 c. red, purple and black	55	10
2181.	–	22 c. red and black	55	10
2182.	–	22 c. purple & blk.	55	10
2183.	–	22 c. red, purple and black	55	10

Designs: No. 2180, Reticulated Helmet. 2181, New England Neptune. 2182, Calico Scallop. 2183, Lightning Whelk.

1985. Greetings Stamp.
2184. **1479.** 22 c. multicoloured 35 10

1480. American Bald Eagle and Moon.

1985.
2185. **1480.** $10.75 multicoloured 13·00 12·00

1481. Electricity Pole and Rural Landscape.

1985. 50th Anniv. of Rural Electrification Administration.

2186. **1481.** 22 c. multicoloured 40 10

1482. 1 c. Franklin Stamp, 1870. **1483.** Abigail Adams.

1985. "Ameripex 86" International Stamp Exhibition, Chicago.

2187. **1482.** 22 c. multicoloured 40 10

1985. Abigail Adams (wife of Pres. John Adams and writer) Commemoration.

2188. **1483.** 22 c. multicoloured 35 10

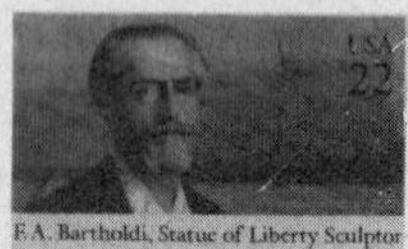

1484. Bartholdi (after J. Frappa) and Statue of Liberty.

1985. Frederic Auguste Bartholdi (sculptor of Statue of Liberty) Commemoration.

2189. **1484.** 22 c. multicoloured 35 10

1485. Troops in Mountain Pass.

1985. Korean War Veterans.

2190. **1485.** 22 c. green and red 55 10

1486. Disabled and Needy People.

1985. 50th Anniv. of Social Security Act.

2191. **1486.** 22 c. blue and deep blue 55 10

1487. Junipero Serra and Mission San Gabriel.

1985. Air. Death Bicentenary (1984) of Father Junipero Serra (missionary).

A2192 1487 44 c. multicoloured 75 20

1488. "Battle of the Marne" (Harvey Dunn).

1985. World War I Veterans.

2193. **1488.** 22 c. green and red 50 10

MORE DETAILED LISTS are given in the Stanley Gibbons Catalogues referred to in the country headings. For lists of current volumes see Introduction.

1489. Quarter Horse. **1493.** Alphabet, Spectacles, Quill and Apple.

1985. Horses. Multicoloured.

2194. 22 c. Type **1489** 70 10
2195. 22 c. Morgan horse .. 70 10
2196. 22 c. Saddlebred horse .. 70 10
2197. 22 c. Appaloosa 70 10

1985. Public Education.

2198. **1493.** 22 c. multicoloured 35 10

1494. Y.M.C.A. Youth Camping (centenary).

1985. International Youth Year. Multicoloured.

2199. 22 c. Type **1494.** .. 40 10
2200. 22 c. Boy Scouts of America (75th Anniv.) 40 10
2201. 22 c. Big Brothers and Big Sisters 40 10
2202. 22 c. Camp Fire Inc. (75th anniv.) 40 10

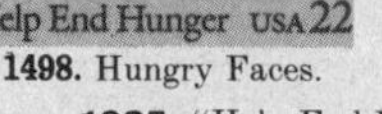

1498. Hungry Faces. **1499.** Envelopes.

1985. "Help End Hunger".

2203. **1498.** 22 c. multicoloured 35 10

1985.

2204 **1499** 21.1. c. multicoloured 50 10

No. 2204 exists both with and without precancel "ZIP+4".

1500. "Genoa Madonna" (Luca della Robbia). **1502.** George Washington (after Stuart) and Washington Monument.

1985. Christmas.

2205. **1500.** 22 c. multicoloured 35 10
2206. – 22 c. red, green and black 35 10

DESIGN—HORIZ. No. 2206, Poinsettias.

1985.

2207 **1502** 18 c. multicoloured .. 35 10

No. 2207 exist both with and without precancel "PRESORTED FIRST-CLASS".

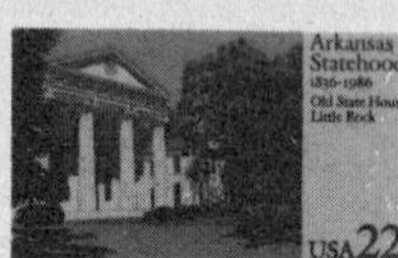

1503. Old State House, Little Rock.

1986. 150th Anniv. of Arkansas State.

2208. **1503.** 22 c. multicoloured 40 10

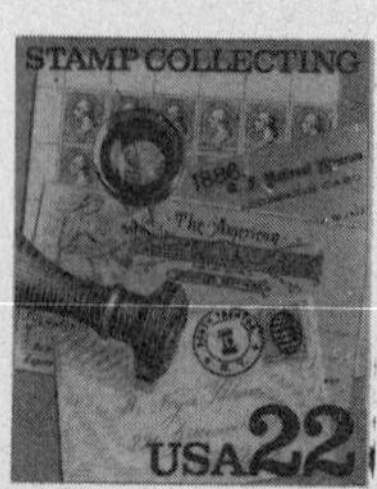

1504. Sheet of Stamps, Handstamp and Magnifying Glass. **1508.** Puppy.

1986. "Ameripex 86" International Stamp Exhibition, Chicago. Stamp Collecting. Multicoloured.

2209. 22 c. Type **1504** 55 10
2210. 22 c. Boy holding stamp in tweezers 55 10
2211. 22 c. Mounted stamps and 3 c. U.S. stamp under glass 55 10
2212. 22 c. "Ameripex" miniature sheet on cover and handstamp .. 55 10

1986. Greetings Stamp.

2213. **1508.** 22 c. multicoloured 40 10

1509. Sojourner Truth. **1510.** Texan Flag and Santa Anna's Spur.

1986. Black Heritage. Sojourner Truth (human rights activist).

2214. **1509.** 22 c. multicoloured 40 10

1986. 150th Anniv. of Battle of San Jacinto.

2215. **1510.** 22 c. red, bl. & blk. 40 10

1511. Muskellunge.

1986. Fishes. Multicoloured.

2216. 22 c. Type **1511** 60 10
2217. 22 c. Atlantic cod .. 60 10
2218. 22 c. Largemouth bass .. 60 10
2219. 22 c. Bluefin tuna .. 60 10
2220. 22 c. Catfish 60 10

1516. Modern Hospital. **1517.** Ellington.

1986. Public Hospitals. 250th Anniv. of Bellevue Hospital Centre, New York.

2221. **1516.** 22 c. multicoloured 40 10

1986. Performing Arts and Artists. Duke Ellington (jazz musician).

2222. **1517.** 22 c. multicoloured 40 10

1519. Elisha Kent Kane and Polar Brig "Advance". **1523.** Head of Statue.

1986. Polar Explorers. Multicoloured.

2224. 22 c. Type **1519** 60 10
2225. 22 c. Adolphus W. Greely 60 10
2226. 22 c. Vilhjalmur Stefansson 60 10
2227. 22 c. Robert E. Peary and Matthew Henson 60 10

1986. Centenary of Statue of Liberty.

2228. **1523.** 22 c. blue and red .. 40 10

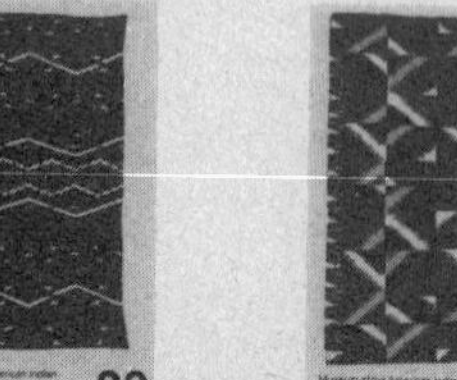

1524. Blanket Designs. **1525.**

1526. Blanket Designs. **1527.**

1986. American Folk Art. Navajo Blankets.

2229. **1524.** 22 c. multicoloured 40 10
2230. **1525.** 22 c. multicoloured 40 10
2231. **1526.** 22 c. multicoloured 40 10
2232. **1527.** 22 c. multicoloured 40 10

1528. T. S. Eliot. **1529.** Highlander Figure (tobacconist).

1986. Literary Arts. Thomas Sterns Eliot (poet).

2233. **1528.** 22 c. red 35 10

1986. American Folk Art. Carved Wooden Figures. Multicoloured.

2234. 22 c. Type **1529** 45 10
2235. 22 c. Ship's figurehead .. 45 10
2236. 22 c. Nautical figure (nautical instrument maker).. .. .. 45 10
2237. 22 c. Indian (cigar store) 45 10

1533. "Madonna" (Il Perugino). **1535.** White Pine and Lake Huron.

1986. Christmas. Multicoloured.

2238. 22 c. Type **1533** 35 10
2239. 22 c. Winter village .. 35 10

1987. 150th Anniv. of Michigan Statehood.

2240. **1535.** 22 c. multicoloured 35 10

1536. Stylized Runner. **1537.** Heart.

1987. 10th Pan-American Games, Indianapolis.

2241 1536 22 c. multicoloured .. 35 10

1987. Greetings Stamp.

2242. **1537.** 22 c. multicoloured 30 10

1538. Du Sable. **1539.** Caruso as Duke of Mantua in "Rigoletto".

1987. Black Heritage. Jean Baptiste Pointe du Sable (founder of Chicago).

2243. **1538.** 22 c. multicoloured 30 10

1987. Performing Arts and Artists. Enrico Caruso (operatic tenor).

2244. **1539.** 22 c. multicoloured 40 10

1540. Badges.

1987. 75th Anniv of Girl Scouts of America.
2245. **1540.** 22 c. multicoloured 30 10

1541. "Congratulations!".

1987. Greetings Stamps. Multicoloured.
2246 22 c. Type **1541** 50 10
2247 22 c. "Get Well!" (18 × 33 mm) 50 10
2248 22 c. "Thank You!" (18 × 33 mm) 50 10
2249 22 c. "Love You, Dad!" 50 10
2250 22 c. "Best Wishes!" (18 × 21 mm) 50 10
2251 22 c. "Happy Birthday!" (18 × 21 mm) 50 10
2252 22 c. "Love You, Mother!" 50 10
2253 22 c. "Keep in Touch!" (18 × 21 mm) 50 10

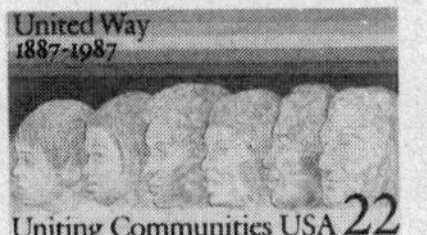

1549. Ethnic Faces.

1550. Flag and Fireworks.

1987. Centenary of United Way Volunteer Organization.
2254. **1549.** 22 c. multicoloured 30 10

1987.
2255. **1550.** 22 c. multicoloured 30 10

1551. Barn Swallows. **1552.** State Seal.

1987. "Capex '87" International Stamp Exhibition, Toronto. North American Wildlife. Multicoloured.
2256 22 c. Type **1551** 45 10
2257 22 c. Monarch butterflies on field thistle .. 45 10
2258 22 c. Bighorn sheep .. 45 10
2259 22 c. Broad-tailed hummingbird on Colorado columbine .. 45 10
2260 22 c. Rabbit and red clover 45 10
2261 22 c. Osprey 45 10
2262 22 c. Mountain lion .. 45 10
2263 22 c. Luna moth on trumpet honeysuckle 45 10
2264 22 c. Mule deer 45 10
2265 22 c. Grey squirrel on red oak 45 10
2266 22 c. Armadillo and Texas prickly pear 45 10
2267 22 c. Eastern chipmunk and European white birch 45 10
2268 22 c. Moose 45 10
2269 22 c. Black bear 45 10
2270 22 c. Tiger swallowtail butterflies on orange milkweed 45 10
2271 22 c. Bobwhite and purple coneflower 45 10
2272 22 c. Ringtail and Cape marigold 45 10
2273 22 c. Red-winged blackbird on common cattail 45 10
2274 22 c. American lobster .. 45 10
2275 22 c. Black-tailed hare and beavertail .. 45 10
2276 22 c. Scarlet tanager and American basswood .. 45 10
2277 22 c. Woodchuck and dandelion 45 10
2278 22 c. Roseate spoonbill and red mangrove .. 45 10
2279 22 c. American bald eagle 45 10
2280 22 c. Alaskan brown bear 45 10
2281 22 c. Iiwi on "Ohia lehua" 45 10
2282 22 c. Badger 45 10
2283 22 c. Pronghorns .. 45 10
2284 22 c. River otter .. 45 10
2285 22 c. Ladybird on rose .. 45 10
2286 22 c. Beaver, maple and quaking aspen .. 45 10
2287 22 c. White-tailed deer .. 45 10
2288 22 c. Blue jays on Table Mountain pine .. 45 10
2289 22 c. Pikas 45 10
2290 22 c. Bison 45 10
2291 22 c. Snowy egret .. 45 10
2292 22 c. Grey wolf 45 10
2293 22 c. Mountain goat .. 45 10
2294 22 c. Deer mouse .. 45 10
2295 22 c. Black-tailed prairie dog 45 10
2296 22 c. Box turtle and Virginia creeper .. 45 10
2297 22 c. Wolverine 45 10
2298 22 c. American elk .. 45 10
2299 22 c. California sea-lion .. 45 10
2300 22 c. Northern mocking-bird on royal poinciana 45 10
2301 22 c. Racoon 45 10
2302 22 c. Bobcat 45 10
2303 22 c. Black-footed ferret 45 10
2304 22 c. Canada goose .. 45 10
2305 22 c. Red fox and red maple 45 10

1987. Bicentenary of Delaware Statehood.
2306. **1552.** 22 c. multicoloured 30 10

1553. Arabesque from Door, Dar Batha Palace, Fez.

1554. Faulkner (after M. L. Goldsborough).

1987. Bicentenary of Diplomatic Relations with Morocco.
2307. **1553.** 22 c. red and black 30 10

1987. Literary Arts. 25th Death Anniv of William Faulkner (novelist).
2308. **1554.** 22 c. green 30 10

1555. Squash Blossoms (Ruth Maxwell).

1556. Floral Design (Mary McPeek).

1557. Floral Design (Leslie Saari).

1558. Dogwood Blossoms (Trenna Ruffner).

1987. American Folk Art. Lacemaking.
2309 **1555** 22 c. white, blue and ultramarine .. 40 10
2310 **1556** 22 c. white, blue and ultramarine .. 40 10
2311 **1557** 22 c. white, blue and ultramarine .. 40 10
2312 **1558** 22 c. white, blue and ultramarine .. 40 10

1559. Independence Hall.

1987. Bicent of Pennsylvania Statehood.
2313. **1559.** 22 c. multicoloured 30 10

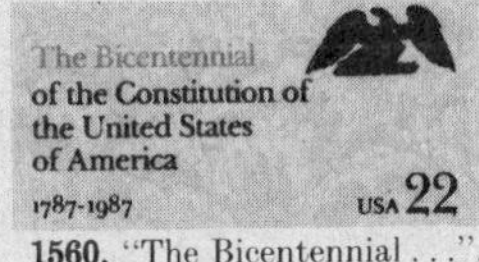

1560. "The Bicentennial . . .".

1987. Bicentenary of United States Constitution (1st issue). Multicoloured.
2314. 22 c. Type **1560** 45 10
2315. 22 c. "We the people . . ." 45 10
2316. 22 c. "Establish justice . . ." 45 10
2317. 22 c. "And secure . . ." .. 45 10
2318. 22 c. "Do ordain . . ." .. 45 10
See also No. 2320.

1565. Farmer with Basket of Produce.

1566. First Page of Constitution and Hand holding Quill Pen.

1987. Bicentenary of New Jersey Statehood.
2319. **1565.** 22 c. multicoloured 30 10

1987. Bicentenary of United States Constitution (2nd issue).
2320. **1566.** 22 c. multicoloured 30 10

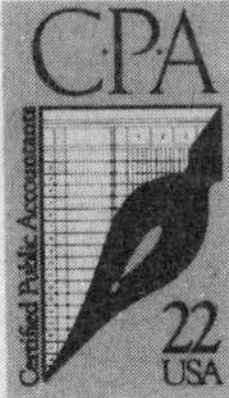

1567. Ledger Page and Pen Nib.

1568. "Stourbridge Lion", 1829.

1987. Centenary of American Institute of Certified Public Accountants.
2321. **1567.** 22 c. multicoloured 1·25 10

1987. Steam Railway Locomotives. Mult.
2322. 22 c. Type **1569** 45 10
2323. 22 c. "Best Friend of Charleston", 1830 .. 45 10
2324. 22 c. "John Bull", 1831 45 10
2325. 22 c. "Brother Jonathan", 1832 .. 45 10
2326. 22 c. "Gowan and Marx", 1839 .. 45 10

1573. "A Gentleman in Adoration Before the Madonna" (detail, Giovanni Battista Moroni).

1575. Oak Tree.

1987. Christmas. Multicoloured.
2327 22 c. Type **1573** 30 10
2328 22 c. Baubles on tree (horiz) 30 10

1988. Bicentenary of Georgia Statehood.
2329. **1575.** 22 c. multicoloured 30 10

1576. "Charles W. Morgan" and Mystic Town.

1577. Slalom.

1988. Bicentenary of Connecticut Statehood.
2330. **1576.** 22 c. multicoloured 30 10

1988. Winter Olympic Games, Calgary.
2331. **1577.** 22 c. multicoloured 30 10

1578. Koala and American Bald Eagle.

1579. Johnson and Music Score.

1988. Bicentenary of Australian Settlement.
2332. **1578.** 22 c. multicoloured 30 10

1988. Black Heritage. James Weldon Johnson (writer, lyricist and diplomat).
2333. **1579.** 22 c. multicoloured 30 10

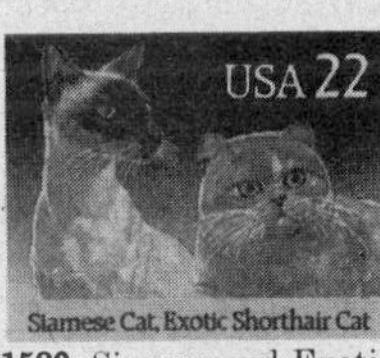

1580. Siamese and Exotic Shorthair Cats.

1584. "A Southwest View of the Statehouse, Boston" (S. Hill).

1988. Cats. Multicoloured.
2334. 22 c. Type **1580** 50 10
2335. 22 c. Abyssinian and Himalayan cats .. 50 10
2336. 22 c. Maine coon and Burmese cats 50 10
2337. 22 c. American shorthair and Persian cats .. 50 10

1988. Bicentenary of Massachusetts Statehood.
2338. **1584.** 22 c. blue, black and red 30 10

1585. St. Anne's Church, "Clarence Crockett" and Statehouse, Annapolis.

1586. Rockne.

1988. Bicentenary of Maryland Statehood.
2339. **1585.** 22 c. multicoloured 30 10

1988. American Sports Personalities. Birth Centenary of Knute Rockne (football player and coach).
2340 **1586** 22 c. multicoloured .. 30 10

1587 Earth

1588 Map, Settlers, Indians, "Calmare Nyckel" and "Fagel Grip"

1988. No value expressed.
2341 **1587** (25 c.) multicoloured 35 10

1988. Air. 350th Anniv of Founding of New Sweden (settlement in America).
2345 **1588** 44 c. multicoloured .. 60 20

1589 Ring-necked Pheasant

1590 Flag and Clouds

1988.
2346 **1589** 25 c. multicoloured .. 35 10

1988.
2347 **1590** 25 c. multicoloured .. 35 10

1591 "Aerodrome 5" and Langley

1593 Flag over Half Dome, Yosemite National Park

1988. Air. Aviation Pioneers. Samuel Pierpont Langley.
A2348 **1591** 45 c. multicoloured 60 20

1988.
2352 **1593** 25 c. blue, red & grn 35 10

1594 Palmetto Trees and Sea Grass

1595 Rose-breasted Grosbeak on Dogwood

1988. Bicentenary of South Carolina Statehood.
2353 **1594** 25 c. multicoloured .. 35 10

1988. Birds. Multicoloured.
2354 25 c. Type **1595** 35 10
2355 25 c. Saw-whet owl on Eastern hemlock .. 35 10

1597 Ouimet

1598 Old Man of the Mountain

1988. American Sports Personalities. 75th Anniv of Francis Ouimet's U.S. Open Golf Championship Victory.
2356 **1597** 25 c. multicoloured .. 35 10

1988. Bicentenary of New Hampshire Statehood.
2357 **1598** 25 c. multicoloured .. 35 10

HAVE YOU READ THE NOTES AT THE BEGINNING OF THIS CATALOGUE?
These often provide answers to the enquiries we receive.

1599 Sikorsky and "VS-300" Helicopter

1600 Carriage and Capitol Building, Williamsburg

1988. Air. Aviation Pioneers. Ignor Sikorsky.
A2358 **1599** 36 c. multicoloured 50 20

1988. Bicentenary of Virginia Statehood.
2359 **1600** 25 c. multicoloured .. 35 10

1601 Rose

1602 Trinity Church, Wall Street and Federal Hall, New York City

1988. Greetings Stamp.
2360 **1601** 25 c. multicoloured .. 35 10

1988. Bicentenary of New York Statehood.
2361 **1602** 25 c. multicoloured .. 35 10

1603 Roses

1604 Gymnast

1988. Greetings Stamp.
2362 **1603** 45 c. multicoloured .. 60 20

1988. Olympic Games, Seoul.
2363 **1604** 25 c. multicoloured .. 35 10

1605 Locomobile, 1928

1610 Honey Bee on Clover

1988. Classic Cars. Multicoloured.
2364 25 c. Type **1605** 40 10
2365 25 c. Pierce-Arrow, 1929 40 10
2366 25 c. Cord, 1931 .. .. 40 10
2367 25 c. Packard, 1932 .. 40 10
2368 25 c. Duesenberg, 1935 .. 40 10

1988.
2369 **1610** 25 c. multicoloured .. 35 10

1611 Nathaniel Palmer (after Samuel Waldo) and "Hero"

1615 Buck (Gustav Dentzel)

1988. Antarctic Explorers. Multicoloured.
2370 25 c. Type **1611** 50 10
2371 25 c. Charles Wilkes (after Samuel Bell Waugh) .. 50 10
2372 25 c. Richard E. Byrd .. 50 10
2373 25 c. Lincoln Ellsworth and "Polar Star" .. 50 10

1988. American Folk Art. Carousel Animals. Multicoloured.
2374 25 c. Type **1615** 45 10
2375 25 c. Armoured horse (Daniel C. Muller) 45 10
2376 25 c. Camel (Charles Looff) 45 10
2377 25 c. Goat (Charles Looff) 45 10

1619 American Bald Eagle and Moon

1988.
2378 **1619** $8.75 multicoloured 11·00 10·00

1620 "Madonna and Child" (detail, Sandro Botticelli)

1622 "Happy Birthday"

1988. Christmas. Multicoloured.
2379 25 c. Type **1620** 35 10
2380 25 c. "White Christmas" (horiz) 35 10

1988. Greetings Stamps. Multicoloured.
2381 25 c. Type **1622** 45 10
2382 25 c. "Thinking of you" 45 10
2383 25 c. "Love you" .. 45 10
2384 25 c. "Best Wishes" .. 45 10

1626 "C. M. Russell and Friends" (Charles M. Russell)

1627 A. Philip Randolph

1989. Centenary of Montana Statehood.
2385 **1626** 25 c. multicoloured .. 40 10

1989. Black Heritage. A. Philip Randolph (trade union activist).
2386 **1627** 25 c. multicoloured .. 30 10

1628 Grain Elevator and Buckboard

1629 Mt. Rainier and Canoe on Reflection Lake

1989. Centenary of North Dakota Statehood.
2387 **1628** 25 c. multicoloured .. 30 10

1989. Centenary of Washington Statehood.
2388 **1629** 25 c. multicoloured .. 30 10

1630 "Experiment", 1788–90

1989. Paddle-steamers. Multicoloured.
2389 25 c. Type **1630** 45 10
2390 25 c. "Phoenix", 1809 .. 45 10
2391 25 c. "New Orleans", 1812 45 10
2392 25 c. "Washington", 1816 45 10
2393 25 c. "Walk in the Water", 1818 .. 45 10

1635 Cancelled 1869 90 c. Lincoln Stamp

1636 Toscanini

1989. "World Stamp Expo'89" International Stamp Exhibition, Washington, D.C.
2394 **1635** 25 c. red, black & brn 30 10

1989. Perfoming Arts and Artists. Arturo Toscanini (conductor).
2395 **1636** 25 c. multicoloured .. 40 10

1637 "Car of History" Clock (Carlo Franzoni)

1638 Eagle and Shield over Vice-President's Chair

1989. Bicentenary of House of Representatives.
2396 **1637** 25 c. multicoloured .. 30 10

1989. Bicentenary of Senate.
2397 **1638** 25 c. multicoloured .. 30 10

1639 George Washington (statue, J. Q. A. Ward)

1640 Pasque Flowers, Pioneer Woman and House

1989. Bicentenary of Executive Branch.
2398 **1639** 25 c. multicoloured .. 30 10

1989. Centenary of South Dakota Statehood.
2399 **1640** 25 c. multicoloured .. 30 10

1641 Gehrig

1643 Hemingway

1642 Liberty, Equality and Fraternity

1989. American Sports Personalities. Lou Gehrig (baseball player).
2400 **1641** 25 c. multicoloured .. 45 10

1989. Air. Bicentenary of French Revolution.
A2401 **1642** 45 c. multicoloured 60 20

1989. Literary Arts. Ernest Hemingway (novelist).
2402 **1643** 25 c. multicoloured .. 30 10

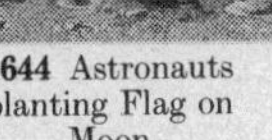
1644 Astronauts planting Flag on Moon

1645 Dogwood Blossoms

1989. 20th Anniv of First Manned Moon Landing.
2403 **1644** $2.40 multicoloured 3·00 2·00

1989. Bicent of North Carolina Statehood.
2404 **1645** 25 c. multicoloured .. 30 10

1646 Letter Carriers

1647 Eagle and Flag as Shield

1989. Centenary of National Association of Letter Carriers.
2405 **1646** 25 c. multicoloured .. 30 10

1989. Bicentenary of Bill of Rights.
2406 **1647** 25 c. black, red & bl 30 10

1648 Tyrannosaurus Rex

1652 Mimbres Ritual Figure

1989. Prehistoric Animals. Multicoloured.
2407 25 c. Type **1648** 60 10
2408 25 c. Pteranodon .. 60 10
2409 25 c. Stegosaurus .. 60 10
2410 25 c. Brontosaurus .. 60 10

1989. America. Pre-Columbian Carvings. Multicoloured.
2411 25 c. Type **1652** (post) 30 10
A2412 45 c. Calusa "Key Marco cat" (air) 55 20

1654 "Dream of St. Catherine of Alexandria" (detail, Ludovico Carracci)

1656 Eagle and Shield

1989. Christmas. Multicoloured.
2413 25 c. Type **1654** 40 10
2415 25 c. Gifts on sleigh (horiz) 30 10

1989. Self-adhesive. Imperf.
2416 **1656** 25 c. multicolured .. 30 10

1658 Western Stagecoach

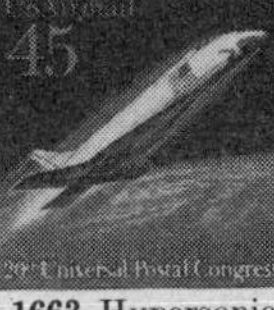
1663 Hypersonic Airplane

1989. 20th U.P.U. Congress, Washington, D.C. (1st issue). Classic Mail Transport. Mult.
2418 25 c. Type **1658** 45 10
2419 25 c. "Chesapeake" (Mississippi river steamer) 45 10
2420 25 c. Curtiss "Jenny" .. 45 10
2421 25 c. Motor car 45 10
See also Nos. A2423/6.

1989. Air. 20th Universal Postal Union Congress, Washington, D.C. (2nd issue). Mail Transport of the Future. Multicoloured.
A2423 45 c. Type **1663** 80 20
A2424 45 c. Hovercar 80 20
A2425 45 c. Rover vehicle delivering mail to space colony 80 20
A2426 45 c. Space shuttle delivering mail to space station 80 20

1668 Mountain Bluebird

1669 Lovebirds

1990. Centenary of Idaho Statehood.
2428 **1668** 25 c. multicoloured .. 40 10

1990. Greetings Stamp.
2429 **1669** 25 c. multicoloured .. 40 10

1670 Ida Wells

1671 John Marshall

1990. Black Heritage. Ida B. Wells (civil rights activist).
2431 **1670** 25 c. multicoloured .. 30 10

1990. Bicentenary of Supreme Court.
2432 **1671** 25 c. multicoloured .. 30 10

1672 Beach Umbrella

1677 Luis Munoz Marin

1990.
2433 **1672** 15 c. multicoloured .. 25 10

1990. Great Americans.
2438 **1677** 5 c. red 10 10
2448 – 29 c. blue 40 10
2449 – 29 c. black 40 10
2452 – 35 c. black 45 10
2454 – 40 c. blue 55 10
2457 – 52 c. lilac 70 10
2462 – 75 c. red .. .. 1·00 15
DESIGNS: 29 c. (2448) Earl Warren; 29 c. (2449) Thomas Jefferson (President, 1801–09); 35 c. Dennis Chavez; 40 c. Lt-Gen. Claire Chennault; 52 c. Hubert Humphrey (Vice-president 1965–69); 75 c. Wendell Wilkie.

1710 "High Mountain Meadows" (Conrad Schwiering)

1990. Centenary of Wyoming Statehood.
2471 **1710** 25 c. multicoloured .. 40 10

1711 Judy Garland ("The Wizard of Oz")

1715 Marianne Moore

1990. Classic Films. Multicoloured.
2472 25 c. Type **1711** 50 10
2473 25 c. Clark Gable and Vivien Leigh ("Gone with the Wind") .. 50 10
2474 25 c. Gary Cooper ("Beau Geste") 50 10
2475 25 c. John Wyane ("Stagecoach") .. 50 10

1990. Literary Arts. Marianne Moore (poet).
2476 **1715** 25 c. multicoloured .. 40 10

1720 Circus Wagon, 1900s

1755 Admiralty Head, Nugent Sound

1990. Transport.
2480 – 4 c. purple 10 10
2481 **1720** 5 c. red 10 10
2504 – 5 c. brown 10 10
2643 – 5 c. red 10 10
2507 – 10 c. green 15 15
2489 – 23 c. blue 30 10
2496 – $1 blue and red .. 1·25 35
DESIGNS: 4 c. Richard Dudgeon steam carriage, 1866; 5 c. (both) Birch bark canoe, 1800s; 10 c. Tractor trailer, 1930s; 23 c. Lunch wagon, 1890s; $1 Benoist Type XIV flying boat.

1990. Lighthouses. Multicoloured.
2516 25 c. Type **1755** 50 10
2517 25 c. Cape Hatteras .. 50 10
2518 25 c. West Quoddy Head 50 10
2519 25 c. American Shoals .. 50 10
2520 25 c. Sandy Hook, New York Harbour .. 50 10

1760 Stars and Stripes

1761 Slater Mill

1990. Self-adhesive. Imperf.
2521 **1760** 25 c. red and blue .. 35 10

1990. Bicentenary of Rhode Island Statehood.
2522 **1761** 25 c. multicoloured .. 35 10

1763 Bobcat

1990. Wildlife.
2524 **1763** $2 multicoloured .. 2·75 85

1769 Jesse Owens

1990. American Olympic Medal Winners. Multicoloured.
2530 25 c. Type **1769** 35 10
2531 25 c. Ray Ewry 35 10
2532 25 c. Hazel Wightman .. 35 10
2533 25 c. Eddie Eagan .. 35 10
2534 25 c. Helene Madison .. 35 10

1774 Assiniboine

1990. American Folk Art. Indian Headdresses. Multicoloured.
2535 25 c. Type **1774** 35 10
2536 25 c. Cheyenne 35 10
2537 25 c. Comanche 35 10
2538 25 c. Flathead 35 10
2539 25 c. Shoshone 35 10

1779 Micronesian Outrigger Canoe and Flag

1990. 4th Anniv of Ratification of Marshall Islands and Micronesia Compacts of Free Association. Multicoloured.
2540 25 c. Type **1779** 35 10
2541 25 c. Marshallese stick chart, outrigger canoe and flag 35 10

1781 Killer Whales

1990. Marine Mammals. Multicoloured.
2542 25 c. Type **1781** 35 10
2543 25 c. Northern sea lions .. 35 10
2544 25 c. Sea otter 35 10
2545 25 c. Common dolphin .. 35 10

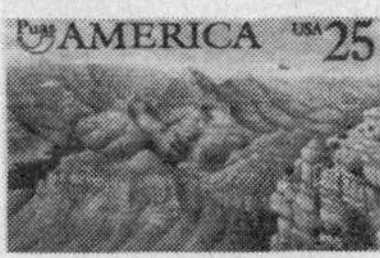

1785 Grand Canyon

1990. America. Natural World. Multicoloured.
2546 25 c. Type **1785** (post) 35 10
A2547 45 c. Tropical island coastline (air) .. 60 15

1787 Eisenhower and Soldiers

1788 "Madonna and Child" (Antonello da Messina)

1990. Birth Centenary of Dwight David Eisenhower (President, 1953—61).
2548 **1787** 25 c. multicoloured .. 35 10

1990. Christmas. Multicoloured.
2549 25 c. Type **1788** 35 10
2551 25 c. Christmas tree .. 35 10

1790 Tulip

This U.S. stamp, along with 25¢ of additional U.S. postage, is equivalent to the 'F' stamp rate
1791

1991. No value expressed.

2552 **1790** (29 c.) multicoloured 40 10

1991. No value expressed. Make-up Rate stamp.

2556 **1791** (4 c.) red and brown 10 10

1792 Stars and Stripes

1991. No value expressed. Self-adhesive. Imperf.

2557 **1792** (29 c.) red, blue & blk 40 15

1794 Federal Palace, Berne, and Capitol, Washington

1795 Farm

1991. 700th Anniv of Swiss Confederation.

2559 **1794** 50 c. multicoloured 65 15

1991. Bicentenary of Vermont Statehood.

2560 **1795** 29 c. multicoloured .. 40 10

1796 Fawn

1797 Flag over Mt. Rushmore

1991.

2561 **1796** 19 c. multicoloured .. 25 10

1991.

2562 **1797** 29 c. red, brown & blk 40 10

1798 Tulip

1799 Wood Duck

1991.

2563 **1798** 29 c. multicoloured .. 40 10

1991. (a) Inscriptions in black.

2565 **1799** 29 c. multicoloured .. 40 15

(b) Inscriptions in red

2566 **1799** 29 c. multicoloured .. 40 15

1800 Flag and Olympic Rings

1801 Quimby and Bleriot Aircraft

1991.

2567 **1800** 29 c. multicoloured .. 40 10

1991. Air. Aviation Pioneers. Harriet Quimby (first American woman pilot).

A2568 **1801** 50 c. multicoloured 65 15

1802 American Bald Eagle

1803 Heart-shaped Globe

1991. 50th Anniv of "E Series" Defence Bonds.

2569 **1802** 29 c. multicoloured .. 40 15

1991. Greetings Stamps. Multicoloured.

2570 29 c. Type **1803** 40 10

2572 52 c. Fischer's lovebirds (21 × 35 mm) 70 20

1805 Hot-air Balloon

1806 Piper and Piper "Cub"

1991.

2573 **1805** 19 c. multicoloured .. 25 10

1991. Air. Aviation Pioneers. William Piper.

A2574 **1806** 40 c. multicoloured 55 15

1807 Saroyan

1808 Flags on Parade

1991. Literary Arts. 10th Death Anniv of William Saroyan (dramatist and novelist).

2575 **1807** 29 c. multicoloured .. 40 10

1991. 125th Anniv of Memorial Day.

2576 **1808** 29 c. multicoloured .. 40 10

1809 Royal Wulff

1814 Porter and Score

1991. Fishing Flies. Multicoloured.

2577 29 c. Type **1809** 40 10

2578 29 c. Jock Scott .. 40 10

2579 29 c. Apte tarpon fly .. 40 10

2580 29 c. Lefty's deceiver .. 40 10

2581 29 c. Muddler minnow .. 40 10

1991. Performing Arts and Artists. Birth Centenary of Cole Porter (composer).

2582 **1814** 29 c. multicoloured .. 40 10

1815 American Bald Eagle

1991. U.S. Olympic Festival.

2583 **1815** $9.95 multicoloured 11·50 4·00

1816 U.S.S. "Glacier" (ice-breaker) near Palmer Station

1817 American Kestrel

1991. Air. 30th Anniv of Antarctic Treaty.

A2584 **1816** 50 c. multicoloured 65 20

1991. Birds. Multicoloured.

2585 1 c. Type **1817** 10 10

2586 3 c. Eastern bluebird .. 10 10

2590 30 c. Common cardinal .. 40 10

1823 Liberty Torch

1824 South-West Asia Service Medal

1991. Self-adhesive. Imperf.

2591 **1823** 29 c. grn, gold & blk 40 10

1991. Operations Desert Shield and Desert Storm (liberation of Kuwait).

2592 **1824** 29 c. multicoloured .. 40 10

1825 American Bald Eagle

1991.

2595 **1825** $2.90 multicoloured 3·75 1·90

1826 Pole Vaulting

1831 Rowing Boat

1991. Olympic Games, Barcelona (1992). Mult.

2596 29 c. Type **1826** 40 10

2597 29 c. Throwing the discus 40 10

2598 29 c. Running .. 40 10

2599 29 c. Throwing the javelin 40 10

2600 29 c. Hurdling 40 10

1991.

2601 **1831** 19 c. multicoloured .. 25 10

1832 Coins and Banknotes

1833 Shot at Goal

1991. Centenary Convention of American Numismatic Association.

2602 **1832** 29 c. multicoloured .. 40 10

1991. Centenary of Basketball.

2604 **1833** 29 c. multicoloured .. 40 10

1834 Stan Laurel and Oliver Hardy

1991. Comedians.

2605 **1834** 29 c. black, vio & red 40 10

2606 – 29 c. black, red & vio 40 10

2607 – 29 c. black, vio & red 40 10

2608 – 29 c. black, vio & red 40 10

2609 – 29 c. black, red & vio 40 10

DESIGNS: No. 2606, Edgar Bergen and Charlie McCarthy; 2607, Jack Benny; 2608, Fanny Brice, 2609, Bud Abbott and Lou Costello.

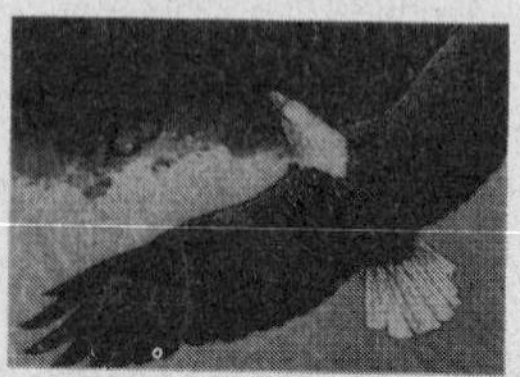

1839 American Bald Eagle

1991.

2610 **1839** $14 multicoloured .. 18·00 5·50

1840 Burma Road Convoy

1991. 50th Anniv of America's Entry into Second World War. Multicoloured.

2611 29 c. Type **1840** 40 15

2612 29 c. America's first peacetime draft .. 40 15

2613 29 c. Lend-Lease Act .. 40 15

2614 29 c. Roosevelt and Churchill (Atlantic Charter) 40 15

2615 29 c. Munitions factory .. 40 15

2616 29 c. Sinking of "Reuben James" (destroyer) .. 40 15

2617 29 c. Gas mask (Civil Defence) 40 15

2618 29 c. Delivery of "Patrick Henry" (first "Liberty" freighter) 40 15

2619 29 c. U.S.S. "West Virginia" and U.S.S. "Tennessee" ablaze, Pearl Harbor .. 40 15

2620 29 c. U.S. Declaration of War on Japan .. 40 15

1850 Pennsylvania Avenue, 1903

1851 Matzeliger

1991. Bicentenary of District of Columbia.

2621 **1850** 29 c. multicoloured .. 40 10

1991. Black Heritage. Jan Ernst Matzeliger (inventor of shoe lasting machine).

2622 **1851** 29 c. multicoloured .. 40 10

1852 Flag

1853 Postal Service Emblem and Olympic Rings

1991.

2623 **1852** 23 c. blue, red & blk 30 30

1991.

2624 **1853** $1 multicoloured .. 1·25 35

1854 "Mariner 10" and Mercury

1991. Space Exploration. Multicoloured.

2625 29 c. Type **1854** 40 10

2626 29 c. Venus and "Mariner 2" 40 10

2627 29 c. Earth and "Landsat" 40 10

2628 29 c. Moon and Lunar Orbiter 40 10

2629 29 c. "Viking" Orbiter and Mars 40 10

2630 29 c. Jupiter and "Pioneer 11" 40 10

2631 29 c. "Voyager 2" and Saturn 40 10

2632 29 c. Uranus and "Voyager 2" 40 10

2633 29 c. Neptune and "Voyager 2" 40 10

2634 29 c. Pluto 40 10

1864 Early Explorers from Asia

1865 "Madonna and Child with Donor" (detail, Antoniazzo Romano)

1991 Air. America. Voyages of Discovery.

A2635 **1864** 50 c. multicoloured 65 15

1991. Christmas. No value expressed. Mult.

2636 (29 c.) Type **1865** .. 40 10
2637 (29 c.) Santa Claus in chimney (horiz) .. 40 10
2639 (29 c.) Santa Claus checking list (horiz) .. 40 10
1640 (29 c.) Santa Claus leaving gifts (horiz) 40 10
2641 (29 c.) Santa Claus leaving by chimney (horiz) .. 40 10
2642 (29 c.) Santa Claus on sleigh (horiz) 40 10

1871 Eagle and Shield

1872 Ice Hockey

1991. Inscr "Bulk Rate USA".

2644 **1871** (10 c.) multicoloured 15 15

For design as T **1871** but inscribed "USA Bulk Rate" see Nos. 2801/2.

1992. Winter Olympic Games, Albertville. Multicoloured.

2645 29 c. Type **1872** 40 10
2646 29 c. Figure skating .. 40 10
2647 29 c. Speed skating .. 40 10
2648 29 c. Skiing 40 10
2649 29 c. Two-man bobsleigh 40 10

1877 1869 15 c. Columbus Stamp

1878 Du Bois

1992. "World Columbian Stamp Expo'92, Chicago.

2650 **1877** 29 c. multicoloured .. 40 10

1992. Black Heritage. William Edward Burghardt Du Bois (founder of Niagara Movement (precursor of National Association for Advancement of Coloured People)).

2651 **1878** 29 c. multicoloured .. 40 10

1879 Heart in Envelope

1880 Catcher and Baserunner

1992. Greetings Stamp.

2652 **1879** 29 c. multicoloured .. 40 10

1992. Addition of Baseball to Olympic Games.

2654 **1880** 29 c. multicoloured .. 40 10

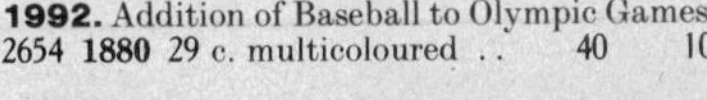

1881 Flag over White House

1882 Seeking Queen Isabella's Support

1992. Bicentenary of White House.

2655 **1881** 29 c. red and blue .. 40 10

1992. 500th Anniv of Discovery of America by Columbus. Multicoloured.

2656 29 c. Type **1882** 40 15
2657 29 c. Crossing the Atlantic 40 15
2658 29 c. Approaching land .. 40 15
2659 29 c. Coming ashore .. 40 15

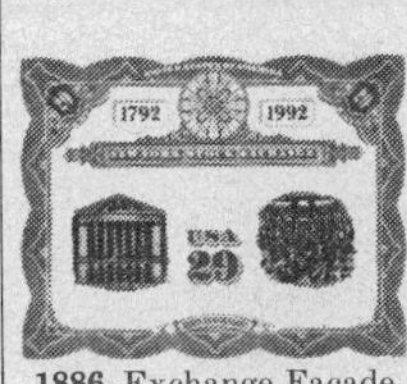

1886 Exchange Facade and Trading Floor

1893 Russian Cosmonaut and Space Shuttle

1992. Bicentenary of New York Stock Exchange.

2660 **1886** 29 c. green, blk & red 40 10

1992. International Space Year. Mult.

2662 29 c. Type **1893** 40 10
2663 29 c. American astronaut and "Mir" space station 40 10
2664 29 c. "Apollo" and "Vostok" spacecraft and Sputnik .. 40 10
2665 29 c. "Soyuz", "Mercury" and "Gemini" spacecraft 40 10

1897 Army Lorry using New Highway

1898 My Old Kentucky Home State Park, Bardstown

1992. 50th Anniv of Alaska Highway.

2666 **1897** 29 c. multicoloured .. 40 10

1992. Bicentenary of Kentucky Statehood.

2667 **1898** 29 c. multicoloured .. 40 10

1899 Football

1904 Ruby-throated Hummingbird

1992. Olympic Games, Barcelona. Mult.

2668 29 c. Type **1899** 40 10
2669 29 c. Gymnastics .. 40 10
2670 29 c. Volleyball .. 40 10
2671 29 c. Boxing 40 10
2672 29 c. Swimming 40 10

1992. Hummingbirds. Multicoloured.

2673 29 c. Type **1094** 40 10
2674 29 c. Broad-billed hummingbird 40 10
2675 29 c. Costa's hummingbird 40 10
2676 29 c. Rufous hummingbird 40 10
2677 29 c. Galliope hummingbird 40 10

1909 Flag in "USA"

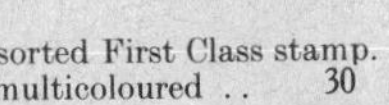

1910 Indian Paintbrush

1992. Presorted First Class stamp.

2678 **1909** 23 c. multicoloured .. 30 30

1992. Wild Flowers. Multicoloured.

2680 29 c. Type **1910** 40 10
2681 29 c. Fragrant water lily 40 10
2682 29 c. Meadow beauty .. 40 10
2683 29 c. Jack-in-the-pulpit .. 40 10
2684 29 c. California poppy .. 40 10
2685 29 c. Large-flowered trillium 40 10
2686 29 c. Tickseed 40 10
2687 29 c. Shooting star .. 40 10
2688 29 c. Stream violet .. 40 10
2689 29 c. Bluets 40 10
2690 29 c. Herb Robert .. 40 10
2691 29 c. Marsh marigold .. 40 10
2692 29 c. Sweet white violet .. 40 10
2693 29 c. Claret cup cactus .. 40 10
2694 29 c. White mountain avens 40 10
2695 29 c. Sessile bellwort .. 40 10
2696 29 c. Blue flag 40 10
2697 29 c. Harlequin lupine .. 40 10
2698 29 c. Twinflower .. 40 10
2699 29 c. Common sunflower 40 10
2700 29 c. Sego lily 40 10
2701 29 c. Virginia bluebells .. 40 10
2702 29 c. Ohi'a lehua .. 40 10
2703 29 c. Rosebud orchid .. 40 10
2704 29 c. Showy evening primrose 40 10
2705 29 c. Fringed gentian .. 40 10
2706 29 c. Yellow lady's slipper 40 10
2707 29 c. Passion flower .. 40 10
2708 29 c. Bunchberry .. 40 10
2709 29 c. Pasqueflower .. 40 10
2710 29 c. Round-lobed hepatica 40 10
2711 29 c. Wild columbine .. 40 10
2712 29 c. Fireweed 40 10
2713 29 c. Indian pond lily .. 40 10
2714 29 c. Turk's cap lily .. 40 10
2715 29 c. Dutchman's breeches 40 10
2716 29 c. Trumpet honeysuckle 40 10
2717 29 c. Jacob's ladder .. 40 10
2718 29 c. Plains prickly pear 40 10
2719 29 c. Moss campion .. 40 10
2720 29 c. Bearberry 40 10
2721 29 c. Mexican hat .. 40 10
2722 29 c. Harebell 40 10
2723 29 c. Desert five spot .. 40 10
2724 29 c. Smooth Solomon's seal 40 10
2725 29 c. Red maids 40 10
2726 29 c. Yellow skunk cabbage 40 10
2727 29 c. Rue anemone .. 40 10
2728 29 c. Standing cypress .. 40 10
2729 29 c. Wild flax 40 10

1911 Doolittle Raid on Tokyo

1921 Dorothy Parker

1992. United States Participation in Second World War. Multicoloured.

2730 29 c. Type **1911** 40 15
2731 29 c. Ration stamps .. 40 15
2732 29 c. Airplane on aircraft carrier (Battle of Coral Sea) 40 15
2733 29 c. Japanese occupation of Corregidor 40 15
2734 29 c. Japanese invasion of Aleutian Islands .. 40 15
2735 29 c. Allies decipher enemy codes 40 15
2736 29 c. U.S.S. "Yorktown" ablaze (Battle of Midway) 40 15
2737 29 c. Woman engaged on war effort 40 15
2738 29 c. Marines landing at Guadalcanal 40 15
2739 29 c. Allied tanks in North Africa 40 15

1992. Literary Arts. Dorothy Parker (short story writer, poet and critic).

2740 **1921** 29 c. multicoloured .. 40 10

1922 Von Karman and Rocket

1923 Flag and "I pledge allegiance..."

1992. Theodore von Karman (space pioneer).

2741 **1922** 29 c. multicoloured .. 40 10

1992. Centenary of Pledge of Allegiance.

2742 **1923** 29 c. multicoloured (value in black) .. 40 10
2788 29 c. multicoloured (value in red) .. 40 10

1924 Azurite

1928 Eagle and Shield

1992. Minerals. Multicoloured.

2743 29 c. Type **1924** 40 10
2744 29 c. Copper 40 10
2745 29 c. Variscite 40 10
2746 29 c. Wulfenite 40 10

1992. Self-adhesive. Imperf.

2747 **1928** 29 c. multicoloured (inscr in red) .. 40 15
2748 29 c. multicoloured (inscr in green) .. 40 15
2749 29 c. multicoloured (inscr in brown) .. 40 15

1929 Spanish Galleon, Map and Cabrillo

1930 Giraffe

1992. 450th Anniv of Discovery of California by Juan Rodriguez Cabrillo.

2750 **1929** 29 c. multicoloured .. 40 15

1992. Wild Animals. Multicoloured.

2751 29 c. Type **1930** 40 10
2752 29 c. Giant panda .. 40 10
2753 29 c. Flamingo 40 10
2754 29 c. King penguins .. 40 10
2755 29 c. White Bengal tiger 40 10

1935 "Madonna and Child with Saints" (Giovanni Bellini)

1940 Pumpkinseed Sunfish

1992. Christmas. Multicoloured.

2756 29 c. Type **1935** 40 10
2757 29 c. Wheeled racing horse (horiz) 40 10
2758 29 c. Locomotive (horiz) 40 10
2759 29 c. Steam engine (horiz) 40 10
2760 29 c. Steamer (horiz) .. 40 10

No. 2758 also comes imperf and self-adhesive.

1992.

2766 **1940** 45 c. multicoloured .. 60 10

1941 Rooster

1992. New Year.
2768 1941 29 c. multicoloured .. 40 10

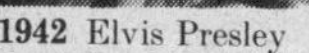

1942 Elvis Presley
1943 Spacecraft and Ringed-planet

1993. Elvis Presley (rock singer and actor).
2769 1942 29 c. multicoloured .. 40 10
For similar design but inscr "ELVIS PRESLEY" see Type **1987**.

1993. Space Fantasy. Multicoloured.
2770 29 c. Type **1943** 40 10
2771 29 c. Space capsules .. 40 10
2772 29 c. Astronauts .. 40 10
2773 29 c. Spaceship 40 10
2774 29 c. Spacecraft and planet 40 10

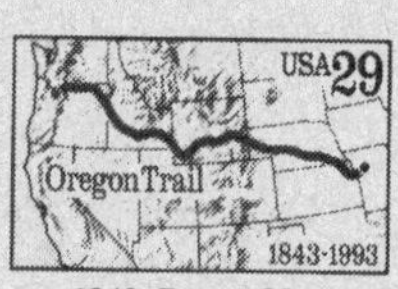

1948 Julian
1949 Route Map

1993. Black Heritage. Percy Lavon Julian (research chemist).
2775 1948 29 c. multicoloured .. 40 10

1993. 150th Anniv of Oregon Trail.
2776 1949 29 c. multicoloured .. 40 10

1950 Athletes
1951 Princess Grace

1993. World University Games, Buffalo.
2777 1950 29 c. multicoloured .. 40 10

1993. 10th Death Anniv of Princess Grace of Monaco (former Grace Kelly).
2778 1951 29 c. blue 40 10

1952 "Oklahoma"

1993. Broadway Musicals. Multicoloured.
(a) No frame. Size 36 × 28 mm.
2779 29 c. Type **1952** 40 10
(b) With frame. Size 35 × 27 mm.
2780 29 c. "Show Boat" .. 40 10
2781 29 c. "Porgy & Bess" .. 40 10
2782 29 c. Type **1952** 40 10
2783 29 c. "My Fair Lady" .. 40 10

1956 Clown

1993. Bicentenary of First Circus Performance in America. Multicoloured.
2784 29 c. Type **1956** 40 10
2785 29 c. Ringmaster .. 40 10
2786 29 c. Trapeze artiste .. 40 10
2787 29 c. Elephant 40 10

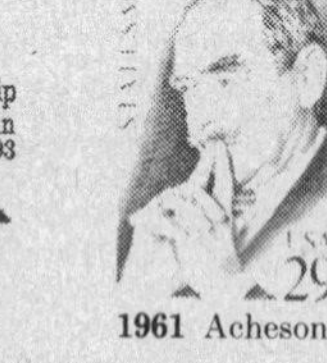

1960 Pioneers racing to Cherokee Strip
1961 Acheson

1993. Centenary of Cherokee Strip Land Run.
2789 1960 29 c. multicoloured .. 40 10

1993. Birth Centenary of Dean Acheson (Secretary of State, 1949–53).
2790 1961 29 c. green 40 10

1962 Steeplechase
1966 Hyacinths

1993. Equestrian Sports. Multicoloured.
2791 29 c. Type **1962** 40 10
2792 29 c. Thoroughbred racing 40 10
2793 29 c. Harness racing .. 40 10
2794 29 c. Polo 40 10

1993. Garden Flowers. Multicoloured.
2796 29 c. Type **1966** 40 10
2797 29 c. Daffodils 40 10
2798 29 c. Tulips 40 10
2799 29 c. Irises 40 10
2800 29 c. Lilac 40 10

1971 Eagle and Shield
1972 Atlantic Convoy

1993. Coil stamps. Inscr "USA Bulk Rate". Multicoloured, colours of eagle given.
2801 1971 (10 c.) yellow & brn 10 10
2802 (10 c.) gold & brown 10 10
For design as Type **1971** but inscr "Bulk Rate USA" see No. 2644.

1993. United States Participation in Second World War. Multicoloured.
2803 29 c. Type **1972** 40 10
2804 29 c. Treating the wounded 40 10
2805 29 c. Allied attack on Sicily 40 10
2806 29 c. "B-24"s bombing Ploesti refineries .. 40 10
2807 29 c. G.I.s with mail from home 40 10
2808 29 c. Allied invasion of Italy 40 10
2809 29 c. War savings stamps and bonds 40 10
2810 29 c. Willie and Joe (cartoon characters) .. 40 10
2811 29 c. Gold Star emblem 40 10
2812 29 c. Marine assault on Tarawa, Gilbert Islands 40 10

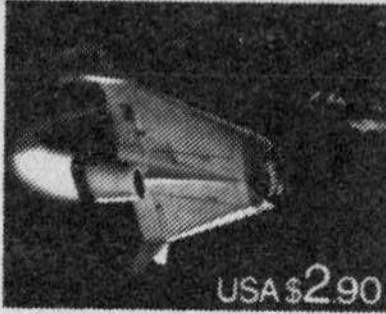

1982 Futuristic Space Shuttle

1993.
2813 1982 $2.90 multicoloured 3·75 1·50

1983 Hank Williams

1993. Country Music. Multicoloured. (a) No frame.
2815 29 c. Type **1983** 40 10
2816 29 c. Patsy Cline .. 40 10
2817 29 c. Carter Family .. 40 10
2818 29 c. Bob Wills 40 10
(b) With frame.
2819 29 c. Type **1983** 40 10
2820 29 c. Carter Family .. 40 10
2821 29 c. Patsy Cline .. 40 10
2822 29 c. Bob Wills 40 10

1987 Elvis Presley
1994 Louis

1993. Rock and Rhythm and Blues Music. Multicoloured. (a) No frame.
2823 29 c. Type **1987** 40 10
2824 29 c. Buddy Holly .. 40 10
2825 29 c. Ritchie Valens .. 40 10
2826 29 c. Bill Haley 40 10
2827 29 c. Dinah Washington 40 10
2828 29 c. Otis Redding .. 40 10
2829 29 c. Clyde McPhatter .. 40 10
(b) With frame.
2830 29 c. Type **1987** 40 10
2831 29 c. Bill Haley 40 10
2832 29 c. Clyde McPhatter .. 40 10
2833 29 c. Ritchie Valens .. 40 10
2834 29 c. Otis Redding .. 40 10
2835 29 c. Buddy Holly .. 40 10
2836 29 c. Dinah Washington 40 10

1993. Joe Louis (boxer).
2837 1994 29 c. multicoloured .. 40 10

1995 Red Squirrel
1996 Benjamin Franklin, Liberty Hall, Philadelphia, Post Rider and Printing Press

1993. Self-adhesive. Imperf.
2838 1995 29 c. multicoloured .. 40 10

1993. Inauguration of National Postal Museum, Washington. Multicoloured.
2840 29 c. Type **1996** 40 10
2841 29 c. Pony Express rider, Civil War soldier and stagecoach 40 10
2842 29 c. "Jenny" biplane, pilot, railway mail carriage and mail truck 40 10
2843 29 c. Gold rush miner's letter and stamps .. 40 10

2000 Rose
2001 Mother signing "I Love You"

1993. Self-adhesive. Imperf.
2844 2000 29 c. multicoloured .. 40 10

1993. Deaf Communication. Multicoloured.
2845 29 c. Type **2001** 40 10
2846 29 c. "I Love You" in sign language 40 10

2003 African Violet

1993.
2847 2003 29 c. multicoloured .. 40 10

2004 "Madonna and Child in a Landscape" (Giovanni Battista Cima de Conegliano)
2005 Snowman

1993. Christmas.
(a) Type **2004**
2848 29 c. multicoloured 40 10
(b) As T **2005**. Multicoloured. Perf or imperf (self-adhesive).
2849 29 c. Type **2005** 40 10
2850 29 c. Toy soldier .. 40 10
2851 29 c. Jack-in-the-box .. 40 10
2852 29 c. Reindeer 40 10
All designs come in more than one version which differ slightly in size.

2009 "Rebecca of Sunnybrook Farm" (Kate Douglas Wiggin)

1993. Classic Children's Books. Mult.
2863 29 c. Type **2009** 40 10
2864 29 c. "Little House on the Prairie" (Laura Ingalls Wilder) 40 10
2865 29 c. "The Adventures of Huckleberry Finn" (Mark Twain) 40 10
2866 29 c. "Little Women" (Louisa May Alcott) .. 40 10

2013 Latte Stones and Flag
2014 Pine Cone

1993. 15th Anniv of Commonwealth of Northern Mariana Islands.
2867 2013 29 c. multicoloured .. 40 10

1993. Self-adhesive. Imperf.
2868 2014 29 c. red, green & blk 40 10

2015 Caravels off Puerto Rico

2016 Emblem

1993. 500th Anniv of Columbus's Landing at Puerto Rica.

2869	**2015**	29 c. multicoloured ..	40	10

1993. World AIDS Day.

2870	**2016**	29 c. red and black ..	40	10

2017 Skiing

2022 Murrow

1994. Winter Olympic Games, Lillehammer. Multicoloured.

2872	29 c. Type **2017**	40	10
2873	29 c. Luge	40	10
2874	29 c. Ice dancing ..	40	10
2875	29 c. Cross-country skiing	40	10
2876	29 c. Ice hockey	40	10

1994. 29th Death Anniv of Edward Murrow (radio and television journalist).

2877	**2022**	29 c. brown	40	10

2023 Heart-shaped Sun

BLACK HERITAGE

2024 Davis

1994. Greetings Stamp. Self-adhesive. Imperf.

2878	**2023**	29 c. multicoloured ..	40	10

1994. Black Heritage. Dr. Allison Davis (educationist).

2879	**2024**	29 c. sepia and brown	40	10

2025 Eagle

2026 Pekinese

1994. Self-adhesive. Imperf.

2880	**2025**	29 c. multicoloured ..	40	10

1994. New Year.

2881	**2026**	29 c. multicoloured ..	40	10

ADD.
Aug'94
Feb'95
Mar'95
Apr'95

CERTIFIED MAIL

C 524. Postman.

1955.

C 1070.	C **524.**	15 c. red	35	25

NEWSPAPER STAMPS

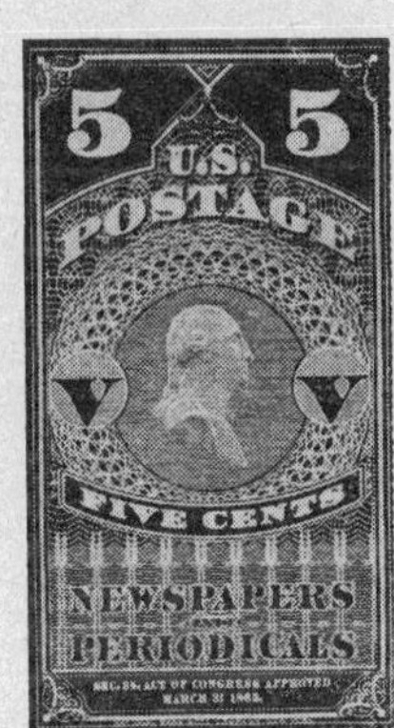

N 21 Washington
(½-size illustration)

1865. 5 c. with coloured or white border.

N78a	N **21**	5 c. blue	22·00	18·00
N80	–	10 c. green ..	25·00	
N81	–	25 c. red	48·00	

DESIGNS: 10 c. Franklin. 25 c. Lincoln.

N 42 "Freedom"

N 87 "Freedom"

1875. Different Frames.

N252	N **42**	1 c. black	5·50	3·00
N291	N **87**	1 c. black	2·25	1·75
N228	N **42**	2 c. black	4·00	3·00
N292	N **87**	2 c. black	2·50	1·25
N229	N **42**	3 c. black	5·00	3·25
N230		4 c. black	5·50	3·25
N293	N **87**	5 c. black	4·00	3·00
N231	N **42**	6 c. black	10·00	7·00
N232		8 c. black	10·00	7·00
N185		9 c. black	42·00	38·00
N233		10 c. black ..	10·00	6·00
N294	N **87**	10 c. black ..	2·50	1·75
N253	A	12 c. red	19·00	8·50
N254		24 c. red	22·00	10·00
N295		25 c. red	5·50	5·50
N255		36 c. red	30·00	12·00
N256		48 c. red	42·00	20·00
N296		50 c. red	6·50	8·00
N191		60 c. red	55·00	30·00
N258		72 c. red	70·00	32·00
N240		84 c. red	£120	60·00
N241		96 c. red	75·00	42·00
N242	–	$1. 92 brown ..	60·00	38·00
N297	–	$2 red	7·50	11·00
N243	–	$3 red	60·00	38·00
N298	–	$5 blue	13·00	18·00
N244	–	$6 blue	£110	65·00
N245	–	$9 orange ..	75·00	42·00
N299	–	$10 green	12·00	18·00
N246	–	$12 green	£110	55·00
N300	–	$20 black	13·00	19·00
N247	–	$24 purple ..	£140	75·00
N248	–	$36 red	£180	90·00
N249	–	$48 brown ..	£225	£120
N301	–	$50 red	16·00	22·00
N250	–	$60 violet ..	£225	£120
N302	–	$100 violet ..	18·00	27·00

DESIGNS: A, Astraea or "Justice"; $1.92, Ceres; $2, $3, "Victory"; $5, $6, Clio; $9, Mineva; $10, $12, Vesta; $20, $24, "Peace"; $36, $50, "Commerce"; $48, Heba; $60, $100, Minnehaha.

OFFICIAL STAMPS

For list of stamps used on correspondence from individual Government Departments, between 1873 and 1879, see the Stanley Gibbons' Part 22 (U.S.A.) Catalogue.

O **1315.** Eagle.

O **1438.**

O **1588.**

1983.

O2008	O **1315**	1 c. blue, red and black ..	10	10
O2009		4 c. blue, red and black ..	10	15
O2010		13 c. blue, red and black ..	15	45
O2011		14 c. blue, red and black ..	25	50
O2012		17 c. blue, red and black ..	25	30
O2015		20 c. blue, red and black ..	1·75	65
O2016		22 c. blue, red and black ..	55	50
O2013		$1 blue, red and black ..	1·50	70
O2014		$5 blue, red and black ..	6·00	4·00

1985. No value expressed.

(a) Inscr. "Postal Card Rate D".

O 2140	(14 c.) blue, red & black	3·00	70

(b) Inscr. "Domestic Letter Rate D".

O 2141	(22 c.) blue, red & black	2·75	70

1988. No value expressed.

O2344	O **1588**	(25 c.) blue, black and red	35	15

O **1592.**

O **1793**

1988.

O2348	O **1592**	1 c. bl, blk & red	10	10
O2349		4 c. bl, blk & red	10	10
O2350		10 c. blue, black and red ..	10	10
O2354		15 c. blue, black and red ..	25	10
O2351		19 c. blue, black and red ..	25	35
O2355		20 c. blue, black and red ..	30	10
O2352		23 c. blue, black and red ..	30	15
O2356		25 c. blue, black and red ..	35	10
O2357		29 c. blue, black and red ..	40	15
O2353		$1 bl, blk & red	1·25	25

The 10 c. and $1 have an additional inscription ("USA1993" repeated several times) above the face value.

1991. No value expressed.

O2558	O **1793**	(29 c.) blue, black & red ..	40	15

PARCEL POST STAMPS

P **134.** Post Office Clerk.

1912.

P 423.	P **134.**	1 c. red	2·75	80
P 424.	–	2 c. red	2·75	50
P 425.	–	3 c. red	11·00	4·50
P 426.	–	4 c. red	20·00	1·50
P 427.	–	5 c. red	35·00	1·25
P 428.	–	10 c. red	40·00	1·50
P 429.	–	15 c. red	50·00	7·00
P 430.	–	20 c. red	85·00	13·00
P 431.	–	25 c. red	75·00	4·25
P 432.	–	50 c. red	£180	28·00
P 433.	–	75 c. red	50·00	20·00
P 434.	–	$1 red	£250	16·00

DESIGNS: 2 c. City carrier. 3 c. Railway postal clerk. 4 c. Rural carrier. 5 c. Steam mail train. 10 c. "Kronprinz Wilhelm" (liner) and mail tender. 15 c. Automobile service. 20 c. Airplane carrying mail. 25 c. Manufacturing (Pullman works). 50 c. Dairying. 75 c. Harvesting. $1 Fruit growing.

PARCEL POST POSTAGE DUE STAMPS

PD **134.**

1912.

PD 423.	PD **134.**	1 c. green ..	6·50	2·50
PD 424.		2 c. green ..	50·00	12·00
PD 425.		5 c. green ..	8·00	2·50
PD 426.		10 c. green ..	£120	28·00
PD 427.		25 c. green ..	55·00	2·75

POSTAGE DUE STAMPS

D **43.**

D **87.**

1879.

D207	D **43**	1 c. brown ..	18·00	3·50
D222		2 c. brown ..	28·00	1·50
D209		3 c. brown ..	16·00	1·75
D224		5 c. brown ..	£180	7·50
D225		10 c. brown ..	£160	4·50
D226		30 c. brown ..	75·00	16·00
D213		50 c. brown ..	£170	26·00

1891.

D 235.	D **43.**	1 c. red	8·50	35
D 236.		2 c. red	11·00	30
D 237.		3 c. red	24·00	2·50
D 238.		5 c. red	26·00	2·50
D 239.		10 c. red	48·00	6·50
D 240.		30 c. red	£180	60·00
D 241.		50 c. red	£200	65·00

1894.

D 529.	D **87.**	½ c. red	40	10
D 530.		1 c. red	1·25	10
D 531.		2 c. red	1·00	10
D 532.		3 c. red	6·00	10
D 533.		5 c. red	6·00	10
D 534a		10 c. red	9·00	10
D 535a		30 c. red	38·00	30
D 536		50 c. red	60·00	10

D **201.** D **202.**

D **581.**

1931.

D 702	D **201.**	½ c. red	75	10
D 703		1 c. red	15	10
D 704		2 c. red	20	10
D 705		3 c. red	25	10
D 706		5 c. red	35	10
D 707		10 c. red	1·10	10
D 708		30 c. red	8·00	10
D 709		50 c. red	8·50	10
D 699a	D **202.**	$1 red	22·00	10
D 700a		$5 red	32·00	15

1959. Centres in black.

D 1130	D **581**	½ c. red ..	1·25	1·25
D 1131		1 c. red ..	15	10
D 1132		2 c. red ..	15	10
D 1133		3 c. red ..	15	10
D 1134		4 c. red ..	15	10
D 1135		5 c. red ..	15	10
D 1136		6 c. red ..	15	10
D 1137		7 c. red ..	15	10
D 1138		8 c. red ..	15	10
D 1139		10 c. red ..	15	10
D 1140		11 c. red ..	25	15
D 1141		13 c. red ..	25	15
D 1142		17 c. red ..	30	25
D 1143		30 c. red ..	50	10
D 1144		50 c. red ..	75	10
D 1145		$1 red	1·60	10
D 1146		$5 red	7·50	15

In the dollar values the numerals are double-lined and vertical.

REGISTERED LETTER STAMP

R **133.** American Bald Eagle.

1911.

R 404.	R **133.**	10 c. blue	75·00	3·00

SPECIAL DELIVERY AIR STAMPS

AE 247. Great Seal of U.S.A.

1934.

AE 750.	AE 247.	16 c. blue ..	60	70
AE 751.		16 c. blue & red	40	15

SPECIAL DELIVERY STAMPS

E 46. Messenger Running.

1885. Inscr "AT A SPECIAL DELIVERY OFFICE".

E 217.	E 46.	10 c. blue	£160	20·00

1888. As Type E 46. but inscr. "AT ANY POST OFFICE".

E 283	E 46.	10 c. blue	90·00	1·75
E 251		10 c. orange ..	£110	8·50

E 117. Messenger on Bicycle.

1917.

E 529.	E 117.	10 c. blue ..	11·00	15

E 129. Hat of Mercury and Olive-branch.

E 143. Delivery by Motor Cycle.

1908.

E 374.	E 129.	10 c. green ..	48·00	20·00

1922.

E 648	E 143	10 c. blue ..	60	10
E 648a		10 c. violet ..	60	10
E 649		13 c. blue ..	45	10
E 650		15 c. orange ..	65	10
E 651		17 c. yellow ..	3·00	2·75

E 144. Delivery by Van.

1925.

E652	E 144	20 c. black ..	1·50	10

E 520. Delivery by Hand.

1954.

E 1066.	E 520.	20 c. blue ..	60	10
E 1067.		30 c. lake ..	70	10

E 799. Arrows.

1969.

E 1374.	E 799.	45 c. red & blue	1·40	15
E 1375.		60 c. blue & red	1·40	10

SPECIAL HANDLING STAMPS

SH 173.

1925.

SH 624	SH 173.	10 c. green ..	1·00	80
SH 625		15 c. green ..	1·10	80
SH 626		20 c. green ..	1·50	25
SH 628		25 c. green ..	16·00	6·00

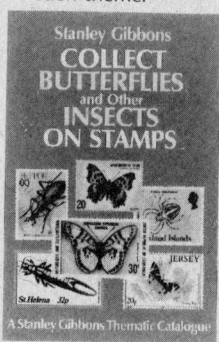

UNITED STATES POSTAL AGENCY IN SHANGHAI Pt. 17

These stamps were valid for use on mail despatched from the U.S. Postal Agency in Shanghai to addresses in the United States. This agency was closed 31st December 1922.

100 cents = 1 dollar (Chinese).

1919. United States stamps of 1908–12 surch **SHANGHAI CHINA** and new value.

1	**128**	2 c. on 1 c. green	13·00	16·00
17		2 Cts. on 1 c. green ..	75·00	80·00
2		4 c. on 2 c. pink ..	13·00	16·00
18		4 Cts. on 2 c. red ..	75·00	75·00
3		6 c. on 3 c. violet ..	25·00	38·00
4		8 c. on 4 c. brown ..	28·00	38·00
5		10 c. on 5 c. blue ..	32·00	40·00
6		12 c. on 6 c. orange ..	42·00	55·00
7		14 c. on 7 c. black ..	45·00	60·00
8	**133**	16 c. on 8 c. olive ..	32·00	40·00
9		18 c. on 9 c. orange ..	32·00	40·00
10		20 c. on 10 c. yellow ..	30·00	40·00
11a		24 c. on 12 c. red ..	38·00	50·00
12		30 c. on 15 c. grey ..	45·00	60·00
13		40 c. on 20 c. blue ..	75·00	95·00
14		60 c. on 30 c. red ..	70·00	90·00
15		$1 on 50 c. lilac ..	£500	£400
16		$2 on $1 black ..	£325	£325

UPPER SENEGAL AND NIGER Pt. 6

A French Colony in W. Africa, E. of Senegal, formerly called Senegambia and Niger, and became part of French Sudan in 1920.

1906. "Faidherbe", "Palms" and "Balay" key-types inscr "HT-SENEGAL-NIGER" in blue (10, 40 c., 5 f.) or red (others).

35.	I.	1 c. grey	50	60
36.		2 c. brown	50	65
37.		4 c. brown on blue ..	70	70
38.		5 c. green	2·50	1·25
39.		10 c. red	2·50	95
40.		15 c. violet	3·25	2·25
41.	J.	20 c. black on blue ..	1·00	2·25
42.		25 c. blue	6·50	4·50
43.		30 c. brown on pink ..	2·75	4·00
44.		35 c. black on yellow ..	2·50	1·75
45.		40 c. red on blue ..	4·00	4·00
46.		45 c. brown on green ..	4·75	5·25
47.		50 c. violet	4·50	4·00
48.		75 c. green on orange ..	5·00	5·50
49.	K.	1 f. black on blue ..	10·00	10·00
50.		2 f. blue on red	30·00	30·00
51.		5 f. red on yellow ..	50·00	60·00

7. Touareg.

1914.

59	**7**	1 c. violet and purple ..	10	25
60		2 c. purple and grey ..	10	25
61		4 c. blue and black ..	10	25
62		5 c. green and light green	10	25
63		10 c. carmine and red ..	10	90
64		15 c. yellow and brown ..	25	60
65		20 c. black and purple ..	30	70
66		25 c. blue and ultramarine	40	80
67		30 c. chocolate and brown	40	80
68		35 c. violet and red ..	30	1·00
69		40 c. red and grey ..	80	85
70		45 c. brown and blue ..	30	65
71		50 c. green and black ..	50	75
72		75 c. brown and yellow ..	40	85
73		1 f. purple and brown ..	1·40	1·75
74		2 f. blue and green ..	60	1·40
75		5 f. black and violet ..	6·75	4·75

1915. Red Cross. Surch **5c** and red cross.

76	**7**	10 c. + 5 c. carmine and red	50	55

POSTAGE DUE STAMPS

1906. "Natives" key-type inscr "HT-SENEGAL-NIGER".

D52	L	5 c. green and red ..	1·25	1·25
D53		10 c. purple and blue	3·75	3·00
D54		15 c. blue & red on blue	5·50	4·75
D55		20 c. black & red on yell	6·00	3·25
D56		50 c. violet and red ..	15·00	11·00
D57		60 c. black & red on buff	9·75	9·00
D58		1 f. black & red on flesh	25·00	18·00

1915. "Figures" key-type inscr. "HT. SENEGAL-NIGER".

D 77.	M.	5 c. green	60	70
D 78.		10 c. red	60	70
D 79.		15 c. grey	65	70
D 80.		20 c. brown	65	70
D 81.		30 c. blue	1·25	1·50
D 82.		50 c. black	1·00	1·25
D 83.		60 c. orange	3·00	3·25
D 84.		1 f. violet	2·25	3·00

For later issues see **FRENCH SUDAN**.

UPPER SILESIA Pt. 7

Stamps issued during a Plebiscite held in 1921 to decide the future of the district.

100 pfenning = 1 mark.

1. 9. Coal-mine in Silesia.

1920.

1.	**1.**	2½ f. grey	35	50
2.		3 pf. brown	30	65
3.		5 pf. green	15	25
4.		10 pf. brown	15	30
5.		15 pf. violet	15	25
6.		20 pf. blue	15	25
7.		50 pf. brown	3·50	4·75
8.		1 m. red	3·50	6·50
9.		5 m. orange	3·50	6·50

1920. Surch.

10.	**1.**	5 pf. on 15 pf. violet ..	6·50	18·00
12.		5 pf. on 20 pf. blue ..	10	15
14.		10 pf. on 20 pf. blue ..	10	10
17.		50 pf. on 5 m. orange ..	10·00	22·00

1920.

19.	**9.**	2½ pf. grey	15	10
20.		3 pf. red	20	10
21.		5 pf. green	10	10
22.		10 pf. red	10	10
23.		15 pf. violet	10	10
24.		20 pf. blue	10	10
25.		25 pf. brown	15	10
26.		30 pf. yellow	10	10
27.		40 pf. olive	10	10

Same design, but larger.

28.	**9.**	50 pf. grey	10	10
29.		60 pf. blue	20	15
30.		75 pf. green	60	40
31.		80 pf. red	50	40
32.		1 m. purple	30	15
33.		2 m. brown	30	30
34.		3 m. violet	50	30
35.		5 m. orange	1·10	85

1921. Optd. **Plebiscite 20 mars 1921.**

36.	**9.**	10 pf. red	1·50	5·50
37.		15 pf. violet	1·50	5·50
38.		20 pf. blue	1·50	7·00
39.		25 pf. brown	4·25	12·00
40.		30 pf. yellow	4·25	12·00
41.		40 pf. olive	4·25	14·00
42.		50 pf. grey	4·00	16·00
43.		60 pf. blue	5·50	14·00
44.		75 pf. green	5·50	17·00
45.		80 pf. red	6·00	22·00
46.		1 m. purple	10·00	38·00

1922. As last, new colours, surch.

47.	**9.**	4 m. on 60 pf. green ..	45	85
48.		10 m. on 75 pf. red ..	70	1·50
49.		20 m. on 80 pf. orange ..	3·50	9·00

OFFICIAL STAMPS

1920. Official stamps of Germany (Types as O 31 and O 32 with figures "21" in corners) optd. **C.G.H.S.**

O 25.	5 pf. green	15	25
O 26.	10 pf. red	15	25
O 27.	15 pf. brown	15	25
O 28.	20 pf. blue	15	25
O 29.	30 pf. orange on buff ..	15	25
O 30.	50 pf. violet on buff ..	30	50
O 31.	1 m. red on buff ..	4·25	7·00

1920. Official stamps of Germany, without figs. "21" in corners, optd. **C.G.H.S.**

O 32.	5 pf. green	55	1·75
O 33.	10 pf. red	10	10
O 34.	15 pf. purple	10	10
O 35.	20 pf. blue	10	10
O 36.	30 pf. orange on buff ..	10	10
O 37.	40 pf. red	10	10
O 38.	50 pf. violet on buff ..	10	10
O 39.	60 pf. brown	10	10
O 40.	1 m. red on buff ..	10	10
O 41.	1 m. 25 blue on yellow ..	10	10
O 43.	2 m. blue	10	20
O 44.	5 m. brown on yellow ..	10	20

UPPER VOLTA Pt. 6; Pt. 14

Formerly part of Upper Senegal and Niger, Upper Volta was created a separate colony in 1919. In 1932 it was divided among French Sudan, Ivory Coast and Niger but was reconstituted as a separate territory in 1947 from when it used the stamps of French West Africa.

In 1958 it became an autonomous republic within the French Community and attained full independence in 1960.

In 1984 the name of the state was changed to Burkina Faso.

100 centimes = 1 franc.

1920. Stamps of Upper Senegal and Niger optd **HAUTE-VOLTA**.

1	**7**	1 c. violet and purple	10	30
2		2 c. purple and grey	10	30
3		4 c. blue and black	10	30
4		5 c. green and light green	30	65
18		5 c. chocolate and brown	10	30
5		10 c. carmine and red ..	35	65
19		10 c. green & light green	15	30
20		10 c. blue and mauve ..	25	55
6		15 c. yellow and brown ..	35	65
7		20 c. black and purple ..	50	1·00
8		25 c. blue & ultramarine	60	1·00
21		25 c. green and black ..	45	75
9		30 c. chocolate and brown	1·10	1·50
22		30 c. carmine and red ..	40	80
23		30 c. red and violet ..	40	80
23a		30 c. turquoise and green	60	1·00
10		35 c. violet and red ..	45	95
11		40 c. red and grey ..	45	1·00
12		45 c. brown and blue ..	35	85
13		50 c. green and black ..	1·50	3·00
24		50 c. blue & ultramarine	20	45
25		50 c. blue and orange ..	35	80
26		60 c. red	20	40
26a		65 c. blue and brown ..	65	1·25
14		75 c. brown and yellow ..	70	1·50
15		1 f. purple and brown ..	70	1·25
16		2 f. blue and green ..	90	1·75
17		5 f. black and violet ..	2·00	3·00

1922. Surch in figures and bars.

27	**7**	0,01 on 15 c. yellow & brn	45	1·00
28		0,02 on 15 c. yellow & brn	45	1·00
29		0,05 on 15 c. yellow & brn	45	1·00
30		25 c. on 2 f. blue & green	50	1·00
31		25 c. on 5 f. black & vio	50	1·00
32		60 on 75 c. violet on pink	35	75
33		65 on 45 c. brown & blue	50	1·00
34		85 on 75 c. brown & yell	70	1·40
35		90 c. on 75 c. pink & red	90	1·75
36		1 f. 25 on 1 f. lt blue & bl	45	1·00
37		1 f. 50 on 1 f. ultram & bl	1·25	2·00
37a		3 f. on 5 f. brown & pink	1·75	2·75
38		10 f. on 5 f. pink & green	7·75	10·00
39		20 f. on 5 f. violet & brn	10·00	15·00

3. Hausa Man. 5. Hausa Warrior.

1928.

40	**3**	1 c. blue and green ..	10	35
41		2 c. brown and mauve ..	10	35
42		4 c. black and yellow ..	15	35
43		5 c. indigo and blue ..	20	40
44		10 c. blue and pink ..	50	1·00
45		15 c. brown and blue ..	95	1·50
46		20 c. brown and green ..	95	1·50
47	–	25 c. brown and yellow ..	1·00	1·40
48	–	30 c. deep green and green	1·00	1·60
49	–	40 c. black and pink ..	1·00	1·90
50	–	45 c. brown and blue ..	1·25	2·00
51	–	50 c. black and green ..	1·25	1·40
52	–	65 c. indigo and blue ..	1·50	2·00
53	–	75 c. black and mauve ..	1·25	2·00
54	–	90 c. red and mauve ..	1·25	2·00
55	**5**	1 f. brown and green ..	1·10	1·90
56		1 f. 10 blue and mauve ..	1·25	1·90
57		1 f. 50 blue	1·90	3·00
58		2 f. black and blue ..	2·00	3·00
59		3 f. brown and yellow ..	2·25	3·50
60		5 f. brown and mauve ..	2·25	3·50
61		10 f. black and green ..	8·25	12·00
62		20 f. black and pink ..	14·00	18·00

DESIGN—VERT. 25 c. to 90 c. Hausa woman.

1931. "Colonial Exhibition" key-types inscr "HAUTE-VOLTA".

63	E	40 c. green and black ..	1·75	3·00
64	F	50 c. mauve and black ..	1·75	3·00
65	G	90 c. red and black ..	1·75	3·00
66	B	1 f. 50 blue and black ..	2·75	4·25

6. President Coulibaly. 7. Antelope Mask. 8. President Yameogo.

1959. 1st Anniv. of Republic.

67.	**6.**	25 f. purple and black ..	30	20

1960. Animal Masks.

68.	**7.**	30 c. violet and red ..	10	10
69.		40 c. purple and ochre ..	10	10
70.		50 c. olive and turquoise ..	10	10
71.	–	1 f. black, brown and red	10	10
72.	–	2 f. multicoloured ..	10	10
73.	–	4 f. black, violet and blue	10	10
74.	–	5 f. red, brown and bistre	15	10
75.	–	6 f. purple and turquoise ..	15	10
76.	–	8 f. brown and red ..	20	15
77.	–	10 f. purple and green ..	25	20
78.	–	15 f. blue, brown and red	35	25
79.	–	20 f. green and blue ..	40	30
80.	–	25 f. purple, green & blue	50	30
81.	–	30 f. black, brown & turq.	65	30
82.	–	40 f. black, red and blue ..	90	40
83.	–	50 f. brn., grn. & mauve	1·10	45
84.	–	60 f. blue and brown ..	1·25	45
85.	–	85 f. blue and turquoise ..	2·00	60

MASKS: 1 f. to 4 f. Wart-hog. 5 f. to 8 f. Monkey. 10 f. to 20 f. Buffalo. 25 f. Antelope. 30 f. to 50 f. Elephant. 60 f., 85 f. Secretary bird.

1960.

86.	**8.**	25 f. purple and grey ..	50	25

1960. 10th Anniv. of African Technical Co-operation Commission. As T 4 of Malagasy Republic.

87.		25 f. indigo and blue ..	50	40

1960. 1st Anniv. of Conseil de l'Entente. As T 9 of Niger.

88.		25 f. multicoloured	65	40

9.

1960. Proclamation of Independence.

89.	**9.**	25 f. brown, red and black	55	40

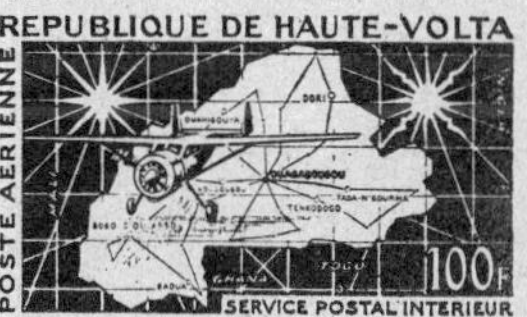

10. Aircraft and Map.

1961. Air.

90.	**10.**	100 f. blue, green and red	1·90	80
91.	–	200 f. brown, red & green	4·75	1·40
92.	–	500 f. multicoloured ..	11·00	5·00

DESIGNS: 200 f. Scene at Ouagadougou Airport. 500 f. Aerial view of Champs Elysees, Ouagadougou.

11. W.M.O. Emblem, Sun and Meteorological Instruments.

1961. 1st World Meteorological Day.

93.	**11.**	25 f. red, blue and black ..	55	35

12. Arms of Republic.

1961. Independence Festival.

94.	**12.**	25 f. multicoloured ..	45	30

1962. Air. "Air Afrique" Airline. As T 42 of Mauritania.

95.		25 f. mauve, green & purple	55	30

13. W.M.O. Emblem, Weather Station and Crops.

1962. World Meteorological Day.

96.	**13.**	25 f. blue, green and black	55	40

1962. Malaria Eradication. As T 43 of Mauritania.

97.		25 f. + 5 f. red	70	

14. Nurse and Hospital.

1962. Establishment of Red Cross in Upper Volta.
98. **14.** 25 f. brown, blue & red 60 40

15. African Buffalo at Water-hole.

DESIGNS—VERT. 15 f. Waterbuck. 85 f. Kob. HORIZ. 10 f. Lion and lioness. 25 f. Arly Camp. 50 f. Diapaga Camp.

1962. Hunting and Tourism.
99. **15.** 5 f. green, blue & sepia 35 20
100. – 10 f. green, yell. & brn. 45 35
101. – 15 f. green, yell. & brn. 1·10 60
102. – 25 f. grn., blue & mauve 1·10 60
103. – 50 f. grn., blue & mauve 1·60 1·40
104. – 85 f. grn., blue & brown 3·75 2·40

1962. Abidjan Games, 1961. As T **13** of Niger Republic. Multicoloured.
105. 20 f. Football 45 30
106. 25 f. Cycling 65 35
107. 85 f. Boating .. .. 1·40 70

1962. 1st Anniv. of Union of African and Malagasy States. As T **45** of Mauritania.
108. **72.** 30 f. multicoloured .. 1·10 75

16. Flag and U.N. Emblem.

1962. Air. Admission to U.N. 2nd Anniv.
109. **16.** 50 f. multicoloured .. 65 35
110. 100 f. multicoloured .. 1·40 65

17. G.P.O., Ouagadougou.

1962. Air. Opening of Ouagadougou P.O.
111. **17.** 100 f. multicoloured .. 1·40 60

1963. Freedom from Hunger. As T **51** of Mauritania.
112. 25 f.+5 f. bl., brn. & myrtle 70 70

18. Rainfall Map.

20. "Argyreia nervosa". **19.** Basketball.

1963. World Meteorological Day.
113. **18.** 70 c. multicoloured .. 85 55

1963. Dakar Games. Centres in black and red.
114. **19.** 20 f. violet 35 20
115. – 25 f. ochre (Discus) .. 45 20
116. – 50 f. blue (Judo) .. 90 40

1963. Flowers. Multicoloured.
117. 50 c. "Hibiscus rosa sinensis" 10 10
118. 1 f. "Oldenandia grandiflora" .. 10 10
119. 1 f. 50 "Portulaca grandiflora" 10 10
120. 2 f. "Nicotiana tabacum" 10 10
121. 4 f. "Ipomaea stolonifera" 15 10
122. 5 f. "Striga senegalensis" 15 10
123. 6 f. "Vigna" 20 10
124. 8 f. "Lepidagathis heudelotiana" 30 20
125. 10 f. "Euphorbia splendens" 30 15
126. 15 f. "Hippeastrum equestre" 40 30
127. 25 f. Type **20** 55 30
128. 30 f. "Quisqualis indica" 70 35
129. 40 f. "Nymphea lotus" .. 1·25 50
130. 50 f. "Plumeria alba" .. 1·40 55
131. 60 f. "Crotalaria retusa" 1·75 80
132. 85 f. "Hibiscus esculentus" 2·40 1·10
The 50 c. to 10 f. are vert.

21. Jetliner in Flight.

1963. Air. 1st Jet-flight, Ouagadougou-Paris.
133. **21.** 200 f. multicoloured .. 4·25 1·25

1963. Air. African and Malagasy Post and Telecommunications Union. As T **56** of Mauritania.
134. 85 f. multicoloured .. 1·25 60

22. Centenary Emblem and Globe. **24.** "Declaration universelle . . .".

1963. Red Cross Centenary.
135. **22.** 25 f. multicoloured .. 90 65

1963. Air. "Air Afrique". 1st Anniv. Surch. **AIR AFRIQUE 19-11-63 50F.**
136. **21.** 50 f. on 200 f. mult. .. 1·10 65

1963. Declaration of Human Rights. 15th Anniv.
137. **24.** 25 f. multicoloured .. 60 40

25. "Europafrique".

26. "Telecommunications".

28. Barograph, Landscape and W.M.O. Emblem. **27.** Rameses II, Abu Simbel.

1964. Air. "Europafrique".
138. **25.** 50 f. multicoloured .. 1·25 70

1964. Admission of Upper Volta to I.T.U.
139. **26.** 25 f. multicoloured .. 45 30

1964. Air. Nubian Monuments Preservation.
140. **27.** 25 f. purple and green .. 65 45
141. 100 f. brown and blue .. 2·25 1·75

1964. World Meteorological Day.
142. **28.** 50 f. mauve, blue & grn. 85 55

29. Dove and Letters.

1964. 1st Anniv. of Admission to U.P.U.
143. **29.** 25 f. sepia and blue .. 45 30
144. – 60 f. sepia and orange .. 90 65
DESIGN: 60 f. Aircraft and letters.

30. Head of Athlete (bronze). **31.** Symbols of Solar Research.

1964. Air. Olympic Games, Tokyo.
145. **30.** 15 f. green, red & sepia 35 15
146. – 25 f. green, red & sepia 50 20
147. – 85 f. green, red & brown 1·10 70
148. – 100 f. choc., red & brn. 1·60 85
DESIGNS: 25 f. Seated athlete (bronze). 85 f. "Victorious athlete" (bronze). 100 f. Venus de Milo.

1964. Int. Quiet Sun Years.
149. **31.** 30 f. red, ochre & green 60 40

32. Grey Woodpecker. **33.** President Kennedy.

1964. Air.
150. **32.** 250 f. multicoloured .. 7·25 4·00

1964. French, African and Malagasy Co-operation. As T **68** of Mauritania.
151. 70 f. brown, red and blue 1·00 55

1964. Air. Pres. Kennedy Commem.
152. **33.** 100 f. multicoloured .. 1·60 1·10

34. Independence Hotel. **35.** Pygmy Sunbird.

1964. Opening of Independence Hotel, Ouagadougou.
153. **34.** 25 f. multicoloured .. 1·75 65

1965. Birds. Multicoloured.
154. 10 f. Type **35** (postage) .. 1·60 55
155. 15 f. Olive-bellied Sunbird 1·75 75
156. 20 f. Splendid Sunbird .. 3·00 1·10
157. 500 f. Abyssinian Roller (27 × 48 mm.) (air) .. 35·00 11·00

36. Sun and Emblems.

1965. Air. World Meteorological Day.
158. **36.** 50 f. multicoloured .. 85 35

37. Grand Cascade, Banfora.

1965. Banfora Waterfalls.
159. – 5 f. brown, blue & green 15 10
160. **37.** 25 f. blue, green & red 55 20
DESIGN—VERT. 5 f. Comoe Cascade.

38. Hughes Telegraph and Modern Telephone.

1965. Air. I.T.U. Cent.
161. **38.** 100 f. red, green & turq. 1·90 85

39. I.C.Y. Emblem.

1965. Air. Int. Co-operation Year.
162. **39.** 25 f. multicoloured .. 45 20
163. 100 f. multicoloured .. 1·25 50

40. Football, Boots and Net. **42.** "Early Bird" Satellite in Orbit.

41. Sacred Alligator of Sabou.

1965. 1st African Games, Brazzaville.
164. **40.** 15 f. green, red & purple 30 20
165. – 25 f. purple, orge. & blue 40 25
166. – 70 f. red and green .. 1·00 55
DESIGNS: 25 f. Boxing-gloves and ring. 70 f. Tennis-racquets, ball and net.

1965. Air. Fauna.
167. **41.** 60 f. grn., turq. & brown 2·25 65
168. – 85 f. brn., bistre & green 2·75 85
DESIGN—VERT. 85 f. Lion.

1965. Air. Space Telecommunications.
169. **42.** 30 f. red, brown and blue 55 30

43. Lincoln. **45.** Dromedary.

44. President Yameogo.

1965. Death Cent. of Abraham Lincoln.
170. **43.** 50 f. multicoloured .. 65 40

1965. Pres. Yameogo.
171. **44.** 25 f. multicoloured .. 45 20

1966. Insects and Fauna. Multicoloured.
172. 1 f. "Nemopistha imperatrix" (vert.) 10 10
173. 2 f. Python (vert.) .. 10 10
174. 3 f. "Sphodromantis lineola" 10 10
175. 4 f. "Staurocleis magnifica occidentalis" 15 10
176. 5 f. Warthog (vert.) .. 20 10
177. 6 f. "Pandinus imperator" 20 10
178. 8 f. Savanna monkey (vert.) 35 15
179. 10 f. Type **45** 35 20
180. 15 f. Leopard (vert.) .. 65 25
181. 20 f. African buffalo .. 90 30
182. 25 f. Pygmy hippopotamus (vert.) .. .. .. 1·00 35
183. 30 f. Agama (lizard) .. 70 35
184. 45 f. Viper (vert.) .. .. 1·40 40
185. 50 f. Chameleon (vert.) .. 1·75 55
186. 60 f. "Ugada limbata" (vert.) .. .. .. 2·25 80
187. 85 f. African elephant .. 2·40 1·00
The 1, 3, 4, 6 and 60 f. are Insects, the remainder are Fauna.

46. Communications Satellite. 47. Ritual Mask.

1966. Air. World Meteorological Day.
188. 46. 50 f. black, lake & blue 55 30

1966. World Festival of Negro Arts, Dakar. Multicoloured.
189. 20 f. Type 47 .. .. 40 15
190. 25 f. Plumed head-dress .. 45 20
191. 60 f. Dancer .. .. 1·10 40

48. Bobo-Dioulasso Mosque.

1966. Religious Buildings. Multicoloured.
192. 25 f. Type 48 .. .. 45 30
193. 25 f. Po Church 45 30

49. Satellite "FR 1" and Ouagadougou Tracking Station.

1966. Air. Inauguration of Ouagadougou Tracking Station.
194. 49. 250 f. lake, brn. and blue 4·00 1·90

50. W.H.O. Building.

1966. Air. Inauguration of W.H.O. Headquarters, Geneva.
195. 50. 100 f. black, blue & yell. 1·60 70

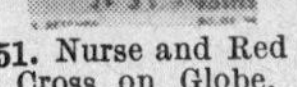

51. Nurse and Red Cross on Globe. 52. Scouts by Camp Fire.

1966. Red Cross.
196. 51. 25 f. multicoloured .. 55 30

1966. Scouting.
197. 52. 10 f. multicoloured .. 35 15
198. – 15 f. black, brown & buff 35 15
DESIGN: 15 f. Scouts on cliff.

53. Inoculating Cattle.

1966. Prevention of Cattle Plague Campaign.
199. 53. 25 f. black, yellow & blue 85 45

1966. Air. Inaug. of "DC-8" Air Services. As T 87 of Mauritania.
200. 25 f. olive, black and brown 55 35

54. Ploughing with Donkey.

1966. Rural Education (25 f.) and 3rd Anniv. of Kamboince Centre (30 f.). Multicoloured.
201. 25 f. Type 54 .. .. 40 20
202. 30 f. "Rotation of crops", Kamboince Centre .. 45 20

55. Sir Winston Churchill.

1966. Air. Churchill Commem.
203. 55. 100 f. green and red .. 1·60 65

56. Pope Paul and Dove over U.N. General Assembly Building.

1966. Air. Pope Paul's Peace Appeal before U.N.
204. 56. 100 f. violet and blue .. 1·60 65

57. U.N.E.S.C.O. Emblem.

1966. 20th Anniv. of U.N.E.S.C.O. and U.N.I.C.E.F.
205. 57. 50 f. red, blue & black.. 65 40
206. – 50 f. violet, purple & red 65 40
DESIGN: No. 206, U.N.I.C.E.F. emblem and child-care theme.

58. Arms of Upper Volta. 59. Man and Woman holding Emblems.

1967.
207. 58. 30 f. multicoloured .. 55 15

1967. Europafrique.
208. 59. 60 f. multicoloured .. 90 40

60. Acclaiming Lions Emblem.

1967. Air. 50th Anniv. of Lions Int.
209. 60. 100 f. ultram., bl. & brn. 1·60 65

61. W.M.O. Emblem and Landscape. 62. "Diamant" Rocket.

1967. Air. World Meteorological Day.
210. 61. 50 f. grn., turq. & blue 85 40

1967. Air. French Space Achievements.
211. 62. 5 f. green, orange & blue 15 10
212. – 20 f. lilac, purple & blue 40 15
213. – 30 f. green, blue and red 55 20
214. – 100 f. grn., violet & pur. 1·40 60
DESIGNS—HORIZ. 20 f. "FR–1" satellite. 100 f. "D1–D" satellite. VERT. 30 f. "D1–C" satellite.

63. Dr. Schweitzer and Organ Pipes. 64. Scout waving Hat.

1967. Air. 2nd Death Anniv. of Dr Albert Schweitzer.
215. 63. 250 f. black and purple 4·00 1·90

1967. World Scout Jamboree, Idaho. Mult.
216. 5 f. Type 64 (postage) .. 35 10
217. 20 f. Scouts' handclasp .. 80 45
218. 100 f. Jamboree emblem and world map (48 × 27 mm.) (air) .. .. 1·40 65

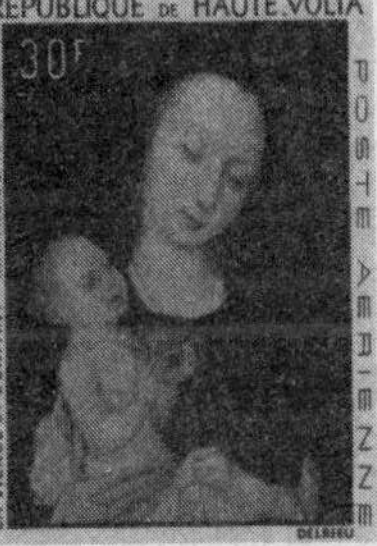

65. "Virgin and Child" (by 15th century master). 67. Postman on Cycle.

66. Bank Book and Coins.

1967. Air. Religious Paintings. Mult.
219. 30 f. Type 65 .. .. 50 30
220. 50 f. "The Deposition of Christ" (Dirk Bouts) .. 85 40
221. 100 f. "Christ giving Blessing" (Bellini) .. .. 1·40 80
222. 250 f. "The Evangelists" (Jordaens) .. .. 4·00 1·90
See also Nos. 237/40.

1967. National Savings Bank.
223. 66. 30 f. grn., brn. and orge. 45 20

1967. Air. 5th Anniv. of U.A.M.P.T. As T 101 of Mauritania.
224. 100 f. green, lake and blue 1·40 55

1967. Stamp Day
225. 67. 30 f. brown, green & blue 65 45

1967. 5th Anniv. of West African Monetary Union. As T 103 of Mauritania.
226. 30 f. violet and blue .. 30 15

68. "The Two Alps". 69. Human Rights Emblem.

1967. Winter Olympic Games, Grenoble (1968).
227. – 15 f. green, blue & brown 40 30
228. 68. 50 f. blue and green .. 70 40
229. – 100 f. green, blue & red 1·60 1·00
DESIGNS—HORIZ. 15 f. St. Nizier-du-Moucherotte. 100 f. Cable-car, Villard-de-Lans.

1968. Human Rights Year.
230. 69. 20 f. red, gold and blue 40 15
231. 30 f. red, gold and green 45 20

70. Student and School.

1968. National School of Administration.
232. 70. 30 f. blue, turq. & brn. 45 20

71. Caravelle Airliner "Ouagadougou".

1968. Air.
233. 71. 500 f. blk., blue & purple 9·00 4·50

72. W.M.O. Emblem, Sun and Cloud-burst.

1968. Air. World Meteorological Day.
234. 72. 50 f. blue, red and green 85 35

73. Human Figures and W.H.O. Emblem.

1968. 20th Anniv. of W.H.O.
235. 73. 30 f. indigo, red & blue 45 20
236. 50 f. blue, brown & grn. 65 35

1968. Air. Paintings. Old Masters in the Louvre. Multicoloured. As T 65. Sizes given in millimetres.
237. 20 f. "Still Life" (Gauguin) (36 × 50) .. 35 30
238. 60 f. "Anne of Cleves" (Holbein the Younger) (36 × 50) 65 50
239. 90 f. "The Pawnbroker and His Wife" (Quentin Metsys) (38 × 40) .. 1·00 70
240. 200 f. "The Cart" (Le Nain) (50 × 37) .. .. 2·40 1·60

74. "Europafrique".

1968. Air. "Europafrique".
241. 74. 50 f. red, black and ochre 70 35

75. Telephone Exchange.

1968. Inauguration of Automatic Telephone Exchange, Bobo-Dioulasso.
242. 75. 30 f. multicoloured .. 55 30

76. Colima Acrobat with Bells.

1968. Air. Olympic Games, Mexico.
243. 76. 10 f. brown, yell. & red 35 20
244. – 30 f. blue, red and green 50 30
245. – 60 f. lake, brown & blue 1·10 45
246. – 100 f. lake, blue & green 1·40 70
DESIGNS—VERT. 30 f. Pelota-player (Veracruz). 60 f. Javelin thrower (Colima). HORIZ. 100 f. Athlete with cape (Jalisco).
The designs represent early Mexican statuary.

77. Weaving.

1968. Handicrafts.
247. – 5 f. blk., pur. & brown (postage) 20 10
248. 77. 30 f. brown, orange and mauve 50 20
249. – 100 f. purple, red and yellow (air) .. .. 1·40 65
250. – 150 f. blk., yellow & brn. 2·25 1·00
DESIGNS—As Type 77. 5 f. Metal-work. 48 × 27 mm. 100 f. Pottery. 150 f. Basket-making.

1968. Air. "Philexafrique" Stamp Exn., Abidjan (Ivory Coast, 1969). (1st issue). As T **113a** of Mauritania. Multicoloured.
251. 100 f. "Too Late" or "The Letter" (A. Cambon) 2·50 2·25
See also No. 256.

78. Mahatma Gandhi. **79.** "Grain for the World".

1968. Air. "Workers for Peace".
252. **78.** 100 f. blk., yell & grn. 1·40 80
253. – 100 f. blk., light green and green .. .. 1·40 80
DESIGN: No. 253, Albert Luthuli.

1969. World Food Programme.
255. **79.** 30 f. purple, slate & blue 45 20

1969. Air. "Philexafrique" Stamp Exn., Abidjan (Ivory Coast) (2nd issue). As T **114a** of Mauritania. Multicoloured.
256. 50 f. Dancers of Tengrela and stamp of 1928 .. 2·50 2·25

80. Loom and I.L.O. Emblem.

1969. 50th Anniv. of I.L.O.
257. **80.** 30 f. blue, lake & green 50 30

81. Cattle and Labourer.

1969. Air. World Meteorological Day.
258. **81.** 100 f. brn., blue & grn. 2·50 1·40

82. "Lions" Emblem within Eye.

1969. Air. 12th Congress of 403 District, Lions Int., Ouagadougou.
259. **82.** 250 f. multicoloured .. 2·75 1·40

83. Blood Donor.

1969. 50th Anniv. of League of Red Cross Societies.
260. **83.** 30 f. black, red and blue 60 40

84. "Mormyrops curviceps".

1969. Fishes.
261. – 20 f. buff, brn. and blue (postage) 80 35
262. – 25 f. pur., brn. and blue 80 35
263. **84.** 30 f. black and olive .. 1·10 50
264. – 55 f. olive, yellow & grn. 1·40 65
265. – 85 f. blue, mauve & brn. 2·50 1·40
266. – 100 f. blue, yellow and purple (air) .. .. 1·60 85
267. – 150 f. blue, black & red 2·50 1·10
DESIGNS: 20 f. "Nannocharax gobioides". 25 f. "Hemigrammocharax polli". 55 f. "Alestes luteus". 85 f. "Micralestes voltae". LARGER (48 × 27 mm.): 100 f. "Phenacogrammus pabrensis". 150 f. "Synodontis arnoulti".

85. Astronaut and Moon.

1969. Air. Moon flight of "Apollo 8". Embossed on gold foil.
268. **85.** 1,000 f. gold .. .. 18·00

1969. Air. 1st Man on the Moon. No. 214 optd. **L'HOMME SUR LA LUNE JUILLET 1969** and "Apollo 11".
269. 100 f. green, violet & purple 3·25 3·25

1969. Air. Birth Bicent. of Napoleon Bonaparte. As T **114b** of Mauritania. Mult.
270. 50 f. "Bonaparte crossing the Great St. Bernard" (J. L. David) .. 1·60 80
271. 150 f. "First presentation of the Legion of Honour" (Debret) .. .. 5·00 2·00
272. 250 f. "Napoleon before Madrid" (C. Vernet) .. 6·75 3·25

1969. 5th Anniv. of African Development Bank.
273. 30 f. brown, emerald and green 35 15

88. Millet. **89.** Stylised Tree.

1969. Agricultural Produce.
274. **88.** 15 f. brown, green and yellow (postage) .. 45 20
275. – 30 f. blue and mauve .. 55 35
276. – 100 f. brn. & violet (air) 1·40 40
277. – 200 f. green and red .. 2·50 80
DESIGNS: 30 f. Cotton. LARGER (48 × 27 mm.): 100 f. Ground-nuts. 200 f. Rice.

1969. Air. Europafrique.
278. **89.** 100 f. multicoloured .. 90 55

1969. 10th Anniv. of Aerial Navigation Security Agency for Africa and Madagascar (A.S.E.C.N.A.). As T **94a** of Niger.
279. 100 f. brown .. .. 1·25 75

90. "Niadale". **91.** Lenin.

1970. Figurines and Masks in National Museum.
280. **90.** 10 f. brn., orge. and red 20 10
281. – 30 f. brown, blue and violet 40 20
282. – 45 f. brn., blue & green 70 30
283. – 80 f. brn., pur. & violet 1·25 60
DESIGNS: 30 f. "Niaga". 45 f. "Iliu bara". 80 f. "Karan weeba".

1970. Air. Birth Cent. of Lenin.
284. **91.** 20 f. brown and ochre 35 20
285. – 100 f. red, blue & green 1·25 80
DESIGN—HORIZ.: 100 f. "Lenin addressing workers" (A. Serov.).

92. African Huts and City Buildings. **93.** Cauris Dancers.

1970. Linked Cities' Day.
286. **92.** 30 f. brown, blue & red 50 30

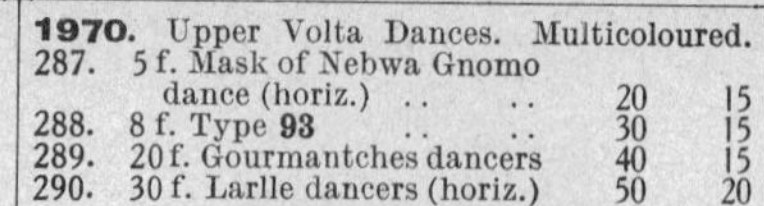
1970. Upper Volta Dances. Multicoloured.
287. 5 f. Mask of Nebwa Gnomo dance (horiz.) 20 15
288. 8 f. Type **93** 30 15
289. 20 f. Gourmantches dancers 40 15
290. 30 f. Larlle dancers (horiz.) 50 20

94. "Pupils", Sun and Emblem of Education Year.

1970. Int. Education Year. Multicoloured.
291. 40 f. Type **94** 40 20
292. 90 f. Visual Aids and emblem 95 45

95. New U.P.U. Headquarters Building, U.P.U. Monument and Abraham Lincoln.

1970. New U.P.U. Headquarters Building.
293. **95.** 30 f. grey, red and brown 50 20
294. 60 f. purple, grn. & brn. 85 35

96. Footballers and Cup.

1970. Air. World Cup Football Championships, Mexico.
295. **96.** 40 f. lake, green & brn. 45 30
296. – 100 f. brn., pur. & grn. 1·10 55
DESIGN: 100 f. Goalkeeper saving ball, Globe and footballers.

97. Franklin D. Roosevelt. **98.** Naval Construction.

1970. Air. 25th Anniv. of Roosevelt's Death.
297. **97.** 10 f. brn., blk. and grn. 20 20
298. – 200 f. red, violet & grey 1·60 80
DESIGN—HORIZ. 200 f. Roosevelt with his stamp collection.

1970. Hanover Fair.
299. **98.** 15 f. multicoloured .. 50 35
300. – 45 f. green, blue & black 60 35
301. – 80 f. pur., brown & blk. 1·40 50
DESIGNS: 45 f. Test-tubes and retorts ("Chemistry"). 80 f. Power transmission lines and pylons ("Electro-techniques").

99. Inoculating Cattle.

1970. National Veterinary School.
302. **99.** 30 f. multicoloured .. 55 35

100. "Manchurian Cranes and Seashore" and Expo Monorail Coach. **101.** Nurse attending Patient.

1970. Air. World Fair "EXPO 70" Osaka Japan.
303. 50 f. Type **100** 55 35
304. 150 f. "Geisha", rocket and satellite .. .. 1·40 80

1970. Upper Volta Red Cross.
305. **101.** 30 f. brown, red & grn. 60 35

102. "Nurse and Child" (F. Hals). **103.** U.N. Emblem and Dove.

1970. "Europafrique". Multicoloured.
306. 25 f. Type **102** 50 20
307. 30 f. "Courtyard in Delft" (Hoogh) 60 35
308. 150 f. "Christina of Denmark" (Holbein) .. 2·25 90
309. 250 f. "Hofburg Courtyard, Innsbruck" (Durer) 4·00 1·40

1970. Air. 25th Anniv. of U.N.O.
310. **103.** 60 f. ultram, blue & grn. 65 30
311. – 250 f. vio., brn. & grn. 2·75 1·10
DESIGN—HORIZ. 250 f. U.N. emblem and two doves.

104. Front of Car.

1970. Paris Motor Show.
312. **104.** 25 f. green, lake & brn. 90 35
313. – 40 f. blue, pur. & green 1·10 55
DESIGN: 40 f. Old and new cars.

105. "Holy Family".

1970. Air. Christmas.
314. **105.** 300 f. silver .. .. 6·75
315. 1000 f. gold .. .. 18·00

106. Centre Buildings.

1970. Inaug. of Austro-Voltaic Centre.
316. **106.** 50 f. orange, grn. & red 55 30

107. Arms and Stork.

1970. 10th Anniv. of Independence.
317. **107.** 30 f. mult. (postage) 45 20
318. – 500 f. blk., red and gold (air) .. .. 5·50
DESIGN—VERT. (27 × 37 mm.) Family and flag. No. 318 is embossed on gold foil.

108. U.N. "Key" and Split Globe.

1970. 10th Anniv. of U.N. Declaration on Colonies.
319. **108.** 40 f. red, blue & brown 60 35
320. – 50 f. multicoloured .. 55 30
DESIGN: 50 f. Two maps of Africa showing African" and "European" areas.

109. Pres. Nasser.

111. Heads of Different Races.

110. Beingolo Hunting Horn.

1971. Air. Pres. Nasser Commem.
321. **109.** 100 f. multicoloured .. 90 40

1971. Musical Instruments.
322. **110.** 5 f. brn., red and blue 20 15
323. – 15 f. brn., red & green 35 20
324. – 20 f. red, grey and blue 65 20
325. – 25 f. drab, green and red 80 40
INSTRUMENTS—VERT. 15 f. Mossi "guitar". 20 f. Gurunssi "flutes". HORIZ. 25 f. Lunga "drum".

1971. Racial Equality Year.
326. **111.** 50 f. brn., red & turq. 55 30

112. "The Purple Herons" (Egypt, 1354).

1971. Air. Muslim Miniatures. Multicoloured.
327. 100 f. Type **112** .. .. 1·10 55
328. 250 f. Page from the Koran (Egypt c. 1368-88) (vert.) 2·75 1·25

113. Telephone and Hemispheres.

115. Cutting Cane and Sugar Factory, Banfora.

114. Olympic Rings and Events.

1971. World Telecommunications Day.
329. **113.** 50 f. vio., grey & brn. 60 30

1971. Air. "Pre-Olympic Year".
330. **114.** 150 f. red, vio. and bl. 2·25 1·10

1971. Local Industries. Multicoloured.
331. 10 f. Type **115** 20 10
332. 35 f. Cotton-plant and textiles ("Voltex" project) 35 20

116. "Gonimbrasia hecate".

117. Scout and Pagodas.

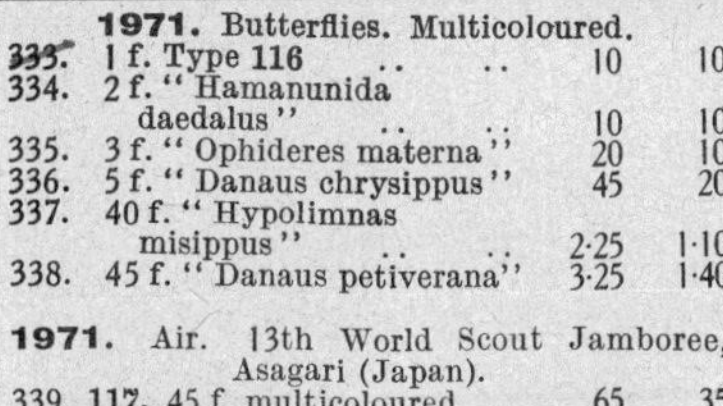

1971. Butterflies. Multicoloured.
333. 1 f. Type **116** 10 10
334. 2 f. "Hamanunida daedalus" 10 10
335. 3 f. "Ophideres materna" 20 10
336. 5 f. "Danaus chrysippus" 45 20
337. 40 f. "Hypolimnas misippus" .. .. 2·25 1·10
338. 45 f. "Danaus petiverana" 3·25 1·40

1971. Air. 13th World Scout Jamboree, Asagari (Japan).
339. **117.** 45 f. multicoloured .. 65 35

118. Actor with Fan.

119. African with Seed-packet.

1971. "Philatokyo" Stamp Exhib., Tokyo. Multicoloured.
340. 25 f. Type **118** 35 20
341. 40 f. Actor within mask .. 50 25

1971. National Seed-protection Campaign. Multicoloured.
342. 35 f. Grading seeds (horiz.) 40 20
343. 75 f. Type **119** 60 30
344. 100 f. Harvesting crops (horiz.) 60 35

1971. 10th Anniv. of Volta Red Cross. Surch. **Xe ANNIVERSAIRE** and new value.
345. **101.** 100 f. on 30 f. brn., red and purple .. .. 1·25 65

121. Teacher and Class

122. Soldier and Tractors.

1971. "Women's Access to Education". Multicoloured.
346. 35 f. Type **121** 45 20
347. 50 f. Family learning alphabet 60 35

1971. Dakiri Project. Military Aid for Agriculture. Multicoloured.
348. 15 f. Type **122** 45 15
349. 40 f. Soldiers harvesting (horiz.) 65 40

123. General De Gaulle and Map.

1971. Air. De Gaulle Commemoration.
350. **123.** 40 f. multicoloured .. 55 55
351. – 500 f. gold and green 10·50 9·50
DESIGN—VERT. (30 × 40 mm.)—500 f. De Gaulle. No. 351 is embossed on gold foil.

1971. Air. 10th Anniv. of African and Malagasy Posts and Telecommunications Union. As T **139a** of Mauritania. Mult.
352. 100 f. U.A.M.P.T. H.Q. and Mossi dancer .. .. 1·10 ·50

124. "Simulium damnosum" and Preventative Measures.

1971. Regional Anti-Onchocercose Campaign.
353. **124.** 40 f. multicoloured .. 55 35

125. Pres. Lamizana.

126. Children acclaiming Emblem.

1971.
354. **125.** 35 f. multicoloured .. 30 20

1971. U.N.I.C.E.F. 25th Anniv.
355. **126.** 45 f. multicoloured .. 50 35

127. Peulh Straw Hut.

1971. Traditional Housing (1st series). Mult.
356. 10 f. Type **127** 15 10
357. 20 f. Gourounsi house .. 30 15
358. 35 f. Mossi huts 45 30
See also Nos. 370/2.

128. Town Halls of Bobo-Dioulasso and Chalons-sur-Marne, France.

1971. "Twin Cities" Co-operation.
359. **128.** 40 f. multicoloured .. 65 40

129. Ice-hockey.

130. Running.

1972. Air. Winter Olympic Games, Sapporo, Japan.
360. **129.** 150 f. pur., bl. and red 1·90 1·00

1972. Air. U.N.E.S.C.O. "Save Venice" Campaign. As T **145** of Senegal. Mult.
361. 100 f. "La Musica" (P. Longhi) (vert.) .. .. 1·90 1·00
362. 150 f. "Panorama da Ponte della Marina" (detail-Caffi) (horiz.) .. .. 2·75 1·25

1972. Air. Olympic Games, Munich.
363. **130.** 65 f. brown, blue & grn. 60 45
364. – 200 f. brown and blue 1·90 1·25
DESIGN: 200 f. Throwing the discus.

131. Louis Armstrong.

1972. Famous Negro Musicians. Mult.
366. 45 f. Type **131** (postage) 1·25 65
367. 500 f. Jimmy Smith (air) 6·75 4·50

132. Globe and Emblems.

1972. World Red Cross Day.
368. **132.** 40 f. mult. (postage) .. 55 40
369. 100 f. mult. (air) .. 1·10 45

133. Bobo House.

134. Hair Style.

1972 Traditional Housing (2nd series). Mult.
370. 45 f. Type **133** 55 30
371. 50 f. Dagari house .. 65 35
372. 90 f. Interior of Bango house (horiz.) .. .. .. 1·25 50

1972. Upper Volta Hair Styles.
373. **134.** 25 f. multicoloured .. 35 15
374. – 35 f. multicoloured .. 50 20
375. – 75 f. multicoloured .. 1·10 45
DESIGNS: 35 f., 75 f. Similar hair styles.

135. "Teaching".

1972. 2nd Nat. Development Plan.
376. **135.** 10 f. mauve, green and turquoise (postage) 10 10
377. – 15 f. brn., orge. & grn. 20 15
378. – 20 f. brn., grn. & blue 30 15
379. – 35 f. brn., blue & grn. 50 20
380. – 40 f. brn., green & pur. 55 30
381. – 85 f. blk., red & bl. (air) 70 50
DESIGNS: 15 f. Doctor and patient ("Health"). 20 f. Factory and silos ("Industry"). 35 f. Cattle ("Cattle-raising"). 40 f. Rice-planting ("Agriculture"). 85 f. Road-making machine ("Infrastructure").

1972. 10th Anniv. of West African Monetary Union. As T **149** of Mauritania.
382. 40 f. grey, blue & mauve .. 45 20

136. Lottery Building.

1972. 5th Anniv. of Nat. Lottery.
383. **136.** 35 f. multicoloured .. 50 20

137. Pres. Pompidou and Lamizana.

1972. Air. Visit of Pres. Pompidou to Upper Volta.
384. **137.** 40 f. multicoloured .. 1·60 1·60
385. – 250 f. multicoloured .. 6·00 6·00
DESIGN: 250 f. As T **137** but frame differs and portraits are embossed on gold.

138. Mary Peters (pentathlon).

1972. Air. Gold Medal-winners, Olympic Games, Munich. Multicoloured.
386. 40 f. Type **138** 35 15
387. 65 f. Ragno-Lonzi (fencing) 55 20
388. 85 f. Touritcheva (gymnastics) 80 30
389. 200 f. Maury (sailing) .. 1·60 65
390. 300 f. Meyfarth (high-jumping) .. .. .. 2·75 1·10

139. Donkeys.

1972. Animals. Multicoloured.
392. 5 f. Type **139** 10 10
393. 10 f. Spur-winged geese .. 10 10
394. 30 f. Goat 55 20
395. 50 f. Bull 80 30
396. 65 f. Dromedaries .. .. 1·10 40

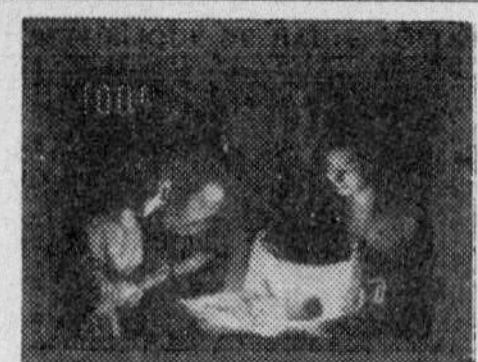

140. " The Nativity " (Della Notte).

1972. Air. Christmas. Religious Paintings. Multicoloured.

397. 100 f. Type **140** .. .. 1·10 65
398. 200 f. " The Adoration of the Magi " (Durer) .. 2·25 1·60

141. Mossi Hair-style and Village.

1973. Air.

399. **141.** 5 f. multicoloured .. 10 10
400. 40 f. multicoloured .. 55 20

1973. 25th Anniv. of W.H.O. No. 353 surch. **O. M. S. 25· Anniversaire** and value.

401. **124.** 45 f. on 40 f. mult. .. 50 30

1973. African and Malagasy Posts and Telecommunications Union. As T **155** of Mauritania.

402. 100 f. purple, red & yellow 1·00 55

1974. 15th Anniv. of Council of Accord. As T **184** of Niger.

403. 40 f. multicoloured .. 30 20

143. Map and Harvester.

1974. Kou Valley Project.

404. **143.** 35 f. multicoloured .. 55 35

144. Woman, Globe and I.W.Y. Emblem.

1975. International Women's Year.

405. **144.** 65 f. multicoloured .. 65 45

145. Mgr. Joanny Thevenoud and Cathedral.

1975. 75th Anniv. of Evangelization of Upper Volta.

406. **145.** 55 f. blk., brn. and grn. 65 35
407. – 65 f. black, brn. and red 80 45

DESIGNS: 65 f. Father Guillaume Templier and Cathedral.

146. Farmer's Hat, Hoe and Emblem. **147.** Diseased People.

1975. Development of the Volta Valleys.

408. **146.** 15 f. multicoloured .. 15 10
409. 50 f. multicoloured .. 50 25

1976. Campaign against Onchocerciasis (round-worm).

410. **147.** 75 f. mve., orge. & grn. 85 35
411. 250 f. sepia, orge. and brown .. .. 2·50 1·10

148. Globe and Emblem.

1976. Non-aligned Countries' Summit Conference, Colombo, Sri Lanka. Mult.

412. 55 f. Type **148** 45 20
413. 100 f. Globe, dove and emblem 90 50

149. Washington at Trenton.

1976. " Interphil '76 " International Stamp Exhibition, Philadelphia. Multicoloured.

414. 60 f. Type **149** (postage) .. 55 15
415. 90 f. Seat of Government, Pennsylvania 80 20
416. 100 f. Siege of Yorktown (air) 80 30
417. 200 f. Battle of Cape St. Vincent .. .. 1·60 60
418. 300 f. Peter Francisco's act of bravery .. .. 2·40 80

150. U.P.U. and U.N. Emblems.

1976. 25th Anniv. of U.N. Postal Administration.

420. **150.** 200 f. blue, bronze & red 1·60 90

151. Tenkodogo Commune. **152.** Bronze Statuette.

1977. Arms. Multicoloured.

421. 10 f. Type **151** 15 10
422. 20 f. Ouagadougou 20 10
423. 55 f. Type **151** 55 20
424. 100 f. As 20 f. 70 35

1977.

425. **152.** 55 f. multicoloured .. 45 20
426. – 65 f. multicoloured .. 45 20

DESIGN: 65 f. Bronze statuette of Woman with bowl.

153. Samo Granary. **154.** Gouin Basket.

1977. Millet Granaries. Multicoloured.

427. 5 f. Type **153** 10 10
428. 35 f. Boromo 30 20
429. 45 f. Banfora 45 20
430. 55 f. Mossi 55 30

1977. Local Handicrafts. Baskets and Bags. Multicoloured.

431. 30 f. Type **154** 20 15
432. 40 f. Bissa 30 15
433. 60 f. Lobi 50 20
434. 70 f. Mossi 55 30

155. " Crinum ornatum ". **156.** General De Gaulle.

1977. Multicoloured.

435. 2 f. " Cordia myxa " .. 10 10
436. 3 f. " Opilia celtidifolia " 15 10
437. 15 f. Type **155** 20 10
438. 25 f. " Haemanthus multiflorus " 20 10
439. 50 f. " Hannoa undulata " 10 10
440. 90 f. " Cochlospermum planchonii " .. .. 1·00 40
441. 125 f. " Clitoria ternatea " 1·10 50
442. 150 f. " Cassia alata " .. 1·40 90
443. 175 f. " Nauclea latifolia " (horiz.) .. .. 1·60 1·00
444. 300 f. " Bombax costatum " (horiz.) .. .. 2·50 1·40
445. 400 f. " Eulophia cucullata " 4·25 1·40

1977. Personalities. Multicoloured.

446. 100 f. Type **156** .. .. 1·60 50
447. 200 f. King Baudouin .. 1·60 50

157. Queen Elizabeth II.

1977. Silver Jubilee of Queen Elizabeth II. Multicoloured.

448. 200 f. Type **157** .. .. 1·60 50
449. 300 f. Queen Elizabeth II taking salute at Trooping the Colour .. .. 2·25 60

158. Cars on " Road " of Banknotes.

1977. 10th Anniv. of National Lottery.

451. **158.** 55 f. multicoloured .. 55 40

159. Selma Lagerlof and Bean Geese.

1977. Nobel Prize Winners. Multicoloured.

452. 55 f. Type **159** (Literature, 1909) 65 20
453. 65 f. Guglielmo Marconi and early transmitter (Physics, 1909) .. 45 20
454. 125 f. Bertrand Russell, laurel, book and dove (Literature, 1950) .. 95 30
455. 200 f. L. C. Pauling, formula and atomic explosion (Chemistry, 1954) .. 1·40 50
456. 300 f. Robert Koch, slide and X-ray plate (Medicine, 1905) .. .. 2·40 70

160. " The Three Graces ".

1977. 400th Birth Anniv. of Rubens.

458. 55 f. "Heads of Four Negroes" (horiz.) .. 40 10
459. 65 f. Type **160** 50 15
460. 85 f. "Bathsheba at the Fountain" 50 20
461. 150 f. "The Drunken Silenus" .. .. 1·25 45
462. 200 f. "The Story of Maria de Medici" (detail) .. .. 1·60 55
463. 300 f. "The Story of Maria de Medici" (detail—different) .. .. 2·50 70

161. Lenin.

1977. 60th Anniv. of Russian Revolution. Multicoloured.

465. 10 f. Type **161** 15 10
466. 85 f. Lenin Monument and Kremlin 65 40
467. 200 f. Lenin with children (horiz.) .. .. 1·90 1·10
468. 500 f. Lenin and Pres. Brezhnev (horiz.) .. 4·50 2·25

162. Stadium and Brazil 5 cr. 80 Stamp of 1950.

1978. World Cup Football Championship, Argentina. Multicoloured.

469. 55 f. Type **162** 35 10
470. 65 f. Brazil 1969 Pele stamp 45 15
471. 125 f. G.B. 1966 England Winners stamp .. 90 30
472. 200 f. Chile 1962 World Cup stamp .. 1·40 45
473. 300 f. Switzerland 1954 World Cup stamp .. 2·00 65

163. Jean Mermoz.

1978. Aviation History. Multicoloured.

475. 65 f. Type **163** 60 20
476. 75 f. Anthony Fokker .. 65 30
477. 85 f. Wiley Post 75 35
478. 90 f. Otto Lilienthal (vert.) 85 35
479. 100 f. " Concorde " .. 1·10 40

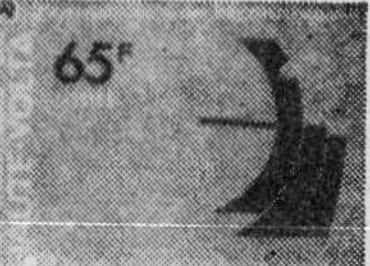

164. " Crateva religiosa ". **165.** Microwave Antennae.

1978. Trees of Upper Volta. Multicoloured.

481. 55 f. Type **164** 55 35
482. 75 f. " Ficus sp " 65 45

1978. World Telecommunications Day.
483. **165.** 65 f. multicoloured .. 55 40

166. Bobo Fetish Portals.

1978. Sacred Objects. Multicoloured.
484. 55 f. Type **166** 55 30
485. 65 f. Mossi fetish 65 40

167. U.P.U. Emblem over Globe.

1978. Air. Cent. of Paris Congress.
486. **167.** 350 f. multicoloured .. 2·75 1·60

168. Capt. Cook and H.M.S. "Endeavour".

1978. 250th Birth Anniv. of Captain James Cook. Multicoloured.
487. 65 f. Type **168** .. .. 1·00 40
488. 85 f. Death of Captain Cook 55 15
489. 250 f. Cook and navigation instruments .. .. 1·60 55
490. 350 f. Cook and H.M.S. "Resolution" .. .. 3·50 2·25

169. Yuri Gagarin and Spacecraft.

1978. "Conquest of Space". Multicoloured.
491. 50 f. Type **169** 40 20
492. 60 f. Jules Verne, "Apollo 11" badge and Neil Armstrong in space-suit .. 45 20
493. 100 f. Montgolfier medallion and balloon, Bleriot's monoplane and "Concorde" 85 40

170. I.A.Y. Emblem.

1978. Air. Anti-Apartheid Year.
494. **170.** 100 f. multicoloured .. 80 45

1978. 25th Anniv. of Coronation of Queen Elizabeth II. Nos. 448/9 optd. **ANNIVERSAIRE DU COURONNEMENT 1953-1978.**
495. **157.** 200 f. multicoloured .. 1·40 90
496. – 300 f. multicoloured .. 2·25 1·40

1978. Air. "Philexafrique" Stamp Exhibitions, Libreville (Gabon), and Int. Stamp Fair, Essen, West Germany (1st series). As T **262** of Niger. Multicoloured.
498. 100 f. Common Kingfisher and Hanover 1850 1 ggr. stamp .. .. .. 1·50 1·25
499. 100 f. Hippopotamus and 1964 250 f. Grey Woodpecker stamp .. .. 1·50 1·25
See also Nos. 518/9.

172. "Trent Castle".

1978. 450th Death Anniv. of Albrecht Durer. Multicoloured.
500. 65 f. Type **172** 55 15
501. 150 f. "Virgin and Child" (vert.) .. .. .. 1·10 35
502. 250 f. "Saints George and Eustace" (vert.) .. 1·90 60
503. 350 f. "H. Holzschuher" (vert.) .. .. .. 2·75 90

173. Horus.

174. Jules Verne.

1978. Air. U.N.E.S.C.O. Campaign: "Save the Philae Temples". Multicoloured.
504. 200 f. Type **173** .. .. 1·40 65
505. 300 f. Stylised falcon .. 2·00 1·00

1978. 150th Birth Anniv of Jules Verne (author).
506 **174** 20 f. purple, blue & grn 1·60 90

175. Human Rights Flame.

1978. 30th Anniv. of Declaration of Human Rights.
507. **175.** 55 f. multicoloured .. 50 30

1979. World Cup Football Championship Winners. Nos. 469/73 optd.
508. **162.** 55 f. multicoloured .. 45 25
509. – 65 f. multicoloured .. 50 30
510. – 125 f. multicoloured .. 95 55
511. – 200 f. multicoloured .. 1·40 85
512. – 300 f. multicoloured .. 2·10 1·10
OPTS.: 55 f. **VAINQUEURS 1950 URUGUAY 1978 ARGENTINE.** 65 f. **VAINQUEURS 1970 BRESIL 1978 ARGENTINE.** 125 f. **VAINQUEURS 1966 GRANDE BRETAGNE 1978 ARGENTINE.** 200 f. **VAINQUEURS 1962 BRESIL 1978 ARGENTINE.** 300 f. **VAINQUEURS 1954 ALLEMAGNE (RFA) 1978 ARGENTINE.**

177. Radio Station.

179. Wave Pattern and Human Figures.

178. Children listening to Story.

1979. 10th Anniv. of Posts and Telecommunications Organization. Multicoloured.
514. 55 f. Type **177** 40 20
515. 65 f. Loading mail aboard aircraft 50 30

1979. International Year of the Child.
516. **178.** 75 f. multicoloured .. 85 45

1979. World Telecommunications Day.
517. **179.** 70 f. multicoloured .. 55 35

180. Basket Weaving and Upper Volta 50 c. stamp of 1963.

1979. "Philexafrique 2" Exhibition, Libreville, Gabon (2nd series). Multicoloured.
518. 100 f. Type **180** .. .. 1·60 1·40
519. 100 f. "Concorde", van, shouting man and U.P.U. emblem .. 1·60 1·40

181. "Synodontis voltae".

183. Kob.

182. Steam Train.

1979. Freshwater Fish. Multicoloured.
520. 20 f. Type **181** 35 20
521. 50 f. "Micralestes comoensis" .. .. .. 1·00 45
522. 85 f. "Silurus" .. .. 1·40 70

1979. Death Cent. of Sir Rowland Hill. Multicoloured.
523. 65 f. Type **182** 55 15
524. 165 f. Diesel train .. 1·40 40
525. 200 f. Diesel train (different) .. .. .. 1·60 50
526. 300 f. French High-speed train .. .. .. 2·75 60

1979. Endangered Animals. Multicoloured.
528. 30 f. Type **183** 20 10
529. 40 f. Roan antelope .. 35 10
530. 60 f. Caracal 65 10
531. 100 f. African elephant .. 1·00 35
532. 175 f. Hartebeest .. .. 1·60 45
533. 250 f. Leopard .. .. 2·50 55

184. Teacher and Class.

1979. World Literacy Day. Multicoloured.
534. 55 f. Farmer reading book (vert.) 45 35
535. 250 f. Type **184** .. .. 2·00 1·25

185. Telecommunications.

1979. 3rd World Telecommunications Exhibition, Geneva.
536. **185.** 200 f. multicoloured .. 1·40 70

186. King Vulture.

187. Airport.

1979. Protected Birds. Multicoloured.
537. 5 f. Type **186** 20 10
538. 10 f. Hoopoe 20 10
539. 15 f. Ruppell's Griffon .. 25 15
540. 25 f. Intermediate Egret .. 40 15
541. 35 f. Ostrich 60 20
542. 45 f. Crowned Crane .. 70 25
543. 125 f. Cassin's Hawk Eagle 1·60 1·00

1979. 20th Anniv. of A.S.E.C.N.A. (Air Navigation Security Agency).
544. **187.** 65 f. multicoloured .. 60 40

188. Headquarters Building.

1979. Opening of West African Savings Bank Building, Dakar, Senegal.
545. **188.** 55 f. multicoloured .. 50 30

189. Jamot, Map and Tsetse Fly.

1979. Birth Cent. of Eugene Jamot (discoverer of cure for sleeping sickness).
546. **189.** 55 f. multicoloured .. 85 45

190. Stamp under Magnifying Glass.

1980. Stamp Day.
547. **190.** 55 f. multicoloured .. 50 25

191. Electric Locomotives. **192.** Pope John Paul II.

1980. 25th Anniv. of World Locomotive Speed Record.
548. **191.** 75 f. multicoloured .. 1·00 45
549. 100 f. multicoloured .. 1·50 65

1980. Papal Visit. Multicoloured.
550. 55 f. Pres. Lamizana, Pope and Cardinal Pau Zoungrana (horiz.) 85 35
551. 100 f. Type **192** .. .. 1·40 85

193. Telephone. **194.** Mountains and Statue.

1980. World Telecommunications Day.
552. **193.** 50 f. multicoloured .. 40 20

1980. Solar Energy. Multicoloured.
553. 65 f. Sun and Earth 50 20
554. 100 f. Type **194** 80 40

195. Downhill Skiing (L. Stock).

1980. Winter Olympic Games Winners. Mult.
555. 65 f. Type **195** 45 15
556. 100 f. Women's downhill skiing (A. Moser-Proell) 65 20
557. 200 f. Figure skating (A. Poetzsch) .. .. 1·40 35
558. 350 f. Slalom (I. Stenmark) (vert.) .. .. .. 2·25 60

196. Map of Europe and Africa. **197.** Hand pushing back Sand Dune.

1980. Europafrique.
560. **196.** 100 f. red, blk. & green 90 45

1980. Operation "Green Sahara". Mult.
561. 50 f. Type **197** 50 20
562. 55 f. Hands planting saplings 60 35

198. Cyclists.

1980. Air. Olympic Games, Moscow. Cycling.
563. **198.** 65 f. multicoloured .. 55 15
564. 150 f. multicoloured .. 1·10 40
565. 250 f. multicoloured .. 1·90 55
566. 350 f. multicoloured .. 2·75 90

199. Installation of Chief.

1980. National History. Multicoloured.
568. 30 f. Type **199** 35 15
569. 55 f. Moro Naba, Emperor of Mossis 55 30
570. 65 f. Princess Guimbe Ouattara (vert.) .. 60 30

200. Gourounsi Mask. **201.** Tractor, Cattle and Grain (Agriculture).

1980. World Tourism Conference, Manila.
571. **200.** 65 f. multicoloured .. 55 30

1980. 5th Anniv. of West African Economic Council. Multicoloured.
572. 55 f. Type **201** 35 15
573. 65 f. "Communication" .. 40 30
574. 75 f. Dam and highway .. 45 30
575. 100 f. "Industry" .. 80 40

1980. Air. Olympic Winners. Nos. 563/6 optd.
576. **198.** 65 f. multicoloured .. 30 25
577. – 150 f. multicoloured .. 75 50
578. – 250 f. multicoloured .. 1·25 90
579. – 350 f. multicoloured .. 1·60 1·00
OVERPRINTS: 65 f. **SOUKHOROUCHENKOV (URSS).** 150 f. **"HESSLICH (RDA)".** 250 f. **"LANG (POL)".** 350 f. **"DILLBUNDI (SUISSE)".**

203. Coat of Arms and Map.

1980. 20th Anniv. of Independence.
581. **203.** 500 f. multicoloured .. 4·25 2·50

204. "Sistine Madonna" (detail). **205.** "Scarabaeus sacer".

1980. Christmas. Multicoloured.
582. 60 f. Type **204** 45 15
583. 150 f. "Virgin de l'Impannata" .. .. 1·10 40
584. 250 f. "Alba Madonna" 1·75 55

1980. 5th Anniv. of African Posts and Telecommunications. As T **292** of Niger.
585. 55 f. multicoloured .. 50 30

1981. Insects. Multicoloured.
586 5 f. Type **205** 10 10
587 10 f. "Gryllus campestris" 10 10
588 15 f. Termites 15 10
589 20 f. "Mantis religiosa" (vert) 25 10
590 55 f. "Nyctaon pyri" .. 75 25
591 65 f. "Locusta migratorius" (vert) .. 85 35

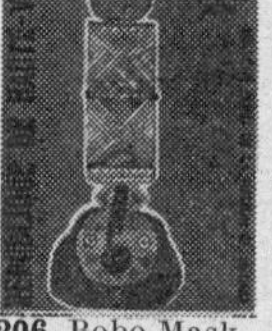

206. Bobo Mask, Hounde. **207.** College Emblem.

1981. Masks. Multicoloured.
592. 45 f. Type **206** 40 15
593. 55 f. Bwa mask 45 20
594. 85 f. Kouroumba mask .. 60 35
595. 105 f. Gourounsi mask .. 80 40

1981. Notre-Dame College, Kologh'naba. 25th Anniv.
596. **207.** 55 f. multicoloured .. 45 20

208. Von Stephan and U.P.U. Emblem.

1981. 150th Birth Anniv. of Heinrich von Stephan (founder of U.P.U.).
597. **208.** 65 f. multicoloured .. 60 35

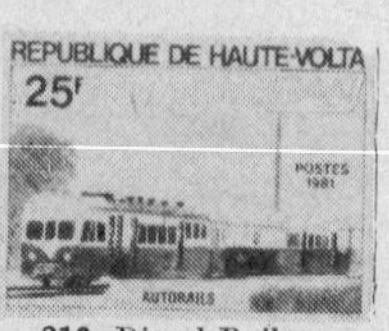

209. Ribbons forming Caduceus, I.T.U. and W.H.O. Emblems. **210.** Diesel Railcar.

1981. World Telecommunications Day.
598. **209.** 90 f. multicoloured .. 60 35

1981. Abidjan-Niger Railway. Multicoloured.
599. 25 f. Type **210** 30 15
600. 30 f. Diesel train "La Gazelle" 45 20
601. 40 f. Diesel locomotive "Le Belier" 55 35

211. Group of Trees.

1981. Tree Month.
602. **211.** 70 f. multicoloured .. 70 40

212. Nurse and Doctor with Medical Equipment. **213.** Handicapped Sculptor.

1981. 25th Anniv. of Upper Volta Red Cross.
603. **212.** 70 f. multicoloured .. 60 40

1981. International Year of Disabled People.
604. **213.** 70 f. multicoloured .. 60 35

214. Koudougou.

1981. Landscapes. Multicoloured.
605. 35 f. Type **214** 30 15
606. 45 f. Toma 40 20
607. 85 f. Volta Noire 65 30

215. Agricultural Scenes within Map.

1981. World Food Day.
608. **215.** 90 f. multicoloured .. 70 45

216. Topi.

1981. Wildlife Protection. Multicoloured.
609. 5 f. Type **216** 10 10
610. 15 f. Waterbuck 15 15
611. 40 f. Roan antelopes .. 35 20
612. 60 f. Dorcas gazelle .. 60 35
613. 70 f. African elephant .. 1·00 55

217. Campaign Emblem. **219.** Donkey.

218. Papaya.

1981. Anti-Apartheid Campaign.
614. **217.** 90 f. red 60 35

1981. Fruit and Vegetables. Multicoloured
615. 20 f. Type **218** 15 10
616. 35 f. Fruit and vegetables 30 15
617. 75 f. Mangoes (vert.) .. 50 30
618. 90 f. Melons 60 35

1981. Stock Breeding. Multicoloured.
619. 10 f. Type **219** 10 10
620. 25 f. Pig 20 10
621. 70 f. Cow 55 20
622. 90 f. Helmet guineafowl (vert.) .. .. .. 1·25 55
623. 250 f. Rabbit .. .. 1·75 90

220. Woman carrying Rice. **221.** Father and Son.

1981. 10th Anniv. of West African Rice Development Association.
625. **220.** 90 f. multicoloured .. 90 45

1982. 20th Anniv. of World Food Programme.
626. **221.** 50 f. multicoloured .. 40 15

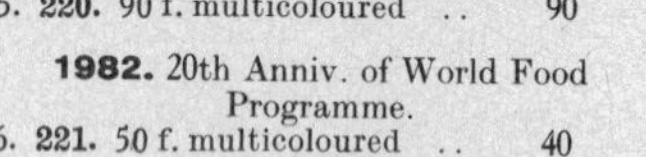

222. Morhonaba Palace, Ouagadougou.

1982. Traditional Houses. Multicoloured.
627. 30 f. Type **222** 20 10
628. 70 f. Bobo 50 20
629. 100 f. Gourounsi 70 30
630. 200 f. Peulh .. .. 1·40 60
631. 250 f. Dagari .. .. 1·60 65

223. Hexagonal Pattern.

1982. World Telecommunications Day.
632. **223.** 90 f. multicoloured .. 85 40

224. Symbols of National Life.

1982. National Life.
633. **224.** 90 f. multicoloured .. 60 30

225. Passing Ball. **226.** Water Lily.

1982. Air. World Cup Football Championship Spain. Multicoloured.
634. 70 f. Type **225** 50 15
635. 90 f. Tackle 60 30
636. 150 f. Running with ball .. 1·10 40
637. 300 f. Receiving ball .. 2·00 85

1982. Flowers. Multicoloured.
639. 25 f. Type **226** 15 10
640. 40 f. Kapoka 35 10
641. 70 f. Frangipani 60 35
642. 90 f. "Cochlospermum planchonii" 80 45
643. 100 f. Cotton 90 45

227. Symbols of Communication on Map of Africa.

228. Children holding Torch.

1982. African Post and Telecommunications Union.

644.	**227.**	70 f. multicoloured ..	45	15
645.		90 f. multicoloured ..	65	35

1982. 25th Anniv. of Cultural Aid Fund.

646.	**228.**	70 f. multicoloured ..	50	30

229. Hairstyle.

1983.

647.	**229.**	90 f. multicoloured ..	65	30
648.		120 f. multicoloured ..	90	35
649.		170 f. multicoloured ..	1·25	50

230. Audience watching Film.

1983. 8th Film Festival, Ouagadougou. Mult.

650.	90 f. Type **230**	85	55
651.	500 f. Dumarou Ganda ..	4·25	2·50

231. J.-M. Montgolfier and First Demonstration of Hot-air Balloon, 1783.

1983. Bicent. of Manned Flight. Mult.

652.	15 f. Type **231** (postage) ..	10	10
653.	25 f. F. Pilatre de Rozier and first manned flight, 1783	15	10
654.	70 f. J. Charles and hydrogen balloon, 1783 ..	50	10
655.	90 f. J. Jeffries and first Channel crossing, 1785 ..	65	20
656.	100 f. Wilhelmine Reichardt and ascent on a horse, 1798 (air)	85	30
657.	250 f. S.A. Andree and Spitzberg Expedition, 1797	1·60	55

232. Campaign Emblem and River.

233. Man reading Letter.

1983. International Drinking Water Decade. Multicoloured.

659.	60 f. Type **232**	45	20
660.	70 f. Woman carrying water	55	35

1983. World Communications Year. Multicoloured.

661.	30 f. Type **233**	20	15
662.	35 f. Type **233**	30	15
663.	45 f. Canoe and aircraft ..	40	20
664.	90 f. Woman on telephone	65	35

234. Space Shuttle " Challenger ".

1983. Air. World Events. Multicoloured.

665.	90 f. Type **234**	60	20
666.	120 f. World Cup football final	85	30
667.	300 f. World Cup football final (different)	1·90	60
668.	450 f. Royal wedding ..	2·50	85

235. " Synodontis gambiensis ".

1983. Fishery Resources. Multicoloured.

670.	20 f. Type **235**	15	15
671.	30 f. " Palmatochromis guntheri "	35	15
672.	40 f. Line fishing (vert.) ..	35	15
673.	50 f. Net fishing	40	15
674.	75 f. Trap fishing	55	20

236. Soling Class Yacht.

1983. Air. Pre-Olympic Year. Multicoloured.

675.	90 f. Type **236**	65	20
676.	120 f. Type 470 yacht ..	1·00	30
677.	300 f. Windsurfing ..	2·25	60
678.	400 f. Windsurfing (diff.) ..	2·75	85

237. Planting a Sapling.

1983. Campaign for Control of the Desert. Multicoloured.

680.	10 f. Type **237**	15	10
681.	50 f. Plantation	40	10
682.	100 f. Control of forest fires	90	35
683.	150 f. Woman cooking ..	1·40	60
684.	200 f. Control of timber trade (vert.)	1·60	90

238. Arms of Upper Volta.

1983. 25th Anniv. of Republic. Mult.

685.	90 f. Type **238**	55	30
686.	500 f. Family with flag ..	3·25	1·40

239. " Self-portrait " (Picasso).

1983. Celebrities' Anniversaries. Multicoloured.

687.	120 f. Type **239**	1·40	35
688.	185 f. " Self-portrait with a Palette " (Manet (1832-1883))	1·40	45
689.	300 f. Fresco detail (Raphael (1483-1520)) (horiz.) ..	2·25	60
690.	350 f. Fresco detail (Raphael) (different) (horiz.) ..	2·50	85
691.	500 f. J. W. Goethe (1749-1832) (portrait by Georg Oswald)	3·50	1·10

240. " Adoration of the Shepherds ".

242. Handball.

1983. Air. Christmas. Multicoloured.

692.	120 f. Type **240**	85	30
693.	350 f. " Virgin of the Garland "	2·40	65
694.	500 f. " Adoration of the Magi "	3·00	1·00

1984. Air. Olympic Games, Los Angeles. Multicoloured.

695.	90 f. Type **242**	55	20
696.	120 f. Volleyball	80	30
697.	150 f. Handball (horiz.) ..	1·10	35
698.	250 f. Basketball (horiz.) ..	1·60	50
699.	300 f. Football (horiz.) ..	2·00	65

243. Greater Flamingo.

1984. Air. Birds. Multicoloured.

701.	90 f. Type **243**	1·00	40
702.	185 f. Kori bustard (vert.)	1·75	1·00
703.	200 f. Red-billed oxpecker (vert.)	1·90	1·10
704.	300 f. Southern ground hornbill	2·50	1·75

244. Pres. Houari Boumedienne of Algeria.

1984. Air. Celebrities. Multicoloured.

705.	5 f. Type **244**	10	10
706.	125 f. Gottlieb Daimler (automobile designer) and car	90	30
707.	250 f. Louis Bleriot (aviator) and "14-Bis" airplane	1·60	50
708.	300 f. Pres. Abraham Lincoln of U.S.A. and White House	2·25	55
709.	400 f. Henry Dunant (founder of Red Cross), red cross and battle of Solferino	2·75	70
710.	450 f. Auguste Piccard and bathyscape "Trieste" ..	3·00	1·40
711.	500 f. Robert Baden-Powell (founder of Boy Scout movement) and scouts ..	3·25	95
712.	600 f. Anatole Karpov, 1978 world chess champion ..	3·75	1·10

245. Seedling and Clasped Hands within Circle of Flags.

246. "Polystictus leoninus".

1984. 25th Anniv. of Council of Unity.

714.	**245.**	90 f. multicoloured ..	65	30
715.		100 f. multicoloured ..	80	35

1984. Fungi and Flowers. Multicoloured.

716.	25 f. Type **246** (postage) ..	20	10
717.	185 f. "Pterocarpus lucens"	1·60	60
718.	200 f. "Phlebopus colossus sudanicus"	1·90	65
719.	250 f. "Cosmos sulphureus"	2·25	85
720.	300 f. "Trametes versicolour" (air)	2·50	95
721.	400 f. "Ganoderma lucidum"	3·50	1·25

247. Cheetah with Cubs.

1984. Protected Animals. Multicoloured.

723.	15 f. Type **247** (postage) ..	10	10
724.	35 f. Two cheetahs ..	30	10
725.	90 f. Cheetah ..	65	20
726.	120 f. Cheetah with cubs (different)	90	35
727.	300 f. Baboons (air) ..	2·25	55
728.	400 f. Marabou stork and African white-backed vulture	2·75	65

248. "CC2400 ch".

1984. Transport. Multicoloured.

(a) Locomotives.

730	40 f. Type **248**	30	10
731	100 f. Steam locomotive No. 1806	75	30
732	145 f. "Livingstone" ..	1·25	50
733	450 f. Pacific class "C51" steam locomotive ..	3·25	1·60

(b) Ships.

734.	20 f. "Maiden Queen" ..	15	5
735.	60 f. "Scawfell" ..	45	15
736.	120 f. "Harbinger" ..	90	35
737.	400 f. "True Briton" ..	3·00	1·25

For later issues see **BURKINA FASO**.

OFFICIAL STAMPS

O 18. African Elephant.

1963.

O 112.	**O 18.**	1 f. sepia and brown	10	10
O 113.		5 f. sepia and green	12	12
O 114.		10 f. sepia and violet	20	20
O 115.		15 f. sepia & orange	25	25
O 116.		25 f. sepia and purple	35	35
O 117.		50 f. sepia and green	65	65
O 118.		60 f. sepia and red ..	75	75
O 119.		85 f. sepia and myrtle	1·25	1·25
O 120.		100 f. sepia and blue	1·50	1·50
O 121.		200 f. sepia and mve.	2·75	2·75

POSTAGE DUE STAMPS

1920. Postage Due stamps of Upper Senegal and Niger, "Figures" key-type, optd. **HAUTE-VOLTA.**

No.	Type	Description		
D 18.	M.	5 c. green	25	50
D 19.		10 c. red	25	50
D 20.		15 c. grey	25	50
D 21.		20 c. brown	30	60
D 22.		30 c. blue	45	90
D 23.		50 c. black	70	1·40
D 24.		60 c. orange	65	1·40
D 25.		1 f. violet	90	1·90

1927. Surch.

No.	Type	Description		
D40	M	2 f. on 1 f. mauve	2·25	3·50
D41		3 f. on 1 f. brown	2·50	3·75

1928. "Figures" key-type inscr. "HAUTE-VOLTA".

No.	Type	Description		
D 63.	M.	5 c. green	35	75
D 64.		10 c. red	35	75
D 65.		15 c. grey	50	95
D 66.		20 c. brown	50	95
D 67.		30 c. blue	65	1·25
D 68.		50 c. black	1·75	3·00
D 69.		60 c. orange	2·25	4·00
D 70.		1 f. violet	3·50	6·50
D 71.		2 f. purple	6·75	10·00
D 72.		3 f. brown	7·50	11·00

D 13. Red-fronted Gazelle.

1962. Figures of value in black.

No.	Type	Description		
D 95.	D 13.	1 f. blue	10	10
D 96.		2 f. orange	10	10
D 97.		5 f. blue	15	15
D 98.		10 f. purple	30	30
D 99.		20 f. green	55	55
D 100.		50 f. red	1·40	1·40

APPENDIX

The following stamps have either been issued in excess of postal needs or have not been available to the public in reasonable quantities at face value. Such stamps may later be given full listing if there is evidence of regular postal use.

1973.

Gold Medal Winners, Munich Olympic Games (2nd series). Air 50, 60, 90, 150, 350 f.

Christmas 1972. Paintings of the Madonna and Child. Air 50, 75, 100, 125, 150 f.

Moon Mission of "Apollo 17". Air 50, 65, 100, 150, 200 f.

Gold Medal Winners, Munich Olympic Games (3rd series). Air 35, 45, 75, 250, 400 f.

Exploration of the Moon. Air 50, 65, 100, 150, 200 f.

Wild Animals. Air 100, 150, 200, 250, 500 f.

10th Anniv. of Organization of African Unity. Air 45 f.

Europafrique. European Paintings. Air 50, 65, 100, 150, 200 f.

Historic Railway Locomotives, French Railway Museum, Mulhouse. Air 10, 40, 50, 150, 250 f.

Upper Volta Boy Scouts. Postage 20 f.; Air 40, 75, 150, 200 f.

Pan-African Drought Relief. Surch. on values of 1973 Europafrique issue. Air 100 f. on 65 f., 200 f. on 150 f.

10th Death Anniv. of President John Kennedy. Rockets. Postage 5, 10, 30 f.; Air 200, 300 f.

50th Anniv. of International Police Organization (Interpol). 50, 65, 70, 150 f.

Tourism. Postage 35, 40 f.; Air 100 f.

Religious Buildings Postage 35, 40 f.; Air 200 f.

Folk-dancers. Postage 35, 40 f.; Air 100, 225 f.

Famous Men. 5, 10, 20, 25, 30, 50, 60, 75, 100, 175, 200, 250 f.

1974.

World Cup Football Championship, Munich (1st issue). Postage 5, 40 f.; Air 75, 100, 250 f.

Pres. De Gaulle Commemoration. Postage 35, 40, 60 f.; Air 300 f.

World Cup Football Championship (2nd issue). Postage 10, 20, 50 f.; Air 150, 300 f.

Centenary of Universal Postal Union. Postage 35, 40, 85 f.; Air 100, 200, 300 f.

World Cup Football Championship (3rd issue). Previous Finals. Postage 10, 25, 50 f.; Air 150, 200, 250 f.

Centenary of Berne Convention. 1974 U.P.U. issue optd. Postage 35, 40, 85 f.; Air 100, 200, 300 f.

Bouquets of Flowers. Postage 5, 10, 30, 50 f.; Air 300 f.

1975.

Birth Centenary of Sir Winston Churchill. 50, 75, 100, 125, 300 f.

Bicentenary of American Revolution (1st issue). 35, 40, 75, 100, 200, 300 f.

Railway Locomotives. Postage 15, 25, 50 f.; Air 100, 200 f.

Vintage and Veteran Cars. Postage 10, 30, 35 f.; Air 150, 200 f.

Bicent. of American Revolution (2nd issue). Postage 30, 40, 50 f.; Air 200, 300 f.

Birth Cent. of Dr Albert Schweitzer. Postage 5, 15 f.; Air 150, 175, 200 f.

"Apollo - Soyuz" Joint Space Test Project. Postage 40, 50 f.; Air 100, 200, 300 f.

Paintings by Picasso. Postage 50, 60, 90 f.; Air 150, 350 f.

"Expo '75" Exhibition, Okinawa, Japan. Postage 15, 25, 45, 50, 60 f.; Air 150 f.

Winter Olympic Games, Innsbruck. Postage 35, 45, 85 f.; Air 100, 200 f.

1976.

Olympic Games, Montreal (1st issue). "Pre-Olympic Year" (1975). Postage 40, 50, 100 f.; Air 125, 150 f.

Olympic Games, Montreal (2nd issue). Postage 30, 55, 75 f.; Air 150, 200 f.

Zeppelin Airships. Postage 10, 40, 50 f.; Air 100, 200, 300 f.

"Viking" Space Flight. Postage 30, 55, 75 f.; Air 200, 300 f.

1977.

Olympic Games Medal Winners, 1976 Olympic Games issue. Optd. Postage 30, 55, 75 f.; Air 150, 200 f.

1983.

Bicentenary of Manned Flight. Air 1500 f.

UPPER YAFA — Pt. 19

A Sultanate of South Arabia, formerly part of the Western Aden Protectorate. Independent from September to December 1967 and then part of the People's Democratic Republic of Yemen.

1000 fils = 1 dinar.

1. Flag and Map.

1967.

No.	Type	Description		
UY 1.	1.	5 f. multicoloured (post.)	15	15
UY 2.		10 f. multicoloured	15	15
UY 3.		20 f. multicoloured	20	20
UY 4.		25 f. multicoloured	25	20
UY 5.		40 f. multicoloured	40	25
UY 6.		50 f. multicoloured	50	30
UY 7.	–	75 f. multicoloured (air)	65	50
UY 8.	–	100 f. multicoloured	85	60
UY 9.	–	250 f. multicoloured	2·00	2·00
UY 10.	–	500 f. multicoloured	3·50	3·50

DESIGNS: UY 7/10, Arms of Sultanate.

APPENDIX

The following stamps have either been issued in excess of postal needs or have not been available to the public in reasonable quantities at face value. Such stamps may later be given full listing if there is evidence of regular postal use.

1967.

Olympic Games, Mexico (1968). Postage 15, 25, 50, 75 f.; Air 150 f.

Sculptures. Postage 10, 30 60, 75 f.; Air 150 f.

Paintings from the Louvre. Postage 50 f.; Air 100, 150, 200, 250 f.

World Cup Football Championships, England (1966). Postage 5, 10, 50 f.; Air 100 f.

Paintings by Old Masters. Postage 10, 15, 20, 25, 30, 40, 50, 60, 75 f.; Air 150 f.

Human Rights Year and 5th Death Anniv. of J. F. Kennedy. Postage 5, 10, 50 75 f.; Air 125 f.

Persian Miniatures. 10, 20, 30, 40, 50 f.

Ballet Paintings. 20, 30, 40, 50, 60 f.

Portraits by Old Masters. Postage 25, 50, 75 f.; Air 100, 125, 150, 175, 200, 225, 250 f.

Winter Olympic Games, Grenoble (1968). 1967 World Cup issue optd. Postage 5 f. × 2, 10 f. × 2, 50 f. × 2; Air 100 f. × 2.

20th Anniv. of UNICEF. Paintings. Postage 50, 75 f.; Air 100, 125, 250 f.

Flower Paintings. Postage 5, 10, 50 f.; Air 100, 150 f.

URUGUAY — Pt. 20

A republic in S. America, bordering on the Atlantic Ocean, independent since 1828.

1856. 120 centavos = 1 real.
1859. 1000 milesimos = 100 centesimos = 1 peso.

1.

1856. Imperf.

No.	Type	Description		
1.	1.	60 c. blue	£190	
2.		80 c. green	£170	
3.		1 r. red	£150	

3.

4.

1858. Imperf.

No.	Type	Description		
5.	3.	120 c. blue	£130	£120
6.		180 c. green	38·00	55·00
7.		240 c. red	38·00	£225

1859. Imperf.

No.	Type	Description		
15.	4.	60 c. purple	15·00	13·50
16.		80 c. yellow	£130	25·00
17.		100 c. red	38·00	29·00
18.		120 c. blue	25·00	9·50
12.		180 c. green	9·50	11·50
13.		240 c. red	35·00	35·00

6.

8.

9.

1864. Imperf.

No.	Type	Description		
20a.	6.	6 c. red	5·75	3·75
21.		8 c. green	9·75	9·75
22.		10 c. yellow	13·50	9·25
23.		12 c. blue	5·75	4·50

1866. Surch. in figures. Imperf.

No.	Type	Description		
24.	6.	5 c. on 12 c. blue	9·50	19·00
25.		10 c. on 8 c. green	9·50	25·00
26.		15 c. on 10 c. yellow	11·50	29·00
27a.		20 c. on 6 c. red	13·50	29·00

1866. Imperf.

No.	Type	Description		
28.	8.	1 c. black	95	1·50
29.	9.	5 c. blue	1·50	85
30.		10 c. green	5·50	2·25
31.		15 c. yellow	9·25	3·75
32.		20 c. red	11·00	3·75

1866. Perf.

No.	Type	Description		
37.	8.	1 c. black	2·25	2·25
33.	9.	5 c. blue	2·00	35
34.		10 c. green	3·75	35
35.		15 c. yellow	2·00	1·40
36.		20 c. red	4·50	1·10

10.

11.

1877. Roul. Various frames.

No.	Type	Description		
42.	10.	1 c. brown	25	20
43.	11.	5 c. green	30	15
44.	10.	10 c. red	40	15
45.		20 c. bistre	60	25
46.		50 c. black	3·00	1·10
47.		1 p. blue	17·00	5·50

15. J. Suarez.

16.

1881. Perf.

No.	Type	Description		
60a	15	7 c. blue	75	90

1882.

No.	Type	Description		
62.	16.	1 c. green	40	40
63.	–	2 c. red	35	35

The central device on the 2 c. is a mountain.

18. Arms.

20. Gen. Maximo Santos.

21. General Artigas.

26.

1883.

No.	Type	Description		
66.	18.	1 c. green	50	30
67.		2 c. red	60	40
68.	20.	5 c. blue	75	60
69.	21.	10 c. brown	1·10	75

1883. Optd. **1883 Provisorio.** Roul.

No.	Type	Description		
75.	11.	5 c. green	50	40

1884. Optd. **PROVISORIO 1884** or surch. **1 CENTESIMO** also.

No.	Type	Description		
76.	10.	1 c. on 10 c. red	15	15
77.	–	2 c. red (No. 63)	50	50

1884.

No.	Type	Description		
79.	26.	5 c. blue	1·00	50

28.

29.

31. Gen. Artigas.

32. M. Santos.

33.

34.

1884. Roul.

No.	Type	Description		
100	28	1 c. green	20	20
83a		1 c. grey	40	30
101	29	2 c. red	20	25
85a	28	5 c. blue	1·00	15
86		5 c. lilac	25	10
87	31	7 c. brown	95	60
103		7 c. orange	60	40
88	32	10 c. brown	20	20
89	33	20 c. mauve	75	30
105		20 c. brown	75	40
90	34	25 c. lilac	1·40	50
106		25 c. red	1·10	60

35.

36.

1887. Roul.

No.	Type	Description		
99.	35.	10 c. mauve	70	40

1888. Roul.

No.	Type	Description		
104.	36.	10 c. violet	25	25

1889. Optd. **Provisorio.** Roul.

No.	Type	Description		
114.	28.	5 c. lilac	15	15

38. 39. 40.

41.

42.

43.

44. Figure of Justice. 45. Mercury. 46.

1889. Perf.

115 **38.** 1 c. green 40 20
116 **39.** 2 c. red 20 25
117 **40.** 5 c. blue 20 15
118 **41.** 7 c. brown 60 25
119 **42.** 10 c. green .. .. 1·50 25
120 **43.** 20 c. orange .. .. 1·10 30
121 **44.** 25 c. brown .. .. 2·00 40
122 **45.** 50 c. blue .. .. 3·50 1·10
123 **46.** 1 p. violet .. .. 8·50 2·00

See also Nos. 142/52, 220, 222, 224 and 236/7.

1891. Optd. **Provisorio 1891.** Roul.

133. **28.** 5 c. lilac 10 10

1892. Optd. **Provisorio 1892** or surch. also in words.

135. **28.** 1 c. green 40 40
137. **43.** 1 c. on 20 c. orange .. 15 10
136. **41.** 5 c. on 7 c. brown .. 15 30

50. 51. 52.

53. 54. 55.

1892. Perf.

138. **50.** 1 c. green 20 15
139. **51.** 2 c. red 25 20
140. **52.** 5 c. blue 20 15
141. **53.** 10 c. orange 90 40

1894.

142. **38.** 1 c. blue 20 25
143. **39.** 2 c. brown 25 25
144. **40.** 5 c. red 50 20
145. **41.** 7 c. green .. .. 2·75 1·10
146. **42.** 10 c. orange .. .. 1·50 30
147. **43.** 20 c. brown .. .. 2·75 75
148. **44.** 25 c. red .. .. 3·50 1·50
149. **45.** 50 c. purple .. .. 6·25 2·25
150. **46.** 1 p. blue .. .. 11·00 3·00
151. **54.** 2 p. red .. .. .. 11·50 7·00
152. **55.** 3 p. purple .. .. 11·50 7·00

56. Gaucho. 57. Solis Theatre. 58. Steam Locomotive.

59. Bull's Head. 60. Ceres. 61. Steamer "Elbe".

62. Amazon. 63. Mercury.

64. 65. Montevideo Fortress.

66. Montevideo Cathedral.

1895.

153. **56.** 1 c. bistre 20 20
154. **57.** 2 c. blue 20 20
155. **58.** 5 c. red 20 20
156. **59.** 7 c. green .. .. 3·75 1·00
157. **60.** 10 c. brown 85 30
158. **61.** 20 c. black and green .. 6·00 55
159. **62.** 25 c. black and brown .. 2·75 60
160. **63.** 50 c. black and blue .. 3·50 1·50
161. **64.** 1 p. black and brown .. 5·50 2·00
162. **65.** 2 p. green and violet .. 11·50 7·75
163. **66.** 3 p. blue and red .. 11·50 6·25

For further stamps in these types, see Nos. 183/93 and 221.

67. J. Suarez. 68. J. Suarez Monument. 72.

1896. Unveiling of President Joaquin Suarez Monument.

177. **67.** 1 c. black and red .. 20 15
178. **68.** 5 c. black and blue .. 25 20
179. – 10 c. black and lake .. 45 25

DESIGN: 10 c. Larger stamp showing whole Suarez Monument.

1897. Optd. **PROVISORIO 1897.**

180. **67.** 1 c. black and red .. 30 30
181. **68.** 5 c. black and blue .. 40 30
182. – 10 c. black and lake .. 50 50

1897.

183. **56.** 1 c. blue 20 15
184. **57.** 2 c. purple 30 20
185. **58.** 5 c. green 30 15
186. **59.** 7 c. orange .. .. 1·75 60
187. **72.** 10 c. red 85 35
188. **61.** 20 c. black and mauve .. 5·50 40
189. **62.** 25 c. blue and red .. 1·50 35
190. **63.** 50 c. brown and green .. 2·75 70
191. **64.** 1 p. blue and brown .. 4·50 1·40
192. **65.** 2 p. red and yellow .. 4·50 65
193. **66.** 3 p. red and lilac .. 4·25 1·10

See also No. 223.

1897. End of Civil War. Optd. with palm leaf and **PAZ 1897.**

197. **56.** 1 c. blue 40 30
198. **57.** 2 c. purple 55 55
199. **58.** 5 c. green 85 75
200. **72.** 10 c. red .. .. 1·40 1·40

1898. Surch. **PROVISIONAL ½ CENTESIMO.**

209. **38.** ½ c. on 1 c. blue .. 15 15
210. **56.** ½ c. on 1 c. bistre .. 15 15
211. **67.** ½ c. on 1 c. black and red 15 15
212. **57.** ½ c. on 2 c. blue .. 15 15
213. **68.** ½ c. on 5 c. black & blue 20 15
214. **59.** ½ c. on 7 c. green .. 20 15

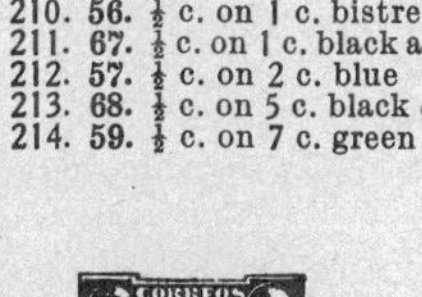

75. Liberty. 76. Monument to Gen. Artigas.

1898.

215. **75.** 5 m. red 20 20
216. 5 m. violet 25 25

1899.

217. **76.** 5 m. blue 25 15
218. 5 m. orange 25 15
220. **39.** 2 c. orange 20 20
221a. **58.** 5 c. blue .. .. 1·50 15
222. **41.** 7 c. red .. .. 2·25 1·10
223. **72.** 10 c. purple 30 25
224. **43.** 20 c. blue .. .. 1·10 20

1900. No. 182 surch. **1900 5 CENTESIMOS** and bar.

229. 5 c. on 10 c. black and lake 25 15

MORE DETAILED LISTS
are given in the Stanley Gibbons Catalogues referred to in the country headings.
For lists of current volumes see Introduction.

78. 79. 80.

81. 82.

1900.

230 **78.** 1 c. green 30 15
231a **79.** 2 c. red 10 15
232b **80.** 5 c. blue 60 15
233 **81.** 7 c. brown 85 30
234 **82.** 10 c. lilac 45 20
236 **45.** 50 c. red .. .. 3·50 35
237 **46.** 1 p. green .. .. 11·00 75

85. General Artigas. 86. 87.

88. 89.

90. 91.

1904.

251 **85.** 5 m. yellow 30 15
252 **86.** 1 c. green 50 15
253a **87.** 2 c. orange 20 15
254b **88.** 5 c. blue 40 10
255 **89.** 10 c. lilac 40 20
256 **90.** 20 c. green .. .. 1·40 40
257 **91.** 25 c. bistre .. .. 1·50 40

1904. End of the Civil War. Optd. **Paz-1904.**

258. **86.** 1 c. green 35 30
259. **87.** 2 c. orange 40 35
260. **88.** 5 c. blue .. .. 1·00 50

95. 96.

1906.

268. **95.** 5 c. blue 50 15

1906.

269. **96.** 5 c. blue 20 10
270. 7 c. brown 40 25
271. 50 c. red .. .. 2·25 40

98. Cruiser "Montevideo" and Cadet Ship "Diez-y-Ocho de Julio".

1908. 83rd Anniv. of Revolt of the "Immortal 33" under Levalleja. Roul.

279. **98.** 1 c. green and red .. 1·10 85
280. 2 c. green .. .. 1·10 85
281. 5 c. green and orange .. 1·10 85

99. Montevideo Port. 103. Centaur.

1909. Opening of the Port of Montevideo.

282. **99.** 2 c. black and brown .. 1·50 80
283. 5 c. black and red .. 1·50 80

1909. Surch. **Provisorio** and value.

284. **82.** 8 c. on 10 c. violet .. 40 30
285. **44.** 23 c. on 25 c. brown .. 75 30

1910. Cent. of 1810 Argentine Revolution.

286. **103.** 2 c. red 30 20
287. 5 c. blue 30 20

1910. Surch. **PROVISORIO 5 MILESIMOS** (or **CENTESIMOS**) **1910.**

294. **78.** 5 m. on 1 c. green .. 10 20
295. **45.** 5 c. on 50 c. red .. 15 30
296. **96.** 5 c. on 50 c. red .. 40 30

107. Artigas. 108.

1910.

297. **107.** 5 m. purple 15 10
298. 1 c. green 15 10
299. 2 c. red 20 10
324. 2 c. pink 25 10
319. 4 c. yellow 30 10
300. 5 c. blue 20 10
301. 8 c. black 40 15
327. 8 c. blue 25 10
302. 20 c. brown 70 20
303. **108.** 23 c. blue .. .. 1·10 25
330. 50 c. orange .. .. 1·50 60
331. 1 p. red .. .. 4·50 40

109. 114. Liberty offering Peace to Uruguay.

1911. First Pan-American Postal Congress.

306. **109.** 5 c. black and red .. 35 25

1911. Cent. of Battle of Las Piedras. Surch. **ARTIGAS,** value and **1811-1911.**

314. **81.** 2 c. on 7 c. brown .. 35 25
315. 5 c. on 7 c. brown .. 35 20

1913. Cent. of 1813 Conference. Optd. **CENTENARIO DE LAS INSTRUCCIONES DEL ANO XIII.**

332. **107.** 2 c. brown 30 40
333. 4 c. yellow 30 40
334. 5 c. blue 30 40

1918. Promulgation of New Constitution.

347. **114.** 2 c. brown and green .. 35 25
348. 5 c. blue and brown .. 35 25

115. Montevideo Harbour. 116. Statue of Liberty, New York. 118. J. E. Rodo.

1919.

349. **115.** 5 m. grey and violet .. 15 10
350. 1 c. grey and green .. 20 10
351. 2 c. grey and red .. 20 10
352. 4 c. grey and orange .. 50 10
353. 5 c. grey and blue .. 60 10
354. 8 c. brown and blue .. 70 20
355. 20 c. grey and brown .. 2·50 35
356. 23 c. brown and green .. 3·50 70
357. 50 c. blue and brown .. 4·00 3·25
358. 1 p. blue and red .. 9·50 2·75

1919. Peace Commemoration.

359.	116.	2 c. brown and red	20	10
360.		4 c. brown and orange	30	10
361.		5 c. brown and blue	35	10
362.		8 c. blue and brown	50	20
363.		20 c. black and bistre	1·40	40
364.		23 c. black and green	2·00	70

1920. Honouring J. E. Rodo (writer).

372.	118.	2 c. black and lake	35	45
373.		4 c. blue and orange	40	30
374.		5 c. brown and blue	50	35

1921. Air. Optd. with aeroplane and **CORREO AEREO.**

377	44.	25 c. brown	2·10	1·50

120. Mercury. 122. Damaso A. Larranaga.

1921.

378	120.	5 m. mauve	30	10
410		5 m. black	20	10
380		1 c. green	30	10
411a		1 c. violet	25	10
411		1 c. mauve	25	10
412		2 c. orange	35	10
412a		2 c. red	40	10
384		3 c. green	40	20
385		4 c. yellow	25	10
386		5 c. blue	25	10
413		5 c. brown	40	10
414		8 c. red	55	50
388		12 c. blue	1·10	50
389		36 c. olive	4·50	1·50

1921. 150th Birth Anniv. of D. A. Larranaga.

390.	122.	5 c. slate	75	55

127. Artigas Monument. 128. Chilian Lapwing.

1923. Unveiling of Monument to Artigas.

418.	127.	2 c. brown and red	30	10
419.		5 c. brown and violet	30	10
420.		12 c. brown and blue	40	20

1923. Various sizes.

450	128.	5 m. grey	15	10
422		1 c. yellow	10	15
451		1 c. pink	25	15
477		1 c. purple	50	20
528		1 c. violet	10	20
423		2 c. mauve	10	15
529		2 c. red	10	20
~~453~~		3 c. green	35	15
454		5 c. blue	25	10
455		8 c. red	35	15
456		10 c. green	25	10
457		12 c. blue	40	15
458		15 c. mauve	30	15
459		20 c. brown	70	15
429		36 c. green	1·50	65
460		36 c. red	2·25	55
430		50 c. orange	3·00	1·00
461		50 c. olive	3·00	75
431		1 p. red	12·50	7·75
462		1 p. buff	4·75	1·75
432		2 p. green	12·50	7·75
463		2 p. lilac	9·50	5·00

130. 131.

1923. Cent. of Battle of Sarandi.

433.	130.	2 c. green	35	25
434.		5 c. red	35	25
435.		12 c. blue	35	25

1924. Air.

436.	131.	6 c. blue	75	85
437.		10 c. red	1·10	1·25
438.		20 c. green	2·00	2·00

134. "Victory" of Samothrace.

1924. Uruguayan Football Victory in Olympic Games.

464	134.	2 c. red	8·50	6·25
465		5 c. purple	8·50	6·25
466		12 c. blue	8·50	6·25

135. Landing of Lavalleja.

1925. Cent. of Rising against Brazilian Rule.

467.	135.	2 c. grey and red	60	70
468.		5 c. grey and mauve	60	70
469.		12 c. grey and blue	60	70

136. Parliament House. 137. White-necked heron.

1925. Inaug. of Parliament House.

470.	136.	5 c. black and violet	60	40
471.		12 c. black and blue	60	40

1925. Air. Cent of Assembly of Florida.

(a) Inscr. "MONTEVIDEO"

472	137	14 c. black and blue	15·00	7·75

(b) Inscr "FLORIDA"

473	137	14 c. black and blue	15·00	7·75

138. Gen. F. Rivera. 139. Gaucho Cavalryman at Rincon.

1925. Cent. of Battle of Rincon.

474.	138.	5 c. pink (postage)	40	30
475.	139.	45 c. green (air)	—	4·50

140. Battle of Sarandi.

1925. Cent. of Battle of Sarandi.

482.	140.	2 c. green	60	55
483.		5 c. mauve	60	55
484.		12 c. blue	75	60

141. Albatross. 145. New G.P.O. Montevideo.

1926. Air. Imperf.

495.	141.	6 c. blue	70	70
496.		10 c. red	95	95
497.		20 c. green	1·40	1·40
498.		25 c. violet	1·40	1·40

See also Nos. 569/80.

1927. Philatelic Exn., Montevideo. Imperf.

534.	145.	2 c. green	2·00	2·00
535.		5 c. red	2·00	2·00
536.		8 c. blue	2·00	2·00

1928. Opening of San Carlos-Rocha Railway. Surch. **Inauguracion Ferrocarril SAN CARLOS a ROCHA 14/1/928** and value.

537.	128.	2 c. on 12 c. blue	85	85
538.		5 c. on 12 c. blue	85	85
539.		10 c. on 12 c. blue	85	85
540.		15 c. on 12 c. blue	85	85

147. Gen. F. Rivera (after M. Bucasso).

1928. Cent. of Conquest of Las Misiones.

541.	147.	5 c. red	30	15

148. Artigas. 149. Artigas Statue, Paysandu.

1928.

542.	148.	5 m. black	10	10
762.		5 m. brown	10	10
868.		5 m. orange	10	10
~~543.~~		1 c. violet	10	10
544.		1 c. purple	10	10
869.		1 c. blue	10	10
687.		15 m. black	25	15
545.		2 c. green	10	10
764.		2 c. brown	10	10
870.		2 c. red	10	10
546.		3 c. bistre	20	10
~~871.~~		3 c. green	10	10
548.		5 c. red	15	10
549.		5 c. olive	15	10
766.		5 c. blue	15	10
767.		5 c. turquoise	30	10
872.		5 c. violet	10	10
550.		7 c. red	15	10
551.		8 c. blue	20	10
552.		8 c. brown	20	10
553.		10 c. orange	30	15
~~768.~~		12 c. blue	30	10
556.		15 c. blue	45	10
557.		17 c. violet	40	15
558.		20 c. brown	55	15
757.		20 c. buff	70	35
770.		20 c. red	40	30
771.		20 c. violet	35	10
560.		24 c. red	70	40
561.		24 c. yellow	40	35
562.		36 c. olive	70	40
563.		50 c. grey	1·75	95
564.		50 c. black	2·25	85
772.		50 c. sepia	1·10	45
566.		1 p. green	4·00	1·50
567.	149.	2 p. brown and blue	5·00	2·75
568.		3 p. black and red	6·25	6·25

1928. Air. Re-issue of T **141.** Perf.

634.	141.	4 c. brown	1·50	1·50
569.		10 c. green	75	70
570.		20 c. orange	1·10	85
571.		30 c. blue	1·10	85
572.		38 c. green	1·75	1·50
573.		40 c. yellow	2·10	2·00
574.		50 c. violet	2·25	2·25
575.		76 c. orange	4·25	4·25
576.		1 p. red	3·50	3·50
577.		1 p. 14 c. blue	10·00	8·75
578.		1 p. 52 c. yellow	15·00	15·00
579.		1 p. 90 c. violet	18·00	17·00
580.		3 p. 80 c. red	50·00	45·00

150. Goal Posts. 151. General Garzon.

1928. Uruguayan Football Victories in 1924 and 1928 Olympic Games.

581.	150.	2 c. purple	4·50	3·75
582.		5 c. red	4·50	3·75
583.		8 c. blue	4·50	3·75

1928. Unveiling of Monument to Gen. Garzon. Imperf.

584.	151.	2 c. red	75	75
585.		5 c. green	75	75
586.		8 c. blue	75	75

154. Artigas. 156. Pegasus.

1929.

759	154	1 p. brown	3·00	1·40
596		2 p. green	5·00	2·75
597		2 p. red	11·00	7·75
760		2 p. blue	5·75	5·50
598		3 p. blue	7·00	5·00
761		3 p. black	8·75	7·00
600		4 p. violet	11·00	8·50
601		4 p. green	11·00	7·75
602		5 p. red	13·50	11·00
603		5 p. orange	11·00	7·75
604		10 p. blue	38·00	35·00
605		10 p. red	38·00	35·00

1929. Air. Size 34½ × 23½ mm.

617.	156.	1 c. mauve	25	25
659.		1 c. blue	25	25
618.		2 c. yellow	25	25
660.		2 c. olive	25	25
619.		4 c. blue	45	40
661.		4 c. lake	45	40
620.		6 c. violet	25	40
662.		6 c. brown	25	40
621.		8 c. orange	1·10	1·10
663.		8 c. grey	1·25	1·10
664.		8 c. green	35	30
622.		16 c. blue	1·10	75
665.		16 c. red	1·10	1·10
623.		24 c. purple	95	95
666.		24 c. violet	1·25	1·10
624.		30 c. brown	1·10	1·10
667.		30 c. green	60	30
625.		40 c. brown	2·00	2·00
668.		40 c. orange	2·00	1·75
626.		60 c. blue	1·75	1·25
669.		60 c. green	3·00	2·25
670.		60 c. red	95	60
627.		80 c. blue	3·00	3·00
671.		80 c. green	5·00	4·00
628.		90 c. blue	3·00	2·10
672.		90 c. olive	5·00	4·00
629.		1 p. red	2·25	2·00
630.		1 p. 20 olive	7·00	7·00
673.		1 p. 20 red	11·00	9·25
631.		1 p. 50 purple	7·00	5·50
674.		1 p. 50 sepia	3·75	3·50
632.		3 p. red	11·50	11·00
675.		3 p. blue	7·75	7·75
633.		4 p. 50 black	20·00	18·00
676.		4 p. 50 lilac	14·00	12·50
677.		10 p. blue	7·00	5·50

For stamps as Type **156**, but smaller, see Nos. 725/44.

157. Rio Negro Bridge. 159. "Peace".

1930. Independence Cent.

639.	157.	5 m. black	20	15
640.	–	1 c. sepia	20	15
641.	159.	2 c. lake	20	15
642.	–	3 c. green	25	20
643.	–	5 c. blue	25	20
644.	–	8 c. red	35	20
645.	–	10 c. violet	25	35
646.	–	15 c. green	30	25
647.	–	20 c. blue	1·40	70
648.	–	24 c. lake	60	30
649.	–	50 c. red	3·25	1·75
650.	–	1 p. black	3·00	1·50
651.	–	2 p. blue	7·00	4·50
652.	–	3 p. red	10·00	7·00
653.	–	4 p. orange	11·50	8·50
654.	–	5 p. lilac	17·00	10·00

DESIGNS—HORIZ. 1 c. Gaucho Horse-breaker. 5 c. Head of Liberty and Uruguayan flag. 10 c. "Artigas", from picture by Blanes. 15 c. Seascape. 20 c. Montevideo Harbour, 1830. 24 c. Head of Liberty and Arms of Uruguay. 50 c. Montevideo Harbour, 1930. VERT. 3 c. Montevideo. 8 c. Allegorical figure with torch. 1 p. to 5 p. Artigas Monument.

161. 163. J. Zorrilla de San Martin.

1930. Fund for Old People.

655.	161.	1 c.+1 c. violet	20	15
656.		2 c.+2 c. green	25	25
657.		5 c.+5 c. red	30	30
658.		8 c.+8 c. blue	30	30

1932.

679.	163.	1½ c. purple	20	10
680.		3 c. green	30	10
681.		7 c. blue	35	10
682.		12 c. blue	30	35
683.		1p. brown	9·25	6·25

1932. Surch.

684.	161.	1½ c. on 2 c.+2 c. green	25	15

167. J. Zorrilla de San Martin. 168. Flag of the Race.

1933. Various portraits.

689.	148.	15 m. red (Lavalleja)	15	10
690.		3 c. green (Rivera)	10	10
~~691.~~	167.	7 c. grey	15	10

1933. 441st Anniv. of Columbus' Departure from Palos.

692 168 3 c. green 15 20
693 5 c. pink 20 25
694 7 c. blue 20 20
695 8 c. red 60 30
696 12 c. blue 25 25
697 17 c. violet 75 40
698 20 c. brown .. .. 1·50 95
699 24 c. bistre .. .. 2·00 95
700 36 c. red .. .. 2·25 1·10
701 50 c. brown .. .. 2·75 1·40
702 1 p. brown .. .. 7·75 3·50

169. Sower. 170. Map and Albatross.

1933. Opening of the 3rd National Assembly.

703. 169. 3 c. green 20 15
704. 5 c. violet 35 25
705. 7 c. blue 30 20
706. 8 c. red 40 40
707. 12 c. blue 75 45

1933. 7th Pan-American Conference, Montevideo.

708. 170. 3 c. grn., brn. & black 1·10 1·10
709. 7 c. blue, blk. & brown 60 45
710. 12 c. blue, red & grey 95 75
711. 17 c. red, blue & grey 2·10 2·10
712. 20 c. yell., grn. & blue 2·25 2·25
713. 36 c. red, yell. & black 3·00 3·00

1934. Air. Closure of the 7th Pan-American Conference. Optd. **SERVICIO POSTAL AEREO 1-1-34** in circle.

714. 170. 17 c. red, blue and grey 7·75 6·25
715. 36 c. red, yell. & black 7·25 6·25

172.

1934. 1st Anniv. of Third Republic.

716. 172. 3 c. green 25 35
717. 7 c. red 25 35
718. 12 c. blue 60 30
719. 17 c. brown and pink 75 70
720. 20 c. yellow and grey 95 75
721. 36 c. violet and green 95 95
722. 50 c. grey and blue .. 2·50 2·00
723. 1 p. red and mauve .. 6·25 4·00

1935. Air. As T **156**, but size $31\frac{1}{2} \times 21\frac{1}{2}$ mm.

725. 15 c. yellow 95 75
726. 22 c. red 60 50
727. 30 c. purple 95 75
728. 37 c. purple 50 40
729. 40 c. red 75 50
730. 47 c. red .. .. 1·50 1·40
731. 50 c. blue 50 50
732. 52 c. blue .. .. 1·50 1·40
733. 57 c. blue 75 70
734. 62 c. green 70 50
735. 87 c. green .. .. 2·10 1·75
736. 1 p. olive .. .. 1·40 85
737. 1 p. 12 brown .. .. 1·40 85
738. 1 p. 20 brown .. .. 4·50 3·75
739. 1 p. 27 brown .. .. 4·50 3·75
740. 1 p. 62 red .. .. 3·00 3·00
741. 2 p. lake .. .. 5·00 4·50
742. 2 p. 12 grey .. .. 5·00 4·50
743. 3 p. blue .. .. 4·50 4·50
744. 5 p. orange .. .. 16·00 16·00

173. Friendship of Uruguay and Brazil.

174. Florencio Sanchez.

1935. Visit of President Vargas of Brazil.

747. 173. 5 m. brown 50 30
748. 15 m. black 25 25
749. 3 c. green 30 25
750. 7 c. orange 35 20
751. 12 c. blue 50 50
752. 50 c. brown .. .. 2·00 1·50

INDEX

Countries can be quickly located by referring to the index at the end of this volume.

1935. 25th Death Anniv. of F. Sanchez (dramatist).

753. 174. 3 c. green 15 10
754. 7 c. brown 20 10
755. 12 c. blue 55 35

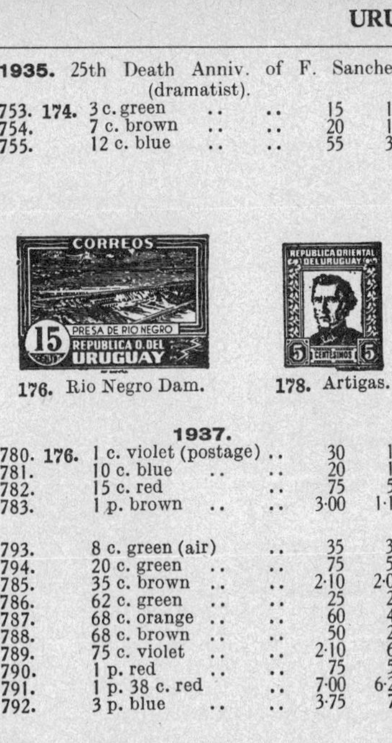

176. Rio Negro Dam. 178. Artigas.

1937.

780. 176. 1 c. violet (postage) .. 30 10
781. 10 c. blue 20 10
782. 15 c. red 75 50
783. 1 p. brown .. .. 3·00 1·10
793. 8 c. green (air) .. 35 35
794. 20 c. green 75 50
785. 35 c. brown .. .. 2·10 2·00
786. 62 c. green 25 20
787. 68 c. orange 60 40
788. 68 c. brown 50 20
789. 75 c. violet .. .. 2·10 60
790. 1 p. red 75 55
791. 1 p. 38 c. red .. 7·00 6·25
792. 3 p. blue .. .. 3·75 75

1939. (a) Plain background.

806. 178. 5 m. orange 10 10
807. 1 c. blue 10 10
808. 2 c. violet 10 10
809. 5 c. brown 15 10
810. 8 c. red 20 10
811. 10 c. green 35 10
812. 15 c. blue 40 30
813. 1 p. brown .. .. 1·25 30
1008. 1 p. purple .. .. 1·25 30
814. 2 p. lilac .. .. 3·00 1·25
815. 4 p. orange .. .. 3·75 1·50
816. 5 p. red .. .. 5·25 2·50

Nos. 806/12 are size 16 × 19 mm. No. 1008 is 18 × 22 mm. and Nos. 813/6 are $24 \times 29\frac{1}{2}$ mm.

(b) Lined background. (i) Size 17 × 22 mm.

835 178 5 m. orange 10 10
848 5 m. black 10 10
849 5 m. blue 10 10
836 1 c. blue 10 10
837 1 c. purple 10 10
838 2 c. violet 10 10
839 2 c. orange 15 10
840a 2 c. brown 10 10
1152 2 c. grey 10 10
841 3 c. green 15 10
842 5 c. brown 15 10
843b 7 c. blue 10 10
844 8 c. red 25 10
845 10 c. green 15 10
851 10 c. brown 25 10
852 12 c. blue 25 10
853 20 c. mauve 70 15
846 50 c. bistre .. .. 3·00 60
847 50 c. green .. .. 2·10 75
1153 50 c. brown 10 10

(ii) Size $23\frac{1}{2} \times 29\frac{1}{2}$ mm.

1024. 178. 2 p. brown .. .. 3·50 1·50

180. Aeroplane over "La Carreta" (sculpture, Jose Bellini).

1939. Air.

817 180 20 c. blue 30 25
818 20 c. violet 20 25
820 35 c. red 25 20
821 50 c. orange 25 20
822 75 c. pink 30 15
823 1 p. blue 85 10
824 1 p. 38 violet .. .. 1·50 60
825 1 p. 38 orange .. .. 1·40 1·25
826a 2 p. blue .. .. 2·25 45
827 5 p. lilac .. .. 3·00 60
828 5 p. green .. .. 3·75 1·50
829 10 p. red .. .. 23·00 15·00

181. Congress of Montevideo.

1939. 50th Anniv. of 1st Int. Juridical Congress, Montevideo.

830. 181. 1 c. red 20 10
831. 2 c. green 25 20
832. 5 c. red 25 20
833. 12 c. blue 30 35
834. 50 c. violet .. .. 1·10 75

183. Juan Manuel Blanes (artist).

185. Fransisco Acuna de Figueroa.

1941. 40th Death Anniv of Blanes.

855. 183. 5 m. brown 20 10
856. 1 c. brown 20 10
857. 2 c. green 20 10
858. 5 c. red 50 10
859. 12 c. blue 60 45
860. 50 c. violet .. .. 2·75 2·10

1942. 80th Death Anniv of Figueroa (author of words of National Anthem).

863 185 1 c. brown 15 15
864 2 c. green 15 15
865 5 c. red 30 15
866 12 c. blue 60 40
867 50 c. violet .. .. 1·75 1·50

1943. Surch **Valor $ 0.005.**

873. 178. 5 m. on 1 c. blue ..

187.

189. Clio.

1943.

874. 187. 1 c. on 2 c. brown .. 10 10
875. 2 c. on 2 c. brown .. 15 10

1943. Centenary of Historical and Geographical Institute. Montevideo.

878. 189. 5 m. violet 20 10
879. 1 c. blue 20 10
880. 2 c. red 35 15
881. 5 c. brown 35 20

191.

192. Emblems of Y.M.C.A.

1944. 75th Anniv of Founding of Swiss Colony.

889. 191. 1 c. on 3 c. green .. 10 10
890. 5 c. on 7 c. brown .. 20 10
891. 10 c. on 12 c. blue .. 40 25

1944. Cent. of Young Men's Christian Assn.

892. 192. 5 c. blue 10 10

1944. Air. Air stamps of 1935, Nos. 730, etc., surch.

893. 40 c. on 47 c. red 25 40
894. 40 c. on 57 c. blue .. 30 25
895. 74 c. on 1 p. 12 brown .. 30 25
896. 79 c. on 87 c. green .. 1·10 75
897. 79 c. on 1 p. 27 brown .. 1·50 1·25
898. 1 p. 20 on 1 p. 62 red .. 85 60
899. 1 p. 43 on 2 p. 12 grey .. 1·10 75

194. Legislative Palace.

1945. Air.

900. 194. 2 p. blue .. .. 1·75 70

195. Book.

198. Statue.

1945. Birth Centenary of Jose Pedro Varela (writer).

901 195. 5 m. green 15 10
902 – 1 c. brown (Varela) .. 15 10
903 – 2 c. red (Statue) .. 15 10
904a 198. 5 c. blue 15 10

Nos. 902/3 are vert.

205. Eduardo Acevedo (statesman).

200. Jose Pedro Varela (writer).

1945.

905. – 5 m. violet 10 10
911. – 1 c. brown 10 10
912. 205. 2 c. purple 10 10
945. – 3 c. green 10 10
906. 200. 5 c. red 15 10
907. – 10 c. blue 25 15
946. – 20 c. brown and green 55 30

PORTRAITS: 5 m. Santiago Vazquez (statesman). 1 c. Sylvestre Blanco (statesman). 3 c. Bruno Mauricio de Zabala (founder of Montevideo). 10 c. Jose Ellauri (President, 1873–75). 20 c. Col. Luis de Larrobla (first Postmaster).

206. Full-rigged Ship "La Eolo".

1945. Air.

913. 206. 8 c. green .. .. 1·75 35

1945. Air. Victory. Surch. figure as "Victory of Samothrace", **1945** and new value. No. 908 optd. **VICTORIA** also.

914 810 14 c. on 50 c. orange 35 30
915 23 c. on 50 c. orange 40 35
916 23 c. on 1 p. 38 orange 50 40
908 156 44 c. on 75 c. brown 70 40
917 180 1 p. on 1 p. 38 orange 2·00 1·10

1946. Inaug of Rio Negro Hydro-electric Power Plant. Optd **INAUGURACION DICIEMBRE, 1945**, No. 918 also surch **CORREO 20 CENTS.**

918. 176. 20 c. on 68 c. brown (postage) .. 80 35
919. 62 c. green (air) .. 50 45

1946. As T 187. (a) Postage. Optd. **CORREOS** and Caduceus.

920. 187. 5 m. orange 10 10
921. 2 c. brown 10 10
922. 3 c. green 10 10
923. 5 c. blue 10 10
924. 10 c. brown 15 10
925. 20 c. green 50 15
926. 50 c. brown .. .. 1·10 60
927. 3 p. red .. .. 4·25 2·25

(b) Air. Optd. **SERVICIO AEREO** and an aeroplane.

928. 187. 8 c. red 10 10
929. 50 c. brown 40 25
930. 1 p. blue 50 30
931. 2 p. olive .. .. 2·25 1·10
932. 3 p. red .. .. 2·25 1·10
933. 5 p. red .. .. 4·50 3·00

217. Four-Engined Aeroplane.

215. National Airport.

1947. Air.

947 217 3 c. brown 10 10
948 8 c. red 15 10
949 10 c. black 10 10
950 10 c. red 10 10
951 14 c. blue 25 15
952 15 c. brown 15 10
953 20 c. purple 15 15
954 21 c. lilac 20 15
955 23 c. green 25 20
956 27 c. green 20 10
957 31 c. brown 30 15
958 36 c. blue 20 10
959 36 c. black 20 15
960 50 c. turquoise 35 25
961 50 c. blue 25 10
962 62 c. blue 40 25
963 65 c. red 40 25
964 84 c. orange 55 40
941 215 1 p. brown and red .. 95 20
965 217 1 p. 08 plum .. 65 45
966 2 p. blue .. .. 1·10 40
942 215 3 p. brown and blue .. 1·75 95
967 217 3 p. orange .. .. 1·25 50
943 215 5 p. brown and green 3·75 2·00
968 217 5 p. green .. .. 2·50 1·10
969 5 p. grey .. .. 1·50 75
944 215 10 p. brown and purple 4·00 3·00
970 217 10 p. green .. .. 6·25 3·50

1947. As T 187 but surch. in figures above shield and wavy lines.

976. 2 c. on 5 c. blue .. 10 10
977. 3 c. on 5 c. blue .. 10 10

219. "Ariel".

221. Bas-reliefs.

1948. Unveiling of Monument to J. E. Rodo (writer).
978. 219. 1 c. brown and olive .. 10 10
979. – 2 c. brown and violet 10 10
980. 221. 3 c. brown and green 15 10
981. 5 c. brown and mauve 20 10
982. 10 c. brown and red .. 20 10
983. 12 c. brown and blue 25 15
984. 219. 20 c. brown and purple 55 35
985. – 50 c. brown and red .. 1·50 70
DESIGN: 2 c., 50 c. Bust of J. E. Rodo.
The 5 c. and 12 c. are as Type **221** but inscr "UN GRAN AMOR ES EL ALMA MISMA DE QUIEN AMA".

1948. Air. As T **187**, optd. **AVIACION** and aeroplane.
986. 12 c. blue 20 10
987. 24 c. green 35 15
988. 36 c. grey 50 25

223. Paysandu. 225. River Santa Lucia Bridge.

1948. Industrial and Agricultural Exhibitions, Paysandu.
989. 223. 3 c. green 15 10
990. – 7 c. blue 20 10
DESIGN—HORIZ. 7 c. Livestock, sower and arms of Paysandu.

1948. Uruguayan-Brazilian Friendship.
991. 225. 10 c. blue 30 15
992. 50 c. green .. .. 1·25 50

226. Ploughing.

1949. 4th American Labour Conf.
993. 226. 3 c. green 15 10
994. – 7 c. blue 20 10
DESIGN—HORIZ. 7 c. Horseman herding cattle.

DESIGNS: 15 c. Architectural faculty. 31 c. Engineering faculty. 36 c. View of University.

227. Medical Faculty.

1949. Air. Cent. of Montevideo University.
995. – 15 c. red 10 10
996. 227. 27 c. brown 15 10
997. – 31 c. blue 25 10
998. – 36 c. green 30 10

228. Cannon and Buildings. 229. Kicking Football.

1950. Bicentenary of Cordon (district of Montevideo).
1003. 228. 1 c. mauve 10 10
1004. 3 c. green 10 10
1005. 7 c. blue 15 10

1951. 4th World Football Championship.
1006. 229. 3 c. green 50 15
1007. 7 c. blue 75 35

230. Gen. Artigas. 231. Emigration from Eastern Provinces.

1952. Cent. of Death of Artigas. Dated "1950".
1009. 230. 5 m. blue 10 10
1010. – 1 c. black and blue .. 10 10
1011. – 2 c. brown and violet 10 10
1012. 231. 3 c. sepia and green .. 10 10
1013. – 5 c. black and orange 15 10
1014. 231. 7 c. black and olive .. 15 10
1015. – 8 c. black and red .. 25 10
1016. – 10 c. red, blue & brn. 25 10
1017. – 14 c. blue 30 10
1018. – 20 c. red, blue & yell. 45 20
1019. – 50 c. olive and brown 80 35
1020. – 1 p. olive and blue .. 1·75 70
DESIGNS (all show Artigas except 10 c. and 20 c.)—As Type **230**: 1 c. at Las Huerfanas. 2 c. at Battle of Las Piedras. 5 c. in Cerrito. 14 c. at Ciudadela. 20 c. Arms. 50 c. in Paraguay. 1 p. Bust. As Type **231**: 7 c. Dictating instructions. 8 c. in Congress. 10 c. Flag.

232. Aeroplane over Mail Coach. 234. Franklin D. Roosevelt.

1952. 75th Anniv. of U.P.U. (1949).
1021. 232. 3 c. green 10 10
1022. 7 c. black 15 10
1023. 12 c. blue 20 10

1953. 5th Postal Congress of the Americas and Spain.
1025. 234. 3 c. green 10 10
1026. 7 c. blue 15 10
1027. 12 c. brown 25 15

235. Ceibo (National Flower). 236. Ombu Tree.

237. Parliament House. 239. Exhibition Entrance.

1954.
1028. 235. 5 m. multicoloured .. 10 10
1029. – 1 c. black and red .. 10 10
1030. 236. 2 c. green and brown 10 10
1031. – 3 c. multicoloured 10 10
1032. 237. 5 c. brown and lilac .. 10 10
1033. – 7 c. green and brown 10 10
1034. – 8 c. blue and red .. 20 10
1035. 236. 10 c. green and orange 20 10
1036. – 12 c. sepia and blue 15 10
1037. – 14 c. black and purple 20 10
1038. 235. 20 c. multicoloured .. 25 10
1039. – 50 c. multicoloured .. 55 20
1040. 237. 1 p. brown and red .. 95 30
1041. – 2 p. sepia and red .. 2·00 80
1042. – 3 p. green and lilac .. 2·10 60
1043. – 4 p. blue and brown .. 5·50 2·50
1044. 236. 5 p. green and blue .. 5·00 2·00
DESIGNS—As T **235**: 3 c. 50 c. Passion flower. As T **236**—HORIZ. 1 c., 14 c. Gaucho breaking-in horse. VERT. 7 c., 3 p. Montevideo Citadel. As T **237**—VERT. 8 c., 4 p. Isla de Lobos lighthouse and southern sealions. HORIZ. 12 c., 2 p. Outer Gateway of Montevideo, 1836.

1956. 1st National Production Exn.
1050. 239. 3 c. green (postage) .. 10 10
1051. 7 c. blue 10 10
1052. – 20 c. blue (air) .. 30 20
1053. – 31 c. green 35 30
1054. – 36 c. red 60 35
DESIGN—HORIZ. Nos. 1052/4, Exn. symbol and two 'planes.

241. Uruguay's First Stamp and "Diligencia". 242. Pres. Jose Batlle y Ordonez.

1956. Air. Centenary of Uruguay Stamp. Stamp in blue.
1055. 241. 20 c. green & yellow 35 20
1056. 31 c. brown and blue 40 25
1057. 36 c. red and pink .. 50 35

1956. Birth Centenary of Jose Batlle y Ordonez (President, 1903–07 and 1911–15).
1058. 242. 3 c. red (postage) .. 10 10
1059. – 7 c. sepia 10 10
1060. – 10 c. mauve (air) .. 10 10
1061. 242. 20 c. slate 15 10
1062. – 31 c. brown 20 15
1063. – 36 c. green 30 20
PORTRAIT OF PRESIDENT—VERT. 7 c. Wearing overcoat. 10 c. Similar to Type **242**. 36 c. Profile, facing right. HORIZ. 31 c. Seated at desk.

1957. Surch. **5** or **10 Cts.**
1071. 242. 5 c. on 3 c. red .. 10 10
1072. – 10 c. on 7 c. sepia (No. 1059) 10 10

248. High Diver. 249. Dr. E. Acevedo.

1958. 14th S. American Swimming Championships, Montevideo. Inscr. as in T **248**.
1073. 248. 5 c. green 15 10
1074. – 10 c. blue 35 15
DESIGN—HORIZ. 10 c. Diving.

1958. Birth Centenary of Dr. Eduardo Acevedo (lawyer).
1075. 249. 5 c. black and green 10 10
1076. 10 c. black and blue 15 10

250. Flags. 251. Baygorria Dam.

1958. Air. Day of the Americas.
1077. 250. 23 c. black and blue .. 15 15
1078. 34 c. black and green 20 15
1079. 44 c. black and mauve 35 20

1958. Inauguration of Baygorria Hydro-Electric Power Station.
1080. 251. 5 c. black and green .. 10 10
1081. 10 c. black and brown 10 10
1082. – 1 p. black and blue .. 40 15
1083. – 2 p. black and mauve 60 35
DESIGN: 1 p., 2 p. Aerial view of dam.

252. "Flame of Freedom". 254. Statue on Capt. Boiso Lanza Monument.

1958. Air. 10th Anniv. of Declaration of Human Rights.
1084. 252. 23 c. black and blue 15 10
1085. 34 c. black and green 20 15
1086. 44 c. black and red .. 35 25

1958. Nos. 1028, 1031 and 1033 surch. with Caduceus and value.
1087. 5 c. on 3 c. multicoloured 10 10
1088. 10 c. on 7 c. grn. and brn. 10 10
1089. 20 c. on 5 m. multicoloured 15 10

1959. Air. Centres in black.
1090. 254. 3 c. brown 10 10
1091. 8 c. mauve 10 10
1092. 38 c. black 10 10
1093. 50 c. yellow 15 10
1094. 60 c. violet 15 10
1095. 90 c. olive 20 15
1096. 1 p. blue 30 15
1097. 2 p. orange 70 50
1098. 3 p. green 85 50
1099. 5 p. purple .. .. 1·10 85
1100. 10 p. red .. .. 3·75 2·50
See also Type **266**.

255. Santos Dumont and his Aeroplane.

1959. Air. Santos Dumont Commem.
1101. 255. 31 c. multicoloured .. 15 15
1102. 36 c. multicoloured .. 15 15

257. "Tourism in Uruguay". 258. Gabriela Mistral (poet).

1959. Air. Tourist Publicity and 50th Anniv. of Punta de Este.
1103. 257. 10 c. blue and ochre .. 10 10
1104. – 38 c. buff and green .. 15 10
1105. – 60 c. buff and violet 25 15
1106. 257. 90 c. green and red .. 30 20
1107. – 1 p. 05 buff and blue 35 25
DESIGN: 38 c., 60 c., 1 p. 05, Beach and compass.

1959. 2nd Death Anniv of Gabriela Mistral.
1108. 258. 5 c. green 10 10
1109. 10 c. blue 10 10
1110. 20 c. red 15 10

259. Dr. Vaz Ferreira. 260. Emblem of Y.M.C.A.

1959. Honouring Dr. Carlos Vaz Ferreira (philosopher).
1111. 259. 5 c. black and blue .. 10 10
1112. 10 c. black and ochre 10 10
1113. 20 c. black and red .. 10 10
1114. 50 c. black and violet 25 10
1115. 1 p. black and green .. 40 20

1959. Air. 50th Anniv. of Y.M.C.A. in Uruguay.
1116. 260. 38 c. blk., grey & green 25 25
1117. 50 c. blk., grey & blue 30 20
1118. 60 c. black, grey & red 35 35

261. Boy and Dam. 262. Artigas and Washington.

1959. National Recovery.
1119. 261. 5 c. + 10 c. green and orange (postage) .. 10 10
1120. 10 c. + 10 c. blue & orge. 10 10
1121. 1 p. + 10 c. vio. & orge. 40 30
1122. 38 c. + 10 c. brown and orange (air) .. 20 20
1123. 60 c. + 10 c. grn. & orge. 30 30

1960. Air. Visit of President Eisenhower.
1124. 262. 38 c. black and red .. 15 15
1125. 50 c. black and blue .. 20 15
1126. 60 c. black and green .. 25 15

1960. Air. Surch. with Caduceus and value.
1128. 217. 20 c. on 27 c. green .. 10 10

265. Dr. M. C. Martinez. 266. Statue on Lanza Monument.

1960. Birth Cent. of Dr. Martin C. Martinez.
1129. 265. 3 c. black and purple 10 10
1130. 5 c. black and violet 10 10
1131. 10 c. black and blue 10 10
1132. 20 c. black and brown 10 10
1133. 1 p. black and grey .. 25 10
1134. 2 p. black and orange 55 15
1135. 3 p. black and olive .. 85 30
1136. 4 p. black and brown 1·10 65
1137. 5 p. black and red .. 1·25 70

1960. Air.
1138. 266. 3 c. black and lilac .. 10 10
1139. 20 c. black and red .. 10 10
1140. 38 c. black and blue .. 10 10
1141. 50 c. black and buff .. 10 10
1142. 60 c. black and green 15 10
1143. 90 c. black and red .. 25 15
1144. 1 p. black and grey .. 30 15
1145. 2 p. black and green .. 45 25
1146. 3 p. black and purple 40 20
1147. 5 p. black and salmon 60 40
1148. 10 p. black and yellow 1·10 65
1149. 20 p. black and blue .. 2·50 1·25

267. Refugees. 268. Scene of Revolution.

1960. World Refugee Year.

1150.	–	10 c. blk. & blue (post.)	10	10
1151.	267.	60 c. black & mve. (air)	20	20

DESIGN: 10 c. "Uprooted tree".

1960. 150th Anniv. of Argentine May Revolution.

1154.	268.	5 c. blk., & blue (post.)	10	10
1155.		10 c. brown and blue	10	10
1156.		38 c. olive & blue (air)	15	10
1157.		50 c. red and blue ..	15	12
1158.		60 c. violet and blue	25	15

269. Pres. M. Oribe 270. Pres. Gronchi.

1961. 104th Death Anniv of Manuel Oribe (President, 1835–38).

1159.	269.	10 c. black and blue	10	10
1160.		20 c. black and brown	10	10
1161.		40 c. black and green	15	10

1961. Air. Visit of President of Italy.

1162.	270.	90 c. multicoloured ..	25	20
1163.		1 p. 20 multicoloured	30	25
1164.		1 p. 40 multicoloured	35	30

271. Carrasco Airport Building.

1961. Air. Carrasco National Airport.

1165.	271.	1 p. grey and violet ..	20	20
1166.		2 p. grey and olive ..	45	10
1167.		3 p. grey and yellow..	35	35
1168.		4 p. grey and dull purple	55	20
1169.		5 p. grey and turquoise	60	30
1170.		10 p. grey and blue..	1·10	45
1171.		20 p. grey and red ..	2·00	1·25

272. "Charging Horsemen" (by C. M. Herrera). 273. Welfare, Justice and Education.

1961. 150th Anniv of February 28th Revolution.

1172.	272.	20 c. black and blue..	15	10
1173.		40 c. black and green	25	10

1961. Latin-American Economic Commission Conference, Punta del Este. (a) Postage. Centres in bistre.

1174.	273.	2 c. violet	10	10
1175.		5 c. orange	10	10
1176.		10 c. red	10	10
1177.		20 c. green	10	10
1178.		50 c. lilac	10	10
1179.		1 p. blue	25	15
1180.		2 p. yellow	55	35
1181.		3 p. grey	55	35
1182.		4 p. blue	85	45
1183.		5 p. brown	95	60

(b) Air. Centres in black.

1184.	273.	20 c. orange	10	10
1185.		45 c. green	15	10
1186.		50 c. purple	15	10
1187.		90 c. violet	20	15
1188.		1 p. red	25	20
1189.		1 p. 40 lilac	35	25
1190.		2 p. ochre	20	25
1191.		3 p. blue	30	35
1192.		4 p. yellow	40	50
1193.		5 p. blue	55	40
1194.		10 p. green	1·10	70
1195.		20 p. mauve	2·00	1·50

274. Gen. Rivera. 275. Symbols of Swiss Settlers.

1962. Honouring Gen. Fructuoso Rivera (first President, 1830–35).

1196.	274.	10 c. black and red ..	10	10
1197.		20 c. black and ochre	10	10
1198.		40 c. black and green	15	10

1962. Cent. of First Swiss Settlers.

1199.	275.	10 c. red, black and blue (postage) ..	10	10
1200.		20 c. red, black & green	10	10
1201.	–	90 c. black, red and orange (air) ..	20	20
1202.	–	1 p. 40 blk., red & blue	30	30

DESIGN—HORIZ. 90 c., 1 p. 40, Wheatsheaf, harvester and Swiss flag.

276. B. P. Berro. 277. Red-crested Cardinal.

1962. Bernardo Prudencio Berro (President, 1860–64).

1203	276	10 c. black and blue	10	10
1204		20 c. black and brown	10	10

1962. Birds.

1205.	–	2 c. brown, pink and black (postage) ..	25	10
1206.	–	50 c. brown & black	60	15
1207.	–	1 p. brown and black	95	35
1208.	–	2 p. blk., brn. & grey	2·25	65
1209.	277.	20 c. red, black and grey (air)	25	15
1210.	–	45 c. red, bl. & blk.	40	15
1211.	–	90 c. brn., blk. & red	95	15
1212.	–	1 p. bl., blk. & brn.	60	25
1213.	–	1 p. 20 multicoloured	1·25	25
1214.	–	1 p. 40 brown, black and blue	1·90	40
1215.	–	2 p. yell., blk. & brn.	1·25	40
1216.	–	3 p. blk., yell. & brn.	1·90	60
1217.	–	5 p. blk., bl. & grn.	3·00	85
1218.	–	10 p. multicoloured	5·00	1·75
1219.	–	20 p. orange, black and grey	11·00	6·00

BIRDS—HORIZ. 2 c. Rufous-bellied Thrush. 45 c. Diademed Tanager. 50 c. Rufous Hornero. 1 p. (1207). Chalk-browed Mockingbird. 1 p. (1212). Common Cowbird. 1 p. 20, Great Kiskadee. 2 p. (1208), Rufous-Collared Sparrow. 2 p. (1215), Yellow Cardinal. 3 p. Hooded Siskin. 5 p. Sayaca Tanager. 10 p. Blue and Yellow Tanager. 20 p. Scarlet-headed Blackbird. VERT. 90 c. Vermilion Flycatcher. 1 p. 40, Fork-tailed Flycatcher.

Nos. 1208, 1210, 1212 and 1215 have no frame; Nos. 1206 and 1214 have a thin frame line; the others are as Type **277**.

278. D. A. Larranaga.

1963. 85th Death Anniv of Damaso Antonio Larranaga (founder of National Library).

1220.	278.	20 c. sepia and turquoise	10	10
1221.		40 c. sepia and drab ..	10	10

279. U.P.A.E. Emblem. 280. Campaign Emblem.

1963. 50th Anniv. of Postal Union of the Americas and Spain.

1222.	279.	20 c. blue & black (post.)	10	10
1223.		45 c. green & blk. (air)	10	10
1224.		90 c. red and black ..	20	15

1963. Freedom from Hunger.

1225.	280.	10 c. yell. & grn. (post.)	10	10
1226.		20 c. yellow and brown	10	10
1227.	280.	90 c. yellow & red (air)	20	15
1228.		1 p. 40 yellow & violet	25	20

281. Anchors. 282. Large Intestine, Congress Emblem.

1963. World Voyage of "Alferez Campora".

1229.	281.	10 c. vio. & orge. (post).	10	10
1230.		20 c. grey and red ..	10	10
1231.	–	90 c. grn. & orge. (air)	20	10
1232.	–	1 p. 40 blue and yellow	30	25

DESIGN: 90 c., 1 p. 40, Sailing ship "Alferez Campora".

1963. 1st Uruguayan Proctological Congress, Punta del Este.

1233.	282.	10 c. red, black & green	10	10
1234.		20 c. red, black & ochre	10	10

283. Centenary Emblem.

1964. Red Cross Centenary.

1235.	283.	20 c. red and blue ..	10	10
1236.		40 c. red and grey ..	15	10

284. L. A. Herrera.

1964. 5th Death Anniv. of Luis A. de Herrera (statesman).

1237.	284.	20 c. black, green & blue	10	10
1238.		40 c. black and blue..	10	10
1239.		80 c. black, yell. & blue	15	10
1240.		1 p. black, lilac & blue	15	10
1241.		2 p. black, slate & blue	25	20

285. Pres. de Gaulle.

1964. Air. Visit of President of France. Multicoloured.

1242.	1 p. 50 Type **285** ..	40	15
1243.	2 p. 40 Flags of France and Uruguay	50	40

286. Reliefs from Abu Simbel.

1964. Nubian Monuments Preservation. Multicoloured.

1244.	20 c. Type **286** (postage)	10	10
1245.	1 p. 30 Sphinx, Sebua (air)	30	15
1246.	2 p. Rameses II, Abu Simbel	65	30

Nos. 1245/6 are vert.

292. Arms. 288. Pres. Kennedy.

1965. Air.

1261.	292.	20 p. multicoloured	1·25	70
1248.	–	50 p. blue, yell. & grey	3·75	3·00

DESIGN—HORIZ. (38 × 27 mm.): 50 p. National flag.

1965. Pres. Kennedy Commem. Frame and laurel in gold.

1249.	288.	20 c. black & grn. (post.)	10	10
1250.		40 c. black and brown	10	10
1251.		1 p. 50 blk. & lilac (air)	20	10
1252.		2 p. 40 black and blue	30	15

289. "Tete-beche" Pair of Uruguayan 8 c. Stamps of 1864.

290. 6 c. "Arms-type" of 1864.

1965. 1st River Plate Stamp Exn., Montevideo.

(a) Postage. T **289**.

1253.	40 c. green and black ..	10	10

(b) Air. As T **290** showing Arms-type stamps of 1864 (values in brackets).

1254.	1 p. black and blue (12 c.)	10	10
1255.	1 p. black & orange (T **290**)	10	10
1256.	1 p. black & green (8 c.)..	10	10
1257.	1 p. black & bistre (10 c.)	10	10
1258.	1 p. black and red (6 c.)..	10	10

Nos. 1254/8 were issued together in sheets of 10 (5 × 2), each design arranged in a vertical pair with "URUGUAY" either at top or bottom.

291. B. Nardone.

1965. 1st Death Anniv. of Benito Nardone (statesman).

1259.	291.	20 c. black and green..	10	10
1260.	–	40 c. black and green..	10	10

DESIGN—VERT. 40 c. Portrait as Type **291**, but Nardone with microphone.

293. Part of Artigas' speech before the 1813 Congress.

1965. Birth Bicent. (1964) of Gen. Jose Artigas.

1262.	293.	20 c. red, blue and yellow (postage) ..	10	10
1263.	–	40 c. olive, black & blue	10	10
1264.	–	80 c. multicoloured	10	10
1265.	–	1 p. multicoloured (air)	10	10
1266.	–	1 p. 50 multicoloured	15	10
1267.	293.	2 p. 40 multicoloured	25	20

DESIGNS—HORIZ. 40 c. Bust of Artigas. 80 c. Artigas and his army flag. 1 p. 50, Bust, flag and exodus of his followers to Argentina. VERT. 1 p. Artigas' statue.

295. Football.

1965. Olympic Games, Tokyo (1964).

1269.	295.	20 c. orange, black and green (postage) ..	10	10
1270.	–	40 c. olive, black & brn.	10	10
1271.	–	80 c. red, black & drab	10	10
1272.	–	1 p. green, black & blue	10	10
1273.	–	1 p. grey, blk. & red (air)	10	10
1274.	–	1 p. 50 blue, blk. & grn.	15	15
1275.	–	2 p. blue, blk. and red	15	15
1276.	–	2 p. 40 orge., blk. & bl.	20	15
1277.	–	3 p. yellow, blk. & lilac	25	20
1278.	–	20 p. pink, blue & indigo	70	50

DESIGNS: 40 c. Basketball. 80 c. Cycling. 1 p. (No. 1272) Swimming. 1 p. (No. 1273) Boxing. 1 p. 50, Running. 2 p. Fencing. 2 p. 40, Sculling. 3 p. Pistol-shooting. 20 p. Olympic "Rings".

1965. Surch. with Caduceus and value.

1280.	178	10 c. on 7 c. blue ..	10	10

1966. 50th Anniv. of Uruguay Architects Assn. Surch. **CINCUENTENARIO Sociedad Arquitectos del Uruguay** and value.
1281. **261.** 4 c. on 5 c.+10 c. green and orange .. 10 10

298. I.T.U. Emblem and Satellite.

1966. Air. Cent. of I.T.U.
1282. **298.** 1 p. deep bl., red & blue 15 10

299. Sir Winston Churchill.

1966. Churchill Commem.
1283. **299.** 40 c. brown, red and blue (postage) .. 10 10
1284. – 2 p. brn., red & gold (air) 20 10
DESIGN—VERT. 2 p. Churchill—full-face portrait and signed quotation.

300. Arms and View of Rio de Janeiro.

1966. 400th Anniv. of Rio de Janeiro.
1285. **300.** 40 c. grn. & brn. (post.) 10 10
1286. 80 c. red & brown (air) 10 10

301. I.C.Y. Emblem.

1966. Air. I.C.Y.
1287. **301.** 1 p. black and green .. 15 10

302. Army Engineer. **304.** Pres. Shazar.

1966. 50th Anniv. of Army Engineers.
1288. **302.** 20 c. multicoloured .. 15 10

1966. Air. Visit of President of Israel.
1291. **304.** 7 p. multicoloured .. 40 30

305. Crested Screamer. **306.** Jules Rimet Cup, Ball and Globe.

1966. Air.
1292. **305.** 100 p. multicoloured 4·50 2·50

1966. Air. World Cup Football Championships.
1293. **306.** 10 p. yellow and violet 50 30

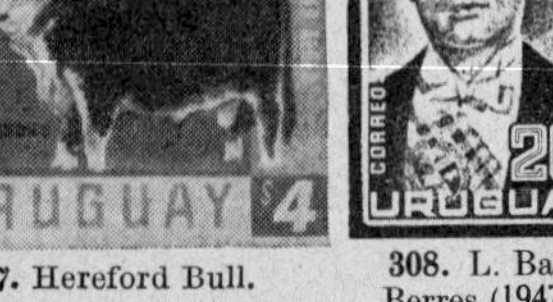
307. Hereford Bull. **308.** L. Batlle Berres (1947–51 and 1955–56).

1966. Air. Cattle-breeding.
1294. **307.** 4 p. brn., chest. & sepia 15 10
1295. – 6 p. blk., grn. & turq. 25 10
1296. – 10 p. mve., grn. & turq. 35 20
1297. – 15 p. blk., red & orge. 30 30
1298. – 20 p. brn., yell. & grey 50 40
1299. – 30 p. brown & yellow 75 55
1300. – 50 p. brn., grey & grn. 1·25 85
DESIGNS (Cattle breeds): 6 p. Dutch. 10 p. Shorthorn. 15 p. Aberdeen Angus. 20 p. Norman. 30 p. Jersey. 50 p. Charolais.

1966. Former Uruguayan Presidents.
1301. **308.** 20 c. black and red .. 10 10
1302. – 20 c. black and blue 10 10
1303. – 20 c. brown and blue 10 10
PRESIDENTS: No. 1302, Daniel Fernandez Crespo (1963–64). No. 1303, Dr. Washington Beltran (1965–66).

309. Gutenberg Press. **310.** Capt. Boiso Lanza.

1966. 50th Anniv. of State Printing Works.
1304. **309.** 20 c. sepia, grn. & brn. 10 10

1966. Air. Honouring Boiso Lanza (pioneer military aviator).
1305. **310.** 25 c. blk., bl. & ultram. 75 55

311. Fireman. **313.** General J. A. Lavalleja.

1966. 50th Anniv. of Firemen's Corps.
1306. **311.** 20 c. black and red .. 25 15

1966. 2nd River Plate Stamp Exn., Montevideo.
(a) Postage. No. 1253 optd. **Segunda Muestra y Jornados Rioplatenses,** etc.
1307. **187.** 40 c. green and black 10 10

(b) Air. Nos. 1254/8 optd. **CENTENARIO DEL SELLO ESCUDITO RESELLADO,** etc.
1308 1 p. blue 10 10
1309 1 p. orange 10 10
1310 1 p. green 10 10
1311 1 p. bistre 10 10
1312 1 p. red 10 10
Nos. 1308/12 commemorate the centenary of Uruguay's first surcharged stamps.

1966. Heroes of War of Independence.
1313. **313.** 20 c. brn., red & blue 10 10
1314. – 20 c. blue, black & grey 10 10
1315. – 20 c. black and blue .. 10 10
DESIGNS—VERT. No. 1314, Gen. L. Gomez. HORIZ. 1315, Gen. A. Saravia on horseback.

1966. Air. 40th Anniv of Uruguayan Philatelic Club. No. 1036 surch **40 ANIVERSARIO Club Filatelico del Uruguay $ 1.00 aereo.**
1316. 1 p. on 12 c. sepia & blue 10 10

315. Dante. **316.** Sunflower.

1966. Air. 700th Birth Anniv (1965) of Dante (writer).
1317. **315.** 50 c. brown and sepia 10 10

1967. 20th Anniv. of Young Farmers' Movement.
1318. **316.** 40 c. sepia, yell. & brn. 10 10

317. Planetarium.

1967. 10th Anniv. of Montevideo Planetarium.
1319. **317.** 40 c. blk. & mve. (post.) 15 10
1320. – 5 p. black & blue (air) 35 15
DESIGN: 5 p. Planetarium projector.

318. Pres. Makarios. **319.** Dr. Schweitzer.

1967. Air. Visit of President of Cyprus.
1321. **318.** 6 p. 60 black & mauve 20 15

1967. Air. Schweitzer Commem.
1322. **319.** 6 p. multicoloured .. 20 15

320. Corriedale Ram. **322.** Church, San Carlos.

321. Uruguayan Flag and Globe.

1967. Air. Uruguayan Sheep-breeding.
1323. **320.** 3 p. blk., bistre & red 10 10
1324. – 4 p. blk., bistre & grn. 15 10
1325. – 5 p. blk., bistre & blue 20 10
1326. – 10 p. blk., bis. & yell. 35 30
DESIGNS (sheep breeds): 4 p. "Ideal". 5 p. Romney Marsh. 10 p. Australian merino.

1967. Air. Heads of State Meeting, Punta del Este.
1327. **321.** 10 p. gold, blue & blk. 25 20

1967. Bicent. of San Carlos.
1328. **322.** 40 c. black, red & blue 10 10

323. E. Acevedo (lawyer and statesman). **325.** Ansina.

324. " Numeral " Stamps of 1866.

1967. Eduardo Acevedo Commem.
1329. **323.** 20 c. brown and green 10 10
1330. 40 c. green and orange 10 10

1967. Air. Cent. of "Numeral" Stamps of 1866.
1331. **324.** 3 p. blue, grn. & blk. 20 10
1332. – 6 p. ochre, red & blk. 35 15
DESIGN: 6 p. As T **324**, but depicting 15 c. and 20 c. stamps of 1866.

1967. Air. Honouring Ansina (servant of Gen. Artigas).
1334. **325.** 2 p. red, blue and black 10 10

326. Aircraft over Runway. **327.** Making Basket.

1967. Air. 30th Anniv. of PLUNA Airline.
1335. **326.** 10 p. multicoloured .. 35 25

1967. Air. World Basketball Championships, Montevideo. Multicoloured.
1336. 5 p. Type **327** 20 10
1337. 5 p. Running 20 10
1338. 5 p. Holding 20 10
1339. 5 p. Pivot 20 10
1340. 5 p. Dribbling 20 10

1967. Air. Nos. 1210 and 1223 surch. with new value in figures only.
1343. – 5 p. 90 on 45 c. red, blue and black .. 45 15
1344. **279.** 5 p. 90 on 45 c. green and black 20 15

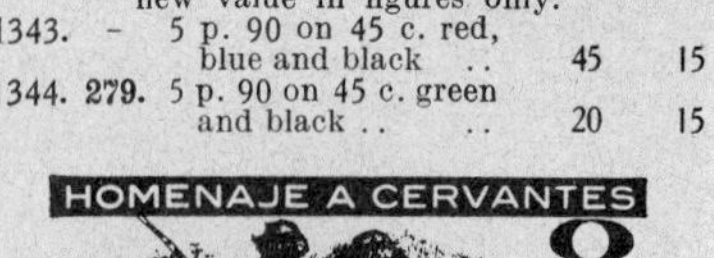

330. " Don Quixote and Sancho Panza ". (after Denry Torres).

1967. Air. 420th Birth Anniv of Cervantes (writer).
1345. **330.** 8 p. brown and bistre 25 15

331. Arms of Carmelo. **332.** J. E. Rodo.

1967. 150th Anniv. of Founding of Carmelo.
1346. **331.** 40 c. deep blue, ochre and blue 10 10

1967. 50th Death Anniv. of Jose E. Rodo (writer). Multicoloured.
1347. 1 p. Type **332** 10 10
1348. 2 p. Portrait and sculpture 10 10
The 2 p. is horiz.

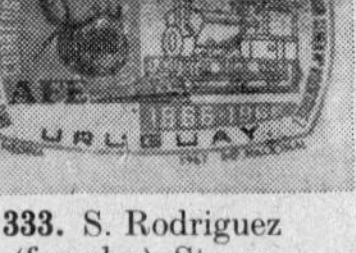
333. S. Rodriguez (founder), Steam Locomotive and Diesel Railcar. **334.** Child and Map of Americas.

1967. Centenary of 1st National Railway Company in Uruguay.
1349. **333.** 2 p. brown and ochre 30 10

1967. 40th Anniv. of Inter-American Children's Institute.
1350. **334.** 1 p. red and violet .. 15 10

1967. No. 1033 surch. **1.00 PESO** and Caduceus.
1351. 1 p. on 7 c. green & brown 10 10

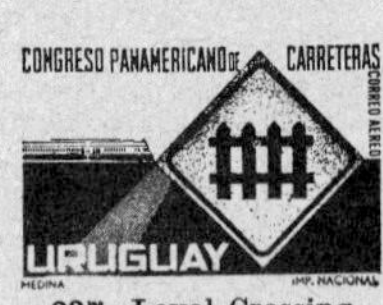
336. Primitive Club. **337.** Level Crossing and Traffic Sign.

1967. Air. Archaeological Discoveries. Each black and grey.
1352. 15 p. Type **336** 10 10
1353. 20 p. Lance-head .. 20 10
1354. 30 p. Axe-head 45 15
1355. 50 p. Sculptured " bird of El Polonio " 60 25
1356. 75 p. Cooking pot .. 60 40
1357. 100 p. Sculptured " bird " of Balizas (horiz.) .. 85 35
1358. 150 p. Bolas .. .. 1·10 40
1359. 200 p. Arrow-heads .. 1·50 85

1967. Air. Pan American Highways Congress.
1360. **337.** 4 p. black, yellow & red 10 10

338. Lions Emblem and Map. **339.** Boy Scout.

1967. Air. 50th Anniv. of Lions Int.
1361. **338.** 5 p. violet, yell. & grn. 15 10

1968. Air. Lord Baden-Powell Commem.
1362. **339.** 9 p. brown & orange 15 10

340. Cocoi Heron. **341.** Sun, Transport and U.N. Emblem.

1968. Birds.
1363. – 1 p. brown and buff.. 20 10
1364. **340.** 2 p. black and green 20 10
1365. – 3 p. pur., blk. & orge. 25 10
1366. – 4 p. black and brown 50 20
1367. – 4 p. black and orange 50 20
1368. – 5 p. black, yell. & brn. 60 30
1369. – 10 p. violet & black 1·10 30
BIRDS—VERT. 1 p. Great horned owl. 4 p. (No. 1367). Black-tailed stilt. HORIZ. 3 p. Brown-hooded gull. 4 p. (No. 1366), White-faced whistling duck. 5 p. Wattled jacana. 10 p. Snowy egret.

1968. Air. Int. Tourist Year (1967).
1370. **341.** 10p. multicoloured.. 40 15

342. Presidents of Uruguay and Brazil, and Concord Bridge. **343.** Footballer.

1968. Opening of Concord Bridge between Uruguay and Brazil.
1371. **342.** 6 p. brown 15 10

1968. Penarol Club's Victory in Inter-continental Soccer Championships.
1372. **343.** 1 p. black and lemon 15 10

344. St. John Bosco.

1968. 75th Anniv. of "Don Bosco Workshops".
1373. **344.** 2 p. black and brown 10 10

345. Octopus.

1968. Air. Uruguayan Marine Fauna.
1374. **345.** 15 p. black, blue and turquoise 20 15
1375. – 20 p. brn., blue & grn. 25 15
1376. – 25 p. multicoloured.. 30 20
1377. – 30 p. blk., grn & blue 35 25
1378. – 50 p. salmon, blue and green 60 35
DESIGNS—HORIZ. 20 p. Mackerel. 25 p. "Dorado". VERT. 30 p. "Surubi". 50 p. Squid.

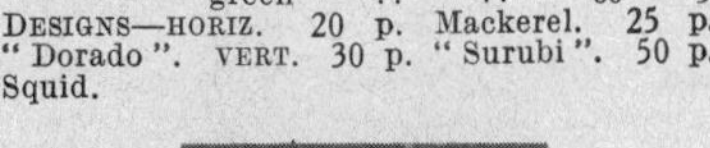

346. Sailors' Monument, Montevideo.

1968. 150th Anniv. of Uruguayan Navy.
1379. **346.** 2 p. black and green (postage) 10 10
1380. – 6 p. black and green.. 10 10
1381. – 12 p. black and blue.. 35 15
1382. – 4 p. blk., red & bl. (air) 10 10
1383. – 6 p. multicoloured .. 10 10
1384. – 10 p. red, yell. & blue 15 10
1385. – 20 p. black and blue.. 65 15
DESIGNS—HORIZ. 4 p. Tailplane (Naval Air Force). 6 p. (No. 1383), Naval Arms. 12 p. Screw gunboat "Suarez". 20 p. Artigas's privateer "Isabel". VERT. 6 p. (No. 1380), Buoy and lighthouse. 10 p. Mast-head and signal flags.

347. President Gestido.

1968. 1st Death Anniv. of President Oscar D. Gestido.
1386. **347.** 6 p. brown, red & blue 10 10

348. Sculling.

1969. Air. Olympic Games, Mexico.
1387. **348.** 30 p. black, brn. & bl. 30 20
1388. – 50 p. black, brn. & yell. 45 30
1389. – 100 p. blk., brn. & grn. 75 50
DESIGNS: 50 p. Running. 100 p. Football.

349. Cogwheel, Ear of Wheat and Two Heads.

1969. 25th Anniv. of Uruguay Trades University.
1390. **349.** 2 p. black and red .. 10 10

350. Cycling.

1969. World Cycling Championships, Montevideo (1968).
1391. **350.** 6 p. blue, orange and green (postage) .. 20 10
1392. – 20 p. mult. (air) .. 30 15
DESIGN—VERT. 20 p. Cyclist and globe.

351. Efimex "Stamp" on Easel.

1969. Air. "EFIMEX" Stamp Exn., Mexico City (1968).
1393. **351.** 20 p. red, grn. & blue 20 15

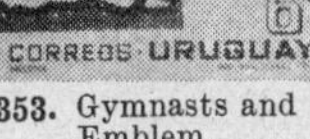

353. Gymnasts and Emblem. **354.** President Baltasar Brum.

1969. 75th Anniv. of "L'Avenir" Gymnastics Club.
1395. **353.** 6 p. black and red .. 15 10

1969. 36th Death Anniv of Baltasar Brum (President, 1919–23).
1396. **354.** 6 p. black and red .. 15 10

356. Sun and Fair Emblem.

1969. 2nd World Industrial Fair, Montevideo.
1399. **356.** 2 p. multicoloured .. 15 5

357. Emblem, Quill and Book. **358.** Modern Diesel Locomotive.

1969. Air. 10th Latin-American Notaries' Congress, Montevideo.
1400. **357.** 30 p. blk., orge. & grn. 35 25

1969. Cent. of Uruguayan Railways.
1401. **358.** 6 p. blk. red & blue.. 30 25
1402. – 6 p. blk., red & blue.. 30 25
DESIGN: No. 1402, Early locomotive and diesel train.

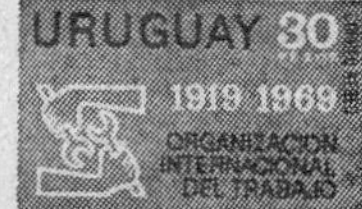

360. Automobile Club Badge. **362.** I.L.O. Emblem.

361. Belloni and "Combat" (monument). (Reduced size illustration. Actual size: 72 × 23 mm.).

1969. Air. 50th Anniv. of Uruguay Automobile Club.
1404. **360.** 10 p. blue and red .. 15 10

1969. 4th Death Anniv of Jose Belloni (sculptor).
1405. **361.** 6 p. grn., black & gold 10 10

1969. Air. 50th Anniv. of I.L.O.
1406. **362.** 30 p. turquoise & black 30 20

363. Training Centre Emblem. **364.** Exhibition Emblem.

1969. 25th Anniv (1967) of Reserve Officers' Training Centre.
1407. **363.** 1 p. lemon and blue 10 10
1408. 2 p. brown and blue 15 10
DESIGN: 2 p. Reservist in uniform and civilian dress.

1969. Air. "ABUEXPO 69" Philatelic Exn., Sao Paulo, Brazil.
1409. **364.** 20 p. yell., blue & grn. 25 10

365. Rotary Emblem and Hemispheres. **366.** Dr. Morquio and Child.

1969. Air. South American Regional Rotary Conf., and 50th Anniv. of Rotary Club, Montevideo.
1410. **365.** 20 p. gold, ult. & blue 40 10

1969. Air. Birth Cent. (1967) of Dr. Luis Morquio (pediatrician).
1411. **366.** 20 p. brown and red.. 20 10

1969. Air. New Year. No. 1345 surch. **FELIZ ANO 1970** and value.
1412 **330** 6 p. on 8 p. brn & bis 10 10

368. Pres. Tomas Berreta. **369.** Mahatma Gandhi.

1969. 22nd Death Anniv of Dr. Tomas Berreta (President, 1947).
1413. **368.** 6 p. red and black .. 15 10

1970. Air. Birth Cent. (1969) of Mahatma Gandhi.
1414. **369.** 100 p. brn., ochre & blue 85 85

370. Teju Lizard. **371.** Dr. E. C. Ciganda.

1970. Air. Fauna.
1415. – 20 p. blk., grn. & pur. 45 15
1416. **370.** 30 p. blk., grn. & yell. 40 20
1417. – 50 p. blk., brn. & yell. 40 35
1418. – 100 p. brown, bistre and orange .. 60 55
1419. – 150 p. brown & green 95 80
1420. – 200 p. blk., brn. & red 1·25 1·25
1421. – 250 p. blk., bl. & grey 1·50 1·50
DESIGNS—VERT. 20 p. Greater rhea. HORIZ. 50 p. Capybara. 100 p. Mulita armadillo. 150 p. Puma. 200 p. Coypu. 250 p. South American fur seal.

1970. Air. Birth Cent. of Evaristo C. Ciganda (pioneer of teachers' pensions law).
1422. **371.** 6 p. brown and green 10 10

372. Garibaldi. **373.** Bank Emblem.

1970. Air. Centenary of Garibaldi's Participation in Defence of Uruguay against Brazil and Argentina.
1423. **372.** 20 p. mauve and pink 15 10

1970. 11th Inter-American Development Bank Governors' Meeting, Punta del Este.
1424. **373.** 10 p. blue and gold .. 15 10

374. Stylised Tree. **375.** Footballer and Emblem.

1970. 2nd National Forestry Exn
1425. **374.** 2 p. black, grn. & red 10 10

1970. Air. World Cup Football Championships, Mexico.
1426. **375.** 50 p. multicoloured.. 55 30

376. Artigas' House, Sauce. **377.** "U.N.".

1970. 120th Death Anniv. of Artigas.
1427. **376.** 15 p. black, blue & red 15 10

1970. Air. 25th Anniv. of United Nations.
1428. **377.** 32 p. blue, gold and light blue 25 15

378. Sun, Sea and Map.

1970. Tourist Publicity.
1429. **378.** 5 p. blue 10 10

379. Eisenhower and U.S. Flag.

1970. Air. 1st Death Anniv. of Dwight D. Eisenhower (American soldier and statesman).
1430. **379.** 30 p. blue, red and grey 30 15

380. First Man on the Moon.

1970. Air. 1st Anniv. of Moon Landing from "Apollo 11".

1431. **380.** 200 p. multicoloured 1·50 1·50

381. Mt. Fuji.

1970. "EXPO 70" World Fair, Osaka, Japan. Each with EXPO emblem and arms of Uruguay.

1432.	**381.**	25 p. blue, grn. & yell.	25	15
1433.	–	25 p. blue, orge. & grn.	25	15
1434.	–	25 p. blue, yell. & vio.	25	15
1435.	–	25 p. blue, vio. & orge.	25	15

DESIGNS: No. 1433, Geishas. No. 1434, Sun tower. No. 1435, Youth totem.

382. Flag of 1825.

1970. Air. 145th Anniv. of "Immortals" Revolt.

1436. **382.** 500 p. blk., red & blue 3·50 3·50

383. Rheumatology Congress Emblem. 384. Street Scene.

1970. Air. 5th Pan-American Rheumatology Congress, Punta del Este.

1437. **383.** 30 p. deep blue, blue and yellow .. 30 15

1970. 290th Anniv. of Colonia del Sacramento (first European settlement in Uruguay).

1439. **384.** 5 p. multicoloured .. 10 10

385. "Mother and Son" (statue, E. Prati). 386. Flags of Member Countries.

1970. "Homage to Mothers".

1440. **385.** 10 p. black and green 15 10

1970. Air. 10th Anniv. of Founding of Latin-American Association for Free Trade by the Montevideo Treaty.

1441. **386.** 22 p. multicoloured .. 30 15

387. "Stamp" Emblem. 389. Dr. Alfonso Espinola.

388. "Playing Ring-o-Roses" (Ana Gaye).

1970. "URUEXPO 70" Stamp Exhib., Montevideo.

1442. **387.** 15 p. vio., blue & brn. 15 10

1970. Int. Education Year. Children's Drawings. Multicoloured.

1443.	10 p. Type **388**	20	15
1444.	10 p. "Two Girls" (Andrea Burcatovsky) (vert.) ..	20	15
1445.	10 p. "Boy at Desk" (Humberto Abel Garcia) (vert.)	20	15
1446.	10 p. "Spaceman" (Aquiles Vaxelaire)	20	15

1971. 125th Birth Anniv (1970) of Dr. Alfonso Espinola (physician and philanthropist).

1447. **389.** 5 p. black & orange 15 10

391. "Stamps" and Poster.
(Illustration reduced. Actual size 71 × 23 mm.)

1971. "EFU 71" Stamp Exhib., Montevideo.

1449. **391.** 15 p. multicoloured .. 20 10

392. 5 c. Coin of 1840 (obverse). 393. Dr. Domingo Arena (from carricature by A. Sifredi).

1971. Numismatics Day.

1450.	**392.**	25 p. blk., brn. & blue	40	30
1451.	–	25 p. blk., brn. & blue	40	30

DESIGN: No. 1451, Reverse of coin showing "Sun" emblem.

1971. Birth Centenary (1970) of Arena (lawyer and statesman).

1452. **393.** 5 p. lake 10 10

394. Opening Bars of Anthem. 395. Dr. Jose Arias.

1971. National Anthem Commem.

1453. **394.** 15 p. blk., bl. & gold 40 25

1971. 1st Death Anniv. of Dr Jose Arias (statesman).

1454. **395.** 5 p. brown 15 10

396. "Yellow Fever" (J. M. Blanes).

1971. Air. 70th Death Anniv. of Juan Blanes (artist).

1455. **396.** 50 p. multicoloured .. 30 30

397. Eduardo Fabini.

1971. 21st Death Anniv of Eduardo Fabini (composer).

1456 **397** 5 p. black and red .. 40 10

398. "Two Races".

1971. Air. Racial Equality Year.

1457. **398.** 27 p. blk., pink & gold 30 15

399. Congress Emblem.

1971. Air. 12th Pan-American Gastro-enterological Congress, Punta del Este.

1458. **399.** 58 p. orge., blk. & grn 55 35

400. J. E. Rodo and U.P.A.E. Emblem.

1971. Birth Centenary of Jose E. Rodo (writer and first delegate to U.P.A.E).

1459. **400.** 15 p. black and blue 20 15

401. Old Water-cart and Tap.

1971. Cent. of Montevideo's Water Supply.

1460. **401.** 5 p. multicoloured .. 15 10

402. Sheep and Roll of Cloth.

1971. Wool Production.

1461.	**402.**	5 p. grn., grey & lt. grn.	10	10
1462.	–	15 p. grey, vio. & blue	20	15

DESIGN: 15 p. Sheep, and loading bales of cloth.

403. Dr. Jose Elorza and Sheep.

1971. 12th Death Anniv of Dr. Jose Elorza (sheep-breeder).

1463. **403.** 5 p. blk., grn. & blue 15 10

404. Creole Horse.

1971. Uruguayan Horse-breeding.

1464. **404.** 5 p. blk., bl. and orge. 20 10

405. Bull, Sheep and Ears of Corn.

1971. Cent. of Uruguayan Rural Association.

1465. **405.** 20 p. multicoloured .. 30 15

406. Police Emblem.

1971. Honouring Police Heroes.

1466.	**406.**	10 p. bl., blk. & grey	25	10
1467.	–	20 p. multicoloured ..	45	15

DESIGN: 20 p. Policeman and flag.

407. 1896 10 Peso Banknote (obverse).

1971. 75th Anniv. of Uruguayan State Bank.

1468.	**407.**	25 p. grn., blk. & gld.	30	25
1469.	–	25 p. grn., blk. & gld.	30	25

DESIGNS: No. 1469, Reverse of banknote showing rural scene.

408. Labourer and Arms.

1971. 150th Anniv of Town of Durazno.

1470. **408.** 20 p. multicoloured .. 25 10

409. Shield and Laurel.
(Illustration reduced. Actual size 72 × 24½ mm.)

1971. Uruguay's Victory in Liberators' Cup Football Championships.

1471. **409.** 10 p. gold, red & blue 20 10

411. Voter and Ballot-box.

1971. General Election.

1473.	**411.**	10 p. black and blue	10	10
1474.	–	20 p. black and blue	25	15

DESIGN—HORIZ. 20 p. Voters in line.

412. C.I.M.E. Emblem and Globe.

1971. Air. 20th Anniv. of Inter-Governmental Committee for European Migration (C.I.M.E.).

1475. **412.** 30 p. multicoloured .. 35 25

413. Exhibition Emblem and Map of Uruguay. 414. Juan Lindolfo Cuestas (1897-1903).

1971. "EXPO LITORAL" Industrial Exhib., Paysandu.

1476. **413.** 20 p. purple and blue 35 12

1971. Uruguayan Presidents. Each brown and blue.

1477	10 p. Type **414**	10	10
1478	10 p. J. Herrera y Obes (1890–94)	10	10
1479	10 p. Claudio Williman (1907–11)	10	10
1480	10 p. Jose Serrato (1923–27)	10	10
1481	10 p. Andres Martinez Trueba (1951–55) ..	10	10

415. Llama Emblem.

417. Olympic Symbols.

1971. Air. "EXFILIMA" Stamp Exhib., Lima, Peru.
1482. 415. 37 p. multicoloured .. 35 30

1972. Air. Olympic Games, Munich (1st issue).
1484 417 50 p. black, red & yell 20 10
1485 – 100 p. multicoloured 40 30
1486 – 500 p. grey, red & bl 1·10 1·10
DESIGNS: 100 p. Athlete and torch. 500 p. Discus-thrower.
See also Nos. 1493/4.

418. Chemical Jar.

419. Bartolome Hidalgo.

1972. Air. 50th Anniv. of Discovery of Insulin.
1487. 418. 27 p. multicoloured .. 20 10

1972. 150th Death Anniv (1973) of Bartolome Hidalgo (Gaucho poet).
1488 419 5 p. black, red & brn 20 10

420. " Flagship ".

421. " Face " on Beethoven Score.

1972. Air. American Stamp Day.
1489. 420. 37 p. multicoloured .. 25 15

1972. 12th Eastern Uruguay Choral Festival.
1491. 421. 20 p. blk., grn. & pur. 25 10

422. Dove supporting Wounded Bird (after Maria Mullin).

424. Columbus Monument, Colon.

423. Footballer and 1928 Gold Medal.

1972. Dionisio Diaz (9 year-old hero) Commemoration.
1492 422 10 p. multicoloured .. 15 10

1972. Air. Olympic Games, Munich. Mult.
1493. 100 p. Type 423 .. .. 40 30
1494. 300 p. Olympic flag (vert.) 70 75

1972. Cent of Colon (suburb of Montevideo).
1495 424 20 p. black, blue & red 10 10

1972. Uruguay's Victory in Intercontinental Football Cup Championships. No. 1471 surch **COPA INTER CONTINENTAL 1971** and football cup.
1496. 409. 50 p. on 10 p. gold, red and blue 35 30

426. Sapling and Spade.

428. U.N.C.T.A.D. Emblem.

427. Cross of Remembrance.

1972. Tree Planting Campaign.
1497. 426. 20 p. blk., myrtle & grn. 15 10

1972. Air. 2nd Death Anniv. of Dan Mitrione (U.S. police instructor assassinated by terrorists in Uruguay).
1498. 427. 37 p. violet and gold 15 10

1972. Air. 3rd United Nations Conference on Trade and Development (U.N.C.T.A.D.), Santiago, Chile.
1499. 428. 30 p. multicoloured .. 15 10

429. Brazilian "Bull's-Eye" Stamp of 1843.

1972. Air. "EXFILBRA 72" Stamp Exhib., Rio de Janeiro.
1500. 429. 50 p. multicoloured .. 20 10

430. Compass Rose and Map of South America.

431. " Birds' Nests in Tree ".

1972. Air. Campaign for Extension of Territorial Waters to 200 Mile Limit.
1501. 430. 37 p. multicoloured .. 15 10

1972. Nat., Building Project for Communal Dwellings.
1502. 431. 10 p. multicoloured .. 10 10

432. Amethyst.

1972. Uruguayan Mineralogy. Rocks and Gems.
1503. 432. 5 p. multicoloured .. 15 10
1504. – 9 p. multicoloured .. 20 10
1505. – 15 p. grn., brn. & blk. 35 15
DESIGNS: 9 p. Agate. 15 p. Chalcedony.

433. "The Three Holy Kings" (R. Barradas).

1972. Air. Christmas.
1506. 433. 20 p. multicoloured .. 20 15

435. Infantry Uniform of 1830.

436. Red Cross over Map.

1972. Military Uniforms. Multicoloured.
1509. 10 p. Type 435 .. .. 15 10
1510. 20 p. Artigas cavalry regiment uniform .. 30 15

1972. 75th Anniv. of Uruguayan Red Cross.
1511. 436. 30 p. multicoloured .. 30 10

438. Open Book.

439. General Jose Artigas.

1972. 25th Anniv of Full Civil Rights for Uruguayan Women.
1513. 438. 10 p. gold, bl. & light bl. 10 8

1972.
1514. 439. 5 p. yellow 10 10
1515. 10 p. brown 10 10
1516. 15 p. green 10 10
1517. 20 p. lilac 10 10
1518. 30 p. blue 20 10
1519. 40 p. orange 20 10
1520. 50 p. red 15 10
1521. 75 p. green 25 15
1522. 100 p. green 30 15
1523. 150 p. brown .. 15 25
1524. 200 p. blue 25 30
1525. 250 p. violet 30 35
1526. 500 p. grey 60 75
1527. 1000 p. blue .. .. 1·10 1·10

440. Cup and Ear of Wheat on Map.

441. E. Fernandez and J. P. Varela (founders).

1973. 30th Anniv of Interamerican Institute for Agricultural Sciences.
1531. 440. 30 p. blk., yell. & red 15 10

1973. Centenary (1968) of Friends of Popular Education Society.
1532. 441. 10 p. blk., green & brn. 10 10

442. Columbus and Map.

1973. American Tourist Year.
1533. 442. 50 p. purple .. 20 15

443. Carlos Ramirez.

1973. Eminent Uruguayan Jurists. Each black, brown and bistre.
1534 10 p. Type 443 .. .. 10 10
1535 10 p. Justino Jimenez de Arechaga 10 10
1536 10 p. Juan Ramirez .. 10 10
1537 10 p. Justino E. Jimenez de Arechaga 10 10

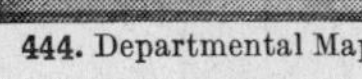
444. Departmental Map.

447. Priest, Indians and Soriano Church.

446. Francisco de los Santos and Artigas.

1973. Uruguayan Departments.
1538. 444. 20 p. multicoloured 30 15
See also No. 1844.

1973. Francisco de los Santos (courier). Commem.
1540. 446. 20 p. emerald, black and green 20 10

1973. Villa Santo Domingo Soriano (first Spanish Settlement in Uruguay). Commem.
1541. 447. 20 p. blk., violet & blue 15 10

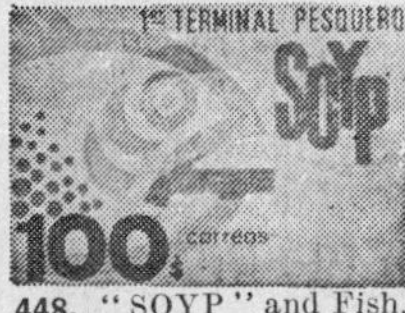
448. " SOYP " and Fish.

1973. Inauguration of 1st Fishery Station of Oceanographic and Fishery Service (S.O.Y.P.).
1542. 448. 100 p. multicoloured 35 15

449. Flower and Sun.

451. Luis A. de Herrera.

1973. Italian Chamber of Commerce in Uruguay.
1543. 449. 100 p. multicoloured 25 15

1973. Birth Centenary of Luis A. de Herrera (Conservative leader).
1545. 451. 50 p. brn., sepia & grey 20 10

452. Festival Emblem.

1973. "Festival of Nations", Montevideo.
1546. 452. 50 p. multicoloured .. 20 10

453. Artery and Heart within " Arm)'.

454. " Madonna " (R. Barradas).

1973. 3rd Pan-American Voluntary Blood Donors' Congress.
1547. 453. 50 p. blk., red & pink 20 10

1973. Christmas.
1548. 454. 50 p. blk., yell. & grn. 15 10

455. Copernicus.

1973. 500th Birth Anniv. of Nicholas Copernicus (astrologer).
1549. 455. 50 p. multicoloured .. 15 10

456. Hands in Prayer, and Andes.

457. O.E.A. Emblem and Map.

1973. Rescue of Survivors from Andes Air-crash.

1550. **456.** 50 p. grn., bl. & blk. 15 10
1551. – 75 p. multicoloured.. 20 15

DESIGN: 75 p. Flower with broken stem, and Christ of the Andes statue.

1974. 25th Anniv. of Organization of American States (O.E.A).

1552. **457.** 250 p. multicoloured 40 50

458. Games' Emblem.

1974. 1st International Scout Games. Montevideo.

1553. **458.** 250 p. multicoloured 40 50

459. Hector Sedes and Motor-car.

462. "The Three Gauchos".

1974. Hector Sedes (motor-racing driver). Commemoration.

1554 **459** 50 p. brown, blk & grn 15 10

1974. Centenary of Antonio Lussich's Poem "Los Tres Gauchos".

1560. **462.** 50 p. multicoloured.. 15 10

463. Rifle, Target and Swiss Flag.

1974. Centenary of Swiss Rifle Club, Nueva Helvecia.

1561. **463.** 100 p. multicoloured 30 15

464. Compass Rose on Map.

465. Emblem and Stadium.

1974. Military Geographical Service.

1562. **464.** 50 p. blk., emer. & grn. 15 10

1974. World Cup Football Championships, Munich. Multicoloured.

1563. 50 p. Type **465** 15 10
1564. 75 p. Emblem and footballer (horiz.) 20 15
1565. 1000 p. Emblem and footballer (diff.) (horiz.) .. 11·00 7·50

466. Old and New School Buildings, and Founders.

1974. Centenary of Osimani-Llerena Technical School, Salto.

1566. **466.** 75 p. black & brown 20 15

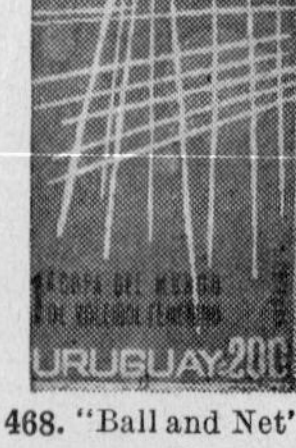

467. Carlos Gardel.

468. "Ball and Net".

1974. 39th Death Anniv of Carlos Gardel (singer).

1567. **467.** 100 p. multicoloured 35 15

1974. 1st Women's World Cup Volleyball Championships.

1568. **468.** 200 p. pur., yell. & blk. 45 25

469. "Protect Your Heart".

470. Vidal and Statue.

1974. Uruguayan "Pro Cardias" Heart Foundation.

1569. **469.** 75 p. red, yell. & grn. 20 15

1974. Bicentenary (1973) of Founding of San Jose by Eusebio Vidal.

1570. **470.** 75 p. blue & new blue 15 10

No. 1570 is incorrectly inscr. "1873–1973".

471. Artigas Monument.

472. W.P.Y. Emblem.

1974. Dedication of Artigas Monument, Buenos Aires, Argentine Republic.

1571. **471.** 75 p. multicoloured.. 15 10

1974. Air. World Population Year.

1572. **472.** 500 p. red, black and grey 55 70

473. Montevideo Citadel Gateway and Emblems.

474. Mast and Radio Waves.

1974. Air. Events of 1974.

1573. **473.** 200 p. multicoloured 55 40
1574. 300 p. multicoloured 70 60

1974. 50th Anniv. of Broadcasting in Uruguay.

1575. **474.** 100 p. multicoloured 20 10

475. "Sheet of Stamps" and "URUEXPO 74" Emblem.

1974. 10th Anniv. of "Circulo Filatelico" Journal of Montevideo Stamp Club.

1576. **475.** 100 p. bl., red & blk. 20 10

476. Envelopes and Emblem.

1974. Cent. of Universal Postal Union.

1577. **476.** 100 p. multicoloured 10 10
1578. – 200 p. blk., gold & lilac 20 10

DESIGN—VERT. 200 p. U.P.U. emblem on envelope, laurel and globe.

477. Mexican Official Stamp of 1884 and Arms.

1974. Air. "EXFILMEX" Interamerican Philatelic Exn., Mexico City.

1579. **477.** 200 p. multicoloured 20 10

478. Artigas Monument.

1974. Dedication of Artigas Monument, Ventura Hill, Minas.

1580. **478.** 100 p. multicoloured 10 10

479. Early Map of Montevideo.

1974. 250th Anniv. of Montevideo's Fortifications.

1581. **479.** 300 p. brn., red & grn. 50 20

480. Naval Vessel in Dry-dock and Badge.

1974. Cent. of Montevideo Naval Arsenal.

1582. **480.** 200 p. multicoloured 40 30

481. Balloon.

1974. History of Aviation. Multicoloured.

1583. 100 p. Type **481** 25 15
1584. 100 p. Farman biplanes.. 25 15
1585. 100 p. Castaibert monoplane 25 15
1586. 100 p. Bleriot monoplane 25 15
1587. 150 p. Military and civil pilots' "wings" .. 35 20
1588. 150 p. Nieuport biplane 35 20
1589. 150 p. Breguet-Bidon biplane 35 20
1590. 150 p. Caproni biplane .. 35 20

482. Pan de Azucar Mountain and Cross.

1974. Cent. of Pan de Azucar (town).

1591. **356.** 150 p. multicoloured 25 20

483. Adoration of the Kings.

1974. Christmas. Multicoloured.

1592. 100 p. Type **483** (postage) 10 10
1593. 150 p. Kings with Gifts.. 15 10
1594. 240 p. Kings following the Star (air) 20 15

484. Rowers, Fireworks and Nike of Samothrace Statue.

1975. Cent. of Montevideo Rowing Club.

1596. **484.** 150 p. multicoloured 15 10

485. "Treaty of Purificacion, 1817" (J. Zorrilla de San Martin).

1975. Recognition of Artigas Government by Great Britain in Treaty of Purificacion, 1817.

1597. **485.** 100 p. multicoloured 10 10

486. Spanish 6 c. Stamp of 1850, and National Colours.

1975. Air. "ESPANA 75" Stamp Exhibition, Madrid.

1598. **486.** 400 p. multicoloured 35 20

487. Rose.

1975. Bicentenary of Rosario.

1600. **487.** 150 p. multicoloured 20 10

488. "The Oath of the Thirty-three" (J. M. Blanes).

1975. 150th Anniv. of 1825 Liberation Movement.

1601. **488.** 150 p. multicoloured 20 10

489. Michelangelo's Motif for Floor of Capitol, Rome.

1975. Air. 500th Birth Anniv. of Michelangelo.
1602. **489.** 1 p. multicoloured .. 60 50

490. Columbus and Caravel.

492. Emblem of Montreal Olympics (1976) and World Cup Football Championship Finals (Argentina, 1978)

491. Sun and 4 p. 50 Air Stamp of 1929.

1975. Spanish-American Stamp Day.
1603. **490.** 1 p. multicoloured .. 1·00 60

1975. Air. Uruguayan Stamp Day.
1604. **491.** 1 p. blk., yell. and grey 2·00 70

1975. Air. "Exfilmo-Espamer 75" Stamp Exhibition, Montevideo. Multicoloured.
1605. 1 p. Type **492** 40 60
1606. 1 p. "Independence" (U.S. & Uruguayan flags) 40 60
1607. 1 p. Emblems of U.P.U. and Spanish-American Postal Union 40 60

493. Jose Artigas and J. Francisco de Larrobla.

1975. 150th Anniv. of Independence.
1608. **493.** 50 c. multicoloured .. 40 35

494. Col. L. Olivera and Fortress.

1975. 150th Anniv. of Capture of Santa Teresa Fortress.
1609. **494.** 10 c. multicoloured .. 20 10

495. Battle Scene from Painting by D. Hequet.

1975. 150th Anniv. of Battle of Rincon.
1610. **495.** 15 c. black and gold 20 10
See also Nos. 1620/1.

496. Florencio Sanchez.

1975. Birth Cent. of Florencio Sanchez (dramatist). Multicoloured.
1611 20 c. Type **496** 30 10
1612 20 c. "En Familia" .. 30 10
1613 20 c. "Barranca Abajo" 30 10
1614 20 c. "Mi Hijo el Doctor" 30 10
1615 20 c. "Canillita" .. 30 10
Nos. 1612/15 show scenes from plays and are horiz, 38 × 26 mm.

1975. Surch in revalued currency.
1616. **439.** 10 c. on 20 p. lilac .. 10 10
1617. 15 c. on 40 p orange 10 10
1618. 50 c. on 50 p. red .. 35 20
1619. 1 p. on 1000 p. blue 40 40

1975. 150th Anniv. of Artigas' Exile and Battle of Sarandi. As T **495.** Multicoloured.
1620. 15 c. Artigas' house, Ibiray (Paraguay) .. 20 10
1621. 25 c. Battle scene .. 40 20

498. Maria E. Vaz Ferreira (poetess).

1975. Birth Centenaries.
1622. **498.** 15 c. blk., yell. & pur. 20 10
1623. – 15 c. blk., orge. & pur. 20 10
DESIGN: No. 1623, Julio Herrera y Reissig (poet).

499. "Virgin and Child" (stained-glass window).

500. Colonel L. Latorre.

1975. Christmas. Multicoloured.
1624. 20 c. Type **499** 35 15
1625. 30 c. "Virgin and Child" (different) .. 50 30
1626. 60 c. "Fireworks" (horiz.) 40 40

1975. 59th Death Anniv of Col. Lorenzo Latorre (President, 1876–80).
1627. **500.** 15 c. multicoloured .. 15 10

501. "Ariel", Stars and Book.

1976. 75th Anniv. of Publication of "Ariel" (by Jose Rodo).
1628. **501.** 15 c. multicoloured .. 15 10

502. "Oncidium bifolium" (orchid).

1976. Air. Multicoloured.
1629. 50 c. Type **502** 45 20
1630. 50 c. Geoffroy's cat .. 45 20

503. "Water Sports".

504. Telephone Receiver.

1976. 23rd South American Swimming, Diving and Water-polo Championships, Maldonado
1631. **503.** 30 c. multicoloured... 20 15

1976. Telephone Centenary.
1632. **504.** 83 c. multicoloured .. 30 25

505. "Plus Ultra" Flying-boat.

506. Aircraft rising around Hour-glass.

1976. 50th Anniv. of "Plus Ultra" Spain–South America Flight.
1633. **505.** 63 c. multicoloured .. 60 25

1976. 50th Anniv. of Lufthansa Airline.
1634. **506.** 83 c. multicoloured .. 55 35

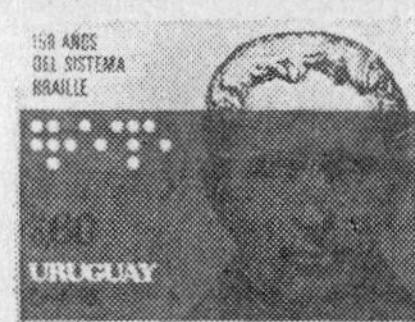

507. Louis Braille and word "Braille".

1976. 150th Anniv. of Braille System for the Blind.
1635. **507.** 60 c. black and brown 40 25

508. Signing of Declaration of Independence.

1976. Bicent. of American Revolution.
1636. **508.** 1 p. 50 multicoloured 1·25 95

509. "Candombe" (Pedro Figari).

1976. 150th Anniv. of Abolition of Slavery.
1637. **509.** 30 c. multicoloured .. 15 10

510. Rivera Monument.

511. Chilian Lapwing.

1976. General Rivera Monument. Dedication.
1638. **510.** 5 p. on 10 p. mult. .. 2·00 95

1976.
1639. **511.** 1 c. violet 30 10
1640. – 5 c. green 10 10
1641. – 15 c. red 15 10
1642. – 20 c. black 10 10
1643. – 30 c. grey 15 10
1644. – 45 c. blue 10 10
1645. – 50 c. green 25 10
1646. – 1 p. brown 45 10
1646b. – 1 p. yellow 25 10
1647. – 1 p. 75 green .. 35 10
1648. – 1 p. 95 grey 40 10
1649. – 2 p. green 90 70
1649a. – 2 p. mauve 35 10
1650. – 2 p. 65 violet .. 45 15
1651. – 5 p. blue .. .. 2·00 2·00
1651a. – 10 p. brown .. .. 3·25 2·00
DESIGNS—VERT. 5 c. Passion flower. 15 c. National flower. 20 c. Indian lancehead. 30 c. Indian statue. 45 c., 1 p. (No. 1646b), 1 p. 75, 1 p. 95, 2 p. (both), 2 p. 65, 5 p., 10 p., Artigas. 1 p. (No. 1646) "At Dawn" (J.M. Blanes). HORIZ. 50 c. "Branding Cattle" (J.M. Blanes).

513. Office Building and Reverse of First Uruguayan Coin of 1840.

514. Hand-pump within Flames.

516. Championship Emblem.

515. Uruguay 60 c. Stamp of 1856 and "Commemorative Postmark".

1976. 150th Anniv. of State Accounting Office.
1652. **513.** 30 c. blk., brn. & blue 25 15

1976. Centenary of Fire Service.
1653. **514.** 20 c. black and red .. 15 10

1976. 50th Anniv of Uruguay Philatelic Club.
1654. **515.** 30 c. red, blue & bistre 15 10

1976. 5th World Universities' Football Championships, Montevideo.
1655. **516.** 83 c. multicoloured .. 40 20

517. Human Eye and Spectrum.

1976. Prevention of Blindness.
1656. **517.** 20 c. multicoloured .. 25 10

518. Map of Montevideo.

1976. 250th Anniv. of Montevideo. Mult.
1657. 30 c. Type **518** 15 10
1658. 45 c. Montevideo panorama. 1842 .. .. 20 10
1659. 70 c. First Settlers 1726 .. 35 15
1660. 80 c. Montevideo coin (vert.) 40 20
1661. 1 p. 15 Montevideo's first arms (vert.) 55 30

519. " VARIG " Emblem.

1977. 50th Anniv. of VARIG Airline.
1662. **519.** 80 c. multicoloured .. 50 40

520. Artigas Mausoleum. 521. Arch on Map.

1977. Mausoleum of General Jose Artigas.
1663. **520.** 45 c. multicoloured .. 30 10

1977. Cent. of Salesian Education in Uruguay.
1664. **521.** 45 c. multicoloured .. 30 10

522. Globe and Emblems. 523. Children.

1977. Air. 150th Anniv. of Uruguayan Postal Services.
1665. **522.** 8 p. multicoloured .. 2·75 2·50

1977. 50th Anniv. of Inter-American Children's Institute.
1667. **523.** 45 c. multicoloured .. 30 10

524. " Windmills ". 525. Sun on " Stamp " and Stripes of Uruguayan Flag.

1977. Hispanidad Day.
1668. **524.** 70 c. red, yell. & blk. 35 15

1977. Stamp Day.
1669. **525.** 45 c. multicoloured .. 20 10

527. Globe and Aircraft. 528. " The Holy Family ".

1977. 30th Anniv. of International Civil Aviation Organization.
1670. **527.** 45 c. multicoloured .. 15 10

1977. Christmas.
1671. **528.** 45 c. multicoloured .. 15 10
1672. – 70 c. red, yell. & blk. 20 10

DESIGN—HORIZ. (45 × 26 mm) 70 c. "Santa Claus".

MINIMUM PRICE

The minimum price quoted is 5p which represents a handling charge rather than a basis for valuing common stamps. For further notes about prices see introductory pages.

529. Arms, Map and Products. 530. Postman clearing Mail-box.

1977. Rio Negro Department.
1673. **529.** 45 c. multicoloured .. 15 10

1977. 150th Anniv. of National Mail Service. Multicoloured.
1674. 50 c. Type **530** 15 10
1675. 50 c. Loading mail-van .. 15 10
1676. 50 c. Post Office counter, Montevideo G.P.O. .. 15 10
1677. 50 c. Post-boxes area .. 15 10
1678. 50 c. Sorting mail .. 15 10
1679. 50 c. Postal sorters .. 15 10
1680. 50 c. Postmen sorting " walks " 15 10
1681. 50 c. Postman on rounds 15 10
1682. 50 c. Postmen on motor-scooters 15 10
1683. 50 c. Postal counter, Carrasco Airport .. 15 10

531. Edison's First " Phonograph ".

1977. Cent. of Sound Recording.
1684. **531.** 50 c. purple & yellow 15 10

532. " R " and Spectrum.

1977. World Rheumatism Year.
1685. **532.** 50 c. multicoloured .. 15 10

533. Emblem, Diploma, Sword and Flag.

1978. 50th Anniv. of Military College.
1686. **533.** 50 c. multicoloured .. 15 10

534. Arms and Map. 537. " Wandering Angels " (detail).

1978. Department of Artigas.
1687. **534.** 45 c. multicoloured .. 30 10

1978. Air. " Riccione " and " Europhil 78 " Stamp Exhibitions, Italy. Optd. **EUROPA 1978 ITALIA Riccione 78 Eurphila 78**
1689. **522.** 8 p. multicoloured .. 3·00 2·50

1978. National Artists. Luis A. Solari. Multicoloured.
1690. 1 p. 50 Type **537** .. 30 20
1691. 1 p. 50 " Wandering Angels " (horiz. 38 × 30 mm.) .. 30 20
1692. 1 p. 50 " Wandering Angels " (detail) .. 30 20

538. Bernardo O'Higgins.

1978. Birth Bicentenary of Bernardo O'Higgins (national hero of Chile).
1693. **538.** 1 p. multicoloured .. 25 10

539. Telephone Dials and " Antel " Emblem.

1978. Telephone Automatisation.
1694. **539.** 50 c. multicoloured .. 10 10

540. San Martin and Army of the Andes Monument (J. M. Ferrari). 541. Spanish Tiles.

1978. Birth Bicentenary of General Jose de San Martin.
1695. **540.** 1 p. multicoloured .. 25 10

1978. " Hispanidad ".
1696. **541.** 1 p. blue, yell. & blk. 25 10

542. Corners of " Stamps ".

1978. Stamp Day.
1697. **542.** 50 c. multicoloured .. 10 10

543. Boeing " 727 " in Flight. 545. Flag Monument, Montevideo.

544. Angel blowing Trumpet.

1978. PLUNA Airline Inaugural Boeing " 727 " Flight.
1698. **543.** 50 c. multicoloured .. 15 10

1978. Christmas.
1699. **544.** 50 c. grn., orge. & blk. 10 10
1700. 1 p. blue, red & black 20 10

1978. Homage to the National Flag.
1701. **545.** 1 p. multicoloured .. 25 10

546. Horacio Quiroga. 547. Arms and Map of Paysandu.

1978. Birth Centenary of Horacio Quiroga (playwright).
1702. **546.** 1 p. black, yell. & red 25 10

1979. Department of Paysandu.
1703. **547.** 45 c. multicoloured .. 10 10

548. Olympic Rings and Ciudadela.

1979. Olympic Games, Moscow (1980) and Winter Olympics, Lake Placid (1980). Multicoloured.
1704. 5 p. Type **548** 90 85
1705. 7 p. Lake Placid emblem 1·10 1·25

See also Nos. 1728/9.

549. Arms and Map of Salto. 550. Artilleryman, 1830.

1979. Department of Salto.
1706. **549.** 45 c. multicoloured .. 10 10

1979. Uruguayan Military Uniforms. Mult.
1707. 5 p. Type **550** 85 85
1708. 5 p. Sapper, 1837 .. 85 85

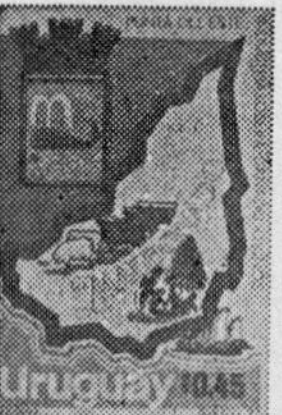

551. Arms and Map of Maldonado. 553. Centenary Symbol and Branch.

552. Salto Grande Dam.

1979. Department of Maldonado.
1709. **551.** 45 c. multicoloured .. 10 10

1979. Salto Grande Dam.
1710. **552.** 2 p. multicoloured .. 50 15

1979. Centenary of Crandon Uruguayan-American High School.
1711. **553.** 1 p. blue and violet .. 20 10

554. Kites.

1979. International Year of the Child (1st issue).
1712. **554.** 2 p. multicoloured .. 35 15

See also Nos. 1715, 1718 and 1720.

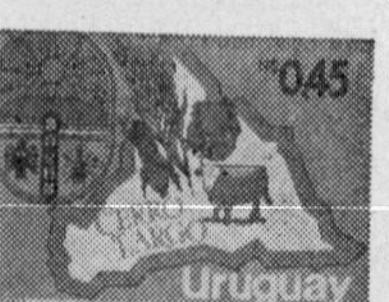

555. Arms and Map of Cerro Largo.

1979. Department of Cerro Largo.
1713. **555.** 45 c. multicoloured .. 10 10

556. Arms and Map of Trienta y Tres. **557.** Cinderella.

1979. Department of Trienta y Tres.
1714. **556.** 50 c. multicoloured . . 10 10

1979. International Year of the Child (2nd issue).
1715. **557.** 2 p. multicoloured . . 35 20

558. National Coat of Arms.

1979. 150th Anniv. of First National Coat of Arms.
1716. **558.** 8 p. multicoloured . . 1·10 1·10

559. U.P.U. Emblem and Arrow.

1979. 18th U.P.U. Congress, Rio de Janeiro.
1717. **559.** 5 p. multicoloured . . 85 50

560. " Chico Carlo " (Juana de Ibarbourou). **561.** Drawing by J. Torres-Garcia.

1979. International Year of the Child (3rd issue).
1718. **560.** 1 p. multicoloured . . 20 10

1979. 31st Death Anniv of Joaquin Torres-Garcia (artist).
1719. **561.** 10 p. yellow and black 1·40 1·25

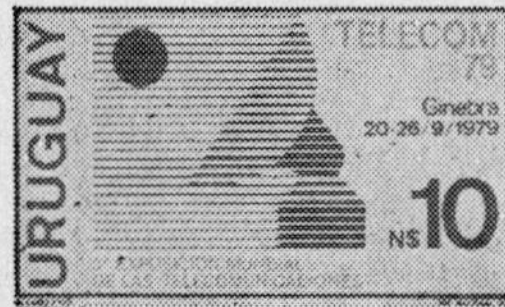

562. Madonna and Child. **563.** Arms and Map of Durazno.

1979. Christmas and International Year of the Child (4th issue).
1720. **562.** 10 p. multicoloured . . 1·40 1·25

1979. Department of Durazno.
1721. **563.** 50 c. multicoloured . . 15 10

565. Caravel.

1979. Hispanidad Day.
1723. **565.** 10 p. multicoloured . . 1·75 85

566. 10 c. Coin of 1877.

1979. Centenary of First Silver Coinage. Multicoloured.
1724. **566.** 10 c. silver, blk. & grn. 10 10
1725. – 20 c. silver, blk. & grn. 10 10
1726. – 50 c. silver, blk. & blue 10 10
1727. – 1 p. silver, blk. & blue 20 10
DESIGNS: 20 c. 1877 20 c. coin. 50 c. 1877 50 c. coin 1 p. 1877 1 p. coin.

1980. Events. Multicoloured.
1728 3 p. Type **548** 60 25
1729 3 p. As No. 1705 . . . . 60 25
1730 5 p. Olympic rings . . 90 40
1731 5 p. "Uruguay 79" stamp exhibition emblem . . 90 40
1732 7 p. Chessboard and rook (23rd Chess Olympiad, Buenos Aires, 1978) . . 1·25 55
1733 7 p. Detail from Greek vase (Olympic Games) 1·25 55
1734 10 p. Detail from Greek vase (different) . . 1·75 80

568. Thomas Edison and Lamp.

1980. Centenary of Electric Light.
1736. **568.** 2 p. multicoloured . . 40 20

569. Arms of Colonia. **571.** Association Emblem.

1980. Colonia.
1737. **569.** 50 c. multicoloured . . 15 10

1980. 50th Anniv. of Uruguayan Printers' Association.
1739. **571.** 1 p. yell., mve. & blue 20 12

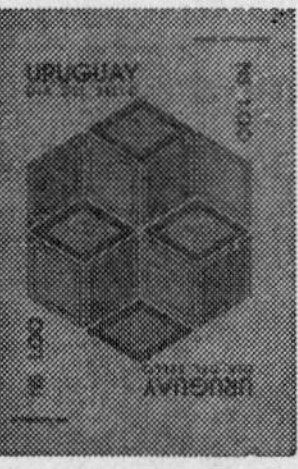

572. Geometric Design. **573.** Zorilla de San Martin and Page of " La Leyenda Patria ".

1980. Stamp Day.
1740. **572.** 1 p. multicoloured . . 20 10

1980. " La Leyenda Patria ".
1741. **573.** 1 p. multicoloured . . 20 10

574. Lufthansa Cargo Plane.

1980. Inauguration of Lufthansa Cargo Container Service.
1742. **574.** 2 p. multicoloured . . 40 20

575. Conference Emblem and Flags.

1980. 8th World Hereford Conference, Punta del Este, and Livestock Exhibition, Prado, Montevideo.
1743. **575.** 2 p. multicoloured . . 40 20

576. Lions Emblem and Map of South America.

1980. Ninth Latin-American Lions Forum.
1744. **576.** 1 p. multicoloured . . 20 10

579. Rotary Emblem on Globe. **580.** Hand stubbing out Cigarette.

1980. 75th Anniv. of Rotary International.
1747. **579.** 5 p. multicoloured . . 85 70

1980. World Health Day. Anti-smoking Campaign.
1748. **580.** 1 p. pink, blk. and grn. 20 10

581. Jose Artigas. **582.** Angel blowing Trumpet.

1980.
1749 **581.** 10 c. blue 10 10
1750 20 c. orange . . 10 10
1751 50 c. red 10 10
1752 60 c. yellow . . 10 10
1753 1 p. grey 15 15
1754 2 p. brown 35 15
1755 3 p. green 55 30
1756 4 p. blue 65 40
1757 5 p. green 30 10
1757a 6 p. orange 10 10
1758 7 p. purple 95 70
1759 10 p. blue 50 25
1760 12 p. black 20 10
1761 15 p. 50 green . . 25 15
1762 20 p. purple . . 1·00 85
1763 30 p. brown . . 1·25 1·25
1764 50 p. blue . . . . 2·00 2·00

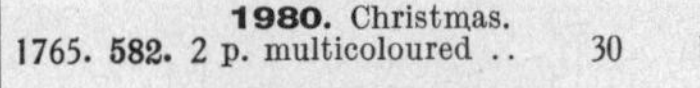

1980. Christmas.
1765. **582.** 2 p. multicoloured . . 30 15

583. Title Page of Constitution.

1980. 150th Anniv. of Constitution.
1766. **583.** 4 p. blue and gold . . 70 35

MORE DETAILED LISTS
are given in the Stanley Gibbons Catalogues referred to in the country headings.
For lists of current volumes see Introduction.

584. Montevideo Football Stadium. **585.** Conquistador.

1980. Gold Cup Football Championship, Montevideo.
1767. **584.** 5 p. multicoloured . . 50 35
1768. – 5 p. yell., blk. and red 50 35
1769. – 10 p. multicoloured . . 1·10 1·10
DESIGNS: As T **584**. No. 1768, Gold cup. 25 × 79 mm. No. 1769, Mascot and flags of participating countries.

1981. Hispanidad Day.
1771. **585.** 2 p. multicoloured . . 35 15

586. U.P.U. Emblem. **587.** Alexander von Humboldt.

1981. Centenary of U.P.U. Membership.
1772. **586.** 2 p. multicoloured . . 35 15

1981 122nd Death Anniv of Alexander von Humboldt (naturalist).
1773. **587.** 2 p. multicoloured . . 40 15

588. Trophy and Open Book. **589.** Flags and Trophy.

1981. International Education Exhibition and Congress, Montevideo.
1774. **588.** 2 p. grn., blk. & lilac 35 15

1981. Uruguayan Victory in Gold Cup Football Championship.
1775. **589.** 2 p. multicoloured . . 40 15
1776. 5 p. multicoloured . . 60 35

590. Musical Notes over Map of the Americas. **592.** Cavalryman of Gen. Manuel Oribe, 1843.

591. Boeing " 737 ".

1981. 40th Anniv. of Interamerican Institute of Musicology.
1777. **590.** 2 p. multicoloured . . 40 15

1981. Inaugural Flight to Madrid of Pluna Airline.
1778. **591.** 2 p. multicoloured . . 40 15
1779. 5 p. multicoloured . . 60 40
1780. 10 p. multicoloured . . 1·25 70

1981. Army Day. Multicoloured.
1781. 2 p. Type **592** 40 15
1782. 2 p. Infantry of Montevideo, 1843 . . . . . . 40 15

593. Conference Emblem on Suitcase.

1981. World Tourism Conference, Manila (1980).
1783. **593.** 2 p. multicoloured .. 35 15

594. Peace Dove and Atomic Emblem.

595. Footballer.

1981. 25th Anniv. of National Atomic Energy Commission.
1784. **594.** 2 p. multicoloured .. 35 15

1981. Europe-South America Football Cup.
1785. **595.** 2 p. multicoloured .. 40 15

596. Arms and Map of Rocha.

597. Carved Stone Tablets.

1981. Department of Rocha.
1786. **596.** 2 p. multicoloured .. 40 15

1981. Salto Grande Archaeological Rescue Excavations.
1787. **597.** 2 p. multicoloured .. 40 15

598. Artigas Monument, Minas.

599. A.N.C.A.P. Anniversary Emblem.

1981. 10th Lavalleja Week.
1788. **598.** 4 p. multicoloured .. 70 35

1981. 50th Anniv. of National Administration for Combustible Fuels, Alcohol and Portland Cement.
1789. **599.** 2 p. multicoloured .. 35 15

600. I.Y.D.P. Emblem.

1981. International Year of Disabled Persons.
1790. **600.** 2 p. deep blue, red and blue 35 15

601. Sun Disc.

1981. Senior Level Meeting on Environm tal Law, Montevideo.
1791. **601.** 5 p. multicoloured .. 60 35

602. Hands holding Knife and Fork.

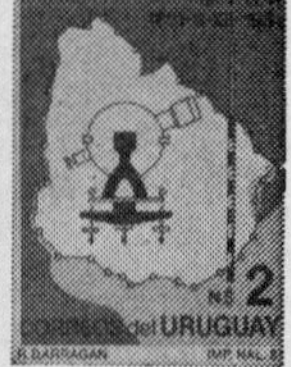

603. Theodolite and Measuring Rod on Map of Uruguay.

1981. World Food Day.
1792. **602.** 2 p. multicoloured .. 40 15

1981. 150th Anniv. of Topographic Survey.
1793. **603.** 2 p. multicoloured .. 40 15

604. Bank of Uruguay.

1981. 85th Anniv. of Bank of Uruguay.
1794. **604.** 2 p. multicoloured .. 40 15

605. Palmar Dam.

1981. Palmar Central Hydroelectric Project.
1795. **605.** 2 p. multicoloured .. 40 15

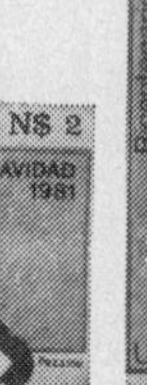

606. Father Christmas 607. Joaquin Suarez.

1981. Christmas.
1796. **606.** 2 p. multicoloured .. 40 15

1982. Birth Bicent. of Joaquin Suarez.
1797. **607.** 5 p. multicoloured .. 60 35

608. Lockheed "L 1049 G Super Constellation" and Route Map.

1982. 25th Anniv. of First Germany-Uruguay, Lufthansa Flight. Multicoloured.
1798. 3 p. Type **608** 50 30
1799. 7 p. "Boeing 747" and Route Map 90 70

609. American Air Forces Co-operation Emblem.

610. Private, Florida Battalion, 1865.

1982. 22nd American Air Force Commanders Conference.
1800. **609.** 10 p. multicoloured .. 1·25 80

1982. Army Day. Multicoloured.
1801. 3 p. Type **610** 55 20
1802. 3 p. Captain of Artillery, 1872 .. .. .. 55 20

611. Face and Satellite in Outer Space.

612. Pinocchio.

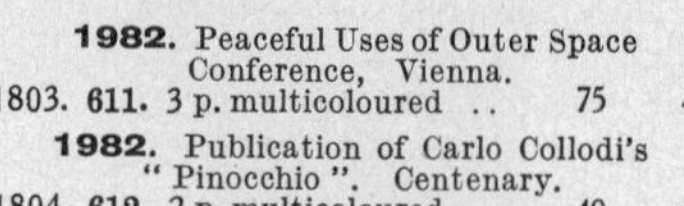

1982. Peaceful Uses of Outer Space Conference, Vienna.
1803. **611.** 3 p. multicoloured .. 75 40

1982. Publication of Carlo Collodi's "Pinocchio". Centenary.
1804. **612.** 2 p. multicoloured .. 40 15

613. Arms of Flores.

1982. Department of Flores.
1805. **613.** 2 p. multicoloured .. 40 15

614. Zorilla de San Martin.

1982. 50th Death Anniv. of Juan Zorilla de San Martin (writer).
1806. **614.** 3 p. multicoloured .. 60 35

615. Cadet Schooner "Capitan Miranda" (after J. Rivera).

1982. 165th Anniv. of Navy.
1807. **615.** 3 p. multicoloured .. 75 20

616. Figures reading Book.

617. Scales of Justice.

1982. National Literacy Campaign.
1808. **616.** 3 p. blue, deep blue and yellow 25 10

1982. Stamp Day.
1809. **617.** 3 p. green 30 15
1810. – 6 p. red 30 15
Design: No. 1810, Volcano.

618. Star, Family and Symbols of Economic Progress.

1982. Christmas.
1811. **618.** 3 p. multicoloured .. 30 15

619. Fabini.

1983. Birth Centenary of Eduardo Fabini (composer).
1812. **619.** 3 p. deep brn. & brn. 30 15

620. 2nd Cavalry Regiment, 1885.

621. "Santa Maria" on Globe.

1983. Army Day. Multicoloured.
1813. 3 p. Type **620** 40 15
1814. 3 p. Military College, 1885 40 15

1983. Visit of King and Queen of Spain. Multicoloured.
1815 3 p. Type **621** .. .. 1·50 30
1816 7 p. Royal couple and Uruguayan and Spanish flags (44 × 31 mm) .. 80 40

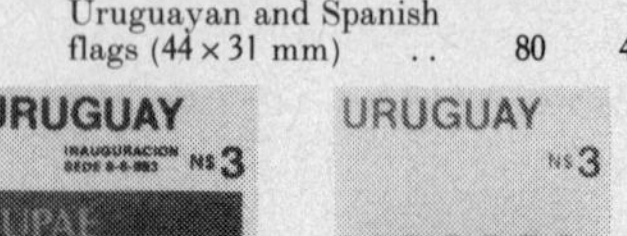

622. Headquarters Building.

623. Exhibition Emblem.

1983. Inauguration of Postal Union of the Americas and Spain H. Q., Montevideo.
1817. **622.** 3 p. blk., blue & brn. 30 15

1983. "Brasiliana 83" International Stamp Exhibition, Rio de Janeiro.
1818. **623.** 3 p. multicoloured .. 30 15

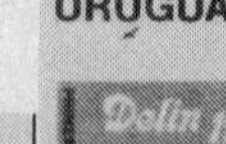

624. Space Shuttle "Columbia".

625. "Delin 1900" Car.

1983. First Flight of Space Shuttle "Columbia".
1819. **624.** 7 p. multicoloured .. 65 30

1983. First Imported Car.
1820. **625.** 3 p. blue and black .. 30 15

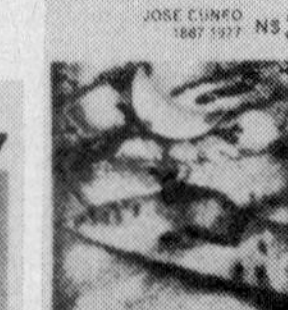

626. Goethe and Scene from "Faust".

627. "Moonlit Landscape".

1983. 150th Death Anniv (1982) of Johann Wolfgang von Goethe (writer).
1821. **626.** 7 p. blue and black .. 65 30

1983. 6th Death Anniv of Jose Cuneo (artist).
1822. **627.** 3 p. multicoloured .. 30 15

628. Statue of Lavelleja.

629. W.C.Y. Emblem.

1983. Bicentenary of Minas City.
1823. **628.** 3 p. multicoloured .. 30 15

1983. World Communications Year.
1824. **629.** 3 p. multicoloured .. 20 10

630. Garibaldi.

1983. Death Centenary (1982) of Giuseppe Garibaldi (Italian revolutionary).
1825. **630.** 7 p. multicoloured .. 50 30

631. "Graf Zeppelin".

1983. Zeppelin Flight over Montevideo (1934).
1826 **631** 7 p. black, blue & mve 90 35

632. Footballers, World Cup and Italian Team Badge.

1983. Italy's Victory in World Cup Football Championship (1982).
1827. **632.** 7 p. multicoloured .. 65 30

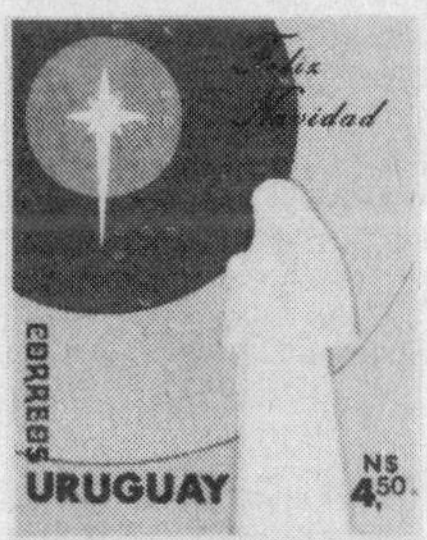

633. Virgin, Child and Star.

1983. Christmas.
1828. **633.** 4 p. 50 multicoloured 25 10

634. "50" on Telephone Dial.

635. Leandro Gomez.

1984. 50th Anniv. of Automatic Telephone Dialling.
1829. **634.** 4 p. 50 multicoloured 25 10

1984. General Leandro Gomez Commem.
1830. **635.** 4 p. 50 blue, light blue and black 25 10

636. Emblem, Map, Flag and Tanker.

637. Flags and Emblem.

1984. 25th Anniv (1983) of International Maritime Organization.
1831. **636.** 4 p. 50 multicoloured 50 15

1984. American Women's Day.
1832. **637.** 4 p. 50 multicoloured 25 10

638. Map of Uruguay and Bank Emblem.

1984. 25th Annual Meeting of Governors of International Development Bank, Punta del Este.
1833 **638** 10 p. blue, gold & blk 55 20

639. Simon Bolivar.

1984. Birth Bicent (1983) of Simon Bolivar.
1834. **639.** 4 p. 50 lt. brn. & brn. 25 10

640. Club Emblem and Radio Waves.

641. Monument.

1984. 50th Anniv (1983) of Uruguay Radio Club.
1835. **640.** 7 p. multicoloured .. 40 20

1984. 1930 World Cup Football Championship Monument.
1836. **641.** 4 p. 50 multicoloured 25 10

642. National Emblem within "200"

1984. Bicent. (1983) of San Jose de Mayo.
1837. **642.** 4 p. 50 multicoloured 25 10

643. Emblem.

1984. 50th Anniv. of Tourist Organization.
1838. **643.** 4 p. 50 gold, violet and blue 25 10

644. Artillery Uniform, 1895.

645. Artigas on Horseback.

1984. Army Day. Multicoloured.
1839 4 p. 50 Type **644** .. 25 15
1840 4 p. 50 2nd Battalion Cazadores uniform, 1894 25 15

1984.
1841. **645.** 4 p. 50 black & blue .. 25 15
1842. 8 p. 50 brown & blue 45 25

646. Trophy.

1984. Penarol Athletic Club, Winners of European–South American Football Cup, 1982.
1843. **646.** 4 p. 50 black, yellow and deep yellow .. 25 10

1984. Uruguayan Departments.
1844. **444.** 4 p. 50 multicoloured 25 10

647. Child holding Flower and "50 ANOS".

1984. 50th Anniv. of Children's Council.
1845. **647.** 4 p. 50 multicoloured 25 10

648. Christmas Tree with Candles.

649. Pelota Player and Flags.

1984. Christmas.
1846. **648.** 6 p. multicoloured .. 30 10

1985. 1st Junior Pelota World Championship.
1847 **649** 4 p. 50 multicoloured 25 10

650. Bruno Mauricio de Zabala.

652. Carlos Gardel.

651. Emblems of Los Angeles and Sarajevo Games and Olympic Rings.

1985. 300th Birth Anniv (1983) of Don Bruno Mauricio de Zabala (Governor of Buenos Aires and founder of Montevideo).
1848. **650.** 4 p. 50 multicoloured 25 10

1985. 90th Anniv. of International Olympic Committee.
1849. **651.** 12 p. multicoloured .. 45 25

1985. 50th Death Anniv. of Carlos Gardel (entertainer).
1850. **652.** 6 p. grey, blue and brown 25 10

INDEX

Countries can be quickly located by referring to the index at the end of this volume.

653. Emblem and Flags of Member States.

1985. 25th Anniv. of American Air Forces' Co-operation System.
1851. **653.** 12 p. multicoloured 20 10

654. Icarus.

1985. 40th Anniv of I.C.A.O.
1852. **654.** 4 p. 50 deep blue, green and blue .. 10 10

655. Stylised Factory and "50".

656. Cross and Clasped Hands.

1985. 50th Anniv. of FUNSA Tyre Factory.
1853. **655.** 6 p. multicoloured .. 10 10

1985. Cent. of Catholic Workers Circle.
1854. **656.** 6 p. multicoloured .. 10 10

657. I.Y.Y. Emblem.

659. Books forming "8".

658. Peace Dove and Sun.

1985. International Youth Year.
1855. **657.** 12 p. red and black 20 10

1985. "Return to Democracy".
1856. **658.** 20 p. blue, yellow and violet .. 30 15

1985. 8th International Book Exhibition.
1857. **659.** 20 p. multicoloured 30 15

660. Emblem.

661. Map and Arms.

1985. Centenary of Military School.
1858. **660.** 10 p. multicoloured 20 10

1985. Centenary of Flores Department.
1859. **661.** 6 p. multicoloured .. 10 10

662. Father Christmas.

1985. Christmas.
1860. **662.** 10 p. multicoloured 20 10
1861. 22 p. multicoloured 35 20

663. Monument to Isabel the Catholic.

1985. Hispanidad Day.
1862. **663.** 12 p. black, red and brown 15 10

664. Emblem and Meeting Logo.

1986. 3rd Inter-American Agriculture Co-operation Institute Meeting.
1863. **664.** 12 p. yell., red & blk. 20 10

665. Emblem and Flag.

1986. World Post Day.
1864. **665.** 15 p. 50 mult. .. 25 10

666. Map and Symbolic House.

1986. 6th Population and 4th Housing Census (1985).
1865. **666.** 10 p. black, blue and yellow 20 10

667. Emblem.

1986. 50th Anniv. (1985) of Conaprole Milk and Cattle Co-operative.
1866. **667.** 10 p. gold, blue and light blue 20 10

668. U.N. Emblem and Population Diagram.

1986. 40th Anniv. (1985) of U.N.O.
1867. **668.** 20 p. multicoloured 30 15

669. Emblem. **670.** Manuel Oribe.

1986. 50th Anniv. (1985) of National Brokers and Auctioneers Association.
1868. **669.** 10 p. black, deep blue and blue 15 10

1986. Liberation Heroes.

1869	**670**	1 p. green (postage)	10	10
1870		2 p. red	10	10
1871	A	3 p. blue	10	10
1872		5 p. blue	10	10
1872a	**670**	5 p. blue	10	10
1873		7 p. brown	10	10
1874	B	10 p. mauve ..	10	10
1875	C	10 p. green	10	10
1875a	**670**	10 p. green	10	10
1876		15 p. blue	10	10
1877	B	17 p. blue	15	10
1877a	**670**	20 p. brown ..	15	10
1877b	A	25 p. orange ..	10	10
1878	B	26 p. brown ..	10	10
1879	C	30 p. orange ..	20	15
1879a	A	30 p. blue	10	10
1879b	B	45 p. red	25	20
1880	C	50 p. ochre	30	20
1880a	A	50 p. mauve ..	30	20
1881	C	60 p. grey	40	40
1881a	A	60 p. orange ..	10	20
1881b	B	60 p. mauve ..	10	10
1881c		75 p. red	10	10
1881d		90 p. red	10	10
1882	C	100 p. red	60	75
1882a		100 p. brown ..	30	30
1882b		150 p. green ..	35	35
1883		200 p. green ..	1·25	1·10
1883a		300 p. blue	60	60
1883b		500 p. red	1·25	1·25
1883c		1000 p. red	2·00	2·00
1884	B	22 p. violet (air) ..	15	10

DESIGNS: A, Lavelleja. B, Jose Fructuoso Rivera. C, Jose Gervasio Artigas.

671. Mosaic in National Colours.

1986. Italian Chamber of Commerce in Uruguay.
1885. **671.** 20 p. multicoloured 20 10

672. American Flag and Monument. **673.** Emblem and Footballer.

1986. 71st Anniv. of Armenian Genocide.
1886. **672.** 10 p. blk., red & bl. 10 10

1986. World Cup Football Championship, Mexico.
1887. **673.** 20 p. multicoloured 20 15

674. Newspaper Page. **675.** Alan Garcia.

1986. Centenary of "El Dia".
1888. **674.** 10 p. gold, blk. & red 10 10

1986. Visit of President of Peru.
1889. [illegible] p. brn., red & bl. 15 15

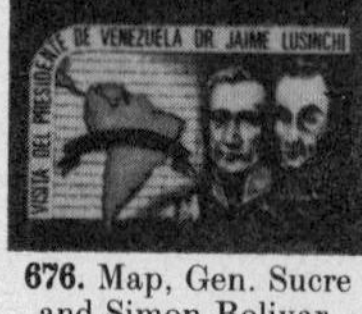

676. Map, Gen. Sucre and Simon Bolivar. **677.** Jose Sarney.

1986. Visit of Pres. Jaime Lusinchi of Venezuela.
1890. **676.** 20 p. multicoloured 15 15

1986. Visit of President of Brazil.
1891. **677.** 20 p. multicoloured 15 15

678. Michelini. **679.** Menorah and "50".

1986. 10th Death Anniv. of Zelmar Michelini (senator).
1892. **678.** 10 p. blue and red .. 10 10

1986. 50th Anniv. of B'nai B'rith in Uruguay.
1893. **679.** 10 p. brn., gold & red 10 10

680. Handshake across "GATT". **681.** Dr. Raul Alfonsin.

1986. General Agreement on Tariffs and Trade Assembly, Punta del Este.
1894. **680.** 10 p. multicoloured 10 10

1986. Visit of President of Argentina.
1895. **681.** 20 p. orge., blk. & bl. 15 15

682. Fishes in Sea.

1986. Quality Exports. Multicoloured.
1896. 20 p. Type **682** 15 15
1897. 20 p. Lambs 15 15

683. Flags and Dr. Blanco. **684.** Dr. Pertini.

1986. Visit of Dr Salvador Jorge Blanco, President of Dominican Republic.
1898. **683.** 20 p. multicoloured 15 15

1986. Visit of Dr. Sandro Pertini, President of Italy.
1899. **684.** 20 p. yellow & green 15 15

685. Airplanes and Flags.

1986. 40th Anniv. of First Scheduled Spain–Uruguay Flight.
1900. **685.** 20 p. multicoloured 45 15

686. Statue of Sts. Philip and John and Montevideo Cathedral.

1987. Hispanidad Day.
1901. **686.** 10 p. red and black 10 10

687. Emblem. **688.** Ruiz.

1987. 50th Anniv (1986) of Juventus Catholic Cultural Organization.
1902. **687.** 10 p. yellow, black and blue 10 10

1987. 10th Death Anniv (1986) of Hector Gutierrez Ruiz (Chamber of Deputies member).
1903. **688.** 10 p. brown and red 10 10

689. Emblem. **690.** "Arrowhead" of Flying Doves.

1987. International Science and Technology Symposium, Montevideo and Punta del Este (1986).
1904. **689.** 20 p. multicoloured 15 15

1987. Visit of Pope John Paul II.
1905. **690.** 50 p. orange and grey 35 45

291. Dr. Arias and Emblem. **692.** "70" and Menorah

1987. Birth Centenary of Dr. Jose F. Arias (founder of Uruguay Trades University).
1906. **691.** 10 p. multicoloured 10 10

1987. 70th Anniv of Uruguayan Jewish Community.
1907 **692** 10 p. blue, orge & blk 10 10

693 "Dragon Fly"

1987. 50th Anniv (1986) of Pluna National Airline. Multicoloured.
1908 10 p. Type **693** 10 10
1909 20 p. Douglas "DC-3" .. 15 10
1910 25 c. Vickers "Viscount" 15 15
1911 30 p. Boeing "707" .. 20 15

694 Artigas Antarctic Base

1987.

1912 **694** 20 p. multicoloured .. 15 15

695 Sun, Symbolic House and "75"

1987. 75th Anniv of Uruguayan Mortgage Bank.

1913 **695** 26 p. multicoloured .. 20 15

696 Dairy Products

697 "Holy Family"

1987. Uruguayan Quality Exports. Mult.

1914 51 p. Type **696** 35 20
1915 51 p. Map and cattle .. 35 20

1987. Christmas. Stained Glass Windows. Multicoloured.

1916 17 p. Type **697** 15 10
1917 66 p. "Angels" 45 55

698 Pres. Duarte

699 Airplane and Globe forming "60"

1988. Visit of Pres. Jose Napoleon Duarte of El Salvador.

1918 **698** 20 p. blue and yellow 15 15

1988. 60th Anniv (1987) of VARIG (airline).

1919 **699** 66 p. blue, yell & blk 45 50

700 Emblem and Globe

1988. International Peace Year (1986).

1920 **700** 10 p. multicoloured .. 10 10

701 Flags and Beret

702 Airplane within Aircraft Wing

1988. 75th Anniv (1987) of Basque Immigration.

1921 **701** 66 p. multicoloured .. 45 45

1988. 75th Anniv of Air Force.

1922 **702** 17 p. multicoloured .. 20 10

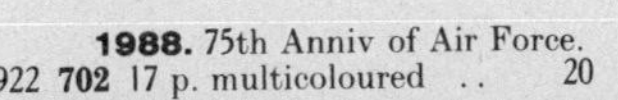

703 Lantern and "75"

1988. 75th Anniv (1987) of UTE (hydro-electric dam programme).

1923 **703** 17 p. multicoloured .. 15 10
1924 – 17 p. black, bl & grn 15 10
1925 – 51 p. black and blue 35 20
1926 – 51 p. black, bl & red 35 20
1927 – 66 p. blue, blk & yell 45 25

DESIGNS: No.1924, Baygorria Dam; 1925, Dr. Gabriel Terra Dam; 1926, Constitucion Dam; 1927, Map showing dam sites on River Negro.

704. Flag and Globe

1988. 75th Anniv (1986) of Postal Union of the Americas and Spain.

1928 **704** 66 p. multicoloured .. 45 45

705 Menorah in "40"

1988. 40th Anniv of Israel.

1929 **705** 66 p. blue and black .. 45 45

706 Airmail Envelope and Postman

1988. "Post, Messenger of Peace".

1930 **706** 66 p. multicoloured .. 45 45

707 Emblem on Map

708 Matos Rodriguez

1988. 60th Anniv of Interamerican Institute for the Child.

1931 **707** 30 p. lt grn, grn & blk 20 15

1988. Gerardo H. Matos Rodriguez (composer) Commemoration.

1932 **708** 17 p. black and violet 15 10
1933 – 51 p. brown on pale brown 35 20

DESIGN: 51 p. Matos Rodriguez and score of "La Cumparsita".

709 Col. Pablo Banales (founder)

711 Citrus Fruits

710 Route Map and "Capitan Miranda"

1988. Centenary (1987) of Fire Service. Mult.

1934 17 p. Type **709** 15 10
1935 26 p. Fireman, 1900 .. 20 15
1936 34 p. Emblem (horiz) .. 20 15
1937 51 p. Merryweather fire engine, 1907 (horiz) .. 35 20
1938 66 p. 8-man hand pump, 1888 (horiz) 45 25
1939 100 p. Magirus mechanical ladder, 1921 (44 × 25 mm) 70 40

1988. 1st World Voyage of "Capitan Miranda".

1940 **710** 30 p. multicoloured .. 50 20

1988. Exports. Multicoloured.

1941 30 p. Type **711** 20 15
1942 45 p. Rice 35 20
1943 55 p. Shoes 40 20
1944 55 p. Clothes 40 20

712 "Toxodon platensis" (mammal bone)

713 Bird posting Letter

1988. 150th Anniv of National Natural History Museum, Montevideo.

1945 – 30 p. brn, yell & blk 20 15
1946 **712** 90 p. brown, bl & blk 65 60

DESIGN: 30 p. "Usnea densirostra" (moss).

1988. Postal Officers' Day. Unissued stamp surch.

1947 **713** 30 p. on 10 p. + 5 p. yellow, black & bl 10 10

714 Abstract

1988. 150th Anniv (1986) of Battle of Carpinteria.

1948 **714** 30 p. multicoloured .. 10 10

715 Virgin and Child

716 "Self-portrait" (Joaquin Torres Garcia)

1988. Christmas.

1949 **715** 115 p. multicoloured .. 55 55

1988. Uruguayan Painters. Multicoloured.

1950 115 p. Type **716** 50 50
1951 115 p. Poster for Pedro Figari exhibition, Montevideo 50 50
1952 115 p. "Squares and Rectangles LXXVIII" (Jose P. Costigliolo) .. 50 50
1953 115 p. "Manolita Pina, 1920" (Joaquin Torres Garcia) 50 50

717 "Santa Maria"

1989. Hispanidad Day.

1954 **717** 90 p. multicoloured .. 40 40
1955 115 p. multicoloured 50 50

718 Emblem

1989. Centenary of Armenian Organization Hnchakian.

1956 **718** 210 p. blue, yell & red 40 35

719 Plumb Line suspended on Frame

1989. Bicentenary of French Revolution. Each black, red and blue.

1957 50 p. Type **719** .. 10 10
1958 50 p. Tree of liberty .. 10 10
1959 210 p. Eye in centre of sunburst 40 35
1960 210 p. "Liberty", "Equality", "Fraternity" around phrygian cap 40 35

720 Map

1989. "Use the Post Code". Each black and red.

1961 50 p. Type **720** 10 10
1962 210 p. Map showing numbered zones (vert) 40 35

721 Map, Cow, Factory and Baby

722 "Tiradentes"

CORREOS N$
URUGUAY 170

1989. 3rd Pan-American Milk Congress.

1963 **721** 170 p. dp blue & blue 30 25

1989. Birth Bicentenary of Joaquin Jose da Silva Xavier.

1964 **722** 170p. multicoloured .. 30 25

MINIMUM PRICE

The minimum price quoted is 5p which represents a handling charge rather than a basis for valuing common stamps. For further notes about prices see introductory pages.

723 Emblem and Flag

1989. Interparliamentary Union Centenary Conference, London.

1965	**723**	210 p. red, blue & blk	40	35

724 F.A.O. Emblem, Map and Fruit Slices

1989. 8th Intergovernmental Group on Citrus Fruits Meeting.

1966	**724**	180 p. multicoloured ..	30	25

725 Flower, Hand and Emblem

1989. U. N. Decade for Disabled People. Mult.

1967	50 p. Type **725**	10	10
1968	210 p. Disabled people and emblem	40	35

726 Nacurutu Artefact

727 Virgin of the Thirty Three

1989. America. Pre-Columbian Culture.

1969	**726**	60 p. multicoloured ..	10	10
1970		180 p. multicoloured	30	25

1989. Christmas. Multicoloured.

1971	70 p. Type **727**	10	10
1972	210 p. "Adoration of the Animals" (Barradas) (horiz)	15	15

728 Old and Modern Buildings

1989. Bicentenary of Pando.

1973	**728**	60 p. multicoloured ..	10	10

729 Hospital Building

1990. Bicentenary of Charity Hospital.

1974	**729**	60 p. flesh, black & brn	10	10

730 Map and Arms of Soriano

731 Luisa Luisi

1990. Departments. Multicoloured.

1975	70 p. Type **730**	10	10
1976	70 p. Florida (vert) ..	10	10
1977	90 p. San Jose (vert) ..	10	10
1978	90 p. Canelones ..	10	10
1979	90 p. Lavalleja (vert) ..	10	10
1980	90 p. Rivera	10	10

1990. Writers. Multicoloured.

1981	60 p. Type **731**	10	10
1982	60 p. Javier de Viana ..	10	10
1983	75 p. J. Zorilla de San Martin	10	10
1984	75 p. Dekmira Agustini ..	10	10
1985	170 p. Julio Casal ..	45	45
1986	170 p. Alfonsina Storni ..	45	45
1987	210 p. Juana de Ibarbourou	55	55
1988	210 p. Carlos Roxlo ..	55	55

732 Mercedes Church

733 Ear of Wheat and Tractor

1990. Bicentenary of Mercedes.

1989	**732**	70 p. multicoloured ..	10	10

1990. 10th Anniv of International Agricultural Fund.

1990	**733**	210 p. multicoloured ..	55	55

734 Glass and Smashed Car

1990. Road Safety. Multicoloured.

1991	70 p. Type **734**	70	70
1992	70 p. Traffic waiting at red light	70	70
1993	70 p. Road signs ..	70	70
1994	70 p. Children crossing road at green light ..	70	70

735 Sculpture of Artigas

736 Woman

1990. Artigas Day.

1995	**735**	60 p. blue and red ..	10	10

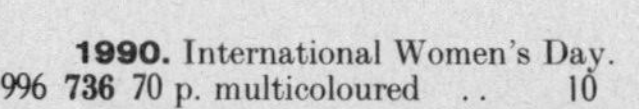

1990. International Women's Day.

1996	**736**	70 p. multicoloured ..	10	10

737 Gonzalo Ramirez

738 Microphone and Radio Mast

1990. Centenary of First International Juridical Congress, Montevideo.

1997	**737**	60 p. blk, yell & mve	55	55
1998	–	60 p. black, bl & mve	55	55
1999	–	60 p. multicoloured ..	55	55
2000	–	60 p. multicoloured ..	55	55

DESIGNS: No. 1998, Ildefonso Garcia; 1999, Flags and left half of 50th anniversary memorial; 2000, Flags and right half of memorial.

1990. The Media. Multicoloured.

2001	70 p. Type **738**	70	70
2002	70 p. Newspaper vendor	70	70
2003	70 p. Television screen, camera and aerial	70	70
2004	70 p. Books and type ..	70	70

739 Burning Trees

741 "Nativity" (Juan B. Maino)

740 American Deer

1990. Fire Prevention.

2005	**739**	70 p. black, yell & red	70	70

1990. America. The Natural World. Mult.

2006	120 p. Type **740**	10	10
2007	360 p. "Peltophorum dubium" (vert) ..	85	85

1990. Christmas.

2008	**741**	170 p. multicoloured	40	40
2009		830 p. multicoloured	2·00	2·00

742 Carlos Federico Saez

1990. Artists. Multicoloured.

2010	90 p. Type **742**	10	10
2011	90 p. Pedro Blanes Viale	10	10
2012	210 p. Edmundo Prati ..	55	55
2013	210 p. Jose L. Zorrilla de San Martin	55	55

743 Mechanical Digger

1991. 75th Anniv of Army Engineers Division.

2014	**743**	170 p. multicoloured ..	40	40

744 Drum and Masks

1991. Carnival.

2015	**744**	170 p. multicoloured ..	40	40

745 Campaign Emblem

1991. Campaign against Aids.

2016	**745**	170 p. multicoloured	40	40
2017		830 p. multicoloured	2·00	2·00

746 Anniversary Emblem

1991. Centenary of Organization of American States.

2018	**746**	830 p. yellow, bl & blk	2·00	2·00

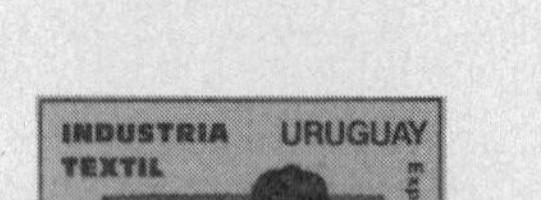

747 Textiles

1991. Uruguayan Quality Exports. Mult.

2019	120 p. Type **747**	10	10
2020	120 p. Clothes (vert) ..	10	10
2021	400 p. Semi-precious stones and granite ..	55	60

748 Flint Axe and Stone Monument

1991. Education. Multicoloured.

2022	120 p. Type **748**	10	10
2023	120 p. Wheel and pyramids	10	10
2024	330 p. Printing press and diagram of planetary orbits	45	45
2025	330 p. Space probe and computer diagram ..	45	45

749 Sword piercing Crab

1991. Anti-Cancer Day.

2026	**749**	360 p. red and black ..	45	45

750 College Arms

751 College Building

1991. Centenary of Holy Family College.
2027 **750** 360 p. multicoloured . . 45 45

1991. Centenary of Immaculate Heart of Mary College.
2028 **751** 1370 p. multicoloured 1·60 1·60

752 Emblem

1991. 7th Pan-American Maccabiah Games.
2029 **752** 1490 p. multicoloured 1·75 1·75

753 World Map and Flying Boat

1991. "Espamer '91" Spain–Latin America Stamp Exhibition, Buenos Aires.
2030 **753** 1510 p. multicoloured 2·00 2·00

754 "Oath of the Constitution" (P. Blanes Viale)

1991. 1830 Constitution.
2031 **754** 360 p. multicoloured . . 45 45

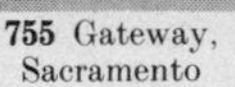

755 Gateway, Sacramento

756 "William Tell" (statue) and Flags

1991.
2032 **755** 360 p. brown & yellow 45 45
2033 – 540 p. grey and blue 65 65
2034 **755** 600 p. brn, yell & blk 55 55
2035 – 825 p. grey, blue & blk 75 75
2036 – 1510 p. brown & green 2·00 2·00
2037 – 2500 p. brn, grn & blk 2·00 2·00
DESIGNS: 540, 825 p. First locomotive, 1869; 1510, 2500 p. Horse-drawn tram.

1991. 700th Anniv of Swiss Confederation.
2038 **756** 1510 p. multicoloured 2·50 2·50

MORE DETAILED LISTS
are given in the Stanley Gibbons Catalogues referred to in the country headings.
For lists of current volumes see Introduction.

757 Yacht

758 Emblem

1991. Whitbread Regatta.
2040 **757** 1510 p. multicoloured 1·75 1·75

1991. 50th Anniv of Uruguay Society of Actors.
2041 **758** 450 p. black and red . . 50 50

759 Camera and Photograph

1991. 150th Anniv of First Photograph in Rio de la Plata.
2042 **759** 1370 p. multicoloured 1·50 1·50

760 Anniversary Emblem

1991. 25th Anniv of CREA (livestock organization).
2043 **760** 450 p. multicoloured . . 50 50

761 Margarita Xirgu

1991. 22nd Death Anniv of Margarita Xirgu (actress).
2044 **761** 360 p. brown, light brown and yellow 40 40

762 "General Rivera" (gunboat)

1991. Centre for Study of Naval and Maritime History. Multicoloured.
2045 450 p. Type **762** 45 45
2046 450 p. "Salto" (coastguard patrol boat) 45 45
2047 1570 p. "Uruguay" (cruiser) . . . . 1·60 1·60
2048 1570 p. "Pte. Oribe" (tanker) . . . . 1·60 1·60

763 "Rio de la Plata, 1602" (woodcut)

1991. America. Voyages of Discovery.
2049 **763** 450 p. brown & yellow 50 50
2050 – 1740 p. green & brown 1·90 1·90
DESIGN—HORIZ. 1740 p. Amerigo Vespucci.

764 "The Tree is the Fountain of Life"

1991. World Food Day.
2051 **764** 1740 p. multicoloured 1·75 1·75

765 "The Table" (Zoma Baitler)

1991.
2052 **765** 360 p. multicoloured . . 40 40

766 Gladiator, 1902

1991. Old Cars. Multicoloured.
2053 360 p. Type **766** 40 40
2054 1370 p. E.M.F., 1909 . . 1·50 1·50
2055 1490 p. Renault, 1912 . . 1·50 1·50
2056 1510 p. Clement-Bayard, 1903 (vert) . . . . 1·75 1·75

767 Emblem

768 Club Badge and Trophy

1991. 60th General Assembly of Interpol, Punta del Este.
2057 **767** 1740 p. multicoloured 1·75 1·75

1991. Nacional Football Club, Winners of World Club Football Cup, 1988, and the Toyota Cup. Multicoloured.
2058 450 p. Type **768** 50 50
2059 450 p. Trophies on football pitch (horiz) . . 50 50

769 School and Pupils

1991. Centenary of Maria Auxiliadora Institute.
2060 **769** 450 p. blue, blk & red 50 50

770 "LATU"

1991. 25th Anniv of Uruguay Technological Laboratory.
2061 **770** 1570 p. blue & dp blue 1·50 1·50

771 Emblem and Couple

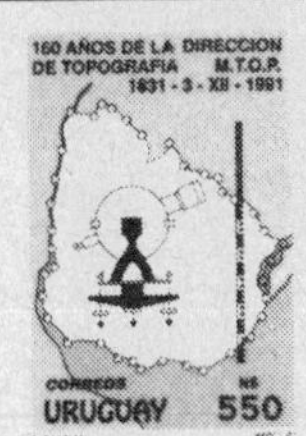

772 Theodolite and Measuring Rod on Map of Uruguay

1991. World AIDS Day.
2062 **771** 550 p. black, yell & bl 55 55
2063 2040 p. blk, lilac & grn 2·00 2·00

1991. 160th Anniv of Topographic Survey.
2064 **772** 550 p. multicoloured . . 55 55

773 Angel

1991. Christmas. Multicoloured.
2065 550 p. Type **773** 55 55
2066 2040 p. "Adoration of the Angels" . . . . 1·90 1·90

774 Anibal Troilo

1992. Musicians.
2067 **774** 450 p. black, mve & bl 40 40
2068 – 450 p. blk, orge & red 40 40
2069 – 450 p. black, light green and green . . 40 40
2070 – 450 p. black, bl & mve 40 40
DESIGNS: No. 2068, Francisco Canaro; 2069, Pintin Castellanos; 2070, Juan de Dios Filiberto.

775 Worker and Factory Building

1992. Quality Exports.
2071 **775** 120 p. multicoloured . . 15 15

776 Pres. Aylwin

777 Trophy

1992. Visit of President Patricio Aylwin of Chile.
2072 **776** 550 p. multicoloured . . 50 50

1992. Penarol F.C., Three-times World Club Football Champions.
2073 **777** 600 p. black and yellow 55 55

778 Hands holding Hammer and Chisel

779 No Smoking Emblem

1992. 120th Anniv of La Paz.
2075 **778** 550 p. multicoloured . . 50 50

1992. World No Smoking Day.
2076 **779** 2500 p. red, blk & brn 2·00 2·00

780 Heart and Emblems

1992. World Health Day. "Health in Rhythm with the Heart".
2077 **780** 2500 p. ultramarine, blue and red . . 2·10 2·10

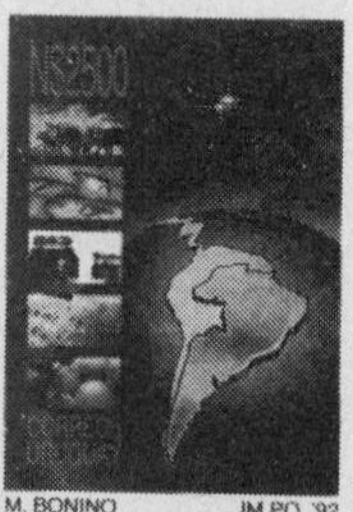

781 Map of South America and Food Products

1992. Mercosur (South American economic organization).
2078 **781** 2500 p. multicoloured 2·10 2·10

782 Stamp

1992. "Olymphilex 92" International Olympic Stamps Exhibition, Barcelona.
2079 **782** 2900 p. multicoloured 2·25 2·25

783 Emblems

1992. 22nd Latin American–Caribbean Regional Conference of Food and Agricultural Organization.
2080 **783** 2500 p. multicoloured 1·75 1·75

784 Children with Basket of Food

1992. International Nutrition Conference, Rome.
2081 **784** 2900 p. multicoloured 2·10 2·10

785 Vallejo

1992. Birth Centenary of Cesar Vallejo (painter and poet).
2082 **785** 2500 p. brown & lt brn 1·75 1·75

786 Monument and Route Map

787 Ruins of Sacramento and Lighthouse

1992. Centenary of Christopher Columbus Monument, Durazno.
2083 **786** 700 p. black, bl & grn 50 50

1992. 500th Anniv of Discovery of America by Columbus.
2084 **787** 700 p. multicoloured . . 50 50

788 Caravel

789 Emblem

1992. America. 500th Anniv of Discovery of America by Columbus. Multicoloured.
2085 700 p. Type **788** 50 50
2086 2900 p. Globe showing Americas and old map (horiz) . . . . 2·10 2·10

1992. Centenary of Christopher Columbus Philanthropic Society.
2087 **789** 700 p. black, mauve and magenta . . 50 50

790 Emblem

1992. 500th Anniv of Presence of Jews in America.
2088 **790** 2900 p. multicoloured 2·10 2·10

791 Arms

1992. 50th Anniv of Jose Pedro Varela Teachers' College.
2089 **791** 700 p. multicoloured . . 50 50

792 Cambadu Building

793 Emblem

1992. Centenary of Chamber of Wholesale and Retail Traders.
2090 **792** 700 p. grey, blk & red 50 50

1992. 50th Anniv of Lebanon Club of Uruguay.
2091 **793** 2900 p. multicoloured 2·10 2·10

794 Nativity

796 Immigrant

795 Map and Emblem

1992. Christmas. Multicoloured.
2092 800 p. Type **794** 55 55
2093 3200 p. Star . . . . 2·10 2·10

1992. 22nd Latin American and Caribbean Lions Clubs Forum.
2094 **795** 2700 p. multicoloured 1·75 1·75

1992. Immigrants Day.
2095 **796** 800 p. green and black 55 55

797 Oribe

799 Anniversary Emblem

798 Anniversary Emblem

1992. Birth Bicentenary of Manuel Oribe (Liberation hero). Multicoloured.
2096 800 p. Type **797** 55 55
2097 800 p. Oribe (founder) and Eastern University (horiz) 55 55

1992. 90th Anniv of Pan-American Health Organization.
2098 **798** 3200 p. multicoloured 2·10 2·10

1992. 50th Anniv of Jose H. Molaguero S.A.
2099 **799** 800 p. brown and stone 55 55

800 Satellite and Map

1992. 70th Anniv of ANDEBU (association of broadcasting stations).
2100 **800** 2700 p. multicoloured 1·75 1·75

801 Emblem and Shanty Town

1992. 30th Anniv of Caritas Uruguaya.
2101 **801** 3200 p. multicoloured 2·00 2·00

802 Gonzalez Pecotche (founder) and Emblem

1992. 60th Anniv of Logosofia.
2102 **802** 800 p. yellow and blue 55 55

LATE FEE STAMPS

L 175.

1936.
L 774. L 175. 3 c. green 10 10
L 775. 5 c. violet 15 10
L 776. 6 c. green 15 10
L 777. 7 c. brown 20 10
L 778. 8 c. red 40 25
L 779. 12 c. blue 60 50

NEWSPAPER STAMPS

1922. Optd. **PRENSA** (=Printed Matter) or surch. also.
N 519.128. 3 c. olive (imperf.) .. 40 25
N 447.118. 3 c. on 2 c. black and lake (perf.) 40 35
N 403.120. 3 c. on 4 c. yellow (perf.) 20 30
N 448.118. 6 c. on 4 c. blue and orange (perf.) 40 35
N 449. 9 c. on 5 c. brown and blue (perf.) .. 40 35
N 520.128. 9 c. on 10 c. green (imp.) 45 35
N 521. 15 c. mauve (imperf.) 60 40

OFFICIAL STAMPS

1880. Optd. **OFICIAL.** Perf.
O 51. 9. 15 c. yellow .. .. 2·00 2·00

1880. Optd. **OFICIAL.** Roul.
O 48 10. 1 c. brown .. .. 1·10 1·10
O 49 11. 5 c. green 45 45
O 61 15. 7 c. blue (perf.) .. 1·50 1·50
O 50 10. 10 c. red 70 70
O 52 20 c. bistre 95 95
O 53 50 c. black .. .. 6·25 6·25
O 55 1 p. blue .. .. 6·25 6·25

1883. Optd. **OFICIAL.**
O 64. 16. 1 c. green .. .. 2·00 2·00
O 65. – 2 c. red (No. 63) .. 3·75 3·00

1883. Optd. **OFICIAL.**
O 70. 18. 1 c. green .. .. 11·50 11·50
O 71. 2 c. red .. .. 3·70 3·75
O 72. 20. 5 c. blue .. .. 1·10 85
O 73. 21. 10 c. brown .. .. 2·75 1·40

1884. Optd. **FRANCO** in frame.
O 74. 18. 1 c. green .. .. 13·50 11·50

1884. Optd. **OFICIAL.**
O 80. 10. 1 c. on 10 c. (No. 76) 80 80
O 81. – 2 c. red (No. 77) .. 2·25 2·25
O 82. 26. 5 c. blue 95 70

1884. Optd. **OFICIAL.** Roul.
O 91a 28. 1 c. grey .. .. 3·75 2·00
O 91 1 c. green 75 45
O 92 29. 2 c. red 45 30
O 93a 28. 5 c. blue .. .. 1·25 1·40
O 94 5 c. lilac .. .. 1·50 1·25
O 95 31. 7 c. brown .. .. 1·10 65
O 110 7 c. orange .. .. 1·10 75
O 96 32. 10 c. brown 60 35
O 111 36. 10 c. violet .. .. 5·75 3·00
O 97 33. 20 c. mauve .. .. 1·10 65
O 112 20 c. brown .. .. 5·75 2·25
O 98 34. 25 c. lilac .. .. 1·10 75
O 113 25 c. red .. .. 5·75 2·25

1890. Optd. **OFICIAL.** Perf.
O 124. 38. 1 c. green 40 20
O 125. 39. 2 c. red 40 20
O 126. 40. 5 c. blue 75 80
O 127. 41. 7 c. brown 60 60
O 128. 42. 10 c. green 60 50
O 129. 43. 20 c. orange 60 50
O 130. 44. 25 c. brown 60 50
O 131. 45. 50 c. blue .. .. 2·75 2·75
O 132. 46. 1 p. violet .. .. 3·00 2·75

1891. Optd. **OFICIAL.**
O 134 28 5 c. lilac (No. 133) .. 75 75

1895. Optd. **OFICIAL.**
O 164. 38. 1 c. blue 85 85
O 165. 39. 2 c. brown .. .. 1·10 1·10
O 166. 40. 5 c. red .. .. 1·50 1·50
O 167. 45. 50 c. purple .. .. 3·00 3·00

1895. Optd. **OFICIAL.**
O 168. 56. 1 c. bistre 20 20
O 169. 57. 2 c. blue 20 20
O 170. 58. 5 c. red 40 25
O 171. 59. 7 c. green 40 40
O 172. 60. 10 c. brown 40 40
O 173. 61. 20 c. black and green 1·25 60
O 174. 62. 25 c. black and brown 60 60
O 175. 63. 50 c. black and blue 55 55
O 176. 64. 1 p. black and brown 2·75 2·75

1897. Nos. 180/2 optd. **OFICIAL.**
O 194. 67. 1 c. black and red .. 60 60
O 195. 68. 5 c. black and blue .. 70 60
O 196. – 10 c. black and lake 95 75

1897. Optd. **OFICIAL.**
O 201. 56. 1 c. blue 35 30
O 202. 57. 2 c. purple 60 55
O 203. 58. 5 c. green 60 35
O 204. 72. 10 c. red .. .. 2·00 1·10
O 205. 61. 20 c. black and mauve 5·50 2·00
O 206. 62. 25 c. blue and red .. 2·25 1·10
O 207. 63. 50 c. brown and green 3·00 1·10
O 208. 64. 1 p. blue and brown .. 4·50 3·00

1899. Optd. **OFICIAL.**
O 226. 39. 2 c. orange 50 25
O 227a. 58. 5 c. blue 60 50
O 228. 72. 10 c. purple 95 95
O 243. 43. 20 c. blue .. .. 3·00 2·25

1901. Optd. **OFICIAL.**
O 238. 78. 1 c. green 20 25
O 239. 79. 2 c. red 25 25
O 240. 80. 5 c. blue 25 30
O 241. 81. 7 c. brown 30 30
O 242. 82. 10 c. lilac 35 35
O 245. 46. 1 p. green .. .. 3·75 3·00

1904. Optd **OFICIAL.**
O 272. 86. 1 c. green 20 15
O 262. 87. 2 c. orange 20 20
O 263. 88. 5 c. blue 20 20
O 275. 89. 10 c. lilac 20 15
O 276. 90. 20 c. green .. .. 1·10 70
O 277. 91. 25 c. bistre 75 35

1907. Optd. **OFICIAL.**
O 273. 96. 5 c. blue 20 15
O 274. 7 c. brown 20 15
O 278. 50 c. red 45 40

1910. Optd. **OFICIAL 1910.**
O 288. 79. 2 c. red .. .. 3·75 2·25
O 289. 80. 5 c. blue .. .. 2·25 2·00
O 290. 82. 10 c. lilac .. .. 1·10 70
O 291. 43. 20 c. green .. .. 1·10 70
O 292. 44. 25 c. brown .. .. 2·00 1·40
O 293. 96. 50 c. red .. .. 2·50 1·40

O 110.

1911.
O 307. O 110. 2 c. brown 25 25
O 308. 5 c. blue 25 20
O 309. 8 c. slate 25 20
O 310. 20 c. brown 40 30
O 311. 23 c. red 60 40
O 312. 50 c. orange 75 45
O 313. 1 p. red .. .. 2·00 70

1915. Optd. **Oficial.**
O 340 107 2 c. pink 40 45
O 341 5 c. blue 40 45
O 342 8 c. blue 40 45
O 343 20 c. brown 85 35
O 344 108 23 c. blue .. .. 2·25 2·00
O 345 50 c. orange .. .. 3·75 2·00
O 346 1 p. red .. .. 4·50 2·00

1919. Optd. **Oficial.**
O 365. 115. 2 c. grey and red .. 60 30
O 366. 5 c. grey and blue .. 70 25
O 367. 8 c. brown and blue .. 70 25
O 368. 20 c. grey and brown 1·40 45
O 369. 23 c. brown & green .. 1·40 45
O 370. 50 c. blue and brown 2·00 95
O 371. 1 p. blue and red .. 5·00 1·50

1924. Optd. **OFICIAL** in frame. (a) Perf.
O 439. 128. 2 c. mauve 40 15
O 440. 5 c. blue 40 15
O 593. 8 c. red 95 25
O 594. 10 c. green .. .. 1·40 25
O 441. 12 c. blue 25 15
O 442. 20 c. brown 25 25
O 443. 36 c. green 95 70
O 444. 50 c. orange .. .. 2·10 1·50
O 445. 1 p. red .. .. 3·50 2·75
O 446. 2 p. green .. .. 6·25 5·00

(b) Imperf.
O 499. 128. 2 c. mauve 45 10
O 500. 5 c. blue 40 15
O 501. 8 c. red 45 20
O 502. 12 c. blue 60 20
O 503. 20 c. brown 95 40
O 504. 36 c. pink .. .. 2·00 60

PARCEL POST STAMPS

P 123. P 144.

1922. (a) Inscr. "EXTERIOR".
P 391. P 123. 5 c. green on buff 20 10
P 516. 5 c. black on yellow 30 10
P 392. 10 c. green on blue 35 10
P 517. 10 c. black on blue 40 10
P 393. 20 c. grn. on rose .. 1·10 50
P 518. 20 c. black on pink 85 15
P 394. 30 c. green on grn. 1·10 20
P 395. 50 c. green on blue 2·00 30
P 396. 1 p. grn. on orge. 2·75 70

(b) Inscr. "INTERIOR".
P 397. P 123. 5 c. green on buff 25 10
P 512. 5 c. black on yell. 30 10
P 398. 10 c. green on blue 25 10
P 513. 10 c. black on blue 35 10
P 399. 20 c. grn. on pink 50 25
P 514. 20 c. black on pink 45 15
P 400. 30 c. green on green 85 25
P 515. 30 c. black on grn. 85 25
P 401. 50 c. green on blue 1·10 30
P 402. 1 p. grn. on orge. 3·00 60

1927.
P 522 P 144. 1 c. blue 10 10
P 606 1 c. violet .. 10 10
P 523 2 c. green .. 10 10
P 524 4 c. violet .. 15 10
P 609a 5 c. red 15 10
P 526 10 c. brown .. 30 10
P 527 20 c. orange .. 40 20

P 152. P 155. P 177. Sea and Rail Transport.

1928.
P 587. P 152. 5 c. blk. on yellow 10 10
P 588. 10 c. blk. on blue 15 10
P 589. 20 c. blk. on red .. 35 10
P 590. 30 c. blk. on grn. 55 10

1929. Agricultural parcels.
P 610. P 155. 10 c. orange .. 30 20
P 611. 15 c. blue .. 30 20
P 612. 20 c. brown .. 45 30
P 613. 25 c. red 50 35
P 614. 50 c. grey .. 95 45
P 615. 75 c. violet .. 3·75 3·75
P 616. 1 p. olive .. .. 2·75 1·40

1938.
P 971 P 177 5 c. orange .. 10 35
P 801 10 c. red .. 40 25
P 972 10 c. purple .. 15 10
P 1066 10 c. green .. 20 40
P 973 20 c. red .. 35 35
P 1067 20 c. blue .. 25 30
P 974 30 c. blue .. 40 10
P 1068 30 c. purple .. 55 20
P 1069 50 c. green .. 85 30
P 805 1 p. red .. 1·40 10
P 975 1 p. blue .. 20 20
P 1070 1 p. green .. 70 90

P 188. P 204. University.

1943.
P 876 P 188 1 c. red 10 10
P 877 2 c. green 10 10

1944. Optd. **ANO 1943.**
P 882. P 155. 10 c. orange .. 20 10
P 883. 15 c. blue .. 20 20
P 884. 20 c. brown .. 30 20
P 885. 25 c. red .. 50 30
P 886. 50 c. grey .. 70 50
P 887. 75 c. violet .. 1·40 95
P 888. 1 p. olive .. 1·75 1·40

1945.
P 909. A. 1 c. green .. 10 10
P 999. P 204. 1 c. red .. 10 10
P 910. 2 c. violet .. 10 10
P 1000. A. 2 c. blue .. 10 10
P 1047. B. 5 c. grey .. 35 10
P 1045. 5 c. brown .. 10 10
P 1001. A. 10 c. turquoise .. 10 10
P 1002. 10 c. olive .. 10 10
P 1048. C. 20 c. yellow .. 10 10
P 1049. 20 c. brown .. 15 10
P 1046. D. 1 p. blue .. 1·50 1·10
P 1290. 1 p. brown .. 10 10

DESIGNS—HORIZ. A, Bank. VERT. B, Custom House. C. Solis Theatre. D. Montevideo Railway Station.

P 211. Custom House. P 212. Mail Coach (Guillermo Rodriguez).

1946.
P 934. P 211. 5 c. blue & brown 15 10

1946.
P 935. P 212. 5 p. brown & red 7·00 2·25

1946. Armorial type as T 187 obliterated by arrow-head device. (a) Optd. **IMPUESTO** and **ENCOMIENDAS.**
P 936. 1 c. mauve 10 10
P 937. 2 c. brown 10 10
P 938. 5 c. blue 10 10

(b) Optd. **ENCOMIENDAS** only.
P 939. 1 p. blue 75 20
P 940. 5 p. red .. .. 2·50 95

1957. No. P 1047 surch. **$0.30.**
P 1064. 30 c. on 5 c. grey 20 10

P 263. National Printing Works.

1960.
P 1127. P 263. 30 c. green .. 10 10

1965. Surch. with Caduceus and **$5.00 ENCOMIENDAS.**
P 1268. 217. 5 p. on 8 c. orange 30 15

1966. No. 1092 surch. with Caduceus **ENCOMIENDAS** and value.
P 1289. 254. 1 p. on 38 c. black 10 10

P 355. Airliner and Motor-coach.

1969.
P 1397. P 355. 10 p. blk., red & grn. 15 10
P 1398. – 20 p. yell., blk. & bl. 30 20

DESIGN: 20 p. Side views of airliner and motor-coach.

1971. No. 1121 surch. **Encomiendas $0·60.**
P 1448. 261. 60 c. on 1 p. + 10 c. violet and orange 45 30

1971. No. 1380 surch. **IMPUESTOS A ECOMIENDAS,** diesel-engine and value.
P 1472. 60 c. on 6 p. blk. & grn. 30 25

1972. Nos. 1401/2 surch. **IMPUESTO A ENCOMIENDAS,** emblem and value.
P 1507 358 1 p. on 6 p. black, red and blue .. 40 25
P 1508 – 1 p. on 6. p. black, red and blue .. 40 25

P 460. Parcels and Arrows.

1974.
P 1555. P 460. 75 p. multicoloured 15 10

P 461. Mail-van.

1974. Old-time Mail Transport.
P 1556. P 461. 100 p. multicoloured 30 20
P 1557. – 150 p. multicoloured 1·25 1·25
P 1558. – 300 p. blk., bl. & orge. 75 50
P 1559. – 500 p. multicoloured 1·25 70

DESIGNS: 150 p. Steam locomotive. 300 p. Paddle-steamer. 500 p. Monoplane.

POSTAGE DUE STAMPS

D 84.

1902.
D 795 D 84. 1 c. green 10 10
D 405 2 c. red 25 15
D 796 2 c. brown 10 10
D 491 3 c. brown 35 25
D 797 3 c. red 10 10
D 798 4 c. violet 10 10
D 799 5 c. blue 10 10
D 746 5 c. red 35 20
D 494 6 c. brown 40 30
D 800 8 c. red 15 10
D 249 10 c. blue 45 35
D 409a 10 c. green 30 15
D 250 20 c. orange 85 45

1904. Surch. **PROVISORIO UN cent'mo.**
D 267. D 84. 1 c. on 10 c. blue 45 45

SPECIAL DELIVERY STAMPS

1921. Overprinted **MENSAJERIAS.**
E 389 120 2 c. orange 50 20

E 126. Caduceus. E 153.

1923.
E 415. E 126. 2 c. red 30 10
E 416. 2 c. blue 30 10

1928.

E 591. E 153. 2 c. blk. on green 15 10
E 635a. 2 c. green .. 15 10
E 636. 2 c. blue 15 10
E 637. 2 c. pink 15 10
E 638. 2 c. brown .. 10 10

1957. Surch. **$0.05.**

E 1065. E 153. 5 c. on 2 c. brn. 15 10

VATHY — Pt. 6

A town on the island of Samos, where there was a French Post Office which closed in 1914.

25 centimes = 1 piastre.

1893. Stamps of France optd **Vathy** or surch also.

82 10 5 c. green .. .. 3·25 4·25
84 10 c. black and lilac .. 6·75 6·75
86 15 c. blue .. .. 6·75 6·75
87 1 pi. on 25 c. blk on pink 5·50 6·25
88 2 pi. on 50 c. pink .. 16·00 17·00
89 4 pi. on 1 f. green .. 18·00 11·50
90 8 pi. on 2 f. brown on bl 50·00 45·00
91 20 pi. on 5 f. mauve .. 70·00 65·00

VATICAN CITY — Pt. 8

A small area in Rome under the independent sovereignty of the Pope since 1929.

100 centesimi = 1 lira.

1. Papal Tiara and St. Peter's Keys. 2. Pope Pius XI. 4.

1929.

1. 1. 5 c. brown on red .. 10 25
2. 10 c. green on green .. 15 35
3. 20 c. violet on lilac .. 60 50
4. 25 c. blue on blue .. 70 35
5. 30 c. black on yellow .. 75 60
6. 50 c. black on pink .. 1·10 60
7. 75 c. red on grey .. .. 1·50 1·10
8. 2. 80 c. red .. .. 1·25 40
9. 1 l. 25 blue .. .. 1·50 65
10. 2 l. brown .. .. 5·00 1·75
11. 2 l. 50 red .. .. 4·50 3·25
12. 5 l. green .. .. 5·50 12·00
13. 10 l. black .. .. 8·50 20·00

1931. Surch. **C. 25** and bars.

14. 1. 25 c. on 30 c. blk. on yell. 1·25 70

1933. "Holy Year".

15. 4. 25 c.+10 c. green .. 4·50 5·50
16. 75 c.+15 c. red .. .. 7·00 13·00
17. 80 c.+20 c. brown .. 26·00 20·00
18. 1 l. 25+25 c. blue .. 7·00 16·00

The 80 c. and 1 l. 25 have inscriptions and frame differently arranged.

6. Arms of Pope Pius XI. 9. Pope Pius XI.

1933.

19. 6. 5 c. red 10 10
20. – 10 c. black and brown .. 10 10
21. – $12\frac{1}{2}$ c. black and green .. 10 10
22. – 20 c. black and orange .. 10 10
23. – 25 c. black and olive .. 10 10
24. – 30 c. brown and black .. 10 10
25. – 50 c. brown and purple .. 10 10
26. – 75 c. brown and red .. 10 10
27. – 80 c. brown and red .. 10 10
28. 9. 1 l. black and violet .. 4·00 75
29. 1 l. 25 black and blue .. 13·00 4·00
30. 2 l. black and brown .. 22·00 14·00
31. 2 l. 75 black and purple .. 24·00 24·00
32. – 5 l. green and brown .. 20 35
33. – 10 l. green and blue .. 25 45
34. – 20 l. green and black .. 30 60

DESIGNS—As Type **6**: 10 c. to 25 c. Wing of Vatican Palace. 30 c. to 80 c. Vatican Gardens and Dome of St. Peter's. As Type **9**: 5 l. to 20 l. St. Peter's Basilica.

1934. Surch.

35. 2. 40 c. on 80 c. red .. 2·00 1·50
36. 1 l. 30 on 1 l. 25 blue .. 80·00 25·00
37. 2 l. 05 on 2 l. brown .. £150 5·50
38. 2 l. 55 on 2 l. 50 red .. 80·00 £140
39. 3 l. 05 on 5 l. green .. £300 £300
40. 3 l. 70 on 10 l. black .. £275 £350

13. Tribonian presenting Pandects to Justinian. 15. Doves and Bell.

1935. International Juridical Congress, Rome. Frescoes by Raphael.

41. 13. 5 c. orange 20 40
42. 10 c. violet 20 40
43. 25 c. green .. .. 2·00 3·50
44. – 75 c. red .. .. 28·00 18·00
45. – 80 c. brown .. .. 20·00 17·00
46. – 1 l. 25 blue .. .. 24·00 12·00

DESIGN: 75 c. to 1 l. 25, Pope Julius II (wrongly inscr as representing Pope Gregory IX).

1936. Catholic Press Exhibition, Rome.

47. 15. 5 c. green 25 60
48. – 10 c. black 25 60
49. – 25 c. green .. .. 13·00 4·00
50. 15. 50 c. purple 25 60
51. – 75 c. red .. .. 30·00 22·00
52. – 80 c. brown .. .. 50 1·75
53. – 1 l. 25 blue .. .. 60 1·75
54. – 5 l. brown .. .. 60 6·00

DESIGNS: 10 c., 75 c. Church and Bible. 25 c., 80 c. St. John Bosco. 1 l. 25, 5 l. St. Francis of Sales.

16. Statue of St. Peter. 17. Ascension of Elijah.

1938. Air.

55. 16. 25 c. brown 10 15
56. – 50 c. green 10 15
57. 17. 75 c. red 15 20
58. – 80 c. blue 25 40
59. 16. 1 l. violet 35 45
60. – 2 l. blue 55 65
61. 17. 5 l. black .. .. 1·25 1·90
62. – 10 l. purple .. .. 1·25 1·90

DESIGNS: 50 c., 2 l. Dove with olive branch and St. Peter's Square. 80 c., 10 l. Transportation of the Holy House.

18. Crypt of Basilica of St. Cecilia. 20. Coronation.

1938. Int. Christian Archaeological Congress. Inscr. "CONGRESSVS INTERNAT. ARCHAEOLOGIAE CHRIST".

63. 18. 5 c. brown 20 20
64. 10 c. orange 20 20
65. 25 c. green 20 20
66. – 75 c. red .. .. 6·00 6·00
67. – 80 c. violet .. .. 14·00 16·00
68. – 1 l. 25 blue .. .. 17·00 13·00

DESIGN: 75 c., 80 c., and 1 l. 25 Basilica of Saints Nereus and Achilles in the Catacombs of Domitilla.

1939. Death of Pope Pius XI. Optd. **SEDE VACANTE MCMXXXIX.**

69. 1. 5 c. brown on red .. 25·00 3·50
70. 10 c. green on green .. 20 20
71. 20 c. violet on lilac .. 20 20
72. 25 c. blue on blue .. 40 3·50
73. 30 c. black on yellow .. 40 20
74. 50 c. black on pink .. 40 20
75. 75 c. red on grey .. 40 20

1939. Coronation of Pope Pius XII.

76. 20. 25 c. green 85 20
77. 75 c. red 15 30
78. 80 c. violet .. .. 1·90 2·10
79. 1 l. 25 blue 15 30

21. Arms of Pope Pius XII. 22. Pope Pius XII.

1940. 1st Anniv. of Coronation of Pope Pius XII.

80. 21. 5 c. red 10 10
99. 5 c. grey 10 10
100. 30 c. brown 10 10
101. 50 c. green 10 10
81. 22. 1 l. black and violet .. 15 10
102. – 1 l. black and brown .. 10 10
82. – 1 l. 25 black and blue .. 15 10
103. – 1 l. 50 black and red .. 15 15
83. 22. 2 l. black and brown .. 60 1·00
104. – 2 l. 50 black and blue .. 15 15
84. – 2 l. 75 black and purple 60 1·50
105. 22. 5 l. black and lilac .. 20 20
106. 20 l. black and green .. 35 45

DESIGN: 1 l. (No. 102) 1 l. 25, 1 l. 50, 2 l. 50 and 2 l. 75 as Type **22** but with portrait of Pope facing left.

23. 24. Consecration of Archbishop Pacelli.

1942. Prisoners of War Relief Fund. 1st series. Inscr. "MCMXLII".

85. 23. 25 c. green 10 15
86. 80 c. brown 10 15
87. 1 l. 25 blue 10 15

See also Nos. 92/4 and 107/9.

1943. Pope's Episcopal Silver Jubilee.

88 24 25 c. turquoise and green 10 10
89 80 c. chocolate and brown 10 20
90 1 l. 25 blue & ultramarine 10 20
91 5 l. blue and black .. 15 45

1944. Prisoners of War Relief Fund. 2nd series. Inscr. "MCMXLIII".

92. 23. 25 c. green 10 10
93. 80 c. brown 10 15
94. 1 l. 25 blue 15 25

25. Raphael. 27. St. Ignatius of Loyola.

1944. 4th Cent. of Pontifical Academy of the Virtuosi of the Pantheon.

95. 25. 25 c. olive and green .. 10 10
96. – 80 c. violet and lilac .. 20 20
97. – 1 l. 25 c. blue and violet 20 20
98. – 10 l. bistre and yellow .. 40 1·75

PORTRAITS: 80 c. Antonio da Sangallo (architect). 1 l. 25, Carlo Maratti (painter) (after Francesco Maratta). 10 l. Antonio Canova (sculptor, self-portrait).

1945. Prisoners of War Relief Fund. 3rd series. Inscr. "MCMXLIV".

107. 23. 1 l. green 10 15
108. 3 l. red 10 15
109. 5 l. blue 10 15

1946. Surch in figures between bars.

110 21 20 c. on 5 c. grey .. 10 10
111 25 c. on 30 c. brown .. 10 10
112 1 l. on 50 c. green .. 10 10
113 – 1 l. 50 on 1 l. black and brown (No. 102) .. 10 10
114 – 3 l. on 1 l. 50 black and red (No. 103) .. 15 15
115 – 5 l. on 2 l. 50 black and blue (No. 104) .. 20 20
116 22 10 l. on 5 l. black & lilac 1·25 55
117 30 l. on 20 l. black & grn 3·50 1·40

1946. 400th Anniv of Inauguration of Council of Trent.

118 – 5 c. brown and bistre 15 15
119 – 25 c. brown and violet 15 15
120 – 50 c. sepia and brown .. 15 15
121 27 75 c. brown and black .. 15 15
122 – 1 l. brown and purple .. 15 15
123 – 1 l. 50 brown and red .. 15 15
124 – 2 l. brown and green .. 15 15
125 – 2 l. 50 brown and blue 15 15
126 – 3 l. brown and red .. 15 15
127 – 4 l. brown and bistre .. 15 15
128 – 5 l. brown and blue .. 15 15
129 – 10 l. brown and red .. 15 15

DESIGNS: 5 c. Trent Cathedral. 25 c. St. Angela Merici. 50 c. St. Anthony Maria Zaccaria. 1 l. St. Cajetan of Thiene. 1 l. 50, St. John Fisher, Bishop of Rochester. 2 l. Cristoforo Madrussi, Bishop of Trent. 2 l. 50, Reginald Pole, Archbishop of Canterbury. 3 l. Marcello Cervini. 4 l. Giovanni Maria Del Monte. 5 l. Emperor Charles V. 10 l. Pope Paul III Farnese.

28. Dove with Olive Branch over St. Peter's Forecourt.

29. Barn Swallows circling Spire of St. Peter's Basilica.

DESIGN—VERT. As Type 28: 4 l., 25 l. Transportation of the Holy House.

30. "Raphael accompanying Tobias" (after Botticelli).

1947. Air.

130. 28. 1 l. red 10 10
131. – 4 l. brown 10 10
132. 28. 5 l. blue 10 10
133. 29. 15 l. violet 90 75
134. – 25 l. green .. .. .. 3·50 1·40
135. 29. 50 l. black .. .. .. 5·00 2·25
136. 100 l. orange .. .. .. 18·00 4·25
137. 30. 250 l. black .. .. .. 11·00 2·00
138. 500 l. blue £375 £250

31. St. Agnes's Basilica. 32. Pope Pius XII.

1949.

139 31 1 l. brown 10 10
140 – 3 l. violet 10 10
141 – 5 l. orange 10 10
142 – 8 l. green 15 15
143 – 13 l. green .. .. 2·25 2·25
144 – 16 l. grey 25 25
145 – 25 l. red .. .. 4·50 55
146 – 35 l. mauve .. .. 22·00 9·50
147 – 40 l. blue 25 15
148 32 100 l. black .. .. 3·50 3·50

DESIGNS (Basilicas)—VERT. 3 l. St. Clement. 5 l. St. Praxedes. 8 l. St. Mary in Cosmedin. HORIZ. 13 l. Holy Cross. 16 l. St. Sebastian. 25 l. St.Laurence's. 35 l. St. Paul's. 40 l. Sta. Maria Maggiore.

33. Angels over Globe. 34. "I Will Give You the Keys of the Kingdom".

1949. Air. 75th Anniv. of U.P.U.

149. 33. 300 l. blue .. .. 20·00 10·00
150. 1,000 l. green .. .. 90·00 55·00

1949. "Holy Year".

151 34 5 l. brown and lt brown 10 10
152 – 6 l. brown and black .. 10 10
153 – 8 l. green and blue .. 60 60
154 – 10 l. blue and green .. 10 10
155 34 20 l. brown and green .. 90 40
156 – 25 l. blue and brown .. 60 30
157 – 30 l. purple and green .. 1·60 1·25
158 – 60 l. red and brown .. 1·40 1·25

DESIGNS: 6, 25 l. Four Basilicas. 8, 30 l. Pope Boniface VIII. 10, 60 l. Pope Pius XII opening the Holy Door.

35. Guards Marching. 36. Pope Proclaiming Dogma.

1950. Centenary of Papal Guard.

159. 35. 25 l. sepia .. .. 7·00 4·50
160. 35 l. green .. .. 3·75 4·50
161. 55 l. brown .. .. 2·25 4·50

1951. Proclamation of Dogma of the Assumption.

162. 36. 25 l. purple .. .. 7·00 80
163. – 55 l. blue .. .. 4·50 10·00

DESIGN: 55 l. Angels over St. Peter's.

37. Pope Pius X. 38. Final Session of Council (fresco).

1951. Beatification of Pope Pius X.

164. 37. 6 l. gold and violet .. 10 15
165. 10 l. gold and green .. 15 15
166. – 60 l. gold and blue .. 5·00 5·00
167. – 115 l. gold and brown .. 12·00 12·00

DESIGN: 60 l., 115 l. Pope looking left.

1951. 1500th Anniv of Council of Chalcedon.

168 38 5 l. grey 15 15
169 – 25 l. red .. .. 2·25 1·40
170 38 35 l. red .. .. 3·25 3·00
171 – 60 l. blue .. .. 12·00 11·00
172 38 100 l. brown .. .. 30·00 22·00

DESIGN: 25, 60 l. "Pope Leo I meeting Attila" (Raphael).

39. Gratian. 41. Mail Coach and First Stamp.

1951. Air. 800th Anniv. of Decree of Gratian.

173. 39. 300 l. purple £160 £130
174. 500 l. blue .. .. 30·00 13·00

1952. No. 143 surch. **L. 12** and bars.

175. – 12 l. on 13 l. green 1·90 1·25

1952. Cent. of First Papal States' Stamp.

176. 41. 50 l. black and blue .. 5·00 5·00

42. St. Maria Goretti. 43. St. Peter and Inscription.

1953. 50th Anniv. of Martyrdom of St. Maria Goretti.

177. 42. 15 l. violet and brown .. 4·25 2·75
178. 25 l. brown and red .. 2·75 2·75

1953. St. Peter's Basilica. Medallions in black.

179 43 3 l. red 10 10
180 – 5 l. grey 10 10
181 – 10 l. green 10 10
182 – 12 l. brown 10 10
183 – 20 l. violet 25 15
184 – 25 l. brown 10 10
185 – 35 l. red 10 10
186 – 45 l. brown 25 20
187 – 60 l. blue 10 10
188 – 65 l. red 35 25
189 – 100 l. purple 10 10

DESIGNS—VERT. 5 l. Pius XII and Roman sepulchre. 10 l. St. Peter's tomb. 12 l. St. Sylvester I and Constantine's basilica (previous building). 20 l. Julius II and Bramante's design. 25 l. Paul III and apse. 35 l. Sixtus V and cupola. 45 l. Paul V and facade. 60 l. Urban VIII and baldaquin. 65 l. Alexander VII and colonnade. 100 l. Pius VI and sacristy.

44. Dome of St. Peter's. 45. St. Clare of Assisi (after Giotto).

1953. Air.

190 44 500 l. brown & dp brn 20·00 6·00
190a 500 l. green & turquoise 10·00 4·50
191 1000 l. blue and dp blue 55·00 11·00
191a 1000 l. red and lake .. 85 85

1953. 700th Death Anniv of St. Clare (founder of Poor Clares Order).

192 45 25 l. dp brown, brn & bl 1·75 75
193 35 l. brn, lt brn & red 12·00 12·00

46. "St. Bernard" (after Lippi). 47. Lombard's Episcopal Seal.

1953. 800th Death Anniv. of St. Bernard of Clairvaux.

194. 46. 20 l. mauve and olive .. 75 75
195. 60 l. myrtle and blue .. 7·50 6·00

1953. 800th Anniv of "Libri Sententiarum" (theological treatise by Peter Lombard, Bishop of Paris).

196 47 100 l. yellow, blue & red 23·00 17·00

48. Pope Pius XI and Vatican City.

1954. 25th Anniv of Lateran Treaty.

197 48 25 l. red, brown and blue 1·40 90
198 60 l. blue, grey & brown 2·75 2·25

49. Pope Pius XII.

1954. Marian Year and Cent. of Dogma of the Immaculate Conception.

199. – 3 l. violet 10 10
200. 49. 4 l. red 10 10
201. – 6 l. red 10 10
202. 49. 12 l. turquoise .. .. 1·50 1·25
203. – 20 l. brown .. .. 1·00 1·00
204. 49. 35 l. blue .. .. 1·75 1·50

DESIGN: 3 l., 6 l., 20 l. Pope Pius IX facing right with different inscr. and dates "1854–1954".

50. St. Pius X. 51. Basilica of St. Francis of Assisi.

1954. Canonization of Pope Pius X.

205 50 10 l. yellow, red & brn 20 20
206 25 l. yellow, red & violet 2·75 2·25
207 35 l. yellow, red & black 4·00 3·50

1954. Bicentenary of Elevation of Basilica of St. Francis of Assisi to Papal Chapel.

208 51 20 l. black and cream .. 2·25 1·25
209 35 l. brown and cream 1·90 2·25

52. "St. Augustine" (after Botticelli). 53. Madonna of Ostra Brama, Vilna.

1954. 1600th Birth Anniv. of St. Augustine.

210. 52. 35 l. green .. .. 1·25 75
211. 50 l. brown .. .. 2·25 1·75

1954. Termination of Marian Year.

212. 53. 20 l. multicoloured .. 75 75
213. 35 l. multicoloured .. 6·00 5·00
214. 60 l. multicoloured .. 10·00 8·00

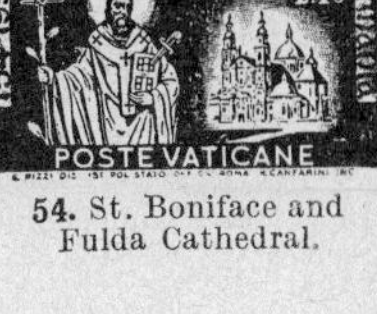

54. St. Boniface and Fulda Cathedral. 55. "Pope Sixtus II and St. Lawrence" (fresco, Niccolina Chapel).

1955. 1200th Anniv. of Martyrdom of St. Boniface.

215. 54. 10 l. black 10 10
216. 35 l. violet 65 55
217. 60 l. turquoise .. 90 70

1955. 500th Death Anniv of Fra Giovanni da Fiesole, "Fra Angelico" (painter).

218 55 50 l. red and blue .. 4·75 2·75
219 100 l. blue and flesh .. 2·75 2·75

56. Pope Nicholas V. 57. St. Bartholomew.

1955. 5th Death Cent. of Pope Nicholas V.

220. 56. 20 l. brown and blue .. 35 20
221. 35 l. brown and red 45 35
222. 60 l. brown and green .. 90 90

1955. 900th Death Anniv. of St. Bartholomew the Young.

223. 57. 10 l. black and brown .. 10 10
224. 25 l. black and red 60 40
225. 100 l. black and green 2·75 2·00

58. "Annunciation" (Melozzo da Forli). 59. Corporal of the Guard.

1956. Air.

226. 58. 5 l. black 10 10
227. A. 10 l. green 10 10
228. B. 15 l. orange 10 10
229. 58. 25 l. red 10 10
230. A. 35 l. red 35 35
231. B. 50 l. sepia 10 10
232. 58. 60 l. blue .. .. 3·00 3·00
233. A. 100 l. brown 10 10
234. B. 300 l. violet 70 70

PAINTINGS: A, "Annunciation" (P. Cavallini). B, "Annunciation" (Leonardo da Vinci).

1956. 450th Anniv. of Swiss Guard.

235. – 4 l. red 10 10
236. 59. 6 l. orange 10 10
237. – 10 l. blue 10 10
238. – 35 l. brown 65 65
239. 59. 50 l. violet 90 90
240. – 60 l. green 95 95

DESIGNS: 4 l., 35 l. Captain Roust. 10 l., 60 l. Two drummers.

60. St. Rita. 61. St. Ignatius presenting Jesuit Constitution to Pope Paul III.

1956. 5th Death Cent. of St. Rita at Cascia.

241. 60. 10 l. grey 10 10
242. 25 l. brown 70 70
243. 35 l. blue 50 50

1956. 4th Death Cent. of St. Ignatius of Loyola.

244. 61. 35 l. brown 65 65
245. 60 l. slate .. .. 1·10 1·10

62. St. John of Capistrano.

63. Madonna and Child.

1956. 5th Death Centenary of St. John of Capistrano.

246 62 25 l. green and black .. 2·50 2·50
247 35 l. brown and purple 90 90

1956. " Black Madonna " of Czestochowa Commemoration.

248. 63. 35 l. black and blue .. 50 50
249. 60 l. blue and green .. 60 60
250. 100 l. lake and sepia .. 85 85

64. St. Domenico Savio.

65. Cardinal D. Capranica (founder) and Capranica College.

1957. Death Cent. of St. Domenico Savio.

251. 64. 4 l. brown 10 10
252. – 6 l. red 10 10
253. 64. 25 l. green 10 10
254. – 60 l. blue .. .. 1·40 1·40

Design: 6 l., 60 l. St. Domenico Savio and St. John Bosco.

1957. 5th Cent. of Capranica College.

255. 65. 5 l. lake.. .. .. 10 10
256. – 10 l. brown 10 10
257. 65. 35 l. slate 20 20
258. – 100 l. blue 90 90

Designs—horiz. 10 l., 100 l. Pope Pius XII and plaque.

66. Pontifical Academy of Science.

1957. 20th Anniv. of the Pontifical Academy of Science.

259. 66. 35 l. green and blue .. 75 75
260. 60 l. blue and brown .. 75 75

67. Mariazell Basilica.

68. Apparition of the Virgin Mary.

1957. 8th Cent. of Mariazell Basilica.

261. 67. 5 l. green 10 10
262. – 15 l. slate 10 10
263. 67. 60 l. blue 85 85
264. – 100 l. violet .. .. 1·10 1·10

Design: 15 l., 100 l. Statue of the Virgin of Mariazell within Sanctuary.

1958. Centenary of Apparition of the Virgin Mary at Lourdes.

265. 68. 5 l. blue 10 10
266. – 10 l. green 10 10
267. – 15 l. brown 10 10
268. 68. 25 l. red 10 10
269. – 35 l. sepia 10 10
270. – 100 l. violet 10 10

Designs—vert. 10 l., 35 l. Invalid at Lourdes. 15 l., 100 l. St. Bernadette.

MINIMUM PRICE

The minimum price quoted is 5p which represents a handling charge rather than a basis for valuing common stamps. For further notes about prices see introductory pages.

69. " Civitas Dei " (" City of God " at Exhibition).

70. Pope Clement XIII (from sculpture by A. Canova).

1958. Brussels International Exhibition.

271 – 35 l. purple 25 25
272 69 60 l. red 55 55
273 100 l. violet .. .. 2·00 2·00
274 – 300 l. blue .. .. 1·10 1·75

Design: 35, 300 l. Pope Pius XII.

1958. Birth Bicentenary of Antonio Canova (sculptor).

275 70 5 l. brown 10 10
276 – 10 l. red 10 10
277 – 35 l. green 35 25
278 – 100 l. blue .. .. 1·25 1·25

Sculptures: 10 l. Pope Clement XIV. 35 l. Pope Pius VI. 100 l. Pope Pius VII.

71. St. Peter's Keys.

72. Pope John XXIII.

1958. " Vacant See ".

279. 71. 15 l. sepia on yellow .. 1·40 1·40
280. 25 l. sepia 10 10
281. 60 l. sepia on lavender.. 10 10

1959. Coronation of Pope John XXIII. Inscr. " IV-XI MCMLVIII ".

282. 72. 25 l. multicoloured .. 10 10
283. – 35 l. multicoloured .. 10 10
284. 72. 60 l. multicoloured .. 10 10
285. – 100 l. multicoloured .. 10 10

Design: 35 l., 100 l. Arms of Pope John XXIII.

73. St. Lawrence.

74. Pope Pius XI.

1959. 1700th Death Annivs (15 to 100 l in 1958) of Martyrs under Valerian.

286. 73. 15 l. brown, yell. & red 10 10
287. – 25 l. brown, yell. & lilac 20 20
288. – 50 l. multicoloured .. 35 35
289. – 60 l. brown, yell. & grn. 25 25
290. – 100 l. brn., yell. & pur. 35 35
291. – 300 l. sepia and buff .. 40 40

Portraits: 25 l. Pope Sixtus II. 50 l. St. Agapitus. 60 l. St. Filisissimus. 100 l. St. Cyprian. 300 l. St. Fructuosus.

1959. 30th Anniv. of Lateran Treaty.

292. 74. 30 l. brown 10 10
293. 100 l. blue 20 15

75. Radio Mast.

76. Obelisk and St. John Lateran Basilica.

1959. 2nd Anniv. of St. Maria di Galeria Radio Station Vatican City.

294. 75. 25 l. red, yell. & black.. 10 10
295. 60 l. yellow, red and blue 25 25

1959. Air. Roman Obelisks.

296. 76. 5 l. violet 10 10
297. – 10 l. green 10 10
298. – 15 l. sepia 10 10
299. – 25 l. green 10 10
300. – 35 l. blue 10 10
301. 76. 50 l. green 15 15
302. – 60 l. red 15 15
303. – 100 l. blue 20 20
304. – 200 l. brown 25 25
305. – 500 l. brown 50 50

Designs: 10, 60 l. Obelisk and Church of Sta. Maria Maggiore. 15, 100 l. Vatican Obelisk and Apostolic Palace. 25, 200 l. Obelisk and Churches of St. Mary in Montesanto and St. Mary of the Miracles, Piazza del Popolo. 35, 500 l. Sallustian Obelisk and Trinita dei Monti Church.

77. St. Casimir, Vilna Palace and Cathedral.

78. " Christ Adored by the Magi " (after Raphael).

1959. 500th Birth Anniv. of St. Casimir (patron saint of Lithuania).

306. 77. 50 l. brown 15 15
307. 100 l. green 15 15

1959. Christmas.

308. 78. 15 l. black 10 10
309. 25 l. red 10 10
310. 60 l. blue 20 20

79. " St. Antoninus " (after Dupre).

80. Transept of St. John Lateran Basilica.

1960. 500th Death Anniv. of St. Antoninus of Florence.

311. 79. 15 l. blue 10 10
312. – 25 l. turquoise 10 10
313. 79. 60 l. brown 25 25
314. – 110 l. red 40 40

Design: 25 l., 110 l. " St. Antoninus preaching sermon " (after Portigiani).

1960. Roman Diocesan Synod.

315 80 15 l. brown 10 10
316 60 l. black 20 20

81. " The Flight into Egypt " (after Beato Angelico).

82. Cardinal Sarto (Pius X) leaving Venice for Conclave in Rome.

1960. World Refugee Year.

317. 81. 5 l. green 10 10
318. – 10 l. sepia 10 10
319. – 25 l. red 15 15
320. 81. 60 l. violet 25 25
321. – 100 l. blue .. .. 1·25 1·50
322. – 300 l. turquoise .. 70 75

Designs: 10, 100 l. "St. Peter giving Alms" (Masaccio). 25, 300 l. "Madonna of Mercy" (Piero della Francesca).

1960. 1st Anniv. of Transfer of Relics of Pope Pius X from Rome to Venice.

323. 82. 15 l. brown 10 10
324. – 35 l. red 65 65
325. – 60 l. turquoise .. 1·40 1·40

Designs: 35 l. Pope John XXIII kneeling before relics of Pope Pius X. 60 l. Relics in procession across St. Mark's Square, Venice.

83. " Feeding the Hungry ".

1960. " Corporal Works of Mercy ". Della Robbia paintings. Centres in sepia.

326. 83. 5 l. brown 10 10
327. – 10 l. green 10 10
328. – 15 l. black 10 10
329. – 20 l. red 10 10
330. – 30 l. violet 10 10
331. – 35 l. brown 10 10
332. – 40 l. orange 10 10
333. – 70 l. ochre 10 10

Designs: 10 l. " Giving drinks to the thirsty ". 15 l. " Clothing the naked ". 20 l. " Sheltering the homeless ". 30 l. " Visiting the sick ". 35 l. " Visiting the imprisoned ". 40 l. " Burying the dead ". 70 l. Pope John XXIII between " Faith " and " Charity ".

84. " The Nativity " after Gerard Honthurst (Gherardo delle Notte).

85. St. Vincent de Paul.

1960. Christmas.

334 84 10 l. black and green .. 10 10
335 15 l. dp brown & brown 10 10
336 70 l. blue and turquoise 15 15

1960. Death Tercent. of St. Vincent de Paul and St. Louise de Marillac.

337. 85. 40 l. violet 15 15
338. – 70 l. black 25 25
339. – 100 l. brown 35 35

Designs: 70 l. St. Louise de Marillac. 100 l. St. Vincent giving child to care of St. Louise.

86. St. Meinrad.

87. "Pope Leo I meeting Attila" (Algardi).

1961. 11th Death Cent. of St. Meinrad.

340. 86. 30 l. black 35 35
341. – 40 l. lilac 70 80
342. – 100 l. brown .. .. 1·25 1·50

Designs—vert. 40 l. The "Black Madonna", Einsiedeln Abbey. horiz. 100 l. Einsiedeln Abbey, Switzerland.

1961. 15th Death Cent. of Pope Leo I.

343. 87. 15 l. lake 10 10
344. 70 l. green 40 40
345. 300 l. sepia .. .. 1·00 1·25

88. Route of St. Paul's Journey to Rome.

1961. 1900th Anniv of St. Paul's Arrival in Rome.

346 88 10 l. green 10 10
347 – 15 l. black and brown .. 10 10
348 – 20 l. black and red .. 15 15
349 88 30 l. blue 20 20
350 – 75 l. black and brown .. 45 45
351 – 200 l. black and blue .. 95 1·10

Designs: 15, 75 l. St. Paul's arrival in Rome (after sculpture by Maraini). 20, 200 l. Basilica of St. Paul-outside-the-Walls, Rome.

89. "L'Osservatore Romano," 1861 and 1961. **90.** St. Patrick (ancient sculpture).

1961. Centenary of "L'Osservatore Romano" (Vatican newspaper).

352. **89.** 40 l. black and brown .. 20 20
353. – 70 l. black and blue .. 50 50
354. – 250 l. black and yellow 1·10 1·10

DESIGNS: 70 l. "L'Osservatore Romano" offices. 250 l. Printing machine.

1961. 15th Death Cent. of St. Patrick.

355. **90.** 10 l. green and buff .. 10 10
356. – 15 l. sepia and blue .. 10 10
357. **90.** 40 l. green and yellow .. 20 20
358. – 150 l. brown & turquoise 50 65

DESIGN: 15, 150 l. St. Patrick's Sanctuary, Lough Derg.

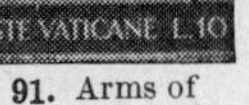

91. Arms of Roncalli Family. **92.** "The Nativity".

1961. Pope John XXIII's 80th Birthday.

359. **91.** 10 l. brown and black .. 10 10
360. – 25 l. green & bistre .. 10 10
361. – 30 l. violet and blue .. 10 10
362. – 40 l. blue and violet .. 15 15
363. – 70 l. brown and grey .. 20 20
364. – 115 l. black and brown 30 30

DESIGNS: 25 l. Church of St. Mary, Sotto il Monte. 30 l. Church of St. Mary, Monte Santo. 40 l. Church of Saints Ambrose and Charles, Rome. 70 l. St. Peter's Chair, Vatican Basilica. 115 l. Pope John XXIII.

1961. Christmas. Centres multicoloured.

365 **92** 15 l. turquoise 10 10
366 40 l. black 10 10
367 70 l. purple 15 15

93. "Annunciation" (after F. Valle). **94.** "Land Reclamation" Medal of 1588.

1962. Air.

368. **93.** 1000 l. brown .. .. 1·25 1·25
369. 1500 l. blue .. .. 1·75 1·75

1962. Malaria Eradication.

370. **94.** 15 l. violet 10 10
371. – 40 l. red 10 10
372. **94.** 70 l. brown 20 20
373. – 300 l. green 40 45

DESIGN: 40 l., 300 l. Map of Pontine Marshes reclamation project (at time of Pope Pius VI).

95. "The Good Shepherd" (statue, Lateran Museum). **96.** St. Catherine (after Il Sodoma (Bazzi)).

1962. Religious Vocations.

374. **95.** 10 l. black and violet .. 10 10
375. – 15 l. brown and blue .. 10 10
376. **95.** 70 l. black and green .. 30 30
377. – 115 l. brown and red .. 1·10 1·10
378. **95.** 200 l. black and brown 1·10 1·10

DESIGN: 15 l., 115 l. Wheatfield ready for harvest.

1962. 5th Centenary of St. Catherine of Siena's Canonization.

379. **96.** 15 l. brown 10 10
380. 60 l. violet 30 30
381. 100 l. blue 40 40

97. Paulina M. Jaricot. **98.** St. Peter and St. Paul (from graffito on child's tomb).

1962. Death Centenary of Paulina M. Jaricot (founder of Society for the Propagation of the Faith). Multicoloured centres.

382. **97.** 10 l. lilac 10 10
383. 50 l. turquoise 25 20
384. 150 l. grey 50 60

1962. 6th Int. Christian Archaeology Congress, Ravenna.

385. **98.** 20 l. sepia and violet .. 10 10
386. – 40 l. green and brown .. 10 10
387. **98.** 70 l. sepia and turquoise 10 10
388. – 100 l. green and red .. 15 15

DESIGN: 40 l., 100 l. "The Passion" (from bas relief on tomb in Domitilla cemetery, near Rome).

99. "Faith" (after Raphael). **100.** "The Nativity".

1962. Ecumenical Council.

389. **99.** 5 l. sepia and blue .. 10 10
390. – 10 l. sepia and green .. 10 10
391. – 15 l. sepia and red .. 10 10
392. – 25 l. grey and red .. 10 10
393. – 30 l. black and mauve .. 10 10
394. – 40 l. sepia and red .. 10 10
395. – 60 l. brown and green .. 10 10
396. – 115 l. red 10 10

DESIGNS—Divine Virtues: 10 l. "Hope"; 15 l. "Charity" (both after Raphael). 25 l. Arms of Pope John XXIII and symbols of Evangelists (frontispiece of "Humanae Salutis" by Arrigo Bravi). 30 l. Central Nave, St. Peter's (council venue). 40 l. Pope John XXIII. 60 l. "St. Peter" (bronze in Vatican Basilica). 115 l. The Holy Ghost in form of dove.

1962. Christmas. Centres multicoloured.

397. **100.** 10 l. grey 10 10
398. 15 l. drab 10 10
399. 90 l. green 15 15

101. "Miracle of the Loaves and Fishes" (after Murillo). **102.** Pope John XXIII.

1963. Freedom from Hunger.

400. **101.** 15 l. sepia and brown .. 10 10
401. – 40 l. green and red .. 10 10
402. **101.** 100 l. sepia and blue .. 10 10
403. – 200 l. green and turq. .. 10 10

DESIGN: 40 l., 200 l. "Miracle of the Fishes" (after Raphael).

1963. Award of Balzan Peace Prize to Pope John XXIII.

404. **102.** 15 l. brown 10 10
405. 160 l. black 20 20

103. St. Peter's Keys. **104.** Pope Paul VI.

1963. "Vacant See".

406. **103.** 10 l. sepia 10 10
407. 40 l. sepia on yellow .. 10 10
408. 100 l. sepia on violet 10 10

1963. Coronation of Pope Paul VI.

409. **104.** 15 l. black 10 10
410. – 40 l. red 10 10
411. **104.** 115 l. brown 15 15
412. – 200 l. grey 15 15

DESIGN: 40 l., 200 l. Arms of Pope Paul VI.

105. "The Nativity" (African terracotta statuette). **106.** St. Cyril.

1963. Christmas.

413. **105.** 10 l. brown and bistre .. 10 10
414. 40 l. brown and blue .. 10 10
415. 100 l. brown and olive .. 10 10

1963. 1100th Anniv. of Conversion of Slavs by Saints Cyril and Methodius.

416. **106.** 30 l. purple 10 10
417. – 70 l. brown 15 15
418. – 150 l. red 20 20

DESIGNS: 70 l. Map of Moravia. 150 l. St. Methodius.

107. Pope Paul VI. **108.** St. Peter, Pharoah's Tomb, Wadi-es-Sebua.

1964. Pope Paul's Visit to the Holy Land.

419. **107.** 15 l. black 10 10
420. – 25 l. red 10 10
421. – 70 l. sepia 10 10
422. – 160 l. blue 15 15

DESIGNS: 25 l. Church of the Nativity, Bethlehem. 70 l. Church of the Holy Sepulchre, Jerusalem. 160 l. Well of the Virgin Mary, Nazareth.

1964. Nubian Monuments Preservation.

423. **108.** 10 l. brown and blue .. 10 10
424. – 20 l. multicoloured .. 10 10
425. **108.** 70 l. brown and olive .. 10 10
426. – 200 l. multicoloured .. 20 20

DESIGN: 20 l., 200 l. Philae Temple.

109. Pope Paul VI. **110.** Michelangelo.

1964. Vatican City's Participation in New York World's Fair.

427. **109.** 15 l. blue 10 10
428. – 50 l. sepia 10 10
429. **109.** 100 l. blue 10 10
430. – 250 l. brown 25 25

DESIGNS: 50 l. Michelangelo's "Pieta". 250 l. Detail of Madonna's head from "Pieta".

1964. 400th Death Anniv. of Michelangelo. Paintings in the Sistine Chapel.

431. **110.** 10 l. black 10 10
432. – 25 l. red 10 10
433. – 30 l. olive 10 10
434. – 40 l. violet 10 10
435. – 150 l. green 10 10

PAINTINGS: 25 l. Prophet Isaiah. 30 l. Delphic Sibyl. 40 l. Prophet Jeremiah. 150 l. Prophet Joel.

111. "The Good Samaritan" (after Emilio Greco). **112.** "Christmas Scene" (after Kimiko Koseki).

1964. Red Cross Cent. (1963). Cross in red.

436. **111.** 10 l. brown 10 10
437. 30 l. blue 10 10
438. 300 l. sepia 30 30

1964. Christmas.

439. **112.** 10 l. multicoloured .. 10 10
440. 15 l. multicoloured .. 10 10
441. 135 l. multicoloured .. 10 10

113. Cues's Birthplace. **114.** Pope Paul at prayer.

1964. 500th Death Anniv. of Nicholas Cues (Cardinal Cusanus).

442. **113.** 40 l. green 10 10
443. – 200 l. red 20 20

DESIGN: 200 l. Cardinal Cusanus's sepulchre, St. Peter's (relief by A. Bregno).

1964. Pope Paul's Visit to India.

444. **114.** 15 l. purple 10 10
445. – 25 l. green 10 10
446. – 60 l. sepia 10 10
447. – 200 l. purple 20 20

DESIGNS—HORIZ. 25 l. Public altar, "The Oval", Bombay. 60 l. "Gateway to India", Bombay. VERT. 200 l. Pope Paul walking across map of India.

115. Sts. Mbaga Tuzinde, Carolus Lwanga and Kizito. **116.** Dante (after Raphael).

1965. Ugandan Martyrs. T **115** and similar portrait designs.

448. – 15 l. turquoise .. 10 10
449. **115.** 20 l. brown 10 10
450. – 30 l. blue 10 10
451. – 75 l. black 10 10
452. – 100 l. red 10 10
453. – 160 l. violet 15 15

DESIGNS: 15 l. St. Joseph Mukasa and six other martyrs. 30 l. Sts. Matthias Mulumba, Noe Mawagalli and Lucas Banabakintu. 75 l. Sts. Gonzaga Gonza Athanasius Bazzekuketta, Pontianus Ngondwe and Bruno Serunkuma. 100 l. Sts. Anatolius Kiriggwajjo, Andreus Kaggwa and Adulphus Mukasa. 160 l. Sts. Mukasa Kiriwananvu and Gyavira.

1965. Dante's 700th Birth Anniv.

454. **116.** 10 l. brn. & light brn. 10 10
455. – 40 l. brown and red .. 10 10
456. – 70 l. brown and green 15 15
457. – 200 l. brown and blue 20 20

DESIGNS—After drawings by Botticelli: 40 l. "Inferno", 70 l. "Purgatory". 200 l. "Paradise".

117. St. Benedict (after Perugino). **118.** Pope Paul.

1965. Declaration of St. Benedict as Patron Saint of Europe.

458. **117.** 40 l. brown 10 10
459. – 300 l. green 25 25

DESIGN: 300 l. Monte Cassino Abbey.

1965. Pope Paul's Visit to the U.N., New York.

460. **118.** 20 l. brown 10 10
461. – 30 l. blue 10 10
462. – 150 l. green 10 10
463. **118.** 300 l. purple 25 25

DESIGN: 30 l., 150 l. U.N.O. Headquarters, New York.

119. "The Nativity" (Peruvian setting).

120. Pope Paul.

1965. Christmas.
464. **119.** 20 l. lake 10 10
465. 40 l. brown 10 10
466. 200 l. green .. 15 15

1966.
467 **120** 5 l. brown 10 10
468 – 10 l. violet 10 10
469 – 15 l. brown 10 10
470 – 20 l. green 10 10
471 – 30 l. brown 10 10
472 – 40 l. turquoise .. 10 10
473 – 55 l. blue 10 10
474 – 75 l. purple 10 10
475 – 90 l. mauve 10 10
476 – 130 l. green 10 10
DESIGNS (SCULPTURES): 10 l. "Music". 15 l. "Science". 20 l. "Painting". 30 l. "Sculpture". 40 l. "Building". 55 l. "Carpentry". 75 l. "Agriculture". 90 l. "Metallurgy". 130 l. "Learning".

121. Queen Dabrowka and King Mieszko I.

122. Pope John XXIII and St. Peter's, Rome.

1966. Poland's Christian Millennium.
477. **121.** 15 l. black 10 10
478. – 25 l. violet 10 10
479. – 40 l. red 10 10
480. – 50 l. red 10 10
481. – 150 l. slate 10 10
482. – 220 l. brown 15 15
DESIGNS: 25 l. St. Adalbert (Wojciech) and Wroclaw and Gniezno Cathedrals. 40 l. St. Stanislas, Skalka Cathedral and Wawel Royal Palace, Cracow. 50 l. Queen Jadwiga (Hedwig), Ostra Brama Gate with Mater Misericordiae, Wilno and Jagellon University Library, Cracow. 150 l. "Black Madonna", Jasna Gora Monastery (Czestochowa) and St. John's Cathedral, Warsaw. 220 l. Pope Paul VI greeting Poles.

1966. 4th Anniv. of Opening of Ecumenical Council.
483. **122.** 10 l. black and red .. 10 10
484. – 15 l. green and brown 10 10
485. – 55 l. mauve and sepia 10 10
486. – 90 l. black and green.. 10 10
487. – 100 l. yellow and green 10 10
488. – 130 l. sepia and brown 10 10
DESIGNS: 15 l. Book of Prayer, St. Peter's. 55 l. Mass. 90 l. Pope Paul with Patriarch Athenagoras. 100 l. Episcopal ring. 130 l. Pope Paul at closing ceremony (12.10.65).

123. "The Nativity" (after sculpture by Scorzelli).

124. Aircraft over St. Peter's.

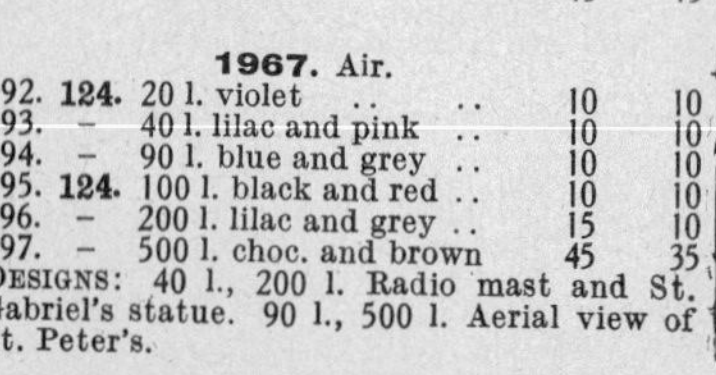
1966. Christmas.
489. **123.** 20 l. purple 10 10
490. 55 l. green 10 10
491. 225 l. brown 15 15

1967. Air.
492. **124.** 20 l. violet 10 10
493. – 40 l. lilac and pink .. 10 10
494. – 90 l. blue and grey .. 10 10
495. **124.** 100 l. black and red .. 10 10
496. – 200 l. lilac and grey .. 15 10
497. – 500 l. choc. and brown 45 35
DESIGNS: 40 l., 200 l. Radio mast and St. Gabriel's statue. 90 l., 500 l. Aerial view of St. Peter's.

125. St. Peter.

126. "The Three Shepherd Children" (sculpture).

1967. 1900th Anniv. of Martyrdom of Saints Peter and Paul. Multicoloured.
498. 15 l. Type **125** 10 10
499. 20 l. St. Paul 10 10
500. 55 l. The two Saints .. 10 10
501. 90 l. Bernini's baldachin, St. Peter's 10 10
502. 220 l. Arnolfo di Cambio's tabernacle, St. Paul's Basilica 20 20

1967. 50th Anniv. of Fatima Apparitions. Multicoloured.
503. 30 l. Type **126** .. 10 10
504. 50 l. Basilica of Fatima .. 10 10
505. 200 l. Pope Paul VI praying before Virgin's statue at Fatima 20 20

127. Congress Emblem.

128. "The Nativity" (Byzantine carving).

1967. Third World Apostolic Laity Congress, Rome.
506. **127.** 40 l. red 15 15
507. 130 l. blue 15 15

1967. Christmas.
508. **128.** 25 l. multicoloured .. 10 10
509. 55 l. multicoloured .. 10 10
510. 180 l. multicoloured .. 15 15

129. "Angel Gabriel" (detail from "The Annunciation" by Fra Angelico).

130. Pope Paul VI.

1968. Air.
511. **129.** 1000 l. red on cream.. 70 80
512. 1500 l. black on cream 90 1·10

1968. Pope Paul's Visit to Colombia.
513. **130.** 25 l. brown and black 10 10
514. – 55 l. ochre, grey & blk. 10 10
515. – 220 l. sepia, blue & blk. 20 20
DESIGNS: 55 l. Monstrance (Raphael's "Disputa"). 220 l. Map of South America.

131. "The Holy Child of Prague".

132. "The Resurrection" (Fra Angelico).

1968. Christmas.
516. **131.** 20 l. purple and red .. 10 10
517. 50 l. violet and lilac .. 10 10
518. 250 l. blue 20 20

1969. Easter.
519 **132** 20 l. red and buff .. 10 10
520 90 l. green and buff .. 19 10
521 180 l. blue and buff .. 15 15

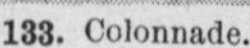

133. Colonnade.

134. Pope with Young Africans.

1969. Europa.
522. **133.** 50 l. brown and slate.. 10 10
523. 90 l. brown and red .. 15 15
524. 130 l. brown and green 15 15

1969. Pope Paul's visit to Uganda.
525. **134.** 25 l. brown and ochre 10 10
526. – 55 l. brown and red 10 10
527. – 250 l. multicoloured .. 20 20
DESIGNS: 55 l. Pope with African bishops. 250 l. Map of Africa and olive branch.

135. Pope Pius IX.

136. "Expo 70" Emblem.

1969. Cent. of St. Peter's Circle Society.
528. **135.** 30 l. brown 10 10
529. – 50 l. slate 10 10
530. – 220 l. purple 20 20
DESIGNS: 50 l. Monogram of Society. 220 l. Pope Paul VI.

1970. "Expo 70" World's Fair, Osaka. Mult.
531 25 l. Type **136** 10 10
532 40 l. Osaka Castle .. 10 10
533 55 l. "Madonna and Child" (Domoto) 10 10
534 90 l. Vatican pavilion .. 10 10
535 110 l. Mt. Fuji 10 10

137. Commemorative Medal of Pius IX.

138. "Christ" (Simone Martini).

1970. Centenary of 1st Vatican Council.
536. **137.** 20 l. brown and orange 10 10
537. – 50 l. multicoloured .. 10 10
538. – 180 l. purple and red.. 15 15
DESIGNS: 50 l. Arms of Pius IX. 180 l. Council souvenir medal.

1970. 50th Anniv. of Pope Paul's Ordination as Priest. Multicoloured.
539. 15 l. Type **138** 10 10
540. 25 l. "Christ" (R. v. d. Weyden) 10 10
541. 50 l. "Christ" (Durer) .. 10 10
542. 90 l. "Christ" (El Greco) 10 10
543. 180 l. Pope Paul VI .. 15 15

139. "Adam" (Michelangelo).

140. Pope Paul VI.

1970. 25th Anniv. of United Nations.
544. 20 l. Type **139** 10 10
545. 90 l. "Eve" (Michelangelo) 10 10
546. 220 l. Olive branch .. 20 20

1970. Pope Paul's Visit to Asia and Oceania. Multicoloured.
547. 25 l. Type **140** 10 10
548. 55 l. "Holy Child of Cebu" (Philippines) 10 10
549. 100 l. "Madonna and Child", Darwin Cathedral (G. Hamori) 10 10
550. 130 l. Manila Cathedral .. 10 10
551. 220 l. Sydney Cathedral.. 15 15

141. "Angel with Lectern".

142. "Madonna and Child" (F. Gnissi).

1971. Racial Equality Year. Multicoloured.
552. 20 l. Type **141** 10 10
553. 40 l. "Christ Crucified, and Doves" 10 10
554. 50 l. Type **141** 10 10
555. 130 l. As 40 l. 10 10

1971. Easter. Religious Paintings. Mult.
556. 25 l. Type **142** 10 10
557. 40 l. "Madonna and Child" (Sassetta—S. di Giovanni) 10 10
558. 55 l. "Madonna and Child" (C. Crivelli) 10 10
559. 90 l. "Madonna and Child" (C. Maratta) 10 10
560. 180 l. "The Holy Family" (G. Ceracchini).. .. 15 15

143. "St. Dominic Guzman" (Sienese School).

144. "St. Matthew".

1971. 800th Birth Anniv. of St. Dominic Guzman (founder of Preaching Friars Order). Multicoloured.
561. 25 l. Type **143** 10 10
562. 55 l. Portrait by Fra Angelico 10 10
563. 90 l. Portrait by Titian .. 10 10
564. 180 l. Portrait by El Greco 15 15

1971. Air.
565. **144.** 200 l. blk. and green.. 25 25
566. – 300 l. blk. and brown 35 35
567. – 500 l. black and pink 80 65
568. – 1,000 l. blk. and mve. 90 75
DESIGNS: "The Four Evangelists" (ceiling frescoes by Fra Angelico in the Niccolina Chapel, Vatican City)—300 l. "St. Mark". 500 l. "St. Luke". 1,000 l. "St. John".

145. "St. Stephen" (from chasuble, Szekesfehervar Church, Hungary).

146. Bramante's Design for Cupola, St. Peter's.

1971. Millennium of St. Stephen, King of Hungary.
569. **145.** 50 l. multicoloured .. 10 10
570. – 180 l. black and yell. 20 20
DESIGN: 180 l. "Madonna, Patroness of Hungary", (sculpture, circa 1511).

1972. Bramante Celebrations.
571 **146** 25 l. black and yellow 10 10
572 – 90 l. black and yellow 10 10
573 – 130 l. black and yellow 15 15
DESIGNS: 90 l. Donato Bramante (architect) from medal. 130 l. Spiral staircase, Innocent VIII's Belvedere, Vatican.

147. "St. Mark at Sea" (mosaic).

1972. U.N.E.S.C.O. "Save Venice" Campaign. Multicoloured.
574. 25 l. Type **147** 25 25
575. 50 l. } Map of Venice, 1581 (fresco) 15 15
576. 50 l. } 15 15
577. 50 l. } 15 15
578. 50 l. } 15 15
579. 180 l. St. Mark's Basilica.. 1·00 1·00
Nos. 575/8 are smaller (39 × 28 mm) and were issued together, se-tenant, forming a composite design.

148. Gospel of St. Mark (from codex "Biblia dell'Aracoeli").

1972. International Book Year. Illuminated Manuscripts. Multicoloured.

581 30 l. Type **148** 10 10
582 50 l. Gospel of St. Luke ("Biblia dell'Aracoeli") 10 10
583 90 l. 2nd Epistle of St. John (Bologna codex) .. 10 10
584 100 l. Revelation of St. John (Bologna codex) .. 10 10
585 130 l. Epistle of St. Paul to the Romans (Italian codex) 20 20

149. Luigi Orione (founder of "Caritas").

1972. Birth Centenaries. Multicoloured.

586. 50 l. Type **149** 10 10
587. 180 l. Lorenzo Perosi (composer) 25 30

150. Cardinal Bassarione (Roselli fresco, Sistine Chapel). **151.** Congress Emblem.

1972. 500th Death Anniv of Cardinal Bassarione.

588 – 40 l. green 10 10
589 **150** 90 l. red 10 10
590 – 130 l. black 15 15

DESIGNS: 40 l. "Reading to Bull of Union" (relief). 130 l. Arms of Cardinal Bassarione.

1973. Int. Eucharistic Congress, Melbourne. Multicoloured.

591. 25 l. Type **151** 10 10
592. 75 l. Michelangelo's "Pieta" 10 10
593. 300 l. Melbourne Cathedral 30 30

152. St. Theresa's Birthplace. **153.** Torun (birthplace).

1973. Birth Cent. of St. Theresa of Lisieux.

594. **152.** 25 l. black and red .. 10 10
595. – 55 l. black and yellow 10 10
596. – 220 l. black and blue .. 25 25

DESIGNS: 55 l. St. Theresa. 220 l. Basilica of Lisieux.

1973. 500th Birth Anniv. of Copernicus.

597. **153.** 20 l. green 10 10
598. – 50 l. brown 10 10
599. **153.** 100 l. purple 15 15
600. – 130 l. blue 15 20

DESIGN: 50 l., 130 l. Copernicus.

154. "St. Wenceslas".

1973. Millennium of Prague Diocese. Mult.

601. 20 l. Type **154** 10 10
602. 90 l. Arms of Prague Diocese 10 10
603. 150 l. Tower of Prague Cathedral 15 15
604. 220 l. "St. Adalbert" .. 25 25

155. Church of St. Hripsime. **156.** "Angel" (porch of St. Mark's, Venice).

1973. 800th Death Anniv of St. Narsete Shnorali (Armenian patriarch).

605 **155** 25 l. brown and ochre 10 10
606 – 90 l. black and lilac .. 10 10
607 – 180 l. purple and green 20 20

DESIGNS: 90 l. Armenian "khatchkar" (stone stele) inscribed "Victory". 180 l. St. Narsete Shnorali.

1974. Air.

608. **156.** 2500 l. multicoloured .. 1·75 2·00

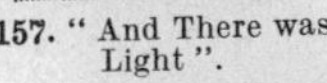

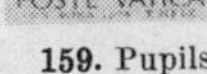

157. "And There was Light". **159.** Pupils.

158. Noah's Ark and Dove.

1974. Int. Book Year (1973). "The Bible". Biblical Texts. Multicoloured.

609. 15 l. Type **157** 10 10
610. 25 l. "Noah entrusts himself to God" (horiz.) 10 10
611. 50 l. "The Annunciation" 10 10
612. 90 l. "The Nativity" .. 10 10
613. 180 l. "The Lord feeds His People" (horiz.) .. 20 20

1974. Centenary of Universal Postal Union. Mosaics. Multicoloured.

614. 50 l. Type **158** 15 15
615. 90 l. Sheep in landscape .. 15 15

1974. 700th Death Anniv of St. Thomas Aquinas (founder of Fra Angelico School). "The School of St. Thomas" (painting, St. Mark's Convent, Florence). Each brown and gold.

616 50 l. Type **159** 10 10
617 90 l. St. Thomas and pupils (24×40 mm) 15 15
618 220 l. Pupils (different) .. 20 20

Nos. 616/18 were issued together, se-tenant, forming a composite design.

160. "Civita" (medieval quarter), Bagnoregio. **161.** Christus Victor.

1974. 700th Death Anniv of St. Bonaventura of Bagnoregio. Wood-carvings. Mult.

619. 40 l. Type **160** 10 10
620. 90 l. "Tree of Life" (13th-century motif) 15 15
621. 220 l. "St. Bonaventura (B. Gozzoli) 20 20

1974. Holy Year (1975). Multicoloured.

622. 10 l. Type **161** 10 10
623. 25 l. Christ 10 10
624. 30 l. Christ, different .. 10 10
625. 40 l. Cross and dove .. 10 10
626. 50 l. Christ enthroned .. 10 10
627. 55 l. St. Peter 10 10
628. 90 l. St. Paul 10 10
629. 100 l. St. Peter 10 10
630. 130 l. St. Paul 10 10
631. 220 l. Arms of Pope Paul VI 20 20
632. 250 l. Pope Paul VI giving blessing 20 20

162. Fountain, St. Peter's Square.

1975. European Architectural Heritage Year. Vatican Fountains.

633 **162** 20 l. black and brown 10 10
634 – 40 l. black and lilac .. 10 10
635 – 50 l. black and pink .. 10 10
636 – 90 l. black and green .. 10 10
637 – 100 l. black and green 10 10
638 – 200 l. black and blue .. 15 15

FOUNTAINS: 40 l. Piazza St. Martha. 50 l. Del Forno. 90 l. Belvedere courtyard. 100 l. Academy of Sciences. 200 l. Galley fountain.

163. "Pentecost" (El Greco). **164.** "Miracle of Loaves and Fishes" (gilt glass).

1975. Pentecost.

639 **163** 300 l. orange and red .. 30 30

1975. 9th International Christian Archaeological Congress. 4th-century Art. Mult.

640. 30 l. Type **164** 10 10
641. 150 l. Christ (painting) .. 10 10
642. 200 l. Raising of Lazarus (gilt glass) 20 20

165. Pope Sixtus IV investing Bartolomeo Sacchi as First Librarian (fresco).

1975. 500th Anniv of Apostolic Library.

643 **165** 70 l. red and violet .. 10 10
644 – 100 l. green & lt green 10 10
645 – 250 l. red and blue .. 25 25

DESIGNS—VERT: 100 l. Pope Sixtus IV (codex). HORIZ. 250 l. Pope Sixtus IV visiting library (fresco).

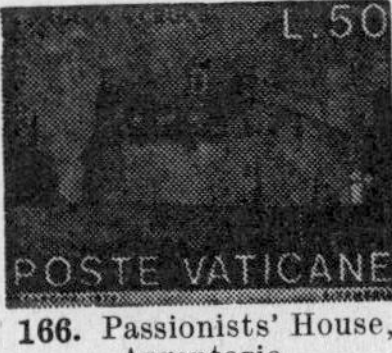

166. Passionists' House, Argentario. **167.** Detail from painting.

1975. Death Bicentenary of St. Paul of the Cross (founder of Passionist religious order). Multicoloured.

646. 50 l. Type **166** 10 10
647. 150 l. "St. Paul" (D. della Porta) (26×31 mm.) .. 15 15
648. 300 l. Basilica of Saints John and Paul 30 30

1975. International Women's Year. Painting by Fra Angelico. Multicoloured.

649. 100 l. Type **167** 15 15
650. 200 l. Detail from painting (different) 25 25

168. "The Last Judgement" (detail). **170.** Eucharist and Ear of Wheat and Globe.

169. "Madonna in Glory with the Child Jesus and Six Saints" (detail).

1976. Air.

651. **168.** 500 l. brown and blue 1·25 1·00
652. – 1,000 l. brown and blue 1·40 1·00
653. – 2,500 l. brown and blue 1·90 1·50

DESIGNS: 1,000 l. and 2,500 l. show different motifs from Michelangelo's "The Last Judgment".

1976. 400th Death Anniv. of Titian. Details from "The Madonna in Glory with the Child Jesus and Six Saints"

654. **169.** 100 l. red 20 20
655. – 300 l. red 30 30

1976. 41st Int. Eucharistic Congress. Philadelphia.

656. **179.** 150 l. multicoloured .. 15 15
657. – 200 l. gold and blue .. 20 20
658. – 400 l. gold and green .. 40 40

DESIGNS: 200 l. Eucharist within protective hands. 400 l. Adoration of the Eucharist.

171. "Transfiguration" (detail).

1976. Details of Raphael's "Transfiguration". Multicoloured.

659. 30 l. Type **171** ("Moses") 10 10
660. 40 l. "Christ Transfigured" 10 10
661. 50 l. "Prophet Elijah" .. 10 10
662. 100 l. "Two Apostles" .. 10 10
663. 150 l. "The Relatives" .. 15 15
664. 200 l. "Landscape" .. 20 20

172. St. John's Tower and Fountain.

1976. Architecture.

665 **172** 50 l. brown and lilac .. 10 10
666 – 100 l. brown & lt brown 10 10
667 – 120 l. black and green 10 10
668 – 180 l. black and grey .. 20 20
669 – 250 l. brown and ochre 25 25
670 – 300 l. purple 30 30

DESIGNS: 100 l. Fountain of the Sacrament. 120 l. Fountain at entrance to Gardens. 180 l. Cupola of St. Peter's and Sacrity Basilica. 250 l. Borgia Tower, Sistine Chapel and Via della Fondamenta. 300 l. Apostolic Palace, Courtyard of St. Damasius.

173. "Canticles of Brother Sun" (detail).

1977. 750th Death Anniv of St. Francis of Assisi. Details from "Canticles of Brother Sun" by D. Cambellotti. Multicoloured.

671. 50 l. Type **173** ("The Lord's Creatures") 10 10
672. 70 l. "Brother Sun" .. 10 10
673. 100 l. "Sister Moon and Stars" 10 10
674. 130 l. "Sister Water" .. 15 15
675. 170 l. "Praise in Infirmities and Tribulations" 20 25
676. 200 l. "Praise for Bodily Death" 20 25

174. Detail from Fresco. **175.** "Death of the Virgin".

1977. 600th Anniv. of Return of Pope Gregory from Avignon. Fresco by G. Vasari. Multicoloured.

677. 170 l. Type **174** 30 35
678. 350 l. Detail from fresco (different) 40 40

1977. Festival of Assumption. Miniatures from Apostolic Library. Multicoloured.

679. 200 l. Type **175** 25 25
680. 400 l. " Assumption of Virgin into Heaven" .. 45 45

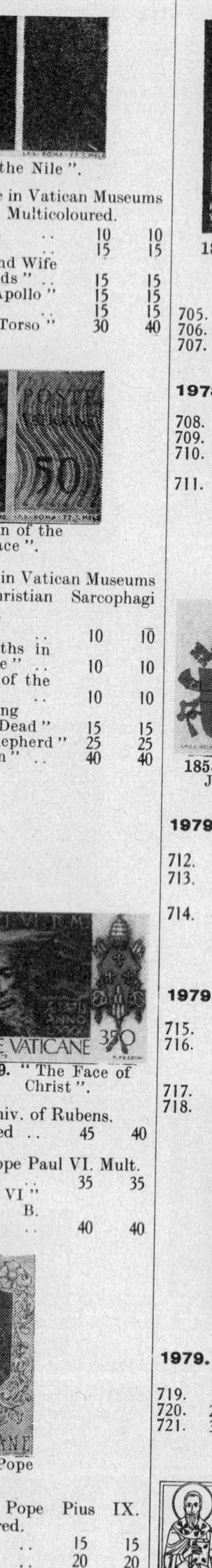

176. " God of the Nile ".

1977. Classical Sculpture in Vatican Museums (1st series). Statues. Multicoloured.

681. 50 l. Type **176** 10 10
682. 120 l. " Pericles " 15 15
683. 130 l. " Husband and Wife with joined Hands " .. 15 15
684. 150 l. " Belvedere Apollo " 15 15
685. 170 l. " Laocoon " .. 15 15
686. 350 l. " Belvedere Torso " 30 40

See also Nos. 687/92.

177. " Creation of the Human Race ".

1977. Classical Sculpture in Vatican Museums (2nd series). Paleo-Christian Sarcophagi Carvings. Multicoloured.

687. 50 l. Type **177** 10 10
688. 70 l. " Three Youths in the Fiery Furnace " .. 10 10
689. 100 l. " Adoration of the Magi " 10 10
690. 130 l. " Christ raising Lazarus from the Dead " 15 15
691. 200 l. " The Good Shepherd " 25 25
692. 400 l. " Resurrection " .. 40 40

178. " Madonna with the Parrot " (detail). **179.** " The Face of Christ ".

1977. 400th Birth Anniv. of Rubens.

693. **178.** 350 l. multicoloured .. 45 40

1978. 80th Birthday of Pope Paul VI. Mult.

694. 350 l. Type **179** 35 35
695. 400 l. " Pope Paul VI " (drawing by L. B. Barriviera) 40 40

180. Arms of Pope Pius IX.

1978. Death Cent. of Pope Pius IX. Multicoloured.

696. 130 l. Type **180** 15 15
697. 170 l. Seal of Pius IX .. 20 20
698. 200 l. Portrait of Pius IX 25 25

181. Microwave Antenna and Radio Vatican Emblem. **182.** St. Peter's Keys.

1978. Air. Tenth World Telecommunications Day.

699. **181.** 1000 l. multicoloured 90 75
700. 2000 l. multicoloured 2·25 2·00
701. 3000 l. multicoloured 3·25 2·50

1978. " Vacant See ".

702. **182.** 120 l. blue and violet .. 15 15
703. 150 l. pink and violet 15 15
704. 250 l. yellow and violet 20 20

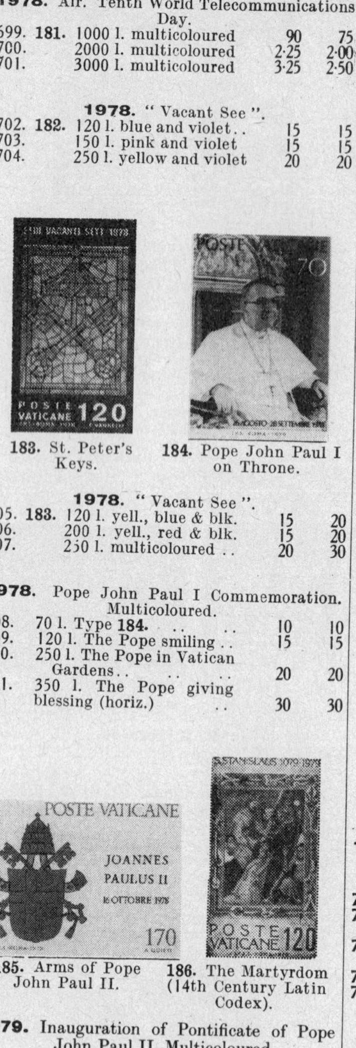

183. St. Peter's Keys. **184.** Pope John Paul I on Throne.

1978. " Vacant See ".

705. **183.** 120 l. yell., blue & blk. 15 20
706. 200 l. yell., red & blk. 15 20
707. 250 l. multicoloured .. 20 30

1978. Pope John Paul I Commemoration. Multicoloured.

708. 70 l. Type **184**. 10 10
709. 120 l. The Pope smiling .. 15 15
710. 250 l. The Pope in Vatican Gardens 20 20
711. 350 l. The Pope giving blessing (horiz.) .. 30 30

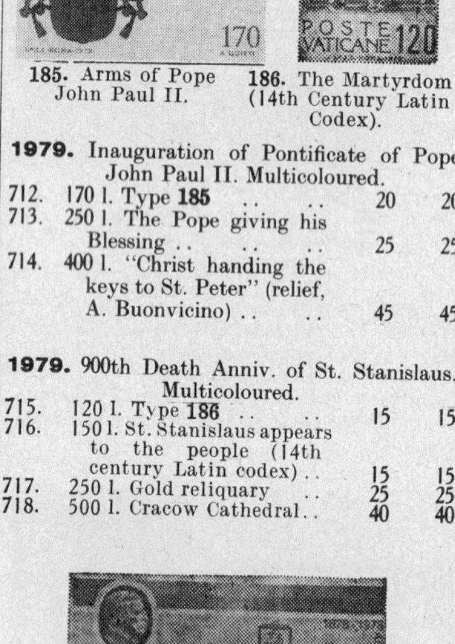

185. Arms of Pope John Paul II. **186.** The Martyrdom (14th Century Latin Codex).

1979. Inauguration of Pontificate of Pope John Paul II. Multicoloured.

712. 170 l. Type **185** 20 20
713. 250 l. The Pope giving his Blessing 25 25
714. 400 l. "Christ handing the keys to St. Peter" (relief, A. Buonvicino) .. 45 45

1979. 900th Death Anniv. of St. Stanislaus. Multicoloured.

715. 120 l. Type **186** 15 15
716. 150 l. St. Stanislaus appears to the people (14th century Latin codex) .. 15 15
717. 250 l. Gold reliquary .. 25 25
718. 500 l. Cracow Cathedral .. 40 40

187. Meteorograph.

1979. Death Centenary of Angelo Secchi (astronomer). Multicoloured.

719. 180 l. Type **187** 20 20
720. 220 l. Spectroscope .. 25 25
721. 300 l. Telescope 30 30

188. St. Basil and Vignette " Handing Monastic Laws to a Hermit". **189.** Aerial View of Vatican City.

1979. 160th Death Anniv. of St. Basil the Great. Multicoloured.

722. 150 l. Type **188** 15 15
723. 520 l. St. Basil & Vignette " Caring for the Sick " .. 45 55

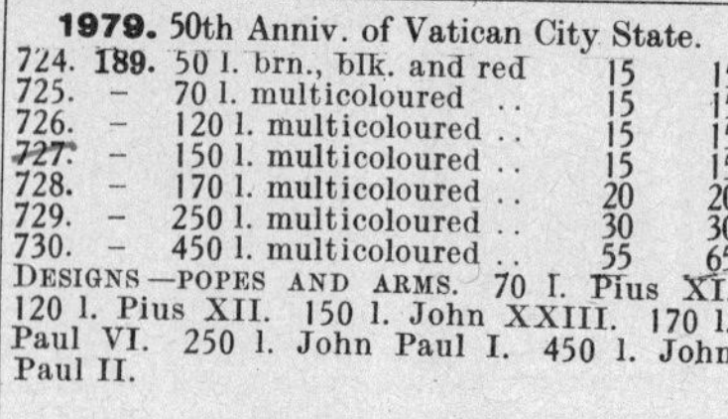

1979. 50th Anniv. of Vatican City State.

724. **189.** 50 l. brn., blk. and red 15 15
725. – 70 l. multicoloured .. 15 15
726. – 120 l. multicoloured .. 15 15
727. – 150 l. multicoloured .. 15 15
728. – 170 l. multicoloured .. 20 20
729. – 250 l. multicoloured .. 30 30
730. – 450 l. multicoloured .. 55 65

DESIGNS—POPES AND ARMS. 70 l. Pius XI. 120 l. Pius XII. 150 l. John XXIII. 170 l. Paul VI. 250 l. John Paul I. 450 l. John Paul II.

190. Child in Swaddling Clothes (relief, Foundling Hospital, Florence).

1979. International Year of the Child. Sculptures by Della Robbia.

731. **190.** 50 l. multicoloured .. 10 10
732. – 120 l. multicoloured .. 20 20
733. – 200 l. multicoloured .. 25 25
734. – 350 l. multicoloured .. 40 45

DESIGNS: 120 l. to 350 l. Similar sculptures.

191. Abbot Desiderius offering Codices to St. Benedict.

1980. 1500th Birth Anniv. of St. Benedict of Nursia (founder of Benedictine Order). Multicoloured.

735. 80 l. Type **191** 10 10
736. 100 l. St. Benedict composing rules of the Order 10 10
737. 150 l. Page of St. Benedict's Rules 15 15
738. 220 l. Death of St. Benedict 20 20
739. 450 l. Montecassino Abbey (after Paul Bril) .. 50 50

192. Hands reaching out to Pope and Arms of Santo Domingo.

1980. Air. Pope John Paul II's Journeys (1st series). Different coats of arms.

740. **192.** 200 l. multicoloured .. 25 25
741. – 300 l. multicoloured .. 35 35
742. – 500 l. vio., red & blk. 60 60
743. – 1000 l. multicolured .. 1·25 90
744. – 1500 l. multicoloured 1·75 1·40
745. – 2000 l. red, bl. & blk. 2·25 2·00
746. – 3000 l. blk., red & bl. 3·50 3·00

COATS OF ARMS: 300 l. Mexico. 500 l. Poland. 1000 l. Ireland. 1500 l. United States. 2000 l. United Nations. 3000 l. Pope John Paul II and Archbishop Dimitrios of Turkey.

See also Nos. 768/78, 814/25, 862/9, 886/93, 912/16, 940/4, 963/6, 992/6 and 1019/22.

193. Bernini (self-portrait) and Medallion showing Baldacchino, St. Peter's. **194.** St. Albertus on Mission of Peace.

1980. 300th Death Anniv of Gian Lorenzo Bernini (artist and architect). Mult.

747 80 l. Type **193** 10 10
748 170 l. Bernini and medallion showing his plan for St. Peter's .. 20 15
749 250 l. Bernini, medallion of bronze chair and group "Doctors of the Church", St. Peter's .. 25 25
750 350 l. Bernini and medallion of Apostolic Palace stairway .. 35 35

1980. 700th Death Anniv. of St. Albertus Magnus. Multicoloured.

751. 300 l. Type **194** 35 35
752. 400 l. St. Albertus as Bishop 45 45

195. Communion of the Saints.

1980. Feast of All Saints. Multicoloured.

753. 250 l. Type **195** 30 30
754. 500 l. Christ and saints .. 55 55

196. Marconi, Pope Pius XI and Radio Emblem.

1981. 50th Anniv of Vatican Radio. Mult.

755 100 l. Type **196** 10 10
756 150 l. Microphone .. 15 15
757 200 l. Antenna of Santa Maria di Galeria Radio Centre and Statue of Archangel Gabriel .. 20 20
758 600 l. Pope John Paul II .. 65 65

197. Virgil and his Writing-desk.

1981. Death Bimillenary of Virgil (Roman poet). Multicoloured.

759 350 l. Type **197** 40 50
760 600 l. As Type **197** but inscr "P. VERGILI MARONIS AENEIDOS LIBRI" 50 65

198. Congress Emblem and Apparition of St. Bernadette. **199.** Jan van Ruusbroec writing Treatise.

1981. 42nd International Eucharistic Congress, Lourdes. Multicoloured.

761. 80 l. Congress emblem .. 10 10
762. 150 l. Type **198** .. 20 20
763. 200 l. Emblem and pilgrims going to Lourdes .. 25 25
764. 500 l. Emblem and Bishop and faithful venerating the Virgin 60 60

1981. 600th Death Anniv. of Jan van Ruusbroec (Flemish mystic). Multicoloured.

765. 200 l. Type **199** 30 30
766. 300 l. Ruusbroec 35 35

200. Turin Shroud and I.Y.D.P. Emblem. **201.** Arms of John Paul II.

1981. International Year of Disabled Persons

767. **200.** 600 l. multicoloured .. 70 70

1981. Pope John Paul II's Journeys (2nd series). Multicoloured.

768 50 l. Type **201** 10 10
769 100 l. Crucifix and map of Africa 10 10
770 120 l. Hands holding crucifix 15 15
771 150 l. Pope performing baptism 20 20
772 200 l. Pope embracing African bishop 25 25
773 250 l. Pope blessing sick man 30 30
774 300 l. Notre Dame Cathedral, Paris .. 40 40
775 400 l. Pope addressing U.N.E.S.C.O., Paris .. 60 60
776 600 l. "Christ of the Andes", Rio de Janeiro 90 90
777 700 l. Cologne Cathedral .. 1·00 1·00
778 900 l. Pope giving blessing 1·25 1·25

202. Agnes handing Church to Grand Master of the Crosiers of the Red Star.

203. "Pueri Cantores" (left panel).

1982. 700th Death Anniv. of Blessed Agnes of Prague. Multicoloured.

779. 700 l. Type **202** 90 90
780. 900 l. Agnes receiving letter from St. Clare .. 1·00 1·00

1982. 500th Death Anniv. of Luca della Robbia (sculptor).

781. **203.** 1000 l. green and blue 1·10 1·10
782. – 1000 l. multicoloured 1·10 1·10
783. – 1000 l. green and blue 1·10 1·10

DESIGNS—As T **203**: No. 783, "Pueri Cantores" (right panel). 44 × 36 mm: No. 782, "Virgin Mary in Prayer".

1582-1982 200

POSTE VATICANE

204. Virgin Mary and St. Joseph clothe St. Theresa.

205. Examining Globe.

1982. 400th Death Anniv. of St. Theresa of Avila.

784. **204.** 200 l. orange, grey and red 25 25
785. – 600 l. grey, orange and blue 75 75
786. – 1000 l. grey, orange and mauve .. .. 1·25 1·25

DESIGNS: 600 l. Ecstasy of St. Theresa. 1000 l. St. Theresa writing "The Interior Castle".

1982. 400th Anniv. of Gregorian calendar. Details from Pope Gregory XIII's tomb.

787. **205.** 200 l. green 20 20
788. – 300 l. black 35 35
789. – 700 l. purple .. .. 1·00 1·00

DESIGNS: 300 l. Presenting proposals to Pope Gregory XIII. 700 l. Kneeling figures.

206. "Nativity" (Veit Stoss).

1982. Christmas.

791 **206** 300 l. stone, brn & gold 40 40
792 – 450 l. lilac, purple & sil 60 60

DESIGN: 450 l. "Nativity with Pope John Paul II" (Enrico Manfrini).

207. Crucifixion.

209. "Theology".

1983. Holy Year. Multicoloured.

793. 300 l. Type **207** 40 40
794. 350 l. Christ the Redeemer 45 45
795. 400 l. Pope bringing message of redemption to world 55 55
796. 2000 l. Dove of the Holy Spirit passing through Holy Door .. .. 2·50 2·50

1983. 500th Birth Anniv of Raphael (artist).

798 **209** 50 l. blue & ultram .. 10 10
799 – 400 l. purple & mauve 50 50
800 – 500 l. brown & chestnut 65 65
801 – 1200 l. green & turq .. 1·50 1·50

DESIGNS—Allegories on the Segnatura Room ceiling: 400 l. "Poetry". 500 l. "Justice". 1200 l. "Philosophy".

210. "Moses explaining the Law to the People" (Luca Signorelli).

1983. Air. World Communications Year. Multicoloured.

804. 2000 l. Type **210** .. .. 2·50 2·00
805. 5000 l. "St. Paul preaching in Athens" (Raphael) .. 5·50 4·75

211. Mendel and Hybrid Experiment.

212. St. Casimir and Vilna Cathedral and Castle.

1984. Death Centenary of Gregor Johan Mendel (geneticist).

806. **211.** 450 l. multicoloured .. 75 75
807. 1500 l. multicoloured 2·00 2·00

1984. 500th Death Anniv. of St. Casimir (patron saint of Lithuania).

808. **212.** 550 l. multicoloured .. 75 75
809. 1200 l. multicoloured 1·75 1·75

213. Pontifical Academy of Sciences.

1984. Cultural and Scientific Institutions.

810. **213.** 150 l. yellow and brn. 25 25
811. – 450 l. multicoloured .. 65 65
812. – 550 l. yellow and vio. 80 80
813. – 1500 l. yellow and blue 1·90 1·90

DESIGNS: 450 l. Seals and document from Vatican Secret Archives. 550 l. Entrance to Vatican Apostolic Library. 1500 l. Vatican Observatory, Castelgandolfo.

214. Pope in Karachi.

215. Damasus and Sepulchre of Sts. Marcellinus and Peter.

1984. Pope John Paul II's Journeys (3rd series). Multicoloured.

814. 50 l. Type **214** 10 10
815. 100 l. Pope and image of Our Lady of Penafrancia, Philippines .. 10 10
816. 150 l. Pope with Crucifix (Guam) 20 20
817. 250 l. Pope and Tokyo Cathedral 50 50
818. 300 l. Pope at Anchorage, Alaska 30 30
819. 400 l. Crucifix, crowd and map of Africa 40 40
820. 450 l. Pope and image of Our Lady of Fatima (Portugal) 45 45
821. 550 l. Pope, Archbishop of Westminster and Canterbury Cathedral .. .. 1·25 1·25
822. 1000 l. Pope and image of Our Lady of Lujan (Argentina) .. .. 2·00 2·00
823. 1500 l. Pope, Lake Leman and Geneva .. .. 3·00 3·00
824. 2500 l. Pope and Monte Titano (San Marino) .. 5·00 5·00
825. 4000 l. Pope and Santiago de Compostela Cathedral (Spain) .. .. .. 8·00 8·00

1984. 1600th Death Anniv. of Pope St. Damasus. Multicoloured.

826. 200 l. Type **215** 30 30
827. 500 l. Damasus and epigraph from St. Januarius's tomb 90 90
828. 2000 l. Damasus and basilica ruins .. .. 4·00 4·00

216. More (after Holbein) and Map.

217. St. Methodius holding Religious Paintings.

1985. 450th Death Anniv. of Saint Thomas More. Multicoloured.

829. 250 l. Type **216** 45 45
830. 400 l. St. Thomas More and title page of "Utopia" .. 85 85
831. 2000 l. St. Thomas More and title page of "Life of Thomas More" by Domenico Regi .. .. 3·50 3·50

1985. 1100th Death Anniv. of Saint Methodius. Multicoloured.

832. 500 l. Type **217** 90 90
833. 600 l. Saints Cyril and Methodius with Pope Clement I's body .. 1·25 1·25
834. 1700 l. Saints Benedict, Cyril and Methodius .. 2·75 2·75

218. Cross on Map of Africa.

219. Eagle (from Door, St. Paul's Basilica, Rome).

1985. 43rd International Eucharistic Congress, Nairobi. Multicoloured.

835. 100 l. Type **218** 20 20
836. 400 l. Assembly of bishops 60 60
837. 600 l. Chalice 90 90
838. 2300 l. Family gazing at cross .. .. .. 3·50 3·50

1985. 900th Death Anniv. of Pope Gregory VII. Multicoloured.

839. 150 l. Type **219** 25 25
840. 450 l. Pope Gregory VII .. 75 75
841. 2500 l. Pope Gregory's former sarcophagus (horiz.) .. .. .. 4·00 4·00

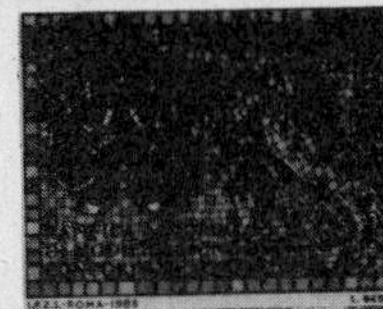

220. Mosaic Map of Italy and Symbol of Holy See.

1985. Ratification of Modification of 1929 Lateran Concordat.

842. **220.** 400 l. multicoloured .. 60 60

221. Carriage.

222. "Nation shall not Lift up Sword against Nation. . .".

1985. "Italia '85" International Stamp Exhibition, Rome.

843 **221** 450 l. red and blue .. 65 65
844 – 1500 l. blue and mauve 2·10 2·10

DESIGN: 1500 l. Carriage (different).

1986. International Peace Year. Mult.

846. 50 l. Type **222** 10 10
847. 350 l. Messenger's feet ("How beautiful . . . are the feet. . .") 50 50
848. 450 l. Profiles and olive branch ("Blessed are the peacemakers . . .") .. 80 80
849. 650 l. Dove and sun ("Glory to God in the highest. . .") .. .. 1·00 1·00
850. 2000 l. Pope's hand releasing dove over rainbow ("Peace is a value with no frontiers. . .") .. 3·00 3·00

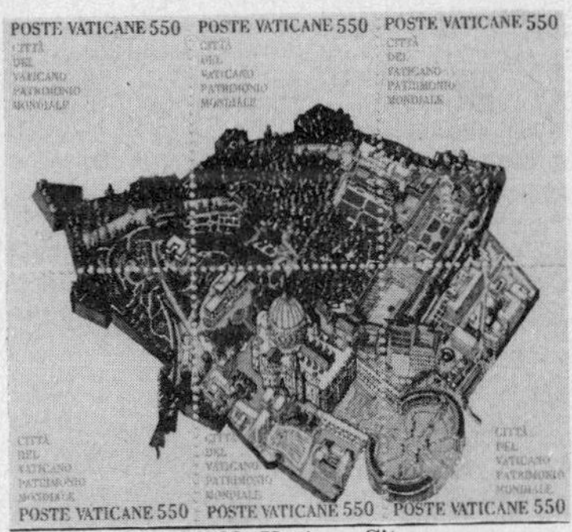

223/228. Vatican City. (illustration reduced. actual size 89 × 80 mm.)

1986. World Heritage. Vatican City. Mult.

851. **223.** 550 l. multicoloured .. 1·00 1·00
852. **224.** 550 l. multicoloured .. 1·00 1·00
853. **225.** 550 l. multicoloured .. 1·00 1·00
854. **226.** 550 l. multicoloured .. 1·00 1·00
855. **227.** 550 l. multicoloured .. 1·00 1·00
856. **228.** 550 l. multicoloured .. 1·00 1·00

Nos. 851/6 were printed together, se-tenant, forming the composite design illustrated.

229. St. Camillus saving Invalid from Flood (after Pierre Subleyras).

230. "The Philosophers".

1986. Centenary of Proclamation of St. Camillus de Lellis and St. John of God as Patron Saints of Hospitals and the Sick.

857. **229.** 700 l. green, vio. & red 1·25 1·25
858. – 700 l. blue, grn. & red 1·25 1·25
859. – 2000 l. multicoloured .. 3·75 3·75

DESIGNS: No. 858, St. John supporting the sick (after Gomez Moreno). 859, Emblems of Ministers of the Sick and Brothers Hospitallers, and Pope John Paul II talking to patient.

1986. 50th Anniv of Pontifical Academy of Sciences. Details from fresco "School of Athens" by Raphael. Multicoloured.
860. 1500 l. Type **230** .. .. 2·25 2·25
861. 2500 l. "The Scientists" .. 3·25 3·25

231. Pope and Young People (Central America).

232. "St. Augustine reading St. Paul's Epistles" (fresco, Benozzo Gozzoli).

1986. Air. Pope John Paul II's Journeys (4th series). Multicoloured.
862 350 l. Type **231** 55 55
863 450 l. Pope in prayer, Warsaw Cathedral and Our Lady of Czestochowa (Poland) .. 70 70
864 700 l. Pope kneeling and crowd at Lourdes (France) .. .. 1·00 90
865 1000 l. Sanctuary of Mariazell and St. Stephen's Cathedral, Vienna (Austria) .. 1·50 1·25
866 1500 l. Pope and representatives of nations visited (Alaska, Asia and Pacific Islands) .. 2·25 1·75
867 2000 l. Image of St. Nicholas of Flue, Basilica of Einsiedeln and Pope (Switzerland) 3·00 2·25
868 2500 l. Crosses, Notre Dame Cathedral, Quebec, and Pope (Canada) .. .. 3·50 2·75
869 5000 l. Pope, bishop and young people with cross (Spain, Dominican Republic and Puerto Rico) .. .. .. 7·00 5·50

1987. 1600th Anniv of Conversion and Baptism of St. Augustine. Multicoloured.
870 300 l. Type **232** 50 50
871 400 l. "Baptism of St. Augustine" (Bartolomeo di Gentile) 60 60
872 500 l. "Ecstasy of St. Augustine" (fresco, Benozzo Gozzoli) .. 70 70
873 2200 l. "Dispute of the Sacrament" (detail of fresco, Raphael) .. 3·50 3·50

233. Statue of Christ, Lithuanian Chapel, Vatican Crypt.

234. Chapter of Riga Church Seal.

1987. 600th Anniv. of Conversion to Christianity of Lithuania. Multicoloured.
874. 200 l. Type **233** 40 40
875. 700 l. Statue of Virgin Mary with body of Christ and two angels .. 1·10 1·10
876. 3000 l. Lithuanian shrine .. 4·25 4·25

1987. 800th Anniv. of Conversion to Christianity of Latvia. Multicoloured.
877. 700 l. Type **234** .. .. 1·00 1·00
878. 2400 l. Basilica of the Assumption, Aglona .. 3·50 3·50

235. Judge.

236. Stamp Room and 1929 5 c. Stamp.

1987. "Olymphilex '87" Olympic Stamps Exhibition, Rome. Figures from Caracalla Baths floor mosaic. Multicoloured.
879. 400 l. Type **235** 60 60
880. 500 l. Runner 80 80
881. 600 l. Discus-thrower .. 90 90
882. 2000 l. Athlete .. .. 3·00 3·00

1987. Inauguration of Philatelic and Numismatic Museum. Multicoloured.
884. 400 l. Type **236** 60 60
885. 3500 l. Coin room and reverse of 1000 l. 1986 coin .. .. .. 4·75 4·75

1987. Pope John Paul II's Journeys (5th series). As T **231**. Multicoloured.
886 50 l. Youths, Pope and Machu Picchu (Venezuela, Ecuador, Peru, Trinidad and Tobago) 20 20
887 250 l. Antwerp Cathedral, smoke stacks and Pope (Netherlands, Luxembourg and Belgium) .. 50 50
888 400 l. People, buildings and Pope (Togo, Ivory Coast, Cameroun, Central African Republic, Zaire, Kenya and Morocco) 85 85
889 500 l. Pope holding Cross and youths (Liechtenstein) .. .. .. 1·00 1·00
890 600 l. Pope, Indians and Delhi Mosque (India) .. 1·40 1·40
891 700 l. Pope, people, ceramic and Bogota Cathedral (Colombia and St. Lucia) 1·50 1·50
892 2500 l. Pope, Cure d'Ars and Lyon Cathedral (France) .. .. 5·00 5·00
893 4000 l. Hands releasing dove and symbols of countries visited (Bangladesh, Singapore, Fiji, New Zealand, Australia and Seychelles) 8·00 8·00

237. Arrival of Relics.

238. Children and Sister of Institute of the Daughters of Mary Help of Christians.

1987. 900th Anniv. of Transfer of St. Nicholas's Relics from Myra to Bari. Multicoloured.
894. 500 l. Type **237** 90 90
895. 700 l. St. Nicholas giving purses of gold to save from dishonour the three daughters of a poor man 1·40 1·40
896. 3000 l. St. Nicholas saving a ship .. .. .. 8·50 8·50

1988. Death Centenary of St. John Bosco (founder of Salesian Brothers). Mult.
897 500 l. Type **238** 75 75
898 1000 l. Bosco and children 1·25 1·25
899 2000 l. Children and Salesian lay brother .. 2·50 2·50
Nos. 897/9 were printed together, se-tenant, forming a composite design.

239 The Annunciation

240 Prince Vladimir the Great (15th-century icon)

1988. Marian Year. Multicoloured.
900 50 l. Type **239** 10 10
901 300 l. Nativity 40 40
902 500 l. Pentecost 65 65
903 750 l. The Assumption .. 85 85
904 1000 l. Mother of the Church .. .. 1·25 1·25
905 2400 l. Refuge of Sinners .. 3·00 3·00

1988. Millenary of Conversion to Christianity of Rus of Kiev. Multicoloured.
906 450 l. Type **240** 60 60
907 650 l. St. Sophia's Cathedral, Kiev .. 90 90
908 2500 l. "Mother of God in Prayer" (mosaic, St. Sophia's Cathedral) .. 3·25 3·25

241 "Marriage of Cana" (detail)

242 Angel with Olive Branch

1988. 400th Death Anniv of Paolo Veronese (painter).
909 **241** 550 l. blue and red .. 80 80
910 – 650 l. multicoloured .. 1·25 1·25
911 – 3000 l. red and brown 3·25 3·25
DESIGNS—HORIZ. 650 l. "Self-portrait". VERT. 3000 l. "Marriage of Cana" (different detail).

1988. Air. Pope John Paul II's Journeys (6th series). As T **231**. Multicoloured.
912 450 l. Hands releasing dove, St. Peter's, Rome, Santiago Cathedral and Sanctuary of Our Lady, Lujan (Uruguay, Chile and Argentina) .. 75 75
913 650 l. Pope in act of blessing, Speyer Cathedral and youths (German Federal Republic) .. 90 90
914 1000 l. Hands releasing dove, Gdansk altar and intertwined flowers and thorns (Poland) .. 1·25 1·25
915 2500 l. Skyscrapers and Pope blessing youths (U.S.A.) .. .. 3·25 3·25
916 5000 l. Hands releasing dove, tepee at Fort Simpson and American Indians (Canada) .. 6·00 6·00

1988. Christmas. Multicoloured.
917 50 l. Type **242** 10 10
918 400 l. Angel holding olive branch in both hands .. 50 50
919 500 l. Angel with olive branch (flying from right) 70 70
920 550 l. Shepherds 75 75
921 850 l. Nativity .. .. 1·00 1·00
922 1500 l. Wise Men .. .. 1·75 1·75

244 The Annunciation

245 Yellow-bibbed Lory

1989. 600th Anniv of Feast of Visitation of Virgin Mary. Illuminated initials. Mult.
925 550 l. Type **244** 75 75
926 750 l. Virgin Mary and St. Elizabeth .. 85 85
927 2500 l. Virgin Mary and St. Elizabeth with Jesus and John the Baptist as babies .. .. 3·00 3·00

1989. Birds featured in "Histoire Naturelle des Oiseaux" by Eleazar Albin. Multicoloured.
928 100 l. Type **245** 15 15
929 150 l. Green woodpecker .. 20 20
930 200 l. Goldcrest ("Crested wren") and common wren 30 30
931 350 l. Common kingfisher 45 45
932 500 l. Common cardinal ("red Gros Beak of Virginia") 65 65
933 700 l. Bullfinch 90 90
934 1500 l. Lapwing ("Lapwing Plover") .. .. 2·25 2·25
935 3000 l. Green-winged teal ("French Teal") .. 4·50 4·50

246 Broken Bread (Congress emblem)

247 Pope's Arms, Map of South America and Pope

1989. 44th International Eucharistic Congress, Seoul.
936 **246** 550 l. red and green .. 65 65
937 – 850 l. multicoloured .. 1·10 1·10
938 – 1000 l. multicoloured 1·25 1·25
939 – 2500 l. green, pink and violet .. .. 3·00 3·00
DESIGNS: 850 l. Cross; 1000 l. Cross and fishes; 2500 l. Small cross on wafer.

1989. Pope John Paul II's Journeys (7th series). Multicoloured.
940 50 l. Type **247** 15 15
941 550 l. Austria 75 75
942 800 l. Southern Africa .. 1·25 1·25
943 1000 l. France .. .. 1·50 1·50
944 4000 l. Italy .. .. 4·75 4·75

248 Basilica of the Assumption, Baltimore

249 Vision of Ursulines on Mystical Stair

1989. Bicentenary of First Catholic Diocese in U.S.A. Each deep brown and brown.
945 450 l. Type **248** 55 55
946 1350 l. John Carroll (first Archbishop of Baltimore) .. .. .. 1·75 1·75
947 2400 l. Cathedral of Mary Our Queen, Baltimore (after Martin Barry) .. 3·25 3·25

1990. 450th Death Anniv of St. Angela Merici (founder of Company of St. Ursula). Multicoloured.
948 700 l. Type **249** 80 80
949 800 l. St. Angela teaching Ursulines .. .. 1·10 1·10
950 2800 l. Ursulines .. .. 3·75 3·75

250 Ordination and Arrival in Frisia

251 Abraham

1990. 1300th Anniv of Beginning of St. Willibrord's Missions. Multicoloured.
951 300 l. Type **250** 35 35
952 700 l. St. Willibrord in Antwerp, creation as bishop by Pope Sergius I and gift of part of Echternach by Abbess of Euren 85 85
953 3000 l. Gift of Echternach by King Pepin and St. Willibrord's death .. 3·75 3·75

1990. 40th Anniv of Caritas Internationalis. Details of mosaic from Basilica of Sta. Maria Maggiore, Rome. Multicoloured.
954 450 l. Type **251** 50 50
955 650 l. Three visitors .. 75 75
956 800 l. Sarah making bread 90 90
957 2000 l. Visitors seated at Abraham's table .. 2·25 2·25

INDEX

Countries can be quickly located by referring to the index at the end of this volume.

252 Fishermen on Lake Peking

253 Pope and African Landscape

1990. 300th Anniv of Peking-Nanking Diocese. Details of two enamelled bronze vases given by Peking Apostolic Delegate to Pope Pius IX. Multicoloured.

959 500 l. Type **252** 60 60
960 750 l. Church of the Immaculate Conception (first Peking church, 1650) 90 90
961 1500 l. Lake Peking .. 1·75 1·75
962 2000 l. Church of the Redeemer, Peking, 1703 2·50 2·50

1990. Air. Pope John Paul II's Journeys (8th series). Multicoloured.

963 500 l. Type **253** 60 60
964 1000 l. Northern European landscape (Scandinavia) 1·10 1·10
965 3000 l. Cathedral (Santiago de Compostela, Spain) 3·25 3·25
966 5000 l. Oriental landscape (Korea, Indonesia and Mauritius) .. .. 5·50 5·50

254 Choir of Angels

1990. Christmas. Details of painting by Sebastiano Mainardi. Multicoloured.

967 50 l. Type **254** 15 15
968 200 l. St. Joseph 25 25
969 650 l. Holy Child .. 70 70
970 750 l. Virgin Mary .. 85 85
971 2500 l. "Nativity" (complete picture) (vert) 3·00 3·00

255 "Eleazar" (left half)

1991. Restoration of Sistine Chapel. Details of "Lunettes of the Ancestors of Christ" by Michelangelo. Multicoloured.

972 50 l. Type **255** 15 15
973 100 l. "Eleazar" (right half) 15 15
974 150 l. "Jacob" (left half) .. 15 15
975 250 l. "Jacob" (right half) 30 30
976 350 l. "Josiah" (left half) 45 45
977 400 l. "Josiah" (right half) 55 55
978 500 l. "Asa" (left half) .. 60 60
979 650 l. "Asa" (right half) .. 80 80
980 800 l. "Zerubbabel" (left half) .. .. .. 1·00 1·00
981 1000 l. "Zerubbabel" (right half) .. .. .. 1·40 1·40
982 2000 l. "Azor" (left half) .. 2·50 2·50
983 3000 l. "Azor" (right half) 3·75 3·75

256 Title Page and Pope Leo XIII's Arms

1991. Centenary of "Rerum Novarum" (encyclical on workers' rights).

984 **256** 600 l. black and green 75 75
985 – 750 l. green and brown 90 90
986 – 3500 l. purple and black 4·50 4·50

DESIGNS: 750 l. Allegory of Church, workers and employers (from Leo XIII's 15th Anniv medal, 1892); 3500 l. Profile of Pope Leo XIII (from same medal).

257 Astrograph (astronomical camera)

258 "Apparition of Virgin Mary" (Biagio Puccini)

1991. Cent of Vatican Observatory. Mult.

987 750 l. Type **257** 90 90
988 1000 l. Castelgandolfo observatory (horiz) .. 1·40 1·40
989 3000 l. Vatican Observatory telescope, Mount Graham, Tucson, U.S.A. 4·25 4·25

1991. 600th Anniv of Canonization of St. Bridget (founder of Order of the Holy Saviour). Multicoloured.

990 1500 l. Type **258** .. .. 2·00 2·00
991 2000 l. "Revelation of Christ" (Biagio Puccini) 2·50 2·50

259 Cathedral of the Immaculate Conception, Ouagadougou

260 Colonnade of St. Peter's Cathedral, Rome

1991. Pope John Paul II's Journeys (9th series). Multicoloured.

992 200 l. Type **259** (Cape Verde, Guinea-Bissau, Mali, Burkina Faso and Chad) 30 30
993 550 l. St. Vitus's Cathedral, Prague (Czechoslovakia) 70 70
994 750 l. Basilica of Our Lady of Guadaloupe (Mexico and Curacao) 95 95
995 1500 l. Ta' Pinu Sanctuary, Gozo (Malta) .. .. 2·00 2·00
996 3500 l. Cathedral of Christ the King, Giteca (Tanzania, Burundi, Rwanda and Ivory Coast) .. .. .. 5·00 5·00

1991. Synod of Bishops' Special Assembly for Europe. Each black and blue.

997 300 l. Type **260** 45 45
998 500 l. St. Peter's Cathedral and square 70 70
999 4000 l. Apostolic Palace and colonnade .. .. 6·00 6·00

Nos. 997/9 were issued together, se-tenant, forming a composite design.

261 Christopher Columbus

262 "Our Lady of Childbirth"

1992. 500th Anniv of Discovery of America by Columbus. Multicoloured.

1000 500 l. Type **261** 65 65
1001 600 l. St. Pedro Claver .. 75 75
1002 850 l. "Virgin of the Catholic Kings" .. 1·10 1·10
1003 1000 l. Bortolome de las Casas .. .. 1·40 1·40
1004 2000 l. Junipero Serra .. 2·75 2·75

1992. 500th Death Anniv of Piero della Francesca (painter). Multicoloured.

1006 300 l. Type **262** 35 35
1007 750 l. "Our Lady of Childbirth" (detail) .. 80 80
1008 1000 l. "The Resurrection" .. .. 1·25 1·25
1009 3000 l. "The Resurrection" (detail) .. 3·25 3·25

263 St. Giuseppe comforting the Sick

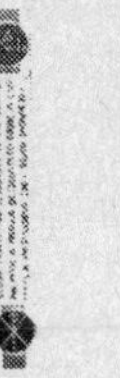

264 Maize

1992. 150th Death Anniv of St. Giuseppe Benedetto Cottolengo. Multicoloured.

1010 650 l. Type **263** 70 70
1011 850 l. St. Giuseppe holding Piccola Casa della Divina Provvidenza (infirmary), Turin .. 90 90

1992. Plants of the New World. Illustrations from the 18th-century "Phytanthoza Iconographia". Multicoloured.

1012 850 l. Type **264** 85 85
1013 850 l. Tomatoes 85 85
1014 850 l. Cactus 85 85
1015 850 l. Cacao 85 85
1016 850 l. Peppers 85 85
1017 850 l. Pineapple 85 85

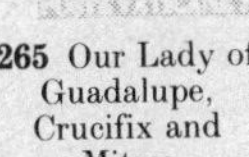

265 Our Lady of Guadalupe, Crucifix and Mitres

266 Pope, Dove and Map of Europe

1992. 4th Latin American Espiscopal Conference, Santo Domingo.

1018 **265** 700 l. gold, emerald and green .. .. 2·50 2·50

1992. Air. Pope John Paul II's Journeys (10th series). Multicoloured.

1019 500 l. Type **266** (Portugal) 50 50
1020 1000 l. Map of Europe highlighting Poland .. 1·00 1·00
1021 4000 l. Our Lady of Czestochowa and map highlighting Poland and Hungary .. .. 4·00 4·00
1022 6000 l. Map of South America highlighting Brazil .. .. .. 6·00 6·00

267 "The Annunciation"

268 "St. Francis healing the Man from Ilerda" (fresco by Giotto in Upper Church, Assisi)

1992. Christmas. Mosaics in Church of Sta. Maria Maggiore, Rome. Multicoloured.

1023 600 l. Type **267** 60 60
1024 700 l. "Nativity" .. 70 70
1025 1000 l. "Adoration of the Kings" .. .. 1·00 1·00
1026 1500 l. "Presentation in the Temple" .. .. 1·50 1·50

1993. "Peace in Europe" Prayer Meeting, Assisi.

1027 **268** 1000 l. multicoloured 1·00 1·00

269 Dome of St. Peter's Basilica

270 "The Sacrifice of Isaac"

1993. Architectural Treasures. Multicoloured.

1028 200 l. Type **269** 15 15
1029 300 l. St. John Lateran Basilica 25 25
1030 350 l. Sta. Maria Maggiore Basilica 30 30
1031 500 l. St. Paul's Basilica 40 40
1032 600 l. Apostolic Palace, Vatican 50 50
1033 700 l. Apostolic Palace, Lateran (Rome) .. 60 60
1034 850 l. Papal Palace, Castelgandolfo .. 70 70
1035 1000 l. Chancery Palace, Rome 85 85
1036 2000 l. Palace of Propagation of the Faith, Rome .. .. 1·60 1·60
1037 3000 l. San Calisto Palace 2·50 2·50

1993. Ascension Day. Multicoloured.

1038 200 l. Type **270** 15 15
1039 750 l. Jesus handing New Law to St. Peter .. 60 60
1040 3000 l. Christ watching servant washing Pilate's hands .. 2·50 2·50

Nos. 1038/40 were issued together, se-tenant, forming a composite design of the bas-relief "Traditio Legis" from 4th-century sarcophagus.

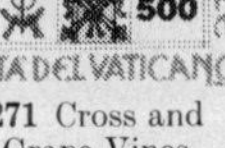

271 Cross and Grape Vines

273 St. John, Cross, Fish and Moldava River

272 "Crucifixion" (Felice Casorati)

1993. 45th International Eucharistic Congress, Seville. Multicoloured.

1041 500 l. Type **271** 40 40
1042 700 l. Cross and hands offering broken bread 60 60
1043 1500 l. Hands holding chalice .. .. 1·25 1·25
1044 2500 l. Cross, banner and ears of wheat .. .. 2·10 2·10

1993. Europa. Contemporary Art. Mult.

1045 750 l. Type **272** 60 60
1046 850 l. "Rouen Cathedral" (Maurice Utrillo) 70 70

1993. 600th Death Anniv of St. John of Nepomuk (patron saint of Bohemia). Mult.

1047 1000 l. Type **273** 85 85
1048 2000 l. Charles Bridge, Prague .. .. 1·60 1·60

274 Pope praying

1993. Pope John Paul II's Journeys (11th series). Multicoloured.
1049 600 l. Type **274** (Senegal, Gambia and Guinea) .. 50 50
1050 1000 l. Pope with Pastoral Staff (Angola and St. Thomas and Prince Islands) 85 85
1051 5000 l. Pope with hands clasped in prayer (Dominican Republic) 4·25 4·25

HANS HOLBEIN IL GIOVANE 1543-1993
CITTA DEL VATICANO 700

275 "Madonna of Solothurn" (detail)

1993. 450th Death Anniv of Hans Holbein the Younger (artist). Multicoloured.
1052 700 l. Type **275** 60 60
1053 1000 l. "Madonna of Solothurn" 85 85
1054 1500 l. "Self-portrait" .. 1·25 1·25

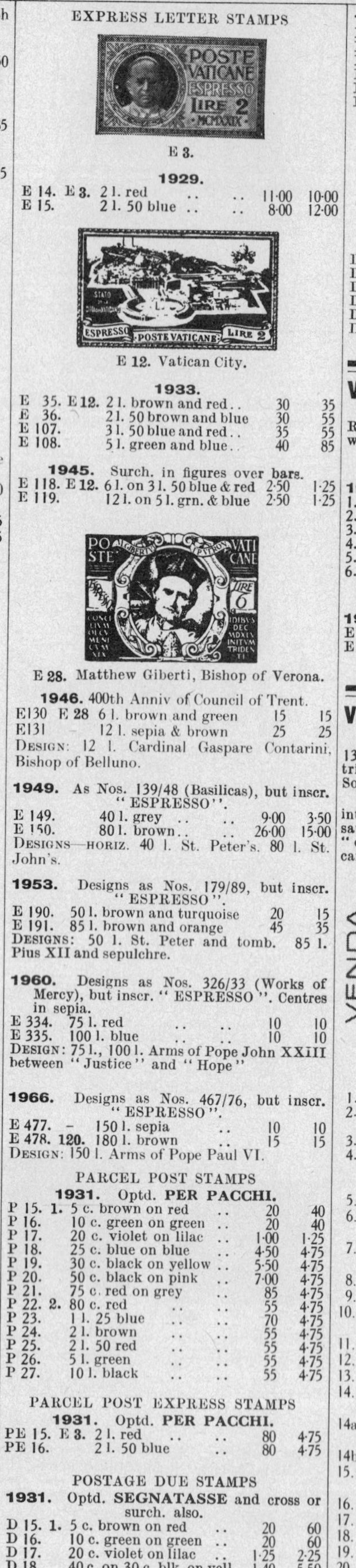

EXPRESS LETTER STAMPS

POSTE VATICANE ESPRESSO LIRE 2 MCMXXIX

E 3.

1929.
E 14. E **3.** 2 l. red .. .. 11·00 10·00
E 15. 2 l. 50 blue .. .. 8·00 12·00

STATO DI CITTA DEL VATICANO ESPRESSO POSTE VATICANE LIRE 2

E 12. Vatican City.

1933.
E 35. E **12.** 2 l. brown and red .. 30 35
E 36. 2 l. 50 brown and blue .. 30 55
E 107. 3 l. 50 blue and red .. 35 55
E 108. 5 l. green and blue .. 40 85

1945. Surch. in figures over bars.
E 118. E **12.** 6 l. on 3 l. 50 blue & red 2·50 1·25
E 119. 12 l. on 5 l. grn. & blue 2·50 1·25

POSTE VATICANE LIRE 6

E 28. Matthew Giberti, Bishop of Verona.

1946. 400th Anniv of Council of Trent.
E130 E **28** 6 l. brown and green 15 15
E131 – 12 l. sepia & brown 25 25
DESIGN: 12 l. Cardinal Gaspare Contarini, Bishop of Belluno.

1949. As Nos. 139/48 (Basilicas), but inscr. "ESPRESSO".
E 149. 40 l. grey .. .. 9·00 3·50
E 150. 80 l. brown .. .. 26·00 15·00
DESIGNS—HORIZ. 40 l. St. Peter's. 80 l. St. John's.

1953. Designs as Nos. 179/89, but inscr. "ESPRESSO".
E 190. 50 l. brown and turquoise 20 15
E 191. 85 l. brown and orange 45 35
DESIGNS: 50 l. St. Peter and tomb. 85 l. Pius XII and sepulchre.

1960. Designs as Nos. 326/33 (Works of Mercy), but inscr. "ESPRESSO". Centres in sepia.
E 334. 75 l. red 10 10
E 335. 100 l. blue 10 10
DESIGN: 75 l., 100 l. Arms of Pope John XXIII between "Justice" and "Hope"

1966. Designs as Nos. 467/76, but inscr. "ESPRESSO".
E 477. – 150 l. sepia .. 10 10
E 478. **120.** 180 l. brown .. 15 15
DESIGN: 150 l. Arms of Pope Paul VI.

PARCEL POST STAMPS

1931. Optd. **PER PACCHI.**
P 15. **1.** 5 c. brown on red .. 20 40
P 16. 10 c. green on green .. 20 40
P 17. 20 c. violet on lilac .. 1·00 1·25
P 18. 25 c. blue on blue .. 4·50 4·75
P 19. 30 c. black on yellow .. 5·50 4·75
P 20. 50 c. black on pink .. 7·00 4·75
P 21. 75 c. red on grey .. 85 4·75
P 22. **2.** 80 c. red .. .. 55 4·75
P 23. 1 l. 25 blue .. .. 70 4·75
P 24. 2 l. brown .. .. 55 4·75
P 25. 2 l. 50 red .. .. 55 4·75
P 26. 5 l. green .. .. 55 4·75
P 27. 10 l. black .. .. 55 4·75

PARCEL POST EXPRESS STAMPS

1931. Optd. **PER PACCHI.**
PE 15. E **3.** 2 l. red .. .. 80 4·75
PE 16. 2 l. 50 blue .. .. 80 4·75

POSTAGE DUE STAMPS

1931. Optd. **SEGNATASSE** and cross or surch. also.
D 15. **1.** 5 c. brown on red .. 20 60
D 16. 10 c. green on green .. 20 60
D 17. 20 c. violet on lilac .. 1·25 2·25
D 18. 40 c. on 30 c. blk. on yell. 1·40 5·50
D 19. **2.** 60 c. on 2 l. brown .. 32·00 24·00
D 20. 1 l. 10 on 2 l. 50 red .. 4·75 18·00

POSTE VATICANE SEGNATASSE

D 26.

POSTE VATICANE LIRE SEGNATASSE 20

D 49. State Arms.

1945. Coloured network shown in brackets.
D 107. D **26.** 5 c. black (yellow) 10 10
D 108. 20 c. black (violet) 10 10
D 109. 80 c. black (red) .. 10 10
D 110. 1 l. black (green) .. 10 10
D 111. 2 l. black (blue) .. 10 15
D 112. 5 l. black (grey) .. 10 15

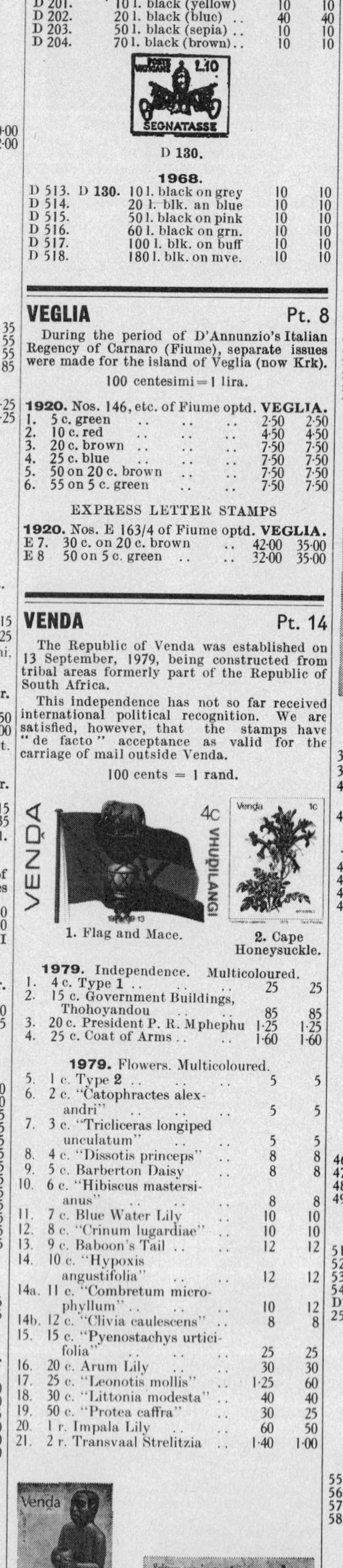

1954. Coloured network shown in brackets.
D 199. D **49.** 4 l. black (red) .. 10 10
D 200. 6 l. black (green) .. 20 20
D 201. 10 l. black (yellow) 10 10
D 202. 20 l. black (blue) .. 40 40
D 203. 50 l. black (sepia) .. 10 10
D 204. 70 l. black (brown) .. 10 10

POSTE VATICANE L.10 SEGNATASSE

D 130.

1968.
D 513. D **130.** 10 l. black on grey 10 10
D 514. 20 l. blk. on blue 10 10
D 515. 50 l. black on pink 10 10
D 516. 60 l. black on grn. 10 10
D 517. 100 l. blk. on buff 10 10
D 518. 180 l. blk. on mve. 10 10

VEGLIA Pt. 8

During the period of D'Annunzio's Italian Regency of Carnaro (Fiume), separate issues were made for the island of Veglia (now Krk).

100 centesimi = 1 lira.

1920. Nos. 146, etc. of Fiume optd. **VEGLIA.**
1. 5 c. green .. .. .. 2·50 2·50
2. 10 c. red .. .. .. 4·50 4·50
3. 20 c. brown .. .. .. 7·50 7·50
4. 25 c. blue .. .. .. 7·50 7·50
5. 50 on 20 c. brown .. .. 7·50 7·50
6. 55 on 5 c. green .. .. 7·50 7·50

EXPRESS LETTER STAMPS

1920. Nos. E 163/4 of Fiume optd. **VEGLIA.**
E 7. 30 c. on 20 c. brown .. 42·00 35·00
E 8 50 on 5 c. green .. .. 32·00 35·00

VENDA Pt. 14

The Republic of Venda was established on 13 September, 1979, being constructed from tribal areas formerly part of the Republic of South Africa.

This independence has not so far received international political recognition. We are satisfied, however, that the stamps have "de facto" acceptance as valid for the carriage of mail outside Venda.

100 cents = 1 rand.

VENDA 4c VHUḒILANGI

1. Flag and Mace.

Venda 1c

2. Cape Honeysuckle.

1979. Independence. Multicoloured.
1. 4 c. Type **1** 25 25
2. 15 c. Government Buildings, Thohoyandou 85 85
3. 20 c. President P. R. Mphephu 1·25 1·25
4. 25 c. Coat of Arms .. .. 1·60 1·60

1979. Flowers. Multicoloured.
5. 1 c. Type **2** 5 5
6. 2 c. "Catophractes alexandri" 5 5
7. 3 c. "Tricliceras longipedunculatum" 5 5
8. 4 c. "Dissotis princeps" .. 8 8
9. 5 c. Barberton Daisy .. 8 8
10. 6 c. "Hibiscus mastersianus" 8 8
11. 7 c. Blue Water Lily .. 10 10
12. 8 c. "Crinum lugardiae" .. 10 10
13. 9 c. Baboon's Tail 12 12
14. 10 c. "Hypoxis angustifolia" 12 12
14a. 11 c. "Combretum microphyllum" 10 12
14b. 12 c. "Clivia caulescens" .. 8 8
15. 15 c. "Pycnostachys urticifolia" 25 25
16. 20 c. Arum Lily 30 30
17. 25 c. "Leonotis mollis" .. 1·25 60
18. 30 c. "Littonia modesta" .. 40 40
19. 50 c. "Protea caffra" .. 30 25
20. 1 r. Impala Lily 60 50
21. 2 r. Transvaal Strelitzia .. 1·40 1·00

Venda woodcarving

3. Man drinking beer.

Tea processing 5c

4. Tea Plants in Nursery.

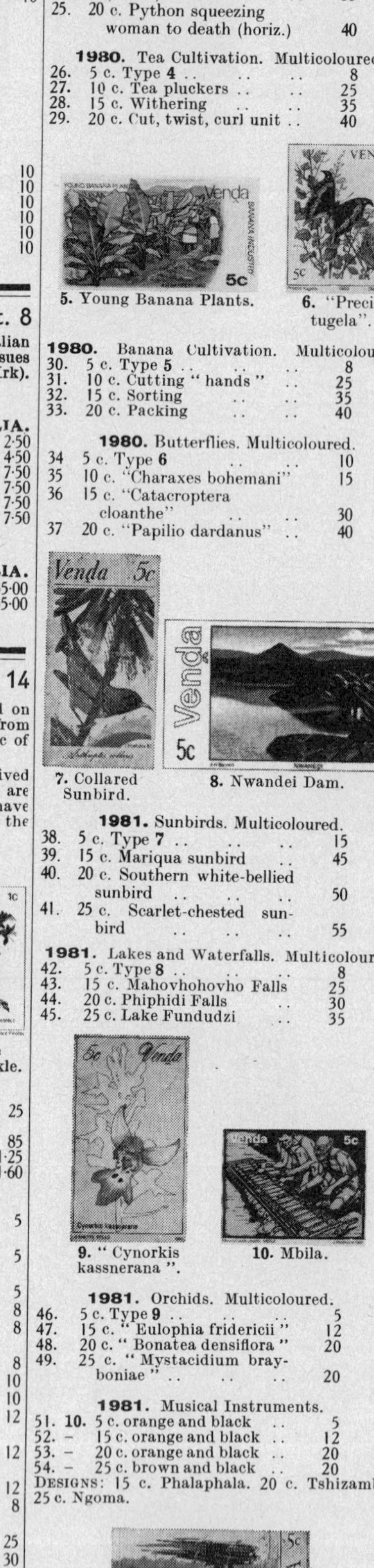

1980. Wood Carving. Multicoloured.
22. 5 c. Type **3** 8 8
23. 10 c. Frying mealies in gourd 25 20
24. 15 c. King Nebuchadnezzar (horiz.) 35 30
25. 20 c. Python squeezing woman to death (horiz.) 40 40

1980. Tea Cultivation. Multicoloured.
26. 5 c. Type **4** 8 8
27. 10 c. Tea pluckers 25 20
28. 15 c. Withering 35 30
29. 20 c. Cut, twist, curl unit .. 40 40

Venda BANANA INDUSTRY 5c

5. Young Banana Plants.

VENDA 5c

6. "Precis tugela".

1980. Banana Cultivation. Multicoloured.
30. 5 c. Type **5** 8 8
31. 10 c. Cutting "hands" .. 25 20
32. 15 c. Sorting 35 30
33. 20 c. Packing 40 40

1980. Butterflies. Multicoloured.
34 5 c. Type **6** 10 8
35 10 c. "Charaxes bohemani" 15 12
36 15 c. "Catacroptera cloanthe" 30 30
37 20 c. "Papilio dardanus" .. 40 35

Venda 5c

7. Collared Sunbird.

Venda 5c

8. Nwandei Dam.

1981. Sunbirds. Multicoloured.
38. 5 c. Type **7** 15 8
39. 15 c. Mariqua sunbird .. 45 35
40. 20 c. Southern white-bellied sunbird 50 30
41. 25 c. Scarlet-chested sunbird 55 40

1981. Lakes and Waterfalls. Multicoloured.
42. 5 c. Type **8** 8 8
43. 15 c. Mahovhohovho Falls 25 25
44. 20 c. Phiphidi Falls .. 30 30
45. 25 c. Lake Fundudzi .. 35 35

5c Venda

9. "Cynorkis kassnerana".

Venda 5c

10. Mbila.

1981. Orchids. Multicoloured.
46. 5 c. Type **9** 5 5
47. 15 c. "Eulophia fridericii" 12 12
48. 20 c. "Bonatea densiflora" 20 20
49. 25 c. "Mystacidium braybonae" 20 20

1981. Musical Instruments.
51. **10.** 5 c. orange and black .. 5 5
52. – 15 c. orange and black .. 12 12
53. – 20 c. orange and black .. 20 20
54. – 25 c. brown and black .. 20 20
DESIGNS: 15 c. Phalaphala. 20 c. Tshizambi. 25 c. Ngoma.

5c VENDA

11. Gathering Sisal.

1982. Sisal Cultivation. Multicoloured.
55. 5 c. Type **11** 5 5
56. 10 c. Drying 10 10
57. 20 c. Grading 20 20
58. 25 c. Baling 25 25

12. Bison Petrograph, Spain.

1982. History of Writing (1st series). Multicoloured.
59. 8 c. Type **12** 8 8
60. 15 c. Petroglyph, Eastern California 15 15
61. 20 c. Pictograph Script (Sumerian tablet) .. 20 20
62. 25 c. Bushman burial stone, Humansdorp 25 25
See also Nos. 75/8, 87/90, 107/10, 139/42, 171/4 and 203/6.

13. "Euphorbia ingens".

1982. Indigenous Trees (1st series). Mult.
63. 8 c. Type **13** 8 8
64. 15 c. "Pterocarpus angolensis" 15 15
65. 20 c. "Ficus ingens" .. 20 20
66. 25 c. "Andansonia digitata" 25 25
See also Nos. 79/82, 95/8 and 227/30.

14. "Rana angolensis".

1982. Frogs. Multicoloured.
67. 8 c. Type **14** 8 8
68. 15 c. "Chiromantis xerampelina" 15 15
69. 20 c. "Leptopelis sp" .. 20 20
70. 25 c. "Ptychadena anchietae" 25 25

15. European Bee Eater.

1983. Migratory Birds. Multicoloured.
71. 8 c. Type **15** 20 15
72. 20 c. Tawny Eagle 60 45
73. 25 c. Violet Starling .. 70 50
74. 40 c. Abdim's Stork .. 1·25 90

1983. History of Writing (2nd series). As T **12**. Multicoloured.
75. 10 c. Indus Valley script .. 10 10
76. 20 c. Sumerian cuneiform .. 20 20
77. 25 c. Egyptian hieroglyphics 25 25
73. 40 c. Chinese handscroll .. 45 45

1983. Indigenous Trees (2nd series). Multicoloured.
79. 10 c. "Gardenia spatulifolia" 10 10
80. 20 c. "Hyphaene natalensis" 20 20
81. 25 c. "Albizia adianthifolia" 25 25
82. 40 c. "Sesamothamnus lugardii" 45 45

16. Avocado.

17. African Paradise Flycatcher.

1983. Subtropical Fruit. Multicoloured.
83. 10 c. Type **16** 10 10
84. 20 c. Mango 20 20
85. 25 c. Papaya 25 25
86. 40 c. Litchi 45 45

1983. History of Writing (3rd series). Multicoloured.
87. 10 c. Evolution of cuneiform sign 10 10
88. 20 c. Evolution of Chinese character 20 20
89. 25 c. Development of Cretan hieroglyphics .. 25 25
90. 40 c. Development of Egyptian hieroglyphics 45 45

1984. Migratory Birds (2nd series). Mult.
91. 11 c. White stork 20 15
92. 20 c. Type **17** 35 30
93. 25 c. Black kite 45 40
94. 30 c. Wood sandpiper 60 55

1984. Indigenous Trees (3rd series). As T **13**. Multicoloured.
95. 11 c. "Afzelia quanzensis" 10 10
96. 20 c. "Peltophorum africanum" 15 15
97. 25 c. "Gyrocarpus americanus" 15 15
98. 30 c. "Acacia sieberana" .. 35 35

18. Dzata Ruins, Nzhelele Valley.

19. White-browed Robin Chat.

1984. 5th Anniv. of Independence. Mult.
99. 11 c. Type **18** 10 10
100. 25 c. Traditional hut 15 15
101. 30 c. Sub-economical house 25 25
102. 45 c. Modern home .. 35 35

1985. Songbirds. Multicoloured.
103. 11 c. Type **19** (inscr "Heuglin's Robin") 20 15
104. 25 c. Black-collared barbet 25 25
105. 30 c. African black-headed oriole 45 40
106. 50 c. Kurrichane thrush .. 70 65

1985. History of Writing (4th series). As T **12**. Multicoloured.
107. 11 c. Southern Arabic characters 10 10
108. 25 c. Phoenician characters 15 15
109. 30 c. Aramaic characters .. 25 25
110. 50 c. Canaanite characters 40 40

20. Transvaal Red Milkwood.

21. "Pellaea dura".

1985. Food from the Veldt. Multicoloured.
111. 12 c. Type **20** 8 8
112. 25 c. Buffalo thorn .. 15 15
113. 30 c. Wild water melon .. 20 20
114. 50 c. Brown ivory 35 35

1985. Ferns. Multicoloured.
115. 12 c. Type **21** 8 8
116. 25 c. "Actiniopteris radiata" 15 15
117. 30 c. "Adiantum hispidulum" 20 20
118. 50 c. "Polypodium polypodioides" 35 35

22. Three-lined Grass Snake.

23. Etruscan Dish.

1986. Reptiles. Multicoloured.
119 1 c. Type **22** 5 5
120 2 c. Mole snake 5 5
121 3 c. Ornate scrub lizard .. 5 5
122 4 c. Puff adder 5 5
123 5 c. Three-lined skink .. 5 5
124 6 c. Egyptian cobra .. 5 5
125 7 c. Blue-tailed kopje skink 5 5
126 8 c. Spotted bush snake 5 5
127 9 c. Yellow-throated plated lizard 8 8
128 10 c. Northern lined shovelsnout 8 8
129 14 c. Transvaal flat lizard 10 10
130 15 c. Soutpansberg lizard 10 10
131 16 c. Iguana water leguan 10 10
132 18 c. Black mamba .. 10 10
133 20 c. Transvaal flat gecko 15 15
133a 21 c. Flap-necked chameleon 15 15
134 25 c. Longtailed garter snake 20 20
135 30 c. Tigroid thick-toed gecko 20 20
136 50 c. Cape file snake .. 35 35
137 1 r. Soutpansberg girdled lizard 70 70
138 2 r. African python .. 1·40 1·40

1986. History of Writing (5th series). Multicoloured.
139. 14 c. Type **23** 10 10
140. 20 c. Greek inscription, AD 70 .. .. 15 15
141. 25 c. Roman inscription .. 20 20
142. 30 c. Cyrillic inscription (Byzantine mosaic) .. 20 20

24. Planting Pine Seedlings.

26. Comb Duck.

25. Maxwell, 1910.

1986. Forestry. Multicoloured.
143. 14 c. Type **24** 10 10
144. 20 c. Mule hauling logs .. 12 12
145. 25 c. Off-loading logs at sawmill 15 15
146. 30 c. Using timber in construction 20 20

1986. FIVA International Veteran Car Rally. Multicoloured.
147. 14 c. Type **25** 10 10
148. 20 c. Bentley 4½ l., 1929 .. 12 12
149. 25 c. Plymouth Coupe, 1933 15 15
150. 30 c. Mercedes Cabriolet, 1958 .. .. .. 20 20

1987. Waterfowl. Multicoloured.
151. 14 c. Type **26** 25 20
152. 20 c. White-faced whistling duck 30 25
153. 25 c. Spur-winged goose (horiz.) 40 30
154. 30 c. Egyptian goose (horiz.) 50 40

27. "Iron Master".

28. Tigerfish.

1987. Wood Sculptures by Meshack Matamela Raphalalani. Multicoloured.
155. 16 c. Type **27** 8 8
156. 20 c. "Distant Drums" .. 12 12
157. 25 c. "Sunrise" 15 15
158. 30 c. "Obedience" 15 15

1987. Freshwater Fish. Multicoloured.
159. 16 c. Type **28** 8 8
160. 20 c. Barred minnow .. 12 12
161. 25 c. Mozambique tilapia 15 15
162. 30 c. Sharptooth catfish .. 15 15

29. Cross-berry.

30. Picking Berries.

1987. Food from the Veldt. Multicoloured.
163. 16 c. Type **29** 8 8
164. 30 c. Wild date palm .. 15 15
165. 40 c. Tree fuchsia 25 25
166. 50 c. Wild cucumber .. 30 30

1988. Coffee Industry. Multicoloured.
167. 16 c. Type **30** 8 8
168. 30 c. Weighing bags of berries 15 15
169. 40 c. Drying beans in sun 25 25
170. 50 c. Roasting graded beans 30 30

31 "Universal Love" in Chinese

1988. History of Writing (6th series).
171 **31** 16 c. stone, blk & red .. 8 8
172 – 30 c. stone, blk & red .. 15 15
173 – 40 c. stone, blk & red .. 20 20
174 – 50 c. black and gold .. 25 25
DESIGNS: 30 c. "Picture of a lion on a stone" in Devanagari (Indian script); 40 c. "Information" in Russian; 50 c. "Peace be upon you" in Thuluth (Arabic script).

32 College

1988. 5th Anniv of Shayandima Nurses' Training College. Multicoloured.
175 16 c. Type **32** 8 8
176 30 c. Students using microscope 15 15
177 40 c. Anatomy class .. 20 20
178 50 c. Clinical training .. 25 25

33 "Fetching Water"

1988. Watercolours by Kenneth Thabo. Mult.
179 16 c. Type **33** 8 8
180 30 c. "Grinding Maize" .. 15 15
181 40 c. "Offering Food" .. 20 20
182 50 c. "Kindling the Fire" 25 25

34 Ndongwana (clay bowls)

1989. Traditional Kitchenware. Mult.
183 16 c. Type **34** 8 8
184 30 c. Ndilo (wooden porridge bowls) .. 15 15
185 40 c. Mufaro (basket with lid) 20 20
186 50 c. Muthatha (dish woven from ilala palm) 25 25

35 Domba

36 Southern Ground Hornbill

1989. Traditional Dances. Multicoloured.
187 18 c. Type **35** 8 8
188 30 c. Tshinzerere 15 15
189 40 c. Malende 20 20
190 50 c. Malombo 25 25

1989. Endangered Birds. Multicoloured.

191	18 c. Type **36**	15	15
192	30 c. Lappet-faced vulture	25	25
193	40 c. Bateleur	35	35
194	50 c. Martial eagle	40	40

37 Pres. Gota F. N. Ravele

38 Lion

1989. 10th Anniv of Independence. Mult.

195	18 c. Type **37**	10	10
196	30 c. Presidential offices	15	15
197	40 c. President's residence	20	20
198	50 c. Thohoyandou Sports Stadium	25	25

1990. Nwanedi National Park. Multicoloured.

199	18 c. Type **38**	10	10
200	30 c. Common zebra	15	15
201	40 c. Cheetah	20	20
202	50 c. White rhinoceros	25	25

39 Calligraphy

40 "Aloe globuligemma"

1990. History of Writing (7th series).

203	**39**	21 c. black and grey	10	10
204	–	30 c. black and brown	10	10
205	–	40 c. black and green	15	15
206	–	50 c. dp blue, blue & blk	20	20

DESIGNS: 30 c. Part of score for Beethoven's "Moonlight Sonata"; 40 c. Characters from personal computer; 50 c. Television picture of message transmitted into outer space from Arecibo 1000 radio telescope.

1990. Aloes. Multicoloured.

207	21 c. Type **40**	10	10
208	35 c. "Aloe aculeata"	15	15
209	40 c. "Aloe lutescens"	15	15
210	50 c. "Aloe angelica"	20	20

41 "Pseudacraea boisduvali"

42 Cape Puff-back Flycatchers

1990. Butterflies. Multicoloured.

211	21 c. Type **41**	10	10
212	35 c. "Papilio nireus"	15	15
213	40 c. "Charaxes jasius"	20	20
214	50 c. "Aeropetes tulbaghia"	25	25

1991. Birds. Paintings by Claude Gibney Finch-Davies. Multicoloured.

215	21 c. Type **42**	20	20
216	35 c. Red-capped robin chat	30	30
217	40 c. Collared sunbirds	30	30
218	50 c. Yellow-streaked greenbul	40	40

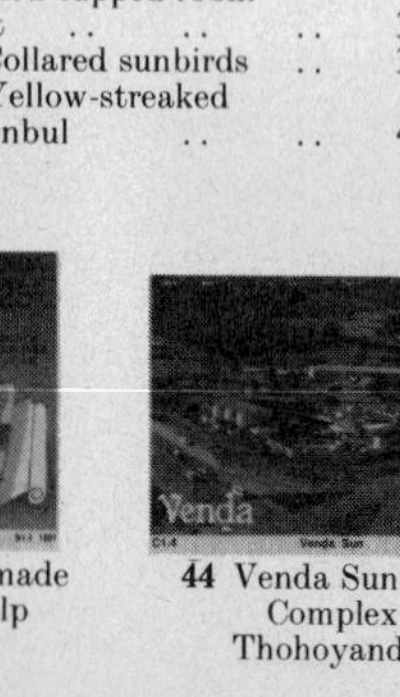

43 Paper made from Pulp

44 Venda Sun Hotel Complex, Thohoyandou

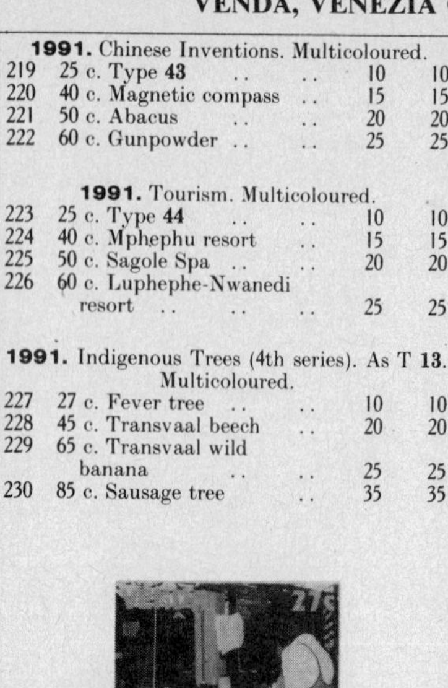

1991. Chinese Inventions. Multicoloured.

219	25 c. Type **43**	10	10
220	40 c. Magnetic compass	15	15
221	50 c. Abacus	20	20
222	60 c. Gunpowder	25	25

1991. Tourism. Multicoloured.

223	25 c. Type **44**	10	10
224	40 c. Mphephu resort	15	15
225	50 c. Sagole Spa	20	20
226	60 c. Luphephe-Nwanedi resort	25	25

1991. Indigenous Trees (4th series). As T **13**. Multicoloured.

227	27 c. Fever tree	10	10
228	45 c. Transvaal beech	20	20
229	65 c. Transvaal wild banana	25	25
230	85 c. Sausage tree	35	35

45 Setting the Web

1992. Clothing Factory. Multicoloured.

231	27 c. Type **45**	10	10
232	45 c. Knitting	20	20
233	65 c. Making up garment	25	25
234	85 c. Inspection of finished product	35	35

46 Honey Bee

1992. Bees. Multicoloured.

235	35 c. Type **46**	15	15
236	70 c. Carder bee	30	30
237	90 c. Leafcutter bee	40	40
238	1 r. 05 Carpenter bee	45	45

47 Egyptian Plough

1992. Inventions. Multicoloured.

239	35 c. Type **47**	15	15
240	70 c. Early wheel, Mesopotamia	30	30
241	90 c. Making bricks, Egypt	40	40
242	1 r. 05 Early Egyptian sailing ship	45	45

48 Nile Crocodile

1992. Crocodile Farming. Multicoloured.

243	35 c. Type **48**	15	15
244	70 c. Egg laying	30	30
245	90 c. Eggs hatching	40	40
246	1 r. 05 Mother carrying young	45	45

49 Burmese

1993. Domestic Cats. Multicoloured.

247	45 c. Type **49**	15	15
248	65 c. Tabby	25	25
249	85 c. Siamese	30	30
250	1 r. 05 Persian	40	40

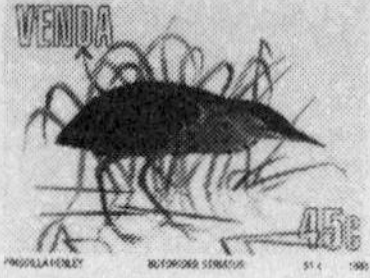

50 Green Heron

51 Punching out Sole Lining

1993. Herons. Multicoloured.

251	45 c. Type **50**	15	15
252	65 c. Black-crowned night heron	25	25
253	85 c. Purple heron	30	30
254	1 r. 05 Black-headed heron	40	40

1993. Shoe Factory. Multicoloured.

255	45 c. Type **51**	15	15
256	65 c. Shaping heel	25	25
257	85 c. Joining the upper to inner sole	30	30
258	1 r. 05 Forming sole	40	40

52 Axes

1993. Inventions. Multicoloured.

259	45 c. Type **52**	15	15
260	65 c. Armour	25	25
261	85 c. Arches	30	30
262	1 r. 05 Pont du Gard aqueduct	40	40

53 Cocker Spaniel

1994. Dogs. Multicoloured.

263	45 c. Type **53**	15	15
264	65 c. Maltese	25	25
265	85 c. Scottish terrier	30	30
266	1 r. 05 Miniature schnauzer	40	40

54 Savanna Monkey

1994. Monkeys. Multicoloured.

267	45 c. Type **54**	15	15
268	65 c. Lesser bushbaby	25	25
269	85 c. Diademed monkey	30	30
270	1 r. 05 Thick-tailed bush-baby	40	40

VENEZIA GIULIA AND ISTRIA Pt. 3

Formerly part of Italy. Stamps issued during Allied occupation, 1945-47. The Peace Treaty of 1947 established the Free Territory of Trieste (q.v.) and gave the rest of the territory to Yugoslavia.

For stamps of Austria overprinted Venezia Giulia see under Italian Austria.

100 centesimi = 1 lira.

A. YUGOSLAV OCCUPATION PROVISIONAL ISSUES

Issue for Trieste.

1945. Stamps of Italian Social Republic 1944, surch **1.V.1945 TRIESTE TRST,** five-pointed star and value.

4	–	20 c.+1 l. on 5 c. brown (No. 106)	10	30
5	**13**	+1 l. on 25 c. green	10	30
6	–	+1 l. on 30 c. brown (No. 110)	10	30
7	–	+1 l. on 50 c. violet (No. 111)	10	30
8	–	+1 l. on 1 l. violet (No. 113)	10	30
9	–	+2 l. on 1 l. 25 blue (No. 114)	10	30
2	**12**	2+2 l. on 25 c. green	10	15
10	–	+2 l. on 3 l. green (No. 115)	10	30
11	–	5+5 l. on 1 l. violet (No. 113)	10	30
12	–	10+10 l. on 30 c. brown (No. 110)	70	1·10
13	–	20+20 l. on 5 c. brown (No. 106)	1·50	2·25

Issue for Istria.

In 1945 various stamps of Italy were overprinted "ISTRA" and further surcharged for use in Istria and Pola but they were not issued. However, four of these were further surcharged and issued later.

1945. Stamps of Italy (No. 14) or Italian Social Republic (others) surch. **ISTRA** with new value and bars obliterating old surch.

14.	**99.**	4 l. on 2 l. on 1 l. (No. 249) violet	15	30
15.	–	6 l. on 1.50 l. on 75 c. (No. 112) red	2·00	2·75
16.	–	10 l. on 0.10 l. on 5 c. (No. 106) brown	8·00	10·00
17.	**103.**	20 l. on 1 l. on 50 c. (No. 59) violet	3·00	3·50

Issue for Fiume.

1945. Stamps of Italian Social Republic 1944, surch. **3-V-1945 FIUME RIJEKA,** five-pointed star over rising sun and new value.

18.	**12.**	2 l. on 25 c. green	10	30
20.	–	4 l. on 1 l. vio. (No. 113)	10	30
21.	–	5 l. on 10 c. brn. (No. 107)	10	30
22.	–	6 l. on 10 c. brn. (No. 107)	10	30
23.	**13.**	10 l. on 25 c. green	10	30
19.	–	16 l. on 75 c. red (No. 112)	2·75	3·50
25.	E **16.**	20 l. on 1 l. 25 c. green	40	75

B. ALLIED MILITARY GOVERNMENT

1945. Stamps of Italy optd. **A.M.G. V.G.** in two lines.

(a) Imperial Series.

26	–	10 c. brown (No. 241) (post.)	15	15
27	–	10 c. brown (No. 633)	15	15
28	**99**	20 c. red (No. 243)	15	30
29		20 c. red (No. 640)	15	15
31	–	60 c. orange (No. 636)	15	15
32	**103**	60 c. green (No. 641)	15	15
33	**99**	1 l. violet (No. 642)	20	15
34	–	2 l. red (No. 644)	20	15
35	**98**	5 l. red (No. 645)	40	25
36	–	10 l. violet (No. 646)	50	70
37	**99**	20 l. green (No. 257)	1·25	1·90

(b) Stamps of 1945-48.

38.	–	25 c. turquoise (No. 649)	15	20
39.	–	2 l. brown (No. 656)	35	40
40.	–	3 l. red (No. 657)	25	15
41.	–	4 l. red (No. 658)	40	20
42.	**195.**	6 l. violet (No. 660)	1·10	1·40
43.	–	20 l. purple (No. 665)	20·00	1·00
44.	**196.**	25 l. green (No. 666)	2·50	3·50
45.		50 l. purple (No. 668)	3·00	4·25
46.	**197.**	100 l. red (No. 669)	10·00	14·00

1945. Air stamps of Italy, optd as above.

47	**110**	50 c. brown (No. 271)	15	25
48	**198**	1 l. slate (No. 670)	20	25
49	–	2 l. blue (No. 671)	15	25
50	–	5 l. green (No. 673)	1·10	1·40
51	**198**	10 l. red (No. 674)	1·10	1·40
52	–	25 l. blue (No. 675)	1·10	1·40
53	–	25 l. brown (No. 676)	10·00	12·00
54	**198**	50 l. green (No. 677)	2·00	3·00

EXPRESS LETTER STAMPS

1946. Express Letter Stamps of Italy optd. **A.M.G. V.G.** in two lines.

E 55.	–	10 l. blue (No. E 680)	2·00	2·75
E 56.	E **200.**	30 l. vio. (No. E 683)	5·00	7·50

C. YUGOSLAV MILITARY GOVERNMENT

6. Grapes.

7. Roman Amphitheatre, Pula.

8. Tunny.

1945. Inscr. "ISTRA SLOVENSKO PRIMORJE — ISTRIA LITTORALE SLOVENO".

74 6 0.25 l. green 10 10
58 – 0.50 l. brown 10 10
59 – 1 l. red 10 10
76 – 1 l. green 10 10
77 – 1.50 l. olive 10 10
61 – 2 l. green 10 10
100 – 3 l. red 15 10
62 7 4 l. blue 10 10
79 4 l. red 10 10
80 – 5 l. black 10 10
101 7 6 l. blue 20 15
81 – 10 l. brown 10 10
65 8 20 l. purple .. .. 2·25 2·25
82 . 20 l. blue .. .. 1·00 30
66 – 30 l. mauve .. .. 1·50 1·50

Designs—As Type 6: 0.50 l. Donkey and view. 1 l. Rebuilding damaged homes. 150 l. Olive branch. 2, 3 l. Duino Castle near Trieste. As Type 7: 5 l. Birthplace of Vladimir Gortan at Piran. 10 l. Ploughing. As Type 8: 30 l. Viaduct over the Solkan.

1946. Nos. 82 and 66 surch.

96 8 1 on 20 l. blue 30 15
97 – 2 on 30 l. mauve .. .. 2·75 2·25

1947. As Nos. 514 and O 540 of Yugoslavia with colours changed, surch. **VOJNA UPRAVA JUGOSLAVENSKE ARMIJE** and new value.

102. 1 l. on 9 d. pink .. 10 10
103. 1.50 l. on 50 p. blue .. 10 10
104. 2 l. on 9 d. pink .. 10 10
105. 3 l. on 50 p. blue .. 10 10
106. 5 l. on 9 d. pink .. 10 10
107. 6 l. on 50 p. blue .. 10 10
108. 10 l. on 9 d. pink .. 10 10
109. 15 l. on 50 p. blue .. 10 10
110. 35 l. on 9 d. pink .. 10 10
111. 50 l. on 50 p. blue .. 10 10

POSTAGE DUE STAMPS

1945. Stamps of 1945 surch. **PORTO** and value in "Lit".

D 72. 8. 0.50 l. on 20 l. purple .. 20 20
D 67. 6. 1 l. on 0.25 l. green .. 1·00 40
D 73. – 2 l. on 30 l. mauve .. 50 50
D 68. – 4 l. on 0.50 l. brown .. 30 15
D 69. – 8 l. on 0.50 l. brown .. 30 15
D 70. – 10 l. on 0.50 l. brown .. 1·00 40
D 71. – 20 l. on 0.50 l. brown .. 1·25 60

1946. Stamps of 1945 surch **PORTO** and value expressed in "Lira".

D90 6 1 l. on 0.25 l. green .. 10 10
D84 – 1 l. on 1 l. green (No. 76) 10 10
D91 6 2 l. on 0.25 l. green .. 10 10
D85 – 2 l. on 1 l. green (No. 76) 10 10
D92 6 4 l. on 0.25 l. green .. 10 10
D86 – 4 l. on 1 l. green (No. 76) 10 15
D93 8 10 l. on 20 l. blue .. 30 15
D87 – 10 l. on 30 l. mauve (No. 66) .. .. .. 2·00 1·50
D94 8 20 l. on 20 l. blue .. 1·50 55
D88 – 20 l. on 30 l. mauve (No. 66) .. .. .. 3·25 2·75
D95 8 30 l. on 20 l. blue .. 1·50 55
D89 – 30 l. on 30 l. mauve (No. 66) .. .. .. 3·25 2·75

1947. No. D 528 of Yugoslavia with colour changed and surch. **Vojna Uprava Jugoslavenske Armije** and value.

D 112. 1 l. on 1 d. green .. 10 10
D 113. 2 l. on 1 d. green .. 10 10
D 114. 6 l. on 1 d. green .. 10 10
D 115. 10 l. on 1 d. green .. 10 10
D 116. 30 l. on 1 d. green .. 10 10

VENEZUELA Pt. 20

A republic in the N. of S. America, independent since 1811.

1859. 100 centavos=8 reales=1 peso.
1879. 100 centesimos=1 venezolano.
1880. 100 centimos=1 bolivar.

1. 2. 3.

1859. Imperf.

7. 1. ½ r. orange .. .. 6·75 2·50
8. 1 r. blue .. .. 11·50 7·25
3. 2 r. red .. .. 27·00 9·25

1862. Imperf.

13. 2. ¼ c. green .. .. 11·50 65·00
14. ½ c. lilac .. .. 19·00 £120
15. 1 c. brown .. .. 27·00 £140

1863. Imperf.

16. 3. ½ c. red .. .. 32·00 55·00
17a. 1 c. grey .. .. 38·00 60·00
21. ½ r. yellow .. .. 2·50 1·50
19. 1 r. blue .. .. 11·00 5·00
20. 2 r. green .. .. 15·00 13·50

4. 5. Bolivar. 7.

1866. Imperf.

22. 4. ½ c. green £140 £200
23. 1 c. green £140 £170
24. ½ r. red .. .. 5·50 1·60
26. 1 r. red .. .. 27·00 10·00
27a. 2 r. yellow .. .. 90·00 50·00

1871. Optd with inscription in very small letters. Imperf.

58 5. 1 c. yellow 65 30
59d 2 c. yellow .. .. 1·00 35
60 3 c. yellow .. .. 1·60 40
61 4 c. yellow .. .. 2·00 40
62b 5 c. yellow .. .. 2·00 40
63b 1 r. red .. .. 2·00 30
64a 2 r. red .. .. 3·25 75
65a 3 r. red .. .. 3·75 75
66a 5 r. red .. .. 3·75 85
52a 7 r. red .. .. 4·50 1·60
53a 9 r. green .. .. 11·50 3·00
54 15 r. green .. .. 23·00 6·25
68 20 r. green .. .. 55·00 10·50
56 30 r. green .. .. £250 85·00
70 50 r. green £850 £225

1873. Optd. with inscription in very small letters. Imperf.

74a. 4. 1 c. lilac .. .. 4·50 12·50
75a. 2 c. green .. .. 27·00 35·00
76a. ½ r. pink .. .. 19·00 2·50
77a. 1 r. red .. .. 23·00 6·25
78a. 2 r. yellow .. .. 80·00 32·00

1879. New Currency. Optd. with inscription in small letters. Imperf.

83. 7. 1 c. yellow .. .. 2·00 15
84. 5 c. yellow .. .. 3·00 30
85. 10 c. blue .. .. 4·25 40
86. 30 c. blue .. .. 5·25 1·00
87. 50 c. blue .. .. 6·25 1·00
88. 90 c. blue .. .. 25·00 5·25
89. 1 v. red .. .. 55·00 7·25
90. 3 v. red .. .. 90·00 29·00
91. 5 v. red .. .. £160 55·00

1880. New Currency. Without opt. Perf.

92. 7. 5 c. yellow .. .. 1·00 15
93. 10 c. yellow .. .. 1·60 15
94. 25 c. yellow .. .. 1·50 20
95. 50 c. yellow .. .. 3·00 25
96. 1 b. blue .. .. 7·25 60
97. 2 b. blue .. .. 11·50 70
98. 5 b. blue .. .. 27·00 60
99. 10 b. red .. .. £140 45·00
100. 20 b. red £850 £140
101. 25 b. red £3500 £425

8. 9. Bolivar. 10.

1880.

107 8. 5 c. blue .. .. 6·25 3·25
108 10 c. red .. .. 10·50 6·25
109 25 c. yellow .. .. 6·25 3·25
110 50 c. brown .. .. 32·00 17·00
106 1 b. green .. .. 50·00 25·00

1882. Various frames. Perf. or roul.

111. 9. 5 c. green 10 10
112. 10 c. brown 10 10
113. 25 c. orange 10 10
114. 50 c. blue 15 10
115. 1 b. red 20 10
116. 3 b. violet 20 30
117. 10 b. brown 40 50
118. 20 b. purple 55 55

1882. Various frames. Perf. or roul.

119. 10. 5 c. blue 20 10
120. 10 c. brown 20 10
121. 25 c. brown 40 20
122. 50 c. green .. .. 1·25 25
123. 1 b. violet .. .. 2·10 70

1892. Surch. **RESOLUCION DE 10 DE OCTUBRE DE 1892** and value in circle.

134. 9. 25 c. on 5 c. green .. 8·25 5·00
138. 10. 25 c. on 5 c. blue .. 25·00 25·00
135. 9. 25 c. on 10 c. brown .. 8·25 5·00
139. 10. 25 c. on 10 c. brown .. 10·00 10·00
136. 9. 1 b. on 25 c. orange .. 10·50 5·75
140. 10. 1 b. on 25 c. brown .. 10·00 10·00
137. 9. 1 b. on 50 c. blue .. 14·50 5·75
141. 10. 1 b. on 50 c. green .. 11·00 11·00

1893. Optd. with coat of arms and diagonal shading.

142. 9. 5 c. green 10 10
150. 10. 5 c. blue 20 10
143. 9. 10 c. brown 10 10
151. 10. 10 c. brown 55 65
144. 9. 25 c. orange 10 10
152. 10. 25 c. brown 35 25
145. 9. 50 c. blue 10 10
153. 10. 50 c. green 50 20
146. 9. 1 b. red 55 20
154. 10. 1 b. violet .. .. 1·25 50
147. 9. 3 b. violet 50 35
148. 10 b. brown .. .. 1·50 1·25
149. 20 b. purple .. .. 1·25 1·25

13. Bolivar. 14. Bolivar.

1893. Schools Tax stamps.

155. 13. 5 c. grey 10 10
156. 10 c. green 10 10
157. 25 c. blue 10 10
158. 50 c. orange 10 10
159. 1 b. purple 30 10
160. 3 b. red 45 20
161. 10 b. violet 55 60
162. 20 b. brown .. .. 1·60 1·50

See also Nos. 227/35.

1893.

163. 14. 5 c. brown 60 10
164. 10 c. blue .. .. 2·10 65
165. 25 c. mauve .. .. 10·00 20
166. 50 c. purple .. .. 2·10 20
167. 1 b. green .. .. 2·75 65

15. Landing of Columbus.

1893. Columbian Exposition, Chicago, and 400th Anniv of Discovery of America by Columbus.

168. 15. 25 c. purple .. .. 6·75 40

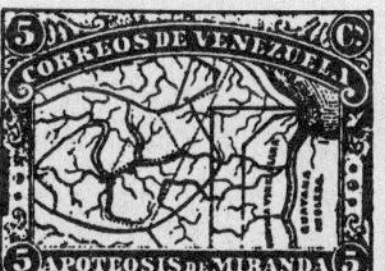

16. Map of Venezuela. 18. Bolivar.

1896. 80th Death Anniv. of Gen. Miranda.

169. 16. 5 c. green .. .. 2·10 1·60
170. 10 c. blue .. .. 2·10 1·60
171. 25 c. yellow .. .. 2·50 3·25
172. 50 c. red .. .. 32·00 17·00
173. 1 b. mauve .. .. 25·00 17·00

1899.

179. 18. 5 c. green 65 15
180. 10 c. red 85 15
181. 25 c. blue .. .. 1·00 50
182. 50 c. black .. .. 1·25 60
183. 50 c. orange .. .. 1·00 30
184. 1 b. green .. .. 21·00 10·50
185. 2 b. yellow £250 £160

(21). "R.T.M." = Ramon Tellos Mendoza, Minister of Interior. (23).

1900. Stamps of 1893 optd. with T 21.

191. 13. 5 c. grey 10 10
192. 10 c. green 10 10
193. 25 c. blue 10 10
194. 50 c. orange 10 10
195. 1 b. purple 20 10
196. 3 b. red 30 10
197. 10 b. violet 65 40
198. 20 b. brown .. .. 4·25 4·25

1900. Stamps of 1899 optd. with T 21.

199. 18. 5 c. green 60 30
200. 10 c. red 60 35
201. 25 c. blue .. .. 4·25 60
202. 50 c. black .. .. 2·10 50
203. 1 b. green 85 40
204. 2 b. yellow .. .. 1·50 1·00

1900. Stamps of 1893 optd. **1900.** Colours changed.

206. 13. 5 c. orange 10 10
207. 10 c. blue 10 10
208. 25 c. purple 10 10
209. 50 c. green 60 10
210. 1 b. black .. .. 4·75 55
211. 3 b. brown .. .. 1·25 60
212. 10 b. red .. .. 5·00 1·40
213. 20 b. violet .. .. 10·00 2·75

1900. Stamps of 1899 optd. **1900.**

214. 18. 5 c. green £120 £120
215. 10 c. red £120 £120
216. 25 c. blue £250 £120
217. 50 c. orange .. .. 15·00 85
218. 1 b. black 85 60

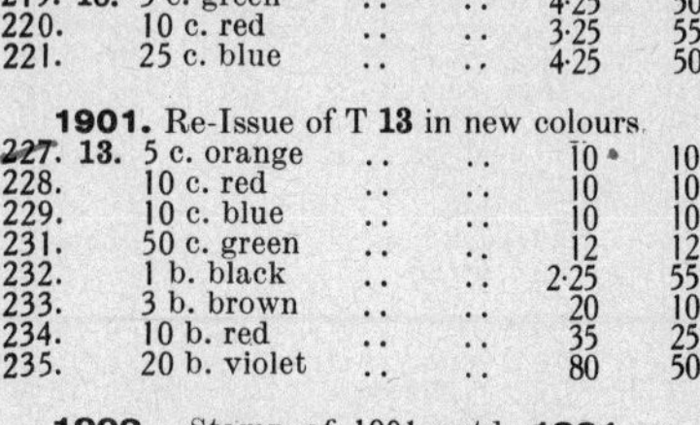

1900. Stamps of 1899 optd. with T 23.

219. 18. 5 c. green .. .. 4·25 50
220. 10 c. red .. .. 3·25 55
221. 25 c. blue .. .. 4·25 50

1901. Re-Issue of T 13 in new colours.

227. 13. 5 c. orange 10 10
228. 10 c. red 10 10
229. 10 c. blue 10 10
231. 50 c. green 12 12
232. 1 b. black .. .. 2·25 55
233. 3 b. brown 20 10
234. 10 b. red 35 25
235. 20 b. violet 80 50

1902. Stamp of 1901 optd. **1901.**

236. 13. 1 b. black 45 30

1904. No. 231 surch. **CORREOS Vale B 0,05 1904.**

310. 13. 5 c. on 50 c. green .. 40 55

38. General Sucre. 39. Bolivar.

1904.

311. 38. 5 c. green 40 15
312. 10 c. red 25 15
313. 15 c. violet 45 30
314. 25 c. blue .. .. 3·25 30
315. 50 c. red 45 40
316. 1 b. red 50 40

1904.

317. 39. 5 c. green 8 8
318. 10 c. grey 8 8
319. 25 c. red 10 10
320. 50 c. yellow 10 10
321. 1 b. red .. .. 1·90 25
322. 3 b. blue 35 15
323. 10 b. violet 45 25
324. 20 b. red .. .. 1·10 35

41. President Castro. 42. Liberty.

1905. 6th Anniv. of General Castro's Revolt.

330 41. 5 c. red .. .. 2·10 2·10
331a 10 c. blue .. .. 3·25 2·75
332a 25 c. yellow .. .. 1·00 1·00

1910. Independence Cent.

333. 42. 25 c. blue .. .. 8·25 45

43. F. de Miranda. 44. 46. Bolivar.

1911. Portraits as T 43.

340 43. 5 c. green 25 12
341 10 c. red 35 5
342 – 15 c. grey (Urdaneta) .. 3·25 20
343 – 25 c. blue (Urdaneta) .. 1·60 25
344 – 50 c. violet (Bolivar) .. 2·10 25
339 – 1 b. orange (Bolivar) .. 2·10 1·00

1911. Portraits as T 44.

345. – 5 c. blue (Vargas) .. 8 8
346. – 10 c. yellow (Avila) .. 8 8
347. – 25 c. grey (Sanz) .. 8 8
348. 44. 50 c. red (Blanco) .. 8 8
349. – 1 b. green (Bello) .. 8 8
350. – 2 b. brown (Sanabria) .. 55 35
351. – 3 b. violet (Paez) .. 55 25
352. – 10 b. purple (Sucre) .. 1·10 50
353. – 20 b. blue (Bolivar) .. 1·10 70

1914.

359. 46. 5 c. green .. .. 20·00 25
360. 10 c. red .. .. 17·00 40
361. 25 c. blue .. .. 3·25 20

47. Bolivar. 48. Bolivar and Sucre.

1915. Various frames.
362a 47. 5 c. green .. .. 2·75 25
379 5 c. brown 55 10
570 7½ c. green 60 35
571 10 c. red .. .. 2·10 30
380 10 c. green 20 10
381 15 c. olive .. .. 1·25 50
382 15 c. brown 30 10
383 25 c. blue .. .. 1·25 10
384 25 c. red 20 10
368 40 c. green .. .. 14·50 6·25
385 40 c. blue 55 20
369 50 c. violet .. .. 3·75 40
386 50 c. blue 55 20
371 75 c. turquoise .. 38·00 12·50
387 1 b. black 55 25
388 3 b. orange .. .. 8·25 2·75
389 5 b. violet .. .. 10·00 5·50
See also Nos. 414/25.

1924. Cent. of Battle of Ayacucho.
390. 48. 25 c. blue .. .. 1·90 35

1926. Fiscal stamps surch. **CORREOS VALE 1926** and value.
392. 0,05 b. on 1 b. olive .. 40 35
393. 0,25 b. on 5 c. brown .. 40 40
DESIGNS: No. 392, Portrait of Sucre. No. 393, Numeral.

50. General J. V. Gomez and Ciudad Bolivar. **51.** Aeroplane and Venezuela.

1928. 25th Anniv. of Capture of Ciudad Bolivar and Peace in Venezuela.
394. 50. 10 c. green .. .. 1·10 55

1930. Air.
395. 51. 5 c. brown 15 10
575. 5 c. green 30 10
396. 10 c. yellow 15 10
576. 10 c. orange .. .. 1·10 55
577. 12½ c. purple 50 30
397. 15 c. grey 15 10
578. 15 c. blue 70 15
398. 25 c. violet 15 10
579. 25 c. brown .. .. 2·40 65
399. 40 c. green 15 10
581. 70 c. red .. .. 17·00 5·25
400. 75 c. red 45 15
401. 1 b. blue 55 15
402. 1 b. 20 green 50 35
403. 1 b. 70 blue 70 40
404. 1 b. 90 green 75 50
405. 2 b. 10 blue .. .. 1·25 40
406. 2 b. 30 red .. .. 1·25 50
407. 2 b. 50 blue .. .. 1·25 50
408. 3 b. 70 green .. .. 1·25 45
409. 10 b. purple .. .. 3·25 1·10
410. 20 b. green .. .. 5·50 2·50
See also Nos. 426/49.

52. Simon Bolivar. **53.**

1930. Death Cent. of Bolivar.
411. 52. 5 c. yellow 60 40
412. 10 c. blue 60 30
413. 25 c. red 60 30

1932. Stamps of 1915 on paper printed with pattern as T 53.
414. 47. 5 c. violet 40 10
415. 7½ c. green 50 40
416. 10 c. green 25 10
417. 15 c. yellow 65 25
418. 22½ c. red .. .. 1·60 35
419. 25 c. red 55 10
420. 37½ c. blue .. .. 2·10 1·00
421. 40 c. blue .. .. 2·10 30
422. 50 c. olive .. .. 2·10 40
423. 1 b. blue .. .. 2·75 45
424. 3 b. brown .. .. 21·00 8·25
425. 5 b. brown .. .. 27·00 11·00

1932. Air. Air stamps as 1930 on paper printed with pattern as T **53**.
426. 51. 5 c. brown 40 10
427. 10 c. yellow 40 10
428. 15 c. grey 40 10
429. 25 c. blue 55 10
430. 40 c. green 50 10
431. 70 c. red 65 10
432. 75 c. orange 70 25
433. 1 b. slate 85 10
434. 1 b. 20 green .. .. 1·50 60
435. 1 b. 70 brown .. .. 3·00 40
436. 1 b. 80 blue .. .. 1·50 30
437. 1 b. 90 green .. .. 3·50 2·50
438. 1 b. 95 blue .. .. 4·25 2·10
439. 2 b. brown .. .. 3·00 1·75
440. 2 b. 10 blue .. .. 6·25 4·25
441. 2 b. 30 red .. .. 3·00 1·60
442. 2 b. 50 blue .. .. 3·50 1·00
443. 3 b. violet .. .. 3·50 60
444. 3 b. 70 green .. .. 5·00 4·25
445. 4 b. orange .. .. 3·50 1·00
446. 5 b. black .. .. 5·00 1·60
447. 8 b. red .. .. 9·75 3·25
448. 10 b. violet .. .. 20·00 5·25
449. 20 b. green .. .. 42·00 15·00

54. Arms of Bolivar.

1933. 150th Birth Anniv. of Bolivar.
450. 54. 25 c. red .. .. 1·60 1·25

1934. Surch. **1933** and figures of value and old value blocked out.
451. 47. 7½ on 10 c. green (380) .. 55 30
453. 22½ on 25 c. red (384) .. 1·10 60
452. 22½ on 25 c. red (419) .. 1·00 1·00
454. 37½ on 40 c. blue (385) .. 1·25 60

1937. Air. Air stamps of 1932 surch. **1937. VALE POR** and new value.
455. 51. 5 c. on 1 b. 70 brown .. 8·00 4·50
456. 10 c. on 3 b. 70 green .. 8·00 4·50
457. 15 c. on 4 b. orange .. 3·50 2·25
458. 25 c. on 5 b. black .. 3·50 2·25
459. 1 b. on 8 b. red .. 2·75 2·25
460. 2 b. on 2 b. 10 blue .. 21·00 15·00

1937. Surch. **1937 VALE POR** and value.
461. 47. 25 c. on 40 c. (No. 421) 4·25 55

59. Nurse and Child. **60.** Ploughing. **61.** " Flight ". **64.** Caribbean Coast

1937. (a) Postage.
463. 59. 5 c. violet 35 25
464. – 10 c. green 80 25
465. – 15 c. brown 65 35
466. 59. 25 c. red 65 40
467. – 50 c. green .. .. 4·25 2·75
468. 60. 3 b. red .. .. 7·25 5·00
469. 59. 5 b. brown .. .. 15·00 10·00
DESIGNS—VERT. 10 c. Sailing barges on Orinoco. 15 c. Women gathering cocoa-beans. HORIZ. 50 c. Rounding up cattle.

(b Air.
470. 61. 5 c. brown 35 35
471. – 10 c. orange 20 10
472. – 15 c. black 40 35
473. 64. 25 c. violet 50 35
474. – 40 c. green 70 40
475. 61. 70 c. red 70 35
476. – 75 c. bistre .. .. 1·60 65
477. 61. 1 b. grey .. .. 1·00 45
478. – 1 b. 20 green .. .. 4·25 1·90
479. 61. 1 b. 80 blue .. .. 2·10 90
480. – 1 b. 95 blue .. .. 6·25 3·75
481. 64. 2 b. brown .. .. 2·50 1·50
482. 2 b. 50 blue .. .. 7·50 4·75
483. – 3 b. lilac .. .. 4·25 2·25
484. 64. 3 b. 70 red .. .. 6·00 5·00
485. – 10 b. purple .. .. 16·00 6·50
486. 61. 20 b. black .. .. 17·00 11·50
DESIGNS—HORIZ. 10 c., 40 c., 1 b. 20, 3 b. Puerto Cabello. 15 c., 75 c., 1 b. 95, 10 b. Caracas.

65. " Venezuela " welcoming La Guaira. **67.** Bolivar.

1937. Acquisition of La Guaira Harbour.
487. 65. 25 c. blue (postage) .. 85 55
488. – 70 c. green (air) .. 2·25 80
489. – 1 b. 80 blue .. .. 4·00 1·50
DESIGN: 70 c., 1 b. 80, Statue of Bolivar and La Guaira Harbour.

1937. Red Cross Fund.
490. 67. 5 c. green 75 50

1937. Stamps of 1937 optd. **RESELLADO 1937-1938.**
491. 59. 5 c. violet (postage) .. 3·00 1·60
492. – 10 c. green .. .. 1·40 65
493. 59. 25 c. red 60 55
494. 60. 3 b. red .. .. £120 60·00
495. – 10 c. orange (air) .. 85 55
496. 64. 25 c. violet .. .. 1·60 75
497. – 40 c. green .. .. 1·60 1·10
498. 61. 70 c. red .. .. 1·25 75
499. 1 b. grey .. .. 1·60 1·10
500. – 1 b. 20 green .. .. 25·00 15·00
501. 61. 1 b. 80 blue .. .. 4·25 1·90
502. – 1 b. 95 blue .. .. 6·50 3·75
503. 64. 2 b. brown .. .. 4·200 19·00
504. 2 b. 50 blue .. .. 42·00 15·00
505. – 3 b. lilac .. .. 25·00 9·50
506. – 10 b. purple .. .. 60·00 32·00
507. 61. 20 b. black .. .. 65·00 38·00

69. Gathering Coffee Beans. **72.** La Guaira.

1938. (a) Postage. As T 69.
508 69 5 c. green 40 15
509 A 10 c. red 40 15
510 B 15 c. violet 85 25
544 15 c. green 55 30
511 A 25 c. blue 40 15
546 37½ c. blue .. .. 1·60 55
513 B 40 c. sepia .. .. 12·50 3·25
547 40 c. black .. .. 10·50 3·25
514 69 50 c. olive .. .. 17·00 3·25
548 50 c. violet .. .. 5·75 55
515 A 1 b. brown .. .. 6·75 3·25
516 69 3 b. orange .. .. 60·00 22·00
517 B 5 b. black .. .. 7·25 3·25
750 5 b. orange .. .. 27·00 13·50
751 5 b. brown .. .. 9·25 3·50
DESIGNS: A, Bolivar. B, G.P.O., Caracas.

(b) Air. As T 72.
550 72 5 c. green 65 40
551 C 10 c. red 20 10
552 72 12½ c. violet 35 30
520 D 15 c. violet .. .. 2·00 75
553 15 c. blue 60 10
521 72 25 c. blue .. .. 2·00 75
554 25 c. brown 25 10
555 D 30 c. violet .. .. 1·40 20
522 C 40 c. violet .. .. 2·25 85
556 40 c. brown .. .. 1·60 20
557 72 45 c. green 65 20
558 C 50 c. blue 75 10
523 D 70 c. red 60 40
524 72 75 c. brown .. .. 4·50 1·25
559 75 c. green 90 25
560 D 90 c. red 65 20
525 C 1 b. green .. .. 4·50 1·75
561 1 b. violet 75 20
526 D 1 b. 20 orange .. .. 13·00 4·25
562 1 b. 20 green .. .. 1·40 60
527 72 1 b. 80 blue .. .. 1·40 35
528 C 1 b. 90 black .. .. 3·25 2·10
529 D 1 b. 95 blue .. .. 2·75 1·90
530 72 2 b. green .. .. 29·00 10·00
563 2 b. red .. .. 1·10 50
531 C 2 b. 50 brown .. .. 29·00 12·00
564 2 b. 50 orange .. .. 7·25 2·10
565 D 3 b. green .. .. 3·25 1·25
533 72 3 b. 70 black .. .. 4·75 3·50
556 D 5 b. red .. .. 4·75 1·25
771 5 b. green .. .. 3·50 1·60
534 C 10 b. purple .. .. 14·50 1·75
773 10 b. yellow .. .. 4·50 1·75
535 D 20 b. orange .. .. 40·00 19·00
DESIGNS: C, National Pantheon. D, Oil Wells.

1938. Surch. **VALE BS. 0,40 1938.**
536. 59. 40 c. on 5 b. brown .. 5·75 2·50

1938. Air. Postage stamps surch. **1938 VALE CINCO** (or other value) **CENTIMOS.**
537. 61. 5 c. on 1 b. 80 blue .. 70 50
538. 64. 10 c. on 2 b. 50 blue .. 2·10 60
539. 15 c. on 2 b. brown .. 1·00 60
540. – 25 c. on 40 c. green (474) 1·10 70
541. 64. 40 c. on 3 b. 70 red .. 2·25 1·25

77. Teresa Carreno. **78.** Allegory of Labour and Statue of Bolivar.

1938. Repatriation of Ashes of Teresa Carreno (concert pianist).
567. 77. 25 c. blue .. .. 3·25 55

1938. Labour Day.
568. 78. 25 c. blue .. .. 3·75 55

80. Monuments at Carabobo. **81.** **82.** Gen. J. I. Paz Castillo.

1938. Air. Independence Issue.
583. – 20 c. brown 25 35
584. 80. 30 c. violet 35 35
585. 81. 45 c. blue 55 25
586. – 50 c. blue 45 25
587. 81. 70 c. red .. .. 8·25 4·50
588. 80. 90 c. orange 75 30
589. 81. 1 b. 35 black 90 45
590. – 1 b. 40 slate .. .. 3·75 1·50
591. 80. 2 b. 25 green .. .. 1·90 1·00
DESIGN: 20 c., 50 c., 1 b. 40, Aeroplane over Sucre Monument.

1939. 80th Anniv. of Venezuelan Posts.
592. 82. 10 c. red .. .. 1·50 55

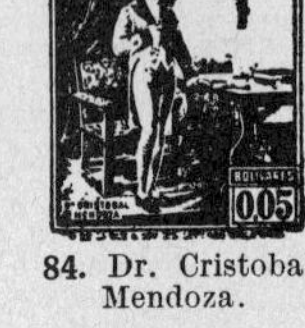

83. View of Ojeda. **84.** Dr. Cristobal Mendoza.

1939. Founding of Ojeda.
593. 83. 25 c. blue .. .. 5·50 40

1939. Cent. of Death of Dr. Mendoza.
594. 84. 5 c. green 25 30
595. 10 c. red 25 30
596. 15 c. violet 65 40
597. 25 c. blue 55 30
598. 37½ c. blue .. .. 10·00 5·00
599. 50 c. olive .. .. 10·00 3·25
600. 1 b. brown .. .. 4·25 2·75

85. Diego B. Urbaneja. **86.** Bolivar and Carabobo Monument.

1940. Independence Issue.
601. 85. 5 c. green (postage) .. 50 15
602. 7½ c. green 40 25
603. 15 c. olive 55 25
604. 37½ c. blue 85 40
605. 40 c. blue 60 30
745. 40 c. mauve 30 25
746. 40 c. orange 30 25
606. 50 c. violet .. .. 3·25 85
607. 1 b. brown .. .. 1·60 55
748. 1 b. blue .. .. 1·00 25
608. 3 b. red .. .. 5·00 2·00
749. 3 b. grey .. .. 2·10 55
609. 86. 15 c. blue (air) .. 25 15
610. 20 c. olive 20 10
611. 25 c. brown .. .. 1·40 35
612. 40 c. brown .. .. 1·00 15
613. 1 b. lilac .. .. 2·25 25
614. 2 b. red .. .. 4·22 35

87. Foundation of Greater Colombia.

1940. Air. 50th Anniv. of Pan-American Union.
615. 87. 15 c. brown 60 30

88. Battle of Carabobo. **89.** " The Crossing of the Andes " (after Salas).

1940. 150th Birth Anniv. of Gen. Paez.
616. 88. 25 c. blue .. .. 3·75 55

1940. Death Cent. of Gen. Santander.
617. 89. 25 c. blue .. .. 3·75 55

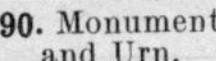

90. Monument and Urn. **91.** Statue of Bolivar at Caracas.

1940. 110th Anniv of Death of Simon Bolivar. (a) Postage.

738 90 5 c. green 10 10
739 5 c. blue 15 10
619 – 10 c. pink 30 10
620 – 15 c. green 40 15
741 – 15 c. red 30 10
621 – 20 c. blue 70 10
622 – 25 c. blue 40 10
742 – 25 c. violet 25 10
623 – 30 c. mauve 1·00 25
743 – 30 c. black 50 35
744 – 30 c. purple 1·00 15
624 – 37½ c. blue 2·10 70
625 – 50 c. violet 1·25 50
747 – 50 c. green 55 25

DESIGNS—VERT. 15 c. Bolivar's Baptism. 25 c. Simon Bolivar on horseback. HORIZ. 10 c. Bolivar's bed. 20 c. House where Bolivar was born. 30 c. Courtyard and Bolivar's baptismal font. 37½ c. Courtyard of house where Bolivar was born. 50 c. "Rebellion of 1812".

(b) Air.

626. 91. 5 c. green 10 10
752. 5 c. orange 10 10
627. 10 c. red 10 10
753. 10 c. green 10 10
628. 12½ c. violet 45 35
754. 12½ c. brown 25 45
629. 15 c. blue 25 10
755. 15 c. grey 15 10
630. 20 c. brown 35 10
756. 20 c. violet 20 10
631. 25 c. brown 25 10
757. 25 c. green 15 10
632. 30 c. violet 25 10
758. 30 c. blue 20 10
633. 40 c. brown 35 10
759. 40 c. green 35 10
634. 45 c. green 50 10
760. 45 c. red 30 15
635. 50 c. blue 50 10
761. 50 c. claret 30 15
636. 70 c. pink 1·00 35
762. 70 c. red 55 30
637. 75 c. olive 4·25 75
763. 75 c. orange 2·75 1·60
764. 75 c. violet 30 15
638. 90 c. orange 65 35
765. 90 c. black 45 40
639. 1 b. mauve 35 10
766. 1 b. blue 35 20
640. 1 b. 20 green 1·40 35
767. 1 b. 20 brown 65 45
641. 1 b. 35 black 5·50 2·50
642. 2 b. red 1·10 20
643. 3 b. black 1·60 35
768. 3 b. brown 6·75 2·50
769. 3 b. blue 1·00 35
644. 4 b. black 1·40 35
645. 5 b. brown 11·00 4·00

1941. No. 622 surch. **HABILITADO 1941 VALE BS.0.20.**

646. 20 c. on 25 c. blue 40 15

1941. Optd. **HABILITADO 1940.**

647. 59. 5 c. violet 1·25 50
648. – 10 c. green (No. 464) 1·25 35

94. Bolivar's Funeral. **95.** Condor.

1941. Cent. of Arrival of Bolivar's Ashes at Caracas and Liberator's Monument Fund.

649. 94. 20 c.+5 c. blue (postage) 3·25 35
650. 95. 15 c.+10 c. brown (air) 1·10 45
651. 30 c.+5 c. violet 1·10 60

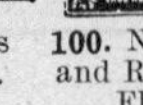

96. Symbolical of industry. **97.** Caracas Cathedral. **100.** National and Red Cross Flags.

1942. National Industrial Exhibition.

652. 96. 10 c. red 60 25

1943.

653. 97. 10 c. red 40 15
740. 10 c. orange 10 10

1943. Surch. **Habilitado Vale Bs. 0.20.**

654. 59. 20 c. on 25 c. red 15·00 15·00
655. 65. 20 c. on 25 c. blue 42·00 32·00
656. 77. 20 c. on 25 c. blue 8·25 8·25
657. 78. 20 c. on 25 c. blue 8·25 8·25

1943. Optd. **Resellado 1943.**

658. 59. 5 c. violet 7·50 4·25
659. – 10 c. green (No. 464) 5·00 3·50
660. – 50 c. green (No. 467) 4·00 2·10
661. 60. 3 b. red 25·00 9·25

1943. Air. Optd. **Resellado 1943.**

662. – 10 c. orange (No. 471) 85 55
663. 64. 25 c. violet 85 60
664. – 40 c. green (No. 474) 1·00 60
665. 61. 70 c. red 85 60
666. – 70 c. green (No. 488) 1·00 60
667. – 75 c. bistre (No. 476) 1·10 75
668. 61. 1 b. grey 1·10 75
669. – 1 b. 20 green (No. 478) 1·60 90
670. 61. 1 b. 80 blue 1·50 75
671. – 1 b. 80 blue (No. 489) 2·10 1·00
672. – 1 b. 95 blue (No. 480) 2·25 1·10
673. 64. 2 b. brown 2·25 1·90
674. – 2 b. 50 blue 2·75 1·90
675. – 3 b. lilac (No. 483) 3·25 2·10
676. 64. 3 b. 70 red 38·00 27·00
677. – 10 b. purple (No. 485) 14·00 8·25
678. 61. 20 b. black 22·00 17·00

1944. Air. 80th Anniv. of Int. Red Cross and 37th Anniv. of Adherence of Venezuela.

680. 100. 5 c. green 10 10
681. 10 c. mauve 15 10
682. 20 c. blue 15 10
683. 30 c. blue 35 10
684. 40 c. brown 50 15
685. 45 c. green 90 35
686. 90 c. orange 85 30
687. 1 b. black 1·25 25

101. Baseball Players. **103.** Charles Howarth.

1944. Air. 7th World Amateur Baseball Championship Games, Caracas. Optd. **AEREO.**

688. 101. 5 c. brown 35 25
689. 10 c. green 40 25
690. 20 c. blue 50 35
691. 30 c. red 40 50
692. 45 c. purple 1·00 45
693. 90 c. orange 1·90 90
694. 1 b. grey 2·10 90
695. 1 b. 20 green 6·25 4·75
696. 1 b. 80 yellow 8·25 6·50

1944. Air. No. 590, surch. **Habilitado 1944 VALE Bs.0.30.**

697. 30 c. on 1 b. 40 c. slate 35 35

1944. Air. Cent. of Rochdale Co-operative Society.

698. 103. 5 c. black 25 15
699. 10 c. violet 25 15
700. 20 c. brown 50 30
701. 30 c. green 35 35
702. 1 b. 20 brown 1·60 1·50
703. 1 b. 80 blue 3·00 1·90
704. 3 b. 70 red 3·75 3·00

104. Antonio Jose de Sucre. **105.** Antonio Jose de Sucre and Aeroplane.

1945. 150th Anniv. of Birth of Gen. Sucre.

705. 104. 5 c. yellow (postage) 75 35
706. 10 c. blue 1·00 70
707. 20 c. red 1·25 70
708. 105. 5 c. orange (air) 20 15
709. 10 c. purple 25 20
710. 20 c. black 35 25
711. 30 c. green 55 40
712. 40 c. olive 55 35
713. 45 c. brown 70 35
714. 90 c. brown 1·25 45
715. 1 b. mauve 90 35
716. 1 b. 20 black 2·10 1·90
717. 2 b. yellow 3·00 1·50

106. Andres Bello. **107.** Gen. Rafael Urdaneta.

1946. 80th Death Anniv. of A. Bello (educationalist).

718. 106. 20 c. blue (postage) 55 35
719. 30 c. green (air) 40 30

1946. Death Cent. of Gen. R. Urdaneta.

720. 107. 20 c. blue (postage) 55 35
721. 30 c. green (air) 40 30

108. Allegory of Republic. **110.** Western Hemisphere and Anti-Tuberculosis Inst., Maracaibo.

1946. 1st Anniv. of Revolution.

722. 108. 20 c. blue (postage) 55 35
723. – 15 c. blue (air) 20 30
724. – 20 c. bistre 25 30
725. – 30 c. violet 30 25
726. – 1 b. red 2·10 1·50

Nos. 723/6 are as Type **108**, but vert.

1947. 12th Pan-American Health Conf., Caracas.

727 110 20 c. yell & blue (post) 50 35
728 – 15 c. yellow & bl (air) 35 25
729 – 20 c. yellow and brown 35 40
730 – 30 c. yellow and violet 35 25
731 – 1 b. yellow and red 2·50 2·10

Nos. 728/31 are as Type **110** but vert.

1947. Surch. **J.R.G. CORREOS Vale Bs. 0.15 1946.**

732. 85. 15 c. on 1 b. brown 55 35

1947. Air. Surch. **J.R.G. AEREO Vale Bs.**, new value, and **1946.**

733. 47. 10 c. on 22½ c. red (No. 418) 20 10
734. – 15 c. on 25 c. blue (No. 622) 45 15
735. 91. 20 c. on 50 c. blue 40 25
736. 85. 70 c. on 1 b. brown 50 35
737. – 20 b. on 20 b. orange (No. 535) 17·00 9·50

1947. Nos. 743 and 624 surch. **CORREOS Vale Bs.**, new value, and **1947.** (a) Postage.

776. 5 c. on 30 c. black 25 8
777. 5 c. on 37½ c. blue 30 8

(b) Air. No. 621 with **AEREO** instead of **CORREOS.**

778. 5 c. on 20 c. blue 40 5
779. 10 c. on 20 c. blue 40 5

116. Freighter "Republica de Venezuela" **117.** and Ship's Wheel.

1948. 1st Anniv. of Greater Colombia Merchant Marine. Frame size 37½ × 22½ mm. or 22½ × 37½ mm. Inscr. "AMERICAN BANK NOTE COMPANY" at foot.

780. 116. 5 c. blue (postage) 20 5
781. 7½ c. red 70 35
782. 10 c. red 55 5
783. 15 c. grey 75 15
784. 20 c. sepia 40 8
785. 25 c. violet 75 20
786. 30 c. yellow 4·75 1·90
787. 37½ c. brown 2·00 1·40
788. 40 c. olive 3·00 1·75
789. 50 c. mauve 85 25
790. 1 b. green 2·00 50
791. 117. 5 c. brown (air) 10 5
792. 10 c. green 10 5
793. 15 c. buff 15 5
794. 20 c. purple 20 5
795. 25 c. grey 25 8
796. 30 c. olive 35 12
797. 45 c. blue 60 25
798. 50 c. black 80 35
799. 70 c. orange 1·75 35
800. 75 c. blue 3·00 45
801. 90 c. red 1·75 1·00
802. 1 b. violet 2·00 70
803. 2 b. slate 2·25 1·00
804. 3 b. green 8·50 3·25
805. 4 b. blue 4·00 3·25
806. 5 b. red 17·00 5·50

For stamps as T **116/17** in larger size and inscribed "COURVOISIER S.A." at foot, see Nos. 1012/7.

118. Arms of Venezuela.

1948. New Constitution Promulgation.

807. 118. 5 c. blue 1·00 55
808. 10 c. red 1·25 60

120. Santos Michelena. **121.**

1949. 110th Anniv. of 1st Int. Postal Convention, Bogota.

810. 120. 5 c. blue (postage) 25 15
811. 10 c. red 25 15
812. 20 c. sepia 1·00 35
813. 1 b. green 3·25 1·60
814. 121. 5 c. brown (air) 20 15
815. 10 c. grey 25 15
816. 15 c. orange 30 15
817. 25 c. green 60 30
818. 30 c. purple 60 30
819. 1 b. violet 3·00 1·25

122. Columbus, Indian, "Santa Maria" and map. **123.**

1949. 450th Anniv. of Columbus's Discovery of America.

820. 122. 5 c. blue (postage) 75 15
821. 10 c. red 3·50 60
822. 20 c. sepia 4·75 90
823. 1 b. green 10·00 3·25
824. 123. 5 c. brown (air) 70 10
825. 10 c. grey 75 25
826. 15 c. orange 1·40 30
827 25 c. green 2·50 65
828. 30 c. mauve 3·50 90
829. 1 b. violet 14·00 2·75

124. Hand, Bird, Aeroplane and Globe. **125.** Francisco de Miranda.

126. Declaration of Independence.

1950. Air. 75th Anniv. of U.P.U.

830. 124. 5 c. lake 20 10
831. 10 c. green 10 10
832. 15 c. brown 20 10
833. 25 c. grey 25 40
834. 30 c. olive 35 20
835. 50 c. black 25 25
836. 60 c. blue 75 35
837. 90 c. red 1·00 45
838. 1 b. violet 1·10 30

1950. Birth Bicent. of Miranda.

839. 125. 5 c. blue (postage) 25 10
840. 10 c. green 30 10
841. 20 c. brown 60 25
842. 1 b. red 2·75 1·25
843. 126. 5 c. red (air) 35 15
844. 10 c. brown 35 15
845. 15 c. violet 30 35
846. 30 c. blue 45 25
847. 1 b. green 2·50 1·10

127. Tubebuia (National tree). **128.** Map and Statistics.

1950. Air. Protection of flora. Centres in yellow.

848. 127. 5 c. brown 35 20
849. 10 c. green 25 10
850. 15 c. mauve 35 15
851. 25 c. green 2·50 1·00
852. 30 c. orange 2·75 1·40
853. 50 c. grey 1·50 35
854. 60 c. blue 2·50 65
855. 90 c. red 4·50 1·40
856. 1 b. violet 5·50 1·60

1950. Census of the Americas.

857. 128. 5 c. blue (postage) 20 10
858. 10 c. grey 20 10
859. 15 c. sepia 30 10
860. 25 c. green 25 15
861. 30 c. red 35 25
862. 50 c. violet 65 25
863. 1 b. brown 1·60 85

864. 128. 5 c. grey (air) 15 10
865. 10 c. green 10 10
866. 15 c. olive 30 15
867. 25 c. black 25 25
868. 30 c. orange 35 20
869. 50 c. brown 25 25
870. 60 c. blue 25 35
871. 90 c. red 90 35
872. 1 b. violet 1·50 1·10

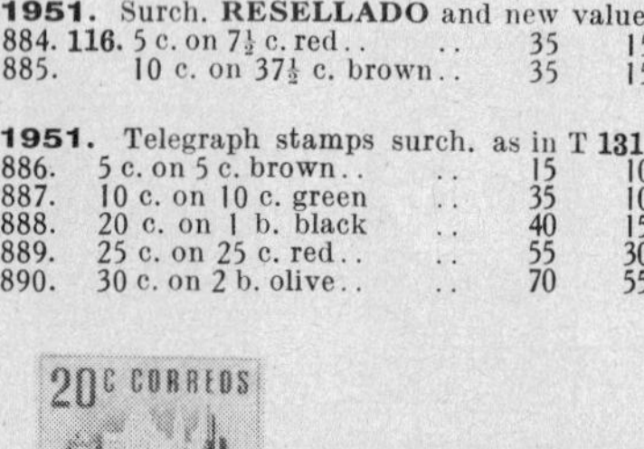

129. Alonso de Ojeda. 131.

1950. 450th Anniv. of Discovery of Lake Maracaibo.
873. 129. 5 c. blue (postage) 25 15
874. 10 c. red 35 15
875. 15 c. grey 40 20
876. 20 c. blue 1·00 40
877. 1 b. green 4·25 2·10
878. 5 c. brown (air) 25 10
879. 10 c. red 35 15
880. 15 c. sepia 45 20
881. 25 c. purple 45 40
882. 30 c. orange 90 35
883. 1 b. green 3·75 1·90

1951. Surch. **RESELLADO** and new value.
884. 116. 5 c. on 7½ c. red 35 15
885. 10 c. on 37½ c. brown 35 15

1951. Telegraph stamps surch. as in T 131.
886. 5 c. on 5 c. brown 15 10
887. 10 c. on 10 c. green 35 10
888. 20 c. on 1 b. black 40 15
889. 25 c. on 25 c. red 55 30
890. 30 c. on 2 b. olive 70 55

132. Arms of Caracus and View. 133. Statue of Bolivar, New York.

1951. Arms issue. Federal District of Caracas.
891. 132. 5 c. green (postage) 30 10
892. 10 c. red 40 10
893. 15 c. brown 1·00 25
894. 20 c. blue 2·10 25
895. 25 c. brown 3·00 55
896. 30 c. blue 2·75 60
897. 35 c. violet 27·00 16·00
898. 5 c. turquoise (air) 40 15
899. 7½ c. green 1·60 60
900. 10 c. red 25 25
901. 15 c. brown 3·75 40
902. 20 c. blue 2·50 40
903. 30 c. blue 4·25 85
904. 45 c. purple 2·50 55
905. 60 c. green 8·25 1·00
906. 90 c. red 5·00 4·25
See also Nos. 922/37, 938/53, 954/69, 970/85, 991/1006, 1018/33, 1034/49, 1050/65, 1066/81, 1082/97, 1098/113, 1137/52, 1153/68, 1169/1184, 1185/1200, 1201/16, 1217/32, 1258/73, 1274/89, 1290/1305, 1306/21, 1322/37, and 1338/53.

1951. Transfer of Statue of Bolivar to Central Park, New York.
907. 133. 5 c. green (postage) 35 10
908. 10 c. red 35 25
909. 20 c. blue 35 25
910. 30 c. grey 45 40
911. 40 c. green 60 40
912. 50 c. brown 1·25 45
913. 1 b. black 4·00 2·10
914. 5 c. violet (air) 40 15
915. 10 c. green 25 15
916. 20 c. grey 25 15
917. 25 c. olive 30 20
918. 30 c. red 35 25
919. 40 c. brown 35 25
920. 50 c. slate 1·10 45
921. 70 c. orange 1·90 1·10

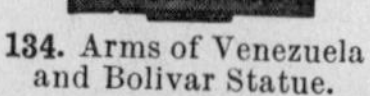

134. Arms of Venezuela and Bolivar Statue. 138. Isabella the Catholic.

1951. Arms issue. National Arms of Venezuela.
922. 134. 5 c. green (postage) 25 10
923. 10 c. red 35 10
924. 15 c. brown 1·90 35
925. 20 c. blue 1·90 45
926. 25 c. brown 3·00 70
927. 30 c. blue 3·00 70
928. 35 c. violet 17·00 12·50
929. 5 c. turquoise (air) 25 5
930. 7½ c. green 70 55
931. 10 c. red 35 15
932. 15 c. brown 1·60 55
933. 20 c. blue 2·25 40
934. 30 c. blue 4·25 90
935. 45 c. purple 1·90 35
936. 60 c. green 9·25 1·90
937. 90 c. red 5·75 4·25

1951. Arms issue. State of Tachira. As T 132 showing Arms of Tachira and agricultural products.
938. 5 c. green (postage) 25 10
939. 10 c. red 30 25
940. 15 c. brown 60 20
941. 20 c. blue 1·50 35
942. 50 c. orange 90·00 11·50
943. 1 b. green 1·50 55
944. 5 b. purple 3·75 2·10
945. 5 c. turquoise (air) 15 15
946. 10 c. red 25 10
947. 15 c. brown 55 25
948. 30 c. blue 7·50 90
949. 60 c. green 5·75 90
950. 1 b. 20 lake 5·75 4·25
951. 3 b. green 1·50 75
952. 5 b. purple 3·25 1·60
953. 10 b. violet 4·75 3·25

1951. Arms issue. State of Zulia. As T 132 showing Arms of Zulia and Oil Well.
954. 5 c. green (postage) 25 10
955. 10 c. red 25 10
956. 15 c. brown 55 25
957. 20 c. blue 70 35
958. 50 c. orange 4·25 3·00
959. 1 b. green 1·50 55
960. 5 b. purple 3·00 2·10
961. 5 c. turquoise (air) 30 15
962. 10 c. red 15 10
963. 15 c. brown 35 35
964. 30 c. blue 2·50 1·00
965. 60 c. green 1·40 35
966. 1 b. 20 lake 5·75 4·25
967. 3 b. green 1·50 65
968. 5 b. purple 2·50 1·60
969. 10 b. violet 4·25 3·25

1951. Arms issue. State of Carabobo. As T 132 showing Arms of Carabobo and agricultural produce.
970. 5 c. green (postage) 15 10
971. 10 c. red 15 10
972. 15 c. brown 20 20
973. 20 c. blue 30 30
974. 25 c. brown 35 35
975. 30 c. blue 70 30
976. 35 c. violet 2·75 2·25
977. 5 c. turquoise (air) 10 10
978. 7½ c. green 25 25
979. 10 c. red 15 10
980. 15 c. brown 20 20
981. 20 c. blue 30 30
982. 30 c. blue 1·00 35
983. 45 c. purple 45 40
984. 60 c. green 90 45
985. 90 c. red 2·50 1·50

1951. Air. 500th Birth Anniv. of Isabella the Catholic.
986. 138. 5 c. green and pale green 25 15
987. 10 c. red and yellow 25 15
988. 20 c. blue and grey 45 25
989. 30 c. blue and grey 45 20

1951. Arms issue. State of Anzoategui. As T 132 showing Arms of Anzoategui and globe.
991. 5 c. green (postage) 15 10
992. 10 c. red 20 10
993. 15 c. brown 55 25
994. 20 c. blue 90 30
995. 40 c. orange 1·90 90
996. 45 c. purple 5·50 3·00
997. 3 b. blue 2·10 1·00
998. 5 c. turquoise (air) 25 10
999. 10 c. red 20 10
1000. 15 c. brown 25 25
1001. 25 c. black 35 15
1002. 30 c. blue 90 65
1003. 50 c. orange 90 35
1004. 60 c. green 1·40 20
1005. 1 b. violet 1·60 65
1006. 2 b. violet 3·00 1·50

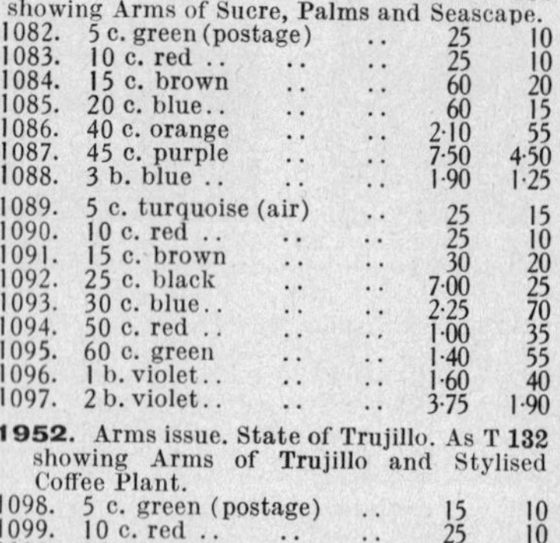

140. National Stadium. 147. Juan de Villegas.

1951. Air. 3rd Bolivarian Games, Caracas.
1007. 140. 5 c. green 55 25
1008. 10 c. red 60 25
1009. 20 c. brown 70 35
1010. 30 c. blue 90 45

1951. As Nos. 780/806 but frame size 38 × 23½ mm. or 23½ × 38 mm. Inscr. " COURVOISIER S.A." at foot.
1012. 116. 5 c. green (postage) 55 10
1013. 10 c. red 90 10
1014. 15 c. slate 3·00 10
1015. 117. 5 c. brown (air) 75 10
1016. 10 c. brown 1·10 10
1017. 15 c. olive 1·50 10

1952. Arms issue. State of Aragua. As T 132 showing Arms of Aragua and Stylised Farm.
1018. 5 c. green (postage) 20 10
1019. 10 c. red 15 10
1020. 15 c. brown 35 10
1021. 20 c. blue 30 30
1022. 25 c. brown 75 40
1023. 30 c. blue 75 35
1024. 35 c. violet 4·25 3·00
1025. 5 c. turquoise (air) 35 12
1026. 7½ c. green 25 60
1027. 10 c. red 15 5
1028. 15 c. brown 85 40
1029. 20 c. blue 45 40
1030. 30 c. blue 1·40 25
1031. 45 c. purple 1·10 40
1032. 60 c. green 2·25 35
1033. 90 c. red 11·50 6·75

1952. Arms issue. State of Bolivar. As T 132 showing Arms of Bolivar and Iron Foundry.
1034. 5 c. green (postage) 15 10
1035. 10 c. red 25 10
1036. 15 c. brown 25 20
1037. 20 c. blue 55 30
1038. 40 c. orange 2·10 70
1039. 45 c. purple 5·50 3·75
1040. 3 b. blue 2·50 1·60
1041. 5 c. turquoise (air) 2·50 25
1042. 10 c. red 15 10
1043. 15 c. brown 30 15
1044. 25 c. black 25 10
1045. 30 c. blue 1·50 75
1046. 50 c. red 1·00 35
1047. 60 c. green 1·90 45
1048. 1 b. violet 1·50 35
1049. 2 b. violet 3·00 1·50

1952. Arms issue. State of Lara. As T 132 showing Arms of Lara and Sisal Industry.
1050. 5 c. green (postage) 25 10
1051. 10 c. red 25 10
1052. 15 c. brown 20 30
1053. 20 c. blue 50 35
1054. 25 c. brown 60 45
1055. 30 c. blue 1·00 35
1056. 35 c. violet 4·25 3·00
1057. 5 c. turquoise (air) 35 15
1058. 7½ c. green 25 25
1059. 10 c. red 15 10
1060. 15 c. brown 55 20
1061. 20 c. blue 75 30
1062. 30 c. blue 1·90 35
1063. 45 c. purple 75 30
1064. 60 c. green 1·90 55
1065. 90 c. red 11·00 8·25

1952. Arms issue. State of Miranda. As T 132 showing Arms of Miranda and Agricultural Products.
1066. 5 c. green (postage) 20 10
1067. 10 c. red 25 10
1068. 15 c. brown 35 20
1069. 20 c. blue 40 30
1070. 25 c. brown 55 40
1071. 30 c. blue 90 40
1072. 35 c. violet 5·50 3·75
1073. 5 c. turquoise (air) 35 10
1074. 7½ c. green 45 25
1075. 10 c. red 15 10
1076. 15 c. brown 35 30
1077. 20 c. blue 55 40
1078. 30 c. blue 90 35
1079. 45 c. purple 75 30
1080. 60 c. green 1·90 45
1081. 90 c. red 10·00 6·75

1952. Arms issue. State of Sucre. As T 132 showing Arms of Sucre, Palms and Seascape.
1082. 5 c. green (postage) 25 10
1083. 10 c. red 25 10
1084. 15 c. brown 60 20
1085. 20 c. blue 60 15
1086. 40 c. orange 2·10 55
1087. 45 c. purple 7·50 4·50
1088. 3 b. blue 1·90 1·25
1089. 5 c. turquoise (air) 25 15
1090. 10 c. red 25 10
1091. 15 c. brown 30 20
1092. 25 c. black 7·00 25
1093. 30 c. blue 2·25 70
1094. 50 c. red 1·00 35
1095. 60 c. green 1·40 55
1096. 1 b. violet 1·60 40
1097. 2 b. violet 3·75 1·90

1952. Arms issue. State of Trujillo. As T 132 showing Arms of Trujillo and Stylised Coffee Plant.
1098. 5 c. green (postage) 15 10
1099. 10 c. red 25 10
1100. 15 c. brown 75 25
1101. 20 c. blue 75 35
1102. 50 c. orange 4·25 2·50
1103. 1 b. green 1·00 45
1104. 5 b. purple 2·50 1·60
1105. 5 c. turquoise (air) 3·75 30
1106. 10 c. red 15 10
1107. 15 c. brown 90 15
1108. 30 c. blue 4·25 90
1109. 60 c. green 3·25 85
1110. 1 b. 20 lake 3·00 2·00
1111. 3 b. green 1·40 85
1112. 5 b. purple 3·00 1·50
1113. 10 b. violet 5·00 3·25

1952. 4th Cent. of Barquisimeto.
1114. 147. 5 c. green (postage) 35 10
1115. 10 c. red 35 10
1116. 20 c. slate 55 35
1117. 40 c. orange 2·50 1·25
1118. 50 c. brown 1·40 65
1119. 1 b. violet 2·50 85
1120. 5 c. turquoise (air) 30 10
1121. 10 c. red 30 10
1122. 20 c. blue 35 10
1123. 25 c. black 35 25
1124. 30 c. blue 45 20
1125. 40 c. orange 2·50 1·25
1126. 50 c. bronze 85 35
1127. 1 b. purple 3·25 1·60

148. Our Lady of Coromoto. 157. G.P.O., Caracas.

1952. 300th Anniv. of Apparition of Our Lady of Coromoto.
1128. 148. 1 b. red (17 × 26½ mm.) 4·25 65
1129. 1 b. red (26½ × 41 mm.) 3·00 65
1130. 1 b. red (36 × 56 mm.) 1·40 55

1952. National Objective Exn. Telegraph stamps as T 131 surch. **Correos Exposicion Objetiva Nacional 1948-1952** and new value.
1131. 5 c. on 25 c. red 35 8
1132. 10 c. on 1 b. black 35 8

1952. Telegraph stamps as T 131 surch. **CORREOS HABILITADO 1952** and new value.
1133. 20 c. on 25 c. red 45 15
1134. 30 c. on 2 b. olive 1·60 1·00
1135. 40 c. on 1 b. black 60 50
1136. 50 c. on 3 b. orange 2·10 1·25

1953. Arms issue. State of Merida. As T 132 showing Arms of Merida and Church.
1137. 5 c. green (postage) 15 10
1138. 10 c. red 15 10
1139. 15 c. brown 20 25
1140. 20 c. blue 55 25
1141. 50 c. orange 2·50 1·00
1142. 1 b. green 65 45
1143. 5 b. purple 2·50 1·40
1144. 5 c. turquoise (air) 20 15
1145. 10 c. red 20 10
1146. 15 c. brown 35 15
1147. 30 c. blue 3·00 65
1148. 60 c. green 1·40 35
1149. 1 b. 20 lake 2·50 1·60
1150. 3 b. green 1·40 65
1151. 5 b. purple 3·00 1·60
1152. 10 b. violet 4·25 2·75

1953. Arms issue. State of Monagas. As T 132 showing Arms of Monagas and Horses.
1153. 5 c. green (postage) 15 10
1154. 10 c. red 20 10
1155. 15 c. brown 25 25
1156. 20 c. blue 35 35
1157. 40 c. orange 1·60 60
1158. 45 c. purple 5·25 3·00
1159. 3 b. blue 2·10 1·60
1160. 5 c. turquoise (air) 20 15
1161. 10 c. red 15 10
1162. 15 c. brown 35 20
1163. 25 c. black 25 15
1164. 30 c. blue 2·50 75
1165. 50 c. red 90 35
1166. 60 c. green 1·10 35
1167. 1 b. violet 1·60 45
1168. 2 b. violet 2·25 1·40

1953. Arms issue. State of Portuguesa. As T 132 showing Arms of Portuguesa and Woodland.
1169. 5 c. green (postage) 12 10
1170. 10 c. red 15 10
1171. 15 c. brown 20 20
1172. 20 c. blue 45 20
1173. 50 c. orange 2·25 1·50
1174. 1 b. green 60 25
1175. 5 b. purple 2·50 1·60
1176. 5 c. turquoise (air) 90 40
1177. 10 c. red 35 10
1178. 15 c. brown 40 25
1179. 30 c. blue 3·00 1·25
1180. 60 c. green 2·10 40
1181. 1 b. 20 lake 5·25 3·00
1182. 3 b. green 1·60 85
1183. 5 b. purple 3·00 1·60
1184. 10 b. violet 4·50 3·75

1953. Arms issue. Federal Territory of Delta Amacuro. As T 132 showing Arms of Delta Amacuro and map.
1185. 5 c. green (postage) 15 10
1186. 10 c. red 20 10
1187. 15 c. brown 25 15
1188. 20 c. blue 40 25
1189. 40 c. orange 1·40 85
1190. 45 c. purple 6·25 3·75
1191. 3 b. blue 1·60 1·25
1192. 5 c. turquoise (air) 25 10
1193. 10 c. red 25 10
1194. 15 c. brown 35 20
1195. 25 c. black 55 40
1196. 30 c. blue 1·90 55
1197. 50 c. red 90 40
1198. 60 c. green 1·50 40
1199. 1 b. violet 1·90 60
1200. 2 b. violet 3·00 2·25

1953. Arms issue. State of Falcon. As T 132 showing Arms of Falcon and Stylised Oil Refinery.
1201. 5 c. green (postage) 15 10
1202. 10 c. red 20 10
1203. 15 c. brown 35 15
1204. 20 c. blue 35 20
1205. 50 c. orange 1·60 85
1206. 1 b. green 1·00 65
1207. 5 b. purple 3·00 1·60
1208. 5 c. turquoise (air) 40 30
1209. 10 c. red 15 10
1210. 15 c. brown 35 25
1211. 30 c. blue 3·00 75
1212. 60 c. green 2·25 75
1213. 1 b. 20 lake 3·00 2·50
1214. 3 b. green 3·00 1·60
1215. 5 b. purple 5·00 3·25
1216. 10 b. violet 5·00 3·75

1953. Arms issue. State of Guarico. As T **132** showing Arms of Guarico and Factory.

1217. 5 c. green (postage) 15 10
1218. 10 c. red 15 10
1219. 15 c. brown 30 25
1220. 20 c. blue.. .. .. 35 30
1221. 40 c. orange .. .. 1·60 1·10
1222. 45 c. purple .. .. 3·75 2·25
1223. 3 b. blue .. .. .. 1·60 1·00

1224. 5 c. turquoise (air) .. 25 10
1225. 10 c. red 35 10
1226. 15 c. brown 35 20
1227. 25 c. black 55 25
1228. 30 c. blue.. .. .. 2·10 85
1229. 50 c. red .. .. .. 1·00 50
1230. 60 c. green .. .. 1·25 55
1231. 1 b. violet.. .. .. 2·10 55
1232. 2 b. violet.. .. .. 3·00 1·60

1953. Inscr. "EE. UU. DE VENEZUELA".

1233. **157.** 5 c green (postage) .. 15 10
1234. 7½ c. green 30 20
1235. 10 c. red 35 10
1236. 15 c. black 30 10
1237. 20 c. blue 40 15
1238. 25 c. mauve 30 10
1239. 30 c. blue .. .. 1·60 25
1240. 35 c. mauve 70 25
1241. 40 c. orange .. .. 1·00 35
1242. 45 c. violet .. .. 1·60 55
1243. 50 c. orange .. .. 1·00 35

1244. 5 c. orange (air) .. 10 10
1245. 7½ c. green 20 20
1246. 15 c. purple 15 10
1247. 20 c. slate 20 10
1248. 25 c. sepia 60 10
1249. 30 c. brown .. .. 3·50 1·50
1250. 40 c. red 60 15
1251. 45 c. purple 60 15
1252. 50 c. red 85 10
1253. 60 c. red .. .. 3·50 1·75
1254. 70 c. myrtle .. .. 2·00 85
1255. 75 c. blue .. .. 3·00 1·25
1256. 90 c. brown .. .. 1·60 70
1257. 1 b. violet .. .. 1·60 60

See also Nos. 1365/82.

1953. Arms issue. State of Cojedes. As T **132** showing Arms of Cojedes and Cattle.

1258. 5 c. green (postage) .. 12 10
1259. 10 c. red 25 10
1260. 15 c. brown 25 10
1261. 20 c. blue.. .. .. 30 15
1262. 25 c. brown 75 35
1263. 30 c. blue.. .. .. 1·10 35
1264. 35 c. violet .. .. 1·50 90

1265. 5 c. turquoise (air) .. 2·10 45
1266. 7½ c. green 55 50
1267. 10 c. red 20 10
1268. 15 c. brown 35 15
1269. 20 c. blue.. .. .. 40 20
1270. 30 c. blue.. .. .. 2·75 40
1271. 45 c. purple .. .. 1·00 35
1272. 60 c. green .. .. 2·10 35
1273. 90 c. red .. .. .. 2·50 1·50

1954. Arms issue. Federal Territory of Amazonas. As T **132** showing Arms of Amazonas and Orchid.

1274. 5 c. green (postage) .. 40 10
1275. 10 c. red 40 10
1276. 15 c. brown 90 20
1277. 20 c. blue.. .. .. 2·50 40
1278. 40 c. orange .. .. 3·00 90
1279. 45 c. purple .. .. 4·50 2·25
1280. 3 b. blue .. .. .. 6·75 2·50

1281. 5 c. turquoise (air) .. 70 10
1282. 10 c. red 40 10
1283. 15 c. brown 70 25
1284. 25 c. black .. .. 1·50 25
1285. 30 c. blue.. .. .. 3·75 35
1286. 50 c. red .. .. .. 3·00 60
1287. 60 c. green .. .. 3·75 60
1288. 1 b. violet.. .. .. 14·50 2·10
1289. 2 b. violet.. .. .. 5·75 2·50

1954. Arms issue. State of Apure. As T **132** showing Arms of Apure, Horse and Bird.

1290. 5 c. green (postage) .. 15 10
1291. 10 c. red 15 10
1292. 15 c. brown 25 20
1293. 20 c. blue.. .. .. 1·50 25
1294. 50 c. orange .. .. 1·90 1·50
1295. 1 b. green.. .. .. 60 55
1296. 5 b. purple .. .. 3·75 2·10

1297. 5 c. turquoise (air) .. 35 15
1298. 10 c. red 15 10
1299. 15 c. brown 35 20
1300. 30 c. blue.. .. .. 1·60 65
1301. 60 c. green .. .. 1·60 35
1302. 1 b. 20 lake .. .. 2·50 1·60
1303. 3 b. green.. .. .. 1·60 65
1304. 5 b. purple .. .. 3·00 1·40
1305. 10 b. violet .. .. 4·25 3·00

1954. Arms issue. State of Barinas. As T **132** showing Arms of Barinas, Cow and Horse.

1306. 5 c. green (postage) .. 15 10
1307. 10 c. red 15 10
1308. 15 c. brown 20 20
1309. 20 c. blue.. .. .. 1·50 35
1310. 50 c. orange .. .. 1·60 1·00
1311. 1 b. green.. .. .. 45 35
1312. 5 b. purple .. .. 3·75 1·90

1313. 5 c. turquoise (air) .. 35 15
1314. 10 c. red 15 10
1315. 15 c. brown 60 25
1316. 30 c. blue.. .. .. 2·10 85
1317. 60 c. green .. .. 2·10 40
1318. 1 b. 20 lake .. .. 3·00 1·60
1319. 3 b. green.. .. .. 1·90 85
1320. 5 b. purple .. .. 3·00 1·00
1321. 10 b. violet .. .. 4·50 3·25

1954. Arms issue. State of Nueva Esparta. As T **132** showing Arms of Nueva Esparta and Fishes.

1322. 5 c. green (postage) .. 15 10
1323. 10 c. red 15 10
1324. 15 c. brown 35 25
1325. 20 c. blue.. .. .. 40 15
1326. 40 c orange .. .. 1·90 70
1327. 45 c. purple .. .. 4·50 2·75
1328. 3 b. blue .. .. .. 2·10 1·50

1329. 5 c. turquoise (air) .. 30 15
1330. 10 c. red 20 10
1331. 15 c. brown 55 20
1332. 25 c. black 90 35
1333. 30 c. blue.. .. .. 1·90 40
1334. 50 c. red .. .. .. 1·90 40
1335. 60 c. green .. .. 1·90 40
1336. 1 b. violet.. .. .. 2·75 60
1337. 2 b. violet.. .. .. 3·75 1·90

1954. Arms issue. State of Yaracuy. As T **132** showing Arms of Yaracuy and Tropical Foliage.

1338. 5 c. green (postage) .. 30 10
1339. 10 c. red 15 10
1340. 15 c. brown 25 20
1341. 20 c. blue.. .. .. 35 30
1342. 25 c. brown 55 40
1343. 30 c. blue.. .. .. 60 30
1344. 35 c. violet .. .. 1·50 90

1345. 5 c. turquoise (air) .. 35 20
1346. 7½ c. green .. .. 5·00 5·00
1347. 10 c. red 20 10
1348. 15 c. brown 55 15
1349. 20 c. blue.. .. .. 70 15
1350. 30 c. blue.. .. .. 1·50 40
1351. 45 c. purple .. .. 1·00 40
1352. 60 c. green .. .. 1·00 40
1353. 90 c. red .. .. .. 3·00 2·10

164. Simon Rodriguez.

165. Bolivar and 1824 Edict.

1954. Air. Death Cent. of Rodriguez (Bolivar's tutor).

1354. **164.** 5 c. turquoise.. .. 35 10
1355. 10 c. red 50 10
1356. 20 c. blue 35 10
1357. 45 c. purple 55 35
1358. 65 c. green .. .. 1·90 85

1954. Air. 10th Pan-American Conf., Caracas.

1359. **165.** 15 c. black and brown 15 10
1360. 25 c. brown and grey.. 45 15
1361. 40 c. brown and orange 35 15
1362. 65 c. black and blue.. 90 45
1363. 80 c. brown and red.. 75 35
1364. 1 b. violet and mauve 1·50 30

1954. As T **157** but inscr. "REPUBLICA DE VENEZUELA".

1365. 5 c. green (postage) .. 15 10
1366. 10 c. red 15 10
1367. 15 c. black 30 10
1368. 20 c. blue 35 10
1369. 30 c. blue 55 50
1370. 35 c. mauve 55 20
1371. 40 c. orange 85 30
1372. 45 c. violet .. .. 1·00 40

1373. 5 c. yellow (air) .. 15 10
1374. 10 c. bistre 15 10
1375. 15 c. purple 20 10
1376. 20 c. slate 35 10
1377. 30 c. brown 35 10
1378. 40 c. red 60 30
1379. 45 c. purple 60 40
1380. 70 c. green .. .. 1·60 70
1381. 75 c. blue .. .. 1·00 40
1382. 90 c. brown 55 30

166.

167.

1955. 400th Anniv. of Valencia Del Rey.

1383 **166.** 5 c. green (postage) .. 25 10
1384. 20 c. blue 50 10
1385. 25 c. brown 55 10
1386. 50 c. orange 85 35

1387. 5 c. turquoise (air) .. 10 10
1388. 10 c. red 15 10
1389. 20 c. blue 25 10
1390. 25 c. black 25 10
1391. 40 c. violet 35 35
1392. 50 c. red 35 35
1393. 60 c. olive 75 35

1955. 1st Postal Convention, Caracas.

1394. **167.** 5 c. green (postage) .. 25 10
1395. 20 c. blue 80 10
1396. 25 c. lake 65 10
1397. 50 c. orange 85 10

1398. 5 c. yellow (air) .. 15 10
1399. 15 c. brown 35 10
1400. 25 c. black 35 10
1401. 40 c. red 35 20
1402. 50 c. orange 35 25
1403. 60 c. red 75 50

168. O'Leary College, Barinas.

DESIGNS—HORIZ. A, University Hospital, Caracas. B, Caracas–La Guaira Highway. C, Simon Bolivar Centre.

1956. Air. Public Works.

1404. **168.** 5 c. yellow 15 10
1405. 10 c. sepia 15 10
1406. 15 c. brown 20 10
1407. A. 20 c. blue 20 10
1408. 25 c. black 25 10
1409. 30 c. brown 25 15
1410. B. 40 c. red 30 20
1411. 45 c. brown 20 15
1412. 50 c. orange 35 15
1413. C. 60 c. olive 35 25
1414. 65 c. blue 60 35
1415. **168.** 70 c. green 60 25
1416. C. 75 c. blue 65 30
1417. A. 80 c. red 75 35
1418. B. 1 b. purple 45 20
1419. C. 2 b. red 90 60

169.

170.

1956. First American Book Festival, Caracas

1420. **169.** 5 c. turquoise and green (postage) 10 10
1421. 10 c. purple and red.. 10 10
1422. 20 c. blue and ultram. 25 10
1423. 25 c. grey and green.. 35 15
1424. 30 c. blue & bright blue 35 15
1425. 40 c. sepia and brown 50 25
1426. 50 c. brown and red.. 55 35
1427. 1 b. slate and violet .. 85 40

1428. **170.** 5 c. brown & orge. (air) 10 10
1429. 10 c. sepia and brown 15 10
1430. 20 c. blue and turquoise 15 10
1431. 25 c. slate and violet.. 35 10
1432. 40 c. purple and red .. 50 15
1433. 45 c. brn. and chocolate 35 15
1434. 60 c. grey and olive .. 75 35

171. Tamanaco Hotel, Caracas.

172. Simon Bolivar.

1957. Tamanaco Hotel, Caracas Commem.

1435. **171.** 5 c. green (postage) .. 10 10
1436. 10 c. red 10 10
1437. 15 c. black 40 10
1438. 20 c. blue 25 10
1439. 25 c. purple 25 10
1440. 30 c. blue 45 35
1441. 35 c. lilac 25 15
1442. 40 c. orange 35 25
1443. 45 c. purple 45 35
1444. 50 c. yellow 60 25
1445. 1 b. myrtle 85 35

1446. 5 c. yellow (air) .. 10 10
1447. 10 c. brown 10 10
1448. 15 c. brown 15 10
1449. 20 c. slate 30 10
1450. 25 c. brown 25 10
1451. 30 c. blue 15 20
1452. 40 c. red 20 15
1453. 45 c. brown 25 15
1454. 50 c. orange 25 20
1455. 60 c. green 45 25
1456. 65 c. orange .. .. 1·25 60
1457. 70 c. black 65 30
1458. 75 c. turquoise .. 75 35
1459. 1 b. purple 75 35
1460. 2 b. black .. .. 1·25 45

1957. 150th Anniv. of Oath of Monte Sacro and 125th Anniv. of Death of Bolivar.

1461. **172.** 5 c. green (postage).. 10 10
1462. 10 c. red 15 10
1463. 20 c. blue 50 15
1464. 25 c. red 50 15
1465. 30 c. blue 40 15
1466. 40 c. orange 60 25
1467. 50 c. yellow 85 40

1468. 5 c. orange (air) .. 15 10
1469. 10 c. brown 20 10
1470. 20 c. blue 45 20
1471. 25 c. purple 50 25
1472. 40 c. red 45 20
1473. 45 c. purple 55 35
1474. 65 c. brown 90 35

173. G.P.O., Caracas.

174. Arms of Santiago de Merida.

1958.

1475. **173.** 5 c. green (postage).. 10 10
1476. 10 c. red 10 10
1477. 15 c. grey 10 10
1478. 20 c. blue 20 10
1479. 25 c. yellow 20 10
1480. 30 c. grey 25 10
1481. 35 c. purple 30 10
1482. 40 c. red 50 15
1483. 45 c. violet .. .. 1·00 70
1484. 50 c. yellow 45 15
1485. 1 b. olive 60 50

1486. 5 c. yellow (air) .. 10 10
1487. 10 c. brown 10 10
1488. 15 c. brown 10 10
1489. 20 c. blue 10 10
1490. 25 c. grey 20 10
1491. 30 c. blue 20 10
1492. 35 c. olive 30 10
1493. 40 c. green 30 10
1494. 50 c. red 30 10
1495. 55 c. olive 45 20
1496. 60 c. mauve 15 20
1497. 65 c. red 20 20
1498. 70 c. green 55 25
1499. 75 c. brown 80 20
1500. 80 c. brown 80 35
1501. 85 c. red .. .. 1·00 50
1502. 90 c. violet 30 35
1503. 95 c. purple 90 50
1504. 1 b. mauve 35 35
1505. 1 b. 20 brown .. 4·50 3·60

1958. 400th Anniv of Santiago de Merida de los Caballeros.

1506. **174.** 5 c. green (postage).. 10 10
1507. 10 c. red 10 10
1508. 15 c. grey 10 10
1509. 20 c. blue 20 10
1510. 25 c. purple 35 10
1511. 30 c. violet 35 15
1512. 35 c. violet 40 15
1513. 40 c. orange 50 35
1514. 45 c. purple 25 15
1515. 50 c. yellow 45 35
1516. 1 b. grey .. .. 1·25 45

1517. 5 c. ochre (air) .. 10 10
1518. 10 c. brown 10 10
1519. 15 c. brown 15 10
1520. 20 c. blue 15 10
1521. 25 c. olive 40 15
1522. 30 c. blue 35 10
1523. 40 c. red 50 15
1524. 45 c. purple 50 20
1525. 50 c. orange 35 35
1526. 60 c. olive 50 25
1527. 65 c. brown 90 35
1528. 70 c. black 55 50
1529. 75 c. blue .. .. 1·00 55
1530. 80 c. violet 65 50
1531. 90 c. green 65 30
1532. 1 b. lilac 75 35

175. G.P.O. Caracas.

176. Arms of Trujillo and Bolivar Monument.

178. "Eternal Flame".

177. Caracas Stadium.

1958.

1533. **175.** 5 c. green (postage).. 35 10
1534. 10 c. red 50 10
1535. 15 c. black 40 10

1536. 5 c. yellow (air) .. 35 10
1537. 10 c. brown 50 10
1538. 15 c. brown 40 10

1958. 400th Anniv. of Trujillo.

1539. **176.** 5 c. green (postage).. 10 10
1540. 10 c. red 10 10
1541. 15 c. grey 10 10
1542. 20 c. blue 15 10
1543. 25 c. mauve 35 10
1544. 30 c. blue 50 15
1545. 35 c. lilac 55 25
1546. 45 c. purple 40 35
1547. 50 c. yellow 40 25
1548. 1 b. olive .. .. 1·00 55

1549. 176. 5 c. buff (air) 10 10
1550. 10 c. brown 10 10
1551. 15 c. brown 25 10
1552. 20 c. blue 30 15
1553. 25 c. grey 40 20
1554. 30 c. blue 40 20
1555. 40 c. green 25 25
1556. 50 c. orange 25 30
1557. 60 c. mauve 35 40
1558. 65 c. red .. .. 1·10 55
1559. 1 b. violet 75 25

1959. 8th C. American and Caribbean Games.
1560. 177. 5 c. green (postage) .. 25 10
1561. 10 c. mauve 25 10
1562. 20 c. blue 35 35
1563. 30 c. blue 45 40
1564. 50 c. lilac 65 35
1565. 178. 5 c. yellow (air) .. 15 10
1566. 10 c. brown 35 15
1567. 15 c. orange 40 20
1568. 30 c. slate 35 40
1569. 50 c. green 45 50

179. Venezuelan ½ Real Stamp of 1859, Gen. J. I. Paz Castillo and Postman.
180. Alexander von Humboldt.

1959. Cent. of First Venezuelan Postage Stamps.
1570. 179. 25 c. ochre (postage) 25 15
1571. – 50 c. blue 45 35
1572. – 1 b. red 85 35
1573. 179. 25 c. ochre (air) .. 25 15
1574. – 50 c. blue 35 35
1575. – 1 b. red 75 35
DESIGNS: 50 c. (2), 1 real stamp of 1859, Don Jacinto Gutierrez and postman on mule. 1 b. (2), 2 reales stamp of 1859, Don Miguel Herrera, and steam mail train and 'plane.

1960. Death Centenary of Von Humboldt (naturalist).
1576. 180. 5 c. olive & grn. (post.) 35 10
1577. 30 c. violet and blue 85 20
1578. 40 c. brown & orange 1·00 50
1579. 5 c. brown & bistre (air) 35 10
1580. 20 c. turquoise & blue 85 20
1581. 40 c. bronze and olive 1·10 50

181. Bolivar Peak, Merida.

1960. Tourist issue.
1582. 181. 5 c. green & emerald (postage) 85 85
1583. – 15 c. deep grey and grey .. .. 2·25 2·25
1584. – 35 c. purple & bright purple .. .. 1·90 1·90
1585. 181. 30 c. blue and deep blue (air) .. .. 1·75 1·60
1586. – 50 c. brown & orange 1·75 1·60
1587. – 65 c. brown & orange 1·75 1·60
DESIGNS: 15 c., 50 c. Caroni Falls, Bolivar. 35 c., 65 c. Cuacharo Caves, Monagas.

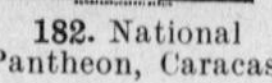

182. National Pantheon, Caracas. **183.** A. Eloy Blanco.

1960. Pantheon in olive.
1588. 182. 5 c. green (postage) .. 10 10
1589. 20 c. blue 50 15
1590. 25 c. olive 70 20
1591. 30 c. grey 85 25
1592. 40 c. light brown .. 1·25 50
1593. 45 c. violet .. .. 1·25 50
1594. 5 c. bistre (air) .. 10 10
1595. 10 c. brown 25 10
1596. 15 c. brown 35 10
1597. 20 c. blue 50 15
1598. 25 c. grey .. .. 1·10 35
1599. 30 c. violet .. .. 1·25 55
1600. 40 c. green 50 15
1601. 45 c. violet 75 20
1602. 60 c. mauve 75 25
1603. 65 c. red 75 40
1604. 70 c. grey 90 35
1605. 75 c. blue .. .. 1·90 60
1606. 80 c. blue .. .. 1·60 50
1607. 1 b. 20 yellow .. 1·90 70

1960. 5th Death Anniv. of Blanco (poet). Portrait in black.
1608. 183. 5 c. green (postage) .. 15 5
1609. 30 c. grey 35 15
1610. 50 c. yellow 60 30
1611. 20 c. blue (air) .. 35 15
1612. 75 c. turquoise .. 1·00 40
1613. 90 c. violet .. .. 1·00 40

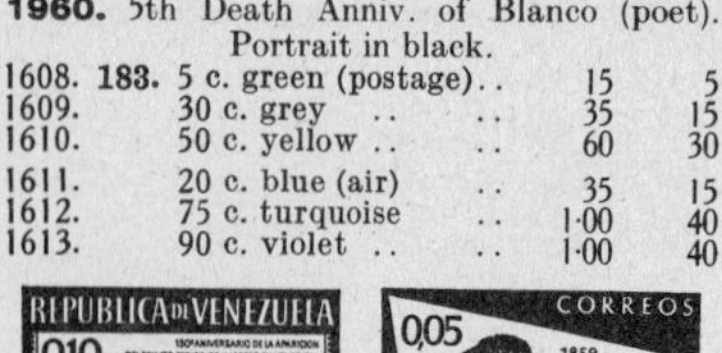

184. 1808 Newspaper and Caracas, 1958. **185.** A. Codazzi.

1960. 150th Anniv. of "Gazeta de Caracas". Centres in black.
1614. 184. 10 c. red (postage) .. 35 15
1615. 20 c. blue 45 20
1616. 35 c. violet 85 70
1617. 5 c. yellow (air) .. 1·50 65
1618. 15 c. brown .. .. 1·00 35
1619. 65 c. orange .. .. 1·25 60

1960. Death Cent. of Codazzi (geographer).
1620. 185. 5 c. deep green and light green (post.) 8 5
1621. 15 c. black and grey .. 45 15
1622. 20 c. blue & light blue 40 15
1623. 45 c. purple and lilac 45 30
1624. 5 c. brown & orge. (air) 8 5
1625. 10 c. sepia and brown 15 8
1626. 25 c. black and grey .. 35 10
1627. 30 c. deep blue & blue 45 15
1628. 50 c. deep brown and light brown .. 70 30
1629. 70 c. black and brown 1·25 45

186. Declaration of Independence.

1960. 150th Anniv. of Independence. Centres multicoloured.
1630. 186. 5 c. green (postage) .. 50 10
1631. 20 c. blue .. .. 1·00 30
1632. 30 c. blue .. .. 1·00 40
1633. 50 c. orange (air) .. 80 30
1634. 75 c. turquoise .. 1·00 35
1635. 90 c. violet .. .. 1·25 40

187. Drilling for Oil. **188.** L. Caceres de Arismendi.

190. Gen. A. J. de Sucre. **189.** Gen. J. A. Anzoategui.

1960. Oil Industry.
1636. 187. 5 c. myrtle and turq. (postage) .. .. 1·40 70
1637. 10 c. brown and red .. 70 25
1638. 15 c. mauve and purple 85 30
1639. – 30 c. indigo & blue (air) 50 20
1640. – 40 c. olive and green 85 35
1641. – 50 c. brown & orange 1·00 40
DESIGN: Nos. 1639/41, Oil refinery.

1960. 94th Death Anniv. of Luisa Caceres de Arismendi. Centres multicoloured.
1642. 188. 20 c. blue (postage) .. 1·00 30
1643. 25 c. yellow 85 30
1644. 30 c. blue .. .. 1·10 40
1645. 5 c. bistre (air) .. 80 30
1646. 10 c. brown .. .. 1·00 45
1647. 60 c. red .. .. 1·90 55

1960. 140th Death Anniv. of Gen. Anzoategui.
1648. 189. 5 c. olive & green (post.) 20 5
1649. 15 c. purple & brown 40 5
1650. 20 c. deep blue & blue 45 15
1651. 25 c. brn. & grey (air) 40 20
1652. 40 c. olive and yellow 40 40
1653. 45 c. purple & mauve 60 30

1960. 130th Death Anniv. of Gen. A. J. de Sucre.
1654. 190. 10 c. mult. (postage) 35 15
1655. 15 c. multicoloured .. 40 20
1656. 20 c. multicoloured .. 60 30
1657. 190. 25 c. mult. (air) .. 60 30
1658. 30 c. multicoloured .. 85 40
1659. 50 c. multicoloured .. 1·25 60

191. Skyscraper. **192.** "Population and Farming".

1961. National Census. Skyscraper in orange.
1660. 191. 5 c. green 5 5
1661. 10 c. red 5 5
1662. 15 c. grey 10 5
1663. 20 c. blue 15 5
1664. 25 c. brown 25 12
1665. 30 c. blue 25 10
1666. 35 c. purple 35 12
1667. 40 c. brown 50 25
1668. 45 c. violet 70 35
1669. 50 c. yellow 50 20

1961. Air. 9th Population Census and 3rd Farming Census. Animal's head and inscr. in black.
1670. 192. 5 c. yellow 10 10
1671. 10 c. brown 10 10
1672. 15 c. orange 10 10
1673. 20 c. blue 15 10
1674. 25 c. grey 20 10
1675. 30 c. blue 25 10
1676. 40 c. green 35 15
1677. 45 c. violet 35 20
1678. 50 c. orange 40 25
1679. 60 c. mauve 50 25
1680. 65 c. red 45 35
1681. 70 c. deep grey .. 65 25
1682. 75 c. turquoise .. 60 40
1683. 80 c. violet 60 35
1684. 90 c. violet 90 35

193. R. M. Baralt. **195.** Arms of San Cristobal.

1961. Death Cent. of R. M. Baralt (writer).
1685. 193. 5 c. turq. & grn. (post.) 10 5
1686. 15 c. brown and grey 25 5
1687. 35 c. violet and mauve 40 15
1688. 25 c. sepia & grey (air) 45 30
1689. 30 c. violet and blue .. 55 35
1690. 40 c. bronze and green 65 35

1961. Air. 4th Cent. of San Cristobal. Arms in red, yellow and blue.
1692. 195. 5 c. sepia and orange 8 5
1693. 55 c. black and green 45 25

196. Yellow-crowned Amazon. **197.** J. J. Aguerrevere (first College President).

1961. Birds. Multicoloured.
1694. 30 c. Type 196 (postage) 90 40
1695. 40 c. Snowy Egret .. 1·10 40
1696. 50 c. Scarlet Ibis .. 2·40 80
1697. 5 c. Troupial (air) .. 1·75 1·10
1698. 10 c. Guianan Cock of the Rock 90 60
1699. 15 c. Tropical Mockingbird .. .. 1·10 65

1961. Engineering College Cent.
1700. 197. 25 c. blue 15 8

198. Battle Scene.

1961. 140th Anniv. of Battle of Carabobo. Centres multicoloured.
1702. 198. 5 c. green (postage) .. 10 8
1703. 40 c. brown 70 30
1704. – 50 c. blue (air) .. 70 15
1705. – 1 b. 05 orange .. 1·10 60
1706. – 1 b. 50 mauve .. 1·60 60
1707. – 1 b. 90 violet .. 1·90 85
1708. – 2 b. sepia .. .. 2·10 85
1709. – 3 b. blue .. .. 2·75 1·00
DESIGN: 50 c. to 3 b. Cavalry charge.

199. Cardinal's Arms. **200.** Archbishop Blanco.

1962. Air. Elevation to Cardinal of Jose Humberto Quintero.
1710. 199. 5 c. mauve 5 5

1962. Air. 4th Anniv. of Archbishop Blanco's Pastoral Letter.
1712. 200. 75 c. mauve .. 70 30

201. "Oncidium papilio Lindl".

1962. Orchids. Multicoloured.
1713. 5 c. Type 201 (postage) .. 10 10
1714. 10 c. "Caularthron bilamellatum (Rchb. f.) R. E. Schultes" 15 10
1715. 20 c. "Stanhopea Wardii Lodd. ex Lindl" .. 40 10
1716. 25 c. "Catasetum pileatum Rchb. f." 35 10
1717. 30 c. "Masdevallia tovarensis Rchb. f." 40 15
1718. 35 c. "Epidendrum Stamfordianum Batem" (horiz.) 45 25
1719. 50 c. "Epidendrum atropurpureum Willd" .. 55 35
1720. 3 b. "Oncidium falcipetalum Lindl." .. .. 3·00 1·60
1721. 5 c. "Oncidium volvox Rchb. f." (air) .. 10 10
1722. 20 c. "Cycnoches chlorochilon Kl." 20 10
1723. 25 c. "Cattleya Gaskelliana Rchb. f. var. alba" 30 15
1724. 30 c. "Epidendrum difforme Jacq." (horiz.) 20 12
1725. 40 c. "Catasetum callosum Lindl." (horiz.) .. 30 20
1726. 50 c. "Oncidium bicolor Lindl." 35 30
1727. 1 b. "Brassavola nodosa Lindl." (horiz.) .. 60 25
1728. 1 b. 05 "Epidendrum lividum Lindl." .. 1·60 85
1729. 1 b. 50 "Schomburgkia undulata Lindl." .. 1·90 90
1730. 2 b. "Oncidium zebrinum Rchb. f." .. .. 2·25 1·40

202. Signing of Independence.

1962. 150th Anniv. of Declaration of Independence. Mult. centres; frame colours given.
1731. 202. 5 c. green (postage) .. 15 5
1732. 20 c. blue 35 15
1733. 25 c. orange 55 30
1735. 55 c. green (air) .. 45 20
1736. 1 b. 05 mauve .. 1·50 60
1737. 1 b. 50 violet .. 1·25 55

1962. Air. Bicentenary of Upata. Surch. **BICENTENARIO DE UPATA 1762-1962 RESELLADO AEREO VALOR Bs 2,00.**
1739. 173. 2 b. on 1 b. olive .. 1·60 75

204. Putting the Shot.

1962. 1st National Games, Caracas, 1961.
1740. **204.** 5 c. green (postage) .. 8 5
1741. – 10 c. mauve 15 5
1742. – 25 c. blue 30 15
1744. – 40 c. grey (air) .. 40 25
1745. – 75 c. brown 60 35
1746. – 85 c. red .. .. 1·40 55
SPORTS: 10 c. Football. 25 c. Swimming. 40 c. Cycling. 75 c Baseball. 85 c. Gymnastics.
Each value is arranged in blocks of 4 within the sheet, with the top corners of each stamp converging to the centre of the block.

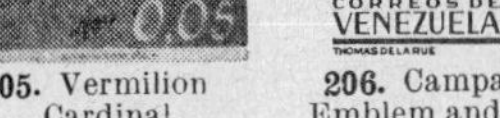

205. Vermilion Cardinal. **206.** Campaign Emblem and Map.

1962. Birds. Multicoloured.
1748 5 c. Type **205** (postage) .. 20 10
1749 10 c. Great kiskadee .. 40 10
1750 20 c. Glossy-black thrush 95 20
1751 25 c. Collared trogon .. 1·10 30
1752 30 c. Swallow tanager .. 1·50 35
1753 40 c. Long-tailed sylph .. 1·90 50
1754 3 b. Black-necked stilt .. 10·50 5·00
1755 5 c. American kestrel (air) 40 15
1756 20 c. Red-billed whistling duck (horiz) .. 95 20
1757 25 c. Amazon kingfisher 1·10 30
1758 30 c. Rufous-vented chachalaca .. .. 1·40 35
1759 50 c. Oriole blackbird .. 2·10 55
1760 55 c. Pauraque .. .. 3·75 1·00
1761 2 b. 30 Red-crowned woodpecker .. .. 10·50 4·25
1762 2 b. 50 White-faced quail dove .. .. 10·50 4·00

1962. Malaria Eradication.
1763. **206.** 50 c. brn. & blk. (post.) 40 20
1764. – 30 c. grn. & blk. (air) 35 20
DESIGN: As T **206** but size 26 × 36 mm.

207. Collared Peccary. **208.** Fisherman.

1963. Venezuelan Wild Life. Multicoloured.
1766. 5 c. White-tailed deer (postage) 10 10
1767. 10 c. Type **207** 10 10
1768. 35 c. Widow monkey .. 25 10
1769. 50 c. Giant otter .. 35 25
1770. 1 b. Puma .. .. 1·60 85
1771. 3 c. Capybara .. .. 3·25 1·60
1772. 5 c. Spectacled bear (vert.) (air) 20 10
1773. 40 c. Paca 60 25
1774. 50 c. Pale-throated sloth 80 35
1775. 55 c. Giant anteater .. 1·00 40
1776. 1 b. 50 Brazilian tapir .. 2·75 1·60
1777. 2 b. Jaguar .. .. 4·25 2·10

1963. Freedom from Hunger.
1778. **208.** 25 c. bl. on pink (post.) 20 15
1779. – 40 c. red on green (air) 50 25
1780. – 75 c. sepia on yellow 30 40
DESIGNS: 40 c. Farmer with lambs. 75 c. Harvester.

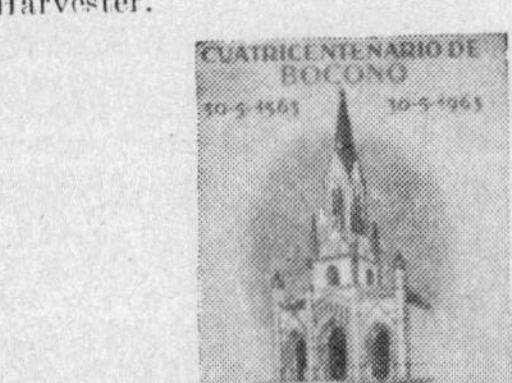

209. Bocono Cathedral.

1963. 400th Anniv. of Bocono.
1781. **209.** 50 c. mult. on buff (postage) 45 20
1782. – 1 b. mult. on buff (air) 1·25 40
DESIGNS: 1 b. Bocono Arms.

210. St. Peter's Basilica, Vatican City. **211.** Flag.

1963. Ecumenical Council, Vatican City.
1783. **210.** 35 c. brn. & blue (post.) 35 15
1784. 45 c. brown and green 35 20
1785. – 80 c. multicoloured (air) 85 35
1786. – 90 c. multicoloured .. 85 40
DESIGN: 80 c., 90 c. Arms of Vatican City and Venezuela.

1963. National Flag and Arms Cent. Mult.
1787. 30 c. Type **211** (postage) 20 15
1788. 70 c. Venezuela Arms (vert.) (air) 85 50

212. Maracaibo Bridge. **213.** Arms, Map and Guardsman.

1963. Opening of Higher Bridge, Lake Maracaibo.
1789. **212.** 30 c. brn. & bl. (post.) 55 10
1790. 35 c. brown and green 65 20
1791. 80 c. brown and green 1·25 40
1792. – 90 c. ochre, brown and green (air) .. .. 1·00 50
1793. – 95 c. ochre, brn. & blue 1·00 55
1794. – 1 b. ochre, brn. & blue 95 50
DESIGN—HORIZ. 90 c. to 1 b. Aerial view of bridge and mainland.

1963. 25th Anniv. of National Guard.
1795. **213.** 50 c. green, red & blue on cream (postage) 40 20
1796. 1 b. blue and red on cream (air) .. 1·25 70

214. Dag Hammarskjold and Atlantic Map.

1963. 1st Death Anniv (1962) of Dag Hammarskjold (U.N. Secretary-General, 1953–61).
1797. **214.** 25 c. ind. & blue (post.) 20 12
1798. 55 c. green & turquoise 75 35
1799. 80 c. light blue and deep blue (air) .. 75 45
1800. 90 c. violet and blue 1·00 60

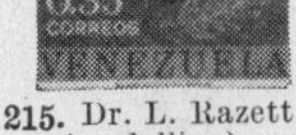

215. Dr. L. Razetti (medallion). **216.** Dr. F. A. Risquez (Venezuelan Red Cross President, 1922–23).

1963. Birth Centenary (1962) of Dr. Luis Razetti (founder of University School of Medicine and of Vargas Hospital).
1802. **215.** 35 c. brown, ochre and blue (postage) .. 35 20
1803. 45 c. brn., ochre & mve. 50 20
1804. – 95 c. blue & mauve (air) 90 60
1805. – 1 b. 05 sepia and green 1·25 70
DESIGN: 95 c., 1 b. 05, Portrait of Dr. Razetti.

1963. Red Cross Centenary. Multicoloured.
1806 15 c. Type **216** (postage) 15 8
1807 20 c. Dr. Carlos J. Bello (President of Venezuelan Red Cross, 1928–31) 20 10
1808 40 c. Sir Vincent K. Barrington (first President of Venezuelan Red Cross) (air) 40 35
1809 75 c. Nurse and Child .. 70 50
All designs show centenary emblem.

217. Labourer. **218.** Pedro Gual.

1964. Cent. of Venezuelan Ministry of Works and National Industries Exhibition, Caracas. Multicoloured.
1810. 5 c. Type **217** (postage) .. 8 5
1811. 10 c. Petrol industry .. 20 5
1812. 15 c. Building construction 25 8
1813. 30 c. Road & rail transport 25 35
1814. 40 c. Agricultural machine 60 25
1815. 5 c. Loading ship (air) .. 8 5
1816. 10 c. Tractor and maize .. 10 5
1817. 15 c. Type **217** 15 8
1818. 20 c. Petrol industry .. 20 8
1819. 50 c. Building construction 60 30

1964. Death Cent. (1962) of Pedro Gual (statesman).
1820. **218.** 40 c. olive (post.) .. 40 20
1821. 50 c. brown 45 25
1822. 75 c. turquoise (air) .. 60 25
1823. 1 b. mauve 70 30

219. Dr. C. Arvelo. **220.** Blast Furnace.

1964. Death Cent. (1962) of Carlos Arvelo (physician).
1824. **219.** 1 b. black and blue .. 1·00 40

1964. Inaug. of Orinoco Steel Works. Mult.
1825. 20 c. Type **220** (postage) 25 10
1826. 50 c. Type **220** 50 20
1827. 80 c. Cauldron & map (air) 85 35
1828. 1 b. As 80 c. .. .. 1·10 40
The 80 c. and 1 b. are vert.

221. Arms of Ciudad Bolivar. **222.** R. Gallegos.

1964. Air. Bicent. of Ciudad Bolivar.
1829. **221.** 1 b. multicoloured .. 1·10 70

1964. 80th Birth Anniv. of Romulo Gallegos (novelist).
1830. **222.** 5 c. green and yellow (postage) 8 5
1831. 10 c. blue & light blue 12 5
1832. 15 c. purple & mauve 25 15
1833. – 30 c. brown & yell. (air) 30 15
1834. – 40 c. purple and pink 40 20
1835. – 50 c. brown and orange 55 30
DESIGN: No. 1833/5, Gallegos and book.

223. Angel Falls (Bolivar State). **224.** Eleanor Roosevelt.

1964. Tourist Publicity. Inscr. "Conozca a Venezuela Primera" ("See Venezuela First"). Multicoloured.
1836. 5 c. Type **223** 10 5
1837. 10 c. Tropical Landscape (Sucre) 15 5
1838. 15 c. Rocks, San Juan (Guarico) 20 8
1839. 30 c. Fishermen casting nets (Anzoategui) .. 40 12
1840. 40 c. Mountaineering (Merida) 60 15

1964. Air. 15th Anniv. (1963) of Declaration of Human Rights.
1841. **224.** 1 b. orange and violet 70 40

1965. Various stamps surch. **RESELLADO VALOR** and new value. (a) Postage.
1842. 5 c. on 1 b. (No. 1485) .. 50 8
1843. 10 c. on 45 c. (1668) .. 15 10
1844. 15 c. on 55 c. (1798) .. 12 8
1845. 20 c. on 3 b. (1754) .. 80 15
1846. 25 c. on 45 c. (1623) .. 20 15
1847. 25 c. on 3 b. (1720) .. 25 15
1848. 25 c. on 1 b. (1770) .. 35 15
1849. 25 c. on 3 b. (1771) .. 20 15
1850. 30 c. on 1 b. (1516) .. 25 10
1851. 40 c. on 1 b. (1824) .. 70 20
1852. 60 c. on 80 c. (1791) .. 85 35

(b) Air.
1853. 5 c. on 55 c. (1495) .. 8 5
1854. 5 c. on 70 c. (1498) .. 10 5
1855. 5 c. on 80 c. (1500) .. 12 8
1856. 5 c. on 85 c. (1501) .. 8 5
1857. 5 c. on 90 c. (1502) .. 8 5
1858. 5 c. on 95 c. (1503) .. 8 5
1859. 5 c. on 1 b. (1796) .. 50 35

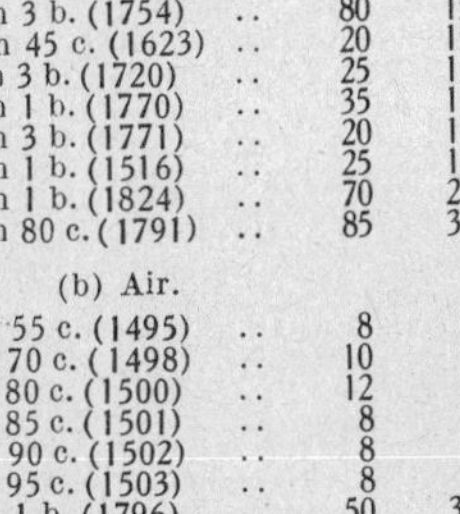

1860. 10 c. on 3 b. (804) .. 15 8
1861. 10 c. on 4 b. (805) .. 70 35
1862. 10 c. on 70 c. (1681) .. 35 15
1863. 10 c. on 90 c. (1684) .. 25 10
1864. 10 c. on 1 b. 05 (1705) .. 50 25
1865. 10 c. on 1 b. 90 (1707) .. 25 15
1866. 10 c. on 2 b. (1708) .. 35 15
1867. 10 c. on 3 b. (1709) .. 35 15
1868. 10 c. on 80 c. (1785) .. 15 5
1869. 10 c. on 90 c. (1786) .. 15 5
1870. 15 c. on 3 b. (769) .. 35 15
1871. 15 c. on 90 c. (1613) .. 25 10
1872. 15 c. on 80 c. (1799) .. 25 10
1873. 15 c. on 90 c. (1800) .. 25 10
1874. 15 c. on 1 b. (1829) .. 35 15
1875. 20 c. on 2 b. (1460) .. 40 15
1876. 20 c. on 55 c. (1693) .. 30 10
1877. 20 c. on 55 c. (1760) .. 1·25 25
1878. 20 c. on 2 b. 30 (1761) .. 80 15
1879. 20 c. on 2 b. 50 (1762) .. 1·25 25
1880. 20 c. on 70 c. (1788) .. 50 35
1881. 25 c. on 70 c. (1629) .. 55 30
1882. 25 c. on 1 b. 05 (1728) .. 35 15
1883. 25 c. on 1 b. 50 (1729) .. 35 15
1884. 25 c. on 2 b. (1730) .. 50 25
1885. 25 c. on 1 b. 50 (1776) .. 50 15
1886. 25 c. on 2 b. (1777) .. 50 25
1887. 25 c. on 95 c. (1804) .. 45 25
1888. 25 c. on 1 b. 05 (1805) .. 50 25
1889. 30 c. on 1 b. (1782) .. 70 35
1890. 40 c. on 1 b. 05 (1736) .. 50 25
1891. 50 c. on 65 c. (1603) .. 25 12
1892. 50 c. on 1 b. 20 (1607) .. 70 35
1893. 50 c. on 1 b. (1841) .. 35 15
1894. 60 c. on 90 c. (1792) .. 1·00 50
1895. 60 c. on 95 c. (1793) .. 75 35
1896. 75 c. on 85 c. (1746) .. 75 40

(c) Revenue stamps additionally optd. **CORREOS.**
1897. 5 c. on 5 c. green .. 8 5
1898. 5 c. on 20 c. brown .. 8 5
1899. 10 c. on 10 c. bistre .. 8 5
1900. 15 c. on 40 c. green .. 8 5
1901. 20 c. on 3 b. blue .. 35 15
1902. 25 c. on 5 b. 70 35
1903. 25 c. on 5 b. blue .. 35 15
1904. 60 c. on 3 b. blue .. 60 40

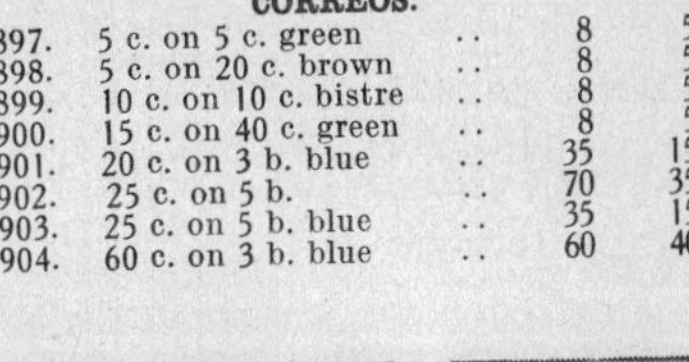

226. Pres. Kennedy and Alliance Emblem. **227.** Federation Emblem.

1965. "Alliance for Progress".
1905. **226.** 20 c. black (postage) 35 15
1906. 40 c. violet 50 20
1907. 60 c. turquoise (air) 70 30
1908. 80 c. brown 85 35

1965. Air. 20th Anniv. of Venezuelan Medical Federation.
1909. **227.** 65 c. red and black .. 1·00 45

228. Venezuelan Pavilion. **229.** Andres Bello.

1965. Air. New York World's Fair.
1910. **228.** 1 b. multicoloured .. 65 35

1965. Air. Death Cent. of Andres Bello (poet).
1911. **229.** 80 c. brown & orange 75 60

230. Restrepo's Map 1827. **232.** Bolivar and Part of Letter.

231. I.T.U. Emblem, Satellite, and Aerials of 1865 and 1965. **233.** Children on "Magic Carpet" and "Three Kings"

1965. Guyana Claim. Multicoloured.

1912. 5 c. Codazzi's map, 1840 (vert.) (postage) .. 10 5
1913. 15 c. Type **230** 30 10
1914. 40 c. L. de Surville's map, 1778 .. .. .. 55 15
1915. 25 c. Cruz Cano's map, 1775 (air) 40 15
1916. 40 c. (50 c.) Map stamp of 1896 (vert.) 55 15
1917. 75 c. Foreign Relations Ministry map 75 35

1965. Air. I.T.U. Cent.

1919. **231.** 75 c. black and green 70 30

1965. Air. 150th Anniv. of Bolivar's Letter from Jamaica.

1920. **232.** 75 c. black and blue .. 60 30

1965. Air. Children's (Christmas) Festival.

1921. **233.** 70 c. blue and yellow 80 55

234. Father F. Toro. **235.** Sir Winston Churchill.

1965. Air. Death Cent. of Father Fermin Toro.

1922. **234.** 1 b. black and orange 60 30

1965. Air. Churchill Commem.

1923. **235.** 1 b. black and lilac .. 90 40

236. I.C.Y. Emblem. **237.** Emblem and Map.

1965. Air. Int. Co-operation Year.

1924. **236.** 85 c. violet and gold 1·00 40

1965. Air. 75th Anniv. of Organization of American States.

1925. **237.** 50 c. gold, black & blue 85 35

238. "Eurytides protesilaus". **239.** Farms of 1936 and 1966.

1966. Butterflies. Multicoloured.

1926 20 c. Type **238** (postage) 40 15
1927 30 c. "Morpho peleides" 55 20
1928 50 c. "Papilio zagreus" .. 80 30
1929 65 c. "Anaea marthesia" (air) .. .. .. 1·00 40
1930 85 c. "Anaea clytemnestra" .. .. 1·60 55
1931 1 b. "Caligo atreus" .. 2·10 60

1966. Air. 30th Anniv. of Ministry of Agriculture and Husbandry.

1932. **239.** 55 c. blk., grn. & yell. 60 25

240. 19th-century Sailing Packet crossing Atlantic.

1966. Bicent. of Maritime Mail.

1933. **240.** 60 c. black, blue & brn. 1·50 50

241. Sebucan Dance.

1966. "Popular Dances". Multicoloured.

1934. 5 c. Type **241** (postage) .. 10 5
1935. 10 c. Candlemas 20 8
1936. 15 c. Chichamaya 30 10
1937. 20 c. Carite 40 15
1938. 25 c. "Round Drum" .. 60 25
1939. 35 c. Devil Dance, Feast of Corpus Christi .. 65 35
1940. 40 c. Tamunanque (air) 50 35
1941. 50 c. Parranda de San Pedro 60 40
1942. 60 c. Las Turas 35 25
1943. 70 c. Joropo 85 55
1944. 80 c. Chimbanguele .. 90 35
1945. 90 c. "The Shepherds" 1·10 50

242. Title Page.

1966. Air. 150th Death Anniv. (1964) of Jose Lamas (composer).

1946. **242.** 55 c. blk., bistre & grn. 60 30
1947. 95 c. blk., bistre & mve. 60 40

243. A. Michelena (self-portrait). **244.** Lincoln.

1966. Birth Cent. (1963) of Arturo Michelena (painter). Multicoloured.

1948. 95 c. sepia and cream (Type **243**) (postage) .. 85 35
1949. 1 b. "Pentesilea" (battle scene) 75 35
1950. 1 b. 05 "La Vara Rota" ("The Red Cloak") .. 85 35
1951. 95 c. "Escena de Circo" ("Circus Scene") (air) 60 35
1952. 1 b. "Miranda in La Carraca" 75 35
1953. 1 b. 05 "Carlota Corday" 85 35
Nos. 1949/53 are horiz.

1966. Air. Death Cent. (1965) of Abraham Lincoln.

1954. **244.** 1 b. black and drab .. 70 55

245. Construction Worker. **246.** Dr. Hernandez.

1966. 2nd O.E.A. Labour Ministers Conf.

1955. **245.** 10 c. black and yellow 8 5
1956. 20 c. black and turq. 20 8
1957. – 30 c. violet and blue 15 15
1958. – 35 c. olive and yellow 25 15
1959. – 50 c. purple and pink 40 20
1960. – 65 c. purple and red 60 30

DESIGNS: 30 c., 65 c. Labour Monument. 35 c. Machinist. 50 c. Car assembly line.

1966. Air. Birth Centenary (1964) of Dr. Jose Hernandez (physician).

1961. **246.** 1 b. deep blue & blue 1·00 45

247. Dr. M. Dagnino (founder) and Hospital.

1966. Air. Centenary of Chiquinquira Hospital, Maracaibo.

1962. **247.** 1 b. deep green & green 1·00 40

248. Marbled Cichlid. **249.** R. Arevalo Gonzalez.

1966. Fishes. Multicoloured.

1963. 15 c. Type **248** (postage) 15 10
1964. 25 c. Eye spot cichlid .. 25 15
1965. 45 c. Piranha 70 30
1966. 75 c. Head-standing fish (vert.) (air) 90 50
1967. 90 c. Swordtail characin 90 50
1968. 1 b. Butterfly dwarf cichlid 90 50

1966. Air. Birth Centenary of Rafael Arevalo Gonzalez.

1969. **249.** 75 c. black and yellow 65 35

250. Simon Bolivar, 1816 (after anonymous artist). **251.** "Justice".

1966. Air. Bolivar Commemoration.

1970. **250.** 5 c. multicoloured .. 10 10
1971. 10 c. multicoloured .. 10 10
1972. 20 c. multicoloured .. 10 10
1973. – 25 c. multicoloured .. 15 10
1974. – 30 c. multicoloured .. 20 10
1975. – 35 c. multicoloured .. 15 10
1976. – 40 c. multicoloured .. 30 15
1977. – 50 c. multicoloured .. 30 15
1978. – 60 c. multicoloured .. 30 15
1979. – 80 c. multicoloured .. 60 30
1980. – 1 b. 20 multicoloured 80 60
1981. – 4 b. multicoloured .. 3·00 1·90

BOLIVAR PORTRAITS: 25 c., 30 c., 35 c. After paintings by Jose Gil de Castro, 1825. 40 c., 50 c., 60 c. Anonymous artist, 1825. 80 c., 1 b. 20, 4 b. Anonymous artist, circa 1829.

1966. Air. 50th Anniv. of Political and Social Sciences Academy.

1982. **251.** 50 c. purple and lilac 55 25

252. The Nativity. **253.** Globe and Communications Emblems.

1966. Christmas.

1983. **252.** 65 c. black and violet 50 25

1960. 30th Anniv. of Venezuelan Communications Ministry.

1984. **253.** 45 c. multicoloured . 40 20

254. Angostura Bridge.

1967. Air. Opening of Angostura Bridge, Orinoco River.

1985. **254.** 40 c. multicoloured .. 35 20

255. Ruben Dario (poet). **256.** University Building and Arms.

1967. Birth Cent. of Ruben Dario.

1986. **255.** 70 c. indigo and blue 85 35

1967. 75th Anniv. of Zulia University.

1987. **256.** 80 c. black, red & gold 85 35

257. Venezuelan Pavilion.

1967. Air. World Fair, Montreal.

1988. **257.** 1 b. multicoloured .. 60 30

258. Cacique Guaicaipuro (statue). **259.** Francisco Esteban Gomez.

1967. Air. 400th Anniv. of Caracas. Mult.

1989. 10 c. Palace of the Academies (horiz.) .. 8 5
1990. 15 c. Type **258** 8 5
1991. 45 c. Capt. F. Fajardo .. 35 15
1992. 50 c. St. Teresa's Church 35 15
1993. 55 c. Diego de Losada (founder) 45 20
1994. 60 c. Constellations over Caracas (horiz.) .. 50 25
1995. 65 c. Arms of Caracas .. 55 30
1996. 70 c. Federal Legislative Building (horiz.) .. 55 25
1997. 75 c. University City (horiz.) 70 30
1998. 85 c. El Pulpo road junction (horiz.) 70 35
1999. 90 c. Map of Caracas (horiz.) 75 35
2000. 1 b. Plaza Mayor, Caracas, c. 1800 (horiz.) .. 85 45
2001. 2 b. Avenida Libertador (horiz.) .. .. .. 2·00 65

1967. Air. 150th Anniv. of Battle of Matasiete.

2003. **259.** 90 c. multicoloured 70 35

260. J. V. Gonzalez. **261.** Child with Toy Windmill.

1967. Air. Death Centenary of Juan Gonzalez (journalist).

2016. **260.** 80 c. black and yellow 55 30

1967. Air. Children's Festival.

2017. **261.** 45 c. multicoloured .. 40 20
2018. 75 c. multicoloured .. 60 25
2019. 90 c. multicoloured .. 70 35

262. "The Madonna of the Rosary" (Lochner). **263.** Dr. J. M. Nunez Ponte (educator).

1967. Air. Christmas.

2020. **262.** 1 b. multicoloured .. 80 40

1968. Air. 3rd Death Anniv of Dr. Jose Manuel Nunez Ponte.

2021. **263.** 65 c. multicoloured 35 25

264. General Miranda and Printing Press.

1968. Air. 150th Death Anniv. of General Francisco de Miranda. Multicoloured.

2022. 20 c. Type **264** 20 10
2023. 35 c. Portrait and Houses of Parliament, London 35 15
2024. 45 c. Portrait and Arc de Triomphe, Paris .. 55 30
2025. 70 c. Portrait (vert.) .. 65 25
2026. 80 c. Bust and Venezuelan flags (vert.) 80 45

HAVE YOU READ THE NOTES AT THE BEGINNING OF THIS CATALOGUE?

These often provide answers to the enquiries we receive.

265. Title Page and Printing Press.

1968. 150th Anniv. of Newspaper "Correo del Orinoco".
2027. **265.** 1 b. 50 multicoloured 1·25 50

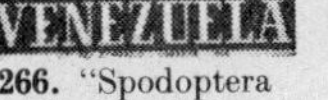

266. "Spodoptera frugiperda". 267. Keys.

1968. Insects. Multicoloured.
2028 20 c. Type **266** (postage) 50 20
2029 75 c. "Anthonomus grandis" 60 30
2030 90 c. "Manduca sexta" .. 80 40
2031 5 c. "Atta sextens" (air) 15 10
2032 15 c. "Aeneolamia varia" 35 15
2033 20 c. "Systena sp." 50 20
The 20 (air), 75 and 90 c. are horiz.

1968. Air. 30th Anniv. of Office of Controller-General.
2034. **267.** 95 c. multicoloured 65 30

268. Pistol-shooting. 269. Guayana Sub-station.

1968. Air. Olympic Games, Mexico. Mult.
2035 5 c. Type **268** 10 10
2036 15 c. Running (horiz) .. 25 10
2037 30 c. Fencing (horiz) .. 35 20
2038 75 c. Boxing (horiz) .. 75 35
2039 5 b. Sailing .. .. 3·75 1·40

1968. Rural Electrification. Multicoloured.
2040. 15 c. Type **269** 15 8
2041. 45 c. Encantado Dam .. 40 20
2042. 50 c. Macagua Dam .. 55 20
2043. 80 c. Guri Dam .. 85 40
The 45 and 50 c. are horiz.

270. "The Holy Family" (F. J. de Lerma). 271. House and Savings Bank.

1968. Air. Christmas.
2044. **270.** 40 c. multicoloured .. 35 15

1968. National Savings System.
2045. **271.** 45 c. multicoloured .. 30 20

272. Children and Star. 273. Planting a Tree.

1968. Air. Children's Festival.
2046. **272.** 80 c. orange and violet 55 25

1968. Conservation of Natural Resources. Multicoloured designs each incorporating central motif as in T **273**.
2047. 15 c. Type **273** (postage) 8 5
2048. 20 c. Plantation 15 8
2049. 30 c. Waterfall 30 12
2050. 45 c. Logs 35 15
2051. 55 c. Cultivated land .. 70 35
2052. 75 c. Bonito (fish) .. 50 25
2053. 15 c. Marbled wood quail (air) 50 15
2054. 20 c. Scarlet ibis, jabiru, great blue heron and red-billed whistling duck 60 15
2055. 30 c. Wood-carving .. 25 10
2056. 90 c. Brown trout .. 75 35
2057. 95 c. Mountain highway 1·25 55
2058. 1 b. Red-eyed vireo and common cowbird (young) .. .. 1·25 50
The 15 c. (both), 20 c. (air), 30 c. (both) and 55 c. are vert. the remainder are horiz.

274. Colorada Beach, Sucre. 276. Dr. Martin Luther King.

275. Bolivar addressing Congress.

1969. Tourism. Multicoloured.
2059. 15 c. Type **274** (postage) .. 15 8
2060. 45 c. San Francisco de Yare Church, Miranda 50 15
2061. 90 c. Houses on Stilts, Zulia 75 55
2062. 15 c. Desert lansdcape, Falcon (air) 20 10
2063. 30 c. Humboldt Hotel, Caracas 25 15
2064. 40 c. Mountain cable-car, Merida 45 25

1969. 150th Anniv. of Angostura Congress.
2066. **275.** 45 c. multicoloured .. 40 20

1969. 1st Death Anniv. of Martin Luther King (American Civil Rights Leader).
2067. **276.** 1 b. multicoloured .. 50 25

277. "Tabebuia pentaphylla".

1969. Nature Conservation. Trees. Mult.
2068. 50 c. Type **277** (postage) .. 50 20
2069. 65 c. "Erythrina poeppigiana" 70 30
2070. 90 c. "Platymiscium sp." 1·00 50
2071. 5 c. "Cassia grandis" (air) 8 5
2072. 20 c. "Triplaris caracasana" 25 10
2073. 25 c. "Samanea saman" 35 15

278. "On the Balcony" (C. Rojas).

1969. Paintings by Cristobal Rojas. Mult.
2074. 25 c. Type **278** 20 15
2075. 35 c. "The Pheasant" .. 35 20
2076. 45 c. "The Christening" 55 30
2077. 50 c. "The Empty Place" 70 35
2078. 60 c. "The Tavern" .. 85 40
2079. 1 b. "The Arm" (27 × 55 mm.) .. .. .. 1·25 70
Nos. 2075/2078 are horiz.

279. I.L.O. Emblem.

1969. 50th Anniv. of I.L.O.
2080. **279.** 2 b. 50 black and brown 1·40 1·10

280. Charter and Arms of Guayana.

1969. Industrial Development. Multicoloured.
2081. 45 c. Type **280** 45 20
2082. 1 b. SIDOR steel-works .. 65 30

281. Arcade, Casa del Balcon.

1969. 400th Anniv. of Carora. Mult.
2083. 20 c. Type **281** 15 8
2084. 25 c. Ruins of La Pastora Church 25 12
2085. 55 c. Chapel of the Cross .. 60 30
2086. 65 c. Museum and library building 70 35

282. "Alexander Von Humboldt" (J. Stieler). 283. A. Alfinger, A. Pacheco and P. Maldonado (founders).

1969. Air. Birth Bicent. of Alexander von Humboldt (German naturalist).
2087. **282.** 50 c. multicoloured .. 50 20

1969. Air. 400th Anniv. of Maracaibo. Mult.
2088. 20 c. Type **283** 20 12
2089. 25 c. Map of Maracaibo, 1562 25 15
2090. 40 c. City coat-of-arms .. 30 20
2091. 70 c. University Hospital 60 35
2092. 75 c. Cacique Mara Monument 70 40
2093. 1 b. Baralt Plaza .. 80 50
Nos. 2089/92 are horiz.

284. Bolivar's Wedding (T. Salas).

1969. "Bolivar in Spain".
2094. **284.** 10 c. multicoloured .. 10 5
2095. – 15 c. black and red .. 20 10
2096. – 35 c. multicoloured .. 35 15
DESIGNS—VERT. 15 c. "Bolivar as a Student" (artist unknown). 35 c. Bolivar's statue, Madrid.

285. Astronauts and Moon Landing.

1969. Air. 1st Man on the Moon.
2098. **285.** 90 c. multicoloured 1·00 45

286. "Virgin of the Rosary" (17th cent. Venetian School).

1969. Air. Christmas. Multicoloured.
2100. 75 c. Type **286** 60 25
2101. 80 c. "The Holy Family" (Landaeta School, Caracas, 18th cent.) 65 30

287. "Children and Birds".

1969. Children's Day. Multicoloured.
2102. 5 c. Type **287** 8 5
2103. 45 c. "Children's Camp" 55 30

288. Map of Greater Colombia.

1969. 150th Anniv. of Greater Colombia Federation.
2104. **288.** 45 c. multicoloured .. 50 20

289. San Antonio Church, Clarines.

1970. Architecture of the Colonial Era. Mult.
2105. 10 c. Type **289** 8 5
2106. 30 c. Church of the Conception, Caroni .. 25 12
2107. 40 c. San Miguel Church, Burbusay 50 25
2108. 45 c. San Antonio Church, Maturin 70 35
2109. 75 c. San Nicolas Church, Moruy 85 40
2110. 1 b. Coro Cathedral .. 1·00 50

290. Seven Hills of Valera. 291. "Simon Bolivar" (M. N. Bate).

1970. 150th Anniv. of Valera.
2112. **290.** 95 c. multicoloured .. 65 30

1970. Air. Portraits of Bolivar. Stamps in brown on buff; inscriptions in green; colours of country name and value given below.
2113. **291.** 15 c. brown 15 10
2114. 45 c. blue 35 15
2115. 55 c. orange 50 25
2116. – 65 c. brown 50 25
2117. – 70 c. blue 55 35
2118. – 75 c. orange 60 40
2119. – 85 c. brown 60 45
2120. – 90 c. blue 65 25
2121. – 95 c. orange 75 25
2122. – 1 b. brown 75 25
2123. – 1 b. 50 blue 90 55
2124. – 2 b. orange .. .. 1·90 90
PORTRAITS BY: 65, 70, 75 c. F. Roulin. 85, 90, 95 c. J. M. Espinoza (1828). 1, 1 b. 50, 2 b. J. M. Espinoza (1830).

292. Gen. A. Guzman Blanco and Dr. M. J. Sanabria.

1970. Air. Centenary of Free Compulsory Education in Venezuela.
2125. **292.** 75 c. black, grn. & brn. 50 30

293. Map of Venezuela.

1970. States of Venezuela. Maps and Arms of the various States. Multicoloured.
2126. 5 c. Federal District (post.) 10 10
2127. 15 c. Monagas 15 10
2128. 20 c. Nueva Esparta .. 20 10
2129. 25 c. Portuguesa (vert.) .. 25 10
2130. 45 c. Sucre 35 15
2131. 55 c. Tachira (vert.) .. 20 20
2132. 65 c. Trujillo 30 25
2133. 75 c. Yaracuy 45 35
2134. 85 c. Zulia (vert.) .. 60 35
2135. 90 c. Amazbonas Federal Territory (vert.) .. 90 40
2136. 1 b. Federal Island Dependencies .. .. 1·10 45
2137. 5 c. Type **293** (air) .. 10 10
2138. 15 c. Apure 20 10
2139. 20 c. Aragua 25 10
2140. 20 c. Anzoategui .. 25 10
2141. 25 c. Barinas 25 10
2142. 25 c. Bolivar 25 10
2143. 45 c. Carabobo 55 20
2144. 55 c. Cojedes (vert.) .. 60 25
2145. 65 c. Falcon 65 25
2146. 75 c. Guarico 60 30
2147. 85 c. Lara 95 35
2148. 90 c. Merida (vert.) .. 95 40
2149. 1 b. Miranda 95 50
2150. 2 b. Amacuro Delta Federal Territory .. .. 2·00 80

294. " Monochaetum humboldtianum ".

295. " The Battle of Boyaca " (M. Tovar y Tovar).

1970. Flowers of Venezuela. Multicoloured.
2151. 20 c. Type **294** (postage) 30 10
2152. 25 c. " Symbolanthus vasculosus " 60 15
2153. 45 c. " Cavendishia splendens " 80 35
2154. 1 b. " Befaria glauca " .. 1·10 50
2155. 20 c. " Epidendrum secundum " (air) .. 25 10
2156. 25 c. " Oyedaea verbesinoides " .. 35 15
2157. 45 c. " Heliconia villosa " 80 35
2158. 1 b. " Macleania nitida " 1·10 50

1970. 150th Anniv. (1969) of Battle of Boyaca.
2159. **295.** 30 c. multicoloured .. 35 15

296. Archiepiscopal Cross.

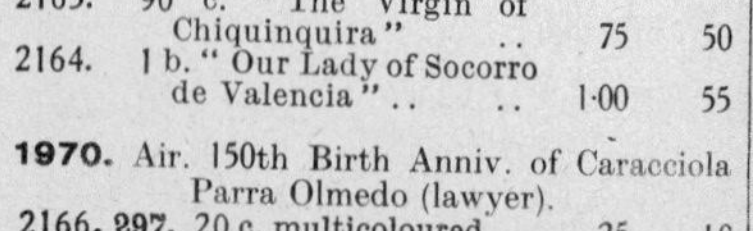

297. " Caracciolo Parra Olmedo" (T. Salas).

1970. Religious Art. Multicoloured.
2160. 35 c. Type **296** 35 15
2161. 40 c. " Our Lady of the Valley " 45 25
2162. 60 c. " Our Lady of Belen de San Mateo " .. 65 35
2163. 90 c. " The Virgin of Chiquinquira " .. 75 50
2164. 1 b. " Our Lady of Socorro de Valencia " .. 1·00 55

1970. Air. 150th Birth Anniv. of Caracciola Parra Olmedo (lawyer).
2166. **297.** 20 c. multicoloured .. 25 10

298. National Flags and Exhibition Emblem. **299.** "Guardian Angel" (J. P. Lopez).

1970. " EXFILCA 70 " Philatelic Exhib., Caracas. Multicoloured.
2167. 20 c. Type **298** 20 8
2168. 25 c. 1871 1 c. stamp and emblem (horiz.) .. 30 12
2169. 70 c. 1930 2 b. 50 air stamp and emblem .. 50 30

1970. Christmas.
2171. **299.** 45 c. multicoloured .. 35 15

300. Aircraft of 1920, and Modern Jet.

1970. 50th Anniv. of Venezuelan Air Force.
2172. **300.** 5 c. multicoloured .. 20 10

301. People in Question Mark. **302.** Battle Scene.

1971. National Census.
2173. **301.** 30 c. black, green and red (postage) .. 60 30
2174. – 70 c. multicoloured (air) 65 45
DESIGN: 70 c. National flag and " pin-men ".

1971. 150th Anniv. of Battle of Carabobo.
2175. **302.** 2 b. multicoloured 1·10 80

303. " Cattleya percivaliana ". **304.** Adoration of the Child.

1971. Air. Venezuelan Orchids. Mult.
2176. 20 c. Type **303** 25 15
2177. 25 c. Cattleya gaskelliana (horiz.) 30 20
2178. 75 c. " Cattleya mossiae " 60 40
2179. 90 c. " Cattleya violacea o superba " (horiz.) .. 65 35
2180. 1 b. " Cattleya lawrenceana " (horiz.) 80 40

1971. Christmas. Multicoloured.
2181. 25 c. Type **304** 25 15
2182. 25 c. Madonna and Child 25 15

305. Dr. Luis D. Beauperthuy. **306.** Constitution and Government Building.

1971. Death Centenary of Luis P. Beauperthuy (scientist).
2183. **305.** 1 b. multicoloured .. 70 30

1971. Air. 10th Anniv. of 1961 Constitution.
2184. **306.** 90 c. multicoloured .. 80 35

307. Heart-shaped Globe. **308.** Arms of Venezuela and National Flags.

1972. World Heart Month.
2185. **307.** 1 b. blk., red & blue .. 60 40

1972. " Venezuela in the Americas ". Mult.
2186. 3 b. Type **308** .. .. 1·40 85
2187. 4 b. Venezuelan flag .. 1·60 1·40
2188. 5 b. National anthem .. 2·10 1·60
2189. 10 b. " Araguaney " (national tree) .. .. 4·25 2·50
2190. 15 b. Map of the Americas 6·25 3·50

309. Tower Blocks.

1972. Central Park Housing Project. Mult.
2191. 30 c. Type **309** 25 15
2192. 30 c. View from ground level 25 15
2193. 30 c. Aerial view 25 15

310. Mahatma Gandhi.

1972. Birth Cent. (1969) of Mahatma Gandhi.
2194. **310.** 60 c. multicoloured .. 50 35

311. Children making Music.

1972. Christmas. Multicoloured.
2195. 30 c. Type **311** 25 15
2196. 30 c. Children roller-skating 25 15
Nos. 2195/6 were issued together se-tenant within the sheet, forming a composite design.

312. Head of " Drymarchon corais ". **313.** Planetary System.

1972. Snakes. Multicoloured.
2197. 10 c. Type **312** 10 5
2198. 15 c. " Spilotes pullatus " 15 8
2199. 25 c. " Bothrops venezuelensis " 40 15
2200. 30 c. " Micrurus dumerili carinicaudus " .. 50 20
2201. 60 c. " Crotalus vegrandis " 50 35
2202. 1 b. Boa constrictor .. 75 50

1973. 500th Birth Anniv. of Copernicus (astronomer). Multicoloured.
2203. 5 c. Type **313** 10 5
2204. 10 c. Copernicus 20 8
2205. 15 c. Book-" De Revolutionibus Orbium Coelestium " 25 10

314. The Sun. **315.** Part of Solar System (left-hand).

1973. 10th Anniv. of Humboldt Planetarium. Multicoloured.
(a) As Type **314**.
2206. 5 c. Type **314** 10 10
2207. 5 c. Earth 10 10
2208. 20 c. Mars 35 10
2209. 20 c. Saturn 25 10
2210. 30 c. Asteroids 30 15
2211. 40 c. Neptune 35 20
2212. 50 c. Venus 50 35
2213. 60 c. Jupiter 60 40
2214. 75 c. Uranus 75 50
2215. 90 c. Pluto 90 40
2216. 90 c. Moon .. .. 1·00 70
2217. 1 b. Mercury .. .. 1·25 60
(b) As Type **315**.
2218. 10 c. Type **315** 30 10
2219. 15 c. Solar Systems (centre) 40 10
2220. 15 c. Solar System (right-hand) 40 10
Nos. 2218/20 form a composite design of the Solar System.

316. O.A.S. Emblem and Map.

1973. 25th Anniv. of Organization of American States.
2221. **316.** 60 c. multicoloured .. 50 20

317. General Paez in Uniform. **319.** Bishop Ramos de Lora.

318. Admiral Padilla, Gen. Montilla and Gen. Manrique.

1973. Death Cent. of General Jose A. Paez.
2222. **317.** 10 c. multicoloured .. 8 5
2223. – 30 c. gold, black & red 25 12
2224. – 50 c. black, ultram. and blue 50 25
2225. – 1 b. multicoloured .. 75 50
2226. – 2 b. multicoloured .. 1·25 75
DESIGNS—VERT. 30 c. Paez and horse (old engraving). 50 c. Gen. Paez in civilian dress. 1 b. Street of the Lancers, Puerto Cabello. HORIZ. 2 b. " The Charge at Centauro ".

1973. 150th Anniv. of Maracaibo Naval Battle. Multicoloured.
2227. 50 c. Type **318** 40 20
2228. 1 b. "Battle of Maracaibo (M. F. Rincon) 60 40
2229. 2 b. Plan of opposing fleets 1·10 60

1973. 250th Birth Anniv. (1972) of Bishop Ramos de Lora.
2230. **319.** 75 c. gold and brown 45 20

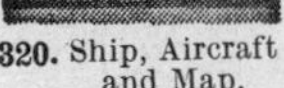

320. Ship, Aircraft and Map.

322. General Paez Dam.

321. Waterfall and Map.

1973. Margarita Island, Free Zone.
2231. **320.** 5 c. multicoloured .. 15 10

1973. Completion of Golden Highway. Multicoloured.
2232. 5 c. Type **321** 5 5
2233. 10 c. Map and Scarlet Macaw 65 10
2234. 20 c. Map and Santa Elena Church, Uairen .. 25 8
2235. 50 c. Map and Ancient mountain sanctuary .. 65 25
2236. 60 c. As 50 c. 65 25
2237. 90 c. Map and Santa Teresita church, Cabanayen 85 35
2238. 1 b. Map and flags of Venezuela and Brazil .. 90 40

1973. Completion of General Paez Dam, Merida.
2239. **322.** 30 c. multicoloured .. 30 10

323. Child on Slide.

1973. Children's Festival. Multicoloured.
2240. 10 c. Type **323** 25 15
2241. 10 c. Fairy tale animals .. 25 15
2242. 10 c. "Paginas Para Imaginar" (Children's book) 25 15
2243. 10 c. Holidaymakers leaving aircraft 25 15

324. King on White Horse.

326. Vase and Lace ("Handicrafts").

325. Regional Map.

1973. Christmas. Multicoloured.
2244. 30 c. Type **324** 25 10
2245. 30 c. Two Kings 25 10

1973. Regional Development.
2246. **325.** 25 c. multicoloured .. 30 8

1973. Venezuelan Industrial Development Commission. Multicoloured.
2247. 15 c. Type **326** 15 8
2248. 35 c. Industrial estate ("Construction") .. 35 10
2249. 45 c. Cogwheels and chimney ("Small and medium industries") 50 20

327. Map and Revellers.

1974. 10th Anniv. of Carupano Carnival.
2250. **327.** 5 c. multicoloured .. 8 5

328. Congress Emblem.

1974. 9th Venezuelan Engineering Congress, Maracaibo.
2251. **328.** 50 c. multicoloured .. 50 15

329. "Law of the Sea" Emblem.

1974. 3rd Law of the Sea Conference, Caracas. Multicoloured.
2252. 15 c. Type **329** 10 5
2253. 35 c. Fish in sea-weed .. 20 10
2254. 75 c. Sea-bed scene .. 50 25
2255. 80 c. Underwater grotto 55 35

330. Pupil and New School.

1974. "Pay Your Taxes" Campaign.
2256. **330.** 5 c. multicoloured .. 5 5
2257. 10 c. multicoloured .. 8 5
2258. 15 c. multicoloured .. 8 5
2259. 20 c. multicoloured .. 10 5
2260. A. 25 c. multicoloured .. 12 5
2261. 30 c. multicoloured .. 40 20
2262. 35 c. multicoloured .. 20 8
2263. 40 c. multicoloured .. 35 12
2264. B. 45 c. multicoloured .. 35 15
2265. 50 c. multicoloured .. 35 15
2266. 55 c. multicoloured .. 55 30
2267. 60 c. multicoloured .. 45 20
2268. C. 65 c. multicoloured .. 1·00 50
2269. 70 c. multicoloured .. 50 20
2270. 75 c. multicoloured .. 50 25
2271. 80 c. multicoloured .. 50 25
2272. D. 85 c. multicoloured .. 50 25
2273. 90 c. multicoloured .. 70 25
2274. 95 c. multicoloured .. 1·00 70
2275. 1 b. multicoloured .. 70 35

DESIGNS: A, Suburban housing project. B, City centre motorway. C, Sports stadium. D, Surgical team in operating theatre.

331. "Bolivar at Junin" (A. H. Tovar).

1974. 150th Anniv. of Battle of Junin.
2276. **331.** 2 b. multicoloured .. 1·25 70

332. World Map.

1974. Centenary of U.P.U. Multicoloured.
2227 45 c. Type **332** 35 15
2278 50 c. Mounted courier, sailing packet, modern liner and jet airliner .. 40 20

333. Rufino Blanco-Fombona and Books.

334. Children on Paper Dart.

1974. Birth Centenary of Rufino Blanco-Fombona (writer).
2279. **333.** 10 c. multicoloured .. 8 5
2280. – 30 c. multicoloured .. 20 10
2281. – 45 c. multicoloured .. 30 15
2282. – 90 c. multicoloured .. 50 25

DESIGNS: Nos. 2280/2, Portraits of Rufino Blanco-Fombona against a background of books similar to Type **333**.

1974. Children's Festival.
2283. **334.** 70 c. multicoloured .. 40 20

335. Marshal Sucre.

336. "Shepherd".

1974. 150th Anniv. of Battle of Ayacucho. Multicoloured.
2284. 30 c. Type **335** 20 10
2285. 50 c. South American flags on globe 30 25
2286. 1 b. Map showing battle sites 55 35
2287. 2 b. "Battle of Ayacucho" (43¼ × 22 mm.) .. 1·00 70

1974. Christmas. Details from "The Adoration of the Shepherds" (J. B. Mayno). Multicoloured.
2288. 30 c. Type **336** 25 15
2289. 30 c. "Holy Family" .. 25 15

Nos. 2288/9 were issued se-tenant, forming a composite design.

337. Road Construction, 1905, and El Ciempies Junction, 1972.

1974. Centenary of Ministry of Public Works. Multicoloured.
2290. 5 c. Type **337** 10 5
2291. 20 c. J. Munoz Tebar (first Minister of Public Works) 25 5
2292. 25 c. Bridges on Caracas-La Guaira Road, 1912 and 1953 .. .. .. 30 5
2293. 40 c. Views of Caracas, 1874 and 1974 .. .. 30 15
2294. 70 c. Tucacas Railway Station, 1911, and projected Caracas terminal 70 20
2295. 80 c. Anatomical Institute, 1911, and Social Security Hospital, 1969 .. .. 85 30
2296. 85 c. Quininari River bridge, 1904, and Orinoco River bridge, 1967 .. .. .. 1·00 35
2297. 1 b. As 20 c. .. .. 1·40 50

MINIMUM PRICE

The minimum price quoted is 5p which represents a handling charge rather than a basis for valuing common stamps. For further notes about prices see introductory pages.

338. Women in Profile. **340.** The Nativity.

339. Emblem and "Tents".

1975. International Women's Year.
2298. **338.** 90 c. multicoloured .. 50 30

1975. 14th World Scout Jamboree.
2299. **339.** 20 c. multicoloured .. 15 8
2300. 80 c. multicoloured .. 55 25

1975. Christmas. Multicoloured.
2301. 30 c. Type **340** 20 10
2302. 30 c. "The Shepherds" 20 10

Nos. 2301/2 were issued se-tenant, forming a composite design.

341. Red Cross Nurse. **342.** Altar.

1975. Venezuelan Red Cross.
2303. **341.** 30 c. + 15 c. mult. .. 35 20
2304. 50 c. + 25 c. mult. .. 50 30

1976. Centenary of National Pantheon.
2305. **342.** 30 c. grey and blue .. 15 8
2306. – 1 b. 05 brown and red 50 25

DESIGN: 1 b. 05 Pantheon building.

343. Coloured Panels. **344.** "Charting from Aircraft".

1976. 150th Anniv. of Bolivian Independence (1975).
2307. **343.** 60 c. multicoloured .. 25 15

1976. 40th Anniv. of Nat. Cartographic Institute (1975).
2308. **344.** 1 b. black and blue .. 50 20

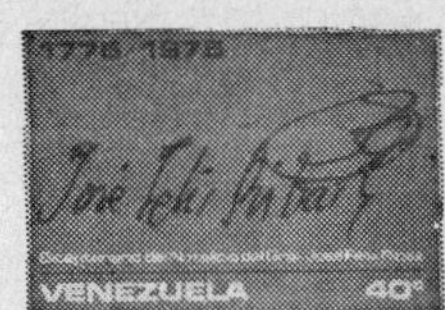

345. Signature of General Jose Felix Ribas.

1976. Birth Bicent. of General Jose Ribas. Multicoloured.
2309. **345.** 40 c. green and red .. 25 10
2310. – 55 c. multicoloured .. 35 15

DESIGN—HORIZ. (40 × 30 mm.). 55 c. General Jose Felix Ribas.

346. "Musicians of Chacao School" (A. Barrios).

1976. Birth Bicentenary (1975) of Jose Angel Lamas (composer).
2311. **346.** 75 c. multicoloured .. 45 25
2312. – 1 b. 25 red, grey and buff 65 35

DESIGN—(40 × 28 mm.). 1 b. 25 Lamas' colophon.

347. " Bolivar " (J. M. Espinoza).

349. C. A. Fernadez de Leoni (founder).

348. Maze Symbolising Opportunity.

1976.

No.	Type	Description		Unused	Used
2313	347	5 c. turquoise	..	5	5
2314		10 c. red	..	5	5
2315		15 c. brown	..	5	5
2316		20 c. black ..	..	8	5
~~2317~~		25 c. orange	..	10	5
2613		25 c. red ..	..	5	5
2318		30 c. blue ..	..	5	5
2319		45 c. lilac ..	..	15	5
2320		50 c. orange	..	20	8
2614		50 c. blue ..	..	5	5
2321		65 c. blue ..	..	25	10
2615		75 c. mauve	..	8	5
2322		1 b. red ..	..	35	15
2616		1 b. orange	..	8	5
2323		2 b. grey ..	..	70	35
2617		2 b. yellow	..	15	5
2324		3 b. blue ..	..	65	50
2618		3 b. green ..	..	8	5
2325		4 b. orange	..	85	45
2619		4 b. brown	..	12	5
2620		5 b. red ..	..	15	5
2327		10 b. lilac ..	..	2·25	1·10
2621		10 b. yellow	..	65	15
2328		15 b. blue ..	..	3·50	1·60
2622		15 b. purple	..	1·00	15
2329		20 b. red ..	..	4·50	2·25
2623		20 b. blue ..	..	1·40	65
2329a		25 b. blue ..	..	4·25	2·25
2623a		25 b. bistre	..	1·60	85
2329b		30 b. blue ..	..	5·50	2·75
2623b		30 b. lilac ..	..	2·00	1·00
2329c		50 b. purple	..	8·75	4·25
2623c		50 b. red ..	..	3·25	1·60

Nos. 2323/9 are larger, 27 × 33 mm.

1976. 250th Anniv. of Central University.
2330. 348. 30 c. multicoloured .. 15 5
2331. – 50 c. blk., orge. & yell. 25 15
2332. – 90 c. yellow and black 50 30
DESIGNS: 50 c. University building. 90 c. Faculty symbols.

1976. Children's Foundation. Multicoloured.
2333. 30 c. + 15 c. Type 349 .. 25 20
2334. 50 c. + 25 c. Children in " home " (31 × 44 mm.) 45 30

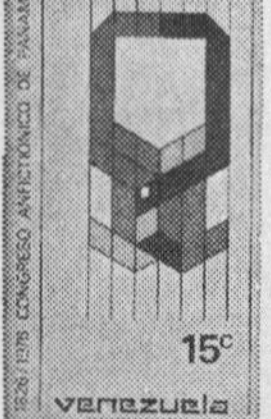

350. "Unity" Emblem.

351. George Washington.

1976. 150th Anniv. of Panama Amphictyonic Congress.
2335. 350. 15 c. multicoloured .. 10 5
2336. – 45 c. multicoloured .. 25 5
2337. – 1 b. 25 multicoloured 55 30
DESIGN: 45 c., 1 b. 25 As Type 275, but with different " Unity " emblems.

1976. Bicent. of American Revolution.
2338. 351. 1 b. black and brown 55 35
2339. – 1 b. black and green 55 35
2340. – 1 b. black and purple 55 35
2341. – 1 b. black and blue .. 55 35
2342. – 1 b. black and brown 55 35
DESIGNS: No. 2339, Thomas Jefferson. No. 2340, Abraham Lincoln. No. 2341, Franklin D. Roosevelt. No. 2342, John F. Kennedy.

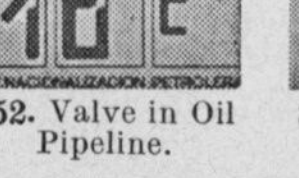

352. Valve in Oil Pipeline.

353. " The Nativity " (B. Rivas).

1976. Oil Nationalization.
2343. 352. 10 c. multicoloured .. 5 5
2344. – 30 c. multicoloured .. 15 8
2345. – 35 c. multicoloured .. 20 10
2346. – 40 c. multicoloured .. 20 5
2347. – 55 c. multicoloured .. 30 15
2348. – 90 c. multicoloured .. 55 25
DESIGNS: 30 c. to 90 c. Various computer drawings of valves and pipelines.

1976. Christmas.
2349. 353. 30 c. multicoloured .. 25 5

354. Patient.

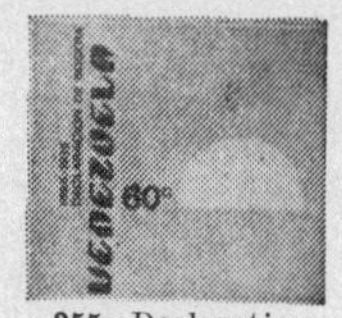

355. Declaration Emblem.

1976. Anti-tuberculosis Society Fund.
2350. 354. 10 c. + 5 c. mult. .. 15 15
2351. 30 c. + 10 c. mult. .. 20 20

1976. 10th Anniv. of Bogota Declaration.
2352. 355. 60 c. black and yellow 30 15

356. Arms of Barinas.

1977. 400th Anniv. of Barinas.
2353. 356. 50 c. multicoloured .. 30 15

357. " Christ Crucified ".

358. Coro Settlement.

1977. 400th Anniv (1976) of La Grita.
2354. 357. 30 c. multicoloured .. 15 10

1977. 450th Anniv. of Coro.
2355. 358. 1 b. multicoloured .. 35 15

359. I.P.C.T.T. Emblem and Stylised Dove.

1977. Ninth Inter-american Postal and Telecommunications Staff Congress, Caracas.
2356. 359. 85 c. multicoloured .. 35 15

360. Cable Links to Domestic Equipment.

361. "VENEZUELA" and Value as Rolled Steel.

1977. Inauguration of " Columbus " Submarine Cable.
2357. 360. 95 c. grey, blue & grn. 35 15

1977. 1st Anniv. of Nationalization and Exploitation of Steel.
2358 361 30 c. black and yellow 15 5
2359 – 50 c. black and orange 25 8
2360 – 80 c. black and grey 35 15
2361 – 1 b. 05 black and red 40 20
2362 – 1 b. 25 black & yellow 45 20
2363 – 1 b. 50 black and grey 65 25
DESIGNS: 50 c. to 1 b. 50, Similar to Type 361 but each differently arranged.

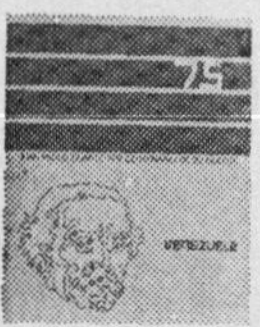

362. J. P. Duarte.

363. " The Holy Family ".

1977. Death Cent. (1976). of Juan Pablo Duarte.
2364. 362. 75 c. black and mauve 30 15

1977. Christmas.
2365. 363. 30 c. multicoloured .. 15 5

364. O.P.E.C. Emblem.

365. Cyclists Racing.

1977. 50th O.P.E.C. Conference, Caracas.
2366. 364. 1 b. 05 black and blue 50 15

1978. World Cycling Championships, San Cristobal, Tachira. Multicoloured.
2367. 5 c. Type 365 .. .. 5 5
2368. 1 b. 25 Cyclist racing .. 65 20

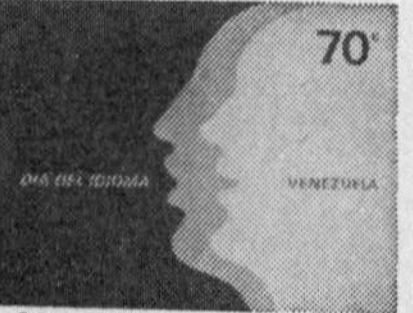

366. Heads in Profile.

1978. Language Day.
2369. 366. 70 c. blk., grey & mauve 25 15

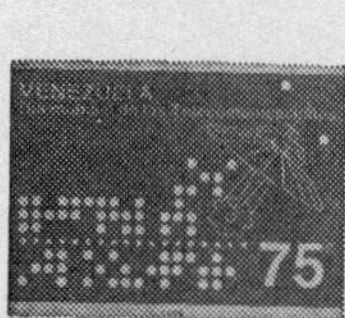

367. Computer Tape and Satellite.

368. " 1777–1977 ".

1978. Tenth World Telecommunications Day.
2370. 367. 75 c. blue 30 20

1978. Bicent. of Venezuelan Unification. Multicoloured.
2381. 30 c. Type 368 .. .. 10 5
2382. 1 b. Computer print of Goya's " Carlos III " 40 15

369. Bolivar in Nurse Hipolita's Arms.

1978. Birth Bicent. (1983) of Simon Bolivar (1st issue).
2383. 369. 30 c. blk., brn. & grn. 15 5
2384. – 1 b. blk., brn. & blue 40 25
DESIGN: 1 b. Juan Vicente Bolivar (father).
See also Nos. 2399/40, 2408/9, 2422/3, 2431/2, 2467/8, 2480/1, 2483/4, 2494/5, 2498/9, 2518/19 and 2521/2.

370. " T " (" Trabajadores ").

371. Medical Abstract.

1978. Workers' Day.
2385. 370. 30 c. red and black .. 10 5
2386. – 30 c. blue and black .. 10 5
2387. – 30 c. yell., blue & blk. 10 5
2388. – 30 c. red, blue & blk. 10 5
2389. – 30 c. red and black .. 10 5
2390. – 95 c. black and red .. 10 5
2391. – 95 c. grey and blue .. 30 15
2392. – 95 c. black and red .. 30 15
2393. – 95 c. blue and black 30 15
2394. – 95 c. multicoloured .. 30 15
DESIGNS: Nos. 2386/2394 based on the letter " T ", also inscribed " CTV ".

1978. Birth Centenary (1977) of Rafael Rangel (physician and scientist).
2395. 371. 50 c. brown 40 20

372. Drill Head and Map of Tachira Oilfield.

1978. Centenary of Venezuelan Oil Industry. Multicoloured.
2396. 30 c. Type 372 .. .. 15 5
2397. 1 b. 05 Letter " P " as pipeline 50 20

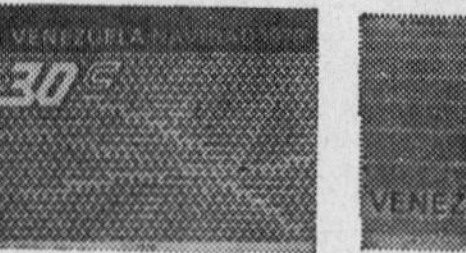

373. Christmas Star.

375. Dam holding back Water.

374. " P T ".

1978. Christmas.
2398. 373. 30 c. multicoloured .. 15 5

1978. Birth Bicentenary (1983) of Simon Bolivar (2nd issue). As T 369.
2399. 30 c. blk., brn. & pur. .. 10 5
2400. 1 b. blk., grey & red .. 30 15
DESIGNS: 30 c. Bolivar at 25 (after M. N. Bate). 1 b. Simon Rodriguez (Bolivar's tutor).

1979. Creation of Postal and Telegraph Institute.
2402. 374. 75 c. blk. & red on cream 25 15

1979. 10th Anniv. of Guri Dam.
2403. 375. 2 b. silver, grey & blk. 70 30

376. " General San Martin " (E. J. Maury).

1979. Birth Bicentenary of General Jose de San Martin. Multicoloured.
2404. 40 c. Type 376 .. .. 15 5
2405. 60 c. Portrait by Mercedes San Martin 25 10
2406. 70 c. San Martin Monument, Guayaquil 30 15
2407. 75 c. San Martin's signature 35 20

1979. Birth Bicentenary (1983) of Simon Bolivar (3rd series). As T 369.
2408. 30c. black, violet and red 10 5
2409. 1b. black, orange and red 30 15
DESIGNS: 30 c. Alexandre Sabes Petion (President of Haiti). 1 b. Bolivar's signature.

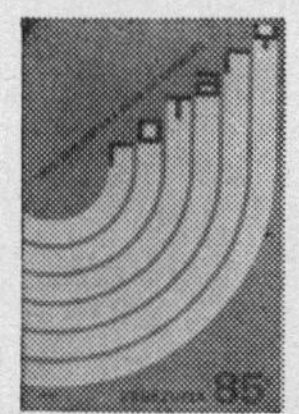

377. " Rotary " and Curves.

378. Statue of Virgin working Miracles, 1654.

1979. 50th Anniv. of Rotary Club of Caracas.
2411. 377. 85 c. black and gold 25 15

1979. 25th Anniv. of Canonization of Virgin of Coromoto.
2412. 378. 55 c. black and red .. 20 10

379. Miranda, London Residence and Arms.

1979. Acquisition by Venezuela of Francisco de Miranda's House in London.
2413. 379. 50 c. multicoloured .. 20 8

380. O'Leary and Maps.

1979. 125th Death Anniv. of Daniel O'Leary (publisher of Bolivar's memoirs).
2414. 380. 30 c. multicoloured .. 10 5

381. Boy with Nest.

382. Candle.

1979. International Year of the Child.
2415. 381. 70 c. black and blue .. 25 12
2416. – 80 c. multicoloured .. 30 15
DESIGN: 80 c. Boys playing in sea.

1979. Christmas.
2417. 382. 30 c. multicoloured .. 10 5

383. Caudron Bomber.

1979. " Exfilve 79 " National Stamp Exhibition and 59th Anniv. of Air Force. Mult.
2418. 75 c. Type 383 .. .. 35 20
2419. 75 c. Stearman Biplane 35 20
2420. 75 c. " UH-1H " helicopter 35 20
2421. 75 c. " CF-5 " jet fighter 55 20

1979. Birth Bicentenary (1983) of Simon Bolivar (4th series). As T 369.
2422. 30 c. black, red and turq. 10 5
2423. 1 b. black, blue and red .. 30 15
DESIGNS: 30 c. Bolivar. 1 b. Slave.

384. Emblem and World Map.

1979. Introduction of New Emblem for Postal and Telegraph Institute.
2425. 384. 75 c. multicoloured .. 25 15

385. Queen Victoria and Hill.

1980. Death Centenary of Sir Rowland Hill (1979).
2426. 385. 55 c. multicoloured .. 20 10

386. Augusto Pi Suner.

1980. Birth Centenary (1979) of Dr. Augusto Pi Suner (physiologist).
2426. 386. 80 c. multicoloured .. 30 15

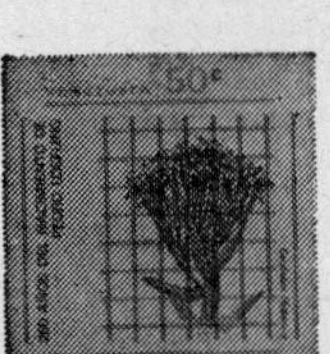

387. " Cotyledon hispanica ".

388. Lovera (self portrait).

1980. 250th Birth Anniv. of Pedro Loefling (Swedish botanist).
2428. 387. 50 c. multicoloured .. 20 8

1980. Birth Bicentenary (1978) of Juan Lovera (artist).
2429. 388. 60 c. blue and red .. 20 10
2430. 75 c. violet and orange 25 15

1980. Birth Bicentenary (1983) of Simon Bolivar (5th issue). As Type 369.
2431. 30 c. blk., green & purple 10 5
2432. 1 b. blk., deep brn. & brn. 30 15
DESIGNS: 30 c. Signing document. 1 b. Congress House, Angostura.

389. " Self Portrait with Children " (detail).

390. Bernardo O'Higgins.

1980. 25th Death Anniv. (1979) of Armando Reveron (artist). Multicoloured.
2434 50 c. Type 389 .. .. 20 8
2435 65 c. "Self Portrait" (26 × 41 mm) 35 20

1980. 204th Birth Anniv of Bernardo O'Higgins.
2436. 390. 85 c. black, red & blue 50 25

391. Frigate " Mariscal Sucre ".

1980. Venezuelan Navy. Multicoloured.
2437. 1 b. 50 Type 391 .. 1·00 40
2438. 1 b. 50 Submarine "Picua" 1·00 40
2439. 1 b. 50 Naval School .. 1·00 40
2440. 1 b. 50 Cadet barque "Simon Bolivar" (33 × 52 mm.) .. .. 1·00 40

392. Figures supporting O.P.E.C. Emblem.

1980. 20th Anniv. of Organization of Petroleum Exporting Countries. Mult.
2441. 1 b. 50 Type 392 .. 50 25
2442. 1 b. 50 O.P.E.C. emblem and globe 50 25

393. " The Death of Bolivar " (Antonio Herrera Toro).

1980. 150th Death Anniv. of Simon Bolivar.
2443. 393. 2 b. multicoloured .. 70 30

394. Antonio Jose de Sucre.

395. " The Adoration of the Shepherds " (Rubens).

1980. 150th Death Anniv. of Marshal Antonio Jose de Sucre.
2444. 394. 2 b. multicoloured .. 70 30

1980. Christmas.
2445. 395. 1 b. multicoloured .. 20 10

396. Helen Keller's Initials in Braille and Print.

1981. Birth Cent. (1980) of Helen Keller.
2446. 396. 1 b. 50 grey, orge. & blk. 40 15

INDEX

Countries can be quickly located by referring to the index at the end of this volume.

397. Gateway, San Felipe.

398. Jean Baptiste de la Salle (founder).

1981. 250th Anniv. of San Felipe.
2447. 397. 3 b. blue, grey and red 70 35

1981. 300th Anniv. (1980) of Brothers of Christian Schools.
2448. 398. 1 b. 25 silver, red & blk. 30 15

399. Municipal Theatre.

1981. Cent. of Caracas Municipal Theatre.
2449. 399. 1 b. 25, pink, blk. & lilac 30 15

400. U.P.U. Emblem, Map of Venezuela and Envelope.

401. People on Map.

1981. Centenary of Admission to Universal Postal Union.
2450. 400. 2 b. multicoloured .. 50 20

1981. 11th National Population and Housing Census.
2451. 401. 1 b. lilac, vio., and blk. 30 15

402. Games Emblem.

404. Musicians.

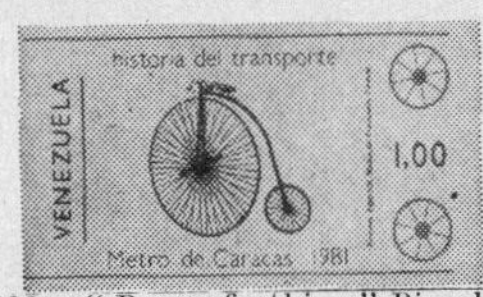

403. " Penny-farthing " Bicycle.

1981. 9th Bolivarian Games, Barquismeto.
2452. 402. 95 c. multicoloured .. 30 15

1981. Transport History (1st series). Mult.
2453. 1 b. Type 403 .. .. 35 20
2454. 1 b. 05 Steam locomotive, 1926 .. .. 90 60
2455. 1 b. 25 Buick car, 1937 .. 40 25
2456. 1 b. 50 Horse-drawn cab 50 25
See also Nos. 2490/3 and 2514/7.

1981. Christmas.
2457. 404. 1 b. multicoloured .. 25 10

405. Mt. Autana.

407. " Landscape ".

406. Calligraphic Script and Arms.

1982. 50th Anniv. of Venezuelan Natural Sciences Society. Multicoloured.
2458. 1 b. Type 405 .. .. 30 20
2459. 1 b. 50 Sarisarinama .. 50 20
2460. 2 b. Guacharo Cave .. 40 35

1982. 20th Anniv. of Constitution.
2461. 406. 1 b. 85 gold and black 40 25

1982. 20th Anniv. of Agricultural Reform.
2462. 407. 3 b. multicoloured .. 70 40

408. Jules Verne.

410. Rose.

409. Bars of National Anthem.

1982. Jules Verne (writer) Commemoration.
2463. 408. 1 b. deep blue and blue 30 15

1982. Cent. of National Anthem (1981).
2464. 409. 1 b. multicoloured .. 30 15

1982. 1300th Anniv. of Bulgarian State.
2465. 410. 65 c. multicoloured .. 20 10

411. Flags.

412. Cecilio Acosta.

1982. Sixth National Plan.
2466. 411. 2 b. multicoloured .. 35 12

1982. Birth Bicentenary (1983) of Simon Bolivar (6th issue). As T 369.
2467. 30 c. black, brown and orange 10 5
2468. 1 b. black, brown and grn. 25 15
DESIGNS: 30 c. Col. Rondon. 1 b. General Anzoategui.

1982. Death Centenary (1981) of Cecilio Acosta (statesman).
2469. 412. 3 b. black, blue and violet 35 25

413. " Fourcroya humboldtiana ".

1982. Flora and Fauna. Multicoloured.
2471. 1 b. 05 Type 413 .. 35 15
2472. 2 b. 55 Turtle ("Podocnemis expansa") .. 85 30
2473. 2 b. 75 "Oyedaea verbesinoides" .. 90 35
2474. 3 b. Oilbird .. .. 2·75 85

414. Andres Bello and Initials.

1982. Birth Bicent. of Andres Bello (1981).
2475. 414. 1 b. 05 light blue, blue and black 25 15
2476. 2 b. 55 yellow, violet and black 45 30
2477. 2 b. 75 blue, deep blue and black 50 35
2478. 3 b. olive, deep olive and black 55 40

415. " Nativity ".

416. Bermudez.

1982. Christmas.
2479. **415.** 1 b. multicoloured .. 20 5

1982. Birth Bicentenary (1983) of Simon Bolivar (7th issue). As T **369**.
2480. 30 c. black, grey & red .. 10 5
2481. 1 b. black, grey & red .. 25 15
DESIGNS: 30 b. Carabobo Monument. 1 b. Gen. Jose Antonio Paez.

1982. Birth Bicentenary (1983) of Simon Bolivar (8th issue). As T **369**.
2483. 30 c. blk., bl. & deep blue 10 5
2484. 1 b. black, violet & red .. 25 15
DESIGNS: 30 c. Commemorative plaque to the meeting at Guayaquil. 1 b. Bolivar and San Martin (detail of monument).

1982. Birth Bicentenary of General Jose Francisco Bermudez (statesman).
2486. **416.** 3 b. multicoloured .. 35 30

417. Briceno.

1982. Birth Bicentenary of Antonio Nicolas Briceno (liberation hero).
2487. **417.** 3 b. multicoloured .. 35 30

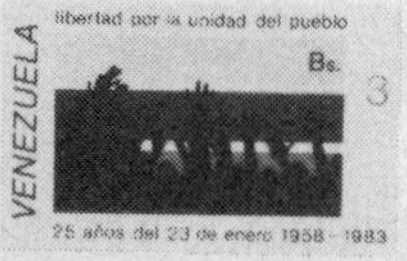

418. Rejoicing Crowd and Flag.

1983. 25th Anniv. of 1958 Reforms.
2488. **418.** 3 b. multicoloured .. 35 30

419. Police Badge.

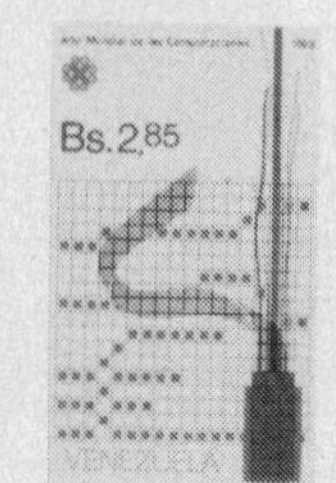

420. Cable and Computer Circuitboard.

1983. 25th Anniv. of Judicial Police Technical Department.
2489. **419.** 4 b. red and green .. 40 30

1983. Transport History (2nd series). As T **403**. Multicoloured.
2490. 75 c. Lincoln touring car, 1923 .. .. 20 10
2491. 80 c. Steam locomotive No. 129. 1889 .. .. 1·50 90
2492. 85 c. Willys truck, 1927 25 10
2493. 95 c. Cleveland motor-cycle, 1920 .. .. 25 10

1983. Birth Bicentenary of Simon Bolivar (9th issue). As T **369**.
2494. 30 c. black, red & blue .. 10 5
2495. 1 b. black, gold & blue .. 25 15
DESIGNS: 30 c. Gen. Antonio Sucre. 1 b. Sword hilt.

1983. World Communications Year.
2497. **420.** 2 b. 85 multicoloured 25 30

1983. Birth Bicentenary of Simon Bolivar (10th issue). As T **369**.
2498. 30 c. multicoloured .. 10 5
2499. 1 b. black, yellow & blue 25 15
DESIGNS: 30 c. Flags. 1 b. " Ascent of Potosi ".

421. Map of the Americas.

422. Power Pylon.

1983. 9th Pan-American Games, Caracas. Multicoloured.
2501. 2 b. Type **421** 30 20
2502. 2 b. Swimming 30 20
2503. 2 b. 70 Cycling 15 30
2504. 2 b. 70 Fencing 15 30
2505. 2 b. 85 Weightlifting .. 20 15
2506. 2 b. 85 Running 20 15

1983. 25th Anniv. of State Electricity Authority.
2508. **422.** 3 b. blue, silver & red 70 30

423. Nativity.

1983. Christmas.
2509. **423.** 1 b. multicoloured .. 10 5

424. Erecting a Tent.

1983. 75th Anniv. (1982) of Scout Movement. Multicoloured.
2510. 2 b. 25 Type **424** .. 30 12
2511. 2 b. 55 Nature watch .. 30 12
2512. 2 b. 75 Mountaineering.. 35 15
2513. 3 b. Camp at night .. 35 15

1983. Transport History (3rd series). Caracas Underground Railway. As T **403**. Mult.
2514 55 c. black, orge & silver 30 10
2515 75 c. black, yell & silver 45 15
2516 95 c. black, green & silver 55 20
2517 2 b. black, blue and silver 1·25 45
DESIGNS: 55 c. Central computer building. 75 c. Maintenance bay. 95 c. Train on elevated section. 2 b. Train at Cano Amarillo station.

1984. Birth Bicentenary of Simon Bolivar (11th issue). As T **369**.
2518 30 c. black, red and brown 5 5
2519 1 b. black, green and blue 10 5
DESIGNS: 30 c. Open volume of "Opere" by Raimondo Montecuccoli. 1 b. Dr. Jose Maria Vargas (President, 1835–36).

1984. Birth Bicentenary of Simon Bolivar (12th issue). As T **369**.
2521. 30 c. blk., red and lilac .. 5 5
2522. 1 b. blk., green & orange 10 5
DESIGNS: 30 c. Pedro Gual (President, 1859 and 1861). 1 b. Jose Faustino Sanchez Carrion.

425. Radio Mast and Waves.
426. Doves and Hands covering Eyes.

1984. 50th Anniv. of Venezuela Radio Club.
2524 **425** 2 b. 70 multicoloured 35 15

1984. "Intelligentsia for Peace". Mult.
2525. 1 b. Type **426** 10 5
2526. 2 b. 70 Profile head .. 30 15
2527. 2 b. 85 Profile head, flower and hexagonal nut .. 35 15

427. Romulo Gallegos.
428. Emblem and Digital Design.

1984. Birth Centenary of Romulo Gallegos (writer and President, 1948). Mult.
2528 **427** 1 b. 70 multicoloured 25 12
2529 – 1 b. 70 multicoloured 25 12
2530 – 1 b. 70 green, grey and black .. 25 12
2531 – 1 b. 70 deep green, green and black .. 25 12
DESIGNS: Nos. 2529/31, Different portraits of Gallegos.

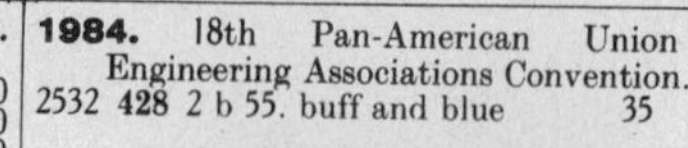

1984. 18th Pan-American Union of Engineering Associations Convention.
2532 **428** 2 b 55. buff and blue 35 15

429. "Nativity" (Maria Candelaria de Ramirez).

1984. Christmas.
2533 **429** 1 b. multicoloured .. 10 5

430. Pope and "Virgin of Coromoto".

1985. Visit of Pope John Paul II (1st issue).
2534 **430** 1 b. multicoloured .. 20 8
See also Nos. 2628/33.

431. Cross, Hand holding Candle and Agricultural Scene.

1985. Bicent. of Valle de la Pascua City.
2535 **431** 1 b. 50 multicoloured 20 10

432. St. Vincent de Paul.

1985. Centenary of Venezuelan Society of St. Vincent de Paul.
2536 **432** 1 b. brown, yell & red 15 8

433. Text and "SELA".

1985. 10th Anniv. of Latin American Economic System.
2537 **433** 4 b. black and red .. 70 35

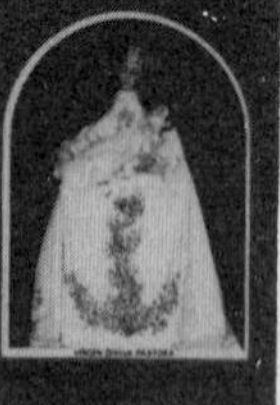

434. Divine Shepherdess.

435. Map and Emblem.

1985. 2000th Birth Anniv. of Virgin Mary. Multicoloured.
2538 1 b. Type **434** 20 12
2539 1 b. "Virgin of Chiquinquira" 20 12
2540 1 b. "Virgin of Coromoto" 20 12
2541 1 b. "Virgin of the Valley" 20 12
2542 1 b. "Virgin of Perpetual Succour" .. 20 12
2543 1 b. "Virgin of Peace" .. 20 12
2544 1 b. "Virgin of the Immaculate Conception" 20 12
2545 1 b. "Virgin of Solitude" 20 12
2546 1 b. "Virgin of Consolation" 20 12
2547 1 b. "Virgin of the Snow" 20 12

1985. 25th Anniv. of Organization of Petroleum Exporting Countries.
2548. **435.** 6 b. black, blue and light blue 70 35

436. Dr Briceno-Iragorry.

1985. 27th Death Anniv. of Dr. Mario Briceno-Iragorry (politician)
2549. **436.** 1 b. 25 silver and red 15 8

437. Museum.

1985. 10th Anniv (1983) of Museum of Modern Art, Caracas.
2550. **437.** 3 b. multicoloured .. 35 20

438. Emblem and Dove as Hand.

1985. 40th Anniv. of U.N.O.
2551. **438.** 10 b. blue and red .. 1·10 60

439. Rainbow and Emblem.

1985. International Youth Year.
2552. **439.** 1 b. 50 multicoloured 20 8

440. Shepherds and Camels.

1985. Christmas. Multicoloured.
2553. 2 b. Type **440** 25 10
2554. 2 b. Holy family and the Three Kings 25 10
Nos. 2553/4 were printed together, se-tenant, forming a composite design of the Nativity.

441. Petroleos de Venezuela Emblem.

1985. 10th Anniv. of National Petrochemical Industry.
2555 **441** 1 b. blue and black .. 15 10
2556 – 1 b. multicoloured .. 15 10
2557 – 2 b. multicoloured .. 25 15
2558 – 2 b. multicoloured .. 25 15
2559 – 3 b. multicoloured .. 35 20
2560 – 3 b. multicoloured .. 80 30
2561 – 4 b. multicoloured .. 50 25
2562 – 4 b. multicoloured .. 50 25
2563 – 5 b. multicoloured .. 60 30
2564 – 5 b. multicoloured .. 60 30
DESIGNS: No. 2556, Refinery and Isla S. A. emblem. 2557, Bariven oil terminal. 2558, Pequiven storage tank. 2559, Corpoven drilling site. 2560, Support vessel, oil rig and Maraven emblem. 2561, Meneven refinery. 2562, Intervep scientist. 2563, "Nodding Donkey". 2564, Lagoven refinery.

442. Five Reales Silver Coin, 1873.

443. Drago

1985. Coins with Portrait of Simon Bolivar. Multicoloured.

2565 2 b. Type **442** 25 12
2566 2 b. 70 Five bolivares gold coin, 1886 .. .. 30 15
2567 3 b. Birth bicentenary gold proof coin, 1983 .. 35 20

1985. 125th Birth Anniv (1984) of Dr. Luis Maria Drago (Argentine Politician)

2568 **443** 2 b. 70 blk, orge & red 30 15

444. Guayana City.

1985. 25th Anniv. of Guayana Development Corporation. Multicoloured.

2569. 2 b. Type **444** 25 12
2570. 3 b. Orinoco steel mill .. 35 20
2571. 5 b. Raul Leoni-Guri dam 60 35

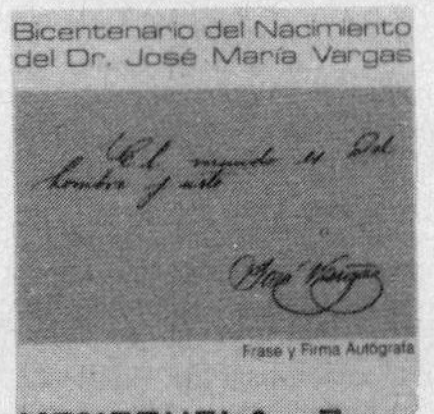

445. Signature.

1985. Birth Bicentenary of Dr. Jose Maria Vargas (President, 1835–36). Multicoloured.

2572. 3 b. Type **445** 30 15
2573. 3 b. "Vargas" (Martin Tovar y Tovar) (vert.) 30 15
2574. 3 b. Statue at Palace of Academies (vert.) .. 30 15
2575. 3 b. "Exfilbo '86" National Stamp Exhibition emblem and flags 30 15
2576. 3 b. Facade of Vargas Hospital, Caracas .. 30 15
2577. 3 b. Title page of Vargas's "Manual and Compendium of Surgery" (vert.) .. 30 15
2578. 3 b. "Vargas" (Alirio Palacios) (vert.) .. 30 15
2579. 3 b. "Gesneria vargasii" (flower) 30 15
2580. 3 b. Portraits of Vargas and Bolivar on Sixth Venezuelan Congress of Medical Sciences medal 30 15
2581. 3 b. "Vargas" (anonymous) (vert.) .. 30 15

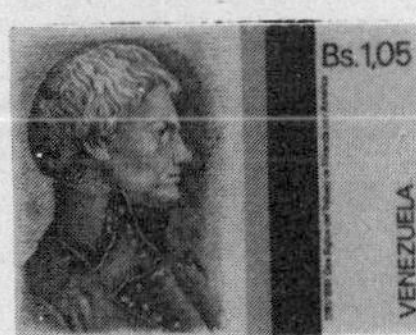

446. Francisco Miranda.

1986. Bicent (1981) of Francisco Miranda's Work for Latin American Liberation.

2583 **446** 1 b. 05 multicoloured 10 5

447. Children painting Wall.

448. Lorries and Processing Plant.

1986. Foundation for Educational Buildings and Equipment. Multicoloured.

2584 3 b. Type **447** 25 12
2585 5 b. Boys at woodwork class 35 15

1986. 45th Anniv. of Venezuelan Dairy Industry Corporation. Multicoloured.

2586. 2 b. 55 Type **448** .. 20 12
2587. 2 b 70 Map and milk containers 25 12
2588. 3 b. 70 Processing plant Machiques, Edo Zulia (horiz.) 35 15

449. Emblem.

1986. 25th Anniv of VIASA (airline). Mult.

2589. 3 b. Type **449** 35 20
2590. 3 b. Airplane in flight .. 35 20
2591. 3 b. Airplane on ground 35 20
2592. 3 b. Jumbo jet flying out to sea 35 20
2593. 3 b. Tail fins 35 20
2594. 3 b. 25 Hemispheres .. 35 20
2595. 3 b. 25 Airplane flying through cloud .. 35 20
2596. 3 b. 25 Airplanes on ground.. .. .. 35 20
2597. 3 b. 25 Airplane flying over mountains .. 35 20
2598. 3 b. 25 Manned flight deck 35 20

450. Giant Armadillo.

1986. Flora and Fauna. Dated "1983". Mult.

2599 70 c. Type **450** 5 5
2600 85 c. "Espeletia angustifolia" 5 5
2601 2 b. 70 Orinoco crocodile 20 10
2602 3 b. Mountain rose .. 20 10

451 Romulo Betancourt.

452 Library Entrance.

1986. 5th Death Anniv of Romulo Betancourt (President, 1959–64). Each black, deep brown and brown.

2603 2 b. Type **451** 20 10
2604 2 b 70. Betancourt in armchair 20 10
2605 2 b. 70 Betancourt and inscription 20 10
2606 2 b. 70 Betancourt wearing sash 20 10
2607 2 b. 70 Betancourt working 20 10
2608 3 b. As No. 2606 .. 25 12
2609 3 b. As No. 2607 .. 25 12
2610 3 b. As No. 2605 .. 25 12
2611 3 b. Type **451** .. 25 12
2612 3 b. As No. 2604 .. 25 12

1986. 40th Anniv. of Re-opening of Zulia University. Each grey, black and blue.

2624 2 b. 70 Type **452** .. 20 10
2625 2 b. 70 University building 20 10

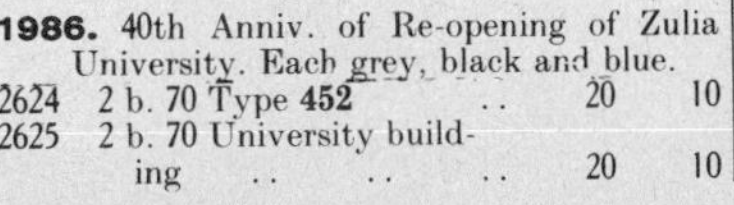

453. Map and Droplets.

1986. 11th Venezuelan Engineers, Architects and Affiliated Professions Congress.

2626 **453** 1 b. 40 bl, blk & yell 25 12
2627 1 b. 55 multicoloured 25 12

454. Pope and Andes.

455. "United Families" (Vianny Hernandez).

1986. Visit of Pope John Paul II (1985) (2nd issue). Multicoloured.

2628 1 b. Type **454** 8 5
2629 1 b. Pope and Maracaibo bridge 15 8
2630 3 b. Pope kissing ground 25 12
2631 3 b. Pope and "Virgin of Coromoto" 25 12
2632 4 b. Pope holding Crucifix, Caracas .. 35 15
2633 5 b. 25 Pope and waterfall 40 20

1986. 20th Anniv. of Children's Foundation. Childrens' paintings. Multicoloured.

2634 2 b. 55 Type **455** .. 20 10
2635 2 b. 55 "Love and Peace" (Yuraima L. Jimenez) 20 10
2636 2 b. 55 "Woodland Animals" (Maria Valentina Arias) .. 20 10
2637 2 b. 55 "Noah's Ark" (Andreina Acero) .. 20 10
2638 2 b. 55 House on hillside (Yenelsa) 20 10
2639 2 b. 70 "Flowers on Table" (Yenny Jimenez) 20 10
2640 2 b. 70 "Peace Lover" (Ramon Briceno) .. 20 10
2641 2 b. 70 "Children for World Peace" (Blanca Yesenia Hernandes) .. 20 10
2642 2 b. 70 "Lighthouse and Cable Railway" (Julio V. Hernandez) .. 20 10
2643 2 b. 70 "Flowers of a Thousand Colours" (with butterfly) (Maryolin Rodrigue Ortega) .. 20 10

456. Three Kings.

1986. Christmas. Crib figures modelled by Eliecer Alvarez. Multicoloured.

2644. 2 b. Type **456** 15 5
2645. 2 b. Nativity 15 5

Nos. 2644/5 were printed together, se-tenant, forming a composite design.

457. Treating Accident Victim.

1986. 17th Anniv. of Caracas City Police. Multicoloured.

2646. 2 b. 70 Type **457** .. 20 10
2647. 2 b. 70 On duty at sporting event .. 20 10
2648. 2 b. 70 Computer identification bar code .. 20 10
2649. 2 b. 70 Cadets on parade 20 10
2650. 2 b. 70 Motor cycle police 20 10

458. Prehispanic Musical Instrument.

1987. Native Art. Multicoloured.

2651. 2 b. Type **458** 15 8
2652. 2 b. Woven fabric .. 15 8
2653. 3 b. Prehispanic ceramic bottle 25 12
2654. 3 b. Basket design .. 25 12

459. Robert Koch (discoverer) and Bacillus Symbol.

1987. Centenary (1982) of Discovery of Tubercle Bacillus.

2655. **459.** 2 b. 55 multicoloured 20 10

460. "Entry of Jesus into Jerusalem" (Antonio Herrera Toro).

1987. Holy Week. Multicoloured.

2656 2 b. Type **460** 15 10
2657 2 b. "Christ at the Pillar" (statue, Jose Francisco Rodriguez) 15 10
2658 2 b. "Jesus of Nazareth" (wood carving, school of Seville) 15 10
2659 2 b. "Descent from the Cross" (Jose Rivadefrecha, El Campeche) .. 15 10
2660 2 b. "Virgin of Solitude" (sculpture) 15 10
2661 2 b. 25 "The Last Supper" (Arturo Michelena) .. 15 10
2662 2 b. 25 "Ecce Homo" (sculpture) 15 10
2663 2 b. 25 "The Crucifixion" (sculpture, Gregorio de Leon Quintana) .. 15 10
2664 2 b. 25 "Holy Sepulchre" (sculpture, Sebastian de Ochoa Montes) .. 15 10
2665 2 b. 25 "The Resurrection" (attr. Peter Paul Rubens) 15 10

461. "Bolivar and Bello" (Marisol Escobar).

1987. World Neurochemical Congress. Mult.

2666. 3 b. Type **461** 25 12
2667 4 b. 25 Retinal cells .. 30 15

462. Barquisimeto Hilton Hotel.

1987. Tourism Development. Multicoloured.

2668	6 b. Type **462**	35	15
2669	6 b. Lake Hotel Inter-continental, Maracaibo	35	15
2670	6 b. Macuto Sheraton Hotel, Carballeda	35	15
2671	6 b. Melia Caribe Hotel, Caraballeda	35	15
2672	6 b. Melia Hotel, Puerto la Cruz	55	20
2673	6 b. 50 Pool, Barquisimeto Hilton Hotel	35	15
2674	6 b. 50 Lake Hotel Inter-continental, Maracaibo, at night	35	15
2675	6 b. 50 Macuto Sheraton Hotel, Caraballeda, and marina	55	20
2676	6 b. 50 Melia Caribe Hotel, Caraballeda (different)	35	15
2677	6 b. 50 Melia Hotel, Puerto la Cruz (different)	55	20

463. Amazon Federal Territory Map and Ship's Bow.

1987. 35th Anniv. of National Canals Institute. Multicoloured.

2678.	2 b. Type **463**	10	5
2679.	4 b. 25 Map of River Orinoco and buoy	25	12

464. Music School, Caracas.

1987. Birth Centenary of Vicente Emilio Sojo (composer). Each deep brown and brown.

2680	2 b. Type **464**	12	8
2681	4 b. Conducting choir	25	12
2682	5 b. Score of "Hymn to Bolivar"	30	15
2683	6 b. Standing beside blackboard	40	20
2684	7 b. Sojo and signature	50	25

465. "Simon Bolivar Academician" (Roca Rey).

1987. 20th Anniv. of Simon Bolivar University. Multicoloured.

2685.	2 b. Type **465**	10	5
2686.	3 b. "Solar Delta" (sculpture, Alejandro Otero)	15	8
2687.	4 b. Rector's residence	20	10
2688.	5 b. Laser beam	25	12
2689.	6 b. Owl sculpture	30	15

466. Motor Vehicles.

1987. 10th Anniv. of Ministry of Transport and Communications. Multicoloured.

2690.	2 b. Type **466**	10	10
2691.	2 b. Bulk carrier and crane	20	10
2692.	2 b. Electric local train	10	10
2693.	2 b. Envelopes and telegraph key	10	10
2694.	2 b. Transmission masts and globe	10	10
2695.	2 b. 25 Motorway interchange system	10	10
2696.	2 b. 25 Airplane	30	15
2697.	2 b. 25 Electric mainline train	10	10
2698.	2 b. 25 Dish aerial	10	10
2699.	2 b. 25 Globe and communications satellite	10	10

Nos. 2690/9 were printed together, se-tenant, each horizontal pair forming a composite design.

467. Administration Building, Caracas.

1987. 70th Anniv. of Venezuelan Navigation Company. Multicoloured.

2700	2 b. Type **467**	10	10
2701	2 b. Containers being loaded	10	10
2702	3 b. Company emblem on ship's funnel	15	10
2703	3 b. Ship's engine-room	15	10
2704	4 b. "Zulia" (freighter) at sea	40	20
2705	4 b. "Guarico" (freighter) off Venezuelan coast	50	20
2706	5 b. "Cerro Bolivar" (bulk carrier)	55	20
2707	5 b. Ship's bridge	25	15
2708	6 b. Map	30	15
2709	6 b. Containers being loaded onto ro-ro ferry	30	15

468. Air-sea Rescue.

1987. 50th Anniv of National Guard. Mult.

2710	2 b. Type **468**	35	10
2711	2 b. Traffic Patrol	10	10
2712	2 b. Guard on horseback	10	10
2713	2 b. Guard with children	10	10
2714	2 b. Armed guard on industrial site	10	10
2715	4 b. As No. 2714	20	10
2716	4 b. As No. 2713	20	10
2717	4 b. As No. 2712	20	10
2718	4 b. As No. 2711	20	10
2719	4 b. Type **468**	60	20

469. "Departure from Puerto Palos" (detail, Jacobo Borges).

1987. 500th Anniv. (1992) of Discovery of America by Columbus. Multicoloured.

2720	2 b. Type **469**	10	5
2721	7 b. "Discovery of America" (Tito Salas)	30	15
2722	11 b. 50 "Fr. de las Casas, Protector of the Indians" (detail, Tito Salas)	50	25
2723	12 b. "Trade in Venezuela during the Time of the Conquest" (detail, Tito Salas)	70	25
2724	12 b. 50 "Rout of Guaicaipuro" (Jacobo Borges)	55	25

470. "Annunciation" (Juan Pedro Lopez).

1987. Christmas. Multicoloured.

2725.	2 b. Type **470**	10	5
2726.	3 b. "Nativity" (Jose Francisco Rodriguez)	15	8
2727.	5 b. 50 "Adoration of the Kings" (anon)	30	15
2728.	6 b. "Flight into Egypt" (Juan Pedro Lopez)	30	15

471. Steel Plant Building.

1987. 25th Anniv. of Steel Production by National SIDOR Mills.

2729.	471.	2 b. multicoloured	10	5
2730.	–	2 b. multicoloured	10	5
2731.	–	6 b. multicoloured	30	15
2732.	–	6 b. multicoloured	30	15
2733.	–	7 b. multicoloured	30	15
2734.	–	7 b. multicoloured	30	15
2735.	–	11 b. 50 mult.	75	25
2736.	–	11 b. 50 mult.	75	25
2737.	–	12 b. black	80	25
2738.	–	12 b. multicoloured	80	25

DESIGNS: No. 2730, Rolling strip. 2731, Walkways and towers of plant. 2732, Drawing steel bars. 2733, Walkway, towers and buildings. 2734, Slab mill. 2735, Building and towers. 2736, Steel bar production; 2737, Company emblem. 2738, Anniversary emblem.

Nos. 2729/38 were printed together, se-tenant, Nos. 2729, 2731, 2733 and 2735 forming a composite design of the SIDOR steel plant.

472. Flags.

1987. 1st Meeting of Eight Latin-American Presidents of Contadora and Lima Groups, Acapulco.

2739.	472.	6 b. multicoloured	30	15

473. Plastics.

474. St. John Bosco and People on Map.

1987. 10th Anniv. of Petro-Chemical Company of Venezuela. Multicoloured.

2740.	2 b. Type **473**	10	5
2741.	6 b. Formulae (oil refining)	30	15
2742.	7 b. Leaves (fertilizers)	30	15
2743.	11 b. 50 Pipes (installations)	75	25
2744.	12 b. Expansion	80	25

1987. Birth Centenary of St. John Bosco (founder of Salesian Brothers). Multicoloured.

2745	2 b. Type **474**	10	5
2746	3 b. National Temple, Caracas	12	5
2747	4 b. Vocational training	15	8
2748	5 b. Church of Maria Auxiliadora	20	10
2749	6 b. Missionary work	25	12

475 Emblem

1988. 29th Governors' Meeting of Inter-American Development Bank.

2750	**475**	11 b. 50 multicoloured	60	30

476 Bank Branch

1988. 30th Anniv of Banco Republica. Mult.

2751	2 b. Type **476**	10	5
2752	2 b. Pottery (small businesses finance)	10	5
2753	2 b. Factory and security guards (industrial finance)	10	5
2754	2 b. Laboratory workers (technology finance)	10	5
2755	2 b. Quay-side scene (exports and imports)	10	5
2756	6 b. Farm workers (agricultural finance)	35	15
2757	6 b. Fishing boat (fisheries finance)	35	15
2758	6 b. Milk production (livestock development)	35	15
2759	6 b. Building site (construction finance)	35	15
2760	6 b. Tourist bus (tourism development)	35	15

477 "Mother and Children" and Emblems

1988. Rotary International Anti-polio Campaign Victory Day.

2761	**477**	11 b. 50 multicoloured	65	35

478 Carlos Eduardo Frias (publicist)

1988. 50th Anniv of Publicity Industry. Mult.

2762	4 b. Three profiles of Frias	30	15
2763	10 b. Type **478**	60	30

479 Smelter

481 Bolivar in Dress Uniform, 1828

480 Red Siskins

1988. 10th Anniv of Venalum (aluminium company).

2764	**479**	2 b. multicoloured	10	5
2765	–	6 b. black	30	15
2766	–	7 b. multicoloured	30	15
2767	–	11 b. 50 multicoloured	65	35
2768	–	12 b. multicoloured	65	35

DESIGNS: 6 b. Plan of electrolytic cell; 7 b. Aluminium pipes; 11 b. 50, Loading ship with aluminium for export; 12 b. Workers playing football.

1988. Endangered Birds. Multicoloured.

2769	2 b. Type **480**	15	10
2770	6 b. Scarlet ibis	45	25
2771	11 b. 50 Harpy eagle	95	45
2772	12 b. Greater flamingoes	95	45
2773	12 b. 50 Northern helmeted curassow	1·00	55

1988. Army Day. Multicoloured.

2774	2 b. Type **481**	10	5
2775	2 b. Lieutenant in ceremonial uniform, 1988	10	5
2776	6 b. Gen. Jose Antonio Paez in dress uniform, 1821	30	15

2777 6 b. Major-General in No. 1 dress, 1988 . . . . 30 15
2778 7 b. Major-General, 1820 30 15
2779 7 b. Line infantryman, 1820 . . . . . . 30 15
2780 11 b. 50 Brigadier-General, 1820 . . . . . . 60 30
2781 11 b. 50 Garrison infantryman, 1820 . . 60 30
2782 12 b. Artilleryman, 1836 60 30
2783 12 b. Light cavalryman, 1820 . . . . . . 60 30

482 Urdaneta (after Salas)

1988. Birth Bicentenary of General Rafael Urdaneta. Multicoloured.
2784 2 b. Sword and scabbard 10 5
2785 4 b. 75 "Wedding of the General" (Tito Salas) . . 20 10
2786 6 b. Type **482** 30 15
2787 7 b. "Siege of Valencia" (Tito Salas) 30 15
2788 12 b. "Retreat from San Carlos" (Tito Salas) . . 65 35

483 Marino (after Martin Tovar y Tovar)

484 Games Emblem

1988. Birth Bicentenary of General Santiago Marino.
2789 **483** 4 b. 75 multicoloured 20 10

1988. Olympic Games, Seoul.
2790 **484** 12 b. multicoloured . . 60 30

485 "Virgin of Copacabana" (Bolivia)

1988. Marian Year. Multicoloured.
2791 4 b. 75 Type **485** . . 25 12
2792 4 b. 75 "Virgin of Chiquinquira" (Colombia) . . 25 12
2793 4 b. 75 "Virgin of Coromoto" (Venezuela) 25 12
2794 4 b. 75 "Virgin of the Cloud" (Ecuador) . . 25 12
2795 4 b. 75 "Virgin of Antigua" (Panama) . . 25 12
2796 6 b. "Virgin of Evangelisation" (Peru) 30 15
2797 6 b. "Virgin of Lujan" (Argentina) 30 15
2798 6 b. "Virgin of Altagracia" (Dominican Republic) 30 15
2799 6 b. "Virgin of Aparecida" (Brazil) . . 30 15
2800 6 b. "Virgin of Guadelupe" (Mexico) . . 30 15

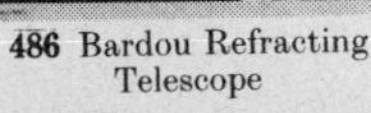
486 Bardou Refracting Telescope

487 Keys

1988. Centenary of Juan Manuel Cagigal Observatory. Multicoloured.
2801 2 b. Type **486** 20 5
2802 4 b. 75 Universal "AUZ-27" theodolite . . 25 12
2803 6 b. Bust of Cagigal . . 30 15
2804 11 b. 50 Boulton Cupola and night sky over Caracas in September 60 30
2805 12 b. Satellite photographing Hurricane Allen . . 65 35

1988. 50th Anniv of Controller-General's Office.
2806 **487** 10 b. multicoloured . . 45 25

488 Commemorative Medal

1988. Centenary of National Historical Museum. Multicoloured.
2807 6 b. Type **488** 30 15
2808 6 b. 50 Juan Pablo Rojas Paul (founder) (after Cristobal Rojas) . . 30 15

489 First Headquarters

1988. Centenary of Electricity Industry. Mult.
2809 2 b. Type **489** 10 5
2810 4 b. 75 "Electrical Plant, 1888" (Jaime Carrillo) 20 12
2811 10 b. Plaza Bolivar, 1888 45 25
2812 11 b. 50 Baralt Theatre, 1888 . . . . . . 60 30
2813 12 b. 50 Ramon Laguna Central Thermo-electricity Station . . 60 30

490 "Nativity" (Tito Salas, left-hand detail)

1988. Christmas. Multicoloured.
2814 4 b. Type **490** 20 10
2815 6 b. "Christ Child" (anonymous) 30 15
2816 15 b. "Nativity" (Salas, right-hand detail) . . 65 35
Nos. 2814 and 2816 form a composite design.

491 "Bolivar and Ricardo" (John de Pool)

1989. "The Liberator at Curacao". Mult.
2817 10 b. Type **491** 60 15
2818 10 b. "The Octagon" (John de Pool) . . 60 15
2819 11 b. "Doctor Mordechay Ricardo" 75 20
Nos. 2817/19 were printed together se-tenant, Nos. 2817/8 forming a composite design.

492 Cardinal Quintero, (Archbishop of Caracas, 1960–80)

494 Dish

493 "Cacao Harvest" (Tito Salas)

1989. 25th Anniv of Convention with Holy See. Multicoloured.
2820 4 b. Type **492** 12 5
2821 4 b. Dr. Raul Leoni (President, 1964–69) . . 12 5
2822 12 b. Arms of Luciano Storero (Papal Nuncio) 70 20
2823 12 b. Arms of Cardinal Lebrun (Archbishop of Caracas) 70 20
2824 16 b. Pope Paul VI . . 90 25

1989. Cent of Bank of Venezuela. Mult.
2825 4 b. Type **493** 12 5
2826 4 b. "Teaching Sowing Time of Coffee" (Tito Salas) 12 5
2827 4 b. Head Office, Caracas 12 5
2828 4 b. Archive of the Liberator, Caracas . . 12 5
2829 4 b. Tree-planting programme 12 5
2830 4 b. Family planting tree 12 5
2831 8 b. Left-hand side of 50 b. banknote . . 25 15
2832 8 b. Right-hand side of 50 b.bank note . . 25 15
2833 8 b. Portrait of Bolivar on left-hand side of 500 b. banknote . . 25 15
2834 8 b. Right-hand side of 500 b. banknote . . 25 15
Nos. 2825/34 were printed together se-tenant, Nos. 2831/2 and 28833/4 forming composite designs.

1989. America. Pre-Columbian Artefacts. Multicoloured.
2835 6 b. Type **494** 20 10
2836 24 b. Figure . . . . 2·00 1·00

495 Shepherds and Sheep

1989. Christmas. Multicoloured.
2837 5 b. As Type **495** but inscr at top 10 5
2838 5 b. Type **495** 10 5
2839 6 b. Angel and shepherds (inscr at top) . . 15 8
2840 6 b. As No. 2839 but inscr at bottom . . 15 8
2841 6 b. Nativity (inscr at top) 15 8
2842 6 b. As No. 2841 but inscr at bottom . . 15 8
2843 12 b. Shepherds (inscr at top) 70 15
2844 12 b. As No. 2843 but inscr at bottom . . 70 15
2845 15 b. Adoration of the Magi (inscr at top) . . 85 15
2846 15 b. As No. 2845 but inscr at bottom . . 85 45
Nos. 2837/46 were printed together, each horizontal strip forming a composite design.

496 Araguaney Tree and State Arms

1990. 20th Anniv of Bank of Venezuela Foundation. Multicoloured.
2847 10 b. Type **496** 20 10
2848 10 b. Silk-cotton tree and Federal District arms 20 10
2849 10 b. "Myrospermum frutescens" and Anzoategui State arms 20 10
2850 10 b. "Pithecellobium saman" and Aragua State arms . . 20 10
2851 10 b. West Indian cedar and Barinas State arms 20 10
2852 10 b. "Dipteryx punctata" and Bolivar State arms 20 10
2853 10 b. Pink trumpet tree and Cojedes State arms 20 10
2854 10 b. "Prosopis juliflora" and Falcon State arms 20 10
2855 10 b. "Copernicia tectorum" and Guarico State arms . . 20 10
2856 10 b. Mountain immortelle and Merida State arms 20 10
2857 10 b. "Brawnea leucantha" and Miranda State arms . . 20 10
2858 10 b. "Mauritia flexuosa" and Monagas State arms 20 10
2859 10 b. Mahogany and Portuguesa State arms 20 10
2860 10 b. "Platymiscium diadelphum" and Sucre State arms 20 10
2861 10 b. "Prumnopitys montana de Laub" and Tachira State arms . . 20 10
2862 10 b. "Roystonea venezuelana" and Yaracuy State arms . . 20 10
2863 10 b. Coconut palm and Zulia State arms . . 20 10
2864 10 b. "Hevea benthamiana" and Amazonas Federal Territory arms . . 20 10
2865 40 b. "Licania pyrofolia" and Apure State arms 1·60 85
2866 40 b. "Malpighia glabra" and Lara State arms . . 1·60 85
2867 40 b. "Erythrina fusca" and Trujillo State arms 1·60 85
2868 50 b. "Sterculia apetala" and Carabobo State arms . . . . . . 2·10 1·00
2869 50 b. "Lignum vitae" and Nueva Esparta State arms . . . . . . 2·10 1·00
2870 50 b. Mangrove and Amacuro Federal Territory arms . . 2·10 1·00

497 Dr. Francisco Ochoa (founder)

1990. Centenary of Zulia University.
2871 **497** 10 b. black and blue 20 10
2872 – 10 b. black and blue 20 10
2873 – 15 b. multicoloured . . 60 15
2874 – 15 b. multicoloured . . 60 15
2875 – 20 b. multicoloured . . 85 25
DESIGNS: No. 2872, Dr. Jesus E. Lossada (Rector, 1946–47); 2873, Research into acid soils; 2874, Petroleum research; 2875, Transplant surgery.

498 Santa Capilla, 1943

1990. 50th Anniv of Central Bank. Mult.
2876 10 b. Type **498** 20 10
2877 10 b. Headquarters, 1967 20 10
2878 10 b. Left half of 1940 500 b. note 20 10
2879 10 b. Right half of 1940 500 b. note 20 10
2880 10 b. "Sun of Peru" decoration, 1825 .. 20 10
2881 10 b. Medals 20 10
2882 15 b. Peruvian sword, 1825 60 15
2883 15 b. Cross, Bucaramanga, 1830 .. .. .. 60 15
2884 40 b. Medallion of George Washington, 1826 .. 1·60 85
2885 50 b. Gen. O'Leary (enamel portrait) .. 2·10 1·00
Nos. 2876/85 were printed together, se-tenant, Nos. 2878/9 forming a composite design.

500 "St. Joseph and the Child" (Juan Pedro Lopez)

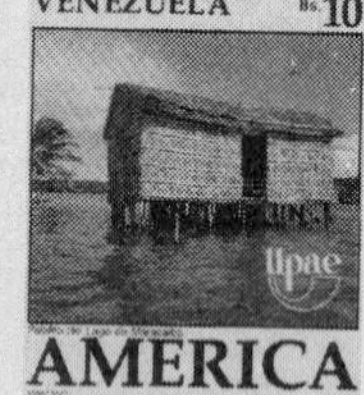

501 Lake House, Maracaibo

1990. Christmas. Multicoloured.
2887 10 b. Type **500** 20 10
2888 10 b. "Nativity" (Juan Pedro Lopez) 20 10
2889 10 b. "Return from Egypt" (Matheo Moreno) 20 10
2890 20 b. "Holy Family" (anon) 85 25
2891 20 b. "Nativity" (Juan Pedro Lopez) (different) 85 25

1990. America. The Natural World. Mult.
2892 10 b. Type **501** 20 10
2893 40 b. East Venezuelan shore .. .. .. 1·60 80

502 Globe and "30"

503 Death Mask

1990. 30th Anniv of O.P.E.C. Multicoloured.
2894 10 b. Type **502** 20 10
2895 10 b. O.P.E.C. emblem .. 20 10
2896 20 b. Anniversary emblem 85 25
2897 30 b. O.P.E.C. emblem and dates .. .. 1·25 60
2898 40 b. Members' flags around O.P.E.C. emblem .. .. 1·60 85

1991. 500th Birth Anniv of St. Ignatius de Loyola (founder of Society of Jesus). Mult.
2899 12 b. Type **503** 25 15
2900 12 b. St. Ignatius de Loyola College, Caracas 25 15
2901 40 b. Silver statue of Loyola by Francisco de Vergara .. .. 1·50 75
2902 50 b. "Our Lady of Montserrat" (wooden statue) .. .. 1·90 95

504 Elisa Elvira Zuloaga (painter and engraver)

1991. 50th Anniv of American–Venezuelan Cultural Centre. Designs showing Centre directors.
2903 **504** 12 b. green & black 25 15
2904 – 12 b. violet & black 25 15
2905 – 12 b. red and black 25 15
2906 – 40 b. blue & black 1·50 80
2907 – 40 b. brown & blk 1·50 80
DESIGNS: No. 2904, Gloria Stolk (writer); 2905, Caroline Lloyd (composer); 2906, Jules Waldman (linguist and journalist); 2907, William Coles (entrepreneur).

505 "Acineta alticola"

1991. Orchids. Multicoloured.
2908 12 b. Type **505** 25 15
2909 12 b. "Brassavola nodosa" 25 15
2910 12 b. "Brachionidium brevicaudatum" .. 25 15
2911 12 b. "Bifrenaria maguirei" 25 15
2912 12 b. "Odontoglossum spectatissimum" .. 25 15
2913 12 b. "Catasetum macrocarpum" 25 15
2914 40 b. "Mendocella jorisiana" 80 40
2915 40 b. "Cochleanthes discolor" 80 40
2916 50 b. "Maxillaria splendens" .. .. 1·00 50
2917 50 b. "Pleurothallis dunstervillei" .. .. 1·00 50

506 Voters at Ballot Box

1991. 50th Anniv of Democratic Action Party.
2919 **506** 12 b. multicoloured 25 15
2920 – 12 b. multicoloured 25 15
2921 – 12 b. multicoloured 25 15
2922 – 12 b. black & blue 25 10
DESIGNS: No. 2920, Agrarian reform; 2921, Education; 2922, Nationalization of petroleum industry.

507 Rodrigues Suarez and Terepaima Chieftain

1991. America. Voyages of Discovery. Showing paintings by Pedro Centeno. Mult.
2923 12 b. Type **507** 25 15
2924 40 b. Paramaconi chieftain and Garcia Gonzalez .. .. 1·60 80

508 Family in House

1991. 25th Anniv of Children's Foundation. Multicoloured.
2925 12 b. Type **508** 20 10
2926 12 b. Children's playground 20 10
2927 12 b. Fairground 20 10
2928 12 b. Mother and daughter 20 10
2929 12 b. Boy in hospital .. 20 10
2930 12 b. Children and tree .. 20 10
2931 40 b. Girls at home .. 65 35
2932 40 b. Children in classroom 65 35
2933 50 b. Children acting in play 80 40
2934 50 b. Children playing ring-a-ring of roses .. 80 40

INDEX

Countries can be quickly located by referring to the index at the end of this volume.

509 "Stable" (Barbaro Rivas)

1991. Christmas. Multicoloured.
2935 10 b. Type **509** 15 10
2936 12 b. "Nativity" (Elsa Morales) 20 10
2937 20 b. "Nativity" (model, Glenda Mendoza) .. 30 15
2938 25 b. "Shepherds watching flock" (Maritza Marin) 40 20
2939 30 b. "Nativity" (Antonia Azuaje) 50 25

1991. Nos. 2613/15 surch **RESELLADO** and value.
2940 **347** 5 b. on 25 c. red .. 10 5
2941 5 b. on 75 c. mauve .. 10 5
2942 10 b. on 25 c. red 15 10
2943 10 b. on 75 c. mauve 15 10
2944 12 b. on 50 c. blue .. 20 10
2945 12 b. on 75 c. mauve 20 10
2946 20 b. on 50 c. blue .. 30 15
2947 20 b. on 75 c. mauve 30 5
2948 40 b. on 50 c. blue .. 65 35
2949 40 b. on 75 c. mauve 65 35
2950 50 b. on 50 c. blue .. 80 40
2951 50 b. on 75 c. mauve 80 40

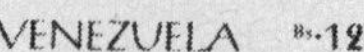

512 Columbus's Arms

1991. 500th Anniv (1992) Discovery of America by Columbus.
2953 **512** 12 b. multicoloured .. 20 10
2954 – 12 b. black, bl & orge 20 10
2955 – 12 b. multicoloured .. 20 10
2956 – 40 b. blk, brn & orge 65 35
2957 – 50 b. black and orange 80 40
DESIGNS: No. 2954, "Santa Maria"; 2955, Juan de la Cosa's map; 2956, Sighting land; 2957, Columbus before King Ferdinand and Queen Isabella the Catholic.

513 Anniversary Emblem

1992. "Expo 92" World's Fair, Seville. 500th Anniv of Discovery of America by Columbus.
2958 **513** 12 b. black, red & blue 20 10
2959 – 12 b. multicoloured .. 20 10
2960 – 12 b. multicoloured .. 20 10
2961 – 12 b. multicoloured .. 20 10
2962 – 12 b. multicoloured .. 20 10
2963 – 12 b. multicoloured .. 20 10
2964 – 40 b. multicoloured .. 65 35
2965 – 40 b. multicoloured .. 65 35
2966 – 50 b. multicoloured .. 80 40
2967 – 50 b. black and brown 80 40
DESIGNS: No. 2959, Venezuelan pavilion at "Expo 92"; 2960, Landmarks and map of southern Spain; 2961, Columbus; 2962, "Encounters"; 2963, "0x500 America"; 2964, "Imago-Mundi"; 2965, "The Grand Voyage"; 2966, "Golden Beach"; 2967, Idols.

514 Red-footed Tortoise

1992. Tortoises. Multicoloured.
2969 12 b. Type **514** 20 10
2970 12 b. Red-footed tortoise ("Geochelone carbonaria") (different) .. 20 10
2971 12 b. South American river turtle ("Podocnemis expansa") (on land) .. 20 10
2972 12 b. South American river turtle (swimming) 20 10

515 Native Hut

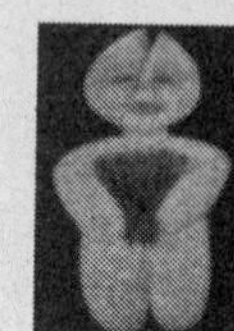

516 Figure holding Sheaf of Wheat

1992. Electricity Distribution in the South.
2973 **515** 12 b. multicoloured .. 20 10
2974 – 12 b. black and blue 20 10
2975 – 12 b. multicoloured .. 20 10
2976 – 40 b. multicoloured .. 65 35
2977 – 50 b. multicoloured .. 80 40
DESIGNS: No. 2974, Pylons; 2975, Horses galloping through water; 2976, Engineers working on pylon; 2977, Traditional baskets beside lake.

1992. "Offering to My Race" (Mateo Manaure). Designs showing various "mother" figures. Multicoloured.
2978 12 b. Type **516** 20 10
2979 12 b. Orange figure .. 20 10
2980 12 b. Yellow figure .. 20 10
2981 12 b. Pink figure .. 20 10
2982 40 b. Brown figure .. 65 35
2983 40 b. Purple and orange figures 65 35
2984 50 b. Three-quarter length figure 80 40
2985 50 b. Head and shoulders 80 40

517 Catechism in Venezuela, 1975

518 "And on the Third Voyage" (Elio Caldera)

1992. Beatification of Josemaria Escriva (founder of Opus Dei).
2986 **517** 18 b. multicoloured .. 20 10
2987 – 18 b. multicoloured .. 20 10
2988 – 18 b. multicoloured .. 20 10
2989 – 18 b. black and yellow 20 10
2990 – 18 b. multicoloured .. 20 10
2991 – 18 b. multicoloured .. 20 10
2992 – 60 b. multicoloured .. 70 35
2993 – 60 b. multicoloured .. 70 35
2994 – 75 b. multicoloured .. 85 45
2995 – 75 b. multicoloured .. 85 45
DESIGNS: No. 2987, Celebrating mass; 2988, Jose Escriva and Dolores Albas (parents); 2989, Text and autograph; 2990, With statuette of Madonna and Child; 2991, Commemorative medal; 2992, With Pope Paul VI, 1964; 2993, Writing at desk; 2994, Portrait; 2995, Portrait in St. Peter's Square, 17 May 1992.

1992. America. 500th Anniv of Discovery of America by Columbus. Multicoloured.
2996 18 b. Type **518** 20 10
2997 60 b. "Descontextura" (Juan Pablo Nascimiento) 70 35

519 "Adoration of the Shepherds"

520 Simon Bolivar

1992. Christmas. Paintings by Lucio Rivas. Multicoloured.
2998 18 b. Type **519** 20 10
2999 75 b. "Adoration of the Magi" 85 45

1993. Portraits and Monuments.
3001 **520** 1 b. silver 10 10
3002 – 2 b. blue 10 10
3005 – 5 b. red 10 10
3007 – 10 b. purple 10 10
3009 – 20 b. green 25 15
3011 – 50 b. orange 60 30
3013 – 100 b. brown .. 1·10 55
DESIGNS: 5 b. National Pantheon, Caracas; 10 b. War of Independence Memorial, Carabobo; 20 b. General Jose Antonio de Paez (President, 1830–35, 1837–43 and 1861–63); 50 b. National Library; 100 b. Bolivar (different).

521 "Cattleya percivaliana"

1993. Orchids. Multicoloured.
3016 20 b. Type **521** 25 15
3017 20 b. "Anguloa ruckeri" 25 15
3018 20 b. "Chondrorhyncha flaveola" 25 15
3019 20 b. "Stenia pallida" .. 25 15
3020 20 b. "Zygosepalum lindeniae" 25 15
3021 20 b. "Maxillaria triloris" 25 15
3022 80 b. "Stanhopea wardii" 90 45
3023 80 b. "Oncidium papilio" 90 45
3024 100 b. "Oncidium hastilabium" .. .. 1·10 55
3025 100 b. "Sobralia cattleya" 1·10 55

522 Woman

1993. 150th Anniv of Tovar Colony, Aragua State. Multicoloured.
3027 24 b. Type **522** 30 15
3028 24 b. Children 30 15
3029 24 b. Catholic church .. 30 15
3030 24 b. St. Martin of Tours (patron saint) 30 15
3031 24 b. Vegetables and fruit 30 15
3032 24 b. School 30 15
3033 80 b. House of Augustin Codazzi (founder) .. 90 45
3034 80 b. House of Alexander Benitz 90 45
3035 100 b. Breidenbach mill 1·10 55
3036 100 b. Procession of Jokili (carnival group) .. 1·10 55

523 Tucacas Steam Locomotive, 1813

524 Smoker and Non-Smoker

1993. 19th Pan-American Railways Congress. Multicoloured.
3037 24 b. Type **523** 30 15
3038 24 b. Halcon steam locomotive, 1894, on Las Mostazas bridge .. 30 15
3039 24 b. Maracaibo steam locomotive 30 15
3040 24 b. Tender and carriages in Palo Grande station 30 15
3041 24 b. Fiat diesel locomotive, 1957 .. 30 15
3042 24 b. "GP-9-L" diesel locomotive, 1957 .. 30 15
3043 80 b. "GP-15-L" diesel locomotive, 1982 .. 90 45
3044 80 b. Underground train, Caracas 90 45
3045 100 b. Electric locomotive 1·10 55
3046 100 b. Carriages .. .. 1·10 55
Nos. 3037/46 were issued together, se-tenant, Nos. 3039/40 and 3043/4 forming composite designs.

1993. World No Smoking Day. Each black, blue and red.
3047 24 b. Type **524** .. 30 15
3048 80 b. No smoking sign .. 90 45

525 Yellow-shouldered Amazon

1993. America. Endangered Animals. Mult.
3049 24 b. Type **525** 30 15
3050 80 b. Scarlet macaw .. 90 45

EXPRESS LETTER STAMPS

E 119.

E 194.

1949.
E 809. E **119.** 30 c. lake .. 30 25

1961.
E 1691. E **194.** 30 c. orange .. 50 25

OFFICIAL STAMPS

O 17.

1898.
O 174. O **17.** 5 c. black & green 30 50
O 175. 10 c. black & red .. 60 65
O 176. 25 c. black & blue 85 90
O 177. 50 c. black & yellow 1·60 1·60
O 178. 1 b. black & mauve 1·60 1·50

1899. Surch. **1899** and new value.
O 187. O **17.** 5 c. on 50 c. black and yellow .. 3·00 2·75
O 188. 5 c. on 1 b. black and mauve .. 11·50 10·50
O 189. 25 c. on 50 c. black and yellow .. 11·50 10·50
O 190. 25 c. on 1 b. black and mauve .. 6·75 6·25

1900. Optd. **1900** in upper corners.
O 222. O **17.** 5 c. black & green 35 35
O 223. 10 c. black & red .. 45 45
O 224. 25 c. black & blue 45 45
O 225. 50 c. black & yellow 50 50
O 226. 1 b. black & mauve 55 55

O **40.** With Stars.

O **41.** Without Stars.

1904.
O 325. O **40.** 5 c. black & green 25 25
O 326. 10 c. black and red 50 50
O 327. 25 c. black & blue 50 50
O 328. 50 c. black & red .. 2·10 1·90
O 329. 1 b. black & lake .. 1·00 90

1912.
O 354. O **41.** 5 c. black & green 15 25
O 355. 10 c. black & red .. 15 25
O 356. 25 c. black & blue 15 25
O 357. 50 c. black & violet 20 35
O 358. 1 b. black & yellow 40 35

REGISTRATION STAMPS

R **19.** Bolivar.

1899.
R 186. R **19.** 25 c. brown .. 2·10 1·60

1899. Optd. with T **21.**
R 205. R **19.** 25 c. brown .. 1·25 1·25

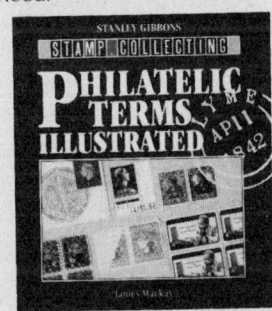

VIETNAM Pt. 21

A. DEMOCRATIC REPUBLIC

The Democratic republic was proclaimed by the Viet Minh Nationalists on 2 September 1945 and recognised by France on 6 March, 1946, as a free state within the Indo-China Federation. It consisted of Tongking, Annam and Cochin-China

Currency: 1945. 100 cents = 1 piastre.
1945. 100 xu = 10 hao = 1 dong.

Stamps of Indo-China overprinted.

VIET-NAM
DAN-CHU CONG-HOA
DOC-LAP
TU-DO HANH-PHUC
BUU-CHINH III
(1.)

("DAN-CHU CONG-HOA" = Democratic Republic: "DOC-LAP TU-DO HANH-PHUC = Independence, Freedom, Happiness; "BUU-CHINH" = Postage.)

1945. Independence. Variously optd. as T 1 (all with **DOC-LAP TU-DO HANH-PHUC** in opt.).
1. **53.** 1 c. brown 20 20
2. – 2 c. mauve (No. 315) .. 15 15
3. – 3 c. brown (Courbet) .. 15 15
4. – 4 c. brown (No. 316) .. 15 15
5. – 5 c. sepia (De Genouilly) 15 15
6. – 6 c. red (No. 304) .. 15 15
7. – 6 c. red (No. 305) .. 35 35
8. – 10 c. green (No. 307) .. 35 35
9. – 10 c. green (No. 322) .. 20 20
10. – 20 c. red (No. 309) .. 1·10 35
11. **64.** 40 c. blue 45 45
12. – $1 green (No. 311) .. 35 35

Nos. 3 and 5 were not issued without opt. and are as Nos. 304 and 305 of Indo-China respectively.

1945. Variously optd. as follows:—
(a) **VIET-NAM DAN-CHU CONG-HOA.**
13. **69.** 10 c. purple and yellow .. 85 80
14. – 15 c. purple (No. 292) .. 15 15
15. – 30 c. brown (No. 294) .. 20 20
16. **69.** 50 c. red .. .. 1·90 1·90
17. – $1 green (No. 295) .. 20 20

(b) **VIET-NAM DAN-CHU CONG-HOA BUU-CHINH.**
18. **53.** 3 c. brown 15 15
19. – 4 c. yellow (No. 317) .. 20 20
20. **53.** 6 c. red 20 20
21. 10 c. green 35 35
22. – 10 c. green (No. 320) .. 35 35
23. – 20 c. red (Pavie) .. 15 15
24. **53.** 40 c. blue 30 30
25. 40 c. grey 50 50

No. 23 was not issued without opt. and is as No. 320 of Indo-China.

VIET-NAM
3$00 DAN-CHU
CONG-HOA

CUU-DOI
(2.)

("CUU-DOI" = Famine Relief.)

1945. Famine Relief. Surch. as T **2.**
26. **70.** "2 $00" on 15 c. + 60 c. purple .. .. 2·75 2·75
27. "3 $00" on 40 c. + 1 $10 c. blue .. .. 2·75 2·75

1945. War wounded. Surch. as T 2 but with **Binh-si Bi-nan** (= Fund for War Wounded).
28. **70.** "5 $00" on 15 c. + 60 c. purple .. .. .. 3·50 3·50

1945. Surch in new currency and variously optd. as before (except Nos. 43/7).
(a) **VIET-NAM DAN-CHU CONG-HOA BUU-CHINH.**
29. **64.** 30 x. on 1 c. brown .. 20 20
30. – 30 x. on 15 c. purple (Garnier) 15 15
31. **67.** 50 x. on 1 c. brown .. 75 75
32. – 60 x. on 1 c. brown (313) 40 40
33. – 1 d. on 5 c. brown (303) .. 85 85
34. – 1 d. 60 x. on 10 c. green (319) 20 20
35. **64.** 3 d. on 15 c. purple .. 45 45
36. **67.** 3 d. on 15 c. purple .. 1·00 1·00
37. – 4 d. on 1 c. brown (302) 35 35
38. – 5 d. on 1 c. brown (301) .. 30 30

(b) **VIET-NAM DAN-CHU CONG-HOA.**
39. – 1 d. on 5 c. purple (318) 20 20
40. **49.** 2 d. on 3 c. brown .. 4·00 4·00
41. – 2 d. on 10 c. green (321) .. 35 35
42. **49.** 4 d. on 6 c. red .. .. 4·00 4·00

(c) Surch. only.
43. **56.** 50 x. on 1 c. brown .. 35 35
44. 2 d. on 6 c. red .. 2·75 2·75
45. **48.** 5 d. on 1 c. orange .. 4·00 4·00
46. 10 d. on 6 c. violet .. 4·00 4·00
47. 15 d. on 25 c. blue .. 4·00 4·00

No. 30 was not issued without opt. and is as No. 301 of Indo-China.

OVERPRINT. Nos. 48/55 are all optd. **VIET-NAM DAN-CHU CONG-HOA** with varying additional words as noted in headings.

1945. National Defence (**Quoc-Phong**).
48. **49.** "+5 d." on 3 c. brown .. 65 70
49. "+10 d." on 6 c. red .. 65 70

1946. People's Livelihood. (**DAN SINH**).
50. **57.** "30 xu. +3 d." on 6 c. red 35 35
51. **55.** "30 xu. +3 d." on 6 c. red 35 35

1946. Campaign against Illiteracy (**Chong nan mu chu**).
52. **59.** "+4 dong" on 6 c. red .. 45 45

1946. New Life Movement (**Doi song moi**).
53. **66.** "+4 dong" on 6 c. red .. 85 85

1946. Child Welfare (**Bao-Anh**).
54. – "+2 dong" on 6 c. red (290) 45 45

1946. War Wounded (**Binh si bi nan**).
55. – "+3 dong" on 20 c. red (293) 85 85

Definitive issues.

3. Ho Chi Minh.

1946.
56. **3.** 1 h. green 20 20
57. 3 h. red 20 20
58. 9 h. yellow 20 20

1946. National Defence.
59. **3.** 4+6 h. blue 45 45
60. 6+9 h. brown 45 45

The Viet-Minh Government was at war with the French from 19 December, 1946, until July, 1954, and the stamps issued by the Democratic Republic in this period are listed as North Viet-Nam Nos. N 1/13, NO 1/9 and ND 1/4.

B. INDEPENDENT STATE

On 14 June, 1949, Vietnam, comprising Tongking, Annam and Cochin-China, became an independent state within the French Union under Emperor Bao-Dai. Until the 1951 issue Indo-Chinese stamps continued in use.

By the Geneva Declaration of 21 July 1954, Vietnam was partitioned near the 17th Parallel, and all authority of Bao-Dai's Government north of that line ended. Later issues are therefore those of SOUTH VIETNAM and NORTH VIETNAM.

Currency: 100 cents = 1 piastre.

4. Bongour Falls, Dalat.

1951.
61. **4.** 10 c. bronze 8 5
62. – 20 c. purple 15 8
63. – 30 c. blue 15 8
64. – 50 c. red 30 10
65. **4.** 60 c. sepia 15 8
66. – 1 p. brown 15 5
67. – 1 p. 20 c. brown .. 1·10 70
68. – 2 p. violet 40 15
69. – 3 p. blue .. .. 1·10 15
70. **4.** 5 p. green 85 20
71. – 10 p. red .. .. 2·25 40
72. – 15 p. brown .. .. 8·00 2·40
73. – 30 p. green .. .. 17·00 3·00

DESIGNS—HORIZ. 20 c., 2 p., 10 p. Imperial Palace, Hue. 30 c., 15 p. Small Lake, Hanoi. 50 c., 1 p. Temple of Remembrance, Saigon. VERT. 1 p. 20, 3 p. 30 p. Emperor Bao Dai.

9.

1952. Air.
74. **9.** 3 p. 30 c. green and lake .. 35 20
75. 4 p. yellow and brown .. 45 15
76. 5 p. 10 c. pink and blue 40 35
77. 6 p. 30 c. red and yellow (symbolic of airlines) .. 45 40

10. Empress Nam Phuong.

11. Globe and Lightning.

1952.
78. **10.** 30 c. brown, yell. & purple 20 30
79. 50 c. brown, yell. & blue 45 30
80. 1 p. 50 brown, yell. & olive 70 30

1952. 1st Anniv. of Admission of Vietnam into I.T.U.
81. **11.** 1 p. blue .. .. .. 2·75 1·40

12. Dragon.

1952. Air. Day of Wandering Souls.
82. **12.** 40 c. red 55 40
83. 70 c. green 65 40
84. 80 c. blue 65 40
85. 90 c. brown 65 50
86. – 3 p. 70 c. purple 80 55

DESIGN—VERT. 3 p. 70 c. Dragon.

13. U.P.U. Monument, Berne, and Coastline.

1952. 1st Anniv. of Admission of Vietnam into U.P.U.
87. **13.** 5 p. brown .. .. 2·50 1·00

1952. Red Cross. T 10 surch, with red cross and **+50 c.**
88. **10.** 1 p. 50 + 50 c. brown, yellow and blue .. 2·75 2·75

15. Emperor Bao Dai and Gateway.

16. Sabres and Flag.

17. Crown Prince Bao Long.

1952. 40th Birthday of Emperor.
89. **15.** 1 p. 50 purple .. .. 1·60 70

1952. Wounded Soldiers' Relief Fund.
90. **16.** 3 p. 30 + 1 p. 70 lake .. 1·25 1·25

1959.
91. **17.** 40 c. turquoise 55 45
92. 70 c. lake 85 55
93. 80 c. sepia .. .. 1·10 65
94. – 90 c. green .. .. 1·90 1·60
95. – 20 p. red .. .. 9·00 5·00
96. – 50 p. violet .. .. 20·00 10·00
97. **17.** 100 p. blue .. .. 42·00 23·00

PORTRAIT: 90 c. to 50 p. Crown Prince in uniform.

POSTAGE DUE STAMPS

D 10. Dragon.

1952.
D 78. **D 10.** 10 c. green and red .. 8 8
D 79. 20 c. yellow & green .. 8 8
D 80. 30 c. orange & violet 8 8
D 81. 40 c. pink and green .. 8 8
D 82. 50 c. grey and lake .. 15 15
D 83. 1 p. silver and blue .. 20 20

C. SOUTH VIETNAM

Currency: 100 cents = 1 piastre.

INDEPENDENT STATE
(Within the French Union)

1. Turtle.

1955. 1st Anniv. of Govt. of Ngo Dinh Diem.
S 1. **1.** 30 c. purple 30 20
S 2. 50 c. green .. .. 2·40 85
S 3. 1 p. 50 c. blue 85 35

2. Phoenix.

1955. Air.
S 4. **2.** 4 p. mauve and violet .. 45 15

3. Refugees.

1955. 1st Anniv. of Arrival of Refugees from North Vietnam.
S 5. **3.** 70 c. red 45 30
S 6. 80 c. purple .. .. 1·10 70
S 7. 10 p. blue .. .. 2·10 1·25
S 8. 20 p. brn., orge. & violet 3·50 1·60
S 9. 35 p. sepia, yell. & blue 8·00 6·50
S 10. 100 p. pur., orge. & grn. 18·00 12·00

No. S 9 is incribed "CHEIN-DICH-HUYNE-DE" in margin at foot. See also No. S 26.

REPUBLIC
(from 26th October, 1955)

4. G.P.O., Saigon.

5. Pres. NgoDinh Diem.

1956. 5th Anniv. of Entry of Vietnam into U.P.U.
S 11. **4.** 60 c. green 55 35
S 12. 90 c. violet .. .. 1·10 55
S 13. 3 p. brown .. .. 1·90 80

1956.
S 14. **5.** 20 c. brown 5 5
S 15. 30 c. purple 10 10
S 16. 50 c. red 5 5
S 17. 1 p. violet 15 10
S 18. 1 p. 50 c. violet .. 30 10
S 19. 3 p. sepia 30 10
S 20. 4 p. blue 45 15
S 21. 5 p. brown 65 15
S 22. 10 p. blue 85 35
S 23. 20 p. black .. .. 2·10 55
S 24. 35 p. green .. .. 5·00 1·40
S 25. 100 p. brown .. .. 11·00 4·75

1956. No. S 9 with bottom marginal inscription obliterated by bar.
S 26. **3.** 35 p. sepia, yell. & blue 4·50 3·25

1956. Optd. **Cong-thu Buu-dien** (="Government Postal Building").
S 27. **4.** 60 c. green 65 35
S 28. 90 c. violet .. .. 1·10 35
S 29. 3 p. brown .. .. 1·75 55

7. Bamboo. 8. Refugee Children.

1956. 1st Anniv. of Republic.

S 30.	7.	50 c. red	15	15
S 31.		1 p. 50 c. purple	20	15
S 32.		2 p. green	30	20
S 33.		4 p. blue	50	30

1956. United Nations "Operation Brotherhood".

S 34.	8.	1 p. mauve	20	15
S 35.		2 p. turquoise	30	15
S 36.		6 p. violet	60	15
S 37.		35 p. blue	4·00	1·75

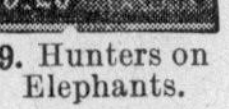

9. Hunters on Elephants. 10. Ship's Cargo being off-loaded at Saigon.

1957. 3rd Anniv. of Govt. of Ngo Dinh Diem.

S 38.	9.	20 c. purple and green	20	8
S 39.		30 c. red and bistre	20	8
S 40.	–	90 c. sepia and green	30	15
S 41.	–	2 p. blue and green	45	20
S 42.	–	3 p. brown and violet	65	30

DESIGN—VERT. 90 c. to 3 p. Mountain hut.

1957. 9th Colombo Plan Conf., Saigon.

S 43.	10.	20 c. purple	8	8
S 44.		40 c. olive	8	8
S 45.		50 c. red	10	10
S 46.		2 p. blue	25	20
S 47.		3 p. green	30	20

11. Torch and Constitution. 12. Youth Felling Tree.

1957. Inaug. of National Assembly.

S 48.	11.	50 c. salmon, grn. & blk.	5	5
S 49.		80 c. pur., blue & black	10	5
S 50.		1 p. red, green & black	20	10
S 51.		4 p. brn., myrtle & blk.	30	15
S 52.		5 p. olive, turq. & black	35	20
S 53.		10 p. brown, blue and black	65	50

1958. Better Living Standards.

S 54.	12.	50 c. green	15	15
S 55.		1 p. violet	20	15
S 56.		2 p. blue	30	15
S 57.		10 p. red	80	40

13. Young Girl with Chinese Lantern. 14.

1958. Children's Festival.

S 58.	13.	30 c. lemon	15	15
S 59.		50 c. red	15	15
S 60.		2 p. red	15	15
S 61.		3 p. green	30	15
S 62.		4 p. olive	40	20

1958. United Nations Day.

S 63.	14.	1 p. light brown	15	15
S 64.		2 p. turquoise	20	15
S 65.		4 p. red	25	15
S 66.		5 p. purple	60	30

15. U.N.E.S.C.O. Emblem and Building. 16. U.N. Emblem and "Torch of Freedom".

1958. Inauguration of U.N.E.S.C.O. Headquarters Building, Paris.

S 67.	15.	50 c. blue	15	15
S 68.		2 p. red	15	15
S 69.		3 p. purple	30	15
S 70.		6 p. violet	45	30

1958. 10th Anniv. of Declaration of Human Rights.

S 71.	16.	50 c. blue	15	10
S 72.		1 p. lake	20	15
S 73.		2 p. green	35	15
S 74.		6 p. purple	60	35

17. PhuCam Cathedral. 18. Saigon Museum.

1958.

S 75.	17.	10 c. slate	10	5
S 76.	–	30 c. green	20	15
S 77.	18.	40 c. green	10	10
S 78.	–	50 c. green	15	10
S 79.	–	2 p. blue	20	15
S 80.	–	4 p. lilac	30	20
S 81.	18.	5 p. red	35	20
S 82.	17.	6 p. brown	45	20

DESIGNS—HORIZ. 30 c., 4 p. ThienMu Pagoda. 50 c., 2 p. Palace of Independence, Saigon.

19. Trung Sisters (national heroines) on Elephants.

1959. Trung Sisters Commem.

S 83.	19.	50 c. multicoloured	55	45
S 84.		2 p. multicoloured	85	55
S 85.		3 p. multicoloured	1·60	95
S 86.		6 p. multicoloured	2·50	1·40

20. 21. Diesel-electric Train.

25. Scout climbing Mountain. 22. Tilling the Land.

1959. Agricultural Reform.

S 87.	20.	70 c. purple	15	10
S 88.		2 p. green and blue	15	10
S 89.		3 p. olive	20	10
S 90.		6 p. red and deep red	45	35

1959. Re-opening of Trans-Vietnam Railway. Centres in green.

S 91.	21.	1 p. violet	50	25
S 92.		2 p. grey	60	35
S 93.		3 p. blue	70	30
S 94.		4 p. lake	1·75	50

1959. 4th Anniv. of Republic.

S 95.	22.	1 p. brn., grn. & blue	20	15
S 96.		2 p. violet, grn. & orge.	25	15
S 97.		4 p. indigo, blue & bistre	55	35
S 98.		5 p. brown, olive and light brown	65	45

1959. 1st National Scout Jamboree, Trang Bom.

S 99.	25.	3 p. green	35	15
S 100.		4 p. mauve	45	20
S 101.		8 p. mauve & purple	90	45
S 102.		20 p. deep turq. & turq.	2·25	1·10

26. "Family Code".

1960. 1st Anniv. of Family Code.

S 103.	26.	20 c. green	10	10
S 104.		30 c. blue	15	15
S 105.		2 p. red and orange	15	15
S 106.		6 p. violet and red	35	25

27. Refugee Family in Flight. 28. Henri Dunant.

1960. World Refugee Year.

S 107.	27.	50 c. mauve	30	10
S 108.		3 p. green	20	15
S 109.		4 p. red	45	20
S 110.		5 p. violet	55	30

1960. Red Cross Day. Cross in red.

S 111.	28.	1 p. blue	25	15
S 112.		3 p. green	35	20
S 113.		4 p. red	50	25
S 114.		6 p. mauve	65	40

29. Co-operative Farm.

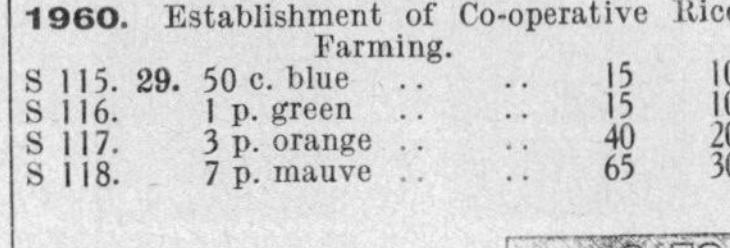

1960. Establishment of Co-operative Rice Farming.

S 115.	29.	50 c. blue	15	10
S 116.		1 p. green	15	10
S 117.		3 p. orange	40	20
S 118.		7 p. mauve	65	30

30. X-Ray Camera and Patient. 31. Flag and Map.

1960. National T.B. Relief Campaign Day.

S 119.	30.	3 p.+50 c. grn. & red	45	45

1960. 5th Anniv. of Republic. Flag and map in red and yellow.

S 120.	31.	50 c. turquoise	10	8
S 121.		1 p. blue	15	10
S 122.		3 p. violet	20	10
S 123.		7 p. green	35	15

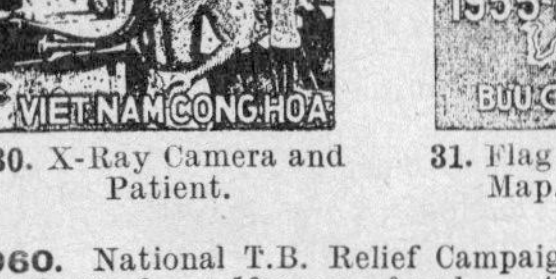

32. Woman with Rice.

1960. F.A.O. Regional Conf., Saigon.

S 124.	32.	2 p. turquoise & green	30	20
S 125.		4 p. ultram. and blue	40	25

33. Crane carrying Letter.

1960. Air.

S 126.	33.	1 p. green	35	15
S 127.		4 p. blue & turquoise	55	30
S 128.		5 p. violet and brown	95	45
S 129.		10 p. mauve	1·50	80

34. Farm Tractor.

35. Child and Plant.

36. Pres. Ngo Dinh Diem. 37. Young People and Torch.

1961. Agricultural Development and Pres. Diem's 60th Birthday.

S 130.	34.	50 c. brown	15	10
S 131.		70 c. mauve	15	10
S 132.		80 c. red	15	15
S 133.		10 p. mauve	55	30

1961. Child Welfare.

S 134.	35.	70 c. blue	15	10
S 135.		80 c. blue	15	10
S 136.		4 p. bistre	20	15
S 137.		7 p. green & turquoise	55	30

1961. 2nd Term of President.

S 138.	36.	50 c. blue	20	15
S 139.		1 p. red	30	15
S 140.		2 p. purple	35	15
S 141.		4 p. violet	65	20

1961. Sports and Youth.

S 142.	37.	50 c. red	10	8
S 143.		70 c. mauve	15	8
S 144.		80 c. mauve and deep red	15	10
S 145.		8 p. purple and red	40	20

38. Bridge over Mekong.

1961. Inaug. of Saigon-Bien Hoa Motor Highway.

S 146.	38.	50 c. green	15	15
S 147.		1 p. brown	15	10
S 148.		2 p. blue	25	15
S 149.		5 p. purple	35	20

39. Alexander of Rhodes. 40. Vietnamese with Torch.

1961. Death Tercent. of Alexander of Rhodes.

S 150.	39.	50 c. red	10	8
S 151.		1 p. purple	10	8
S 152.		3 p. bistre	15	8
S 153.		6 p. green	35	20

1961. Youth Moral Rearmament.

S 154.	40.	50 c. red	15	10
S 155.		1 p. green	15	10
S 156.		3 p. red	20	15
S 157.		8 p. brown & purple	35	20

41. Gateway of Van Mieu Temple, Hanoi. 42. Tractor and Cottages.

1961. 15th Anniv. of U.N.E.S.C.O.

S 158.	41.	1 p. green	15	10
S 159.		2 p. red	15	15
S 160.		5 p. olive	30	15

1961. Rural Reform.

S 161.	42.	50 c. green	15	10
S 162.		1 p. lake and blue	15	15
S 163.		2 p. brown and green	20	15
S 164.		10 p. turquoise	55	35

43. Attack on Mosquito. 44. Postal Cheque Building, Saigon.

1962. Malaria Eradication.

S 165.	43.	50 c. mauve	15	10
S 166.		1 p. orange	15	10
S 167.		2 p. green	20	15
S 168.		6 p. blue	50	30

1962. Inaug. of Postal Cheques Service.

S 169.	44.	70 c. green	20	15
S 170.		80 c. brown	20	15
S 171.		4 p. purple	25	15
S 172.		7 p. red	40	30

45. St. Mary of La Vang.

46. Armed Guards and Fortified Village.

1962. St. Mary of La Vang Commem.
S 173. 45. 50 c. red and violet .. 15 10
S 174. 1 p. blue and brown 15 10
S 175. 2 p. lake and brown 25 10
S 176. 8 p. blue & turquoise 65 30

1962. Strategic Villages.
S 177. 46. 50 c. red 15 10
S 178. 1 p. bronze 15 10
S 179. 1 p. 50 purple .. 20 10
S 180. 7 p. blue 40 25

47. Gougah Waterfalls, Dalat.

48. Trung Sisters Monument.

1963. Pres. Ngo Dinh Diem's 62nd Birthday and Spring Festival.
S 181. 47. 60 c. red 15 10
S 182. 1 p. blue 20 10

1963. Women's Day.
S 183. 48. 50 c. green 15 10
S 184. 1 p. red 15 10
S 185. 3 p. purple 20 15
S 186. 8 p. blue 50 35

49. Harvester.

1963. Freedom from Hunger.
S 187. 49. 50 c. red 10 10
S 188. 1 p. red 15 10
S 189. 3 p. purple 20 15
S 190. 5 p. violet 40 30

50. Sword and Fortress.

51. Soldier and Emblem.

1963. Communal Defence and 9th Anniv. of Inaug. of Pres. Diem.
S 191. 50. 30 c. bistre 15 8
S 192. 50 c. mauve 15 10
S 193. 3 p. green 30 15
S 194. 8 p. red 45 30

1963. Republican Combatants.
S 195. 51. 50 c. red 10 8
S 196. 1 p. green 15 10
S 197. 4 p. violet 25 15
S 198. 5 p. orange 45 35

52. Centenary Emblem and Globe.

53. Scales of Justice and Book.

1963. Red Cross Centenary. Cross in Red.
S 199. 52. 50 c. blue 15 10
S 200. 1 p. red 20 15
S 201. 3 p. orange 25 15
S 202. 6 p. brown 50 35

1963. 15th Anniv. of Declaration of Human Rights.
S 203. 53. 70 c. orange 15 10
S 204. 1 p. mauve 15 10
S 205. 3 p. green 20 10
S 206. 8 p. ochre 55 25

54. Danhim Hydro-Electric Station.

1964. Inauguration of Danhim Hydro-Electric Station.
S 207. 54. 40 c. red 10 5
S 208. 1 p. brown 15 10
S 209. 3 p. violet 20 15
S 210. 8 p. green 40 20

55. Atomic Reactor.

1964. Peaceful Uses of Atomic Energy.
S 211. 55. 80 c. olive 15 10
S 212. 1 p. 50 brown 15 5
S 213. 3 p. brown 35 15
S 214. 7 p. blue 45 30

56. "Meteorology".

57. "Unification".

1964. World Meteorological Day.
S 215. 56. 50 c. ochre 15 8
S 216. 1 p. red 15 15
S 217. 1 p. 50 lake 20 15
S 218. 10 p. green 45 30

1964. 10th Anniv. of Partition of Vietnam.
S 219. 57. 30 c. blue & green .. 10 5
S 220. 50 c. blue, lake & yell. 15 8
S 221. 1 p. 50 ind., bl. & orge. 15 10

58. Hatien Beach.

1964.
S 222. 58. 20 c. blue 15 5
S 223. 3 p. green 20 10

59. "Support of the People".

1964. 1st Anniv. of Revolution of 1 November 1963.
S 224. 59. 50 c. blue and purple 15 8
S 225. – 80 c. brown and lilac 20 15
S 226. – 3 p. brown and blue .. 35 15
DESIGNS—HORIZ. 80 c. Solider breaking chain. VERT. 3 p. Allergory of Revolution.

60. Temple and Monument, Botanic Gardens, Saigon.

1964. Monuments and views.
S 227. 60. 50 c. brn., grn. & blue 15 10
S 228. – 1 p. slate and bistre 20 10
S 229. – 1 p. 50 green and drab 30 15
S 230. – 3 p. red, green & violet 45 20
DESIGNS: 1 p. Tomb of Minh Mang, Hue. 1 p. 50, Phan Thiet waterfront. 3 p. General Le Van Duyet Temple, Gia Dinh.

61. Face of bronze drum.

1965. Hung Vuong (legendary founder of Vietnam, 2000 B.C.).
S 231. 61. 3 p. orange and lake 1·10 45
S 232. 100 p. violet & purple 10·00 5·00

62. Dharmachakra and "Fire of Clemency".

63. I.T.U. Emblem and Symbols.

1965. Buddhism.
S 233. 62. 50 c. red 15 10
S 234. – 1 p. 50 orange, blue & deep blue .. 15 10
S 235. – 3 p. deep brown, sepia and brown .. 20 15
DESIGNS—HORIZ. 1 p. 50, Dharmachakra, lotus and globe. VERT. 3 p. Dharmachakra and flag.

1965. I.T.U. Cent.
S 236. 63. 1 p. red and bistre .. 15 10
S 237. 3 p. red, mve. & brn. 20 15

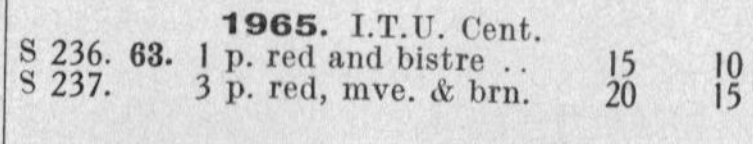

64. "World Solidarity".

65. Ixora.

1965. Int. Co-operation Year.
S 238. 64. 50 c. blue and brown 15 10
S 239. 1 p. sepia and brown 15 10
S 240. 1 p. 50 red and grey .. 15 10

1965. Mid-Autumn Festival.
S 241. 65. 70 c. red, grn. & deep green 15 10
S 242. – 80 c. pur., grn. & mve. 20 15
S 243. – 1 p. yell., light blue and deep blue .. 30 15
S 244. – 1 p. 50 green and olive 40 15
S 245. – 3 p. orange and green 60 30
FLOWERS—VERT. 80 c. Orchid. 1 p. Chrysanthemum. 3 p. "Ochna harmandii". HORIZ. 1 p. 50, Nenuphar.

66. Student and University Building.

67. Young Farmers.

1965. Re-opening of Vietnam University.
S 246. 66. 50 c. brown 10 10
S 247. 1 p. green 15 15
S 248. 3 p. red 20 15
S 249. 7 p. violet 30 20

1965. 10th Anniv. of "4-T" Rural Youth Clubs.
S 250. 67. 3 p. red and green .. 40 20
S 251. – 4 p. violet, blue & pur. 40 20
DESIGNS. 4 p. Young farmer and club banner.

68. Basketball.

69. Aerial Mast and Equipment.

1965. 3rd S.E. Asia Peninsular Games, Kuala Lumpur (Malaysia).
S 252. 68. 50 c. bistre, brown and red 20 8
S 253. – 1 p. lake and brown .. 30 15
S 254. – 1 p. 50 green .. 40 20
S 255. – 10 p. lake and purple 1·10 55
DESIGNS: 1 p. Throwing the javelin. 1 p. 50, "Physical Culture" (gymnasts and Olympic Games' symbols). 10 p. Pole-vaulting.

1966. 1st Anniv. of Saigon Microwave Station.
S 256. 69. 3 p. sepia, blue & brn. 15 10
S 257. – 4 p. pur., red & grn. .. 20 15
DESIGN: 4 p. Aerial mast, Telephone dial and map.

INDEX

Countries can be quickly located by referring to the index at the end of this volume.

70. Hook and Hemispheres.

71. Help for Refugees.

1966. "Free World's Aid to Vietnam".
S 258. 70. 3 p. lake and slate .. 10 5
S 259. 4 p. violet and brown 15 10
S 260. 6 p. blue and green .. 20 15

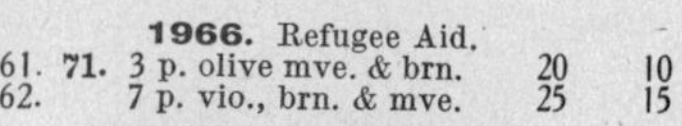

1966. Refugee Aid.
S 261. 71. 3 p. olive mve. & brn. 20 10
S 262. 7 p. vio., brn. & mve. 25 15

72. Paper "Soldiers".

1966. Wandering Soul's Festival.
S 263. 72. 50 c. bistre, brn. & red 15 10
S 264. – 1 p. 50 red, grn. & brn. 20 10
S 265. – 3 p. verm., crim. & red 35 15
S 266. – 5 p. brown, ochre and deep brown .. 40 20
DESIGNS: 1 p. 50, Obeisance. 3 p. Pool of candles. 5 p. Votive offering.

73. "Violinist".

1966. Ancient Musical Instruments.
S 267. 73. 1 p. deep brown, mauve and brown .. 10 5
S 268. – 3 p. violet and purple 15 10
S 269. – 4 p. brown and red .. 20 15
S 270. – 7 p. deep blue & blue 45 20
DESIGNS: 3 p. "Harpist". 4 p. Small band. 7 p. "Flautists".
For 3 p. in smaller size, see No. S 302.

74. W.H.O. Building.

1966. Inaug. of W.H.O. Headquarters, Geneva.
S 271. 74. 50 c. pur., violet & red 10 5
S 272. – 1 p. 50 blk., blue & lake 15 10
S 273. – 8 p. blue, sepia & turq. 20 15
DESIGNS—VERT. 1 p. 50, W.H.O. Building and flag. 8 p. U.N. flag and W.H.O. Building.

75. Spade in Hand, and Soldiers.

76. U.N.E.S.C.O. Emblem and Tree.

1966. 3rd Anniv. of Overthrow of Diem Government.
S 274. 75. 80 c. brown & bistre 15 10
S 275. – 1 p. 50 pur., red & yell. 15 10
S 276. – 3 p. grn., brn. & chest. 15 15
S 277. – 4 p. lake, black & pur. 40 20
DESIGNS—HORIZ. 1 p. 50, Agricultural workers, soldier and flag. VERT. 3 p. Soldier, tractor and labourers. 4 p. Soldier and horseman.

1966. 20th Anniv. of U.N.E.S.C.O.
S 278. 76. 1 p. brown and lake .. 15 10
S 279. – 3 p. brn., turq. & blue 15 15
S 280. – 7 p. blue, turq. & red 40 20
DESIGNS—VERT. 3 p. Globe and laurel sprigs. HORIZ. 7 p. Pagoda.

77. Cashew Apples.

78. Phan Boi Chau.

1967. Exotic Fruits.
S 281. 77. 50 c. red, green & blue 15 8
S 282. – 1 p. 50 orge., grn. & brn. 15 10
S 283. – 3 p. brown, grn. & choc. 35 15
S 284. – 20 p. olive, grn. & lake 1·00 55
FRUITS—HORIZ. 1 p. 50, Bitter "cucumbers". 3 p. Cinnamon apples. 20 p. Areca-nuts.

1967. Vietnamese Patriots.
S 285. 78. 1 p. pur., brn. & red . . 15 10
S 286. – 20 p. blk., vio. & grn. 55 35
DESIGN: 20 p. Phan Chau-Trinh (portrait and making speech).

79. Horse-cab.

80. Pottery-making.

1967. Life of the People.
S 287. – 50 c. ultram., bl. & grn. 15 8
S 288. – 1 p. vio., grn. & myrtle 15 10
S 289. 79. 3 p. lake and red 20 10
S 290. – 8 p. violet and red . . 30 15
DESIGNS: 50 c. Itinerant merchant. 1 p. Market-place. 8 p. Pastoral activities.

1967. Arts and Crafts. Multicoloured.
S 291. 50 c. Type 80 . . . . 15 10
S 292. 1 p. 50 Wicker basket and vase 20 15
S 293. 3 p. Weavers and potters 30 20
S 294. 35 p. Baskets and pottery 1·40 80
The 3 p. is a horiz. design.

81. Wedding Procession.

1967. Vietnamese Wedding.
S 295. 81. 3 p. red, violet & pur. 35 20

82. "Culture".

1967. Foundation of Vietnamese Cultural Institute.
S 296. 82. 10 p. multicoloured . . 35 20

83. "Freedom and Justice".

84. Lions Emblem and Pagoda.

1967. Democratic Elections. Multicoloured.
S 297. 4 p. Type 83 . . . . 20 15
S 298. 5 p. Vietnamese and hands casting votes . . 25 20
S 299. 30 p. Two Vietnamese with Constitution and flaming torch 90 55

1967. 50th Anniv. of Lions Int.
S 300. 84. 3 p. multicoloured . . 60 35

85. Class on Globe.

1967. World Literacy Day (8 Sept.)
S 301. 85. 3 p. multicoloured . . 20 10

1967. Mobile Post Office Inaug. As No. S 268 but smaller size 23 × 17 mm.
S 302. 3 p. violet and purple . . 10·00 8·50

87. Tractor.

89. Flags of Allied Nations.

88. W.H.O. Emblem.

1968. Rural Development. Multicoloured.
S 303. 1 p. Type 87 . . . . 20 15
S 304. 9 p. Bulldozer 20 15
S 305. 10p. Workers with wheel-barrow and tractor . . 30 15
S 306. 20 p. Building construction 65 30

1968. W.H.O. 20th Anniv.
S 307. 88. 10 p. yell., blk. & grn. 40 20

1968. Thanks for International Aid. Mult.
S 308. 1 p. Handclasp, flags and soldiers 15 10
S 309. 1 p. 50 S.E.A.T.O. emblem and flags . . 15 15
S 310. 3 p. Handclasp & flags 25 20
S 311. 50 p. Type 89. . . 90 80

92. Farmers, Farm, Factory and Transport.

93. Human Rights Emblem.

1968. Development of Private Ownership. Multicoloured.
S 318. 80 c. Type 92 . . . . 10 10
S 319. 2 p. Motor vehicles and labourers . . 10 10
S 320. 10 p. Tractor and tri-car 20 15
S 321. 30 p. Motor vehicles and labourers . . 95 50

1968. Human Rights Year. Multicoloured.
S 322. 10 p. Type 93 . . . . 20 15
S 323. 16 p. Men of all races acclaiming Human Rights Emblem . . 40 20

94. Children with U.N.I.C.E.F. "Kite".

1968. U.N.I.C.E.F. Day. Multicoloured.
S 324. 6 p. Type 94 . . . . 30 15
S 325. 16 p. Mother and Child 45 20

95. Diesel Train, Map and Mechanical Loader.

97. Peasant Woman.

1968. Re-opening of Trans-Vietnam Railway. Multicoloured.
S 326. 1 p. 50 Type 95 . . 35 25
S 327. 3 p. Type 95 . . . . 45 25
S 328. 9 p. Diesel train and permanent-way workers . . 1·25 40
S 329. 20 p. As No. S 328 . . 2·40 80

1969. Vietnamese Women.
S 331. 97. 50 c. vio., ochre & bl. 10 10
S 332. – 1 p. brown and green 15 10
S 333. – 3 p. blk., blue & sepia 20 10
S 334. – 20 p. multicoloured . . 50 35
DESIGNS—VERT. 1 p. Tradeswoman. 20 p. "Ladies of fashion". HORIZ. 3 p. Nurse.

98. Soldier and Militiaman.

99. Vietnamese and Scales of Justice.

1969. "Open-arms" National Unity Campaign. Multicoloured.
S 335. 2 p. Type 98 . . . . 20 15
S 336. 50 p. Family welcoming soldier 85 40

1969. 1st Anniv. of New Constitution. Mult.
S 337. 1 p. Type 99 . . . . 15 8
S 338. 20 p. Voters at polling station 30 25

100. Mobile Post Office Van in Street.

1969. Vietnamese Mobile Post Offices System. Multicoloured.
S 339. 1 p. Type 100 . . . . 15 10
S 340. 3 p. Clerk serving customers 15 10
S 341. 4 p. Child with letter, and mobile post office . . 20 15
S 342. 20 p. Queue at mobile post office, and post mark 40 30

101. Djarai Woman.

1969. 2nd Anniv. of Ethnic Minorities' Statute. Multicoloured.
S 343. 1 p. Type 101 . . . . 20 15
S 344. 6 p. Mnong-Gar woman 50 20
S 345. 50 p. Bahnar man . . 2·50 1·10

102. "Civilians to Soldiers".

103. I.L.O. Emblem and Globe.

1969. General Mobilisation.
S 346. 102. 1 p. 50 multicoloured . . 10 8
S 347. – 3 p. multicoloured . . 15 10
S 348. – 5 p. brown, red & yell. 20 15
S 349. – 10 p. multicoloured . . 30 20
DESIGNS: 3 p. Bayonet practice. 5 p. Recruits arriving at depot. 10 p. Happy conscripts.

1969. 50th Anniv. of I.L.O.
S 350. 103. 6 p. black, grey & green 15 8
S 351. 20 p. black, grey & red 45 20

104. Imperial Palace, Hue.

1970. Reconstruction of Hue.
S 352. 104. 1 p. blue and brown . . 1·10 1·10

105. Asian Golden Weaver and Baya Weaver.

1970. Birds of Vietnam. Multicoloured.
S 353. 2 p. Type 105 . . . . 75 25
S 354. 6 p. Chestnut mannikin 1·00 35
S 355. 7 p. Great Indian hornbill 1·10 65
S 356. 30 p. Tree Sparrow . . 4·25 1·75

106. Ruined House and Family.

1970. Aid for Victims of Communist Tet Offensive. Multicoloured.
S 357. 10 p. Type 106 . . . . 30 15
S 358. 20 p. Refugee family, and First Aid 40 25

107. Man, Woman and Priest in Traditional Costume.

108. Builders and Pagoda.

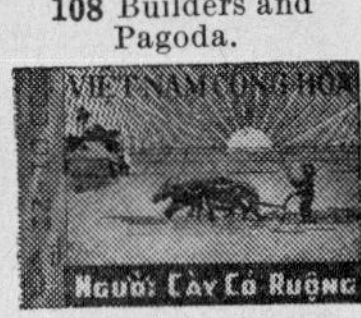

109. Ploughing Paddyfield.

1970. Vietnamese Traditional Costumes. Multicoloured.
S 359. 1 p. Type 107 . . . . 15 10
S 360. 2 p. Seated woman (horiz.) 15 10
S 361. 3 p. Three women with carved lion (horiz.) . . 20 15
S 362. 100 p. Man and woman (horiz.) . . . . 2·25 1·60

1970. Reconstruction of Hue. Mult.
S 363. 6 p. Type 108 . . . . 35 20
S 364. 20 p. Mixing cement . . 60 35

1970. "Land to the Tiller". Agrarian Reform Law.
S 365. 109. 6 p. blk., grn. & brn. 35 20

110. Scaffolding and New Building.

111. A.P.Y. Symbol.

1970. Reconstruction after Tet Offensive. Multicoloured.
S 366. 8 p. Type 110 . . . . 30 15
S 367. 16 p. Construction workers 40 20

1970. Asian Productivity Year.
S 368. 111. 10 p. multicoloured 30 15

112. Nguyen Dinh Chieu and Poems.

113. I.E.Y. Emblem.

1970. Nguyen Dinh Chieu (poet). Commem.
S 369. 112. 6 p. brn., red & violet 15 15
S 370. 10 p. brn., red & grn. 30 20

1970. Int. Education Year.
S 371. 113. 10 p. blk., yell. & brn. 35 15

114. Senate House.

115. Two Dancers.

1970. Ninth Council Meeting and 6th General Assembly of Asiatic Interparliamentary Union, Saigon. Multicoloured.
S 372. 6 p. Type 114 . . . . 20 15
S 373. 10 p. House of Representatives 30 15

1971. Vietnamese Traditional Dances.
S 374. 115. 2 p. multicoloured . . 20 10
S 375. – 6 p. brn., blue & grn. 30 15
S 376. – 7 p. red, blue & brn. . 45 20
S 377. – 10 p. multicoloured . . 55 30
DESIGNS—HORIZ. 6 p. Drum dance. 7 p. Drum dancers in various positions. VERT. 10 p. Flower dance.

116. Paddyfield, Peasants and Agrarian Law.

1971. 1st Anniv. of "Land to the Tiller" Agrarian Reform Law. Multicoloured.

S 378. 2 p. Type **116** 20 15
S 379. 3 p. Tractor and Law .. 20 15
S 380. 16 p. Peasants ringing Law 35 20

117. Postal Courier. 119. Hog-deer.

118. Armed Forces on Map of Vietnam.

1971. History of Vietnam Postal Service. Multicoloured.

S 381. 2 p. Type **117** 15 10
S 382. 6 p. Mounted courier with banner 30 15

1971. Armed Forces Day.

S 383. **118.** 3 p. multicoloured .. 35 15
S 384. 40 p. multicoloured .. 1·25 45

1971. Vietnamese Fauna. Multicoloured.

S 385. 9 p. Type **119** 35 15
S 386. 30 p. Tiger 80 45

120. Rice Harvesters.

1971. "The Rice Harvest".

S 387. **120.** 1 p. multicoloured .. 15 10
S 388. – 30 p. lilac, blk. & red 55 20
S 389. – 40 p. brn., yell. & blue 80 40

DESIGNS: 30p Threshing and winnowing rice. 40 p. Harvesters in paddyfield.

121. New H.Q. Building.

1971. New U.P.U. Headquarters Building, Berne.

S 390. **121.** 20 p. multicoloured .. 60 30

122. Ca Bong. 123. "Local Delivery

1971. Vietnam Fishes. Multicoloured.

S 391. 2 p. Type **122** 15 10
S 392. 10 p. Ca Nau (horiz.) .. 40 15
S 393. 100 p. Ca Ong Tien (horiz.) 3·50 2·25

1971. Development of Rural Post System. Multicoloured.

S 394. 5 p. Type **123** 20 15
S 395. 10 p. Symbolic crane .. 25 15
S 396. 20 p. Cycle postman delivering letter .. 45 20

124. Fishermen in Boat, and Modern Trawler.

1972. Vietnamese Fishing Industry. Mult.

S 397. 4 p. Type **124** 15 10
S 398. 7 p. Fishermen hauling net 15 10
S 399. 50 p. Trawl net .. .. 1·40 60

125. Emperor Quang Trung. 126. Community Workers.

1972. Emperor Quang Trung (victor of Dong Da). Commemoration.

S 400. **125.** 6 p. multicoloured 15 10
S 401. 20 p. multicoloured 40 20

1972. Community Development Projects.

S 403. **126.** 3 p. multicoloured .. 10 10
S 404. 8 p. multicoloured .. 15 10

127. Harvesting Rice.

1972. Farmer's Day. Multicoloured.

S 405. 1 p. Type **127** 15 10
S 406. 10 p. Sowing rice .. 25 15

128. Airliner over Dalat.

1972. 20th Anniv. of Viet-Nam Airlines. Mult.

S 407. 10 p. Type **128** 40 20
S 408. 10 p. Airliner over Ha Tien 40 20
S 409. 10 p. Airliner over Hue 40 20
S 410. 10 p. Airliner over Saigon 40 20
S 411. 25 p. Type **128** 70 35
S 412. 20 p. As. No S 408 .. 70 35
S 413. 25 p. As No. S 409 .. 70 35
S 414. 25 p. As No. S 410 .. 70 35

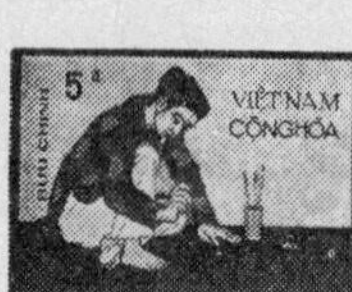

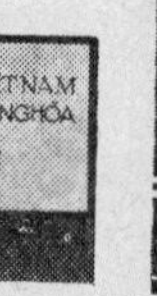

129. Vietnamese Scholar. 130. Sentry.

1972. Vietnamese Scholars. Multicoloured.

S 415. 5 p. Type **129** 10 10
S 416. 20 p. Scholar with pupils 30 20
S 417. 50 p. Scholar with scroll 1·00 45

1972. Civilian Defence Force. Multicoloured.

S 418. 2 p. Type **130** 10 10
S 419. 6 p. Young volunteer and badge (horiz.) .. 15 15
S 420. 20 p. Volunteers at rifle practice 35 25

131. Hands supporting Savings Bank.

1972. Treasury Bonds Savings Scheme.

S 421. **131.** 10 p. multicoloured 15 10
S 422. 25 p. multicoloured 35 15

132. Three Guards with Horse. 133. Wounded Soldier.

1972. Traditional Vietnamese Frontier Guards. Multicoloured.

S 423. 10 p. Type **132** 20 15
S 424. 30 p. Pikeman (vert.) .. 45 30
S 425. 40 p. Guards on parade 70 45

1972. Vietnamese War Veterans. Mult.

S 426. 9 p. Type **133** 10 8
S 427. 16 p. Soldier on crutches 20 15
S 428. 100 p. Veteran's memorial 1·60 90

134. Soldiers on Tank, and Memorial. 135. "Books for Everyone".

1972. Victory at Binh Long. Multicoloured.

S 429. 5 p. Type **134** 10 8
S 430. 10 p. Soldiers on map of An Loc (vert.) .. 15 8

1972. Int. Book Year. Multicoloured.

S 431. 2 p. Type **135** 8 8
S 432. 4 p. Book Year emblems encircling Globe .. 15 8
S 433. 5 p. Emblem, books and Globe 15 12

138. Satellite and Globe.

136. "200,000th Returnees".

139. Programme Emblem and Farm-workers. 137. Soldiers raising Flag.

1973. 200,000th Returnees under "Open Arms" National Unity Campaign.

S 434. **136** 10 p. multicoloured .. 20 15

1973. Victory at Quang Tri. Multicoloured.

S 435. 3 p. Type **137** 10 8
S 436. 10 p. Map and defenders 15 15

1973. World Meteorological Day.

S 437. **138.** 1 p. multicoloured .. 20 15

1973. Five-Year Agricultural Development Programme. Multicoloured.

S 438. 2 p. Type **139** 8 8
S 439. 5 p. Ploughing in paddy-field 10 10

140. Emblem and H.Q. Paris.

1973. 50th Anniv. of International Criminal Police Organization (Interpol). Mult.

S 440. 1 p. Type **140** 8 8
S 441. 2 p. "INTERPOL 1923 1973" 15 10
S 442. 25 p. Emblem and view of Headquarters (different) 40 20

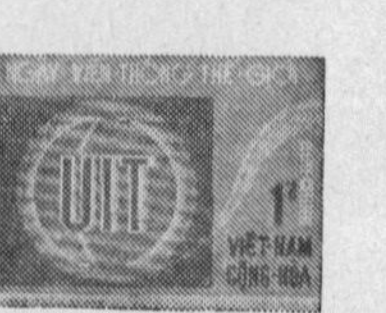

141. I.T.U. Emblem. 142. Lamp in Hand.

1973. World Telecommunications Day.

S 443. **141.** 1 p. multicoloured .. 8 5
S 444. – 2 p. black and blue .. 10 5
S 445. – 3 p. multicoloured .. 15 5

DESIGNS: 2 p. Globe. 3 p. I.T.U. Emblem in frame.

1973. National Development.

S 446. **142.** 8 p. multicoloured .. 15 10
S 447. – 10 p. blue, blk. & brn. 15 10
S 448. – 15 p. multicoloured .. 20 15

DESIGNS: 10 p. "Agriculture, Industry and Fisheries". 15 p. Workers on power pylon.

143. Water Buffaloes. 144. Flame Emblem and "Races of the World".

1973. "Year of the Buffalo". Multicoloured.

S 449. 5 p. Type **143** 20 10
S 450. 10 p. Water buffalo .. 20 15

1973. 25th Anniv. of Declaration of Human Rights. Multicoloured.

S 451. 15 p. Type **144** 25 15
S 452. 100 p. Flame emblem and scales of justice (vert.) 55 30

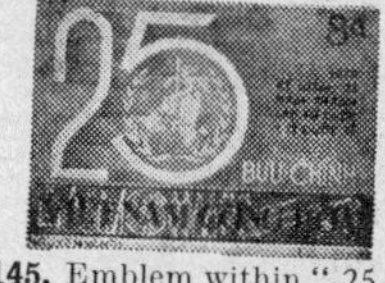

145. Emblem within "25".

1973. 25th Anniv. of W.H.O.

S 453. **145.** 8 p. multicoloured .. 15 10
S 454. – 15 p. blue, red & brn. 25 15

DESIGN: 15 p. W.H.O. emblem and inscription.

146. Sampan crossing River.

1974. Vietnamese Sampan Women. Mult.

S 455. 5 p. Type **146** 15 10
S 456. 10 p. Sampan and passengers 20 15

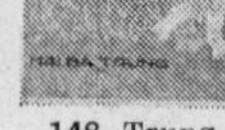

147. Flags and Soldiers of Allies. 148. Trung Sisters on Elephant.

1974. Allies Day. Multicoloured.

S 457. 8 p. Type **147** 15 8
S 458. 15 p. Soldiers and flags .. 15 8
S 459. 15 p. Allied Nations Monument 15 15
S 460. 60 p. Raising South Vietnamese flag, and map (vert.) 45 20

1974. Trung Sisters' Festival.

S 461. **148.** 8 p. grn., yell. & blk. 15 10
S 462. 15 p. red, yell. & blk. 20 15
S 463. 80 p. bl., pink & blk. 45 20

149. Pres. Thieu holding Agrarian Reform Law.

1974. Farmers' Day. Multicoloured.

S 464. 10 p. Type **149** 15 8
S 465. 20 p. Farm-workers (32 × 22 mm.) 15 10
S 466. 70 p. Girl harvesting rice (22 × 32 mm.) 35 20

150. King Hung Vuong.

1974. King Hung Vuong (first Vietnamese monarch). Commemoration. Multicoloured.

S 467.	20 p. Type **150**	20	15
S 468.	100 p. Banner inscribed "Hung Vuong, National Founder"	90	40

151. National Library.

152. Allied Nations Memorial, Saigon.

1974. New National Library Building, Mult.

S 469.	10 p. Type **151**	15	5
S 470.	15 p. Library and Phoenix bas-relief	20	15

1974. Surch.

S 470a.	**142.**	10 p. on 8 p. mult.		
S 470b.	**145.**	10 p. on 8 p. mult.		
S 470c.	**120.**	25 p. on 1 p. mult.		
S 470d.	**140.**	25 p. on 1 p. mult.		
S 470e.	**138.**	25 p. on 1 p. mult.		
S 470f.	**141.**	25 p. on 1 p. mult.		
S 470g.	–	25 p. on 7 p. red, blue and brown (No. S 376) ..		
S 470h.	**147.**	25 p. on 8 p. mult.		
S 470i.	–	25 p. on 16 p. mult. (No. S 427) ..		
S 470j.	–	25 p. on 16 p. mult. (No. S 380) ..		

1974. International Aid Day. Multicoloured.

S 471.	10 p. Type **152**	10	8
S 472.	20 p. Flags on crane (horiz.)	15	10
S 473.	60 p. Crate on hoist ..	35	20

153. "Tourist Attractions".

1974. Tourism. Multicoloured.

S 474.	5 p. Type **153**	15	10
S 475.	10 p. Xom Bong Bridge Nhatrang	10	10
S 476.	15 p. Thien Mu Pagoda, Hue (vert.)	15	10

154. "Rhynchostylis gigantea".

1974. Orchids. Multicoloured.

S 477.	10 p. Type **154**	20	15
S 478.	20 p. "Cypripedium callosum" (vert.) ..	30	15
S 479.	200 p. "Dendrobium nobile"	1·60	85

155. "International Exchange of Mail".

1974. Cent. of U.P.U. Mult.

S 480.	20 p. Type **155**	25	10
S 481.	30 p. "U.P.U. letter" and Hemispheres" ..	35	15
S 482.	300 p. U.P.U. emblem and Vietnamese girl (vert.)	1·90	1·10

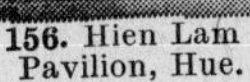

156. Hien Lam Pavilion, Hue.

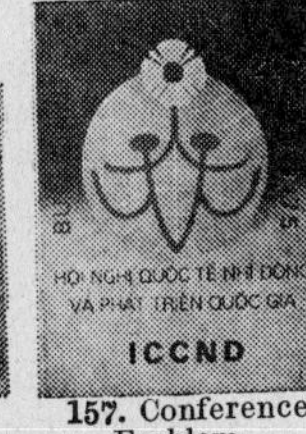

157. Conference Emblem.

1975. Historical Sites. Multicoloured.

S 483.	25 p. Type **156**	15	10
S 484.	30 p. Throne Room, Imperial Palace, Hue	20	15
S 485.	60 p. Tu Duc's Pavilion, Hue	30	20

1975. International Conference on Children and National Development, Saigon. Mult.

S 486.	20 p. Type **157**	20	15
S 487.	70 p. Vietnamese family (32×22 mm.)	25	20

158. Unicorn Dance.

1975. Vietnamese New Year Festival. Mult.

S 488.	20 p. Type **158**	15	10
S 489.	30 p. Letting-off fire-crackers (vert.) ..	20	15
S 490.	100 p. New Year greeting custom (vert.) ..	70	40

159. Military Mandarin ("San Hau" play).

1975. "Hat Bo" Vietnamese Traditional Theatre. Multicoloured.

S 491.	25 p. Type **159**	30	15
S 492.	40 p. Two characters from "Tam Ha Nam Duong" (vert.)	40	20
S 493.	100 p. Heroine, "Luu Kim Giai Gia Tho Chau" (vert.)	1·60	55

160. Produce for Export and Map.

1975. Farmers Day. Multicoloured.

S 494.	10 p. Type **160**	15	10
S 495.	50 p. Ancient and modern irrigation ..	45	20

MILITARY FRANK STAMPS

MF **29.** Soldier and Barracks.

1961. No value indicated. Roul.

SMF 115.	MF **29.** (–) yell., brown, green & black	8·50	6·50
SMF 116.	(–) yell., brown and green ..	8·50	6·50

POSTAGE DUE STAMPS

D **1.** Dragon. D **90.** Butterfly. D **91.** Butterflies.

1955.

SD 1.	D **1.**	2 p. yell. & mauve ..	35	35
SD 2.		3 p. turq. & violet ..	40	40
SD 3.		5 p. yellow & violet	65	55
SD 4.		10 p. red and green	85	60
SD 14.	–	20 p. green and red	2·25	1·40
SD 15.	–	30 p. yellow & grn. ..	3·25	2·25
SD 16.	–	50 p. yellow & brn. ..	7·00	5·00
SD 17.	–	100 p. yellow & vio.	11·00	9·00

The 20 p. to 100 p. are inscribed "BUU-CHINH" instead of "TIMBRE TAXE".

1968.

SD 312.	D **90.**	50 c. multicoloured	50	35
SD 313.		1 p. multicoloured	50	35
SD 314.		2 p. multicoloured	50	35
SD 315.	D **91.**	3 p. multicoloured	1·25	95
SD 316.		5 p. multicoloured	3·00	2·50
SD 317.		10 p. multicoloured	4·25	3·25

1974. Surch.

SD 470k.	D **91.**	5 p. on 3 p. mult.	4·50	
SD 470l.	D **90.**	10 p. on 50 c. mult.	4·50	
SD 470m.		40 p. on 1 p. mult.	4·50	
SD 470n.		60 p. on 2 p. mult.	4·50	

D. NATIONAL FRONT FOR THE LIBERATION OF SOUTH VIETNAM

The National Front for the Liberation of South Vietnam was formed by the Communists, known as the Vietcong, in December 1960. With the support of troops from North Vietnam the Vietcong gradually gained control of more and more territory within South Vietnam until the surrender of the last South Vietnamese Republican forces in May 1975 enabled them to take control of the entire country. The following stamps were used in those areas controlled by the National Liberation Front.

1963. 100 xu = 1 dong.

The value of the N.L.F. dong fluctuated considerably and was not on parity with the North Vietnamese currency.

1. Vietcong Flag.

1963. 3rd Anniv. of National Liberation Front.

NLF 1.	**1.**	20 x. multicoloured (English inscr.) ..	3·00	2·50
NLF 2.		20 x. multicoloured (French inscr.) ..	3·00	2·50
NLF 3.		20 x. multicoloured (Spanish inscr.) ..	3·00	2·50

2. Attack on Village.

1963. 3rd Anniv. of Revolutionary Struggle in South Vietnam. Multicoloured.

NLF 4.	10 x. Type **2**	2·00	1·25
NLF 5.	10 x. Attack on U.S. helicopter	2·50	1·50

3. Demonstrators with Banner.

1964. 4th Anniv. of National Liberation Front.

NLF 6.	10 x. Type **3**	75	75
NLF 7.	20 x. multicoloured ..	1·00	1·00
NLF 8.	30 x. green and blue ..	2·50	1·75

DESIGNS: 20 x. Harvesting rice. 30 x. Sinking of U.S.S. "Card" (destroyer).

4. Attack on Bien Hoa Airfield.

1965. 5th Anniv. of National Liberation Front.

NLF 9.	**4**	10 x. multicoloured ..	70	60
NLF 10.	–	20 x. black, grey & red	75	75
NLF 11.	–	40 x. multicoloured ..	3·50	3·50

DESIGNS: 20 x. Nguyen Van Troi facing firing squad. 40 x. Vietcong flags.

5. Vietcong Soldiers on U.S. Tanks.

6. "Guerrilla".

1967. 7th Anniv. of National Liberation Front. Multicoloured.

NLF 12.	20 x. Type **5**	70	60
NLF 13.	20 x. Vietcong guerrillas (horiz.)	50	50
NLF 14.	30 x. Crowd with banners	90	90

1968. "The Struggle for Freedom". Paintings. Multicoloured.

NLF 15.	10 x. Type **6**	50	50
NLF 16.	20 x. "Jungle Patrol" (horiz.)	75	75
NLF 17.	30 x. "Woman Soldier"	1·00	1·00
NLF 18.	40 x. "Towards the Future" (horiz.) ..	1·50	1·50

7. Casting Votes.

1968. 8th Anniv. of National Liberation Front. Multicoloured.

NLF 19.	20 x. Type **7**	25	25
NLF 20.	20 x. Bazooka crew and burning aircraft ..	30	25
NLF 21.	30 x. Vietcong flag and crowd (French inscr.)	50	50
NLF 22.	30 x. Vietcong flag and crowd (English inscr.)	50	50

8. Lenin and Vietcong Flag.

1970. Birth Cent. of Lenin.

NLF 23.	**8.**	20 x. multicoloured	20	15
NLF 24.		30 x. multicoloured	25	20
NLF 25.		50 x. multicoloured	35	25
NLF 26.		2 d. multicoloured ..	1·25	1·00

9. Ho Chi Minh watering Kainito Plant.

10. Vietcong "Lightning Flash".

1970. 80th Birth Anniv. of Ho Chi Minh.

NLF 27.	**9.**	20 x. multicoloured	20	15
NLF 28.		30 x. multicoloured	25	20
NLF 29.		50 x. multicoloured	35	25
NLF 30.		2 d. multicoloured ..	1·25	1·00

1970. 10th Anniv. of National Liberation Front.

NLF 31.	**10.**	20 x. multicoloured	20	15
NLF 32.		30 x. multicoloured	25	20
NLF 33.		50 x. multicoloured	40	30
NLF 34.		3 d. multicoloured	2·75	1·25

11. Home Guards defending Village.

1971. 10th Anniv. of People's Liberation Armed Forces. Multicoloured.

NLF 35.	20 x. Type **11** ..	50	50
NLF 36.	30 x. Surrender of U.S. tank	75	75
NLF 37.	50 x. Agricultural workers	1·00	1·00
NLF 38.	1 d. Vietcong ambush	1·50	1·50

12. Children in School.

13. Harvesting Rice.

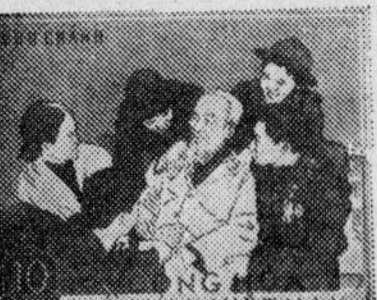

14. Ho Chi Minh with Vietcong Soldiers.

INDEX

Countries can be quickly located by referring to the index at the end of this volume.

1971. 2nd Anniv. of Provisional Government. Life in Liberated Areas. Multicoloured.
NLF 39. 20 x. Type **12** 15 15
NLF 40. 30 x. Women sewing Vietcong flag 25 25
NLF 41. 40 x. Fortifying village 75 75
NLF 42. 50 x. Medical clinic .. 1·00 1·00
NLF 43. 1 d. Harvesting .. 1·50 1·50

1974. 5th Anniv. of Provisional Government. Multicoloured.
NLF 44. 10 d. Type **13** .. 10 10
NLF 45. 10 d. Demonstrators with banner .. 10 10
NLF 46. 10 d. Schoolchildren 10 10
NLF 47. 10 d. Women home guards 10 10
NLF 48. 10 d. Vietcong conference delegate .. 10 10
NLF 49. 10 d. Soldiers and tanks 10 10
NLF 50. 10 d. Type **14** .. 15 15
NLF 51. 20 d. Type **14** .. 40 40
For other values as Type **14**, see Nos. NLF 57/60.

15. Ho Chi Minh watering Kainito Plant.

1975. 85th Birth Anniv. of Ho Chi Minh (1st issue).
NLF52. **15.** 5 d. multicoloured 10 10
NLF53. 10 d. mult. .. 12 12
NLF54. 30 d. mult. (mauve frame) 75 75
NLF54a. 30 d. mult. (green frame) 75 75

1975. National Front for Liberation of South Vietnam. 15th Anniv. As T **14** but $35\frac{1}{2} \times 26$ mm.
NLF55. **14.** 15 d. black & green 25 25
NLF56. 30 d. black and red 50 50
NLF57. 60 d. black and blue 75 75
NLF58. 300 d. black & yell. 2·50 2·50

85th Birth Anniv. of Ho Chi Minh (2nd issue). As T **284** of North Vietnam, but inscr. "MIEN NAM VIET NAM".
NLF 59. 30 d. multicoloured .. 40 40
NLF 60. 60 d. multicoloured .. 75 75

1976. Various stamps surch in South Vietnamese currency.
NLF61. – 10 p. on 1 d. multicoloured (NLF 38) ..
NLF62. – 20 p. on 6 x. yellow and red (NLF 75) ..
NLF63. – 20 p. on 20 x. multicoloured (NLF 27) ..
NLF64. – 20 p. on 40 x. multicoloured (NLF 11) ..
NLF65. **9.** 20 p. on 2 d. multicoloured (NLF 30) ..
NLF66. **15.** 20 p. on 5 d. multicoloured (NLF 52) ..
NLF67. **14.** 20 p. on 10 d. multicoloured (NLF 50) ..
NLF68. **15.** 20 p. on 10 d. multicoloured (NLF 53) ..
NLF69. 20 p. on 30 d. multicoloured (NLF 54) ..
NLF70. 20 p. on 30 d. multicoloured (NLF 54a) ..

17. " Cosos nucifera ".

1976. Fruits. Multicoloured.
NLF71. 20 d. Type **17** .. 50 50
NLF72. 30 d. " Garcinia mangostana " 75 75
NLF73. 60 d. " Mangifera indica " .. 1·50 1·50

1976. First Elections to United National Assembly. As Nos. N 858/60 of North Vietnam, but inscr. " MIEN NAM VIET NAM ".
NLF74. 6 x. red and blue (as N 858) 10 10
NLF75. 6 x. yellow and red (as N 859) 10 10
NLF76. 12 x. red and green (as N 860) 25 25

18. Flag of Provisional Revolutionary Government.

1976. 1st Anniv. of Liberation of South Vietnam.
NLF77. **18.** 30 d. multicoloured 30 25

1976. 1st Session of United National Assembly. As Nos. N 861/2 of North Vietnam, but inscr. "MIEN NAM VIET NAM".
NLF78. 6 x. brn., red & yell. 10 10
NLF79. 12 x. turq., red & yell. 25 25

The unified National Assembly proclaimed the reunification of Vietnam on 2 July 1976 and the united country was then known as the Socialist Republic of Vietnam.

E. NORTH VIETNAM
(Vietnam Democratic Republic)

Issues before April 1954 were made in Tongking and Central Annam, in areas under Viet Minh control. From 21 July 1954 French troops withdrew from north of the 17th Parallel and the Ho Chi Minh Government assumed complete control.

1946. 100 cents. = 1 dong.
1959. 100 xu = 1 dong.

GUM. All stamps were issued without gum unless otherwise stated.

I. TONGKING

1946. No. 190 of Indo-China optd. **V VIET-NAM N DAN-CHU CONG-HOA BUU CHINH.**
N 1. 25 c. blue .. .. .. 32·00 32·00

2. Ho Chi Minh.

3. Ho Chi Minh and Vietnam Map.

1948.
N 2a. **2.** 2 d. brown .. .. 4·00
N 3a. 5 d. red .. .. 4·00

1951. Imperf. or perf.
N 4. **3.** 100 d. green .. .. 2·50 2·50
N 5. 100 d. brown .. .. 2·50 2·50
N 6. 200 d. red .. .. 2·50 2·50

5. Blacksmith.

7. Malenkov, Ho Chi Minh, Mao Tse-tung and Flags.

1953. Production Campaign.
N 11. **5.** 100 d. violet .. .. 2·25 55
N 12. 500 d. brown .. .. 4·50 2·25

1954. Friendship Month.
N 13. **7.** 100 d. red .. .. 11·00 11·00

II. CENTRAL ANNAM

NA 1. Ho Chi Minh.

1950. Figures in white. Imperf.
NA1. **NA1.** 1 d. violet .. ..
NA2. 1 d. green .. ..
NA3. 5 d. green .. ..
NA4. 15 d. brown .. ..
Nos. NA 3 and NA 1

1952. Nos. NA3 and NA1 surch. in figures. Imperf.
NA5. **NA1.** 30 d. on 5 d. green £150 £130
NA6. 60 d. on 1 d. violet £200 £180

1952. Figures of values coloured. Imperf.
NA7. **NA1.** 300 d. blue £250 £250
NA8. 500 d. red £500 £500

III. GENERAL ISSUES

8. Malenkov, Ho Chi Minh & Mao Tse-tung.

1954.
N 14. **8.** 50 d. brown and red .. 9·50 9·50
N 15. 100 d. red and yellow .. 11·00 11·00

9. Battlefield.

1954. Dien Bien Phu Victory. Imperf. or perf.
N 16a. **9.** 10 d. bistre and red .. 6·00 1·75
N 17a. 50 d. ochre and red .. 6·00 2·00
N 18d. 150 d. blue and brown .. 6·00 2·75
See also No. NO 24.

1954. (a) Handstamped thus: **10 dNH.**
N 19. **3.** 10 d. on 100 d. green .. 3·00 3·00
N 20. 10 d. on 100 d. brown .. 4·50 4·50
N 21. 20 d. on 200 d. red .. 3·00 3·00

(b) Handstamped thus: **10 d.**
N 22. **3.** 10 d. on 100 d. green .. 3·25 3·25
N 25. 10 d. on 100 d. brown .. 5·50 5·50
N 28. 20 d. on 200 d. red .. 5·50 5·50
See also Nos. N 46/9.

12. Pagoda of the Lost Sword, Hanoi.

1954. Proclamation of Hanoi as Capital.
N 30. **12.** 10 d. blue .. .. 2·25 2·25
N 31. 50 d. green .. .. 2·25 2·25
N 32. 150 d. red .. .. 4·00 4·00

13. Distribution of Title Deeds.

1955. Land Reform.
N 33. **13.** 5 d. green .. .. 4·00 4·00
N 34. 10 d. grey .. .. 4·00 4·00
N 35. 20 d. orange .. .. 5·00 5·00
N 36. 50 d. mauve .. .. 12·00 12·00
N 37. 100 d. brown .. .. 19·00 19·00

14. Crowd Welcoming Steam Train.

1956. Hanoi-China Railway Re-opening
N 38. **14.** 100 d. blue .. .. 13·00 13·00
N 39. 200 d. turquoise .. 13·50 13·50
N 40. 300 d. violet .. .. 28·00 28·00
N 41. 500 d. brown .. .. 35·00 35·00

15. Parade, Ba Dinh Square, Hanoi.

1956. Return of Govt. to Hanoi.
N 42. **15.** 1,000 d. violet .. 35·00 28·00
N 43. 1,500 d. blue .. .. 50·00 38·00
N 44. 2,000 d. turquoise .. 50·00 38·00
N 45. 3,000 d. turquoise .. 60·00 60·00

1956. Surch. thus: **10 d** in frame.
N 46. **3.** 10 d. on 100 d. green .. 8·00 8·00
N 48. 10 d. on 100 d. brown .. 14·00 14·00
N 49. 20 d. on 200 d. red .. 10·00 10·00

17. Tran Danh Ninh.

18. Mac Thi Buoi.

1956. 1st Death Anniv. of Tran Danh Ninh (patriot).
N 50. **17.** 5 d. green .. .. 2·50 1·10
N 51. 10 d. red .. .. 2·50 1·10
N 52. 20 d. brown .. .. 2·75 1·60
N 53. 100 d. blue .. .. 3·25 2·25

1956. 5th Death Anniv. of Mac Thi Buoi (guerilla heroine).
N 54. **18.** 1,000 d. red .. .. 9·00 6·00
N 55. 2,000 d. brown .. 12·00 6·50
N 56. 4,000 d. green .. 21·00 17·00
N 57. 5,000 d. blue .. .. 30·00 21·00

19. Bai Thuong Dam.

21. Cotton Mill.

1956. Reconstruction of Bai Thuong Dam.
N 58. **19.** 100 d. violet and brown 4·00 4·00
N 59. 200 d. red and black .. 5·50 3·25
N 60. 300 d. red and lake .. 7·50 7·50

1956. Surch. **50 DONG.**
N 61. **2.** 50 d. on 5 d. red .. 18·00 28·00

1957. Opening of Nam-Dinh Mill. 1st Anniv.
N 62. **21.** 100 d. brown and lake 3·25 3·25
N 63. 200 d. slate and blue .. 3·50 3·50
N 64. 300 d. pale grn. & grn. 5·50 5·50

22. Pres. Ho Chi Minh.

23. Arms of Republic.

1957. President's 67th Birthday.
N 65. **22.** 20 d. green .. .. 1·40 85
N 66. 60 d. bistre .. .. 1·40 85
N 67. 100 d. blue .. .. 1·90 1·60
N 68. 300 d. brown .. .. 3·00 2·50
Nos. N 67/8 commemorate President's 67th Birthday.

1957. 12th Anniv. of Democratic Republic.
N 69. **23.** 20 d. green .. .. 1·90 1·40
N 70. 100 d. red .. .. 3·50 2·50

24. Congress Emblem.

1957. 4th World T.U. Congress, Leipzig
N 71. **24.** 300 d. purple .. .. 4·75 3·25
See also Nos. NO 69/72.

25. Presidents Voroshilov and Ho Chi Minh.

1957. 40th Anniv. of Russian Revolution.
N 72. **25.** 100 d. red .. .. 5·00 4·00
N 73. 500 d. brown .. .. 6·00 4·50
N 74. 1,000 d. orange .. 14·00 12·00

26. Open-air Class.

27. Girl Gymnast.

1958. Education Campaign.
N 75. **26.** 50 d. blue .. .. 4·00 2·75
N 76. 150 d. red .. .. 5·50 4·50
N 77. 1,000 d. brown .. 13·00 6·50

1958. Physical Education.
N 78. **27.** 150 d. brown and blue 8·50 5·50
N 79. 500 d. brown and rose 12·00 11·00

28. 29. Congress Emblem.

1958. Labour Day.
N 80. **28.** 50 d. yellow and red.. 2·25 1·60
N 81. 150 d. red and yellow 4·75 2·75

1958. 4th Int. Congress of Democratic Women, Vienna.
N 82. **29.** 150 d. blue .. .. 5·00 4·00

30. Cup, Basket and Lace. 31. Hanoi-Saigon Railway Reconstruction.

1958. Arts and Crafts Fair, Hanoi.
N 83. **30.** 150 d. sepia and turq. 1·60 1·10
N 84. 2,000 d. black and lilac 6·50 4·00

1958. Re-unification of Vietnam Propaganda.
N 85. **31.** 50 d. blue .. .. 4·50 1·50
N 86. 150 d. brown .. .. 1·50 25

32. Revolution in Hanoi.

1958. 13th Anniv. of Vietnamese Revolution.
N 87. **32.** 150 d. red .. .. 1·40 85
N 88. 500 d. blue .. .. 2·75 1·40

33. Woman Potter.

1958. Handicraft Exn.
N 89. **33.** 150 d. lake and red 1·40 1·10
N 90. 1,000 d. brn. & ochre.. 6·50 2·75

34. Vo Thi Sau and Crowd. 35. Tran Hung Dao.

1958. 13th Anniv. of South Vietnam Resistance Movement.
N 91. **34.** 50 d. green and buff .. 1·90 1·00
N 92. 150 d. lake and orange 4·25 1·25

1958. 658th Death Anniv. of Tran Hung Dao.
N 93. **35.** 150 d. grey and blue.. 1·10 55

36. Hanoi Factories. 37. Harvesting Rice.

1958. Hanoi Mechanical Engineering Plant.
N 94. **36.** 150 d. sepia .. .. 1·60 65

1958. Mutual Aid Teams.
N 95. **37.** 150 d. lake .. .. 4·00 1·40
N 96. 500 d. brown .. .. 5·00 2·50

38. Temple of Jade, Hanoi. 39. Furniture-makers.

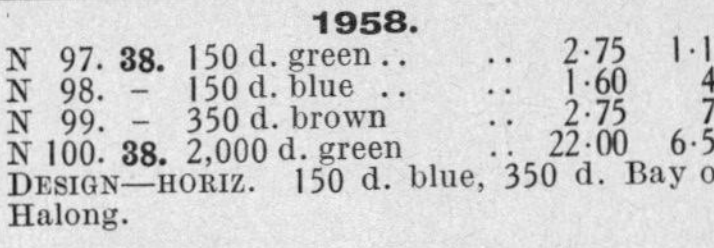

1958.
N 97. **38.** 150 d. green .. .. 2·75 1·10
N 98. – 150 d. blue .. .. 1·60 40
N 99. – 350 d. brown .. 2·75 70
N 100. **38.** 2,000 d. green .. 22·00 6·50
DESIGN—HORIZ. 150 d. blue, 350 d. Bay of Halong.

1958. Furniture Co-operatives.
N 101. **39.** 150 d. blue .. .. 1·60 45

40. Cam Pha Coal Mines. 41. The Trung Sisters.

1959.
N 102. **40.** 150 d. blue .. .. 2·00 50

1959. Trung Sisters Commem.
N 103. **41.** 5 x. red and yellow.. 65 40
N 104. 8 x. deep brown and brown .. .. 1·10 55

42. Mother and Child.

1959. 10th Anniv. of World Peace Movement.
N 105. **42.** 12 x. violet 65 45

43. Xuan Quan Dam.

1959. Bac Hung Hai Irrigation Project.
N 106. **43.** 6 x. yell., green & vio. 1·90 55
N 107. 12 x. ochre, bl. & grey 4·25 80

44. Victims in Phu Loi Concentration Camp.

46. Hien Luong Bridge 45. Radio Mast.

1959. The Phu Loi Massacre on 1 December 1958.
N 108. **44.** 12 x. salmon, ol. & blk. 1·40 35
N 109. 20 x. ochre, grey & blk. 3·00 80

1959. Me Tri Radio Station.
N 110. **45.** 3 x. green & orange.. 85 20
N 111. 12 x. sepia and blue.. 1·60 45

1959. Vietnam Day.
N 112. **46.** 12 x. red and black.. 1·10 60

47. Rifle-shooting.

DESIGNS: 6 x. Swimming. 12 x. Wrestling.

1959. Sports.
N 113. **47.** 1 x. deep blue & blue 80 35
N 114. – 6 x. olive and red .. 1·40 65
N 115. – 12 x. red and rose .. 2·10 95

48. Balloons. 49. Coconuts.

1959. 10th Anniv. of Chinese People's Republic.
N 116. **48.** 12 x. red, yell. & grn. 45 20

1959. Fruits. Multicoloured.
N 117. 3 x. Type **49** 90 40
N 118. 12 x. Bananas .. .. 1·40 70
N 119. 30 x. Pineapple.. .. 4·00 1·60

50. Convair Airliner.

1959. Air.
N 120. **50.** 20 x. black and blue 8·50 4·50

51. Soldiers. 52. Sailing Ship.

1959. 15th Anniv. of N. Vietnam People's Army.
N 121. **51.** 12 x. yell., brn. & blue 1·10 65

1959. 30th Anniv. of N. Vietnam Workers' Party.
N 122. **52.** 2 x. multicoloured .. 85 55
N 123. 12 x. multicoloured.. 1·60 1·10

53. Girl in "E—De" Costume. 54. Women of Vietnam.

1960. National Costumes.
N 124. **53.** 2 x. red, blue & pur. 55 30
N 125. – 10 x. blue, orge. & grn. 90 40
N 126. – 12 x. blue and brown 1·25 55
N 127. – 12 x. blue and buff.. 1·25 55
COSTUMES: No. N 125, "Meo"; No. N 126, 'Thai"; No. N 127, "Tay".

1960. National Census.
N 128. **54.** 1 x. green 20 15
N 129. – 12 x. brown and red 35 20
DESIGN: 12 x. Workers and factories.

55. Emblem and Women. 56. Hung Vuong Temple.

1960. 50th Anniv. of Int. Women's Day.
N 130. **55.** 12 x. multicoloured.. 50 20

1960. Hung Vuong Anniversary Day.
N 131. **56.** 12 x. green and buff 4·50 2·25
N 132. 4 d. brown and blue.. 45·00 22·00

57. Lenin. 58. Ballot Box.

1960. 90th Birth Anniv. of Lenin.
N 133. **57.** 5 x. red and blue .. 35 20
N 134. 12 x. blue and buff .. 60 45

1960. 2nd Election of Parliamentary Deputies.
N 135. **58.** 12 x. multicoloured.. 50 30

59. Red Cross Nurse. 60. Pres. Ho Chi Minh.

1960. Int. Red Cross Commem.
N 136. **59.** 8 x. red, blue & bistre 45 20
N 137. 12 x. green, red & grey 65 35

1960. President Ho Chi Minh's 70th Birthday.
N 138. **60.** 4 x. lilac and green .. 35 20
N 139. 12 x. purple and rose 65 30
N 140. – 12 x. multicoloured.. 65 30
DESIGN. ($24\frac{1}{2}\times39$ mm.): No. N 140, Hồ Chi Minh and children.

61. "New Constitution".

1960. Opening of 2nd National Assembly.
N 141. **61.** 12 x. sepia and ochre 95 55

62. Pres. Ho Chi Minh at Microphone.

1960. 15th Anniv. of Viet-Nam Democractic Republic.
N 142. **62.** 4 x. multicoloured .. 1·60 80
N 143. 12 x. multicoloured.. 2·25 90
N 144. – 12 x. deep blue & blue 2·25 90
N 145. – 12 x. green and yellow 2·25 90
N 146. – 12 x. blue and brown 2·25 90
DESIGNS: No. N 144, Ploughing. No. N 145, Electricity Works, Vietri. No. N 146, Classroom.

63. Workers and Flags.

1960. 3rd Vietnam Workers' Party Congress.
N 147. **63.** 1 x. multicoloured .. 1·40 55
N 148. 12 x. multicoloured.. 1·60 85

64. Handclasp of Three Races.

1960. 15th Anniv. of W.F.T.U.
N 149. **64.** 12 x. black and red.. 4·00 2·75

65. Dragon. 66. Exhibition Entrance.

1960. 950th Anniv. of Hanoi.
N 150. **65.** 8 x. yell., brn. & turq. 1·40 85
N 151. 12 x. yell., brn. & blue 2·25 1·10

1960. "Fifteen Years of Republic" Exn.
N 152. **66.** 2 x. grey and red .. 60 45
N 153. 12 x. green and red .. 1·40 65

67. Badge, Dove and Flag.

1960. 15th Anniv. of World Federation of Democratic Youth.
N 154. **67.** 12 x. multicoloured.. 1·60 1·10

68. Emblem of Vietnamese Trade Unions.

69. Woman, Globe and Dove.

1961. 2nd National Congress of Trade Unions.
N 155. 68. 12 x. red, bl. & yellow 1·25 55

1961. 3rd National Congress of Women.
N 156. 69. 6 x. green and blue .. 1·60 35
N 157. 12 x. green & salmon 1·60 50

IMPERF. STAMPS. Many issues from here onwards also exist imperf.

70. Sambar.

71. Ly Tu Trong (revolutionary).

1961. Vietnamese Fauna.
N 158. 70. 12 x. buff, blk. & olive 2·00 85
N 159. – 20 x. multicoloured .. 2·75 1·40
N 160. – 50 x. grey, blk. & grn. 5·00 2·50
N 161. – 1 d. blk., grey & green 6·00 3·00
DESIGNS: 20 x. Sun bear. 50 x. Indian elephant. 1 d. Crested gibbon.

1961. 3rd Congress of Vietnam Labour Youth Union.
N 162. 71. 2 x. olive and blue .. 60 35
N 163. 12 x. olive and salmon 1·60 80

72. Bugler and Drummer.

73. Disabled Soldier learning to use Crutches.

1961. 20th Anniv. of Vietnam Youth Pioneers.
N 164. 72. 1 x. multicoloured .. 90 55
N 165. 12 x. multicoloured .. 1·90 1·10

1961. 101st Anniv. of Proposal for Int. Red Cross.
N 166. 73. 6 x. multicoloured .. 1·10 55
N 167. 12 x. multicoloured .. 2·50 1·10

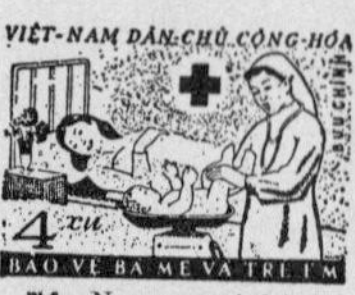

74. Nurse weighing Baby.

75. Major Yuri Gagarin.

1961. Int. Children's Day.
N 168. 74. 4 x. green, blk. & red 1·10 55
N 169. 12 x. yell., blk. & red 2·40 1·25

1961. World's First Manned Space Flight.
N 170. 75. 6 x. red and violet .. 10·00 4·00
N 171. 12 x. red and green .. 10·00 4·00

76.

77. Women.

78. Mother and Child.

79. Prospecting Team.

1961. Vietnam Reunification Campaign.
N 172. 76. 12 x. multicoloured .. 35 35
N 173. 2 d. multicoloured .. 7·00 3·50

1961. Tripling of Hanoi, Hue and Saigon.
N 174. 77. 12 x. multicoloured .. 1·60 1·40
N 175. 3 d. brown, myrtle and green .. .. 17·00 9·50

1961. National Savings, Campaign.
N 176. 78. 3 x. multicoloured .. 65 35
N 177. 12 x. multicoloured .. 1·25 80

1961. Geological Research.
N 178. 79. 2 x. grn., blue & pur. 1·10 35
N 179. 12 x. brn., blk. & turq. 2·25 80

80. Thien Mu Tower, Hue.

81. Workers and Rocket.

1961. Ancient Towers.
N 180. 80. 6 x. brown & chestnut 55 35
N 181. – 10 x. olive and buff .. 1·10 50
N 182. – 12 x. olive and green 1·40 55
N 183. – 12 x. brown and blue 1·40 55
TOWERS: No. N 181, Pen Brush, Bac Ninh. No. N 182, Bihn Son, Vinh Phuc. No. N 183, Cham, Phan Rang.

1961. 22nd Communist Party Congress, Moscow.
N 184. 81. 12 x. red and black .. 1·60 1·10

82. Major Titov and Rocket.

83. Freighter at Haiphong.

1961. 2nd Manned Space Flight.
N 185. 82. 6 x. multicoloured .. 1·40 85
N 186. 12 x. multicoloured .. 2·25 1·60

1961. Haiphong Port Commem.
N 187. 83. 5 x. grey, grn. & myrtle 1·75 45
N 188. 12 x. brown, light brn. and sepia .. .. 3·75 95

84. Cymbalist.

85. Congress Emblem.

1961. Third Writers and Artists Congress. Multicoloured.
N 189. 12 x. Type 84 .. .. 85 55
N 190. 12 x. Flautist .. .. 1·10 85
N 191. 30 x. Fan dancer .. 2·50 1·10
N 192. 50 x. Guitarist .. .. 3·25 2·25

1961. 5th W.F.T.U. Congress, Moscow.
N 193. 85. 12 x. mauve and drab 50 35

86. Resistance Fighters.

87. "Pigs"

1961. 15th Anniv. of National Resistance.
N 194. 86. 4 x. multicoloured .. 30 15
N 195. 12 x. multicoloured .. 55 30

1962. New Year.
N 196. 87. 6 x. multicoloured .. 85 45
N 197. – 12 x. multicoloured .. 1·60 85
DESIGN: 12 x. "Poultry".

88. Watering Tree.

89. Tea Plant.

1962. Tree-Planting Festival.
N 198. 88. 12 x. multicoloured .. 1·40 80
N 199. 40 x. multicoloured .. 1·90 1·40

1962. Multicoloured.
N 200. 2 x. Type 89 .. .. 55 35
N 201. 6 x. Aniseed 55 35
N 202. 12 x. Coffee .. .. 1·90 1·00
N 203. 12 x. Castor-oil .. .. 1·90 1·00
N 204. 30 x. Lacquer-tree .. 4·50 2·40

90. Gong Dance.

91. Hibiscus.

1962. Folk-Dancing. Multicoloured.
N 205. 12 x. Type 90 .. .. 1·60 55
N 206. 12 x. Bamboo Dance .. 1·60 55
N 207. 30 x. Hat Dance .. 3·25 55
N 208. 50 x. Parasol Dance .. 6·50 1·90

1962. Flowers. Multicoloured.
N 209. 12 x. Type 91 .. .. 1·40 55
N 210. 12 x. Frangipani .. 1·40 55
N 211. 20 x. Chrysanthemum .. 2·25 1·40
N 212. 30 x. Lotus .. .. 4·00 1·90
N 213. 50 x. Ipomoea .. .. 6·00 2·75

92. Kim Lien Flats, Hanoi.

93. Workers and Rose.

1962. 1st Five Year Plan (1st issue).
N214 92 1 x. blue, blk & grey 30 15
N215 – 3 x. multicoloured .. 55 30
N216 – 8 x. vio, blk & stone 85 45
DESIGNS: 3 x. State agricultural farm. 8 x. Institute of Hydraulic and Electro-Dynamic Studies.
See also Nos. N245/8, N251/2, N270/1 and N294/6.

1962. 3rd National "Heroes of Labour" Congress.
N 217. 93. 12 x. orge., olive & red 1·10 35

94. Dai Lai Dam.

1962.
N 218. 94. 12 x. turq. and brown 1·40 70

95. "Plough of Perfection".

1962.
N 219. 95. 6 x. black & turquoise 65 35

96. Titov greeting Children.

DESIGNS: 20 x. Pres. Ho Chi Minh pinning medal on Titov. 30 x. Titov in space-suit.

1962. Visit of Major Titov.
N 220. 96. 12 x. sepia and blue .. 65 45
N 221. – 20 x. sepia and salmon 1·10 65
N 222. – 30 x. sepia and green 1·90 85

97. Mosquito and Red Cross.

1962. Malaria Eradication.
N 223. 97. 8 x. red, black & blue 85 45
N 224. 12 x. red, blk. & violet 1·10 65
N 225. 20 x. red, blk. & pur. 1·90 85

98. Factory and Soldiers.

99. Ban Gioc Falls.

1962. 8th Anniv. of Geneva Vietnamese Agreements.
N 226. 98. 12 x. multicoloured .. 50 30

1962. Vietnamese Scenery.
N 227. – 12 x. purple and blue 55 30
N 228. 99. 12 x. sepia & turquoise 55 30
DESIGN—HORIZ. (32½ × 23 mm). No. N 227, Ba Be Lake.

99a. Weightlifting.

1962. Int. Military Sports Festival of Socialist States, Prague.
N 228a. 99a. 12 x. multicoloured 40·00 75·00

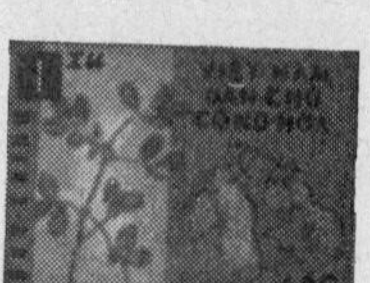

100. Quang Trung.

101. Groundnuts.

1962. National Heroes.
N 229. 100. 3 x. yell., brn. & grey 35 20
N 230. – 3 x. orge., blk. & ochre 35 20
N 231. 100. 12 x. yell., grn. & grey 55 30
N 232. – 12 x. orge., blk. & grey 55 30
PORTRAIT: Nos. N 230, N 232, Nguyen Trai.

1962. Multicoloured.
N 233. 1 x. Type 101 .. .. 20 20
N 234. 4 x. Haricot beans .. 45 25
N 235. 6 x. Sweet potatoes .. 55 30
N 236. 12 x. Maize .. .. 1·60 55
N 237. 30 x. Manioc .. .. 3·00 1·50

102. Girl Feeding Poultry.

DESIGNS: No. N 239, Woman tending pigs. No. N 240, Herdgirl with oxen. No. N 241, Boy feeding buffalo.

1962. Farm Stock-breeding.
N 238. 102. 2 x. red, grey & blue 35 20
N 239. – 12 x. ochre, turquoise and blue 80 30
N 240. – 12 x. brown, pale and deep green .. 80 30
N 241. – 12 x. buff, mauve and sepia 80 30

103. Popovich in "Vostok 4".

DESIGNS—HORIZ. 20 x. Nikolaev in "Vostok 3". VERT. 30 x. "Vostoks 3 and 4".

1962. First "Team" Manned Space Flights.
N 242. 103. 12 x. multicoloured .. 55 45
N 243. – 20 x. ochre, bl. & blk. 1·10 45
N 244. – 30 x. red, blue & blk. 1·40 80

104. Teacher and Students.

1962. 1st Five Year Plan (2nd issue). Higher Education and Land Cultivation.
N 245. 104. 12 x. black & yellow 65 30
N 246. – 12 x. blk., brn. & buff 1·60 85
DESIGN: No. N246, Tree felling.

105. Guerrilla Fighter. 106. Hoang Hoa Tham.

1963. 1st Five Year Plan (3rd issue). National Defence.
N 247. 105. 5 x. green and grey 55 20
N 248. 12 x. brown and buff 85 35

1963. 50th Death Anniv. of Hoang Hoa Tham (freedom fighter).
N 249. 106. 6 x. myrtle and blue 45 35
N 250. 12 x. blk., & light brn. 65 45

107. Workers in Field. 108. Karl Marx.

1963. 1st Five Year Plan (4th issue). Agricultural and Chemical Manufacture.
N 251. 107. 12 x. multicoloured 85 55
N 252. – 12 x red, mauve and black 55 35
DESIGN: No. N 252, Lam Thao Fertiliser Factory.

1963. 80th Death Anniv. of Karl Marx.
N 253. 108. 3 x. black and green 35 25
N 254. 12 x. black and drab on pink 50 30

109. Castro and Vietnamese Soldiers. 111. Nurse tending Child.

110. Doves and Labour Emblem.

1963. Vietnamese–Cuban Friendship.
N 255. 109. 12 x. multicoloured 50 40

1963. Labour Day.
N 256. 110. 12 x. orge., blk. & bl. 55 35

1963. Red Cross Centenary.
N 257. 111. 12 x. red, blk. & blue 90 45
N 258. – 12 x. red, blk. & turq. 90 45
N 259. – 20 x. red, grey and yell. 1·40 65
DESIGNS: No. N 258 Child, and syringe inscr. "BCG". 20 x. (25 × 42 mm.), Centenary emblem.

112. "Mars 1" Interplanetary Station.

1963. Launching of Soviet Rocket "Mars 1". Multicoloured.
N 260. 6 x. Type 112 .. .. 45 30
N 261. 12 x. Type 112 .. .. 65 35
N 262. 12 x. "Mars 1" in space (vert.) 65 35
N 263. 20 x. "Mars 1" in space (vert.) .. .. 1·60 65

113. Carp. 114. Pres. Ho Chi Minh embracing Prof. Nguyen Van Hien of South Vietnam.

1963. Fishing Industry. Multicoloured.
N 264. 12 x. Type 113 .. .. 2·50 1·10
N 265. 12 x. Fishes and trawler 2·75 1·10

1963. Campaign for reunification of Vietnam.
N 266. 114. 12 x. blk., bl. & turq. 55 35

DESIGNS: 20 x. Nikolaev and "eagle" motif. 30 x. Popovich and "phoenix" motif.
115. Globe and "Vostoks 3 and 4".

1963. 1st Anniv. of "Team" Manned Space Flights.
N 267. 115. 12 x. blk., brn. & yell. 45 30
N 268. – 20 x. blk., bl. & grn. 55 45
N 269. – 30 x. blk., vio. & bl. 1·25 80

DESIGN: 12 x. Viet Tri chemical factory.
116. Viet Tri Insecticide Factory.

1963. 1st Five-Year Plan (5th issue).
N 270. 116. 3 x. buff, brn. & blue 20 20
N 271. – 12 x. pink, brown and bistre 50 30

117. Black Amur.

1963. Freshwater Fish Culture. Multicoloured.
N 272. 12 x. Type 117 .. .. 70 45
N 273. 12 x. Carp 70 45
N 274. 12 x. Silver Carp .. 70 45
N 275. 20 x. Snakehead .. 2·00 90
N 276. 30 x. Mozambique mouthbreeder .. .. 3·00 1·90

118. Chinese Francolin. 119. Broken Chain and Map.

1963. Birds. Multicoloured.
N 277 12 x. Type 118 .. .. 2·25 1·10
N 278. 12 x. Chinese jungle mynah .. .. .. 2·25 1·10
N 279. 12 x. White-breasted kingfisher .. .. 2·25 1·10
N 280. 20 x. Siamese fireback pheasant (horiz.) .. 5·50 2·25
N 281. 30 x. Eastern reef heron 9·00 3·25
N 282. 40 x. Slaty-headed parakeet .. .. 12·00 4·75

1963. W.F.T.U. Assembly, Hanoi.
N 283. 119. 12 x. multicoloured 40 30

120. Football. 121. "Rauwolfia verticillata".

1963. "GANEFO" Athletic Games, Jakarta.
N 284. 120. 12 x. blk., grey & ochre 50 30
N 285. – 12 x. blk., grey & orge. 50 30
N 286. – 12 x. blk., grey & blue 50 30
N 287. – 30 x. blk., grey & mag. 1·00 55
DESIGNS—VERT. No. N 285, Volleyball. HORIZ. No. N 286, Swimming. No. N 287, High-jumping.

1963. Medicinal Plants. Multicoloured.
N 288. 6 x. Type 121 (green, yellow and violet) .. 50 30
N 289. 12 x. "Chenopodium ambrosicides" .. 60 30
N 290. 12 x. "Sophora japonica" 60 50
N 291. 12 x. "Fibraurea tinctoria" 60 50
N 292. 20 x. "Momordica cochinchinensis" 3·00 95

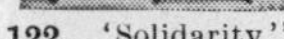
122. 'Solidarity'. 123. Pylon.

1963. South Vietnam Liberation National Front.
N 293. 122. 12 x. blk., brn. & ochre 40 30

1964. 1st Five-Year Plan (6th issue).
N 294. – 6 x. blk., red & pur. 40 25
N 295. – 12 x. multicoloured 1·10 45
N 296. 123. 12 x. blk., grey & orge. 1·10 45
DESIGNS—HORIZ. (40×22½ mm.): 6 x. Tapping cast-iron. No. N 295, Thai Ngyuen Iron and Steel Works.

124. Sun, Globe and Dragon. 125. Twin Space Flights.

1964. Int. Quiet Sun Years.
N 297. 124. 12 x. orge., blk. & grn. 30 20
N 298. 50 x. drab., blk. & pur. 1·10 70

1964. Space Flights of Bykovsky and Tereshkova. Multicoloured.
N 299. 12 x. Type 125 .. 55 30
N 300. 12 x. Bykovsky and "Vostok 5" 55 30
N 301. 30 x. Tereshkova and "Vostok 6" .. .. 1·60 85

126. "Hibiscus mutabilis". 127. Rural Costume.

1964. Flowers. Multicoloured.
N 302. 12 x. Type 126 .. .. 80 35
N 303. 12 x. "Persica vulgaris" 80 35
N 304. 12 x. "Saraca dives" .. 80 35
N 305. 12 x. "Passiflora hispida" 80 35
N 306. 20 x. "Michelia champaca" .. 1·90 1·10
N 307. 30 x. "Camellia amplexicaulis" .. 2·75 1·40

1964. National Costumes. Multicoloured.
N 308. 6 x. Type 127 .. 35 20
N 309. 12 x. "Ceremonial" .. 55 25
N 310. 12 x. "Everyday" .. 55 25

128. Artillery.

1964. 10th Anniv. of Battle of Dien Bien Phu.
N 311. 128. 3 x. black and red .. 35 20
N 312. – 6 x. black and blue .. 40 30
N 313. – 12 x. black & yellow 75 35
N 314. – 12 x. black & purple 75 35
DESIGNS: 6 x. Machine-gun post. No. N 313, Bomb-disposal. No. N 314, Dien Bien Phu and tractor.

129. Ham Rong Bridge.

1964. Inaug. of reconstructed Ham Rong Bridge.
N 315. 129. 12 x. multicoloured 65 30

130. Spotted Deer. 131. Women Fighters, Map, Industrial Scene and Watch-Towers.

1964. Wild Animals. Multicoloured.
N 316. 12 x. Type 130 .. 1·10 50
N 317. 12 x. Malayan tapir (horiz.) .. .. 1·10 50
N 318. 12 x. Tiger .. .. 1·10 50
N 319. 20 x. Water buffalo (horiz.) .. .. 3·00 1·10
N 320. 30 x. Sumatran rhinoceros (horiz.) .. 3·00 1·40
N 321. 40 x. Banteng (horiz.) 3·00 2·10

1964. 10th Anniv. of Geneva Agreements on Vietnam.
N 322. 131. 12 x. multicoloured 45 30
N 323. – 12 x. multicoloured 45 30
DESIGN—VERT. (23×45 mm.): N 323, Map of Vietnam, T.U. emblem and flag, inscr. ("NHAN DAN MIEN NAM") etc.

132. Nhu Quynh Pumping Station.

1964. Irrigation for Agriculture.
N 324. 132. 12 x. slate and black 50 30

133. Populace Greeting Soldiers.

1964. 10th Anniv. of Liberation of Hanoi. Multicoloured.
N 325. 6 x. Type 133 .. .. 30 20
N 326. 12 x. Building construction 50 45

134. Naval Longboat.

1964. "National Defence" Games.
N 327. 134. 5 x. blk., grey & blue 60 20
N 328. – 12 x. blk., grey. & yell. 1·00 40
N 329. – 12 x. blk., brn. & bl. 1·25 40
N 330. – 12 x. multicoloured 1·00 40
DESIGNS—HORIZ. No. N 328, Pistol-shooting. VERT. No. N 329, Gliding. No. N 330, Parachuting.

135. "Guarcinia mangostana".

1964. Tropical Fruits. Multicoloured.
N 331. 12 x. Type 135 .. .. 70 35
N 332. 12 x. "Mangifera indica" 70 35
N 333. 12 x. "Nephelium litchi" 70 35
N 334. 20 x. "Anona squamosa" 1·40 70
N 335. 50 x. "Citrus medica" 3·25 1·60

136. Conference Building.

1964. World Solidarity Conf., Hanoi. Mult.
N 336. 12 x. Type **136** .. 55 30
N 337. 12 x. Soldier greeting workers 55 30
N 338. 12 x. Clenched fist, ships and aircraft 70 30

137. Soldiers with Standard.

138. Cuban Revolutionaries.

1964. 20th Anniv. of Vietnamese People's Army. Multicoloured.
N 339. 12 x. Type **137** .. 55 25
N 340. 12 x. Coastguards .. 65 25
N 341. 12 x. Frontier guards (vert.) 55 25

1965. 6th Anniv. of Cuban Republic.
N 342. **138.** 12 x. blk., red & blue 55 30
N 343. – 12 x. multicoloured 55 30
DESIGN: No. N 343, Flags of Cuba and North Vietnam.

139. Le Hong Phong.

140. Party Flag.

1965. 35th Anniv. of Vietnamese Workers' Party. (a) As T **139**. Portraits and inscr. purple-brown; background colours given.
N 344. **139.** 6 x. grey 20 15
N 345. – 6 x. bistre 20 15
N 346. – 6 x. drab 20 15
N 347. – 6 x. brown 20 15
N 348. – 6 x. lilac 20 15
DESIGNS: No. N 345, Tran Phu. N 346 Hoang Van Thu. N 347, Hgo Gia Tu. N 348 Hguyen van Cu (Party leaders).

(b) As T **140.**
N 349. **140.** 12 x. yellow, red and mauve 40 25
N 350. – 12 x. mauve, yellow and red 40 25
DESIGN: No. N 350, Foundryman and guerilla fighter.

141. Women tending Maize.

142. Locomotive and Nguyen Van Troi (patriot).

1965. Populating Mountain Settlements.
N 351. **141.** 2 x. multicoloured .. 20 15
N 352. 3 x. multicoloured .. 25 20
N 353. – 12 x. indigo, orange and blue 45 30
DESIGN: 12 x. Young girls going to school.

1965. Transport Ministers' Congress, Hanoi.
N 354. **142.** 12 x. blue and red .. 70 15
N 355. – 30 x. black and green 1·50 45
DESIGN: 30 x. As Type **142** but position of locomotive, portrait and value transposed.

143. Cosmonauts Komarov, Feoktistov, Yegorov, and "Voskhod I".

1965. Three-manned Space Flight.
N 356. **143.** 20 x. violet, grn. & bl. 1·10 35
N 357. – 1 d. violet, red & mve. 3·25 1·40
DESIGN: 1 d. "Voskhod I" and cosmonauts.

INDEX
Countries can be quickly located by referring to the index at the end of this volume.

144. Lenin with Red Guards.

145. Pres. Ho Chi Minh.

1965. Lenin's 95th Birth Anniv.
N 358. **144.** 8 x. purple & buff .. 30 20
N 359. 12 x. purple & grey 40 25

1965. Pres. Ho Chi Minh's 75th Birthday.
N 360. **145.** 6 x. vio., yell. & grn. 30 15
N 361. 12 x. vio., yell. & buff 50 20

146. Hands clasping Serpent.

147. Two Soldiers advancing.

1965. 10th Anniv. of Afro-Asian Conf., Bandung.
N 362. **146.** 12 x. multicoloured 45 30

1965. Trade Union Conf., Hanoi.
N 363. **147.** 12 x. blue & purple 45 20
N 364. – 12 x. multicoloured 45 20
N 365. – 12 x. red, blk. & grn. 45 20
DESIGNS—HORIZ. No. N 364, Sea battle. No. N 365, "Peoples of the world" on Globe, and soldiers.

148. Yellow-throated Marten.

1965. Fauna Protection. Multicoloured.
N 366. 12 x. Type **148** .. 80 45
N 367. 12 x. Owston's palm civet 80 45
N 368. 12 x. Chinese pangloin 80 45
N 369. 12 x. Francois' monkey (vert.) .. 80 45
N 370. 20 x. Red giant flying squirrel .. .. 2·50 1·50
N 371. 50 x. Lesser slow loris (vert.) .. .. 3·25 2·75

149. Marx and Lenin.

150. Nguyen Van Troi (patriot).

1965. Postal Ministers Congress, Peking.
N 372. **149.** 12 x. multicoloured 55 30

1965. Nguyen Van Troi Commem.
N 373. **150.** 12 x. sep., brn. & grn. 45 12
N 374. 50 x. sep., brn. & ochre 95 60
N 375. 4 d. sepia and red .. 6·00 3·25

151. "Rhynchocoris humeralis".

152. Revolutionaries.

1965. Noxious Insects. Multicoloured.
N 376. 12 x. Type **151** 75 35
N 377. 12 x. "Tessaratoma papillosa" .. 75 35
N 378. 12 x. "Poecilliocoris latus" .. 75 35
N 379. 12 x. "Tosena melanoptera" .. 75 35
N 380. 20 x. "Cicada sp." .. 2·50 1·40
N 381. 30 x. "Fulgora candelaria" .. 3·25 1·60
Nos. N 379/81 are vert. (20½ × 38 mm.).

1965. 20th Anniv. of August Revolution.
N 382. **152.** 6 x. sep., blk. & blue 20 15
N 383. 12 x. black and red 45 20

153. Prawn.

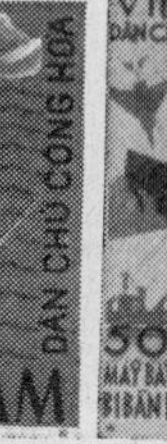
154. Air Battle.

1965. Marine Life. Multicoloured.
N 384. 12 x. Type **153** .. .. 1·25 45
N 385. 12 x. Shrimp .. .. 1·25 45
N 386. 12 x. Swimming Crab .. 1·25 45
N 387. 12 x. Serrate Swimming Crab .. .. 1·25 45
N 388. 20 x. Spiny Lobster .. 3·00 1·25
N 389. 50 x. Fiddler Crab .. 6·00 2·50

1965. "500th U.S. Aircraft Brought Down over North Vietnam".
N 390. **154.** 12 x. green and lilac 5·00 3·25

155. Foundryman ("Heavy Industries").

1965. 20th Anniv. of Republic and Completion of 1st Five Year Plan.
N 391. **155.** 12 x. black & orange 35 20
N 392. – 12 x. black & green 35 15
N 393. – 12 x. black & purple 35 15
DESIGNS: No. N 392, Irrigation, pylon and power station ("Hydro-electric Power"). No. N 393, Nurse examining child ("Social Medicine"). See also Nos. N 417/9.

156. Drummer and Peasants.

1965. 35th Anniv. of Movement of Nghe An and Ha Tinh Soviet Peasants.
N 394. **156.** 10 x. multicoloured 30 15
N 395. 12 x. multicoloured 45 20

157. Girls and Flags.

1965. 16th Anniv. of Friendship between China and Vietnam. Multicoloured.
N 396. 12 x. Type **157** 35 20
N 397. 12 x. Vietnamese and Chinese girls with flags (vert.) 35 20

158. Tsiolkovsky and "Sputnik 1".

1965. Space Flight of "Voskhod 2".
N 398. **158.** 12 x. blue & purple 45 20
N 399. – 12 x. ochre and blue 45 20
N 400. – 50 x. blue & green .. 1·40 65
N 401. – 50 x. blue & turquoise 1·40 65
DESIGNS: No. N 399, Leonov, Beliaiev and "Voskhod 2". No. N 400, Gagarin. No. N 401, Leonov in space.

159. "Cethosia biblis".

1965. Butterflies. Multicoloured.
N402 12 x. Type **159** .. 1·50 35
N403 12 x. "Cethosia cyane" .. 1·50 35
N404 12 x. "Graphium sarpedon" .. 1·50 35
N405 12 x. "Apatura ambica" 1·50 35
N406 20 x. "Papilio paris" .. 4·25 1·40
N407 30 x. "Atrophaneura aristolochiae" .. 6·25 2·25

160. Norman R. Morrison and Demonstrators.

161. Birthplace of Nguyen Du (poet).

1965. Homage to Norman R. Morrison (American Quaker who immolated himself).
N 408. **160.** 12 x. black and red 45 30

1965. Nguyen Du Commem. Multicoloured.
N 409. 12 x. Type **161** 35 20
N 410. 12 x. Nguyen Du Museum 35 20
N 411. 20 x. "Kieu" (volume of poems) .. 65 90
N 412. 1 d. Scene from "Kieu" 1·40 95

162. Pres. Ho Chi Minh.

163. Rice-field and Insecticide-sprayer ("Agriculture").

1965. Engels' 145th Birth Anniv. Mult.
N 413. 12 x. Type **162** .. 35 20
N 414. 12 x. Marx 35 20
N 415. 12 x. Lenin 35 20
N 416. 50 x. Engels .. .. 1·50 80

1965. Completion of First Five-Year Plan (2nd issue).
N 417. **163.** 12 x. orange & green 45 20
N 418. – 12 x. blue and red .. 45 20
N 419. – 12 x. orange & blue 45 20
DESIGNS: No. N 418, Factory-worker ("Light Industries"). No. N 419, Children at play and students ("Social Education").

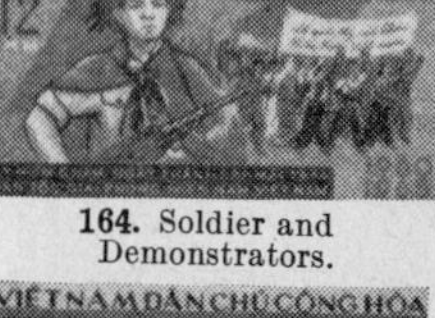
164. Soldier and Demonstrators.

165. Casting Votes.

166. "Dendrobium moschatum".

1965. 5th Anniv. of South Vietnam National Liberation Front.
N 420. **164.** 12 x. violet and lilac 45 20

1966. 20th Anniv. of 1st Vietnamese General Elections.
N 421. **165.** 12 x. black and red 35 15

1966. Orchids. Multicoloured.
N 422. 12 x. Type **166** 65 25
N 423. 12 x. "Vanda teres" .. 65 25
N 424. 12 x. "Dendrobium crystallinum" .. 65 25
N 425. 12 x. "Dendrobium nobile" .. 65 25
N 426. 20 x. "Vandopsis gigantea" .. 1·75 80
N 427. 30 x. "Dendrobium" .. 2·50 1·40

167. Child on Rocking-Horse.

168. "Physignathus cocincinus".

1966. New Year.
N 428. **167.** 12 x. multicoloured 40 15

1966. Protection of Nature—Reptiles. Multicoloured.
N 429. 12 x. Type **168** 65 35
N 430. 12 x. "Trionyx sincensis" 65 35
N 431. 12 x. Gecko (inscr. "GEKKO GECKO") 65 35
N 432. 12 x. "Testudo elongata" 65 35
N 433. 20 x. "Varanus salvator" 1·75 1·40
N 434. 40 x. "Eretmochelys imbricata" .. 2·50 1·40

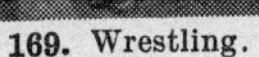
169. Wrestling.

170. Ly Tu Trong (revolutionary), Badge and Banner.

1966. National Games.
N 435. **169.** 12 x. multicoloured 35 20
N 436. – 12 x. multicoloured 35 20
N 437. – 12 x. multicoloured 35 20
GAMES: No. N 436, Archery (with crossbow). No. N 437, "Fencing".

1966. 35th Anniv. of Labour Youth Union.
N 438. **170.** 12 x. multicoloured 35 15

171. Aircraft in Flames.

1966. "1,000th U.S. Aircraft Brought Down over North Vietnam".
N 439. **171.** 12 x. multicoloured 3·25 1·40

172. Worker with Rifle.

174. Children and Banners.

173. Battle Scene on Con Co Island.

1966. Labour Day.
N 440. **172.** 6 x. black, red and salmon 35 20

1966. Defence of Con Co ("Steel Island").
N 441. **173.** 12 x multicoloured 40 15

1966. 25th Anniv. of Vietnam Youth Pioneers.
N 442. **174.** 12 x. black and red 40 20

175. View of Dien An (Yenan).

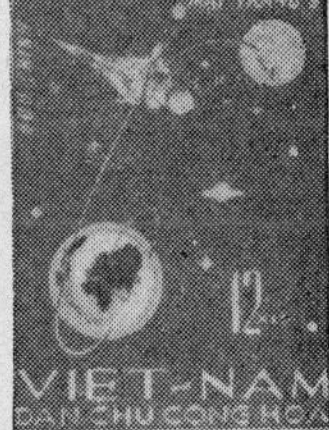
176. "Luna 9" in Space.

1966. 45th Anniv. of Chinese Communist Party. Multicoloured.
N 443. 3 x. Type **175** 20 15
N 444. 12 x. Ho Chi Minh and Mao Tse-tung .. 40 30

1966. "Luna 9". Space Flight. Multicoloured. Inscr. "MAT TRANG 9".
N 445. 12 x. Type **176** 30 20
N 446. 50 x. "Luna 9" on Moon 1·10 85

177. Aircraft in Flames.

178. Liberation Fighter.

1966. "1,500th U.S. Aircraft Brought Down over North Vietnam".
N 447. **177.** 12 x. multicoloured 3·00 2·25
N 448. 12 x. mult. (optd. **NGAY 14.10. 1966**) .. .. 2·25 2·25

1966. Victories of Liberation Army. Inscr. "1965–1966".
N 449. **178.** 1 x. purple 15 15
N 450. 12 x. multicoloured 25 15
N 451. – 12 x. multicoloured 35 20
DESIGN: No. N 451, Soldier escorting prisoners-of-war.
See also No. N 646.

179. Women from different Regions, and Child.

1966. 20th Anniv. of Vietnamese Women's Union.
N 452. **179.** 12 x. black & salmon 40 20

180. Moluccan Pittas.

1966. Birds. Multicoloured.
N 453. 12 x. Type **180** .. .. 1·00 45
N 454. 12 x. Black-naped Orioles 1·00 45
N 455. 12 x. Common Kingfisher 1·00 45
N 456. 12 x. Long-tailed Broadbill .. .. 1·00 45
N 457. 20 x. Hoopoe .. .. 2·75 1·40
N 458. 30 x. Maroon Orioles .. 3·75 1·75
Nos. N 454/5 and N 457 are vert.

181. Football.

1966. Ganefo Games. Multicoloured.
N 459. 12 x. Type **181** 35 20
N 460. 12 x. Rifle-shooting .. 35 20
N 461. 30 x. Swimming .. 80 45
N 462. 30 x. Running 80 45

182. Harvesting Rice.

1967. Agricultural Production.
N 463. **182.** 12 x. multicoloured 45 20

183. Ho Chi Minh Text and Fighters.

1967. Ho Chi Minh's Appeal.
N 464. **183.** 12 x. purple and red 20 15
N 465. – 12 x. purple and red 30 15
DESIGNS: No. N 465, Ho-Chi-Minh text and marchers with banners.
See also Nos. 519/22.

184. Bamboo ("Arundinaria rolleana").

1967. Bamboo. Multicoloured.
N 466. 12 x. Type **184** 35 15
N 467. 12 x. "Arundinaria racemosa" 35 15
N 468. 12 x. "Bambusa bingami" 35 15
N 469. 12 x. "Bambusa arundinaceu" 35 15
N 470. 30 x. "Bambusa nutans" 1·10 85
N 471. 50 x. "Dendrocalamus patellaris" .. 2·25 1·60

185. Dhole.

1967. Wild Animals. Multicoloured.
N472 12 x. Type **185** 70 35
N473 12 x. Binturong .. 70 35
N474 12 x. Hog-badger .. 70 30
N475 20 x. Large Indian civet 1·50 85
N476 40 x. Bear macaque .. 2·10 1·40
N477 50 x. Clouded leopard .. 3·25 2·25

186. Captured Pilot.

187. Rocket Launching and Agricultural Scene.

1967. "2,000th U.S. Aircraft Brought Down over North Vietnam".
N 478. **186.** 6 x. blk. & red on pink 1·50 70
N 479. 12 x. blk. & red on grn. 1·50 70

1967. Launching of Chinese Rocket at Ogive. Multicoloured.
N 480. 12 x. Type **187** 35 20
N 481. 30 x. Rocket launching, and Gate of Heavenly Peace, Peking .. 80 45

188. Siamese Tiger Fish.

189. Lenin and Revolutionary Soldiers.

1967. Vietnamese Fishes. Multicoloured.
N 482. 12 x. Type **188** 35 15
N 483. 12 x. Spanish Mackerel 35 15
N 484. 12 x. Lizard Fish .. 35 20
N 485. 20 x. Spangled Emperor 65 45
N 486. 30 x. German Fish .. 1·40 65
N 487. 50 x. Golden-Striped Snapper .. .. 2·25 85

1967. 50th Anniv. of October Revolution. Multicoloured.
N 488. 6 x. Type **189** 15 15
N 489. 12 x. Lenin and revolutionaries 30 20
N 490. 12 x. Lenin, Marx and Vietnamese soldiers.. 30 20
N 491. 20 x. Cruiser "Aurora" 60 35

190. Air Battle.

1967. "2,500th U.S. Aircraft Brought Down over North Vietnam".
N 492. **190.** 12 x. blk., red & grn. 4·25 1·00
N 493. – 12 x. blk., red & blue 2·25 1·00
DESIGN—VERT. No. N 493, Aircraft falling in flames.

191. Atomic Symbol and Gate of Heavenly Peace, Peking.

1967. First Chinese "H"-Bomb Test. Mult.
N 494. 12 x. Type **191** 45 25
N 495. 20 x. Chinese lantern, atomic symbol & dove (30×35 mm.) .. 65 30

192. Factory Anti-Aircraft Unit.

1967. Anti-aircraft Defences. Multicoloured.
N 496. 12 x. Type **192** 50 20
N 497. 12 x. Rifle-fire from trenches 50 20
N 498. 12 x. Seaborne gun-crew 50 20
N 499. 12 x. Militiawoman with captured U.S. pilot.. 50 20
N 500. 20 x. Air battle .. 80 35
N 501. 30 x. Military anti-aircraft post .. .. .. 1·75 65

193. Chickens.

1968. Domestic Fowl. Multicoloured designs showing cocks and hens.
N 502. 12 x. Type **193** 45 35
N 503. 12 x. Inscr. "Ga ri" .. 45 35
N 504. 12 x. Inscr. "Ga trong thien ri" 45 35
N 505. 12 x. Inscr. "Ga den chanchi" 45 35
N 506. 20 x. Junglefowl .. 1·10 55
N 507. 30 x. Hen .. .. 1·25 90
N 508. 40 x. Hen and chicks .. 1·40 1·10
N 509. 50 x. Two hens .. 2·25 1·40

194. Gorky.

1968. Birth Cent. of Maxim Gorky.
N 510. **194.** 12 x. black & brown 45 20

195. Burning Village.

1968. Victories of 1966–67.
N 511. **195.** 12 x. brown and lake 35 20
N 512. – 12 x. brown and lake 45 20
N 513. – 12 x. brown and lake 35 20
N 514. – 12 x. brown and lake 35 20
N 515. – 12 x. black and violet 35 20
N 516. – 12 x. black and violet 35 20
N 517. – 12 x. black and violet 35 20
N 518. – 12 x. black and violet 35 20
DESIGNS: No. N 512, Firing mortars. No. N 513, Attacking tanks with rocket-gun. No. N 514, Sniping. No. N 515, Attacking gun-site. No. N 516, Escorting prisoners. No. N 517, Interrogating refugees. No. N 518, Civilians demonstrating.

197. Ho Chi Minh Text and Fighters. **198.** Rose.

1968. Intensification of Production.
N 519. **197.** 6 x. blue on yellow .. 20 15
N 520. 12 x. blue 30 20
N 521. 12 x. purple .. 30 20
N 522. 12 x. red 30 20

1968. Roses.
N 523. **198.** 12 x. multicoloured 35 20
N 524. – 12 x. multicoloured 35 20
N 525. – 12 x. multicoloured 35 20
N 526. – 20 x. multicoloured 1·10 55
N 527. – 30 x. multicoloured 1·40 70
N 528. – 40 x. multicoloured 2·10 1·10
DESIGNS: Nos. N 524/8, Different species of rose similar to Type **198.**

199. Ho Chi Minh and Flag. **200.** Karl Marx.

1968. Ho Chi Minh's New Year Message.
N 529. **199.** 12 x. brown & violet 30 15

1968. 150th Birth Anniv. of Karl Marx.
N 530. **200.** 12 x. black & green 40 20

201. Anti-aircraft Machine-gun Crew.

1968. "3,000th U.S. Aircraft Brought Down over North Vietnam". Multicoloured.
N 531. 12 x. Type **201** .. 1·10 55
N 532. 12 x. Women manning anti-aircraft gun .. 1·25 55
N 533. 40 x. Aerial dogfight .. 3·00 1·25
N 534. 40 x. Anti-aircraft missile .. .. 3·00 1·25

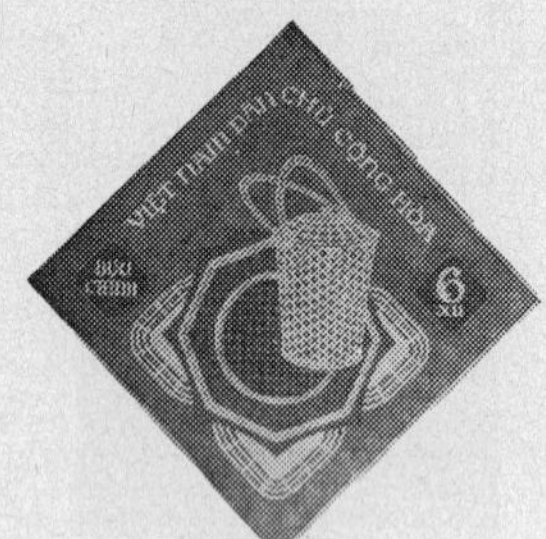

202. Rattan-cane Work.

1968. Arts and Crafts. Multicoloured.
N 535. 6 x. Type **202** 20 15
N 536. 12 x. Bamboo work .. 30 20
N 537. 12 x. Pottery 30 20
N 538. 20 x. Ivory carving .. 55 30
N 539. 30 x. Lacquer work .. 90 40
N 540. 40 x. Silverware .. 1·10 65

203. Quarter-staff Contest.

1968. Traditional Sports. Multicoloured.
N 541. 12 x. Type **203** 35 15
N 542. 12 x. Dagger fighting .. 35 15
N 543. 12 x. Duel with sabres .. 35 15
N 544. 30 x. Unarmed combat 85 45
N 545. 40 x. Scimitar fighting .. 1·40 55
N 546. 50 x. Sword and buckler 1·60 70

205. Temple, Khue.

1968. Vietnamese Architecture. Multicoloured.
N 548. 12 x. Type **205** 35 20
N 549. 12 x. Bell tower, Keo Pagoda 35 20
N 550. 20 x. Bridge, Bonze Pagoda (horiz.) 50 25
N 551. 30 x. Mot Cot Pagoda, Hanoi 50 30
N 552. 40 x. Gateway, Ninh Phuc Pagoda (horiz.) 85 45
N 553. 50 x. Tay Phuong Pagoda (horiz.) .. .. 1·10 55

206. Vietnamese Militia. **207.** "Ploughman with Rifle".

1968. Cuban-North Vietnamese Friendship. Multicoloured. With gum.
N 554. 12 x. Type **206** 20 15
N 555. 12 x. Cuban revolutionary (vert.) 20 15
N 556. 20 x. "Revolutionary Solidarity" (vert.) .. 45 20

1968. "The War Effort". Paintings. With gum.
N 557. **207.** 12 x. blk., bl. & yell. 20 15
N 558. – 12 x. multicoloured 20 15
N 559. – 30 x. brown, blue and turquoise .. 85 30
N 560. – 40 x. multicoloured 90 35
DESIGNS—HORIZ. No. N 558, "Defending the Mines". No. N 559, "Repairing Railway Track". No. N 560, "Crashed Aircraft".

208. Nam Ngai shooting down aircraft.

1969. Lunar New Year. Victories of the National Liberation Front. Multicoloured.
N 561. 12 x. Type **208** 35 15
N 562. 12 x. Tay Nguyen throwing grenade 25 15
N 563. 12 x. Insurrection of Tri Thien 25 15
N 564. 40 x. Insurgents, Tay Ninh 70 35
N 565. 50 x. Home Guards .. 1·10 70

209. Loading Timber Lorries.

1969. North Vietnamese Timber Industry. Multicoloured.
N 566. 6 x. Type **209** .. 15 15
N 567. 12 x. Log raft on River 30 15
N 568. 12 x. Tug "towing log train" 30 15
N 569. 12 x. Elephant hauling logs 25 15
N 570. 12 x. Insecticide spraying 25 15
N 571. 20 x. Buffalo hauling log 80 35
N 572. 30 x. Logs on overhead cable .. .. .. 1·40 65

MINIMUM PRICE
The minimum price quoted is 5p which represents a handling charge rather than a basis for valuing common stamps. For further notes about prices see introductory pages.

210. "Young Guerrilla". (Co Tan Long Chau).

1969. "South Vietnam—Land and People". Paintings. Multicoloured.
N 573. 12 x. Type **210** 35 25
N 574. 12 x. "Scout on patrol" (Co Tan Long Chau) .. 35 25
N 575. 20 x. "Woman guerrilla" (Le Van Chuong) (vert.) 35 25
N 576. 30 x. "Soldiers in Camp" (Co Tan Long Chau) .. 35 25
N 577. 40 x. "Soldiers playing cards" (Co Tan Long Chau) .. .. 1·10 95
N 578. 50 x. "A liberated Hamlet" (Huynh Phuong Dong) 1·40 1·10

211. Woman Soldier, Ben Tre. **213.** Grapefruit.

214. Tribunal Emblem and Falling plane. **212.** Soldier defending Hanoi.

1969. Victories in Tet Offensive (1968).
N 579. **211.** 8 x. blk., grn. & pink 25 15
N 580. 12 x. blk., emer. & green 25 15
N 581. – 12 x. multicoloured 25 15
N 582. – 12 x. multicoloured 25 15
N 583. – 12 x. multicoloured 25 15
DESIGNS—VERT. No. N 581, Urban guerilla and attack on U.S. Embassy, Saigon. No. N 582, Two soldiers with flag, Hue. No. N 583, Mortar crew, Khe Sanh.

1969. 15th Anniv. of Liberation of Hanoi.
N 584. **212.** 12 x. black and red 85 45
N 585. – 12 x. multicoloured 85 45
DESIGN: No. N 585, Children with construction toy.

1969. Fruits. Multicoloured.
N 586. 12 x. Type **213** 30 15
N 587. 12 x. Pawpaw 30 15
N 588. 20 x. Tangerines .. 40 15
N 589. 30 x. Oranges .. 65 80
N 590. 40 x. Lychees .. 1·00 60
N 591. 50 x. Persimmons .. 1·40 90
See also Nos. N 617/21 and N 633/6.

1969. Int. War Crimes Tribunal, Stockholm and Roskilde.
N 592. **214.** 12 x. black, red & brn. 45 15

215. Ho Chi Minh in 1924.

1970. 40th Anniv. of Vietnamese Workers' Party. Multicoloured.
N 593. 12 x. Type **215** 30 15
N 594. 12 x. Ho Chi Minh in 1969 30 15
N 595. 12 x. Le Hong Phong .. 30 15
N 596. 12 x. Tran Phu 30 15
N 597. 12 x. Nguyne van Cu .. 30 15
Nos. N 595/7 are smaller than Type **215**, size 40 × 24 mm.

216. Playtime in Nursery School. **217.** Lenin and Red Flag.

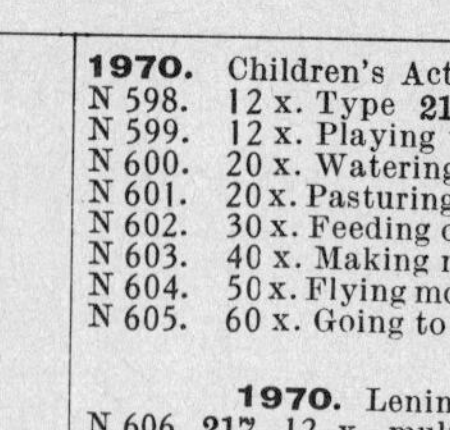

1970. Children's Activities. Multicoloured.
N 598. 12 x. Type **216** .. 25 15
N 599. 12 x. Playing with toys 25 15
N 600. 20 x. Watering plants .. 35 20
N 601. 20 x. Pasturing buffalo .. 35 20
N 602. 30 x. Feeding chickens .. 55 35
N 603. 40 x. Making music .. 70 45
N 604. 50 x. Flying model aircraft 1·10 65
N 605. 60 x. Going to school 1·60 85

1970. Lenin. Birth Cent.
N 606. **217.** 12 x. multicoloured 20 15
N 607. – 1 d. pur., red & yell. 1·40 40
DESIGN: 1 d. Portrait of Lenin.

218. Oc Xa Cu Sea-shell. **219.** Ho Chi Minh in 1930.

1970. Sea-shells. Multicoloured.
N 608. 12 x. Type **218** .. 35 15
N 609. 12 x. Oc Con Lon shell .. 35 15
N 610. 20 x. Oc Tien shell .. 45 15
N 611. 1 d. Oc Tu Va shell .. 1·60 45

1970. Ho Chi Minh's 80th Birth Anniv.
N 612. **219.** 12 x. blk., brn. & flesh 20 10
N 613. – 12 x. blk., bl. & grn. 20 15
N 614. – 2 d. blk., ochre & yell. 1·25 95
PORTRAITS: No. N 613, In 1945 with microphone. No. N 614, In 1969.

220. Vietcong Flag.

1970. 1st Anniv. of National Liberation Front Provisional Government in South Vietnam.
N 616. **220.** 12 x. multicoloured 30 15

221. Water-melon. **222.** Power Linesman.

1970. Fruits. Multicoloured.
N 617. 12 x. Type **221** .. 20 15
N 618. 12 x. Pumpkin .. 20 15
N 619. 20 x. Cucumber .. 30 15
N 620. 50 x. Courgette .. 80 35
N 621. 1 d. Charantais melon 1·60 60

1970. North Vietnamese Industries.
N 622. **222.** 12 x. blue and red 35 20
N 623. – 12 x. red, yell. & bl. 35 20
N 624. – 12 x. blk., orge. & bl. 35 20
N 625. – 12 x. yell., pur. & grn. 35 20
DESIGNS—VERT. No. N 623, Hands winding thread on bobbin ("Textiles"). No. N 624, Stoker and power station ("Electric Power"). No. N 625, Workers and lorry ("More coal for the Fatherland").

223. Peasant Girl with Pigs. **225.** Chuoi Tieu Bananas.

224. Ho Chi Minh proclaiming Republic, 1945.

1970. North Vietnamese Agriculture.
N 626. **223.** 12 x. multicoloured 35 20

1970. 25th Anniv. of Democratic Republic of Vietnam.
N 627. **224.** 12 x. blk., brn. & red 20 10
N 628. – 12 x. dark brown, brown and green 20 10
N 629. – 12 x. brn., grey and red .. 20 10
N 630. – 12 x. dark brown, brown and green 20 10
N 631. – 20 x. brn., red & bistre 30 15
N 632. – 1 d. brown, drab & chestnut .. .. 1·10 55
DESIGNS: No. N 628, Vo Thi Sau facing firing-squad. No. N 629, Nguyen Van Troi and captors. No. N 630, Phan Giot attacking pill-box. No. N 631, Nguyen Viet Xuan encouraging troops. No. N 632, Nguyen Van Be attacking tank.

1970. Bananas. Multicoloured.
N 633. 12 x. Type **225** .. 20 15
N 634. 12 x. Chuoi Tay .. 20 15
N 635. 50 x. Chuoi Ngu .. 80 30
N 636. 1 d. Chuoi Mat .. 1·60 55

226. Flags, and Bayonets in Helmet.

1970. Indo-Chinese People's Summit Conf.
N 637. **226.** 12 x. multicoloured 20 15

227. Engels and Signature.

1970. 150th Birth Anniv. of Friedrich Engels.
N 638. **227.** 12 x. blk. brn. & red 25 15
N 639. 1 d. blk., brn. & grn. 85 55

228. " Akistrodon ciatus ".

229. Mother and Child with Flag.

1970. Snakes. Multicoloured.
N 640. 12 x. Type **228** 35 15
N 641. 20 x. " Calliophis macclellandii " .. 55 30
N 642. 50 x. " Bungarus faciatus " .. .. 1·00 40
N 643. 1 d. " Trimeresurus gramineus " .. 1·40 70

1970. 10th Anniv. of National Front for Liberation of South Vietnam. Multicoloured.
N 644. 6 x. Type **229** 15 10
N 645. 12 x. Vietcong flag and torch (horiz.) 20 10

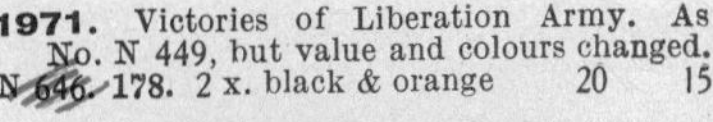

1971. Victories of Liberation Army. As No. N 449, but value and colours changed.
N 646. **178.** 2 x. black & orange 20 15

232. Satellite in Earth Orbit.

1971. 1st Anniv. of Launching of Chinese Satellite.
N 649. **232.** 12 x. multicoloured 20 10
N 650. 50 x. multicoloured 40 15

234. Ho Chi Minh Medal.

1971. Pres. Ho Chi Minh. 81st Birth Anniv.
N 652. **234.** 1 x. multicoloured 5 5
N 653. 3 x. multicoloured 10 5
N 654. 10 x. multicoloured 15 8
N 655. 12 x. multicoloured 20 15

235. Emperor Quang Trung liberating Hanoi.

1971. Bicent. of Tay Son Rising.
N 657. **235.** 6 x. multicoloured 20 15
N 658. 12 x. multicoloured 35 20

236. Karl Marx and Music of " L'Internationale ".

1971. Paris Commune. Cent.
N 659. **236.** 12 x. blk., red & pink 35 15

237. Hai Thuong Lan Ong.

1971. 250th Birth Anniv. of Hai Thuong Lan Ong (physician).
N 660. **237.** 12 x. blk., grn. & brn. 15 8
N 661. 50 x. multicoloured 40 20

238. " Kapimala ".

239. Ho Chi Minh, Banner and Young Workers.

1971. Folk Sculptures in Tay Phuong Pagoda. Multicoloured.
N 662. 12 x. Type **238** .. 40 15
N 663. 12 x. " Sangkayasheta " 40 15
N 664. 12 x. " Vasumitri " .. 40 15
N 665. 12 x. " Dhikaca " .. 40 15
N 666. 30 x. " Bouddha Nandi " 1·10 30
N 667. 40 x. " Rahulata " .. 1·10 45
N 668. 50 x. " Sandha Nandi " 1·10 50
N 669. 1 d. " Cakyamuni " .. 1·10 60

1971. 40th Anniv. of Ho Chi Minh Working Youth Union.
N 670. **239.** 12 x. multicoloured 20 10

240. " Luna 16 " on Moon.

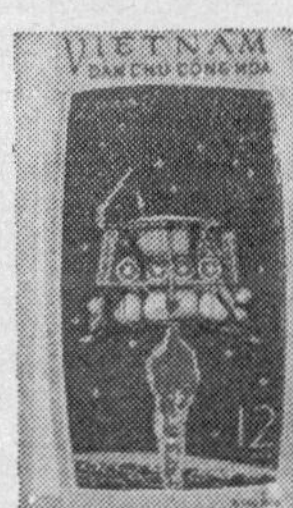

241. " Luna 17 " landing on Moon.

1971. Moon Flight of " Luna 16 ".
N 671. – 12 x. multicoloured 20 10
N 672. – 12 x. multicoloured 20 10
N 673. **240.** 1 d. brn., bl. & turq. 1·10 50
DESIGNS: No. N 671, Flight to Moon. No. N 672, Return to Earth.
Nos. N 671/2 were issued horizontally se-tenant forming a composite design, within the sheet.

1971. Moon Flight of " Luna 17 ".
N 674. **241.** 12 x. red, bl. & grn. 20 15
N 675. – 12 x. pink, green & myrtle 20 15
N 676. – 1 d. pink, brn. & grn. 85 40
DESIGNS—HORIZ. No. N 675, " Luna 17 " on Moon. No. N 676, " Lunokhod 1 " crossing Moon crevasse.

243. " White Tiger ".

1971. " The Five Tigers " (folk-art paintings). Multicoloured.
N 679. 12 x. Type **243** .. 20 15
N 680. 12 x. " Yellow Tiger " 20 15
N 681. 12 x. " Red Tiger " .. 20 15
N 682. 40 x. " Green Tiger " .. 75 30
N 683. 50 x. " Grey Tiger " .. 95 40
N 684. 1 d. " Five Tigers " .. 1·60 85

244. Flags and Gate of Heavenly Peace, Peking.

245. Mongolian Emblem.

1971. 50th Anniv. of Chinese Communist Party.
N 686. **244.** 12 x. multicoloured 20 10

1971. 50th Anniv. of Mongolian People's Republic.
N 687. **245.** 12 x. multicoloured 20 10

246. " Drum Procession ".

1972. Dong Ho Folk Engravings.
N 688. **246.** 12 x. pink, brn. & blk. 20 15
N 689. – 12 x. pink and black 20 15
N 690. – 12 x. multicoloured 20 15
N 691. – 12 x. multicoloured 20 15
N 692. – 40 x. multicoloured 1·10 30
N 693. – 50 x. multicoloured 1·40 55
DESIGNS—HORIZ. No. N 689, " Traditional wrestling ". No. N 692, " Wedding of mice ". No. N 693, " The Toads' school ". VERT. No. N 690, " Jealous Attack ". No. N 691, " Gathering coconuts ".

247. Workers.

248. Planting Rice.

1972. 3rd Vietnamese Trade Unions Congress.
N 694. **247.** 1 x. black and blue 15 8
N 695. – 12 x. black and orange 20 15
DESIGN: 12 x. As Type **247**, but design reversed.

1972. 25th Anniv. of Nat. Resistance.
N 696. **248.** 12 x. multicoloured 15 10
N 697. – 12 x. multicoloured 15 10
N 698. – 12 x. multicoloured 15 10
N 699. – 12 x. turq., red & pink 15 10
DESIGNS: No. N 697, Munitions worker, No. N 698, Soldier with flame-thrower. No. N 699, Text of Ho Chi Minh's Appeal.

249. Ho Chi Minh's Birthplace.

1972. 82nd Birth Anniv. of Ho Chi Minh.
N 700. **249.** 12 x. black, drab & ochre 20 10
N 701. – 12 x. blk., grn. & pink 20 10
DESIGN: No. N 701, Ho Chi Minh's House, Hanoi.

250. Captured Pilot and Falling Aircraft.

251. Georgi Dimitrov.

1972. " 3,500th U.S. Aircraft Brought Down over North Vietnam. "
N 702. **250.** 12 x. green and red 90 55
N 703. 12 x. black & red .. 90 55
No. N 703 has the inscription, amended to record the actual date on which the 3,500th aircraft was brought down–20.4.1972.

1972. 90th Birth Anniv. of Georgi Dimitrov (Bulgarian statesman).
N 704. **251.** 12 x. brown & green 20 10
N 705. – 12 x. black & pink .. 20 10
DESIGN: No. N 705, Dimitrov at Leipzig Court, 1933.

252. Falcated Teal.

253. Anti-Aircraft Gunner.

1972. Vietnamese Birds. Multicoloured.
N 706. 12 x. Type **252** 45 25
N 707. 12 x. Red-wattled Lapwing 45 25
N 708. 30 x. Cattle Egret .. 75 30
N 709. 40 x. Water Cock .. 1·00 50
N 710. 50 x. Purple Swamphen 1·90 70
N 711. 1d. Greater Adjutant Stork .. .. 3·75 1·10

1972. "4,000th U.S. Aircraft Brought Down over North Vietnam".
N712. **253.** 12 x. black, mauve. and pink .. 65 25
N713. – 12 x. green, black and red 65 25

254. Umbrella Dance.

1972. Tay Nguyen Folk Dances. Mult.
N 714. 12 x. Type **254** 15 10
N 715. 12 x. Drum dance .. 15 10
N 716. 12 x. Shield dance .. 15 10
N 717. 20 x. Galloping-horse dance 30 15
N 718. 30 x. Ka-dong dance .. 35 15
N 719. 40 x. Grinding-rice dance 50 20
N 720. 50 x. Gong dance .. 70 45
N 721. 1 d. Cham rong dance 1·25 60

255. " Soyuz 11 " Spacecraft and " Salyut " Space Laboratory.

1972. Space Flight of " Soyuz 11 ".
N 722. **255.** 12x. blue and lilac .. 20 10
N 723. – 1 d. brown and flesh 70 40
DESIGN: 1 d. " Soyuz 11 " astronauts.

256. Dhole.

1973. Wild animals (1st series). Mult.
N724. 12 x. Type **256** .. 20 12
N725. 30 x. Leopard 40 12
N726. 50 x. Leopard cat .. 65 35
N727. 1 d. European otter .. 1·60 55
See also Nos. N 736/9.

257. Copernicus and Globe.

1973. 500th Birth Anniv. of Copernicus (astronomer).

N 728. 257. 12 x. blk., red & brn. 20 15
N 729. – 12 x. blk., red & brn. 20 15
N 730. – 30 x. black & brown 40 20

DESIGNS—HORIZ. 12 x. (No. N 729), Copernicus and sun. VERT. 30 x. Copernicus and facsimile signature.

258. " Drummers ".

1973. Engravings from Ngoc Lu Bronze Drums. Each yellow and green.

N 731. 12 x. Type 258 .. 30 15
N 732. 12 x. " Pounding rice " 30 15
N 733. 12 x. " Folk-dancing " 30 15
N 734. 12 x. " War canoe " .. 30 15
N 735. 12 x. " Birds and beasts " 30 15

259. Lesser Malay Chevrotain.

260. Striated Canegrass Warblers.

1973. Wild Animals (2nd series). Mult.

N 736. 12 x. Type 259 .. 20 10
N 737. 30 x. Mainland serow 25 20
N 738. 50 x. Wild boar .. 55 35
N 739. 1 d. Siberian musk deer 1·25 50

1973. Birds Useful to Agriculture. Mult.

N 740. 12 x. Type 260 .. .. 55 20
N 741. 12 x. Red-whiskered bulbuls 65 20
N 742. 20 x. Magpie robin .. 75 35
N 743. 40 x. White-browed fantails .. .. 1·25 45
N 744. 50 x. Great tits .. .. 1·75 65
N 745. 1 d. Japanese white eyes 3·50 1·10

262. " Ready to Learn ".

1973. " Three Readies " Youth Movement.

N 748. 262. 12 x. brown & green 15 8
N 749. – 12 x. violet and blue 15 8
N 750. – 12 x. green & mauve 15 8

DESIGNS: No. N 749, Soldiers on the march (" Ready to Fight "). No. N 750, Road construction (" Ready to Work ").

263. Flags of North Vietnam and North Korea.

1973. 25th Anniv. of People's Republic of Korea.

N 751. 263. 12 x. multicoloured 15 8

264. Dogfight over Hanoi.

1973. Victory over U.S. Air Force.

N 752. 264. 12 x. multicoloured 30 10
N 753. – 12 x. multicoloured 30 10
N 754. – 12 x. multicoloured 30 10
N 755. – 1 d. black and red .. 1·60 60

DESIGNS: No. N 753, Bomber exploding over Haiphong. No. N 754, Anti-aircraft gun. No. N 755, Aircraft wreckage in China Sea.

266. Elephant hauling logs. 267. Dahlia.

1974. Vietnamese Elephants. Multicoloured.

N 758. 12 x. Type 266 .. .. 20 10
N 759. 12 x. War elephant .. 20 10
N 760. 40 x. Elephant rolling logs 45 20
N 761. 50 x. Circus elephant .. 80 30
N 762. 1 d. Elephant carrying war supplies .. .. 1·60 65

1974. Flowers.

N 763. 267. 12 x. red, lake & grn. 20 8
N 764. – 12 x. red, lake & grn. 20 8
N 765. – 12 x. yell., grn. & bl. 20 8
N 766. – 12 x. multicoloured 20 8
N 767. – 12 x. multicoloured 20 8

FLOWERS: No. N 764, Rose. No. N 765, Chrysanthemum. No. N 766, Bach Mi. No. N 767, Dai Doa.

268. Soldier planting Flag. 269. Armed Worker and Peasant.

1974. 20th Anniv. of Victory at Dien Bien Phu.

N 768. 12 x. Type 268 .. .. 15 8
N 769. 12 x. Victory badge .. 15 8

1974. " Three Responsibilities " Women's Movement.

N 770. 269. 12 x. blue and pink 20 10
N 771. – 12 x. blue and pink 20 10

DESIGN: No. N 771, Woman operating loom.

270. Cuc Nau Chrysanthemum. 271. " Corchorus capsularis ".

1974. Vietnamese Chrysanthemums. Mult.

N 772. 12 x. Type 270 .. .. 25 15
N 773. 12 x. Cuc Vang 25 15
N 774. 20 x. Cuc Ngoc Khong Tuoc 45 20
N 775. 30 x. Cuc Trang 45 25
N 776. 40 x. Kim Cuc 55 35
N 777. 50 x. Cuc Hong Mi .. 85 40
N 778. 60 x. Cuc Gam .. .. 1·00 45
N 779. 1 d. Cuc Tim .. .. 1·50 80

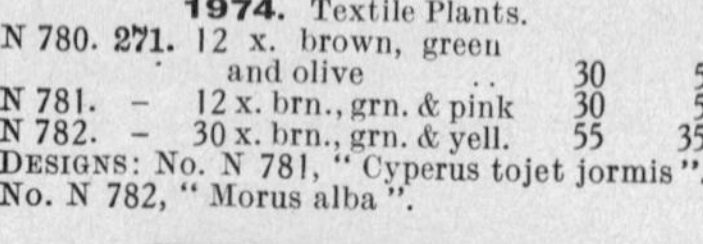

1974. Textile Plants.

N 780. 271. 12 x. brown, green and olive 30 5
N 781. – 12 x. brn., grn. & pink 30 5
N 782. – 30 x. brn., grn. & yell. 55 35

DESIGNS: No. N 781, " Cyperus tojet jormis ". No. N 782, " Morus alba ".

272. Nike Statue, Warsaw.

1974. 30th Anniv. of People's Republic of Poland.

N 783. 272. 1 x. pur., pink and red 20 8
N 784. 2 x. red, pink and red 15 10
N 785. 3 x. brn., pink and red 15 10
N 786. 12 x. lt. red, pink & red 35 15

273. Flags of China and Vietnam.

1974. 25th Anniv. of People's Republic of China.

N 787. 273. 12 x. multicoloured 20 10

274. Handclasp with Vietnamese and East German Flags.

1974. 25th Anniv. of German Democratic Republic.

N 788. 274. 12 x. multicoloured 20 10

275. Woman Bricklayer. 276. Pres. Allende with Chilean Flag.

1974. 20th Anniv. of Liberation of Hanoi. Multicoloured.

N 789. 12 x. Type 275 .. .. 15 5
N 790. 12 x. Soldier with child 15 5

1974. 1st Death Annivs. of Salvador Allende (President of Chile) and Pablo Neruda (Chilean poet).

N 791. 276. 12 x. blue and red .. 15 5
N 792. – 12 x. blue (Pablo Neruda) 15 5

277. "Rhizostoma".

1974. Marine Life. Multicoloured.

N 793. 12 x. Type 277 .. .. 20 10
N 794. 12 x. " Loligo " 20 10
N 795. 30 x. " Haleotis " .. 30 15
N 796. 40 x. " Pteria martensii " 40 20
N 797. 50 x. " Sepia officinalis " 65 30
N 798. 1 d. " Palinurus japonicus " .. 1·40 65

278. Flags of Algeria and Vietnam. 279. Albanian Emblem.

1974. 20th Anniv. of Algerian War of Liberation.

N 799. 278. 12 x. multicoloured 20 10

1974. 30th Anniv. of People's Republic of Albania. Multicoloured.

N 800. 12 x. Type 279 .. .. 20 10
N 801. 12 x. Girls from Albania and North Vietnam 20 10

280. Signing of Paris Agreement.

1975. 2nd Anniv. of Paris Agreement on Vietnam.

N 802. 280. 12 x. blk., grn. and emerald 15 8
N 803. – 12 x. blk., blue and grey 15 8

DESIGN: No. N 803, International Conference in session.

281. Tran Phu.

1975. 45th Anniv. of Vietnamese Workers' Party.

N 804. 281. 12 x. brn., red & pink 15 5
N 805. – 12 x. brn., red & pink 15 5
N 806. – 12 x. brn., red & pink 15 5
N 807. – 12 x. brn., red & pink 15 5
N 808. – 60 x. brown, chestnut and pink 55 30

PORTRAITS—HORIZ. No. N 805, Nguyen Van Cu. No. N 806, Le Hong Phong. No. N 807, Ngo Gia Tu. VERT. No. N 808, Ho Chi Minh in 1924.

282. "Costus speciosus". 283. " Achras sapota ".

1975. Medicinal Plants. Multicoloured.

N 809. 12 x. Type 282 .. .. 15 10
N 810. 12 x. " Rosa laevigata " 15 10
N 811. 12 x. " Curcuma zedoaria " 15 10
N 812. 30 x. " Erythrina indica " 30 15
N 813. 40 x. " Lilium brownii " 30 20
N 814. 50 x. " Hibiscus sagittifolius " .. 40 30
N 815. 60 x. " Papaver somniferum " .. 50 35
N 816. 1 d. " Belamcanda chinensis " .. .. 1·40 60

1975. Fruits. Multicoloured.

N 817. 12 x. Type 283 .. .. 15 5
N 818. 12 x. " Persica vulgaris " 15 5
N 819. 20 x. " Eugenia jambos " 15 10
N 820. 30 x. " Chrysophyllum cainito " 20 15
N 821. 40 x. " Lucuma mamosa " 20 15
N 822. 50 x. " Prunica granitum " 35 15
N 823. 60 x. " Durio ziberthinus " 45 30
N 824. 1 d. " Prunus salicina " 90 50

284. Ho Chi Minh. 285. Ho Chi Minh proclaiming Independence, 1945.

1975. 85th Birth Anniv. of Ho Chi Minh.

N 825. 284. 12 x. multicoloured 15 10
N 826. 60 x. multicoloured 30 15

1975. 30th Anniv. of Democratic Republic of Vietnam. Multicoloured.

N 827. 12 x. Type 285 .. .. 10 5
N 828. 12 x. Democratic Republic emblem 10 5
N 829. 12 x. Democratic Republic flag 15 10

286. " Dermochelys coriacea ". 287. Arms of Hungary.

1975. Reptiles. Multicoloured.

N 831. 12 x. Type 286 .. .. 15 5
N 832. 12 x. " Physignathus cocincinus " 15 5
N 833. 20 x. " Hydrophis brookii " 20 10
N 834. 30 x. " Platysternum megacephalum " .. 25 15
N 835. 40 x. " Leiolepis belliana " 40 15
N 836. 50 x. " Python molurus " 45 20
N 837. 60 x. " Naja hannah " 55 30
N 838. 1 d. " Draco maculatus " 1·25 40

1975. 30th Anniv. of Liberation of Hungary.

N 839. 287. 12 x. multicoloured 15 8

288. "Graphium antiphates".

1976. Butterflies. Multicoloured.

No.	Description	Unused	Used
N840	12 x. Type **288**	20	10
N841	12 x. "Danaus genutia"	20	10
N842	20 x. "Gynautocera papilionaria" ..	30	15
N843	30 x. "Eudocima salaminia"	45	20
N844	40 x. "Papilio machaon"	60	20
N845	50 x. "Ixias pyrene" ..	70	20
N846	60 x. "Episteme vetula"	90	35
N847	1 d. "Polyura eudamippus"	1·60	45

289. Lan Hoang Thao Orchid. 290. Masked Palm Civet.

1976. Lunar New Year.

No.	Type	Description	Unused	Used
N 848.	289.	6 x. yell., grn. & blue	15	8
N 849		12 x. yell., grn. & red	20	8

1976. Wild Animals. Multicoloured.

No.	Description	Unused	Used
N 850.	12 x. Type **290** ..	20	5
N 851.	12 x. Belly-banded squirrel	20	8
N 852.	20 x. Rhesus macaque	20	10
N 853.	30 x. Chinese porcupine	40	12
N 854.	40 x. Racoon-dog ..	45	20
N 855.	50 x. Asiatic black bear	50	25
N 856.	60 x. Leopard	75	35
N 857.	1 d. Malayan flying lemur	1·25	55

291. Voters and Map.

1976. 1st Elections of Unified National Assembly.

No.	Type	Description	Unused	Used
N 858.	291.	6 x. red and sepia ..	8	5
N 859.	–	6 x. yellow and red	8	5
N 860.	291.	12 x. red and blue..	15	5

DESIGN: 35×24 mm. No. N 859, Map and ballot box.

See also Nos. NLF 64/6 of National Front for the Liberation of South Vietnam.

292. Map and Text. 293. " Dendrobium devonianum ".

1976. 1st Session of Unified National Assembly.

No.	Type	Description	Unused	Used
N 861.	292.	6 x. pur., red & yell.	8	5
N 862.		12 x. turq., red & yell.	15	5
N 863.	–	12 x. bistre, red & yell.	15	5

DESIGN—VERT. (27×42 mm.) No. N 863, Vietnam map and design from Ngoc Lu Drum'. No. N 862 shows different text from Type **292**.

See also Nos. NLF 68/9 of National Front for the Liberation of South Veitnam.

1976. Orchids. Multicoloured.

No.	Description	Unused	Used
N 864.	12 x. Type **293**	5	5
N 865.	12 x. " Habenaria rhodocheila "	5	5
N 866.	20 x. " Dendrobium tortile "	15	8
N 867.	30 x. " Doritis pulcherrima "	20	8
N 868.	40 x. " Dendrobium farmeri "	30	10
N 869.	50 x. " Dendrobium aggregatum "	35	15
N 870.	60 x. " Eria pannea " ..	45	25
N 871.	1 d. " Paphiopedilum concolor "	65	35

FRANK STAMPS

F 29. F 42. Invalids in Rice-field.

1958. No value indicated.

No.	Type	Description	Unused	Used
NF 82.	F 29.	(–) Red, yellow and green	6·50	2·75

Issued to war-disabled persons for private correspondence.

1959. No value indicated.

No.	Type	Description	Unused	Used
NF 105.	F 42.	(–) Brown	2·25	85
NF 106.		(–) Olive and blue	3·25	1·10

Issued to invalids in agriculture for private correspondence.

F 230. Invalids' Badge.

1971. No value indicated.

No.	Type	Description	Unused	Used
NF 647.	F 230.	(–) Brown and red	25	15

Issued to disabled ex-servicemen for private correspondence.

F 233. Disabled Soldier with Baby. F 261. " Returning Home ".

1971. No value indicated.

No.	Type	Description	Unused	Used
NF 651.	F 233.	(–) Brown, red and yellow ..	25	15

1973.

No.	Type	Description	Unused	Used
NF 746.	F 261.	12 x. blk. and red	15	8
NF 747.	–	12 x. black & bl.	15	8

DESIGN—22×33 mm. No. NF 747, Disabled soldier with drill.

Issued to disabled veterans for private correspondence.

MILITARY FRANK STAMPS

MF 46. Soldier and Steam train.

1959. No value indicated.

No.	Type	Description	Unused	Used
NMF 112.	MF 46.	(–) Black & grn.	6·50	2·25

MF 68. Mounted Frontier Guard. MF 118. Military Medal and Invalid's Badge.

1961. No value indicated.

No.	Type	Description	Unused	Used
NMF 154.	MF 68.	(–) Multicoloured	6·00	3·25

1963.

No.	Type	Description	Unused	Used
NMF 277.	MF 118.	12 x. mult.	1·50	90

For use on disabled soldier's mail.

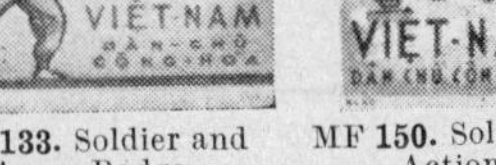
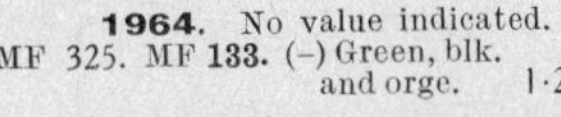

MF 133. Soldier and Army Badge. MF 150. Soldier in Action.

1964. No value indicated.

No.	Type	Description	Unused	Used
NMF 325.	MF 133.	(–) Green, blk. and orge.	1·25	55

1965. No value indicated.

No.	Type	Description	Unused	Used
NMF 373.	MF 150.	(–) Blk. & red	1·10	35
NMF 374.		(–) Blk. & grn.	1·10	35

MF 177. Soldiers and Weapons.

MF 204. Soldiers attacking. MF 189. " Star " Badge of Peoples' Army.

1966. No value indicated.

No.	Type	Description	Unused	Used
NMF 447.	MF 177.	(–) Violet & black ..	25	25

1967. No value indicated.

No.	Type	Description	Unused	Used
NMF 488.	MF 189.	(–) Mult. ..	20	15

1968. No value indicated.

NMF 519. (–) Brown and green

No. NMF 519 is similar in design to No. NMF 447, but shows more modern equipment and is dated "1967".

1968. No value indicated.

No.	Type	Description	Unused	Used
NMF 547.	MF 204.	(–) Lilac ..	35	20

1969. Type MF **177**. but undated. No value indicated.

No.	Type	Description	Unused	Used
NMF 579.	MF 177.	(–) Brown & green	25	15

MF 231. Nguyen Van Be attacking Tank.

1971. No value indicated.

No.	Type	Description	Unused	Used
NMF 648.	MF 231.	(–) Blk., red & drab ..	35	15

MF 252. Nguyen Viet Yuan and Anti-aircraft Gun.

1971. No value indicated.

No.	Type	Description	Unused	Used
NMF 677.	MF 252.	(–) Blk., pink and buff	20	15
NMF 678.		(–) Brown & green	20	15

MF 265. Soldier with Bayonet advancing.

1974. No value indicated.

No.	Type	Description	Unused	Used
NMF 756.	MF 265.	(–) Blk., yell. and blue ..	15	8
NMF 757.	–	(–) Blk., red and brown	15	8
NMF 758.	MF 265.	(–) Blk., flesh and red ..	15	8

DESIGN: No. NMF 757. Soldier with sub-machine gun, and tanks. No. NMF 757 is 40×24 mm.; No. NMF 758 31×21 mm.

OFFICIAL STAMPS

The values on Official stamps issued 1952 to 1954 are in kilogrammes of rice, the basis of the State's economy.

A. Tongking.

O 6. Rice-harvester.

1953. Production and Economy Campaign.

No.	Type	Description	Unused	Used
NO 17.	O 6.	0.600 k. red ..	2·25	1·10
NO 18.		1.000 k. brown ..	2·25	1·60
NO 19.		2.000 k. orange ..	3·25	2·25
NO 20.		5.000 k. slate ..	4·50	4·00

B. Central Annam.

NAO 3. "Family Left Behind".

1952. Issue for Central Annam. Imperf.

No.	Type	Description	Unused	Used
NAO 9.	NAO 3.	0.050 k. red ..	—	£120
NAO 10.		0.300 k. red ..	—	£120
NAO 11.		0.300 k. violet	—	£120
NAO 12.		0.600 k. green	—	£120
NAO 13.		0.600 k. blue ..		£120
NAO 14.		1,000 k. green	—	£190

1954. NO. NA 5 surch. **TEMSU VU O. k 300 THOC.**

No.	Type	Description	Unused	Used
NAO 15.	NA 1.	0.300 k. on 30 d on 5 d. green	£275	£190

1954. Nos. 56/7 of Vietnam Democratic Republic surch, No. NAO 17 also optd. "LKV" at top and "THOC" below value.

No.	Type	Description	Unused	Used
NAO 16.	3.	0 kg 05 on 1 h. green		£140
NAO 17.		0 kg 050 on 3 h. red		£140

C. General issues

1954. Dien-Bien-Phu Victory. As T **9** but value in " KILO ". Imperf.

No.	Description	Unused	Used
NO 24.	0.600 k. ochre and sepia	7·00	4·50

1955. Surch. **O k, 100 THOC.**

No.	Type	Description	Unused	Used
NO 33.	2.	0.100 k. on 2 d. brown	£140	90·00
NO 34.		0.100 k. on 5 d. red ..	£140	90·00

1955. Land Reform. As T **13** but inscr. " SU VU ".

No.	Description	Unused	Used
NO 38.	40 d. blue	6·00	3·25
NO 39.	80 d. red	9·50	4·00

O 17. Cu Chinh Lan (Tank Destroyer).

1956. Cu-Chinh-Lan Commem.

No.	Type	Description	Unused	Used
NO 50.	O 17.	20 d. green & turq...	1·60	1·60
NO 51.		80 d. mauve & red	1·90	1·90
NO 52.		100 d. sepia & drab	2·25	2·25
NO 53.		500 d. bl. & pale bl.	7·50	7·50
NO 54.		1,000 d. brn. & salm.	14·00	14·00
NO 55.		2,000 d. pur. & grn.	28·00	28·00
NO 56.		3,000 d. lake & lilac	55·00	55·00

1957. 4th World T.U. Conf., Leipzig. As T **24** but inscr. " SU VU ".

No.	Description	Unused	Used
NO 69.	20 d. green ..	1·40	85
NO 70.	40 d. blue ..	1·60	85
NO 71.	80 d. lake	2·50	1·40
NO 72.	100 d. brown ..	2·75	1·90

O 26. Moi Cot Pagoda, Hanoi. O 30. Lathe.

1957.

No.	Type	Description	Unused	Used
NO 75.	O 26.	150 d. brown & grn.	4·50	2·25
NO 76.		150 d. black & yell.	6·00	4·00

1958. Arts and Crafts Fair, Hoi.

No.	Type	Description	Unused	Used
NO 83.	O 30.	150 d. black & pink	1·40	90
NO 84.		200 d. blue & orange	1·90	1·40

O 31. Congress Symbol.

1958. 1st World Congress of Young Workers, Prague.
NO 85. O **31.** 150 d. red and green 1·60 85

O **34.** Soldier, Factory and Crops.

1958. Military Service.
NO 91. O **34.** 50 d. blue, and purple 1·00 45
NO 92. 150 d. brown & green 1·25 55
NO 93. 200 d. red and yellow 1·90 65

O **40.** Footballer and Hanoi Stadium.

1958. Opening of New Hanoi Stadium.
NO 102. O **40.** 10 d. lilac and blue 45 20
NO 103. 20 d. olive & salmon 65 35
NO 104. 80 d. brn. & ochre 1·10 20
NO 105. 150 d. brn. & turq. 1·60 65

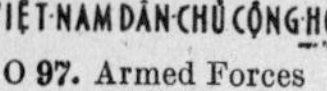
O **97.** Armed Forces on Boat. O **100.** Woman with Rice-planter.

1962. Military Service.
NO 223. O **97.** 12 x. multicoloured 2·75 1·40

1962. Rural Service.
NO 229. O **100.** 3 x. red 35 15
NO 230. 6 x. turquoise .. 45 20
NO 231. 12 x. olive .. 60 30

O **176.** Postman delivering Letter.

1966. Rural Service.
NO 445. O **176.** 3 x. purple, bistre and lilac .. 20 20
NO 446. – 6 x. purple, bistre and turquoise .. 35 20
DESIGN: 6 x. As Type O **11** but design reversed.

POSTAGE DUE STAMPS

1952. Handstamped **TT** in diamond frame.
ND 33. **3.** 100 d. green .. .. 20·00 20·00
ND 34. 100 d. brown .. .. 20·00 20·00
ND 35. **5.** 100 d. violet .. .. 28·00 28·00
ND 36. **3.** 200 d. red .. .. 28·00 28·00

D**13.** Letter Scales. D **39.**

1955.
ND 40. D **13.** 50 d. brown & lemon 7·00 6·00

1958.
ND 101. D **39.** 10 d. red and violet 55 55
ND 102. 20 d. green & orange 1·10 85
ND 103. 100 d. red and slate 2·25 1·90
ND 104. 300 d. red and olive 3·25 2·75

F. SOCIALIST REPUBLIC OF VIETNAM

Following elections held in April 1976 a National Assembly representing the whole of Vietnam met in Hanoi on 24th June 1976 and on 2 July proclaimed the reunification of the country as the Socialist Republic of Vietnam, with Hanoi as capital.

100 xu = 1 dong.

18. Red Cross and Vietnam Map on Globe.

1976. 30th Anniv. of Vietnamese Red Cross.
99. **18.** 12 x. red, blue and green 15 10

20. " Lutjanus sebae ".

1976. Marine Fishes. Multicoloured.
102. 12 x. Type **20** 5 5
103. 12 x. " Dampieria melanotaenia " 5 5
104. 20 x. " Therapon theraps " 10 8
105. 30 x. " Amphiprion bifasciatus " 15 8
106. 40 x. " Abudefduf sexfasciatus " 25 8
107. 50 x. " Heniochus acuminatus " 35 15
108. 60 x. " Amphiprion macrostoma " 45 25
109. 1 d. " Symphorus spilurus " 80 35

22. Party Flag and Map. **23.** Workers and Flag.

1976. 4th Congress of Vietnam Workers' Party (1st issue). Flag in yellow and red background colours given below.
111. **22.** 2 x. turquoise 5 5
112. 3 x. purple 5 5
113. 5 x. turquoise 8 5
114. 10 x. green 8 5
115. 12 x. myrtle 8 5
116. 20 x. green 15 10

1976. 4th Congress of Vietnam Workers' Party (2nd issue).
117. **23.** 12 x. blk., red & yell. 10 5
118. 12 x. red, orge. & blk. 10 5

24. Ho Chi Minh and map of Vietnam.

1976. " Unification of Vietnam.
119. **24.** 6 x. multicoloured .. 8 5
120. 12 x. multicoloured .. 10 5

25. Soldiers seizing Buon Me Thuot.

1976. Liberation of South Vietnam. Mult.
121. 2 x. Type **25** 5 5
122. 3 x. Soldiers on Son Tra Peninsula, Da Nang .. 5 5
123. 6 x. Soldiers attacking Presidential Palace, Saigon 15 5
124. 50 x. Type **25** 30 15
125. 1 d. As 3 x. 50 35
126. 2 d. As 6 x. .. .. 1·00 70

1976. As Nos. N848/9 but inscr. **"VIET NAM 1976"** at foot and background colours changed.
126a. **289.** 6 x. yell. grn. & orge. 20 15
126b. 12 x. yellow, light green and green .. 25 15

26. "Ictinogomphus clavatus" (Bao).

1977. Dragonflies. Multicoloured.
127 12 x. Type **26** 10 8
128 12 x. "Crocothemis servillia" (Ho) 10 8
129 20 x. "Rhinocypha fenestrella" 20 10
130 30 x. "Neurothemis tullia" 25 10
131 40 x. "Neurobavis chinensis" 30 10
132 50 x. "Neurothemis fulvia" 45 10
133 60 x. "Rhyothemis variegata" 60 35
134 1 d. "Rhymothemis fuliginosa" .. .. 1·00 45

27. Great Indian Hornbill and Emblem of Protection. **28.** Thang Long Tower and Bronze Drum.

1977. Protection of Rare Birds. Multicoloured
135. 12 x. Type **27** .. 25 15
136. 12 x. Tickell's Hornbill .. 25 15
137. 20 x. Long-crested Hornbill 35 20
138. 30 x. Wreathed Hornbill .. 45 20
139. 40 x. Indian Pied Hornbill 45 30
140. 50 x. Black Hornbill .. 75 30
141. 60 x. Great Indian Hornbill 95 35
142. 1 d. Rufous-necked Hornbill 1·75 65

1977. 1st Anniv. of National Assembly General Election. Multicoloured.
143. 4 x. Type **28** 5 5
144. 5 x. Map of Vietnam .. 5 5
145. 12 x. Lotus flower .. 8 5
146. 50 x. Vietnamese flag .. 25 15
Each design shows a bronze drum in the background.

29. "Anopolophora bowringii". **30.** " Thevetia peruviana ".

1977. Beetles. Multicoloured.
147 12 x. Type **29** 10 10
148 12 x. "Anopolophora horsfieldi" 10 10
149 20 x. "Aphrodisum griffithi" 15 10
150 30 x. "Aromia moschata" 20 15
151 40 x. "Calloplophora tonkinea" 30 20
152 50 x. "Thysia wallacei" .. 45 20
153 60 x. "Aristobia approximator" .. 55 25
154 1 d. "Batocera rubus" .. 90 45

1977. Wild Flowers. Multicoloured.
155. 12 x. Type **30** 8 8
156. 12 x. " Broussonetia papyrifera " 8 8
157. 20 x. " Aleurites montana " 10 10
158. 30 x. " Cerbera manghes " 15 10
159. 40 x. " Cassia multijuga " 25 15
160. 50 x. " Cassia nodosa " .. 35 15
161. 60 x. " Hibiscus schizopetalus " 45 25
162. 1 d. " Lagerstroesnia speciosa " 80 45

31. Pink Dahlias (Hoa Dong Tien). **32.** Children drawing Map of Vietnam.

1977. Flowers. Multicoloured.
163. 6 x. Type **31** 8 5
164. 6 x. Orange cactus dahlias (Bong tien kep) .. 8 5
165. 12 x. Type **31** 10 5
166. 12 x. As No. 164 .. .. 10 5

1977. Unification of Vietnam.
167. **32.** 4 x. multicoloured .. 5 5
168. 5 x. multicoloured .. 5 5
169. 10 x. multicoloured .. 10 5
170. 12 x. multicoloured .. 10 5
171. 30 x. multicoloured .. 20 10

33. Goldfish (Dong Nai Hoa).

1977. Goldfish. Multicoloured.
172. 12 x. Type **33** 8 5
173. 12 x. Hoa nhung 8 5
174. 20 x. Tau xanh 15 8
175. 30 x. Mat rong 20 8
176. 40 x. Cam trang 20 15
177. 50 x. Ngu sac 35 15
178. 60 x. Dong nai 55 25
179. 1 d. Thap cam 85 40

34. Ho Chi Minh and Lenin Banner. **35.** Hill Myna.

1977. 60th Anniv. of Russian October Revolution. Multicoloured.
180. 12 x. Type **34** (blue background) 8 5
181. 12 x. Type **34** (brown background) 8 5
182. 50 x. Mother holding child with flag .. 20 15
183. 1 d. Workers and banner 50 35

1978. Vietnamese Songbirds. Multicoloured.
184. 12 x. Type **35** 50 20
185. 20 x. Spotted dove .. 75 25
186. 20 x. Hwamei 75 25
187. 30 x. Black-headed shrike 90 35
188. 40 x. Crimson-winged laughing thrush .. 90 35
189. 50 x. Black-throated laughing thrush .. 95 55
190. 60 x. Chinese jungle mynah 1·75 90
191. 1 d. Yersin's laughing thrush .. .. 2·75 1·40

1978. Flowers. As Type **31.** Multicoloured.
192. 5 x. Sunflower 5 5
193. 6 x. Marguerites 5 5
194. 10 x. As 5 x. 8 8
195. 12 x. As 6 x. 15 8

36. Vietnamese Children. **37.** Throwing the Discus.

1978. International Children's Day.
196. **36.** 12 x. multicoloured .. 5 5

1978. Athletic Sports. Multicoloured.
197. 12 x. Type **37** 8 5
198. 12 x. Long-jumping .. 8 5
199. 20 x. Hurdling 8 8
200. 30 x. Throwing the hammer 20 10
201. 40 x. Putting the shot .. 20 15
202. 50 x. Throwing the javelin 35 15
203. 60 x. Sprinting 50 20
204. 1 d. High-jumping .. 80 40

38. Ho Chi Minh and Workers. **39.** Ho Chi Minh.

1978. 4th Vietnamese Trades Union Congress. Multicoloured.
205. 10 x. Trade Union Emblem 8 8
206. 10 x. Type **38** 8 8

1978. 88th Birth Anniv. of Ho Chi Minh. Multicoloured.
207. 10 x. Type **39** 8 5
208. 12 x. Ho Chi Minh Monument (38 × 22 mm.) .. 8 5

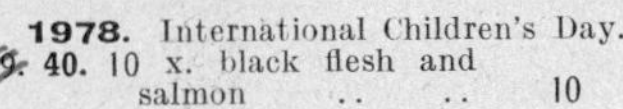

40. Young Pioneers' Cultural House, Hanoi. **41.** Sanakavasa.

1978. International Children's Day.
209. **40.** 10 x. black flesh and salmon 10 5

1978. Sculptures from Tay Phoung Pagoda. Multicoloured.
210. 12 x. Type **41** 10 5
211. 12 x. Parsva 10 5
212. 12 x. Punyasas 10 5
213. 20 x. Kumarata 10 5
214. 20 x. Nagarjuna 10 5
215. 30 x. Yayata 15 5
216. 40 x. Cadiep 20 10
217. 50 x. Ananda 25 10
218. 60 x. Buddhamitra .. 30 15
219. 1 d. Asvaghosa 35 35

42. Cuban Flag. **43.** Worker, Peasant, Soldier and Intellectual.

1978. 25th Anniv. of Cuban Revolution.
220. **42.** 6 x. red, black and blue 5 5
221. 12 x. red, black and blue 8 5

1978. 33rd Anniv. of August Revolution.
222. **43.** 6 x. red, mauve & yell. 5 5
223. – 6 x. turq. and pale green 5 5
224. **43.** 12 x. red, mauve & yell. 10 5
225. – 12 x. red and pink .. 10 5
DESIGN: Nos. 223 and 225, Symbols of agriculture and industry.

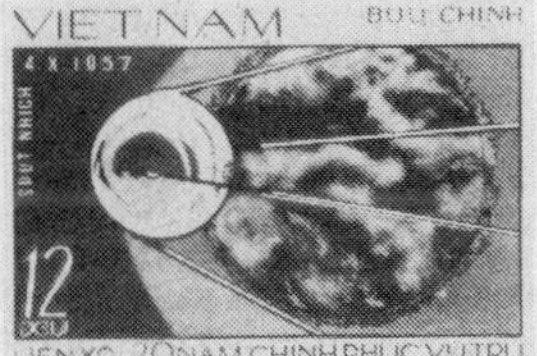

44. " Sputnik ".

1978. Space Research. Multicoloured.
226. 12 x. Type **44** 10 5
227. 12 x. " Venus 1 " 10 5
228. 30 x. Space capsules docking 15 10
229. 40 x. " Molniya 1 " .. 20 15
230. 60 x. " Soyuz " 30 20
231. 2 d. A. Gubarev and G. Grechko .. .. .. 1·10 65

45. Printed Circuit. **47.** Chrysanthemum " Cue Tim ".

46. Telephone Dial and Letter.

1978. International Telecommunications Day.
232. **45.** 12 x. orange and brown 15 5
233. – 12 x. brown and orange 15 5
DESIGN: No. 233, I.T.U. emblem.

1978. 20th Congress Socialist Countries Postal Ministers.
234. **46.** 12 x. multicoloured .. 10 5

1978. Chrysanthemums. Multicoloured.
235. 12 x. Type **47** 10 5
236. 12 x. " Cuc Kim Tien " .. 10 5
237. 20 x. " Cuc Hong " .. 10 8
238. 30 x. " Cuc Van Tho " .. 15 10
239. 40 x. " Cuc Vang " .. 20 10
240. 50 x. " Cuc Thuy Tim " 25 15
241. 60 x. " Cuc Vang Mo " .. 50 20
242. 1 d. " Cuc Nau Do " .. 80 35

48. Plesiosaurus. **49.** Cuban and Vietnamese Flags and Militiawomen.

1979. Prehistoric Animals. Multicoloured.
243. 12 x. Type **48** 10 5
244. 12 x. Brontosaurus .. 10 5
245. 20 x. Iguanodon 10 8
246. 30 x. Tyrannosaurus .. 15 10
247. 40 x. Stegosaurus .. 15 10
248. 50 x. Mozadaurus .. 20 15
249. 60 x. Triceratop 50 20
250. 1 d. Pteranodon .. 70 35

1979. 20th Anniv. of Cuban Republic.
251. **49.** 12 x. multicoloured .. 10 5

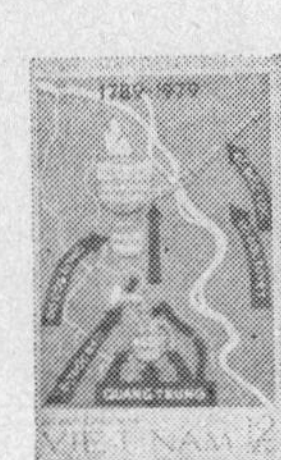

50. Battle Plan. **51.** Einstein.

1979. 190th Anniv. of Quang Trung's Victory over the Thanh.
252. **50.** 12 x. green, red and blue 10 5
253. – 12 x. multicoloured .. 10 5
DESIGN: No. 253, Quang Trung.

1979. Birth Centenary of Albert Einstein (physicist).
254. **51.** 12 x. black, brn. and bl. 15 5
255. – 60 x. multicoloured .. 40 25
DESIGN: 60 x. Equation, sun and planets.

52. Ram. **53.** Emblem.

1979. Domestic Animals. Multicoloured.
256. 10 x. Type **52** 10 5
257. 12 x. Ox 10 5
258. 20 x. Ewe and lamb .. 10 8
259. 30 x. White buffalo (vert.) 15 10
260. 40 x. Cow 20 10
261. 50 x. Goat 30 15
262. 60 x. Buffalo and calf .. 45 20
263. 1 d. Young goat (vert.) .. 80 35

1979. Five Year Plan.
264. **53.** 6 x. purple and pink .. 5 5
265. – 6 x. green and buff .. 5 5
266. – 6 x. green and lilac .. 5 5
267. – 6 x. orange and blue .. 5 5
268. – 6 x. blue and yellow .. 5 5
269. **53.** 12 x. red and pink .. 10 5
270. – 12 x. brown and pink .. 10 5
271. – 12 x. green and yellow 10 5
272. – 12 x. blue and brown 10 5
273. – 12 x. red and blue .. 10 5
DESIGNS: Nos. 265, 270, Worker. Nos. 266, 271, Peasant. Nos. 267, 272, Soldier. Nos. 268, 273, Intellectual.

54. " Philaserdica '79 " Emblem. **55.** Ho Chi Minh and Children.

1979. " Philaserdica '79 " International Stamp Exhbition, Sofia, Bulgaria.
274. **54.** 12 x. blue, brown & orge. 10 5
275. 30 x. blue, brn. and pink 20 5

1979. International Year of the Child. Mult.
276. 12 x. Type **55** 10 5
277. 20 x. Nurse, mother and child 15 5
278. 50 x. Children with aeroplane 30 10
279. 1 d. Children of different races 65 30

56. Silver Pheasant. **57.** " Dendrobium heterocacpum ".

1979. Ornamental Birds. Multicoloured.
280. 12 x. Siamese fireback pheasant (horiz.) .. 30 15
281. 12 x. Temminck's tragopan (horiz.) 30 15
282. 20 x. Ring-necked pheasant (horiz.) .. 30 15
283. 30 x. Edward's pheasant (horiz.) 40 20
284. 40 x. Type **56** 50 20
285. 50 x. Germain's peacock-pheasant 65 30
286. 60 x. Rheinard's pheasant 85 30
287. 1 d. Green peafowl .. 1·40 65

1979. Orchids. Multicoloured.
288. 12 x. Type **57**. 10 5
289. 12 x. " Cymbidium hybridum " 10 5
290. 20 x. " Rhynghostylis gigantea " 10 5
291. 30 x. " Dendrobium nobile " 15 8
292. 40 x. " Aerides falcatum " 20 8
293. 50 x. " Paphiopedilum callosum " 35 15
294. 60 x. " Vanda teres " .. 45 15
295. 1 d. " Dendrobium phalaenopsis " 80 35

58. Cat (Meo Muop).

1979. Cats. Multicoloured.
296. 12 x. Type **58** 10 5
297. 12 x. Meo Tam The (horiz.) 10 5
298. 20 x. Meo Khoang .. 10 5
299. 30 x. Meo Dom Van (horiz.) 15 8
300. 40 x. Meo Muop Dom .. 20 8
301. 50 x. Meo Vang 35 15
302. 60 x. Meo Xiem (horiz.) .. 45 15
303. 1 d. Meo Van Am (horiz.) .. 80 35

60. Citizens greeting Soldiers. **62.** Red and Pink Roses.

1979. 35th Anniv. of Vietnam People's Army.
306. **60.** 12 x. brown and green 10 8
307. – 12 x. brown and green 10 8
DESIGN: No. 307, Soldiers in action.

1980. Roses. Multicoloured.
311. 1 x. Type **62** 5 5
312. 2 x. Single Pink Rose .. 5 5
313. 12 x. Type **62** 10 5
314. 12 x. As No. 312 .. .. 10 5

63. " Nelumbium nuciferum ".

1980. Water Flowers. Multicoloured.
315. 12 x. Type **63** 10 5
316. 12 x. " Nymphala stellata " 10 5
317. 20 x. " Ipomola reptans " 10 5
318. 30 x. " Nymphoides indicum " 15 8
319. 40x. " Jussiala repens " .. 20 8
320. 50 x. " Eichhornia crassipes " 35 15
321. 60 x. " Monochoria voginalis " 50 15
322. 1 d. " Nelumbo nucifera " 70 35

64. Peasants with Banner and Implements as Weapons.

1980. 50th Anniv. of Vietnamese Communist Party. Multicoloured.
323. 12 x. Type **64** 8 5
324. 12 x. Ho Chi Minh proclaiming independence .. 8 5
325. 20 x. Victory of Dien Bien Phu 10 5
326. 20 x. Unification of North and South Vietnam .. 10 5
327. 2 d. Ho Chi Minh and armed Vietnamese .. .. 1·00 50

65. Lenin.

1980. 110th Birth Anniv. of Lenin.
328. **65.** 6 x. green and flesh .. 5 5
329. 12 x. red and flesh .. 8 5
330. 1 d. blue and flesh .. 45 30

66. Running. **67.** Ho Chi Minh in 1924.

1980. Olympic Games, Moscow. Multicoloured.
331. 12 x. Type **66** 5 5
332. 12 x. Hurdles 5 5
333. 20 x. Basketball 10 5
334. 30 x. Football 15 8
335. 40 x. Wrestling 20 10
336. 50 x. Gymnastics (horiz.) 30 10
337. 60 x. Swimming (horiz.) .. 40 20
338. 1 d. Sailing (horiz.) .. 65 35

1980. President Ho Chi Minh's 90th Birthday. Multicoloured.
339. 12 x. Type **67** 5 5
340. 40 x. Ho Chi Minh .. 25 15

68. Children dancing around Globe. **69.** Soviet and Vietnamese Cosmonauts.

1980. International Day of the Child.
341. **68.** 5 x. multicoloured .. 5 5

1980. Soviet-Vietnamese Space Flight. Mult.
342. 12 x. Type **69** 5 5
343. 12 x. Rocket 5 5
344. 20 x. " Soyuz 37 " .. 10 5
345. 40 x. Space station .. 20 10
346. 1 d. " Soyuz " returning to Earth 45 20
347. 2 d. Capsule landing by parachute 95 45

70. " Rhincodon typus ".

1980. Fishes. Multicoloured.

349.	12 x. Type **70**	5	5
350.	12 x. "Galeocerdo cuvier"	5	5
351.	20 x. "Orectolobus japonicus"	10	5
352.	30 x. "Heterodontus zebra"	15	8
353.	40 x. "Dasyatis uarnak"	20	10
354.	50 x. "Pristis microdon"	30	15
355.	60 x. "Shpyrna lewini" ..	40	15
356.	1 d. "Myliobatis tobijei"	65	30

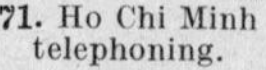

71. Ho Chi Minh telephoning.　**72.** Pink Rose (Hong Bach).

1980. Posts and Telecommunications Day. Multicoloured.

357.	12 x. Ho Chi Minh reading newspaper "Nhan Dan"	8	5
358.	12 x. Type **71**	12	5
359.	50 x. Kim Dong "the heroic postman" carrying magpie robin in cage	75	30
360.	1 d. Dish aerial	60	30

1980. Flowers.

361.	**72.**	12 x. pink and green ..	10	5
362.	–	12 x. red and green ..	10	5
363.	–	12 x. pink, mve. and grn.	10	5

DESIGNS: No. 362, Red Roses (Hong nhung). 15×20 mm. No. 363, Camellia.

73. Telephone Switchboard Operator.　**74.** Ho Chi Minh.

1980. National Telecommunications Day. Multicoloured.

364.	12 x. Type **73**	10	5
365.	12 x. Diesel train and railway route map	15	10

1980. 35th Anniv. of Republic of Vietnam. Multicoloured.

366.	12 x. Type **74**	8	5
367.	12 x. Arms of Vietnam (29×40 mm.)	8	5
368.	40× Pac Bo cave (29×40 mm.)	20	10
369.	1 d. Source of Lenine (40×29 mm.)	55	35

75. Vietnamese Arms.　**76.** Nguyen Trai.

1980. National Emblems.

370.	**75.**	6 x. multicoloured ..	10	5
371.	–	12 x. yell., red and blk.	10	5
372.	–	12 x. blk., yell. and orge.	10	5

DESIGNS—VERT. No. 371, National Anthem. HORIZ. No. 372, National flag.

1980. 600th Birth Anniv. of Nguyen Trai (national hero).

373.	**76.**	12 x. yellow and black	8	5
374.	–	50 x. black and blue ..	30	15
375.	–	1 d. brown and black	60	35

DESIGNS—HORIZ. 50 x. Three books by Nguyen Trai. VERT. 1 d. Ho Chi Minh reading commemorative stele.

MORE DETAILED LISTS
are given in the Stanley Gibbons Catalogues referred to in the country headings.
For lists of current volumes see Introduction.

77. Ho Chi Minh with Women.　**78.** "Biguoniaceae venusta".

1980. 50th Anniv. of Vietnamese Women's Union.

376.	**77.**	12 x. green, blue & lilac	10	5
377.	–	12 x. blue and lilac ..	10	5

DESIGN: No. 377, Group of women.

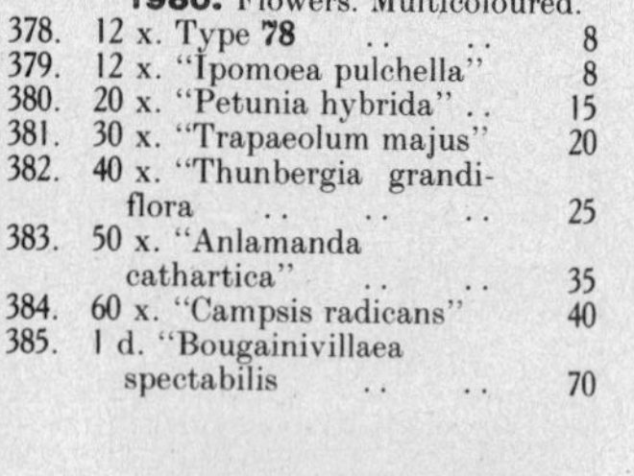

1980. Flowers. Multicoloured.

378.	12 x. Type **78**	8	5
379.	12 x. "Ipomoea pulchella"	8	5
380.	20 x. "Petunia hybrida" ..	15	5
381.	30 x. "Trapaeolum majus"	20	8
382.	40 x. "Thunbergia grandiflora	25	10
383.	50 x. "Anlamanda cathartica"	35	15
384.	60 x. "Campsis radicans"	40	20
385.	1 d. "Bougainivillaea spectabilis	70	35

79. "Symphysodon aequifasciata".

1981. Ornamental Fishes. Multicoloured.

386.	12 x. Type **79**	8	5
387.	12 x. "Betta splendens" ..	8	5
388.	20 x. "Poecilobrycon eques"	15	5
389.	30 x. "Gyrinocheilus aymonieri"	20	8
390.	40 x. "Barbus tetrazona"	25	10
391.	50 x. "Pterophyllum eimekei"	35	15
392.	60 x. "Xiphophorous helleri"	40	20
393.	1 d. "Trichopterus sumatranus	70	35

80. Rocket, Flowers and Flag.　**82.** Green Imperial Pigeon.

81. Bear Macaque.

1981. 26th U.S.S.R. Communist Party Congress. Multicoloured.

394.	20 x. Type **80**	10	5
395.	50 x. Young citizens with flag	30	15

1981. Animals of Cue Phuong Forest. Mult.

396.	12 x. Type **81**	10	5
397.	12 x. Crested gibbons ..	10	5
398.	20 x. Asiatic black bears ..	20	5
399.	30 x. Dhole	25	8
400.	40 x. Wild boar	40	10
401.	50 x. Sambars	50	15
402.	60 x. Leopard	55	20
403.	1 d. Tiger	95	35

1981. Turtle Doves. Multicoloured.

404.	12 x. Type **82**	25	15
405.	12 x. White-bellied wedge-tailed green pigeon (horiz.)	25	15
406.	20 x. Red turtle dove ..	45	25
407.	30 x. Bar-tailed cuckoo dove	55	25
408.	40 x. Mountain imperial pigeon	75	30
409.	50 x. Pin-tailed green pigeon (horiz.)	1·00	50
410.	60 x. Emerald dove (horiz.)	1·10	55
411.	1 d. White-bellied pin-tailed green pigeon (horiz.)	1·90	95

83. Yellow-backed Sunbird.　**85.** "Elaeagnus latifolia".

1981. Nectar-sucking Birds. Multicoloured.

412.	20 x. Type **83**	25	15
413.	20 x. Ruby-cheeked Sunbird	25	15
414.	20 x. Black-throated Sunbird	50	25
415.	40 x. Mrs Gould's Sunbird	60	30
416.	50 x. Macklot's Sunbird ..	90	50
417.	50 x. Blue-naped Sunbird	90	50
418.	60 x. Van Hasselt's Sunbird	1·00	55
419.	1 d. Green-tailed Sunbird	1·75	80

1981. Fruits. Multicoloured.

422.	20 x. Type **85**	10	5
423.	20 x. "Fortunella japonica"	10	5
424.	30 x. "Nephelium lappaceum"	20	8
425.	40 x. "Averrhoa bilimbi"	25	10
426.	50 x. "Ziziphus mauritiana"	35	15
427.	50 x. "Fragaria vesca" ..	35	15
428.	60 x. "Bouea oppositifolia"	40	20
429.	1 d. "Syzygium aqueum"	70	35

86. Girl with Rice Sheaf.　**87.** Ho Chi Minh planting Tree.

1981. World Food Day.

430.	**86.**	30 x. green	15	10
431.	–	50 x. green	20	10
432.	–	2 d. orange	85	35

DESIGN: 2 d. F.A.O. emblem and rice.

1981. Tree Planting Festival.

433.	**87.**	30 x. orange and blue	20	15
434.	–	30 x. red and blue ..	20	15

DESIGN: No. 434, Family planting tree.

88. European Bison.

1981. Animals. Multicoloured.

435.	30 x. Type **88**	20	8
436.	30 x. Orang-utan	20	8
437.	40 x. Hippopotamus ..	30	15
438.	40 x. Red kangaroo ..	30	15
439.	50 x. Giraffe	50	15
440.	50 x. Javan rhinoceros ..	50	15
441.	60 x. Common zebra ..	55	20
442.	1 d. Lion	85	40

INDEX
Countries can be quickly located by referring to the index at the end of this volume.

89. Congress Emblem.　**90.** Ho Chi Minh and Party Flag.

1982. Tenth World Trade Unions Congress, Havana, Cuba.

443.	**89.**	50 x. multicoloured ..	20	10
444.		5 d. multicoloured ..	2·25	1·00

1982. Fifth Communist Party Congress (1st issue). Multicoloured.

445.	30 x. Type **90**	30	15
446.	30 x. Hammer, sickle and rose	30	15

See also Nos. 455/6.

91. "Thyreus decorus".

1982. Bees. Multicoloured.

447	20 x. Type **91**	25	10
448	20 x. "Vespa affinis" ..	25	10
449	30 x. "Eumenes esuriens"	30	20
450	40 x. "Polistes sp." ..	40	20
451	50 x. "Sphex sp." ..	55	30
452	50 x. "Chlorion lobatum"	55	30
453	60 x. "Xylocopa sp." ..	70	30
454	1 d. "Apis mellifera" ..	1·10	50

92. Electricity Worker and Pylon.

1982. Fifth Communist Party Congress (2nd issue).

455.	**92.**	30 x. yell., blk. & red	30	15
456.	–	50 x. multicoloured ..	30	15

DESIGN: 50 x. Women harvesting rice.

93. Football.

1982. Football Training Movement.

457.	**90.**	30 x. multicoloured ..	20	10
458.	–	30 x. multicoloured ..	20	10
459.	–	40 x. multicoloured ..	30	15
460.	–	40 x. multicoloured ..	30	15
461.	–	50 x. multicoloured ..	35	15
462.	–	50 x. multicoloured ..	35	15
463.	–	60 x. multicoloured ..	45	35
464.	–	1 d. multicoloured ..	65	35

DESIGNS: Nos. 458/64, Various football scenes.

94. Militia woman.　**95.** Arms of Bulgaria.

1982.

465.	**94.**	30 x. multicoloured ..	20	5

1982. 1300th Anniv. of Bulgarian State.

468.	**95.**	30 x. pink and red	20	5
469.		50 x. brown and red ..	35	12
470.		2 d. orange and red ..	1·40	70

96. Map of Vietnam and Red Cross.

97. Georgi Dimitrov.

1982. 35th Anniv. of Vietnam Red Cross.

471. **96.** 30 c. red, blue and blk. 20 12
472. 1 d. red, green and blk. 90 45

DESIGN: 1 d. Red Cross.

1982. Death Centenary of Georgi Dimitrov (Bulgarian Statesman).

473. **97.** 30 x. orange and black 20 12
474. 3 d. brown and black .. 2·00 85

98. Rejoicing Women.

99. Common Kestrel.

1982. Fifth National Women's Congress. Multicoloured.

475. 12 x. Type **98** 20 10
476. 12 x. Congress emblem and three women 20 20

1982. Birds of Prey. Multicoloured.

477. 30 x. Type **99** 45 35
478. 30 x. Pied Falconet .. 45 35
479. 40 x. Black Baza 75 40
480. 50 x. Black Kite 85 45
481. 50 x. Lesser Fishing Eagle 85 45
482. 60 x. Fieldens Falconet (horiz.) 95 50
483. 1 d. Black-shouldered Kite (horiz.) .. .. .. 1·75 1·10
484. 1 d. Short-toed Eagle .. 1·75 1·10

100. Red Dahlia.

101. Dribble.

1982. Dahlias. Multicoloured.

485. 30 x. Type **100** 20 10
486. 30 x. Orange dahlia .. 20 10
487. 40 x. Rose dahlia 30 10
488. 50 x. Red decorative dahlia 35 15
489. 50 x. Yellow dahlia .. 35 15
490. 60 x. Red single dahlia .. 40 15
491. 1 d. White dahlia 80 35
492. 1 d. Pink dahlia 80 35

1982. World Cup Football Championship, Spain. Multicoloured.

493. 50 x. Type **101** 35 15
494. 50 x. Tackle 35 15
495. 50 x. Passing Ball 35 15
496. 1 d. Heading ball 70 30
497. 1 d. Goalkeeper saving ball 70 30
498. 2 d. Shooting .. .. 1·10 55

102. Cuban Flag.

104. Rabindranath Tagore.

103. Ho Chi Minh and Children planting Tree.

1982. 120th Anniv. of Cuban Victory at Giron.

499. **102.** 30 x. multicoloured .. 20 12

1982. World Environment Day.

500. **103.** 30 x. green and black 20 12
501. – 30 x. green and black 20 12

DESIGN: No. 501, U.N. environment emblem and plants.

1982. 120th Birth Anniv. (1981) of Rabindranath Tagore (Indian poet).

502. **104.** 30 x. orange, brown and black 20 12

105. "Sycanus falleni".

106. Lenin and Cruiser "Aurora".

1982. Harmful Insects. Multicoloured.

503 30 x. Type **105** 30 8
504 30 x. "Catacanthus incarnatus" 30 8
505 40 x. "Nezara viridula" .. 35 10
506 50 x. "Helcomeria spinosa" 50 15
507 50 c. "Lohita grandis" .. 50 15
508 60 x. "Chrysocoris stolli" 55 25
509 1 d. "Tiarodes ostentans" 95 40
510 1 d. "Pterygamia grayi" .. 95 40

1982. 65th Anniv. of Russian Revolution.

511. **106.** 30 x. red and black .. 20 15
512. – 30 x. red and black .. 20 15

DESIGN: No. 512 Russian man and woman, Lenin and space station.

108. Swimming.

1982. Ninth South East Asian Games, New Delhi.

514. **108.** 30 x. blue and lilac .. 20 12
515. – 30 x. blue and mauve 20 12
516. – 1 d. orange and blue 70 35
517. – 2 d. green and brown 1·40 60

DESIGNS: 30 x. (No. 515) Table tennis. 1 d. Wrestling. 2 d. Rifle shooting.

109. "Samaris cristatus".

1982. Fishes. Soles. Multicoloured.

518. 30 x. Type **109** 20 8
519. 30 x. "Tephrinectes sinensis" 20 8
520. 40 x. "Psettodes erumei" 30 10
521. 40 x. "Zebrias zebra" 30 10
522. 50 x. "Pardachirus pavoninus" 40 15
523. 50 x. "Cynoglossus puncticeps" 40 15
524. 60 x. "Brachirus orientalis" 50 30
525. 1 d. "Psettina iijimae" .. 80 40

110. Foundry and Textile Workers.

112. Sampan.

111. Lenin on Map.

1982. "All for Socialist Fatherland, All for Happiness of People".

526. **110.** 30 x. blue & deep blue 20 12
527. – 30 x. brown and yellow 20 12
528. – 1 d. brown and green 70 35
529. – 2 d. pink and purple .. 1·40 60

DESIGNS: 30 x. Women holding sheaf of wheat and basket of grain. 1 d. Soldiers. 2 d. Nurse with children holding books.

1982. 60th Anniv. of U.S.S.R.

530. **111.** 30 x. multicoloured .. 20 12

1983. Boats. Multicoloured.

531. 30 x. Type **112** 15 10
532. 50 x. Junk with striped sails 20 10
533. 1 d. Houseboats 35 20
534. 3 d. Junk 55 25
535. 5 d. Sampan with patched sails .. .. .. 1·00 35
536. 10 d. Sampan (horiz.) .. 1·75 80

113. Class "231–300".

1983. Steam Locomotives. Multicoloured.

537. 30 x. Type **113** 15 8
538. 50 x. Class "230–000" .. 20 8
539. 1 d. Class "140–601" .. 35 20
540. 2 d. Class "241–000" .. 45 25
541. 3 d. Class "141–500" .. 55 25
542. 5 d. Class "150–000" .. 1·00 35
543. 8 d. Class "40–300" .. 1·50 60

114. Montgolfier Balloon.

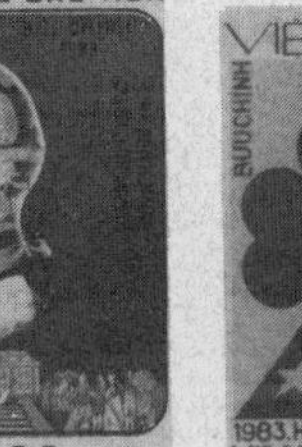

115. Flags and Dove.

1983. Bicentenary of Manned Flight. Mult.

544. 30 x. Type **114** 15 8
545. 50 x. Hydrogen balloon .. 20 8
546. 1 d. Balloon No. CA-11 .. 35 20
547. 2 d. Hot-air balloon .. 45 25
548. 3 d. Balloon over harbour 55 25
549. 5 d. "Le Geant" .. .. 1·00 35
550. 8 d. Balloon .. .. 1·40 55

1983. Laos-Kampuchea-Vietnam Summit Conference.

552. **115.** 50 x. red, yell. & bl. 20 15
553. 5 d. red, bl. & yell. 1·90 1·25

116. Robert Koch.

1983. Centenary of Discovery of Tubercle Bacillus.

554. **116.** 5 d. blk, bl. & red .. 1·90 1·25

117. "Teratolepis fasciata".

1983. Reptiles. Multicoloured.

555. 30 x. Type **117** 12 5
556. 30 x. Jackson's chameleon 12 5
557. 50 x. Spiny-tailed agamid 20 8
558. 80 x. "Heloderma suspectum" 25 8
559. 1 d. "Chamaeleo meileri" 35 20
560. 2 d. "Amphibolurus barbatus" 55 25
561. 5 d. "Chlamydosaurus kingi" .. .. .. 1·00 35
562. 10 d. "Phrynosoma coronatum" .. .. 2·00 70

118. A. Gubatev and V. Remek.

1983. Cosmonauts. Multicoloured.

563. 30 x. Type **118** 12 8
564. 50 x. P. Klimuk and Miroslaw Hermaszewski 20 8
565. 50 x. V. Bykovsky and Sigmund Jahn 20 8
566. 1 d. Nikolai Rukavishnikov and Georgi Ivanov 30 12
567. 1 d. Bertalan Farkas and V. Kubasov 30 12
568. 2 d. V. Gorbatko and Pham Tuan 55 25
569. 2 d. Arnaldo Tamayo Mendez and I. Romanenko 55 25
570. 5 d. V. Dzhanibekov and Gurragcha .. .. 1·00 35
571. 8 d. L. Popov and D. Prunariu .. .. 1·40 50

119. "Madonna of the Chair".

120. Burmese King and Rook.

1983. 500th Birth Anniv. of Raphael (artist). Multicoloured.

573. 30 x. Type **119** 12 5
574. 50 x. "Madonna of the Grand Duke" 20 8
575. 1 d. "Sistine Madonna" .. 30 12
576. 2 d. "The Marriage of Mary" 55 25
577. 3 d. "The Beautiful Gardener" 80 30
578. 5 d. "Woman with Veil" .. 1·10 40
579. 8 d. "Self-portrait" .. 1·50 55

1983. Chess Pieces. Multicoloured.

581 30 x. Type **120** 12 5
582 50 x. 18th-century Delhi king (elephant) .. 20 8
583 1 d. Lewis knight and bishop 30 12
584 2 d. 8th/9th-century Arabian king (elephant) 55 25
585 3 d. 12th-century European knight 75 30
586 5 d. 16th-century Russian rook (sailing boat) .. 1·00 40
587 8 d. European Chinese-puzzle bishop and rook (fool and elephant) .. 1·40 55

123. Long Jumping.

125. "Terias hecabe".

1983. Olympic Games, Los Angeles (1984). Multicoloured.

591. 30 x. Type **123** 12 5
592. 50 x. Running 20 8
593. 1 d. Javelin throwing .. 30 12
594. 2 d. High jumping (horiz.) 55 25
595. 3 d. Hurdling (horiz.) .. 75 30
596. 5 d. Putting the shot 1·00 40
597. 8 d. Pole vaulting .. .. 1·40 55

1983. Butterflies and Moths. Multicoloured.

600 30 x. Type **125** 25 10
601 30 x. "Lamproptera meges" 25 10
602 40 x. "Lyssa patroclus" .. 25 10
603 40 x. "Graphium agamemnon" 35 10
604 50 x. "Precis almana" .. 50 20
605 50 x. "Papilio nephelus" .. 50 20
606 60 x. "Thauria aliris" .. 50 20
607 1 d. "Kallima inachus" .. 95 35

128. Postman.

1983. World Communications Year. Mult.

617. 50 x. Type **128** 20 5
618. 2 d. Mail sorting office .. 55 25
619. 8 d. Telephonists .. .. 1·40 45
620. 10 d. Wireless operator and dish aerial .. .. 1·90 70

129. Running, Stadium and Sports Pictograms.

1983. National Youth Sports Festival.

622. **129.** 30 x. dp. blue and blue 20 15
623. 1 d. brown and orange 70 45

130. Karl Marx.

1983. Death Centenary of Karl Marx.

624. **130.** 50 x. black and red .. 25 15
625. 10 d. black and red .. 2·00 1·60

131. Child with Fish. **132.** "Pleurotus ostreatus".

1983. World Food Day. Multicoloured.

626. 50 x. Type **131** 20 8
627. 4 d. Family 95 40

1983. Fungi. Multicoloured.

628. 50 x. Type **132** 30 5
629. 50 x. "Coprinus atramentarius" 30 5
630. 50 x. "Flammulina velutipes" 30 5
631. 50 x. "Catharellus cibarius" 30 5
632. 1 d. "Volvariella volvacea" 40 12
633. 2 d. "Agoricus silvaticus" 65 25
634. 5 d. "Morchella esculenta" 1·25 40
635. 10 d. "Amanita caesarea" 2·50 75

133. Building Dam.

1983. 5th Anniv of U.S.S.R.-Vietnam Co-operation.

638 **133** 4 d. grey and black .. 95 40

134. Envelope with I.T.U. Emblem.

1983. World Telecommunications Day and Year.

640. **134.** 50 x. + 10 x. blue, green and red .. 40 25
641. – 50 x. + 10 x. red, light brown and brown .. 40 25

DESIGN: No. 641, W.C.Y. emblem and dish aerial.

135. Girl with Flowers.

1983. 5th Trade Union Congress.

642. **135.** 50 x. bl., orge. & blk. 15 5
643. – 2 d. blk., bl. & brn. 35 25
644. – 30 d. blk., bl. & red 4·50 2·50

DESIGNS: 2, 30 d. Worker and industrial complex.

136. Conference Emblem and Hands. **137.** Grey Herons.

1983. World Peace Conference, Prague.

645. – 50 x. bl., red & yell. 12 5
646. **136.** 3 d. grn., red & yell. 70 45
647. 5 d. lilac, red & yell. 1·25 75
648. 20 d. bl., red & yell. 5·00 2·75

DESIGN: 50 x. Conference emblem and woman.

1983. Birds. Multicoloured.

649. 50 x. Type **137** 40 10
650. 50 x. Painted storks .. 40 10
651. 50 x. Black storks 40 10
652. 50 x. Purple herons .. 40 10
653. 1 d. Common cranes .. 65 30
654. 2 d. Black-faced spoonbills 1·25 60
655. 5 d. Black-crowned night herons .. .. 2·25 1·00
656. 10 d. Asian open-bill storks 4·25 1·90

138. Biathlon.

1984. Winter Olympic Games, Sarajevo. Multicoloured.

657. 50 x. Type **138** 20 5
658. 50 x. Cross-country skiing 20 5
659. 1 d. Speed skating .. 30 12
660. 2 d. Bobsleighing 50 25
661. 3 d. Ice hockey (horiz.) .. 70 30
662. 5 d. Ski jumping (horiz.) .. 1·00 40
663. 6 d. Slalom (horiz.) .. 1·10 55

139. Marbled Cat.

1984. Protected Animals. Multicoloured.

665. 50 x. Type **139** 20 5
666. 50 x. Leopard 20 5
667. 50 x. Tiger 20 5
668. 1 d. Common gibbon .. 30 12
669. 1 d. Slow loris 30 12
670. 2 d. Indian elephant .. 50 25
671. 2 d. Gaur 50 25

140. "Banhinia variegata". **141.** "Brasse cattleya".

1984. Flowers. Multicoloured.

672. 50 x. Type **140** 20 5
673. 50 x. "Caesalpinia pulcherrima" 20 5
674. 1 d. "Cassia fistula" .. 30 12
675. 2 d. "Delonix regia" .. 50 25
676. 3 d. "Artabotrys uncinatus" 70 30
677. 5 d. "Corchorus olitorius" 1·00 40
678. 8 d. "Banhinia grandiflora" .. .. .. 1·10 55

1984. Orchids. Multicoloured.

680. 50 x. Type **141** 20 5
681. 50 x. "Cymbidium sp." .. 20 5
682. 1 d. "Cattleya dianx" var. "alba" 30 12
683. 2 d. "Cymbidium sp." (different) 55 25
684. 3 d. "Cymbidium hybridum" 80 30
685. 5 d. Phoenix winged orchids .. .. .. 1·10 40
686. 8 d. Yellow Queen orchids 1·40 55

142a. "Cypselwius spilopterus".

1984. Deep Sea Fish. Multicoloured.

686a. 30 x. Type **142a** 12 5
686b. 30 x. "Ostracion cornutus" 12 5
686c. 50 x. "Diodon hystrix" 20 5
686d. 80 x. "Chelmon rostratus" 25 10
686e. 1 d. "Antennarius bidens" 30 12
686f. 2 d. "Pterois russelli" .. 55 25
686g. 5 d. "Mola mola" .. 1·10 40
686h. 10 d. "Minous monodactylus" .. .. 2·00 75

144. Ho Chi Minh discussing Battle Plan.

1984. 30th Anniv. of Battle of Dien Bien Phu. Multicoloured.

689. 50 x. Type **144** 20 10
690. 50 x. Vietnamese soldiers and truck 20 10
691. 1 d. Students carrying provisions 30 15
692. 2 d. Pulling field gun up hill 50 25
693. 3 d. Anti-aircraft gun and crashed airplane .. 1·00 40
694. 5 d. Fighting against tanks 1·40 50
695. 8 d. Vietnamese soldiers with flag on bunker .. 1·40 55

146. "Trichogaster trichopterus". **148.** Nguyen Duc Canh.

1984. Fishes. Multicoloured.

698. 50 x. Type **146** 20 5
699. 50 x. "Brachydanio rerio" 20 5
700. 1 d. "Macropodus opercularis" 30 12
701. 2 d. "Gymnocorymbus ternetzi" 55 25
702. 3 d. "Hyphessobrycon serpae" 80 30
703. 5 d. "Labeo bicolor" .. 1·10 40
704. 8 d. "Betta splendens" .. 1·40 55

1984. Nos. 362 and 373 surch.

705. – 50 x. on 12 x. red and green 20 20
706. **76.** 50 x. on 12 x. yellow and black 20 20

1984. 55th Anniv. of Vietnamese Trade Union Movement.

707. **148.** 50 x. red and black .. 12 5
708. – 50 x. red and black .. 12 5
709. – 1 d. multicoloured .. 25 10
710. – 2 d. multicoloured .. 55 25
711. – 3 d. multicoloured .. 75 30
712. – 5 d. multicoloured .. 1·25 50

DESIGNS:—VERT. No. 708, Founder's house. HORIZ. No. 709, Workers presenting demands to employer. 711, Factory. 712, Workers, procession and doves.

149. Hon Dua.

1984. Coastal Scenes. Multicoloured.

714. 50 x. Type **149** 20 5
715. 50 x. Hang con gai .. 20 5
716. 50 x. Hang Bo Nau .. 20 5
717. 50 x. Nui Yen Ngua .. 20 5
718. 1 d. Hon Ga Choi 30 12
719. 1 d. Hon Coc 30 12
720. 2 d. Hon Dinh Huong .. 55 25
721. 3 d. Hon Su Tu 80 30
722. 5 d. Hon Am .. .. 1·10 40
723. 8 d. Nui Bai Tho .. .. 1·40 55

150. Styracosaurus.

1984. Prehistoric Animals. Multicoloured.

724. 50 x. Type **150** 20 5
725. 50 x. Diplodocus 20 5
726. 1 d. Rhamphorhynchus .. 30 12
727. 1 d. Corythosaurus .. 30 12
728. 2 d. Seymouria 55 25
729. 3 d. Allosaurus 80 30
730. 5 d. Dimetrodon .. .. 1·10 40
731. 8 d. Brachiosaurus .. 1·40 55

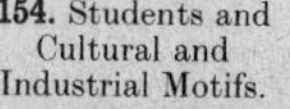

152. Dove and Flags. **154.** Students and Cultural and Industrial Motifs.

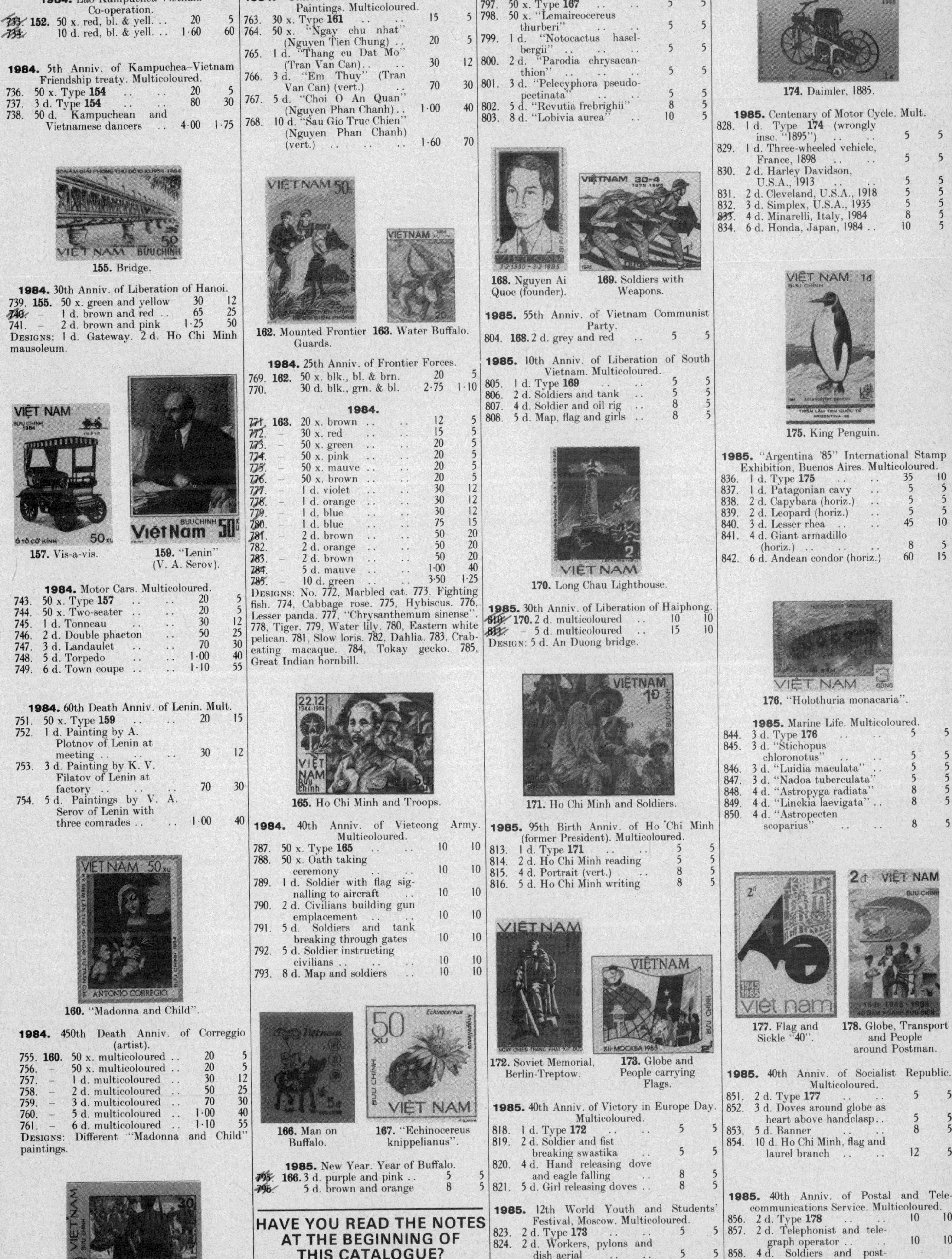

1984. Lao-Kampuchea-Vietnam Co-operation.
733. **152.** 50 x. red, bl. & yell. .. 20 5
734. 10 d. red, bl. & yell. .. 1·60 60

1984. 5th Anniv. of Kampuchea–Vietnam Friendship treaty. Multicoloured.
736. 50 x. Type **154** 20 5
737. 3 d. Type **154** 80 30
738. 50 d. Kampuchean and Vietnamese dancers .. 4·00 1·75

155. Bridge.

1984. 30th Anniv. of Liberation of Hanoi.
739. **155.** 50 x. green and yellow 30 12
740. – 1 d. brown and red .. 65 25
741. – 2 d. brown and pink 1·25 50
DESIGNS: 1 d. Gateway. 2 d. Ho Chi Minh mausoleum.

157. Vis-a-vis.

159. "Lenin" (V. A. Serov).

1984. Motor Cars. Multicoloured.
743. 50 x. Type **157** 20 5
744. 50 x. Two-seater 20 5
745. 1 d. Tonneau 30 12
746. 2 d. Double phaeton .. 50 25
747. 3 d. Landaulet 70 30
748. 5 d. Torpedo .. .. 1·00 40
749. 6 d. Town coupe .. .. 1·10 55

1984. 60th Death Anniv. of Lenin. Mult.
751. 50 x. Type **159** 20 15
752. 1 d. Painting by A. Plotnov of Lenin at meeting 30 12
753. 3 d. Painting by K. V. Filatov of Lenin at factory 70 30
754. 5 d. Paintings by V. A. Serov of Lenin with three comrades .. .. 1·00 40

160. "Madonna and Child".

1984. 450th Death Anniv. of Correggio (artist).
755. **160.** 50 x. multicoloured .. 20 5
756. – 50 x. multicoloured .. 20 5
757. – 1 d. multicoloured .. 30 12
758. – 2 d. multicoloured .. 50 25
759. – 3 d. multicoloured .. 70 30
760. – 5 d. multicoloured .. 1·00 40
761. – 6 d. multicoloured .. 1·10 55
DESIGNS: Different "Madonna and Child" paintings.

161. "Giu Lay Hoa Binh" (Le Quoc Loc).

1984. United Nations Children's Fund. Paintings. Multicoloured.
763. 30 x. Type **161** 15 5
764. 50 x. "Ngay chu nhat" (Nguyen Tien Chung) .. 20 5
765. 1 d. "Thang cu Dat Mo" (Tran Van Can) 30 12
766. 3 d. "Em Thuy" (Tran Van Can) (vert.) .. 70 30
767. 5 d. "Choi O An Quan" (Nguyen Phan Chanh) .. 1·00 40
768. 10 d. "Sau Gio Truc Chien" (Nguyen Phan Chanh) (vert.) .. .. .. 1·60 70

162. Mounted Frontier Guards.

163. Water Buffalo.

1984. 25th Anniv. of Frontier Forces.
769. **162.** 50 x. blk., bl. & brn. 20 5
770. 30 d. blk., grn. & bl. 2·75 1·10

1984.
771. **163.** 20 x. brown 12 5
772. – 30 x. red 15 5
773. – 50 x. green 20 5
774. – 50 x. pink 20 5
775. – 50 x. mauve 20 5
776. – 50 x. brown 20 5
777. – 1 d. violet 30 12
778. – 1 d. orange 30 12
779. – 1 d. blue 30 12
780. – 1 d. blue 75 15
781. – 2 d. brown 50 20
782. – 2 d. orange 50 20
783. – 2 d. brown 50 20
784. – 5 d. mauve .. .. 1·00 40
785. – 10 d. green .. .. 3·50 1·25
DESIGNS: No. 772, Marbled cat. 773, Fighting fish. 774, Cabbage rose. 775, Hybiscus. 776, Lesser panda. 777, "Chrysanthemum sinense". 778, Tiger. 779, Water lily. 780, Eastern white pelican. 781, Slow loris. 782, Dahlia. 783, Crab-eating macaque. 784, Tokay gecko. 785, Great Indian hornbill.

165. Ho Chi Minh and Troops.

1984. 40th Anniv. of Vietcong Army. Multicoloured.
787. 50 x. Type **165** 10 10
788. 50 x. Oath taking ceremony 10 10
789. 1 d. Soldier with flag signalling to aircraft .. 10 10
790. 2 d. Civilians building gun emplacement 10 10
791. 5 d. Soldiers and tank breaking through gates 10 10
792. 5 d. Soldier instructing civilians 10 10
793. 8 d. Map and soldiers .. 10 10

166. Man on Buffalo.

167. "Echinocereus knippelianus".

1985. New Year. Year of Buffalo.
795. **166.** 3 d. purple and pink .. 5 5
796. 5 d. brown and orange 8 5

HAVE YOU READ THE NOTES AT THE BEGINNING OF THIS CATALOGUE?
These often provide answers to the enquiries we receive.

1985. Flowering Cacti. Multicoloured.
797. 50 x. Type **167** 5 5
798. 50 x. "Lemaireocereus thurberi" 5 5
799. 1 d. "Notocactus haselbergii" 5 5
800. 2 d. "Parodia chrysacanthion" 5 5
801. 3 d. "Pelecyphora pseudopectinata" 5 5
802. 5 d. "Revutia frebrighii" 8 5
803. 8 d. "Lobivia aurea" .. 10 5

168. Nguyen Ai Quoc (founder).

169. Soldiers with Weapons.

1985. 55th Anniv. of Vietnam Communist Party.
804. **168.** 2 d. grey and red .. 5 5

1985. 10th Anniv. of Liberation of South Vietnam. Multicoloured.
805. 1 d. Type **169** 5 5
806. 2 d. Soldiers and tank .. 5 5
807. 4 d. Soldier and oil rig .. 8 5
808. 5 d. Map, flag and girls .. 8 5

170. Long Chau Lighthouse.

1985. 30th Anniv. of Liberation of Haiphong.
810. **170.** 2 d. multicoloured .. 10 10
811. – 5 d. multicoloured .. 15 10
DESIGN: 5 d. An Duong bridge.

171. Ho Chi Minh and Soldiers.

1985. 95th Birth Anniv. of Ho Chi Minh (former President). Multicoloured.
813. 1 d. Type **171** 5 5
814. 2 d. Ho Chi Minh reading 5 5
815. 4 d. Portrait (vert.) .. 8 5
816. 5 d. Ho Chi Minh writing 8 5

172. Soviet Memorial, Berlin-Treptow.

173. Globe and People carrying Flags.

1985. 40th Anniv. of Victory in Europe Day. Multicoloured.
818. 1 d. Type **172** 5 5
819. 2 d. Soldier and fist breaking swastika .. 5 5
820. 4 d. Hand releasing dove and eagle falling .. 8 5
821. 5 d. Girl releasing doves .. 8 5

1985. 12th World Youth and Students' Festival, Moscow. Multicoloured.
823. 2 d. Type **173** 5 5
824. 2 d. Workers, pylons and dish aerial 5 5
825. 4 d. Sailor, soldier and lighthouse 8 5
826. 5 d. Youths and balloons 8 5

174. Daimler, 1885.

1985. Centenary of Motor Cycle. Mult.
828. 1 d. Type **174** (wrongly insc. "1895") 5 5
829. 1 d. Three-wheeled vehicle, France, 1898 .. .. 5 5
830. 2 d. Harley Davidson, U.S.A., 1913 .. .. 5 5
831. 2 d. Cleveland, U.S.A., 1918 5 5
832. 3 d. Simplex, U.S.A., 1935 5 5
833. 4 d. Minarelli, Italy, 1984 8 5
834. 6 d. Honda, Japan, 1984 .. 10 5

175. King Penguin.

1985. "Argentina '85" International Stamp Exhibition, Buenos Aires. Multicoloured.
836. 1 d. Type **175** 35 10
837. 1 d. Patagonian cavy .. 5 5
838. 2 d. Capybara (horiz.) .. 5 5
839. 2 d. Leopard (horiz.) .. 5 5
840. 3 d. Lesser rhea 45 10
841. 4 d. Giant armadillo (horiz.) 8 5
842. 6 d. Andean condor (horiz.) 60 15

176. "Holothuria monacaria".

1985. Marine Life. Multicoloured.
844. 3 d. Type **176** 5 5
845. 3 d. "Stichopus chloronotus" 5 5
846. 3 d. "Luidia maculata" .. 5 5
847. 3 d. "Nadoa tuberculata" 5 5
848. 4 d. "Astropyga radiata" 8 5
849. 4 d. "Linckia laevigata" .. 8 5
850. 4 d. "Astropecten scoparius" 8 5

177. Flag and Sickle "40".

178. Globe, Transport and People around Postman.

1985. 40th Anniv. of Socialist Republic. Multicoloured.
851. 2 d. Type **177** 5 5
852. 3 d. Doves around globe as heart above handclasp .. 5 5
853. 5 d. Banner 8 5
854. 10 d. Ho Chi Minh, flag and laurel branch 12 5

1985. 40th Anniv. of Postal and Telecommunications Service. Multicoloured.
856. 2 d. Type **178** 10 10
857. 2 d. Telephonist and telegraph operator 10 10
858. 4 d. Soldiers and postwoman Nguyen Thi Nghia 10 10
859. 5 d. Dish aerial 10 10

179. Profile of Ho Chi Minh and Policeman.

1985. 40th Anniv. of People's Police.
860. **179.** 10 d. orange and black .. 12 5

180. Gymnasts.

1985. 1st National Sports and Gymnastics Games. Multicoloured.
862. 5 d. Type **180** 8 5
863. 10 d. Badminton player, gymnast, athlete and swimmer 12 5

181. Oil Rig, Derrick and Helicopter.

1985. 30th Anniv. of Geological Service.
864. **181.** 1 d. blue and purple .. 15 10
865. – 1 d. green and brown .. 15 10
DESIGN: No. 865, Airplane over coastline.

182. Alfa Romeo, 1922.

1985. "Italia '85" International Stamp Exhibition, Rome. Motor Cars. Mult.
866. 1 d. Type **182** 5 5
867. 1 d. Bianchi "Berlina", 1932 .. .. .. 5 5
868. 2 d. Isotta Fraschini, 1928 5 5
869. 2 d. Bugatti, 1930 .. .. 5 5
870. 3 d. Itala, 1912 .. .. 5 5
871. 4 d. Lancia "Augusta", 1934 .. .. .. 8 5
872. 6 d. Fiat, 1927 .. .. 10 5

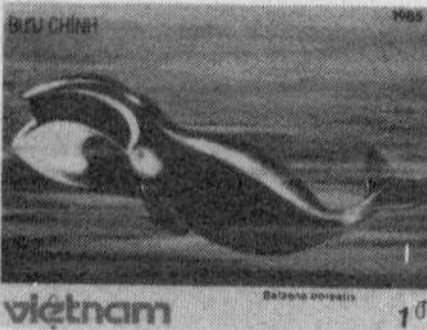

183. Sei Whale.

1985. Marine Mammals. Multicoloured.
874. 1 d. Type **183** 5 5
875. 1 d. Blue whale 5 5
876. 2 d. Killer whale 5 5
877. 2 d. Common dolphin .. 5 5
878. 3 d. Humpback whale .. 5 5
879. 4 d. Fin whale 8 5
880. 6 d. Black right whale .. 10 5

184. Goalkeeper attempting to save Ball.

1985. World Cup Football Championship, Mexico (1986) (1st issue). Various footballing scenes. Multicoloured.
881. **184.** 1 d. multicoloured .. 5 5
882. – 1 d. multicoloured .. 5 5
883. – 2 d. multicoloured .. 5 5
884. – 2 d. mult. (vert.) .. 5 5
885. – 3 d. mult. (vert.) .. 5 5
886. – 4 d. mult. (vert.) .. 8 5
887. – 6 d. mult. (vert.) .. 10 5
See also Nos. 912/8.

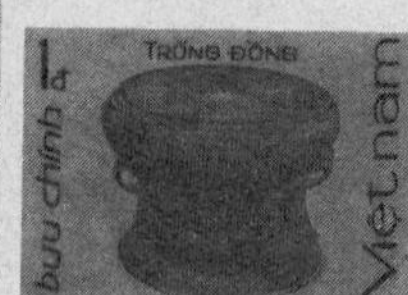

185. Laotian Girl and Dove. **186.** Decorated Drum.

1985. 10th Anniv. of Laos People's Democratic Republic. Multicoloured.
889. 1 d. Type **185** .. 5 5
890. 1 d. Laotian girl and arms 5 5

1985. Traditional Musical Instruments. Multicoloured
891. 1 d. Type **186** 5 5
892. 1 d. Xylophone 5 5
893. 2 d. Double-ended drum .. 5 5
894. 2 d. Flutes 5 5
895. 3 d. Single-stringed instrument 5 5
896. 4 d. Four-stringed instrument 8 5
897. 4 d. Double-stringed instrument with bow .. 10 5

187. "Reuth" Steam Locomotive, 1840.

1985. 150th Anniv. of German Railways. Multicoloured.
898 1 d. Type **187** 20 5
899 1 d. Steam tank locomotive, 1990 .. .. 20 5
900 2 d. Locomotive "Der Adler", 1835 .. .. 35 8
901 2 d. Passenger locomotive, 1850 .. .. .. 35 8
902 3 d. Steam locomotive No. 2024, 1910 .. .. 50 12
903 4 d. Tank locomotive, 1920 70 15
904 6 d. Bavarian State locomotive No. 659, 1890 .. 1·00 30

188. Agriculture. **189.** Hands, Emblem and Dove.

1985. 40th Anniv of Independence.
906 10 d. Type **188** .. .. 5·00 2·50
907 10 d. Industry .. .. 5·00 2·50
908 20 d. Health care .. 10·00 5·00
909 30 d. Education .. .. 15·00 7·50

1985. 40th Anniv. of U.N.O.
910. **189.** 1 d. multicoloured .. 5 5

190. Ho Chi Minh, Map, Line of Voters and Ballot Box.  **191.** Isaac Newton.

1986. 40th Anniv. of First Assembly Elections.
911. **190.** 50 x. mauve and black 5 5
912. 1 d. orange and black 5 5

1986. Appearance of Halley's Comet.
913 2 d. Type **191** 35 15
914 2 d. Edmond Halley .. 35 15
915 3 d. Launch of "Vega" space probe and flags .. 50 25
916 5 d. Comet and planet .. 85 40

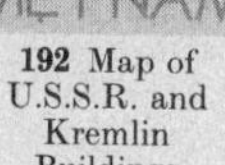

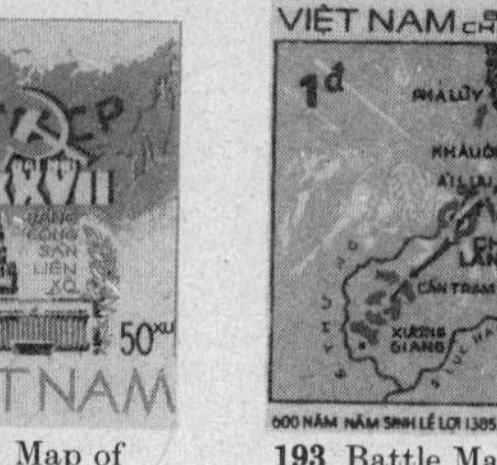

192 Map of U.S.S.R. and Kremlin Buildings **193** Battle Map

1986. 27th Communist Party Congress, Moscow. Multicoloured.
917 50 x. Type **192** 5 5
918 1 d. Lenin on flag, transport, industrial and scientific motifs .. 5 5

1986. 600th Anniv. of Battle of Xuong Giang.
919 **193** 1 d. multicoloured .. 5 5

194 Footballer

1986. World Cup Football Championship, Mexico (2nd issue). Multicoloured.
920 1 d. Type **194** 5 5
921 1 d. Two players 5 5
922 2 d. Player heading ball .. 5 5
923 3 d. Player tackling .. 5 5
924 3 d. Two players chasing ball 5 5
925 5 d. Footballer (different) 8 5
926 5 d. Two players (different) 8 5

195 Konstantin Tsiolkovski and "Sputnik I"

1986. 25th Anniv. of First Man in Space. Multicoloured.
928 1 d. Type **195** 5 5
929 1 d. Rocket on launch vehicle, Baikanur cosmodrome 5 5
930 2 d. Yuri Gagarin and "Vostok I" 5 5
931 3 d. Valentina Tereshkova and "Vostok VI" on launch vehicle (vert) .. 5 5
932 3 d. Cosmonaut Leonov and cosmonaut on space walk 5 5
933 5 d "Soyuz"–"Apollo" link and astronauts .. 8 5
934 5 d. "Salyut"–"Soyuz" link and cosmonauts .. 8 5

196 Thalmann and Flag

1986. Birth Centenary of Ernst Thalmann (German Communist leader).
936 **196** 2 d. red and brown .. 5 5

197 Flag, Hammer and Glove in Sickle

1986. Centenary of May Day.
937 **197** 1 d. red and blue .. 5 5
938 5 d. red and brown .. 8 5

198 Hawker Hart

1986. "Expo '86" World's Fair, Vancouver. Historic Aircraft. Multicoloured.
939 1 d. Type **198** 10 10
940 1 d. Curtiss-Jenny .. 10 10
941 2 d. PZL.P23 .. .. 10 10
942 3 d. Yak-11 .. .. 10 10
943 3 d. Fokker "Dr.1" .. 10 10
944 5 d. Boeing "P-12", 1920 .. 20 10
945 5 d. ND.29C1, 1929 .. 20 10

199 Black and White Cat

1986. Cats. Multicoloured.
946 1 d. Type **199** 5 5
947 1 d. Grey and white cat .. 5 5
948 2 d. White cat 5 5
949 3 d. Brown-faced cat .. 5 5
950 3 d. Beige cat 5 5
951 5 d. Black-faced cat (vert) 8 5
952 5 d. Beige and cream cat 8 5

200 Ho Chi Minh and People working on Barriers

1986. 40th Anniv. of Foundation of Committee for Protection of Flood Barriers.
953 **200** 1 d. red and brown .. 5 5

201 Thai Den House

1986. Traditional Architecture. Mult.
954 1 d. Type **201** 5 5
955 1 d. Nung house 5 5
956 2 d. Thai Trang house .. 5 5
957 3 d. Tay house 5 5
958 3 d. H'mong house .. 5 5
959 5 d. Dao house 8 5
960 5 d. Tay Nguyen house (vert) 8 5

202 European Bee Eater **203** Plymouth Rock Cock

1986. "Stockholmia 86" International Stamp Exhibition. Birds. Multicoloured.
962 1 d. Type **202** 15 10
963 1 d. Green magpie .. 15 10
964 2 d. Shrike babbler .. 15 10
965 3 d. White-crested laughing thrush 15 10
966 3 d. Long-tailed broadbill (horiz) 15 10
967 5 d. Pied wagtail 20 10
968 5 d. Azure-winged magpie (horiz) 20 10

1986. Domestic Fowl. Multicoloured.
970 1 d. Type **203** 5 5
971 1 d. Common turkey .. 5 5
972 2 d. Rhode Island Red cock 5 5
973 2 d. White Plymouth Rock cock 5 5
974 3 d. Rhode Island Red hen 5 5
975 3 d. White Leghorn cock 5 5
976 3 d. Rhode Island Red cock (different) .. 5 5
977 5 d. Barred Plymouth Rock cock 8 5

204 Emblem

1986. 11th World Federation of Trades Union Congress, Berlin.
978 **204** 1 d. blue and red .. 5 5

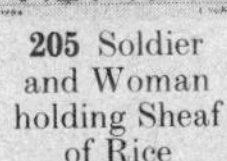

205 Soldier and Woman holding Sheaf of Rice

206 Woman-shaped Sword Handle

1986.
979 **205** 1 d. brown and black .. 5 5

1986. Historic Bronzes Excavated at Mt. Do. Multicoloured.
980 1 d. Type **206** 5 5
981 1 d. Seated figure with man on back 5 5
982 2 d. Saddle pommel (horiz) 5 5
983 3 d. Shoe-shaped hoe (horiz) 5 5
984 3 d. Bowl (horiz) 5 5
985 5 d. Vase (horiz) 8 5
986 5 d. Pot with lid (horiz) .. 8 5

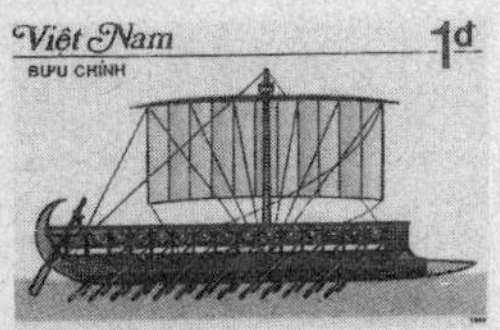

207 Greek Bireme

1986. Sailing Ships. Multicoloured.
988 1 d. Type **207** 20 10
989 1 d. Viking longship .. 20 10
990 2 d. Medieval kogge (36 × 46 mm) 20 10
991 3 d. Greek cargo galley .. 20 10
992 3 d. Phoenician war galley with ram 20 10
993 5 d. Ancient Mediterranean cargo ship 20 10
994 5 d. Roman trireme .. 20 10

208 Hands cupping Red Cross in Flower

1986. 40th Anniv. of Vietnamese Red Cross.
995 **208** 3 d. mauve and blue .. 5 5

MORE DETAILED LISTS
are given in the Stanley Gibbons Catalogues referred to in the country headings.
For lists of current volumes see Introduction.

209 "Catopsilia scylla"

1986. Butterflies. Multicoloured.
996 1 d. Type **209** 15 12
997 1 d. "Euploea midamus" 15 12
998 2 d. "Appias nero" .. 15 12
999 3 d. "Papilio polytes stichius" 15 12
1000 3 d. "Danaus chrysippus" 15 12
1001 5 d. 'Charaxes polyxena" 30 12
1002 5 d. "Euploea diocletianus" 30 12

210 Red Flag and Symbols of Industry and Agriculture

1986. 6th Vietnamese Communist Party Congress. Multicoloured.
1003 1 d. Type **210** 5 5
1004 2 d. Red flag and weapons 5 5
1005 4 d. Red flag and Ho Chi Minh 5 5
1006 5 d. Red flag and symbols of peace 8 5

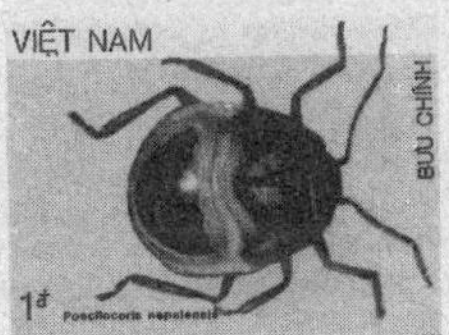

211 "Poecilocoris nepalensis"

1986. Insects. Multicoloured.
1008 1 d. Type **211** 10 10
1009 1 d. "Bombus americanorum" (bee) 10 10
1010 2 d. "Romalea microptera" (beetle) 10 10
1011 3 d. "Chalcocoris rutilans" (beetle) 15 10
1012 3 d. "Chrysocoris sellatus" (beetle) 15 10
1013 5 d. "Crocisa crucifera" (fly) 25 10
1014 5 d. "Paranthrene palmii" (moth) 25 10

212 Dove and Emblem

213 "Ficus glomerata"

1986. International Peace Year.
1015 **212** 1 d. green and black 5 5
1016 3 d. pink and black 5 5

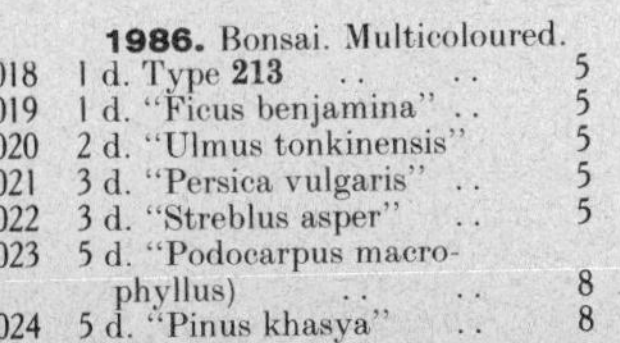
1986. Bonsai. Multicoloured.
1018 1 d. Type **213** 5 5
1019 1 d. "Ficus benjamina" .. 5 5
1020 2 d. "Ulmus tonkinensis" 5 5
1021 3 d. "Persica vulgaris" .. 5 5
1022 3 d. "Streblus asper" .. 5 5
1023 5 d. "Podocarpus macrophyllus) 8 5
1024 5 d. "Pinus khasya" .. 8 5

214 Basket

1986. Basketry and Wickerwork. Mult.
1026 1 d. Type **214** 5 5
1027 1 d. Tall basket with lid and handles 5 5
1028 2 d. Stool 5 5
1029 3 d. Handbag 5 5
1030 3 d. Dish 5 5
1031 5 d. Tall basket for carrying on back 8 5
1032 5 d. Square basket with star-shaped foot .. 8 5

215 Soldiers and Women

216 "Fokienia hodginsii"

1986. 40th Anniv. of National Resistance.
1034 **215** 2 d. brown and green 5 5

1986. Fruits of Conifers. Multicoloured.
1035 1 d. Type **216** 5 5
1036 1 d. "Amentotaxus yunnanensis" .. 5 5
1037 2 d. "Pinus kwangtungensis" .. 5 5
1038 3 d. "Cupressus torulosa" 5 5
1039 3 d. "Taxus chinensis" .. 5 5
1040 5 d. "Tsuga yunnanensis" 8 5
1041 5 d. "Ducampopinus krempfii" 8 5

217 Mother and Calf

1986. Elephants.
1043 1 d. Type **217** 5 5
1044 1 d. Two elephants .. 5 5
1045 3 d. Elephant (vert) .. 5 5
1046 3 d. Elephant feeding .. 5 5
1047 5 d. Working elephant (vert) 8 5
1048 5 d. Elephants by water (68 × 27 mm) 8 5

218 Girl watering Tree

219 Young Girl

1987. New Year. Year of the Cat.
1049 **218** 3 d. brown and mauve 5 5

1987. "Son Tinh-Thuy Tinh" (folk tale). Multicoloured.
1050 3 d. Type **219** 10 10
1051 3 d. Young man bearing gift and leading horse 10 10
1052 3 d. Elephants carrying materials for flood barrier 10 10
1053 3 d. Men working against flood through the night 10 10
1054 3 d. Men felling trees .. 10 10
1055 3 d. Pounding rice .. 10 10
1056 3 d. Canoes bringing fruit and grain to store .. 10 10
1057 3 d. Canoe 10 10
Nos. 1050/7 were printed together, se-tenant, forming a composite design.

220 "Nymphaea lotus"

222 Temple, Da Nang

221 National Liberation Army attacking Building (August 1945)

1987. Water Lilies. Multicoloured.
1058 5 d. Type **220** 10 5
1059 10 d. "Nymphaea nouchali" 20 10
1060 10 d. "Nymphaea pubescens" 20 10
1061 20 d. "Nymphaea rubra" 40 20
1062 20 d. "Nymphaea gigantea" 40 20
1063 30 d. "Nymphaea laydekeri" 55 20
1064 50 d. "Nymphaea capensis" 85 40

1987. 8th National Assembly. Multicoloured.
1065 10 d. Type **221** 20 10
1066 20 d. Proclamation of Democratic Republic (Sept 1945) 40 20
1067 30 d. Fall of Dien Bien Phu (May 1954) .. 55 20
1068 50 d. Tank entering Saigon (April 1975) .. 85 40

1987. Cham Culture. Multicoloured.
1069 3 d. Type **222** 5 5
1070 10 d. Temple, Phu Khanh 20 10
1071 15 d. Temple, Da Nang (different) 30 15
1072 20 d. Figure of dancer, Nghia Binh 40 20
1073 25 d. Bust, Da Nang .. 45 20
1074 30 d. Woman playing flute (statuette), Nghia Binh 55 20
1075 40 d. Figure of dancer on capital, Da Nang .. 75 35

223 Hanoi

1987. Tourism. Multicoloured.
1077 5 d. Type **223** 10 5
1078 10 d. Hai Phong 20 10
1079 15 d. Pagoda, Mu Hue .. 30 15
1080 20 d. Da Nang 40 20
1081 25 d. Nha Trang .. 45 20
1082 30 d. Waterfall, Da Lat .. 55 20
1083 40 d. Ho Chi Minh City .. 75 35

224 Cactus

226 Man from Bana

225 People on Globe

1987. Cacti. Showing various flowering cacti. Multicoloured.

1085 **224** 5 d. multicoloured .. 10 5
1086 10 d. multicoloured .. 20 10
1087 15 d. multicoloured .. 30 15
1088 20 d. multicoloured .. 40 20
1089 25 d. multicoloured .. 45 20
1090 30 d. multicoloured .. 55 20
1091 40 d. muticoloured .. 75 35
DESIGNS: 10 to 40 d. Various flowering cacti.

1987. Day of Five Billion Inhabitants of Earth.

1093 **225** 5 d. mauve and blue 10 5

1987. Costumes. Multicoloured.

1094 5 d. Type **226** 10 5
1095 20 d. Woman from Bana 40 20
1096 20 d. Woman from Gia Rai 40 20
1097 30 d. Man from Gia Rai 55 20
1098 30 d. Man from Ede .. 55 20
1099 40 d. Woman from Ede .. 75 35

227 Silhouettes of Soldiers and Disabled Soldier

228 Rose

1987. 40th Anniv of Association of Disabled Soldiers Association.

1100 **227** 5 d. red and violet .. 10 5

1987. Roses. Showing various roses.

1101 **228** 5 d. multicoloured .. 10 5
1102 – 10 d. multicoloured .. 20 10
1103 – 15 d. multicoloured .. 30 15
1104 – 20 d. multicoloured .. 40 20
1105 – 25 d. multicoloured .. 45 20
1106 – 30 d. multicoloured .. 55 20
1107 – 40 d. multicoloured .. 75 35
DESIGNS: 10 to 40 d. Various roses.

229 Postwoman and Mail Transport

1987. 40th Anniv of Postal Trade Union.

1109 **229** 5 d. black and red .. 15 10
1110 – 30 d. black and green 55 20
DESIGNS: 30 d. Linesman, dish aerial and telephonist.

230 Siamese Fighting Fish

1987. Fishes. Multicoloured.

1111 5 d. Type **230** 10 5
1112 10 d. Red-tailed black labeo 20 10
1113 15 d. "Puntis tetrazona" 30 15
1114 20 d. Pearl danio .. 40 20
1115 25 d. "Puntis conchonius" 45 20
1116 30 d. Siamese fighting fish (different) 55 20
1117 40 d. "Botia lecontei" .. 75 35

231 Emblem

1987. International Year of Shelter for the Homeless.

1118 **231** 5 d. black and blue .. 10 5

232 Armed Forces Personnel and Flag

1987.

1119 **232** 5 d. red and brown .. 10 5

233 Crested Gibbons

235 Industrial and Agricultural Symbols

234 "Musicians"

1987. Monkeys. Multicoloured.

1120 5 d. Type **233** 10 5
1121 5 d. Variegated langurs .. 10 5
1122 15 d. Crested gibbon (different) 30 15
1123 40 d. Variegated langur (different) 75 35

1987. Paintings by Picasso. Multicoloured.

1124 3 d. Type **234** 5 5
1125 20 d. Horse-drawn wagon 40 20
1126 20 d. Winged horse on shore 40 20
1127 30 d. "Child with Dove" (vert) 55 20
1128 30 d. "Gertrude Stein" (vert) 55 20
1129 40 d. "Guernica" (44 × 27 mm) 75 35

1987. 70th Anniv of Russian Revolution. Multicoloured.

1131 5 d. Type **235** 10 5
1132 20 d. Soviet Memorial, Berlin-Treptow, "Aurora" and Lenin .. 40 20
1133 30 d. "70" and symbols of progress 55 20
1134 50 d. Ho Chi Minh and building 85 40

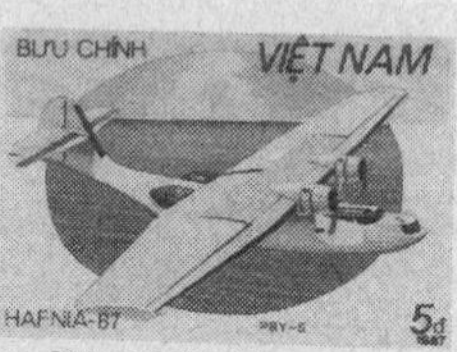

236 PBY-5 Flying Boat

1987. "Hafnia 87" International Stamp Exhibition, Copenhagen. Flying Boats and Seaplanes. Multicoloured.

1136 5 d. Type **236** 15 10
1137 10 d. L.O-246 flying boat 25 10
1138 15 d. DO-18 flying boat .. 40 15
1139 20 d. Short Sunderland flying boat 50 20
1140 25 d. 1923 seaplane .. 60 20
1141 30 d. ARK-3 flying boat 70 20
1142 40 d. Cant Z.509 seaplanes 1·00 40

237 "Epanouis"

1987. Corals. Multicoloured.

1144 5 d. Type **237** 10 5
1145 10 d. "Acropora" 20 10
1146 15 d. "Rhizopsammia" .. 30 15
1147 20 d. "Acropora" (diff) .. 40 20
1148 25 d. "Alcyone" 45 20
1149 30 d. "Corollum" 55 20
1150 40 d. "Cristatella" 75 35

238 Doves as Clasped Hands forming Heart

1987. 5th Anniv of Vietnam–Czechoslovak Friendship Treaty. Each blue, yellow and red.

1151 10 d. Type **238** 20 10
1152 50 d. Flags and buildings 85 40

239 Symbols of Industry and Agriculture

1987. Soviet–Vietnam Friendship Treaty. Each red, brown and yellow.

1153 5 d. Type **239** 10 5
1154 50 d. National emblems and buildings 85 40

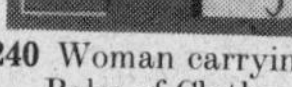

240 Woman carrying Bales of Cloth

242 "Polyporellus squamosus"

241 Coloured Circles

1987. 6th Party Congress Decisions.

1155 **240** 5 d. green and brown 10 5
1156 – 20 d. orange & brown 40 20
1157 – 30 d. violet and blue 55 20
DESIGNS: 20 d. Tractor driver; 30 d. Loading crate on freighter.

1987. Peace.

1158 **241** 10 d. multicoloured .. 20 10

1987. Fungi. Multicoloured.

1159 5 d. Type **242** 10 5
1160 10 d. "Clitocybe geotropa" 20 10
1161 15 d. "Tricholoma terreum" 30 15
1162 20 d. "Russula aurata" .. 40 20
1163 25 d. "Collybia fusipes" .. 45 20
1164 30 d. "Cortinarius violaceus" 55 20
1165 40 d. "Boletus aereus" .. 75 35

243 Dove on Open Hands

1987. 30th Anniv of Africa–Asia Co-operation Committee.

1166 **243** 10 d. blue, blk & yell 20 10
1167 – 30 d. black, brn & yell 55 20
DESIGNS: VERT—Hands and map.

244 Wrecked Bomber and Girl watering Flowers

1987. 15th Anniv of of U.S. Air Bombardment of Vietnam.

1168 **244** 10 d. black and yellow 30 10
1169 – 30 d. black & orange 55 20
DESIGNS: 30 d. Young Pioneers and weapons.

245 Junk, Man blowing Horn and Map

1988. Paracel and Spratley Islands.

1170 **245** 10 d. blk, red & pink 30 15
1171 – 100 d. lt brown, black and brown .. 2·75 1·40
DESIGN: 100 d. Maps showing Paracel Islands.

246 Anniversary Emblem and Dove

248 Oil Rig Platform

247 Fleet

1988. 125th Anniv of International Red Cross.

1172 **246** 10 d. red, black & blue 5 5

1988. 700th Anniv of Battle of Bach Dang River.

1173 **247** 80 d. blk, pink & red 40 15
1174 – 200 d. multicoloured 2·10 60
DESIGN: 200 d. Battle scene.

1988. Oil Industry.

1175 **248** 1000 d. black, bl & red 6·25 1·75

249 Blue and Yellow Macaw **250** Map

1988. Parrots. Multicoloured.

1176 10 d. Type **249** 40 20
1177 10 d. Slaty-headed parakeet 40 20
1178 20 d. Red-winged parrot 90 35
1179 20 d. Green-winged macaw 90 35
1180 30 d. Moustached parakeet .. .. 1·50 65
1181 30 d. Military macaw .. 1·50 65
1182 50 d. Vernal hanging parrot .. .. .. 2·75 85

1988. 33rd Council for Mutual Economic Assistance Meeting and 10th Anniv of Vietnam's Membership.

1184 **250** 200 d. multicoloured 80 20
1185 – 300 d. blue and bistre 1·25 35

DESIGN: 300 d. Headquarters building, Moscow.

251 Child and Syringe **252** Emblem and Building

1988. Child Vaccination Campaign.

1186 **251** 60 d. orange, blk & bl 60 30

1988. 30th Anniv of "Peace and Socialism" (magazine).

1187 **252** 20 d. multicoloured .. 45 20

253 Ton Duc Thang **254** Emblem

1988. Birth Centenary of Ton Duc Thang (politician).

1188 **253** 150 d. multicoloured .. 1·40 60

1988. 6th Trade Unions Congress. Mult.

1189 50 d. Type **254** 65 30
1190 100 d. "VI" and couple 1·40 60

255 Family

1988. Children's Drawings. Multicoloured.

1191 10 d. Type **255** 20 10
1192 10 d. Couple and house (Phuong Ti) 20 10
1193 20 d. Fishermen (Lam Hoang Thang) .. 50 15
1194 20 d. Children flying kite (Nguyen Xuan Anh) .. 50 15
1195 30 d. Couple (Hong Hanh) (vert) 80 25
1196 30 d. Animals and girl playing guitar (Quynh May) 80 25
1197 50 d. Woman holding dove (Ta Phuong Tra) (vert) .. .. .. 1·25 35

256 Tri An

1988. U.S.S.R.–Vietnam Co-operation. Hydro-electric Power Stations.

1199 **256** 2000 d. blk, orge & red 4·00 1·50
1200 — 3000 d. black, bistre and red .. .. 6·00 2·50

DESIGN: 3000 d. Hoa Binh.

257 Kamov "KA-26"

1988. Helicopters. Multicoloured.

1201 10 d. Type **257** 25 10
1202 10 d. Boeing "Chinook" 25 10
1203 20 d. MBB "BO 105" .. 55 15
1204 20 d. MIL "MI-10 (V-10)" 55 15
1205 30 d. Kawasaki-Hughes "369 HS" 95 30
1206 30 d. Bell "Jetranger" .. 95 30
1207 50 d. MIL "MI-8" .. 1·50 40

258 Gaur **259** Flower and Banners

1988. Animals. Multicoloured.

1209 10 d. Type **258** 20 10
1210 10 d. Banteng 20 10
1211 20 d. Malayan tapir .. 45 15
1212 20 d. Hog deer 45 15
1213 30 d. Mainland serow .. 75 25
1214 30 d. Wild boar 75 25
1215 50 d. Water buffalo .. 1·25 35

1988. 10th Anniv of U.S.S.R.–Vietnam Friendship.

1217 **259** 50 d. multicoloured .. 45 20

260 Indian Star Tortoise **261** Skaters

1988. Turtles and Tortoises.

1218 10 d. Type **260** 20 20
1219 10 d. Three-banded box turtle 20 10
1220 20 d. Big-headed turtle .. 45 15
1221 20 d. Hawksbill turtle .. 45 15
1222 30 d. Indian Ocean green turtle 75 25
1223 30 d. Leatherback turtle 75 25
1224 50 d. Loggerhead turtle 1·25 35

1988. Ice Skating. Multicoloured.

1226 **261** 10 d. multicoloured .. 20 10
1227 – 10 d. multicoloured .. 20 10
1228 – 20 d. multicoloured .. 45 15
1229 – 20 d. mult (horiz) .. 45 15
1230 – 30 d. multicoloured .. 75 25
1231 – 30 d. mult (horiz) .. 75 25
1232 – 50 d. mult (horiz) .. 1·25 35

DESIGNS: Nos. 1227/32 Different skating scenes.

262 Pointed-scaled Pit Viper

1988. Snakes. Multicoloured.

1234 10 d. Type **262** 20 10
1235 10 d. Pope's pit viper .. 20 10
1236 20 d. Banded krait .. 45 15
1237 20 d. Malayan krait .. 45 15
1238 30 d. Coral snake .. 75 25
1239 30 d. Striped beaked snake 75 25
1240 50 d. King cobra (vert) .. 1·25 35

263 Bowden "Spacelander" **264** Fidel Castro

1988. Bicycles. Multicoloured.

1241 10 d. Type **263** 20 10
1242 10 d. Rabasa Derbi with red tyres 20 10
1243 20 d. Huffy 45 15
1244 20 d. Rabasa Derbi with black tyres 45 15
1245 30 d. VMX-PL 75 25
1246 30 d. Premier 75 25
1247 50 d. Columbia RX5 .. 1·25 35

1988. 30th Anniv of Cuban Revolution. Mult.

1248 100 d. Type **264** 25 5
1249 300 d. National flags and Cuban and Vietnamese workers 55 10

265 Cosmonauts on Spacecraft Wing

1988. Cosmonauts Day. Multicoloured.

1250 10 d. Type **265** 20 10
1251 10 d. Spacecraft moving across surface of planet 20 10
1252 20 d. Space rocket heading for planet .. 45 15
1253 20 d. Spacecraft and cosmonauts on planet with Earth in sky .. 45 15
1254 30 d. Spacecraft hovering over surface 75 25
1255 30 d. "Soyuz"-"Salyut" complex 75 25
1256 50 d. Space "bubble" and rocket .. .. .. 1·25 35

266 "Conus miles"

1988. Sea Shells. Multicoloured.

1258 10 d. Type **266** 20 10
1259 10 d. "Strombus lentiginosus" 20 10
1260 20 d. "Bursa rana" .. 50 15
1261 20 d. Turban shell .. 50 15
1262 30 d. "Oliva erythrostoma" 80 25
1263 30 d. "Nautilus" 80 25
1264 50 d. "Mitra episcopalis" (wrongly inscr "eriscopalis") .. .. 1·25 35

The inscriptions on Nos. 1261 and 1263 have been transposed.

267 Class "VL85" Locomotive, U.S.S.R.

1988. Electric Locomotives. Multicoloured.

1266 20 d. Type **267** 45 15
1267 20 d. LRC, Canada .. 45 15
1268 20 d. Monorail, Japan .. 45 15
1269 20 d. KIHA 80, Japan .. 45 15
1270 30 d. Class "DR 1A", U.S.S.R. 75 20
1271 30 d. Class "RC 1" .. 75 20
1272 50 d. Class "TE-136", U.S.S.R. .. .. 1·25 50

268 Gourd

1988. Fruits. Multicoloured.

1274 10 d. Type **268** 20 10
1275 10 d. "Momordica charantia" 20 10
1276 20 d. Pumpkin 50 15
1277 20 d. Eggplant 50 15
1278 30 d. "Benincasa hispida" 80 25
1279 30 d. Luffa gourd .. 80 25
1280 50 d. Tomatoes .. .. 1·25 35

269 Soldiers and Field Workers

1989. 10th Anniv of People's Republic of Kampuchea. Multicoloured.

1281 100 d. Type **269** 25 5
1282 500 d. Crowd greeting soldier and mother with child .. .. .. 1·00 20

270 "Junonia evarete"

1989 "India-89" International Stamp Exhibition, New Delhi (1st issue). Butterflies. Multicoloured.

1283 50 d. Type **270** 25 15
1284 50 d. "Anaea echemus" .. 25 15
1285 50 d. "Ascia monuste" .. 25 15
1286 100 d. "Phoebis avellaneda" 70 25
1287 100 d. "Eurema proterpia" 70 25
1288 200 d. "Papilio palamedes" .. .. 1·10 55
1289 300 d. "Danaus plexippus" .. .. 2·00 70

See also Nos. 1291/4.

271 Flag and Telecommunications **273** Emblems on Banner

272 Festival

1989. "India-89" International Stamp Exhibition, New Delhi (2nd issue).

1291 **271** 100 d. multicoloured .. 20 5
1292 – 100 d. multicoloured .. 20 5
1293 – 300 d. multicoloured .. 70 15
1294 – 600 d. brn, orge & grn 1·25 40

DESIGNS: 100 d. (No. 1292), Oil and electricity industries; 300 d. Government Secretariat and Asokan capital; 600 d. Jawaharlal Nehru (Indian statesman, birth centenary).

1989. Bicentenary of Battle of Dongda.

1295 **272** 100 d. violet and green 25 5
1296 – 1000 d. mauve and red 2·10 65

DESIGN: 1000 d. Battle scene.

1989. Cent of Interparliamentary Union.

1297 **273** 100 d. multicoloured 30 5
1298 – 200 d. gold, ultram and blue 60 10

DESIGN: 200 d. "100" on banner.

274 Junk from Quang-Nam

1989 Regional Fishing Junks. Multicoloured.

1299 10 d. Type **274** 30 10
1300 10 d. Quang-Tri 30 10
1301 20 d. Thua-Thien 50 10
1302 20 d. Da-Nang 50 10
1303 30 d. Quang-Tri (different) 90 40
1304 30 d. Da-Nang (different) 90 40
1305 50 d. Hue .. .. 1·50 55

275 Dachshunds

1989. Dogs. Multicoloured.

1306 50 d. Type **275** 15 5
1307 50 d. Basset hounds .. 15 5
1308 50 d. Setter (vert) .. 15 5
1309 100 d. Hunting dog (vert) 40 10
1310 100 d. Basset hounds (66 × 25 mm) 40 10
1311 200 d. Hound (vert) .. 75 20
1312 300 d. Basset hound puppy .. .. 1·40 35

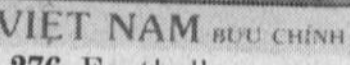

276 Footballers

277 Jug

1989. World Cup Football Championship, Italy (1st issue). Multicoloured.

1313 50 d. Type **276** 15 5
1314 50 d. Striker and goal-keeper 15 5
1315 50 d. Goalkeeper .. 15 5
1316 100 d. Player No. 5 tackling 40 10
1317 100 d. Tackling (vert) .. 40 10
1318 200 d. Player No. 3 (vert) 80 20
1319 300 d. Players heading ball (vert) .. .. 1·25 35

See also Nos. 1382/8.

1989. Pottery. Multicoloured.

1321 50 d. Type **277** 15 5
1322 100 d. Bowl with geometric pattern .. 40 10
1323 100 d. Round pot with flower decoration .. 40 10
1324 200 d. Tall pot with animal decoration .. 75 20
1325 300 d. Vase .. .. 1·10 30

278 Baby Thanh Giong with Mother

1989. Legend of Thanh Giong. Multicoloured.

1326 50 d. Type **278** 15 5
1327 100 d. Thanh Giong as boy 40 10
1328 100 d. Thanh Giong at head of army .. 40 10
1329 200 d. Thanh Giong beating out flames .. 75 20
1330 300 d. Thanh Giong riding to heaven .. .. 1·10 30

279 Appaloosa

1989. Horses. Multicoloured.

1331 50 d. Type **279** 25 5
1332 50 d. Tennesse walking horse 25 15
1333 50 d. Tersky 25 15
1334 100 d. Kladruber .. 55 30
1335 100 d. Welsh cob .. 55 30
1336 200 d. Pinto 85 50
1337 300 d. Pony and bridle (68 × 27 mm) .. .. 1·50 65

280 "Fuchsia fulgens"

281 Bird carrying Envelope above Dish Aerial

1989. Flowers. Multicoloured.

1338 50 d. Type **280** 10 5
1339 50 d. Bird-of-paradise flower 10 5
1340 100 d. Glory Lily .. 40 10
1341 100 d. Orange day lily .. 40 10
1342 200 d. "Paphiopedilum siamense" 75 20
1343 300 d. "Iris sp." .. .. 1·10 30

On Nos. 1339and 1342 the inscriptions have been transposed.

1989. Communications.

1344 **281** 100 d. brown 40 10

282 Birds

283 "Return from Varennes"

1989. Bicentenary of French Revolution.

(a) As T **282**. Multicoloured.

1345 100 d. Type **282** 20 5
1346 500 d. "Liberty guiding the People" (detail, Eugene Delacroix) .. 75 15

(b) As T **283**

1347 50 d. Type **283** 15 5
1348 50 d. "Revolutionary Court" 15 5
1349 50 d. "Oath of the Tennis Court" (Jacques-Louis David) (vert) 15 5
1350 100 d. "Assassination of Marat" (David) (vert) 35 10
1351 100 d. "Storming the Bastille" (vert) .. 35 10
1352 200 d. Two children (Pierre-Paul Prud'hon) (vert) 80 35
1353 300 d. Models (Jean-Leon Gerome) .. .. 1·40 45

284 Man and Ox

1989. Rice Cultivation. Multicoloured.

1355 50 d. Type **284** 10 5
1356 100 d. Ploughing with ox 30 10
1357 100 d. Flooding fields .. 40 10
1358 200 d. Fertilizing .. 75 20
1359 300 d. Harvesting crop .. 1·10 30

285 Brandenburg Gate, Flag and Emblem

1989. 40th Anniv of German Democratic Republic.

1360 **285** 200 d. yell, blk & mve 85 35

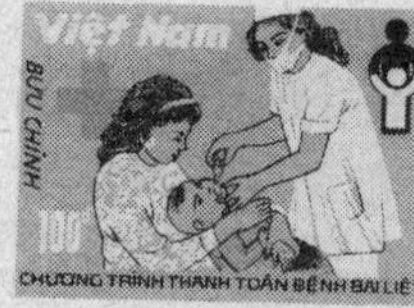

286 Polio Oral Vaccination

1989. Immunization Campaign.

1361 **286** 100 d. brn, blk & red 35 10
1362 – 100 d. pink, blk & grn 35 10
1363 – 100 d. grn, blk & red 35 10

DESIGNS: No. 1362, Vaccinating pregnant woman; 1363, Health clinic.

287 Horse

1989. Paintings of Horses by Hsu Pei-Hung. Multicoloured.

1364 100 d. Type **287** 5 5
1365 200 d. Two horses galloping 10 5
1366 300 d. Three horses grazing 15 5
1367 500 d. Horse galloping (horiz) 25 5
1368 800 d. Galloping horse .. 40 10
1369 1000 d. Two horses under tree 50 15
1370 1500 d. Galloping horse (different) 75 25

288 "Nina", "Pinta" and "Santa Maria" and Mochica Ceramic Figure

1989. Discovery of America by Columbus. Multicoloured.

1372 50 d. Type **288** 10 10
1373 100 d. Columbus and Ferdinand the Catholic and Peruvian ceramic bottle 20 10
1374 100 d. Columbus's arrival at Rabida and Mexican decorated vessel .. 20 10
1375 100 d. Columbus offering gifts (18th-century engraving) and human-shaped jug 20 10
1376 200 d. Early map and Peruvian ceramic .. 40 10
1377 200 d. Portrait and arms of Columbus and Nazca ceramic 40 10
1378 300 d. Chart by Toscanelli and Chimu vessel .. 60 25

289 Tank, Crowd, Hammer and Sickle and Ho Chi Minh

1990. 60th Anniv of Vietnamese Communist Party. Multicoloured.

1380 100 d. Type **289** 10 5
1381 500 d. Industry, workers, hammer and sickle and flag 20 10

290 Players

1990. World Cup Football Championship, Italy (2nd issue). Multicoloured.

1382 100 d. Type **290** 10 5
1383 200 d. Argentina player with possession .. 10 5
1384 300 d. Netherlands and Scotland players .. 15 5
1385 500 d. Soviet Union player tackling 20 10
1386 1000 d. Scotland and West Germany player .. 40 20
1387 2000 d. Soviet Union player losing possession 80 30
1388 3000 d. Goalkeeper .. 1·25 30

291 Hybrids of Mallard and Local Species

1990. Ducks. Multicoloured.

1390 100 d. Type **291** 25 10
1391 300 d. European mallard 25 10
1392 500 d. Mallards 40 10
1393 1000 d. Red-billed pintails 65 20
1394 2000 d. White duck preening 80 30
1395 3000 d. African yellow-bills .. .. .. 1·60 30

292 Mack Truck and Trailer

1990. Trucks. Multicoloured.
1396 100 d. Type **292** 10 5
1397 200 d. Volvo "F89" tipper 15 10
1398 300 d. Tatra "915 S1" tipper 15 10
1399 500 d. Hino "KZ30000" lorry 20 10
1400 1000 d. Italia Iveco 40 20
1401 2000 d. Leyland-Daf "Super Comet" tipper 80 30
1402 3000 d. Kamaz "53212" lorry 1·25 30

293 8th–9th Century Viking Longship

1990. Sailing Ships. Multicoloured.
1403 100 d. Type **293** 10 10
1404 500 d. 15th-century caravel 15 10
1405 1000 d. 15th-century carrack (vert) 30 15
1406 1000 d. 14th–15th-century carrack 30 15
1407 1000 d. 17th-century frigate 30 15
1408 2000 d. 16th-century galleons (vert) 70 25
1409 3000 d. 16th-century galleon 1·10 35

294 Red-bodied Goldfish

1990. Goldfish.
1411 **294** 100 d. multicoloured 10 5
1412 – 300 d. multicoloured 15 10
1413 – 500 d. multicoloured 20 10
1414 – 1000 d. mult (vert) 40 20
1415 – 2000 d. mult (vert) 80 30
1416 – 3000 d. mult (vert) 1·25 30
DESIGNS: 300 d. to 3000 d. Different goldfish.

295 Gate of Noble Mankind

1990. Hu Temples. Multicoloured.
1417 100 d. Type **295** 25 10
1418 100 d. Lotus pool at tomb of Emperor Tu Duc 25 10
1419 200 d. Southern Gate 60 20
1420 300 d. Thien Pagoda 90 30

296 "Antonia Zarate" (Francisco de Goya)

1990. "Stamp World London 90" International Stamp Exhibition. Portraits of women by painters named. Multicoloured.
1422 100 d. Type **296** 10 5
1423 200 d. Auguste Renoir 10 5
1424 300 d. "Janet Grizel" (John Russell) 15 10
1425 500 d. Joshua Reynolds 20 10
1426 1000 d. George Romney (wrongly inscr "Omney") 40 20
1427 2000 d. Vincent van Gogh 80 30
1428 3000 d. Thomas Gainsborough 1·10 30

297 Henry Giffard's Airship, 1851

1990. "Helvetia 90" International Stamp Exhibition, Geneva. Airships. Multicoloured. With or without gum.
1430 100 d. Type **297** 10 10
1431 200 d. Lebandy's airship, 1910 10 10
1432 300 d. "Graf Zeppelin", 1924 15 10
1433 500 d. "R-101", 1930 30 15
1434 1000 d. "Osoaviakhim", 1936 45 30
1435 2000 d. Tissandier's airship, 1883 95 40
1436 3000 d. U.S. Navy airship 1·50 45

298 Silver Tabby and White Cat

1990. Cats. Multicoloured.
1438 100 d. Type **298** 10 5
1439 200 d. Black cat (vert) 10 5
1440 300 d. Black and white cat 15 10
1441 500 d. Brown tabby and white (vert) 25 10
1442 1000 d. Silver tabby 40 20
1443 2000 d. Tortoiseshell and white (vert) 80 30
1444 3000 d. Tortoiseshell tabby and white (vert) 1·25 30

299 Ho Chi Minh, 1923

300 King Charles Spaniel

1990. Birth Cent of Ho Chi Minh. Mult.
1446 100 d. Type **299** 10 5
1447 300 d. Ho Chi Minh, 1945 10 5
1448 500 d. Dove, hand holding rifle, and Ho Chi Minh 20 10
1449 1000 d. Ho Chi Minh conducting 40 20
1450 2000 d. Ho Chi Minh embracing child 80 30
1451 3000 d. Globe and Ho Chi Minh 1·25 30

1990. "New Zealand 90" International Stamp Exhibition, Auckland. Dogs. Mult.
1453 100 d. Type **300** 10 5
1454 200 d. Spaniel 10 5
1455 300 d. Saluki 15 10
1456 500 d. Dachshund 25 10
1457 1000 d. Dalmatian 40 20
1458 2000 d. Highland terrier 80 30
1459 3000 d. Boxer 1·25 30

301 Gorgosaurus

1990. Prehistoric Animals. Multicoloured.
1461 100 d. Type **301** 10 5
1462 500 d. Ceratosaurus 25 10
1463 1000 d. Ankylosaurus 40 20
1464 2000 d. Ankylosaurus (different) 80 30
1465 3000 d. Edaphosaurus 1·25 30

302 High Jumping

303 Golden Mushroom ("Flammulina velutipes")

1990. 11th Asian Games, Peking. Mult.
1466 100 d. Type **302** 10 5
1467 200 d. Basketball 10 5
1468 300 d. Table tennis 15 10
1469 500 d. Volleyball 25 10
1470 1000 d. Gymnastics 40 20
1471 2000 d. Tennis 80 30
1472 3000 d. Judo 1·25 30

1990. "Dulich '90". Fungi. Multicoloured.
1474 50 x. Type **303** 5 5
1475 50 x. Common ink cap ("Coprinus atramentarius") 5 5
1476 50 x. Oyster fungus ("Pleurotus ostreatus") 5 5
1477 50 x. Chanterelle ("Cantharellus cibarius") 5 5
1478 1 d. Chinese mushroom 10 5
1479 2 d. Red-staining mushroom 20 10
1480 5 d. Common morel 55 20
1481 10 d. Caesar's mushroom 1·10 45

1990. World Cup Football Championship, Italy (3rd series). Nos. 457/64 optd **ITALIA '90** and ball.
1482 30 x. multicoloured 15 5
1483 30 x. multicoloured 15 5
1484 40 x. multicoloured 20 10
1485 40 x. multicoloured 20 10
1486 50 x. multicoloured 25 10
1487 50 x. multicoloured 25 10
1488 60 x. multicoloured 35 15
1489 1 d. multicoloured 55 20

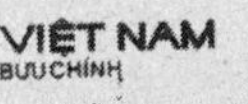

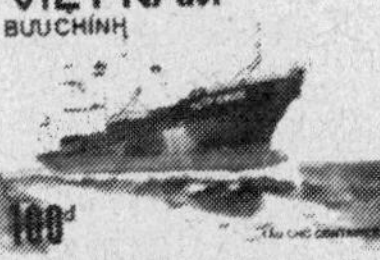

305 "Pyotr Emtsov" (container ship)

1990. Ships. Multicoloured.
1490 100 d. Type **305** 10 10
1491 300 d. Mexican Lines container ship 10 10
1492 500 d. Liner 20 10
1493 1000 d. "Ben Nevis" (tanker) 35 15
1494 2000 d. "RoRo" ferry 70 30
1495 3000 d. Sealink train ferry 1·00 40

306 Emblem, Globe and Dove

1990. 45th Anniv of Postal Service. Mult.
1496 100 d. Type **306** 10 10
1497 1000 d. Emblem, dish aerial and globe 40 15

307 Red Flags and Symbols of Construction and Agriculture

308 Thach Sanh collecting Wood

1990. 45th Anniv of Independence. Mult.
1498 100 d. Type **307** 5 5
1499 500 d. Crowd before Hanoi building, map and revolutionaries with tank 15 5
1500 1000 d. Ship, dish aerial and "VI" 35 15
1501 3000 d. Hammer and sickle, industrial symbols and couple 1·00 40

1990. Legend of Thach Sanh. Multicoloured.
1503 100 d. Type **308** 5 5
1504 300 d. Ly Thong 10 5
1505 500 d. Thach Sanh fighting fire-breathing snake 20 10
1506 1000 d. Thach Sanh shooting down bird 35 15
1507 2000 d. Thach Sanh in prison 70 30
1508 3000 d. Thach Sanh and wife 1·00 40

1990 World Cup Football Championship Results. Nos. 1382/1388 optd **1. GERMANY 2. ARGENTINA 3. ITALY.**
1509 100 d. multicoloured 5 5
1510 200 d. multicoloured 5 5
1511 300 d. multicoloured 10 5
1512 500 d. multicoloured 20 10
1513 1000 d. multicoloured 35 15
1514 2000 d. multicoloured 70 30
1515 3000 d. multicoloured 1·00 40

1990. Red Cross. Child Welfare. Nos. N598/605 optd, with red cross and **FOR THE FUTURE GENERATION** in various languages (given in brackets).
1517 12 x. mult (Italian) 10 5
1518 12 x. mult (Chinese) 10 5
1519 20 x. mult (German) 25 10
1520 20 x. mult (Vietnamese) 25 10
1521 30 x. mult (English) 35 15
1522 40 x. mult (Russian) 50 20
1523 50 x. mult (French) 60 25
1524 60 x. mult (Spanish) 70 30

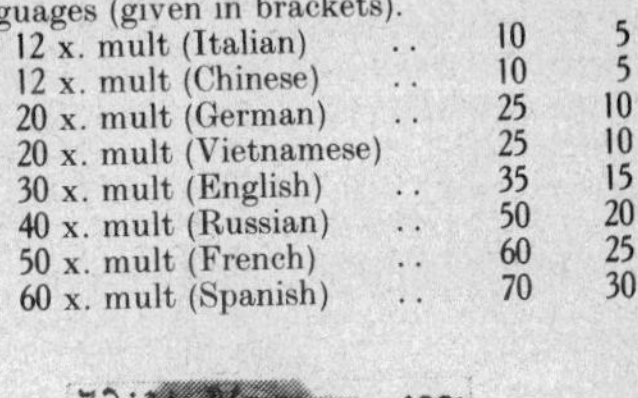

311 Soldier

1990. 60th Anniv of Vietnamese Women's Union. Multicoloured.
1525 100 d. Type **311** 5 5
1526 500 d. Women in various occupations 20 10

312 Emblems

1990. 20th Anniv of Asian–Pacific Postal Training Centre, Bangkok.
1527 **312** 150 d. multicoloured 30 10

313 Hands holding Forest and City

1990. Preservation of Forests. Multicoloured.
1528 200 d. Type **313** 5 5
1529 1000 d. Forest fire, "S.O.S." and river .. 10 5

314 Pather Cap

315 Yachting

1991. Poisonous Fungi. Multicoloured.
1530 200 d. Type **314** 5 5
1531 300 d. Death cap .. 5 5
1532 1000 d. Destroying angel 10 5
1533 1500 d. Fly agaric .. 20 10
1534 2000 d. "Russula emetica" 25 10
1535 3000 d. Satan's mushroom 35 15

1991. Olympic Games, Barcelona (1992). Multicoloured.
1536 200 d. Type **315** 5 5
1537 300 d. Boxing 5 5
1538 400 d. Cycling 5 5
1539 1000 d. High jumping .. 10 5
1540 2000 d. Show jumping .. 25 10
1541 3000 d. Judo 35 15
1542 3000 d. Wrestling (horiz) 35 15

316 Nguyen Binh Khiem

1991. 500th Birth Anniv of Nguyen Binh Khiem (poet).
1544 **316** 200 d. black, brown and ochre 5 5

317 "Marisiliana"

318 Woman in Blue Tunic

1991. 500th Anniv (1992) of Discovery of America by Columbus. Multicoloured.
1545 200 d. Type **317** 5 5
1546 400 d. "Venetien" .. 5 5
1547 400 d. "Cromster" (vert) 5 5
1548 2000 d. "Pinta" 25 10
1549 2000 d. "Nina" 25 10
1550 3000 d. "Howker" (vert) 35 15
1551 5000 d. "Santa Maria" .. 60 25

1991. Golden Heart Charity.
1553 **318** 200 d. multicoloured 5 5
1554 – 500 d. multicoloured 5 5
1555 – 1000 d. multicoloured 10 5
1556 – 5000 d. multicoloured 60 25
DESIGNS: 500 d. to 5000 d. Traditional women's costumes.

319 Japanese White-necked Crane

1991. Birds. Multicoloured.
1557 200 d. Type **319** 5 5
1558 300 d. Sarus crane chick (vert) 5 5
1559 400 d. Manchurian crane (vert) 5 5
1560 1000 d. Sarus cranes (adults) (vert) .. 10 5
1561 2000 d. Black-necked crane (vert) 25 10
1562 3000 d. South African crowned cranes (vert) 35 15
1563 3000 d. Great white crane 35 15

320 Blacktip Reef Shark

1991. Sharks. Multicoloured.
1564 200 d. Type **320** 5 5
1565 300 d. Grey reef shark .. 5 5
1566 400 d. Leopard shark .. 5 5
1567 1000 d. Great hammer-head 10 5
1568 2000 d. Whitetip reef shark 25 10
1569 3000 d. "Carcharias laurus" 35 15
1570 3000 d. Bull shark .. 35 15

321 Lobster

1991. Shellfish. Multicoloured.
1571 200 d. Type **321** 5 5
1572 300 d. "Alpheus bellulus" 5 5
1573 400 d. "Periclemenes brevicarpalis" .. 5 5
1574 1000 d. Lobster (different) 10 5
1575 2000 d. Lobster (different) 25 10
1576 3000 d. Lobster (different) 35 15
1577 3000 d. "Astacus sp." .. 35 15

322 "Fusee", 1829

323 Ho Chi Minh, "VII" and Building

1991. Early Locomotives. Multicoloured.
1578 400 d. Type **322** 5 5
1579 400 d. Hedley's "Puffing Billy", 1811 .. .. 5 5
1580 500 d. John Stevens locomotive, 1825 (horiz) 5 5
1581 1000 d. Crampton No. 80 locomotive, 1852 (horiz) 10 5
1582 2000 d. "Locomotion", 1825 (horiz) 25 10
1583 3000 d. "Saint-Lo", 1843 (horiz) 35 15
1584 3000 d. "Coutances", 1855 (horiz) 35 15

1991. 7th Vietnamese Communist Party Congress. Multicoloured.
1586 200 d. Type **323** 5 5
1587 300 d. Workers 5 5
1588 400 d. Mother and children 5 5

324 Pioneers

1991. 50th Anniv of Vietnam Youth Pioneers (200 d.) and United Nations Convention on Children's Rights (400 d.). Multicoloured.
1589 200 d. Type **324** 5 5
1590 400 d. Child's face and U.N. emblem .. 5 5

INDEX
Countries can be quickly located by referring to the index at the end of this volume.

325 Lada

1991. Rally Cars. Multicoloured.
1591 400 d. Type **325** 5 5
1592 400 d. Nissan 5 5
1593 500 d. Ford Sierra RS Cosworth 5 5
1594 1000 d. Suzuki 10 5
1595 2000 d. Mazda "323" .. 25 10
1596 3000 d. Peugeot 35 15
1597 3000 d. Lancia 35 15

326 Yellow-banded Poison-arrow Frog

328 Speed Skating

1991. Frogs. Multicoloured.
1599 200 d. Type **326** 5 5
1600 400 d. Edible frog .. 5 5
1601 500 d. Golden mantella .. 5 5
1602 1000 d. Dyeing poison-arrow frog 10 5
1603 2000 d. Tree frog .. 25 10
1604 3000 d. Red-eyed tree frog 35 15
1605 3000 d. Golden tree frog 35 15

1991. Winter Olympic Games, Albertville (1992). Multicoloured.
1607 200 d. Type **328** 5 5
1608 300 d. Freestyle skiing .. 5 5
1609 400 d. Four-man bobsleighing (horiz) .. 5 5
1610 1000 d. Biathlon (rifle shooting) (horiz) .. 10 5
1611 2000 d. Skiing (horiz) .. 25 10
1612 3000 d. Cross-country skiing 35 15
1613 3000 d. Ice skating .. 35 15

329 "Arsinoitherium zitteli"

1991. Prehistoric Animals. Multicoloured.
1615 200 d. Type **329** 5 5
1616 500 d. "Elephas primigenius" 5 5
1617 1000 d. "Baluchitherium" 10 5
1618 2000 d. "Deinotherium giganteum" 25 10
1619 3000 d. Brontops .. 35 15
1620 3000 d. Uintatherium .. 35 15

330 Pawn

1991. Chess. Staunton Pieces.
1621 200 d. Type **330** 5 5
1622 300 d. Knight 5 5
1623 1000 d. Rook 10 5
1624 2000 d. Queen 25 10
1625 3000 d. Bishop 35 15
1626 3000 d. King 35 15

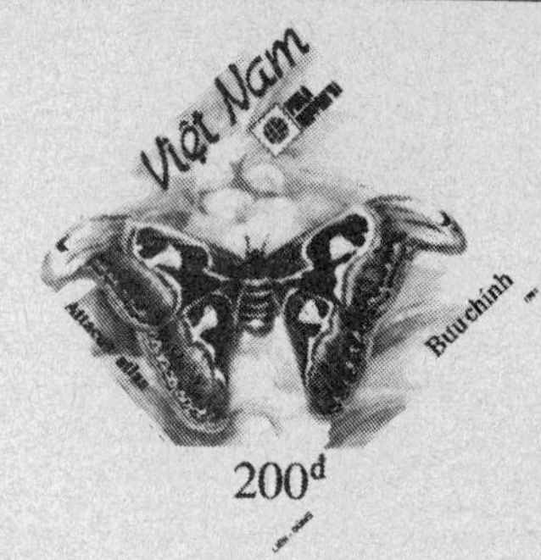

331 Atlas Moth

1991. "Phila Nippon '91" International Stamp Exhibition, Tokyo. Moths and Butterflies. Multicoloured.
1628 200 d. Type **331** 5 5
1629 400 d. Blue morpho .. 5 5
1630 500 d. Birdwing 5 5
1631 1000 d. Red admiral .. 10 5
1632 1000 d. "Papilio demetrius" 10 5
1633 3000 d. "Papilio weiskei" 35 15
1634 5000 d. Lesser purple emperor 60 25

332 Means of Communication

333 Eye and Clasped Hands

1991. 25th Anniv of Posts and Telecommunications Research Institute.
1636 **332** 200 d. multicoloured .. 5 5

1991. Golden Heart Charity for Disabled People.
1638 **333** 200 d. bl, lilac & orge 5 5
1639 – 3000 d. ultramarine, blue and light blue 35 15
DESIGN: 3000 d. Tennis player in wheelchair.

334 Gymnastics

1992. Olympic Games, Los Angeles (1984). Multicoloured.
1640 50 x. Type **334** 5 5
1641 50 x. Football (vert) .. 5 5
1642 1 d. Wrestling 5 5
1643 2 d. Volleyball (vert) .. 5 5
1644 3 d. Hurdling 5 5
1645 5 d. Basketball (vert) .. 5 5
1646 8 d. Weightlifting .. 5 5

1992. "Expo '92" World's Fair, Seville. Nos. 1372/8 optd **SEVILLA '92** and emblem.
1648 **288** 50 d. mult 5 5
1649 – 100 d. mult (No. 1373) 5 5
1650 – 100 d. mult (No. 1374) 5 5
1651 – 100 d. mult (No. 1375) 5 5
1652 – 200 d. mult (No. 1376) 5 5
1653 – 200 d. mult (No. 1377) 5 5
1654 – 300 d. mult 5 5

336 Chu Van An teaching

1992. 700th Death Anniv of Chu Van An.
1656 **336** 200 d. multicoloured .. 5 5

337 Atomic Symbol, Communications, Industry and Agriculture

1992. Resolutions of 7th Communist Party Congress. Multicoloured.

1657	200 d. Type **337**	5	5
1658	2000 d. Hands clasped and map of Asia	25	10

338 Biathlon

1992. Winter Olympic Games, Albertville. Multicoloured.

1659	200 d. Type **338**	5	5
1660	2000 d. Ice hockey ..	25	10
1661	4000 d. Skiing (slalom) ..	50	20
1662	5000 d. Ice skating ..	60	25
1663	6000 d. Skiing (downhill)	75	30

339 Columbus's Fleet

1992. 500th Anniv of Discovery of America by Columbus. Multicoloured.

1664	400 d. Type **339**	5	5
1665	3000 d. "Santa Maria" ..	35	10
1666	4000 d. Columbus and flag on land ..	50	20
1667	6000 d. Columbus offering gifts to Amerindians ..	75	30
1668	8000 d. Ship returning home	1·00	40

340 Tupolev Tu-154M

1992. Aircraft. Multicoloured.

1670	400 d. Type **340**	5	5
1671	500 d. "Concorde" ..	5	5
1672	1000 d. A-320 Airbus ..	10	5
1673	3000 d. A340-300	35	10
1674	4000 d. Boeing Dash 8-400	50	20
1675	5000 d. Boeing 747-200 ..	60	25
1676	6000 d. MD-11CF ..	75	30

341 Weather System and Forecasting Equipment

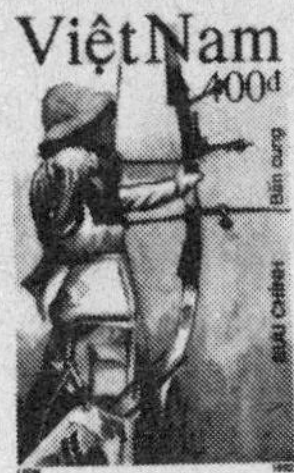

342 Archery

1992. International Decade for Natural Disaster Reduction. Multicoloured.

1677	400 d. Type **341**	5	5
1678	4000 d. Man taking depth readings	50	20

1992. Olympic Games, Barcelona. Mult.

1679	400 d. Type **342**	5	5
1680	600 d. Volleyball ..	5	5
1681	1000 d. Wrestling ..	10	5
1682	3000 d. Fencing	35	15
1683	4000 d. Running ..	50	20
1684	5000 d. Weightlifting ..	60	25
1685	6000 d. Hockey	75	30

343 Suzuki "500 F"

1992. Racing Motor Cycles. Multicoloured.

1687	400 d. Type **343**	5	5
1688	500 d. Honda "CBR 600F	5	5
1689	1000 d. Honda "HRC 500F"	10	5
1690	3000 d. Kawasaki "250F" (vert)	35	15
1691	4000 d. Suzuki "RM 250 F" (vert)	50	20
1692	5000 d. Suzuki "500F" ..	60	25
1693	6000 d. BMW "1000F" ..	75	30

344 Shuttle Launch

346 Footballer

345 Main Entrance

1992 International Space Year. Mult.

1695	400 d. Type **344**	5	5
1696	500 d. Launch of space shuttle "Columbia" ..	5	5
1697	3000 d. "Columbia" in space (horiz)	35	15
1698	4000 d. Projected shuttle "Hermes" docked at space station (horiz) ..	50	20
1699	5000 d. "Hermes" in space with solar panel (horiz)	60	25
1700	6000 d. Astronauts repairing Hubble space telescope	75	30

1992. Centenary of Saigon Post Office.

1701	**345** 200 d. multicoloured ..	5	5

1992. European Cup Football Championship. Multicoloured.

1703	200 d. Type **346**	5	5
1704	2000 d. Goalkeeper ..	25	10
1705	4000 d. Two players with ball on ground ..	50	20
1706	5000 d. Two players with ball in air	60	25
1707	6000 d. Three players ..	75	30

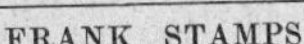

FRANK STAMPS

F 19. Invalid's Badge.

F 158. Children and Disabled Teacher.

1976. For use by disabled veterans. Dated " 27.7.75 ". No value indicated.

F 100.	F 19. (–) Red and blue ..	25	15
F 101.	– (–) Myrtle, light green and olive	25	15

DESIGN: No. F 101, Disabled veteran in factory.

1984. Disabled and Invalids. No value indicated.

F 750.	F 158. (–) brn. & ochre	25	15

No value indicated. As T 179.

F 861.	(–) Policeman and militia members ..	25	15

MILITARY FRANK STAMP

MF 21. Soldier and Map of Vietnam.

MF 59. Pilot.

1976. No value indicated.

MF 110.	MF 21. (–) black and red	20	15

1979. No value indicated. Vietnam People's Army. 35th Anniv.

MF 304.	MF 59. (–) red and pink	15	10
MF 305.	– (–) red and pink	15	10

DESIGN: No. MF 305, Badge of People's Army.

MF 61. Tank Driver and Tanks

MF 84. Ho Chi Minh in Naval Uniform.

1979. No value indicated.

MF 308.	MF 61. (–) black and mauve ..	15	10
MF 309.	– (–) violet and green ..	15	10
MF 310.	– (–) black and red	15	10

DESIGNS: MF 309, Sailor and ship. MF 310, Pilot and aircraft.

1981. No value indicated.

MF 420.	MF 84. (–) pink & blue	15	15
MF 421.	– (–) multicoloured	15	15

DESIGN—VERT. (13×17 mm.) No. MF 421, Factory Militiawomen.

1982. Multicoloured. No value indicated.

MF 466.	(–) Soldier and militiawoman ..	15	8
MF 467.	(–) Type **94**	15	8

MF 107. Disabled Soldier.

1982. 35th Anniv. of Disabled Soldiers' Day. No value indicated.

MF 513.	MF 107. (–) purple and green ..	20	12

MF 122. Militia.

1983. No value indicated.

MF 590.	MF 122. (–) mult. ..	30	20

MF 143. Star and Soldiers on Bunker.

MF 151. Coastal Militia.

1984. 30th Anniv. of Battle of Dien Bien Phu.

MF 688.	MF 143. (–) yellow, orange and brown ..	25	20

1984. No value indicated.

MF 732.	MF 151. (–) brown, orange and yellow ..	25	20

MF 164. Soldiers and Emblem.

1984. No value indicated.

MF 786.	MF 164. (–) orange, red and black ..	25	20

WALLIS AND FUTUNA ISLANDS Pt. 6

A group of French Islands in the Pacific Ocean north-east of Fiji Islands. Attached to New Caledonia for administrative purposes in 1888. In 1961 they became a French Overseas Territory.

100 centimes = 1 franc.

1920. Stamps of New Caledonia optd **ILES WALLIS et FUTUNA**.

1 15 1 c. black on green .. 25 35
2 2 c. brown .. 30 40
3 4 c. blue on orange .. 30 40
4 5 c. green .. 40 45
18 5 c. blue .. 40 55
5 10 c. red .. 50 45
19 10 c. green .. 50 60
6 15 c. lilac .. 50 50
7 16 20 c. brown .. 50 60
8 25 c. blue on green .. 60 60
21 25 c. red on yellow .. 50 50
9 30 c. brown on orange .. 70 70
22 30 c. red .. 50 50
24 30 c. green .. 1·10 1·10
10 35 c. black on yellow .. 55 55
11 40 c. red on green .. 55 55
12 45 c. purple .. 60 60
13 50 c. red on orange .. 60 60
25 50 c. blue .. 70 70
26 50 c. grey .. 90 90
27 65 c. blue .. 2·25 2·25
14 75 c. green .. 1·25 1·25
15 17 1 f. blue on green .. 2·00 2·00
28 1 f. 10 brown .. 1·60 1·75
16 2 f. red on blue .. 3·25 3·25
17 5 f. black on orange .. 5·50 5·50

1922. As last surch.

29 15 0,01 on 15 c. lilac .. 40 50
30 0,02 on 15 c. lilac .. 40 50
31 0,04 on 15 c. lilac .. 40 50
32 0,05 on 15 c. lilac .. 40 50
33 17 25 c. on 2 f. red on blue .. 50 60
34 25 c. on 5 f. black on orge .. 50 60
35 16 65 on 40 c. red on green .. 60 60
36 85 on 75 c. green .. 60 60
37 90 on 75 c. red .. 90 90
38 17 1 f. 25 on 1 f. blue .. 50 50
39 1 f. 50 on 1 f. blue on blue .. 1·75 1·75
40 3 f. on 5 f. mauve .. 3·50 3·50
41 10 f. on 5 f. grn on mve .. 14·00 14·00
42 20 f. on 5 f. red on yell .. 20·00 20·00

1930. Stamps of New Caledonia, some with colours changed, optd **ILES WALLIS et FUTUNA**.

43 22 1 c. blue and purple .. 20 30
44 2 c. green and brown .. 30 35
45 3 c. blue and red .. 35 40
46 4 c. green and red .. 30 35
47 5 c. brown and blue .. 35 25
48 10 c. brown and lilac .. 30 40
49 15 c. blue and brown .. 30 40
50 20 c. brown and red .. 35 45
51 25 c. brown and green .. 50 60
52 23 30 c. turquoise and green .. 45 55
53 35 c. green and dp green .. 55 65
54 40 c. green and red .. 45 55
55 45 c. red and blue .. 50 60
56 45 c. green and turquoise .. 45 55
57 50 c. brown and mauve .. 45 55
58 55 c. red and blue .. 1·25 1·25
59 60 c. red and blue .. 40 50
60 65 c. blue and brown .. 80 80
61 70 c. brown and mauve .. 50 60
62 75 c. drab and blue .. 1·25 1·25
63 80 c. green and purple .. 50 50
64 85 c. brown and green .. 2·00 2·00
65 90 c. carmine and red .. 1·10 1·10
66 90 c. red and brown .. 45 55
67 24 1 f. red and drab .. 2·00 2·00
68 1 f. carmine and red .. 85 80
69 1 f. green and red .. 35 45
70 1 f. 10 brown and green .. 15·00 15·00
71 1 f. 25 green and brown .. 1·10 1·25
72 1 f. 25 carmine and red .. 45 55
73 1 f. 40 red and blue .. 60 60
74 1 f. 50 blue & ultramarine .. 45 55
75 1 f. 60 brown and green .. 65 65
76 1 f. 75 red and blue .. 6·25 6·25
77 1 f. 75 blue .. 1·25 1·25
78 2 f. brown and orange .. 80 80
79 2 f. 25 blue & ultramarine .. 65 65
80 2 f. 50 brown .. 65 65
81 3 f. brown and purple .. 80 80
82 5 f. brown and blue .. 80 80
83 10 f. brn & mve on pink .. 1·50 1·50
84 20 f. brown & red on yell .. 2·25 2·25

1931. "Colonial Exhibition" key-types.

85. E. 40 c. green and black .. 3·00 3·00
86. F. 50 c. mauve and black .. 3·00 3·00
87. G. 90 c. red and black .. 3·00 3·00
88. H. 1 f. 50 blue and black .. 3·00 3·00

1939. New York World's Fair. As T **28** of Mauritania.

89 1 f. 25 red .. .. .. 1·00 1·00
90 2 f. 25 blue .. .. .. 1·00 1·00

1939. 150th Anniv. of French Revolution. As T **29** of Mauritania.

91. 45 c.+25 c. green and black 7·50 7·50
92. 70 c.+30 c. brown and black 7·50 7·50
93. 90 c.+35 c. orange & black 7·50 7·50
94. 1 f. 25 c.+1 f. red and black 7·50 7·50
95. 2 f. 25 c.+2 f. blue & black 7·50 7·50

1941. Adherence to General de Gaulle. Stamps of 1930 optd **France Libre**.

96 22 1 c. blue and purple .. 70 70
97 2 c. green and brown .. 70 70
97a 3 c. blue and red .. 60·00 60·00
98 4 c. green and orange .. 70 70
99 5 c. brown and blue .. 70 70
100 10 c. brown and lilac .. 70 70
101 15 c. blue and brown .. 70 70
102 20 c. brown and red .. 1·40 1·40
103 25 c. brown and green .. 1·40 1·40
104 23 30 c. green .. .. 1·40 1·40
105 35 c. green 70 70
106 40 c. green and red .. 1·40 1·40
107 45 c. red and blue .. 1·40 1·40
107a 45 c. green & turquoise .. 60·00 60·00
108 50 c. brown and mauve .. 70 70
109 55 c. red and blue .. 70 70
109a 60 c. red and blue .. 60·00 60·00
110 65 c. blue and brown .. 70 70
111 70 c. brown and mauve .. 70 70
112 75 c. drab and blue .. 1·40 1·40
113 80 c. green and purple .. 70 70
114 85 c. brown and green .. 1·40 1·40
115 90 c. carmine and red .. 70 70
116 24 1 f. carmine and red .. 1·40 1·40
117 1 f. 25 green and brown .. 1·40 1·40
118 1 f. 50 blue and dp blue .. 70 70
119 1 f. 75 blue 70 70
120 2 f. brown and orange .. 1·40 1·40
121 2 f. 50 brown £110 £110
122 3 f. brown and purple .. 70 70
123 3 f. brown and blue .. 2·75 2·75
124 10 f. brown and mauve on pink .. 35·00 35·00
125 20 f. brn & red on yell .. 55·00 55·00

5. Native Ivory Head.

1944. Free French Administration.

126. 5. 5 c. brown 15 30
127. 10 c. blue 15 30
128. 25 c. green 15 30
129. 30 c. orange 15 30
130. 40 c. green 30 30
131. 80 c. purple 30 45
132. 1 f. purple 35 40
133. 1 f. 50 c. red 20 30
134. 2 f. black 25 35
135. 2 f. 50 blue 45 60
136. 4 f. violet 40 50
137. 5 f. yellow 40 50
138. 10 f. brown 85 90
139. 20 f. green .. .. 1·10 1·25

1944. Mutual Aid and Red Cross Funds. As T **31** of New Caledonia.

140. 5 f.+20 f. orange .. 1·10 1·10

1945. Surch.

141 5 50 c. on 5 c. brown .. 50 60
142 60 c. on 5 c. brown .. 50 60
143 70 c. on 5 c. brown .. 45 55
144 1 f. 20 on 5 c. brown .. 40 50
145 2 f. 40 on 35 c. green .. 40 50
146 3 f. on 25 c. green .. 60 70
147 4 f. 50 on 25 c. green .. 1·10 1·25
148 15 f. on 2 f. 50 blue .. 1·10 1·25

1946. Air. Victory. As T **34** of New Caledonia.

149. 8 f. violet 50 75

1946. Air. From Chad to the Rhine. As Nos. 300/305 of New Caledonia.

150. 5 f. violet 80 90
151. 10 f. green 80 90
152. 15 f. brown 80 90
153. 20 f. blue .. .. .. 1·00 1·25
154. 25 f. orange .. .. .. 1·25 1·50
155. 50 red .. .. .. 1·75 2·00

1949. Air. 75th Anniv of Universal Postal Union. As T **38** of New Caledonia.

156 10 f. multicoloured .. 4·25 5·00

1949. Air. Nos. 325/6 of New Caledonia, with colours changed, optd. **WALLIS ET FUTUNA.**

157. 37. 50 f. red and yellow .. 4·75 4·75
158. – 100 f. brown and yellow 6·75 7·00

1952. Centenary of Military Medal. As T **40** of New Caledonia.

159. 2 f. turquoise, yell & green 1·90 1·75

1954. Air. 10th Anniv of Liberation. As T **42** of New Caledonia.

160 3 f. brown and deep brown 4·25 4·50

7. Making Tapa (cloth).

9. "Charonia tritonis".

8. Father Chanel.

1955. (a) Postage as T **7**.

161. – 3 f. pur., mve. & lilac 75 80
162. 7. 5 f. choc., brn. & grn. 75 80
163. – 7 f. brown and turq. 1·10 1·10
164. – 9 f. deep purple, purple and blue .. 1·50 1·50
165. – 17 f. multicoloured .. 1·90 1·90
166. – 19 f. green and red .. 2·00 2·00

(b) Air, as T **8**.

167. 8. 14 f. bl., grn. & ind.. 2·00 1·40
168. – 21 f. grn., brn. & bl. 3·50 2·75
168a. – 27 f. grn., bl. & brn. 3·50 2·00
169. – 33 f. brn., bl. & turq. 5·50 5·00

DESIGNS—HORIZ. 3, 9 f. Wallisian and island view. 7 f. Preparing kava. 17 f. Dancers. 21 f. View of Mata-Utu, Queen Amelia and Mgr. Bataillon. 27 f. Wharf, Mata-Utu. 33 f. Map of Wallis and Futuna Islands and "Stella Matutina" (full-rigged ship). VERT. 19 f. Paddle dance.

1958. Tropical Flora. As T **47** of New Caledonia.

170. 5 f. multicoloured .. 2·75 2·00

DESIGN—HORIZ. 5 f. "Montrouziera".

1958. 10th Anniv. of Declaration of Human Rights. As T **48** of New Caledonia.

171. 17 f. blue and ultramarine 3·50 3·50

1962. 5th South Pacific Conference. Pago Pago. As T **49d** of New Caledonia.

172. 16 f. multicoloured .. 2·75 2·25

1962. Marine Fauna.

173 9 25 c. brown and green (postage) 55 55
174 – 1 f. red and green .. 55 55
175 – 2 f. brown and blue .. 1·10 1·10
176 – 4 f. brown and blue .. 1·60 1·60
177 – 10 f. multicoloured .. 3·50 3·50
178 – 20 f. brown and blue .. 6·50 6·50
179 – 50 f. brown, bl & pur (air) 7·75 5·00
180 – 100 f. black, green & pur 15·00 11·00

DESIGNS—As T **9**: 1 f. "Mitra episcopalis". 2 f. "Cypraecassis rufa". 4 f. "Murex tenuispina". 10 f. "Oliva erythrostoma". 20 f. "Cypraea tigris". 26½ × 48 mm: 50 f. "Harpa ventricosa". 48 × 26½ mm: 100 f. Fishing under water for trochus shells.

1962. Air. 1st Trans-Atlantic TV Satellite Link. As T **50** of New Caledonia.

181. 12 f. blue, purple and violet 2·50 2·50

1963. Red Cross Cent. As Type **53** of New Caledonia.

182. 12 f. red, grey and purple .. 2·50 1·60

1963. 15th Anniv. of Declaration of Human Rights. As T **54** of New Caledonia.

183. 29 f. ochre and red .. 5·50 4·50

1964. "PHILATEC 1964" Int. Stamp Exn., Paris. As T **54c** of New Caledonia.

184. 9 f. red, green and deep green .. .. .. 2·50 1·75

10. Throwing the Javelin.

11. Inter-island Ferry "Reine Amelia".

1964. Air. Olympic Games, Tokyo.

185. 10. 31 f. purple, red & green 15·00 10·00

1965.

186. 11. 11 f. multicoloured .. 5·00 4·00

1965. Air. Centenary of I.T.U. As T **56** of New Caledonia.

187 50 f. brown, purple and red 16·00 12·00

1966. Air. Launching of 1st French Satellite. As Nos. 398/9 of New Caledonia.

188. 7 f. red, claret & vermilion 2·75 2·75
189. 10 f. red, claret & vermilion 3·50 3·50

1966. Air. Launching of Satellite "D1". As T **56e** of New Caledonia.

190. 10 f. red, lake and green .. 2·50 2·50

12. W.H.O. Building.

1966. Air. Inauguration of W.H.O. Headquarters, Geneva.

191. 12. 30 f. red, yellow & bl. 3·00 3·00

13. Art Students.

1966. Air. 20th Anniv of U.N.E.S.C.O.

192 13 50 f. brown, green & orge 4·50 3·50

14. Athlete and Decorative Pattern.

1966. Air. South Pacific Games, Noumea.

193. 14. 32 f. multicoloured .. 3·50 2·50
194. – 38 f. green and mauve .. 4·00 3·00

DESIGN: 38 f. Woman with ball, and decorative pattern.

15. Samuel Wallis's Frigate H.M.S. "Dolphin" at Uvea.

1967. Air. Bicentenary of Discovery of Wallis Island.

195. 15. 12 f. multicoloured .. 5·00 3·50

1968. 20th Anniv. of W.H.O. As T **68** of New Caledonia.

196. 17 f. purple, orange & green 4·00 3·50

1968. Human Rights Year. As T **69** of New Caledonia.

197. 19 f. brn., mauve & purple 2·50 2·50

1969. Air. 1st Flight of "Concorde". As T **75** of New Caledonia.

198. 20 f. black and purple .. 10·00 6·50

16. Gathering Coconuts.

18. Weightlifting.

1969. Scenes of Everyday Life. Mult.

199. 1 f. Launching outrigger canoe (35 × 22 mm.) (postage) 80 80
200. 20 f. Type **16** (air) .. .. 1·75 1·00
201. 32 f. Horse-riding .. .. 3·00 1·50
202. 38 f. Wood-carving .. 3·50 1·90
203. 50 f. Fishing .. .. 5·00 3·50
204. 100 f. Marketing fruit .. 10·00 5·50

1969. 50th Anniv. of Int. Labour Organization. As T **79** of New Caledonia.

205. 9 f. blue, brown and salmon 2·00 2·00

1970. Inaug of New U.P.U. Headquarters Building, Berne. As T **81** of New Caledonia.

206 21 f. brown, blue & purple 2·50 2·50

1971. Surch.

207. 12 f. on 19 f. (No. 166) (postage) .. .. 1·10 1·10
208. 21 f. on 33 f. (No. 169) (air) 3·50 2·75

1971. 4th South Pacific Games, Papeete, Tahiti.

209. 18. 24 f. brown, blue and green (postage) .. 3·00 2·25
210. – 36 f. blue, olive and red 3·75 2·75
211. – 48 f. brown, green and lilac (air) .. .. 4·25 2·25
212. – 54 f. red, pur. and blue 4·50 3·50

DESIGNS—As T **12**: 36 f. Basketball. 47 × 27 mm: 48 f. Pole vaulting. 54 f. Archery.

1971. 1st Death Anniv of General Charles de Gaulle. As Nos. 493/4 of New Caledonia.

213. 30 f. black and blue .. 5·00 2·75
214. 70 f. black and blue .. 9·00 5·50

1972. Air. 25th Anniv. of South Pacific Commission. As T **96** of New Caledonia.

215. 44 f. multicoloured .. 4·50 2·75

20. Pacific Island Dwelling.

21. Model Pirogue.

1972. Air. South Pacific Arts Festival, Fiji.
216. **20.** 60 f. violet, grn. & red 5·50 3·50

1972. Sailing Pirogues. Multicoloured.
217. 14 f. Type **21** (postage) .. 4·00 2·25
218. 16 f. Children with model pirogues .. .. 4·00 2·25
219. 18 f. Racing pirogue .. 4·50 3·50
220. 200 f. Pirogue race (47×27 mm.) (air) .. .. 25·00 14·00

22. La Perouse and "La Boussole".

1973. Air. Explorers of the Pacific.
221. **22.** 22 f. brn., grey & red 2·40 1·60
222. – 28 f. grn., red & blue.. 3·00 2·25
223. – 40 f. brown, blue and bright blue .. 5·00 3·50
224. – 72 f. brn., blue & violet 7·50 4·50
Designs: 28 f. Samuel Wallis and H.M.S. "Dolphin". 40 f. Dumont d'Urville and "L'Astrolabe". 72 f. Bougainville and "La Boudeuse".

23. General De Gaulle.

1973. Air. 3rd Death Anniv of General Charles de Gaulle.
225 **23** 107 f. purple and brown 9·50 6·00

24. "Plumeria rubra".

1973. Air. Flora of Wallis Islands. Mult.
226. 12 f. Type **24** .. .. 1·10 75
227. 17 f. "Hibiscus tiliaceus" 1·40 90
228. 19 f. "Phaeomeria magnifica" .. .. 1·60 1·00
229. 21 f. "Hibiscus rosa sinensis" .. .. 1·60 1·00
230. 23 f. "Allamanda cathartica" .. 2·00 1·50
231. 27 f. "Barringtonia asiatica" .. 2·00 2·00
232. 39 f. Bouquet in vase .. 5·50 3·50

25. Rhinoceros Beetle.

1974. Insects. Multicoloured.
233 15 f. Type **25** .. .. 1·40 90
234 25 f. "Cosmopolites sordidus" (weevil) .. 2·00 1·40
235 35 f. Tropical fruit-piercer 2·75 1·60
236 45 f. "Pantala flavescens" (darter) .. .. 4·50 2·75

26. "Flower Hand" holding Letter.

27. "Holy Family" (Kamalielf-Filimoehala).

1974. Air. Cent. of Universal Postal Union.
237. **26.** 51 f. purple, brn. & grn. 4·50 2·75

1974. Air. Christmas.
238. **27.** 150 f. multicoloured .. 8·50 5·50

28. Tapa Pattern.

1975. Air. Tapa Mats. Each brown, gold and yellow.
239. 3 f. Type **28** 55 45
240. 24 f. "Villagers" .. .. 1·60 1·10
241. 36 f. "Fishes" .. .. 2·75 1·75
242. 80 f. "Fishes and Dancers" 5·50 4·00

29. Aircraft in Flight.

30. Volleyball.

1975. Air. First Regular New Caledonia Air Service.
243. **29.** 100 f. multicoloured .. 5·00 4·00

1975. Air. Fifth South Pacific Games, Guam. Multicoloured.
244. 26 f. Type **30** .. .. 1·50 85
245. 44 f. Football .. .. 1·75 1·25
246. 56 f. Throwing the javelin 3·00 2·00
247. 105 f. Aqua-diving .. 6·00 4·50

1976. Pres. Pompidou Commemoration. As T **125** of New Caledonia.
248. 50 f. grey and blue .. 4·00 2·50

31. Lalolalo Lake, Wallis.

1976. Landscapes. Multicoloured.
249. 10 f. Type **31** (postage) .. 80 40
250. 29 f. Vasavasa, Futuna (air) 2·00 1·10
251. 41 f. Sigave Bay, Futuna 2·75 1·50
252. 68 f. Gahi Bay, Wallis .. 4·00 2·50

32. "Concorde".

1976. Air. First Commercial Flight of "Concorde".
253. **32.** 250 f. multicoloured .. 18·00 11·00

33. Washington and Battle of Yorktown.

1976. Bicent. of American Revolution.
254. **33.** 19 f. green, blue and red 1·40 90
255. – 47 f. purple, red and blue 3·00 2·25
Design: 47 f. Lafayette and sea battle of the Virginia Capes.

34. Throwing the Hammer.

1976. Air. Olympic Games, Montreal.
256. **34.** 31 f. purple, blue and red 2·00 1·50
257. – 39 f. mauve, red & purp. 3·00 2·00
Design: 39 f. High-diving.

35. "Conus ammiralis".

1976. Sea Shells. Multicoloured.
258. 20 f. Type **35** .. .. 1·40 1·25
259. 23 f. "Cypraea assellus" .. 1·40 1·25
260. 43 f. "Turbo petholatus" 3·00 2·50
261. 61 f. "Mitra papalis" .. 4·50 4·00

36. Father Chanel and Sanctuary Church, Poi.

1977. Father Chanel Memorial. Mult.
262. 22 f. Type **36** .. .. 1·25 85
263. 32 f. Father Chanel and map 1·60 1·00

36a. De Gaulle Memorial.

1977. 5th Anniv. of General de Gaulle Memorial.
264. **36a.** 100 f. multicoloured .. 6·00 4·50

37. Tanoa (bowl), Lali (mortar trough) and Ipu (coconut shell).

1977. Handicrafts. Multicoloured.
265 12 f. Type **37** 65 30
266 25 f. Wallis and Futuna kumetes (bowls) and tuluma (box) .. .. 1·25 60
267 33 f. Milamila (comb), ike (club) and tutua (model outrigger) .. .. 1·50 80
268 45 f. Kolo (Futana clubs) 1·60 1·25
269 69 f. Kailao (Wallis and Futuna lances) .. 2·75 2·00

1977. Air. First Commercial Flight of "Concorde". Optd **PARIS NEW-YORK 22.11.77 1er VOL COMMERCIAL.**
270 **32** 250 f. multicoloured .. 13·50 10·00

39. Post Office, Mata-Utu.

1977. Building and Monuments. Mult.
271. 27 f. Type **39** .. .. 1·40 80
272. 50 f. Sia Hospital, Mata-Utu 1·75 1·25
273. 57 f. Government Buildings, Mata-Utu .. .. 2·00 2·00
274. 63 f. St. Joseph's Church, Sigave .. .. 2·75 2·00
275. 120 f. Royal Palace, Matu-Utu .. .. 5·00 3·00

1977. Bicentenary of Captain Cook's Discovery of Hawaii. Nos. 254/5 optd **JAMES COOK Bicentenaire de la decouverte des Iles Hawaii 1778–1978.**
276 **33** 19 f. green, blue and red 2·50 1·60
277 – 47 f. purple, red & blue 4·50 2·75

41. "Balistes niger".

1977. Air. Fishes. Multicoloured.
278 26 f. Type **41** .. .. 1·00 55
279 35 f. Anemone fish .. 1·40 1·75
280 49 f. Emperor angelfish .. 2·00 1·75
281 51 f. Moorish idol .. 2·75 2·00

42. Map of Futuna and Alofi.

1978. Maps of Wallis and Futuna Islands.
282. **42.** 300 f. turquoise, blue and ultramarine .. 12·00 9·50
283. – 500 f. brown, blue and ultramarine .. .. 16·00 12·75
Design—vert. 500 f. Map of Wallis Island.

43. Father Bataillon and Churches.

1978. Air. Arrival of First French Missionaries. Multicoloured.
284. 60 f. Type **43** .. .. 2·00 1·50
285. 72 f. Monsgr. Pompallier and map .. .. 2·50 2·00

44. I.T.U. Emblem and Antennae.

1978. Air. World Telecommunications Day.
286. **44.** 66 f. multicoloured .. 2·50 1·60

45. "Triomphant" (destroyer).

1978. Free French Pacific Naval Force, 1940–1944. Multicoloured.
287 150 f. Type **45** .. .. 7·25 5·00
288 200 f. "Cap des Palmes" and "Chevreuil" (patrol boats) .. .. 10·00 6·50
289 280 f. "Savorgnan de Brazza" (destroyer) .. 14·00 10·00

46. "Solanum seaforthianum". 47. Eastern Reef Heron.

1978. Tropical Flowers. Multicoloured.
290. 16 f. Type **46** 80 40
291. 24 f. " Cassia alata " .. 90 55
292. 29 f. " Gloriosa superba " 1·50 80
293. 36 f. " Hymenocallis littoralis " .. .. 2·00 1·10

1978. Ocean Birds. Multicoloured.
294. 17 f. Type **47** 65 40
295. 18 f. Red-footed Booby .. 65 40
296. 28 f. Brown Booby .. 1·40 80
297. 35 f. White Tern .. .. 1·90 1·25

48. Costumed Carpet-sellers.

1978. Costumes and Traditions. Mult.
298. 53 f. Type **48** .. .. 1·75 1·10
299. 55 f. " Festival of God " procession .. .. 2·25 1·50
300. 59 f. Guards of honour .. 2·75 1·50

49. Nativity Scene.

1978. Air. Christmas.
301. **49.** 160 f. multicoloured .. 5·50 3·50

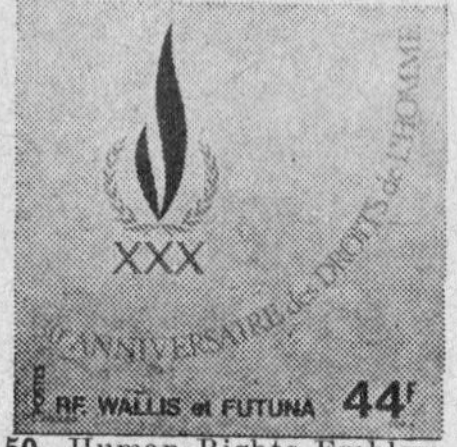

50. Human Rights Emblem.

1978. 30th Anniv. of Declaration of Human Rights.
302. **50.** 44 f. multicoloured .. 1·50 1·00
303. 56 f. multicoloured .. 2·00 1·50

51. Pope Paul VI.

1979. Air. Popes. Multicoloured.
304 37 f. Type **51** .. .. 1·40 1·00
305 41 f. Pope John-Paul I .. 1·60 1·40
306 105 f. St. Peter's, Rome, and Popes Paul IV and John-Paul I (horiz) .. 4·00 2·50

52. Aircraft of UTA Airline.

1979. Air. Inter-Island Communications (1st series). Multicoloured.
307 46 f. Type **52** .. .. 1·40 90
308 68 f. Freighter "Moana II" 1·75 1·40
309 80 f. Hihifo Airport .. 2·50 1·60
See also Nos. 349/51.

53. Fishing Boat.

1979. Tagging Bonita Fish. Multicoloured.
310. 10 f. Type **53** 40 30
311. 30 f. Weighing bonito .. 90 55
312. 34 f. Young fishes .. .. 1·00 75
313. 38 f. Tagging bonito .. 1·40 85
314. 40 f. Angling for bonito .. 1·50 1·10
315. 48 f. Bonito fish .. .. 2·00 1·60

54. Boy with Model Outrigger Canoe.

1979. International Year of the Child. Multicoloured.
317. 52 f. Type **54** .. .. 1·50 95
318. 58 f. Girl on horseback .. 1·75 1·00

55. " Bombax ellipticum ".

1979. Flowering and Fruiting Trees. Mult.
319. 50 f. Type **55** .. .. 1·25 90
320. 64 f. " Callophyllum inophyllum " .. .. 2·10 1·00
321. 76 f. " Pandanus odoratissimus " .. 2·75 1·75

56. French 1876 5 c. Stamp and " Eole " Meteorological Satellite.

1979. Air. Death Centenary of Sir Rowland Hill.
322. **56.** 5 f. multicoloured .. 55 30
323. – 70 f. multicoloured .. 1·75 1·10
324. – 90 f. black and red .. 2·50 1·50
325. – 100 f. brn., yell. & blue 2·75 2·00
DESIGNS—VERT: 70 f. Hibiscus and Wallis and Futuna 1920 1 f. stamp. HORIZ: 90 f. Sir Rowland Hill and Great Britain Penny Black. 100 f. "Birds" (Kano School) and Japan 1872 ½ s. stamp.

57. Normal and Distorted Landscapes.

1979. Anti-Alcoholism Campaign.
326. **57.** 22 f. multicoloured .. 1·10 90

58. Heads looking at Cross of Lorraine.

1978. Air. 39th Anniv. of 18 June Appeal by General De Gaulle.
327. **58.** 33 f. red, blue and grey 1·40 1·00

59. " Crinum moorei ". 60. Map of Islands and French Arms.

1979. Flowers (1st series). Multicoloured.
328. 20 f. Type **59** 50 30
329. 42 f. Passion flower .. 1·50 90
330. 62 f. " Canna indica " .. 2·00 1·40
See also Nos 392/4.

1979. Air. Presidential Visit
331. **60.** 47 f. multicoloured .. 1·90 1·10

61. Cook and Death Scene, Hawaii.

1979. Air. Death Bicent. of Captain Cook.
332. **61.** 130 f. grey, blue & brn. 4·00 2·75

62. Swimmers.

1979. Sixth South Pacific Games, Fiji.
333. **62.** 31 f. olive, lake & green 1·50 80
334. – 39 f. brn., turq. and grn. 2·00 1·00
DESIGN: 39 f. High jumper.

63. Garlands.

1979. Necklaces. Multicoloured.
335. 110 f. Type **63** .. .. 2·50 2·00
336. 140 f. Coral necklaces .. 4·50 2·50

64. Satellite and Dish Aerial.

1979. Air. Third World Telecommunications Exhibition, Geneva.
337. **64.** 120 f. multicoloured .. 3·50 2·50

65. Detail of Painting by Mme. Sutita.

1979. Works of Local Artists. Multicoloured.
338. 27 f. Painting by Mme. Sutita (detail) (different) 1·00 90
339. 65 f. Painting by M. A. Pilioko (detail) (vert.) .. 1·75 1·40
340. 78 f. Type **65** .. .. 2·50 1·75

66. Squilla.

1979. South Pacific Fauna. Multicoloured.
341. 15 f. Type **66** 50 30
342. 23 f. "Hexabranchus sanguineus" 60 50
343. 25 f. "Spondylus barbatus" 1·00 65
344. 43 f. Sea Fan .. .. 1·25 65
345. 45 f. Starfish .. .. 1·40 80
346. 63 f. "Tridacna squamosa" 2·50 1·75

67. " Virgin of the Crescent Moon " (detail Durer).

1979. Air. Christmas.
347. **67.** 180 f. black and red .. 5·50 4·00
See also No. 554.

68. "Concorde", Map and Rotary Emblem.

1980. Air. 75th Anniv. of Rotary International.
348. **68.** 86 f. multicoloured .. 3·50 2·50

1980. Inter-Island Communications (2nd series). As Nos. 307/9.
349. 1 f. Type **52** 15 15
350. 3 f. As No. 308 .. .. 15 15
351. 5 f. As No. 309 .. .. 25 15

69. Radio Station.

1980. 1st Anniv. of Radio Station FR3.
352. **69.** 47 f. multicoloured .. 1·50 1·00

70. "Jesus laid in the Tomb" (Maurice Denis).

1980. Easter.
353. **70.** 25 f. multicoloured .. 1·10 65

71. Rochambeau and Soldiers. 73. " Gnathodentex mossambicus ".

72. Flags and Island.

1980. Air. Bicentenary of Rochambeau's Landing at Newport, Rhode Island.
354. **71.** 102 f. sepia, bl. and brn. 3·50 2·75

1980. Air. National Day.
355. **72.** 71 f. multicoloured .. 1·75 1·00

1980. Fishes. Multicoloured.
356 23 f. Type **73** 70 40
357 27 f. Blue-spotted snapper 85 55
358 32 f. Ruby snapper .. 1·25 90
359 51 f. Rock cod .. .. 1·75 1·25
360 59 f. Flame snapper .. 2·50 2·00

74. Mermoz and "Arc en Ciel".

1980. Air. 50th Anniv. of 1st South Atlantic Airmail Flight.
361. **74.** 122 f. bl., dp. bl. and red 3·50 2·50

1980. "Sydpex 80" International Stamp Exhibition, Sydney. No. 315 surch. **50F SYDPEX 80 29 Septembre**.
362 50 f. on 48 f. multicoloured 2·00 2·10

76. Fleming and Penicillin Slide.

1980. Air. 25th Death Anniv. of Alexander Fleming (discoverer of penicillin).
363. **76.** 101 f. blue, brn. and red 2·50 1·75

77. Charles de Gaulle.

1980. Air. 10th Death Anniv. of Charles de Gaulle (French statesman).
364. **77.** 200 f. green and brown 5·50 4·00

78. "The Virgin, Child and St. Catherine" (Lorenzo Lotto).

1980. Air. Christmas.
365. **78.** 150 f. multicoloured 3·50 2·50

79. Alan Shepard and "Freedom 7". **80.** Ribbons and I.T.U. and W.H.O. Emblems forming Caduceus, and Satellite.

1981. Air. 20th Anniv. of First Men in Space. Multicoloured.
366. 37 f. Type **79** 1·00 65
367. 44 f. Yuri Gagarin and "Vostok I" 1·25 90

1981. World Telecommunications Day.
368. **80.** 49 f. multicoloured 1·25 90

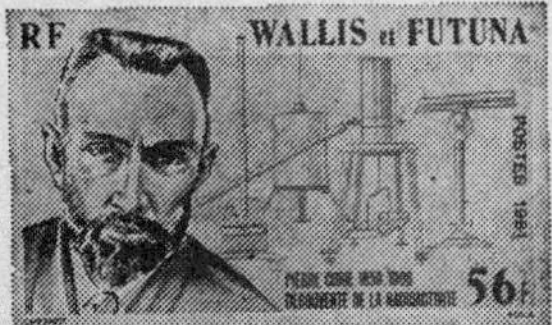

81. Curie and Laboratory Equipment.

1981. 75th Death Anniv. of Pierre Curie (physicist and discoverer of radium).
369. **81.** 56 f. multicoloured 1·40 1·00

82. Coral. **84.** Section of Globe.

83. Doctor inoculating Child.

1981. Undersea Fauna. Multicoloured.
370. 28 f. Type **82** 85 60
371. 30 f. Blue-green algae 85 60
372. 31 f. "Ceratium vultur" (dinoflagellate) 1·00 65
373. 35 f. "Amphiprion frenatus" (fish) 1·10 65
374. 40 f. "Conus textile" (mollusc) 1·25 90
375. 55 f. Feather-star (echinoderm) 1·75 1·00

1981. 60th Anniv. of First B.C.G. Anti-tuberculosis Inoculation.
376. **83.** 27 f. multicoloured 75 50

1981. International Year of Disabled Persons.
377. **84.** 42 f. multicoloured 1·40 75

85. Edison and Phonograph.

1981. 50th Death Anniv. of Thomas Edison (inventor).
378. **85.** 59 f. black, blue & red 1·40 1·00

1981. No. 341 surch **5F**.
379 5 f. on 15 f. multicoloured 30 20

87. Battle Scene. **88.** "Vase of Flowers" (Cezanne).

1981. Bicent of Battle of "Virginia Capes".
380. – 66 f. purple, blue & slate 1·40 1·10
381. **87.** 74 f. green, violet and light green 2·00 1·10

DESIGN: 66 f. Admiral Francois de Grasse and battle scene.

1981. Air. 75th Death Anniv of Paul Cezanne and Birth Cent of Pablo Picasso (artists).
382. 53 f. Type **88** 1·50 1·00
383. 135 f. "Harlequin leaning" (Picasso) 3·50 2·25

89. Football.

1981. Air. World Cup Football Championship, Spain (1982).
384. **89.** 120 f. brown, black & green 2·50 2·00
385. 120 f. brown, mauve and green 2·50 2·00

90. Patrol Boat "La Dieppoise".

1981. Surveillance of 200-mile zone. Mult.
386. 60 f. Type **90** 1·40 1·00
387. 85 f. Frigate "Protet" 2·00 1·50

91. Crib.

1981. Air. Christmas.
388. **91.** 180 f. multicoloured 4·00 2·75

92. "Pilioko Alio" (tapestry). **93.** Dr. Robert Koch at Microscope.

1982. Air.
389. **92.** 100 f. multicoloured 2·25 1·75

1982. Centenary of Discovery of Tubercle Bacillus.
390. **93.** 45 f. multicoloured 1·10 90

94. "Fishing Boats at Collioure".

1982. Air. Death Centenary of Georges Braque (painter).
391. **94.** 300 f. multicoloured 6·50 4·50

1982. Flowers (2nd series). Multicoloured.
392. 1 f. As Type **59** 10 10
393. 2 f. As No. 329 15 10
394. 3 f. As No. 330 15 10

95. 1930 Stamp.

1982. "Philexfrance" International Stamp Exhibition, Paris.
395. **95.** 140 f. violet, blue and red 2·50 1·75

96. "Acanthe phippium".

1982. Orchids. Multicoloured.
396. 34 f. Type **96** 80 55
397. 68 f. "Acanthe phippium" (different) 1·75 1·25
398. 70 f. "Spathoglottis pacifica" 2·00 1·25
399. 83 f. "Mussaenda raiateensis" 2·50 1·75

97. Lord Baden-Powell.

1982. 125th Birth Anniv. of Lord Baden-Powell (founder of Boy Scout Movement).
400. **97.** 80 f. multicoloured 2·00 1·25

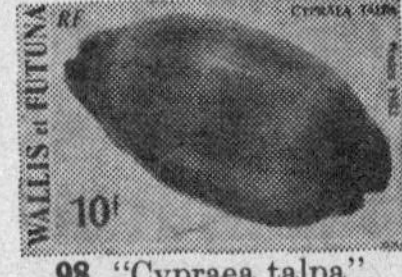

98. "Cypraea talpa".

1982. Sea Shells (1st series). Multicoloured.
401. 10 f. Type **98** 20 15
402. 15 f. "Cypraea vitellus" 30 15
403. 25 f. "Cypraea argus" 40 30
404. 27 f. "Cypraea carneola" 55 40
405. 40 f. "Cypraea mappa" 80 55
406. 50 f. "Cypraea tigris" 1·10 80

See also Nos. 428/33, 440/5, 459/64, 481/6 and 510/15.

99. Santos-Dumont, Airship No. 14 and Aircraft "14 bis".

1982. Air. 50th Death Anniv. of Alberto Santo-Dumont (aviation pioneer).
407. **99.** 95 f. brown, green and blue 2·25 1·40

1982. Air. World Cup Football Championship Result. No. 384 optd. **ITALIE VAINQUEUR 1982.**
408. **89.** 120 f. brown, black and green 2·75 2·00

101. Beach.

1982. Air. Overseas Week.
409. **101.** 105 f. multicoloured 2·25 1·75

102. Coral.

1982. Marine Life. Multicoloured.
410 32 f. Type **102** 65 45
411 35 f. Starfish 75 45
412 46 f. "Hexabranchus sanguineus" 1·00 75
413 63 f. "Spondylus barbatus" 1·40 1·10

103. Hands reaching towards Eye. **104.** St. Theresa of Avila.

1982. Air. Blind Day.
414 **103** 130 f. blue, scarlet & red 2·25 2·00

1982. 400th Death Anniv. of St. Theresa of Avila.
415. **104.** 31 f. brown, green and deep brown .. 80 55
See also No. 447.

105. "Adoration of the Virgin" (Correggio).

1982. Air. Christmas.
416. **105.** 170 f. multicoloured .. 3·50 2·50

106. Wallis Meeting House.

1983.
417. **106.** 19 f. multicoloured .. 55 30

107. Eiffel and Eiffel Tower under Construction.

1983. 60th Death Anniv. of Gustave Eiffel (engineer).
418. **107.** 97 f. purple, red and green .. .. 2·00 1·60

108. Windsurfing. **110.** Early Balloon.

109. Island Scene and U.P.U. Emblem.

1983. Air.
419. **108.** 270 f. multicoloured .. 5·50 3·25

1983. Air. World U.P.U. Day.
420. **109.** 100 f. multicoloured .. 2·25 1·40

1983. Air. Bicent of Manned Flight.
421. **110.** 205 f. multicoloured .. 4·25 2·75

111. "Cat".

1983. Air. 150th Death Anniv. of Foujita (painter).
422. **111.** 102 f. multicoloured .. 2·25 1·40

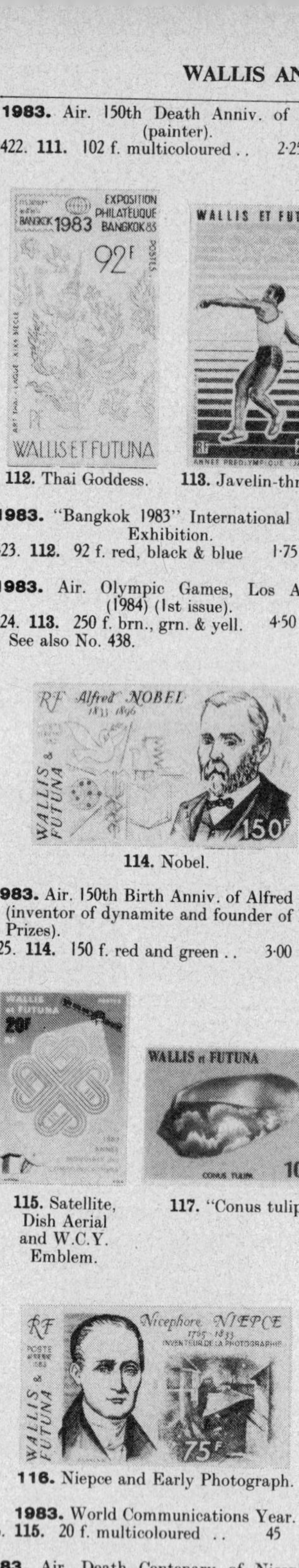

112. Thai Goddess. **113.** Javelin-thrower.

1983. "Bangkok 1983" International Stamp Exhibition.
423. **112.** 92 f. red, black & blue 1·75 1·10

1983. Air. Olympic Games, Los Angeles (1984) (1st issue).
424. **113.** 250 f. brn., grn. & yell. 4·50 3·50
See also No. 438.

114. Nobel.

1983. Air. 150th Birth Anniv. of Alfred Nobel (inventor of dynamite and founder of Nobel Prizes).
425. **114.** 150 f. red and green .. 3·00 2·00

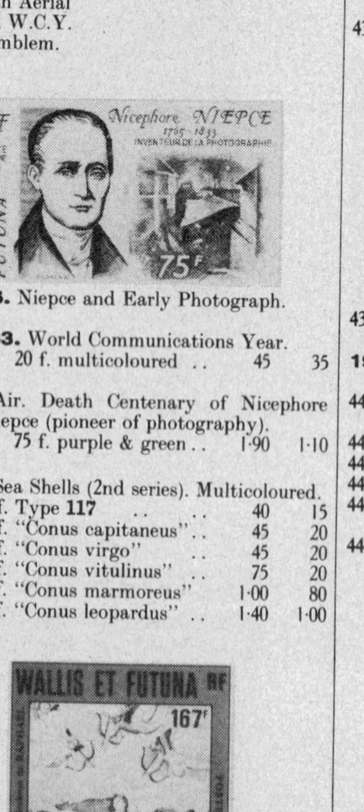

115. Satellite, Dish Aerial and W.C.Y. Emblem. **117.** "Conus tulipa".

116. Niepce and Early Photograph.

1983. World Communications Year.
426. **115.** 20 f. multicoloured .. 45 35

1983. Air. Death Centenary of Nicephore Niepce (pioneer of photography).
427. **116.** 75 f. purple & green .. 1·90 1·10

1983. Sea Shells (2nd series). Multicoloured.
428. 10 f. Type **117** 40 15
429. 17 f. "Conus capitaneus" .. 45 20
430. 21 f. "Conus virgo" .. 45 20
431. 39 f. "Conus vitulinus" .. 75 20
432. 52 f. "Conus marmoreus" 1·00 80
433. 65 f. "Conus leopardus" .. 1·40 1·00

118. "Triumph of Galatea".

1983. Air. 500th Birth Anniv. of Raphael (artist).
434. **118.** 167 f. multicoloured .. 3·25 2·50

119. Pandanus Tree.

1983. Air.
435. **119.** 137 f. multicoloured .. 2·75 1·75

120. "Madonna and Pope Sixtus" (Raphael).

1983. Air. Christmas.
436. **120.** 200 f. multicoloured .. 4·25 2·75

121. Frigate "Commandant Bory".

1984. Air.
437. **121.** 67 f. multicoloured .. 1·50 1·00

122. Weightlifting.

1984. Air. Olympic Games, Los Angeles (2nd issue).
438. **122.** 85 f. multicoloured .. 2·00 1·40

123. Frangipani.

1984. Air.
439. **123.** 130 f. multicoloured .. 2·75 1·75

1984. Sea Shells (3rd series). As T **117**. Multicoloured.
440. 22 f. "Strombus lentiginosus 40 30
441. 25 f. "Lambis chiragra" .. 40 30
442. 35 f. "Strombus dentatus" 75 40
443. 43 f. "Lambis scorpius" .. 1·10 65
444. 49 f. "Strombus aurisdianae .. .. .. 1·40 90
445. 76 f. "Lambis crocata" .. 1·90 1·40

124. "Deposition of Christ" (Alele Chapel).

1984. Air. Easter.
446. **124.** 190 f. multicoloured .. 3·50 2·50

1984. "Espana 84" International Stamp Exhibition, Madrid. As T **104** but with "Espana 84" emblem.
447 70 f. sepia, green and brown 1·50 1·10

125. Diderot and Title Page of Encyclopedia. **126.** Killer Whale.

1984. Death Bicent. of Denis Diderot (encyclopedist).
448. **125.** 100 f. brown & blue .. 2·00 1·40

1984. Nature Protection.
449. **126.** 90 f. multicoloured .. 2·00 1·40

127. Painting. **128.** Tiki.

1984. Air. 95th Birth Anniv. of Jean Cocteau (artist).
450. **127.** 150 f. multicoloured .. 3·00 2·25

1984. Air. Soane Hoatau Sculpture.
451. **128.** 175 f. multicoloured .. 3·25 2·50

129. "Alice". **130.** "Pilioko Aloi" (tapestry).

1984. Air. Birth Centenary of Amedeo Modigliani (painter).
452. **129.** 140 f. multicoloured .. 3·00 2·00

1984. Air. "Ausipex 84" International Stamp Exhibition, Melbourne.
453. **130.** 180 f. multicoloured .. 3·50 2·25

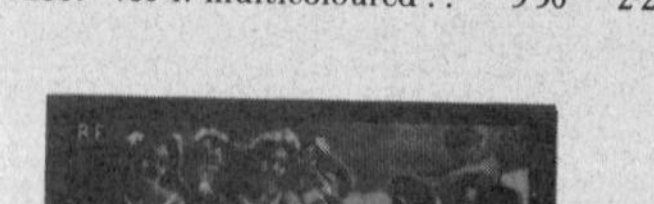

131. "Local Dances" (Jean Michon).

1984. Air.
454. **131.** 110 f. multicoloured .. 2·50 1·75

132. Altar, Mount Lulu Chapel.

1984. Air.
455. **132.** 52 f. multicoloured .. 1·10 75

133. Islanders wearing Leis.

1985. 4th Pacific Arts Festival.

456. **133.**	160 f. multicoloured ..	3·00	2·25

134. Conch Shell and Virgin and Child.

1984. Air. Christmas.

457. **134.**	260 f. multicoloured ..	5·00	2·75

135. Lapita Pottery.

136. Victor Hugo.

1985. Archaeological Expedition.

458. **135.**	53 f. multicoloured ..	1·00	55

1985. Sea Shells (4th series). As T **117**. Multicoloured.

459.	2 f. "Nautilus pompilius"	10	10
460.	3 f. "Murex bruneus" ..	10	10
461.	41 f. "Casmaria erinaceus"	75	45
462.	47 f. "Conus vexillum" ..	1·00	65
463.	56 f. "Harpa harpa" ..	1·10	75
464.	71 f. "Murex ramosus" ..	1·60	1·00

1985. Death Centenary of Victor Hugo (writer).

465. **136.**	89 f. deep blue, blue and red	2·00	1·25

137. "Pilioko Aloi" (tapestry).

1985. Air.

466. **137.**	500 f. multicoloured ..	8·50	5·50

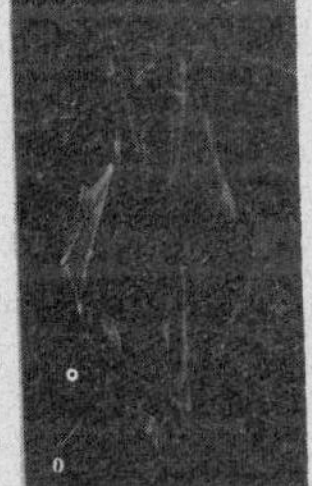

138. Flying Fox.

139. Children.

1985.

467. **138.**	38 f. multicoloured ..	1·00	55

1985. International Youth Year.

468. **139.**	64 f. multicoloured ..	1·25	80

140. "The Post Office".

1985. Air. 30th Death Anniv. of Maurice Utrillo (artist).

469. **140.**	200 f. multicoloured ..	3·50	2·25

141. Hands and U.N. Emblem.

1985. 40th Anniv. of U.N.O.

470. **141.**	49 f. grn., bl. & red ..	1·00	65

142. Sailing Canoe.

1985. Air.

471. **142.**	350 f. multicoloured ..	6·00	3·25

143. Ronsard, Organist and Muse of Poetry.

1985. 400th Death Anniv. of Pierre de Ronsard (poet).

472. **143.**	170 f. brown, deep brown and blue ..	3·50	2·25

144. Landing Ship "Jacques Cartier".

145. "Portrait of Young Woman" (Patrice Nielly).

1985. Air.

473. **144.**	51 f. deep blue, blue and turquoise ..	1·00	65

1985. Air.

474. **145.**	245 f. multicoloured ..	4·25	2·25

146. Schweitzer, African Boy and Cathedral Organ.

1985. 20th Death Anniv. of Dr. Albert Schweitzer (missionary).

475. **146.**	50 f. blk., pur. & brn.	1·00	65

147. "Virgin and Child" (Jean Michon).

1985. Air. Christmas.

476. **147.**	330 f. multicoloured ..	6·00	4·00

148. Bread-fruit.

1986. Food and Agriculture Organization.

477. **148.**	39 f. multicoloured ..	90	55

149. Flamboyant Flower.

1986.

478. **149.**	38 f. multicoloured ..	90	55

150. Comet and "Giotto" Space Probe.

1986. Air. Appearance of Halley's Comet.

479. **150.**	100 f. multicoloured ..	2·00	1·40

151. Vianney praying.

1986. Air. Birth Bicentenary of Cure d'Ars.

480. **151.**	200 f. light brown, brown and black ..	4·00	2·50

1986. Sea Shells (5th series). As T **117**. Multicoloured.

481.	4 f. "Lambis truncata" ..	10	10
482.	5 f. "Charonia tritonis" ..	10	10
483.	10 f. "Oliva miniacea" ..	20	15
484.	18 f. "Distorsio anus" ..	30	20
485.	25 f. "Mitra mitra" ..	55	35
486.	107 f. "Conus distans" ..	2·00	1·40

152. Players and Boy with Football.

1986. World Cup Football Championship, Mexico.

487. **152.**	95 f. multicoloured ..	2·00	1·25

153. Willem Schouten and "Eendracht".

1986. 370th Anniv of Discovery of Horn Islands. Each purple, green and blue.

488	8 f. Type **153**	20	15
489	9 f. Jacob le Maire and "Hoorn"	20	15
490	155 f. Map of Futuna and Alofi Islands	3·00	2·50

154. Watt and Steam Engine.

1986. 250th Birth Anniv. of James Watt (inventor).

491. **154.**	74 f. red and black ..	1·50	1·10

155. Queen Amelia.

1986. Air. Centenary of Request for Protectorate and 25th Anniv. of French Overseas Territory Status. Each purple, red and blue.

492.	90 f. Type **155**	1·75	1·75
493.	137 f. Law of 1961 bestowing Overseas Territory status ..	2·50	2·50

156. Patrol Boat "La Lorientaise".

1986. Naval Ships.

494. **156.**	6 f. red, purple & blue	15	10
495. –	7 f. violet, orge. & red	15	10
496. –	120 f. turq., red & bl.	2·25	1·60

DESIGNS: 7 f. Frigate "Commandant Blaison". 120 f. Frigate "Balny".

157. Oleander.

1986.

497. **157.**	97 f. multicoloured ..	2·00	1·40

158. U.P.U. Emblem and Dove carrying Envelope.

1986. Air. World Post Day.

498. **158.**	270 f. multicoloured ..	5·00	3·50

MINIMUM PRICE

The minimum price quoted is 5p which represents a handling charge rather than a basis for valuing common stamps. For further notes about prices see introductory pages.

159. New York, Statue and Paris.

1986. Air. Centenary of Statue of Liberty.
499. **159.** 205 f. multicoloured .. 4·00 2·50

160. "Virgin and Child" (Botticelli).

1986. Christmas.
500. **160.** 250 f. multicoloured .. 4·50 3·00

161. "Papilio montrouzieri".

162. Father Chanel and Basilica.

1987. Butterflies. Multicoloured.

501	2 f. Type **161**	30	20
502	42 f. Caper white	75	45
503	46 f. "Delias ellipsis" ..	90	55
504	50 f. "Danaus pumila" ..	1·00	65
505	52 f. "Lutbrodes cleotas"	1·00	65
506	59 f. Meadow argus ..	1·40	90

1987. Air. 1st Anniv. of Poi Basilica.
507. **162.** 230 f. multicoloured .. 4·50 2·50

163. "Telstar", Globe and Pleumeur-Bodou.

1987. Air. World Communications Day. 25th Anniv. of Launch of "Telstar" Communications Satellite.
508. **163.** 200 f. blue, black and red .. .. .. 3·50 2·00

164. Wrestlers.

1987. World Wrestling Championships, Clermont-Ferrand.
509. **164.** 97 f. multicoloured .. 1·90 1·25

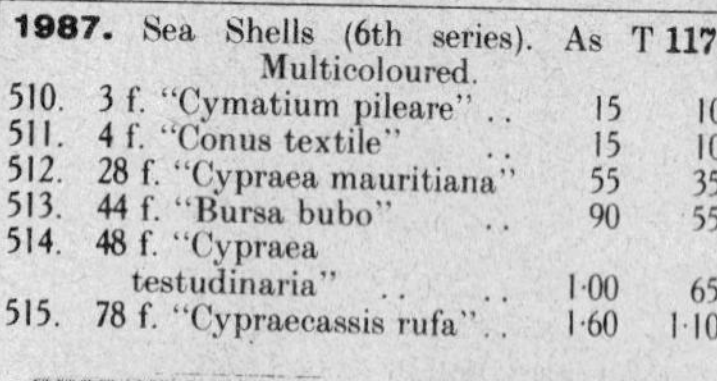

1987. Sea Shells (6th series). As T **117**. Multicoloured.

510.	3 f. "Cymatium pileare" ..	15	10
511.	4 f. "Conus textile" ..	15	10
512.	28 f. "Cypraea mauritiana"	55	35
513.	44 f. "Bursa bubo" ..	90	55
514.	48 f. "Cypraea testudinaria"	1·00	65
515.	78 f. "Cypraecassis rufa" ..	1·60	1·10

165. Piccard, Stratosphere Balloon F.N.R.S. and Bathyscaphe.

167. Bust of Girl.

1987. Air. 25th Death Anniv. of Auguste Piccard (physicist).
516. **165.** 135 f. deep blue, blue and green .. .. 2·50 1·60

1987. "Olymphilex '87" Olympic Stamps Exhibition, Rome. No. 509 optd. **OLYMPHILEX '87 ROME** and Olympic rings.
517. **164.** 97 f. multicoloured .. 1·90 1·25

1987. 70th Death Anniv. of Auguste Rodin (sculptor).
518. **167.** 150 f. purple .. .. 2·75 1·75
See also No. 557.

168. Letters between Globes and Postbird.

1987. World Post Day.
519. **168.** 116 f. blue, deep blue and yellow .. .. 2·25 1·40

169. Spotbill Duck.

1987. Birds. Multicoloured.

520.	6 f. Type **169**	10	10
521.	19 f. American golden plover	35	20
522.	47 f. Friendly quail dove ..	90	55
523.	56 f. Turnstone	1·00	65
524.	64 f. Banded rail	1·25	65
525.	68 f. Bar-tailed godwit ..	1·40	90

170. Mgr. Bataillon, French Frigate and Islands.

1987. Air. 150th Anniv. of Arrival of First Missionaries.
526. **170.** 260 f. turquoise, blue and brown .. .. 4·75 3·00

171. Nativity Scene.

1987. Air. Christmas.
527. **171.** 300 f. multicoloured .. 5·50 3·50

172. Carco and Parisian Scenes.

1988. 30th Death Anniv. of Francis Carco (writer).
528. **172.** 40 f. multicoloured .. 80 45

173. "Bleriot" Airplane and Garros.

1988. Air. 70th Death Anniv. of Roland Garros (aviator).
529. **173.** 600 f. deep blue, brown and blue .. 10·50 6·75

174 La Perouse, "L'Astrolabe" and "La Boussole"

1988. Bicentenary of Disappearance of La Perouse's Expedition.
530 **174** 70 f. green, blue & brn 1·50 90

175 "Self-Portrait wearing Lace Jabot"

1988. Air. Death Bicentenary of Maurice Quentin de la Tour (painter).
531 **175** 500 f. multicoloured .. 9·00 6·00

176 Arrows and Dish Aerial

1988. Air. World Telecommunications Day.
532 **176** 100 f. multicoloured .. 1·75 1·25

177 Map and Bishop with Crosier

1988. Air. South Pacific Episcopal Conference.
533 **177** 90 f. multicoloured .. 1·75 1·10

178 Nurse, Child and Anniversary Emblem

1988. 125th Anniv of International Red Cross.
534 **178** 30 f. black, green & red 60 45

179 Throwing the Javelin

1988. Olympic Games, Seoul. Each brown, red and blue.

535	11 f. Type **179**	35	20
536	20 f. Volleyball	45	35
537	60 f. Windsurfing ..	1·25	1·00
538	80 f. Yachting	1·60	1·40

180 Envelopes forming Map

1988. World Post Day.
539 **180** 17 f. yellow, blue & blk 40 20

181 Becquerel

1988. Birth Bicentenary of Antoine Becquerel (physicist).
540 **181** 18 f. black and blue .. 40 20

182 Nativity Scene

1988. Air. Christmas.
541 **182** 400 f. multicoloured .. 7·25 4·50

183 "Amiral Charner" (frigate)

1989. International Maritime Organization.
542 **183** 26 f. multicoloured .. 75 45

184 Renoir and Scene from "The Great Illusion"

1989. 10th Death Anniv of Jean Renoir (film director).
543 **184** 24 f. brown, mve & orge 50 35

185 Royal Throne (Aselo Kulimoetoke)

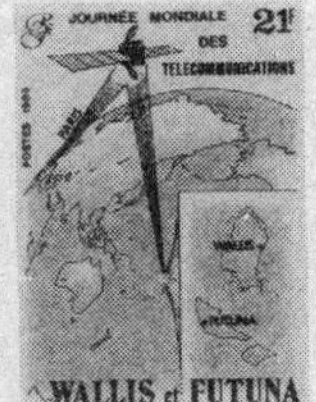

186 Map

1989. Air.
544 **185** 700 f. multicoloured .. 12·00 7·25

1989. Futuna Hydro-electric Power Station.
545 **186** 25 f. multicoloured .. 50 35

188 Satellite above Earth

1989. International Telecommunications Day.
546 **188** 21 f. multicoloured .. 45 35

189 Mural (H. Tailhade)

1989.
547 **189** 22 f. multicoloured .. 45 35

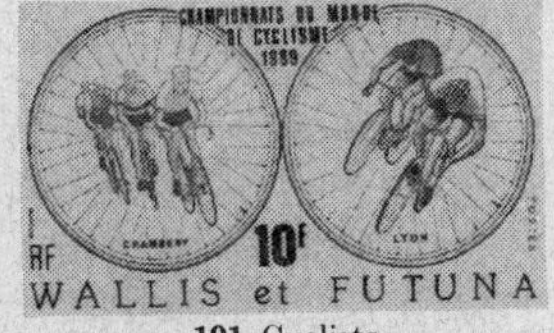

190 Globe and Emblem

1989. "Philexfrance '89" International Stamp Exhibition, Paris (548) and Bicentenary of Declaration of Rights of Man and South Pacific Youth Meeting (549). Multicoloured.
548 29 f. Type **190** (postage) .. 50 35
549 900 f. Sportsmen (air) .. 14·50 11·50

191 Cyclists

1989. World Cycling Championships, France.
551 **191** 10 f. black, brown & grn 30 15

192 Envelopes around Globe of Flags

1989. World Post Day.
552 **192** 27 f. multicoloured .. 50 35

193 Landscape

1989.
553 **193** 23 f. multicoloured .. 75 60

1989. Air. Christmas. As No. 347 but date, value and colour changed.
554 **67** 800 f. mauve .. .. 14·00 9·00

194 "Star of Bethlehem"

1990.
555 **194** 44 f. multicoloured .. 80 55

195 Tortoise Fossil

1990.
556 **195** 48 f. multicoloured .. 80 55

1990. 150th Birth Anniv of Auguste Rodin (sculptor). As No. 518 but value and colour changed.
557 **167** 200 f. blue .. .. 4·00 2·25

197 Footballers

1990. World Cup Football Championship, Italy.
558 **197** 59 f. multicoloured .. 1·10 80

198 Orchids

1990. Mothers' Day.
559 **198** 78 f. multicoloured .. 1·60 1·10

199 Aircraft and Clement Ader

1990. Air. Cent of First Heavier-than-Air Flight and 1st Anniv of Wallis–Tahiti Air Link.
560 **199** 56 f. brown, mve & red 1·10 65

200 Red-tailed Tropic Bird

1990. Multicoloured.
561 300 f. Type **200** .. .. 5·50 3·25
562 600 f. South Pacific islet 11·50 6·75

201 "Moana II" (inter-island freighter)

1990. Ships.
563 **201** 40 f. brown, green & bl 90 60
564 – 50 f. brown, blue & grn 1·10 80
DESIGN: 50 f. "Moana III" (container ship) at jetty.

202 Traditional Dwellings

1990.
565 **202** 28 f. multicoloured .. 55 35

203 Doves and Globe

204 Outrigger Canoe

1990. Stamp Day.
566 **203** 97 f. multicoloured .. 1·90 1·40

1990.
567 **204** 46 f. multicoloured .. 1·25 65

205 De Gaulle

1990. Air. Birth Centenary of Charles de Gaulle (French statesman).
568 **205** 1000 f. multicoloured .. 17·00 10·00

206 Palm Trees

1990. "Best Wishes".
569 **206** 100 f. multicoloured .. 1·90 1·40

207 Patrol Boat "La Glorieuse"

1991.
570 **207** 52 f. blue, green and red 1·50 85
See also No. 578.

208 Warrior

1991.
571 7 f. Breadfruit gatherer .. 10 10
572 54 f. Taro planter .. 1·00 55
573 63 f. Spear fisherman .. 1·10 65
574 72 f. Type **208** .. .. 1·25 65
575 90 f. Kailao dancer .. 1·60 80

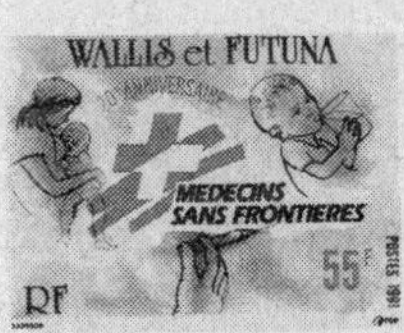

209 Aspects of Health Care

1991. 20th Anniv of Medecins sans Frontieres (medical charity).
577 **209** 55 f. multicoloured .. 1·00 65

1991. Patrol Boat "La Moqueuse". As T **207**.
578 42 f. black, blue and red .. 1·25 65

210 Chanel and Reliquary

1991. Air. 150th Death Anniv of Father Chanel (missionary).
579 **210** 235 f. multicoloured .. 4·50 2·75

211 Players through the Ages ($\frac{1}{2}$-size illustration)

1991. Air. Centenary of French Open Tennis Championships.
580 **211** 250 f. black, orge & grn 4·75 2·75

212 Map and Aircraft

1991. Ultralight Aircraft Flying in Wallis and Futuna.
581 **212** 85 f. multicoloured .. 1·75 1·10

213 "Portrait of Jean"

1991. 150th Birth Anniv of Pierre Auguste Renoir (painter). Perf or imperf (self-adhesive).
582 **213** 400 f. multicoloured .. 7·25 4·00

214 Map

1991. 30th Anniv of French Overseas Territory Status.
584 **214** 102 f. multicoloured .. 1·60 1·10

215 Islanders in Festive Dress and Angel

1991. Feast of the Assumption.
585 **215** 30 f. multicoloured .. 55 35

216 Mozart and Scene from "The Marriage of Figaro"

1991. Air. Death Bicentenary of Wolfgang Amadeus Mozart (composer).
586 **216** 500 f. blue, lilac and red 8·25 4·50

217 Imprisoned Figure

1991. 30th Anniv of Amnesty International.
587 **217** 140 f. yellow, violet & bl 2·75 1·40

218 House and Generator

1991. 50th Anniv of Central Economic Co-operation Bank.
588 **218** 10 f. multicoloured .. 15 10

219 "Allamanda cathartica"

1991. Flowers. Multicoloured.
589 1 f. Type **219** 10 10
590 4 f. "Hibiscus rosa sinensis" (vert) .. 10 10
591 80 f. Water lily .. .. 1·40 90

220 Santa Claus on Beach

1991. Christmas.
592 **220** 60 f. multicoloured .. 1·00 55

221 Ski Jumping

1992. Winter Olympic Games, Albertville.
593 **221** 150 f. multicoloured .. 2·75 1·60

222 Map, Plants and Airplane

1992. "Escadrille 9S" Maritime Surveillance Service.
594 **222** 48 f. multicoloured .. 90 45

223 Canadian 1938 $1 and Wallis & Futuna 1920 2 f. Stamps (½-size illustration)

1992. "Canada 92" International Youth Philatelic Exhibition, Montreal.
595 **223** 35 f. black, red & violet 45 30

224 Throwing the Javelin

1992. Olympic Games, Barcelona.
596 **224** 106 f. indigo, bl & grn 1·60 95

225 Spanish 1975 4 p. Stamp and Wallis Post Office

1992. "Granada 92" International Stamp Exhibition.
597 **225** 100 f. black, blue & pur 1·40 85

226 Columbus's Fleet, Pavilion and Seville

1992. "Expo 92" World's Fair, Seville.
598 **226** 200 f. green, blue & orge 2·75 2·10

227 Saddleback Butterfly Fish

1992. Butterfly and Angel Fishes. Mult.
599 21 f. Type **227** 25 20
600 22 f. Threadfin butterfly fish 30 20
601 23 f. Horned coachman .. 30 20
602 24 f. Royal angelfish .. 30 20
603 25 f. Spectacled angelfish 30 20
604 26 f. One spot butterfly fish 35 25

228 Columbus and Map

1992. Air. "World Columbian Stamp Expo '92", Chicago.
605 **228** 100 f. multicoloured .. 1·25 80
See also No. 612.

229 Three Spearmen

1992. Wallis Islands. Multicoloured.
606 70 f. Type **229** 90 55
607 70 f. Two spearmen and palm trees 90 55
608 70 f. Pirogues 90 55
609 70 f. Two fishermen and palm trees 90 55
610 70 f. Three fishermen and palm trees 90 55
Nos. 602/6 were issued together, se-tenant, forming a composite design.

1992. Air. "Genova '92" International Thematic Stamp Exhibition. As T **228** but with different Exhibition emblem.
612 800 f. multicoloured .. 10·00 6·25

230 Victorious Marianne

1992. Air. Bicentenary of Year One of First French Republic.
613 **230** 350 f. black, blue & red 4·50 2·75

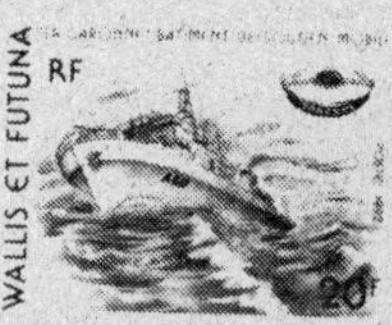
231 "La Garonne" (supply vessel)

1992.
614 **231** 20 f. multicoloured .. 25 15

232 "L'Idylle d'Ixelles"

1992. 75th Death Anniv of Auguste Rodin (sculptor).
615 **232** 300 f. black and mauve 3·75 2·40

233 "Mirabilis jalapa"

1992.
616 **233** 200 f. multicoloured .. 2·50 1·60

234 Airplane, Frigate and Native Canoes

1993. French Naval Forces in the Pacific.
617 **234** 130 f. multicoloured .. 1·75 1·25

235 Abstract (J. E. Korda)

1993. School Art.
618 **235** 56 f. multicoloured .. 1·60 1·00
See also Nos. 635/6.

236 Banded Rail

1993. Birds. Multicoloured.

619	50 f. Type **236**	65	40
620	60 f. Purple swamphen ..	75	50
621	110 f. Grey's fruit dove ..	1·40	85

237 Building Facade

1993. Air. Bicentenary of the Louvre, Paris.

622 **237** 315 f. ultramarine, red and blue .. .. 4·00 2·50

238 Copernicus and Planetary Model

1993. Air. "Polska '93" International Stamp Exhibition, Poznan. 450th Death Anniv of Nicolas Copernicus (astronomer).

623 **238** 600 f. red, brown and crimson .. .. 7·75 4·75

239 Hibiscus

1993. Mothers' Day. Multicoloured.

624	95 f. Type **239**	1·25	75
625	120 f. Bouquet of stephanotis	1·50	95

240 Sailfin surgeon fish

1993. Fishes. Multicoloured.

626	27 f. Spinefoot	35	25
627	35 f. Type **240**	45	30
628	45 f. Flag-tailed surgeon fish	60	40
629	53 f. Fox-face	70	45

241 D'Entrecasteaux and Flagship

1993. Death Bicentenary of Bruni d'Entrecasteaux (explorer).

630 **241** 170 f. red, blue & black 2·25 1·40

242 Symbols of Taiwan

1993. "Taipei '93" International Stamp Exn.

631 **242** 435 f. multicoloured .. 5·50 3·25

243 Tepa Church, Wallis Island

1993. Churches. Multicoloured.

632	30 f. Type **243**	40	25
633	30 f. Vilamalia Church, Futuna Island	40	25

244 "La Marseillaise"

1993. Air. Bicentenary of Year Two of First French Republic.

634 **244** 400 f. red, blue & black 5·00 3·00

1993. School Art. As T **235**.

635	28 f. blue, black & grey	35	25
636	52 f. multicoloured ..	65	40

DESIGNS—HORIZ. 28 f. Palm trees (T. Tuhimutu). VERT. 52 f. People (M. Hakula).

245 Nativity

1993. Christmas.

637 **245** 80 f. multicoloured .. 1·00 60

POSTAGE DUE STAMPS

1920. Postage Due Stamps of New Caledonia optd **ILES WALLIS et FUTUNA**.

D18	D **18**	5 c. blue	60	70
D19		10 c. brown on buff	60	70
D20		15 c. green ..	60	70
D21		20 c. black on yellow	70	80
D22		30 c. red	70	80
D23		50 c. blue on cream	1·00	1·25
D24		60 c. green on blue ..	1·40	1·50
D25		1 f. green on cream	1·75	1·75

1927. As Postage Due stamp of New Caledonia, but colour changed, surch.

D43	D **18**	2 f. on 1 f. mauve ..	6·50	7·00
D44		3 f. on 1 f. brown ..	6·50	7·00

1930. Postage Due stamps of New Caledonia optd **ILES WALLIS et FUTUNA**.

D85	D **25**	2 c. brown and blue	20	30
D86		4 c. green and red ..	25	35
D87		5 c. blue and red ..	25	35
D88		10 c. blue and purple	25	35
D89		15 c. red and green	30	40
D90		20 c. brown & purple	30	45
D91		25 c. blue and brown	30	45
D92		30 c. brown & green	60	75
D93		50 c. red and brown	40	50
D94		60 c. red and mauve	1·00	1·25
D95		1 f. green and blue ..	75	85
D96		2 f. brown and red ..	75	90
D97		3 f. brown & mauve	75	90

1943. Nos. D85/97 optd **FRANCE LIBRE**.

D126	D **25**	2 c. brown and blue	18·00	25·00
D127		4 c. green and red	18·00	25·00
D128		5 c. blue and red ..	18·00	25·00
D129		10 c. blue & purple	18·00	25·00
D130		15 c. red and green	18·00	25·00
D131		20 c. brown & pur	18·00	25·00
D132		25 c. blue and brown	18·00	25·00
D133		30 c. brown & green	18·00	25·00
D134		50 c. red and brown	18·00	25·00
D135		60 c. red and mauve	18·00	25·00
D136		1 f. green and blue	20·00	27·00
D137		2 f. brown and red	20·00	27·00
D138		3 f. brown & mauve	20·00	27·00

D **18.** Moorish Idol.

1963. Fishes.

D182	D **18**	1 f. black, yell & bl	65	65
D183	–	3 f. red, green & bl	1·00	1·00
D184	–	5 f. orange, blk & bl	1·60	1·60

DESIGNS—HORIZ. 3 f. Green wrasse. 5 f. Orange anemone fish.

WENDEN Pt. 10

Formerly part of W. Russia but later became part of Latvia. Issued stamps for use within the district until 1903.

100 kopeks = 1 rouble.

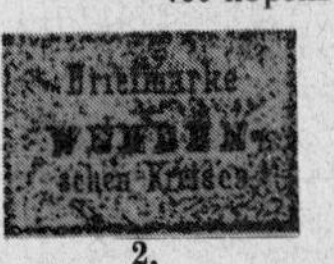

2. **3.**

1863. Inscr "Briefmarke des WENDEN-schen Kreises". Imperf.

1 **2** 2 k. black and red £180 £225

1863. Inscr "Packenmarke des WENDEN-schen Kreises". Imperf.

2 **3** 4 k. black and green .. £120 £200

6. **7.** **8.**

1863. Imperf.

6. **6.** 2 k. green and red .. .. 20·00 24·00

1864. As T **6**, but with horse in central oval. Imperf.

5. 2 k. green and red .. .. 60·00 £120

1871. Imperf.

7. **7.** 2 k. green and red .. .. 15·00 18·00

1872. Perf.

8. **8.** 2 k. red and green .. .. 20·00 27·00

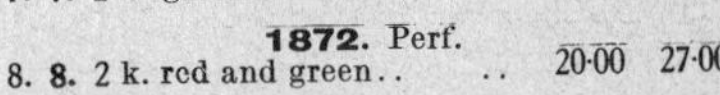

9. Arms of Wenden. **10.** **11.** Castle of Wenden.

1875.

9. **9.** 2 k. green and red .. .. 5·00 7·00

1878.

10. **10.**	2 k. green and red	5·00	9·00
11.	2 k. red, brown and green	5·00	9·00
13.	2 k. green, black and red ..	6·00	15·00

1901.

14. **11.**	2 k. brown and green ..	4·00	10·00
15.	2 k. red and green ..	4·00	10·00
16.	2 k. purple and green ..	4·00	10·00

WEST IRIAN Pt. 21

The following stamps superseded Nos. 1/19 of West New Guinea, after the former Dutch territory became part of Indonesia. From 1971 Indonesian stamps have been used.

100 cents or sen = 1 rupiah.

1963. Stamps of Indonesia optd. **IRIAN BARAT**, or surch. also.

1.	–	1 s. on 70 s. red (No. 724)	10	10
2.	–	2 s. on 90 s. grn. (No. 727)	10	10
3.	–	5 s. grey (No. 830) ..	5	5
4.	–	6 s. on 20 s. bistre (No. 833)	5	5
5.	–	7 s. on 50 s. blue (No. 835)	5	5
6.	–	10 s. brown (No. 831) ..	5	5
7.	–	15 s. purple (No. 832) ..	5	5
8.	**134.**	25 s. green	10	10
9.	–	30 s. on 75 s. red (No. 836)	12	12
10.	–	40 s. on 1 r. 15 red (No. 837)	15	15
11.	**99.**	1 r. mauve	35	35
12.		2 r. green	75	75
13.		3 r. blue	95	95
14.		5 r. brown	1·60	1·60

1a. Indonesia, from Atjeh to Merauke.

1963. Acquisition of West Irian.

21.	**1a.**	12 s. orge., red and blk.	5	5
22.		17 s. orge., red and blk.	8	8
23.	–	20 s. blue, green & grey	12	12
24.	–	50 s. blue, green & grey	20	20
25.	–	60 s. brn., yell. & green	75	35
26.	–	75 s. brn., yell. & green	95	40

DESIGNS: 20 s., 50 s. Parachutist. 60 s., 75 s. Greater Bird of Paradise.

2. "Maniltoa gemmipara". **4.** Mother and Child Figurine.

3. Map of Indonesia.

1968. Flora and Fauna.
27. 2. 5 s. purple and green .. 10 10
28. – 15 s. violet and green .. 20 20
29. – 30 s. green and orange .. 25 25
30. – 40 s. violet and yellow .. 45 45
31. – 50 s. black and red .. 55 55
32. – 75 s. black and blue .. 1·25 75
33. – 1 r. black and brown .. 1·10 1·10
34. – 3 r. black and green .. 2·40 1·60
35. – 5 r. multicoloured .. 1·10 50
36. – 10 r. multicoloured .. 2·25 1·10
DESIGNS: 15 s. "Dendrobium lancifolium". 30 s. "Gardenia gjelleripii". 40 s. "Manitoa gemmipara" (blossom). 50 s. Common phalanger. 75 s. One-wattled cassowary. 1 r. Common forest wallaby. 3 r. Blue crown pigeons. 5 r. Black capped lory. 10 r. Great bird of paradise.

1968. West Irian People's Pledge of 9 May 1964.
43. 3. 10 s. gold and blue .. 20 20
44. 25 s. gold and red .. 25 25

1970. West Irian Wood-carvings. Mult.
45. 5 s. Type 4 .. .. 5 5
46. 6 s. Carved shield 5 5
47. 7 s. Man and serpents .. 5 5
48. 10 s. Drum 5 5
49. 25 s. Seated warrior .. 8 8
50. 30 s. "Female" drum .. 8 8
51. 50 s. Bamboo vessel .. 12 12
52. 75 s. Seated man and tree .. 20 20
53. 1 r. Decoratedshield .. 30 30
54. 2 r. Seated figure 55 55
Nos. 45/54 are inscr. "I.B." ("Irian Barat").

POSTAGE DUE STAMPS.

1963. Postage Due Stamps as Type D 100 of Indonesia, optd. **IRIAN BARAT.**
D 15. 1 s. slate 5 5
D 16. 5 s. olive 5 5
D 17. 10 s. turquoise 5 5
D 18. 25 s. slate 12 15
D 19. 40 s. orange 20 25
D 20. 100 s. brown 50 55

1968. As Type D 100 of Indonesia, but with coloured network background incorporating "1968", optd. **IRIAN BARAT.**
D 37. 1 s. blue and green .. 5 5
D 38. 5 s. green and pink .. 8 8
D 39. 10 s. red and grey .. 12 12
D 40. 25 s. green and yellow .. 20 20
D 41. 40 s. purple and green .. 25 25
D 42. 100 s. red and olive .. 45 45

WEST NEW GUINEA Pt. 4

U.N. Administration of former Netherlands New Guinea from 1 Oct. 1962 to 30 April 1963, when it became known as West Irian and became part of Indonesia.

100 cents = 1 gulden.

1962. "United Nations Temporary Executive Authority". Stamps of Netherlands New Guinea optd **UNTEA**.
1 5 1 c. yellow and red .. 1·10 1·25
21 – 2 c. orange .. 1·10 1·40
3 5 5 c. yellow and brown .. 1·10 1·40
4 – 7 c. pur, bl & brn (No. 60) 1·50 1·60
5 – 10 c. brown & bl (No. 27) 1·10 1·40
6 – 12 c. pur, bl & grn (No. 61) 1·60 1·90
7 – 15 c. brown & yell (No. 28) 1·60 1·90
8 – 17 c. pur, bl & blk (No. 62) 1·60 1·60
9 – 20 c. brown & grn (No. 29) 1·60 1·60
10 6 25 c. red .. .. 2·75 2·75
11 30 c. blue .. .. 2·75 2·75
12 40 c. orange .. .. 2·75 2·75
13 45 c. green .. .. 3·25 4·00
14 55 c. turquoise .. .. 3·25 4·00
34 80 c. grey .. .. 21·00 18·00
16 85 c. brown .. .. 8·50 8·00
17 1 g. purple .. .. 8·50 7·50
18 – 2 g. brown (No. 20) .. 25·00 20·00
19 – 5 g. green (No. 21) .. 20·00 17·00

For later issues see **WEST IRIAN**.

WEST UKRAINE Pt. 10

Before the 1914/18 War this district, known as E. Galicia, was part of Austria. It achieved temporary independence after the war when stamps were issued. In June 1919 it became part of Poland but was transferred to the Ukraine in 1945.

100 heller = 1 krone.

(5.)

1919. Stamps of Austria 1916 optd. with T 5.
70. 49. 3 h. violet 30
71. 5 h. green 30
72. 6 h. orange 30
73. 10 h. red 30
74. 12 h. blue 30
75. 60. 15 h. red 30
76. 20 h. green 30
77. 25 h. blue 30
78. 30 h. violet 30
79. 51. 40 h. olive 40
80. 50 h. green 40
81. 60 h. blue 40
82. 80 h. brown 50
83. 90 h. purple 50
84. 1 k. red on yellow .. 55
85. 52. 2 k. blue 65
86. 3 k. red 90
87. 4 k. green .. .. 5·00
88. 10 k. violet .. .. 6·50

For other issues, which were mainly of a local character, see Part 10 (Russia) of the standard catalogue.

WURTTEMBERG Pt. 7

Formerly an independent kingdom, Wurttemberg became part of the German Empire in 1902.

1851. 60 kreuzer = 1 gulden.
1875. 100 pfennige = 1 mark.

1.

2.

1851. Imperf.
1. 1. 1 k. black on buff .. £600 80·00
3. 3 k. black on yellow .. £170 3·00
5. 6 k. black on green .. £800 26·00
7. 9 k. black on red .. .. £4000 24·00
9. 18 k. black on lilac .. £950 £600

1857. Imperf.
10. 2. 1 k. brown .. .. £375 55·00
24. 3 k. orange .. .. £200 3·25
15. 6 k. green .. .. £450 45·00
17. 9 k. red .. .. £750 38·00
19. 18 k. blue £1400 £950
85. 70 k. purple £1400 £3000

1859. Perf.
37. 2. 1 k. brown £475 £130
40. 3 k. yellow .. .. 55·00 19·00
41. 6 k. green .. .. £225 45·00
42. 9 k. red £650 £140
43. 9 k. purple £750 £190
44. 18 k. blue £900 £900

1863. Perf. or Roul.
60. 2. 1 k. green .. .. 32·00 5·50
63. 3 k. red .. .. 25·00 1·40
54. 6 k. blue .. .. £110 35·00
66. 7 k. blue £800 £130
57. 9 k. brown .. .. £190 42·00
59. 18 k. orange £900 £325

3.

4.

1869. Roul. or perf. (1 k.).
72. 3. 1 k. green .. .. 20·00 1·40
74. 2 k. orange .. .. £120 85·00
77. 3 k. red .. .. 10·00 70
78. 7 k. blue .. .. 55·00 15·00
80. 9 k. bistre .. .. 70·00 35·00
82. 14 k. yellow .. .. 70·00 35·00

1875. Perf.
123. 4. 2 pf. grey .. .. 1·75 80
89. 3 pf. green .. .. 10·00 1·50
124. 3 pf. brown 60 10
91. 5 pf. mauve .. .. 6·50 30
127. 5 pf. green .. .. 1·75 10
93. 10 pf. red .. .. 1·00 10
95. 20 pf. blue .. .. 1·00 10
97. 25 pf. brown .. .. 70·00 8·50
130. 25 pf. orange .. .. 3·00 70
151. 30 pf. black and orange 4·00 3·25
152. 40 pf. black and red .. 4·25 7·00
99. 50 pf. grey .. .. £500 27·00
101. 50 pf. green .. .. 45·00 3·75
132. 50 pf. brown .. .. 3·00 60
102. 2 m. yellow £650 £225
103. 2 m. red on orange .. £1500 £110
121. 2 m. black and orange .. 7·50 10·00
122. 5 m. black and blue .. 55·00 £130

For issues of 1947–49 see Germany (French Zone).

MUNICIPAL SERVICE STAMPS

M 5.

1875.
M168 M 5 2 pf. grey .. .. 40 1·00
M169 2½ pf. grey 40 65
M170 3 pf. brown 40 40
M104 5 pf. mauve .. .. 19·00 1·00
M171 5 pf. green 40 40
M172 7½ pf. orange 40 65
M173 10 pf. red 40 40
M261 10 pf. orange 15 85
M174 15 pf. brown .. .. 1·25 75
M262 15 pf. violet 15 90
M176 20 pf. blue 40 70
M263 20 pf. green 15 85
M177 25 pf. orange 40 70
M178 25 pf. black & brown .. 60 65
M179 35 pf. brown .. .. 3·50 17·00
M264 40 pf. red 15 15
M265 50 pf. purple 30 85
M266 60 pf. green .. .. 50 1·00
M267 1 m. 25 green 30 90
M268 2 m. grey 35 85
M269 3 m. brown 35 85

1906. Cent. of Wurttemberg becoming a Kingdom. Optd. **1806 - 1906** under crown.
M 153. M 5. 2 pf. grey .. .. 40·00 85·00
M 154. 3 pf. brown .. .. 14·00 10·00
M 155. 5 pf. green .. .. 3·75 1·25
M 156. 10 pf. red .. .. 3·75 1·25
M 157. 25 pf. orange .. .. 48·00 80·00

1916. Surch **25 Pf.**
M199 M 5 25 pf. on 25 pf. orange 3·00 3·50

M 9.

M 14.

1916. Jubilee of King William.
M 202. M 9. 2½ pf. grey .. .. 3·75 12·00
M 203. 7½ pf. red .. .. 3·00 60
M 204. 10 pf. red .. .. 3·00 7·50
M 205. 15 pf. bistre .. .. 3·00 1·40
M 206. 20 pf. blue .. .. 3·00 6·50
M 207. 25 pf. grey .. .. 8·00 15·00
M 208. 50 pf. brown .. .. 14·00 80·00

1919. Surch. with large figure **2**.
M 219. M 5. 2 on 2½ pf. grey .. 1·10 1·50

1919. Optd. **Volksstaat Wurttemberg.**
M 222. M 5. 2½ pf. grey .. .. 20 1·25
M 223. 3 pf. brown .. .. 12·00 14·00
M 224. 5 pf. green 20 30
M 225. 7½ pf. orange .. .. 50 3·25
M 226. 10 pf. red 20 30
M 227. 15 pf. violet 20 30
M 228. 20 pf. blue 20 30
M 229. 25 pf. black & brown 20 1·40
M 230. 35 pf. brown .. .. 4·50 14·00
M 231. 50 pf. purple .. .. 5·50 5·50

1920.
M 245. M 14. 10 pf. red .. .. 2·00 7·50
M 246. 15 pf. brown .. .. 2·00 3·25
M 247. 20 pf. blue .. .. 2·00 1·25
M 248. 30 pf. green .. .. 3·00 17·00
M 249. 50 pf. yellow .. .. 3·00 38·00
M 250. 75 pf. bistre .. .. 6·50 85·00

1922. Surch.
M 270. M 5. 5 m. on 10 pf. orange 10 65
M 271. 10 m. on 15 pf. mauve 10 65
M 272. 12 m. on 40 pf. red .. 20 1·40
M 273. 20 m. on 10 pf. orange 20 5·50
M 274. 25 m. on 20 pf. green 10 60
M 275. 40 m. on 20 pf. green 30 5·00
M 276. 50 m. on 60 pf. olive 10 60
M 277. 60 m. on 1 m. 25 grn. 10 90
M 278. 100 m. on 40 pf. red 10 85
M 279. 200 m. on 2 m. grey 10 85
M 280. 300 m. on 50 pf. pur. 15 85
M 281. 400 m. on 3 m. brown 20 1·75
M 282. 1000 m. on 60 pf. olive 20 1·75
M 283. 2000 m. on 1 m. 25 grn. 20 60

1923. Surch with new value (T = Tausend (thousand); M = Million; Md. = Milliard).
M 284. M 5. 5 T. on 10 pf. orange 20 6·50
M 285. 20 T. on 40 pf. red .. 20 3·50
M 286. 50 T. on 15 pf. mauve 1·25 15·00
M 287. 75 T. on 2 m. grey .. 5·00 65
M 288. 100 T. on 20 pf. green 20 6·50
M 289. 250 T. on 3 m. brown 20 85
M 290. 1 M. on 60 pf. olive .. 2·50 20·00
M 291. 2 M. on 50 pf. purple 20 65
M 292. 5 M. on 1 m. 25 green 30 4·50
M 293. 4 Md. on 50 pf. purple 7·00 £100
M 294. 10 Md. on 3 m. brn. 1·00 12·00

1923. Surch. in figures, representing gold pfennige.
M 295. M 5. 3 pf. on 25 pf. orange 2·00 8·00
M 296. 5 pf. on 25 pf. orange 30 85
M 297. 10 pf. on 25 pf. orange 30 85
M 298. 20 pf. on 25 pf. orange 60 2·50
M 299. 50 pf. on 25 pf. orange 3·00 £950

OFFICIAL STAMPS

O 16. Ulm.

VIEWS: 10 pf., 50 pf., 2 m. 50, 3 m. Stuttgart, 20 pf., 1 m. Tubingen. 30 pf., 1 m. 25, Ellwangen.

1881.
O181 O 5 2 pf. grey 40 15
O182 2½ pf. grey 45 40
O108 3 pf. green .. .. 5·00 2·75
O183 3 pf. brown 40 15
O112 5 pf. mauve .. .. 3·25 60
O184 5 pf. green 40 15
O185 7½ pf. orange 45 40
O186 10 pf. red 40 15
O187 15 pf. brown 45 40
O188 15 pf. purple 90 20
O189 20 pf. blue 40 15
O117 25 pf. brown .. .. 12·00 3·75
O191 25 pf. orange 40 15
O192 25 pf. black & brown .. 35 15
O193 30 pf. black & orange .. 40 15
O194 35 pf. brown .. .. 1·60 22·00
O195 40 pf. black and red .. 40 15
O119 50 pf. green .. .. 22·00 4·50
O141 50 pf. brown £180 £1200
O196 50 pf. purple 40 20
O120 1 m. yellow .. .. 90·00 £190
O197 1 m. violet .. .. 3·00 4·50
O198 1 m. black and grey .. 5·50 17·00

1906. Optd **1806-1906** under crown.
O 158. O 5. 2 pf. grey .. .. 32·00 60·00
O 159. 3 pf. brown .. .. 6·00 3·25
O 160. 5 pf green .. .. 4·50 60
O 161. 10 pf. red .. .. 4·50 75
O 162. 20 pf. blue .. .. 4·50 2·00
O 163. 25 pf. orange .. .. 12·00 11·00
O 164. 30 pf. black & orange 12·00 11·00
O 165. 40 pf. black and red 35·00 45·00
O 166. 50 pf. purple .. .. 35·00 45·00
O 167. 1 m. violet .. .. 75·00 85·00

1916. Surch.
O 200. O 5. 25 pf. on 25 pf. orge. 3·50 3·25
O 201. 50 pf. on 50 pf. pur. 3·50 15·00

1916. 25th Year of Reign.
O 209. O 10. 2½ pf. grey .. .. 3·75 11·00
O 210. 7½ pf. red .. .. 2·50 75
O 211. 10 pf. red .. .. 2·50 2·25
O 212. 15 pf. bistre .. .. 2·50 75
O 213. 20 pf. blue .. .. 2·50 3·00
O 214. 25 pf. grey .. .. 3·75 10·00
O 215. 30 pf. green .. .. 3·75 17·00
O 216. 40 pf. red .. .. 5·50 17·00
O 217. 50 pf. brown .. .. 7·50 30·00
O 218. 1 m. mauve .. .. 7·50 55·00

1919. Surch. in large figures.
O 220. O 5. 2 on 2½ pf grey .. 1·10 5·50
O 221. 75 on 3 pf. brn. (O 183) 2·25 35·00

1919. Optd. **Volksstaat Wurttemberg.**
O 232. O 5. 2½ pf. grey .. .. 35 1·25
O 233. 3 pf. brown .. .. 10·00 13·00
O 234. 5 pf. green 20 30
O 235. 7½ pf. orange .. .. 35 2·25
O 236 10 pf. red 20 30
O 237. 15 pf. purple 20 30
O 238. 20 pf. blue 35 30
O 239. 25 pf. black & brown 35 85
O 240. 30 pf. black & orange 75 1·50
O 241. 35 pf. brown .. .. 35 7·00
O 242. 40 pf. black and red 60 3·00
O 243. 50 pf. purple .. .. 70 3·00
O 244. 1 m. black and grey 1·00 6·50

1920.
O 251. – 10 pf. red .. .. 1·50 5·50
O 252. O 16. 15 pf. brown .. 1·50 7·50
O 253. – 20 pf. blue .. .. 1·50 1·75
O 254. – 30 pf. green .. 1·50 17·00
O 255. – 50 pf. yellow .. 1·50 32·00
O 256. O 16. 75 pf. bistre .. 2·25 27·00
O 257. – 1 m. red .. .. 2·25 27·00
O 258. – 1 m. 25 violet .. 2·25 40·00
O 259. – 2 m. 50 blue .. 3·75 42·00
O 260. – 3 m. green .. .. 3·75 60·00

O 5.

O 10. King Wilhelm II.

YEMEN Pt. 19

A republic in S.W. Arabia, ruled as a kingdom and imamate until 1962. From 1962 stamps were issued concurrently by the Republican Government and the Royalists. The latter are listed after the Republican issues.

In 1990 the Yemen Arab Republic and Yemen People's Democratic Republic united (see YEMEN REPUBLIC (combined)).

1926. 40 bogaches = 1 imadi.
1964. 40 bogaches = 1 rial.
1975. 100 fils = 1 riyal.

KINGDOM

1. (2½ b.)

2.

1926. Imperf. or perf.
1. 1. 2½ b. black on white .. 35·00 45·00
2. 2½ b. black on orange .. 35·00 45·00
3. 5 b. black on white .. 35·00 45·00

1930. The 6 b. to 1 im. values are larger.

10	2	½ b. orange	20	20
11		1 b. green	25	25
5		2 b. green	50	40
12		2 b. brown	40	40
13		3 b. lilac	50	50
14		4 b. red	65	65
15		5 b. grey	45	45
16		6 b. blue	1·00	65
17		8 b. purple	1·50	1·00
18		10 b. brown	1·50	1·00
19		20 b. green	6·00	5·00
9		1 im. blue and brown	12·00	9·50
20		1 im. green and purple	12·00	9·00

4. Flags of Saudi Arabia, Yemen and Iraq.

7.

6.

8.

1939. 2nd Anniv. of Arab Alliance.

21.	4.	4 b. blue and red	1·00	70
22.		6 b. blue and slate	1·00	75
23.		10 b. blue and brown	1·50	1·00
24.		14 b. blue and olive	2·25	1·75
25.		20 b. blue and green	2·75	2·50
26.		1 im. blue and purple	6·00	4·50

1939. Surch. with T **6**.

27.	2.	4 b. on ½ b. orange	7·50	2·00
65.		4 b. on 1 b. olive	2·00	1·00
66.		4 b. on 2 b. brown	8·00	3·25
67.		4 b. on 3 b. lilac	2·00	1·00
68.		4 b. on 5 b. grey	2·00	1·00

1940.

28.	7.	½ b. blue and orange	40	20
29.		1 b. red and green	40	20
30.		2 b. violet and bistre	40	20
31.		3 b. blue and mauve	40	20
32.		4 b. green and red	40	20
33.		5 b. bistre and green	60	30
34.	8.	6 b. orange and blue	60	30
35.		8 b. blue and purple	1·00	50
36.		10 b. olive and orange	1·00	50
37.		14 b. violet and olive	1·50	75
38.		18 b. black and green	1·75	90
39.		20 b. red and green	3·00	1·50
40.		1 im. red, olive and purple	7·00	3·00

The 5 b. (for which there had originally been no postal use) was released in 1957 to serve as 4 b., without surcharge.

9.

10.

1942.

41.	9.	1 b. olive and orange	20	15
42.		2 b. olive and orange	25	15
43.		4 b. olive and orange	35	25
44.		6 b. blue and orange	45	30
45.		8 b. blue and orange	75	45
46.		10 b. blue and orange	1·00	60
47.		12 b. blue and orange	1·25	90
48.		20 b. blue and orange	2·00	1·50

These stamps, formerly listed under Nos. D 1/8, although inscribed "TAXE A PERCEVOIR" were only used for ordinary postage purposes as there is no postage due system in Yemen.

1945. Surch with T **6**.

49a	7.	4 b. on ½ b. blue & orange	2·00	80
50		4 b. on 1 b. red and green	2·00	1·00
51a		4 b. on 2 b. violet & bistre	1·25	90
52a		4 b. on 3 b. blue & mauve	1·50	1·00
53		4 b. on 5 b. bistre and green	2·00	1·00

1949. Inauguration of Yemenite Hospital.

54.	10.	4 b. black and green	75	75
55.		6 b. red and green	1·00	1·00
56.		10 b. blue and green	1·90	1·90
57.		14 b. olive and green	2·25	2·25

11. Coffee Plant.

13. View of Sana'a Parade Ground.

12. Aeroplane over Sana'a.

1947.

58.	11.	½ b. brown (postage)	65	65
59.		1 b. purple	1·50	1·50
60.		2 b. violet	3·00	3·00
61.	–	4 b. red	3·00	3·00
62.	–	5 b. blue	3·00	3·00
62a.	11.	6 b. green	3·00	3·00
63.	12.	10 b. blue (air)	5·50	5·50
64.		20 b. green	7·50	7·50

DESIGN—VERT. 4 b., 5 b. Palace, Sana'a.

The 5 b. was put on sale in 1957 to serve as 4 b., without surcharge.

1949. Surch. as T **6**.

68a	11.	4 b. on ½ b. brown	1·75	1·10
69a		4 b. on 1 b. purple	1·60	1·10
70b		4 b. on 2 b. violet	2·00	50

1951. (a) Postage.

71.	13.	1 b. brown	35	20
72.		2 b. brown	75	45
73.		3 b. purple	1·00	60
74.	–	5 b. red and blue	1·50	1·10
75.	–	6 b. red and purple	1·50	1·25
76.	–	8 b. green and blue	1·75	1·40
77.	–	10 b. purple	1·75	1·50
78.	–	14 b. turquoise	3·00	2·25
79.	–	20 b. red	4·00	3·00
80.	–	1 im. violet	10·00	5·50

DESIGNS—HORIZ. 5 b. Yemeni flag. 10 b. Mosque, Sana'a. 14 b. Walled city of Sana'a. 20 b., 1 im. Taiz and Citadel. VERT. 6 b. Eagle and Yemeni flag. 8 b. Coffee plant.

(b) Air. With aeroplane.

81.	6 b. blue	1·75	1·40
82.	8 b. sepia	2·50	1·75
83.	10 b. green	5·00	3·75
84.	12 b. blue	3·25	2·50
85.	16 b. purple	3·25	2·50
86.	20 b. orange	5·00	3·75
87.	1 im. red	13·00	8·00

DESIGNS—HORIZ. 6 b., 8 b. Sana'a. 10 b. Trees. 16 b. Taiz Palace. VERT. 12 b. Palace of the Rock, Wadi Dhahr. 20 b. Crowd of people. 1 im. Landscape.

The 5 b. postage stamp was released in 1956 to serve as 4 b. without surcharge and it was again put on sale as 8 b. in 1957. The 6 b. and 8 b. air stamps were released in 1957 to serve as ordinary postage stamps.

14. Flag and View of Sana'a and Hodeida.

1952. 4th Anniv. of Accession of King Ahmed. Flag in red. Perf. or imperf.

88.	14.	1 im. blk. & lake (post.)	12·00	12·00
89.		1 im. blue & brown (air)	9·00	9·00

1952. 4th Anniv. of Victory. As T **14**, but inscr. "COMMEMORATION OF VICTORY". Flag in red. Perf. or imperf.

90.	30 b. green & lake (post.)	7·50	8·50
91.	30 b. blue & green (air)	7·50	10·00

1952. Surch as T **6**.

91a	13	4 b. on 1 b. brown	3·00	2·75
92		4 b. on 2 b. brown	2·50	2·50
93		4 b. on 3 b. purple	3·25	2·50

15. Palace of the Rock, Wadi Dhahr.

1952. Sky in blue. Perf. or imperf.

94	15.	12 b. grn. & sepia (post.)	7·50	7·50
95	–	20 b. brown and red	8·50	10·00
96	15.	12 b. brn. & green (air)	9·00	9·00
97	–	20 b. brown and blue	7·50	7·50

DESIGN: 20 b. (2). Walls of Ibb.

1953. Surch as T **6**.

98.	9.	4 b. on 1 b. olive & orge.	7·70	5·00
99.		4 b. on 2 b. olive & orge.	7·50	4·00

16.

16a. Bab al-Yemen Gate, Sana'a.

1953.

100.	16.	4 b. orange (postage)	1·75	1·75
101.		6 b. blue	2·25	2·25
102.		8 b. turquoise	2·75	2·75
103.		10 b. red (air)	3·00	3·00
104.		12 b. blue	3·50	3·50
105.		20 b. bistre	6·50	6·50

1956. Unissued official stamps issued for ordinary postal use without surch.

105a.	16a.	1 b. brown	85	3·50
105b.		5 b. turquoise	95	2·75
105c.		10 b. blue	1·25	2·75

The 1 and 5 b. were each sold for use as 4 b. and the 10 b. as 10 b. for inland registered post.

1957. Arab Postal Union. As T **96a** of Syria but inscr. "YEMEN" at top and inscriptions in English.

106.	4 b. brown	1·75	1·75
107.	6 b. green	2·00	2·00
108.	16 b. violet	4·00	4·00

1959. 1st Anniv. of Proclamation of United Arab States (U.A.R. and Yemen). As T **139a** of Syria.

109.	1 b. black and lake (postage)	30	25
110.	2 b. black and green	45	35
111.	4 b. red and green	55	45
112.	6 b. black and orange (air)	1·25	85
113.	10 b. black and red	1·75	1·50
114.	16 b. red and violet	2·00	1·75

1959. Arab Telecommunications Union Commem. As T **138a** of Syria.

115.	4 b. red	1·75	90

1959. Inaug of Automatic Telephone, Sana'a. Optd **AUTOMATIC TELEPHONE INAUGURATION SANAA MARCH 1959** in English and Arabic.

116.	2.	6 b. blue	2·00	2·00
117.		8 b. red	2·50	2·50
118.		10 b. orange	3·25	3·25
119.		20 b. olive	6·50	6·50
120.		1 im. olive and red	9·00	9·00

1960. Air. Optd. **AIR MAIL 1959** in English and Arabic and aeroplane.

121.	2.	6 b. blue	2·00	2·00
122.		10 b. brown	3·50	3·50

1960. Inaug. of Arab League Centre, Cairo. As T **154a** of Syria but with different arms.

123.	4 b. black and green	75	60

IMPERF. STAMPS. From this point many issues also exist imperf. This applies also to Republican and Royalist issues.

1960. World Refugee Year. As T **155a** of Syria.

124.	4 b. brown	1·00	1·25
125.	6 b. green	1·25	1·75

19. Olympic Torch.

1960. Olympic Games, Rome.

126.	19.	2 b. red and black	1·25	1·25
127.		4 b. yellow and black	1·40	1·40
128.		6 b. orange and black	2·00	2·00
129.		8 b. turquoise and black	2·50	2·50
130		20 b. orange and violet	5·00	5·00

20. U.N. Emblem.

1961. 15th Anniv. of U.N.

131.	20.	1 b. violet	30	30
132.		2 b. green	35	35
133.		3 b. turquoise	40	40
134.		4 b. blue	45	45
135.		6 b. purple	55	55
136.		14 b. red	1·25	1·25
137.		20 b. sepia	1·75	1·75

21. Hodeida Port and Freighter.

1961. Hodeida Port Inaug.

138.	21.	4 b. multicoloured	75	60
139.		6 b. multicoloured	75	60
140.		16 b. multicoloured	2·00	2·00

22. Alabaster Death-mask.

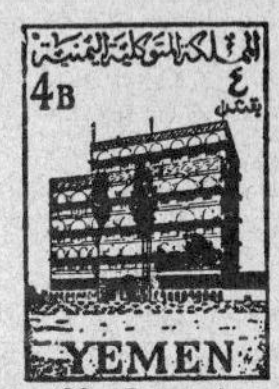

23. Imam's Palace, Sana'a.

1961. Statues of Marib.

141.	1 b. black & orange (post.)	30	20
142.	2 b. black and violet	45	25
143.	4 b. black and brown	60	35
144.	8 b. black and purple	75	50
145.	10 b. black and yellow	1·25	80
146.	12 b. black and violet	1·50	1·00
147.	20 b. black and grey	1·75	1·25
148.	1 im. black and green	3·75	2·50
149	6 b. black & turquoise (air)	75	45
150.	16 b. black and blue	2·50	1·50

DESIGNS: 1 b. Type 22. 2 b. Horned head (8th-century B.C. frieze, Temple of the Moon God). 4 b. Bronze head of the Himyaritic emperor, of 1st or 2nd-century. 6 b. "Throne of Bilqis" (8th-century B.C. limestone columns, Moon God Temple). 8 b. Bronze figure of Himyaritic Emperor Dhamar Ali, 2nd or 3rd-century. 10 b. Alabaster statuette of 2nd or 3rd-century child. 12 b. Entrance to Moon God Temple. 16 b. Control tower and spillway, Marib dam. 20 b. 1st-century alabaster relief of boy with dagger riding legendary monster, Moon God Temple. 1 im. 1st-century alabaster relief of woman with grapes, Moon God Temple.

1961. Yemeni Buildings.

151.	4 b. blk., grn. & turq. (post.)	30	30
152.	8 b. black, green and red	50	50
153.	10 b. black, green & orange	80	80
154.	6 b. black, grn. & blue (air)	55	55
155.	16 b. black, green and red	1·75	2·00

DESIGNS—VERT. 4 b. Type **23**. 10 b. Palace of the Rock, Wadi Dhahr. 16 b. Palace of the Rock (different view). HORIZ. 6 b. Bab al-Yemen Gate, Sana'a. 8 b. Imam's Palace, Sana'a (different view).

24. Hodeida-Sana'a Highway.

1961. Inaug. of Hodeida-Sana'a Highway.

156.	24.	4 b. multicoloured	60	45
157.		6 b. multicoloured	75	70
158.		10 b. multicoloured	1·25	85

25. Nubian Temple.

1962. U.N.E.S.C.O. Campaign for Preservation of Nubian Monuments.

159.	25.	4 b. brown	2·50	1·75
160.		6 b. green	4·50	2·50

1962. Arab League Week. As T **76** of Libya.

161.	4 b. green	55	55
162.	6 b. blue	65	65

26. Nurse weighing Child.

26a. Campaign Emblem.

1962. Maternity and Child Centre. Mult.
163. 2 b. Putting child to bed .. 60 40
164. 4 b. Type **26** 80 50
165. 6 b. Taking child's temperature 90 65
166. 10 b. Weighing baby .. 1·60 80

1962. Malaria Eradication.
167. **26a.** 4 b. orange and black 60 45
168. – 6 b. green and brown 90 65
DESIGN: 6 b. As T **26a** but with laurel and inscription around emblem.

1962. 17th Anniv. of U.N. Nos. 131/7 optd. **1945–1962** in English and Arabic with bars over old dates.
169. **20.** 1 b. violet . 1·75 1·75
170. 2 b. green . . 1·75 1·75
171. 3 b. turquoise . 1·75 1·75
172. 4 b. blue . . 1·75 1·75
173. 6 b. purple .. 1·75 1·75
174. 14 b. red . .. 1·75 1·75
175. 20 b. sepia .. 1·75 1·75

RE. ,IC

الجمهورية العربية اليمنية
١٩٦٢/٩/٢٧-١٣٨٢/٤/٢٨
Y.A.R. 27.9.1962
(28.)

1963. Various issues optd. as T **28**.
(a) Nos. 141/50.
176. 1 b. black & orange (post.) 15 15
177. 2 b. black and violet .. 15 15
178. 4 b. black and brown .. 45 45
179. 8 b. black and mauve .. 90 90
180. 10 b. black and yellow .. 1·25 1·25
181. 12 b. black and violet .. 1·25 1·25
182. 20 b. black and grey .. 1·40 1·40
183. 1 im. black and grey .. 3·75 3·75
184. 6 b. black & turquoise (air) 90 90
185. 16 b. black and blue .. 1·40 1·40

(b) Nos. 151/5.
186. 4 b. blk., grn. & turq. (post.) 35 35
187. 8 b. black, green and red .. 90 90
188. 10 b. black, green & orange 1·50 1·50
189. 6 b. blk., green & blue (air) 70 70
190. 16 b. black, green and red 1·75 1·75

(c) Nos. 163/6.
191. 2 b. multicoloured .. 35 35
192. 4 b. multicoloured .. 40 40
193. 6 b. multicoloured .. 60 60
194. 10 b. multicoloured .. 1·40 1·40

29. "Torch of Freedom".

1963. "Proclamation of Republic".
195. – 4 b. brn. & purple (post.) 70 70
196. – 6 b. red and blue .. 70 70
197. – 8 b. black & purple (air) 1·00 1·00
198. **29.** 10 b. red & deep violet 1·00 1·00
199. – 16 b. red and green .. 1·75 1·75
DESIGNS—VERT. 4 b. Soldier with flag. 6 b. Tank and flag. 8 b. Bayonet and torch. HORIZ. 16 b. Flag and torch.

29a. Cow and Emblems.

1963. Freedom from Hunger.
200. **29a.** 4 b. brown and red .. 40 25
201. – 6 b. yellow and violet 60 40
DESIGN: 6 b. Corncob and ear of wheat.

1963. Various issues optd.

١٩٦٢/٩/٢٧-١٣٨٢/٤/٢٨
27-9-1962
(30.)

الجمهورية
العربية اليمنية
١٣٨٢/٤/٢٨
١٩٦٢/٩/٢٧
Y. A. R.
27. 9. 1962
بريد اليمن
(31.)

(a) With T **30**. On Nos. 161/2.
202. 4 b. green .. .. .. 2·50 2·50
203. 6 b. blue .. .. .. 4·75 4·75

(b) With T **31**.
207. **2.** 5 b. grey .. .. .. 1·25 1·25
204. 6 b. blue .. .. .. 1·75 1·75
208. 8 b. red .. .. .. 1·50 1·50
205. 10 b. brown .. .. 2·25 2·25
209. 10 b. orange .. .. 1·75 1·75
210. 20 b. olive .. .. 2·50 2·50
206. 1 im. blue and brown .. 6·00 6·00
211. 1 im. olive and red .. 4·25 4·25

(c) As T **31** but with lowest line of inscription at top.
212. **7.** 6 b. red and green .. 1·90 1·90
213. 10 b. blue and green .. 3·25 3·25
214. 14 b. olive and green .. 5·50 5·50

(d) As T **31**, but with lowest line of inscription omitted and bar at top. On Nos. 167/8.
215. 4 b. orange and black .. 2·75 2·75
216. 6 b. green and sepia .. 3·50 3·50

الجمهورية العربية اليمنية
١٩٦٢-٩-٢٧ — ١٣٨٢-٤-٢٨
Y. A. R 27. 9. 1962
(32.)

(e) With T **32**. (i) On Nos. 139/40.
217. **21.** 6 b. multicoloured .. 1·25 1·25
218. 16 b. multicoloured .. 2·00 2·00

(ii) On Nos. 157/8.
219. **24.** 6 b. multicoloured .. 1·25 1·25
220. 10 b. multicoloured .. 1·75 1·75

(f) As T **32**, but with only one bar over old inscription. (i) Nos. 126/8.
221. **19.** 2 b. red and black 5·50 5·50
222. 4 b. yellow and black 5·50 5·50
223. 6 b. orange and black 5·50 5·50

(ii) Nos. 159/60.
224. **25.** 4 b. brown .. 8·50 8·50
225. 6 b. green .. .. 9·00 9·00

(34.)

35. Flag and Laurel Sprig.

(g) Air. With T **34**.
226. **4.** 6 b. blue and slate .. 1·00 1·00
227. 10 b. blue and brown .. 1·25 1·25
228. 14 b. blue and olive .. 1·60 1·60
229. 20 b. blue and green .. 2·25 2·25
230. 1 im. blue and purple .. 4·25 4·25

1963. 1st Anniv. of Revolution.
231 – 2 b. red, green and black 30 15
232 – 4 b. red, black and green 45 25
233 **35** 6 b. red, black and green 95 55
DESIGNS—HORIZ. 4 b. Flag, torch and broken chain. VERT. 2 b. Flag, torch and candle.

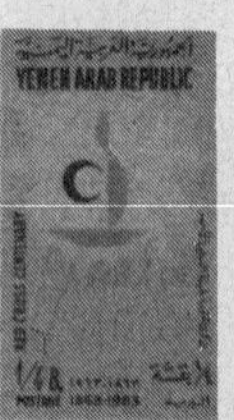

36. Hands reaching for Centenary Emblem.

38. Globe and Scales of Justice.

37.

1963. Red Cross Centenary. Crescent red; inscriptions black.
234. **36.** ¼ b. blue 90 30
235. ⅓ b. brown 90 40
236. ½ b. grey 90 45
237. – 4 b. lilac .. .. 1·25 65
238. – 8 b. ochre .. .. 1·50 80
239. – 20 b. green .. .. 4·00 1·75
DESIGN: 4 b. to 20 b. Centenary emblem.

1963. Air. "Honouring Astronauts". T **31** and similar designs showing rockets, etc.
240. **37.** ¼ b. multicoloured .. 75 50
241. – ⅓ b. multicoloured .. 75 50
242. – ½ b. multicoloured .. 75 50
243. – 4 b. multicoloured .. 1·25 90
244. – 20 b. multicoloured .. 6·00 3·75

1963. 15th Anniv. of Declaration of Human Rights.
245. – 4 b. black, orge. & lilac 25 15
246. **38.** 6 b. black and green .. 35 25
DESIGN: 4 b. As Type **38** but differently arranged.

39. Darts.

1964. Olympic Games, Tokyo (1st issue). T **39** and similar designs.
247. ¼ b. bronze, brown and orange (postage) .. 20 15
248. ⅓ b. brown, blue and violet 20 15
249. ½ b. brown, blue and mauve 20 15
250. 1 b. brown, green and blue 35 15
251. 1½ b. red, brown and grey 50 15
252. 4 b. brn., blk. & blue (air) 50 25
253. 20 b. blue, indigo & brown 1·50 1·00
254. 1 r. red, brn. & turquoise 3·25 2·25
DESIGNS—HORIZ. ¼ b. Type 39. ⅓ b. Table tennis. 4 b. Horse-racing. 20 b. Pole vaulting. VERT. ½ b. Running. 1 b. Volleyball 1½ b. Football. 1 r. Basketball. All designs include the Olympic "Rings" symbol.
See also Nos. 272/80.

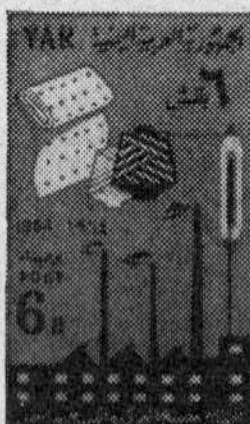

40. Factory, Bobbins and Cloth.

42. Aircraft on Runway.

1964. Inauguration of Bagel Spinning and Weaving Factory.
255 – 2 b. blue & yellow (post) 20 10
256 – 4 b. blue and yellow .. 30 15
257 **40** 6 b. green and brown .. 40 25
258 – 16 b orange, blue and grey (air) 90 65
DESIGNS—VERT. 2 b. Factory, bobbins and cloth (different). 4 b. Loom. HORIZ. 16 b. Factory and lengths of cloth.

1964. Air. President Kennedy Memorial Issue. Nos. 240/2 optd. **JOHN F. KENNEDY 1917 1963** in English and Arabic and with portrait and laurel.
259 **37.** ¼ b. multicoloured .. 75 75
260 – ⅓ b. multicoloured .. 75 75
261 – ½ b. multicoloured .. 75 75

1964. Inaug of Hodeida Airport.
262 **42** 4 b. yellow and blue .. 35 20
263 – 6 b. green and blue .. 45 30
264 – 10 b. blue, yellow and indigo 60 40
DESIGNS: 6 b. Control tower and aircraft on runway. 10 b. Control tower, aircraft and ship.

43. Aircraft, New York and Sana'a.

1964. New York World's Fair.
265. **43.** ¼ b. brn., bl. & grn. (post.) 15 10
266. – ⅓ b. black, red & green 20 15
267. – ½ b. turquoise, red & blue 25 20
268. **43.** 1 b. indigo, blue & green 35 25
269. – 4 b. blue, red & green .. 50 35
270. – 16 b. brn., red & bl. (air) 1·75 1·25
271. **43.** 20 b. purple, blue & grn. 2·25 1·40
DESIGNS: ⅓ b., 4 b. Flag, Empire State Building, New York and Mosque, Sana'a. ½ b., 16 b. Liner, freighter, Statue of Liberty, New York and Harbour, Hodeida.

44. Globe and Flags.

45. Scout hoisting Flags.

1964. Olympic Games, Tokyo (2nd issue). Multicoloured.
272. ¼b. Type **44** (postage) .. 15 10
273. ⅓b. Olympic Torch .. 20 10
274. ½b. Discus-thrower .. 25 15
275. 1 b. Yemeni flag 35 20
276. 1½ b. Swimming (horiz.) .. 40 25
277. 4 b. Swimming (horiz.) (air) 55 40
278. 6 b. Olympic Torch .. 60 45
279. 12 b. Type **44** .. .. 1·50 1·00
280. 20 b. Discus-thrower .. 2·75 1·50

1964. Yemeni Scouts. Multicoloured.
281. ¼ b. Type **45** (postage) .. 20 10
282. ⅓ b. Scout badge and scouts guarding camp 25 15
283. ½ b. Bugler 25 20
284. 1 b. As No. 282 .. .. 30 20
285. 1½ b. Scouts by camp-fire 40 25
286. 4 b. Type **45** (air) 40 25
287. 6 b. As No. 282 .. .. 45 25
288. 16 b. Bugler .. .. 1·25 75
289. 20 b. Scouts by camp-fire 1·75 1·25

46. Hamadryas Baboons.

47. Gentian.

1964. Animals.
290. **46.** ¼ b. brn. & lilac (post.) 20 10
291. – ⅓ b. brown and blue .. 25 15
292. – ½ b. sepia and orange .. 25 15
293. – 1 b. brown and blue .. 40 15
294. – 1½ b. brown and blue .. 45 15
295. – 4 b. red & green (air) .. 70 30
296. – 12 b. drab and buff .. 2·25 95
297. – 20 b. brown and blue .. 3·50 1·50
ANIMALS: ½ b. Arab horses. ½ b., 12 b. Bullock. 1 b., 20 b. Lion and lioness. 1½ b., 4 b. Mountain gazelles.

1964. Flowers. Multicoloured.
298. ¼ b. Type **47** (postage) .. 20 10
299. ⅓ b. Lily 25 10
300. ½ b. Poinsettia 30 15
301. 1 b. Rose 40 15
302. 1½ b. Viburnum 45 20
303. 4 b. Rose (air) 70 30
304. 12 b. Poinsettia .. .. 2·25 90
305. 20 b. Viburnum .. .. 3·50 1·75

48. Aircraft over Mountains.

49. A.P.U. Emblem.

1964. Inaug. of Sana'a Int. Airport.

306. **48.** 1 b. brn. & blue (post.) 10 10
307. – 2 b. brown and blue .. 15 10
308. – 4 b. brown and blue .. 35 20
309. **48.** 8 b. brown and blue .. 55 45
310. – 6 b. brown & blue (air) 40 30

DESIGNS: 2 b., 4 b. Aircraft over runway. 6 b. Aircraft in flight and on ground.

1964. 10th Anniv. of Arab Postal Union.

311. **49.** 4 b. black, red and orange (postage) .. 45 40
312. 6 b. black, green and turquoise (air) .. 65 50

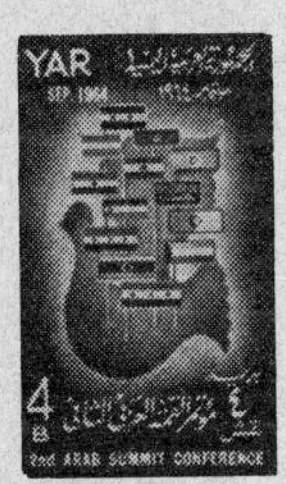

50. Flags and Dove.  **51.** Flaming Torch.

1964. 2nd Arab Summit Conf.

313. **50.** 4 b. green 45 40
314. – 6 b. brown 65 50

DESIGN: 6 b. Arms within conference emblem and map.

1964. 2nd Anniv. of Revolution.

315. **51.** 2 b. ochre and blue .. 25 20
316. – 4 b. green and yellow .. 50 40
317. – 6 b. rose, red and green 50 40

DESIGNS: 4 b. Yemeni soldier. 6 b. Candles on map.

52. Western Reef Herons.  **52a.** Dagger on Deir Yassin, Palestine.

1965. Birds. Multicoloured.

318. ¼ b. Type **52** (postage) .. 55 25
319. ½ b. Arabian chukar .. 55 25
320. ¾ b. Eagle owl (vert.) .. 75 25
321. 1 b. Hammerkop 55 25
322. 1½ b. Yemini linnets .. 60 35
323. 4 b. Hoopoes 95 45
324. 6 b. Violet starlings (air) .. 1·10 55
325. 8 b. Waldrapp (vert.) .. 1·90 1·00
326. 12 b. Arabian woodpecker (vert.) .. .. 3·25 1·60
327. 20 b. Bateleur (vert.) .. 4·25 2·25
328. 1 r. Yellow-bellied green pigeon .. .. 5·50 3·00

1965. Deir Yassin Massacre.

329. **52a.** 4 b. purple and blue (postage) .. 70 30
330. 6 b. red and orange (air) 80 45

53. I.T.U. Emblem and Symbols.

1965. I.T.U. Cent.

331. – 4 b. red and blue .. 75 35
332. **53.** 6 b. green and red .. 85 45

DESIGN—VERT. 4 b. As Type **53** but rearranged.

53a. Lamp and Burning Library.

1965. Burning of Algiers Library.

333. **53a.** 4 b. green, red & black (postage) 40 30
334. 6 b. blue and red (air) 50 40

54. Tractor and Agricultural Produce.  **55.** I.C.Y. and U.N. Emblems.

1965. 3rd Anniv. of Revolution.

335. **54.** 4 b. blue and yellow .. 40 35
336. – 6 b. blue and yellow .. 50 45

DESIGN: 6 b. Tractor and landscape.

1965. Int. Co-operation Year.

337. **55.** 4 b. green and orange .. 75 35
338. – 6 b. brown and blue .. 85 45

DESIGN: 6 b. U.N. Headquarters and General Assembly Building, New York.

56. Pres. Kennedy, Map and Rocket-launching.  **57.** Belyaev and Rocket.

1965. Pres. Kennedy Commem. Designs each include portraits of Pres. Kennedy. Multicoloured.

339. ¼ b. Type **56** (postage) .. 25 20
340. ¼ b. Rocket gantries .. 25 20
341. ¼ b. Rocket 25 20
342. ⅓ b. Type **56** 25 20
343. ½ b. Rocket 25 20
344. 4 b. Capsule and U.S. flag 50 40
345. 8 b. Capsule in ocean (air) 1·50 1·25
346. 12 b. Rocket gantries .. 2·40 2·00

1965. Space Achievements. Multicoloured.

347. ¼ b. Type **57** (postage) .. 10 8
348. ¼ b. Leonov and rocket .. 10 8
349. ¼ b. Scott and capsule .. 10 8
350. ⅓ b. Carpenter and rocket gantry 10 8
351. ½ b. Scott and capsule .. 10 8
352. 4 b. Leonov and rocket (air) 65 65
353. 8 b. Type **57** .. .. 1·40 1·40
354. 16 b. Carpenter and rocket gantry .. .. .. 2·50 2·50

1966. Anti T.B. Campaign. Nos. 200/1 optd. **Tuberculous Campaign 1965** in English and Arabic.

356. 4 b. brown and red .. 60 60
357. 6 b. yellow and violet 80 80

59. Torch Signalling.

1966. Telecommunications.

359. **59.** ¼ b. black & red (postage) 15 12
360. – ¼ b. black and blue .. 15 12
361. – ¼ b. black and ochre .. 15 12
362. – ⅓ b. black and red .. 15 12
363. – ½ b. black and blue .. 15 12
364. – 4 b. black & green (air) 50 40
365. – 6 b. black and brown .. 1·00 90
366. – 20 b. black and blue .. 2·25 2·00

DESIGNS: No. 360. Morse telegraphy. No. 361, Early telephone. No. 362, Wireless telegraphy. No. 363, Television. No. 364, Radar. No. 365, Telex. No. 366, "Early Bird" Satellite.

1966. Prevention of Cruelty to Animals. Nos. 318/20 optd. **Prevention of Cruelty to Animals** in English and Arabic.

368. **52.** ¼ b. multicoloured .. 50 25
369. – ½ b. multicoloured .. 50 25
370. – ¾ b. multicoloured .. 90 55

1966. 3rd Arab Summit Conference Nos. 313/14 optd **3rd. Arab summit Conference 1965** in English and Arabic.

371. **50.** 4 b. green 65 65
372. – 6 b. brown .. .. 1·25 1·25

INDEX

Countries can be quickly located by referring to the index at the end of this volume.

62. Pres. Kennedy and Globe.

1966. "Builders of World Peace".

(a) Postage. Size 39 × 28½ mm.

374. **62.** ¼ b. brown 20 15
375. – ¼ b. green 20 15
376. – ¼ b. blue 20 15
377. – ⅓ b. brown 20 15
378. – ½ b. purple 25 15
379. **62.** 4 b. purple 50 25

(b) Air. Size 51 × 38 mm.

381. – 6 b. brown and green .. 1·00 75
382. – 10 b. brown and blue .. 1·25 90
383. – 12 b. brown and mauve 2·25 1·00

PORTRAITS: Nos. 375, 377, Dag Hammarskjold. Nos. 376, 378, Nehru. No. 381, Ralph Bunche. No. 382, U Thant. No. 383, Pope Paul VI

63. Cockerel.

1966. Animals and Insects.

(a) Postage. Multicoloured.

385. ¼ b. Type **63** 30 20
386. ¼ b. Brown hare 30 20
387. ¼ b. Pony 30 20
388. ⅓ b. Cat 30 20
389. ½ b. Sheep and lamb .. 30 20
390. 4 b. Dromedary 75 40

(b) Air. Butterflies.

391 6 b. "Vanessa atalanta" .. 3·00 90
392 8 b. "Papilio machaon" .. 3·50 1·10
393 10 b. "Arctia caja" .. 4·00 1·25
394 16 b. "Papilio dardanus" 5·50 1·75

1966. Space Flight of "Luna 9". Nos. 347/54 optd. **LUNA IX 3 February 1966** in English and Arabic, and space-craft.

396. **57.** ¼ b. multicoloured (post.) 25 20
397. – ¼ b. multicoloured .. 25 20
398. – ¼ b. multicoloured .. 25 20
399. – ⅓ b. multicoloured .. 25 20
400. – ½ b. multicoloured .. 25 20
401. – 4 b. multicoloured (air) 50 40
402. **57.** 8 b. multicoloured .. 1·00 75
403. – 16 b. multicoloured .. 1·75 1·40

65. Jules Rimet Cup.  **66.** Traffic Signals.

1966. World Cup Football Championships, England.

405. **65.** ¼ b. multicoloured (post) 25 20
406. – ¼ b. multicoloured .. 25 20
407. – ¼ b. multicoloured .. 25 20
408. – ⅓ b. multicoloured .. 25 20
409. – ½ b. multicoloured .. 25 20
410. – 4 b. multicoloured (air) 65 50
411. – 5 b. multicoloured .. 1·00 90
412. – 20 b. multicoloured .. 2·25 2·00

DESIGNS: Nos. 406/11 Footballers in play (all different). No. 412, World Cup emblem.

1966. Traffic Day.

414. **66.** 4 b. red, deep grn. & grn. 85 40
415. 6 b. red, deep grn. & grn. 1·25 60

1966. Space Flight of "Surveyor 1". Nos. 347/51 surch. **SURVEYOR 1 2 June 1966** space-craft and new value in English and Arabic.

417. **57.** 1 b. on ¼ b. multicoloured 65 65
418. – 1 b. on ¼ b. multicoloured 65 65
419. – 1 b. on ¼ b. multicoloured 65 65
420. – 3 b. on ⅓ b. multicoloured 1·90 1·90
421. – 4 b. on ½ b. multicoloured 2·25 2·25

68. Yemeni Flag.

1966. 4th Anniv. of Revolution.

422. **68.** 2 b. black, red and green 20 15
423. – 4 b. multicoloured .. 40 25
424. – 6 b. multicoloured .. 60 40

DESIGNS—VERT. (25×42 mm.): 4 b. Automatic weapon. 6 b. "Agriculture and Industry"

1966. "World Fair, Sana'a, 1965". Nos. 265/71 optd. **1965 SANA'A** in English and Arabic.

425. **43.** ¼ b. brn., bl. & grn. (post.) 20 15
426. – ⅓ b. black, red and green 20 15
427. – ½ b. green, red and blue 20 15
428. **43.** 1 b. indigo, blue & green 35 25
429. – 4 b. blue, red and green 50 30
430. – 16 b. brn., red & bl. (air) 2·50 2·00
431. **43.** 20 b. purple, blue & green 3·25 2·75

70. Galen, Helianthus and W.H.O. Building.

1966. Inauguration of W.H.O. Headquarters, Geneva. Multicoloured designs incorporating W.H.O. Building.

433 ¼ b. Type **70** (postage) .. 30 20
434 ¼ b. Hippocrates and ipomoeas 30 20
435 ¼ b. Ibn Sina (Avicenna) and peonies 30 20
436 4 b. Type **70** (air) .. 85 45
437 8 b. As No. 434 .. 1·25 75
438 16 b. As No. 435 .. 2·75 2·00

71. Space-craft Launching.

1966. Space Flight of "Gemini 6 and 7". Multicoloured.

440. ¼ b. Type **71** (postage) .. 15 15
441. ¼ b. Astronauts .. 15 15
442. ¼ b. "Gemini" space-craft (horiz.) 15 15
443. ⅓ b. "Gemini 6 and 7" (horiz.) 15 15
444. ½ b. Recovery operations at sea 15 15
445. 2 b. As ½ b. 40 25
446. 8 b. As ½ b. (air) .. 95 75
447. 12 b. "Gemini 6 and 7" link (horiz.) .. .. 1·40 95

1966. Space Flight of "Gemini 9". Nos. 440/7 optd. **GEMINI IX CERNAN-STAFFORD JUNE 3-1966** in English and Arabic.

449. **71.** ¼ b. multicoloured (post) 15 15
450. – ¼ b. multicoloured .. 15 15
451. – ¼ b. multicoloured .. 15 15
452. – ⅓ b. multicoloured .. 15 15
453. – ½ b. multicoloured .. 15 15
454. – 2 b. multicoloured .. 40 25
455. – 8 b. multicoloured (air) 1·40 1·00
456. – 12 b. multicoloured .. 1·75 1·40

73. Figs.

1967. Fruits. Multicoloured.
458. ¼ b. Type **73** (postage) .. 20 10
459. ¼ b. Quinces 20 10
460. ¼ b. Grapes 20 10
461. ⅓ b. Dates 20 10
462. ½ b. Apricots 20 15
463. 2 b. Quinces 60 25
464. 4 b. Oranges .. .. 1·25 60
465. 6 b. Bananas (air) .. .. 1·50 75
466. 8 b. Type **73** .. .. 1·75 90
467. 10 b. Grapes .. .. 2·00 95

1967. Arab League Day. As T **328** of Egypt.
471. 4 b. brown and violet .. 50 50
472. 6 b. brown and violet .. 1·00 1·00
473. 8 b. brown and violet .. 1·40 1·40
474. 20 b. brown and green .. 2·00 1·75
475. 40 b. black and green .. 5·00 4·50

73a. Women in Factory.

1967. Labour Day.
475a. **73a.** 2 b. blue and violet .. 45 40
475b. 4 b. green and red .. 90 75
475c. 6 b. red and green .. 1·50 1·00
475d. 8 b. olive and blue .. 1·75 1·00

74. Ploughing and Sunset.

1967.
476. **74.** 1 b. multicoloured .. 15 15
477. 2 b. multicoloured .. 20 15
478. 4 b. multicoloured .. 35 15
479. 6 b. multicoloured .. 45 15
480. 8 b. multicoloured .. 75 15
481. 10 b. multicoloured .. 1·25 30
482. 12 b. multicoloured .. 1·50 50
483. 16 b. multicoloured .. 1·75 60
484. 20 b. multicoloured .. 2·50 90
485. 40 b. multicoloured .. 4·75 2·25

75. Pres. Al-Salal and Soldiers.

1968. 6th Anniv. of Revolution. Mult.
486. 2 b. Type **75** 12 12
487. 4 b. Yemen Arab Republic flag 30 30
488. 6 b. Pres. Abdullah al-Salal (vert.) 50 50

76. Map of Yemen and Dove.

1969. 7th Anniv. of Revolution. Mult.
490. 2 b. Type **76** .. 10 10
491. 4 b. Government building (horiz.) 20 20
492. 6 b. Yemeni workers (horiz.) 50 50

77. " Lenin addressing Crowd ".

1970. Air. Birth Cent. of Lenin. Mult.
494. 6 b. Type **77** .. .. 1·25 80
495. 10 b. " Lenin with Arab Delegates " .. .. 2·50 2·00

78. Arab League Flag, Arms and Map.

1970. 25th Anniv. of Arab League.
496. **78.** 5 b. purple, green & pink 25 25
497. 7 b. brown, green & blue 30 30
498. 16 b. blue, grn. & olive 90 90

1971. Various 1968 issues listed in Appendix surch.
499a. 40 b. on 10 b. black, red and green on gold foil (Yemen Red Crescent issue) .. .. 4·50 4·50
499b. 60 b. on 15 b. multicoloured on gold foil (Olympics — Chariot Racing issue) .. .. 6·00 6·00
499c. 80 b. on 10 b. multicoloured on gold foil (International Human Rights and U Thant issue) .. 8·00 8·00

79. Yemeni Castle.

1971. 8th Anniv (1970) of Revolution. Mult.
500. 5 b. Type **79** (postage) .. 90 50
501. 7 b. Yemeni workers and soldier (air) .. .. 1·10 65
502. 16 b. Clasped hands, flag and torch .. .. 1·50 90

1971. Air. Proclamation of first Permanent Constitution. No. 502 optd **PROCLAMATION OF THE INSTITUTION 1/11/1390 H. 28/12/1970 C.** in English and Arabic.
504. 16 b. multicoloured .. 4·00 3·25

81. U.N. Emblems and Globe.

1971. 25th Anniv. (1970) of U.N.O.
505. **81.** 5 b. purple, green and olive 40 25
506. 7 b. deep blue, green and blue 50 35

82. View of Sana'a.

1972. 9th Anniv (1971) of Revolution.
508. 7 b. Type **82** 60 60
509. 18 b. Military parade .. 2·00 2·00
510. 24 b. Mosque, Sana'a .. 2·50 2·50

83. A.P.U. Emblem and Flags.

1972. 25th Anniv. (1971) of Founding of Arab Postal Union at Sofar Conference.
512. **83.** 3 b. multicoloured .. 40 25
513. 7 b. multicoloured .. 60 45
514. 10 b. multicoloured .. 80 70

84. Arms and Flags.

85. Skeleton and Emblem.

1972. 10th Anniv. of Revolution.
516. **84.** 7 b. mult. (postage) .. 60 40
517. 10 b. multicoloured .. 90 65
518. 21 b. multicoloured (air) 2·50 2·00

1972. 25th Anniv. of W.H.O.
519. **85.** 2 b. multicoloured .. 50 30
520. 21 b. multicoloured .. 2·00 1·50
521. 37 b. multicoloured .. 3·00 2·50

86. Dome of the Rock, Jerusalem.

1973. 2nd Anniv. of Burning of Al-Aqsa Mosque, Jerusalem.
522. **86.** 7 b. multicoloured (post.) 85 55
523. 18 b. multicoloured .. 2·50 1·50
524. 24 b. multicoloured (air) 3·00 2·25

87. Arab Child with Book.

1973. 25th Anniv. (1971) of U.N.I.C.E.F.
526. **87.** 7 b. multicoloured (post.) 70 50
527. 10 b. multicoloured .. 90 65
528. 18 b. multicoloured (air) 1·40 90

88. Modern Office Building.

1973. Air. 11th Anniv. of Revolution.
530. **88.** 7 b. red and green .. 45 30
531. – 10 b. pink and green .. 90 75
532. – 18 b. violet and green .. 1·25 90
DESIGNS: 10 b. Factory. 18 b. Flats.

89. U.P.U. Emblem. **90.** Yemeni Town and Emblem.

1974. Cent. of U.P.U.
533. **89.** 10 b. red, blk. & blue .. 35 25
534. 30 b. red, black & green 85 85
535. 40 b. red, black & yell. 1·00 1·10

1975. 10th Anniv. of F.A.O. World Food Programme.
536. **90.** 10 b. multicoloured .. 45 30
537. 30 b. multicoloured .. 1·50 1·00
538. 63 b. multicoloured .. 2·75 2·25

91. Janad Mosque.

1975. 12th Anniv (1974) of Revolution. Mult.
539. 25 f. Type **91** 50 30
540. 75 f. Althawra Hospital .. 1·75 1·25

1975. Various stamps surch.
541 **84** 75 f. on 7 b. mult (post) 1·40 1·40
542 **86** 75 f. on 7 b. mult .. 1·25 70
542a **85** 75 f. on 21 b. mult .. 1·40 1·40
542b **89** 160 f. on 40 b. red, black and yellow .. 2·50 2·50
543 **86** 278 f. on 7 b. mult .. 4·75 4·75
544 **87** 75 f. on 18 b. mult (air) 1·50 1·50
544a **84** 75 f. on 21 b. mult .. 1·50 1·50
545 **88** 90 f. on 7 b. red & grn 1·50 1·50
546 – 120 f. on 18 b. violet and green (No. 532) 2·25 2·25

93. Early and Modern Telephones. **94.** Coffee Beans.

1976. Telephone Centenary.
547. **93.** 25 f. black and purple .. 40 25
548. 75 f. black and green .. 1·25 80
549. 160 f. black and brown 2·00 1·60

1976.
551. **94.** 1 f. multicoloured .. 10 15
552. 3 f. multicoloured .. 10 15
553 5 f. multicoloured .. 10 10
554. 10 f. multicoloured .. 15 10
555. 25 f. multicoloured .. 40 25
556. 50 f. multicoloured .. 75 45
557. 75 f. multicoloured .. 1·25 70
558. 1 r. multicoloured .. 1·50 90
559. 1 r. 50 multicoloured .. 2·25 1·75
560. 2 r. multicoloured .. 2·75 2·50
561. 5 r. multicoloured .. 6·50 6·00
Nos. 558/61 are larger, 22 × 30 mm.

95. Industrial Scaffolding. **96.** Emblem of National Institute of Public Administration.

1976. 2nd Anniv. of Reformation Movement. Multicoloured.
562. 75 f. Type **95** .. 1·00 80
563. 135 f. Hand holding pick .. 1·75 1·50

1976. 14th Anniv. of Revolution. Mult.
565. 25 f. Type **96** 35 30
566. 75 f. Yemeni family (Housing and population census) 1·00 80
567. 160 f. Shield emblem (Sana'a University) .. 2·00 1·75

97. President Ibrahim M. al-Hamdi.

1977. 1st Anniv of Assassination of Pres. Ibrahim al-Hamdi.
569. **97.** 25 f. green and black .. 35 30
570. 75 f. brown and black .. 80 70
571. 160 f. blue and black .. 1·50 1·40

98. Sa'ada and Sana'a.

1978. 15th Anniv (1977) of Revolution. Mult.
573. 25 f. Type **98** 35 25
574. 75 f. Television and transmitter 75 60
575. 160 f. Type **98** .. .. 1·40 1·25

99. A.P.U. Emblem.

100. Dish Aerial.

1978. 25th Anniv. of Arab Postal Union.

577.	**99.**	25 f. multicoloured ..	50	45
578.		60 f. multicoloured ..	1·25	1·10

1978. 3rd Anniv. of Correction Movement. Multicoloured.

580.	25 f. Type **100**	30	20
581.	75 f. Operating a computer	70	35

101. View of Sana'a.

1979. 30th Anniv. of I.C.A.O.

583.	**101.**	75 f. multicoloured ..	90	45
584.		135 f. multicoloured ..	1·60	1·00

102. Koran on Map of World.

1979. The Arabs.

586.	**102.**	25 f. multicoloured ..	30	20
587.		75 f. multicoloured ..	85	55

103. Viewers and Video-screen.

104. Dome of the Rock, Jerusalem.

1980. World Telecommunications Day (1979). Multicoloured.

589.	75 f. Type **103**	90	45
590.	135 f. As No. 589 but horiz.	1·60	1·00

1980. Palestinian Welfare.

592.	**104.**	5 f. multicoloured ..	35	10
593.		10 f. multicoloured ..	45	10

105. Girl and Chaffinch.

1980. International Year of the Child. (1979). Multicoloured.

594.	25 f. Type **105** (postage) ..	1·10	30
595.	50 f. Girl and Great Tit ..	1·60	65
596.	75 f. Child and butterfly ..	1·60	90
597.	80 f. Girl and Bullfinch (air)	2·25	1·10
598.	100 f. Child and butterfly	1·75	90
599.	125 f. Child and butterfly ..	2·75	1·25

Each stamp shows a different variety of bird or butterfly.

106. Scoring a Goal (Austria v. Spain).

1980. World Cup Football Championship, Argentina (1978). Multicoloured.

601.	25 f. Type **106** (postage) ..	35	35
602.	30 f. Tunisia v. Mexico ..	40	35
603.	35 f. Netherlands v. Iran ..	55	35
604.	50 f. Brazil v. Sweden ..	80	50
605.	60 f. Peru v. Scotland (air)	85	65
606.	75 f. Italy v. France ..	1·00	80
607.	80 f. Argentina v. Hungary	1·25	95
608.	100 f. West Germany v. Poland	1·60	1·00

107. Scout Fishing.

1980. World Scout Jamboree. Multicoloured.

610.	25 f. Type **107** (postage) ..	50	25
611.	35 f. Scouts and " Concorde "	1·10	45
612.	40 f. Parade and Scout on horseback	80	35
613.	50 f. Scouts with telescope	1·00	50
614.	60 f. Parade and cycling (air)	1·25	55
615.	75 f. Poppy and fencer ..	1·75	75
616.	120 f. Scouts catching butterflies	2·25	1·00

108. Match Scene and Flag of Poland.

1980. World Cup Football Championship Quarter-finalists. Match scenes and Flags. Multicoloured.

617.	25 f. Type **108** (postage) ..	45	25
618.	30 f. Peru	55	30
619.	35 f. Brazil	65	35
620.	50 f. Austria	95	60
621.	60 f. Italy (air)	1·00	60
622.	75 f. Netherlands	1·40	70
623.	80 f. West Germany ..	1·50	80
624.	100 f. Argentina (winners)	1·90	1·00

109. Kaaba, Mecca.

1980. Pilgrimage to Mecca. Multicoloured.

625.	25 f. Type **109**	30	20
626.	75 f. Type **109**	80	55
627.	160 f. Pilgrims around the Kaaba	1·90	70

110. Government Buildings, Sana'a.

1980. 17th Anniv. of Revolution. Mult.

629.	25 f. Arm and cogwheel encircling flower and factories (vert.)	45	30
630.	75 f. Type **110**	1·25	70

111. Al-Rawdah Mosque.

112. Figure clothed in Palestinian Flag.

1980. 1400th Anniv. of Hejira. Mult.

632.	25 f. Type **111**	30	20
633.	75 f. Al-Aqsa Mosque ..	85	55
634.	100 f. Al-Nabawi Mosque	1·90	75
635.	160 f. Al-Haram Mosque ..	2·25	1·25

1980. International Day of Solidarity with Palestinian People.

637.	**112.**	25 f. multicoloured ..	75	35
638.		75 f. multicoloured ..	2·25	1·25

113. Al-Aamiriya Mosque.

1981. 9th Arab Archaeological Conference. Multicoloured.

639	75 f. Type **113**	1·50	75
640	125 f. Al-Hadi Mosque ..	2·00	1·40

114. Tower and Ramparts.

1981. Sir Rowland Hill Commemoration. Multicoloured.

1981. World Tourism Conference, Manila. Multicoloured.

642.	25 f. Type **114**	35	15
643.	75 f. Mosque and houses ..	1·00	45
644.	100 f. Columns (horiz.) ..	1·25	60
645.	135 f. Bridge	1·75	85
646.	160 f. View of Sana'a (horiz.)	1·90	1·00

115. Hill and U.P.U. Emblem.

648	25 f. Type **115** (postage) ..	85	45
649	30 f. U.P.U. and A.P.U. emblems and Y.A.R. 4 b. stamp of 1963 ..	90	55
650	50 f. Hill, magnifying glass and stamps	1·40	85
651	75 f. Hill and airplane circling globe (air) ..	2·25	1·40
652	100 f. Hill, album and hand holding stamp with tweezers	3·00	1·75
653	150 f Air letter, aircraft and Y.A.R. 160 f. stamp of 1976	4·50	2·75

1981. Nos. 551/5 surch.

654.	**94.**	125 f. on 1 f. mult. ..	1·50	80
655.		150 f. on 3 f. mult. ..	1·75	1·00
656.		325 f. on 5 f. mult. ..	4·00	2·25
657.		350 f. on 10 f. mult. ..	4·50	2·50
658.		375 f. on 25 f. mult. ..	4·75	2·75

117. Map of Yemen.

1982. Air. 19th Anniv (1981) of Revolution. Multicoloured.

659.	75 f. Type **117**	70	40
660.	125 f. Yemenis looking towards map within sun	1·00	55
661.	325 f. Sun, fist, dove with flags for wings and industrial scene ..	2·50	1·75
662.	400 f. Air display	3·50	2·25

118. Al-Hasan ibn Ahmed al-Hamadani.

1982. Air. Birth Millenary of Al-Hasan ibn Ahmed al-Hamadani (philosopher).

664.	**118.**	125 f. multicoloured ..	1·00	55
665.		325 f. multicoloured ..	2·25	1·50

119. Common Rabbits.

1982. World Food Day. Multicoloured.

667.	25 f. Type **119**	70	30
668.	50 f. Cock and hens ..	1·50	60
669.	60 f. Turkeys	1·75	75
670.	75 f. Sheep	1·90	90
671.	100 f. Cow and calf ..	2·00	1·25
672.	125 f. Red deer	2·50	1·50

120. Gymnast.

1982. Air. Olympic Games, Moscow (1980). Multicoloured.

674.	25 f. Type **120**	50	20
675.	50 f. Pole vault	1·00	40
676.	60 f. Throwing the javelin	1·25	55
677.	75 f. Runner	1·40	70
678.	100 f. Basketball	1·60	80
679.	125 f. Football	1·90	1·00

121. Hang Glider and Satellite.

1982. Air. Progress in Air Transport.

681.	**121.**	25 f. multicoloured ..	40	20
682.	–	50 f. multicoloured ..	60	35
683.	–	60 f. multicoloured ..	70	45
684.	–	75 f. multicoloured ..	80	50
685.	–	100 f. multicoloured ..	1·00	65
686.	–	125 f. multicoloured ..	1·40	85

DESIGNS: 50 f. to 125 f. Early airplane and satellites.

122. Crocuses and Nurse pushing Wheelchair.

1982. Air. International Year of Disabled People (1981). Each shows nurse with wheelchair and different flowers.

688.	25 f. Type **122**	50	25
689.	50 f. Roses	80	45
690.	60 f. Pasque flowers ..	90	55
691.	75 f. Mixed arrangement	1·25	70
692.	100 f. Lilies	1·50	80
693.	125 f. Gladioli	1·75	1·25

123. Aerials and Satellite circling Globe.

1982. Air. Telecommunications Progress. Multicoloured.

695. 25 f. Modern radio communications 35 20
696. 50 f. Type **123** 55 35
697. 60 f. Radio masts, watch and dish aerials 65 45
698. 75 f. Dish aerials and landscape 85 60
699. 100 f. Dish aerials, satellites and morse transmitter 1·00 65
700. 125 f. Aerials, airplane and globe .. .. .. 1·75 1·25

124. Oranges, "T B" and Cross of Lorraine.

1982. Air. Centenary of Discovery of Tubercle Bacillus. Multicoloured.

702. 25 f. Type **124** 40 20
703. 50 f. Blossom, pears, cross of Lorraine and Robert Koch 65 35
704. 60 f. Pomegranates, flowers and cross of Lorraine .. 80 50
705. 75 f. Roses, grapes and bacillus 95 65
706. 100 f. Cherries, blossom and microscope .. .. 1·25 70
707. 125 f. Lemons, cross of Lorraine and microscope 1·50 1·00

125. Tackling.

1982. Air. World Cup Football Championship, Spain. Multicoloured.

709. 25 f. Type **125** 30 15
710. 50 f. Marking the opposition 50 25
711. 60 f. Players with ball .. 70 35
712. 75 f. Scoring a goal .. 85 45
713. 100 f. Dribbling .. .. 1·00 55
714. 125 f. Intercepting the ball 1·25 70

126. Map, Boy with Flag, Tents and Dome of the Rock.

1982. Air. Palestinian Children's Day. Multicoloured.

716. 75 f. Type **126** .. .. 1·25 60
717. 125 f. As Type **126** but girl with flag .. .. 2·00 1·25
718. 325 f. As Type **126** but boy and girl .. .. .. 4·50 2·50

127. Map under Grid and Airplane.

1982. Air. 30th Anniv. of Arab Postal Union. Multicoloured.

720. 75 f. Type **127** 85 45
721. 125 f. Map under grid and ship .. .. .. 1·40 70
722. 325 f. Map under grid and emblem .. .. .. 3·75 1·50

128. Passengers and Aircraft.

1983. 20th Anniv. of Yemen Airways.

724. **128.** 75 f. multicoloured .. 1·00 60
725. 125 f. multicoloured .. 1·75 90
726. 325 f. multicoloured .. 3·75 2·00

129. Man with Donkey and Foal.

1983. Traditional Costumes. Multicoloured.

727. 50 f. Type **129** (postage) .. 1·75 90
728. 50 f. Woman in embroidered veil carrying jug on head .. .. 1·75 90
729. 50 f. Shepherds in country 1·75 90
730. 50 f. Man walking through city and shepherds .. 1·75 90
731. 75 f. Woman at well (horiz.) (air) .. .. 2·50 1·40
732. 75 f. Woman sitting by shore (horiz.) .. .. 2·50 1·40
733. 75 f. Man ploughing with camel (horiz.) .. .. 2·50 1·40
734. 75 f. Man reading (horiz.) 2·50 1·40

130. Map of Yemen.

1983. 20th Anniv (1982) of Revolution. Mult.

736 100. f Houses, aircraft, telephone and dish aerial 1·25 70
737 150 f. Literacy campaign emblem .. .. 1·75 1·00
738 325 f. Tree and houses .. 4·00 2·25
739 400 f. Type **130** .. 6·00 2·75

131. Emblems, Satellite, Dish Aerial and Telephone on Flag.

1983. World Communications Year.

741. **131.** 150 f. multicoloured .. 2·00 1·25
742. 325 f. multicoloured .. 4·50 2·50

132. Man at Window and Men planting Tree.

1984. 21st Anniv (1983) of Revolution. Mult.

744. 100 f. Type **132** .. .. 1·50 70
745. 150 f. Fist and bust .. 1·75 95
746. 325 f. Sun, tank and open gates .. .. .. 4·00 2·00

133. Woman in Bombed Street.

134. Profiles and Clasped Hands as Doves.

1984. "Israeli Aggression against Lebanon".

748. **133.** 150 f. multicoloured .. 2·00 1·00
749. 325 f. multicoloured .. 4·50 2·50

1985. International Anti-apartheid Year (1978).

751. **134.** 150 f. multicoloured .. 1·75 1·00
752. 325 f. multicoloured .. 4·25 2·25

135. Winged Figure and Globe.

1985. 40th Anniv. of I.C.A.O.

754. **135.** 25 f. multicoloured .. 40 20
755. 50 f. multicoloured .. 70 30
756. 150 f. multicoloured .. 1·75 1·00
757. 325 f. multicoloured .. 3·75 2·00

136. Monument of Unknown Soldier.

1985. 22nd Anniv (1984) of Revolution. Mult.

759. 50 f. Type **136** 70 30
760. 150 f. Reconstruction of Marem Dam .. .. 2·00 1·25
761. 325 f. Althawrah Sports Stadium .. .. .. 4·00 2·25

137. Wrestling.

1985. Air. Olympic Games, Los Angeles (1984). Multicoloured.

763. 20 f. Type **137** 25 15
764. 30 f. Boxing 35 20
765. 40 f. Running 45 30
766. 60 f. Hurdling 55 40
767. 150 f. Pole vaulting .. 1·10 70
768. 325 f. Javelin throwing .. 2·75 1·50

138. Emblem and Satellite over Globe.

1986. 1st Anniv. of "Arabsat" Satellite.

770. **138.** 150 f multicoloured .. 2·00 1·25
771. 325 f. multicoloured .. 4·50 2·50

139. Dish Aerial and Cables.

1986. 120th Anniv of World Telecommunications.

773. **139.** 150 f. multicoloured .. 2·00 1·25
774. 325 f. multicoloured .. 4·50 2·50

140. Emblem.

1986. 2nd Anniv. of General People's Conference.

776. **140.** 150 f. multicoloured .. 1·75 1·25
777. 325 f. multicoloured .. 3·50 2·50

141. Emblem and Sana'a.

142. Emblem and Dove.

1986. 15th Islamic Foreign Ministers Conference, Sana'a (1984).

779. **141.** 150 f. multicoloured .. 1·75 1·25
780. 325 f. multicoloured .. 3·50 2·50

1986. 40th Anniv. of U.N.O.

782. **142.** 150 f. multicoloured .. 1·75 1·25
783. 325 f. multicoloured .. 3·50 2·50

143. Members' Flags, Map and Emblem.

1986. 39th Anniv (1984) of Arab League Foundation.

785. **143.** 150 f. multicoloured .. 1·75 1·25
786. 325 f. multicoloured .. 3·50 2·50

144. Anniversary Emblem.

1987. 25th Anniv. of Revolution.

787. **144.** 100 f. multicoloured .. 55 30
788. 150 f. multicoloured .. 80 55
789. 425 f. multicoloured .. 2·25 1·75
790. 450 f. multicoloured .. 2·50 2·00

145. Dove, Emblems and Open Hands.

1987. International Youth Year (1985).

792 **145** 150 f. multicoloured .. 70 45
793 425 f. multicoloured .. 2·00 1·50

146 Burning Oil

1987. 3rd Anniv of Discovery of Oil in Yemen Arab Republic. Multicoloured.

795 150 f. Type **146** 70 45
796 425 f. Oil derrick and refinery .. .. 2·00 1·50

147 Numbers and Emblem

1987. General Population and Housing Census (1986).
798 **147** 150 f. multicoloured .. 70 45
799 425 f. multicoloured .. 2·00 1·50

148 Footballers and Pique (mascot)

149 Skin Diving

1988. World Cup Football Championship, Mexico (1986). Multicoloured.
801 100 f. Type **148** 40 25
802 150 f. Goalkeeper saving ball 65 45
803 425 f. Players and Pique (horiz) .. .. .. 1·75 1·25

1988. 17th Scout Conference, Sana'a. Scout Activities. Multicoloured.
805 25 f. Type **149** 15 10
806 30 f. Table tennis .. 15 10
807 40 f. Tennis 20 15
808 50 f. Game with flag .. 20 15
809 60 f. Volleyball .. 25 20
810 100 f. Tug-of-war 40 30
811 150 f. Basketball 65 50
812 425 f. Archery .. .. 1·75 1·50

150 Old City.

1988. International Campaign for Preservation of Old Sana'a. Multicoloured.
814 **150** 25 f. multicoloured .. 15 10
815 50 f. multicoloured .. 20 15
816 100 f. multicoloured .. 40 30
817 150 f. multicoloured .. 65 50
818 425 f. multicoloured .. 1·75 1·50

151 Horseman

1988. 800th Anniv (1987) of Battle of Hattin.
820 **151** 150 f. multicoloured .. 2·25 1·10
821 425 f. multicoloured .. 5·50 2·25

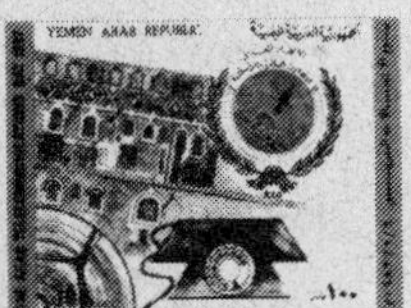
152 Building, Dish Aerial, Telephone and Emblem

1988. Arab Telecommunications Day (1987).
823 **152** 100 f. multicoloured .. 1·50 75
824 150 f. multicoloured .. 2·25 1·10
825 425 f. multicoloured .. 3·50 1·75

153 Torch and Symbols of Development

1989. 26th Anniv (1988) of Revolution. Multicoloured.
827 300 f. Type **153** .. .. 1·10 45
828 375 f. Type **153** .. .. 1·40 55
829 850 f. Flag, Koran and symbols of agriculture and industry (vert) .. 3·00 1·10
830 900 f. As No. 829 (vert) .. 3·50 1·40

154 Old and New Cities and Crowd

1989. 25th Anniv of 14th October Revolution. Multicoloured.
831 300 f. Type **154** .. .. 1·10 45
832 375 f. Type **154** .. .. 1·40 55
833 850 f. City street and crowd (vert) .. .. .. 3·00 1·10
834 900 f. As No. 833 (vert) .. 3·50 1·40

155 Sports

1989. Olympic Games, Seoul (1988). Mult.
835 300 f. Type **155** .. .. 1·25 45
836 375 f. Football .. .. 1·50 55
837 850 f. Football and judo (vert) .. .. .. 3·00 1·10
838 900 f. Emblem and torch bearer .. .. .. 4·25 1·40

156 Flag, Couple and Fist

1989. Palestinian "Intifida" Movement. Multicoloured.
840 300 f. Type **156** .. .. 1·10 45
841 375 f. Soldier raising flag (vert) .. .. .. 1·40 55
842 850 f. Dome of the Rock, youths and burning tyres .. .. .. 3·00 1·10
843 900 f. Crowd of youths (vert) .. .. .. 3·50 1·40

157 Emblem

1990. 1st Anniv of Arab Co-operation Council.
845 **157** 300 f. multicoloured .. 1·10 45
846 375 f. multicoloured .. 1·40 55
847 850 f. multicoloured .. 3·00 1·10
848 900 f. multicoloured .. 3·50 1·40

158 Loading Tanker

159 Emblem

1990. 1st Shipment of Oil. Multicoloured.
850 300 f. Type **158** .. .. 1·10 45
851 375 f. Type **158** .. .. 1·40 1·10
852 850 f. Pipeline around globe and tanker .. 3·00 1·10
853 900 f. As No. 852 .. .. 3·50 1·40

1990. 10th Anniv (1989) of Arab Board for Medical Specializations.
855 **159** 300 f. multicoloured .. 75 30
856 375 f. multicoloured .. 90 40
857 850 f. multicoloured .. 2·10 1·00
858 900 f. multicoloured .. 2·75 1·25

160 Woman feeding Baby

1990. Immunization Campaign. Mult.
860 300 f. Type **160** .. .. 1·10 45
861 375 f. Type **160** .. .. 1·25 55
862 850 f. Nurse weighing baby (horiz) .. .. .. 3·00 1·10
863 900 f. As No. 862 (horiz) .. 3·50 1·40

For further issues see **YEMEN REPUBLIC (combined)**.

POSTAGE DUE STAMPS

1964. Designs as Nos. 291, 295/6 (Animals), but inscr. " POSTAGE DUE ".
D 298. 4 b. brown and green .. 2·00 70
D 299. 12 b. brown and orange 3·75 2·50
D 300. 20 b. black and violet .. 6·00 3·25
DESIGNS: 4 b. Mountain gazelles. 12 b. Bullock. 20 b. Arab horses.

1964. Designs as Nos. 303/5, but inscr. " POSTAGE DUE ". Multicoloured.
D 306. 4 b. Roses .. .. 1·75 60
D 307. 12 b. Poinsettia .. .. 4·25 1·75
D 308. 20 b. Viburnum .. .. 6·00 5·50

1966. Nos. 324/8 optd. **POSTAGE DUE** in English and Arabic.
D 371. 6 b. multicoloured .. 2·25 1·50
D 372. 8 b. multicoloured .. 2·50 1·90
D 373. 12 b. multicoloured .. 3·25 2·40
D 374. 20 b. multicoloured .. 5·50 4·25
D 375. 1 r. multicoloured .. 11·50 8·50

1966. Designs as Nos. 410/12 (Football), but inscr. " POSTAGE DUE ".
D 414. 4 b. multicoloured .. 1·60 1·00
D 415. 5 b. multicoloured .. 4·00 2·00
D 416. 20 b. multicoloured .. 9·00 4·00

1967. Designs as Nos. 465/7, but inscr. " POSTAGE DUE " instead of " AIR MAIL ". Multicoloured.
D 468. – 6 b. Bananas .. .. 2·50 1·25
D 469. **73.** 8 b. Figs .. .. 3·25 1·75
D 470. – 10 b. Grapes .. .. 4·25 2·25

ROYALIST ISSUES

Fighting continued between the Royalists and Republicans until 1970. In 1970 Saudi Arabia recognised the Republican government as the rulers of Yemen, and the royalist position crumbled.

1962. Various issues optd. (i) Optd. **FREE YEMEN FIGHTS FOR GOD, IMAM, COUNTRY** in English and Arabic.
R 1. **19.** 2 b. red and black .. 2·25 4·00
R 3. 4 b. yellow and black .. 2·25 4·00

(ii) Optd. **FREE YEMEN FIGHTS FOR GOD, IMAM & COUNTRY** in English and Arabic. (a) Nos. 156/8.
R 5. **24.** 4 b. multicoloured .. 3·00 4·50
R 6. 6 b. multicoloured .. 3·00 4·50
R 7. 10 b. multicoloured .. 5·00 6·00

(b) Nos. 159/60.
R 8. **25.** 4 b. brown .. .. 18·00 18·00
R 9. 6 b. green .. .. 18·00 18·00

(c) Nos. 161/2.
R 10. 4 b. green .. .. 2·50 3·50
R 11. 6 b. blue .. .. .. 2·50 3·50

(d) Nos. 167/8.
R 12. 4 b. orange and black .. 2·25 3·50
R 13. 6 b. green and sepia .. 2·25 3·50

(e) Nos. 126/30.
R 14. **19.** 2 b. red and black ..
R 15. 4 b. yellow and black ..
R 16. 6 b. orange and black
R 17. 8 b. turquoise and black
R 18. 20 b. orange and violet
Set of 5 .. .. 90·00 90·00

(f) Nos. 169/75.
R 19. **20.** 1 b. violet .. .. 1·50 1·50
R 20. 2 b. green .. .. 1·50 1·50
R 21. 3 b. turquoise .. .. 1·60 1·60
R 22. 4 b. blue .. .. 3·00 3·00
R 23. 6 b. purple .. .. 3·75 3·75
R 24. 14 b. red .. .. 5·00 5·00
R 25. 20 b. sepia .. .. 6·50 6·50

R 6. Five Ears of Wheat.

1963. Air. Freedom from Hunger.
R 26. **R 6.** 4 b. red, grn. & ochre 2·25 2·75
R 27. 6 b. red, green & blue 2·25 2·75

(R 7.)

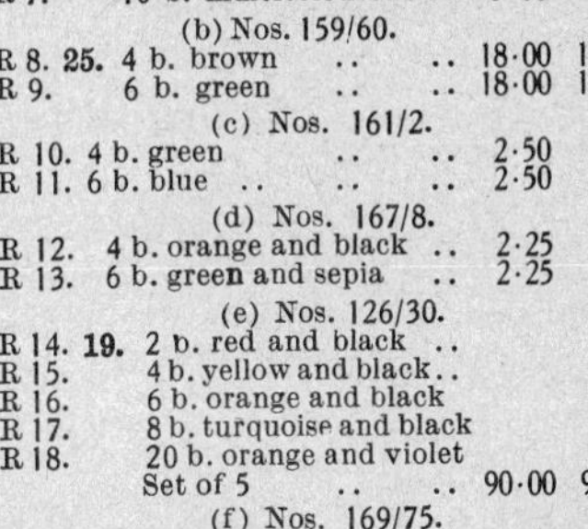
(R 8.)

1963. Nos. 195/6 variously optd.
(a) No. 195 optd. with Type R 7.
R 28. 4 b. brown and mauve .. 40·00 45·00
(b) No. 196 optd. with Type R 7 with first line of Arabic inscr. repeated at foot.
R 29. 6 b. red and blue .. 40·00 45·00
(c) No. 196 optd. with Types R 7 and R 8.
R 30. 6 b. red and blue .. 50·00 60·00

1963. Surch. in figures with stars over old value, for use on circulars.
R 31. **R 6.** 1 b. on 4 b. red, green and ochre .. .. 1·50 1·75
R 32. 2 b. on 6 b. red, green and blue .. .. 1·50 2·25

R 10. Red Cross Field Post.

1963. Red Cross Cent. Flags in red; inscr. in black.
R 33. **R 10.** ⅛ b. violet (postage) .. 60 65
R 34. ¼ b. mauve 60 65
R 35. ½ b. brown 60 65
R 36. 4 b. turquoise .. 85 1·50
R 37. 6 b. blue (air) .. 2·25 2·50

R 11.

1963. Consular Fee stamp optd **YEMEN** in English and "POSTAGE 1383" (Moslem Year) in Arabic with bar over old inscr. as in Type R 11.

R 38 R 11 10 b. black and red 65·00 65·00

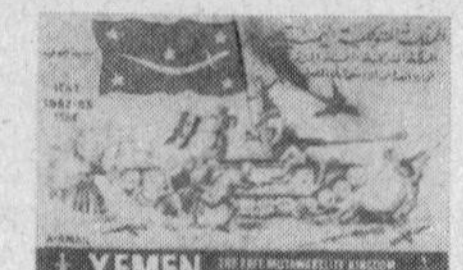

R 12. Troops in Action.

1964. Air. "The Patriotic War". Flags and emblem in red.

R 39. R 12. ½ b. green 50 75
R 40. 1 b. black 50 75
R 41. 2 b. slate 50 75
R 42. 4 b. turquoise .. 75 1·00
R 43. 6 b. blue .. .. 1·25 1·75

1964. Air. Surch. **AIR MAIL**, red cross, **1963-64 HONOURING BRITISH RED CROSS SURGICAL TEAM** and value and Arabic equivalent.

R 44. R 12. 10 b. on 4 b. turquoise 3·75 3·75
R 45. 18 b. on ½ b. green .. 5·00 5·00

1964. Air. Surch. **AIR MAIL** and value in English and Arabic with aeroplane motif.

R 46. R 10. 10 b. on ⅛ b. violet .. 3·25 3·75
R 47. 18 b. on ½ b. purple .. 5·00 6·00
R 48. 28 b. on ½ b. brown .. 7·50 7·50

1964. Air. Surch. **4 REVALUED** in English and Arabic with dotted frameline around stamp.

R 49. R 12. 4 b. on ½ b. green .. 7·50 7·50
R 50. 4 b. on 1 b. black .. 7·50 7·50
R 51. 4 b. on 2 b. slate .. 7·50 7·50

R 16. Olympic Flame and "Rings".

1964. Olympic Games, Tokyo.

R 52. R 16. 2 b. blue (postage) .. 1·50 1·50
R 53. 4 b. violet .. 2·50 2·50
R 54. 6 b. brown (air) .. 3·75 3·75

R 17. Rocket.

1964. Astronauts.

R 55. R 17. 2 b. brown, violet and black (postage) .. 1·50 1·50
R 56. 4 b. brown, blue and black .. .. 3·25 3·25
R 57. 6 b. yellow & blk. (air) 5·00 5·00

R 18. (Actual size 80 × 26 mm.).

1964. Consular Fee stamps optd across a pair as in Type R 18.

R 58. R 18. 10 b. (5b.+5 b.) pur.

Owing to a shortage of 10 b. postage stamps, 5 b. Consular Fee stamps were optd. across pairs with **YEMEN** in English and "POSTAGE 1383" (Moslem Year) in Arabic, in frame, together with the Ministry of Communications' Royal Arms seal and a bar over old inscription at foot. Price is for horiz. or vert. pair.

1965. Air. British Yemen Relief Committee. Nos. R 46/8 additionally optd. **HONOURING BRITISH YEMEN RELIEF COMMITTEE 1963 1965**, in English and Arabic.

R 59. R 10. 10 b. on ⅛ b. violet .. 2·50 2·50
R 60. 18 b. on ½ b. magenta 5·00 5·00
R 61. 28 b. on ½ b. brown .. 6·50 6·50

R 20. Seif-al-Islam Ali.

R 21. Kennedy as Young Man.

1965. Prince Seif al-Islam Ali Commem.

R 62. R 20. 4 b. grey and red .. 1·75 1·75

1965. Pres. Kennedy Commem.

R 63. R 21. ⅛ b. black, mauve and gold (postage) .. 40 40
R 64. – ¼ b. vio., turq. & gold 40 40
R 65. – ½ b. brn., blue & gold 50 50
R 66. – 4 b. sep., yell. & gold 3·25 3·25
R 67. – 6 b. black, apple and gold (air) .. 5·00 5·00

DESIGNS (Kennedy): ¼ b. As naval officer. ½ b. Sailing with Mrs. Kennedy. 4 b. In rocking-chair. 6 b. Full-face portrait.

1965. Churchill Commem. (1st issue). No. R 62, with colours changed, optd. **IN MEMORY OF SIR WINSTON CHURCHILL 1874-1965**, in English and Arabic.

R 68. R 20. 4 b. blue and red .. 8·00 8·00

R 23. Satellite and Emblems.

1965. I.T.U. Cent.

R 69. R 23. 2 b. yellow, violet and black (postage) .. 3·00 2·25
R 70. 4 b. red, blue and blk. 3·75 2·50
R 71. 6 b. green, violet and black (air) .. .. 5·50 5·00

R 24. Hammerkop.

1965. Birds. Multicoloured.

R 72 ⅛ b. Type R 24 (post) 90 30
R 73 ¼ b. Golden-winged grosbeak 90 30
R 74 ½ b. Hoopoe 90 30
R 75 4 b. Arabian woodpecker .. .. 2·75 1·10
R 76 6 b. Violet starling (air) 4·75 1·75

R 25. Sir Winston Churchill and St. Paul's Cathedral.

1965. Churchill Commemoration (2nd issue). Multicoloured.

R 77. ⅛ b. Type R 25 .. .. 50 25
R 78. ¼ b. Churchill and Houses of Parliament .. 50 25
R 79. ½ b. Full-face portrait .. 60 30
R 80. 1 b. Type R 25 .. .. 80 40
R 81. 2 b. Churchill and Houses of Parliament .. 1·50 70
R 82. 4 b. Full-face portrait .. 3·25 1·25

R 26. Imam Al-Badr.

DESIGNS—VERT. 2 b., 18 b. Royal arms. HORIZ. 6 b., 24 b. Flag.

1965.

R 83. R 26. 1 b. blk. & blue (post.) 45 35
R 83a. 1½ b. black & green 20 25
R 84. – 2 b. red and green .. 1·00 75
R 85. R 26. 4 b. black and purple 1·50 1·00
R 86. – 6 b. red & violet (air) 1·75 1·40
R 87. – 18 b. red and brown 4·50 3·75
R 88. – 24 b. red and blue .. 7·50 6·50

1965. Space Flight of "Mariner 4". Nos. R 55/7 optd. **MARINER 4** in English and Arabic.

R 89. R 17. 2 b. brown, violet and black (postage) .. 1·90 1·90
R 90. 4 b. brown, blue & blk. 4·50 4·50
R 91. 6 b. yell. and blk. (air) 7·00 7·00

R 28. I.C.Y. Emblem, King Faisal of Saudi Arabia and Imam Al-Badr.

1965. Int. Co-operation Year.

R 92. R 28. 2 b. blue and brown (postage) .. .. 1·75 1·50
R 93. 4 b. lake and green .. 3·00 2·50
R 94. 6 b. sepia & blue (air) 4·50 4·25

1965. Space Flight of "Gemini 5". Nos R 69/71 optd. **'GEMINI -V' GORDON COOPER & CHARLES CONRAD AUGUST 21-29, 1965** and space capsule.

R 95. R 23. 2 b. yellow, violet and black (postage) 1·50 1·50
R 96. 4 b. red, blue and black .. .. 3·00 3·00
R 97. 6 b. green, violet and black (air) .. 5·50 5·50

R 30. Black Persian.

1965. Cats. Multicoloured.

R 99. ⅛ b. Type R 30 .. .. 50 25
R 100. ¼ b. Tortoise-shell .. 50 25
R 101. ½ b. Seal Point Siamese 70 40
R 102. 1 b. Silver Tabby Persian 80 50
R 103. 2 b. Cream Persian .. 1·75 75
R 104. 4 b. Red Tabby .. 3·00 1·50

Nos. R 102/4 are vert.

R 31. Red Saxifrage.

1965. Flowers. Multicoloured.

R 106. ⅛ b. Verbena 45 25
R 107. ¼ b. Dianthus 45 25
R 108. ½ b. Dahlia 65 40
R 109. 1 b. Nasturtium .. 75 50
R 110. 2 b. Type R 31 .. 1·50 65
R 111. 4 b. Wild rose .. 2·75 1·25

Nos. R 106/8 are vert.

R 32. Flag and Globe.

1965. Pope Paul's Visit to U.N. Organization.

R 113. R 32. 2 b. red, blk. & grn. 2·00 1·25
R 114. 4 b. red, blk. & vio. 3·50 2·50
R 115. 6 b. red, blk. & blue 4·25 3·75

R 33. Moon Landing.

1965. Space Achievements. Multicoloured.

(a) Postage. (i) Size as Type R 33.

R 117. ⅛ b. Type R 33 .. 25 25
R 118. ¼ b. Astronauts on Moon 25 25
R 119. ½ b. Pres. Kennedy and Cape Kennedy (vert.) 40 40

(ii) Size 48 × 28 mm.

R 120 4 b. Belyaev and Leonov in space .. 2·50 1·25

(b) Air. Size 48 × 28 mm.

R 121. 6 b. White and Mcdivitt in space .. .. 3·75 1·75

R 34. Football and Gold Medal.

1965. "Winners of Olympic Games, Tokyo" (1964). Each design showing a sport with a gold medal. Multicoloured.

R 123. ⅛ b. Type R 34 (postage) 25 25
R 124. ¼ b. Running .. 25 25
R 125. ¼ b. Throwing the discus 40 40
R 126. 2 b. Judo .. .. 1·00 70
R 127. 4 b. Wrestling .. .. 2·50 1·25
R 128. 6 b. Horse-jumping (air) 3·75 1·75

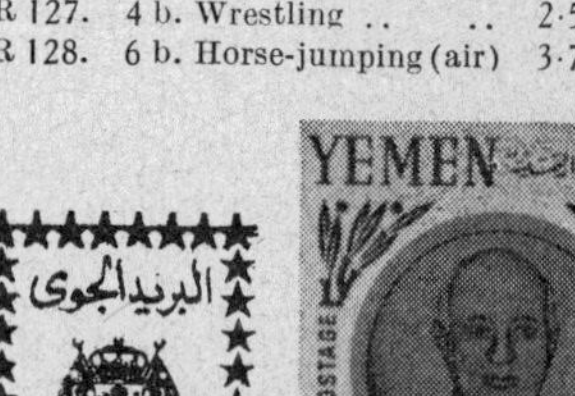

R 35. Arms. R 36. Nehru.

1966. Air. Imperf.

R 130. R 35. 10 b. red on white
R 131. 10 b. violet on white
R 132. 10 b. red on yellow
R 133. 10 b. violet on orange
R 134. 10 b. violet on mag.

These handstamps were also applied directly to envelopes and aerogrammes.

1966. "Builders of World Peace" (1st Series). Portraits in gold and black; inscr. in black.

R 136. R 36. ⅛ b. green 25 25
R 137. – ¼ b. brown 25 25
R 138. – ½ b. grey 75 40
R 139. – 1 b. blue .. .. 1·25 50
R 140. – 4 b. green .. .. 2·50 1·00

DESIGNS: ¼ b. Dag Hammarskjold. ½ b. Pope John XXIII. 1 b. Sir Winston Churchill. 4 b. Pres. Kennedy.

See also Nos. R 146/51.

1966. Nos. R 63/5 and R 67 surch. with new values in English and Arabic.

R 142 R 21 4 b. on ⅛ b. black, mauve and gold (postage) .. 1·00 75
R 143 – 8 b. on ¼ b. violet, blue and gold .. 2·00 1·50
R 144 – 10 b. on ½ b. brown, blue and gold .. 2·50 2·00
R 145 – 1 r. on 6 b. black, green and gold (air) .. 7·00 6·00

1966. "Builders of World Peace" (2nd series). As Type R 36. Portraits in black and gold; inscr in black.

R 146. ⅛ b. yellow 25 25
R 147. ¼ b. flesh 25 25
R 148. ½ b. mauve 75 40
R 149. 1 b. blue 60 50
R 150. 1 b. turquoise .. 60 45
R 151. 4 b. green .. .. 2·50 1·00

PORTRAITS: ⅛ b. Pres. Lubke. ¼ b. Pres. De Gaulle. ½ b. Pope Paul VI. 1 b. (R 149) Pres. Johnson. 1 b. (R 150) King Faisal of Saudi Arabia. 4 b. U Thant.

1966. Newspaper Stamps. Optd. **PERIODICALS** in English and Arabic in frame.

(a) Similar to Nos. R 26/7, but imperf.

R 153. R 6. 4 b. red, grn. & ochre 10·00
R 154. 6 b. red, green & blue 10·00

(b) Unissued 1963 Red Cross Cent. issue (Nos. R 26/7 surch.)

R 155. R 6. 1 b. on 4 b. red, green and ochre .. 10·00
R 156. 2 b. on 6 b. red, green and blue .. 18·00

1966. Air. Olympic Games Preparation, Mexico (1968). Nos. R 123/5 in new colours surch. **AIR MAIL OLYMPIC GAMES PREPARATION MEXICO 1968** and new value in English and Arabic with aircraft and flag.

R 158. R 34. 12 b. on ½ b. mult. 1·90 1·90
R 159. – 28 b. on ½ b. mult. 3·75 3·75
R 160. – 34 b. on ½ b. mult. 5·00 5·00

R 40. Yemeni Cannon.

1966. Shaharah Fortress. Frame and stars in red.

R 162. R 40. ½ b. bistre (postage) 25 15
R 163. – 1 b. grey 35 25
R 164. – 1½ b. blue .. 55 40
R 165. – 2 b. brown .. 70 50
R 166. – 4 b. green .. 1·25 1·00
R 167. – 6 b. violet (air) .. 1·75 1·50
R 168. – 10 b. black .. 2·25 2·00

DESIGNS—VERT. 1 b. Bombed Mosque. 2 b. Victory Gate. 4 b. Yemeni cannon (different). 10 b. Bombed houses. HORIZ. 1½ b. Shararah Fortress. 6 b. Yemeni cannon (different).

1966. Nos. R 33/5 surch. **4 B REVALUED** in English and Arabic within border of stars. Flags red; inscr. in black.

R 170. R 10. 4 b. on ⅛ b. violet.. 25·00 25·00
R 171. 4 b. on ¼ b. mauve.. 25·00 25·00
R 172. 4 b. on ½ b. brown.. 25·00 25·00

R 42. President Kennedy.

1967. 3rd Anniv. of Pres. Kennedy's Death. and Inaug. of Arlington Grave.

R 173. R 42. 12 b. multicoloured 1·90 1·90
R 174. 28 b. multicoloured 3·75 3·75
R 175. 34 b. multicoloured 5·00 5·00

1967. England's Victory in World Cup Football Championships (1966). Nos. R 123/8 optd. **WORLD CHAMPIONSHIP CUP ENGLAND 1966** in English and Arabic, **ENGLAND WINNER** in English only and World Cup emblem.

R 177. R 34. ⅛ b. mult. (postage) 25 25
R 178. – ¼ b. multicoloured 25 25
R 179. – ½ b. multicoloured 25 25
R 180. – 2 b. multicoloured 2·00 2·00
R 181. – 4 b. multicoloured 3·50 3·50
R 182. – 6 b. mult. (air) .. 4·00 4·00

1967. Surch. **4 B REVALUED** in English and Arabic within border of stars.

(a) Nos. R 123/5.

R 183. R 34. 4 b. on ⅛ b. mult...
R 184. – 4 b. on ¼ b. mult...
R 185. – 4 b. on ½ b. mult...

(b) Nos. R 177/9.

R 186. R 34. 4 b. on ⅛ b. mult...
R 187. – 4 b. on ¼ b. mult...
R 188. – 4 b. on ½ b. mult...

R 44. Bazooka.

1967. "Freedom Fighters". Designs showing Freedom Fighters with various weapons. Multicoloured.

R 189 4 b. Type R 44 .. 75 30
R 190 4 b. Fighter in fez with rifle 75 30
R 191 4 b. Bare-headed man with rifle .. 75 30
R 192 4 b. Fighters holding bazooka and round 75 30
R 193 4 b. Anti-aircraft gun 75 30
R 194 4 b. Heavy machine-gun 75 30
R 195 4 b. Light machine-gun 75 30
R 196 4 b. Fighter with bazooka on mount and rifle 75 30

R 45. Rembrandt—Self Portrait.

1967. "AMPHILEX" Stamp Exn., Amsterdam. Rembrandt Paintings. Multicoloured.

(a) Borders in gold.

R 198. 2 b. "An Elderly Man as St. Paul" 15 15
R 199. 4 b. Type R 45 .. 25 25
R 200. 6 b. "Portrait of Jacob Trip" 30 25
R 201. 10 b. "An Old Man in an Armchair" 50 40
R 202. 12 b. Self-portrait (different) 75 45
R 203. 20 b. "A Woman Bathing" .. .. .. 1·00 1·75

(b) Borders in silver.

R 205. 2 b. As No. R 198 .. 20 20
R 206. 4 b. Type R 45.. .. 35 35
R 207. 6 b. As No. R 200 .. 40 40
R 208. 10 b. As No. R 201 .. 60 50
R 209. 12 b. As No. R 202 .. 90 55
R 210. 20 b. As No. R 203 .. 1·50 65

1967. Pres. Kennedy's 50th Birth Anniv. Nos. R 173/5 optd **50th. ann. 29 MAY** in English only.

R 212. R 42. 12 b. multicoloured 1·10 1·10
R 213. 28 b. multicoloured 2·50 2·50
R 214. 34 b. multicoloured 3·00 3·00

R 47. Trigger Fish.

1967. Red Sea Fish. Multicoloured.

R 216. ⅛ b. Type R 47 (postage) 40 10
R 217. ¼ b. Rudder fish .. 40 10
R 218. ½ b. Butterfly fish .. 40 10
R 219. 1 b. Grouper 45 10
R 220. 4 b. Dragon fish .. 60 10
R 221. 6 b. Dark Clown fish .. 75 10
R 222. 10 b. Violet-hued Berycid 1·25 10
R 224. 12 b. As No. R 222 (air) 1·00 10
R 225. 14 b. Cuckoo Wrasse .. 1·25 10
R 226. 16 b. Deepwater Squirrel fish .. .. 1·50 10
R 227. 18 b. As No. R 221 1·75 15
R 228. 24 b. As No. R 220 2·00 25
R 229. 34 b. As No. R 219 2·50 35

Nos. R 216/22 are are Type R 47; Nos. R 224/9 are larger, size 58 × 42 mm.

R 48. "The Gipsy Girl" (Frans Hals).

1967. Air. Famous Paintings. Mult.

R 230. 8 b. Type R 48.. .. 35 15
R 231. 10 b. "The Zouave" (Van Gogh) 40 15
R 232. 12 b. Self portrait (Rubens) 50 15
R 233. 14 b. "Boys Eating Melon" (Murillo) .. 75 20
R 234. 16 b. "The Knight's Dream" (Raphael) .. 1·00 20
R 235. 20 b. "St. George and the Dragon" (Ucello) .. 1·25 25

The 20 b. is a horiz.

1967. "For Poison Gas Victims". Surch. **FOR POISON GAS VICTIMS** and surcharge in English and Arabic, with skull and Crossbones within frame.

R 236. R 40. ½ b. + 1 b. (No. R162) (postage) ..
R 237. – 1 b. + 1 b. (R 163)
R 238. – 1½ b. + 1 b. (R 164)
R 239. – 2 b. + 1 b. (R 84) ..
R 240. – 2 b. + 1 b. (R 126)
R 241. – 2 b. + 1 b. (R 165)
R 242. R 20. 4 b. + 2 b. (R 62)
R 243. – 4 b. + 2 b. (R 66)
R 244. R 20. 4 b. + 2 b. (R 68)
R 245. R 26. 4 b. + 2 b. (R 85)
R 246. R 34. 4 b. + 2 b. (R 93)
R 247. – 4 b. + 2 b. (R 127)
R 248. – 4 b. + 2 b. (R 166)
R 249. – 6 b. + 3 b. (R 86) (air)
R 250. – 6 b. + 3 b. (R 128)
R 251. – 6 b. + 3 b. (R 167)
R 252. R35. 10 b. + 5 b. (R 130)
R 253. – 10 b. + 5 b. (R 168)
R 254. R 32. 12 b. + 6 b. (R 158)
R 255. – 18 b. + 9 b. (R 87)
R 256. R 12. 24 b. + 12 b. red and blue (Imperf. Size 57 × 36 mm.)
R 257. – 24 b. + 12 b. (R 88)
R 258. – 28 b. + 14 b. (R 159)
R 259. – 34 b. + 17 b. (R 160)

The amount of surcharge was 50 per cent of the face value of each stamp (except Nos. R 236/8 where the surcharge was 1 b. each). Some of the higher values have two handstamps, which, when added together make up the 50 per cent.

1967. Jordan Relief Fund. Surch **JORDAN RELIEF FUND** and value in English and Arabic with Crown.

(a) No. R 66 (Kennedy).

R 261. – 4 b. + 2 b. sepia, yellow and gold 5·00 5·00

(b) Nos. R 75/6 (Birds).

R 262. – 4 b. + 2 b. mult. (post.) 1·50 1·00
R 263. – 6 b. + 3 b. mult. (air) 2·25 1·75

(c) Nos. R 92/4 (I.C.Y.).

R 265. R 34. 2 b. + 1 b. blue and brown (postage) 1·00 1·00
R 266. 4 b. + 2 b. lake and green .. .. 1·00 1·00
R 267. 6 b. + 3 b. sepia and blue (air) 1·00 1·00

(d) Nos. R 102/4 (Cats).

R 269. – 1 b. + 1 b. mult. .. 1·00 1·00
R 270. – 2 b. + 1 b. mult. .. 1·00 1·00
R 271. – 4 b. + 2 b. mult. .. 1·00 1·00

(e) R 109/11 (Flowers).

R 273. – 1 b. + 1 b. mult. .. 1·00 1·00
R 274. R 30. 2 b. + 1 b. mult. .. 1·00 1·00
R 275. – 4 b. + 2 b. mult. .. 1·00 1·00

(f) Nos. R 136/40 ("Builders").

R 277. R 36. ⅛ b. + 1 b. gold, black and green .. 70 70
R 278. – ¼ b. + 1 b. gold, black and brown .. 70 70
R 279. – ½ b. + 1 b. gold, black and grey .. 70 70
R 280. – 1 b. + 1 b. gold, black and blue .. 1·00 1·00
R 281. – 4 b. + 2 b. gold, black and green .. 3·00 3·00

(g) Nos. R 146/51 ("Builders").

R 283. – ⅛ b. + 1 b. gold, black and yellow .. 30 30
R 284. – ¼ b. + 1 b. gold, black and flesh .. 30 30
R 285. – ½ b. + 1 b. gold, black and mauve .. 30 30
R 286. – 1 b. + 1 b. gold, black and blue .. 50 50
R 287. – 1 b. + 1 b. gold, black and turquoise .. 50 50
R 288. – 4 b. + 2 b. gold, black and green .. 75 75

R 51. "The Pharmacy".

1967. Air. Paintings. Multicoloured.

(a) Asiatic Paintings.

R 290 ⅛ b. "Mountains and Forests" (Wang Hwei) 10 10
R 291 ¼ b. "Tiger" (Sim Sajoug) 10 10
R 292 ½ b. "Mountain Views" (Tony K'itch'ang) .. 10 10
R 293 ¾ b. "Rama Lakshama and Shiva" (Indian 16th century) 15 10
R 294 1 b. "Ladies" (T. Kiyomitsu) .. 15 10

(b) Arab Paintings.

R295 1½ b. "Bayad plays the Oud and sings" .. 20 10
R296 2 b. Type R 51 .. 25 10
R297 3 b. "Dioscorides and a Student" .. 30 10
R298 4 b. "The Scribe" .. 50 20
R299 6 b. "Abu Zayd asks to be taken over by boat" 90 25

The ⅛ b., 1½ b. and 6 b. are horiz and the remainder vert.

R 52. Bugler.

1967. World Scout Jamboree. Idaho. Mult.

R 301 ¼ b. Type R 52 (post) 15 10
R 302 ½ b. Campfire .. 15 10
R 303 4 b. Type R 52 55 10
R 304 6 b. As ¼ b .. 75 15
R 305 ⅛ b. Scout badge and Yemeni flag (air) .. 15 10
R 306 10 b. As ⅛ b. 75 15
R 307 20 b. Scout and satellite .. .. 2·00 20

1967. Jordan Refugees Relief Fund. Surch **JORDAN REFUGEES RELIEF FUND** and value in English and Arabic, and Refugee Emblem.

(a) Nos. R 52/4 (Olympic Games).

R 309. R 16. 2 b. + 2 b. blue (post.) 50 50
R 310. 4 b. + 4 b. violet .. 70 70
R 311. 6 b. + 6 b. brown (air) 1·25 1·25

(b) Nos. R 55/7 (Astronauts).

R 313. R 17. 2 b. + 2 b. brown, violet & blk. (post.) 50 50
R 314. 4 b. + 4 b. brown, blue and black .. 70 70
R 315. 6 b. + 6 b. yellow and black (air) .. 1·25 1·25

(c) Nos. R 63/7 (Kennedy).

R 317. R 21. ⅛ b. + ⅛ b. black, mve. & gold (post.) 20 20
R 318. – ¼ b. + ¼ b. violet, turquoise & gold 20 20
R 319. – ½ b. + ½ b. brown, blue and gold .. 20 20
R 320. – 4 b. + 4 b. sepia, yellow and gold 2·00 2·00
R 321. 6 b. + 6 b. black, green & gold (air) 3·00 3·00

(d) No. R 68 (Churchill opt.).

R 323. R 20. 4 b. + 4 b. bl. & red 12·00 12·00

(e) R 69/71 (I.T.U.).

R 324. R 23. 2 b. + 2 b. yell., violet and black (post.) 40 40
R 325. 4 b. + 4 b. red, blue and black .. 70 70
R 326. 6 b. + 6 b. grn., violet and black (air).. 2·50 2·50

(f) R 77/82 (Churchill).

R 328. R 25. ⅛ b. + ⅛ b. mult. .. 25 25
R 329. – ¼ b. + ¼ b. mult. .. 25 25
R 330. – ½ b. + ½ b. mult. .. 30 30
R 331. R 25. 1 b. + 1 b. mult. .. 40 40
R 332. – 2 b. + 2 b. mult. .. 70 70
R 333. – 4 b. + 4 b. mult. .. 1·00 1·00

R 54. Gaucho.

1967. Olympic Games, Mexico (1968). Multicoloured.

R 335. ⅛ b. Type R 54 (post.) 10 10
R 336. ¼ b. Fishermen on Lake Patzcuaro .. 10 10
R 337. ½ b. Football .. 10 10
R 338. 4 b. Avenida de la Reforma, Mexico City .. 30 10
R 339. 8 b. Fine Arts Theatre, Mexico City .. 60 10
R 340. 12 b. Mayan ruins (air).. 80 10
R 341. 16 b. Type R 54 .. 1·10 15
R 342. 20 b. As ¼ b. .. 2·00 60

The ½ b. is vert.

R 55. Battle Scene.

1967. Moorish Art in Spain. Multicoloured.

R344	2 b. Moor slaying knight (horiz) (postage) ..	10	10
R345	4 b. Arab kings of Granada (horiz) ..	15	10
R346	6 b. Diagram of chess game (from King Alfonso X's "Book of Chess, Dice and Tablings") (horiz) ..	50	10
R347	10 b. Type R 55 ..	50	10
R348	12 b. Moors with prisoners	70	10
R349	20 b. Meeting of Moor and Christian (air) ..	1·75	10
R350	22 b. Bullfight	1·75	10
R351	24 b. Lute-players ..	2·00	15

APPENDIX

The following stamps have either been issued in excess of postal needs or have not been available to the public in reasonable quantities at face value. Such stamps may later be given full listing if there is evidence of regular postal use.

REPUBLIC

1967.

5th Anniv of Revolution Nos. 476/81 optd in Arabic 1, 2, 4, 6, 8, 10 b.

Paintings by Flemish Masters. Postage ¼, ⅓, ½ b.; Air 3, 6 b.

Paintings by Florentine Masters. Postage ¼, ⅓, ½ b.; Air 3, 6 b.

Paintings by Spanish Masters. Postage ¼, ⅓, ½ b.; Air 3, 6 b.

Winter Olympic Games, Grenoble (1968) (1st issue). Embossed on gold foil. Air 5, 10, 15, 50 b.

Winter Olympic Games, Grenoble (1968) (2nd issue). Sports ¼, ⅓, ½, 3, 6 b.

Chancellor Adenauer Commemoration (1st issue). Embossed on gold foil. Air 50 b.

1968.

Yemen Red Cresent. Embossed on gold foil. Air 5, 10, 15, 50 b.

Paintings by Gauguin. Postage ¼, ¼, ⅓, ⅓, ½, ½ b.; Air 3, 3, 6, 6 b.

Paintings by Van Gogh. Postage ¼, ¼, ⅓, ⅓, ½, ½ b.; Air 3, 3, 6, 6 b.

Paintings by Rubens. Postage ¼, ¼, ⅓, ⅓, ½, ½ b.; Air 3, 3, 6, 6 b.

Provisionals. Various 1930/31 values optd. "Y.A.R." and date in English and Arabic. ½, 1, 1, 2, 2, 3, 4, 4, 5, 6, 6, 10, 10, 20 b., 1, 1 i.

Gold Medal Winners, Winter Olympic Games, Grenoble (1st issue). 1967 Winter Olympic Games (1st issue) optd. with names of various winners. Air 50 b. × 4.

1st Death Anniv. of Vladimir Komarov (Russian cosmonaut). Air 5, 10, 15, 50 b.

International Human Rights Year and U Thant Commemoration. Embossed on gold foil. Air 5, 10, 15, 50 b.

Chancellor Adenauer Commemoration (2nd issue). Air 5, 10, 15 b.

Refugee Relief. Adenauer (2nd issue) optd. in Arabic only. Air 5, 10, 15, 50 b.

Olympic Games, Mexico (1st issue). Chariot-racing. Embossed on gold foil. Air 5, 10, 15, 50 b.

Paintings of Horses. Postage ¼, ⅓, ½ b.; Air 3, 6 b.

Paintings by Raphael. Postage ¼, ⅓, ½ b.; Air 3, 6 b.

Paintings by Rembrandt. Postage ¼, ⅓, ½ b.; Air 3, 6 b.

Dr. Martin Luther King Commemoration (1st issue). Human Rights issue optd. Air 50 b.

Gold Medal Winners, Winter Olympic Games, Grenoble (2nd issue). Postage ¼, ⅓, ½, 2 b.; Air 3, 4 b.

Olympic Games, Mexico (2nd issue). Greek and Mexican Folk-lore. Postage ¼, ⅓, ½, 2 b.; Air 3, 4 b.

Gold Medal Winners, Olympic Games, Mexico (1st issue). Mexico Olympics (1st issue) optd. with names of various winners. Air 50 b. × 4.

Gold Medal Winners Olympic Games, Mexico (2nd issue) Postage ¼, ⅓, ½, 2 b.; Air 3, 4 b.

Dr. Martin Luther King Commemoration (2nd issue). Embossed on gold foil. 16 b.

Emblems of Winter Olympic Games. Postage ¼, ⅓, ½, 2 b.; Air 3, 4 b.

Emblems of Olympic Games. Postage ¼, ⅓, ½ 2 b.; Air 3, 4 b.

Dag Hammarskjold and Kennedy Brothers Commemoration. ½, 2, 6, 14 b.

Dr. Christian Barnard's Heart Transplant Operations. ¼, ¾, 8, 10 b.

Dr. Martin Luther King Commemoration (3rd issue). 1, 4, 12, 16 b.

John and Robert Kennedy Commemoration. Embossed on gold foil. 10 b.

1969.

Paintings from the Louvre, Paris. Postage ¼, ⅓, ½, 2 b.; Air 3, 4 b.

1st Death Anniv. of Yuri Gagarin (Russian cosmonaut). Optd. on 1968 Komarov issue. Air 50 b.

Paintings from the Uffizi Gallery, Florence. Postage ¼, ⅓, ½, 2 b.; Air 3, 4 b.

Paintings from the Prado, Madrid. Postage ¼, ⅓, ½, 2 b.; Air 3, 4 b.

Birth Bicentenary of Napoleon (1st issue). Embossed on gold foil. Air 4 b.

Space Exploration (1st series). Inscr. "DISCOVERIES OF UNIVERSE". Postage ¼, ¼, ⅓, ⅓ b.; Air 3, 6, 10 b.

Space Exploration (2nd series). Inscr. "FLIGHTS TO THE PLANETS". Postage ¼, ¼, ⅓, ⅓ b.; Air 2, 4, 22 b.

First Man on the Moon. Embossed on gold foil. Air 10 b.

50th Anniv. of International Labour Organization. Postage 1, 2, 3, 4 b.; Air 6, 8, 10 b.

Space Exploration (3rd series). Inscr. "MAN IN SPACE". Postage ¼, ¼, ⅓, ⅓ b.; Air 3 6, 10 b.

Birth Bicentenary of Napoleon (2nd issue). Postage ¼, ⅓, ½, ¾ b.; Air 4, 8, 10 b.

Space Exploration (4th series). "Apollo" Moon Flights. Postage ¼, ¼, ⅓, ⅓ b.; Air 2, 4, 22 b.

Winter Olympic Games, Sapporo (1972) Preparation. Optd. on 1967 Grenoble Winter Olympics issue. Air 50 b.

Olympic Games, Munich (1972) Preparation. Optd. on 1968 Mexico Olympics issue. Air 50 b.

Paintings from the National Gallery, Washington. Postage ¼, ⅓, ½, 2 b.; Air 3, 4 b.

Paintings from the National Gallery, London. Postage ¼, ⅓, ½, 2 b.; Air 3, 4 b.

French Monarchs and Statesmen. Postage 1¾, 2 2¼, 2½ b.; Air 3½, 5, 6 b.

1970.

Tutankhamun Exhibition, Paris. Postage ¼, ⅓, ½, 2 b.; Air 3, 4 b.

Siamese Sculptures. Postage ¼, ⅓, ½, 2 b.; Air 3, 4 b.

"EXPO 70" World Fair, Osaka, Japan (1st issue). Japanese Paintings. Postage ¼, ⅓, ½, 2 b.; Air 3, 4 b.

"EXPO 70" World Fair, Osaka, Japan (2nd issue). Japanese Puppets. Postage ¼ ⅓, ½, 2 b.; Air 3, 4 b.

World Cup Football Championships, Mexico (1st issue). Views and Maps. Postage 1¾, 2, 2¼, 2½ b.; Air 3½, 5, 6, 7, 8 b.

World Cup Football Championships, Mexico (2nd issue). Jules Rimet. Embossed on gold foil. Air 10 b.

"United Europe". Postage 1⅓, 1¾, 2¼, 2½, 5 b.; Air 7, 8, 10 b.

25th Anniv. of Victory in Second World War. Gen. De Gaulle. Embossed on gold foil. Air 6 b.

Moon Mission of "Apollo 12". Postage 1, 1¼, 1⅓, 1½ b.; Air 4, 4½, 7 b.

World Cup Football Championships, Mexico (3rd issue). Teams. Postage ¼, ⅓, ½, ¾ b.; Air 4, 4½ b.

World Cup Football Championships, Mexico (4th issue). Beckenbauer and Pele. Embossed on gold foil. Air 10 b.

World Cup Football Championships, Mexico (5th issue). Footballers and Mexican Antiquities. Postage 1, 1¼, 1⅓, 1½ b.; Air 3, 10 b.

Interplanetary Space Travel. Postage 1¾, 2, 2¼, 2½ b.; Air 5, 8, 10, 22 b.

Inauguration of New U.P.U. Headquarters Building, Berne. Postage ⅓, 1¼, 1½, 2 b.; Air 3½, 4½, 6 b.

"Philympia 70" Stamp Exhibition, London. Postage ¼, ½, ¾, 1, 3 b.; Air 4 b.

8th Anniv. of Revolution. Flowers. ¼ b. × 5.

Olympic Games, Munich (1972) (1st issue). Buildings. Postage 1, 1¾, 2½, 3, 3½ b.; Air 8, 10 b.

Olympic Games, Munich (2nd issue). Statue. Embossed on gold foil. Air 6 b.

25th Anniv. of United Nations. Human Rights Year issue of 1968 optd. Air 50 b.

Winter Olympic Games, Sapporo (1st issue). Buildings and Emblem. Postage 1½, 2½, 4½, 5, 7 b.; Air 8, 10 b.

Winter Olympic Games, Sapporo (2nd issue). Snow Sculpture. Embossed on gold foil. Air 4 b.

General Charles de Gaulle Commemoration. 1970 25th Anniv of Victory issue optd. Air 6 b.

German Gold Medal Winners in Olympic Games. Postage ¼, ¾, ⅓, ⅓ b.; Air 6 b.

1971.

Pres. Gamal Nasser of Egypt Commemoration, Postage ¼ b. × 4, ½ b. × 2; Air 1, 2, 5, 7, 10, 16 b.

International Sporting Events. Postage ¼, ⅓, ½, 2 b.; Air 3, 4 b.

Olympic Games, Munich (3rd issue). Theatre Productions. Postage ½, 1¼, 1¾, 2¼, 4½ b.; Air 5, 6 b.

Moon Mission of "Apollo 14" 1969 Moon Landing issue optd. Air 10 b.

Olympic Games, Munich (4th issue). Paintings from the Pinakothek. Postage ¼, ⅓, ¾, 1½, 2 b.; Air 4, 7 b.

Chinese Paintings. Postage ¼, ⅓, ½, 2 b.; Air 3, 4 b.

Winter Olympic Games, Sapporo (3rd issue). Winter Sports and Japanese Works of Art. Postage ¼, ½, 1, 1⅓, 2 b.; Air 3, 4 b.

Winter Olympic Games, Sapporo (4th issue) Japanese Skier. Embossed on gold foil. Air 8 b.

Launching of Soviet "Salyut" Space Station. Interplanetary issue of 1970 optd. Air 22 b.

Olympic Games, Munich (5th issue). Sports and Sculptures. Postage ⅓, 1, 1⅓, 1¾, 2¼ b.; Air 4½, 7, 10 b.

Olympic Games, Munich (6th issue). Gold Medals. Embossed on gold foil. Air 8 b.

Exploration of Outer Space. Postage ¼, ⅓, ½, ¾ b.; Air 3, 3½, 6 b.

Birth Bicentenary of Beethoven. Postage ¼ b. × 4, ½ b. × 2; Air 1, 2, 5, 7, 10 b.

Indian Paintings. Postage ¼, ⅓, ½, 2 b.; Air 3, 4 b.

Olympic Games, Munich (7th issue). Sailing Events at Kiel. Postage ¼, ½, 1¼, 2, 3 b.; Air 4 b.

Winter Olympic Games, Sapporo (5th issue). Sports. Postage ⅓, ¾, 1¼, 1¾, 2¼ b.; Air 3½, 6 b.

Winter Olympic Games, Sapporo (6th issue). Slalom Skier. Embossed on gold foil. Air 10 b.

Persian Miniatures. Postage ¼, ⅓, ½, 2 b.; Air 3, 4 b.

Olympic Games, Munich (8th issue). Sports. Postage ¾, 1½, 2½, 3½, 5 b.; Air 6, 8 b.

Olympic Games, Munich (9th issue). Discus-thrower. Embossed on gold foil. Air 10 b.

Italian Gold Medal Winners in Olympic Games. Postage ¼ b. × 2, ⅓ b. × 2; Air 22 b.

1972.

French Gold Medal Winners in Olympic Games. Postage 2, 3 b.; Air 4, 10 b.

Works of Art. Postage 1, 1¼, 1⅓, 1½ b.; Air 3, 4½, 7 b.

ROYALIST ISSUES

1967.

Visit of Queen of Sheba to Solomon. ⅛, ¼, ½, 4, 6, 20, 24 b.

Arab Horses. ⅛, ¼, ½, 4, 10 b.

1968.

Winter Olympic Games, Grenoble (1st issue). Nos. R216/29 optd. Postage ⅛, ¼, ½, 1, 4, 6, 10 b.; Air 12, 14, 16, 24, 34 b.

Butterflies. Air 16, 20, 40 b.

Postage Due. Butterflies and Horse. 4, 16, 20 b.

Winter Olympic Games, Grenoble (2nd issue). Sports. Postage 1, 2, 3, 4, 6 b.; Air 10, 12, 18, 24, 28 b.

Gold Medal Winners, Grenoble Winter Olympics. Winter Olympic Games, Grenoble (2nd issue) optd. with names of various medal winners. Postage 1, 2, 3, 4, 6 b.; Air 10, 12, 18, 24, 28 b.

20th Anniv. of UNESCO. ½, 1, 1½, 2, 3, 4, 6, 10 b.

Mothers' Day. Paintings. Postage 2, 4, 6 b.; Air 24, 28, 34 b.

Olympic Games, Mexico (1st issue) Sports. Postage 1, 2, 3, 4, 6 b.; Air 10, 12, 18, 24, 28 b.

UNESCO. "Save Florence" Campaign. Paintings. Postage 2, 4, 6 b.; Air 10, 12, 18 b.

UNESCO. "Save Venice" Campaign. Paintings. Postage ½, 1, 1½, 24 b.; Air 28, 34 b.

Olympic Games, Mexico (2nd issue). Athletes and Flags. 4 b. × 11.

Winter Olympic Games since 1924. Competitors and Flags. Postage 1, 2, 3, 4, 6 b.; Air 10, 12, 18, 24, 28 b.

International Human Rights Year. 2 b. × 4, 4 b. × 4, 6 b. × 4.

Paintings by European and American Artists. Postage 1, 2, 3, 4, 6, 10 b.; Air 12, 18, 24, 28 b.

Coronation of Shah of Iran. Postage 1, 2, 3, 4 b.; Air 24, 28 b.

International Philately. Postage 1, 2, 3, 4, 6 b.; Air 10, 12, 18, 24, 28 b.

World Racial Peace. Postage 4, 6, 18 b.; Air 10 b.

Children's Day. Paintings. Postage 1, 2, 3, 4 b.; Air 6, 10, 12, 18, 24, 28 b.

Gold Medal Winners, Mexico Olympic Games (1st issue). Mexico Olympics (1st issue) optd. with names of various medal winners. Postage 1, 2, 3, 4, 6 b.; Air 10, 12, 18, 24, 28 b.

Gold Medal Winners, Mexico Olympics (2nd issue). Athletes and Medals. Air 12, 18, 24, 28, 34 b.

Gold Medal Winners. Mexico Olympics (3rd issue). Embossed on gold foil. 28 b.

"EFIMEX 68" Stamp Exhibition, Mexico City. Air 12, 18, 24, 28, 34 b.

1969.

Motor-racing Drivers. Postage 1, 2, 3, 4, 6 b.; Air 10, 12, 18, 24, 28 b.

Space Flight of "Apollo 7". 4, 8, 12, 24, 28 b.

Space Flight of "Apollo 8" (1st issue). 4, 6, 10, 18, 34 b.

Space Flight of "Apollo 8" (2nd issue). Embossed on gold foil. 28 b.

5th Anniv. of Imam's Meeting with Pope Paul VI at Jerusalem (1st issue). Scenes from Pope's Visit. ⅛, ¼, ¼, 1, 1½, 2, 3, 4, 5, 6 b.

5th Anniv. of Imam's Meeting with Pope Paul VI at Jerusalem (2nd issue). Paintings of the Life of Christ. Postage 1, 2, 3, 4, 5, 6, 7, 8, 9, 10 b.; Air 11, 12, 13, 14, 15, 16, 17, 18, 19, 20, 21, 22, 23, 24, 25, 26, 27, 28, 29, 30 b.

5th Anniv. of Imam's Meeting with Pope Paul VI at Jerusalem (3rd issue). Abraham's Tomb, Hebron. 4 b.

Paintings by Rembrandt (1st series). Postage 1, 2, 4 b.; Air 6, 12 b., 1 i.

Paintings by Rembrandt (2nd series). Embossed on gold foil. 20 b.

Paintings by European Artists. Postage ½, 1½, 3, 5 b; Air 10, 18, 24, 28, 34 b.

"Apollo" Moon Programme. Postage 1, 2, 3, 4, 5 b.; Air 6, 7, 8, 9, 10, 11, 12, 13, 14, 15 b.

Moon Flight of "Apollo 10". Postage 2, 4, 6 b.; Air 8, 10, 12, 18, 24, 28, 34 b.

Olympic Games, Munich (1972). Athletes and Olympic Rings. Postage 1, 2, 4, 5, 6 b.; Air 10, 12, 18, 24, 34 b.

World Wildlife Conservation. Postage ½ b. × 2, 1 b. × 2, 2 b. × 2, 4 b. × 2, 6 b. × 2; Air 8 b. × 2, 10 b. × 2, 18 b. × 2.

First Man on the Moon (1st issue). Air 6, 10, 12, 18 b.

First Man on the Moon (2nd issue). Air 6, 10, 12, 18, 24 b.

First Man on the Moon (3rd issue). Embossed on gold foil. 24 b. × 2.

First Man on the Moon (4th issue). Embossed on gold foil. 28 b.

First Man on the Moon (5th issue). Air 10, 12, 18, 24 b.

Palestine Holy Places. Postage 4 b. × 6 6 b. × 10; Air 12 b. × 8.

Famous Men. Postage 4 b. × 4, 6 b. × 10, Air 12 b. × 2.

History of Space Exploration. Air 6 b. × 27.

Olympic Sports. Postage 1, 2, 4, 5, 6 b.; Air 10, 12, 18, 24, 34 b.

World Cup Football Championships, Mexico. Air 12 b. × 8.

Christmas. Ikons. Postage ½, 1, 1½, 2, 4, 5, 6 b.; Air 10, 12, 18, 24, 28, 34 b.

Burning of Al-Aqsa Mosque, Jerusalem. Postage 4 b. + 2 b., 6 b. + 3 b.; Air 10 b. + 5 b.

1970.

Brazil's Victory in World Cup Football Championships, Mexico. 1969 World Cup issue optd. Air 12 b. × 3.

Dogs. Postage 2, 4, 6 b.; Air 8, 12 b.

Paintings of Horses. Postage 2, 4, 6 b.; Air 8, 12 b.

We close the Appendix with stamps believed to have been issued prior to July 1970, when first Saudi Arabia and then the United Kingdom recognised the Republican government in Yemen.

YEMEN PEOPLE'S DEMOCRATIC REPUBLIC Pt. 19

The former People's Republic of Southern Yemen was known by the above title from 30 November 1970.

In 1990 it united with Yemen Arab Republic (see YEMEN REPUBLIC (combined)).

1000 fils = 1 dinar.

22. Temple of Isis, Philae, Egypt.

1971. Preservation of Philae Temples Campaign.

65.	22.	5 f. multicoloured ..	10	10
66.		35 f. multicoloured ..	45	25
67.		65 f. multicoloured ..	90	55

23. Symbols of Constitution.

1971. Introduction of First Constitution.

68.	23.	10 f. multicoloured ..	10	10
69.		15 f. multicoloured ..	15	15
70.		35 f. multicoloured ..	30	30
71.		50 f. multicoloured ..	40	40

24. Heads of Three Races and Flame.

1971. Racial Equality Year.

72. 24. 20 f. multicoloured .. 15 15
73. 35 f. multicoloured .. 30 30
74. 75 f. multicoloured .. 55 55

25. Map, Flag and Products.

26. Hand holding Sub-machine Gun and Map.

1971.

75. 25. 5 f. multicoloured .. 10 10
76. 10 f. multicoloured .. 10 10
77. 15 f. multicoloured .. 15 10
78. 20 f. multicoloured .. 15 10
79. 25 f. multicoloured .. 20 10
80. 35 f. multicoloured .. 25 15
81. 40 f. multicoloured .. 35 15
82. 50 f. multicoloured .. 55 20
82a. 60 f. multicoloured .. 60 20
83. 65 f. multicoloured .. 75 25
84. 80 f. multicoloured .. 85 30
84a. 90 f. multicoloured .. 85 30
84b. – 110 f. multicoloured .. 90 35
85. – 125 f. multicoloured .. 1·00 60
86. – 250 f. multicoloured .. 2·00 1·40
87. – 500 f. multicoloured .. 3·75 3·00
88. – 1 d. multicoloured .. 7·00 6·00

DESIGNS—HORIZ. (42 × 25 mm): Nos 84b/8, "Dam-al-Khawain" tree, Socotra.

1971. 6th Anniv. of Revolutionary Activity in Arabian Gulf Area. Multicoloured.

89. 15 f. Type 26 .. .. 20 15
90. 45 f. Girl guerilla and emblem (horiz.) 55 35
91. 50 f. Guerilla on the march 75 50

27. Hands supporting Cogwheel.

29. Gamal Nasser.

28. Eagle and Flags.

1971. 2nd Anniv. of "Corrective Move" in Revolutionary Government. Multicoloured.

92. 15 f. Type 27 .. .. 15 10
93. 25 f. Torch and revolutionary emblems 25 20
94. 65 f. Salt-works and windmill 60 45

1971. 9th Anniv. of 26th September Revolution. Multicoloured.

95 10 f. Type 28 .. .. 10 10
96 40 f. Flag on "United Jemen" 35 30

1971. 1st Death Anniv. of Gamal Nasser (Egyptian statesman).

97. 29. 65 f. multicoloured .. 50 35

30. "Children of the World".

31. Domestic Pigeons.

32. Dhow-building.

1971. 25th Anniv. of U.N.I.C.E.F.

98. 30. 15 f. black, red & orange 10 10
99. 40 f. black, pur. & blue 20 15
100. 50 f. black, red & green 35 30

1971. Birds.

101. 31. 5 f. black, pur. & blue .. 30 20
102. – 40 f. multicoloured .. 85 40
103. – 65 f. black, red & green 1·25 75
104. – 100 f. multicoloured .. 2·40 1·10

DESIGNS: 40 f. Arabian chukar. 65 f. Helmet guineafowl and Arabian chukar. 100 f. Black kite.

1972. Dhow-building in Aden. Multicoloured

105. 25 f. Type 32 .. .. 50 20
106. 80 f. Dhow at sea (vert.) .. 1·50 90

33. Singer with Oud (lute), and Band.

1972. Folk Dances. Multicoloured.

107. 10 f. Type 33 .. .. 20 10
108. 25 f. Yemeni girls dancing 35 15
109. 40 f. Dancing teams .. 70 30
110. 80 f. Festival dance .. 1·50 90

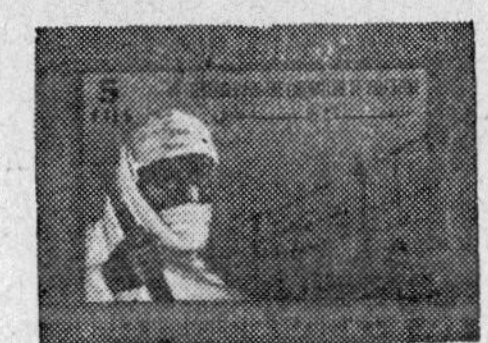

34. Palestinian Guerrilla and Barbed-wire.

1972. Palestine Day.

111. 34. 5 f. multicoloured .. 20 15
112. 20 f. multicoloured .. 45 15
113. 65 f. multicoloured .. 1·50 90

35. Police Colour Party.

1972. Police Day. Multicoloured.

114. 25 f. Type 35 .. .. 50 20
115. 80 f. Girls of People's Militia on parade .. .. 2·00 1·00

36. Start of Cycle Race.

1972. Arab Youth Week. Multicoloured.

117. 10 f. Type 36 .. .. 15 10
118. 15 f. Girls on parade .. 20 10
119. 40 f. Guides and scouts .. 35 35
120. 80 f. Acrobatic team (vert.) 1·25 80

37. Turtle.

1972. Marine Life. Multicoloured.

121. 15 f. Type 37 .. .. 40 20
122. 40 f. Sailfish 75 45
123. 65 f. Kingfish .. .. 1·00 75
124. 125 f. Lobster .. .. 1·75 1·25

38. Book Year Emblem.

1972. Int. Book Year.

125. 38. 40 f. multicoloured .. 50 35
126. 65 f. multicoloured .. 75 55

39. Farmworkers and Field.

1972. Agriculture Day.

127. 39. 10 f. multicoloured .. 15 15
128. 25 f. multicoloured .. 25 15
129. 40 f. multicoloured .. 60 45

40. Soldiers advancing.

1972. 5th Anniv. of Independence. Mult.

130. 5 f. Type 40 .. .. 15 15
131. 20 f. Soldier and town .. 35 15
132. 65 f. Vignettes of Yemeni Life (vert.) 80 50

41. Population Graph.

1973. Population Census.

134. 41. 25 f. deep grn., red & grn. 25 15
135. 40 f. new blue, red and blue 45 30

42. W.H.O. Emblem within "25".

43. Taweela Tanks, Aden.

1973. 25th Anniv. of W.H.O. Mult.

136. 5 f. Type 42 .. .. 15 15
137. 25 f. W.H.O. emblem on globe (horiz.) 25 15
138. 125 f. "25" and W.H.O. emblem (horiz.) .. .. 1·25 1·00

1973. Tourism. Multicoloured.

139. 20 f. Type 43 .. .. 20 15
140. 25 f. Shibam Town (horiz.) 25 15
141. 40 f. Elephant Bay, Aden (horiz.) 55 35
142. 100 f. Al-Mohdar Mosque, Tarim (horiz.) .. .. 1·25 90

44. Modern Apartments and Slum Clearance.

1973. Nationalization of Buildings (1972). Multicoloured.

143. 20 f. Type 44 .. .. 20 15
144. 80 f. Street scene (vert.) .. 70 60

45. Women's Corps on Parade.

1973. People's Army. Multicoloured.

145. 10 f. Type 45 .. .. 20 20
146. 20 f. Soldiers marching .. 35 20
147. 40 f. Naval contingent .. 90 50
148. 80 f. Column of tanks .. 1·75 1·00

46. Quayside Crane.

1973. 10th Anniv. of World Food Programme. Multicoloured.

149. 20 f. Type 46 .. .. 25 10
150. 80 f. Granary workers .. 1·25 75

47. "U.P.U. Letter".

1974. Cent. of U.P.U. Mult.

151. 5 f. Type 47 .. .. 10 10
152. 20 f. "100" formed of people and U.P.U. emblems 15 15
153. 40 f. U.P.U. emblem and Yemeni flag (vert.) .. 30 30
154. 125 f. Map of People's Republic (vert.) 65 65

48. Irrigation Canal.

1974. Agricultural Progress. Multicoloured.

155. 10 f. Type 48 .. .. 15 15
156. 20 f. Bulldozers clearing land 25 15
157. 100 f. Tractors with harrows 85 55

49. Lathe Operator.

50.

1975. Industrial Progress. Multicoloured.

158 10 f. Type 49 .. .. 15 15
159. 40 f. Workers in clothing factory 40 25
160. 80 f. Women textile workers (horiz.) 75 35

1975. Women's Costumes.

161. 50. 5 f. brown and black .. 15 15
162. – 10 f. violet and black .. 15 15
163. – 15 f. yellow and black .. 20 15
164. – 25 f. purple and black .. 40 25
165. – 40 f. blue and black .. 65 40
166. – 50 f. brown and black .. 75 55

DESIGNS: Nos. 162/6 show different costumes.

51. Women in Factory.

1975. Int. Women's Year

167. 51. 40 f. brown and black .. 40 25
168. 50 f. green and black .. 50 35

52.

53. Lunar Launch.

1976. Yemeni Football.
169. 52. 5 f. multicoloured .. 10 10
170. – 40 f. multicoloured .. 40 25
171. – 80 f. multicoloured .. 70 40
DESIGNS: Nos. 170/1 show footballers in different positions.

1976. Russian Space Exploration. Mult.
172 10 f. Type **53** 10 10
173 15 f. V. A. Shatalov (cosmonaut) 15 10
174 40 f. Luna vehicle (horiz) 45 25
175 65 f. Valentina Tereshkova and rocket 75 45

54. Members of Presidential Council.

1977. 1st Anniv. of Unification Congress. Multicoloured.
176 25 f. Type **54** 15 15
177 35 f. Text of document .. 25 25
178 65 f. Girls of People's Militia 35 35
179 95 f. Aerial view of textile factory 45 45

55. Traffic Policeman and Woman Trainee.

1977. Traffic Change to Right.
180. **55.** 25 f. black and red .. 40 20
181. 60 f. black and yellow .. 1·00 70
182. 75 f. black and green .. 1·50 90
183. 110 f. black and blue .. 2·25 1·75

56. A.P.U. Emblem within Flags of Member States.

1977. 25th Anniv. of Arab Postal Union.
184. **56.** 20 f. multicoloured .. 15 15
185. 60 f. multicoloured .. 45 35
186. 70 f. multicoloured .. 50 40
187. 90 f. multicoloured .. 55 50

57. "Festilyria duponti". **58.** Dove of Peace and Flag.

1977. Cowries. Multicoloured.
188. 60 f. Type **57** 45 35
189. 90 f. "Afrivoluta pringlei" (horiz.) .. 60 50
190. 110 f. "Conus splendidulus" (horiz.) .. 90 65
191. 180 f. "Cypraea broderipii" (horiz.) .. 1·40 1·10

1977. 10th Anniv. of Independence. Mult.
192. 5 f. Type **58** .. 10 10
193. 20 f. Man with broken manacle .. 15 10
194. 90 f. Oil pipeline .. 45 45
195. 110 f. "Pillar of Freedom" 60 60

59. Dome of the Rock, Jerusalem.

1978. Palestinian Welfare.
196. **59.** 5 f. multicoloured .. 30 10
For smaller design with value at top right, see No. 264.

60. Almarfaa (drum).

1978. Musical Instruments. Multicoloured.
197. 35 f. Type **60** .. 20 15
198. 60 f. Almizmar (pipes) .. 40 35
199. 90 f. Alquboos (fiddle) .. 55 45
200. 110 f. Simsimiya (lyre) .. 80 70

61. Almotl (armbands).

1978. Silver Ornaments. Multicoloured.
201 10 f. Type **61** 10 10
202 15 f. Aloodhad (ring) .. 15 15
203 20 f. Al Hizam (necklace) 20 15
204 60 f. Alhoogaalah (bangle) 35 30
205 90 f. Al Muk-Hala (perfume flask) .. 50 45
206 110 f. Al Janbiya (dagger) 70 60

62. Palm Tree Emblem. **63.** "V" for Vanguard and Cogwheel.

1978. 11th World Youth Festival, Cuba. Multicoloured.
207. 5 f. Type **62** 10 10
208. 60 f. Global emblem .. 30 30
209. 90 f. Flower emblem .. 40 40
210. 110 f. Girl, youth and emblems 50 50

1978. First Conference of Vanguard Party.
211. **63.** 5 f. multicoloured .. 10 10
212. 20 f. multicoloured .. 15 10
213. 60 f. multicoloured .. 25 25
214. 180 f. multicoloured .. 65 65

64. Calligraphic Emblem, Symbols of Peace and Freedom.

1978. 15th Anniv. of 14 Oct. Revolution. Multicoloured.
215. 10 f. Type **64** .. 10 10
216. 35 f. Emblems of growth (vert.) .. 15 15
217. 60 f. Candle and figure "15" (vert). 20 20
218. 110 f. Revolutionaries and figure "15" (vert.) .. 40 40

65. Map of Yemen, Child with Olive-branch and Dove. **66.** "Agricultural Progress".

1979. International Year of the Child.
219. **65.** 15 f. multicoloured .. 15 15
220. 20 f. multicoloured .. 15 15
221. 60 f. multicoloured .. 25 25
222. 90 f. multicoloured .. 35 35

1979. 10th Anniv of "Corrective Move" in Revolutionary Government. Multicoloured.
223. 20 f. Type **66** 10 10
224. 35 f. "Industrial Progress" 15 15
225. 60 f. Students 25 20
226. 90 f. Woman with star and doves 35 30

67. Sir Rowland Hill and Yemeni Costume Stamp of 1970.

1979. Death Cent. of Sir Rowland Hill. Mult.
227. 90 f. Type **67** 35 30
228. 110 f. Yemeni camel stamp of 1970 .. .. .. 40 30

68. World Map, Koran and Symbols of Arab Achievements. **69.** Emblem of Yemeni Socialist Party.

1979. The Arabs.
230. **68.** 60 f. multicoloured .. 30 20

1979. 1st Anniv. of Yemeni Socialist Party.
231. **69.** 60 f. multicoloured .. 25 20

70. "Cassia adenensis". **71.** Ayatollah Khomeini and Crowd.

1979. Flowers. (1st series). Multicoloured.
232. 20 f. Type **70** .. 15 15
233. 90 f. "Nerium oleander" 55 35
234. 110 f. "Calligonum comosum" 60 55
235. 180 f. "Adenium obesum" 90 80
See also Nos. 265/8.

1980. 1st Anniv of Iranian Revolution.
236. **71.** 60 f. multicoloured .. 75 60

72. "Dido". **73.** Woman Basketmaking.

1980. Screw Steamers. Multicoloured.
237. 110 f. Type **72** 70 50
238. 180 f. "Anglia" .. .. 1·00 75
239. 250 f. "India" .. .. 1·60 1·25

1980. "London 1980". Handicrafts. Mult.
240. 60 f. Type **73** 20 20
241. 90 f. Making a hubble-bubble pipe .. 35 25
242. 110 f. Man at loom .. 40 35
243. 250 f. Boy making clay pot 80 70

74. Skink. **75.** Misha the Bear (Olympic Mascot).

1980. Reptiles. Multicoloured.
244. 20 f. Type **74** 20 15
245. 35 f. Mole Viper 25 15
246. 110 f. Carter's Day Gecko 65 50
247. 180 f. Cobra .. .. 1·10 80

1980. Olympic Games, Moscow.
248. **75.** 110 f. multicoloured .. 45 30

76. Farming. **77.** Lenin.

1980. 10th Anniv. of Peasants' Uprising. Multicoloured.
249. 50 f. Type **76** .. 20 15
250. 90 f. Peasants 35 25
251. 110 f. Corn sickle and fist 45 40

1980. 110th Birth Anniv. of Lenin.
252. **77.** 35 f. multicoloured .. 30 15

78. Douglas "DC 3".

1981. Democratic Yemen Airlines. Mult.
253. 60 f. Type **78** 50 25
254. 90 f. Boeing "707" .. 80 35
255. 250 f. DHC "Dash 7" .. 2·25 1·50

79. Map, Dish Aerial and Satellite. **80.** "Conocarpus lancifolius".

1981. Ras Boradli Satellite Station.
256. **79.** 60 f. multicoloured .. 60 30

1981. Trees. Multicoloured.
257. 90 f. Type **80** 55 25
258. 180 f. "Ficus vasta" .. 1·25 70
259. 250 f. "Maerua crassifolia" 1·75 1·25

81. Council Building, Citizens and Flag.

1981. 10th Anniv. of Supreme People's Council.
260. **81.** 180 f. multicoloured .. 1·00 75

82. Sand Fox.

1981. Wildlife Conservation. Multicoloured.
261. 50 f. Type **82** 40 35
262. 90 f. Leopard .. .. 1·25 85
263. 250 f. Ibex .. .. 2·50 2·00

1981. Palestinian Welfare. As T **59**, but smaller 25×27 mm. and value at top right.
264. 5 f. multicoloured .. 25 10

1981. Flowers (2nd series). As T **70**. Mult.
265. 50 f. "Tephrosia apollinea" 45 20
266. 90 f. "Citrullus colocynthis" 75 50
267. 110 f. "Aloe squarrosa" 95 65
268. 250 f. "Lawsonia inermis" 2·00 1·50

83. Blind People Basket-weaving and Typing.

1982. International Year of Disabled Persons
269. **83.** 50 f. multicoloured .. 30 20
270. 100 f. multicoloured .. 70 35
271. 150 f. multicoloured .. 1·10 80

84. Microscope Slides and Lungs.

1982. Cent. of Discovery of Tubercle Bacillus.
272. **84.** 50 f. black, orange and red 60 25

85. A.P.U. Emblem and Map within Heart.

1982. 30th Anniv. of Arab Postal Union.
273. **85.** 100 f. red, black and blue 85 65

86. Footballers.

1982. World Cup Football Championship, Spain. Multicoloured.
274. 50 f. Type **86** 40 25
275. 100 f. Match scene .. 70 55
276. 150 f. Players and shield .. 1·10 75
277. 290 f. Player and flags .. 1·40 1·10

87. Emblems and Flags of Russia and Yemen.

1982. 60th Anniv. of U.S.S.R.
279. **87.** 50 f. multicoloured .. 35 25

1982. World Cup Football Championship Result. Nos. 274/7 optd. **WORLD CUP WINNERS 1982 1st ITALY 2nd W-GERMANY 3rd POLAND 4th FRANCE.** Multicoloured.
280. 50 f. Type **86** 40 30
281. 100 f. Match scene .. 70 60
282. 150 f. Players and shield .. 1·10 85
283. 200 f. Player and flags .. 1·40 1·25

89. Yasser Arafat.

1983. Palestinian Solidarity. Multicoloured.
285. 50 f. Type **89** 75 25
286. 100 f. Yasser Arafat and Dome of the Rock .. 1·25 75

1983. "Tembal 83" Stamp Exhibition, Basel. No. 248 optd. **TEMBAL 83 MAY 21st-29th, 1983.**
288. **75.** 110 f. multicoloured .. 2·50 1·75

91. Man with Letter, Postal Barge and Postman.

1983. World Communications Year.
289. **91.** 50 f. black and blue .. 50 35
290. – 100 f. black and red .. 90 55
291. – 150 f. black, light green and green .. .. 1·25 1·00
292. – 200 f. multicoloured .. 1·50 1·25

DESIGNS: 100 f. Postman, stage coach and morse code equipment. 150 f. Motor coach and telephones. 200 f. Transmitter, airplane, satellite, television, envelope and dish aerial.

92. "The Poor Family".

1983. 10th Death Anniv. of Picasso (artist). Multicoloured.
294. 50 f. Type **92** 45 25
295. 100 f. "Woman with Crow" 75 50

93. Show Jumping.

1983. Olympic Games, Los Angeles (1st issue). Equestrian Events. Multicoloured.
297. 25 f. Type **93** 20 15
298. 50 f. Show jumping (different) 35 25
299. 100 f. Horse crossing water (Three-day event) .. 65 40

See also Nos. 316/18.

94. "P 8" Steam Engine, 1905.

1983. Railway Locomotives. Multicoloured.
301. 25 f. Type **94** 70 35
302. 50 f. "880" steam engine, 1915 .. .. 1·25 50
303. 100 f. "Gt 2×4/4" locomotive, 1923 .. .. 2·25 80

95. "Europa".

1983. Liners. Multicoloured.
305. 50 f. Type **85** .. .. 1·00 45
306. 100 f. "World Discoverer" 1·50 95

96. "20" and Hand holding Sheaf of Corn.

1983. 20th Anniv. of Revolution. Mult.
308. 50 f. Type **96** 45 25
309. 100 f. Flag, man with gun and "XX" 80 45

97. Balloon carrying Man on Horseback.

1983. Bicent. of Manned Flight. Mult.
310. 50 f. Type **97** 60 25
311. 100 f. Unmanned balloon 1·00 50

98. Skiing.

1983. Winter Olympic Games, Sarajevo. Multicoloured.
313. 50 f. Type **98** 40 25
314. 100 f. Bobsleigh 70 40

99. Fencing.

1984. Olympic Games, Los Angeles (2nd issue). Multicoloured.
316. 25 f. Type **99** 25 20
317. 50 f. Fencing (different) .. 45 25
318. 100 f. Fencing (different) .. 75 45

100. "Soyuz 10"–"Salyut 1" Link-up, 1971.

1984. Space. Multicoloured.
320. 15 f. Type **100** 15 15
321. 20 f. "Apollo 8" and moon, 1968 .. .. .. 20 15
322. 50 f. "Apollo 2" and first man on moon, 1969 .. 50 35
323. 100 f. "Soyuz–"Apollo" link-up, 1975 .. .. 90 55

1984. Nos. 83 and 84b surch.
325. **25.** 50 f. on 65 f. mult. .. 50 40
326. – 100 f. on 110 f. mult. .. 90 70

102. "Abalistes stellaris".

1984. Fishes. Multicoloured.
327. 10 f. Type **102** 10 10
328. 15 f. "Caranx speciocus" .. 10 10
329. 20 f. "Pomadasys maculatus" 15 10
330. 35 f. "Chaetodon fasciatus" 15 10
331. 35 f. Imperial angelfish .. 25 15
332. 50 f. "Rastrelliger kanagurta" 35 20
333. 100 f. Wavyback skipjack 70 40
334. 150 f. Longfin butterfly fish 1·10 65
335. 200 f. Blue moon angelfish 1·40 80
336. 250 f. "Pterois russelli" .. 1·75 1·00
337. 400 f. "Argyrops spinifer" 2·75 1·50
338. 500 f. "Dasyatis uarnak" 3·50 1·90
339. 1 d. "Epinephelus chlorostigma" .. .. 7·00 3·75
340. 2 d. "Drepane longimana" 14·00 8·00

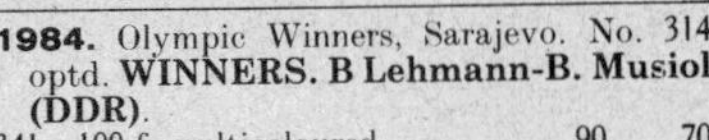
1984. Olympic Winners, Sarajevo. No. 314 optd. **WINNERS. B Lehmann-B. Musiol (DDR).**
341 100 f. multicoloured .. 90 70

104. Women writing.
105. Victory Parade, Red Square.

1985. National Literacy Campaign. Mult.
343 50 f. Type **104** 50 35
344 100 f. Pen held in manacled hand 90 60

1985. 40th Anniv. of End of Second World War.
345. **105.** 100 f. multicoloured .. 1·00 55

106. Flag within Emblem.
107. Modern Buildings.

1985. 12th World Youth and Students' Festival, Moscow. Multicoloured.
346. 50 f. Type **106** 50 35
347. 100 f. Hand holding emblem as placard .. 90 60

1985. U.N.E.S.C.O. World Heritage Site. Shibam City. Multicoloured.
348. 50 f. Type **107** 50 40
349. 50 f. View of city 50 40
350. 100 f. Screen 90 70
351. 100 f. Gate (vert.) 90 70

108. Industrial Symbols.
109. Mother feeding Child.

1985. Third Yemen Socialist Party General Congress. Multicoloured.
352. 25 f. Type **108** 25 20
353. 50 f. Crane loading ship .. 50 35
354. 100 f. Combine harvesters 90 65

1985. U.N.I.C.E.F. Child Survival Campaign. Multicoloured.
355 50 f. Type **109** 50 40
356 50 f. Immunization .. 50 40
357 100 f. Breastfeeding .. 90 70
358 100 f. Oral rehydration therapy 90 70

110. Wheat and Al-Mohdar Mosque, Tarim.
111. Lenin addressing Crowd in Red Square.

1986. World Food Day. 40th Anniv. (1985) of F.A.O. Multicoloured.
359. 20 f. Type **110** 40 25
360. 180 f. Palm trees .. .. 2·25 1·50

1986. 27th Russian Communist Party Congress. Multicoloured.

361. **111.** 75 f. multicoloured .. 70 50
362. 250 f. multicoloured .. 2·40 1·75

112. Bride in Yashmak.

113. Ali Ahmed N. Antar.

1986. Brides and Bridegrooms of Yemen. Multicoloured.

363. 50 f. Type **112** 75 45
364. 50 f. Bride with striped shawl 70 45
365. 50 f. Bride with long dressed hair 70 45
366. 100 f. Bridegroom in modern jacket with knife 1·25 70
367. 100 f. Bridegroom in traditional clothes with gun 1·25 70
368. 100 f. Bride in modern dress .. .. .. 1·25 70

1986. "Party and Homeland Martyrs". Multicoloured.

369. 75 f. Type **113** 60 50
370. 75 f. Saleh Musleh Kasim 60 50
371. 75 f. Ali Shayaa Hadi .. 60 50
372. 75 f. Abdul Fattah Ismail 60 50

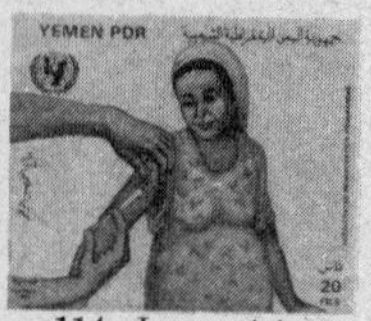

114. Immunizing Pregnant Woman against Tetanus.

1987. U.N.I.C.E.F. Immunization Campaign. Multicoloured.

373 20 f. Type **114** 15 15
374 75 f. Immunizing baby .. 50 35
375 140 f. Nurse giving oral poliomyelitis vaccine to baby 90 60
376 150 f. Pregnant woman and children carrying syringes .. .. 1·00 70

115. Party Emblem and Worker.

116. Lenin and Soldier.

1987. Yemeni Socialist Party General Conference.

377. **115.** 75 f. multicoloured .. 55 35
378. 150 f. multicoloured .. 1·00 75

1987. 70th Anniv. of Russian October Revolution.

379. **116.** 250 f. multicoloured .. 1·60 1·25

117. Steps to King's Court.

1987. Shabwa Remains. Multicoloured.

380 25 f. Type **117** 15 15
381 75 f. Royal Palace .. 45 30
382 140 f. Winged lion, King's Court (vert) 80 60
383 150 f. Inscribed bronze plaque (vert) 90 70

INDEX

Countries can be quickly located by referring to the index at the end of this volume.

118. Students and College Buildings.

1987. 20th Anniv. of Independence. Mult.

384. 25 f. Type **118** 15 15
385. 75 f. Family and housing 45 30
386. 140 f. Workers, oil derrick and power station .. 80 60
387. 150 f. Party headquarters and members 90 70

119 Tank and Liberty Monument, Sana'a

1988. 25th Anniv. (1987) of 26th September Revolution in Yemen.

388. **119.** 75 f. multicoloured .. 55 30

120 Tap, Boy and Rainbow (safe water)

121 Weightlifting

1988. World Health Day. 40th Anniv of W.H.O. Multicoloured.

389 40 f. Type **120** 25 20
390 75 f. Child with globe as head breaking cigarette (No Smoking day) .. 45 30
391 140 f. Nurse immunizing baby (immunization campaign) 80 65
392 250 f. Red Crescent worker instructing group (Health for all) .. 1·50 1·25

1988. Olympic Games, Seoul. Multicoloured.

393 40 f. Type **121** 25 20
394 75 f. Running 40 30
395 140 f. Boxing 70 55
396 150 f. Football 75 60

122 Crowd and Flag

123 Yellow-bellied Green Pigeon

1988. 25th Anniv of 14 October Revolution.

397 **122** 25 f. black and red .. 15 15
398 — 75 f. multicoloured .. 40 30
399 — 300 f. multicoloured .. 1·50 1·25

DESIGNS—HORIZ. 75 f. Radfan mountains and revolutionary. VERT—300 f. Anniversary emblem.

1988. Birds. Multicoloured.

400 40 f. Type **123** 40 25
401 50 f. Lilac-breasted roller (vert) 50 30
402 75 f. Hoopoe (vert) 75 40
403 250 f. Houbara bustard .. 2·25 1·50

124 Incense Burner

125 Shipping entering Old Harbour

1988. Traditional Crafts. Multicoloured.

404 25 f. Type **124** 15 15
405 70 f. Mashjub (rack used when impregnating dresses with incense) .. 40 30
406 150 f. Cosmetic basket made of palm fibre with cowrie shell decoration 75 60
407 250 f. Woman making palm fibre basket .. .. 1·25 1·00

1988. Centenary of Port of Aden. Mult.

408 75 f. Type **125** 60 40
409 300 f. Section of new harbour project .. 1·90 1·50

126 Old City

1988. International Campaign for Preservation of Old Sana'a. Multicoloured.

410 75 f. Type **126** 40 30
411 250 f. City (different) .. 1·25 1·00

127 Sand Cat Kitten

1989. Endangered Animals. Multicoloured.

412 20 f. Type **127** 10 10
413 25 f. Adult sand cat .. 15 10
414 50 f. Fennec fox cub .. 30 20
415 75 f. Adult fennec fox .. 40 30

128 Symbols of War in Star

129 Ismail

1989. 20th Anniv of "Corrective Movement" in Revolutionary Government. Multicoloured.

416 25 f. Type **128** 15 10
417 35 f. Industrial symbols in hook 20 10
418 40 f. Agricultural symbols 25 15

1989. 50th Birth Anniv of Adbul Fattah Ismail (founder of People's Socialist Party).

419 **129** 75 f. multicoloured .. 40 30
420 150 f. multicoloured .. 75 60

130 "Children at Play" (Abeer Anwer)

131 Sana'a and Fighters

1989. 15th Anniv of Ali Anter Pioneer Organization. Multicoloured.

421 10 f. Type **130** 10 10
422 25 f. Girl pioneer 15 10
423 75 f. Pioneers parading at Khormaksar (horiz) .. 40 30

1989. 22nd Anniv of Siege of Sana'a.

424 **131** 150 f. multicoloured .. 50 40

132 Taj Mahal and Nehru

133 Coffee Plant

1989. Birth Centenary of Jawaharlal Nehru (Indian statesman).

425 **132** 250 f. black and brown 90 75

1989. Cent of Interparliamentary Union.

426 **133** 300 f. multicoloured .. 1·00 80

134 Seera Rock, Aden, Birds and Arc de Triomphe, Paris

1989. Bicentenary of French Revolution.

427 **134** 250 f. multicoloured .. 90 75

135 U.S.A. v Belgium (Uruguay, 1930)

1990. World Cup Football Championship, Italy. Matches from previous championships. Multicoloured.

428 5 f. Type **135** 10 10
429 10 f. Switzerland v Netherlands (Italy, 1934) 10 10
430 20 f. Italy v France (France, 1938) 10 10
431 35 f. Sweden v Spain (Brazil, 1950) 10 10
432 50 f. West Germany v Austria (Switzerland, 1954) 15 10
433 60 f. Brazil v England (Sweden, 1958) 15 10
434 500 f. U.S.S.R. v Uruguay (Chile, 1962) .. .. 1·10 85

YEMEN REPUBLIC (combined)

Pt.19

A draft joint constitution was ratified by the parliaments of Yemen Arab Republic and the Yemen People's Democratic Republic on 21 May 1990 and the unification of the two countries was declared the following day.

The currencies of both the previous republics have legal validity throughout Yemen.

100 fils = 1 rial (North Yemen).
1000 fils = 1 dinar (South Yemen).

1 Scouts supporting Globe

1990. 60th Anniv of Arab Scout Movement. Multicoloured.

1 300 f. Type **1** 85 40
2 375 f. Type **1** .. .. 1·10 50
3 850 f. Oil derrick, scouts with flag, anniversary emblem and tower .. .. 2·00 95
4 900 f. As No. 3 .. .. 2·40 1·25

Nos. 1/4 are inscribed "YEMEN ARAB REPUBLIC".

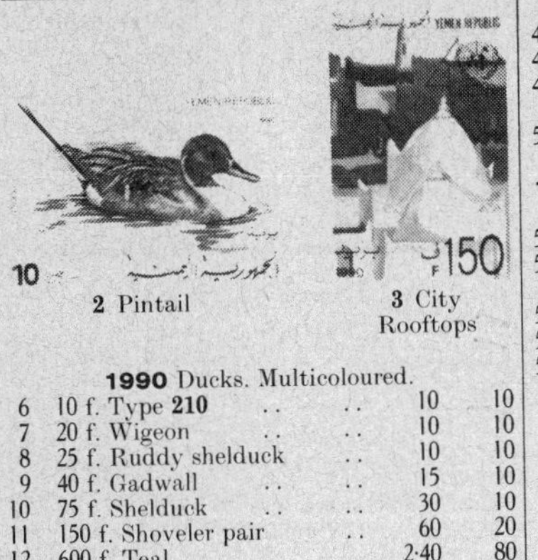

2 Pintail   3 City Rooftops

1990 Ducks. Multicoloured.

6	10 f. Type **210**	10	10
7	20 f. Wigeon	10	10
8	25 f. Ruddy shelduck	10	10
9	40 f. Gadwall	15	10
10	75 f. Shelduck	30	10
11	150 f. Shoveler pair	60	20
12	600 f. Teal	2·40	80

1990. 40th Anniv of U.N. Development Programme.

14 **3**	150 f. multicoloured	60	30

4 "Dirphia multicolor"

5 Protembolotherium

1990. Moths and Butterflies. Multicoloured.

15	5 f. Type **4**	10	10
16	20 f. "Automeris sp."	10	10
17	25 f. Swallowtail	10	10
18	40 f. Bhutan glory	15	10
19	55 f. Silver king shoemaker	20	10
20	75 f. Tiger moth	30	15
21	700 f. "Attacus edwardsii" (moth)	2·75	85

1990. Prehistoric Animals. Multicoloured.

23	5 f. Type **5**	10	10
24	10 f. Diatryma	10	10
25	35 f. Mammoth (horiz)	15	10
26	40 f. Edaphosaurus (horiz)	15	10
27	55 f. Dimorphodon (horiz)	20	10
28	75 f. Phororhacos (horiz)	30	10
29	700 f. Ichthyosaurus (wrongly inscr "Ichtyosaurus")	3·00	90

6 Abyssinian Kitten   7 "Boletus aestivalis"

1990. Cats. Multicoloured.

31	5 f. Type **6**	10	10
32	15 f. Blue longhair	10	10
33	35 f. Siamese	15	15
34	55 f. Burmese	25	10
35	60 f. Sealpoint colourpoint	25	10
36	150 f. Red British shorthair	65	10
37	600 f. Leopard cat	2·50	80

1991. Fungi. Multicoloured.

39	50 f. Type **7**	10	10
40	60 f. Butter mushroom	25	10
41	80 f. Beefsteak morel	30	10
42	100 f. Brown birch bolete	40	15
43	130 f. Fly agaric	55	20
44	200 f. Flaky-stemmed witches' mushroom	80	25
45	300 f. Red cap	1·25	60

8 State Arms

9 Shaking Hands

1991. 1st Anniv of Yemen Republic. Mult.

47	300 f. Type **8**	45	15
48	375 f. Type **8**	70	25
49	850 f. Hand holding flag, map and sun	1·10	45
50	900 f. As No. 49	1·40	60

1991. Signing of Unity Agreement (in November 1989) Commemoration. Mult.

52	225 f. Type **9**	65	20
53	300 f. Hand holding flag over map	85	30
54	375 f. As No. 53	1·10	45
55	650 f. Type **9**	1·50	60
56	850 f. As No. 53	2·40	1·10

10 Cigarettes and Skull on Globe

1991. World Anti-smoking Day. Mult.

58	225 f. Type **10**	30	10
59	300 f. Skull smoking and man	45	15
60	375 f. As No. 59	60	20
61	650 f. Type **10**	1·00	40
62	850 f. As No. 59	1·25	50

11 Emblem

1991. 45th Anniv of U.N.O.

64 **11**	5 r. multicoloured	1·10	45
65	8 r. multicoloured	1·25	50
66	10 r. multicoloured	1·40	60
67	12 r. multicoloured	1·75	70

1993. Various stamps surch. (a) Stamps of Yemen Arab Republic. (i) Postage.

69 **94**	5 r. on 75 f. mult	60	25
70 **144**	8 r. on 425 f. mult	1·00	45
71 **150**	8 r. on 425 f. mult	1·00	45
72 –	10 r. on 900 f. mult (No. 830)	1·40	65
73 –	10 r. on 900 f. mult (No. 834)	1·40	65
74 –	10 r. on 900 f. mult (No. 838)	1·40	65
75 –	10 r. on 900 f. mult (No. 843)	1·40	65
76 **157**	10 r. on 900 f. mult	1·40	65
77 –	10 r. on 900 f. mult (No. 853)	1·40	65
78 **159**	10 r. on 900 f. mult	1·40	65
79 –	10 r. on 900 f. mult (No. 863)	1·40	65
80 –	12 r. on 850 f. mult (No. 829)	1·75	80
81 –	12 r. on 850 f. mult (No. 833)	1·75	80
82 –	12 r. on 850 f. mult (No. 837)	1·75	80
83 –	12 r. on 850 f. mult (No. 842)	1·75	80
84 **157**	12 r. on 850 f. mult	1·75	80
85 –	12 r. on 850 f. mult (No. 852)	1·75	80
86 **159**	12 r. on 850 f. mult	1·75	80

(ii) Air. Additionally optd **AIR MAIL** (except for No. 87)

87 **118**	3 r. on 125 f. mult	60	25
88 –	3 r. on 125 f. mult (No. 672)	60	25
89 –	3 r. on 125 f. mult (No. 679)	60	25
90 –	3 r. on 125 f. mult (No. 686)	60	25
91 –	3 r. on 125 f. mult (No. 700)	60	25
92 –	3 r. on 125 f. mult (No. 707)	60	25
93 –	5 r. on 75 f. mult (No. 670)	60	25
94 –	5 r. on 75 f. mult (No. 677)	60	25
95 –	5 r. on 75 f. mult (No. 684)	60	25
96 –	5 r. on 75 f. mult (No. 691)	60	25
97 –	5 r. on 75 f. mult (No. 698)	60	25
98 –	5 r. on 75 f. mult (No. 705)	60	25
99 **145**	8 r. on 425 f. mult	1·00	45
100 –	8 r. on 425 f. mult (No. 796)	1·00	45
101 **147**	8 r. on 425 f. mult	1·00	45
102 –	8 r. on 425 f. mult (No. 803)	1·00	45
103 –	8 r. on 425 f. mult (No. 812)	1·00	45
104 **151**	8 r. on 425 f. mult	1·00	45
105 **152**	8 r. on 425 f. mult	1·00	45
106 –	12 r. on 850 f. mult (No. 862)	1·75	80

(b) Stamps of Yemen Republic (combined)

107	10 r. on 900 f. mult (No. 4)	1·40	65
108	10 r. on 900 f. mult (No. 50)	1·40	65
109	12 r. on 850 f. mult (No. 3)	1·75	80
110	12 r. on 850 f. mult (No. 49)	1·75	80
111	12 r. on 850 f. mult (No. 56)	1·75	80
112	12 r. on 850 f. mult (No. 62)	1·75	80

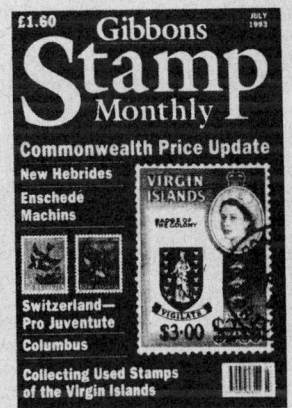

YUGOSLAVIA Pt. 3

The kingdom of the Serbs, Croats and Slovenes, in S.E. Europe, established after the 1914–18 war and comprising Serbia, Montenegro, Bosnia, Herzegovina and parts of pre-war Hungary.

From 1945 it was a Federal Republic comprising six republics. In 1991 four of these republics seceded, leaving Serbia and Montenegro.

A. KINGDOM OF THE SERBS, CROATS AND SLOVENES

I. ISSUES FOR BOSNIA AND HERZEGOVINA

100 heller = 1 kruna.

1918. 1910 commem. stamps of Bosnia (with date labels) optd. **DRZAVA S.H.S. 1918 Bosna i Hercegovina** or the same in Cyrillic characters or surch. also.

1. 3 h. olive (No. 345) .. 50 1·00
2. 5 h. green .. 30 45
3. 10 h. red .. 30 45
4. 20 h. sepia .. 30 45
5. 25 h. blue .. 30 45
6. 30 h. green .. 30 45
7. 40 h. orange .. 30 45
8. 45 h. red .. 30 45
9. 50 h. purple .. 20 25
10. 60 h. on 50 h. purple .. 12 25
11. 80 h. on 6 h. brown .. 10 75
12. 90 h. on 35 h. green .. 10 20
13. 2 k. green .. 20 50
14. 3 k. on 3 h. olive .. 1·50 1·00
15. 4 k. on 1 k. lake .. 3·00 3·00
16. 10 k. on 2 h. violet .. 7·50 3·75

1918. Newspaper stamps of Bosnia for Express: 5 h. optd. as last and **HELERA** and 2 h. the same but in Cyrillic.

17. N 35. 2 h. red .. 2·50 4·00
18. 5 h. green .. 1·75 2·00

These were issued for use as ordinary postage stamps.

1918. Bosnian War Invalids Fund stamps optd. **DRAVA S.H.S. Bosna Hercegovina** or the same in Cyrillic characters.

19. 31. 5 h. (+2 h.) green .. £130 £160
20. – 10 h. (+2 h.) red .. 85·00 £140
21. – 10 h. (+2 h.) blue .. 75 3·75
22. 31. 15 h. (+2 h.) brown .. 1·25 3·25

6a.

(7.)

1918. Newspaper stamps of Bosnia of 1913 (as T 6a) surch. Imperf.

50. 6a. 2 on 6 h. mauve .. £120 £150
51. 2 on 10 h. red .. 60·00 90·00
52. 2 on 20 h. green .. 7·50 15·00
23. 3 on 2 h. blue .. 10 20
24. 5 on 6 h. mauve .. 10 20

Most of these were used for ordinary postage purposes.

1919. Perf.

25. 6a. 2 h. blue .. 10 25
26. 6 h. mauve .. 75 1·25
27. 10 h. red .. 25 25
28. 20 h. green .. 20 25

The above were issued for use as ordinary postage stamps.

These stamps imperforate were issued as Newspaper stamps for Bosnia q.v.

1919. Types of Bosnia optd. with T 7 or similar type with wording **KRALJEVSTVO S.H.S.**, or surch. also.

29. 25. 3 h. lake .. 5 1·10
30. 5 h. green .. 5 8
31. 10 on 6 h. black .. 5 5
32. 26. 20 on 35 h. green .. 5 12
33. 25. 25 h. blue .. 5 12
34. 30 h. red .. 75 25
35. 26. 45 h. brown .. 10 25
36. 33. 45 on 80 h. brown .. 5 5
37. 26. 50 h. blue .. 40·00 50·00
38. 50 on 72 h. blue .. 5 5
39. 60 h. purple .. 5 25
40. 33. 80 h. brown .. 5 25
41. 90 h. purple .. 8 25
42. – 2 k. green (No. 200) .. 12 25
43. 26. 3 k. red on green .. 25 50
44. 34. 4 k. red on green .. 1·00 1·50
45. 26. 5 k. lilac on grey .. 1·00 1·75
46. 34. 10 k. violet on grey .. 2·40 3·00

1919. War Victims' Fund. Stamps of Bosnia of 1906 surch. **KRALJEVSTVO Srba. Hrvata i Slovenaca** or same in Cyrillic characters and new value.

47. – 10 x. + 10 x. on 40 h. orange (No. 196) .. 1·25 2·25
48. – 20 x. + 10 x. on 20 h. sepia (No. 192) .. 65 1·50
49. 5. 45 x. + 15 x. on 1 k. lake 3·75 6·00

II. ISSUES FOR CROATIA

100 filir (heller) = 1 kruna (krone).

The provisional issues on Hungarian stamps were sold in Yugoslavian "heller" and "krone" currency, but as this is not expressed on the stamps (except for Nos. 69/73) we have retained the Hungarian descriptions to facilitate reference to the original stamps.

1918. Various issues of Hungary optd. **HRVATSKA SHS** and bar or wheel.

"Turul" issue of 1900.

53. 7. 6 f. olive .. 75 1·25
54. 50 f. lake on blue .. 1·00 1·90

"Harvesters" and "Parliament" issue of 1916

55. 18. 2 f. brown .. 5 12
56. 3 f. red .. 5 5
57. 5 f. green .. 5 10
58. 6 f. green .. 5 5
59. 10 f. red .. 6·00 4·50
60. 15 f. violet (No. 244) .. 45·00 60·00
61. 15 f. violet (No. 251) .. 5 5
62. 20 f. brown .. 8 5
63. 25 f. blue .. 5 20
64. 35 f. brown .. 8 5
65. 40 f. olive .. 12 30
66. 19. 50 f. purple .. 5 5
67. 75 f. blue .. 5 5
68. 80 f. green .. 5 20
69. 1 k. lake .. 5 5
70. 2 k. brown .. 8 10
71. 3 k. grey and violet .. 20 30
72. 5 k. brown .. 1·00 1·25
73. 10 k. lilac and brown .. 7·50 9·00

The kroner values are overprinted **KRUNA** or **KRUNE** also.

"Charles" and "Zita" issue of 1918.

74. 27. 10 f. red .. 5 12
75. 20 f. brown .. 5 12
76. 25 f. blue .. 10 40
77. 28. 40 f. olive .. 8 12

1918. Stamps of Hungary optd. **HRVATSKA SHS. ZF. ZA NAROD. VIJECE.**

War Charity issue of 1916.

78. 20. 10+2 f. red .. 20 30
79. – 15+2 f. violet .. 5 25
80. 22. 40+2 f. lake .. 8 25

Coronation issue of 1916.

81. 23. 10 f. mauve .. 22·00 55·00
82. – 15 f. red .. 22·00 55·00

20. "Freedom of Croatia".

1918. Freeing of the Yugoslavs.

83. 20. 10 h. lake .. 2·40 2·50
84. 20 h. violet .. 2·40 4·25
85. 25 h. blue .. 6·00 7·50
86. 45 h. black .. 35·00 40·00

21. Angel of Peace.

22. Sailor with Standard and Falcon.

23. Falcon ("Liberty")

1919.

87. 21. 2 h. brown .. 8 25
88. 3 h. mauve .. 8 30
89. 5 h. green .. 8 8
90. 22. 10 h. red .. 8 8
91. 20 h. brown .. 8 8
92. 25 h. blue .. 8 8
93. 45 h. olive .. 10 10
94. 23. 1 k. red .. 15 15
95. – 3 k. purple .. 75 65
96. – 5 k. brown .. 75 55

DESIGN: 3 k., 5 k. as Type 5 but light background behind falcon.

III. ISSUES FOR SLOVENIA

1919. 100 vinar (heller) = 1 kruna (krone).
1920. 100 paras = 1 dinar.

25.

Chainbreakers. 26.

27. "Yugoslavia" with Three Falcons.
28. Angel of Peace.

29. King Peter I.

1919. Perf. or rouletted.

97a. 25. 3 v. violet .. 10 5
127. 3 v. purple .. 10 8
98a. 5 v. green .. 12 5
99b. 10 v. red .. 20 8
100. 15 v. blue .. 10 5
101. 26. 20 v. brown .. 30 10
102. 25 v. blue .. 25 5
103. 30 v. pink .. 25 5
111. 30 v. red .. 25 10
104a. 40 v. yellow .. 25 5
122. 27. 50 v. green .. 15 8
113b. 60 v. violet .. 60 25
114b. 28. 1 k. red .. 35 20
120. 2 k. blue .. 35 12
126. 29. 5 k. red .. 35 15
139a. 10 k. blue .. 2·00 55
105. 15 k. green .. 5·25 12·50
106. 20 k. purple .. 1·00 1·40

31. Chainbreaker.

32. "Yugoslavia" with Three Falcons.

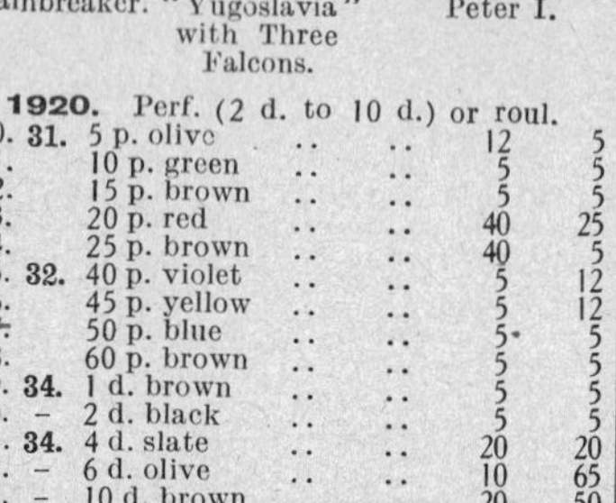

34. King Peter I.

1920. Perf. (2 d. to 10 d.) or roul.

150. 31. 5 p. olive .. 12 5
151. 10 p. green .. 5 5
152. 15 p. brown .. 5 5
153. 20 p. red .. 40 25
154. 25 p. brown .. 40 5
155. 32. 40 p. violet .. 5 12
156. 45 p. yellow .. 5 12
157. 50 p. blue .. 5 5
158. 60 p. brown .. 5 5
159. 34. 1 d. brown .. 5 5
160. – 2 d. black .. 5 5
161. 34. 4 d. slate .. 20 20
162. – 6 d. olive .. 10 65
163. – 10 d. brown .. 20 50

The 2, 6 and 10 d. are as Type 34 but larger.

1920. Carinthian Plebiscite. Newspaper stamps of Yugoslavia of 1919 surch. **KGCA** and new value. Imperf.

163a. N 30. 5 p. on 4 v. grey .. 5 12
163b. 15 p. on 4 v. grey .. 5 15
163c. 25 p. on 4 v. grey .. 5 20
163d. 45 p. on 2 v. grey .. 12 40
163e. 50 p. on 2 v. grey .. 10 25
163f. 2 d. on 2 v. grey .. 90 3·50

These stamps were sold at three times face value in aid of the Plebiscite Propaganda Fund.

IV. ISSUES FOR THE WHOLE KINGDOM

100 paras = 1 dinar.

35. King Alexander when Prince.

37. Kosovo Maiden, 1389.

1921. Inscr. "KRALJEVSTVO" at foot.

164. 35. 2 p. brown .. 10 5
165. 5 p. green .. 10 5
166. 10 p. red .. 10 5
167. 15 p. purple .. 10 5
168. 20 p. black .. 10 5
169. 25 p. blue .. 10 5
170. 50 p. olive .. 10 5
171. 60 p. red .. 20 5
172. 75 p. violet .. 10 5
173. – 1 d. orange .. 20 5
174. – 2 d. olive .. 40 5
175. – 4 d. green .. 90 8
176. – 5 d. red .. 2·50 15
177. – 10 d. brown .. 5·50 50

DESIGN: 1 d. to 10 d. as Type 35, but portrait of King Peter I.

1921. Disabled Soldiers' Fund.

178. 37. 10+10 p. red .. 8 10
179. – 15+15 p. brown .. 8 10
180. – 25+25 p. blue .. 10 15

DESIGNS: 10 p. Kosovo maiden, 1389. 15 p. Albanian retreat, 1915. 25 p. National Unity.

1922. Nos. 178/80 surch.

181. 1 d. on 10 p. red .. 5 5
183. 1 d. on 15 p. brown .. 8 8
182. 1 d. on 25 p. blue .. 20 8
184. 3 d. on 15 p. brown .. 25 8
186. 8 d. on 15 p. brown .. 1·00 25
187. 20 d. on 15 p. brown .. 9·00 75
188. 30 d. on 15 p. brown .. 12·50 2·25

1923. As T 35, but inscr. "KRALJEVINA" at foot.

189. 35. 1 d. brown .. 1·25 5
190. 5 d. red .. 6·50 30
191. 8 d. purple .. 7·50 30
192. 20 d. green .. 30·00 75
193. 30 d. orange .. 90·00 2·50

1924. Nos. 171 and 191 surch.

195. 35. 20 p. on 60 p. red .. 25 5
196. 5 d. on 8 d. purple .. 8·00 65

44. King Alexander.

46.

1924.

197. 44. 20 p. black .. 10 5
198. 50 p. brown .. 10 5
199. 1 d. red .. 10 5
200. 2 d. green .. 30 5
201. 3 d. blue .. 30 5
202. 5 d. brown .. 3·00 8
203. – 10 d. violet .. 15·00 10
204. – 15 d. olive .. 10·50 20
205. – 20 d. orange .. 10·50 20
206. – 30 d. green .. 7·50 1·25

The 10 d. to 30 d. have the head in a square panel.

1925. Surch.

207. 44. 25 p. on 3 d. blue .. 12 5
208. 50 p. on 3 d. blue .. 12 5

1926.

209. 46. 25 p. green .. 8 5
210. 50 p. sepia .. 8 5
211. 1 d. red .. 20 5
212. 2 d. black .. 20 5
213. 3 d. blue .. 35 5
214. 4 d. orange .. 70 5
215. 5 d. violet .. 1·40 5
216. 8 d. brown .. 4·50 10
217. 10 d. olive .. 2·50 5
218. 15 d. brown .. 12·00 5
219. 20 d. purple .. 15·00 15
220. 30 d. yellow .. 75·00 50

1926. Danube Flood Fund. Surch.

221. 46. 25 p.+0.25 green .. 5 5
222. 50 p.+0.50 sepia .. 5 5
223. 1 d.+0.50 red .. 20 5
224. 2 d.+0.50 black .. 40 8
225. 3 d.+0.50 blue .. 25 15
226. 4 d.+0.50 orange .. 40 10
227. 5 d.+0.50 violet .. 60 10
228. 8 d.+0.50 brown .. 90 40
229. 10 d.+1.00 olive .. 3·00 12
230. 15 d.+1.00 brown .. 6·50 50
231. 20 d.+1.00 purple .. 5·00 40
232. 30 d.+1.00 yellow .. 22·00 1·25

1928. Nos. 223/32 optd. **XXXX** over previous surch.

233. 46. 1 d. red .. 50 10
234. 2 d. black .. 75 10
235. 3 d. blue .. 1·40 25
236. 4 d. orange .. 2·75 30
237. 5 d. violet .. 2·00 12
238. 8 d. brown .. 9·00 50
239. 46. 10 d. olive .. 18·00 12
240. 15 d. brown .. 90·00 1·90
241. 20 d. purple .. 55·00 1·90
242. 30 d. yellow .. £120 11·50

B. KINGDOM OF YUGOSLAVIA

100 paras = 1 dinar.

49. Duvno Cathedral.

DESIGNS—As Type 49: 3 d. King Tomislav. HORIZ. (34×23 mm.): 1 d. Kings Tomislav and Alexander I.

1929. Millenary of Croatian Kingdom (1925)

243. 49. 50 p.+50 p. olive .. 30 25
244. – 1 d.+50 p. red .. 70 35
245. – 3 d.+1 d. blue .. 1·25 65

52. Dobropolje.

53. Serbian War Memorial, Paris.

1931. Serbian War Memorial (Paris) Fund.

246. 52. 50 p.+50 p. green .. 5 5
247. 53. 1 d.+50 p. red .. 8 15
248. – 3 d.+1 d. blue .. 12 25

DESIGN—As Type 52: 3 d. Kajmaktchalan.

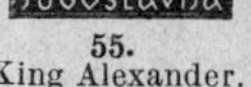

55. King Alexander.

57. Rowing "four" on Lake Bled.

1931.

249. **55.** 25 p. black 12 5
250. 50 p. green 12 5
262. 75 p. green 25 5
251. 1 d. red 15 5
263. 1 d. 50 red 50 5
263b. 1 d. 75 red .. .. 1·00 45
252. 3 d. blue .. .. 1·00 5
263c. 3 d. 50 blue .. .. 1·25 12
253. 4 d. orange .. .. 3·75 5
254. 5 d. violet .. .. 4·50 8
255. 10 d. olive .. .. 12·00 5
256. 15 d. brown .. .. 11·00 8
257. 20 d. purple .. .. 22·00 12
258. 30 d. red .. .. 13·50 55

1931. Optd. **KRALJEVINA JUGOSLAVIJA** and also in Cyrillic characters.

259. **49.** 50 p.+50 p. olive .. 5 5
260. – 1 d.+50 p. red 5 5
261. – 3 d.+1 d. blue 35 20

1932. European Rowing Championship. Inscr. ending "EUROPE 1932".

264. – 75 p.+50 p. green .. 65 1·00
265. **57.** 1 d.+½ d. red .. .. 1·00 1·25
266. – 1½ d.+½ d. red .. .. 1·00 1·25
267. – 3 d.+1 d. blue .. .. 1·75 2·50
268. – 4 d.+1 d. blue & orge. 5·25 12·00
269. – 5 d.+1 d. lilac & violet 5·25 10·00

DESIGNS—HORIZ. 75 p. Single-sculler on Danube at Smederevo. 1½ d. Rowing "eight" on Danube at Belgrade. 3 d. Rowing "pair" at Split harbour. VERT. 4 d. Rowing "pair" on river and Zagreb Cathedral. 5 d. Prince Peter.

1933. 11th Int. Pen Club Congress, Dubrovnik. As T **25** with additional value and **XI. int. kongres Pen-Klubova u Dubrovniku 1933** below in Roman or Cyrillic characters.

270. **55.** 50 p.+25 p. black .. 3·75 7·00
271. 75 p.+25 p. green .. 3·75 7·00
272. 1 d. 50+50 p. red .. 3·75 7·00
273. 3 d+1 d. blue .. .. 3·75 7·00
274. 4 d.+1 d. green .. 3·75 7·00
275. 5 d.+1 d. yellow .. 3·75 7·00

60. Crown Prince Peter in "Sokol" Uniform.

62.

1933. "Sokol" Meeting, Ljubljana.

276. **60.** 75 p.+25 p. green .. 25 30
277. 1½d.+½ d. red 25 30

1933. Optd. **JUGOSLAVIJA** in Roman and Cyrillic characters. (a) Postage.

278. **46.** 25 p. green 15 5
279. 50 p. sepia 15 5
280. 1 d. red 50 5
281. 2 d. black 55 15
282. 3 d. blue .. .. 1·90 10
283. 4 d. orange .. .. 1·00 10
284. 5 d. violet .. .. 1·90 10
285. 8 d. brown .. .. 4·75 1·25
286. 10 d. olive .. .. 9·25 10
287. 15 d. brown .. .. 14·00 1·40
288. 20 d. purple .. .. 24·00 50
289. 30 d. yellow .. .. 23·00 50

(b) Charity stamps, Nos. 221/3.

290. **46.** 25 p.+0.25 green .. 35 25
291. 50 p.+0.50 sepia .. 35 15
292. 1 d.+0.50 red .. .. 1·40 45

1933. Obligatory Tax. Red Cross.

293. **62.** 50 p. red and blue .. 12 5

63. Osprey over R. Bosna.

64. Athlete and Falcon (from sculpture by Krsinic).

1934. 20th Anniv. of "Sokol" Games, Sarajevo.

294. **63.** 75 p.+25 p. green .. 6·25 4·50
295. 1 d. 50+50 p. red .. 6·75 5·25
296. 1 d. 75+25 p. brown .. 17·00 7·00

1934. 60th Anniv. of Croat "Sokol" Games, Zagreb.

297. **64.** 75 p.+25 p. green .. 2·50 2·50
298. 1 d. 50+50 p. red .. 3·75 5·00
299. 1 d. 75+25 p. brown .. 10·00 6·00

65. Dubrovnik.

69. Mostar Bridge.

1934. Air.

300. **65.** 50 p. purple 15 20
301. – 1 d. green 12 20
302. – 2 d. red 35 25
303. – 3 d. blue .. .. 1·25 40
304. **69.** 10 d. orange .. .. 2·25 2·00

DESIGNS: 1 d. Lake of Bled. 2 d. Waterfall at Jajce. 3 d. Oplenats.

1934. King Alexander Mourning issue. With black margins.

305. **55.** 25 p. black (postage) .. 8 5
306. 50 p. green 8 5
307. 75 p. green 8 5
308. 1 d. red 8 5
309. 1 d. 50 red 8 5
310. 1 d. 75 red 8 8
311. 3 d. blue 10 5
312. 3 d. 50 p. blue 30 5
313. 4 d. orange 30 5
314. 5 d. violet 40 5
315. 10 d. olive .. .. 2·10 5
316. 15 d. brown .. .. 4·00 15
317. 20 d. purple .. .. 7·00 15
318. 30 d. red .. .. 4·00 40
319. – 3 d. blue (No. 303) (air) 3·75 2·00

70. King Peter II.

71. King Alexander.

1935.

320. **70.** 25 p. black 10 5
321. 50 p. orange 10 5
322. 75 p. green 15 5
323. 1 d. brown 15 5
324. 1 d. 50 red 15 5
325. 1 d. 75 red 30 5
325a. 2 d. red 15 5
326. 3 d. orange 15 5
327. 3 d. 50 blue 50 5
328. 4 d. green .. .. 1·10 5
329. 4 d. blue 30 5
330. 10 d. violet 90 5
331. 15 d. brown 90 10
332. 20 d. blue .. .. 2·75 25
333. 30 d. pink .. .. 2·25 25

1935. 1st Anniv. of King Alexander's Assassination.

334. **71.** 75 p. green 20 25
335. 1 d. 50 red 20 25
336. 1 d. 75 brown 25 50
337. 3 d. 50 blue .. .. 1·60 2·10
338. 7 d. 50 red .. .. 1·00 2·10

72.

73. Queen Marie.

1935. Winter Relief Fund.

339. **72.** 1 d. 50+1 d. brown .. 1·00 1·75
340. 3 d. 50+1 d. 50 blue .. 2·10 2·75

1936. Child Welfare.

341. **73.** 75 p.+25 p. green .. 45 40
342. 1 d. 50+50 p. red .. 45 40
343. 1 d. 75+75 p. brown .. 1·10 75
344. 3 d. 50+1 d. blue .. 1·60 1·10

74. Nicola Tesla.

75. Prince Paul.

76. Dr. V. Georgevitch.

1936. 80th Birthday of Dr Tesla (physicist).

345. **74.** 75 p. brown and green .. 15 20
346. 1 d. 75 black and blue .. 25 25

1936. Red Cross Fund.

347. **75.** 75 p.+50 p. green .. 10 30
348. 1 d. 50+50 p. red .. 15 40

1936. Obligatory Tax. Jubilee of Serbian Red Cross.

349. **76.** 50 p. brown 15 5

MORE DETAILED LISTS
are given in the Stanley Gibbons Catalogues referred to in the country headings.
For lists of current volumes see Introduction.

77. Princes Tomislav and Andrew.

78. Oplenats.

1937. Child Welfare. T **77** and similar horiz. portrait.

350. – 25 p.+25 p. brown .. 15 25
351. – 75 p.+75 p. orange .. 35 50
352. **77.** 1 d. 50+1 d. orange .. 65 50
353. 2 d.+1 d. purple .. 75 75

1937. Little Entente.

354. **78.** 3 d. green 75 20
355. 4 d. blue 75 30

80. St. Naum Convent, Lake Ochrida.

83. Arms of Yugoslavia, Greece, Rumania and Turkey.

1937. Air.

360. **80.** 50 p. brown 15 10
361. – 1 d. green 15 10
362. – 2 d. blue 15 10
363. – 2 d. 50 red 25 15
364. **80.** 5 d. violet 30 20
365. – 10 d. red 50 25
366. – 20 d. green 75 65
367. – 30 d. blue .. .. 1·40 1·10

DESIGNS—VERT. 1 d., 10 d. Rab (Arbe) Harbour. HORIZ. 2 d., 20 d. Sarajevo. 2 d. 50, 30 d. Laibach (Ljubljana).

1937. Balkan Entente.

368. **83.** 3 d. green 55 15
369. 4 d. blue 80 50

84.

85.

1938. Child Welfare.

370. **84.** 50 p.+50 p. brown .. 20 30
371. **85.** 1 d.+1 d. green .. 20 30
372. **84.** 1 d. 50+1 d. 50 red .. 45 60
373. **85.** 2 d.+2 d. mauve .. 1·00 1·10

86. Searchlight Display and Parachute Tower.

87. Entrance to Demir Kapija Cliff.

1938. Int. Aeronautical Exn., Belgrade and Yugoslav Air Club Fund.

374. **86.** 1 d.+50 p. green .. 30 60
375. 1 d. 50 p.+1 d. red .. 1·00 75
376. 2 d.+1 d. mauve .. 2·25 1·50
377. 3 d.+1 d. 50 p. blue .. 2·75 2·25

1938. Railway Employees' Hospital Fund.

378. **87.** 1 d.+1 d. green .. 40 45
379. – 1 d. 50+1 d. 50 red .. 1·10 95
380. – 2 d.+2 d. mauve .. 2·00 2·10
381. – 3 d. + 3 d. blue .. 2·40 2·40

DESIGNS—HORIZ. 1 d. 50 p. Demir Kapija Hospital. VERT. 2 d. Runner carrying torch. 3 d. King Alexander.

DESIGNS-HORIZ. 1 d. 50 p. Pole vaulting. VERT. 50 p. Runner. 2 d. Putting the Shot.

90. Hurdling.

1938. IX Balkan Games.

382. – 50 p.+50 p. orange .. 75 1·00
383. **90.** 1 d.+1 d. green .. 1·50 1·50
384. – 1 d. 50+1 d. 50 mauve 2·25 2·00
385. – 2 d.+2 d. blue .. .. 3·00 3·00

91. Maiden of Kosovo (after P. Jovanovic).

1938. Red Cross.

386. **91.** 50 p. multicoloured .. 15 5
386a. 50 p. red and blue .. 20 5

1938. Child Welfare. Optd. **SALVATE PARVULOS.**

387. **84.** 50 p.+50 p. brown .. 30 30
388. **85.** 1 d.+1 d. green .. 30 50
389. **84.** 1 d. 50+1 d. 50 red .. 60 85
390. **85.** 2 d.+2 d. mauve .. 1·25 2·00

DESIGNS: 50 p. Mounted postmen. 1 d. 50, Mail train. 2 d. Mail coach. 4 d. Mail plane.

93. Mail-carrier.

1939. Postal Cent. and Railway Benevolent Association Fund.

391. – 50 p.+50 p. orange and brown 50 75
392. **93.** 1 d.+1 d. green & black 50 75
393. – 1 d. 50 p.+1 d. 50 p. red 2·75 1·25
394. – 2 d.+2 d. purple & violet 1·40 2·75
395. – 4 d.+4 d. blue .. .. 2·25 4·50

94. Meal-time.

95. Milosh Obilich.

1939. Child Welfare.

396. **94.** 1 d.+1 d. green .. 40 75
397. – 1 d. 50 + 1 d. 50 red and brown .. .. 2·00 3·50
398. – 2 d.+2 d. mauve & brn. 1·25 2·40
399. – 4 d.+4 d. blue .. .. 2·40 4·75

DESIGNS—HORIZ. 2 d. Young carpenter. VERT. 1 d. 50, Children playing on sands. 4 d. Children whispering.

1939. 550th Anniv. of Battle of Kosovo.

400. – 1 d.+1 d. green .. 1·00 1·25
401. **95.** 1 d. 50+1 d. 50 red .. 1·00 1·25

DESIGN: 1 d. King Lazar.

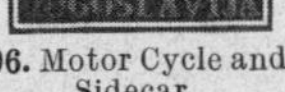

96. Motor Cycle and Sidecar.

97. Cadet Barquentine "Jadran".

1939. 1st International Motor Races, Belgrade. Inscr. "I. MEDUNARODNE AUTO I MOTO", etc.

402. **96.** 50 p. + 50 p. orange and brown .. .. 1·10 85
403. – 1 d.+1 d. green & black 1·40 1·25
404. – 1 d. 50+1 d. 50 red .. 2·00 2·00
405. – 2 d.+2 d. blue .. .. 3·00 3·00

DESIGNS—HORIZ. 1 d., 2 d. Racing cars. VERT. 1 d. 50, Motor cycle.

1939. King Peter's Birthday and Adriatic Guard Fund Inscr. "ZA JADRANSKU STRAZU".

406. **97.** 50 p.+50 p. red .. 65 60
407. – 1 d.+50 p. green .. 85 60
408. – 1 d. 50+1 d. red .. 1·50 1·25
409. – 2 d.+1 d. 50 blue .. 2·40 2·00

DESIGNS: 1 d. Liner "King Alexander". 1 d. 50 Freighter "Triglav". 2 d. Destroyer "Dubrovnik".

98. Unknown Warrior's Tomb, Avala.

99. King Peter II.

1939. 5th Death Anniv. of King Alexander. War Invalids' Fund.

410. **98.** 50 p.+50 p. green .. 1·10 1·25
411. 1 d. 50+1 d. red .. 1·10 1·25
412. 2 d.+1 d. 50 purple .. 1·60 1·60
413. 3 d.+2 d. blue .. .. 2·50 2·50

1939.

414. 99. 25 p. black 15 5
415. 50 p. orange 15 5
416. 1 d. green 15 5
417. 1 d. 50 red 15 5
418. 2 d. mauve 15 5
419. 3 d. brown 20 5
420. 4 d. blue 20 5
420a. 5 d. blue 20 20
420b. 5 d. 50 violet 50 5
421. 6 d. blue 90 5
422. 8 d. brown 90 5
423. 12 d. violet .. .. 1·90 5
424. 16 d. purple .. .. 2·00 20
425. 20 d. blue .. .. 2·00 20
426. 30 d. pink .. .. 6·00 35

100. Postman delivering Letters. 101. Arrival of Thorval.

1940. Belgrade Postal Employees' Fund. Inscr. "ZA DOM P.T.T. ZVAN. I SLUZ'".

427. 100. 50 p.+50 p. orge. & brn. 50 1·10
428. – 1 d.+1 d. green & black 50 1·10
429. – 1 d. 50+1 d. 50 red and brown .. .. 1·00 2·40
430. – 2 d.+2 d. mauve & pur. 5·00 3·75
431. – 4 d.+4 d. blue and grey 3·75 6·00

DESIGNS—VERT. 1 d. Postman collecting letters. 4 d. Telegraph linesman. HORIZ. 1 d. 50, Mail-van. 2 d. Mail-train.

1940. Zagreb Postal Employees' Fund. Inscr. "ZA DOM P.T.T. CINOV U ZAGREBU".

432. 101. 50 p.+50 p. brown .. 35 40
433. – 1 d.+1 d. green .. 35 40
434. – 1 d. 50 p.+1 d. 50 p. red 55 75
435. – 2 d.+2 d. red .. 1·00 1·25
436. – 4 d.+2 d. blue.. .. 1·50 1·75

DESIGNS—VERT. 1 d. King Tomislav enthroned. 1 d. 50 p, Death of Matthew Gubac. HORIZ. 2 d. Radich Brothers. 4 d. Divisional map of Yugoslavia.

DESIGB — VERT. 1 d., 2 d. Children at seaside (Summer games).

102. Winter Games.

1940. Child Welfare. Inscr. "ZA NASU DECU".

437. 102. 50 p. + 50 p. orange and brown .. 20 25
438. – 1 d.+1 d. green .. 20 30
439. 102. 1 d. 50+1 d. 50 red and brown .. 50 60
440. – 2 d.+2 d. mauve .. 1·25 1·40

103. Arms of Yugoslavia, Greece, Rumania and Turkey. 104. Zagreb Cathedral and Junkers "JU 86".

1940. Balkan Entente. Inscr. "JUGOSLAVIJA" alternately at top in Cyrillic (I) or Roman (II) throughout the sheet.

		I.		II.	
441. 103.	3 d. blue	90	55	90	55
442.	4 d. blue	90	55	90	55

1940. Air.

443. 104. 40 d. green .. .. 1·25 2·00
444. – 50 d. blue .. .. 1·75 2·50

DESIGN: 50 d. Suspension Bridge at Belgrade and Fokker "F VII".

105. Obod, scene of early Press, 1493.

1940. 5th Centenary of Invention of Printing Press by Johannes Gutenberg.

445. 105. 5 d. 50 green .. .. 1·50 3·50

1940. Anti-T.B. Fund. Nos. 364/7 surch.

446. 80. 50 p.+50 p. on 5 d. violet 20 35
447. – 1 d.+1 d. on 10 d. red 20 35
448. – 1 d. 50+1 d. 50 on 20 d. green .. .. 80 1·10
449. – 2 d.+2 d. on 30 d. blue 1·25 2·10

107. St. Peter's Cemetery, Ljubljana. 109. Kamenita Gate, Zagreb.

1941. Ljubljana War Veterans' Fund.

450. 107. 50 p.+50 p. green .. 20 25
451. – 1 d.+1 d. red .. 20 25
452. – 1 d. 50+1 d. 50 green 80 75
453. – 2 d.+2 d. lilac and blue 1·25 2·10

DESIGNS—HORIZ. 2 d. War Memorial, Bresje. VERT. 1 d. National costumes. 1 d. 50, Memorial Chapel, Kajmakcalan.

1941. Philatelic Exhibs.

(a) 2nd Croatian Philatelic Exhib., Zagreb.

454. 109. 1 d. 50+1 d. 50 brown.. 50 1·50
455. – 4 d.+3 d. black .. 50 1·50

(b) 1st Philatelic Exhib., Slav Brod.

456. 109. 1 d. 50+1 d. 50 black.. 7·50 18·00
457. – 4 d.+3 d. brown .. 7·50 18·00

DESIGNS: 4 d. (2) Old Cathedral, Zagreb.

NOTE. From 1941 until 1945 Yugoslavia ceased to exist as a stamp-issuing entity, except for the following series, Nos. 468/81, which were issued by the exiled government for the use of the Yugoslav Merchant Navy working with the Allies.

110. King Peter II. 112. Vodnik.

1943. 2nd Anniv. of Overthrow of Regency and King Peter's Assumption of Power.

468. 110. 2 d. blue 12 12
469. 3 d. grey 15 20
470. 5 d. red 20 35
471. 10 d. black 30 70

1943. Red Cross Fund. Surch. CRVENI KRST + 12.50.

472. 110. 2 d.+12 d. 50 blue .. 70 1·25
473. 3 d.+12 d. 50 grey .. 70 1·25
474. 5 d.+12 d. 50 red .. 70 1·25
475. 10 d.+12 d. 50 black 70 1·25

1944. 25th Anniv. of Formation of Yugoslavia. 19th-century Patriots and Writers.

476. 112. 1 d. black and red .. 10
477. – 2 d. black and green .. 15
478. – 3 d. black and blue .. 15
479. – 4 d. black and violet .. 40
480. – 5 d. brown and purple .. 40
481. – 10 d. brown .. 1·10

PORTRAITS: 2 d. Njegos. 3 d. Gaj. 4 d. Karadjic. 5 d. Strosmajer. 10 k. Karageorge.

C. DEMOCRATIC FEDERATION OF YUGOSLAVIA

I. REGIONAL ISSUES

Bosnia and Herzegovina

Currency: Croatian Kunas

1945. Mostar Issue. Stamps of Croatia surch. **Demokratska Federativna Jugoslavija 50 KUNA 50.**

(a) Pictorial stamps of 1941-43.

R 1. 10 k. on 25 b. red .. 35 35
R 2. 10 k. on 50 b. green .. 20 20
R 3. 10 k. on 2 k. red .. 25 25
R 4. 10 k. on 3 k. 50 brown.. 60 60
R 5. 40 k. on 1 k. green .. 20 20
R 6. 50 k. on 4 k. blue .. 3·00 3·00
R 7. 50 k. on 5 k. blue .. 16·00 16·00
R 8. 50 k. on 6 k. green .. 3·00 3·00
R 9. 50 k. on 7 k. red .. 90·00 90·00
R 10. 50 k. on 8 k. brown .. £110 £110
R 11. 50 k. on 10 k. violet .. 60 60

(b) Famous Croats issue of 1943.

R 12. 30 k. on 1 k. blue .. 25 25
R 13. 30 k. on 3 k. 50 red .. 20 20

(c) Boskovic issue of 1943.

R 14. 28. 30 k. on 3 k. 50 brown 75 75
R 15. 30 k. on 12 k. 50 purple 1·50 1·50

(d) War Victims Charity Tax stamps of 1944.

R 16. 34. 20 k. on 1 k. green .. 15 15
R 17. 35. 20 k. on 2 k. red .. 15 15
R 18. 20 k. on 5 k. green .. 25 25
R 19. 20 k. on 10 k. blue .. 25 25
R 20. 20 k. on 20 k. brown .. 70 70

Croatia

Currency: Kunas.

DEMOKRATSKA FEDERATIVNA

20 KUNA

JUGOSLAVIJA

(R 2.)

1945. Split issue. Stamps of Croatia 1941-43 surch as Type R 2.

R 21. 10 k. on 25 b red .. 5 5
R 22. 10 k. on 50 b. green .. 5 5
R 23. 10 k. on 75 b. green .. 5 5
R 24. 10 k. on 1 k. green .. 5 5
R 25. 20 k. on 2 k. red .. 5 5
R 26. 20 k. on 3 k. brown .. 15 15
R 27. 20 k. on 3 k. 50 brown .. 5 5
R 28. 20 k. on 4 k. blue .. 5 5
R 29. 20 k. on 5 k. blue .. 15 15
R 30. 20 k. on 6 k. green .. 8·50 8·50
R 31. 30 k. on 7 k. red .. 5 5
R 32. 30 k. on 8 k. brown .. 9·25 9·25
R 33. 30 k. on 10 k. violet .. 5 5
R 34. 30 k. on 12 k. 50 black .. 5 5
R 35. 40 k. on 20 k. brown .. 15 15
R 36. 40 k. on 30 k. brown .. 20 20
R 37. 50 k. on 50 k. green .. 12 12

1945. Zagreb issue. Stamps of Croatia, 1941-43, surch. **DEMOKRATISKA FEDERATIVNA JUGOSLAVIJA KN 80 KN** and star.

R 38. 20 k. on 5 k. blue .. 12 12
R 39. 40 k. on 1 k. green .. 5 5
R 40. 60 k. on 3 k. 50 brown .. 5 5
R 41. 80 k. on 2 k. red .. 5 5
R 42. 160 k. on 50 b. green .. 15 15
R 43. 200 k. on 12 k. 50 black 20 20
R 44. 400 k. on 25 b. red .. 20 20

Montenegro

Currency: Italian Lire.

Демократска 
Федеративна
Југославија
Лира 3.— Лира 3.—

(R 4.)

1945. Cetinje issue. Stamps of Italian Occupation surch. with Type R 4.

(a) National Poem Issue on 1943.

R 50. 1 l. on 10 c. green .. 65 80
R 51. 2 l. on 25 c. green .. 40 50
R 52. 3 l. on 50 c. mauve .. 40 50
R 53. 5 l. on 1 l. 25 blue .. 40 50
R 54. 10 l. on 15 c. brown .. 80 1·00
R 55. 15 l. on 20 c. orange .. 80 1·00
R 56. 20 l. on 2 l. green .. 80 1·00

(b) Air stamps of 1943, for use as ordinary postage stamps.

R 57. 3 l. on 50 c. brown .. 3·00 3·00
R 58. 6 l. on 1 l. blue .. 3·00 3·00
R 59. 10 l. on 2 l. red .. 3·00 3·00
R 60. 20 l. on 5 l. green .. 3·00 3·00

Serbia

Currency: Hungarian Filler.

1944. Senta issue. Various stamps of Hungary optd. with a large Star, **8.X.1944** and "Yugoslavia" in Cyrillic characters.

R 63. 1 f. grey .. .. 6·25 4·75
R 64. 2 f. red .. .. 6·25 4·75
R 65. 3 f. blue .. .. 6·25 4·75
R 66. 4 f. brown .. .. 6·25 4·75
R 67. 5 f. red .. .. 6·25 4·75
R 68. 8 f. green .. .. 6·25 4·75
R 69. 10 f. brown £120 £120
R 70. 24 f. brown £150 £150
R 71. 24 f. purple .. .. 9·25 9·25
R 72. 30 f. red £120 £120

Slovenia

Currencies: Italian (Ljubljana)
German (Maribor)
Hungarian (Murska Sobota)

(R 5.)

1945. Ljubljana issue. Pictorial stamps of German Occupation, 1945, optd. as Type R 5.

R 74. 5 c. brown 5 5
R 75. 10 c. orange 5 5
R 76. 20 c. brown 5 5
R 77. 25 c. green 5 5
R 78. 50 c. violet 5 5
R 79. 75 c. red 40 40
R 80. 1 l. green 12 5
R 81. 1 l. 25 blue 25 20
R 82. 1 l. 50 green 10 10
R 83. 2 l. blue 20 15
R 84. 2 l. 50 brown 8 8
R 85. 3 l. mauve 25 35
R 86. 5 l. brown 40 35
R 87. 10 l. green 30 35
R 88. 20 l. blue .. .. 3·00 3·00
R 89. 30 l. red .. .. 20·00 20·00

1945. Maribor issue. Hitler stamps of Germany, 1941-44, optd. **SLOVENIJA 9.5.1945 JUGOSLAVIJA** and star.

R 90. 173. 1 pf. grey .. .. 2·75 2·75
R 91. 3 pf. brown 25 25
R 92. 4 pf. grey .. .. 2·00 2·00
R 93. 5 pf. green .. .. 1·75 1·75
R 94. 6 pf. violet 25 15
R 95. 8 pf. red 50 50
R 96. 173. 10 pf. brown (775) 1·75 1·75
R 97. 12 pf. red (776) .. 12 12
R 98. 15 pf. brown .. 3·75 3·75
R 99. 20 pf. blue .. 2·50 2·50
R 100. 24 pf. brown .. 2·00 2·00
R 101. 25 pf. blue .. 6·00 6·00
R 102. 30 pf. green .. 50 50
R 103. 40 pf. mauve .. 50 50
R 104. 225. 42 pf. green .. 40 40
R 105. 173. 50 pf. green .. 1·25 1·25
R 106. 60 pf. brown .. 50 50
R 107. 80 pf. blue .. 1·00 1·00

1945. Murska Sobota issue. Various stamps of Hungary optd. as Nos. R 90/107.

R 108. 1 f. grey.. .. .. 5·00 5·00
R 109. 4 f. brown 35 35
R 110. 5 f. red .. .. 4·50 4·50
R 111. 10 f. brown 35 35
R 112. 18 f. black 35 35
R 113. 20 f. brown 35 35
R 114. 30 f. red.. .. .. 35 35
R 115. 30 f. red.. .. .. 35 35
R 116. 50 f. blue .. .. 7·50 7·50
R 117. 70 f. brown .. .. 7·50 7·50
R 118. 80 f. brown .. .. 42·00 42·00
R 119. 1 p. green .. .. 6·25 6·25

II. GENERAL ISSUES

100 paras = 1 dinar.

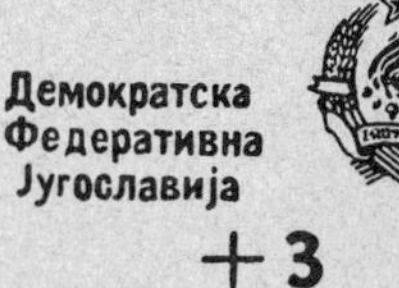

(113.)

1944. Stamps of Serbia, 1942, surch. as T 113.

482. – 3 d.+2 d. pink (No. 64) 5 20
485. – 4 d.+21 d. bl. (No. 65) 5 20
483. – 7 d.+3 d. grn. (No. 66) 5 20

114. Marshal Tito. 115. Chapel at Prohor Pcinjski.

1945.

491. 114. 25 p. green 35 15
492. 50 p. green 35 5
493. 1 d. red .. .. 4·50 40
494. 2 d. red 35 5
495. 4 d. blue 75 5
487. 5 d. green 5 5
496. 6 d. violet 80 5
497 9 d. brown .. .. 1·40 20
488. 10 d. red 8 5
498. 20 d. yellow .. .. 5·00 1·40
489. 25 d. violet 12 12
490. 30 d. blue 25 15

1945. 1st Anniv. of Anti-Fascist Chamber of Deputies, Macedonia.

499. 115. 2 d. red 70 25

116. Partisans. 119. Partisans. 120. Marshal Tito.

1945. Red Cross Fund.

500. 116. 1 d.+4 d. blue.. .. 90 80
501. – 2 d.+6 d. red 90 80

DESIGN—VERT. Child's head.

1945. Partisans.

502 119 50 p. brown 10 8
503 1 d. green 15 5
504 1 d. 50 brown 20 8
505 120 2 d. red 15 8
506 – 2 d. 50 red 60 5
507 – 3 d. brown .. .. 1·00 8
508 – 3 d. red 60 8
509 120 4 d. blue 30 5
510 – 5 d. green .. .. 1·00 8
511 – 5 d. blue .. .. 1·75 8
512 – 6 d. black 60 5
513 – 8 d. yellow 65 8
514 – 9 d. mauve 55 10
515 – 12 d. blue .. .. 1·00 8
516 119 16 d. blue .. .. 1·00 10
517 – 20 d. red .. .. 2·25 20

DESIGNS—As Type 119: 1 d. 50, 12, 20 d., Riflemen. VERT. 3, 5 d. Town of Jajce, inscr. "29-XI-1943". HORIZ. 2 d. 50 p., 6, 8, 9 d. Girl with flag.

122. Russian and Yugoslav Flags.

1945. 1st Anniv. of Liberation of Belgrade.

No.	Type	Description	Unused	Used
518.	122.	2 d.+5 d. mult.	70	40

124. "Industry and Agriculture". 126.

1945. Meeting of the Constituent Assembly. Inscr. in Cyrillic at top and Roman characters at foot (I) or vice versa (II).

No.	Type	Description	I	I	II	II
519.	124.	2 d. red	3·00	3·00	3·00	3·00
520.		4 d. blue	3·00	3·00	3·00	3·00
521.		6 d. green	3·00	3·00	3·00	3·00
522.		9 d. orange	3·00	3·00	3·00	3·00
523.		16 d. blue	3·00	3·00	3·00	3·00
524.		20 d. brown	3·00	3·00	3·00	3·00

D. FEDERAL PEOPLE'S REPUBLIC

100 paras = 1 dinar.

1946. Type of 1945 (Girl with flag), surch.

No.	Type	Description	Unused	Used
525.		2 d. 50 on 6 d. red	60	5
526.		8 d. on 9 d. orange	1·00	10

1946. 1st Anniv. of Victory over Fascism. Star in red.

No.	Type	Description	Unused	Used
527.	126.	1 d. 50 orange	40	50
528.		2 d. 50 red	60	70
529.		5 d. blue	1·75	1·50

127. Symbolic of Communications. 128. Railway Construction. 129. Svetozar Markovic.

1946. Postal Congress.

No.	Type	Description	Unused	Used
530.	127.	1 d. 50+1 d. green	4·50	4·50
531.		2 d. 50+1 d. 50 red	4·50	4·50
532.		5 d.+2 d. blue	4·50	4·50
533.		8 d.+3 d. 50 brown	4·50	4·50

1946. Volunteer Workers' Railway Reconstruction Fund.

No.	Type	Description	Unused	Used
534.	128.	50 p.+50 p. brown, red and blue	3·50	2·00
535.		1 d. 50+1 d. green, blue and red	3·50	1·75
536.		2 d. 50+2 d. lilac, red and blue	3·50	1·75
537.		5 d.+3 d. grey, red & bl.	3·50	2·25

1946. Birth Centenary of S. Markovic (socialist writer).

No.	Type	Description	Unused	Used
538.	129.	1 d. 50 green	75	40
539.		2 d. 50 purple	75	45

130. Theatre in Sofia. 131. Roofless Houses.

1946. Slav Congress.

No.	Type	Description	Unused	Used
540.	130.	½ d. brown	8	5
541.	–	1 d. green	10	5
542.	–	1½ d. red	12	5
543.	–	2½ d. orange	20	10
544.	–	5 d. blue	75	60

DESIGNS—HORIZ. 1 d. Charles Bridge and Hradcany, Prague. VERT. 1½ d. Sigismund Monument, Warsaw. 2½ d. Victory Monument, Belgrade. 5 d. Kremlin Tower, Moscow.

1947. Obligatory Tax. Red Cross.

No.	Type	Description	Unused	Used
545.	131.	50 p. brown	15	5

132. Aeroplane over Kalimegdan Terrace, Belgrade. 133. "Wreath of Mountains". 134. P. P. Njegos.

1947. Air. Inscr. in Cyrillic at top and Roman characters at foot (I) or vice versa (II).

No.	Type	Description	I	I	II	II
546.	132.	50 p. olive and lake	15	15	15	15
547.	–	1 d. red & olive	25	20	25	20
548.	132.	2 d. blue & blk.	40	25	40	25
549.	–	5 d. grn. & grey	45	30	45	30
550	–	10 d. brn. & sep.	55	40	55	40
551.	132.	20 d. blue & ol.	1·00	65	1·00	65

DESIGN: 1 d., 5 d., 20 d. Aeroplane over Dubrovnik.

1947. Centenary of Publication of "Wreath of Mountains".

No.	Type	Description	Unused	Used
552.	133.	1½ d. black & green	15	10
553.	134.	2 d. 50 red and buff	20	12
554.	133.	5 d. black and blue	35	20

135. Girl Athlete, Star and Flags. 137. Gymnast.

1947. Federal Sports Meeting.

No.	Type	Description	Unused	Used
555.	–	1 d. 50 brown	12	10
556.	135.	2 d. 50 red	20	12
557.	–	4 d. blue	50	40

DESIGNS—VERT. 1 d. 50, Physical training groups. HORIZ. 4 d. Parade of athletes.

1947. Balkan Games.

No.	Type	Description	Unused	Used
558.	137.	1 d. 50+50 p. green	15	10
559.		2 d. 50+50 p. red	30	20
560.		4 d.+50 p. blue	40	35

138. Star and Map of Julian Province. 139. Railway Construction.

1947. Annexation of Julian Province to Yugoslavia.

No.	Type	Description	Unused	Used
561.	138.	2 d. 50 red and blue	12	5
562.		5 d. brown and green	15	5

1947. Juvenile Labour Organizations' Relief Fund.

No.	Type	Description	Unused	Used
563.	139.	1 d.+50 p. orange	30	15
564.		1 d. 50+1 d. green	35	25
565.		2 d. 50+1 d. 50 red	60	30
566.		5 d.+2 d. blue	1·25	70

140. Music Book and Fiddle. 141. Vuk Karadzic (poet).

1947. Centenary of Serbian Literature.

No.	Type	Description	Unused	Used
567.	140.	1 d. 50 green	10	10
568.	141.	2 d. 50 red	15	12
569.	140.	5 d. blue	20	20

142. "B.C.G. Vaccine Defeating Tuberculosis". 143. "Illness and Recovery".

144. "Fight against Tuberculosis". 145. Map of Yugoslavia and Symbols of Industry and Agriculture.

1948. Anti-T.B. Fund.

No.	Type	Description	Unused	Used
570.	142.	1 d. 50+1 d. green & red	10	10
571.	143.	2 d. 50+2 d. green & red	15	12
572.	144.	5 d.+3 d. blue and red	25	20

1948. Int. Fair, Zagreb.

No.	Type	Description	Unused	Used
573.	145.	1 d. 50 grn., blue & red	5	5
574.		2 d. 50 pur., blue & red	8	5
575.		5 d. indigo, blue and red	15	8

146. Flag-bearers. 147. Djura Danicic.

1948. 5th Yugoslav Communist Party Congress, Belgrade.

No.	Type	Description	Unused	Used
576.	146.	2 d. green	20	15
577b.		3 d. red and lake	20	15
578a.		10 d. blue	45	45

1948. 80th Anniv. of Yugoslav Academy.

No.	Type	Description	Unused	Used
579.	147.	1 d. 50+50 p. green	15	15
580.	–	2 d. 50+1 d. red	25	15
581.	–	4 d.+2 d. blue	35	30

PORTRAITS: 2 d. 50, Franjo Racki. 4 d. Josip J. Strasmajer.

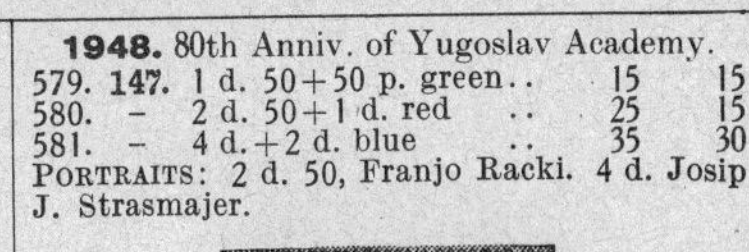

148. Danube Bridge and "Krajina" (former royal yacht).

1948. Danube Conf.

No.	Type	Description	Unused	Used
582.	148.	2 d. green	2·50	2·50
583.		3 d. red	3·75	3·75
584.		5 d. blue	4·50	4·50
585.		10 d. brown	8·50	8·50

149. Laurence Kosir. 150. Kosir and his Birthplace.

1948. 80th Death Anniv. of Laurence Kosir ("Ideological creator of first postage stamp").

No.	Type	Description	Unused	Used
586.	149.	3 d. purple (postage)	12	8
587.		5 d. blue	15	15
588.		10 d. orange	20	10
589.		12 d. green	35	25
590.	150.	15 d. mauve (air)	90	45

151. Putting the shot. 152. 153. Arms of Montenegro.

1948. Projected Balkan Games.

No.	Type	Description	Unused	Used
591.	151.	2 d.+1 d. green	30	20
592.	–	3 d.+1 d. red	30	20
593.	–	5 d.+2 d. blue	50	40

DESIGNS: 3 d. Girl hurdler. 5 d. Pole-vaulting

1948. Obligatory Tax. Red Cross.

No.	Type	Description	Unused	Used
594.	152.	50 p. red and blue	15	5

1948. 5th Anniv. of Republic.

No.	Type	Description	Unused	Used
595.	–	3 d. blue (Serbia)	40	30
596.	–	3 d. red (Croatia)	40	30
597.	–	3 d. orange (Slovenia)	40	30
598.	–	3 d. green (Bosnia and Herzegovina)	40	30
599.	–	3 d. mauve (Macedonia)	40	30
600.	153.	3 d. black	40	30
601.	–	10 d. red (Yugoslavia)	2·00	2·00

No. 601 is larger (24½×34½ mm.)

154. F. Presern. 155. Ski-jump, Planica.

1949. Death Cent. of Franc Presern (author).

No.	Type	Description	Unused	Used
602.	154.	3 d. blue	20	12
603.		5 d. orange	25	20
604.		10 d. sepia	1·50	35

1949. Ski-jumping Competition, Planica.

No.	Type	Description	Unused	Used
605.	155.	10 d. mauve	90	65
606.	–	12 d. slate (Ski-jumper)	1·25	65

156. Soldiers. 158. Globe, Letters and Forms of Transport.

1949. 5th Anniv. of Liberation of Macedonia.

(a) Postage.

No.	Type	Description	Unused	Used
607.	156.	3 d. red	50	40
608.	–	5 d. blue	1·25	65
608a.	–	12 d. brown	2·75	2·50

DESIGNS: 5 d. Industrial and agricultural workers. 12 d. Arms and flags of Yugoslavia and Macedonia.

(b) Air. Optd. with aeroplane and AVIONSKA POSTA.

No.	Type	Description	Unused	Used
609.	156.	3 d. red	2·50	2·50
610.	–	5 d. blue (No. 608)	2·50	2·50
610a.	–	12 d. brown (608a)	2·50	2·50

1949. 75th Anniv. U.P.U.

No.	Type	Description	Unused	Used
611.	158.	3 d. red	2·75	2·75
612.	–	5 d. blue	45	45
613.	158.	12 d. brown	45	45

DESIGN—HORIZ. 5 d. Aeroplane, train and mail-coach.

1949. Surch. with bold figures and bars.

No.	Type	Description	Unused	Used
614.	O 130.	3 d. on 8 d. brown	40	8
615.		3 d. on 12 d. violet	50	12

160. Nurse and Child.

1949. Obligatory Tax. Red Cross.

No.	Type	Description	Unused	Used
616.	160.	50 p. brown and red	15	5

ФНР ЈУГОСЛАВИЈА

≡ D3 FNR JUGOSLAVIJA (161.)

F N R D10 JUGOSLAVIJA (162.)

1949. Surch. with T 161 or 162.

No.	Type	Description	Unused	Used
617.	–	3 d. on 8 d. yellow (No. 513)	50	8
618.	–	10 d. on 20 d. red (No. 517)	65	8

FNR JUGOSLAVIJA (163.)

Ф Н Р

F N R JUGOSLAVIJA (165.)

F N R (164.)

1949. Optd. with T 163 on 2 d., 164 on 3 d. and 5 d., or 165 on others.

No.	Type	Description	Unused	Used
619.	119.	50 p. olive	5	5
620.		1 d. green	5	5
621.		1 d. orange	30	5
622.	120.	2 d. red	15	5
623.		2 d. green	30	5
624.	–	3 d. red (No. 508)	15	5
625.	–	3 d. pink	30	5
626.	–	5 d. blue (No. 511)	40	20
627.	–	5 d. light blue	50	10
628.	–	12 d. violet (No. 515)	35	5
629.	119.	16 d. light blue	1·25	40
630.		20 d. red	85	15

166. Steam Loco of 1849. 167. Surveying.

1949. Cent. of National Railways.

No.	Type	Description	Unused	Used
631.	166.	2 d. green	1·25	35
632.	–	3 d. red	1·25	35
633.	–	5 d. blue	5·00	65
633a.	–	10 d. orange	23·00	8·00

DESIGNS: 3 d. Modern steam locomotive. 5 d. Diesel train. 10 d. Electric loco.

1950. Completion of Belgrade-Zagreb Road

No.	Type	Description	Unused	Used
634.	167.	2 d. green	40	12
635.	–	3 d. pink	25	15
636.	–	5 d. blue	1·00	70

DESIGNS: 3 d. Map, road and car. 5 d. Youth, road and flag.

168. Marshal Tito. 169. A Child Eating.

1950. May Day.

No.	Type	Description	Unused	Used
637.	168.	3 d. red	2·10	40
638.		5 d. blue	2·10	40
639.		10 d. brown	35·00	21·00
640.		12 d. black	2·10	2·00

1950. Child Welfare.

No.	Type	Description	Unused	Used
641.	169.	3 d. red	35	8

170. Launching Model Glider. 171. Chessboard and Bishop.

1950. 3rd Aeronautical Meeting.
642. **170.** 2 d. green 80 90
643. – 3 d. red 85 90
644. – 5 d. violet .. .. 2·10 90
645. – 10 d. brown .. .. 2·25 2·10
646. – 20 d. blue .. .. 15·00 15·00
DESIGNS—VERT. 3 d. Glider in flight. 5 d. Parachutists landing. 10 d. Woman pilot. 20 d. Glider on water.

1950. 9th Chess Olympiad, Dubrovnik.
647. **171.** 2 d. red 90 40
648. – 3 d. bistre, sepia and drab 90 30
649. – 5 d. multicoloured .. 1·75 50
650. – 10 d. multicoloured .. 2·40 1·25
651. – 20 d. yellow and blue 30·00 20·00
DESIGNS—VERT. 3 d. Rook and flags. 5 d. Chessboard showing position in 1924 Capablanca v. Lasker game, pieces and globe. 10 d. Chequered globe and map. 20 d. Knight and flags.

172. Girl Harvester. **173.** Train and Map.

1950.
652. – 50 p. brown 10 5
653. – 1 d. green 20 5
705. – 1 d. grey 20 5
654. **172.** 2 d. orange 20 5
718. 2 d. red .. .. 3·00 12
655. – 3 d. red 20 5
656. – 5 d. blue .. .. 1·25 5
719. – 5 d. orange .. .. 1·40 12
657. – 7 d. grey .. .. 1·25 8
720. – 8 d. blue .. .. 4·50 25
658. – 10 d. brown .. .. 1·50 5
721. – 10 d. green .. .. 7·50 12
722. – 12 d. purple .. .. 45·00 25
723. – 15 d. red .. .. 18·00 10
660. – 16 d. blue .. .. 3·50 12
723a. – 17 d. purple .. .. 6·00 20
661. – 20 d. olive .. .. 3·50 15
710. – 20 d. purple .. .. 7·50 5
711a. **172.** 25 d. bistre .. .. 13·50 5
662. – 30 d. brown .. .. 9·00 35
712. – 30 d. blue .. .. 1·75 5
713. – 35 d. brown .. .. 2·50 10
662a. – 50 d. violet .. .. 45·00 16·00
714. – 50 d. green .. .. 2·00 10
715. – 75 d. violet .. .. 3·00 10
716. – 100 d. sepia .. .. 10·50 20
DESIGNS—VERT. 50, 100 d. Metallurgy. 1 d. Electrical supply engineer. 3 d., 35 d. Man and woman with wheelbarrow. 5 d. Fishing. 7 d., 8 d. Mining. 10 d. Apple-picking. 12 d., 75 d. Lumbering. 14 d., 15 d., 16 d. Picking sunflowers. 17 d., 20 d. Woman and farm animals. 30 d. Girl printer. 50 d. Dockers unloading cargo.

1950. Zagreb Exhibition.
663. **173.** 3 d. lake .. .. 1·25 50

174. Girl in National Costume. **175.** Galleon.

1950. Obligatory Tax. Red Cross.
664. **174.** 50 p. green and red .. 15 5

1950. Navy Day.
665. **175.** 2 d. purple 30 15
666. – 3 d. brown 30 10
667. – 5 d. green .. .. 1·40 10
668. – 10 d. blue 80 15
669. – 12 d. grey .. .. 1·90 50
670. – 20 d. red .. .. 4·25 2·00
DESIGNS: 3 d. Partisan patrol boat. 5 d. Freighter discharging cargo. 10 d. "Zagreb" (freighter) and globe. 12 d. Yachts. 20 d. Sailor, gun and "Golesnica" (torpedo boat).

176. Patriots of 1941. **177.** Stane-Rozman.

1951. 10th Anniv. of Revolt against Pact with Axis.
671. **176.** 3 d. lake and red .. 3·75 2·25

1951. 10th Anniv. of Partisan Rising in Slovenia.
672. **177.** 3 d. brown 50 25
673. – 5 d. blue (Boy courier) 75 35

178. Children Painting.

1951. International Children's Day.
674. **178.** 3 d. red .. .. 1·10 25

179. "Iron Gates", Danube. **181.** Z. Jovanovic.

1951. Air.
675. **179.** 1 d. orange 15 10
676. – 2 d. green 25 10
677. – 3 d. red 25 10
677a. – 5 d. brown 30 10
678. – 6 d. blue .. .. 4·50 4·50
679. – 10 d. brown 50 10
680. – 20 d. grey 75 10
681. – 30 d. red .. .. 2·50 10
682. – 50 d. violet .. .. 3·75 10
683. – 100 d. grey (40 × 27 mm.) .. .. 60·00 5·00
683a. – 100 d. green .. .. 1·40 15
683b. – 200 d. red .. .. 1·75 25
683c. – 500 d. blue (39½ × 26 mm.) .. .. 7·00 1·25
DESIGNS—HORIZ. All show aeroplane. 2 d., 5 d. Pitvice Cascades. 3 d. 100 d. (green) Gozd-Martuljak (mountain village). 6 d., 200 d. Old Bridge Mostar. 10 d. Ohrid. 20 d. Kotor Bay. 30 d. Dubrovnik. 50 d. Bled. 40 × 27 mm. 100 d. (grey) 500 d. Belgrade.

1951. Air. Zagreb Philatelic Exn., No. 678 in new colour optd. **ZEFIZ 1951.**
684. 6 d. green 90 70

1951. 10th Anniv. of Serbian Insurrection.
685. **181.** 3 d. brown 75 40
686. – 5 d. blue .. .. 1·10 65
DESIGN—HORIZ. 5 d. Armed insurgents.

183. Mt. Kopaonik, Serbia. **184.** S. Kovacevic.

1951. Air. Int. Mountaineering Assn. Meeting, Bled. Inscr. "UIAA–1951".
687. **183.** 3 d. mauve .. .. 1·60 1·60
688. – 5 d. blue .. .. 1·60 1·60
689. – 20 d. green .. .. 95·00 65·00
DESIGNS: 5 d. Mt. Triglav. 20 d. Mt. Kalnik.

1951. 10th Anniv. of Montenegrin Insurrection.
690. **184.** 3 d. red .. .. 1·00 75
691. – 5 d. blue .. .. 1·75 1·00
DESIGN—HORIZ. 5 d. Partisan and mountains.

185. M. Oreskovic Statue. **186.** S. Solaj.

1951. 10th Anniv. of Croatian Insurrection.
692. **185.** 3 d. red 75 35
693. – 5 d. dark green .. 1·25 65
DESIGN—VERT. 5 d. Statue: "Transport of a Wounded Man".

1951. 10th Anniv. of Insurrection of Bosnia and Herzegovina.
694. **186.** 3 d. red 90 40
695. – 5 d. blue .. .. 1·25 65
DESIGN—VERT. 5 d. Group of insurgents.

187. Parachutists Landing. **189.** P. Trubar (author).

1951. Air. 1st World Parachute Jumping Championship, Bled.
696. **187.** 6 d. lake .. .. 5·00 2·00

As No. 682 in new colour optd **I SVETSKO TAKMICENJE PADOBRANACA 1951.**
697 50 d. blue .. .. 80·00 45·00

1951. Cultural Annivs.
698 **189** 10 d. black 40 25
699 – 12 d. orange 40 25
700 – 20 d. violet .. .. 5·75 4·75
PORTRAITS: 12 d. M. Marulic (poet). 20 d. Tsar Stefan Duzan.

190. National Products. **191.** Hoisting the Flag.

1951. Zagreb Int. Fair.
701. **190.** 3 p. yellow, red & blue 1·10 35

1951. Obligatory Tax. Red Cross.
702. **191.** 50 p. blue and red .. 15 5

192. M. Acev. **193.** P. P. Njegos.

1951. 10th Anniv. of Macedonian Insurrection.
703. **192.** 3 d. mauve 75 40
704. – 5 d. violet .. .. 1·75 1·10
DESIGN—HORIZ. 5 d. War Victims' Monument, Skopje.

1951. Death Cent. of Njegos (poet).
724. **193.** 15 d. purple .. .. 1·75 55

194. Soldier and Badge. **195.** Marshal Tito.

1951. Army Day.
725. **194.** 15 d. red (postage) .. 60 8

726. **195.** 150 d. blue (air) .. 15·00 9·00

196. Marshal Tito. **197.**

1952. Marshal Tito's 60th Birthday.
727. **196.** 15 d. brown .. .. 1·00 1·00
728. **197.** 28 d. lake .. .. 1·75 1·75
729. – 50 d. green .. .. 45·00 42·00
DESIGN—As Type **196**: 50 d. Statue of Marshal Tito.

198. **199.** Gymnastics.

1952. Children's Week.
730. **198.** 15 d. red .. .. 7·50 40

1952. 15th Olympic Games, Helsinki. Inscr. "XV OLIMPIJADA 1952".
731. **199.** 5 d. brown on buff .. 40 25
732. – 10 d. brown on yellow 40 25
733. – 15 d. blue on pink .. 90 30
734. – 28 d. brown on flesh .. 1·25 90
735. – 50 d. green on green .. 6·00 3·00
736. – 100 d. brown on mauve 60·00 23·00
DESIGNS: 10 d. Running. 15 d. Swimming. 28 d. Boxing. 50 d Basketball. 100 d. Football.

200. "Fishing-boat" (from relief by Krsinic). **200a.** Belgrade (XVI Cent.).

1952. Navy Day. Views inscr. "1952".
737. – 15 d. purple .. .. 1·75 60
738. **200.** 28 d. brown .. .. 3·25 90
739. – 50 d. black .. .. 23·00 19·00
DESIGNS: 15 d. Split, Dalmatia. 50 d. Sveti Stefan, Montenegro.

1952. Philatelic Exn., Belgrade.
739a. **200a.** 15 d. purple .. 9·00 9·00
No. 739a was only sold at the Exhibition at 35 d. (20 d. entrance fee).

201. **202.** Workers in Procession (from fresco by S. Pengov). **203.** N. Tesla.

1952. Obligatory Tax. Red Cross.
740. **201.** 50 p. red, grey & black 30 8

1952. 6th Yugoslavia Communist Party Congress.
741. **202.** 15 d. brown .. .. 1·50 1·10
742. 15 d. turquoise .. 1·50 1·10
743. 15 d. brown .. .. 1·50 1·10
744. 15 d. blue .. .. 1·50 1·10

1953. 10th Death Anniv. of Tesla (inventor).
745. **203.** 15 d. lake .. .. 1·25 15
746. 30 d. blue .. .. 4·00 40

204. Fresco, Sopocani Monastery. **205.**

1953. United Nations. Commemoration.
747. **204.** 15 d. green .. .. 1·50 60
748. – 30 d. blue .. .. 3·00 60
749. – 50 d. lake .. .. 18·00 4·75
DESIGNS—VERT. 30 d. Fresco, St. Panteleimon Church, Nerezim, Skopje. 50 d. Fresco, St. Dimitri Church, Pec.

1953. Adriatic Car and Motor-cycle Rally.
750. **205.** 15 d. lake and pink .. 25 8
751. – 30 d. deep blue & blue 70 10
752. – 50 d. brown and yellow 1·60 10
753. – 70 d. green & turquoise 5·00 80
DESIGNS—HORIZ. 30 d. Motor-cyclist and coastline. 50 d. Racing car and flags. 70 d. Saloon car descending mountain roadway.

206. Marshal Tito **207.**

1953. Marshal Tito. Commem.
754. **206.** 50 d. violet .. .. 9·00 1·25

1953. 38th Esperanto Congress, Zagreb.
755. **207.** 15 d. grn. & blk. (post.) 4·50 1·50
756. 300 d. grn. & blue (air) £300 £275

208. "Insurrection" (from painting by B. Lazevski). **209.**

1953. 50th Anniv. of Macedonian Insurrection.
757. **208.** 15 d. purple .. .. 1·00 75
758. – 30 d. green .. .. 3·25 2·00
DESIGN: 30 d. N. Karev (revolutionary).

1953. 10th Anniv. of Liberation of Istria and Slovene Coast.
759. **209.** 15 d. green .. .. 12·50 1·75

210. B. Radicevic. **211.** Blood-transfusion.

1953. Death Cent. of Radicevic (poet).
760. **210.** 15 d. purple .. .. 6·00 1·00

1953. Obligatory Tax. Red Cross.
761. **211.** 2 d. red and purple .. 35 35

212. Jajce. **213.** European Souslik.

1953. 10th Anniv. of 1st Republican Legislative Assembly.
762. **212.** 15 d. green .. .. 1·50 45
763. – 30 d. red .. .. 2·00 1·00
764. – 50 d. sepia .. .. 11·50 9·00
DESIGNS: 30 d. Assembly building. 50 d. Marshal Tito addressing assembly.

1954. Animals.
765. **213.** 2 d. slate, buff & green 20 10
766. – 5 d. brown and green .. 35 15
767. – 10 d. brown and slate 60 25
768. – 15 d. brown and blue .. 80 30
769. – 17 d. sepia and purple 1·40 30
770. – 25 d. yell., blue & violet 2·50 30
771. – 30 d. sepia and blue .. 4·50 35
772. – 35 d. black and brown 6·00 90
773. – 50 d. brn. and bronze 15·00 1·75
774. – 65 d. black and lake .. 21·00 12·00
775. – 70 d. brown and turq. 18·00 12·00
776. – 100 d. black and blue .. 60·00 32·00
DESIGNS—HORIZ. 5 d. Lynx. 10 d. Red deer. 15 d. Brown bear. 17 d. Chamois. 25 d. Eastern white pelican. VERT. 30 d. Lammergeier. 35 d. "Procerus gigas" (black beetle). 50 d. "Callimeniu microgaster" (grasshopper). 65 d. Black Dalmatian lizard. 70 d. Blind cave-dwelling salamander. 100 d. Trout.

214. Ljubljana (XVII cent.).

1954. Philatelic Exn., Ljubljana.
777. **214.** 15 d. brn., grn. & blk. 15·00 11·00
No. 777 was only sold at the Exhibition at 35 d. (20 d. entrance fee).

215. Cannon, 1804.

1954. 150th Anniv. of Serbian Insurrection. Multicoloured.
778. 15 d. Serbian flag .. .. 1·25 40
779. 30 d. Type **215** .. .. 2·00 75
780. 50 d. Seal of insurgents council .. .. .. 3·75 90
781. 70 d. Karageorge .. .. 35·00 10·00

215a. **216.**

1954. Children's Week.
781a. **215a.** 2 d. red 35 60

1954. Obligatory Tax. Red Cross.
782. **216.** 2 d. red and green .. 20 5

217. V. Lisinski (composer). **218.** "Midsummer Night's Dream" (Shakespeare).

1954. Cultural Anniversaries.
783. **217.** 15 d. green .. .. 3·00 45
784. – 30 d. brown .. .. 2·25 1·00
785. – 50 d. purple .. .. 2·50 1·60
786. – 70 d. blue .. .. 5·00 3·00
787. – 100 d. violet .. .. 22·00 18·00
PORTRAITS—VERT. 30 d. A. Kacic-Miosic (writer). 50 d. J. Vega (mathematician). 70 d. Z. J. Jovanovic (poet). 100 d. F. Visnjic (poet and musician).
See also Nos. 975/80.

1955. Dubrovnik Festival.
788. – 15 d. lake .. .. 1·00 35
789. **218.** 30 d. blue .. .. 3·50 1·10
DESIGN—VERT. 15 d. Scene from "Robinja" by Hanibal Lucic.

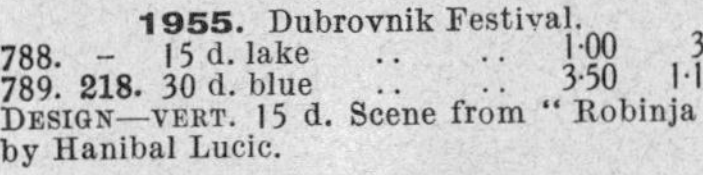

219. **220.**

1955. 1st Int. Exn. of Engraving, Ljubljana.
790. **219.** 15 d. brown and green on grey .. .. 3·75 75

1955. 2nd World Congress of the Deaf and Dumb.
791. **220.** 15 d. lake .. .. 1·90 35

221. Hops. **222.** Laughing Girl.

1955. Vert. floral designs as T **221.**
792. 5 d. green & brown (T **221**) 12 10
793. 10 d. purple, green & buff 15 10
794. 15 d. multicoloured 20 10
795. 17 d. buff, green and lake .. 30 12
796. 25 d. yell., green and blue 30 12
797. 30 d. multicoloured .. 70 45
798. 50 d. red, green and brown 3·75 1·75
799. 70 d. orange, green & brown 5·00 3·00
800. 100 d. multicoloured .. 26·00 15·00
FLOWERS—10 d. Tobacco. 15 d. Poppy. 17 d. Linden. 25 d. Camomile. 30 d. Sage. 50 d. Wild rose. 70 d. Gentian. 100 d. Adonis.

1955. Obligatory Tax. Children's Week.
801. **222.** 2 d. red 15 5

223. Peace Monument, U.N. Building, New York (A. Augustincic). **224.** Red Cross Nurse.

1955. 10th Anniv. of United Nations.
802. **223.** 30 d. black and blue .. 1·40 55

1955. Obligatory Tax. Red Cross.
803. **224.** 2 d. grey and red .. 20 5

225. Woman and Dove. **226.** St. Donat's Church, Zadar.

1955. 10th Anniv. of Republic.
804. **225.** 15 d. violet 40 20

1956. Yugoslav Art.
805. **226.** 5 d. grey 40 10
806. – 10 d. myrtle 40 10
807. – 15 d. brown 45 10
808. – 20 d. lake 45 15
809. – 25 d. sepia 55 15
810. – 30 d. red 55 20
811. – 35 d. olive .. .. 1·10 30
812. – 40 d. lake .. .. 2·00 40
813. – 50 d. brown .. .. 5·00 30
814. – 70 d. green .. .. 12·00 7·50
815. – 100 d. purple .. 32·00 18·00
816. – 200 d. blue .. .. 48·00 30·00
DESIGNS—VERT. 10 d. Bas-relief of Croat King, Diocletian Palace, Split. 15 d. Church portal, Studenica, Serbia. 20 d. Master Radovan's portal, Trogir Cathedral. 25 d. Fresco, Sopocani, Serbia. 30 d. Monument, Radimlje, Herzegovina. 50 d. Detail from Bozidarevic Triptych, Dubrovnik. 70 d. Carved figure, Belec Church, Croatia. 100 d. Self-portrait of R. Jakopic. 200 d. Peace Monument by A. Augustincic, New York. HORIZ. 35 d. Heads from Cathedral cornice, Sibenik, Dalmatia. 40 d. Frieze, Kotor Cathedral, Montenegro.

227. Zagreb through the Centuries. **228.** Houses ruined by Avalanche.

1956. Yugoslav Int. Philatelic Exn., Zagreb.
817. **227.** 15 d. brown, orange & black (postage) .. 30 12
818. 30 d. blue, red and black (air) .. 1·50 55

1956. Obligatory Tax. Red Cross.
819. **228.** 2 d. sepia and red .. 15 5

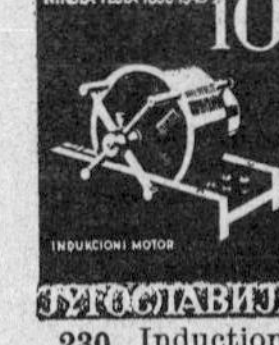
229. "Technical Education". **230.** Induction Motor.

1956. Air. 10th Anniv. of Technical Education.
820. **229.** 30 d. red and black .. 1·25 90

1956. Birth Cent. of Tesla (inventor).
821. **230.** 10 d. olive 15 5
822. – 15 d. brown 40 5
823. – 30 d. blue 70 15
824. – 50 d. purple .. .. 2·25 40
DESIGNS: 15 d. Transformer. 30 d. "Telekomanda" (invention). 50 d. Portrait.

231. Sea-horse. **232.**

1956. Adriatic Sea Creatures. Multicoloured.
825. 10 d. Type **231** 12 5
826. 15 d. Paper nautilus .. 15 5
827. 20 d. Rock lobster .. 20 5
828. 25 d. "Sea-prince" .. 30 10
829. 30 d. Perch 40 10
830. 35 d. Red mullet .. 80 15
831. 50 d. Scorpion fish .. 3·25 75
832. 70 d. Wrasse .. .. 4·75 1·25
833. 100 d. Dory .. .. 14·00 3·50

1956. Obligatory Tax. Children's Week.
834. **232.** 2 d. green 15 5

233. Running. **234.**

1956. Olympic Games. Figures, values and country name in ochre.
835. **233.** 10 d. red 5 5
836. – 15 d. blue (Canoeing) .. 8 5
837. – 20 d. blue (Skiing) .. 20 5
838. – 30 d. green (Swimming) 30 5
839. – 35 d. sepia (Football) .. 45 8
840. – 50 d. green (Water-polo) 1·25 12
841. – 70 d. purple (Table-tennis) .. .. 3·75 1·25
842. – 100 d. red (Shooting) .. 6·50 2·50

1957. Obligatory Tax. Red Cross.
843. **234.** 2 d. red, black and blue 15 10

235. Centaury. **236.** Factory in Worker's Hand.

1957. Flowers. Multicoloured.
844. 10 d. Type **235** 10 5
845. 15 d. Belladonna .. 12 5
846. 20 d. Autumn crocus .. 15 8
847. 25 d. Marsh-mallow .. 20 8
848. 30 d. Valerian 25 12
849. 35 d. Woolly foxglove .. 50 12
850. 50 d. Fern .. .. 1·50 40
851. 70 d. Green-winged orchid 3·00 75
852. 100 d. Pyrethrum .. .. 16·00 9·00

1957. 1st Congress of Workers' Councils. Belgrade.
853. **236.** 15 d. lake 40 5
854. 30 d. blue 85 25

237. Gymnastics.

1957. 2nd Gymnastics Festival, Zagreb. Vert. designs as T **237.**
855. **237.** 10 d. olive and black .. 25 5
856. – 15 d. brown and black 25 5
857. – 30 d. blue and black .. 65 5
858. – 50 d. brown and black 2·00 1·50

239. Musician and Dancers of Slovenia. **240.** Children.

1957. Yugoslav Costumes (1st series).
860. – 10 d. multicoloured .. 20 5
861. – 15 d. multicoloured .. 30 5
862. – 30 d. multicoloured .. 30 5
863. – 50 d. grn., brn. & buff 1·00 2·00
864. – 70 d. blk., brn. & buff 1·25 35
865. **239.** 100 d. multicoloured .. 6·00 2·50
DESIGNS—HORIZ. 10 d. Montenegrin musician, man and woman. 15 d. Macedonian dancers. 30 d. Croatian shepherdess and shepherd boys. VERT. 50 d. Serbian peasants. 70 d. Bosnian villagers.
See also Nos. 1020/5.

1957. Obligatory Tax. Children's Week.
866. **240.** 2 d. slate and red .. 15 5

241. Revolutionaries. **242.** S. Gregorcic (poet).

1957. 40th Anniv. of Russian Revolution.
867. **241.** 15 d. red and ochre .. 40 20

1957. Cultural Anniversaries.
868. **242.** 15 d. sepia 30 5
869. – 30 d. blue 40 5
870. – 50 d. brown 90 5
871. – 70 d. violet .. .. 8·50 2·25
872. – 100 d. green .. .. 14·00 13·00
PORTRAITS—VERT. 30 d. A. Linhart (dramatist) 50 d. O. Kucera (physicist). 70 d. S. Mokranja (composer). 100 d. J. Popovic (writer).

244. **245.** Fresco of Sopocani Monastery.

1958. 7th Yugoslav Communist Party Congress.
877. **244.** 15 d. purple 20 10

1958. Obligatory Tax. Red Cross.
878. **245.** 2 d. multicoloured .. 20 5

246. Mallard. **247.** Pigeon.

1958. Yugoslav Game Birds. Birds in natural colours. Background colours given below.

879. **246.** 10 d. brown 10 5
880. – 15 d. mauve (Capercaillie) 15 5
881. – 20 d. blue (Ring-necked Pheasant) 30 5
882. – 25 d. green (Common Coot) 35 5
883. – 30 d. turquoise (Water Rail) 55 12
884. – 35 d. bistre (Great Bustard) 65 12
885. – 50 d. purple (Rock Partridge) .. .. 2·75 65
886. – 70 d. blue (Woodcock) 4·75 1·50
887. – 100 d. brown & black (Common Crane) .. 10·50 3·50

The 25, 35, 50 and 100 d. values are vert.

1958. Opening of Postal Museum, Belgrade.

888. **247.** 15 d. black 20 15

248. Battle Flag. **249.** Pomet, hero of Drzic's comedy "Dundo Maroje", and ancient fountain at Dubrovnik.

1958. 15th Anniv. of Battle of Sutjeska River.

889. **248.** 15 d. lake 25 10

958. 450th Birth Anniv. of Marin Drzic (writer).

890. **249.** 15 d. brown and black 40 12

243. Steel Plant, Sisak. **250.** Children at play.

1958.

891 – 2 d. green 10 10
892 – 5 d. red 15 10
983 – 5 d. orange 30 10
893 – 8 d. purple 25 10
984 – 8 d. violet 30 10
894 **243** 10 d. green 35 10
985 10 d. brown 30 10
896 – 15 d. red 30 10
986 – 15 d. green 35 10
898 – 17 d. purple 15 10
899 – 20 d. red 75 10
987 – 20 d. blue 45 10
987a – 20 d. green 45 10
900 – 25 d. grey 35 10
988 – 25 d. red 30 10
901 – 30 d. blue 30 10
989 – 30 d. brown .. .. 4·50 10
989a – 30 d. red 75 10
902 – 35 d. red 30 10
903 – 40 d. red 35 10
904 – 40 d. blue .. .. 1·75 10
990 – 40 d. purple 30 10
905 – 50 d. blue 35 10
991 – 50 d. blue 75 10
906 – 55 d. red .. .. 3·00 10
992 – 65 d. green 20 10
907 – 70 d. red .. .. 1·00 10
908 – 80 d. red .. .. 7·00 10
909 – 100 d. green .. .. 9·00 10
993 – 100 d. green .. .. 3·00 10
994 – 150 d. red .. .. 1·00 15
910 – 200 d. brown .. 3·25 15
995 – 200 d. blue 70 10
996 – 300 d. green .. .. 1·75 30
911 – 500 d. blue .. .. 6·00 35
997 – 500 d. violet .. .. 1·60 10
998 – 1000 d. brown .. 3·00 15
999 – 2000 d. purple .. 7·50 40

DESIGNS—VERT. 2, 100 (993) d. Oil derricks, Nafta. 5 d. Shipbuilding. 8, 17 d. Timber industry, cable railway. 15 (896), 20 d. Jablanica Dam. 15 (986), 25 (900) d. Ljubljana–Zagreb motor road. 25 (988) d. Cable industry. 30 d. "Litostroj" turbine factory, Ljubljana. 35, 40 (990) d. Coke plant, Lukavac. 50 (991) d. Iron foundry, Zenica. 65 d. Furnace, Sovojno. HORIZ. 40 (903/4), 150 d. Hotel, Titograd. 50 (905), 55, 200 (995) d. Skopje. 70, 80, 300 d. Sarajevo railway station and obelisk. 100 (909), 500 (997) d. Bridge, Ljubljana. 200 (910), 1000 d. Theatre, Zagreb. 500 (911), 2000 d. Parliament House, Belgrade.

See also Nos. 1194/1204.

1958. Obligatory Tax. Children's Week.

912. **250.** 2 d. black, olive & yell. 15 5

251. Ship with Oceanographic equipment. **252.** "Human Rights".

1958. I.G.Y.

913. **251.** 15 d. purple (postage) 55 15
914. – 300 d. blue (air) .. 7·50 2·25

DESIGN: 300 d. Moon and earth with orbital tracks of artificial satellites.

1958. 10th Anniv. of Declaration of Human Rights.

915. **252.** 30 d. green 65 45

253. Old City, Dubrovnik. **254.** Communist Party Emblem and Red Flags.

1959. Tourist Publicity (1st series). Views.

916. **253.** 10 d. yellow and red .. 10 5
917. – 10 d. blue and green .. 10 5
918. – 15 d. violet and blue .. 10 5
919. – 15 d. green and blue .. 10 5
920. – 20 d. green and brown 15 5
921. – 20 d. green & turquoise 15 5
922. – 30 d. violet and buff .. 1·00 5
923. – 30 d. green and blue .. 1·00 5
924. – 70 d. black & turquoise 3·00 1·00

DESIGNS: No. 917, Bled. No. 918, Postojna grottoes. No. 919, Ohrid. No. 920, Plitvice Lakes. No. 921, Opatija. No. 922, Split. No. 923, Sveti Stefan. No. 924, Belgrade.

See also Nos. 1033/41, 1080/5 and 1165/70.

1959. 40th Anniv. of Yugoslav Communist Party.

925. **254.** 20 d. multicoloured .. 15 5

255. "Family Assistance". **256.** Dubrovnik (XV Cent.).

1959. Obligatory Tax. Red Cross.

926. **255.** 2 d. blue and red .. 15 5

1959. Philatelic Exhibition, Dubrovnik ("JUFIZ IV").

927. **256.** 20 d. myrtle, green and blue 75 65

257. Lavender. **258.** Tug-of-War.

1959. Medicinal Plants.

928. **257.** 10 d. vio., grn. & blue 10 5
929. – 15 d. multicoloured .. 10 5
930. – 20 d. pur., grn. & bistre 10 5
931. – 25 d. lilac, grn. & olive 20 8
932. – 30 d. grn., blue & pink 25 12
933. – 35 d. blue, grn. & brn. 50 15
934. – 50 d. yell., grn. & brn. 2·00 40
935. – 70 d. multicoloured .. 3·00 75
936. – 100 d. grey, grn. & brn. 5·00 2·00

FLOWERS: 15 d. Black alder. 20 d. Scopolia. 25 d. Monk's-head. 30 d. Bilberry. 35 d. Juniper. 50 d. Cowslip. 70 d. Pomegranate. 100 d. Thorn-apple.

1959. "Partisan" Physical Culture Festival, Belgrade.

937. **258.** 10 d. black and ochre 5 5
938. – 15 d. blue and sepia .. 5 5
939. – 20 d. violet and brown 5 5
940. – 35 d. purple and grey .. 12 5
941. – 40 d. violet and grey .. 20 5
942. – 55 d. green and brown 35 10
943. – 80 d. olive and slate .. 75 40
944. – 100 d. violet and ochre 2·25 75

DESIGNS—HORIZ. 15 d. High-vaulting and running. 20 d. Gymnasium exercise. 35 d. Female exercises with hoops. 40 d. Sailors' exercises. 55 d. Handball and basketball. 80 d. Swimming and diving. VERT. 100 d. "Partisan" Association insignia.

259. Fair Emblem. **260.**

1959. Zagreb Int. Fair.

945. **259.** 20 d. black and blue .. 45 12

1959. Obligatory Tax. Children's Tax.

946. **260.** 2 d. slate and yellow .. 15 5

261. Athletes. **262.** "Reconstruction" (sculpture by L. Dolinar).

1960. Olympic Games.

947. **261.** 15 d. yellow, buff and violet 5 5
948. – 20 d. drab., lav. & blue 8 5
949. – 30 d. bl., stone & ultram. 15 5
950. – 35 d. grey, brn. & purple 15 8
951. – 40 d. drab, green & bronze 20 10
952. – 55 d. blue, drab & grn. 35 12
953. – 80 d. ochre, grey & red 50 25
954. – 100 d. ochre, drab and violet 60 30

DESIGNS: 20 d. Swimming. 30 d. Skiing. 35 d. Graeco-Roman wrestling. 40 d. Cycling. 55 d. Yachting. 80 d. Horse-riding. 100 d. Fencing.

Nos. 948, 950, 952 and 954 are inscr. in Cyrillic characters.

1960. Obligatory Tax. Red Cross.

955. **262.** 2 d. blue and red .. 15 5

1960. Yugoslav Forest Mammals. As T **213.** Animals in natural colours. Background colours given.

956 15 d. blue (West European hedgehog) 10 5
957 20 d. olive (Eurasain red squirrel) 12 5
958 25 d. turq (Pine marten) 15 5
959 30 d. olive (Brown hare) .. 20 5
960 35 d. brown (Red fox) .. 25 10
961 40 d. lake (Eurasian badger) 30 10
962 55 d. blue (Wolf) 45 20
963 80 d. violet (Roe deer) .. 70 20
964 100 d. red (Wild boar) .. 1·25 90

263. Lenin. **264.** Accelerator.

1960. 90th Birth Anniv. of Lenin.

965. **263.** 20 d. grey and green .. 12 5

1960. Nuclear Energy Exn., Belgrade.

966. **264.** 15 d. green 10 5
967. – 20 d. red 10 5
968. – 40 d. blue 20 12

DESIGNS: 20 d. Neutron generator. 40 d. Nuclear reactor.

265. Young Girl. **266.** Serbian National Theatre. Novi Sad (Centenary).

1960. Obligatory Tax. Children's Week.

969. **265.** 2 d. red 12 5

1960. Jubilee Annivs.

970. **266.** 15 d. black 10 10
971. – 20 d. sepia 10 10
972. – 40 d. blue 10 10
973. – 55 d. purple 15 10
974. – 80 d. green 15 10

DESIGNS: 20 d. Part of "Illyrian Renaissance" (allegorical figure), after V. Bukovac (Cent. of Croat National Theatre, Zagreb). 40 d. Edward Rusijan and "Bleriot" plane (50th Anniv. of 1st Flight in Yugoslavia). 55 d. Symbolic hand holding fruit (15th Anniv. of Republic). 80 d. Symbol of nuclear energy (15th Anniv. of U.N.O.).

1960. Cultural Annivs. Portraits as T **217.**

975. 15 d. green 5 5
976. 20 d. brown 8 5
977. 40 d. bistre 12 5
978. 55 d. red 20 5
979. 80 d. blue 40 5
980. 100 d. turquoise 40 15

PORTRAITS: 15 d. I. Cankar (writer). 20 d. S. S. Kranjcevic (poet). 40 d. P. Jovanovic (painter). 55 d. D. Jaksic (writer). 80 d. M. Pupin (physician). 100 d. R. Boskovic (astronomer).

268. "Blood Transfusion". **269.** "Atomic Energy".

1961. Obligatory Tax. Red Cross. Perf. or imperf.

981. **268.** 2 d. multicoloured .. 15 5

1961. Int. Nuclear Electronic Conf., Belgrade.

982. **288.** 25 d. blue, red and grey 15 5

271. Stevan Filipovic (statue by V. Bakic). **273.** St. Clement (14th-century wood-carving).

272.

1961. Medicinal Plants. As T **257.** Mult.

1000. 10 d. Yellow foxglove .. 5 5
1001. 15 d. Marjoram 5 5
1002. 20 d. Hyssop 8 5
1003. 25 d. Whitethorn .. 10 5
1004. 40 d. Rosemallow .. 12 5
1005. 50 d. Soapwort 15 5
1006. 60 d. Clary-sage 25 10
1007. 80 d. Blackthorn .. 40 10
1008. 100 d. Marigold 90 40

See also Nos. 1074/9.

1961. 20th Anniv. of Yugoslav Insurrection. Inscriptions in gold.

1009. **271.** 15 d. brown and red .. 5 5
1010. – 20 d. yellow and sepia 8 5
1011. – 25 d. green and turq. 10 5
1012. – 60 d. violet and blue 15 10
1013. – 100 d. indigo and blue 30 20

DESIGNS: 20 d. Insurrection Monument, Bosansko Grahovo (relief by S. Stojanovic). 25 d. Executed Inhabitants Monument, Kragujevac (by A. Grzetic). 60 d. Nova Gradiska Victory Monument (by A. Augustincic). 100 d. Marshal Tito (Revolution Monument, Titovo Uzice, statue by F. Krsinic).

1961. Non-Aligned Countries Conf., Belgrade.

1014. **272.** 25 d. sepia (postage) 10 5
1015. – 50 d. green 20 5

1016. **272.** 250 d. purple (air) .. 1·00 50
1017. – 500 d. blue .. .. 2·50 1·25

DESIGN: 50 d., 500 d. National Assembly Building, Belgrade.

1961. 12th Int. Congress of Byzantine Studies, Ochrida.

1018. **273.** 25 d. sepia and olive 20 5

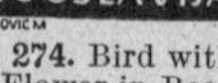

274. Bird with Flower in Beak. **275.** L. Vukalovic (revolutionary leader).

1961. Obligatory Tax. Children's Week.

1019. **274.** 2 d. orange and violet 12 5

1961. Yugoslav Costumes (2nd series). As T **239**. Inscr. "1941–1961".
1020. 15 d. multicoloured .. 15 5
1021. 25 d. black, red & brown 15 5
1022. 30 d. sepia, red & brown 25 5
1023. 50 d. multicoloured .. 35 8
1024. 65 d. multicoloured .. 45 10
1025. 100 d. multicoloured .. 1·60 50
DESIGNS—HORIZ. Costumes of: 15 d. Serbia. 25 d. Montenegro. 30 d. Bosnia and Herzegovina. 50 d. Macedonia. 65 d. Croatia. 100 d. Slovenia.

1961. Cent. of Herzegovina Insurrection.
1026. **275.** 25 d. black 15 10

276. Hands holding Flower and Rifle. **277.** Miladinovci Brothers.

1961. Yugoslav Partisan Army. 20th Anniv.
1027. **276.** 25 d. blue and red .. 20 5

1961. Centenary of Macedonian National Songs by brothers Miladinovci.
1028. **277.** 25 d. purple and buff 20 5

278. "Mother's Play" (after F. Krainio). **279.** Mosquito.

1962. 15th Anniv. of U.N.I.C.E.F.
1029. **278.** 50 d. black on buff .. 12 5

1962. Malaria Eradication.
1030 **279** 50 d. black on blue .. 15 10

280. Goddess Isis (from temple at Kalabscha). **281.** Bandages and Symbols.

1962. 15th Anniv. of U.N.E.S.C.O.
1031 **280.** 25 d. green on cream 10 5
1032. – 50 d. brown on buff .. 20 8
DESIGN: 50 d. Rameses II (Nubian monument) and U.N.E.S.C.O. emblem.

1962. Tourist Publicity (2nd series). Views as T **253**. Inscr. "1941–1961".
1033. 15 d. olive and blue .. 15 5
1034. 15 d. olive and turq .. 15 5
1035. 25 d. brown and blue .. 20 5
1036. 25 d. blue and light blue 20 5
1037. 30 d. blue and brown .. 30 5
1038. 30 d. blue and purple .. 50 5
1039. 50 d. turq. and bistre .. 1·25 5
1040. 50 d. blue and bistre .. 1·25 5
1041. 100 d. grey and green .. 5·00 60
VIEWS: No. 1033, Portoroz. No. 1034, Jajce. No. 1035, Zadar. No. 1036, Popova Sapka. No. 1037, Hvar. No. 1038, Kotor Bay. No. 1039, Derdap. No. 1040, Rab. No. 1041, Zagreb.

1962. Obligatory Tax. Red Cross.
1042. **281.** 5 d. red, brn. & grey 12 5

282. Marshal Tito (after sculpture by A. Augustincic). **283.** Pole-vaulting.

1962. Marshal Tito's 70th Birthday.
1043. **282.** 25 d. turquoise .. 10 5
1044. – 50 d. brown 20 5
1045. **282.** 100 d. blue 65 20
1046. – 200 d. myrtle .. 1·50 75
DESIGN: 50 d., 200 d. As Type **282** but profile view of bust.

1962. Yugoslav Amphibians and Reptiles. As T **213**. Inscr. "1962". Animals in natural colours. Background colours given.
1047. 15 d. green (Crested Newt) 12 5
1048. 20 d. violet (Spotted salamander) 12 5
1049. 25 d. brown (Yellow-bellied toad) 12 5
1050. 30 d. blue (Marsh frog) 15 5
1051. 50 d. brown (Pond Tortoise) 20 5
1052. 65 d. green (Wall lizard) 25 10
1053. 100 d. black (Green Lizard) 40 25
1054. 150 d. brn. (Leopard snake) 1·00 50
1055. 200 d. red (Common viper) 2·25 1·10

1962. 7th European Athletic Championships, Belgrade. Sportsmen in black.
1056. **283.** 15 d. blue 5 5
1057. – 25 d. purple 8 5
1058. – 30 d. green 10 5
1059. – 50 d. red 10 5
1060. – 65 d. bright blue .. 15 5
1061. – 100 d. turquoise .. 25 12
1062. – 150 d. orange .. 35 20
1063. – 200 d. brown .. 65 40
DESIGNS—HORIZ. 25 d. Throwing the discus. 50 d. Throwing the javelin. 100 d. Start of sprint. 200 d. High jumping. VERT. 30 d. Running. 65 d. Putting the shot. 150 d. Hurdling.

284. Physical Culture. **285.** "Bathing the Newborn Child" (Decani Monastery).

1962. Children's Week.
1064. **284.** 25 d. black and red 15 5

1962. Yugoslav Art. Multicoloured.
1065. 25 d. Situla of Vace (detail from bronze vessel) .. 8 5
1066. 30 d. Golden Mask of Trebiniste (5th-cent. burial mask) (horiz.) .. 10 5
1067. 50 d. The God Kairos (Trogir Monastery) .. 15 5
1068. 65 d. Pigeons of Nerezi (detail from series of frescoes, "The Visitation", Nerezi Church, Skopje) 25 20
1069. 100 d. Type **285** 55 30
1070. 150 d. Icon of Ohrid (detail from 14th-cent. icon, "The Annunciation") 1·10 75
The 25 d., 30 d. and 150 d. are horiz.
See also Nos. 1098/1103.

286. Ear of Wheat and Parched Earth. **287.** Dr. A. Mohorovicic (meteorologist).

1963. Freedom from Hunger.
1071. **286.** 50 d. purple on stone 20 5

1963. World Meteorological Day.
1072. **287.** 50 d. blue on grey .. 20 5

288. Centenary Emblem. **289.** Partisans in file.

1963. Obligatory Tax. Red Cross Cent. and Red Cross Week.
1073. **288.** 5 d. red, grey and ochre 20 5

1963. Medicinal Plants. As T **257** but dated "1963". Flowers in natural colours. Colours of backgrounds, panels and inscr. given.
1074. 15 d. dull grn., grn. & blk. 12 5
1075. 25 d. cobalt, blue & violet 12 5
1076. 30 d. grey and blue .. 12 5
1077. 50 d. pale brown & brown 20 10
1078. 65 d. pale brown & brown 40 15
1079. 100 d. slate and deep slate 1·40 40
FLOWERS: 15 d. Lily of the Valley. 25 d. Iris. 30 d. Bistort. 50 d. Henbane. 65 d. St. John's wort. 100 d. Caraway.

1963. Tourist Publicity (3rd series). Views as T **253**. Inscr. "1963". Multicoloured.
1080. 15 d. Pula 10 5
1081. 25 d. Vrnjacka Banja .. 10 5
1082. 30 d. Crikvenica .. 10 5
1083. 50 d. Korcula 15 8
1084. 65 d. Durmitor 15 12
1085. 100 d. Ljubljana 90 25

1963. 20th Anniv. of Battle of Sutjeska River.
1086. **289.** 15 d. green and drab 10 5
1087. – 25 d. green 10 5
1088. – 50 d. violet & pale brn. 20 5
DESIGNS—VERT. 25 d. Sutjeska Gorge. HORIZ. 50 d. Partisans in battle.
See also No. 1125.

290. Gymnast on "Horse". **291.** "Mother".

1963. 5th European Cup Gymnastic Championships.
1089. **290.** 25 d. green and black 8 5
1090. – 50 d. blue and black .. 15 12
1091. – 100 d. brown and black 50 45
DESIGNS (Gymnast): 50 d. on parallel bars. 100 d. exercising with rings.

1963. Sculptures by Ivan Mestrovic.
1092. **291.** 25 d. bistre on pale brn. 10 5
1093. – 50 d. olive on pale olive 15 10
1094. – 65 d. green on pale blue 50 30
1095. – 100 d. blk. on pale grey 65 50
SCULPTURES: 50 d. "Reminiscence" (nude female figure). 65 d. "Kraljevic Marko" (head). 100 d. "Indian on horseback".

292. Children with Toys. **293.** Soldier and Emblem.

1963. Children's Week.
1096. **292.** 25 d. multicoloured .. 25 5

1963. 20th Anniv. of Yugoslav Democratic Federation.
1097. **293.** 25 d. red, olive & drab 12 5

1963. Yugoslav Art. Designs as T **285**. Inscr. "1963". Multicoloured.
1098. 25 d. "Man", relief on Radimlje tombstone (13th–15th cents.) .. 10 5
1099. 30 d. Detail of relief on door of Split Cathedral, after A. Buvina (13th-cent.) 10 5
1100. 50 d. Detail of fresco in Beram Church (15th cent.) 15 8
1101. 65 d. Archangel Michael, from plaque in Dominican Monastery, Dubrovnik (15th-cent.) .. 20 12
1102. 100 d. Figure of man on Baroque fountain, by F. Robba, Ljubljana (18th-cent.) 25 15
1103. 150 d. Archbishop Eufraise—detail of mosaic in Porec Basilica (6th-cent.) 70 70
The 30 d. and 50 d. are horiz.

294. D. Obradovic (writer). **295.** Parachute.

1963. Cultural Celebrities.
1104. **294.** 25 d. blk. on pale buff 10 5
1105. – 30 d. blk. on pale blue 10 5
1106. – 50 d. blk. on pale cream 15 5
1107. – 65 d. blk. on pale lilac 25 20
1108. – 100 d. blk. on pale pink 40 35
PORTRAITS: 30 d. V. S. Karadzic (language reformer). 50 d. F. Miklosic (philologist) 65 d. L. Gaj (writer). 100 d. P. P. Njegos (poet).
See also Nos. 1174/9.

1964. Obligatory Tax. Red Cross Week and 20th Anniv. of Yugoslav Red Cross.
1109. **295.** 5 d. red, purple & blue 15 5

296. "Inachis io.". **297.** Fireman saving Child.

1964. Butterflies. Multicoloured.
1110 25 d. Type **296** 10 5
1111 30 d. "Nymphalis antiopa" 10 5
1112 40 d. "Daphnis nerii" .. 10 5
1113 50 d. "Parnassius apollo" 12 5
1114 150 d. "Nyctaon pyri" .. 45 25
1115 200 d. "Papilio machaon" 65 35

1964. Cent. of Voluntary Fire Brigade.
1116. **297.** 25 d. sepia and red .. 20 5

298. Running. **299.** "Reconstruction".

1964. Olympic Games, Tokyo.
1117. **298.** 25 d. yell., blk. & grey 5 5
1118. – 30 d. vio., blk. & grey 5 5
1119. – 40 d. grn., blk. & grey 8 5
1120. – 50 d. multicoloured .. 12 5
1121. – 150 d. multicoloured 20 15
1122. – 200 d. blue, blk. & grey 30 25
DESIGNS: 30 d. Boxing. 40 d. Rowing. 50 d. Basketball. 150 d. Football. 200 d. Water-polo.

1964. 1st Anniv. of Skopje Earthquake.
1123. **299.** 25 d. brown .. 15 5
1124. – 50 d. blue 20 5
DESIGN: 50 d. "International Aid" (U.N. flag over town).

1964. 20th Anniv. of Occupation of Vis Island. As T **289** but inscr. "VIS 1944–1964" at foot.
1125. 25 d. lake and grey .. 12 5

300. Costumes of Kosovo-Metohija (Serbia). **301.** F. Engels.

1964. Yugoslav Costumes (3rd series). As T **300**. Multicoloured.
1126. 25 d. Type **300** 10 5
1127. 30 d. Slovenia 12 5
1128. 40 d. Bosnia and Herzegovina 15 5
1129. 50 d. Hrvatska (Croatia) 15 5
1130. 150 d. Macedonia .. 65 25
1131. 200 d. Crna Gora (Montenegro) 85 40

1964. Cent. of "1st International".
1132. **301.** 25 d. black on cream 8 5
1133. – 50 d. black on lilac .. 15 5
DESIGN: 50 d. Karl Marx.

302. Children on Scooter. **303.** "Victor" (after Ivan Mestrovic).

1964. Children's Week.
1134. **302.** 25 d. grn., blk. & red 20 5

1964. 20th Anniv. of Liberation of Belgrade.
1135. **303.** 25 d. black and olive on pink 10 5

304. Initial of Hilander's Gospel (13th cent.). **305.** "Hand of Equality".

1964. Yugoslav Art. Inscr. "1964". Mult.
1136. 25 d. Type **304** 10 5
1137. 30 d. Initial of Miroslav's gospel (12th cent.) .. 10 5
1138. 40 d. Detail from Cetinje octateuch (15th cent.) 10 5
1139. 50 d. Miniature from Trogir's gospel (13th cent.) .. 10 5
1140. 150 d. Miniature from Hrvoe's missal (15th cent.) 30 10
1141. 200 d. Miniature from Herman Priory, Bistrica (14th cent.) (horiz.) .. 55 40

1964. 8th Yugoslav Communist League Congress. Multicoloured.
1142. 25 d. Type **305** 5 5
1143. 50 d. Dove and factory ("Peace & Socialism") 10 5
1144. 100 d. Industrial plant ("Socialism") .. 25 20

306. Table-tennis Player. **307.** Children around Red Cross.

1965. World Table-tennis Championships Ljubljana.
1145. **306.** 50 d. multicoloured .. 15 5
1146. – 150 d. multicoloured 35 20
DESIGN: 150 d. As Type **306** but design arranged in reverse.

1965. Obligatory Tax. Red Cross Week.
1147. **307.** 5 d. red and brown .. 10 5

308. Titograd. **309.** Young Partisan (after D. Andrejevic-Kun).

1965. 20th Anniv. of Liberation. Yugoslav Capitals.
1148. **308.** 25 d. purple 10 5
1149. – 30 d. brown 10 5
1150. – 40 d. violet 10 5
1151. – 50 d. green 10 5
1152. – 150 d. violet 25 10
1153. – 200 d. blue 50 45
CAPITALS: 30 d. Skopje. 40 d. Sarajevo. 50 d. Ljubljana. 150 d. Zagreb. 200 d. Belgrade.

1965. "Twenty Years of Freedom" Pioneer Games.
1154. **309.** 25 d. blk. & brn. on buff 12 5

310. T. V. Tower, Avala (Belgrade). **311.** Yarrow.

1965. Centenary of I.T.U.
1155. **310.** 50 d. blue 12 5

1965. Inauguration of Djerdap Hydro-Electric Project. As Nos. 3271/2 of Rumania.
1156. – 25 d. (30 b.) grn. & grey 15 5
1157. – 50 d. (55 b.) red & grey 30 5
DESIGN: 25 d. Djerdap Gorge. 50 d. Djerdap Dam.
Nos. 1156/7 were issued simultaneously in Rumania.

1965. Medicinal Plants. Multicoloured.
1158. 25 d. Type **311** 12 5
1159. 30 d. Rosemary 12 5
1160. 40 d. Inula 12 5
1161. 50 d. Belladonna 20 8
1162. 150 d. Mint 35 12
1163. 200 d. Digitalis 70 40

312. I.C.Y. Emblem. **313.** Sibenik.

1965. Int. Co-operation Year.
1164. **312.** 50 d. violet, indigo and blue 12 5

1965. Tourist Publicity (4th series). Mult.
1165. 25 d. Rogaska Slatina .. 10 5
1166. 30 d. Type **313** 10 5
1167. 40 d. Prespa Lake .. 10 5
1168. 50 d. Prizren 10 5
1169. 150 d. Skadar Lake .. 25 10
1170. 200 d. Sarajevo 40 40

314. Cat. **316.** Marshal Tito.

1965. Children's Week.
1171. **314.** 30 d. lake and yellow 40 5

1965. Nos. 984 and 988 surch.
1172. 5 d. on 8 d. violet .. 40 5
1173. 50 d. on 25 d. red .. 40 8

1965. Cultural Celebrities. Portraits as T **294**.
1174. 30 d. red on pink .. 5 5
1175. 50 d. slate on blue .. 8 5
1176. 60 d. sepia on brown .. 10 5
1177. 85 d. indigo on blue .. 12 5
1178. 200 d. olive on pale olive 15 15
1179. 500 d. mauve on purple 35 30
PORTRAITS: 30 d. B. Nusic (author and dramatist). 50 d. A. G. Matos (poet). 60 d. I. Mazuranic (author). 85 d. F. Levstik. 200 d. J. Pancic (botanist). 500 d. D. Tucovic (politician).

(Currency revalued. 100 paras = 1 dinar (= 100 old dinars).)

1966.
1180. **316.** 20 p. green 25 5
1181. 30 p. red 45 5

317. Jumping (Balkan Games, Sarajevo). **318.** "T", 15th-cent. Psalter.

1966. Sports Events.
1182. **317.** 30 p. red 5 5
1183. – 50 p. violet 8 5
1184. – 1 d. green 10 5
1185. – 3 d. brown 20 12
1186. – 5 d. blue 45 35
DESIGNS AND EVENTS: 50 p. Ice-Hockey and 3 d. Ice-hockey sticks and puck. (World Ice-hockey Championships—Jesenice, Ljubljana, Zagreb). 1 d. Rowing and 5 d. Oras (World Rowing Championships, Bled).

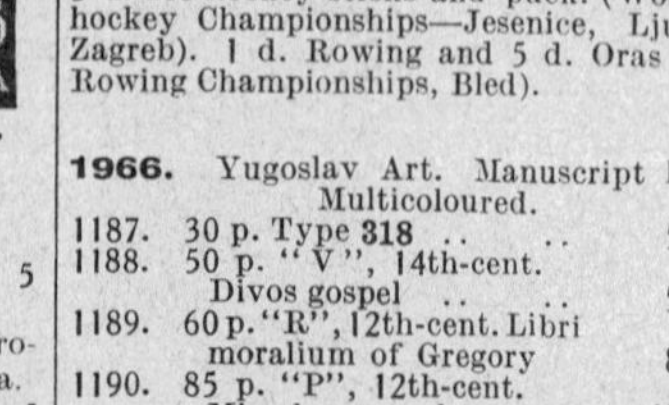

1966. Yugoslav Art. Manuscript Initials. Multicoloured.
1187. 30 p. Type **318** 5 5
1188. 50 p. "V", 14th-cent. Divos gospel 5 5
1189. 60 p. "R", 12th-cent. Libri moralium of Gregory 8 5
1190. 85 p. "P", 12th-cent. Miroslav gospel .. 15 12
1191. 2 d. "B", 13th-cent. Radomir gospel .. 25 15
1192. 5 d. "F", 11th-cent. passional 45 30

319. Red Cross Emblem. **320.** Beam Aerial on Globe.

1966. Obligatory Tax. Red Cross Week.
1193. **319.** 5 p multicoloured .. 10 5

1966. As Nos. 983, etc., but values expressed "0.05" etc., colours changed and new values.
1194. 5 p. orange 10 10
1195. 10 p. brown 10 10
1196. 15 p. blue 20 10
1197. 20 p. green 25 10
1198. 30 p. red 75 10
1199. 40 p. purple 30 10
1200. 50 p. blue 30 10
1201. 60 p. brown 30 10
1202. 65 p. green 30 10
1203. 85 p. purple 40 10
1204. 1 d. olive 65 10
NEW VALUES: 60 p. as No. 988, 85 p. as No. 984.

1966. Int. Amateur Radio Union Regional Conf., Opatija.
1205. **320.** 85 p. blue 15 5

321. "Lucanus cervus". **322.** Serbian 1 para Stamp of 1866.

1966. Insects. Multicoloured.
1206 30 p. Type **321** 10 5
1207 50 p. "Cetonia aurata" .. 10 5
1208 60 p. "Meloe violaceus" .. 10 5
1209 85 p. "Coccinella septempunctata" .. 12 5
1210 2 d. "Rosalia alpina" .. 25 15
1211 5 d. "Dytiscus marginalis" .. 55 25

1966. Serbian Stamp Cent.
1212. **322.** 30 p. green, lake & brn. 5 5
1213. – 50 p. lake, bis. & ochre 8 5
1214. – 60 p. orange and green 10 5
1215. – 85 p. red and blue .. 15 15
1216. – 2 d. bl., bronze & grn. 45 25
DESIGNS (Serbian stamps of 1866): 50 p. 2 p. 50 p.—10 p. 85 p.—20 p. 2 d.—40 p.

323. Rebels on Shield. **324.** Strossmayer and Racki (founders).

1966. 25th Anniv. of Yugoslav Insurrection.
1218. **323.** 20 p. brn., gold & grn. 5 5
1219. 30 p. mve., gold & buff 5 5
1220. 85 p. blue, gold & stone 10 5
1221. 2 d. violet, gold & blue 15 15

1966. Cent. of Yugoslav Academy.
1222. **324.** 30 p. black and drab 15 5

325. Old Bridge, Mostar. **325a.** Medieval View of Sibenik.

1966. 400th Anniv of Old Bridge, Mostar.
1223 **325** 30 p. purple .. 75 5

1966. 900th Anniv. of Sibenik.
1224. **325a.** 30 p. purple .. 20 10

326. "The Girl in Pigtails".

1966. Children's Week.
1225. **326.** 30 p. multicoloured 50 5

327. U.N.E.S.C.O. Emblem. **328.** Stylised Winter Landscape.

1966. 20th Anniv. of U.N.E.S.C.O.
1226. **327.** 85 p. blue 20 10

1966. Christmas.
1227. **328.** 15 p. yellow and blue 5 5
1228. – 20 p. yellow and blue 5 5
1229. – 30 p. yellow and green 5 5
DESIGNS: 20 p. Father Christmas. 30 p. Stylised Christmas tree.
See also Nos. 1236/8.

329. Dinar of Durad I Balsic. **330.** Flower between Red Crosses.

1966. Yugoslav Art. Designs showing different coins.
1230. **329.** 30 p. multicoloured .. 10 5
1231. – 50 p. multicoloured .. 10 5
1232. – 60 p. multicoloured .. 10 5
1233. – 85 p. multicoloured .. 10 5
1234. – 2 d. multicoloured .. 30 12
1235. – 5 d. multicoloured .. 70 30
MEDIEVAL COINS (Dinars of): 50 p. King Stefan Tomasevic. 60 p. Durad Brankovic. 85 p. Ljubljana. 2 d. Split. 5 d. Emperor Stefan Dusan.

1966. New Year. As Nos. 1227/9 but colours changed.
1236. 15 p. gold, blue & indigo 15 12
1237. 20 p. gold, red and pink 15 12
1238. 30 p. gold, myrtle & green 15 12

1967. Obligatory Tax. Red Cross Week.
1239. **330.** 5 p. red, green & blue 8 5

331. "Arnica montana". **332.** President Tito.

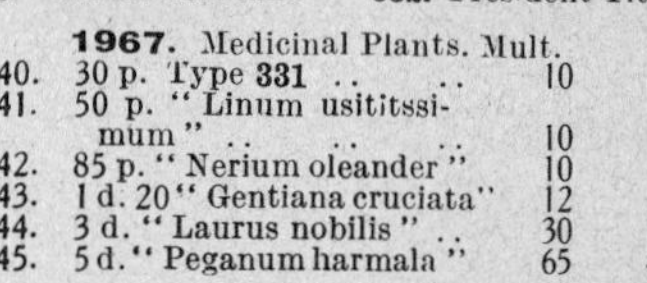

1967. Medicinal Plants. Mult.
1240. 30 p. Type **331** 10 5
1241. 50 p. "Linum usititssimum" .. 10 5
1242. 85 p. "Nerium oleander" 10 5
1243. 1 d. 20 "Gentiana cruciata" 12 5
1244. 3 d. "Laurus nobilis" .. 30 10
1245. 5 d. "Peganum harmala" 65 40

1967. Pres. Tito's 75th Birthday.
(a) Size as Type **332.**
1256. **332.** 5 p. orange 12 5
1257. 10 p. brown 12 5
1258. 15 p. violet 12 5
1259. 20 p. green 15 5
1260. 20 p. blue .. .. 1·50 5
1261. 25 p. red 15 5
1262a. 30 p. red .. .. 1·50 5
1263. 30 p. myrtle 30 5
1264. 40 p. black 15 5
1265. 50 p. turquoise .. 2·00 5
1266a. 50 p. red 30 5
1267. 60 p. purple 15 5
1268. 70 p. sepia 40 5
1269. 75 p. green 50 5
1270. 80 p. brown .. .. 2·25 5
1270a. 80 p. red 45 5
1271. 85 p. blue 50 5
1272. 90 p. brown 35 5
1273. 1 d. lake 25 15
1274. 1 d. 20 blue 75 5
1274a. 1 d. 20 green 70 5
1275. 1 d. 25 blue 55 5
1276 1 d. 50 green 50 5
(b) Size 20 × 30 mm.
1277. **332.** 2 d. sepia .. .. 1·50 5
1278. 2 d. 50 green .. .. 1·50 5
1279. 5 d. purple .. .. 1·25 20
1280. 10 d. purple .. .. 3·00 35
1281. 20 d. green .. .. 2·75 40

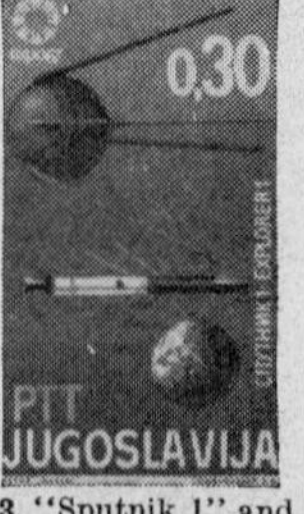

333. "Sputnik 1" and "Explorer 1". **334.** St. Tripun's Church, Kotor.

1967. World Fair, Montreal. Space Achievements. Multicoloured.
1282. 30 p. Type **333** 5 5
1283. 50 p. "Tiros", "Telstar" and "Molyna" .. 8 5
1284. 85 p. "Luna 9" and lunar orbiter 10 5
1285. 1 d. 20 "Mariner 4" and "Venus 3" .. 12 5
1286. 3 d. "Vostok 1" and Gemini-Agena space vehicle 15 15
1287. 5 d. Leonov in space .. 50 50

1967. Int. Tourist Year.
1288. **334.** 30 p. olive and blue .. 5 5
1289. – 50 p. violet and brown 5 5
1290. – 85 p. purple and blue 10 5
1291. – 1 d. 20 brown & purple 15 5
1292. – 3 d. olive and brown 40 10
1293. – 5 d. brn. & olive-brn. 60 55
DESIGNS: 50 p. Town Hall, Maribor. 85 p. Trogir Cathedral. 1 d. 20, Fortress gate, Nis. 3 d. Bridge, Visegrad. 5 d. Ancient bath, Skopje.

335. Bobwhite. **336.** Congress Emblem.

1967. Int. Hunting and Fishing Exn. and Fair, Novi Sad. Multicoloured.
1294. 30 p. Type **335** 40 10
1295. 50 p. Pike 15 5
1296. 1 d. 20 Red deer 25 10
1297. 5 d. Peregrine falcon .. 2·00 55

1967. Int. Astronautical Federation Congress, Belgrade.
1298. **336.** 85 p. gold light blue and blue 15 5

337. Old Theatre Building. **338.** "Winter Landscape" (A. Becirovic).

1967. Centenary of Slovene National Theatre, Ljubljana.
1299. **337.** 30 p. brown and green 12 5

1967. Children's Week.
1300. **338.** 30 p. multicoloured 50 5

339. "Lenin" (from bust by Ivan Mestrovic). **340.** Four-leaved Clover.

1967. 50th Anniv. of October Revolution.
1301. **339.** 30 p. violet 5 5
1302. 85 p. brown 15 5

1967. New Year. Inscr. "1968".
1304. **340.** 20 p. gold, blue & grn. 5 5
1305. – 30 p. gold, violet and yellow 5 5
1306. – 50 p. gold, red and lilac 10 5
DESIGNS: 30 p. Sweep with ladder. 50 p. Horseshoe and flower.
See also Nos. 1347/9.

341. "The Young Sultana" (V. Bukovac).

1967. Yugoslav Paintings (1st series). Multicoloured.
1307. 85 p. "The Watchtower" (D. Jaksic) 10 8
1308. 1 d. Type **341** 12 10
1309. 2 d. "At Home" (J. Petkovsek) .. 20 15
1310. 3 d. "The Cock-fight" (P. Jovanovic) .. 30 25
1311. 5 d. "Summer" (I. Kobilca) 50 40
The 85 p. and 5d. are vert.
See also Nos. 1337/41, 1399/1404, 1438/43 1495/1500, 1535/40, 1570/5, 1616/19, 1750/5 and 1793/8.

MINIMUM PRICE

The minimum price quoted is 5p which represents a handling charge rather than a basis for valuing common stamps. For further notes about prices see introductory pages.

342. Ski-jumping.

1968. Winter Olympic Games. Grenoble.
1312. **342.** 50 p. purple and blue 5 5
1313. – 1 d. olive and brown 10 5
1314. – 2 d. lake and black .. 15 10
1315. – 5 d. blue and olive .. 50 40
DESIGNS: 1 d. Figure-skating (pairs). 2 d. Downhill skiing. 5 d. Ice-hockey.

343. "The Madonna and Child" (St. George's Church, Prizren). **344.** Honeycomb on Red Cross.

1968. Medieval Icons. Multicoloured.
1316. 50 p. Type **343** 5 5
1317. 1 d. "The Annunciation" (Ohrid Museum) .. 15 5
1318. 1 d. 50 "St. Sava and St. Simeon" (Belgrade Museum) 20 8
1319. 2 d. "The Descent" (Ohrid Museum) .. 30 20
1320. 3 d. "The Crucifixion" (St. Clement's Church, Ohrid) 35 25
1321. 5 d. "The Madonna and Child" (Gospe od zvonika Church, Split) .. 75 75

1968. Obligatory Tax. Red Cross Week.
1322. **344.** 5 p. multicoloured .. 8 5

345. Bullfinch. **346.** Running (Women's 800 metres).

1968. Song Birds. Multicoloured.
1323. 50 p. Type **345** 12 5
1324. 1 d. Goldfinch 15 5
1325. 1 d. 50 Chaffinch 30 8
1326. 2 d. Greenfinch 35 12
1327. 3 d. Red Crossbill .. 75 15
1328. 5 d. Hawfinch .. .. 1·10 50

1968. Olympic Games, Mexico.
1329. 50 p. pur. & brn. on cream 8 5
1330. 1 d. olive & turq. on grn. 10 5
1331. 1 d. 50 sep. & bl. on flesh 12 5
1332. 2 d. grn. & bistre on cream 15 10
1333. 3 d. indigo & violet on blue 15 10
1334. 5 d. pur. & grn. on mauve 35 40
DESIGNS: 50 p. Type **346**. 1 d. Basketball. 1 d. 50, Gymnastics. 2 d. Sculling. 3 d. Water-polo. 5 d. Wrestling.

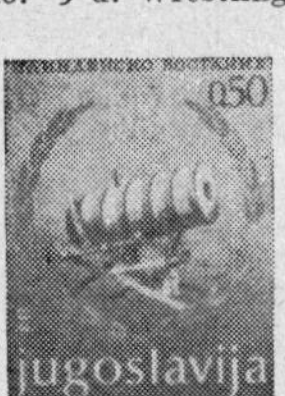

347. Rebel Cannon. **348.** "Mother and Children" (fresco in Hrastovlje Church, Slovenia).

1968. 65th Anniv. of Ilinden Uprising.
1335. **347.** 50 p. brown and gold 12 5

1968. 25th Anniv. of Partisan Occupation of Istria and Slovenian Littoral.
1336. **348.** 50 p. multicoloured .. 10 5

349. "Lake of Klansko" (M. Pernhart).

1968. Yugoslav Paintings (2nd series). 19th-cent. Landscapes. Multicoloured.
1337. 1 d. Type **349** 10 5
1338. 1 d. 50 "Bavarian Landscape" (M. Popovic) .. 15 5
1339. 2 d. "Gateway, Zadar" (F. Quiquerez) .. 25 5
1340. 3 d. "Triglav from Bohinj" (A. Karinger) .. 35 20
1341. 5 d. "Studenica Monastery" (D. Krstic) .. 85 90

350. A. Santic. **351.** "Promenade" (Marina Cudov).

1968. Birth Cent. of Aleksa Santic (poet).
1342. **350.** 50 p. blue 10 5

1968. Children's Week.
1343. **351.** 50 p. multicoloured 15 5

352. Karl Marx (after sculpture by N. Mitric). **353.** Aztec Emblem and Olympic Rings.

1968. 150th Birth Anniv. of Karl Marx.
1344. **352.** 50 p. lake 10 5

1968. Obligatory Tax. Olympic Games Fund.
1345. **353.** 10 p. multicoloured 5 5

354. Old Theatre and view of Kalimegdan. **355.** Hasan Brkic.

1968. Centenary of Serbian National Theatre, Belgrade.
1346. **354.** 50 p. bistre and green 10 5

1968. New Year. Designs as Nos. 1304/6 but colours changed and inscr. "1969".
1347. 20 p. gold, blue and lilac 5 5
1348. 30 p. gold, violet & green 5 5
1349. 50 p. gold, red and lemon 10 5

1968. Yugoslav National Heroes.
1350. **355.** 50 p. violet 8 5
1351. – 75 p. black 12 5
1352. – 1 d. 25 brown .. 15 8
1353. – 2 d. blue 20 10
1354. – 2 d. 50 green .. 25 15
1355. – 5 d. lake 60 60
PORTRAITS: 75 p. Milutinovic. 1 d. 25, R. Koncar. 2 d. K. Josifovski. 2 d. 50, T. Tomsic. 5 d. M. Pijade.

356. "Family" (sculpture by J. Soldatovic) and Human Rights Emblem. **357.** I.L.O. Emblem.

1968. Human Rights Year.
1357. **357.** 1 d. 25 blue 10 5

1969. 50th Anniv. of I.L.O.
1358. **357.** 1 d. 25 black and red 10 5

358. Dove on Hammer and Sickle Emblem **359.** "St. Nikita" (Manasija Monastery).

1969. 50th Anniv. of Yugoslav Communist Party.
1359. **358.** 50 p. red and black .. 10 5
1360. – 75 p. black and ochre 10 5
1361. – 1 d. 25 black and red 15 8
DESIGNS: 75 p. "Tito" and star (wall graffiti). 1 d. 25 Five-pointed crystal formation.

1969. Medieval Frescoes in Yugoslav Monasteries. Multicoloured.
1363. 50 p. Type **359** 10 5
1364. 75 p. "Jesus and the Apostles" (Sopocani) .. 10 5
1365. 1 d. 25 "The Crucifixion" (Studenica) 12 5
1366. 2 d. "Cana Wedding Feast" (Kalenic) .. 20 5
1367. 3 d. "Angel guarding Tomb" (Milesava) .. 20 5
1368. 5 d. "Mourning over Christ" (Nerezi) .. 90 90

360. Roman Memorial and View of Ptuj. **361.** Vasil Glavinov.

1969. 1900th Anniv. of Ptuj (Poetovio) (Slovene town).
1369. **360.** 50 p. brown 8 5

1969. Birth Centenary of Vasil Glavinov (Macedonian revolutionary).
1370. **361.** 50 p. purple & brown 8 5

362. Globe between Hands. **363.** Single Peony.

1969. Obligatory Tax. Red Cross Week.
1371. **362.** 20 p. black, red and deep red 8 5

1969. Flowers. Multicoloured.
1372. 50 p. Type **363** 10 5
1373. 75 p. Coltsfoot 15 5
1374. 1 d. 25 Primrose .. 15 5
1375. 2 d. Christmas Rose .. 25 8
1376. 2 d. 50 Violet 30 10
1377. 5 d. Pasque flower .. 85 75

364. "Eber" (V. Ivankovic).

1969. Dubrovnik Summer Festival. Sailing Ships. Multicoloured.
1378. 50 p. Type **364** 10 5
1379. 1 d. 25 "Tare in Storm" (Franasovic) 15 5
1380. 1 d. 50 "Brig Sela" (Ivankovic) 25 5
1381. 2 d. 50 "16th-century Drubrovnik Galleon" 30 20
1382. 3 d. 25 "Frigate Madre Mimbelli" (A. Roux) 60 25
1383. 5 d. "Shipwreck" (16th-century icon) .. 1·40 1·25

365. Games' Emblem. **366.** Bosnian Mountain Horse.

1969. 9th World Deaf and Dumb Games, Belgrade.
1384. **385.** 1 d. 25 lilac and lake 20 5

1969. 50th Anniv. of Veterinary Faculty, Zagreb. Multicoloured.
1385. 75 p. Type **366** 12 5
1386. 1 d. 25 Lipizzaner Horse 15 5
1387. 3 d. 25 Ljutomer trotter 40 8
1388. 5 d. Yugoslav Half-breed 85 75

367. Children and Chicks. **368.** Arms of Belgrade.

1969. Children's Week.
1389. **367.** 50 p. multicoloured .. 12 5

1969. 25th Anniv. of Yugoslav Liberation. Arms of Regional Capitals. Multicoloured.
1390. 50 p. Type **368** 15 5
1391. 50 p. Skopje 15 5
1392. 50 p. Titograd (Podgorica) 15 5
1393. 50 p. Sarajevo 15 5
1394. 50 p. Zagreb 15 5
1395. 50 p. Ljubljana 15 5

369. Dr. Josip Smodlaka. **370.** Torch, Globe and Olympic Rings.

1969. Birth Centenary of Dr. Josip Smodlaka (politician).
1397. **369.** 50 p. blue 8 5

1969. Obligatory Tax. Olympic Games Fund.
1398. **370.** 10 p. multicoloured .. 5 5

371. " Gipsy Girl " (N. Martinoski).

1969. Yugoslav Nude Paintings (3rd series). Multicoloured.
1399. 50 p. Type **371** 12 5
1400. 1 d. 25 " Girl in Red Armchair " (S. Sumanovic) 20 5
1401. 1 d. 50 " Girl Brushing Hair " (M. Tartaglia) .. 25 10
1402. 2 d. 50 " Olympia " (M. Kraljevic) 40 20
1403. 3 d. 25 " The Bather " (J. Bijelic) 70 40
1404. 5 d. " Woman on a Couch " (M. Sternen) .. .. 1·50 1·50
Nos. 1402 and 1404 are horiz.

372. University Building.

1969. 50th Anniv. of Ljubljana University.
1405. **372.** 50 p. green 8 5

373. University "Seal". **374.** Colonnade.

1969. 300th Anniv. of Zagreb University.
1406. **373.** 50 p. gold, pur. & blue 8 5

1969. Europa.
1407. **374.** 1 d. 25 brown & green 3·00 3·00
1408. 3 d. 25 blue, grey & pur. 9·00 9·00

375. Jovan Cvijic (geographer). **376.** " Punishment of Dirka " (4th-cent mosaic).

1970. Famous Yugoslavs.
1409. **375.** 50 p. purple 8 5
1410. – 1 d. 25 black .. 12 5
1411. – 1 d. 50 purple .. 15 5
1412. – 2 d. 50 olive 15 12
1413. – 3 d. 25 brown .. 25 15
1414. – 5 d. blue 30 40
CELEBRITIES: 1 d. 25, Dr. A. Stampar (hygienist). 1 d. 50, J. Krcovski (author). 2 d. 50, M. Miljanov (soldier). 3 d. 25, V. Pelagic (socialist revolutionary). 5 d., O. Zupancic (poet).

1970. Mosaics. Multicoloured.
1415. 50 p. Type **376** 5 5
1416. 1 d. 25 " Cerberus " (5th cent.) (horiz.) .. 15 5
1417. 1 d. 50 " Angel of Annunciation " (6th-cent.) .. 15 5
1418. 2 d. 50 " Hunters " (4th-cent.) 25 10
1419. 3 d. 25 " A Bull beside Cherries " (5th-cent.) (horiz.) 35 15
1420. 5 d. " Virgin and Child Enthroned" (6th cent.) 90 90

377. Lenin (after sculpture by S. Stojanovic). **378.** Trying for Goal.

1970. Birth Centenary of Lenin.
1421. **377.** 50 p. lake 10 5
1422. – 1 d. 25 blue 15 10
DESIGN: 1 d. 25. As Type **377**, but showing left side of Lenin's bust.

1970. 6th World Basketball Championships.
1423. **378.** 1 d. 25 red 15 8

379. Red Cross Trefoil. **380.** "Flaming Sun".

1970. Obligatory Tax. Red Cross Week.
1424. **379.** 20 p. multicoloured .. 8 5

1970. Europa.
1425. **380.** 1 d. 25 blue & turq... 15 8
1426. 3 d. 25 brn., vio. & pur. 35 40

381. Istrian Short-haired Hound. **382.** Olympic Flag.

1970. Yugoslav Dogs. Multicoloured.
1427. 50 p. Type **381** 10 5
1428. 1 d. 25 Yugoslav tricolour hound 15 5
1429. 1 d. 50 Istrian hard-haired hound 15 5
1430. 2 d. 50 Balkan hound .. 25 12
1431. 3 d. 25 Dalmatian .. 40 15
1432. 5 d. Shara mountain dog 1·10 1·00

1970. Obligatory Tax. Olympic Games Fund.
1433. **382.** 10 p. multicoloured .. 8 5

383. Telegraph Key. **384.** " Bird in Meadow ".

1970. Montenegro Telegraph Cent.
1434. **383.** 50 p. gold, blk. & brn. 8 5

1970. Children's Week.
1435. **384.** 50 p. multicoloured 15 5

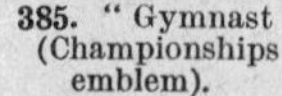

385. " Gymnast " (Championships emblem). **386.** " Hand Holding Dove " (Macota).

1970. 17th World Gymnastic Championships, Ljubljana.
1436. **385.** 1 d. 25 blue & purple 12 5

1970. 25th Anniv. of United Nations.
1437. **386.** 1 d. 25 multicoloured 12 5

1970. Yugoslav Paintings (4th series). Baroque Period. Designs as T **341.** Mult.
1438. 50 p. " The Ascension " (T. D. Kracun) 10 5
1439. 75 p. " Abraham's Sacrifice " (F. Benkovic) .. 10 5
1440. 1 d. 25 " The Holy Family " (F. Jelovsek) 15 5
1441. 2 d. 50 " Jacob's Dream " (H. Zefarovic) .. 25 15
1442. 3 d. 25 " Christ's Baptism " (Serbian village artist) 35 15
1443. 5 d. 75 " Coronation of the Virgin " (T. Kokolja) .. 75 75

388. Rusty-leaved Alpenrose. **389.** F. Supilo.

1970. Nature Conservation Year. Mult.
1444. 1 d. 25 Type **388** .. .. 1·00 1·00
1445. 3 d. 25 Lammergeier .. 15·00 7·50

1971. Birth Cent. of Frano Supilo (politician).
1446. **389.** 50 p. brown and buff 8 5

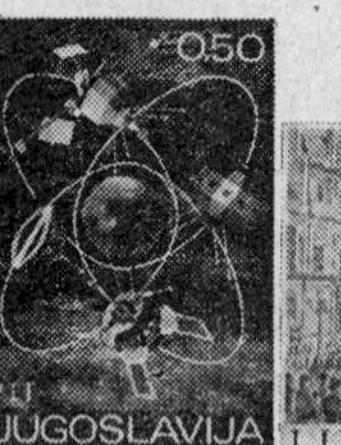

390. Different Nations' Satellites (" International Co-operation "). **391.** " Proclamation of the Commune " (A. Dodenarde, after A. Lamy).

1971. Space Exploration. Multicoloured.
1447. 50 p. **390** 12 5
1448. 75 p. Telecommunications satellite 15 5
1449. 1 d. 25 Unmanned Moon flights 20 5
1450. 2 d. 50 Exploration of Mars and Venus (horiz.) 35 15
1451. 3 d. 25 Space-station (horiz.) 50 30
1452. 5 d. 75 Astronauts on the Moon (horiz.) .. 1·75 1·75

1971. Centenary of Paris Commune.
1453. **391.** 1 d. 25 brn. & orge. 15 8

392. Red Cross Ribbon.

1971. Obligatory Tax. Red Cross Week.
1454. **392.** 20 p. multicoloured .. 8 5

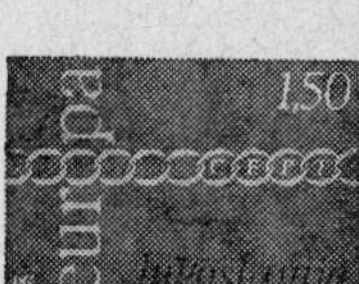

393. Europa Chain. **394.** Congress Emblem (A. Pajvancic).

1971. Europa.
1455. **393.** 1 d. 50 multicoloured 12 10
1456. 4 d. pink, pur. & mve. 55 55

1971. 20th Anniv. of Yugoslav "Self-Managers" Movement.
1457. **394.** 50 p. red, blk. & gold 12 5
1458. – 1 d. 25 red, blk. & gold 60 60
DESIGN: 1 d. 25, "Self-Managers" emblem (designed by M. Miodragovic).

395. Common Mallow. **396.** Olympic " Spiral" and Rings.

1971. Flowers. Multicoloured.
1459. 50 p. Type **395** 12 5
1460. 1 d. 50 Buckthorn .. 12 5
1461. 2 d. Water-lily 20 5
1462. 2 d. 50 Wild poppy .. 40 10
1463. 4 d. Wild chicory .. 50 12
1464. 6 d. Bladder-herb .. 90 70

1971. Obligatory Tax. Olympic Games Fund.
1465. **396.** 10 p. blk., pur. & blue 5 5

397. Krk, Dalmatia. **398.** " Prince Lazar Hrebeljanovic " (from fresco, Lazarica Church).

1971. Tourism.
1641. – 5 p. orange 5 5
1642. – 10 p. brown 5 5
1468. – 20 p. lilac 12 5
1644. – 25 p. red 20 5
1469. **397.** 30 p. green 55 10
1645. 30 p. olive 5 5
1646. – 35 p. red 15 5
1647. – 40 p. olive 5 5
1473. – 50 p. red .. .. 1·00 15
1474. – 50 p. green 20 5
1650. – 60 p. purple 5 5
1476. – 75 p. green 50 10
1652. – 75 p. purple 20 5
1477. – 80 p. red .. .. 1·10 5
1478. – 1 d. red .. .. 2·25 30
1656. – 1 d. lilac 15 5
1657. – 1 d. green 15 5
1479. – 1 d. 20 green .. 1·40 12
1480. – 1 d. 25 blue 65 12
1481. – 1 d. 50 blue 30 5
1660. – 1 d. 50 red 20 5
1482. – 2 d. turquoise .. 60 5
1661. – 2 d. 10 green .. 25 10
1483. – 2 d. 50 violet .. 60 12
1662a. – 2 d. 50 red 20 5
1663. – 2 d. 50 blue 20 5
1664a. – 3 d. grey 10 5
1665. – 3 d. 20 blue 45 5
1666. – 3 d. 40 green .. 20 5
1667. – 3 d. 50 red 20 5
1668a. – 4 d. red 10 5
1669. – 4 d. 90 blue 35 5
1670. – 5 d. green 10 5
1671. – 5 d. 60 olive 25 5
1672. – 6 d. brown 10 8
1673a. – 6 d. 10 green .. 20 5
1674. – 8 d. grey 30 5
1675a. – 8 d. 80 grey 25 10
1676. – 10 d. purple 20 5
1677. – 16 d. 50 blue .. 25 10
1678. – 26 d. blue 30 10
1679. – 38 d. mauve 50 10
1680. – 70 d. blue 45 10
DESIGNS: 5 p. Krusevo, Macedonia. 10 p. Gradacac. 20 p., 75 p. Bohinj, Slovenia. 25 p. Budva. 35 p. Omis, Dalmatia. 40 p. Pec. 50 p. (1473/4), Krusevac, Serbia. 60 p. Logarska Valley. 75 p. (1652), Rijeka. 80 p. Piran. 1 d. (1478), Bitola, Macedonia. 1 d. (1656/7). 16 d. 50

Ohrid. 1 d. 20, 4 d. Pocitelj. 1 d. 25, 1d. 50 (1481), 8 d. 80, Herceg Novi. 1 d. 50 Bihac, 2 d. Novi Sad. 2 d. 10, 6 d. 10 Hvar. 2 d. 50 Rijeka Cronjevica, Montenegro. 2 d. 50 (1662a/3), Kragujevac., 3 d., 3 d. 20 Skofja Loka. 3 d. 40 Vranje. 3 d. 50 Vrsac. 4 d. 90 Perast. 5 d. Osijek. 5 d. 60 Travnik. 6 d. Kikinda. 8 d. Dubrovnik. 10 d. Sarajevo. 26 d. Korcula. 38 d. Maribor. 70 d. Zagreb.

1971. City of Krusevac. 600th Anniv.
1487. **396.** 50 p. multicoloured 10 5

399. " Satyr ". **400.** Children in Balloon.

1971. Bronze Archaeological Discoveries. Multicoloured.
1488. 50 p. Head of Emperor Constantine 5 5
1489. 1 d. 50 "Boy with Fish" (statuette) 8 5
1490. 2 d. "Hercules" (statuette) 12 5
1491. 2 d. 50 Type **399** .. 30 10
1492. 4 d. "Goddess Aphrodite" (head) .. 40 15
1493. 6 d. "Emona Citizen" (statue) 70 70

1971. Children's Week and 25th Anniv. of U.N.I.C.E.F.
1494. **400.** 50 p. multicoloured 25 5

1971. Yugoslav Portraits (5th series). As T **371.** Multicoloured.
1495. 50 p. " Girl in Serbian Dress " (K. Ivanovic) 5 5
1496. 1 d. 50 " Ivanesevic the Merchant " (A. Bocaric) 12 5
1497. 2 d. " Anna Kresic " (V. Karas) 15 8
1498. 2 d. 50 " Pavla Jagodic " (K. Danil) 20 10
1499. 4 d. " Louise Pasjakova " (M. Stroj) 30 12
1500. 6 d. " Old Man at Ljubljana " (M. Langus) 90 75

402. "Postal Codes". **403.** Dame Gruev.

1971. Introduction of Postal Codes.
1501. **402.** 50 p. multicoloured .. 5 5

1971. Birth Centenary of Dame Gruev (Macedonian revolutionary).
1502. **403.** 50 p. blue 8 5

404. Speed-skating.

1972. Winter Olympic Games. Sapporo, Japan. Multicoloured.
1503. 1 d. 25 Type **404** .. 60 45
1504. 6 d. Slalom-skiing .. 2·00 2·25

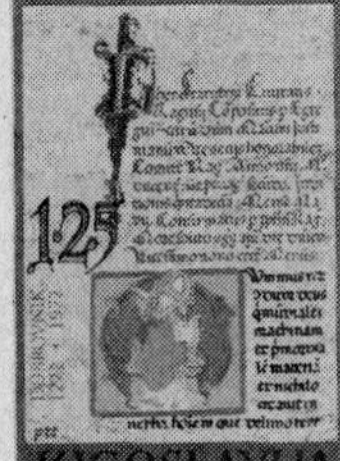

405. First Page of Statute. **406.** Ski-jump, Planica.

1972. 700th Anniv. of Dubrovnik Law Statutes.
1505. **405.** 1 d. 25 multicoloured 15 8

1972. 1st World Ski-jumping Championships, Planica.
1506. **406.** 1 d. 25 multicoloured 20 8

407. Water-polo. **408.** Red Cross and Hemispheres.

1972. Olympic Games, Munich. Multicoloured.
1507. 50 p. Type **407** 5 5
1508. 1 d. 25 Basketball .. 10 5
1509. 2 d. 50 Swimming .. 15 5
1510. 3 d. 25 Boxing 20 5
1511. 5 d. Running 30 15
1512. 6 d. 50 Sailing 60 55

1972. Obligatory Tax. Red Cross Week.
1513. **408.** 20 p. multicoloured .. 8 5

409. " Communications ". **410.** Wallcreeper.

1972. Europa.
1514. **409.** 1 d. 50 multicoloured 25 20
1515. 5 d. multicoloured 1·10 1·00

1972. Birds. Multicoloured.
1516. 50 p. Type **410** 15 10
1517. 1 d. 25 Little Bustard .. 15 10
1518. 2 d. 50 Chough 30 15
1519. 3 d. 25 White Spoonbill .. 70 20
1520. 5 d. Eagle Owl .. 1·25 20
1521. 6 d. 50 Rock Ptarmigan 3·00 95

411. President Tito. **412.** Communications Tower, Olympic Rings and 1972 Games' Emblems.

1972. President Tito's 80th Birthday.
1522. **411.** 50 p. brown and buff 12 10
1523. 1 d. 25 blue and grey 50 25

1972. Obligatory Tax. Olympic Games Fund.
1525. **412.** 10 p. multicoloured .. 5 5

413. Locomotive No. 1 " King of Serbia ", 1882. **415.** Pawn.

414. Glider in Flight.

1972. 50th Anniv. of Int. Railway Union. Multicoloured.
1526. 1 d. 50 Type **413** 20 10
1527. 5 d. Modern " Bo-Bo " electric locomotive .. 80 40

1972. 13th World Gliding Championships, Vrasac.
1528. **414.** 2 d. black, blue & gold 20 15

1972. 20th Chess Olympiad, Skopje.
1529 **415** 1 d. 50 brn, vio & pur 35 12
1530 – 6 d. black, bl & dp bl 80 75
DESIGN: 6 d. Stylised king and queen on board.

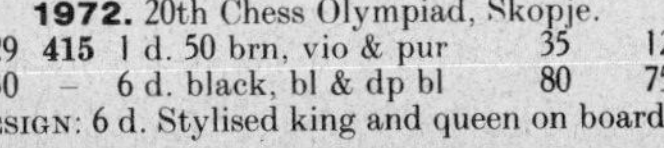

416. " Child on Horse " (B. Zlatec). **417.** G. Delcev.

1972. Children's Week.
1531. **416.** 80 p. multicoloured .. 15 5

1972. Birth Centenary of Goco Delcev (Macedonian revolutionary).
1532. **417.** 80 p. black and green 10 5

418. Father Martica.

1972. 180th Birth Anniv. of Father Grge Martica. (politician).
1533. **418.** 80 p. black, green & red 10 5

419. National Library.

1972. 140th Anniv. of and Re-opening of National Library, Belgrade.
1534. **419.** 50 p. brown 8 5

420. " Fruit Dish and Broken Majolica Vase " (M. Tenkovic).

1972. Yugoslav Art (6th series). Still Life. Multicoloured.
1535. 50 p. Type **420** 5 5
1536. 1 d. 25 " Mandoline and Book " (J. Petkovsek) (vert.) 10 5
1537. 2 d. 50 " Basket with Grapes " (K. Javanovic) 20 5
1538. 3 d. 25 " Water-melon " (K. Danil) 35 15
1539. 5 d. " In a Stable " (N. Masic) (vert.) .. 45 20
1540. 6 d. 50 " Scrap-books " (C. Medovic) .. .. 1·00 1·00

421. Battle of Stubica.

1973. 500th Anniv. of Slovenian Peasant Risings and 400th Anniv. of Croatian-Slovenian Rebellion. Multicoloured.
1541. 2 d. Type **421** 20 5
1542. 6 d. Battle of Krsko .. 1·25 75

422. R. Domanovic. **424.** "Novi Sad" (P. Demetrovic).

423. Skofja Loka.

1973. Birth Centenary of Radoje Domanovic (Serbian satirist).
1543. **422.** 80 p. brown and drab 25 10

1973. Millenary of Skofja Loka.
1544. **423.** 80 p. brown 20 8

1973. Old Engravings of Yugoslav Towns. Each black and gold.
1545. 50 p. Type **424** 10 10
1546. 1 d. 25 "Zagreb" (J. Szeman) 10 10
1547. 2 d. 50 "Kotor" (P. Montier) 15 10
1548. 3 d. 25 "Belgrade" (Mancini) 20 15
1549. 5 d. "Split" (L. F. Cassas) 30 15
1550. 6 d. 50 "Kranj" (M. Merian) 60 45

425. Table-tennis Bat and Ball.

1973. 32nd World Table-tennis Championships, Sarajevo.
1551. **425.** 2 d. multicoloured .. 30 10

426. Red Cross Emblem. **427.** Europa "Posthorn".

1973. Obligatory Tax. Red Cross Week.
1552. **426.** 20 p. multicoloured .. 5 5

1973. Europa.
1553. **427.** 2 d. lilac, grn. & bl. 15 10
1554. 5 d. 50 pink, green & purple .. .. 1·40 1·25

428. " Aristolochia clematatis ". **429.** Globe and Olympic Rings.

1973. Flora. Medicinal Plants. Mult.
1555. 80 p. Type **428** 12 5
1556. 2 d. " Echinops ritro " .. 20 5
1557. 3 d. " Olea europaea " .. 30 5
1558. 4 d. " Corydalis cava " .. 45 15
1559. 5 d. " Viscum album " .. 65 20
1560. 6 d. " Symphytum officinale " .. .. 2·00 2·00

1973. Obligatory Tax. Olympic Games Fund.
1561. **429.** 10 p. multicoloured .. 5 5

430. A. Jansa and Bee. **431.** Aquatic Symbol.

1973. Death Bicentenary of Anton Jansa (apiculturist).
1562. **430.** 80 p. black 10 5

1973. 1st World Aquatic Championships, Belgrade.
1563. **431.** 2 d. multicoloured .. 20 5

432. " Child on Boat ". **433.** Posthorn.

1973. Children's Week.
1564. **432.** 80 p. multicoloured 25 5

1973.

1565. **433.** 30 p. brown 12 5
1565a. 50 p. blue 12 5
1566. 80 p. red 12 5
1566a. 1 d. green 12 5
1567. 1 d. 20 red 15 5
1567a. 1 d. 50 red 15 5

434. J. Dalmatinac (from sculpture by I. Mestrovic).

435. "N. Petrovic" (self portrait).

1973. 500th Death Anniv. of Juraj Dalmatinac (sculptor and architect).

1568. **434.** 80 p. olive and green 10 5

1973. Birth Centenary of Nadezda Petrovic (painter).

1569. **435.** 2 d. multicoloured .. 20 15

436. "The Plaster Head" (M. Celebonovic).

1973. Yugoslav Art (7th series). Interiors Multicoloured.

1570. 80 p. Type **436** .. 5 5
1571. 2 d. "St. Duja Church" (E. Vidovic) .. 10 5
1572. 3 d. "Slovenian House-wife" (M. Tartaglia).. 15 5
1573. 4 d. "Dedicated at Karas"—painter at easel (M. Stancic) 30 15
1574. 5 d. "My Studio" (M. Konjovic).. 50 15
1575. 6 d. "Tavern in Stara Loka" (F. Slana) .. 70 60

437. D. Dudic.

438. "M" for "Metrication".

1973. National Heroes.

(a) Each black.

1576. 80 p. Type **437** 10 10
1577. 80 p. S. Pindzur .. 10 10
1578. 80 p. B. Kidric 10 10
1579. 80 p. D. Dakic 10 10

(b) Each red.

1580. 2 d J. Mazar-sosa .. 15 15
1581. 2 d Z. Zrenjanin 15 15
1582. 2 d D. Emin 15 15
1583. 2 d I. Lola Ribar .. 15 15

1974. Centenary of Introduction of Metric System in Yugoslavia.

1584. **438.** 80 p. multicoloured 10 5

439. Skater.

440. Statjeska Monument.

1974. European Figure-skating Championships Zagreb.

1585. **439.** 2 d. multicoloured .. 40 20

1974. Monuments.

1586. – 3 d. green 75 8
1587. – 4 d. 50 brown .. 1·25 10
1588. – 5 d. violet .. .. 1·25 10
1589. **440.** 10 d. green .. 1·50 20
1590. – 20 d. purple .. 1·75 20
1591. – 50 d. blue .. 4·00 90

DESIGNS—VERT. 3 d. Ljubljana. 4 d. 50, Kozara. 5 d. Belcista. HORIZ. 20 d. Podgaric. 50 d. Kragujevac.

441. Mailcoach.

1974. Cent. of Universal Postal Union.

1592. **441.** 80 p. black & yellow 10 5
1593. – 2 d. black and red .. 10 8
1594. – 8 d. black and blue.. 40 45

DESIGNS: 2 d. U.P.U. H.Q., Building. 8 d. Yugoslav jetliner.

442. Montenegro 25 n. stamp of 1874.

1974. Montenegro Stamp Centenary. Mult.

1595. 80 p. Montenegrin 2 n. stamp of 1874 .. .. 12 5
1596. 6 d. Type **442** 35 35

443. President Tito.

444. Lenin.

1974.

1597. **443.** 50 p. green 12 5
1598. 80 p. red 20 5
1599. 1 d. 20 green .. 25 5
1600. 2 d. blue 30 5

1974. 50th Death Anniv. of Lenin.

1601. **444.** 2 d. black and silver 15 10

445. Red Cross Emblems.

1974. Obligatory Tax. Red Cross Week.

1602. **445.** 20 p. multicoloured.. 5 5

446. "Dwarf" (Lepensk settlement, c. 4950 B.C.).

447. Great Tit.

1974. Europa. Sculptures. Multicoloured.

1603. 2 d. Type **446** 15 12
1604 6 d. "Widow and Child" (I. Mestrovic) .. .. 1·00 1·25

1974. Youth Day. Multicoloured.

1605 80 p. Type **447** 70 15
1606 2 d. Roses 50 15
1607 6 d. "Pieris brassicae" (butterfly) .. .. 2·00 1·10

448. Congress Poster.

449. Olympic Rings and Stadium.

1974. 10th Yugoslav League of Communists' Congress, Belgrade.

1608. **448.** 80 p. multicoloured.. 8 5
1609. 2 d. multicoloured .. 12 8
1610. 6 d. multicoloured .. 35 30

1974. Obligatory Tax. Olympic Games Fund.

1611. **449.** 10 p. multicoloured.. 5 5

450. Dish Aerial, Ivanjica.

451. World Cup.

1974. Inauguration of Satellite Communications Station, Ivanjica.

1612. **450.** 80 p. blue 20 5
1613. – 6 d. lilac .. .. 1·25 70

DESIGN: 6 d. "Intelstat 4" in orbit.

1974. World Cup Football Championships, West Germany.

1614. **451.** 4 d. 50 multicoloured 70 50

452. Edelweiss and Klek Mountain.

1974. Centenary of Croatian Mountaineers' Society.

1615. **452.** 2 d. multicoloured .. 15 10

453. "Children's Dance" (J. Knjazovic).

1974. Paintings (8th series). Multicoloured.

1616. 80 p. Type **453** .. 10 8
1617. 2 d. "Crucified Rooster" (I. Generalic) .. 15 12
1618. 5 d. "Laundresses" (I. Lackovic) .. 35 20
1619. 8 d. "Dance" (J. Brasic) 1·10 1·25

Nos. 1617/18 are vert.

454. "Rooster and Flower" (K. Milinojsin).

455. Interior of Library.

1974. Children's Week and 6th "Joy of Europe" Meeting, Belgrade. Children's Paintings. Multicoloured.

1620. 1 d. 20 Type **454** .. 15 5
1621. 3 d. 20 "Boy and Girl" (E. Mednecka) (vert.).. 25 10
1622. 5 d. "Cat and kitten" (J. Anastasyevic) .. 70 40

1974. Bicentenary of National and University Library.

1623. **455.** 1 d. 20 black .. 10 5

456. "White Peonies" (P. Dobrovic).

458. Dove and Map of Europe.

457. Title page of Volume 1.

1974. Floral Paintings. Mult.

1624. 80 p. Type **456** .. 5 5
1625. 2 d. "Carnations" (V. Gecan) 12 12
1626. 3 d. "Flowers" (M. Konjovic) 15 15
1627. 4 d. "White Vase" (S. Sumanovic) 35 20
1628. 5 d. "Branching Lark-spurs" (S. Kregar) .. 40 20
1629. 8 d. "Roses" (P. Lubarda) 70 50

1975. 150th Anniv. of "Matica Sirpska" Annals.

1630. **457.** 1 d. 20 green .. 8 5

1975. 2nd European Security and Co-operation Conf., Belgrade.

1631. **458.** 3 d. 20 multicoloured 20 5
1632. 8 d. multicoloured .. 90 65

459. Gold-plated Bronze Ear-ring (14th-15th-century), Alisici, Bosnia.

460. S. Markovic (sculpture by S. Bodnarov).

1975. Archeological Discoveries. Mult.

1633. 1 d. 20 Type **459** .. 10 5
1634. 2 d. 10 Silver bracelet (19th-century), Kosovo .. 10 5
1635. 3 d. 20 Gold-plated silver buckle (18th-century), Bitola 15 5
1636. 5 d. Gold-plated ring (14th-century), Novi Sad .. 30 10
1637. 6 d. Silver-and-paste neck-lace (17th-century), Kosovo 45 15
1638. 8 d. Gold-plated bronze and jewelled bracelet (18th-century), Bitola .. 75 70

1975. Death Centenary of Svetozar Markovic (writer and statesman).

1639. **460.** 1 d. 20 blue 8 5

461. "Fettered" (sculpture by F. Krsinic).

1975. International Women's Year.

1640. **461.** 3 d. 20 brn. and gold 15 12

462. Red Cross and Hands.

1975. Obligatory Tax. Red Cross Week.

1681. **462.** 20 p. multicoloured.. 5 5

463. "Still Life with Eggs" (M. Pijade).

1975. Europa. Paintings. Multicoloured.

1682. 3 d. 20 Type **463** .. 15 12
1683. 8 d. "The Three Graces" (I. Radovic) 50 50

464. "Liberation" Monument (Dzamonja).

465. Garland-flower.

1975. 30th Anniv. of Liberation.

1684. **464.** 3 d. 20 multicoloured 12 8

1975. National Youth Day. Flowers. Mult.

1685. 1 d. 20 Type **465** .. 12 5
1686. 2 d. 10 Touch-me-not .. 12 5
1687. 3 d. 20 Rose-mallow .. 20 5
1688. 5 d. Mourning widow .. 40 10
1689. 6 d. Crocus .. 50 15
1690. 8 d. Rose-bay .. 75 50

466. Games Emblem. **467.** Canoeing.

1975. Obligatory Tax. Olympic Games Fund.
1691. **466.** 10 p. multicoloured .. 5 5

1975. World Canoeing Championships. Macedonia.
1692. **467.** 3 d. 20 multicoloured 20 10

468. " Herzegovinian Insurgents in Ambush ".

1975. Centenary of Bosnian-Herzegovinian Uprising.
1693. **468.** 1 d. 20 multicoloured 12 5

469. " Skopje Earthquake ". **470.** S. M. Ljubisa.

1975. Obligatory Tax. Solidarity Week.
1694. **469.** 30 p. blk., grey & bl. 10 5
See also Nos. 1885 and 1933.

1975. Writers.
1695. **470.** 1 d. 20 black and lake 8 5
1696. – 2 d. 10 blk. and grn. 12 5
1697. – 3 d. 20 blk. & brown 15 5
1698. – 5 d. black and orange 20 8
1699. – 6 d. black and green 20 10
1700. – 8 d. black and blue .. 35 50
PORTRAITS: 2 d. 10 I. Prijatelj. 3 d. 20 J. Ignjatovic. 5 d. D. Jarnevic. 6 d. S. Corivic. 8 d. I. Brlic-Mazuranic.

471. " Young Lion " (A. Savic). **472.** Peace Dove within " EUROPA ".

1975. Children's Week and 7th "Joy of Europe" meeting, Belgrade. Children's Paintings. Multicoloured.
1701. 3 d. 20 Type **471** .. 20 5
1702. 6 d. " Baby in Pram " .. 90 50

1975. European Security and Co-operation Conference, Helsinki.
1703. **472.** 3 d. 20 multicoloured 15 5
1704. 8 d. multicoloured .. 50 30

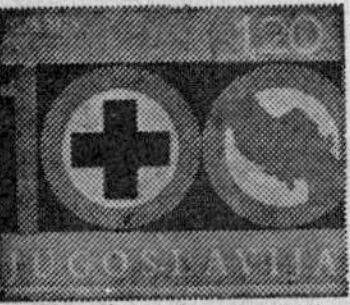

473. Red Cross and Map within " 100 ".

475. Diocletian's Palace, Split (3rd-century). **474.** "Folk Kitchen" (D. Andrejevic-Kun).

1975. Cent. of Red Cross. Mult.
1705. 1 d. 20 Type **473** .. 15 5
1706. 8 d. Red Cross and people 50 25

1975. Republic Day. Paintings. Mult.
1707. 1 d. 20 Type **474** .. 5 5
1708. 2 d. 10 "On the Doorstep" (V. Grdan) 10 5
1709. 3 d. 20 " The Drunken Coach-load" (M. Detoni) (horiz.) 15 5
1710. 5 d. " Lunch " (T. Kralj) (horiz.) 20 10
1711. 6 d. " Waterwheel " (L. Licenoski) 30 12
1712. 8 d. " Justice " (K. Hegedusic) .. 55 60

1975. European Architectural Heritage Year.
1713. **475.** 1 d. 20 brown .. 12 10
1714. – 3 d. 20 black .. 15 10
1715. – 8 d. blue 50 50
DESIGNS—VERT. 3 d. 20 House of Ohrid (19th-century). HORIZ. 8 d. Gracanica Monastery, Kosovo (14th-century).

476. Ski-jumping. **477.** Red Flag.

1976. Winter Olympic Games, Innsbruck.
1716. **476.** 3 d. 20 blue 15 5
1717. – 8 d. lake 55 50
DESIGN: 8 d. Figure-skating.

1976. Cent. of "Red Flag" Insurrection (workers' demonstrations), Kragujevac.
1718. **477.** 1 d. 20 multicoloured 12 5

478. S. Miletic. **479.** B. Stankovic.

1976. 150th Birth Anniv. of Svetozar Miletic (politician).
1719. **478.** 1 d. 20 grn. & grey .. 12 5

1976. Birth Cent. of Boran Stankovic (writer).
1720. **479.** 1 d. 20 red, brown and yellow .. 12 5

480. " King Matthias " (sculpture, J. Pogovelec). **481.** I. Cankar.

1976. Europa. Handicrafts. Multicoloured.
1721. 3 d. 20 Type **480** .. 10 10
1722. 8 d. Base of a beaker .. 40 40

1976. Birth Centenary of Ivan Cankar (Slovenian writer).
1723. **481.** 1 d. 20 purple, brown and pink .. 10 5

482. Stylized Figure. **483.** Train crossing Viaduct.

1976. Obligatory Tax. Red Cross Week.
1724. **482.** 20 p. multicoloured 60 60

1976. Inauguration of Belgrade-Bar Railway.
1725. **483.** 3 d. 20 brown .. 25 15
1726. – 8 d. blue 65 45
DESIGN: 8 d. Train crossing bridge.

484. "Anax imperator". **485.** V. Nazor.

1976. Youth Day. Freshwater Fauna. Multicoloured.
1727. 1 d. 20 Type **484** .. 10 10
1728. 2 d. 10 Snail 10 5
1729. 3 d. 20 Rudd 15 5
1730. 5 d. Common frog .. 30 10
1731. 6 d. Ferruginous Duck .. 1·25 20
1732. 8 d. Muskrat 60 60

1976. Birth Cent. of Vladimir Nazor (writer).
1733. **485.** 1 d. 20 blue and lilac 10 5

486. " Battle of Vucji Dol " (from " Eagle " journal of 1876).

1976. Centenary of Montenegrin Liberation Wars.
1734. **486.** 1 d. 20 multicoloured 10 5

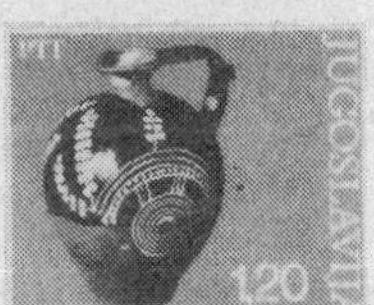

487. Jug, Aleksandrova, Serbia.

1976. Ancient Pottery. Multicoloured.
1735. 1 d. 20 Type **487** .. 5 5
1736. 2 d. 10 Pitcher, Ptuj, Slovenia 10 5
1737. 3 d. 20 Coffee-pot, Visnjica, Sarajevo 15 5
1738. 5 d. Pitcher, Backi Breg, Vojvodina 30 15
1739. 6 d. Goblet, Vranestice, Macedonia 40 15
1740. 8 d. Jug, Prizren, Kosovo 75 50

488. N. Tesla Monument and Niagara Falls. **489.** Long-jumping.

1976. 120th Birth Anniv. of Nikola Tesla (scientist).
1741. **488.** 5 d. blue and green 25 10

1976. Olympic Games, Montreal.
1742. **489.** 1 d. 20 purple .. 8 5
1743. – 3 d. 20 brown .. 15 5
1744. – 5 d. brown 20 10
1745. – 8 d. blue 40 35
DESIGNS: 3 d. 20 Handball. 5 d. Shooting. 8 d. Rowing.

490. Stadium and Olympic Rings. **491.** Globe.

1976. Obligatory Tax. Olympic Games Fund.
1746. **490.** 10 p. blue 5 5

1976. 5th Non-aligned Nations' Summit Conf., Colombo.
1747. **491.** 4 d. 90 multicoloured 20 10

492. " Navy Day " (N. Mitar).

1976. Children's Week. 8th " Joy of Europe " Meeting, Belgrade. Children's Paintings. Multicoloured.
1748. 4 d. 90 Type **492** .. 12 5
1749. 8 d. " Children's Trains " (W. Gulbrandsen) .. 50 40

493. " Battle of Montenegrins " (D. Jaksic). **495.** " Prota Mateja Nenadovic " (U. Kenezevic).

1976. Paintings (9th series). Historical Events. Multicoloured.
1750. 1 d. 20 Type **493** .. 8 5
1751. 2 d. 10 " Nikola Subic Zrinjski at Siget " (O. Ivelovic) 12 5
1752. 3 d. 20 " Herzegovinian Fugitives " (U. Predic) (horiz.) 20 5
1753. 5 d. " The Raziovci Uprising " (B. Lazeki) (horiz.) 25 15
1754. 6 d. " Enthronement of the Slovenian Duke, Gosposvetsko Field " (A. G. Kos) (horiz.) .. 40 20
1755. 8 d. " Breach of the Solun Front " (V. Stanojevic) (horiz.) 50 45

1976. No. 1203 surch.
1756. 1 d. on 85 p. plum .. 12 5

1977. Birth Bicentenary of P. M. Nenadovic (soldier and diplomat).
1757. **495.** 4 d. 90 multicoloured 25 25

496. R. Zinzifov. **497.** Phlox.

1977. Death Cent. of Raiko Zinzifov (writer).
1758. **496.** 1 d. 50 brn. & sepia. 8 5

1977. Flowers. Multicoloured.
1759. 1 d. 50 Type **497** .. 8 8
1760. 3 d. 40 Tiger-lily .. 20 10
1761. 4 d. 90 Dicentra 25 10
1762. 6 d. Zinnia 30 12
1763. 8 d. Marigold 40 15
1764. 10 d. Horseshoe geranium 65 60

498. Institute Building. **499.** Alojz Kraigher.

1977. 150th Anniv. of Croatian Music Institute.
1765. **498.** 4 d. 90 blue & brn. .. 20 8

1977. Birth Centenary of Alojz Kraigher (author).
1766. **499.** 1 d. 50 brn. & buff .. 8 5

500. " Boka Kotorske ". (Milo Milunovic).

1977. Europa. Landscapes. Multicoloured.
1767. 4 d. 90 Type **500** .. 12 10
1768. 10 d. " Zagorje in November " (Ljubo Babic) 40 40

501. Figure and Emblems.

1977. Obligatory Tax. Red Cross Week.
1769. **501.** 20 p. red and brown 1·75 70
1770. 50 p. red and olive .. 50 20
1771. 1 d. red and blue .. 25 5

502. " President Tito " (O. Mujadzic). **503.** Alpine Scene.

1977. 85th Birthday of President Tito.
1772. **502.** 1 d. 50 brown, olive and gold 8 5
1773. 4 d. 90 brown, pink and gold 20 15
1774. 8 d. brn., olive & gold 50 45

1977. International Environment Protection Day. Multicoloured.
1775. 4 d. 90 Type **503** .. 20 5
1776. 10 d. Plitvice waterfall and red-breasted fly-catcher .. .. 2·25 55

504. Petar Kocic. **505.** Dove and Map of Europe.

1977. Birth Cent. of Petar Kocic (writer).
1777. **504.** 1 d. 50 mauve & grn. 8 5

1977. European Security and Co-operation Conference, Belgrade (1st issue).
1778. **505.** 4 d. 90 multicoloured 30 15
1779. 10 d. multicoloured .. 1·50 1·50
See also Nos. 1784/5.

506. Tree. **507.** "Bather" (M. Franci).

1977. Obligatory Tax. Anti-tuberculosis. Week.
1780. **506.** 50 p. multicoloured 3·00 3·00
1781. 1 d. multicoloured .. 45 45

1977. Children's Week and 9th "Joy of Europe" meeting, Belgrade. Children's Paintings. Multicoloured.
1782. 4 d. 90 Type **507** .. 20 5
1783. 10 d. "One Fruit into Pail—the other into Mouth" (T. Ilinskaja) 70 50

508. Congress Building, Belgrade. **509.** Exhibition Emblem.

1977. European Security and Co-operation Conference, Belgrade (2nd issue).
1784. **508.** 4 d. 90 grey, blue & gold 25 15
1785. 10 d. red, rose & gold 1·50 1·50

1977. "Balkanphila 6" Stamp Exhibition, Belgrade.
1786. **509.** 4 d. 90 multicoloured 12 10

510. Double Flute.

511. Ivan Vavpotic. **512.** Globe and Olympic Rings.

1977. Musical Instruments in Ethnographical Museum, Belgrade.
1787. **510.** 1 d. 50 brn. & yellow 8 5
1788. – 3 d. 40 brn. & green .. 20 5
1789. – 4 d. 90 yell. & brown 25 5
1790. – 6 d. brown and blue .. 30 15
1791. – 8 d. brown & orange 50 25
1792. – 10 d. brown & green .. 65 55
DESIGNS: 3 d. 40, Tamburitza. 4 d. 90, Fiddle. 6 d. Lijerica. 8 d. Bagpipe. 10 d. Pan's flute.

1977. Self-portraits (10th series). Mult.
1793. 1 d. 50 Type **511** 8 5
1794. 3 d. 40 Mihailo Vukotic .. 15 10
1795. 4 d. 90 Kosta Hakman .. 20 10
1796. 6 d. Miroslav Kraljevic .. 25 15
1797. 8 d. Nikola Martinovski 35 20
1798. 10 d. Milena Pavlovic-Barili 60 65

1977. Obligatory Tax. Olympic Games Fund.
1799. **512.** 10 p. yell., tur. and bl. 5 5

513. "Ceremony of Testaccio" (miniature from Officium Virginis). **514.** Pre-stamp Letter (Bavaniste-Kubin).

1978. 400th Death Anniv. of Julije Klovic (Croat miniaturist). Multicoloured.
1800. 4 d. 90 Type **513** 20 5
1801. 10 d. "Portrait of Klovic" (El Greco) 50 35

1978. Post Office Museum Exhibits. Mult.
1802. 1 d. 50 Type **514** .. 8 5
1803. 3 d. 40 19th century mail box 12 5
1804. 4 d. 90 Ericsson induction table telephone 20 10
1805. 10 d. Morse's first electromagnetic telegraph set 40 40

515. Battle of Pirot.

1978. Centenary of Serbo-Turkish War.
1806. **515.** 1 d. 50 multicoloured 90 45

516. "S-49" Fighter.

1978. Aeronautical Day.
1807. **516.** 1 d. 50 pink, brown and orange .. 10 10
1808. – 3 d. 40 blue, black and slate 15 10
1809. – 4 d. 90 black and brn. 30 10
1810. – 10 d. yellow, brown and olive .. 55 50
DESIGNS: 3 d. 40, "Gull" trainer. 4 d. 90, "Wild Duck" jet trainer. 10 d. "Eagle" jet fighter.

517. Golubac. **518.** Boxing Glove on Glove.

1978. Europa. Multicoloured.
1811. 4 d. 90 Type **517** .. 20 15
1812. 10 d. St. Naum Monastery 1·00 1·00

1978. Second World Amateur Boxing Championship, Belgrade.
1813. **518.** 4 d. 90 brown, blue and deep blue 20 10

519. Symbols of Red Crescent, Red Cross and Red Lion. **520.** "Apis mellifera".

1978. Obligatory Tax. Red Cross Week. No. 1814 surch.
1814. **519.** 20 p. on 1 d. bl. & red 30 5
1815. 1 d. blue and red .. 10 5

1978. Bees. Multicoloured.
1816 1 d. 50 Type **520** .. 10 5
1817 3 d. 40 "Halictus scabiosae" 25 10
1818 4 d. 90 "Xylocopa violacea" 40 15
1819 10 d. "Bombus terrestris" 85 65

521. Filip Filipovic and Radovan Dragovic. **522.** President Tito (poster).

1978. Birth Centenaries of F. Filipovic and R. Dragovic (socialist movement leaders).
1820. **521.** 1 d. 50 green and red 8 5

1978. 11th Communist League Congress. Multicoloured.
1821. 2 d. Type **522** 10 5
1822. 4 d. 90 Hammer and Sickle (poster) 25 10

1978. Various stamps surch.
1829. – 35 p. on 10 p. brown (No. 1642) .. 12 5
1830. **332.** 60 p. on 85 p. blue (No. 1271) 12 5
1831. **443.** 80 p. on 1 d. 20 green (No. 1599) 12 5
1832. – 2 d. on 1 d. green (No. 1657) .. 12 5
1833. – 3 d. 40 on 2 d. 10 green (No. 1662) 20 8

524. Conference Emblem over Belgrade. **525.** Championship Emblem.

1978. Conference of Foreign Ministers of Non-aligned Countries.
1834. **524.** 4 d. 90 blue and pale blue 10 5

1978. 14th Kayak and Canoe "Still Water" World Championships, Belgrade.
1835. **525.** 4 d. 90 black, blue and light blue .. 20 10

526. North Face, Mount Triglav. **527.** Hand holding Flame.

1978. Bicent. of First Ascent of Mount Triglav.
1836. **526.** 2 d. multicoloured .. 12 5

1978. Obligatory Tax. Anti-tuberculosis Week.
1837. **527.** 1 d. multicoloured .. 20 10

528. Black Lake, Durmitor. **529.** Olympic Rings on Map of World.

1978. Protection of the Environment. Multicoloured.
1838. 4 d. 90 Type **528** .. 25 10
1839. 10 d. River Tara .. 60 40

1978. Obligatory Tax. Olympic Games Fund.
1840. **529.** 30 p. multicoloured .. 10 5

530. Star Map.

1978. 29th International Astronautical Federation Congress, Dubrovnik.
1841. **530.** 4 d. 90 multicoloured 20 10

531. "People in Forest" (I. Balen). **532.** Seal.

1978. Children's Week and 10th "Joy of Europe" Meeting, Belgrade. Mult.
1842. 4 d. 90 Type **531** .. 20 5
1843. 10 d. "Family round a Pond" (V. Christel) .. 70 40

1978. Centenary of Kresna Uprising.
1844. **532.** 2 d. black, brown and gold 12 5

533. Old College Building. **534.** Red Cross.

1978. Bicentenary of Teachers' Training College, Sombor.
1845. **533.** 2 d. brn., yell. & gold 12 5

1978. Cent. of Croatian Red Cross.
1846. **534.** 2 d. red, blue & black 12 5

535. Metallic Sculpture "XXII" (D. Dzamonja).

1978. Modern Sculpture.
1847. **535.** 2 d. blk., brn. & silver 10 5
1848. – 3 d. 40 blue, grey and silver 15 8
1849. – 4 d. 90 olive, brown and silver 15 10
1850. – 10 d. brown, buff and silver 40 45
DESIGNS—VERT. 3 d. 40, "Circulation in Space I" (V. Bakic). 4 d. 90, "Tectonic Octopode" (O. Jevric). HORIZ. 10 d. "The Tree of Life" (D. Trsar).

536. "Crossing the Neretva". (I. Mujezinovic). **537.** "People from the Seine" (Marijan Detoni).

1978. 35th Anniv. of Battle of Neretva.
1851. **536.** 2 d. multicoloured .. 15 5

1978. Republic Day. Graphic Art.
1852. **537.** 2 d. black, stone and gold 10 5
1853. – 3 d. 40 black, grey and gold 12 5
1854. – 4 d. 90 black, yellow and gold 15 10
1855. – 6 d. black, flesh and gold 20 12
1856. – 10 d. black, flesh and gold 35 40
DESIGNS: 3 d. 40, "Labourers" (Maksim Sedej). 4 d. 90, "Felling of Trees" (Daniel Ozmo). 6 d. "At a Meal" (Pivo Karamatijevic). 10 d. "They are not afraid even at a most loathsome crime" (Djordje Andrejevic Kun).

538. Eurasian Red Squirrel. **539.** Masthead.

1978. New Year. Multicoloured.
1857. 1 d. 50 Type **538** .. 15 10
1858. 1 d. 50 Larch 15 10
1859. 2 d. Red deer 15 10
1860. 2 d. Sycamore 15 10
1861. 3 d. 40 Rock partridge (pink background) 75 15
1861a. 3 d. 40 Rock partridge (green background) 50 25
1862. 3 d. 40 Alder (pink background) 25 10
1862a. 3 d. 40 Alder (green background) 40 12
1863. 4 d. 90 Capercaillie (green background) 85 15
1863a. 4 d. 90 Capercaillie (yellow background) .. 70 25
1864. 4 d. 90 Oak (green background) 30 10
1864a. 4 d. 90 Oak (yellow background) 55 25

1979. 75th Anniv. of "Politika" Newspaper.
1865. **539.** 2 d. black and gold 12 5

540. Flags. **541.** Games Mascot.

1979. 10th Anniv. of Self-Managers' Meeting.
1866. **540.** 2 d. multicoloured .. 12 5

1979. Obligatory Tax. Mediterranean Games, Fund.
1867. **541.** 1 d. blue & deep blue 12 5
See also No. 1886.

542. Child. **543.** Sabre, Mace and Enamluk (box holding Koranic texts).

1979. Int. Year of the Child.
1868. **542.** 4 d. 90 blue and gold 40 30

1979. Ancient Weapons from Ethnographic Museum, Belgrade. Multicoloured.
1869. 2 d. Type **543** 10 5
1870. 3 d. 40 Pistol and ammunition stick .. 15 10
1871. 4 d. 90 Carbine and powder-horn .. 25 10
1872. 10 d. Rifle and cartridge-pouch 55 45

544. Hammer and Sickle on Star. **545.** Kiril-Metodij University.

1979. 60th Anniv. of Yugoslav Communist Party and League of Communist Youth.
1873. **544.** 2 d. multicoloured .. 10 8
1874. 4 d. 90 multicoloured 25 12

1979. 30th Anniv. of Kiril-Metodij University.
1875. **545.** 2 d. brown, buff & pink 10 5

546. " Panorama of Belgrade " (C. Goebel). **547.** Stylized Bird.

1979. Europa. Multicoloured.
1876. 4 d. 90 Type **546** .. 12 12
1877. 10 d. Postilion and view of Ljubljana (after Jan van der Heyden) .. 40 40

1979. Obligatory Tax. Red Cross Week.
1878. **547.** 1 d. turq., blue and red 12 5

548. " Cicerbita alpina ". **549.** Milutin Milankovic (after Paja Jovanovic).

1979. Alpine Flowers. Multicoloured.
1879. 2 d. Type **548** 10 5
1880. 3 d. 40 " Anemone narcissiflora " 15 10
1881. 4 d. 90 " Astragalus sempervirens " .. 30 12
1882. 10 d. " Trifolium alpinum " 60 40

1979. Birth Centenary of Milutin Milankovic (scientist).
1883. **549.** 4 d. 90 multicoloured 20 10

550. Kosta Abrasevic. **551.** Rowing Crew.

1979. Birth Cent. of Kosta Abrasevic (poet).
1884. **550.** 2 d. grey, pink & blk. 10 5

1979. Obligatory Tax. Solidarity Week. As T **469** but inscribed "1.-7.VI".
1885. 30 p. blk., grey and blue 12 5

1979. Obligatory Tax. Mediterranean Games Fund. As No. 1867 but colour changed.
1886. **541.** 1 d. blue & deep blue 10 5

1979. Ninth World Rowing Championships. Lake Bled.
1887. **551.** 4 d. 90 multicoloured 30 10

552. Games Emblem. **553.** Girl playing Hopscotch.

1979. Eighth Mediterranean Games. Mult.
1888. 2 d. Type **552** 10 8
1889. 4 d. 90 Mascot and emblem 20 10
1890. 10 d. Map and flags of participating countries 45 40

1979. Obligatory Tax. Anti-tuberculosis Week.
1891. **553.** 1 d. multicoloured .. 10 5

554. Arms of Zagreb. **555.** Lake Palic.

1979. 450th Anniv. of Zagreb Postal Service.
1892. **554.** 2 d. grey and red .. 12 5

1979. Environment Protection. Mult.
1893. 4 d. 90 Type **555** .. 20 10
1894. 10 d. Lake in Prokletije range 55 30

556. Emblems. **557.** Street in Winter (Mirjana Markovic).

1979. Meeting of International Bank for Reconstruction and Development and of International Monetary Fund.
1895. **556.** 4 d. 90 multicoloured 20 10
1896. 10 d. multicoloured 40 30

1979. 11th " Joy of Europe " Meeting, Belgrade. Children's Paintings. Mult.
1897. 4 d. 90 Type **557** .. 20 10
1898. 10 d. House and Garden (Jacques An) 65 45

558. Mihailo Pupin. **559.** Olympic Rings.

1979. 125th Birth Anniv. of Mihailo Pupin (scientist).
1899. **558.** 4 d. 90 brown, light blue and blue .. 20 10

1979. Obligatory Tax. Olympic Games Fund.
1900. **559.** 30 p. red and blue .. 8 5

560. Marko Cepenkov. **561.** Pristina University.

1979. 150th Birth Anniv. of Marko Cepenkov (author and folklorist).
1901. **560.** 2 d. multicoloured .. 15 5

1979. 10th Anniv. of Pristina University.
1902. **561.** 2 d. multicoloured .. 10 5

562. Lion on Column (Trogir Cathedral). **563.** Sarajevo University.

1979. Romanesque Sculpture. Multicoloured.
1903. 2 d. Type **562** 10 5
1904. 3 d. 40 Apostle (detail of choir stall, Split Cathedral) 15 5
1905. 4 d. 90 Window (Church of the Ascension, Deconi) 20 10
1906. 6 d. Detail of Buvina door (Split Cathedral) 30 15
1907. 10 d. Virgin and child (West door, Church of the Virgin, Studenica) 40 40

1979. 30th Anniv. of Sarajevo University.
1908. **563.** 2 d. blk., brn. & grey 10 5

564. Djakovic and Hecimovic.

1979. 50th Death Anniv. of Djuro Djakovic and Nikola Hecimovic (leaders of socialist movement).
1909. **564.** 2 d. multicoloured .. 10 5

565. Paddle Steamer " Serbia ".

1979. Danube Conference. Multicoloured.
1910. 4 d. 90 Paddle steamer " Deligrad " 75 50
1911. 10 d. Type **565** .. .. 1·50 1·00

566. Milton Manaki. **567.** Edvard Kardelj.

1980. Birth Centenary of Milton Manaki (first Balkan film maker).
1912. **566.** 2 d. purple and ochre 12 5

1980. 70th Birth Anniv. of Edvard Kardelj (revolutionary).
1913. **567.** 2 d. multicoloured .. 10 5

1980. Renaming of Ploce as Kardeljevo. No. 1913 optd. with **PLOCE—1980—KARDELJEVO.**
1914. **567.** 2 d. multicoloured .. 12 12

569. Speed Skating.

1980. Winter Olympic Games, Lake Placid. Multicoloured.
1915. 4 d. 90 Type **569** .. 15 10
1916. 10 d. Skiing 75 70

570. Belgrade University.

1980. 75th Anniv. of Belgrade University.
1917. **570.** 2 d. multicoloured .. 10 5

571. Fencing.

1980. Olympic Games, Moscow. Multicoloured.
1918. 2 d. Type **571** 8 5
1919. 3 d. 40 Cycling 15 5
1920. 4 d. 90 Hockey 20 10
1921. 10 d. Archery 40 40

572. President Tito (relief by Antun Augustincic). **573.** Pres. Tito.

1980. Europa. Multicoloured.
1922. 4 d. 90 Type **572** .. 25 25
1923. 13 d. Portrait of Tito by Djordje Prudnikov .. 1·75 1·75

1980. Death of President Tito. Portraits by Bozidar Jakac.
1924. **573.** 2 d. 50 purple .. 12 5
1925. – 4 d. 90 black .. 30 20
DESIGN: 4 d. 90 Different portrait of President Tito.

574. Sculpture by S. Kovacevic. **575.** Sava Kovacevic.

1980. Obligatory Tax. Red Cross Week.
1926. **574.** 1 d. multicoloured .. 12 8

1980. 75th Birth Anniv. of Sava Kovacevic (partisan).
1927. **575.** 2 d. brown, orange and yellow .. 10 5

576. Estafette and Letter from Youth of Belgrade, 1945.

1980. 35th Anniv. of Tito's First Estafette (youth celebration of Tito's birthday).
1928. **576.** 2 d. multicoloured .. 12 10

577. Flying Gurnard. **578.** Decius Trajan (249–51).

1980. Adriatic Sea Fauna. Multicoloured.
1929. 2 d. Type **577** 12 10
1930. 3 d. 40 Turtle 25 15
1931. 4 d. 90 Little tern 80 15
1932. 10 d. Common dolphin .. 45 40

1980. Obligatory Tax. Solidarity Week. As No. 1885.
1933. **469.** 1 d. blk., grey and blue 12 8

1980. Roman Emperors on Coins. Multicoloured.
1934. 2 d. Type **578** 12 5
1935. 3 d. 40 Aurelian (270–5) 20 10
1936. 4 d. 90 Probus (276–82) 30 12
1937. 10 d. Diocletian (284–305) 55 40

1980. Nos. 1660 and 1652 surch.
1938. 2 d. 50 on 1 d. 50 red .. 12 5
1939. 5 d. on 75 p. purple .. 40 10

580. Lipica Horses.

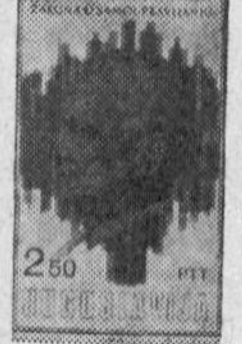
581. Tito.

1980. 400th Anniv. of Lipica Stud Farm.
1940. **580.** 2 d. 50 black .. 20 10

1980. 30th Anniv. of Self-Management Law.
1941. **581.** 2 d. dp. red and red 10 5

582. Novi Sad University.

583. Mljet.

1980. 20th Anniv. Novi Sad University.
1942. **582.** 2 d. 50 green .. 10 5

1980. Protection of the Environment. Mult.
1943. 4 d. 90 Type **583** .. 25 10
1944. 13 d. Galicica, Ohrid .. 65 50

584. Pyrrhotine.

585. Lake.

1980. Crystals. Multicoloured.
1945. 2 d. 50 Type **584** .. 10 5
1946. 3 d. 40 Dolomite .. 15 8
1947. 4 d. 90 Sphalerite .. 25 12
1948. 13 d. Wulfenite 50 40

1980. Obligatory Tax. Anti-Tuberculosis Week.
1949. **585.** 1 d. multicoloured .. 12 5

586. Kotor.

1980. 21st Session of U.N.E.S.C.O. General Conference, Belgrade.
1950. **586.** 4 d. 90 blue, gold and deep blue 20 10

587. "Children with Balloons" (Gabrijela Radojevic).

588. Olympic Flag and Globe.

1980. 12th "Joy of Europe" Meeting, Belgrade. Multicoloured.
1951. 4 d. 90 Type **587** .. 20 10
1952. 13 d. "Face" (Renata Pisarcikova) .. 65 40

1980. Obligatory Tax. Olympic Games Fund.
1953. **588.** 50 p. multicoloured .. 5 5

589. Dove and Madrid. **590.** Flag of Bosnia and Herzegovina Socialist Republic.

1980. European Security and Co-operation Conference, Madrid.
1954. **589.** 4 d. 90 green and deep green 20 12
1955. 13 d. bistre and brown 40 40

1980. Flags of Yugoslavian Socialist Republics and of Federal Republic.
1956. 2 d. 50 multicoloured .. 10 8
1957. 2 d. 50 multicoloured .. 10 8
1958. 2 d. 50 multicoloured .. 10 8
1959. 2 d. 50 multicoloured .. 10 8
1960. 2 d. 50 multicoloured .. 10 8
1961. 2 d. 50 red, gold and grey 10 8
1962. 2 d. 50 multicoloured .. 10 8
1963. 2 d. 50 multicoloured .. 10 8

DESIGNS: No. 1956, Type **590**. 1957, Montenegro. 1958, Croatia. 1959, Yugoslavia (inscr. in Roman alphabet). 1960, Yugoslavia (inscr. in Cyrillic alphabet). 1961, Macedonia. 1962, Slovenia. 1963, Serbia.

591. "Complaint" (Milos Vuskovic).

1980. Paintings. Multicoloured.
1964. 2 d. 50 "Woman in a Straw Hat" (Stojan Aralica) (horiz.) .. 10 5
1965. 3 d. 40 "Atelier No. 1" (Gabrijel Stupica) (horiz.) 15 5
1966. 4 d. 90 "To the Glory of Sutjeska Fighters" (detail, Ismet Mejezinovic) (horiz.) .. 20 8
1967. 8 d. "Serenity" (Marino Tartaglia) 35 12
1968. 13 d. Type **591** 50 45

592. Sports Complex, Novi Sad.

593. Ivan Ribar.

1980. Obligatory Tax. World Table Tennis Championships, Novi Sad.
1969. **592.** 1 d. grn., yell. & bl. 12 5

1981. Birth Cent. of Ivan Ribar (politician).
1970. **593.** 2 d. 50 black and red 10 5

594. "Cementusa" Hand Bomb.

1981. Partisan Arms in Belgrade Military Museum.
1971. **594.** 3 d. 50 black & red .. 15 5
1972. – 5 d. 60 black & green 25 5
1973. – 8 d. black and brown 30 10
1974. – 13 d. black & purple 45 35

DESIGNS: 5 d. 60, "Partizanka" rifle. 8 d. Cannon. 13 d. Tank.

595. Virgin of Eleousa Monastery.

596. Table Tennis.

1981. 900th Anniv. of Virgin of Eleousa Monastery, Veljusa, Macedonia.
1975. **595.** 3 d. 50 grey, brown and blue 12 5

1981. "SPENS '81" World Table Tennis Championships, Novi Sad.
1976. **596.** 8 d. multicoloured .. 30 15

597. "Lamp".

598. "Herzegovinian Wedding" (detail).

1981. Obligatory Tax. Red Cross Week.
1977. **597.** 1 d. multicoloured .. 10 5

1981. Europa. Paintings by Nikola Arsenovic. Multicoloured.
1978. 8 d. Type **598** 25 10
1979. 13 d. "Witnesses at a Wedding" 50 30

599. Tucovic and Dimitrije Tucovic Square.

600. Tito (after Milivoje Unkovic).

1981. Birth Centenary of Dimitrije Tucovic (socialist leader).
1980. **599.** 3 d. 50 blue and red 12 5

1981. 89th Birth Anniv. of Tito.
1981. **600.** 3 d. 50 multicoloured 35 15

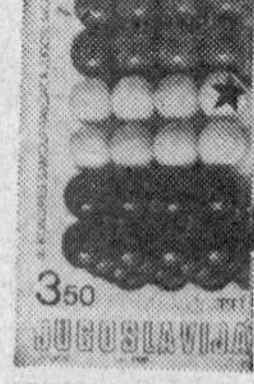

601. Sunflower.

602. Congress Emblem.

1981. Cultivated Plants. Multicoloured.
1982. 3 d. 50 Type **601** .. 15 5
1983. 5 d. 60 Hop 20 12
1984. 8 d. Corn 30 15
1985. 13 d. Wheat 60 35

1981. 3rd Congress of Self-Managers.
1986. **602.** 3 d. 50 multicoloured 12 5

603. Djordje Petrov. **604.** Star.

1981. 60th Death Anniv. of Djordje Petrov (politician).
1987. **603.** 3 d. 50 black & brn. 12 5

1981. 40th Anniv. of Yugoslav Insurrection.
1988. **604.** 3 d. 50 yellow & red 12 5
1989. 8 d. orange and red 25 15

605. Apple and Target.

1981. Obligatory Tax. "Spet '81" European Shooting Championships, Titograd.
1991. **605.** 1 d. blue, red & orge. 3·00 3·00

1981. Nos. 1666 and 1669 surch.
1992. 3 d. 50 on 3 d. 40 green .. 25 5
1993. 5 d. on 4 d. 90 blue .. 25 5

606. Varazdin (18th-century illustration).

1981. 800th Anniv. of Varazdin.
1994. **606.** 3 d. 50 yellow & blue 12 5

607. Parliament Building, Belgrade.

608. "Flower".

1981. 20th Anniv. of 1st Non-aligned Countries Conference, Belgrade.
1995. **607.** 8 d. blue and red .. 25 10

1981. Obligatory Tax. Anti-Tuberculosis Week.
1996. **608.** 1 d. red, yellow & bl. 12 5

609. Printing Press and Serbian Newspaper.

1981. 150th Anniv. of First Serbian Printing House.
1997. **609.** 3 d. 50 pink and blue 12 5

610. Fran Levstik.

1981. 150th Birth Anniv. of Fran Levstik (writer).
1998. **610.** 3 d. 50 grey and red 12 5

611. Village Scene (Saso Arsovski).

1981. 13th "Joy of Europe" Meeting, Belgrade. Multicoloured.
1999. 8 d. Type **611** 20 10
2000. 13 d. Skiers (Aino Jokinen) 55 45

612. Pusher "Karlovac".

1981. 125th Anniv. of European Danube Commission. Multicoloured.
2001. 8 d. Type **612** 50 25
2002. 13 d. Sip Canal .. .. 1·25 70

613. Postal Savings Bank Emblem.

614. Emblem.

1981. 60th Anniv. of Postal Savings Bank.
2003. **613.** 3 d. 50 red & yellow 12 5

1982. World Intellectual Property Organization. Conference.
2004. **614.** 8 d. red and gold .. 25 15

615. Forsythia and Rugovo Ravine. **616.** August Senoa.

1981. Protection of Nature. Multicoloured.
2005. 8 d. Type **615** 25 10
2006. 13 d. Lynx and Prokletije 60 40

1981. Death Centenary of August Senoa (writer).
2007. **616.** 3 d. 50 purple and brown 12 5

617. "Still-life with Fish" (Jovan Bijelic).

1981. Paintings of Animals. Multicoloured.
2008. 3 d. 50 Type **617** 12 5
2009. 5 d. 60 "Raven" (Milo Milunovic) 35 10
2010. 8 d. "Bird on Blue Background" (Marko Celebonovic) 45 10
2011. 10 d. "Horses" (Peter Lubarda) 40 15
2012. 13 d. "Sheep" (Nikola Masic) 40 35

618. Mosa Pijade (politician).

1982. 40th Anniv. of Foca Regulations.
2013. **618.** 3 d. 50 blue & mve. 12 5

619. Mastheads. **620.** Cetinje.

1982. 60th Anniv. of "Borba" (newspaper).
2014. **619.** 3 d. 50 black and red 12 5

1982. 500th Anniv. of City of Cetinje.
2015. **620.** 3 d. 50 brown & blk. 12 5

621. Visin's Ship "Splendido".

1982. Europa. Multicoloured.
2016. 8 d. Capt. Ivo Visin (first Yugoslav to sail round world) and naval chart 25 15
2017. 15 d. Type **621** 80 25

622. Clasped Hands. **624.** House Sparrow (male).

1982. Obligatory Tax. Red Cross Week.
2018. **622.** 1 d. black and red .. 10 5

1982. Multicoloured.
2020. 3 d. 50 Type **624** 30 10
2021. 5 d. 60 House Sparrow (female) 35 15
2022. 8 d. Spanish sparrow (female) 55 25
2023. 15 d. Tree sparrow (male) 1·40 40

625. "Tito" (after Dragan Dosen). **626.** Poster (Dobrilo Nikolic).

1982. 90th Birth Anniv. of Tito.
2024. **625.** 3 d. 50 multicoloured 12 5

1982. 12th Communist League Congress, Belgrade.
2025. **626.** 3 d. 50 brown, orange and red 12 5
2026. 8 d. light grey, grey and red 25 12

627. Jaksic (self-portrait). **628.** Kayaks.

1982. 150th Birth Anniv. of Dura Jaksic (writer and painter).
2028. **627.** 3 d. 50 multicoloured 12 5

1982. Sport Championships.
2029. **628.** 8 d. light blue and blue 25 12
2030. – 8 d. light green and green 25 12
2031. – 8 d. pink and red .. 25 12

DESIGNS AND EVENTS: No. 2029, Type **628** (17th World Kayaks and Canoe Still Water Championships, Belgrade). 2030, Weightlifting (36th World Weightlifting Championships, Ljubljana). 2031, Gymnastics (6th World Gymnastics Cup, Zagreb).

629. Ivan Zajc. **630.** "Breguet XIX" and Potez "XXV" Aircraft.

1982. 150th Birth Anniv. of Ivan Zajc (composer).
2032. **629.** 4 d. orange & brown 15 5

1982. 40th Anniv. of Air Force, Anti-aircraft Defence and Navy.
2033. **630.** 4 d. black and blue 20 10
2034. – 6 d. 10 multicoloured 30 10
2035. – 8 d. 80 black & grn. 50 15
2036. – 15 d. multicoloured 90 30

DESIGNS: 6 d. 10, "Super Galeb-4" jet. 8 d. 80, National Liberation Army armed tug. 15 d. "Rade Koncar" (missile gunboat).

631. Tara National Park and Pine Cones.

1982. Nature Protection. Multicoloured.
2037. 8 d. 80 Type **631** .. 25 15
2038. 15 d. Kornati National Park and Mediterranean monk seal .. 50 40

632. Dr. Robert Koch.

1982. Obligatory Tax. Anti-Tuberculosis Week.
2039. **632.** 1 d. orge., blk. & red 10 5

633. "Traffic" (Tibo Bozo).

1982. 14th "Joy of Europe" Meeting, Belgrade. Children's Drawings. Mult.
2040. 8 d. 80 Type **633** 25 15
2041. 15 d. "In the Bath" (Heiko Jakel) .. 50 35

634. Small Onofrio Fountain, Dubrovnik.

1982. 16th World Federation of Travel Agents' Associations Congress, Dubrovnik.
2042. **634.** 8 d. 80 multicoloured 25 12

635. Herceg Novi (from old engraving).

1982. 600th Anniv. of Herceg Novi.
2043. **635.** 4 d. multicoloured .. 15 8

636. Bridge, Miljacka. **637.** Bihac.

1982. Winter Olympic Games, Sarajevo. Each black, light blue and blue.
2044. 4 d. Type **636** 25 15
2045. 6 d. 10 Mosque tower and cable cars, Sarajevo .. 30 20
2046. 8 d. 80 Evangelical Church, Sarajevo .. 40 25
2047. 15 d. Old Street, Sarajevo 55 40

1982. 40th Anniv. of Avnoj-a (anti-fascist council) Session, Bihac.
2048. **637.** 4 d. brown & orange 15 8

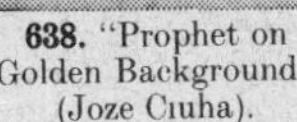

638. "Prophet on Golden Background" (Joze Ciuha). **639.** Predic (self-portrait).

1982. Modern Art. Multicoloured.
2049. 4 d. Type **638** 15 8
2050. 6 d. 10 "Journey to the West" (Andrej Jemec) 20 10
2051. 8 d. 80 "Black Comb with Red Band" (Riko Debenjak) 25 15
2052. 10 d. "Manuscript" (Janez Bernik) (horiz.) 30 20
2053. 15 d. "Display Case" (Adriane Maraz) (horiz.) 50 35

1982. 125th Birth Anniv. of Uros Predic (painter).
2054. **639.** 4 d. orange and brn. 15 8

1983. Nos. 1663 and 1667 surch.
2057. 30 p. on 2 d. 50 blue .. 10 5
2055a. 50 p. on 2 d. 50 blue .. 5 5
2058. 60 p. on 2 d. 50 blue .. 10 5
2059a. 1 d. on 3 d. 50 red .. 10 5
2060. 2 d. on 2 d. 50 red .. 5 5

641. Pioneer Badge. **644.** Lead Pitcher (16th century).

1982. 40th Anniv. of Pioneer League.
2056. **641.** 4 d. brown, silver and red 15 8

1983. Museum Exhibits.
2061. **644.** 4 d. black, bistre and silver 10 5
2062. – 6 d. 10 black, brown and silver 15 8
2063. – 8 d. 80 gold, purple and grey 20 12
2064. – 15 d. gold, purple and grey 40 25

DESIGNS: 6 d 10, Silver-plated tin jar (18th century). 8 d. 80, Silver-gilt dish (16th century). 15 d. Bronze mortar (15th century).

645. Jalovec Mountain Peak and Edelweiss. **646.** Ericsson Wall Telephone and War Ministry, Belgrade.

1983. 90th Anniv. of Slovenian Mountaineering Society.
2065. **645.** 4 d. blue, light blue and deep blue .. 10 5

1983. Centenary of Telephone in Serbia.
2066. **646.** 3 d. brown and blue 8 5

647. I.M.O. Emblem and Freighters. **648.** Field Mushroom.

1983. 25th Anniv. of International Maritime Organization.
2067. **647.** 8 d. 80 multicoloured 35 15

1983. Edible Mushrooms. Multicoloured.
2068. 4 d. Type **648** 15 5
2069. 6 d. 10 Morel 25 10
2070. 8 d. 80 Cep 40 15
2071. 15 d. Chanterelle .. 80 30

649. Series "401" Steam Locomotive. **650.** Monument, Landovica.

1983. 110th Anniv. of Rijeka Railway.
2072. **649.** 4 d. grey and red .. 20 10
2073. – 23 d. 70 on 8 d. 80 red and grey 60 30

DESIGN: 23 d. 70 Series "442" electric locomotive.

No. 2073 was only issued surcharged.

1983. 40th Death Annivs. of Boro Vukmirovic and Ramiz Sadiku (revolutionaries).
2074. **650.** 4 d. grey and violet 10 5

651. Nobel Prize Medal and Manuscript of "Travnik Chronicle" by Andric.

1983. Europa. Multicoloured.
2075. 8 d. 80 Type **651** .. 20 15
2076. 20 d. Ivo Andric (author and Nobel Prize winner) and bridge over the Drina .. 50 40

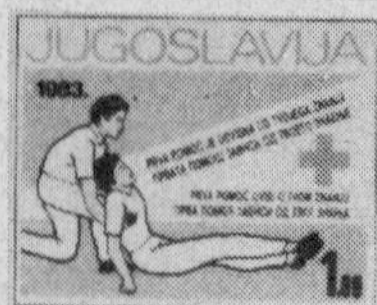

652. First Aid.

1983. Obligatory Tax. Red Cross Week.
2077. 652. 1 d. deep brown, brown and red .. 12 8
2078. 2 d. deep brown, brown and red .. 15 8

653. Combine Harvester.
654. " Assault " (Pivo Karamatijevic).

1983. 50th International Agriculture Fair, Novi Sad.
2079. 653. 4 d. green and purple 10 5

1983. 40th Anniv. of Battle of Sutjeska.
2080. 654. 3 d. pink and brown 8 5

655. Tito (after Bozidar Jakac) and Parliament Building.
656. Delahaye Postbus 1903.

1983. 30th Anniv. of Tito's Election to Presidency.
2081. 655. 4 d. brown and green 10 5

1983. 80th Anniv. of Postbus Service in Montenegro.
2082. 656. 4 d. black and brown 10 5
2083. – 16 d. 50 brown & black 40 25
DESIGN: 16 d. 50, Road used by first postbus.

657. Statue by V. Bakic, Valjevo.
658. Graph.

1983. Monuments.
2084. 657. 100 d. orge. & blue .. 1·25 50
2085. – 200 d. orge. & green .. 2·25 50
DESIGN—HORIZ. 200 d. Triumphal arch, Titograd.

1983. Sixth U.N. Conference for Trade and Development Session, Belgrade.
2086. 658. 23 d. 70 multicoloured 50 30

659. Pazin (after engraving by Valvasor).
660. Skopje.

1983. Millenary of Pazin.
2087. 659. 4 d. brown & green 10 5

1983. 20th Anniv. of Skopje Earthquake.
2088. 660. 23 d. 70 red 50 30

661. "The Victor".
662. Gentian and Kupaonik National Park.

1983. Birth Cent. of Ivan Mestrovic (sculptor).
2089. 681. 6 d. deep brown, brown and blue .. 15 8

1983. Nature Protection. Multicoloured.
2090. 16 d. 50 Type 662 .. 40 25
2091. 23 d. 70 Chamois and Sutjeska National Park 50 30

663. Apple.
664. "Newly Weds". (Vesna Paunkovic).

1983. Obligatory Tax. Anti-Tuberculosis Week.
2092. 663. 1 d. red blk. & turq. 10 5
2093. 2 d. red, blk. & turq. 12 5

1983. 15th "Joy of Europe" Meeting Belgrade.
2094. 664. 16 d. 50 yellow, black and red 40 25
2095. – 23 d. 70 mult. .. 50 30
DESIGN: 23 d. 70, "Andres and his Mother" (Marta Lopez-Ibor).

665. School and Seal.
666. Monument by Antun Augustincic.

1983. 150th Anniv. of Kragujevac Grammar School.
2096. 665. 5 d brown & blue .. 10 5

1983. Cent. of Uprising Timocka Buna.
2097. 686. 5 d. blue & purple .. 10 5

667. Skier and Games Emblem.
668. Zmaj and "Neven" Periodical

1983. Obligatory Tax. Winter Olympic Games, Sarajevo.
2098. 667. 2 d. blue & deep blue 15 5

1983. 150th Birth Anniv. of Jovan Jovanovic Zmaj (poet and editor).
2099. 668. 5 d. red and green .. 10 5

669. Ski Jump, Malo Polje, Mt. Igman.

1983. Winter Olympic Games, Sarajevo (1st issue).
2100. 669. 4 d. blk., grn. & brn. 8 5
2101. – 4 d. dp. bl., bl. & brn. 8 5
2102. – 16 d. 50 lilac, deep brown and brown 35 20
2103. – 16 d. 50 grn., bl. & brn. 35 30
2104. – 23 d. 70 deep brown, green and brown .. 45 30
2105. – 23 d. 70 black, green and brown .. 45 30
DESIGNS: No. 2101, Women's slalom run, Mt. Jahorina. 2102, Bob-sleigh and luge run, Mt. Trebevic. 2103, Men's alpine downhill ski run, Mt. Bjelasnica. 2104, Olympic Hall (for ice hockey and figure skating, Zetra. 2105, Speed skating rink, Zetra.

670. "The Peasant Wedding" (Brueghel the Younger).
671. Jajce.

1983. Paintings. Multicoloured.
2107. 4 d. Type 670 .. .. 8 5
2108. 16 d. 50 " Susanna and the Elders " (Master of " The Prodigal Son ") 35 20
2109. 16 d. 50 " The Allegory of Wisdom and Strength " (Veronese) 35 20
2110. 23 d. 70 " The Virgin Mary from Salamanca " (Robert Campin) .. 45 30
2111. 23 d. 70 " St. Anne with the Madonna and Jesus " (Durer) 45 30

1983. 40th Anniv. of 2nd Avnoja (anti-fascist council) Session, Jajce.
2112. 671. 5 d. red and blue .. 10 5

672. Drawing by Hasukic Sabina.
673. Koco Racin.

1983. World Communications Year.
2114 672 23 d. 70 multicoloured 40 25

1983. 75th Birth Anniv. of Koco Racin (writer).
2115 673 5 d. blue and brown .. 10 5

674. First Issue of " Politika ".
675. Veljko Petrovic.

1984. 80th Anniv. of "Politika" (daily newspaper).
2116. 674. 5 d. black and red .. 10 5

1984. Birth Cent. of Veljko Petrovic (writer).
2117. 675. 5 d. brown, orange & grey 10 5

676. Giant Slalom.

1984. Winter Olympic Games, Sarajevo (2nd issue). Multicoloured.
2118. 4 d. Type 676 .. .. 8 5
2119. 4 d. Biathlon 8 5
2120. 5 d. Slalom 10 5
2121. 5 d. Bobsleigh 10 5
2122. 16 d. 50 Speed skating .. 25 15
2123. 16 d. 50 Ice hockey .. 25 15
2124. 23 d. 70 Ski jump .. 35 20
2125. 23 d. 70 Downhill skiing 35 20

677. Marija Bursac.
678. Bond and Banknote.

1984. Women's Day. National Heroines. Each grey, blue and black.
2127. 5 d. Type 677 .. 10 5
2128. 5 d. Jelena Cetkovic .. 10 5
2129. 5 d. Nada Dimic .. 10 5
2130. 5 d. Elpida Karamandi .. 10 5
2131. 5 d. Toncka Cec Olga .. 10 5
2132. 5 d. Spasenija Babovic Cana 10 5
2133. 5 d. Jovanka Radivojevic Kica 10 5
2134. 5 d. Sonja Marinkovic .. 10 5

1984. 40th Anniv. of Slovenian Monetary Institute.
2135. 678. 5 d. blue and red .. 10 5

MORE DETAILED LISTS
are given in the Stanley Gibbons Catalogues referred to in the country headings.
For lists of current volumes see Introduction.

679. Belgrade Central Station and Steam Mail Train, 1884.
680. Jure Franko and Silver Medal.

1984. Centenary of Serbian Railway.
2136. 679. 5 d. brown and deep brown 10 5

1984. First Yugoslav Winter Olympics Medal.
2137. 680. 23 d. 70 mult. .. 35 20

681. Bridge.
682. Globe as Jigsaw Pieces.

1984. Europa. 25th Anniv. of European Post and Telecommunications Conference.
2138. 681. 23 d. 70 multicoloured 35 20
2139. 50 d. multicoloured 75 40

1984. Obligatory Tax. Red Cross Week.
2140. 682. 1 d. multicoloured .. 8 5
2141. 2 d. multicoloured .. 15 8
2142. 4 d. multicoloured .. 30 12
2143. 5 d. multicoloured .. 35 25

683. Basketball.

1984. Olympic Games, Los Angeles. Multicoloured.
2144. 5 d. Type 683 .. .. 10 5
2145. 16 d. 50 Diving 25 15
2146. 23 d. 70 Equestrian .. 35 20
2147. 50 d. Running 70 40

684. Tito (after Bozidar Jakac).
685. "Skopje Earthquake".

1984. 40th Anniv. of Failure of German Attack on National Liberation Movement's Headquarters at Drvar.
2148. 684. 5 d. brown and light brown 10 5

1984. Obligatory Tax. Solidarity Week.
2149. 685. 1 d. 50 blue and red

686. Mt. Biokovo Natural Park and "Centaurea gloriosa".

1984. Nature Protection. Multicoloured.
2150 26 d. Type 686 .. .. 40 25
2151 40 d. Pekel Cave and "Anophthalmus schmidti" 60 35

687. Great Black-backed Gull.

1984. Birds. Multicoloured.

2152. 4 d. Type **687** 15 5
2153. 5 d. Black-headed gull .. 15 8
2154. 16 d. 50 Herring gull .. 40 20
2155. 40 d. Common tern .. 90 45

688. Cradle from Bihac, Bosnia and Herzegovina.

1984. Museum Exhibits. Cradles.

2156. **688.** 4 d. green 8 5
2157. – 5 d. purple and red 10 5
2158. – 26 d. light brown and brown 35 20
2159. – 40 d. ochre and orge. 60 40

DESIGNS: Cradles from—5 d. Montenegro. 26 d. Macedonia. 40 d. Rasina, Serbia.

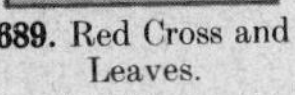

689. Red Cross and Leaves. **691.** National Costume (Erika Sarcevic).

690. Olive Tree, Mirovica.

1984. Obligatory Tax. Anti-tuberculosis Week.

2160. **689.** 1 d. multicoloured .. 5 5
2161. 2 d. multicoloured .. 8 5
2162. 2 d. 50 multicoloured 10 8
2163. 4 d. multicoloured .. 20 10
2164. 5 d. multicoloured .. 25 12

1984.

2165. **690.** 5 d. multicoloured .. 10 5

1984. 16th "Joy of Europe" Meeting, Belgrade. Children's paintings. Mult.

2166. 26 d. Type **691** .. 35 20
2167. 40 d. Girl pushing bear in buggy (Eva Gug) .. 60 40

692. Virovitica (17th-century engraving).

1984. 750th Anniv. of Virovitica.

2168. **692.** 5 d. orange and black 10 5

693. Map and Radio Waves. **694.** "Flower".

1984. 80th Anniv. of Radio-Telegraphic Service in Montenegro.

2169. **693.** 6 d. blue and green 12 10

1984. Veteran's Conference on Security, Disarmament and Co-operation in Europe, Belgrade.

2170. **694.** 26 d. pink, black and violet 90 90
2171. 40 d. green, black and blue 90 90

695. City Arms and "40". **696.** Milojevic and Music Score.

1984. 40th Anniv. of Liberation of Belgrade.

2172. **695.** 6 d. red, silver and blue 12 10

1984. Birth Centenary of Miloje Milojevic (composer).

2173. **696.** 6 d. lilac and green .. 12 10

697. Issues of 1944 and 1984.

1984. 40th Anniv. of "Nova Makedoniya" (newspaper).

2174. **697.** 6 d. blue and red .. 12 10

698. Boxing.

1984. Yugoslav Olympic Games Medal Winners. Each blue and red.

2175. 26 d. Type **698.** 35 20
2176. 26 d. Wrestling 35 20
2177. 26 d. Canoeing 35 20
2178. 26 d. Handball 35 20
2179. 26 d. Football 35 20
2180. 26 d. Basketball 35 20
2181. 26 d. Water polo .. 35 20
2182. 26 d. Rowing 35 20

699. "Madame Tatichek" (Ferdinand Waldmuller).

1984. Paintings. Multicoloured.

2183. 6 d. Type **699** 12 10
2184. 26 d. "The Bathers" (Pierre-Auguste Renoir) 35 20
2185. 26 d. "At the Window" (Henri Matisse) .. 35 20
2186. 38 d. "The Tahitians" (Paul Gauguin) (horiz.) 40 25
2187. 40 d. "The Ballerina" (Edgar Degas) (horiz.) 60 40

1984. Nos. 1675a, 1668a and 2088 surch.

2188a. 2 d. on 8 d. 80 grey .. 5 5
2189. 6 d. on 4 d. red 8 5
2190. 20 d. on 23 d. 70 red .. 25 10

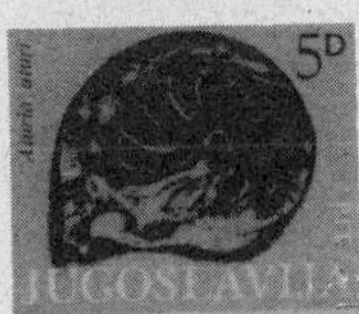

701. "Aturia aturi" (cephalopod).

1985. Museum Exhibits. Fossils.

2191. **701.** 5 d. purple and blue 8 5
2192. – 6 d. brown and light brown .. 10 5
2193. – 33 d. brown & yellow 40 25
2194. – 60 d. brown & orange 65 45

DESIGNS: 6 d. "Pachyophis woodwardi" (snake). 33 d. "Chaetodon hoeferi" (fish). 60 d. Skull of Neanderthal man.

702. Hopovo Church. **703.** Three Herons in Flight.

1985. 40th Anniv. of Organized Protection of Yugoslav Cultural Monuments.

2195. **702.** 6 d. red, yell. & grn. 10 5

1985. 50th Anniv. of Planica Ski-jump.

2196. **703.** 6 d. multicoloured .. 90 30

704. Lammergeier and Airplane over Mountains. **705.** Osprey.

1985. Air. Multicoloured.

2197. 500 d. Type **704.** .. 5·00 2·00
2199. 1000 d. Swallow and airplane at airport .. 10·00 4·50

1985. Nature Protection. Birds. Mult.

2202. 42 d. Type **705.** .. .. 1·25 55
2203. 60 d. Hoopoe .. .. 1·60 80

706. Three Herons in Flight. **707.** "St. Methodius" (detail, "Seven Slav Saints") (St. Naum's Church, Ohrid).

1985. Obligatory Tax. 50th Anniv. of Planica Ski-jump.

2204. **706.** 2 d. blue and green 10 5

1985. 1100th Death Anniv. of Saint Methodius, Archbishop of Moravia.

2205. **707.** 10 d. multicoloured 1·10 60

708. Handshake.

1985. Osimo Agreements between Yugoslavia and Italy.

2206. **708.** 6 d. blue & dp. blue 10 5

709. Flute, Darabukka and Josip Slavenski (composer).

1985. Europa. Multicoloured.

2207. 60 d. Type **709.** .. 60 60
2208. 80 d. Score of "Balkanophonia" (Slavenski) .. 60 60

710. Red Cross and Faces. **711.** Vujic (after Dimitrije Auramovic).

1985. Obligatory Tax. Red Cross Week.

2209. **710.** 1 d. violet and red .. 5 5
2210. 2 d. violet and red .. 5 5
2211. 3 d. violet and red .. 8 5
2212. 4 d. violet and red .. 15 8

1985. 150th Anniv. of Joakim Vujic Theatre, Kragujevac.

2213. **711.** 10 d. multicoloured 12 5

712. Order of Liberty.

1985. 40th Anniv. of V.E. (Victory in Europe) Day. Multicoloured.

2214. 10 d. Type **712** 12 5
2215. 10 d. Order of National Liberation 12 5

713. Franjo Kluz and Rudi Cajavec (pilots) and Breguet "19" Airplane. **714.** Tito (after Bozidar Jakac).

1985. Air Force Day.

2216 **713** 10 d. blue, pur & brn 30 10

1985. 93rd Birth Anniv. of Tito.

2217. **714.** 10 d. multicoloured 45 5

715. Red Cross and "Skopje Earthquake". **716.** Villa, Map of Islands and Arms.

1985. Obligatory Tax. Solidarity Week.

(a) As Nos. 1885 and 1933.

2218. 2 d. 50 blk., grey & bl. .. 10 5
2219. 3 d. black, grey and blue 10 5

(b) Type **715.**

2220. **715.** 3 d. blue and red .. 60 60

See also Nos. 2315/16, 2460 and 2532.

1985. Centenary of Tourism in Cres-Losinj Region.

2221. **716.** 10 d. multicoloured 12 5

717. U.N. Emblem and Rainbow. **718.** Regatta Emblem.

1985. 40th Anniv. of U.N.O.

2222. **717.** 70 d. multicoloured 35 35

1985. 30th Anniv. of International European Danubian Regatta.

2223. **718.** 70 d multicoloured .. 35 35

719. Aerial View of Yacht.

720. Type "F1B" Aeromodel.

1985. Nautical Tourism. Multicoloured.
2225. 8 d. Type **719**. 10 8
2226. 10 d. Windsurfing .. 15 8
2227. 50 d. Yacht in sunset .. 55 30
2228. 70 d. Yacht by coastline 75 45

1985. World Free Flight Aeromodels Championships, Livno.
2229. **720.** 70 d. multicoloured 80 35

721. Emblem and Text.

722. Boy with Football.

1985. Obligatory Tax. 20th European Shooting Championships, Osijek.
2230. **721.** 3 d. blue 10 10

1985. Obligatory Tax. Anti-Tuberculosis Week.
2231. **722.** 2 d. blk., orge. & red 8 5
2232. 3 d. blk., orge. & red 8 5
2233. 4 d. blk., orge. & red 10 5
2234. 5 d. on 2 d. black, orange and red .. 15 5

723. "Corallina officinalis" and seahorses.

725. Selling Vegetables from Cart (Branka Lukie).

724. Federation Emblem.

1985. Marine Flora. Multicoloured.
2235. 8 d. Type **723** 5 5
2236. 10 d. "Desmarestia viridis" 10 5
2237. 50 d. Bladder wrack seaweed 45 25
2238. 70 d. "Padina pavonia" 75 75

1985. 73rd International Stomatologists Federation Congress, Belgrade.
2239. **724.** 70 d. multicoloured 60 35

1985. 17th "Joy of Europe" Meeting, Belgrade. Children's Paintings. Multicoloured.
2240. 50 d. Type **725** 40 20
2241. 70 d. "Children playing" (Suzanne Straathof) .. 90 90

726. Detail of Theatre Facade.

1985. 125th Anniv. of Croatian National Theatre, Zagreb.
2242. **726.** 10 d. multicoloured 10 5

INDEX
Countries can be quickly located by referring to the index at the end of this volume.

727. Miladin Popovic.

728. State Arms.

1985. 75th Birth Anniv. and 40th Death Anniv. of Miladin Popovic (communist party worker).
2243. **727.** 10 d. brown & orange 10 5

1985. 40th Anniv. of Federal Republic.
2244. **728.** 10 d. multicoloured 10 5

729. "Royal Procession" (Iromie Wijewardena).

1985. Paintings. Multicoloured.
2246. 8 d. Type **729** 5 5
2247. 10 d. "Return from Hunting" (Mama Cangare) 8 5
2248. 50 d. "Drum of Coca" (Agnes Ovando Sanz de Franck) 35 20
2249. 50 d. "The Cock" (Mariano Rodriguez) (vert.) 35 20
2250. 70 d. "Three Women" (Quamrul Hassan) (vert.) 80 80

1985. Nos. 1641, 1644, 1646, 1671, 1672 and 1677/9, surch.
2251. 1 d. on 25 p. red .. 60 5
2252. 2 d. on 5 p. orange .. 35 5
2253. 3 d. on 35 p. red .. 5 5
2254. 4 d. on 5 d. 60 olive .. 5 5
2255. 8 d. on 6 d. brown .. 10 5
2256. 20 d. on 26 d. blue .. 15 5
2257. 50 d. on 16 d. 50 blue .. 60 15
2258. 70 d. on 38 d. mauve .. 90 20

731. Zagreb Exhibition Hall.

1986.
2259. **731.** 100 d. violet & yell. 40 40

732. Patrol Car.

1986. 40th Anniv. of Yugoslav Automobile Association. Multicoloured.
2260. 10 d. Type **732** 10 10
2261. 70 d. Emergency first aid helicopter .. .. 1·25 75

733. Wildlife on River Bank.

734. Church of the Virgin.

1986. Nature Protection. River Tara. Mult.
2262. 100 d. Type **733** .. .. 2·50 60
2263. 150 d. Bridge over river 90 90

1986. 800th Anniv. of Studenica Monastery.
2264. **734.** 10 d. red, green & bl. 60 30

735. Postman on Motor Cycle.

736. Player and Ball in Goal.

1986. Post Services.
2265 735 20 d. purple 10 10
2266 – 30 d. brown 10 10
2267 – 40 d. red 10 10
2268 – 50 d. violet 10 10
2269 – 60 d. green 10 10
2273 – 93 d. blue 10 10
2275 – 100 d. purple .. 10 10
2276 – 106 d. red 10 10
2277 – 106 d. brown .. 10 10
2277a – 120 d. green 10 10
2277b – 140 d. red 10 10
2277c – 170 d. green .. 10 10
2278 – 200 d. blue 10 10
2278c – 220 d. brown .. 10 10
2278d – 300 d. red 10 10
2280 – 500 d. blue and brown 15 10
2281 – 500 d. blue & yellow 15 10
2282 735 800 d. blue 10 10
2284 – 1000 d. violet & green 30 10
2284b – 2000 d. green & orge 10 10
2285 – 5000 d. blue and red 1·50 40
2285b – 10000 d. violet & orge 30 20
2285c – 20000 d. brown & grn 65 35

DESIGNS—VERT. 30, 10000 d. Postman giving letters to man. 60 d. Posting letters. 93 d. Envelope and leaflet. 106 d. (No. 2276) Woman working at computer and woman filling envelope. 106 d. (No. 2277) Woman working at computer. 120 d. Woman with Valentine card. 140 d. Woman working at computer. 170, 300 d. Flower and post box. 220 d. Mail coach and cover. 500 d. Postal sorter. 1000 d. Woman using public telephone. 5000 d. Posthorn, globe and bird with stamp. HORIZ. 40 d. Forklift truck. 50, 20000 d. Train. 200 d. Freighter. 2000 d. Telephone card, tokens and handset. (20 × 18 mm). 100 d. Postman and van.

See also Nos. 2586/99.

1986. World Cup Football Championship Mexico. Multicoloured.
2286. 70 d. Type **736** 60 60
2287. 150 d. Players and ball in goal 60 60

737. St. Clement and Model of Ohrid (fresco, Church of St. Spas).

1986. 1100th Anniv. of Arrival of St. Clement of Ohrid in Macedonia.
2288. **737.** 10 d. multicoloured 1·00 60

1986. No. 1674 surch.
2289. 5 d. on 8 d. grey .. 5 5

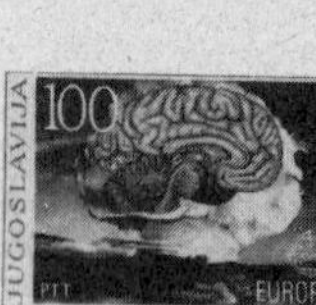
739. Human Brain as Nuclear Cloud

740. Judo.

1986. Europa. Multicoloured.
2290. 100 d. Type **739** 50 30
2291. 200 d. Injured deer on road 90 50

1986. European Men's Judo Championships, Belgrade.
2292. **740.** 70 d. brn., pink & bl. 30 20

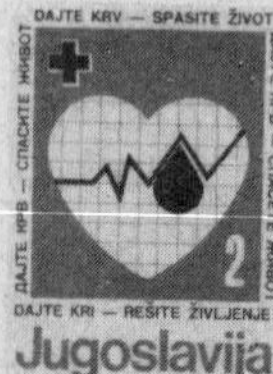
741. Graph and Blood Drop within Heart.

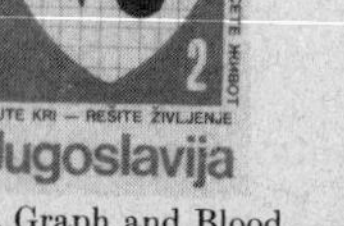
742. Costume of Slovenia.

1986. Obligatory Tax. Red Cross Week.
2293. **741.** 2 d. blk., bl. and red 5 5
2294. 3 d. blk., bl. and red 5 5
2295. 4 d. blk., bl. and red 5 5
2296. 5 d. blk., bl. and red 8 8
2297. 11 d. black, bl. & red 10 8
2298. 20 d. black, bl. & red 15 10

1986. Yugoslav Costumes. Multicoloured.
2299. 50 d. Type **742** 25 15
2300. 50 d. Voivodina (woman with red apron) .. 25 15
2301. 50 d. Croatia (man in embroidered trousers) 25 15
2302. 50 d. Macedonia (woman hand spinning) 25 15
2303. 50 d. Serbia (woman in bolero) 25 15
2304. 50 d. Montenegro (man with rifle) 25 15
2305. 50 d. Kosovo (woman carrying basket) .. 25 15
2306. 50 d. Bosnia and Herzegovina (man carrying bag on back) 25 15

743. Sailing Boats.

744. Tito (after Safet Zec).

1986. "Flying Dutchman" Class European Sailing Championships, Moscenicka Draga. Multicoloured.
2307. 50 d. Type **743** 25 15
2308. 80 d. Sailing boats (different) 35 25

1986. 94th Birth Anniv. of Tito.
2310. **744.** 10 d. multicoloured 5 5

745. "Eudia pavonia".

746. "Skopje Earthquake".

1986. Butterflies and Moths. Multicoloured.
2311 10 d. Type **745** 10 5
2312 20 d. "Inachis io" .. 15 5
2313 50 d. "Parnassius apollo" 20 20
2314 100 d. "Apatura iris" .. 25 35

1986. Obligatory Tax. Solidarity Week.
(a) As No. 2200
2315. **715.** 10 d. blue and red .. 10 5
(b) As Type **715** but inscr. "Solidarity Week" in four languages
2316. 10 d. blue and red .. 10 5
(c) Type **746**
2317. **746.** 10 d. lilac and red .. 10 5

747. Bosancica manuscript.

1986. Museum Exhibits. Ancient Manuscripts. Multicoloured.
2319. 10 d. Type **747** 5 5
2320. 20 d. Leontije's Gospel .. 10 5
2321. 50 d. Astrological writing, Mesopotamia 25 15
2322. 100 d. Hagada (ritual book), Spain 50 30

748. Congress Poster (B. Dobanovacki).

1986. 13th Communist League Congress, Belgrade.
2323. **748.** 10 d. black and red 5 5
2324. – 20 d. black and red 10 5
DESIGN: 20 d. Another part of the Congress poster.

749. Trubar and Title Page of "Abecedari".

1986. 400th Death Anniv. of Primoz Trubar (founder of Slovenian literary language and religious reformer).
2326. **749.** 20 d. multicoloured 45 25

750. Emblem.

751. Dancers.

1986. 125th Anniv. of Serbian National Theatre, Novi Sad.
2327. **750.** 40 d. multicoloured 20 10

1986. Rugovo Dance.
2328. **751.** 40 d. multicoloured 20 10

753. Crosses forming Earth and Sky.

1986. Obligatory Tax. Anti-tuberculosis Week.
2330. **753.** 2 d. multicoloured .. 5 5
2331. 5 d. multicoloured .. 10 5
2332. 6 d. multicoloured .. 10 5
2333. 7 d. multicoloured .. 15 10
2334. 8 d. multicoloured .. 15 10
2335. 10 d. multicoloured 15 10
2336. 11 d. multicoloured 20 15
2337. 14 d. multicoloured 20 15
2338. 20 d. multicoloured 20 15

754. Volleyball.

755. Bird and Child running on globe (Tanja Faletic).

1986. "Universiade '87" University Games, Zagreb. Multicoloured.
2339. 30 d. Type **754** 10 5
2340. 40 d. Canoeing 15 5
2341. 100 d. Gymnastics .. 40 25
2342. 150 d. Fencing .. 60 35

1986. 18th "Joy of Europe" Meeting, Belgrade. Children's Paintings. Mult.
2343. 100 d. Type **755** 40 25
2344. 150 d. City of the Future (Johanna Kraus) .. 60 35

756. Diagram of Rotary Selector and Bled.

1986. 50th Anniv. of Automatic Telephone Exchange Network.
2345. **756.** 40 d. multicoloured 12 5

757. Criminal in Stocking Mask.

758. Brigade Member addressing Crowd (after D. Andrejevic-Kun).

1986. 55th Interpol General Assembly Session, Belgrade.
2346. **757.** 150 d. multicoloured 60 35

1986. 50th Anniv. of Formation of International Brigades in Spain.
2347. **758.** 40 d. brown, gold and orange 12 5

759. Academy.

1986. Centenary of Servian Academy of Arts and Sciences.
2348. **759.** 40 d. multicoloured 12 5

760. People riding on Doves (Branislav Barnak).

1986. International Peace Year.
2349. **760.** 150 d. multicoloured 65 35

761. "Portrait" (Bernard Buffet).

762. European Otter.

1986. Paintings in Museum of Contemporary Arts, Skopje. Multicoloured.
2350. 30 d. "Still Life" (Frantisek Muzika) (horiz.) 10 5
2351. 40 d. "Disturbance" (detail, Rafael Canogar) (horiz.) .. 12 5
2352. 100 d. Type **761** 40 25
2353. 100 d. "IOL" (Victor Vasarely) 40 25
2354. 150 d. "Woman's Head" (Pablo Picasso) 60 35

1987. Protected Animals. Multicoloured.
2355. 30 d. Type **762** 10 5
2356. 40 d. Goat 12 5
2357. 100 d. Red deer 40 25
2358. 150 d. Brown bear .. 60 35

763. Boskovic, Brera Observatory and Solar Eclipse.

764. Mountains, Woodland and Animal Feeder.

1987. Death Bicentenary of Ruder Boskovic (astronomer).
2359. **763.** 150 d. multicoloured 60 35

1987. Nature Protection. Triglav National Park. Multicoloured.
2360. 150 d. Type **764** 90 90
2361. 400 d. Mountains, woodland and glacial lake 90 90

765. Potez "29".

1987. 60th Anniv. of Civil Aviation in Yugoslavia. Multicoloured.
2362. 150 d. Type **765** 75 40
2363. 400 d. Douglas "DC-10" 1·75 1·00

766. Mateja Svet.

1987. Yugoslav Medals at World Alpine Skiing Championships, Crans Montana.
2364. **766.** 200 d. multicoloured 50 50

767. Kole Nedelkovski.

1987. 75th Birth Anniv. of Kole Nedelkovski (poet and revolutionary).
2365. **767.** 40 d. multicoloured 12 5

768. Battle Flags and Gusle.

1987. 125th Anniv. of Liberation Wars of Montenegro.
2366. **768.** 40 d. multicoloured 12 5

769. "Founding the Party at Cebine, 1937" (Anton Gojmir Kos).

1987. 50th Anniv. of Slovenian Communist Party.
2367. **769.** 40 d. multicoloured 12 5

770. Tito Bridge (Ilija Stojadinovic).

771. Children of Different Races in Flower.

1987. Europa. Architecture. Multicoloured.
2368. 200 d. Type **770** .. .. 1·50 60
2369. 400 d. Bridges over River Ljubljanica (Joze Plecnik) 85 75

1987. Obligatory Tax. Red Cross Week.
2370. **771.** 2 d. multicoloured .. 5 5
2371. 4 d. multicoloured .. 5 5
2372. 5 d. multicoloured .. 5 5
2373. 6 d. multicoloured .. 5 5
2374. 7 d. multicoloured .. 5 5
2375. 8 d. multicoloured .. 5 5
2376. 10 d. multicoloured 5 5
2377. 11 d. multicoloured 5 5
2378. 12 d. multicoloured 5 5
2379. 14 d. multicoloured 5 5
2380. 17 d. multicoloured 5 5
2381. 20 d. multicoloured 5 5

772. Almonds.

773. "Josip Broz Tito" (Mosa Pijade).

1987. Fruit. Multicoloured.
2382. 60 d. Type **772** 5 5
2383. 150 d. Pears 12 5
2384. 200 d. Apples 45 35
2385. 400 d. Plums 75 75

1987. 95th Birth Anniv. of Tito.
2386. **773.** 60 d. multicoloured 5 5

774. "Skopje Earthquake".

776. Mail Coach in Zrenjanin.

775. Bust of Karadzic (Petar Ubavkic), Trsic (birthplace) and Vienna.

1987. Obligatory Tax. Solidarity Week.
2387. **774.** 30 d. multicoloured 5 5

1987. Birth Bicentenary of Vuk Stefanovic Karadzic (linguist and historian). Mult.
2388. 60 d. Type **775** 5 5
2289. 200 d. Serbian alphabet and Karadzic (portrait by Uros Knezevic) .. 20 8

1987. 250th Anniv. of Postal Service in Zrenjanin.
2390. **776.** 60 d. multicoloured 5 5

777. Emblem and Mascot.

778. Hurdling.

1987. Obligatory Tax. "Universiade '87" University Games, Zagreb.
2391. **777.** 20 d. blue and green 5 5

1987. "Universiade '87" University Games, Zagreb. Multicoloured.
2392. 60 d. Type **778** 5 5
2393. 150 d. Basketball .. 12 5
2394. 200 d. Gymnastics .. 20 8
2395. 400 d. Swimming .. 75 75

779. Canadair "CL-215" Airplane spraying Forest Fire.

780. Monument, Anindol Park.

1987. Fire Fighting. Multicoloured.
2396. 60 d. Type **779** 20 10
2397. 200 d. Fire-fighting tug 20 10

1987. 50th Anniv. of Croatian Communist Party.
2398. **780.** 60 d. multicoloured 5 5

781. School and Foundation Document.

782. Crosses and Children's Head.

1987. 150th Anniv. of Sabac High School.
2399. **781.** 80 d. brown, orange and blue 8 5

1987. Obligatory Tax. Anti-Tuberculosis Week.
2400. **782.** 2 d. multicoloured .. 5 5
2401. 4 d. multicoloured .. 5 5
2402. 6 d. multicoloured .. 5 5
2403. 8 d. multicoloured .. 5 5
2404. 10 d. multicoloured 5 5
2405. 12 d. multicoloured 5 5
2406. 14 d. multicoloured 5 5
2407. 20 d. multicoloured 5 5
2408. 25 d. multicoloured 5 5
2409. 40 d. multicoloured 5 5

783. Emblem, Map and Flowers.

785. "Children playing amongst Trees" (Bedic Aranka).

1987. "Balkanphila XI" International Stamp Exhibition, Novi Sad.
2410. **783.** 250 d. multicoloured 20 8

1987. No. 2269 surch. **80.**
2412. 80 d. on 60 d. green .. 8 5

1987. 19th "Joy of Europe" Meeting. Mult.
2413. 250 d. Type **785** 60 60
2414. 400 d. "Child and scarecrow in orchard" (Ingeborg Schaffer) .. 60 60

786. Arslanagica Bridge Trebinje.

1987. Bridges. Multicoloured.
2415. 80 d. Type **786** 8 5
2416. 250 d. Terzija bridge, Djakovica 20 8

787. Tug in Canal.

788. SPRAM Emblem.

1987. 600th Anniv. of Titov Vrbas.
2417. **787.** 80 d. multicoloured 15 10

1987. Obligatory Tax.
2418. **788.** 20 d. blue 5 5

789. Eclipse, Telescope and Old Observatory Building.

1987. Centenary of Astronomical and Meteorological Observatory, Belgrade.
2419. **789.** 80 d. multicoloured 8 5

790. "St. Luke the Evangelist" (Raffaello Santi).

1987. Paintings in Mimara Museum, Zegreb. Multicoloured.
2420. 80 d. Type **790** 8 5
2421. 200 d. "Infanta Maria Theresa" (Diego Velazquez) 20 8
2422. 250 d. "Nicolaes Rubens" (Peter Paul Rubens) 20 8
2423. 400 d. "Louise Laure Sennegon" (Camille Corot) 35 20

791. Bull Fighting (Grmec).

1987. Museum Exhibits. Folk Games. Multicoloured.
2424. 80 d. Type **791** 8 5
2425. 200 d. Sword used in Ljuvicevo Horse Games 20 8
2426. 250 d. Crown worn at Moresca Games (Korcula) 20 8
2427. 400 d. Sinj Iron Ring .. 60 60

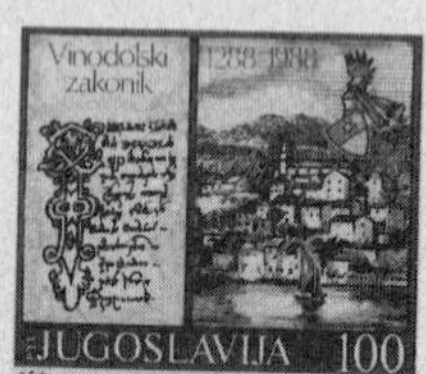

792. Foundation Document, View of Town and Arms.

1988. 700th Anniv. of Vinodolski.
2428. **972.** 100 d. multicoloured 8 5

793. Skier.

794. Cub.

1988. 25th Anniv. of Golden Fox Skiing Competition, Maribor.
2429. **793.** 350 d. multicoloured 30 15

1988. Protected Wildlife. Brown Bear. Multicoloured.
2430. 70 d. Type **794** 8 5
2431. 80 d. Bears among branches 8 5
2432. 200 d. Adult bear .. 20 8
2433. 350 d. Adult stalking prey 30 15

795. Slalom Skier.

797. Basketball.

1988. Winter Olympic Games, Calgary. Multicoloured.
2434. 350 d. Type **795** 60 55
2435. 1200 d. Ice hockey .. 60 55

1988. Olympic Games, Seoul. Multicoloured.
2437. 106 d. Type **797** 10 5
2438. 450 d. High jumping .. 35 20
2439. 500 d. Gymnastics .. 40 25
2440. 1200 d. Boxing .. .. 1·00 55

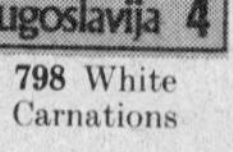

798 White Carnations

799 "INTELSAT V-A", Globe and Dish Aerials, Ivanjica

1988. Obligatory Tax. Anti-Cancer Campaign. Multicoloured.
2442 4 d. Type **798** 5 5
2443 8 d. Red flowers .. 5 5
2444 12 d. Red roses .. 5 5

1988. Europa. Transport and Communications. Multicoloured.
2445 450 d. Type **799** 15 5
2446 1200 d. Woman using mobile telephone and methods of transport .. 40 25

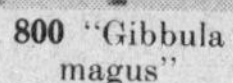

800 "Gibbula magus"

801 Anniversary Emblem

1988. Molluscs. Multicoloured.
2447 106 d. Type **800** 45 45
2448 550 d. "Pecten jacobaeus" 45 45
2449 600 d. "Tonna galea" .. 45 45
2450 1000 d. "Argonauta argo" 55 45

1988. Obligatory Tax. 125th Anniv of Red Cross.
2451 **801** 4 d. blue, red & grey 5 5
2452 8 d. blue, red & grey 5 5
2453 10 d. blue, red & grey 5 5
2454 12 d. blue, red & grey 5 5
2455 20 d. blue, red & grey 5 5
2456 30 d. blue, red & grey 5 5
2457 50 d. blue, red & grey 5 5

802 Josip Broz Tito

803 "Skopje Earthquake"

1988. 60th Anniv of Trial of Tito.
2458 **802** 106 d. brown and black 5 5

1988. Obligatory Tax. Solidarity Week.
(a) Type **803**.
2459 **803** 50 d. grey, brn & red 5 5

(b) As No. 2220 but value changed.
2460 **715** 50 d. blue and red .. 5 5

(c) No. 2387 surch.
2461 **774** 50 d. on 30 d. mult .. 5 5

1988. Nos. 2273 and 2277 surch.
2462 120 d. on 93 d. blue .. 5 5
2463 140 d. on 106 d. brown .. 5 5

806 First Lyceum Building

807 Krleza

1988. 150th Anniv of Belgrade University.
2464 **806** 106 d. multicoloured .. 5 5

1988. Obligatory Tax. Culture Fund. 95th Birth Anniv of M. Krleza (writer).
2465 **807** 30 d. brown & orange 5 5

808 "Phelypaea boissieri"

809 Globe and Flags

1988. Nature Protection Macedonian Plants. Multicoloured.
2466 600 d. Type **808** 60 60
2467 1000 d. "Campanula formanekiana" .. 60 60

1988. Cent of Esperanto (invented languague).
2468 **809** 600 d. blue and green 20 5

810 Shipping on the Danube

811 Globe as Ball in Basket

1988. 40th Anniv of Danube Conference.
2469 **810** 1000 d. multicoloured 30 15

1988. 13th European Junior Basketball Championship, Tito Vrbas and Srbobran.
2471 **811** 600 d. multicoloured .. 20 8

812 Horse Racing

1988. 125th Anniv of Belgrade Horse Races. Multicoloured.
2472 140 d. Type **812** 5 5
2473 600 d. Show-jumping event 20 8
2474 1000 d. Trotting race .. 30 15

813 Airplane and Globe

1988. Air.
2475 **813** 2000 d. multicoloured 80 30

814 Museum and Bosnian Bellflower

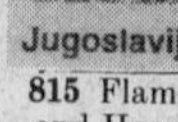

815 Flame and Hand

1988. Centenary of Bosnia and Herzegovina Museum, Sarajevo.
2476 **814** 140 d. multicoloured .. 5 5

1988. Obligatory Tax. Anti-Tuberculosis Week.
2477 **815** 4 d. multicoloured .. 5 5
2478 8 d. multicoloured .. 5 5
2479 12 d. multicoloured .. 5 5
2480 20 d. multicoloured .. 5 5
2481 50 d. multicoloured .. 5 5
2482 70 d. multicoloured .. 5 5

1988. Obligatory Tax. No. 2039 surch **1988 12**.
2483 **632** 12 d. on 1 d. orange, black and red .. 5 5

817 Arm and Crab's Claw (Anti-cancer)

818 "Daughter of the Artist" (Peter Ranosovic)

1988. Health Campaigns. Multicoloured.
2484 140 d. Type **817** 5 5
2485 1000 d. Screaming mouth in splash of blood (Anti-AIDS) 30 15

1988. 20th "Joy of Europe" Meeting. Mult.
2486 1000 d. Type **818** . . 60 60
2487 1100 d. "Girl with Straw Hat" (Pierre-Auguste Renoir) 60 60

819 1701 Arms and Present Emblem

1988. 50th Anniv of Slovenian Academy of Arts and Sciences.
2488 **819** 200 d. multicoloured . . 8 5

820 Galicnik Wedding

1988. Museum Exhibits. Traditional Crafts and Customs. Multicoloured.
2489 200 d. Type **820** 8 5
2490 1000 d. Weapons from Bokelji 30 15
2491 1000 d. Vojvodina embroidery (horiz) . . 30 15
2492 1100 d. People wearing masks, Kurenti (horiz) 35 20

821 Title Page of "Gorski Vijenac" and Njegos (after J. Boss)

1988. 175th Birth Anniv of Prince-Bishop Petar II of Montenegro. Multicoloured.
2493 200 d. Type **821** 8 5
2494 1000 d. Njegos Mausoleum, Loveen and Njegos in bishop's robes (after Josip Tominc) . . 30 15

822 "Girl with Lyre"

1988. Greek Terracotta Figures from Josip Broz Tito Memorial Centre Collection. Multicoloured.
2495 200 d. Type **822** 8 5
2496 1000 d. "Girl on a Stone" 30 15
2497 1000 d. "Eros and Psyche" 30 15
2498 1100 d. "Girl by the Stele" 35 20

823 Krsmanovic House, Belgrade

1988. 70th Anniv of Yugoslavian State.
2499 **823** 200 d. multicoloured . . 8 5

1988. Nos. 2277a and 2277b surch.
2500 170 d. on 120 d. green . . 5 5
2501 220 d. on 140 d. red . . 8 5

825 Pistol shooting

826 Gundulic and Dubrovnik

1988. Yugoslavian Medals at Olympic Games. Multicoloured.
2502 500 d. Type **825** (2 gold, 1 bronze) 15 5
2503 500 d. Handball (bronze) 15 5
2504 500 d. Table tennis (silver and bronze) 15 5
2505 500 d. Wrestling (silver) 15 5
2506 500 d. Rowing (bronze) . . 15 5
2507 500 d. Basketball (2 silver) 15 5
2508 500 d. Waterpolo (gold) . . 15 5
2509 500 d. Boxing (bronze) . . 15 5

1989. 400th Birth Anniv of Ivan Gundulic (poet).
2510 **826** 220 d. multicoloured . . 8 5

827 Mallard

828 Valvasor and Wagensperg Castle

1989. Wild Ducks. Multicoloured.
2511 300 d. Type **827** 15 10
2512 2100 d. Green-winged teal 85 40
2513 2200 d. Pintail 90 45
2514 2200 d. Common shoveller 90 45

1989. 300th Anniv of Publishing of "The Glory of the Duchy of Kranjska" by Johann Weickhard Valvasor.
2515 **828** 300 d. multicoloured . . 10 5

829 "Bulbocodium vernum"

832 Competitor

830 Envelopes and Dish Aerial

1989. Flowers. Multicoloured.
2516 300 d. Type **829** 10 5
2517 2100 d. White water-lily 65 35
2518 2200 d. "Fritillaria degeniana" (vert) . . 70 40
2519 3000 d. "Orchis simia" (vert) 90 45

1989. Air.
2520 **830** 10000 d. blue, mauve and yellow . . 1·50 90
2521 – 20000 d. orange, violet and red . . . . 1·40 1·40
DESIGN: 20000 d. Map and satellite.

1989. No. 1657 surch **100 d.**
2522 100 d. on 1 d. green . . 5 5

1989. 6th World Air Gun Championships, Sarajevo.
2523 **832** 3000 d. multicoloured 40 40

833 Girl looking through Magic Cube.

834 Anniversary Emblem

1989. Europa. Children's Games and Toys. Multicoloured.
2524 3000 d. Type **833** . . 90 75
2525 6000 d. Boy playing with marbles and paper boats 90 90

1989. Obligatory Tax. 125th Anniv of Red Cross Movement (1988).
2526 **834** 20 d. bl, silver & red 5 5
2527 80 d. bl, silver & red 5 5
2528 150 d. bl, silver & red 5 5
2529 160 d. bl, silver & red 5 5

835 Tito

836 "Skopje Earthquake"

1989. 70th Anniv of Yugoslavian Communist Party.
2530 **835** 300 d. multicoloured . . 5 5

1989. Obligatory Tax. Solidarity Week.
(a) Type **836**.
2531 **836** 250 d. silver and red . . 5 5

(b) As T **715**.
2532 **715** 400 d. blue and red . . 5 5

837 Pole Vaulting

838 Racers

1989. 15th European Trophy Athletic Clubs Championship, Belgrade.
2533 **837** 4000 d. multicoloured 12 5

1989. Motor Cycle Grand Prix, Rijeka. Mult.
2534 500 d. Type **838** 5 5
2535 4000 d. Racers (different) 12 5

839 Flags of Netherlands, Italy, USSR and Spain and Ball

1989. 26th European Men's Basketball Championship, Zagreb. Multicoloured.
2537 2000 d. Type **839** . . 8 5
2538 2000 d. Flags of France, Yugoslavia, Greece and Bulgaria and ball . . 8 5

840 Ancient Greek Galleys

1989. Sailing Ships. Multicoloured.
2539 1000 d. Type **840** . . 15 10
2540 1000 d. Roman warships 15 10
2541 1000 d. 13th-century Crusader nefs 15 10
2542 1000 d. 16th-century Dubrovnik navas . . 15 10
2543 1000 d. 17th-century French warships . . 15 10
2544 1000 d. 18th-century ships of the line . . 15 10

841 "Battle of Kosovo" (lithograph, Adam Stefanovic)

1989. 600th Anniv of Battle of Kosovo.
2546 **841** 500 d. multicoloured . . 5 5

842 Danilovgrad

1989. Centenary of First Reading Room at Danilovgrad.
2547 **842** 500 d. multicoloured . . 5 5

1989. No. 2278c surch **700**.
2548 700 d. on 220 d. brown . . 5 5

1989. Nos. 2266 and 2277c surch.
2549 400 d. on 30 d. brown . . 5 5
2550 700 d. on 170 d. green . . 5 5

845 Stone Tablet, Detail of Charter and Mule Train

1989. 800th Anniv of Kulin Ban Charter (granting free trade to Dubrovnik).
2551 **845** 500 d. multicoloured . . 5 5

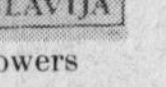

846 Rowers

847 Houses of Parliament, London

1989. World Rowing Championship, Bled.
2552 **846** 10000 d. multicoloured 30 15

1989. Cent of Interparliamentary Union.
2553 10000 d. Type **847** . . 30 15
2554 10000 d. Notre Dame Cathedral, Paris . . 30 15

848 Belgrade and Cairo

849 Emblem

1989. 9th Non-aligned Conference, Belgrade. Multicoloured.

2555	10000 d. Type **848** ..		30	15
2556	10000 d. Lusaka and Algiers		30	15
2557	10000 d. Colombo and Havana		30	15
2558	10000 d. New Delhi and Harare		30	15

1989. Obligatory Tax. USAOJ-A Conference, Bihac.

2560	**849**	400 d. blue and red ..	5	5

850 Brezovica-Jazinac Lake, Kosovo

851 Crosses as Basket of Flowers

1989. Nature Protection. Multicoloured.

2561	8000 d. Type **850** ..	25	12
2562	10000 d. Mirusa Canyon, Kosovo	30	15

1989. Obligatory Tax. Anti-tuberculosis Week.

2563	**851**	20 d. red and black ..	5	5
2564		200 d. red and black .	5	5
2565		250 d. red and black	5	5
2566		400 d. red and black	5	5
2567		650 d. red and black	5	5

852 "Child with Lamb" (Jovan Popovic)

853 Men Fighting

1989. 21st "Joy of Europe" Meeting. Mult.

2568	10000 d. Type **852** ..	30	15
2569	10000 d. "Girl feeding Dog" (Aelbert Cuyp) ..	30	15

1989. 300th Anniv of Karpos Insurrection.

2570	**853**	1200 d. multicoloured	5	5

854 Cancelled 100 d. Stamp, Quill and Seal

1989. Stamp Day.

2571	**854**	1200 d. multicoloured	5	5

855 Packsaddle Maker

1989. Museum Exhibits. Traditional Crafts. Multicoloured.

2572	1200 d. Type **855** ..	5	5
2573	14000 d. Cooper ..	45	25
2574	15000 d. Wine maker ..	50	25
2575	30000 d. Weaver	95	50

856 Airplane, Arrows and Map

857 "Apostle Mathias"

1989. Air.

2576	**856**	50000 d. blue & orange	1·60	80

1989. Frescoes by Iohannes de Kastua from Holy Trinity Church, Hrastovlje, Slovenia. Multicoloured.

2577	2100 d. Type **857** ..	8	5
2578	21000 d. "St. Barbara" ..	35	35
2579	30000 d. "Creation of the Universe, the Fourth Day" (horiz)	60	50
2580	50000 d. "Creation of the Universe, the Fifth Day" (horiz)	90	80

858 Barn Swallow, Envelope and Flower

860 Colour Spectrum entering Star

1989.

2581	**858**	100000 d. green & orge	1·75	1·50

1989. No. 1680 surch.

2582	700 d. on 70 d. blue ..	5	5

1990. 14th Extraordinary Congress of League of Communists of Yugoslavia.

2583	**860**	10000 d. multicoloured	30	15
2584	–	50000 d. multicoloured	40	40

DESIGN: 50000 d. Hammer and sickle on V.D.U. screen.

1990. Postal Services. As T **735** but in revised currency.

2586	10 p. violet and green ..	5	5
2587	20 p. red and yellow ..	5	5
2588	30 p. green and orange ..	5	5
2589	40 p. green and purple ..	5	5
2590	50 p. green and violet ..	5	5
2591	60 p. mauve and red ..	8	5
2595	1 d. blue and purple ..	10	5
2596	2 d. blue and red ..	20	10
2597	3 d. blue and red ..	30	15
2599	5 d. ultramarine and blue	50	25
2603	10 d. blue and red ..	1·50	60
2605	20 d. red and orange ..	1·10	55

DESIGNS—VERT. 10 p. Man posting letters; 20 p. Postal sorter; 30 p. Postman giving letters to man; 40 p., 20 d. Woman telephoning; 50 p. Posthorn, globe and bird; 60 p. Telephone card, tokens and handset; 3 d. Post-box; 5 d. Airplane, letters and map; 10 d. Barn swallow, flower and envelope. HORIZ. 1 d. Train; 2 d. Freighter.

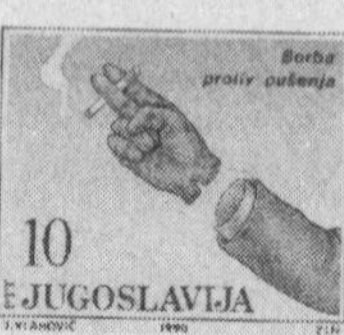
861 Gloved Hand holding Lighted Cigarette

1990. Anti-smoking Campaign.

2610	**861**	10 d. multicoloured ..	1·00	85

862 Northern Pike

1990. Endangered Fishes. Multicoloured.

2611	1 d. Type **862**	10	5
2612	5 d. European catfish ..	50	25
2613	10 d. Burbot	1·00	85
2614	15 d. River perch ..	1·50	1·25

863 Zabljak Fortress, Printed Page and Arms

1990. 500th Anniv of Enthronement of Djuradj Crnojevic.

2615	**863**	50 p. multicoloured ..	5	5

864 Telegraphist and V.D.U. Screen

1990. 125th Anniv of I.T.U.

2616	**864**	6 d. 50 multicoloured	65	35

865 Footballers

866 Skopje Posts and Telecommunications Centre

1990. World Cup Football Championship, Italy.

2617	–	6 d. 50 multicoloured	65	30
2618	**865**	10 d. multicoloured ..	1·00	50

DESIGN: 6 d. 50, Footballers (different).

1990. Europa. Post Office Buildings. Mult.

2619	6 d. 50 Type **866** ..	65	30
2620	10 d. Belgrade Telephone Exchange	1·00	50

867 Chicago Water Tower and Carnation

868 Record, Notes and Pen

1990. Centenary of Labour Day.

2621	**867**	6 d. 50 multicoloured	65	30

1990. Eurovision Song Contest, Zagreb. Mult.

2622	6 d. 50 Type **868** ..	65	30
2623	10 d. Conductor and score of "Te Deum" ..	1·00	50

869 Cross and Leaves

870 Large Yellow Flowers

1990. Obligatory Tax. Red Cross Week.

2624	**869**	10 p. red and green ..	5	5
2625		20 p. red and green ..	5	5
2626		30 p. red and green ..	5	5

(b) 45th Anniv of Macedonian Red Cross. Flower paintings by Zivko A. Popovski. Mult.

2627	20 p. Type **870**	5	5
2628	20 p. Arrangement of small yellow flowers ..	5	5
2629	20 p. Anniversary emblem	5	5

See also Nos. 2636/7.

871 Server

873 Tito (bronze, Antun Augustincic)

1990. Yugoslav Open Tennis Championship, Umag. Multicoloured.

2630	6 d. 50 Type **871** ..	65	30
2631	10 d. Receiver ..	1·00	50

1990. No. 2282 surch **0,50**.

2632	**735**	50 p. on 800 d. blue ..	5	5

1990. 98th Birth Anniv of Tito.

2633	**873**	50 p. multicoloured ..	5	5

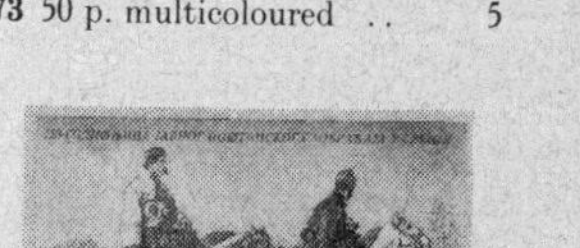

874 "Tartar Post Riders" (Carl Goebel)

1990. 150th Anniv of Public Postal Service in Serbia.

2634	**874**	50 p. multicoloured ..	5	5

875 "Skopje Earthquake" 876

1990. Obligatory Tax. Solidarity Week.

2635	**875**	20 p. brn, red & silver	5	5
2636	–	20 p. multicoloured ..	5	5
2637	–	20 p. multicoloured ..	5	5
2638	**876**	20 p. blue and red ..	5	5
2639	**715**	30 p. blue and red ..	5	5

DESIGNS—As T **870**. No. 2636, Mauve flowers; 2637, Red and yellow flowers.

877 Fantail

878 Idrija Town

1990. Pigeons. Multicoloured.

2640	50 p. Type **877**	5	5
2641	5 d. Serbian high flier ..	50	25
2642	6 d. 50, Carrier pigeon (vert)	65	30
2643	10 d. Pouter (vert) ..	1·00	50

1990. 500th Anniversaries of Idrija Town (2644) and Mercury Mine (2645). Mult.

2644	50 p. Type **878**	5	5
2645	6 d. 50 Mine	65	30

879 Newspaper Offices, Museum and Mastheads

881 Runners leaving Blocks

1990. 50th Anniv of "Vjesnik" (newspaper).

2646	**879**	60 p. multicoloured ..	5	5

1990. Nos. 2587 and 2588 surch.

2647		50 p. on 20 p. red & yellow	5	5
2648		1 d. on 30 p. green & orge	10	5

1990. European Athletics Championships, Split. Multicoloured.

2649		1 d. Type **881**	10	5
2650		6 d. 50 Runners' feet ..	65	30

882 Nurse and Sun

883 Flower in Vase and Birds

1990. Obligatory Tax. Anti-tuberculosis Week.

2652	**882**	20 p. yellow, bl & red	5	5
2653		25 p. yellow, bl & red	5	5
2654		50 p. yellow, bl & red	5	5
2655	**883**	50 p. brn, red & grey	5	5

884 "Pec Patriachate" (D. Cudov)

1990. 300th Anniv of Great Migration of Serbs. Multicoloured.

2656		1 d. Type **884**	10	5
2657		6 d. 50 "Migration of Serbs" (Paja Jovanovic)	65	30

1990. No. 2589 surch **2**.

2658		2 d. on 40 p. grn & pur	20	10

887 "Little Sisters" (Ivana Kobilca)

888 Chess Pieces

1990. 22nd "Joy of Europe" Meeting. Mult.

2660		6 d. 50 Type **887** ..	65	30
2661		10 d. "Willem III of Orange as a Child" (Adriaen Hanneman) (vert)	1·00	50

1990. 29th Chess Olympiad, Novi Sad. Mult.

2662		1 d. Type **888**	10	5
2663		5 d. Rook, bishop, knight and chessboard ..	50	25
2664		6 d. 50 Knights, queen, king, pawn and chess-board	65	30
2665		10 d. Chess pieces and symbols	1·00	50

889 "St. Vlaho and Ragusa" (detail of triptych, Nikola Bozidarevic) and Penny Black

1990. Stamp Day.

2667	**889**	2 d. multicoloured ..	20	10

890 Vransko Lake

1990. Nature Protection. Multicoloured.

2668		6 d. 50 Type **890** ..	65	30
2669		10 d. Griffon vulture ..	1·50	60

891 "King Milutin" and Notre Dame Monastery, Ljeviska

1990. Monastery Frescoes. Multicoloured.

2670		2 d. Type **891**	20	10
2671		5 d. "St. Sava" and Mileseva Monastery ..	50	25
2672		6 d. 50 "St. Elias" and Moraca Monastery ..	65	30
2673		10 d. "Jesus Christ" and Sopocani Monastery ..	1·00	50

892 Milanovic and Kringa (birthplace)

1990. Birth Centenary of Dr. Bozo Milanovic (politician).

2674	**892**	2 d. multicoloured ..	20	10

893 Bringing Mary into the Temple

894 Lapwing

1990. Iconostasis of St. Jovan Bigorski Monastery. Multicoloured.

2675		2 d. Type **893**	20	10
2676		5 d. Nativity	50	25
2677		6 d. 50 Flight into Egypt (horiz)	65	30
2678		10 d. Entry into Jerusalem (horiz) ..	1·00	50

1991. Protected Birds. Multicoloured.

2679		2 d. Type **894**	20	10
2680		5 d. Woodchat shrike ..	50	25
2681		6 d. 50 Common crane ..	65	30
2682		10 d. Goosander	1·00	50

895 "Crocus kosaninii"

896 Bishop Josip Juraj Strossmayer (founder) (after Vlaho Bukovac)

1991. Crocuses. Multicoloured.

2683		2 d. Type **895**	20	10
2684		6 d. "Crocus scardicus" ..	60	30
2685		7 d. 50 "Crocus rujanensis"	75	35
2686		15 d. "Crocus adamii" ..	1·50	75

1991. 125th Anniv of Yugoslav Academy of Arts and Sciences.

2687	**896**	2 d. multicoloured ..	20	10

897 Mozart (after P. A. Lorenzoni)

898 Edvard Rusjan (Slovenian pioneer)

1991. Death Bicentenary of Wolfgang Amadeus Mozart (composer).

2688	**897**	7 d. 50 multicoloured	75	35

1991. Centenary of First Heavier-than-Air Flight by Lilienthal. Multicoloured.

2689		7 d. 50 Type **898** ..	75	35
2690		15 d. Otto Lilienthal ..	1·50	75

899 Route of Climb and Cesen

1991. 1st Anniv of Tomo Cesen's Ascent of South Face of Lhotse Peak.

2691	**899**	7 d. 50 multicoloured	75	35

900 Satellite and Earth

1991. Europa. Europe in Space. Mult.

2692		7 d. 50 Type **900** ..	75	35
2693		15 d. Telecommunications	1·50	75

901 Figures

902 Red Cross and Rays

1991. Obligatory Tax. Red Cross Week.

2694	**901**	60 p. multicoloured ..	5	5
2695		1 d. 20 multicoloured	5	5
2696		2 d. 50 multicoloured	15	10
2697	–	1 d. 70 multicoloured	10	5
2698	**902**	1 d. 70 multicoloured	10	5
2699	–	1 d. 70 multicoloured	10	5
2700	–	1 d. 70 multicoloured	10	5
2701	–	1 d. 70 multicoloured	10	5

DESIGNS—29 × 24 mm: No. 2697, similar to T **901** but differently inscribed. As T **902**: No. 2699, Pink flowers; 2700, Children on globe; 2701, Yellow flowers.

903 Miraculous Icon of St. Mary of Trsat (14th-century)

904 River Steamer

1991. 700th Anniv of Franciscan Monastery, Rijeka.

2702	**903**	3 d. 50 multicoloured	20	10

1991. Community of Danubian Regions Conference, Belgrade. Multicoloured.

2703		7 d. 50 Type **904** ..	70	25
2704		15 d. River at sunset ..	1·40	50

905 Woman with Horse

1991. Obligatory Tax. Solidarity Week.

2706	**876**	2 d. green and orange	10	5
2707	–	2 d. brown, red & gold	10	5
2708	**905**	2 d. brown, red & gold	10	5
2709	–	2 d. brown, red & gold	10	5
2710	–	2 d. brown, red & gold	10	5
2711	**715**	2 d. 20 blue and red ..	10	5

DESIGNS—As T **905**: No. 2707, "Skopje Earth- quake"; 2709, Woman and tree; 2710, Woman holding cockerel.

906 "Karawanke Pass" (17th-century engraving, J. Valvasor)

1991. Karawanke Road Tunnel. Mult.

2712		4 d. 50 Type **906** ..	25	15
2713		11 d. Tunnel entrance ..	60	35

907 Balls and Baskets

908 Order of the Partisan Star

1991. Centenary of Basketball. Multicoloured.

2714		11 d. Type **907**	60	35
2715		15 d. Aerial view of baskets	80	50

1991. 50th Anniversaries of Yugoslav Insurrection and National Army. Mult.

2716		4 d. 50 Type **908** ..	25	15
2717		11 d. Order for Bravery ..	60	35

909 Ujevic

910 Score and Gallus

1991. Birth Centenary of Tin Ujevic (writer).

2718	**909**	4 d. 50 multicoloured	25	15

1991. 400th Death Anniv of Jacobus Gallus (composer).

2719	**910**	11 d. multicoloured ..	60	35

911 Savudrija, 1818

1991. Lighthouses of the Adriatic and the Danube. Multicoloured.

2720 10 d. Type **911** 50 30
2721 10 d. Sveti Ivan na Pucini, 1853 .. .. 50 30
2722 10 d. Porer, 1833 .. .. 50 30
2723 10 d. Stoncica, 1865 .. .. 50 30
2724 10 d. Olipa, 1842 .. .. 50 30
2725 10 d. Glavat, 1884 .. .. 50 30
2726 10 d. Veli Rat, 1849 .. .. 50 30
2727 10 d. Vir, 1881 .. .. 50 30
2728 10 d. Tajerske Sestrice, 1876 .. .. 50 30
2729 10 d. Razanj, 1875 .. .. 50 30
2730 10 d. Derdap, Danube .. 50 30
2731 10 d. Tamis, Danube .. 50 30

912 "Sremski Karlovci School" (Ljubica Sokic)

1991. Bicent of Sremski Karlovci High School.

2732 **912** 4 d. 50 multicoloured 25 15

913 Girl

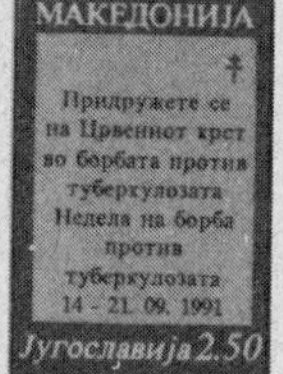

914 Inscription

1991. Obligatory Tax. Anti-tuberculosis Week.

2733 **913** 1 d. 20 blue, red & yell 5 5
2734 2 d. 50 blue, red & yell 15 10
2735 **914** 2 d. 50 blk, yell & mve 15 10
2736 – 2 d. 50 multicoloured 15 10
2737 – 2 d. 50 multicoloured 15 10
2738 – 2 d. 50 blk, yell & mve 15 10

DESIGNS—As T **914** No. 2736, Doctor; 2737, Children; 2738, Girls with birds and flowers.

915 Mayfly

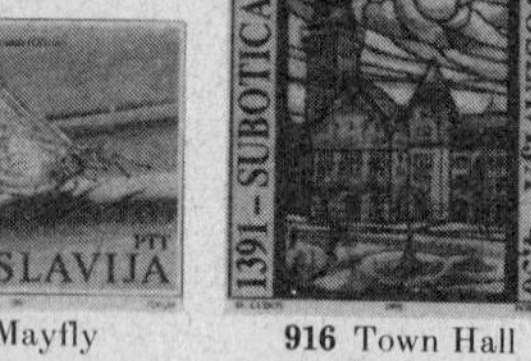

916 Town Hall (stained glass)

1991. Nature Protection. Multicoloured.

2739 11 d. Type **915** 60 35
2740 15 d. Pigmy cormorants 80 40

1991. 600th Anniv of Subotica.

2741 **916** 4 d. 50 multicoloured 25 15

917 Honey Bees and Congress Emblem

918 "Little Dubravka" (Jovan Bijelic)

1991. "Apimondia" 33rd International Bee Keeping Congress, Split.

2742 **917** 11 d. multicoloured .. 60 35

1991. 23rd "Joy of Europe" Meeting. Mult.

2743 5 d. Type **918** 25 15
2744 30 d. "Little Girl with a Cat" (Mary Cassatt) .. 1·60 95

919 Statue of Prince Michael Obrenovich and Serbian 1866 1 p. Newspaper Stamp

1991. Stamp Day.

2745 **919** 4 d. 50 multicoloured 25 15

920 Battle of Vucji Flag and Medal for Military Valour

921 Angel carring Sun (Andrija Raicevic) (17th century)

1991. Cetinje Museum Exhibits. Montenegrin Flags and Medals. Multicoloured.

2746 20 d. Type **920** .. .. 1·10 65
2747 30 d. Battle of Grahovo flag and medal .. 1·60 95
2748 40 d. State flag and Medal for bravery .. .. 2·10 1·25
2749 50 d. Court flag and Petrovic dynasty commemorative medal 2·60 1·60

1991. Illustrations from Ancient Manuscripts. Multicoloured.

2750 20 d. Type **921** .. .. 1·10 65
2751 30 d. "April" (Celnica Gospel) (14th century) 1·60 95
2752 40 d. "Annunciation" (Trogir Evangeliarum) (13th century) .. 2·10 1·25
2753 50 d. Mary Magdalene in initial V (Miroslav Gospel) (12th century) 2·60 1·60

1991. Nos. 2591 and 2586 surch.

2754 5 d. on 60 p. mauve & red 25 15
2755 10 d. on 10 p. violet & grn 50 30

923 Delcev

924 Trophies and Club Emblem

1992. 120th Birth Anniv of Goce Delcev (revolutionary).

2756 **923** 5 d. multicoloured .. 25 15

1992. Victories of Red Star Club, Belgrade, in European and World Football Championships.

2757 **924** 17 d. multicoloured .. 90 55

925 Luge

1992. Winter Olympic Games, Albertville. Multicoloured.

2758 80 d. Type **925** .. .. 4·00 2·40
2759 100 d. Acrobatic skiing .. 5·25 3·25

926 European Hare

927 "Mary feeding Jesus" (fresco, Pec Patriarchate)

1992. Protected Animals. Multicoloured.

2760 50 d. Type **926** .. .. 2·50 1·50
2761 60 d. Siberian flying squirrels .. .. 3·00 1·75
2762 80 d. Forest dormouse .. 4·00 2·50
2763 100 d. Common hamsters 5·25 3·25

1992. United Nations Children's Fund Breastfeeding Campaign.

2764 **927** 80 d. multicoloured .. 4·00 2·50

928 Skier

1992. Centenary of Skiing in Montenegro.

2765 **928** 8 d. multicoloured .. 40 25

929 Fountain, Belgrade

930 "Titanic"

1992.

2766 **929** 50 d. violet .. .. 2·50 1·50

1992. 80th Anniv of Sinking of "Titanic".

2785 **930** 150 d. multicoloured .. 8·00 4·75

931 La Barqueta Bridge and Seville (engraving)

1992. "Expo '92" World's Fair, Seville.

2786 **931** 150 d. multicoloured .. 8·00 4·75

EXPRESS LETTER STAMP

CROATIA

1918. Express Letter stamp of Hungary optd. **HRVATSKA SHS ZURNO.**

E 84. E **18.** 2 f. olive and red .. 5 12

NEWSPAPER STAMPS

CROATIA

1918. Newspaper stamp of Hungary optd. **HRVATSKA SHS.**

N83. N **9.** 2 f. orange 5 12

N **25.**

1919. Imperf.

N 97. N **25.** 2 h. yellow 8 75

SLOVENIA

N **30.** Cherub with Newspapers.

1919. Imperf.

N 150. N **30.** 2 v. grey 5 12
N 155. 2 v. blue 5 5
N 151. 4 v. grey 8 25
N 156. 4 v. blue 8 12
N 152. 6 v. grey .. .. 3·00 3·75
N 157. 6 v. blue .. .. 2·50 3·00
N 153. 10 v. grey 5 12
N 158. 10 v. blue 5 8
N 154. 30 v. grey 8 25

(N **35.**)

(N **36.**)

1920. Surch. as Type N **35** (2 to 6 p.) or Type N **36** (10 p. and 30 p.).

N 164. N **30.** 2 p. on 2 v. grey .. 30 65
N 169. 2 p. on 2 v. blue .. 5 5
N 165. 4 p. on 2 v. grey .. 30 65
N 170. 4 p. on 2 v. blue .. 5 5
N 166. 6 p. on 2 v. grey .. 45 65
N 171. 6 p. on 2 v. blue .. 5 5
N 167. 10 p. on 2 v. grey .. 65 75
N 172. 10 p. on 2 v. blue .. 12 40
N 168. 30 p. on 2 v. grey .. 65 1·00
N 173. 30 p. on 2 v. blue .. 20 50

OFFICIAL STAMPS

O **130.**

1946.

O 540. O **130.** 50 p. orange .. 15 5
O 541. 1 d. green 15 5
O 542. 1 d. 50 olive .. 30 5
O 543. 2 d. 50 red 30 5
O 544. 4 d. brown 60 10
O 545. 5 d. blue 80 10
O 546. 8 d. brown .. .. 1·10 15
O 547. 12 d. violet .. 1·40 30

POSTAGE DUE STAMPS

BOSNIA AND HERZEGOVINA

ДРЖАВА С.Х.С.
БОСНА И
ХЕРЦЕГОВИНА

хелера

(D 5.)

КРАЉЕВСТВО
СРБА. ХРВАТА
И СЛОВЕНАЦА

ПОРТО

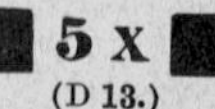

(D 13.)

1918. Postage Due stamps of Bosnia optd. as Type D 5 or **DRZAVA S.H.S. BOSNA I HERCEGOVINA HELERA.**

D 19. D **35.** 2 h. red 5 5
D 20. 4 h. red 30 50
D 21. 5 h. red 5 5
D 22. 6 h. red 50 35
D 23. 10 h. red 5 5
D 24. 15 h. red .. .. 5·25 5·25
D 25. 20 h. red 5 5
D 26. 25 h. red 35 35
D 27. 30 h. red 35 35
D 28. 40 h. red 12 12
D 29. 50 h. red 70 70
D 30. 1 k. blue 35 35
D 31. 3 k. blue 25 25

1919. "Eagle" type of Bosnia surch. as Type **D 13** or **KRALJEVSTVO SRBA, HRVATA I SLOVENACA PORTO** and value.

D 50.	**2.**	2 h. on 35 h. blue ..	25	15
D 51.		5 h. on 45 h. blue ..	45	75
D 52.		10 h. on 10 h. red ..	5	5
D 53.		15 h. on 40 h. orange ..	25	30
D 54.		20 h. on 5 h. green ..	5	5
D 55.		25 h. on 20 h. pink ..	20	2[illegible]
D 56.		30 h. on 30 h. brown ..	20	25
D 57.		1 k. on 50 h. purple ..	10	35
D 58.		3 k. on 25 h. blue ..	25	35

КРАЉЕВСТВО
СРБА, ХРВАТА
И СЛОВЕНАЦА
40
40 хелера 40
(D 14.)

1919. Postage Due stamps of Bosnia surch. or optd. as Type **D 14** or **KRALJEVSTVO SRBA HRVATA SLOVENACA** and value.

D 59.	**D 4.**	40 h. on 6 h. black, red and yellow ..	5	5
D 60.		50 h. on 8 h. black, red and yellow ..	5	5
D 61.		200 h. blk., red & grn.	6·25	5·25
D 62.		4 k. on 7 h. black, red and yellow ..	20	35

CROATIA

1919. Postage Due stamps of Hungary, with figures in red (except 50 f. in black), optd. **HRVATSKA SHS.**

D 85.	**D 9.**	1 f. green (No. D 190)	22·00	28·00
D 86.		2 f. green	90	90
D 87.		10 f. green	65	65
D 88.		12 f. green	85·00	95·00
D 89.		15 f. green	50	50
D 90.		20 f. green	50	50
D 91.		30 f. green	1·60	1·60
D 92.		50 f. green (No. D 177)	25·00	30·00

SLOVENIA

D 30.

1919.

D 150.	**D 30.**	5 v. red	5	5
D 151.		10 v. red	5	5
D 152.		20 v. red	5	5
D 153.		50 v. red	5	5
D 154.		1 k. blue	25	25
D 155.		5 k. blue	45	25
D 156.		10 k. blue	80	65

ПОРТО 50 PORTO
(D 35.)

ПОРТО 8 PORTO
(D 36.)

1920. Stamps of 1919 issue surch. as Types **D 36** or **D 36.**

D 164.	**25.**	5 p. on 15 v. blue ..	5	5
D 165.		10 p. on 15 v. blue ..	50	40
D 166.		20 p. on 15 v. blue ..	12	8
D 167.		50 p. on 15 v. blue ..	5	5
D 168.	**26.**	1 d. on 30 v. pink (or red)	15	12
D 169.		3 d. on 30 v. pink (or red)	30	15
D 170.		8 d. on 30 v. pink (or red)	75	45

GENERAL ISSUES

D 39. King Alexander I when Prince.

D 40.

1921.

D 182.	**D 39.**	10 on 5 p. green ..	12	5
D 183.		30 on 5 p. green ..	20	5

1921.

D 184.	**D 40.**	10 p. red	5	5
D 185.		30 p, green ..	15	5
D 197.		50 p. violet ..	5	5
D 187.		1 d. brown	10	5
D 188.		2 d. blue	20	5
D 189.		5 d. orange ..	1·60	5
D 190.		10 d. brown ..	7·50	25
D 191.		25 d. pink	30·00	1·00
D 192.		50 d. green ..	30·00	1·50

There are two issues in this type, differing in the lettering, etc.

1928. Surcharged **10.**

D 233.	**D 40.**	10 on 25 d. pink ..	3·75	25
D 234.		10 on 50 d. green ..	3·75	25

D 56.

ЈУГОСЛАВИЈА JUGOSLAVIJA
(D 62.)

1931.

D 259.	**D 56.**	50 p. violet ..	5	5
D 260.		1 d. red	5	5
D 261.		2 d. blue	5	5
D 262.		5 d. orange ..	10	8
D 263.		10 d. brown ..	20	10

1933. Optd. with Type **D 62.**

D 293a.	**D 40.**	50 p violet	12	5
D 294a.		1 d brown	15	5
D 295b.		2 d. blue	30	5
D 296.		5 d. orange	90	35
D 297a.		10 d. brown ..	3·50	10

1933. Red Cross. As T **62**, but inscr. "PORTO" in Latin and Cyrillic characters.

D 298.	**62.**	50 p. red and green	25	5

DEMOCRATIC FEDERATION OF YUGOSLAVIA

(a) REGIONAL ISSUES.

CROATIA

1945. Zagreb issue. Croatian Postage Due stamps of 1942 surch. **DEMOKRATSKA FEDERATIVNA JUGOSLAVIJA KN 80 KN** and star.

RD 45.	**D 15.**	40 k. on 50 b. brn. and blue ..	5	5
RD 46.		60 k. on 1 k. brown and blue	5	5
RD 47.		80 k. on 2 k. brown and blue	10	10
RD 48.		100 k. on 5 k. brown and blue	12	12
RD 49.		200 k. on 6 k. brown and blue	20	20

MONTENEGRO

1945. Cetinje issue. National Poem issue of Italian Occupation surch as Type R **4**, with "PORTO" in addition.

RD 61.	10 l. on 5 c. violet ..	62·00	£225
RD 62.	20 l. on 5 l. red on brn.	90·00	85·00

SERBIA

1944. Senta issue. No. D 684 of Hungary optd. with a large Star, **8.X.1944** and "Yugoslavia" in Cyrillic characters. and surch. in addition.

RD 73.	**D 115.**	10 (f.) on 2 f. brn.	45·00	45·00

(b) GENERAL ISSUES.

D **114.** D **115.** D **126.**

1944. Postage Due stamps of Serbia optd. in Cyrillic characters, as Type D **114.**

D 487.	10 d. red	30	50
D 488.	20 d. blue	30	50

1945. (a) Value in black.

D 489.	**D 115.**	2 d. brown ..	5	5
D 490.		3 d. violet	5	5
D 491.		5 d. green	5	5
D 492.		7 d. brown ..	5	5
D 493.		10 d lilac	15	5
D 494.		20 d. blue	20	5
D 495.		30 d. green ..	35	15
D 496.		40 d. red	40	20

(b) Value in colour.

D 497.	**D 115.**	1 d. green	8	5
D 498.		1 d. 50 blue ..	8	5
D 499.		2 d. red	15	5
D 500.		3 d. brown	30	10
D 501.		4 d. violet	40	20

1946.

D 527.	**D 126.**	50 p. orange ..	5	5
D 528.		1 d. orange ..	5	5
D 724.		1 d. brown ..	25	5
D 529.		2 d. blue	8	5
D 725.		2 d. green ..	25	5
D 530.		3 d. green ..	15	5
D 531.		5 d. violet ..	15	5
D 726.		5 d. blue	40	5
D 532.		7 d. red	65	10
D 533.		10 d. pink ..	1·00	20
D 727.		10 d. red	1·60	5
D 534.		20 d. lake ..	2·25	45
D 1030.		20 d. violet ..	2·40	10
D 1031.		30 d. orange ..	5·25	10
D 1032.		50 d. blue ..	26·00	40
D 1033.		100 d. purple ..	10·50	95

1947. Red Cross. As No. 545, but with "PORTO" added. Colour changed.

D 546.	**131.**	50 p. green and red	30	8

1948. Red Cross. As No. 594, but inscr. "PORTO".

D 595.	**152.**	50 p. red and green	25	8

1949. Red Cross. As T **160** but inscr. "PORTO".

D 617.	**160.**	50 p. purple & red	40	8

ФНР ЈУГОСЛАВИЈА
FNR JUGOSLAVIJA
(D **168.**)

D **175.** Map.

D **202.**

1950. Optd. with Type D **168.**

D 637.	**D 115.**	1 d. 50 p. blue ..	5	5
D 638.		3 d. brown ..	10	5
D 639.		4 d. violet ..	20	15

1950. Red Cross.

D 665.	**D 175.**	50 p. brown & red	30	8

1951. Red Cross. Inscr. "PORTO".

D 703.	**191.**	50 p. green and red	30	8

1952. Red Cross.

D 741.	**D 202.**	50 p. red and grey	30	8

1953. Red Cross. Inscr. "PORTO".

D 762.	**211.**	2 d. red and brown ..	50	10

1954. Red Cross. Inscr. "PORTO".

D 783.	**216.**	2 d. red and lilac ..	45	10

1955. Children's Week. Inscr. "PORTO".

D 802.	**222.**	2 d. green	35	8

1955. Red Cross. Inscr. "PORTO".

D 804.	**224.**	2 d. brn., deep red and red	50	10

1956. Red Cross. Inscr. "PORTO".

D 820.	**228.**	2 d. green and red ..	35	8

1956. Children's Week. Inscr. "PORTO".

D 835.	**232.**	2 d. brown	30	8

1957. Red Cross. Inscr. "PORTO".

D 844.	**234.**	2 d. red, black, grey	35	10

1957. Children's Week. Inscr. "PORTO".

D 867.	**240.**	2 d. brown and blue	30	8

1958. Red Cross. Inscr. "PORTO".

D 879.	**245.**	2 d. multicoloured ..	50	10

D **251.** Child with Toy.

1958. Children's Week.

D 913.	**D 251.**	2 d. black and blue	40	5

1959. Red Cross. Inscr. "PORTO".

D 927.	**255.**	2 d. orange and red	30	8

1959. Children's Week. As T **260.** Inscr. "PORTO".

D 947.	2 d. purple and yellow	25	5

DESIGN: Tree, cockerel and ears of wheat.

1960. Red Cross. Inscr. "PORTO".

D 956.	**262.**	2 d. purple and red	25	10

1960. Children's Week. As T **265.** Inscr. "PORTO".

D 970.	2 d. blue (Young boy)	20	5

1961. Red Cross. Inscr. "PORTO". Perf. or Imperf.

D 982.	**268.**	2 d. multicoloured	25	8

1961. Children's Week. Inscr. "PORTO'

D 1020.	**274.**	2 d. green and sepia	20	5

1962. Red Cross. Inscr. "PORTO"

D 1043.	**281.**	5 d. red, brown and blue	20	5

1963. Red Cross Cent. and Week. Inscr. "PORTO".

D 1074.	**288.**	5 d. red, purple and orange	30	8

YUNNANFU Pt. 17

Yunnanfu (formerly Yunnansen), the chief city of the Chinese province of Yunnan, had an Indo-Chinese Post Office from 1900 to 1922.

1901. 100 centimes = 1 franc.
1918. 100 cents = 1 piastre.

Stamps of Indo-China surcharged.

1903. "Tablet" key-type surch. **YUNNANSEN** and value in Chinese.

1.	D.	1 c. black on blue ..	1·75	1·50
2.		2 c. brown on yellow ..	1·40	1·40
3.		4 c. red on grey ..	1·40	1·75
4.		5 c. green	1·40	1·10
5.		10 c. red	1·40	1·10
6.		15 c. grey	1·75	1·40
7.		20 c. red on green ..	1·90	1·60
8.		25 c. blue	1·75	1·60
9.		30 c. brown on drab ..	2·25	1·60
10.		40 c. red on yellow ..	18·00	11·00
11.		50 c. red on rose ..	£110	£110
12.		50 c. brown on blue ..	60·00	60·00
13.		75 c. brown on orange ..	15·00	12·00
14.		1 f. olive	17·00	17·00
15.		5 f. mauve on lilac ..	40·00	40·00

1906. Surch. **Yunnan-Fou** and value in Chinese.

16.	**8.**	1 c. olive	60	60
17.		2 c. red on yellow ..	70	70
18.		4 c. purple on blue ..	80	80
19.		5 c. green	80	80
20.		10 c. red	80	80
21.		15 c. brown on blue ..	1·40	1·40
22.		20 c. red on green ..	1·10	1·10
23.		25 c. blue	1·10	1·10
24.		30 c. brown on cream ..	1·10	1·10
25.		35 c. black on yellow ..	1·60	1·60
26.		40 c. black on grey ..	1·40	1·40
27.		50 c. brown on cream ..	1·40	1·40
28.	D.	75 c. brown on orange ..	15·00	15·00
29.	**8.**	1 f. green	7·00	7·00
30.		2 f. brown on yellow ..	10·00	10·00
31.	D.	5 f. mauve on lilac ..	25·00	25·00
32.	**8.**	10 f. red on green ..	32·00	32·00

1908. Native types surch. **YUNNANFOU** and value in Chinese.

33.	**10.**	1 c. black and brown ..	20	20
34.		2 c. black and brown ..	20	20
35.		4 c. black and blue ..	20	20
36.		5 c. black and green ..	45	45
37.		10 c. black and red ..	20	20
38.		15 c. black and violet ..	1·00	80
39.	**11.**	20 c. black and violet ..	1·25	90
40.		25 c. black and blue ..	1·25	1·00
41.		30 c. black and brown ..	1·40	1·25
42.		35 c. black and green ..	1·40	1·25
43.		40 c. black and brown ..	1·90	1·90
44.		50 c. black and red ..	1·90	1·90
45.	**12.**	75 c. black and orange ..	2·25	2·00
46.		1 f. black and red ..	3·75	3·00
47.		2 f. black and green ..	5·50	5·50
48.		5 f. black and blue ..	15·00	12·00
49.		10 f. black and violet ..	32·00	32·00

1919. As last, surch. in addition with value in figures and words.

50.	**10.**	⅖ c. on 1 c. blk. & brown	20	15
51.		⅘ c. on 2 c. blk. & brown	30	30
52.		1⅗ c. on 4 c. black & blue	35	30
53.		2 c. on 5 c. black & grn.	30	30
54.		4 c. on 10 c. black & red	30	25
55.		6 c. on 15 c. blk. & violet	30	25
56.	**11.**	8 c. on 20 c. blk. & violet	45	35
57.		10 c. on 25 c. blk. & blue	60	55
58.		12 c. on 30 c. blk. & brown	50	50
59.		14 c. on 35 c. blk. & grn.	1·00	95
60.		16 c. on 40 c. blk. & brn.	1·10	1·00
61.		20 c. on 50 c. blk. & red	60	60
62.	**12.**	30 c. on 75 c. blk. & orge.	1·10	95
63.		40 c. on 1 f. blk. & red ..	1·25	1·10
64.		80 c. on 2 f. blk. & grn.	1·90	1·90
65.		2 p. on 5 f. black & blue	15·00	15·00
66.		4 p. on 10 f. blk. & violet ..	5·50	5·00

ZAIRE Pt. 14

In 1971 the Congo Republic (Kinshasa), formerly Belgian Congo, changed its name to Zaire.

100 sengi = 1 (li) kuta. 100 (ma) kuta = 1 zaire.

176. Nurse tending Child.

177. Pres. Mobutu, Memorial and Emblem.

1971. 25th Anniv. of U.N.I.C.E.F. Mult.

788.	4 k. Type **176**	30	20
789.	14 k. Zaire Republic on map of Africa	85	55
790.	17 k. Child in African village	1·10	90

1972. 5th Anniv. of Revolution.

791.	**177.**	4 k. multicoloured ..	3·25	2·75
792.		14 k. multicoloured ..	3·25	2·75
793.		22 k. multicoloured ..	4·50	3·25

177a. Arms.

177b. Pres. Mobutu.

1972.

794.	**177a.**	10 s. orange and black	10	10
795.		40 s. blue and black	10	10
796.		50 s. yellow and black	10	10
797.	**177b.**	1 k. multicoloured ..	10	10
798.		2 k. multicoloured ..	10	10
799.		3 k. multicoloured ..	10	10
800.		4 k. multicoloured ..	10	10
801.		5 k. multicoloured ..	15	10
802.		6 k. multicoloured ..	15	10
803.		8 k. multicoloured ..	20	15
804.		9 k. multicoloured ..	30	15
805.		10 k. multicoloured ..	35	15
806.		14 k. multicoloured ..	45	20
807.		17 k. multicoloured ..	50	35
808.		20 k. multicoloured ..	65	40
809.		50 k. multicoloured ..	1·75	85
810.		100 k. multicoloured ..	3·50	2·00

178. Inga Dam.

1973. Inga Dam. Completion of 1st Stage.
811. **178.** 0.04 z. multicoloured 10 10
812. 0.14 z. multicoloured 45 35
813. 0.18 z. multicoloured 80 45

1973. As T **177b**, but face values in Zaires.
814 0.01 z. multicoloured .. 10 10
815. 0.02 z. multicoloured .. 10 10
816. 0.03 z. multicoloured .. 10 10
817. 0.04 z. multicoloured .. 10 10
818. 0.10 z. multicoloured .. 45 20
819. 0.14 z. multicoloured .. 80 35

179. Africa on World Map.

1973. Third International Fair, Kinshasa.
820. **179.** 0.04 z. multicoloured 15 10
821. 0.07 z. multicoloured 30 15
822. 0.18 z. multicoloured 80 45

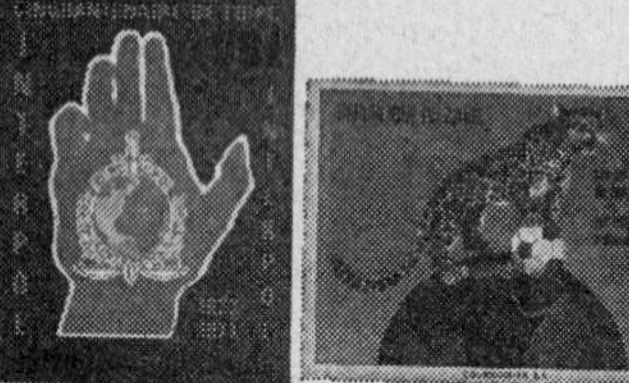

180. Emblem on Hand. 181. Leopard with Football on Globe.

1973. 50th Anniv. of International Criminal Police Organization (Interpol).
823. **180.** 0.06 z. multicoloured 35 20
824. 0.14 z. multicoloured 80 35

1974. World Cup Football Championship, Munich.
825. **181.** 1 k. multicoloured .. 10 10
826. 2 k. multicoloured .. 10 10
827. 3 k. multicoloured .. 15 10
828. 4 k. multicoloured .. 20 10
829. 5 k. multicoloured .. 30 10
830. 14 k. multicoloured .. 1·40 55

182. Muhamed Ali and George Foreman. 185. Waterfall.

1974. World Heavyweight Boxing Title Fight, Kinshasa.
831 **182.** 1 k. multicoloured .. 10 10
832 4 k. multicoloured .. 15 10
833 6 k. multicoloured .. 20 10
834 14 k. multicoloured .. 55 30
835 20 k. multicoloured .. 90 40

1975. World Heavyweight Boxing Title Fight, Kinshasa. As T **182** optd. with amended date **25-9-74**.
836. **182.** 0.01 z. multicoloured 10 10
837. 0.04 z. multicoloured 10 10
838. 0.06 z. multicoloured 20 10
839. 0.14 z. multicoloured 45 15
840. 0.20 z. multicoloured 80 30

Nos. 836/40 differ from Type **182** by having the face values expressed as decimals of the zaire. Both dates are in fact incorrect as the fight was held on 30 October, 1974.

1975. 12th U.I.C.N. General Assembly, Kinshasa.
858 **185** 1 k. multicoloured .. 10 10
859 2 k. multicoloured .. 10 10
860 3 k. multicoloured .. 20 10
861 4 k. multicoloured .. 30 10
862 5 k. multicoloured .. 40 10

186. Okapis.

1975. 50th Anniv. of Virunga National Park.
863. **186.** 1 k. multicoloured .. 10 10
864. 2 k. multicoloured .. 20 10
865. 3 k. multicoloured .. 35 10
866. 4 k. multicoloured .. 45 10
867. 5 k. multicoloured .. 55 10

187. Woman Judge with Barristers.

1975. Int. Women's Year.
868. **187.** 1 k. multicoloured .. 10 10
869. 2 k. multicoloured .. 10 10
870. 4 k. multicoloured .. 20 10
871. 14 k. multicoloured .. 65 20

188. Sozacom Building. 189. Pende Statuette.

1976. 10th Anniv. of "New Regime". Mult.
872. 1 k. Type **188** .. 10 10
873. 2 k. Siderma Maluku Industrial Complex (horiz.) .. 10 10
874. 3 k. Flour-mill, Matadi .. 10 10
875. 4 k. Women parachutists (horiz.) .. 20 10
876. 8 k. Pres. Mobutu with Mao Tse-Tung .. 35 10
877. 10 k. Soldiers clearing vegetation along the Salongo (horiz.) .. 45 20
878. 14 k. Pres. Mobutu addressing U.N. General Assembly, 4 October 1973 (horiz.) 65 30
879. 15 k. Rejoicing crowd (horiz.) 80 20

1977. Masks and Statuettes. Multicoloured.
880. 2 z. Type **189** 10 10
881 4 z. Type **189** 10 10
882. 5 z. Tshokwe mask .. 10 10
883. 7 z. As 5 k. 15 10
884. 10 z. Suku mask 20 10
885. 14 z. As 10 k. 35 15
886. 15 z. Kongo statuette .. 40 15
887. 18 z. As 15 k. 45 30
888. 20 z. Kuba mask 65 35
889. 25 z. As 20 k. 80 45

190. U.P.U. Emblem on Map. 192. " Pantodon buchholzi ".

1977. Cent. of Universal Postal Union.
890. **190.** 1 k. multicoloured .. 10 10
891. 4 k. multicoloured .. 20 10
892. 7 k. multicoloured .. 50 35
893. 50 k. multicoloured .. 4·25 2·25

1977. Various stamps of Congo (Kinshasa) and Zaire, surch. **REPUBLIQUE DE ZAIRE** or with new value only (No. 904).
894. **158.** 1 k. on 10 s. red & blk. 10 10
895. **152.** 2 k. on 9.6 k. blk. on red 10 10
896. **158.** 5 k. on 30 s. grn. & blk. 10 10
897. **173.** 10 k. on 10 s. mult. .. 35 10
898. **158.** 10 k. on 15 s. blue & blk. 15 10
899. – 20 k. on 9.6 k. mult. (No. 673) 35 15
900. **167.** 25 k. on 10 s. mult. .. 65 30
901. **174.** 30 k. on 12 k. mult. .. 65 35
902. **159.** 40 k. on 9.6 k. mult. 1·00 50
903. **168.** 48 k. on 10 s. mult. 1·10 55
904. **158.** 100 k. on 40 s. bl. & blk. 2·40 95

1978. Fishes. Multicoloured.
905. 30 s. Type **192** 10 10
906. 70 s. " Aphyosemion striatum " 10 10
907. 5 k. " Ctenopoma fasciolatum " 10 10
908. 8 k. " Malaterurus electricus " 20 10
909. 10 k. " Hemichromis bimaculatus " .. 35 10
910. 30 k. " Marcusenius isidori " 55 40
911. 40 k. " Synodontis nigriventris " 90 50
912. 48 k. " Julidochromis ornatus " .. .. 1·10 65
913. 100 k. " Nothobranchius brieni " .. .. 2·75 1·25

193. Argentina v. France. 194. Mama Mobutu.

1978. World Cup Football Championship, Argentina. Multicoloured.
915. 1 k. Type **193** 10 10
916. 3 k. Austria v Brazil .. 10 10
917. 7 k. Scotland v Iran .. 10 10
918. 9 k. Netherlands v Peru .. 10 10
919. 10 k. Hungary v Italy .. 15 10
920. 20 k. West Germany v Mexico 35 20
921. 50 k. Tunisia v Poland .. 85 45
922. 100 k. Spain v Sweden .. 1·90 1·00

1978. Mama Mobutu Sese Seko (wife of President). First Death Anniv.
924. **194.** 8 k. multicoloured .. 20 10

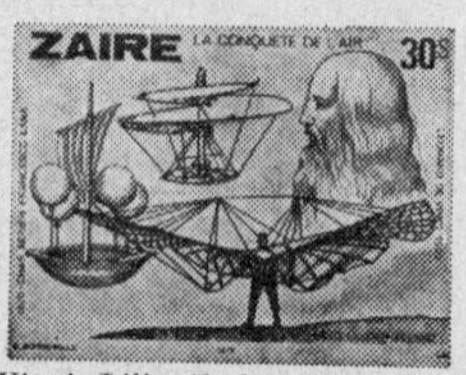

197. Da Vinci, Lilienthal and Flying Machines.

1978. History of Aviation. Multicoloured.
927. 30 s. Type **197** 10 10
928. 70 s. Wright Brothers' " Flyer III " and Santos Dumont's " 14 Bis " .. 10 10
929. 1 k. Farman " F 60 " and Bleriot " XI " 10 10
930. 5 k. Junkers " G 38 " and " Spirit of St. Louis " .. 10 10
931. 8 k. Macchi-Castoldi " MC 72 " and Sikorski " S–42 B " (Clipper) 15 15
932. 10 k. Boeing " 707 " and Fokker " F VII " .. 30 20
933. 50 k. " Apollo XI " space capsule and " Concorde " 1·10 55
934. 75 k. British Airways helicopter and Douglas " DC 10 " .. .. .. 1·40 90

198. President Mobutu. 199. " Phylloporus ampliporus ".

1979.
936. **198.** 2 k. multicoloured .. 10 10
937. 5 k. multicoloured .. 10 10
938. 6 k. multicoloured .. 10 10
939. 8 k. multicoloured .. 10 10
940. 10 k. multicoloured .. 10 10
941. 25 k. multicoloured .. 10 10
942. 48 k. multicoloured .. 35 15
942a. 50 k. reddish lilac .. 20 10
943. 1 z. multicoloured .. 80 30
943a. 2 z. brown 65 35
943b. 5 z. blue .. .. 1·50 85

1979. Mushrooms. Multicoloured.
944. 30 s. Type **199** 10 10
945. 5 k. " Engleromyces goetzei " 10 10
946. 8 k. " Scutellinia virungae " 10 10
947. 10 k. " Pycnoporus sanguineus " 20 10
948. 30 k. " Cantharellus miniatescens " 55 20
949. 40 k. " Lactarius phlebonemus " 90 20
950. 48 k. " Phallus indusiatus " 1·40 35
951. 100 k. " Ramaria moelleriana " .. .. 2·25 70

200. Ntore Dancer.

1979. Zaire River Expedition. Multicoloured.
952. 1 k. Type **200** 10 10
953. 3 k. Regal sunbird .. 10 10
954. 4 k. African elephant .. 10 10
955. 10 k. Diamond, cotton boll and tobacco 10 10
956. 14 k. Hand holding flaming torch 15 10
957. 17 k. Lion and water lily .. 20 15
958. 25 k. Inzia Falls .. 30 15
959. 50 k. Wagenia fishermen .. 55 35

201. President Mobutu and Flag.

1979. 5th Anniv. (1970) of 2nd Republic.
961. **201.** 3 z. gold, red and blue 22·00

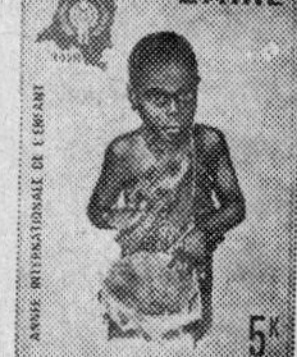

203. Globe and Drummer. 204. Boy with Drum.

1979. Sixth International Fair, Kinshasa.
963. **203.** 1 k. multicoloured .. 10 10
964. 9 k. multicoloured .. 10 10
965. 90 k. multicoloured .. 65 30
966. 100 k. multicoloured .. 80 35

1979. International Year of the Child. Mult.
968. 5 k. Type **204** 10 10
969. 10 k. Girl 10 10
970. 20 k. Boy 20 10
971. 50 k. Laughing boy .. 40 20
972. 100 k. Two children .. 85 35
973. 300 k. Mother and child .. 3·00 1·60

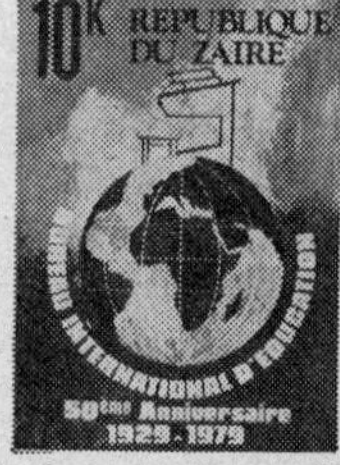

205. Desk standing on Globe.

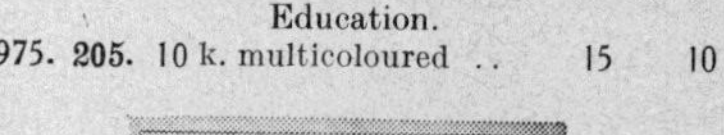

1979. 50th Anniv. of International Bureau of Education.
975. **205.** 10 k. multicoloured .. 15 10

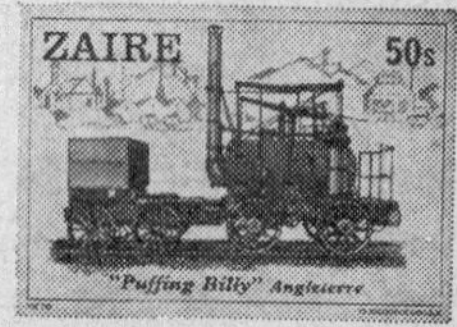

207. " Puffing Billy ", England.

1980. Locomotives. Multicoloured.
977 50 s. Type **207** 15 15
978 1 k. 50 Buddicom No. 33, France 15 15
979 5 k. "Elephant", Belgium 25 25
980 8 k. No. 601, Zaire .. 25 25
981 50 k. "Slieve Gullion", Ireland 50 50
982 75 k. "Black Elephant", Germany 95 95
983 2 z. Type "1-15", Zaire .. 2·75 2·75
984 5 z. "Golden State", U.S.A. 6·75 6·75

208. Sir Rowland Hill and Congo 5 f. Stamp, 1886.

1980. Death Cent. of Sir Rowland Hill. Mult.
986. 2 k. Type **208** 10 10
987. 4 k. Congo 10 f. stamp 1887 10 10
988. 10 k. Congo 1 f. African elephant stamp, 1884 .. 10 10
989. 20 k. Belgian Congo overprinted 3 f. 50 stamp, 1909 .. .. .. 15 10
990. 40 k. Belgian Congo 10 f. African elephant stamp, 1925 .. .. .. 20 10
991. 150 k. Belgian Congo 1 f. 50+1 f. 50 Chimpanzees stamp, 1939 .. .. 85 40
992. 200 k. Belgian Congo 1 f. 75 Leopard stamp, 1942 .. 1·25 60
993. 250 k. Belgian Congo 2 f. 50 Railway stamp, 1948 .. 2·50 2·50

209. Einstein.

1980. Birth Cent. of Albert Einstein (physicist).

995. 209. 40 s. brn., black & mauve 10 10
996. 2 k. brn., blk. and grn. 10 10
997. 4 k. brn., blk. and yell. 10 10
998. 15 k. brn., blk. & blue 15 10
999. 50 k. brn., blk. & red .. 35 20
1000. 300 k. brn., blk. & lilac 2·00 1·00

210. Booth Memorial Medical Centre, Flushing, New York.

1980. Centenary of Salvation Army in the United States. Multicoloured.

1002. 50 s. Type 210 .. .. 10 10
1003. 4 k. 50 Arrival of Railton in America 10 10
1004. 10 k. Mobile dispensary, Masian, Zaire 10 10
1005. 20 k. General Evangeline Booth and salvationist holding child (vert.) .. 10 10
1006. 40 k. Army band .. 20 15
1007. 75 k. Mobile clinic in bush, Zaire 45 20
1008. 1 z. 50 Canteen serving firefighters 90 40
1009. 2 z. American unit marching with flags (vert.) .. .. .. 1·40 55

212. Musical Instrument.

1980. 75th Anniv. of Rotary International. Multicoloured.

1013. 50 k. Drawing of mother and child (kamba) .. 30 15
1014. 100 k. Type 212 .. .. 55 30
1015. 500 k. Statuette (Liyolo) (vert.) .. .. 2·00 1·40

213. " Chaetodon collaris ".

1980. Tropical Fish. Multicoloured.

1017. 1 k. Type 213 .. .. 10 10
1018. 5 k. " Zebrasoma veliferum " 10 10
1019. 10 k. " Euxiphipops xanthometapon " .. 10 10
1020. 20 k. " Pomacanthus annularis " 10 10
1021. 50 k. " Centropyge loriculus " 15 10
1022. 150 k. " Oxymonacanthus longirostris " 50 30
1023. 200 k. " Balistoides niger " 95 50
1024. 250 k. " Rhinecanthus aculeatus " .. .. 1·25 60

214. Belgium 40 c. Congo Independence Stamp, 1960, and " Phibelza ".

1980. " Phibelza ". Belgian-Zaire stamp Exhibition, Kinshasha. Multicoloured.

1026. 1 z. Type 214 .. .. 40 30
1027. 1 z. Congo 20 f. Independence stamp, 1960 .. 40 30
1028. 2 z. Belgium 10 f. + 5 f. Zoo stamp, 1968 .. 85 55
1029. 2 z. Congo 40 c. Birds stamp, 1963 .. .. 85 40
1030. 3 z. Belgium 10 f. + 5 f. Brussels stamp, 1971 1·25 85
1031. 3 z. Zaire 22 k. stamp, 1972 1·25 85
1032. 4 z. Belgium 25 f. + 10f. stamp, 1980 .. .. 1·60 1·10
1033. 4 z. Congo 24 f. stamp, 1966 1·60 1·10

Nos. 1026/33 exist in two versions with the exhibition logo either at the right or the left of the design. Prices are the same for either version.

1980. 29th Anniv of Independence. Various stamps optd **20e Anniversaire-Independance-1960—1980.**

1034. 207. 50 s. "Puffing Billy" 10 10
1035. – 1 k. 50 Locomotive Buddicom No. 33 (No. 978) 25 25
1036. – 10 k Boeing 707 and Fokker "F VII" (No. 932) 10 10
1037. – 50 k. "Slieve Gullion" (No. 981) 25 25
1038. – 75 k. British Airways helicopter and Douglas "DC-10" (No. 934) 35 15
1039. 203. 100 k. Globe and drummer 45 25
1040. – 1 z. on 5 z. on 100 k. Two children (No. 972) 45 25
1041. – 250 k. Rowland Hill and railway stamp of 1948 (No. 993) .. 2·25 2·25
1042. – 5 z. on 100 k. Two children (No. 972) 2·75 1·25

216. Leopold I and 1851 Map of Africa.

1980. 150th Anniv. of Belgian Independence.

1043. 216. 10 k. green and blue 10 10
1044. – 75 k. brown and blue 45 20
1045. – 100 k. violet and blue 45 20
1046. – 145 k. blue & deep blue 1·00 35
1047. – 270 k. red and blue .. 1·60 85

DESIGNS: 75 k. Leopold II and Stanley's expedition. 100 k. Albert I and Colonial troops of 1914–18 War. 145 k. Leopold III and African animals. 270 k. Baudouin I and visit to Zaire of King Baudouin and Queen Fabiola.

217. Angels appearing to Shepherds.

1980. Christmas. Multicoloured.

1048. 10 k. Type 217 .. .. 10 10
1049. 75 k. Flight into Egypt .. 35 20
1050. 80 k. Three Kings .. 45 20
1051. 145 k. In the stable .. 80 45

218. Girl dancing to Cello.

1981. Norman Rockwell Paintings. Mult.

1053. 10 k. Type 218 .. .. 10 10
1054. 20 k. Couple with saluting boy scout 10 10
1055. 50 k. Sorter reading mail 20 10
1056. 80 k. Cupid whispering into youth's ear .. 35 15
1057. 100 k. Signing Declaration of Independence .. 50 20
1058. 125 k. Boy looking through telescope held by sailor 80 25
1059. 175 k. Boy in armchair playing trumpet .. 1·00 40
1060. 200 k. Weakling exercising with dumb bells .. 1·10 50

219. Pope John-Paul II and Pres. Mobutu.

220. Footballers.

1981. Papal Visit. Multicoloured.

1061. 5 k. Pope kneeling at shrine (horiz.) 10 10
1062. 10 k. Pres. Mobutu greeting Pope (horiz.) .. 10 10
1063. 50 k. Type 219 .. .. 20 10
1064. 100 k. Pope talking to child (horiz.) 65 35
1065. 500 k. Pope leading prayers 2·75 1·25
1066. 800 k. Pope making speech (horiz.) .. .. 4·00 2·00

1981. World Cup Football Championship. Spain, (1982)

1067. 220. 2 k. multicoloured .. 10 10
1068. – 10 k. multicoloured .. 10 10
1069. – 25 k. multicoloured .. 10 10
1070. – 90 k. multicoloured .. 35 15
1071. – 2 z. multicoloured .. 65 35
1072. – 3 z. multicoloured .. 1·25 55
1073. – 6 z. multicoloured .. 2·40 1·10
1074. – 8 z. multicoloured .. 3·25 1·60

DESIGNS: 1068/1074, Similar Football scenes.

221. Archer in Wheelchair.

1981. International Year of Disabled People. Multicoloured.

1076. 2 k. Type 221 .. .. 10 10
1077. 5 k. Ear and sound wave 10 10
1078. 10 k. One-legged person with crutch 10 10
1079. 18 k. Glasses, Braille and white cane 10 10
1080. 50 k. Crippled legs .. 20 10
1081. 150 k. Sign language .. 45 20
1082. 500 k. Hand and model showing joints .. 1·60 90
1083. 800 k. Dove shedding feathers .. .. 2·50 1·60

222. Children performing Carols.

224. Red Cross Helicopters.

1981. Christmas. Multicoloured.

1084. 25 k. Type 222 .. .. 10 10
1085. 1 z. Boy lighting candle .. 35 15
1086. 1 z. 50 Boy praying .. 45 20
1087. 3 z. Girl with presents .. 95 45
1088. 5 z. Children admiring baby .. .. 1·75 85

1982. Telecommunications and Health. Multicoloured.

1091. 1 k. Type 224 .. .. 10 10
1092. 25 k. Doctor and telephone 10 10
1093. 90 k. Antenna and map .. 20 15
1094. 1 z. Patient 35 15
1095. 1 z. 70 Teleprinter .. 45 20
1096. 3 z. Nurse and television 90 35
1097. 4 z. 50 Tape recorder .. 1·60 85
1098. 5 z. Babies and walkie-talkie .. .. 1·75 85

225. U.P.U. Emblem.

1982. 20th Anniv. (1981) of African Postal Union.

1099. 225. 1 z. green and gold .. 45 20

226. Salvador v Hungary.

1982. World Cup Football Championship, Spain. Multicoloured.

1100 2 k. Type 226 .. .. 10 10
1101 8 k. Cameroun v Peru .. 10 10
1102 25 k. Brazil v Russia .. 10 10
1103 50 k. Kuwait v Czechoslovakia 10 10
1104 90 k. Yugoslavia v Northern Ireland .. 30 15
1105 1 z. Austria v Chile .. 35 15
1106 1 z. 45 France v England 45 15
1107 1 z. 70 West Germany v Algeria 55 35
1108 3 z. Spain v Honduras .. 1·00 50
1109 3 z. 50 Belgium v Argentina .. .. 1·10 60
1110 5 z. Scotland v New Zealand .. .. 1·60 85
1111 6 z. Italy v Poland .. 2·00 95

228. Hands reaching towards Zaire.

1982. Ninth French and African Heads of State conference, Kinshasa.

1113. 228. 75 k. multicoloured .. 20 10
1114. 90 k. multicoloured .. 30 15
1115. 1 z. multicoloured .. 35 15
1116. 1 z. 50 multicoloured 45 20
1117. 3 z. multicoloured .. 95 50
1118. 5 z. multicoloured .. 1·60 85
1119. 8 z. multicoloured .. 2·50 1·10

229. Lions.

1982. Virunga National Park. Multicoloured.

1120. 1 z. Type 229 .. .. 35 20
1121. 1 z. 70 African buffalo .. 55 35
1122. 3 z. 50 African elephant 1·10 65
1123. 6 z. 50 Topi .. .. 2·00 1·00
1124. 8 z. Hippopotamus .. 2·75 1·40
1125. 10 z. Savanna Monkey .. 4·00 1·60
1126. 10 z. Leopard .. .. 4·00 1·60

230. Scout Camp.

233. Malachite.

231. Red-billed Quelea.

1982. 75th Anniv. of Boy Scout Movement. Multicoloured.

1127. 90 k. Type 230 .. .. 30 15
1128. 1 z. 70 Camp-fire .. 55 25
1129. 3 z. Scout 95 45
1130. 5 z. Scout carrying injured person .. .. 1·75 85
1131. 8 z. Scout signalling with flags .. .. .. 2·75 1·10

1982. Birds. Multicoloured.

1133. 25 k. Type **231** 20 15
1134. 50 k. African Pygmy Kingfisher 30 20
1135. 90 k. Kynsna Turaco .. 50 25
1136. 1 z. 50 Three-banded Plover 80 45
1137. 1 z. 70 Temminck's Courser 90 50
1138. 2 z. Bennett's Wood-pecker .. .. .. 1·10 65
1139. 3 z. Little Grebe .. 1·40 75
1140. 3 z. 50 Lizard Buzzard (vert.) .. .. .. 1·75 1·00
1141. 5 z. Black Crake .. 2·50 1·40
1142. 8 z. White-headed Vulture (vert.) .. 4·00 2·40

1983. Malachite. Multicoloured.

1144. 2 k. Type **233** 10 10
1145. 45 k. Quartz (horiz.) .. 20 10
1146. 75 k. Gold (horiz.) .. 35 10
1147. 1 z. Uranium and pitch-blende (horiz.) .. 45 15
1148. 1 z. 50 Bournonite .. 55 30
1149. 3 z. Cassiterite (horiz.) .. 1·10 50
1150. 6 z. Dioptase .. .. 2·25 95
1151. 8 z. Cuprite .. .. 3·25 1·40

234. Dr. Koch and Microscope.

1983. Centenary (1982) of Discovery of Tubercle Bacillus.

1153. **234.** 80 k. multicoloured 20 15
1154. 1 z. 20 multicoloured 35 20
1155. 3 z. 60 multicoloured 1·10 55
1156. 9 z. 60 multicoloured 2·75 1·40

235. " Zaire Diplomat " (Lufwa Mawidi).

1983. Kinshasa Monuments. Multicoloured.

1157. 50 k. Type **235** 15 10
1158. 1 z. " Echo of Zaire " .. (Lufwa Mawidi) (horiz.) 25 15
1159. 1 z. 50 " Messengers " (Liyolo Limbe Mpuanga) 40 20
1160. 3 z. " Shield of Revolution " (Liyolo Limbe Mpuanga) 85 50
1161. 5 z. " Weeping Woman " (Wuma Mbambila) (horiz.) 1·40 85
1162. 10 z. "The Militant" (Liyolo Limbe Mpuanaga) .. 2·50 1·25

236. Satellites over Globe.

1983. I.T.U. Delegates' Conference, Nairobi. Multicoloured.

1163. 2 k. Type **236** 10 10
1164. 4 k. Dish aerial 10 10
1165. 25 k. Dish aerial (different) 10 10
1166. 1 z. 20 Satellite and micro-wave antenna 45 15
1167. 2 z. 05 Satellite 65 30
1168. 3 z. 60 Satellite and micro-wave antenna (different) 1·10 45
1169. 6 z. Map of Zaire .. 1·60 70
1170. 8 z. Satellite (different) .. 2·40 1·40

238. Giant Eland.

1984. Garamba National Park. Multicoloured.

1172. 10 k. Type **238** 10 10
1173. 15 k. Tawny eagles .. 40 15
1174. 3 z. Servals 20 10
1175. 10 z. White rhinoceros .. 80 35
1176. 15 z. Lions .. .. 1·00 55
1177. 37 z. 50 Warthogs .. 2·75 1·10
1178. 40 z. Kori bustards .. 3·50 2·00
1179. 40 z. South African crowned cranes and game lodge .. .. 3·50 2·00

239. Visual Display Unit and Ferry.

1984. World Communications Year. Multicoloured.

1180. 10 k. Type **239** 10 10
1181. 15 k. Communications satellite 10 10
1182. 8 z.50 Radio telephone .. 45 30
1183. 10 z. Satellite and aerial .. 55 35
1184. 15 z. Video camera .. 1·00 55
1185. 37 z.50 Satellite and dish antenna .. .. 2·75 1·25
1186. 80 z. Switchboard operator 5·50 2·75

240. "Hypericum revolutum".

241. Basketball.

1984. Flowers. Multicoloured.

1187. 10 k. Type **240** 10 10
1188. 15 k. "Borreria dibrachiata" 10 10
1189. 3 z. "Disa erubesens" .. 20 10
1190. 8 z. 50 "Scaevola plumieri" 55 35
1191. 10 z. "Clerodendron thompsonii" 80 35
1192. 15 z. "Thumbergia erecta" .. .. 1·10 65
1193. 37 z. 50 "Impatiens niamniamesis" .. 2·75 1·60
1194. 100 z. "Canarina eminii" 7·75 3·25

1984. Olympic Games, Los Angeles. Multicoloured.

1195. 2 z. Type **241** 15 10
1196. 3 z. Equestrian 20 10
1197. 10 z. Running 70 35
1198. 15 z. Long jump .. 1·10 50
1199. 20 z. Football .. 1·60 80

242. Montgolfier Balloon, 1783.

243. Okapi Feeding.

1984. Bicentenary of Manned Flight. Mult.

1201. 10 k. Type **242** 10 10
1202. 15 k. Charles and Robert Balloon, 1783 .. .. 10 10
1203. 3 z. "La Gustave", 1784 15 10
1204. 5 z. "Santos Dumont III", 1899 .. .. 30 15
1205. 10 z. Picard's strato-spheric balloon, 1932 .. 70 40
1206. 15 z. Zeppelin "LZ129", 1936 .. .. 1·10 60
1207. 37 z. 50 "Double Eagle II", 1978 .. .. 2·50 1·40
1208. 80 z. Hot air balloons .. 6·00 3·00

1984. Wildlife Protection. Okapi. Mult.

1209. 2 z. Type **243** 15 10
1210. 3 z. Okapi resting .. 30 10
1211. 8 z. Okapi and foal .. 65 35
1212. 10 z. Okapi crossing stream 85 35

1985. 50th Anniv. of SABENA Brussels-Kinshasa Air Service. Nos. 927/34 surch. **SABENA/1935-1985** and new value.

1214. 2 z. 50 on 30 s. mult. .. 15 10
1215. 5 z. on 5 k. mult. .. 40 20
1216. 6 z. on 70 s. mult. .. 45 30
1217. 7 z. 50 on 1 k. mult. .. 55 35
1218. 8 z. 50 on 1 k. mult. .. 65 40
1219. 10 z. on 8 k. mult. .. 80 45
1220. 12 z. 50 on 75 k. mult. .. 90 60
1221. 30 z. on 50 k. mult. .. 2·25 1·25

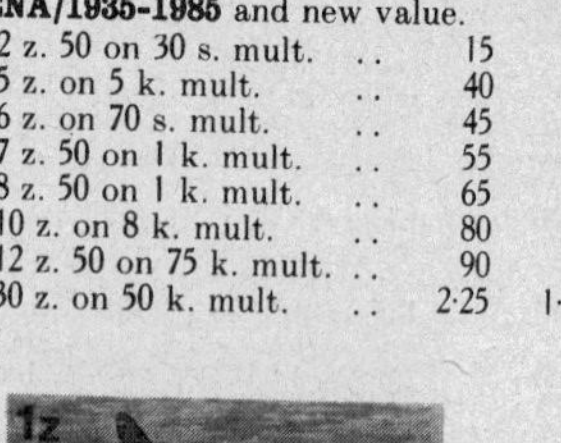

245. Swimming.

1985. "Olymphilex '85" Olympic Stamps Exhibition, Lausanne. Multicoloured.

1223. 1 z. Type **245** 10 10
1224. 2 z. Football (vert.) .. 15 10
1225. 3 z. Boxing 20 10
1226. 4 z. Basketball (vert.) .. 30 15
1227. 5 z. Show jumping .. 35 20
1228. 10 z. Volleyball (vert.) .. 70 45
1229. 15 z. Running .. .. 1·00 65
1230. 30 z. Cycling (vert.) .. 2·25 1·25

1985. Second Papal Visit. Nos. 1061/5 surch. **AOUT 1985.**

1231. 2 z. on 5 k. multicoloured 15 10
1232. 3 z. on 10 k. mult. .. 20 15
1233. 5 z. 50 k. multicoloured 45 20
1234. 10 z. on 100 k. mult. .. 90 50
1235. 15 z. on 500 k. mult. .. 1·40 65
1236. 40 z. on 800 k. mult. .. 3·00 1·40

247. Great Egrets.

1985. Birth Bicentenary of John J. Audubon (ornithologist). Multicoloured.

1238. 5 z. Type **247** 45 25
1239. 10 z. Common scoter .. 90 50
1240. 15 z. Black-crowned night heron .. .. 1·50 75
1241. 25 z. Surf scoter .. .. 2·25 1·25

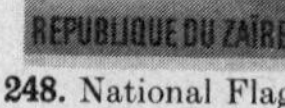

248. National Flag and "25" on Flag.

249. U.N. and Zaire Flags.

1985. 25th Anniv. of Independence.

1242. **248.** 5 z. multicoloured .. 20 10
1243. 10 z. multicoloured .. 45 20
1244. 15 z. multicoloured .. 65 35
1245. 20 z. multicoloured .. 90 40

1985. 40th Anniv of U.N.O. and 25th Anniv of Zaire Membership. Multicoloured.

1247. 10 z. Type **249** 45 30
1248. 50 z. U.N. building and emblem .. .. 2·25 1·10

1985. International Youth Year. Nos. 1127/31 optd. **1985** and I.Y.Y. emblem and surch. also.

1249. 3 z. on 3 z. multicoloured 10 10
1250. 5 z. on 5 z. multicoloured 20 10
1251. 7 z. on 90 k. mult. .. 35 15
1252. 10 z. on 90 k. mult. .. 45 15
1253. 15 z. on 1 z. 70 mult. .. 55 25
1254. 20 z. on 8 z. mult. .. 1·10 45
1255. 50 z. on 90 k. mult. .. 2·75 1·00

HAVE YOU READ THE NOTES AT THE BEGINNING OF THIS CATALOGUE?
These often provide answers to the enquiries we receive.

252. "Kokolo" (pusher tug).

1985. 50th Anniv of National Transport Office.

1258 7 z. Type **252** 30 10
1259 10 z. Early steam locomotive 45 20
1260 15 z. "Luebo" (pusher tug) 55 35
1261 50 z. Modern diesel locomotive .. .. 1·75 85

253. Pope John Paul II.

1985. Beatification of Sister Anuarite Nengapeta. Multicoloured.

1262. 10 z. Type **253** 45 20
1263. 15 z. Sister Anuarite .. 65 35
1264. 25 z. Pope and Sister Anuarite (horiz.) .. 1·10 55

254. Map and 1886 25 c. Stamp.

1986. Centenary of 1st Congo Free State Stamp.

1266. **254.** 25 z. blue, grey and deep blue .. .. 1·10 55

255. Congo Free State 1898 10 f. Stamp.

1986. "Cenzapost" Stamp Centenary Exhibition. Multicoloured.

1267. 7 z. Type **255** 30 10
1268. 15 z. Belgian Congo 1939 1 f. 25 + 1 f. 25 stamp 55 30
1269. 20 z. Belgian Congo 1942 50 f. stamp (vert.) .. 65 30
1270. 25 z. Zaire 1982 8 k. stamp 80 35
1271. 40 z. Zaire 1984 37 z. 50 stamp (vert.) .. .. 1·40 65

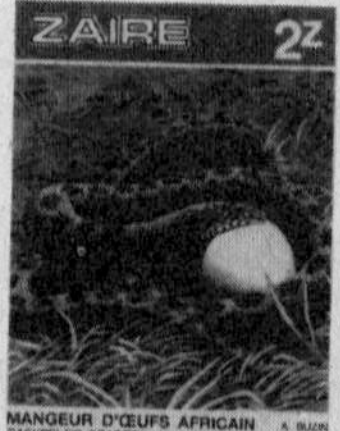

256. African Egg Eater.

1987. Reptiles. Multicoloured.

1273. 2 z. Type **256** 10 10
1274. 5 z. Rainbow lizard .. 10 10
1275. 10 z. Royal python .. 20 10
1276. 15 z. Cape chameleon .. 45 15
1277. 25 z. Green mamba .. 65 30
1278. 50 z. Black-necked cobra 1·25 55

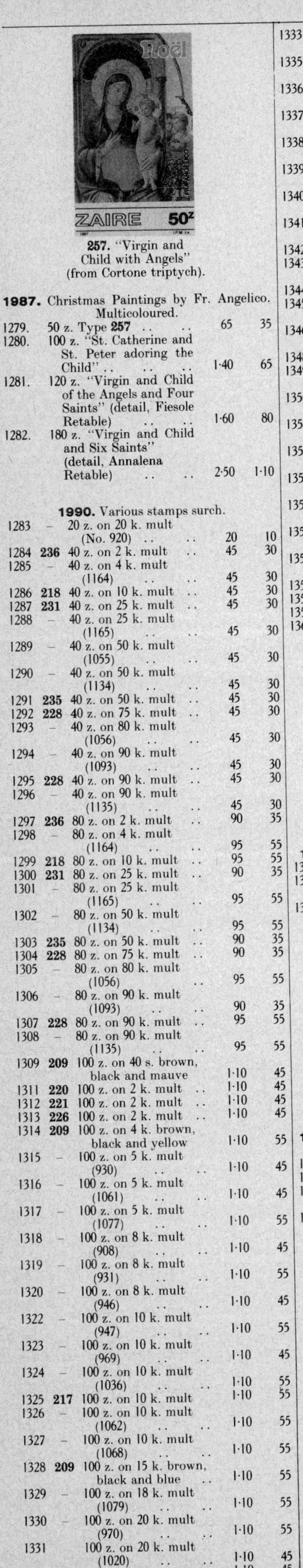

257. "Virgin and Child with Angels" (from Cortone triptych).

1987. Christmas Paintings by Fr. Angelico. Multicoloured.

No.	Description	Mint	Used
1279.	50 z. Type **257**	65	35
1280.	100 z. "St. Catherine and St. Peter adoring the Child"	1·40	65
1281.	120 z. "Virgin and Child of the Angels and Four Saints" (detail, Fiesole Retable)	1·60	80
1282.	180 z. "Virgin and Child and Six Saints" (detail, Annalena Retable)	2·50	1·10

1990. Various stamps surch.

No.	Type	Description	Mint	Used
1283	–	20 z. on 20 k. mult (No. 920)	20	10
1284	**236**	40 z. on 2 k. mult ..	45	30
1285	–	40 z. on 4 k. mult (1164)	45	30
1286	**218**	40 z. on 10 k. mult ..	45	30
1287	**231**	40 z. on 25 k. mult ..	45	30
1288	–	40 z. on 25 k. mult (1165)	45	30
1289	–	40 z. on 50 k. mult (1055)	45	30
1290	–	40 z. on 50 k. mult (1134)	45	30
1291	**235**	40 z. on 50 k. mult ..	45	30
1292	**228**	40 z. on 75 k. mult ..	45	30
1293	–	40 z. on 80 k. mult (1056)	45	30
1294	–	40 z. on 90 k. mult (1093)	45	30
1295	**228**	40 z. on 90 k. mult ..	45	30
1296	–	40 z. on 90 k. mult (1135)	45	30
1297	**236**	80 z. on 2 k. mult ..	90	35
1298	–	80 z. on 4 k. mult (1164)	95	55
1299	**218**	80 z. on 10 k. mult ..	95	55
1300	**231**	80 z. on 25 k. mult ..	90	35
1301	–	80 z. on 25 k. mult (1165)	95	55
1302	–	80 z. on 50 k. mult (1134)	95	55
1303	**235**	80 z. on 50 k. mult ..	90	35
1304	**228**	80 z. on 75 k. mult ..	90	35
1305	–	80 z. on 80 k. mult (1056)	95	55
1306	–	80 z. on 90 k. mult (1093)	90	35
1307	**228**	80 z. on 90 k. mult ..	95	55
1308	–	80 z. on 90 k. mult (1135)	95	55
1309	**209**	100 z. on 40 s. brown, black and mauve	1·10	45
1311	**220**	100 z. on 2 k. mult ..	1·10	45
1312	**221**	100 z. on 2 k. mult ..	1·10	45
1313	**226**	100 z. on 2 k. mult ..	1·10	45
1314	**209**	100 z. on 4 k. brown, black and yellow	1·10	55
1315	–	100 z. on 5 k. mult (930)	1·10	45
1316	–	100 z. on 5 k. mult (1061)	1·10	45
1317	–	100 z. on 5 k. mult (1077)	1·10	55
1318	–	100 z. on 8 k. mult (908)	1·10	45
1319	–	100 z. on 8 k. mult (931)	1·10	55
1320	–	100 z. on 8 k. mult (946)	1·10	45
1322	–	100 z. on 10 k. mult (947)	1·10	55
1323	–	100 z. on 10 k. mult (969)	1·10	45
1324	–	100 z. on 10 k. mult (1036)	1·10	55
1325	**217**	100 z. on 10 k. mult	1·10	55
1326	–	100 z. on 10 k. mult (1062)	1·10	55
1327	–	100 z. on 10 k. mult (1068)	1·10	55
1328	**209**	100 z. on 15 k. brown, black and blue ..	1·10	55
1329	–	100 z. on 18 k. mult (1079)	1·10	55
1330	–	100 z. on 20 k. mult (970)	1·10	55
1331		100 z. on 20 k. mult (1020)	1·10	45
1332	**177**	100 z. on 22 k. mult	1·10	45
1333	–	100 z. on 25 k. mult (1069)	1·10	55
1335	–	100 z. on 48 k. mult (912)	1·10	55
1336	–	100 z. on 48 k. mult (950)	1·10	55
1337	–	100 z. on 50 k. mult (1013)	1·10	45
1338	–	100 z. on 50 k. mult (1080)	1·10	55
1339	–	100 z. on 50 k. mult (1103)	1·10	55
1340	–	100 z. on 75 k. mult (1038)	1·10	45
1341	–	100 z. on 75 k. mult (1049)	1·10	45
1342	**203**	100 z. on 90 k. mult	1·10	45
1343	–	100 z. on 80 k. mult (1050)	1·10	55
1344	**234**	100 z. on 80 k. mult	1·10	45
1345	–	100 z. on 90 k. mult (1070)	1·10	55
1346	–	100 z. on 90 k. mult (1104)	1·10	55
1348	**233**	300 z. on 2 k. mult ..	3·50	1·60
1349	–	300 z. on 8 k. mult (980)	3·50	1·60
1350	**216**	300 z. on 10 k. green and blue ..	3·50	1·60
1351	–	300 z. on 14 k. mult (789)	3·50	1·60
1352	**159**	300 z. on 17 k. mult (807)	3·50	1·60
1353	–	300 z. on 20 k. mult (989)	3·50	1·60
1354	–	300 z. on 45 k. mult (1145)	3·50	1·60
1355	–	300 k. on 75 k. brown and blue (1044) ..	3·50	1·60
1356	–	300 z. on 75 k. mult (1146)	3·50	2·00
1357	**198**	500 z. on 8 k. mult ..	6·00	3·25
1358		500 z. on 10 k. mult	6·00	2·75
1359		500 z. on 25 k. mult	6·00	2·75
1360		500 z. on 48 k. mult	6·25	2·75

259 "Sida" forming Owl's Face

1990. Anti-AIDS Campaign. Multicoloured.

No.	Description	Mint	Used
1361	30 z. Type **259**	50	20
1362	40 z. Skeleton firing arrow through "SIDA" ..	60	35
1363	80 z. Leopard	1·10	80

260 Administration Building

1990. 50th Anniv of Regideso (development organization). Multicoloured.

No.	Description	Mint	Used
1365	40 z. Type **260**	55	35
1366	50 z. Modern factory ..	65	45
1367	75 z. Old water treatment plant	1·00	65
1368	120 z. Communal water tap	1·40	80

261 Maps of France and Zaire and Birds

1990. Bicentenary of French Revolution Mult.

No.	Description	Mint	Used
1369	40 z. Type **261**	55	35
1370	50 z. Article 1 of Declaration of Rights of Man and the Citizen within outline of person	65	45
1371	100 z. Crowd	1·25	65
1372	120 z. Globe	1·40	80

262 Stairs of Venus, Mount Hoyo

1990. Tourist Sites. Multicoloured.

No.	Description	Mint	Used
1373	40 z. Type **262**	45	20
1374	60 z. Scenic road to village	65	35
1375	100 z. Lake Kivu ..	1·25	55
1376	120 z. Niyara Gongo volcano	1·60	25

1991. Various stamps surch.

No.	Type	Description	Mint	Used
1379	–	1000 z. on 100 k. mult (1064)	15	15
1380	–	1000 z. on 1 z. mult (1105)	15	15
1381	**214**	1000 z. on 1 z. mult (1026)	15	15
1383	–	1000 z. on 1 z. mult (1027)	15	15
1385	–	2000 z. on 100 k. violet and blue (1045) ..	30	30
1386	–	2000 z. on 1 z. mult (1147)	30	30
1387	**228**	2500 z. on 1 z. mult ..	40	40
1388	**225**	3000 z. on 1 z. green and gold	45	45
1389	–	4000 z. on 1 z. mult (1158)	60	60
1390	–	5000 z. on 1 z. mult (1158)	75	75
1391	**228**	10000 z. on 1 z. mult	1·50	1·50
1392	**225**	15000 z. on 1 z. green and gold	2·25	2·25

Nos. 1381 and 1383 exist in two versions with the exhibition logo either at right or left of design.

OFFICIAL STAMPS

1975. Optd. **SP.**

No.	Type	Description	Mint	Used
O 841.	**172.**	10 s. orange & black	10	10
O 842.		40 s. blue and black	10	10
O 843.		50 s. yellow & black	10	10
O 844.	**177b.**	1 k. multicoloured..	10	10
O 845.		2 k. multicoloured..	10	10
O 846.		3 k. multicoloured..	10	10
O 847.		4 k. multicoloured..	15	10
O 848.		5 k. multicoloured..	20	10
O 849.		6 k. multicoloured..	20	10
O 850.		8 k. multicoloured..	35	15
O 851.		9 k. multicoloured..	35	20
O 852.		10 k. multicoloured	45	20
O 853.		14 k. multicoloured	55	25
O 854.		17 k. multicoloured	80	45
O 855.		20 k. multicoloured	1·00	50
O 856.		50 k. multicoloured	2·50	1·00
O 857.		100 k. multicoloured	6·75	2·75

ZAMBEZIA Pt. 9

Formerly administered by the Zambezia Co. This district of Portuguese E. Africa was later known as Quelimane and is now part of Mozambique.

1000 reis = 1 milreis.

1894. "Figures" key-type inscr. "ZAMBEZIA"

No.	Description	Mint	Used
1. R.	5 r. orange	15	15
2.	10 r. mauve	20	20
3.	15 r. brown	25	25
4.	20 r. lilac	25	25
12.	25 r. green	40	30
13.	50 r. blue	40	30
14.	75 r. red	90	90
15.	80 r. green	75	60
8.	100 r. brown on buff ..	70	60
16.	150 r. red on rose ..	90	75
17.	200 r. blue on blue ..	90	80
18.	300 r. blue on brown ..	1·75	1·50

1898. "King Carlos" key-type inscr "ZAMBEZIA". Name and value in red (500 r.) or black (others).

No.	Description	Mint	Used
20. S.	2½ r. grey	20	15
21.	5 r. orange	20	15
22.	10 r. green	20	15
23	15 r. brown	45	40
55.	15 r. green	60	50
24.	20 r. lilac	40	35
25.	25 r. green	40	35
56.	25 r. red	40	30
26.	50 r. blue	50	40
57.	50 r. brown	1·00	90
58.	65 r. blue	2·50	2·00
27.	75 r. red	2·75	1·90
59.	75 r. purple	1·25	95
28.	80 r. mauve	1·75	1·50
29.	100 r. blue on blue ..	80	75
60.	115 r. brown on pink ..	3·25	2·50
61.	130 r. brown on yellow ..	3·25	2·50
30.	150 r. brown on yellow ..	1·75	1·40
31.	200 r. purple on pink ..	1·75	1·40
32.	300 r. blue on pink ..	2·00	1·50
62.	400 r. blue on yellow ..	3·50	3·00
33.	500 r. black on blue ..	3·00	2·50
34.	700 r. mauve on yellow ..	3·50	3·00

1902. Surch.

No.	Description	Mint	Used
63. S.	50 r. on 65 r. blue ..	2·00	1·25
35. R.	65 r. on 10 r. mauve ..	2·00	1·75
36.	65 r. on 15 r. brown ..	2·00	1·75
37.	65 r. on 20 r. lilac	2·00	1·75
38.	65 r. on 300 r. blue on brn.	2·00	1·75
40.	115 r. on 5 r. orange ..	2·00	1·75
41.	115. r. on 25 r. green ..	2·00	1·75
42.	115 r. on 80 r. green ..	2·00	1·75
46. V.	130 r. on 2½ r. brown ..	2·00	1·75
43. R.	130 r. on 75 r. red ..	2·00	1·75
45.	130 r. on 150 r. red on rose	1·75	1·40
47.	400 r. on 50 r. blue ..	80	70
49.	400 r. on 100 r. brn. on buff	80	70
50.	400 r. on 200 r. blue on bl.	80	70

1902. 1898 issue optd. **PROVISORIO.**

No.	Description	Mint	Used
51. S.	15 r. brown	65	50
52.	25 r. blue	65	50
53.	50 r. blue	65	50
54.	75 r. red	2·00	1·40

1911. 1898 issue optd. **REPUBLICA.**

No.	Description	Mint	Used
64. S.	2½ r. grey	10	10
65.	5 r. orange	10	10
66.	10 r. green	15	15
67.	15 r. green	15	15
68.	20 r. lilac	20	10
69.	25 r. red	45	20
108.	25 r. green	4·00	3·00
70.	50 r. brown	15	15
71.	75 r. purple	35	25
72.	100 r. blue on blue ..	35	25
73.	115 r. brown on pink ..	40	30
74.	130 r. brown on yellow ..	40	30
75.	200 r. purple on pink ..	40	30
76.	400 r. blue on cream ..	70	55
77.	500 r. black on blue ..	70	55
78.	700 r. mauve on yellow ..	70	55

1914. 1902 **PROVISORIO** issue optd **REPUBLICA.**

No.	Description	Mint	Used
94. S.	50 r. blue	25	20
81.	75 r red	50	40

1914. Provisionals of 1902 optd. **REPUBLICA.**

No.	Description	Mint	Used
95. S.	50 r. on 65 r. blue ..	1·00	80
96. R.	115 r. on 5 r. orange ..	25	20
97.	115 r. on 25 r. green ..	25	20
98.	115 r. on 80 r. green ..	25	20
99. V.	130 r. on 2½ r. brown ..	25	20
100. R.	130 r. on 75 r. red ..	25	20
102.	130 r. on 150 r. red on rose	20	20
90.	400 r. on 50 r. blue ..	70	60
92.	400 r. on 100 r. brn. on buff	80	60
93.	400 r. on 200 r. bl. on blue	80	70

NEWSPAPER STAMP

1893. "Newspaper" key-type inscr. "ZAMBEZIA".

No.	Description	Mint	Used
N 1. V.	2½ r. brown	20	15

ADDENDA AND CORRIGENDA

KOREA

SOUTH KOREA

1256 "Twin Tigers" (military officials, 1st to 3rd rank)

1260 Campaign Emblem

1993. Korean Beauty (3rd series). Hyoongbae (embroidered insignia of the Chosun dynasty). Multicoloured.
2068 110 w. Type **1256** 20 10
2069 110 w. "Single Crane" (civil officials, 4th to 9th rank) 20 10
2070 110 w. "Twin Cranes" (civil officials, 1st to 3rd rank) 20 10
2071 110 w. "Dragon" (King) 20 10

1993. Anti-litter Campaign.
2072 **1260** 110 w. multicoloured 20 10

1261 "Eggplant and Oriental Long-nosed Locust" (Shin Sa-im Dang)

1262 "Weaving"

1993. Philatelic Week.
2073 **1261** 110 w. multicoloured 20 10

1993. 21st Universal Postal Union Congress, Seoul. Paintings by Kim Hong Do. Mult.
2075 110 w. Type **1262** 20 10
2076 110 w. "Musicians and a Dancer" (vert) .. 20 10

1263 Ribbon and Globe as "30", Freighter and Airplane

1993. 30th Trade Day.
2078 **1263** 110 w. multicoloured 20 10

1264 Sapsaree and Kite

1993. Lunar New Year ("Year of the Dog"). Multicoloured.
2079 110 w. Type **1264** 20 10
2080 110 w. Puppy with New Year's Greetings Bow 20 10

1993. Wild Flowers (4th series). As T **1166**.
2082 110 w. "Weigela hortensis" 20 10
2083 110 w. "Iris ruthenica" .. 20 10
2084 110 w. "Acериphyllum rosii" 20 10
2085 110 w. Marsh marigold ("Caltha palustris") .. 20 10

NORTH KOREA

1079 King Tongmyong shooting Bow

1081 "Cyrtopodium andresoni"

1993. Restoration of King Tongmyong of Koguryo's Tomb. Multicoloured.
N3339 10 ch. Type **1079** .. 10 10
N3340 20 ch. King Tongmyong saluting crowd .. 15 10
N3341 30 ch. Restoration monument 20 10
N3342 40 ch. Temple of the Tomb of King Tongmyong (horiz) .. 25 10
N3343 50 ch. Tomb (horiz) .. 30 10

1993. Orchids. Multicoloured.
N3346 10 ch. Type **1081** .. 10 10
N3347 20 ch. "Cattleya CV" .. 15 10
N3348 30 ch. "Cattleya intermedia" "Oculata" .. 20 10
N3349 40 ch. Potinaria "Maysedo godensia" 25 10
N3350 50 ch. Kimilsungia .. 30 10

LITHUANIA

New Currency
100 centu = 1 litas

125 Klaipeda Post Office

1993. 75th Anniv of First Lithuanian Postage Stamps.
545 **125** 60 c. multicoloured .. 20 20
546 – 60 c. multicoloured .. 20 20
547 – 80 c. multicoloured .. 30 30
548 – 1 l. black, brown & grn 35 35
DESIGNS: No. 546, Kaunas post office; 547, Ministry for Post and Information, Vilnius; 548, First Lithuanian stamp.

126 "The Ladle Carver" (A. Gudaitis)

127 European Pond Turtle

1993. Europa. Contemporary Art.
549 **126** 80 c. multicoloured .. 30 30

1993. Pond Life. Multicoloured.
550 80 c. Type **127** 30 30
551 1 l. Running toad .. 35 35

128 Games Emblem and Team Colours

1994. Winter Olympic Games, Lillehammer, Norway.
552 **128** 1 l. 10 multicoloured .. 35 35

129 Antanas Smetona (President 1919–22 and 1926–40)

1994. National Day.
553 **129** 1 l. red and black .. 35 35
554 – 1 l. brown and black .. 35 35
DESIGN: No. 554, Aleksandras Stulginskis (President 1922–26).

LUXEMBOURG

Add to Nos. 1332/45 (Grand Duke Jean):
1330 **388** 1 f. black and yellow 10 10
1338 15 f. black and green 55 35
1341 20 f. black and red .. 75 45
1349 100 f. black and brown 3·75 2·25

1993. National Welfare Fund. Birds (2nd series). As T **387**. Multicoloured.
1364 14 f.+2 f. Snipe ("Becassine") 60 45
1365 14 f.+2 f. Kingfisher ("Martin-Pecheur") (vert) 60 45
1366 18 f.+3 f. Little ringed plover ("Petit Gravelot") 80 80
1367 22 f.+7 f. Sand martin ("Hirondelle de Rivage") (vert) .. 1·10 1·10

397 "Snow-covered Landscape" (Joseph Kutter)

1994. Artists' Birth Centenaries. Mult.
1368 14 f. Type **397** 55 35
1369 14 f. "The Moselle" (Nico Klopp) 55 35

MACAO

187 Chow-chow and Moon

1994. New Year. Year of the Dog.
828 **187** 5 p. multicoloured .. 85 60

188 Map and Prince Henry (½-size illustration)

1994. 600th Birth Anniv of Prince Henry the Navigator.
829 **188** 3 p. multicoloured .. 50 35

MONACO

669 King Charles Spaniels

1994. International Dog Show, Monte Carlo.
2165 **669** 2 f. 40 multicoloured 55 35

670 Couple, Leaves and Pollution

671 Iris

1994. Monaco Committee of Anti-tuberculosis and Respiratory Diseases Campaign.
2166 **670** 2 f. 40+60 c. mult .. 70 45

1994. Monte Carlo Flower Show.
2167 **671** 4 f. 40 multicoloured 1·00 60

672 Levitation Trick

1994. 10th Monte Carlo Magic Grand Prix.
2168 **672** 5 f. blue, black and red 1·10 70

673 Ingredients and Dining Table overlooking Harbour

1994. 35th Anniv of Brotherhood of Cordon d'Or French Chefs.
2169 **673** 6 f. multicoloured .. 1·40 85

NETHERLANDS

Add to Nos. 1594/1605 (Queen Beatrix):
1708 **428** 10 g. green .. .. 7·00 10

466 Candle

1993. Christmas. Multicoloured.
1711 55 c. Type **466** 40 10
1712 55 c. Fireworks 40 10
Both designs have a number of punched holes.

467 "Composition"

1994. 50th Death Anniv of Piet Mondriaan (artist). Multicoloured.
1713 70 c. "The Red Mill" (detail) 50 15
1714 80 c. Type **467** 55 10
1715 90 c. "Broadway Boogie Woogie" (detail) .. 65 30

HAVE YOU READ THE NOTES AT THE BEGINNING OF THIS CATALOGUE?
These often provide answers to the enquiries we receive.

468 Barnacle Goose

1994. "Fepapost 94" European Stamp Exhibition, The Hague. Mult.
1716 70 c.+60 c. Type **468** .. 90 60
1717 80 c.+70 c. Bluethroat .. 1·00 35
1718 90 c.+80 c. Garganey .. 1·25 85

NETHERLANDS ANTILLES

293 "Mother and Child" (mosaic)

294 Basset Hound

1993. Christmas. Works by Lucilia Engels-Boskaljon. Multicoloured.
1112 30 c. Type **293** 20 15
1113 115 c. "Madonna and Christ" (painting) .. 85 70

1994. Dogs. Multicoloured.
1114 65 c. Type **294** 50 40
1115 75 c. Pit bull terrier .. 60 50
1116 90 c. Cocker spaniel .. 70 60
1117 175 c. Chow-chow .. 1·25 1·00

NEW CALEDONIA

370 Bourail

1993. Town Arms. Multicoloured.
981 70 f. Type **370** 90 55
982 70 f. Noumea 90 55
983 70 f. Canala 90 55
984 70 f. Kone 90 55
985 70 f. Paita 90 55
986 70 f. Dumbea 90 55
987 70 f. Koumac 90 55
988 70 f. Ponerihouen .. 90 55
989 70 f. Kaamoo Hyehen .. 90 55
990 70 f. Mont Dore 90 55
991 70 f. Thio 90 55
992 70 f. Kaala-Gomen .. 90 55
993 70 f. Touho 90 55

1994. No value expressed.
994 **321** (60 f.) red 80 50

371 Dog, Exhibition Emblem and Chinese Horoscope Signs (New Year)

1994. Air. "Hong Kong '94" International Stamp Exhibition.
995 **371** 60 f. multicoloured 80 50

NIGER REPUBLIC

450 Jerusalem

1993. "Jerusalem, Holy City".
1268 **450** 110 f. multicoloured .. 25 15

451 People of Different Races

1994. Award of Nobel Peace Prize to Nelson Mandela and F. W. de Klerk (South African statesmen).
1269 **451** 270 f. multicoloured .. 65 35

NORWAY

Add to Nos. 1125 etc. (King Harald):
1132 **355** 6 k. 50 emerald, green and turquoise .. 1·25 25

1994. Butterflies (2nd series). As T **364**. Multicoloured.
1173 3 k. 50 Northern clouded yellow ("Colias hecla") 65 10
1174 3 k. 50 Freya's fritillary ("Colssiana freija") 65 10

374 Flags

375 Cross-country Skiing

1994. Winter Olympic Games, Lillehammer (8th issue). Multicoloured.
1175 3 k. 50 Type **374** .. 65 10
1176 3 k. 50 Flags (different) .. 65 10
1177 3 k. 50 Lillehammer (church) and rings .. 65 10
1178 3 k. 50 Lillehammer (ski jump) and rings .. 65 10
1179 4 k. 50 Flags of European countries 85 25
1180 5 k. 50 Flags of non-European countries .. 1·00 40
Nos. 1175/8 were issued together, forming a composite design.

1994. Paralympic Games, Lillehammer. Mult.
1181 4 k. 50 Type **375** .. 80 20
1182 5 k. 50 Downhill skiing .. 1·00 25

376 King Christian VII's Signature and Seal

1994. Bicentenary of Tromso.
1183 **376** 3 k. 50 red, bis & brn 65 10
1184 – 4 k. 50 blue, yellow and light blue .. 85 25
DESIGN: 4 k. 50, Tromsdalen church.

377 Mount Floy Incline Railway, Bergen

1994. Tourism. Multicoloured.
1185 4 k. Type **377** 70 20
1186 4 k. 50 "Svolvaer Goat" (rock formation), Lofoten 85 25
1187 5 k. 50 Beacon, World's End, Tjome .. .. 1·00 40

PALAU

84 "After Child-birth Ceremony" (Charlie Gibbons)

1993. International Year of Indigenous Peoples. Multicoloured.
641 29 c. Type **84** 40 30
642 29 c. "Village in Early Palau" (Charlie Gibbons) 40 30

85 Flukes of Whale's Tail

1993. Jonah and The Whale. Multicoloured.
644 29 c. Type **85** 40 30
645 29 c. Bird and part of fluke 40 30
646 29 c. Two birds 40 30
647 29 c. Kaeb (canoe) .. 40 30
648 29 c. Sun, birds and dolphin 40 30
649 29 c. Shark and whale's tail 40 30
650 29 c. Shoal of brown fishes and part of whale 40 30
651 29 c. Hammerhead shark, shark's tail and fishes .. 40 30
652 29 c. Two species of fish and shark's head .. 40 30
653 29 c. Dolphin and fishes .. 40 30
654 29 c. Small brown and large striped fishes and part of whale .. 40 30
655 29 c. Two turtles swimming across whale's body .. 40 30
656 29 c. Shoal of pink fishes and whale's back .. 40 30
657 29 c. Rays, fishes and top of whale's head .. 40 30
658 29 c. Two large and shoal of small brown fishes .. 40 30
659 29 c. Jellyfish and blue fish 40 30
660 29 c. Fishes and whale's dorsal fin 40 30
661 29 c. Whale's eye and corner of mouth .. 40 30
662 29 c. Opened mouth .. 40 30
663 29 c. Jonah 40 30
664 29 c. Yellow and black striped fish and corals on sea bed 40 30
665 29 c. Three fishes and sea anenome 40 30
666 29 c. Blue-striped fish and corals on sea bed .. 40 30
667 29 c. Brown and red striped fish, corals and part of whale's jaw .. 40 30
668 29 c. Spotted fishes on sea bed 40 30
Nos. 644/68 were issued together, se-tenant, forming a composite design.

PANAMA

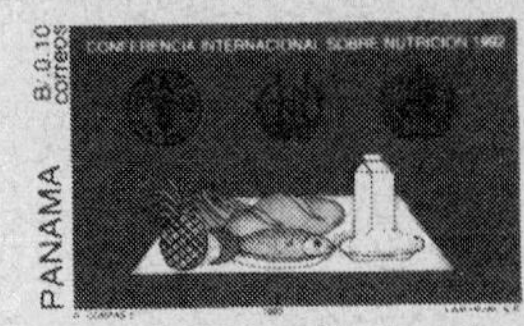

414 Nutritious Foods and Emblems

1993. International Nutrition Conference, Rome.
1549 **414** 10 c. multicoloured .. 15 10

POLAND

1047 Daisy shedding Petals

1994. Greetings Stamp.
3504 **1047** 1500 z. multicoloured 10 10

PORTUGAL

501 Oliveira Martins (historian)

1994. Centenaries. Multicoloured.
2363 45 e. Type **501** (death) .. 35 15
2364 100 e. Florbela Espanca (poet, birth) 80 40

502 Map and Prince Henry (½-size illustration)

1994. 600th Birth Anniv of Prince Henry the Navigator.
2365 **502** 140 e. multicoloured .. 1·10 55

QATAR

197 Girls playing

1993. Children's Games. Multicoloured.
923 25 d. Type **197** 10 10
924 50 d. Boys playing with propeller (vert) .. 20 15
925 75 d. Wheel and stick race (vert) 30 25
926 1 r. 50 Skipping 55 45

198 Lanner Falcon

1993. Falcons. Multicoloured.
928 25 d. Type **198** 10 10
929 50 d. Saker falcon .. 20 15
930 75 d. Barbary falcon .. 30 25
931 1 r. 50 Peregrine falcon .. 55 45

RUMANIA

1993. 35th Annivs of Rumanian Philatelic Association and Rumanian Philatelic Federation. No. 5445 surch **35 ANI DE ACTIVITATE AFR-FFR 1958—1993 70L+45L.**

5562 **1122** 70 l. + 45 l. on 10 l. + 4 l. pink, violet and blue .. 40 10

RUSSIA

2578 Seasonal Decorations

1993. New Year.

6448 **2578** 25 r. multicoloured .. 10 10

2579 Indian Elephant

2580 Rimsky-Korsakov and Scene from "Sadko"

1993. Animals. Multicoloured.

6449 250 r. Type **2579** .. 40 20
6450 250 r. Japanese white-necked crane 40 20
6451 250 r. Giant panda .. 40 10
6452 250 r. American bald eagle 40 20
6453 250 r. Dall's porpoise .. 40 20
6454 250 r. Koala 40 20
6455 250 r. Hawaiian monk seal 40 20
6456 250 r. Grey whale .. 40 20

1994. 150th Birth Anniv of Nikolai Rimsky-Korsakov (composer). Scenes from his operas. Multicoloured.

6457 250 r. Type **2580** .. 40 20
6458 250 r. "The Golden Cockerel" 40 20
6459 250 r. "The Tsar's Bride" 40 40
6460 250 r. "The Snow Maiden" 40 20

ST.- PIERRE ET MIQUELON

207 Player lining up Shot

1994. 1st French Overseas Territories Petanque Championship.

710 **207** 5 f. 10 multicoloured .. 1·25 75

208 "Cristalis tenax" on Dandelion

1994.

711 **208** 3 f. 70 multicoloured .. 85 50

209 Drying Cod

1994.

712 **209** 1 f. 50 black and green 35 20
713 1 f. 80 multicoloured .. 40 25

SAN MARINO

408 Long-haired Dachshund

1994. 10th International Dog Show. Mult.

1466 350 l. Type **408** 30 30
1467 400 l. Afghan hound .. 35 35
1468 450 l. Belgian tervuren shepherd dog 40 40
1469 500 l. Boston terrier .. 40 40
1470 550 l. Mastiff 45 45
1471 600 l. Malamute 50 50

410 Gate

411 Olympic Flags

1994. Gardens. Multicoloured.

1473 100 l. Type **410** 10 10
1474 200 l. Pergola 15 15
1475 300 l. Well 25 25
1476 450 l. Gazebo 40 40
1477 1850 l. Pond .. .. 1·50 1·50

1994. Centenary of International Olympic Committee.

1478 **411** 600 l. multicoloured .. 50 50

1994. 100 Years of Radio (4th issue). As T **389**. Multicoloured.

1479 750 l. Aleksandr Stepanovich Popov .. 65 65

Popov was the first to use a suspended wire as an aerial.

SENEGAL

399 Decorated Tree, Children playing and Father Christmas

1993. Christmas. Multicoloured.

1240 5 f. Type **399** 5 5
1241 80 f. Children decorating tree and Father Christmas 20 15
1242 145 f. Children visiting Father Christmas .. 35 25
1243 150 f. Girl tugging Father Christmas's beard .. 35 25

SLOVAKIA

Add to No. 163:

164 50 k. black, blue & orange 2·10 65

DESIGN—VERT. 50 k. Bratislava.

50 Canal Lock, Gabcikovo

1993. Rhine–Main–Danube Canal.

170 **50** 10 k. multicoloured .. 40 15

MINIMUM PRICE

The minimum price quoted is 5p which represents a handling charge rather than a basis for valuing common stamps. For further notes about prices see introductory pages.

51 Child's Face in Blood-drop

52 "Madonna and Child" (Jozef Klemens)

1993. Red Cross.

171 **51** 3 k. + 1 k. red and blue 15 10

1993. Christmas.

172 **52** 2 k. multicoloured .. 10 10

54 "The Labourer's Spring" (Jozef Kostka)

1993. Art.

174 **54** 9 k. multicoloured .. 35 35

55 Ski Jumping

1994. Winter Olympic Games, Lillehammer, Norway.

175 **55** 2 k. black, mauve & blue 10 10

SLOVENIA

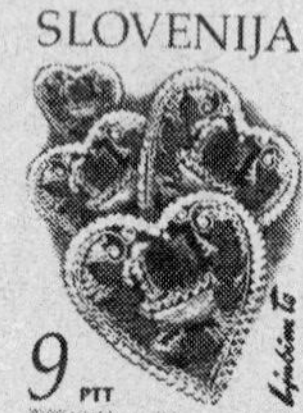

52 Illustration from "The Vagabond"

53 Hearts

1994. 150th Anniversaries. Multicoloured.

222 8 t. Type **52** (birth anniv of Josip Jurcic (writer)) .. 10 10
223 9 t. Nightingale and bridge over river (birth anniv of Simon Gregorcic, poet) 10 10
224 55 t. Book showing Slovenian vowels (birth anniv of Stanislav Skrabec, philologist) .. 55 55
225 65 t. Cover of grammar book (death anniv of Jernei Kopitar, philologist) 65 65

1994. Greetings Stamp.

226 **53** 9 t. multicoloured .. 10 10

SOUTH AFRICA

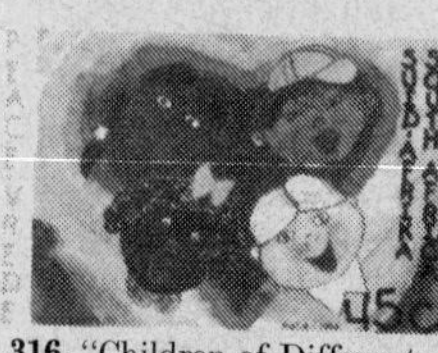

316 "Children of Different Races" (Nicole Davies)

1994. Peace Campaign. Children's Paintings. Multicoloured.

836 45 c. Type **316** 20 25
837 70 c. "Dove and Tree" (Robynne Lawrie) .. 30 35
838 95 c. "Children and Dove" (Batami Nothmann) .. 40 45
839 1 r. 15 "Multi-racial Crowd" (Karen Uys) .. 45 50

317 Pres. Mandela

1994. Inauguration of President Nelson Mandela. Multicoloured.

840 45 c. Type **317** 20 25
841 70 c. South African national anthems .. 30 35
842 95 c. New national flag .. 40 45
843 1 r. 15 Union Buildings, Pretoria 45 50

318 T. S. "McEwen" towing "Winchester Castle" (liner), 1935

1994. Tugboats. Multicoloured.

844 45 c. Type **318** 20 25
845 70 c. "Sir William Hoy" with "Karanja" (liner), 1970 .. .. 30 35
846 95 c. "Sir Charles Elliott" and wreck of "Dunedin Star" (liner), 1942 .. 40 45
847 1 r. 15 "Eland" and freighter at wharf, 1955 45 50
848 1 r. 35 "Pioneer" (paddle tug) and sailing ships, 1870 .. .. .. 55 60

SPAIN

1994. Fungi (2nd series). As T **859**. Mult.

3256 18 p. Cep ("Boletus edulis") 20 10
3257 18 p. Satan's mushroom ("Boletus saganas") .. 20 10
3258 29 p. Death cap ("Amanita phalloides") 30 10
3259 29 p. Saffron milk cap ("Lactarius deliciosus") 30 10

880 Cinnabar

1994. Minerals.

3260 **880** 29 p. multicoloured .. 30 10
3261 – 29 p. multicoloured .. 30 10
3262 – 29 p. multicoloured .. 30 10
3263 – 29 p. black and blue 30 10

DESIGNS: 3261, Blende (inscr "Esfalerita"); 3262, Pyrites; 3263, Galena.

SWEDEN

491 Siamese

492 Illustration from "Le Roman de la Rose"

1994. Cats. Multicoloured.

1724	4 k. 50 Type **491** ..	75	45
1725	4 k. 50 Persian	75	45
1726	4 k. 50 European ..	75	45
1727	4 k. 50 Abyssinian ..	75	45

1994. Franco–Swedish Cultural Relations. Multicoloured.

1728	5 k. Type **492**	85	50
1729	5 k. Swedish and French flags	85	50
1730	5 k. Sketch by De la Vallee of Knight's House (40 × 43 mm) ..	85	50
1731	5 k. "Household Chores" (Pehr Hillestrom) ..	80	50
1732	5 k. "Banquet for Gustav III at the Trianon, 1784" (Niclas Lafrensen the younger) (40 × 43 mm)	85	90
1733	5 k. "Carl XIV Johan" (Francois Gerard) ..	85	50

SWITZERLAND

Add to Nos. 1168/75 (Occupations):

1173a	4 f. multicoloured ..	4·75	1·40

DESIGN: 4 f. Vine grower.

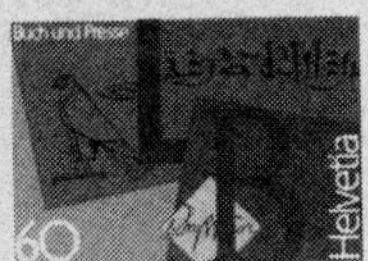

321 Hieroglyphic, Cuneiform and Roman Scripts

1994. "Books and the Press" Exhibition, Geneva. Multicoloured.

1277	60 c. Type **321**	55	15
1278	80 c. Gothic letterpress script	75	40
1279	100 c. Modern electronic fonts	95	85

322 Athletes

1994. Publicity Issue. Multicoloured.

1280	60 c. Type **322** (50th anniv of National Sports School, Magglingen) ..	55	15
1281	80 c. Jakob Bernoulli (after Nicolas Bernoulli) and formula and diagram of the law of large numbers (Int Mathematicians Congress, Zurich) ..	75	40
1282	100 c. Heads, Unisource emblem, globe and flags (collaboration of Swiss, Dutch and Swedish telecommunications companies)	95	85
1283	180 c. Radar image, airliner and globe (50th anniv of International Civil Aviation Organization)	1·75	1·60

323 Footballers

1994. World Cup Football Championship, U.S.A., and Centenary (1995) of Swiss Football Association.

1284	**323** 80 c. multicoloured ..	75	40

TUNISIA

478 "7"

479 Tapestry

1993. 6th Anniv of Declaration of 7 November 1987. Multicoloured.

1253	180 m. Type **478** ..	25	15
1254	450 m. "7"s and waves ..	60	30

1993. Kairouan Carpets.

1255	**479** 100 m. multicoloured	15	10
1256	– 120 m. multicoloured	15	10
1257	– 180 m. multicoloured	25	15
1258	– 350 m. multicoloured	45	25

DESIGNS: 120 m. to 350 m. Different carpets.

TURKEY

749 Satellite, Globe and Map

750 Ears of Corn

1994. "Turksat" Communications Satellite. Multicoloured.

3209	1500 l. Type **749**	10	10
3210	5000 l. Satellite and map showing satellite's "footprint"	20	10

1994. 40th Anniv of Water Supply Company.

3211	**750** 1500 l. multicoloured	10	10

UNITED STATES

2027 Dove on Heart-shaped Bouquet of Roses

2029 Troopers on Western Frontier

1994. Greetings Stamps. Multicoloured.

2882	29 c. Type **2027**	40	10
2883	52 c. Doves on flower arrangement (horiz) ..	70	25

1994. "Buffalo Soldiers" (U.S. Army black regiments).

2884	**2029** 29 c. multicoloured ..	40	10

2030 Rudolph Valentino

2040 Lilies

1994. Silent Screen Stars.

2885	**2030**	29 c. black, vio & red	40	10
2886	–	29 c. black, vio & red	40	10
2887	–	29 c. black, red & vio	40	10
2888	–	29 c. black, red & vio	40	10
2889	–	29 c. black, vio & red	40	10
2890	–	29 c. black, red & vio	40	10
2891	–	29 c. black, vio & red	40	10
2892	–	29 c. black, vio & red	40	10
2893	–	29 c. black, red & vio	40	10
2894	–	29 c. black, red & vio	40	10

DESIGNS: No. 2886, Clara Bow; 2887, Charlie Chaplin; 2888, Lon Chaney; 2889, John Gilbert; 2890, Zasu Pitts; 2891, Harold Lloyd; 2892, Keystone Cops; 2893, Theda Bara; 2894, Buster Keaton.

1994. Garden Flowers. Multicoloured.

2895	29 c. Type **2040**	40	10
2896	29 c. Zinnias	40	10
2897	29 c. Gladioli	40	10
2898	29 c. Marigolds	40	10
2899	29 c. Roses	40	10

WALLIS AND FUTUNA ISLANDS

246 "Wallis Landscape" (P. Legris)

1994. Air.

638	**246** 400 f. multicoloured ..	5·00	3·00

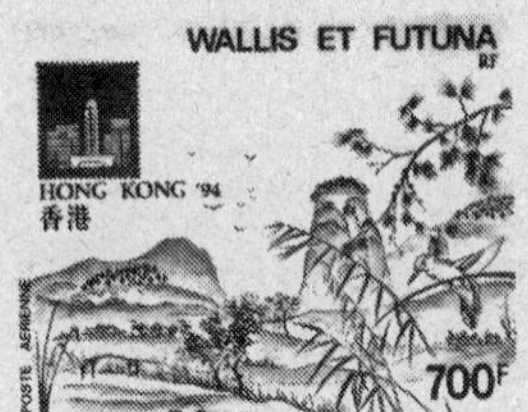

247 Landscape and Emblem

1994. Air. "Hong Kong '94" International Stamp Exhibition.

639	**247** 700 f. multicoloured ..	9·00	5·50

NOTE. The first supplement containing new issues not in this catalogue or the Addenda appeared in the September 1994 number of *Gibbons Stamp Monthly.*

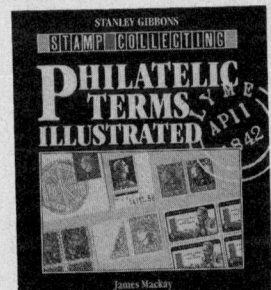

INDEX

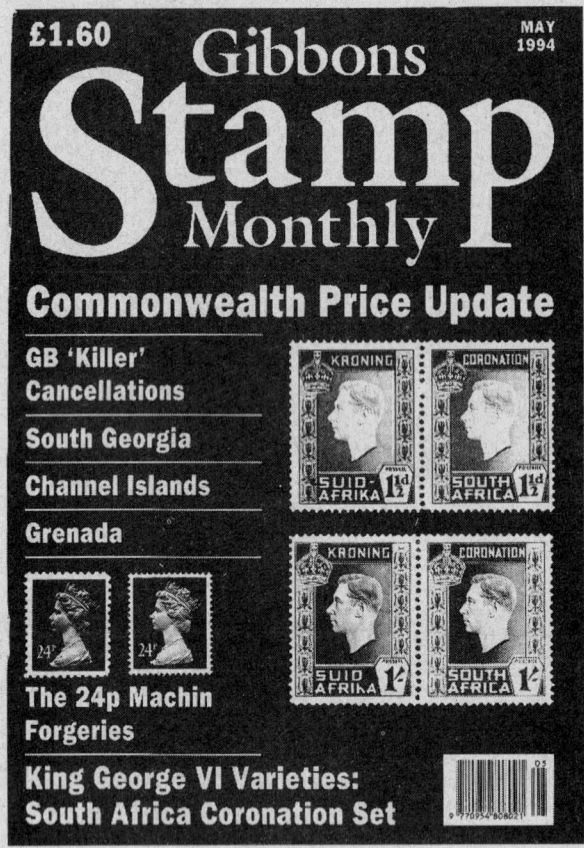